Mer[illegible]

To

Tom and Peggy Thompson

Charlie [illegible]

Letters to Dear Dan

by

Dr. Charles M. Stebner

1989

Laramie, Wyoming

FOREWORD

In this book Dr. Stebner has realized a long-cherished project. Starting with some scattered memories, addressed to his grandson, he found himself involved in a threefold ambition only recently in his 80th year achieved: namely, a family history, the story of Hanna, Wyoming, from its very beginnings, and, he has noted, an affirmation of the reality of the American dream of an opportunity for the neediest of the Ellis-Island immigrants.

Before the Hanna story there was Carbon, Wyoming. Encouraged by the Transcontinental Railroad, Dr. Stebner's paternal grandparents left Germany to seek the American west and mine coal. From 1868 to the turn of the century we see a raucous mining camp of Carbon, which was replaced by the new town of Hanna.

Dr. Stebner maternal grandfather, Charles Hughes and two children arrived in Hanna after hailing from a mid-England small mining village, must have found at first in Hanna little change in their status. More tragically, the early death of the strong father in a mine accident, left in the mother a growing determination that her son should have both an education and a career.

This book then, is unique in its combination of biography, history, and final optimism. It should attract two type of readers: first, friends and neighbors and former residents of Hanna; and second, less involved but nevertheless students of Wyoming's history in both its local and its larger reaches. Dr. Stebner has also recovered some valid illustrations to accompany his story.

Dr. Stebner makes no pretense of being a trained writer. It is his material that has pushed him to the effort. The small assistance requested of Dr. T. A. Larson and of me has consisted only of a red-pencil reading for possible errors of spelling or punctuation. We have had no hand in editing Stebner's material. Its author, long an active citizen in Laramie's city, has dedicated its returns to Wyoming's Community Center enterprises. We join willingly in the hope that the book will have a merited reception, and that its author can take a justifiable pride in a goal accomplished.

Wilson O. Clough

Wilson O. Clough
Professor Emeritus

PREFACE

About six years ago our first grandchild, Dan, was born. We visited with his great grandmother, Mary Hughes Stebner Ford, and she held him long enough for a photograph.

Then, I bought a computer and began to write about that unique lady, and also record my own personal experiences. Finally, what began as "Letters to Danny" slowly grew into this volume. Now I realize that a century has passed during the lives of my mother and myself. Most of our personal experiences and philosophies seem to be recorded. Together they include living during four wars and the Great Depression.

We know George Washington did not cut down the cherry tree. It was fabricated by others to add to his legend of truthfulness. In this volume I have used the real names of individuals. If any of them are either pleased, or disturbed, I cannot help it.

Charles Martin Stebner

TABLE OF CONTENTS

TABLE OF PHOTOGRAPHS

CREDITS

Photo no. 1, Richardson family; no. 3, Sue Mangan family, Laramie; no. 9 & 10, Klassen family, Wheatland; no. 11, John Traeger, Rock Springs; no. 22-27, Sam Thompson Collection, American Heritage Center; 30 & 31, Laramie Plains Museum; no. 28, Dr. Alan R. Schneider, Beverly Hills, CA; no. 34, Dr. Ben Chesebro, Laramie. The rest of the photographs are credited to the Charles Stebner family.

Old Carbon

CREIGHTON AND CARBON

Dear Dan:

When Carbon, Wyoming was only sagebrush, rocks and sand Edward Creighton of Omaha, Nebraska discovered a vein of coal at that location. This signaled the end of wood-burning in the new railroad which was being built to unite America from the Atlantic to the Pacific Ocean. Edward Creighton, and his brother John, endowed Creighton University in Omaha, Nebraska. Edward died in 1874, but his wife, Mary Lucretia Creighton, later added to his bequest.

These brothers made a fortune as they contracted and worked with the Union Pacific and the Government. They helped unite the country, both by establishing telegraphic lines and finding coal. The Catholic brothers spent considerable time in Old Carbon where they aided Thomas Wardell, of the Union Pacific, to open Wyoming's first coal mine. Today, there is an area of Rock Springs named after Wardell.

Ultimately, there was some criticism from the Federal Government and, through litigation, the Union Pacific Coal Company was organized to take over such holdings on railroad property. Later, Creighton's philanthropy encouraged them to build hospitals and a University in Omaha. They were knighted and made Counts of the Pope. This, I did not know when I entered the School of Dentistry at Creighton University.

IMMIGRANTS TO CARBON

During the time of unlimited immigration which was necessary for the development of Wyoming, only those from England spoke a language we could understand. I will quote from the history of the Union Pacific Coal Mines, Colonial Press, Omaha, Nebraska:

"Most of the miners were Lankies, as they were called, big, rawboned men, quick to take offense, as earnest at their play as at their work.

"They came to America from England's heavy coal producing county, Lancashire, and they were well able to handle the job of mining in Wyoming. Sport-loving men, they were not long in exploring the amusement possibilities of the country-side. Hunting as a pastime they discarded in short order. With two to three hundred elk grazing in the mule pasture with the company mules a half mile from camp, shooting elk held about the same wild zest for a sportsman as shooting a Guernsey cow. As for sage chickens, a man could find them in boring abundance a few hundred yards outside of camp.

"Horse racing was the mine workers favorite sport. One of their first activities after moving to No. Five Mine was to clear the sagebrush for a quarter mile stretch of prairie near the camp and call it a race track. Horses were raced there every Sunday.

"Second only to the horse races was pigeon shooting, with live pigeons as targets. They had an infallible system for encouraging the bird to fly to the right or to the left. . .They would jab a pigeon's eye out. Of course the pigeon would fly in the opposite direction for a shooter who shot poorly in that direction. . . They resorted to squirting tobacco juice in the pigeon's eye."

The German Stebner family fished and hunted, both in Carbon and then later in Hanna. There I remember sacks full of fish or sage chicken that my Dad Bruno brought home. There was no refrigeration then, so I carried game to our neighbors in small lard pails.

BILL RICHARDSON

A survivor was tough and colorful--Bill Richardson. Bill arrived in this country in the earliest days of Carbon and realized that other members of his English family should leave the Mother Country and follow him to Wyoming. He helped finance their passage. This he could not have done if he were not frugal. Most of the rowdy Lankies loved life and spent their earnings--not Richardson! Bill had a vision!

He came to Carbon from Durham, England, which is a neighbor of Lancashire. He was very opposite in temperament from his niece Sue Mangan. Perhaps we could identify him as an adventurous workaholic. As I remember him he seemed to have no sense of humor. Sue also knew hard work, but her attitude was always optimistic and tempered with humor.

In structure he was small, tough and wiry. Other miners were often big and strong in comparison, but they could not keep up with Bill in producing coal. He had the reputation of mining more coal in a day than any other miner. They were paid accordingly.

Concerning finances, very many miners were satisfied to get along from pay-day to pay-day. They understood they would never have much money. Their needs were few. They expected to work hard, to eat well, and have some fun.

Richardson did not fit that pattern. He loved the outdoors and wanted to own a ranch above the town of Elk Mountain. To him the pay in the mines was worth the hard work. During Richardson's sessions as a miner he and an Irish partner, Pat Murphy, set a record for coal mined in a single shift. They drew their semimonthly pay on a tonnage basis. These miners drew $500.00. That was a lot of tax-free money in those days.

But when the bright green leaves budded out on the Cottonwood trees, Bill headed for his homestead on Medicine Bow River. The Indians discovered that the best willows to make their bows were also found there.

BILL RICHARDSON FIRST IN CANADA

Some Englishmen first immigrated to Canada and Bill Richardson used this route. That was an easier way to enter the continent. Then it was simple to enter the United States.

First, Bill worked in a coal mine. When he could, Bill found jobs with farmers in the nearby fields or forests, for his heart was always on the land--not underground. One day in the forest he was listening to the birds and enjoying the outdoor sounds. Finally his boss asked him what he was contemplating, and Richardson told him he was listening to the song birds. Then, he asked a question: "What kind of bloody bird is that, making that funny damn cracking noise?" The amused native took Bill down the hill to a pond and showed him the source. His first frog!

RICHARDSON THE HORSETRADER

When Bill Richardson was not working the mine or improving his homestead on the upper Medicine Bow River, he joined other Carbonites in collecting and buying cattle or horses.

In the early days of Carbon a man could get ahead financially if he was sharp enough to buy and sell livestock. This trade sometimes included deals with the desperadoes, particularly Tom McCarthy whose gang often hid out in the area that is now Baggs, Wyoming. McCarthy had good contact with the Indians.

Bill Richardson homesteaded on the Medicine Bow River. He worked in the coal mines only to finance his livestock business and to buy land.

Bill Richardson and John Milliken heard that the Ute Indian Chief, Half Moon, wanted to sell horses they had collected--perhaps from other tribes, or white travelers and ranchers. Those two left Carbon with a packstring to buy horses which they could sell in the Elk Mountain area, or even in western Nebraska where they were in demand.

They met McCarthy who acted as their guide to meet Half Moon, the Ute Chief. Earlier, the Indians would demand payments for the horses only in gold or silver coin. But the weight of hard money on a long pack trip was not desirable. After McCarthy's explanation that paper money was even better for the Indians, they accepted it. This proved to be a good idea for the Indians because they could braid it in their hair and travel lighter. Milliken and Richardson no doubt lost a few animals returning to the Carbon area. Nevertheless, the risky trip paid off.

When Richardson and Milliken made the trip to buy horses, they saw two men fighting over a calf. Richardson asked, "Why in 'ell should a fella get bloodied up fer a five-dollar calf?" Someone answered, "'ell Billie, hits not the five, but hits the twenty that hits worth after he lets it run in the hills a year." This easy profit gave the young man an idea that carried him a long way from the mine pit.

RICHARDSON AND FRIENDS BUY CATTLE

Richardson, Milliken, Bob Jackson and Duncan Jack went into Utah to buy cattle from the Mormon settlers. They purchased 1200 head of stock. On there way home a stampede at night claimed some cattle. Another forty drowned when they started to swim in a circle half-way across the Green River. Later they realized that they were in danger as they skirted Brown's Hole, which was a well-known bandit hangout. Their fortune was good because Richardson had previously been guided thru that area by the questionable character named McCarthy.

Carbon was in confusion when they arrived with their cattle because these Elk Mountain men were very popular in the area. Richardson sold most of his cattle after wintering them in the upper Platte Valley and was ready to work that winter in the pursuit for a grubstake to buy more ranch land.

RICHARDSON SHIPS CATTLE TO OMAHA

On one occasion he drank more than he needed to celebrate his cattle sale in Omaha. When he tried to board the train he fell and many silver dollars rolled out of his pockets over the platform. The train was moving, and rather than retrieving the silver he boarded the train. Being hung-over when the train arrived at destination Percy, he placed a penalty on himself and walked the entire eighteen miles back to the ranch.

Bill Richardson seldom drank whiskey and that was something his sons ignored, too, partly because they had to work regularly and they saved their money carefully. Yet, when Bill shipped his cattle to Omaha during the autumn he became a spendthrift. At Brandeis Store he bought fancy clothes for the woman at home, always remembering which color looked best on her.

. . . .

Richardson once told his family of the first black man he ever saw. He was working on the roundup one summer when a stranger rode into camp. He was hungry and joined the cowboys at chow. When he was asked where he worked previously, he said, Texas. The roundup boss was also a Texan. He was promised a job as horse wrangler if he could ride. The cowboys selected the meanest bronc in camp. They blindfolded and saddled the horse. When the stranger was well seated in the saddle the blindfold was removed and the bronc came apart. The horse pitched and ran in circles, but the black cowboy was still in the saddle. Then the new hired hand rode to collect the rest of the string.

The roundup boss asked the new cowboy what he thought of his mount. Sam said, "Boss, that is one of the hardest trotting horses I ever rode." He got the job and later became a foreman himself. As time went on he was one of the most famous cowboys in the area. Certainly he was respected by all who drank and ate with him. They fondly called him "Nigger Sam."

. . . .

Both Richardson and Milliken were still alive when I was a kid in Hanna. I was fascinated by Richardson when I saw him on his ranch at Elk

Mountain and Milliken had a blacksmith shop in Hanna. I remember being there with other kids to watch Milliken shoe horses.

WATER WAS HAULED TO CARBON

The area upon which Carbon was built lacked water. A team of horses hauled water from the Medicine Bow River. This mountain stream is about twelve miles east of Carbon. It cost the family twenty-five cents a barrel for the precious water. None was wasted.

The locomotives were finally fired with coal. The training the miners had in the 'Old Country' paid off for both themselves and the Union Pacific. Hard manual labor was nothing new to the many poor people of the Industrial Revolution. Yet, one phase of their life was different. When they had a day off the miners could roam endlessly over the hills and mountains fishing and hunting. That was sport and freedom which was new to them.

In the Carbon area there were many elk in the fields where the company's mules and horses were pastured. These they hunted, along with deer and antelope, and they fished for trout in the streams. For the men it was a life which was enjoyed only by the ruling classes of Europe. But the miner's wives were not yet liberated. Women worked as hard as ever; cooking, washing clothes, keeping house and raising children. These pioneer wives and their daughters had the strength of character we admire. Yes, Wyoming women were the first to vote and take their place in our history.

SUE IN CARBON

One such lady was Sue Mangan, a life-long friend of my Mother Mary Ford and a good friend of mine, too. I helped her celebrate her 100th birthday.

Sue Mangan, was quite a gal! Even at one hundred and two years old, her mind continued to be sharp and entertaining. I loved her because she was such a great friend of my Mother, but especially because she was Sue. She told me stories that were often risque and humorous.

Sue was not a Lanky, and she let you know it! She was born in Durham, a neighboring county to

Lancashire. Her background was also from a coal mining area, but she believed herself a bit above the Lancashire crowd. Her uncle, Bill Richardson, Sue and others in her family to come to Carbon.

Also, the Union Pacific recruited laborers from other countries, particularly Japan and China. You should read something about the Chinese massacre which occurred in Rock Springs, Wyoming because so many Chinese had been imported here and they would work for less than the white miners.

In old Carbon and in Hanna we had a great example of how the various nationalities worked, and appreciated one another. It was the ideal of the lack of prejudice from which the United Nations Organization could learn much. In these coal mining camps everyone was equal. We helped each other when they were in trouble. And very often even as the various groups lived more closely because they could understand their next door neighbor's speech. Where I was born in Hanna we had several Italian families as our closest friends, along with my Finnish buddies. They mixed with the only German family of Bruno Stebner. He married an English girl. I suppose if I had followed my father into the mines, I would have married a Finn girl--they were blond and beautiful. The fact is that I had been conditioned so strongly by my mother that I was going to continue an education. When anyone asked what I was going to do when I graduated from High School the answer was built in! "Oh, I am going to College." I was the first member of the Stebner-Hughes Clan to be born in the USA, and the first to graduate from High School. Few laborer's sons had that chance or their Mother's influence.

AN INDIAN SCARE IN CARBON

Sue told me that as a young girl who had just arrived in Carbon from England she was frightened by the threat of an Indian invasion. Although most of the Indians which roamed the area were peaceful, there were a few bands who hated the white invaders. Horses and mules were used in and around the mines to haul coal and supplies in Carbon. A stable boss was searching for some missing mules near the edge of town when he was attacked by Indians. He staggered back to town wounded with arrows, and he later died. All of the women and children were hurried into the open mouth of the mine while the men patrolled the mining camp carrying their hunting rifles. They expected an attack, but the few Indians who were there were not to be found. Sue told me of her anxiety which lasted several days.

DESPERADOES IN CARBON

The payday accounts for the miners were paid in gold coins. Payday was a time to drink in the several saloons. The best time meant a bare-fisted fight between the miners and the cowboys. The Lankies were best at drinking and singing the ribald songs they learned in England. It is interesting that no person ever thought of robbing the payroll. Men who robbed for a living were not comfortable in Carbon.

Desperadoes Dutch Charlie and Bignose George were around, but they gave Carbon a wide berth, even though they must have patronized some of the saloons in their travels. They and their gang were being trailed through the area by lawmen. They held up trains for the gold but they never bothered Carbon pay rolls. One wonders why? The Carbon miners gold coin pay rolls were handled so casually.

A Carbon County deputy sheriff named Widdowfield was very popular in the area of Carbon and Elk Mountain. He and a man named Vincent were part of a group who were trailing members of the Dutch Charlie and Big Nose George gang near Rattle Snake Creek. They were close to the group. Widdowfield got off his horse to check ashes of a camp fire. To his partner he said, "They must be near because these ashes are still hot as hell!" A voice from dense brush spoke out, saying, "I'll show you just how hot hell is." Sudden gunfire killed Widdowfield and Vincent. Others escaped to tell the people of Carbon of the murder.

The miners and cowboys formed a posse, but the desperadoes eluded them. Men of the area were dedicated to ultimately settling the score.

Months passed but finally good news came to Carbon. Dutch Charlie was captured and in the Laramie jail. Then better news came: the prisoner was to go to the Carbon County Court House in Rawlins for trial. This news was exactly what the Carbon citizens wanted. That meant the train he rode would have to stop for coal in Carbon. A neck-tie party was hastily organized and a strong lariat was ready. Among the greeting party were friends of Widdowfield's widow.

Men armed with rifles and six-shooters climbed on the locomotive and took over the crew. Others boarded the rest of the train. They were sure the train would not move. Armed men escorted the Train Conductor to the car where the hand-cuffed Dutch Charlie was under surveillance of Sheriff Rankin and his Deputy. The boarding party relieved the officers of his prisoner.

As they stepped off the train a determined group of men and older boys were ready with a lariat. He pleaded for a chance to prove his innocence, but they were determined to give as much chance as was given to Widdowfield.

Without a convenient tree they selected a prominent telegraph pole. The loop fit Dutch Charlie's neck firmly. He was placed standing on a beer barrel for all to observe. A short husky Finlander had the honor. He kicked the barrel away. The next morning, January 23, 1875, the body swayed in the wind, and taller boys could reach his feet and swing the body around. He remained there for all to see the next day.

Recently, I showed a friend the beautiful white marble marker above the body of Widdowfield in the Carbon cemetery, which notes: "Erected By His Friends".

After hanging from the pole overnight, Dutch Charlie's body was lowered so that the natives could get souvenirs from Dutch's body. I knew a fellow in Hanna by the name of Choate who used to show us kids an amputated finger which he kept in a little box which he carried with him. Very impressive!

Later, Big Nose George was caught and transported to Rawlins for his trial. He broke out of his cell, but an alert mob caught him in the street. He pleaded to be shot rather than hanged. As he made a break he was accommodated. Souvenirs from his body are artifacts in the Rawlins Museum.

Now I understand why there was little fear of robbery with the citizens in Carbon. Often on paydays there was a sack of $150,000 or $200,000 casually unloaded on the train platform, which was left there until a store clerk picked it up. Still, none was ever stolen.

FUN IN OLD CARBON

The Old Carbon Fire Department was an elite group. I saw a picture of the proud men, of which my own Dad was a member. It was disappointing because in the names printed on the photo his name was misspelled. I recognized his face but he was listed as 'Bruno Stevens'--not Stebner. Mary Ford also saw the problem, and she changed it when the photo she had was used in the Union Pacific History.

The firemen were sporting fellows who had to make their own entertainment. They conducted a rather severe initiation and it was an honor to be asked to join the group. The night before initiation they celebrated with a banquet. Earlier, members of the brigade stole twenty chickens from the coops of Joe who was a new initiate. Like other Lankies he raised the birds to breed fighting cocks, a popular sport in both England and Carbon. That evening Joe and the members enjoyed the chicken dinner.

Later Joe thanked the group for the fine banquet. After a few drinks he returned home to find that his prize breeding cocks had been stolen by his firemen brothers for the dinner. His violent objections availed him nothing but laughter.

Another element of the initiation was a bit rough. The brothers at Milliken's saloon passed a rope through the initiate's belt and using pulleys, they hoisted the initiate into the air. When he was helpless they paddled his rear end to be sure he could stand the height and pain necessary to be a fireman.

MRS. STIMPSON

Mrs. Stimpson was an excellent cook at Dana and Percy, which were railroad stops about ten miles west of the present-day Hanna. Stimpson ran a restaurant and boarding house at those two stops on the railroad. Apparently Richardson liked her cooking. He took her as his bride to his ranch in Elk Mountain where they raised three sons, Tom, Willing, and Ted. I knew them all.

Stimpson was a hardy woman besides being known for her meals. At Percy wooden products were cut from the forest of Elk Mountain to the south for the new railroad. The lumber was hauled from Elk Mountain to Percy by oxen or horse teams.

Certainly, a good cook like Mrs. Stimpson had the culinary expertise to attract anyone, and especially Bill Richardson. From Percy Mrs. Stimpson went by wagon with a picnic party toward Elk Mountain. There she fell in love with the valley as they picked wild berries. On the way home she remarked that a lake (later to be called Bloody Lake) was a dangerous area where the terrain could easily conceal Indians.

Her hunch was right, because a few weeks later two timber wagons were ambushed and the driver of leading wagon was killed by Indian arrows. A second driver of the trailing slower ox team could see what faced him. He left the wagon and headed on foot to the hills. He escaped and found his way back to Percy where groups were organized to hunt for the elusive Indians. They went to the lake and learned that the Indians had taken all the firearms and axes, and had driven the mules and other animals into the lake. Here they cut their hamstring tendons and harnesses. Most of them had drowned, but a few had freed themselves to make the bank where they had to be destroyed. The body of the driver was also found in the lake and the arrows were removed to later be displayed at the Percy Section House by Mrs. Stimpson.

She used them to warn UP passengers who stopped there that they should not wander into the surrounding hills. Today, we find a body of water near a high hill between Hanna and Elk Mountain. For a while the lake was red, and was named "Bloody Lake".

MRS. STIMPSON LEAVES PERCY

Mrs. Stimpson had a daughter from a former marriage who was also a rugged woman, and also a business person. She drove her own four-horse team from the railroad at the old Rock River Station on the Union Pacific.

Her mother left Percy and thought she might relocate where her daughter freighted. Richardson followed her there. I suppose he missed her cooking. Bill liked the terrain, and thought of selling his Elk Mountain property and moving to northern Wyoming. Bill did not find Stimpson, even though he made a trip to the states of Oregon and Washington.

Bill returned to the Carbon area where he found his favorite cook in a kitchen at Medicine Bow. Like many other men, who had been free to roam where-ever they wished, Bill married Stimpson and settled down on the ranch he homesteaded on the upper Medicine Bow river.

Stimpson worked as hard as her husband on the ranch. Together they dug irrigation ditches, cleared the land and built fences. They raised three sons, Tom, Ted and Willing. The Richardsons became successful ranchers.

NOTES ON STIMPSON

Richardson said about his wife, Stimpson, "She was not afraid of God, Man, or the Devil" . . . She proved it on many occasions.

. . . .

There were bad feelings between the Richardsons and their neighbor, Josh Widdowfield. It showed up often. On one occasion Richardson had a contract with the Union Pacific Coal Company in Carbon to deliver hay to them for their horses and mules which moved cars in the mine. Josh swore he would kill anyone who attempted to haul the hay across his land.

Stimpson had a hired man drive her through the fence toward Carbon with a load of hay. She sat on the wagon seat with a shotgun plainly in sight on her lap. Those who saw the gun knew she would use it. Stimpson completed the delivery of hay to Carbon.

. . . .

Sue Mangan remembers that Stimpson rode side-saddle on the open range. Her ample skirts covered half of her mount. Often when she arrived back at the ranch she would release an unbranded newborn calf from under her skirts. The relatives were amused that the calf was the only animal which had a mule for a mother.

. . . .

Apparently, Grandma Stimpson had charm which also influenced another man who ate her meals. His name was Stryker. He built his own mortuary in Laramie. It still bears his name. With no charge, Stimpson was buried in style on her last trip to Laramie.

TWO OLD CARBONITES WHO STAYED

Only two early bachelors continued to live in Carbon and never moved away when the mines closed. They did not work in the mines. Rather they lived off the land. I presume that they trapped, hunted and also traded with the Indians before coal entered the picture. Still, Nels Sargent and Hugo Miller failed to communicate with one another.

My grandfather Martin Stebner, who had been Carbon's blacksmith, often visited each of them separately. On a trip following the death of my father, granddad Martin Stebner invited me and a pal to ride with him to Carbon where he spent time with each of the two friends. Tom Rodda and I sat on the single seat with Martin as we traveled twelve miles to Carbon. My dad's horse, Old Joe, trotted along pulling the little hunting cart Bruno built.

Martin spent time with each of them in their dug-out houses. While he was there Tom and I had a great day playing in the old remaining buildings. In the broken down Milliken dance hall and saloon we found gambling cards and poker chips in the basement. There were whiskey bottles and other memorabilia we should have saved, but did not realize that they were history.

We also found the remains of a building which must have been a photographer's home or office. In one corner there was a mass of glass negatives, which in themselves recorded the history of Carbon. Now I know we should have saved those plates. We could see clear images as we held them to the sky. They showed images of the photographer's customers. Tom and I were too immature to understand the damage we were doing as we ran up and down a pile in the corner of a room to hear the glass crackle. We broke hundreds of them.

Hugo Miller was then an old man who had been in the area for many years even before there was a city of Carbon. Years after our visit with him, before my grandpa Martin died, Uncle Adolph kept in touch with Miller. The transportation changed because Adolph drove one of Hanna's first automobiles from Hanna to Carbon to visit with Miller. Before Hugo died he gave Adolph most of his prized possessions. Now I have one item from it--a hand made wooden box which contains a few arrow heads and other interesting things. This I am saving for my only grandson, Danny.

My grandfather drove me to Carbon when I was about seven years old. There the dance hall and bar were standing, as were a few other dilapidated structures.

Coffee John's Restaurant and Bar in Old Carbon.

Early Carbon

THE GERMAN FAMILY

Dear Dan:

The Stebner family probably arrived in America in the early 1880s. They had relatives somewhere in the state of New York who were their contact. Stebner is an unusual name, although I found a barber and his son in Powell, Wyoming. There is a street named Stebner in Duluth, Minnesota. There are a few, and they could be considered Polish in Chicago, Illinois. Those were the only contacts I had until I heard from a man by the name of 'Dan Stebner' in California. He has made many contacts with people named Stebner. None of these have any proven relationship. I talked to those in Powell, and played golf with the old granddad. He and his son were fine people.

The Polish relationship makes sense, although the name Stebner, ending "er" is definitely German. The history of Germany and Poland is often mixed because the borders changed following the wars which have always plagued that area--sometimes a town is German, and later becomes Polish. I know our Stebners came from Posnen, Germany, but since WW-II it is now in Poland.

In a book authored by James A. Michener, called 'Poland', we can understand that some Germans were settled there. My wife, Mary, and I had the pleasure of meeting Michener at Chesapeake Bay, and again in our house when he was in Laramie as he dedicated our new library. We had a cocktail party for him and his interesting wife.

Martin Stebner, after whom I was named was the oldest Stebner I ever knew. He was an imposing figure being severe, militaristic, and a disciplinarian. He had a full beard and I doubt that he ever smiled. Still, his wife Amelia was the type of a grandmother any child would appreciate. Any gentleness and kindness that ever came to our genes on that side of the family must have been from her, and the harsher and tougher part had to come from Martin.

When I was only four or five years old I sat on Martin's lap, and I foolishly pulled his beard. My grandfather then pulled my hair vigorously to let me know how it felt. I was sure I never bothered the old man again.

Martin's sons told a story how he lost a finger which he smashed in the Hanna blacksmith shop. They took him to the young doctor's office with the bone exposed. Martin made the physician's job easier when he took the bone shears from the fumbling doctor, in his other hand, and cut his own finger off. Then he let the doctor bandage it up and went back to work.

Martin was not a laborer who worked in the mine. He had a most respected position as a blacksmith. In those days blacksmiths were the highest rated of the uneducated class. They were much in demand and could do anything with metal that was needed in those days. They could shoe a horse (that was before the automobile) repair a wagon, fix a rail, and in general build anything made of metal.

Martin was an early first blacksmith in old Carbon. He taught his sons many of his talents. All could work well with their hands. At first they worked down in the mines, but soon their experience and talent brought them to the surface where they would work in the sunlight.

Martin Stebner, as a 28 year-old blacksmith fought in the Franco-Prussian War in 1870 and 1871. They needed blacksmiths to repair the wagons, gun carriages, shoe the horses, and generally work with metal. He was born in 1842 and died in 1915. I wish I could have been older so he could tell me the war stories of his day. My Uncle Sharrer, a German who could speak the language, often visited with Martin, and he told me of a conversation he had with the old man. He said that during the campaign against the French Army he remembered a critical incident. And Sharrer passed the experience on to me.

Martin's unit was invading France. As the Germans advanced they entered a heavily wooded area. There was suddenly an eerie atmosphere. The birds, squirrels, and other forest animals were quiet or had disappeared. This warned the Germans that the French forces were close by waiting in ambush. They silently withdrew and formed a flanking attack around the waiting French, who themselves were surprised as artillery and rifle shots decimated the foe from both sides. Germans won that battle, and ultimately the War.

I am sure that the Stebner family was fed up with the European wars and came here to give their kids a better break.

. . . .

Martin's sons, as tradition suggested, were taught to do skilled labor. Their hands were talented. When I was in high school I wondered if perhaps I could work with my hands in dentistry. The genes must have been there, but unfortunately I had no father to teach me

My dad Bruno was called to repair one of the first cars that drove from New York to San Francisco. Then the Lincoln Highway was only a single dirt road which had a lot of rocks and high centers which were hazards. The car developed a leaky radiator. Bruno soldered the damage to hold water and the car drove on west.

. . . .

The Stebner daughters inherited their mother's talents and training to be wonderful cooks. All of my own children remember Aunt Tillie, who came to Laramie each Thanksgiving. Her mother, Amelia, taught her how to cook a great turkey dinner. She baked a big bird, which she called "Old Oscar." Her potato dumplings and dressing were something wonderful to be thankful for each holiday. Aunt Tillie Sharrer was a loving person we remember each Thanksgiving. Yes, we call our turkey "Old Oscar."

The Stebner family in Carbon in 1888 were Tillie, Max, Fritz, Bruno, Adolph and Martha standing. Seated are Martin and Amelia.

THE PRUSSIANS

There was a place for my grandfather on the estate of German-Prussia. Or should we say 'Polish' estate? Since reading James Michener's book POLAND-- that is where Posnen was then located. German nobility moved east into Poland. There he met little Amelia who worked in the kitchen, and Martin Stebner was a blacksmith, when they were married. My grandparents like many other Europeans, were tired of endless wars on the continent. With the Martin Stebner family they decided to leave Europe and make their home in America. After a short stay with relatives in New York, Martin learned about the need for workmen in the new town of Carbon, Wyoming. They rode on a new railroad, the Union Pacific, westward!

Once, when working at the dental chair for a good friend of mine I lead with my chin when I mentioned that my grandfather was a blacksmith. I guess he had just undergone a little rough treatment: he said, "Sure, Charlie, I can believe that."

Tradition of a family preserves our history. A wise man once said, "Tradition is to Human Beings, is what instinct is to animals." Often times we have trouble in separating tradition from heredity. If one has a weakness in a family which suffers from heart attacks, then that individual must work harder to improve his condition. Perhaps, favorable inherited talents might become a beneficial family tradition.

In the original Stebner family there were eight people. This was not considered a big group in those days. There were good reasons for large families. Manpower was essential, especially before the Industrial Revolution in Europe--more than one paycheck was needed. The other reasons for large families were the lack of birth control and religion. Earlier generations were heavy on religion and naive on birth control.

Now families are smaller and that is good. Man could easily over populate the world. Today we are concerned with the hunger in Africa. Large families have been traditional in Central and South America. The same is true in India and China. Control of the family size in China is controlled by the government. In the future you will see a trend in this direction. It is a must!

. . . .

Max was born in 1878 and he was the shortest of the group and was never married. I had little contact with him because he traveled to other mining towns in the state. Max was always changing jobs. I guess we would classify him as an introvert.

My Dad, Bruno, must have been about 12 or 14 years old when he worked as a 'sprag boy' in the Carbon mine. It was a most dangerous job because he had to push heavy wooden spikes between the running wheels of moving mine cars to work as a brake. Many sprag boys lost arms, hands or fingers between the wheels of running mine cars. It was not long before he worked himself up to a job above the mine.

INGE

This morning I went to the hospital to have my good friend Dr. Larry Greene cut out a few warts, or moles, from my face and back. We call them lesions. They were not bothering me, but every time I shaved I was aware of them. So, I decided that they should be in a placed in a bottle and sent to the pathologist for a scientific diagnosis. Often times they are ignored or burned off. This could be a gamble. I walked into the surgical room, and in an hour later I was finished. The next day I was informed the lesion was benign.

Now, I will tell you about Inge who assisted in the operation. She is an excellent surgical nurse who came to Laramie from Germany. While she and Doctor Green were working on my face, she told me a story about our name 'Stebner.' She said:

"Vell, zo yur name iss Shtebener? Yhu know daats Cherman!" I answered affirmatively and Inge continued, saying that in Germany she once dated a young man named Stebner, and went on to say . . . "Py Got gott he zas the stingest guy I effer saw!. Vonce he took me to da show, and maype to a dunce or something pefore. He vas nice lookin und sossiable und vas boilite tooo! Put like I sed he was tite vit his mooney. Ven we vas at tu show vindow he unley pout his own ticket. None for me, because he was too tite. Yu vont pelive it, put I ad to puy mine own ticket! You know, Tocter Stebbener, dat was delast tate I had vit yer relative!"

Well, Dan, some day you may someday travel to Germany, but don't look up anyone just because his name is Stebner. He will not entertain you quite as well as my mother's family treated us in England. They were much like my Mary Ford--generous to a fault! But, Danny, his name could really be Scrooge Stebner. He could be rich, but I doubt he would be generous. Take you own travel checks with you because he could insist you buy your own meal.

THE STEBNERS LEAVE CARBON

In 1900 the mines were closed in Carbon. Then most of the people moved to Hanna, which was only 16 miles away. There were a few early Carbonites who chose other areas and the Stebner family decided to move to the mines in Cambria, which was in eastern Wyoming near Newcastle. They were there for only a few years--long enough to miss the explosion of the Number One mine of Hanna. Again they decided to make their home in Carbon County.

About that time the Charles Hughes family left Liverpool, England, enroute to Hanna. Charles' brother, William, was established in Hanna and wrote to England encouraging Charles to follow him because the Union Pacific needed experienced miners from Europe. Charles was assured of a job in this new mining town. It was important to get out of the oppressing, unpleasant life of Lancashire. The wages were better and the working conditions were improved. Especially in Wyoming there was more freedom from the oppression of the working man in England.

. . . .

You cannot strengthen the weak
by weakening the strong.
You cannot help the wage earner
by pulling down the wage payer.
You cannot further the brotherhood of men
by encouraging class hatred.
You cannot help the poor
by discouraging the rich.
You cannot build character and courage
by taking away a man's initiative
and independence.

A. Lincoln

1903 Mine Explosion

1903 MINE EXPLOSION

Dear Dan:

In 1903, after the new Hanna No. 1 mine had operated, for only three or four years, there was a tragic accident. Here I quote a few lines from a "HISTORY OF UNION PACIFIC COAL MINES". . 1868-1940.

"Mine No. One was a pathetic story of grief for the company, its employees and their families. Work was progressing as usual on June 30, 1903, with no warning of the horrible catastrophe that was almost upon them. At ten o'clock in the morning people outside the mine heard an ear-splitting crash, which has been described as sounding like the explosion of a heavy charge of dynamite in rock. Timber, masonry, and earth, coal and rock were catapulted from the two portals of the mine. Heavy smoke poured out into the air.

"Rescue crews sped into the mine as quickly as they could be organized, but the inner workings had been caved in badly and soon, with the pumps stopped, water began to rise in the lower reaches of the mine. It was revealed that one hundred and sixty-nine men had been killed, including John Battle, the Foreman. It was not until the following November that the last caved-in workings had been uncovered and the last body removed. Early in 1904 the mine was reopened."

Dan, that paragraph leaves me stunned and cold. I realize the quote in the coal company history is too brief for those who lost their family workers, but not enough for me. In this small town of less than a thousand people nearly every family lost many men in a single day. John Battle, the foreman, was one of the 169. I think of the husbands and sons all of whom had families that grieved and suffered economically, with little or no money.

It is unfortunate but they seemed to be considered expendable, and I suppose they were, because there were more needy men still left in foreign lands who could easily replace them. Only for a short time the mine was not operating. As soon as the bodies were removed the mine was again produced coal.

Old Carbon Dies

OLD CARBON DIES--HANNA IS BORN

Dear Dan:

The coal mines in Old Carbon were closed by the Union Pacific in 1900 because a better seam of coal was found in the area which became Hanna. There were two reasons for this. The railroad bed could be shortened in an area of less snow, and the thickness of the seam of coal and its quality were better sixteen miles northwest.

The new railroad bed would be directed to Hanna on the way to Rawlins. Previously, at Carbon there was better access to the wood near Elk Mountain, which at an earlier time was important to the Union Pacific. The importance of Hanna coal was a factor.

MARCUS ALONZO HANNA

Marcus Alonzo Hanna was a political giant. Records show him as a leader of the Conservative branch of the Republican Party in Washington D.C. Hanna was a Senator from Ohio and considered as a possible Presidential candidate. His prominence suggested the name, Hanna, to the Union Pacific Railroad built the new mining town. Marcus operated coal and iron mines and was known for solving capital and labor problems.

Mary Comes to Hanna

LITTLE MARY COMES TO HANNA

Dear Dan:

When Little Mary Hughes was about 14, in 1904, she arrived in Wyoming. It was a disturbing moment for Little Mary to leave the only world she ever had known to venture so far from the home she knew so well. She was timid and insecure and had cousins and a few aunts and uncles with whom she was comfortable- -and, especially her Church! English nobility came to America for the adventure. They read of Indians, Cowboys and wild animals. Few Lancashire coal miners could even read about glamour in America.

Leaving her cousins was devastating to Little Mary. To leave her mother's grave, her cousins, and the Methodist Church must have shaken her foundation. Her father, Charles Hughes was promised a good job which was an improvement of the conditions he suffered in Lancashire. Charles wanted a better life for his two children.

There was another problem that they had to face. Charles had promised his deceased wife that he would assume the responsibility of moving three of mother's male cousins from an orphan's home in Lancashire. Their parents died when they were very young children. He kept his promise and also brought the Mellor boys along with his own son and daughter to America.

Mother told me of the day they left the train to board British ship, the LUCANIA, in Liverpool, that she was ashamed to say "good-bye" to her cousins who came to see them to start their long journey. Mary hid around every possible obstacle so they could not see her cry.

One man with five young children must have been an odd sight, and probably made many of the other passengers wonder. Their luggage was meager. They had only a few family mementos precious enough to carry.

The Hughes family quarters were in "steerage," which was at the bottom of the ship where the mechanical equipment is housed. For Little Mary the ship, which traveled about six days, was an arduous experience. She suffered sea-sickness the entire voyage, and became so ill that another English family took her into their better accommodations the last part of the voyage. All of her life thereafter she was plagued with motion sickness. Only in her later years could she even ride in the back seat of an automobile. She conquered this when she learned to drive her own little red Plymouth automobile.

I do not know how long I'll live,
but while I live, Lord let me give.

Some comfort to some one in need
by smile or nod--kind word--or deed.

And let me do whatever I can,
To ease things for my fellow man.

I want naught, but to do my part
to lift a tired weary heart.

To change folks frown to smile again,
Then I will not have lived in vain.

And I'll not care how long I'll live,
If I can give--and give and give.

MARY ON THE SHIP

The boat trip from Liverpool to New York was unlike anything you, Danny, will ever know. The experience of Little Mary was arduous and long. She suffered sea-sickness the entire voyage, then another couple who had a cabin moved her into their quarters because they were sorry for the young girl.

The ship, named 'LUCANIA' was at sea six days before it reached New York, much less time than the cruise ships which are common today. They were assigned to an area called 'steerage', in the bottom of the ship where the mechanics of steering takes place. Breeding cattle shipped from England could have shared the same area. Certainly there were no port-holes for them to see the sunshine or rain at that level. Mother was so ill these conditions didn't matter.

There must also have been lice and other vermin in the hold of that ship. When my Mother arrived in Hanna her Aunt Alice, Uncle Bill's wife, burned all of her clothes which she wore on the trip, and she also cut all the hair from her body to eliminate the lice which infested her. Her bald head did not help the appearance that scrawny little girl who could not have weighed more than 90 pounds.

In any energy based economy like Hanna's there are booms and busts. Communities grow rapidly and finally end up as ghost towns. The boom was on in the last part of 1800's and the early part of the 1900's when my two Grandparents arrived in this country.

New small, four-room houses were being built rapidly near the first mine. It's hard to imagine the thoughts that must have gone through their heads as they slept under the same roof for the first time in the USA. For a while the three boy cousins stayed with Charles, Mary and her brother John.

HOUSES IN HANNA

When Charles Hughes, my grandfather arrived in One Town there were three or four rows of identical houses, but they were all numbered so that the tenants could tell them apart. Ours was the seventh house in the first long row facing the railroad track. The number was No. 77! I presume that there were about 60 other houses there. Later more homes were built behind them so there were five or six rows. To the rear of the house was an with outdoor toilet which was over a large pit to contain the refuse.

The photo taken in the 1920's records Hanna north of the railroad tracks. The largest two-story building toward the west is the Hanna Hotel where Mary and Ford served boarders. This was my home until my graduation from high school in 1927. A row of miners houses were moved from One Town now runs north toward the hills. The smaller four-room houses have added additional space to serve as a kitchen and bathroom.

There was no indoor water supply, but we carried buckets of water from a faucet sticking out of the ground near the toilet. Here residents of several homes would carry their water to their rented houses. I believe that each tenant paid the coal company about twelve dollars each month rent, which was deducted from their paychecks. This did not include the coal we burned for heat and cooking--this cost each home about $2.50 for a ton.

Soon after, Mary and her dad, and her younger brother John, were settled in their new home. The older Mellor boys were hired to work outside the mines and on neighboring ranches. That was a better life than being in the orphan home in England. Charles Hughes and Little Mary cooked for the expanded family. At first there was little cash. But they charged the bare necessities from the UP store. The expenses were deducted along with their rent from payroll checks by the company. What was left purchased a few clothes from the Sears-Roebuck and Montgomery Ward catalogues. As meager as this was it was a great improvement from what they had known in England.

For about three years all went well for the Hughes family. With the mining experience of Charles, he was valuable to the Coal Company between 1904 and 1908. Uncle John, was enrolled in the Hanna Schools system which terminated at the eighth grade. The Mellor boys worked on ranches for their board and room, and later in the mines.

. . . .

Forcing one's will on someone who is incapable of resisting may be to deny that person his free will, and even his freedom. And, Freedom is the most precious right of a man! *CMS*

ETTIE D. HALASEY

(This was written by Etta Halasey in June, 1986--She was the eldest daughter of Sue Mangan. Etta often listened to Sue and Mary talk of Hanna and their past and she furnished the following information.)

. . . .

"Sue lost a thumb as a child in England. It was wrapped too tightly with a bandage by her older sister. This bandage stopped the circulation, and the thumb dropped like a burnt stick." (CMS . . Visitors to Sue's home discouraged their very young children from sucking their thumbs. Sue cautioned them by showing them her stub, and telling the child that the habit was the cause.) Sue was sponsored to America by her uncle, Bill Richardson. He also brought the Watson family to Elk Mountain, Wyoming. Mary Ford and Sue Mangan were great friends who often visited in Laramie and in their homes. Mary's father and Sue's husband were killed in the mine explosion at Hanna in 1908.)

"Mary had to miss a lot of school trying to do the work at home. School was a must for children but often she was tardy or absent. Then she was punished with some stinging wacks on the hand with a stick."

"After the explosion, the UP Coal Company told Mary to get what staples she needed at the company store. She was not much more than a child herself, so her brother John and Jack Mellor accepted the invitation and found a treat they liked, called "Mother's Cookies." Also, they had other treats they seldom enjoyed previously. The company did not consider desserts as necessary staples. When the statement came at the end of the month the kids were charged for the desserts.

"A few months after the explosion the company suggested to Mary that she give up her house and move a mile to Three Town. Mary refused and then the company began to charge her rent for their present home. This cost Mary twelve dollars a month, which she could hardly afford."

FINANCING THEIR PASSAGE

I do not know how my family financed their passage across the Atlantic, but there were several ways this could be done. Charles Hughes might have planned and saved for the passage. This does not seem possible because their income was so inadequate. Labor troubles in England often prevented them from planning steady work and regular paychecks. There were frequent strikes and lockouts. The first was brought about by the workers who were doing their best to organize unions. The second was a technique of the mine owners who would lock-up the mines when they had plenty of coal in reserve. This kept the workers lean and hungry so that they would be more subservient.

Mary Ford's father, and perhaps all of his brothers, were non-drinkers because of their nature and their church. Mary's Uncle Bill and Aunt Alice were devout Methodists. Uncle Bill was a foreman in one of the Hanna mines. They saved their money. It is possible that he helped Charles finance the tickets for his brother and the five children he brought to Hanna.

Many Europeans came to Hanna because they were recruited by the Union Pacific. Some might have paid that debt from paychecks they later earned. There was an enterprising Englishman from Lancashire by the name of Sam Dickinson who came here earlier. I knew him well because he owned the only store in Hanna that wasn't operated by the Coal Company. It was a small place right on the main street of the town and I guess we could say it was a dry-goods store which sold sewing material, a few dolls and trinkets, that were not available elsewhere.

Sam Dickinson was a special man for the Union Pacific. It was rare that anyone could do business in Hanna, but he had a small store which the UP permitted. He had contacts in Lancashire and recruited English miners. He would finance their passage which they would repay with interest.

I don't know how the Finlanders, Greeks, and Italians financed their passage. There were others who came to Hanna from their native lands, but it is obvious that the Union Pacific was the ultimate source. For the most part the railroad did recruit many of them, but there were exceptions. Some were personally dedicated to be leaving their native land and find their way in this free country.

VARVANDAKIS

One was Anthony N. Varvandakis who eventually came to Hanna on his own. He borrowed money from relatives for his passage, but ultimately paid it back. He was not a mainland Greek, but was proud to be known as a native of Crete. He was a career soldier who fought in the Balkan wars of 1914-1919, where he lost an eye in combat. Much like my grandfather Stebner, he had enough of European wars. No doubt he wanted something better for his children--FREEDOM! He simply wanted to become a USA citizen and he accomplished that ambition. After various locations and jobs he came to Hanna and invited his childhood bride to join him. They raised their children in Wyoming and today his daughter, Mrs. Edgar (Peggy) Smith is proud of his struggles and determination.

. . . .

Consider that your life is divided into three areas. So if you will live to be 90 years old, give the first 30 years to education and travel. Perhaps, the next 30 to your work, and enjoy the last third for retirement doing something useful.

CMS

Mary's Family

MY GRANDFATHER'S GENES

Dear Dan:

In Europe before 1850 the life of uneducated people was dismal. At birth they were guided to serve nobility. Poor people were stifled to keep them from getting an education. During the many wars they served as soldiers and often were cannon fodder. In peace times they worked for very minimal wages.

During the beginning of the Industrial Revolution, which began slowly in the early 1700's, water power was used in unique situations, but this was rare and undependable. More often both men and women were needed to produce industrial products.

James Watt, a young Scottish engineer, began experiments while he studied the Newcomen steam engine during 1764. The idea was good, but the engine was inefficient. In 1769 Watt patented the forerunner of the modern steam engine, and the Industrial Revolution became a reality.

The mining of coal to produce steam was a top priority. This allowed many agricultural laborers to leave the fields and work for wages in industrial plants. Even though wages were meager they had taken a major step in society. They were no longer serfs!

England led the Industrial Revolution because she had the coal and a world market. My mother's grand father, Job Hughes, left his home in Wales to seek work in the Lancashire coal fields. One wonders why teen- age boy would leave home. Perhaps his genes demanded an adventurous change. He gambled on the unknown rather than to exist in a secure environment. So my similarly adventurous grandfathers of both England and Germany gambled to leave Europe to seek a better life in Old Carbon.

MARY FORD RETURNS TO ENGLAND

Soon after World War Two, Mary had another adventuous experience. She rode an airplane to England! There she renewed acquaintances with friends of her aunts and cousins. It was a most beneficial experience for all of the family. For many years Mary was a faithful correspondent to her English family--especially to a cousin, Hilda. Before she returned to Hanna she and Hilda spent time in London and Paris. It was an adventure for both of them.

Mary Ford's experience with the various modes of transportation covered every phase during her 93 years. Before she left England at the age of fifteen she simply walked everywhere. Then, she came by ship, in her own little cloggers and a pair of buttoned shoes. Later, when she married my Dad, she saw much of the area around Hanna riding with a horse and buggy which he owned. Of course, she rode the Union Pacific passenger train from New York to Wyoming. Following my father's death we had automobiles at the hotel, and she drove her own little bright red Plymouth around the state. Certainly, flying to England in a transport plane was much easier than the big ship across the Atlantic. Finally, mother saw our astronauts on the moon. If she had the chance, she would have volunteered to be part of the crew.

She left the Hanna Hotel in good hands and flew by air to the place of her English birth. When she arrived in New York she remembered the day her father brought her to the 'Land of Opportunity'. Then she was a scrawny fifteen year-old, unhappy, undernourished frightened girl at Ellis Island. But, this time it was different. Now, leaving for England, Mary was a confident, capable, and well-dressed lady.

Her cousin, Hilda, with whom she had faithfully corresponded for 69 years, and various others of the family met her at the train in Wigan. They treated her as though she were Royalty! In her childhood Mary only knew one town, Crawford Village, where she was born in 1890. It is a small coal mining town a mile or two from Wigan. Later

Hilda and Mary visited both London and Paris. It was a thrill for a woman who knew no other European place than the mining town in which she was born.

. . . .

Mary Ford visited the school she was privileged to attend for only two years. At that point in her childhood she took her mother's place in the home--she became her mother's nurse and housekeeper for her father and her little brother John.

When my wife, Mary, and I went to England we were met by Bryan Hughes. After a dinner in his home we saw his sister Nora and their retired parents. Then, Bryan and Nora drove us around the area of Wigan. We saw the house where mother was born and lived until she came to America. And we learned that during the last several generations Bryan was the first of the family who refused to work in the coal mines. Rather, he drove a bus for the city and this made him an excellent guide. We discovered a great deal of my mother's early days in England.

We wanted to find the grave of my greatgrandmother. It was a great disappointment not to find the headstone, but learned it had been destroyed by young vandals. I was especially interested in other old graves. There were two bodies buried together--a 27 year-old father who died in a mine accident. With him was his nine year-old son who worked with him. I was shocked to learn that fathers and their young sons worked together. This was a common practice because of insufficient income in a family.

Bryan had a great sense of humor, and told us many stories. Some we could not understand because of his heavy Lancashire dialect. Years later, Bryan and Nora came to visit Mary Ford in Laramie. There he told us ribald Lanky stories and he sang rare miner songs. Nora was timid in comparison.

CHARLIE AND MARY IN LANCASHIRE

When your grandmother and I were on a trip to England we rode a train to Wigan, Lancashire. Only a mile from there was a little mining town in which my mother was born. She lived there the first 14 years of her life.

We rode the train from London to Wigan and checked into the quaint Queen Ann hotel. We called Bryan Hughes, a second cousin of my mother. We soon learned that Bryan was dedicated to the history of mother's family, and fascinated with Mary Hughes Stebner Ford. He had met her when she went to England several years before.

We had dinner in his home where we met his sister, Nora, and their parents. Bryan and Nora drove us around Wigan and the surrounding area. We saw the house in which my Mother was born, and she lived there until she came to America.

Bryan was the first member of several generations of Hugheses who did not work in the coal mines. His job was driving a bus for the city of Wigan, and this made him an excellent guide. Bryan was considerably younger than I but had never been far from his home, but he had carefully researched the Hughes family.

Through Bryan we learned that the original Job Hughes was born in 1834 at Wellington, Shropshire Wales. In 1846 Job came to Lancashire and married Louisa Seymour. He worked as a coal miner in Staffordshire. Six sons were produced from this marriage, four of them born in West Bromwich.

Bryan and Nora came to the United States to visit my cousin Gordon Hughes in North Carolina. Then, of course, they came to Laramie to see Mary Ford. I took them to the Elk Mountain area and along the road we saw some pumping oil wells. I said that we had some oil in the area. He said, "We've got some of 'em in Hingland--we call 'em bluddy nodin' donkies."

THE HUGHES FAMILY HISTORY

Bryan researched the Hughes family history, which began with Job Hughes the First, born in 1834 at Wellington, Shropshire, Wales. In 1847 he married Louisa Seymour. Job was working as a Coal Miner in Strafffordshire. Six sons were born to this marriage, four of them born in West Bromwich. Charles Hughes, my grandfather, was born during 1859. Then came Job in 1862, William in 1864, and John in 1867.

It was a period of unrest among the working class, at the time of the European Industrial

Revolution. Strikes and job lockouts caused Job to move his family back to Cefn Mawr Wales where he had previously worked in the mines during 1869.

My grandfather, Charles, was only ten years old, but he and his younger brother Job, also worked with their Father in the mines. They remained there until 1878. The wages of the father was insufficient to care for a family, so it was necessary for his children to work with him. At that time the Cefn miners were the poorest paid, and often treated brutally by the pit owners.

The family attempted to improve their luck by moving to the Wigan coal fields in 1878. Then the two older sons were working in the mines with their father. They were not men, but mere boys. Although they worked more than ten hours a day in a six day work week, even then the family was still exceedingly poor.

The education of the miners' sons and daughters was meager. Until they were eight or ten years old they were listed as "scholars". But soon their title became "miners" and they suffered the same fate as did their fathers.

My grandfather Charles Hughes, was one of these young boys who survived the mines of England. There was no such thing as child-labor laws in those days. Often a few women and young males worked in the mines. Bryan's mother showed us pictures of herself working on the tipple where she emptied smaller mining cars into larger cars.

The home in which my mother was born and where she lived during her early years was solidly built in red brick, and attached on either side by identical structures where other families lived. There was no plumbing nor central heating and the stoves for cooking and heat burned coal.

My mother often spoke of her own mother, Sarah Annie Britles, who married Charles Hughes. Sarah was constantly in poor health so her daughter was forced to leave school after two or three years. Her father needed the child Mary at home. Legally, an excuse was necessary to get her out of school. He arranged for a doctor's certificate which suggested Mary had weak eyes. (Yet, when she died at the age of 93 she could read without glasses). In England she became a "housewife" for the men, and a nurse for her fragile mother. It seems that schooling for a girl was considered to be a waste of time.

Sarah's real pleasure was her own daughter. They called her "Little Mary", and that name followed her to Hanna. Her Mother was pleased to have her home from school, saying, "Now, I have my own little nurse who will take care of me from now on." I am not sure of her illness but surmise it was tuberculosis, which was common in England at that time. Her death certificate mentions inflammation of the bowel, and could have even been appendicitis. In the mining community medical attention was very poor. She died when Mary was about thirteen years old. The young girl was now challenged to be full time housewife.

"Little Mary", a name her family bestowed on her which followed her when she moved to Wyoming, had a somber and unexciting childhood. Dinner had to be ready when the men arrived in the late afternoon. Meals were plain and meager, and what little she learned about cooking came from her dad's instruction. But Little Mary took her lot seriously and she was dependable. She did what was expected of the oldest and only daughter, and became a full time maid and cook. It was a form of servitude, without pay, but she accepted it.

All of this little girl's clothes were dark and heavy--nothing bright or pretty and certainly nothing with frills. When new clothing was urgently needed, her father took her shopping. He would hold the garment up to the sun, and if he could see any light he would not buy them. He wanted them to wear like iron. Little Mary's clothes were also purchased too large so that she could wear them for several years. Family photographs show her in the thick and practical clothes. She looked like an old fashioned lady. Perhaps this explains why, in later life, she chose bright and fluffy dresses.

The earliest picture of Mary Hughes, as a young infant in her mother's arms along with a proud father. This was in England during the 1880's.

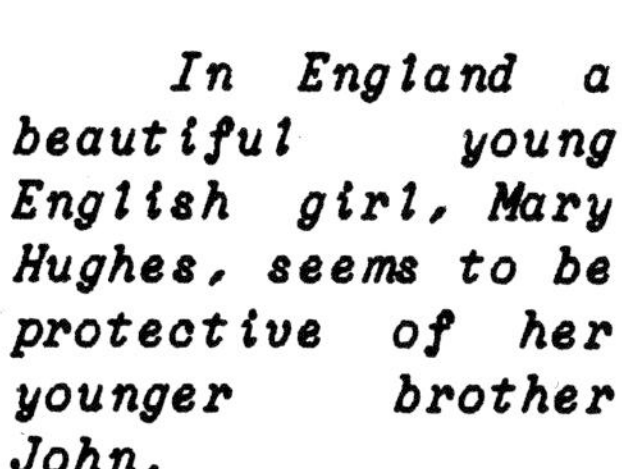

In England a beautiful young English girl, Mary Hughes, seems to be protective of her younger brother John.

Funerals in England, and those who mourned the death, were photographed with many relatives and close friends. The 15 year-old Mary Hughes is shown in black mourner clothes. She sits between two aunts (who wore lighter colors). Behind her was her tall father on the porch of their rented stone home. Her younger brother John, is the youngest boy on a small chair near an aunt. The three Mellor cousins are on the opposite side of the front line. Two kneel on

My mother remembered a fancy doll which was given to her. It was considered too beautiful to play with and was kept under a glass bowl for protection. Often, against all rules, she would sneak it out when her father was in the mine and Uncle John was in school. For a short and precious time Mary would carefully remove the protective glass and hold and talk to her doll. She carefully put it under the glass cover before anyone came home.

Her only social life was her church and she enjoyed every minute of it. As she grew older it is easy to understand why the Methodist church meant so much to her. It was the only time that she was able to be with children her age.

In England we know that Little Mary had her hands full with her ill mother and hard working father and her little brother John. That would have been enough but she still had a problem with her grandfather Job. He lived next door. He was the original leader of the Hughes clan. Even with his hard life of drinking and working it allowed him to live beyond the age of 72, and it was done in reasonable comfort, while his six sons worked and even died in the mines. Old Job seems to have retired rather early and demanded much attention. Most of his sons and families were devout Methodists and they gave their musical talents to their communities and church. Apparently old Job did not share their dedication.

Mother once told me this story: "I had a difficult chore every day for grandpa. He insisted that I go to the saloon and fetch him his daily bucket of beer. With the old lunch pail that he used to carry into the mine, and a small coin in it, he sent me on my way." Perhaps her destination was the Dull Pick Saloon, which was near her home. (It was called the Dull Pick because it was also near a blacksmith shop where miners brought their dull picks to be sharpened. And while that operation was performed on their picks they would enter the saloon, also feeling the need to sharpen their senses of humor and the dulled spirits which came from ten hours picking coal!)

Little Mary might be considered an early "feminist!" She resisted the demands of her chauvinistic grandfather, for in her Methodist

Sunday School she was enlisted in a group (I believe it was called "JACOBEANS") which was apparently a temperance organization. They, with other groups, would parade through the mining area on Sundays with drums and other band instruments. (In fact, when your grandmother and I were in England, we observed just such a meager parade.) No doubt the Jacobeans encouraged little Mary to avoid the saloon. Old Job ranted and swore about the Jacobeans until he died because Mary would no longer fetch him his daily beer.

Little Mary, ever since her earliest childhood days until she died at age ninety-three, worked and loved her church and the God she believed in.

THE MINERS' WIVES

Today, we read and hear much about the many problems wives suffer from battering husbands, especially when they are drinking. It shocks our younger generations but I assure you that it is nothing new, especially in the last generations of working people in England. Yes, and even in Hanna!

Women had a tough life. It was expected that they bear children, cook, wash the clothes and be subjective to their husbands. The men were free to drink and fight with one another, because they worked in such difficult surroundings, and anything they did was excusable. . . A song they sang said this . . .

The miner he is strong and bold.
A gallant toiler is he;
He toils in dark chambers in the earth's hold
And do ye grudge his fee?
He toils hard where he can't stand,
And danger is no stay;
But death and danger is at every hand,
And do ye grudge his pay?

Raymond Challinor notes that the miners have neither the time nor inclination for change. Their main pastime appears to have been drinking, often heavy drinking. Mine owners complained that alcohol resulted in a high absentee rate, and even some of them stumbled to work. They relaxed with games like whipper-racing and cock-fighting. In public houses with the heavy drinking, "young courting couples were invited to parade in front of the assembled drinkers, running a gauntlet of ribald comment. The customary prize for the most attractive girl was a pint of rum and a sixpenny pasty while the ugliest female competitor received a pound of black pudding."

Also 'purring' was a game of football without the ball, and here is Challinor's explanation..."It is all up and down fighting here. They fought quite naked, excepting their cloggers. (Cloggers were shoes carved out of wood, and they had metal pieces over the toes and on the soles, much like mule shoes.) When one has the other down on the ground, he first endeavors to choke him by squeezing his throat, then he kicks him on the head with his cloggers. Sometimes they are very severely injured." Like boxing it was done for money, and often the loser was killed.

News items from surrounding Lancashire towns on 'purring' are reported..."A collier kicked a woman to death. Received five years penal servitude. . .A man kicked to death by his workmates. . .Sixty-year-old woman kicked to death by her husband, who had been drinking. . .Three men attacked a fourth, kicking out his teeth. . .A man 'purred' for the price of a quart. He was also turned upside down, and two shillings and an eight pence stolen. . A six-year-old child kicked and paralyzed in the leg. . .

When 'purring' was questioned a defender of the sport argued, "The clog is the traditional Lancashire method of duelling". And it was compared to be "less dangerous than other forms of duelling, as was my Lord Tom Noddy's pistol or sword." Some felt that it was as honorable as the duel of the aristocrats. I guess all strata of each society must endure what other people consider fun.

Discipline in the family was autocratic. The man was the head of the house and his decisions were final. No doubt, the wife could cleverly intervene for her children and be a quiet influence, but the children never argued with the old man. We seldom see the happy kids such as we have today. Especially in their rare family photos when they hired accomplished photographers there was never a smile.

It was much different than in our day, when you appear much happier with smiles and laughter, natural and encouraged. You kids have a much happier environment than was displayed in the old pictures of my grandparents. Yes, life was less frivolous and disciplined then. Perhaps we were less secure and it left a mark. When you hear people say, "Give me the good old days," don't believe them, because life is less arduous and more fun than it used to be.

FILTH IN ENGLAND

Sanitation in that older neighborhood was nil. They had no indoor plumbing and most of the human refuse was dumped in the street where the kids would play. Infection and illness among children was general and infant mortality was high. Both in England, and later in Hanna where I was a child, sanitary conditions were similar. But little Mary was tough! Both Uncle John and Mary survived poor sanitary and educational facilities.

As difficult as it was to be a miner in early Carbon and Hanna, it was a vast improvement compared to the conditions they remembered in England. Fredrick Engels visited the coal fields of England, and described the conditions this way:

> Deansgate, which serves as a market, and is even in the finest weather a dark, unattractive hole in spite of the fact that, except for the factories, its sides are formed by low one and two-storied houses. Here, as everywhere, the older part of the town is especially ruinous and miserable. A dark-colored body of water, which leaves the beholder in doubt whether it is a brook or a long string of stagnant puddles, flows through the town and contributes its share to the total pollution of the air, by no means pure without it.

And Matthew Arnold said,.."Those children rolling on the heaps of black and slimy ground, mixed with brickbats, broken plates and bottles...the children themselves, black and in rags evermore, and the only water near them either boiling or gathered in unctuous pools, covered with rancid clots of scum, in the lowest holes are the earth-heaps...." In Wigan the death rate was 42.1 per one thousand, but the national average was only 27.2. Human life was cheap!

Sanitation was certainly improved when English miners came to Hanna. Still, their children had a long way to go. When I was about six or eight years old I remember a very unsanitary game we played--perhaps it was brought from England. You have heard the term, "I got the dirty end of the stick." Well, that expression was invented in England or Hanna. I got it once in One Town. After dark a gang of kids played near the outdoor toilets. One boy, who was it placed one of two sticks into fecal matter. Another kid, who was blindfolded, had to choose and hold one of the two sticks. If he missed the clean stick, then he was it!

THE UNIONS--I

In the early days of unions in England, and perhaps even in this country, men were often fired because of their complaints. This was an insidious tactic used against the organizers. Their homes were owned by the coal company and the miners were constantly afraid of being evicted. Also, they were often blackballed and their names were given to other mining companies. Then they were considered trouble- makers and kept from employment elsewhere.

Certainly, we can see the need for unions in America. When my own father worked to form a union in Hanna his freedom was limited. The penalties were less stringent in America than in England, but they remained a factor.

First William and then Job Hughes left England and came to the mines of Iowa. The town was called 'WHATT CHEER'. I presume that there was little to cheer about at that locality. Job was soon killed in a dynamite blast which he had set to loosen coal. William decided to bring Job's widow and two children back to the United Kingdom. After a time William returned to mine coal at Hanna, Wyoming.

I quote from the Lancashire & Cheshire Miners by Raymond Challinor "A large quantity of gravel and water suddenly burst in upon the workings. The survivors rushed out and called on neighboring pits for assistance. Together they cleared 70 yards of roadway which, by the force of water, was rapidly filled again. Driven back, the rescuers adopted a new tactic and cut through six yards of coal. There they discovered the bodies of an old man and his two daughters. After cutting another eleven yards, they discovered a further corpse. It was a wet and dangerous task. The men were to work night and day until they found the bodies. But when all the work was finished and the men came to be paid, they received only 1s. ed. per day." (about $2.00)

Dan, you should know something about the thickness of coal seams in that area of England. They are very shallow, probably no more than a couple of feet, so most of the miners' work was done as they lay on their bellies. Those of the Lankies who left there and came to Hanna could not believe that they could stand up and work all day. The veins of coal in Hanna would average about 28 feet--not inches that they were used to. Many of them told me that at first they were worried about coal falling from the ceiling, and quite often it did kill or injure them. In Wyoming in the later years large pieces of equipment worked to loosen and load the coal into the cars, but in England they were paid by the quantity of coal they could produce, sometimes even with a Dull Pick.

. . . .

THE COMPANY ONE KEEPS

One night in late October,
When I was far from sober,
Returning with my load with manly pride,
So I lay down in the gutter,
And a pig came near and lay down by my side.
A lady passing by was then heard plain to say,
"You can tell a man who boozes,
By the company he chooses,"
At which the pig got up and slowly walked away.

Bruno

BRUNO WORKED ON DAVE WEST'S RANCH

Dear Dan:

Dave West was a prominent Elk Mountain rancher who welcomed young men to fish and hunt on his land, and they reciprocated during haying season. My dad Bruno Stebner was one of those young kids. Dave's son Edgar West, who now lives in Rock River, told me of an accident which occurred in their hay field. A friend of my dad, Johnnie Veatch, was working in the same area, when Bruno lost control of his reins and his team and equipment ran into Johnnie's equipment. Both young men were thrown away from the wreck, but a horse had his leg cut off in the sickle bar equipment. Neither man was injured. Of course the horse had to be shot. Today, we all fear car accidents, but in that time accidents caused by horses were very common.

. . . .

In the coal mines of old Carbon some of the older miners abused the young sprag boys unreasonably. One miner would hold the kid by the shirt, while others rubbed coal slack on his back just to toughen him up. Often they opened the neophytes lunch pail and stole his pie or cake. (Incidentally, Bruno was about 16 years old when he entered the mine in Carbon as a 'sprag boy'. There were no brakes on the smaller coal cars, but to stop them a boy would lie on his belly and force a wooden sprag into the spokes of the wheel to slow, or stop, a moving car. Many of these young miners lost fingers or hands on that particular job.)

. . . .

BRUNO, A FRIEND OF RICHARDSONS

My Dad, Bruno, was a fisherman and a hunter. It was natural he would become a good friend of Richardson and his three sons. Bruno had a good horse we called Old Joe, and he built a light weight buggy that would carry him, with a friend, into the hills in the Elk Mountain area. There my Dad joined the ODD FELLOWS LODGE at Elk Mountain. This was a popular fraternal organization with the ranchers. When the Richardsons came to town they often ate a meal or two at our house. I was impressed with the big, strong son, Tom Richardson. I remember his dynamic jaws and powerful teeth when he took such an enormous bite out of an apple.

Sue admitted that old Bill Richardson was not very popular with his ranching neighbors, saying, "Ede sure they 'ave a good bunch of cattle, but hits odd that 'e got started with a duzzen calves that 'ad nothin' fer a muther but a damn mule." Sue explained the success on his courageous and opportunistic wife, which she explained this way, "Thu hold woman was responsible--shed 'ave a big aperun and would ride a horse like the very devil, and when shed get 'ome there'd be more likely a calf hin hit."

I remember a particular day during the early 1920's when our family visited the Ted Richardson ranch. At that time, Bill was probably 75 years old and was crustier and tougher than most older men I ever knew. He refused to leave his little old log cabin and would not move into his son's home.

That day I watched him milk a cow. The image of that day comes through loud and clear. I stood in the door of the milking shed observing a process I had never seen. The old boy's rough hands seemed to irritate the cow's udder as he tried to get a little more milk. The cow violently objected. She kicked the stool from under Bill and placed the other hind hoof into the pail of milk. Then the air turned blue with profanity. Bill's vocabulary of cuss words was endless and complete. No miner I knew was more eloquent. He immediately kicked the cow in the belly and jerked her tail as he headed to the ranch house urging Ted to shoot the cow.

BRUNO STEBNER THE BACHELOR

Bruno Stebner was a bachelor who taught himself how to read and write with very little schooling. He was fascinated by anything mechanical. For years I had his book on practical mechanics which was well read. He learned to repair watches and clocks. He hunted and worked on guns, and he could build anything. With his experience he would not be working down in the mines very long.

His hobbies after working hours augmented his income. He ran the first movie at the old Opera House with those old machines. There were many breakdowns which slowed the pleasure of the audience that followed the humor of Fatty Arbuckle and the heroics of William S. Hart. But Bruno could improvise repairs on the spot!

CHARLES AND BRUNO ARE FRIENDS

The Stebners lived near the Charles Hughes family in Number One Town, and it seems that Bruno and Charles were good friends. To observe Little Mary must have fascinated Bruno. Yet, he was a confirmed bachelor like his three brothers who shared their bunkhouse. He was occupied with the repair of the Stebner brothers Indian Motorcycles. When they were not working in the mine, hunting and fishing took their leisure time. Available girls did not interest any of them. Bruno was twenty-six years old and Mary was only sixteen and they were an unlikely match.

Bruno repaired the radiator of the first automobile in Hanna. It was in an international race across the United States, Asia and Europe. Bruno welded the radiator after it had been hit by a rock a few miles beyond the town.

The Second Explosion

THE SECOND EXPLOSION . . 1908

Dear Dan:

It was March 28, 1908, a Sunday, and Charles Hughes could stay home with Mary and John. Mary remembered that her dad was telling her how to make a pudding which was common in England. She was mixing the recipe as he sat in the kitchen, explaining the ingredients. I presume that Uncle John was outdoors playing. It was a time for the two of them to visit and relax after his hard week of toil in the mine. It was quiet of the little kitchen. Suddenly, the entire house shook and it felt like thunder under the house. There was a deep rumble throughout the entire town.

An old friend of mine, Tommy Dodds, who was about my mother's age, told me he had a good view of the mine. Tom worked outside the mine at various odd jobs for the coal company and that day he was on the streets of Hanna.

As the ground rumbled he saw a great ground-swell of dust, debris, and flying heavy objects come from the entrance of the mine. It made Tom think of a giant explosion from the mouth of an enormous cannon. He saw large objects shoot into the air covering a very big area. Tom Dodds wrote the following:

"The day of the explosion, March 28, 1908, I remember going from our house, No. 113 in No. 1 town, to get my statement at the mine office, as payday would be the next day. I heard a loud explosion, I looked around and saw a 'Ball of Fire' and black smoke. Mine timbers were in the air at No. 1 mine, and they were falling through the tipple, and scattered across the tracks.

"I ran to the mine and could see that the mouth of the mine was closed with dirt. The air-fan was off its foundation, but was still working drawing air from the mine. I went to the East Side (an auxiliary entrance to the mine) and saw that the explosion had blown the timbers out of the mouth of that slope. But this slope was open, and this was where the rescue crew would be working.

"They were calling for workers to open the mouth of the west slope. I then returned to the west portal, which I said was previously closed. And I saw my father Tony Dodds a few minutes before he left to go to the west side, as a rescuer.

"Mr. Jones a mine clerk, was telling us to work faster. But that is what we were doing. But we could not open the slope because there was too much dirt and timbers. I worked shoveling dirt and moving timbers with other men until 10:30 that night when it exploded again. I heard the bump and knew it had exploded again. I was lucky that we had not opened the Portal, or we would have all been killed.

"I went home and had to tell my mother that the mine exploded again, and that my father had been killed. It was a very hard job."

. . . .

Immediately, Charles Hughes left his daughter with her partially prepared pudding. He hurried for the mine entrance to join others who were already there. They had a little dog which always followed every time Charles left the house. Of course, it chased after his master that day. Whatever happened to the faithful pet no one ever knew. It was the last time Little Mary ever saw her dad or the dog!

Charles, and his friend Bruno Stebner, were with nearly every other able-bodied man who entered the mine entrance and began to organize a rescue party. Few even changed into their mine clothes as they entered the clear East Side entrance hoping to find trapped or wounded men. They planned to dig through the debris of fallen coal, mine ties, and twisted rails and find someone who was alive or trapped. It was an unselfish wish that they might save them. The rescue party did not know that all had died in that enormous blast.

As they worked their way into the mine they discovered a few crushed and burned bodies. With the tools and stretchers and with teams of four they began to carry their burdens toward the surface.

As Charles and Bruno entered the mine with other rescuers--no men were drafted, but all were volunteers who hoped to save at least one life of their fellow workers--they separated preparing to do different tasks. The two of them entered and again came to the surface with bodies. Finally, Charles was one of a team of four carrying a body up the steep mine slope toward the surface.

When some of the rescue crews arrived in the mine they noticed that the lighted lamps which they wore on their caps suddenly increased in the volume of flame. One said, "We are in pretty heavy gas, and there will be more trouble." So they retreated to the surface. The prediction was right because the second explosion of the day occurred, killing many others who were elsewhere in various entries and rooms. Few bodies were not located. The body of one of the victims was completely blown out of the entrance of the mine.

Soon women and children arrived, each wanting to know about their own family. Each hoped that their family was not among the corpses. Weeping, tears, and condolences were many for bereaved new widows and young orphans as the bodies were identified.

Little Mary stayed at home with her brother John as her departing Father had instructed. She worked in the kitchen to complete her first pudding, knowing that her father would be pleased to eat it when he returned later that night.

Bruno, who was mechanical, was carrying tools and bradish into the mine to seal off escaping gases which might be ignited. In a narrow passage he met his older friend Charles who, with others, was carrying a miner's body out of the mine. Someone suggested that Bruno and Charles trade places because a younger man could handle the heavy body up the steep incline. Charles descended to deliver the tools deeper into the mine. As they separated neither dreamed he would not see the other man again.

As Bruno and his three companions deposited the body hastily in a mining shack he hurried again to the mine entrance at the same moment Charles was delivering the tools in the deeper area full of the debris and water, fire, and escaping gas; the ultimate catastrophe suddenly occurred with the second blast.

All rescuers then in the mine were immediately killed; only a lucky few, including Bruno, were on the safety of the surface. There was one exception! A single individual miner was standing at the opening of the mine when the second explosion occurred. The blast was like the opening of a shotgun throwing its deadly pellets of rock, coal, and lumber into the air. That miner never knew what hit him because his decapitated body lay close by. There was no head by which to identify him. There were others that were never accounted for.

. . . .

This was the main entry to Number One mine following the explosion in Hanna. It was sealed with debris, lumber, distorted steel rails, coal and soil. The second opening, the East Side Entrance, was clear and served for rescue parties who hoped to save three trapped miners.

Two horsemen, and the American flag, led mourners to the East Side Entrance to attend a Memorial Service. The group crossed the prairie in a long line from Hanna. Most of the walkers lost their fathers, sons and friends who were entombed within the mine.

The mourners listen to a speaker and join in a prayer. At this point in time the opening is sealed with concrete.

The sixteen year old girl pushed the pudding toward the back of the stove as she tried to explain to her brother John that it would not be much longer until their father would soon be home for his supper. Then they could all eat together. It was dark when someone knocked on the kitchen door, but it was not Charles--it was his friend Bruno Stebner!

I am sure at that moment Bruno knew Mary and her young brother would not be alone very long. Soon he planned to marry the girl, who was ten years younger than he. There was much empathy in the community and many of the widows were married to eligible bachelors who raised their children.

QUOTATIONS FROM UNION PACIFIC HISTORY

"The second disaster to No. One Mine occurred on March 28, 1908, as suddenly and unexpectedly as the first. The second explosion was much like the first, coming at one o'clock in the afternoon."

This was a Sunday afternoon and a non-working day in the mine. In my opinion there must have been a severe problem because there were 18 officials, bosses and administrative people consulting in the mine. Spontaneous fire and gas were common. Air was shut off from the fire by bradish, which is a canvas curtain. It was hung strategically to keep oxygen and gas away from smoldering flames on the miners' carbide hat lamps.

Now I continue quote from the Union Pacific History . . .

"Rescue crews once more assembled to carry on their grim task. The workings were found to have caved in badly, and smoke and gas were pouring up from the depths in such volume that the lives of the rescuers were in peril. At ten-thirty that same evening, a second explosion shook the mine, snuffing out the lives of forty-one members of the rescue crew. The company's officials agreed that no one in the mine could have possibly survived the two explosions, and that human life was too precious to be risked in any further attempt to recover the bodies of the men whose lives had already been claimed by the mine. Rescue attempts were, therefore, abandoned for the time being and the mine was closed."

(CMS opinion)...You know Dan, it is easy to second-guess any decision. Yet, one wonders why they waited until a second explosion occurred. In fact, why did they even open the same mine after the 1903 explosion?

In 1908, all 18 officials were killed when the explosion occurred. Unfortunately, there was no person in authority to deny eager rescue workers entrance into the mine. It was possible that trapped men might still be alive. There was a chance some could be saved. Rescue workers accomplished much that was important in retrieving bodies from the mine. As hopeless as it was, the work of the rescue workers was important to the unfortunate widows and their families.

Later the mine was opened to retrieve bodies. Another Union Pacific quotation. . . .

"On July 10th of that year, after extended conferences held between the officials of the State Mine Inspection Department and the officers of The Union Pacific Coal Company, the mine was reopened and twenty-seven bodies of men who died in the two explosions were recovered, and today No. One Mine remains the tomb of twenty-seven of those who died therein. The toll of this disaster was fifty-nine lives. Superintendent Alexander Briggs, Foreman Joseph Burton, and the entire underground staff were among those killed, as was State Coal Mine Inspector D. M. Elias, leading a rescue crew. In recent years the coal company's engineers located a site for a monument, directly above the place where the ashes of the twenty seven men rest within the mine, and on each recurring Memorial Day services are held in memory of those who died in the scorching flame that wrecked the mine on that memorable March 28, 1908."

Muriel Kitchings, a Hanna resident and historian, is a granddaughter of a miner who worked with rescuers. She inquired at the Union Pacific Offices in Omaha, Nebraska, and learned their records are rather incomplete. Muriel recently organized a memorial to all of the Hanna miners who lost their lives; also it was dedicated on Memorial Day in 1985. Since then she has heard of at least two men who are not recorded by the Union Pacific. Some of these miners had been recently hired, and had no relatives to report them missing. In those days human life was cheap.

The Union Pacific History of Coal Mines, which was printed in 1940, tells us that in the explosion of 1903, 169 miners lost their lives; also, that in the disaster of 1908 fifty-nine were added to total 228 lives lost to Number One mine.

From the March explosion until July, more than forty bodies remained in the mine. At that time the mine was reopened and all but twenty-seven bodies were recovered. The last one to be recovered was Charles Hughes. He was identified by a watch he brought from England. It was not an expensive timepiece, but it was one that was wound with a key which was attached by a chain. For many years Mary Ford saved the watch. Its face had turned an unusual green color which came from the gas of the mine. I gave it to Uncle John's son, Gordon Hughes.

Years ago Mary Ford worked with a few friends in Hanna who made and painted white metal crosses to mark unknown graves of the victims of the explosions in the Hanna cemetery.

Mary and Bruno

THE UNIONS--II

Dear Dan:

I visited an interesting man in Rock Springs. He had lived to a ripe old age. He didn't stay in Hanna very long. The man named John Traeger knew Bruno. With a few others they received the Hanna Charter of the United Mine Workers of America in 1908.

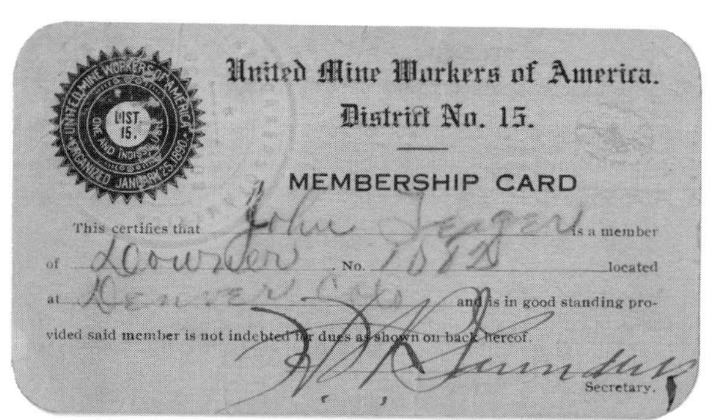

United Mine Workers of America.
District No. 15.

MEMBERSHIP CARD

This certifies that John [illegible] is a member of [illegible] No. [illegible] located at [illegible] and is in good standing provided said member is not indebted for dues as shown on back hereof.

[illegible]
Secretary.

A membership card of John Treager which he gave to me. This was the beginning of the United Mine Workers of America in Hanna.

This small group met secretly at the Home Ranch which was only a few miles east of Hanna. This location was a secret because they had to be away from Union Pacific property. Otherwise they might lose their jobs and the houses in which they lived. It took courage to attend such organizational meetings.

At that time, as in England, there were strikes and lock-outs to prevent Union programs. In 1890 there was pressure from the Unions to establish the 'Eight Hour Day.' Also, there was a pay-raise which averaged four dollars a day.

During the time Bruno and Traeger were active with the Union in Hanna, they were well aware that the coal companies were also on the offensive. A Union was needed in Hanna. It took guts to be an organizer at that time. I am proud that Bruno Stebner, then a bachelor, was among the first to gain a U. M. W. of A. charter.

Recently I visited the area between Walsenburg and Trinidad, Colorado, where there is a statue to the coal miners and their families who were killed at the old town of Ludlow. Here the Colorado National Guard massacred coal miners and their families in 1914. The Colorado Fuel & Iron Company coal mine operators were crude in their dealings with mining families. This was documented by Alvin R. Sunseri, professor of History at the University of Northern Iowa.

The Ludlow massacre in our neighboring state occurred on April 20, 1914, my fifth birthday, shortly before my Father's death at the Hanna mines. The Colorado Fuel and Iron company owned mines in the area. They encouraged the Colorado National Guard to put pressure on union miners, and some shots were fired by the Guard into tents which housed strikers and their families. Two women and eleven children were suffocated in a pit where the miners had taken refuge. Ten miners lost their lives in the conflict.

. . . .

When I was fifteen years old and living in my mother's boarding house a man visited there who fascinated me! He was John L. Lewis who was President of the National U.M.W.A. and he visited with Hanna miners in our Cottage Home. To some he was a national hero. He was an imposing figure with bushy, wavy hair and piercingly prominent eyes beneath heavy, bushy black eyebrows. He talked with local union officials behind a closed door. I sneaked close to listen to the "big boys" talk. He was a heroic figure.

But like so many men, Lewis became too powerful, and almost ruined what men like my father had started as a good movement. Following World War II, Lewis called unnecessary strikes to raise the miner's pay. It seemed to please his ego to be able to do this. Finally, these actions made coal so expensive and undependable that the Union Pacific began using locomotives which burned oil rather than coal. Hanna almost became a ghost town! Later, Hanna revived as the low-sulphur western coal proved to meet more of the environmental standards. Today Hanna became a boom-or-bust community. With coal the only product produced it is not a consistent place to make a living.

Well, Dan, the union which my dad helped organize many years ago was necessary for the working man. But the egos of Lewis and others created a problem, and today unions suffer from the influence of gangsters and other dishonest men. Some even rob their own union treasuries. Many unions, which had their beginning fighting for better lives, have been destroyed by the power and greed of a few bad leaders.

. . . .

Sometimes, the family fails; sometimes, the home; sometimes the community. But Americans can reduce these "sometimes."

Bruno and his bride.

MARY THE BRIDE

Two of the four Stebner brothers were bachelors. Uncle Adolph married late in life, but Bruno was the first to challenge matrimony. Mary often said that he married her because of sympathy after her dad died in the mine explosion. Yet, she was a lovely young girl and he was attracted to her. Uncle Bill Hughes had to give his approval because in those days young girls were seldom married without parental consent.

Their wedding picture shows the young bride as the center of attraction. Her face and figure were young and beautiful. An enormous white hat with many white plumes and copious feathers, which were like a cloud above her small and serious face. Her long lacy dress reached to the floor, and she wore long white gloves showing her folded hands. A simple white ribbon encircled the waist of the young seventeen year old beauty. During her lifetime Mary's weight was never more than a hundred pounds.

Bruno was seated in a comfortable chair, with his black suit and baggy pants. He wore a stiff white collar and a black tie with a white vest. In his lap strong hands held a black derby hat. A trace of a smile showed Bruno was a proud and happy bridegroom.

The bride was delicate and active. She loved to dance! In the photo she sits gracefully balanced on a stool a little higher than the proud groom's left arm. They both wore white carnations. I presume her dress was the best available in Montgomery Ward. Bruno bought most of their new clothes mail-order. The money came from his extra earnings gained from repairing watches during his evenings and on Sundays.

They rode the passenger train to Denver for a long weekend honeymoon. Few Hanna newlyweds could enjoy such an auspicious start in married life, but that was the way he treated his new bride--nothing was too good for her. For Little Mary it must have seemed like a dream. Bruno cared for her as though she were English nobility. With his great sense of humor he teased and kidded her. They enjoyed the social activities Denver had to offer--especially dancing. He worshiped her.

CHARLIE IS BORN

Within the year Mary was pregnant and was naive about the entire miracle because she had no mother or older sister to tell her about the intimate relations of married life. These conversations were unspeakable in England, and especially in her father's home. Mother told me of an incident that occurred during her pregnancy.....

She had a neighbor who was married several months after the Stebners. Both of the new brides were pregnant. But, Mary was disturbed when the neighbor's baby arrived two months ahead of my birthdate. She was extremely excited about becoming a mother in April, but Mary said she was even ashamed to have people know Bruno and she had intercourse on their honeymoon. Once again Bruno found it necessary to explain to Little Mary the facts of life, which included the nine-month wait. Then, she finally understood that often marriage is necessary to establish legitimacy.

Mary was less than 100 pounds and shorter than five feet. It is natural she would have trouble delivering a husky ten pound boy. She tells of a long labor session where she was encouraged to walk around the house continuously. The company doctor came to our house only during the last hour. Dan, your birth was easier because of a modern hospital with an especially trained physician and talented nurses to help.

When I was born the Stebners finally had their first new child since they left Germany. I had three Stebner bachelor uncles--Adolph, Max and Fritz Stebner. Of course there was my Uncle John, who was not much older than I. I also had two German Aunts, Martha and Tillie. Tillie was later to marry O. G. Sharrer. Uncle Sharrer was the only educated man in our family. He was a mining engineer who had recently graduated from a college in Pennsylvania. The youngest was Aunt Martha who became the bride of a Hanna miner, J. R. Mann.

Tradition was meaningful to Hanna European families. The Stebners were elated with a baby boy who might preserve the family name. This phenomenon was a big deal in the history of Europe. I presume some filtered down even to the working man. When I entered the back door years later of Mary Ford's apartment in Laramie, I could hear her say, "There comes Sir Charles."

My dad would lift me above his head and announce, "This little guy will grow up to be the President of the United States." English friends made snide remarks, and everybody had fun. All of the immigrants of that day believed that in this free country anything was possible for those who were born poor. I wish my dad could have lived to see I settled for less than he predicted--I was elected President of the Wyoming Dental Society!

As ridiculous as my proud father must have been, today I am aware of the many wonderful things that have happened to me. Gosh, Dan, although I fortunately stayed out of politics, I was recently one of ten dentists who were honored by Northwestern University as a Legend in the field of general dentistry. And, yes Danny, I did make it to become the President of the American Academy of Gold Foil Operators, which is a small group of dentists dedicated toward perfection in a technical area. Your grandmother and I were surprised when the Foil Academy invited us to San Francisco in 1985 where I received their Distinguished Member Award. It was a thrill for us because they paid all of our expenses for the trip and we had a great time.

Bruno would have liked that! That, and the other fine honors that have come to me certainly would have made Bruno proud if he had lived longer. Danny, because of Mary Ford, you and I have come a long way from digging coal! Now, to get back to the year of 1909 . . . . . .

THE DOTING AUNTS

The doting Stebner aunts, uncles and grandparents enjoyed the event of my arrival, and finally when my little sister Elsie was born two years later there had to be another celebration. And then a little girl the women could dress and pamper! They were happier when another boy named LeRoy arrived two years later. The family of three children seemed to please all of the Stebner family. Leroy--another heir to carry on the Stebner name?

Aunt Tillie and Aunt Martha with Mary on the right.

I mentioned earlier that there were no cars in Hanna then but there were bicycles and the Stebner boys all drove Indian motorcycles, after which the company was named. The Stebner men drove them down the animal paths that were in the hills near Hanna where they hunted sage chicken and rabbits. Grandmother Amelia learned to cook wild game to perfection when she was a young girl working for nobility in Germany.

The Stebner boys were not too popular because of the new noise which spooked the horses which other people drove. Wagons were the accepted way to deliver coal, bakery goods, and all heavy materials.

The situation was not always peaceful because the grown men had their problems. Once Fritz encouraged his little mother to ride in a sidecar that he had added to his Indian motorcycle, so he placed her in the sidecar for a ride out of town. No doubt she enjoyed the new experience until Fritz turned a corner too sharply and threw my grandmother into the sagebrush. She was not dressed for the occasion. Grandmother always wore a little white apron which covered part of a long heavy black skirt. She had a little white bonnet which covered her black braided hair. Her wrinkled bright face was a picture I will always remember.

Amelia refused Fritz's invitation to ride back. She came to our house and reported the accident to Bruno. He took her home and afterwards there were strong words during which my dad threatened to whip his younger brother. It created an episode which excited me. I thought I was going to see a fight!

BRUNO THE BENEFACTOR

Bruno was a benefactor to the three or four Italian families who were our neighbors in One-Town. Each year on Christmas Eve four Italian laborers carried their string instruments to our lighted tree and entertained us. They were grateful because my Dad helped them cash their pay checks. Then, with the Sears Roebuck and Montgomery Ward catalogue they explained the items they wanted to order. With his help they made Postal Money Orders for payment. They were grateful because he understood their problems.

When I was in Hanna High School I remember a tribute to my dad by an Italian friend, Joe Marinaro. Joe was a bachelor who worked for the Union Pacific repairing the walls of company houses. On that Memorial Day, the band in which I played was on the crest of a hill above the old No. 1 mine. There is a small stone marker which tells the story of the 27 miners who are entombed beneath that point. Each of the various speakers talked in their native tongues as a memorial to those still in the mine. A Finlander, a Greek, and certainly a Lanky, shared the podium with Joe Marinaro. Joe said: 'Memory of Georgia Washiton, Abrahan Lencon, and Bruno Stebanor.' For me it was an emotional experience to hear his name.

Joe Marinaro was a cultured Italian and musician. Today, I still have a piece of sheet music he composed. An Italian classmate told me Joe left Europe to escaped persecution from the Italian Government. There he was an outspoken Mason, and that did not go well in Italy. I remember his large scarred and callused hands of a plasterer. It was incongruous that those hands could play the violin so delicately.

For many years Bruno fished and hunted in the Elk Mountain area. Before there were any game limits or refrigeration we gave wild game to our neighbors. When Bruno died our Italian friends requested that he be buried on the summit of Elk Mountain, and they carry his casket to burial. Our family did not agree. Sometimes I wish the Italians had been allowed to make that tribute.

. . . .

I can still see my first rainbow. It followed a rain shower and sunshine was taking over from the clouds. I was about four years old and I was sitting with my dad on our little porch facing the railroad. A rainbow suddenly appeared in the few clouds which was mixed with sunshine. As I admired it, my dad said, "Well, Charlie, that is a beautiful rainbow, and where it disappear over the hills there is a pot of gold for anyone who finds it." Well, I was young enough to believe it! Now at age 80 I understand that he meant; if I worked hard enough with proper planning, the gold would be waiting.

CMS

Bruno In An Accident

BRUNO IN ACCIDENT

Dear Dan:

On May 10th, 1914, Bruno met with a tragic accident. He had a good permanent job outside the mine because of his experience and ability. His work was in the engine room where he operated the steam generated cables that pulled the loaded mine cars out of the depths of the mine to a tipple above ground.

There on this structure the smaller mining cars came to a point above the large railroad cars. Here they were tipped sideways on metal shakers and coal was finally dumped into shipping coal cars. Then, the engineer, my dad, would lower the empties back down the main slope into the mine to be filled again.

I suppose Bruno's unselfish nature was his most serious problem. A friend of Bruno's, by the name of Ryburn, was recuperating from an illness. My dad's regular work was a more pleasant chore of running the hoist which pulled coal to the surface from the mine. This boiler was being prepared to generate steam in a few days and the scale had to be removed. There was a small manhole at the top of the boiler which was to accommodate anyone entering or exiting from the boiler. As my dad worked, someone, I hope inadvertently, turned on the steam valve from another boiler into the cool boiler. Live steam surrounded Bruno, and men who later were amazed that he was strong enough to climb out of the manhole. He walked out of the building into the cooler atmosphere before he collapsed from critical scaled wounds.

There was no ambulance other than a team of horses which pulled a canvas covered wagon. When I was in school we called it the "dead wagon." Most of the miners who rode in it were seriously injured. When we saw it all the kids wondered if one of their family was in it. Our house in One Town, number 77, was where it was driven that day. At that time there was very little medical help other than first-aid.

Various members of our family visited with Bruno in that small darkened bedroom. The company doctor was present apparently to relieve the pain. Bruno was rational and conscious. We all know that there are few injuries more excruciating than steam burns. Any time we feel the steam from a tea kettle on our hand we develop empathy for a painful burn of our skin.

I was only five years old, but I remember entering his room when he called for me. He smiled and put a hand on my head while I stood there crying. I saw patches of skin on his hands and face. I was disturbed to notice his denuded Adam's apple in his throat moving as he spoke to me. His voice was clear and calm when he spoke, saying: "Charlie, you are the man of the house now. Take good care of your mother!" I still remember all of the details of those few minutes. He took my small hand in his bruised fist. For the next seventy years I never forgot his challenge.

Often since then I wondered why the Union Pacific punctually arranged to have a special engine and a caboose to hurry him 40 miles to the nearest hospital in Rawlins. Perhaps others thought he was something special. The following day he died.

. . . .

Opportunity for distinction lies in doing ordinary things extraordinarily well.

William Feather

The Young Widow

MARY FORD AFTER BRUNO
(stealing coal)

Dear Dan:

After Bruno died there was sympathy and some help for Little Mary and her children--Charlie five years old, Elsie age three, and LeRoy a six month old baby. Money, food, and coal for cooking and heat, were problems for the 23 year old 'Little Mary'. The little English girl had lost the capable German. Bruno was ten years older and treated her like she was a princess. He gave her confidence and taught her to read and write. They were the best six years of her life. He spent his paychecks to make her home the best in town, and didn't worry about the future he planned. But there was very little immediate cash because his job was secure. Mary had all she wanted--comfort, food, and clothes she never expected to have.

In the mining towns the Union Pacific Coal Company had no liability insurance for miners. Bruno bought a New York Life policy for about a thousand dollars which seemed like a fortune. Also the United Mine Workers Union, which Bruno had helped to organize, contributed about eight hundred dollars to the widow of the wife whose husband was killed in the mines. In those days there was no federal funds for widows or orphans. Those meager funds disappeared rapidly, as did Bruno's watch repairing tools, guns, and fishing tackle. Only Old Joe, Bruno's horse, which was used for family transportation and hunting and fishing excursions, remained. Mother's desire to help others prevailed. People borrowed and failed to return items. They were not malicious but simply forgetful. Mary had many other things to worry about such as providing groceries and clothes for her children. Thoughtfully, the Union Pacific Coal Company temporarily ignored the twelve dollars a month rent for the little company house we lived in.

Fuel was no serious problem. Mary's kids picked up pieces of coal that had fallen from the cars at the railroad coal chute. Perhaps you could say we stole it. Coal was generally available in a mining camp. Usually it sold for about two dollars a ton when it was purchased by Hanna citizens. Mary Stebner and her children didn't have that two dollars.

Very often a few of the pieces of coal fell off the cars onto the ground. When there was not enough we climbed up into the cars and threw off enough to fill our wagon, or in the winter, a box on our little sled. It was a short distance to our coal shed near the kitchen.

Elsie, Charlie and LeRoy, about four years after Bruno's death.

Climbing onto the cars was frowned on by UP workmen because it was thievery. And it was dangerous. I remember we had a near crisis as my little sister climbed onto a loaded car of coal and was throwing coal off so I could load the wagon. The switch-engine suddenly appeared and the engineer decided to move the cars. Elsie screamed as her car moved. There was some neighborhood noise which brought my mother from the kitchen, and in her little apron she ran toward us and captured the attention of the train crew.

Mother was young and beautiful and many of the train crews often waved when she was in the yard hanging clothes. She had no trouble stopping a train; especially, when her child was being carried away. Elsie was soon back on solid ground and we gathered all of the coal lumps she had thrown off and took the loot home as usual.

. . . .

I have a vivid recollection of another near crisis which occurred about that same time. The Union Pacific hired a very large black detective who wore a conspicuous gun on his belt. We weren't terribly afraid of him--only cautious when he made his rounds on the railroad property. On this particular day, he suddenly walked around a railroad car and accosted Elsie and me. We were terrified that he might arrest us and take us away. Someone saw what was going on and alerted Little Mary. She ran to the scene carrying her small clothes-washing stick, which was made from part of a broom handle. It was used to stir her clothes as she washed them. All her life she armed herself with this weapon when she smelled trouble.

Little Mary had no fear of the big bully! She was simply belligerent, and shook her stick in his face. The gun hanging on the watchman's belt made no impression on mother, who was less than five feet tall. It was a great display of woman power. She forcefully explained that both her father and husband were killed mining Union Pacific coal. Now, she believed she had the right to get all the coal she needed. Sheepishly, the watchman backed away, saying, "Yes ma'am, I don't blame you, go right ahead!" From that time on, my Saturday chore of collecting coal continued without further problems.

THE BATH

When I was a boy this computer and printer was an unbelievable wonder. And yet when you enroll in high school, the equipment I work with will fascinate you as did the first automobile I saw in Hanna about 70 year ago. I predict you will speak into a tube and out of the equipment will come written copies which will be corrected and printed.

In my high school days I was amazed at the electric typewriter. Now I use the computer, and before long even this will be antique. You ask, "What has this to do with THE BATH?"

Let me recall the first baths I remember. I must have been about three years old. My dad was self- educated in many areas, and one was the need for cleanliness. He was a coal miner, and coal miners become black and grimy in the mines. Of course, that may be considered _clean_ dirt. But I have reasons to believe he understood something about filth and bacteria, which are _dirty_ dirt!

My mother told me of the men and boys who worked in the mines and boys who came home from the coal mines of Lancashire, England--they were very black. Their homes had no indoor bath facilities. Only the rich enjoyed running water. The miners carried water from a hydrant which served many homes. This was the situation I remember when I was a kid in Hanna. Running water in the laborer's homes just did not exist.

We carried water in buckets from the hydrants into the kitchen, where it was heated on the same cooking stove used to prepare meals. Then it was tempered with cold water and placed in a small round galvanized wash tub. An English miner who worked long hours would come home, and roll up his sleeves and only wash his face and his arms from the elbows down. He ate a meager meal and carried his tired body to bed. I assure you that there were no pajamas, so usually he went to bed in long underwear, and also with some coal dust.

For me, as a kid in Hanna, Saturday was the day to get the human body _really_ clean. The bath was not only a family event, but often a social event. Historically, this was true when the Romans occupied England in the second century A.D. When we visited England we stopped at a town called Bath. Here we viewed the ruins of a Roman bath house constructed centuries before. Roman invaders of the British Isles brought their engineering and culture. A natural hot spring was available and they used lead pipes to circulate water in their community bath house. Just as today, many believed there was medicinal value in drinking the hot water. Well, that wasn't true, and lead poisoning did more to end the Roman invasion than did the warring English natives. That water was a health hazard.

Dan, it just could be that while the Romans died, or became insane, the English coal miners were saved because they had no plumbing. They did not drink water from the lead-lined pipes the Romans imported for their bath houses. Later miners perished from overwork, undernourishment and accidents in the mines. Miners were expected to be victims of a short life expectancy.

Anyway, I remember the pleasure of my early baths on our kitchen floor, where on Saturday evening, the water was heated and placed in a tin bath tub. All three of us Stebner kids were dunked into the sudsy bath where we played and were scrubbed until we were pink and tired. Then we said our prayers and were tucked between newly-washed blankets.

My dad was an inventive and talented mechanic. He designed and built the first indoor water system in Number One Town, laying a pipeline from the community hydrant into Mother's kitchen. This eliminated our bucket brigade. Can you imagine the thrill just to turn on a faucet and have water? He also wound water pipes through the fire box and out again into a home- made storage tank he built so we always had hot water when we needed. His love for his family provided us with the best that he could make available. Like others we previously carried coal from the coal shed into the kitchen. He cut a hole through the kitchen wall and made a narrow tin chute with a trap door that emptied coal into a bucket on the side of the stove. All we had to do was to fill a coal bin in the outdoor shed with enough coal for a day supply. Then, all Mother had to do was to lift the lid with her little shovel to stoke the cooking stove.

When I was six years old, after my dad's death, I figured a better way to have a weekly bath. I had a few Finnish friends known for their neat and clean homes. Their children were scrubbed more regularly than most of my classmates. This was true especially on Saturday. They had built a Finnish bath house at the edge of No. One Town, and I soon discovered I could have a bath which could last all day for twenty-five cents. I went there each Saturday and I was the only one who did not speak Finnish. Their bath ritual was a cultural and social event.

The men and boys used half of the building, divided by a pine partition in the middle, and the girls and women used the other half. We peeled off the clothes we had worn all week, and placed them under the bench which ran around the inside walls. Then we put our clean clothes neatly on the bench. We arrived at about ten in the morning and would not leave until about three that afternoon. I guess we must have figured that the cleaner we got on Saturday, the better others could endure us during the rest of the week.

Each of us selected a bucket of cold water and a bar of black tar soap. I can still smell that fragrant bar. Then we would leave the resting area and enter the steam room through a tight fitting door. (Today Americans are very taken with the 'sauna'.) Especially during the winter the steam would roll out to meet you. You didn't need the water bucket because your own perspiration glands took over. There was a series of benches which made a stairway to the ceiling. First we started on the lower row, and worked our way upward. Most of us got all the heat we needed on the second or third bench. Only a few tough little old Finns relaxed at the top.

The person who amazed us all was Eric Lepponen's father. He was an energetic little weasel of a guy who was also a blacksmith at the mines, and whether it was the heat of the bath or the Polka on the dance floor he endured more than anyone I have ever known. Old Pete made a lie of our theory that smoking will kill you! He chain-smoked Camels, inhaling more than two packages a day, for over thirty years and lived to be 87. He would be in the upper sauna for an hour or more and then come down, drink a bottle of soda pop, run bare naked about 50 yards in the snow. And then come back into steam heat again. I've seen pictures of the Finns in Europe who leave the sauna and jump into icy water for a little swim. Physiology and experience indicate to me that such a shock should overtax the circulatory system and might kill most of us.

In the steam room they used little bundles of willow leaves to switch their bodies to increase the circulation. We try to accomplish this with wash-cloth and heavy towels, but their way was more effective.

All of us boys soon learned that if we punched out a few knots in the pine partition, we could view little blond girls bathing on the other side. Still no one seemed to care, for traditionally the Finns are not secretive about sex. They were very frank in their discussions, and with some of the songs they taught me. I learned to speak Finnish rather well and sing along with them.

Now many of us have two or three bath tubs or showers which we use every day. I appreciate that luxury more than many because I remember our outdoor toilet and no bathroom. We used these outdoor facilities until we moved from the Cottage Home to the Hanna Hotel where we had a single bath tub for everyone. Such a luxury was new to me until we built a new school in Hanna.

Now I wonder about the odor which faced a new teacher in Hanna when she had room full of kids who bathed only once a week. I presume she looked forward to Monday and dreaded Friday--today it seems to be the other way around.

THE STOLEN SLED

In the winter one of our thrills was to slide down snowy hills on a small sled. That is, when we had our own sled. Ours was missing and that led to trouble with a Finnish housewife. When I looked for our sled, upon which we also hauled coal from the railroad to our home, I found it on the outside wall of a Finnish neighbor. I hurried home and reported my find.

Mother's Lanky temper ignited. She said, "Let's go and git it!" We lifted it off the wall, and identified it with with the letter 'S' we marked with a hot wire on the wood. Suddenly, the neighbor woman, about twice the size of Little Mary, came storming out of her kitchen door, with one of her larger sons, to help retrieve the sled. Mother and I held onto one end of the sled and the two Finns pulled on the other end. The winter air was filled with Finnish and Lanky obscenities.

The superior man and womanpower carried the sled into their house. When we arrived home my little brother and sister joined me and Mother as we shed a few tears. You might wonder why we didn't call the police. Well, in Hanna there were no phones, and also no police--we simply had to fight it out ourselves. I remembered that encounter, and there came a time when I got even!

THE GOATS

I remember the day mother baked several loaves of bread, and for some reason, she set it on a bench at our back door, to cool it.

That was a mistake because our next door neighbors, the Italian family the D'Andreas, had a couple of goats which they milked. They were loose and parading the area for what little forage in barren mining town. You guessed it, Dan! They saw Little Mary's bread and helped themselves to a treat. There were a few tears and some shouts as we chased the goats back into their own yard. Mrs. D'Andreas' Italian temper was acute. She shouted at mother, who fired back some Lanky threats. Neither could understand what the other said. It was a heated discussions the entire neighborhood heard.

MARY SELLS BEER

Before we moved into the Cottage Home mother made a little money by getting into the beer business. . . root-beer that is! I don't know how she arrived at the formula, but it was good and I think that all the kids in our area who helped me wash bottles and fill them drank most of the profit. In washing them we placed the quart-size bottles in a big tub. Then we placed lead B-B shot and then covered the opening with our hand and shook them. The warm soapy suds and our shaking did the cleaning job.

While we did this she made the root beer out of plain water and some yeast and tablets which she bought from some mail-order house. Then, we had a small rubber tube which we used to siphon the root beer into the bottles. The bottles were capped with an ingenious wire around the neck of the bottle. The wire incorporated a rubber stopper which securely sealed the bottle while we forced the wire handle down.

Then, Dan, there were none of the colas or other flavored cans or bottles. We had to manufacture our own product which we sold during the July 4th celebration, or on Labor Day. On those two days business was good and so was the root-beer! The town of Hanna made their own entertainment by the men of our town's baseball team played the Rawlins men's team. I remember Uncle John playing first base and I could talk my mother out of another bottle of that good soft drink when he got a hit.

There were games for the kids too, especially on Labor Day or the Fourth of July. We used to get into a gunny-sack that was tied around our waist so when the gun went off we were hobbled as we tried to run fifty yards. The winner got a quarter, and the rest of us were paid a nickel when we finished.

The feature of the day was the horse races. Nearly everyone had some sort of a plug, and there were even some better animals that Old Joe Lucas, the Norris family and the Jacksons owned. These Lankies brought that sport with them from England, where it is known as the "Sport of Kings". Here it was just as important as the sport of the miners. I never remember a horse race which did not have a foul claimed. They would violently argue who was guilty, and to whom the enormous purse of twenty-five dollars would go. I remember when Gal Norris thought the Jacksons should be penalized. He knew of illegal training of 'Little Blue' he said, "Aw knew dalm well, every morn they putt a blouddy heg in 'is hoaats."

During those years mother had many ideas to make a little extra money to care for her little brood. One thing was to sell ice cream around town. She ordered ice cream from Laramie, and they would ship it on the train to Hanna. Then, she would hitch up Old Joe to the buggy and canvass the neighborhood. Her own kids and their pals rang a bell to announce Mary was selling ice cream cones. It did not work out too well because all of her kids and their pals and close friends ate most of the profit. It kept us all busy and we had fun!

Mother would cater the food at community dances and dinners--usually they occurred the same night, and it was a break for me because I was older than the other two children who were at home with a baby sitter. The food was great during the dancing intermission and I could eat all of the fantastic cake and desserts we never had at home. I especially remember very thin layer cakes six or seven layers deep which were made with chocolate, pineapple, or other goodies between each layer.

Our desire for the sweets led to much dental decay, which I am sure would not have occurred if Bruno had lived. He was conscious away ahead of his time concerning vitamins and healthful food, although I am sure that they never used the word 'vitamins.' His reading and German appreciation of simple and wholesome dishes were a way of life. I remember the odor of the sauer-kraut that he made from cabbage which fermented on our back porch. I have loved it ever since. In those early days the fancy cakes and sweetened ice cream caused me to have three or four permanent teeth extracted soon after they erupted.

GRANDPA AND GRANDMA NORRIS

When mother worked outside our home in the community she would take Elsie and myself to stay with an older couple we called Grandpa and Grandma Norris. We often stayed there through the noon-hour.

At their house we enjoyed a treat. Grandma Norris gave each of us a piece of her homemade bread with ample real butter and covered with home-made jam. To us the ecstasy of that treat was not known to us. Perhaps other kids in Hanna, who had fathers, could afford such luxuries; but not our family. I can still taste that combination which simply delicious to me. Many times I have lovingly thought of that quaint old English couple. A visit to their little house was an event long remembered.

Grandpa and Grandma Norris who cared for Elsie and myself while mother was busy making a living for her family.

LEROY AND THE ROCKS

Mother needed baby-sitters as she had to leave home to work on any job. With Bruno gone she needed help, especially with LeRoy. Often, her help was Siama Ojala, a trusted Finnish girl.

When little LeRoy was four years old he had an accident. He was industrious, often climbing and throwing rocks, as healthy kids are likely to do.

There was an old bedspring, which should have been thrown away, against the side of the house. He tried to climb up to the top using the wire coils to assist him. With his right hand caught in a coil, his feet slipped and he hung there with one hand trapped in a coil.

Of course he screamed, but by the time someone came to his aid his shoulder was pulled out of the socket, and from that time on his arm withered and became useless. We were too poor to seek help beyond our company physician, who put the arm in a sling. Certainly, the tendons and nerves must have separated. He was simply a one-armed kid!

Today, our orthopedic surgeons could have easily repaired the damage and the arm would be useful. Mother loved and cared for the little guy in every way she knew, or could afford. She took him to the neighboring town of Rawlins where there were more experienced doctors, but to no avail. Finally, our company doctor suggested that she take him to Omaha, more than six hundred miles away, to the Union Pacific surgeon.

She boarded a train, and I will never know how she financed the trip. When she returned home she had a mechanical gadget which we hoped would restore the nerves and tendons by stimulation. There were two brass bars the patient would put in the palms of his hands, and wires were attached to them running to a battery. They were all in a nicely varnished box which impressed us. Within that box there was a battery which was hooked up to a crank-handle which came from the box to the outside. We turned the handle for about five minutes three times a day. An electric current ran through LeRoy's arms and shoulders. He held the brass bars in his hands to complete the circuit.

The pain was excruciating. We wondered why he cried and often screamed. We tried it and learned. I often wondered if the inventor of that box lived during the Spanish Inquisition. It was not long before we mailed the box back to Omaha. For the rest of his short life his back right arm withered and dangled helplessly at his side. LeRoy played and mixed with the other kids and seemed contented and happy.

During this time friends encouraged mother to take Bruno's case to court to provide some of the financial help she needed. There were three reasons she decided against the advice. She had no money to pay a lawyer. The Stebner boys were afraid they might lose their jobs with the Coal Company, and we might be asked to leave the house in which we lived. It seemed reasonable that we should not be forced to move from Hanna where friends and relatives might help.

But for the first time in her life she knew what lawyers might accomplish. Then she set her strong will to plan steps to see that LeRoy would become a lawyer. It was apparent he could not be a coal miner. He was her top priority to receive an education. Somehow, she would get that job accomplished. Unfortunately, LeRoy would live only another two years.

When my brother was about four years old he suffered another terrible accident. With Mother working elsewhere Siama was again our baby-sitter, and she helped with household chores. There were no indoor toilets in town and our needs were served by a simple row of outdoor privies behind the houses. (When I was older we celebrated Halloween by dumping them over, and then the company outdoor crews made a little extra money setting them up until the next Halloween.)

On a particular summer day, which I well remember, my little crippled brother was taken to the outdoor toilet, then Siama returned to the house. After his chore, LeRoy started to return to the kitchen, but he noticed a few rocks, or perhaps the ever present lumps of coal in the yard. He wanted to see them splash in the excrement under the toilet seat. He returned to the toilet. There was a rock in his strong left hand and more ammunition in his pockets. He looked down to see them splash in the fluid below.

Soon, Siama wondered why he had not returned, and she went to investigate. She heard his screams as she entered the outhouse and looked down to see only his head above the awful mess of human excrement. Her call for help soon brought neighbors running to our outdoor toilet. My uncle, J. R. Mann, who had just married Bruno's younger sister Martha, lived very near our house. He came running half-naked following his day's work in the mines. Someone handed him an ax and splintered the two-hole seat to make room for his big body to enter. Others held his legs and he reached LeRoy's good arm and pulled him out. By that time a larger group had gathered; there were no phones in Hanna but everyone helped, especially the Finnish women who knew what to do. They took buckets of warm water from their stoves and grabbed blankets and towels from their homes and placed the little boy in them and rolled him around.

It worked. He was soon clean and still breathing. He was soon in our home and in bed. There was little the doctor could do for him but wait to see if he was blind. In all toilets was a bucket of lime, which is a strong detergent, and a shovel. This white material is often placed in the toilet debris to discourage the flies and odors. Lime, being a caustic, injured the boy's eyeballs so he could not see. We were well aware that if he had two functioning arms he would not have fallen into the toilet. Now, we worried that he might also become blind.

The days passed slowly in that darkened bedroom. We hoped that the drops we placed in his eyes would let them heal. It was a great thrill when he finally noted that it was daytime. He had seen the light. Soon after he could see his mother's face. We all prayed and thanked God that he would be able to read law books later.

BAD BOOTS

Seldom did we get new clothes. Neighbors and friends, those who had fathers, would pass on clothes their children outgrew. There was an exception when I did have a new pair of boots. They were ordered from Sears or Montgomery Ward and were cheap and stiff, but they were all my mother could afford. I was pleased with them because they were high-topped like my Uncle Sharrer's engineer boots.

I presume they were not made of sterile leather as boots are now.

Perhaps they came from some cheap supplier who failed to treat the leather carefully. There must have been some sort of animal organism contaminating the inside of the boot. Of course, they were large. We purchased shoes and clothes larger so they could be passed on. When they were outgrown the next in line would get them. One of the boots rubbed a blister on my heel and it became infected. Then, later they were given to LeRoy.

In those days we heard a lot about "Blood Poison." but today it is simply a bacterial infection that invades the blood stream. We were exposed to numerous flies and virulent bacteria. Today, I know that the white corpuscles and our built-in immunity, usually defeat and eliminate infection. It was probably true in my body, but unfortunately LeRoy was not so fortunate. He developed an infection on his heel as I had. Later, his ear became very sore and infected.

The doctor used wires which were wrapped with a saturated gauze to clean out the pus. I remember how he would scream with each treatment. This continued for a while, but ultimately it was diagnosed as a fatal 'mastoiditis." This was a common diagnosis among children in Hanna. Now I believe LeRoy died from meningitis infection when he was only five years-old.

. . . .

In college I had a teacher who often became disgusted with our class. He said his grandson learned much faster than we did, because he kept asking, "Why, Grandpa, Why?" *CMS*

CHILDHOOD INFECTIONS

Little Mary early understood the desirability of an education. And she set priorities for her three children.

I remember the withered right arm that dangled on my brother LeRoy's right side. Because of it mother had visions that he should become a lawyer--probably because she could not afford a lawyer to gain compensation when her father and husband were killed in the mines.

It was seldom that the family's oldest boy went to college. He had to support the family by working in the mines. I thought that my sister Elsie was a good choice because she was an excellent student and had the personality to go with it. She was beautiful, much like her mother, and the teachers who boarded with us made much over her. She had many young girl friends and applied herself to the studies, much to the opposite of her brother.

Later, my sister Elsie died at age thirteen as she suffered from a disease they then diagnosed as Bright's disease. Today it is simply noted as a renal infection. I feel it was the result of tonsillitis. Bacteria from her tonsils could have been carried in the blood to her kidneys. Virulent bacteria were ever present in Hanna because of the many flies and open toilets behind every house. There was none of the sewage disposal which is legislated today.

Dan, fear of those childhood infections made the doctors deny my playing any sports other than baseball. This was difficult for me, but they were aware that in the winter time I might catch cold, and my kidneys might not withstand it. When I was in the sixth grade, albumin and blood were found in my urine. The Doctor realized that I had developed a serious kidney infection which kept me out of school for six weeks.

My tonsils were surgically removed after I came to Laramie to practice dentistry. Following that operation I gained twelve pounds because I was free from bacterial foci.

When I graduated from college there were specialists who operated as they treated mastoiditis, and also some general practitioners. On one occasion I helped a physician on one of these cases. Dr. Maurey Leake chiseled the mastoid process as he worked to eliminate a discharge behind the ear. Usually, the infection found its way into the skull. There was no surgical effort for my brother.

Contagious infection--you name it and we had it in Hanna. In retrospect, I now conclude that there were several reasons for that. Our diets were inadequate. The sanitary conditions were horrible. And we knew little about contact with infected individuals. Like every other family, we expected to acquire measles, chicken pox, diptheria, and tonsillitis. We saw others with influenza and poliomyelitis.

LITTLE MARY AND EMPATHY

There are few people who communicate with others immediately, and with action, if a person has suffered a tragic situation. But my mother was one of them. I suppose that it was because of her problems early in life. I remember only a few of many when someone would first suggest: "Call Mary--she will know what to do!"

The Gus Collins sadness was one of them. He was a lean wiry coal miner, and she an overweight broad- smiling red-faced Irish lady. They had three children from the oldest, who was about 14 years of age, down to the youngest who must have been age six.

On that sad day the father was at home while the mother attended a lady's group at the Catholic church. He worked in the kitchen to feed himself and his three children a lunch, which consisted of some home-canned meat. It was later determined that the meat was contaminated with the botulism bacteria. That night and the next morning all three children were dead and the father was also near death, but he survived.

In Hanna the usual thing happened, someone said, "Call Mary, she will know what to do!" She was among the first to arrive at their little house. As long as the Collins couple were alive they ate with us in our boarding house nearly every Sunday evening.

. . . .

Another tragedy I remember was following a suicide of a prominent Hanna citizen in his home. When the news broke someone said, "Call Mary, she will know what to do!" Because of her empathy, she cleaned up the mess and consoled the family as long as they needed her.

. . . .

What is life?

It is the flash of a firefly in the night.
It is the breath of a buffalo in the winter time.
It is the little shadow which runs across the grass
and loses itself in the sunset.

The Indian Chief, Crowfoot...1890

My Uncle Fritz and Adolph

FRITZ AND PATRIOTISM

Dear Dan:

During World War One, my Uncle Fritz Stebner had problems simply because his name was 'Fritz'. A tough mining town did not make a ten-year-old boy's life less arduous. An unfair sense of patriotism was generally encouraged. It seemed to be popular to hate Germans. I remember a patriotic song which started like this, "Keep your head down Fritzy boy." The song promised that the American soldiers would shoot him. Some of the tougher Lankies kids sang that song to me.

Don't get me wrong about that word PATRIOTISM. During times of war the philosophy is essential. It is a noble cause, and we should respond favorable. I was glad when I boarded a train as I wore my Navy Lieutenant's uniform following Pearl Harbor. Also, I encouraged your dad to do the same thing during the unpopular Vietnam War. Your generation and mine were lucky to be born in this country, and when our President calls on us in a worthy cause, we should respond patriotically. But when extreme and phony patriots take charge of a citizen, as they did in Hanna, we lose the real meaning of patriotism.

I sincerely believe that we should answer the call for volunteers when the country is in trouble. With that philosophy in mind I encouraged Ken to respond patriotically during the Vietnam war--even though it was a mistake which he didn't believe in. That is what <u>real</u> patriotism is all about.

The Stebner family was shocked and embarrassed during the heated days of World War I. Today, I believe that if my dad alive there would have been trouble simply because the family spoke German to their parents in their home.

I remember the day when men, under the guise of patriotism, embarrassed and shocked the Stebner family. Uncle Fritz returned from a day's work at the mine and was shaving in a little bunkhouse beside our home. A group of men, their leader in uniform, came to harass Fritz, perhaps because his name was 'Fritz'. (Incidentally, their leader never left Wyoming during the war.) They dragged him out to the street to lead a straggling crowd. My mother was there with her three little children, and there were tears because we wondered what they do with our Uncle Fritz. In those days they talked about tar-and-feathers. He had to carry the flag to please the assembled crowd. I remember a bass drum and a few instruments playing. The object was to force him to purchase War Bonds. When Fritz returned he was not bodily harmed, but those of us with the Stebner name suffered emotionally.

Later we learned that Fritz had bought more War Bonds than some of his tormentors. Today I am concerned with the way we treated those Japanese heritage. Certainly, it was under the guise of patriotism.

Uncle Fritz leaning on his Model T Ford.

CHUCK MELLOR

There is irony in the fact that Chuck Mellor's father and my mother were cousins. During 1905 my Grandfather, Charles Hughes, brought two of Mary's cousins' to Hanna, Wyoming, from a Lancashire, England orphans facility. Tom Mellor's son, Chuck, acted patriotically as any teen-age boy would. In later years Chuck and I became very good friends, but it didn't start that way.

Chuck and a couple of his friends caught me in my mother's Cottage Home wash-shed. They held me and took off my shirt, and Chuck grabbed and twisted the nipples on my chest. Of course they laughed because I had an Uncle Fritz and was 50% German. Certainly, Chuck had no pangs of conscience. Since then I have thought of the way we treated American Japanese during WW II. When it happened I didn't even tell my little Mother about that experience--she had enough troubles of her own.

FRITZ IS A COWBOY

I liked Uncle Fritz. After a few years he left the mines to become a Cowboy on a ranch. The glamour of that appeals to young kids even today. The early movies made heros of William S. Hart and later Tom Mix. There was nothing exciting about having uncles working in the coal mines, but to have a Stebner who was a cowboy raised my status in No. One Town.

Cowboys were romantic heroes in the dime-store novels and the early movies. They caught the bad guys and won the leading ladies. All young boys worshiped them and few saw much glamour in being miners like the fathers. But young boys usually grew up to be miners like their father because their wages were better than that of cowboys.

On one occasion Fritz had a lady friend who got him in trouble. He had a serious affair with a miner's wife whom he visited now and then when her husband was working in the mine. Perhaps the miner advised Fritz to leave town permanently. At any rate Fritz spent most of his time on the ranch near Elk Mountain.

When my dad died from his mine accident Fritz was notified of the funeral date. He had to come to Hanna. His lady friend's husband was waiting for him at the edge of town. Well, Fritz paid for all of his previous pleasure. When he finally showed up at our house he was not a pretty sight. Mother said she was embarrassed when he attended the funeral because his face was a mess with black eyes, a broken nose and other evidence that the husband must have been a pugilist in his younger days.

BILL CARLISLE AND FRITZ

A few years after my dad's death I heard the news that an 18-year-old train robber had given the Union Pacific a bad time. I remember the excitement in Hanna when Bill Carlisle held up a Union Pacific passenger train.

Bill left his home in Pennsylvania and came to Wyoming to work on ranches. Between ranch jobs he was standing on the platform of the depot in Green River. Without money, cold and hungry on that dark night, Bill could see people comfortably eating their evening meal.

Impulsively, Bill got aboard the train and walked into the dining car. He sat down and ordered a complete meal. When the conductor came to collect, Bill stood next to the fat man in his dark blue suit and shoved his .22 pistol into his belly and demanded cash from everyone in the car. Then he entered the adjoining Pullman car where the passengers had plenty of money. He instructed the trembling porter to pass his cap to take up the collection. Finally, Bill entered the chair car. He shared some of his recently good fortune with those who looked less prosperous.

After this action was reported Bill became sort of a folk-hero to many. The Union Pacific coal miners liked his style because they believed themselves underpaid. And the ranchers perhaps thought of him as a modern Robin Hood. It seemed to them the railroad charged them too much to ship their cattle.

Carlisle plagued the UP officials for weeks. He even told them, in letters he wrote to the Denver Post newspaper, which train he would rob next. He went to Colorado and bought himself a new wardrobe. He kept his promise and they placed detectives on all trains to apprehend the train robber. He held up two more trains before a posse cornered him in the hills along the Platte River. Then he went to the Penitentiary in Rawlins.

After a few years as a model prisoner, Bill planned a unique way to ride another train. The state had prisoners make and ship shirts from the Penitentiary to the market.

Carlisle worked in the shipping area and built himself a special box. When the truck came to take the order to the depot Bill was in one of them. Later, at the depot they found one box lighter than it should be. Bill was missing!

He left Rawlins on his usual conveyance--a UP freight train. The sheriff and his deputies, with company detectives, searched every train. Some sat near him without recognizing the man they desperately wanted. After he held up a passenger car or two Bill had departed sometimes from a moving train. Once they got near him in the hills where he had just eaten his breakfast with a sheepherder in his covered wagon. When they left, Bill disappeared.

After his fourth successful train robbery Carlisle headed to the ranches in the Laramie Peak area where he had many friends. He ran on foot and hid in the rocks and sagebrush to stay a few miles ahead of the horsemen. Several ranchers and their wives who had fed and sheltered him lied to the posse and said they had not seen him. Finally, one must have told the truth and Bill was cornered in a rancher's bedroom where he was trying to get some much needed rest. When a sheriff beat on his door he came out with his hands up. A trigger happy, perhaps frightened officer, shot him in the shoulder.

. . . .

When I arrived in Laramie in 1932 to practice dentistry, I knew Dr. Lee Storey who treated Bill's wound in the Douglas hospital. Fear of infection in the patient led Dr. Storey to plead to keep him hospitalized longer, but the law overruled him. They took him to Rawlins and he survived to become a long term prisoner.

With the help and encouragement of a Catholic priest, Carlisle was a model prisoner and took an oath to live within the law. After 20 years he was paroled, much to the objections of the Union Pacific. He followed the priest to Kemmerer, Wyoming, and there met the nurse who had cared for him in Douglas. They were married and the couple built a tourist home in Laramie. Bill became a respected business man, and was an avid bowler in tournaments.

He wrote a great book on his life, and when I bought one from him he autographed it for me. Bill was frank and honest when I visited with him. Somehow I loaned the book and lost it. (My advice is that you loan none of your favorite books, but if you do keep a good record on them.)

. . . .

Now, you might ask just what did my Uncle Fritz have to do with the story of Carlisle? Well, as a Hanna kid I remember the a day or two before Bill was captured. Of course, Dan, at that time there was no radio or TV. Hanna phones belonged to the Coal Company and were not available to us. But news spread effectively throughout the town. Cowboys and their horses were recruited from the surrounding ranches by the Railroad to search for the train robber. I remember when they assembled as a posse which rode out of town searching for Carlisle. Among them was my Uncle Fritz.

When news came to Hanna that Carlisle was captured it was announced loudly by train and mine whistles. I was glad that Uncle Fritz was not at the scene of Bill's final arrest.

UNCLE ADOLPH STEBNER

The Stebner men were capable of working with anything mechanical. As a young boy I found it fascinating to go into their bachelor quarters where they slept and worked. It was next door to the to the home in which their parents and their sisters, Tillie and Martha lived. The entire family had their meals together cooked by my grandmother with the help of her daughters.

I was entranced with the bachelors quarters. There was a long work bench which held big vices, wrenches, hammers, saws and a variety of tools. The scene and the smell of oil and wood made a little boy's nerves tingle. There was always a gun, an Indian motorcycle, or a bicycle being repaired.

Adolph took me hunting before I had a gun of my own. We went to the Old Carbon area, which he knew so well, and there he shot sage chicken with an old double barrel 12 gauge shotgun. I thought he must have been the best shot in Wyoming.

He cherished his bachelorhood, but on a trip to Denver he met a frail woman whose devoted care helped him out-live his other two bachelor brothers. They were married late in life and had no children. Her name was Blanche and she provided him with a good home. When Uncle Adolph died my mother looked out for Blanche.

Uncle Adolph saw me graduate from high school, and was very proud because someone in the family made it. He stretched his budget to present me with a marvelous pocket watch, which I eventually presented to Ken Stebner. This prize will eventually go to you Danny. Adolph also lived long enough to visit my dental office in Laramie.

The first radio I ever saw was in Adolph's home after my dad died. It was weird box with five or six dials. Also there was a set of ear pieces we used to hear scratchy music and other voices which were being broadcast. If we had all of the dials turned right it was good entertainment. My uncle spent many evening hours working with that radio.

ADOLPH TAUGHT ME TO SWIM

Hanna youth had no opportunity to learn about swimming but Uncle Adolph planned for me to be confident in a body of water. His job outside of the mine was running the power plant which generated electricity for the mine and the town.

Hot water coming from the boilers was sprayed into the air to be cooled before it returned to the boilers. The cooler water was stored in a concrete basin which was quite deep. This left a narrow area outside the sprays. Aldolph bought some inflatable "Water-Wings" and put them across the chests of myself and one of my pals so that we could float and dog-paddle around the edges of the pond. Adolph's hand was available to lift us out if we got into trouble. Eventually I was able to paddle across a shallow a few miles from town, without the water-wings.

After I joined the Navy during WW II and moved my family to Spirit Lake, Idaho, with other Navy personnel and friends, we swam in the lake. At first I could swim no more than thirty feet, but I decided that before the summer was over I would improve. This I did!

It was evident that at the navy base many recruits were unable to swim. Many drowned in the Pacific Ocean because they could not even swim to a nearby life-boat. I expected orders to a Navy ship and made up my mind I did not want to be one of them. My swimming style amateurish, but, before that summer ended, with the assurance of a nearby boat, I swam completely across Spirit Lake, which was about a third of a mile. Then I felt more confident about getting sea duty.

This experience caused me realize that Laramie kids deserved a better opportunity to learn to save themselves in water. When I returned from the service I was pushing the city for its first swimming pool. Despite considerable opposition, a group of us worked to build a pool in the High School. Today Laramie High School excels among Wyoming swim teams.

. . . .

Don't let too many people run through your life.
Warren W. Grothe

The Cottage Home

MARY AND WORLD WAR ONE

Dear Dan:

During World War One mother became a business woman and served her country and community at the same time. A new school was built in Hanna, and the old one provided space that could be used for bedrooms and a large kitchen and dining room. The Coal Company remodeled it for boarders, who would help mine the coal that was desperately needed to carry troop trains and military supplies in our war effort. Mother became the boarding house proprietor for single miners, many imported from the Appalachian coal fields. She called it the 'Cottage Home,' and it was a fine home for dozens of miners. Beyond that it was a place where she could feed and clothe her children. Her hard work provided an income she desperately needed.

Hanna imported experienced miners from the coal fields of Pennsylvania and West Virginia, and many of them lived at mother's Cottage Home. Some were pretty good guys, but others were tough and crude. They drank moonshine whiskey during that Prohibition era. It was wild, especially on pay-days when they gathered on the cement floor in the wash house. It was a great place to shoot craps for money. I often heard them sing ribald songs and some played string musical instruments. Often they fought one another just to see who was the toughest.

Some who ate at our table were even on the lam from the law. Occasionally an officer came to our boarding house and picked up a fugitive for crimes commited elsewhere.

MARY FORD, PIONEER INNKEEPER

Quotations from Erne Linford (LARAMIE BOOMERANG) when Mary Ford had moved to Laramie. And, also a story written by Rebecca Northen, who wrote in an article which was featured in the DENVER POST magazine section 33 years previously.

(Linford) "Even though a broken hip slowed down her many activities several years ago, Mrs. Ford now gets around without a cane and is a stalwart in the Senior Citizens movement. That organization held an annual picnic in her backyard on North Eight street each July. An ardent fan, this diminutive bundle of energy, is a familiar figure at football and basketball games at the University and served as cheerleader for the older fans. She was a state officer of the Pythian Sisters lodge and traveled around the state to visit all local lodges until her driver's license came under question."

. . . .

(Northen) "The center of life in Hanna is its one hotel, Mary Ford's hotel. There from 4:30 a.m. often to midnight, Mary ministers to the needs of about 30 miners. She feeds them, packs their lunch pails, tends to their finances, referees their fights, is confessor of their misdeeds. She ministers also to the needs of the whole town. And if Mary were to leave, the heart of the people would go with her."

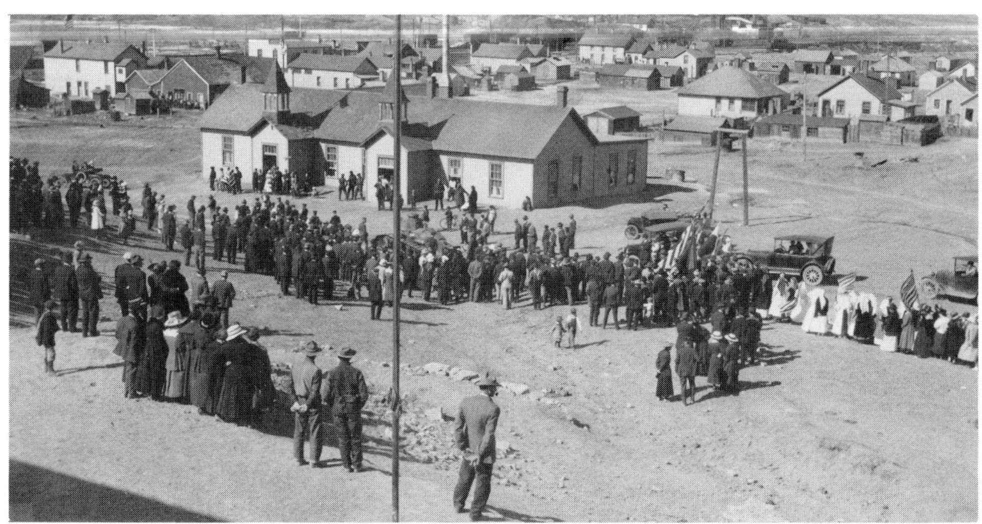

A Liberty Bond drive and parade passed in front of Cottage Home during WW I.

(Linford describing Mary's arrival to Hanna in 1906.) "Everything was so bare, so unfriendly. No fences, no grass, no trees. Just the town, the mines, and space." Mary "believed that only her sense of humor kept her afloat in these days of grief and hardship. Also important was the sense of being needed. She helped nurse the community through the memorable influenza epidemic of World War I, turning her boarding house into a hospital with cots crowded into every room. After this siege, Mary was in demand and on call for family illnesses and accidents."

Northen reports, "During World War II it was Mary who practically kept the mine open."

An Austrian miner known as Mike, told Northen, "She makes us all go to work. We no get up. Miss Mary come and knock on the door. She says, 'Mike, you get up.' I say I gon' sleep some more. She say, 'Mike, you get up and go to work today, there's a war goin' on. So I get up. Like that. She tell me to do it."

MARY FORD IN COTTAGE HOME

Little Mary was running the Cottage Home long before Ford came into the picture, and she had a lot of fans among the boarders. She was still young and beautiful, with a lot of enthusiasm and a sense of humor. She had two young children who were sometimes in the way and discouraged those who were most interested in her.

One day, in her usual hurried way she was about to do her weekly washing in the shower and wash room which was a separate building at the back of the boarding house. As she sang, or whistled, about 9:30 AM, after all the miners were at work, she busily opened the door of the laundry and men's shower room. When she entered she was shocked to see one of her younger boarders, who came home early that day, standing and facing her during his shower. Of course, both of them were embarrassed and shocked seeing the other in that situation. She screamed and rapidly retreated back to the safety of her kitchen to tell the hired help of her awkward experience. They all laughed and kidded her.

Later, as she told me and others, she said, "It was awful. If the damn fool had just held the wash cloth in front of his face, I would have never known who he was!" I was old enough to understand, and asked the question for which she would never forgive me. "Really, mother, are you sure you wouldn't know him?" She took the rolling pin and ran me out of the house as everyone present howled!

BUGS AT THE COTTAGE HOME

When Mary established herself in the old cottage home during World War I and began to accept transient boarders, some of them were not too clean. A few of them carried little red bedbugs with them. That presented Mary with a problem concerning her desire for cleanliness.

I remember working with her and Elsie as we tried to eliminate them from the new mattresses upon which the boarders slept. I can still see the lines of their little red bodies in the seams around the edges of the mattresses--there were endless rows of the little devils. Each of us had small cloths which we dipped into solutions of kerosene and attempted to dislodge them. They reminded me of the sage-ticks that we would find on our clothes or our bodies when we had been out of town walking in the sage-brush. In the summer we would carry the bedding out into the sunshine where we could easily see the little pests. Somehow, we finally eliminated the last of them. Those we did not kill with the kerosene probably attached themselves to one of the many boarders who came to Hanna.

ALEXANDER THE BOARDER

The miners were generally a rough and sometimes crude group but some even became our good friends. At least I had many big brother and father images among them. But they would drink bootleg whiskey, fight among themselves, shoot craps, and play real hard baseball. In those boom days they worked hard to produce the needed coal.

Alexander and a big guy named Mike decided to fight just to see who was the toughest. Soon after supper they decided to fight for the title. Each weighed about 200 pounds, and with their bare fists they slugged it out in the dirt of the front yard of the Cottage Home. Each had a cheering team who watched the fun. They were both drinking from the same bottle of bootleg whiskey.

When the sun went down they entered their rooms for a rest. No one bothered them as they rested on their own blood-soaked beds. We all would have called the struggle a draw, but during the night they awakened and started to fight in the building. Then my mother finally called me out of bed to "go and get Snapper". He was the only law officer, the Deputy Sheriff. He was tougher than any guy in town. We had no phones in Hanna then, so I climbed Tipperay hill to call him.

Snapper broke up the friendly fight. He threw both of them in the little building called the jail where there was only one cell. Of course they slept it off until they had sobered up and were again good friends. Then he simply freed them. For several days each sported black eyes, missing teeth, bruised knuckles.

ALEXANDER AND THE BLACK BASEBALL

Alexander was my favorite boarder at the Cottage Home. The big red-headed Irishman sometimes played catch with me in the front yard. I had a catcher's mitt and he used a pitcher's glove. We would play for an hour or more after supper. He was patient and helpful and in time I improved to catch the ball which he threw with increasing speed. He bragged about my technique. To demonstrate to one of his friends he said, "Now, look as I really pour it on." I was ready and eager to show-off and he threw about as hard as he could. I still can feel how heavy my catcher's mitt was, as I tried to raise it to my face. The glove did not get there in time. The baseball hit me in the left eye, and the lights simply went out.

Later, I awakened on my mother's bed. Alexander was there trying to tell how he was sorry. I opened the only eye that would work and tried to smile at him. For days there were cold wet packs on the black eye. When it did open everything seemed blurry. We were happy that I was not blinded.

THE BLACK BASEBALL

The rubber ball we played with was larger and softer than a regular baseball. The difference was important as we played catch. If we used a real hard baseball it might have damaged some of our delicate home decorations. As it was we were careful and we broke nothing.

When I was a youngster the only balls we ever saw were black baseballs. Now, I am sure you will ask, "weren't they white?" Well, when I was a kid in Hanna we played only with black baseballs. We couldn't afford white ones.

Recently, Mary and I were vacationing in San Diego, California. There I was with my good friend, and adopted brother, Jim Vernetti. Jim never had a brother, and I lost LeRoy when he was only five years old. So, Jim and I agreed to mentally adopt each other--great idea wasn't it? Jim was a perfect host and wanted me to know his own grandchildren. Finally, we found his son Ron and Jim's youngest grandson who were having batting practice on one of their baseball fields.

We watched the father and son, whose name was Tony. The whole procedure was new to me. Ron had more than a dozen baseballs (and they were white) and he would place them, one at a time, into a machine which would literally fire the ball at home plate. Tony would hit it in the direction his Dad suggested. That was quite different than when I played baseball in One Town in Hanna. Then, the only practice I remember was on a rocky field and the balls were thrown by an opposing team pitcher.

Finally, I shook Ron's hand and met Tony. I told them that I was surprised to see that their practice balls were white. The only time I saw white balls was when the Hanna men played Rawlins but I never touched one of those horsehide covers. We kids were poor and could not buy white balls. The men gave us balls that had lost their cover. We made an improvised cover with black friction tape.

I only played when they needed a ninth man. Batting averages were never heard of, but mine would have been very low. I believe I was smallest and lightest member of our high school and fraternity team in college. My position was that of catcher. Today, the biggest team member seems to be the catcher, possibly because he is tougher and more durable to take the beating around home plate. In Hanna we had no mask, or other protective equipment.

Now, I think I know why they selected me for that position. It took nine players to make a team and I was the last chosen. Many of the kids in One Town who had fathers had baseball gloves, and even black baseballs and a bat. Any extra equipment belonged to the Ojala family, Gus and George. They were a Finnish family and apparently their dad had a good job in the mines. At least they were enterprising and knew how to save their money. They were the only family that I knew who had an early automobile which took them fishing toward the Elk Mountain area.

The Ojala family had control of the other kids because of various reasons. They had a few cows and were the only producers of milk which they peddled to who couldn't afford a cow. I was proud when I helped them gather the cows and peddle some of their milk. It seems that they had a concession with Tom Love to carry drinking water in buckets for picture show patrons. Sometimes they helped me get in to see the show. All of these efforts on my part were to butter them up so that I could play on their One Town baseball team.

Finally, I was selected as the catcher with their big mitt. There was no mask, no body pad or shin guards. The catcher was selected on guts to take foul- tips or pitches in the dirt. I guess I had the fortitude and the desire to be chosen for that position. Later, in High School, they did furnish me with a mask.

I have vivid memories of times when I was hit with that black baseball which skipped into my unprotected body when I was behind the plate. It seemed that all the big, strong guys were the pitchers. I was an easy out at bat when they wound up and cut loose. This was especially true when the pitcher was a big raw-boned ranch kid from Saratoga. His name was Grooman. He made that black baseball look like it was the size of a pea. I think it would have been easier if the ball had been white.

Doctor Jim Vernetti and I visit often. Once I had a package from his lawyer son, Ron. He and young Tony sent me a present. When I opened it, we laughed as we found a black baseball. I am saving it for my Grandson. He should know all baseballs are <u>not white</u>!

TROOP TRAINS AND THE COTTAGE HOME

In 1918 Hanna was a busy place because the UP was mining all the coal they could. Many passenger trains were full of our troops while their engines took on coal and water in Hanna. With the window and doors open we could see the men in uniform as they headed for training, or to ship to France. Wives and mothers greeted them with knitted gloves and scarfs that they would need in the trenches of Europe. Also, we passed out all of the Camel and Lucky Strike cigarettes which we could scarcely afford. There were sincere cheers and happy waving between the townspeople and the soldiers.

We knew they soon would be on a ship to carry them to England, and then to France, to face the Kaiser's battle-tested German army. It was the same kind of troop train that carried Uncle John to a training camp.

UNCLE JOHN ENLISTS

Mother had no sister, but one fine brother, my Uncle John. I guess that you could say that he was a hero image of mine. He was the kind of a person especially young boys might imitate. Although he worked in the coal mine he always looked clean, unlike many of the miners who were not as careful about removing the coal dust when their day's work was over. He and mother were taught to scrub themselves. (I think that mother over-did it at times. She abhorred blackheads on one's face and when she scrubbed me with a rough wash-cloth and they did not disappear she used a brass pot scratcher with just enough pressure that there was no bleeding. Just the threat of having it handy made me work harder.)

When my parents were married, my dad informally adopted Uncle John, who was about 15 years of age. This family relationship was common in Hanna following the tragic explosion. Bachelor men seemed to feel some unexplained duty to marry a widow and raise her children. Perhaps, that explains why Uncle John tried to assume the father image. There was no high school in Hanna. John left school as soon as the Company would let him work in the mine.

Uncle John, in his youth, was a well coordinated left-handed first baseman on the Hanna men's baseball team. He worked on ranches during the summer and rode Bruno's horse Old Joe in the Fourth of July races.

Later, he dated a Hanna school teacher--Georgia Weston. Soon, the United States became involved in WW I, and Uncle John and a few of his buddies joined the Army. I have fond recollections of John and a few of his friends standing in a crowd at the depot with the unfurled Stars and Stripes, as they waited for the train which would eventually take him to France. It was a proud and patriotic moment for a ten-year-old Charlie. Years later I found that Uncle John had received a summons from England; "The King needs your services in the British Army." He chose to be an American, and was granted his citizenship papers at the time of his discharge.

In 1917 the Hanna American Legion group at the Funeral of Bill Jones, who was killed in France. Soon after this Uncle John Hughes enlisted in the Army and left Hanna on a troop train.

Standing are Mike Stravakis, Alex Greenwood, Bill Wright, Eli Johnson, unknown..., Albin Klaseen, Lynn Smith, unknown..., John Hughes in the white shirt before he was issued a uniform, unknown..., Killison, unknown..., Dr. Stoddard (Hanna dentist), Red Hapbood, Joe Jackson, Pete Owen.

UNCLE JOHN RETURNS FROM FRANCE

It was a great day when the returning train brought Uncle John back to the Hanna depot. He was in full uniform. It was great for him and me--he married Georgia Weston, and I got his steel helmet! Uncle John moved to his and Georgia's home in Hanna. They called it 'Tipperary' because it was separate from the post office, the railroad and the center of town. The name came from the song British soldiers sang, saying , "It's a long way to Tipperary." It seemed a long way in Hanna from the railroad, the post office and the Cottage Home when it was built for miners who increased the population during the war.

I was disappointed that the helmet showed no battle scars. I fixed that--I took it out into the prairie and shot it with a .22 rifle. It made an impressive dent, which I could show to my pals. It raised my status, especially with the individuals who gave me a bad time because of my German name.

Soon, following the Armistice, Uncle John and my new Aunt Georgia moved to California to work in the ship yards. After a few years the desire for employment in the mines caused them to return to Hanna. Perhaps that generation of the Hughes family realized the importance of an education. They raised two unique and successful college graduates, my cousins Gordon and Elaine. They were both successful in their chosen fields.

Uncle John worked and studied diligently to eventually be recognized as management material. This was accomplished with very limited schooling. Ultimately, he worked his way into the management strata of Union Pacific Coal Company.

These responsibilities allowed him very little time for recreation and fun. After his retirement he was still lean and healthy, and my family included him in all our hunting camps. He loved the outdoors and we enjoyed those days together. My own three children and wife were very attached to Uncle John. Like his sister he had a keen sense of Lanky humor. He died after a short illness at the home of his son in Winston Salem.

Friends

SCHOOL PALS

Dear Dan:

I want to tell you about a couple of Hanna families I knew well when I was a kid. The Hanna Lanky Cleggs, the Italian Scarpellis, and most of the Finlanders.

As a kid I admired, and often envied most of them. They were huskier and healthier than I. They were families with mothers, dads and sisters and brothers. I had a mother, for which I was always thankful--but no father after I was five years old. Most of all, I noticed they had a regular dinner hour when they all congregated at the table. This happened during the big evening meal, which we called supper.

My mother worked pretty hard at the Cottage Home boarding house and later at the Hanna Hotel, but the atmosphere was different. At five o'clock I would go to the kitchen and load my plate with gravy, meat, and peas--the rest was canned food which didn't interest me. There were few salads like we have today. We had no fresh milk, and I didn't enjoy the canned milk which was diluted with water. I drank plenty of water with my meals. Bread and butter were staples for me. When I was in school some fellow said that he knew what my middle name 'M' stood for he was sure it meant 'More bread'! The Italians, the Finns, and some Lankies planted vegetable gardens.

In One Town some of the Finns had a few cows, which they milked each day. After I had eaten my supper alone in the big kitchen I remember walking past my friends little four-room homes and watching through the windows, as they all ate together in their lighted kitchens. When it was dark during the winter I was envious. Then I realized that I was bothered because I was not part of a similar family.

Often I'd meet one the guys to accompany me to a basketball game, or go to a play practice, but more often to the pool hall. The loneliness was not because I wasn't socially active. I had plenty of pals and top girl friends. I was involved in every activity because I took the lead in most of our school plays, and I was a better shot than most of them at the pool hall. If there was mischief to be done, I led the group. At that age it hurt a lot not be allowed to be athletically involved. Now, I know that my problem was infected tonsils which caused kidney infections. This affected me physically and mentally.

My health picture improved. It was a matter of basics in diet and exercise. I turned out to be a tough and wiry guy as I miraculously reached my 79th birthday.

LASTING FRIENDSHIPS

Treasure your <u>real</u> friends! Some one said that in a life-time a person is lucky to be able to count them on a single hand. Sure, there will be hundreds of acquaintances you will enjoy. But few of these will be classified as friends. The few loyal friends understand you, and you can tell them what is on your mind. A definition of a real friend that person who knows all your faults and is forever loyal.

Mutuality is the key! Friendship is never one-sided. Each must know the other person's ambitions, accomplishments and goals. Often they share disappointments and troubles. Longevity is another necessity we must measure for a prolonged time of the relationship. Eric Lepponen's and my friendship began in grade school and lasted more than 60 years, until he died. Eric Lepponen and I met all of these qualifications. We could predict one another's ideas and actions.

Perhaps it began with music. Eric was a talented pianist, and I was a mediocre clarinetist. I was the only one who was not a Finn, but was still accepted in the Hanna Finnish Symphony Orchestra. Our older director did not speak

English, so I had to learn some of his language. Eric and myself joined other Finn boys to form a Jazz Band during the mid-1920's. This group played for the first dance at the old Elk Mountain Garden Spot dance hall. After I went to college Mark Jackson, a well known Hanna Lanky, reorganized the group. He included a fine Italian musician who worked in the mine--Bert Tavelli. I suppose they were an international group who played for dances in the area.

Besides our interest in music Eric and I spent countless hours fishing and hunting, and later had our first dates with girls. When we were seniors in high school we drank alcohol in the form of wine which we stole from a Greek miner. We had our first hangover together. During those high school years that was my first and only experience. But it was just the beginning for Eric. Very many years later he became an alcoholic, and later still a self-cured alcoholic.

Following our high school graduation, we worked as partners on manual labor jobs to save money to further our educations. Eric spent a year at the Chicago Conservatory of Music and I went away to study dentistry. When Eric was drinking heavily we were not able to communicate very well. But when he sobered up again we fished, and hunted. Years later, I dug out my clarinet and visited him, and we played together just as we did 55 years before when we were in high school. We saw one another often and again enjoyed our long friendship, until he died.

. . . .

When I came to practice dentistry in Laramie I found another great friend--Warren Grothe. He and his father owned a lumber yard. Although he was a few years older than I, we shared the same interests. That friendship carried on with our wives, our children and grandchildren. It didn't only endure, it developed into marvelous fruition!

BILL CLEGG and KAT KANDOLIN

My health picture improved. It was a matter of basics in diet and exercise. I turned out to be a tough and wiry guy as I miraculously reached my 78th birthday. Others I knew were not so lucky.

Bill Clegg was a Hanna High school athlete. He was a year older than I, but we were good friends. I admired him. Both the girls and fellows liked Bill. He was a good student and an fine athlete. Never in his life did he abuse himself in any way. He was the star on our basketball team, and I was the Cheer Leader! Later, when Hanna began to play football Bill was the captain. Red Grange was the best athlete Illinois University ever had, and it seemed natural that Bill would go there where he learned to be a coach.

Following our senior year in high school, Bill worked for the Wyoming Timber Company, and when they needed more help with the loading of railroad ties, he encouraged his brother Jim, Eric, Kat Kandolin and myself to apply. We worked mostly at the Fort Steele loading plant for several years.

Bill was a purist. Neither did the girls or mischief distract his clean living. As an example, Bill ignored a beautiful blonde girl. If she had flicked an eyelash in my direction I would have fallen in love. No luck for me! She was awe-struck with Bill.

Bill saved every cent he earned at work, but even then it must have been a sacrifice for his coal mining Dad to send him to Illinois. I saw him only once after he went to Salt Lake City where he married a fine Mormon girl. At that time he worked at the University of Utah physical education staff and was also a sports reporter for the newspaper there. In spite of his careful living and strong body he died at a rather young age.

. . . .

Another all around athlete who was more fun to be around was Wilho Kandolin. He was in our class, played the drums in our orchestra and was the fastest kid on our high school teams. He and I double-dated two swell young girls and he was a good all around sport. We called him Kat--after Crazy Kat in the funnies. We never knew what idea would appeal to him next. It was unbelievable that he would die young with a weak heart.

When I remember those two fine athletes, both who died a long while ago, it is hard to understand the cheer-leader would survive both of them. Good genes, I guess!

HANNA ITALIANS

And now, Dan, I want to tell you about the Italian family which made a great impression on me. With their Catholic background, the Scarpelli family knew nothing of birth control. They were a family of about 15 kids. Sam was older, but Ralph was in my class. I really enjoyed them and would visit their house each time I came home from College. I was always most eager to see their wonderful mother and father.

They were exuberant and stimulating. They all talked at once and made me feel good. Their dialect was wonderful and I have told many stories as I tried to imitate their broken Italian.

My father befriended them when they came to this country. They thought he was a saint for his kindness to them, and Mrs. Scarpelli seemed to place me on a pedestal. My great friend, Dr. Jim Vernetti came to hunt sage grouse and antelope with me, and I wanted him for meet some Hanna Italians, of course with a name like his I wanted him to feel at home. They had a good visit as they spoke in their native tongue, but finally Jim started to give me a bad time, but Mrs. Scarpelli didn't realize Jim was kidding. She said, "Donta you say bad tings bout my Sharlie. Hesa gooda boy." It's great to have old friends who stand up for you!

RALPH SCARPELLI II

In my college days my first stop during the Christmas holidays was to see the Scarpellis and Besignanos. They opened a new bottle of their home-made wine, known as Dago Red, in my honor. Often, my mother, at the hotel, would send someone to get me home for the Christmas dinner. She knew that I should not have another water glass full of wine.

Ralph Scarpelli was in my high school class, and I've been able see him more often than I have other classmates. After our graduation he worked at the Hanna railroad coal chutes where trains stopped to take on coal and water. A few years ago I taped him at our house after we played golf. Some time, Dan, you can listen to it. These were his words. . . .

"I was above the coal car and had a bar trying to loosen the coal on the shakers. Finally the coal jam broke and I fell into the traveling shakers and was carried to the car and dumped with the coal. Much coal began to follow me until I was being covered by tons of coal. It all happened so fast, but before the coal covered my head, I screamed for help. There were tons of coal under my feet and more tons of coal fell around me and over my head. I was in a tomb!

"My brother, Sam, who was working with me, finally shut off the shakers and it was still and very quiet. I began to think it was a wild dream and maybe I thought I was going crazy. I knew I'd had it!

"I was not hurt but I had coal in my mouth and I was frozen with coal and immovable. Eventually I passed out.

"What happened above me was unbelievable. A passenger train was next to the car I was trapped in, and they unhooked its engine to pull my car into the open where they could unload it to recover my body. The coal which trapped me was fortunately not powdered slack, but there were lumps and chunks which allowed some air near my head.

"Eager workmen, especially Sam, began to uncover the coal above my head. My mother and father lived very close and the excitement brought them to the area. I regained consciousness enough to hear a shovel near me and I was afraid it would hit me. It didn't! When I was completely uncovered they put me on the ground and soon I could see my weeping mother. Yes, I was bruised, but had no broken bones or dangerous cuts. I think the Lord had something for me to accomplish during the future."

Ralph had enough of the coal in a mining camp. Soon he enlisted to join the Army to fight against Hitler. His charmed life protected him in Europe where he was with a tank crew that approached the Rhine. Without any more education than his Hanna High school diploma, he adapted himself and was advanced to get many breaks few enlisted men accomplish.

His commanding officer got him a pass into the courtroom where Nazi criminals were on trial. There, Ralph watched Goering and dozens of Hitler's men being prosecuted. It was a rare moment in our history which he witnessed.

Later, Ralph saw action in the Korean War and still has strong feelings about military and political mistakes. He especially condemns our lack of political action which kept his group from entering Berlin.

During WW II the Scarpelli family had four sons serve in the Army. Their father was very proud of them, because, even with his dialect, he considered himself 100% all American. Some Hanna immigrants sent money back to their original home country. Not the old man Scarpelli because he loved America.

Ralph is the guy who whipped me in one of the fair fights we had in Hanna. Yes, when we play a game of golf, he continues to beat me on the course each summer.

At times I wonder how my early experiences affected me. Maybe courage comes to guys like Ralph and myself from our early difficult environment. Or, we became the individual we are because of the genes we inherited.

. . . .

Don't go out of your way to step on a stink-bug. You will carry the odor with you.

Warren W. Grothe

Fights

UNITED NATIONS--FIGHTS

Dear Dan:

In Hanna we were, in fact, a little United Nations. We learned to amalgamate as mixed groups. I don't want anyone to get the idea that we never had any fights--we had plenty of them, but they were never based on color or nationality.

The fights were personal, usually just to see who was the best man. Kids fought often so that they could establish a pecking order. In other words, we could say, "Last week I whipped Joe and Joe whipped Urho, so there's no need for us to fight." Winning one good fight could take you a long way up the ladder and save a lot of tears, and sometimes a bloody nose. If two kids got into an argument, we often settled it by placing a little stick on the shoulder of one of them. If the other guy refused to knock it off, he was a step down the ladder by admitting that the fellow with the stick on his shoulder was the better man. Now you know, Dan, what is meant when people speak of somebody always going around with a "chip on his shoulder." But if he keeps it up, he will eventually be challenged and finally find someone tougher.

If you are wondering about my fights, then, the answer is yes! I had too many fights, and I won some and lost a few others. I will tell you some one of each category.

Being without a father or a big brother, I think that I had to become a pretty good salesman and a bit of a bluffer and that kept me from too many fights. I won one with one punch. A new kid had just come to town and he was about my size so we had to fit him into our pecking order. The other guys talked me into checking him. Luckily he was timid, and before he could get his dukes up I landed a punch as hard as possible into his softly rounded solar plexus. Well, he lost all of his air and folded up crying on the ground. From then on he was known as "soft belly".

All kids in Hanna started at the bottom of the pecking order by fighting kids in their grade. We had a real big kid in our room who'd been held back several grades, but he was also timid and easy to bluff. Now and then, I would write him a few notes in school and threaten to get him when school was out. It was always fun to chase him home. One day however, it was different because I cornered him between a fence and a house. With no way to escape he turned around and beat the hell out of me! He went up in the pecking order and I dropped. From that time on, I never challenged a kid that big unless I had a rock or a club.

Another boy much taller and stronger than I was several years older. I thought I had a score to settle for something I had said about him. He caught me alone and threw me on the only grass we had in town. It was near the band stand where adults played weekly band concerts. With his knees on my small arms, he sat on my stomach and laughed while he spit in my face. I struggled and cried a lot, to no avail. When he tired of the trauma he caused me by spitting in my face, he left laughing. That day I promised myself no guy would ever humiliate me so crudely without paying for it.

A few weeks later there was a kids' baseball game going in One Town. The bully had his arms folded and standing with others waiting his turn to bat. I sneaked up behind him and grabbed a baseball bat and hit the big bully across the shoulders and neck. He went down in a heap and I hurried home thinking that he might be dead. When he recovered, he and the others who witnessed it said, "That Chuck Stebner is crazy. He will kill someone one day." That episode kept me from many fights. That reputation was just what a skinny kid without another male in his family needed.

Yes, Dan, there was another fight I should have avoided. Ralph Scarpelli. He is a good friend of mine even after more than 60 years. We had good Italian friends who were our neighbors. We knew and appreciated one another's families. It happened on a day when things must have been dull. Someone suggested that Ralph and I should see who was the best fighter. If I had been smarter I would simply have let him move up in the pecking order, with no contest. He was tough and probably heavier than I, and after a good struggle he whipped me! Since that time we have been good friends. Things haven't changed much because when he comes to Laramie we play a game of golf. Sure, he beats me there too!

When the kids fought, none seemed to get hurt, but the better fights were between grown men. These were rare and often both the loser and winner showed signs of serious encounters. It was the same in a few fights I observed among older girls and women. I remember two young women fighting over a boy-friend. After some screaming spiced with profanity they took off their shoes and used them as weapons. Hair was pulled and blows were struck. Finally the men broke it up. Women get pretty vicious and are pretty scary to watch.

When I was only about seven or eight years old I witnessed a tragic gun fight between two imported Greek miners. My mother and I were enjoying the early summer sunrise as we sat on our small porch. Running from the direction of the mine the first Greek passed us and entered a house several doors down from us. We wondered about his hurry, but mother thought he had forgotten something at his house that he was expected to take to work that morning. There was a train on the tracks where it took on coal and water, and mother and I a second miner sneaking to board a car to leave town.

Suddenly, the first Greek came out of his house with a revolver in his hand and pointed it toward the man who was sneaking near the train. There were several shots fired and the fellow by his house fell over. The winner of that fight calmly kept walking eastward to the edge of town and headed for the hills.

Mother and I hurried into the house and when the train pulled away she sent me to the Depot to tell the agent Mr. Tolliver to call the sheriff because a man was killed in the street. Well, the sheriff was in Rawlins forty miles away. During that time the dead man, who was shot through the head, lay there in a puddle of blood. There was a good group of kids around the body and I remember that we were throwing pebbles into the blood where the flies had gathered.

About noon the lawman arrived and arranged for a coal company wagon to load the body and take it to the cemetery for a quick burial. We later heard the two men had an argument at the mine about some sort of family feud originating in Greece. No one made any effort to follow the killer.

THE DANCE HALL FIGHT

When I was about a freshman or sophomore in high school I saw a fight following a dance which should have been photographed. They could use the real thing in a tough western movie. Many of those old pictures built a romantic theme around a desirable girl.

I am not sure of the summer when it occurred but 1924 or 1925 is not far off. A good-looking young man came to Hanna and was one of our boarders when he worked in the coal mines. I seem to remember that he was from some place in Pennsylvania. He had some pugilist training there--that was his first mistake. His second mistake was to go to the dances every Saturday night at the Garden Spot Dance Hall in Elk Mountain, where I played in an orchestra with Jack Cook's jazz band. There he did something no Hanna native would ever do and that was to date a beautiful Elk Mountain girl. Some of the young cowboys seemed to resent the coal-mining Hanna men getting out of his territory.

Of course it started out with a few words, which often ended up with bare knuckles. During the intermission it was announced that the young miner and a tough cowboy would fight concerning a grievance in the dance hall. Women and children were to leave the hall immediately after the last dance. This they did!

The orchestra had plenty of time to pack our instruments and we sat on benches which surrounded the dance floor. It was to be a fair fight, with timed rounds, just like prize-fighters obeyed in the big cities. There was no referee, but someone was appointed timer and when the cymbal crashed the fighters would separate and go to their corners.

It was brutal and some blood showed up early on the faces of the contestants. In an allotted minute they squared off again in the center of the floor. There was wild cheering from the cowboys and the miners'. As the base drummer hit the cymbal the two fighters quit swinging at each other. There were a lot of women and girls screaming as they watched them breaking windows and the doors. This bedlam continued only two or three timed rounds. Then there was punching and wrestling which involved many of the crowd.

Jack Cook and I stood on the bench seats to be protected. We were looking for the crowded door to make our escape to our cars, but there was no way we could make the trip without getting smacked. At one time there was one cowboy holding the arms of a miner we knew, as another rancher kept hammering at him. Jack swung his foot and ask me if he should swing. I nodded yes, and the side of Jack's foot knocked the holder to the floor so our friend could freely enter the fray.

There had to be fifteen or more men and boys fighting around the dance floor. Teeth and blood on the floor told the story. About that time someone shouted that the deputy sheriff, Jay Johnson, had gone to his car for his gun. He was known for his temper and toughness. Suddenly, people poured out of the exits. Some of the losers were helpless on the floor.

The last thing I saw was the back of the Hanna pugilist's head which was against breaking windows. He was out and lost the fight as far as I was concerned. I think I heard a shot fired outside. Suddenly the crowd disappeared.

The next day the Pennsylvania guy was in the hospital where he stayed a few days before he checked out of the mine to go back east.

I have tried to explain my view of the fight to others who were there. Everyone saw and heard different things. It appeared that the cowboys won the fight, and also the hand of the maiden. It should have been filmed!

Mary and Fred

MARY THE HOTEL PROPRIETOR

Dear Dan:

After Ford's death many Hannaites thought that my mother should move to Laramie and give up the Hotel. Good friends believed Ford had managed the hotel very well, and that Little Mary was simply the cook. They thought she should move to Laramie where her son could take care of her. They really didn't understand the extent of her capacities.

Mary making pies at the Hotel.

With all of her experience, she didn't want to give it up and I encouraged her to do as she liked. It was only a few months later that she started to save money. Still, she only charged seventy-five cents for home cooked meals. The boarders and others could have as many helpings as they wished. We were all amazed at that little girl. She made it pay. It was not hard to understand that all of the profit had been going to booze, cars, and Ford's guns. She worked just as hard, but now began to accomplish a considerable savings.

As Little Mary's savings increased, I suggested that she plan a trip to her old home in England while she still had cousins living there. Surprisingly, she was in the mood and we arranged things at the hotel so it would work. With new luggage we put her on an airplane for the first time in her life. It was the total experience for a person who had known every form of transportation during her amazing life. As a girl she only walked, then a train took her to Liverpool, a ship to America, a horse and buggy that Bruno had for her to enjoy, then her own Buick with Ford; and now a big plane to carry her back to the place of her birth. Yes, she lived to see American astronauts walk on the moon. She was adventurous and I believe that she would have welcomed the opportunity to be the first lady senior citizen to ride in space!

FRED FORD THE BOARDER

Boarders came to work in Hanna, but often some only stayed there a few days. In retrospect, I think that in those days, because there were no Social Security numbers, a few of these men who had questionable records and were just a step ahead of law officers. (In fact, the Sheriff came to our boarding house several times to pick up characters.) One these who might have had a past went by his last name only. He never liked the name "Fred," and was simply known as "Ford."

He was a complex man, and one I did not fully appreciate because of some of his characteristics. He was a great salesman and charmer, and finally sold Little Mary. She married him! I was not happy about having a stepfather when I was only eleven years old. I suppose he was jealous of me, and perhaps I was jealous of him.

I always resented him after they were married, but for Elsie it was different. She thought it was great because he solved her father image problem for a short time.

Soon Elsie became ill. Both she and I developed chronic kidney problems. Later, when I attended college, I learned more about the human body. I understood that the infection the doctors called Bright's disease, was really nephritis. Both Elsie and I had the same problem--very badly infected tonsils. We had sore throats constantly. I now believe that the toxins were carried to our kidneys. During my sixth grade I missed a lot of school because there was blood in my urine. The doctor ordered that I not attend school for weeks. That made me give up all winter sports. It bothered me because I was on the sixth grade basketball team. My urine contained albumin and blood cells even after I graduated from Creighton. Then finally two of my Laramie physician friends, Leake and Hunt, removed my tonsils. That took care of the kidney problems. Immediately, I gained weight when the infection I had carried so many years disappeared.

Unfortunately, the solution of our tonsil problem came too late for Elsie and her fragile body. She died at the age of thirteen. Her death bothered my little mother more than any of the other family deaths she had endured. Mother planned that she would sacrifice, and save the needed money to see that her daughter would enter college and become a teacher. There was little understanding from Ford. He was little help in mother's bereavement. Ford was pragmatic and suggested that many children die and one must accept the loss. His attitude encouraged me to dislike the guy even more.

During my sister's illness and death I didn't shed a tear. Elsie and I had regularly attended the Methodist Sunday school as mother insisted. Every week we sang a song, "God will take care of you." My mother's faith was unshaken, but I reacted differently. I wondered why he hadn't taken care of Elsie, and why my mother had to suffer another cruel blow. I have not recovered from that thought even today.

The day of Elsie's funeral Uncle John could see I was keeping too much within myself. He took my by the hand and encouraged me to cry. Without a word we wept together.

. . . .

Ford had some good qualities, and in many ways he helped my mother. He even taught me to hunt and fish. It was sad that at other times, the opposite side dominated his personality, especially when he was drunk. Then, no one could appreciate him.

He was secretive concerning his past. There were a loaded six-shooter and brass-knuckles in his dresser drawer. He brought these weapons with him when he came west to work for a sheep rancher in the Bear Lake area of eastern Idaho. He had also worked in the mines of Pennsylvania before coming to Wyoming. At that time there was considerable conflict between the Unions and the mine operators in Pennsylvania. I believe he left there to escape his past.

Although Ford worked in the coal mines for a while he soon gave that up to become the proprietor of the Cottage Home. Later, we learned his home had been in Leavenworth, Kansas, where he had been married and divorced.

An early Buick belonging to Ford, who stands at the rear wheel. Charlie is at the steering wheel, but was too young to drive. In the back seat are Uncle John, Aunt Georgia and Elsie.

FORD DANCES AND PLAYS BRIDGE

Both Ford and Mother loved to dance and Ford was good at it. They went to all the area balls, especially at Elk Mountain where some of the Big Name Bands played during the 1930's. They played bridge with couples that we'd call the 'upper-crust'--the owner of the Wyoming Timber Company, the manager of the UP company store, the superintendent of schools, the physician and the dentist. Theirs was a good social life in that little town.

As I look back at those days when I was in school, I appreciate what I learned from Ford on hunting and fishing trips. At first I shot a single-shot small .410 gauge gun, and Ford used a 12 gauge gun. He liked that because he was able to fill most of my limit of sage grouse, as well as his own. When we fished he caught his own limit and part of mine. As he bought new shotguns and I was old enough to carry his cast-off gun, things changed. Once, Ford confiscated the ammunition he allotted me and insisted I go to the car because I was killing his chickens.

He was real tough when he provided me with fishing flies. Mine were his rejects.

MY FIRST TROUT

I finally caught a fish! When I showed it to Ford, he ridiculed me until I nearly shed tears. He said it wasn't a fish, rather it was a sucker. After all trout were the only real fish. He made me throw it away in the brush.

About a week later Eric, Ford and I went fishing on Mill Creek near Elk Mountain. I got on my knees and worked my way through the willows to the small stream. There I found a deep secluded pool into which I tossed my worm-baited hook into the crystal clear water. As the worm swung slowly toward the floor of the wide pool floor, out dashed a BIG TROUT. He grabbed the hook and took off!

I had been taught that when this happened I was to set the hook firmly and carefully play the fish toward the surface. I didn't follow that technique. In my excitement I placed the pole over my shoulder and ran for the road. The fish was well hooked and the line and leader held. When I looked around, the fish was dangling from the line about eight feet high from a willow branch. It was about 20 feet from the pool that had been his home.

When I pulled him down where I could reach his head, I hurried to show that big brookie to Ford and Eric who were fishing above me. I could hardly wait to get to Hanna, and show the biggest fish any of us caught that day. After all it was an honest-to-God trout. Certainly not a sucker!

MARY LEARNS TO DRIVE

Mother finally learned to drive a car. Ford had always discouraged mother from ever learning how to drive. Perhaps, that was a way to keep her from being more independent, but it didn't work. A couple of years before his death they traded the old Model T in for a Chevrolet Coupe, and mother was determined to learn to drive it. She watched how Ford would start it and shift gears, and one day when he was not around she asked Jessie, who worked for us, to get in and drive to Number Three town, which was about a mile out of town. Jessie was afraid to get into the car with her because she realized it was Mary's maiden voyage.

The two of them got the car started and mother forgot what to do next, but a friend of ours was passing the hotel at that moment and she asked him to come over and answer a few questions. He did, and she turned the car around and started down the main street toward Elmo (Three Town). No doubt, she shifted gears with a little grinding and steered in the middle of the road. When she arrived in Elmo she knew that she had to turn around to get home, and there was no turnaround place. So the crisis-oriented driver turned off the road into the sagebrush and began to circle, still in high gear, back toward home. They hit a larger bush that bounced both of them to the roof and the motor, still in high gear, stalled! As the dust settled they sat there and laughed until the tears rolled down their cheeks.

Mother had spunk! When she thought over a problem, and knew she was right, she worked until it was accomplished. She wanted to come to Laramie whenever she felt it was necessary. It was not pleasant to have Ford drive her here. She decided she would learn to drive the little Chevrolet and accomplish the trip without any help.

On her first trip to Laramie she drove with confidence down the highway, but when she came into the city traffic she could find no place to park diagonally. Mary and Jennie continued to drive around the block where my downtown office was located. There was a vacant spot in front of the Albany National Bank. It was a favorite area for older men to lean against the building and gossip. Mother made another trip around the block and the space was still waiting for her Chevy. She headed into the space too fast. The front wheels bounced onto the sidewalk and the motor died. Well, by that time the men had run for cover. Mary rolled the window down and called for these fellows to come and push the Chevy back off the sidewalk. They did!

The two gals came into my office giggling about the men Mary ran off the sidewalk, but who came back to help her out. I said to mother, "Mother, the city does not hire men to push cars off the sidewalk."

. . . .

From that experience and getting out of the sagebrush in Elmo on her own, she had complete confidence. She visited all of the Pythian Sisters lodges in the State of Wyoming, and often had several of her sisters as passengers. On one occasion she drove on a trip to Newcastle, several hundred miles away, and returned on what she thought was a marvelous trip. After that trip Ford walked into the yard the day after her return and came back into the kitchen after he noticed the right front fender was caved in. He said, "What in the hell did you do to the fender?" She had forgotten a minor incident, and followed him into the yard to see what he was talking about. "Oh yes, I guess it was that bull." "What bull?" Ford asked. Mother said, "It was his fault, he walked right in front of me and I had to push him off!" It was no problem in her mind.

She drove that car for many years, mostly to Laramie and then back to Hanna. Several times she would come here to stay with her grandchildren when we went on short trips. She loved the children, but had her bags packed at the door when we came home.

She learned three grandchildren were more trouble than the boarders she had left.

Later when she moved to Laramie we sold the Chevy and bought her a new 1958 fire-engine-red in color sedan. This was her favorite automobile and she drove it thousands of miles around the state to 'lodge doins', as she called those excursions.

The last four years of her life we finally found it necessary to cancel her driving license. An unexpected cerebral mini-stroke caused her to black out on the University Campus as she parked her car to attend a concert. Later, she reluctantly presented the title to the car to our son Ron. He babied that red car until it finally wore out.

When we decided that she should not drive anymore she gave her Doctor, and me, a lot of trouble. It was hard for her give up her wheels at age 90.

The Comedian

HUMOR

Dear Dan:

Perhaps by now you have learned, as all young people should, that life is often a bit difficult, and sometimes a challenge. In other words, things do not always work out exactly the way you wish they would. I will give you an example which was very real to some people in Chicago.

Sports is a very frustrating area in our life for many of us. Here in Laramie we believe athletic contests, and this last week-end we lost a football game we thought we should have won. Well, that is a minor disappointment compared to what happened to the Chicago Cubs baseball team. In that city. It had been thirty years since they appeared in the World Series and it looked like their jinx was broken. They played very well all season and worked their way to the play-off series against the San Diego team, where they only had to win three games out of five to get into the World Series. They easily won the first two and needed another. Well, of course all Chicago Cubs fans elsewhere were unbelievably ecstatic. Tickets were sold for the Series, and unbelievable amounts of series memorabilia trinkets were stocked by merchants who hoped to make big profits. Well, sadly for the Cubs fans and team, the San Diego Padres accomplished the unbelievable odds of winning the next three games. San Diego celebrated and Chicago was sick!

What can we learn from that? Certainly, we should not take ourselves or our favorite teams too seriously. It's important that we place everything in our lives in their proper perspective. People put extreme emphasis on petty things, and sometimes these things even drive people crazy. This morning

on the TV I heard a discussion on the subject of 'agoraphobia' which is the fear of being in a large open space. Very often it causes panic and destroys some people. Now, that is a helluva disease--growing up in your family you will love the open spaces! Others suffer from claustrophobia which is the fear of enclosed spaces like an elevator. A few extreme cases simply have to stay at their home. Now, they are being treated by specialists to prevent simple stress or even panic.

When I was in the 'muddy trap' as I was on that fishing trip I guess these two phobias must have neutralized each other. Rather than treating stress as a destroyer, it could be that some stress drives some of us on to successful lives.

I see we have strayed from the title of the subject . . . HUMOR! If a person has any sense of humor he might make a wise crack in the elevator to keep others from freezing up. Try to find something which causes a smile wherever you are to relax other individuals. Humor is an antidote for any awkward situation.

Mary Ford was a genius at getting people to relax, smile or even laugh. Humor made her life more pleasant and helped everyone relax in her presence. When she first came to Laramie she agreed to drive with other ladies to a meeting. When they returned and opened the car door she began to approach the door, then the driver said, "Wait a minute Mary I will go in with you." "Why?" Mother questioned. Her friend asked "Aren't you afraid someone may have entered the back door and is waiting for you to come home. He could be waiting in your bedroom, what would you do?" The 80 year-old lady answered, without hesitation, "Gosh, I'd lock the door so he wouldn't get away!" There was no fear of the dark in that little Lanky girl! Her sense of humor brought laughter from everyone in the car.

. . . .

Our family has always appreciated humor, and to show you how this true this is. I remember something your dad said, which pleased me. That day our group were on a ski trip near Sheridan, and in the evening the entire group had a good social hour telling various entertaining stories. Ken heard me tell many stories (some true) that the group enjoyed. On the way back to our cabin he said . . .

"Dad, when you make your will I will be happy if you just leave me your sense of humor." Well, I think he has it! I have been in groups with our three kids, Marilyn, Ron and Ken, and noted their sense of humor caused much laughter. Ron's humor is not as ribald as the other two, but is more subtle--he says, "There is very little bad humor; the worst is no humor at all."

You know Dan, when you want to get any of us to take you someplace you said, "But it be fun, Uncle Ron." You worked that on Ron several times. He reports that when his alarm clock goes off at 4 A.M. to get him to work in the dark, especially when he was celebrating late the night before, he remembers your encouragement, "it be fun Uncle Ron." Then he thinks of his three year-old nephew. He smiles but does not laugh aloud.

Dan, your wonderful little mother also has a great sense of humor. She tells a few great stories which capture the fun of a group--especially if they happen to be on her father-in-Law. Your sense of humor is apparent even at the age of four, and little Ann is a fun-loving little lady. Some unfortunately did not inherit those genes.

I once heard someone say that the best sense of humor is shown when the joke you tell is on yourself. I have good reason to believe that. Too many like to poke fun about other's mistakes, and that is all right if it is done in good taste--especially, if the joke is on a good friend. But the best humor is when you encourage the story of your own faux pas.

JACK MELLOR

Jack Mellor was a bachelor and the youngest of the group which came here from England with my mother and Uncle John. I'm sure that he was mother's favorite cousin even though he was a bit of an alcoholic, and usually undependable, but fun-loving, witty, and most unpredictable of the group.

Jack and his cousin Mary were on the same wave-length, especially where humor was concerned. He never had a serious girl friend. Jack would live in Hanna enjoying Mother's cooking and a bed for a year or so, and then the wanderlust would take him to San Francisco for a while.

Jack's Lancashire humor earned him many friends. His Lancashire dialect was ribald and unpredictable. He was a born actor and entertainer. If he had lived fifty years later he could have been a TV comedian.

JACK AND PETE'S PIGS

At the Cottage Home boarding house Jack avoided the kitchen chores which my mother tried to thrust on him some kitchen work to earn his board. She insisted, for example, that he help throw away the left-over hot cakes from breakfast. These scraps were placed in a container to be picked up by Pete Puro to feed his hogs. One morning Mother noticed this was taking Jack more time than usual. On checking his work, mother she saw black spots in the discarded hotcakes. She saw a box of carpet tacks in front of Jack, and asked what he was doing. Jack answered without a smile, "I am doing it so that Pete's pigs will think the tacks are raisins!"

Well, Dan, mother was a good friend of Pete and his pigs, and Jack lost his job as Garbage Man in the kitchen. The demotion suited Jack perfectly!

JACK MELLOR ON THE ANTELOPE HUNT

A Navy buddy of mine, Doctor Jim Sommers, and his friend, a U. S. Senator from Iowa named Hickenlooper, brought their two sons to hunt antelope with me in the Red Desert. It was at a time when my little, long suffering mother wanted to get Jack a long way from the hotel. Although I knew Jack could cause me trouble, I reluctantly agreed that he might be some help around our camp.

All was going well until Jack found a bottle in our guests' supplies. When we were in bed after a hard day hunting, Jack kept nipping at the whiskey. He was no hunter, and he insisted on staying up at night with the excuse of keep the fire burning. Then, he said he wouldn't have to build a new fire to cook breakfast. At that point we didn't know he had found the bottle, so I agreed.

Late into the night he sang, told stories, recited poetry, and kept all of us awake in spite of my threats and pleading that he shut up. Finally, he decided to get a bucket of water from a rather deep, and very cold, spring. We heard the splash as Jack fell into the pool. As he floundered he called, "Churlie, Churlie, cum and save yer coosin." I thought he was still entertaining our guests, so my only response was to threaten to come and hold him under if he didn't shut up. Finally, he crawled up the grassy bank, shivering badly, to spend what was left of the night with wet clothes. He needed a big fire to dry out. Jack cussed me, and swore I pushed him into the pond. I didn't--but I should have!

Jack sobered up enough to prepare the breakfast. As we drove the car away to hunt a big buck antelope, he informed my friends: "Churlie pushed me in the spring, and then 'eld me 'ead under tryin' to drown 'is purr coosin." He added that I told him, "Drown, damn ye drown--it's a good way to get rid of yuh." And then he threatened, "I'll tell thee muther on thee." He did!

The comedian, Jack Mellor with Uncle John. Jack's nickname was 'Hooky' because of his bent nose.

JACK, BESSIE AND THE PYTHIAN SISTERS

My mother was at a meeting in Parco (now Sinclair) for a meeting with her Pythian Sisters Lodge when she realized that their white ritual uniforms were still in Hanna. She called and asked that I drive the Model T around town and gather them. I put Bessie, Mother's hired girl at the hotel, in the front seat with me, but I failed to close the door properly. So, as I pressed the pedal for low gear executing a U turn with the hand throttle down, I lost Bessie. That sawed-off automobile was like a saddle horse--ready for emergencies! Poor Bessie slid off the seat and into the dirt road. I was in such a hurry I did not miss her until I had driven about a half block. Then, I pressed the reverse pedal and charged back to get her. In a blur she saw the rear end of the car rapidly approaching and she quickly retrieved her glasses and upper denture, which had fallen into the ashes which we used for pavement. She scrambled as fast as possible for the safety of the kitchen door. There Jack looking through the window where he drank coffee, saw the whole escapade, and was laughing and pointing a finger at me, saying, "I'll tell thee muther on thee--I'll tell 'er when I see'er that it's not safe fer a decent woman to ride with yuh. You were puttin' yer 'and on 'er knee, and now look 'ow its scratched. You're getting too damned fresh, and the only proper thing fer a decent woman to do was to git out uff the car!"

Well, when Bessie got all of the loose parts back in place she got in the car again, and this time I checked to see the door was properly latched. We picked up all the clothes Mother wanted and we got it off in time for the Pythians' ritual. You can bet that Jack told everyone in town that no decent girl should ride with Charlie!

JACK MELLOR AND SNAPPER

One terribly cold and wintry morning I was in the Hanna Hotel kitchen and saw Jack Mellor as he sat watching the swirling snow. The temperature was below zero and Jack enjoying his cigarette and hot coffee.

Snapper Jones, our deputy sheriff, entered the warm kitchen. He was bundled up against the blizzard and on an errand of mercy. Snapper spoke: "Jack, do you remember our old school pal Arthur Olsen?" Jack answered affirmatively, and Snapper reported that Arthur had committed suicide the night before, and he was recruiting good friends like Jack to go to the frozen cemetery and dig the grave. Jack gave the suggestion thoughtful consideration, had a swallow of coffee, and answered, "No, Snapper, I can't make it today." Snapper pleaded, "Look Jack--he was a good friend of yours. Others are going to help." Jack spoke, "If he were a friend uf mine' 'ed 'ave waited till spring." When Snapper prevailed, Jack said, "Aw, put 'im in the bloody wood shed--hits cold enough, e'll keep till hits a fit day." I don't know who dug Arthur's grave, but Jack had no part in it!

JACK IN WORLD WAR ONE

Jack Mellor was probably the first Hanna native to join the Allied Armies to fight against the Kaiser during the First World War. Being a bachelor and an adventurer as well as an Englishman, he joined the Canadian forces. He was determined to see action rather than waiting for the United States to get involved.

Jack saw a lot of action in the trenches against the better organized German army. He began as lowly private and ended with that same rank because of his unorthodox behavior. Through some valiant action with his group he became a corporal or a sergeant, but was finally busted back to his original status.

Jack was a victim of the mustard gas used by the Germans and was sent on medical leave to England, where he enjoyed the English nurses. Then he was returned to the trenches of France. He found the action there dull, and after a few months Jack used some risky ingenuity and he again was a casualty.

He related to me: 'During a lull in action we were pinned down by the Jerries. They knew where we were and we knew all their positions. If you kept out of sight there was no real danger. From our trench near a little village we were secure, but we knew that in some high point there was an accurate German sniper. I figured out that if I made a short run to a nearby tree he would see me and it could draw his fire. This I did, and when I got behind the behind the tree, he fired into the protective trunk. Each time I moved he would respond. I waited until it was nearly dark and then I stuck one leg out as a target and he shot me through the calf of my left leg. When it was dark enough I dragged myself back into our trenches and became a casualty and got the Purple Heart. The real payoff was another trip back to England. There was a long rehabilitation leave and the care of good looking English nurses. But when the report was written up I once again lost my stripes and returned to my unit. It was worth the risk!"

JACK IN WORLD WAR TWO

Jack was no young man during WW II or he would have again been in uniform. Still, as an older man he volunteered and was accepted to serve as a sailor in the Pacific against Japan. His merchant ship was torpedoed and his life boat spent several days at sea. He was almost thrown overboard because of his levity. Others in the boat could see nothing funny about drifting on the high waves.

On Memorial day the Canadian flag flies over Jack Mellor's grave in Hanna.

JACK'S LAST TRIP TO SAN FRANCISCO

Jack's favorite location was my mother's kitchen, where he could get free food and a bed, was San Francisco. He could always find a few odd jobs there. In Hanna, his favorite fans, whom he loved to entertain, were my mother and her best friend Sue Mangan. As Jack prepared to travel to San Francisco for his last trip there he suggested to Mary and Sue that if he chanced to die there he wanted to be buried in Hanna. He said, "I'll have a few bobs in me pocket book and just 'ave em ship me back so I can 'ave one more chance to go to the Methodist Church, 'cause when Preacher is a sayin' all them nice lies 'bout me at my funeral, I want no tears at my funeral! I'll just sit up a moment and wink at two of you and then lay back."

There were no tears! Mary and Sue were in the front row both about ready to see Jack sit up and wink. Many friends simply thanked him for the laughter he gave them. Mary Ford and Sue especially smiled and thought they saw him wink.

LANKY HUMOR

Dear Dan:

In Lancashire, England, the humor it ribald and hilarious. Your great grandmother provided a good example of a person who could laugh at herself and other Lankies. I presume that humor in the British Isles is a trademark. Often times it is a dry-humor which takes some people a while before it sinks in. There have been many great English comedians in the show business, and in politics. Both the Scotch and Irish share this talent.

I believe part of the reason is that in the Coal fields of Lancashire humor is a necessary antidote for the harsh lives of the coal miners. They had to have some fun, rather than concentrating on their troubles.

. . . .

STORIES

I saw a fight one day when I was a kid. The contestants were a tough Hanna Lanky and a newcomer. They were wrestling and punching at the same time in the dirt near the hotel. We made a circle around the fighters, and a tough Lanky, Joe, was cheering for his friend. As they rolled in the dust, Joe shouted:. . . "oose dawn now---eer side! Let 'im oop, let 'im oop! EEE, 'oose dawn now---thoother side! Purr 'is bloody ribs!" (In Lancashire 'purr' means kick with your clogs.) I don't remember who won the fight, but from that time on we mocked Joe when there was a fight.

. . . .

A Hanna old timer tells the story of the time during early WW I when there when there was an effort to whip up a little war spirit. The Liberty Bell came through Hanna on a railroad car and some old Lanky was trying to get close enough to touch it--probably to work the clapper and see if it would ring. He wasn't satisfied to observe it from the ground, but he was restrained by one of the guards. In a loud voice he said: "Liberty Bell, Liberty 'ell--there's no bloody liberty 'ere."

. . . .

Hanna's deadly baseball rival, Rawlins, was being tested on a Sunday afternoon. At a tense moment when a Rawlins player was at bat, Joe shouted through a little megaphone which he always took to the games. (I suppose he feared that his encouragement to the home team might be lost, or that his jibes at the enemy might not find their mark.) This day he continued repeating the following words when the Rawlins men were at bat: "E caun't 'it hit. 'E caun't 'it hit. 'E caun't 'it hit a bloody balloon cumin' down hout u the herr!" But occasionally he did hit it, and then Joe had unkind remarks for the Hanna pitcher.

. . . .

Once while hunting sage chicken in the hills south of Hanna we came upon an automobile belonging to an old Lanky and his young son. This was during prohibition and we sat on the ground near his car for a drink. His home-brew was strong and even warm, but it tasted good on that dry desert. He entertained us with stories of when he was a young man living in Lancashire.

He talked incessantly, but his kid said not a word. The old boy told of a man he remembered as the deafest person he ever knew. He said repeatedly and with emphasis: "'E didn't know when you were a shoutin' at 'im. Eee wus like a bloody fence post. Ye'd 'ave to go oop and shake 'im when you wanted 'is 'tendon. 'e'd talk back at yuh, but ee didn't know a damn thing ye was a-sayin'." The old boy repeated this several times to make the point solid, and finally his son asked incredulously, "Couldn't 'e 'ear Paw?"

Well, without a word the old man got up and kicked the boy over the nearest sagebrush. I guess you can say he 'purred' his kid in the seat of the pants beyond the sage!

. . . .

One of the Joes of Hanna was a notable character. He was known as the house boss in charge of repairs of the company's houses. He was checking property in the Lanky neighborhood when a Lanky woman came out on the porch and shouted, " 'ay Joe, hits about time fer you to fettle me ass." Now Dan in our American language she meant. . . Hey Joe, its about time for you to fix my house. Well, his answer was shouted for all neighbors to hear, "If thee needs thou ass fettled (fixed), thou should go to the bloody hoffice.and.git.ha border."

Hank Jones told me of a Lanky named Joe. During a summer evening at a band concert in the Hanna's little park and band stand, Joe mixed with the audience, and the men in the band. Some of the kids were teasing Joe became he used a cane. He was particularly upset with the handicapped Peekin boy. Joe made a pass at the kid with his cane, and was reprimanded by Jones. The bass drummer who worked in the mine office, reprimanded the irritated old man. Then, Joe shook his finger under Frank's nose and said, "Thou's not fettled me ass for three bloody years, and finally I wunt sommit done'! I knew thee muther, I knew thee father, and they worked 'ard all their bloody lives, but thou're not like 'em cuse thouve not done a bloody tap since I've known thee." Well, after he had properly put Hank in his place, he marched away militantly to the approval of the crowd. That provided more entertainment than the band concert.

. . . .

Two newly arrived Englishmen, Gal and Joe, were enjoying many new experiences in their adopted country. On one occasion they were investigating the mysteries of the first banana they had ever encountered. The coal miners had little or no experience with the fresh fruit which was suddenly displayed at the company store. One asked the manager, "Hey Stear, whut in 'ell is that bunch of stuff", as he pointed to a stock of bananas hanging in the butcher shop. "Aw, you bloody Lankies, its bananas" "What's a damn banana?" Stear handed them one and suggested that they divide and eat it. Gal started to peel it, and when he finished he handed the fruit to his pal as he started to chew the peeling, saying to Joe, " 'ere ye bloody Lanky--guts is bloody good enough for thee."

. . . .

Two Lankies had heard of the natives hunting sage- chicken, and, deciding that they would enjoy the sport, they borrowed a shotgun. But they really didn't know much about the bird they were to pursue. Eventually, they approached a bunch of willows in the draw and noticed a bird perched there, which eyed them suspiciously. But they called to Gal, who had the gun, and when he shot, the bird hit the ground. Joe picked it up and said, "Gal, ere's sommit, hits uh bloody 'en!" but Gal disagreed saying, "no, hit haint no 'en--hits a bloody howl!" Joe objected, "Howl 'ell-- hits a broad faced bloody 'en--that's wut it were." They brought the trophy back to Hanna. Experts testified that it was an owl.

. . . .

Hank Jones told me of a practical joke which went on for weeks during World War I. Old John Milliken, an American who used to rib his illiterate Lanky friends, often read aloud reports of the sea battle England was conducting against the Germans. Among his daily audience as he read from the Rawlins Republican newspaper was Joe, who believed all the paper reported. Although he couldn't read he listened intently. Sometimes Milliken would fabricate the story in a most colorful way that was sure to disturb the militant Englishman. Hank happened to overhear a particular account which falsely reported the sinking of several of Britain's capital ships. Joe was about to dissolve in tears as he listened, but Hank Jones interrupted the scene saying, "Stop it, John! Can't you see your lies are about to get to the poor fellow?"

The loyal Englishman didn't appreciate anyone defending him. The Lanky's fist was shaking at Hank as he shouted, "Damn hit, stay hout of this--hits true! Can't ye see whut he's readin' hit frum? We are tuff enuf to take a bit of bad news now and then even if yer not." That retort convinced Hank not to intercede in private affairs or problems.

. . . .

Coal was cheap in Hanna at $2.50, but many of us couldn't afford it at any price. Some stole it from the railroad cars just because it was so readily available. Things got a little out of hand and it was decided to set up an account at the mine office for those who were caught throwing pieces from the parked coal cars.

One such account that Hank Jones had to charge was a particular Lanky who was upset when he got the bill on his statement the next pay day. It was explained to him after he stormed into Hank's office that he had bought no coal for more than a year, and that his boys were caught in the act so he was rightly being charged for two tons of coal. He immediately blew the short fuse which most Lankies have, saying, "I've bought no bloody coal, but yer deducting hit anyhow! Do ye know what I think? I think when they talk about bloody Roosia, that's where ye should be--you've bin around 'ere too bloody long!" He left the office feeling better , but then there was no small claims court to hear his case then.

. . . .

Dan, in those days I guess we had a Justice of Peace court which heard a few minor cases. When I assisted your dad at a banquet of law enforcement officers in Rawlins last year, an old time law officer told me about the Justice of Peace, a Lanky named Bob Moulinex, of Hanna. I knew him well and gave him a bad time when I was a janitor in Hanna High School. He said that when he was a young deputy sheriff he brought in a man who was charged with breaking an ordinance. Bob immediately asked the prisoner whether he would plead guilty or not guilty. The guy said not guilty! Bob blew his fuse, and said: "Wot ye mean 'not guilty, they brought ye in 'ere, didn't they? Of course yer guilty!"

That case reminds me of an other Justice of Peace in Rawlins who would start a hearing by saying to the arresting officer, "Bring the prisoner in."

NICK-NAMES

Few Lankies were ever known by what they would term their 'proper' name, but all had nicknames that were often expressive. Tinser, Softbelly, Dumpy, Swat, Boots, and Pickles because he ate a whole jar on the way home from the store; Lim because he did the same thing with limburger cheese. Then there was a group who moved into Hanna later, and their names were Flat, Spec, Jake and Moe.

. . . .

The school programs were wonderful! Once I heard Jimmy recite the following before an audience that was being entertained by the English department. With great concentration, in a halting voice, he coaxed these words out, "Good Hinglish his uh a'bit, git the a'bit!"

. . . .

None of us ever dreamed that the Beatels from Lancashire, would be such a hit in the USA. I guess we should have expected it because we had similar humor and entertainment constantly in early Hanna.

. . . .

The Lankies had many new things to learn when they came to this country, but they were willing to take a run at the challenge. In England my grandmother died of 'inflammation of the bowel', but I am convinced it might have been appendicitis. The Lankies made a lot out that diagnosis.

. . . .

A Lanky by the name of Watson ran the candy store and was as near to being as a pharmacist as Hanna ever had. He also sold patented medicine, which one could buy for nearly any illness. One day a countryman entered and announced, "'our Sara's hawful sick...she must 'ave happendicitis...hits hall oop 'er in 'ead and nose." Watson disagreed on the diagnosis, saying "EEE no, hits not happendecitis--hits newralgia, she's got." The husband's diagnosis was not affirmed and experience suggested a different patented medication.

FI HING

I think you should know how tactless your father, Ken, can be. Often, I get little respect in this family. Some kids never give their dad bad times, but we are not like the average group.

When Ken was about ten we were on a trip somewhere west of Laramie. We stopped for refreshment in a town east of Rawlins where there is an oil refinery. It was then called Parco, but today is Sinclair. I was telling the family about the tragic explosion at the refinery when I was a kid in Hanna. About 15 or 20 workmen were killed at the refinery in Parco.

We were in a hurry to have our treat and be back on the road. As I led them to the soda fountain, we passed a small sports shop which was advertising fishing flies in the window. There was a sign in the window read, FI HING TACKLE. Ken, being the fisherman, wanted to go in. His window shopping was delaying us, and to get them moving I said: "Oh, yes, I know the guy who makes those flies. He is a Chinese fellow who moved from Hanna and has that shop."

Everybody followed me, except Ken, who was still looking into the window at the tackle. Then he called us back and said, "Dad, look! The letter 'S' fell out of that sign." He pointed on the floor of the window, and said, "That sign meant FISHING TACKLE."

Everybody, but me, laughed hilariously. Through the years the entire family loved to tell this story. Incidentally, each person adds a bit to it and they make it worse than it was.

Too often now when I tell a <u>true</u> story in a group someone says, "Yah, that another FI HING story!

BURTON DELONEY

When I was thirty-two years old Mary and I drove Burton Deloney and his wife to a dance at Elk Mountain, and we stayed overnight at the Hanna Hotel. The next morning Burt, who was a former news reporter, wanted to know something of the local color which made Hanna unique. I simply couldn't think of anything unusual, but decided to take him for a drive around town that Sunday morning.

It was dull with none on the streets, so we entered Love's bar and movie hall, and decided to go into the bar and have a drink. There were two old Catholic Lankies who had been up all night drinking and possibly afraid to go home and face their long-suffering wives. I recognized them, but at the bar I turned my back toward them as Burt and I ordered a couple of beers. I just did not want to get involved with them.

As I explained to my friend that there was no local color worth looking for at that hour on a Sunday, I heard one of the Lankies say to the other: "Eee, hits Churlie Stebner." He moved closer, apparently looking for me to buy them a beer, and said, "Eee be God, Churlie, 'ow are ye?"

I told him that I lived in Laramie now, and I felt great! I ordered beer for both of them. Joe said, "Aw, thee tell me you 'ave a young won?" I verified the news that we had our first son and his name was Ron. "Eee," said Joe, "Me and tha old woman 'ad fourteen of the little buggers, but all of a sudden 'er up and quit. 'er quit, I didn't! Yuh know Churlie, a woman is like a bloody 'en--they lay so many bloody heggs und then they quit. Not a damn thing you kin do bout it. 'hif I had it to do over again there'd not be fourteen of the little devils, but two, or maybe three, und then you know what I'd do...I'd learn a bloody Yankee trick, that whut I' do, by God."

It was easy for Burt to see what the local color was. When we came back to Laramie, he would get me to tell the conversation I had with Joe.

. . . .

Concerning the greatest man of our time...
WINSTON CHURCHILL

A backward boy...he was a frail, freckle-faced boy who refused to study. It took him three full terms to get out of the lowest prep school grade. His father decided he'd never master law and suggested an army career. The boy failed a military college entrance exam three times before he was admitted. Then he took stock of himself, tackled his weakness, a speech defect, and became an inspired orator. He developed leadership, courage, faith. Who was the stubborn young rebel who became a world renowned statesman? Winston Churchill.

The Tie Hacks

TIE HACKS

Dear Dan:

I never thought about the possibility of working for the timber industry when I graduated from High School. But suddenly in the summer of 1927, following my high school graduation, I had a chance to join some classmates for a job in Fort Steele, Wyoming. There railroad ties were loaded from the Platte River into cars for shipment.

It was a thrill to work with a group of Scandinavians. I had often heard exciting stories of these real 'he-men.' I considered myself too small physically, but here was an opportunity to prove I had grown up. I needed the money for college tuition. At that time it seemed a long way from Hanna to the forests of Fox Park and Keystone where ties were made.

In the summer of 1927, C. D. Williamson of Hanna, president of the Wyoming Timber Company promised a job to my good friend Bill Clegg. Bill had just returned from his first year at the University of Illinois. Bill suggested to my classmates, Eric Lepponen, Wilho Kandolin and myself, that perhaps we could join him. We applied and were accepted as part of the crew.

Many years previously the Carbon Timber Company floated logs down the river to Fort Steele to be processed into wood products. Now, tiehacks made ties in the forest. They were floated to the loading plant at the railroad in Fort Steele.

Later, I had the opportunity to work at the Keystone commissary for a month after the loading season. There I observed tie hacks at their trade.

The tools they used included a heavy cross-cut saw and double-bladed ax, with which they felled and trimmed the tree. Then, they used a very heavy broadax. Their action was something beautiful to watch. As a tiehack worked the big ax, he took a step backwards after each swing. Each time the ax hit the tree a smooth area about four to eight inches long was exposed. When he had walked backwards the length of the tree one side was as smooth as it had been planed. He would reverse himself to work on the opposite side of the tree.

After the ties were cut into eight feet lengths they were piled nearby. Then a company tie-checker counted and credited the tiehack for payment. Later the finished ties were bunched in groups of six or eight ties and a chain placed around them. Finally, a horse dragged them to the banks of Douglas Creek to wait for Spring run-off.

THE KEYSTONE COMMISSARY

Following one season after the ties were loaded at Fort Steele I worked for a couple of weeks as a clerk at the Keystone store. It was rare to see anyone other than the Scandinavians working as tie-hacks. I became friends with a young man who had bristly red hair and a mustache. He came here from Yugoslavia and was proud of his physique. To me he was very sociable, but the Scandinavians had little to do with him. He was a physical culture addict. When he came home from the timber each day where he made ties, he lifted heavy stones to build stronger muscles.

Tie Hacks never complained about the hours or pay. On rare occasions they made trips to Laramie where in those days of prohibition, they drank lots of bootleg whiskey. Few of them were married and these bachelors cashed their hard earned money with the bootleggers. The girls of First Street got the rest. When they sobered up, they returned to work in the timber. Many of the cutters remained in the mountains all winter to work in deep snow. It was here I saw my first pair of skis which they used in their work.

A friend of mine, Elmer Wick of Elk Mountain, told me, "Those guys were lucky--especially during the depression when they hacked ties, they never made less than five dollars a day."

. . . .

When I came to Laramie I met Louis Schilt, was about my age, he lived on a ranch in the Saratoga area. Louie contracted with the timber company to use a team of horses and a chain to drag groups of ties back into the river during the tie drive. Most of us had only simple manpower.

THE TIE DRIVE

These Scandinavians were masters with the saw and the ax. In 1930, our group of us who loaded ties in Fort Steele were drafted to fight a fire on French Creek. (Recently, I drove through that area and the scars are there for all to see.) During the height of the destruction we were fascinated by these experienced workmen as they worked in two-man teams. They rapidly cut fire lanes around the approaching fire. The rest of us we removed the slash and cleared the fallen trees.

It was rare to see a workman other than the Scandinavians. But there was one amazing Yugoslavian. He worked alone and was more sociable than the Swedes. He was also more muscular than most of the tiehacks, and wore a bristly red mustache. I especially enjoyed his stories of his experiences as a young man in eastern Europe.

He was very proud of his physique. After a day cutting ties he came back to camp and lifted stones, much as some of our weight-lifters work today. Each day he worked to lift slightly heavier stones to build muscles.

Louis Schilt, Senior was about my age, and lived on a ranch near Saratoga. There he contracted with the Timber company to use a team of horses to drag groups of ties back to the river. But most of us worked with pike-poles and picaroons to drag ties, one at a time, back to the stream.

The pikepole had a sharpened point in the heavy end of a long thin tree. It was about eight or ten feet long. At the thick end there was a metal unit with two sharpened points; one was a hook for pulling a tie toward the worker, the other with a point for pushing the tie forward. Another helpful tool was the picaroon. It was made from a short axe head had been cut away leaving a single curved point which with a small hook driven into the tie. We used it to drag ties from the banks.

TIE JAMS ON UPPER RIVER

On the upper Platte River big boulder would catch floating ties and form log jams. Sometimes many ties caught behind the obstruction created serious problems. These jams extended forty to fifty yards upstream. This problem called for experienced tie drivers. With flat bottom boat three men would land at the upper end of the jam. One would remain in the boat and the other two, with steel spikes in their shoes, would walk toward the obstructing boulder, being careful not to slip.

They would pry a few offending key ties loose with their pike poles. Suddenly, the entire mass of trapped ties began to move. This was very dangerous work and we were excited as we watched the two men run cautiously toward the rear where they would jump into the boat. There was immense pressure on some of the ties and the force would break a few into separate pieces. One wondered what might happen if these men ever fell in that rushing mass of ties. But we never saw anyone injured on the drive.

Most of our work was mundane and tiresome as we dragged ties off the sand banks to float freely in the stream. Our boots were built of special leather which resisted constant water. The soles had sharp steel spikes, similar to golf shoes of today. This feature kept us from slipping on wet ties.

It was difficult to wake up on cold mornings and climb into wet sox and boots. At night, after supper we would sit around a big camp fire, and the old timers would back up to the fire to dry their clothes, but my collegiate partner and I would immediately change into dry clothes for the evening. The Swedes had an idea that if the clothes dried out on their bodies around the fire they would avoid catching cold.

In some places where ties were buried in sloughs a considerable distance from the stream, two men carried a broad hand-hewed tie on our shoulders back to the river. I remember an occasion when that challenge almost got me fired. After working for several hours in a particularly difficult mud hole we noted several dozen heavy water-soaked ties buried in the mud. These ties were heavier than the average. Our group worked this area late in the day until only a few ties remained. I counted which particular tie might be our unpleasant challenge. Sure enough, the biggest one came to Bill Clegg and me.

Two Swedes dug it out of the mud and lifted it onto our shoulders. Bill led the way out of the hole and up an slick incline. I tried to follow with my end, but my feet slipped and I fell to my knees. The pressure was painful.

Both Swede loaders lifted it off my shoulder and waited for me to get up on the ledge where they again replaced the tie. I can still feel the mud running down my neck as we struggled toward the stream. The weight of that big tie hurt. We made it to the embankment and rolled it down hill into the water. I fell the other way and simply lay there.

After I rested for about five minutes, not far from tears, Bill said, "Charlie, you had better get up, because our boss Sam Thompson will be coming down stream and he might fire you." He helped me to my feet. There were no more ties in that mud hole. So we dragged easier ones and soon it was quitting time.

Even today, my memory is still fresh. Years later I recalled that experience on a special day at the dude ranch--the famous A-Bar-A. I remembered that day we reached that spot. I recalled rich dudes sitting on the corral fence watching the 'river rats' as we dragged ties into the stream for $4.00 a day. Some of them smiled and spoke to us. I said to Bill Clegg, "Damnit, Bill some day I will be the guy on that fence."

I related that experience to the ranch manager, John Echhart, who incidentally was my dental patient. We were attending a wedding at the ranch. John laughed and said, "Charlie, it looks like you finally made it."

Tie driver releasing ties which were hung up on a boulder in the upper Platte River during the early 1930's.

Sam Thompson (standing, with mustache)

BOOTLEGGERS VISIT CAMP

As we approached the town of Saratoga we expected trouble with the Swedes. We heard bootleggers and their girl friends would be waiting for us. This could delay the progress of the drive for several days.

Sam Thompson made camp in an inaccessible area well above the town. The next day we traveled farther below Saratoga for the second night. This camp placed us in an area where it would be impossible for the tie hacks to walk to Saratoga. But after supper the bootleggers drove several Model T Fords into camp and loaded all willing tie drivers to make the trip to Saratoga. No doubt the girls were eager to work overtime. Certainly there was plenty of moonshine whiskey available.

During the early morning hours we heard much commotion as they unloaded their inebriated customers. They simply dumped their cargo at our campsite. We heard a terrible scream, and then a moan! Those who had been asleep hurried from their bedrolls to discover that the last car ran over a small, but wiry, tie hack. Two wheels of the Ford crossed over his body. Surprisingly, there was no obvious damage. He was dragged to his sleeping bag. When, it was time to go to work the next morning he was complaining about his sore ribs. It seemed that his pain was no worse than the hangovers suffered by the rest of his pals.

IMMIGRANTS CROSSING

About half way between Saratoga and Fort Steele the immigrants crossed the Platte River on their way west. We camped there one night also.

Bill and I walked on a steep rock cliff and saw names of some of the early pioneers which were scratched in the sandstone. On some of the simple graves were crude headstones who people who didn't make it across the river. A few were of infants and older children. There were rattlesnakes in this region so one had to be aware.

THE FRENCH CREEK FIRE

The Scandinavians were masters with the saw and the ax. In 1931 a group of us who loaded ties in Fort Steele were drafted to fight a forest fire on French Creek. Recently, I drove through that area and the scars are there for all to see--so is the regrowth. During the height of the destruction we were fascinated by the experienced tie-hacks as they worked in two-man teams. They cut all the trees as they developed a fire-break about thirty yards wide ahead of the fire. Using a double bit ax and a two-man saw they chopped the trees rapidly. Then there were no power saws. The rest of us were muckers who removed the slash and cleared the fallen trees. Then we used shovels to rake the forest floor so that hot brush and needles could not carry sparks into unburned areas. The ties-hacks had all the glamour and we had the mess!

We slept in our bedrolls about five or six hours each night. The food was not the best. Two railroad cars from the Saratoga and Encampment railroad (this railroad was known by the natives as the S & E for Slow and Easy) was sidetracked for emergency food. One car had nothing but cheese, and the other only canned peaches. Pack horses supplied these items of food to the fire line. We had nothing but our shovels to open a can of wonderful juicy peaches. For several years I refused to eat either cheese or peaches.

The most obnoxious part of that experience was the smoke which drifted into our eyes and nostrils while we patrolled the fire line. After five or six days the fire was controlled and we returned to the Fort Steele loading plant. There we would again live like humans.

THE TIE LOADING PLANT

It was a great thrill to reach old Highway 30 above Fort Steele, and to see all the hundreds of ties riding on the river ready for loading. Here those who were on the drive had first choice for the loading crew, which included Bill Clegg and myself. The others were Jim, Eric and Kat Kandolin. The rest were all Swedes. During the eight hour day we fed hundreds of ties from the river onto the chains which carried them up into the car. Husky experienced men stacked the ties neatly in the rail road cars. Each day they were moved to the creosote treatment plant in Laramie.

This was easier and more pleasant work compared to the tie drive. We had our own cabin with mattresses on the floor, and we could go for a swim in the river every evening before the dinner bell rang. The meals were great because of their indoor facilities. We sat at tables on long benches rather than on the ground with a plate in our laps, which was how we ate our meals on the tie drive.

But the cook was the master of the cookhouse. There were no unnecessary words during meals. One time before I knew the rules I mentioned to Eric that if he turned around he could see the locomotive hauling away the ties we had loaded that day. That was against the rules, and the cook tapped me on the shoulder and suggested that I save my comments until we were out of the cook house. It was a good rule, because the cooks could clean up the place early and prepare for the next meal. Also, I am sure that with conversation there might be a fight or other trouble.

If we worked efficiently, it was possible to get off early Saturday. On that afternoon the older tie hacks headed to Rawlins to be greeted by the bootleggers and the girls. The Hanna guys would drive home so that we could go to Elk Mountain for a dance. Some took dates and others played in the orchestra. Sunday evening we drove back to Fort Steele for another week of work and that important pay check.

It was a great experience to work for Sam Thompson on the drive. He was tough. But with a shortage of jobs available he would not hesitate to fire anyone who loafed. He was respected because he was fair. His son Albert worked with us on the tie drive and I am sure that his father was harder on him than the rest of us. Albert was a great guy and a friend of mine. Later we worked together for our Lions Club in Laramie.

At the loading plant we had a more relaxed boss in the person of Mandy Matson. His wife was the assistant cook, and treated college kids more like family. Her daughter and a girl friend added to the environment compared to the all male cast we had on the drive.

Because of my experience working with tie drive, I had a moment of empathy in my dental office during the Depression. A man came suffering from an infected tooth. I was aware from his characteristic clothing and his accent that was a Scandinavian, but did not remember seeing him before. As he paid me the usual fee of four dollars when he was leaving, he asked if had ever been on the tie drive.

I answered affirmatively, and we had a good visit of the days we worked together. When he closed the reception door as he left, I looked at the four silver dollars in my hand and it bothered me greatly. Yes, I thought that money was a full day's pay, which had taken me less than an hour to earn. Then I wish that I had only charged him a dollar.

A GOOD TIME AT WOODS LANDING

I developed great admiration for the Scandinavians who worked for the timber companies summer and winter. They never complained about the hours or pay. On rare occasions they made trips to Laramie to celebrate during the days of prohibition where they drank whiskey and visited the girls on First Street. When they sobered up, they returned to work in the timber.

When I graduated from dental school I came to Laramie to begin my practice. Along with other unmarried men, I attended a Saturday night dances in Woods Landing. Part of the entertainment there were fights between the townspeople and the tie hacks. More often though, the tiehacks would fight among themselves just to see who was the better man.

I had a friend who once arrived there on the wrong night. Some old Swede who had trained too heavily on bootleg whiskey asked him; "Have ya had a good fight tonight?" My friend foolishly answered, "No." The Swede said, as he hit him on the jaw, "Vell yuh got von now." We took him home and he never danced at Wood's Landing again.

College

AIMS

Dear Dan:

To gain in this race of life we must have a target and carefully aim at it. But first we must be realistic. Problems arise because too few know what is realistic. It helps to consult with someone we trust. I know a person who consults with nearly everyone and listens carefully, but he follows none.

The individual who early knows what his aims are, and has the confidence and determination to keep his eye on the target until he is successful, is fortunate. Often, even when people are told their objective is unrealistic, they sometimes keep driving with dogged determination, and make a fortune in what others thought was an impossible dream.

Not many years ago it was unrealistic to think that any of us could ever walk on the surface of the moon. Many would have called that dreaming. Others worked, and the dream became a reality.

In any endeavor we must respect experience, but not entirely be controlled by it. I remember a time when I lectured at a dental meeting back East. When I was not busy I went with a friend who lived there to listen to another lecture. The fellow at the podium seemed rather young and constantly referred to his years of experience. I asked my host, who was a classmate of his, and lived in the area, about his remarks. "Yes," came the answer, "He had only one year of experience 20 times." We left the lecture hall seeking something more substantial.

Even though some may think our aims too ambitious, we ourselves must keep a ray of hope and the belief they can be achieved. Long ago I learned that we should not underrate anyone. Certainly not ourselves. We admire those who have made major accomplishments. They believed in themselves. Few are pleased with cockiness, but we must have confidence in ourselves.

Yesterday, I received a letter from a good friend, a person of many accomplishments. But I would not use him as a model, because his self image is unrealistic. He admires persons who are financially successful and for the prestige they have.

Those areas where his success was the greatest should have been his principal aim in life--not the prestige that only money can buy. He missed the boat when he did not think that perhaps his health was more important than the money and prestige which governed his life. Without a healthy body, and the mind that goes with it, life can indeed be rough. Surely, Dan, we need enough money to be comfortable and live well, but beyond that it becomes a disease which destroys us. How much money is necessary?

Well, no person has the answer to that in dollars. Inflation and other economic factors will affect the answer. An idea of saving for the future, which my mother achieved, worked out real well. Each month she paid herself first by buying a Government War Bond, Sometimes for only twenty-five dollars.

Once I made the trip to Hanna to help her with her income taxes, I told her she had no business saving each month when she had a stack of unpaid bills. She told me to mind my own savings and she would take care of hers. She was right!

One will be surprised by benefits resulting from compounding interest on a safe financial investment. If you develop such an investment, promise yourself <u>not</u> to invade this account. It is hard to do, but smart! Everyone should have a chance to save for unexpected needs. I would like to see a young person get into the habit of paying themselves first. When you earn money, save one dime out of each dollar you earn.

Sports, relaxation, and entertainment are necessary for the healthy body and mind, but work and savings are also important. I am reminded of early rulers. They say Nero fiddled while his Rome burned. I guess he had fun, but his work ethic was poor. To quote a philosopher, Chesterfield said, "Aim at perfection in everything, though in most things it is not attainable; however, those who aim at it, and persevere, will come much nearer to it, than those whose laziness and despondence make them give it up as unattainable."

J. Hawes noted, "Aim at the sun, and you may never reach it but your arrow will fly higher than if you aimed at an object on the level with yourself."

CHARLIE ENTERS COLLEGE

Dan, I will share with you a big moment in my life. I went to college in the autumn of 1927. Really going to college was for me like being one of the astronauts who flew to the moon. Although we anticipated it, but was not sure of the atmosphere.

It was a thrilling, but still a scary feeling, as I joined that long line on the Denver University campus during registration. An upperclassman walked down the line and placed a bright green cap with a yellow beak on my head. Freshmen wore the cap for identification, but I did not need it. I was really green. I wanted everyone to know I was actually in college. I knew I would work very hard to become a dentist. As a pre- dental student, my required courses were English, Chemistry, and I believe something about basic science. My one elective should have been an easy course, but I innocently chose algebra. That was a crucial mistake, because I had no mathematics in Hanna High School. The only time I used numbers was to keep score when I played pool. Numbers never fascinated me. Even the grades on my report card were of little interest in my life.

In the Hanna school system I had concentrated on enjoying myself. Of course I liked dramatics, music and girls. I was woefully ill-prepared for the University. Several times I thought that my stepfather Ford insisted that I have a course in mathematics to repay me for all the grief I gave him. Every available course would be tough for a kid who was already a year behind other freshmen who graduated from bigger and better Colorado schools.

Before my folks left me on the campus they found a place for me to sleep, a little house right across from the campus, owned by a little old couple. They had a simple bedroom for rent. I very seldom saw either of them. They had a coal burning stove in the kitchen, but I think they wanted all the heat for themselves. Little escaped to my room that winter. After the bustle of the hotel in Hanna it was very lonesome. But, with all of the reading and writing I needed for my classes, I still played my clarinet to survive. No wonder they kept the door to their warm kitchen closed!

In fact, things started out pretty well, or so I thought. I had a meal ticket to a little eating place across the street. And I went to all of the football games where I played with the Denver University Band. Going to classes became routine. All I had to do was to listen to lectures, and the teacher didn't give us any assignments. I did work on themes for English and read what I could understand in the books.

The real shock came when exams started. My grades were horrible, someplace in the 50s and the low 60s. Hell, I was flunking! I found that was hard to understand, because I had 80s and 90s in High School, and I never had any homework after school. Some might wonder why I registered at Denver University. After all they had a school of dentistry downtown, and I was advised that it would help for me to get into dentistry for the single pre-dental year that was required at that time.

I soon found out, after visiting with a few of my professors about my lousy grades, that I should have been taking notes and following the material in the books I purchased. Fortunately, I had a little portable typewriter and I began using it to write notes which I typed every day. This helped a little, but I was so far behind the rest of the class. It was a difficult for me to realize I did know how to study. Still I was determined not to fail. I remembered older Hanna kids who hurried home from college to work in the coal mines.

I was also disturbed because my mother had planned and worked very hard for this chance to help me gain a college education. If I were to fail, I promised myself that I would travel east and not show up in Hanna. I would look for a job and become successful at something worthwhile. Only then could I face mother again.

Meals were cheap and simple. For my breakfast and noon meal I ate food from the shelf where I stored groceries. Mostly, I had packages of breakfast food and a bottle of milk, and at noon there were a few goodies that my mother mailed me from the Hanna Hotel, like fruit-cake, cookies and an apple or orange. Laundry was a cinch. I mailed soiled clothes home every week. I almost spoiled this privilege the following year when I enclosed a cadaver's ear home in an undershirt. Well, for the evening meal I used my meal ticket at the little restaurant across the street.

I was lonely and homesick most of that first semester, and the only thing that saved me was my clarinet and the DU band. There will be times when you can work out a lot of frustration that way. For me it was good therapy.

My landlord and his wife had a friend who was a lady pharmacist who worked in a nearby drug store. She was raising her young son alone because her husband had been killed in a coal mine in Leadville, Colorado. When I related my past to her, we had something in common, so she helped me with chemistry. Boy, did I need her friendship! She encouraged me to go and talk to my professors and tell them my situation.

Two of those professors understood. My English teacher was a young and understanding person whose name was Mr. Gunn. I still have some the themes he had us write. He complimented me on my ideas and description, but destroyed me on spelling, and sentence structure. He helped and encouraged me, and I knew I would pass his course because he was complimentary of some of my descriptions. I remember a theme I wrote about my friend Eric, and on one page with red ink he circled six or eight times the misspelled word-- "freind". Then, the professor encircled the misspelled word which I used many times, because Eric was a <u>very</u> good friend. Then Mr. Gunn connected the words with his red pencil until the page looked like a cobweb. At first I could not understand his reason until I looked it up in the dictionary.

My chemistry teacher also directed the Denver University band, and I played clarinet in it. He was both helpful and understanding of a kid who was poorly prepared for college. He encouraged me to stop after class and he would explain a point that was not clear to me during his lecture. This man reminded me of Ottis Rechard, a great man and teacher at the University of Wyoming. Ottis became a most treasured friend when I came to Laramie to practice dentistry. He and I worked together in many groups in Laramie. I recall being in his home when he left a dinner party and patiently consulted with a student who phoned to get some help on a mathematical problem. Rechard was a compassionate teacher.

But my algebra teacher used a different approach. I asked that he sign a drop-slip which would keep me from failing his course. He asked what course I would substitute to get the fifteen hours I needed to get into dental school. I mentioned archaeology because it came at the same time as did the algebra class. Then, he asked what archaeology meant. I couldn't answer his question, and he insisted I continue the class. He mentioned that if I continued working as hard as he observed I would pass his the course. I did, and he did! I passed the course with a minimum grade--the benevolent guy must have padded my grades from a 55 or 60 to average a 70%. That got me Dean's Mudd List!

At the end of the semester I took my first trip home on the train. What a thrill! I had barely passed all of the courses without a failure. The second semester I pledged the Sigma Phi Epsilon fraternity and moved into the house. I was more confident and made good friends. I was on my way! When I entered the dental school in Denver, the work was surprisingly easy. We had a bunch of characters in that class, and we caused enough trouble that they closed the school during the depression. I transferred to Creighton for my sophomore year.

FOOD AND CHURCH

Eating out at boarding houses, the tie loading plant, and the restaurants and fraternity houses when I was in college was simply human need, but it lacked something.

I remember well that while at Denver University I made friends of a fine Christian family. The older girl, who was in one of my classes, invited me to her church, and to a family dinner. I was always hungry and I accepted the dinner even though I had to go to church first. This girl had a younger brother and sister. These two younger children were twins, and I must admit that the young sister was most attractive. I soon found out that her youth and personality pleased me, so I enjoyed that family nearly every Sunday.

It worked out very well for me, but when the little girl became romantically inclined I shied off. I was determined to get my education before getting seriously involved. Anyhow, the family relationship was most pleasing. The preacher failed to impress me!

After I graduated and came to Laramie, I was eating out all the time in restaurants before returning to the little rooming house. I suppose I was hungry for food and a home of my own. When my bills were finally paid, and I had a few hundred dollars in the bank and a brand new Chevrolet, I seriously began to make plans for a different lifestyle. The most fundamental objective was to find someone to share it with me.

Your grandmother Mary had no chance! Nor did I! Mary's mother often invited me in for an occasional meal. I hunted her daughter with the persistence of an old caveman. Mary had no serious idea of matrimony and was still in college, wishing to work for the clothes and a few luxuries she had never been able to enjoy. Well, Dan, I'm sure that you know I am persistent and determined. I waited a year or two and convinced her to marry me. Then, the biggest thrill I ever enjoyed was to move into the first home I had ever had since my Dad died when I was five years old. It was a well furnished apartment which cost us only $35.00 a month. But it was ours!

The most important furnishing was a big beer mug and ten beautifully painted smaller steins which graced our second story window for all to see. Your grandmother saved and bought them it for me as a wedding present. It is still my most prized possession. I seldom use it, but I do like to show it off after the more than 50 years we have been married. I guess it might be a secret symbol which reminds me of the Scarpelli family who shared their Dago Red with me in a water glass. To have friends come and share our home today means as much to me as it did as when I visited the Scarpelli family.

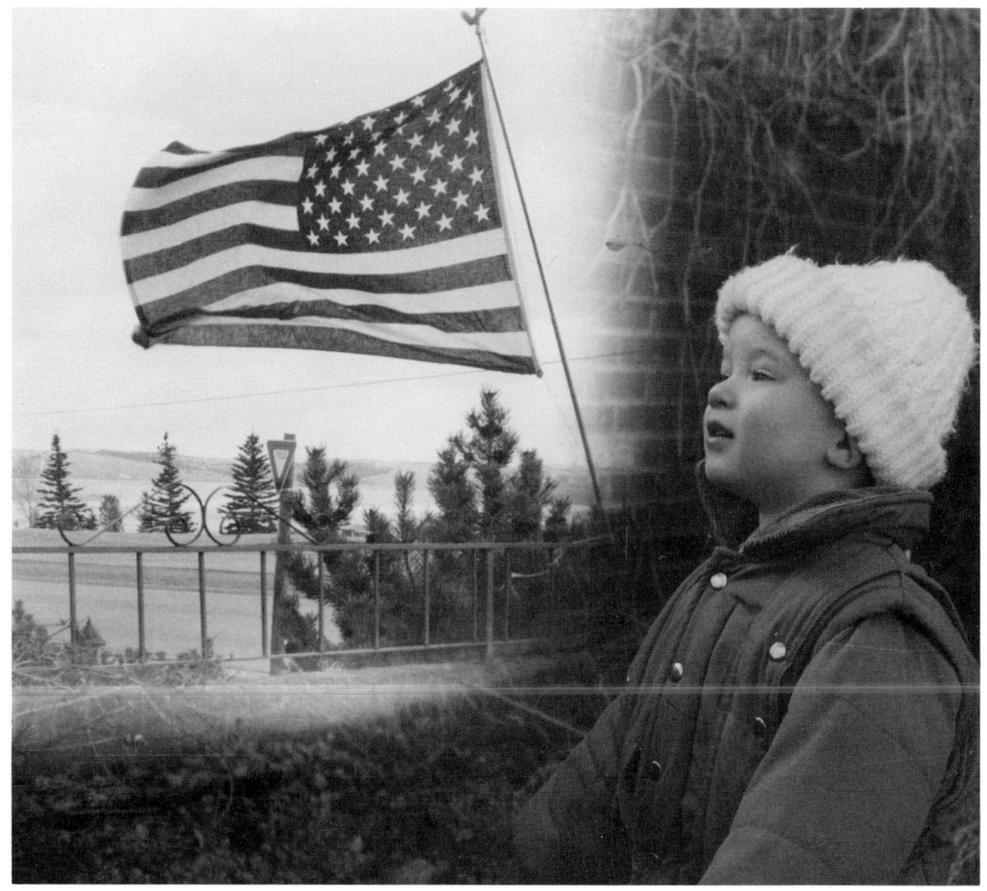

. . . .

How to be rich and happy as we mature is no secret. All we have to do is be child-like and reverent. Simply, enjoy and pause to observe the beauty created by God and Man. It is registered in the wonderment of children as they see their first sunset, love the colors of the rainbow, and watch the flag flying in the wind. *CMS*

Relationships

GIRLS

Dear Dan:

You will note that this session is on girls. I am sticking my neck out because no man can ever understand the mysteries of women. It is ridiculous that we even call them the weaker sex. At age 78 I have had considerable time to do research on this subject. But facts are hard to come by. Most of what I report is unproven research. We just can't explain the female.

I fell in love with my first school teacher! At that time I was perhaps in the first or second grade in the Hanna schools. She was Crystal Scott, and I remember her as a beautiful young lady who had recently received her teachers certificate and come to Hanna to teach.

Years later, I realized she was from a family who owned a store, and finally the Virginian Hotel, in Medicine Bow. Miss Scott was different! I remember that she wore bright colors while Hanna women dressed in plain and practical clothes. The air around her in the classroom was also different. Eventually, I found out that it was her favorite perfume--the odor of lilacs. If all of my teachers impressed me as she did, perhaps I might have been an honor student, but I was never motivated scholastically in Hanna.

THE YOUNG LOVE

The word love is perhaps the most commonly used, and abused, word. Its meaning is ambiguous. Some people say they love chocolate cake; others talk of their love for their country, and many have died for it. We must eliminate most of this hog-wash concerning love.

Dan, it is obvious you love your mom, dad and also little Lady Ann. I am pleased that you show it. Too many youngsters fail to tell parents just how you feel. I am concerned that I might have taken my little mother for granted in my early years.

Many would say that they love all of their friends. Perhaps they are using the word too broadly. I had a great friend Eric, but I think it would have embarrassed him if I said that I loved him. Hell, I liked the guy very much and respected nearly all of his qualities. (At this time, I want to keep that boy loves boy, or girl loves girl stuff out of this discussion, that homosexual business makes me ill.) Eric and I understood, respected, and admired the other guy's qualities. There was an element of trust and compassion in our relationships.

In my mind love exists between the male and female. Young people are biologically attracted to members of the opposite sex. Love is even more profound. Character, admiration, respect, and loyalty are cornerstones of love. Young love, I believe, can be real.

Sex is a biological urge to protect the species but often this has nothing to do with love. Nature finds sex necessary to multiply and protect the species. Women, and the lower species, have the mothering instinct. Little happens until the female beings show the early signs of maturation. Then, she gives the biological message. Of course, the male then becomes aggressive. Young boys should be aware of this procedure.

When I was in high school I had a marvelous girl friend. Perhaps, like all kids that age, we thought we loved one another without using the word 'love'. I think we both were afraid to admit we were seriously in love. This girl had everything any guy would appreciate. We had a lot of fun together, picnics, dances, driving around town, dramatics, and pleasant days. She was bright, athletic and humorous--sort of a tomboy type. Baseball was my sport and I had a couple of baseball mitts and often during the noon hour we would play catch. She threw the ball overhand, about as hard as any boy. To be ornery I often increased the speed of the return until the velocity made her glove sting. Incidentally, I used my catcher's mitt and she used the pitcher's thinner glove. This was a little unfair. Often, when it hurt her hand she reciprocated and threw the ball over my head. Then it was time to go back to school. She was a good sport!

At that time we were knowledgeable, in an amateurish way, and understood that too much steady company could lead us into trouble. That is something all young girls and boys should understand. I remember some of my friends who had to get married--they had to work in the mines to support a family.

This situation worried both of us. I presume that our mothers were quietly responsible. Most of the credit should go to mothers. In our case they steered us away from trouble. I had great respect for her mother, but avoided her tough-acting dad.

I promised my mother that I would go to college and become a professional man. Certainly, her mother also was a positive influence. We knew we were too young for sex, because there was a better life available to work toward. About graduation time we talked frankly about our plans. Mutually we decided that this was our last date. Sure it was tough and we shed a few mutual tears. Yes, Dan, ours was an honest 'young love'.

Throughout my college years I dated many fine and attractive girls, but when things began to get serious I shied away. Some were more experienced than I, so I found another girl to date. I was determined to graduate as a dentist and satisfy my mother. Until my financial debts were paid I was glad to be a bachelor.

Your grandmother, Mary was in college when I met her. It was her plan to also graduate and help her family, and also buy her own clothes to be independent. When she was age 24, I was a bit of a salesman and I sold 'Mom Conwell' that I might be a good son-in-law. Yes, Dan, ours was mature love--it produced a better life!

SEX and LOVE

When I was a kid we seldom even talked about these subjects, much less wrote candidly about them. Then we were careful and secretive in our conversations. The subject of sex was taboo. Today we know ignorance in these personal matters is dangerous.

My little mother was married at the age of 17 but first learned from her husband that she would have to wait nine months for a child. Today, nearly all young girls have better information than that. Most of my sexual education was gained in pool hall conversations. Ignorance in sexual matters is dangerous, and too many young girls are having infants out of wedlock. Could it be that they had old fashioned parents who did not provide their children with sexual education?

Chastity before marriage is often considered old- fashioned. Yet, after watching the problems of many young people I can tell you they are not the only ones involved. We have friends who are grandparents of very young children born out of wedlock. It is not fair for them to help raise and worry about children who are not their own, but often they do.

Today, the entire world is disturbed by a new and different disease known as Acquired Immune Deficiency Syndrome, or AIDS. This virus destroys nature's ability to resist other infections. It terminates in death of the patient. It is particularly rampant today among homosexuals and is becoming more common among promiscuous heterosexuals. For years people were infected by gonorrhea and syphilis. These two infections are caused by bacterial infections. Young people should read the description of them in a medical dictionary. Persons tempted with illicit romance will then refuse to gamble with their own health.

Young people should be factual and objective. There is nothing wrong about being a virgin. Other guys and girls often ridicule the informed and cautious person. It takes knowledge and character to stay out of trouble. Peer-pressure influences the weaker person.

As a healthy and normal teen-ager I reacted as did most of my pals. The urge for sex is natural, for both the female and the male. Otherwise, all of the species would disappear. Nature encourages reproduction, but that urge has nothing to do with real love. Often people fail to properly define their emotions.

I was biologically normal and had the sexual urge in the company of girls I dated long before marriage, but somehow I never told a girl that I 'loved' her. Sure I was sexually stimulated by the presence of a lovely female. Yet, to tell a girl I loved her seemed to be impossible. I guess that would mean commitment-- maybe a proposal for marriage and I wasn't ready for that responsibility. I was not mature enough for parenting. First, I had to graduate from college and be making enough money to support them and perhaps raise a family. Sure, I had the sexual urge but not the commitment. Too often men, and even boys, take advantage of an innocent young girl by telling her they love her--that is usually a lie. There is a big difference between LOVE and SEX!

Especially on the radio we hear songs repeating, "Tonight I want to love you." Why don't they be honest and simply say, "Tonight I want to have sex with you." Fortunately, I understood the difference between love and sex. And again, maybe I was lucky!

I USED FORD'S BUICK

Buicks were Ford's favorite car , and he traded for a new one often--more often than mother and the hotel could afford. Ford found good reasons to keep me away from the steering wheel of his Buicks when I was in high school. I sometimes persuaded my mother to allow me to take the Buick out to drive one of my girl friends around the area when Ford was out of town fishing or hunting. But every time I put my hands on the Buick something unpleasant happened. Most of the time Ford had the evidence I had driven his car. This caused my little mother added problems with Ford.

Ford encouraged Mother to close the Cottage Home and purchase the Hanna Hotel. It was a good move because there was more room and different clientele. There was also a Model T Ford with a single seat and a box on the rear for hauling supplies from the depot to the Hotel. This was used for fishing and hunting by both Ford and myself. I had a car to drive! Ultimately, I used that Model T for many interesting things that a high school boy does. I never damaged it, but I tried! The Buick was different.

Once I took a girl named Grace for a spin in that impressive Buick on a Sunday afternoon when Ford was fishing. I was always careful with it--sometimes too careful. We drove all around the area, and sneaked it into the garage as my mother insisted before Ford came back into town. The next day Ford was in the garage, and on the wrong side of the Buick he saw tell-tale speckles of paint all over. It was yellow and showed too well on the blue Buick. You see, Dan, they were painting a row of houses between my girl's home and the hotel. The painter was using a spray gun and the west wind blew little specks of yellow paint to the east while I carefully drove the car home. No luck! Both mother and I caught hell. I was used to it, but it was tougher on her.

Yet another time mother let me drive another date, named Helen, around the area on a Saturday afternoon. Ford was again fishing. It was several days before Ford found out about my bad luck. A fellow in Number Three town came to Ford and asked him to pay for his prize hunting dog. It seems that the dog ran under the back wheels of the Buick. I am sure that we did not pay for the dog, but again I caught hell. Ford never hit me, although he sometimes had a good reason. That is something I can say for him. And, as far as I know he never touched my mother when angered. For that he probably felt I might accidentally shoot him when we hunted together.

Once again, I told my mother I would be especially careful if I could use the Buick to impress my new gal, whose name was Leona. My old buddy Eric went along with his girl Ellen. It was unique because nothing happened on this impressive Sunday drive. We waved to most of the kids in the neighborhood. I needed all the credibility I could get! Finally, I wanted to get that big car into the garage but the doors would not close so we decided to place the shift in neutral and then push it in. Eric, being stronger than I, pulled too hard and broke the door handle off. It just snapped off! Wouldn't you think Buicks of that day could be built with tougher handles? When, days later, Ford discovered the broken handle my mother was on the spot with Ford.

One more time, though, I did talk mother into letting me drive the Buick when Ford was out of town. On this trip I had a great tomboy girl,

Billie, who was well worth impressing. Another pal we called Kat and his girl-friend, Maybelle, went for a ride in the Buick. All went well until we took the girls home and backed out of the final yard. There was a telephone pole that just missed the rear bumper and crushed the back fender.

That was last time I ever drove the Buick. Ford, Mother and I had a peace truce, and I agreed to drive only the Model T Ford, which was unimpressive. If there were driver's licenses I would have lost mine because we had heard of Barney Oldfield, the race driver. Often I was a bit wild with the Model T, but it would not go over 30 miles an hour, except down hill! My pal Eric demanded the care of my favorite knife, which we agreed he could keep if I drove too fast. Now, Dan, I am not bragging about this, but as I survey that action I believe it was to prove that I had guts. It was not good judgment, rather, I guess it was another way I could be productive. We drove fast on the gravel roads we had then. Sometimes around curves the gravel would fly and we often tore off a tire. My advice is that you don't act stupidly in automobiles. There are other ways to prove yourself.

We did have a lot of fun in that old open Model T truck. I was the Fourth of July when Kat and I drove the model T to the rodeo in Saratoga. We rode around town with all four of us in pain because we didn't have the good sense to tell the opposite sex, "Excuse me, I will be right back." Then, we headed for the men's room. On the main street, near the bridge I was so uncomfortable that I got out of the car and raced around the corner where they were selling fireworks and behind their display I unbuttoned my pants, (no zippers then) and after I was about half finished taking a leak I looked up and found myself in view of all who drove down a side street--too late, so I finished! The four of us cuddled up in that small front seat and my recent experience gave us something to giggle about.

. . . .

During my last few years in high school, and each summer during college, I worked for the Wyoming Timber Company at a loading plant in Fort Steele where we loaded railroad ties. One weekend a young friend from Denver came to visit me in Hanna.

That Sunday afternoon I drove the Model T around the area of Old Carbon.

On the way home I followed the old railroad grade which we sometimes used to go home, which was about eight miles from Hanna. As we reached the middle of the overpass I suddenly realized that the bridge, which crossed a deep draw, had been washed out since I had last been there. We were so high that I could go neither right nor left. As I used all the brakes the Model T had, we shuddered directly to the washed out area. It looked like we were headed for a helluva fall into the chasm. The front tires disappeared beyond the trail. We high-centered on the automobile frame with the radiator pointing to the bottom of the gulch.

I advised my guest to open the door gently, step carefully onto the running board and then into the truck box, then move back to the safe ground. I wanted him to pull the end-gate backwards while I did the same thing from the driver's side. When we were safe we were aware the Ford was headed downward, at about a 45 degree angle, into the deep gulch.

Earlier we had passed Johnnie Jack's ranch where he was putting up his hay about a mile from the road. I hurried to him and asked if he would unhitch his team and pull us backwards. He hooked up but then he worried that if the ground broke away his team of horses might be pulled into chasm with the car. Instead he offered to drive us to the Hanna Hotel.

There we ate supper as I waited for the crew to arrive and take me back to the tie loading plant at Fort Steele. Only then, I handed the keys to Ford and suggested that he drive to Johnnie Jack's ranch and get his help to retrieve the Model T. Ford muttered and said he would go the next day. Knowing me, he decided to take his old Kodak box camera with him. He and Johnnie Jack worked an hour or two and with the team and shovels and successfully saved the truck. From that time on when I asked about borrowing his Buick, he would just show me the pictures he took of the stranded Model T.

CONFESSIONS

Dear Dan:

Now, Dan, I have some confessions to make. Many of my actions as a kid in Hanna now seem unforgivable. Some say that confession is good for the soul, and as I watch some of my Catholic friends I am sure it's true. They tell God, through their priest, about their unpleasant actions. I couldn't do that, so I have to live with mine. Others are disturbed by their past. A psychiatrist gets paid very well for simply having the patient lie down on a couch and spill their guts, or tell the doctor, what's bothering them. I guess that writing this family history may serve the same function for me. As the years go on, just getting this down on paper for you will make you my "psychiatrist."

I promised myself that these letters would be honest, even though they may be painful. Your Uncle Ron tells everyone who will listen about the stupid things he has done, but most of us keep our sins secret. Ron is probably right. He gets things off of his chest and kids nobody.

Often alcoholism and drugs are screens people hide behind when they get depressed from thinking of the unpleasant things they have been a part of. I guess it's important to realize that no person is really perfect, and we're each entitled to some weakness. In the bible there is a story of Christ running the money changers out of the Temple. History acknowledges His influence changed the course of history of man.

O.K. Dan, here goes....I was a thief! I stole things from others. When I was about ten or twelve years old, several of us entered the little Hanna bakery shop which was run by a fine Finlander by the name of Pete Puro. As one of us bought a few doughnuts, I, or my pals would slip a pie or two under our jacket. Then we would slip out laughing about how slick we were to fool poor trusting Pete. Hell, nowadays they put kids in court for shop-lifting. There were no policemen in Hanna so Pete would have kicked our asses out of the bakery.

. . . .

Yes, we often suffered a little corporal punishment in some places of business, or in school. In the sixth grade a teacher beat me on the back of the head with a book. I was sure I deserved the experience and the resulting nose bleed. It is doubtful that this taught me much. With the help from my obnoxious friends she had a nervous breakdown and didn't return to Hanna the following year.

. . . .

We had a cash drawer in the bedroom where Ford and my mother slept, from which we made change for transients who often ate in the dining room. Without Ford knowing it mother let me slip in there and get a silver dollar so I could go and take a girl to the show, or perhaps play pool with the guys. We didn't let Ford in on it because it would cause a family battle. Now, when I thought I really had to have a buck I would slip into the drawer and pick up the silver dollar myself--not even asking my mother! Hell, that was stealing, wasn't it? This is the first time I have ever told anyone about that because it was such a shameful thing to do.

. . . .

In Hanna a Greek miner was known to pay a few cents for empty beer bottles. We collected them and when we had enough we sold them to him. We noticed that he put the bottles in a shack near his home. There was a loose board around the back of the building and I was smaller than the others so at the right time I squeezed in and pushed bottles out to my buddies. Then, after a few weeks, we again sold some of the bottles back to the Greek bootlegger. We didn't think there was anything really dishonest--we thought it was a slick trick!

Some time after high school I stopped doing such stupid things. Maybe I was simply afraid of hurting my mother. Her influence caused me to improve my character. Even today my heart aches when I read of some punk who commits a crime and gets in trouble, because I feel empathy for his mother and father.

WE ALWAYS HURT THE ONE WE LOVE

I believe we all have thoughts sometime during the 24 hours of a day which we should record, but if we don't do it NOW it is usually forgotten. Some of the greatest ideas come from diaries, and perhaps we should all keep one. You would love it and understand yourself better. Maybe with this computer I now have one! Worthwhile thought often comes to our minds unexpectedly. If we do not write them down at that moment the valuable ideas can be lost forever.

As I ran this morning the title of an old song came to me.."We always hurt the one we love!" You know, Dan it is true! Two people who are very much in love seldom injure one another's feelings until after they are married. Another old adage could apply . . . Familiarity breeds contempt! Whoever first wrote these words had difficult experiences and understood human nature.

We seldom say things to a neighbor or a casual classmate which makes them feel horrible. But we often speak unkindly to members of our own family, whom we love. An easy way to eliminate family fights, divorces, and personal injuries someone should apologize first. We should be happier, wiser and kinder and we must concentrate and avoid the things that disturb them. For no good reason, we should put our arms around someone in the family, and tell the other person we love them.

Often when a single couple become too familiar in personal or sexual ways, their love and friendship often goes on the rocks. Those in successful marriages and friendships seem to keep a few more intimate secrets from one another. Hate is often the result of sharing one's past secrets.

Whenever a person selfishly develops an alcohol, drug or tobacco habit, which often destroys a mind and body, he hurts those he loves.

PATIENCE--FRUSTRATION--STRESS

I admire individuals who have been born with the ability to control difficult emotional problems. I wonder how they were so endowed to handle frustration? Did they inherit the genes that make them more patient? Are they freer from stress than the average person? I don't know! Could it be that their formative years were better controlled.

Again we come to the problems of deciding which is the more important--heredity or environment? No doubt we are products of both of these influences which are developed at an early age. Surely the intelligent person can modify his behavior.

On the door of my study I printed in large letters the words, TEMPER, ANGER, CONTROL. Often I am working on my computer when my poor little wife calls me to breakfast, and I become frustrated. I suppose it would be well if I would read the words I see on my door.

FORD'S BETTER SIDE

You will learn that there are no perfect people. The most conscientious persons never achieve perfection. I am sure that we would have to live with them for only a few days to see their character flaws.

No doubt I saw his Ford's behavioral actions which caused me and my mother difficulties. Certainly, Ford was well aware of mine. I remember the times he treated both mother and my sister Elsie very well. Elsie, in her short life with a stepfather, thought he was a pretty good addition to our family.

My younger cousin, Gordon Hughes, remembers that Ford drove him, and his buddies to see the rodeo at Cheyenne, and both he and the kids had a ball. Certainly, there were times like those that he seemed generous and had fun with younger kids.

Ford was an expert fisherman and hunter, and being with him as a teenager, I learned how to handle a gun safely, and observed how to cast a fly on the stream. My pal, Eric, and I had many good trips hunting with Ford.

Dan, you will learn, as time goes by, everyone has both their good and bad traits. Certainly, I have my share of the latter.

OUR GOLDEN WEDDING ANNIVERSARY

On September 22, 1935, your grandmother and I were married. This year we have celebrated in various ways over several weeks, but yesterday was special! You and your folks and the rest of our family were together. Also, Leah Grothe and Dan's wife Roberta were invited to your Uncle Byra and Aunt Marilyn's home for a real feast--presents and all!

Fifty years is a long while to be married. Too often divorces, or premature deaths, prevent Golden Anniversaries. We were lucky! There are valid reasons for divorces. I know a divorced couple who work together in a successful business venture. Today, they are better friends than when they were married. Very often divorced couples simply marry too young.

Younger people ask how we made it. Well, luck and health were factors, but so was patience and real love. Mary and I are far from perfect. But who isn't? Sure, there were many disagreements during those fifty years, and some were serious. The key was we made mutual adjustments. Also, we loved one another and our children. We apologized and forgave each other.

Finances, liquor, and extramarital relationships are most of the factors which destroy most marriages. Sure, we partied with a group of young people, and I occasionally drank more alcohol than I needed. Mary and I had trouble paying our bills during the depression even though we were conservative. I simply worked harder to earn the most important things we needed, and my little wife was a wonderful homemaker.

Yes, we borrowed money for essentials in our home--like furniture, vacations and other things we wanted and never had before. We protected our credit rating. Items like automobiles had to wait until we had the cash. We refused the installment buying approach and saved the interest. Many financial problems in the home can be avoided with good planning. Before we had a child we borrowed enough money to add to our savings and built our first home. As years passed we purchased other property and this established the foundation for our savings.

Often couples marry before they are ready to take such an important step. I was twenty-seven years old and your grandmother was about four years younger. Each of us graduated from college where we dated other people. Some individuals begin to think that they might have missed something by not dating different people. Then, they begin to experiment and are not loyal to their wedding vows. Their actions often keep them from celebrating a Golden Wedding Anniversary.

Incidentally, Dan, on our Anniversary our three children, and their spouses, financed an expense-free trip to the fabulous Broadmoor Hotel in Colorado Springs. We played golf and lived-it-up on that second honeymoon.

Wait a minute Dan! It just occurred to me that you might someday be a bachelor like your Uncle Ron. There is nothing wrong with that! Today, Ron is glad that he never married--he says that he enjoys his freedom and is glad he has no wife or children to support.

A SEQUEL TO GOLDEN ANNIVERSARY

Try as we may, but in life we should never say <u>never</u>. Time and situation constantly change and we must prepare ourselves for change.

It has been only exactly five years since I wrote to tell you of our Golden Wedding Anniversary. At that time I made a case against divorce. Then, I never dreamed that there might be a divorce in our family. Well, it happened!

Your aunt Marilyn and uncle Byra have been divorced. This was a shock to your Grandmother and myself, but in retrospect we should have thought it was possible. In the first place we are grateful that they were not parents. Children suffer more from divorce more than do their mother and father.

Their mutual decision to be divorced finally makes sense to all of us. Their life-style was necessarily very different because both of them had work which did not lend itself to the normal home-life that made our Golden Anniversary successful.

Marilyn is devoted to her work which is that of a very successful lawyer who works with Holland and Hart law firm in Denver. She must attend meetings and plead cases all around the country. She drives and flies most of her time around the entire United States. Byra Kite, our son-in-law, has a similar work problem. He is in charge of planning and accomplishes the needs of our Senator Malcolm Wallop in Washington D. C. He also must drive or fly regularly around Wyoming, with many trips to Washington. I often noted much of the time they had together was in airports where they flew in opposite directions.

Their decision to apply for divorce came as a blow to Mary and myself. We love that couple dearly. I relied on Byra especially for my hunting excursions. He was, and will be, my guide and partner. We had much in common.

It was difficult for Marilyn to tell us their mutual decision to apply for divorce. It took some time for me to recover because everyone knew of my firm conviction against divorces. Today, we are proud of both of them for making that decision. We were grateful that there was no other man or woman involved in the life they enjoyed together.

Marilyn was eager that Byra remain an important member of the Stebner family. He will because he means so much to the rest of our family. Remember Dan, when you see Byra you should call him "Uncle Byra."

Yes, Dan, there is an important place for divorce in our society.

The Early Dentist

DR McDERMOTT

Dear Dan:

Finally, Hanna hired a good surgeon, Dr. McDermott, who incidentally stimulated me to attend Creighton. When I was home from college I assisted him in surgery because he could not trust his alcoholic physician partner. Doctor McDermott was a master surgeon, but had little to do with diagnosis or postoperative care--he simply liked to operate.

Once I saw him make an immediate diagnosis which allowed him to work in the operating room the coming Monday morning. A patient entered to see McDermott and said, as he entered the open doorway, and remarked to the good Doctor: : "Doc, I feel that perhaps I should get rid of my appendix." Between puffs on his pipe the doctor nodded his head and said, "I guess you're right, Jack. Come in early Monday morning and we will operate." Both Doctor McDermott and the patient were both satisfied. At that time there were no second opinions or laboratory tests needed.

. . . .

Doctor McDermott had many qualities which impressed myself. He was well trained at Creighton University, and prepared himself for the good life he was to enjoy. Certainly he was a man of courage, and one who believed in himself. McDermott was a most honest man and a good family person. He was married to a pleasant, striking blonde woman, and they had a pretty blonde daughter about my age. This girl attracted me! Several times I went to their ranch north of Hanna, and she and I would ride horses in the hills. It was quite romantic, but there was nothing serious between us--maybe I held her hand on occasions. She had a more serious boy-friend who was a freshman, basketball player here at University Prep, and she finally married him. That was just as well, because I had a lot of time and plenty of available girls who were available.

When I left Denver University during the early 1920,s and was attending Creighton, where he advised me to go, he treated me like a member of his family. I drove him in his Packard touring car to the State Medical Meeting in Casper. Then it was an oil boom community. It was my first trip there and I was impressed by the flavor of the boisterous little city on the Wyoming plains. I am sure that the famous illicit Sand Bar was functioning, but I didn't even drink, let alone think of the girls who were there, although we all knew about it.

McDermott invited me to go with him to a surgical demonstration at the hospital. Several well-known surgeons were operating. It was a simple appendectomy, and it was my first time in an operating room even though I was a junior student at Creighton. At that time some Wyoming doctors didn't wear a gloves or a mask. McDermott, myself and other observers leaned against the open window with me and watched and asked questions. We were dressed in the clothes we wore into Casper as we discussed the procedure and asks questions. It was very informal and less than antiseptic.

Those two or three men who actually worked on the patient <u>did</u> have gowns, masks and rubber gloves. In those days this attempt at sterility impressed many people there, and one in particular. As I remember, this doctor was from a small towns in northeast Wyoming, probably only doctor in that area. He was not the picture of the modern physician. His hair was uncombed and his face unshaven, and even I was impressed that he was chewing tobacco and would often spit out of the open window.

I,m sure he was the oldest doctor in the room, and I was the youngest observer. He came to Doctor McDermott and asked, "Doctor, what do you really think about this germ theory." McDermott assured him that the theory had been proven by Pasteur, and, yes, he really did agree that the masks and rubber gloves should be worn during the operation.

I am sure that this old doctor had only a year or two of medical education. Nevertheless, he was practicing medicine and no doubt saving a few lives and delivering many babies in his community.

You know, Dan, in a way he had a break because most of his older patients had lived through many accidents and infections and had built up a lot of immunity to the germs. You could probably operate on many of them with a pocket knife and a drink of whiskey for an anesthetic. In those days only the tougher survivors lived into adulthood. The weaklings died early. It was the survival of the fittest.

Another thing Dr. McDermott did for me, which I cherished and for which I will always be grateful, was that he paid the registration fee of $25.00 for my Wyoming State Board. This was in 1932 --the worst of the depression!

Mother seemed concerned by the good Doctor's desire to use his scalpel too readily. Some one repeated the news that her friend Jennie had her appendix removed that week by McDermott. Mother thought of others who had the same treatment during the last month, and said: "Eee, if I kin just keep away from him a bit longer, I'll be in a class by myself, and then they will call me 'Smooth-belly Mary' because I'll be the only woman in town no scar."

. . . .

One summer vacation day before I went to work at the tie-loading plant, I received news that McDermott wanted me at the hospital urgently. When I arrived they wheeled in the patient in who had an attack in the mine. It was my Uncle John! He was in great pain had a history of a stomach ulcer. Apparently it had ruptured into the abdominal area. The nurses were preparing for the operation, I told the doctor that I was reluctant to help operate on my favorite uncle. McDermott said, "Hell, you gotta, my assistant is drunk and he'll be lucky to pour the ether."

The operation was a success and Uncle John lived another fifty years with no more ulcers.

. . . .

Dr. McDermott abhorred postoperative care--he just wanted to operate! But his intuitive wisdom and his experience were great. I remember helping him operate on a rather large Mexican woman, whose husband worked on the section for the railroad. She was an emergency, and the doctor's diagnosis--that she had a ruptured appendix was correct. A quick look at her allowed him to diagnose, without all of the tests, laboratory findings, and other scientific aids we must have today.

I also recall is that his alcoholic physician assistant performed a poor job of pouring the ether. The patient was never really out! Although unconscious, she still groaned and strained, but that didn't bother the scalpel of McDermott.

When he opened the stomach the evidence was there: the foul smelling, darkened fluid squirted out. I was the towel man. The nurses brought me large warm towels with which I soaked up all the fluid and controlled the intestines which attempted to escape their home and get into my arms. Ultimately, McDermott found the diseased appendix and cut it off, sutured and stopped the flow of intestinal fluids.

Closing the field of operation was a difficult chore. Usually, most of the viscera simply stays home, but with this patient's straining, I literally had most of her intestines in the towel and in my arms. It took McDermott's hands and mine place the intestines into the abdominal cavity. As we pushed a foot of intestine in, six inches seemed to come out. When they were all returned home, and I hoped in their proper relationship, I held them there while McDermott sutured. In this case he placed several feet of a wide gauze drain into the abdominal cavity with the end sticking out of the sutures to allow all foreign fluids to escape exteriorly.

The poor gal was placed in her room and after he watched her for a day or two, he announced that he was going to drive to his ranch and stay there for a week. The ranch was about thirty miles north of Hanna.

He asked me to check her every day or two to see how she was doing. I was an undergraduate student at Creighton School of Dentistry. I felt rather uncomfortable being in charge of the post-operative care. McDermott said, "Hell, Charlie, you can do it. All you have to do is notice when you go into her room to see if the odor still remains. If it does then the drain is working. If there is no strong odor and if you can't smell too bad, ask the nurse if her pulse has increased Maybe then you had better call me, and I'll come into town." The stench remained foul until he returned. The lady lived. Her husband and I were both happy! McDermott knew it all the time.

I AM A DENTIST

There was no doubt that Ford was pleased when I graduated from dental school. Among other things, it meant that he would no longer have to wonder what happened to his neck ties. Mother regularly stole them and mailed them to Omaha. Anything he seldom used disappeared. My classmates couldn't understand how I could afford so many nice ties during the worst of the Depression.

Ford was eager to see me practice dentistry following my graduation in 1932. But that period was the most difficult time to start a new business. Even men who had thrived during the 1920's were having trouble paying their obligations. Somehow he thought that, as a professional man, I could pay off the five thousand dollars mother had sent me during the five years since my high school graduation. To my mother it was not a debt I owed, but to Ford it was.

It was known that some dental equipment was available in the office of a Doctor Fitch, who had died. I might be able to purchase that cheaply and move it to Medicine Bow, Walden, or any place which had no dentist. Most of my classmates in Nebraska or Iowa followed that procedure starting in small towns, perhaps their hometown.

I came to Laramie to talk to the father of the former dentist, Mr. E. E. Fitch. He agreed to let me have the entire office-there was no x-ray machine-for one thousand dollars cash. I knew of no person who had entered dental practice for less. 'Ned' Fitch became a good friend and advisor for as long as he lived.

I drove the old Model T Ford I borrowed to the Hanna Hotel and visited with my uncle, O. G. Sharrer, who was the only college graduate in the family. He had married Bruno's sister and was superintendent at the Hanna mines. He wrote me a check which I signed over to Fitch and the contents of the office was mine.

An experienced business person, Fitch was wiser than I, and suggested that I might leave the equipment in the Roach building and build my practice in Laramie. He had a hunch that without the obligation of being married, I might make it. I was able to find a room near the office and borrow a few dollars for meal tickets. The rent was only fifty dollars, but that seemed a lot then.

For the first six weeks no person opened my reception room door. During the morning I polished the shiny equipment that was now mine, and sat in the dental chair to read scientific journals. The reading habit paid off for me during the rest of my professional life.

My old office ledger book tells the story. Slowly, very slowly, I was doing a little dentistry. Gradually I was able to pay off debts I owed. The supply houses made me pay for all materials C.O.D. During the next two or three years I was making enough money to save. I borrowed a car from Howard Penny, an old Hanna friend. I used it for a few dates. He let me take his car to visit to my Uncle Sharrer. This time it was a pleasant business trip.

I had saved one thousand dollars, and could hardly wait to pay off the debt to my uncle. I paid no interest--it was simply a loan. As we visited he suggested that he did not need the money right then, and that I buy my own car with those savings. That I did! It was a brand new 1935 Chevrolet four-door green sedan with yellow wire wheels.

I remember the pleasure I had when I entered the show room of the garage. Business was slow there too, and the owner Ray Pizolli and his salesman Elmer Redburn were sitting in the office playing cards. I told them I liked that sedan, and wondered how much it would cost. First, they asked me about the car I wished to trade in. Then, they asked how I was going to finance it. But when I told them I had the cash in my pocket, both of them came out of their seats. When would the car be ready to drive out? Their answer was about thirty minutes! I was very proud when I drove it away to my office.

Ford was my only financial problem now. He and my mother disagreed on my liability. Ford kept track of all the money Mother saved to invest in my college expenses. He wanted it back! I presume he would have liked to buy another Buick.

I PLAN MY WEDDING

When I was 27 years old, and finally out of debt and in love with a beautiful girl who was four years younger than myself, I proposed marriage to your grandmother Mary. She had graduated from the business college at the University of Wyoming, and was planning to live with her mother and help with her two younger sisters. Finally, with my persistence Mary accepted. We set the date of our wedding--September 22, 1936!

I had another hurdle to overcome. My step-father Ford opposed my marriage. He came to Laramie and I made him a new set of dentures. He was difficult as he insisted on telling me how I should select the color, size and alignment of the artificial teeth I was making for him. Then I realized that his main objection was that I should pay both him and my mother the $4,500 mother had spent on my entire college education. He also did not agree with my choice of a bride. It was a stormy dental appointment.

When he arrived in Hanna he upset my mother with his version of our difficult visit. When I talked to her on the phone I realized that I must immediately drive to Hanna and face mother and Ford. Mother told both of us that she never considered any financial repayment necessary. Then I told Ford that if he ever came between me and my mother I would make another trip home and beat the hell out of him. That was the last time we spoke to one another.

. . . .

Several months later both Ford, my mother, Uncle John and Aunt Georgia drove in Ford's Buick to Laramie to attend my wedding. It was a happy time with the beautiful wedding, but it was a tense time for my little mother. Following the wedding Mary and I left the church that we had decorated beautifully with autumn leaves we had collected from our colorful Snowy Range.

Mother's trip back through that same Snowy Range. toward Hanna was not so pleasant. Ford had been drinking whiskey and still insisted that he was able to drive his Buick on that mountain road. The first part of the trip was hazardous because Ford drove dangerously. When he stopped for another drink from his bottle, Uncle John asked for the keys. He had to threaten Ford that he would forcefully take the keys if necessary. With Ford in the back seat they finished my wedding trip safely home.

. . . .

At a dental meeting where I lectured a person said that I reminded him of this Bible quotation. I hope he was a good judge of character...

ECCLESIASTICS 5:18-20

Behold, what I have seen to be good and to be fitting is to eat and drink and find enjoyment in all the toil with which one toils under the sun the few days of his life which God has given him, for this is his lot. Every man also to whom God has given wealth and possessions and power to enjoy them and to accept his lot and find enjoyment in his toil--this is the gift of God. For he will not much remember the days of his life because God keeps him occupied with joy in his heart.

Widowed Again

DR. MAUREY LEAKE

Dear Dan:

At the height of the Depression I was fortunate enough to be sort of adopted by a fine physician who was much older than I. Maurey Leake came to Laramie from his home in Tennessee to practice medicine in Wyoming with his younger partner, Dr. Richard DeKay. They both guided me and helped me build my practice.

Dr. Leake had been divorced and seemed lonely and I helped fill a void when he needed companionship. At first I lived in various rooming houses until Maurey invited me to share his bachelor's apartment on the fifth floor of our office building. Of course besides the companionship, I saved what little money I had--he paid the rent. Both Dr. Leake and his junior partner Dick DeKay were practical jokers and had a lot of fun with tricks they played on me.

Maurey told a history of the largest professional fee he received during the Depression. A lady patient presented herself because of her abdominal growth--she was older but still often thought she was pregnant. Rightly, Dr. Leake decided to operate her to determine the cause of the consistent growth of her belly. There he found and removed a large sack of fluid. It was an ovarian cyst which weighed 60 pounds. Maurey was amazed! When she asked for her bill the good doctor thought she should pay $10.00 a pound to get rid of all that fluid. Gladly she wrote out a check for $600.00 dollars.

A HANNA RELATIVE ON THE TRAIN

The name of the new mining town was chosen to honor Senator Hanna of Ohio. He was a member of the Board which established the Union Pacific Railroad. When I was in Creighton University I rode the train from Omaha to Hanna. In the roof of the observation car I noticed a pleasant grey-haired lady who was most interested in watching out of the window with her camera ready to shoot something which seemed important to her. As we approached Medicine Bow I asked what her interest was. She said Hanna! She wanted a picture of the town as we traveled west.

I assured her that we were quite a few miles away and for the time being she could relax. She introduced herself as a 'Mrs. Hanna', and said that her family was responsible for the origin of the town. Then I told her what Hanna meant to me and she was surprised. I kidded her that my family had helped make her's wealthy. She laughed and explained her side of the family did not get any of the Senator's inheritance. But she was interested in a photo so she could show it to her richer relatives.

Well, Dan you can be assured I gave her some of Hanna's more unpleasant history concerning the explosions and other sad things that Hanna meant to me. She no doubt took home an accurate history to add to the pictures of the depot, the mine, and the Hanna Hotel as I disembarked. I should have mentioned that my mother was Mrs. Ford, and that Henry did not leave us any money either.

MARY FORD AFTER FORD'S DEATH

Little Mary again became the Big Mary after Ford was buried in the family lot in Hanna with a much smaller stone than the one for Bruno. Petty? Yes, I know.

The Hanna Hotel business went on. But, the big difference was that now a profit showed in the business account. I encouraged mother to sell all of the tools, guns, and fishing equipment. My thought was that was that she should start a clean slate now that Ford was no longer there to make decisions. Her past permitted to work harder and allowed her to face a better future.

In the Navy

FARRAGUT

Dear Dan:

When I was a dentist in the Navy during WW II, I had to miss those traditional family Christmases for a while. Later, our little family left Laramie to join me and continue our Christmas tradition.

Your grandmother drove to Farragut, Idaho where I was stationed, in our old Chevrolet. Your great grandmother, Martha Conwell, was with her, and they had to worry about gasoline, which was rationed at that time. Mary called me at the dental infirmary where I boarded a bus. I was proud to have them see me in my officer's uniform when I met them at the railroad station. The railroad station was named 'ATHOL', and the recruits felt that if they changed the spelling a little it could mean the end of the line for their freedom when they got off the train.

I had desperately missed my four-year-old son, your Uncle Ron, with whom I had played by the hour. It was a new experience to see your dad Ken; we were strangers to one another! I can't say he was a beautiful baby, as I remembered Ron being when he was born. Ken was wrinkled, crying and looked like an unhappy little old man. He wasn't happy to be greeted by the man in uniform, and I had to give him to his Grandma Conwell before he was satisfied. I assure you that he blossomed into a happy boy very soon.

I took them to the little town of Spirit Lake, where I had rented a small home. At any time I expected to be assigned to sea duty, which never happened. We lived at Spirit Lake until the war was over and I was discharged. Then we came back to our home which we had rented to the Petri family.

Yet, without the conveniences we knew in Laramie we were happy and carefree. Our rented home had a wood burning kitchen stove, which was our only source of heat. The refrigerator was an old ice-box, and we carried ice from Athol, a station on the railroad. Spirit Lake was built on the shores of a beautiful body of clear water. I road a bicycle with an extra tricycle seat attached for Ron. When I was not on duty at Farragut, Ron and I rode on the unpaved roads around the town, fishing, swimming. Ron enjoyed visiting the horses which which is still his favorite pleasure.

Ron, Ken and parents at Farragut.

Our lifestyle was much like a vacation even though we knew that at any day I might have been assigned to the Fleet Marines, or a big navy ship. At that time we were having difficulties fighting the Japanese in the terrible battles of the Pacific Ocean. We had good friends at Farragut who shared the same problems, especially the Walter Dowler family we knew in Laramie.

We made the best of our life and played the game of waiting for orders. Your grandmother was relaxed and happy to remain in that little house. There she played by the hour with her new son Kenny on the floor or the bed, the two of them laughing and squealing together, while Ron and I were on the bicycle built for two.

My work at the Navy base was frustrating at times but still very rewarding. The young recruits came from all over the country and many desperately needed my professional services. Farragut was built swiftly to accommodate navy recruits in the forest wilderness on the shores of Lake Coeur D'Alene. The base accommodated about 60,000 Navy personnel. At one time there were more than 250 dentists, and even more medical personnel. There were more than six large camps. I was assigned to Camp Ward.

The only ship in evidence was something they called a 'whale boat'. The new recruits were known as 'Boots'. Their early training was rowing these boats on the lake. Most of the Boots arrived in poor physical condition. Dan, if you could have seen the way many suffered trying to get ready to go to sea within six weeks, you would keep yourself in good physical condition to obtain toughness and save your own life and those of your buddies.

On arrival, the recruits went to a receiving center which reminded me of a sheep shearing pen where I worked soon after high school. Barbers, if you could call them that, made beautiful locks hit the deck. Their skulls all looked the same--like peeled onions. Some recruits shed a tear or two, and others pointed at their buddies and laughed. They came from big cities, small towns and from the farms and ranches.

I figured that there were two good reasons for that haircut. First, many of those kids needed a good cleaning to eliminate vermin, and the haircut was followed by a thorough shower. The second reason was to discourage them from going AWOL. Those 'peeled onions' would be easy for the military police to spot them. I understand that the same thing then went on with some of the Catholic Nuns when they enter a convent. It is understandable that many become discouraged and think of sneaking back into the bigger world. But by the time their hair grows out they will have made an adjustment to a new life.

Most of the recruits were quite adaptable and patriotic because of the memories of Pearl Harbor. They enjoyed a lot of horse-play with others who soon became devoted friends. They were forced to work very hard, and discipline was tough! There was no junk food, and they were exercised to the limit. They lost fat and replaced it with muscle. Many were fortunate to leave the ghetto or parents who spoiled them. Each of them had teeth repaired, or removed when they were hopeless. Many had never been to a dentist. It was important they should have few or no dental emergencies when on board a fighting ship. The rapid enforcement of discipline was rough but necessary before the Boot was assigned to a fighting ship.

Before I volunteered I attended two month course in Oral Surgery at Northwestern University in Chicago. This, combined with my ten years in practice, benefited both myself and the Navy. Most of the younger dentists I worked with had been pushed through dental school with limited experience. At first I worked right along with them until higher officers assigned me to more meaningful assignments. Soon I was in charge of surgery in our dispensary. There I was able to help inexperienced young graduates to whom I taught surgery. I also used the rubber dam, and challenged new dental officer to perform better dentistry on the Boots.

In a short time I was a dentist's dentist as I treated my fellow officers. Also, I taught the dental corpsmen who assisted dentists at the chair. It was important to help these men who would soon be going to sea on our fighting ships.

One of my favorite courses when I was an undergraduate was Bacteriology. Soon my experience this field was needed at Farragut. A streptococcus organism caused great problems. Scarlet fever finally became rampant with many badly infected throats among navy personnel. The Medical Corps in Washington issued an order that a Sulpha drug be given indiscriminately to all new recruits at Farragut. At first this seemed to be effective in controlling the organism, but soon the bacteria adjusted to the medicine. It became apparent that eventually the organism converted the sulpha into a nutrient.

We realized that the dental handpieces, used almost continuously by several shifts of dentists, were infecting more individuals. I was appointed to help work out a method for sterilizing handpieces in hot oil sterilizers. This bateriological project pleased me. I also worked with physicians and used a microscope with the Dark-Field illumination. I could soon identify the spirochetes of syphilis. This was necessary in diagnosing the organisms which cause syphilis.

My experience at Farragut was broad. I took advantage of every available experience and I read and learned very much. Eventually, I wrote a paper on some of these bacteriological results, which was published.

As time passed it became apparent that Farragut wasn't the place for a Navy Training Base. This was partly because of the scarlet fever problem, and also because we were training fewer Boots as we caught up with the ship building operations. The war was winding down. The Japanese had with their backs toward their own homeland. Soon, we dropped the atom bomb! At that time we celebrated in Spirit Lake. I remember making that statement there would never be another World War because there would never be a winner. It was obvious Captain Rehraurer canceled orders to go to sea because he could use me in Farragut.

The reputation I gained in Farragut proved to be a real bonus for me in the years following the war. Dentists around the country suggested that I lecture at their dental meetings. This exposure soon made me a teacher around the country.

IT WAS FOR THE BEST--A NEW OFFICE

An incident which proves Mother's point that things very often work out for the best happened when I returned from the Navy after the Japanese surrendered in the Pacific. Anyone who was in uniform then remembers the personal euphoria of coming home. I was eager to greet my friends and former patients but there was no office space available for me. The office space I had left to join the Navy had been unethically usurped by a younger dentist I had taken into my practice. We had agreed that he would care for my patients until I returned. But it did not work as we planned. He reneged on our agreement. After a short time he refused to pay my wife $150.00 a month for the use of my office upon which we agreed. When I was in uniform on my way to Farragut my wife was expecting our second son Ken. I wrote him letters and made phone calls, but received only weak excuses. I had no chance of getting a leave from the military at that time. In the meantime, my former trusted friend made a deal with another older dentist and they both moved into the office I left.

I was bitter and spent some time in the Navy gymnasium learning the fundamentals of boxing, because I knew that after a year I would be entitled to a leave from the service. When I did arrive for a week I immediately went to the office and confronted both dentists. I challenged both of them and forced an agreement to grant me a few hundred dollars for cabinets I had installed. I left no question of my attitude and what I expected concerning the payment for the cabinets. A check was written to pay the amount I asked. Frankly, I was disappointed that there were none of the fisticuffs for which I had carefully prepared in the Navy gym.

Well, Dan, when I was returned home following the capitulation of the Japanese, and could find no office to rent, I was bitter. Dr. Jack Rowlett, a physician friend of mine, who also gave up his practice to join the Navy, reminded me of an old cliche, saying I should have been prepared because, "NOTHING is too good for the returning veteran."

For a while I shared a room with Dr. Petri, another returning veteran who sympathetically allowed me to use a room in his office until I could find something better. When I complained about office space my mother said, "Don't worry about it, Charlie--everything happens for the best." Mother's promise proved to be correct. Having no office made me look for property elsewhere.

I had dreamed of an office on my own property nearer the residential area. This was impossible in Laramie because the ordinance allowed nothing to be built away from the established business district. I was forced to fight the City Council to change the ordinance. This was one of my many battles with the City Council. On a close vote I was successful. I was forced to borrow what then seemed to be a lot of money for a returning service man.

Although it seemed expensive then it turned out to be my best business venture. An older man was sympathetic to my problems. Babe Mohr had a soft spot for the returning service person, and he gave me a break. He owned a couple of vacant houses and a barn at Ninth and Grand. I gambled, and borrowed more money to purchase the land and build a modern dental office near the University of Wyoming. Today, 41 years later, I realize I gained about 525% on the money I borrowed.

It is easy to see that the person who failed to pay Mary the $150.00 per month and welcome me home really did me a great benefit. When you are down, Dan, realize that "Everything happens for the best"!

Ron and Ken are happy to have a sister, Marilyn.

The Laramie Fire

A FIRE TO REMEMBER

Dear Dan:

It happened soon after I returned from my service with the Navy. The BIG BOMB had caused the Japanese to surrender, and I and others were glad to be back in our hometown. Laramie looked great, and others, including Russ Allbaugh and Jim Hull, came to this city to make this their home. Their newspaper had something big to report--a 1.5 million dollars downtown fire. It began at the Holliday General Merchandise store. The total loss of that store, merchandise and building, was estimated at more than $500,000 dollars. There was excitement and despair on the downtown streets.

On that night, April 14, 1948, the fire was reported by Harold Olson, a Union Pacific railroad employee who was returning from work at 2 a.m.

I had found it impossible to find an office in the overcrowded business district. My dental office had been taken over by others. Dr. Ken Petri was discharged from the service and decided not to return to Illinois, because Laramie looked better. He rented the few rooms remaining in the Roach Building. Petri understood my need to find a place to rebuild the dental practice that I left to join the Navy. I was grateful to accept his offer, and that the single room was adequate for the dental chair, which had been in storage.

Another good medical friend, Dr. Jack Rowlett, who had returned from his service in the Navy, called me to make a dental appointment for his wife Ruth. Following WW II she was my first patient. I constructed a dental bridge for her and made an appointment to seat the restoration the next day.

When the fire was at its height I went to my one room office in the Roach (now Wagner) building and placed a few favorite gold foil dental instruments in my pocket along with Ruth's bridge. To the larger fixtures I said, "Goodbye" because at the rate of the spreading fire I felt sure that this block would also be in flames. However, the fire missed that building.

The lone occupants of the Holliday building were Mrs. E. H. Walker and her 19-year-old daughter, Beverly, who had an apartment there. Mr. Walker was the manager of the Holliday Store and was in Denver that night. The BOOMERANG reported Mrs. Walker's statement:

"My first impression when I awoke early this morning was I smelled smoke in the building. It was completely dark, but when I became more awake, I got up and looked out the back window of the apartment into the alley. All I could see was a fence burning next to the building across the way, but that was enough to frighten me. I called Beverly, my daughter, and told her there was a fire in the alley, and that we'd better get dressed. We had nearly completed dressing when someone started beating on the door and shouting for us to get out, the building was on fire. It was Frank Kirnig, and he told me to get out.

"I realized then that the thing was more serious than just the fire in the alley. but I wanted to get some of our things together to take out. We were gathering some things up when another man came up and said to drop everything and get out of the building. We were dressed and out on the street before the fire department ever arrived, but all we got out with were the clothes we had on. We lost everything we had in the fire. After the firemen came, we just stood on the sidewalk and watched and kept getting pushed back into the crowd. The building was completely gutted within 45 minutes of the time we got out of it. I'm really glad that Mr. Walker wasn't here, because he would probably have tried to get into the office and save the records, and the way the building went up I'm afraid it just couldn't have been done."

Our little family (Ron age eight, Ken four, and six-month-old Marilyn) were all asleep when the Grothes called us. The Grothes lived near the downtown area, and they called us for help--our part of town was not in danger. Warren and Leah were awakened by fire engines. There was a glow of flames on their bedroom window.

As we looked out of our window we knew it was something unusual because about fifteen blocks away we could see flames and smoke in the downtown area. We dressed, leaving our kids safely asleep. The flames were not headed toward our home.

We hurried to the Grothes and found them watering the roof of their home to extinguish falling embers. It seemed that they would have to begin removing their personal belongings from their home. The wind carried burning embers many blocks toward the University. Eight blocks from the source of the fire the American Legion Hall roof was burning. The wind threatened a large area of private homes toward the University.

It was an eerie sight on that dark night as the flames and smoke erupted from all of the four stories of that bulky building. There was no way the Laramie fire department could do anything other than to spray a limited amount of water on surrounding buildings. Fire engines from Cheyenne and Fort Collins were called and on their way, but they were too late to stem the tide. The real problem was Laramie's water supply and the wind that blew out of the southeast. Fortunately the wind subsided during the morning.

For years before the war I and others had been fighting reactionary public officials to encourage them to improve our obsolete water supply, and also the water mains which delivered it. A group that I chaired repeatedly encouraged the public to pass bond issues on several occasions. The public voted down our suggested projects. While I was in the service, my good friend, H. T. Person, Dean of Engineering (who later served temporarily as University of Wyoming President) wired me: "You asked for WATER, and we voted you WATER." Unfortunately, the water project was not completed before the fire.

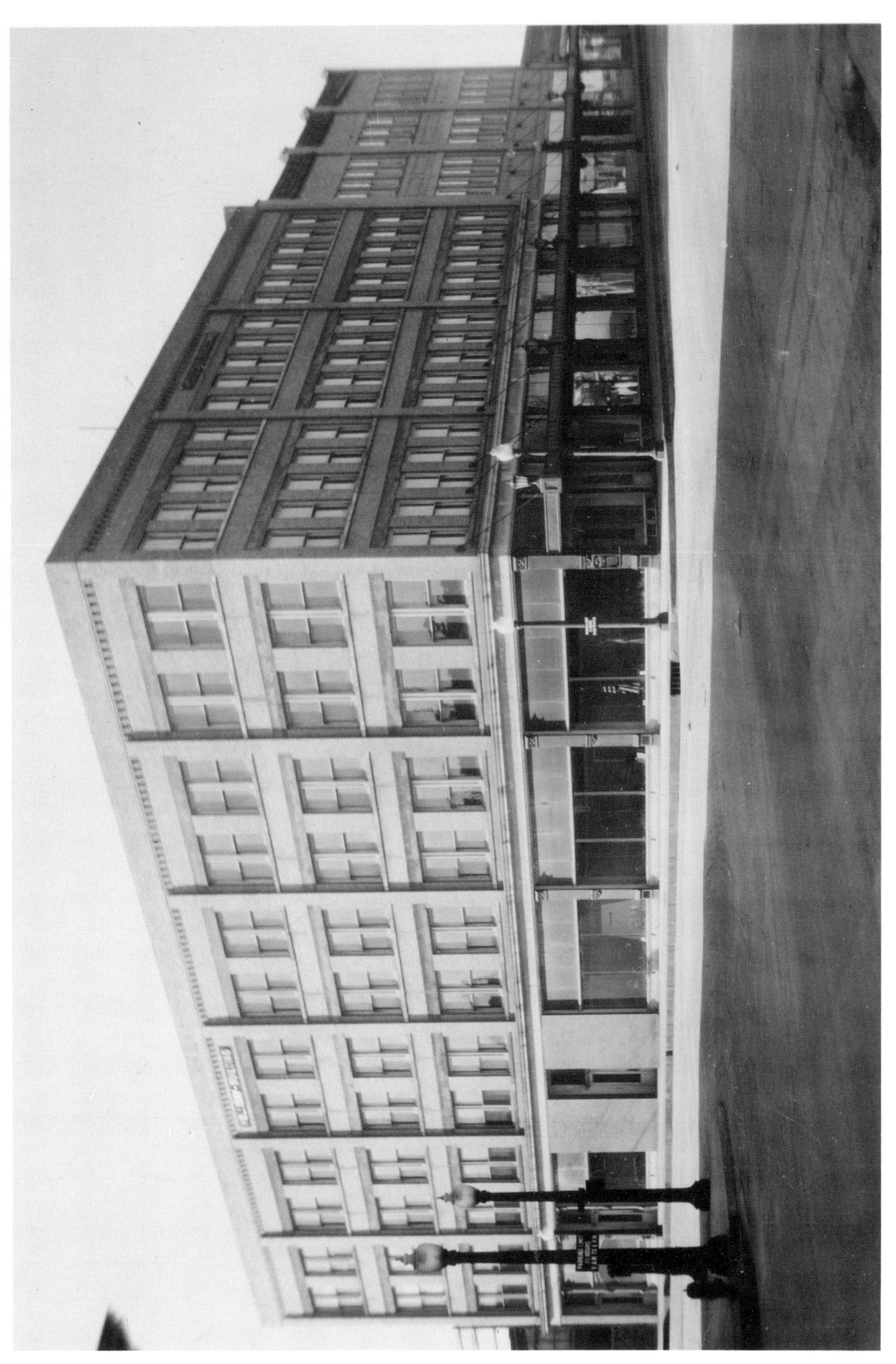

The W. H. Holliday Building before the fire.

The W. H. Holliday Building after the fire.

The day before the fire during a Laramie Chamber of Commerce meeting, there were two quotations in our newspaper, the Daily BOOMERANG. Jim Steele said: "The town is not only dirty, but filthy." And, he added we should clean up the town to attract new business and industry. Charlie Stebner was also quoted: "We should devote a special meeting to the question of promotion of new buildings and the abandoned, unsightly old structures, as one means of improving the city's general appearance."

The BOOMERANG reported that 29 businesses were destroyed that night. Those listed were as follows:

Mehse-Baker Company, Ford Dealers
W. H. Holliday & Company
De Vore Sheet Metal Works
John & Jakes Shoe Repair
Weick Refrigerator
Linde's Gun Shop
National Cash Register
Culligan Soft Water Company
Fred Wood Plumbing & Heating
Gambles
Laramie Hotel
Garrod Radio Service
Kett's Battery
Mountain States Lithographics
Rabb Garage
Dulco Refrigeration
Killian Florist
Rosedale Dairy
Laramie Feed & Implement
Sam Smith's Furniture
Holley Laycock Motor
Laramie Automotive Parts
Halverson Upholstery
Maple Way Bowling Alley
Bill Knight Shoe Shop
Murphey's Barber Shop
The American Legion Hall roof

Eddie Rassmusen, Fireman, received the only injury--a broken ankle.

Under the leadership of the Chamber of Commerce President, Oscar Hammond, the community raised thirty thousand dollars to loan to burned out victims. This was called the "Little Marshall Plan."

Gifts came from Cheyenne, Rawlins, Greeley, Fort Collins, and the rural community. It was estimated that the reconstruction cost would be three million dollars. Now, forty years later, the costs would have doubled many times because of inflation.

CHUCK STREET and THE FIRE

Chuck Street, a long time Laramie resident, was a very successful businessman, operating the Mountain States Lithographing Company. During World War II he had a great desire to join the Air Force and become a pilot. However, he was forty years old and that ruled him out. Still eager to serve his country in time of war, he left his printing business to his competent staff and joined the Navy to become a Navy recruiter until the end of the war. Upon returning to Laramie and his printing business, he immediately took over and began to build his business to greater heights. His business was located across from the Holliday Building where Laramie's most disastrous fire broke out. It completely destroyed his entire business, together with many others.

Chuck and his staff had ordered a brand new Miehle printing press and waited 21 months for its delivery. This equipment had been placed on the floor of his shop and ready for operation when the Holliday fire occurred. A friend called Street out of bed and told him of the conflagration across from his printing shop. Chuck told of his experience that early morning:

"I put my clothes on over my pajamas and hurriedly went to the street opposite the fire. There I watched the fire spread across the street and in twenty minutes I watched my business burn down. First I saw the standard for the street lights, which had a big white cover melt, and saw the standard topple over leaving only the base. I tried to get in the back door of our shop to recover my records and other valuable material I had in the safe.

"The police wouldn't let me enter and I had to give up on that idea. Everything in that building was burned! Even that brand new Miehle Press which we hadn't even used once. We didn't have any insurance on it yet. Insurance was almost prohibitive because we were surrounded by other inflammable materials--a battery shop, a paint shop and a garage. Across the street was the Holliday Building which was condemned. Holliday was a lumber man and the building was constructed almost entirely of wood with a brick outside. "The

Laramie Community and the Chamber of Commerce responded to aid the disaster victims. A Hollywood Premiere staged at the University as a highly successful fund raiser, as well as were other projects. Oscar Hammond was president of the Chamber of Commerce at that time, and he and Ernie Smith were the two fine people the community desperately needed at that time. (Previously, when I was president of the Chamber we hired Ernie Smith, a newcomer to Laramie, as the first manager of the new Chamber of Commerce.)

Local bankers offered Chuck an opportunity to borrow money, but only for six months. This was impossible because he needed something between $75,000. and $100,000. to get back in business. This was too much money to be repaid in a short time. He was forced to investigate elsewhere for a longer loan.

Dean Dearinger was working in the Albany National Bank, and he suggested that Chuck investigate the RFC--Reconstruction Finance Administration--located in Omaha, Nebraska. Dean said: "I would like to give you some pertinent advice. The normal procedure would be for you to fill out an application and mail it to them in Omaha. I advise you not to do that. Rather, prepare your written application, then get on the train and go to Omaha and apply in person. It will pay off to do it that way." Chuck noted, "I organized most of the facts and figures, but they were not complete. On the Streamliner, which travels pretty fast I was unable to complete the material because it rocked around and I became sea-sick! But when I arrived in Omaha I was able to use the portable typewriter in my room and finalize the report.

"I made my appointment and was assigned to two examiners. At their conference table I gave my written report. One of them kept making notes while I was giving my oral report to the other person. After a few minutes the first fellow interrupted and said, 'I am sorry but we can't consider your application.' I asked, 'Why, why?' 'Your report indicates that some monies already have been made available, and that precludes us from considering your application.' I was stunned, and said, 'You mean to tell me that because I have friends who wanted to help me get back into business, who know me and have faith in me, my abilities and contributed a few thousand dollars, (which is only a drop in the bucket, which I <u>must</u> have to start up in business) then that precludes consideration for my application? Do I understand you correctly?' They said, 'That is the case.'

"Then I asked who was their manager. They answered Mr. Johnson. 'I would like to see him.' They told me it would not do any good because that is one of the regulations. But they took me into Mr. Johnson's office. There I explained what happened in the other office. 'I want to ask you, Mr. Johnson, that since I have established a reputation that is worthy, and that my friends who believe in me and want to get me back in business, I have received $4,000. from ranchers and another $1000 from another friend--because they had enough faith in me to give me that money, does that preclude your consideration on my application?' I said, I just cannot understand that!' Mr. Johnson stopped and thought for a few minutes and said, to the two examiners, 'Go ahead and process this application and bring it to me.'

"Then, I could see the wisdom of Dean Dearinger's advice that I should make application in person. Had I mailed it, they would have refused my application. I got the loan but I had to abide by stringent regulations. To get equipment then we had to scour the country, but I had people in Denver with whom I had done business and they gave me valuable help.

"This government loan worked well for a year or two even though the paper work was burdensome. The Chamber of Commerce leased some downtown land and welcomed all who could not find a location to set up their burned out business in Butler Huts on what was called 'Comeback Corner.' We were among those who gratefully accepted their offer.

"During the period of rebuilding the business, Howard Rhodes, highly proficient in the art of printing and publishing, studied the operation and its potential, purchased an interest in the business and moved his family to Laramie from Missouri.

"Vital equipment was difficult to find but, through the efforts of many friends in the industry, equipment was located, purchased and assembled in Laramie. The business started to make progress. Then our good friend Ernie Smith called me into his office and said, 'Chuck, loans from other fire victims are being paid off more rapidly than anticipated. Why don't you make application to the Chamber for a substantial loan, pay off the government loan and get in gear!' I accepted his suggestion, the application was overwhelmingly approved and things looked brighter."

Chuck continued to remain active in the community and was a member of the "Boomerangs," a male quartet of distinction which included Floyd Foreman, Cecil Cupps and Ward Husted. (All four of them were my dental patients.) They were popular throughout the region. Chuck, in addition to his many community contributions, received the National Kappa Sigma Award for the outstanding service to his fraternity.

After retirement, he and his wife Billie continue to be active in the community and remain in the city that had the BIG FIRE!

. . . .

Truth is violated by falsehood,
but is outraged by silence.
A Swiss Philosopher.

Bank of Laramie Story

BANK OF LARAMIE STORY

Dear Dan:

Life is not always pleasant! If you live long enough life's messes will take over. Then if you are patient, the mess will take care of itself. That is if you act honorably! I know these things are easy to say, but difficult to accomplish.

I'll tell you now about a problem I experienced nearly thirty years ago. The difficulty arose in Laramie, but it concerned people also in Cheyenne, Hanna, Elk Mountain, Medicine Bow, Rock River, Walden, and the entire area. Speculation and uninformed rumors made the situation worse.

I became involved, along with Warren Grothe, who was one of the best friends I ever had. Soon after WW II, Warren realized there was need for a second bank in Laramie. The First National bank had no competition, and new business or professional people who came into town often found it difficult for them to get a loan.

With Warren's urging, I joined him in the founding of a second bank in Laramie in 1956. We knew that if Laramie were to grow and prosper, we needed competitive banking. During the Depression there were three banks in Laramie. One failed. The Albany National bank was purchased by the First National Bank, and all accounts were transferred there. Now, growth was stifled!

Warren was a successful lumber yard owner and builder, and could see the need for business opportunities. We agreed to organize others, form a nucleus of support, and apply for a Bank Charter.

About this time Hanna's mines were being closed and the entire town was threatened with following Old Carbon to become a second ghost mining town. My mother had recently sold her hotel and moved to Laramie,and other Hanna residents were leaving to find employment elsewhere. We needed a banker, and I suggested C. D. Williamson who was closing his Hanna bank, and was also owner of the Wyoming Timber Company.

Williamson had considerable business experience. He also had safety deposit bank boxes and other banking materials and supplies he was eager to sell. He knew some Laramie men through the Masonic Lodge. (Previously he had failed in an effort to become governor of Wyoming.) My mother, Mary Ford, did all she could to get him elected.

The three of us, Warren, Williamson and I, tried to sell stock in the new enterprise to others in the community, but this didn't work out, largely because many qualified stockholders felt a loyalty to the older established Laramie bankers. Even within our group there was a weakness because, as it turned out, even Williamson was reluctant to make an adequate investment, which he could well afford.

After a concerted effort by Warren and me to sell enough stock in Laramie, we were forced to go to Cheyenne. There we found aggressive business men who bought more than 50% of the stock. They could see the opportunity! Finally, we were granted a charter in the name of "Bank of Laramie." This was a name I suggested.
Grothe had purchased most of the burned out lots from the big fire, and on this land we planned and built our new bank.

Williamson was elected the bank president, not because of the stock shares he bought, but because of his banking experience. Warren, 'Doc' Vass of the University College of Agriculture, our President Williamson and I were directors of the Bank. Also, the five Cheyenne men who bought the majority of stock were elected to the board.

The bank grew slowly. And for the next few years <u>too slowly</u>. Trouble began to develop. Williamson being of the old school, did not believe in advertising. He expected his friends, and others, to move accounts from the older bank into ours because of loyalty. His approach did not work. The pragmatic philosophy of successful Cheyenne business men was at odds with the conservative 72-year-old bank president. Williamson's outdated attitude was not in tune with the modern banking world. The venture was a disappointment to all of us.

Another problem centered around Williamson's fire insurance accounts, which he had serviced in Hanna. These were old policies which he brought with him when he moved to Laramie. Established local insurance agents were upset, for it seemed the bank was in the insurance business. Many of the board members thought that Williamson should be on the main floor greeting customers, or better yet, be out the street getting acquainted and seeking new accounts.

State bank examiners who regularly come to banks questioned loans and complained of loans which were granted on a personal basis without adequate collateral. These banking practices were probably sufficient in Hanna where a single person practically owned the bank, but they could not be tolerated in a larger town, and where the president was only a very minor stockholder.

Meetings at the board of directors were awkward because the Cheyenne stockholders complained. We hired a younger person from Denver as a vice-president thinking that he could take over most of Williamson's duties. But he was not able to accomplish this task. The Cheyenne board members often expressed their complaints to Warren Grothe, but usually avoided me because of my mother's long-time friendship with Williamson. Even the Laramie board members left me out of their conversations for of the same reason. After all, I was only a minor stockholder and my vote would not count when the chips were down.

The Cheyenne men and Grothe were experienced business men and finally decided that, as majority stockholders, they would not wait as patiently as the minority of stockholders. They felt they could make better investments with their bank stock funds, and with less hassle.

One Monday evening my friend Warren came to my home and, reluctantly, told me that he and the majority Cheyenne stockholders had a buyer for the bank. They were going to sell it!

I did not sleep very much that night. I told my wife of their decision, and we worried about how it would effect both Williamson and my mother. Mary suggested I tell them both before the news hit the paper. On Tuesday I went to mother's house with the news. She was disturbed and insisted that I warn Williamson so that he could be prepared before the monthly meeting on Thursday afternoon.

. . . .

(Note: During the last few years the bank has again been sold. And the name changed from Bank of Laramie, to First Wyoming Bank. As I remember, our original stock cost me about $150.00 a share. When we sold it we made $50.00 per share. Those who refused to sell have multiplied their earnings perhaps several hundreds of times. The amount I received was less than the $30,000 for my stock.)

. . . .

Although I had promised Warren otherwise, I finally went to Williamson's home Wednesday evening and visited with him and his wife. I told them I knew what would happen at the next day's meeting. It was not a pleasant session, even though both of them knew the majority stockholders were unhappy.

I explained to the Williamsons that I was disgusted with the whole bank deal, and would sell my stock to whomever the new owners were. They agreed that they would also sell.

We had worked together and provided the community with some banking competition, which was my original purpose. At least we accomplished that much. We agreed to sell our stock because we did not know at that time who was buying the bank.

That afternoon at three o'clock I hurried from my office and entered the banks back door because it was after banking hours. But the first person I saw behind the counter was Jack Guthrie working on stock certificates. I was surprised because I had expected to see strangers from out of town. This was the first indication that I had that the original banking family was back in business. They had recently sold their First National Bank to a national banking firm, and had announced they were leaving the banking business.

Most of the local people bought small amounts of stock because of friendship and confidence. Many were patients and friends of mine. Later, when I told some of them that I sold my stock, they did the same. I especially remember that Ottis Rechard, Al Larson, and "Doc" Vass, and others, were among my close friends. The first two sold their stock when I did, but not Vass--he played it cool and kept his to ultimately achieve great financial benefits.

On my way to the directors' meeting room I passed Williamson's office and went in to see how he was doing. I received a cold stare and no word, which I could not understand. When all the directors were assembled the announcement was made that all who wanted to sell their stock would receive $175.00 per share. The board members knew that because of management procedures and increased expenses, the stock had depreciated well below the $150.00 we had paid for it. Later, I wondered if the State of Wyoming bank examiners had suggested the need for more experienced bankers to the Cheyenne people. Anyway, that is the way it worked out!

When the news hit the papers the next morning, there were signs of bitterness. People who left the old First National Bank to open accounts with us were again depositors with the Guthrie-Forbes bank. Much of the criticism was directed to Grothe and Stebner. They seemed to be encouraged by Williamson and his friends.

A vindictive gossip campaign was launched, and I was the primary target. There was little I could do without pointing a finger at Williamson. As president, he was responsible for the bank's condition, but he needed a scapegoat and I was available. It was not my option to tell the truth publicly. The only choice I had was to remain silent.

Former Hanna and Elk Mountain people consoled my mother. Many wondered why Charlie did not protect Williamson and keep him on as president. Others were sincerely offering Mother their uninformed condolences. Their concern for my mother left me in a dilemma. She was devastated and ill over the whole thing, wondering just what her son had done. I even had difficulty explaining the atmosphere to my own kids.

Some of Williamson's lodge brothers and friends worked on me pretty hard. Anonymous phone callers, at all hours of the night, called me "Judas."

There were people who canceled their appointments and selected other dentists. I felt it was my responsibility to inform local stockholders of the situation. I suggested meeting a few of them for lunch so that we could have a more effective discussion. Most refused! One, after filthy language at three o'clock in the morning, refused the invitation. I thought I knew a particular voice, but when I called him later, he called me a son-of-a-bitch for not protecting Williamson. This person retained his stock and eventually made money out of it, even though he did not like the new bankers.

From that experience I decided that anonymous letters and phone calls are cowardly. Dan, never be ashamed of <u>your</u> name when you call or write a letter.

. . . .

At the time of Williamson's dismissal, I had organized the Stebner Dental Group, with five dentists and two hygienists in my building at 9th and Grand Ave. The group, all of whom I had invited to share my dental practice, were from out of town. They had a ten year lease to rent my building. For eight years the group functioned smoothly to everyone's advantage. Most of them learned a different way to practice better dentistry. But during the last year or two friction developed. This occurred about the same time the Bank of Laramie was sold.

Before their lease was about to be terminated they asked to buy into the building or threatened to move out. I encouraged them to move. Well, they moved leaving me with just one loyal associate. You might be surprised to learn that they moved with the blessing of one person. Yes, it was Williamson! His picture was displayed on their reception room wall. I had cause to believe that they planned to run me out of town. But it didn't work. My friends and patients, for the most part, believed in me and were loyal.

Bill Breslin, who was manager of the Power Company and a popular member of the business community, had worked with me on several community projects. He gave me a lift when I tried to explain the bank deal while the scuttlebutt heat was at its high point. I wanted him to hear my view, because he was closely associated with Williamson. Bill interrupted my early remarks, saying that he had already visited with a close Williamson friend.

I said, "Bill, I want to tell you my side of the story." He smiled and patted me on the shoulder and said this: "Yes, I did hear from one of them and he called you a son-of-a-bitch. I stopped him right there, and said 'tell me no more; sure, you might be right, but you know Charlie is my kind of a son-of-a-bitch.' We both laughed and the conversation ended. Bill and others resented the gossip. Since then Bill and I have remained loyal friends.

At that time, our newspaper allowed various favored ministers to regularly submit biblical verses as they related to modern times. This was printed in our BOOMERANG newspaper on November 26, 1957.

A Thought for the Day

Please Read Psalm 54

Psalm 54:3 "For strangers are risen up against me, and oppressors seek after my soul: They have not set God before them."

Verse 3 makes us think that the author of this psalm might have been a banker whose directors sold their stock out from under him and effectively put him out of business. God doesn't really have much to do with the affairs of men, unless they let Him.

--Otis Jackson, Dean, St. Matthew's Cathedral

Now, Dan, I don't believe in revenge, but I do believe in retribution. I also believe in the facts of history. The person who authored those lines was a fine, well-meaning minister. But he was closely connected with Williamson, who was a pillar in his church. Nevertheless, he should have checked both sides of the issue.

When this was printed I was literally fighting mad, I called the church and was answered by Bishop Hunter, a man I always admired. I strongly suggested to him, with emphasis, that on the following Thursday I should meet him, Dean Jackson, and Williamson, in his office. I told him that they had only heard on side of the story, and I was coming to tell the other side, and refute the implication of the news column.

Bishop Hunter tried to calm me and said he would speak to the responsible parties. But I assured him that would not satisfy me. I told him that if he did not arrange the meeting I would go to his church the next Sunday and at the proper moment I would stand and speak out against the column's innuendo, which was intended for me. Only then did the Bishop promise that he would call the meeting I suggested.

I arrived at the church at the appointed time on Thursday afternoon. But instead of the four people there were only three--the pastor, the Bishop and me. They explained that Williamson chose not to be present. But I told the two of them the entire story as it happened. I placed the need for the sale on Williamson's personal problems.

I let them know if was any confusion in my statements I would again come and repeat what I had said. My point was that I was disappointed that Williamson did not show because I wanted get it over with. The Pastor was very apologetic and disturbed, admitting that he had not had enough facts. With the Bishop's suggestion he made up his mind to visit with my disturbed mother the next day. He told her that I had done nothing wrong, and let her know she should be proud of me for what I had done for the community. A day or so later I visited my mother and she had made a remarkable recovery. Her depression suddenly disappeared, and we never discussed the bank deal again.

But the vindication came 21 years later, long after Williamson's death. A handsome young father, whom I knew from Lions Club, asked to come and visit with me. He was Richard Tyler, and a

"Tailtwister" in the club. Rich had a great sense of humor and he kept the meetings moving. He asked to come and visit with me and talk about the bank fiasco because he was Williamson's grandson. As a youngster he couldn't understand the family animosity toward me. Richard was a young carefree father who was very religious and compassionate. After his grandfather died he needed to settle his own thoughts.

Richard came to my study where he listened attentively to my side of the story. He asked many questions which I answered. The factor which disturbed Rich most was that his grandfather had all the money he needed to buy much more bank stock than he agreed to purchase. Had he done so, nobody could have fired him!

Richard enjoyed his son, with whom he played with by the hour. He became my best friend in the Lions Club. Rich and his wife, Janet, had three very young children. Mary and I visited them in their home. He was a religious, idealistic husband and father. I found him fun to be around.

Richard was proud of his young son, and loved his girls and wonderful wife. Mary and I visited them in their home. When his boy was only four years-old, he was in his Dad's lap as they were in a swing over concrete floor in his father's warehouse. The rope broke. As he protected his son, Richard's head hit the the floor. He died too young. I suffered from empathy because my father died when I was only five years old. I knew what it meant to grow up without a father.

At Home in the Sagebrush

THE SAGEBRUSH DENTIST

Dear Dan:

When I came to Laramie in 1932, I was no doubt the youngest dentist in Wyoming, but soon I had the privilege of meeting the oldest--an historian and character, Dr. Will Frackelton, who was still practicing in Sheridan.

He greeted me generously and autographed his book, "The Sagebrush Dentist." At that time I was the Wyoming Dental Society's historian, and I wanted to get all the information that I could from the man. Many years ago he traveled throughout Wyoming in his horse and buggy, which was his office. His patients were ranchers, cowboys and those living in small towns. He was also a dentist for some of the Indians and outlaws. At the time I visited with him, he had a permanent office in Sheridan, Wyoming. His equipment was slightly more modern than his former tread-pedaled drill. His home was in the same building in which he worked. He even had a younger wife to do his cooking. I bought the book, which I still treasure. I pressed him for a story he might not have written.

He told me about the mobile horsepowered office he drove on a stretch of isolated ground south of Buffalo, Wyoming. He came to a fork in the roads, which had a bar and an eating place. A wild group of cowboys were drinking and shooting at targets behind the building. After a drink or two he was invited to join the game and with his six-shooter he won a few dollars from them. Later, he learned they were a group of outlaws known as the Hole-in-the Wall gang. That night he made camp near them, but he felt uneasy being around those people, and he awakened early the next morning to go on on his way to Casper. Later, one of them needed dental work and Will cared for him. He was paid liberally with stolen money.

When his wife was out of hearing range he told me of a visit to an Indian village, where he was treated as a blood-brother to the chief. He often stopped at their camp to fish and visit as he extracted a troublesome tooth or two. His plans were to be there only a few days before moving on his route.

Dr. Frackelton almost whispered the following, when his wife was in the kitchen: "When I got there it was late in the afternoon and I joined the chief at the fire in front of his tent. We smoked the pipe together. After our visit my host told me to that my meal was being prepared at my own tent and he would see me in the morning before I began to fish.

"My tent was pitched and there was a handsome young squaw who cooked my dinner at the campfire. While I ate she disappeared, but when I entered the tent, in my bedroll was my young cook. You know Dr. Stebner, fishing was so good that I stayed there a full week!"

. . . .

Many of his experiences are recorded in the book he autographed for me, where he wrote: "To Dr. C. M. Stebner, here's one for you historians, Will Frackelton, Sage Brush Dentist, 10-1-41. Ka-He, Crow Indian talk for. . Welcome to our land."

MARTHA EDWARDS CONWELL

Martha Edwards Conwell was my mother-in-law and I loved her. Everyone felt that she was a sincere and tolerant person. Mom, as everyone called her, came from her home in Iowa to Wyoming as a young bride of Patrick Conwell. He established a ranch at Merna on the upper Horse Creek. Mom arrived at Opal Junction near Kemmerer, Wyoming in the summer of 1906.

When mom and her two young children boarded a horse-drawn stage they were faced with a trip about 100 miles to Merna on the Upper Horse Creek. She told me of a tortuous area down a long steep hill where for safety's sake the passengers walked down the hill to board again. There they made their home in a log cabin and carried buckets of water from Horse Creek. Although the nearest doctor to serve the area was in Pinedale, he delivered four more children who went to a ranch school. Both Irene and Donald died at early ages. Mom raised George, Mary, Helen and Alice June.

During the economically depressed days of the late 1920s Pat Conwell lost the ranch he worked so hard to establish. Ralph, the oldest son, made up his mind to go to the University of Wyoming. Patrick never adjusted to life away from his ranch and roamed around the state seeking odd jobs. When Ralph graduated from the University of Wyoming he became a professor in Economics under the tutelage of Grace Raymond Hebard. Mom brought her family to Laramie and the diligent Ralph purchased a home and a little grocery store which Mom operated to care for her five younger children.

I remember Mom, who became my good friend when I began to date her oldest daughter, your grandmother Mary. She and I were great friends. She tolerated my pranks, fed me many meals with groceries from her store. Later Mary and I were married as we had much in common. Eventually she gave up the store when her children were able to work for themselves and retired visiting friends and relatives. On her last trip, at age 65, she was visiting relatives in Canada where she died of a sudden heart attack.

RALPH CONWELL

There are many success stories of poor, but ambitious people, who lived in the small towns and on our Wyoming ranches.

A poor ranch kid, Ralph was able to do a hired man's work with his Father at an early age. He rode a horse to school, branded cattle, put up hay for their horses and cattle and worked through the most difficult winters in Wyoming. Sub-zero temperatures were common at their ranch, and the summers were simply hard work as they fought mosquitoes. The entire family worked with their parents as each accomplished daily ranch chores.

The bank foreclosed on a loan for the ranch in 1924. Meanwhile Ralph saw the educational possibilities in Laramie.

When the depression began in 1929 Ralph decided to travel to Laramie, where he finished his last two years of high school, and also began taking some courses at the University of Wyoming. He worked a nighttime job at the small refinery and went to school during the days. There was no money from home for Ralph. He had to earn his own! Today, when I see the cars students drive as they go to college, and hear them sometimes complain when government loans are terminated, I think of Ralph. He was determined to work his way through college.

He graduated in Liberal Arts and married Margaret O'Neil, a ranch girl from Big Piney, whom he had known in western Wyoming. Ralph was asked to teach a few classes, and with his modest income, frugal Ralph purchased two small houses near the University--one for his mother and brothers and sisters who left the ranch. A smaller house was purchased across the street where he and his family lived. This was ideal because there was a very small grocery store attached to the home where Mom Conwell and her children lived. Mom became a storekeeper!

Ralph and Margaret were parents of a bright daughter, Barbara. One might say she was really the "apple of her father's eye". That father-daughter combination was a pleasure to observe during the rest of Ralph's life. Margaret suffered ill health, but was aided by Barbara and Mom Conwell who proved to be helpful and attentive to her.

When Ralph was financially able, the banker in Rock Springs, John Hayes, suggested that once again he should own the original Conwell ranch. Ralph bought it back!

During Ralph's college days he was interested in dramatics. He wrote and directed plays. One summer he attended a special course in dramatics at the Pasadena Playhouse in California. Later, this paid off when he lectured to his own classes, because he acted as he taught and was known as a stimulating teacher. Dr. Grace Raymond Hebard did much to encourage Ralph. She suggested that he graduate from the school of law following his Bachelor of Arts degree--this he did, but teaching was his love. He is remembered by students for his dramatics in the lecture hall. With Dr. Hebard's help and encouragement, he became the head of economics at the University of Wyoming Later, Ralph loved to travel, especially in Central America. The economics of this area became his teaching specialty.

Dramatics was an interesting side-line to Ralph. He enjoyed directing plays of the 'Jester's Club', which was made up of local business men who who also enjoyed dramatics. There I knew Ralph well as I played the lead in "Our Town" and "The Drunkard" under his direction.

Many instructors ably teach a particular subject, but Ralph used the economic theories for personal gain. Gradually he bought stocks which he knew would advance in the market. With his success in the stock market he converted the old ranch into a summer project where he boarded other people's stock on a weight-gain basis. It pleased Ralph to finally make it profitable.

Ralph never lived as though he earned considerable money. His most expensive cars were Chevrolets which he drove until they gave up. Several times he and I rode the same train to Chicago. He had considerable investments there, and I attended dental meetings at the same time. I stayed in the better hotels, which I could hardly afford, but Ralph found a cheaper room elsewhere. He rode in the chair car and I rode in the Pullman as we rode the same train. He was frugal!

A mutual friend of ours told me that when Ralph visited him in Arizona Ralph's car battery became dead. went dead, but that didn't worry him because he had another battery in the trunk. So, his friend pushed him a few blocks to a filling station to have them both recharged.

Ralph had a great sense of humor. On his ranch on Horse Creek he often hired his young nephews to work with him. They were a long way from a confectionery store, but one day when your dad, Ken, was working for him he decided to have a little fun with his nephew. It was a very hot summer day and Ken was thirsty and hungry. Ralph knew Ken would appreciate a Hershey candy bar. Well, Ralph planted a bar under a dry cow- flop where Ken was working. Then he said, "Ken, you would be surprised what you might find if you were to turn over a few dried cow-pies which are baked in the sun." Ken thought the heat was getting to the old man, but with Ralph's encouragement he decided he would please him. After kicking over a few he found, to his surprise, a Hershey bar! When other kids worked for Ralph they won at the candy bar game.

Ralph was an enthusiastic fisherman and skier who loved both sports until he died of cancer at age 82. Unlike many wills he left all of his brother and sisters a generous amount of valuable stocks. Today his his daughter, Barbara Gildea and her husband Vern, run the Conwell ranch where they board cattle each summer, as Ralphy taught them.

Prior to Ralph's death his sister Helen. and her husband Bob Montgomery, had been active in helping the Gildeas keep the ranch home-fires burning on the old Conwell homestead.

. . . .

If you would thoroughly know anything, teach it to others. *Tyron Edwards*

Education

ALPHABET AND MULTIPLICATION

Dear Dan:

This might sound like ancient history to you, but I hope that with your sharp mind you will thoroughly learn two basic of knowledge, the alphabet and multiplication tables. They are simple to learn at the right age, but when one reaches seventy-five it might be hopeless.

Today we have computers like the one I am now working with to write your letter. You will be a long way ahead of this, but nevertheless the alphabet and multiplication tables are tools upon which you will rely. Your pals may give you a bad time for working on these skills, but when no electric gadget is available the natural computer of your mind will serve you.

I have a definite problem with my spelling. Today I waste a lot of time and energy because of these deficiencies. During the next few years you would be ahead of many of your classmates if you efficiently if practice quick recall of the dictionary and the multiplication tables. These two things are only tools which will save you a lot of time--time which I now waste. Time is our most precious commodity. I resent the time I waste each day.

Today I wish I could recall the alphabet spontaneously. Oh sure, Dan, I do know my ABCDEFs, but working on this book with the dictionary, I have trouble. Valuable time is wasted as I recite the letter after the "ts", or whether "J" is before or after "G". Hell, if I had those early years again I would study harder to use the dictionary automatically, rather than constantly starting with my ABC's.

I promise you I would <u>really</u> learn the multiplication tables. Right now I do fairly well through the sixes...and then I have trouble! Yes, Dan, I can figure it pretty well until I get to the 7's 8's and 9's. Now, I go back to the 5's and add them to come up with the right answer with the 8's. Stupid, isn't it?

SLIDES TO NORTHWESTERN

During the last couple of months, I have been organizing a slide file cabinet. When I started to practice dentistry I was interested in keeping records of my patients. There were not so many of them then and I had a lot of time between appointments. First, I wondered why they chose me and I found out that a friend or another patient encouraged them to come to the office. I made it a point to thank the reference.

At first I did not have an x-ray machine. Later, it became impossible to believe that anybody could practice without one, but I simply could not afford it. Then, I saved interesting x-rays and also soon bought a camera which would take pictures of the patient's mouth. That way I learned many things that had not been taught me when I was in college.

Well, Dan, when I finally had a full appointment book I used the x-rays and colored slides to document my work. Colored slides from various cameras built up until I closed my office about four years ago. Now I have an unusual library of slides on all phases of dentistry and I have used this material to demonstrate and show various techniques to dentists all around the country and in six or seven foreign countries. Also, this material has helped me write many professional papers.

One day I counted and organized this material to learn that I had accumulated 1280 colored slides. I realized that when I disappear from life's scene neither my family nor any of my dentist friends could explain the stories they tell. I wrote 52 pages of descriptions in which I explained all 1280 slides.

Then I contacted five schools of dentistry where I know professors and deans, offering one of them this collection. Now, I have decided on the one school who pleased me most in their plans to use these slides for the benefit of their students and instructors. That school is Northwestern University School of Dentistry.
They plan to make copies available to other schools.

TEACHERS AND STUDENTS

Teaching is the oldest and most noble of all professions. Even in nature the mother and father teach the offspring to function. With the help parents and older brothers and sisters the youngest people learn to eat with a spoon, to use the toilet, to walk, to speak the language, and to avoid dangerous hazards.

At age four to six they will have their first professional teacher, either in preschool, kindergarten, or grade one. From then on many people will teach children.

Dan, this learning experience of mine, as I approach my 80th birthday, I will pass along information that should help you. Most young guys are not good listeners. Often they're impatient and want to move quickly from one experience to another. Not until I was in dental school did I realize that we should absorb as much as possible from every older teacher, and take advantage of their experience. Finances for tuition were important, and I wanted my money's worth, so I concentrated on my older teachers.

I attached myself to Dr. Charlie Woodbury, and especially to Dr. Lester Myers, who became my role model after graduation. Later I became a friend of a great dentist, Dr. George Hollenback. Perhaps the early loss of my dad made me appreciate these older dentists. When I became older these three men became my life-long friends.

I had a hunger for knowledge and also realized that I could acquire what I needed from great professionals. I might have pestered a few, but I did get their attention and it paid off!

Later, when I was more experienced, I sought younger dentists I could stimulate and teach. When

I joined the Navy during World War II, there were many younger dentists I helped at Farragut Naval Base. I was at least ten years older than most of them. Like many older professional people, I appreciated the attention and stimulation of youth.

Experience has taught me that a receptive student is a person who has worked in a field for a few years. Good students are hungry for information and knowledge.

For years I have wondered how it would work if our youth went to school for only three years of High School, then entered their chosen field, as employees for a single year, and then come back to finish their last year before graduation. I believe they would have the right desire to learn.

Years ago a good friend and my dental patient, Bill Thomas was in my office. I complained about the lack of compassion by one of his younger peers on the University of Wyoming faculty. They seemed to make learning harder than necessary. I noted that older professors seemed more humane. Bill smiled and said, "You know, Charlie, that's a human trait noticed by the early Romans several thousand years ago when they had slaves in the glory days of Rome. He said that it was observed that; "None are more vindictive as the newly freed slave." Bill noted that the young Ph.D. who comes to his first teaching job is often more severe than are the older teachers. He has a fresh memory of how hard he worked for his Ph.D. degree and he wants to share similar unpleasant experiences.

Physical Fitness

THE HEALTHY BODY

Dear Dan:

When I was in dental school, I was fortunate enough to dissect a human body. I admired the perfection of the body, the way it functions and the beauty of design. I later thought of the times I abused my own body. I tried to smoke tobacco a few times, but today I am grateful the habit didn't stick. Certainly, I ate many foods which I should have ignored. Both in college, and later I drank a lot more alcohol than was wise.

That course in anatomy taught me something of the way human bodies function and I was impressed by nature's beautiful design. I learned the basic fundamentals of anatomy, physiology, and the complicated nervous system. During my sixty years as a health professional I understood only a minute portion of the body's marvelous function.

Thoughtful scientists must smile as they review the artificial heart. And we know the human brain is even more complicated. Young people should appreciate the beautifully built, rugged, strong and alert body.

I taught classes in which I encouraged others to protect and appreciate healthy bodies. It seems that less than one-fourth ever changed their lifestyle for the better. I wasted my time and effort on the 75% who would be as well off if they had gone to the bar and skipped the lecture. Most took better care of their lawns and automobiles than their hearts.

It might help if we think of our hearts as machines. Hearts function much they same as do our automobile carburetors. If they are gummed up the vehicle fails to run. Even many scientists fail to place themselves under the microscope. They see the problems of others and fail in self-evaluation. We all know when our friends suffer a heart attack. It always happens to the other guy. But we should understand that no one is immune.

Today, we observe unique and heroic surgery to replace diseased hearts with by-pass artery implants, and even plastic hearts that will pump blood in the chests of victims whose heart has failed. These are not the ultimate answer. The entire vascular system is diseased and continues to threaten the patient. Only diet, exercise and habit correction can make us well.

HERB GILLARD

A good friend of mine rebuilt his own circulatory system. He is Dr. Herb Gillard of Houston, Texas. He and Jim Vernetti, were co-authors with me as we wrote a paper on coronary problems in the Journal of the American Dental Association, September 1972.

I promise you Dan, there will be no new plastic pump in your grandpa's chest. I am doing all I can to keep my vessels elastic and clean by means of diet and alot of running every day.

Today I recalled my friend Gillard had his first heart attack at age 53. Also, he suffered through two other coronary emergencies before he was 56 years old. He realized he would live only a short time in a lethargic atmosphere, having no fun, unless he changed his habits. He chose exercise and diet and is in good health more than twenty-seven years later. He rebuilt his entire vascular system.

The article co-authored by these good friends and myself tells one how to keep his heart young so he will not need repairs when he is only fifty years old. Someday you may have a friend who is a little overweight, and also has a poor diet. You might find out that he might also have an elevated blood pressure. Then, you might let him read the enclosed paper.

(Reprint from JADA, vol. 85, September 1972.)

PHYSICAL FITNESS FOR THE PREVENTION OF CORONARY ATTACKS

Charles M. Stebner, DDS, Laramie, Wyo
James P. Vernetti, DDS, Coronado, Calif
Herbert F. Gillard, DDS, Houston

During his working day the professional who practices sit-down dentistry is almost immobilized in his operatory. Inactivity, along with stress, obesity, smoking, and a high fat intake contribute to the deterioration of the circulatory and pulmonary systems. The deterioration, however, can be prevented to some degree with regular exercise. It will improve one's resistance to stress, develop endurance and vascular flexibility, and provide general physical and mental well-being.

Acute coronary insufficiency! Herb Gillard, a 54-year-old dentist from Houston, suffered acute chest pains while on a pleasure fishing boat in October 1963. When he arrived on shore an ambulance carried him to a nearby hospital where his condition was diagnosed. An angiogram showed extensive narrowing of a branch of the coronary artery, resulting in insufficient supply of oxygen to the coronary muscle.

Previously, after a busy day in the office, he would be overly fatigued, but he had not been aware of impending disaster. His worried wife often would call attention to his slightly pasty, grayish appearance. Like many individuals prone to coronary disorders, Gillard had paid no attention to the sympathetic nervous system signals, but had dismissed them simply as the result of his age and work.

Gillard's story

I should have known the symptoms to be a warning of advancing atherosclerosis, which often precedes heart attack. I also noted a high degree of irritability, nervousness, and sensibility, and a lack of physical endurance.

At the end of my hospitalization, the cardiologist suggested a low fat diet, walking a mile each day, resting at noon, and practicing dentistry no more than five or six hours a day; he instructed me to leave my office by 5 PM. This routine was carried out every working day for a year and a half. I had previously read that "ordinarily, 20 percent of middle-aged men with a single uncomplicated heart attack died within five years, usually from a second attack!"[1] I thought of little else but his possibility until the second attack occurred!

I had a myocardial infarct and was hospitalized. The infarct caused a sudden drop of systolic blood pressure of 80 mm Hg and I required constant intravenous infusions of a pressor substance for several days to gain stabilization of the circulation. I returned home after two weeks, and began an uncomplicated convalescence of only ten days.

My third cardiac emergency (atrial fibrillation) occurred without warning. Again the blood pressure dropped dangerously low and support with continuous intravenous infusions of a pressor substance was required. The diagnosis was congestive heart failure. Some years later my wife told me that the doctor had prepared her to accept the likely possibility of my death. Statistically, the warning was sound because the odds were against me after the first attack, and they were vastly greater after the second--but after this more serious episode, the odds were enormous. Added to these complications was the heredity factor--two brothers had suffered fatal attacks.

During this convalescent period, I was informed that I would probably never practice dentistry again. This threw me into depression for months--including sieges of uncontrollable weeping for hours at a time. I had deteriorated into a human vegetable. Fortunately, only 30% of patients with postcoronary conditions have this experience. I believe that if I previously cared for myself better through physical conditioning, I might not have entirely prevented this coronary attack but I would have been in better condition to resist the emotionally and physical trauma. For the conditioned person, a recovery period is shorter and depression is less often experienced.

The depression devastated me more than the physical debilitation. I now understand how important it is for the patient with coronary failure to solve his psychological problems. One of my friends, a psychologist, suggested that i begin therapy under his guidance. This proved very helpful and after five months I was again at work on a limited basis.

My physician suggested that I begin walking short distances. At first I could barely walk a block but I finally got back to a mile. Because an electrocardiogram showed only slight improvement in my condition, and because I tired easily and often suffered prolonged tachycardia, I realized that a more adequate physical fitness program should be considered. I asked my physician for guidance in a more extensive exercise program, but he was neither encouraging nor informative. Although he though I was doing enough, I joined a health club in which exercise gadgets were emphasized. After six months during which I worked out about 20 to 25 minutes a day, seven days a week, and walked a mile a day, I concluded I was not improving. My physician indicated the electrocardiograms did not reflect satisfactory progress.

I had heard of Cureton's work on physical fitness at the University of Illinois and found that a YMCA in Houston sponsored a Cureton fitness program. I read his book, "Physical Fitness and Dynamic Health,"[2] which opens with the sentence "Old age comes by invitation and most of us extend the invitation too soon." This man's experience and philosophy impressed me greatly. I was amazed to learn from his book and his experience that people of various ages and conditions could be improved physically by adequate exercise.

I entered the "low gear" program for beginners of the 20-to- 40 year age group, which was certainly not designed for patients with post-coronary conditions. The athletic director suggested that I should attend a noon class that would take me out of the office 1 1/2 to 2 hours a day, three times a week. Although I was reluctant, I realized there was little to lose. The program consisted of trying to jog a half mile and do 20 minutes of moderate calisthenics. At first I could not jog three laps around the gym--only a seventh of a mile. However, at my next examination in three months, the cardiologist was astonished by my electrocardiogram; he wanted to know what I was doing because this was the first improvement he noted. He was impressed with my schedule and thought it would be all right to continue, if I took it easy. Many physicians today are encouraging physical activity for patients with postcoronary conditions.[3,4] Now I began a calisthenics and jogging program on my own four days a week when not under YMCA class supervision. After a year I could finally jog a mile without stopping and graduated to the "intermediate gear" of the Cureton program. This meant jogging two miles in 16 to 17 minutes, plus 30 minutes of calisthenics. By this time my electrocardiogram was normal and my pulse rate had dropped from 72 beats a minute to the high 50s. Paroxysms of tachycardia diminished in number and were much shorter.

After I had been on the daily program of jogging five miles and doing 30 minutes of calisthenics for two years, my cardiologist agreed that it would be safe to stop all medication.

Among other fringe benefits from the physical fitness program were my ability to work again full time without tiring, almost nonexistent tachycardia, peace of mind that I never knew existed, absence of apprehension, confidence in overcoming any problem, and the ability to survive any mental trauma. Feeling alive instead of half alive! This experience convinced me that, because of the stressful nature of our work, all dentists should work out an hour a day.

I became aware that a practical and efficient test for oxygen consumption, designed by Astrand,[5] was available. The test is performed on a stationary bicycle equipped with an ergometer. This test creates a controlled amount of foot-pounds of resistance which requires six minutes of pedaling. Pulse rate is checked before the test begins and at the end of each minute as the bicycle is operated. A chart is available, prepared from extensive research, with which to compute the amount of oxygen that is used at the tissue level. The percentage of pulse rate increase is compared with the selected work load.

The "low" category charted for my age group, (61), measuring aerobic work capacity, is 21 ml of oxygen consumption per minute. A recent test showed that my oxygen consumption was 42 ml--100% more than my previous reading of 21 ml. The "excellent" category is listed at 40 ml. My experience proves that only a few months on a jogging program significantly improve oxygen consumption in repeated tests.

Finally, nine years after my first coronary emergency, I am working full time and really living. I am convinced that I need not have another coronary problem.

Prevention of coronary disorders

The philosophy of prevention is a noble and rewarding way of life for any person. Civilized society and the individual have no choice for survival other than through prevention. Prevention of disease, war, crime, and environmental disaster must replace desperate attempts to control and treat emergencies and crises. We must evaluate the problem and redirect our efforts and intelligence to prevention.

Because we treat the ravages of dental disease, we have learned to appreciate the preventive approach to dental care. We are in a favorable position to transfer this philosophy of prevention to our personal health problems associated with circulatory disease.

More than 50% of dentists die of circulatory disease. Still, many other persons suffer coronary attacks that are undetected. It was determined in a study of 5,127 person that a fourth of nonfatal heart attacks were unrecognized.[6] We believe that these people could reduce the likelihood of a second and more serious attack if they were to reverse circulatory deterioration by physical conditioning.

Stebner thinks that he was one of these people when in 1968, at the age of 57, he was motivated by the experience of Gillard to begin running every day. He recalls, "There were many mornings when there was personal doubt if it was all worthwhile, as I arose a 5:30 AM and dressed in about ten pounds of clothing, including hunting boots and a wool face mask to prevent the inhalation of sub-zero Wyoming winds. But the conditioned person knows that the procrastination and rationalization of the unconditioned individual are not valid. At the beginning, half a block was about as far as I could jog because my oxygen consumption was blocked out, even though I did not smoke, by partially plugged vessels of minimum elasticity. Finally, after considerable time, effort, and discomfort, a nonstop mile was no problem."

Vernetti relates his routine: "My personal routine is a five-minute warm-up period followed by a two-mile run on the beach. This is done at 5:30 AM four days a week. Two other days I do about 20 minutes of calisthenics. In addition I ride a bicycle to work about three miles a day. My age is 57, my blood pressure is 120/80, and my pulse rate is 58 beats per minute--I feel great, with an abundance of energy. This was not so before 1965, when Cureton motivated me to this new way of life. The chest and arm pains that I worried about have long ago disappeared. There is no doubt in my mind that I had a coronary condition."

Physical activity benefits circulatory system

The four components of a blood vessel are endothelial lining, elastin fibers, collagen fibers, and smooth muscle. In the unconditioned person, the endothelial lining is probably intact, but often some plaque covers it internally, making the lumen smaller. Also there may be deposits beneath the endothelial lining. The function on the elastin fibers in the walls is negated, by an increasing proportion of collagen fibers. The action of the smooth muscle within the walls is inhibited by a deterioration of the stretching response that is necessary during exercise, stress and emergency.

A continuous program of running can improve the percentages against probable cardiac emergency, because the conditioned person by daily persistence, has changed the physiologic function of the vessels. Histology and pathology help us explain the improvement in the elasticity of these vessels, the gain in the lumen caliber, and also the development of new vessels in the form of collateral arteries and capillaries. The cardiac muscle and oxygen supply to it are generally improved. An increase in the efficiency and capacity of the lungs in notable.

All types of physical activity are beneficial but many are overrated. They all burn calories and increase the heart beat rate. Calisthenics also are helpful, with benefits related to the time and effort spent. Cooper[7] said, "The best exercises are running, swimming, cycling, walking, stationary running, handball, basketball, and squash, and in just about that order." It would be most beneficial if individuals would exercise enough to perspire freely every day.

There is no easy way to improve the physical powers of the heart. Casually played sports, such as weekend golf, bowling, or even occasional tennis, are often ineffective. Our objective must be to improve resistance to stress, to develop endurance and vascular flexibility, and to provide general physical and mental well-being. This can be done only if one undergoes a systematic, comprehensive, and vigorous conditioning program.

Conditioning program

More realistic than the expression "one is only as old as he feels" may be the fact that a person is only as young as the elasticity of his vessels permits him to be. If under physical activity the blood pressure and the heart rate increase rapidly, and especially if recovery is unusually delayed after exertion--the patient is older physiologically regardless of his chronological age. Fortunately, we can grow young physiologically, to some degree, through a well-planned program of running. By slow and rather painful steps, we can increase the elastic response of the blood vessels.

At first, the unconditioned person should walk a lot, and then walk and jog alternately according to his comfort. Gradually, he will be able to decrease his walking and to jog farther until a longer slow jog is no problem. Later he should run short spurts at greater speed. The use of this new approach of conditioning athletes could well be followed by older men, but with caution and in moderation. Each person should have a complete physical examination, including and electrocardiogram, before starting such a program. Intelligently planned conditioning is considered safe for those with no specific organic circulatory disability. Ellestad and co- workers,[8] reported on more than 4,000 subjects who were tested on a treadmill in a controlled program. They noted: "No deaths occurred during the testing ...ventricular asystole and ventricular fibrillation were not seen. Transient ventricular tachycardia, lasting less than 20 seconds and reverting spontaneously, occurred nine times. Only one patient required any therapy for ventricular tachycardia." This study is convincing evidence of the feasibility of a strenuous exercise program for the average person.

*Effect on pulse rate: Rapid pulse rates are important because they may be a warning sign. A ten-year study of 1,329 Chicago men between the ages of 40 and 59 was reported by Berkson and co-workers.[9] They found a higher incidence of coronary problems among persons with high pulse rates than among others. Significantly, the death rate was 71 per 1,000 for the group whose pulse rate exceeded 80 beats a minute; in the group with lower pulse rates, the fatalities dropped to 32 per 1,000.

A heart that beats 88 times per minute will beat 1,800 more times an hour than does a better conditioned heart that beats 58 times per minute. The less efficient, weaker heart must beat more rapidly to deliver the necessary oxygen to the tissue level. But the heart of the well-conditioned person, by means of a greater stroke volume, will eject much more blood per beat. Burton[10] noted that in the well-conditioned athlete with a resting pulse of 40, four times the normal volume of blood per stroke is delivered under the demand of exercise. But in the average person with the resting pulse of 70, only 2 1/2 to 3 times the normal volume is delivered under exercise. We must conclude that the delivery of blood volume (and oxygen) is much greater per stroke when the pulse rate of the individual is usually slower.

*Effect on pulmonary system: The average person seldom uses his lungs to much more than 75% of their capacity, and the sedentary individual uses his even less. The obvious function of the lungs is to permit an interchange between oxygen and carbon dioxide. They do no more work than is absolutely necessary. The alveoli and lining of blood vessels then must be challenged daily so they will function more effectively when a signal for emergency oxygen delivery is given. Jogging or other vigorous exercise will open the alveoli to perform at the peak of their capacity, thereby enabling them to maintain constant physiologic efficiency. Nature recognizes the need to aerate the 25% of lung alveoli that are seldom used. Involuntarily induced actions such as yawns, sighing, and sneezing keep them from becoming nonfunctional. An oxygen deficiency, caused by inactivity, necessitates that a yawn be invoked so that more oxygen can be made available to the brain and other vital organs. Continuous, vigorous exercise is a form of lung insurance.

Dentist's work patterns

One's work and daily life pattern are important considerations. The recent trend toward sit-down dentistry, although it has some merit, immobilized the dentist in the operating room. He operates from static position, with minimum of body movement. The dentist with two operative assistants, all instruments within inches of his fingers, and the patient in one specific chair position, engages in little dynamic movement. Increased static pressures are exerted on the muscles and this effects his circulatory system.

Isometrics, a static form of exercise in which muscles are contracted by the exertion of pressure with little or no motion, can be observed in sit-down dentistry: pressure is place on a foot control; hands and arms are maintained in a fixed operation position; back and neck muscles often are contracted with little or no movement observed. Such isometrics should be discouraged as much as possible; they do not beneficially substitute for dynamic exercise.

Physiologists will question the wisdom of keeping the operative dentist immobile. The physics of circulation demands that we make vigorous use of the large muscles of the body, especially the legs. When an oxygen demand is created on the muscles by vigorous exercise, the action of the muscle aids the heart in its work. An increased volume of blood is forced through the tissues and little-used capillary beds are opened to deliver oxygen and to eliminate waste products. The dentist's dynamic movements such a walking to the laboratory or climbing stairs, rather than simply turning around on a stool, will cause the circulation to be stimulated occasionally to his benefit.

In the traditional position the operator stands for prolonged periods in a contorted and strained position with most of his weight on one leg. This is not beneficial because blood pools excessively in the venous system of the legs. Many dentists have been forced to retire early because of circulatory problems in the lower extremities.

The legs have been considered a second heart because of the action of the large muscles in aiding the return of blood to the heart. The valves in the large veins of the legs are often damaged by sluggish circulation that results from lack of exercise. Many dentists have a pathologic condition in the vessels of the legs that is similar to a condition in many women. The condition may require a vein-stripping operation, not a particularly simple or pleasant experience. In an examination of the affected tissue in the laboratory, one sees that nonfunctioning valves are covered with rough, fatty, fibrous material. Blood clots are obvious. They often completely block the lumen or reduce the carrying capacity to minimum effectiveness. This problem could become less frequent if more vigorous and frequent use were made of the lower limbs.

As much movement as possible will benefit the dentist. Those who have little physical activity outside the office should especially consider this.

In regard to isometric exercise, Burton[11] wrote, "The increase in heart rate was twice as great as for purely dynamic exercise, such as running on a treadmill." He also said, "Blood pressure, particularly the diastolic pressure, rises more in the performance of static work than in dynamic work, even if the former requires less oxygen.... The cardiac patient should be warned not to exert himself (with static pressure exercise) but he need not necessarily be prohibited from dynamic exercise...." Burton notes that dynamic motion and muscular contraction that aid circulation are not dangerous. The cardiac patient has more risk if he has a heated argument with his wife.

Other contributing factors

*Stress: The tensions of modern living--competition, schedules, and operative procedures--are stressful and affect the individual's circulation responses. Selye [12] defined stress as anything that tends to disturb a man's equilibrium. Many physicians agree that often a correlation exists between stress and coronary emergencies. Recently, Roseman and Friedman[13] reported findings on stress as an important factor in coronary heart disease. They call attention to an increased incidence of coronary heart disease, created by stress of our modern industrialized way of life. The authors also report that coronary heart disease in twice as common in individuals who show extra stress patterns. These people, they say, "appear to be living habitually under time pressure."

Nevertheless, Dimond[14] said: "I work and drive as hard as I am capable, and fully believe that I would have found, or made, life just as stressful had I lived in ancient Egypt, in Greece, or in Rome....I do not personally feel stressed and do not believe modern living, or my version of it, has changed my survival time one day."

Stress probably is not a primary cause of coronary emergency; rather it is a contributing factor, especially for the individual who smokes, is obese, or is poorly conditioned. Many well-conditioned individuals have no problem in coping with stress.

Dentists, and other professional people who live with pressures must condition their bodies and minds to withstand the stresses. Black[15] said that we cannot always rid ourselves of the butterflies in our stomachs, but we can try to have them fly in formation.

*Obesity: There seems to be no disagreement that obesity is a major cause of coronary disease because it severely burdens the circulatory system.

Skin fold measurements are a quick way to indicate obesity. If an inch or more of skin on the back of the upper arm can be pinched, fat will be found within the muscles and around the internal organs. One pound of fat, which must be nourished and drained by blood vessels, has about five miles of capillaries. This places an extra burden on the heart and other organs.

Obesity is usually created by the consumption of more calories each day than are expended. Foods, especially carbohydrates, consumed in excess of need will result in the storage of fat. In America, the land of honey and money, obesity is a particular hazard. Mechanization has brought many people below the level of energy expenditure at which food intake is properly regulated.

*Smoking: Persons who smoke have a high incidence of circulatory disease. The well-known nicotinic effect results in the increase of blood pressure, an increase in pulse rate, and a lowering of the temperature in extremities. These symptoms occur because nicotine causes noradrenalin to be released. This triggers the sympathetic nervous system to close the capillary beds. These conditions have a generally deleterious effect on the entire circulatory system, particularly in the skin, lung, brain, and kidneys.[16]

Phibbs[17] noted that, "Framingham study researchers found that the death rate from coronary artery disease was 300 percent higher in cigarette smokers than in nonsmokers."

*Cholesterol: Although the role of cholesterol in coronary disease is not yet clear, it is known that a correlation exists between high cholesterol content of the blood and circulatory problems. Atherosclerosis, a high saturated fat intake, and an elevated cholesterol blood content are also related. Cholesterol is manufactured normally in the body and is necessary for physiologic function. Excess cholesterol, however, is a danger signal. Other fats, triglycerides, and lipids are being given more attention in physical examinations as causative factors in atherosclerosis.

The Framingham, Mass, study[6] of 3,000 families over 20 years showed that a man between 30 and 59 years of age, who had a serum cholesterol level of more than 260 mg/100 ml (compared with a high normal of 250 mg/100) had a 94% greater chance of heart disease. If his blood pressure was more than 180 mm Hg, his chance of heart disease increased by 117%. Smokers double their chances of trouble.

Prolonging the working years

Persons who greatly concerned with dental manpower must be aware of the importance of prolonged service to society by those currently practicing, and also of the health of future generations of dentists. Those interested in public health, union dental programs, and federally financed programs also should consider the longevity of the dentist's career. Dental educators request more financial grants for new dental schools and additions to old ones. However, they do not include gymnasiums and specific conditioning programs in the schools to prevent the waste of dental man-hours--and years--that often are destroyed by early circulatory and cardiac problems.

We can all point to professional men who had just begun service to society when their life was cut short because of coronary attacks. A contemporary dentist, who died at the age of 45, should have lived to retire at 65 or more and could have served society by an increase of 100%. This is a total gain in patient service of 20 years and a partial solution to the manpower problem. Dental students should apply their knowledge of physiology and pathology to their own circulatory systems. Society would greatly benefit if we were to motivate dental students, medical students, and the combined faculties to prepare themselves physically for a longer life of professional service.

We cannot refuse to act positively because we are fatalistic, casual, or brave. We dare not defy scientific facts and research in circulation. We owe it to others to be selfish and protective of our lives. We need motivation. Ovid, a Roman philosopher of the second century, AD, wrote: "Video meliora proboque, deteriora sequor," The translation is "I know the better and I want it, but I continue to follow the worse." We can explain our lethargy in many areas with this observation on human nature.

Ovid knew what was right and wanted it, but failed to follow up his knowledge. We know something of the needs of our bodies, particularly of our circulatory system, and certainly we each want the best. Still we smoke, overeat, and overdrink and, especially, we sit watching television when we should do a little jogging. We all have mental commitments to ourselves, which we do not deliver, and we suffer psychologically when we fail to act. The mental benefits derived from a daily running program are only known to those who do it.

This paper is a compilation of three papers presented by the authors at the Academy of Restorative Dentistry, Feb 13, 1971, in Chicago.

Drs. Stebner, Vernetti and Gillard are general practitioners. Dr. Stebner's address is 903 Grand Ave., Laramie, Wyo. Dr. Vernetti's address is 543 Orange Ave., Coronado, Calif. Dr. Gillard's address is 1714 Medical Towers, Houston.

1. Blakeslee, A., and Stamler,.J. Your heart has nine lives. New York, Pocket Books, Inc. 1963, p 183

2. Cureton. T. Physical fitness and dynamic health. New York, Dial Press, 1965.

3. Boyer, J.L. Physical activity programs following myocardial infarction. Hosp Med. March 1972, p. 95.

4. Report of committee on exercise and physical fitness, AMA. Evaluation for exercise participation. JAMA 219:900 Feb 14, 1972.

5. Astrand, I. Aerobic work capacity in men and women with special reference to age. Acta Physiol Scand 49:1 1960.

6. Kannel, W., and McNamara, P. The evidence for excessive risk. Read before Minnesota Symposium on Prevention in Cardiology, May 2-3, 1968, Rochester.

7. Cooper, K. Aerobics. New York, Bantam Books, Inc., 1968, p 517.

8. Ellestad, M., and others. Maximal treadmill stress testing for cardiovascular evaluation. Circulation 39:517 April 1969.

9. Berkson, D., and others. Heart rate: an important risk factor for coronary mortality. Ten year experience of Peoples Gas Co., epidemiologic study (1958-68). In Jones, R.L. Atherosclerosis. Proceedings of the second international symposium. New York, Springer-Verlag, 1970.

10. Burton, A. Physiology and biophysics of circulation. Chicago, Year Book Medical Publishing Co., 1965, p 165.

11. Burton, A. Physiology and biophysics of circulation. Chicago, Year Book Medical Publishing Co., 1965, p 100.

12. Selye, H. Syndrome produced by diverse nocuous agents. Nature 138:32 July 4, 1936.

13. Roseman, R., and Friedman, H. Observations on the pathogenesis of coronary heart disease. Nutr News 34:9 Oct 1971.

14. Dimond, E. Cited in Blakeslee, A., and Stamler, J. Your heart has nine lives. New York, Pocket Books, Inc. 1963, p 140.

15. Black, H. Physical fitness of the dentist. Read before American Academy of Gold Foil Operators, November 1970, Los Angeles.

16. Burton, A. Physiology and biophysics of circulation. Chicago, Year Book Medical Publishing Co., 1965, p 179, 196.

17. Phibbs, B. The human heart: a guide to heart disease. St. Louis, C.V. Mosby Co., 1967, p 101.

STRESS TEST

In 1983 I underwent a Stress Test at the University of Wyoming. Others preceded me. One was a 38-year-old law officer who was a smoker and overweight. His tests were far inferior to mine. And sill my results were questioned. When my pulse exceeded 150, there appeared to be a slight narrowing in an artery of my heart.

I requested that this same test be repeated during the spring of 1986 because I was planning my big run. This time there was no evidence of any problem with pulse rates higher than 150. Perhaps my increased conditioning had been effective.

I am fortunate to have two fine physician friends. Both cautioned me against running so far, especially in hunting boots. One said, "You had better take your doctor along with you." The other said, "Don't go too far from the road, because someone should be there with the necessary equipment in case of an emergency."

First I wanted to test my fortitude. Second, I admit having a reasonable amount of ego. No one wishes to be known as "egotistical". Still all persons I know who have accomplished something worthwhile have a good measure of pride.

Finally, there is a missionary factor, especially in our better teachers. When we speak of missionaries we think of religion, but this is not part of me. Nevertheless, if a person considers longevity and health, then I am a missionary. I simply want to be an example to help prevent unnecessary heart attacks.

Friday I will jog in hunting boots across those 25 miles of prairie. Yes, I will walk a few steps if I feel too much stress, or through rocks, sagebrush, or in difficult areas. I may change boots and drink some refreshing orange juice, and a volume of cool water.

I will not be running against time or any other person--just myself!

MY RUNNING

Dan, at your age you we think you we are going to live forever, and it is good that young people do not think of ever dying. It would be a hell of a life to think otherwise. But, when one has lived to be 80, as I will be next April then one becomes more realistic and understands that he is playing the third act of life's production.

None of the males of the Stebner clan have lived as long as I. The reasons: mine accidents and archaic medical help. I lucked out! I was fortunate to have graduated into the professional world, and realized that good health and luck are factors. There is no use kidding myself. Hunting and fishing accidents, and the 'other driver' could have ended my life. Life is a gamble and to date I have won the game.

About 25 years ago, I think I became the first jogger in Laramie. I was stimulated by the examples of two dental friends--Herb Gillard and Jim Vernetti.

During the last few months I have been planning to gamble on running from Centennial, Wyoming, to Laramie. It's been on my mind for a long time. You might wonder why I have planned to cover that thirty miles on foot. I can think of a few reasons.

I heard of a person who planned to climb one of the world's highest mountains, and when he was asked why he said, "Because the mountain is there." I'm sure many people could not understand what he meant, but I think I can. Once a person has such a fixation it becomes hard to get it out of his mind. More often though, reasonable individuals chooSe to erase it from their minds.

About twelve years ago, I tried to imagine how it would feel to run east of Laramie to the summit of the Laramie Range, where we see an air communication tower. It is about nine miles from Laramie. I was in the mood to run on a cool cloudy day and I took off in my hunting boots. On the steeper area near the top I had to walk. Two men were working on the tower and asked me where my car was parked. When I said it was at home they simply shook their heads in disbelief. It was a great day! The rest was all down hill. Rain drops hit my face, and I enjoyed the exhilaration. It felt as though I were flying.

Often, during the past few years, as I have driven toward Snowy Range, I wondered how it would feel to run the miles from Centennial to Laramie. Also during our autumn on the Sweetwater River of the Red Desert we might have car trouble. If we needed help because someone was injured, could I run the thirty miles to Wamsutter? I don't know! I guess I would have to try.

It would be great to think that one has the physical and mental conditioning, and the guts to endure. In most of our lives we have to dig deep in own resources if we are to accomplish such a feat.

. . . .

In two days, Friday the 27th day of June, a good friend, Mark Marquardt, will drive me to the Little Laramie bridge, which is about five miles east of Centennial, Wyoming. He will drive or run and contact me as I run across country to Laramie, about 25 miles away. He will be the person to check my physical condition and supply me with liquids as I need them.

This run has been on my mind for a long while. Although I am 77 years old, I must do it. My reasons to endure the run are several:

1. A test of guts
2. Ego
3. Missionary zeal
4. Signs of insanity

In 1984 I demonstrated the benefits of running by doing just that during the entire meeting at a pre-coronary seminar.

Your Heart

FOLLOWING MY RUN

Dear Dan:

A week ago, in my Red Wing hunting boots, I ran 25 miles. Now, comes a sequel following my run from the Little Laramie River bridge.

. . . .

My friend Mark Marquardt followed my Chevy pickup which I parked in West Laramie, near the area I hoped I would conclude my running adventure. Then, I got into the seat of his vehicle. Neither of us had small talk, and it seemed there was tension. Neither of us knew what might happen that morning. Many times as I drove an automobile on that road I surveyed my route across the hills and prairie. This plan I conveyed to Mark. He knew where I would cross the steep hill, and that I would follow a telephone line, and that I would cross the road twice.

We arrived at the Little Laramie bridge at 5.10 A.M. in the early light. It was pretty cool, but I knew I would not need the shirt with hood and gloves very long. When I started to run the rays of sunrise permitted me to see the many rocks in the first field I had to traverse. I was keyed up as I began to jog toward Laramie.

It was serious business for a 77 year-old man to commit himself to the challenge of running that far. Sure, I thought of the warnings of my conscientious physician friends to whom I told my plans. But my present physician, a young man who runs himself, thought I could make it. He realized I knew some of the signs that might mean trouble, and I promised him that I would abort the run if I did not feel well.

I must record the gut-feelings I had a week after the run. One cannot plan such an excursion without some misgivings. Previously, the longest distance I had run on the prairie near Laramie was about twelve miles, and even then I was leg-weary and perspiring from the heat.

The program I had planned had haunted me during the last several years. I was not sure that I could accomplish the entire 25 miles, but I had to try. I knew that I could, at any time, get into the car with Mark and ride into Laramie if my energy played out. That was my escape!

The idea of simply making the effort was important. I hoped it would be stimulating and exhilarating, and give me an inner view of my psychic and physical being.

During the first six or eight miles it was steeply uphill. Yet my energy level was excellent. Several times I could not see Mark's car because I was about a mile away from the road. Reassuringly he jogged over the hill to meet me with orange juice, or water, and some salted soda crackers. That was my breakfast, but I ate sparingly. The first rays of the sun warmed me and I gave the shirt and gloves to Mark as he returned to the car to meet me later.

Meeting tight barb-wire fences was a problem when I was alone. But, usually, Mark would show up and hold the wires or open a gate for me. When I was some distance from the road I saw wild game. First, six deer crossed casually in front of me. Also, an inquisitive single buck antelope followed me, remaining close for a mile or two. There were fat cattle who seemed to wonder what I was doing in their pasture as I followed the telephone lines along my route.

When I had covered about eight miles Mark was waiting for me with more liquid and crackers. I sat on the edge of the seat and exchanged wet sox for dry ones. There I laced on my second pair of Red Wing hunting boots. This refreshed me as I crossed the pavement to run about two or three hundred yards on the left side of the highway. It was reassuring to be able to see Mark in his automobile.

The running seemed to be more difficult, even though it was generally downhill. When I began the early morning run I had no problem running uphill. Then it was cool and I was fresh. It was difficult before I had covered fifteen miles. Now, the heat was noticeable, and I perspired. Mosquitoes were annoying and I was glad that Mark showed up with an effective repellent. Always he asked how I was doing. I lied a little as I said I was feeling great. Now I could see the town of Laramie, and it was still a long way off.

In the distance I saw Mark's car and another automobile. As I approached I recognized the Sports Editor of the BOOMERANG newspaper, my long-time friend Bob Hammond. He had a camera and focused in on me. When I ran near Bob I made up my mind to really smile. Often, friends who want an excuse to not run say they never see a jogger smile. I made up my mind to change that pattern so I forced a smile as I approached the camera. When I passed them I am sure a more pained expression was evident.

Then, Mark told me he was driving to the airport to phone four of his co-workers. He had converted them to become runners. Mark himself had already run in two marathons and knew what I was going through at this point of my jaunt.

Being alone made it seem like Mark was gone a long while, but it could not have been more than a half an hour. He showed up with his friends in their car. They gave my spirits a lift! We spent about ten minutes together as they took pictures and encouraged me. One of the young men went to get his running clothes and ran along on the road while I was out in the grass. He kept pace with me for for about a mile. Then he ran to his car.

Finally, I reached a lumber mill five miles from Laramie. I had driven past this enterprise and thought it was compact and only covered about a hundred yards. I was eager to get it out of my sight, but it went on and on. It seemed to be opposite to me for a full mile. I was glad when it disappeared.

Eventually, I could see the airport building which is only two miles from Laramie. As I ran, and occasionally walked a short distance, the airport seemed slow getting to me. Mark was there and suggested that I had done a good job, and it was no crime if I got in the car with him and rode the last two miles. His suggestion was tempting.

"No," I reluctantly answered. I had invested too much time and energy to quit at this point. I suggested that he drive to the skeleton of a stone church, which had been my final target at the edge of Laramie. When I hit the last mile I must have walked about as much as I jogged.

The sight of his car at the stone church was more than welcome. I entered the front seat with Mark's help. During the last few miles I imagined what it would be like to have a cold beer. Could I buy one in West Laramie, or would I have to wait until I got home?

Then came a surprise reward! Mark had hidden a gold colored can of MICHELOB beer on ice. He opened it for me. I nearly choked as the liquid failed to clear my parched and swollen throat. The second swallow made it. I never tasted a better beer!

Ordinarily, I crush and save aluminum cans, but not this one. It is hanging on a nail in my garage--a trophy for a great day!

THE ARTIFICIAL HEART

Well, Dan, I am irritated with the surgeon who placed artificial hearts in the two very ill men, because they failed to understand the factors McGaw understood.

When a deceased heart is removed he seems to be not a man but a vegetable, regardless of the replacement. The patient may exist but he is not having any fun. The first transplant patient finally died. And his son, who is a doctor, said that if they had it to do over again he would not have agreed to it. He said something like this: He was not the man I knew as a father. He was in pain and general discomfort-- surely he was only partially alive a week or two. The son didn't think it was fair.

The inventor of the artificial heart is a surgeon who has a vested interest in his invention. Also, the hospital received much favorable publicity. It looked great for a while, even if it did cost several hundred thousand dollars. For these patients after a week or two the news was not good. The poor guys usually have a stroke. Even with anticoagulation medication, a piece of crud lodges in a small artery of the brain. Then they become a vegetable and no longer a person who enjoys life.

Dan, now you know where the problem lies. Sure, crud broke loose in the pipes. The pump worked well, perhaps too well, and the pressure it created knocked loose pieces of material which had obstructed a vessel. Hell, the guy needed a new set of vessels and only God can do that. Now we have learned that with the help of exercise and diet this can be accomplished. It takes a long while and patience to accomplish that. I recently learned that of five artificial hearts that have been implanted, all five patients died without a decent life style. The experiment cost our society about 24 million dollars. It <u>might</u> be worthwhile as a patient to wait for a human implant. Even this I doubt! Recently several organs were transplanted for a little girl who was born without them. It was a blessing her heart stopped!

SURGEONS ARE CURRENT EVENTS

Right now medical history is being made--today it's part of current events, or news. Almost daily, in the newspapers and on television physicians, especially surgeons, make the headlines.

Previously, I wrote you about the modern trend for some members of our medical profession to try to "Play God". They select a person who has developed a diseased heart and needs a new one. The new healthy heart probably comes from a donor who was an accident victim. It is transplanted to take place of the diseased heart. As I mentioned, the artificial plastic heart also works pretty well pumping blood.

I believe such operations are ridiculous. Usually the guy who got the new heart had a lousy lifestyle and will become even more of a vegetable. He probably didn't take care of his original organ, so what makes them think he will do any better with the new gift? In most of these cases the patient simply acts alive, but he isn't really <u>LIVING</u>. I presume this foolishness will end when doctors stop competing for notoriety. These operations cost hundreds of thousands of dollars--whatta waste of money and talent!!

THE CABIN PUMP

Let me tell you about the water supply at a cabin we owned in Snowy Range. Your Dad should show you the place our family enjoyed when he was young. We needed a better source of water when we were there. Finally, I decided to pump water up the steep hill to a little well-type structure upon which we hung a water pail on a pipe.

I did not know what type or size pump to buy. But I designed a couple of water tanks which were welded together, and we dug a six foot hole in sand a few feet from the creek that flowed at the base of the hill. I punctured the lower tank so that water could percolate. As the water in the tank raised to ground level it compressed the air in the top half of the tank and tripped a switch which started the pump working.

I discarded all the old iron pipe which obstructed the water flow, for in it were rust, lumps of metal and a few rocks. These made the inside diameter much smaller than it was originally. The clean pipes required less effort to carry the full load of water up the hill when the pump worked.

What size pump should I buy? I went to a friend, an expert in the field of engineering at the University, and asked him about the pump. First, he had to know how many feet of pipe we needed and the dimension of the pipe. Then, he asked for more information on the length and grade of the hill, which I measured for him.

When my friend, Mike McGaw, had this information he said it would take a one-third horse power pump. But before the pump order went in, I decided perhaps I might wish to get water into the kitchen. When I told him the added height and distance for that purpose he increased the horse power of the pump. Finally, before we bought the pump, it occurred to me that it would be good to have enough pressure so that we could place a hose on the pipe and water the roof, which might save the cabin if we had a forest fire.

Then my engineer more than doubled the size of the pump, which I purchased. He noted that if the pump worked too hard it would overheat and probably burn out. It stayed cool and efficient for more than 20 years.

Someday you may have a friend who is a little overweight, with a poor diet, you might find out that he also has elevated blood pressure. Then you might let him read this paper.

You know, Dan, when there are problems in the circulatory system, the heart gets bigger because it has to work harder. You can't buy a larger pump! I guess we can say--THEIR PUMP IS HOT!

BUILD YOUR OWN BYPASS

The medical profession is accomplishing much to prevent tragic heart failure. We all know people who have had by-pass surgery because of heart disease where vessels are narrow, or blocked, by cholesterol plaques. Surgeons often take another clear vessel from elsewhere in the body and attach it to bypass fresh blood to areas of heart muscle which are undernourished.

I know a man who had three unprecedented heart attacks more than 25 years ago. He also had a poor medical history in his family. With the aid of exercise and diet he is alive today. Herb Gillard runs every day. He built his own Bypass through exercise and diet. He challenged all of his arteries to demand more oxygen beginning with a slow walk, and later turned into a jog.

Nature used the technique called 'anastomosis'. This simply means that the body has the ability to create a Bypass around restricted, or blocked, arteries of the heart. With natures help the entire heart finally receives life-saving oxygen.

If climbing stairs bothers one, then that person should talk with his physician. A good physical examination is in order. It must include some exercise immediately preceding an electrocardiograph. This is a must! Then we can plan to build our <u>own</u> non-surgical Bypass.

GEORGE MILLETT'S HEART

George Millett was one of my first patients when he was in the University of Wyoming law school 53 years ago. He was my kind of a lawyer, and I was his kind of a dentist. Our sense of ethics is similar. We have hunted, fished, and golfed together. We also share a keen interest in the University of Wyoming, especially as sports fans. There are few people in whom one can really put their trust. They are important because everyone must occasionally visit confidentially. George and I can discuss sensitive problems and often use one another as sounding boards.

For many years my friend, George and I drove to a favorite hunting area on a farm near the town of Torrington, Wyoming. We always had good luck there finding enough beautiful cock pheasants to fill our limit.

We arrived the evening before the season and rented a motel room while old Beaver, my first German Shorthair pointer, slept in an old second hand GMC bus of mine. The car was old when I paid $100.00 for it, but it was all I could afford at that time. It was a banged up brown car which I could use for hunting and fishing, and also for transportation to the office.

We had a conversation concerning a physical examination George recently had. Also, with friends, Drs. Vernetti and Gillard, I authored a paper on the prevention of heart attacks. We discussed the early symptoms.

George was concerned because of his negative family history, in which several men suffered fatal heart attacks. At that time he was smoking a cigarette and I explained that was his first liability. George was not particularly worried because his doctor gave him a clean bill of health.

I encouraged him to have another examination in which a stress test might be included. In those days physicians used a couple of steps in their office to function as a stress test. I suggested that the next week he should return and ask the doctor to check his electrocardiograph after he had exercised a little. He thought he would. I knew he should because there is no complete physical examination without some sort of a stress test.

The opening morning of the season was bright, cold and clear. We had some coffee and rolls (which is incidentally a poor diet for hunters.) But it was important to beat other hunters to the fields we knew so well.

The hunt started out as expected, and the irrigation ditch around the farmhouse produced several birds. Soon we each had a bird or two in our hunting jackets and all was going well, especially for me. It seemed that George was slowing his pace, and as I waited for him to catch up he complained of a little indigestion which he attributed to the coffee and rolls. I was concerned about him because of some symptoms he had told me about on our trip to Torrington.

Well, Dan, I was concerned when indigestion still seemed to bother George. I looked around and could see my Uncle John Hughes, who was hunting with us as he drove his pickup truck toward the farm house where we had planned to meet. Then, I casually suggested to George that he sit down by the fence, while I hunted a little pocket of weeds as Uncle John approached. George seemed comfortable in the warm sunrise as he smoked another cigarette and watched me hunt. He waved encouragement as old Beaver went on point and I approached the dog. The cock pheasant was flushed. I hit the bird and Beaver retrieved for me. George seemed relaxed as I waved Uncle John to drive to the spot where George was waiting. I held his gun and carried his hunting coat which was heavy with birds.

I asked Uncle John to drive to my parked old brown bus and told George that perhaps we should go to Torrington and check with the doctor. That idea didn't sit well with him. He wanted to go to the farmhouse so he could have some coffee and visit with the farmer and his wife. He believed the slight pain would disappear, as it always had previously, if he rested in the warm kitchen.

To this I agreed, but I suggested we all might feel better if we went to Torrington and visited with a doctor. Finally George consented and we were soon in my car headed for the pavement and on our way to town. After a few high-speed miles and light conversation George slumped down in pain. I was sure my suspected diagnosis was true. George was having a heart attack!

The old GMC traveled faster than I knew was possible. I followed the big blue "H" signs to the hospital, and drove up to the emergency entrance. George opened his eyes and I told him I was going for a wheel chair. I asked him to sit still because I would soon be back. In the entrance I grabbed a wheel chair, and a nurse asked what I was doing. I said that we needed it for a patient who just had a heart attack. She asked, "Who is your doctor?" I hurriedly wheeled the chair to the entrance, I said, "I am Doctor Stebner, and you had better get the oxygen ready."

When I wheeled George in everything was in order and when we had him breathing oxygen, I said, "You had better call a physician." She looked at my hunting clothes which were messed up with feathers, and a little blood and crap. Later, I wondered if the nurse thought I was perhaps a surgeon who had operated in the corn field. Later, I told her I really was a doctor of dentistry. As we undressed George, I threw his opened package of cigarettes away. I knew he had just quit smoking.

His physician arranged with a specialist in Casper to listen over the phone to George's electrocardiograph. The next morning George was diagnosed as having had a massive heart attack. Today, 17 years later George's heart is still ticking away as he beats me playing golf.

A FRIEND DESCRIBES A HEART ATTACK

In April, 1984 I organized a PRECORONARY clinic at the University of Wyoming, where I encouraged health scientists to lend their expertise. During the entire time of the lectures (one and a half hours) I ran around the ballroom as a demonstration. I also encouraged a friend who had just recovered from a serious heart attack to tell his story. Here, in part, are statements from the paper read by Murray Carroll. . . . .

"My heart attack, according to the records, was a lower transverse myocardial infarction with cardiac arrest. I remember nothing of my heart attack: as a matter of fact, I have little or no memory of the four days before nor the ten days after it happened.

"In terms of life style before my attack, I was probably the classic prime candidate, sort of an accident looking for a place to happen. I operated under stress; I was not particularly careful about my diet; I did not have a regular exercise program; and although I stopped smoking over four years ago, I had been a two-pack-a-day smoker for some 30 years.

"Perhaps more important than the stressful environment, since my attack, I have been taking a good look at myself. I have demanded levels of performance of myself and unfortunately, frequently of those around me, that were unrealistic, and frequently unnecessary. This created an environment of stress both for me and for those around me.

In terms of diet, in so far as possible, I have always tried to eat balanced meals including all the basic food groups. I paid little attention to cholesterol or to sodium content. I dismissed what I heard and read as not really pertaining to me. I grew up in a period when you were told that eggs, dairy products, liver, shell fish, all of the high cholesterol foods, were good for you. When possible, I drank a quart of milk a day, ate two or three pounds of cheese a week, and butter, eggs, liver, shrimp, were a regular part of what I considered to be a healthy diet.

"Exercise. I am not athletic, except for skiing, ice skating and swimming, and when I was growing up I did not participate in any athletic programs. During my military career, I did not participate in any athletic programs. I did make an effort to keep reasonably fit because I had an annual physical exam, and semi-annual physical fitness tests, and because it was part of my duty and responsibility.

"After I retired from the Army, I did walk with some regularity, swam when I could, and occasionally bicycled, but because of pressure of school, then work, and probably as much as anything--sheer laziness, I became less conscientious about exercising on a regular basis.

"After I stopped smoking, I gained about ten pounds, extra weight I intended to get rid of, but could never quite get around to doing.

"I was feeling over-extended--sort of 'pushed to the limit' so to speak. Ironically, I resigned my position at the Museum just a few days prior to my attack.

"In the last paragraph of my letter of resignation I said: 'I am feeling a strong sense of my own mortality and although I have enjoyed thoroughly every minute of the last two and a half years, I now feel the need to free myself of some of the more demanding obligations I have incurred for the sake of both my physical and mental health.'

"Since my release from the hospital, I have been living under a regimen of hard and fast rules set for me by my doctor. I am on a low cholesterol, 4-gram sodium, no caffeine diet. This has meant some rather radical changes in my eating habits.

"Perhaps the most difficult thing I had to do was reduce the stress in my life. This has required a major reassessment of myself, my approach to life, and my relationships with those around me--in some ways, a stressful situation in itself. I realize that if not a classic type "A" personality, I come fairly close to it. I am trying to be more realistic in my goals, avoid situations that are apt to create stress, and learn to relax, move more slowly, and enjoy and savor life. It is not easy, but like exercise and diet, it is essential. In fact, of the three, I feel that for me, it is probably the most essential.

"There are some problems that are a little hard to handle. One is an acceptance of the reality of death. This is something I learned many years ago in combat, but have conveniently forgotten. Having been as close to death as I was, and recognizing that my life expectancy is now probably less than I expected, this is something I have to face. I still relish my privacy at times, but I prefer not to be too far from people. I feel that I am the best judge of what my limits are, and I want to be the one to decide. I appreciate the concern and the caring it represents, but it does get smothering.

"I expect that my life span has probably been shortened, but I do intend to improve the quality of the balance of my life, and I am grateful that I live in a community which has the medical facilities and the dedicated people that together have given me a second chance."

. . . .

A wise professor said he would give an A to any student who would ask one intelligent question.

Healthy Habits

ARTHRITIS

Dear Dan:

I shall tell you of an unpleasant challenge I I experienced fifteen years ago. An acute attack of arthritis on my otherwise healthy body.

Well, what is arthritis? Sometimes it is known as rheumatism--that was the name the English used. It is hard to define because the cause is unknown even though it is a very common disease and in most every country. Usually, its victims are older adults, but sometimes even young children suffer this way can become invalids and in some cases die.

Arthritis has many forms and symptoms. Usually it attacks knuckles to grow more bone and the joints to form lumps which restrict normal function. I now have two joints so affected on the middle fingers of each hand. With pressure I can straighten them to nearly match the other digits. Today it is seldom tender.

You might know that I read much about the disease that attacked me. I traveled to Denver to learn about arthritis in the library of the University of Colorado School of Medicine and spent many hours reading about arthritis. The best book I could find was published in England, and I believe it listed about 85 varieties of the disease. Many authorities wrote on the various areas of their expertise.

It was disturbing to learn that some forms were fatal, while others were only minor diseases with less pain. I learned that my problem could have been have been a form of tendonitis. This is accompanied by considerable inflammation of particular tendons. You see, Dan, there are tendons at each end of a muscle which and they are attached into the bone perform functions of movement and locomotion. I can assure you that all of my tendons were very tender!

I remember the morning the morning when my trouble began. As usual I ran outside early on that November morning, which was my usual routine even though it was about 15 degrees above zero outside. At times like that I dress with woolens and a face mask, so there is no danger from the cold. The problem occurred when I failed to cool off gradually in the warm house. Rather, I was feeling so good that I decided to shovel about eight inches of snow from our walks which had fallen the night before.

I cooled off too rapidly as I shoveled, affecting every large muscle muscle I stressed with the shovel. When I came in I was chilled. Your Grandmother Mary suggested I use her bath tub rather than my usual shower. The water seemed to be quite hot and I had difficulty entering it. Suddenly I noticed my toes had turned very white. The same blanching occurred to my fingers. There was no blood in the extremities. No doubt, this shock set off a series of physiological reactions. The result was an acute attack of arthritis!

I didn't dress that morning but stayed in bed. The next morning I could hardly rise because of the pain which affected the larger muscles and their tendons that I used while shoveling.

The pain and the lack of mobility increased constantly over the next few months. It is difficult for me realize I was frightened at the possibility that I might become an invalid, to even be unable to find a comfortable position. Sleeping in any bed was painful. My family supported me as they continued to insist I would conquer the problem.

Sometime after Christmas was the worst. I gave up sleeping one night and walked into the living room where we have a soft and beautiful blue carpet. It looked better than the bed I left, and with some effort I was able to lie down and enjoyed the firm yet soft surface.

After a half hour I became cold and thought I should return to bed, but I was physically unable to stand. I realized that all of my limbs were too painful to pull myself in an erect position. I crawled around the room for what seemed to be a long while, and tried unsuccessfully to pull myself to my feet. I actually cried. That was the first time I wept as a grown man, and I was emotionally disturbed. Yes, I eventually did crawl to a chair, painfully stood up and shuffled into the bedroom. That experience is one I will never forget.

From that point on I believed, with the help of pain pills and cortisone, that there was some improvement. I tried physical therapy and it was not the answer because the pressure the therapist exerted on my shoulder bothered me too much. I could see that he was trying to lengthen my muscles and their tendons, but he did not seem to note where the pain started. So I came home and did the same therapy because I knew when to stop the extension.

Each day I slowly raised my arms and hands away from my sides, and stretched my legs apart, but it was all I could do was to could stand erect. I felt that if I could raise my hands to a certain point, then the next day I would work to go a little higher. Each day, I promised myself, I would stand the pain. Then I felt they wouldn't shorten any more. I was determined that I would raise my arms and legs a little more each week. It worked! My range of action slowly improved.

That summer my wife drove us to a dental meeting meeting in Denver. There I visited Cheraskin, whom I had known. We had lectured on other programs together. He was well known for his research on diet and vitamins. He advised me to stop using the pain pills and the cortisone, which we knew could cause more serious complicating problems. I followed his advice even if it caused more pain and unpleasant symptoms.

Ultimately, I gained some mobility. One morning I found that my arms raised a little higher as I went through my regular exercises. With renewed hope I promised everyone that I would lick that arthritis. I told them I would be able to go hunting pheasants with them in the autumn. I did! I was slow and stiff as I carried my Model 12 shotgun and shot a few birds. From then until now I force my arms and legs to go to their complete extension.

Years later I continued to improve. Some asked me if the megadoses of vitamin pills, which Cheraskin advised cured the problem. No I don't think so, I gave that after a short time. I think exercise was the key!

Recent research on arthritis has explained, for me the first time, what happened when I forced myself to get into the hot bath which turned my feet completely white. Now they know that our white blood cells, which ordinarily protect us from infection, rebel. The shock I gave my immune system caused some of my protective immune cells to focus into my tendons and joints.

At the present time, during the last few weeks I have had tenderness and swelling which had only been in my right hand, reappear in my left hand. This has happened after about fifteen years. Now the knuckle in the left hand matches the older right hand.

This time, though, I know how to control it--forced exercise and stretching!

HABITS and SNUFF

Life should be a continual learning process, and although I already knew much about the tobacco habit, I learned more from an article in the Miami Herald by Steve Sternberg . . . He said: "The bulging tobacco- packed cheeks of America's youth suggest that for some teens, at least, manhood no longer is measured in Marlboros. The effect, doctors warn, may be a distressing, painful mid-life crisis: cancer of the gums.

"Though they say it is too early to document the trend with statistics, many doctors, researchers and health experts believe teens are chewing tobacco in record numbers. Worse, they say, a recent study reports worrisome changes in the gums of teenage "snuff dippers."

"We have had an increase in inquiries from mothers from South Florida through Georgia," says Carlos Ugarte, associate director of the University of Miami Cancer Information Network, sponsored by the National Cancer Institute in Bethesda, Md.

"They're worried about their children using smokeless tobacco," Ugarte said. "Especially young children.

"Just a pinch between the gum and the lip more than doubles the risk of oral cancer over that of cigarette smokers." This was reported in the October issue of the American Cancer Society Journal.

William C. Wampler, lobbyist for the Smokeless Tobacco Council in Washington, says: "Oral cancer is unproved, but there also are connections between oral cancer, alcohol, poor dental care, and ill-fitting dentures. The majority of smokeless tobacco users never develop oral cancer."

Larry Alan, a spokesman for 'moist snuff' of the U. S. Tobacco in Greenwich, Connecticut, says: "The advertisements, using professional athletes and actors, are broadcast during the major sports events as Monday night football, are doing quite well, in fact."

. . . .

Well, Dan, as a retired dentist I have seen frightening changes in the mouths of my young patients. There are other ways to prove you are a man rather than to get involved with tobacco or drug habits.

NATURE'S STERILIZATION

No matter how careless humans are it seems that as we try to ruin the environment, Nature does her best to save it. When I was in the Navy in WW II I worked with bacterial sterilization. In fact bacteriology was my best subject when I was in school, and I have held that interest.

We had a lot of trouble controlling certain organisms at Farragut which the Indians called Fever Valley. I am sure it had something to do with the cold damp weather. Still, I determined to learn if there were certain pathological bacteria in the soil. I learned that Nature would not let that happen.

We know that most bacteria divide and double themselves in about twenty minutes when things are favorable. If one compiles the figures of one organism multiplying that rapidly, our soil and the land would soon have virile stacked bacteria as high as a man is tall.

But obviously that doesn't happen. Through elements of nature, the soil is sterilized constantly by the freezing, heat, wind, sunshine, and rapid changes in them.

For some time I was concerned that individuals spit and sneeze when outdoors. People in the small towns, or in the wide-open spaces urinate and defecate on the soil, but there is no chance for the extreme division of organisms.

Still, in the cities where there is overcrowding and pavement, there is more chance of some organisms producing, but there is little danger even there. During the last several months we read of a barge of man-made garbage that some people would like to dump in the ocean. There is much opposition to this, and it keeps coming back to the United States and we have no place to dispose of it. Recently, we have also read of the contamination of Boston harbor which has suffered from man's pollution. This is a problem in New York and many of the other large cities around the world.

To add to that we are well aware that the population of this earth will soon be doubled because of the increase in world-wide baby booms. Unless we control man and his birth rate intelligently, the earth we are now using will see more disease and pestilence.
When we control a particular organism, man is attacked with new diseases. A good example is AIDS!

POPULUTION

Don't look in the dictionary for this word. It should be there; but people are slow to catch on. The word is a good one--why don't you call the dictionary publishers and tell them your Grandpa coined it?

Published in the CONGRESSIONAL RECORD by Sen.McGee:
Mr. President, we are all becoming increasingly aware of a pair of problems which are closely associated; namely, the problems of over population and pollution. One gives rise to the other, surely, Dr. Charles M Stebner, of Laramie, Wyo., is a man deeply concerned with our environment and with the

quality of life. He has coined a word which fits the very special problem shared by all men in the 1970's. I ask unanimous consent that a brief explanation by Dr. Stebner of his word "populution" be printed in the Congressional Record. (June 3, 1970)

There being no objection, the statement was ordered to be printed in the Record, as follows:

Need for a New Word

We remember the statement, "The Greeks had a word for it." Well, we need a new word for a very special problem to be shared by all men in the 1970's.

There are two selfish drives of man that threaten our environment. First, man's exploitation of the blessings of earth in the name of something called progress; and the abuse of the sex drive which was designed to perpetuate the species rather than destroy it. These drives are responsible for the multitude of problems that we could call populution.

If we read, listen, look, smell, and finally think, we must become aware of an alarming growth in both population and pollution. They are inseparable in thought and in the symbol--a new word.

Yes, we need it! How else can we effectively discuss the urgent problems of populution?

Charles M. Stebner, D.D.S. Laramie, Wyo. April 20, 1970

DEAD EPITHELIAL CELLS

Now Dan, I will tell you what an interesting kid your Dad was. When he was about age nine, he had an aversion to soap and water. He played freely in the dirt and mud during the summer vacation, but when it was time to go to school he resented being polished with soap and a brush. He fought the daily cleansing ritual planned by his mother. She imagined that his teacher would appreciate her efforts.

We set a rule that he wash his hands before coming to the dinner table, even though he did not realize the entire reason for the rule. One evening his mother noticed that his hands needed attention. She made him return to the bath room again. Well, he turned clean palms over and said, "I did! Look, they are are clean. This is the side I eat with."

. . . .

Ken's sister Marilyn defended her older brother when we insisted on showers. After the glorious summer days when little boys play in the mud and change their socks seldom, there had to be a new rule of cleanliness in our home when school started. We had many family sessions during our dinner hours. This one I particularly remember . . . . .

Again, Marilyn defended her brother Ken. She asked, "But Dad, Kenny has a point. Why should he need a bath every day now that school started? He doesn't play in the mud like he did all summer."

I thought it was necessary to use a scientific approach. So I went to the blackboard and picked up a piece of chalk, saying, "Well, your point is well taken. I will show you why!" Then I attempted to draw a layer of epithelial cells, and said: "Below these cells there are blood vessels and above them are live cells, each having a nucleus, and this living quality decreases until there are no nuclei in the outside layers. The old cells die off. That is why he needs a bath, just to get rid of the dead ones." This seemed to satisfy all concerned, especially Marilyn. Ken and Ron could not care less!

A week or so later Marilyn came home all smiles because she received a good grade for telling a story that seemed to please her teacher. When we asked what the story was about, she told her explanation of why windows should be opened when it's warm outside. She had gone to the school blackboard and demonstrated about dead epithelial cells.

She noted that the teacher kept encouraging her to exceed her allotted time. (No doubt the teacher was aware of the story's truth in those warm rooms which had no air conditioning.) So Marilyn ended, saying: "And when it is so warm all of us have so many dead cells in our sox, the dead cells just smell bad."

As parents we were proud that she remembered the story so well, but it was not so pleasant for Kenny. He burst into angry tears and tried to reach his little sister, saying, . . . "and she mentioned my name, now all the kids will be calling me dead-cells Kenny."

Remember, Dan, that without a bath dead epithelial cells are not clean just because there is no evidence of dirt!

CONVERSATION WITH A CILIATED EPITHELIAL

The human body is unbelievably complex, and is served well by the protective covering of epithelium, both externally and internally. This tough tissue is callused and rough in some areas, but sometimes it is very delicate. Always it is tough enough to ward off invasions which would soon destroy all animals, including us.

In the nose, sinuses, the bronchial tubes and lungs, we have ciliated epithelial cells. These have a specialized function, unique even among epithelial cells. Cilia are microscopic hair-like, movable feelers. They can move fluids, toxins and bacteria toward the outside to be expelled from the body. They are garbage collectors.

Danny, let you and I play a game! OK? Imagine we are only one of my ciliated cells and we can understand a conversation. This cell is unlike most ciliated epithelial cells in that it lives a very long time, while in life epithelial cells are routinely replaced. We are good friends . . . Listen to this special cell!

. . . .

"You know, Dan, I have a real tough job! I have a lot of help other from millions of ciliated epithelium. This damn pollution gets to us! If it were not for us, this old host of mine would have been dead long before his 80th year, but because of me he is still very much alive and active. The thing that bothers most of us epithelial cells is that he seldom thanks us for our unceasing efforts. Oh, he respects us and seems to understand us better than most humans do, but still he takes me and my buddies for granted most of the time.

"When Charlie (that's what they call my host) was born, we were resting. We knew we would endlessly be busy when the doctor brought him into the air. I had an awful shock when there was a slap, a loud cry, and the wind rushed in. The first words I ever heard were, "It's a boy." There was great confusion, it was very annoying. But I knew I was trained for a very important job because my cilia started flagellating. My first taste of oxygen was very exciting! I have always liked that taste--it stimulates me! There were clean fluids all over my cilia and I just loved to move in one direction we will call, "out." It was something like swimming, but I stayed in one place and the fluids moved above me.

"But soon I noticed odors and tastes which offended me. One was smoke! It seemed to come from a heater. When the guy I slave for swallowed the smoky air I noticed that my moving cilia lost their pretty white tips and turned slightly yellow. But that was not too bad, because when oxygen was inhaled the yellow stain disappeared.

"Worse than the smoke from the heater, which they called a pipe, produced an unpleasant odor. Later, I heard a nice guy called Bruno ask for his favorite pipe. Gosh, someone helped him find it and then I heard a scratch of a firestick (later I found out it was a match). Boy, suddenly the air was awful and my flagella became more active, but the worst was yet to come. I found out it was tobacco smoke. Dan, the first smoke was bad enough, but when the burned tobacco came in clouds--ugg! It simply made me ill, and my sensor spun around and then I had a hard time controlling my cilia. Gosh, it was lucky for Charlie that my many friends and I were adaptable. We stroked faster than I ever imagined was possible. Still, yellow stains were moved toward the outside. I'm glad we had a lot of fluid to float the stuff out. I guess that extra fluid, which is called mucous, always appears when there is an emergency. This time the problem was the toxin nicotine. It was mixed with sticky tar which is hard to handle.

"Dan, you would be amazed if you could have seen how many of my friends, other epithelial cells, I have seen killed by those products--billions of them! They often made me seriously ill, but I was dedicated to Charlie and I fought to help him. I found out that sometimes they even killed the entire host. I'm glad Charlie was tough enough to survive, or I would have been a goner, too.

"Often I thought we would never get enough oxygen to help me clean the tar from my cilia. And, of course, there was dust, pollen, bacteria and basic filth I had to handle.

"My fellow epithelial celia and I fought many foreign invasions. One of the worst was when Charlie decided he would smoke a cigarette. That day I expected my host might die--and he nearly did! That would have been the end of me also. What good is such a ciliated cell with no oxygen?

"They tell me that young males eager to become adults often smoke cigarettes. Boy, they don't understand, do they? Ughhh! That seems foolish because an intelligent person should know better than to mess up valuable epithelium. If a guy is an honest person he should learn to protect us so we can save his life.

"Anyhow, Charlie and a guy he called Tom wanted to try smoking cigarettes. They were poor kids, especially Charlie, who had no dad to warn him against making his body vulnerable. They had no money to buy a package of clean cigarettes. Rather, they noticed that the Greek coal miners in Hanna smoked a lot. They found a place to pick up some snipes, which are short pieces of unfinished cigarettes, at the Greek pool and smoking hall. There were plenty of dry snipes, and some still wet, on the floor or near the spittoons. Had they known anything about germs, they might have looked elsewhere.

"The adventurous, but stupid boys who were only ten or twelve years old then began to look for a place to start smoking. There were a couple of old boilers left near the Number One mine, which had exploded killing many miners twelve or fourteen years before my host was born. It was a mass of empty junk. In it were something called flue holes, openings at the end of the boiler through which the heat of the fire could enter and make steam. Here Charlie and his pal would hide. They spaced the cigarettes in the flue holes. Each boy had matches and lit their smokes at opposite ends and worked towards the center.

"The kids began to get dizzy, and it did not take long because the tobacco was strong. Then they became sick in their stomachs. There were still many unsmoked snipes in the flue holes, but they headed to an old barn where Charlie's folks used to keep a horse. There they lay on the hay and vomited. They were a mess!

"Well, Dan, they didn't know, it seems, that all of us epithelial cells were disturbed--those who had cilia were overworked. Our entire oxygen delivery system was in turmoil. Never was I closer to death! My cilia were drowning in the food Charlie had eaten for lunch. It was flowing out of the stomach into our area. It was horrible! Even since the first snipe was lit I had been busy trying to move mucous away from the lung area. My cilia were in disarray with no smooth movement. Some of the fluids seemed to be traveling both ways. It was a losing battle. There was a mess of tars, and the poison nicotine was attacking my cilia. The odors were horrible! Both of the boys were retching and convulsing. Even though the hosts might make it, I nearly gave up and felt I would wash out as part of the mess. Many cells of various kinds died and were expelled from the mouth and the anus. I lucked out!

"I don't know how many hours it took before my tired cilia could get enough oxygen to straighten up. Charlie stumbled home after dark and sneaked into his bedroom, where he opened the window real wide. Boy, that fresh air felt great! Finally, most of us epithelial cells relaxed when Charlie went to sleep.

"You might guess that it was years before I ever was poisoned again by tobacco. It was not as abusive when my host once again tried to smoke a cigar. You wouldn't think that grown men would put friends like us through that punishment after all we have done for them. I suppose he was more of an adult, and hesitated to overdo bad habits. Only on rare occasions was I ever abused with tobacco. That was when Charlie was in the Navy where friends encouraged him to buy a pipe. Gosh, were they <u>really friends</u>?

"Only on two other occasions did my cilia get stained with tobacco. Once was when Charlie was driving his adult son, Ron, home from a Cheyenne hospital following a leg operation. Ron gave my host a cigar and he foolishly lit it trying to please Ron. Well, it didn't please me! The first signs of poisoning appeared. Just a little nausea and then dizziness followed. Of course, by this time the cigar was thrown away and then soon the car stopped. Charlie opened the door and ran a few hundred yards up a side road for about fifteen minutes. I loved the smell of that oxygen, and my flagella calmed down.

"My last encounter with tobacco smoke was what they called 'second hand smoke'. The host had good friends and relatives visiting them when this happened. Charlie was helping them with clerical work. Barb and Vern were downstairs on a cold and refreshing morning, and Charlie was running in the basement before his shower. Most of these mornings I like this early morning ritual but on this day I just did not feel like I was enjoying the running effort.

"Listen, Dan, as a trained ciliated epithelia, I said 'Oh, oh, I sense danger!' Most people don't know how sensitive and dedicated I am. Gosh, I can smell any invader who might injure my host. I'm wired into the sympathetic nervous system, and when danger approaches my cilia are activated and even the adrenalin flows, speeding up the heart. They can talk about warning systems hooked up to computers, but we cells are so far ahead of them they will never catch up.

"As Charlie ran that morning I was inhaling nicotine from the air he was breathing. Yes, he was getting ill--nausea and shortening of breath. Of course, the heart beat was noticeably faster. Poor little Barbara, in her intense pressure and responsibility was smoking more cigarettes than usual. Even during the night the nicotine was present in very small amounts and then because Charlie was running, all of us cells needed more oxygen. That day there was no breakfast. He told Mary he had to rest the balance of the morning. Charlie wasn't aware of the cause but I knew there was smoke in the basement. I could tell by my cilia's increased action--it was nicotine poisoning!

"Dan, once I heard Charlie say that some day he would be cremated--that means he will turn into smoke and a few ashes. Well, I have served him for more than 77 years and seen hundreds of my ciliated friends fold up and be pushed out by newer cells. I was as tough as my host, but when he is burned I will be glad to go with him. You know Dan, I have had some close calls, but enjoyed a lot of fun too. When we leave together I will be a minute bit of pollution and maybe I will get even with a few careless people.

"One bit of advice for you Dan: Take care of your ciliated epithelia better than my host did!

Dan, I have an interesting experiment for you. Test how acutely your own cilia will function if you urgently need their action. In the spring of the year you will often smell a new weed that might be a bit toxic to you, and when you smell it you may sneeze. That could be your ciliated epithelia saying, "Stay away from that pollen."

I hope that you will not have hay-fever, from which I suffered in high school and college. Then I could not stay away from the many pollen which irritated my cilia--I had to work in the grass when I was loading railroad ties in Fort Steele. Many nights I was unable to sleep. I would get out of bed and go for a walk to relieve my eyes and nose. Finally, my symptoms improved and I could back to bed.

Dan, simply test yourself with the fresh pepper your mother uses when she cooks. Just take a good whiff and you will see your ciliated epithelial in action!

DON'T BREAK A LEG

Recently I observed your Uncle Ron as recuperates from a fractured femur, the largest bone of the body. He is having <u>no</u> fun! Ron's always been attracted to horses, and although he seems to continue to enjoy them at age 44, I doubt that the pleasure he had from this hobby is worth the risk. The same might be said for his Uncle George Conwell, who suffered the same injury and nearly cost him his life.

Many years ago Ron had his other leg injured played high school football. The damage from that experience wrecked his knee, and he has had to have several operations. As a proud father I pressed Ron to join his High School football team. I wanted to learn the benefits of working with the team concept. With his strength, endurance and coordination, he could have been an excellent wrestler.

When I was a kid in grade school our physician discouraged me from even playing basketball because of a kidney infection. Right now I have two good legs and arms at the age of 78, and I am glad!

In my experience I have seen many old coal miners and cowboys who had their share of injured legs and they are not as agile as I am. They pay for it as they age. Those areas are more vulnerable to arthritis. Injured joints often keep them from hunting, fishing and even enjoying a nice walk. These activities are most important later in life.

Dan, you have many good reasons to be proud of your Uncle Ron. He is all <u>man</u>, compassionate, courageous and kind. When he was in the hospital more people were calling him, visiting and encouraging him. No one in this town enjoys so many sincere friends of all ages.

I am reminded of your Grandmother's brother, George Conwell. He had an most difficult experience as he rode a horse when his frenum was fractured. Your Uncle Byra suffered a severe broken leg as he rode a horse while hunting elk. Byra had no injuries from playing football in high school and college, but was the victim of a horse. Yes, our family knows much about broken legs and hospitals. A physician in the hospital emergency room said horses and motorcycles cause the same number of broken legs in this area.

HORSES AND HOSPITALS

Your Uncles Ron and Byra, those two hunters and horsemen in our family, were working a new quarter horse that Ron recently bought, and the big mule of Byra's named Jimmy Carter. They were training it for elk hunting camp in the fall. A rope from Jimmy's halter which was attached to the saddle of Ron's horse named Hacksaw.

Jimmy fell and Ron's horse started bucking due to the pressure around his cinch. Well, as Byra said, "Ron really cowboyed Hacksaw real well, until the horse fell backward with Ron in the saddle." It seems that the cantle of the saddle broke Ron's largest bone of the body, the femur!

They both realized that an ambulance was necessary and apparently Byra scrambled fast by horse to a phone while Ron lay helpless until the ambulance arrived on the prairie.

Your old Uncle Ron stands pain very well and acted rather nonchalant. He took all the blame for the problem. We blamed the horse but Ron denied the animal was dangerous. As usual Ron blamed himself for <u>any</u> of his problems, of which he has had his share. With metal implants and a cast, he was again on crutches.

Previously, Ron had suffered from operations on the other leg. When he was in High School I encouraged him to go out for football. Perhaps, if he had been more aggressive, and not worried about the other guy, that leg would not have been injured.

Dan, you will be proud of Ron. He is all man, compassionate, courageous and kind. Many of his friends visit and sent him cards and flowers. Yes, we remembered George Conwell and his ordeal with a horse and a broken leg! Uncle Byra had similar a accident and also felt empathy for Ron.

. . . .

Many years ago my older friend read that I was involved in a rather bitter community confrontation. Milward L. Simpson mailed me the enclosed quotation attributed to Charles Mackay (1814-1889).

. . . .

NO ENEMIES ?

You have no enemies, you say?
   Alas! my friend, the boast is poor.
He who has mingled in the fray
   Of duty that the brave endure,
Must have made foes! If you have none,
   Small is the work that you have done;
You've hit no traitor on the hip;
   You've dashed no cup from perjured lip;
You've never turned the wrong to right,
   You've been a coward in the fight!

HEROES

Dear Dan:

Once I heard someone say that he would rather be a live coward than a dead hero. That is one of those dogmatic statements we should guard against. Couldn't there be something between those extremes?

Some individuals are daredevils and they make a living that way, as do stunt pilots. They may ride motorcycles across a canyon, or dive a hundred feet into a shallow tank of water. At the moment of the event they have the adulation of the crowd. But the cheering crowd soon passes them by. They are not real heroes!

Every war we've have has produced at least one well-known hero; an individual who accomplishes something unbelievable. In most of those remarkable events, the person simply acted impulsively without any intention of becoming heroic. No doubt they deserve the acclaim of being heroes.

In most of us there is a dangerous urge to want to 'show off'. Today's word for it is "macho". I have to plead guilty to that urge in the past. I know my old pal Eric would agree. He would point his finger at me and laugh as he recalled some of my antics when we were in school. Now I know it was a symptom of immaturity! I have seen so many unnecessary deaths in my life by people who simply wanted to be 'macho'.

Intelligent individuals have an inborn wish to protect their lives. To do this, they need a little cool and calculated thought, rather than an impulsive act to show-off for those who may be watching our action.

Great acts of heroism must be of considerable magnitude. This act was known by only the hero and myself. No doubt he has forgotten the day! One spring spring day I was driving to the west on Highway 30, toward Hanna, when I saw a semitrailer truck parked without a driver. I had just passed a band of sheep grazing on the prairie. Then, I came to the burly truck driver who was carrying something which rested on his ample chest. It was a little lamb, which had lost it's mother! Then, I passed the big truck and stopped my car to figure out what was going on. Finally, the driver crossed the road and went to the barbwire fence where he gently laid the lamb down on the other side of the fence. As he walked back to his truck I saw an old ewe running to the lamb.

Surely he saved he saved the life of the little stranded lamb. It was the most gentle act of heroism I ever witnessed. That big man seemed happy as he drove his truck along the road and passed me on his way toward Hanna. Sure, Dan, he was a hero!

Recently, I read of a twelve year-old black boy in a Saint Louis ghetto, who heard a girl screaming as he was passing an open and vacated house. He went to investigate, and saw a tall black man who was trying to undress a ten year old girl he was about to rape. First, the went into the street and told a passerby to call the police, then he picked up a heavy board and re-entered the building calling for the man to free the girl. As he approached the scene he was swinging the club and threatening to hit the man who was more than twice his size. Then the police arrived and arrested the man. Later, the boy was honored by President Reagen as a hero!

. . . .

Similar efforts do not always have such a happy ending. We like to hear of David-Goliath stories. But often the hero gets himself in trouble and loses his life. Dan, I am sure that your mother and dad will train you to care for yourself. Remember Nature is an unforgiving master, and will not tolerate stupid decisions. Knowing that, it is important for each of us to keep in good physical condition. Then, you can save your <u>own</u> life when you are challenged. Often you may be able to save the lives of others.

Our family have a good friend who is a deputy sheriff was riding with a low-flying airplane as they searched for lost snowmobilers on our Snowy Range. They hit a tree. The pilot was killed and our friend was taken to the hospital with a broken back. He has since recovered. If the people they were trying to rescue had any judgment they would not have caused this tragic accident. At that time others found the snowmobilers as they approached their own car.

Sure, Dan, there are heros who die because of the stupidity of careless people. Since the day I was trapped in the "Muddy Trap" I try to be more cautious.

THE FIRST ENVIRONMENTALIST

Yes, I consider myself an environmentalist. But long before the term was generally used I believe that the rancher and farther east the farmer, accomplished much to protect and preserve the better qualities of our environment.

Yet, there is such a person who is a practical environmentalist. I am one of these. In all groups there are extremists who give the group a bad name. During the summer of 1988 we had a tragic fire in the Yellowstone National Park. Most of the damage could have been prevented. I presume that there were individuals, considering themselves environmentalists, who believed that we must let Nature (or we might say God) establish a course for refusing to fight a fire which was started by lightning.

A year earlier a tornado knocked down a large swath of standing timber. The forest officials refused to allow private enterprise to salvage fallen timber. Again, environmental philosophers were blamed. I am not one of <u>them</u>. Intelligent man is expected to help nature in every way we can. We have to fight fires early and save scarce timber for public benefit.

When someone owns the land, even Yellowstone Park which we all own, it is understandable that we must protect and preserve the good qualities of nature. Our dictionary defines the word environment this way: "The aggregate of our surroundings; things, conditions or influences." I would put it simply that we want as much purity and beauty of our air and water as we can possibly have. Those individuals who are aware of their environment abhor contamination of air and water.

In this world, perhaps, there is an excess of human beings, because masses of population ruin a favorable environment. In early America the environment was excellent, but today it has gravely deteriorated.

I am aware that the western rancher was the primary environmentalist because I observed his influence when I was a young boy. During the 1920's we hunted and fished in an area where the land, water and air were uncontaminated. Then we could drink water from the stream and breath clean air. It is not so today. Now the hills and streams show signs that careless people have preceded us.

Only a single rancher refused to allow us to fish on his land. Then I resented his attitude. Today, I realize he was a remarkable early environmentalist. This rancher, Sam Johnson protected the fish on the Medicine Bow river. That was before the Fish and Game Commission effective.

Today, as an outdoor sportsman, I have learned a good approach. First, one should go to the ranchhouse and let them know who you are, then ask for permission to hunt or fish. Park your car where they suggest, and when you are ready to leave, gather your debris and take it home with you. Most ranchers are helpful and courteous, especially if you are alone. No person welcomes a group.

Many years ago, with my two young boys, I visited the ranch of a good friend and asked if we could fish there. Generously he pointed to a grove of trees where we could park our car. We soon learned that he had sent other fishermen to this spot because of the papers and cans which were on the ground. This mess I pointed out to my sons, ages eight and twelve. They agreed that others had been thoughtless, but were eager to get their fishing poles rigged up. I had another idea, and said, "Get that shovel in the back of the car, dig a hole and bury all that crap, and only then get your fishing tackle ready and join me--I am going fishing!" Reluctantly, they cleaned up the mess left by a previous fisherman. Never again did I have to repeat this lesson--they are both strong environmentalists and leave campsites as nature intended.

On another occasion, Ken and I chanced to meet a friend from Texas whom I had previously introduced to the Red Desert area. As we talked for a while we each had a can of beer, and the visitor threw his can into the sagebrush across the trail. My son quietly walked over and picked up the empty can and tossed it in our truck. That was the last can our visitor haphazardly threw on the desert floor--he placed his cans into the back of his own truck.

I fish with a rancher who posts "NO FISHING" signs on his property. He and I often fish together and retrieve empty beer cans along a stretch of river. Can you blame my rancher friend for his signs?

A visiting tourist asked if he could place his recreational vehicle near a stream on a rancher's property. He was told to park near a stream by a fence which separated his land from his neighbor's. But he was told to pick up his trash when he left. A few weeks later when the rancher was checking his fence line he noted that his own property was clean, but the tourist had thrown all of his trash across the fence on the neighbor's property.

The irritated rancher now moved the mess into the back of his own pickup. While he was doing this he noticed a prescription bottle which contained the name and address of his departed guest. He chose a large box in which he carefully packed empty cans, paper, and assorted trash. This he mailed COD back east. It was accepted and much to the tourist's surprise he received his neglected trash. Who could blame the rancher who posted signs saying, "No Trespassing!"

. . . .

Another environmental problem exists between the land owner and the State Game & Fish Department. I believe sometimes both are at fault. The G & F has restored our native antelope herds and have improved the habitat of all game and fish. But at times they are too insensitive to the landowner, and also to the sportsmen! Scientifically, they have accomplished much as an environmentalist, but too often their status and regulations lack human qualities and understanding.

Yes, the early rancher was the <u>very</u> first environmentalist. Both the Game and Fish people and the sportsman can learn from him.

BELONGING

Discipline, Belonging and Education

Let us talk about "Belonging"...humans and all animals know we must belong to something for our mutual benefit. Man's earliest ancestors had to belong to a family or they would not exist. In some way Nature gave us the message. Could it have been sex? That was necessary if we were going to propagate and save our species. Families had to form in groups to defend them- selves against other humans and animals. Finally, the group became a tribe. And people ultimately developed the United Nations.

Today, environmentalists have influential groups. That is good because we must protect the world we live in. I have joined several, one was the Instream Group. We were able to activate Flow legislation. It took a group to accomplish the project. Some years ago I put pressure on the city of Laramie to form our first Laramie environmental committee. Belonging was a factor. Others joined my group because they also wanted to protect our environment.

We all need and love the company of others who share our beliefs. Before we get involved we should know our cause is just and noble. It must be moral! Each cause must have a leader. Most sadistic terrorists kill one another and innocent people because they are a negative group.

For various reasons, I have early aspired to leadership. I was elected as the president of my high school graduating class, my college fraternity, my college graduating class, the Wyoming Dental Association, Laramie's first Chamber of Commerce, the American Academy of Gold Foil Operators, and other groups.

The key to belonging is to believe in yourself and the cause of the group you work for. Dedication is thinking and working for ideals and needs, rather than satisfying your own ego. But let us be honest we all have a reasonable amount of ego which is built into rational people through our genes.

Dan, I suggest that you accept opportunities which will come to you to play a part in various group activities. But to be determined to control your group too long is dangerous. After a short time you would be wise to turn the reins over to someone else, usually younger, and find another group with a needy cause. There is much we can each do for the benefit of our community, government, or even the world, and we should accept the challenge.

Many of my friends, people whom I admire, are dedicated members of various fraternal organizations. I think I can understand them because when I was in college I was a member of a fraternity, in fact two of them, the Sigma Phi Epsilon at Denver University in my pre-dental year and the Delta Sigma Delta which is a dental school organization. I worked hard at it and doubt that I did any single thing significant for the organizations, but they did much for me.

In Hanna our cultural experiences were meager and there was much for me to gain from my fraternity, including some discipline I needed. I got both from the organization. Big fancy paddles were ever present and the older brothers were eager to use them on the pledges. With my ignorance and enthusiasm I had to bend over and hold my ankles while the paddle was used. It was corporal punishment which kept me from making the same blunder twice. I had to learn to answer the phone correctly, as we had none in Hanna for our use.

Also I learned that on a date I should walk up to the door and introduce myself to the parents. It was simple in Hanna. We drove up and honked our horn, and the girl came running out and opened the the car door and climbed in. Before long, I rented a formal suit and learned to tie the black tie. My fraternity brother used the paddle to impress me that I should talk respectfully to upper classmen and visitors at the fraternity house. I also learned to rush new recruits and pledge them. The fraternities had a tough time teaching me any culture.

This education was gained with the aid of group discipline, which I needed. That culture aspect never did rub off on me completely. Perhaps it came a little late in my life. I hope that some of my fraternity brothers might have called me a diamond in the rough.

Later in life I hope that I accomplished that which we might read in the Bible . . "when I was a child, I acted as a child. When I became a man I put away childish things" . . . For the sake of history I was encouraged, and with some reluctance, to join the Elks Lodge. They are a great and respected group of men and accomplish much for communities, but it was not the group I particularly wanted to work with. It might be just the group that I might someday enjoy. I guess I did not give them a chance because I only attended one or two meetings.

Now, Danny, as I recollect the Bank fiasco which I wrote you about I was reminded of another fraternal organization--the Masons. You will learn they also accomplish many services for people in need, especially crippled children. I have many respected friends who have gained much from this group. Do not hesitate to join if you feel the desire. But today I am glad that I did not become a member, and I am sure many of them are also equally happy.

Later I thought of all the time which would have been necessary to attend their meetings and function as any member. Rather, I was able to concentrate on my wife, children, dentistry and working for community service. This approach was more profitable for me and others.

It is only fair that I tell you about my experience with the Masons. They are a secret organization. First, they say that you must approach them to become a member and that they invite no one to join. That is not exactly true. I was approached by two people. Ken Briggs, a person your dad knows well, can verify my experience. He and I discussed that application only a few years ago. Jim Steele, who built my office, and someone else, perhaps it was Ken Briggs, approached me and suggested I apply for membership. I was apparently the type of person they were looking for, a professional man of some promise who was interested in the community. These are good qualities which most Masons have.

Good friends of mine were eager to enter my name for membership. But a former patient of mine named Elmer black-balled me. I guess I should have felt insulted. Later I realized he did both me and the lodge a favor. He was a difficult patient who complained about the fees he was billed for. Those who proposed my name understood Elmer and suggested that at future meeting when they would again submit my name when Elmer was not present. When I considered their suggestion I withdrew my name permanently. Since then I have been grateful to Elmer. All fraternal organizations accomplish much good for the community and their members. The Masonic lodge accomplishes many worthwhile and charitable projects for public benefit. It was a pleasure to see my friend Charlie Street, an active Mason, when he entered my office and sold me tickets for worthy causes. The cause was good if it was for a circus or the all-state Wyoming High School football game. In this way the Masons accomplish much for Crippled Children Hospitals, which they could not accomplish alone.

On the positive side favoring fraternal organizations, was the marvelous opportunity the auxiliary of the Knights of Pythias accomplished for my little mother Mary Ford. She gave much of her life to principles of the Pythian Sisters. And in return they helped her gain an informal education which was important. She was elected to all of their offices and worked hard for them. With the help of her lodge sisters she was instrumental in establishing a Nursing Scholarship at the University of Wyoming. Belonging to this group gave her the confidence and training to conduct meetings and express herself beautifully. Yes, Dan, most fraternal organizations often accomplish notable benefits for society. It simply did not fit my style.

Bob Montgomery in WW II

BOB MONTGOMERY IN WW II

Dear Dan:

To really understand war experiences we must listen to the enlisted men rather than to read history as written by the Admiral or General. But it is difficult to get them to tell their story. Finally, I was able to interview my brother-in-law and tape some of his experiences.

. . . .

Charlie: Bob, how old were you when you enlisted in the Navy soon after you married Helen?

Bob: I was twenty-one.

C. Had you been working on the railroad then?

B. No, I was working in the oil field as a truck driver. It was in 1942. I had only eighteen days of Boot training. Our group learned to do a little drilling and exercise. We were in San Diego, and went from there to Pearl Harbor. It was sure a mess there.

C. Years later Mary and I saw the Arizona still sticking out of the water.

B. Then it made me mad as hell, and I wished I had been in the Navy then, but who wants action when you might never come back. But we didn't worry about that. Sure, that's a kid for you, and that is why they are the best fighting men. All they wanted to do was to kill Japs.

B. Well, I'll tell you that when we got to Pearl Harbor and tried to pull in we could hardly get through because of the damaged ships. They had bottled up the bay. There were ships in dry docks which couldn't get out because the Japs damaged them. Man, it was bad. Quite a mess! Our gang failed to muster. So, they had no record of us. So we just laid around in this three bedroom barracks, which had been officer's quarters. Finally, they found us after two weeks. (Laughter) . . . No doubt someone caught hell for that. There were five of us from Laramie--Lee Kruppa, Red Nottage, Charlie Klouda, Stanley Potmesil, and me. There were two guys from Cheyenne. There must have been 12 or 15 all together. As soon as they found us they shipped us all out to schools. They said, "you are going here, you're going there." They put me in me in a torpedo school. Lee Kruppa went to a barge that operated in the harbor. Klouda went to some ocean-going tug. And we all went to different schools.

C. Sure, Bob, you remember the five brothers who were on the same ship and they were lost together.

B. And from that time on they would not even let brothers be together. They were the Sullivan brothers. Well, I went to torpedo school for sixty days. And then I was assigned to a destroyer. And then the battle of Midway came up and they slapped me aboard a ship right now! We headed there and did not see much because we were sort of a standby there. The others of our group took the beating.

B. Then we came back to Pearl Harbor for about thirty days. Finally, they sent a little group of ships out to sea. We were getting ready for the Coral Sea battle, rating exam, and I don't know how it happened, but my exam was 3.8 out of a possible 4.0. I never did that well in school in Laramie.

C. Well, Bob, this was something you really wanted to do, and that made the difference.

B. We rendezvoused some place down south. Then the skipper in charge of the Task Force picked two destroyers to go ahead and knock off these Japanese patrol boats. They drew our name, and we took off at about 9 o'clock at night. The next morning we were near the Marshall Gilbert islands.

B. The Japs didn't have many airplanes available, so our radar showed these patrol boats. So we went after them. They only had a little three-inch gun, and we had four five-inch guns.

C. Let's see. Those patrol boats are sort of scouts?

B. Yes, that's what they were. We could see them on our radar, and we could easily knock off four or five of these little boats. Every time we could see one, we would stop and lie dead in the water. It was a cinch!

C. Sure, it was like shooting sitting ducks on the water. (laughter)

B. When we were lying dead in the water we could easily get our five-inch guns on them. It was easy, then the radar showed something much bigger ahead. No doubt they radioed back to their group. Well, I happened to be in the control room when this big object showed up. It turned out to be a floating machine shop. Then the planes showed up and flew over us dropping bombs all around us, but none hit us.

C. The Japs should have sent something with a torpedo.

B. Yes, we were a sitting duck and it would have been a cinch for them to hit us. We hit him and watched him go down. Our Captain was a Mustang (that means he came up through the ranks) and he made a circle through the area. There were Japs floating around their boats and as we went through them we dropped some depth charges into the water, and that got rid of them.

C. Of course you didn't pick any of them up...you didn't have room for any, did you?

B. No, we had room for no prisoners. We had about 180 in our crew. It was quite a new sensation to most of us to watch the crew of the big ship as it went down. First the nose went down and then the rest of it followed under the surface.

C. I presume most of you stood on deck for that big moment? What was your reaction, did you all holler then?

B. No, it was pretty damn serious business and was awfully quiet. Then we went on down further and got two more patrol boats. They should have been warned that we were out there by now. See, we had two destroyers and we worked together at about 1000 yards apart. I kept pretty close to the radar room to see what was going on. Here a formation of

Japanese bombers showed up, and things got pretty tense. They made a run over us but nothing hit. They were high, about 32,000 feet above the surface. They must have dropped about 100 ton of bombs, but never got a hit. It sure was close at times.

C. I bet it shook your ship now and then.

B. Oh, Jesus, yes! Our five-inch guns reached up there pretty high and we put a good barrage in front of them. Then they circled around and we thought they would make another run over us again, but they headed home.

B. We knew we were in trouble and the skipper ordered flank-speed. We traveled at 32 knots for 28 hours to get out of the area. Finally, we caught our Task Force the next morning.

B. Now, we were out of fuel. And then we had to take on sea water to stabilize the ship. Well, we pulled along side the carrier with the 150 foot, six-inch line attached to our coupling. Then, on the carrier there was a butter-fingered guy who dropped the Goddamn thing overboard. It swung right back along side our ship. And, believe it or not it tangled in our screws.

B. Oh, my God! And the carrier knew we were disabled. So they cut all the lines and said adieus, and the carrier and the rest of them went over the horizon. If I could have gone over the hill, I would have gone. (Laughter!)

C. So there was no hill, was there Bob?

B. Here we are, dead in the water!

C. You had no fuel, did you Bob?

B. Oh, yes we had a little, but they worked on the shaft which was about 16 inches thick. We had no diving gear, just a diving lung which helped. We had a difficult time keeping sharks from attacking our crew who worked on the screw. Charlie, you might not believe this, but with all of the firepower we had we used 30-40 rifles like you hunt with. Although we didn't kill any sharks, the concussion of the bullets we fired discouraged the four or five of them who circled our divers. But they finally got the screw free, we were no longer a sitting duck in the water. We could not travel very fast, but we finally caught our Task Force. We had another stroke of good luck. They were at a little island where there was a floating dry-dock. It was built by the Japanese. In a previous engagement it was a spoil of war they left undamaged for our use. They took us right in and lifted us up and dumped the water out of the dry-dock. Then they straightened the shaft. Well, we took off and found our Task Force just about in time to be in on the Coral Sea battle.

C. Well, I'll be damned! That ship was doomed to make it! You were lucky. Yours was destined to be a very lucky ship.

. . . .

C. What was the name of your ship?

B. Our's was the USS LAMPSON, DD367. Our sister ship was the MAHON.

C. Boy, Bob, your war experience started off plenty fast. How long had you been in the service at that time.

B. Oh, about four months.

C. Bob what was your duty besides being the torpedo man?

B. Well, I was responsible for my twelve torpedoes. But, sometimes I would relieve someone on the wheel, or someone on the radar. And if we were under an air attack I would fire one of the five 20 millimeter guns. I was pretty lucky when we were practicing shooting star shells. They would open up about 1500 yards in the air and you fire at them. I picked two out of the air. The Gunnery Officer thought I was a pretty good shot. That is why I was put on a 20 millimeter.

C. Bob, after your ship was repaired, you again caught up with your task force as they were engaging the larger Japanese force. Tell us about that battle, what was the name of that engagement? How come you got near the enemy? Why did you get so close?

B. Well, with torpedoes we had to be near. Yes, we lost one Heavy Cruiser and six Light Cruisers were damaged. Still, we got some hits, but if we sunk anything we did not know it. Our planes picked up their Task Force the next day and they were headed for Rabaul, which might be some place in the Marianas. Our planes told us of the number of ships and airplanes the Japs had. On our radar I never saw so much air cover. We did not match up with the information we had on our Radar. Soon, we had a great turkey-shoot! These flights of Japanese planes came over in formation. They were not interested in small ships like the destroyers but were after larger ships. They had to fly over us and we fired into their formation. We knocked a lot of Zeros down that day. Those planes were not protected and a hit anywhere was fatal. They just came apart, but our planes were slower because they had better armor. The Zeros were great in a dog-fight because of their speed.

B. But on this day we raised hell with the Jap planes and we had a rain of shrapnel on our decks. Still, we lost a lot of ships that day!

. . . .

B. Charlie, did I ever tell you about the time we were at anchor in a port called Buna in New Guinea? We were partly hidden under big overhanging trees. Everybody was just loafing around and I was laying there by the gun reading. It was in the shade, and boy it was hot! And, here came this damn seaplane with pontoons and the Rising Sun on it. He went on a ways and dropped a bomb. He went further and turned around to come back. I was waiting for him. I loaded my 20 millimeter gun let him have a burst.

C. Oh, you knocked him down!

B. No, I didn't knock him down, but I could see I hit him because he was smoking, and he made a turn to go into the trees. I damn near got a court martial for that.

C. How come?

B. Because nobody issued me orders to fire. Dammit, this Lieutenant JG, right out of the states, raised hell. But we had a Jewish guy who was the Senior Officer, except for the Skipper, and he encouraged the JG to drop the charges. The Lieutenant was fresh from Annapolis and was going by the book. His name was, uh, Horsepool.

. . . .

B. We often hit other ships, but couldn't stick around and check the damage we did. You know, Charlie, if the enemy scores a direct hit on one of our destroyers, usually we have had it! This is because there was only one-quarter inch steel plate on the sides. Some times an armor piercing shell might go right through the ship doing very little damage. But with ammunition and a time fuse, if it strikes one of the beams, then it explodes inside and we have had it!

. . . .

C. Bob, when you are on the torpedo tubes do you get a view of the action?

B. Oh, yes, after you get the information the rest is done in your head. You gotta lead them!

C. Sure, it is like shooting a bird with a shotgun so that the projectile and the target get to the same point at the same time. You gotta lead 'em!

B. After the projectile goes 400 feet then it arms itself. In school we had to tear them apart and then put it back together. There are five gallons of alcohol and water. Well, the alcohol burns so hot and it turns the gyro. Those things are something. You can hold it but the centrifugal force straightens it out. In school we had a Japanese instructor who really knew his stuff. He had been in our Navy for about 30 years.

A torpedo has a 2000 pound war head with T.N.T. After the torpedo travels 400 feet in the water it arms itself. They can be set at three different speeds, 22, 25, or 30 knots. Usually they were set at a slower speed. It didn't make such a big wake as it moved through the water. They were also set at different depths, which depended on the type of ship you were shooting at.

C. Bob, after this last engagement, did you join your Task Force?

B. Yes, we were under Mitschner. Halsey was there, but we were under him for a while. Boy, he went out and fought a war, that was his plan. He was like Patton. If you are in War you had better fight it and get it over with.

. . . .

B. Halsey had a few more destroyers than needed and he thought some were expendable. So, he gave orders for our ship to enter Rabaul Harbor which was a big Japanese stronghold. It was after we had Guadalcanal under control so we left the Task Force. So our two destroyers sneaked into their harbor. The entrance was about a mile-and-a half wide at the entrance. But then it went through another narrow area and ran into a larger body of water that ran about 25 miles and was five to six miles wider. We left Guadalcanal about four in the morning and got to Rabaul after dark. We caught them by surprise. There were targets on our both sides, so we launched a few torpedoes and started hammering away with our five inch guns until the paint melted off the barrels. I guess there was so much confusion among the sleeping Japs who thought they were secure.

C. Perhaps, they thought there would be more ships and they were scrambling. I suppose you were shooting at the beaches.

B. Sure, we shot at anything that moved. Sometimes if there was a group of men moving we would fire at them. Then we knew we hit a lot of aviation fuel tanks, and we knew what they were because the explosions were just a big ball of fire which would blow up a hundred feet in the air.

C. You were trying to neutralize the area?

B. Oh, no, we didn't neutralize anything, but we sure raised hell there. It sure gave them something to think about to see how vulnerable they were. Especially, if two ships could cause all that damage.

B. When we made our circle and shot up the other side as we were going out--Oh, God, they really opened up on us then. We took a lot of near hits, but we were glad to get out of the harbor.

B. We showed the results of their fire when we got back to Guadalcanal alongside of our Tender. We showed the results of concussion, but nothing serious. You know those old destroyers were sometimes just held together with rust! (Laughter)

B. Our task force was waiting outside for us,

and it was fun. By God, it was so much fun I really began to like the Navy. (laughter)

. . . .

B. When we were in New Guinea the Japs were trying to go down the beach at night in barges and attack the Australians from the rear. In each barge they would crowd about 300 men. So our destroyer showed up about 100 yards off the beach and started shooting at the barges which would sink easily. One night we sank twelve barges, with their soldiers and their rifles overboard. While they were struggling we would intercept them and drop depth charges. Hell, they died by the hundreds. Later, the the Australian soldiers said it was a mess, the smell was so bad that you couldn't get within a mile of the place.

C. I can imagine that it was bad because in that water they would get bloated and float to the surface. I am sure the sharks had a picnic.

B. That is right, there are a lot of sharks in that area. We operated in New Guinea a long time. I thought the Navy had it in for our group.

. . . .

B. You know, Charlie, these unpleasant situations were not one-sided. I remember a place called Buna where we had to land to take some men and supplies to those who were left after the allies had driven the Japanese out of the island. Myself and others left the ship with them. Here we saw, and smelled the filth of a battlefield. There we witnessed a machine gun emplacement with two dead Japs still there. But in front of them were the remains of 38 Australians who had died in the struggle. The sight and odor made me sick. There is nothing worse than the smell of decaying human flesh. In cases like this it was the policy to send machinery which simply covered the bodies. I guess this is what we call "missing in action".

. . . .

C. Well, Bob, back to Okinawa. . .

B. Yes, Charlie, we were hit by a Kamakazi, and we were lucky too. We could see that plane coming right at us. He came in right over the fan-tail. He must not have been too interested in his work. He almost missed the ship. Anyhow, he took off both stacks! He hit the radio room and killed everybody on the bridge. And he got 38 people. As he left the ship his plane exploded because their bomb was set to go off about two seconds after impact with a time delay fuse. By then, he was past the ship, which saved the rest of us. What seemed funny later was the skipper we had then was from Annapolis and jumped overboard.

C. Well, I guess he was going to save his own life, which is contrary to his training.

B. Sure, Charlie, but how can you criticize a guy who acts on instinct? He didn't have time to think it over. About four hours later they picked him up. And some little Junior Officer put him under arrest and confined him to quarters. Then they sent him to Halsey's ship the next day for his Court Martial. We never heard what happened to him.

C. Well, I don't know, Bob. But if he goes over the side, he will never be a hero, because there are a lot of instincts in war.

B. That is right, but if he hadn't jumped he would have been dead. Everyone else on the bridge was killed.

C. I guess that is where that old saying came from, "I would rather be a live coward, than a dead hero."

B. Well, it wasn't my time, because I have two hours on the wheel and the next two hours on the fantail where I was. I saw that damn Kamikazi come right over the top of me. I ducked, because I thought he was going to hit me. Some of those old heads in the Navy would tell you not to worry about it because when it hits, hell your gone!

B. This was in the Philippine Sea at Layte. When you are under general quarters because of an air attack, the heat is on! When you have that five-inch gun and you are shooting straight up it is hard to load it.

. . . .

B. Another time we were under heavy air attack and I worked so hard I got cold. I had to run down and get my pea-jacket. The sweat was just running off of me, but I was cold. Then I looked around to see if anybody was noticing. I was so damn scared I was just shivering. I didn't realize the panic at the time, but I just had to have that coat.

C. It must have been about ninety degrees.

B. Oh, yes it was a hot sunshine day! But I was scared, damn scared. Until then I didn't think anything could really scare me. Finally, I realized it!

C. Usually, I think that a man is responsible for his own good or bad breaks, and I know it is usually the case. But when you were at the fantail rather than the two hours you might have been at the wheel, then that is simply luck. No real injuries or psychological problems came your way. You were simply fortunate.

B. As close as I came was a piece of shrapnel cut right in front of me. It cut my pants like a scissors on both legs, and just scratched me enough to leave a slight scar.

C. Hell, Bob, you should have made something of it, you could have gotten the Purple Heart. (Laughter)

. . . .

B. We were going for a landing at New Britain, and we had a <u>Life</u> reporter, and a <u>Time</u> reporter. They were going to cover the landing. All the time they were around the deck patting everybody on the back. They wanted to see some action. Well, I went into the radar room because I had an attack of appendicitis and didn't feel too well.

B. Well, Charlie, the screen was just full of airplanes. I would guess there must have been about 280 of them. We had never seen any of those reporters on board when there was any action. And as we reported the area, boy, we saw no reporters on board. They headed down to the Ward room. That is where the Doctor who was on board wanted me because he thought I had a bad appendix. The reporters and I just traded places.

B. There was a Japanese plane which would come down and dive bomb you when they could. Well, on this day one of our planes was chasing him at about 2,000 feet. We started using our 20 millimeter guns and we hit the Jap, but we also knocked down our own plane too. Both of them had plenty of time to open their chutes.

B. Finally, we could see that the American was OK and we picked him up. He was glad to be on deck. Then, we saw a guy out there waving at us, so we headed his way. Here was the Japanese pilot. He swam over to the side of the ship and began to climb up to the deck. He just climbed to the deck level, and here came that American pilot over there. Well, the American pilot just kicked him in the face and knocked him back into the water.

B. The two reporters there saw it all, and I think that they got pictures of the whole thing. Well, the old skipper hollered for us to take up the ladder, and called for full steam ahead. This was the only thing to do because when you lie dead in the water you are too good a target.

B. Those reporters were eager for action, but as it got tougher they spent more time in the Ward room. But you can't blame them, because no matter how tough you are, that kind of action makes you protect yourself when you can.

C. You know, Bob, some of these kids today would gain much if they had to serve their country for about two years in the Army or the Navy, as you did.

B. Boy, that's true. You know when the things get tough it is great to see how young kids mature. You know at that age you do a lot of things that older people seem cautious about. Most of the kids I knew showed a lot of guts.

B. You know, Charlie, one day we surfaced a submarine with depth charges. And, when it came up, the tower opened up and they started climbing out of there like rats as fast as they could as they tried to get their guns ready. We already had them in our sights and we let them have it. As some swam near our ship within hearing distance, we had a Mexican kid who was a real character who always kept us laughing. He greeted the one nearest, saying, "Hey, Mac, what ship there?"

B. That is quite a deal when you can get right over the submarine, and if you are lucky enough to get depth charges on both sides of him. He will come up.

C. What makes them surface?

B. Oh, it is the concussion in the water that does it. That's powerful! They can't control their equipment, and he just pops up. Then, they get busy and try to mount their guns, but with them it was too late. We poured enough 20 millimeter fire to take care of that maneuver. Sure, it is easy because we were zeroed in on them.

B. But, I can tell you it doesn't happen that way all the time. When we were at Guadalcanal the Navy was unloading two ships right on the beach, and a Jap submarine hit both of these ships while we had destroyers all around there. It was a mystery; how he got in there nobody ever knew. We had five destroyers there he must have sneaked by. But there were a lot of reefs there, and apparently he got under one of them. It is hard for a skipper to explain a deal like that. We picked him up on his way out, but we couldn't zero on him. We must have dropped depth charges around there for about two hours.

C. Maybe he got hit and went to the bottom.

D. Naw, it wasn't that deep right there, because we found it was shallow when one of our ships hit a reef and damaged his bottom. We could never understand how he could hide there.

C. Well, I guess he was just lucky.

B. And still, you can be a way out in the ocean and you can sometimes pick up a submarine on your sonar. Lots of time you can spot 'em. They have lots tricks that help them hide. Sometimes they just lie still. Then, it's hard to tell them from a big fish or something similar.

C. In a case like that how would you know whether it was an American or an enemy sub?

B. Oh, all of our forces have to have their identification radar on, which means he is ours. That is on all of our ships, subs and planes. But if they come within 5,000 feet and don't have it on--just let them have it!

B. You know old Dug-out-Doug (MacArthur) covered a landing in an Australian plane, and didn't have his identification radar on, and they fired hell on him. Boy, he let them know in no uncertain terms. Damn, I was on the radar and it was pretty strong.

C. I had never known that he was known as Dug-out-Doug.

B. Yah, that's what the Navy called him. It is too bad he couldn't have cooled it after the war. You know old Harry Truman cooled him. Then, he was nothing but a dirty dog. Too bad! He could have come home a hero.

. . . .

C. I am sure that it wasn't always serious business. You were a young kid, and I know they let their hair down and had a good bit of fun also.

B. Oh, yes, sometimes to get rid of built-up tension. That was the opposite side of being a sailor.

B. Once, we decided to celebrate. You know alcohol was in the torpedoes, and now and then we would drain it off for medicinal purposes. So we had been drinking a little alcohol, and we got over on the beach, and this officer wouldn't give me my beer ration. He said I was too drunk already. Hell, I was just happy! Instead he handed me a salami sandwich, so I spread it apart and shoved it in his ear. His name was Bob Apple. He was a Navy Lieutenant from Cheyenne and I knew him from Wyoming. We had a helluva laugh. You know even the officers needed a drink once in a while, and then we let our hair down.

B. You know being in charge of the torpedoes myself, I almost got in trouble. Once, we came up to a sub tender and as usual he took our old torpedoes and gave us new ones. So, with the help of some of the Chiefs we would drain off too much alcohol from the old ones. Then, we would smuggle enough to take when we went on Liberty in Australia. Well, we would give it to a bartender, and hell, we never had to buy any drinks there. Several times I worried about this, because I could see Leavenworth staring me in the face.

B. Once, we got orders to go to General Quarters to pull the anchor and leave because of a submarine scare. Well, we started maneuvering making curves because we we wanted to make it tough for the submarine. Well, on one of the turns, this joker was resting on an ammunition box and he rolled off into the drink. Finally, someone missed him and we reversed our selves, and here he was swimming toward us. Well, we picked him up. And boy did that guy take a ribbing! He sometimes wished he had stayed in the Ocean.

B. When we were in port in Sydney, Australia, half of the crew had ten days shore leave. Well, I knew I would live it up because I had about $900.00 back pay, and I was rich because their money was worth less than ours. Hell, I was a millionaire! Of course, I got in a lot of parties and when I sobered up I headed for the ship, but it was on its way to another port. Boy, was I sick?

There was no Shore Patrol there. So I turned myself over to the Army MPs. They made it as easy for me as possible. I was in the brig, but they left the door open and I had a lot of freedom. Finally, they found out where my ship was headed for another port. It took three days to go about 400 miles. The Army was good and gave me a train ticket and ten dollars. When I arrived no ship was there. And no Army. I had no money. All I could do was to go to the police. They fed me and gave me a place to sleep.

B. I was there for four or five days while they were deciding what to do with me. Then, in came my own ship! Immediately, I reported on deck. Hell, they could have court marshaled me and sent me to the States. Well, the skipper was as light as he could be on me and assigned me to restricted duty. No more shore leaves!

B. Boy, I sure learned a lesson. The skipper was a Mustanger, who came up through the ranks. He fined me $250 bucks and confined me to the ship for one year. That was the least he could get by with. It is a good thing he was not from Annapolis.

B. Well, I survived it! We went back to the war, headed for the Philippines, New Guinea and other spots. That wasn't so bad because nobody else got any liberty either.

B. As time went on, and I was a good boy, I realized that the mail-orderly had a good duty. So I put in for that and got it. When we hit a beach I got off the ship to deliver the mail and pick up ours. I thought I outsmarted the old Skipper, but he used to grin at me every time I brought the mail back. He probably did the same thing when he was coming up too.

. . . .

C. Bob, when I was at Farragut late during the war we had a lot of prisoners, mostly Marines. They were in the brig, and usually they were sentenced for jumping ship. I found out that they were tight-lipped and mean as hell. Sometimes they wouldn't even open their mouths when we have to give them a dental check. They were waiting trial, waiting discharge--perhaps dishonorable. Few would even talk to me because I was a Navy Lieutenant. But one young guy did let his hair down one day. He said that he got a letter from his wife and she was leaving him for another guy. He simply got on the train and hurried home. When he got back his ship had left port without him. He was bitter.

B. Besides missing one's ship the next most severe penalty is for getting sunburned. They furnished you a uniform for several good reasons and you understood it should not happen to you. A badly sunburned body is only a liability that can not function in battle.

. . . .

C. Bob, were you in Okinawa when the Japs were making a desperate last stand?

B. Oh, no, I got orders to the States. First, I was in San Diego where they brought us up-to-date on all the new materials and techniques. Then I went to Boston. Boy, I liked that town. We picked up a new destroyer at Bath, Maine. I was on a shake-down cruise. Suddenly, we heard that Truman dropped the BIG BOMB. We knew that was the end of the War.

. . . .

C. Gosh, Bob, you saw practically all of it! Let's see Bob, you had about three years in action. Did you get elevated in your rank?

B. Oh, yes, I was at the top of my rank. Torpedoman 1st Class.

C. Did you ever get any compensation or pension?

B. Oh, no, I didn't need any.

C. Of course you got your medals when you were discharged?

B. Oh, yes. I still have the medals in a drawer somewhere.

C. You know Bob, we took our son Ken's medals when he came back from Vietnam, and we put them in a little case for him. But he was not interested then, but I think they mean more now, especially since he has his son, Danny, who arrived on the scene. You must care for them properly.

B. Yah, I have been thinking about it. I might do something with them one of these days.

Tight Spots in the Field

ERIC'S MODEL T

Dear Dan:

When I was about 15 years old my pal Eric was the only Hanna kid who owned a car. There were no license restrictions, and the roads were unpaved and rarely used. His Model T Ford had a single seat behind the gas tank and just over the rear wheels. I suppose it was a factor in cementing our relationship.

Together we drove that car all over the county. In its box we placed the few possessions we needed to fish and camp in the hills during the summer. When the old car lost compression, or the brake-bands were worn we could take the engine apart, grind the valves and clean the spark plugs. When it was difficult to start (which was often) we would check the spark and gas, which were on levers under the steering wheel. One of us would be in front of the radiator where the choke wire and the crank were. Eric was usually at the steering wheel because he thought I was a rather wild driver. I did most of the cranking! Ultimately, the motor would take off.

The transmission was under the floor boards. Sometimes we would open the gear box and when they needed it, we would replace the three bands, which were round and covered with heavy felt material. The bands were connected to three pedals on the floor of the car. The one on the left engaged the low gear and was used to move the car forward, the middle one was reverse, and the right petal was the brake. Sometimes we let it go without changing the bands--this often caused emergencies. There was a hand break lever that stuck up through the floor boards--we had to use it too often. This was to operate the emergency brake. We used it when the foot brake bands were nearly worn out. It was a simple automobile which Henry Ford designed, perhaps he thought about the kids like Eric and me.

We must have been about 16 years of age the summer we drove Eric's Model T nearly to the headwaters of the Medicine Bow river because we heard there was excellent fishing there at Stillwater Park. The trail wandered around large boulders among the pine trees. It was made by tall wheeled wagons and strong horses--not for automobiles. Eric hit a big boulder with the middle of the front axle. The impact bent that straight piece of metal into a 'V'. This left the front wheels pointed at each other. It was the end of the road as far as we were concerned.

We unloaded our bed rolls, cooking gear, and most important, our fishing gear. Our minds were made up by that boulder, so we took our poles and reels and headed up hill the last few miles to the gorgeous Stillwater Park we had heard so much about. It was a wide meadow surrounded by pine trees, but only grass grew around the slowly moving water. At the lower end of the park the still water tumbled into a roaring torrent winding toward the town of Elk Mountain 18 miles away.

The still water was an easy place to fish for nice fat speckled brookie trout and some bigger rainbows. We enjoyed throwing the smaller fish back, but we kept all of the nicer fish because we knew we would camp where the Ford was waiting with the pigeon-toed front wheels.

That night we cooked a fresh fish dinner and never worried about the dishes. After a good night's sleep we wandered around the area and found an interesting high firetower where we climbed the ladder to the crows nest at the top. We sat there the next morning and watched beaver playing around in a small pond nearby. When it was about dinner time we went back to the Ford, fried fish and potatoes and relaxed around the camp fire.

We had plenty of time to plan the repair of the front axle--that is if it would work! We jacked the front end up and removed the wheels, and then the axle and tie-rod. The next day we built a big bunch of coals and placed the 'V' into the center of the heat. When the metal was red hot we carried it to a spot where the apex of the 'V' was higher and then we dropped a big rock on it. Slowly it started to straighten. This went on a day or two because we didn't work steadily as we were out of fish; that gave us another day in the meadows at Stillwater Park catching more fish.

But the diet was becoming unpleasant. We depended on the bread we bought in town. As we had driven over the rocks, a little gas had bounced out of the gas cap and soaked some of the bread. The gas flavored bread was not to our liking but we ate it anyhow. We wondered what would happen if we got too close to the fire and inhaled.

The mosquitoes were horrible, and back then there was no bottled repellent to shoo them off. We just killed a few and let the others feed. At night we slept on a tarpaulin which had a few blankets in it. What bothered me most were the wood-ticks. It seemed that there was some deterrent in Eric's skin that discouraged them, so he would not even pick them off and they would come to me. I picked many of them off with Eric's help. It seemed only fair to me that he should get those that had originally left him for me. Then we had never heard of tick fever.

As we ran out of groceries and tired of fish, we finished straightening the front axle and tie rod. When we replaced the wheels, we were ready to back the car up until we found a place to turn around and head for Hanna. We were tired of gas flavored bread!

KEN & KAREY IN THE WIND RIVERS

One day we will be known as Pioneers! History is different for each generation. There is a most important reason why we should read history. We must <u>learn</u> from it. In my lifetime I have seen World War I, World War II, the Korean War, and the Vietnam War. Now some talk of WW III. In my 78 years I know we should prepare for the unexpected, using our experience, and history.

I will tell you some history of your parents. Ken and Karey love the outdoors, especially their annual backpacking trip in the Wyoming Wind River Mountains. Soon after they were married they traveled by maps to an areas they wished to see. One day they walked through heavy timber when they suddenly came to an opening in the forest. Rather, if they didn't enter the large grassy parklike area which seemed to invite them to cross on their route, they would have to circle around by the pine trees for a greater distance. Usually when we see a grassy area the sunshine it is a relief from the dark timber.

With Ken in the lead and your Mother following him, they entered the park. Soon they noticed that their shoes were moist, but that was nothing new in old lake beds. But as they traveled it was simply soggy underfoot and they continued. Suddenly, Ken noticed it was springy and he bounced and staggered. Karey thought he was horsing around and she laughed.

He shouted for her to go back. Ken knew he was in trouble, but he kept moving with all his strength and agility to keep from falling. He exerted as he danced and stumbled trying to keep his balance, while his boots were sucked into the mud. Finally, he was able to retrace his steps to solid footing.

Of course, they had to rest and be grateful for their good fortune. At that point they realized they should have taken the longer trip around the grassy park.

Later, your dad had a job working as a lawyer for the government assisting the Indians of Fort Washakie. He told his Indian friends about his trip, and especially of the grassy trap. This area was not new to them. From the recent history of the Indian hunters they knew of the muddy trap forest. Several of them were in the area hunting elk. One of them wounded a Bull Elk that had an enormous set of antlers. As they chased him for another shot he also tried to cross that grassy park. First they noticed it floundering around about where Ken must have been. As it thrashed around, it slowly sank into the grass. The last thing they saw was the antlers!

A NIGHT AT LARAMIE PEAK

Forty years ago I had an experience in which hypothermia might have threatened me, but did not because I finally relaxed and controlled a tendency to panic.

I had a friend by the name of George Gorsuch. Even today we exchange Christmas cards. He and I fished and hunted together, and our wives were sorority sisters in college. George was a Forest Ranger stationed near Laramie Peak, which is a very confusing area. It's confusing because various streams flow in different directions so you cannot follow a stream to locate your position.

George and I were to meet at Esterbrook Ranger Station at about ten o'clock but George had other duties and failed to show up, so I drove to a fire-tower to look over the general area. After waiting a while I decided to hunt for a buck deer. I left my car there and got into the timber. Soon I found fresh deer tracks and began to follow them. The buck led me out of the area I had surveyed from the fire-tower.

At about five o'clock I thought I would climb a hill and locate my car, which was on a high point. But by that time there was a complete cloud cover and it was impossible to tell north from south, or east from west. I was lost. As it got darker, I thought I would travel in the direction I thought was west, toward my car. I pressured myself to get to the car because I had written a note to George telling him I was hunting. (As he later told me, he found my car at the fire-tower. He said that he was not worried about me because he knew I had been in the forest many times alone. And if he heard no shots calling for help, then I was not injured.)

Well, Dan, when it was very dark I found myself in extremely dense small pines, in an area burned over by a previous forest fire. Traveling at night was impossible. Apparently, I was fighting the timber pretty vigorously because I was perspiring and out of breath. I fell backwards in the timber and thought, "Hey, don't panic! You aren't far from your car and you'll just have to wait to get out of here!" Then I remembered that a few minutes before I had crossed through a park--simply a grassy area where no timber grew.

So I backtracked to it and decided to wait there. Soon after I left the boundary of trees and entered the open space, my heart started to pound because there was the outline of a black bear which faced me, standing on its hind legs. My old 30-40 rifle was cocked and at my shoulder automatically and I pointed the barrel right at the chest of the black object, but didn't fire because there was no movement. I waited a few more seconds and then decided to check a little closer . . . Hell, it wasn't a bear, but a burned out base of an old tree that had perished in a fire many years ago. I guess I panicked a little but not enough to shoot until I was sure.

Let's see, did I have any matches? Not being a smoker, I wondered. Sure enough, there was a package of paper matches in my shirt pocket. The early October night was getting cold and needed a fire. I gathered some bits of grass and small sticks and stacked them up and tried to light a match. Having been near my sweaty body they were moist and wouldn't strike. So I found a rock on which to place them to dry. Now I gathered some dry grass and little pieces of wood.

The next match flamed and I had a fire started. I knew how fires get started in an area like that--the wind fans the flames into other grass and finally through a forest. I wasn't going to let that happen because years before I had fought on a crew to help control a fire on French Creek in the Snowy Range, and I remembered how rapidly flames spread. So, as nearby dry grasses began to burn, I stomped them out. Soon I had a burned clearance around me. Gradually, I built up my fire and felt secure and relaxed.

I had known of others lost in the timber at night who panicked. They fall off into a canyon, break a leg or kill themselves one way or another. I knew of a young football player from Indiana who was lost in the same area. When they found his body during good weather they found that he died from stress. I decided that would not happen to me.

As I lay by the fire into the night, my back would get too warm and my front would grow cold. Then I would reverse the process to warm my belly. I kept the fire good and warm with an old log which burned slowly and I had time to think of many things. First, I thought of little old Ron who was less than a year old asleep in his little crib as you are now. And of his mother who felt sure that I was hunting with George Gorsuch all day and was now in his ranger station home, resting up for tomorrow.

Yes, and I thought of my young dental practice and office which would make me a good living. I knew I was foolish to let that deer lead me into trouble. I felt sure I would reach my car tomorrow--that was if it didn't snow tonight! The sky was cloud-covered as it often happens to be in those mountains at that time of the year. If a storm were to begin, I promised myself that I wouldn't leave the fire. There was plenty of wood near and I felt sure that I could prevent hypothermia (although I didn't use that word then). I would make plenty of smoke to guide George and others who would be looking for me later. I could even shoot my old 30-40 into the air to guide them to me if I found it necessary.

It was a long night! I tried not to look at my watch often, but at about three o'clock in the morning stars began to appear and the cloud-cover parted. I lay my gun pointing toward the North Star and decided that the next morning I might walk in that direction because I knew a well-traveled road was there. But I changed that plan when the sun appeared and I decided I would go west where I expected to climb a steep hill and see the fire-tower. This time I could navigate through that dense group of trees which had resisted me the night before, and as I climbed toward a high hill I could see the glass on the fire tower where my car was parked.

I wasn't long getting there because I'd had nothing to eat since breakfast the day before and remembered some cheese and crackers which were awaiting me. Especially, I was thirsty and grabbed a bottle of beer which had been on ice. I drank too fast and choked as the beer made its exit through my nostrils. I cleared that problem quickly and placed the rest of that cold beer where it belonged.

I drove the car to the Ranger Station and was pleased to see smoke coming out of the chimney which meant George was there. Sure enough he was making a big breakfast, ready to go and hunt for me. He added to the breakfast with hotcakes, eggs, and bacon, and I placed that where it belonged.

Of course, we were glad to be together many hours later than we had planned. George had found my car the morning before. He ate his dinner and went to bed. He was not worried because he knew I would not panic. He heard no shots calling for help, but assumed that I had decided to wait out the darkness. He was right!

Then he asked if I wanted to hunt the rest of the day or go to bed. I chose hunting and later that afternoon I shot the most beautiful buck of my life.

THE MUDDY TRAP ON THE BOW

It was a critical day in my life when I went fishing alone on August 9, 1984. I told my first 'little white lie' of the day--it seemed innocuous then--when I left I told my wife I perhaps would fish after dark, to go to bed and not wait up for me. It was a day I almost lost my life.

In our family, early August dates are significant. On August 8, 1880 Mary Hughes Stebner Ford was born in England. Then, on August 9, 1912, my wife, Mary, was born in Merna, Wyoming. And on August 9, our first grandchild made his appearance in Rawlins.

I planned to have my fish in the cooler with iced cans of beer, and be back home in time so Mary and I could do something together. That would make her birthday complete. However, the lie I told her as I placed my fishing gear in the pickup was a serious mistake. I suggested that she shouldn't plan dinner because I didn't want her to cook. So I said I could be very late. I also said that I might even eat at the ranch, or even drive into the famous old Virginian hotel in Medicine Bow to eat one of their big steaks. Neither of these thing I planned to do--I just wanted to surprise her by getting home early! I actually lied to surprise her on her birthday.

The day before , your grandmother had agreed to let me miss her birthday morning if I would help her celebrate with a festive dinner in one of our better restaurants. Too much rain had fallen during the previous days, but August 9th I saw a change for better fishing weather. So, I planned to drive to Elk Mountain early and catch some larger trout on the Medicine Bow river near my hometown of Hanna.

Finally, I was on my way to the beautiful river I remembered so well. I was going to an area of the river I had never fished, and was eager to get my limit of big German Brown trout while I spent the entire day alone. To be on a beautiful stream with no other person is a spiritual experience I thoroughly enjoy.

When I arrived at the McKee ranch I found Pete repairing haying equipment and after a short visit I told him not to worry about me, but encouraged him to continue with his important work. Then I went to the ranch house to greet his pretty wife.

Dan, you will learn that Wyoming ranch wives are often gracious, and excellent cooks. I had many sumptuous meals after fishing, often eating with the family after they finished in the hay field. I usually avoided taking another fisherman with me because often we were both invited to the dinner table, and later they might return with another buddy. That could put me on the spot with the rancher. I don't want to be the originator of an embarrassing situation. This is the second reason I prefer to fish alone.

This particular day I didn't want to take advantage of Betty McKee's hospitality. I told her I would fish a while and then drive to Laramie because I had plans for Mary's birthday. That was my second "white lie."

I parked my car at a bridge about a mile below Pete's so as not to interfere with their business. I also suggested to them that I wouldn't return to the ranch home later to let them know I was leaving their property--which was not true.

You will see now one simple lie can cause trouble. The way it worked out, they wouldn't have checked my car to see that I had really taken off for Laramie. It was also my mistake to tell Mary that I might eat at the Virginian hotel in Medicine Bow--really, I did <u>not</u> ever plan to do that. I simply wanted nothing to disturb a great day for fishing.

In low gear I steered the truck down a very rocky road to my favorite bridge, a place where I once fished and camped when I was a kid in the Hanna schools. Near that bridge is one of the nicest stretches of fly- fishing water you'll ever see. I guess I should have stayed there! But dry fly fishermen are always eager to see different lazy pools of water and tantalizing rapids.

I wasn't familiar with the river below the bridge and the idea intrigued me. Arriving early I took my time tying my favorite Rio Grande King fly carefully onto the leader. I didn't want to lose a BIG one. I even enjoyed myself as I fought the dense brush, walking several miles downstream. Now and then I caught views of exciting water. I slowly worked my way through tough brush until I crossed the stream. But I resisted fishing there because I promised myself to go at least another mile or two. Then I could choose the most ideal places to fish as I worked back toward the car.

On the east side, I came to a place where the river divided and the lesser stream formed a slough, a swamp-like section of the main river. The slow flowing slough water flows back into the principal river bed, and a small island is created between the two streams. As I walked along the slough I approached a chalky cliff. At this point I realized I should have followed the main river, but I didn't want to disturb the fish I planned to catch on the way back toward the car.

Yes, I made a poor choice following the slough. It led me to a steep sandy hill on my right, capped with a barren rock outcropping which rose skyward more than fifty feet. On my left was the ominous slow running slough water. My only choice seemed to be to climb part way up this steep sandy cliff.

I noticed that the lower part of the cliff bank was moist, while the upper two-thirds was sun-baked and barren. The moist third grew a few scattered weeds and sparse grass, particularly closer to the slow moving water. The water in the slough was dangerous to cross because it has characteristics of quick-sand. Humans and animals do not go into that sort of water. There were no animal tracks across the area and that should have made me cautious. Actually, I thought of backtracking. But I didn't like the heavy brush I'd just been through, and thought I would save some time, if I passed through the cliff area.

As I walked parallel to the steep bank and the line which separated the wet area from the dry baked soil, the steep angle carried me toward the lower wet area. All of a sudden, I found my left foot embedded in mud. I tried to turn around, but my other foot became stuck in the wet goo.

Then I tried to free my boots, but instead fell forward facing the dry material. For support I reached for the dry bank, where rains had caused cracks to form. The clay broke off in my hands. I couldn't free my boots. The harder I worked the deeper the boots sank. Buddy, I realized that I was trapped by some insidious muddy devil in that damp ground.

At first I was not particularly concerned. My watch said 9:30 A.M. The only thing which really disturbed me was that I was going to be late getting to some beautiful pool in the main river a couple of hundred yards downstream.

So that I could have both hands free, and lighten the load I was carrying, I tossed my favorite fishing rod up onto the dry baked surface high and to the left. I fully believed I soon would be headed toward the next beautiful pool I could visualize downstream.

Leaning against the baked upper area, and hanging onto a crack the rain had made, I continued to work to free my boots. That failing, I tried to reduce my weight by removing my fishing jacket. It was heavy. In it were two cans of Old Milwaukee beer which I hoped to consume during the next five or six hours, simply to make room for the fat German Browns which I anticipated catching during that time. Usually, before heading for the car I cleaned the fish and placed them in the jacket with the crushed beer cans. Not so today! I threw the jacket on the bank where my fishing pole taunted me.

But there was no time to day-dream. First I had to get my boots out of this gooey mess. As I worked with my fingers around the boot soles to free them, I sank deeper. My plans were not working the way I wished. I threw mud from my feet to each side and behind me. It was replaced by water seeping to replace the mud. A pool formed in front of me. I worked steadily, with no luck, as I worked to get my fingers under the boot soles.

It was evident that I had lost contact with the dry baked material; I was slipping down hill.

When I looked behind me, I saw I was slowly moving toward the water in the slough. If I reached that, I was fully aware I would soon have water up to my neck.

At this point the water did not bother me because I could feel the tops of my boots, even though the water in the pool I created had reached my belt. I felt it would only be a short time until I could free my feet. Then, I planned to roll out to a spot where I could again stand on a firm footing.

I thought of it as a challenge, sort of a silly game which would take just a little longer. Maybe, I could still fish for an hour or two before I would be headed home. Gosh, maybe I was winning! First the mud I threw out was thicker, but as more water entered my pool more mud ran through my fingers.

Dan, I thought of your dad, Ken. When he returned home from Vietnam he gave me his jungle boots. They lasted me several years. Finally, I found a military surplus catalogue, and I replaced them, and the new ones were now on my feet in the Muddy Trap.

As I worked to free these boots I was also reminded of the day he came home. That was also a great day in my life. He left Laramie and served his year as an infantryman in the jungles for which such boots were designed. And I smiled as I was trapped in my own jungle.

I considered the GI boots ideal for fishing in Wyoming streams, and preferred them to the heavy waders most of my friends use. Waders are too hot when you walk through the brush to get to lower areas where I like to start fishing. Also, I have punctured them going through barbwire fences. With those heavy waders I was concerned about crossing a difficult rapid and stumbling, filling them with water. Then, a fisherman might wash into a deep hole and drown. In a situation like that I believe I could swim to the bank with the Vietnam boots.

During my college days I worked on the tie drive with the Swedes. There we all wore short boots which were constantly wet. Still, they dried out as we walked on the bank of the prairie. The tie-drivers have been able to survive because of these short boots. It was really hazardous during the early run-off in the Platte River. These thoughts ran through my mind as I worked to get out of the Muddy Trap!

I realized that I had been there too long to think about fishing. I could see my hat, muddied glasses, fishing pole and vest on the dry bank above and to the left of me. They were no longer important to me, even though I knew I would get out of that trap! I looked at the large mound of mud I had thrown around me and wanted to get myself up there.

There was a large dead pine tree at the left of the dry bank and a scavenger magpie flew to the top of it and began to squawk for his neighbors. He seemed interested in me. I looked at him and said aloud, "Damnit, get out of here! I am not dead yet!" He was looking for fresh meat and I was still moving. One encouraging thought came to me. I realized that my daily exercise of running each day sustained me to fight the mud.

Then, I had another thought--Hell, I was running out of options! I was not tired, nor did I panic. I realized that could be the worst thing I could do. To call for help could have done no good. I was well aware that no one would hear me. I had to go it alone. Somehow I was sure I would get out of that trap.

After my the little 'white lie', I wasn't concerned that Mary would worry about me today. And, I knew my good friends, the McKees, were cutting hay and would not expect me later. I could even hear the mower in the field a long way off. Now and then I heard a car on the main road about a quarter of a mile from me.

Several times I tried to unlace my mud covered boots, but the knots were impossible. I wondered what would happen if I was still in the muddy trap when the sun went down. Maybe Mary might try to call the McKee ranch, and sometime that night I would hear their voices. I would be resting in my mud puddle then and could I answer their calls?

Now, I thought of the 'little white lies' that I had told them. These I regretted! Such thoughts made me the more determined to extricate myself. I was confident as I rested for a while.

I had a new idea! My only fishing tool, not on the bank out of reach was my little hunting and fishing knife which hung on my belt. If I could work it down into the water and mud and slip the blade under the laces, I might cut them loose. Perhaps I might be able to roll out of that mess barefooted.

It worked on the left foot, but not on the right. I could feel the sock move freely in the left boot. In the murky water I must have missed a knot on the right side, and although there was some movement, it was not enough. Now, I carefully pulled the sock out of the left boot and placed it on the toes of the right boot. I was afraid to allow my bare left foot to once again stick in the mud. So I carefully placed it on toes of the right boot.

My right foot was looser but not free. So, I placed as much weight as possible on my right foot. And, with all my remaining strength, and using my left hand on the banked mud for extra leverage, I heaved my body up and to the left. The left foot flew out of the water. Somehow the partly laced right boot followed it. I kicked it free.

In my stocking feet, I rolled through the wet surface to the higher dry bank where my fishing gear was waiting. But I ignored all possessions and on my hands and knees I reached some willows which was my target some hours earlier. There seemed to be some sort of animal path in the brush and I was soon on it.

Only now did I pause to look back at the pool I created. One boot lay on top of the mud I had stacked, and the other will remain forever in about three feet of water.

Then I had a strange feeling! For the first time since I was trapped, I had the urge to take a leak. As a matter of habit, I reached for the muddy zipper. No way! Muddy sore fingers would not function. It was ridiculous!

A brilliant thought came to my relieved mind. I said aloud with a smile, "Hell, go ahead and piss your pants! You can't add to that mess!" I didn't realize that the water I'd had been in was at least fifty degrees lower than my body heat. I was amused when that warm body water began to trickle down my legs into my ragged and cold socks. (Hey, Dan, not a bad feeling, was it?)

I can't explain the relief I felt after I left my muddy bath and crawled without shoes, or other personal gear which I walked through, to the only exit which would take me to my car.

Before I faced that steep hill which led to the road, I wanted to know what time it was. I had trouble looking at my watch because the face was mud-caked. With a willow leaf I partially cleaned the glass to see. I had been in the mud trap four-and-a-half hours.

On my hands and knees I climbed the very steep hill toward the gravel road. I was forced to pull at weeds and plants to keep from slipping back. It was a long way to the top and the gravel road. Then, a slight breeze hit me. I was cold and began to shiver. It didn't seem to make sense, because the temperature was at least 75 degrees that day. I didn't realize it was a hypothermic symptom which suddenly struck me. I'd been running on adrenalin.

For about four hours, while I sat in that cool muddy water, I had enough calories to keep my temperature normal. But it would been only a matter of time until my fueling mechanism would run out of calories. Then my temperature would slowly drop. Because of osmosis my body fluids would leave my body through the permeable membrane of my skin. Ultimately they would equal the temperature of the mud and water around me, which must have been about 60 degrees. There was too much of that foreign fluid near me so my body fluids were being diluted. Then I would become hypothermic and my vital signs would disappear. I would black out and the heart would slowly cease beating. Hell, I would be dead. This osmosis and hypothermia business is very serious. Nature tells you that you should work to keep warm in the winter and cool in the summer. The loss of body fluid (osmosis) is the key to hypothermia!

I stumbled my way through the gravel until I saw the trail on which I had driven to the bridge which crossed the river. All the time on the road I hoped a car would come along to take me to the pickup. None appeared, so I walked through the stones and weeds in stocking feet the last quarter-mile to the bridge. My vehicle was in sight. When I reached it, with a muddy hand I slapped the hood because it waited for my return.

The first thing I did was to get into the back of my truck where I had some clean and dry clothes. I had trouble unbuttoning the muddy ones. My knife was still at the mud trap or I would have used it to cut buttons. Warm dry clothes and clean sox and dry leather boots were a blessing!

I forced myself to take a few steps to the water's edge near the bridge. I looked at the rapids I had hoped to fish. I got into the pickup's front cab, I started the motor and turned on the heater, even though it was a warm summer day.

With a beer in one hand I wolfed down a sandwich Mary had made for me. At first I was shivering badly. I remained there for a long while, but eventually, I was able to drive the car. In low gear, I traveled those six miles to the town of Elk Mountain and kept the heater running. I stopped at the store there hoping no person would recognize me. The way I looked, not even a good friend would know me.

I bought a few things to eat with a twenty dollar bill and I'm sure the clerk wondered how it happened to be water soaked when I had it in a dry shirt pocket.

I stalled until the phone was available. Then I called Betty McKee and thanked her for letting me fish on their ranch. I had to explain that I would talk to her later about the fish--that I didn't catch!

Yes, Dan, I lied again when I told her that I enjoyed the day--I could see no reason to worry her by telling her the truth.

OSMOSIS AND HYPOTHERMIA

Edmund R. Leach wrote "We Scientists have the right to play God." That was a pretty deep subject for a little guy like you who is now only one year old. You may become a musician, an artist, a politician, an athlete or a preacher. You might become an honest laborer or a garbage collector (as a little boy, your dad aspired for this, rather than the Judge he became.) Our society needs all these, and many others to assure us reasonably happy and healthy lives. Perhaps that's why we exist.

Nevertheless, we all should know something about science. Today I will try to give some scientific information that might just save your life. I hope you will understand the relationship of osmosis and hypothermia. As I review my experience in the Muddy Trap I realize that I was an unpleasant practical guinea pig for those two phenomena.

Let's define them. Osmosis is the passage of a fluid through a semipermeable membrane into a solution where its concentration is lower, thus equalizing the conditions on both sides of the membrane.

To illustrate this, in college we used an animal skin from an orchestra drum. (Today drums are made of plastic, and that would not work in the experiment). On one side, in an enclosed vessel, was a salt solution and on the other side was plain water. We waited a while, and then tested the solutions which had been separated by the skin. Now we learned that some of the salt penetrated through the skin, and water entered toward the other side. This left the same percentage of salty water on both sides of the skin. Osmosis accomplished this phenomenon. This is a quality of all molecules, whether the media is a liquid or the air. Molecules want to balance the books!

Hypothermia is defined this way, "A state of low body temperature occurring because of decreased metabolism of tissues, due to dysfunction of the central nervous system and the endocrine glands.

Now, Dan, you should know that the normal body temperature is 98.6 F or 37 degrees C. The complicated thermostats of the body fight really hard to maintain that normal temperature. But if you get a bug which infects you, the body temperature will rise and the doctor knows you are sick. We call that 'hypothermia' but if the body temperature goes lower than normal we call that 'hypothermia'.

If your body is immersed in water much cooler than it is (as I was in the Muddy Trap) then the normal blood loses calories. For a short time it works pretty well, but ultimately the body runs out of stored calories. Then you chill and may finally die. The same thing can happen in very warm weather and when you perspire to cool yourself. Your body thermostat gets fouled up as you can suffer from serious hypothermia. Nature does her best to keep temperatures normal!

As I said earlier, you just can't screw around with hypothermia. Nature makes every effort to control normal temperature. We have to understand and help her!

BENTONITE

Since I wrote about the Muddy Trap I've learned something about the formation in which I was trapped. It is BENTONITE! It is a clay, a mineral, formed by the decomposition of volcanic ash, having the ability to absorb large quantities of water and to expand to several times its normal volume. It is common in this area and is now being mined in the Green River area of Wyoming, and is used for many commercial purposes. Bentonite is even used for various foods, for an example in peanut butter, because it keeps the materials it is mixed with soft. We also find it in tooth-paste. As an afterthought, wouldn't it be a news item if a dentist who had spent a large part of his life trying to get people to use toothpaste met his demise being drowned in one of its ingredients? I learned about bentonite on a recent trip to the Conwell ranch in Merna. I had just described my experience in the Muddy Trap to Mary's sister Helen and her husband Bob Montgomery. I had shown them the pictures that Steve Stocker and I took when we returned to the bank of the Medicine Bow river where I retrieved my abandoned fishing rod, my hat, my fishing creel, and my life-saving knife.

As I took my very best fishing pole out of the case, I noticed that it still had an ample supply of the trap's mud on parts of it. I showed it to Bob and Helen, and they spoke almost in unison, "Hell, Charlie that is BENTONITE!" They'd just used some of it on the ranch to seal leaks on an irrigation dam. It's often confused with mud or clay because is about the same yellow color. It's very smooth and penetrating, and once you've worked with it you will not confuse it with anything else.

Bob had worked for some years in the oil well fields, where it is an important factor. Bentonite is usually pumped down into well casings to seal off water and lubricate the drilling bits. Bob told of a near tragic accident at one rig he worked on. One of the shorter men on the job was asked to go out and see how the bentonite pump was working. His co-workers later heard him calling for help, and when they arrived at the bentonite crib (where the clay is mixed with water) they could just see the head of the small workman, who was being pulled toward the pump. Several of them hurried to grab the workman before the pump could destroy him. Apparently, while mixing the solution, he fell into the bentonite pool and there was no way he could get out of the mud by himself.

Now, Danny, remember that in the dry state it looks like a pale smooth and soft chalk. Without water it appears as any simple clay. The moral of this story is that even though you should brush your teeth, don't use too much paste or peanut butter!

PANIC AND SURVIVORS

The greatest enemy most people have when they encounter emergencies is panic. When they become confused and fail to think or act rationally, then the mind and the body are in danger. I have a feeling that God (nature) gave us various qualities which encourage individuals and even our whole species to survive. All animals have the reaction for "fight or flight," and that's intended to stimulate us to survive suddenly surprising events. Without thinking, our muscles react to face the antagonist and fight back against the danger, or, more sensibly, run away from it. When the involuntary fight or flight reaction takes place in a man or other animal, there's an immediate infusion of adrenalin into the blood. This causes the heart and respiration to increase and pours oxygen-rich blood into the muscles so that the entire organism reacts-- all this is without any thought process.

If you have ever been startled by someone in a darkened room where you expected no one, then you've felt this infusion. You might have even struck out at the unknown. (By the way, people get hurt when they play practical jokes on others, like startling them. If the frightened person has a weak heart, the sudden release of adrenalin can kill them on the spot. There is a good reason why it is against the law to falsely shout "FIRE" in a theatre or other public places. People can panic and kill one another as they rush to the exits.)

Well, Dan, to get us back to the subject, your Grandmother Mary paid me the best compliment ever when she told someone that I did not panic when I realized I was stuck in the Muddy Trap. To survive, guard against panic.

I think survival could be a family gene, and I think you are going have that gene! As you read the story of my mother you recall she was a survivor. I hope you can say the same for me, and I think after reviewing your dad's Vietnam history, you'll know that he , too, is a survivor. He came out when many of his buddies did not. And I know that your Uncle Ron is one because he has had many reasons to give up in defeat, for example when he was all alone for days but found his way to camp. Many of his classmates have not survived as well as he.

My Muddy Trap experience was enlightening in several ways which you, Dan, would not expect. I found that you and I have more things in common that even I realized. I found out why you simply smile when you wet you pants.

THE GIRL IN THE DESERT

I was very surprised one day when I was driving alone near our camp in the Red Desert of Wyoming. From the makings of the old Overland Trail I saw a bright red object at the turn off to our camp.

That morning I had seen nothing but sage chicken, a few eagles, elusive antelope, a coyote, coy rabbits who thought they were hidden, and several groups of wild horses. But nothing like this--a girl alone!

When I approached she stood up by her bright backpack. She had a long braid of black hair down her back, and she must have been at least six-feet tall. She was lean, muscular and tan from being in the hot sun.

She smiled and asked me if I knew where the Hadsell cabin crossing was. Sure, I knew that this area was about 25 miles away, through a endless maze of trails that I could not describe. It was a question no person could intelligently answer.

To be traveling on the Red Desert on foot a with a minimum amount of food and potable water for 90 miles of tough country, where few vehicles encountered seemed impossible to me. She had maps in her hand, but they meant nothing to me, and perhaps less to her.

I had hunted in the Red Desert for forty-nine years, and although I thought I knew most of the trails and landmarks, but it seemed impossible for me to give her any intelligent answers to how she could get to Hadsell crossing and then on to Wamsutter--that was about 45 miles of desert with many hunter and sheepherder trails she would have to choose from.

The only thing I could think of to do to offer her a ride to our camp which was five miles away. There I had agreed to meet Ron and Steve. I knew that if I went in alone and told them that I had found an Amazon woman at Eagle-Shit-Rock they would not believe me. No gal could possibly get there with an eighty-pound pack on her back! They wouldn't believe my story and would accuse me of drinking too much beer in the hot sunshine on the desert.

It took lots of explanation and all of the charm of an old man with days of whiskers and bloody clothes from cleaning out antelope and sage chicken, to sell her into riding with me to our camp. She agreed to go for a good meal and camp there that night.

As I drove in they wondered who would be sitting in the front seat with me. Could it be my hunting dog Bella? No, they decided. It must be a lost hunter! You should see their faces when a tall, strong, and gorgeous girl with braids, a visor cap and hiking shorts stepped out.

After the introduction of our guest, Theresa, one of them lifted her pack out of the shell of the pickup because I couldn't lift it. We asked her to select a spot to pitch her plastic tent. She had agreed to stay for supper, because she needed pure drinking water to help her on her route following the Continental Divide the next morning. As the two cousins were about to carry that pack to the selected area, the girl lifted and swung it back over her strong shoulders and walked to the selected spot. All three of us were amazed how expertly she lifted and carried that eighty-three pound burden. We were more amazed that she carried it through the mountains, timber, streams, and now the desert!

When we were seated around our campfire, she told us that she traveled about fifteen miles every day, except at pre-arranged spots where she would get mail from her father, or replenish the dried foods and what fresh water she could carry. Her father seemed to know where she would be almost every day.

Theresa had flown from her home in New England to the Continental Divide at the U.S/Canadian border where she would follow that high area all the way to the Mexican border. This trek had been a dream she had prepared herself for during the past years. Now, after two national parks she had walked to the Red Desert-- about half-way on her adventurous endurance trip.

We learned she was being partly financed by outdoor equipment companies, whose materials were in her pack. But she was mostly financing herself from her own modest savings, and from the proceeds from the sale of many photos she was taking along the way. She said she would give slide shows later, and might even plan another excursion. Who knows?

Ron is the Stebner cowboy, and on this trip had brought two horses and a great riding mule named "Jimmy Carter." We agreed that our guest should see the Sweetwater River Canyon and watch Steve and me catch her favorite food--TROUT! She was no horseperson, but agreed to ride Jimmy down a steep and difficult canyon. Steve and Ron rode the two horses, and I walked to lead the way because I'd made the trip before and knew a little about the path the cattle and game had made. I walked in my fishing shoes trying to stay out of the way of the horses, which the riders had to prod through difficult areas.

When we arrived at the river I started to fish and the other two encouraged Theresa to try to catch a trout in the turbulent white water with her spinner and fly rod. She had no luck, as it required more expertise to entice beautiful trout to take the flies Steve and I offered them. Ron and Theresa sat on the sagebrush banks and visited about the area and some of her experiences in the National Parks where she encountered four grizzly bears. Yes, she had been worried, but made a lot of noise to make them think she also belonged there. Steve and I caught about four nice trout for dinner. I rode Steve's horse back. He got bucked off at one crossing, but got aboard Ron's horse and we all rode back to camp. Theresa had some trouble with the mule at difficult crossings, but she made it to camp. That evening Byra arrived at camp and was surprised to see we had a guest. He took some pictures of our enlarged group the next morning.

We cooked trout for Theresa, which was a break for her. She even had a beer during dinner. She told us of many of her experiences she had since leaving the Canadian border. She pitched her tent with ease that night, and we realized how efficient she was. We knew that she could sell a group with her equipment and expertise traveling along the Continental divide.

The next morning I drove her to Hadsell crossing, but on the way even I missed a trail that should have taken us there. Still we got near a band of wild horses and took some excellent pictures of that group. We had trouble with my truck because it would stall. Finally we stopped at Hadsell crossing. There I decided to drive on to Wamsutter where I found out that the truck had a filter that was giving us trouble. Then I drove her on to Rawlins where she had to call her father. I drove her to meet Karey Stebner and Danny. She checked in at the Jade Motel where she had a rare shower. Then I took her to dinner, and I am sure that she enjoyed sitting at a real table. The next day she began walking along the Continental Divide toward Mexico. She promised to send me a card telling of her progress, but we didn't hear from her again.

(We learned that Theresa did <u>not</u> make it to the Mexican border. She got stranded in the early snows near the Colorado border and was forced to go home.)

. . . .

SPEARS AND ANTELOPE

One year we nearly ruined the season! I invited Avery Spear of Houston, Texas to hunt antelope in the Red Desert. I drove a Chevrolet sedan into an area which demanded a truck. We drove too fast for the trails we were on because we wanted to get ahead of a bunch of Wyoming antelope. I made a sharp turn in the sand and when the tie-rod between the front wheels buckled we were stranded. The front wheels twisted toward one another and we could not move!

Avery was a city boy who had never traveled off the pavement. We were about 40 miles from the nearest telephone, and 100 from a garage! When we surveyed our predicament, he smiled and said, "I will wait here, Charlie, and you can walk down to the corner drug store and telephone for a new tie rod." After a few profane remarks, I informed my hunting party that the nearest drug store was about forty miles away.

We took the rod off and carried it along with our guns, and we headed toward a major trail about five or six miles from our disabled car. There chances were good that other hunters might drive by and take us about 25 miles to Wamsutter. Perhaps some filling station attendant could help us straighten the rod. If that failed we would look for a ride to Rawlins to buy a new one.

After we walked about an hour in the desert, we came to some sagebrush near a pond of water. There we rested, still thinking that a big buck antelope might wander in and give Avery a good shot. That didn't happen, but there was another bit of good luck. I noticed a few rocks in the area. These rocks are rare in that area where there was only sand.

I remembered the stunt where Eric and I straightened a bigger piece of metal--an axle in the forest. I had Avery help me gather bigger stones and we placed the two ends of our rod in the sand with the obtuse V upright. While one of us held the rod the other dropped a heavy stone at the bend. Finally, we straightened it out and returned to the car where we bolted it back in place. We continued our hunt and the next day Avery finally killed his buck, which he proudly carried back to Houston. The mounted head adorned his office wall.

Danny, now when you are learning to talk you seem to be having trouble saying TRUCK . But later when you have to repair one, these examples might get you out of bad Trouble!

THE SAGE GROUSE HUNT

Yesterday I returned from a trip where I hunted SAGE CHICKEN. That's what I've called them since I was about five years old. I do remember the fish my dad, Bruno, brought home before his death, and I am sure he also hunted sage chicken for us to eat. The first time I went hunting with a gun was with my dad's brother, my Uncle Adolph. I didn't hunt because I was too young to carry a gun, but I remember the thrill of it all.

We went to the Old Carbon area where the Stebner family lived when they first arrived from Germany. All of the four Stebner brothers were hunters, and they liked to eat young sage chicken. Hanna people never heard the name sage grouse, which is the term used by the Wyoming Game and Fish Commission.

After my dad's death, and before I was old enough to shoot a shotgun, I hunted with a slingshot made using rubber from some of the early automobile innertubes. A pal and I walked a couple of miles south of Hanna and found a little spring which was a natural place for a mother bird to raise her young chicks. We had our slingshots and pockets full of rocks which were deadly at close range, and we carefully approached the spring. There we found a hen and her half-grown chicks eating clover. I shot my first sage chicken and proudly took it home for my mother to fry.

Well, yesterday I returned from hunting the young sage chicken. My base was on a unique spring in the sagebrush hills which surround the old deserted town that was once Carbon, Wyoming. There is a solitude to that place and seldom do we see another person. The only sound is the hum of a high flying transport plane enroute from the North Pacific area to Denver.

During the first morning your uncle, Byra Kite, showed up to hunt with me a few hours. I told

Byra, and also your dad, as well as others, that when I leave this life I wish to be cremated and have the ashes placed beneath an old weather-beaten tree near our spring.

I chose to hunt alone in the rough hills. Our family for many years often camped at a box spring in one of the canyons. The area is important to me, because I have a feeling that my dad, Bruno, hunted there when he was a young kid from Germany long before I was born.

When I first saw that spring, Eric, my step-dad Ford, and I found it during the early 1920's. We drank cold, clear water from it. I presume that an early sheepherder dug away some rocks and soil where underground water bubbled up. He placed a big box about five feet high into the source of the water and left the top open for cold, clear water to escape and form a stream, which found its way down the canyon where his sheep and antelope drank. The stream meandered down the grassy area, and the banks were surrounded by copious sagebrush. Sage chicken could find water in an ideal place and that is where we hunt them.

As the years passed the old box deteriorated, and I finally removed it. And one year, before hunting season, I carried in building materials for a more stable enclosure. It took some digging in the mud and sand. Finally, your dad came to help me place good redwood two-by-fours lengthwise into the area, and we made a wooden lid to cover the box so that animals wouldn't fall in. We also placed a cup there for others to drink this pure, cold water whenever they came that way in their travels.

Above this spot, on a dim road, there's a moist area where automobiles have often no doubt become stuck. Thoughtless people have found they needed boards and planks to remove their vehicles from the mud. I'm sad to report that they repeatedly tore the top of my box away and used it to help free their mired wheels. This week I found the entire area nearly wrecked. One night when I slept at the area alone I retrieved most of the broken lid from the dried mud and again placed it haphazardly over the foundation. Then, as usual, I used a shovel to remove moss and mud so that the clear water could drain down hill. People we sometimes call "sportsmen" can destroy a healthy and beautiful environment. This angers me! Maybe next year I will again try to rebuild the box for the benefit of any person who would like to drink from that cold, clear spring.

Well, Dan, after a good night's sleep in our old camping place, I hunted again along the few meandering trails made by early sheepherder wagons and early automobiles which twisted their way through the rough hills. It was the same view Indians enjoyed more than a century ago, except for the old Carbon cemetery on the hill some miles away. Outside of my German Shorthair hunting dog (and the sage chicken I hoped to find) I was alone! Today few people anywhere in this world can enjoy that experience. In fact, most would be terrified of such solitude.

Experience led me into the little grassy draw, where, after miles of walking among majestic wind-carved sandstone monuments, my dog Bella led me to find sagechicken. Yes, Dan in two days I shot my legal limit of those wonderful birds which I then brought home to grace our dinner table.

. . . .

Bella and I had a bit of a scare when she worked her way, smelling for sage chicken, into an area guarded by another kind of animal. It soon became apparent Bella had entered forbidden ground. An ill-tempered animal lived there. Ordinarily, when you see a badger in the hills they run away and speedily crawl into their protective holes.

I sensed the situation was not normal when Bella came running back toward me. I was in deep sagebrush, but she brushed by me after she hurried across the grassy drainage bottom. Bella brushed by me as she retreated behind me. Then I saw a fast-moving brown object on the grassy bottom as it chased the dog from the sagebrush. It climbed rapidly up the bank to the sagebrush about fifteen feet ahead of me. There it froze when she caught my scent. It was the largest badger I had ever seen. There the animal showed its teeth and hissed violently like a very big tomcat. I could just see the head and neck of the badger through the tops of heavy sagebrush.

I had never seen such an antagonistic and speedy challenge. The badger showed no signs of retreating when we faced one another. I could only see her neck through the thick sagebrush which separated us. By instinct I had released the safety on my sixteen gauge shotgun and pointed the barrel at the animal which stared at me. I fired and the badger disappeared.

When Bella heard the shotgun fire she returned, she might have thought I killed a sage chicken and wanted her to retrieve it. Together we cautiously circled to climb down to the grassy bottom. There was badger on its back. As I walked around her I was amazed at her size, with claws and teeth which could have easily cut my hunting dog to pieces. Yes, Dan, I was glad I pulled the trigger.

STORY OF OLD SHOTGUNS

When a man lives beyond his 79th year and has a treasured shotgun returned, he is lucky! First, my uncle John had the foresight to save my dad's double barrel 12 gauge gun, which he later gave me. It had a Damascus steel barrel. My father, Bruno, hunted sage grouse at the turn of the Century in the Old Carbon area.

Then, many years later his son Gordon Hughes returned a single-shot .410 gun to me. Some day, Danny, you might shoot your first sage grouse with that small gun. This particular gun has an interesting history. When I was about eleven years old my uncle John and Aunt Georgia mailed it to Hanna from California. They moved there for a short time following his discharge from the Army in 1919.

My sister Elsie and I found the gun, along with a doll for her, which were Christmas presents for us. They were stored in a linen closet in the Cottage Home boarding house. Several times before Christmas in about 1920, we climbed the shelves of the Old Cottage Home boarding house, when our mother was out of the building. There we played with our intended presents. Of course, we acted surprised when we opened the gifts on Christmas morning.

Finally I had my own real shotgun! After Ford married mother, I hunted with him, using my .410 for several years. It would hold only one shell at a time and I couldn't load fast enough to shoot my share of birds. Of course, Ford had a 12 gauge automatic pump gun also shot part of my limit as well as his own. Eventually, Ford bought another more modern gun for himself and the pump gun came to me. That was the last time I used the little .410 weapon.

When your Uncle Ron was born I saved the .410 for him and he learned to hunt with it, but birds were not his favorite game. He is a rifle man who only hunts big game. Later, your dad Ken, shot his first sage grouse with the .410 until he outgrew it. I suppose I helped him fill part of his limit also.

When Bruce Hughes was born I was pleased to send the .410 to Uncle John's grandson. Like Ron, Bruce was not a bird hunter. About all Gordon accomplished was to shoot mistletoe from the trees. There were no sage grouse there.

Later, after you were born Gordon drove to Wyoming, accompanied by his wife Virginia and Gordon's sister Elaine, to visit us. Gordon handed me the .410 shotgun. It was marked "TO DANNY"!

George Conwell and the Cow

GEORGE CONWELL AND THE COW

Dear Dan:

The Conwell family had three sons, Ralph, Donald and George. There were four girls Irene, Mary (your Grandmother), Helen and Alice June.

The Conwell kids had a teacher, Ethel Shipton, in their ranch-school house at Daniel, on Horse Creek twenty miles west of Pinedale. All of the Conwell kids were mentally bright, but Ethel told me that George had the sharpest mind. His personality and humor made him very many friends.

George was a real cowboy character. He left school sometime in high school and hired out as a ranch hand. But his real love was the rodeo. Today there are big purses to be made in rodeo. Then most of those who traveled the rodeo circuit made little more than their expenses. George rodeoed for the thrill and fun. He spent his young life working on ranches and could see no need for an education.

He and I had many experiences camping, hunting, fishing and riding horseback when George was a guide for big game hunting parties. He tested the greenhorn with a sadistic vengeance, but they loved him in spite of their discomfort. His ready smile and sense of humor are his saving graces. Most of us were bucked off horses he saddled. I remember the day I flew too high for a comfortable landing. Rather than blaming the green horse he saddled for me, George said that it was the fishing flies in my hat which scared the animal. There was nothing malicious in my brother-in- law's nature. He just liked action.

George rode broncs in the Cheyenne Frontier Days, the Denver Stock Show, Arizona, Oklahoma, and Canada and elsewhere. He has a scar on his forehead when he bucked against the retaining wall in Madison Square Garden and many others. George joined artist friends Sprague and Walt LaRue, stunt men who drove run-away stages in western movies in Hollywood.

George got a break, from his rodeoing experiences when he married a younger and wonderful girl, Joann Smith. She was the Riverton Rodeo Queen and could ride a horse well enough to keep up with George. They raised a fine daughter, Susie. Without a doubt George and Joann loved one another, and she made him a marvelous home which kept the wandering and adventurous man from wandering too far. Often times I am amazed how she has handled his antics.

It is ironic that, with all of his wild exploits, George was to wait until 1982, when he was 68 years old, to have his most harrowing experience on horseback. He had a summer job which he loved cowboying for about twenty ranchers that kept their cattle on the summer range near Green River Lake above Pinedale.

Your Grandmother Mary and I visited him at his typical mountain cabin where George had everything he wanted. He batched and rode one of his five different horses every day to check on the cattle he was responsible for. He said the solitude and quietness made the job better than anything he had ever done. He had no other person to talk to and argue with--this was all on the plus side for George. That was great until he had a near fatal accident.

. . . .

The following are excerpts from a tape he helped me make:

George: I was moving about ten or twelve head up to another area away from the river. Then I wanted to get another bunch to join them, and I was just about ready turn them up hill.

Charlie: Did you say there was a bull fight?
George: No there was only one bull but I guess it was a cow which chased the dog and he came back toward my horse. I tried to push her off, and somehow I was pushed back of the saddle about the

time something hit me on the leg. It just happened so God-damn quick, there's no way you can put it all together. It couldn't have been more than two or three seconds and it was all over. And I was trying to get out of there--off that damn hill. I was down on the ground and saw the dogs under my horse. Everything just happened all at once. I remember that I had my foot on the cow.

C: You had your foot on the cow?

G: After I hit the ground, I never saw a thing--not a dog, horse or a cow.

C: You put your foot on the cow?

G: Yah, that's a habit of mine, when a cow crowds me, even in a corral, I just take my foot out of the stirrup and push against the cow. I don't know why I do it, and I'll probably never do it again. I don't believe anyone watching would know any more than I did.

C: If you had stayed on the horse until you got down to the gate, you couldn't have opened the gate.

G: Hell, I couldn't have stayed on the horse. I was in so damn much pain. Charlie, someone asked, that if I had some matches, could I have built a fire. Hell, that was the last thing I would have thought of-- I was in too damn much pain! Some guy said to me, that horse bucked you off. I thought to hell with you, you were thirty miles from me and you know more about it than I do. I guess he thought if it had, then I wouldn't have a suit against them. Hell, no it wouldn't buck just to be bucking--I had ridden him all summer, and there was no chance of him bucking me off. There are only two things I know that are accurate. I know I put my foot down on the cow, and then I went back in the saddle and then reached back with my hand on the coat that was tied on the back, but I never remember getting hold of it.

C: What time of the day was that?

G: I guess it was sometime between two and four o'clock. And I wasn't on the ground very long, and then I just wanted to get down off that hill. I do remember that I had to get my spurs off. And, then I thought that I should get my hat to keep my bald head warm. Then, I decided to leave them both there so I could later get them. I just had to crawl grabbing sagebrush or a rock to pull myself forward.

C: You were trying to get down to that trail?

G: Yes, there are hunters and others going back and forth there and they might see me.

G: Buddy Summers went back up there later and said it was about half-a-mile. When you keep dragging yourself forward by grabbing a sagebrush or a rock, you don't make much time. Maybe, if I could get a hold of something solid I could make a foot each move. Then, between movements I would rest quite a while.

C: Were there any trees there?

G: Yes, when I got down there I saw a few trees off to the right. I lined up with them, and that was after I ran out of sagebrush, so I just decided how fast I was going by watching them. After, I pulled myself forward fourteen or twenty times I looked at them. It was slow. I was thinking about that bottle of whiskey I had at camp. I wanted to get to that whiskey!

G: I wanted to see how far I could go in ten pulls. I could still see those same trees. Boy, it was disappointing! I just quit counting. It got dark and my mind was jumbled and finally it was morning. I made it to the trail and now it was level with no more downhill.

G: At the beginning I had a flannel shirt and long underwear, with brown overalls over them. I had a big scab from my elbows to my hands. When I hit that trail I just couldn't go anywhere.

G: The guy who went up there the next day to get my hat and spurs, couldn't believe it--his wife told my wife Joann that they didn't have any trouble finding where I had been because of all the rock and sagebrush I had moved.

C: Well, George, if that guy hadn't been hauling hay to you and had seen your saddled horse, no one would have known anything about you for days.

G: Maybe so, but someone had to open the gate the next day and turn my horse into the pasture where the other horses were. But Bud Sommers was finished with his haying and could have come up--he was the only one who ever came up. And if he had seen my horse with the saddle, he would have known damn well something was wrong, and he would have found me.

C: Let's see, George, you got to the trail about daylight?

G: Yes, that was my goal. I thought some hunter might be coming up there about then. You know, the thing that I kept thinking about was that bottle of booze that was in camp.

C: George, do you think that you slept a little that first night?

G: Oh, I don't really know how much, but I guess I was sort of in and out. I can remember I was sure in pain, and damn it I would sure groan and moan. I think that scared the dog--I guess he was afraid of me and he wouldn't come close. A couple of times I tried to put my arm around him, but he wouldn't let me.

C: Do you think it was the blood on your arms that bothered him?

G: No, I don't think it was that but the noise I made. I remember once when I tried to see how God damn much noise I could make just to relieve the pain. That dog came back and forth a dozen times, but half of the time I couldn't turn my head and follow him.

C: You said you heard voices that night, didn't you?

G: Oh, hell Charlie, early in the morning there were those two guys there watching me, and I would tell them to go and get me that bottle of whiskey. They said, "Oh hell no, we are not going to get you any whiskey." Then, I would turn over to look at them and the bastards would move around to the other side. That went on most of the afternoon, and I could hear them talk. Then, I remember when the plane was flying over us, I told them to wave at the plane and let them know I was in distress. And they said, "Oh no, that's your "responsibility." And I cussed them...blankety, blank!

C: (We both laughed.) Well, George, at least you had company! You would talk to them and they would talk back to you.

G: Oh yes, but the trouble with them was that I had to do most of the talking...sometimes they would just clam up and walk around saying nothing.

C: (Laughing!) Well, that was damn unsociable of them.

. . . .

(George was wearing coveralls that were about the same color as the ground, and I think that the dog was moving around and got the attention of the plane which was looking for George)

. . . .

C: George, it was about dark when the plane spotted you, and I presume it was the movement of the dog, because you sure were not moving.

G. It is hard to see something on the ground when you are flying around. But, I know that the last pass they made they were flying pretty low and

I was worried about them. I couldn't figure out what those bastards were doing! No, they didn't come back again, but now I am sure they spotted that dog moving around.

C: Well, George, they radioed to Pinedale and set the rescue in motion and came in an ambulance.

G: No, those guys came in a four-wheeler. Oh, yes, Carl and some of those guys were there first, they came to me and went down to the river and got me a couple drinks of water. They must have been there a good half-hour first. It was awfully steep right there to the river. There were other guys there, but Albert Summers was the only guy I knew.

C: Who was the guy who brought the hay the day the before?

G: That was Roy Steele. I knew him for years--he and his father had that same job I had years before.

C: How many cattle were you guys responsible for there?

G: About 76,000! You know that a pretty big job. I guess I was responsible for half of it.

C: Well, with 20 ranchers wouldn't they have more cattle than that?

G: Oh, yes, but some of them had to be somewhere else, that's all that range could have. I think that there were 22 brands, like Stan Murdock and his mother--that's two brands. I could name all of them.

C: George, did you say that if you had a gun you would have used it on yourself?

G: Why, hell yes! I'd of used it on my dog, or horse if they were in the same shape. Christ, I wouldn't have seen him suffer. And, if they would have to be in the same condition that I was.

G: Well, Charlie, he thought of his leg dangling along behind him. He thought he might loose his leg.

G: Well, it was that awful pain! You talk about Byra hollering in the hospital, but he was no worse than I was. You know, its a funny thing I don't remember it hurting after I got in the ambulance. First in the four-wheeler I remember it hurting when we hit some of them bumps. I remember trying to slow that driver down and said, there's no reason to be in a hurry now.

C: You know, George, the first thing they gave you was morphine, and that is why you were comfortable.

G: Even in the hospital I don't remember that leg hurting, but I sure as hell remember it hurting in my back and my arms, and especially in my back--there was no way you could get to it.

C: Let's see, George, you had to be on your own for about 27 or 28 hours. And then there was more time until you arrived at the hospital.

G: Yes, somebody said we didn't get there until about 11 o'clock. Yah, I remember the Doctor told me they were going to operate the next morning. But they didn't do it until the next night.

C: Sure, George, you were in no shape for it because you were dehydrated, and they had to get some of those fluids into you.

G: Yah, that's the way I lost so much weight, Charlie. You know I wouldn't recommend that treatment to fat people.

C: George, you were in good physical shape then, and you can be glad about that.

G: Oh, yes Charlie, I guess I was about 165 pounds before. I was in good shape.

C: Sure, its a damn good thing or you wouldn't have made it. You know, George, when some people have an experience like that they say, "You know in those moments my whole life passed before me. Or I thought of all the things I should have done, or the things I should have said." Or they wished they had made peace with their Lord?

G: Oh, Charlie, I didn't think of any things like that. I was thinking too much of old George. I was wondering what George could do--not what the Lord could do.

MUCH LAUGHTER . . . . .

My Son Ken

KEN GETS GREETING FROM PRESIDENT

Dear Dan:

Ken was no youngster when he was drafted by the army to fight in the Vietnam war. He was 24 years old and had graduated with a major in history from Wyoming University. Most of the men he served with were 18 and 20 years old. These younger fellows were adventurous and made better soldiers. To them there was a worthy cause because President Johnson thought we should resist the communists of North Vietnam. Danny, your father, Ken, had little faith in President Johnson's decision.

But I remembered when my Uncle John enlisted, as a young man, to fight the Kaiser in France. I reminded Ken that our family had been consistently patriotic to answer the call of our President. He is our leader and should have more information which, for security reasons, he cannot communicate with the public.

Also Ken knew why I left my dental practice, and more importantly, my family. Your grandmother was left with your older brother Ron, and was expecting Ken to be born in a few months. Nevertheless, it was a very different war. The Japanese had bombed Pearl Harbor and America was forced to declare war. I wanted to be part of it. I was 34 years old, but I left my dental practice and studied oral surgery at Northwestern University in Chicago. With my age and experience I knew I could be valuable in caring for our sailors.

I explained this to Ken and encouraged him to accept the draft summons because we were certainly a patriotic family. Still both of us knew the Vietnam War was considerably different. Ken's

Laramie buddies were involved and on their way to serve because they were in the reserve forces. Ken could see that he would be drafted even though he had a minor experience with the Naval reserve in Cheyenne. It was not enough, so the letter summoning him to appear to the draft board had to be faced.

(a taped interview between son and father)

KEN'S BASIC TRAINING

Charlie . . When you were through with your basic training and ready to get on the plane for Vietnam, we went fishing near Walden, Colorado. We traveled over some spongy ground. The character of that field was nothing compared to Vietnam. I presume some of those kids you trained with would panic. Tell us about your training!

Ken . . Yes, some of those guys had never before been outside the city they were born in. But most of the guys at Fort Ord in California were from the West. Many of them went through AIT with me. There you receive training in specialized areas such as a cook, mechanic, or whatever. Here they tried to simulate combat and probably did a pretty good job. But the truth is it can't be done. When a fellow arrives in Vietnam it is entirely different. Here it included wading through ponds, and they also shot guns over your head. You learned about avoiding booby-traps. We worked with the M-16 which is smaller and faster than your 308 rifle. This weapon was fully automatic. It is only little bigger than the .22. You can see the expense and problems of carrying heavier ammunition like we use to kill big game in Wyoming. We were trained to use a variety of other weapons, such as LAWS--anti-tank guns.

In basic training , whether you were going to be a cook, or whatever, you were trained to use basic weapons. When your MOS was eleven bravo, you knew you were going to grub it out in Vietnam--that was mine! You paid attention to the training because Vietnam was getting closer. Most of us hoped that we would be lucky and be assigned as a cook, a mechanic, or something safer. Then they needed soldiers and about half the people who were drafted would go into the infantry. I guess the Army could not have trained you any better. They knew how to do it--the guys who trained you were

ones who had been there. So you listened to them; it was a very serious business. Nobody fooled around like they did in Basic. This was different! There was no harassment by the drill sergeants. In Basic they wanted to get you in shape and get your mind to a point where you could be properly trained. Then in the AIT you get it or you don't. If you didn't get it then it might cost you.

C . . Ken, some place along the line, didn't someone say, "Hey, with your background you should be an officer."

K . . Well, yes, I had been through college, and if I had been smart, which I wasn't back then, I would have stayed in ROTC like Thomas, Ben, and Rick Ward. They all went through ROTC and became officers. But I hated ROTC. I managed to stay in college and avoid the draft. Finally, when I graduated I was drafted. Then, I would have had the option to sign up and go to Officer's Training School.

C . . Well, they thought you were smart enough, and that you were officer material.

K . . You did not have to be smart to be an officer, but you had to sign up for two years for basic training, infantry training, and then get sent to one of the Officer Training Schools, which was a real miserable experience. It was like a small version of West Point. Ben Alexander went through Infantry OCS. In about 16 months you come out as a Second Lieutenant. The four schools were Infantry, Armor, Artillery and Engineering. So I signed the thing and that meant I was going to OCS after AIT. Once you became a Second Lieutenant, that committed you to another year in the Army. That would be three years in the Army! Then I was sent to Fort Belvoir in Virginia, to be trained as an officer, an engineer.

C . . Kenny, you weren't an engineer--but yours was a B.A. degree.

K . . No, they just placed you wherever they needed officers. After OCS, let's see--after I was drafted in September 1968, and went through all this basic training and AIT at Fort Ord in Monterey, California, and then in the summer I got a month leave and came home in the spring before I went to OCS.

C . . Yes, that is probably when we went fishing.

K . . When I went out there I was put in a holding company, which is the best thing that ever happened to me. All that time I wondered why I should go through OCS, where they break you down mentally and make an officer. That would be more of the same that I had already been through. And to go through all that just for the privilege of being in the Army for another year. It didn't make sense--I would go to Vietnam anyway. Fortunately they were so jammed up you just sat waiting to get into a class.

C . . So you had time to do some thinking?

K . . Yes, I had already been thinking about it . . Why do I have to go through this for another year in the Army. There were others there who thought that way too. My priority was to get it over as fast as I could. I had listened to you all of my life about being an officer rather than an enlisted man. There is a difference between being an officer and a private. They were a world apart--this was true generally. But then I decided against being an officer, even though I had signed to do it. The slogan then was, "What can they do, send me to Vietnam?"

So I talked to this Colonel and said I am not going to go to Officers Training. Others were doing the same and that made him mad as hell. He said, "You signed that contract, didn't you?" I said that I had changed my mind. Then he said: "I'll tell you what I am going to do if that's the way you want to play it. I am going to see that you get orders immediately for Vietnam." I said, "What you're telling me--that if I went through OCS, I wouldn't go to Vietnam?" He was furious. Before that he tried to talk me into being an officer. But I said no. Then, I remember calling you on the phone, and mom and you were upset. But it was the best decision I ever made.

C . . Well, that is the way it worked out!

K . . There is another reason, but I didn't know about it until I got over there. If you were a Second Lieutenant, and you had the responsibility to carry out orders. You had the possibility of getting killed by your own men. But if you were a draftee, enlisted man, you could just slide and get through it. But you don't have orders from the Captain to a second Lieutenant which says: "I ordered you to do it." That gives you no choice. In some cases like this, officers who were fragged by their own men. Also, officers were the ones the VC wanted to shoot first. If you were an officer and had a year to do there, the possibility of having a bad time, to get killed, was greater than if you were a grunt.

I received orders for Vietnam. My sister, Marilyn was in Washington working on Senator McGee's staff. I had a great time because she was there and we got to see Washington, D. C. Marilyn would line me up with girls. I stayed at Fort Belvoir for a month. That was before I told them I wasn't going to O.C.S.

C . . Sure that was good because it takes them time to get the paper work done because you changed your mind.

K . . Then they had to give me another month leave so I came home again that summer. I don't remember whether we went fishing again. But I remember that Wyoming played their first football game, and I was supposed to be at Fort Lewis to fly to Vietnam. Well, I decided to see Wyoming play football. I was two weeks late, and thought the only thing they could do was to send me to Vietnam.

C . . Well, it didn't make much difference because you were already at the bottom of the totem pole.

K . . Yes, I stayed for the football game and was about a couple of weeks late. Other guys were doing the same thing--some of them bailed out and went to Canada. I thought, "What could they do to me if I don't show on time." When I showed up, they didn't care. They didn't want to discipline me or court-martial me. They didn't have time to screw with a guy who was only a few weeks late--they were still hunting for guys who were more than a year late. Hell, they just shoved me on the next plane for Vietnam.

K . . Something you said was not exactly right, Dad. You said I signed up. I didn't--I was drafted, and that was different. There were only a few things that could keep you from being drafted. One was to somehow flunk the physical. I didn't! (Ron, four years older than Ken failed his physical because of fractured bad legs.)

K. . That is what happened to Byra my brother-in-law. He was All-American football player who played in the Sugar Bowl game. He was in the best physical shape of anyone in our family. His weight was 230 pounds and he was a physical animal. He was too short for that weight according to the charts. But they took me, a scrawny kid--I didn't have any weight problem. When we went to Denver to take our physical, a bunch of us got as drunk as we could to raise our blood pressure--but that didn't work.

The other options were to do something like becoming a "conscientious objector", moving to Canada, or go to Vietnam.

C . . But that is not your style, Ken!

K . . Well, it wasn't patriotism. It was a rational decision. I had to decide. Someday I would have to come back, and I knew that would be harder on me. The only thing to do was to wear the uniform and hope that your luck holds out. That is what I did and it wasn't any brave thing. Those thoughts were in my mind and if there was another option available I would have done it. You were right, Dad, when you said it was different in WW II. Totally different! Most of the guys with whom I went to college, including those who were committed to ROTC, had no choice. Fellows like Thomas, Ben Alexander, Rick Ward, or some who were married and had kids. Or fellows like Bill Horn who was 4F. I think that I was the only one of my close friends who really got drafted. I remember how I felt then, that I was the most stupid guy in the world, because I thought it would not happen--I thought that somehow I would get out of it. I even thought that the war would be over by then, but it was still going on. Everyone was betting on a short war. I was unique in being a 24 year old guy with a college degree to get drafted.

C . . But Ken, you never wanted to play soldier as a kid. You were not military minded. It is great that it is glamorous to some kids, and I am grateful that we have them.

K . . Well, I don't like to look back, but those who stayed in ROTC did the right thing. I guess I was too irresponsible to hedge my bet. I got caught. Still, the way it worked out I was in the service for 16 or 17 months--I don't know anybody who had less.

C . . So you got out in a minimum time?

K . . Yah, one full year in Vietnam, and the rest was training and screwing around. Yes, it wouldn't have been a good decision if I had got shot. But a lot of my memories of Vietnam were not bad. I was one of the lucky ones. You remember Rick who was a Second Lieutenant, he was shot through the legs. I was lucky!

C . . I remember one young fellow who went to Canada, and I can't believe that was the thing to do.

K . . Well, the guys who did go to Canada had their reasons for it. I don't feel badly toward them, and certainly don't look down on them.

C . . Well, you know I would have discouraged Canada if you considered it.

K . . Well, the fathers that were in WW II just couldn't understand the problem.

C . . What happened to those guys who went to Canada? After the war was over, did they come home?

K . . You remember the amnesty law that a lot of the people were outraged about? After the war was over draft dodgers were granted amnesty. They might have then been given some time doing civil service. Well, there was a lot of outrage by the parents whose sons had gone to Vietnam. They thought it was terrible, especially for those who had sons killed there. But if I did go to Canada, then I would have to worry about how I would get back, and I wanted to come back home. But, I don't look down on them.
C . . No, I'm sure you don't. But you are a helluva lot more fair-minded that your Dad was. I resented it!
K . . It was harder on the older generation.
C . . Yes, amnesty was harder on the father than the kids.
C . . Do you remember the date you left the country?
K . . Not exactly, but it was in September, 1969.

KEN FLIES TO VIETNAM

C . . Ken, tell me your first reaction when you landed there. Could you hear the big guns and planes?
K . . Well, you fly from Fort Lewis, Washington to Vietnam, but you have to stop somewhere to refuel because it is so far. When I went over it was night when we left and it stayed dark all the way because we were following the sun.

Everybody was scared as hell all the way. Nobody talked because we knew this was it! It was serious business. When we landed in Vietnam, in Chu Lai, we noticed an overpowering smell. The stench was indescribable--a combination of heat, and burning human sewage. This had to be burned with diesel as there was no indoor plumbing available.
C . . In that damp tropical atmosphere it must have been overpowering.
K . . Well, yes, when you have a big concentration of bodies you can't dig outhouses. The filth was contained in big metal drums, and the contents had to be burned. When you were there you finally got used to the odor--it became part of the atmosphere which lasted as long as I was there.
C. . Where did you go when you left that area?
K. . Then they flew us to a combat center for about two weeks, and there I got more training with the use of the radio and general information. They gave us ammunition and guns, flack jackets, and helmets. From here we were assigned to our outfit. We were part of the Americal Division. There were three

infantry battalions, the 196th, the 198th, and the 11th. The 11th was in the area south of Chu Lai near Mea Lai where Lieutenant Calley got in trouble. The other two were up north with the Marines. My MOS was infantry, and it took two or three weeks to get your final assignment. All this while you go through more combat training.

C . . Well, Ken I thought you were with an artillery unit?

K . . Well, that is another story. But before that we had better have another beer. That's right. I was in the infantry when we got over there, but things just happen and you trust your luck. On the plane going over there I sat next to a young guy, a 19-year-old kid from Ohio. He was gung-ho--John Wayne. He wanted to go over there and fight. I wasn't excited about my orders to the 196th. We sat together and compared orders--a bunch of us got them for that unit, and the guys who knew more than new recruits said, "You're screwed!" The 196th had been taking 90% casualties.

C . . So our group was going to be their replacements?

K . . They were in the thick of it. We might have about a 10% chance of not being a casualty (The 196th were in some of the heaviest stuff while I was there.)

K . . This kid next to me had orders to go to the artillery; they didn't care how you had been trained-- they just wanted bodies on these hills. They took 200 of us for the 196th, and the next ten guys went to the artillery, which is one step up because you are not out in the bush. On a hill it is not pleasant, but you're not out wading through the water and sleeping in the mud. Sometimes, the L.Z. would get hit, but we were sleeping in a hooch most of the time. When we got our orders we were standing there looking at them, and he was mad. He said, "I am an infantryman and I want to be in the action. I came here to fight. I don't want to be a Gun Bunnie." He knew I wasn't happy with my orders, and suggested that we trade. I thought, "Well you dumb son- of-a-bitch!" I could hardly talk to him, but he kept it up, and others said they would trade with him. I thought they wouldn't change these orders, but still they might. So, he and I went to the First Sergeant with our orders, and the kid explained he wanted to go to the 196th and said I would change with him.

I will never forget the look on the sergeant's face when he looked at the kid and then at me. He said to him, "You stupid son-of-a-bitch," and he crossed out the numbers and made the change. I still have those orders. He got the 196th and I went to the 1st of the 82nd Artillery . So I spent my whole year with the artillery. That change probably saved me.

C . . Did you ever know what happened to that kid?

K . . That is the amazing thing. If you go over on a certain date, you stay there exactly one year to the day. So the day after I spent my year, I got back on the plane to go back to the world. Then, the same guys you went over with, or what was left of them, are there. At first I didn't recognize any of them. But sure as hell I saw this kid. I could tell that he didn't want to come over and talk to me. Finally, I went over there and said, "You made it--you did well!" He said, "You did too." Then I asked him how it was and he didn't want to talk much. But another fellow told me that as soon they got into a fire-fight and some of them were killed, he was plenty scared. He re- upped for another year and got reassigned to a rear job. Well, he didn't like it when he saw guys of his group get blown to hell. I might have felt bad if he had been killed, but he wasn't. That trade was just a stroke of my good luck!

C . . Well, Ken, it was his decision. I have found out that during my life we have to live by our own decisions.

K . . I would have gone to the 196th, an officer might have selected me as their radio man because I had been to college. That was not good because you had an antenna showing and the VC know you are with an officer, a captain or lieutenant, and they go for those two men. Then, you never know. I might have never been scratched. I might have been assigned elsewhere.

C . . You went to that artillery unit.

K . . The very first night we got hit at the combat center with rockets and mortars in a supposedly secure area. When they hit us all hell broke loose and we started scrambling and didn't know what was going on. We FNGS.

C . . What does that mean?

K . . It stands for Fucking New Guys. We were in hooch with new guys who had seen no real action. There was chaos, with people running to get into the bunkers and stuff, and two or three guys got hurt from falling off the beds and running into things. One guy got cut on something, and he was a casualty They shipped him back home. (Laughter)

C . . That was the end of his war experience, and he got the purple heart!

K . . I thought that was ironic our first night there. I remember him--he was a big fat guy! I resented the fact that he got a free ride home. (Laughter!) It was pandemonium during that first night. Later, at this combat center, I woke up one night with a rat on my chest.

Then, I went to the artillery battalion, 1st of the 82nd. There were four companies and each had four a big gun, 155 mm, or 8 inch on different hills out in the boonies. There were LZ Snoopie, LZ Gator, and I can't remember the others. The Colonel and other brass were located near Chu Lai where we had ammo dumps. I got the best area because I wasn't on one of the hills, but at headquarters battery. Those on the farther hills were getting hit all the time. At Headquarters we were not hit as often.

About that time, they saw I was a college graduate, and the Captain of the Headquarters Battery-- the little jerk, said, "I want that guy in my office as a clerk." I didn't know how to type, or do any of those things. When they put me in there I hated it, but I met a guy who was a Second Lieutenant who was in charge of ammo. Nobody wanted that because you had to go out on convoys. He was my age too, and said, "Hell, we have a good time driving around." And I said, "I'd go anywhere to get out of this office," I didn't want to go and get killed, but I sure didn't want that office work. I was transferred to ammo. The Captain never liked me when he found I wanted to get away from him. So I transferred to ammo, and stayed there the rest of the year. We convoyed ammo to the LZs and slung ammo to choppers to be delivered to the LZs farther out.

C . . Well, Ken, anyhow, you had experiences driving through the villages. Tell us about your barber.

K . . Well, I forgot about that, but you didn't know if they were friendly or not. Some of them worked for the VC.

C . . Well, what was that about your barber?

K . . The Vietnamese would come into our wire to work there, doing KP or other odd jobs during the day, but at night it was sealed off. One guy who came in was a barber and seemed to be a good guy. But we got hit real bad one night with rockets. The Russian rockets were real crude, but if they hit this house here, nothing would be left. They put them between two sticks like we do with firecrackers on the fourth of July and fired them. But this time we got the hell knocked out of us,

and we could see where they were coming from. The next day our choppers blasted the area. Among the other bodies, we found our barber. He had been firing at us.
C . . In other words, the guy who was cutting your hair during the day and being friendly. But they would go home and try to kill you at night.
K . . Well, people who were working there during the day would go out and work with the VC at night. The VC ruled the area at night, and we took over during the day.

JACK THOMAS--A VISIT

C . . There is one thing I want to record. That is about your old Laramie buddy, Jack Thomas. When he said he wanted you to come down to your area. What happened?
K . . Jack Thomas found out where I was. He was an Air Force Pilot and was in Cameron Bay. He was a Captain. This little squirt Captain we had came down to our hooch and said, "You got a call from some Captain in Cameron Bay." When I picked up the phone I'll be damned if it wasn't Jack Thomas. I don't think I even knew he was there.
C . . I'll bet you thought you were dreaming!
K . . We talked on the phone and he said he was going to come up where I was. He wanted to know just where I was. I told him that he had better stay on his Air Force Base.
C . . We know Jack Thomas though, and he would work it out someway.
K . . Jack worked it out--by God he did!
M . . Did he fly a plane?
K . . Yes, those guys knew how to get around. He got in his own plane at Cameron Bay. He had a better picture of the area than I did. They can pull strings and work it out. He just said, "Hell, I am going to stay with you a couple of days." You have to understand that the grunts hated the Army sometimes more than the enemy. You hated officers, and sergeants. It was us against the lifers. Where we stayed, no officers would dare to come there at night. If they came, they came in force. So I said, "Jack, you don't understand. These guys I am with aren't going to like you. I don't know what they are going to think about having an officer here." I told them, "I got this friend of mine, a captain in the Air Force." They said, "You got a captain who is your friend?" They said, "He ain't coming here!" I told them he was a good guy. Then, I told Thomas what they said. These guys were combat tough--they

were from the big cities and the hills of Tennessee. But that didn't stop Jack. He walked in and shook all of those black guys' hands and they were buddies. They couldn't believe it and pretty soon he had his bars off and they liked him. He stayed a couple of nights with me. He and I went down to this ammo shack and got a couple of bottles of whiskey and got drunker than hell. And you'll not believe it, we got hit that night too, but that didn't bother us. Sure, he got shot at when he was flying, but this was the first action he had seen on the ground. He outranked most of our officers. Captain Smith wanted Thomas to stay in the officers quarters, but he made up his mind he was going to be with me. He pointed to me and said, "This is the guy I came to see." This bothered our officers because it was against protocol. But you know Thomas, he had so much guts that he did his thing. He took pictures of us and they were the only ones I got from Vietnam. The
Air Force was different because they are more of a team and they fraternize. Thomas had never had any experience with grunts.

KEN GETS RID OF HIS OFFICER

C . . Tell us about the Captain that you didn't like; so you went above his head to his superior officer and complained.
K .. Well, after I had been over there a long time we lost the Lieutenant and our Sergeant.
C . . Did you work with a bunch of teen-agers as privates?
K . . Oh no, they were a bunch of hard core guys--good people, but it was just that there were no officers in charge. Then, there was a big operation just before I was supposed to come home. We went into Cambodia or Laos. Well, it was a big operation where we airlifted our guns. We were trying to stop them from coming from those areas into South Vietnam. Well, this Second Lieutenant, who was giving us hell, was put in charge for this operation.
C . . Was he a West Pointer?
K . . No he was OCS. But our Colonel was a good guy. The higher you go up in the Army, the officers are pretty sharp or they wouldn't be there. But our trouble was with the lieutenants and captains. Well, the Colonel was a guy I knew, and he liked our outfit because we were getting the job done. Ours was kind of a renegade group but we did our

job. The Colonel knew it and we had been working our butts off. We had been working day and night.

All they had to do was just to leave us alone and the job would get done. But they put this officer in there who really started to screw things up, and the Colonel could see what was happening. He came to me to see what was wrong. I told him what was wrong.

K . . So I told him that he should get this Lieutenant off our backs, so we could get the job done. I told him that the guy was incompetent. Usually a Spec 4 could get court-martialed for complaining to a Colonel. But the Colonel listened to me, and got rid of the Lieutenant immediately. That was unusual for an officer to be relieved of a command, and it would never happen State-side. Here in the states it couldn't happen, but it did in combat. We got rid of him fast. They didn't care, they just wanted to get the job done fast. He was a good Colonel and he listened. We pulled it off and we worked like hell. The operation was a success.

C . . I think that you told me that you were lying in your bunk just fagged out, and someone came and said we want you on the parade ground.

K . . No, it wasn't a parade ground. We didn't have any parades there! It was just a formation and I didn't think I had to be there, but they woke me up.

K . . Yah, the Colonel liked me, and gave me a medal because we did well--others were given medals too.

C . . Well, I was proud of that because it took a lot of guts to tell the Colonel about the trouble.

K . . Well, I don't remember it being so remarkable. But the amazing thing was that I was able to talk to the Colonel. I didn't care if a General walked up. Some Generals came out there. The only time I saw a General was on this operation. He came out there and talked to all of us. High officers seemed to be decent guys. The lifers were just petrified by that high brass. They were afraid to talk to them. The Bird Colonel, or a general, knows that if he talks to a Captain or Lieutenant he is not going to get a straight answer. They will tell him what they think he wants to hear. But if he goes out and talks to the grunts it is different. Hell, I didn't give a damn. In deals like that, what's he going to do to me? They knew that. The grunts had nothing to lose in telling it like it was.

KEN FLIES FIRST CLASS

Then Thomas arranged for me to come to Cameron Bay to visit him, and I did. I am probably about the only guy who went to Vietnam and didn't take an R and R leave. That is rest and recovery, and you got two weeks. Most of them went to Hong Kong, Shanghai and Bangkok and Australia.

C . . How come you didn't think of it?

K . . Well, I made a mistake. I should've gone, but most of the guys wanted to go to Australia. I should have taken advantage of it and gone to Bangkok, because I will never be in the Far East again. But then there was a waiting list for Australia. I put in during my eleventh month, but that was when that big operation took place and they airlifted our entire unit to Laos.

KEN PLAYS OFFICER IN VIETNAM

K . . Oh, yes, I never took an R&R (rest and recovery) but I was about the only draftee who moved around in the country and that was because of Thomas. He worked it out and I got to Cameron Bay to visit with him there. I had a couple of days visiting him. But first Thomas had come to my outfit and stayed overnight to see a "grunt" in the Army. The environment in Cameron Bay was unbelievable in my eyes.

C . . Sure, like an officer's club?

K . . Oh, Yes, more like a hotel in Denver. It blew my mind!

C . . Yes, Ken, but how did you get in there as an enlisted man? I'll bet you couldn't believe you were still in Vietnam when he flew you down there in his small plane. K . . Oh, there was nothing wrong about me being in his quarters. It was private, like an apartment. A TV and everything. But then he took me to the Officers Club, and there weren't supposed to be enlisted men there. Thomas gave me one of those flight suits like part of the jet set--a hot stick! Thomas wasn't a fighter pilot, but he flew a smaller plane. When we were in the Officer's Club having some drinks, and I asked Thomas if it would be ok? He said, "Oh don't pay attention, just act like you're a Captain." Finally, I didn't care even if I did get caught. I changed clothes in his apartment and he gave me a new flight suit to wear. Hell, what are they going to do- -send me back to the States? I didn't give a damn, they couldn't do anything to me there. Jack wasn't worried--why should I?

C . . I guess regulations were nil?
K . . I didn't worry, but if there had been any trouble it would have been between Thomas and the officers. While we were drinking beer in the club Thomas's boss, a bird Colonel, came over and stopped when he saw me. I was wearing this newer flight suit when Thomas introduced me. He said, "I don't think I know you, what do you think of that new suit. Do you think it is cooler?" I smiled and said, 'Yah, I really like it.' I was comfortable and these other guys just had sweat pouring off them in their older issue. So then the Colonel walked away and we had another drink.
K . . You know Thomas, he never worried about anything--he always did what he wanted. You know that even if I had known Thomas was in Vietnam, I am sure I wouldn't have looked him up. But he was so aggressive, and if he wants something he will make it happen. He had to look me up!
C . . Well, that was a great experience for you.
K . . One thing about Jack Thomas, he doesn't let anybody walk over him. You know being with him was a very strange thing for me. After being in Vietnam for eight months you get to be like an animal. As far as the officers, I hated them! You know there was a camaraderie among the draftees--it was us against everyone else. It was weird how I felt--just like I had died and now I was a different being. Then to have Thomas walk out as a Captain just brought back where, and who I was. It was important that happened to me then. You know when I saw an officer I froze up.
C . . Yes, Ken, I can understand but we need them in our society, and some of them are pretty good guys. Your attitude is understandable, but you must remember that in WW II I was an officer.

DEATH OF A CAPTAIN IN CAMBODIA

Ken . . When I was in Cambodia that was my greatest exposure to combat. Yes, we knew it was a real war there. But just about a month before I was to come home we came back to a safer base. We had another commanding officer, a captain got fragged--killed!
C . . By his own men?
K . . I was on guard duty and was in the bunker that night, and I can't just remember all the details. We had a bad day, and the officer had been giving the guys a lot of trouble about petty stuff. When he was changing his boots someone slipped a grenade under his chair. . .
C . . Was he a West Pointer?

K . . Yah, or maybe an OCS . . He lived a little while that night. But he died on the chopper.
C . . They didn't know who did it?
K . . No, but they sealed the hill off and had an investigation. None of us moved from the area for a week or two. When that mess was over, I was almost ready to go home.
K . . Yes, that is the first time I thought of that. I should have known. I am a college graduate and my family is upper middle class.
C . . Thank God you were not an officer in that mess!
K . . Yes, Dad, you are right I am glad I wasn't an officer. The men I served with were the guys I have more respect for.
C . . You know Ken, that there were some good human beings who were officers. In all groups only about 10% are bad.
K . . Oh, yes, dad, I know that's true.

DAD'S CONCERN

There were two situations concerning Ken in Vietnam, and his father was responsible for both of them. First, we had not received much mail for a long while and we were concerned because Ken thought he had written regularly. So, we blamed that on the Army, and I called my friend and dental patient, Gale McGee, who was then our Wyoming Senator in Washington, and at that time was Chairman of the Postal department. He called the Postmaster General, who then called the Armed Forces in Vietnam. Then they called Ken into the Colonel's office for objecting to the poor service. Ken was on the spot and wrote us to say that now the mail service to our men in Vietnam was excellent.

The second problem was again my fault. I knew that Ken would be thinking of the smell of the sagebrush when we went fishing in the spring. So I clipped off some of the fragrant blossoms of the sage, which I wrapped in a plastic envelope. I knew he would be thrilled when he smelled the sage. When he opened his mail in his hutch where all his crew were reading their own mail, he sniffed the sage. The other guys thought his generous father had sent his son some marijuana to smoke. Each asked for a blossom of sage to add to their cigarettes. None of them got much of a kick out of their treat! Finally Ken told them that it came from his favorite Wyoming bush.

KEN BACK IN USA

You know, Ken, there is something I will never forget, and I am sure your mother will remember. Finally, you called us from Fort Lewis in Seattle area where you left the United States a year earlier. You called us and said you were there. We immediately got in our car and drove to Denver to meet your plane. We drove from Laramie to Leah Grothe's house--Warren was still alive then. The four of us drove to the airport and could hardly wait for that plane to arrive.

When you got off that plane and walked out where we could see you, it was the most thrilling experience we ever had. Your Mother and I were in tears, and so were Warren and Leah. We could see you before you saw us. We were all in tears except you. You were a different person than when you left. You were not the Kenny Stebner we knew before you left while you and I went fishing on the fork of the Platte just before you left for Vietnam. Still you were our son and it was a thrilling experience for us to see you--to see your arms and your legs were moving. Your life changed over there. I know it was a helluva experience, but you were not changed for the worse, but for the better. We ate at a little Italian restaurant near Grothes. The conversation was difficult and guarded but we were all serious as we talked about nothing important.

Then, I drove us home to Laramie and we talked of unimportant details on the trip home. But when we arrived late that night at our house there was still not a personal connection between us. We drove into the garage and carried your few belongings into the house. You said, "Dad, I can't go to bed right now--I just want to go for a walk." So you and I walked a mile or so beyond Gray's Gables. It was a very dark night with many stars showing in a beautiful quiet sky. You stopped in the street and looked into the sky and said, "I didn't think I would ever see this again." It was a very emotional experience for both of us. You returned to our house and you said, "It's so quiet! I had never before heard the quietness and stillness and remembered the stars like this."

I didn't realize what you meant because it was a good experience I had always known. I had always

seen nights like this, and it was normal to me, but to you it was eerie and abnormal. Because the minute you got on that plane in Seattle to fly you to Vietnam, the roaring of the motors and other unpleasant sounds, with that odor you described when you landed there, with the many planes and the flashes of guns, where you would walk over to areas where you would go sound asleep. Then you heard those noises for a whole damn year, constantly smelling and feeling the heat. Then it was suddenly so different the night you came home.
K . . Yes, that sudden change when I came home was almost too abrupt. I think that they later found out that they should keep you in the Seattle area to let you debrief, seeing cars in the streets and the other normal things in America. Sort of debriefing with psychologists and other trained people helping in making the adjustment.

The first thing I knew was meeting some fellows, some who said, "Hey, I am glad you're back", and others would say, "Oh, I hadn't seen you, where were you?" I really didn't want to go down town for a while.

KEN AND THE NEWS REPORTER

I remember the first summer Ken was home. We spent many hours fishing and there was little discussion of his experience in Vietnam. He was not the same carefree young man he had been.

One day a lady newspaper reporter came to interview him just when he was working with his bedroll and a few of our camping pots and pans as he planned to go to the Platte River just to fish and be alone. She asked a few questions about his war experience, and it was not a generous interview. I don't remember the question she asked, but he seemed particularly disturbed that day. Unlike the old Ken we knew before, his answers were abrupt and this disturbed me.

Later that fall he again made a camp on a stream near Saratoga and planned to be gone four or five days. It was during the antelope season and when he returned after one night alone. When I asked him why he shortened his trip he said that the rifle shots in the area bothered him. He had enough of firearms and just felt better in town.

Each year our family hunts antelope in the Red Desert where we enjoy a family camp that lasts most of the week. Ken did not get a license and just drove us around the area. Someone wounded a nice buck antelope with a trophy head, but the antelope stayed out of range and we wanted to get in the car and drive for a better shot. Finally, I encouraged Ken to shoot at the animal. Reluctantly he fired only one shot and the antelope was down. Now, many years later, Ken and his wonderful wife seldom hunt with the rest of us. Today Ken enjoys the sport.

KEN SEARCHES FOR OIL

When Ken came home from the service he had a helluva adjustment to make. He had to clear his mind of the Vietnam experience. He failed to register in the autumn, but again worked through the winter with a crew who searched for oil. He couldn't settle down. Nearly all men who fought in Vietnam came back emotionally disturbed. There was no lack of intelligence, but he was not the student I hoped he would be on the campus. He struggled through the first year but dropped out to again work in the desert for an oil company.

BOOG POWELL IN LARAMIE

C . . Ken, do you remember that guy who came here to see you. He was an enlisted man from someplace down south. He told us his story of getting a dishonorable discharge. He was one of those real tough guys who had no respect for anyone. When it was time for him to go out and take a leak he just walked across the street and relieved himself on the golf course.

K . . Oh sure, he was one of those guys who had to serve another year after he came back from Vietnam. His name was Boog Powell. I can understand him because he hated the service so much he would do anything. I don't know but I hated the service so much I might have acted as he did. You can't expect those guys who were in Vietnam to come back and act decently when you tell them that they must polish their boots. When I came back if I had even one day to serve I might have deserted. Here you have to salute and go through all that stuff after you have been in Vietnam. You hate it so much you can't stand it anymore. You can't put guys back in Fort Carson and expect them to respond like a green recruit. They take you over there and make an

animal out of you and when you get back the expect you to change. It can't be done!
C . .Yes, after his story I wrote a letter about him to his commanding officer, and he answered that if Boog just came back, after a little discipline he could avoid a dishonorable discharge.

A BUDDIE FOUND IN WYOMING

K . . You know, Dad, that reminds me of another time I realized how lucky I was. You know, I had my times over there, but not as bad as some other guys. There was another boy from up there in Gillette who was a younger kid than I was, and one day later he called me. He was from North Dakota, a farm kid, but ended up in Gillette. He called me when I was up there in Sheridan and wanted to get together with me, but I didn't follow up with him. He was a real good kid by the name of Rich Bonsess. He was probably my best friend over there. He came over after I had been there six month, so he had another six months to do when I left. I talked to him on the phone three or four times. He said that right after I left they changed everything into a real bad deal. They moved them up near the DMZ and a bunch of the guys I was with got killed. They got hit every night.
C . . You gotta find him Kenny!
K . . Sure, I would like to. The guys I was with saw a lot of fire soon after I left. For me the timing was good.
C..It was timing.It was fate.Yes,you were lucky!
K . . Well, Rick was really disturbed when I talked to him. He was really confused and I felt sorry for him. I would like to get to Gillette some time and be with him again.
C . . Boy, you had better make an effort to see him.
K . . Yes, but I guess that when I got back I just didn't want to talk to anyone about that mess. He was wanted to come to Sheridan and we were going to play golf and talk.
C . . You just gotta shake his hand and see him.
K . . Sure, that is what I want to do now. But Rick named the guys I had been with, and they took a beating for about four months after I left. He named them and some of them got blown apart. Boy, they were living out there in the mud. I never had anything that bad--I guess I just lucked out!
C . . I don't know how we can explain it, only to say it was luck. Every break you had just worked out for you!

KEN BECOMES A LAWYER AND MARRIES

The following year he returned to become a lawyer. Still he was not interested in private practice. Ken worked with the Indians at Fort Washakie near Riverton. There he met and married a great girl, Karey Huff. Kary, a Wyoming graduate from the College of Journalism, was working on the Riverton newspaper. Of course, Danny, she is your wonderful mother.

Ken's Vietnam experience, as tough as it was, made him a compassionate judge. Also, he gained a rugged strength while in the army which few others have. In the Rawlins court Judge Stebner seems to be able to separate the wheat from the chaff.

WE TAKE MARILYN TO EUROPE

Dear Dan:

Our first trip, beyond Mexico and Canada, was in Europe where I lectured on dental subjects in London, Paris and Italy. We were thrilled with the Parthenon and the Greek Islands. All three of us were at the right age to make the most of an entirely new adventure.

We have pleasant memories of a dinner in London with a dentist friend of mine, Dr. Max Walter. Incidentally, our former Secretary of State Henry Kissinger was a cousin of Max Walter. Both of them lived on the family farm in Germany but they escaped the wrath of Hitler before World War One. At Walter's home, on a Jewish holiday, all three of us were grateful to enjoy the culture and friendship of the Walters.

In Paris we had an exciting day driving through the country side. The Cathedral of Chartres was a high point. That day our guide and driver conversed in French with Marilyn. They both laughed at Mary and me because we couldn't partake in their hilarious conversation.

The American Dental Society of Europe served us a fabulous dinner on the roof-top of our hotel in Florence, Italy. Marilyn sat with young people of various nations. Their waiter clowned to keep them laughing. When we traveled through the Swiss Alps and listened to a young girl who was our guide, she yodeled and sang folk songs we will never forget.

To travel with a teenage girl who spoke fluent

French often helped get us out of annoying problems.

THE EXCITING BALTIC SEA

To live the complete life, young people must first rely on good books. But when they are able, they should travel.

The Scandinavian Countries were one area of Europe I had never seen, but it was especially important to me. I'd worked with the Swedes and Norwegians on the tie drive, and you know my close relationship with Eric Lepponen, a Finlander.

Every day I ran on deck while we were on board our Scandinavian cruise. Few passengers get up as early as I do and I had a lot of freedom at dawn. I presume that I have made a ritual of that for more than 25 years. Through habit I seem to have developed a built- in alarm clock. As we planned our cruises I was concerned that I would lose my running. At that hour the crew was busy washing the decks, rearranging chairs, cleaning rugs and getting ready for breakfast. When my run was about half finished a few persons watched the sunrise and looked through their binoculars at ships and islands. The seagulls gathered as they followed the ship to pick up their breakfast.

Often we disembarked at a Ports-of-Call destination when most of the passengers were finishing their breakfast. It was a time of great interest because few had ever seen that port. In my youth history, as it was taught, became a dull bore. But being there, especially in Scandinavia, was exciting history as passengers were stimulated. I felt close to the Vikings. A vivid imagination helps! Living in Hanna with many Finns, made me feel at home. These people had a quiet composure which was built on physical strength--this I lacked. They exuded a sense of assurance.

We awakened in Copenhagen, Denmark. After breakfast, we boarded a tour bus which drove us through beautiful gardens to a famous statue of the Mermaid (with the tail of a fish) looking wistfully out to sea. She is a character in the Fairy Tales written by the poet, Hans Christian Andersen. That evening we ate in the most charming amusement park called the Tivoli, geared not only to children, but adults loved it. Children love the trains and other fun things, but with music and fine food it is a glorious place for adults to relax. The flowers and gardens are unbelievable. The next day we shopped and saw much of the city before we had to be back on our ship for dinner. Again, we took off into the Baltic sea.

It took us two days to reach the Russian port city of Leningrad, called Saint Petersburg before Communism. It is a fabulous and historic city with an exciting past. The city was fascinating with all its churches and palaces. They say their Hermitage Art Museum is the largest in the world, a magnificent building blocks long. We toured part of it. When we came out to the square we sat on a great base of some statue to rest. A military guard brusquely asked us to stand up and move. So we entered the hot bus. That hardly seemed hospitable. Nevertheless Leningrad is worth seeing, but it was past generations of Russians who were responsible for the beauty and charm.

I was reminded of cities we visited in China--artistic and beautiful many years ago, even though there were slaves and peons among the poor. I believe the masses are better off now, but they seem to be slaves without freedom. In Leningrad there were few smiles on the faces of the people. There were no private automobiles hurrying around as in western countries. Some streets seemed deserted, with only big fast-moving tourist buses moving. The natives walked without any apparent conversations and somber faces. Most of the side street seemed to be without people.

A government store built especially for tourists, was the only place we could shop. Here we bought a doll for your little sister Ann. Only the day before we received a telegram telling us of her birth and we were real happy that you had a sister. On board ship Ken and Karey called to tell us the good news that there was a little girl in the family.

That night we attended an excellent dinner and a theatre of very well trained dancers. The cast was excellent in a plush theatre which could challenge best. There were no Russians in the crowded theatre. It was all for show, and dreamed up to attract the tourist dollars. I was glad to leave Russia.

FINLAND

After being in Russia the contrast to arriving in Finland was acute! Hooray for the Finns! We only saw Helsinki, but sometime I want to see the rest of the country.

This Port-of-Call was especially important to me because I had known so many Finnish people when I was a kid in Hanna. This was a great contrast, and everyone on the ship wanted to go where the people were free and happy.

Finland is a proud country. And I am also proud for them because they are the only country I have even known to honor their War Debts to both the United States and Russia. All the Finns I have ever known had the pride to meet their obligations. They also should be proud of their country's defense which gave the Russians more military resistance than was expected. Their pride is shown to the visitor who see no rubbish and filth anywhere.

In Helsinki we visited an architecturally unbelievable new church which was built into a granite hill--only the beautiful dome shows slightly above the rocks. It is bright and marvelous inside, and the construction is amazing.

People who lived nearby had complained that a big church on the horizon would detract from their view. The architects understood and built it underground. One would not know there was a church there if not for the small dome which shows slightly above the native rocks. Inside the walls were all stone which had always been there. The organ was wonderful!

In Finland everyone has at least a small garden. Grass, flowers and sometimes vegetables are grown around their homes. Adjacent home never touch one another and this give the homes owners a sense of freedom. The Finns love the outdoors and nearly everyone has a boat because the country has more lakes than land. I would love to go there for a month in the summer and learn to speak the language I knew in Hanna. I was sad when we sailed on to the next port.

STOCKHOLM AND THE WASA

Stockholm Sweden is a marvelous city with similar flavor we tasted in Finland. Buildings here were quaint and picturesque. The Scandinavian countries they have many Lutheran churches, and I was impressed with one very old Church. It contained a famous statue of St. George slaying the Dragon.

In Stockholm we could hardly believe our own eyes when we found a very large ship, which was recovered from the depths of their harbor. There had always been a legend of a ship which sank there on its maiden voyage.

This ship tells a story of both man's genius and stupidity. It was built between 1625 and 1628 by the King of Sweden, Gustavus Adolphus II. No doubt he suffered from a great Ego! It was raised from its grave, after lying intact at the Ocean floor remained undisturbed for 333 years.

This ancient battleship was named the WASA, was designed and adorned with the most impressive wooden art work. On board, among other things, were 64 cannons. Intricate art work and cannons just don't seem to go together, do they? One might suppose that if the King couldn't destroy the enemy with firepower, he might woo them with the art work!

The powerful Viking King hired Holland's best ship builders and commissioned them to build the most formidable Battleship afloat. As it neared completion he got news an even greater ship recently built elsewhere. His ego had to be satisfied, so he added more hardware and art work. These additions caused the weight to exceed the original specifications. He was warned that it might not float, but he was The King, and he would not be discouraged by science. He ordered his men to make the ship heavier, and they reluctantly followed his orders.

With great fanfare the docks, covered with cheering people the ship, with all banners flowing, moved out of its dry-dock. Still, sailing within the harbor with bright sails in the wind too many of the crew moved toward the waving people on the beach. WASA capsized in the water! The sea rushed in as it sank down to the sea bed 110 feet below.

The ship rested there for 333 years, until a crude diving bell was produced for men to reach it. Finally, the ship was raised almost intact. Usually, after that length of time salt water, or fresh water, causes extensive deterioration. But here the glacier soft water was an ideal blend to preserve the WASA.

Dan, we walked around this treasure and watched the workmen carefully restoring the ship to its original beauty and magnificence. No doubt it will long remain for others to witness and appreciate the exclusive art work and the massive construction. But it is also a monument to the stupidity of a powerful ruler.

GOTHENBURG, NORWAY

Many Vikings sailed from Gothenburg to other parts of the Atlantic Ocean and into the Baltic Sea. In zest for plunder and excitement hundred of adventurers left to invade the weaker river ports of Europe and Britain. The brave history of hardy Norsemen is significant to Europe, and even America.

Gothenburg is a beautiful city of many parks and interesting artwork. We visited an old house with the original furniture. The early owners were affluent. But crude stoves prove they had considerable trouble keeping warm during the long severe winter months.

As we cruised northward we constantly changed our watches as the days became longer. We were there in the summer. But during the winter, we understand the natives see the sun only a few hours in the middle of the day. The long darkness leads to considerable depression, and is though to be a cause of problems with alcoholism and suicide.

Our ship carried us northerly along the Norwegian coast until we entered the famous Stavanger Fjord. Here rocky cliffs rise out of the ocean, covered with brush and trees. There seems to be no flat land, except that, now and then, we saw colorful homes and cottages on the shore. The inhabitants are few, and they try to raise crops against the sheer mountains. One couldn't call them farmers, because there is little to live on. They depend upon the fish they catch, and dairy products from small herds of cows.

It was most colorful as we traveled into the fjord. On this particular day clouds covered the top of the mountains surrounding us. We could see islands and even more narrow waterways which extended out of sight. There were fascinating views of little villages and lonely houses dotting the steep landscape. Often there was fog, and this is perhaps why so many bright colors were used on the buildings. Many people are isolated, but they all have boats for transportation, and sometimes Ferry-boats between communities.

For many years Norway was the poorest Scandinavian country, with its economy based on fishing and some dairy production. This has changed. Now it is the most wealthy because of the oil discovered in its waters of the North Sea. At one point on this cruise, I counted three oil rig platforms in one view on the ocean. For too many years our oil importing sources were from the Arab countries. But this new oil source has helped Europe and England economically.

We had an exciting experience as our ship made its way into the Stavanger Fjord. We would have gone a bit farther inland, but because of the extreme size of our ship, the captain decided to go only part way, leaving no room to turn around. Nevertheless, it was spectacular to ride on the ocean so near the very large mountains which rose from sea level. At one point we counted seven waterfalls coming down the mountains.

We reached the port of Bergen, Norway, which our tour guide said was only a fishing village in 1057. But in 1350 a group of German merchants saw the possibilities of commercial trade with Scandinavia. They simply moved in and joined the natives. These merchants became community leaders and made this area part of Europe. The new merchants, influential and prosperous, formed the Hanseatic League,a commercial alliance. Bergen began to grow, and Lutheranism from Germany became the dominant church.

American tourists are interested to find that Knut Rockne, the famous American football coach, emigrated from this area. In fact, from the latter part of the last century and the first part of this century, more Norwegians came to America than now live in Norway!

During WW II the Nazi Germans again found it desirable to occupy the country. The difficult terrain, which had always kept Norway poor, was just the place the Germans needed. They could hide submarines in the Norwegian fjords.

In Bergen harbor a fully-loaded Nazi ammunition ship disappeared in a single destructive explosion and obliterated buildings for many nearby blocks. Without success, I tried to learn how the explosion was sparked. It destroyed many buildings. We would have been told if allied planes or ships had successfully destroyed it. I guessed that loyal Norwegians deserved the credit.

ON TO HOLLAND

When our ship reached Amsterdam the next morning we had a unique experience. The city is below sea level by some fifteen feet. Our big ship could not have entered the Amsterdam harbor without locks. As we entered the area our ship was lowered to meet the Holland sea level.

You may have heard the folklore of the little Amsterdam boy who saved the city because he noticed a leak in the dike which protected the city from the ocean and kept the ocean out of the town. He put his arm into the void and stopped the water until help arrived. The boy prevented a wash out of the dam. Suddenly he became a national Hero!

In Amsterdam the streets are canals. Rather than trucks delivering passengers and products, boats take their place. We rode on such tourist boats as we toured the city. You can easily understand that with so much water in the canals the little remaining land is very valuable.

The houses are built one against their neighbor and they are tall and narrow, only two windows wide. This means a lot of narrow stairs. It's impossible to carry a piano, or other heavy furniture upstairs. So, each building has a big strong hook near the roof. They take the materials off the boat with pulleys and raise them up to a window wide enough to let the furniture swing into the room.

You can easily understand that with so much water in the canals the little remaining land is very valuable. The people in Amsterdam are friendly and cosmopolitan, although in some areas a bit "squirrelly" with weird hair styles and orange hair. Various cultures and lifestyles are tolerated, but these unconventional individuals are few in number compared with the general population.

The atmosphere was pleasant, and there were a great many small shops and businesses. We drank some very strong coffee and ate wonderful pastries in one area. That diet made me think of the stereotyped Hollander, who is a short fat, happy man. I wish I had time to inquire about his coronary problems, and his dental caries.

Both Mary and I loved Amsterdam, where we made interesting purchases, but we didn't have enough time to visit the surrounding area. As our ship left I was fascinated to watch the big ship become elevated through a series of locks so that we could enter the open sea. Now, we were on our way to London!

INDESCRIBABLE LONDON

The city of London is LARGE. This was our third time to see this city. In London there is so much to see that one wants to be there for weeks. It was like enjoying a dessert after a wonderful meal, but fun after returning from the Baltic Sea voyage.

Our first stop was at Herrod's famous store. I am not much of a shopper, but this block is exciting just to see the merchandise and other shoppers. I believe that it is impossible to be there for a short hour and not make a purchase.

Then we again visited Hyde Park, where on a Sunday afternoon free speech is freer! Dozens of self- appointed orators constantly lecture on most any subject. Here you can pick your own subject, and as you stroll around someone will have an audience that you can join. Yes, there are hecklers encourage a few laughs. It seems that this is a place to blow off steam and frustration.

CAIRO EGYPT AND ANTIBIOTICS

Some years ago Mary and I had a wonderful trip through the Mediterranean area. We owe much to the early Greeks, especially for our form of of democratic government. The city of Athens has many treasures but our few days were not enough. Every Greek island where our cruise ship stopped made us eager to return.

Of course we enjoyed the Holy Land and the impressive history of Jesus had a profound effect on us as we walked where He carried His cross. It was an overwhelming experience.

Our ship was anchored at Cairo, Egypt and there we were overcome by the great mass of humanity who call that enormous city their home. As our bus driver drove toward Jerusalem I asked him about the many people who lived in that overcrowded area where men were trying to sleep along the streets.

His answer shocked me. He blamed the congestion and apparent hunger on the United States of America, although he admitted many poor and homeless people had been that way for very many years. But he said too many mothers have too many children. At first I thought we should supply more information on birth control. It was not the answer he gave me.

The bus driver said: "You Americans are responsible for the fact that most babies now live because of the antibiotics you send to Egypt. Some years ago half of the children died early. That is not the case now, because nearly all of the fifteen or sixteen babies live to become adults. Your antibiotics are now our problem of overpopulation."

Recently, I have reflected that horrible death rate of little children who starve in Africa. Our churches and Red Cross agencies send food to Africa which is only a drop in the bucket. The history of Africa tells us hunger and drought have long threatened to wipe out native tribes. All we have done by teaching birth control, and delivery of free food, makes no permanent difference.

THE AMERICAN DREAM IS REAL

About five or six years ago your grandma Mary and I joined our good friends Dr. Jim Vernetti and his wife Beth, on a trip to China. There we lectured at various medical and dental schools where we hoped to give them a view of the practice of the healing professions in our country. Also, it was an exchange because we learned much about the professions in China.

For many years I did not eat the noon meal, but enjoyed larger meals for breakfast and later dinners. This created a problem for our tour guides, who were usually females, who spoke good English. Every city we visited made it a point to take us to a special restaurant which by far exceeded eating places where the native Chinese frequented.

The communist guide was certain to keep all of the bus grouped tightly together. It was obvious that we were to see only the places which were planned in advance. It was obvious that I was the only member in our bus who refused to enter the building in which we were supposed to eat. I explained to her I would wait in the bus alone with the bus driver because I was not hungry. Certainly, this disturbed our guide who was carefully following the rules she had been specifically trained for.

Well, Dan, this left me free to leave the bus. When they were in the restaurant I slipped out and walked around several blocks taking photos that most of our group missed. I was careful to be back at the bus when they left the eating place. On this particular day one of our party saw something unusual in the street and took a photo which he later sent to me.

. . . .

As I stood waiting for arrival of our guide and group to board the bus two young Chinese college students approached me and said in English: "You an American?" Of course I was surprised that he knew any English, and later I found out that his partner was in school studying Dutch. It was my impression that the government was training them to converse with other new groups.

Then, he asked, "You rich American?" This I rightfully denied. After we conversed I asked about his friend and found out that he could not follow our conversation. So, I asked that he interpret our conversation so that his friend would understand what we were talking about. This he did, and I was amazed that many other people began to gather around to listen.

Perhaps because I was the first American he had talked to, he was full of questions which I answered. It went like this . . . .

"How come you here, if not rich?" I explained that I was a dentist there to teach Chinese dentists about American technics. He still continued to talk about rich Americans, and asked: "If not rich, how come you afford the airplane ticket?

I told him that I had financed my own fare. Again he insisted I had to be rich. Then, he asked: "If not rich, how come you to get educated in dentistry--the government send you to school to be a dentist?"

At this point I decided a little background work was in order. We had recently been visiting in northern China where they had industrial development in coal and steel. I told him, and the larger group who were listening to his interpreting for his friend--that my dad was a coal miner in our country and was killed at the mine. Then, that my little uneducated mother ran a boarding house for miners to save money so that I could study dentistry. I also mentioned that I worked at manual labor to save enough for my college expenses.

When I mentioned coal mines, he said: "Oh, that is dangerous and dirty work--I no like to work there!" About that time the truth had finally sunk in for the Chinese friend. He seemed convinced, and asked his final incredulous question, "The American Dream is <u>real</u>? I assured him it was!

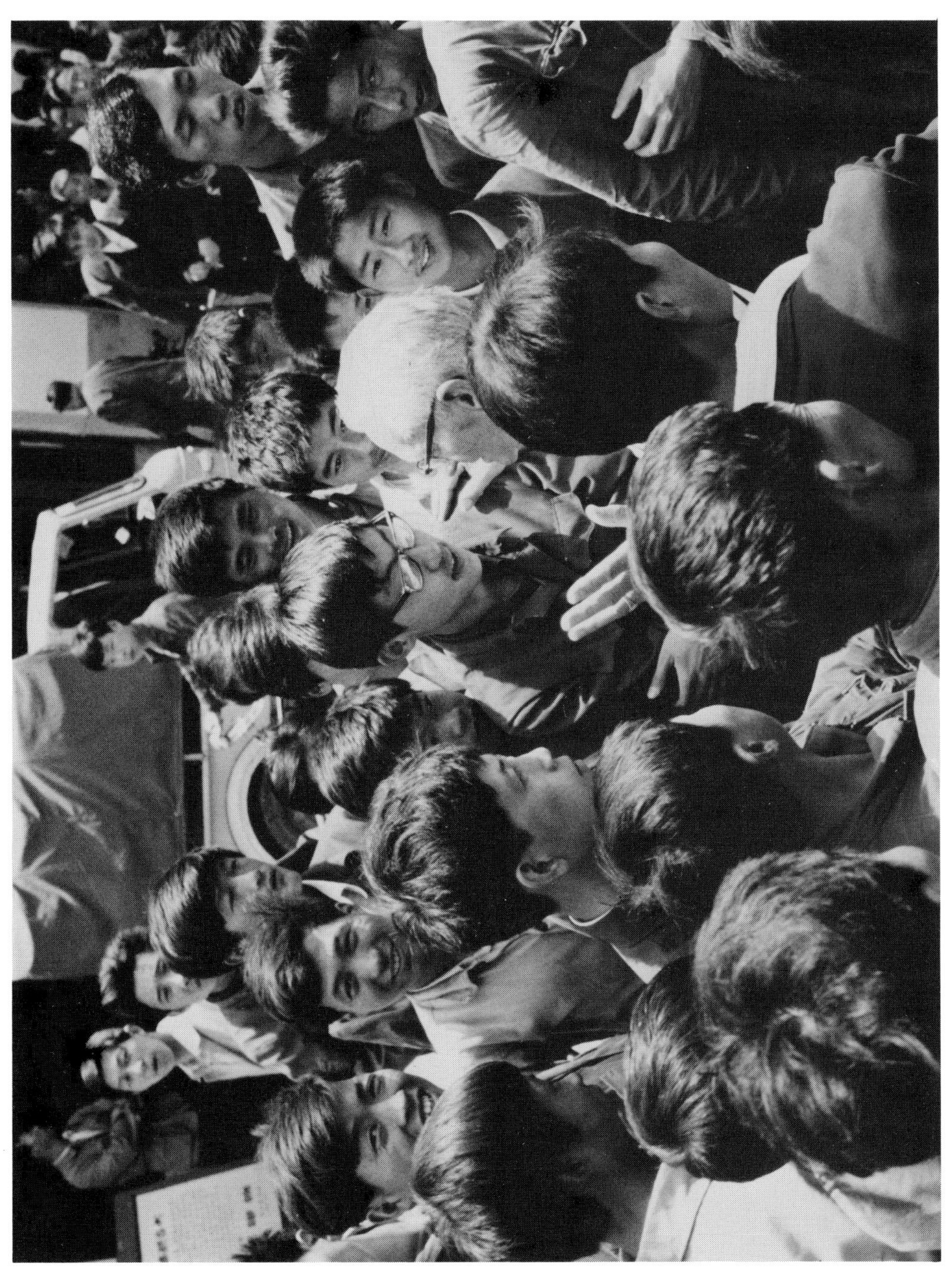

The American Dream is Real?

"As seen from Abroad"

"How Dr. Hamilton's escape in viewed in Chicago. The Chicago Tribune prints the following experience with range stock across the River."

"Men who are posted in the ways of western range cattle, and especially those of the Texas breed, know it is extremely hazardous to approach them on foot or in any unusual manner. Mounted cowboys ride through and around the herds without trouble because the animals are accustomed to seeing men and on horseback, but the appearance within close range and any strange object arouses their curiosity and ire. Pedestrians are a rarity on cattle ranches, like-wise bicyclists.

Dr. A. B. Hamilton of Laramie, Wyoming should have known better than to try to cross the range near a big bunch of steers on his bicycle, but it seems he didn't, and now the doctor had occasion to visit a patient on the Little Laramie River and was within four miles of Laramie when he ran into a herd of Texans. It was probably the first wheelman the cattle had ever seen for they pawed the ground and snorted viciously for a moment and then made a concerted charge for the doctor, who realized his danger, pedaled away at top rate of speed in an effort to escape.

There are few living things except a race horse of high class that can out run a Texas range steer when it once is in full motion. Dr. Hamilton made a brave race, but the cattle gained on him at every jump and he could feel the hot breath of the leaders almost at his side before he had covered half a mile. Just as he thought one particular vicious-looking beast was about to pick him off with his horns the wheel struck a hummock and the doctor took a header which landed him safe in a buffalo wallow, where he lay quiet while the cattle jumped over him. The steers were under such headway they couldn't stop and besides it isn't the nature of western steers to stop when they have once started on a stampede until they drop from exhaustion.

The bicycle did not escape. It lay directly in the path of the maddened animals and was crushed into a worthless wreck." (From Gertrude Gould)

Our Family

THE FAMILY

Dear Dan:

Some one said that tradition in humans is like instinct in animals. Tradition in our lives begins when we are newborn babies. Most of the time it is a blessing centered around the family. Highly respected and disciplined families are admired by our society, our country, and the entire world.

You, Danny, are lucky to be born to a family in which your parents wanted and loved you. My family showed their love and embraced their children as does yours. My little mother built a sound base that became our tradition. It endured in spite of many difficulties because of love and respect.

Not all families are so fortúnate. Yesterday on a cold wintry morning, I awakened at about 4:00, dressed in my running clothes and ran downstairs in my stocking feet. I listen to television as I work out. The program was special. It described street derelicts on the streets of Boston. I will relate the story for you.

. . . .

The subject was derelicts in the city of Boston, Massachusetts. They showed scenes of bums, mostly men, without homes--people who sleep in shelters or in the alleys. They are homeless and usually hopeless alcoholics. They exist in every large city, but we don't have them here in Laramie. Sure, we have individuals who drink too much, but we don't see them unless they bum their way through town. Usually, they go to the Salvation Army for a bed or meal and leave to be with more of their kind in any city. They are known as 'street people,' and in their ragged clothes and unshaven beards they slouch along looking for a place to eat--or rather drink. Often they steal, or beg enough for a little food, or preferably for a bottle of cheap wine.

Sure, they are homeless and are a problem for the Salvation Army or other relief agencies. Most of them accept just enough to keep them alive and warm and seldom say thanks to those who feel sorry for them and give them a hand-out! Usually, they seldom speak or really look at you. Yes, it is tragic.

But it is not a new problem. We have always had people like that in our society, whether our economy is good or bad. When I was a kid in Hanna more than 60 years ago, and especially during the depression, such people rode the freight trains that passed through Hanna. We called them bums because they would come to the homes near the railroad tracks and knock on our doors and ask for something to eat. Surely, they were out of work but few of them would accept a job of manual labor if it were offered to them.

The story I watched on TV bothered me, not because of my sympathy for the homeless men, but for their families. In the documentary we were shown a daughter and a son of one of these men. They sometimes leave their home and drive to seamy Boston neighborhoods looking for their father.

The daughter was an attractive well-dressed young woman on the subway where she saw a derelict sitting opposite her. She thought she recognized the features of her dad. He didn't look at her, but through her. Neither of them were sure who the other was and they did not speak or smile. Later she was quite sure it was her father, and she wished that she had spoken to him and told him who she was. This bothered the young lady, since she has been looking for him on the unpleasant dirty streets.

She told the audience that she remembered her father when she was considerably younger, and he was a pleasant, adaptable man. But later he became a heavy drinker. That changed him and the rest of the family because he became abusive. The change in his personality and actions were difficult, especially for her mother. Neither she or brother was happy. They remember how their father packed some clothes and left home.

The brother told a similar story. As a young man he was bitter, and there were times when he threatened to beat the family troublemaker because of the problems he caused. Like his sister, he was relieved when the man left and vanished.

Later they became concerned about their father. It bothered them and developed a guilt complex in the son. He too began looking at the street people wondering if one of them could be his father whom he might help.

During the efforts they learned that their father had spent some time in the acute alcoholic ward of a hospital. The records indicated that he had no family. Learning this, one can understand how it disturbed the members of the family he left.

As a television viewer it left me believing that many street people we try to help are living the life they find comfortable. We have always had these people on the streets. Each generation faces an insoluble problem. Most derelicts seem to have found a way to escape our society and they really don't want to be helped, or even found.

DADS ARE GREAT

Dads are great! Especially, if they have character, honesty, ability, imagination, dependability, and even ambition, personality and confidence. It is a bonus if he is an outdoorsman with a sense of humor and lots of love. You will note that lots of money would be great, but even a little would help. But no one should underrate the influence and direction that a Dad may have passed on to his children.

Let's talk about Bruno Stebner--your great grandfather. My father and I were together for only the first five years of my life. But he was a profound influence in my life. Many people do not understand just what happens to the minds of infants and very young children. But they remember!

All of my life, over and over again, I think of Bruno whenever I am honored. He deserves his share! It might seem a little corny, but I often feel he shares the pride.

For that short time Bruno Stebner was a great dad. He had all of the qualities I have mentioned. I am not saying that everyone loved him. He was a positive leader among other miners and he spoke his mind. People did respect the man. Of all the people we know it would be foolhardy to infer that many really loved us. To be respected is enough.

MOTHERS ARE WONDERFUL

I want you to know that mothers are the most important family member to kids. You know that I lost my dad when I was only five years old, but a mother is often able to partially take the place of both parents.

When my son Ken married your mother we all lucked out. Mary and I love her as though she were our own child. Stebner you lucked out! It's been thrilling for us to observe her good nature, sense of humor. Watching her care for you and little lady Ann, and feeling the love she has for her family gratifies us.

You will know that I had a wonderful sister who was two years younger than I. When she died I lost much in my life. There are exceptions, but children without siblings are often spoiled and selfish. I know that won't happen to you. Already you are sharing everything with her. The way you two play together is hard to understand. Your little sister learns very much from you. Yes, Dan, sisters are wonderful too, and already at age five you seem to understand.

We're looking forward to the next month because your Dad and Mother are going to take a vacation to California and you will be coming to stay at our house for a full week. Now that you're older running and talking you will keep your grandparents on our toes. But we'll love the challenge and all the many rewards of getting to know you even better.

DAN'S FIRST CHRISTMAS AND TRANSPORTATION

Christmas gifts thrill a little boy, but there is another gift we often take for granted. That gift is the unbelievable body in which we live. Today, we are amazed at highly scientific and mechanical Christmas gifts.

Man is ingenious and his endless projects cause us to wonder what you will see in your lifetime. During my early days we didn't even have an automobile. I remember the horse and buggy and we were most fortunate to have this transportation. Few coal miners were that lucky. My father was proud to be sitting in the leather seat with the reins in his big hands.

The first automobile I remember appeared in Hanna soon after my father's death. Of course we didn't own it. It was a dream with rubber tires, brass head lights and a crank ahead of the radiator which they spun to start the motor. It was a big open car with black leather seats. Although at that time my dad was not alive, I imagined him sitting behind that steering wheel. It would take a big hand like his to work the brass emergency brake on the driver's side. I am not sure, but I think there was a brass plate on the front of the radiator, which said, BUICK. It was parked at the old movie house and we all gathered around that mechanical miracle!

Then, there was the airplane! It must have been soon after my thirteenth Christmas when our classes were dismissed so that we could go out on the playground to watch the first airplane to fly over Hanna. The pilot was so low we could see his goggles! He waved to us from his open cockpit. The flight path was the UP railroad tracks and we were lucky to have him pass through Hanna. On this historic day he was flying the first mail across the country following World War One.

I knew that these things were man-made but I was thrilled by them. But, you know Dan, they were nothing compared to the feeling I had when I looked at your uncle Ron when he was born, also I recalled the early morning we drove to Rawlins when you were born. That day I saw the same silent wonderment on the face of your dad.

MEMORIES OF CHARLIE'S EARLY CHRISTMAS

My first Christmas was happy as was your first Christmas in Rawlins. I personally remember no more than you do of yours. Gosh, who can remember that far back? Mine was in my parents' little miner's house in Hanna. My dad drove our horse, Old Joe, sixteen miles to Elk Mountain. There he cut an evergreen tree and brought it back home. The project involved the entire family. It was a big deal--the entire Stebner family--my grandparents, four Stebner uncles, two aunts and my parents.

They decorated the tree in our small living room with all sorts of strings of popcorn and cranberries. There were a few sparkling tinsels purchased from the Montgomery Ward catalogue. They also had a few red and white candles which were fastened to the tree branches. It was spectacular when matches lit all of the candles at the magic moment on Christmas eve. Still, it was sobering to see that there was a bucket of water placed near in the event the branches caught fire. Immediately, there was music in the kitchen as Italian musicians, playing Silent Night, entered the crowded living room.

Our Italian neighbors revered my dad. Every year they carried their string instruments. Joe Marinaro was an accomplished musician, and led a few other who accompanied him. They had a jug of home-made wine. My Dad furnished the beer. They sang Italian songs which were traditional in their country--the words we could not understand. Nobody got drunk! After they wished us a Merry Christmas, with warm handshakes they went to their own trees and families.

My dad disappeared momentarily, but soon there was banging on the kitchen door, and in come Santa Claus ringing a cow bell. He had a bulging sack over his shoulder. Years later I learned it was it was my dad in the red suit and the white whiskers. He was convincing as he checked to see if I had been a good boy all year. Of course, I lied a little.

After my dad's death there was another really generous and loving annual visitor with pillows in a smaller red suit--Mary Stebner Ford. She was the greatest giver of goodwill. Often she rode a stick-horse around the room as she gave everyone a special gift. Mother performed every Christmas until she passed her 90th birthday. Many people saw her and a laughed at her ho-hos in our home, at the Lady's Club, the retirement homes, churches, and other Christmas parties, both in Hanna and in

Laramie. Her Christmas was heavily scheduled. She loved Christmas, and kids of all ages loved her!

DAN'S FIRST CHRISTMAS

Today I left Laramie to be with you and the rest of our family to celebrate your first Christmas. Your Grandmother Mary, Uncle Byra, Aunt Marilyn, and your Uncle Ron drove to Rawlins. It was extremely cold and the roads were dangerously icy, but with Byra at the wheel we felt safe.

We introduced you to a typical Stebner Christmas and your mother had prepared a marvelous breakfast for us. Your home showed all the signs of a traditional holiday with papers, boxes and presents everywhere! I was euphoric in the presence of my first grandchild, and we happily watched as you, a little four-month-old guy, tried to tear the bright papers away. Finally I began to help you, and then you took over with enthusiasm.

A high point was when you saw the wooden elk your Aunt Marilyn found while shopping in Texas. Although your face lit up as you watched Uncle Byra assemble this beast, you were a little timid as I helped you mount.

Dan, with all the wonderful things about that day, I'm sorry to report there was one little problem--and I was it! Before our Christmas meal, your dad served "Tom and Jerries," which are very tasty traditional alcoholic Christmas drinks. I was a little keyed-up about being with my grandson, and I'm afraid I drank too many of them too fast!

I'm sorry to report my lack of judgment. I was a bit carried away--you may say intoxicated! I wish it had been my first experience of that type, but during my college days and even later I and others thought that was the best way to have a good time. Well, Dan, I now believe that one or two drinks on any social occasion should be enough. Maybe none would be better!

Drinking alcohol is a serious problem. Those who drink and drive cause many fatal accidents. Your dad fines drunken drivers. Innocent people are killed every day by alcoholics. A juvenile alcoholic will ruin his life and also the lives of those he loves.

Alcohol and narcotics are evils we should fight. Our society must face this issue, and I guess we should start working on our personal habits. Today in Russia, although the government is supposed to control the populace, they have a most serious problem with alcoholism. This situation might be their most serious problem. Many of us think their communistic government is impractical and will eventually fail because of the lack of freedom. I may not be around to see it, but you will be here to witness what alcohol and other drug habits can do to any society. The effect of drugs is simply to blot out reality. We know we must face the realties of life. I hope you and Ann will avoid such crutches. Noble and respected men learn from the experiences of others.

Now, to get back to the first Christmas you and I ever enjoyed together. I thought of your great grandmother, Mary Ford, who died at age ninety-three only a few months before your first Christmas. She lived long enough to hold you in her in her arms. It is great that you share the same date of birth.

As you know my dad died when I was only five years old, but still has been a great influence in my life. I hope that somehow having a living contact with Mary Ford might influence you. Who knows?

Your first Christmas I told everyone in your living room that I would begin writing letters to 'Dear Danny' so that some day you would know your heritage, and especially my mother, Mary Ford.

And on Christmas Day it's important that kids (and grown-ups too) pause to remember the reason for this holiday. Sure there are toys for kids and gifts adults appreciate. But in our country, which is labeled "Christian," we have the freedom to go to <u>any</u> church. Or if we question the relation between Christ and God, we are free to avoid celebrating Christmas. In the western world, Christ and Christmas are synonymous, and for that reason we should pay homage to the One who gave us Christmas.

DAN'S FIRST WEEK IN LARAMIE

What a week! Your grandmother and I had you to ourselves for seven days. Some day you will know that it changed our lives--our regular routine was shot.

Your mother went to Denver to take a course that will make her a better teacher for her class at Sinclair and your dad traveled to Reno to learn with others how to be a better judge. So they had to get rid of you, and we were happy to be near enough to have you move in with us.

It had been very many years since we had a little one in our house for so long. Boy, you changed our life-style plenty! You kept both of us moving day and night. You demanded food (lots of it), changing pants (often), and then the reward of playing games, laughter, and hugging.

We learned a lot about you as a person. First, we found out that you are lovable, and you trust us. It's hard to realize that a one-year-old has already developed a distinct personality. You have many good qualities, and of course your grandmother and I think the genes came from us. But then, we seemed to realize that your mother's parents might also have been responsible. We know they are wonderful people, so reluctantly we can't take all the credit for your many good qualities. Yes, Dan, we saw enough good qualities in your young personality for all of us to share.

I'm a person who has lived 75 years with many varied experiences--some good and others painful. But in all I have been fortunate to have lived a wonderful life. A person my age has the right to draw upon his experiences and make a few predictions. So, being the author, I shall now claim my senior prerogative--O. K. ?

. . . .

Personality! I really don't know exactly how that is developed, or inherited. We often use that word ambiguously. Let's check it out. Some say aspect of one's character as it impresses others. But it is more than that--it's the embodiment of a collection of mental, physical, and social characteristics and qualities. It has something to do with the quality of a person as we see it.

Some people are actors and can fool the observer. There are very good salesmen, who are not what they first seem to be. Often, they actually fool the casual observer. Perhaps it takes time to see them in varying situations to really know them. We should be slow to make judgments and that takes time. Many of us make snap judgments and accept others as our close friends.

We have to be careful, especially at social meetings when alcohol is being served. On these occasions, we often judge personality rather character.

People's character is often revealed when they are drinking. Alcohol makes often makes people let their guard down and then you can see their true colors show. One who wants to fight and be obnoxious should be guarded against because his true character overcomes his personality.

Well, Dan, even at age one, you have a warm and wonderful personality. Little kids and dogs seldom act out of character. Your personality seems to be inherited, and unless you are inhibited unfairly by others it will work for your benefit. Let your natural personality carry you to be free and open like a wild horse we see in the Red Desert.

I base my predictions on being with you the last week. You were a naturally happy little guy. Smiles and laughter come easily with you and even the casual visitor to our house were impressed and pleased. If you feel good you show it! But when you were tired and couldn't go to sleep, you bawled and roared, as you should. That lets you let off a little steam that you should not attempt to keep inside. Then, if we left you alone, you rolled over and went to sleep.

It was a thrill early in the morning when you awakened. You pulled yourself up in the crib and talked to yourself good naturedly. There was no pretense in your manner. You enjoyed your little animals and talked to them as you looked at the new lights and colors around the room. The radio music seemed to please you.

Then I picked you up and took you to our bed where your grandmother was waiting for you. We had a great time there as the three of us visited and played. Eventually, you were held down as we changed your diapers and then you struggled to get away by crawling toward the edge of the bed.

I predict that you are going to have a fine body because you are so vigorous and have an endless amount of energy. Some of your early teachers will have a few problems with all of your enthusiasm. But they will love you almost as much as do your grandparents.

During your life, I believe you will be impressed by the personalities of those you meet. It does not mean that you will react positively because some will leave you cold, and most of the others will be impressed by your smile which is free and natural.

WELCOME LITTLE ANN

Dear Dan: (and now I also say Ann)

Earlier I wrote you that dads are great, and also that moms are great. Now, I want to tell you that sisters are equally great!

You know Dan, when we get a little older it seems harder for us to give up the old habits and ways and adjust to new situations.

Your little sister who is only about a month old is a new situation. Even though you are just two years old, you will understand the process of adjusting to a new situation, and with me being 76, you can understand my problem.

Little Ann Elizabeth is <u>our</u> situation! First, we must remember she is a miracle of nature who has come to live with us, and that this little being did not ask to be born into this complicated world. Maybe, we could say that God thought the best place for her to be is in our Stebner family. I agree with Him! And knowing your compassionate nature and native intelligence I am sure that you will agree.

As well as I know your mother and dad, your other grandparents, and your aunts and uncles, I am sure that there is enough love and sharing to more than satisfy you, little Ann, and the rest of us.

Being a male myself, it is easier for me to find my way into the fears, ambitions and pleasures of a boy like you. But I am hopeful that many things I have written to you previously will also apply to little Ann. After all, when I began this material it was to emphasize the life of my mother,

Mary Ford. I knew her intimately for more than three-quarters of a century, and now your grandmother Mary for fifty years. Also, I have been very close to my wonderful daughter Marilyn. I feel that I know much about the female of our species.

This much I know about women and girls--they are human. They share all of the pleasures of this wonderful world that we enjoy. But there are a few mysteries about women that the male will never know. Often times even other girls don't understand. They are more subtle in devious ways than you and I. Someone wiser than I said that women are different, but he added, "Thank God for the difference."

We should not be proud to note that in the past history of men, women have been poorly treated as unequals. We can be proud that we live in Wyoming which is a state that gave women the right to vote for our leaders. At our capital in Cheyenne there is a statue of Esther Hobart Morris, the leader of the movement which legalized women as voters.

Before that time when we recognized women as equals, there is a sordid history of the abuse men perpetrated on women. As I read the history of coal miners in England it seemed that women only served to produce children, cook, sew, and wash their husbands dirty clothes. They were often beaten by their husbands who demanded much of them. Today we hear much of unfortunate battered women. This is too often done by some husbands even today, but there is a valid campaign against such treatment.

Let's you and I, and other respectable men, do all that we can to eliminate anything which degrades women and girls. We can be thankful that little Ann is born in a country where she will have the same chance that you have to become educated and respected.

Dan, by now you know how much we love our grandson, but we love your little sister every bit as much as we love you.

LITTLE ANN'S FIRST BIRTHDAY

Doesn't <u>every</u> little girl have a First Birthday? One might think that every little girl has a First Birthday, but that is not true! Sure, all of the little girls you know have probably had first birthday parties.

It is painful to report this. Too many children die before they are one year old. In many parts of the world they are too fragile and poorly cared for and they soon cease to exist. This is even true in our United States, but is much more common in foreign countries.

Throughout Central and South America, and elsewhere, too many children are born. Infants receive poor medical care, and their diets aren't adequate in quality and volume. Poor health care and preventable diseases will continue to exist. Sanitation seems impossible there.

In Communist China, where we visited, a female child is not welcome. When the first child is born there is a slight increase in the pay for the parents. But the excess stipend is reduced if the mother becomes pregnant again. There is no "third child," because if the mother becomes pregnant a third time, she is forced to have an abortion. The Chinese are very pragmatic in this approach. Their population approaches one billion people and their economy simply cannot feed that many.

Ann, you were more than welcome when you arrived on the scene. We all wanted a little girl. Your Grandma and I were parents of two boys and finally a darling, talented and beautiful little girl blessed us. Your Aunt Marilyn is our great treasure. So are you!

Today I went to the bank and, as we have done for your big brother, Dan, we established a fund in your name which will grow each birthday and Christmas. Today, there's only $500.00 in your account. It will be there until you graduate from high school. If things are tough financially it might encourage you to go to college, buy a car, or finance a honeymoon. Who knows what your needs will be then?

SISTERS ARE GREAT

For me it was a great personal loss when my own sister, Elsie, died at the age of thirteen. I felt cheated! My strong little mother considered that loss her heaviest blow. She had already endured four deaths in her immediate family, but she said this was her greatest loss.

Elsie's death made me question the Sunday school stories that God is kind and good to all who deserve his blessing. If God had anything to do with taking her away, then, I lost a little faith. As I matured I believe God had nothing to do with my sister's death. Now I believe she was the victim of poor medical care. Our doctors then just did not have the information and trainings that became available later. I am sure that my mother encouraged me to enter the health professions because even she did not blame God.

I felt repaid when my own little girl was born. My sons, Ron and Ken, had a great sister--Marilyn. The three of them grew up together and as adults they have great times together. It seems that the books were finally balanced in my family. As much as I have enjoyed my sons, it was always a different experience to have that curly-haired blonde girl climb up into her father's lap for me to read her a story.

You will realize that men are suckers to be manipulated by girls--mothers, sweethearts, and especially sisters like little Ann!

LITTLE ANN'S FIRST CHRISTMAS

Dear Ann:

When you were born your big brother was four years old and your father and your mother called you "Baby Ann". Well, that was expected, but it did not last long because soon that energetic bundle was no longer a baby. So, I started to call you "Lady Ann." You are just a little doll your first Christmas, and not even six months old! But by the time you learn to read, I may not be here to explain all this to you. So I'll do it now.

All four of your grandparents love you very much. Your mom and dad adore their little girl, and your big brother Dan is ecstatic. We are lucky people who have both a fine boy and a girl. You will learn that I like the gals even though I pal around with the guys. Soon you will run to your dad and cuddle up on his lap. It will be a thrill for him have a little girl--I have a warm thrill today when I remember how your aunt Marilyn ran to me with her curly hair bouncing when I came home from the office. Those quiet moments are reserved only for little girls.

Several days ago I mailed you a little pure golden finger which matches yours perfectly! I made it especially for you! When you are older you can wear it on the chain around your neck and brag it was made by your grandfather who loved you very much.

Also, I am mailing a box in which there is a silver dollar, minted in the last century--that makes it more valuable than a paper dollar.

Of course, there is another silver dollar for Dan. With it is a watch-fob of great history and sentiment. His silver dollar is much older even than your grandpa. The watch-fob functioned as a key to wind the pocket watch. When my grandfather Hughes was killed in the 1908 mine explosion, he was identified by the watch and this key. Dan will appreciate it!

MICKEY, THE HOUSE GUEST

Last week we had a most interesting house guest. You would have been proud of the way he acted when he visited us. Now I hear you are coming to stay with us next month while your parents vacation in California. We are glad! But, even though we think you are great, you will have a hard time being as good a houseguest as the one I am going to tell you about.

That guest made a marvelous adjustment and seemed to like everything we had to offer--no complaints. She was totally black, and when I brag about her as a guest you know your grandfather is not color biased. Regardless of her color I must admit that we never had a better guest.

The guest's name was "Mickey", and her last name was Labrador. I am sure you know and love her very much, even, though you are not two years old--just a little young to be in love, but I started thinking I was in love with the girls when I, too, was quite young.

Your dad brought her down to stay with us while he went to Cheyenne on business and then also went skiing. I am sure that he didn't know how well she would behave in new surroundings. Some individuals worry and make a fuss when they go traveling and don't have all the comforts of home. Many are nervous and do not adjust well away from their natural surroundings.

Ken thought she was one who liked to stay in a warm house most of the time, but I found out that she was most adaptable, and was even perfectly happy to sleep in our back yard. Of course, she had company who made her feel welcome. Her friend liked her and played with her, sharing a few toys like bones and a tennis ball. They chased one another around in circles, wrestled, and played hide-and-seek around a big iron stove I have in the back yard, and also around a little house there.

When it was time to feed a girl we call Bella and her guest, I served them in separate dishes but neither of them was concerned about table manners. I thought they might argue over their shares of the meal, or even fight. But not them! In fact, they were perhaps better about cleaning up their plates than they were when alone. Mickey gets into the house in Rawlins, but I kept her in the back yard with my dog. It was a cold and wintry night and I was concerned about your dog when I saw no animal moving the next morning. When I stepped onto the back porch Bella poked her nose out of her house and Mickey followed right behind.

I was pleased that Bella invited Mickey to share her house. You can tell your dad how well our pets got along. Your dog can come anytime and Bella will be her baby-sitter.

The Great Depression

THE GREAT DEPRESSION

Dear Dan:

Few people who are in business today KNOW about the major financial depression of the 1930's. Those of us who remember have failed to record our personal experiences. My recollections are still sharp. The preceding decade was called the "Roaring Twenties," and then the economy was great. Those were the days of the bootleggers, new cars and jobs for everyone who wanted to work. Still, many did not! Even then there were men we called "hoboes" who rode freight trains through Hanna. Later, there were even more bums on the trains. Even later, came the same type of individual we called "hippies." Regardless of the times this element is ever present and wants to live off the rest of us.

During the Depression many left the freight train and came to my mother's hotel to ask for food. She was always generous, but often asked them to chop a little wood first. I remember one guy who apparently didn't like swinging an ax while Mother was making him some sandwiches. She was too slow, and he came to the door, and handed her the ax, saying: "Lady, here is your ax. My train is moving and I gotta go."

When the stock market collapsed suicides were common among people who had been in the market. Some who had been wealthy suddenly were paupers. This economic collapse eventually trickled on down to Wyoming. Many high school graduates could not pay their college tuition and buy books, and dropped out of school.

About that time we elected Franklin D. Roosevelt as President and he created the CCC (Civilian Conservation Corps), which encouraged many young men to work in the forest and benefit this area. Also created was the WPA (Works Project Administration). They built golf courses, parks and other beneficial public facilities. But these government-created jobs went too far. Now many individuals expect too much in government subsidies.

In Laramie and other communities, we experienced depressed economics. In 1932 I graduated from dental school. Neither Laramie nor any other city encouraged a young dentist. Here in Laramie we suffered closures at a refinery, the railroad shops, a cement plant and layoffs at the University. Women who worked at the University were laid off if their husbands were employed by the school. It was thought that there should be only one on the payroll for each family. All professional people in the community suffered. Ranchers were forced to sell their cattle at any price.

It was a poor time to graduate because even established professional people were having financial troubles. Students at the University did anything they could to stay in school, because there were no jobs after graduation. One was a friend of mine, George Fowler, who, like others, joined the ROTC (Reserve Officer Training Corps). Patriotic? Well, yes, but it was also a source of income while in school. Finally, during World War Two he served with the Marines with honor until he retired.

Law students like George Millett and Clifford Hansen (future governor and senator from Wyoming) were patients of mine and they had trouble paying my modest dental bills. There was Quinton Blair, who worked his way singing in a student orchestra and later become an owner of Wyoming motels. All of them fought and worked hard to get their education during the depression.

During the first few years of my practice I showed more interest in the co-eds on the campus than the guys on the campus. There were girls like Kay, Ila, Peg, Martha and Mary, but when they found out I was a professional man with an office downtown (only age 23) they were not interested. It seemed that a man who had already graduated from college couldn't even dance.

I have an old ledger which tells a rather sad story of my income from patients during the early 1930's. During the first six weeks after I rented an office absolutely no person even opened the reception room door. Finally, I did get a patient! I had a plan which worked.

I had never seen Wyoming play football but it would take a dollar and fifty-cents of borrowed money to get into the gate and I hated to spend it. . . . . . On this particular Saturday afternoon I waited, hoping some patient might enter our office building. Perhaps some one with a toothache might be looking for an older dentist whose office was locked. I must have been the only person in the old Roach office building. After the game had already started I decided it was so lonely that I would spend the borrowed $1.50 and go to Corbett field.

When I reached the street door I found a distraught mother holding the hand of a crying six-year old girl who had suffered all night with an infected tooth. The mother had been awake all night with the crying daughter and she was headed for the office of a dentist friend of mine, Doctor McCalla on the second floor. I turned around and guided them into the elevator. The mother returned to the elevator where she asked, while I continued to hold the door open, if Doctor Shoemaker had an office on the fourth floor. I stayed in the elevator while they tried to enter another locked door.

Now came my chance! I told the mother that I was also a dentist with an office on the second floor. She looked at me with disbelief. I was only 23 years old, and guess my abundance of curly hair made me look even younger. To prove I was a real professional man I had to show her that the key I had indeed unlocked the door marked "Dr. C. M. Stebner, Dentist". Reluctantly, she and the crying little girl entered the reception room.

Gosh, Dan, my very first patient! I hadn't made an injection since I was in school, where a teacher would be present to advise me on where the mandibular nerve was. Luckily I hit the nerve with my needle and the little girl stopped crying. The pain was gone, thank goodness. I removed the tooth without any pain for my first patient.

I called the mother into the operating room and showed her the tooth which had been the culprit all the previous night. There were smiles were on the faces of the relieved mother and her daughter.

Now, the fee, what was it worth? I remembered it would take $1.50 to get into the game. I held my hand out and the Mother put a silver dollar and a fifty-cent piece in it. I could hardly wait for them to leave the building. I burst through the door and ran to Corbett field to spend the first fee I ever earned.

Well, Dan, let's get back to the story the ledger tells. The first month, after that initial patient, I received exactly $90.00 in cash, but granted $58.49 in credit. It was not good news to realize the expenses were $171.49, and left me $81.49 further in debt. That was the last time I used red ink. But the average was not good because during the first year my total income was $95.97 per month. That didn't mean I was not busy most of the time, but the fees per patient were so small because people just didn't have the money. Of course, my meals and room came from borrowed money.

Things changed for the better (or did they) when the University students heard I would allow anyone credit just to keep the dental chair warm, more of them accommodated me.

Something bothered me. I had practically no cute co-eds as patients, but the fellows appeared without cash. I soon realized that at my age of 23 the girls were not interested in an older person who was known as "Doctor Stebner." The girls dated fellows who were younger. I needed better contacts with co-eds!

H. E. GROTHE AND THE DEPRESSION

The senior Mr. Grothe built the Grothe Lumber Company in Laramie in about 1930. He had previously been in the Omaha area and had a lumber yard in Idaho. His experience taught him much about small communities and the people who lived in them. he was a pillar in the Baptist church--a devoted Christian.

At the depth of the Great Depression I attended an important community meeting designed to help business and the city government of Laramie. There was a big debate about the issuance of a money substitute we called 'script.' There were heated discussions among the City Council and the public. The script which was later issued by the city government was colored paper about the size of a dollar bill.

The city employees were to be paid with the script bills and would spend them with local merchants as though they were paper dollars. Then each merchant would place a two-cent postage stamp on the script and purchase a product from another merchant. This continued until there were fifty two-cent stamps attached. Then the script was really worth a dollar because it could be taken to the bank or the post office for a real dollar bill.

The theory was that the city, which didn't have enough money to pay their employees with real money, would be able to afford to maintain all city services with no cost. I was only twenty-five years old, and hadn't had enough experience in the business world, nor in understanding human nature to object. Most of the people in the room and the community, agreed to try the script plan. The only person who thought it would not work gave an eloquent speech--Mr. Grothe. He was much older than the rest of us. And, as it turned out, he certainly knew more about human nature than myself or the majority who voted for the script plan. His basic argument was that it would not work because the greedy would spend the script with neighbors without adding their own two-cents worth on the script.

For a while our sadly depressed town was pleased because the plan seemed to be working. Some of the "phony money" did receive the required fifty stamps. Finally, most of the script was circulated with stamps added. Still, too many were circulated without the necessary stamps being added. Then it was not worth a dollar. The last merchant who gave a dollar's worth of merchandise was stuck!

But, sad to say, Mr. Grothe's prediction was right. The script kept circulating with only ten or fifteen stamps. The script began to look sad, with only a few stamps applied, long before it became legal tender. If, as we had assumed, we had been dealing with 100% normally honest people, then we had a good weapon to help us defeat the depression.

H. E. Grothe knew more about the character of people than we did. As he promised, at least two percent were uncooperative, or dishonest.

MONEY HABITS

We are creatures of habit! All of us regularly take actions that even we fail to understand. The other day I was in our Overland Cafe and a favorite girl was at the cash register when I cashed a check to cover the bill and have a little extra money in my billfold. The amount of the check was exactly $80.00. This was not new for me, but she mentioned that during the years she has seen other checks from me for exactly that amount.

Mary Parker asked: "For years, when I have been checking out receipts at the end of the day I find that your checks are always for that amount. How come?" No other person had ever asked me that question.

I finally asked myself the same question, and tried to find the answer. As I dug deeper in my memory I think I came up with the answer. Habits are formed early in our lives and they stick with us. That is the reason young boys like you should form the most beneficial habits when you are very young. It will pay off.

My explanation to Mary is as follows: When I graduated from high school and left Hanna to go to the University, I had very limited funds in my checking account. I am sure that during the five years I was in school I never wrote a check for more than $80.00 to spend for my current needs. I spent carefully as though that were all the money I had. Eighty bucks has always been a lot of money for me to carry around. Maybe I could lose it or have my pocket picked--that would have been tragic! How could I replace it? That was during the depression more than sixty years ago. My mother and I worked very hard to handle that much money, so that we wouldn't lose it or spend it recklessly.

In those days a buck was a buck, and it would go a long way! Since then we have experienced considerable inflation, and now when I write a check for $80.00 I realize it does not last too long and then I write another for the same amount, so I guess the people at my bank wonder why I don't write them for larger amounts. Now I can afford it, but then when I developed the habit, I had to watch every dollar.

Another reason I stick with that magic figure is that somehow I am a bit offended when I am out with the boys and a few of them open their billfold and I see stacks of one-hundred dollar bills. I think maybe they are making a lot more money than I, or maybe they are being macho! I don't know, but it doesn't make sense to me.

I suppose my "eighty" habit is with me until I die, or hit a jack pot in a wild gambling deal and there is more money in my account and I don't know what to do with all that money.

BUYING STOCKS

I recently found out something that you might use when you get a little cash and have someone give you a good tip on stock purchases.

Ten or twelve years ago I had an idea that I now pass on to you. My good friend Warren Grothe gave me a guarded tip on a new pharmaceutical stock that had just reached the market.

Warren had the tip from a friend that in a reasonably short time the stock (which sold for eighteen dollars a share) would soon double because the company had a new drug which would soon hit the market and there would probably be a run on the stock.

Well, it was a gamble! I had a stock that had never increased in value and had paid poor dividends, so I sold it for $2,200.00 and took a gamble on the pharmaceutical company. But I hedged! I told the broker that if that stock ever doubled in value to sell half of it and send the $2,200.00 back to me.

As predicted the stock was a hot stock and I watched it increase from $22 to $44 a share. The broker called me and asked if I would still cash half of it in. I did! Another friend with much more money had received the same tip and invested much more than I had. He kidded me when the stock finally reached $55. At first I thought I had made a mistake, but then it began to drop in value to the $44 I had sold it for, and much lower! The last time I checked it was down to $8 a share, and on its way back up. I was playing on the company's money and had nothing to lose.

That stock never paid me a dividend, but it was not important because I still had the stock I had originally invested. Finally, it got down even farther to $1 a share. It didn't owe me anything so I simply forgot it.

I knew that company was working on a drug that would be a great help to arthritic patients, and there are a lot of them. I suffered from that disease for more than a year, but I finally recovered with few problems to show for the experience.

This last month, through persistence, good management, and good luck it seems that the company has developed and patented a drug which will be a God-send for arthritic patients. Now, the stock has gone from one to seven dollars per share. I am sure it will soon be paying dividends on the original stock I purchased.

This reminds me of a news article I read years ago. A stock broker in Chicago reached his retirement and was very successful and wealthy. At a testimonial dinner for the man, his company gave him a beautiful watch. On the back was engraved, "To Bill, the guy who always sold too soon."

That was a fitting tribute to the old guy's wisdom. Apparently, he was satisfied with a reasonable profit, then sold and got out. He was not as greedy as his compatriots who usually held out for a greater profit, but were caught as are many frustrated gamblers by holding out too long.

PYRAMIDING

We should discuss a the recent trend to make money in an unethical manner. Often it is considered unethical, and one often declared illegal. The structure is named after the Great Pyramids of Egypt.

Many people working at the base of the pyramid get small incomes, but they support the originator who moves to the top. But the structure of the pyramid inevitably crumbles.

Today we have companies built on the pyramid principle. The wise, and often dishonest, person starts a program with himself at the peak of the pyramid. Then he builds a substructure of friends and relatives further away from the apex, and they build an even larger power structure.

One day, Dan, you may be contacted to be a member of a chain letter fraud. In my time I have received many chain letters. I predict they will surface again in one form or another.

With the chain letter you send a dollar (or even a bottle of whiskey) to the person who mailed the chain letter to you. If he is in the right spot, perhaps he will have four or five others mailing him dollar bills. So it looks good and he invests only one dollar and gains four or five times that much. But those who are on the bottom of the pyramid lose. I lost money as most people do. It's a racket!

On only one occasion was I near enough to the apex to chance an investment. I invested five dollars, and ultimately received twenty-two in exchange. I guess we took advantage of friends who were also greedy and expected to get something for nothing. When this happens--look out.

Other quasi pyramid deals!

Now the national emphasis is on Health. They even have established health pyramids. Many are asked to lose excess pounds of fat. Some diets are even rackets today! Television ads encourage us to buy books on the subject. Hundreds of pills, which are often candies promise to decrease your appetite. Many of these can actually destroy your teeth and your health. If you eat that junk and neglect to eat wholesome, nutritious food, you <u>do</u> lose weight, but the benefit is only temporary. No adequate substitute exists for exercise and eliminating calories.

THE GREEDY ARE SUCKERS

I have always been interested in people who are much younger than I. This has brought me many lasting friendships. One of them was Dan Grothe, the son of Warren, who is at present a statistician and consultant for public groups who wish to float bond issues for public needs. Since Dan's college days he has been involved a great variety of businesses. He understands much about human nature.

Dan said: "As I recall, we were standing around the campfire during one of our many hunting trips, exchanging pearls of wisdom. The conversation evolved around the current devious confidence games being perpetrated on the public. You will note the victims of any scam are greedy. I observed the one common character flaw that confidence men depend on is greed. In other words, the schemes and setting might change, but the sucker had to be greedy to be cheated."

I agree with Dan! It seems to be the technic of confidence men is to locate a person who wants to make money the easy way. That person is usually a sucker and is more easily sold on most any scam. On the other hand, individuals who realize that there is seldom anything we can gain without hard work and personal effort.

THE GROTHE FAMILY

This morning I received a phone call from a great friend (another Danny). Dan Grothe is a guy I hope you get to know. He lives in Denver and has three sons of his own, and also grandchildren.

Dan was born in 1937 and I was with Warren at the hospital to give him support at that critical event. So you can see that I saw him very early. Our first home was next door to the Grothes. Dan is also one of my best friends even though he is 53 years younger than I. Someone once described a real friend this way, "It is one who knows all of your faults, and still loves you." Warren and Dan fit that description.

During Warren's life in Laramie he was well-respected, and did much for the community. He was a very intelligent person. He gave me some good advice on many occasions. Once he cautioned me against becoming too socially involved. He said, "Charlie, don't let too many people run through your life." I can pass that thought on to you. Many are simply acquaintances, not true friends.

Dan Grothe's mother was formerly Leah Nelson, an attractive University girl from Evanston, Wyoming. She worked for me some months in the dental office when I could no longer keep my set of meager books. Like most students during the depression, she needed part time employment. Sometimes, rather than paying Leah I gave her credit for her dental bill.

Leah also worked part time for a lawyer who ran the credit agency. There Warren noticed the cute trick, and asked me who she was. I arranged a date between them. That was fatal. Warren and Leah were soon married, just a few days before our wedding.

The Grothes and Stebners were therefore newlyweds in Laramie together, and the four of us remained devoted to one another. Warren and I fished and worked for the community together, and our wives were always close friends. The Stebner children and the two Grothe kids, Dan and Lorna, have also shared one another as friends all of their lives.

Dan Grothe was the first new baby in our two families, and I had a lot of fun with him. Once I fed him licorice when he was in his high chair--he made a beautiful mess of himself and we took his picture. Dan is now an excellent amateur photographer and wants to photograph you in the same situation.

I hunted more than Warren did and introduced Dan to guns. At Warren's suggestion I selected Dan's first shotgun, which he still uses, especially when he comes to Wyoming and hunts with us. He and I hunted sage-chickens together for many years.

Several times Dan sent his three boys to our camp and they are also my friends. Recently one of Dan's sons, Shad, came to Laramie to fish with me. We camped in an isolated area and caught some little fish which we ate over the camp-fire. We both had fun, but I was disappointed that he didn't get a BIG trout. On the way home I had a hunch that really paid off. We stopped at the Little Laramie and I used dry flies to show him the technique of fly casting. He fished without luck while I caught a few nice browns, and eventually we came to a spot where I knew a big brown trout must be waiting.

I instructed him where to throw his worm and watch it float downstream. I left him and fished above with my dry-fly, until I heard him shout . .

. "Charlie, I think I finally hooked a big one!" I hurried back to see if he was right, and sure as the dickens he was working as the pole was bent double. I coached him as he got the fish to surface, and with care he backed up on the sand bar and we were both excited to find he had landed a 18 inch brown trout.

You know Dan, with your wonderful mother and a great fisherman like your dad, you will have the experience that Shad and I had. I hope I can be there when it happens.

I hope you will understand the communication between the younger generation and the older ones is so important to both of them. You can learn so much without painful experimentation if you will just encourage it and listen carefully. It will save you many heart-aches. But, equally important, you will make the earlier generation both proud and happy.

This seldom happens, but because of the Stebner-Grothe relationship, I was the dentist for four generations of Grothes. I loved those kids and their teeth. But most of all today I think of Dan and the phone call he made just to visit with me.

DAN GROTHE--MY HUNTING PARTNER

Recently my good friend wrote the following for me. . .

"It was the last day of the hunting season, all the other guys had packed and headed for Laramie. Someone was kind enough to leave us a half pot of chili to eat. After hunting that morning we were hungry and ready for a meal. We started a fire and warmed the chili, but noticed all the utensils had been packed and were enroute to town. Well, we just let the chili cool and dug into it with dirty hands. We were sitting on the ground, with a beer and chili, but with ample conversation. Then, I spotted a coyote (Canis latrans) watching us from the ridge. We looked at the coyote, and you mused, "I wonder what he is thinking?" I answered: "He is probably saying; I could <u>not</u> live like that!"

Character and the American Flag

SOME OF MY DENTAL FRIENDS

Dear Dan:

In my experience as a dental officer at Farragut, Idaho, during WW II, I met many professional friends. One was Avery Spears. He was a conscientious dentist, but did not have my background. Our families also became friends. I taught a class in Gold Foil at his hometown, Houston, Texas. He joined me and was elected Secretary at the first meeting of the American Academy of Gold Foil Operators, and I was the first Vice- President. He came to see me shortly before he died of cancer.

More than forty years ago I listened to a dental lecturer in Denver. Like myself he was a dental officer in the Navy but unfortunately our paths never crossed. He was a handsome large man who held his audience with scientific facts, and especially with his humor. His audience had lots of good laughs. I did not! I was infuriated as he ridiculed principles I was teaching. At the conclusion of his presentation I was on this big guy's neck. I challenged him to learn more about the fundamentals of dentistry. I mailed him some of the published articles I had written. He responded in kind, but was not easily discouraged. I continued to harass him by mail. This I did because of the man's potential to influence other men to practice better dentistry.

It took many letters and phone calls and a meeting where we shared the podium in California. There my philosophy of practice got to him. He was Dr. John M. Mosteller of Mobile, Alabama.

John had much talent as a practitioner, a lecturer, and a notable author. He introduced me to many of his friends in the profession. One was his classmate, Dr. Ray Bassich of New Orleans, who was a dentist I admired. Ray and his buddie often came to hunt big game with me in Wyoming.

As the years passed Stebners and Mostellers grew to know each other and they became our treasured friends. His wonderful wife, Janet, allowed their youngest son to be named Charles Stebner Mosteller.

During my Navy experience in World War II I grew close to another dental officer, and an excellent friendship was nourished. Avery Spears, who was already a fine dentist, changed his practice and image because of our friendship. When he suffered from terminal cancer I flew to Houston for a last visit.

Perhaps because I lost my dad at such an early age I needed a father image when I entered Creighton. There I found the right person. Lester Myers who was one of the few premier dental artisans of America. He took me under his wing and influenced my entire professional life. Years later I had an opportunity to encourage his son, Jim, to attend the University of Wyoming. This changed his life work. Today, he is a renowned psychologist and author.

During the early years of World War II, I went to Northwestern to study dental surgery so I could better serve our enlisted men after I joined the Navy. In that class was a dentist from New York City who was older than I, but we cemented another friendship which has lasted for more 38 years. Earlier Joe Lenzner was discouraged, and a loner and not proud of his dentistry. I helped and encouraged him to change his technique. Finally, when he retired from practice he had the right to be proud of his dentistry, and I am proud of him. He adapted to new procedures with my help and encouragement. Both Lenzner and Mosteller accomplished critical and difficult Gold Foils and learned the importance of the rubber dam. This allowed them to become members of a unique Academy.

Easterners Jack Freese and Lionel Bergeron traveled by rail from Boston to my office in Laramie. After a week they returned home and organized study clubs. They invited me to lecture for a full week at Tufts University. Freese and others became my good friends. They and others in that class are among my many dental friends.

In West Virginia, I gained professional friendships with Loflin, Bridgeman, and others. They, too, organized study clubs. Some of that group take time off to teach at their University. This group was organized after a session we had in Chicago.

In Dallas, Texas is an outstanding dental specialist. Adrian Sampeck began his practice in my office. At every opportunity, I look forward to being with him and watching his accomplishments.

Today, I often cross paths with a highly respected dentist in Houston, Texas. Ralph Boelsche and I have counted more than 40 years of friendship. He feels that our relationship changed his philosophy of general practice. Ralph is a benefactor to dentists around the country. Since we first met, he sends me a case of grapefruit every Christmas.

It was exciting for me when Dr. Miles Markley of Denver recommended that a dentist from London visit my office and watch my procedures for a week. Max Walter, who practiced in London, became my friend. He was originally from Germany--he escaped Hitler's wrath. He spent a week in my office and became dedicated to me and my dental philosophy. Max was a cousin of our Secretary of State, Henry Kissinger. In Europe Dr. Walter was well known and respected. I lectured to dental friends in his office, and we were devoted friends.

Dr. George Hollenback was known to every American dentist for his research, and as an inventor and author of many publications. When he retired from practice he wanted me to move to California and be heir of his practice. It was difficult for me to say I wanted to live and raise my children in Wyoming.

John Mosteller encouraged many dentists to visit me in Laramie. One was Freese and another outstanding professional, Ray Stevens, of Grand Rapids, Michigan. Ray taught and influenced changes at his University. All of these and others have been my good friends for more than twenty-five years. Yes, there are others that I treasure as friends in dentistry!

. . . and then there is Vernetti . . .

UNITED WAY HONOR

During 1987 Mary and I went to Washington D.C. for the 100th a celebration of the United Way. Sixty-three of us were honored in a large group of about 4,000 workers. They came from most states and places beyond our borders, like Puerto Rico. There I enjoyed a casual lunch with two men, one from Japan and another from Australia.

I had just celebrated my 78th birthday, but still not heard of Alexis de Tocqueville. Later, I learned he came to America following France's revolution in 1830. The United Way was celebrating their 100th year of service in his name.

The medallion I received said: "The Alexis de Tocqueville Society Award was created by United Way of America to recognize persons who have rendered outstanding service as volunteers in their own community or on a national level."

Earlier we were entertained by the Army Band on the steps of the Lincoln Memorial. Finally, the crowd moved endlessly to walk around the mall. We joined a line at the head of the memorial of Vietnam Veterans. I didn't realize so many young men died in their vain effort to bring freedom to another nation. Many of our group searched, for family names. I was most grateful that son Ken's name was not on those tablets.

Then came the BIG NIGHT where those of us received the Alexis de Toqueville Award. In previous years both President Gerald Ford and Gregory Peck had received the Award. Now each of them confirmed our awards. I was pleased to visit with Gerald Ford during rehearsals and at the news briefing. When he read my citation I could not remember what he said that night when the medallion was placed around my neck. At that moment I remembered my mother. Was she listening--who knows?

OTHER HONORS

This is a very tough subject for me to address. At a dental meeting in San Francisco my friend Jim Vernetti read a citation which was awarded to me by the American Academy of Gold Foil Operators. This is a group of very special dentists who have dedicated themselves a most difficult procedure--one which saves many teeth for a lifetime. I was an originator and past-president of that group which served dentistry, and their patients for nearly forty years. When Jim read the citation Mary and I were both pleased to be honored by that distinguished group.

Also, Dan I was also honored along with ten other dentists at Northwestern School of Dentistry. They called us the "Legends of Operative Dentistry." All three of our children surprised me by arriving in Chicago for that event. My own Creighton University presented me with the "Alumni Merit Award" in 1967. Many years ago, in 1965, I received "The Distinguished Community Service Award" in Laramie.

The climax of my dental honors was in Las Vegas at the annual American Dental Association meeting in October 1987. During the 124 years of that organization they granted this special distinguished award only 17 times. For a small town general practitioner, from a sparsely populated state, this honor was unique.

Sure, Dan, honors are great, but the best is that it makes your friends and family proud. Many of the finest persons I have known were never honored as I was. Longevity is part of the answer--soon I will celebrate my 80th birthday, I was lucky.

TOO COLD--TOO HOT

Be happy in the climate in which you live! There are many people who could be happier if they could just accept their work or their geographical location.

This is easy if you never travel far from the home in which you were born. Then there is no other place in the world you know much about. I had an experience when I returned from the Navy following WW II. I traveled to visit the Medical College of Virginia (all expenses were paid) to investigate the possibility of teaching dentistry rather than practicing it. I was serious about moving from Laramie to a different location and culture because

I was disgusted when I couldn't find a place to rent a decent office when I came home.

When I arrived in Richmond, fortunately for me, it was about 100 degrees F, hot and muggy! Believe it or not, the Dean's name was Harry Bear! He was congenial and eager to see me because he had heard I was a good teacher and would fit into his faculty well. Dr. Bear was an excellent host and drove me around the area to impress me. When I first entered his office, before the general use of air conditioning, he sat at his desk without a shirt as he perspired under an electric fan. Sure he was uncomfortably hot, and so was I in my light suit coat and a tie. Afterwards another faculty person showed me the facilities of the school.

When we entered the clinic I met one student who discouraged me from teaching undergraduates. He was much taller than I was and in his white gown was disgusted as he fumbled around in the mouth of a distressed patient.

As I had done in the Navy when graduates had trouble with a technique I volunteered, saying: "Look let me help you. I will show a better matrix which can be applied to produce a better restoration for the patient, and it will be easier on you because it is simple and effective." As the noon hour approached the young dentist regularly kept looking out of the window, and at his wrist watch. I held him up while his classmates hurried out for their lunch hour, dismissing their patients rather randomly. I stayed at the chair, as I had always done, without watching the clock and the patient received a decent service.

It seemed apparent to me that this particular student, upon graduation, would be more interested in the clock and the profit he would make in his fee. This guy should not even be tolerated in a professional school. He didn't want to learn, but was there just to earn!

Well, Dan, let's get back to the weather and the geographic location of Richmond. That afternoon the Dean and his wife drove me around the area. I was fascinated with the history of Richmond. Much unlike Laramie it was rather level and there was much interesting profuse vegetation. It was new and exciting, especially with the beautiful period homes.

When my plane arrived in Laramie, without a single tree in view, I knew the answer to the question Mary would asked me, "Are we going to move to Virginia?" Well, I looked around at the Snowy Range, the Colorado mountain peaks, the Laramie mountain range, and the north where the horizon disappears infinitely. I had been away from views I had taken for granted--here I could literally see views that went on for hundreds of miles. My answer to Mary's question was, "Hell, no! The breeze is cool even in July, and the view is wonderful."

I regularly attended the Midwinter Dental Meeting in February. It was held in Chicago and I went for a walk to the Museum, which was only a few blocks from my hotel. There a bitter wind was blowing across the ice from the lake. Even though I was dressed in a warm coat and a fur hat I wore comfortably in Laramie, I was cold! I hailed a taxi to take me the few block to the Museum. When I got in by the heater I complained about the weather. The taxi driver, who had never been out of Chicago where he was born, said: "You are from Wyoming and you complain about the cold here? My radio reported it was 20 degrees below zero there today, and it is only 18 degrees above zero here!" I failed as I tried to explain the difference humidity makes in the weather between the elevation of the Great Lakes and Laramie's 7280 feet. He liked Chicago and I liked Laramie!

We all would be better if we could pay less attention to the weather reports we see on television. All conversation on this subject fails to change anything. I know a person who remarks: "It's too hot." Or, "It's too cold."

Dan, simply learn to live with the weather where you have work or go to school. You should be like an old friend of mine. Ottis Rechard drove a Model T Ford from his native Pennsylvania with his wonderful new bride to the plains and mountains of Wyoming. He came to Wyoming in 1923 where he fished for trout and loved his mountain cabin until his death in 1980. He ignored anyone who complained. Once I heard his retort when someone complained about the heavy wind we have only occasionally. Ottis said with a straight face, asked, "What wind?"

I have observed wealthy people who have several homes so that they can accommodate to the weather, but that doesn't make them particularly happy. They often have poor weather wherever they are.

KAREN AND THE SCALES

When I lectured for the Utah State Dental Association about thirty years ago, an appreciative and generous dental assistant that I once had was there. I introduced her to dentistry soon after she graduated. At that time she needed a job and I needed her. Years later she moved to Utah and married a young Mormon.

When I first saw her she was timid and unsure of herself. When she applied as a dental assistant she desperately needed employment. We were both fortunate when I hired her. At a critical time in her life she gained much confidence in herself and was dedicated to her work and my patients. With encouragement she progressed rapidly. Karen had excellent tactile ability. This was important because I wanted her to bake porcelain. It was a break for me and my patients. She also cast my inlays and learned other laboratory techniques. The porcelain crowns she made soon became better than my own. Karen cast my inlays and worked with me at the chair. The patients loved her!

After seven years, Karen found it necessary to move to Utah. It was difficult for me to lose an employee so dedicated and honest. I encouraged her to continue with her dental pursuits. Soon she had a good position working for a group of dentists baking their porcelain crowns. Karen remarried and they adopted a fine young boy. Her husband was a talented teacher who had a hobby of working with brass.

Karen encouraged him to build a set of scales. At the meeting of her group she presented me with a special gift. It was a delicate set of brass mini-scales with delicate pans and fine chains. In her presentation, Karen recalled her thoughts of the balance of fairness between individuals. She noted the need to obtain balance between the doctor and his patient; the balance of fairness between the doctor and the nurse. Also, she mentioned the need for a fair balance between husband and wife. When Karen described the balance which was present in our office, as I unwrapped the gift, I had trouble controlling tears in my eyes.

After enjoying those scales for years, I was reminded that we would soon see Charles Stebner Mosteller at his wedding in Dallas, Texas. I had the two delicate pans on the balance engraved with the names of the newlyweds, CHARLIE and ALEXA! I was sure that my namesake and his beautiful bride will keep their lives in balance.

VIDEO MELIORA PROBOQUE, DEFERIORA SEQUOR

A Roman philosopher and poet wrote the above, which is translated to mean: "I know the better and I want it, but I continue to follow the worse." This observation of the frailty of human nature is as true today as it was when Ovid wrote it a thousand years ago. Sotar Lahradka, a professor at Wyoming University at the end of WW II, called that quotation to my attention as I lectured him on the importance of saving his teeth. Sure Sotar understood the need for dental hygiene, but he failed in doing anything about it.

Devout Christians believe Jesus Christ was without fault. Yet, he must have lost his temper when he drove the infidels out of the temple. Today, we know that we must not 'blow our top'! Those who know me well are aware that among my many character faults I have good reason to write warning words in my study-- TEMPER, ANGER, and CONTROL! Too often I am ashamed for losing my head over trivial problems.

. . . .

A few people say that we are the product of the food we eat. Often results develop in fad diets and among their followers. Others say the most important factor in our make-up is the genes we inherit, and that lets us blame our ancestors for our troubles. Another group believes that we can build a character, and a healthy body, by creating the proper environment and exercise. Scientifically, all of these are important in our lives.

Perhaps Ovidius was right when he wrote: "We want the best but continue to follow the worse." Every person realizes there is plenty of room for personal improvement in character and health. An intelligent individual should take an honest inventory of himself every day, and not follow Ovid to continue to follow the worse.

PROVINCIALISM

We should avoid provincialism. Very often we are too satisfied at home. We are unwisely narrow in making acquaintances. There was a time in our history where we knew and understood only people who were our neighbors.

Before our three kids entered high school, we packed them and their belonging in our car and nearly toured most of these United States. We did not want them to become provincial. It was important to us that they should understand people who live a long way from our home town, because there are fine people everywhere.

Too many individuals fail to make friends in other sections of this country, or for that matter, elsewhere in the world. During our family's summer trips, our kids saw the beautiful scenery and the generous people on the East Coast as well as Canada. They enjoyed the culture of our southwest Indians, and made friends on the Pacific Coast. We all learned that there are very many good people everywhere, and a very few unpleasant people who are the minority.

A TRIP DOWNTOWN

All of us seem to go down town at least once a week--especially to the Post Office, and while we are there a call to the stores or a bank is necessary. Being retired, I like to make that trip when the traffic is light. It gets me away from home and is a break in the day.

Usually I come back to my house feeling better. Yes, the fresh air stimulates me, but I just like to see people on the streets. Some I know and there are always a few strange faces.

Laramie is a friendly town, but I have a few suggestions that will make it friendlier. Smile! There are too many serious faces, but we can change that by being friendly. When I park the car at the Post Office it is rare that I can't hold the door for someone who least expects it. Especially if some woman is approaching the door I will wait or hurry a bit to hold the door for her and let her enter first. Usually, she will smile and say: "Thank you!" If she doesn't, it is rare and that is her problem. It helps if one says something good about the weather. If there is a waiting line there, let her go first--it's pleasant for both of you. Sure, it helps if she is young and pretty.

But if it is a grouchy old man he will be surprised when you speak and often his face will light up. Women with kids are fun to see and often you can say something complimentary about the youngster. Most of the young guys will be pleased and surprised, and then you have helped to make their day. There should always be a pleasant greeting to the person behind the counter.

Driving around downtown, give the other driver a break and wave him on at the intersection. You both will come home feeling better just because they didn't expect it. A person on the sidewalk should not be ignored as though he were a post. Look him in the eye, and give him a chance to speak!

NONE ARE INDISPENSABLE

History tells of many great rulers. A few were known as worthy because they ruled nobly, but most were crude and unkind to those they ruled. And nearly all were crude to those they conquered.

The frailties of man demand we must be governed. If we were perfect beings, there would no need for a power to govern us. Various countries that had reasonable rulers drew homage from their public. But when a ruler's successor is chosen, we often we fear the unknown. Still life goes on whether the loss is the head of a family or a national ruler.

In the death of respected leaders we ask, "What in the world will happen to us now?" We should remember in times like this that <u>no</u> person is indispensable.

During WW II, when I was a Lieutenant in the Navy Dental Corps, I left your Grandmother at home to care for our two young children. I also left my dental patients with other dentists, and some of them said: "Now what will we do for a dentist who takes care of our family as you have?" Some dedicated patients seemed to think I was indispensable. Of course, I knew that they would find another dentist, and even though some of them lost teeth which I might have saved, I realized I was certainly not indispensable.

As a father too, I knew my little wife would take wonderful care of our children without me. I remembered how my valiant mother found a way to care for her three children when my dad died at the coal mine.

Yet, I and thousands of men in the military seemed to think that our U. S. President was indispensable. Our war-time leader was Roosevelt, and both civilians and those of us in the service thought he was the one man we needed to defeat the enemy. But a tragedy struck all of us when we heard he died of a stroke.

As programmed, the Vice President Harry Truman became President. I, myself, believed Truman was inadequate in comparison to Franklin Roosevelt. No citizen I knew objected to Roosevelt being our first President to serve a third term. We <u>needed</u> him!

Harry Truman surprised nearly everyone, and perhaps even himself, to became a strong President. At the time he was sworn into office I remembered him as a small town politician from Missouri. After all, he had been a haberdasher in a Missouri men's clothing store before he was elected to his high office, with none of the valuable experience that would be needed.

History will list him as a greater President, I believe, than Roosevelt. Truman was a hero to most men man in uniform. He was a valuable leader. Franklin Roosevelt was <u>not</u> indispensable!

All the Christians who witnessed the death of Jesus Christ were devastated when he died. Then he was considered indispensable. His teaching and disciples established Christianity.

VICTORY OR DEFEAT

I suggest, Dan, that you be a reasonable spectator of sports, but don't think your team <u>must win</u>. It's taken me a very long while to become more philosophical about defeat and victory. There were times when my team lost that I would be down in the dumps for several days. I assure you it isn't worth that! It is great to win, but in defeat we must learn to rebound. Spectators, and understandably the participants, take these games too seriously. I will tell you a story about your Uncle Ron--he had a better attitude than your dad or your grandfather.

Ron would work harder at jumping rope than anyone I ever saw. He is strong physically and mentally tough. He is able to cut down trees and load them on a truck with more vigor and strength than anyone we have been around. Yes, I guess he could have been a great wrestler. But Ron was not a team man. Perhaps he worried that his mistakes might hurt his team-mates.

Because I believed that team sports help teach working together, I insisted that he learn to play baseball, but when that didn't work I talked him into trying out for the high school football team. Even now I think that being part of a team would have helped him. One day during a scrimmage, the whistle blew he simply stopped. A member of the opposing unit was more aggressive and he hit Ron at the knees. He never recovered from that act. His knee, regardless of several operations, left him with a degree of damage. Ron blamed himself for not being alert.

During the time Ron was on the football squad, he was disturbed following a football game with Cheyenne. His team members were vitriolic as they referred to the opponents. He asked, "Dad, Why do our guys hate the Cheyenne kids? Gosh, the Cheyenne players come from homes like ours--must be good kids too!" The point Ron made was philosophically sound and mature. Well, anyhow my efforts to make Ron a team player went awry. He can take failures, but he deserves victory!

WIN SOME--LOSE OTHERS

Often each of us has a cause which we encourage for our own desire. We work, dream, and often fight for a specific accomplishment. I presume that when it is all added up in a lifetime effort we should forget the losses and take pleasure in our success.

There was never a President of our country who had his way with congress. We can measure our government, whether it is local, state, or national, and realize we have benefited the citizens. Some decisions were great and others were horrible. But there is general improvement which benefits each of us. We should call that progress!

As you will realize I have been active in my community and my profession. Too many capable people hesitate to speak out, and work for something they believe in. I call myself an activist. I desire to improve the general environment we live in.

Let me recall some of the actions I sponsored. When I came to Laramie I joined the Lion's Club and an organization we called the Boosters Club. It was the depression and a bunch of us younger men made goodwill trips to the surrounding areas. We also boosted the University and their athletic teams. I made many friends from that group, and I think we accomplished quite a little.

In 1934, or 1935, Laramie desperately needed more water. I worked with others to accomplish a project which eventually solved our problem. I call that a WIN! H. T. Person telegraphed me in 1944 when I was in the Navy at Farragut, Idaho, saying, "Shawlie, you asked for wattah, we got yuh wattah." This announced to me that a bond issue we worked for passed to acquire water from the Big Laramie River.

When I was in the Navy I saw the need for a swimming pool that would benefit our youth. We really had a community battle over that. A group, with which I disagreed, suggested an outdoor pool for Laramie. Myself and others opted for an indoor facility. It was a bitter dispute. We won that battle and the year- around facility benefited all of our children. It was a bitter fight because our opposition collected about twenty or thirty thousand dollars, which they spent for land on which they built a cement foundation. With the help of our school Superintendent Jack Corbett we erected an indoor pool the community still uses. That was a WIN.

We needed a new form of city government, and I suggested and worked for a new City Manager Form of Government. We WON that battle and we have improved our situation.

More recently, we had another controversy at the Ivinson Hospital. Previously I served on that board for thirteen years. I struggled with the County Commissioners to have well people pay more of the hospital costs. This would benefit ill people. Chalk up a DEFEAT!

In dentistry I put on a one-man campaign to discourage blatant advertisements in my profession of dentistry. Since that time I have seen a major change for the worse. Crude advertisements and the general use of plastics bother me, still they keep coming. Another DEFEAT.

Eight or ten years ago, I worked hard to prevent the building of an annex to our hospital, but I only delayed it a year or so. I fought the project nearly alone, with just one physician, Dr. Shine, who helped me. Yes, the board, with assistance of the County Commissioners, built the private structure on hospital grounds. It turned to be sort of a 'white elephant' and caused later boards and administrative officers a lot of problems. Originators of the project suffered heavy financial losses to the community and the banks who loaned funds--not only that, but they messed up the hospital land. The building was poorly planned and constructed. I guess you can call it another DEFEAT for myself.

Dan, you know I am an environmentalist. That does not mean all the negative things a few people try to apply to environmentalist. I am not negative--but positive! To me it means we believe in clean air and safe water. I would like to know some who enjoy dirty air and foul water. Well, I am disgusted with the cities of Laramie and Cheyenne--I suppose we could also include every town in the state which allows plastic waste to escape to the surrounding areas. We don't seem to know how to handle rubbish and garbage. It is visible everywhere for tourists and visitors to view. God gave us a beautiful area. One might believe we are doing our best to destroy it with our waste.

Some eight or ten years ago I suggested to our city and county officials that we do something about the mess we create. They were too busy with other things less important than cleanliness. They dragged their feet when I suggested an Environmental Council be appointed. Finally, they did make such an appointment and I was one of those appointed. I served as a member for several years, but was disgusted that they didn't follow our suggestions. Many ordinances we passed were shoved into the background and were seldom enforced. I resigned!

Three or four years ago I beat on the council to set a "Laramie Cleanup Day." It worked fairly well that beautiful spring day. We deposited much debris from the streets and alleys to the city dumps. More could have been accomplished if there had been more concerned citizens involved.

In the spring of 1988 the cleanup day was a flop. Weather was a factor, but there are many ways it could have been better. I was disappointed even though I did not work in any official capacity, I personally cleaned up a small section of the polluted stream that runs thru town.

A friend of mine suggested that the city should name a street in my name. Hell, Dan, I have had enough honors in the past. Still nothing would mean more to me if the City endorsed two days a year which they could call "Charlie trash and garbage cleanup days." One day is <u>not</u> enough to suit me! We need one in the autumn, when the UW students and local school kids can help. One should be in the spring and the other in the autumn. I have been DEFEATED as a successful organizer.

But Dan, we can't WIN them all. Just keep trying!

SELF ESTEEM

In the year 1987 we hear this term, "Self Esteem" as a desirable quality people should cultivate. There was a day when some one who showed confidence was berated as being too cocky. He was considered to be a braggart, or had too much "macho." But now the psychologists inform us that rather than being degrading, self esteem is healthful and we should encourage it.

I am worried about individuals who think poorly of themselves and their accomplishments. I don't know of a worthwhile person who did not have a healthy view of you can! And if you are realistic you will work harder to accomplish a particularly difficult task.

History abounds with men and women, boys and girls, who believed in themselves and dreamed of accomplishing things that others previously thought were impossible. Not many years ago, to ridicule someone a person might say, "Ah hell, that guy is shooting at the moon!" Long after I became a dentist, none of us thought we could escape the earth's atmosphere and land a person right on the surface of the moon. And it seemed equally impossible that the rest of us could witness those actions and hear their words.

For as long as man's history has been recorded, we have had reason to believe that there have always been wars between various groups of men. Many say war in inevitable. But is it?

There is a way out, and perhaps it is the atom bomb. When we turned loose that deadly weapon, I said to some of my friends in the Navy, "This will make war impossible because there are no winners." Now, our leaders have to have confidence in themselves to take these steps necessary for peaceful solutions. They must have "Self Esteem." Yes, that is not an impossible task. I hope for more honest Self Esteem, and less Macho!

CHARACTER

For some reason my mind has wandered to the word CHARACTER. I guess it might have been my experience with Theresa, the girl I met on the desert. She was an impressive physical specimen, but I am a little too old to be impressed by that. I guess that as we get older we are more impressed by one's character.

Character has been defined as....Genetics, any trait, function, structure or substance of an organism resulting from the effect of one or more genes as modified by the environment. Or, it could be defined as the moral qualities and ethical principles to which one adheres. I presume character is the sum total of all the qualities which make a person different from anyone else who ever lived. It's great that Nature, or God, designed each of our fingerprints uniquely. Nobody is just like you! That is a distinctly wonderful thought. Although other persons can have some important influences on us, they can never really transform us into being exactly like another person. Sure, one can strengthen or weaken his basic character. Consciously one may dream nobly to improve an already strong character.

I think of Mary Ford--she had the kind of a character we all appreciate. As I look at women, we know that their character was built, in part, by the hardships of their lives. I have seen some like your Aunt Marilyn who built their desirable character without any noticeable drudgery, or painful hardships. I am sure that her genes took over her desire to accomplish something wonderful; but she is unusual! My wife, Mary, had a Mother who homesteaded in a difficult area of western Wyoming. Her hardships were notable, but they helped to build a remarkable character.

ASSUME NOTHING

You should live long enough to eliminate the word, "assume" from your vocabulary. The dictionary says . . to take for granted or without proof . . to suppose or postulate.

My friend, Jimmy Stocker, has a better definition than the dictionary. He once told me that when that one should never assume anything, because it usually makes an Ass out of You and Me.

Recently, I made a promised to meet your Dad and we would have lunch at a restaurant. I arrived early and waited for him on the lawn outside the building. He parked in another area and didn't see my car so he went into the restaurant, finally ordered his meal and ate it while I still waited outside. After forty-five minutes I assumed he was held up at the office. He assumed I had ignored the appointment. Really, I was on a hunting trip and I wanted to be in camp before dark so I drove away.

Each of us assumed too much. Rather we should have agreed on complete details in our previous phone conversations. Then, we might have enjoyed one another that noon hour. One of us should have said either inside or outside of the restaurant.

Assume nothing, rather be specific!

TAKE 'EM TO LUNCH

If you get involved in any cause, you should know that there are a few who will resent you and your position. Still, you must speak out! Too many individuals fail to express themselves on controversial problems. Each of us has adequate intelligence to make intelligent decisions. There are areas of black or white, but often areas of grey make it difficult to make firm decisions.

Nevertheless, you must take a stand even if it involves controversy. When you become involved, especially in a large group, some will often violently challenge your stand. This has also happened to me on a one-on-one basis with a friend. There you must have a way to protecting your former relationship.

I have a prescription that will often work. A few days after the confrontation, call them on the phone and invite them to have lunch with you. You can tell them that after the heated session you now realize that there were differences of opinion, and that there is room for compromise.

Usually, they will accept the suggestion that you have lunch together. Then, after you greet one another each of you will be in a better environment as you order the lunch and begin to eat with one another. This gives the host a chance to explain his position. While the guest is eating he will listen more reasonably. When you are eating he can have his say and explain his position.

Both parties can see the other's position and there will be very few differences that can't be resolved. In several cases I did not lose a friend, but gained one. (This has happened with my own children. They say, "If Dad asks you go to lunch--DON'T GO!") I remember two who refused my invitation and we no longer speak. Still, many others who did accept saved our friendship.

PROCRASTINATION

Someone once said: " Procrastination is the thief of time; year after year it steals" . . .

Many people put off accomplishing a task they know needs their attention. Most of us to some degree are procrastinators, but we all admire that rare individual who disciplines himself to constantly attack and finish projects.

Right now as I approach my 80th birthday my procrastination is a luxury I can not afford. It is a luxury only young people can afford. We feel that time is running out and we are not able to accomplish our plans. I feel driven to write our family history each day. Mary often suggests that I leave this study and notes that there is no time limit on this project. After my experience in the Muddy Trap, I realize that life is fragile and may end on any day.

Very young children do not procrastinate. When they are hungry they cry and often scream. If we continued to do this as we get older some say we have a temper--that is not good! Others might call it determination, or simply being bull-headed, because we charge ahead on a project we believe is important. In activities like writing this book there is no place for procrastination. I think persons should analyze themselves and try to make adjustments to allow each to proceed with the determination to become successful.

I suggest, Danny, that when you come home from school on a nice spring day there is a tendency to procrastinate about getting your chores, or home-work done. Then it takes a bit of will-power to begin the unpleasant task immediately. Finally, after the that task is finished you can enjoy your play without your conscience bothering you.

VOTING

Because of a heated discussion I had with Steve, a cousin of my adult children, I've been thinking of Patriotism. Maybe the subject should be responsibility to one's country, or even community.

Today, I reflect upon a conversation I had with Steve on our annual antelope and sage chicken hunting trip at the north edge of Wyoming's Red Desert. The problem began as we discussed the upcoming Presidential election between our President, Ronald Reagan, and his opponent Walter Mondale.

We're usually out there hunting for about a week and often have enough guests to form a party of nearly a dozen people. We seldom discuss politics or other serious subjects. We are there for fun, with a lot of good natured razzing and humor. I'm often the butt of their jokes but I enjoy it. I like it when they laugh at me and tell stories on me, which in part are usually true. I abhor the senior member who is often too serious for their ribald humor, and I want to put-out and receive ribbing. I refuse to be any different in that than any of the younger individuals.

At the time Steve and I got involved in the political argument, we had a surprise guest, a girl of twenty-six years old. I don't know why both Steve and I were unconsciously trying to impress that unique young lady, but that could have been part of our volatile argument.

Steve is the son of my wife's sister, Alice June Stocker, and both Mary and I think highly of him and his cousins. But like any person, young or old, I will often disagree on almost any subject, and I'm not shy about voicing my strong opinions. Steve began to berate President Reagan and I objected! As our voices filled the desert silence it was probably embarrassing to the only others there--your Uncle Ron and the new guest, Theresa.

I asked Steve whether he would vote for Reagan or Mondale and he said he didn't like the choice and would vote for neither. I voiced my opinion about his cop- out, and suggested that everyone should vote. In a case where we like neither, we should vote for the person with the fewer negative characteristics. It's my opinion that you should use your God-given judgment and vote for a man who has the fewer negative characteristics. It's my opinion that you should always use your instinctive gut-feelings about a particular candidate. At least, you should use your God-given judgment of achieving the office. But, to refuse to make that choice is simply throwing one's vote into the waste basket. Someone has said that a mind is a terrible thing to waste. I believe a vote is also a terrible thing to waste. The United States is one of very few countries in this world that gives all its citizens the right to choose their leaders. Many brave and well-meaning people have given their lives so that we have the freedom to vote. and we should not take our vote lightly. This idea is what I tried to convey to Steve, but I presume it got lost in the heat and non-objective shouting on the desert. Hell, yes, he should vote for the person, and also the Vice- President, who will do the best to fill the highest office in this country. Voting for the Vice-President is equally important.

PHRASEOLOGY

Now and then we hear a few words that are meaningful to each of us. The other day I heard someone complain about walking up-hill. That is life and no matter where we walk we must first go up-hill before we have the pleasure of walking down-hill. I presume that some individuals would always choose to walk down-hill or perhaps on the level. It takes a little more effort to travel up-hill. But the way this planet evolved there are many hills on which we must travel.

When in our life things are tough for a while, and we must expend much effort to travel through life. After difficult up-hill battles, we must struggle and smile because if we tough it out we will get a break and things will vastly improve as we get a down-hill break. The guy who wrote the poem which wished the Cowboy, "May the wind always be at your back." Hell, Dan, that is asking too much, sometimes it has to be in your face when you travel horseback!

Some of us had a difficult up-hill early life, but with patience and hard work the great day will come late in life where everything is on a pleasant down-hill path.

Dan, in my life and my mother's life we had a tough first half, but then a most generous second half. I must admit that some others do it the other way around.

. . . .

If we observe several generations of a particular family, we can learn something which often happens.

The first generation originates,

The second generation operates,

And the third liquidates the fortune!

I can't remember where I first heard the above wisdom, but during the years I have observed its truth.

BEWARE THE BIG COMMITTEE

When many of us returned home following WW II, we realized Laramie needed a golf course. About 20 enthusiastic men were organized to accomplish the task. But it didn't work! Little happened until my good friend Warren Grothe disbanded the organization. He had the wisdom to know that BIG committees are ineffective. Quietly he selected Phil Tilgner and Harry Tatham to work with him. They met often with only one purpose in mind...BUILD IT, and they did!

Warren had a lumber yard, dedication and know how, and the other two were experienced workers. To get the title to unused land, Grothe got on the train and visited the headquarters of the Union Pacific in Omaha. He came away with a 99 year lease on the ground that is now Jacoby Golf Course. Warren also had a friend with experience in designing courses in the Salt Lake area, and he drew the plans, which were financed by Warren. Tilgner started building bunkers and Harry staked out fairways.

Others of the original committee were assigned projects. Railroad employee John Flippin and I started planting twigs along 30th street where a heavy caragana hedge now grows. My young sons, Ron and Ken, became tired of digging holes and watering the plants. Gene Flippin, John's younger brother, also worked with us and played the course before he moved to California. Others picked up rocks and assumed various chores. It was truly a community effort. Later, when it was roughly established the City of Laramie assumed responsibility for maintenance and of the course.

The rough course struggled along and finally the City Fathers were eager to give it to the University of Wyoming. "Red' Jacoby, the UW athletic director, really made a fine course from that awkward beginning. He transplanted big evergreens which were crowded on the campus and also built an underground watering system. "Red" was dedicated to produce the course we have today. We were all proud when it was dedicated as the Jacoby Golf Course.

THE DEADLINE

When my little wife Mary sees me working long hours in an attempt to finish my 'Dear Danny' book she discourages the hours I spend by saying, "You have been working too long on that. There is no deadline on that project."

I suggest that on every project we have in mind, or are working on, there <u>is</u> a deadline. But the real problem is that we don't know when <u>our</u> deadline really is! When I think of mine I recall the nice summer day when I got stuck in the bentonite bank on the Medicine Bow River. It was obvious to me, as I was trapped in that muddy pool that when the sun went down I would be dead. I would be found the next morning as a victim of hypothermia and I wouldn't have finished the book which means so much to me, and perhaps to you.

The other day we read of a young healthy sober man who was killed in his own car on a routine trip because a semitruck suddenly crossed the median line and ran over the smaller touring car. When he started driving down the road that day and hour, it was his deadline. These things happen when lightning hits a golfer, or for others who are caught in an earthquake. That was there deadline! This is true when a heavy truck accidentally crosses the median and runs into one's automobile.

I had a friend who shot himself when he learned he had terminal cancer. He did not wish to die, but to avoid a bitter end for himself and his family, he willing chose his own deadline with his six-shooter. When a criminal is electrocuted the warden sets his deadline. Yes, each of us has a deadline, but most of us have little choice when it will occur.

I will be 80 years old next April, and I know the odds are much smaller at my age than those of a person who is ready to celebrate his 20th birthday. Insurance companies bet on that factor.

DISCIPLINE

Discipline! In our society, at home and in the world, there must be personal discipline on the part of all human beings. Society will suffer without it. We must discipline our children and ourselves. Otherwise we will lose the benefits that come from discipline.

I remember reading about the "Zodiac Killer" in Los Angeles. He was simply a clerk and was reported to be a quiet, inoffensive, nonviolent young student, but he was sick. As I read of him I thought he might have been normal if as a kid, he had grown up in Wyoming as I did. On the school grounds he would have seen a few bloody noses. Or during the hunting season he might have had the experience of dissecting and cleaning his game. The blood he created in sadistic crimes in California might not have happened.

When radical groups are arrested on the streets, they often claim they have been denied their right to free speech. We should be realistic when we survey such disruptive factors. It could be that those who oppose the military draft are misled. Surely, they should be aware that there is no freedom of speech without discipline. Good judgment on their part would allow plenty of freedom not observed in Russia, China or Cuba. Discipline is necessary to permit the life of freedom.

Charles De Montesquieu wrote in his Spirit of Laws that in the evaluation of laws and liberties of western civilization: "It is true that in the democracies the people seem to act as they please; but political liberty does not consist in unlimited freedom. Governments do not consist in an unlimited freedom. In governments, that consist only in the power of doing what we ought to will, and in not being constrained to do what we ought not to will."

ETHICS IN THE PROFESSIONS

Every individual at this meeting should review the ethical basis of the professions. We owe it to the students who will hopefully join us in practice. Our professional heritage should make us proud. Ethical dentists must pass that heritage on to future generations so that they will share our pride.

My dictionary describes ETHICS as follows . . . a body of moral principles or values. . . pertaining to or dealing with morals or the principles of morality . . . pertaining to right rules or standards for right conduct of practice . . . the standards of a profession.

Basically, we are an offspring of the early Greek philosophers and early ethical physicians. Early lawyers and nurses were also founded by thoughtful and generous people who believed it was their obligation to care for unfortunate individuals who needed care and help.

We know that dentistry was the first group who taught public PREVENTION in this country. Our recall lists were functioning to prevent disease in the last century. We taught dental hygiene many years ago. We researched fluoride and fought to get it in public water supplies. We have done our best to eliminate refined carbohydrates which destroy natural dentitions.

There is considerable evidence that dentists are altruistic individuals. Above all we have worked together to form legislation to benefit the public, and we have served on State Boards of Dental Examiners to protect the public. The practicing dentists developed a philosophy of service which influences our dental schools. Of course schools must teach science and techniques. Also they must also teach Ethics!

OUR GENES AND DISCIPLINE

There are personal situations which we hesitate to discuss even with those who are dear to us. Today, I am undergoing such an experience.

You, Baby Ann and your mother and dad visited us to see a University of Wyoming basket-ball game yesterday. But this morning when you were ready to leave for your home I was both pleased and reminiscently thoughtful. We received the BOOMERANG Sunday newspaper, and in it was a long and involved article about me. It was most complimentary as it told of the many civic activities in which I was involved during the last fifty years. One day you will read it and I am sure will be as pleased as the adults in our family were today.

You will learn that I am not much of a church-goer. It isn't that I don't believe in God. I do, but I feel that there is a supreme being that programmed us to function. I think it might be to develop a Utopia for humanity.

Then, what about the spirit and after-life which most religions believe in. Well, I have a personal image. Several times in my 77 years I pause when I imagine that perhaps my deceased mother and father are looking down on this world in which I live. And, when we accomplish something noteworthy I look into the sky and think they are smiling approvingly at me.

When I graduated from high school and dentistry I had that satisfied feeling. And when I am honored as I was during the last year or two, and in the news article which was printed today, I feel that they know about it and are again smiling their approval. Perhaps they can communicate with one another and are sharing in my accomplishments, just as my little wife and our family are also pleased.

I know that anything good that pleases my family is partly because of the genes I inherited, and that my little wife and I also passed on to you and Ann. That is our biological heritage! Still, that in itself is not enough. There is the discipline of our daily efforts to teach our offspring what is right and what is wrong!

MY GRANDFATHER'S GENES

In Europe before 1850 the life of uneducated people was dismal. At birth they were guided to serve nobility. Poor people were stifled to keep them from getting an education. During the many wars they served as soldiers and often were cannon fodder. In peace times they worked for very minimal wages.

During the beginning of the Industrial Revolution, which began slowly in the early 1700s, water power was used in unique situations, but this was rare and undependable. More often both men and women were needed to produce industrial products.

James Watt, a young Scottish engineer, began experiments while he studied the Newcomen steam engine during 1764. The idea was good, but the engine was inefficient. In 1769 Watt patented the forerunner of the modern steam engine, and the Industrial Revolution became a reality.

The mining of coal to produce steam was a top priority. This allowed many agricultural laborers to leave the fields and work for wages in industrial plants. Even though wages were meager they had taken a major step in society. They were no longer serfs!

England led the Industrial Revolution because she had the coal and a world market. My mother's grandfather Job Hughes, left his home in Wales to seek work in the Lancashire coal fields. One wonders why teen-age boy would leave home. Perhaps his genes demanded an adventurous change. He gambled on the unknown rather than to exist in a secure environment. So my similarly adventurous grandfathers of both England and Germany gambled to leave Europe to seek a better life in Old Carbon.

HEREDITY

Of course you have four Grandparents, and you will be a product of each one of them. You will not be exactly like anyone of them in any phase of your personality, size, intelligence, courage, humor, complexion, or athletic ability.

But you will inherit genes from all four. No one can completely duplicate individuals, although it is attempted in the selective breeding of all animals. This is especially true when experts try to select the sires and dams in their efforts to breed a colt that will win the next Kentucky Derby. They have problems when they try to make the Mendelian research work for them. Someday you should read about Johann Gregor Mendel, a monk in the Augustinian monastery of Brunn Moravia. Mendel was born in 1822, and later became interested in heredity. His theory is still valid today.

I guess it is an amazing planning of God! No two people have the same finger-prints. Each of us is completely unique and in the history of any animals there was never a complete individual that perfectly matched another one. That's true even in twins or quadruplets. Sure, they have similar qualities that seem to match up, but there are subtle differences that are not always evident. They even have different talents and flaws, and yes, different finger-prints!

The pattern is even more complicated because you have eight great-grandparents from whom you will inherit genes, and then sixteen other people beyond that who have different genes. And so on, and so on! If you study more about heredity you will learn about dominant genes and recessive genes. As it ends up, both you and your sister Ann are closely related, though very different in various ways, but hereditarily you have more in common than you have with the neighbor kids.

You are the result of heredity, but much can still be done by your environment. That is the home you live in, and that depends on the intelligence and care Ken and Karey will provide. The rest depends only on <u>YOU</u>!

HAVE A NICE DAY

"Thanks, have a nice day." This a trite expression which seems to be in vogue now. It should be possible for anyone to greet one another without that phrase! I would rather simply see people simply smile. When I go to the post office, I try see who else is about to use that door, and then I hold it for them and smile. Both of us feel better.

When I am on the streets I like to look into the face of someone approaching me and smile, and perhaps say something pleasant. Nothing is gained if you ignore a stranger, or to look through them as though they didn't exist. And when I am driving it pleases me to slow down and motion a jay-walker to cross the street ahead of me. They usually smile or wave, and we both feel better. Dan, it is a good habit to get into!

It gives you a 'nice day' to slow down in traffic and motion to a person in another car, or a jaywalker, to continue on their way.

SEE THE CLOUDS

All around us, especially in Wyoming, there are graphic examples of ARTWORK OF GOD. We should simply pause, and drink in the beauty of pure white billowing clouds against an intensely blue sky.

On a marvelous spring day at our cabin on the Snowy Range, our four-year-old son Kenny was lying on his back in the wooded area while he looked at fleecy bundles of little clouds as they floated across the sky.

At that time we had on our bed a similar tufted chenille bed cover, with little balls of cotton raised above the fabric. As Ken watched the sky and asked me, as he pointed skyward, "Daddy is that God's bedspread?"
His was a wonderful childlike innocence.

. . . .

Often times Mary and I drive to a nearby hill at sunset and watch the many changing colors of the clouds which surround our plains and mountains. Every thirty seconds we see something new and beautiful in an endless panorama. A day or two later the view has entirely changed. Sometimes we see a sheet of rain descending but elsewhere are varieties of other moving clouds.

Years ago I visited with a lady who teaches on the UW campus. When she first came here she missed the trees she had always known. New England was her early home, and then she received her Ph.D in California. She believed the horizon began about twenty-degrees above the earth's surface in the north and ended at twenty-degrees in the south. One day while driving to Casper, where she taught a class, she stopped to stretch her legs on a high hill. Suddenly she reached her arm toward the horizon it was at right angle to her body. Then she realized why it is known as the BIG SKY COUNTRY. In the Rocky Mountain west the horizon covers ninety degrees, and we can see areas clearly more than a hundred miles.

NEW YEAR'S RESOLUTIONS

When a baby is born we are thrilled perhaps because we are part of God's creation. You will learn, as you grow older, that a New Year is also born on January the First. At that moment we seldom think seriously. Most of us are concerned with going out and celebrating just because our friends are doing the same,

The New Year should be a time for us to review our experiences the past twelve months and often plan to do better next year. We think of the mistakes we made during the old year. In other words, Dan, it's a time to take inventory of ourselves. Someone said "Only a damn fool makes the same mistake twice, but a wise man only once." Still none of are perfect, but as we grow older we should learn from our, and others' mistakes.

. . . .

The first time I was aware of a New Year was in 1919, when I was ten years old. Some of my Finnish friends had a barn upon which they painted the four figures each New Year. When I saw that 1919, I thought, "Hey...that is the last time we will ever see that again in my life--both number are the same!"

The next time this will occur will be in the year 2020 and you will be 17 years old! I will not be around then, so let me give you a little advice while I have the chance! Wait another ten years before you propose to <u>any</u> girl! I was 27 when I was married, and I can tell you that was soon enough.

LEARN TO PLAY A MUSICAL INSTRUMENT

Every youngster should learn something about music, and the best way to do that is to take lessons on some instrument whose sound pleases you. Now, of course, only a few have enough desire or natural ability to become proficient in the music area.

When I was as a youngster about ten years old, my mother sent to one of her favorite catalogues and bought me a clarinet. I read the lessons from the practice book that came with the instrument and followed the chart that explained the notes and keys. Then I went once a week to visit a man named Sharrett who led the Hanna Band which played at the bandstand in the little park we had there. He worked in the mines and played the cornet but knew little about the clarinet.

Eventually I learned enough to join the Finnish Orchestra. I chose because of my friendship with the piano playing Eric. (Incidentally, I was the only non- Finnish speaking in the group.) I soon realized my musical talent was mediocre, but I made up for that with enthusiasm and diligent practice. I just did not have the gifted ear of a musician. Often, I had to call for help in tuning the instrument to be in key with the rest of the orchestra or the town band.

I don't know how my mother could afford it, but one summer when I was in high school she sent me to Denver and I lived with a wonderful Italian couple. They had lost a son years before and nearly adopted me. His name was Sam Satriano, and for a living he played in the Denver band and orchestra. I worked hard with his instruction, but I think that both of us knew I could not make a living as a musician. After a month living with these fine people I returned to Hanna and could play rather well. Eric and I organized the first Jazz band with two of the Kandolin brothers and Urho Maki--all Finlanders. Hanna always had a good band and I enjoyed the marches.

When I was at Denver University as a pre-dental student, I played in the university band. While there, I had the thrill of my life by attending a concert of the John Phillip Sousa traveling band. He was known as the March King of music. His orchestra ended the concert to a standing ovation as they played the Stars and Stripes Forever.

As a young dentist in Laramie, I joined the band and also the University of Wyoming Symphony Orchestra. At that time there were few students and some of us non-students were invited to play in the group. Today, I could not compete with the students.

When our three children were youngsters, I gave up the clarinet and did the other things that kids enjoy. For about thirty years I neglected the clarinet, but on retirement, I had the instrument repaired and again started trying to play some of the music I dug out of my memorabilia. For some years I tried to play some of the music but never as well as before. Nevertheless, it was a great relaxing pastime for me before the dinner hour. Finally, Dan, I did not touch it again as I started working with computer and writing my book. Soon I will again dig out the clarinet.

The greatest benefit any young child can gain from playing a musical instrument is that he becomes a more appreciative audience at various musical concerts. I love the old jazz recordings and have an appreciation for classical music because I am always amazed at the technique and versatility of professional musicians.

LEARN TO WRITE

Few people have the desire or talent to write. But many want to try. I believe one should make an effort to write some of his thoughts or experiences, especially as we grow older. Everyone has had unique experiences which are different from all other individuals. Whether it is success or failure our writing might help others.

It is unfortunate that our society seems to make the same mistakes of those who preceded us. But by reading and writing we should try to prevent failure, and also stimulate positive benefits. One who only reads, but never writes, reminds me of a sponge who soaks up knowledge and amusement, but never contributes.

Well, Dan, let's you and I place this on a one-to-one basis. Perhaps this is why I've written these many "Dear Dan" letters.

WHITE LIES AND THE TRUTH

A Swiss philosopher once said, "Truth is violated by falsehood, but is outraged by silence." I am involved in a civic confrontation because I want our officials to construct a new Post Office, and a needed Department of Justice building. I know I am taking a lot of heat from some, but I am outraged by the silent majority who simply fail to become involved. Few of the majority fail make waves; or are they just lazy? Earning the respect of one's peers should be our goal in life.

You will observe that some people habitually tell little white lies just to keep from offending others. But at what point does a little lie become a big one? In my time lies led our Federal Government into the Watergate scandal of President Nixon. He and other bureaucrats told white lies to protect themselves and the government. I have told a few which always fouled me up. Later I feel badly. . White lies often have a boomerang effect.

Well, Dan, you should be proud of your Uncle Ron. In a sticky situation when a little white lie seems indicated, he simply disappears. At other times when someone puts him on the spot, he often speaks with a truth. This often and shocks a few individuals.

Dan, when you are caught in a situation where you have to dance with a girl classmate, afterwards simply thank her, but don't tell her she sweats a lot. Perhaps, you should rather tell her that she has beautiful hair. That is, if it's true!

SHOULD AND MUST

The individual who accomplishes tasks because he <u>must</u> will be ordinary. He will vegetate, taking up his allotted space in society until he becomes a vital statistic. History will not remember him.

But each of us has a chance to accomplish something to benefit future generations. This is our challenge. Those who meet this challenge have an inner drive which sets them apart. They are governed by an impulse for intellectual honesty. These people who react to the pilot SHOULD, rather than MUST, refuse to be a mass of connective tissue. Seldom are these individuals inwardly directed to analyze their actions and accomplishments. Rather, they have empathy for others. Their MUST counterparts have only sympathy. The SHOULD people allow their conscience to guide them. These unique individuals lead us along toward Utopia.

THE AMERICAN FLAG

Of course, after saying daddy and mommie, your next two words were 'ball' and 'flag.' When you were two years old you seemed profoundly fascinated by the American flag in our yard, which I fly when you visit us. That day as you watched the flag, I photographed the scene. Your expression caused me to write:

"How to be rich and happy as we mature is no secret. All we have to do is to be child-like and reverent. Simply enjoy and pause to observe the beauty created by God and Man. It is registered in the wonderment of children as they see their first sunset, love the colors of the rainbow, and watch the flag flying in the wind."

The Afterlife

SCIENCE IS A PROVEN FACT

Dear Dan:

When you think of the word science, you must think, "Is true?" Today many things are known as scientific, but many are not proven beyond all doubt, and then they are not really scientific.

As an example, water becomes ice at 32 degrees Fahrenheit. That is a indisputable fact! But before facts really are unquestionable, they must be proven. Scientists often begin their investigations with a hypothesis or theory. That means they simply have ideas for which they seek evidence. Whatever the true scientist expects, until it is proven, it is simply a working hypothesis. And it must further be proven by enough other scientific persons before it is really scientific.

Perhaps in every generation there are pseudo-scientists who act as if they were true scientists. I have had personal contacts with a dentist who mistakenly believes he is a scientist. I believe he is a pseudo-scientist. He cannot get the help of others because they do not believe mercury poisoning is caused by silver amalgam dental fillings. On the new media statements we hear every day individuals who claim to be true scientists. Their ideas are only theories or hypothesis. They need indisputable scientific research to establish fact.

PHILOSOPHICAL CONCEPTS

Anyone examining philosophical concepts will note that philosophy, ethics and religion overlap in many areas. In times of personal tragedy religious inquiry often solves problems. Many individuals should ask, "What is the reason for each of us being born?" For a simple mind like mine, I have a simple answer. It is the progressive search of man for Utopia--the better life for all! That is a goal which can only be achieved by small progressive steps in which everyone can contribute.

Since the first of our species appeared, man has worked to improve his family's lives, and then likewise wanted something better for his grandchildren. True, many philosophers have also striven for better life styles for their neighbors.

The Utopian drive suggests that we share our enthusiasm and knowledge. If it were not so, most of us would never conduct research, teach classes, or encourage others to follow us. We would not have added to the professional literature for the benefit of our contemporaries and their posterity. (How about Ego? Well, could it have been built into some of us to encourage the drive toward Utopia?)

The philosophical ethic encourages us toward Utopian goals. It directs the activities of the professional person beyond his office or laboratory. People work relentlessly, as they should, to improve the political, charitable, legal, religious, civic, and educational life of their communities--as well as their country.

However it would be well if during our activities, we did not take ourselves and our projects too seriously. There is an important place in life for fun, sports, and humor. To make and hear laughter, cause a smile on a stranger's face, exercise, hunt and fish, and to enjoy good music and literature, and also to love and communicate with friends and family, this is good therapy!

All worthy human beings, must practice personal discipline, otherwise community can be damaged. We must appreciate discipline, either as children and adults. The need is great!

Perhaps, in my search for personal answers, I have not given our Christian churches their full credit they deserve. As we know the history of the United States is tied to the basics of our Judeo-Christianity history. Our churches provide a humane influence on our society. I, for one, am grateful for the pleasure and consolation Mary Ford received from her church. Long before she died she contributed to all churches equally. Yes I would hate to live in a community that had no Church!

SOLVING PHILOSOPHICAL PROBLEMS

Years ago I read of the "Zodiac Killer," who was convicted in Los Angeles. He was a post office clerk and those who knew him remarked that he was reserved, inoffensive, and a good student. But he was sick! When I read of him I wondered what would have happened if he had grown up on a ranch in Wyoming and as a boy had a few bloody noses on the school grounds, and even hunted antelope which he would kill, dissect and clean. Then perhaps he would not have shed the blood of innocent victims, as did the young man in California. Perhaps he would not become so crudely seductive.

We all tire of the individuals who make an effort to defend themselves with pleas of their right to free speech; or plead insanity at the moment of ugly action. Realistically, these disruptive factions deserve little sympathy. Often they oppose the military conscription act and as blatantly demand their individual rights. They refuse to discipline themselves. Would they trade this for their counterparts in Russia, China or Cuba?

RELIGION I
SPEAKING OUT--EDMUND R. LEACH

In an old volume of a magazine SPEAKING OUT, Edmund R. Leach wrote "We Scientists have the Right to Play God." I was impressed and wish to copy it:

"Human scientists now have it in their power to redesign the face of the earth, and to decide what kind of species shall survive to inherit it. How they actually use this terrible potentiality must depend on moral judgments, not on reason. But who shall decide, and how shall we judge? The answer to these questions seems to me repugnant but quite plain: There can be no source for these moral judgments except the scientist himself. In traditional religion, morality was held to derive from God, but God was only credited with the authority to establish and enforce moral rules because He was also credited with supernatural powers of creation and destruction. Those powers have now been usurped by man, and he must take on the moral responsibility that goes with them.

"Our idea of God is a product of history. What I now believe about the supernatural is derived from parents, and what they taught me was derived from what we were taught, and so on. But such beliefs are justified by faith alone, never by reason, and the true believer is expected to go on reaffirming his faith in the same verbal formula, even if the passage of history and growth of scientific knowledge should have turned the words into plain nonsense. Everyone now knows that the cosmology that is presupposed by the language of Christian utterance is quite unrelated to any empirical reality. This explains why so many religious-minded people exhibit an extreme reluctance to inquire at all closely into the meaning of basic religious concepts.

"But just what do we mean by the word God? In Christian mythology, as represented by the Bible, God is credited with a variety of functions. He is the creator who first set the cosmological clock in motion; He is the lawgiver who establishes the principles of the moral code; He is the judge who punishes sinners even when human law fails to do so; He is also a kind of a trickster who intervenes in human affairs in a quite arbitrary way so as to test the faith of the righteous; and, finally, He is a mediator between sinful man and his destiny. He is not only the judge of sinners but their salvation. These attributes of God are by definition "superhuman," but they are nevertheless qualities of an essentially human kind. The God of Judeo-Christianity is, in all His aspects, whether creator, judge, trickster or mediator, quite explicitly anthropomorphic. And the converse is equally true: There is necessarily something godlike about every human being.

"Anthropologists, who make it their business to discover just how human beings perceive themselves as differing from one another and from other natural species, will tell you that every community conceives of itself as being uniquely "human." This humanity is always felt to be a quality of civilization and orderliness that "we" foreigners and animals, are members of inferior species and are described by labels such as "savage," "wild," "lawless," "heathen," "dangerous," "mysterious."

"There is a paradox here: When we affirm that we are civilized and that the others are savage, we are claiming superiority over the others, but the mythology always explains the origin of this superiority by a story of Adam and Eve type. "In the beginning God created our first ancestors and gave them the moral rules that are the basis of our present civilization." But this "God" himself belongs to the category of "others:" He is nonhuman, He is above the law, He is dangerous and mysterious, He existed even before the beginning. He is Nature itself. So we find that, in religious terms, culture--that is, civilization--stands in a curiously ambivalent relationship to nonculture--that is, nature. At one level we, the men of culture, are dominant over nature, but at another level God and nature merge together and become dominant over us.

"All this is more relevant to my title than might at first appear, for scientists, like God, have now become mediators between culture and nature. Modern science grew out of medieval alchemy, and the alchemists were quite explicitly men who sought to do what only gods might properly do--to transform one element into another and to discover the elixir of immortal life. They pursued these revolutionary objectives in the atmosphere of a very conservative society. Official doctrine held that the order of nature had been established once and for all in the first six days of Creation, and that the proper station and destiny of every individual had been preordained by God. The alchemists , therefore, were very properly regarded as blasphemous heretics, for they were attempting to tamper with God's handiwork, they were claiming that "laws of nature" could be altered by human intervention, they were playing at being God. Moreover, they lived in a world of fantasy. The heretical miracles that they claimed to perform were imaginary."

"But at the present time the ordinary every day achievements of science, which we take quite for granted, are precisely the kind that our medieval forebears considered to be supernatural. We can fly through the air, we can look in on events that are taking place on the other side of the earth, we can transplant organs from corpses to living bodies, we can even produce a chemical mimicry of living tissue itself."

(And since this was written, we now fertilize ovum with sperm in the laboratory and transplant them to produce babies, and even split chromosomes to affect heredity. --C. M. Stebner)

"In the traditional mythology, the performance of miracles is only a part (and on the whole a minor part) of God's function. God's major role is mortal--He is the source of the rules. He can now play God in this role as wonder-worker, but can he-- and should he--also play God as moral arbiter? If you put this question to any group of actual scientists, the majority will answer it with an unhesitating "No," for it is one of the most passionately held formal dogmas of modern science that research procedures should be objective and not tendentious. The scientist must seek to establish the truth for truth's sake, and not as an advocate of any particular creed. And on the face of it, this principle is self-evident: If we are to attain scientific objectivity, moral detachment is absolutely essential.

"Yet this viewpoint, too, is a product of history. Modern science can be said to have begun when Copernicus and Galileo established the fundamental base of modern astronomy. In order to do this, they had to achieve moral detachment and deny the truth of the Ptolemaic cosmology, which at that time had the official sanction of the Church. As both these men were good Catholics, and several of the cardinals, including Galileo's Pope, were excellent scientists. And so it has continued even down to the present. Again and again leaders of the Church have felt themselves compelled to declare that some finding of science--such as evolution by natural selection, or the chemical origin of life, or the capacity of the human to reproduce itself beyond the limits of its food supply--is contrary to religious doctrine, and they have demanded that the scientist recant. Against this coercion the scientists have erected their own counterdogma: The pursuit of scientific truth must be free of all moral or religious restraints.

"But the claim to moral detachment is not absolute. In actual practice all scientists draw the line somewhere, and they usually draw it between culture and nature. Freedom from moral restraint applies only to the study of nature, not to study of culture. Even the Nazi scientists who experimented with human beings as if they were monkeys, rats or guinea pigs, would not have challenged this distinction. They merely drew their line in a different place: From their point of view the Jews were not really human, but just a part of nature.

"But discriminations of this sort are very ungodlike. God is the creator and protector of all things: He does not destroy one part of His creation in order to give benefit to another; creation is a totality, one and indivisible. In contrast, we human beings habitually act as if all other living species, whether animals or plants, exist only for our own convenience; we feel free to exploit and destroy them as we think fit. It is true that some sentimental laymen have moral qualms about vivisection, but no orthodox scientist could ever have any hesitation about experiments involving "mere animals." All the same, there are always some kinds of experiments that any particular research worker would not be prepared to carry out. Each individual does, in practice, "draw the line somewhere," so the question arises whether he might not with advantage draw it somewhere else.

"The moral doubts of those who helped to design the first atomic bombs have become notorious, and today there must be thoughts of highly qualified scientists engaged on hundreds of different chemical and biological research projects who face similar difficulties. It is not simply a matter of trying to measure the positive value of a gain in human knowledge against the negative value of merits and demerits of our whole biological history are at stake. It is no good for the scientist to suppose that there is some outside authority who can decided whether his experiments are legitimate or illegitimate. It has become useless to appeal to God against the Devil; the scientist must be the source of his own morality.

"Because God traditionally had unlimited power to intervene and alter the natural course of events, it made sense to treat Him as the ultimate moral authority as well. But today when the molecular biologists are rapidly unraveling the genetic chemistry of all living things--while the radio astronomers are deciphering the program of an evolving cosmos--all the marvels of creation are seen to be mechanisms rather than mysteries. Since even the human brain is nothing more than an immensely complicated computer, it is no longer necessary to invoke metaphysics to explain how it works. In the resulting mechanistic universe all that remains of the divine will is the moral consciousness of man himself.

"So we must now learn to play God in a moral as well as in a creative or destructive sense. To do this effectively, we shall have to educate our children in quite a different way. In the past, education has always been designed to inculcate a respect for the wisdom and experience of the older generation, whose members have been credited with an intuitive understanding of wisdom and experiences of the older generation, whose members have been credited with an intuitive understanding of the wishes of an omniscient God. From this point of view, the dogmas of religion represent the sum of our historical experience. So long as it appeared that "natural law" was eternal and unalterable--except by God--it was quite sensible to use history in this way as a guide to virtue. But in our changed circumstances, ground rules of the game, excessive deference to established authority could well be an invitation to disaster. For example, as long as medical science was virtually impotent--except by God-- it was quite sensible to use history in this way as a guide to virtue. But in our changing circumstances, when we ourselves can alter all the ground rules of the game, excessive deference to established authority could well be an invitation to disaster. For example, as long as medical science was virtually impotent--as it was until the beginning of this century--it made perfect sense to accept the traditional theological principle that it is always virtuous to save a life. But today the doctors, provided they are given sufficient resources, can preserve alive all manner of deformed infants and senile invalids who would, in the natural course of events, have been dead long ago. But the cost of preserving these defective lives is ultimately borne by those who are normal and healthy, and at some point the burden will become intolerable, and saving life will become morally evil. When we are faced with moral paradoxes of this kind--and science presents us with new ones every day--it is useless to console ourselves with the conventional religious formulas. We ourselves have to decide what is sin and what is virtue, and we must do so on the basis of our modern knowledge and not on the basis of traditional categories. This implies that we must all share in a kind of immediate collective responsibility for any action that any one individual performs. Perhaps this all sounds like a pie-in-the-sky doctrine. But unless we teach those of the next generation that they can afford to be atheists only if they assume the moral responsibilities of God, the prospects for the human race are decidedly bleak."

(End of SPEAKING OUT BY LEACH)

SCIENCE, SPIRITUALITY, and RELIGION

James R. Collins

For me spirit is life. While spirituality expressed within a religious structure is not necessary, it is at the core of the expression of my spiritual life in the culture I know. First, some informal definitions--my own.

Spirituality: A person's relationship with God.
Religion: An institutional mechanism to live out one's spirituality.
Faith: Belief or trust even in the absence of knowledge.

I know a few who deny a sense of spirituality in spirit in their life. While often undefined, even unexamined, most people I know would acknowledge a creator--God. In most of our scientific work to deny a creator, a first cause if you will, means to believe in a universe that is an accident of some sort. Such an accident certainly is a possibility but one with a very small probability. In fact, it would be an accident so rare that if most scientists would stop to consider the evidence and the probabilities, I believe they would reject the null hypothesis "there is no creator of the universe" or "the universe is an accident" well beyond the .01 level of significance. Together you and I have expressed our amazement at new life, be it the formation of a cell, the unfolding of a leaf, or the spark of new human life. And I think we both have concluded that those moments lead us to believe in a source greater than ourselves, greater than the world of science in which we work. But the consideration of the probabilities of either a creator or an accident and concluding in favor of one does not prove the conclusion is correct. My hunch is that in our lifetime the question will remain open for debate. We all live our lives based on faith of one sort or another. More importantly, while in some cases belief or lack of belief in a creator may imply different procedures for a given scientific investigation or drawing different conclusion for given evidence, my contention is that such differences are rare in the day-to-day activities of scientists. Most scientists would approach their work and draw their conclusions independent of their spiritual beliefs. But those cases where believers and non-believers would differ are usually critical ones. So, just as I have heard you say that you would not want to live in a community that had no churches, I would not want live in a scientific community that was devoid of spirituality.

In many cases I sense concern over control by some, particularly scientists, in arguing against spirituality. If there is a perfect, omnipotent, omniscient God, then why can not--does not--that God take charge? Or, how can God's secrets of the universe be unfolding through scientific investigation at the whim of mere humans? I can only describe the God I know. The God I know is perfect, omnipotent, and omniscient. But the God I know delights in our discoveries of the secrets of the universe. For the most part, the God I know chooses to leave the laws of nature alone to determine the outcome of this world's activities on both the large scale and the small scale. It is not that my God is not interested, it is just that the principle of free will means for me that we carry both the rights and responsibilities of life in this God-created and God-given world. My God weeps and rejoices right along with us as things go ill or well. My God gave us our intellect and the principles of scientific investigation and expects us to use them to their fullest for an evolving understanding and control of the universe for the good of all.

For scientists to refuse to consider spirituality in their lives because it would somehow acknowledge a limitation on their own control seems arrogant, egotistical, and inconsistent with the reality of scientific investigation where we are asked to keep an open mind about all sorts of things we can not control. At times I suspect that some really are interested in being able to explain phenomenon so that they can build their sense of personal control over the world. The ability to work as a scientist who does acknowledge one's spirituality requires a degree of both faith and humility--but then so does the ability to work credibly as a scientist who does not acknowledge one's spirituality.

I have yet to consider the questions related to spirituality that focus on religion. Those questions are important and ones I have pondered, some to my personal satisfaction, many to my continuing personal confusion. I feel one's commitment to a religion is heavily influenced by circumstances, the culture in which that person exists. For the most part religion represents for me the gathering of those who believe, who have faith in similar things. Most of that common base rests on the lived traditions or the written records that are shared together. In general, religion is a product of humans and in that sense is tainted by the fallibility of humans. If one wants perfection, it is best found somewhere other than in human activities. But I tolerate imperfection in most parts of my life: my profession, my relationships, my society, my government, certainly in myself--and I tolerate imperfections in my religion. My call to that group is the same as my call to the other sources of imperfection listed above, and that is that we trust, that we try, that we correct ourselves when we are wrong, and we reconcile when errors are made. I expect my religion to lead the way in all of this. Sometimes it does; sometimes it does not. But as long as there remains my fundamental belief and faith in what my religion represents and as long as my religion represents what I profess, I continue to embrace my Church. Anything else would bring me back to the control issues I mentioned above, namely, an attitude that unless I have complete control, I will not enter in.

At times it would seem that both my spirituality and my religion are like a monkey on my back--one that I could not shake if I wanted to. Part of the good news is I do not want to.

ALBERT EINSTEIN

In the March issue of the American Scientist, 1988 Abraham Pais presents an interesting paper on Einstien. He notes that the noted person who is credited with the Theory of Relativity was in his early days a devout believer as a Jewish student.

When Einstein was asked about his thoughts concerning God, he said, "Spinoza's God who reveals himself in the orderly harmony of what exists, not in a God who concerns himself with fates and actions of human beings. When he was pressed he noted, as he compared God with Science, he said: "Science without religion is lame, religion without science is blind."

(I was impressed by Einstein's quotation.)

. . . .

People who are using the word "God" might say "NATURE." They should think of that the next time they see a Butterfly.

CMS

SCIENTISTS ARE PLAYING GOD

As Edmund R. Leach, a British scientist and philosopher, has suggested, scientists are playing God, and they often miss the need for a keen sense of morality. He believes we should educate our children differently, because they will be able to write the rules of life for the game of the future. He notes that economically and practically we cannot ignore birth control. It seems to me that we are housing and feeding criminals who have been condemned to die. Our society cannot feed and protect them in increasing numbers.

Today, we must question the radical transplanting of baboon and mechanical hearts into the chests of those who neglected their own. We must agree with the logic of Leach who says our scientists and surgeons are playing God. Often this is an immoral and unethical act.

WE ARE A CHRISTIAN NATION

The United States is a Christian country. Or are we? On an average Sunday, a majority of us do not celebrate the Christian Sabbath. Certainly not during the summer months. We take the day off for recreation. It was different for our Founding Fathers.

Much like the average American family, we sent our young children to Sunday School. Perhaps we did not set a good example, because in the summer we took them to our mountain cabin. In the winter we taught them how to ski on Sundays.

Another problem was that we had trouble finding a minister we all liked. We started out as Baptists because Mary and I were married in that church. This seemed normal because Mary's mother was a Baptist.

At times we went to Mary Ford's Methodist Church and our family enjoyed being with their grandmother. She was devout and never missed a Sunday service when she was able. She knew all the old hymns, and benefited much from her religion. She often sang a song she learned in her childhood days in England-- "I will be a Methodist until I die." At age 93 she was buried from the Laramie Methodist Church. Also, there followed a service in the Hanna Methodist Church, which she helped to found and prosper. Mother worked, not only for her own church, but also for the Episcopalian and the Catholic churches in Hanna. She believed in her God, but still loved those who had no church as well.

Like most Americans, we were as good Christians, as were our grandparents. Still, our kids were baptized when they were old enough to understand the ritual.

Today we support the Presbyterian church financially and continue our membership, but are far from attending regularly. It's likely that my wife, Mary, will request traditional Christian funeral services.

Christian churches are traditional in the families of Mary and myself. Yes, there will be a Memorial service, and the minister will say a prayer for us if we continue to serve others well. For me it is cremation! I know of a high hill near old Carbon where I want my ashes--there I hunt each autumn. I wonder if my parents are aware of me as I climb the hill to that weather-beaten gnarled tree which was there when my dad and granddad hunted sage-chickens a hundred years ago. Like most people I think about the hereafter, but no human knows the answer.

Like all human beings I wonder what will happen to our soul, or spirit, when we die. But while I am alive I enjoy taking a step toward the Utopian goal and make this earth a better place in which to live. I'm not concerned with Heaven or Hell. It doesn't concern me.

Many who are scientifically oriented, as I am, have trouble in understanding the Virgin Birth or the Resurrection. To me the union between the sperm and the ovum are all the wonderful mystery I need. The formation and birth of a healthy baby amazes me. Millions of intelligent Christians accept these miracles as facts. Who knows?

PHILOSOPHY--RELIGION and UTOPIA

If one examines philosophical concepts it will be noted that there are many grey areas between philosophy, ethics, and religion. In times of personal tragedy, religious inquiry often solves problems. Philosophers have asked, "What is the supreme plan for our existence?" Or, "What is the reason for each of us being born"? For me, there's a simple answer.

I believe it is the search of man for Utopia. No doubt it is the desire to achieve a better life for all mankind. That is a goal which can only be achieved by small progressive steps taken by everyone. Individually we can contribute!

Since the first man appeared I think that he worked to improve his family's lives. And that he wanted something better for his offspring. True professionals and philosophers have also striven for better lifestyles for our neighbors.

The utopian drive suggests that we share our enthusiasm and knowledge. If that were not so, we would not have conducted research, taught classes, or encouraged others to do the same. Many contributors would not have added to professional literature for the benefit of our contemporaries and posterity. How about our Ego? Perhaps that characteristic was instilled in most of us to produce the drive to search for Utopia.

The philosophical ethic pushes each of us toward utopian goals. It stimulates the idealistic professional person to work outside of his office or laboratory. Many people work relentlessly to improve political, charitable, legal, religious, civic, and educational benefits to lives of others.

It would be well however, during such activities a person did not take himself and his projects too seriously. There must be an important place in life for fun, sports and humor. Good therapy makes laughter, causes a smile on a stranger's face. We should also enjoy good music and literature, and be pleased to communicate with friends and family.

MANNA FROM HEAVEN

This morning, I awakened early. The clock said 4:40--that seems to be my usual time. That must be the hour for me because I felt great! After my session in the bathroom where I drink two big glasses of hot water, I came down stairs and ran in my stocking feet. As usual I went to watch the news on TV while I did my stretching exercises.

This program started off with a preacher giving his daily message. Often I hear a person say something I've long believed. His message was one we can gain without experience. I am no Bible student, but there are many lessons we can learn from material written more than 2,000 years ago.

It goes like this . . .

Before the time of Christ the Jews had a tough time existing in the desert of the Near East. But hunger and starvation were imminent. Still there were many Jews who faced starvation. Yet they were tough and intelligent. They believed in the Lord profoundly. Their blessing was the seeds which were found in the desert. It became a special food which they named MANNA. To the Jews this source of food became an ancient bread which saved the lives of their ancestors. The word is anthropological--and means a generalized supernatural force of power, which may be concentrated in objects or persons. Now we understand why early Jews called it, "manna, a blessing from heaven."

Well, the story goes that those who ate only manna became very tired of the menu! They complained because it was often stale and tasteless, even though it was a blessing from the Lord. Perhaps, they griped because it was simply given to them.

I've noticed that rich kids rarely appreciate the many things that their parents give them, such as a TV, or a new automobile. That is because they had not worked to earn the money which paid for it. You can bet that those who worked to develop manna thought it was wonderful. They gathered and planted the seeds, carried water necessary for growth, then ground the grains in a mortar and pestle, which was made of stones they had fashioned. Later, they carried more water to make it into a paste. Finally, the collected scarce wood and built a fire. Then they ate it from pottery they had fashioned. After the meal was eaten they ate the finished product and said prayers because their bodies were nourished. It saved their lives! Sure, those who earned it with hard work! They said their prayers for the gift from the Lord they worshiped.

. . . .

In a few days I plan to go to Denver, and in court will insist that the kids who broke into our automobile at the airport and stole my radio <u>should</u> pay the damages. It may not work as well if their parents, one a psychiatrist and the other an engineer, pay the damages their kids created. If their parents were intelligent they would have insisted their offspring found a tough job and earned the money to finance a new radio. Then they would understand the effort it takes to buy a new radio. They are not gifts from heaven.

Dan, the many benefits I have today are the result of an education that my mother and I worked hard to accomplish, and also because of the many long hours I spent in the dental office. Today, they are having a big fight in the congress in order to balance the national debt. Part of the argument suggests it is necessary to remove federal benefits we have given to kids in college. The federal government, and the taxpayers cannot finance educations for all.

Generally, we have indulged youths creating many problems for all concerned. Even their parents cry like spoiled children when they are in trouble. It was quite different when I was in college. Then my little mother and I worked hard for our ultimate benefit without expecting "Manna from heaven.'

MARY FORD RETIRES

The years between 1953 and 1983 Mary Ford was actually retired. She had her own apartment and when she felt the need for heat, simply reached for her own thermostat. No longer did she have to lift the heavy coal bucket to fire the big stove in the hotel kitchen.

She had a lot of company in Laramie and people loved her as they did in Hanna. During the last five years she had a live-in companion, Jessie Gerald, to whom she gave her bedroom while mother slept too in another bed. For them we hired a practical nurse to live across the hall to cook and care for their needs.

Mary earned her abandoned 30 year retirement!

Mary Ford retired and moved to Laramie.

THE YOUNG SAMARITAN

At my age everyone seems too young to marry. Yet, I was twenty-seven when I was married--that was young enough.

We were invited to his wedding party, where I met many whom I had not seen before. The bride was alluring, petite and beautiful. Then I was introduced to the groom, who rates lesser at affairs like this!

The groom impressed me by his clean-cut appearance. He was polite and acted interested in me and others he had just met. And when he heard my name he casually said, "I met your mother."

Years before, when he was on his way to a University Wyoming class, he saw a bewildered little lady standing on a street corner. She seemed distressed. Then, he saw blood on her face, and when he asked where she lived she could not answer. She lived near the campus, and was out for a walk around the block. She seemed distressed!

It was my mother! She was bleeding and in shock and could not tell him where she lived. She fractured her nose and also broke her dentures, which he helped her retrieve. Then, he helped her into his car and drove her to the hospital. When they were treating her she mentioned that her son was Doctor Stebner. Then the young man went to his class!

At the wedding he casually mentioned how he met my Mother. Mary and I had been touring China, but finally the hospital contacted our son Ron. When we returned from our trip I made several efforts to locate that young man. I knew that because of his empathy, both he and his parents were people I wanted to know. Years later I met them just before he was married.

It was good to know that even in our busy times, there are still young SAMARITANS in our midst! His name was Donald Budd.

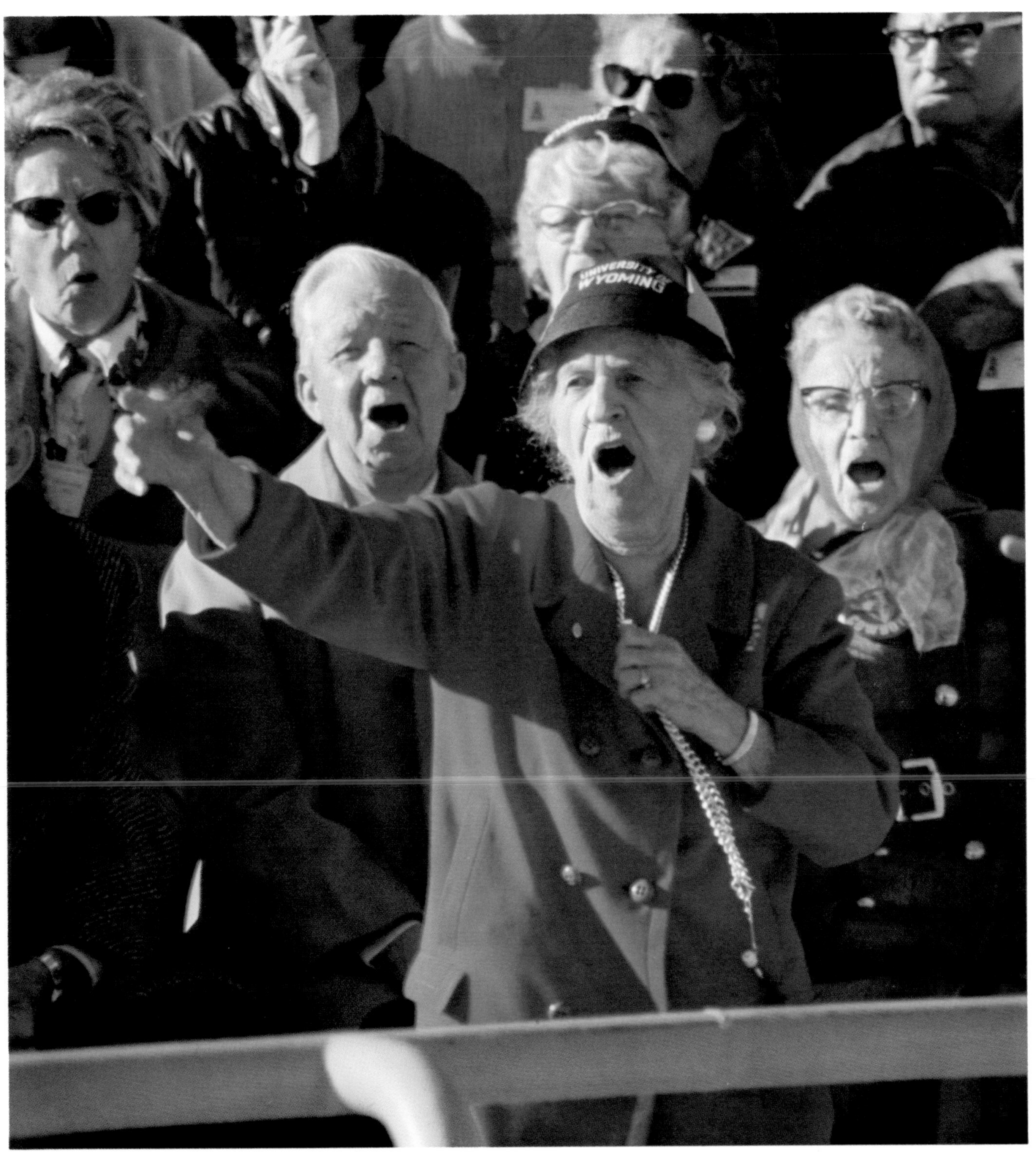
UNIVERSITY OF
WYOMING

RALPH HOLLAND DIES

Today I read the news that I had lost a good younger friend, Ralph Holland. He was in excellent health, but died from an unnecessary accident. I thought of the loss of my dad when I was five years old.

Friends and families say prayers to God--in other areas they would call on Mohammed, or other Deities, but none of them have an answer for me. Situations like this have too many unanswered questions.

Still, as a scientist, I learned a little of the genes, the sperm, and the ovum. Yet, I am astounded with the <u>real</u> miracle of the birth of a healthy child, and the death of a fine and healthy person. Some simply say it is God's way.

When I was in Sunday school we were told that God will take care of YOU! But, today we are told that we are responsible first and must buckle our seat belt.

I wonder why such an unnecessary death would come to Ralph, when He allows dastardly crude criminals to avoid capital punishment. If it is God's way, and someone must die at that moment, then I question His choice!

THE RIGHT TO DIE WITH DIGNITY

The Right to Die by Louis Cassels (United Press International) was the author of a plea for Euthanasia.

That word reminds of the day I was about to enter the Wyoming University library for information on a paper I was writing for my group called the Peripatetics. I met my son Ken, and some his college pals. They wanted to know what I was doing on their campus. I told them I was searching for material on Euthanasia. I asked them for a definition of the word 'Euthanasia'. They laughed as Ken answered, "Sure Dad it is a study of young people in China!"

Well, Cassels had these things to say about Euthanasia: "the writers of the constitution might have suggested the fourth basic human right: the right to die with dignity. . . dying is a universal human experience. Like all other experiences, it has content and quality. It can be done bravely or cravenly; reluctantly or with serene acceptance. It can take place in the warmly supportive setting of a home and a family, or in the coldly impersonal atmosphere of an institution". He quotes a Boston physician, of the Equinox Institute, people who die in institutions have, "little opportunity to be assisted in working out meaningful details of the dying experience."

And also Kant says, we need to "review and explore the meaning of control of one's dying." By this, he does not necessarily mean people should be encouraged to end their own lives by suicide, or that terminally ill people be ushered out by deliberate medical execution. Since most people move slowly into death, the right to control their dying experience really means that they are allowed to retain power of decision "over those few remaining choices and options" which may determine how long they'll linger or where they'll die.

Cassels says that most doctors are imbued with the idea they should never stop fighting to maintain technical life--no matter how hopeless or costly the battle may be, or how the patient or his family may feel about the matter. The contemporary society often robs people of the right to control their own dying and thus to die with dignity.

In this age we are well aware that for the first time in our evolutionary history we are progressing more rapidly than we can imagine. But are we advancing as fast as necessary in the development of the human dignity? Substantiating the idea of many philosophers it would do little good to combat the mechanical and scientific progress of today. Now we should improve our moral standards. The rapid progress of pure science and medicine should not be neglected. But we need rational instruction in the science and medical schools to adopt thoughtful philosophical principles. Progress in this area is feeble.

There is great need among younger professional people to react for the needs of society. Today the mercenary trends among the professions makes us look more like business men. Even some of our churches are criticized, and rightly so, for demonstrating various degrees of intolerance and dogmas. Too often the churches have not kept pace with the moral evolution and science. We must teach our children to adapt to human dignity. Then, we should expect our political leaders to join them.

MARY FORD'S DEATH

In early 1987 I realized that mother's struggles, and immense happiness and enthusiasm were at an end. She was slowly drifting away. There was no pain or medication indicated. Often I thought that a sudden heart attack would be the way to go. Still, most of us are faced with little we can control.

I abhor dramatic efforts to prolong life when there is nothing to be gained. Most aged individuals have had all the pleasures and difficulties they deserve. It seems that the so-called ethics of the medical profession, and our hospitals, have gone too far in prolonging life. Most old people sincerely wish that nature should take its course.

The first 90 years she was healthy and active, but during her last three years she was subject to accidental falling. Finally, she was forced to spend some time in the hospital. She was always healthy and active, but the abrupt change in her life-style was discouraging. After her last falling accident I decided that I would plan to have her expire naturally her own apartment which she loved.

Across the hall from her lived a nurse aide who had experience in caring for older people. We furnished her with her own apartment and some groceries to care for mother and her companion, Jessie. The nurse served their meals, and also did general household work.

During mother's last week I told my wife it would not be long because her respiration was labored. Much of her time was spent sleeping. I saw her every day, and she was aware who I was. When she could no longer respond to my conversation, she gripped my hand. Each day I hoped that she would cease to breathe during the night. We had a had an understanding physician who knew mother well. He told me that she would drift away peacefully. She soon was unable to swallow fluids or soft foods. I was determined to not have her force fed.

Very early the next morning her nurse called me and said Mother had died peacefully in her sleep. Sure there were a few tears, but it was rewarding to know that she died in dignity--without pain!

Her funeral was in the her Methodist church and there were few tears. Our family was grateful to see the large crown who knew and loved her.

. . . .

A second funeral service for her was held in the little Methodist church mother helped to build. We traveled to the Cemetery on a clear cool afternoon with bright sunshine on the sagebrush. But unlike many of the trips she made to bury others of her family there was little sadness.

That day Spring snow was piled on the sides of the road and melting water ran toward us. It was difficult for automobiles to climb that steep hill. A tractor on the hill pulled cars to drier ground. For us it because Byra, our son-in-law, drove his high powered automobile to the family lot. Later, on the head stone I had her poem engraved:

"I'll care not how long I'll live, If I can give, and give, and give, and give."

. . . .

We had trouble leaving the cemetery. Her sentimental grandson Ken was reluctant to leave her there alone, but finally we drove down and decided to stop near a place where our family hunts sagechicken during fall. Our three or four cars rendezvoused. The wind was a little too cool as we stood together in the sagebrush. Someone had a bottle of whiskey and a few beers, and had a wake. Many stories were told about Mary Ford--most of them hilarious!

PROBLEM-SOLVING STRATEGIES

Extended Edition includes Chapters 1–44. Standard Edition includes Chapters 1–37.
Three-volume edition: *Volume 1 includes Chapters 1–20, Volume 2 includes Chapters 21–37, and Volume 3 includes Chapters 37–44.*

ACTIVPHYSICS ONLINE™ ACTIVITIES

ActivPhysics ONLINE **www.mastering physics.com**

1.1 Analyzing Motion Using Diagrams
1.2 Analyzing Motion Using Graphs
1.3 Predicting Motion from Graphs
1.4 Predicting Motion from Equations
1.5 Problem-Solving Strategies for Kinematics
1.6 Skier Races Downhill
1.7 Balloonist Drops Lemonade
1.8 Seat Belts Save Lives
1.9 Screeching to a Halt
1.10 Pole-Vaulter Lands
1.11 Car Starts, Then Stops
1.12 Solving Two-Vehicle Problems
1.13 Car Catches Truck
1.14 Avoiding a Rear-End Collision
2.1.1 Force Magnitudes
2.1.2 Skydiver
2.1.3 Tension Change
2.1.4 Sliding on an Incline
2.1.5 Car Race
2.2 Lifting a Crate
2.3 Lowering a Crate
2.4 Rocket Blasts Off
2.5 Truck Pulls Crate
2.6 Pushing a Crate Up a Wall
2.7 Skier Goes Down a Slope
2.8 Skier and Rope Tow
2.9 Pole-Vaulter Vaults
2.10 Truck Pulls Two Crates
2.11 Modified Atwood Machine
3.1 Solving Projectile Motion Problems
3.2 Two Balls Falling
3.3 Changing the x-Velocity
3.4 Projectile x- and y-Accelerations
3.5 Initial Velocity Components
3.6 Target Practice I
3.7 Target Practice II
4.1 Magnitude of Centripetal Acceleration
4.2 Circular Motion Problem Solving
4.3 Cart Goes Over Circular Path
4.4 Ball Swings on a String
4.5 Car Circles a Track
4.6 Satellites Orbit
5.1 Work Calculations
5.2 Upward-Moving Elevator Stops
5.3 Stopping a Downward-Moving Elevator
5.4 Inverse Bungee Jumper
5.5 Spring-Launched Bowler
5.6 Skier Speed
5.7 Modified Atwood Machine
6.1 Momentum and Energy Change
6.2 Collisions and Elasticity
6.3 Momentum Conservation and Collisions
6.4 Collision Problems
6.5 Car Collision: Two Dimensions
6.6 Saving an Astronaut
6.7 Explosion Problems
6.8 Skier and Cart
6.9 Pendulum Bashes Box
6.10 Pendulum Person-Projectile Bowling
7.1 Calculating Torques
7.2 A Tilted Beam: Torques and Equilibrium
7.3 Arm Levers
7.4 Two Painters on a Beam
7.5 Lecturing from a Beam
7.6 Rotational Inertia
7.7 Rotational Kinematics
7.8 Rotoride–Dynamics Approach
7.9 Falling Ladder
7.10 Woman and Flywheel Elevator–Dynamics Approach
7.11 Race Between a Block and a Disk
7.12 Woman and Flywheel Elevator–Energy Approach
7.13 Rotoride–Energy Approach
7.14 Ball Hits Bat
8.1 Characteristics of a Gas
8.2 Maxwell-Boltzmann Distribution–Conceptual Analysis
8.3 Maxwell-Boltzmann Distribution–Quantitative Analysis
8.4 State Variables and Ideal Gas Law
8.5 Work Done By a Gas
8.6 Heat, Internal Energy, and First Law of Thermodynamics
8.7 Heat Capacity
8.8 Isochoric Process
8.9 Isobaric Process
8.10 Isothermal Process
8.11 Adiabatic Process
8.12 Cyclic Process–Strategies
8.13 Cyclic Process–Problems
8.14 Carnot Cycle
9.1 Position Graphs and Equations
9.2 Describing Vibrational Motion
9.3 Vibrational Energy
9.4 Two Ways to Weigh Young Tarzan
9.5 Ape Drops Tarzan
9.6 Releasing a Vibrating Skier I
9.7 Releasing a Vibrating Skier II
9.8 One-and Two-Spring Vibrating Systems
9.9 Vibro-Ride
9.10 Pendulum Frequency
9.11 Risky Pendulum Walk
9.12 Physical Pendulum
10.1 Properties of Mechanical Waves
10.2 Speed of Waves on a String
10.3 Speed of Sound in a Gas
10.4 Standing Waves on Strings
10.5 Tuning a Stringed Instrument: Standing Waves
10.6 String Mass and Standing Waves
10.7 Beats and Beat Frequency
10.8 Doppler Effect: Conceptual Introduction
10.9 Doppler Effect: Problems
10.10 Complex Waves: Fourier Analysis
11.1 Electric Force: Coulomb's Law
11.2 Electric Force: Superposition Principle
11.3 Electric Force Superposition Principle (Quantitative)
11.4 Electric Field: Point Charge
11.5 Electric Field Due to a Dipole
11.6 Electric Field: Problems
11.7 Electric Flux
11.8 Gauss's Law
11.9 Motion of a Charge in an Electric Field: Introduction
11.10 Motion in an Electric Field: Problems
11.11 Electric Potential: Qualitative Introduction
11.12 Electric Potential, Field, and Force
11.13 Electrical Potential Energy and Potential
12.1 DC Series Circuits (Qualitative)
12.2 DC Parallel Circuits
12.3 DC Circuit Puzzles
12.4 Using Ammeters and Voltmeters
12.5 Using Kirchhoff's Laws
12.6 Capacitance
12.7 Series and Parallel Capacitors
12.8 *RC* Circuit Time Constants
13.1 Magnetic Field of a Wire
13.2 Magnetic Field of a Loop
13.3 Magnetic Field of a Solenoid
13.4 Magnetic Force on a Particle
13.5 Magnetic Force on a Wire
13.6 Magnetic Torque on a Loop
13.7 Mass Spectrometer
13.8 Velocity Selector
13.9 Electromagnetic Induction
13.10 Motional emf
14.1 The *RL* Circuit
14.2 The *RLC* Oscillator
14.3 The Driven Oscillator
15.1 Reflection and Refraction
15.2 Total Internal Reflection
15.3 Refraction Applications
15.4 Plane Mirrors
15.5 Spherical Mirrors: Ray Diagrams
15.6 Spherical Mirror: The Mirror Equation
15.7 Spherical Mirror: Linear Magnification
15.8 Spherical Mirror: Problems
15.9 Thin-Lens Ray Diagrams
15.10 Converging Lens Problems
15.11 Diverging Lens Problems
15.12 Two-Lens Optical Systems
16.1 Two-Source Interference: Introduction
16.2 Two-Source Interference: Qualitative Questions
16.3 Two-Source Interference: Problems
16.4 The Grating: Introduction and Qualitative Questions
16.5 The Grating: Problems
16.6 Single-Slit Diffraction
16.7 Circular Hole Diffraction
16.8 Resolving Power
16.9 Polarization
17.1 Relativity of Time
17.2 Relativity of Length
17.3 Photoelectric Effect
17.4 Compton Scattering
17.5 Electron Interference
17.6 Uncertainty Principle
17.7 Wave Packets
18.1 The Bohr Model
18.2 Spectroscopy
18.3 The Laser
19.1 Particle Scattering
19.2 Nuclear Binding Energy
19.3 Fusion
19.4 Radioactivity
19.5 Particle Physics
20.1 Potential Energy Diagrams
20.2 Particle in a Box
20.3 Potential Wells
20.4 Potential Barriers

SEARS AND ZEMANSKY'S

UNIVERSITY PHYSICS

12TH EDITION

HUGH D. YOUNG
CARNEGIE MELLON UNIVERSITY

ROGER A. FREEDMAN
UNIVERSITY OF CALIFORNIA, SANTA BARBARA

CONTRIBUTING AUTHOR
A. LEWIS FORD
TEXAS A&M UNIVERSITY

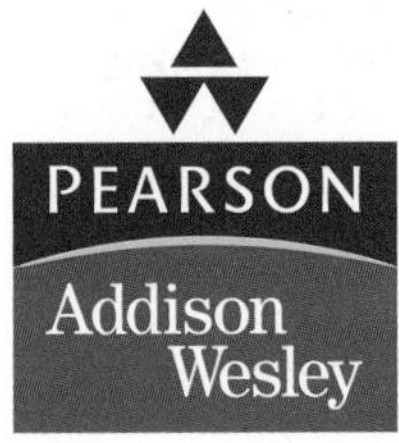

San Francisco Boston New York
Cape Town Hong Kong London Madrid Mexico City
Montreal Munich Paris Singapore Sydney Tokyo Toronto

Vice President and Editorial Director: Adam Black, Ph.D.
Senior Development Editor: Margot Otway
Editorial Manager: Laura Kenney
Associate Editor: Chandrika Madhavan
Media Producer: Matthew Phillips
Director of Marketing: Christy Lawrence
Managing Editor: Corinne Benson
Production Supervisor: Nancy Tabor
Production Service: WestWords, Inc.
Illustrations: Rolin Graphics
Text Design: tani hasegawa
Cover Design: Yvo Riezebos Design
Manufacturing Manager: Pam Augspurger
Director, Image Resource Center: Melinda Patelli
Manager, Rights and Permissions: Zina Arabia
Photo Research: Cypress Integrated Systems
Cover Printer: Phoenix Color Corporation
Printer and Binder: Courier Corporation/Kendallville
Cover Image: The Millau Viaduct, designed by Lord Norman Foster, Millau, France.
Photograph by Jean-Philippe Arles/Reuters/Corbis

Photo Credits: See page C-1.

Library of Congress Cataloging-in-Publication Data
Young, Hugh D.
Sears and Zemansky's university physics : with modern physics.— 12th ed. Hugh D. Young, Roger A. Freedman ; contributing author, A. Lewis Ford.
p. cm.
Includes index.
ISBN 0-8053-2187-X
I. Freedman, Roger A. II. Sears, Francis Weston, 1898–1975. University physics. III. Title. IV. Title: University physics.

QC21.3.Y68 2007
530--dc22

2006032537

ISBN-13: 978-0-321-50147-9
ISBN-10: 0-321-50147-0

www.aw-bc.com

1 2 3 4 5 6 7 8 9 10—CRK—09 08

BRIEF CONTENTS

ABOUT THE AUTHORS

Hugh D. Young is Emeritus Professor of Physics at Carnegie Mellon University in Pittsburgh, PA. He attended Carnegie Mellon for both undergraduate and graduate study and earned his Ph.D. in fundamental particle theory under the direction of the late Richard Cutkosky. He joined the faculty of Carnegie Mellon in 1956 and has also spent two years as a Visiting Professor at the University of California at Berkeley.

Prof. Young's career has centered entirely around undergraduate education. He has written several undergraduate-level textbooks, and in 1973 he became a co-author with Francis Sears and Mark Zemansky for their well-known introductory texts. With their deaths, he assumed full responsibility for new editions of these books until joined by Prof. Freedman for *University Physics.*

Prof. Young is an enthusiastic skier, climber, and hiker. He also served for several years as Associate Organist at St. Paul's Cathedral in Pittsburgh, and has played numerous organ recitals in the Pittsburgh area. Prof. Young and his wife Alice usually travel extensively in the summer, especially in Europe and in the desert canyon country of southern Utah.

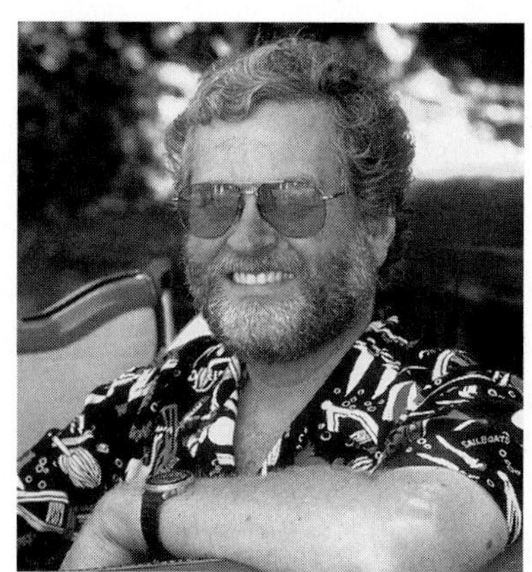

Roger A. Freedman is a Lecturer in Physics at the University of California, Santa Barbara. Dr. Freedman was an undergraduate at the University of California campuses in San Diego and Los Angeles, and did his doctoral research in nuclear theory at Stanford University under the direction of Professor J. Dirk Walecka. He came to UCSB in 1981 after three years teaching and doing research at the University of Washington.

At UCSB, Dr. Freedman has taught in both the Department of Physics and the College of Creative Studies, a branch of the university intended for highly gifted and motivated undergraduates. He has published research in nuclear physics, elementary particle physics, and laser physics. In recent years, he has helped to develop computer-based tools for learning introductory physics and astronomy.

When not in the classroom or slaving over a computer, Dr. Freedman can be found either flying (he holds a commercial pilot's license) or driving with his wife, Caroline, in their 1960 Nash Metropolitan convertible.

A. Lewis Ford is Professor of Physics at Texas A&M University. He received a B.A. from Rice University in 1968 and a Ph.D. in chemical physics from the University of Texas at Austin in 1972. After a one-year postdoc at Harvard University, he joined the Texas A&M physics faculty in 1973 and has been there ever since. Professor Ford's research area is theoretical atomic physics, with a specialization in atomic collisions. At Texas A&M he has taught a variety of undergraduate and graduate courses, but primarily introductory physics.

TO THE STUDENT

HOW TO SUCCEED IN PHYSICS BY REALLY TRYING

Mark Hollabaugh *Normandale Community College*

Physics encompasses the large and the small, the old and the new. From the atom to galaxies, from electrical circuitry to aerodynamics, physics is very much a part of the world around us. You probably are taking this introductory course in calculus-based physics because it is required for subsequent courses you plan to take in preparation for a career in science or engineering. Your professor wants you to learn physics and to enjoy the experience. He or she is very interested in helping you learn this fascinating subject. That is part of the reason your professor chose this textbook for your course. That is also the reason Drs. Young and Freedman asked me to write this introductory section. We want you to succeed!

The purpose of this section of *University Physics* is to give you some ideas that will assist your learning. Specific suggestions on how to use the textbook will follow a brief discussion of general study habits and strategies.

Preparation for This Course

If you had high school physics, you will probably learn concepts faster than those who have not because you will be familiar with the language of physics. If English is a second language for you, keep a glossary of new terms that you encounter and make sure you understand how they are used in physics. Likewise, if you are farther along in your mathematics courses, you will pick up the mathematical aspects of physics faster. Even if your mathematics is adequate, you may find a book such as Arnold D. Pickar's *Preparing for General Physics: Math Skill Drills and Other Useful Help (Calculus Version)* to be useful. Your professor may actually assign sections of this math review to assist your learning.

Learning to Learn

Each of us has a different learning style and a preferred means of learning. Understanding your own learning style will help you to focus on aspects of physics that may give you difficulty and to use those components of your course that will help you overcome the difficulty. Obviously you will want to spend more time on those aspects that give you the most trouble. If you learn by hearing, lectures will be very important. If you learn by explaining, then working with other students will be useful to you. If solving problems is difficult for you, spend more time learning how to solve problems. Also, it is important to understand and develop good study habits. Perhaps the most important thing you can do for yourself is to set aside adequate, regularly scheduled study time in a distraction-free environment.

Answer the following questions for yourself:

- Am I able to use fundamental mathematical concepts from algebra, geometry and trigonometry? (If not, plan a program of review with help from your professor.)
- In similar courses, what activity has given me the most trouble? (Spend more time on this.) What has been the easiest for me? (Do this first; it will help to build your confidence.)

- Do I understand the material better if I read the book before or after the lecture? (You may learn best by skimming the material, going to lecture, and then undertaking an in-depth reading.)
- Do I spend adequate time in studying physics? (A rule of thumb for a class like this is to devote, on the average, 2.5 hours out of class for each hour in class. For a course meeting 5 hours each week, that means you should spend about 10 to 15 hours per week studying physics.)
- Do I study physics every day? (Spread that 10 to 15 hours out over an entire week!) At what time of the day am I at my best for studying physics? (Pick a specific time of the day and stick to it.)
- Do I work in a quiet place where I can maintain my focus? (Distractions will break your routine and cause you to miss important points.)

Working with Others

Scientists or engineers seldom work in isolation from one another but rather work cooperatively. You will learn more physics and have more fun doing it if you work with other students. Some professors may formalize the use of cooperative learning or facilitate the formation of study groups. You may wish to form your own informal study group with members of your class who live in your neighborhood or dorm. If you have access to e-mail, use it to keep in touch with one another. Your study group is an excellent resource when reviewing for exams.

Lectures and Taking Notes

An important component of any college course is the lecture. In physics this is especially important because your professor will frequently do demonstrations of physical principles, run computer simulations, or show video clips. All of these are learning activities that will help you to understand the basic principles of physics. Don't miss lectures, and if for some reason you do, ask a friend or member of your study group to provide you with notes and let you know what happened.

Take your class notes in outline form, and fill in the details later. It can be very difficult to take word for word notes, so just write down key ideas. Your professor may use a diagram from the textbook. Leave a space in your notes and just add the diagram later. After class, edit your notes, filling in any gaps or omissions and noting things you need to study further. Make references to the textbook by page, equation number, or section number.

Make sure you ask questions in class, or see your professor during office hours. Remember the only "dumb" question is the one that is not asked. Your college may also have teaching assistants or peer tutors who are available to help you with difficulties you may have.

Examinations

Taking an examination is stressful. But if you feel adequately prepared and are well-rested, your stress will be lessened. Preparing for an exam is a continual process; it begins the moment the last exam is over. You should immediately go over the exam and understand any mistakes you made. If you worked a problem and made substantial errors, try this: Take a piece of paper and divide it down the middle with a line from top to bottom. In one column, write the proper solution to the problem. In the other column, write what you did and why, if you know, and why your solution was incorrect. If you are uncertain why you made your mistake, or how to avoid making it again, talk with your professor. Physics continually builds on fundamental ideas and it is important to correct any misunderstandings immediately. Warning: While cramming at the last minute may get you through the present exam, you will not adequately retain the concepts for use on the next exam.

TO THE INSTRUCTOR

PREFACE

This book is the product of more than half a century of leadership and innovation in physics education. When the first edition of University Physics by Francis W. Sears and Mark W. Zemansky was published in 1949, it was revolutionary among calculus-based physics textbooks in its emphasis on the fundamental principles of physics and how to apply them. The success of University Physics with generations of (several million) students and educators around the world is a testament to the merits of this approach, and to the many innovations it has introduced subsequently.

In preparing this new Twelfth Edition, we have further enhanced and developed *University Physics* to assimilate the best ideas from education research with enhanced problem-solving instruction, pioneering visual and conceptual pedagogy, the first systematically enhanced problems, and the most pedagogically proven and widely used online homework and tutorial system in the world.

New to This Edition

- **Problem solving.** The acclaimed, research-based **four-step problem-solving framework** (Identify, Set Up, Execute, and Evaluate) is now used throughout every Worked Example, chapter-specific Problem-Solving Strategy, and every Solution in the Instructor and Student Solutions Manuals. Worked Examples now incorporate black-and-white Pencil Sketches to focus students on this critical step—one that research shows students otherwise tend to skip when illustrated with highly rendered figures.

- **Instruction followed by practice.** A streamlined and systematic learning path of instruction followed by practice includes **Learning Goals** at the start of each chapter and **Visual Chapter Summaries** that consolidate each concept in words, math, and figures. Popular **Test Your Understanding** conceptual questions at the end of each section now use **multiple-choice and ranking formats** to allow students to instantly check their knowledge.

- **Instructional power of figures.** The instructional power of figures is enhanced using the research-proven technique of **"annotation"** (chalkboard-style commentary integrated into the figure to guide the student in interpreting the figure) and by **streamlined use of color and detail** (in mechanics, for example, color is used to focus the student on the object of interest while the rest of the image is in grayscale and without distracting detail).

- **Enhanced end-of-chapter problems.** Renowned for providing the most wide-ranging and best-tested problems available, the Twelfth Edition goes still further: It provides **the first library of physics problems systematically enhanced** based on student performance nationally. Using this analysis, more than 800 new problems make up the entire library of 3700.

- **MasteringPhysics™** (www.masteringphysics.com). Launched with the Eleventh Edition, MasteringPhysics is now the most widely adopted, educationally proven, and technically advanced online homework and tutorial system in the world. For the Twelfth Edition, MasteringPhysics provides a wealth of new content and technological enhancements. In addition to a library of more than 1200 tutorials and all the end-of-chapter problems, MasteringPhysics

Standard, Extended, and Three-Volume Editions

With MasteringPhysics™:

- **Standard Edition:** Chapters 1–37 (ISBN-13: 978-0-321-50161-5) (ISBN-10: 0-321-50161-6)
- **Extended Edition:** Chapters 1–44 (ISBN-13: 978-0-8053-2187-6) (ISBN-10: 0-8053-2187-X)
- **Volume 1:** Chapters 1–20 (ISBN-13: 978-0-321-50056-4) (ISBN-10: 0-321-50056-3)
- **Volume 2:** Chapters 21–37 (ISBN-13: 978-0-321-50039-7) (ISBN-10: 0-321-50039-3)
- **Volume 3:** Chapters 37–44 (ISBN-13: 978-0-321-50040-3) (ISBN-10: 0-321-50040-7)

Without MasteringPhysics™:

- **Standard Edition:** Chapters 1–37 (ISBN-13: 978-0-321-50147-9) (ISBN-10: 0-321-50147-0)
- **Extended Edition:** Chapters 1–44 (ISBN-13: 978-0-321-50121-9) (ISBN-10: 0-321-50121-7)
- **Volume 1:** Chapters 1–20 (ISBN-13: 978-0-321-50062-5) (ISBN-10: 0-321-50062-8)
- **Volume 2:** Chapters 21–37 (ISBN-13: 978-0-321-50076-2) (ISBN-10: 0-321-50076-8)
- **Volume 3:** Chapters 37–44 (ISBN-13: 978-0-321-50077-9) (ISBN-10: 0-321-50077-6)

now also provides specific tutorials for every Problem-Solving Strategy and key Test Your Understanding questions from each chapter. Answer types include algebraic, numerical, and multiple-choice answers, as well as ranking, sorting, graph drawing, vector drawing, and ray tracing.

Key Features of *University Physics*

A Guide for the Student Many physics students experience difficulty simply because they don't know how to use their textbook. The section entitled "How to Succeed in Physics by Really Trying," which precedes this preface, is a "user's manual" to all the features of this book. This section, written by Professor Mark Hollabaugh (Normandale Community College), also gives a number of helpful study hints. *Every* student should read this section!

Chapter Organization The first section of each chapter is an *Introduction* that gives specific examples of the chapter's content and connects it with what has come before. There are also a *Chapter Opening Question* and a list of *Learning Goals* to make the reader think about the subject matter of the chapter ahead. (To find the answer to the question, look for the ? icon.) Most sections end with a *Test Your Understanding Question,* which can be conceptual or quantitative in nature. At the end of the last section of the chapter is a *Visual Chapter Summary* of the most important principles in the chapter, as well as a list of *Key Terms* with reference to the page number where each term is introduced. The answers to the Chapter Opening Question and Test Your Understanding Questions follow the Key Terms.

Questions and Problems At the end of each chapter is a collection of *Discussion Questions* that probe and extend the student's conceptual understanding. Following these are *Exercises,* which are single-concept problems keyed to specific sections of the text; *Problems,* usually requiring one or two nontrivial steps; and *Challenge Problems,* intended to challenge the strongest students. The problems include applications to such diverse fields as astrophysics, biology, and aerodynamics. Many problems have a conceptual part in which students must discuss and explain their results. The new questions, exercises, and problems for this edition were created and organized by Wayne Anderson (Sacramento City College), Laird Kramer (Florida International University), and Charlie Hibbard.

Problem-Solving Strategies and Worked Examples Throughout the book, *Problem-Solving Strategy* boxes provide students with specific tactics for solving particular types of problems. They address the needs of any students who have ever felt that they "understand the concepts but can't do the problems."

All Problem-Solving Strategy boxes follow the ISEE approach (Identify, Set Up, Execute, and Evaluate) to solving problems. This approach helps students see how to begin with a seemingly complex situation, identify the relevant physical concepts, decide what tools are needed to solve the problem, carry out the solution, and then evaluate whether the result makes sense.

Each Problem-Solving Strategy box is followed by one or more worked-out *Examples* that illustrate the strategy. Many other worked-out Examples are found in each chapter. Like the Problem-Solving Strategy boxes, all of the quantitative Examples use the ISEE approach. Several of the examples are purely qualitative and are labeled as *Conceptual Examples;* see, for instance, Conceptual Examples 6.5 (Comparing kinetic energies, p. 191), 8.1 (Momentum versus kinetic energy, p. 251) and 20.7 (A reversible adiabatic process, p. 693).

"Caution" paragraphs Two decades of physics education research have revealed a number of conceptual pitfalls that commonly plague beginning physics students. These include the ideas that force is required for motion, that electric current is "used up" as it goes around a circuit, and that the product of an object's mass and its acceleration is itself a force. The "Caution" paragraphs alert students to these and other pitfalls, and explain why the wrong way to think about a certain situation (which may have occurred to the student first) is indeed wrong. (See, for example, pp. 118, 159, and 559.)

Notation and units Students often have a hard time keeping track of which quantities are vectors and which are not. We use boldface italic symbols with an arrow on top for vector quantities, such as $\vec{v}$, $\vec{a}$, and $\vec{F}$; unit vectors such as $\hat{\imath}$, have a caret on top. Boldface **+**, **−**, **×**, and **=** signs are used in vector equations to emphasize the distinction between vector and scalar mathematical operations.

SI units are used exclusively (English unit conversions are included where appropriate). The joule is used as the standard unit of energy of all forms, including heat.

Flexibility The book is adaptable to a wide variety of course outlines. There is plenty of material for a three-semester or a five-quarter course. Most instructors will find that there is too much material for a one-year course, but it is easy to tailor the book to a variety of one-year course plans by omitting certain chapters or sections. For example, any or all of the chapters on fluid mechanics, sound and hearing, electromagnetic waves, or relativity can be omitted without loss of continuity. In any case, no instructor should feel constrained to work straight through the entire book.

Instructor Supplements

The **Instructor Solutions Manuals,** prepared by A. Lewis Ford (Texas A&M University), contain complete and detailed solutions to all end-of-chapter problems. All solutions follow consistently the same Identify/Set Up/Execute/Evaluate problem-solving framework used in the textbook. The *Instructor Solutions Manual for Volume 1* (ISBN 0-321-49968-9) covers Chapters 1–20, and the *Instructor Solutions Manual for Volumes 2 and 3* (ISBN 0-321-49210-2) covers Chapters 21–44.

The cross-platform **Media Manager CD-ROM** (ISBN 0-321-49916-6) provides a comprehensive library of more than 220 applets from ActivPhysics OnLine™ as well as all line figures from the textbook in JPEG format. In addition, all the key equations, Problem-Solving Strategies, tables, and chapter summaries are provided in editable Word format. In-class weekly multiple-choice questions for use with various Classroom Response Systems (CRS) are also provided, based on the Test Your Understanding questions in the text. The CD-ROM also provides the Instructor Solutions Manual in convenient editable Word format and as PDFs.

MasteringPhysics™ (www.masteringphysics.com) is the most advanced, educationally effective, and widely used physics homework and tutorial system in the world. It provides instructors with a library of extensively pretested end-of-chapter problems and rich, Socratic tutorials that incorporate a wide variety of answer types, wrong-answer feedback, and adaptive help (comprising hints or simpler sub-problems upon request). MasteringPhysics™ allows instructors to quickly build wide-ranging homework assignments of just the right difficulty and duration and provides them with efficient tools to analyze class trends—or the work of any student—in unprecedented detail and to compare the results either with the national average or with the performance of previous classes.

Five Easy Lessons: Strategies for Successful Physics Teaching (ISBN 0-8053-8702-1) by Randall D. Knight (California Polytechnic State University, San Luis

Obispo) is packed with creative ideas on how to enhance any physics course. It is an invaluable companion for both novice and veteran physics instructors.

The **Transparency Acetates** (ISBN 0-321-50034-2) contain more than 200 key figures from *University Physics,* Twelfth Edition, in full color.

The **Printed Test Bank** (ISBN 0-321-50035-0) provides more than 2000 multiple-choice questions.

The **Computerized Test Bank** (ISBN 0-321-50126-8) includes all of the questions from the Printed Test Bank on a cross-platform CD-ROM. More than half the questions have numerical values that can be randomly assigned for each student.

Student Supplements

The **Study Guide,** by James R. Gaines, William F. Palmer, and Laird Kramer, reinforces the text's emphasis on problem-solving strategies and student misconceptions. The *Study Guide for Volume 1* (ISBN 0-321-50033-4) covers Chapters 1–20, and the *Study Guide for Volumes 2 and 3* (ISBN 0-321-50037-7) covers Chapters 21–44.

The **Student Solutions Manual,** by A. Lewis Ford (Texas A&M University), contains detailed, step-by-step solutions to more than half of the odd-numbered end-of-chapter problems from the textbook. All solutions follow consistently the same Identify/Set Up/Execute/Evaluate problem-solving framework used in the textbook. The *Student Solutions Manual for Volume 1* (ISBN 0-321-50063-6) covers Chapters 1–20, and the *Student Solutions Manual for Volumes 2 and 3* (ISBN 0-321-50038-5) covers Chapters 21–44.

MasteringPhysics™ (www.masteringphysics.com) is the most advanced, widely used, and educationally proven physics tutorial system in the world. It is the result of eight years of detailed studies of how real students work physics problems, and of precisely where they need help. Studies show that students who use MasteringPhysics™ significantly improve their scores on final exams and conceptual tests such as the Force Concept Inventory. MasteringPhysics™ achieves this by providing students with instantaneous feedback specific to their wrong answers, simpler sub-problems upon request when they get stuck, and partial credit for their method. This individualized, 24/7 tutor system is recommended by nine out of ten students to their peers as the most effective and time-efficient way to study.

ActivPhysics OnLine™ (www.masteringphysics.com), now included in the self-study area of MasteringPhysics, provides the most comprehensive library of applets and applet-based tutorials available. ActivPhysics OnLine was created by the educational pioneer Alan Van Heuvelen of Rutgers. Throughout *University Physics,* Twelfth Edition, in-margin icons direct the student to specific applets in ActivPhysics OnLine in for additional interactive help.

ActivPhysics OnLine™ Workbooks, Volume 1 (0-8053-9060-X) and **Volume 2** (0-8053-9061-8) by Alan Van Heuvelen, Rutgers, and Paul d'Alessandris, Monroe Community College, provide a range of tutorials that use the critically acclaimed ActivPhysics OnLine applets to help students develop understanding and confidence. In particular, they focus on developing intuition, making predictions, testing assumptions experimentally, drawing effective diagrams, understanding key equations both qualitatively and quantitatively, and interpreting graphical information. These workbooks can be used for labs, homework, or self-study.

The **Addison-Wesley Tutor Center** (www.aw.com/tutorcenter) provides one-on-one tutoring via telephone, fax, e-mail, or interactive website. Qualified instructors answer questions and provide instruction with examples, problems, and other content from *University Physics,* Twelfth Edition, as well as help with MasteringPhysics™.

Acknowledgments

We would like to thank the hundreds of reviewers and colleagues who have offered valuable comments and suggestions over the life of this textbook. The continuing success of *University Physics* is due in large measure to their contributions.

Edward Adelson (Ohio State University), Ralph Alexander (University of Missouri at Rolla), J. G. Anderson, R. S. Anderson, Wayne Anderson (Sacramento City College), Alex Azima (Lansing Community College), Dilip Balamore (Nassau Community College), Harold Bale (University of North Dakota), Arun Bansil (Northeastern University), John Barach (Vanderbilt University), J. D. Barnett, H. H. Barschall, Albert Bartlett (University of Colorado), Paul Baum (CUNY, Queens College), Frederick Becchetti (University of Michigan), B. Bederson, David Bennum (University of Nevada, Reno), Lev I. Berger (San Diego State University), Robert Boeke (William Rainey Harper College), S. Borowitz, A. C. Braden, James Brooks (Boston University), Nicholas E. Brown (California Polytechnic State University, San Luis Obispo), Tony Buffa (California Polytechnic State University, San Luis Obispo), A. Capecelatro, Michael Cardamone (Pennsylvania State University), Duane Carmony (Purdue University), Troy Carter (UCLA), P. Catranides, John Cerne (SUNY at Buffalo), Roger Clapp (University of South Florida), William M. Cloud (Eastern Illinois University), Leonard Cohen (Drexel University), W. R. Coker (University of Texas, Austin), Malcolm D. Cole (University of Missouri at Rolla), H. Conrad, David Cook (Lawrence University), Gayl Cook (University of Colorado), Hans Courant (University of Minnesota), Bruce A. Craver (University of Dayton), Larry Curtis (University of Toledo), Jai Dahiya (Southeast Missouri State University), Steve Detweiler (University of Florida), George Dixon (Oklahoma State University), Donald S. Duncan, Boyd Edwards (West Virginia University), Robert Eisenstein (Carnegie Mellon University), Amy Emerson Missourn (Virginia Institute of Technology), William Faissler (Northeastern University), William Fasnacht (U.S. Naval Academy), Paul Feldker (St. Louis Community College), Carlos Figueroa (Cabrillo College), L. H. Fisher, Neil Fletcher (Florida State University), Robert Folk, Peter Fong (Emory University), A. Lewis Ford (Texas A&M University), D. Frantszog, James R. Gaines (Ohio State University), Solomon Gartenhaus (Purdue University), Ron Gautreau (New Jersey Institute of Technology), J. David Gavenda (University of Texas, Austin), Dennis Gay (University of North Florida), James Gerhart (University of Washington), N. S. Gingrich, J. L. Glathart, S. Goodwin, Rich Gottfried (Frederick Community College), Walter S. Gray (University of Michigan), Paul Gresser (University of Maryland), Benjamin Grinstein (UC San Diego), Howard Grotch (Pennsylvania State University), John Gruber (San Jose State University), Graham D. Gutsche (U.S. Naval Academy), Michael J. Harrison (Michigan State University), Harold Hart (Western Illinois University), Howard Hayden (University of Connecticut), Carl Helrich (Goshen College), Laurent Hodges (Iowa State University), C. D. Hodgman, Michael Hones (Villanova University), Keith Honey (West Virginia Institute of Technology), Gregory Hood (Tidewater Community College), John Hubisz (North Carolina State University), M. Iona, John Jaszczak (Michigan Technical University), Alvin Jenkins (North Carolina State University), Robert P. Johnson (UC Santa Cruz), Lorella Jones (University of Illinois), John Karchek (GMI Engineering & Management Institute), Thomas Keil (Worcester Polytechnic Institute), Robert Kraemer (Carnegie Mellon University), Jean P. Krisch (University of Michigan), Robert A. Kromhout, Andrew Kunz (Marquette University), Charles Lane (Berry College), Thomas N. Lawrence (Texas State University), Robert J. Lee, Alfred Leitner (Rensselaer Polytechnic University), Gerald P. Lietz (De Paul University), Gordon Lind (Utah State University), S. Livingston, Elihu Lubkin (University of Wisconsin, Milwaukee), Robert Luke (Boise State University), David Lynch (Iowa State University), Michael Lysak (San Bernardino Valley College), Jeffrey Mallow (Loyola University), Robert Mania (Kentucky State University), Robert Marchina (University of Memphis), David Markowitz (University of Connecticut), R. J. Maurer, Oren Maxwell (Florida International University), Joseph L. McCauley (University of Houston), T. K. McCubbin, Jr. (Pennsylvania State University), Charles McFarland (University of Missouri at Rolla), James Mcguire (Tulane University), Lawrence McIntyre (University of Arizona), Fredric Messing (Carnegie-Mellon University), Thomas Meyer (Texas A&M University), Andre Mirabelli (St. Peter's College, New Jersey), Herbert Muether (S.U.N.Y., Stony Brook), Jack Munsee (California State University, Long Beach), Lorenzo Narducci (Drexel University), Van E. Neie (Purdue University), David A. Nordling (U. S. Naval Academy), Benedict Oh (Pennsylvania State University), L. O. Olsen, Jim Pannell (DeVry Institute of Technology), W. F. Parks (University of Missouri), Robert Paulson (California State University, Chico), Jerry Peacher (University of Missouri at Rolla), Arnold Perlmutter (University of Miami), Lennart Peterson (University of Florida), R. J. Peterson (University of Colorado, Boulder), R. Pinkston, Ronald Poling (University of Minnesota), J. G. Potter, C. W. Price (Millersville University), Francis Prosser (University of Kansas), Shelden H. Radin, Michael Rapport (Anne Arundel Community College), R. Resnick, James A. Richards, Jr., John S. Risley (North Carolina State University), Francesc Roig (University of California, Santa Barbara), T. L. Rokoske, Richard Roth (Eastern Michigan University), Carl Rotter (University of West Virginia), S. Clark Rowland (Andrews University), Rajarshi Roy (Georgia Institute of Technology), Russell A. Roy (Santa Fe Community College), Dhiraj Sardar (University of Texas, San Antonio), Bruce Schumm (UC Santa Cruz), Melvin Schwartz (St. John's University), F. A. Scott, L. W. Seagondollar, Paul Shand (University of

Northern Iowa), Stan Shepherd (Pennsylvania State University), Douglas Sherman (San Jose State), Bruce Sherwood (Carnegie Mellon University), Hugh Siefkin (Greenville College), Tomasz Skwarnicki (Syracuse University), C. P. Slichter, Charles W. Smith (University of Maine, Orono), Malcolm Smith (University of Lowell), Ross Spencer (Brigham Young University), Julien Sprott (University of Wisconsin), Victor Stanionis (Iona College), James Stith (American Institute of Physics), Chuck Stone (North Carolina A&T State University), Edward Strother (Florida Institute of Technology), Conley Stutz (Bradley University), Albert Stwertka (U.S. Merchant Marine Academy), Martin Tiersten (CUNY, City College), David Toot (Alfred University), Somdev Tyagi (Drexel University), F. Verbrugge, Helmut Vogel (Carnegie Mellon University), Robert Webb (Texas A & M), Thomas Weber (Iowa State University), M. Russell Wehr, (Pennsylvania State University), Robert Weidman (Michigan Technical University), Dan Whalen (UC San Diego), Lester V. Whitney, Thomas Wiggins (Pennsylvania State University), David Willey (University of Pittsburgh, Johnstown), George Williams (University of Utah), John Williams (Auburn University), Stanley Williams (Iowa State University), Jack Willis, Suzanne Willis (Northern Illinois University), Robert Wilson (San Bernardino Valley College), L. Wolfenstein, James Wood (Palm Beach Junior College), Lowell Wood (University of Houston), R. E. Worley, D. H. Ziebell (Manatee Community College), George O. Zimmerman (Boston University)

In addition, we both have individual acknowledgments we would like to make.

I want to extend my heartfelt thanks to my colleagues at Carnegie Mellon, especially Professors Robert Kraemer, Bruce Sherwood, Ruth Chabay, Helmut Vogel, and Brian Quinn, for many stimulating discussions about physics pedagogy and for their support and encouragement during the writing of several successive editions of this book. I am equally indebted to the many generations of Carnegie Mellon students who have helped me learn what good teaching and good writing are, by showing me what works and what doesn't. It is always a joy and a privilege to express my gratitude to my wife Alice and our children Gretchen and Rebecca for their love, support, and emotional sustenance during the writing of several successive editions of this book. May all men and women be blessed with love such as theirs. — H. D. Y.

I would like to thank my past and present colleagues at UCSB, including Rob Geller, Carl Gwinn, Al Nash, Elisabeth Nicol, and Francesc Roig, for their wholehearted support and for many helpful discussions. I owe a special debt of gratitude to my early teachers Willa Ramsay, Peter Zimmerman, William Little, Alan Schwettman, and Dirk Walecka for showing me what clear and engaging physics teaching is all about, and to Stuart Johnson for inviting me to become a co-author of *University Physics* beginning with the 9th edition. I want to express special thanks to the editorial staff at Addison Wesley and their partners: to Adam Black for his editorial vision; to Margot Otway for her superb graphic sense and careful development of this edition; to Peter Murphy and Carol Reitz for their careful reading of the manuscript; to Wayne Anderson, Charlie Hibbard, Laird Kramer, and Larry Stookey for their work on the end-of-chapter problems; and to Laura Kenney, Chandrika Madhavan, Nancy Tabor, and Pat McCutcheon for keeping the editorial and production pipeline flowing. I want to thank my father for his continued love and support and for keeping a space open on his bookshelf for this book. Most of all, I want to express my gratitude and love to my wife Caroline, to whom I dedicate my contribution to this book. Hey, Caroline, the new edition's done at last — let's go flying! — R. A. F.

Please Tell Us What You Think!

We welcome communications from students and professors, especially concerning errors or deficiencies that you find in this edition. We have devoted a lot of time and effort to writing the best book we know how to write, and we hope it will help you to teach and learn physics. In turn, you can help us by letting us know what still needs to be improved! Please feel free to contact us either electronically or by ordinary mail. Your comments will be greatly appreciated.

October 2006

Hugh D. Young
Department of Physics
Carnegie Mellon University
Pittsburgh, PA 15213
hdy@andrew.cmu.edu

Roger A. Freedman
Department of Physics
University of California, Santa Barbara
Santa Barbara, CA 93106-9530
airboy@physics.ucsb.edu
http://www.physics.ucsb.edu/~airboy/

DETAILED CONTENTS

MECHANICS

MODERN PHYSICS

APPENDICES

UNITS, PHYSICAL QUANTITIES, AND VECTORS

LEARNING GOALS

By studying this chapter, you will learn:

- What the fundamental quantities of mechanics are, and the units physicists use to measure them.
- How to keep track of significant figures in your calculations.
- The difference between scalars and vectors, and how to add and subtract vectors graphically.
- What the components of a vector are, and how to use them in calculations.
- What unit vectors are, and how to use them with components to describe vectors.
- Two ways of multiplying vectors.

? Being able to predict the path of a hurricane is essential for minimizing the damage it does to lives and property. If a hurricane is moving at 20 km/h in a direction 53° north of east, how far north does the hurricane move in one h?

The study of physics is important because physics is one of the most fundamental of the sciences. Scientists of all disciplines make use of the ideas of physics, including chemists who study the structure of molecules, paleontologists who try to reconstruct how dinosaurs walked, and climatologists who study how human activities affect the atmosphere and oceans. Physics is also the foundation of all engineering and technology. No engineer could design a flat-screen TV, an interplanetary spacecraft, or even a better mousetrap without first understanding the basic laws of physics.

The study of physics is also an adventure. You will find it challenging, sometimes frustrating, occasionally painful, and often richly rewarding and satisfying. It will appeal to your sense of beauty as well as to your rational intelligence. If you've ever wondered why the sky is blue, how radio waves can travel through empty space, or how a satellite stays in orbit, you can find the answers by using fundamental physics. Above all, you will come to see physics as a towering achievement of the human intellect in its quest to understand our world and ourselves.

In this opening chapter, we'll go over some important preliminaries that we'll need throughout our study. We'll discuss the nature of physical theory and the use of idealized models to represent physical systems. We'll introduce the systems of units used to describe physical quantities and discuss ways to describe the accuracy of a number. We'll look at examples of problems for which we can't (or don't want to) find a precise answer, but for which rough estimates can be useful and interesting. Finally, we'll study several aspects of vectors and vector algebra. Vectors will be needed throughout our study of physics to describe and analyze physical quantities, such as velocity and force, that have direction as well as magnitude.

1.1 The Nature of Physics

Physics is an *experimental* science. Physicists observe the phenomena of nature and try to find patterns and principles that relate these phenomena. These patterns are called physical theories or, when they are very well established and of broad use, physical laws or principles.

CAUTION **The meaning of the word "theory"** Calling an idea a theory does *not* mean that it's just a random thought or an unproven concept. Rather, a theory is an explanation of natural phenomena based on observation and accepted fundamental principles. An example is the well-established theory of biological evolution, which is the result of extensive research and observation by generations of biologists.

The development of physical theory requires creativity at every stage. The physicist has to learn to ask appropriate questions, design experiments to try to answer the questions, and draw appropriate conclusions from the results. Figure 1.1 shows two famous experimental facilities.

1.1 Two research laboratories. (a) According to legend, Galileo investigated falling bodies by dropping them from the Leaning Tower in Pisa, Italy, and he studied pendulum motion by observing the swinging of the chandelier in the adjacent cathedral. (b) The Hubble Space Telescope is the first major telescope to operate outside the earth's atmosphere. Measurements made with this telescope have helped determine the age and expansion rate of the universe.

(a)

(b)

Legend has it that Galileo Galilei (1564–1642) dropped light and heavy objects from the top of the Leaning Tower of Pisa (Fig. 1.1a) to find out whether their rates of fall were the same or different. Galileo recognized that only experimental investigation could answer this question. From examining the results of his experiments (which were actually much more sophisticated than in the legend), he made the inductive leap to the principle, or theory, that the acceleration of a falling body is independent of its weight.

The development of physical theories such as Galileo's is always a two-way process that starts and ends with observations or experiments. This development often takes an indirect path, with blind alleys, wrong guesses, and the discarding of unsuccessful theories in favor of more promising ones. Physics is not simply a collection of facts and principles; it is also the *process* by which we arrive at general principles that describe how the physical universe behaves.

No theory is ever regarded as the final or ultimate truth. The possibility always exists that new observations will require that a theory be revised or discarded. It is in the nature of physical theory that we can disprove a theory by finding behavior that is inconsistent with it, but we can never prove that a theory is always correct.

Getting back to Galileo, suppose we drop a feather and a cannonball. They certainly do *not* fall at the same rate. This does not mean that Galileo was wrong; it means that his theory was incomplete. If we drop the feather and the cannonball *in a vacuum* to eliminate the effects of the air, then they do fall at the same rate. Galileo's theory has a **range of validity:** It applies only to objects for which the force exerted by the air (due to air resistance and buoyancy) is much less than the weight. Objects like feathers or parachutes are clearly outside this range.

Every physical theory has a range of validity outside of which it is not applicable. Often a new development in physics extends a principle's range of validity. Galileo's analysis of falling bodies was greatly extended half a century later by Newton's laws of motion and law of gravitation.

1.2 Solving Physics Problems

At some point in their studies, almost all physics students find themselves thinking, "I understand the concepts, but I just can't solve the problems." But in physics, truly understanding a concept or principle is the same thing as being able to apply it to a variety of practical problems. Learning how to solve problems is absolutely essential; you don't *know* physics unless you can *do* physics.

How do you learn to solve physics problems? In every chapter of this book you will find *Problem-Solving Strategies* that offer techniques for setting up and solving problems efficiently and accurately. Following each *Problem-Solving Strategy* are one or more worked *Examples* that show these techniques in action.

(The *Problem-Solving Strategies* will also steer you away from some *incorrect* techniques that you may be tempted to use.) You'll also find additional examples that aren't associated with a particular *Problem-Solving Strategy.* Study these strategies and examples carefully, and work through each example for yourself on a piece of paper.

Different techniques are useful for solving different kinds of physics problems, which is why this book offers dozens of *Problem-Solving Strategies.* No matter what kind of problem you're dealing with, however, there are certain key steps that you'll always follow. (These same steps are equally useful for problems in math, engineering, chemistry, and many other fields.) In this book we've organized these steps into four stages of solving a problem.

All of the *Problem-Solving Strategies* and *Examples* in this book will follow these four steps. (In some cases we will combine the first two or three steps.) We encourage you to follow these same steps when you solve problems yourself. You may find it useful to remember the acronym ***I SEE***—short for *Identify, Set up, Execute,* and *Evaluate.*

Problem-Solving Strategy 1.1 Solving Physics Problems

IDENTIFY *the relevant concepts:* First, decide which physics ideas are relevant to the problem. Although this step doesn't involve any calculations, it's sometimes the most challenging part of solving the problem. Don't skip over this step, though; choosing the wrong approach at the beginning can make the problem more difficult than it has to be, or even lead you to an incorrect answer.

At this stage you must also identify the **target variable** of the problem—that is, is the quantity whose value you're trying to find. It could be the speed at which a projectile hits the ground, the intensity of a sound made by a siren, or the size of an image made by a lens. (Sometimes the goal will be to find a mathematical expression rather than a numerical value. Sometimes, too, the problem will have more than one target variable.) The target variable is the goal of the problem-solving process; don't lose sight of this goal as you work through the solution.

SET UP *the problem:* Based on the concepts you selected in the *Identify* step, choose the equations that you'll use to solve the problem and decide how you'll use them. If appropriate, draw a sketch of the situation described in the problem.

EXECUTE *the solution:* In this step, you "do the math." Before you launch into a flurry of calculations, make a list of all known and unknown quantities, and note which are the target variable or variables. Then solve the equations for the unknowns.

EVALUATE *your answer:* The goal of physics problem solving isn't just to get a number or a formula; it's to achieve better understanding. That means you must examine your answer to see what it's telling you. Be sure to ask yourself, "Does this answer make sense?" If your target variable was the radius of the earth and your answer is 6.38 centimeters (or if your answer is a negative number!), something went wrong in your problem-solving process. Go back and check your work, and revise your solution as necessary.

Idealized Models

In everyday conversation we use the word "model" to mean either a small-scale replica, such as a model railroad, or a person who displays articles of clothing (or the absence thereof). In physics a **model** is a simplified version of a physical system that would be too complicated to analyze in full detail.

For example, suppose we want to analyze the motion of a thrown baseball (Fig. 1.2a). How complicated is this problem? The ball is not a perfect sphere (it has raised seams), and it spins as it moves through the air. Wind and air resistance influence its motion, the ball's weight varies a little as its distance from the center of the earth changes, and so on. If we try to include all these things, the analysis gets hopelessly complicated. Instead, we invent a simplified version of the problem. We neglect the size and shape of the ball by representing it as a point object, or **particle.** We neglect air resistance by making the ball move in a vacuum, and we make the weight constant. Now we have a problem that is simple enough to deal with (Fig. 1.2b). We will analyze this model in detail in Chapter 3.

To make an idealized model, we have to overlook quite a few minor effects to concentrate on the most important features of the system. Of course, we have to be careful not to neglect too much. If we ignore the effects of gravity completely,

1.2 To simplify the analysis of (a) a baseball in flight, we use (b) an idealized model.

(a) A real baseball in flight

Baseball spins and has a complex shape.

Air resistance and wind exert forces on the ball.

Direction of motion

Gravitational force on ball depends on altitude.

(b) An idealized model of the baseball

Baseball is treated as a point object (particle).

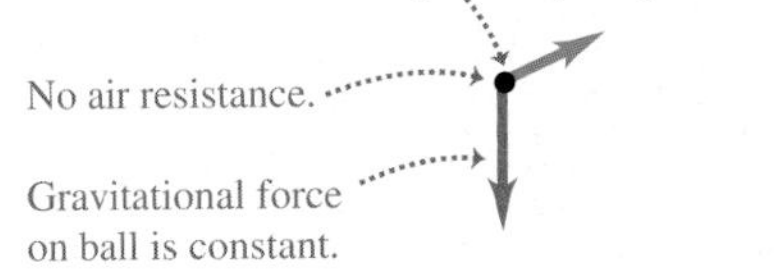
No air resistance.
Gravitational force on ball is constant.

then our model predicts that when we throw the ball up, it will go in a straight line and disappear into space. We need to use some judgment and creativity to construct a model that simplifies a problem enough to make it manageable, yet keeps its essential features.

When we use a model to predict how a system will behave, the validity of our predictions is limited by the validity of the model. For example, Galileo's prediction about falling bodies (see Section 1.1) corresponds to an idealized model that does not include the effects of air resistance. This model works fairly well for a dropped cannonball, but not so well for a feather.

When we apply physical principles to complex systems in physical science and technology, we always use idealized models, and we have to be aware of the assumptions we are making. In fact, the principles of physics themselves are stated in terms of idealized models; we speak about point masses, rigid bodies, ideal insulators, and so on. Idealized models play a crucial role throughout this book. Watch for them in discussions of physical theories and their applications to specific problems.

1.3 Standards and Units

As we learned in Section 1.1, physics is an experimental science. Experiments require measurements, and we generally use numbers to describe the results of measurements. Any number that is used to describe a physical phenomenon quantitatively is called a **physical quantity.** For example, two physical quantities that describe you are your weight and your height. Some physical quantities are so fundamental that we can define them only by describing how to measure them. Such a definition is called an **operational definition.** Two examples are measuring a distance by using a ruler and measuring a time interval by using a stopwatch. In other cases we define a physical quantity by describing how to calculate it from other quantities that we *can* measure. Thus we might define the average speed of a moving object as the distance traveled (measured with a ruler) divided by the time of travel (measured with a stopwatch).

When we measure a quantity, we always compare it with some reference standard. When we say that a Porsche Carrera GT is 4.61 meters long, we mean that it is 4.61 times as long as a meter stick, which we define to be 1 meter long. Such a standard defines a **unit** of the quantity. The meter is a unit of distance, and the second is a unit of time. When we use a number to describe a physical quantity, we must always specify the unit that we are using; to describe a distance as simply "4.61" wouldn't mean anything.

1.3 In 1791 the distance from the North Pole to the equator was defined to be exactly 10^7 m. With the modern definition of the meter, this distance is about 0.02% more than 10^7 m.

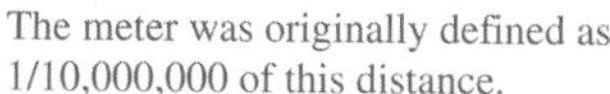

The meter was originally defined as
1/10,000,000 of this distance.

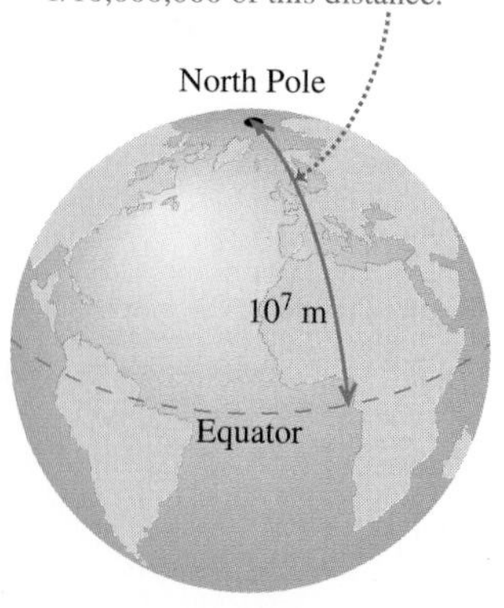

To make accurate, reliable measurements, we need units of measurement that do not change and that can be duplicated by observers in various locations. The system of units used by scientists and engineers around the world is commonly called "the metric system," but since 1960 it has been known officially as the **International System,** or **SI** (the abbreviation for its French name, *Système International*). A list of all SI units is given in Appendix A, as are definitions of the most fundamental units.

The definitions of the basic units of the metric system have evolved over the years. When the metric system was established in 1791 by the French Academy of Sciences, the meter was defined as one ten-millionth of the distance from the North Pole to the equator (Fig. 1.3). The second was defined as the time required for a pendulum one meter long to swing from one side to the other. These definitions were cumbersome and hard to duplicate precisely, and by international agreement they have been replaced with more refined definitions.

Time

From 1889 until 1967, the unit of time was defined as a certain fraction of the mean solar day, the average time between successive arrivals of the sun at its highest point in the sky. The present standard, adopted in 1967, is much more precise. It is based on an atomic clock, which uses the energy difference between the two lowest energy states of the cesium atom. When bombarded by microwaves of precisely the proper frequency, cesium atoms undergo a transition from one of these states to the other. One **second** (abbreviated s) is defined as the time required for 9,192,631,770 cycles of this microwave radiation.

Length

In 1960 an atomic standard for the meter was also established, using the wavelength of the orange-red light emitted by atoms of krypton (^{86}Kr) in a glow discharge tube. Using this length standard, the speed of light in a vacuum was measured to be 299,792,458 m/s. In November 1983, the length standard was changed again so that the speed of light in a vacuum was *defined* to be precisely 299,792,458 m/s. The meter is defined to be consistent with this number and with the above definition of the second. Hence the new definition of the **meter** (abbreviated m) is the distance that light travels in a vacuum in 1/299,792,458 second. This provides a much more precise standard of length than the one based on a wavelength of light.

Mass

The standard of mass, the **kilogram** (abbreviated kg), is defined to be the mass of a particular cylinder of platinum–iridium alloy kept at the International Bureau of Weights and Measures at Sèvres, near Paris (Fig. 1.4). An atomic standard of mass would be more fundamental, but at present we cannot measure masses on an atomic scale with as much accuracy as on a macroscopic scale. The *gram* (which is not a fundamental unit) is 0.001 kilogram.

1.4 The metal object carefully enclosed within these nested glass containers is the international standard kilogram.

Unit Prefixes

Once we have defined the fundamental units, it is easy to introduce larger and smaller units for the same physical quantities. In the metric system these other units are related to the fundamental units (or, in the case of mass, to the gram) by multiples of 10 or $\frac{1}{10}$. Thus one kilometer (1 km) is 1000 meters, and one centimeter (1 cm) is $\frac{1}{100}$ meter. We usually express multiples of 10 or $\frac{1}{10}$ in exponential notation: $1000 = 10^3$, $\frac{1}{1000} = 10^{-3}$, and so on. With this notation, $1\ \text{km} = 10^3\ \text{m}$ and $1\ \text{cm} = 10^{-2}\ \text{m}$.

The names of the additional units are derived by adding a **prefix** to the name of the fundamental unit. For example, the prefix "kilo-," abbreviated k, always means a unit larger by a factor of 1000; thus

$$\begin{aligned} 1\ \text{kilometer} &= 1\ \text{km} = 10^3\ \text{meters} = 10^3\ \text{m} \\ 1\ \text{kilogram} &= 1\ \text{kg} = 10^3\ \text{grams} = 10^3\ \text{g} \\ 1\ \text{kilowatt} &= 1\ \text{kW} = 10^3\ \text{watts} = 10^3\ \text{W} \end{aligned}$$

A table on the inside back cover of this book lists the standard SI prefixes, with their meanings and abbreviations.

Here are several examples of the use of multiples of 10 and their prefixes with the units of length, mass, and time. Figure 1.5 shows how these prefixes help describe both large and small distances.

Length

$$\begin{aligned} 1\ \text{nanometer} &= 1\ \text{nm} = 10^{-9}\ \text{m}\ \text{(a few times the size of the largest atom)} \\ 1\ \text{micrometer} &= 1\ \mu\text{m} = 10^{-6}\ \text{m}\ \text{(size of some bacteria and living cells)} \\ 1\ \text{millimeter} &= 1\ \text{mm} = 10^{-3}\ \text{m}\ \text{(diameter of the point of a ballpoint pen)} \\ 1\ \text{centimeter} &= 1\ \text{cm} = 10^{-2}\ \text{m}\ \text{(diameter of your little finger)} \\ 1\ \text{kilometer} &= 1\ \text{km} = 10^{3}\ \text{m}\ \text{(a 10-minute walk)} \end{aligned}$$

1.5 Some typical lengths in the universe. **(a)** The distance to the most remote galaxies we can see is about 10^{26} m, or 10^{23} km. **(b)** The sun is 1.50×10^{11} m, or 1.50×10^{8} km, from earth. **(c)** The diameter of the earth is 1.28×10^{7} m, or 12,800 km. **(d)** A typical human is about 1.7 m, or 170 cm, tall. **(e)** Human red blood cells are about 8×10^{-6} m (0.008 mm, or 8 μm) in diameter. **(f)** These oxygen atoms, shown arrayed on the surface of a crystal, are about 10^{-10} m, or 10^{-4} μm, in radius. **(g)** Typical atomic nuclei (shown in an artist's impression) have radii of about 10^{-14} m, or 10^{-5} nm.

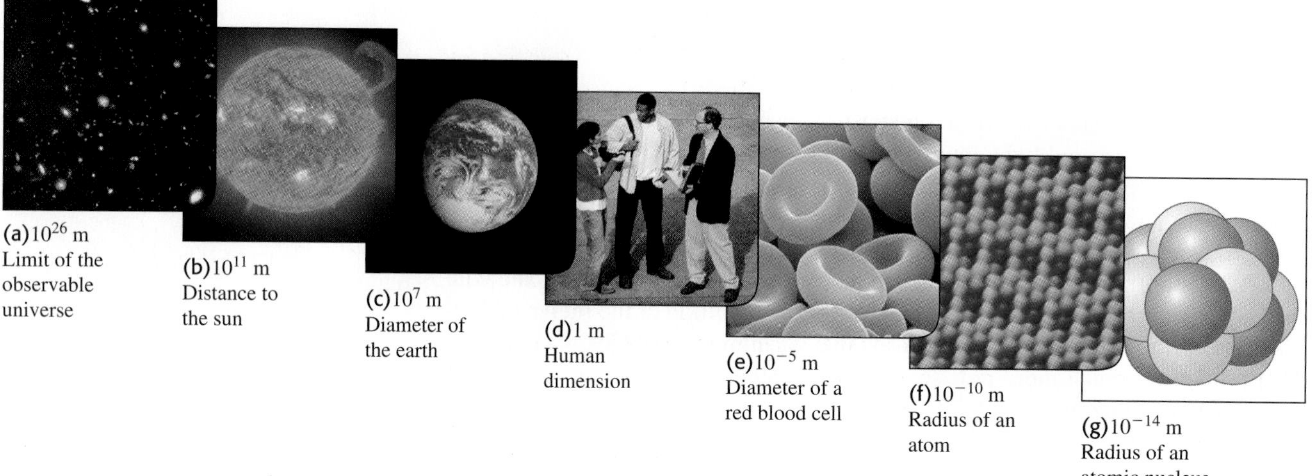

Mass

1 microgram = 1 μg = 10^{-6} g = 10^{-9} kg (mass of a very small dust particle)
1 milligram = 1 mg = 10^{-3} g = 10^{-6} kg (mass of a grain of salt)
1 gram = 1 g = 10^{-3} kg (mass of a paper clip)

Time

1 nanosecond = 1 ns = 10^{-9} s (time for light to travel 0.3 m)
1 microsecond = 1 μs = 10^{-6} s (time for an orbiting space shuttle to travel 8 mm)
1 millisecond = 1 ms = 10^{-3} s (time for sound to travel 0.35 m)

The British System

Finally, we mention the British system of units. These units are used only in the United States and a few other countries, and in most of these they are being replaced by SI units. British units are now officially defined in terms of SI units, as follows:

Length: 1 inch = 2.54 cm (exactly)
Force: 1 pound = 4.448221615260 newtons (exactly)

The newton, abbreviated N, is the SI unit of force. The British unit of time is the second, defined the same way as in SI. In physics, British units are used only in mechanics and thermodynamics; there is no British system of electrical units.

In this book we use SI units for all examples and problems, but we occasionally give approximate equivalents in British units. As you do problems using SI units, you may also wish to convert to the approximate British equivalents if they are more familiar to you (Fig. 1.6). But you should try to *think* in SI units as much as you can.

1.6 Many everyday items make use of both SI and British units. An example is this speedometer from a U.S.-built automobile, which shows the speed in both kilometers per hour (inner scale) and miles per hour (outer scale).

1.4 Unit Consistency and Conversions

We use equations to express relationships among physical quantities, represented by algebraic symbols. Each algebraic symbol always denotes both a number and a unit. For example, d might represent a distance of 10 m, t a time of 5 s, and v a speed of 2 m/s.

An equation must always be **dimensionally consistent.** You can't add apples and automobiles; two terms may be added or equated only if they have the same units. For example, if a body moving with constant speed v travels a distance d in a time t, these quantities are related by the equation

$$d = vt$$

If d is measured in meters, then the product vt must also be expressed in meters. Using the above numbers as an example, we may write

$$10\text{ m} = \left(2\,\frac{\text{m}}{\cancel{\text{s}}}\right)(5\,\cancel{\text{s}})$$

Because the unit $1/\text{s}$ on the right side of the equation cancels the unit s, the product has units of meters, as it must. In calculations, units are treated just like algebraic symbols with respect to multiplication and division.

CAUTION Always use units in calculations When a problem requires calculations using numbers with units, *always* write the numbers with the correct units and carry the units through the calculation as in the example above. This provides a very useful check for calculations. If at some stage in a calculation you find that an equation or an expression has inconsistent units, you know you have made an error somewhere. In this book we will *always* carry units through all calculations, and we strongly urge you to follow this practice when you solve problems.

Problem-Solving Strategy 1.2 Unit Conversions

MP

IDENTIFY *the relevant concepts:* Unit conversion is important, but it's also important to recognize when it's needed. In most cases, you're best off using the fundamental SI units (lengths in meters, masses in kilograms, and time in seconds) within a problem. If you need the answer to be in a different set of units (such as kilometers, grams, or hours), wait until the end of the problem to make the conversion. In the following examples, we'll concentrate on unit conversion alone, so we'll skip the *Identify* step.

SET UP *the problem* and **EXECUTE** *the solution:* Units are multiplied and divided just like ordinary algebraic symbols. This gives us an easy way to convert a quantity from one set of units to another. The key idea is to express the same physical quantity in two different units and form an equality.

For example, when we say that $1\text{ min} = 60\text{ s}$, we don't mean that the number 1 is equal to the number 60; rather, we mean that 1 min represents the same physical time interval as 60 s. For this reason, the ratio $(1\text{ min})/(60\text{ s})$ equals 1, as does its reciprocal $(60\text{ s})/(1\text{ min})$. We may multiply a quantity by either of these factors without changing that quantity's physical meaning. For example, to find the number of seconds in 3 min, we write

$$3\text{ min} = (3\,\cancel{\text{min}})\left(\frac{60\text{ s}}{1\,\cancel{\text{min}}}\right) = 180\text{ s}$$

EVALUATE *your answer:* If you do your unit conversions correctly, unwanted units will cancel, as in the example above. If instead you had multiplied 3 min by $(1\text{ min})/(60\text{ s})$, your result would have been $\frac{1}{20}\text{ min}^2/\text{s}$, which is a rather odd way of measuring time. To be sure you convert units properly, you must write down the units at *all* stages of the calculation.

Finally, check whether your answer is reasonable. Is the result $3\text{ min} = 180\text{ s}$ reasonable? The answer is yes; the second is a smaller unit than the minute, so there are more seconds than minutes in the same time interval.

Example 1.1 Converting speed units

The official world land speed record is 1228.0 km/h, set on October 15, 1997, by Andy Green in the jet engine car *Thrust SSC.* Express this speed in meters per second.

SOLUTION

IDENTIFY AND SET UP: We want to convert the units of a speed from km/h to m/s.

EXECUTE: The prefix k means 10^3, so the speed $1228.0\text{ km/h} = 1228.0 \times 10^3\text{ m/h}$. We also know that there are 3600 s in 1 h. So we must combine the speed of $1228.0 \times 10^3\text{ m/h}$ and a factor of 3600. But should we multiply or divide by this factor? If we treat the factor as a pure number without units, we're forced to guess how to proceed.

The correct approach is to carry the units with each factor. We then arrange the factor so that the hour unit cancels:

$$1228.0\text{ km/h} = \left(1228.0 \times 10^3\,\frac{\text{m}}{\cancel{\text{h}}}\right)\left(\frac{1\,\cancel{\text{h}}}{3600\text{ s}}\right) = 341.11\text{ m/s}$$

If you multiplied by $(3600\text{ s})/(1\text{ h})$ instead of $(1\text{ h})/(3600\text{ s})$, the hour unit wouldn't cancel, and you would be able to easily

Continued

recognize your error. Again, the *only* way to be sure that you correctly convert units is to carry the units throughout the calculation.

EVALUATE: While you probably have a good intuition for speeds in kilometers per hour or miles per hour, speeds in meters per second are likely to be a bit more mysterious. It helps to remember that a typical walking speed is about 1 m/s: the length of an average person's stride is about one meter, and a good walking pace is about one stride per second. By comparison, a speed of 341.11 m/s is rapid indeed!

Example 1.2 Converting volume units

The world's largest cut diamond is the First Star of Africa (mounted in the British Royal Sceptre and kept in the Tower of London). Its volume is 1.84 cubic inches. What is its volume in cubic centimeters? In cubic meters?

SOLUTION

IDENTIFY AND SET UP: Here we are to convert the units of a volume from cubic inches (in.^3) to cubic centimeters (cm^3) and cubic meters (m^3).

EXECUTE: To convert cubic inches to cubic centimeters, we multiply by $[(2.54\text{ cm})/(1\text{ in.})]^3$, not just $(2.54\text{ cm})/(1\text{ in.})$. We find

$$1.84\text{ in.}^3 = (1.84\text{ in.}^3)\left(\frac{2.54\text{ cm}}{1\text{ in.}}\right)^3 = (1.84)(2.54)^3\frac{\cancel{\text{in.}^3}\text{ cm}^3}{\cancel{\text{in.}^3}} = 30.2\text{ cm}^3$$

Also, $1\text{ cm} = 10^{-2}\text{ m}$, and

$$30.2\text{ cm}^3 = (30.2\text{ cm}^3)\left(\frac{10^{-2}\text{ m}}{1\text{ cm}}\right)^3 = (30.2)(10^{-2})^3\frac{\cancel{\text{cm}^3}\text{ m}^3}{\cancel{\text{cm}^3}} = 30.2\times10^{-6}\text{ m}^3 = 3.02\times10^{-5}\text{ m}^3$$

EVALUATE: While 1 centimeter is 10^{-2} of a meter (that is, $1\text{ cm} = 10^{-2}\text{ m}$), our answer shows that a cubic centimeter (1 cm^3) is *not* 10^{-2} of a cubic meter. Rather, it is the volume of a cube whose sides are 1 cm long. So $1\text{ cm}^3 = (1\text{ cm})^3 = (10^{-2}\text{ m})^3 = (10^{-2})^3\text{ m}^3$, or $1\text{ cm}^3 = 10^{-6}\text{ m}^3$.

1.5 Uncertainty and Significant Figures

Measurements always have uncertainties. If you measure the thickness of the cover of this book using an ordinary ruler, your measurement is reliable only to the nearest millimeter, and your result will be 3 mm. It would be *wrong* to state this result as 3.00 mm; given the limitations of the measuring device, you can't tell whether the actual thickness is 3.00 mm, 2.85 mm, or 3.11 mm. But if you use a micrometer caliper, a device that measures distances reliably to the nearest 0.01 mm, the result will be 2.91 mm. The distinction between these two measurements is in their **uncertainty.** The measurement using the micrometer caliper has a smaller uncertainty; it's a more accurate measurement. The uncertainty is also called the **error** because it indicates the maximum difference there is likely to be between the measured value and the true value. The uncertainty or error of a measured value depends on the measurement technique used.

We often indicate the **accuracy** of a measured value—that is, how close it is likely to be to the true value—by writing the number, the symbol $\pm$, and a second number indicating the uncertainty of the measurement. If the diameter of a steel rod is given as 56.47 ± 0.02 mm, this means that the true value is unlikely to be less than 56.45 mm or greater than 56.49 mm. In a commonly used shorthand notation, the number 1.6454(21) means 1.6454 ± 0.0021. The numbers in parentheses show the uncertainty in the final digits of the main number.

We can also express accuracy in terms of the maximum likely **fractional error** or **percent error** (also called *fractional uncertainty* and *percent uncertainty*). A resistor labeled "47 ohms $\pm$ 10%" probably has a true resistance that differs from 47 ohms by no more than 10% of 47 ohms—that is, about 5 ohms. The resistance is probably between 42 and 52 ohms. For the diameter of the steel rod given above, the fractional error is $(0.02\text{ mm})/(56.47\text{ mm})$, or about 0.0004; the percent error is $(0.0004)(100\%)$, or about 0.04%. Even small percent errors can sometimes be very significant (Fig. 1.7).

1.7 This spectacular mishap was the result of a very small percent error—traveling a few meters too far in a journey of hundreds of thousands of meters.

In many cases the uncertainty of a number is not stated explicitly. Instead, the uncertainty is indicated by the number of meaningful digits, or **significant figures,** in the measured value. We gave the thickness of the cover of this book as 2.91 mm, which has three significant figures. By this we mean that the first two digits are known to be correct, while the third digit is uncertain. The last digit is in the hundredths place, so the uncertainty is about 0.01 mm. Two values with the *same* number of significant figures may have *different* uncertainties; a distance given as 137 km also has three significant figures, but the uncertainty is about 1 km.

When you use numbers having uncertainties to compute other numbers, the computed numbers are also uncertain. When numbers are multiplied or divided, the number of significant figures in the result can be no greater than in the factor with the fewest significant figures. For example, $3.1416 \times 2.34 \times 0.58 = 4.3$. When we add and subtract numbers, it's the location of the decimal point that matters, not the number of significant figures. For example, $123.62 + 8.9 = 132.5$. Although 123.62 has an uncertainty of about 0.01, 8.9 has an uncertainty of about 0.1. So their sum has an uncertainty of about 0.1 and should be written as 132.5, not 132.52. Table 1.1 summarizes these rules for significant figures.

Table 1.1 Using Significant Figures

Mathematical Operation	Significant Figures in Result
Multiplication or division	No more than in the number with the fewest significant figures *Example:* $(0.745 \times 2.2)/3.885 = 0.42$ *Example:* $(1.32578 \times 10^7) \times (4.11 \times 10^{-3}) = 5.45 \times 10^4$
Addition or subtraction	Determined by the number with the largest uncertainty (i.e., the fewest digits to the right of the decimal point) *Example:* $27.153 + 138.2 - 11.74 = 153.6$

Note: In this book we will usually give numerical values with three significant figures.

As an application of these ideas, suppose you want to verify the value of π, the ratio of the circumference of a circle to its diameter. The true value of this ratio to ten digits is 3.141592654. To test this, you draw a large circle and measure its circumference and diameter to the nearest millimeter, obtaining the values 424 mm and 135 mm (Fig. 1.8). You punch these into your calculator and obtain the quotient 3.140740741. This may seem to disagree with the true value of π, but keep in mind that each of your measurements has three significant figures, so your measured value of π, equal to $(424 \text{ mm})/(135 \text{ mm})$, can have only three significant figures. It should be stated simply as 3.14. Within the limit of three significant figures, your value does agree with the true value.

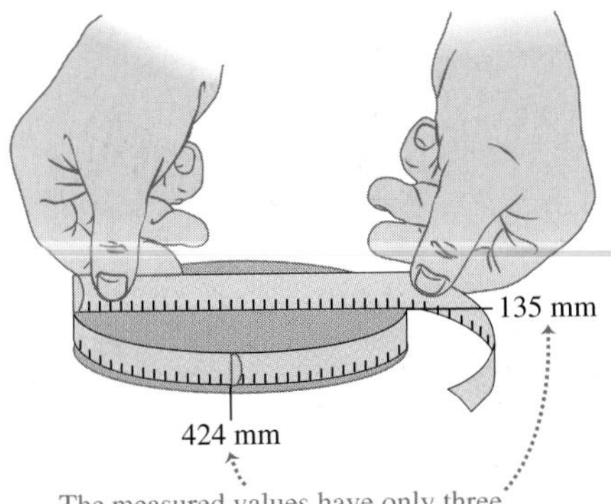
135 mm
424 mm
The measured values have only three significant figures, so their calculated ratio (π) also has only three significant figures.

1.8 Determining the value of π from the circumference and diameter of a circle.

In the examples and problems in this book we usually give numerical values with three significant figures, so your answers should usually have no more than three significant figures. (Many numbers in the real world have even less accuracy. An automobile speedometer, for example, usually gives only two significant figures.) Even if you do the arithmetic with a calculator that displays ten digits, it would be wrong to give a ten-digit answer because it misrepresents the accuracy of the results. Always round your final answer to keep only the correct number of significant figures or, in doubtful cases, one more at most. In Example 1.1 it would have been wrong to state the answer as 341.11111 m/s. Note that when you reduce such an answer to the appropriate number of significant figures, you must *round,* not *truncate.* Your calculator will tell you that the ratio of 525 m to 311 m is 1.688102894; to three significant figures, this is 1.69, not 1.68.

When we calculate with very large or very small numbers, we can show significant figures much more easily by using **scientific notation,** sometimes called **powers-of-10 notation.** The distance from the earth to the moon is about 384,000,000 m, but writing the number in this form doesn't indicate the number of significant figures. Instead, we move the decimal point eight places to the left (corresponding to dividing by 10^8) and multiply by 10^8; that is,

$$384{,}000{,}000 \text{ m} = 3.84 \times 10^8 \text{ m}$$

In this form, it is clear that we have three significant figures. The number 4.00×10^{-7} also has three significant figures, even though two of them are zeros. Note that in scientific notation the usual practice is to express the quantity as a number between 1 and 10 multiplied by the appropriate power of 10.

When an integer or a fraction occurs in a general equation, we treat that number as having no uncertainty at all. For example, in the equation $v_x^2 = v_{0x}^2 + 2a_x(x - x_0)$, which is Eq. (2.13) in Chapter 2, the coefficient 2 is *exactly* 2. We can consider this coefficient as having an infinite number of significant figures $(2.000000\ldots)$. The same is true of the exponent 2 in v_x^2 and v_{0x}^2.

Finally, let's note that **precision** is not the same as *accuracy.* A cheap digital watch that gives the time as 10:35:17 A.M. is very *precise* (the time is given to the second), but if the watch runs several minutes slow, then this value isn't very *accurate.* On the other hand, a grandfather clock might be very accurate (that is, display the correct time), but if the clock has no second hand, it isn't very precise. A high-quality measurement, like those used to define standards (see Section 1.3), is both precise *and* accurate.

Example 1.3 Significant figures in multiplication

The rest energy E of an object with rest mass m is given by Einstein's equation

$$E = mc^2$$

where c is the speed of light in a vacuum. Find E for an object with $m = 9.11 \times 10^{-31}$ kg (to three significant figures, the mass of an electron). The SI unit for E is the joule (J); $1\ \text{J} = 1\ \text{kg}\cdot\text{m}^2/\text{s}^2$.

SOLUTION

IDENTIFY AND SET UP: Our target variable is the energy E. We are given the equation to use and the value of the mass m; from Section 1.3 the exact value of the speed of light is $c = 299{,}792{,}458\ \text{m/s} = 2.99792458 \times 10^8\ \text{m/s}$.

EXECUTE: Substituting the values of m and c into Einstein's equation, we find

$$\begin{aligned} E &= (9.11 \times 10^{-31}\ \text{kg})(2.99792458 \times 10^8\ \text{m/s})^2 \\ &= (9.11)(2.99792458)^2(10^{-31})(10^8)^2\ \text{kg}\cdot\text{m}^2/\text{s}^2 \\ &= (81.87659678)(10^{[-31+(2\times 8)]})\ \text{kg}\cdot\text{m}^2/\text{s}^2 \\ &= 8.187659678 \times 10^{-14}\ \text{kg}\cdot\text{m}^2/\text{s}^2 \end{aligned}$$

Since the value of m was given to only three significant figures, we must round this to

$$E = 8.19 \times 10^{-14}\ \text{kg}\cdot\text{m}^2/\text{s}^2 = 8.19 \times 10^{-14}\ \text{J}$$

Most calculators use scientific notation and add exponents automatically, but you should be able to do such calculations by hand when necessary.

EVALUATE: While the rest energy contained in an electron may seem ridiculously small, on the atomic scale it is tremendous. Compare our answer to 10^{-19} J, the energy gained or lost by a single atom during a typical chemical reaction; the rest energy of an electron is about 1,000,000 times larger! (We will discuss the significance of rest energy in Chapter 37.)

Test Your Understanding of Section 1.5 The density of a material is equal to its mass divided by its volume. What is the density (in kg/m^3) of a rock of mass 1.80 kg and volume $6.0 \times 10^{-4}\ \text{m}^3$? (i) $3 \times 10^3\ \text{kg/m}^3$; (ii) $3.0 \times 10^3\ \text{kg/m}^3$; (iii) $3.00 \times 10^3\ \text{kg/m}^3$; (iv) $3.000 \times 10^3\ \text{kg/m}^3$; (v) any of these—all of these answers are mathematically equivalent.

1.6 Estimates and Orders of Magnitude

We have stressed the importance of knowing the accuracy of numbers that represent physical quantities. But even a very crude estimate of a quantity often gives us useful information. Sometimes we know how to calculate a certain quantity, but we have to guess at the data we need for the calculation. Or the calculation might be too complicated to carry out exactly, so we make some rough approximations. In either case our result is also a guess, but such a guess can be useful even if it is uncertain by a factor of two, ten, or more. Such calculations are often called **order-of-magnitude estimates.** The great Italian-American nuclear physicist Enrico Fermi (1901–1954) called them "back-of-the-envelope calculations."

Exercises 1.18 through 1.29 at the end of this chapter are of the estimating, or "order-of-magnitude," variety. Some are silly, and most require guesswork for the needed input data. Don't try to look up a lot of data; make the best guesses you can. Even when they are off by a factor of ten, the results can be useful and interesting.

Example 1.4 An order-of-magnitude estimate

You are writing an adventure novel in which the hero escapes across the border with a billion dollars' worth of gold in his suitcase. Is this possible? Would that amount of gold fit in a suitcase? Would it be too heavy to carry?

SOLUTION

IDENTIFY, SET UP, AND EXECUTE: Gold sells for around \$400 an ounce. On a particular day the price might be \$200 or \$600, but never mind. An ounce is about 30 grams. Actually, an ordinary (avoirdupois) ounce is 28.35 g; an ounce of gold is a troy ounce, which is 9.45% more. Again, never mind. Ten dollars' worth of gold has a mass somewhere around one gram, so a billion (10^9) dollars' worth of gold is a hundred million (10^8) grams, or a hundred thousand (10^5) kilograms. This corresponds to a weight in British units of around 200,000 lb, or 100 tons. Whether the precise number is closer to 50 tons or 200 tons doesn't matter. Either way, the hero is not about to carry it across the border in a suitcase.

We can also estimate the *volume* of this gold. If its density were the same as that of water $(1\ \text{g/cm}^3)$, the volume would be $10^8\ \text{cm}^3$, or $100\ \text{m}^3$. But gold is a heavy metal; we might guess its density to be 10 times that of water. Gold is actually 19.3 times as dense as water. But by guessing 10, we find a volume of $10\ \text{m}^3$. Visualize 10 cubical stacks of gold bricks, each 1 meter on a side, and ask yourself whether they would fit in a suitcase!

EVALUATE: Clearly, your novel needs rewriting. Try the calculation again with a suitcase full of five-carat (1-gram) diamonds, each worth \$100,000. Would this work?

Test Your Understanding of Section 1.6 Can you estimate the total number of teeth in all the mouths of everyone (students, staff, and faculty) on your campus? (*Hint:* How many teeth are in your mouth? Count them!)

1.7 Vectors and Vector Addition

Some physical quantities, such as time, temperature, mass, and density, can be described completely by a single number with a unit. But many other important quantities in physics have a *direction* associated with them and cannot be described by a single number. A simple example is the motion of an airplane. To describe this motion completely, we must say not only how fast the plane is moving, but also in what direction. To fly from Chicago to New York, a plane has to head east, not south. The speed of the airplane combined with its direction of motion together constitute a quantity called *velocity.* Another example is *force,* which in physics means a push or pull exerted on a body. Giving a complete description of a force means describing both how hard the force pushes or pulls on the body and the direction of the push or pull.

When a physical quantity is described by a single number, we call it a **scalar quantity.** In contrast, a **vector quantity** has both a **magnitude** (the "how much" or "how big" part) and a direction in space. Calculations that combine scalar quantities use the operations of ordinary arithmetic. For example, $6\ \text{kg} + 3\ \text{kg} = 9\ \text{kg}$, or $4 \times 2\ \text{s} = 8\ \text{s}$. However, combining vectors requires a different set of operations.

To understand more about vectors and how they combine, we start with the simplest vector quantity, **displacement.** Displacement is simply a change in position of a point. (The point may represent a particle or a small body.) In Fig. 1.9a we represent the change of position from point P_1 to point P_2 by a line from P_1 to P_2, with an arrowhead at P_2 to represent the direction of motion. Displacement is a vector quantity because we must state not only how far the particle moves, but also in what direction. Walking 3 km north from your front door doesn't get you

1.9 Displacement as a vector quantity. A displacement is always a straight-line segment directed from the starting point to the ending point, even if the path is curved.

(a) Handwritten notation: $\vec{A}$

Ending position: P_2

Displacement $\vec{A}$

Starting position: P_1

(b)

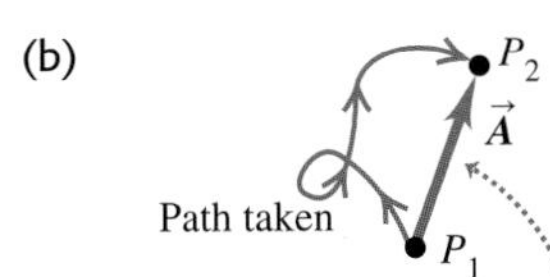

The displacement depends on only the starting and ending positions—not on the path taken.

(c)

P_1

If an object makes a round trip, the total displacement is 0, regardless of the distance traveled.

to the same place as walking 3 km southeast; these two displacements have the same magnitude, but different directions.

We usually represent a vector quantity such as displacement by a single letter, such as $\vec{A}$ in Fig. 1.9a. In this book we always print vector symbols in ***boldface italic type with an arrow above them.*** We do this to remind you that vector quantities have different properties from scalar quantities; the arrow is a reminder that vectors have direction. In handwriting, vector symbols are usually underlined or written with an arrow above them (see Fig. 1.9a). When you write a symbol for a vector, *always* write it with an arrow on top. If you don't distinguish between scalar and vector quantities in your notation, you probably won't make the distinction in your thinking either, and hopeless confusion will result.

We always *draw* a vector as a line with an arrowhead at its tip. The length of the line shows the vector's magnitude, and the direction of the line shows the vector's direction. Displacement is always a straight-line segment, directed from the starting point to the ending point, even though the actual path of the particle may be curved. In Fig. 1.9b the particle moves along the curved path shown from P_1 to P_2, but the displacement is still the vector $\vec{A}$. Note that displacement is not related directly to the total *distance* traveled. If the particle were to continue on past P_2 and then return to P_1, the displacement for the entire trip would be *zero* (Fig. 1.9c).

1.10 The meaning of vectors that have the same magnitude and the same or opposite direction.

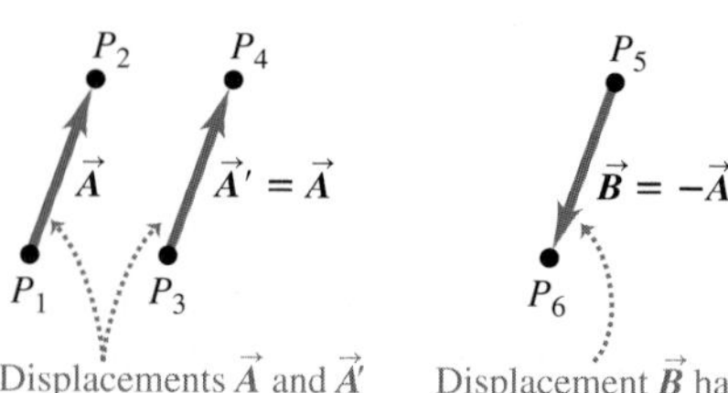
P_2
P_4
P_5
$\vec{A}$
$\vec{A}' = \vec{A}$
$\vec{B} = -\vec{A}$
P_1
P_3
P_6
Displacements $\vec{A}$ and $\vec{A}'$ are equal because they have the same length and direction.
Displacement $\vec{B}$ has the same magnitude as $\vec{A}$ but opposite direction; $\vec{B}$ is the negative of $\vec{A}$.

If two vectors have the same direction, they are **parallel.** If they have the same magnitude *and* the same direction, they are *equal,* no matter where they are located in space. The vector $\vec{A}'$ from point P_3 to point P_4 in Fig. 1.10 has the same length and direction as the vector $\vec{A}$ from P_1 to P_2. These two displacements are equal, even though they start at different points. We write this as $\vec{A}' = \vec{A}$ in Fig. 1.10; the boldface equals sign emphasizes that equality of two vector quantities is not the same relationship as equality of two scalar quantities. Two vector quantities are equal only when they have the same magnitude *and* the same direction.

The vector $\vec{B}$ in Fig. 1.10, however, is not equal to $\vec{A}$ because its direction is *opposite* to that of $\vec{A}$. We define the **negative of a vector** as a vector having the same magnitude as the original vector but the *opposite* direction. The negative of vector quantity $\vec{A}$ is denoted as $-\vec{A}$, and we use a boldface minus sign to emphasize the vector nature of the quantities. If $\vec{A}$ is 87 m south, then $-\vec{A}$ is 87 m north. Thus we can write the relationship between $\vec{A}$ and $\vec{B}$ in Fig. 1.10 as $\vec{A} = -\vec{B}$ or $\vec{B} = -\vec{A}$. When two vectors $\vec{A}$ and $\vec{B}$ have opposite directions, whether their magnitudes are the same or not, we say that they are **antiparallel.**

We usually represent the *magnitude* of a vector quantity (in the case of a displacement vector, its length) by the same letter used for the vector, but in *light italic type* with *no* arrow on top, rather than boldface italic with an arrow (which is reserved for vectors). An alternative notation is the vector symbol with vertical bars on both sides:

$$(\text{Magnitude of } \vec{A}) = A = |\vec{A}| \tag{1.1}$$

By definition the magnitude of a vector quantity is a scalar quantity (a number) and is *always positive.* We also note that a vector can never be equal to a scalar because they are different kinds of quantities. The expression "$\vec{A} = 6$ m" is just as wrong as "2 oranges = 3 apples" or "6 lb = 7 km"!

When drawing diagrams with vectors, we'll generally use a scale similar to those used for maps. For example, a displacement of 5 km might be represented in a diagram by a vector 1 cm long, and a displacement of 10 km by a vector 2 cm long. In a diagram for velocity vectors, we might use a scale in which a vector that is 1 cm long represents a velocity of magnitude 5 meters per second (5 m/s). A velocity of 20 m/s would then be represented by a vector 4 cm long, with the appropriate direction.

Vector Addition

Suppose a particle undergoes a displacement $\vec{A}$ followed by a second displacement $\vec{B}$ (Fig. 1.11a). The final result is the same as if the particle had started at the same initial point and undergone a single displacement $\vec{C}$, as shown. We call displacement $\vec{C}$ the **vector sum,** or **resultant,** of displacements $\vec{A}$ and $\vec{B}$. We express this relationship symbolically as

$$\vec{C} = \vec{A} + \vec{B} \tag{1.2}$$

The boldface plus sign emphasizes that adding two vector quantities requires a geometrical process and is not the same operation as adding two scalar quantities such as $2 + 3 = 5$. In vector addition we usually place the *tail* of the *second* vector at the *head,* or tip, of the *first* vector (Fig. 1.11a).

If we make the displacements $\vec{A}$ and $\vec{B}$ in reverse order, with $\vec{B}$ first and $\vec{A}$ second, the result is the same (Fig. 1.11b). Thus

$$\vec{C} = \vec{B} + \vec{A} \quad \text{and} \quad \vec{A} + \vec{B} = \vec{B} + \vec{A} \tag{1.3}$$

This shows that the order of terms in a vector sum doesn't matter. In other words, vector addition obeys the commutative law.

Figure 1.11c shows another way to represent the vector sum: If vectors $\vec{A}$ and $\vec{B}$ are both drawn with their tails at the same point, vector $\vec{C}$ is the diagonal of a parallelogram constructed with $\vec{A}$ and $\vec{B}$ as two adjacent sides.

CAUTION Magnitudes in vector addition It's a common error to conclude that if $\vec{C} = \vec{A} + \vec{B}$, then the magnitude C should just equal the magnitude A plus the magnitude B. In general, this conclusion is *wrong;* for the vectors shown in Fig. 1.11, you can see that $C < A + B$. The magnitude of $\vec{A} + \vec{B}$ depends on the magnitudes of $\vec{A}$ and $\vec{B}$ *and* on the angle between $\vec{A}$ and $\vec{B}$ (see Problem 1.92). Only in the special case in which $\vec{A}$ and $\vec{B}$ are *parallel* is the magnitude of $\vec{C} = \vec{A} + \vec{B}$ equal to the sum of the magnitudes of $\vec{A}$ and $\vec{B}$ (Fig. 1.12a). By contrast, when the vectors are *antiparallel* (Fig. 1.12b) the magnitude of $\vec{C}$ equals the *difference* of the magnitudes of $\vec{A}$ and $\vec{B}$. If you're careful about distinguishing between scalar and vector quantities, you'll avoid making errors about the magnitude of a vector sum.

When we need to add more than two vectors, we may first find the vector sum of any two, add this vectorially to the third, and so on. Figure 1.13a shows three vectors $\vec{A}$, $\vec{B}$, and $\vec{C}$. In Fig. 1.13b, we first add $\vec{A}$ and $\vec{B}$ to give a vector sum $\vec{D}$; we then add vectors $\vec{C}$ and $\vec{D}$ by the same process to obtain the vector sum $\vec{R}$:

$$\vec{R} = (\vec{A} + \vec{B}) + \vec{C} = \vec{D} + \vec{C}$$

Alternatively, we can first add $\vec{B}$ and $\vec{C}$ to obtain vector $\vec{E}$ (Fig. 1.13c), and then add $\vec{A}$ and $\vec{E}$ to obtain $\vec{R}$:

$$\vec{R} = \vec{A} + (\vec{B} + \vec{C}) = \vec{A} + \vec{E}$$

1.11 Three ways to add two vectors. As shown in (b), the order in vector addition doesn't matter; vector addition is commutative.

(a) We can add two vectors by placing them head to tail.

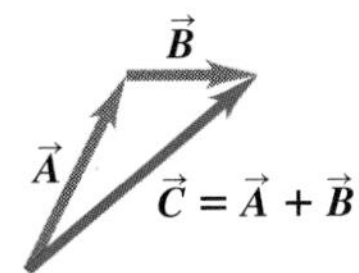

(b) Adding them in reverse order gives the same result.

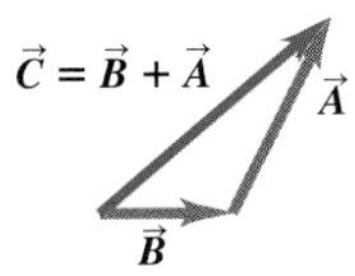

(c) We can also add them by constructing a parallelogram.

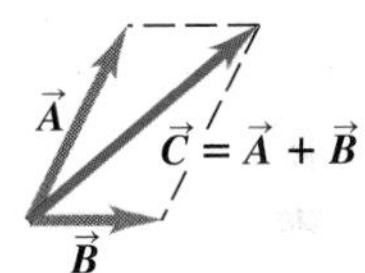

1.12 (a) Only when two vectors $\vec{A}$ and $\vec{B}$ are parallel does the magnitude of their sum equal the sum of their magnitudes: $C = A + B$. (b) When $\vec{A}$ and $\vec{B}$ are antiparallel, the magnitude of their sum equals the *difference* of their magnitudes: $C = |A - B|$.

(a) The sum of two parallel vectors

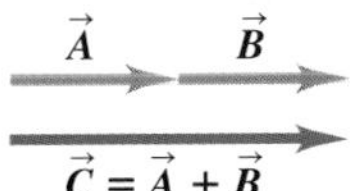

(b) The sum of two antiparallel vectors

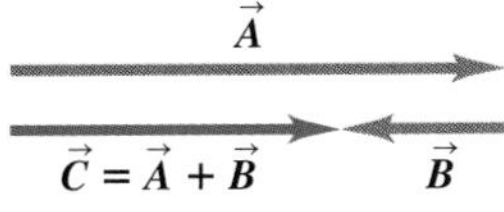

1.13 Several constructions for finding the vector sum $\vec{A} + \vec{B} + \vec{C}$.

(a) To find the sum of these three vectors ...

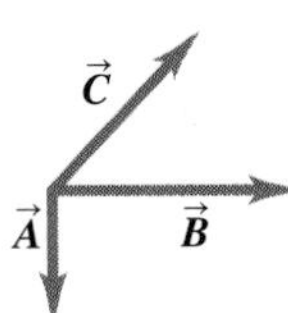

(b) we could add $\vec{A}$ and $\vec{B}$ to get $\vec{D}$ and then add $\vec{C}$ to $\vec{D}$ to get the final sum (resultant) $\vec{R}$, ...

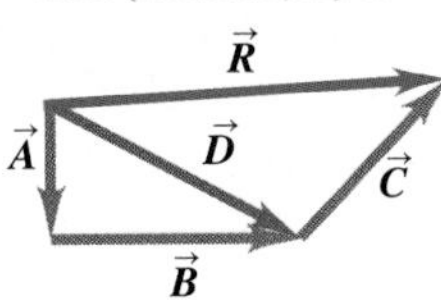

(c) or we could add $\vec{B}$ and $\vec{C}$ to get $\vec{E}$ and then add $\vec{A}$ to $\vec{E}$ to get $\vec{R}$, ...

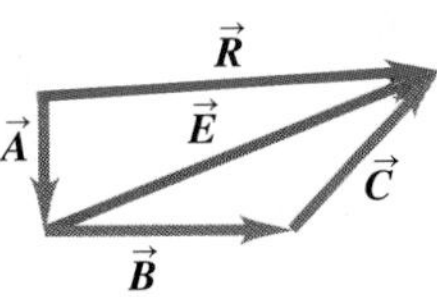

(d) or we could add $\vec{A}$, $\vec{B}$, and $\vec{C}$ to get $\vec{R}$ directly, ...

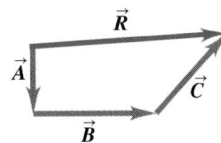

(e) or we could add $\vec{A}$, $\vec{B}$, and $\vec{C}$ in any other order and still get $\vec{R}$.

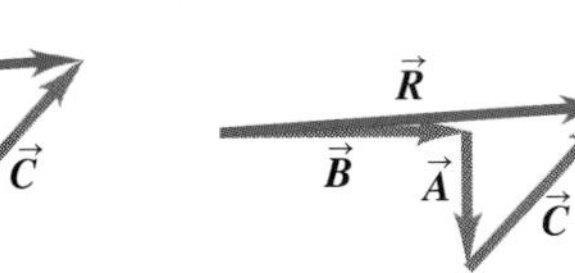

1.14 To construct the vector difference $\vec{A} - \vec{B}$, you can either place the tail of $-\vec{B}$ at the head of $\vec{A}$ or place the two vectors $\vec{A}$ and $\vec{B}$ head to head.

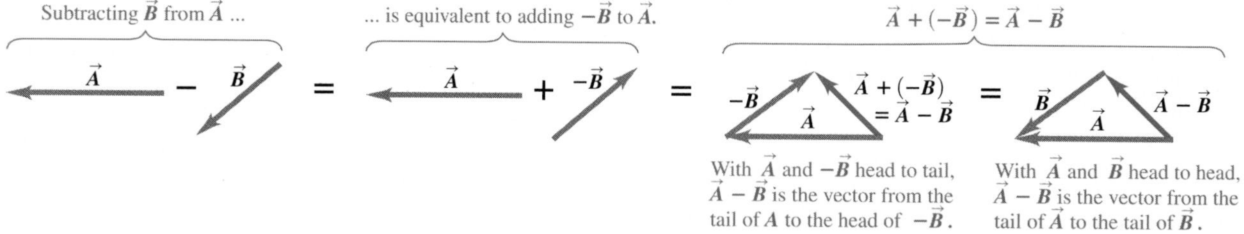

We don't even need to draw vectors $\vec{D}$ and $\vec{E}$; all we need to do is draw $\vec{A}$, $\vec{B}$, and $\vec{C}$ in succession, with the tail of each at the head of the one preceding it. The sum vector $\vec{R}$ extends from the tail of the first vector to the head of the last vector (Fig. 1.13d). The order makes no difference; Fig. 1.13e shows a different order, and we invite you to try others. We see that vector addition obeys the associative law.

We can *subtract* vectors as well as add them. To see how, recall that the vector $-\vec{A}$ has the same magnitude as $\vec{A}$ but the opposite direction. We define the difference $\vec{A} - \vec{B}$ of two vectors $\vec{A}$ and $\vec{B}$ to be the vector sum of $\vec{A}$ and $-\vec{B}$:

$$\vec{A} - \vec{B} = \vec{A} + (-\vec{B}) \tag{1.4}$$

Figure 1.14 shows an example of vector subtraction.

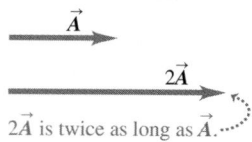

A vector quantity such as a displacement can be multiplied by a scalar quantity (an ordinary number). The displacement $2\vec{A}$ is a displacement (vector quantity) in the same direction as the vector $\vec{A}$ but twice as long; this is the same as adding $\vec{A}$ to itself (Fig. 1.15a). In general, when a vector $\vec{A}$ is multiplied by a scalar c, the result $c\vec{A}$ has magnitude $|c|A$ (the absolute value of c multiplied by the magnitude of the vector $\vec{A}$). If c is positive, $c\vec{A}$ is in the same direction as $\vec{A}$; if c is negative, $c\vec{A}$ is in the direction opposite to $\vec{A}$. Thus $3\vec{A}$ is parallel to $\vec{A}$, while $-3\vec{A}$ is antiparallel to $\vec{A}$ (Fig. 1.15b).

The scalar quantity used to multiply a vector may also be a physical quantity having units. For example, you may be familiar with the relationship $\vec{F} = m\vec{a}$; the net force $\vec{F}$ (a vector quantity) that acts on a body is equal to the product of the body's mass m (a positive scalar quantity) and its acceleration $\vec{a}$ (a vector quantity). The direction of $\vec{F}$ is the same as that of $\vec{a}$ because m is positive, and the magnitude of $\vec{F}$ is equal to the mass m (which is positive and equals its own absolute value) multiplied by the magnitude of $\vec{a}$. The unit of force is the unit of mass multiplied by the unit of acceleration.

1.15 Multiplying a vector (a) by a positive scalar and (b) by a negative scalar.

(a) Multiplying a vector by a positive scalar changes the magnitude (length) of the vector, but not its direction.

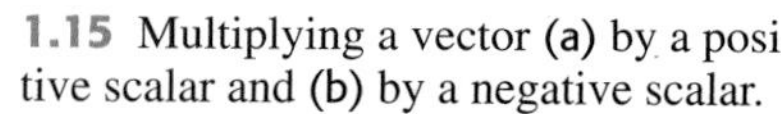

(b) Multiplying a vector by a negative scalar changes its magnitude and reverses its direction.

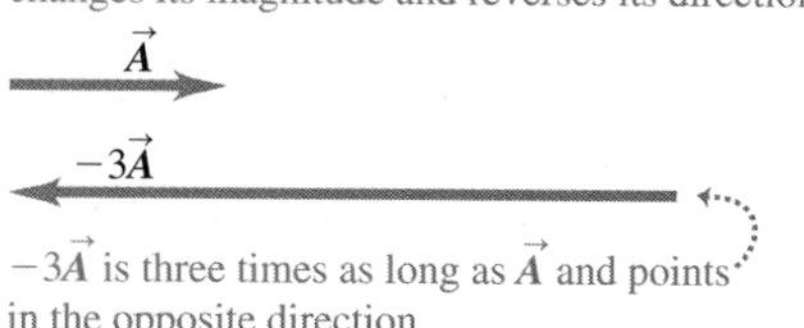

Example 1.5 Vector addition

A cross-country skier skis 1.00 km north and then 2.00 km east on a horizontal snow field. How far and in what direction is she from the starting point?

SOLUTION

IDENTIFY: The problem involves combining displacements, so we can solve it using vector addition. The target variables are the skier's total distance and direction from her starting point. The distance is just the magnitude of her resultant displacement vector from the point of origin to where she stops, and the direction we want is the direction of the resultant displacement vector.

SET UP: Figure 1.16 is a scale diagram of the skier's displacements. We describe the direction from the starting point by the angle ϕ (the Greek letter phi). By careful measurement we find that the distance from the starting point to the ending point is about 2.2 km and that

1.16 The vector diagram, drawn to scale, for a cross-country ski trip.

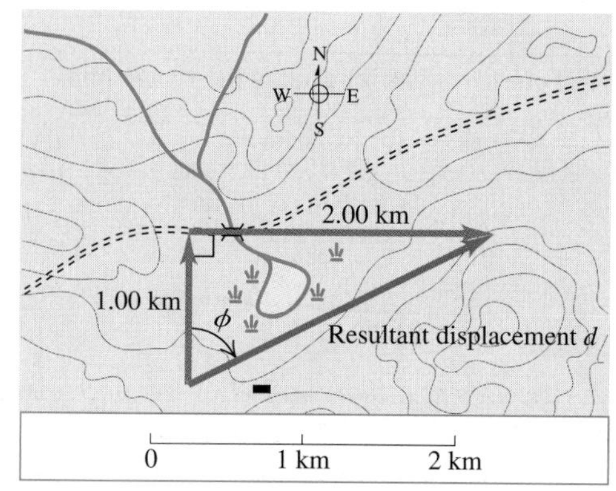

ϕ is about 63°. But we can *calculate* a much more accurate result by adding the 1.00-km and 2.00-km displacement vectors.

EXECUTE: The vectors in the diagram form a right triangle; the distance from the starting point to the ending point is equal to the length of the hypotenuse. We find this length by using the Pythagorean theorem:

$$\sqrt{(1.00\text{ km})^2 + (2.00\text{ km})^2} = 2.24\text{ km}$$

The angle ϕ can be found with a little simple trigonometry. If you need a review, the trigonometric functions and identities are summarized in Appendix B, along with other useful mathematical and geometrical relationships. By the definition of the tangent function,

$$\tan\phi = \frac{\text{opposite side}}{\text{adjacent side}} = \frac{2.00\text{ km}}{1.00\text{ km}}$$
$$\phi = 63.4°$$

We can describe the direction as 63.4° east of north or 90° − 63.4° = 26.6° north of east. Take your choice!

EVALUATE: It's good practice to check the results of a vector-addition problem by making measurements on a drawing of the situation. Happily, the answers we found by calculation (2.24 km and ϕ = 63.4°) are very close to the cruder results we found by measurement (about 2.2 km and about 63°). If they were substantially different, we would have to go back and check for errors.

Test Your Understanding of Section 1.7 Two displacement vectors, $\vec{S}$ and $\vec{T}$, have magnitudes S = 3 m and T = 4 m. Which of the following could be the magnitude of the difference vector $\vec{S} - \vec{T}$? (There may be more than one correct answer.) (i) 9 m; (ii) 7 m; (iii) 5 m; (iv) 1 m; (v) 0 m; (vi) −1 m.

1.8 Components of Vectors

In Section 1.7 we added vectors by using a scale diagram and by using properties of right triangles. Measuring a diagram offers only very limited accuracy, and calculations with right triangles work only when the two vectors are perpendicular. So we need a simple but general method for adding vectors. This is called the method of *components*.

To define what we mean by the components of a vector $\vec{A}$, we begin with a rectangular (Cartesian) coordinate system of axes (Fig. 1.17a). We then draw the vector with its tail at O, the origin of the coordinate system. We can represent any vector lying in the xy-plane as the sum of a vector parallel to the x-axis and a vector parallel to the y-axis. These two vectors are labeled $\vec{A}_x$ and $\vec{A}_y$ in Fig. 1.17a; they are called the **component vectors** of vector $\vec{A}$, and their vector sum is equal to $\vec{A}$. In symbols,

$$\vec{A} = \vec{A}_x + \vec{A}_y \tag{1.5}$$

Since each component vector lies along a coordinate-axis direction, we need only a single number to describe each one. When the component vector $\vec{A}_x$ points in the positive x-direction, we define the number A_x to be equal to the magnitude of $\vec{A}_x$. When the component vector $\vec{A}_x$ points in the negative x-direction, we define the number A_x to be equal to the negative of that magnitude (the magnitude of a vector quantity is itself never negative). We define the number A_y in the same way. The two numbers A_x and A_y are called the **components** of $\vec{A}$ (Fig. 1.17b).

CAUTION **Components are not vectors** The components A_x and A_y of a vector $\vec{A}$ are just numbers; they are *not* vectors themselves. This is why we print the symbols for components in light italic type with *no* arrow on top instead of the boldface italic with an arrow, which is reserved for vectors.

We can calculate the components of the vector $\vec{A}$ if we know its magnitude A and its direction. We'll describe the direction of a vector by its angle relative to some reference direction. In Fig. 1.17b this reference direction is the

1.17 Representing a vector $\vec{A}$ in terms of (a) component vectors $\vec{A}_x$ and $\vec{A}_y$ and (b) components A_x and A_y (which in this case are both positive).

(a)

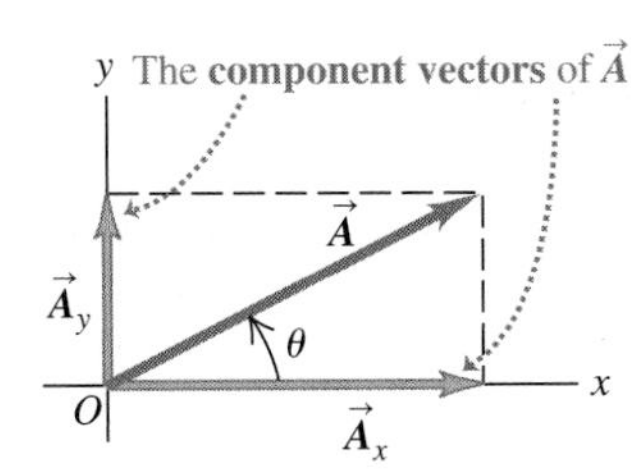

(b)

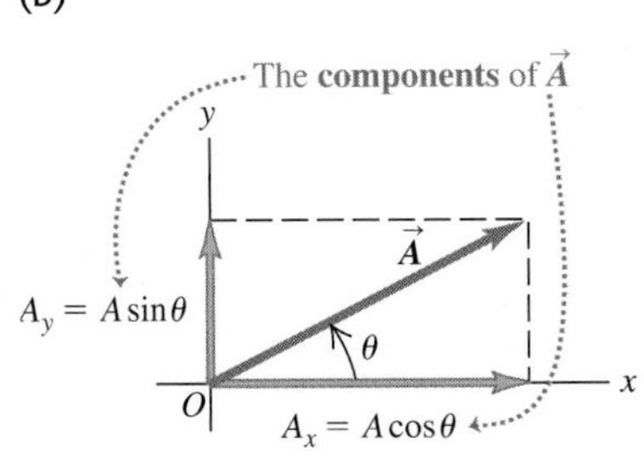

1.18 The components of a vector may be positive or negative numbers.

(a)

B_y is positive: Its component vector points in the $+y$ direction.

B_x is negative: Its component vector points in the $-x$ direction.

(b)

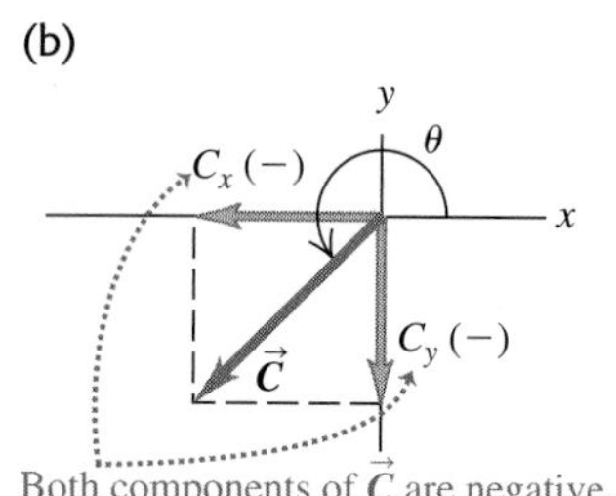

Both components of $\vec{C}$ are negative.

positive x-axis, and the angle between vector $\vec{A}$ and the positive x-axis is θ (the Greek letter theta). Imagine that the vector $\vec{A}$ originally lies along the $+x$-axis and that you then rotate it to its correct direction, as indicated by the arrow in Fig. 1.17b on the angle θ. If this rotation is from the $+x$-axis toward the $+y$-axis, as shown in Fig. 1.17b, then θ is *positive;* if the rotation is from the $+x$-axis toward the $-y$-axis, θ is *negative.* Thus the $+y$-axis is at an angle of 90°, the $-x$-axis at 180°, and the $-y$-axis at 270° (or $-90°$). If θ is measured in this way, then from the definition of the trigonometric functions,

$$\frac{A_x}{A} = \cos\theta \quad \text{and} \quad \frac{A_y}{A} = \sin\theta$$

$$A_x = A\cos\theta \quad \text{and} \quad A_y = A\sin\theta \qquad (1.6)$$

$$(\theta \text{ measured from the } +x\text{-axis, rotating toward the } +y\text{-axis})$$

In Fig. 1.17b, A_x is positive because its direction is along the positive x-axis, and A_y is positive because its direction is along the positive y-axis. This is consistent with Eqs. (1.6); θ is in the first quadrant (between 0° and 90°), and both the cosine and the sine of an angle in this quadrant are positive. But in Fig. 1.18a the component B_x is negative; its direction is opposite to that of the positive x-axis. Again, this agrees with Eqs. (1.6); the cosine of an angle in the second quadrant is negative. The component B_y is positive ($\sin\theta$ is positive in the second quadrant). In Fig. 1.18b, both C_x and C_y are negative (both $\cos\theta$ and $\sin\theta$ are negative in the third quadrant).

CAUTION Relating a vector's magnitude and direction to its components Equations (1.6) are correct *only* when the angle θ is measured from the positive x-axis as described above. If the angle of the vector is given from a different reference direction or using a different sense of rotation, the relationships are different. Be careful! Example 1.6 illustrates this point.

Example 1.6 Finding components

(a) What are the x- and y-components of vector $\vec{D}$ in Fig. 1.19a? The magnitude of the vector is $D = 3.00$ m and the angle $\alpha = 45°$. (b) What are the x- and y-components of vector $\vec{E}$ in Fig. 1.19b? The magnitude of the vector is $E = 4.50$ m and the angle $\beta = 37.0°$.

SOLUTION

IDENTIFY: In each case we are given the magnitude and direction of a vector, and we are asked to find its components.

1.19 Calculating the x- and y-components of vectors.

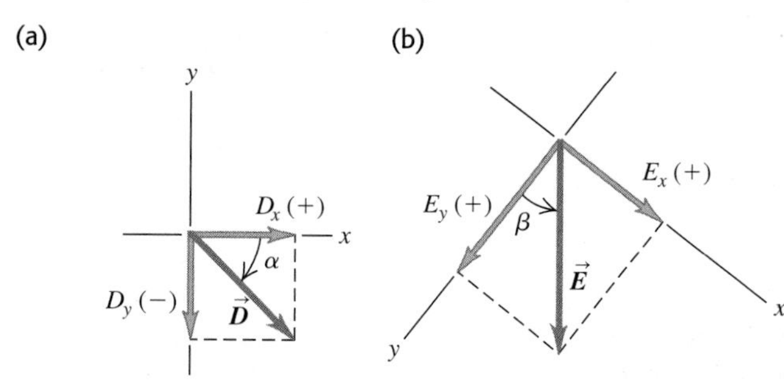

SET UP: It would seem that all we need is Eqs. (1.6). However, we need to be careful because the angles in Fig. 1.19 are *not* measured from the $+x$-axis toward the $+y$-axis.

EXECUTE: (a) The angle between $\vec{D}$ and the positive x-axis is α (the Greek letter alpha), but this angle is measured toward the *negative* y-axis. So the angle we must use in Eqs. (1.6) is $\theta = -\alpha = -45°$. We find

$$D_x = D\cos\theta = (3.00\text{ m})(\cos(-45°)) = +2.1\text{ m}$$
$$D_y = D\sin\theta = (3.00\text{ m})(\sin(-45°)) = -2.1\text{ m}$$

The vector has a positive x-component and a negative y-component, as shown in the figure. Had you been careless and substituted $+45°$ for θ in Eqs. (1.6), you would have gotten the wrong sign for D_y.

(b) The x-axis isn't horizontal in Fig. 1.19b, nor is the y-axis vertical. Don't worry, though: *Any* orientation of the x- and y-axes is permissible, just so the axes are mutually perpendicular. (In Chapter 5 we'll use axes like these to study an object sliding on an incline; one axis will lie along the incline and the other will be perpendicular to the incline.)

Here the angle β (the Greek letter beta) is the angle between $\vec{E}$ and the positive y-axis, *not* the positive x-axis, so we *cannot* use this angle in Eqs. (1.6). Instead, note that $\vec{E}$ defines the hypotenuse of a right triangle; the other two sides of the triangle are the magnitudes of E_x and E_y, the x- and y-components of $\vec{E}$. The sine of β is the opposite side (the magnitude of E_x) divided by the hypotenuse (the magnitude E), and the cosine of β is the adjacent side (the magnitude of E_y) divided by the hypotenuse (again, the magnitude E). Both components of $\vec{E}$ are positive, so

$$E_x = E\sin\beta = (4.50\text{ m})(\sin 37.0°) = +2.71\text{ m}$$
$$E_y = E\cos\beta = (4.50\text{ m})(\cos 37.0°) = +3.59\text{ m}$$

Had you used Eqs. (1.6) directly and written $E_x = E\cos 37.0°$ and $E_y = E\sin 37.0°$, your answers for E_x and E_y would have been reversed!

If you insist on using Eqs. (1.6), you must first find the angle between $\vec{E}$ and the positive x-axis, measured toward the positive y-axis; this is $\theta = 90.0° - \beta = 90.0° - 37.0° = 53.0°$. Then $E_x = E\cos\theta$ and $E_y = E\sin\theta$. You can substitute the values of E and θ into Eqs. (1.6) to show that the results for E_x and E_y are the same as those given above.

EVALUATE: Notice that the answers to part (b) have three significant figures, but the answers to part (a) have only two. Can you see why?

Doing Vector Calculations Using Components

Using components makes it relatively easy to do various calculations involving vectors. Let's look at three important examples.

1. Finding a vector's magnitude and direction from its components. We can describe a vector completely by giving either its magnitude and direction or its x- and y-components. Equations (1.6) show how to find the components if we know the magnitude and direction. We can also reverse the process: We can find the magnitude and direction if we know the components. By applying the Pythagorean theorem to Fig. 1.17b, we find that the magnitude of vector $\vec{A}$ is

$$A = \sqrt{A_x^2 + A_y^2} \quad (1.7)$$

(We always take the positive root.) Equation (1.7) is valid for any choice of x-axis and y-axis, as long as they are mutually perpendicular. The expression for the vector direction comes from the definition of the tangent of an angle. If θ is measured from the positive x-axis, and a positive angle is measured toward the positive y-axis (as in Fig. 1.17b), then

$$\tan\theta = \frac{A_y}{A_x} \quad \text{and} \quad \theta = \arctan\frac{A_y}{A_x} \quad (1.8)$$

We will always use the notation arctan for the inverse tangent function. The notation $\tan^{-1}$ is also commonly used, and your calculator may have an INV or 2ND button to be used with the TAN button.

CAUTION Finding the direction of a vector from its components There is one slight complication in using Eqs. (1.8) to find θ. Suppose $A_x = 2$ m and $A_y = -2$ m as in Fig. 1.20; then $\tan\theta = -1$. But there are two angles that have tangents of -1—namely, 135° and 315° (or −45°). In general, any two angles that differ by 180° have the same tangent. To decide which is correct, we have to look at the individual components. Because A_x is positive and A_y is negative, the angle must be in the fourth quadrant; thus $\theta = 315°$ (or −45°) is the correct value. Most pocket calculators give $\arctan(-1) = -45°$. In this case that is correct; but if instead we have $A_x = -2$ m and $A_y = 2$ m, then the correct angle is 135°. Similarly, when A_x and A_y are both negative, the tangent is positive, but the angle is in the third quadrant. You should *always* draw a sketch like Fig. 1.20 to check which of the two possibilities is the correct one.

1.20 Drawing a sketch of a vector reveals the signs of its x- and y-components.

Suppose that $\tan\theta = \frac{A_y}{A_x} = -1$. What is θ?

Two angles have tangents of -1: 135° and 315°. Inspection of the diagram shows that θ must be 315°.

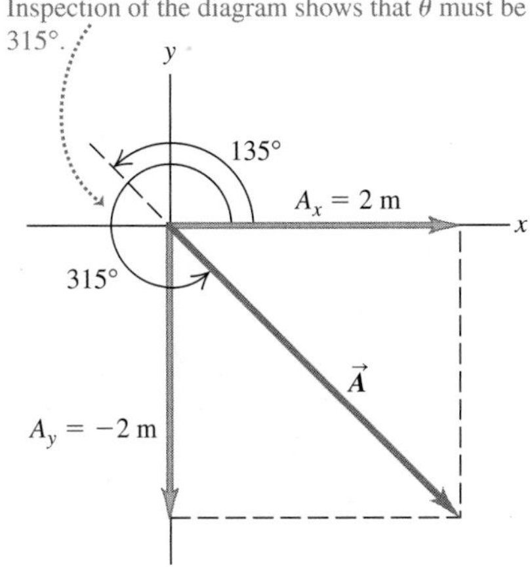

2. Multiplying a vector by a scalar. If we multiply a vector $\vec{A}$ by a scalar c, each component of the product $\vec{D} = c\vec{A}$ is just the product of c and the corresponding component of $\vec{A}$:

$$D_x = cA_x \qquad D_y = cA_y \qquad (\text{components of } \vec{D} = c\vec{A}) \quad (1.9)$$

For example, Eq. (1.9) says that each component of the vector $2\vec{A}$ is twice as great as the corresponding component of the vector $\vec{A}$, so $2\vec{A}$ is in the same direction as $\vec{A}$ but has twice the magnitude. Each component of the vector $-3\vec{A}$ is three times as great as the corresponding component of the vector $\vec{A}$ but has the opposite sign, so $-3\vec{A}$ is in the opposite direction from $\vec{A}$ and has three times the magnitude. Hence Eqs. (1.9) are consistent with our discussion in Section 1.7 of multiplying a vector by a scalar (see Fig. 1.15).

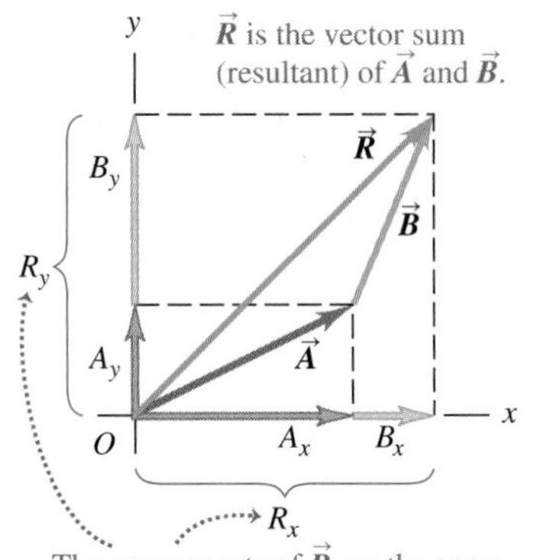
$\vec{R}$ is the vector sum (resultant) of $\vec{A}$ and $\vec{B}$.
y
x
O
$\vec{R}$
$\vec{B}$
$\vec{A}$
B_y
A_y
R_y
A_x
B_x
R_x
The components of $\vec{R}$ are the sums of the components of $\vec{A}$ and $\vec{B}$:
$R_y = A_y + B_y$ $R_x = A_x + B_x$

1.21 Finding the vector sum (resultant) of $\vec{A}$ and $\vec{B}$ using components.

3. Using components to calculate the vector sum (resultant) of two or more vectors. Figure 1.21 shows two vectors $\vec{A}$ and $\vec{B}$ and their vector sum $\vec{R}$, along with the x- and y-components of all three vectors. You can see from the diagram that the x-component R_x of the vector sum is simply the sum $(A_x + B_x)$ of the x-components of the vectors being added. The same is true for the y-components. In symbols,

$$R_x = A_x + B_x \qquad R_y = A_y + B_y \qquad (\text{components of } \vec{R} = \vec{A} + \vec{B}) \tag{1.10}$$

Figure 1.21 shows this result for the case in which the components A_x, A_y, B_x, and B_y are all positive. You should draw additional diagrams to verify for yourself that Eqs. (1.10) are valid for *any* signs of the components of $\vec{A}$ and $\vec{B}$.

If we know the components of any two vectors $\vec{A}$ and $\vec{B}$, perhaps by using Eqs. (1.6), we can compute the components of the vector sum $\vec{R}$. Then if we need the magnitude and direction of $\vec{R}$, we can obtain them from Eqs. (1.7) and (1.8) with the A's replaced by R's.

We can extend this procedure to find the sum of any number of vectors. If $\vec{R}$ is the vector sum of $\vec{A}, \vec{B}, \vec{C}, \vec{D}, \vec{E}, \ldots$, the components of $\vec{R}$ are

$$\begin{aligned} R_x &= A_x + B_x + C_x + D_x + E_x + \cdots \\ R_y &= A_y + B_y + C_y + D_y + E_y + \cdots \end{aligned} \tag{1.11}$$

We have talked only about vectors that lie in the xy-plane, but the component method works just as well for vectors having any direction in space. We introduce a z-axis perpendicular to the xy-plane; then in general a vector $\vec{A}$ has components A_x, A_y, and A_z in the three coordinate directions. The magnitude A is given by

$$A = \sqrt{A_x^2 + A_y^2 + A_z^2} \tag{1.12}$$

Again, we always take the positive root. Also, Eqs. (1.11) for the components of the vector sum $\vec{R}$ have an additional member:

$$R_z = A_z + B_z + C_z + D_z + E_z + \cdots$$

Finally, while our discussion of vector addition has centered on combining *displacement* vectors, the method is applicable to all other vector quantities as well. When we study the concept of force in Chapter 4, we'll find that forces are vectors that obey the same rules of vector addition that we've used with displacement. Other vector quantities will make their appearance in later chapters.

Problem-Solving Strategy 1.3 Vector Addition

MP

IDENTIFY *the relevant concepts:* Decide what your target variable is. It may be the magnitude of the vector sum, the direction, or both.

SET UP *the problem:* Draw the individual vectors being summed and the coordinate axes being used. In your drawing, place the tail of the first vector at the origin of coordinates; place the tail of the second vector at the head of the first vector; and so on. Draw the vector sum $\vec{R}$ from the tail of the first vector to the head of the last vector. Use your drawing to make rough estimates of the magnitude and direction of $\vec{R}$; you'll use these estimates later to check your calculations.

EXECUTE *the solution* as follows:

1. Find the x- and y-components of each individual vector and record your results in a table. If a vector is described by its magnitude A and its angle θ, measured from the $+x$-axis toward the $+y$-axis, then the components are given by

$$A_x = A\cos\theta \qquad A_y = A\sin\theta$$

Some components may be positive and some may be negative, depending on how the vector is oriented (that is, what quadrant θ lies in). You can use this sign table as a check:

Quadrant	**I**	**II**	**III**	**IV**
A_x	+	−	−	+
A_y	+	+	−	−

If the angles of the vectors are given in some other way, perhaps using a different reference direction, convert them to angles measured from the $+x$-axis as described above. Be particularly careful with signs.

2. Add the individual x-components algebraically, including signs, to find R_x, the x-component of the vector sum. Do the same for the y-components to find R_y.

3. Then the magnitude R and direction θ of the vector sum are given by

$$R = \sqrt{R_x^2 + R_y^2} \qquad \theta = \arctan\frac{R_y}{R_x}$$

EVALUATE *your answer:* Check your results for the magnitude and direction of the vector sum by comparing them with the rough estimates you made from your drawing. Remember that the magnitude R is *always* positive and that θ is measured from the positive x-axis. The value of θ that you find with a calculator may be the correct one, or it may be off by 180°. You can decide by examining your drawing.

If your calculations disagree totally with the estimates from your drawing, check whether your calculator is set in "radians" or "degrees" mode. If it's in "radians" mode, entering angles in degrees will give nonsensical answers.

Example 1.7 Adding vectors with components

Three players on a reality TV show are brought to the center of a large, flat field. Each is given a meter stick, a compass, a calculator, a shovel, and (in a different order for each contestant) the following three displacements:

72.4 m, 32.0° east of north
57.3 m, 36.0° south of west
17.8 m straight south

The three displacements lead to the point where the keys to a new Porsche are buried. Two players start measuring immediately, but the winner first *calculates* where to go. What does she calculate?

SOLUTION

IDENTIFY: The goal is to find the sum (resultant) of the three displacements, so this is a problem in vector addition.

SET UP: Figure 1.22 shows the situation. We have chosen the $+x$-axis as east and the $+y$-axis as north, the usual choice for maps. Let $\vec{A}$ be the first displacement, $\vec{B}$ the second, and $\vec{C}$ the third. We can estimate from the diagram that the vector sum $\vec{R}$ is about 10 m, 40° west of north.

1.22 Three successive displacements $\vec{A}$, $\vec{B}$, and $\vec{C}$ and the resultant (vector sum) displacement $\vec{R} = \vec{A} + \vec{B} + \vec{C}$.

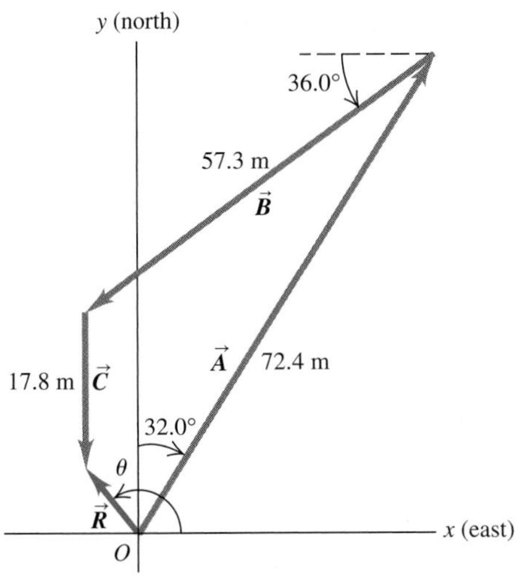

EXECUTE: The angles of the vectors, measured from the $+x$-axis toward the $+y$-axis, are $(90.0° - 32.0°) = 58.0°$, $(180.0° + 36.0°) = 216.0°$, and 270.0°. We have to find the components of each. Because of our choice of axes, we may use Eqs. (1.6), and so the components of $\vec{A}$ are

$$A_x = A\cos\theta_A = (72.4\text{ m})(\cos 58.0°) = 38.37\text{ m}$$
$$A_y = A\sin\theta_A = (72.4\text{ m})(\sin 58.0°) = 61.40\text{ m}$$

Note that we have kept one too many significant figures in the components; we will wait until the end to round to the correct number of significant figures. The table shows the components of all the displacements, the addition of the components, and the other calculations. Always arrange your component calculations systematically like this.

Distance	**Angle**	***x*-component**	***y*-component**
$A = 72.4$ m	58.0°	38.37 m	61.40 m
$B = 57.3$ m	216.0°	−46.36 m	−33.68 m
$C = 17.8$ m	270.0°	0.00 m	−17.80 m
		$R_x = -7.99$ m	$R_y = 9.92$ m

$$R = \sqrt{(-7.99\text{ m})^2 + (9.92\text{ m})^2} = 12.7\text{ m}$$

$$\theta = \arctan\frac{9.92\text{ m}}{-7.99\text{ m}} = 129° = 39° \text{ west of north}$$

The losers try to measure three angles and three distances totaling 147.5 m, one meter at a time. The winner measured only one angle and one much shorter distance.

EVALUATE: Our calculated answers for R and θ are not too different from our estimates of 10 m and 40° west of north; that's good! Notice that $\theta = -51°$, or 51° south of east, also satisfies the equation for θ. But since the winner has made a drawing of the displacement vectors (Fig. 1.22), she knows that $\theta = 129°$ is the only correct solution for the angle.

Example 1.8 A vector in three dimensions

After an airplane takes off, it travels 10.4 km west, 8.7 km north, and 2.1 km up. How far is it from the takeoff point?

SOLUTION

Let the $+x$-axis be east, the $+y$-axis north, and the $+z$-axis up. Then $A_x = -10.4$ km, $A_y = 8.7$ km, and $A_z = 2.1$ km; Eq. (1.12) gives

$$A = \sqrt{(-10.4\text{ km})^2 + (8.7\text{ km})^2 + (2.1\text{ km})^2} = 13.7\text{ km}$$

Test Your Understanding of Section 1.8 Two vectors $\vec{A}$ and $\vec{B}$ both lie in the xy-plane. (a) Is it possible for $\vec{A}$ to have the same magnitude as $\vec{B}$ but different components? (b) Is it possible for $\vec{A}$ to have the same components as $\vec{B}$ but a different magnitude?

1.9 Unit Vectors

1.23 (a) The unit vectors $\hat{\imath}$ and $\hat{\jmath}$. (b) Expressing a vector $\vec{A}$ in terms of its components.

(a) The unit vectors $\hat{\imath}$ and $\hat{\jmath}$ point in the directions of the x- and y-axes and have a magnitude of 1.

(b) We can express a vector $\vec{A}$ in terms of its components as $\vec{A} = A_x\hat{\imath} + A_y\hat{\jmath}$

A **unit vector** is a vector that has a magnitude of 1, with no units. Its only purpose is to *point*—that is, to describe a direction in space. Unit vectors provide a convenient notation for many expressions involving components of vectors. We will always include a caret or "hat" (^) in the symbol for a unit vector to distinguish it from ordinary vectors whose magnitude may or may not be equal to 1.

In an x-y coordinate system we can define a unit vector $\hat{\imath}$ that points in the direction of the positive x-axis and a unit vector $\hat{\jmath}$ that points in the direction of the positive y-axis (Fig. 1.23a). Then we can express the relationship between component vectors and components, described at the beginning of Section 1.8, as follows:

$$\vec{A}_x = A_x\hat{\imath} \qquad \vec{A}_y = A_y\hat{\jmath} \tag{1.13}$$

Similarly, we can write a vector $\vec{A}$ in terms of its components as

$$\vec{A} = A_x\hat{\imath} + A_y\hat{\jmath} \tag{1.14}$$

Equations (1.13) and (1.14) are vector equations; each term, such as $A_x\hat{\imath}$, is a vector quantity (Fig. 1.23b). The boldface equals and plus signs denote vector equality and addition.

When two vectors $\vec{A}$ and $\vec{B}$ are represented in terms of their components, we can express the vector sum $\vec{R}$ using unit vectors as follows:

$$\begin{aligned}\vec{A} &= A_x\hat{\imath} + A_y\hat{\jmath}\\ \vec{B} &= B_x\hat{\imath} + B_y\hat{\jmath}\\ \vec{R} &= \vec{A} + \vec{B}\\ &= (A_x\hat{\imath} + A_y\hat{\jmath}) + (B_x\hat{\imath} + B_y\hat{\jmath})\\ &= (A_x + B_x)\hat{\imath} + (A_y + B_y)\hat{\jmath}\\ &= R_x\hat{\imath} + R_y\hat{\jmath}\end{aligned} \tag{1.15}$$

Equation (1.15) restates the content of Eqs. (1.10) in the form of a single vector equation rather than two component equations.

If the vectors do not all lie in the xy-plane, then we need a third component. We introduce a third unit vector $\hat{k}$ that points in the direction of the positive z-axis (Fig. 1.24). Then Eqs. (1.14) and (1.15) become

1.24 The unit vectors $\hat{\imath}$, $\hat{\jmath}$, and $\hat{k}$.

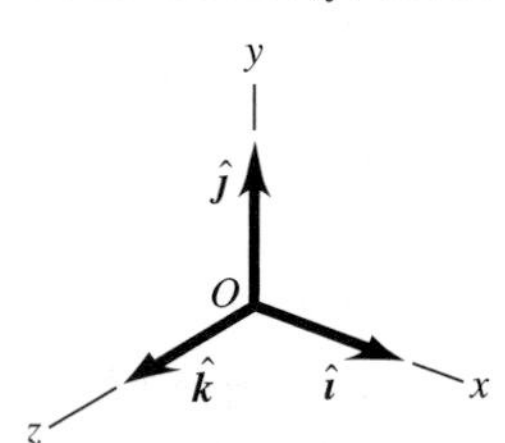

$$\begin{aligned}\vec{A} &= A_x\hat{\imath} + A_y\hat{\jmath} + A_z\hat{k}\\ \vec{B} &= B_x\hat{\imath} + B_y\hat{\jmath} + B_z\hat{k}\end{aligned} \tag{1.16}$$

$$\vec{R} = (A_x + B_x)\hat{\imath} + (A_y + B_y)\hat{\jmath} + (A_z + B_z)\hat{k}$$
$$= R_x\hat{\imath} + R_y\hat{\jmath} + R_z\hat{k} \qquad (1.17)$$

Example 1.9 Using unit vectors

Given the two displacements

$$\vec{D} = (6\hat{\imath} + 3\hat{\jmath} - \hat{k})\text{ m} \qquad \text{and} \qquad \vec{E} = (4\hat{\imath} - 5\hat{\jmath} + 8\hat{k})\text{ m}$$

find the magnitude of the displacement $2\vec{D} - \vec{E}$.

SOLUTION

IDENTIFY: We are to multiply the vector $\vec{D}$ by 2 (a scalar) and then subtract the vector $\vec{E}$ from the result.

SET UP: Equation (1.9) says that to multiply $\vec{D}$ by 2, we simply multiply each of its components by 2. Then Eq. (1.17) tells us that to subtract $\vec{E}$ from $2\vec{D}$, we simply subtract the components of $\vec{E}$ from the components of $2\vec{D}$. (Recall from Section 1.7 that subtracting a vector is the same as adding the negative of that vector.) In each of these mathematical operations, the unit vectors $\hat{\imath}$, $\hat{\jmath}$, and $\hat{k}$ remain unchanged.

EXECUTE: Letting $\vec{F} = 2\vec{D} - \vec{E}$, we have

$$\begin{aligned}\vec{F} &= 2(6\hat{\imath} + 3\hat{\jmath} - \hat{k})\text{ m} - (4\hat{\imath} - 5\hat{\jmath} + 8\hat{k})\text{ m}\\ &= [(12 - 4)\hat{\imath} + (6 + 5)\hat{\jmath} + (-2 - 8)\hat{k}]\text{ m}\\ &= (8\hat{\imath} + 11\hat{\jmath} - 10\hat{k})\text{ m}\end{aligned}$$

The units of the vectors $\vec{D}$, $\vec{E}$, and $\vec{F}$ are meters, so the components of these vectors are also in meters. From Eq. (1.12),

$$\begin{aligned}F &= \sqrt{F_x^2 + F_y^2 + F_z^2}\\ &= \sqrt{(8\text{ m})^2 + (11\text{ m})^2 + (-10\text{ m})^2} = 17\text{ m}\end{aligned}$$

EVALUATE: Working with unit vectors makes vector addition and subtraction no more complicated than adding and subtracting ordinary numbers. Still, be sure to check for simple arithmetic errors.

Test Your Understanding of Section 1.9 Arrange the following vectors in order of their magnitude, with the vector of largest magnitude first. (i) $\vec{A} = (3\hat{\imath} + 5\hat{\jmath} - 2\hat{k})$ m; (ii) $\vec{B} = (-3\hat{\imath} + 5\hat{\jmath} - 2\hat{k})$ m; (iii) $\vec{C} = (3\hat{\imath} - 5\hat{\jmath} - 2\hat{k})$ m; (iv) $\vec{D} = (3\hat{\imath} + 5\hat{\jmath} + 2\hat{k})$ m.

1.10 Products of Vectors

We have seen how addition of vectors develops naturally from the problem of combining displacements, and we will use vector addition for calculating many other vector quantities later. We can also express many physical relationships concisely by using *products* of vectors. Vectors are not ordinary numbers, so ordinary multiplication is not directly applicable to vectors. We will define two different kinds of products of vectors. The first, called the *scalar product,* yields a result that is a scalar quantity. The second, the *vector product,* yields another vector.

Scalar Product

The **scalar product** of two vectors $\vec{A}$ and $\vec{B}$ is denoted by $\vec{A}\cdot\vec{B}$. Because of this notation, the scalar product is also called the **dot product.** Although $\vec{A}$ and $\vec{B}$ are vectors, the quantity $\vec{A}\cdot\vec{B}$ is a scalar.

To define the scalar product $\vec{A}\cdot\vec{B}$ of two vectors $\vec{A}$ and $\vec{B}$, we draw the two vectors with their tails at the same point (Fig. 1.25a). The angle ϕ (the Greek letter phi) between their directions ranges from 0° to 180°. Figure 1.25b shows the projection of the vector $\vec{B}$ onto the direction of $\vec{A}$; this projection is the component of $\vec{B}$ in the direction of $\vec{A}$ and is equal to $B\cos\phi$. (We can take components along any direction that's convenient, not just the x- and y-axes.) We define $\vec{A}\cdot\vec{B}$ to be the magnitude of $\vec{A}$ multiplied by the component of $\vec{B}$ in the direction of $\vec{A}$. Expressed as an equation,

$$\vec{A}\cdot\vec{B} = AB\cos\phi = |\vec{A}||\vec{B}|\cos\phi \qquad \text{(definition of the scalar (dot) product)} \qquad (1.18)$$

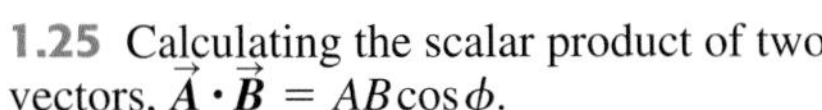

1.25 Calculating the scalar product of two vectors, $\vec{A}\cdot\vec{B} = AB\cos\phi$.

(a)

(b) $\vec{A}\cdot\vec{B}$ equals $A(B\cos\phi)$.

(Magnitude of $\vec{A}$) times (Component of $\vec{B}$ in direction of $\vec{A}$)

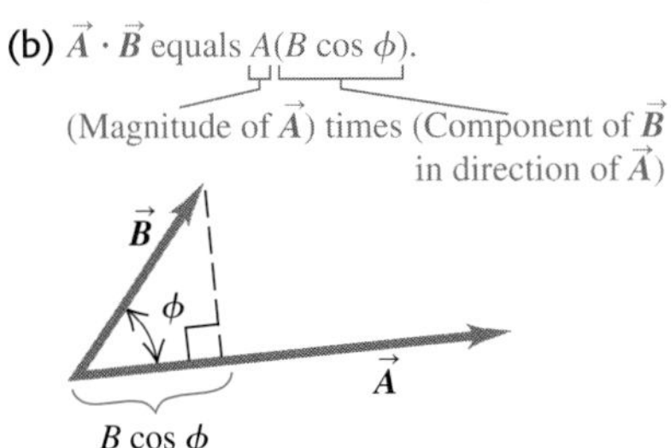

(c) $\vec{A}\cdot\vec{B}$ also equals $B(A\cos\phi)$

(Magnitude of $\vec{B}$) times (Component of $\vec{A}$ in direction of $\vec{B}$)

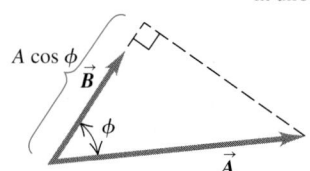

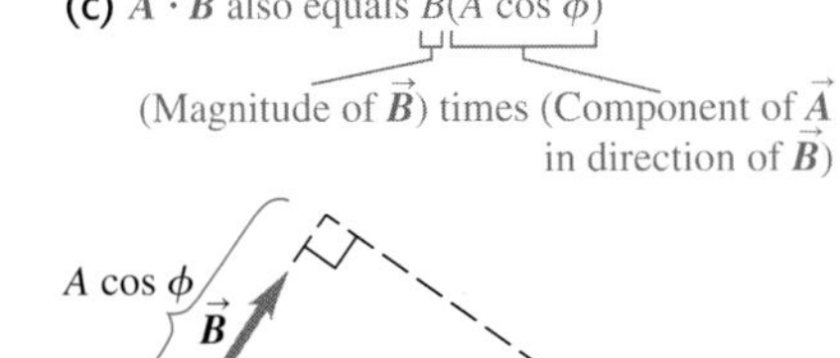

1.26 The scalar product $\vec{A} \cdot \vec{B} = AB\cos\phi$ can be positive, negative, or zero, depending on the angle between $\vec{A}$ and $\vec{B}$.

(a)

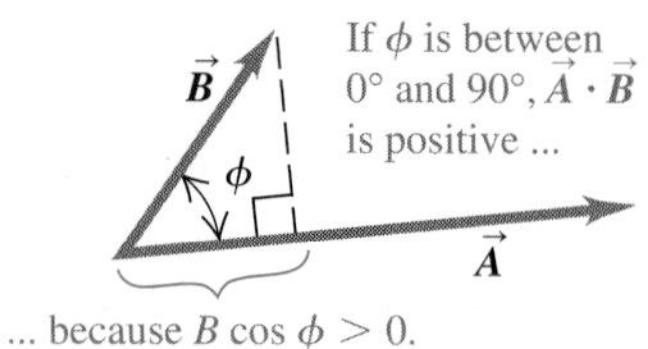

If ϕ is between 0° and 90°, $\vec{A} \cdot \vec{B}$ is positive ...
$\vec{B}$
ϕ
$\vec{A}$
... because $B\cos\phi > 0$.

(b)

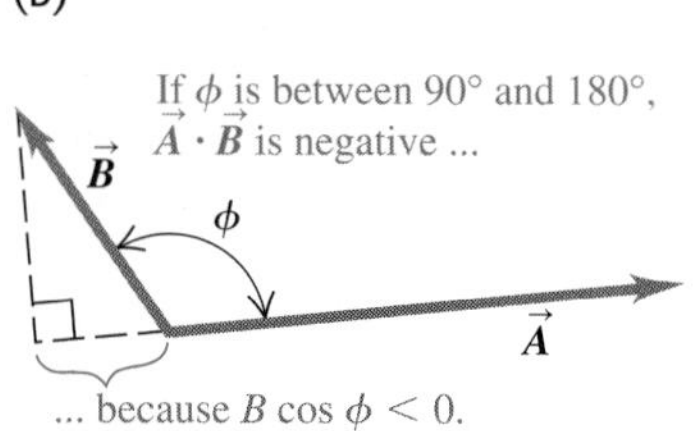

If ϕ is between 90° and 180°, $\vec{A} \cdot \vec{B}$ is negative ...
$\vec{B}$
ϕ
$\vec{A}$
... because $B\cos\phi < 0$.

(c)

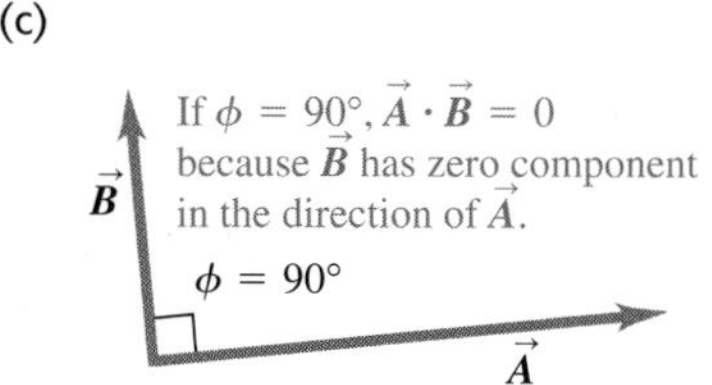

If $\phi = 90°$, $\vec{A} \cdot \vec{B} = 0$ because $\vec{B}$ has zero component in the direction of $\vec{A}$.
$\vec{B}$
$\phi = 90°$
$\vec{A}$

Alternatively, we can define $\vec{A} \cdot \vec{B}$ to be the magnitude of $\vec{B}$ multiplied by the component of $\vec{A}$ in the direction of $\vec{B}$, as in Fig. 1.25c. Hence $\vec{A} \cdot \vec{B} = \vec{A} \cdot \vec{B} = B(A\cos\phi) = AB\cos\phi$, which is the same as Eq. (1.18).

The scalar product is a scalar quantity, not a vector, and it may be positive, negative, or zero. When ϕ is between 0° and 90°, $\cos\phi > 0$ and the scalar product is positive (Fig. 1.26a). When ϕ is between 90° and 180° so that $\cos\phi < 0$, the component of $\vec{B}$ in the direction of $\vec{A}$ is negative, and $\vec{A} \cdot \vec{B}$ is negative (Fig. 1.26b). Finally, when $\phi = 90°$, $\vec{A} \cdot \vec{B} = 0$ (Fig. 1.26c). *The scalar product of two perpendicular vectors is always zero.*

For any two vectors $\vec{A}$ and $\vec{B}$, $AB\cos\phi = BA\cos\phi$. This means that $\vec{A} \cdot \vec{B} = \vec{B} \cdot \vec{A}$. The scalar product obeys the commutative law of multiplication; the order of the two vectors does not matter.

We will use the scalar product in Chapter 6 to describe work done by a force. When a constant force $\vec{F}$ is applied to a body that undergoes a displacement $\vec{s}$, the work W (a scalar quantity) done by the force is given by

$$W = \vec{F} \cdot \vec{s}$$

The work done by the force is positive if the angle between $\vec{F}$ and $\vec{s}$ is between 0° and 90°, negative if this angle is between 90° and 180°, and zero if $\vec{F}$ and $\vec{s}$ are perpendicular. (This is another example of a term that has a special meaning in physics; in everyday language, "work" isn't something that can be positive or negative.) In later chapters we'll use the scalar product for a variety of purposes, from calculating electric potential to determining the effects that varying magnetic fields have on electric circuits.

Calculating the Scalar Product Using Components

We can calculate the scalar product $\vec{A} \cdot \vec{B}$ directly if we know the x-, y-, and z-components of $\vec{A}$ and $\vec{B}$. To see how this is done, let's first work out the scalar products of the unit vectors. This is easy, since $\hat{\imath}$, $\hat{\jmath}$, and $\hat{k}$ all have magnitude 1 and are perpendicular to each other. Using Eq. (1.18), we find

$$\begin{aligned} \hat{\imath} \cdot \hat{\imath} &= \hat{\jmath} \cdot \hat{\jmath} = \hat{k} \cdot \hat{k} = (1)(1)\cos 0° = 1 \\ \hat{\imath} \cdot \hat{\jmath} &= \hat{\imath} \cdot \hat{k} = \hat{\jmath} \cdot \hat{k} = (1)(1)\cos 90° = 0 \end{aligned} \tag{1.19}$$

Now we express $\vec{A}$ and $\vec{B}$ in terms of their components, expand the product, and use these products of unit vectors:

$$\begin{aligned} \vec{A} \cdot \vec{B} &= (A_x\hat{\imath} + A_y\hat{\jmath} + A_z\hat{k}) \cdot (B_x\hat{\imath} + B_y\hat{\jmath} + B_z\hat{k}) \\ &= A_x\hat{\imath} \cdot B_x\hat{\imath} + A_x\hat{\imath} \cdot B_y\hat{\jmath} + A_x\hat{\imath} \cdot B_z\hat{k} \\ &\quad + A_y\hat{\jmath} \cdot B_x\hat{\imath} + A_y\hat{\jmath} \cdot B_y\hat{\jmath} + A_y\hat{\jmath} \cdot B_z\hat{k} \\ &\quad + A_z\hat{k} \cdot B_x\hat{\imath} + A_z\hat{k} \cdot B_y\hat{\jmath} + A_z\hat{k} \cdot B_z\hat{k} \\ &= A_xB_x\hat{\imath} \cdot \hat{\imath} + A_xB_y\hat{\imath} \cdot \hat{\jmath} + A_xB_z\hat{\imath} \cdot \hat{k} \\ &\quad + A_yB_x\hat{\jmath} \cdot \hat{\imath} + A_yB_y\hat{\jmath} \cdot \hat{\jmath} + A_yB_z\hat{\jmath} \cdot \hat{k} \\ &\quad + A_zB_x\hat{k} \cdot \hat{\imath} + A_zB_y\hat{k} \cdot \hat{\jmath} + A_zB_z\hat{k} \cdot \hat{k} \end{aligned} \tag{1.20}$$

From Eqs. (1.19) we see that six of these nine terms are zero, and the three that survive give simply

$$\vec{A} \cdot \vec{B} = A_xB_x + A_yB_y + A_zB_z \quad \text{(scalar (dot) product in terms of components)} \tag{1.21}$$

Thus *the scalar product of two vectors is the sum of the products of their respective components.*

The scalar product gives a straightforward way to find the angle ϕ between any two vectors $\vec{A}$ and $\vec{B}$ whose components are known. In this case, Eq. (1.21) can be used to find the scalar product of $\vec{A}$ and $\vec{B}$. From Eq. (1.18) the scalar product is also equal to $AB\cos\phi$ The vector magnitudes A and B can be found from the vector components with Eq. (1.12), so $\cos\phi$ and hence the angle ϕ can be determined (see Example 1.11).

Example 1.10 Calculating a scalar product

Find the scalar product $\vec{A}\cdot\vec{B}$ of the two vectors in Fig. 1.27. The magnitudes of the vectors are $A = 4.00$ and $B = 5.00$.

SOLUTION

IDENTIFY: We are given the magnitudes and directions of $\vec{A}$ and $\vec{B}$, and we wish to calculate their scalar product.

SET UP: We will calculate the scalar product in two ways: using the magnitudes of the vectors and the angle between them (Eq. 1.18), and using the components of the two vectors (Eq. 1.21).

1.27 Two vectors in two dimensions.

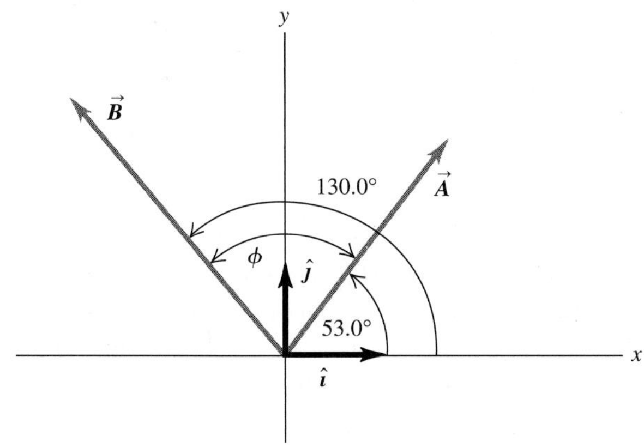

EXECUTE: With the first approach, the angle between the two vectors is $\phi = 130.0° - 53.0° = 77.0°$, so

$$\vec{A}\cdot\vec{B} = AB\cos\phi = (4.00)(5.00)\cos 77.0° = 4.50$$

This is positive because the angle between $\vec{A}$ and $\vec{B}$ is between 0° and 90°.

To use the second approach, we first need to find the components of the two vectors. Since the angles of $\vec{A}$ and $\vec{B}$ are given with respect to the $+x$-axis, and these angles are measured in the sense from the $+x$-axis to the $+y$-axis, we can use Eqs. (1.6):

$$A_x = (4.00)\cos 53.0° = 2.407$$
$$A_y = (4.00)\sin 53.0° = 3.195$$
$$A_z = 0$$
$$B_x = (5.00)\cos 130.0° = -3.214$$
$$B_y = (5.00)\sin 130.0° = 3.830$$
$$B_z = 0$$

The z-components are zero because both vectors lie in the xy-plane. As in Example 1.7, we are keeping one too many significant figures in the components; we'll round to the correct number at the end. From Eq. (1.21) the scalar product is

$$\vec{A}\cdot\vec{B} = A_xB_x + A_yB_y + A_zB_z$$
$$= (2.407)(-3.214) + (3.195)(3.830) + (0)(0) = 4.50$$

EVALUATE: We get the same result for the scalar product with both methods, as we should.

Example 1.11 Finding angles with the scalar product

Find the angle between the two vectors

$$\vec{A} = 2\hat{\imath} + 3\hat{\jmath} + \hat{k} \qquad \text{and} \qquad \vec{B} = -4\hat{\imath} + 2\hat{\jmath} - \hat{k}$$

SOLUTION

IDENTIFY: We are given the x-, y-, and z-components of two vectors. Our target variable is the angle ϕ between them.

SET UP: Figure 1.28 shows the two vectors. The scalar product of two vectors $\vec{A}$ and $\vec{B}$ is related to the angle ϕ between them and to the magnitudes A and B by Eq. (1.18). The scalar product is also related to the components of the two vectors by Eq. (1.21). If we are given the components of the vectors (as we are in this example), we first determine the scalar product $\vec{A}\cdot\vec{B}$ and the values of A and B, and then determine the target variable ϕ.

EXECUTE: We set our two expressions for the scalar product, Eq. (1.18) and Eq. (1.121), equal to each other. Rearranging, we obtain

$$\cos\phi = \frac{A_xB_x + A_yB_y + A_zB_z}{AB}$$

This formula can be used to find the angle between *any* two vectors $\vec{A}$ and $\vec{B}$. For our example the components of $\vec{A}$ are $A_x = 2$,

1.28 Two vectors in three dimensions.

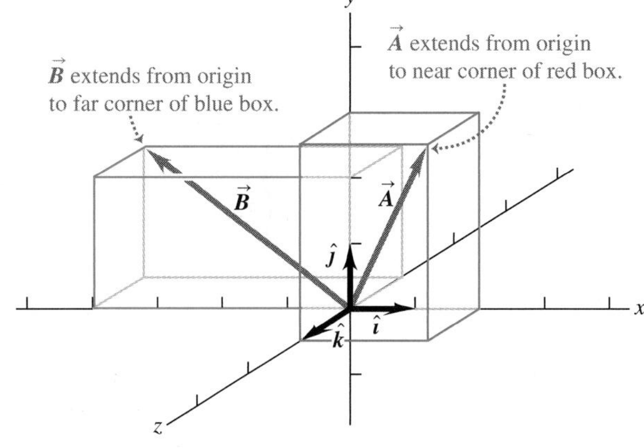

Continued

$A_y = 3$, and $A_z = 1$, and the components of $\vec{B}$ are $B_x = -4$, $B_y = 2$, and $B_z = -1$. Thus

$$\vec{A} \cdot \vec{B} = A_xB_x + A_yB_y + A_zB_z$$
$$= (2)(-4) + (3)(2) + (1)(-1) = -3$$
$$A = \sqrt{A_x^2 + A_y^2 + A_z^2} = \sqrt{2^2 + 3^2 + 1^2} = \sqrt{14}$$
$$B = \sqrt{B_x^2 + B_y^2 + B_z^2} = \sqrt{(-4^2) + 2^2 + (-1)^2} = \sqrt{21}$$

$$\cos\phi = \frac{A_xB_x + A_yB_y + A_zB_z}{AB} = \frac{-3}{\sqrt{14}\sqrt{21}} = -0.175$$
$$\phi = 100°$$

EVALUATE: As a check on this result, note that the scalar product $\vec{A} \cdot \vec{B}$ is negative. This means that ϕ is between 90° and 180° (see Fig. 1.26), in agreement with our answer.

Vector Product

The **vector product** of two vectors $\vec{A}$ and $\vec{B}$, also called the **cross product,** is denoted by $\vec{A} \times \vec{B}$. As the name suggests, the vector product is itself a vector. We will use this product in Chapter 10 to describe torque and angular momentum; in Chapters 27 and 28 we will use it extensively to describe magnetic fields and forces.

To define the vector product $\vec{A} \times \vec{B}$ of two vectors $\vec{A}$ and $\vec{B}$ we again draw the two vectors with their tails at the same point (Fig. 1.29a). The two vectors then lie in a plane. We define the vector product to be a vector quantity with a direction perpendicular to this plane (that is, perpendicular to both $\vec{A}$ and $\vec{B}$) and a magnitude equal to $AB\sin\phi$. That is, if $\vec{C} = \vec{A} \times \vec{B}$, then

$$C = AB\sin\phi \quad \text{(magnitude of the vector (cross) product of } \vec{A} \text{ and } \vec{B}) \quad (1.22)$$

1.29 (a) The vector product $\vec{A} \times \vec{B}$. determined by the right-hand rule. (b) $\vec{B} \times \vec{A} = -\vec{A} \times \vec{B}$; the vector product is anticommutative.

(a)

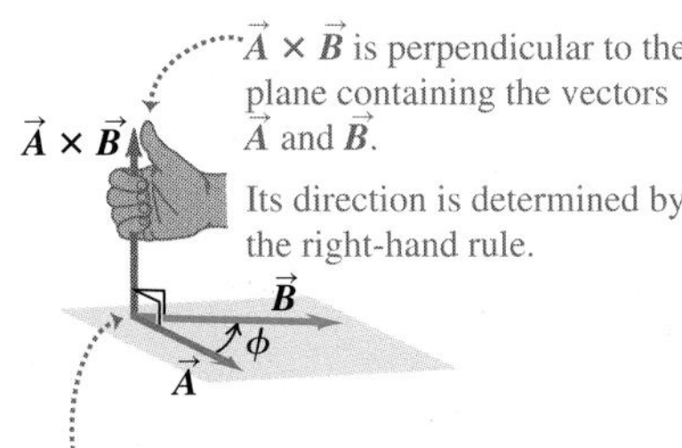
$\vec{A} \times \vec{B}$ is perpendicular to the plane containing the vectors $\vec{A}$ and $\vec{B}$.
Its direction is determined by the right-hand rule.
$\vec{A} \times \vec{B}$
$\vec{B}$
ϕ
$\vec{A}$
Place the vectors tail to tail. They define a plane.

(b)

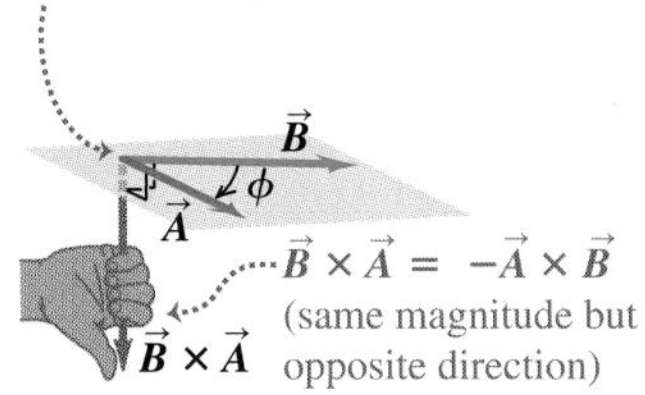
$\vec{B}$
ϕ
$\vec{A}$
$\vec{B} \times \vec{A} = -\vec{A} \times \vec{B}$ (same magnitude but opposite direction)
$\vec{B} \times \vec{A}$

We measure the angle ϕ from $\vec{A}$ toward $\vec{B}$ and take it to be the smaller of the two possible angles, so ϕ ranges from 0° to 180°. Then $\sin\phi \geq 0$ and C in Eq. (1.22) is never negative, as must be the case for a vector magnitude. Note also that when $\vec{A}$ and $\vec{B}$ are parallel or antiparallel, $\phi = 0$ or 180° and $C = 0$. That is, *the vector product of two parallel or antiparallel vectors is always zero.* In particular, *the vector product of any vector with itself is zero.*

CAUTION **Vector product vs. scalar product** Be careful not to confuse the expression $AB\sin\phi$ for the magnitude of the vector product $\vec{A} \times \vec{B}$ with the similar expression $AB\cos\phi$ for the scalar product $\vec{A} \cdot \vec{B}$. To see the contrast between these two expressions, imagine that we vary the angle between $\vec{A}$ and $\vec{B}$ while keeping their magnitudes constant. When $\vec{A}$ and $\vec{B}$ are parallel, the magnitude of the vector product will be zero and the scalar product will be maximum. When $\vec{A}$ and $\vec{B}$ are perpendicular, the magnitude of the vector product will be maximum and the scalar product will be zero.

There are always *two* directions perpendicular to a given plane, one on each side of the plane. We choose which of these is the direction of $\vec{A} \times \vec{B}$ as follows. Imagine rotating vector $\vec{A}$ about the perpendicular line until it is aligned with $\vec{B}$, choosing the smaller of the two possible angles between $\vec{A}$ and $\vec{B}$. Curl the fingers of your right hand around the perpendicular line so that the fingertips point in the direction of rotation; your thumb will then point in the direction of $\vec{A} \times \vec{B}$. Figure 1.29a shows this **right-hand rule.**

Similarly, we determine the direction of $\vec{B} \times \vec{A}$ by rotating $\vec{B}$ into $\vec{A}$ as in Fig. 1.29b. The result is a vector that is *opposite* to the vector $\vec{A} \times \vec{B}$. The vector product is *not* commutative! In fact, for any two vectors $\vec{A}$ and $\vec{B}$,

$$\vec{A} \times \vec{B} = -\vec{B} \times \vec{A} \quad (1.23)$$

Just as we did for the scalar product, we can give a geometrical interpretation of the magnitude of the vector product. In Fig. 1.30a, $B\sin\phi$ is the component of vector $\vec{B}$ that is *perpendicular* to the direction of vector $\vec{A}$ From Eq. (1.22) the magnitude of $\vec{A} \times \vec{B}$ equals the magnitude of $\vec{A}$ multiplied by the component of $\vec{B}$ perpendicular to $\vec{A}$. Figure 1.30b shows that the magnitude of $\vec{A} \times \vec{B}$ also equals the magnitude of $\vec{B}$ multiplied by the component of $\vec{A}$ perpendicular to $\vec{B}$. Note that Fig. 1.30 shows the case in which ϕ is between 0° and 90°; you should draw a similar diagram for ϕ between 90° and 180° to show that the same geometrical interpretation of the magnitude of $\vec{A} \times \vec{B}$ still applies.

1.30 Calculating the magnitude $AB\sin\phi$ of the vector product of two vectors, $\vec{A} \times \vec{B}$.

(a)

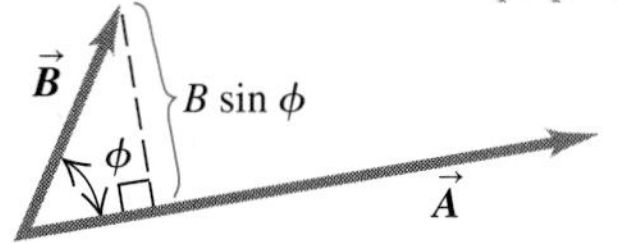

(b)

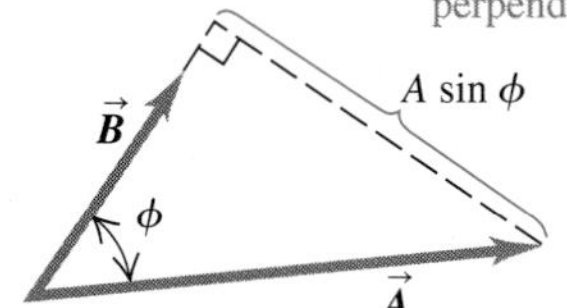

Calculating the Vector Product Using Components

If we know the components of $\vec{A}$ and $\vec{B}$, we can calculate the components of the vector product using a procedure similar to that for the scalar product. First we work out the multiplication table for the unit vectors $\hat{\imath}$, $\hat{\jmath}$, and $\hat{k}$, all three of which are perpendicular to each other (Fig. 1.31a). The vector product of any vector with itself is zero, so

$$\hat{\imath} \times \hat{\imath} = \hat{\jmath} \times \hat{\jmath} = \hat{k} \times \hat{k} = \mathbf{0}$$

The boldface zero is a reminder that each product is a zero *vector*—that is, one with all components equal to zero and an undefined direction. Using Eqs. (1.22) and (1.23) and the right-hand rule, we find

$$\begin{aligned} \hat{\imath} \times \hat{\jmath} &= -\hat{\jmath} \times \hat{\imath} = \hat{k} \\ \hat{\jmath} \times \hat{k} &= -\hat{k} \times \hat{\jmath} = \hat{\imath} \\ \hat{k} \times \hat{\imath} &= -\hat{\imath} \times \hat{k} = \hat{\jmath} \end{aligned} \quad (1.24)$$

You can verify these equations by referring to Fig. 1.31a.

Next we express $\vec{A}$ and $\vec{B}$ in terms of their components and the corresponding unit vectors, and we expand the expression for the vector product:

$$\begin{aligned} \vec{A} \times \vec{B} &= (A_x\hat{\imath} + A_y\hat{\jmath} + A_z\hat{k}) \times (B_x\hat{\imath} + B_y\hat{\jmath} + B_z\hat{k}) \\ &= A_x\hat{\imath} \times B_x\hat{\imath} + A_x\hat{\imath} \times B_y\hat{\jmath} + A_x\hat{\imath} \times B_z\hat{k} \\ &\quad + A_y\hat{\jmath} \times B_x\hat{\imath} + A_y\hat{\jmath} \times B_y\hat{\jmath} + A_y\hat{\jmath} \times B_z\hat{k} \\ &\quad + A_z\hat{k} \times B_x\hat{\imath} + A_z\hat{k} \times B_y\hat{\jmath} + A_z\hat{k} \times B_z\hat{k} \end{aligned} \quad (1.25)$$

We can also rewrite the individual terms in Eq. (1.25) as $A_x\hat{\imath} \times B_y\hat{\jmath} = (A_xB_y)\hat{\imath} \times \hat{\jmath}$, and so on. Evaluating these by using the multiplication table for the unit vectors in Eqs. (1.24) and then grouping the terms, we find

$$\vec{A} \times \vec{B} = (A_yB_z - A_zB_y)\,\hat{\imath} + (A_zB_x - A_xB_z)\hat{\jmath} + (A_xB_y - A_yB_x)\hat{k} \quad (1.26)$$

Thus the components of $\vec{C} = \vec{A} \times \vec{B}$ are given by

$$C_x = A_yB_z - A_zB_y \qquad C_y = A_zB_x - A_xB_z \qquad C_z = A_xB_y - A_yB_x$$
$$(\text{components of } \vec{C} = \vec{A} \times \vec{B}) \quad (1.27)$$

The vector product can also be expressed in determinant form as

$$\vec{A} \times \vec{B} = \begin{vmatrix} \hat{\imath} & \hat{\jmath} & \hat{k} \\ A_x & A_y & A_z \\ B_x & B_y & B_z \end{vmatrix}$$

If you aren't familiar with determinants, don't worry about this form.

With the axis system of Fig. 1.31a, if we reverse the direction of the z-axis, we get the system shown in Fig. 1.31b. Then, as you may verify, the definition of the vector product gives $\hat{\imath} \times \hat{\jmath} = -\hat{k}$ instead of $\hat{\imath} \times \hat{\jmath} = \hat{k}$. In fact, all vector products of the unit vectors $\hat{\imath}$, $\hat{\jmath}$, and $\hat{k}$ would have signs opposite to those in Eqs. (1.24). We see that there are two kinds of coordinate systems, differing in the signs of the vector products of unit vectors. An axis system in which $\hat{\imath} \times \hat{\jmath} = \hat{k}$, as in Fig. 1.31a, is called a **right-handed system.** The usual practice is to use *only* right-handed systems, and we will follow that practice throughout this book.

1.31 (a) We will always use a right-handed coordinate system, like this one. (b) We will never use a left handed coordinate system (in which $\hat{\imath} \times \hat{\jmath} = -\hat{k}$, and so on).

(a) A right-handed coordinate system

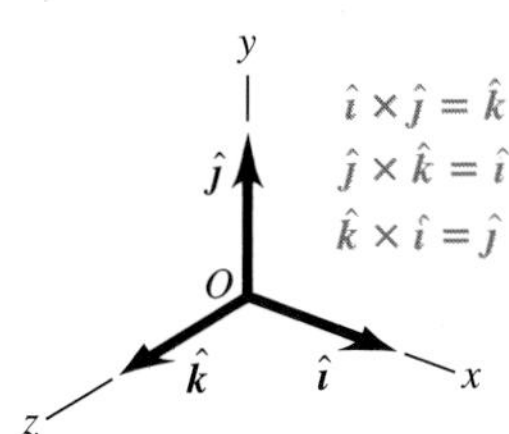

(b) A left-handed coordinate system; we will not use these.

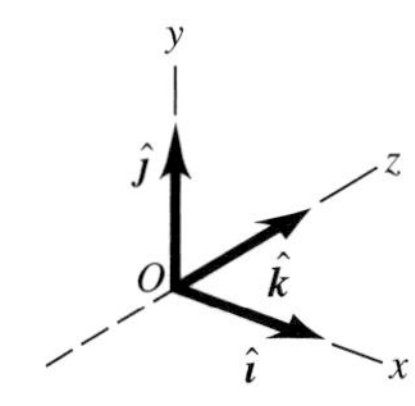

Example 1.12 Calculating a vector product

Vector $\vec{A}$ has magnitude 6 units and is in the direction of the $+x$-axis. Vector $\vec{B}$ has magnitude 4 units and lies in the xy-plane, making an angle of 30° with the $+x$-axis (Fig. 1.32). Find the vector product $\vec{A} \times \vec{B}$.

SOLUTION

IDENTIFY: We are given the magnitude and direction for each vector, and we want to find their vector product.

SET UP: We can find the vector product in one of two ways. The first way is to use Eq. (1.22) to determine the magnitude of $\vec{A} \times \vec{B}$ and then use the right-hand rule to find the direction of the vector product. The second way is to use the components of $\vec{A}$ and $\vec{B}$ to find the components of the vector product $\vec{C} = \vec{A} \times \vec{B}$ using Eqs. (1.27).

1.32 Vectors $\vec{A}$ and $\vec{B}$ and their vector product $\vec{C} = \vec{A} \times \vec{B}$. The vector $\vec{B}$ lies in the xy-plane.

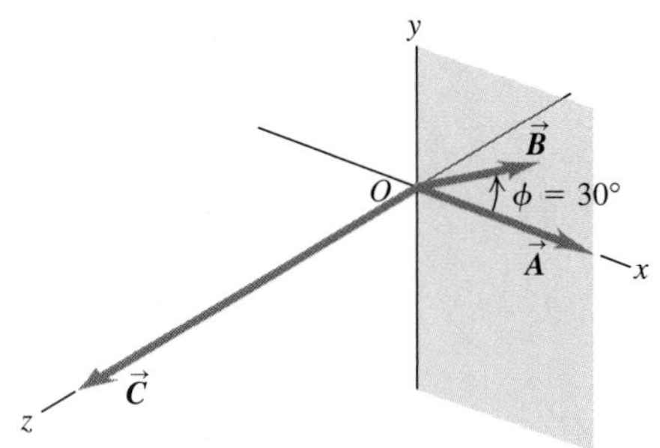

EXECUTE: With the first approach, from Eq. (1.22) the magnitude of the vector product is

$$AB\sin\phi = (6)(4)(\sin 30°) = 12$$

From the right-hand rule, the direction of $\vec{A} \times \vec{B}$ is along the $+z$-axis, so we have $\vec{A} \times \vec{B} = 12\hat{k}$.

To use the second approach, we first write the components of $\vec{A}$ and $\vec{B}$:

$$A_x = 6 \qquad A_y = 0 \qquad A_z = 0$$
$$B_x = 4\cos 30° = 2\sqrt{3} \qquad B_y = 4\sin 30° = 2 \qquad B_z = 0$$

Defining $\vec{C} = \vec{A} \times \vec{B}$, we have from Eqs. (1.27) that

$$C_x = (0)(0) - (0)(2) = 0$$
$$C_y = (0)(2\sqrt{3}) - (6)(0) = 0$$
$$C_z = (6)(2) - (0)(2\sqrt{3}) = 12$$

The vector product $\vec{C}$ has only a z-component, and it lies along the $+z$-axis. The magnitude agrees with the result we obtained with the first approach, as it should.

EVALUATE: For this example the first approach was more direct because we knew the magnitudes of each vector and the angle between them, and furthermore, both vectors lay in one of the planes of the coordinate system. But often you will need to find the vector product of two vectors that are not so conveniently oriented or for which only the components are given. In such a case the second approach, using components, is more direct.

Test Your Understanding of Section 1.10 Vector $\vec{A}$ has magnitude 2 and vector $\vec{B}$ has magnitude 3. The angle ϕ between $\vec{A}$ and $\vec{B}$ is known to be either 0°, 90°, or 180°. For each of the following situations, state what the value of ϕ must be. (In each situation there may be more than one correct answer.) (a) $\vec{A} \cdot \vec{B} = 0$; (b) $\vec{A} \times \vec{B} = \mathbf{0}$; (c) $\vec{A} \cdot \vec{B} = 6$; (d) $\vec{A} \cdot \vec{B} = -6$; (e) (magnitude of $\vec{A} \times \vec{B}$) $= 6$.

CHAPTER 1 SUMMARY

Physical quantities and units: The fundamental physical quantities of mechanics are mass, length, and time. The corresponding basic SI units are the kilogram, the meter, and the second. Derived units for other physical quantities are products or quotients of the basic units. Equations must be dimensionally consistent; two terms can be added only when they have the same units. (See Examples 1.1 and 1.2.)

Significant figures: The accuracy of a measurement can be indicated by the number of significant figures or by a stated uncertainty. The result of a calculation usually has no more significant figures than the input data. When only crude estimates are available for input data, we can often make useful order-of-magnitude estimates. (See Examples 1.3 and 1.4.)

Significant figures in magenta

$$\pi = \frac{C}{2r} = \frac{0.424\text{ m}}{2(0.06750\text{ m})} = 3.14$$

$$123.62 + 8.9 = 132.5$$

Scalars, vectors, and vector addition: Scalar quantities are numbers and combine with the usual rules of arithmetic. Vector quantities have direction as well as magnitude and combine according to the rules of vector addition. The negative of a vector has the same magnitude but points in the opposite direction. (See Example 1.5.)

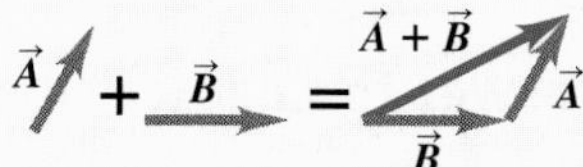

Vector components and vector addition: Vector addition can be carried out using components of vectors. The x-component of $\vec{R} = \vec{A} + \vec{B}$ is the sum of the x-components of $\vec{A}$ and $\vec{B}$, and likewise for the y- and z-components. (See Examples 1.6–1.8.)

$$R_x = A_x + B_x$$
$$R_y = A_y + B_y \qquad (1.10)$$
$$R_z = A_z + B_z$$

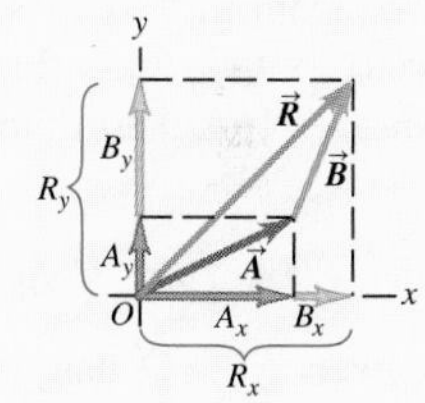

Unit vectors: Unit vectors describe directions in space. A unit vector has a magnitude of one, with no units. The unit vectors $\hat{\imath}$, $\hat{\jmath}$, and $\hat{k}$, aligned with the x-, y-, and z-axes of a rectangular coordinate system, are especially useful. (See Example 1.9.)

$$\vec{A} = A_x\hat{\imath} + A_y\hat{\jmath} + A_z\hat{k} \qquad (1.16)$$

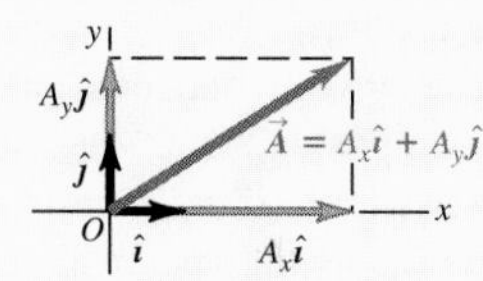

Scalar product: The scalar product $C = \vec{A}\cdot\vec{B}$ of two vectors $\vec{A}$ and $\vec{B}$ is a scalar quantity. It can be expressed in terms of the magnitudes of $\vec{A}$ and $\vec{B}$ and the angle ϕ between the two vectors, or in terms of the components of $\vec{A}$ and $\vec{B}$. The scalar product is commutative; $\vec{A}\cdot\vec{B} = \vec{B}\cdot\vec{A}$. The scalar product of two perpendicular vectors is zero. (See Examples 1.10 and 1.11.)

$$\vec{A}\cdot\vec{B} = AB\cos\phi = |\vec{A}||\vec{B}|\cos\phi \qquad (1.18)$$

$$\vec{A}\cdot\vec{B} = A_xB_x + A_yB_y + A_zB_z \qquad (1.21)$$

Scalar product $\vec{A}\cdot\vec{B} = AB\cos\phi$

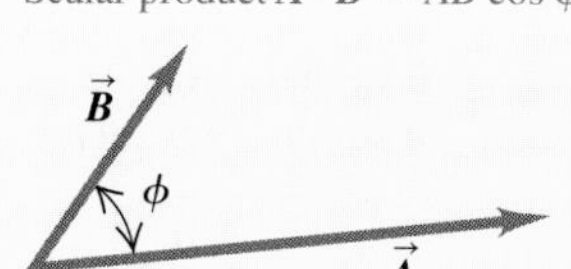

Vector product: The vector product $\vec{C} = \vec{A} \times \vec{B}$ of two vectors $\vec{A}$ and $\vec{B}$ is another vector $\vec{C}$. The magnitude of $\vec{A} \times \vec{B}$ depends on the magnitudes of $\vec{A}$ and $\vec{B}$ and the angle ϕ between the two vectors. The direction of $\vec{A} \times \vec{B}$ is perpendicular to the plane of the two vectors being multiplied, as given by the right-hand rule. The components of $\vec{C} = \vec{A} \times \vec{B}$ can be expressed in terms of the components of $\vec{A}$ and $\vec{B}$. The vector product is not commutative; $\vec{A} \times \vec{B} = -\vec{B} \times \vec{A}$. The vector product of two parallel or antiparallel vectors is zero. (See Example 1.12.)

$$C = AB\sin\phi \qquad (1.22)$$

$$C_x = A_yB_z - A_zB_y$$
$$C_y = A_zB_x - A_xB_z \qquad (1.27)$$
$$C_z = A_xB_y - A_yB_x$$

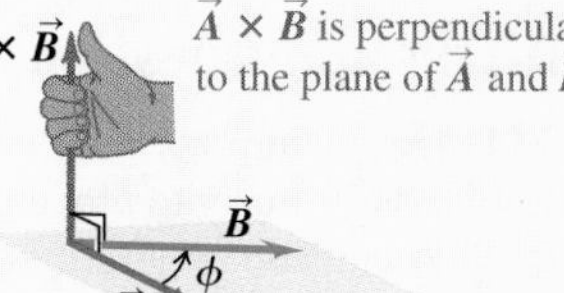

(Magnitude of $\vec{A} \times \vec{B}$) = $AB\sin\phi$

Key Terms

range of validity, *2*
target variable, *3*
model, *3*
particle, *3*
physical quantity, *4*
operational definition, *4*
unit, *4*
International System (SI), *4*
second, 5
meter, *5*
kilogram, *5*
prefix, *5*
dimensionally consistent, *7*
uncertainty (error), *8*
accuracy, *8*
fractional error, *8*
percent error, *8*
significant figures, *9*
scientific (powers-of-10) notation, *9*
precision, *10*
order-of-magnitude estimates, *11*
scalar quantity, *11*
vector quantity, *11*
magnitude of a vector, *11*
displacement, *11*
parallel vectors, *12*
negative of a vector, *12*
antiparallel vectors, *12*
vector sum (resultant), *13*
component vectors, *15*
components, *15*
unit vector, *20*
scalar (dot) product, *21*
vector (cross) product, *24*
right-hand rule, *24*
right-handed system, *25*

Answer to Chapter Opening Question ?

Take the $+x$-axis to point east and the $+y$-axis to point north. Then what we are trying to find is the y-component of the velocity vector, which has magnitude $v = 20\text{ km/h}$ and is at an angle $\theta = 53°$ measured from the $+x$-axis toward the $+y$-axis. From Eqs. (1.6) we have $v_y = v\sin\theta = (20\text{ km/h})\sin 53° = 16\text{ km/h}$. So the hurricane moves 16 km north in 1 h.

Answers to Test Your Understanding Questions

1.5 Answer: (ii) Density $= (1.80\text{ kg})/(6.0 \times 10^{-4}\text{ m}^3) = 3.0 \times 10^3\text{ kg/m}^3$. When we multiply or divide, the number with the fewest significant figures controls the number of significant figures in the result.

1.6 The answer depends on how many students are enrolled at your campus.

1.7 Answers: (ii), (iii), and (iv) The vector $-\vec{T}$ has the same magnitude as the vector $\vec{T}$, so $\vec{S} - \vec{T} = \vec{S} + (-\vec{T})$ is the *sum* of one vector of magnitude 3 m and one of magnitude 4 m. This sum has magnitude 7 m if $\vec{S}$ and $-\vec{T}$ are parallel and magnitude 1 m if $\vec{S}$ and $-\vec{T}$ are antiparallel. The magnitude of $\vec{S} - \vec{T}$ is 5 m if $\vec{S}$ and $-\vec{T}$ are perpendicular, so that the vectors $\vec{S}$, $\vec{T}$, and $\vec{S} - \vec{T}$ form a 3-4-5 right triangle. Answer (i) is impossible because the magnitude of the sum of two vectors cannot be greater than the sum of the magnitudes; answer (v) is impossible because the sum of two vectors can be zero only if the two vectors are antiparallel and have the same magnitude; and answer (vi) is impossible because the magnitude of a vector cannot be negative.

1.8 Answers: (a) yes, (b) no Vectors $\vec{A}$ and $\vec{B}$ can have the same magnitude but different components if they point in different directions. If they have the same components, however, they are the same vector $(\vec{A} = \vec{B})$ and so must have the same magnitude.

1.9 Answer: all have the same magnitude The four vectors $\vec{A}$, $\vec{B}$, $\vec{C}$, and $\vec{D}$ all point in different directions, but all have the same magnitude:

$$A = B = C = D = \sqrt{(\pm 3\text{ m})^2 + (\pm 5\text{ m})^2 + (\pm 2\text{ m})^2}$$
$$= \sqrt{9\text{ m}^2 + 25\text{ m}^2 + 4\text{ m}^2} = \sqrt{38\text{ m}^2} = 6.2\text{ m}$$

1.10 Answers: (a) $\phi = 90°$, (b) $\phi = 0°$ or $\phi = 180°$, (c) $\phi = 0°$, (d) $\phi = 180°$, (e) $\phi = 90°$ (a) The scalar product is zero only if $\vec{A}$ and $\vec{B}$ are perpendicular. (b) The vector product is zero only if $\vec{A}$ and $\vec{B}$ are either parallel or antiparallel. (c) The scalar product is equal to the product of the magnitudes $(\vec{A} \cdot \vec{B} = AB)$ only if $\vec{A}$ and $\vec{B}$ are parallel. (d) The scalar product is equal to the negative of the product of the magnitudes $(\vec{A} \cdot \vec{B} = -AB)$ only if $\vec{A}$ and $\vec{B}$ are antiparallel. (e) The magnitude of the vector product is equal to the product of the magnitudes $[(\text{magnitude of } \vec{A} \times \vec{B}) = AB]$ only if $\vec{A}$ and $\vec{B}$ are perpendicular.

PROBLEMS

For instructor-assigned homework, go to www.masteringphysics.com 

Discussion Questions

Q1.1. How many correct experiments do we need to disprove a theory? How many to prove a theory? Explain.

Q1.2. A guidebook describes the rate of climb of a mountain trail as 120 meters per kilometer. How can you express this as a number with no units?

Q1.3. Suppose you are asked to compute the tangent of 5.00 meters. Is this possible? Why or why not?

Q1.4. A highway contractor stated that in building a bridge deck he poured 250 yards of concrete. What do you think he meant?

Q1.5. What is your height in centimeters? What is your weight in newtons?

Q1.6. The U.S. National Institute of Science and Technology (NIST) maintains several accurate copies of the international standard kilogram. Even after careful cleaning, these national standard kilograms are gaining mass at an average rate of about $1\ \mu\text{g/y}$ $(1\text{ y} = 1\text{ year})$ when compared every ten years or so to the standard international kilogram. Does this apparent change have any importance? Explain.

Q1.7. What physical phenomena (other than a pendulum or cesium clock) could you use to define a time standard?

Q1.8. Describe how you could measure the thickness of a sheet of paper with an ordinary ruler.

Q1.9. The quantity $\pi = 3.14159\ldots$ is a number with no dimensions, since it is a ratio of two lengths. Describe two or three other geometrical or physical quantities that are dimensionless.
Q1.10. What are the units of volume? Suppose another student tells you that a cylinder of radius r and height h has volume given by $\pi r^3 h$. Explain why this cannot be right.
Q1.11. Three archers each fire four arrows at a target. Joe's four arrows hit at points 10 cm above, 10 cm below, 10 cm to the left, and 10 cm to the right of the center of the target. All four of Moe's arrows hit within 1 cm of a point 20 cm from the center, and Flo's four arrows all hit within 1 cm of the center. The contest judge says that one of the archers is precise but not accurate, another archer is accurate but not precise, and the third archer is both accurate and precise. Which description goes with which archer? Explain your reasoning.
Q1.12. A circular racetrack has a radius of 500 m. What is the displacement of a bicyclist when she travels around the track from the north side to the south side? When she makes one complete circle around the track? Explain your reasoning.
Q1.13. Can you find two vectors with different lengths that have a vector sum of zero? What length restrictions are required for three vectors to have a vector sum of zero? Explain your reasoning.
Q1.14. One sometimes speaks of the "direction of time," evolving from past to future. Does this mean that time is a vector quantity? Explain your reasoning.
Q1.15. Air traffic controllers give instructions to airline pilots telling them in which direction they are to fly. These instructions are called "vectors." If these are the only instructions given, is the name "vector" used correctly? Why or why not?
Q1.16. Can you find a vector quantity that has a magnitude of zero but components that are different from zero? Explain. Can the magnitude of a vector be less than the magnitude of any of its components? Explain.
Q1.17. (a) Does it make sense to say that a vector is *negative?* Why? (b) Does it make sense to say that one vector is the negative of another? Why? Does your answer here contradict what you said in part (a)?
Q1.18. If $\vec{C}$ is the vector sum of $\vec{A}$ and $\vec{B}$, $\vec{C} = \vec{A} + \vec{B}$, what must be true if $C = A + B$? What must be true if $C = 0$?
Q1.19. If $\vec{A}$ and $\vec{B}$ are nonzero vectors, is it possible for $\vec{A} \cdot \vec{B}$ and $\vec{A} \times \vec{B}$ *both* to be zero? Explain.
Q1.20. What does $\vec{A} \cdot \vec{A}$, the scalar product of a vector with itself, give? What about $\vec{A} \times \vec{A}$, the vector product of a vector with itself?
Q1.21. Let $\vec{A}$ represent any nonzero vector. Why is $\vec{A}/A$ a unit vector and what is its direction? If θ is the angle that $\vec{A}$ makes with the $+x$-axis, explain why $(\vec{A}/A) \cdot \hat{\imath}$ is called the *direction cosine* for that axis.
Q1.22. Which of the following are legitimate mathematical operations: (a) $\vec{A} \cdot (\vec{B} - \vec{C})$; (b) $(\vec{A} - \vec{B}) \times \vec{C}$; (c) $\vec{A} \cdot (\vec{B} \times \vec{C})$; (d) $\vec{A} \times (\vec{B} \times \vec{C})$; (e) $\vec{A} \times (\vec{B} \cdot \vec{C})$? In each case, give the reason for your answer.
Q1.23. Consider the two repeated vector products $\vec{A} \times (\vec{B} \times \vec{C})$ and $(\vec{A} \times \vec{B}) \times \vec{C}$. Give an example that illustrates the general rule that these two vector products do not have the same magnitude or direction. Can you choose the vectors $\vec{A}$, $\vec{B}$, and $\vec{C}$ such that these two vector products *are* equal? If so, give an example.
Q1.24. Show that, no matter what $\vec{A}$ and $\vec{B}$ are, $\vec{A} \cdot (\vec{A} \times \vec{B}) = 0$. (*Hint:* Do not look for an elaborate mathematical proof. Rather look at the definition of the direction of the cross product.)
Q1.25. (a) If $\vec{A} \cdot \vec{B} = 0$, does it necessary follow that $A = 0$ or $B = 0$? Explain. (b) If $\vec{A} \times \vec{B} = \mathbf{0}$, does it necessary follow that $A = 0$ or $B = 0$? Explain.
Q1.26. If $\vec{A} = \mathbf{0}$ for a vector in the xy plane, does it follow that $A_x = -A_y$? What *can* you say about A_x and A_y?

Exercises

Section 1.3 Standards and Units
Section 1.4 Unit Consistency and Conversions

1.1. Starting with the definition 1 in. = 2.54 cm, find the number of (a) kilometers in 1.00 mile and (b) feet in 1.00 km.
1.2. According to the label on a bottle of salad dressing, the volume of the contents is 0.473 liter (L). Using only the conversions $1\ \text{L} = 1000\ \text{cm}^3$ and 1 in. = 2.54 cm, express this volume in cubic inches.
1.3. How many nanoseconds does it take light to travel 1.00 ft in vacuum? (This result is a useful quantity to remember.)
1.4. The density of lead is $11.3\ \text{g/cm}^3$. What is this value in kilograms per cubic meter?
1.5. The most powerful engine available for the classic 1963 Chevrolet Corvette Sting Ray developed 360 horsepower and had a displacement of 327 cubic inches. Express this displacement in liters (L) by using only the conversions $1\ \text{L} = 1000\ \text{cm}^3$ and 1 in. = 2.54 cm.
1.6. A square field measuring 100.0 m by 100.0 m has an area of 1.00 hectare. An acre has an area of $43{,}600\ \text{ft}^2$. If a country lot has an area of 12.0 acres, what is the area in hectares?
1.7. How many years older will you be 1.00 billion seconds from now? (Assume a 365-day year.)
1.8. While driving in an exotic foreign land you see a speed limit sign on a highway that reads 180,000 furlongs per fortnight. How many miles per hour is this? (One furlong is $\frac{1}{8}$ mile, and a fortnight is 14 days. A furlong originally referred to the length of a plowed furrow.)
1.9. A certain fuel-efficient hybrid car gets gasoline mileage of 55.0 mpg (miles per gallon). (a) If you are driving this car in Europe and want to compare its mileage with that of other European cars, express this mileage in km/L (L = liter). Use the conversion factors in Appendix E. (b) If this car's gas tank holds 45 L, how many tanks of gas will you use to drive 1500 km?
1.10. The following conversions occur frequently in physics and are very useful. (a) Use 1 mi = 5280 ft and 1 h = 3600 s to convert 60 mph to units of ft/s. (b) The acceleration of a freely falling object is $32\ \text{ft/s}^2$. Use 1 ft = 30.48 cm to express this acceleration in units of m/s^2. (c) The density of water is $1.0\ \text{g/cm}^3$. Convert this density to units of kg/m^3.
1.11. Neptunium. In the fall of 2002, a group of scientists at Los Alamos National Laboratory determined that the critical mass of neptunium-237 is about 60 kg. The critical mass of a fissionable material is the minimum amount that must be brought together to start a chain reaction. This element has a density of $19.5\ \text{g/cm}^3$. What would be the radius of a sphere of this material that has a critical mass?

Section 1.5 Uncertainty and Significant Figures

1.12. A useful and easy-to-remember approximate value for the number of seconds in a year is $\pi \times 10^7$. Determine the percent error in this approximate value. (There are 365.24 days in one year.)
1.13. Figure 1.7 shows the result of unacceptable error in the stopping position of a train. (a) If a train travels 890 km from Berlin to Paris and then overshoots the end of the track by 10 m, what is the percent error in the total distance covered? (b) Is it correct to write the total distance covered by the train as 890,010 m? Explain.

1.14. With a wooden ruler you measure the length of a rectangular piece of sheet metal to be 12 mm. You use micrometer calipers to measure the width of the rectangle and obtain the value 5.98 mm. Give your answers to the following questions to the correct number of significant figures. (a) What is the area of the rectangle? (b) What is the ratio of the rectangle's width to its length? (c) What is the perimeter of the rectangle? (d) What is the difference between the length and width? (e) What is the ratio of the length to the width?

1.15. Estimate the percent error in measuring (a) a distance of about 75 cm with a meter stick; (b) a mass of about 12 g with a chemical balance; (c) a time interval of about 6 min with a stopwatch.

1.16. A rectangular piece of aluminum is 5.10 ± 0.01 cm long and 1.90 ± 0.01 cm wide. (a) Find the area of the rectangle and the uncertainty in the area. (b) Verify that the fractional uncertainty in the area is equal to the sum of the fractional uncertainties in the length and in the width. (This is a general result; see Challenge Problem 1.98.)

1.17. As you eat your way through a bag of chocolate chip cookies, you observe that each cookie is a circular disk with a diameter of 8.50 ± 0.02 cm and a thickness of 0.050 ± 0.005 cm. (a) Find the average volume of a cookie and the uncertainty in the volume. (b) Find the ratio of the diameter to the thickness and the uncertainty in this ratio.

Section 1.6 Estimates and Orders of Magnitude

1.18. How many gallons of gasoline are used in the United States in one day? Assume two cars for every three people, that each car is driven an average of 10,000 mi per year, and that the average car gets 20 miles per gallon.

1.19. A rather ordinary middle-aged man is in the hospital for a routine check-up. The nurse writes the quantity 200 on his medical chart but forgets to include the units. Which of the following quantities could the 200 plausibly represent? (a) his mass in kilograms; (b) his height in meters; (c) his height in centimeters; (d) his height in millimeters; (e) his age in months.

1.20. How many kernels of corn does it take to fill a 2-L soft drink bottle?

1.21. How many words are there in this book?

1.22. Four astronauts are in a spherical space station. (a) If, as is typical, each of them breathes about 500 cm^3 of air with each breath, approximately what volume of air (in cubic meters) do these astronauts breathe in a year? (b) What would the diameter (in meters) of the space station have to be to contain all this air?

1.23. How many times does a typical person blink her eyes in a lifetime?

1.24. How many times does a human heart beat during a lifetime? How many gallons of blood does it pump? (Estimate that the heart pumps 50 cm^3 of blood with each beat.)

1.25. In Wagner's opera *Das Rheingold,* the goddess Freia is ransomed for a pile of gold just tall enough and wide enough to hide her from sight. Estimate the monetary value of this pile. The density of gold is 19.3 g/cm^3, and its value is about \$10 per gram (although this varies).

1.26. You are using water to dilute small amounts of chemicals in the laboratory, drop by drop. How many drops of water are in a 1.0 L bottle? (*Hint:* Start by estimating the diameter of a drop of water.)

1.27. How many pizzas are consumed each academic year by students at your school?

1.28. How many dollar bills would you have to stack to reach the moon? Would that be cheaper than building and launching a spacecraft? (*Hint:* Start by folding a dollar bill to see how many thicknesses make 1.0 mm.)

1.29. How much would it cost to paper the entire United States (including Alaska and Hawaii) with dollar bills? What would be the cost to each person in the United States?

Section 1.7 Vectors and Vector Addition

1.30. Hearing rattles from a snake, you make two rapid displacements of magnitude 1.8 m and 2.4 m. In sketches (roughly to scale), show how your two displacements might add up to give a resultant of magnitude (a) 4.2 m; (b) 0.6 m; (c) 3.0 m.

1.31. A postal employee drives a delivery truck along the route shown in Fig. 1.33. Determine the magnitude and direction of the resultant displacement by drawing a scale diagram. (See also Exercise 1.38 for a different approach to this same problem.)

Figure **1.33** Exercises 1.31 and 1.38.

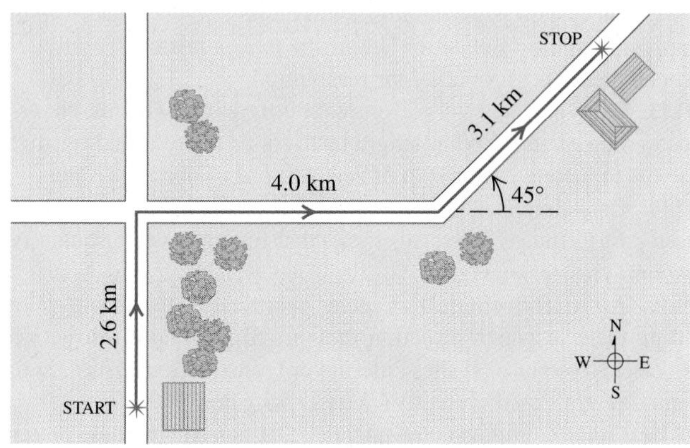

1.32. For the vectors $\vec{A}$ and $\vec{B}$ in Fig. 1.34, use a scale drawing to find the magnitude and direction of (a) the vector sum $\vec{A} + \vec{B}$ and (b) the vector difference $\vec{A} - \vec{B}$. Use your answers to find the magnitude and direction of (c) $-\vec{A} - \vec{B}$ and (d) $\vec{B} - \vec{A}$. (See also Exercise 1.39 for a different approach to this problem.)

Figure **1.34** Exercises 1.32, 1.35, 1.39, 1.47, 1.53, and 1.57, and Problem 1.72.

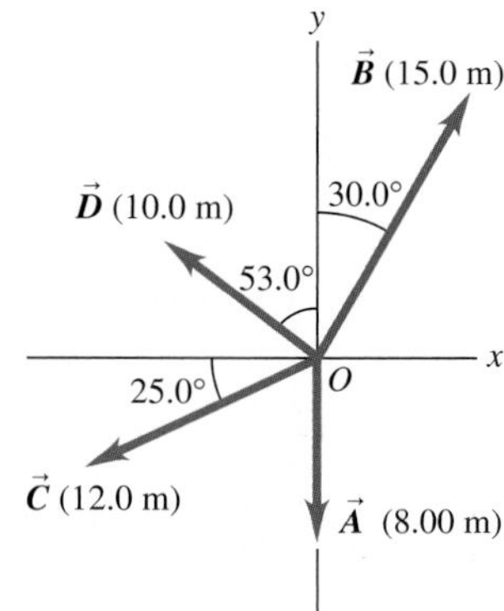

1.33. A spelunker is surveying a cave. She follows a passage 180 m straight west, then 210 m in a direction 45° east of south, and then 280 m at 30° east of north. After a fourth unmeasured displacement, she finds herself back where she started. Use a scale drawing to determine the magnitude and direction of the fourth displacement. (See also Problem 1.73 for a different approach to this problem.)

Section 1.8 Components of Vectors

1.34. Use a scale drawing to find the x- and y-components of the following vectors. For each vector the numbers given are the magnitude of the vector and the angle, measured in the sense from the $+x$-axis toward the $+y$-axis, that it makes with the $+x$-axis: (a) magnitude 9.30 m, angle 60.0°; (b) magnitude 22.0 km, angle 135°; (c) magnitude 6.35 cm, angle 307°.

1.35. Compute the x- and y-components of the vectors $\vec{A}$, $\vec{B}$, $\vec{C}$, and $\vec{D}$ in Fig. 1.34.

1.36. Let the angle θ be the angle that the vector $\vec{A}$ makes with the $+x$-axis, measured counterclockwise from that axis. Find the angle θ for a vector that has the following components: (a) $A_x = 2.00$ m, $A_y = -1.00$ m; (b) $A_x = 2.00$ m, $A_y = 1.00$ m; (c) $A_x = -2.00$ m, $A_y = 1.00$ m; (d) $A_x = -2.00$ m, $A_y = -1.00$ m.

1.37. A rocket fires two engines simultaneously. One produces a thrust of 725 N directly forward, while the other gives a 513-N thrust at 32.4° above the forward direction. Find the magnitude and direction (relative to the forward direction) of the resultant force that these engines exert on the rocket.

1.38. A postal employee drives a delivery truck over the route shown in Fig. 1.33. Use the method of components to determine the magnitude and direction of her resultant displacement. In a vector-addition diagram (roughly to scale), show that the resultant displacement found from your diagram is in qualitative agreement with the result you obtained using the method of components.

1.39. For the vectors $\vec{A}$ and $\vec{B}$ in Fig. 1.34, use the method of components to find the magnitude and direction of (a) the vector sum $\vec{A} + \vec{B}$; (b) the vector sum $\vec{B} + \vec{A}$; (c) the vector difference $\vec{A} - \vec{B}$; (d) the vector difference $\vec{B} - \vec{A}$.

1.40. Find the magnitude and direction of the vector represented by the following pairs of components: (a) $A_x = -8.60$ cm, $A_y = 5.20$ cm; (b) $A_x = -9.70$ m, $A_y = -2.45$ m; (c) $A_x = 7.75$ km, $A_y = -2.70$ km.

1.41. A disoriented physics professor drives 3.25 km north, then 4.75 km west, and then 1.50 km south. Find the magnitude and direction of the resultant displacement, using the method of components. In a vector addition diagram (roughly to scale), show that the resultant displacement found from your diagram is in qualitative agreement with the result you obtained using the method of components.

1.42. Vector $\vec{A}$ has components $A_x = 1.30$ cm, $A_y = 2.25$ cm; vector $\vec{B}$ has components $B_x = 4.10$ cm, $B_y = -3.75$ cm. Find (a) the components of the vector sum $\vec{A} + \vec{B}$; (b) the magnitude and direction of $\vec{A} + \vec{B}$; (c) the components of the vector difference $\vec{B} - \vec{A}$; (d) the magnitude and direction of $\vec{B} - \vec{A}$.

1.43. Vector $\vec{A}$ is 2.80 cm long and is 60.0° above the x-axis in the first quadrant. Vector $\vec{B}$ is 1.90 cm long and is 60.0° below the x-axis in the fourth quadrant (Fig. 1.35). Use components to find the magnitude and direction of (a) $\vec{A} + \vec{B}$; (b) $\vec{A} - \vec{B}$; (c) $\vec{B} - \vec{A}$. In each case, sketch the vector addition or subtraction and show that your numerical answers are in qualitative agreement with your sketch.

Figure 1.35 Exercises 1.43 and 1.59.

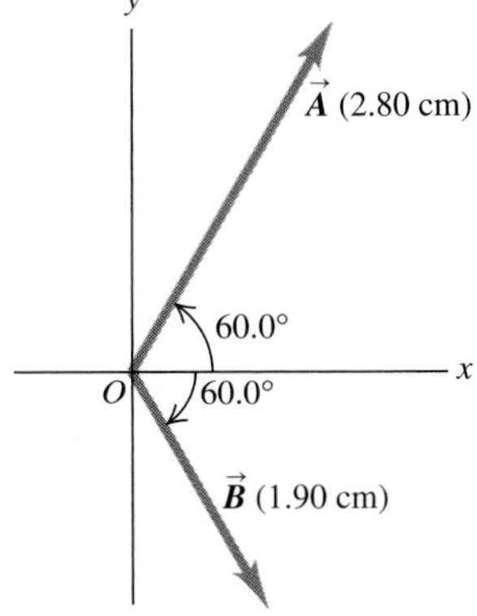

1.44. A river flows from south to north at 5.0 km/h. On this river, a boat is heading east to west perpendicular to the current at 7.0 km/h. As viewed by an eagle hovering at rest over the shore, how fast and in what direction is this boat traveling?

1.45. Use vector components to find the magnitude and direction of the vector needed to balance the two vectors shown in Figure 1.36. Let the 625-N vector be along the $-y$-axis and let the $+x$-axis be perpendicular to it toward the right.

Figure 1.36 Exercise 1.45.

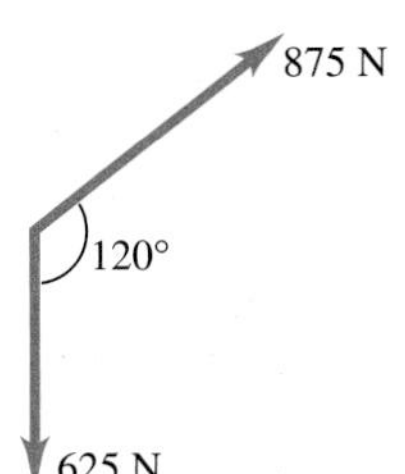

1.46. Two ropes in a vertical plane exert equal magnitude forces on a hanging weight but pull with an angle of 86.0° between them. What pull does each one exert if their resultant pull is 372 N directly upward?

Section 1.9 Unit Vectors

1.47. Write each vector in Fig. 1.34 in terms of the unit vectors $\hat{\imath}$ and $\hat{\jmath}$.

1.48. In each case, find the x- and y-components of vector $\vec{A}$: (a) $\vec{A} = 5.0\hat{\imath} - 6.3\hat{\jmath}$; (b) $\hat{A} = 11.2\hat{\jmath} - 9.91\hat{\imath}$; (c) $\vec{A} = -15.0\hat{\imath} + 22.4\hat{\jmath}$; (d) $\vec{A} = 5.0\vec{B}$, where $\vec{B} = 4\hat{\imath} - 6\hat{\jmath}$.

1.49. (a) Write each vector in Fig. 1.37 in terms of the unit vectors $\hat{\imath}$ and $\hat{\jmath}$. (b) Use unit vectors to express the vector $\vec{C}$, where $\vec{C} = 3.00\vec{A} - 4.00\vec{B}$. (c) Find the magnitude and direction of $\vec{C}$.

Figure 1.37 Exercise 1.49 and Problem 1.86.

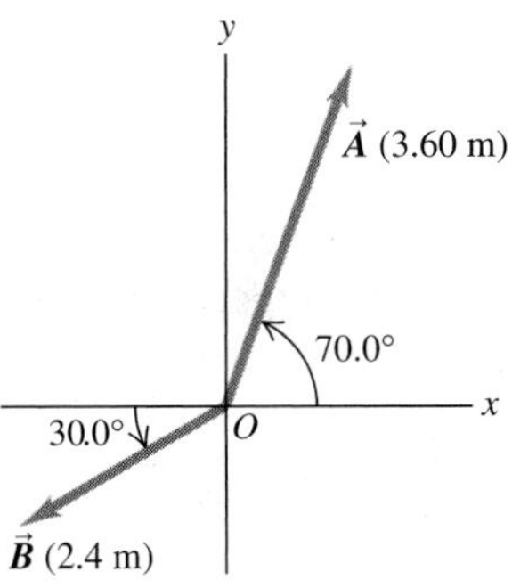

1.50. Given two vectors $\vec{A} = 4.00\hat{\imath} + 3.00\hat{\jmath}$ and $\vec{B} = 5.00\hat{\imath} - 2.00\hat{\jmath}$, (a) find the magnitude of each vector; (b) write an expression for the vector difference $\vec{A} - \vec{B}$ using unit vectors; (c) find the magnitude and direction of the vector difference $\vec{A} - \vec{B}$. (d) In a vector diagram show $\vec{A}$, $\vec{B}$, and $\vec{A} - \vec{B}$, and also show that your diagram agrees qualitatively with your answer in part (c).

1.51. (a) Is the vector $(\hat{\imath} + \hat{\jmath} + \hat{k})$ a unit vector? Justify your answer. (b) Can a unit vector have any components with magnitude greater than unity? Can it have any negative components? In each case justify your answer. (c) If $\vec{A} = a(3.0\hat{\imath} + 4.0\hat{\jmath})$, where a is a constant, determine the value of a that makes $\vec{A}$ a unit vector.

Section 1.10 Products of Vectors

1.52. (a) Use vector components to prove that two vectors commute for both addition and the scalar product. (b) Prove that two vectors *anticommute* for the vector product; that is, prove that $\vec{A} \times \vec{B} = -\vec{B} \times \vec{A}$.

1.53. For the vectors $\vec{A}$, $\vec{B}$, and $\vec{C}$ in Fig. 1.34, find the scalar products (a) $\vec{A} \cdot \vec{B}$; (b) $\vec{B} \cdot \vec{C}$; (c) $\vec{A} \cdot \vec{C}$.

1.54. (a) Find the scalar product of the two vectors $\vec{A}$ and $\vec{B}$ given in Exercise 1.50. (b) Find the angle between these two vectors.

1.55. Find the angle between each of the following pairs of vectors:

(a) $\vec{A} = -2.00\hat{\imath} + 6.00\hat{\jmath}$ and $\vec{B} = 2.00\hat{\imath} - 3.00\hat{\jmath}$

(b) $\vec{A} = 3.00\hat{\imath} + 5.00\hat{\jmath}$ and $\vec{B} = 10.00\hat{\imath} + 6.00\hat{\jmath}$

(c) $\vec{A} = -4.00\hat{\imath} + 2.00\hat{\jmath}$ and $\vec{B} = 7.00\hat{\imath} + 14.00\hat{\jmath}$

1.56. By making simple sketches of the appropriate vector products, show that (a) $\vec{A} \cdot \vec{B}$ can be interpreted as the product of the magnitude of $\vec{A}$ times the component of $\vec{B}$ along $\vec{A}$, or the magnitude of $\vec{B}$ times the component of $\vec{A}$ along $\vec{B}$; (b) $|\vec{A} \times \vec{B}|$ can be interpreted as the product of the magnitude of $\vec{A}$ times the component of $\vec{B}$ perpendicular to $\vec{A}$, or the magnitude of $\vec{B}$ times the component of $\vec{A}$ perpendicular to $\vec{B}$.

1.57. For the vectors $\vec{A}$ and $\hat{D}$ in Fig. 1.34, (a) find the magnitude and direction of the vector product $\vec{A} \times \hat{D}$; (b) find the magnitude and direction of $\hat{D} \times \vec{A}$.

1.58. Find the vector product $\vec{A} \times \vec{B}$ (expressed in unit vectors) of the two vectors given in Exercise 1.50. What is the magnitude of the vector product?

1.59. For the two vectors in Fig. 1.35, (a) find the magnitude and direction of the vector product $\vec{A} \times \vec{B}$; (b) find the magnitude and direction of $\vec{B} \times \vec{A}$.

Problems

1.60. An acre, a unit of land measurement still in wide use, has a length of one furlong ($\frac{1}{8}$ mi) and a width one-tenth of its length. (a) How many acres are in a square mile? (b) How many square feet are in an acre? See Appendix E. (c) An acre-foot is the volume of water that would cover 1 acre of flat land to a depth of 1 foot. How many gallons are in 1 acre-foot?

1.61. An Earthlike Planet. In January 2006, astronomers reported the discovery of a planet comparable in size to the earth orbiting another star and having a mass of about 5.5 times the earth's mass. It is believed to consist of a mixture of rock and ice, similar to Neptune. If this planet has the same density as Neptune ($1.76\ \text{g/cm}^3$), what is its radius expressed (a) in kilometers and (b) as a multiple of earth's radius? Consult Appendix F for astronomical data.

1.62. The Hydrogen Maser. You can use the radio waves generated by a hydrogen maser as a standard of frequency. The frequency of these waves is 1,420,405,751.786 hertz. (A hertz is another name for one cycle per second.) A clock controlled by a hydrogen maser is off by only 1 s in 100,000 years. For the following questions, use only three significant figures. (The large number of significant figures given for the frequency simply illustrates the remarkable accuracy to which it has been measured.) (a) What is the time for one cycle of the radio wave? (b) How many cycles occur in 1 h? (c) How many cycles would have occurred during the age of the earth, which is estimated to be 4.6×10^9 years? (d) By how many seconds would a hydrogen maser clock be off after a time interval equal to the age of the earth?

1.63. Estimate the number of atoms in your body. (*Hint:* Based on what you know about biology and chemistry, what are the most common types of atom in your body? What is the mass of each type of atom? Appendix D gives the atomic masses for different elements, measured in atomic mass units; you can find the value of an atomic mass unit, or 1 u, in Appendix F.)

1.64. Biological tissues are typically made up of 98% water. Given that the density of water is $1.0 \times 10^3\ \text{kg/m}^3$, estimate the mass of (a) the heart of an adult human; (b) a cell with a diameter of 0.5 μm; (c) a honey bee.

1.65. Iron has a property such that a 1.00-m^3 volume has a mass of 7.86×10^3 kg (density equals $7.86 \times 10^3\ \text{kg/m}^3$). You want to manufacture iron into cubes and spheres. Find (a) the length of the side of a cube of iron that has a mass of 200.0 g and (b) the radius of a solid sphere of iron that has a mass of 200.0 g.

1.66. Stars in the Universe Astronomers frequently say that there are more stars in the universe than there are grains of sand on all the beaches on the earth. (a) Given that a typical grain of sand is about 0.2 mm in diameter, estimate the number of grains of sand on all the earth's beaches, and hence the approximate number of stars in the universe. It would be helpful to consult an atlas and do some measuring. (b) Given that a typical galaxy contains about 100 billion stars and there are more than 100 billion galaxies in the known universe, estimate the number of stars in the universe and compare this number with your result from part (a).

1.67. Physicists, mathematicians, and others often deal with large numbers. The number 10^{100} has been given the whimsical name *googol* by mathematicians. Let us compare some large numbers in physics with the googol. (*Note:* This problem requires numerical values that you can find in the appendices of the book, with which you should become familiar.) (a) Approximately how many atoms make up our planet? For simplicity, assume the average atomic mass of the atoms is 14 g/mol. Avogadro's number gives the number of atoms in a mole. (b) Approximately how many neutrons are in a neutron star? Neutron stars are composed almost entirely of neutrons and have approximately twice the mass of the sun. (c) In the leading theory of the origin of the universe, the entire universe that we can now observe occupied, at a very early time, a sphere whose radius was approximately equal to the present distance of the earth to the sun. At that time the universe had a density (mass divided by volume) of $10^{15}\ \text{g/cm}^3$. Assuming that one-third of the particles were protons, one-third of the particles were neutrons, and the remaining one-third were electrons, how many particles then made up the universe?

1.68. Three horizontal ropes pull on a large stone stuck in the ground, producing the vector forces $\vec{A}$, $\vec{B}$, and $\vec{C}$ shown in Fig. 1.38. Find the magnitude and direction of a fourth force on the stone that will make the vector sum of the four forces zero.

Figure 1.38 Problem 1.68.

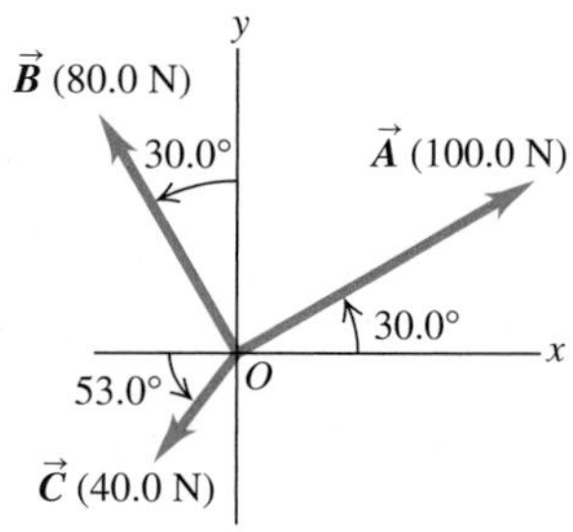

1.69. Two workers pull horizontally on a heavy box, but one pulls twice as hard as the other. The larger pull is directed at 25.0° west of north, and the resultant of these two pulls is 350.0 N directly northward. Use vector components to find the magnitude of each of these pulls and the direction of the smaller pull.

1.70. Emergency Landing. A plane leaves the airport in Galisteo and flies 170 km at 68° east of north and then changes direction to fly 230 km at 48° south of east, after which it makes an immediate emergency landing in a pasture. When the airport sends out a rescue crew, in which direction and how far should this crew fly to go directly to this plane?

1.71. You are to program a robotic arm on an assembly line to move in the xy-plane. Its first displacement is $\vec{A}$; its second displacement is $\vec{B}$, of magnitude 6.40 cm and direction 63.0° measured in the sense from the $+x$-axis toward the $-y$-axis. The resultant $\vec{C} = \vec{A} + \vec{B}$ of the two displacements should also have a magnitude of 6.40 cm, but a direction 22.0° measured in the sense from the $+x$-axis toward the $+y$-axis. (a) Draw the vector addition diagram for these vectors, roughly to scale. (b) Find the components of $\vec{A}$. (c) Find the magnitude and direction of $\vec{A}$.

1.72. (a) Find the magnitude and direction of the vector $\vec{R}$ that is the sum of the three vectors $\vec{A}$, $\vec{B}$, and $\vec{C}$ in Fig. 1.34. In a diagram, show how $\vec{R}$ is formed from these three vectors. (b) Find the magnitude and direction of the vector $\vec{S} = \vec{C} - \vec{A} - \vec{B}$. In a diagram, show how $\vec{S}$ is formed from these three vectors.

1.73. As noted in Exercise 1.33, a spelunker is surveying a cave. She follows a passage 180 m straight west, then 210 m in a direction 45° east of south, and then 280 m at 30° east of north. After a fourth unmeasured displacement she finds herself back where she started. Use the method of components to determine the magnitude and direction of the fourth displacement. Draw the vector addition diagram and show that it is in qualitative agreement with your numerical solution.

1.74. A sailor in a small sailboat encounters shifting winds. She sails 2.00 km east, then 3.50 km southeast, and then an additional distance in an unknown direction. Her final position is 5.80 km directly east of the starting point (Fig. 1.39). Find the magnitude and direction of the third leg of the journey. Draw the vector addition diagram and show that it is in qualitative agreement with your numerical solution.

Figure **1.39** Problem 1.74.

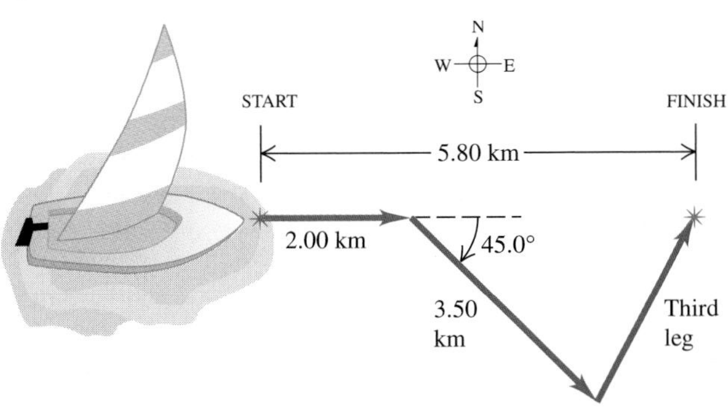

1.75. Equilibrium. We say an object is in *equilibrium* if all the forces on it balance (add up to zero). Figure 1.40 shows a beam weighing 124 N that is supported in equilibrium by a 100.0-N pull and a force $\vec{F}$ at the floor. The third force on the beam is the 124-N weight that acts vertically downward. (a) Use vector components to find the magnitude and direction of $\vec{F}$. (b) Check the reasonableness of your answer in part (a) by doing a graphical solution approximately to scale.

Figure **1.40** Problem 1.75.

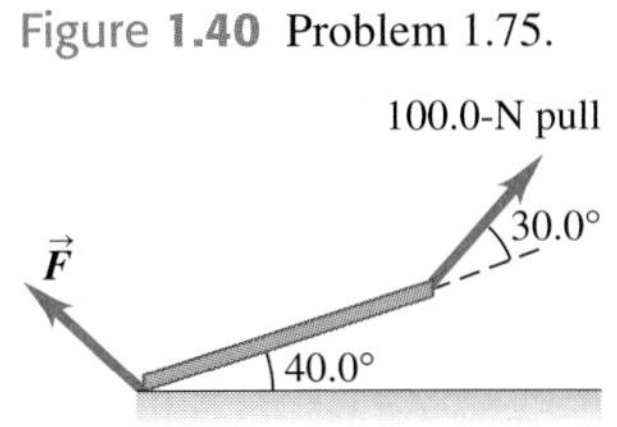

1.76. On a training flight, a student pilot flies from Lincoln, Nebraska to Clarinda, Iowa, then to St. Joseph, Missouri, and then to Manhattan, Kansas (Fig. 1.41). The directions are shown relative to north: 0° is north, 90° is east, 180° is south, and 270° is west. Use the method of components to find (a) the distance she has to fly from Manhattan to get back to Lincoln, and (b) the direction (relative to north) she must fly to get there. Illustrate your solutions with a vector diagram.

Figure **1.41** Problem 1.76.

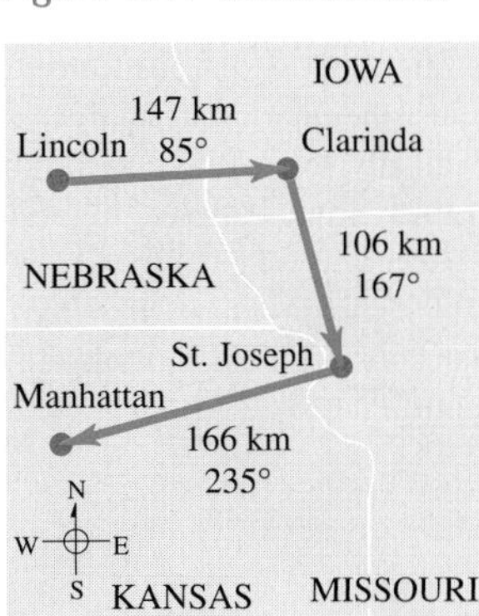

1.77. A graphic artist is creating a new logo for her company's website. In the graphics program she is using, each pixel in an image file has coordinates (x, y), where the origin $(0, 0)$ is at the upper left corner of the image, the $+x$-axis points to the right, and the $+y$-axis points down. Distances are measured in pixels. (a) The artist draws a line from the pixel location $(10, 20)$ to the location $(210, 200)$. She wishes to draw a second line that starts at $(10, 20)$, is 250 pixels long, and is at angle of 30° measured clockwise from the first line. At which pixel location should this second line end? Give your answer to the nearest pixel. (b) The artist now draws an arrow that connects the lower right end of the first line to the lower right end of the second line. Find the length and direction of this arrow. Draw a diagram showing all three lines.

1.78. Getting Back. An explorer in the dense jungles of equatorial Africa leaves his hut. He takes 40 steps northeast, then 80 steps 60° north of west, then 50 steps due south. Assume his steps all have equal length. (a) Sketch, roughly to scale, the three vectors and their resultant. (b) Save the explorer from becoming hopelessly lost in the jungle by giving him the displacement, calculated using the method of components, that will return him to his hut.

1.79. A ship leaves the island of Guam and sails 285 km at 40.0° north of west. In which direction must it now head and how far must it sail so that its resultant displacement will be 115 km directly east of Guam?

1.80. A boulder of weight w rests on a hillside that rises at a constant angle α above the horizontal, as shown in Fig. 1.42. Its weight is a force on the boulder that has direction vertically downward. (a) In terms of α and w, what is the component of the weight of the boulder in the direction parallel to the surface of the hill? (b) What is the component of the weight in the direction perpendicular to the surface of the hill? (c) An air conditioner unit is fastened to a roof that slopes upward at an angle of 35.0°. In order that the unit not slide down the roof, the component of the unit's weight parallel to the roof cannot exceed 550 N. What is the maximum allowed weight of the unit?

Figure **1.42** Problem 1.80.

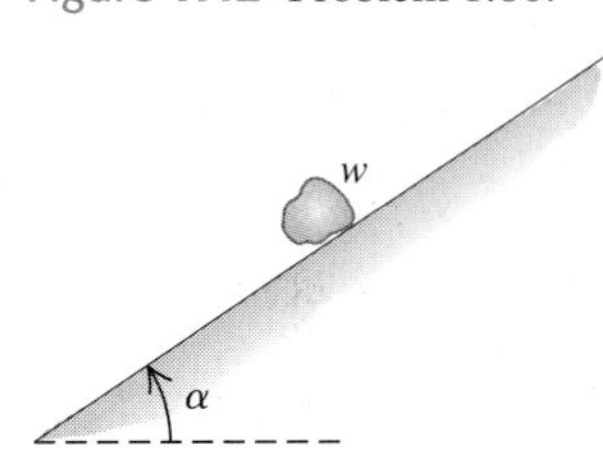

1.81. Bones and Muscles. A patient in therapy has a forearm that weighs 20.5 N and that lifts a 112.0-N weight. These two forces have direction vertically downward. The only other significant forces on his forearm come from the biceps muscle (which acts perpendicularly to the forearm) and the force at the elbow. If the biceps produces a pull of 232 N when the forearm is raised 43° above the horizontal, find the magnitude and direction of the force that the elbow exerts on the forearm. (The sum of the elbow force and the biceps force must balance the weight of the arm and the weight it is carrying, so their vector sum must be 132.5 N, upward.)

1.82. You are hungry and decide to go to your favorite neighborhood fast-food restaurant. You leave your apartment and take the elevator 10 flights down (each flight is 3.0 m) and then go 15 m south to the apartment exit. You then proceed 0.2 km east, turn north, and go 0.1 km to the entrance of the restaurant. (a) Determine the displacement from your apartment to the restaurant. Use unit vector notation for your answer, being sure to make clear your choice of coordinates. (b) How far did you travel along the path you took from your apartment to the restaurant, and what is the magnitude of the displacement you calculated in part (a)?

1.83. While following a treasure map, you start at an old oak tree. You first walk 825 m directly south, then turn and walk 1.25 km at 30.0° west of north, and finally walk 1.00 km at 40.0° north of east, where you find the treasure: a biography of Isaac Newton! (a) To return to the old oak tree, in what direction should you head and how far will you walk? Use components to solve this problem.

(b) To see whether your calculation in part (a) is reasonable, check it with a graphical solution drawn roughly to scale.

1.84. You are camping with two friends, Joe and Karl. Since all three of you like your privacy, you don't pitch your tents close together. Joe's tent is 21.0 m from yours, in the direction 23.0° south of east. Karl's tent is 32.0 m from yours, in the direction 37.0° north of east. What is the distance between Karl's tent and Joe's tent?

1.85. Vectors $\vec{A}$ and $\vec{B}$ are drawn from a common point. Vector $\vec{A}$ has magnitude A and angle θ_A measured in the sense from the $+x$-axis to the $+y$-axis. The corresponding quantities for vector $\vec{B}$ are B and θ_B. Then $\vec{A} = A\cos\theta_A\hat{\imath} + A\sin\theta_A\hat{\jmath}$, $\vec{B} = B\cos\theta_B\hat{\imath} + B\sin\theta_B\hat{\jmath}$, and $\phi = |\theta_B - \theta_A|$ is the angle between $\vec{A}$ and $\vec{B}$. (a) Derive Eq. (1.18) from Eq. (1.21). (b) Derive Eq. (1.22) from Eqs. (1.27).

1.86. For the two vectors $\vec{A}$ and $\vec{B}$ in Fig. 1.37, (a) find the scalar product $\vec{A}\cdot\vec{B}$, and (b) find the magnitude and direction of the vector product $\vec{A}\times\vec{B}$.

1.87. Figure 1.11c shows a parallelogram based on the two vectors $\vec{A}$ and $\vec{B}$. (a) Show that the magnitude of the cross product of these two vectors is equal to the area of the parallelogram. (*Hint:* Area = base × height.) (b) What is the angle between the cross product and the plane of the parallelogram?

1.88. The vector $\vec{A}$ is 3.50 cm long and is directed into this page. Vector $\vec{B}$ points from the lower right corner of this page to the upper left corner of this page. Define an appropriate right-handed coordinate system and find the three components of the vector product $\vec{A}\times\vec{B}$, measured in cm^2. In a diagram, show your coordinate system and the vectors $\vec{A}$, $\vec{B}$, and $\vec{A}\times\vec{B}$.

1.89. Given two vectors $\vec{A} = -2.00\hat{\imath} + 3.00\hat{\jmath} + 4.00\hat{k}$ and $\vec{B} = 3.00\hat{\imath} + 1.00\hat{\jmath} - 3.00\hat{k}$, do the following. (a) Find the magnitude of each vector. (b) Write an expression for the vector difference $\vec{A}-\vec{B}$, using unit vectors. (c) Find the magnitude of the vector difference $\vec{A}-\vec{B}$. Is this the same as the magnitude of $\vec{B}-\vec{A}$? Explain.

1.90. Bond Angle in Methane. In the methane molecule, CH_4, each hydrogen atom is at a corner of a regular tetrahedron with the carbon atom at the center. In coordinates where one of the C—H bonds is in the direction of $\hat{\imath} + \hat{\jmath} + \hat{k}$, an adjacent C—H bond is in the $\hat{\imath} - \hat{\jmath} - \hat{k}$ direction. Calculate the angle between these two bonds.

1.91. The two vectors $\vec{A}$ and $\vec{B}$ are drawn from a common point, and $\vec{C} = \vec{A} + \vec{B}$. (a) Show that if $C^2 = A^2 + B^2$, the angle between the vectors $\vec{A}$ and $\vec{B}$ is 90°. (b) Show that if $C^2 < A^2 + B^2$, the angle between the vectors $\vec{A}$ and $\vec{B}$ is greater than 90°. (c) Show that if $C^2 > A^2 + B^2$, the angle between the vectors $\vec{A}$ and $\vec{B}$ is between 0° and 90°.

1.92. When two vectors $\vec{A}$ and $\vec{B}$ are drawn from a common point, the angle between them is ϕ. (a) Using vector techniques, show that the magnitude of their vector sum is given by

$$\sqrt{A^2 + B^2 + 2AB\cos\phi}$$

(b) If $\vec{A}$ and $\vec{B}$ have the same magnitude, for which value of ϕ will their vector sum have the same magnitude as $\vec{A}$ or $\vec{B}$?

1.93. A cube is placed so that one corner is at the origin and three edges are along the x-, y-, and z-axes of a coordinate system (Fig. 1.43). Use vectors to compute (a) the angle between the edge along the z-axis (line ab) and the diagonal from the origin to the opposite corner (line ad), and (b) the angle between line ac (the diagonal of a face) and line ad.

Figure 1.43 Problem 1.93.

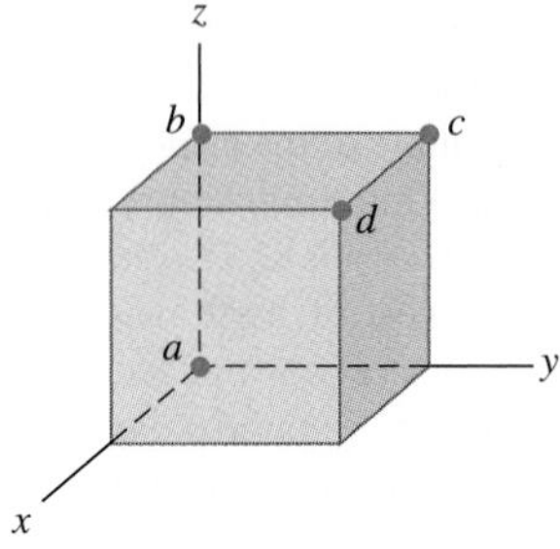

1.94. Obtain a *unit vector* perpendicular to the two vectors given in Problem 1.89.

1.95. You are given vectors $\vec{A} = 5.0\hat{\imath} - 6.5\hat{\jmath}$ and $\vec{B} = -3.5\hat{\imath} + 7.0\hat{\jmath}$. A third vector $\vec{C}$ lies in the xy-plane. Vector $\vec{C}$ is perpendicular to vector $\vec{A}$, and the scalar product of $\vec{C}$ with $\vec{B}$ is 15.0. From this information, find the components of vector $\vec{C}$.

1.96. Two vectors $\vec{A}$ and $\vec{B}$ have magnitude $A = 3.00$ and $B = 3.00$. Their vector product is $\vec{A}\times\vec{B} = -5.00\hat{k} + 2.00\hat{\imath}$. What is the angle between $\vec{A}$ and $\vec{B}$?

1.97. Later in our study of physics we will encounter quantities represented by $(\vec{A}\times\vec{B})\cdot\vec{C}$. (a) Prove that for any three vectors $\vec{A}$, $\vec{B}$, and $\vec{C}$, $\vec{A}\cdot(\vec{B}\times\vec{C}) = (\vec{A}\times\vec{B})\cdot\vec{C}$. (b) Calculate $(\vec{A}\times\vec{B})\cdot\vec{C}$ for the three vectors $\vec{A}$ with magnitude $A = 5.00$ and angle $\theta_A = 26.0°$ measured in the sense from the $+x$-axis toward the $+y$-axis, $\vec{B}$ with $B = 4.00$ and $\theta_B = 63.0°$, and $\vec{C}$ with magnitude 6.00 and in the $+z$-direction. Vectors $\vec{A}$ and $\vec{B}$ are in the xy-plane.

Challenge Problems

1.98. The length of a rectangle is given as $L \pm l$ and its width as $W \pm w$. (a) Show that the uncertainty in its area A is $a = Lw + lW$. Assume that the uncertainties l and w are small, so that the product lw is very small and you can ignore it. (b) Show that the fractional uncertainty in the area is equal to the sum of the fractional uncertainty in length and the fractional uncertainty in width. (c) A rectangular solid has dimensions $L \pm l$, $W \pm w$, and $H \pm h$. Find the fractional uncertainty in the volume, and show that it equals the sum of the fractional uncertainties in the length, width, and height.

1.99. Completed Pass. At Enormous State University (ESU), the football team records its plays using vector displacements, with the origin taken to be the position of the ball before the play starts. In a certain pass play, the receiver starts at $+1.0\hat{\imath} - 5.0\hat{\jmath}$, where the units are yards, $\hat{\imath}$ is to the right, and $\hat{\jmath}$ is downfield. Subsequent displacements of the receiver are $+9.0\hat{\imath}$ (in motion before the snap), $+11.0\hat{\jmath}$ (breaks downfield), $-6.0\hat{\imath} + 4.0\hat{\jmath}$ (zigs), and $+12.0\hat{\imath} + 18.0\hat{\jmath}$ (zags). Meanwhile, the quarterback has dropped straight back to a position $-7.0\hat{\jmath}$. How far and in which direction must the quarterback throw the ball? (Like the coach, you will be well advised to diagram the situation before solving it numerically.)

1.100. Navigating in the Solar System. The *Mars Polar Lander* spacecraft was launched on January 3, 1999. On December 3, 1999, the day that *Mars Polar Lander* touched down on the Martian surface, the positions of the earth and Mars were given by these coordinates:

	x	y	z
Earth	0.3182 AU	0.9329 AU	0.0000 AU
Mars	1.3087 AU	−0.4423 AU	−0.0414 AU

In these coordinates, the sun is at the origin and the plane of the earth's orbit is the xy-plane. The earth passes through the $+x$-axis once a year on the autumnal equinox, the first day of autumn in the northern hemisphere (on or about September 22). One AU, or *astronomical unit,* is equal to 1.496×10^8 km, the average distance from the earth to the sun. (a) In a diagram, show the positions of the sun, the earth, and Mars on December 3, 1999. (b) Find the following distances in AU on December 3, 1999: (i) from the sun to the earth; (ii) from the sun to Mars; (iii) from the earth to Mars. (c) As seen from the earth, what was the angle between the direction to the sun and the direction to Mars on December 3, 1999? (d) Explain whether Mars was visible from your location at midnight on December 3, 1999. (When it is midnight at your location, the sun is on the opposite side of the earth from you.)

1.101. Navigating in the Big Dipper. All the stars of the Big Dipper (part of the constellation Ursa Major) may appear to be the same distance from the earth, but in fact they are very far from each other. Figure 1.44 shows the distances from the earth to each of these stars. The distances are given in light years (ly), the distance that light travels in one year. One light year equals 9.461×10^{15} m. (a) Alkaid and Merak are 25.6° apart in the earth's sky. In a diagram, show the relative positions of Alkaid, Merak, and our sun. Find the distance in light years from Alkaid to Merak. (b) To an inhabitant of a planet orbiting Merak, how many degrees apart in the sky would Alkaid and our sun be?

Figure 1.44 Challenge Problem 1.101.

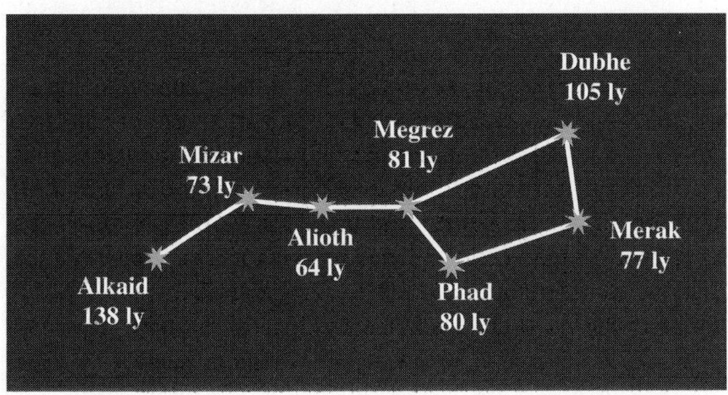

1.102. The vector $\vec{r} = x\hat{\imath} + y\hat{\jmath} + z\hat{k}$, called the *position vector*, points from the origin $(0, 0, 0)$ to an arbitrary point in space with coordinates (x, y, z). Use what you know about vectors to prove the following: All points (x, y, z) that satisfy the equation $Ax + By + Cz = 0$, where A, B, and C are constants, lie in a plane that passes through the origin and that is perpendicular to the vector $A\hat{\imath} + B\hat{\jmath} + C\hat{k}$. Sketch this vector and the plane.

2 MOTION ALONG A STRAIGHT LINE

LEARNING GOALS

By studying this chapter, you will learn:

- How to describe straight-line motion in terms of average velocity, instantaneous velocity, average acceleration, and instantaneous acceleration.
- How to interpret graphs of position versus time, velocity versus time, and acceleration versus time for straight-line motion.
- How to solve problems involving straight-line motion with constant acceleration, including free-fall problems.
- How to analyze straight-line motion when the acceleration is not constant.

? A typical sprinter speeds up during the first third of a race and slows gradually over the rest of the course. Is it accurate to say that a sprinter is *accelerating* as he slows during the final two-thirds of the race?

What distance must an airliner travel down a runway before reaching takeoff speed? When you throw a baseball straight up in the air, how high does it go? When a glass slips from your hand, how much time do you have to catch it before it hits the floor? These are the kinds of questions you will learn to answer in this chapter. We are beginning our study of physics with *mechanics,* the study of the relationships among force, matter, and motion. In this chapter and the next we will study *kinematics,* the part of mechanics that enables us to describe motion. Later we will study *dynamics,* which relates motion to its causes.

In this chapter we concentrate on the simplest kind of motion: a body moving along a straight line. To describe this motion, we introduce the physical quantities *velocity* and *acceleration.* These quantities have simple definitions in physics; however, those definitions are more precise and slightly different than the ones used in everyday language. An important part of how a physicist defines velocity and acceleration is that these quantities are *vectors.* As you learned in Chapter 1, this means that they have both magnitude and direction. Our concern in this chapter is with motion along a straight line only, so we won't need the full mathematics of vectors just yet. But using vectors will be essential in Chapter 3 when we consider motion in two or three dimensions.

We'll develop simple equations to describe straight-line motion in the important special case when the acceleration is constant. An example is the motion of a freely falling body. We'll also consider situations in which the acceleration varies during the motion; in this case, it's necessary to use integration to describe the motion. (If you haven't studied integration yet, Section 2.6 is optional.)

2.1 Displacement, Time, and Average Velocity

Suppose a drag racer drives her AA-fuel dragster along a straight track (Fig. 2.1). To study the dragster's motion, we need a coordinate system. We choose the x-axis to lie along the dragster's straight-line path, with the origin O at the starting line. We also choose a point on the dragster, such as its front end, and represent the entire dragster by that point. Hence we treat the dragster as a **particle.**

A useful way to describe the motion of the particle—that is, the point that represents the dragster—is in terms of the change in the particle's coordinate x over a time interval. Suppose that 1.0 s after the start the front of the dragster is at point P_1, 19 m from the origin, and 4.0 s after the start it is at point P_2, 277 m from the origin. The *displacement* of the particle is a vector that points from P_1 to P_2 (see Section 1.7). Figure 2.1 shows that this vector points along the x-axis. The x-component of the displacement is just the change in the value of x, $(277\text{ m} - 19\text{ m}) = 258\text{ m}$, that took place during the time interval of $(4.0\text{ s} - 1.0\text{ s}) = 3.0\text{ s}$. We define the dragster's **average velocity** during this time interval as a *vector* quantity whose x-component is the change in x divided by the time interval: $(258\text{ m})/(3.0\text{ s}) = 86\text{ m/s}$.

In general, the average velocity depends on the particular time interval chosen. For a 3.0-s time interval *before* the start of the race, the average velocity would be zero because the dragster would be at rest at the starting line and would have zero displacement.

Let's generalize the concept of average velocity. At time t_1 the dragster is at point P_1, with coordinate x_1, and at time t_2 it is at point P_2, with coordinate x_2. The displacement of the dragster during the time interval from t_1 to t_2 is the vector from P_1 to P_2. The x-component of the displacement, denoted Δx, is just the change in the coordinate x:

$$\Delta x = x_2 - x_1 \tag{2.1}$$

The dragster moves along the x-axis only, so the y- and z-components of the displacement are equal to zero.

CAUTION The meaning of Δx Note that Δx is *not* the product of Δ and x; it is a single symbol that means "the change in the quantity x." We always use the Greek capital letter Δ (delta) to represent a *change* in a quantity, equal to the *final* value of the quantity minus the *initial* value—never the reverse. Likewise, the time interval from t_1 to t_2 is Δt, the change in the quantity t: $\Delta t = t_2 - t_1$ (final time minus initial time).

The x-component of average velocity, or **average x-velocity,** is the x-component of displacement, Δx, divided by the time interval Δt during which the displacement occurs. We use the symbol $v_{av\text{-}x}$ for average x-velocity (the

2.1 Positions of a dragster at two times during its run.

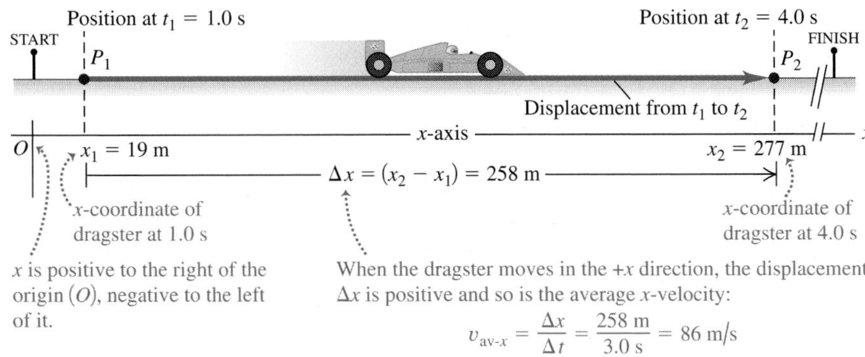
Position at $t_1 = 1.0$ s
Position at $t_2 = 4.0$ s
START
FINISH
P_1
P_2
Displacement from t_1 to t_2
x-axis
x
O
$x_1 = 19$ m
$x_2 = 277$ m
$\Delta x = (x_2 - x_1) = 258$ m
x-coordinate of dragster at 1.0 s
x-coordinate of dragster at 4.0 s
x is positive to the right of the origin (O), negative to the left of it.
When the dragster moves in the $+x$ direction, the displacement Δx is positive and so is the average x-velocity:
$v_{av\text{-}x} = \frac{\Delta x}{\Delta t} = \frac{258\text{ m}}{3.0\text{ s}} = 86\text{ m/s}$

subscript "av" signifies average value and the subscript x indicates that this is the x-component):

$$v_{\text{av-}x} = \frac{x_2 - x_1}{t_2 - t_1} = \frac{\Delta x}{\Delta t} \quad \text{(average } x\text{-velocity, straight-line motion)} \quad (2.2)$$

As an example, for the dragster $x_1 = 19$ m, $x_2 = 277$ m, $t_1 = 1.0$ s, and $t_2 = 4.0$ s, so Eq. (2.2) gives

$$v_{\text{av-}x} = \frac{277\text{ m} - 19\text{ m}}{4.0\text{ s} - 1.0\text{ s}} = \frac{258\text{ m}}{3.0\text{ s}} = 86\text{ m/s}$$

The average x-velocity of the dragster is positive. This means that during the time interval, the coordinate x increased and the dragster moved in the positive x-direction (to the right in Fig. 2.1).

If a particle moves in the *negative* x-direction during a time interval, its average velocity for that time interval is negative. For example, suppose an official's truck moves to the left along the track (Fig. 2.2). The truck is at $x_1 = 277$ m at $t_1 = 16.0$ s and is at $x_2 = 19$ m at $t_2 = 25.0$ s. Then $\Delta x = (19\text{ m} - 277\text{ m}) = -258$ m and $\Delta t = (25.0\text{ s} - 16.0\text{ s}) = 9.0$ s. The x-component of average velocity is $v_{\text{av-}x} = \Delta x/\Delta t = (-258\text{ m})/(9.0\text{ s}) = -29$ m/s.

Here are some simple rules for the average x-velocity. **Whenever x is positive and increasing or is negative and becoming less negative, the particle is moving in the $+x$-direction and $v_{\text{av-}x}$ is positive** (Fig. 2.1). **Whenever x is positive and decreasing or is negative and becoming more negative, the particle is moving in the $-x$-direction and $v_{\text{av-}x}$ is negative** (Fig. 2.2).

CAUTION **Choice of the positive x-direction** You might be tempted to conclude that positive average x-velocity must mean motion to the right, as in Fig. 2.1, and that negative average x-velocity must mean motion to the left, as in Fig. 2.2. But that's correct *only* if the positive x-direction is to the right, as we chose it to be in Figs. 2.1 and 2.2. Had we chosen the positive x-direction to be to the left, with the origin at the finish line, the dragster would have negative average x-velocity and the official's truck would have positive average x-velocity. In most problems the direction of the coordinate axis will be yours to choose. Once you've made your choice, you *must* take it into account when interpreting the signs of $v_{\text{av-}x}$ and other quantities that describe motion!

With straight-line motion we sometimes call Δx simply the displacement and $v_{\text{av-}x}$ simply the average velocity. But be sure to remember that these are really the x-components of vector quantities that, in this special case, have *only* x-components. In Chapter 3, displacement, velocity, and acceleration vectors will have two or three nonzero components.

Figure 2.3 is a graph of the dragster's position as a function of time—that is, an ***x-t* graph.** The curve in the figure *does not* represent the dragster's path in space; as Fig. 2.1 shows, the path is a straight line. Rather, the graph is a pictorial way to represent how the dragster's position changes with time. The points p_1

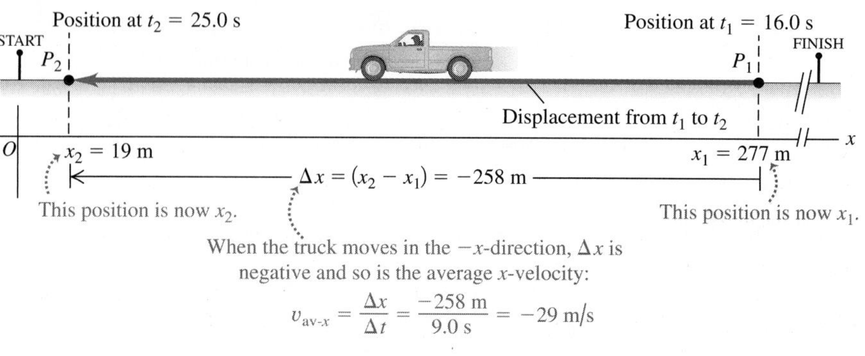

2.2 Positions of an official's truck at two times during its motion. The points P_1 and P_2 now indicate the positions of the truck, and so are the reverse of Fig. 2.1.

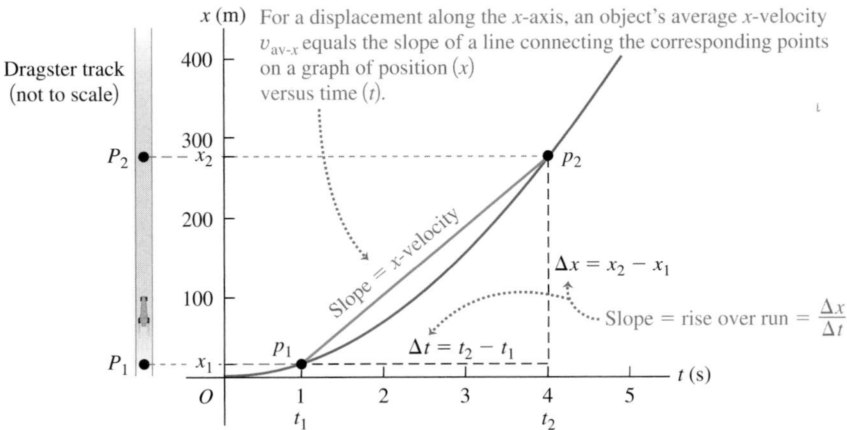

2.3 The position of a dragster as a function of time.

and p_2 on the graph correspond to the points P_1 and P_2 along the dragster's path. Line p_1p_2 is the hypotenuse of a right triangle with vertical side $\Delta x = x_2 - x_1$ and horizontal side $\Delta t = t_2 - t_1$. The average x-velocity $v_{av\text{-}x} = \Delta x/\Delta t$ of the dragster equals the *slope* of the line p_1p_2—that is, the ratio of the triangle's vertical side Δx to its horizontal side Δt.

The average x-velocity depends only on the total displacement $\Delta x = x_2 - x_1$ that occurs during the time interval $\Delta t = t_2 - t_1$, not on the details of what happens during the time interval. At time t_1 a motorcycle might have raced past the dragster at point P_1 in Fig. 2.1, then blown its engine and slowed down to pass through point P_2 at the same time t_2 as the dragster. Both vehicles have the same displacement during the same time interval and so have the same average x-velocity.

If distance is given in meters and time in seconds, average velocity is measured in meters per second (m/s). Other common units of velocity are kilometers per hour (km/h), feet per second (ft/s), miles per hour (mi/h), and knots (1 knot = 1 nautical mile/h = 6080 ft/h). Table 2.1 lists some typical velocity magnitudes.

Table 2.1 Typical Velocity Magnitudes

A snail's pace	10^{-3} m/s
A brisk walk	2 m/s
Fastest human	11 m/s
Running cheetah	35 m/s
Fastest car	341 m/s
Random motion of air molecules	500 m/s
Fastest airplane	1000 m/s
Orbiting communications satellite	3000 m/s
Electron orbiting in a hydrogen atom	2×10^6 m/s
Light traveling in a vacuum	3×10^8 m/s

Test Your Understanding of Section 2.1 Each of the following automobile trips takes one hour. The positive x-direction is to the east. (i) Automobile A travels 50 km due east. (ii) Automobile B travels 50 km due west. (iii) Automobile C travels 60 km due east, then turns around and travels 10 km due west. (iv) Automobile D travels 70 km due east. (v) Automobile E travels 20 km due west, then turns around and travels 20 km due east. (a) Rank the five trips in order of average x-velocity from most positive to most negative. (b) Which trips, if any, have the same average x-velocity? (c) For which trip, if any, is the average x-velocity equal to zero?

2.2 Instantaneous Velocity

Sometimes the average velocity is all you need to know about a particle's motion. For example, a race along a straight line is really a competition to see whose average velocity, $v_{av\text{-}x}$, has the greatest magnitude. The prize goes to the competitor who can travel the displacement Δx from the start to the finish line in the shortest time interval, Δt (Fig. 2.4).

But the average velocity of a particle during a time interval can't tell us how fast, or in what direction, the particle was moving at any given time during the interval. To do this we need to know the velocity at any specific instant of time or specific point along the path. This is called **instantaneous velocity,** and it needs to be defined carefully.

CAUTION How long is an instant? Note that the word "instant" has a somewhat different definition in physics than in everyday language. You might use the phrase "It lasted just an instant" to refer to something that lasted for a very short time interval. But in physics an instant has no duration at all; it refers to a single value of time.

2.4 The winner of a 50-m swimming race is the swimmer whose average velocity has the greatest magnitude—that is, the swimmer who traverses a displacement Δx of 50 m in the shortest elapsed time Δt.

2.5 Even when he's moving forward, this cyclist's instantaneous x-velocity can be negative—if he's traveling in the negative x-direction. In any problem, the choice of which direction is positive and which is negative is entirely up to you.

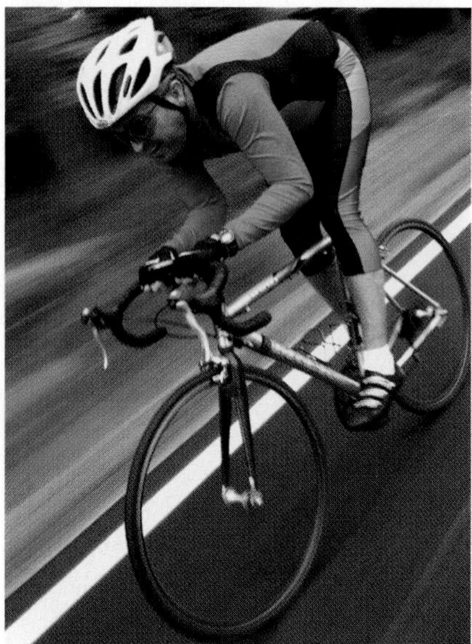

To find the instantaneous velocity of the dragster in Fig. 2.1 at the point P_1, we move the second point P_2 closer and closer to the first point P_1 and compute the average velocity $v_{\text{av-}x} = \Delta x/\Delta t$ over the ever-shorter displacement and time interval. Both Δx and Δt become very small, but their ratio does not necessarily become small. In the language of calculus, the limit of $\Delta x/\Delta t$ as Δt approaches zero is called the **derivative** of x with respect to t and is written dx/dt. *The instantaneous velocity is the limit of the average velocity as the time interval approaches zero; it equals the instantaneous rate of change of position with time.* We use the symbol v_x, with no "av" subscript, for the instantaneous velocity along the x-axis, or the **instantaneous x-velocity:**

$$v_x = \lim_{\Delta t \to 0} \frac{\Delta x}{\Delta t} = \frac{dx}{dt} \quad \text{(instantaneous } x\text{-velocity, straight-line motion)} \quad (2.3)$$

The time interval Δt is always positive, so v_x has the same algebraic sign as Δx. A positive value of v_x means that x is increasing and the motion is in the positive x-direction; a negative value of v_x means that x is decreasing and the motion is in the negative x-direction. A body can have positive x and negative v_x, or the reverse; x tells us where the body is, while v_x tells us how it's moving (Fig. 2.5).

Instantaneous velocity, like average velocity, is a vector quantity; Eq. (2.3) defines its x-component. In straight-line motion, all other components of instantaneous velocity are zero. In this case we often call v_x simply the instantaneous velocity. (In Chapter 3 we'll deal with the general case in which the instantaneous velocity can have nonzero x-, y-, and z-components.) When we use the term "velocity," we will always mean instantaneous rather than average velocity.

The terms "velocity" and "speed" are used interchangeably in everyday language, but they have distinct definitions in physics. We use the term **speed** to denote distance traveled divided by time, on either an average or an instantaneous basis. We use the symbol v with *no* subscripts to denote instantaneous speed. Instantaneous *speed* measures how fast a particle is moving; instantaneous *velocity* measures how fast *and* in what direction it's moving. For example, a particle with instantaneous velocity $v_x = 25$ m/s and a second particle with $v_x = -25$ m/s are moving in opposite directions at the same instantaneous speed 25 m/s. Instantaneous speed is the magnitude of instantaneous velocity, and so instantaneous speed can never be negative.

CAUTION **Average speed and average velocity** Average speed is *not* the magnitude of average velocity. When Alexander Popov set a world record in 1994 by swimming 100.0 m in 46.74 s, his average speed was $(100.0\text{ m})/(46.74\text{ s}) = 2.139$ m/s. But because he swam two lengths in a 50-m pool, he started and ended at the same point and so had zero total displacement and zero average *velocity!* Both average speed and instantaneous speed are scalars, not vectors, because these quantities contain no information about direction.

Example 2.1 Average and instantaneous velocities

A cheetah is crouched 20 m to the east of an observer's vehicle (Fig. 2.6a). At time $t = 0$ the cheetah charges an antelope and begins to run along a straight line. During the first 2.0 s of the attack, the cheetah's coordinate x varies with time according to the equation $x = 20\text{ m} + (5.0\text{ m/s}^2)t^2$. (a) Find the displacement of the cheetah between $t_1 = 1.0$ s and $t_2 = 2.0$ s. (b) Find the average velocity during the same time interval. (c) Find the instantaneous velocity at time $t_1 = 1.0$ s by taking $\Delta t = 0.1$ s, then $\Delta t = 0.01$ s, then $\Delta t = 0.001$ s. (d) Derive a general expression for the instantaneous velocity as a function of time, and from it find v_x at $t = 1.0$ s and $t = 2.0$ s.

SOLUTION

IDENTIFY: We use the definitions of displacement, average velocity, and instantaneous velocity. Using the first two of these involves algebra; the last one requires using calculus to take a derivative.

SET UP: Figure 2.6b shows our sketch of the cheetah's motion. To analyze this problem we use Eq. (2.1) for displacement, Eq. (2.2) for average velocity, and Eq. (2.3) for instantaneous velocity.

EXECUTE: (a) At time $t_1 = 1.0\text{ s}$ the cheetah's position x_1 is

$$x_1 = 20\text{ m} + (5.0\text{ m/s}^2)(1.0\text{ s})^2 = 25\text{ m}$$

At time $t_2 = 2.0\text{ s}$ its position x_2 is

$$x_2 = 20\text{ m} + (5.0\text{ m/s}^2)(2.0\text{ s})^2 = 40\text{ m}$$

The displacement during this interval is

$$\Delta x = x_2 - x_1 = 40\text{ m} - 25\text{ m} = 15\text{ m}$$

(b) The average x-velocity during this time interval is

$$v_{\text{av-}x} = \frac{x_2 - x_1}{t_2 - t_1} = \frac{40\text{ m} - 25\text{ m}}{2.0\text{ s} - 1.0\text{ s}} = \frac{15\text{ m}}{1.0\text{ s}} = 15\text{ m/s}$$

(c) With $\Delta t = 0.1\text{ s}$, the time interval is from $t_1 = 1.0\text{ s}$ to $t_2 = 1.1\text{ s}$. At time t_2, the position is

$$x_2 = 20\text{ m} + (5.0\text{ m/s}^2)(1.1\text{ s})^2 = 26.05\text{ m}$$

The average x-velocity during this interval is

$$v_{\text{av-}x} = \frac{26.05\text{ m} - 25\text{ m}}{1.1\text{ s} - 1.0\text{ s}} = 10.5\text{ m/s}$$

You should follow this same pattern to work out the average x-velocities for the 0.01-s and 0.001-s intervals. The results are 10.05 m/s and 10.005 m/s. As Δt gets smaller, the average x-velocity gets closer to 10.0 m/s, so we conclude that the instantaneous x-velocity at time $t = 1.0\text{ s}$ is 10.0 m/s.

(d) To find the instantaneous x-velocity as a function of time, take the derivative of the expression for x with respect to t. The derivative of a constant is zero, and for any n the derivative of t^n is nt^{n-1}, so the derivative of t^2 is $2t$. Therefore

$$v_x = \frac{dx}{dt} = (5.0\text{ m/s}^2)(2t) = (10\text{ m/s}^2)t$$

At time $t = 1.0\text{ s}$, $v_x = 10\text{ m/s}$ as we found in part (c). At time $t = 2.0\text{ s}$, $v_x = 20\text{ m/s}$.

EVALUATE: Our results show that the cheetah picked up speed from $t = 0$ (when it was at rest) to $t = 1.0\text{ s}$ $(v_x = 10\text{ m/s})$ to $t = 2.0\text{ s}$ $(v_x = 20\text{ m/s})$. This makes sense; the cheetah covered only 5 m during the interval $t = 0$ to $t = 1.0\text{ s}$, but covered 15 m during the interval $t = 1.0\text{ s}$ to $t = 2.0\text{ s}$.

2.6 A cheetah attacking an antelope from ambush. The animals are not drawn to the same scale as the axis.

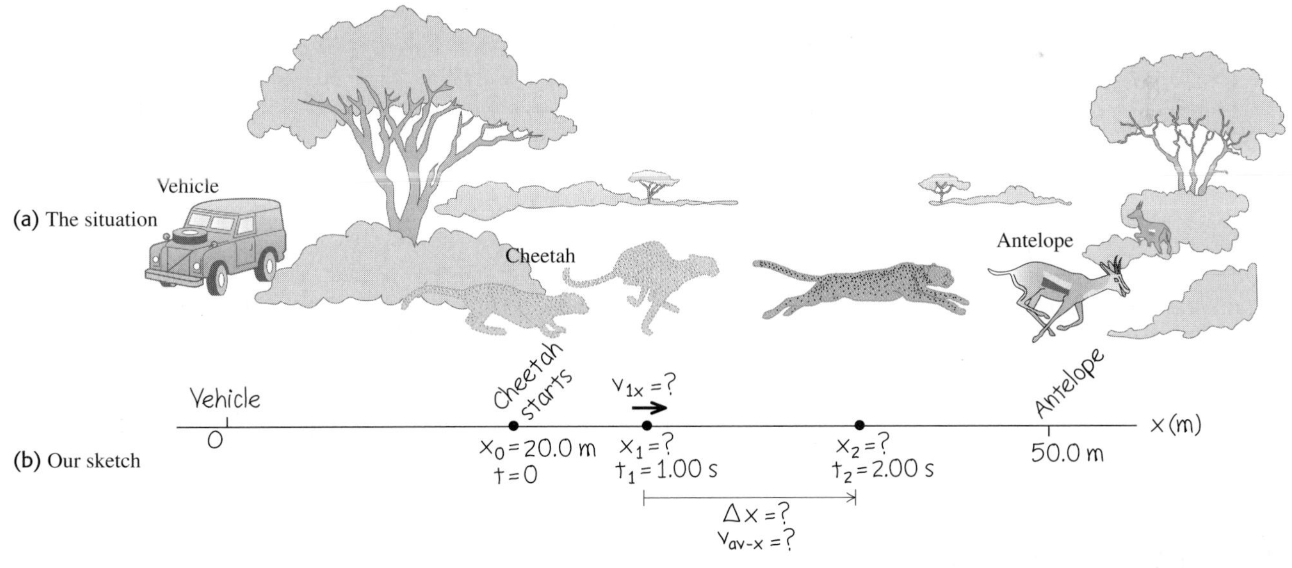

(a) The situation
Vehicle
Cheetah
Antelope
(b) Our sketch
Vehicle
Cheetah starts
v_{1x} = ?
Antelope
x (m)
O
x_0 = 20.0 m
t = 0
x_1 = ?
t_1 = 1.00 s
x_2 = ?
t_2 = 2.00 s
50.0 m
Δx = ?
$v_{av\text{-}x}$ = ?
(c) Our thinking
1 We draw an axis. We point it in the direction the cheetah runs, so that our values will be positive.
2 We choose to place the origin at the vehicle.
3 We mark the initial positions of the cheetah and the antelope. (We won't use the antelope's position—but we don't know that yet.)
4 We're interested in the cheetah's motion between 1 s and 2 s after it begins running. We place dots to represent those points.
5 We add symbols for known and unknown quantities. We use subscripts 1 and 2 for the points at t = 1 s and t = 2 s.

ActivPhysics ONLINE

1.1 Analyzing Motion Using Diagrams

Finding Velocity on an x-t Graph

The x-velocity of a particle can also be found from the graph of its position as a function of time. Suppose we want to find the x-velocity of the dragster in Fig. 2.1 at point P_1. As point P_2 in Fig. 2.1 approaches point P_1, point p_2 in the x-t graphs of Figs. 2.7a and 2.7b approaches point p_1 and the average x-velocity is calculated over shorter time intervals Δt. In the limit that $\Delta t \rightarrow 0$, shown in Fig. 2.7c, the slope of the line p_1p_2 equals the slope of the line tangent to the curve at point p_1. Thus, *on a graph of position as a function of time for straight-line motion, the instantaneous x-velocity at any point is equal to the slope of the tangent to the curve at that point.*

If the tangent to the x-t curve slopes upward to the right, as in Fig. 2.7c, then its slope is positive, the x-velocity is positive, and the motion is in the positive x-direction. If the tangent slopes downward to the right, the slope of the x-t graph and the x-velocity are negative, and the motion is in the negative x-direction. When the tangent is horizontal, the slope and the x-velocity are zero. Figure 2.8 illustrates these three possibilities.

Figure 2.8 actually depicts the motion of a particle in two ways: as (a) an x-t graph and (b) a **motion diagram.** A motion diagram shows the particle's posi-

2.7 Using an x-t graph to go from (a), (b) average x-velocity to (c) instantaneous x-velocity v_x. In (c) we find the slope of the tangent to the x-t curve by dividing any vertical interval (with distance units) along the tangent by the corresponding horizontal interval (with time units).

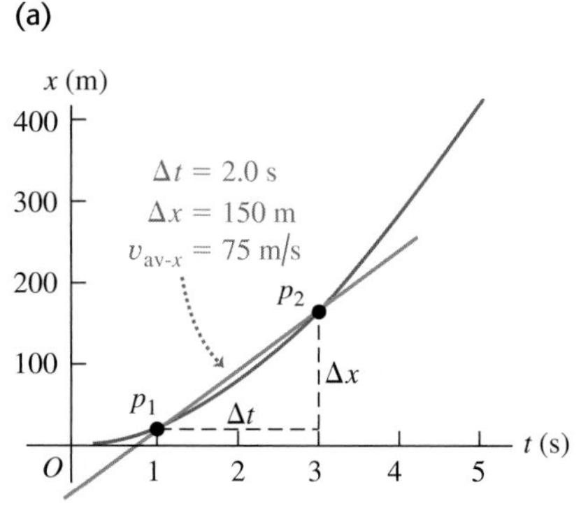

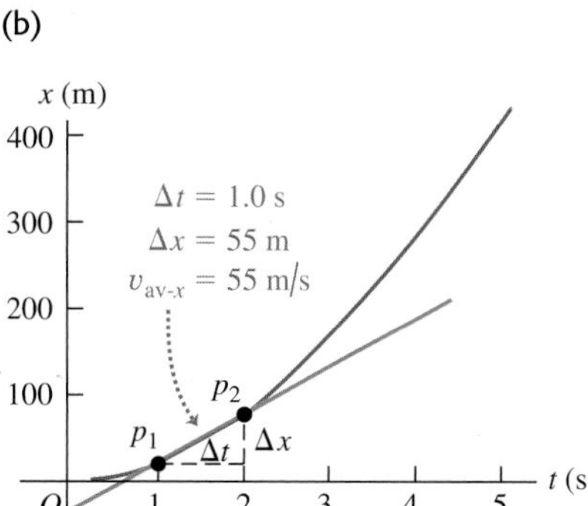

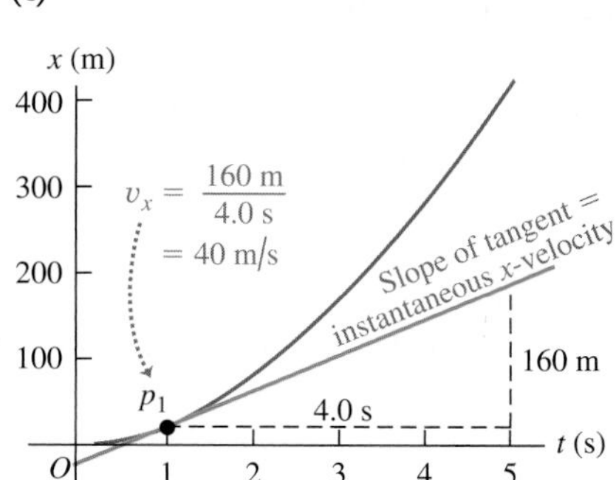

2.8 (a) The x-t graph of the motion of a particular particle. The slope of the tangent at any point equals the velocity at that point. (b) A motion diagram showing the position and velocity of the particle at each of the times labeled on the x-t graph.

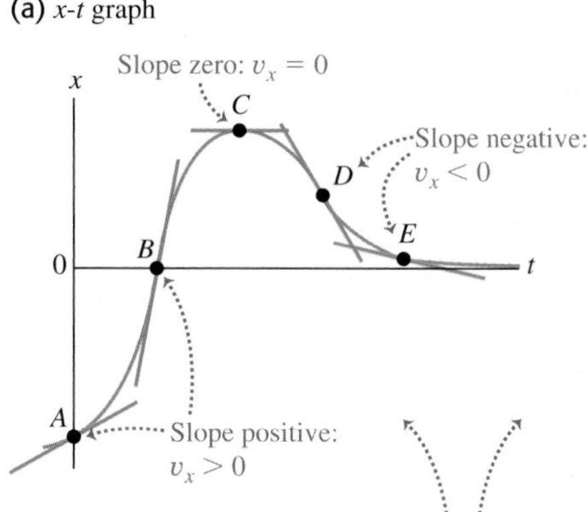

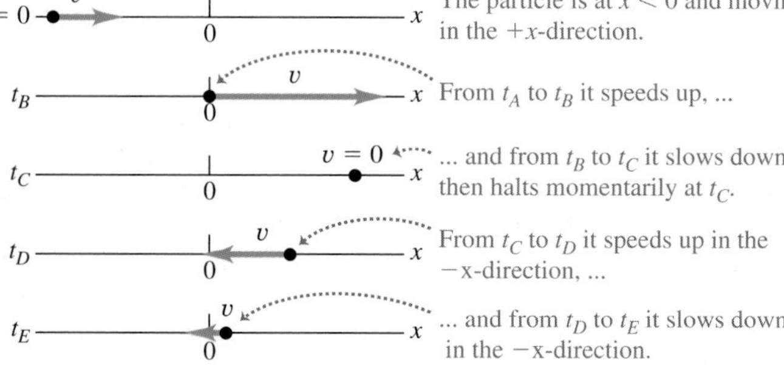

The steeper the slope (positive or negative) of an object's x-t graph, the greater is the object's speed in the positive or negative x-direction.

tion at various times (like frames from a video of the particle's motion) as well as arrows to represent the particle's velocity at each instant. We will use both *x-t* graphs and motion diagrams in this chapter to help you understand motion. You will find it worth your while to draw *both* an *x-t* graph and a motion diagram as part of solving any problem involving motion.

Test Your Understanding of Section 2.2 Figure 2.9 is an *x-t* graph of the motion of a particle. (a) Rank the values of the particle's *x*-velocity v_x at the points *P*, *Q*, *R*, and *S* from most positive to most negative. (b) At which points is v_x positive? (c) At which points is v_x negative? (d) At which points is v_x zero? (e) Rank the values of the particle's *speed* at the points *P*, *Q*, *R*, and *S* from fastest to slowest.

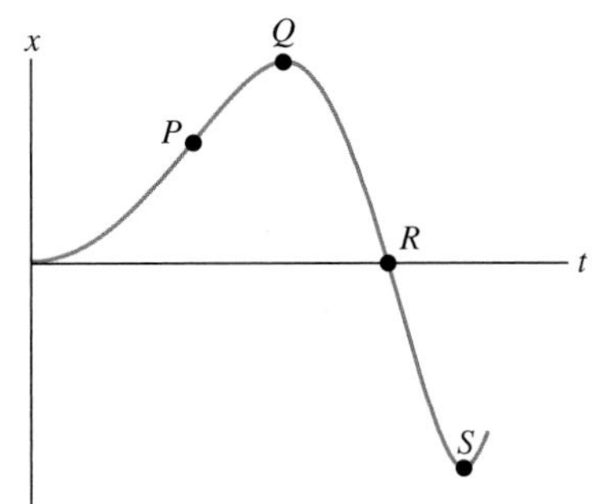

2.9 An *x-t* graph for a particle.

2.3 Average and Instantaneous Acceleration

Just as velocity describes the rate of change of position with time, *acceleration* describes the rate of change of velocity with time. Like velocity, acceleration is a vector quantity. When the motion is along a straight line, its only nonzero component is along that line. As we'll see, acceleration in straight-line motion can refer to either speeding up or slowing down.

Average Acceleration

Let's consider again a particle moving along the *x*-axis. Suppose that at time t_1 the particle is at point P_1 and has *x*-component of (instantaneous) velocity v_{1x}, and at a later time t_2 it is at point P_2 and has *x*-component of velocity v_{2x}. So the *x*-component of velocity changes by an amount $\Delta v_x = v_{2x} - v_{1x}$ during the time interval $\Delta t = t_2 - t_1$.

We define the **average acceleration** of the particle as it moves from P_1 to P_2 to be a vector quantity whose *x*-component $a_{\text{av-}x}$ (called the **average *x*-acceleration**) equals Δv_x, the change in the *x*-component of velocity, divided by the time interval Δt:

$$a_{\text{av-}x} = \frac{v_{2x} - v_{1x}}{t_2 - t_1} = \frac{\Delta v_x}{\Delta t} \qquad \text{(average } x\text{-acceleration, straight-line motion)} \tag{2.4}$$

For straight-line motion along the *x*-axis we will often call $a_{\text{av-}x}$ simply the average acceleration. (We'll encounter the other components of the average acceleration vector in Chapter 3.)

If we express velocity in meters per second and time in seconds, then average acceleration is in meters per second per second, or $(\text{m/s})/\text{s}$. This is usually written as m/s^2 and is read "meters per second squared."

CAUTION **Acceleration vs. velocity** Be very careful not to confuse acceleration with velocity! Velocity describes how a body's position changes with time; it tells us how fast and in what direction the body moves. Acceleration describes how the velocity changes with time; it tells us how the speed and direction of motion are changing. It may help to remember the phrase "acceleration is to velocity as velocity is to position." It can also help to imagine yourself riding along with the moving body. If the body accelerates forward and gains speed, you would feel pushed backward in your seat; if it accelerates backward and loses speed, you would feel pushed forward. If the velocity is constant and there's no acceleration, you would feel neither sensation. (We'll see the reason for these sensations in Chapter 4.)

Example 2.2 Average acceleration

An astronaut has left an orbiting spacecraft to test a new personal maneuvering unit. As she moves along a straight line, her partner on the spacecraft measures her velocity every 2.0 s, starting at time $t = 1.0$ s:

t	v_x	t	v_x
1.0 s	0.8 m/s	9.0 s	−0.4 m/s
3.0 s	1.2 m/s	11.0 s	−1.0 m/s
5.0 s	1.6 m/s	13.0 s	−1.6 m/s
7.0 s	1.2 m/s	15.0 s	−0.8 m/s

Find the average x-acceleration, and describe whether the speed of the astronaut increases or decreases, for each of these time intervals: (a) $t_1 = 1.0$ s to $t_2 = 3.0$ s; (b) $t_1 = 5.0$ s to $t_2 = 7.0$ s; (c) $t_1 = 9.0$ s to $t_2 = 11.0$ s; (d) $t_1 = 13.0$ s to $t_2 = 15.0$ s.

SOLUTION

IDENTIFY: We'll need the definition of average acceleration $a_{av\text{-}x}$. To find the changes in speed, we'll use the idea that speed v is the magnitude of the instantaneous velocity v_x.

SET UP: Figure 2.10 shows our graphs. We use Eq. (2.4) to find the value of $a_{av\text{-}x}$ from the change in *velocity* for each time interval.

EXECUTE: In the upper part of Fig. 2.10, we graph the x-velocity as a function of time. On this v_x-t graph, the slope of the line connecting the points at the beginning and end of each interval equals the average x-acceleration $a_{av\text{-}x} = \Delta v_x/\Delta t$ for that interval. In the lower part of Fig. 2.10, we graph the values of $a_{av\text{-}x}$. We find:

(a) $a_{av\text{-}x} = (1.2\text{ m/s} - 0.8\text{ m/s})/(3.0\text{ s} - 1.0\text{ s}) = 0.2\text{ m/s}^2$. The speed (magnitude of instantaneous x-velocity) increases from 0.8 m/s to 1.2 m/s.

(b) $a_{av\text{-}x} = (1.2\text{ m/s} - 1.6\text{ m/s})/(7.0\text{ s} - 5.0\text{ s}) = -0.2\text{ m/s}^2$. The speed decreases from 1.6 m/s to 1.2 m/s.

(c) $a_{av\text{-}x} = [-1.0\text{ m/s} - (-0.4\text{ m/s})]/(11.0\text{ s} - 9.0\text{ s}) = -0.3\text{ m/s}^2$. The speed increases from 0.4 m/s to 1.0 m/s.

(d) $a_{av\text{-}x} = [-0.8\text{ m/s} - (-1.6\text{ m/s})]/(15.0\text{ s} - 13.0\text{ s}) = 0.4\text{ m/s}^2$. The speed decreases from 1.6 m/s to 0.8 m/s.

2.10 Our graphs of x-velocity versus time (top) and average x-acceleration versus time (bottom) for the astronaut.

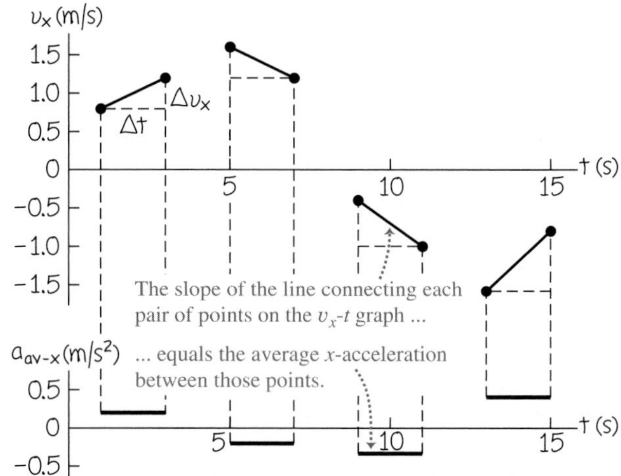

EVALUATE: Our results show that when the average x-acceleration has the *same* direction (same algebraic sign) as the initial velocity, as in intervals (a) and (c), the astronaut goes faster; when it has the *opposite* direction (opposite algebraic sign), as in intervals (b) and (d), she slows down. Thus positive x-acceleration means speeding up if the x-velocity is positive [interval (a)] but slowing down if the x-velocity is negative [interval (d)]. Similarly, negative x-acceleration means speeding up if the x-velocity is negative [interval (c)] but slowing down if the x-velocity is positive [interval (b)].

Instantaneous Acceleration

We can now define **instantaneous acceleration** following the same procedure that we used to define instantaneous velocity. As an example, suppose a race car driver is driving along a straightaway as shown in Fig. 2.11. To define the instantaneous acceleration at point P_1, we take the second point P_2 in Fig. 2.11 to be closer and closer to P_1 so that the average acceleration is computed over shorter and shorter time intervals. *The instantaneous acceleration is the limit of the average acceleration as the time interval approaches zero.* In the language of calculus, *instantaneous acceleration equals the instantaneous rate of change of velocity with time.* Thus

$$a_x = \lim_{\Delta t \to 0} \frac{\Delta v_x}{\Delta t} = \frac{dv_x}{dt} \quad \text{(instantaneous } x\text{-acceleration, straight-line motion)} \tag{2.5}$$

2.11 A Grand Prix car at two points on the straightaway.

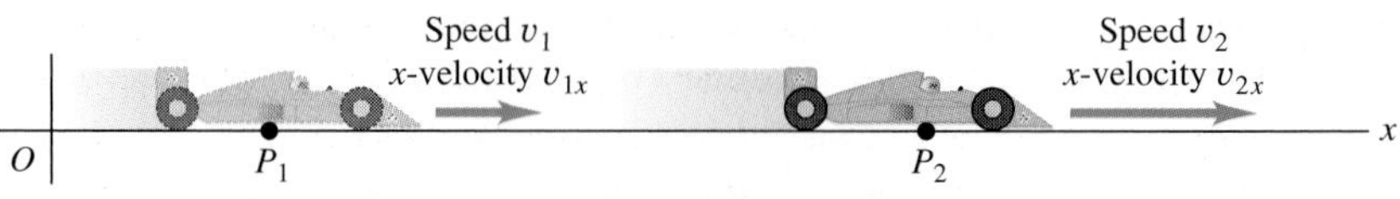

Note that a_x in Eq. (2.5) is really the x-component of the acceleration vector, or the **instantaneous x-acceleration;** in straight-line motion, all other components of this vector are zero. From now on, when we use the term "acceleration," we will always mean instantaneous acceleration, not average acceleration.

Example 2.3 Average and instantaneous accelerations

Suppose the x-velocity v_x of the car in Fig. 2.11 at any time t is given by the equation

$$v_x = 60\ \text{m/s} + (0.50\ \text{m/s}^3)t^2$$

(a) Find the change in x-velocity of the car in the time interval between $t_1 = 1.0$ s and $t_2 = 3.0$ s. (b) Find the average x-acceleration in this time interval. (c) Find the instantaneous x-acceleration at time $t_1 = 1.0$ s by taking Δt to be first 0.1 s, then 0.01 s, then 0.001 s. (d) Derive an expression for the instantaneous x-acceleration at any time, and use it to find the x-acceleration at $t = 1.0$ s and $t = 3.0$ s.

SOLUTION

IDENTIFY: This example is analogous to Example 2.1 in Section 2.2. (Now is a good time to review that example.) There we found the average x-velocity over shorter and shorter time intervals from the change in position, and we determined the instantaneous x-velocity by differentiating the position as a function of time. In this example, we find the *average* x-acceleration from the change in x-velocity over a time interval. Likewise, we find the *instantaneous* x-acceleration by differentiating the x-velocity as a function of time.

SET UP: We'll use Eq. (2.4) for average x-acceleration and Eq. (2.5) for instantaneous x-acceleration.

EXECUTE: (a) We first find the x-velocity at each time by substituting each value of t into the equation. At time $t_1 = 1.0$ s,

$$v_{1x} = 60\ \text{m/s} + (0.50\ \text{m/s}^3)(1.0\ \text{s})^2 = 60.5\ \text{m/s}$$

At time $t_2 = 3.0$ s,

$$v_{2x} = 60\ \text{m/s} + (0.50\ \text{m/s}^3)(3.0\ \text{s})^2 = 64.5\ \text{m/s}$$

The change in x-velocity Δv_x is

$$\Delta v_x = v_{2x} - v_{1x} = 64.5\ \text{m/s} - 60.5\ \text{m/s} = 4.0\ \text{m/s}$$

The time interval is $\Delta t = 3.0\ \text{s} - 1.0\ \text{s} = 2.0$ s.

(b) The average x-acceleration during this time interval is

$$a_{\text{av-}x} = \frac{v_{2x} - v_{1x}}{t_2 - t_1} = \frac{4.0\ \text{m/s}}{2.0\ \text{s}} = 2.0\ \text{m/s}^2$$

During the time interval from $t_1 = 1.0$ s to $t_2 = 3.0$ s, the x-velocity and average x-acceleration have the same algebraic sign (in this case, positive), and the car speeds up.

(c) When $\Delta t = 0.1$ s, $t_2 = 1.1$ s and we find

$$v_{2x} = 60\ \text{m/s} + (0.50\ \text{m/s}^3)(1.1\ \text{s})^2 = 60.605\ \text{m/s}$$
$$\Delta v_x = 0.105\ \text{m/s}$$
$$a_{\text{av-}x} = \frac{\Delta v_x}{\Delta t} = \frac{0.105\ \text{m/s}}{0.1\ \text{s}} = 1.05\ \text{m/s}^2$$

You should do these calculations for $\Delta t = 0.01$ s and $\Delta t = 0.001$ s; the results are $a_{\text{av-}x} = 1.005\ \text{m/s}^2$ and $a_{\text{av-}x} = 1.0005\ \text{m/s}^2$, respectively. As Δt gets smaller, the average x-acceleration gets closer to $1.0\ \text{m/s}^2$, so the instantaneous x-acceleration at $t = 1.0$ s is $1.0\ \text{m/s}^2$.

(d) The instantaneous x-acceleration is $a_x = dv_x/dt$. The derivative of a constant is zero and the derivative of t^2 is $2t$, so

$$a_x = \frac{dv_x}{dt} = \frac{d}{dt}[60\ \text{m/s} + (0.50\ \text{m/s}^3)t^2]$$
$$= (0.50\ \text{m/s}^3)(2t) = (1.0\ \text{m/s}^3)t$$

When $t = 1.0$ s,

$$a_x = (1.0\ \text{m/s}^3)(1.0\ \text{s}) = 1.0\ \text{m/s}^2$$

When $t = 3.0$ s,

$$a_x = (1.0\ \text{m/s}^3)(3.0\ \text{s}) = 3.0\ \text{m/s}^2$$

EVALUATE: Note that neither of the values we found in part (d) is equal to the average x-acceleration found in part (b). That's because the car's instantaneous x-acceleration varies with time. The rate of change of acceleration with time is sometimes called the "jerk."

Finding Acceleration on a v_x-t Graph or an x-t Graph

In Section 2.2 we interpreted average and instantaneous x-velocity in terms of the slope of a graph of position versus time. In the same way, we can interpret average and instantaneous x-acceleration by using a graph with instantaneous velocity v_x on the vertical axis and time t on the horizontal axis—that is, a **v_x-t graph** (Fig. 2.12). The points on the graph labeled p_1 and p_2 correspond to points P_1 and P_2 in Fig. 2.11. The average x-acceleration $a_{\text{av-}x} = \Delta v_x/\Delta t$ during this interval is the slope of the line p_1p_2. As point P_2 in Fig. 2.11 approaches point P_1, point p_2 in the v_x-t graph of Fig. 2.12 approaches point p_1, and the slope of the line p_1p_2 approaches the slope of the line tangent to the curve at point p_1. Thus, *on a graph of x-velocity as a function of time, the instantaneous x-acceleration at any point is equal to the slope of the tangent to the curve at that point.* Tangents drawn at

2.12 A v_x-t graph of the motion in Fig. 2.11.

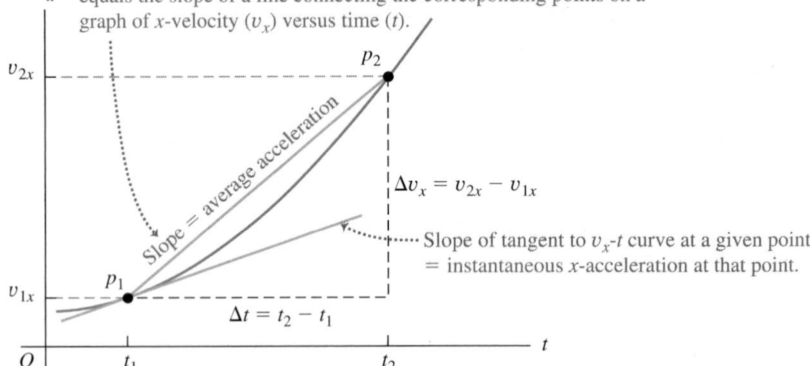
For a displacement along the x-axis, an object's average x-acceleration equals the slope of a line connecting the corresponding points on a graph of x-velocity (v_x) versus time (t).
v_x
v_{2x}
p_2
Slope = average acceleration
$\Delta v_x = v_{2x} - v_{1x}$
Slope of tangent to v_x-t curve at a given point = instantaneous x-acceleration at that point.
p_1
v_{1x}
$\Delta t = t_2 - t_1$
O
t_1
t_2
t

different points along the curve in Fig. 2.12 have different slopes, so the instantaneous x-acceleration varies with time.

CAUTION **The signs of x-acceleration and x-velocity** By itself, the algebraic sign of the x-acceleration does *not* tell you whether a body is speeding up or slowing down. You must compare the signs of the x-velocity and the x-acceleration. When v_x and a_x have the *same* sign, the body is speeding up. If both are positive, the body is moving in the positive direction with increasing speed. If both are negative, the body is moving in the negative direction with an x-velocity that is becoming more and more negative, and again the speed is increasing. When v_x and a_x have *opposite* signs, the body is slowing down. If v_x is positive and a_x is negative, the body is moving in the positive direction with decreasing speed; if v_x is negative and a_x is positive, the body is moving in the negative direction with an x-velocity that is becoming less negative, and again the body is slowing down. Figure 2.13 illustrates some of these possibilities.

The term "deceleration" is sometimes used for a decrease in speed. Because it may mean positive or negative a_x, depending on the sign of v_x, we avoid this term.

We can also learn about the acceleration of a body from a graph of its *position* versus time. Because $a_x = dv_x/dt$ and $v_x = dx/dt$, we can write

$$a_x = \frac{dv_x}{dt} = \frac{d}{dt}\left(\frac{dx}{dt}\right) = \frac{d^2x}{dt^2} \tag{2.6}$$

2.13 **(a)** A v_x-t graph of the motion of a different particle than that shown in Fig. 2.8. The slope of the tangent at any point equals the x-acceleration at that point. **(b)** A motion diagram showing the position, velocity, and acceleration of the particle at each of the times labeled on the v_x-t graph. The positions are consistent with the v_x-t graph; for instance, from t_A to t_B the velocity is negative, so at t_B the particle is at a more negative value of x than at t_A.

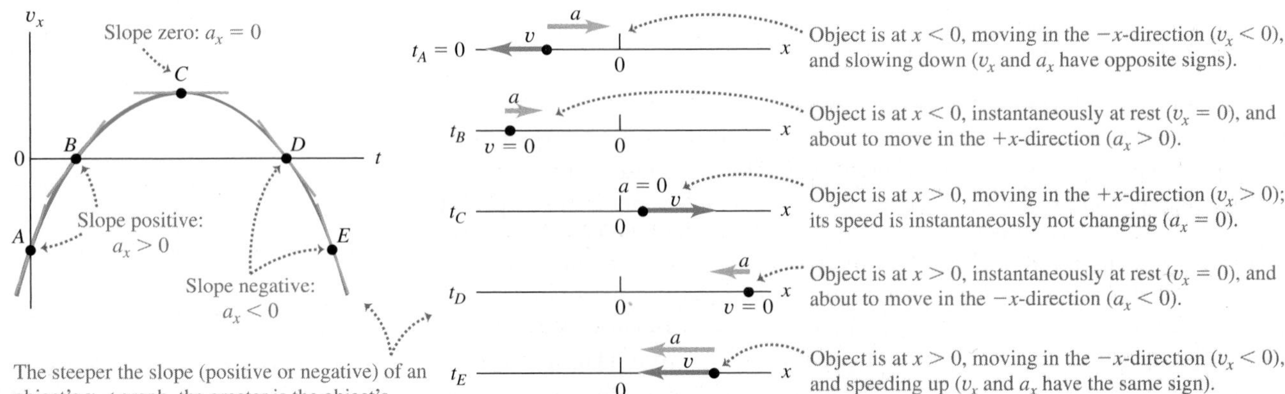
MP
(a) v_x-t graph for an object moving on the x-axis
(b) Object's position, velocity, and acceleration on the x-axis
v_x
Slope zero: $a_x = 0$
C
B
D
0
t
A
E
Slope positive: $a_x > 0$
Slope negative: $a_x < 0$
The steeper the slope (positive or negative) of an object's v_x-t graph, the greater is the object's acceleration in the positive or negative x-direction.
$t_A = 0$
t_B
t_C
t_D
t_E
a
v
$v = 0$
$a = 0$
x
0
Object is at $x < 0$, moving in the $-x$-direction ($v_x < 0$), and slowing down (v_x and a_x have opposite signs).
Object is at $x < 0$, instantaneously at rest ($v_x = 0$), and about to move in the $+x$-direction ($a_x > 0$).
Object is at $x > 0$, moving in the $+x$-direction ($v_x > 0$); its speed is instantaneously not changing ($a_x = 0$).
Object is at $x > 0$, instantaneously at rest ($v_x = 0$), and about to move in the $-x$-direction ($a_x < 0$).
Object is at $x > 0$, moving in the $-x$-direction ($v_x < 0$), and speeding up (v_x and a_x have the same sign).

2.14 (a) The same *x-t* graph as shown in Fig. 2.8a. The *x*-velocity is equal to the *slope* of the graph, and the acceleration is given by the *concavity* or *curvature* of the graph. (b) A motion diagram showing the position, velocity, and acceleration of the particle at each of the times labeled on the *x-t* graph.

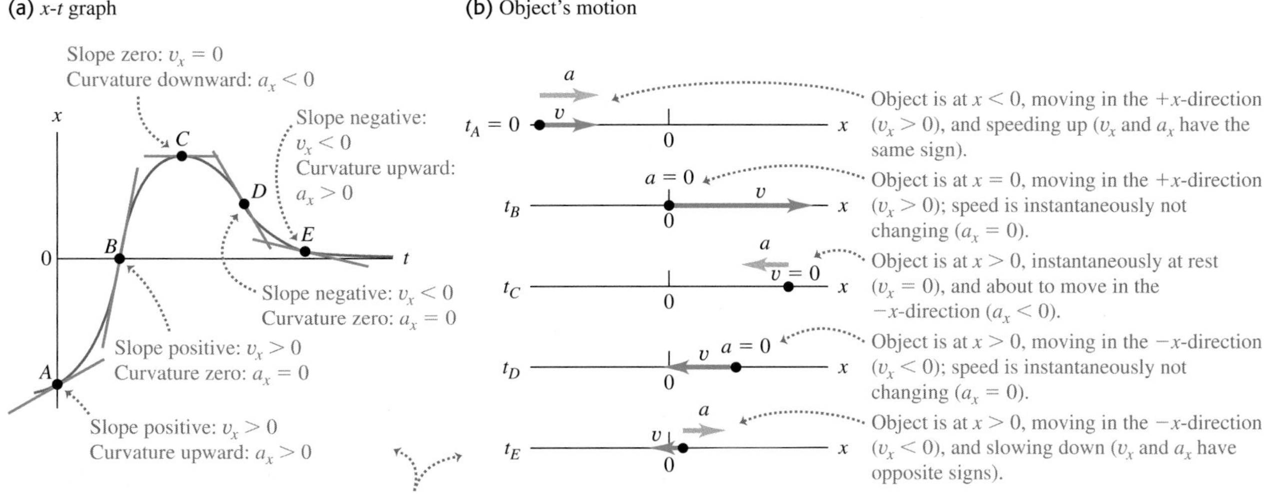

(a) x-t graph
(b) Object's motion
Slope zero: $v_x = 0$
Curvature downward: $a_x < 0$
Slope negative: $v_x < 0$
Curvature upward: $a_x > 0$
Slope negative: $v_x < 0$
Curvature zero: $a_x = 0$
Slope positive: $v_x > 0$
Curvature zero: $a_x = 0$
Slope positive: $v_x > 0$
Curvature upward: $a_x > 0$
The greater the curvature (upward or downward) of an object's x-t graph, the greater is the object's acceleration in the positive or negative x-direction.
$t_A = 0$
t_B
t_C
t_D
t_E
$a = 0$
$v = 0$
Object is at $x < 0$, moving in the $+x$-direction ($v_x > 0$), and speeding up (v_x and a_x have the same sign).
Object is at $x = 0$, moving in the $+x$-direction ($v_x > 0$); speed is instantaneously not changing ($a_x = 0$).
Object is at $x > 0$, instantaneously at rest ($v_x = 0$), and about to move in the $-x$-direction ($a_x < 0$).
Object is at $x > 0$, moving in the $-x$-direction ($v_x < 0$); speed is instantaneously not changing ($a_x = 0$).
Object is at $x > 0$, moving in the $-x$-direction ($v_x < 0$), and slowing down (v_x and a_x have opposite signs).

That is, a_x is the second derivative of x with respect to t. The second derivative of any function is directly related to the *concavity* or *curvature* of the graph of that function. At a point where the *x-t* graph is concave up (curved upward), the *x*-acceleration is positive and v_x is increasing; at a point where the *x-t* graph is concave down (curved downward), the *x*-acceleration is negative and v_x is decreasing. At a point where the *x-t* graph has no curvature, such as an inflection point, the *x*-acceleration is zero and the velocity is not changing. Figure 2.14 shows all three of these possibilities.

Examining the curvature of an *x-t* graph is an easy way to decide what the *sign* of acceleration is. This technique is less helpful for determining numerical values of acceleration because the curvature of a graph is hard to measure accurately.

Test Your Understanding of Section 2.3 Look again at the *x-t* graph in Fig. 2.9 at the end of Section 2.2. (a) At which of the points *P*, *Q*, *R*, and *S* is the *x*-acceleration a_x positive? (b) At which points is the *x*-acceleration negative? (c) At which points does the *x*-acceleration appear to be zero? (d) At each point state whether the speed is increasing, decreasing, or not changing.

2.4 Motion with Constant Acceleration

The simplest kind of accelerated motion is straight-line motion with *constant* acceleration. In this case the velocity changes at the same rate throughout the motion. This is a very special situation, yet one that occurs often in nature. A falling body has a constant acceleration if the effects of the air are not important. The same is true for a body sliding on an incline or along a rough horizontal surface. Straight-line motion with nearly constant acceleration also occurs in technology, such as an airplane being catapulted from the deck of an aircraft carrier.

Figure 2.15 is a motion diagram showing the position, velocity, and acceleration for a particle moving with constant acceleration. Figures 2.16 and 2.17 depict this same motion in the form of graphs. Since the *x*-acceleration is constant, the **a_x-*t* graph** (graph of *x*-acceleration versus time) in Fig. 2.16 is a horizontal line. The graph of *x*-velocity versus time, or v_x-*t* graph, has a constant *slope* because the acceleration is constant, so this graph is a straight line (Fig. 2.17).

2.15 A motion diagram for a particle moving in a straight line in the positive *x*-direction with constant positive *x*-acceleration a_x. The position, velocity, and acceleration are shown at five equally spaced times.

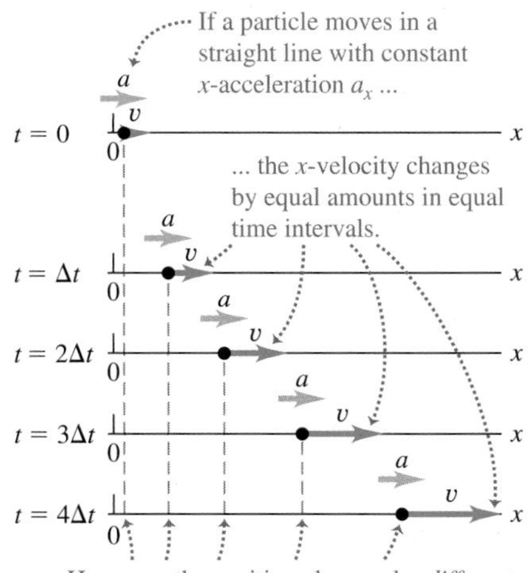

If a particle moves in a straight line with constant x-acceleration a_x ...
... the x-velocity changes by equal amounts in equal time intervals.
$t = 0$
$t = \Delta t$
$t = 2\Delta t$
$t = 3\Delta t$
$t = 4\Delta t$
However, the position changes by *different* amounts in equal time intervals because the velocity is changing.

2.16 An acceleration-time (a_x-t) graph for straight-line motion with constant positive x-acceleration a_x.

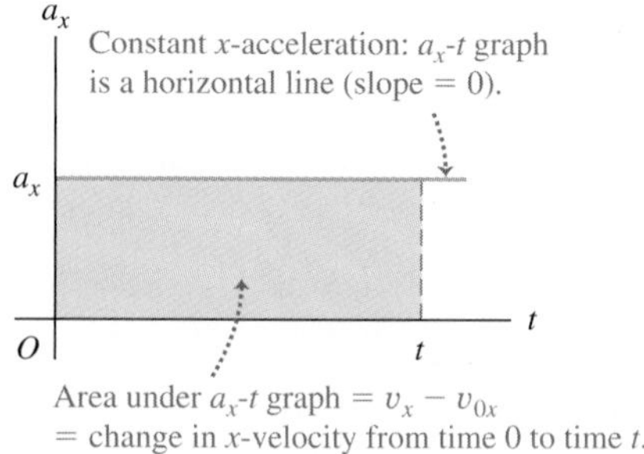
a_x
Constant x-acceleration: a_x-t graph is a horizontal line (slope = 0).
a_x
O
t
t
Area under a_x-t graph = $v_x - v_{0x}$
= change in x-velocity from time 0 to time t.

When the x-acceleration a_x is constant, the average x-acceleration $a_{av\text{-}x}$ for any time interval is the same as a_x. This makes it easy to derive equations for the position x and the x-velocity v_x as functions of time. To find an expression for v_x, we first replace $a_{av\text{-}x}$ in Eq. (2.4) by a_x:

$$a_x = \frac{v_{2x} - v_{1x}}{t_2 - t_1} \tag{2.7}$$

Now we let $t_1 = 0$ and let t_2 be any later time t. We use the symbol v_{0x} for the x-velocity at the initial time $t = 0$; the x-velocity at the later time t is v_x. Then Eq. (2.7) becomes

$$a_x = \frac{v_x - v_{0x}}{t - 0} \quad \text{or}$$

$$v_x = v_{0x} + a_x t \quad \text{(constant } x\text{-acceleration only)} \tag{2.8}$$

2.17 A velocity-time (v_x-t) graph for straight-line motion with constant positive x-acceleration a_x. The initial x-velocity v_{0x} is also positive in this case.

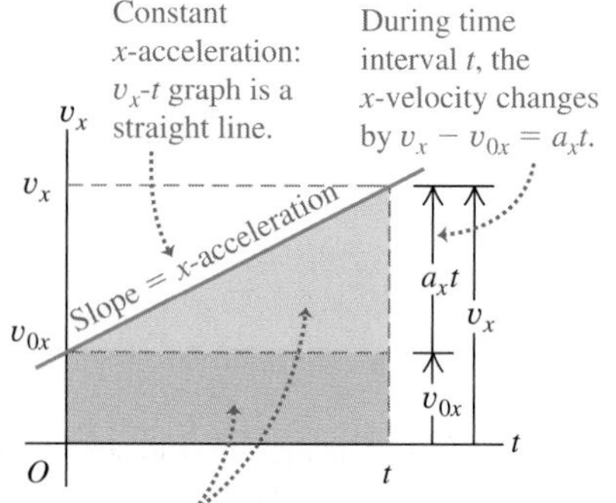
Constant x-acceleration: v_x-t graph is a straight line.
During time interval t, the x-velocity changes by $v_x - v_{0x} = a_x t$.
v_x
v_x
Slope = x-acceleration
$a_x t$
v_x
v_{0x}
v_{0x}
O
t
t
Total area under v_x-t graph = $x - x_0$
= change in x-coordinate from time 0 to time t.

We can interpret this equation as follows. The x-acceleration a_x is the constant rate of change of x-velocity—that is, the change in x-velocity per unit time. The term $a_x t$ is the product of the change in x-velocity per unit time, a_x, and the time interval t. Therefore it equals the *total* change in x-velocity from the initial time $t = 0$ to the later time t. The x-velocity v_x at any time t then equals the initial x-velocity v_{0x} (at $t = 0$) plus the change in x-velocity $a_x t$ (see Fig. 2.17).

Another interpretation of Eq. (2.8) is that the change in x-velocity $v_x - v_{0x}$ of the particle between $t = 0$ and any later time t equals the *area* under the a_x-t graph between those two times. In Fig. 2.16, the area under the graph of x-acceleration versus time is a rectangle of vertical side a_x and horizontal side t. The area of this rectangle is $a_x t$, which from Eq. (2.8) is indeed equal to the change in velocity $v_x - v_{0x}$. In Section 2.6 we'll show that even if the x-acceleration is not constant, the change in x-velocity during a time interval is still equal to the area under the a_x-t curve, although in that case Eq. (2.8) does not apply.

Next we'll derive an equation for the position x as a function of time when the x-acceleration is constant. To do this, we use two different expressions for the average x-velocity $v_{av\text{-}x}$ during the interval from $t = 0$ to any later time t. The first expression comes from the definition of $v_{av\text{-}x}$, Eq. (2.2), which is true whether or not the acceleration is constant. We call the position at time $t = 0$ the *initial position,* denoted by x_0. The position at the later time t is simply x. Thus for the time interval $\Delta t = t - 0$ the displacement is $\Delta x = x - x_0$, and Eq. (2.2) gives

$$v_{av\text{-}x} = \frac{x - x_0}{t} \tag{2.9}$$

We can also get a second expression for $v_{av\text{-}x}$ that is valid only when the x-acceleration is constant, so that the v_x-t graph is a straight line (as in Fig. 2.17) and the x-velocity changes at a constant rate. In this case the average x-velocity during any time interval is simply the arithmetic average of the x-velocities at the beginning and end of the interval. For the time interval 0 to t,

$$v_{av\text{-}x} = \frac{v_{0x} + v_x}{2} \quad \text{(constant } x\text{-acceleration only)} \tag{2.10}$$

(This equation is *not* true if the x-acceleration varies and the v_x-t graph is a curve, as in Fig. 2.13.) We also know that with constant x-acceleration, the x-velocity v_x at any time t is given by Eq. (2.8). Substituting that expression for v_x into Eq. (2.10), we find

$$\begin{aligned} v_{av\text{-}x} &= \frac{1}{2}(v_{0x} + v_{0x} + a_x t) \\ &= v_{0x} + \frac{1}{2}a_x t \quad \text{(constant } x\text{-acceleration only)} \end{aligned} \tag{2.11}$$

ActivPhysics ONLINE

1.1 Analyzing Motion Using Diagrams
1.2 Analyzing Motion Using Graphs
1.3 Predicting Motion from Graphs
1.4 Predicting Motion from Equations
1.5 Problem-Solving Strategies for Kinematics
1.6 Skier Races Downhill

Finally, we set Eqs. (2.9) and (2.11) equal to each other and simplify:

$$v_{0x} + \frac{1}{2}a_x t = \frac{x - x_0}{t} \qquad \text{or}$$

$$x = x_0 + v_{0x}t + \frac{1}{2}a_x t^2 \qquad \text{(constant } x\text{-acceleration only)} \qquad (2.12)$$

Here's what Eq. (2.12) tells us: If at time $t = 0$ a particle is at position x_0 and has x-velocity v_{0x}, its new position x at any later time t is the sum of three terms—its initial position x_0, plus the distance $v_{0x}t$ that it would move if its x-velocity were constant, plus an additional distance $\frac{1}{2}a_x t^2$ caused by the change in x-velocity.

A graph of Eq. (2.12)—that is, an x-t graph for motion with constant x-acceleration (Fig. 2.18a)—is always a *parabola.* Figure 2.18b shows such a graph. The curve intercepts the vertical axis (x-axis) at x_0, the position at $t = 0$. The slope of the tangent at $t = 0$ equals v_{0x}, the initial x-velocity, and the slope of the tangent at any time t equals the x-velocity v_x at that time. The slope and x-velocity are continuously increasing, so the x-acceleration a_x is positive; you can also see this because the graph in Fig. 2.18b is concave up (it curves upward). If a_x is negative, the x-t graph is a parabola that is concave down (has a downward curvature).

If there is zero x-acceleration, the x-t graph is a straight line; if there is a constant x-acceleration, the additional $\frac{1}{2}a_x t^2$ term in Eq. (2.12) for x as a function of t curves the graph into a parabola (Fig. 2.19a). We can analyze the v_x-t graph in the same way. If there is zero x-acceleration this graph is a horizontal line (the x-velocity is constant); adding a constant x-acceleration gives a slope to the v_x-t graph (Fig. 2.19b).

ActivPhysics ONLINE

1.8 Seat Belts Save Lives
1.9 Screeching to a Halt
1.10 Car Starts, Then Stops
1.11 Solving Two-Vehicle Problems
1.12 Car Catches Truck
1.13 Avoiding a Rear-End Collision

(a) A race car moves in the x-direction with constant acceleration.

(b) The x-t graph

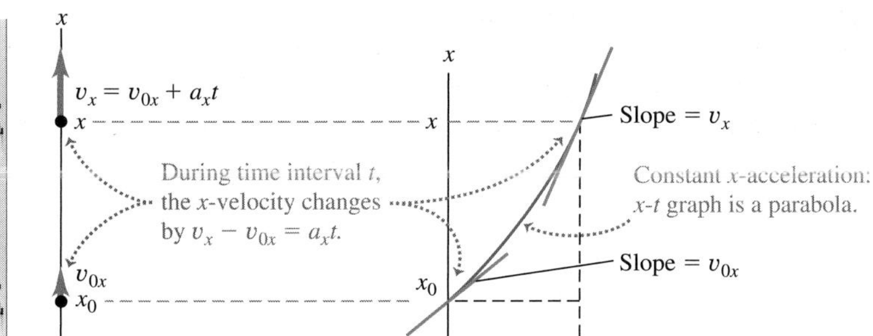

2.18 (a) Straight-line motion with constant acceleration. (b) A position-time (x-t) graph for this motion (the same motion as is shown in Figs. 2.15, 2.16, and 2.17). For this motion the initial position x_0, the initial velocity v_{0x}, and the acceleration a_x are all positive.

(a) An x-t graph for an object moving with positive constant x-acceleration

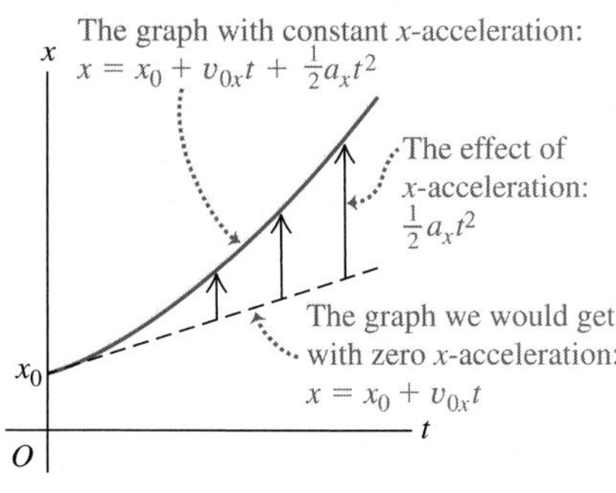

(b) The v_x-t graph for the same object

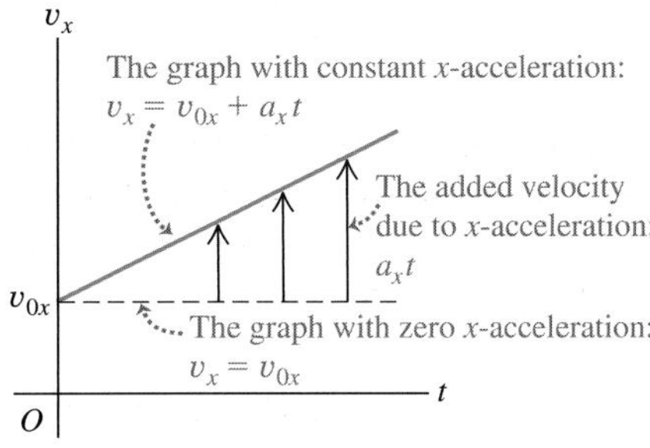

2.19 (a) How a constant x-acceleration affects a body's (a) x-t graph and (b) v_x-t graph.

Just as the change in x-velocity of the particle equals the area under the a_x-t graph, the displacement—that is, the change in position—equals the area under the v_x-t graph. To be specific, the displacement $x - x_0$ of the particle between $t = 0$ and any later time t equals the area under the v_x-t graph between those two times. In Fig. 2.17 the area under the graph is divided into a dark-colored rectangle of vertical side v_{0x} and horizontal side t and a light-colored right triangle of vertical side $a_x t$ and horizontal side t. The area of the rectangle is $v_{0x}t$ and the area of the triangle is $\frac{1}{2}(a_x t)(t) = \frac{1}{2}a_x t^2$, so the total area under the v_x-t graph is

$$x - x_0 = v_{0x}t + \frac{1}{2}a_x t^2$$

in agreement with Eq. (2.12).

The displacement during a time interval can always be found from the area under the v_x-t curve. This is true even if the acceleration is *not* constant, although in that case Eq. (2.12) does not apply. (We'll show this in Section 2.6.)

We can check whether Eqs. (2.8) and (2.12) are consistent with the assumption of constant acceleration by taking the derivative of Eq. (2.12). We find

$$v_x = \frac{dx}{dt} = v_{0x} + a_x t$$

which is Eq. (2.8). Differentiating again, we find simply

$$\frac{dv_x}{dt} = a_x$$

which agrees with the definition of instantaneous x-acceleration.

It's often useful to have a relationship between position, x-velocity, and (constant) x-acceleration that does not involve the time. To obtain this, we first solve Eq. (2.8) for t, then substitute the resulting expression into Eq. (2.12), and simplify:

$$t = \frac{v_x - v_{0x}}{a_x}$$

$$x = x_0 + v_{0x}\left(\frac{v_x - v_{0x}}{a_x}\right) + \frac{1}{2}a_x\left(\frac{v_x - v_{0x}}{a_x}\right)^2$$

We transfer the term x_0 to the left side and multiply through by $2a_x$:

$$2a_x(x - x_0) = 2v_{0x}v_x - 2v_{0x}^2 + v_x^2 - 2v_{0x}v_x + v_{0x}^2$$

Finally, simplifying gives us

$$v_x^2 = v_{0x}^2 + 2a_x(x - x_0) \qquad \text{(constant } x\text{-acceleration only)} \qquad (2.13)$$

We can get one more useful relationship by equating the two expressions for $v_{\text{av-}x}$, Eqs. (2.9) and (2.10), and multiplying through by t. Doing this, we obtain

$$x - x_0 = \left(\frac{v_{0x} + v_x}{2}\right)t \qquad \text{(constant } x\text{-acceleration only)} \qquad (2.14)$$

Note that Eq. (2.14) does not contain the x-acceleration a_x. This equation can be handy when a_x is constant but its value is unknown.

Equations (2.8), (2.12), (2.13), and (2.14) are the *equations of motion with constant acceleration.* By using these equations, we can solve *any* problem involving straight-line motion of a particle with constant acceleration.

For the particular case of motion with constant x-acceleration depicted in Fig. 2.15 and graphed in Figs. 2.16, 2.17, and 2.18, the values of x_0, v_{0x}, and a_x are all positive. We invite you to redraw these figures for cases in which one, two, or all three of these quantities are negative.

A special case of motion with constant x-acceleration occurs when the x-acceleration is *zero.* The x-velocity is then constant, and the equations of motion become simply

$$v_x = v_{0x} = \text{constant}$$
$$x = x_0 + v_x t$$

Problem-Solving Strategy 2.1 Motion with Constant Acceleration

IDENTIFY *the relevant concepts:* In most straight-line motion problems, you can use the constant-acceleration equations. Occasionally, however, you will encounter a situation in which the acceleration *isn't* constant. In such a case, you'll need a different approach (see Section 2.6).

SET UP *the problem* using the following steps:

1. First decide where the origin of coordinates is and which axis direction is positive. It is often easiest to place the particle at the origin at time $t = 0$; then $x_0 = 0$. It helps to make a motion diagram showing the coordinates and some later positions of the particle.
2. Remember that your choice of the positive axis direction automatically determines the positive directions for x-velocity and x-acceleration. If x is positive to the right of the origin, then v_x and a_x are also positive toward the right.
3. Restate the problem in words, and then translate it into symbols and equations. *When* does the particle arrive at a certain point (that is, what is the value of t)? *Where* is the particle when its x-velocity has a specified value (that is, what is the value of x when v_x has the specified value)? Example 2.4 asks, "Where is the motorcyclist when his velocity is 25 m/s?" In symbols, this says "What is the value of x when $v_x = 25$ m/s?"
4. Make a list of quantities such as x, x_0, v_x, v_{0x}, a_x, and t. In general, some of them will be known and some will be unknown. Write down the values of the known quantities, and decide which of the unknowns are the target variables. Be on the lookout for implicit information. For example, "A car sits at a stoplight" usually means $v_{0x} = 0$.

EXECUTE *the solution:* Choose an equation from Eqs. (2.8), (2.12), (2.13), and (2.14) that contains only one of the target variables. Solve this equation for the target variable, using symbols only. Then substitute the known values and compute the value of the target variable. Sometimes you will have to solve two simultaneous equations for two unknown quantities.

EVALUATE *your answer:* Take a hard look at your results to see whether they make sense. Are they within the general range of values you expected?

Example 2.4 Constant-acceleration calculations

A motorcyclist heading east through a small Iowa city accelerates after he passes the signpost marking the city limits (Fig. 2.20). His acceleration is a constant 4.0 m/s^2. At time $t = 0$ he is 5.0 m east of the signpost, moving east at 15 m/s. (a) Find his position and velocity at time $t = 2.0$ s. (b) Where is the motorcyclist when his velocity is 25 m/s?

2.20 A motorcyclist traveling with constant acceleration.

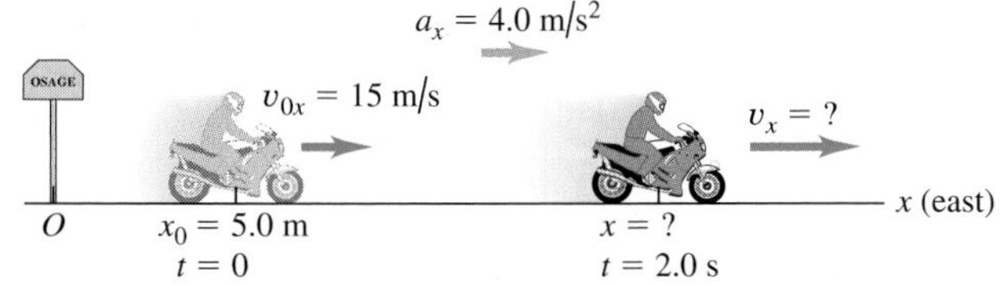

SOLUTION

IDENTIFY: The problem statement tells us that the acceleration is constant, so we can use the constant-acceleration equations.

SET UP: We take the signpost as the origin of coordinates $(x = 0)$, and choose the positive x-axis to point east (see Fig. 2.20, which also serves as a motion diagram). At the initial time $t = 0$, the initial position is $x_0 = 5.0$ m and the initial x-velocity is $v_{0x} = 15$ m/s. The constant x-acceleration is $a_x = 4.0$ m/s^2. The unknown target variables in part (a) are the values of the position x and the x-velocity v_x at the later time $t = 2.0$ s; the target variable in part (b) is the value of x when $v_x = 25$ m/s.

Continued

EXECUTE: (a) We can find the position x at $t = 2.0$ s by using Eq. (2.12), which gives x as a function of time t:

$$x = x_0 + v_{0x}t + \frac{1}{2}a_x t^2$$
$$= 5.0\text{ m} + (15\text{ m/s})(2.0\text{ s}) + \frac{1}{2}(4.0\text{ m/s}^2)(2.0\text{ s})^2$$
$$= 43\text{ m}$$

We can find the x-velocity v_x at this same time by using Eq. (2.8), which gives v_x as a function of time t:

$$v_x = v_{0x} + a_x t$$
$$= 15\text{ m/s} + (4.0\text{ m/s}^2)(2.0\text{ s}) = 23\text{ m/s}$$

(b) We want to find the value of x when $v_x = 25$ m/s, but we don't know the time when the motorcycle has this x-velocity. Hence we use Eq. (2.13), which involves x, v_x, and a_x but does not involve t:

$$v_x^2 = v_{0x}^2 + 2a_x(x - x_0)$$

Solving for x and substituting in the known values, we find

$$x = x_0 + \frac{v_x^2 - v_{0x}^2}{2a_x}$$
$$= 5.0\text{ m} + \frac{(25\text{ m/s})^2 - (15\text{ m/s})^2}{2(4.0\text{ m/s}^2)}$$
$$= 55\text{ m}$$

An alternative but longer route to the same answer is to use Eq. (2.8) to first find the time when $v_x = 25$ m/s:

$$v_x = v_{0x} + a_x t \quad \text{so}$$
$$t = \frac{v_x - v_{0x}}{a_x} = \frac{25\text{ m/s} - 15\text{ m/s}}{4.0\text{ m/s}^2} = 2.5\text{ s}$$

Given the time t, we can find x using Eq. (2.12):

$$x = x_0 + v_{0x}t + \frac{1}{2}a_x t^2$$
$$= 5.0\text{ m} + (15\text{ m/s})(2.5\text{ s}) + \frac{1}{2}(4.0\text{ m/s}^2)(2.5\text{ s})^2$$
$$= 55\text{ m}$$

EVALUATE: Do these results make sense? According to our results in part (a), the motorcyclist accelerates from 15 m/s (about 34 mi/h, or 54 km/h) to 23 m/s (about 51 mi/h, or 83 km/h) in 2.0 s while traveling a distance of 38 m (about 125 ft). This is pretty brisk acceleration, but well within the capabilities of a high-performance bike.

Comparing our results in part (b) with those in part (a) tells us that the motorcycle attains an x-velocity $v_x = 25$ m/s at a later time and after traveling a greater distance than when the motorcycle had $v_x = 23$ m/s. This makes sense, since the motorcycle has a positive x-acceleration and so its x-velocity is increasing.

Example 2.5 Two bodies with different accelerations

A motorist traveling with a constant speed of 15 m/s (about 34 mi/h) passes a school-crossing corner, where the speed limit is 10 m/s (about 22 mi/h). Just as the motorist passes, a police officer on a motorcycle stopped at the corner starts off in pursuit with constant acceleration of 3.0 m/s^2 (Fig. 2.21a). (a) How much time elapses before the officer catches up with the motorist? (b) What is the officer's speed at that point? (c) What is the total distance each vehicle has traveled at that point?

SOLUTION

IDENTIFY: The police officer and the motorist both move with constant acceleration (equal to zero for the motorist), so we can use the formulas we have developed.

SET UP: We take the origin at the corner, so $x_0 = 0$ for both, and we take the positive direction to the right. Let x_P (for police) be the officer's position and x_M (for motorist) be the motorist's position at any time. The initial x-velocities are $v_{P0x} = 0$ for the officer and $v_{M0x} = 15$ m/s for the motorist; the constant x-accelerations are $a_{Px} = 3.0$ m/s^2 for the officer and $a_{Mx} = 0$ for the motorist. Our target variable in part (a) is the time when the officer catches the motorist—that is, when the two vehicles are at the same position. In part (b) we're looking for the officer's speed v (the magnitude of his velocity) at the time found in part (a). In part (c) we want to find the position of either vehicle at this same time. Hence we use Eq. (2.12) (which relates position and time) in

2.21 (a) Motion with constant acceleration overtaking motion with constant velocity. (b) A graph of x versus t for each vehicle.

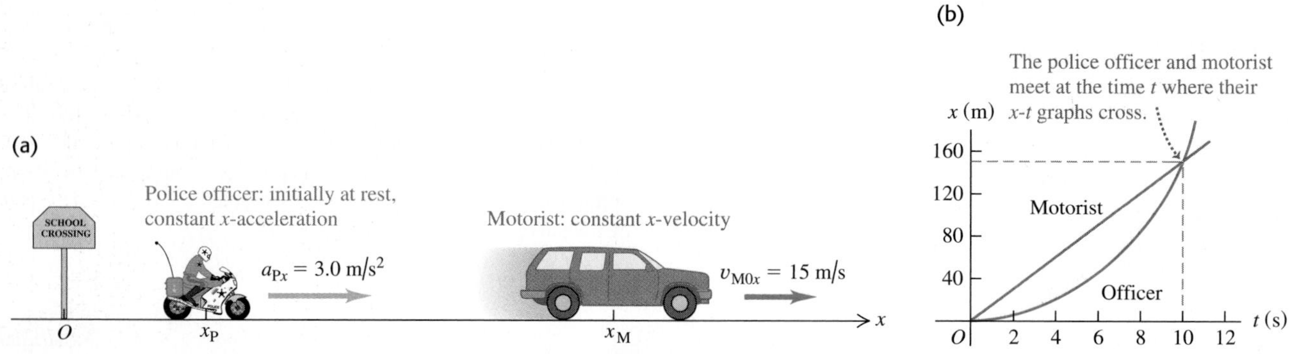

parts (a) and (c), and Eq. (2.8) (which relates velocity and time) in part (b).

EXECUTE: (a) To find the value of the time t when the motorist and the police officer are at the same position, we apply Eq. (2.12), $x = x_0 + v_{0x}t + \frac{1}{2}a_x t^2$, to each vehicle:

$$x_M = 0 + v_{M0x}t + \frac{1}{2}(0)t^2 = v_{M0x}t$$

$$x_P = 0 + (0)t + \frac{1}{2}a_{Px}t^2 = \frac{1}{2}a_{Px}t^2$$

Since $x_M = x_P$ at time t, we set these two expressions equal to each other and solve for t:

$$v_{M0x}t = \frac{1}{2}a_{Px}t^2$$

$$t = 0 \quad \text{or} \quad t = \frac{2v_{M0x}}{a_{Px}} = \frac{2(15\text{ m/s})}{3.0\text{ m/s}^2} = 10\text{ s}$$

There are *two* times when both the vehicles have the same x-coordinate. The first, $t = 0$, is the time when the motorist passes the parked motorcycle at the corner. The second, $t = 10$ s, is the time when the officer catches up with the motorist.

(b) We want the magnitude of the officer's x-velocity v_{Px} at the time t found in part (a). Her velocity at any time is given by Eq. (2.8):

$$v_{Px} = v_{P0x} + a_{Px}t = 0 + (3.0\text{ m/s}^2)t$$

Using $t = 10$ s, we find $v_{Px} = 30$ m/s. When the officer overtakes the motorist, she is traveling twice as fast as the motorist is.

(c) In 10 s the distance the motorist travels is

$$x_M = v_{M0x}t = (15\text{ m/s})(10\text{ s}) = 150\text{ m}$$

and the distance the officer travels is

$$x_P = \frac{1}{2}a_{Px}t^2 = \frac{1}{2}(3.0\text{ m/s}^2)(10\text{ s})^2 = 150\text{ m}$$

This verifies that at the time the officer catches the motorist, they have gone equal distances.

EVALUATE: Figure 2.21b shows graphs of x versus t for each vehicle. We see again that there are two times when the two positions are the same (where the two graphs cross). At neither of these times do the two vehicles have the same velocity (i.e., where the two graphs cross, their slopes are different). At $t = 0$, the officer is at rest; at $t = 10$ s, the officer has twice the speed of the motorist.

Test Your Understanding of Section 2.4 Four possible v_x-t graphs are shown for the two vehicles in Example 2.5. Which graph is correct?

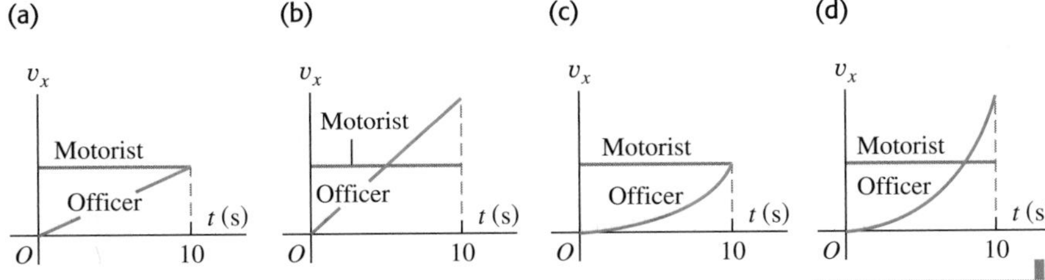

2.5 Freely Falling Bodies

The most familiar example of motion with (nearly) constant acceleration is a body falling under the influence of the earth's gravitational attraction. Such motion has held the attention of philosophers and scientists since ancient times. In the fourth century B.C., Aristotle thought (erroneously) that heavy bodies fall faster than light bodies, in proportion to their weight. Nineteen centuries later, Galileo (see Section 1.1) argued that a body should fall with a downward acceleration that is constant and independent of its weight.

Experiment shows that if the effects of the air can be neglected, Galileo is right; all bodies at a particular location fall with the same downward acceleration, regardless of their size or weight. If in addition the distance of the fall is small compared with the radius of the earth, and if we ignore small effects due to the earth's rotation, the acceleration is constant. The idealized motion that results under all of these assumptions is called **free fall,** although it includes rising as well as falling motion. (In Chapter 3 we will extend the discussion of free fall to include the motion of projectiles, which move both vertically and horizontally.)

Figure 2.22 is a photograph of a falling ball made with a stroboscopic light source that produces a series of short, intense flashes. As each flash occurs, an image of the ball at that instant is recorded on the photograph. There are equal

2.22 Multiflash photo of a freely falling ball.

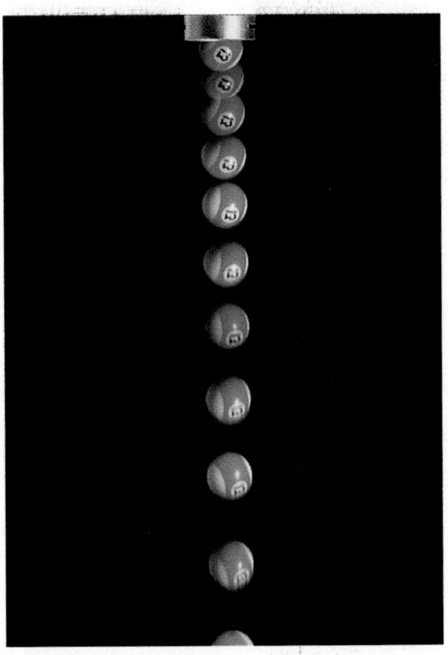

1.7 Balloonist Drops Lemonade
1.10 Pole-Vaulter Lands

time intervals between flashes, so the average velocity of the ball between successive flashes is proportional to the distance between corresponding images. The increasing distances between images show that the velocity is continuously changing; the ball is accelerating downward. Careful measurement shows that the velocity change is the same in each time interval, so the acceleration of the freely falling ball is constant.

The constant acceleration of a freely falling body is called the **acceleration due to gravity,** and we denote its magnitude with the letter g. We will frequently use the approximate value of g at or near the earth's surface:

$$g = 9.8 \text{ m/s}^2 = 980 \text{ cm/s}^2$$
$$= 32 \text{ ft/s}^2 \qquad \text{(approximate value near the earth's surface)}$$

The exact value varies with location, so we will often give the value of g at the earth's surface to only two significant figures. Because g is the magnitude of a vector quantity, it is always a *positive* number. On the surface of the moon, the acceleration due to gravity is caused by the attractive force of the moon rather than the earth, and $g = 1.6 \text{ m/s}^2$. Near the surface of the sun, $g = 270 \text{ m/s}^2$.

In the following examples we use the constant-acceleration equations developed in Section 2.4. You should review Problem-Solving Strategy 2.1 in that section before you study the next examples.

Example 2.6 A freely-falling coin

A one-euro coin is dropped from the Leaning Tower of Pisa. It starts from rest and falls freely. Compute its position and velocity after 1.0 s, 2.0 s, and 3.0 s.

SOLUTION

IDENTIFY: "Falls freely" means "has a constant acceleration due to gravity," so we can use the constant-acceleration equations to determine our target variables.

2.23 A coin freely falling from rest.

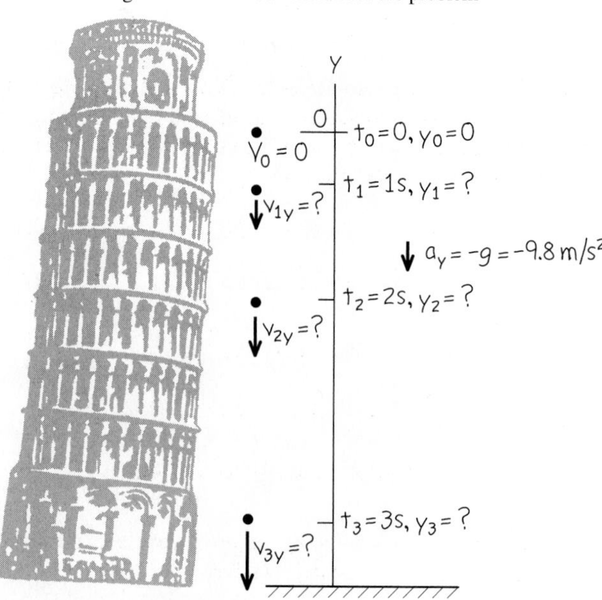

SET UP: The right side of Fig. 2.23 shows our motion diagram for the coin. The motion is vertical, so we use a vertical coordinate axis and call the coordinate y instead of x. Then we replace all the x's in the constant-acceleration equations by y's. We take the origin O at the starting point and the upward direction as positive. The initial coordinate y_0 and the initial y-velocity v_{0y} are both zero. The y-acceleration is downward, in the negative y-direction, so $a_y = -g = -9.8 \text{ m/s}^2$. (Remember that, by definition, g itself is *always* positive.) Our target variables are the values of y and v_y at the three given times. To find these, we use Eqs. (2.12) and (2.8) with x replaced by y.

EXECUTE: At a time t after the coin is dropped, its position and y-velocity are

$$y = y_0 + v_{0y}t + \frac{1}{2}a_y t^2 = 0 + 0 + \frac{1}{2}(-g)t^2 = (-4.9 \text{ m/s}^2)t^2$$

$$v_y = v_{0y} + a_y t = 0 + (-g)t = (-9.8 \text{ m/s}^2)t$$

When $t = 1.0$ s, $y = (-4.9 \text{ m/s}^2)(1.0 \text{ s})^2 = -4.9$ m and $v_y = (-9.8 \text{ m/s}^2)(1.0 \text{ s}) = -9.8$ m/s; after 1 s, the coin is 4.9 m below the origin (y is negative) and has a downward velocity (v_y is negative) with magnitude 9.8 m/s.

The position and y-velocity at 2.0 s and 3.0 s are found in the same way. Can you show that $y = -19.6$ m and $v_y = -19.6$ m/s at $t = 2.0$ s, and that $y = -44.1$ m and $v_y = -29.4$ m/s at $t = 3.0$ s?

EVALUATE: All our answers for v_y are negative because we chose the positive y-axis to point upward. But we could just as well have chosen the positive y-axis to point downward. In that case the acceleration would have been $a_y = +g$ and all our answers for v_y would have been positive. Either choice of axis is fine; just make sure that you state your choice explicitly in your solution and confirm that the acceleration has the correct sign.

Example 2.7 Up-and-down motion in free fall

You throw a ball vertically upward from the roof of a tall building. The ball leaves your hand at a point even with the roof railing with an upward speed of 15.0 m/s; the ball is then in free fall. On its way back down, it just misses the railing. At the location of the building, $g = 9.80\ \text{m/s}^2$. Find (a) the position and velocity of the ball 1.00 s and 4.00 s after leaving your hand; (b) the velocity when the ball is 5.00 m above the railing; (c) the maximum height reached and the time at which it is reached; and (d) the acceleration of the ball when it is at its maximum height.

SOLUTION

IDENTIFY: The words "free fall" in the statement of the problem mean that the acceleration is constant and due to gravity. Our target variables are position [in parts (a) and (c)], velocity [in parts (a) and (b)], and acceleration [in part (d)].

SET UP: In Fig. 2.24 (which is also a motion diagram for the ball) the downward path is displaced a little to the right of its actual position for clarity. Take the origin at the point where the ball leaves your hand, and take the positive direction to be upward. The initial position y_0 is zero, the initial y-velocity v_{0y} is $+15.0\ \text{m/s}$, and the y-acceleration is $a_y = -g = -9.80\ \text{m/s}^2$. We'll again use Eqs. (2.12) and (2.8) to find the position and velocity as functions of time. In part (b) we need to find the velocity at a certain *position* rather than at a certain *time,* so we'll use Eq. (2.13) for that part.

EXECUTE: (a) The position y and y-velocity v_y a time t after the ball leaves your hand are given by Eqs. (2.12) and (2.8) with x's replaced by y's:

$$y = y_0 = v_{0y}t + \frac{1}{2}a_y t^2 = y_0 + v_{0y}t + \frac{1}{2}(-g)t^2$$
$$= (0) + (15.0\ \text{m/s})t + \frac{1}{2}(-9.80\ \text{m/s}^2)t^2$$
$$v_y = v_{0y} + a_y t = v_{0y} + (-g)t$$
$$= 15.0\ \text{m/s} + (-9.80\ \text{m/s}^2)t$$

2.24 Position and velocity of a ball thrown vertically upward.

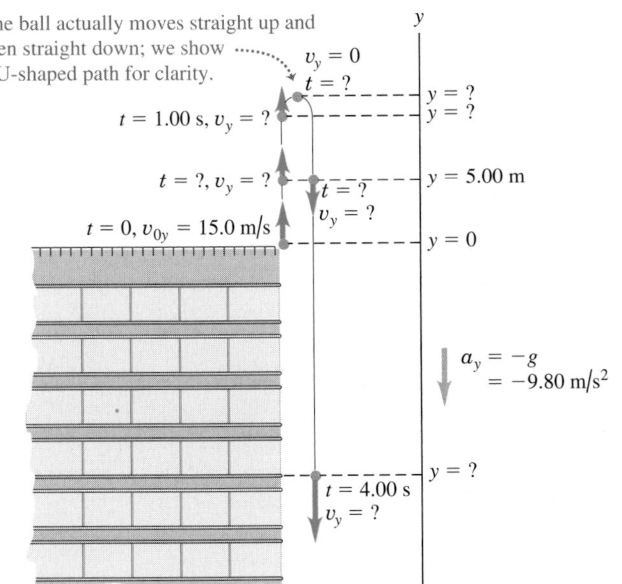

When $t = 1.00$ s, these equations give

$$y = +10.1\ \text{m} \qquad v_y = +5.2\ \text{m/s}$$

The ball is 10.1 m above the origin (y is positive) and moving upward (v_y is positive) with a speed of 5.2 m/s. This is less than the initial speed because the ball slows as it ascends.

When $t = 4.00$ s, the equations for y and v_y as functions of time t give

$$y = -18.4\ \text{m} \qquad v_y = -24.2\ \text{m/s}$$

The ball has passed its highest point and is 18.4 m *below* the origin (y is negative). It has a *downward* velocity (v_y is negative) with magnitude 24.2 m/s. The ball loses speed as it ascends, then gains speed as it descends; it is moving at the initial 15.0-m/s speed as it moves downward past the ball's launching point (the origin), and continues to gain speed as it descends below this point.

(b) The y-velocity v_y at any position y is given by Eq. (2.13) with x's replaced by y's:

$$v_y^2 = v_{0y}^2 + 2a_y(y - y_0) = v_{0y}^2 + 2(-g)(y - 0)$$
$$= (15.0\ \text{m/s})^2 + 2(-9.80\ \text{m/s}^2)y$$

When the ball is 5.00 m above the origin, $y = +5.00$ m, so

$$v_y^2 = (15.0\ \text{m/s})^2 + 2(-9.80\ \text{m/s}^2)(5.00\ \text{m}) = 127\ \text{m}^2/\text{s}^2$$
$$v_y = \pm 11.3\ \text{m/s}$$

We get *two* values of v_y because the ball passes through the point $y = +5.00$ m twice (see Fig. 2.24), once on the way up so v_y is positive and once on the way down so v_y is negative.

(c) Just at the instant when the ball reaches the highest point, it is momentarily at rest and $v_y = 0$. The maximum height y_1 can then be found in two ways. The first way is to use Eq. (2.13) and substitute $v_y = 0$, $y_0 = 0$, and $a_y = -g$:

$$0 = v_{0y}^2 + 2(-g)(y_1 - 0)$$
$$y_1 = \frac{v_{0y}^2}{2g} = \frac{(15.0\ \text{m/s})^2}{2(9.80\ \text{m/s}^2)} = +11.5\ \text{m}$$

The second way is find the time at which $v_y = 0$ using Eq. (2.8), $v_y = v_{0y} + a_y t$, and then substitute this value of t into Eq. (2.12) to find the position at this time. From Eq. (2.8), the time t_1 when the ball reaches the highest point is given by

$$v_y = 0 = v_{0y} + (-g)t_1$$
$$t_1 = \frac{v_{0y}}{g} = \frac{15.0\ \text{m/s}}{9.80\ \text{m/s}^2} = 1.53\ \text{s}$$

Substituting this value of t into Eq. (2.12), we find

$$y = y_0 + v_{0y}t + \frac{1}{2}a_y t^2 = (0) + (15\ \text{m/s})(1.53\ \text{s})$$
$$+ \frac{1}{2}(-9.8\ \text{m/s}^2)(1.53\ \text{s})^2 = +11.5\ \text{m}$$

Notice that the first way of finding the maximum height is easier, since it's not necessary to find the time first.

Continued

(d) **CAUTION** **A free-fall misconception** It's a common misconception that at the highest point of free-fall motion the velocity is zero *and* the acceleration is zero. If this were so, once the ball reached the highest point it would hang there suspended in midair! Remember that acceleration is the rate of change of velocity. If the acceleration were zero at the highest point, the ball's velocity would no longer change, and once the ball was instantaneously at rest, it would remain at rest forever.

At the highest point, the acceleration is still $a_y = -g = -9.80\ \text{m/s}^2$, the same value as when the ball is moving up and when it's moving down. That's because the ball's velocity is continuously changing, from positive values through zero to negative values.

EVALUATE: A useful way to check any motion problem is to draw the graphs of position and velocity versus time. Figure 2.25 shows these graphs for this problem. Since the y-acceleration is constant and negative, the y-t graph is a parabola with downward curvature and the v_y-t graph is a straight line with a negative slope.

2.25 (a) Position and (b) velocity as functions of time for a ball thrown upward with an initial speed of 15 m/s.

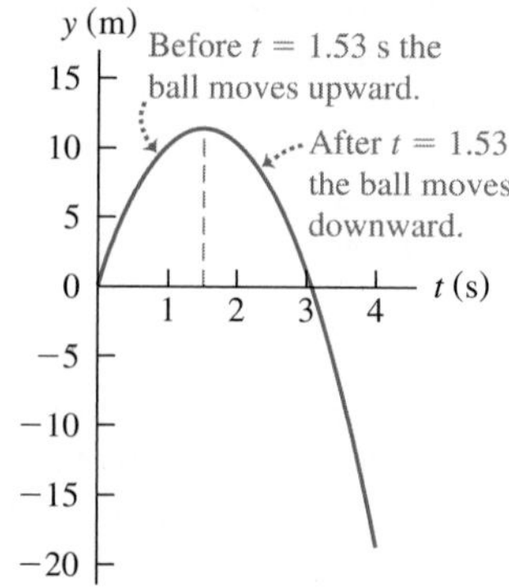

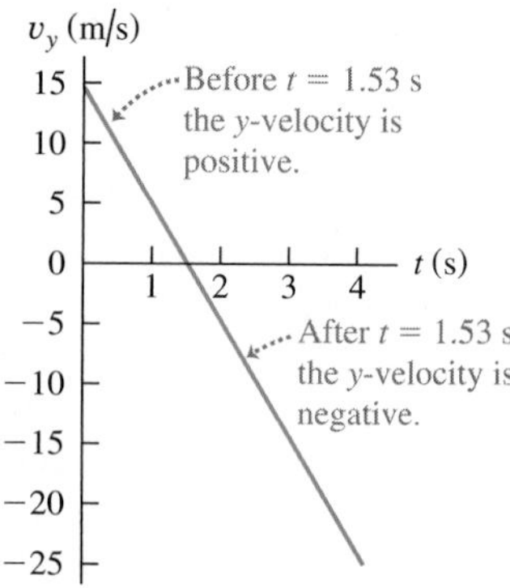

Example 2.8 Two solutions or one?

Find the time when the ball in Example 2.7 is 5.00 m below the roof railing.

SOLUTION

IDENTIFY: Again this a constant-acceleration problem. The target variable is the time when the ball is at a certain position.

SET UP: We again choose the y-axis as in Fig. 2.24, so y_0, v_{0y}, and $a_y = -g$ have the same values as in Example 2.7. The position y as a function of time t is again given by Eq. (2.12):

$$y = y_0 + v_{0y}t + \frac{1}{2}a_y t^2 = y_0 + v_{0y}t + \frac{1}{2}(-g)t^2$$

We want to solve this for the value of t when $y = -5.00$ m. Since this equation involves t^2, it is a *quadratic* equation for t.

EXECUTE: We first rearrange the equation into the standard form of a quadratic equation for an unknown x, $Ax^2 + Bx + C = 0$:

$$\left(\frac{1}{2}g\right)t^2 + (-v_{0y})t + (y - y_0) = At^2 + Bt + C = 0$$

so $A = g/2$, $B = -v_{0y}$, and $C = y - y_0$. Using the quadratic formula (see Appendix B), we find that this equation has *two* solutions:

$$t = \frac{-B \pm \sqrt{B^2 - 4AC}}{2A}$$

$$= \frac{-(-v_{0y}) \pm \sqrt{(-v_{0y})^2 - 4(g/2)(y - y_0)}}{2(g/2)}$$

$$= \frac{v_{0y} \pm \sqrt{v_{0y}^2 - 2g(y - y_0)}}{g}$$

Substituting the values $y_0 = 0$, $v_{0y} = +15.0\ \text{m/s}$, $g = 9.80\ \text{m/s}^2$, and $y = -5.00$ m, we find

$$t = \frac{(15.0\ \text{m/s}) \pm \sqrt{(15.0\ \text{m/s})^2 - 2(9.80\ \text{m/s}^2)(-5.00\ \text{m} - 0)}}{9.80\ \text{m/s}^2}$$

$t = +3.36$ s or $t = -0.30$ s

To decide which of these is the right answer, the key question to ask is, "Are these answers reasonable?" The second answer, $t = -0.30$ s, is simply not reasonable; it refers to a time 0.30 s *before* the ball left your hand! The correct answer is $t = +3.36$ s. The ball is 5.00 m below the railing 3.36 s *after* it leaves your hand.

EVALUATE: Where did the erroneous "solution" $t = -0.30$ s come from? Remember that the equation $y = y_0 + v_{0y}t + \frac{1}{2}(-g)t^2$ is based on the assumption that the acceleration is constant for *all* values of t, whether positive, negative, or zero. Taken at face value, this equation tells us that the ball has been moving upward in free fall ever since the dawn of time; it eventually passes your hand at $y = 0$ at the special instant we chose to call $t = 0$, then continues in free fall. But anything that this equation describes happening before $t = 0$ is pure fiction, since the ball went into free fall only after leaving your hand at $t = 0$; the "solution" $t = -0.30$ s is part of this fiction.

You should repeat these calculations to find the times when the ball is 5.00 m *above* the origin ($y = +5.00$ m). The two answers are $t = +0.38$ s and $t = +2.68$ s. These are both positive values of t, and both refer to the real motion of the ball after leaving your hand. The earlier time is when the ball passes through $y = +5.00$ m moving upward; the later time is when it passes through this point moving downward. [Compare this with part (b) of Example 2.7.]

You should also solve for the times at which $y = +15.0$ m. In this case, both solutions involve the square root of a negative number, so there are *no* real solutions. This makes sense; we found in part (c) of Example 2.7 that the ball's maximum height is only $y = +11.5$ m, so it *never* reaches $y = +15.0$ m. While a quadratic equation such as Eq. (2.12) always has two solutions, in some situations one or both of the solutions will not be physically reasonable.

Test Your Understanding of Section 2.5 If you toss a ball upward with a certain initial speed, it falls freely and reaches a maximum height h a time t after it leaves your hand. (a) If you throw the ball upward with double the initial speed, what new maximum height does the ball reach? (i) $h\sqrt{2}$; (ii) $2h$; (iii) $4h$; (iv) $8h$; (v) $16h$. (b) If you throw the ball upward with double the initial speed, how long does it take to reach its new maximum height? (i) $t/2$; (ii) $t/\sqrt{2}$; (iii) t; (iv) $t\sqrt{2}$; (v) $2t$.

2.6 *Velocity and Position by Integration

This optional section is intended for students who have already learned a little integral calculus. In Section 2.4 we analyzed the special case of straight-line motion with constant acceleration. When a_x is not constant, as is frequently the case, the equations that we derived in that section are no longer valid (Fig. 2.26). But even when a_x varies with time, we can still use the relationship $v_x = dx/dt$ to find the x-velocity v_x as a function of time if the position x is a known function of time. And we can still use $a_x = dv_x/dt$ to find the x-acceleration a_x as a function of time if the x-velocity v_x is a known function of time.

2.26 When you push your car's accelerator pedal to the floorboard, the resulting acceleration is *not* constant: the greater the car's speed, the more slowly it gains additional speed. A typical car takes twice as long to accelerate from 50 km/h to 100 km/h as it does to accelerate from 0 to 50 km/h.

In many situations, however, position and velocity are not known as functions of time, while acceleration is. How can we find the position and velocity from the acceleration function $a_x(t)$? This problem arises in navigating an airliner between North America and Europe (Fig. 2.27). The pilots must know their position precisely at all times, but over the ocean an airliner is usually out of range of both radio navigation beacons on land and air traffic controllers' radar. To determine their position, airliners carry a device called an inertial navigation system (INS), which measures the airliner's acceleration. This is done in much the same way that you can sense changes in the velocity of a car in which you're riding, even when your eyes are closed. (In Chapter 4 we'll discuss how your body detects acceleration.) Given this information, along with the airliner's initial position (say, a particular gate at Miami International Airport) and its initial velocity (zero when parked at the gate), the INS calculates the airliner's current velocity and position at all times during the flight. (Airliners also use the Global Positioning System, or GPS, for navigation, but this supplements INS rather than replacing it.) Our goal in this section is to see how these calculations are done for the simpler case of motion in a straight line with time-varying acceleration.

2.27 The position and velocity of an airliner crossing the Atlantic are found by integrating its acceleration with respect to time.

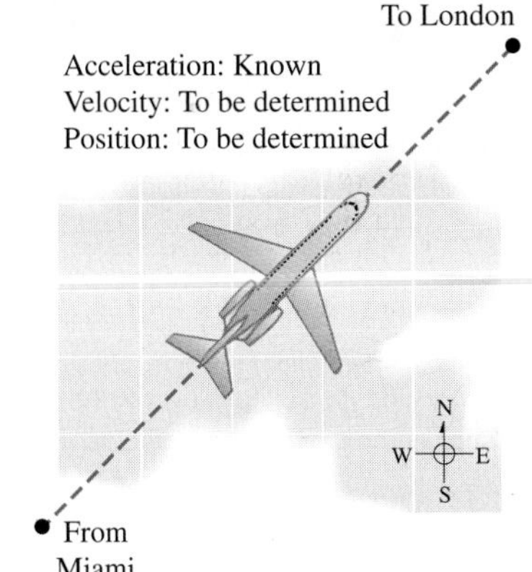

We first consider a graphical approach. Figure 2.28 is a graph of x-acceleration versus time for a body whose acceleration is not constant. We can divide the time interval between times t_1 and t_2 into many smaller intervals, calling a typical one Δt. Let the average x-acceleration during Δt be $a_{\text{av-}x}$. From Eq. (2.4) the change in x-velocity Δv_x during Δt is

$$\Delta v_x = a_{\text{av-}x}\,\Delta t$$

Graphically, Δv_x equals the area of the shaded strip with height $a_{\text{av-}x}$ and width Δt—that is, the area under the curve between the left and right sides of Δt. The total change in x-velocity during any interval (say, t_1 to t_2) is the sum of the x-velocity changes Δv_x in the small subintervals. So the total x-velocity change is represented graphically by the *total* area under the a_x-t curve between the vertical lines t_1 and t_2. (In Section 2.4 we showed this for the special case in which the acceleration is constant.)

2.28 An a_x-t graph for a body whose x-acceleration is not constant.

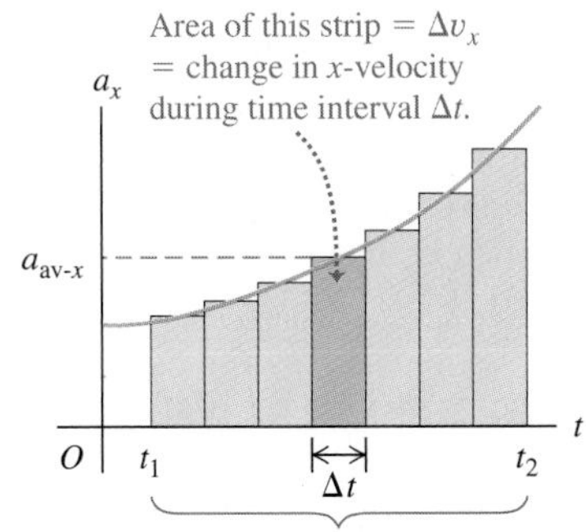

In the limit that all the Δt's become very small and their number very large, the value of $a_{\text{av-}x}$ for the interval from any time t to $t + \Delta t$ approaches the instantaneous x-acceleration a_x at time t. In this limit, the area under the a_x-t curve is the *integral* of a_x (which is in general a function of t) from t_1 to t_2. If v_{1x} is the x-velocity of the body at time t_1 and v_{2x} is the velocity at time t_2, then

$$v_{2x} - v_{1x} = \int_{v_{1x}}^{v_{2x}} dv_x = \int_{t_1}^{t_2} a_x\,dt \qquad (2.15)$$

The change in the x-velocity v_x is the time integral of the x-acceleration a_x.

We can carry out exactly the same procedure with the curve of x-velocity versus time. If x_1 is a body's position at time t_1 and x_2 is its position at time t_2, from Eq. (2.2) the displacement Δx during a small time interval Δt is equal to $v_{\text{av-}x}\,\Delta t$, where $v_{\text{av-}x}$ is the average x-velocity during Δt. The total displacement $x_2 - x_1$ during the interval $t_2 - t_1$ is given by

$$x_2 - x_1 = \int_{x_1}^{x_2} dx = \int_{t_1}^{t_2} v_x\,dt \qquad (2.16)$$

The change in position x—that is, the displacement—is the time integral of x-velocity v_x. Graphically, the displacement between times t_1 and t_2 is the area under the v_x-t curve between those two times. [This is the same result that we obtained in Section 2.4 for the special case in which v_x is given by Eq. (2.8).]

If $t_1 = 0$ and t_2 is any later time t, and if x_0 and v_{0x} are the position and velocity, respectively, at time $t = 0$, then we can rewrite Eqs. (2.15) and (2.16) as follows:

$$v_x = v_{0x} + \int_0^t a_x\,dt \qquad (2.17)$$

$$x = x_0 + \int_0^t v_x\,dt \qquad (2.18)$$

Here x and v_x are the position and x-velocity at time t. If we know the x-acceleration a_x as a function of time and we know the initial velocity v_{0x}, we can use Eq. (2.17) to find the x-velocity v_x at any time; in other words, we can find v_x as a function of time. Once we know this function, and given the initial position x_0, we can use Eq. (2.18) to find the position x at any time.

Example 2.9 Motion with changing acceleration

Sally is driving along a straight highway in her classic 1965 Mustang. At time $t = 0$, when Sally is moving at 10 m/s in the positive x-direction, she passes a signpost at $x = 50$ m. Her x-acceleration is a function of time:

$$a_x = 2.0\ \text{m/s}^2 - (0.10\ \text{m/s}^3)t$$

(a) Find her x-velocity and position as functions of time. (b) When is her x-velocity greatest? (c) What is the maximum x-velocity? (d) Where is the car when it reaches the maximum x-velocity?

SOLUTION

IDENTIFY: The x-acceleration is a function of time, so we cannot use the constant-acceleration formulas of Section 2.4.

SET UP: We use Eqs. (2.17) and (2.18) to find the x-velocity and position as functions of time. Once we have those functions, we'll be able to answer a variety of questions about the motion.

EXECUTE: (a) At $t = 0$, Sally's position is $x_0 = 50$ m and her x-velocity is $v_{0x} = 10$ m/s. Since we are given the x-acceleration a_x as a function of time, we first use Eq. (2.17) to find the x-velocity v_x as a function of time t. The integral of t^n is $\int t^n\,dt = \frac{1}{n+1}t^{n+1}$ for $n \neq -1$, so

$$\begin{aligned} v_x &= 10\ \text{m/s} + \int_0^t [2.0\ \text{m/s}^2 - (0.10\ \text{m/s}^3)t]\,dt \\ &= 10\ \text{m/s} + (2.0\ \text{m/s}^2)t - \frac{1}{2}(0.10\ \text{m/s}^3)t^2 \end{aligned}$$

Then we use Eq. (2.18) to find x as a function of t:

$$\begin{aligned} x &= 50\ \text{m} + \int_0^t \left[10\ \text{m/s} + (2.0\ \text{m/s}^2)t - \frac{1}{2}(0.10\ \text{m/s}^3)t^2\right] dt \\ &= 50\ \text{m} + (10\ \text{m/s})t + \frac{1}{2}(2.0\ \text{m/s}^2)t^2 - \frac{1}{6}(0.10\ \text{m/s}^3)t^3 \end{aligned}$$

Figure 2.29 shows graphs of a_x, v_x, and x as functions of time. Note that for any time t, the slope of the v_x-t graph equals the value of a_x and the slope of the x-t graph equals the value of v_x.

(b) The maximum value of v_x occurs when the x-velocity stops increasing and begins to decrease. At this instant, $dv_x/dt = a_x = 0$. Setting the expression for a_x equal to zero, we obtain

$$\begin{aligned} 0 &= 2.0\ \text{m/s}^2 - (0.10\ \text{m/s}^3)t \\ t &= \frac{2.0\ \text{m/s}^2}{0.10\ \text{m/s}^3} = 20\ \text{s} \end{aligned}$$

(c) We find the maximum x-velocity by substituting $t = 20$ s (when x-velocity is maximum) into the equation for v_x from part (a):

$$\begin{aligned} v_{\text{max-}x} &= 10\ \text{m/s} + (2.0\ \text{m/s}^2)(20\ \text{s}) - \frac{1}{2}(0.10\ \text{m/s}^3)(20\ \text{s})^2 \\ &= 30\ \text{m/s} \end{aligned}$$

2.29 The position, velocity, and acceleration of the car in Example 2.9 as functions of time. Can you show that if this motion continues, the car will stop at $t = 44.5$ s?

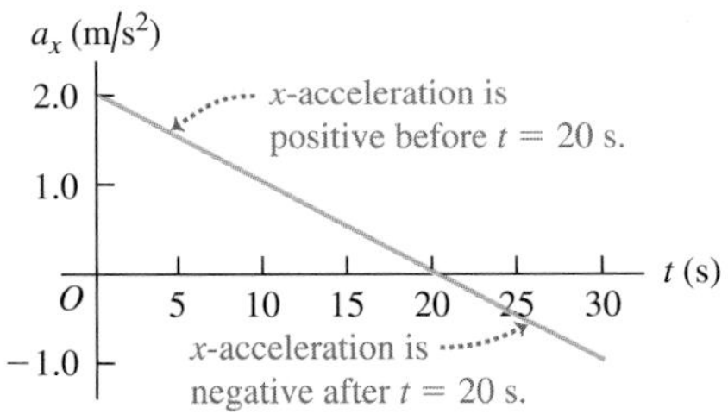

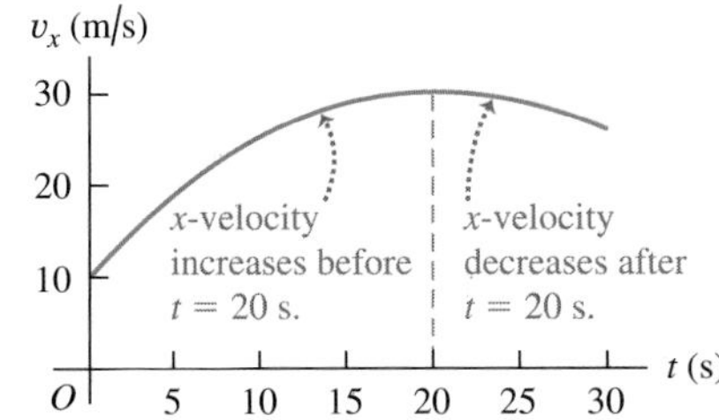

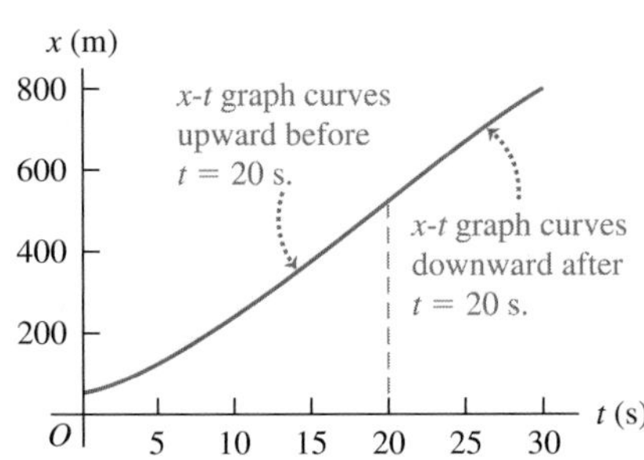

(d) The maximum value of v_x occurs at time $t = 20$ s. To obtain the position of the car at that time, we substitute $t = 20$ s into the expression for x from part (a):

$$x = 50\text{ m} + (10\text{ m/s})(20\text{ s}) + \frac{1}{2}(2.0\text{ m/s}^2)(20\text{ s})^2 - \frac{1}{6}(0.10\text{ m/s}^3)(20\text{ s})^3 = 517\text{ m}$$

EVALUATE: Figure 2.29 helps us interpret our results. The top graph in this figure shows that a_x is positive between $t = 0$ and $t = 20$ s and negative after that. It is zero at $t = 20$ s, the time at which v_x is maximum (the high point in the middle graph). The car speeds up until $t = 20$ s (because v_x and a_x have the same sign) and slows down after $t = 20$ s (because v_x and a_x have opposite signs).

Since v_x is maximum at $t = 20$ s, the x-t graph (the bottom graph in Fig. 2.29) has its maximum positive slope at this time. Note that the x-t graph is concave up (curved upward) from $t = 0$ to $t = 20$ s, when a_x is positive. The graph is concave down (curved downward) after $t = 20$ s, when a_x is negative.

Example 2.10 Constant-acceleration formulas via integration

Use Eqs. (2.17) and (2.18) to find v_x and x as functions of time in the case in which the acceleration is constant.

SOLUTION

IDENTIFY: This example serves as a check on the equations we've derived in this section. If they are correct, we should end up with the same constant-acceleration equations we derived in Section 2.4 without using integration.

SET UP: We follow the same steps as in Example 2.9. The only difference is that a_x is a constant.

EXECUTE: From Eq. (2.17) the x-velocity is given by

$$v_x = v_{0x} + \int_0^t a_x\,dt = v_{0x} + a_x\int_0^t dt = v_{0x} + a_x t$$

We were able to take a_x outside the integral because it is constant. Substituting this expression for v_x into Eq. (2.18), we get

$$x = x_0 + \int_0^t v_x\,dt = x_0 + \int_0^t (v_{0x} + a_x t)\,dt$$

Since v_{0x} and a_x are constants, we can take them outside the integral:

$$x = x_0 + v_{0x}\int_0^t dt + a_x\int_0^t t\,dt = x_0 + v_{0x}t + \frac{1}{2}a_x t^2$$

EVALUATE: Our results are the same as Eqs. (2.8) and (2.12) from Section 2.4, as they should be! Although we developed Eqs. (2.17) and (2.18) to deal with cases in which acceleration depends on time, they can be used just as well when the acceleration is constant.

Test Your Understanding of Section 2.6 If the x-acceleration a_x is increasing with time, will the v_x-t graph be (i) a straight line, (ii) concave up (i.e., with an upward curvature), or (iii) concave down (i.e., with a downward curvature)?

CHAPTER 2 SUMMARY

Straight-line motion, average and instantaneous x-velocity: When a particle moves along a straight line, we describe its position with respect to an origin O by means of a coordinate such as x. The particle's average x-velocity $v_{av\text{-}x}$ during a time interval $\Delta t = t_2 - t_1$ is equal to its displacement $\Delta x = x_2 - x_1$ divided by Δt. The instantaneous x-velocity v_x at any time t is equal to the average x-velocity for the time interval from t to $t + \Delta t$ in the limit that Δt goes to zero. Equivalently, v_x is the derivative of the position function with respect to time. (See Example 2.1)

$$v_{av\text{-}x} = \frac{x_2 - x_1}{t_2 - t_1} = \frac{\Delta x}{\Delta t} \quad (2.2)$$

$$v_x = \lim_{\Delta t \to 0} \frac{\Delta x}{\Delta t} = \frac{dx}{dt} \quad (2.3)$$

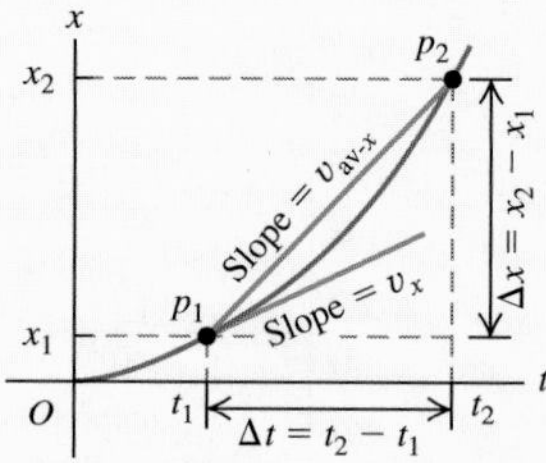

Average and instantaneous x-acceleration: The average x-acceleration $a_{av\text{-}x}$ during a time interval Δt is equal to the change in velocity $\Delta v_x = v_{2x} - v_{1x}$ during that time interval divided by Δt. The instantaneous x-acceleration a_x is the limit of $a_{av\text{-}x}$ as Δt goes to zero, or the derivative of v_x with respect to t. (See Examples 2.2 and 2.3.)

$$a_{av\text{-}x} = \frac{v_{2x} - v_{1x}}{t_2 - t_1} = \frac{\Delta v_x}{\Delta t} \quad (2.4)$$

$$a_x = \lim_{\Delta t \to 0} \frac{\Delta v_x}{\Delta t} = \frac{dv_x}{dt} \quad (2.5)$$

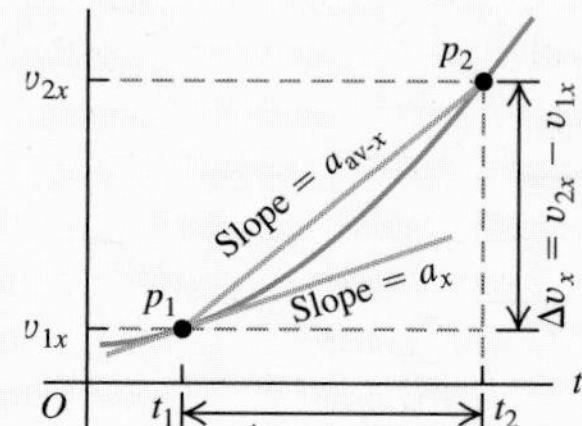

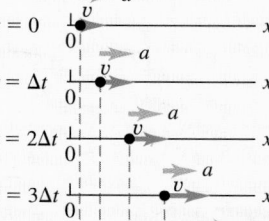

Straight-line motion with constant acceleration: When the x-acceleration is constant, four equations relate the position x and the x-velocity v_x at any time t to the initial position x_0, the initial x-velocity v_{0x} (both measured at time $t = 0$), and the x-acceleration a_x. (See Examples 2.4 and 2.5.)

Constant x-acceleration only:

$$v_x = v_{0x} + a_x t \quad (2.8)$$

$$x = x_0 + v_{0x}t + \frac{1}{2}a_x t^2 \quad (2.12)$$

$$v_x^2 = v_{0x}^2 + 2a_x(x - x_0) \quad (2.13)$$

$$x - x_0 = \left(\frac{v_{0x} + v_x}{2}\right)t \quad (2.14)$$

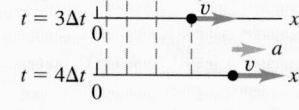

Freely falling bodies: Free fall is a case of motion with constant acceleration. The magnitude of the acceleration due to gravity is a positive quantity, g. The acceleration of a body in free fall is always downward. (See Examples 2.6–2.8.)

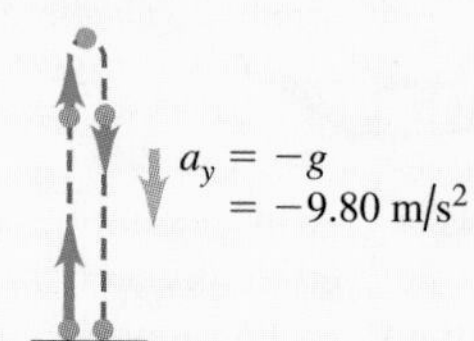

Straight-line motion with varying acceleration: When the acceleration is not constant but is a known function of time, we can find the velocity and position as functions of time by integrating the acceleration function. (See Examples 2.9 and 2.10.)

$$v_x = v_{0x} + \int_0^t a_x\, dt \quad (2.17)$$

$$x = x_0 + \int_0^t v_x\, dt \quad (2.18)$$

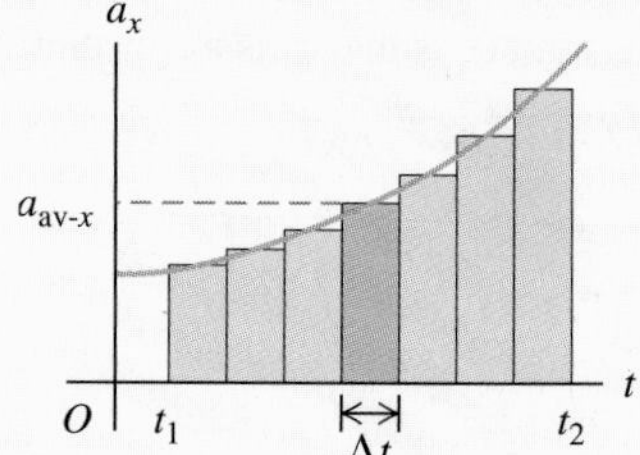

Key Terms

Answer to Chapter Opening Question ?

Yes. Acceleration refers to *any* change in velocity, including both speeding up and slowing down.

Answers to Test Your Understanding Questions

2.1 Answers to (a): (iv), (i) and (iii) (tie), (v), (ii); answer to (b): (i) and (iii); answer to (c): (v) In (a) the average x-velocity is $v_{\text{av-}x} = \Delta x/\Delta t$. For all five trips, $\Delta t = 1$ h. For the individual trips, we have (i) $\Delta x = +50$ km, $v_{\text{av-}x} = +50$ km/h; (ii) $\Delta x = -50$ km, $v_{\text{av-}x} = -50$ km/h; (iii) $\Delta x = 60$ km $- 10$ km $= +50$ km, $v_{\text{av-}x} = +50$ km/h; (iv) $\Delta x = +70$ km, $v_{\text{av-}x} = +70$ km/h; (v) $\Delta x = \Delta x = -20$ km $+ 20$ km $= 0$, $v_{\text{av-}x} = 0$. In (b) both have $v_{\text{av-}x} = +50$ km/h.

2.2 Answers: (a) *P*, *Q* and *S* (tie), *R* The x-velocity is **(b)** positive when the slope of the x-t graph is positive (***P***), **(c)** negative when the slope is negative (***R***), and **(d)** zero when the slope is zero (***Q* and *S***). **(e) *R*, *P*, *Q* and *S* (tie)** The speed is greatest when the slope of the x-t graph is steepest (either positive or negative) and zero when the slope is zero.

2.3 Answers: (a) *S*, where the x-t graph is curved upward (concave up). **(b) *Q*,** where the x-t graph is curved downward (concave down). **(c) *P* and *R*,** where the x-t graph is not curved either up or down. **(d)** At P, $v_x > 0$ and $a_x = 0$ (speed is **not changing**); at Q, $v_x > 0$ and $a_x < 0$ (speed is **decreasing**); at R, $v_x < 0$ and $a_x = 0$ (speed is **not changing**); and at S, $v_x < 0$ and $a_x > 0$ (speed is **decreasing**).

2.4 Answer: (b) The officer's x-acceleration is constant, so her v_x-t graph is a straight line, and the officer's motorcycle is moving faster than the motorist's car when the two vehicles meet at $t = 10$ s.

2.5 Answers: (a) (iii) Use Eq. (2.13) with x replaced by y and $a_y = g$; $v_y^2 = v_{0y}^2 - 2g(y - y_0)$. The starting height is $y_0 = 0$ and the y-velocity at the maximum height $y = h$ is $v_y = 0$, so $0 = v_{0y}^2 - 2gh$ and $h = v_{0y}^2/2g$. If the initial y-velocity is increased by a factor of 2, the maximum height increases by a factor of $2^2 = 4$ and the ball goes to height $4h$. **(b) (v)** Use Eq. (2.8) with x replaced by y and $a_y = g$; $v_y = v_{0y} - gt$. The y-velocity at the maximum height is $v_y = 0$, so $0 = v_{0y} - gt$ and $t = v_{0y}/g$. If the initial y-velocity is increased by a factor of 2, the time to reach the maximum height increases by a factor of 2 and becomes $2t$.

2.6 Answer: (ii) The acceleration a_x is equal to the slope of the v_x-t graph. If a_x is increasing, the slope of the v_x-t graph is also increasing and the graph is concave up.

PROBLEMS

For instructor-assigned homework, go to www.masteringphysics.com 

Discussion Questions

Q2.1. Does the speedometer of a car measure speed or velocity? Explain.

Q2.2. Figure 2.30 shows a series of high-speed photographs of an insect flying in a straight line from left to right (in the positive x-direction). Which of the graphs in Fig. 2.31 most plausibly depicts this insect's motion?

Figure 2.30 Question Q2.2.

● ● ● ● ● ●

Figure 2.31 Question Q2.2.

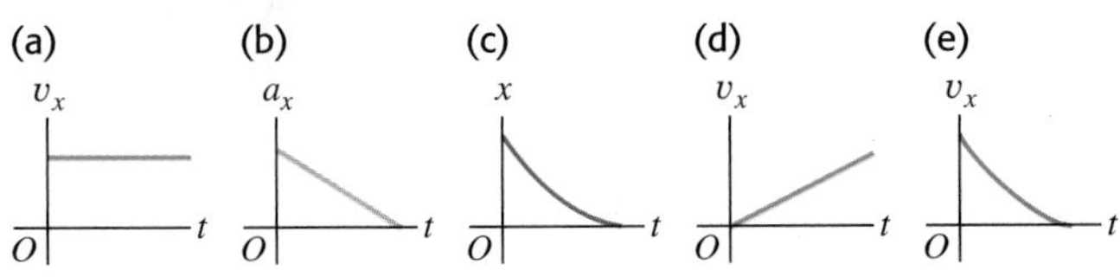

Q2.3. Can an object with constant acceleration reverse its direction of travel? Can it reverse its direction *twice?* In each case, explain your reasoning.

Q2.4. Under what conditions is average velocity equal to instantaneous velocity?

Q2.5. Is is possible for an object (a) to be slowing down while its acceleration is increasing in magnitude; (b) to be speeding up while its acceleration is decreasing? In each case, explain your reasoning.

Q2.6. Under what conditions does the magnitude of the average velocity equal the average speed?

Q2.7. When a Dodge Viper is at Elwood's Car Wash, a BMW Z3 is at Elm and Main. Later, when the Dodge reaches Elm and Main, the BMW reaches Elwood's Car Wash. How are the cars' average velocities between these two times related?

Q2.8. A driver in Massachusetts was sent to traffic court for speeding. The evidence against the driver was that a policewoman observed the driver's car alongside a second car at a certain moment, and the policewoman had already clocked the second car as going faster than the speed limit. The driver argued, "The second car was passing me. I was not speeding." The judge ruled against the driver because, in the judge's words, "If two cars were side by side, you were both speeding." If you were a lawyer representing the accused driver, how would you argue this case?

Q2.9. Can you have a zero displacement and a nonzero average velocity? A nonzero velocity? Illustrate your answers on an *x-t* graph.
Q2.10. Can you have zero acceleration and nonzero velocity? Explain using a v_x-t graph.
Q2.11. Can you have zero velocity and nonzero average acceleration? Zero velocity and nonzero acceleration? Explain using a v_x-t graph, and give an example of such motion.
Q2.12. An automobile is traveling west. Can it have a velocity toward the west and at the same time have an acceleration toward the east? Under what circumstances?
Q2.13. The official's truck in Fig. 2.2 is at $x_1 = 277$ m at $t_1 = 16.0$ s and is at $x_2 = 19$ m at $t_2 = 25.0$ s. (a) Sketch *two* different possible *x-t* graphs for the motion of the truck. (b) Does the average velocity $v_{\text{av-}x}$ during the time interval from t_1 to t_2 have the same value for both of your graphs? Why or why not?
Q2.14. Under constant acceleration the average velocity of a particle is half the sum of its initial and final velocities. Is this still true if the acceleration is *not* constant? Explain.
Q2.15. You throw a baseball straight up in the air so that it rises to a maximum height much greater than your height. Is the magnitude of the acceleration greater while it is being thrown or after it leaves your hand? Explain.
Q2.16. Prove these statements: (a) As long as you can neglect the effects of the air, if you throw anything vertically upward, it will have the same speed when it returns to the release point as when it was released. (b) The time of flight will be twice the time it takes to get to its highest point.
Q2.17. A dripping water faucet steadily releases drops 1.0 s apart. As these drops fall, will the distance between them increase, decrease, or remain the same? Prove your answer.
Q2.18. If the initial position and initial velocity of a vehicle are known and a record is kept of the acceleration at each instant, can you compute the vehicle's position after a certain time from these data? If so, explain how this might be done.
Q2.19. From the top of a tall building you throw one ball straight up with speed v_0 and one ball straight down with speed v_0. (a) Which ball has the greater speed when it reaches the ground? (b) Which ball gets to the ground first? (c) Which ball has a greater displacement when it reaches the ground? (d) Which ball has traveled the greater distance when it hits the ground?
Q2.20. A ball is dropped from rest from the top of a building of height h. At the same instant, a second ball is projected vertically upward from ground level, such that it has zero speed when it reaches the top of the building. When the two balls pass each other, which ball has the greater speed, or do they have the same speed? Explain. Where will the two balls be when they are alongside each other: at height $h/2$ above the ground, below this height, or above this height? Explain.

Exercises

Section 2.1 Displacement, Time, and Average Velocity

2.1. A rocket carrying a satellite is accelerating straight up from the earth's surface. At 1.15 s after liftoff, the rocket clears the top of its launch platform, 63 m above the ground. After an additional 4.75 s, it is 1.00 km above the ground. Calculate the magnitude of the average velocity of the rocket for (a) the 4.75-s part of its flight and (b) the first 5.90 s of its flight.
2.2. In an experiment, a shearwater (a seabird) was taken from its nest, flown 5150 km away, and released. The bird found its way back to its nest 13.5 days after release. If we place the origin in the nest and extend the $+x$-axis to the release point, what was the bird's average velocity in m/s (a) for the return flight, and (b) for the whole episode, from leaving the nest to returning?
2.3. Trip Home. You normally drive on the freeway between San Diego and Los Angeles at an average speed of 105 km/h (65 mi/h), and the trip takes 2 h and 20 min. On a Friday afternoon, however, heavy traffic slows you down and you drive the same distance at an average speed of only 70 km/h (43 mi/h). How much longer does the trip take?
2.4. From Pillar to Post. Starting from a pillar, you run 200 m east (the $+x$-direction) at an average speed of 5.0 m/s, and then run 280 m west at an average speed of 4.0 m/s to a post. Calculate (a) your average speed from pillar to post and (b) your average velocity from pillar to post.
2.5. Two runners start simultaneously from the same point on a circular 200-m track and run in *opposite* directions. One runs at a constant speed of 6.20 m/s, and the other runs at a constant speed of 5.50 m/s. When they first meet, (a) for how long a time will they have been running, and (b) how far will each one have run along the track?
2.6. Suppose the two runners in Exercise 2.5 start at the same time from the same place but run in the *same* direction. (a) When will the fast one first overtake ("lap") the slower one, and how far from the starting point will each have run? (b) When will the fast one overtake the slower one for the *second* time, and how far from the starting point will they be at that instant?
2.7. Earthquake Analysis. Earthquakes produce several types of shock waves. The most well known are the P-waves (P for *primary* or *pressure*) and the S-waves (S for *secondary* or *shear*). In the earth's crust, the P-waves travel at around 6.5 km/s, while the S-waves move at about 3.5 km/s. The actual speeds vary depending on the type of material they are going through. The time delay between the arrival of these two waves at a seismic recording station tells geologists how far away the earthquake occurred. If the time delay is 33 s, how far from the seismic station did the earthquake occur?
2.8. A Honda Civic travels in a straight line along a road. Its distance x from a stop sign is given as a function of time t by the equation $x(t) = \alpha t^2 - \beta t^3$, where $\alpha = 1.50\ \text{m/s}^2$ and $\beta = 0.0500\ \text{m/s}^3$. Calculate the average velocity of the car for each time interval: (a) $t = 0$ to $t = 2.00$ s; (b) $t = 0$ to $t = 4.00$ s; (c) $t = 2.00$ s to $t = 4.00$ s.

Section 2.2 Instantaneous Velocity

2.9. A car is stopped at a traffic light. It then travels along a straight road so that its distance from the light is given by $x(t) = bt^2 - ct^3$, where $b = 2.40\ \text{m/s}^2$ and $c = 0.120\ \text{m/s}^3$. (a) Calculate the average velocity of the car for the time interval $t = 0$ to $t = 10.0$ s. (b) Calculate the instantaneous velocity of the car at $t = 0$, $t = 5.0$ s, and $t = 10.0$ s. (c) How long after starting from rest is the car again at rest?
2.10. A physics professor leaves her house and walks along the sidewalk toward campus. After 5 min it starts to rain and she returns home. Her distance from her house as a function of time is shown in Fig. 2.32. At which of the labeled points is her velocity (a) zero? (b) constant and positive? (c) constant and negative? (d) increasing in magnitude? (e) decreasing in magnitude?

Figure 2.32 Exercise 2.10.

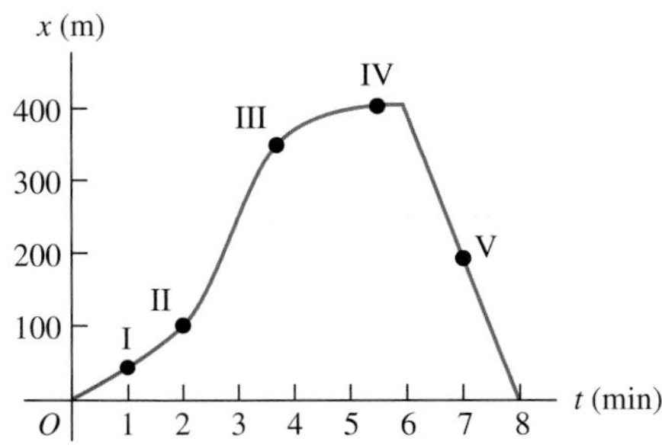

2.11. A ball moves in a straight line (the x-axis). The graph in Fig. 2.33 shows this ball's velocity as a function of time. (a) What are the ball's average speed and average velocity during the first 3.0 s? (b) Suppose that the ball moved in such a way that the graph segment after 2.0 s was $-3.0\ \text{m/s}$ instead of $+3.0\ \text{m/s}$. Find the ball's average speed and average velocity in this case.

Figure 2.33 Exercise 2.11.

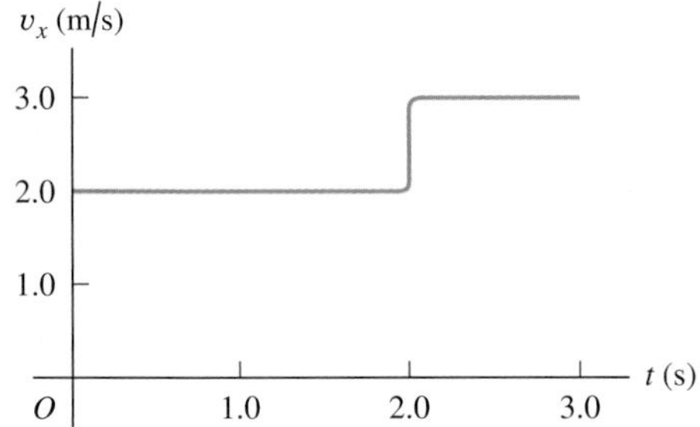

Section 2.3 Average and Instantaneous Acceleration

2.12. A test driver at Incredible Motors, Inc., is testing a new model car with a speedometer calibrated to read m/s rather than mi/h. The following series of speedometer readings was obtained during a test run along a long, straight road:

Time (s)	0	2	4	6	8	10	12	14	16
Speed (m/s)	0	0	2	6	10	16	19	22	22

(a) Compute the average acceleration during each 2-s interval. Is the acceleration constant? Is it constant during any part of the test run? (b) Make a v_x-t graph of the data, using scales of 1 cm = 1 s horizontally and 1 cm = 2 m/s vertically. Draw a smooth curve through the plotted points. By measuring the slope of your curve, find the instantaneous acceleration at $t = 9$ s, 13 s, and 15 s.

2.13. The Fastest (and Most Expensive) Car! The table shows test data for the Bugatti Veyron, the fastest car made. The car is moving in a straight line (the x-axis).

Time (s)	0	2.1	20.0	53
Speed (mi/h)	0	60	200	253

(a) Make a v_x-t graph of this car's velocity (in mi/h) as a function of time. Is its acceleration constant? (b) Calculate the car's average acceleration (in m/s^2) between (i) 0 and 2.1 s; (ii) 2.1 s and 20.0 s; (iii) 20.0 s and 53 s. Are these results consistent with your graph in part (a)? (Before you decide to buy this car, it might be helpful to know that only 300 will be built, it runs out of gas in 12 minutes at top speed, and it costs \$1.25 million!)

2.14. Figure 2.34 shows the velocity of a solar-powered car as a function of time. The driver accelerates from a stop sign, cruises for 20 s at a constant speed of 60 km/h, and then brakes to come to a stop 40 s after leaving the stop sign. (a) Compute the average acceleration during the following time intervals: (i) $t = 0$ to $t = 10$ s; (ii) $t = 30$ s to $t = 40$ s; (iii) $t = 10$ s to $t = 30$ s; (iv) $t = 0$ to $t = 40$ s. (b) What is the instantaneous acceleration at $t = 20$ s and at $t = 35$ s?

Figure 2.34 Exercise 2.14.

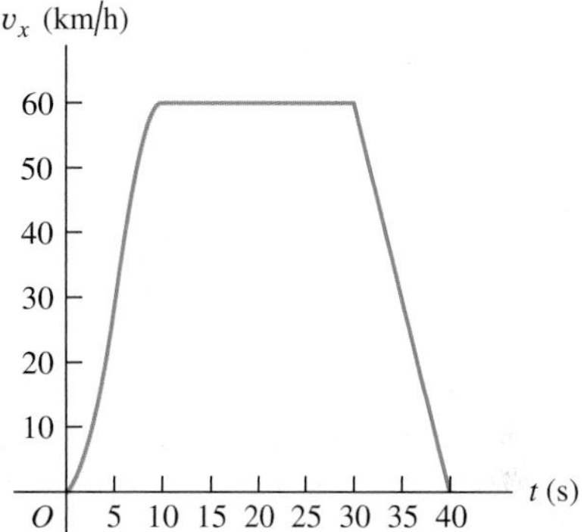

2.15. A turtle crawls along a straight line, which we will call the x-axis with the positive direction to the right. The equation for the turtle's position as a function of time is $x(t) = 50.0\ \text{cm} + (2.00\ \text{cm/s})t - (0.0625\ \text{cm/s}^2)t^2$. (a) Find the turtle's initial velocity, initial position, and initial acceleration. (b) At what time t is the velocity of the turtle zero? (c) How long after starting does it take the turtle to return to its starting point? (d) At what times t is the turtle a distance of 10.0 cm from its starting point? What is the velocity (magnitude and direction) of the turtle at each of these times? (e) Sketch graphs of x versus t, v_x versus t, and a_x versus t, for the time interval $t = 0$ to $t = 40$ s.

2.16. An astronaut has left the International Space Station to test a new space scooter. Her partner measures the following velocity changes, each taking place in a 10-s interval. What are the magnitude, the algebraic sign, and the direction of the average acceleration in each interval? Assume that the positive direction is to the right. (a) At the beginning of the interval the astronaut is moving toward the right along the x-axis at 15.0 m/s, and at the end of the interval she is moving toward the right at 5.0 m/s. (b) At the beginning she is moving toward the left at 5.0 m/s, and at the end she is moving toward the left at 15.0 m/s. (c) At the beginning she is moving toward the right at 15.0 m/s, and at the end she is moving toward the left at 15.0 m/s.

2.17. Auto Acceleration. Based on your experiences of riding in automobiles, estimate the magnitude of a car's average acceleration when it (a) accelerates onto a freeway from rest to 65 mi/h, and (b) brakes from highway speeds to a sudden stop. (c) Explain why the average acceleration in each case could be regarded as either positive or negative.

2.18. A car's velocity as a function of time is given by $v_x(t) = \alpha + \beta t^2$, where $\alpha = 3.00\ \text{m/s}$ and $\beta = 0.100\ \text{m/s}^3$. (a) Calculate the average acceleration for the time interval $t = 0$ to $t = 5.00$ s.

(b) Calculate the instantaneous acceleration for $t = 0$ and $t = 5.00$ s. (c) Draw accurate v_x-t and a_x-t graphs for the car's motion between $t = 0$ and $t = 5.00$ s.

2.19. Figure 2.35 is a graph of the coordinate of a spider crawling along the x-axis. (a) Graph its velocity and acceleration as functions of time. (b) In a motion diagram (like Fig. 2.13b and 2.14b), show the position, velocity, and acceleration of the spider at the five times $t = 2.5$ s, $t = 10$ s, $t = 20$ s, $t = 30$ s, and $t = 37.5$ s.

Figure 2.35 Exercise 2.19.

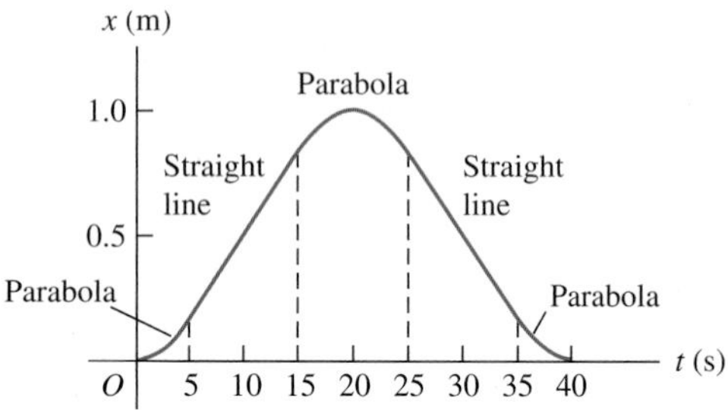

2.20. The position of the front bumper of a test car under microprocessor control is given by $x(t) = 2.17\text{ m} + (4.80\text{ m/s}^2)t^2 - (0.100\text{ m/s}^6)t^6$. (a) Find its position and acceleration at the instants when the car has zero velocity. (b) Draw x-t, v_x-t, and a_x-t graphs for the motion of the bumper between $t = 0$ and $t = 2.00$ s.

Section 2.4 Motion with Constant Acceleration

2.21. An antelope moving with constant acceleration covers the distance between two points 70.0 m apart in 7.00 s. Its speed as it passes the second point is 15.0 m/s. (a) What is its speed at the first point? (b) What is its acceleration?

2.22. The catapult of the aircraft carrier USS *Abraham Lincoln* accelerates an F/A-18 Hornet jet fighter from rest to a takeoff speed of 173 mi/h in a distance of 307 ft. Assume constant acceleration. (a) Calculate the acceleration of the fighter in m/s^2. (b) Calculate the time required for the fighter to accelerate to takeoff speed.

2.23. A Fast Pitch. The fastest measured pitched baseball left the pitcher's hand at a speed of 45.0 m/s. If the pitcher was in contact with the ball over a distance of 1.50 m and produced constant acceleration, (a) what acceleration did he give the ball, and (b) how much time did it take him to pitch it?

2.24. A Tennis Serve. In the fastest measured tennis serve, the ball left the racquet at 73.14 m/s. A served tennis ball is typically in contact with the racquet for 30.0 ms and starts from rest. Assume constant acceleration. (a) What was the ball's acceleration during this serve? (b) How far did the ball travel during the serve?

2.25. Automobile Airbags. The human body can survive an acceleration trauma incident (sudden stop) if the magnitude of the acceleration is less than 250 m/s^2. If you are in an automobile accident with an initial speed of 105 km/h (65 mi/h) and you are stopped by an airbag that inflates from the dashboard, over what distance must the airbag stop you for you to survive the crash?

2.26. Entering the Freeway. A car sits in an entrance ramp to a freeway, waiting for a break in the traffic. The driver accelerates with constant acceleration along the ramp and onto the freeway. The car starts from rest, moves in a straight line, and has a speed of 20 m/s (45 mi/h) when it reaches the end of the 120-m-long ramp. (a) What is the acceleration of the car? (b) How much time does it take the car to travel the length of the ramp? (c) The traffic on the freeway is moving at a constant speed of 20 m/s. What distance does the traffic travel while the car is moving the length of the ramp?

2.27. Launch of the Space Shuttle. At launch the space shuttle weighs 4.5 million pounds. When it is launched from rest, it takes 8.00 s to reach 161 km/h, and at the end of the first 1.00 min its speed is 1610 km/h. (a) What is the average acceleration (in m/s^2) of the shuttle (i) during the first 8.00 s, and (ii) between 8.00 s and the end of the first 1.00 min? (b) Assuming the acceleration is constant during each time interval (but not necessarily the same in both intervals), what distance does the shuttle travel (i) during the first 8.00 s, and (ii) during the interval from 8.00 s to 1.00 min?

2.28. According to recent test data, an automobile travels 0.250 mi in 19.9 s, starting from rest. The same car, when braking from 60.0 mi/h on dry pavement, stops in 146 ft. Assume constant acceleration in each part of the motion, but not necessarily the same acceleration when slowing down as when speeding up. (a) Find the acceleration of this car when it is speeding up and when it is braking. (b) If its acceleration is constant, how fast (in mi/h) should this car be traveling after 0.250 mi of acceleration? The actual measured speed is 70.0 mi/h; what does this tell you about the motion? (c) How long does it take this car to stop while braking from 60.0 mi/h?

2.29. A cat walks in a straight line, which we shall call the x-axis with the positive direction to the right. As an observant physicist, you make measurements of this cat's motion and construct a graph of the feline's velocity as a function of time (Fig. 2.36). (a) Find the cat's velocity at $t = 4.0$ s and at $t = 7.0$ s. (b) What is the cat's acceleration at $t = 3.0$ s? At $t = 6.0$ s? At $t = 7.0$ s? (c) What distance does the cat move during the first 4.5 s? From $t = 0$ to $t = 7.5$ s? (d) Sketch clear graphs of the cat's acceleration and position as functions of time, assuming that the cat started at the origin.

Figure 2.36 Exercise 2.29.

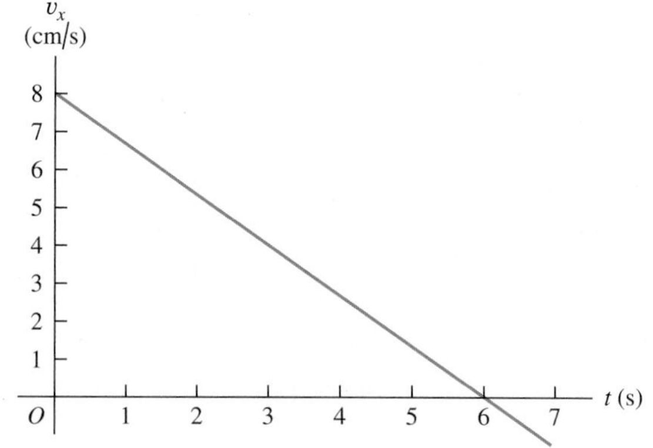

2.30. At $t = 0$ a car is stopped at a traffic light. When the light turns green, the car starts to speed up, and gains speed at a constant rate until it reaches a speed of 20 m/s 8 seconds after the light turns green. The car continues at a constant speed for 60 m. Then the driver sees a red light up ahead at the next intersection, and starts slowing down at a constant rate. The car stops at the red light, 180 m from where it was at $t = 0$. (a) Draw accurate x-t, v_x-t, and a_x-t graphs for the motion of the car. (b) In a motion diagram (like Figs. 2.13b and 2.14b), show the position, velocity, and acceleration of the car at 4 s after the light changes, while traveling at constant speed, and while slowing down.

2.31. The graph in Fig. 2.37 shows the velocity of a motorcycle police officer plotted as a function of time. (a) Find the instantaneous acceleration at $t = 3$ s, at $t = 7$ s, and at $t = 11$ s. (b) How far does the officer go in the first 5 s? The first 9 s? The first 13 s?

Figure **2.37** Exercise 2.31.

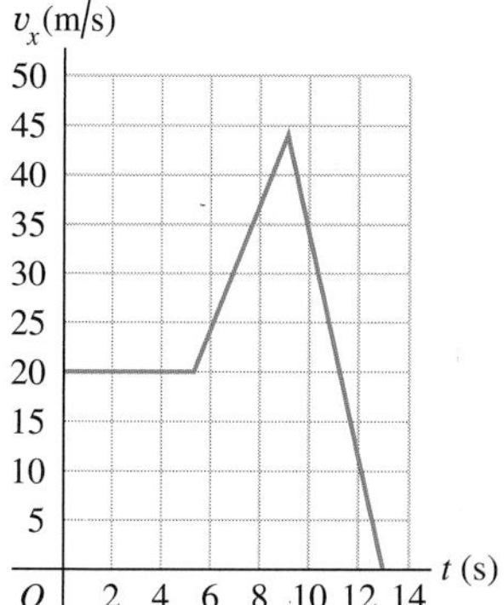

2.32. Figure 2.38 is a graph of the acceleration of a model railroad locomotive moving on the x-axis. Graph its velocity and x-coordinate as functions of time if $x = 0$ and $v_x = 0$ at $t = 0$.

Figure **2.38** Exercise 2.32.

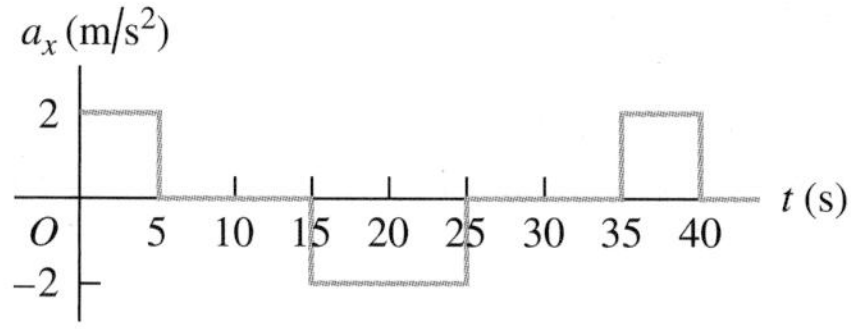

2.33. A spaceship ferrying workers to Moon Base I takes a straight-line path from the earth to the moon, a distance of 384,000 km. Suppose the spaceship starts from rest and accelerates at 20.0 m/s^2 for the first 15.0 min of the trip, and then travels at constant speed until the last 15.0 min, when it slows down at a rate of 20.0 m/s^2, just coming to rest as it reaches the moon. (a) What is the maximum speed attained? (b) What fraction of the total distance is traveled at constant speed? (c) What total time is required for the trip?

2.34. A subway train starts from rest at a station and accelerates at a rate of 1.60 m/s^2 for 14.0 s. It runs at constant speed for 70.0 s and slows down at a rate of 3.50 m/s^2 until it stops at the next station. Find the *total* distance covered.

2.35. Two cars, A and B, move along the x-axis. Figure 2.39 is a graph of the positions of A and B versus time. (a) In motion diagrams (like Figs. 2.13b and 2.14b), show the position, velocity, and acceleration of each of the two cars at $t = 0$, $t = 1$ s, and $t = 3$ s. (b) At what time(s), if any, do A and B have the same position? (c) Graph velocity versus time for both A and B. (d) At what time(s), if any, do A and B have the same velocity? (e) At what time(s), if any, does car A pass car B? (f) At what time(s), if any, does car B pass car A?

Figure **2.39** Exercise 2.35.

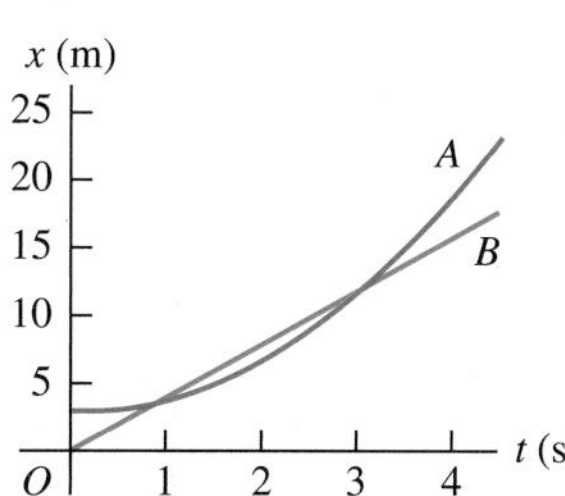

2.36. At the instant the traffic light turns green, a car that has been waiting at an intersection starts ahead with a constant acceleration of 3.20 m/s^2. At the same instant a truck, traveling with a constant speed of 20.0 m/s, overtakes and passes the car. (a) How far beyond its starting point does the car overtake the truck? (b) How fast is the car traveling when it overtakes the truck? (c) Sketch an x-t graph of the motion of both vehicles. Take $x = 0$ at the intersection. (d) Sketch a v_x-t graph of the motion of both vehicles.

2.37. Mars Landing. In January 2004, NASA landed exploration vehicles on Mars. Part of the descent consisted of the following stages:

Stage A: Friction with the atmosphere reduced the speed from 19,300 km/h to 1600 km/h in 4.0 min.

Stage B: A parachute then opened to slow it down to 321 km/h in 94 s.

Stage C: Retro rockets then fired to reduce its speed to zero over a distance of 75 m.

Assume that each stage followed immediately after the preceding one and that the acceleration during each stage was constant. (a) Find the rocket's acceleration (in m/s^2) during each stage. (b) What total distance (in km) did the rocket travel during stages A, B, and C?

Section 2.5 Freely Falling Bodies

2.38. Raindrops. If the effects of the air acting on falling raindrops are ignored, then we can treat raindrops as freely falling objects. (a) Rain clouds are typically a few hundred meters above the ground. Estimate the speed with which raindrops would strike the ground if they were freely falling objects. Give your estimate in m/s, km/h, and mi/h. (b) Estimate (from your own personal observations of rain) the speed with which raindrops actually strike the ground. (c) Based on your answers to parts (a) and (b), is it a good approximation to neglect the effects of the air on falling raindrops? Explain.

2.39. (a) If a flea can jump straight up to a height of 0.440 m, what is its initial speed as it leaves the ground? (b) How long is it in the air?

2.40. Touchdown on the Moon. A lunar lander is making its descent to Moon Base I (Fig. 2.40). The lander descends slowly under the retro-thrust of its descent engine. The engine is cut off when the lander is 5.0 m above the surface and has a downward speed of 0.8 m/s. With the engine off, the lander is in free fall. What is the speed of the lander just before it touches the surface? The acceleration due to gravity on the moon is 1.6 m/s^2.

Figure **2.40** Exercise 2.40.

5.0 m

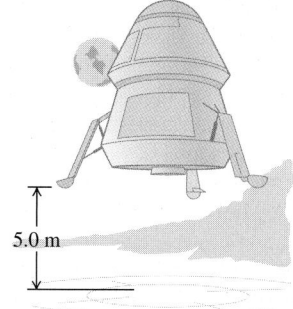

2.41. A Simple Reaction-Time Test. A meter stick is held vertically above your hand, with the lower end between your thumb and first finger. On seeing the meter stick released, you grab it with these two fingers. You can calculate your reaction time from the distance the meter stick falls, read directly from the point where your fingers grabbed it. (a) Derive a relationship for your reaction time in terms of this measured distance, d. (b) If the measured distance is 17.6 cm, what is the reaction time?

2.42. A brick is dropped (zero initial speed) from the roof of a building. The brick strikes the ground in 2.50 s. You may ignore air resistance, so the brick is in free fall. (a) How tall, in meters, is the building? (b) What is the magnitude of the brick's velocity just before it reaches the ground? (c) Sketch a_y-t, v_y-t, and y-t graphs for the motion of the brick.

2.43. Launch Failure. A 7500-kg rocket blasts off vertically from the launch pad with a constant upward acceleration of 2.25 m/s^2 and feels no appreciable air resistance. When it has reached a height of 525 m, its engines suddenly fail so that the only force acting on it is now gravity. (a) What is the maximum height this rocket will reach above the launch pad? (b) How much time after engine failure will elapse before the rocket comes crashing down to the launch pad, and how fast will it be moving just before it crashes? (c) Sketch a_y-t, v_y-t, and y-t graphs of the rocket's motion from the instant of blast-off to the instant just before it strikes the launch pad.

2.44. A hot-air balloonist, rising vertically with a constant velocity of magnitude 5.00 m/s, releases a sandbag at an instant when the balloon is 40.0 m above the ground (Fig. 2.41). After it is released, the sandbag is in free fall. (a) Compute the position and velocity of the sandbag at 0.250 s and 1.00 s after its release. (b) How many seconds after its release will the bag strike the ground? (c) With what magnitude of velocity does it strike the ground? (d) What is the greatest height above the ground that the sandbag reaches? (e) Sketch a_y-t, v_y-t, and y-t graphs for the motion.

Figure 2.41 Exercise 2.44.

2.45. A student throws a water balloon vertically downward from the top of a building. The balloon leaves the thrower's hand with a speed of 6.00 m/s. Air resistance may be ignored, so the water balloon is in free fall after it leaves the thrower's hand. (a) What is its speed after falling for 2.00 s? (b) How far does it fall in 2.00 s? (c) What is the magnitude of its velocity after falling 10.0 m? (d) Sketch a_y-t, v_y-t, and y-t graphs for the motion.

2.46. An egg is thrown nearly vertically upward from a point near the cornice of a tall building. It just misses the cornice on the way down and passes a point 50.0 m below its starting point 5.00 s after it leaves the thrower's hand. Air resistance may be ignored. (a) What is the initial speed of the egg? (b) How high does it rise above its starting point? (c) What is the magnitude of its velocity at the highest point? (d) What are the magnitude and direction of its acceleration at the highest point? (e) Sketch a_y-t, v_y-t, and y-t graphs for the motion of the egg.

2.47. The rocket-driven sled *Sonic Wind No. 2,* used for investigating the physiological effects of large accelerations, runs on a straight, level track 1070 m (3500 ft) long. Starting from rest, it can reach a speed of 224 m/s (500 mi/h) in 0.900 s. (a) Compute the acceleration in m/s^2, assuming that it is constant. (b) What is the ratio of this acceleration to that of a freely falling body (g)? (c) What distance is covered in 0.900 s? (d) A magazine article states that at the end of a certain run, the speed of the sled decreased from 283 m/s (632 mi/h) to zero in 1.40 s and that during this time the magnitude of the acceleration was greater than 40g. Are these figures consistent?

2.48. A large boulder is ejected vertically upward from a volcano with an initial speed of 40.0 m/s. Air resistance may be ignored. (a) At what time after being ejected is the boulder moving at 20.0 m/s upward? (b) At what time is it moving at 20.0 m/s downward? (c) When is the displacement of the boulder from its initial position zero? (d) When is the velocity of the boulder zero? (e) What are the magnitude and direction of the acceleration while the boulder is (i) moving upward? (ii) Moving downward? (iii) At the highest point? (f) Sketch a_y-t, v_y-t, and y-t graphs for the motion.

2.49. A 15-kg rock is dropped from rest on the earth and reaches the ground in 1.75 s. When it is dropped from the same height on Saturn's satellite Enceladus, it reaches the ground in 18.6 s. What is the acceleration due to gravity on Enceladus?

*Section 2.6 Velocity and Position by Integration

***2.50.** The acceleration of a bus is given by $a_x(t) = \alpha t$, where $\alpha = 1.2\ m/s^3$. (a) If the bus's velocity at time t = 1.0 s is 5.0 m/s, what is its velocity at time t = 2.0 s? (b) If the bus's position at time t = 1.0 s is 6.0 m, what is its position at time t = 2.0 s? (c) Sketch a_x-t, v_x-t, and x-t graphs for the motion.

***2.51.** The acceleration of a motorcycle is given by $a_x(t) = At - Bt^2$, where $A = 1.50\ m/s^3$ and $B = 0.120\ m/s^4$. The motorcycle is at rest at the origin at time $t = 0$. (a) Find its position and velocity as functions of time. (b) Calculate the maximum velocity it attains.

***2.52. Flying Leap of the Flea.** High-speed motion pictures (3500 frames/second) of a jumping, 210-μg flea yielded the data used to plot the graph given in Fig. 2.42. (See "The Flying Leap of the Flea" by M. Rothschild, Y. Schlein, K. Parker, C. Neville, and S. Sternberg in the November 1973 *Scientific American.*) This flea was about 2 mm long and jumped at a nearly vertical take-off angle. Use the graph to answer the questions. (a) Is the acceleration of the flea ever zero? If so, when? Justify your answer. (b) Find the maximum height the flea reached in the first 2.5 ms. (c) Find the flea's acceleration at 0.5 ms, 1.0 ms, and 1.5 ms. (d) Find the flea's height at 0.5 ms, 1.0 ms, and 1.5 ms.

Figure 2.42 Exercise 2.52.

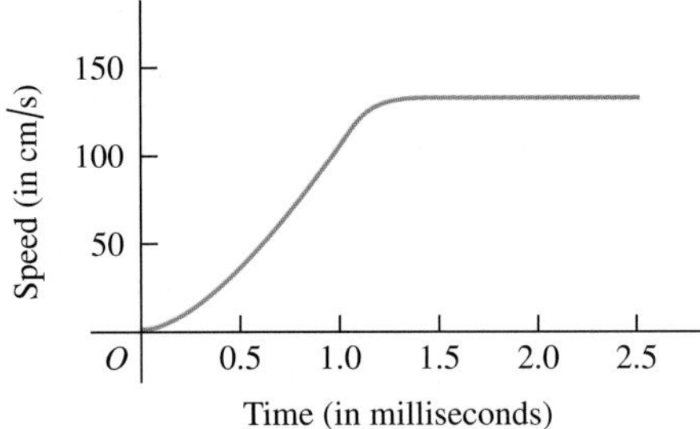

***2.53.** The graph in Fig. 2.43 describes the acceleration as a function of time for a stone rolling down a hill starting from rest. (a) Find

Figure 2.43 Exercise 2.53

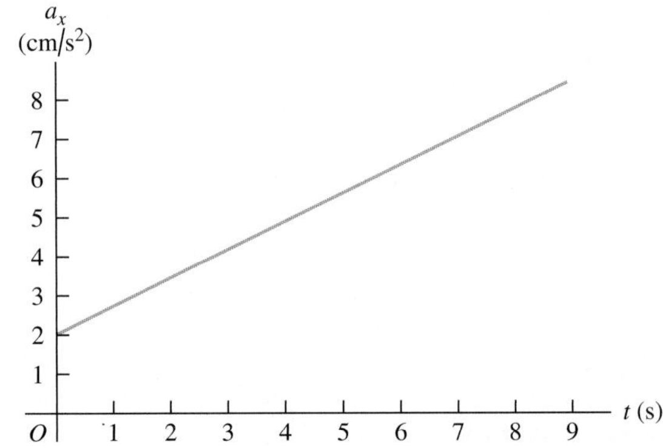

the change in the stone's velocity between $t = 2.5$ s and $t = 7.5$ s. (b) Sketch a graph of the stone's velocity as a function of time.

Problems

2.54. On a 20-mile bike ride, you ride the first 10 miles at an average speed of 8 mi/h. What must your average speed over the next 10 miles be to have your average speed for the total 20 miles be (a) 4 mi/h? (b) 12 mi/h? (c) Given this average speed for the first 10 miles, can you possibly attain an average speed of 16 mi/h for the total 20-mile ride? Explain.

2.55. The position of a particle between $t = 0$ and $t = 2.00$ s is given by $x(t) = (3.00\ \text{m/s}^3)t^3 - (10.0\ \text{m/s}^2)t^2 + (9.00\ \text{m/s})t$. (a) Draw the x-t, v_x-t, and a_x-t graphs of this particle. (b) At what time(s) between $t = 0$ and $t = 2.00$ s is the particle instantaneously at rest? Does your numerical result agree with the v_x-t graph in part (a)? (c) At each time calculated in part (b) is the acceleration of the particle positive or negative? Show that in each case the same answer is deduced from $a_x(t)$ and from the v_x-t graph. (d) At what time(s) between $t = 0$ and $t = 2.00$ s is the velocity of the particle instantaneously not changing? Locate this point on the v_x-t and a_x-t graphs of part (a). (e) What is the particle's greatest distance from the origin $(x = 0)$ between $t = 0$ and $t = 2.00$ s? (f) At what time(s) between $t = 0$ and $t = 2.00$ s is the particle *speeding up* at the greatest rate? At what time(s) between $t = 0$ and $t = 2.00$ s is the particle *slowing down* at the greatest rate? Locate these points on the v_x-t and a_x-t graphs of part (a).

2.56. Relay Race. In a relay race, each contestant runs 25.0 m while carrying an egg balanced on a spoon, turns around, and comes back to the starting point. Edith runs the first 25.0 m in 20.0 s. On the return trip she is more confident and takes only 15.0 s. What is the magnitude of her average velocity for (a) the first 25.0 m? (b) The return trip? (c) What is her average velocity for the entire round trip? (d) What is her average speed for the round trip?

2.57. Dan gets on Interstate Highway I–80 at Seward, Nebraska, and drives due west in a straight line and at an average velocity of magnitude 88 km/h. After traveling 76 km, he reaches the Aurora exit (Fig. 2.44). Realizing he has gone too far, he turns around and drives due east 34 km back to the York exit at an average velocity of magnitude 72 km/h. For his whole trip from Seward to the York exit, what are (a) his average speed and (b) the magnitude of his average velocity?

Figure 2.44 Problem 2.57.

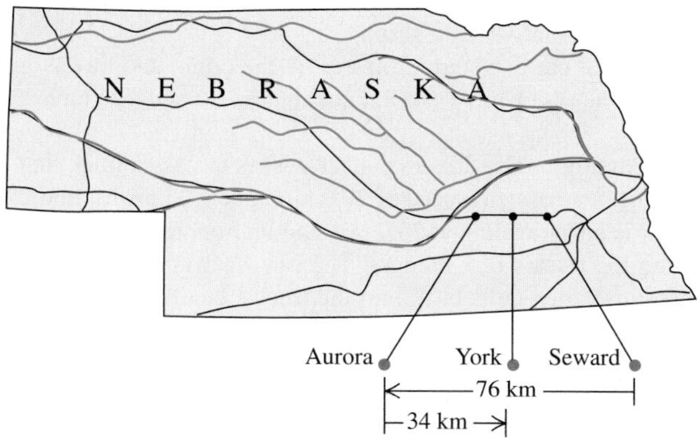

2.58. Freeway Traffic. According to a *Scientific American* article (May 1990), current freeways can sustain about 2400 vehicles per lane per hour in smooth traffic flow at 96 km/h (60 mi/h). With more vehicles the traffic flow becomes "turbulent" (stop-and-go). (a) If a vehicle is 4.6 m (15 ft) long on the average, what is the average spacing between vehicles at the above traffic density? (b) Collision-avoidance automated control systems, which operate by bouncing radar or sonar signals off surrounding vehicles and then accelerate or brake the car when necessary, could greatly reduce the required spacing between vehicles. If the average spacing is 9.2 m (two car lengths), how many vehicles per hour can a lane of traffic carry at 96 km/h?

2.59. A world-class sprinter accelerates to his maximum speed in 4.0 s. He then maintains this speed for the remainder of a 100-m race, finishing with a total time of 9.1 s. (a) What is the runner's average acceleration during the first 4.0 s? (b) What is his average acceleration during the last 5.1 s? (c) What is his average acceleration for the entire race? (d) Explain why your answer to part (c) is not the average of the answers to parts (a) and (b).

2.60. A sled starts from rest at the top of a hill and slides down with a constant acceleration. At some later time it is 14.4 m from the top; 2.00 s after that it is 25.6 m from the top, 2.00 s later 40.0 m from the top, and 2.00 s later it is 57.6 m from the top. (a) What is the magnitude of the average velocity of the sled during each of the 2.00-s intervals after passing the 14.4-m point? (b) What is the acceleration of the sled? (c) What is the speed of the sled when it passes the 14.4-m point? (d) How much time did it take to go from the top to the 14.4-m point? (e) How far did the sled go during the first second after passing the 14.4-m point?

2.61. A gazelle is running in a straight line (the x-axis). The graph in Fig. 2.45 shows this animal's velocity as a function of time. During the first 12.0 s, find (a) the total distance moved and (b) the displacement of the gazelle. (c) Sketch an a_x-t graph showing this gazelle's acceleration as a function of time for the first 12.0 s.

Figure 2.45 Problem 2.61.

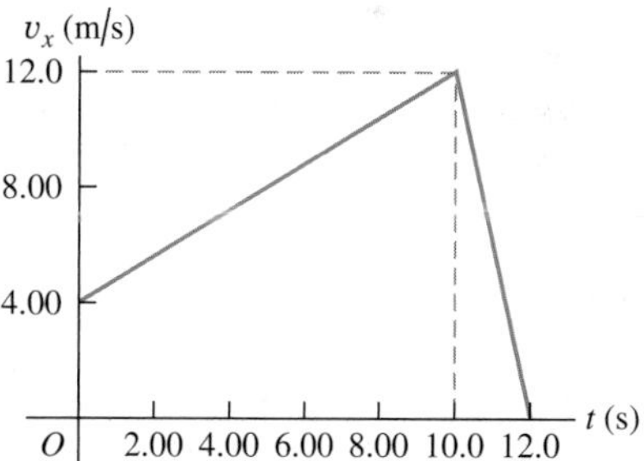

2.62. In air or vacuum light travels at a constant speed of 3.0×10^8 m/s. To answer some of these questions you may need to look up astronomical data in Appendix F. (a) One light year is defined as the distance light travels in 1 year. Use this information to determine how many meters there are in 1 light-year. (b) How far in meters does light travel in 1 nanosecond? (c) When a solar flare occurs on our sun, how soon after its occurrence can we first observe it? (d) By bouncing laser beams off a reflector placed on our moon by the Apollo astronauts, astronomers can make very accurate measurements of the earth–moon distance. How long after it is sent does it take such a laser beam (which is just a light beam) to return to earth? (e) The *Voyager* probe, which passed by Neptune in August 1989, was about 3.0 billion miles from earth at that time. Photographs and other information were sent to earth by radio waves, which travel at the speed of light. How long did it take these waves to reach earth from *Voyager*?

2.63. Use the information in Appendix F to answer the questions. (a) What is the speed of the Galapagos Islands, on the earth's equator, due to our planet's spin on its axis? (b) What is the earth's speed due to its rotation around the sun? (c) If light would bend around the curvature of the earth (which it does not), how many times would a light beam go around the equator in one second?

2.64. A rigid ball traveling in a straight line (the x-axis) hits a solid wall and suddenly rebounds during a brief instant. The v_x-t graph in Fig. 2.46 shows this ball's velocity as a function of time. During the first 20.0 s of its motion, find (a) the total distance the ball moves, and (b) its displacement. (c) Sketch a graph of a_x-t for this ball's motion. (d) Is the graph shown really vertical at 5.00 s? Explain.

Figure 2.46 Problem 2.64.

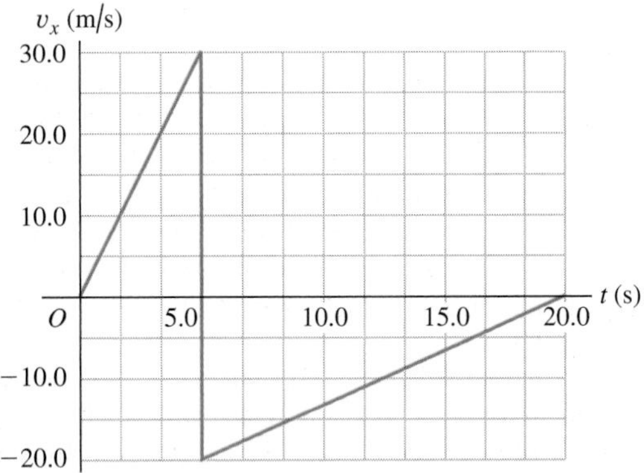

2.65. A ball starts from rest and rolls down a hill with uniform acceleration, traveling 150 m during the second 5.0 s of its motion. How far did it roll during the first 5.0 s of motion?

2.66. Collision. The engineer of a passenger train traveling at 25.0 m/s sights a freight train whose caboose is 200 m ahead on the same track (Fig. 2.47). The freight train is traveling at 15.0 m/s in the same direction as the passenger train. The engineer of the passenger train immediately applies the brakes, causing a constant acceleration of $-0.100\ \text{m/s}^2$, while the freight train continues with constant speed. Take $x = 0$ at the location of the front of the passenger train when the engineer applies the brakes. (a) Will the cows nearby witness a collision? (b) If so, where will it take place? (c) On a single graph, sketch the positions of the front of the passenger train and the back of the freight train.

Figure 2.47 Problem 2.66.

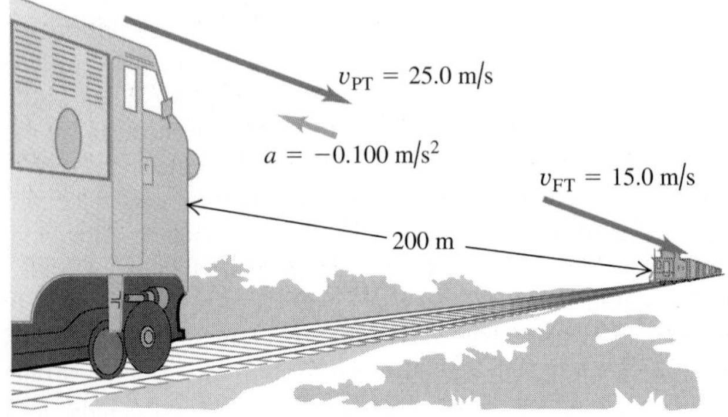

2.67. Large cockroaches can run as fast as 1.50 m/s in short bursts. Suppose you turn on the light in a cheap motel and see one scurrying directly away from you at a constant 1.50 m/s. If you start 0.90 m behind the cockroach with an initial speed of 0.80 m/s toward it, what minimum constant acceleration would you need to catch up with it when it has traveled 1.20 m, just short of safety under a counter?

2.68. Two cars start 200 m apart and drive toward each other at a steady 10 m/s. On the front of one of them, an energetic grasshopper jumps back and forth between the cars (he has strong legs!) with a constant horizontal velocity of 15 m/s relative to the ground. The insect jumps the instant he lands, so he spends no time resting on either car. What total distance does the grasshopper travel before the cars hit?

2.69. An automobile and a truck start from rest at the same instant, with the automobile initially at some distance behind the truck. The truck has a constant acceleration of $2.10\ \text{m/s}^2$, and the automobile an acceleration of $3.40\ \text{m/s}^2$. The automobile overtakes the truck after the truck has moved 40.0 m. (a) How much time does it take the automobile to overtake the truck? (b) How far was the automobile behind the truck initially? (c) What is the speed of each when they are abreast? (d) On a single graph, sketch the position of each vehicle as a function of time. Take $x = 0$ at the initial location of the truck.

2.70. Two stunt drivers drive directly toward each other. At time $t = 0$ the two cars are a distance D apart, car 1 is at rest, and car 2 is moving to the left with speed v_0. Car 1 begins to move at $t = 0$, speeding up with a constant acceleration a_x. Car 2 continues to move with a constant velocity. (a) At what time do the two cars collide? (b) Find the speed of car 1 just before it collides with car 2. (c) Sketch x-t and v_x-t graphs for car 1 and car 2. For each of the two graphs, draw the curves for both cars on the same set of axes.

2.71. A marble is released from one rim of a hemispherical bowl of diameter 50.0 cm and rolls down and up to the opposite rim in 10.0 s. Find (a) the average speed and (b) the average velocity of the marble.

2.72. You may have noticed while driving that your car's velocity does not continue to increase, even though you keep your foot on the gas pedal. This behavior is due to air resistance and friction between the moving parts of the car. Figure 2.48 shows a qualitative v_x-t graph for a typical car if it starts from rest at the origin and travels in a straight line (the x-axis). Sketch qualitative a_x-t and x-t graphs for this car.

Figure 2.48 Problem 2.72.

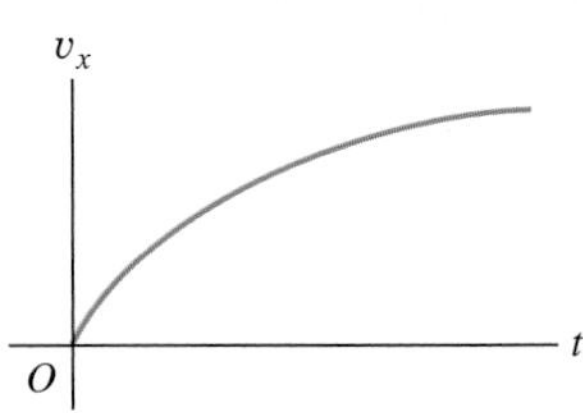

2.73. Passing. The driver of a car wishes to pass a truck that is traveling at a constant speed of 20.0 m/s (about 45 mi/h). Initially, the car is also traveling at 20.0 m/s and its front bumper is 24.0 m behind the truck's rear bumper. The car accelerates at a constant $0.600\ \text{m/s}^2$, then pulls back into the truck's lane when the rear of the car is 26.0 m ahead of the front of the truck. The car is 4.5 m long and the truck is 21.0 m long. (a) How much time is required for the car to pass the truck? (b) What distance does the car travel during this time? (c) What is the final speed of the car?

***2.74.** An object's velocity is measured to be $v_x(t) = \alpha - \beta t^2$, where $\alpha = 4.00\ \text{m/s}$ and $\beta = 2.00\ \text{m/s}^3$. At $t = 0$ the object is at $x = 0$. (a) Calculate the object's position and acceleration as functions of time. (b) What is the object's maximum *positive* displacement from the origin?

***2.75.** The acceleration of a particle is given by $a_x(t) = -2.00\ \text{m/s}^2 + (3.00\ \text{m/s}^3)t$. (a) Find the initial velocity v_{0x} such that the particle will have the same x-coordinate at $t = 4.00$ s as it had at $t = 0$. (b) What will be the velocity at $t = 4.00$ s?

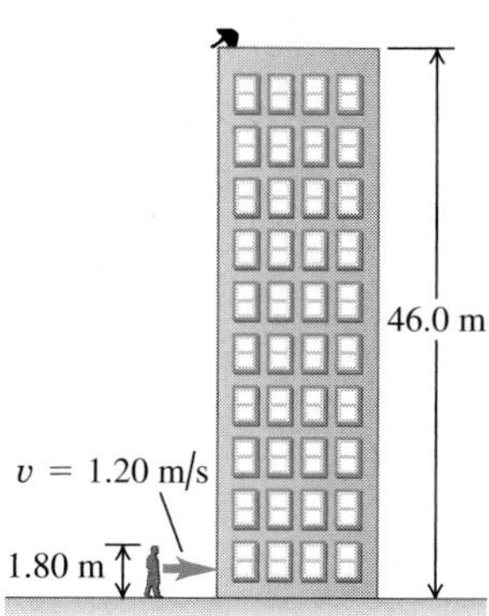

Figure 2.49 Problem 2.76.

2.76. Egg Drop. You are on the roof of the physics building, 46.0 m above the ground (Fig. 2.49). Your physics professor, who is 1.80 m tall, is walking alongside the building at a constant speed of 1.20 m/s. If you wish to drop an egg on your professor's head, where should the professor be when you release the egg? Assume that the egg is in free fall.

2.77. A certain volcano on earth can eject rocks vertically to a maximum height H. (a) How high (in terms of H) would these rocks go if a volcano on Mars ejected them with the same initial velocity? The acceleration due to gravity on Mars is 3.71 m/s^2, and you can neglect air resistance on both planets. (b) If the rocks are in the air for a time T on earth, for how long (in terms of T) will they be in the air on Mars?

2.78. An entertainer juggles balls while doing other activities. In one act, she throws a ball vertically upward, and while it is in the air, she runs to and from a table 5.50 m away at a constant speed of 2.50 m/s, returning just in time to catch the falling ball. (a) With what minimum initial speed must she throw the ball upward to accomplish this feat? (b) How high above its initial position is the ball just as she reaches the table?

2.79. Visitors at an amusement park watch divers step off a platform 21.3 m (70 ft) above a pool of water. According to the announcer, the divers enter the water at a speed of 56 mi/h (25 m/s). Air resistance may be ignored. (a) Is the announcer correct in this claim? (b) Is it possible for a diver to leap directly upward off the board so that, missing the board on the way down, she enters the water at 25.0 m/s? If so, what initial upward speed is required? Is the required initial speed physically attainable?

2.80. A flowerpot falls off a windowsill and falls past the window below. You may ignore air resistance. It takes the pot 0.420 s to pass this window, which is 1.90 m high. How far is the top of the window below the windowsill from which the flowerpot fell?

2.81. Certain rifles can fire a bullet with a speed of 965 m/s just as it leaves the muzzle (this speed is called the *muzzle velocity*). If the muzzle is 70.0 cm long and if the bullet is accelerated uniformly from rest within it, (a) what is the acceleration (in g's) of the bullet in the muzzle, and (b) for how long (in ms) is it in the muzzle? (c) If, when this rifle is fired vertically, the bullet reaches a maximum height H, what would be the maximum height (in terms of H) for a new rifle that produced half the muzzle velocity of this one?

2.82. A Multi-stage Rocket. In the first stage of a two-stage rocket, the rocket is fired from the launch pad starting from rest but with a constant acceleration of 3.50 m/s^2 upward. At 25.0 s after launch, the rocket fires the second stage, which suddenly boosts its speed to 132.5 m/s upward. This firing uses up all the fuel, however, so then the only force acting on the rocket is gravity. Air resistance is negligible. (a) Find the maximum height that the stage-two rocket reaches above the launch pad. (b) How much time after the stage-two firing will it take for the rocket to fall back to the launch pad? (c) How fast will the stage-two rocket be moving just as it reaches the launch pad?

2.83. Look Out Below. Sam heaves a 16-lb shot straight upward, giving it a constant upward acceleration from rest of 45.0 m/s^2 for 64.0 cm. He releases it 2.20 m above the ground. You may ignore air resistance. (a) What is the speed of the shot when Sam releases it? (b) How high above the ground does it go? (c) How much time does he have to get out of its way before it returns to the height of the top of his head, 1.83 m above the ground?

2.84. A physics teacher performing an outdoor demonstration suddenly falls from rest off a high cliff and simultaneously shouts "Help." When she has fallen for 3.0 s, she hears the echo of her shout from the valley floor below. The speed of sound is 340 m/s. (a) How tall is the cliff? (b) If air resistance is neglected, how fast will she be moving just before she hits the ground? (Her actual speed will be less than this, due to air resistance.)

2.85. Juggling Act. A juggler performs in a room whose ceiling is 3.0 m above the level of his hands. He throws a ball upward so that it just reaches the ceiling. (a) What is the initial velocity of the ball? (b) What is the time required for the ball to reach the ceiling? At the instant when the first ball is at the ceiling, the juggler throws a second ball upward with two-thirds the initial velocity of the first. (c) How long after the second ball is thrown did the two balls pass each other? (d) At what distance above the juggler's hand do they pass each other?

2.86. A helicopter carrying Dr. Evil takes off with a constant upward acceleration of 5.0 m/s^2. Secret agent Austin Powers jumps on just as the helicopter lifts off the ground. After the two men struggle for 10.0 s, Powers shuts off the engine and steps out of the helicopter. Assume that the helicopter is in free fall after its engine is shut off, and ignore the effects of air resistance. (a) What is the maximum height above ground reached by the helicopter? (b) Powers deploys a jet pack strapped on his back 7.0 s after leaving the helicopter, and then he has a constant downward acceleration with magnitude 2.0 m/s^2. How far is Powers above the ground when the helicopter crashes into the ground?

2.87. Building Height. Spider-Man steps from the top of a tall building. He falls freely from rest to the ground a distance of h. He falls a distance of $h/4$ in the last 1.0 s of his fall. What is the height h of the building?

2.88. Cliff Height. You are climbing in the High Sierra where you suddenly find yourself at the edge of a fog-shrouded cliff. To find the height of this cliff, you drop a rock from the top and 10.0 s later hear the sound of it hitting the ground at the foot of the cliff. (a) Ignoring air resistance, how high is the cliff if the speed of sound is 330 m/s? (b) Suppose you had ignored the time it takes the sound to reach you. In that case, would you have overestimated or underestimated the height of the cliff? Explain your reasoning.

2.89. Falling Can. A painter is standing on scaffolding that is raised at constant speed. As he travels upward, he accidentally nudges a paint can off the scaffolding and it falls 15.0 m to the ground. You are watching, and measure with your stopwatch that it takes 3.25 s for the can to reach the ground. Ignore air resistance. (a) What is the speed of the can just before it hits the ground? (b) Another painter is standing on a ledge, with his hands 4.00 m above the can when it falls off. He has lightning-fast reflexes and if the can passes in front of him, he can catch it. Does he get the chance?

2.90. Determined to test the law of gravity for himself, a student walks off a skyscraper 180 m high, stopwatch in hand, and starts his free fall (zero initial velocity). Five seconds later, Superman arrives at the scene and dives off the roof to save the student. Superman leaves the roof with an initial speed v_0 that he produces by pushing himself downward from the edge of the roof with his legs of steel. He then falls with the same acceleration as any freely falling body. (a) What must the value of v_0 be so that Superman catches the student just before they reach the ground? (b) On the same graph, sketch the positions of the student and of Superman as functions of time. Take Superman's initial speed to have the value calculated in part (a). (c) If the height of the skyscraper is less than some minimum value, even Superman can't reach the student before he hits the ground. What is this minimum height?

2.91. During launches, rockets often discard unneeded parts. A certain rocket starts from rest on the launch pad and accelerates upward at a steady 3.30 m/s^2. When it is 235 m above the launch pad, it discards a used fuel canister by simply disconnecting it. Once it is disconnected, the only force acting on the canister is gravity (air resistance can be ignored). (a) How high is the rocket when the canister hits the launch pad, assuming that the rocket does not change its acceleration? (b) What total distance did the canister travel between its release and its crash onto the launch pad?

2.92. A ball is thrown straight up from the ground with speed v_0. At the same instant, a second ball is dropped from rest from a height H, directly above the point where the first ball was thrown upward. There is no air resistance. (a) Find the time at which the two balls collide. (b) Find the value of H in terms of v_0 and g so that at the instant when the balls collide, the first ball is at the highest point of its motion.

2.93. Two cars, A and B, travel in a straight line. The distance of A from the starting point is given as a function of time by $x_A(t) = \alpha t + \beta t^2$, with $\alpha = 2.60$ m/s and $\beta = 1.20$ m/s^2. The distance of B from the starting point is $x_B(t) = \gamma t^2 - \delta t^3$, with $\gamma = 2.80$ m/s^2 and $\delta = 0.20$ m/s^3. (a) Which car is ahead just after they leave the starting point? (b) At what time(s) are the cars at the same point? (c) At what time(s) is the distance from A to B neither increasing nor decreasing? (d) At what time(s) do A and B have the same acceleration?

2.94. An apple drops from the tree and falls freely. The apple is originally at rest a height H above the top of the grass of a thick lawn, which is made of blades of grass of height h. When the apple enters the grass, it slows down at a constant rate so that its speed is 0 when it reaches ground level. (a) Find the speed of the apple just before it enters the grass. (b) Find the acceleration of the apple while it is in the grass. (c) Sketch the y-t, v_y-t, and a_y-t graphs for the apple's motion.

Challenge Problems

2.95. Catching the Bus. A student is running at her top speed of 5.0 m/s to catch a bus, which is stopped at the bus stop. When the student is still 40.0 m from the bus, it starts to pull away, moving with a constant acceleration of 0.170 m/s^2. (a) For how much time and what distance does the student have to run at 5.0 m/s before she overtakes the bus? (b) When she reaches the bus, how fast is the bus traveling? (c) Sketch an x-t graph for both the student and the bus. Take $x = 0$ at the initial position of the student. (d) The equations you used in part (a) to find the time have a second solution, corresponding to a later time for which the student and bus are again at the same place if they continue their specified motions. Explain the significance of this second solution. How fast is the bus traveling at this point? (e) If the student's top speed is 3.5 m/s, will she catch the bus? (f) What is the *minimum* speed the student must have to just catch up with the bus? For what time and what distance does she have to run in that case?

2.96. In the vertical jump, an athlete starts from a crouch and jumps upward to reach as high as possible. Even the best athletes spend little more than 1.00 s in the air (their "hang time"). Treat the athlete as a particle and let y_{max} be his maximum height above the floor. To explain why he seems to hang in the air, calculate the ratio of the time he is above $y_{max}/2$ to the time it takes him to go from the floor to that height. You may ignore air resistance.

2.97. A ball is thrown straight up from the edge of the roof of a building. A second ball is dropped from the roof 1.00 s later. You may ignore air resistance. (a) If the height of the building is 20.0 m, what must the initial speed of the first ball be if both are to hit the ground at the same time? On the same graph, sketch the position of each ball as a function of time, measured from when the first ball is thrown. Consider the same situation, but now let the initial speed v_0 of the first ball be given and treat the height h of the building as an unknown. (b) What must the height of the building be for both balls to reach the ground at the same time (i) if v_0 is 6.0 m/s and (ii) if v_0 is 9.5 m/s? (c) If v_0 is greater than some value v_{max}, a value of h does not exist that allows both balls to hit the ground at the same time. Solve for v_{max}. The value v_{max} has a simple physical interpretation. What is it? (d) If v_0 is less than some value v_{min}, a value of h does not exist that allows both balls to hit the ground at the same time. Solve for v_{min}. The value v_{min} also has a simple physical interpretation. What is it?

2.98. An alert hiker sees a boulder fall from the top of a distant cliff and notes that it takes 1.30 s for the boulder to fall the last third of the way to the ground. You may ignore air resistance. (a) What is the height of the cliff in meters? (b) If in part (a) you get two solutions of a quadratic equation and you use one for your answer, what does the other solution represent?

MOTION IN TWO OR THREE DIMENSIONS

3

?If a car is going around a curve at constant speed, is it accelerating? If so, in what direction is it accelerating?

LEARNING GOALS

By studying this chapter, you will learn:

- How to represent the position of a body in two or three dimensions using vectors.
- How to determine the vector velocity of a body from a knowledge of its path.
- How to find the vector acceleration of a body, and why a body can have an acceleration even if its speed is constant.
- How to interpret the components of a body's acceleration parallel to and perpendicular to its path.
- How to describe the curved path followed by a projectile.
- The key ideas behind motion in a circular path, with either constant speed or varying speed.
- How to relate the velocity of a moving body as seen from two different frames of reference.

What determines where a batted baseball lands? How do you describe the motion of a roller coaster car along a curved track or the flight of a circling hawk? If you throw a water balloon horizontally from your window, will it take the same amount of time to hit the ground as a balloon that you simply drop?

We can't answer these kinds of questions using the techniques of Chapter 2, in which particles moved only along a straight line. Instead, we need to extend our descriptions of motion to two- and three-dimensional situations. We'll still use the vector quantities displacement, velocity, and acceleration, but now these quantities will no longer lie along a single line. We'll find that several important kinds of motion take place in two dimensions only—that is, in a *plane.* These motions can be described with two components of position, velocity, and acceleration.

We also need to consider how the motion of a particle is described by different observers who are moving relative to each other. The concept of *relative velocity* will play an important role later in the book when we study collisions, when we explore electromagnetic phenomena, and when we introduce Einstein's special theory of relativity.

This chapter merges the vector mathematics of Chapter 1 with the kinematic language of Chapter 2. As before, we are concerned with describing motion, not with analyzing its causes. But the language you learn here will be an essential tool in later chapters when we study the relationship between force and motion.

3.1 Position and Velocity Vectors

To describe the *motion* of a particle in space, we must first be able to describe the particle's *position.* Consider a particle that is at a point P at a certain instant. The **position vector** $\vec{r}$ of the particle at this instant is a vector that goes from the origin of the coordinate system to the point P (Fig. 3.1). The Cartesian coordinates x, y, and z of point P are the x-, y-, and z-components of vector $\vec{r}$. Using the unit vectors we introduced in Section 1.9, we can write

3.1 The position vector $\vec{r}$ from the origin to point P has components x, y, and z. The path that the particle follows through space is in general a curve (Fig. 3.2).

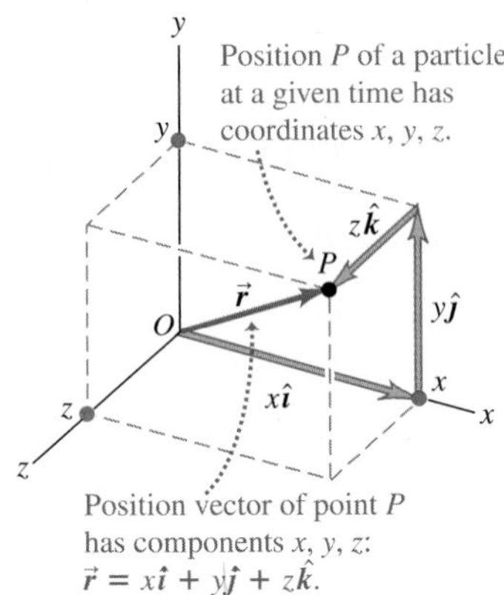

Position P of a particle at a given time has coordinates x, y, z.
y
$z\hat{k}$
P
$\vec{r}$
O
$y\hat{j}$
$x\hat{i}$
x
z
Position vector of point P has components x, y, z:
$\vec{r} = x\hat{i} + y\hat{j} + z\hat{k}$.

$$\vec{r} = x\hat{\imath} + y\hat{\jmath} + z\hat{k} \qquad \text{(position vector)} \tag{3.1}$$

During a time interval Δt the particle moves from P_1, where its position vector is $\vec{r}_1$, to P_2, where its position vector is $\vec{r}_2$. The change in position (the displacement) during this interval is $\Delta\vec{r} = \vec{r}_2 - \vec{r}_1 = (x_2 - x_1)\hat{\imath} + (y_2 - y_1)\hat{\jmath} + (z_2 - z_1)\hat{k}$. We define the **average velocity** $\vec{v}_{av}$ during this interval in the same way we did in Chapter 2 for straight-line motion, as the displacement divided by the time interval:

$$\vec{v}_{av} = \frac{\vec{r}_2 - \vec{r}_1}{t_2 - t_1} = \frac{\Delta\vec{r}}{\Delta t} \qquad \text{(average velocity vector)} \tag{3.2}$$

3.2 The average velocity $\vec{v}_{av}$ between points P_1 and P_2 has the same direction as the displacement $\Delta\vec{r}$.

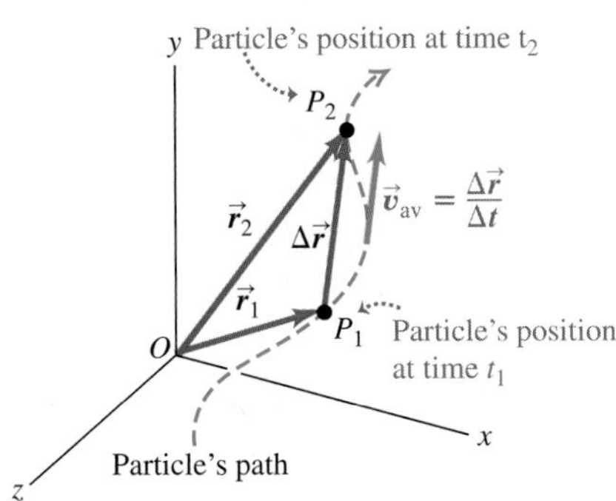

y Particle's position at time t_2
P_2
$\vec{v}_{av} = \frac{\Delta\vec{r}}{\Delta t}$
$\vec{r}_2$
$\Delta\vec{r}$
$\vec{r}_1$
O
P_1 Particle's position at time t_1
x
Particle's path
z

Dividing a vector by a scalar is really a special case of *multiplying* a vector by a scalar, described in Section 1.7; the average velocity $\vec{v}_{av}$ is equal to the displacement vector $\Delta\vec{r}$ multiplied by $1/\Delta t$, the reciprocal of the time interval. Note that the x-component of Eq. (3.2) is $v_{av\text{-}x} = (x_2 - x_1)/(t_2 - t_1) = \Delta x/\Delta t$. This is just Eq. (2.2), the expression for average x-velocity that we found in Section 2.1 for one-dimensional motion.

We now define **instantaneous velocity** just as we did in Chapter 2: It is the limit of the average velocity as the time interval approaches zero, and it equals the instantaneous rate of change of position with time. The key difference is that position $\vec{r}$ and instantaneous velocity $\vec{v}$ are now both vectors:

$$\vec{v} = \lim_{\Delta t \to 0} \frac{\Delta\vec{r}}{\Delta t} = \frac{d\vec{r}}{dt} \qquad \text{(instantaneous velocity vector)} \tag{3.3}$$

The *magnitude* of the vector $\vec{v}$ at any instant is the *speed* v of the particle at that instant. The *direction* of $\vec{v}$ at any instant is the same as the direction in which the particle is moving at that instant.

Note that as $\Delta t \to 0$, points P_1 and P_2 in Fig. 3.2 move closer and closer together. In this limit, the vector $\Delta\vec{r}$ becomes tangent to the path. The direction of $\Delta\vec{r}$ in the limit is also the direction of the instantaneous velocity $\vec{v}$. This leads to an important conclusion: *At every point along the path, the instantaneous velocity vector is tangent to the path at that point* (Fig. 3.3).

3.3 The vectors $\vec{v}_1$ and $\vec{v}_2$ are the instantaneous velocities at the points P_1 and P_2 shown in Fig. 3.2.

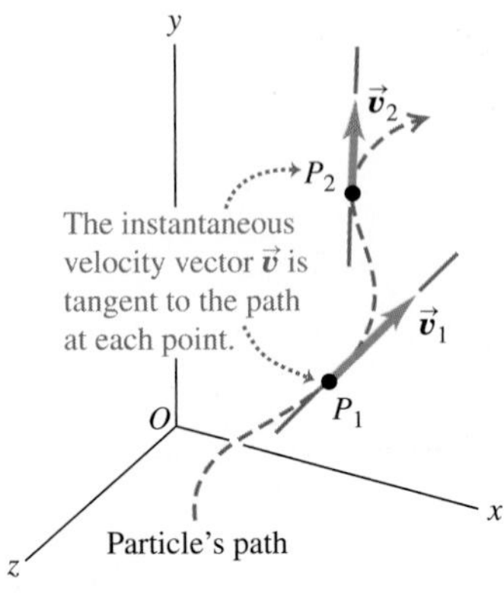

y
$\vec{v}_2$
P_2
The instantaneous velocity vector $\vec{v}$ is tangent to the path at each point.
$\vec{v}_1$
O
P_1
x
Particle's path
z

It's often easiest to calculate the instantaneous velocity vector using components. During any displacement $\Delta\vec{r}$, the changes Δx, Δy, and Δz in the three coordinates of the particle are the *components* of $\Delta\vec{r}$. It follows that the components v_x, v_y, and v_z of the instantaneous velocity $\vec{v}$ are simply the time derivatives of the coordinates x, y, and z. That is,

$$v_x = \frac{dx}{dt} \qquad v_y = \frac{dy}{dt} \qquad v_z = \frac{dz}{dt} \qquad \text{(components of instantaneous velocity)} \tag{3.4}$$

The x-component of $\vec{v}$ is $v_x = dx/dt$, which is the same as Eq. (2.3)—the expression for instantaneous velocity for straight-line motion that we obtained in Section 2.2. Hence Eq. (3.4) is a direct extension of the idea of instantaneous velocity to motion in three dimensions.

We can also get this result by taking the derivative of Eq. (3.1). The unit vectors $\hat{\imath}$, $\hat{\jmath}$, and $\hat{k}$ are constant in magnitude and direction, so their derivatives are zero, and we find

$$\vec{v} = \frac{d\vec{r}}{dt} = \frac{dx}{dt}\hat{\imath} + \frac{dy}{dt}\hat{\jmath} + \frac{dz}{dt}\hat{k} \tag{3.5}$$

This shows again that the components of $\vec{v}$ are dx/dt, dy/dt, and dz/dt.

The magnitude of the instantaneous velocity vector $\vec{v}$—that is, the speed—is given in terms of the components v_x, v_y, and v_z by the Pythagorean relation

$$|\vec{v}| = v = \sqrt{v_x^2 + v_y^2 + v_z^2} \tag{3.6}$$

Figure 3.4 shows the situation when the particle moves in the xy-plane. In this case, z and v_z are zero. Then the speed (the magnitude of $\vec{v}$) is

$$v = \sqrt{v_x^2 + v_y^2}$$

and the direction of the instantaneous velocity $\vec{v}$ is given by the angle α in the figure. We see that

$$\tan\alpha = \frac{v_y}{v_x} \tag{3.7}$$

(We always use Greek letters for angles. We use α for the direction of the instantaneous velocity vector to avoid confusion with the direction θ of the *position* vector of the particle.)

The instantaneous velocity vector is usually more interesting and useful than the average velocity vector. From now on, when we use the word "velocity," we will always mean the instantaneous velocity vector $\vec{v}$ (rather than the average velocity vector). Usually, we won't even bother to call $\vec{v}$ a vector; it's up to you to remember that velocity is a vector quantity with both magnitude and direction.

3.4 The two velocity components for motion in the xy-plane.

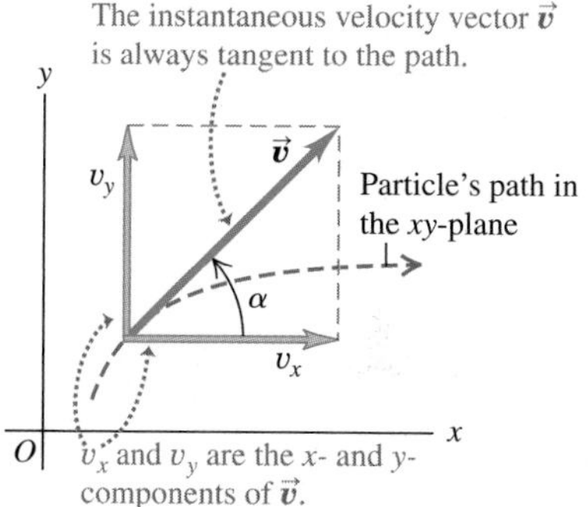

Example 3.1 Calculating average and instantaneous velocity

A robotic vehicle, or rover, is exploring the surface of Mars. The landing craft is the origin of coordinates, and the surrounding Martian surface lies in the xy-plane. The rover, which we represent as a point, has x- and y-coordinates that vary with time:

$$x = 2.0\text{ m} - (0.25\text{ m/s}^2)t^2$$
$$y = (1.0\text{ m/s})t + (0.025\text{ m/s}^3)t^3$$

(a) Find the rover's coordinates and its distance from the lander at $t = 2.0$ s. (b) Find the rover's displacement and average velocity vectors during the interval from $t = 0.0$ s to $t = 2.0$ s. (c) Derive a general expression for the rover's instantaneous velocity vector. Express the instantaneous velocity at $t = 2.0$ s in component form and also in terms of magnitude and direction.

SOLUTION

IDENTIFY: This problem involves motion in two dimensions—that is, in a plane. Hence we must use the expressions for the displacement, average velocity, and instantaneous velocity *vectors* obtained in this section. (The simpler expressions in Sections 2.1 and 2.2 don't involve vectors; they apply only to motion along a straight line.)

SET UP: Figure 3.5 shows the rover's path. We'll use Eq. (3.1) for position $\vec{r}$, the expression $\Delta\vec{r} = \vec{r}_2 - \vec{r}_1$ for displacement, Eq. (3.2) for average velocity, and Eqs. (3.5) and (3.6) for instantaneous velocity and its direction. The target variables are stated in the problem.

3.5 At $t = 0$ the rover has position vector $\vec{r}_0$ and instantaneous velocity vector $\vec{v}_0$. Likewise, $\vec{r}_1$ and $\vec{v}_1$ are the vectors at $t = 1.0$ s; $\vec{r}_2$ and $\vec{v}_2$ are the vectors at $t = 2.0$ s.

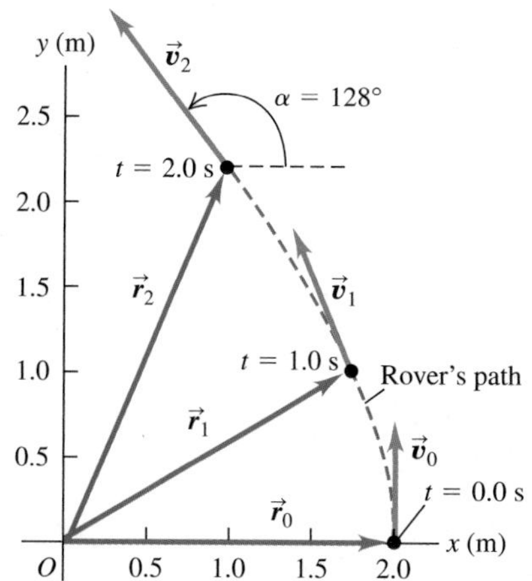

Continued

EXECUTE: (a) At time $t = 2.0$ s the rover's coordinates are

$$x = 2.0\text{ m} - (0.25\text{ m/s}^2)(2.0\text{ s})^2 = 1.0\text{ m}$$
$$y = (1.0\text{ m/s})(2.0\text{ s}) + (0.025\text{ m/s}^3)(2.0\text{ s})^3 = 2.2\text{ m}$$

The rover's distance from the origin at this time is

$$r = \sqrt{x^2 + y^2} = \sqrt{(1.0\text{ m})^2 + (2.2\text{ m})^2} = 2.4\text{ m}$$

(b) To find the displacement and average velocity, we express the position vector $\vec{r}$ as a function of time t. From Eq. (3.1), this is

$$\begin{aligned}\vec{r} &= x\hat{\imath} + y\hat{\jmath}\\ &= [2.0\text{ m} - (0.25\text{ m/s}^2)t^2]\hat{\imath}\\ &\quad + [(1.0\text{ m/s})t + (0.025\text{ m/s}^3)t^3]\hat{\jmath}\end{aligned}$$

At time $t = 0.0$ s the position vector $\vec{r}_0$ is

$$\vec{r}_0 = (2.0\text{ m})\hat{\imath} + (0.0\text{ m})\hat{\jmath}$$

From part (a) the position vector $\vec{r}_2$ at time $t = 2.0$ s is

$$\vec{r}_2 = (1.0\text{ m})\hat{\imath} + (2.2\text{ m})\hat{\jmath}$$

Therefore the displacement from $t = 0.0$ s to $t = 2.0$ s is

$$\begin{aligned}\Delta\vec{r} = \vec{r}_2 - \vec{r}_0 &= (1.0\text{ m})\hat{\imath} + (2.2\text{ m})\hat{\jmath} - (2.0\text{ m})\hat{\imath}\\ &= (-1.0\text{ m})\hat{\imath} + (2.2\text{ m})\hat{\jmath}\end{aligned}$$

During the time interval from $t = 0.0$ s to $t = 2.0$ s, the rover moves 1.0 m in the negative x-direction and 2.2 m in the positive y-direction. From Eq. (3.2), the average velocity during this interval is the displacement divided by the elapsed time:

$$\begin{aligned}\vec{v}_{av} &= \frac{\Delta\vec{r}}{\Delta t} = \frac{(-1.0\text{ m})\hat{\imath} + (2.2\text{ m})\hat{\jmath}}{2.0\text{ s} - 0.0\text{ s}}\\ &= (-0.50\text{ m/s})\hat{\imath} + (1.1\text{ m/s})\hat{\jmath}\end{aligned}$$

The components of this average velocity are

$$v_{av\text{-}x} = -0.50\text{ m/s} \qquad v_{av\text{-}y} = 1.1\text{ m/s}$$

(c) From Eq. (3.4), the components of instantaneous velocity are the time derivatives of the coordinates:

$$v_x = \frac{dx}{dt} = (-0.25\text{ m/s}^2)(2t)$$
$$v_y = \frac{dy}{dt} = 1.0\text{ m/s} + (0.025\text{ m/s}^3)(3t^2)$$

Then we can write the instantaneous velocity vector $\vec{v}$ as

$$\begin{aligned}\vec{v} = v_x\hat{\imath} + v_y\hat{\jmath} &= (-0.50\text{ m/s}^2)t\hat{\imath}\\ &\quad + [1.0\text{ m/s} + (0.075\text{ m/s}^3)t^2]\hat{\jmath}\end{aligned}$$

At time $t = 2.0$ s, the components of instantaneous velocity are

$$v_x = (-0.50\text{ m/s}^2)(2.0\text{ s}) = -1.0\text{ m/s}$$
$$v_y = 1.0\text{ m/s} + (0.075\text{ m/s}^3)(2.0\text{ s})^2 = 1.3\text{ m/s}$$

The magnitude of the instantaneous velocity (that is, the speed) at $t = 2.0$ s is

$$\begin{aligned}v &= \sqrt{v_x^2 + v_y^2} = \sqrt{(-1.0\text{ m/s})^2 + (1.3\text{ m/s})^2}\\ &= 1.6\text{ m/s}\end{aligned}$$

The direction of $\vec{v}$ with respect to the positive x-axis is given by the angle α, where, from Eq. (3.7),

$$\tan\alpha = \frac{v_y}{v_x} = \frac{1.3\text{ m/s}}{-1.0\text{ m/s}} = -1.3 \qquad \text{so} \qquad \alpha = 128°$$

Your calculator will tell you that the inverse tangent of -1.3 is $-52°$. But as we learned in Section 1.8, you have to examine a sketch of a vector to decide on its direction. Figure 3.5 shows that the correct answer for α is $-52° + 180° = 128°$.

EVALUATE: Take a moment to compare the components of *average* velocity that we found in part (b) for the interval from $t = 0.0$ s to $t = 2.0$ s ($v_{av\text{-}x} = -0.50$ m/s, $v_{av\text{-}y} = 1.1$ m/s) with the components of *instantaneous* velocity at $t = 2.0$ s that we found in part (c) ($v_x = -1.0$ m/s, $v_y = 1.3$ m/s). The comparison shows that, just as in one dimension, the average velocity vector $\vec{v}_{av}$ over an interval is in general *not* equal to the instantaneous velocity $\vec{v}$ at the end of the interval (see Example 2.1).

You should calculate the position vector, instantaneous velocity vector, speed, and direction of motion at $t = 0.0$ s and $t = 1.0$ s. Figure 3.5 shows the position vectors $\vec{r}$ and instantaneous velocity vectors $\vec{v}$ at $t = 0.0$ s, 1.0 s, and 2.0 s. Notice that at every point, $\vec{v}$ is tangent to the path. The magnitude of $\vec{v}$ increases as the rover moves, which shows that its speed is increasing.

Test Your Understanding of Section 3.1 In which of these situations *would* the average velocity vector $\vec{v}_{av}$ over an interval be equal to the instantaneous velocity $\vec{v}$ at the end of the interval? (i) a body moving along a curved path at constant speed; (ii) a body moving along a curved path and speeding up; (iii) a body moving along a straight line at constant speed; (iv) a body moving along a straight line and speeding up.

3.2 The Acceleration Vector

Now let's consider the *acceleration* of a particle moving in space. Just as for motion in a straight line, acceleration describes how the velocity of the particle changes. But since we now treat velocity as a vector, acceleration will describe changes in the velocity magnitude (that is, the speed) *and* changes in the direction of velocity (that is, the direction in which the particle is moving).

In Fig. 3.6a, a car (treated as a particle) is moving along a curved road. The vectors $\vec{v}_1$ and $\vec{v}_2$ represent the car's instantaneous velocities at time t_1, when the

3.6 (a) A car moving along a curved road from P_1 to P_2. (b) Obtaining $\Delta\vec{v} = \vec{v}_2 - \vec{v}_1$ by vector subtraction. (c) The vector $\vec{a}_{av} = \Delta\vec{v}/\Delta t$ represents the average acceleration between P_1 and P_2.

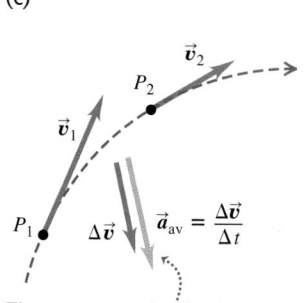

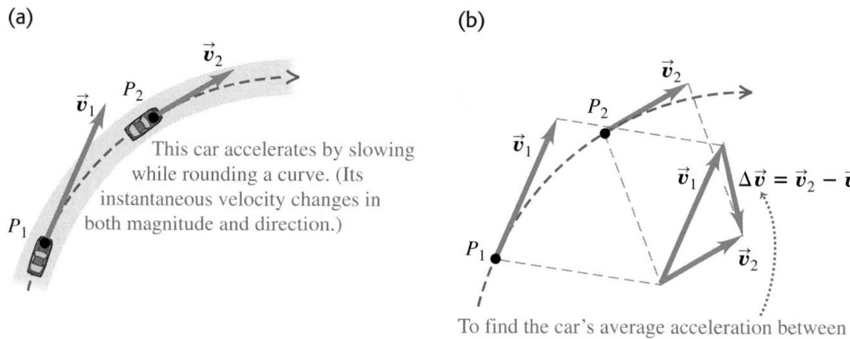
(a)
(b)
(c)
This car accelerates by slowing while rounding a curve. (Its instantaneous velocity changes in both magnitude and direction.)
$\Delta\vec{v} = \vec{v}_2 - \vec{v}_1$
To find the car's average acceleration between P_1 and P_2, we first find the change in velocity $\Delta\vec{v}$ by subtracting $\vec{v}_1$ from $\vec{v}_2$. (Notice that $\vec{v}_1 + \Delta\vec{v} = \vec{v}_2$.)
$\vec{a}_{av} = \frac{\Delta\vec{v}}{\Delta t}$
The average acceleration has the same direction as the change in velocity, $\Delta\vec{v}$.

car is at point P_1, and at time t_2, when the car is at point P_2. The two velocities may differ in both magnitude and direction. During the time interval from t_1 to t_2, the *vector change in velocity* is $\vec{v}_2 - \vec{v}_1 = \Delta\vec{v}$ (Fig. 3.6b). We define the **average acceleration** $\vec{a}_{av}$ of the car during this time interval as the velocity change divided by the time interval $t_2 - t_1 = \Delta t$:

$$\vec{a}_{av} = \frac{\vec{v}_2 - \vec{v}_1}{t_2 - t_1} = \frac{\Delta\vec{v}}{\Delta t} \quad \text{(average acceleration vector)} \quad (3.8)$$

Average acceleration is a *vector* quantity in the same direction as the vector $\Delta\vec{v}$ (Fig. 3.6c). Note that $\vec{v}_2$ is the vector sum of the original velocity $\vec{v}_1$ and the change $\Delta\vec{v}$ (Fig. 3.6b). The x-component of Eq. (3.8) is $a_{av\text{-}x} = (v_{2x} - v_{1x})/(t_2 - t_1) = \Delta v_x/\Delta t$, which is just Eq. (2.4) for the average acceleration in straight-line motion.

As in Chapter 2, we define the **instantaneous acceleration** $\vec{a}$ at point P_1 as the limit of the average acceleration when point P_2 approaches point P_1 and $\Delta\vec{v}$ and Δt both approach zero. The instantaneous acceleration is also equal to the instantaneous rate of change of velocity with time. Because we are not restricted to straight-line motion, instantaneous acceleration is now a vector (Fig. 3.7):

$$\vec{a} = \lim_{\Delta t \to 0} \frac{\Delta\vec{v}}{\Delta t} = \frac{d\vec{v}}{dt} \quad \text{(instantaneous acceleration vector)} \quad (3.9)$$

The velocity vector $\vec{v}$, as we have seen, is tangent to the path of the particle. But Figs. 3.6c and 3.7 show that if the path is curved, the instantaneous acceleration vector $\vec{a}$ always points toward the concave side of the path—that is, toward the inside of any turn that the particle is making.

CAUTION **Any particle following a curved path is accelerating** When a particle is moving in a curved path, it always has nonzero acceleration, even when it moves with constant speed. This conclusion may seem contrary to your intuition, but it's really just contrary to the everyday use of the word "acceleration" to mean that speed is increasing. The more precise definition given in Eq. (3.9) shows that there is a nonzero acceleration whenever the velocity vector changes in any way, whether there is a change of speed, direction, or both.

To convince yourself that a particle has a nonzero acceleration when moving on a curved path with constant speed, think of your sensations when you ride in a car. When the car accelerates, you tend to move inside the car in a

3.7 Instantaneous acceleration $\vec{a}$ at point P_1 in Fig. 3.6.

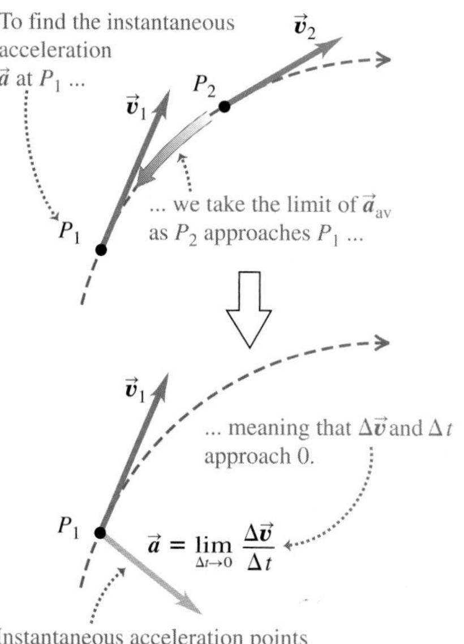
To find the instantaneous acceleration $\vec{a}$ at P_1 ...
... we take the limit of $\vec{a}_{av}$ as P_2 approaches P_1 ...
... meaning that $\Delta\vec{v}$ and Δt approach 0.
$\vec{a} = \lim_{\Delta t \to 0} \frac{\Delta\vec{v}}{\Delta t}$
Instantaneous acceleration points toward concave side of path.

direction *opposite* to the car's acceleration. (We'll discover the reason for this behavior in Chapter 4.) Thus you tend to slide toward the back of the car when it accelerates forward (speeds up) and toward the front of the car when it accelerates backward (slows down). If the car makes a turn on a level road, you tend to slide toward the outside of the turn; hence the car has an acceleration toward the inside of the turn.

We will usually be interested in the instantaneous acceleration, not the average acceleration. From now on, we will use the term "acceleration" to mean the instantaneous acceleration vector $\vec{a}$.

Each component of the acceleration vector is the derivative of the corresponding component of velocity:

$$a_x = \frac{dv_x}{dt} \qquad a_y = \frac{dv_y}{dt} \qquad a_z = \frac{dv_z}{dt} \qquad \text{(components of instantaneous acceleration)} \tag{3.10}$$

In terms of unit vectors,

$$\vec{a} = \frac{dv_x}{dt}\hat{\imath} + \frac{dv_y}{dt}\hat{\jmath} + \frac{dv_z}{dt}\hat{k} \tag{3.11}$$

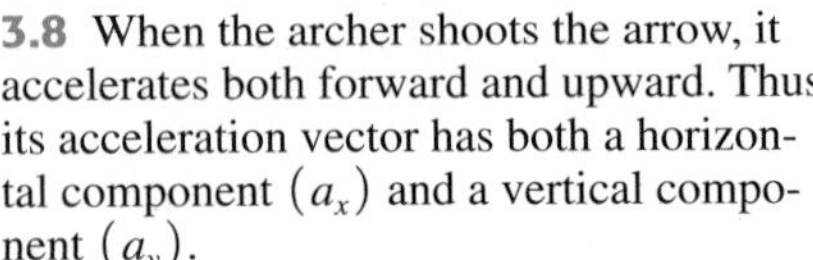

3.8 When the archer shoots the arrow, it accelerates both forward and upward. Thus its acceleration vector has both a horizontal component (a_x) and a vertical component (a_y).

The x-component of Eqs. (3.10) and (3.11), $a_x = dv_x/dt$, is the expression from Section 2.3 for instantaneous acceleration in one dimension, Eq. (2.5). Figure 3.8 shows an example of an acceleration vector that has both x- and y-components.

Since each component of velocity is the derivative of the corresponding coordinate, we can express the components a_x, a_y, and a_z of the acceleration vector $\vec{a}$ as

$$a_x = \frac{d^2x}{dt^2} \qquad a_y = \frac{d^2y}{dt^2} \qquad a_z = \frac{d^2z}{dt^2} \tag{3.12}$$

The acceleration vector $\vec{a}$ itself is

$$\vec{a} = \frac{d^2x}{dt^2}\hat{\imath} + \frac{d^2y}{dt^2}\hat{\jmath} + \frac{d^2z}{dt^2}\hat{k} \tag{3.13}$$

Example 3.2 Calculating average and instantaneous acceleration

Let's return to the motions of the robotic rover in Example 3.1. We found that the components of instantaneous velocity at any time t are

$$v_x = \frac{dx}{dt} = (-0.25\ \text{m/s}^2)(2t)$$

$$v_y = \frac{dy}{dt} = 1.0\ \text{m/s} + (0.025\ \text{m/s}^3)(3t^2)$$

and that the velocity vector is

$$\vec{v} = v_x\hat{\imath} + v_y\hat{\jmath} = (-0.50\ \text{m/s}^2)t\hat{\imath} + [1.0\ \text{m/s} + (0.075\ \text{m/s}^3)t^2]\hat{\jmath}$$

(a) Find the components of the average acceleration in the interval from $t = 0.0$ s to $t = 2.0$ s. (b) Find the instantaneous acceleration at $t = 2.0$ s.

SOLUTION

IDENTIFY: This example uses the vector relationships among velocity, average acceleration, and instantaneous acceleration.

SET UP: In part (a) we first determine the values of v_x and v_y at the beginning and end of the interval, and then use Eq. (3.8) to calculate the components of the average acceleration. In part (b) we determine the instantaneous acceleration components at any time t by taking the time derivatives of the velocity components as in Eq. (3.10).

EXECUTE: (a) If we substitute $t = 0.0$ s or $t = 2.0$ s into the expressions for v_x and v_y, we find that at the beginning of the interval $(t = 0.0\ \text{s})$ the velocity components are

$$v_x = 0.0\ \text{m/s} \qquad v_y = 1.0\ \text{m/s}$$

and that at the end of the interval $(t = 2.0\ \text{s})$ the components are

$$v_x = -1.0\ \text{m/s} \qquad v_y = 1.3\ \text{m/s}$$

(The values at $t = 2.0$ s are the same as we found in Example 3.1.) Thus the components of average acceleration in this interval are

$$a_{\text{av-}x} = \frac{\Delta v_x}{\Delta t} = \frac{-1.0\ \text{m/s} - 0.0\ \text{m/s}}{2.0\ \text{s} - 0.0\ \text{s}} = -0.5\ \text{m/s}^2$$

$$a_{\text{av-}y} = \frac{\Delta v_y}{\Delta t} = \frac{1.3\ \text{m/s} - 1.0\ \text{m/s}}{2.0\ \text{s} - 0.0\ \text{s}} = 0.15\ \text{m/s}^2$$

(b) Using Eq. (3.10), we find

$$a_x = \frac{dv_x}{dt} = -0.50\ \text{m/s}^2 \qquad a_y = \frac{dv_y}{dt} = (0.075\ \text{m/s}^3)(2t)$$

We can write the instantaneous acceleration vector $\vec{a}$ as

$$\vec{a} = a_x\hat{\imath} + a_y\hat{\jmath} = (-0.50\ \text{m/s}^2)\hat{\imath} + (0.15\ \text{m/s}^3)t\hat{\jmath}$$

At time $t = 2.0$ s, the components of instantaneous acceleration are

$$a_x = -0.50\ \text{m/s}^2 \qquad a_y = (0.15\ \text{m/s}^3)(2.0\ \text{s}) = 0.30\ \text{m/s}^2$$

The acceleration vector at this time is

$$\vec{a} = (-0.50\ \text{m/s}^2)\hat{\imath} + (0.30\ \text{m/s}^2)\hat{\jmath}$$

The magnitude of acceleration at this time is

$$a = \sqrt{a_x^2 + a_y^2}$$
$$= \sqrt{(-0.50\ \text{m/s}^2)^2 + (0.30\ \text{m/s}^2)^2} = 0.58\ \text{m/s}^2$$

The direction of $\vec{a}$ with respect to the positive x-axis is given by the angle β, where

$$\tan\beta = \frac{a_y}{a_x} = \frac{0.30\ \text{m/s}^2}{-0.50\ \text{m/s}^2} = -0.60$$
$$\beta = 180° - 31° = 149°$$

EVALUATE: You should use the results of part (b) to calculate the instantaneous acceleration at $t = 0.0$ s and $t = 1.0$ s. Figure 3.9 shows the rover's path and the velocity and acceleration vectors at $t = 0.0$ s, 1.0 s, and 2.0 s. Note that $\vec{v}$ and $\vec{a}$ are *not* in the same direction at any of these times. The velocity vector $\vec{v}$ is tangent to the path at each point, and the acceleration vector $\vec{a}$ points toward the concave side of the path.

3.9 The path of the robotic rover, showing the velocity and acceleration at $t = 0.0$ s ($\vec{v}_0$ and $\vec{a}_0$), $t = 1.0$ s ($\vec{v}_1$ and $\vec{a}_1$), and $t = 2.0$ s ($\vec{v}_2$ and $\vec{a}_2$).

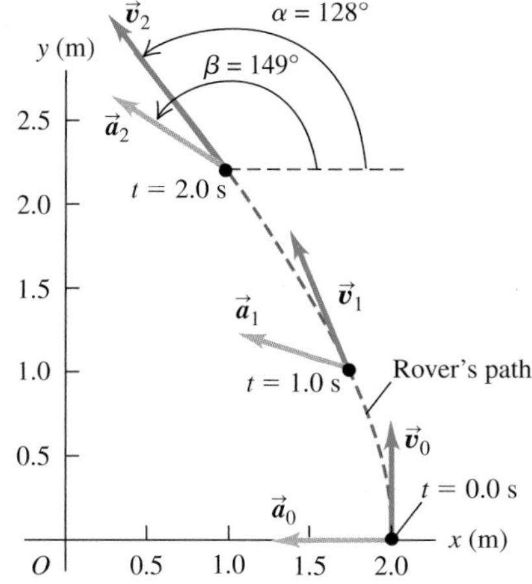

Parallel and Perpendicular Components of Acceleration

The acceleration vector $\vec{a}$ for a particle can describe changes in the particle's speed, its direction of motion, or both. It's useful to note that the component of acceleration *parallel* to a particle's path—that is, parallel to the velocity—tells us about changes in the particle's *speed,* while the acceleration component *perpendicular* to the path—and hence perpendicular to the velocity—tells us about changes in the particle's *direction of motion.* Figure 3.10 shows these components, which we label $a_{\parallel}$ and $a_{\perp}$. To see why the parallel and perpendicular components of $\vec{a}$ have these properties, let's consider two special cases.

In Fig. 3.11a the acceleration vector is in the same direction as the velocity $\vec{v}_1$, so $\vec{a}$ has only a parallel component $a_{\parallel}$ (that is, $a_{\perp} = 0$). The velocity change $\Delta\vec{v}$ during a small time interval Δt is in the same direction as $\vec{a}$ and hence in the same direction as $\vec{v}_1$. The velocity $\vec{v}_2$ at the end of Δt, given by $\vec{v}_2 = \vec{v}_1 + \Delta\vec{v}$, is in the same direction as $\vec{v}_1$ but has greater magnitude. Hence during the time interval Δt the particle in Fig. 3.11a moved in a straight line with increasing speed.

In Fig. 3.11b the acceleration is *perpendicular* to the velocity, so $\vec{a}$ has only a perpendicular component $a_{\perp}$ (that is, $a_{\parallel} = 0$). In a small time interval Δt, the velocity change $\Delta\vec{v}$ is very nearly perpendicular to $\vec{v}_1$. Again $\vec{v}_2 = \vec{v}_1 + \Delta\vec{v}$, but in this case $\vec{v}_1$ and $\vec{v}_2$ have different directions. As the time interval Δt

3.10 The acceleration can be resolved into a component $a_{\parallel}$ parallel to the path (that is, along the tangent to the path) and a component $a_{\perp}$ perpendicular to the path (that is, along the normal to the path).

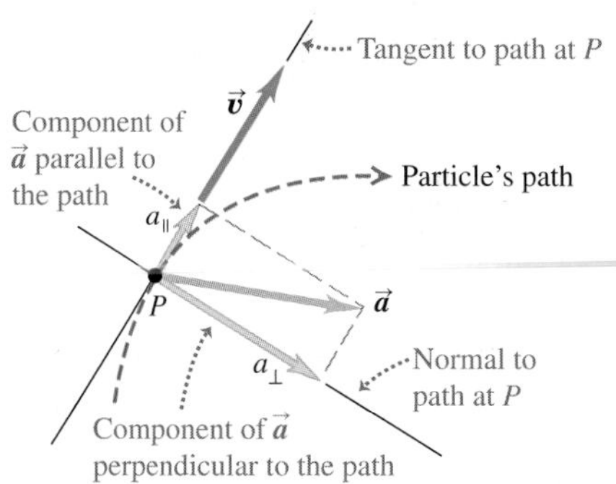

3.11 The effect of acceleration directed (a) parallel to and (b) perpendicular to a particle's velocity.

(a)

Acceleration parallel to particle's velocity:
- Changes *magnitude* but not *direction* of velocity.
- Particle moves in a straight line with changing speed.

(b)

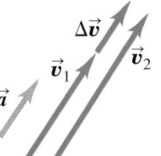

Acceleration perpendicular to particle's velocity:
- Changes *direction* but not *magnitude* of velocity.
- Particle follows a curved path at constant speed.

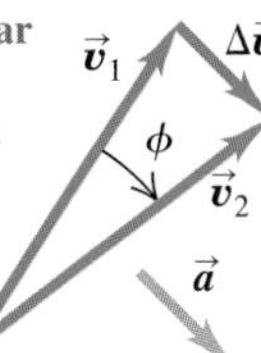

approaches zero, the angle ϕ in the figure also approaches zero, $\Delta\vec{v}$ becomes perpendicular to *both* $\vec{v}_1$ and $\vec{v}_2$, and $\vec{v}_1$ and $\vec{v}_2$ have the same magnitude. In other words, the speed of the particle stays the same, but the direction of motion changes and the path of the particle curves.

In the most general case, the acceleration $\vec{a}$ has components *both* parallel and perpendicular to the velocity $\vec{v}$, as in Fig. 3.10. Then the particle's speed will change (described by the parallel component $a_{\parallel}$) *and* its direction of motion will change (described by the perpendicular component $a_{\perp}$) so that it follows a curved path.

Figure 3.12 shows a particle moving along a curved path for three different situations: constant speed, increasing speed, and decreasing speed. If the speed is constant, $\vec{a}$ is perpendicular, or *normal,* to the path and to $\vec{v}$ and points toward the concave side of the path (Fig. 3.12a). If the speed is increasing, there is still a perpendicular component of $\vec{a}$, but there is also a parallel component having the same direction as $\vec{v}$ (Fig. 3.12b). Then $\vec{a}$ points ahead of the normal to the path. (This was the case in Example 3.2.) If the speed is decreasing, the parallel component has the direction opposite to $\vec{v}$, and $\vec{a}$ points behind the normal to the path (Fig. 3.12c). We will use these ideas again in Section 3.4 when we study the special case of motion in a circle.

3.12 Velocity and acceleration vectors for a particle moving through a point P on a curved path with (a) constant speed, (b) increasing speed, and (c) decreasing speed.

(a) When speed is constant along a curved path ...

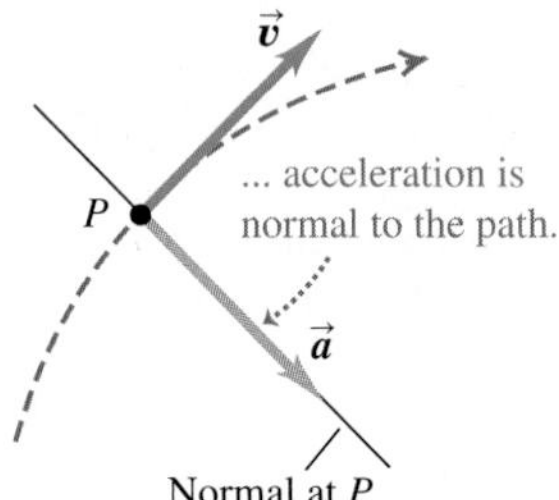

(b) When speed is increasing along a curved path ...

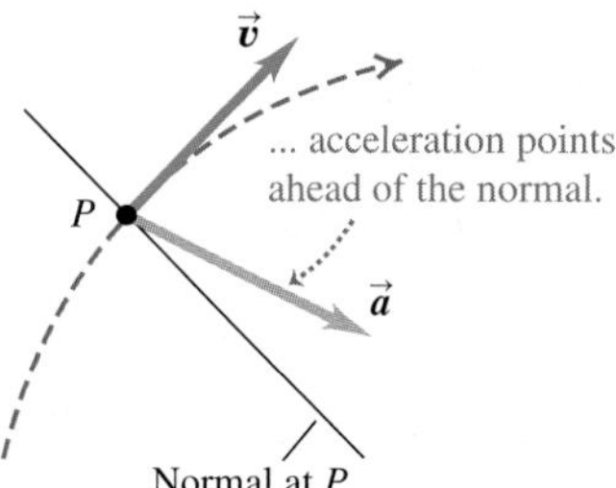

(c) When speed is decreasing along a curved path ...

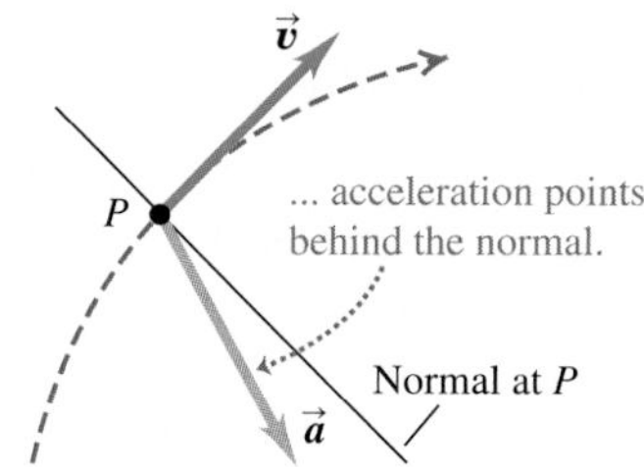

Example 3.3 Calculating parallel and perpendicular components of acceleration

For the rover of Examples 3.1 and 3.2, find the parallel and perpendicular components of the acceleration at $t = 2.0$ s.

SOLUTION

IDENTIFY: We want to find the components of the acceleration vector $\vec{a}$ that are parallel and perpendicular to the velocity vector $\vec{v}$.

SET UP: We found the directions of $\vec{a}$ and $\vec{v}$ in Examples 3.2 and 3.1, respectively. This will allow us to find the angle between the two vectors and hence the components of $\vec{a}$.

EXECUTE: In Example 3.2 we found that at $t = 2.0$ s the particle has an acceleration of magnitude $0.58\ \text{m/s}^2$ at an angle of 149° with respect to the positive x-axis. From Example 3.1, at this same time the velocity vector is at an angle of 128° with respect to the positive x-axis. So Fig. 3.9 shows that the angle between $\vec{a}$ and $\vec{v}$ is $149° - 128° = 21°$ (Fig. 3.13). The parallel and perpendicular components of acceleration are then

$$a_{\parallel} = a\cos 21° = (0.58\ \text{m/s}^2)\cos 21° = 0.54\ \text{m/s}^2$$
$$a_{\perp} = a\sin 21° = (0.58\ \text{m/s}^2)\sin 21° = 0.21\ \text{m/s}^2$$

3.13 The parallel and perpendicular components of the acceleration of the rover at $t = 2.0$ s.

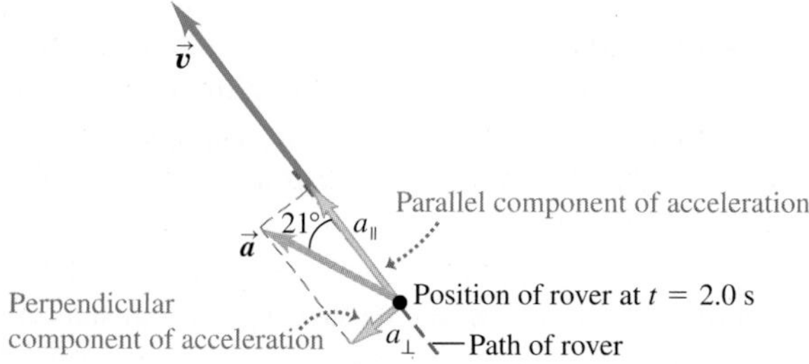

EVALUATE: The parallel component $a_{\parallel}$ is in the same direction as $\vec{v}$, which means that the speed is increasing at this instant; the value of $a_{\parallel} = 0.54\ \text{m/s}^2$ means that the speed is increasing at a rate of 0.54 m/s per second. The perpendicular component $a_{\perp}$ is not zero, which means that at this instant the rover is changing direction and following a curved path; in other words, the rover is turning.

Conceptual Example 3.4 Acceleration of a skier

A skier moves along a ski-jump ramp as shown in Fig. 3.14a. The ramp is straight from point A to point C and curved from point C onward. The skier picks up speed as she moves downhill from point A to point E, where her speed is maximum. She slows down after passing point E. Draw the direction of the acceleration vector at points B, D, E, and F.

SOLUTION

Figure 3.14b shows our solution. At point B the skier is moving in a straight line with increasing speed, so her acceleration points downhill, in the same direction as her velocity.

At point D the skier is moving along a curved path, so her acceleration has a component perpendicular to the path. There is also a component in the direction of her motion because she is still speeding up at this point. So the acceleration vector points *ahead* of the normal to her path at point D.

The skier's speed is instantaneously not changing at point E; the speed is maximum at this point, so its derivative is zero. There is no parallel component of $\vec{a}$, and the acceleration is perpendicular to her motion.

Finally, at point F the acceleration has a perpendicular component (because her path is curved at this point) and a parallel component *opposite* to the direction of her motion (because she's slowing down). So at this point, the acceleration vector points *behind* the normal to her path.

In the next section we'll examine the skier's acceleration after she flies off the ramp.

3.14 (a) The skier's path. (b) Our solution.

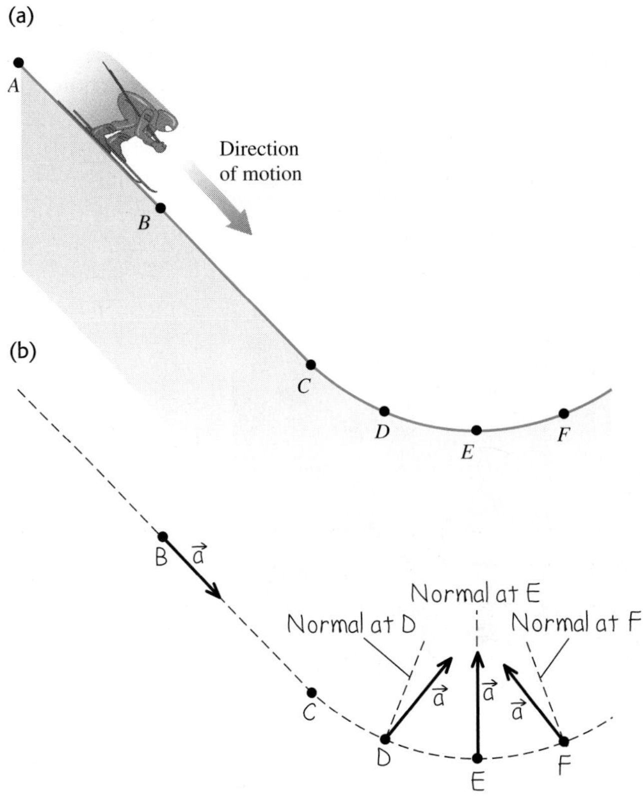

Test Your Understanding of Section 3.2 A sled travels over the crest of a snow-covered hill. The sled slows down as it climbs up one side of the hill and gains speed as it descends on the other side. Which of the vectors (1 through 9) in the figure correctly shows the direction of the sled's acceleration at the crest? (Choice 9 is that the acceleration is zero.)

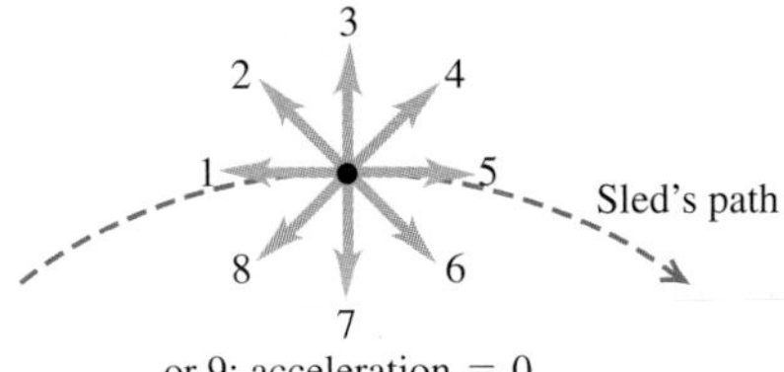

3.3 Projectile Motion

A **projectile** is any body that is given an initial velocity and then follows a path determined entirely by the effects of gravitational acceleration and air resistance. A batted baseball, a thrown football, a package dropped from an airplane, and a bullet shot from a rifle are all projectiles. The path followed by a projectile is called its **trajectory.**

To analyze this common type of motion, we'll start with an idealized model, representing the projectile as a single particle with an acceleration (due to gravity) that is constant in both magnitude and direction. We'll neglect the effects of air resistance and the curvature and rotation of the earth. Like all models, this one has limitations. Curvature of the earth has to be considered in the flight of long-range missiles, and air resistance is of crucial importance to a sky diver. Nevertheless, we can learn a lot from analysis of this simple model. For the remainder of this chapter the phrase "projectile motion" will imply that we're ignoring air resistance. In Chapter 5 we will see what happens when air resistance cannot be ignored.

Projectile motion is always confined to a vertical plane determined by the direction of the initial velocity (Fig. 3.15). This is because the acceleration due to

3.15 The trajectory of a projectile.

- A projectile moves in a vertical plane that contains the initial velocity vector $\vec{v}_0$.
- Its trajectory depends only on $\vec{v}_0$ and on the downward acceleration due to gravity.

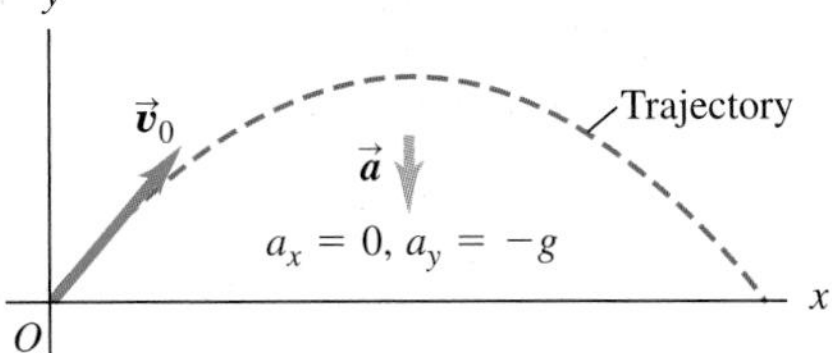

3.16 The red ball is dropped from rest, and the yellow ball is simultaneously projected horizontally; successive images in this stroboscopic photograph are separated by equal time intervals. At any given time, both balls have the same y-position, y-velocity, and y-acceleration, despite having different x-positions and x-velocities.

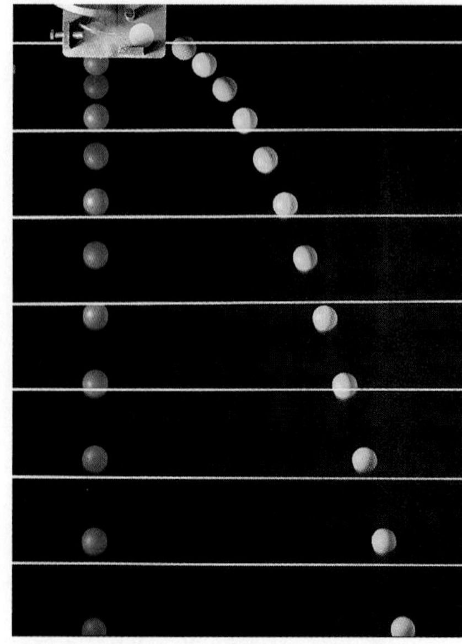

gravity is purely vertical; gravity can't move the projectile sideways. Thus projectile motion is *two-dimensional.* We will call the plane of motion the xy-coordinate plane, with the x-axis horizontal and the y-axis vertically upward.

The key to analyzing projectile motion is that we can treat the x- and y-coordinates separately. The x-component of acceleration is zero, and the y-component is constant and equal to $-g$. (By definition, g is always positive; with our choice of coordinate directions, a_y is negative.) So *we can analyze projectile motion as a combination of horizontal motion with constant velocity and vertical motion with constant acceleration.* Figure 3.16 shows two projectiles with different x-motion but identical y-motion; one is dropped from rest and the other is projected horizontally, but both projectiles fall the same distance in the same time.

We can then express all the vector relationships for the projectile's position, velocity, and acceleration by separate equations for the horizontal and vertical components. The components of $\vec{a}$ are

$$a_x = 0 \qquad a_y = -g \qquad \text{(projectile motion, no air resistance)} \tag{3.14}$$

Since the x-acceleration and y-acceleration are both constant, we can use Eqs. (2.8), (2.12), (2.13), and (2.14) directly. For example, suppose that at time $t = 0$ our particle is at the point (x_0, y_0) and that at this time its velocity components have the initial values v_{0x} and v_{0y}. The components of acceleration are $a_x = 0$, $a_y = -g$. Considering the x-motion first, we substitute 0 for a_x in Eqs. (2.8) and (2.12). We find

$$v_x = v_{0x} \tag{3.15}$$

$$x = x_0 + v_{0x}t \tag{3.16}$$

For the y-motion we substitute y for x, v_y for v_x, v_{0y} for v_{0x}, and $a_y = -g$ for a_x:

$$v_y = v_{0y} - gt \tag{3.17}$$

$$y = y_0 + v_{0y}t - \frac{1}{2}gt^2 \tag{3.18}$$

3.1 Solving Projectile Motion Problems
3.2 Two Balls Falling
3.3 Changing the x-velocity
3.4 Projectile x-y-Accelerations

It's usually simplest to take the initial position (at $t = 0$) as the origin; then $x_0 = y_0 = 0$. This might be the position of a ball at the instant it leaves the thrower's hand or the position of a bullet at the instant it leaves the gun barrel.

Figure 3.17 shows the path of a projectile that starts at (or passes through) the origin at time $t = 0$. The position, velocity, and velocity components are shown

3.17 If air resistance is negligible, the trajectory of a projectile is a combination of horizontal motion with constant velocity and vertical motion with constant acceleration.

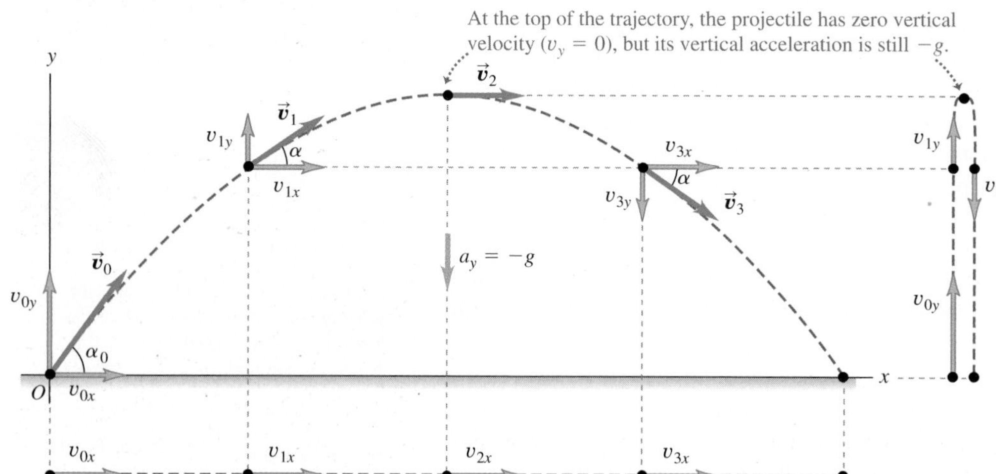

at equal time intervals. The x-component of acceleration is zero, so v_x is constant. The y-component of acceleration is constant and not zero, so v_y changes by equal amounts in equal times, just the same as if the projectile were launched vertically with the same initial y-velocity. At the highest point in the trajectory, $v_y = 0$.

We can also represent the initial velocity $\vec{v}_0$ by its magnitude v_0 (the initial speed) and its angle α_0 with the positive x-axis (Fig. 3.18). In terms of these quantities, the components v_{0x} and v_{0y} of the initial velocity are

$$v_{0x} = v_0 \cos\alpha_0 \qquad v_{0y} = v_0 \sin\alpha_0 \tag{3.19}$$

Using these relationships in Eqs. (3.15) through (3.18) and setting $x_0 = y_0 = 0$, we find

$$x = (v_0 \cos\alpha_0)t \quad \text{(projectile motion)} \tag{3.20}$$

$$y = (v_0 \sin\alpha_0)t - \frac{1}{2}gt^2 \quad \text{(projectile motion)} \tag{3.21}$$

$$v_x = v_0 \cos\alpha_0 \quad \text{(projectile motion)} \tag{3.22}$$

$$v_y = v_0 \sin\alpha_0 - gt \quad \text{(projectile motion)} \tag{3.23}$$

These equations describe the position and velocity of the projectile in Fig. 3.17 at any time t.

We can get a lot of information from these equations. For example, at any time the distance r of the projectile from the origin (the magnitude of the position vector $\vec{r}$) is given by

$$r = \sqrt{x^2 + y^2} \tag{3.24}$$

The projectile's speed (the magnitude of its velocity) at any time is

$$v = \sqrt{v_x^2 + v_y^2} \tag{3.25}$$

The *direction* of the velocity, in terms of the angle α it makes with the positive x-direction (see Fig. 3.17), is given by

$$\tan\alpha = \frac{v_y}{v_x} \tag{3.26}$$

The velocity vector $\vec{v}$ is tangent to the trajectory at each point.

We can derive an equation for the trajectory's shape in terms of x and y by eliminating t. From Eqs. (3.20) and (3.21), which assume $x_0 = y_0 = 0$, we find $t = x/(v_0 \cos\alpha_0)$ and

$$y = (\tan\alpha_0)x - \frac{g}{2v_0^2\cos^2\alpha_0}x^2 \tag{3.27}$$

Don't worry about the details of this equation; the important point is its general form. The quantities v_0, $\tan\alpha_0$, $\cos\alpha_0$, and g are constants, so the equation has the form

$$y = bx - cx^2$$

where b and c are constants. This is the equation of a *parabola.* In projectile motion, with our simple model, the trajectory is always a parabola (Fig. 3.19).

When air resistance *isn't* always negligible and has to be included, calculating the trajectory becomes a lot more complicated; the effects of air resistance

3.18 The initial velocity components v_{0x} and v_{0y} of a projectile (such as a kicked soccer ball) are related to the initial speed v_0 and initial angle α_0.

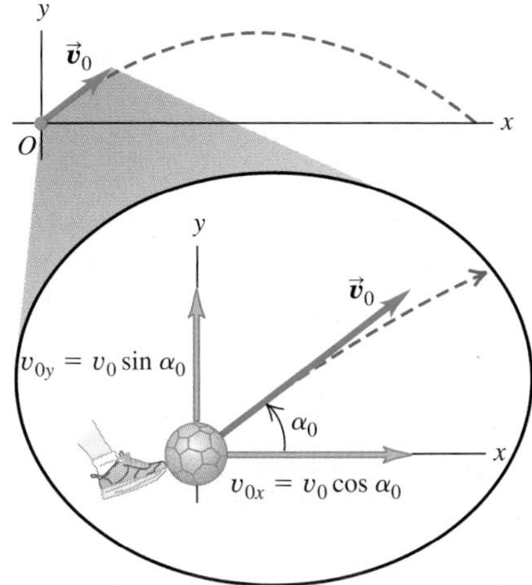
y
$\vec{v}_0$
x
O
y
$\vec{v}_0$
$v_{0y} = v_0 \sin \alpha_0$
α_0
x
$v_{0x} = v_0 \cos \alpha_0$

ActivPhysics ONLINE

3.5 Initial Velocity Components
3.6 Target Practice I
3.7 Target Practice II

3.19 The nearly parabolic trajectories of (a) a bouncing ball and (b) blobs of molten rock ejected from a volcano.

(a) Successive images of ball are separated by equal time intervals.

Successive peaks decrease in height because ball loses energy with each bounce.

(b)

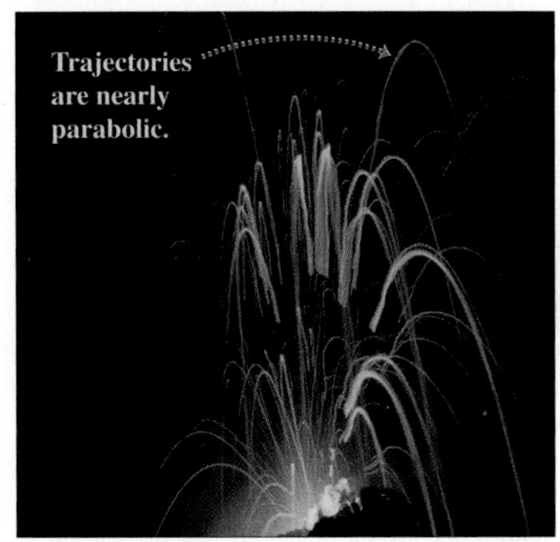
Trajectories are nearly parabolic.

3.20 Air resistance has a large cumulative effect on the motion of a baseball. In this simulation we allow the baseball to fall below the height from which it was thrown (for example, the baseball could have been thrown from a cliff).

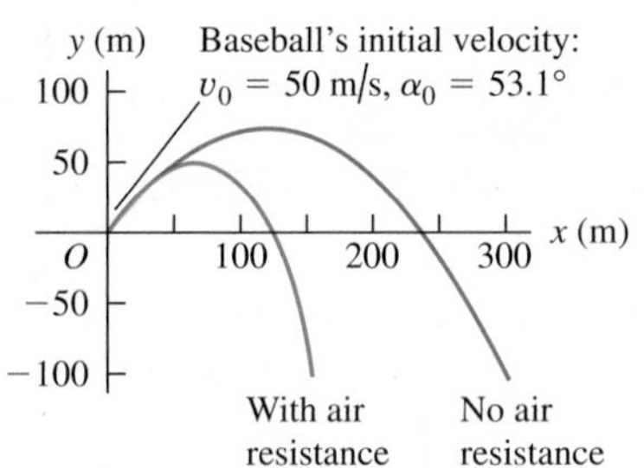

depend on velocity, so the acceleration is no longer constant. Figure 3.20 shows a computer simulation of the trajectory of a baseball both without air resistance and with air resistance proportional to the square of the baseball's speed. We see that air resistance has a very large effect; the maximum height and range both decrease, and the trajectory is no longer a parabola. (If you look closely at Fig. 3.19b, you'll see that the trajectories of the volcanic blobs deviate in a similar way from a parabolic shape.)

Conceptual Example 3.5 Acceleration of a skier, continued

Let's consider again the skier in Conceptual Example 3.4. What is her acceleration at points *G*, *H*, and *I* in Fig. 3.21a *after* she flies off the ramp? Neglect air resistance.

SOLUTION

Figure 3.21b shows our answer. The skier's acceleration changed from point to point while she was on the ramp. But as soon as she leaves the ramp, she becomes a projectile. So at points *G*, *H*, and *I*, and indeed at *all* points after she leaves the ramp, the skier's acceleration points vertically downward and has magnitude g. No matter how complicated the acceleration of a particle before it becomes a projectile, its acceleration as a projectile is given by $a_x = 0$, $a_y = -g$.

3.21 (a) The skier's path during the jump. (b) Our solution.

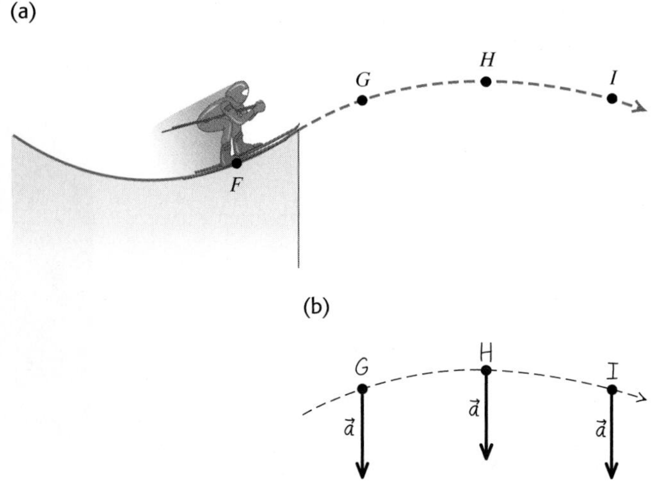

Problem Solving Strategy 3.1 Projectile Motion

NOTE: The strategies we used in Sections 2.4 and 2.5 for straight-line, constant-acceleration problems are also useful here.

IDENTIFY *the relevant concepts:* The key concept to remember is that throughout projectile motion, the acceleration is downward and has a constant magnitude g. Note that the projectile-motion equations don't apply to throwing a ball, because during the throw the ball is acted on by both the thrower's hand and gravity. These equations come into play only after the ball leaves the thrower's hand.

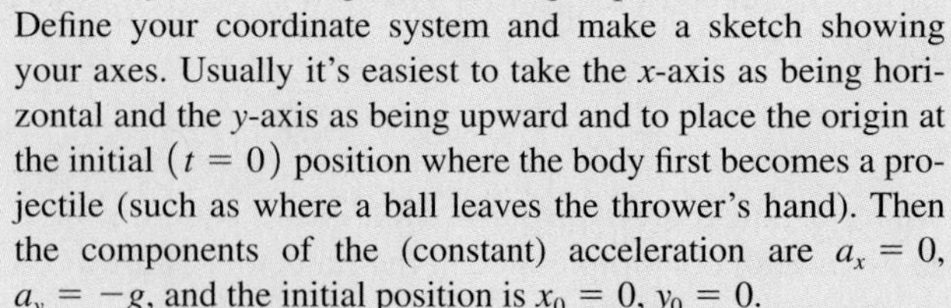

SET UP *the problem* using the following steps:

1. Define your coordinate system and make a sketch showing your axes. Usually it's easiest to take the x-axis as being horizontal and the y-axis as being upward and to place the origin at the initial $(t = 0)$ position where the body first becomes a projectile (such as where a ball leaves the thrower's hand). Then the components of the (constant) acceleration are $a_x = 0$, $a_y = -g$, and the initial position is $x_0 = 0$, $y_0 = 0$.

2. List the unknown and known quantities, and decide which unknowns are your target variables. For example, you might be given the initial velocity (either the components or the magnitude and direction) and asked to find the coordinates and velocity components at some later time. In any case, you'll be using Eqs. (3.20) through (3.23). (Certain other equations given in Section 3.3 may be useful as well.) Make sure that you have as many equations as there are target variables to be found.
3. State the problem in words and then translate those words into symbols. For example, *when* does the particle arrive at a certain point? (That is, at what value of t?) *Where* is the particle when its velocity has a certain value? (That is, what are the values of x and y when v_x or v_y has the specified value?) Since $v_y = 0$ at the highest point in a trajectory, the question "When does the projectile reach its highest point?" translates into "What is the value of t when $v_y = 0$?" Similarly, "When does the projectile return to its initial elevation?" translates into "What is the value of t when $y = y_0$?"

EXECUTE *the solution:* Use Eqs. (3.20) through (3.23) to find the target variables. Resist the temptation to break the trajectory into segments and analyze each segment separately. You don't have to start all over when the projectile reaches its highest point! It's almost always easier to use the same axes and time scale throughout the problem. Use the value $g = 9.8\ \text{m/s}^2$.

EVALUATE *your answer:* As always, look at your results to see whether they make sense and whether the numerical values seem reasonable.

Example 3.6 A body projected horizontally

A motorcycle stunt rider rides off the edge of a cliff. Just at the edge his velocity is horizontal, with magnitude 9.0 m/s. Find the motorcycle's position, distance from the edge of the cliff, and velocity after 0.50 s.

SOLUTION

IDENTIFY: Once the rider leaves the cliff, he is in projectile motion. His velocity at the edge of the cliff is therefore his initial velocity.

SET UP: Figure 3.22 shows our sketch. We place the origin of our coordinate system at the edge of the cliff, where the motorcycle first becomes a projectile, so $x_0 = 0$ and $y_0 = 0$. The initial velocity is purely horizontal (that is, $\alpha_0 = 0$), so the initial velocity components are $v_{0x} = v_0 \cos\alpha_0 = 9.0\ \text{m/s}$ and $v_{0y} = v_0 \sin\alpha_0 = 0$. To find the motorcycle's position at time $t = 0.50$ s, we use Eqs. (3.20) and (3.21), which give x and y as functions of time. We then find the distance from the origin using Eq. (3.24). Finally, we use Eqs. (3.22) and (3.23) to find the velocity components v_x and v_y at $t = 0.50$ s.

3.22 Our sketch for this problem.

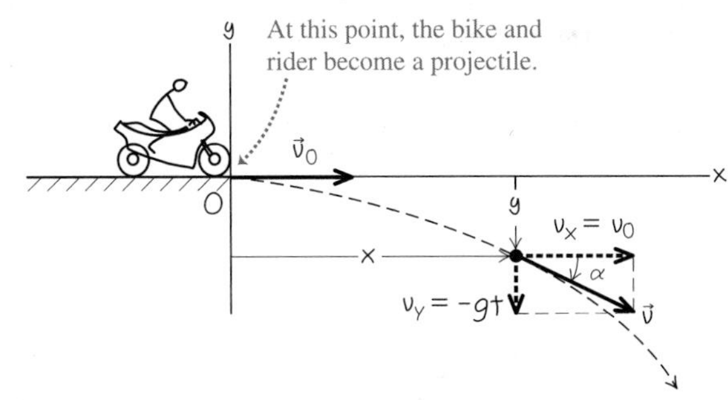

EXECUTE: Where is the motorcycle at $t = 0.50$ s? From Eqs. (3.20) and (3.21), the x- and y-coordinates are

$$x = v_{0x}t = (9.0\ \text{m/s})(0.50\ \text{s}) = 4.5\ \text{m}$$

$$y = -\frac{1}{2}gt^2 = -\frac{1}{2}(9.8\ \text{m/s}^2)(0.50\ \text{s})^2 = -1.2\ \text{m}$$

The negative value of y shows that at this time the motorcycle is below its starting point.

What is the motorcycle's distance from the origin at this time? From Eq. (3.24),

$$r = \sqrt{x^2 + y^2} = \sqrt{(4.5\ \text{m})^2 + (-1.2\ \text{m})^2} = 4.7\ \text{m}$$

What is the velocity at time $t = 0.50$ s? From Eqs. (3.22) and (3.23), the components of velocity at this time are

$$v_x = v_{0x} = 9.0\ \text{m/s}$$

$$v_y = -gt = (-9.8\ \text{m/s}^2)(0.50\ \text{s}) = -4.9\ \text{m/s}$$

The motorcycle has the same horizontal velocity v_x as when it left the cliff at $t = 0$, but in addition there is a downward (negative) vertical velocity v_y. If we use unit vectors, the velocity at $t = 0.50$ s is

$$\vec{v} = v_x\hat{\imath} + v_y\hat{\jmath} = (9.0\ \text{m/s})\hat{\imath} + (-4.9\ \text{m/s})\hat{\jmath}$$

We can also express the velocity in terms of magnitude and direction. From Eq. (3.25), the speed (magnitude of the velocity) at this time is

$$v = \sqrt{v_x^2 + v_y^2} = \sqrt{(9.0\ \text{m/s})^2 + (-4.9\ \text{m/s})^2} = 10.2\ \text{m/s}$$

From Eq. (3.26), the angle α of the velocity vector is

$$\alpha = \arctan\frac{v_y}{v_x} = \arctan\left(\frac{-4.9\ \text{m/s}}{9.0\ \text{m/s}}\right) = -29^\circ$$

At this time the velocity is 29° below the horizontal.

EVALUATE: Just as shown in Fig. 3.17, the horizontal aspect of the motion is unchanged by gravity; the motorcycle continues to move horizontally at 9.0 m/s, covering 4.5 m in 0.50 s. The motorcycle initially has zero vertical velocity, so it falls vertically just like a body released from rest and descends a distance $\frac{1}{2}gt^2 = 1.2$ m in 0.50 s.

Example 3.7 Height and range of a projectile I: A batted baseball

A batter hits a baseball so that it leaves the bat at speed $v_0 = 37.0\ \text{m/s}$ at an angle $\alpha_0 = 53.1°$, at a location where $g = 9.80\ \text{m/s}^2$. (a) Find the position of the ball, and the magnitude and direction of its velocity, at $t = 2.00\ \text{s}$. (b) Find the time when the ball reaches the highest point of its flight and find its height h at this point. (c) Find the *horizontal range* R—that is, the horizontal distance from the starting point to where the ball hits the ground.

SOLUTION

IDENTIFY: As Fig. 3.20 shows, the effects of air resistance on the motion of a baseball aren't really negligible. For the sake of simplicity, however, we'll ignore air resistance for this example and use the projectile-motion equations to describe the motion.

SET UP: Figure 3.23 shows our sketch. We use the same coordinate system as in Fig. 3.17 or 3.18 so we can use Eqs. (3.20) through (3.23) without any modifications. Our target variables are (1) the position and velocity of the ball 2.00 s after it leaves the bat, (2) the elapsed time after leaving the bat when the ball is at its maximum height—that is, when $v_y = 0$—and the y-coordinate at this time, and (3) the x-coordinate at the time when the y-coordinate is equal to the initial value y_0.

The ball leaves the bat a meter or so above ground level, but we neglect this distance and assume that it starts at ground level $(y_0 = 0)$. The initial velocity of the ball has components

$$v_{0x} = v_0 \cos\alpha_0 = (37.0\ \text{m/s})\cos 53.1° = 22.2\ \text{m/s}$$
$$v_{0y} = v_0 \sin\alpha_0 = (37.0\ \text{m/s})\sin 53.1° = 29.6\ \text{m/s}$$

EXECUTE: (a) We want to find x, y, v_x, and v_y at time $t = 2.00\ \text{s}$. From Eqs. (3.20) through (3.23),

$$x = v_{0x}t = (22.2\ \text{m/s})(2.00\ \text{s}) = 44.4\ \text{m}$$
$$y = v_{0y}t - \frac{1}{2}gt^2$$
$$= (29.6\ \text{m/s})(2.00\ \text{s}) - \frac{1}{2}(9.80\ \text{m/s}^2)(2.00\ \text{s})^2$$
$$= 39.6\ \text{m}$$
$$v_x = v_{0x} = 22.2\ \text{m/s}$$
$$v_y = v_{0y} - gt = 29.6\ \text{m/s} - (9.80\ \text{m/s}^2)(2.00\ \text{s})$$
$$= 10.0\ \text{m/s}$$

The y-component of velocity is positive, which means that the ball is still moving upward at this time (Fig. 3.23). The magnitude and direction of the velocity are found from Eqs. (3.25) and (3.26):

$$v = \sqrt{v_x^2 + v_y^2} = \sqrt{(22.2\ \text{m/s})^2 + (10.0\ \text{m/s})^2}$$
$$= 24.3\ \text{m/s}$$
$$\alpha = \arctan\left(\frac{10.0\ \text{m/s}}{22.2\ \text{m/s}}\right) = \arctan 0.450 = 24.2°$$

The direction of the velocity (that is, the direction of motion) is 24.2° above the horizontal.

(b) At the highest point, the vertical velocity v_y is zero. When does this happen? Call the time t_1; then

$$v_y = v_{0y} - gt_1 = 0$$
$$t_1 = \frac{v_{0y}}{g} = \frac{29.6\ \text{m/s}}{9.80\ \text{m/s}^2} = 3.02\ \text{s}$$

3.23 Our sketch for this problem.

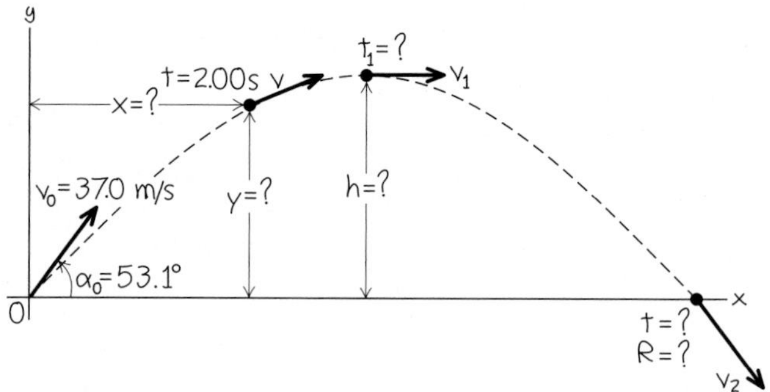

The height h at this time is the value of y when $t = t_1 = 3.02\ \text{s}$:

$$h = v_{0y}t_1 - \frac{1}{2}gt_1^2$$
$$= (29.6\ \text{m/s})(3.02\ \text{s}) - \frac{1}{2}(9.80\ \text{m/s}^2)(3.02\ \text{s})^2$$
$$= 44.7\ \text{m}$$

(c) We'll find the horizontal range in two steps. First, *when* does the ball hit the ground? This occurs when $y = 0$. Call this time t_2; then

$$y = 0 = v_{0y}t_2 - \frac{1}{2}gt_2^2 = t_2\left(v_{0y} - \frac{1}{2}gt_2\right)$$

This is a quadratic equation for t_2. It has two roots:

$$t_2 = 0 \quad \text{and} \quad t_2 = \frac{2v_{0y}}{g} = \frac{2(29.6\ \text{m/s})}{9.80\ \text{m/s}^2} = 6.04\ \text{s}$$

There are two times at which $y = 0$; $t_2 = 0$ is the time the ball *leaves* the ground, and $t_2 = 2v_{0y}/g = 6.04\ \text{s}$ is the time of its return. This is exactly twice the time to reach the highest point that we found in part (b), $t_1 = v_{0y}/g = 3.02\ \text{s}$, so the time of descent equals the time of ascent. This is *always* true if the starting and end points are at the same elevation and air resistance can be neglected.

The horizontal range R is the value of x when the ball returns to the ground—that is, at $t = 6.04\ \text{s}$:

$$R = v_{0x}t_2 = (22.2\ \text{m/s})(6.04\ \text{s}) = 134\ \text{m}$$

The vertical component of velocity when the ball hits the ground is

$$v_y = v_{0y} - gt_2 = 29.6\ \text{m/s} - (9.80\ \text{m/s}^2)(6.04\ \text{s})$$
$$= -29.6\ \text{m/s}$$

That is, v_y has the same magnitude as the initial vertical velocity v_{0y} but the opposite direction (down). Since v_x is constant, the angle $\alpha = -53.1°$ (below the horizontal) at this point is the negative of the initial angle $\alpha_0 = 53.1°$.

EVALUATE: It's often useful to check results by getting them in a different way. For example, we can check our answer for the maximum height in part (b) by applying the constant-acceleration formula Eq. (2.13) to the y-motion:

$$v_y^2 = v_{0y}^2 + 2a_y(y - y_0) = v_{0y}^2 - 2g(y - y_0)$$

At the highest point, $v_y = 0$ and $y = h$. Substituting these, along with $y_0 = 0$, we find

$$0 = {v_{0y}}^2 - 2gh$$

$$h = \frac{{v_{0y}}^2}{2g} = \frac{(29.6\ \text{m/s})^2}{2(9.80\ \text{m/s}^2)} = 44.7\ \text{m}$$

which is the same height we obtained in part (b).

It's interesting to note that $h = 44.7$ m in part (b) is comparable to the 52.4-m height above the playing field of the roof of the Hubert H. Humphrey Metrodome in Minneapolis, and the horizontal range $R = 134$ m in part (c) is greater than the 99.7-m distance from home plate to the right-field fence at Safeco Field in Seattle. (The ball's height when it crosses the fence is more than enough to clear it, so this ball is a home run.)

In real life, a batted ball with the initial speed and angle we've used here won't go as high or as far as we've calculated. (If it did, home runs would be far more common and baseball would be a far less interesting game.) The reason is that air resistance, which we neglected in this example, is actually an important factor at the typical speeds of pitched and batted balls (see Fig. 3.20).

Example 3.8 Height and range of a projectile II: Maximum height, maximum range

For a projectile launched with speed v_0 at initial angle α_0 (between 0° and 90°), derive general expressions for the maximum height h and horizontal range R (Fig. 3.23). For a given v_0, what value of α_0 gives maximum height? What value gives maximum horizontal range?

SOLUTION

IDENTIFY: This is really the same exercise as parts (b) and (c) of Example 3.7. The difference is that we are looking for general expressions for h and R. We'll also be looking for the values of α_0 that give the maximum values of h and R.

SET UP: In part (b) of Example 3.7 we found that the projectile reaches the high point of its trajectory (so that $v_y = 0$) at time $t_1 = v_{0y}/g$, and in part (c) of Example 3.7 we found that the projectile returns to its starting height (so that $y = y_0$) at time $t_2 = 2v_{0y}/g$. (As we saw in Example 3.7, $t_2 = 2t_1$.) To determine the height h at the high point of the trajectory, we use Eq. (3.21) to find the y-coordinate at t_1. To determine R, we substitute t_2 into Eq. (3.20) to determine the x-coordinate at t_2. We'll express our answers in terms of the launch speed v_0 and launch angle α_0 using Eq. (3.19).

EXECUTE: From Eq. (3.19), $v_{0x} = v_0 \cos\alpha_0$ and $v_{0y} = v_0 \sin\alpha_0$. Hence we can write the time t_1 when $v_y = 0$ as

$$t_1 = \frac{v_{0y}}{g} = \frac{v_0 \sin\alpha_0}{g}$$

Then, from Eq. (3.21), the height at this time is

$$h = (v_0 \sin\alpha_0)\left(\frac{v_0 \sin\alpha_0}{g}\right) - \frac{1}{2}g\left(\frac{v_0 \sin\alpha_0}{g}\right)^2$$

$$= \frac{v_0^2 \sin^2\alpha_0}{2g}$$

For a given launch speed v_0, the maximum value of h occurs when $\sin\alpha_0 = 1$ and $\alpha_0 = 90°$—that is, when the projectile is launched straight up. That's what we should expect. If it is launched horizontally, as in Example 3.6, $\alpha_0 = 0$ and the maximum height is zero!

The time t_2 when the projectile returns to the ground is

$$t_2 = \frac{2v_{0y}}{g} = \frac{2v_0 \sin\alpha_0}{g}$$

The horizontal range R is the value of x at this time. From Eq. (3.20),

$$R = (v_0 \cos\alpha_0)t_2 = (v_0 \cos\alpha_0)\frac{2v_0 \sin\alpha_0}{g}$$

We can now use the trigonometric identity $2\sin\alpha_0\cos\alpha_0 = \sin 2\alpha_0$ to rewrite this as

$$R = \frac{v_0^2 \sin 2\alpha_0}{g}$$

The maximum value of $\sin 2\alpha_0$ is 1; this occurs when $2\alpha_0 = 90°$, or $\alpha_0 = 45°$. This angle gives the maximum range for a given initial speed.

EVALUATE: Figure 3.24 is based on a composite photograph of three trajectories of a ball projected from a spring gun at angles of 30°, 45°, and 60°. The initial speed v_0 is approximately the same in all three cases. The horizontal ranges are nearly the same for the 30° and 60° angles, and the range for 45° is greater than either. Can you prove that for a given value of v_0 the range is the same for both an initial angle α_0 and an initial angle $90° - \alpha_0$?

CAUTION Height and range of a projectile We don't recommend memorizing the above expressions for h and R. They are applicable only in the special circumstances we have described. In particular, the expression for the range R can be used *only* when launch and landing heights are equal. There are many end-of-chapter problems to which these equations do *not* apply.

3.24 A launch angle of 45° gives the maximum horizontal range. The range is shorter with launch angles of 30° and 60°.

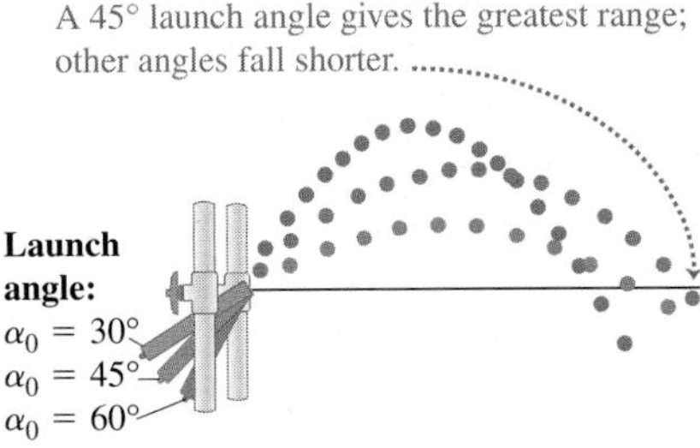
A 45° launch angle gives the greatest range; other angles fall shorter.
Launch angle:
$\alpha_0 = 30°$
$\alpha_0 = 45°$
$\alpha_0 = 60°$

Example 3.9 Different initial and final heights

You toss a ball from your window 8.0 m above the ground. When the ball leaves your hand, it is moving at 10.0 m/s at an angle of 20° below the horizontal. How far horizontally from your window will the ball hit the ground? Ignore air resistance.

SOLUTION

IDENTIFY: As in our calculation of the horizontal range in Examples 3.7 and 3.8, we are trying to find the horizontal coordinate of a projectile when it is at a given value of y. The difference here is that this value of y is *not* equal to the initial y-coordinate.

SET UP: Once again we choose the x-axis to be horizontal and the y-axis to be upward, and we place the origin of coordinates at the point where the ball leaves your hand (Fig. 3.25). We have $v_0 = 10.0\ \text{m/s}$ and $\alpha_0 = -20°$; the angle is negative because the initial velocity is below the horizontal. Our target variable is the value of x at the point where the ball reaches the ground—that is, when $y = -8.0\ \text{m}$. Because the initial and final heights of the ball are different, we can't simply use the expression for the horizontal range found in Example 3.8. Instead, we first use Eq. (3.21) to find the time t when the ball reaches $y = -8.0\ \text{m}$ and then calculate the value of x at this time using Eq. (3.20).

3.25 Our sketch for this problem.

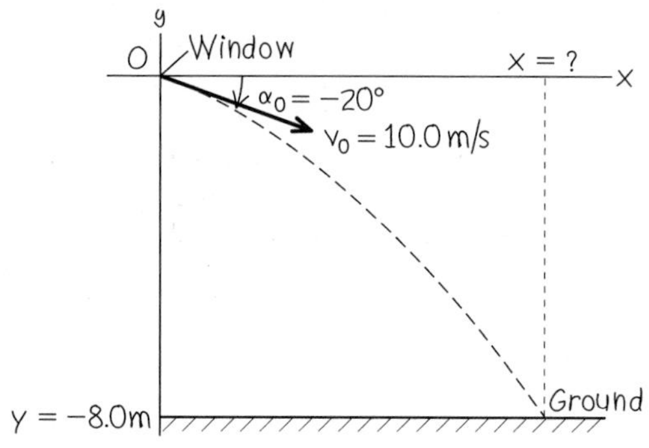

EXECUTE: To determine t, we rewrite Eq. (3.21) in the standard form for a quadratic equation for t:

$$\frac{1}{2}gt^2 - (v_0 \sin\alpha_0)t + y = 0$$

The roots of this equation are

$$t = \frac{v_0\sin\alpha_0 \pm \sqrt{(-v_0\sin\alpha_0)^2 - 4\left(\frac{1}{2}g\right)y}}{2\left(\frac{1}{2}g\right)}$$

$$= \frac{v_0\sin\alpha_0 \pm \sqrt{v_0^2\sin^2\alpha_0 - 2gy}}{g}$$

$$= \frac{\left[\begin{array}{l}(10.0\ \text{m/s})\sin(-20°)\\ \pm\sqrt{(10.0\ \text{m/s})^2\sin^2(-20°) - 2(9.80\ \text{m/s}^2)(-8.0\ \text{m})}\end{array}\right]}{9.80\ \text{m/s}^2}$$

$$= -1.7\ \text{s} \quad \text{or} \quad 0.98\ \text{s}$$

We can discard the negative root, since it refers to a time before the ball left your hand. The positive root tells us that the ball takes 0.98 s to reach the ground. From Eq. (3.20), the ball's x-coordinate at that time is

$$x = (v_0\cos\alpha_0)t = (10.0\ \text{m/s})[\cos(-20°)](0.98\ \text{s})$$
$$= 9.2\ \text{m}$$

The ball hits the ground a horizontal distance of 9.2 m from your window.

EVALUATE: The root $t = -1.7\ \text{s}$ is an example of a "fictional" solution to a quadratic equation. We discussed these in Example 2.8 in Section 2.5; you should review that discussion.

With our choice of origin we had initial and final heights $y_0 = 0$ and $y = -8.0\ \text{m}$. Can you use Eqs. (3.16) and (3.18) to show that you get the same answers for t and x if you choose the origin to be at the point on the ground directly below where the ball leaves your hand?

Example 3.10 The zookeeper and the monkey

A monkey escapes from the zoo and climbs a tree. After failing to entice the monkey down, the zookeeper fires a tranquilizer dart directly at the monkey (Fig. 3.26). The clever monkey lets go at the same instant the dart leaves the gun barrel, intending to land on the ground and escape. Show that the dart *always* hits the monkey, regardless of the dart's muzzle velocity (provided that it gets to the monkey before he hits the ground).

SOLUTION

IDENTIFY: In this example we have *two* bodies in projectile motion: the tranquilizer dart and the monkey. The dart and the monkey have different initial positions and initial velocities, but they go into projectile motion at the same time. To show that the dart hits the monkey, we have to prove that at some time the monkey and the dart have the same x-coordinate and the same y-coordinate.

SET UP: We make the usual choice for the x- and y-directions, and place the origin of coordinates at the end of the barrel of the tranquilizer gun (Fig. 3.26). We'll first use Eq. (3.20) to find the time t when the x-coordinates x_{monkey} and x_{dart} are the same. Then we'll use Eq. (3.21) to check whether y_{monkey} and y_{dart} are also equal at this time; if they are, the dart hits the monkey.

EXECUTE: The monkey drops straight down, so $x_{\text{monkey}} = d$ at *all* times. For the dart, Eq. (3.20) tells us that $x_{\text{dart}} = (v_0\cos\alpha_0)t$. When these x-coordinates are equal, $d = (v_0\cos\alpha_0)t$, or

$$t = \frac{d}{v_0\cos\alpha_0}$$

To have the dart hit the monkey, it must be true that $y_{\text{monkey}} = y_{\text{dart}}$ at this same time. The monkey is in one-dimensional free fall; his position at any time is given by Eq. (2.12), with appropriate symbol changes. Figure 3.26 shows that the monkey's initial height is $d\tan\alpha_0$ (the opposite side of a right triangle with angle α_0 and adjacent side d), and we find

$$y_{\text{monkey}} = d\tan\alpha_0 - \frac{1}{2}gt^2$$

3.26 The tranquilizer dart hits the falling monkey.

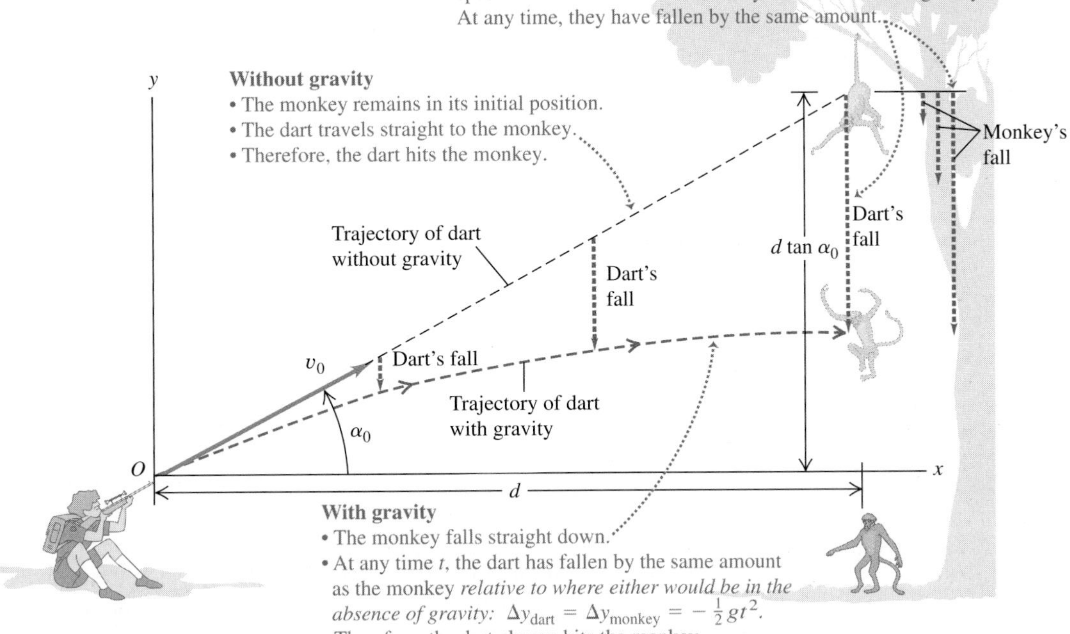
Dashed arrows show how far the dart and monkey have fallen at specific times relative to where they would be without gravity. At any time, they have fallen by the same amount.
Without gravity
• The monkey remains in its initial position.
• The dart travels straight to the monkey.
• Therefore, the dart hits the monkey.
Monkey's fall
Dart's fall
Trajectory of dart without gravity
Dart's fall
d tan α0
Dart's fall
Trajectory of dart with gravity
v0
α0
O
x
y
d
With gravity
• The monkey falls straight down.
• At any time t, the dart has fallen by the same amount as the monkey relative to where either would be in the absence of gravity: Δy_dart = Δy_monkey = −½gt².
• Therefore, the dart always hits the monkey.

For the dart we use Eq. (3.21):

$$y_{\text{dart}} = (v_0 \sin\alpha_0)t - \frac{1}{2}gt^2$$

So we see that if $d\tan\alpha_0 = (v_0\sin\alpha_0)t$ at the time when the two x-coordinates are equal, then $y_{\text{monkey}} = y_{\text{dart}}$, and we have a hit. To prove that this happens, we replace t with $d/(v_0\cos\alpha_0)$, the time when $x_{\text{monkey}} = x_{\text{dart}}$. Sure enough, we find that

$$(v_0\sin\alpha_0)t = (v_0\sin\alpha_0)\frac{d}{v_0\cos\alpha_0} = d\tan\alpha_0$$

EVALUATE: We have proved that at the time the x-coordinates are equal, the y-coordinates are also equal; a dart aimed at the initial position of the monkey *always* hits it, no matter what v_0 is. This result is also independent of the value of g, the acceleration due to gravity. With no gravity $(g = 0)$, the monkey would remain motionless, and the dart would travel in a straight line to hit him. With gravity, both "fall" the same distance $(\frac{1}{2}gt^2)$ below their $g = 0$ positions, and the dart still hits the monkey (Fig. 3.26).

Test Your Understanding of Section 3.3 In Example 3.10, suppose the tranquilizer dart has a relatively low muzzle velocity so that the dart reaches a maximum height at a point P before striking the monkey, as shown in the figure. When the dart is at point P, will the monkey be (i) at point A (higher than P), (ii) at point B (at the same height as P), or (iii) at point C (lower than P)? Ignore air resistance.

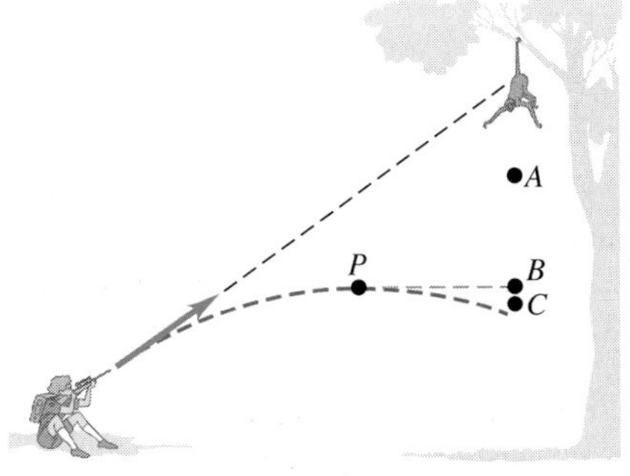
A
P
B
C

3.4 Motion in a Circle

When a particle moves along a curved path, the direction of its velocity changes. As we saw in Section 3.2, this means that the particle *must* have a component of acceleration perpendicular to the path, even if its speed is constant (see Fig. 3.11b). In this section we'll calculate the acceleration for the important special case of motion in a circle.

ActivPhysics ONLINE

4.1 Magnitude of Centripetal Acceleration

3.27 A car in uniform circular motion. The speed is constant and the acceleration is directed toward the center of the circular path.

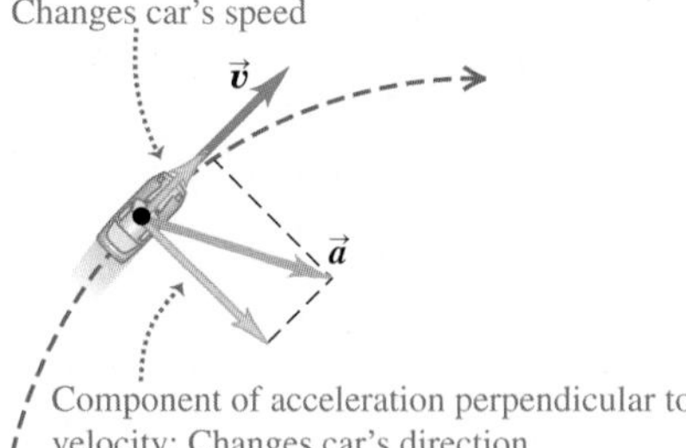
Car speeding up along a circular path
Component of acceleration parallel to velocity: Changes car's speed
$\vec{v}$
$\vec{a}$
Component of acceleration perpendicular to velocity: Changes car's direction

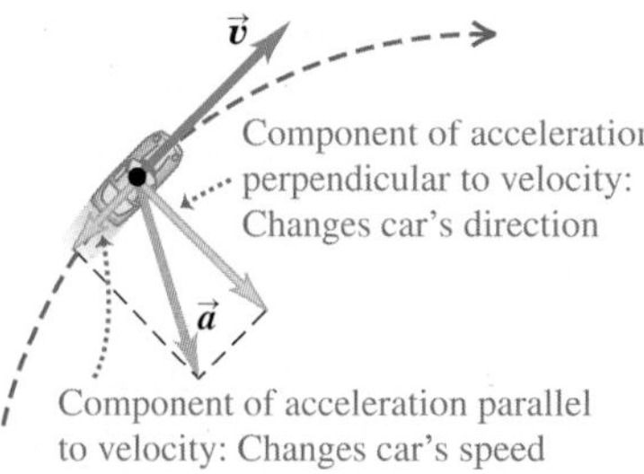
Car slowing down along a circular path
$\vec{v}$
Component of acceleration perpendicular to velocity: Changes car's direction
$\vec{a}$
Component of acceleration parallel to velocity: Changes car's speed

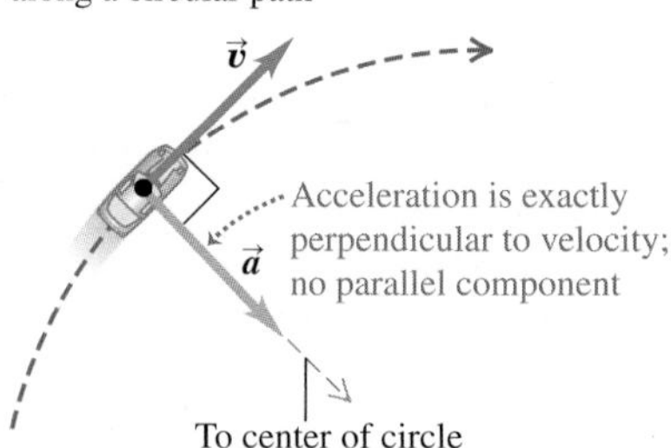
Uniform circular motion: Constant speed along a circular path
$\vec{v}$
$\vec{a}$
Acceleration is exactly perpendicular to velocity; no parallel component
To center of circle

3.28 Finding the velocity change $\Delta\vec{v}$, average acceleration $\vec{a}_{av}$, and instantaneous acceleration $\vec{a}_{rad}$ for a particle moving in a circle with constant speed.

(a) A point moves a distance Δs at constant speed along a circular path.

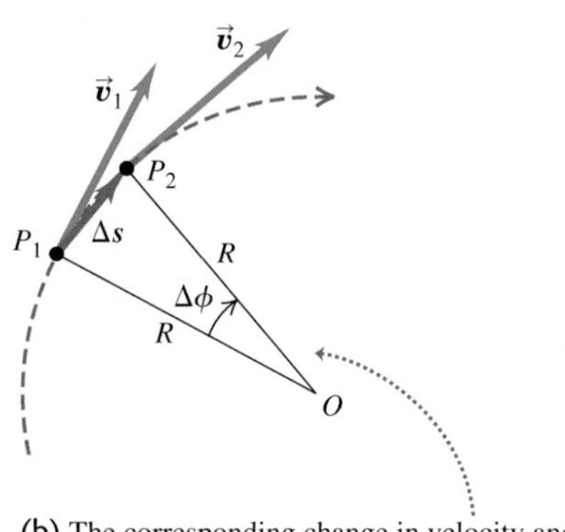
$\vec{v}_2$
$\vec{v}_1$
P_2
P_1
Δs
R
$\Delta\phi$
R
O

(b) The corresponding change in velocity and average acceleration

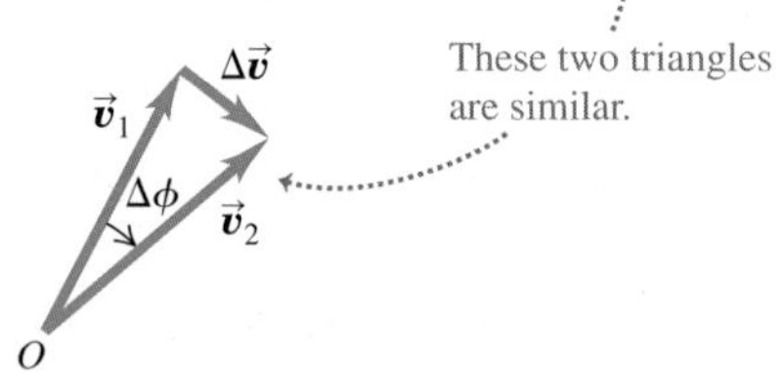
$\Delta\vec{v}$
$\vec{v}_1$
These two triangles are similar.
$\Delta\phi$
$\vec{v}_2$
O

(c) The instantaneous acceleration

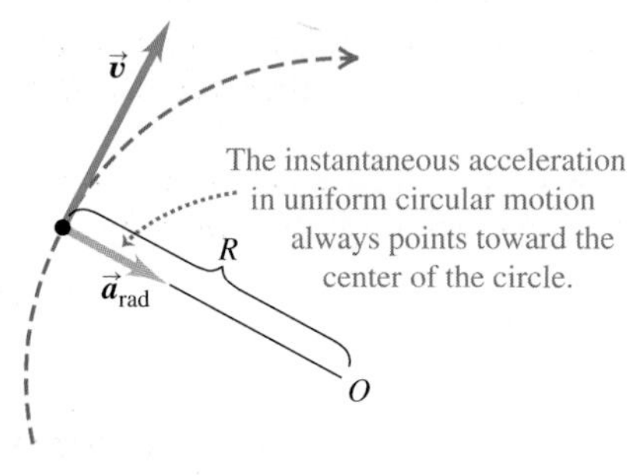
$\vec{v}$
The instantaneous acceleration in uniform circular motion always points toward the center of the circle.
R
$\vec{a}_{rad}$
O

Uniform Circular Motion

When a particle moves in a circle with *constant speed,* the motion is called **uniform circular motion.** A car rounding a curve with constant radius at constant speed, a satellite moving in a circular orbit, and an ice skater skating in a circle with constant speed are all examples of uniform circular motion (Fig. 3.27; compare Fig. 3.12). There is no component of acceleration parallel (tangent) to the path; otherwise, the speed would change. The acceleration vector is perpendicular (normal) to the path and hence directed inward (never outward!) toward the center of the circular path. This causes the direction of the velocity to change without changing the speed. Our next project is to show that the magnitude of the acceleration in uniform circular motion is related in a simple way to the speed of the particle and the radius of the circle.

Figure 3.28a shows a particle moving with constant speed in a circular path of radius R with center at O. The particle moves from P_1 to P_2 in a time Δt. The vector change in velocity $\Delta\vec{v}$ during this time is shown in Fig. 3.28b.

The angles labeled $\Delta\phi$ in Figs. 3.28a and 3.28b are the same because $\vec{v}_1$ is perpendicular to the line OP_1 and $\vec{v}_2$ is perpendicular to the line OP_2. Hence the triangles in Figs. 3.28a and 3.28b are *similar.* The ratios of corresponding sides of similar triangles are equal, so

$$\frac{|\Delta\vec{v}|}{v_1} = \frac{\Delta s}{R} \quad \text{or} \quad |\Delta\vec{v}| = \frac{v_1}{R}\Delta s$$

The magnitude a_{av} of the average acceleration during Δt is therefore

$$a_{av} = \frac{|\Delta\vec{v}|}{\Delta t} = \frac{v_1}{R}\frac{\Delta s}{\Delta t}$$

The magnitude a of the *instantaneous* acceleration $\vec{a}$ at point P_1 is the limit of this expression as we take point P_2 closer and closer to point P_1:

$$a = \lim_{\Delta t \to 0} \frac{v_1}{R}\frac{\Delta s}{\Delta t} = \frac{v_1}{R}\lim_{\Delta t \to 0}\frac{\Delta s}{\Delta t}$$

But the limit of $\Delta s/\Delta t$ is the speed v_1 at point P_1. Also, P_1 can be any point on the path, so we can drop the subscript and let v represent the speed at any point. Then

$$a_{rad} = \frac{v^2}{R} \quad \text{(uniform circular motion)} \qquad (3.28)$$

We have added the subscript "rad" as a reminder that the direction of the instantaneous acceleration at each point is always along a radius of the circle, toward its center. Because the speed is constant, the acceleration is always perpendicular to the instantaneous velocity. This is shown in Fig. 3.28c; compare with the right-hand illustration in Fig. 3.27.

We have found that *in uniform circular motion, the magnitude a of the instantaneous acceleration is equal to the square of the speed v divided by the radius R of the circle. Its direction is perpendicular to $\vec{v}$ and inward along the radius.*

Because the acceleration is always directed toward the center of the circle, it is sometimes called **centripetal acceleration.** The word "centripetal" is derived from two Greek words meaning "seeking the center." Figure 3.29a shows the directions of the velocity and acceleration vectors at several points for a particle moving with uniform circular motion.

3.29 Acceleration and velocity (a) for a particle in uniform circular motion and (b) for a projectile with no air resistance.

(a) Uniform circular motion

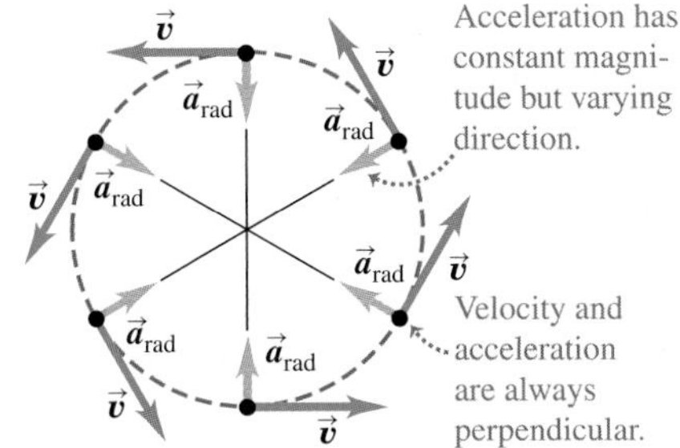
$\vec{v}$
$\vec{a}_{rad}$
Acceleration has constant magnitude but varying direction.
Velocity and acceleration are always perpendicular.

(b) Projectile motion

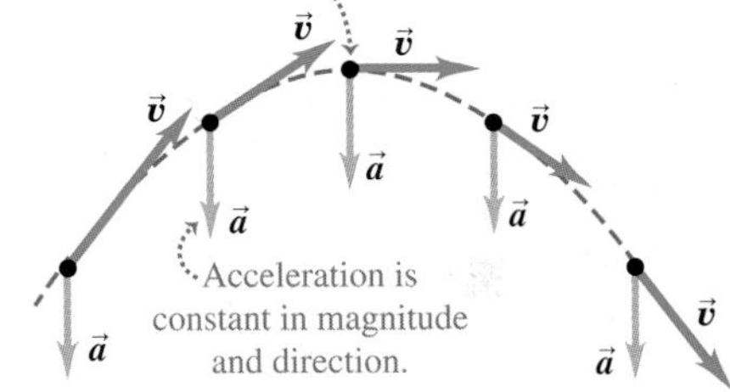
Velocity and acceleration are perpendicular only at the peak of the trajectory.
$\vec{v}$
$\vec{a}$
Acceleration is constant in magnitude and direction.

CAUTION Uniform circular motion vs. projectile motion The acceleration in uniform circular motion has some similarities to the acceleration in projectile motion without air resistance, but there are also some important differences. In both uniform circular motion (Fig. 3.29a) and projectile motion (Fig. 3.29b) the *magnitude* of acceleration is the same at all times. However, in uniform circular motion the *direction* of $\vec{a}$ changes continuously so that it always points toward the center of the circle. (At the top of the circle the acceleration points down; at the bottom of the circle the acceleration points up.) In projectile motion, by contrast, the direction of $\vec{a}$ remains the same at all times.

We can also express the magnitude of the acceleration in uniform circular motion in terms of the **period** T of the motion, the time for one revolution (one complete trip around the circle). In a time T the particle travels a distance equal to the circumference $2\pi R$ of the circle, so its speed is

$$v = \frac{2\pi R}{T} \qquad (3.29)$$

When we substitute this into Eq. (3.28), we obtain the alternative expression

$$a_{rad} = \frac{4\pi^2 R}{T^2} \quad \text{(uniform circular motion)} \qquad (3.30)$$

Example 3.11 Centripetal acceleration on a curved road

An Aston Martin V8 Vantage sports car has a "lateral acceleration" of $0.96g$, which is $(0.96)(9.8\ \text{m/s}^2) = 9.4\ \text{m/s}^2$. This represents the maximum centripetal acceleration that the car can attain without skidding out of the circular path. If the car is traveling at a constant 40 m/s (about 89 mi/h, or 144 km/h), what is the minimum radius of curve it can negotiate? (Assume that the curve is unbanked.)

SOLUTION

IDENTIFY: Because the car is moving at a constant speed along a curve that is a segment of a circle, we can apply the ideas of uniform circular motion.

SET UP: We use Eq. (3.28) to find the target variable R (the radius of the curve) in terms of the given centripetal acceleration a_{rad} and speed v.

EXECUTE: We are given a_{rad} and v, so we solve Eq. (3.28) for R:

$$R = \frac{v^2}{a_{rad}} = \frac{(40\ \text{m/s})^2}{9.4\ \text{m/s}^2} = 170\ \text{m (about 560 ft)}$$

EVALUATE: Our result shows that the required turning radius R is proportional to the *square* of the speed. Hence even a small reduction in speed can make R substantially smaller. For example, reducing v by 20% (from 40 m/s to 32 m/s) would decrease R by 36% (from 170 m to 109 m).

Another way to make the required turning radius smaller is to *bank* the curve. We will investigate this option in Chapter 5.

Example 3.12 Centripetal acceleration on a carnival ride

In a carnival ride, the passengers travel at constant speed in a circle of radius 5.0 m. They make one complete circle in 4.0 s. What is their acceleration?

SOLUTION

IDENTIFY: The speed is constant, so this is a problem involving uniform circular motion.

SET UP: We are given the radius $R = 5.0$ m and the period $T = 4.0$ s, so we can use Eq. (3.30) to calculate the acceleration. Alternatively, we can first calculate the speed v using Eq. (3.29) and then find the acceleration using Eq. (3.28).

EXECUTE: From Eq. (3.30),

$$a_{\text{rad}} = \frac{4\pi^2(5.0\text{ m})}{(4.0\text{ s})^2} = 12\text{ m/s}^2$$

We'll check this answer by using Eq. (3.28) after first determining the speed v. From Eq. (3.29), the speed is the circumference of the circle divided by the period T:

$$v = \frac{2\pi R}{T} = \frac{2\pi(5.0\text{ m})}{4.0\text{ s}} = 7.9\text{ m/s}$$

The centripetal acceleration is then

$$a_{\text{rad}} = \frac{v^2}{R} = \frac{(7.9\text{ m/s})^2}{5.0\text{ m}} = 12\text{ m/s}^2$$

Happily, we get the same answer for a_{rad} with both approaches.

EVALUATE: As in Example 3.11, the direction of $\vec{a}$ is always toward the center of the circle. The magnitude of $\vec{a}$ is greater than g, the acceleration due to gravity, so this is not a ride for the faint-hearted. (Some roller coasters subject their passengers to accelerations as great as $4g$.)

Nonuniform Circular Motion

We have assumed throughout this section that the particle's speed is constant. If the speed varies, we call the motion **nonuniform circular motion.** An example is a roller coaster car that slows down and speeds up as it moves around a vertical loop. In nonuniform circular motion, Eq. (3.28) still gives the *radial* component of acceleration $a_{\text{rad}} = v^2/R$, which is always *perpendicular* to the instantaneous velocity and directed toward the center of the circle. But since the speed v has different values at different points in the motion, the value of a_{rad} is not constant. The radial (centripetal) acceleration is greatest at the point in the circle where the speed is greatest.

In nonuniform circular motion there is also a component of acceleration that is *parallel* to the instantaneous velocity. This is the component $a_{\parallel}$ that we discussed in Section 3.2; here we call this component a_{tan} to emphasize that it is *tangent* to the circle. From the discussion at the end of Section 3.2 we see that the tangential component of acceleration a_{tan} is equal to the rate of change of *speed.* Thus

$$a_{\text{rad}} = \frac{v^2}{R} \quad \text{and} \quad a_{\text{tan}} = \frac{d|\vec{v}|}{dt} \quad \text{(nonuniform circular motion)} \tag{3.31}$$

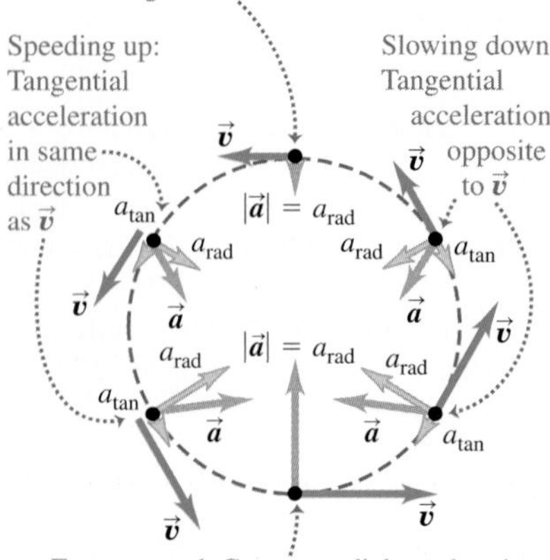
Slowest speed: Least radial acceleration, zero tangential acceleration
Speeding up: Tangential acceleration in same direction as $\vec{v}$
Slowing down: Tangential acceleration opposite to $\vec{v}$
$\vec{v}$
$|\vec{a}| = a_{\text{rad}}$
a_{tan}
a_{rad}
$\vec{a}$
Fastest speed: Greatest radial acceleration, zero tangential acceleration

3.30 A particle moving in a vertical loop with a varying speed, like a roller coaster car.

The vector acceleration of a particle moving in a circle with varying speed is the vector sum of the radial and tangential components of accelerations. The tangential component is in the same direction as the velocity if the particle is speeding up, and in the opposite direction if the particle is slowing down (Fig. 3.30).

In *uniform* circular motion there is no tangential component of acceleration, but the radial component is the magnitude of $d\vec{v}/dt$.

CAUTION Uniform vs. nonuniform circular motion Note that the two quantities

$$\frac{d|\vec{v}|}{dt} \quad \text{and} \quad \left|\frac{d\vec{v}}{dt}\right|$$

are *not* the same. The first, equal to the tangential acceleration, is the rate of change of speed; it is zero whenever a particle moves with constant speed, even when its direction of motion changes (such as in *uniform* circular motion). The second is the magnitude of the vector acceleration; it is zero only when the particle's acceleration *vector* is zero—that is, when the particle moves in a straight line with constant speed. In *uniform* circular motion $|d\vec{v}/dt| = a_{\text{rad}} = v^2/r$; in *nonuniform circular motion* there is also a tangential component of acceleration, so $|d\vec{v}/dt| = \sqrt{a_{\text{rad}}^2 + a_{\text{tan}}^2}$.

Test Your Understanding of Section 3.4 Suppose that the particle in Fig. 3.30 experiences four times the acceleration at the bottom of the loop as it does at the top of the loop. Compared to its speed at the top of the loop, is its speed at the bottom of the loop (i) $\sqrt{2}$ times as great; (ii) 2 times as great; (iii) $2\sqrt{2}$ times as great; (iv) 4 times as great; or (v) 16 times as great.

3.5 Relative Velocity

You've no doubt observed how a car that is moving slowly forward appears to be moving backward when you pass it. In general, when two observers measure the velocity of a moving body, they get different results if one observer is moving relative to the other. The velocity seen by a particular observer is called the velocity *relative* to that observer, or simply **relative velocity.** Figure 3.31 shows a situation in which understanding relative velocity is extremely important.

We'll first consider relative velocity along a straight line, then generalize to relative velocity in a plane.

3.31 Airshow pilots face a complicated problem involving relative velocities. They must keep track of their motion relative to the air (to maintain enough airflow over the wings to sustain lift), relative to each other (to keep a tight formation without colliding), and relative to their audience (to remain in sight of the spectators).

Relative Velocity in One Dimension

A passenger walks with a velocity of 1.0 m/s along the aisle of a train that is moving with a velocity of 3.0 m/s (Fig. 3.32a). What is the passenger's velocity? It's a simple enough question, but it has no single answer. As seen by a second passenger sitting in the train, she is moving at 1.0 m/s. A person on a bicycle standing beside the train sees the walking passenger moving at 1.0 m/s + 3.0 m/s = 4.0 m/s. An observer in another train going in the opposite direction would give still another answer. We have to specify which observer we mean, and we speak of the velocity *relative* to a particular observer. The walking passenger's velocity relative to the train is 1.0 m/s, her velocity relative to the cyclist is 4.0 m/s, and so on. Each observer, equipped in principle with a meter stick and a stopwatch, forms what we call a **frame of reference.** Thus a frame of reference is a coordinate system plus a time scale.

Let's use the symbol A for the cyclist's frame of reference (at rest with respect to the ground) and the symbol B for the frame of reference of the moving train. In straight-line motion the position of a point P relative to frame A is given by $x_{P/A}$ (the position of P with respect to A), and the position of P relative to frame B is given by $x_{P/B}$ (see Fig. 3.32b). The position of the origin of A with respect to the origin of B is $x_{B/A}$. Figure 3.32b shows that

$$x_{P/A} = x_{P/B} + x_{B/A} \tag{3.32}$$

In words, the total distance from the origin of A to point P equals the distance from the origin of B to point P plus the distance from the origin of A to the origin of B.

The x-velocity of P relative to frame A, denoted by $v_{P/A\text{-}x}$, is the derivative of $x_{P/A}$ with respect to time. The other velocities are similarly obtained. So the time derivative of Eq. (3.32) gives us a relationship among the various velocities:

$$\frac{dx_{P/A}}{dt} = \frac{dx_{P/B}}{dt} + \frac{dx_{B/A}}{dt} \quad \text{or}$$

$$v_{P/A\text{-}x} = v_{P/B\text{-}x} + v_{B/A\text{-}x} \quad \text{(relative velocity along a line)} \tag{3.33}$$

Getting back to the passenger on the train in Fig. 3.32, we see that A is the cyclist's frame of reference, B is the frame of reference of the train, and point P represents the passenger. Using the above notation, we have

$$v_{P/B\text{-}x} = +1.0 \text{ m/s} \qquad v_{B/A\text{-}x} = +3.0 \text{ m/s}$$

3.32 (a) A passenger walking in a train. (b) The position of the passenger relative to the cyclist's frame of reference and the train's frame of reference.

(a)

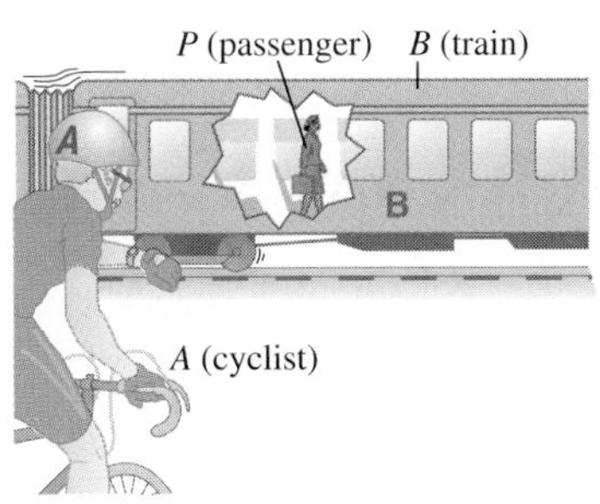

(b)

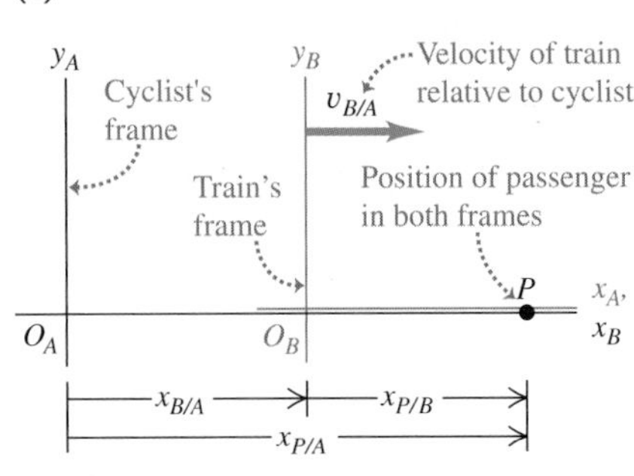

From Eq. (3.33) the passenger's velocity $v_{P/A}$ relative to the cyclist is

$$v_{P/A\text{-}x} = +1.0\text{ m/s} + 3.0\text{ m/s} = +4.0\text{ m/s}$$

as we already knew.

In this example, both velocities are toward the right, and we have taken this as the positive x-direction. If the passenger walks toward the *left* relative to the train, then $v_{P/B\text{-}x} = -1.0\text{ m/s}$, and her x-velocity relative to the cyclist is $v_{P/A\text{-}x} = -1.0\text{ m/s} + 3.0\text{ m/s} = +2.0\text{ m/s}$. The sum in Eq. (3.33) is always an algebraic sum, and any or all of the x-velocities may be negative.

When the passenger looks out the window, the stationary cyclist on the ground appears to her to be moving backward; we can call the cyclist's velocity relative to her $v_{A/P\text{-}x}$. Clearly, this is just the negative of $v_{P/A\text{-}x}$. In general, if A and B are any two points or frames of reference,

$$v_{A/B\text{-}x} = -v_{B/A\text{-}x} \tag{3.34}$$

Problem Solving Strategy 3.2 Relative Velocity

IDENTIFY *the relevant concepts:* Whenever you see the phrase "velocity relative to" or "velocity with respect to," it's likely that the concepts of relative velocity will be helpful.

SET UP *the problem:* Label each frame of reference in the problem. Each moving body has its own frame of reference; in addition, you'll almost always have to include the frame of reference of the earth's surface. (Statements such as "The car is traveling north at 90 km/h" implicitly refer to the car's velocity relative to the surface of the earth.) Use the labels to help identify the target variable. For example, if you want to find the x-velocity of a car (C) with respect to a bus (B), your target variable is $v_{C/B\text{-}x}$.

EXECUTE *the solution:* Solve for the target variable using Eq. (3.33). (If the velocities are not along the same direction, you'll need to use the vector form of this equation, derived later in this section.) It's important to note the order of the double subscripts in Eq. (3.33): $v_{A/B\text{-}x}$ always means "x-velocity of A relative to B." These subscripts obey an interesting kind of algebra, as Eq. (3.33) shows. If we regard each one as a fraction, then the fraction on the left side is the *product* of the fractions on the right sides: $P/A = (P/B)(B/A)$. This is a handy rule you can use when applying Eq. (3.33) to any number of frames of reference. For example, if there are three different frames of reference A, B, and C, we can write immediately

$$v_{P/A\text{-}x} = v_{P/C\text{-}x} + v_{C/B\text{-}x} + v_{B/A\text{-}x}$$

EVALUATE *your answer:* Be on the lookout for stray minus signs in your answer. If the target variable is the x-velocity of a car relative to a bus $(v_{C/B\text{-}x})$, make sure that you haven't accidentally calculated the x-velocity of the *bus* relative to the *car* $(v_{B/C\text{-}x})$. If you have made this mistake, you can recover using Eq. (3.34).

Example 3.13 Relative velocity on a straight road

You are driving north on a straight two-lane road at a constant 88 km/h. A truck traveling at a constant 104 km/h approaches you (in the other lane, fortunately). (a) What is the truck's velocity relative to you? (b) What is your velocity with respect to the truck? (c) How do the relative velocities change after you and the truck have passed each other?

SOLUTION

IDENTIFY: This example is about relative velocities along a line.

SET UP: Let you be Y, the truck be T, and the earth's surface be E, and let the positive x-direction be north (Fig. 3.33). Then your x-velocity relative to the earth is $v_{Y/E\text{-}x} = +88\text{ km/h}$. As the truck is initially approaching you, it must be moving south and its x-velocity with respect to the earth is $v_{T/E\text{-}x} = -104\text{ km/h}$. The target variable in part (a) is $v_{T/Y\text{-}x}$; the target variable in part (b) is $v_{Y/T\text{-}x}$. We'll find both target variables by using Eq. (3.33) for relative velocity.

3.33 Reference frames for you and the truck.

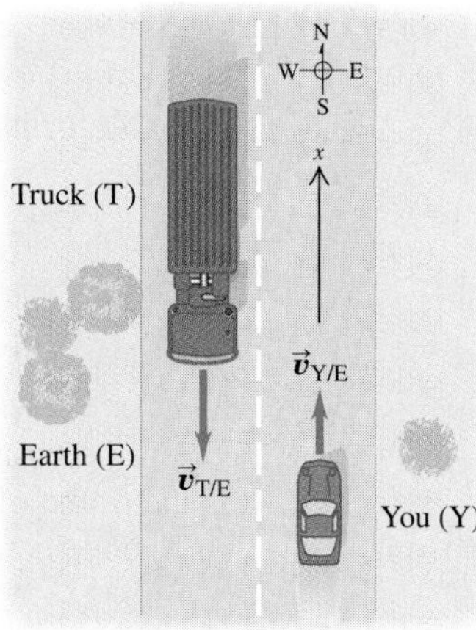

EXECUTE: (a) To find $v_{T/Y\text{-}x}$, we first write Eq. (3.33) for the three frames Y, T, and E, and then rearrange:

$$v_{T/E\text{-}x} = v_{T/Y\text{-}x} + v_{Y/E\text{-}x}$$
$$v_{T/Y\text{-}x} = v_{T/E\text{-}x} - v_{Y/E\text{-}x}$$
$$= -104 \text{ km/h} - 88 \text{ km/h} = -192 \text{ km/h}$$

The truck is moving at 192 km/h in the negative x-direction (south) relative to you.

(b) From Eq. (3.34),

$$v_{Y/T\text{-}x} = -v_{T/Y\text{-}x} = -(-192 \text{ km/h}) = +192 \text{ km/h}$$

You are moving at 192 km/h in the positive x-direction (north) relative to the truck.

(c) The relative velocities do *not* change at all after you and the truck pass each other. The relative positions of the bodies don't matter. The truck is still moving at 192 km/h toward the south relative to you, but it is now moving away from you instead of toward you.

EVALUATE: To check your answer in part (b), try using Eq. (3.33) directly in the form $v_{Y/T\text{-}x} = v_{Y/E\text{-}x} + v_{E/T\text{-}x}$. (Remember that the x-velocity of the earth with respect to the truck is the opposite of the x-velocity of the truck with respect to the earth: $v_{E/T\text{-}x} = -v_{T/E\text{-}x}$.) Do you get the same result?

Relative Velocity in Two or Three Dimensions

We can extend the concept of relative velocity to include motion in a plane or in space by using vector addition to combine velocities. Suppose that the passenger in Fig. 3.32a is walking not down the aisle of the railroad car but from one side of the car to the other, with a speed of 1.0 m/s (Fig. 3.34a). We can again describe the passenger's position P in two different frames of reference: A for the stationary ground observer and B for the moving train. But instead of coordinates x, we use position vectors [&*lcacc*{~bfit~r~normal~}{|Ararr|}&] because the problem is now two-dimensional. Then, as Fig. 3.34b shows,

$$\vec{r}_{P/A} = \vec{r}_{P/B} + \vec{r}_{B/A} \tag{3.35}$$

Just as we did before, we take the time derivative of this equation to get a relationship among the various velocities; the velocity of P relative to A is $\vec{v}_{P/A} = d\vec{r}_{P/A}/dt$ and so on for the other velocities. We get

$$\vec{v}_{P/A} = \vec{v}_{P/B} + \vec{v}_{B/A} \quad \text{(relative velocity in space)} \tag{3.36}$$

Equation (3.36) is known as the *Galilean velocity transformation.* It relates the velocity of a body P with respect to frame A and its velocity with respect to frame B ($\vec{v}_{P/A}$ and $\vec{v}_{P/B}$, respectively) to the velocity of frame B with respect to frame A ($\vec{v}_{B/A}$). If all three of these velocities lie along the same line, then Eq. (3.36) reduces to Eq. (3.33) for the components of the velocities along that line.

If the train is moving at $v_{B/A} = 3.0$ m/s relative to the ground and the passenger is moving at $v_{P/B} = 1.0$ m/s relative to the train, then the passenger's velocity

3.34 (a) A passenger walking across a railroad car. (b) Position of the passenger relative to the cyclist's frame and the train's frame. (c) Vector diagram for the velocity of the passenger relative to the ground (the cyclist's frame), $\vec{v}_{P/A}$.

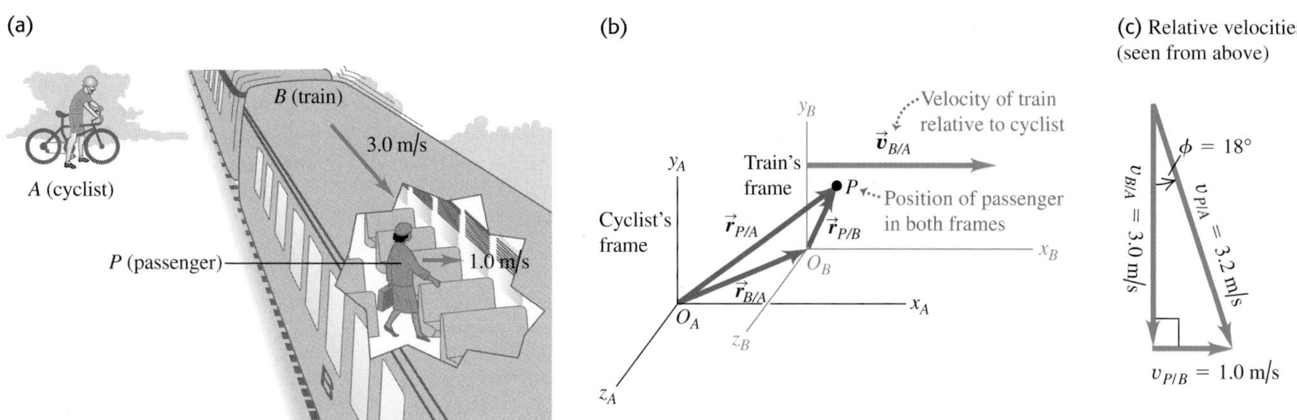

vector $\vec{v}_{P/A}$ relative to the ground is as shown in Fig. 3.34c. The Pythagorean theorem then gives us

$$v_{P/A} = \sqrt{(3.0\ \text{m/s})^2 + (1.0\ \text{m/s})^2} = \sqrt{10\ \text{m}^2/\text{s}^2} = 3.2\ \text{m/s}$$

Figure 3.34c also shows that the *direction* of the passenger's velocity vector relative to the ground makes an angle ϕ with the train's velocity vector $\vec{v}_{B/A}$, where

$$\tan\phi = \frac{v_{P/B}}{v_{B/A}} = \frac{1.0\ \text{m/s}}{3.0\ \text{m/s}} \quad \text{and} \quad \phi = 18^\circ$$

As in the case of motion along a straight line, we have the general rule that if A and B are *any* two points or frames of reference,

$$\vec{v}_{A/B} = -\vec{v}_{B/A} \tag{3.37}$$

The velocity of the passenger relative to the train is the negative of the velocity of the train relative to the passenger, and so on.

In the early 20th century Albert Einstein showed in his special theory of relativity that the velocity-addition relationship given in Eq. (3.36) has to be modified when speeds approach the speed of light, denoted by c. It turns out that if the passenger in Fig. 3.32a could walk down the aisle at $0.30c$ and the train could move at $0.90c$, then her speed relative to the ground would be not $1.20c$ but $0.94c$; nothing can travel faster than light! We'll return to the special theory of relativity in Chapter 37.

Example 3.14 Flying in a crosswind

The compass of an airplane indicates that it is headed due north, and its airspeed indicator shows that it is moving through the air at 240 km/h. If there is a wind of 100 km/h from west to east, what is the velocity of the airplane relative to the earth?

SOLUTION

IDENTIFY: This problem involves velocities in two dimensions (northward and eastward), so it is a relative velocity problem using vectors.

SET UP: We are given the magnitude and direction of the velocity of the plane (P) relative to the air (A). We are also given the magnitude and direction of the wind velocity, which is the velocity of the air (A) with respect to the earth (E):

$$\vec{v}_{P/A} = 240\ \text{km/h} \quad \text{due north}$$
$$\vec{v}_{A/E} = 100\ \text{km/h} \quad \text{due east}$$

Our target variables are the magnitude and direction of the velocity of the plane (P) relative to the earth (E), $\vec{v}_{P/E}$. We'll find these using Eq. (3.36).

EXECUTE: Using Eq. (3.36), we have

$$\vec{v}_{P/E} = \vec{v}_{P/A} + \vec{v}_{A/E}$$

Figure 3.35 shows the three relative velocities and their relationship; the unknowns are the speed $v_{P/E}$ and the angle α. From this diagram we find

$$v_{P/E} = \sqrt{(240\ \text{km/h})^2 + (100\ \text{km/h})^2} = 260\ \text{km/h}$$

$$\alpha = \arctan\left(\frac{100\ \text{km/h}}{240\ \text{km/h}}\right) = 23^\circ\ \text{E of N}$$

EVALUATE: The crosswind increases the speed of the airplane relative to the earth, but at the price of pushing the airplane off course.

3.35 The plane is pointed north, but the wind blows east, giving the resultant velocity $\vec{v}_{P/E}$ relative to the earth.

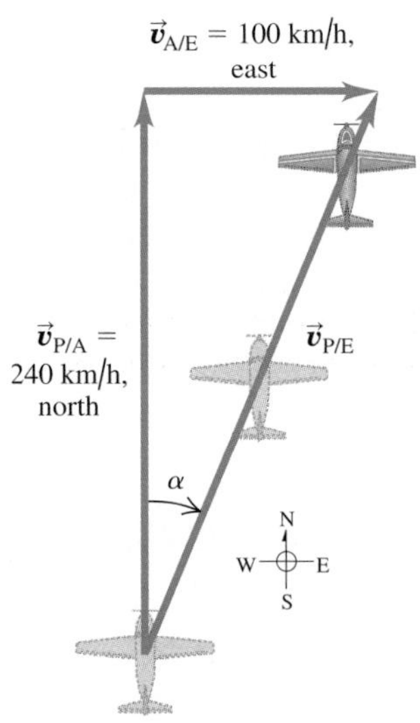

Example 3.15 Correcting for a crosswind

In Example 3.14, in what direction should the pilot head to travel due north? What will be her velocity relative to the earth? (Assume that her airspeed and the velocity of the wind are the same as in Example 3.14.)

SOLUTION

IDENTIFY: Like Example 3.14, this is a relative velocity problem with vectors.

SET UP: Figure 3.36 illustrates the situation. The vectors are arranged in accordance with the vector relative-velocity equation, Eq. (3.36):

$$\vec{v}_{P/E} = \vec{v}_{P/A} + \vec{v}_{A/E}$$

As Fig. 3.36 shows, the pilot points the nose of the airplane at an angle β into the wind to compensate for the crosswind. This angle, which tells us the direction of the vector $\vec{v}_{P/A}$ (the velocity of the airplane relative to the air), is one of our target variables. The other target variable is the speed of the airplane over the ground, which is the magnitude of the vector $\vec{v}_{P/E}$ (the velocity of the airplane relative to the earth). Here are the known and unknown quantities:

$\vec{v}_{P/E}$ = magnitude unknown	due north
$\vec{v}_{P/A}$ = 240 km/h	direction unknown
$\vec{v}_{A/E}$ = 100 km/h	due east

We can solve for the unknown target variables using Fig. 3.36 and trigonometry.

EXECUTE: From the diagram, the speed $v_{P/E}$ and the angle β are given by

$$v_{P/E} = \sqrt{(240\text{ km/h})^2 - (100\text{ km/h})^2} = 218\text{ km/h}^2$$

$$\beta = \arcsin\left(\frac{100\text{ km/h}}{240\text{ km/h}}\right) = 25°$$

3.36 The pilot must point the plane in the direction of the vector $\vec{v}_{P/A}$ to travel due north relative to the earth.

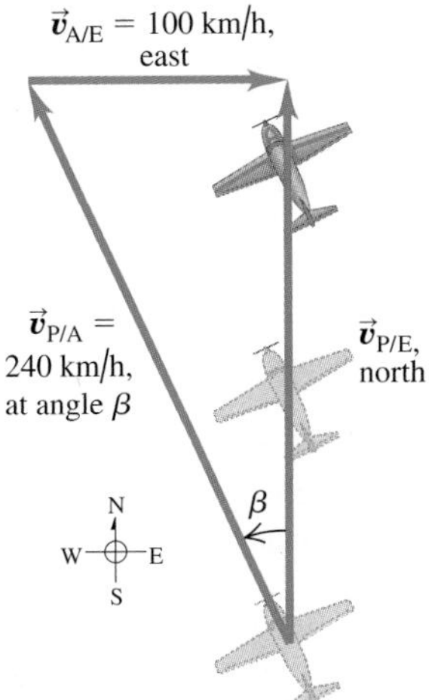

The pilot should point the airplane 25° west of north, and her ground speed is then 218 km/h.

EVALUATE: Note that there were two target variables—the magnitude of a vector and the direction of a vector—in both this example and Example 3.14. The difference is that in Example 3.14, the magnitude and direction referred to the *same* vector ($\vec{v}_{P/E}$), whereas in this example they referred to *different* vectors ($\vec{v}_{P/E}$ and $\vec{v}_{P/A}$).

It's no surprise that a headwind reduces an airplane's speed relative to the ground. This example shows that a *crosswind* also slows an airplane down—an unfortunate fact of aeronautical life.

Test Your Understanding of Section 3.5 Suppose the nose of an airplane is pointed due east and the airplane has an airspeed of 150 km/h. Due to the wind, the airplane is moving due *north* relative to the ground and its speed relative to the ground is 150 km/h. What is the velocity of the air relative to the earth? (i) 150 km/h from east to west; (ii) 150 km/h from south to north; (iii) 150 km/h from southeast to northwest; (iv) 212 km/h from east to west; (v) 212 km/h from south to north; (vi) 212 km/h from southeast to northwest; (vii) there is no possible wind velocity that could cause this.

CHAPTER 3 SUMMARY

Position, velocity, and acceleration vectors: The position vector $\vec{r}$ of a point P in space is the vector from the origin to P. Its components are the coordinates x, y, and z.

The average velocity vector $\vec{v}_{av}$ during the time interval Δt is the displacement $\Delta\vec{r}$ (the change in the position vector $\vec{r}$) divided by Δt. The instantaneous velocity vector $\vec{v}$ is the time derivative of $\vec{r}$, and its components are the time derivatives of x, y, and z. The instantaneous speed is the magnitude of $\vec{v}$. The velocity $\vec{v}$ of a particle is always tangent to the particle's path. (See Example 3.1.)

The average acceleration vector $\vec{a}_{av}$ during the time interval Δt equals $\Delta\vec{v}$ (the change in the velocity vector $\vec{v}$) divided by Δt. The instantaneous acceleration vector $\vec{a}$ is the time derivative of $\vec{v}$, and its components are the time derivatives of v_x, v_y, and v_z. (See Example 3.2.)

The component of acceleration parallel to the direction of the instantaneous velocity affects the speed, while the component of $\vec{a}$ perpendicular to $\vec{v}$ affects the direction of motion. (See Examples 3.3 and 3.4.)

$$\vec{r} = x\hat{\imath} + y\hat{\jmath} + z\hat{k} \quad (3.1)$$

$$\vec{v}_{av} = \frac{\vec{r}_2 - \vec{r}_1}{t_2 - t_1} = \frac{\Delta\vec{r}}{\Delta t} \quad (3.2)$$

$$\vec{v} = \lim_{\Delta t \to 0} \frac{\Delta\vec{r}}{\Delta t} = \frac{d\vec{r}}{dt} \quad (3.3)$$

$$v_x = \frac{dx}{dt} \qquad v_y = \frac{dy}{dt} \qquad v_z = \frac{dz}{dt} \quad (3.4)$$

$$\vec{a}_{av} = \frac{\vec{v}_2 - \vec{v}_1}{t_2 - t_1} = \frac{\Delta\vec{v}}{\Delta t} \quad (3.8)$$

$$\vec{a} = \lim_{\Delta t \to 0} \frac{\Delta\vec{v}}{\Delta t} = \frac{d\vec{v}}{dt} \quad (3.9)$$

$$a_x = \frac{dv_x}{dt} \qquad a_y = \frac{dv_y}{dt} \qquad a_z = \frac{dv_z}{dt} \quad (3.10)$$

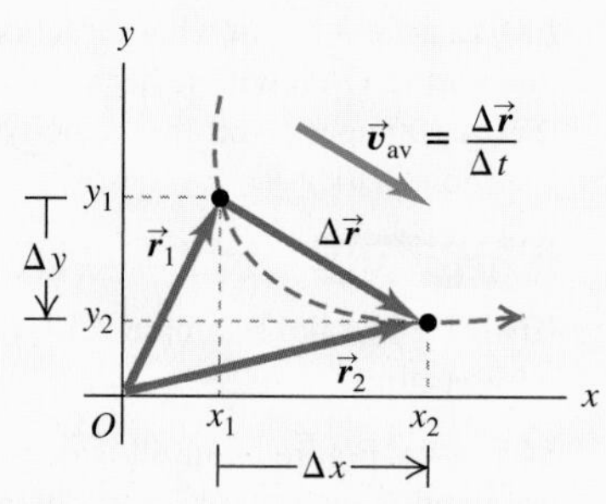

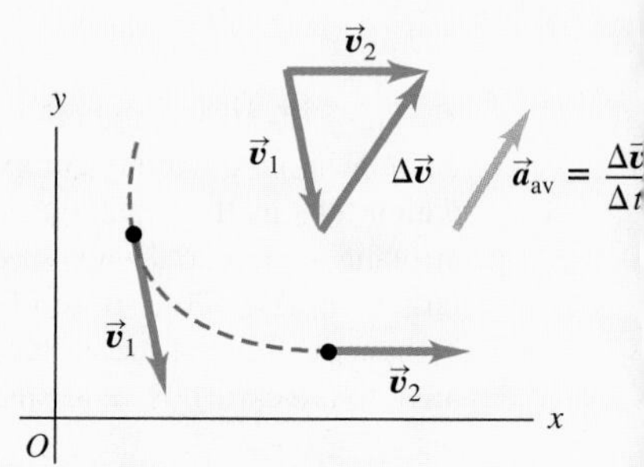

Projectile motion: In projectile motion with no air resistance, $a_x = 0$ and $a_y = -g$. The coordinates and velocity components are simple functions of time, and the shape of the path is always a parabola. We usually choose the origin to be at the initial position of the projectile. (See Examples 3.5–3.10.)

$$x = (v_0 \cos\alpha_0)t \quad (3.20)$$

$$y = (v_0 \sin\alpha_0)t - \frac{1}{2}gt^2 \quad (3.21)$$

$$v_x = v_0 \cos\alpha_0 \quad (3.22)$$

$$v_y = v_0 \sin\alpha_0 - gt \quad (3.23)$$

Uniform and nonuniform circular motion: When a particle moves in a circular path of radius R with constant speed v (uniform circular motion), its acceleration $\vec{a}$ is directed toward the center of the circle and perpendicular to $\vec{v}$. The magnitude a_{rad} of the acceleration can be expressed in terms of v and R or in terms of R and the period T (the time for one revolution), where $v = 2\pi R/T$. (See Examples 3.11 and 3.12.)

If the speed is not constant in circular motion (nonuniform circular motion), there is still a radial component of $\vec{a}$ given by Eq. (3.28) or (3.30), but there is also a component of $\vec{a}$ parallel (tangential) to the path. This tangential component is equal to the rate of change of speed, dv/dt.

$$a_{rad} = \frac{v^2}{R} \quad (3.28)$$

$$a_{rad} = \frac{4\pi^2 R}{T^2} \quad (3.30)$$

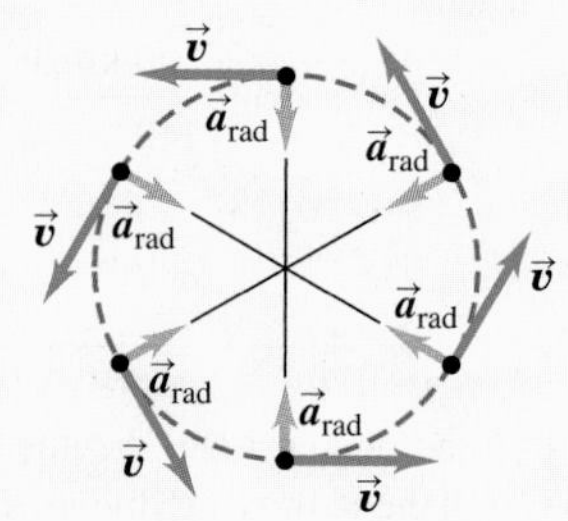

Relative velocity: When a body P moves relative to a body (or reference frame) B, and B moves relative to A, we denote the velocity of P relative to B by $\vec{v}_{P/B}$, the velocity of P relative to A by $\vec{v}_{P/A}$, and the velocity of B relative to A by $\vec{v}_{B/A}$. If these velocities are all along the same line, their components along that line are related by Eq. (3.33). More generally, these velocities are related by Eq. (3.36). (See Examples 3.13–3.15)

$$v_{P/A\text{-}x} = v_{P/B\text{-}x} + v_{B/A\text{-}x} \quad (3.33)$$

(relative velocity along a line)

$$\vec{v}_{P/A} = \vec{v}_{P/B} + \vec{v}_{B/A} \quad (3.36)$$

(relative velocity in space)

Key Terms

position vector, 72
average velocity, 72
instantaneous velocity, 72
average acceleration, 75
instantaneous acceleration, 75
projectile, 79
trajectory, 79
uniform circular motion, 88
centripetal acceleration, 89
period, 89
nonuniform circular motion, 90
relative velocity, 91
frame of reference, 91

Answer to Chapter Opening Question ?

A car going around a curve at constant speed has an acceleration directed toward the inside of the curve (see Section 3.2, especially Fig. 3.12a).

Answers to Test Your Understanding Questions

3.1 **Answer: (iii)** If the instantaneous velocity $\vec{v}$ is constant over an interval, its value at any point (including the end of the interval) is the same as the average velocity $\vec{v}_{av}$ over the interval. In (i) and (ii) the direction of $\vec{v}$ at the end of the interval is tangent to the path at that point, while the direction of $\vec{v}_{av}$ points from the beginning of the path to its end (in the direction of the net displacement). In (iv) $\vec{v}$ and $\vec{v}_{av}$ are both directed along the straight line, but $\vec{v}$ has a greater magnitude because the speed has been increasing.

3.2 **Answer: vector 7** At the high point of the sled's path, the speed is minimum. At that point the speed is neither increasing nor decreasing, and the parallel component of the acceleration (that is, the horizontal component) is zero. The acceleration has only a perpendicular component toward the inside of the sled's curved path. In other words, the acceleration is downward.

3.3 **Answer: (i)** If there were no gravity ($g = 0$), the monkey would not fall and the dart would follow a straight-line path (shown as a dashed line). The effect of gravity is to make the monkey and the dart both fall the same distance $\frac{1}{2}gt^2$ below their $g = 0$ positions. Point A is the same distance below the monkey's initial position as point P is below the dashed straight line, so point A is where we would find the monkey at the time in question.

3.4 **Answer: (ii)** At both the top and bottom of the loop, the acceleration is purely radial and is given by Eq. (3.28). The radius R is the same at both points, so the difference in acceleration is due purely to differences in speed. Since a_{rad} is proportional to the square of v, the speed must be twice as great at the bottom of the loop as at the top.

3.5 **Answer: (vi)** The effect of the wind is to cancel the airplane's eastward motion and give it a northward motion. So the velocity of the air relative to the ground (the wind velocity) must have one 150-km/h component to the west and one 150-km/h component to the north. The combination of these is a vector of magnitude $\sqrt{(150\text{ km/h})^2 + (150\text{ km/h})^2} = 212\text{ km/h}$ that points to the northwest.

PROBLEMS

For instructor-assigned homework, go to **www.masteringphysics.com** (MP)

Discussion Questions

Q3.1. A simple pendulum (a mass swinging at the end of a string) swings back and forth in a circular arc. What is the direction of the acceleration off the mass at the ends of the swing? At the midpoint? In each case, explain how you obtain your answer.

Q3.2. Redraw Fig. 3.11a if $\vec{a}$ is antiparallel to $\vec{v}_1$. Does the particle move in a straight line? What happens to its speed?

Q3.3. A projectile moves in a parabolic path without air resistance. Is there any point at which $\vec{a}$ is parallel to $\vec{v}$? Perpendicular to $\vec{v}$? Explain.

Q3.4. When a rifle is fired at a distant target, the barrel is not lined up exactly on the target. Why not? Does the angle of correction depend on the distance of the target?

Q3.5. At the same instant that you fire a bullet horizontally from a gun, you drop a bullet from the height of the barrel. If there is no air resistance, which bullet hits the ground first? Explain.

Q3.6. A package falls out of an airplane that is flying in a straight line at a constant altitude and speed. If you could ignore air resistance, what would be the path of the package as observed by the pilot? As observed by a person on the ground?

Q3.7. Sketch the six graphs of the x- and y-components of position, velocity, and acceleration versus time for projectile motion with $x_0 = y_0 = 0$ and $0 < \alpha_0 < 90°$.

Q3.8. An object is thrown straight up into the air and feels no air resistance. How is it possible for it to have an acceleration when it has stopped moving at its highest point?

Q3.9. If a jumping frog can give itself the same initial speed regardless of the direction in which it jumps (forward or straight up), how is the maximum vertical height to which it can jump related to its maximum horizontal range $R_{max} = v_0^2/g$?

Q3.10. A projectile is fired upward at an angle θ above the horizontal with an initial speed v_0. At its maximum height, what are its velocity vector, its speed, and its acceleration vector?

Q3.11. In uniform circular motion, what are the *average* velocity and *average* acceleration for one revolution? Explain.

Q3.12. In uniform circular motion, how does the acceleration change when the speed is increased by a factor of 3? When the radius is decreased by a factor of 2?

Q3.13. In uniform circular motion, the acceleration is perpendicular to the velocity at every instant. Is this still true when the motion is not uniform—that is, when the speed is not constant?

Q3.14. Raindrops hitting the side windows of a car in motion often leave diagonal streaks even if there is no wind. Why? Is the explanation the same or different for diagonal streaks on the windshield?

Q3.15. In a rainstorm with a strong wind, what determines the best position in which to hold an umbrella?

Q3.16. You are on the west bank of a river that is flowing north with a speed of 1.2 m/s. Your swimming speed relative to the water is 1.5 m/s, and the river is 60 m wide. What is your path relative to earth that allows you to cross the river in the shortest time? Explain your reasoning.

Q3.17. When you drop an object from a certain height, it takes time T to reach the ground with no air resistance. If you dropped it from three times that height, how long (in terms of T) would it take to reach the ground?

Q3.18. A stone is thrown into the air at an angle above the horizontal and feels negligible air resistance. Which graph in Fig. 3.37 best depicts the stone's *speed* v as a function of time t while it is in the air?

Figure 3.37 Question Q3.18.

(a) (b)

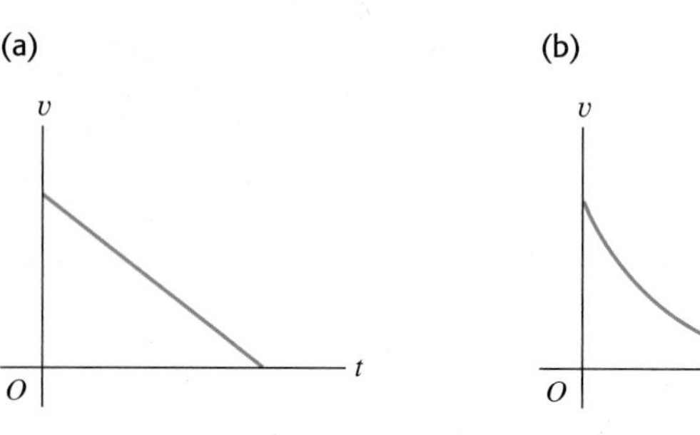

(c)

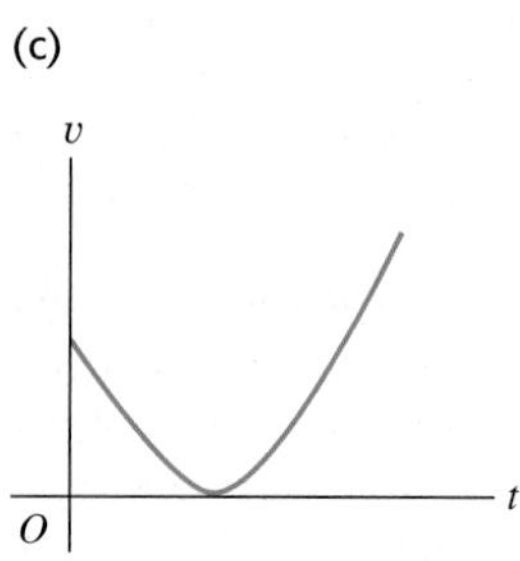

(d)

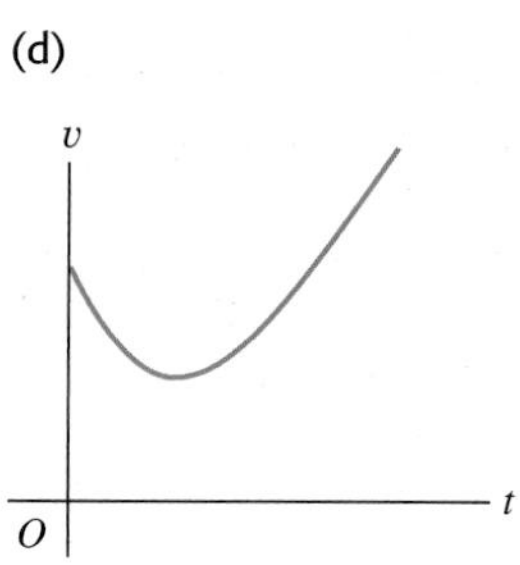

(e)

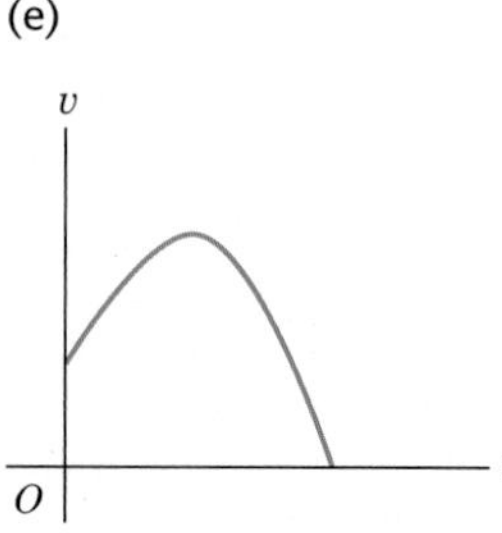

Exercises

Section 3.1 Position and Velocity Vectors

3.1. A squirrel has x- and y-coordinates $(1.1 \text{ m}, 3.4 \text{ m})$ at time $t_1 = 0$ and coordinates $(5.3 \text{ m}, -0.5 \text{ m})$ at time $t_2 = 3.0 \text{ s}$. For this time interval, find (a) the components of the average velocity, and (b) the magnitude and direction of the average velocity.

3.2. A rhinoceros is at the origin of coordinates at time $t_1 = 0$. For the time interval from $t_1 = 0$ to $t_2 = 12.0 \text{ s}$, the rhino's average velocity has x-component -3.8 m/s and y-component 4.9 m/s. At time $t_2 = 12.0 \text{ s}$, (a) what are the x- and y-coordinates of the rhino? (b) How far is the rhino from the origin?

3.3. A web page designer creates an animation in which a dot on a computer screen has a position of $\vec{r} = [4.0 \text{ cm} + (2.5 \text{ cm/s}^2)t^2]\hat{\imath} + (5.0 \text{ cm/s})t\hat{\jmath}$. (a) Find the magnitude and direction of the dot's average velocity between $t = 0$ and $t = 2.0 \text{ s}$. (b) Find the magnitude and direction of the instantaneous velocity at $t = 0$, $t = 1.0 \text{ s}$, and $t = 2.0 \text{ s}$. (c) Sketch the dot's trajectory from $t = 0$ to $t = 2.0 \text{ s}$, and show the velocities calculated in part (b).

3.4. If $\vec{r} = bt^2\hat{\imath} + ct^3\hat{\jmath}$, where b and c are positive constants, when does the velocity vector make an angle of 45.0° with the x- and y-axes?

Section 3.2 The Acceleration Vector

3.5. A jet plane is flying at a constant altitude. At time $t_1 = 0$ it has components of velocity $v_x = 90 \text{ m/s}$, $v_y = 110 \text{ m/s}$. At time $t_2 = 30.0 \text{ s}$ the components are $v_x = -170 \text{ m/s}$, $v_y = 40 \text{ m/s}$. (a) Sketch the velocity vectors at t_1 and t_2. How do these two vectors differ? For this time interval calculate (b) the components of the average acceleration, and (c) the magnitude and direction of the average acceleration.

3.6. A dog running in an open field has components of velocity $v_x = 2.6 \text{ m/s}$ and $v_y = -1.8 \text{ m/s}$ at $t_1 = 10.0 \text{ s}$. For the time interval from $t_1 = 10.0 \text{ s}$ to $t_2 = 20.0 \text{ s}$, the average acceleration of the dog has magnitude 0.45 m/s^2 and direction 31.0° measured from the $+x$-axis toward the $+y$-axis. At $t_2 = 20.0 \text{ s}$, (a) what are the x- and y-components of the dog's velocity? (b) What are the magnitude and direction of the dog's velocity? (c) Sketch the velocity vectors at t_1 and t_2. How do these two vectors differ?

3.7. The coordinates of a bird flying in the xy-plane are given by $x(t) = \alpha t$ and $y(t) = 3.0 \text{ m} - \beta t^2$, where $\alpha = 2.4 \text{ m/s}$ and $\beta = 1.2 \text{ m/s}^2$. (a) Sketch the path of the bird between $t = 0$ and $t = 2.0 \text{ s}$. (b) Calculate the velocity and acceleration vectors of the bird as functions of time. (c) Calculate the magnitude and direction of the bird's velocity and acceleration at $t = 2.0 \text{ s}$. (d) Sketch the velocity and acceleration vectors at $t = 2.0 \text{ s}$. At this instant, is the bird speeding up, is it slowing down, or is its speed instantaneously not changing? Is the bird turning? If so, in what direction?

3.8. A particle moves along a path as shown in Fig. 3.38. Between points B and D, the path is a straight line. Sketch the acceleration vectors at A, C, and E in the cases in which (a) the particle moves with a constant speed; (b) the particle moves with a steadily increasing speed; (c) the particle moves with a steadily decreasing speed.

Figure 3.38 Exercise 3.8.

(a) (b) (c)

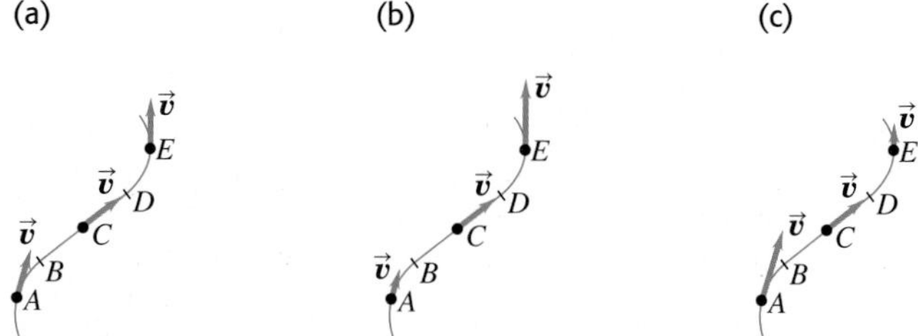

Section 3.3 Projectile Motion

3.9. A physics book slides off a horizontal tabletop with a speed of 1.10 m/s. It strikes the floor in 0.350 s. Ignore air resistance. Find (a) the height of the tabletop above the floor; (b) the horizontal distance from the edge of the table to the point where the book strikes the floor; (c) the horizontal and vertical components of the book's velocity, and the magnitude and direction of its velocity, just before the book reaches the floor. (d) Draw x-t, y-t, v_x-t, and v_y-t graphs for the motion.

3.10. A military helicopter on a training mission is flying horizontally at a speed of 60.0 m/s and accidentally drops a bomb (fortunately not armed) at an elevation of 300 m. You can ignore air resistance. (a) How much time is required for the bomb to reach the earth? (b) How far does it travel horizontally while falling? (c) Find the horizontal and vertical components of its velocity just before it strikes the earth. (d) Draw x-t, y-t, v_x-t, and v_y-t graphs for the bomb's motion. (e) If the velocity of the helicopter remains constant, where is the helicopter when the bomb hits the ground?

3.11. Two crickets, Chirpy and Milada, jump from the top of a vertical cliff. Chirpy just drops and reaches the ground in 3.50 s, while Milada jumps horizontally with an initial speed of 95.0 cm/s. How far from the base of the cliff will Milada hit the ground?

3.12. A daring 510-N swimmer dives off a cliff with a running horizontal leap, as shown in Fig. 3.39. What must her minimum speed be just as she leaves the top of the cliff so that she will miss the ledge at the bottom, which is 1.75 m wide and 9.00 m below the top of the cliff?

Figure 3.39 Exercise 3.12.

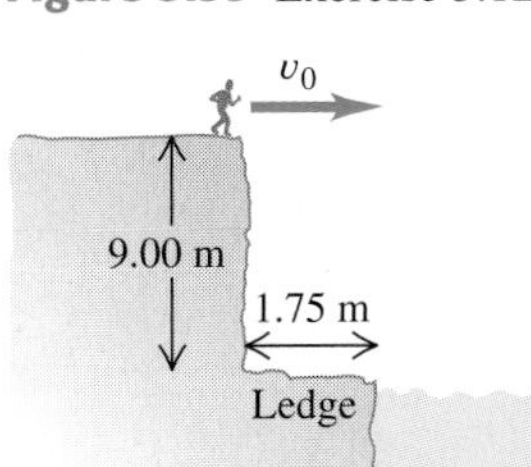

3.13. Leaping the River I. A car comes to a bridge during a storm and finds the bridge washed out. The driver must get to the other side, so he decides to try leaping it with his car. The side of the road the car is on is 21.3 m above the river, while the opposite side is a mere 1.8 m above the river. The river itself is a raging torrent 61.0 m wide. (a) How fast should the car be traveling at the time it leaves the road in order just to clear the river and land safely on the opposite side? (b) What is the speed of the car just before it lands on the other side?

3.14. A small marble rolls horizontally with speed v_0 off the top of a platform 2.75 m tall and feels no appreciable air resistance. On the level ground, 2.00 m from the base of the platform, there is a gaping hole in the ground (Fig. 3.40.) For what range of marble speeds v_0 will the marble land in the hole?

Figure 3.40 Exercise 3.14.

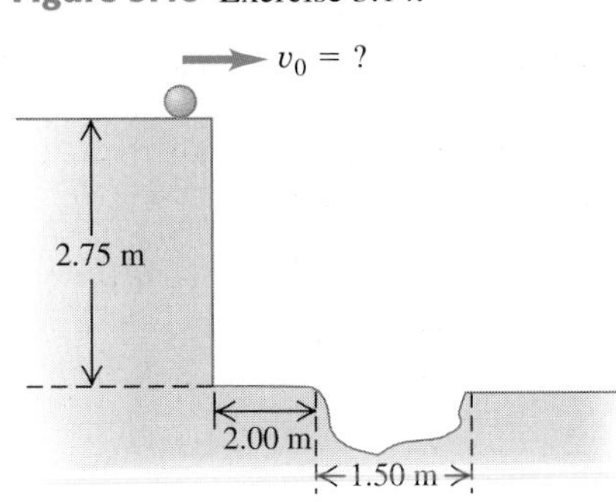

3.15. Inside a starship at rest on the earth, a ball rolls off the top of a horizontal table and lands a distance D from the foot of the table. This starship now lands on the unexplored Planet X. The commander, Captain Curious, rolls the same ball off the same table with the same initial speed as on earth and finds that it lands a distance $2.76D$ from the foot of the table. What is the acceleration due to gravity on Planet X?

3.16. A rookie quarterback throws a football with an initial upward velocity component of 16.0 m/s and a horizontal velocity component of 20.0 m/s. Ignore air resistance. (a) How much time is required for the football to reach the highest point of the trajectory? (b) How high is this point? (c) How much time (after it is thrown) is required for the football to return to its original level? How does this compare with the time calculated in part (a)? (d) How far has the football traveled horizontally during this time? (e) Draw x-t, y-t, v_x-t, and v_y-t graphs for the motion.

3.17. On level ground a shell is fired with an initial velocity of 80.0 m/s at 60.0° above the horizontal and feels no appreciable air resistance. (a) Find the horizontal and vertical components of the shell's initial velocity. (b) How long does it take the shell to reach its highest point? (c) Find its maximum height above the ground. (d) How far from its firing point does the shell land? (e) At its highest point, find the horizontal and vertical components of its acceleration and velocity.

3.18. A pistol that fires a signal flare gives it an initial velocity (muzzle velocity) of 125 m/s at an angle of 55.0° above the horizontal. You can ignore air resistance. Find the flare's maximum height and the distance from its firing point to its landing point if it is fired (a) on the level salt flats of Utah, and (b) over the flat Sea of Tranquility on the Moon, where $g = 1.67\ \text{m/s}^2$.

3.19. A major leaguer hits a baseball so that it leaves the bat at a speed of 30.0 m/s and at an angle of 36.9° above the horizontal. You can ignore air resistance. (a) At what *two* times is the baseball at a height of 10.0 m above the point at which it left the bat? (b) Calculate the horizontal and vertical components of the baseball's velocity at each of the two times calculated in part (a). (c) What are the magnitude and direction of the baseball's velocity when it returns to the level at which it left the bat?

3.20. A shot putter releases the shot some distance above the level ground with a velocity of 12.0 m/s, 51.0° above the horizontal. The shot hits the ground 2.08 s later. You can ignore air resistance. (a) What are the components of the shot's acceleration while in flight? (b) What are the components of the shot's velocity at the beginning and at the end of its trajectory? (c) How far did she throw the shot horizontally? (d) Why does the expression for R in Example 3.8 *not* give the correct answer for part (c)? (e) How high was the shot above the ground when she released it? (f) Draw x-t, y-t, v_x-t, and v_y-t graphs for the motion.

3.21. Win the Prize. In a carnival booth, you win a stuffed giraffe if you toss a quarter into a small dish. The dish is on a shelf above the point where the quarter leaves your hand and is a horizontal distance of 2.1 m from this point (Fig. 3.41). If you toss the coin with a velocity of 6.4 m/s at an angle of 60° above the horizontal, the coin lands in the dish. You can ignore air resistance. (a) What is the height of the shelf above the point where the quarter leaves your hand? (b) What is the vertical component of the velocity of the quarter just before it lands in the dish?

Figure 3.41 Exercise 3.21.

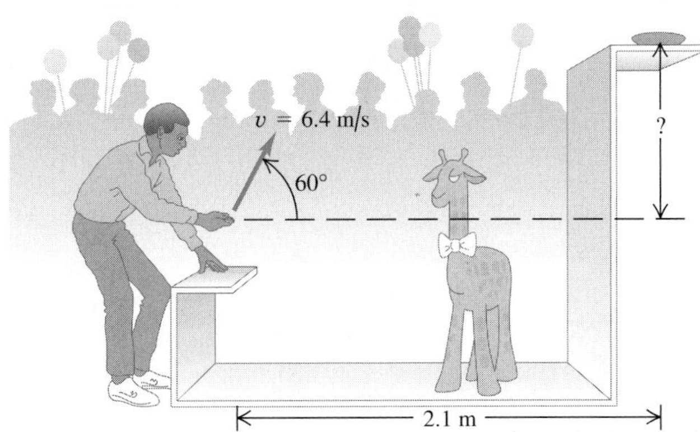

3.22. Suppose the departure angle α_0 in Fig. 3.26 is 42.0° and the distance d is 3.00 m. Where will the dart and monkey meet if the initial speed of the dart is (a) 12.0 m/s? (b) 8.0 m/s? (c) What will happen if the initial speed of the dart is 4.0 m/s? Sketch the trajectory in each case.

3.23. A man stands on the roof of a 15.0-m-tall building and throws a rock with a velocity of magnitude 30.0 m/s at an angle of 33.0° above the horizontal. You can ignore air resistance. Calculate

(a) the maximum height above the roof reached by the rock; (b) the magnitude of the velocity of the rock just before it strikes the ground; and (c) the horizontal range from the base of the building to the point where the rock strikes the ground. (d) Draw x-t, y-t, v_x-t, and v_y-t graphs for the motion.

3.24. Firemen are shooting a stream of water at a burning building using a high-pressure hose that shoots out the water with a speed of 25.0 m/s as it leaves the end of the hose. Once it leaves the hose, the water moves in projectile motion. The firemen adjust the angle of elevation α of the hose until the water takes 3.00 s to reach a building 45.0 m away. You can ignore air resistance; assume that the end of the hose is at ground level. (a) Find the angle of elevation α. (b) Find the speed and acceleration of the water at the highest point in its trajectory. (c) How high above the ground does the water strike the building, and how fast is it moving just before it hits the building?

3.25. A 124-kg balloon carrying a 22-kg basket is descending with a constant downward velocity of 20.0 m/s. A 1.0-kg stone is thrown from the basket with an initial velocity of 15.0 m/s perpendicular to the path of the descending balloon, as measured relative to a person at rest in the basket. The person in the basket sees the stone hit the ground 6.00 s after being thrown. Assume that the balloon continues its downward descent with the same constant speed of 20.0 m/s. (a) How high was the balloon when the rock was thrown out? (b) How high is the balloon when the rock hits the ground? (c) At the instant the rock hits the ground, how far is it from the basket? (d) Just before the rock hits the ground, find its horizontal and vertical velocity components as measured by an observer (i) at rest in the basket and (ii) at rest on the ground.

3.26. A cannon, located 60.0 m from the base of a vertical 25.0-m-tall cliff, shoots a 15-kg shell at 43.0° above the horizontal toward the cliff. (a) What must the minimum muzzle velocity be for the shell to clear the top of the cliff? (b) The ground at the top of the cliff is level, with a constant elevation of 25.0 m above the cannon. Under the conditions of part (a), how far does the shell land past the edge of the cliff?

3.27. An airplane is flying with a velocity of 90.0 m/s at an angle of 23.0° above the horizontal. When the plane is 114 m directly above a dog that is standing on level ground, a suitcase drops out of the luggage compartment. How far from the dog will the suitcase land? You can ignore air resistance.

Section 3.4 Motion in a Circle

3.28. On your first day at work for an appliance manufacturer, you are told to figure out what to do to the period of rotation during a washer spin cycle to triple the centripetal acceleration. You impress your boss by answering immediately. What do you tell her?

3.29. The earth has a radius of 6380 km and turns around once on its axis in 24 h. (a) What is the radial acceleration of an object at the earth's equator? Give your answer in m/s^2 and as a fraction of g. (b) If a_{rad} at the equator is greater than g, objects would fly off the earth's surface and into space. (We will see the reason for this in Chapter 5.) What would the period of the earth's rotation have to be for this to occur?

3.30. A model of a helicopter rotor has four blades, each 3.40 m long from the central shaft to the blade tip. The model is rotated in a wind tunnel at 550 rev/min. (a) What is the linear speed of the blade tip, in m/s? (b) What is the radial acceleration of the blade tip expressed as a multiple of the acceleration of gravity, g?

3.31. In a test of a "g-suit," a volunteer is rotated in a horizontal circle of radius 7.0 m. What must the period of rotation be so that the centripetal acceleration has a magnitude of (a) 3.0g? (b) 10g?

3.32. The radius of the earth's orbit around the sun (assumed to be circular) is 1.50×10^8 km, and the earth travels around this orbit in 365 days. (a) What is the magnitude of the orbital velocity of the earth, in m/s? (b) What is the radial acceleration of the earth toward the sun, in m/s^2? (c) Repeat parts (a) and (b) for the motion of the planet Mercury (orbit radius $= 5.79 \times 10^7$ km, orbital period $= 88.0$ days).

3.33. A Ferris wheel with radius 14.0 m is turning about a horizontal axis through its center (Fig. 3.42). The linear speed of a passenger on the rim is constant and equal to 7.00 m/s. What are the magnitude and direction of the passenger's acceleration as she passes through (a) the lowest point in her circular motion? (b) The highest point in her circular motion? (c) How much time does it take the Ferris wheel to make one revolution?

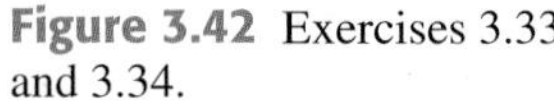

Figure 3.42 Exercises 3.33 and 3.34.

3.34. The Ferris wheel in Fig. 3.42, which rotates counterclockwise, is just starting up. At a given instant, a passenger on the rim of the wheel and passing through the lowest point of his circular motion is moving at 3.00 m/s and is gaining speed at a rate of 0.500 m/s^2. (a) Find the magnitude and the direction of the passenger's acceleration at this instant. (b) Sketch the Ferris wheel and the passenger, showing his velocity and acceleration vectors.

3.35. Hypergravity. At its Ames Research Center, NASA uses its large "20-G" centrifuge to test the effects of very large accelerations ("hypergravity") on test pilots and astronauts. In this device, an arm 8.84 m long rotates about one end in a horizontal plane, and the astronaut is strapped in at the other end. Suppose that he is aligned along the arm with his head at the outermost end. The maximum sustained acceleration to which humans are subjected in this machine is typically 12.5g. (a) How fast must the astronaut's head be moving to experience this maximum acceleration? (b) What is the *difference* between the acceleration of his head and feet if the astronaut is 2.00 m tall? (c) How fast in rpm (rev/min) is the arm turning to produce the maximum sustained acceleration?

Section 3.5 Relative Velocity

3.36. A railroad flatcar is traveling to the right at a speed of 13.0 m/s relative to an observer standing on the ground. Someone is riding a motor scooter on the flatcar (Fig. 3.43). What is the velocity (magnitude and direction) of the motor scooter relative to the flatcar if its velocity relative to the observer on the ground is (a) 18.0 m/s to the right? (b) 3.0 m/s to the left? (c) zero?

Figure 3.43 Exercise 3.36.

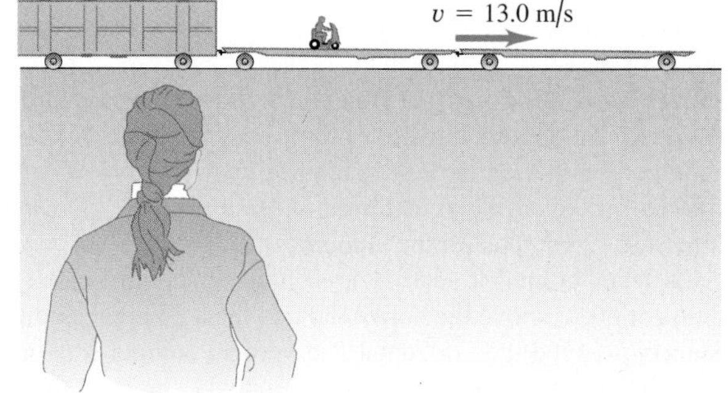

3.37. A "moving sidewalk" in an airport terminal building moves at 1.0 m/s and is 35.0 m long. If a woman steps on at one end and walks at 1.5 m/s relative to the moving sidewalk, how much time does she require to reach the opposite end if she walks (a) in the same direction the sidewalk is moving? (b) In the opposite direction?

3.38. Two piers, *A* and *B*, are located on a river: *B* is 1500 m downstream from *A* (Fig. 3.44). Two friends must make round trips from pier *A* to pier *B* and return. One rows a boat at a constant speed of 4.00 km/h relative to the water; the other walks on the shore at a constant speed of 4.00 km/h. The velocity of the river is 2.80 km/h in the direction from *A* to *B*. How much time does it take each person to make the round trip?

Figure 3.44 Exercise 3.38.

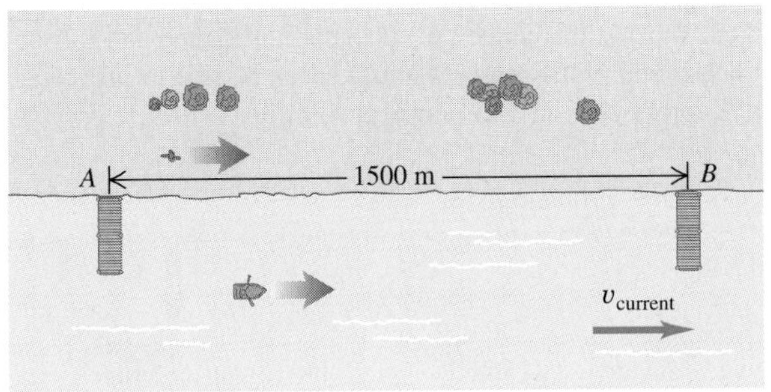

3.39. A canoe has a velocity of 0.40 m/s southeast relative to the earth. The canoe is on a river that is flowing 0.50 m/s east relative to the earth. Find the velocity (magnitude and direction) of the canoe relative to the river.

3.40. An airplane pilot wishes to fly due west. A wind of 80.0 km/h (about 50 mi/h) is blowing toward the south. (a) If the airspeed of the plane (its speed in still air) is 320.0 km/h (about 200 mi/h), in which direction should the pilot head? (b) What is the speed of the plane over the ground? Illustrate with a vector diagram.

3.41. Crossing the River I. A river flows due south with a speed of 2.0 m/s. A man steers a motorboat across the river; his velocity relative to the water is 4.2 m/s due east. The river is 800 m wide. (a) What is his velocity (magnitude and direction) relative to the earth? (b) How much time is required to cross the river? (c) How far south of his starting point will he reach the opposite bank?

3.42. Crossing the River II. (a) In which direction should the motorboat in Exercise 3.41 head in order to reach a point on the opposite bank directly east from the starting point? (The boat's speed relative to the water remains 4.2 m/s.) (b) What is the velocity of the boat relative to the earth? (c) How much time is required to cross the river?

3.43. The nose of an ultralight plane is pointed south, and its airspeed indicator shows 35 m/s. The plane is in a 10-m/s wind blowing toward the southwest relative to the earth. (a) In a vector-addition diagram, show the relationship of $\vec{v}_{P/E}$ (the velocity of the plane relative to the earth) to the two given vectors. (b) Letting *x* be east and *y* be north, find the components of $\vec{v}_{P/E}$. (c) Find the magnitude and direction of $\vec{v}_{P/E}$.

Problems

3.44. A faulty model rocket moves in the *xy*-plane (the positive *y*-direction is vertically upward). The rocket's acceleration has components $a_x(t) = \alpha t^2$ and $a_y(t) = \beta - \gamma t$, where $\alpha = 2.50\ \text{m/s}^4$, $\beta = 9.00\ \text{m/s}^2$, and $\gamma = 1.40\ \text{m/s}^3$. At $t = 0$ the rocket is at the origin and has velocity $\vec{v}_0 = v_{0x}\hat{\imath} + v_{0y}\hat{\jmath}$ with $v_{0x} = 1.00$ m/s and $v_{0y} = 7.00$ m/s. (a) Calculate the velocity and position vectors as functions of time. (b) What is the maximum height reached by the rocket? (c) Sketch the path of the rocket. (d) What is the horizontal displacement of the rocket when it returns to $y = 0$?

3.45. A rocket is fired at an angle from the top of a tower of height $h_0 = 50.0$ m. Because of the design of the engines, its position coordinates are of the form $x(t) = A + Bt^2$ and $y(t) = C + Dt^3$, where *A*, *B*, *C*, and *D* are constants. Furthermore, the acceleration of the rocket 1.00 s after firing is $\vec{a} = (4.00\hat{\imath} + 3.00\hat{\jmath})\ \text{m/s}^2$. Take the origin of coordinates to be at the base of the tower. (a) Find the constants *A*, *B*, *C*, and *D*, including their SI units. (b) At the instant after the rocket is fired, what are its acceleration vector and its velocity? (c) What are the *x*- and *y*-components of the rocket's velocity 10.0 s after it is fired, and how fast is it moving? (d) What is the position vector of the rocket 10.0 s after it is fired?

3.46. A bird flies in the *xy*-plane with a velocity vector given by $\vec{v} = (\alpha - \beta t^2)\hat{\imath} + \gamma t\hat{\jmath}$, with $\alpha = 2.4$ m/s, $\beta = 1.6\ \text{m/s}^3$, and $\gamma = 4.0\ \text{m/s}^2$. The positive *y*-direction is vertically upward. At $t = 0$ the bird is at the origin. (a) Calculate the position and acceleration vectors of the bird as functions of time. (b) What is the bird's altitude (*y*-coordinate) as it flies over $x = 0$ for the first time after $t = 0$?

3.47. A test rocket is launched by accelerating it along a 200.0-m incline at 1.25 m/s² starting from rest at point *A* (Figure 3.45.) The incline rises at 35.0° above the horizontal, and at the instant the rocket leaves it, its engines turn off and it is subject only to gravity (air resistance can be ignored). Find (a) the maximum height above the ground that the rocket reaches, and (b) the greatest horizontal range of the rocket beyond point *A*.

Figure 3.45 Problem 3.47.

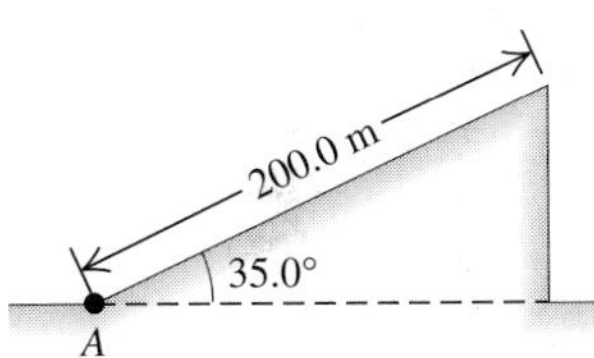

3.48. Martian Athletics. In the long jump, an athlete launches herself at an angle above the ground and lands at the same height, trying to travel the greatest horizontal distance. Suppose that on earth she is in the air for time *T*, reaches a maximum height *h*, and achieves a horizontal distance *D*. If she jumped in *exactly* the same way during a competition on Mars, where g_{Mars} is 0.379 of its earth value, find her time in the air, maximum height, and horizontal distance. Express each of these three quantities in terms of its earth value. Air resistance can be neglected on both planets.

3.49. Dynamite! A demolition crew uses dynamite to blow an old building apart. Debris from the explosion flies off in all directions and is later found at distances as far as 50 m from the explosion. Estimate the maximum speed at which debris was blown outward by the explosion. Describe any assumptions that you make.

3.50. Spiraling Up. It is common to see birds of prey rising upward on thermals. The paths they take may be spiral-like. You can model the spiral motion as uniform circular motion combined with a constant upward velocity. Assume a bird completes a circle of radius 8.00 m every 5.00 s and rises vertically at a rate of 3.00 m/s. Determine: (a) the speed of the bird relative to the ground; (b) the bird's acceleration (magnitude and direction); and (c) the angle between the bird's velocity vector and the horizontal.

3.51. A jungle veterinarian with a blow-gun loaded with a tranquilizer dart and a sly 1.5-kg monkey are each 25 m above the ground in trees 90 m apart. Just as the hunter shoots horizontally at the monkey, the monkey drops from the tree in a vain attempt to escape being hit. What must the minimum muzzle velocity of the dart have been for the hunter to hit the monkey before it reached the ground?

3.52. A movie stuntwoman drops from a helicopter that is 30.0 m above the ground and moving with a constant velocity whose components are 10.0 m/s upward and 15.0 m/s horizontal and toward the south. You can ignore air resistance. (a) Where on the ground (relative to the position of the helicopter when she drops) should the stuntwoman have placed the foam mats that break her fall? (b) Draw x-t, y-t, v_x-t, and v_y-t graphs of her motion.

3.53. In fighting forest fires, airplanes work in support of ground crews by dropping water on the fires. A pilot is practicing by dropping a canister of red dye, hoping to hit a target on the ground below. If the plane is flying in a horizontal path 90.0 m above the ground and with a speed of 64.0 m/s (143 mi/h), at what horizontal distance from the target should the pilot release the canister? Ignore air resistance.

3.54. As a ship is approaching the dock at 45.0 cm/s, an important piece of landing equipment needs to be thrown to it before it can dock. This equipment is thrown at 15.0 m/s at 60.0° above the horizontal from the top of a tower at the edge of the water, 8.75 m above the ship's deck (Fig. 3.46.) For this equipment to land at the front of the ship, at what distance D from the dock should the ship be when the equipment is thrown? Air resistance can be neglected.

Figure 3.46 Problem 3.54.

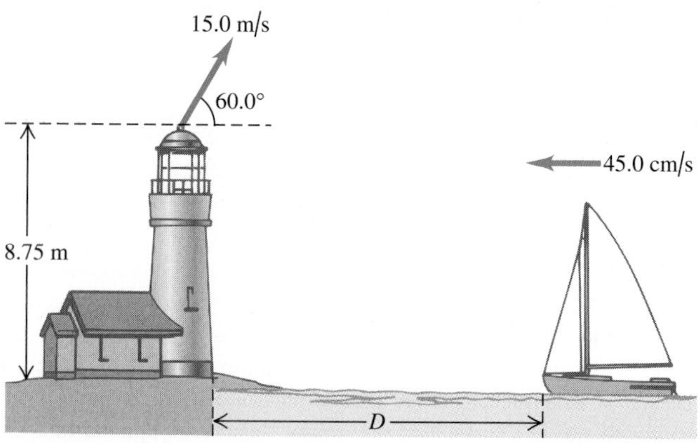

3.55. The Longest Home Run. According to the *Guinness Book of World Records,* the longest home run ever measured was hit by Roy "Dizzy" Carlyle in a minor league game. The ball traveled 188 m (618 ft) before landing on the ground outside the ballpark. (a) Assuming the ball's initial velocity was 45° above the horizontal and ignoring air resistance, what did the initial speed of the ball need to be to produce such a home run if the ball was hit at a point 0.9 m (3.0 ft) above ground level? Assume that the ground was perfectly flat. (b) How far would the ball be above a fence 3.0 m (10 ft) high if the fence was 116 m (380 ft) from home plate?

3.56. A water hose is used to fill a large cylindrical storage tank of diameter D and height $2D$. The hose shoots the water at 45° above the horizontal from the same level as the base of the tank and is a distance $6D$ away (Fig. 3.47). For what *range* of launch speeds (v_0) will the water enter the tank? Ignore air resistance, and express your answer in terms of D and g.

Figure 3.47 Problem 3.56.

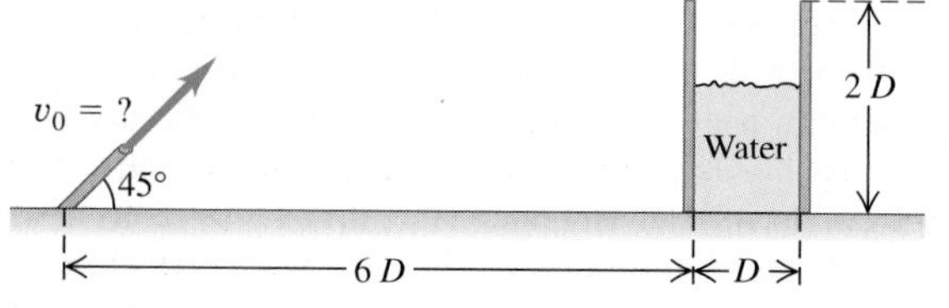

3.57. A projectile is being launched from ground level with no air resistance. You want to avoid having it enter a temperature inversion layer in the atmosphere a height h above the ground. (a) What is the maximum launch speed you could give this projectile if you shot it straight up? Express your answer in terms of h and g. (b) Suppose the launcher available shoots projectiles at twice the maximum launch speed you found in part (a). At what maximum angle above the horizontal should you launch the projectile? (c) How far (in terms of h) from the launcher does the projectile in part (b) land?

3.58. Kicking a Field Goal. In U.S. football, after a touchdown the team has the opportunity to earn one more point by kicking the ball over the bar between the goal posts. The bar is 10.0 ft above the ground, and the ball is kicked from ground level, 36.0 ft horizontally from the bar (Fig. 3.48). Football regulations are stated in English units, but convert to SI units for this problem. (a) There is a minimum angle above the ground such that if the ball is launched below this angle, it can never clear the bar, no matter how fast it is kicked. What is this angle? (b) If the ball is kicked at 45.0° above the horizontal, what must its initial speed be if it to just clear the bar? Express your answer in m/s and km/h.

Figure 3.48 Problem 3.58.

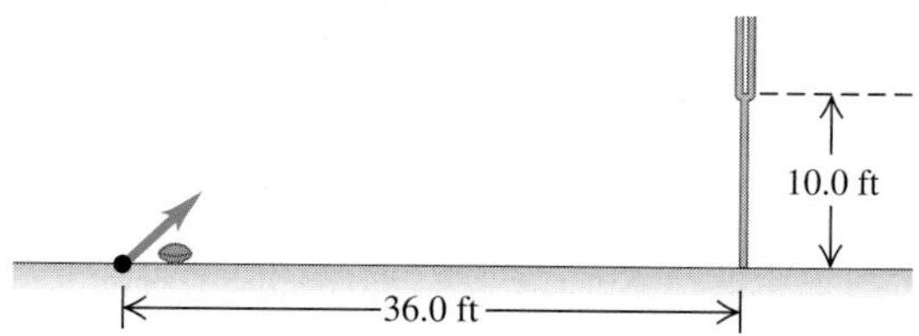

3.59. A projectile is launched with speed v_0 at an angle α_0 above the horizontal. The launch point is a height h above the ground. (a) Show that if air resistance is ignored, the horizontal distance that the projectile travels before striking the ground is

$$x = \frac{v_0 \cos \alpha_0}{g}\left(v_0 \sin \alpha_0 + \sqrt{v_0^2 \sin^2 \alpha_0 + 2gh}\right)$$

Verify that if the launch point is at ground level so that $h = 0$, this is equal to the horizontal range R found in Example 3.8. (b) For the case where $v_0 = 10$ m/s and $h = 5.0$ m, graph x as a function of launch angle α_0 for values of α_0 from 0° to 90°. Your graph should show that x is zero if $\alpha_0 = 90°$, but x is nonzero if $\alpha_0 = 0$; explain why this is so. (c) We saw in Example 3.8 that for a projectile that lands at the same height from which it is launched, the horizontal range is maximum for $\alpha_0 = 45°$. For the case graphed in part (b), is the angle for maximum horizontal distance equal to, less than, or greater than 45°? (This is a general result for the situation where a projectile is launched from a point higher than where it lands.)

3.60. Look Out! A snowball rolls off a barn roof that slopes downward at an angle of 40° (Fig. 3.49). The edge of the roof is 14.0 m above the ground, and the snowball has a speed of 7.00 m/s as it rolls off the roof. Ignore air resistance. (a) How far from the edge of the barn does the snowball strike the ground if it doesn't strike anything else while falling? (b) Draw x-t, y-t, v_x-t, and v_y-t graphs for the motion in part (a). (c) A man 1.9 m tall is standing 4.0 m from the edge of the barn. Will he be hit by the snowball?

Figure 3.49 Problem 3.60.

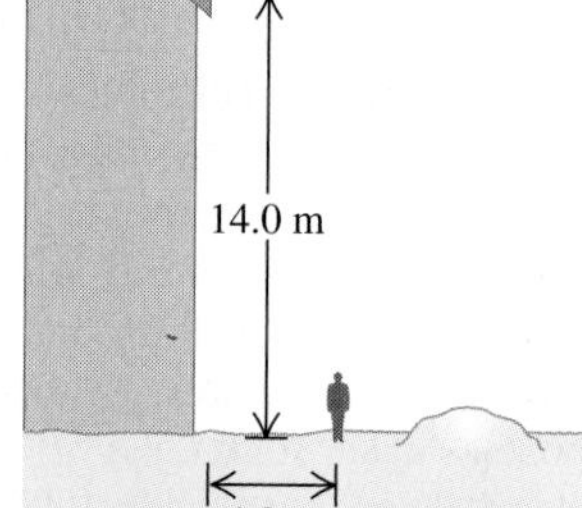

3.61. (a) Prove that a projectile launched at angle α_0 has the same horizontal range as one launched with the same speed at angle $(90° - \alpha_0)$. (b) A frog jumps at a speed of 2.2 m/s and lands 25 cm from its starting point. At which angles above the horizontal could it have jumped?

3.62. On the Flying Trapeze. A new circus act is called the Texas Tumblers. Lovely Mary Belle swings from a trapeze, projects herself at an angle of 53°, and is supposed to be caught by Joe Bob, whose hands are 6.1 m above and 8.2 m horizontally from her launch point (Fig. 3.50). You can ignore air resistance. (a) What initial speed v_0 must Mary Belle have just to reach Joe Bob? (b) For the initial speed calculated in part (a), what are the magnitude and direction of her velocity when Mary Belle reaches Joe Bob? (c) Assuming that Mary Belle has the initial speed calculated in part (a), draw x-t, y-t, v_x-t, and v_y-t graphs showing the motion of both tumblers. Your graphs should show the motion up until the point where Mary Belle reaches Joe Bob. (d) The night of their debut performance, Joe Bob misses her completely as she flies past. How far horizontally does Mary Belle travel, from her initial launch point, before landing in the safety net 8.6 m below her starting point?

Figure 3.50 Problem 3.62.

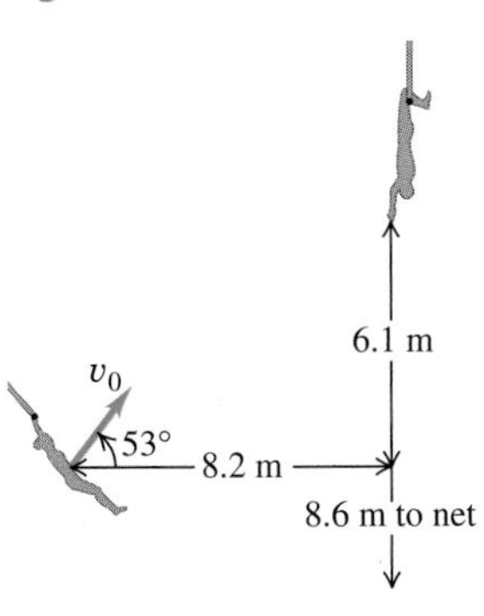

3.63. Leaping the River II. A physics professor did daredevil stunts in his spare time. His last stunt was an attempt to jump across a river on a motorcycle (Fig. 3.51). The takeoff ramp was inclined at 53.0°, the river was 40.0 m wide, and the far bank was 15.0 m lower than the top of the ramp. The river itself was 100 m below the ramp. You can ignore air resistance. (a) What should his speed have been at the top of the ramp to have just made it to the edge of the far bank? (b) If his speed was only half the value found in (a), where did he land?

Figure 3.51 Problem 3.63.

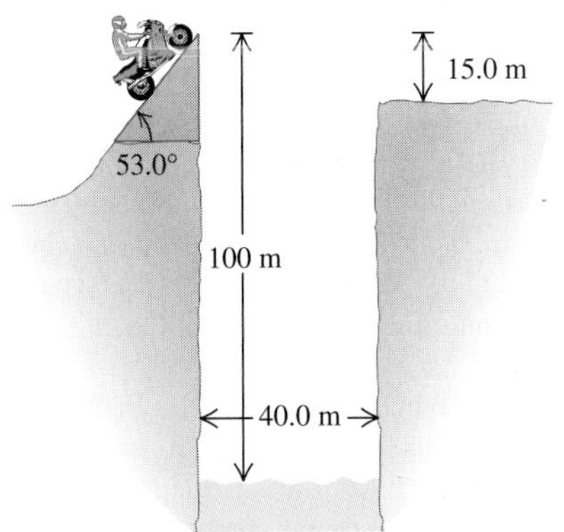

3.64. A rock is thrown from the roof of a building with a velocity v_0 at an angle of α_0 from the horizontal. The building has height h. You can ignore air resistance. Calculate the magnitude of the velocity of the rock just before it strikes the ground, and show that this speed is independent of α_0.

3.65. A 5500-kg cart carrying a vertical rocket launcher moves to the right at a constant speed of 30.0 m/s along a horizontal track. It launches a 45.0-kg rocket vertically upward with an initial speed of 40.0 m/s relative to the cart. (a) How high will the rocket go? (b) Where, relative to the cart, will the rocket land? (c) How far does the cart move while the rocket is in the air? (d) At what angle, relative to the horizontal, is the rocket traveling just as it leaves the cart, as measured by an observer at rest on the ground? (e) Sketch the rocket's trajectory as seen by an observer (i) stationary on the cart and (ii) stationary on the ground.

3.66. A 2.7-kg ball is thrown upward with an initial speed of 20.0 m/s from the edge of a 45.0-m-high cliff. At the instant the ball is thrown, a woman starts running away from the base of the cliff with a constant speed of 6.00 m/s. The woman runs in a straight line on level ground, and air resistance acting on the ball can be ignored. (a) At what angle above the horizontal should the ball be thrown so that the runner will catch it just before it hits the ground, and how far does the woman run before she catches the ball? (b) Carefully sketch the ball's trajectory as viewed by (i) a person at rest on the ground and (ii) the runner.

3.67. A 76.0-kg boulder is rolling horizontally at the top of a vertical cliff that is 20 m above the surface of a lake, as shown in Fig. 3.52. The top of the vertical face of a dam is located 100 m from the foot of the cliff, with the top of the dam level with the surface of the water in the lake. A level plain is 25 m below the top of the dam. (a) What must be the minimum speed of the rock just as it leaves the cliff so it will travel to the plain without striking the dam? (b) How far from the foot of the dam does the rock hit the plain?

Figure 3.52 Problem 3.67.

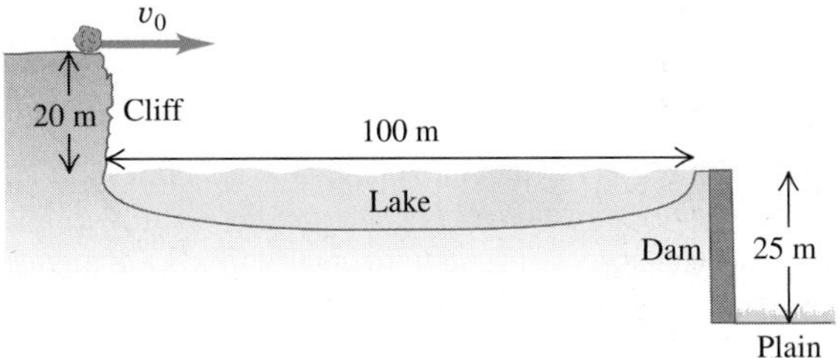

3.68. Tossing Your Lunch. Henrietta is going off to her physics class, jogging down the sidewalk at 3.05 m/s. Her husband Bruce suddenly realizes that she left in such a hurry that she forgot her lunch of bagels, so he runs to the window of their apartment, which is 43.9 m above the street level and directly above the sidewalk, to throw them to her. Bruce throws them horizontally 9.00 s after Henrietta has passed below the window, and she catches them on the run. You can ignore air resistance. (a) With what initial speed must Bruce throw the bagels so Henrietta can catch them just before they hit the ground? (b) Where is Henrietta when she catches the bagels?

3.69. Two tanks are engaged in a training exercise on level ground. The first tank fires a paint-filled training round with a muzzle speed of 250 m/s at 10.0° above the horizontal while advancing toward the second tank with a speed of 15.0 m/s relative to the ground. The second tank is retreating at 35.0 m/s relative to the ground, but is hit by the shell. You can ignore air resistance and assume the shell hits at the same height above ground from which it was fired. Find the distance between the tanks (a) when the round was first fired and (b) at the time of impact.

3.70. Bang! A student sits atop a platform a distance h above the ground. He throws a large firecracker horizontally with a speed v. However, a wind blowing parallel to the ground gives the firecracker a constant horizontal acceleration with magnitude a. This results in the firecracker reaching the ground directly under the student. Determine the height h in terms of v, a, and g. You can ignore the effect of air resistance on the vertical motion.

3.71. A rocket is launched vertically from rest with a constant upward acceleration of 1.75 m/s^2. Suddenly 22.0 s after launch, an unneeded fuel tank is jettisoned by shooting it away from the rocket. A crew member riding in the rocket measures that the initial speed of the tank is 25.0 m/s and that it moves perpendicular to the rocket's path. The fuel tank feels no appreciable air resistance and feels only the force of gravity once it leaves the rocket. (a) How fast is the rocket moving at the instant the fuel tank is jettisoned? (b) What are the horizontal and vertical components of the fuel tank's velocity just as it is jettisoned as measured by (i) a crew member in the rocket and (ii) a technician standing on the ground? (c) At what angle with respect to the horizontal does the jettisoned fuel tank initially move, as measured by (i) a crew member in the rocket and (ii) a technician standing on the ground? (d) What maximum height above the launch pad does the jettisoned tank reach?

3.72. When it is 145 m above the ground, a rocket traveling vertically upward at a constant 8.50 m/s relative to the ground launches a secondary rocket at a speed of 12.0 m/s at an angle of 53.0° above the horizontal, both quantities being measured by an astronaut sitting in the rocket. Air resistance is too small to worry about. (a) Just as the secondary rocket is launched, what are the horizontal and vertical components of its velocity relative to (i) the astronaut sitting in the rocket and (ii) Mission Control on the ground? (b) Find the initial speed and launch angle of the secondary rocket as measured by Mission Control. (c) What maximum height above the ground does the secondary rocket reach?

3.73. In a Fourth of July celebration, a firecracker is launched from ground level with an initial velocity of 25.0 m/s at 30.0° from the *vertical.* At its maximum height it explodes in a starburst into many fragments, two of which travel forward initially at 20.0 m/s at ±53.0° with respect to the horizontal, both quantities measured *relative to the original firecracker just before it exploded.* With what angles with respect to the horizontal do the two fragments initially move right after the explosion, as measured by a spectator standing on the ground?

3.74. In an action-adventure film, the hero is supposed to throw a grenade from his car, which is going 90.0 km/h, to his enemy's car, which is going 110 km/h. The enemy's car is 15.8 m in front of the hero's when he lets go of the grenade. If the hero throws the grenade so its initial velocity relative to him is at an angle of 45° above the horizontal, what should the magnitude of the initial velocity be? The cars are both traveling in the same direction on a level road. You can ignore air resistance. Find the magnitude of the velocity both relative to the hero and relative to the earth.

3.75. A rock tied to a rope moves in the *xy*-plane. Its coordinates are given as functions of time by

$$x(t) = R\cos\omega t \qquad y(t) = R\sin\omega t$$

where R and ω are constants. (a) Show that the rock's distance from the origin is constant and equal to R—that is, that its path is a circle of radius R. (b) Show that at every point the rock's velocity is perpendicular to its position vector. (c) Show that the rock's acceleration is always opposite in direction to its position vector and has magnitude $\omega^2 R$. (d) Show that the magnitude of the rock's velocity is constant and equal to ωR. (e) Combine the results of parts (c) and (d) to show that the rock's acceleration has constant magnitude v^2/R.

3.76. A 400.0-m-wide river flows from west to east at 30.0 m/min. Your boat moves at 100.0 m/min relative to the water no matter which direction you point it. To cross this river, you start from a dock at point A on the south bank. There is a boat landing directly opposite at point B on the north bank, and also one at point C, 75.0 m downstream from B (Fig. 3.53). (a) Where on the north shore will you land if you point your boat perpendicular to the water current, and what distance will you have traveled? (b) If you initially aim your boat directly toward point C and do not change that bearing relative to the shore, where on the north shore will you land? (c) To reach point C: (i) at what bearing must you aim your boat, (ii) how long will it take to cross the river, (iii) what distance do you travel, and (iv) and what is the speed of your boat as measured by an observer standing on the river bank?

Figure 3.53 Problem 3.76.

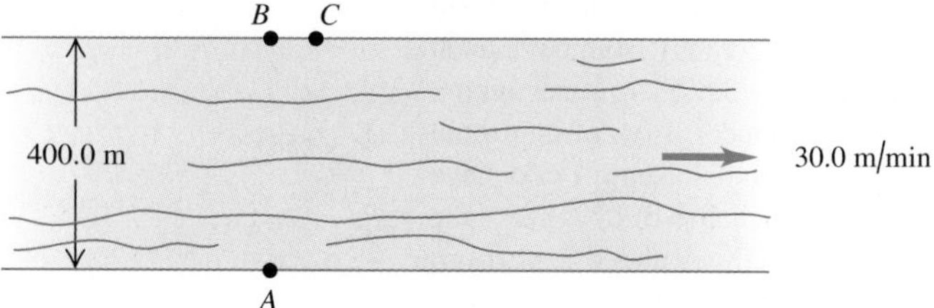

3.77. Cycloid. A particle moves in the *xy*-plane. Its coordinates are given as functions of time by

$$x(t) = R(\omega t - \sin\omega t) \qquad y(t) = R(1 - \cos\omega t)$$

where R and ω are constants. (a) Sketch the trajectory of the particle. (This is the trajectory of a point on the rim of a wheel that is rolling at a constant speed on a horizontal surface. The curve traced out by such a point as it moves through space is called a *cycloid.*) (b) Determine the velocity components and the acceleration components of the particle at any time t. (c) At which times is the particle momentarily at rest? What are the coordinates of the particle at these times? What are the magnitude and direction of the acceleration at these times? (d) Does the magnitude of the acceleration depend on time? Compare to uniform circular motion.

3.78. A projectile is fired from point A at an angle above the horizontal. At its highest point, after having traveled a horizontal distance D from its launch point, it suddenly explodes into two identical fragments that travel horizontally with equal but opposite velocities as measured *relative to the projectile just before it exploded.* If one fragment lands back at point A, how far from A (in terms of D) does the other fragment land?

3.79. Centrifuge on Mercury. A laboratory centrifuge on earth makes n rpm (rev/min) and produces an acceleration of $5.00g$ at its outer end. (a) What is the acceleration (in g's) at a point halfway out to the end? (b) This centrifuge is now used in a space capsule on the planet Mercury, where g_{Mercury} is 0.378 what it is on earth. How many rpm (in terms of n) should it make to produce $5g_{\text{Mercury}}$ at its outer end?

3.80. Raindrops. When a train's velocity is 12.0 m/s eastward, raindrops that are falling vertically with respect to the earth make traces that are inclined 30.0° to the vertical on the windows of the train. (a) What is the horizontal component of a drop's velocity with respect to the earth? With respect to the train? (b) What is the magnitude of the velocity of the raindrop with respect to the earth? With respect to the train?

3.81. An airplane pilot sets a compass course due west and maintains an airspeed of 220 km/h. After flying for 0.500 h, she finds herself over a town 120 km west and 20 km south of her starting point. (a) Find the wind velocity (magnitude and direction). (b) If the wind velocity is 40 km/h due south, in what direction should the pilot set her course to travel due west? Use the same airspeed of 220 km/h.

3.82. An elevator is moving upward at a constant speed of 2.50 m/s. A bolt in the elevator ceiling 3.00 m above the elevator floor works loose and falls. (a) How long does it take for the bolt to fall to the elevator floor? What is the speed of the bolt just as it hits the elevator floor (b) according to an observer in the elevator? (c) According to an observer standing on one of the floor landings of the building? (d) According to the observer in part (c), what distance did the bolt travel between the ceiling and the floor of the elevator?

3.83. Suppose the elevator in Problem 3.82 starts from rest and maintains a constant upward acceleration of 4.00 m/s^2, and the bolt falls out the instant the elevator begins to move. (a) How long does it take for the bolt to reach the floor of the elevator? (b) Just as it reaches the floor, how fast is the bolt moving according to an observer (i) in the elevator? (ii) Standing on the floor landings of the building? (c) According to each observer in part (b), how far has the bolt traveled between the ceiling and floor of the elevator?

3.84. City A lies directly west of city B. When there is no wind, an airliner makes the 5550-km round-trip flight between them in 6.60 h of flying time while traveling at the same speed in both directions. When a strong, steady 225-km/h wind is blowing from west to east and the airliner has the same airspeed as before, how long will the trip take?

3.85. In a World Cup soccer match, Juan is running due north toward the goal with a speed of 8.00 m/s relative to the ground. A teammate passes the ball to him. The ball has a speed of 12.0 m/s and is moving in a direction of 37.0° east of north, relative to the ground. What are the magnitude and direction of the ball's velocity relative to Juan?

Challenge Problems

3.86. A man is riding on a flatcar traveling at a constant speed of 9.10 m/s (Fig. 3.54). He wishes to throw a ball through a stationary hoop 4.90 m above the height of his hands in such a manner that the ball will move horizontally as it passes through the hoop. He throws the ball with a speed of 10.8 m/s with respect to himself. (a) What must the vertical component of the initial velocity of the ball be? (b) How many seconds after he releases the ball will it pass through the hoop? (c) At what horizontal distance in front of the hoop must he release the ball? (d) When the ball leaves the man's hands, what is the direction of its velocity relative to the frame of reference of the flatcar? Relative to the frame of reference of an observer standing on the ground?

Figure 3.54 Challenge Problem 3.86.

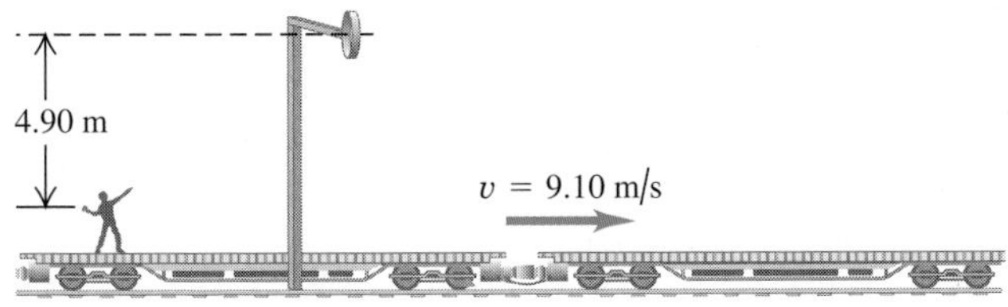

3.87. A shotgun fires a large number of pellets upward, with some pellets traveling very nearly vertically and others as much as 1.0° from the vertical. Assume that the initial speed of the pellets is uniformly 150 m/s, and ignore air resistance. (a) Within what radius from the point of firing will the pellets land? (b) If there are 1000 pellets, and they fall in a uniform distribution over a circle with the radius calculated in part (a), what is the probability that at least one pellet will fall on the head of the person who fires the shotgun? Assume that his head has a radius of 10 cm. (c) Air resistance, in fact, has several effects. It slows down the rising pellets, decreases their horizontal component of velocity, and limits the speed with which they fall. Which of these effects will tend to make the radius larger than calculated in part (a), and which will tend to make it smaller? What do you think the overall effect of air resistance will be? (The effect of air resistance on a velocity component increases as the magnitude of the component increases.)

3.88. A projectile is thrown from a point P. It moves in such a way that its distance from P is always increasing. Find the maximum angle above the horizontal with which the projectile could have been thrown. You can ignore air resistance.

3.89. Projectile Motion on an Incline I. A baseball is given an initial velocity with magnitude v_0 at an angle ϕ above the surface of an incline, which is in turn inclined at an angle θ above the horizontal (Fig. 3.55) (a) Calculate the distance, measured along the incline, from the launch point to where the baseball strikes the incline. Your answer will be in terms of v_0, g, θ, and ϕ. (b) What angle ϕ gives the maximum range, measured along the incline? (*Note:* You might be interested in the three different methods of solution presented by I. R. Lapidus in *Amer. Jour. of Phys.*, Vol. 51 (1983), pp. 806 and 847. See also H. A. Buckmaster in *Amer. Jour. of Phys.*, Vol. 53 (1985), pp. 638–641, for a thorough study of this and some similar problems.)

Figure 3.55 Challenge Problem 3.89.

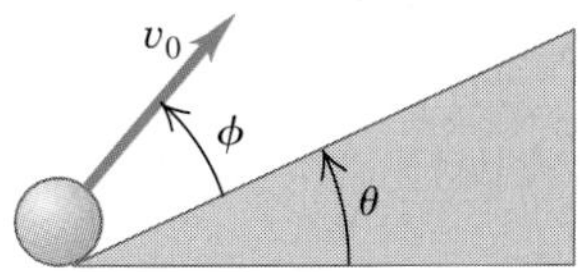

3.90. Projectile Motion on an Incline II. Refer to Challenge Problem 3.89. (a) An archer on ground that has a constant upward slope of 30.0° aims at a target 60.0 m farther up the incline. The arrow in the bow and the bull's-eye at the center of the target are each 1.50 m above the ground. The initial velocity of the arrow just after it leaves the bow has magnitude 32.0 m/s. At what angle above the *horizontal* should the archer aim to hit the bull's-eye? If there are two such angles, calculate the smaller of the two. You might have to solve the equation for the angle by iteration—that is, by trial and error. How does the angle compare to that required when the ground is level, with 0 slope? (b) Repeat the above for ground that has a constant *downward* slope of 30.0°.

3.91. For no apparent reason, a poodle is running at a constant speed of $v = 5.00$ m/s in a circle with radius $R = 2.50$ m. Let $\vec{v}_1$ be the velocity vector at time t_1, and let $\vec{v}_2$ be the velocity vector at time t_2. Consider $\Delta\vec{v} = \vec{v}_2 - \vec{v}_1$ and $\Delta t = t_2 - t_1$. Recall that $\vec{a}_{av} = \Delta\vec{v}/\Delta t$. For $\Delta t = 0.5$ s, 0.1 s, and 0.05 s, calculate the magnitude (to four significant figures) and direction (relative to $\vec{v}_1$) of the average acceleration $\vec{a}_{av}$. Compare your results to the general expression for the instantaneous acceleration $\vec{a}$ for uniform circular motion that is derived in the text.

3.92. A rocket designed to place small payloads into orbit is carried to an altitude of 12.0 km above sea level by a converted airliner. When the airliner is flying in a straight line at a constant speed of 850 km/h, the rocket is dropped. After the drop, the airliner maintains the same altitude and speed and continues to fly in a straight line. The rocket falls for a brief time, after which its rocket motor turns on. Once its rocket motor is on, the combined effects of thrust and gravity give the rocket a constant acceleration of magnitude 3.00g directed at an angle of 30.0° above the horizontal. For reasons of safety, the rocket should be at least 1.00 km in front of the airliner when it climbs through the airliner's altitude. Your job is to determine the minimum time that the rocket must fall before its engine starts. You can ignore air resistance.

Your answer should include (i) a diagram showing the flight paths of both the rocket and the airliner, labeled at several points with vectors for their velocities and accelerations; (ii) an x-t graph showing the motions of both the rocket and the airliner; and (iii) a y-t graph showing the motions of both the rocket and the airliner. In the diagram and the graphs, indicate when the rocket is dropped, when the rocket motor turns on, and when the rocket climbs through the altitude of the airliner.

3.93. Two students are canoeing on a river. While heading upstream, they accidentally drop an empty bottle overboard. They then continue paddling for 60 minutes, reaching a point 2.0 km farther upstream. At this point they realize that the bottle is missing and, driven by ecological awareness, they turn around and head downstream. They catch up with and retrieve the bottle (which has been moving along with the current) 5.0 km downstream from the turn-around point. (a) Assuming a constant paddling effort throughout, how fast is the river flowing? (b) What would the canoe speed in a still lake be for the same paddling effort?

NEWTON'S LAWS OF MOTION

4

? The standing child is pushing the child seated on the swing. Is the seated child pushing back? If so, is he pushing with the same amount of force or a different amount?

LEARNING GOALS

By studying this chapter, you will learn:

- What the concept of force means in physics, and why forces are vectors.
- The significance of the net force on an object, and what happens when the net force is zero.
- The relationship among the net force on an object, the object's mass, and its acceleration.
- How the forces that two bodies exert on each other are related.

We've seen in the last two chapters how to describe motion in one, two, or three dimensions. But what are the underlying *causes* of motion? For example, how can a tugboat push a cruise ship that's much heavier than the tug? Why is it harder to control a car on wet ice than on dry concrete? The answers to these and similar questions take us into the subject of **dynamics,** the relationship of motion to the forces that cause it. In the two preceding chapters we studied *kinematics,* the language for *describing* motion. Now we are ready to think about what makes bodies move the way they do.

In this chapter we will use two new concepts, *force* and *mass,* to analyze the principles of dynamics. These principles can be wrapped up in just three statements that were clearly stated for the first time by Sir Isaac Newton (1642–1727), who published them in 1687 in his *Philosophiae Naturalis Principia Mathematica* ("Mathematical Principles of Natural Philosophy"). These three statements are called **Newton's laws of motion.** The first law states that when the net force on a body is zero, its motion doesn't change. The second law relates force to acceleration when the net force is *not* zero. The third law is a relationship between the forces that two interacting bodies exert on each other.

Newton's laws are not the product of mathematical derivations, but rather a synthesis of what physicists have learned from a multitude of *experiments* about how objects move. (Newton used the ideas and observations of many scientists before him, including Copernicus, Brahe, Kepler, and especially Galileo Galilei, who died the same year Newton was born.) These laws are truly fundamental, for they cannot be deduced or proved from other principles. Newton's laws are the foundation of **classical mechanics** (also called **Newtonian mechanics**); using them we can understand most familiar kinds of motion. Newton's laws need modification only for situations involving extremely high speeds (near the speed of light) or very small sizes (such as within the atom).

Newton's laws are very simple to state, yet many students find these laws difficult to grasp and to work with. The reason is that before studying physics, you've spent years walking, throwing balls, pushing boxes, and doing dozens of things that involve motion. Along the way, you've developed a set of "common sense" ideas about motion and its causes. But many of these "common sense" ideas don't stand up to logical analysis. A big part of the job of this chapter—and of the rest of our study of physics—is helping you to recognize how "common sense" ideas can sometimes lead you astray, and how to adjust your understanding of the physical world to make it consistent with what experiments tell us.

4.1 Force and Interactions

4.1 Some properties of forces.

- A force is a push or a pull.
- A force is an interaction between two objects or between an object and its environment.
- A force is a vector quantity, with magnitude and direction.

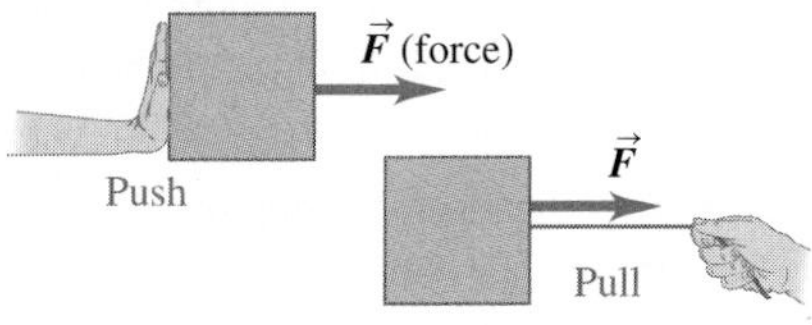

In everyday language, a **force** is a push or a pull. A better definition is that a force is an *interaction* between two bodies or between a body and its environment (Fig. 4.1). That's why we always refer to the force that one body *exerts* on a second body. When you push on a car that is stuck in the snow, you exert a force on the car; a steel cable exerts a force on the beam it is hoisting at a construction site; and so on. As Fig. 4.1 shows, force is a *vector* quantity; you can push or pull a body in different directions.

When a force involves direct contact between two bodies, such as a push or pull that you exert on an object with your hand, we call it a **contact force.** Figures 4.2a, 4.2b, and 4.2c show three common types of contact forces. The **normal force** (Fig. 4.2a) is exerted on an object by any surface with which it is contact. The adjective *normal* means that the force always acts perpendicular to the surface of contact, no matter what the angle of that surface. By contrast, the **friction force** (Fig. 4.2b) exerted on an object by a surface acts *parallel* to the surface, in the direction that opposes sliding. The pulling force exerted by a stretched rope or cord on an object to which it's attached is called a **tension force** (Fig. 4.2c). When you tug on your dog's leash, the force that pulls on her collar is a tension force.

In addition to contact forces, there are **long-range forces** that act even when the bodies are separated by empty space. The force between two magnets is an example of a long-range force, as is the force of gravity (Fig. 4.2d); the earth pulls a dropped object toward it even though there is no direct contact between the object and the earth. The gravitational force that the earth exerts on your body is called your **weight.**

To describe a force vector $\vec{F}$, we need to describe the *direction* in which it acts as well as its *magnitude,* the quantity that describes "how much" or "how hard" the force pushes or pulls. The SI unit of the magnitude of force is the *newton,* abbreviated N. (We'll give a precise definition of the newton in Section 4.3.) Table 4.1 lists some typical force magnitudes.

4.2 Four common types of forces.

(a) **Normal force $\vec{n}$:** When an object rests or pushes on a surface, the surface exerts a push on it that is directed perpendicular to the surface.

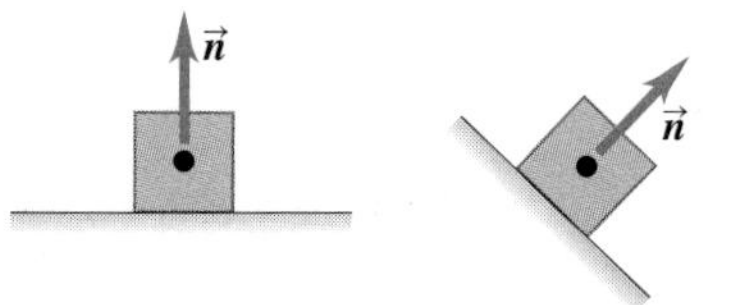

(b) **Friction force $\vec{f}$:** In addition to the normal force, a surface may exert a frictional force on an object, directed parallel to the surface.

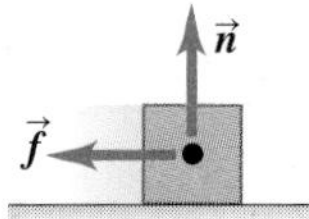

(c) **Tension force $\vec{T}$:** A pulling force exerted on an object by a rope, cord, etc.

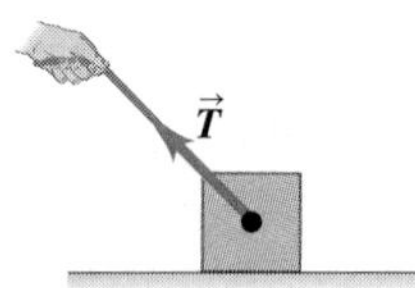

(d) **Weight $\vec{w}$:** The pull of gravity on an object is a long-range force (a force that acts over a distance).

Table 4.1 Typical Force Magnitudes

Sun's gravitational force on the earth	3.5×10^{22} N
Thrust of a space shuttle during launch	3.1×10^{7} N
Weight of a large blue whale	1.9×10^{6} N
Maximum pulling force of a locomotive	8.9×10^{5} N
Weight of a 250-lb linebacker	1.1×10^{3} N
Weight of a medium apple	1 N
Weight of smallest insect eggs	2×10^{-6} N
Electric attraction between the proton and the electron in a hydrogen atom	8.2×10^{-8} N
Weight of a very small bacterium	1×10^{-18} N
Weight of a hydrogen atom	1.6×10^{-26} N
Weight of an electron	8.9×10^{-30} N
Gravitational attraction between the proton and the electron in a hydrogen atom	3.6×10^{-47} N

A common instrument for measuring force magnitudes is the *spring balance*. It consists of a coil spring enclosed in a case with a pointer attached to one end. When forces are applied to the ends of the spring, it stretches by an amount that depends on the force. We can make a scale for the pointer by using a number of identical bodies with weights of exactly 1 N each. When one, two, or more of these are suspended simultaneously from the balance, the total force stretching the spring is 1 N, 2 N, and so on, and we can label the corresponding positions of the pointer 1 N, 2 N, and so on. Then we can use this instrument to measure the magnitude of an unknown force. We can also make a similar instrument that measures pushes instead of pulls.

Figure 4.3 shows a spring balance being used to measure a pull or push that we apply to a box. In each case we draw a vector to represent the applied force. The labels indicate the magnitude and direction of the force. The length of the vector also shows the magnitude; the longer the vector, the greater the force magnitude.

4.3 Using a vector arrow to denote the force that we exert when **(a)** pulling a block with a string or **(b)** pushing a block with a stick.

(a) A 10-N pull directed 30° above the horizontal

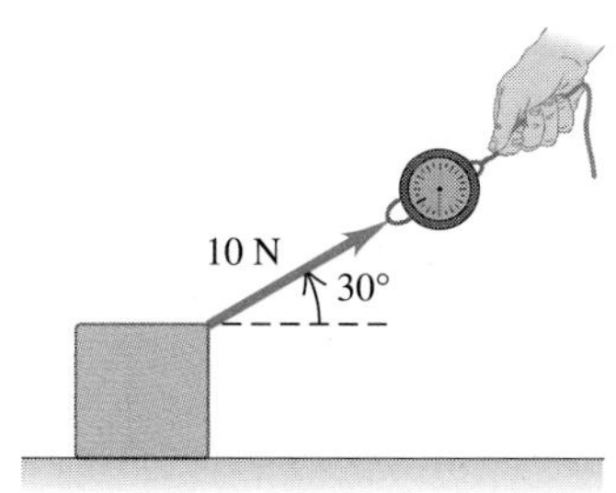

(b) A 10-N push directed 45° below the horizontal

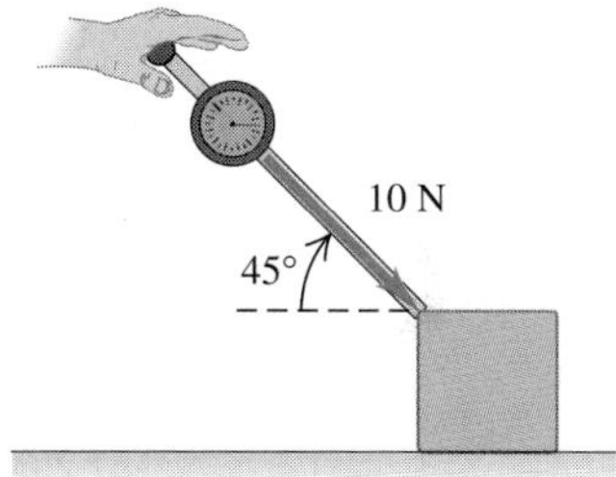

Superposition of Forces

When you throw a ball, there are at least two forces acting on it: the push of your hand and the downward pull of gravity. Experiment shows that when two forces $\vec{F}_1$ and $\vec{F}_2$ act at the same time at a point A of a body (Fig. 4.4), the effect on the body's motion is the same as if a single force $\vec{R}$ were acting equal to the *vector sum* of the original forces: $\vec{R} = \vec{F}_1 + \vec{F}_2$. More generally, *any number of forces applied at a point on a body have the same effect as a single force equal to the vector sum of the forces.* This important principle is called **superposition of forces.**

The experimental discovery that forces combine according to vector addition is of the utmost importance, and we will use this fact throughout our study of physics. It allows us to replace a force by its component vectors, as we did with displacements in Section 1.8. For example, in Fig. 4.5a, force $\vec{F}$ acts on a body at point O. The component vectors of $\vec{F}$ in the directions Ox and Oy are $\vec{F}_x$ and $\vec{F}_y$. When $\vec{F}_x$ and $\vec{F}_y$ are applied simultaneously, as in Fig. 4.5b, the effect is exactly the same as the effect of the original force $\vec{F}$. Hence *any force can be replaced by its component vectors, acting at the same point.*

It's frequently more convenient to describe a force $\vec{F}$ in terms of its x- and y-components F_x and F_y rather than by its component vectors (recall from Section 1.8 that *component vectors* are vectors, but *components* are just numbers). For the case shown in Fig. 4.5, both F_x and F_y are positive; for other orientations of the force $\vec{F}$, either F_x or F_y can be negative or zero.

There is no law that says our coordinate axes have to be vertical and horizontal. Figure 4.6 shows a crate being pulled up a ramp by a force $\vec{F}$, represented by its components F_x and F_y parallel and perpendicular to the sloping surface of the ramp.

4.4 Superposition of forces.

Two forces $\vec{F}_1$ and $\vec{F}_2$ acting on a point A have the same effect as a single force $\vec{R}$ equal to their vector sum.

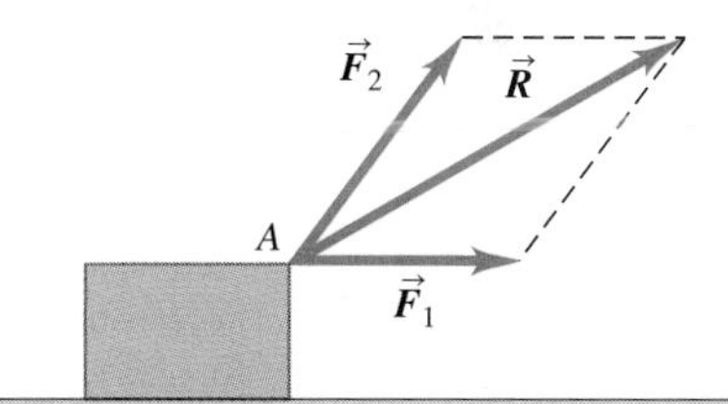

4.5 The force $\vec{F}$, which acts at an angle θ from the x-axis, may be replaced by its rectangular component vectors $\vec{F}_x$ and $\vec{F}_y$.

(a) Component vectors: $\vec{F}_x$ and $\vec{F}_y$
Components: $F_x = F\cos\theta$ and $F_y = F\sin\theta$

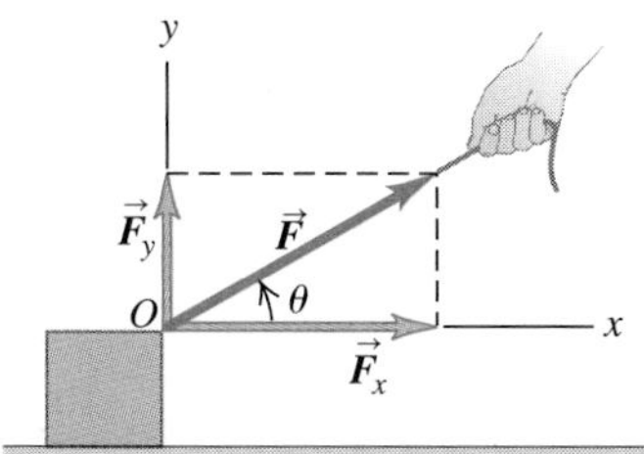

(b) Component vectors $\vec{F}_x$ and $\vec{F}_y$ together have the same effect as original force $\vec{F}$.

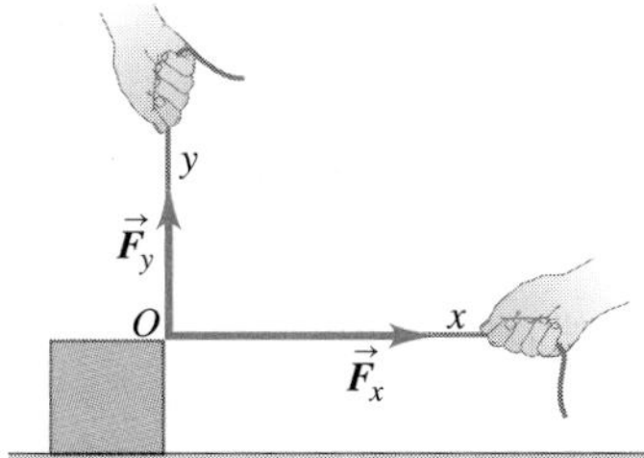

4.6 F_x and F_y are the components of $\vec{F}$ parallel and perpendicular to the sloping surface of the inclined plane.

We cross out a vector when we replace it with its components.

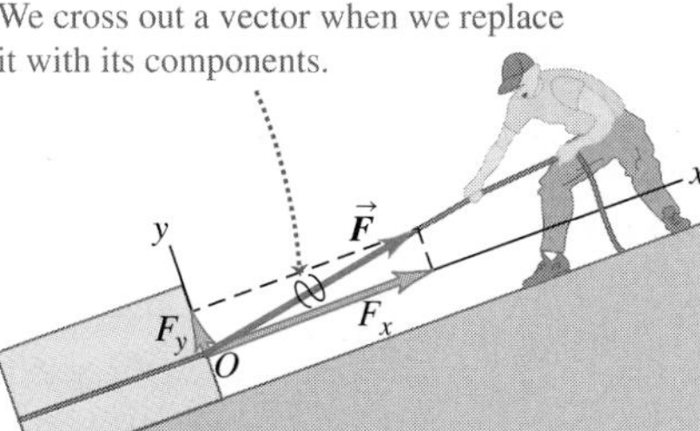

4.7 Finding the components of the vector sum (resultant) $\vec{R}$ of two forces $\vec{F}_1$ and $\vec{F}_2$.

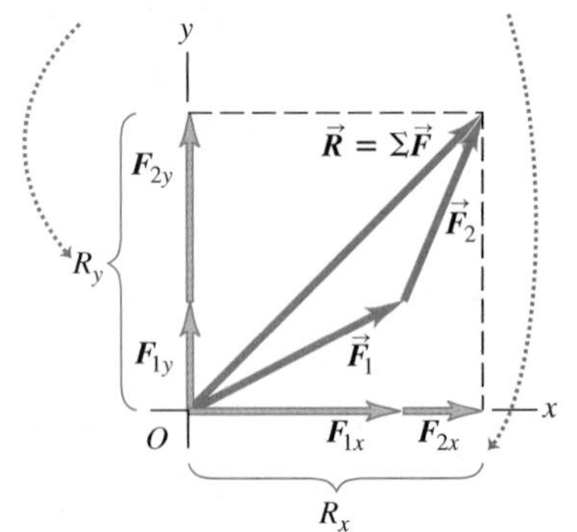

CAUTION **Using a wiggly line in force diagrams** In Fig. 4.6 we draw a wiggly line through the force vector $\vec{F}$ to show that we have replaced it by its x- and y-components. Otherwise, the diagram would include the same force twice. We will draw such a wiggly line in any force diagram where a force is replaced by its components. Look for this wiggly line in other figures in this and subsequent chapters.

We will often need to find the vector sum (resultant) of *all* the forces acting on a body. We call this the **net force** acting on the body. We will use the Greek letter Σ (capital sigma, equivalent to the Roman S) as a shorthand notation for a sum. If the forces are labeled $\vec{F}_1$, $\vec{F}_2$, $\vec{F}_3$, and so on, we abbreviate the sum as

$$\vec{R} = \vec{F}_1 + \vec{F}_2 + \vec{F}_3 + \cdots = \sum\vec{F} \tag{4.1}$$

We read $\sum\vec{F}$ as "the vector sum of the forces" or "the net force." The component version of Eq. (4.1) is the pair of component equations

$$R_x = \sum F_x \qquad R_y = \sum F_y \tag{4.2}$$

Here $\sum F_x$ is the sum of the x-components and $\sum F_y$ is the sum of the y-components (Fig. 4.7). Each component may be positive or negative, so be careful with signs when you evaluate the sums in Eq. (4.2).

Once we have R_x and R_y, we can find the magnitude and direction of the net force $\vec{R} = \sum\vec{F}$ acting on the body. The magnitude is

$$R = \sqrt{R_x^2 + R_y^2}$$

and the angle θ between $\vec{R}$ and the $+x$-axis can be found from the relation $\tan\theta = R_y/R_x$. The components R_x and R_y may be positive, negative, or zero, and the angle θ may be in any of the four quadrants.

In three-dimensional problems, forces may also have z-components; then we add the equation $R_z = \sum F_z$ to Eq. (4.2). The magnitude of the net force is then

$$R = \sqrt{R_x^2 + R_y^2 + R_z^2}$$

Example 4.1 Superposition of forces

Three professional wrestlers are fighting over the same champion's belt. As viewed from above, they apply the three horizontal forces to the belt that are shown in Fig. 4.8a. The magnitudes of the three forces are $F_1 = 250$ N, $F_2 = 50$ N, and $F_3 = 120$ N. Find the x- and y-components of the net force on the belt, and find the magnitude and direction of the net force.

SOLUTION

IDENTIFY: This example is just a problem in vector addition. The only new feature is that the vectors represent forces.

SET UP: We need to find the x- and y-components of the net force $\vec{R}$, so we'll use the component method of vector addition expressed by Eq. (4.2). Once we have the components of $\vec{R}$, we can find its magnitude and direction.

EXECUTE: From Fig. 4.8a, the angles between the three forces $\vec{F}_1$, $\vec{F}_2$, and $\vec{F}_3$ and the $+x$-axis are $\theta_1 = 180° - 53° = 127°$, $\theta_2 = 0°$, and $\theta_3 = 270°$. The x- and y-components of the three forces are

$$F_{1x} = (250\text{ N})\cos 127° = -150\text{ N}$$
$$F_{1y} = (250\text{ N})\sin 127° = 200\text{ N}$$
$$F_{2x} = (50\text{ N})\cos 0° = 50\text{ N}$$
$$F_{2y} = (50\text{ N})\sin 0° = 0\text{ N}$$

4.8 (a) Three forces acting on a belt. (b) The net force $\vec{R} = \sum\vec{F}$ and its components.

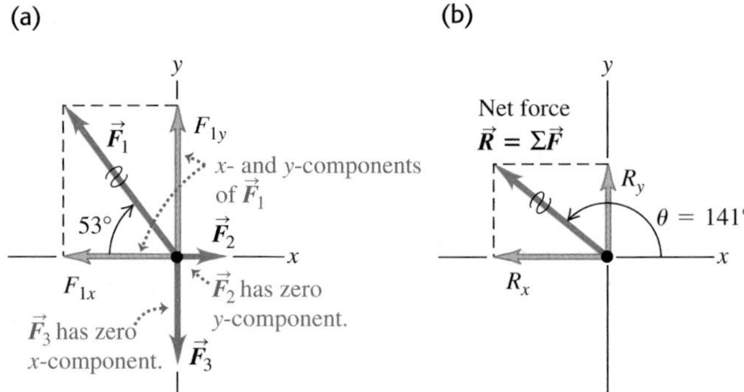

$$F_{3x} = (120\text{ N})\cos 270° = 0\text{ N}$$
$$F_{3y} = (120\text{ N})\sin 270° = -120\text{ N}$$

From Eq. (4.2) the net force $\vec{R} = \sum\vec{F}$ has components

$$R_x = F_{1x} + F_{2x} + F_{3x} = (-150\text{ N}) + 50\text{ N} + 0\text{ N} = -100\text{ N}$$
$$R_y = F_{1y} + F_{2y} + F_{3y} = 200\text{ N} + 0\text{ N} + (-120\text{ N}) = 80\text{ N}$$

The net force has a negative x-component and a positive y-component, so it points to the left and toward the top of the page in Fig. 4.8b (that is, in the second quadrant).

The magnitude of the net force $\vec{R} = \Sigma\vec{F}$ is

$$R = \sqrt{R_x^2 + R_y^2} = \sqrt{(-100\ \text{N})^2 + (80\ \text{N})^2} = 128\ \text{N}$$

To find the angle between the net force and the $+x$-axis, we use the relation $\tan\theta = R_y/R_x$, or

$$\theta = \arctan\frac{R_y}{R_x} = \arctan\left(\frac{80\ \text{N}}{-100\ \text{N}}\right) = \arctan(-0.80)$$

The two possible solutions are $\theta = -39°$ and $\theta = -39° + 180° = 141°$. Since the net force lies in the second quadrant, as mentioned earlier, the correct answer is 141° (see Fig. 4.8b).

EVALUATE: In this situation the net force is *not* zero, and you can see intuitively that wrestler 1 (who exerts the largest force, $\vec{F}_1$, on the belt) is likely to walk away with the belt at the end of the struggle. In Section 4.2 we will explore in detail what happens in situations in which the net force *is* zero.

Test Your Understanding of Section 4.1 Figure 4.6 shows a force $\vec{F}$ acting on a crate. With the x- and y-axes shown in the figure, which statement about the components of the *gravitational* force that the earth exerts on the crate (the crate's weight) is *correct?* (i) The x- and y-components are both positive. (ii) The x-component is zero and the y-component is positive. (iii) The x-component is negative and the y-component is positive. (iv) The x- and y-components are both negative. (v) The x-component is zero and the y-component is negative. (vi) The x-component is positive and the y-component is negative.

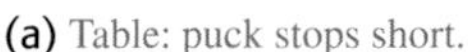

4.2 Newton's First Law

We have discussed some of the properties of forces, but so far have said nothing about how forces affect motion. To begin, let's consider what happens when the net force on a body is *zero.* You would almost certainly agree that if a body is at rest, and if no net force acts on it (that is, no net push or pull), that body will remain at rest. But what if there is zero net force acting on a body in *motion?*

To see what happens in this case, suppose you slide a hockey puck along a horizontal tabletop, applying a horizontal force to it with your hand (Fig. 4.9a). After you stop pushing, the puck *does not* continue to move indefinitely; it slows down and stops. To keep it moving, you have to keep pushing (that is, applying a force). You might come to the "common sense" conclusions that bodies in motion naturally come to rest and that a force is required to sustain motion.

But now imagine pushing the puck across a smooth surface of ice (Fig. 4.9b). After you quit pushing, the puck will slide a lot farther before it stops. Put it on an air-hockey table, where it floats on a thin cushion of air, and it moves still farther (Fig. 4.9c). In each case, what slows the puck down is *friction,* an interaction between the lower surface of the puck and the surface on which it slides. Each surface exerts a frictional force on the puck that resists the puck's motion; the difference in the three cases is the magnitude of the frictional force. The ice exerts less friction than the tabletop, so the puck travels farther. The gas molecules of the air-hockey table exert the least friction of all. If we could eliminate friction completely, the puck would never slow down, and we would need no force at all to keep the puck moving once it had been started. Thus the "common sense" idea that a force is required to sustain motion is *incorrect.*

Experiments like the ones we've just described show that when no net force acts on a body, the body either remains at rest or moves with constant velocity in a straight line. Once a body has been set in motion, no net force is needed to keep it moving. We now call this observation *Newton's first law of motion:*

Newton's first law of motion: A body acted on by no net force moves with constant velocity (which may be zero) and zero acceleration.

4.9 The slicker the surface, the farther a puck slides after being given an initial velocity. On an air-hockey table (c) the friction force is practically zero, so the puck continues with almost constant velocity.

(a) Table: puck stops short.

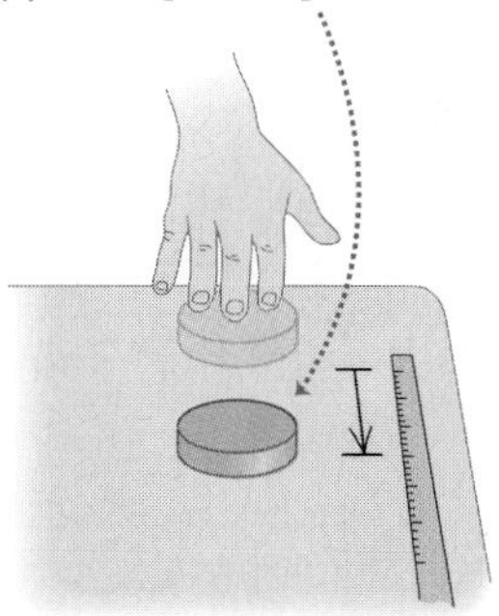

(b) Ice: puck slides farther.

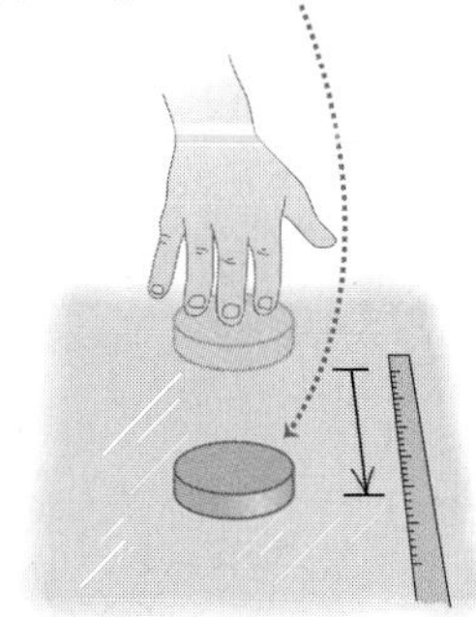

(c) Air-hockey table: puck slides even farther.

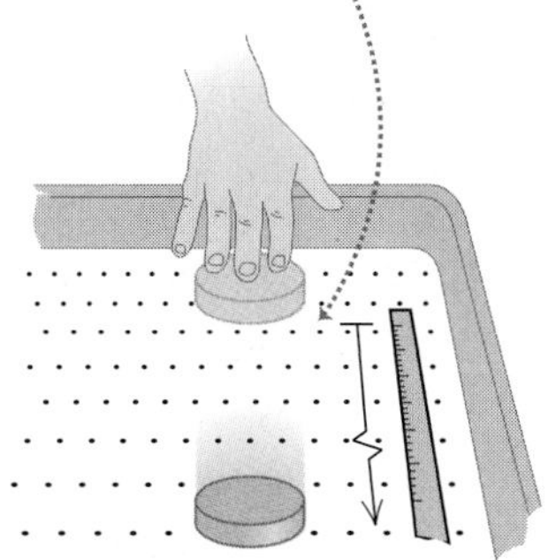

4.10 (a)A hockey puck accelerates in the direction of a net applied force $\vec{F}_1$. (b) When the net force is zero, the acceleration is zero, and the puck is in equilibrium.

(a) A puck on a frictionless surface accelerates when acted on by a single horizontal force.

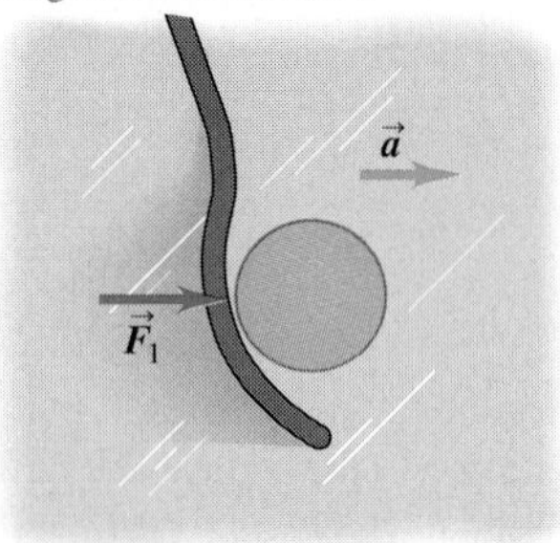

(b) An object acted on by forces whose vector sum is zero behaves as though no forces act on it.

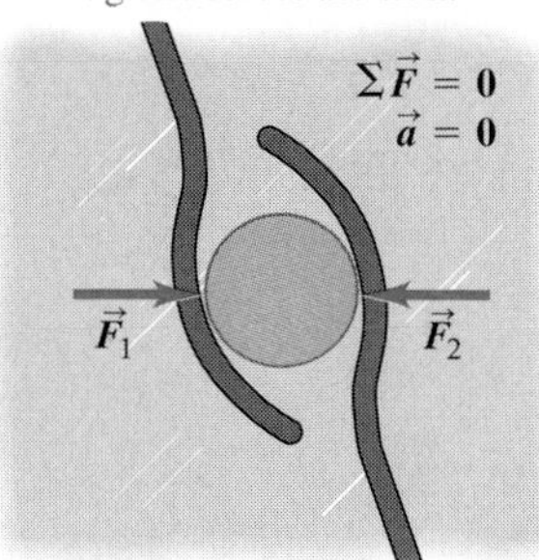

The tendency of a body to keep moving once it is set in motion results from a property called **inertia.** You use inertia when you try to get ketchup out of a bottle by shaking it. First you start the bottle (and the ketchup inside) moving forward; when you jerk the bottle back, the ketchup tends to keep moving forward and, you hope, ends up on your burger. The tendency of a body at rest to remain at rest is also due to inertia. You may have seen a tablecloth yanked out from under the china without breaking anything. The force on the china isn't great enough to make it move appreciably during the short time it takes to pull the tablecloth away.

It's important to note that the *net* force is what matters in Newton's first law. For example, a physics book at rest on a horizontal tabletop has two forces acting on it: an upward supporting force, or normal force, exerted by the tabletop (see Fig. 4.2a) and the downward force of the earth's gravitational attraction (a long-range force that acts even if the tabletop is elevated above the ground; see Fig. 4.2d). The upward push of the surface is just as great as the downward pull of gravity, so the *net* force acting on the book (that is, the vector sum of the two forces) is zero. In agreement with Newton's first law, if the book is at rest on the tabletop, it remains at rest. The same principle applies to a hockey puck sliding on a horizontal, frictionless surface: The vector sum of the upward push of the surface and the downward pull of gravity is zero. Once the puck is in motion, it continues to move with constant velocity because the *net* force acting on it is zero.

Here's another example. Suppose a hockey puck rests on a horizontal surface with negligible friction, such as an air-hockey table or a slab of wet ice. If the puck is initially at rest and a single horizontal force $\vec{F}_1$ acts on it (Fig. 4.10a), the puck starts to move. If the puck is in motion to begin with, the force changes its speed, its direction, or both, depending on the direction of the force. In this case the net force is equal to $\vec{F}_1$, which is *not* zero. (There are also two vertical forces: the earth's gravitational attraction and the upward normal force exerted by the surface. But as we mentioned earlier, these two forces cancel.)

Now suppose we apply a second force $\vec{F}_2$ (Fig. 4.10b), equal in magnitude to $\vec{F}_1$ but opposite in direction. The two forces are negatives of each other, $\vec{F}_2 = -\vec{F}_1$, and their vector sum is zero:

$$\sum\vec{F} = \vec{F}_1 + \vec{F}_2 = \vec{F}_1 + (-\vec{F}_1) = \mathbf{0}$$

Again, we find that if the body is at rest at the start, it remains at rest; if it is initially moving, it continues to move in the same direction with constant speed. These results show that in Newton's first law, *zero net force is equivalent to no force at all.* This is just the principle of superposition of forces that we saw in Section 4.1.

When a body is either at rest or moving with constant velocity (in a straight line with constant speed), we say that the body is in **equilibrium.** For a body to be in equilibrium, it must be acted on by no forces, or by several forces such that their vector sum—that is, the net force—is zero:

$$\sum\vec{F} = \mathbf{0} \quad \text{(body in equilibrium)} \tag{4.3}$$

For this to be true, each component of the net force must be zero, so

$$\sum F_x = 0 \quad \sum F_y = 0 \quad \text{(body in equilibrium)} \tag{4.4}$$

We are assuming that the body can be represented adequately as a point particle. When the body has finite size, we also have to consider *where* on the body the forces are applied. We will return to this point in Chapter 11.

Conceptual Example 4.2 Zero net force means constant velocity

In the classic 1950 science fiction film *Rocketship X-M,* a spaceship is moving in the vacuum of outer space, far from any planet, when its engine dies. As a result, the spaceship slows down and stops. What does Newton's first law say about this event?

SOLUTION

In this situation there are no forces acting on the spaceship, so according to Newton's first law, it will *not* stop. It continues to move in a straight line with constant speed. Some science fiction movies have made use of very accurate science; this was not one of them.

Conceptual Example 4.3 Constant velocity means zero net force

You are driving a Porsche Carrera GT on a straight testing track at a constant speed of 150 km/h. You pass a 1971 Volkswagen Beetle doing a constant 75 km/h. For which car is the net force greater?

SOLUTION

The key word in this question is "net." Both cars are in equilibrium because their velocities are both constant; therefore the *net* force on each car is *zero.*

This conclusion seems to contradict the "common sense" idea that the faster car must have a greater force pushing it. It's true that the forward force on your Porsche is much greater than that on the Volkswagen (thanks to your Porsche's high-power engine). But there is also a *backward* force acting on each car due to road friction and air resistance. The only reason these cars need engines is to counteract this backward force so that the vector sum of the forward and backward forces will be zero and the car will travel with constant velocity. The backward force on your Porsche is greater because of its greater speed, so its engine has to be more powerful than the Volkswagen's.

Inertial Frames of Reference

In discussing relative velocity in Section 3.5, we introduced the concept of *frame of reference.* This concept is central to Newton's laws of motion. Suppose you are in a bus that is traveling on a straight road and speeding up. If you could stand in the aisle on roller skates, you would start moving *backward* relative to the bus as the bus gains speed. If instead the bus was slowing to a stop, you would start moving forward down the aisle. In either case, it looks as though Newton's first law is not obeyed; there is no net force acting on you, yet your velocity changes. What's wrong?

The point is that the bus is accelerating with respect to the earth and is *not* a suitable frame of reference for Newton's first law. This law is valid in some frames of reference and not valid in others. A frame of reference in which Newton's first law *is* valid is called an **inertial frame of reference.** The earth is at least approximately an inertial frame of reference, but the bus is not. (The earth is not a completely inertial frame, owing to the acceleration associated with its rotation and its motion around the sun. These effects are quite small, however; see Exercises 3.29 and 3.32.) Because Newton's first law is used to define what we mean by an inertial frame of reference, it is sometimes called the *law of inertia.*

Figure 4.11 helps us understand what you experience when riding in a vehicle that's accelerating. In Fig. 4.11a, a vehicle is initially at rest and then begins to accelerate to the right. A passenger on roller skates (which nearly eliminate the effects of friction) has virtually no net force acting on her, so she tends to remain at rest relative to the inertial frame of the earth. As the vehicle accelerates around her, she moves backward relative to the vehicle. In the same way, a passenger in a vehicle that is slowing down tends to continue moving with constant velocity relative to the earth, and so moves forward relative to the vehicle (Fig. 4.11b). A vehicle is also accelerating if it moves at a constant speed but is turning (Fig. 4.11c). In this case a passenger tends to continue moving relative to the earth at constant speed in a straight line; relative to the vehicle, the passenger moves to the side of the vehicle on the outside of the turn.

4.11 Riding in an accelerating vehicle.

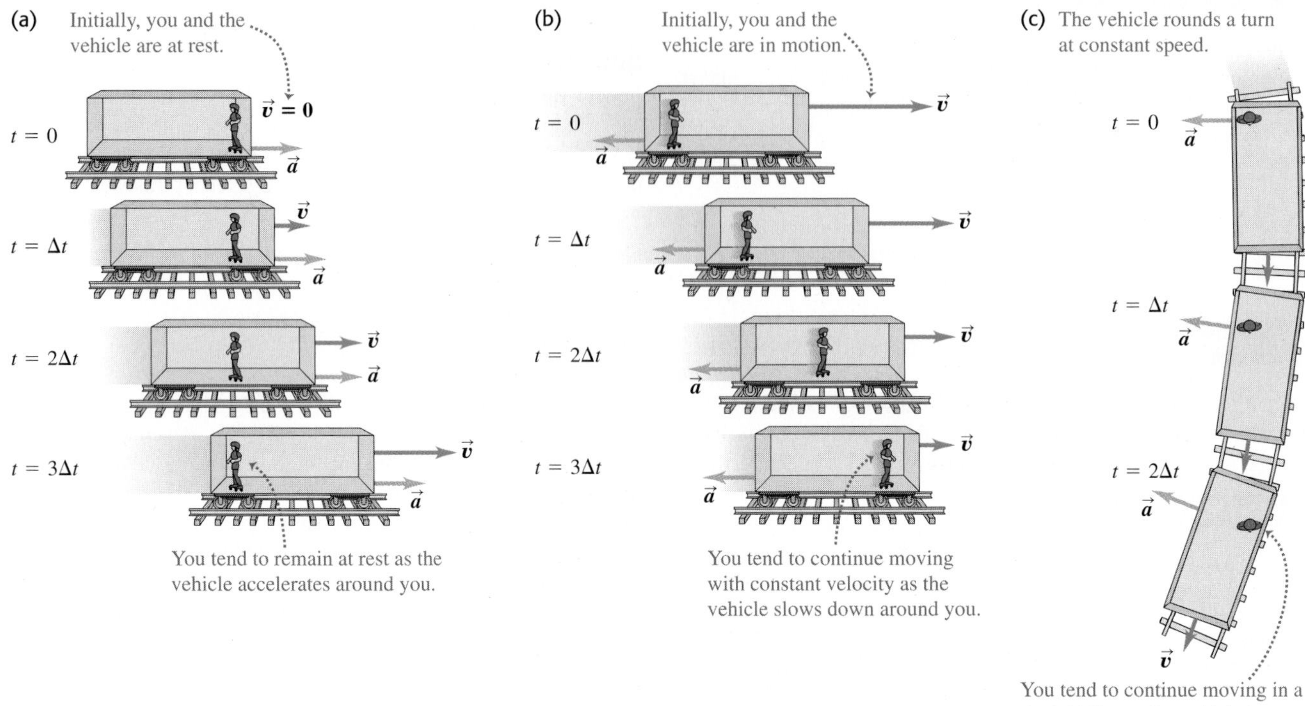
(a) Initially, you and the vehicle are at rest.
$\vec{v} = 0$
$t = 0$
$t = \Delta t$
$t = 2\Delta t$
$t = 3\Delta t$
You tend to remain at rest as the vehicle accelerates around you.
(b) Initially, you and the vehicle are in motion.
You tend to continue moving with constant velocity as the vehicle slows down around you.
(c) The vehicle rounds a turn at constant speed.
You tend to continue moving in a straight line as the vehicle turns.

In each case shown in Fig. 4.11, an observer in the vehicle's frame of reference might be tempted to conclude that there *is* a net force acting on the passenger, since the passenger's velocity *relative to the vehicle* changes in each case. This conclusion is simply wrong; the net force on the passenger is indeed zero. The vehicle observer's mistake is in trying to apply Newton's first law in the vehicle's frame of reference, which is *not* an inertial frame and in which Newton's first law isn't valid (Fig. 4.12). In this book we will use *only* inertial frames of reference.

We've mentioned only one (approximately) inertial frame of reference: the earth's surface. But there are many inertial frames. If we have an inertial frame of reference A, in which Newton's first law is obeyed, then *any* second frame of reference B will also be inertial if it moves relative to A with constant velocity $\vec{v}_{B/A}$. We can prove this using the relative velocity relation Eq. (3.36) from Section 3.5:

$$\vec{v}_{P/A} = \vec{v}_{P/B} + \vec{v}_{B/A}$$

Suppose that P is a body that moves with constant velocity $\vec{v}_{P/A}$ with respect to an inertial frame A. By Newton's first law the net force on this body is zero. The velocity of P relative to another frame B has a different value, $\vec{v}_{P/B} = \vec{v}_{P/A} - \vec{v}_{B/A}$. But if the relative velocity $\vec{v}_{B/A}$ of the two frames is constant, then $\vec{v}_{P/B}$ is constant as well. Thus B is also an inertial frame; the velocity of P in this frame is constant, and the net force on P is zero, so Newton's first law is obeyed in B. Observers in frames A and B will disagree about the velocity of P, but they will agree that P has a constant velocity (zero acceleration) and has zero net force acting on it.

There is no single inertial frame of reference that is preferred over all others for formulating Newton's laws. If one frame is inertial, then every other frame moving relative to it with constant velocity is also inertial. Viewed in this light, the state of rest and the state of motion with constant velocity are not very different; both occur when the vector sum of forces acting on the body is zero.

4.12 From the frame of reference of the car, it seems as though a force is pushing the crash test dummies forward as the car comes to a sudden stop. But there is really no such force: As the car stops, the dummies keep moving forward as a consequence of Newton's first law.

Test Your Understanding of Section 4.2 In which of the following situations is there zero net force on the body? (i) an airplane flying due north at a steady 120 m/s and at a constant altitude; (ii) a car driving straight up a hill with a 3° slope at a constant 90 km/h; (iii) a hawk circling at a constant 20 km/h at a constant height of 15 m above an open field; (iv) a box with slick, frictionless surfaces in the back of a truck as the truck accelerates forward on a level road at 5 $\mathrm{m/s^2}$.

4.3 Newton's Second Law

Newton's first law tells us that when a body is acted on by zero net force, it moves with constant velocity and zero acceleration. In Fig. 4.13a, a hockey puck is sliding to the right on wet ice. There is negligible friction, so there are no horizontal forces acting on the puck; the downward force of gravity and the upward normal force exerted by the ice surface sum to zero. So the net force $\sum\vec{F}$ acting on the puck is zero, the puck has zero acceleration, and its velocity is constant.

But what happens when the net force is *not* zero? In Fig. 4.13b we apply a constant horizontal force to a sliding puck in the same direction that the puck is moving. Then $\sum\vec{F}$ is constant and in the same horizontal direction as $\vec{v}$. We find that during the time the force is acting, the velocity of the puck changes at a constant rate; that is, the puck moves with constant acceleration. The speed of the puck increases, so the acceleration $\vec{a}$ is in the same direction as $\vec{v}$ and $\sum\vec{F}$.

In Fig. 4.13c we reverse the direction of the force on the puck so that $\sum\vec{F}$ acts opposite to $\vec{v}$. In this case as well, the puck has an acceleration; the puck moves more and more slowly to the right. The acceleration $\vec{a}$ in this case is to the left, in the same direction as $\sum\vec{F}$. As in the previous case, experiment shows that the acceleration is constant if $\sum\vec{F}$ is constant.

We conclude that *a net force acting on a body causes the body to accelerate in the same direction as the net force.* If the magnitude of the net force is constant, as in Figs. 4.13b and 4.13c, then so is the magnitude of the acceleration.

4.13 Exploring the relationship between the acceleration of a body and the net force acting on the body (in this case, a hockey puck on a frictionless surface).

(a) A puck moving with constant velocity (in equilibrium): $\sum\vec{F} = \mathbf{0}$, $\vec{a} = \mathbf{0}$

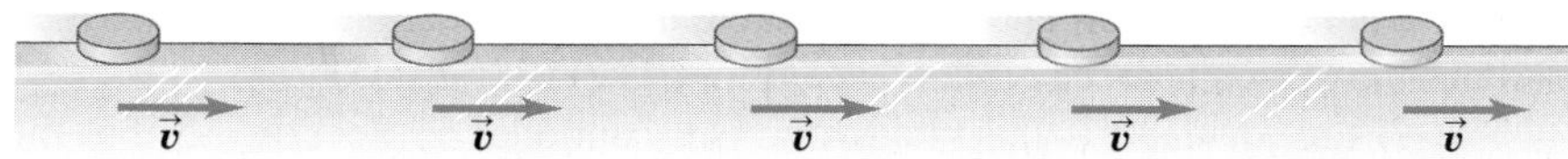

(b) A constant net force in the direction of motion causes a constant acceleration in the same direction as the net force.

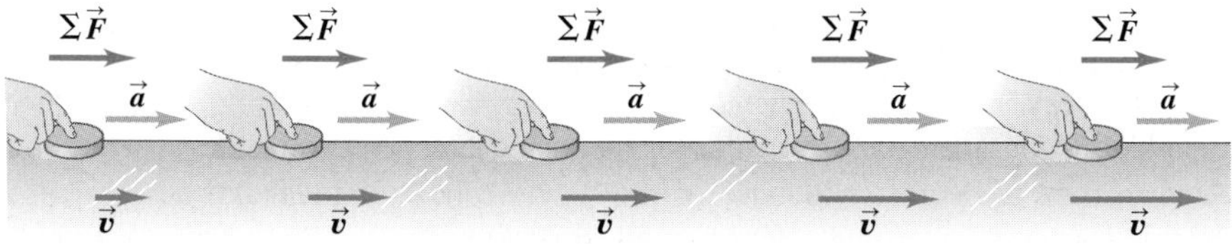

(c) A constant net force opposite the direction of motion causes a constant acceleration in the same direction as the net force.

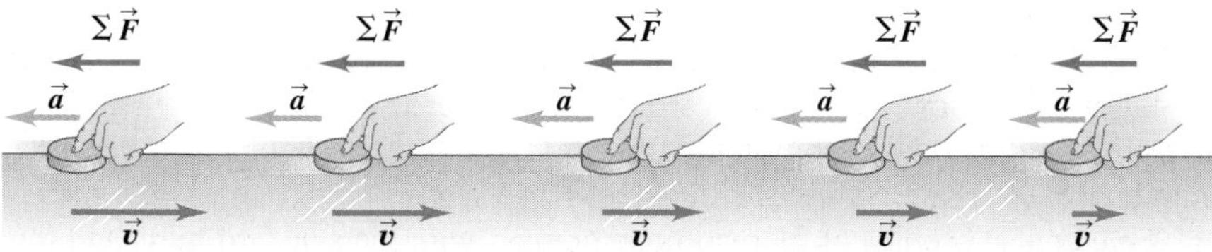

4.14 A top view of a hockey puck in uniform circular motion on a frictionless horizontal surface.

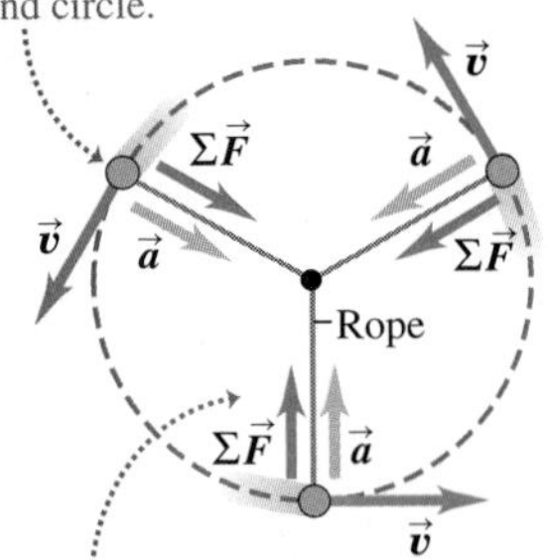
Puck moves at constant speed around circle.
$\vec{v}$
$\Sigma\vec{F}$
$\vec{a}$
Rope
At all points, the acceleration $\vec{a}$ and the net force $\Sigma\vec{F}$ point in the same direction—always toward the center of the circle.

4.15 For a body of a given mass m, the magnitude of the body's acceleration is directly proportional to the magnitude of the net force acting on the body.

(a) A constant net force $\Sigma\vec{F}$ causes a constant acceleration $\vec{a}$.

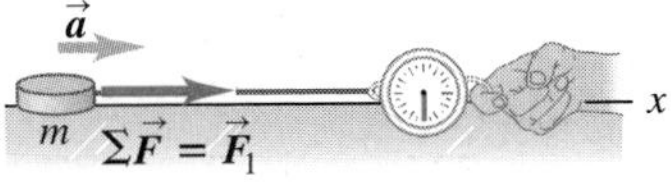
$\vec{a}$
m
$\Sigma\vec{F} = \vec{F}_1$
x

(b) Doubling the net force doubles the acceleration.

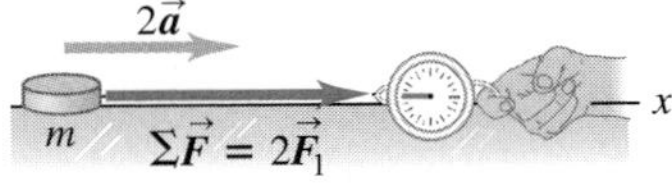
$2\vec{a}$
m
$\Sigma\vec{F} = 2\vec{F}_1$
x

(c) Halving the force halves the acceleration.

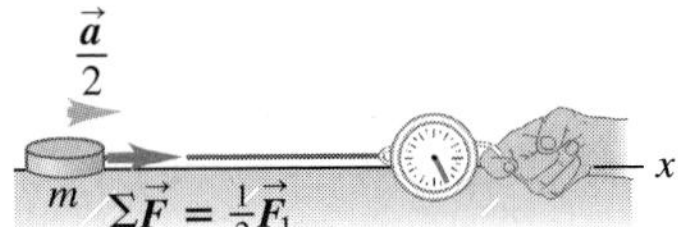
$\frac{\vec{a}}{2}$
m
$\Sigma\vec{F} = \frac{1}{2}\vec{F}_1$
x

These conclusions about net force and acceleration also apply to a body moving along a curved path. For example, Fig. 4.14 shows a hockey puck moving in a horizontal circle on an ice surface of negligible friction. A rope attaching the puck to the ice exerts a tension force of constant magnitude toward the center of the circle. The result is a net force and an acceleration that are constant in magnitude and directed toward the center of the circle. The speed of the puck is constant, so this is uniform circular motion, as discussed in Section 3.4.

Figure 4.15a shows another experiment to explore the relationship between acceleration and net force. We apply a constant horizontal force to a puck on a frictionless horizontal surface, using the spring balance described in Section 4.1 with the spring stretched a constant amount. As in Figs. 4.13b and 4.13c, this horizontal force equals the net force on the puck. If we change the magnitude of the net force, the acceleration changes in the same proportion. Doubling the net force doubles the acceleration (Fig. 4.15b), halving the net force halves the acceleration (Fig. 4.15c), and so on. Many such experiments show that *for any given body, the magnitude of the acceleration is directly proportional to the magnitude of the net force acting on the body.*

Mass and Force

Our results mean that for a given body, the *ratio* of the magnitude $|\Sigma\vec{F}|$ of the net force to the magnitude $a = |\vec{a}|$ of the acceleration is constant, regardless of the magnitude of the net force. We call this ratio the *inertial mass,* or simply the **mass,** of the body and denote it by m. That is,

$$m = \frac{|\Sigma\vec{F}|}{a} \quad \text{or} \quad |\Sigma\vec{F}| = ma \quad \text{or} \quad a = \frac{|\Sigma\vec{F}|}{m} \qquad (4.5)$$

Mass is a quantitative measure of inertia, which we discussed in Section 4.2. The last of the equations in Eq. (4.5) says that the greater its mass, the more a body "resists" being accelerated. When you hold a piece of fruit in your hand at the supermarket and move it slightly up and down to estimate its heft, you're applying a force and seeing how much the fruit accelerates up and down in response. If a force causes a large acceleration, the fruit has a small mass; if the same force causes only a small acceleration, the fruit has a large mass. In the same way, if you hit a table-tennis ball and then a basketball with the same force, the basketball has much smaller acceleration because it has much greater mass.

The SI unit of mass is the **kilogram.** We mentioned in Section 1.3 that the kilogram is officially defined to be the mass of a cylinder of platinum–iridium alloy kept in a vault near Paris. We can use this standard kilogram, along with Eq. (4.5), to define the **newton:**

One newton is the amount of net force that gives an acceleration of 1 meter per second squared to a body with a mass of 1 kilogram.

This definition allows us to calibrate the spring balances and other instruments used to measure forces. Because of the way we have defined the newton, it is related to the units of mass, length, and time. For Eq. (4.5) to be dimensionally consistent, it must be true that

$$1 \text{ newton} = (1 \text{ kilogram})(1 \text{ meter per second squared})$$

or

$$1 \text{ N} = 1 \text{ kg} \cdot \text{m/s}^2$$

We will use this relationship many times in the next few chapters, so keep it in mind.

We can also use Eq. (4.5) to compare a mass with the standard mass and thus to *measure* masses. Suppose we apply a constant net force $\Sigma\vec{F}$ to a body having a known mass m_1 and we find an acceleration of magnitude a_1 (Fig. 4.16a). We then apply the same force to another body having an unknown mass m_2, and we find an acceleration of magnitude a_2 (Fig. 4.16b). Then, according to Eq. (4.5),

$$m_1 a_1 = m_2 a_2$$
$$\frac{m_2}{m_1} = \frac{a_1}{a_2} \quad \text{(same net force)} \tag{4.6}$$

For the same net force, the ratio of the masses of two bodies is the inverse of the ratio of their accelerations. In principle we could use Eq. (4.6) to measure an unknown mass m_2, but it is usually easier to determine mass indirectly by measuring the body's *weight.* We'll return to this point in Section 4.4.

When two bodies with masses m_1 and m_2 are fastened together, we find that the mass of the composite body is always $m_1 + m_2$ (Fig. 4.16c). This additive property of mass may seem obvious, but it has to be verified experimentally. Ultimately, the mass of a body is related to the number of protons, electrons, and neutrons it contains. This wouldn't be a good way to *define* mass because there is no practical way to count these particles. But the concept of mass is the most fundamental way to characterize the quantity of matter in a body.

4.16 For a given net force $\sum\vec{F}$ acting on a body, the acceleration is inversely proportional to the mass of the body. Masses add like ordinary scalars.

(a) A known force $\sum\vec{F}$ causes an object with mass m_1 to have an acceleration $\vec{a}_1$.

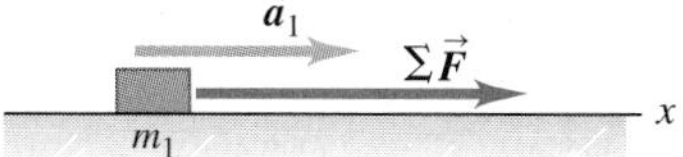

(b) Applying the same force $\sum\vec{F}$ to a second object and noting the acceleration allow us to measure the mass.

(c) When the two objects are fastened together, the same method shows that their composite mass is the sum of their individual masses.

Stating Newton's Second Law

We've been careful to state that the *net* force on a body is what causes that body to accelerate. Experiment shows that if a combination of forces $\vec{F}_1, \vec{F}_2, \vec{F}_3$, and so on is applied to a body, the body will have the same acceleration (magnitude and direction) as when only a single force is applied, if that single force is equal to the vector sum $\vec{F}_1 + \vec{F}_2 + \vec{F}_3 + \cdots$. In other words, the principle of superposition of forces (see Fig. 4.4) also holds true when the net force is not zero and the body is accelerating.

Equation (4.5) relates the magnitude of the net force on a body to the magnitude of the acceleration that it produces. We have also seen that the direction of the net force is the same as the direction of the acceleration, whether the body's path is straight or curved. Newton wrapped up all these relationships and experimental results in a single concise statement that we now call *Newton's second law of motion:*

Newton's second law of motion: If a net external force acts on a body, the body accelerates. The direction of acceleration is the same as the direction of the net force. The mass of the body times the acceleration of the body equals the net force vector.

In symbols,

$$\sum\vec{F} = m\vec{a} \quad \text{(Newton's second law of motion)} \tag{4.7}$$

An alternative statement is that the acceleration of a body is in the same direction as the net force acting on the body, and is equal to the net force divided by the body's mass:

$$\vec{a} = \frac{\sum\vec{F}}{m}$$

Newton's second law is a fundamental law of nature, the basic relationship between force and motion. Most of the remainder of this chapter and all of the next are devoted to learning how to apply this principle in various situations.

Equation (4.7) has many practical applications (Fig. 4.17). You've actually been using it all your life to measure your body's acceleration. In your inner ear, microscopic hair cells sense the magnitude and direction of the force that they must exert to cause small membranes to accelerate along with the rest of your body. By Newton's second law, the acceleration of the membranes—and hence

4.17 The design of high-performance motorcycles depends fundamentally on Newton's second law. To maximize the forward acceleration, the designer makes the motorcycle as light as possible (that is, minimizes the mass) and uses the most powerful engine possible (thus maximizing the forward force).

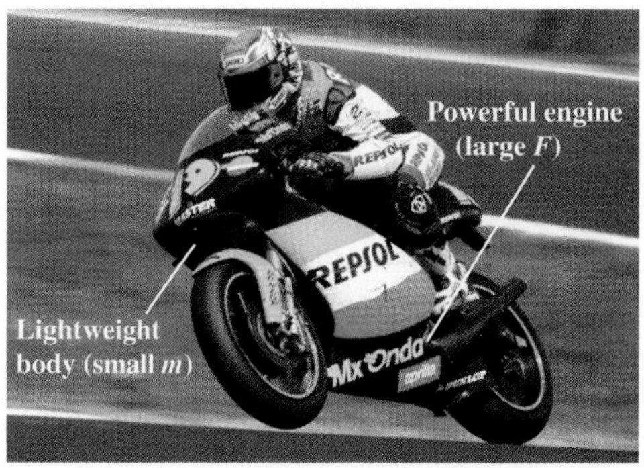

that of your body as a whole—is proportional to this force and has the same direction. In this way, you can sense the magnitude and direction of your acceleration even with your eyes closed!

ActivPhysics ONLINE
2.1.3 Tension Change
2.1.4 Sliding on an Incline

Using Newton's Second Law

There are at least four aspects of Newton's second law that deserve special attention. First, Eq. (4.7) is a *vector* equation. Usually we will use it in component form, with a separate equation for each component of force and the corresponding acceleration:

$$\sum F_x = ma_x \qquad \sum F_y = ma_y \qquad \sum F_z = ma_z \qquad \text{(Newton's second law of motion)} \qquad (4.8)$$

This set of component equations is equivalent to the single vector equation (4.7). Each component of the net force equals the mass times the corresponding component of acceleration.

Second, the statement of Newton's second law refers to *external* forces. By this we mean forces exerted on the body by other bodies in its environment. It's impossible for a body to affect its own motion by exerting a force on itself; if it were possible, you could lift yourself to the ceiling by pulling up on your belt! That's why only external forces are included in the sum $\sum\vec{F}$ in Eqs. (4.7) and (4.8).

Third, Eqs. (4.7) and (4.8) are valid only when the mass m is *constant.* It's easy to think of systems whose masses change, such as a leaking tank truck, a rocket ship, or a moving railroad car being loaded with coal. But such systems are better handled by using the concept of momentum; we'll get to that in Chapter 8.

Finally, Newton's second law is valid only in inertial frames of reference, just like the first law. Thus it is not valid in the reference frame of any of the accelerating vehicles in Fig. 4.11; relative to any of these frames, the passenger accelerates even though the net force on the passenger is zero. We will usually assume that the earth is an adequate approximation to an inertial frame, although because of its rotation and orbital motion it is not precisely inertial.

CAUTION **$m\vec{a}$ is not a force** You must keep in mind that even though the vector $m\vec{a}$ is equal to the vector sum $\sum\vec{F}$ of all the forces acting on the body, the vector $m\vec{a}$ is *not* a force. Acceleration is a *result* of a nonzero net force; it is not a force itself. It's "common sense" to think that there is a "force of acceleration" that pushes you back into your seat when your car accelerates forward from rest. But *there is no such force;* instead, your inertia causes you to tend to stay at rest relative to the earth, and the car accelerates around you (see Fig. 4.11a). The "common sense" confusion arises from trying to apply Newton's second law where it isn't valid, in the noninertial reference frame of an accelerating car. We will always examine motion relative to *inertial* frames of reference only.

In learning how to use Newton's second law, we will begin in this chapter with examples of straight-line motion. Then in Chapter 5 we will consider more general cases and develop more detailed problem-solving strategies.

Example 4.4 Determining acceleration from force

A worker applies a constant horizontal force with magnitude 20 N to a box with mass 40 kg resting on a level floor with negligible friction. What is the acceleration of the box?

SOLUTION

IDENTIFY: This problem involves force and acceleration. Whenever you encounter a problem of this kind, you should approach it using Newton's second law.

SET UP: In *any* problem involving forces, the first steps are to choose a coordinate system and then identify all of the forces acting on the body in question.

It's usually convenient to take one axis either along or opposite the direction of the body's acceleration, which in this case is horizontal. Hence we take the $+x$-axis to be in the direction of the applied horizontal force (that is, the direction in which the box accelerates) and the $+y$-axis to be upward (Fig. 4.18). In most

4.18 Our sketch for this problem. The tiles under the box are freshly waxed, so we assume that friction is negligible.

The box has no vertical acceleration, so the vertical components of the net force sum to zero. Nevertheless, for completeness, we show the vertical forces acting on the box.

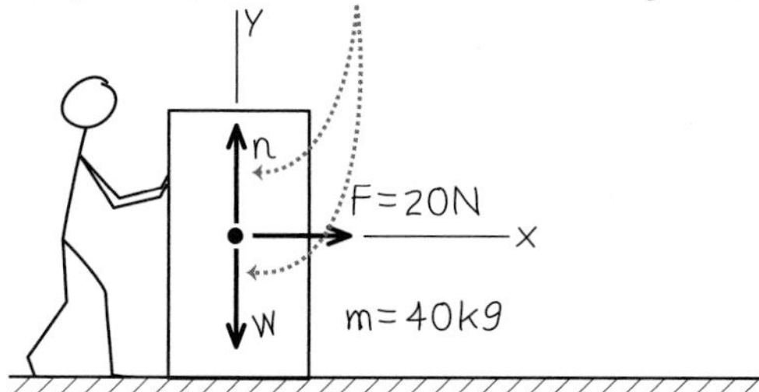

force problems that you'll encounter (including this one), the force vectors all lie in a plane, so the z-axis isn't used.

The forces acting on the box are (i) the horizontal force $\vec{F}$ exerted by the worker, of magnitude 20 N; (ii) the weight $\vec{w}$ of the box—that is, the downward gravitational force exerted by the earth; and (iii) the upward supporting force $\vec{n}$ exerted by the floor. As in Section 4.2, we call $\vec{n}$ a *normal* force because it is normal (perpendicular) to the surface of contact. (We use an italic letter n to avoid confusion with the abbreviation N for newton.) We are told that friction is negligible, so no friction force is present.

Since the box doesn't move vertically at all, the y-acceleration is zero: $a_y = 0$. Our target variable is the x-component of acceleration, a_x. We'll find it using Newton's second law in component form as given by Eq. (4.8).

EXECUTE: From Fig. 4.18, only the 20-N force has a nonzero x-component. Hence the first relation in Eqs. (4.8) tells us that

$$\sum F_x = F = 20\text{ N} = ma_x$$

Hence the x-component of acceleration is

$$a_x = \frac{\sum F_x}{m} = \frac{20\text{ N}}{40\text{ kg}} = \frac{20\text{ kg}\cdot\text{m/s}^2}{40\text{ kg}} = 0.50\text{ m/s}^2$$

EVALUATE: The acceleration is in the $+x$-direction, the same direction as the net force. The net force is constant, so the acceleration is also constant. If we are given the initial position and velocity of the box, we can find the position and velocity at any later time from the equations of motion with constant acceleration we derived in Chapter 2.

Notice that to determine a_x, we didn't have to use the y-component of Newton's second law from Eq. (4.8), $\sum F_y = ma_y$. By using this equation, can you show that the magnitude n of the normal force in this situation is equal to the weight of the box?

Example 4.5 Determining force from acceleration

A waitress shoves a ketchup bottle with mass 0.45 kg to the right along a smooth, level lunch counter. The bottle leaves her hand moving at 2.8 m/s, then slows down as it slides because of the constant horizontal friction force exerted on it by the counter top. It slides a distance of 1.0 m before coming to rest. What are the magnitude and direction of the friction force acting on the bottle?

SOLUTION

IDENTIFY: Like Example 4.4, this problem involves forces and acceleration (the slowing of the ketchup bottle), so we'll use Newton's second law to solve it.

SET UP: As in Example 4.4, we first choose a coordinate system and then identify the forces acting on the body (in this case, the ketchup bottle). As Fig. 4.19 shows, we choose the $+x$-axis to be in the direction that the bottle slides, and we take the origin to be where the bottle leaves the waitress's hand moving at 2.8 m/s. Figure 4.19 also shows the forces acting on the bottle. The friction force $\vec{f}$ acts to slow the bottle down, so its direction must be opposite the direction of velocity (see Fig. 4.13c).

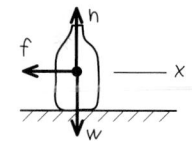

Our target variable is the magnitude f of the friction force. We'll find it using the x-component of Newton's second law from Eq. (4.8). To do so, we'll first need to know the x-component of the bottle's acceleration, a_x. We aren't told the value of a_x in the problem, but we are told that the friction force is constant. Hence the acceleration is constant as well, and we can calculate a_x by using one of the constant-acceleration formulas from Section 2.4. Since we know the bottle's initial x-coordinate and x-velocity ($x_0 = 0$, $v_{0x} = 2.8$ m/s) as well as its final x-coordinate and x-velocity ($x = 1.0$ m, $v_x = 0$), the easiest equation to use to determine a_x is Eq. (2.13), $v_x^2 = v_{0x}^2 + 2a_x(x - x_0)$.

4.19 Our sketch for this problem.

We draw one diagram for the bottle's motion and one showing the forces on the bottle.

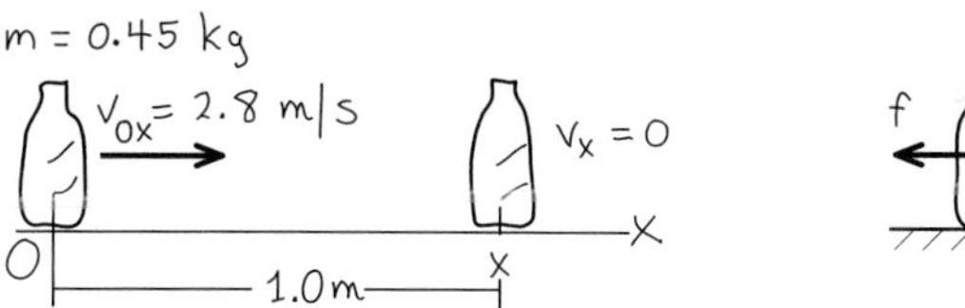

EXECUTE: From Eq. (2.13),

$$v_x^2 = v_{0x}^2 + 2a_x(x - x_0)$$

$$a_x = \frac{v_x^2 - v_{0x}^2}{2(x - x_0)} = \frac{(0\text{ m/s})^2 - (2.8\text{ m/s})^2}{2(1.0\text{ m} - 0\text{ m})} = -3.9\text{ m/s}^2$$

The negative sign means that the acceleration is toward the *left;* the velocity is in the opposite direction to acceleration, as it must be, since the bottle is slowing down. The net force in the x-direction is the x-component $-f$ of the friction force, so

$$\sum F_x = -f = ma_x = (0.45\text{ kg})(-3.9\text{ m/s}^2)$$
$$= -1.8\text{ kg}\cdot\text{m/s}^2 = -1.8\text{ N}$$

Continued

Again the negative sign shows that the force on the bottle is directed toward the left. The magnitude of the friction force is $f = 1.8$ N. Remember that magnitudes are *always* positive!

EVALUATE: We chose the $+x$-axis to be in the direction of the bottle's motion, so that a_x was negative. As a check on the result, try repeating the calculation with the $+x$-axis directed *opposite* to the motion (to the left in Fig. 4.19) so that a_x is positive. In this case you should find that ΣF_x is equal to $+f$ (because the friction force is now in the $+x$-direction), which in turn is equal to $+1.8$ N. Your answers for the *magnitudes* of forces (which are always positive numbers) should never depend on your choice of coordinate axes!

4.20 Despite its name, the English unit of mass has nothing to do with the type of slug shown here. A common garden slug has a mass of about 15 grams, or about 10^{-3} slug.

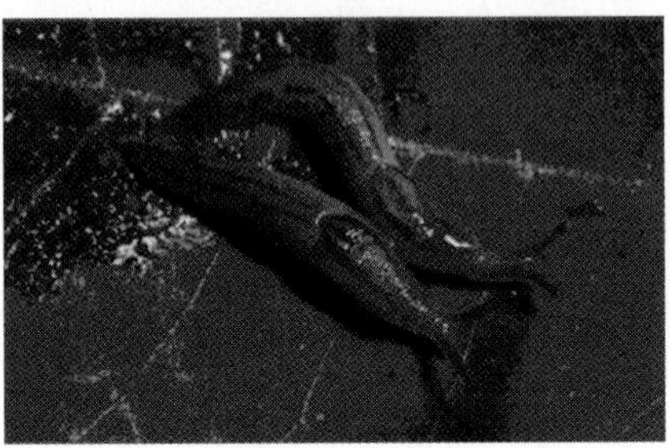

Some Notes on Units

A few words about units are in order. In the cgs metric system (not used in this book), the unit of mass is the gram, equal to 10^{-3} kg, and the unit of distance is the centimeter, equal to 10^{-2} m. The cgs unit of force is called the *dyne:*

$$1 \text{ dyne} = 1 \text{ g} \cdot \text{cm/s}^2 = 10^{-5} \text{ N}$$

In the British system, the unit of force is the *pound* (or pound-force) and the unit of mass is the *slug* (Fig. 4.20). The unit of acceleration is 1 foot per second squared, so

$$1 \text{ pound} = 1 \text{ slug} \cdot \text{ft/s}^2$$

The official definition of the pound is

$$1 \text{ pound} = 4.448221615260 \text{ newtons}$$

It is handy to remember that a pound is about 4.4 N and a newton is about 0.22 pound. Next time you want to order a "quarter-pounder," try asking for a "one-newtoner" and see what happens. Another useful fact: A body with a mass of 1 kg has a weight of about 2.2 lb at the earth's surface.

Table 4.2 summarizes the units of force, mass, and acceleration in the three systems.

Table 4.2 Units of Force, Mass, and Acceleration

System of Units	Force	Mass	Acceleration
SI	newton (N)	kilogram (kg)	m/s^2
cgs	dyne (dyn)	gram (g)	cm/s^2
British	pound (lb)	slug	ft/s^2

Test Your Understanding of Section 4.3 Rank the following situations in order of the magnitude of the object's acceleration, from lowest to highest. Are there any cases that have the same magnitude of acceleration? (i) a 2.0-kg object acted on by a 2.0-N net force; (ii) a 2.0-kg object acted on by an 8.0-N net force; (iii) an 8.0-kg object acted on by a 2.0-N net force; (iv) an 8.0-kg object acted on by a 8.0-N net force.

4.4 Mass and Weight

One of the most familiar forces is the *weight* of a body, which is the gravitational force that the earth exerts on the body. (If you are on another planet, your weight is the gravitational force that planet exerts on you.) Unfortunately, the terms *mass* and *weight* are often misused and interchanged in everyday conversation. It is absolutely essential for you to understand clearly the distinctions between these two physical quantities.

Mass characterizes the *inertial* properties of a body. Mass is what keeps the china on the table when you yank the tablecloth out from under it. The greater the mass, the greater the force needed to cause a given acceleration; this is reflected in Newton's second law, $\Sigma\vec{F} = m\vec{a}$.

Weight, on the other hand, is a *force* exerted on a body by the pull of the earth. Mass and weight are related: Bodies having large mass also have large weight. A large stone is hard to throw because of its large *mass,* and hard to lift off the ground because of its large *weight.*

To understand the relationship between mass and weight, note that a freely falling body has an acceleration of magnitude g. Newton's second law tells us that a force must act to produce this acceleration. If a 1-kg body falls with an acceleration of 9.8 m/s^2, the required force has magnitude

$$F = ma = (1 \text{ kg})(9.8 \text{ m/s}^2) = 9.8 \text{ kg} \cdot \text{m/s}^2 = 9.8 \text{ N}$$

ActivPhysics Online

2.9 Pole-Vaulter Vaults

The force that makes the body accelerate downward is its weight. Any body near the surface of the earth that has a mass of 1 kg *must* have a weight of 9.8 N to give it the acceleration we observe when it is in free fall. More generally, a body with mass m must have weight with magnitude w given by

$$w = mg \qquad \text{(magnitude of the weight of a body of mass } m\text{)} \qquad (4.9)$$

Hence the magnitude w of a body's weight is directly proportional to its mass m. The weight of a body is a force, a vector quantity, and we can write Eq. (4.9) as a vector equation (Fig. 4.21):

$$\vec{w} = m\vec{g} \qquad (4.10)$$

Remember that g is the *magnitude* of $\vec{g}$, the acceleration due to gravity, so g is always a positive number, by definition. Thus w, given by Eq. (4.9), is the *magnitude* of the weight and is also always positive.

CAUTION **A body's weight acts at all times** It is important to understand that the weight of a body acts on the body *all the time,* whether it is in free fall or not. If we suspend an object from a chain, it is in equilibrium, and its acceleration is zero. But its weight, given by Eq. (4.10), is still pulling down on it (Fig. 4.21). In this case the chain pulls up on the object, applying an upward force. The *vector sum* of the forces is zero, but the weight still acts.

4.21 The relationship of mass and weight.

Falling body, mass m — $\vec{a} = \vec{g}$ — Weight $\vec{w} = m\vec{g}$ — $\Sigma\vec{F} = \vec{w}$

Hanging body, mass m — $\vec{T}$ — $\vec{a} = 0$ — Weight $\vec{w} = m\vec{g}$ — $\Sigma\vec{F} = 0$

- The relationship of mass to weight: $\vec{w} = m\vec{g}$.
- This relationship is the same whether a body is falling or stationary.

Conceptual Example 4.6 Net force and acceleration in free fall

In Example 2.6 (Section 2.5) a one-euro coin was dropped from rest from the Leaning Tower of Pisa. If the coin falls freely, so that the effects of the air are negligible, how does the net force on the coin vary as it falls?

SOLUTION

In free fall, the acceleration $\vec{a}$ of the coin is constant and equal to $\vec{g}$. Hence by Newton's second law the net force $\Sigma\vec{F} = m\vec{a}$ is also constant and equal to $m\vec{g}$, which is the coin's weight $\vec{w}$ (Fig. 4.22). The coin's velocity changes as it falls, but the net force acting on it remains constant. If this surprises you, perhaps you still believe in the erroneous "common sense" idea that greater speed implies greater force. If so, you should reread Conceptual Example 4.3.

The net force on a freely falling coin is constant even if you initially toss it upward. The force that your hand exerts on the coin to toss it is a contact force, and it disappears the instant that the coin loses contact with your hand. From then on, the only force acting on the coin is its weight $\vec{w}$.

4.22 The acceleration of a freely falling object is constant, and so is the net force acting on the object.

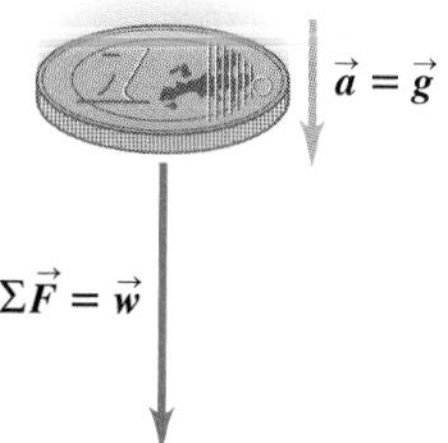

Variation of g with Location

We will use $g = 9.80\ \text{m/s}^2$ for problems on the earth (or, if the other data in the problem are given to only two significant figures, $g = 9.8\ \text{m/s}^2$). In fact, the value of g varies somewhat from point to point on the earth's surface, from about 9.78 to 9.82 m/s^2, because the earth is not perfectly spherical and because of effects due to its rotation and orbital motion. At a point where $g = 9.80\ \text{m/s}^2$, the weight of a standard kilogram is $w = 9.80$ N. At a different point, where $g = 9.78\ \text{m/s}^2$, the weight is $w = 9.78$ N but the mass is still 1 kg. The weight of a body varies from one location to another; the mass does not.

If we take a standard kilogram to the surface of the moon, where the acceleration of free fall (equal to the value of g at the moon's surface) is 1.62 m/s^2, its

4.23 The weight of a 1-kilogram mass (a) on earth and (b) on the moon.

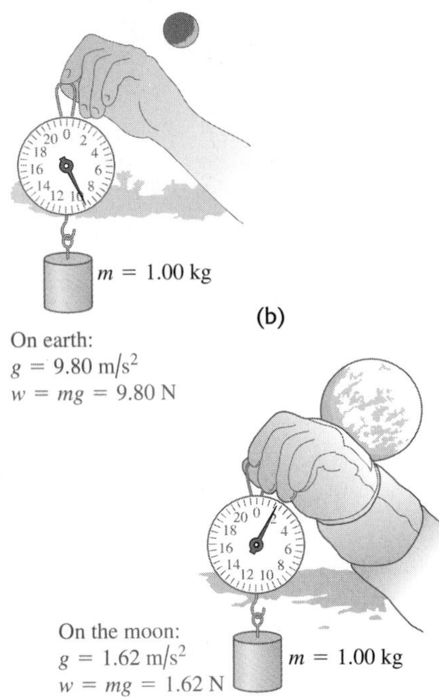

weight is 1.62 N, but its mass is still 1 kg (Fig. 4.23). An 80.0-kg astronaut has a weight on earth of $(80.0\ \text{kg})(9.80\ \text{m/s}^2) = 784\ \text{N}$, but on the moon the astronaut's weight would be only $(80.0\ \text{kg})(1.62\ \text{m/s}^2) = 130\ \text{N}$. In Chapter 12 we'll see how to calculate the value of g at the surface of the moon or on other worlds.

Measuring Mass and Weight

In Section 4.3 we described a way to compare masses by comparing their accelerations when subjected to the same net force. Usually, however, the easiest way to measure the mass of a body is to measure its weight, often by comparing with a standard. Equation (4.9) says that two bodies that have the same weight at a particular location also have the same mass. We can compare weights very precisely; the familiar equal-arm balance (Fig. 4.24) can determine with great precision (up to 1 part in 10^6) when the weights of two bodies are equal and hence when their masses are equal. (This method doesn't work in the apparent "zero-gravity" environment of outer space. Instead, we apply a known force to the body, measure its acceleration, and compute the mass as the ratio of force to acceleration. This method, or a variation of it, is used to measure the masses of astronauts in orbiting space stations as well as the masses of atomic and subatomic particles.)

The concept of mass plays two rather different roles in mechanics. The weight of a body (the gravitational force acting on it) is proportional to its mass; we call the property related to gravitational interactions *gravitational mass.* On the other hand, we call the inertial property that appears in Newton's second law the *inertial mass.* If these two quantities were different, the acceleration due to gravity might well be different for different bodies. However, extraordinarily precise experiments have established that in fact the two *are* the same to a precision of better than one part in 10^{12}.

CAUTION **Don't confuse mass and weight** The SI units for mass and weight are often misused in everyday life. Incorrect expressions such as "This box weighs 6 kg" are nearly universal. What is meant is that the *mass* of the box, probably determined indirectly by *weighing,* is 6 kg. Be careful to avoid this sloppy usage in your own work! In SI units, weight (a force) is measured in newtons, while mass is measured in kilograms.

Example 4.7 Mass and weight

A 2.49×10^4 N Rolls-Royce Phantom traveling in the $+x$-direction makes a fast stop; the x-component of the net force acting on it is -1.83×10^4 N. What is its acceleration?

SOLUTION

IDENTIFY: Again we will use Newton's second law to relate force and acceleration. To use this relationship, we need to know the car's mass. However, because the newton is a unit for force, we know that 2.49×10^4 N is the car's weight, not its mass. So we'll also have to use the relationship between a body's mass and its weight.

SET UP: Our target variable is the x-component of acceleration of the car, a_x. (The motion is purely in the x-direction.) We use Eq. (4.9) to determine the car's mass from its weight and then use the x-component of Newton's second law from Eq. (4.8) to determine a_x.

EXECUTE: The mass m of the car is

$$m = \frac{w}{g} = \frac{2.49 \times 10^4\ \text{N}}{9.80\ \text{m/s}^2} = \frac{2.49 \times 10^4\ \text{kg} \cdot \text{m/s}^2}{9.80\ \text{m/s}^2} = 2540\ \text{kg}$$

Then $\sum F_x = ma_x$ gives

$$a_x = \frac{\sum F_x}{m} = \frac{-1.83 \times 10^4\ \text{N}}{2540\ \text{kg}} = \frac{-1.83 \times 10^4\ \text{kg} \cdot \text{m/s}^2}{2540\ \text{kg}} = -7.20\ \text{m/s}^2$$

EVALUATE: The negative sign means that the acceleration vector points in the negative x-direction. This makes sense: The car is moving in the positive x-direction and is slowing down.

Note that the acceleration can alternatively be written as $-0.735g$. It's of interest that -0.735 is also the ratio of -1.83×10^4 N (the x-component of the net force) to 2.49×10^4 N (the weight). Indeed, the acceleration of a body expressed as a multiple of g is always equal to the ratio of the net force on the body to its weight. Can you see why?

Test Your Understanding of Section 4.4 Suppose an astronaut landed on a planet where $g = 19.6\ \text{m/s}^2$. Compared to earth, would it be easier, harder, or just as easy for her to walk around? Would it be easier, harder, or just as easy for her to catch a ball that is moving horizontally at 12 m/s? (Assume that the astronaut's spacesuit is a lightweight model that doesn't impede her movements in any way.)

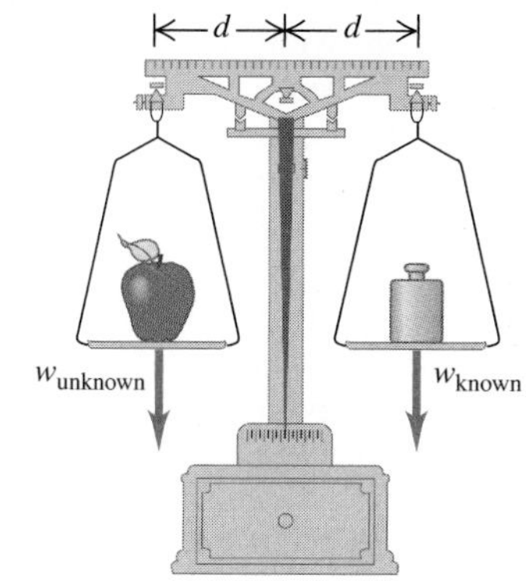

4.24 An equal-arm balance determines the mass of a body (such as an apple) by comparing its weight to a known weight.

4.5 Newton's Third Law

A force acting on a body is always the result of its interaction with another body, so forces always come in pairs. You can't pull on a doorknob without the doorknob pulling back on you. When you kick a football, the forward force that your foot exerts on the ball launches it into its trajectory, but you also feel the force the ball exerts back on your foot. If you kick a boulder, the pain you feel is due to the force that the boulder exerts on your foot.

In each of these cases, the force that you exert on the other body is in the opposite direction to the force that body exerts on you. Experiments show that whenever two bodies interact, the two forces that they exert on each other are always *equal in magnitude* and *opposite in direction*. This fact is called *Newton's third law of motion:*

Newton's third law of motion: If body A exerts a force on body B (an "action"), then body B exerts a force on body A (a "reaction"). These two forces have the same magnitude but are opposite in direction. These two forces act on *different* bodies.

For example, in Fig. 4.25 $\vec{F}_{A \text{ on } B}$ is the force applied *by* body A (first subscript) *on* body B (second subscript), and $\vec{F}_{B \text{ on } A}$ is the force applied *by* body B (first subscript) *on* body A (second subscript). The mathematical statement of Newton's third law is

$$\vec{F}_{A \text{ on } B} = -\vec{F}_{B \text{ on } A} \quad \text{(Newton's third law of motion)} \tag{4.11}$$

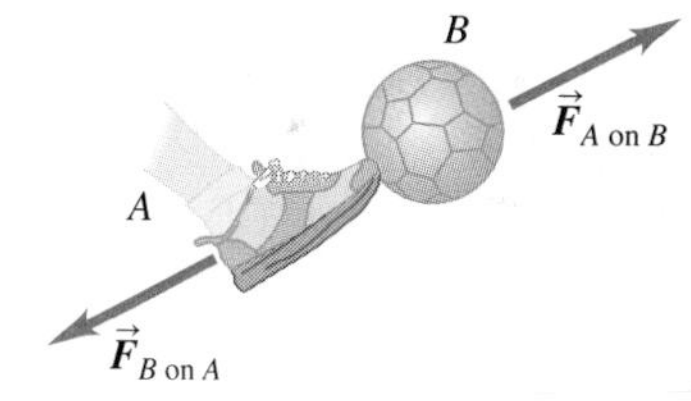

4.25 If body A exerts a force $\vec{F}_{A \text{ on } B}$ on body B, then body B exerts a force $\vec{F}_{B \text{ on } A}$ on body A that is equal in magnitude and opposite in direction: $\vec{F}_{A \text{ on } B} = -\vec{F}_{B \text{ on } A}$.

It doesn't matter whether one body is inanimate (like the soccer ball in Fig. 4.25) and the other is not (like the kicker): They necessarily exert forces on each other that obey Eq. (4.11). ?

In the statement of Newton's third law, "action" and "reaction" are the two opposite forces (in Fig. 4.25, $\vec{F}_{A \text{ on } B}$ and $\vec{F}_{B \text{ on } A}$); we sometimes refer to them as an **action–reaction pair.** This is *not* meant to imply any cause-and-effect relationship; we can consider either force as the "action" and the other as the "reaction." We often say simply that the forces are "equal and opposite," meaning that they have equal magnitudes and opposite directions.

CAUTION **The two forces in an action–reaction pair act on different bodies** We stress that the two forces described in Newton's third law act on *different* bodies. This is important in problems involving Newton's first or second law, which involve the forces that act on a body. For instance, the net force acting on the soccer ball in Fig. 4.25 is the vector sum of the weight of the ball and the force $\vec{F}_{A \text{ on } B}$ exerted by the kicker. You would not include the force $\vec{F}_{B \text{ on } A}$ because this force acts on the kicker, not on the ball.

In Fig. 4.25 the action and reaction forces are *contact* forces that are present only when the two bodies are touching. But Newton's third law also applies to *long-range* forces that do not require physical contact, such as the force of gravitational attraction. A table-tennis ball exerts an upward gravitational force on the earth that's equal in magnitude to the downward gravitational force the earth exerts on the ball. When you drop the ball, both the ball and the earth accelerate toward each other. The net force on each body has the same magnitude, but the earth's acceleration is microscopically small because its mass is so great. Nevertheless, it does move!

Conceptual Example 4.8 Which force is greater?

After your sports car breaks down, you start to push it to the nearest repair shop. While the car is starting to move, how does the force you exert on the car compare to the force the car exerts on you? How do these forces compare when you are pushing the car along at a constant speed?

SOLUTION

In *both* cases, the force you exert on the car is equal in magnitude and opposite in direction to the force the car exerts on you. It's true that you have to push harder to get the car going than to keep it going. But no matter how hard you push on the car, the car pushes just as hard back on you. Newton's third law gives the same result whether the two bodies are at rest, moving with constant velocity, or accelerating.

You may wonder how the car "knows" to push back on you with the same magnitude of force that you exert on it. It may help to remember that the forces you and the car exert on each other are really interactions between the atoms at the surface of your hand and the atoms at the surface of the car. These interactions are analogous to miniature springs between adjacent atoms, and a compressed spring exerts equally strong forces on both of its ends.

Fundamentally, though, the reason we know that objects of different masses exert equally strong forces on each other is that *experiment tells us so.* Never forget that physics isn't merely a collection of rules and equations; rather, it's a systematic description of the natural world based on experiment and observation.

Conceptual Example 4.9 Applying Newton's third law: Objects at rest

An apple sits on a table in equilibrium. What forces act on it? What is the reaction force to each of the forces acting on the apple? What are the action–reaction pairs?

SOLUTION

Figure 4.26a shows the forces acting on the apple. In the diagram, $\vec{F}_{\text{earth on apple}}$ is the weight of the apple—that is, the downward gravitational force exerted *by* the earth (first subscript) *on* the apple (second subscript). Similarly, $\vec{F}_{\text{table on apple}}$ is the upward force exerted *by* the table (first subscript) *on* the apple (second subscript).

As the earth pulls down on the apple, the apple exerts an equally strong upward pull $\vec{F}_{\text{apple on earth}}$ on the earth, as shown in Fig. 4.26b. $\vec{F}_{\text{apple on earth}}$ and $\vec{F}_{\text{earth on apple}}$ are an action–reaction pair, representing the mutual interaction of the apple and the earth, so

$$\vec{F}_{\text{apple on earth}} = -\vec{F}_{\text{earth on apple}}$$

Also, as the table pushes up on the apple with force $\vec{F}_{\text{table on apple}}$, the corresponding reaction is the downward force $\vec{F}_{\text{apple on table}}$ exerted by the apple on the table (Fig. 4.26c). So we have

$$\vec{F}_{\text{apple on table}} = -\vec{F}_{\text{table on apple}}$$

The two forces acting on the apple are $\vec{F}_{\text{table on apple}}$ and $\vec{F}_{\text{earth on apple}}$. Are they an action–reaction pair? No, they aren't, despite being equal and opposite. They do not represent the mutual interaction of two bodies; they are two different forces acting on the *same* body. *The two forces in an action–reaction pair* ***never*** *act on the same body.* Here's another way to look at it. Suppose we suddenly yank the table out from under the apple (Fig. 4.26d). The two forces $\vec{F}_{\text{apple on table}}$ and $\vec{F}_{\text{table on apple}}$ then become zero, but $\vec{F}_{\text{apple on earth}}$ and $\vec{F}_{\text{earth on apple}}$ are still there (the gravitational interaction is still present). Since $\vec{F}_{\text{table on apple}}$ is now zero, it can't be the negative of $\vec{F}_{\text{earth on apple}}$, and these two forces can't be an action–reaction pair.

4.26 The two forces in an action–reaction pair always act on different bodies.

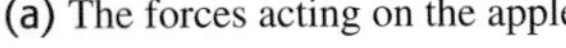
(a) The forces acting on the apple

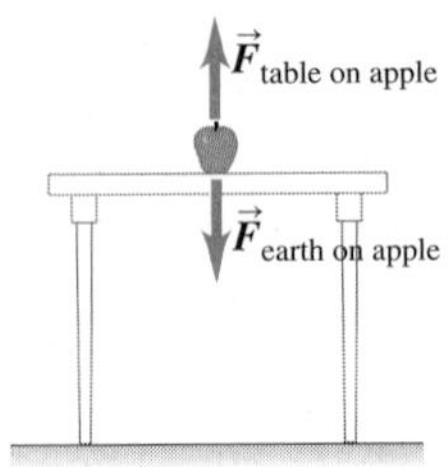

(b) The action–reaction pair for the interaction between the apple and the earth

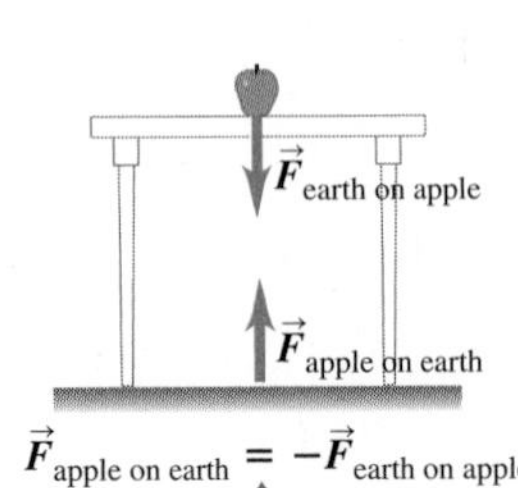

(c) The action–reaction pair for the interaction between the apple and the table

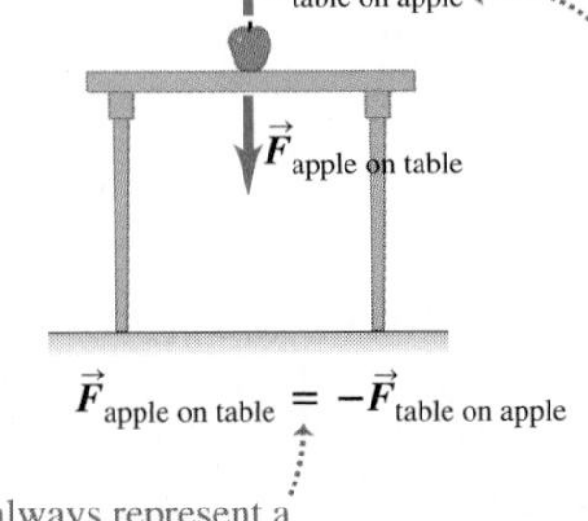

Action–reaction pairs always represent a mutual interaction of two different objects.

(d) We eliminate one of the forces acting on the apple

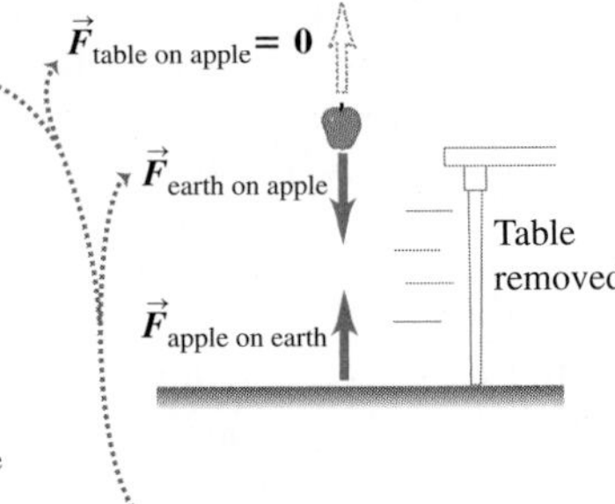

The two forces on the apple CANNOT be an action–reaction pair because they act on the same object. We see that if we eliminate one, the other remains.

Conceptual Example 4.10 Applying Newton's third law: Objects in motion

A stonemason drags a marble block across a floor by pulling on a rope attached to the block (Fig. 4.27a). The block may or may not be in equilibrium. How are the various forces related? What are the action–reaction pairs?

SOLUTION

We'll use subscripts on all the forces to help explain things: B for the block, R for the rope, and M for the mason. Vector $\vec{F}_{\text{M on R}}$ represents the force exerted by the *mason* on the *rope*. Its reaction is the equal and opposite force $\vec{F}_{\text{R on M}}$ exerted by the *rope* on the *mason*. Vector $\vec{F}_{\text{R on B}}$ represents the force exerted by the *rope* on the *block*. The reaction to it is the equal and opposite force $\vec{F}_{\text{B on R}}$ exerted by the *block* on the *rope*. For these two action-reaction pairs (Fig. 4.27b), we have

$$\vec{F}_{\text{R on M}} = -\vec{F}_{\text{M on R}} \quad \text{and} \quad \vec{F}_{\text{B on R}} = -\vec{F}_{\text{R on B}}$$

Be sure you understand that the forces $\vec{F}_{\text{M on R}}$ and $\vec{F}_{\text{B on R}}$ are *not* an action–reaction pair (Fig. 4.27c) because both of these forces act on the *same* body (the rope); an action and its reaction *must* always act on *different* bodies. Furthermore, the forces $\vec{F}_{\text{M on R}}$ and $\vec{F}_{\text{B on R}}$ are not necessarily equal in magnitude. Applying Newton's second law to the rope, we get

$$\sum \vec{F} = \vec{F}_{\text{M on R}} + \vec{F}_{\text{B on R}} = m_{\text{rope}}\vec{a}_{\text{rope}}$$

If the block and rope are accelerating (that is, speeding up or slowing down), the rope is not in equilibrium, and $\vec{F}_{\text{M on R}}$ must have a different magnitude than $\vec{F}_{\text{B on R}}$. By contrast, the action–reaction forces $\vec{F}_{\text{M on R}}$ and $\vec{F}_{\text{R on M}}$ are always equal in magnitude, as are $\vec{F}_{\text{R on B}}$ and $\vec{F}_{\text{B on R}}$. Newton's third law holds whether or not the bodies are accelerating.

In the special case in which the rope is in equilibrium, the forces $\vec{F}_{\text{M on R}}$ and $\vec{F}_{\text{B on R}}$ are equal in magnitude. But this is an example of Newton's *first* law, not his *third*. Another way to look at this is that in equilibrium, $\vec{a}_{\text{rope}} = \mathbf{0}$ in the preceding equation. Then $\vec{F}_{\text{B on R}} = -\vec{F}_{\text{M on R}}$ because of Newton's first or second law.

This is also true if the rope is accelerating but has negligibly small mass compared to the block or the mason. In this case, $m_{\text{rope}} = 0$ in the above equation, so again $\vec{F}_{\text{B on R}} = -\vec{F}_{\text{M on R}}$. Since $\vec{F}_{\text{B on R}}$ *always* equals $-\vec{F}_{\text{R on B}}$ by Newton's third law (they are an action–reaction pair), in these same special cases, $\vec{F}_{\text{R on B}}$ also equals $\vec{F}_{\text{M on R}}$ (Fig. 4.27d). In other words, in these cases the force of the rope on the block equals the force of the mason on the rope, and we can then think of the rope as "transmitting" to the block, without change, the force the person exerts on the rope. This is a useful point of view, but you have to remember that it is valid *only* when the rope has negligibly small mass or is in equilibrium.

If you feel as though you're drowning in subscripts at this point, take heart. Go over this discussion again, comparing the symbols with the vector diagrams, until you're sure you see what's going on.

4.27 Identifying the forces that act when a mason pulls on a rope attached to a block.

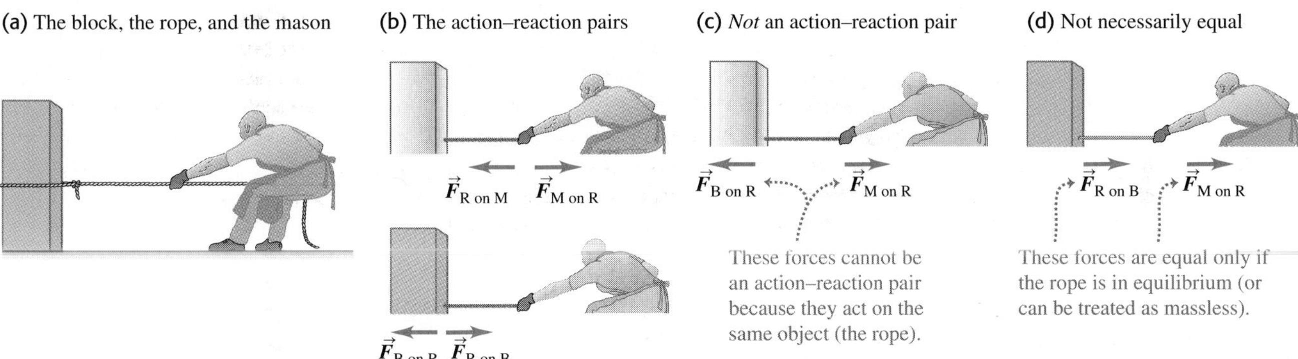
(a) The block, the rope, and the mason
(b) The action–reaction pairs
(c) Not an action–reaction pair
(d) Not necessarily equal
$\vec{F}_{\text{R on M}}$ $\vec{F}_{\text{M on R}}$
$\vec{F}_{\text{B on R}}$ $\vec{F}_{\text{R on B}}$
$\vec{F}_{\text{B on R}}$ $\vec{F}_{\text{M on R}}$
These forces cannot be an action–reaction pair because they act on the same object (the rope).
$\vec{F}_{\text{R on B}}$ $\vec{F}_{\text{M on R}}$
These forces are equal only if the rope is in equilibrium (or can be treated as massless).

Conceptual Example 4.11 A Newton's third law paradox?

We saw in Conceptual Example 4.10 that the stonemason pulls as hard on the rope–block combination as that combination pulls back on him. Why, then, does the block move while the stonemason remains stationary?

SOLUTION

The way out of this seeming conundrum is to keep in mind the difference between Newton's *second* law and his *third* law. The only forces involved in Newton's second law are those that act *on* that body. The vector sum of these forces determines how the body accelerates (and whether it accelerates at all). By contrast, Newton's third law relates the forces that two *different* bodies exert on each other. The third law alone tells you nothing about the motion of either body.

If the rope–block combination is initially at rest, it begins to slide if the stonemason exerts a force $\vec{F}_{\text{M on R}}$ that is *greater* in magnitude than the friction force that the floor exerts on the block (Fig. 4.28). (The marble block has a smooth underside, which helps to minimize friction.) Hence there is a net force on the rope–block combination to the right, and so it accelerates to the right. By contrast, the stonemason *doesn't* move because the net force acting on him is *zero*. His shoes have nonskid soles that don't

Continued

slip on the floor, so the friction force that the floor exerts on him is strong enough to exactly balance the pull of the rope, $\vec{F}_{\text{R on M}}$. (Both the block and the stonemason also experience a downward force of gravity and an upward normal force exerted by the floor. These balance each other and cancel out, so we haven't included them in Fig. 4.28.)

Once the block is moving, the stonemason doesn't need to pull quite so hard; he need exert only enough force to exactly balance the friction force on the block. Then the net force on the moving block is zero, and the block continues to move toward the mason at a constant velocity in accordance with Newton's first law.

We conclude that the block moves while the stonemason doesn't because different amounts of friction act on them. If the floor were freshly waxed, so that there was little friction between the floor and the stonemason's shoes, pulling on the rope would start the block sliding to the right *and* start him sliding to the left.

4.28 The horizontal forces acting on the block–rope combination (left) and the mason (right). (The vertical forces are not shown.)

These forces are an action–reaction pair. They have the same magnitude but act on different objects.
Friction force of floor on block
$\vec{F}_{\text{M on R}}$
$\vec{F}_{\text{R on M}}$
Friction force of floor on mason
Block + rope
Mason
The block begins sliding if $\vec{F}_{\text{M on R}}$ overcomes the friction force on the block.
The mason remains at rest if $\vec{F}_{\text{R on M}}$ is balanced by the friction force on the mason.

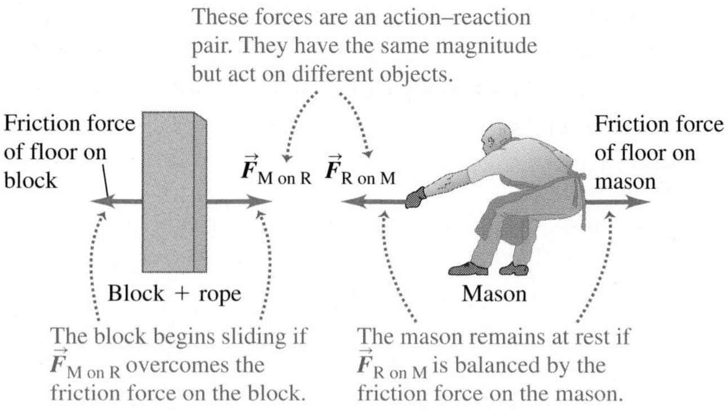

The moral of this example is that when analyzing the motion of a body, remember that only forces acting *on* the body determine its motion. From this perspective, Newton's third law is merely a tool that can help you determine what those forces are.

A body, such as the rope in Fig. 4.27, that has pulling forces applied at its ends is said to be in *tension.* The **tension** at any point is the magnitude of force acting at that point (see Fig. 4.2c). In Fig. 4.27b the tension at the right end of the rope is the magnitude of $\vec{F}_{\text{M on R}}$ (or of $\vec{F}_{\text{R on M}}$), and the tension at the left end equals the magnitude of $\vec{F}_{\text{B on R}}$ (or of $\vec{F}_{\text{R on B}}$). If the rope is in equilibrium and if no forces act except at its ends, the tension is the *same* at both ends and throughout the rope. Thus, if the magnitudes of $\vec{F}_{\text{B on R}}$ and $\vec{F}_{\text{M on R}}$ are 50 N each, the tension in the rope is 50 N (*not* 100 N). The *total* force vector $\vec{F}_{\text{B on R}} + \vec{F}_{\text{M on R}}$ acting on the rope in this case is zero!

We emphasize once more a fundamental truth: The two forces in an action–reaction pair *never* act on the same body. Remembering this simple fact can often help you avoid confusion about action–reaction pairs and Newton's third law.

Test Your Understanding of Section 4.5 You are driving your car on a country road when a mosquito splatters itself on the windshield. Which has the greater magnitude, the force that the car exerted on the mosquito or the force that the mosquito exerted on the car? Or are the magnitudes the same? If they are different, how can you reconcile this fact with Newton's third law? If they are equal, why is the mosquito splattered while the car is undamaged?

4.6 Free-Body Diagrams

ActivPhysics ONLINE
2.1.1 Force Magnitudes

Newton's three laws of motion contain all the basic principles we need to solve a wide variety of problems in mechanics. These laws are very simple in form, but the process of applying them to specific situations can pose real challenges. In this brief section we'll point out three key ideas and techniques to use in any problems involving Newton's laws. You'll learn others in Chapter 5, which also extends the use of Newton's laws to cover more complex situations.

1. *Newton's first and second laws apply to a specific body.* Whenever you use Newton's first law, $\sum\vec{F} = \mathbf{0}$, for an equilibrium situation or Newton's second law, $\sum\vec{F} = m\vec{a}$, for a nonequilibrium situation, you must decide at the

beginning to which body you are referring. This decision may sound trivial, but it isn't.

2. *Only forces acting on the body matter.* The sum $\sum\vec{F}$ includes all the forces that act *on* the body in question. Hence, once you've chosen the body to analyze, you have to identify all the forces acting on it. Don't get confused between the forces acting on a body and the forces exerted by that body on some other body. For example, to analyze a person walking, you would include in $\sum\vec{F}$ the force that the ground exerts on the person as he walks, but *not* the force that the person exerts on the ground (Fig. 4.29). These forces form an action–reaction pair and are related by Newton's third law, but only the member of the pair that acts on the body you're working with goes into $\sum\vec{F}$.
3. *Free-body diagrams are essential to help identify the relevant forces.* A **free-body diagram** is a diagram showing the chosen body by itself, "free" of its surroundings, with vectors drawn to show the magnitudes and directions of all the forces applied to the body by the various other bodies that interact with it. We have already shown some free-body diagrams in Figs. 4.18, 4.19, 4.21, and 4.26a. Be careful to include all the forces acting *on* the body, but be equally careful *not* to include any forces that the body exerts on any other body. In particular, the two forces in an action–reaction pair must *never* appear in the same free-body diagram because they never act on the same body. Furthermore, forces that a body exerts on itself are never included, since these can't affect the body's motion.

4.29 The simple act of walking depends crucially on Newton's third law. To start moving forward, you push backward on the ground with your foot. As a reaction, the ground pushes forward on your foot (and hence on your body as a whole) with a force of the same magnitude. This *external* force provided by the ground is what accelerates your body forward.

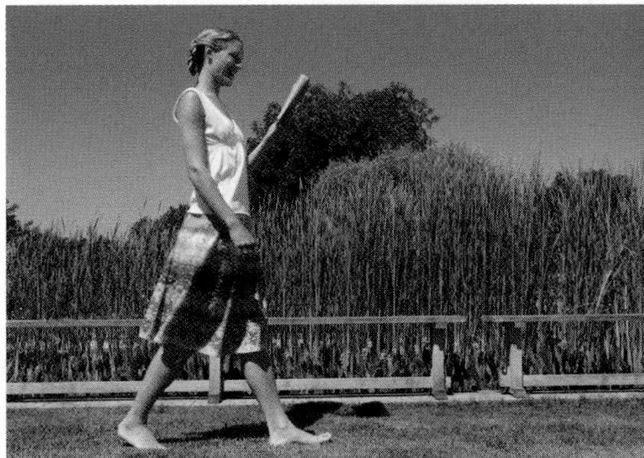

CAUTION **Forces in free-body diagrams** When you have a complete free-body diagram, you *must* be able to answer for each force the question: What other body is applying this force? If you can't answer that question, you may be dealing with a nonexistent force. Be especially on your guard to avoid nonexistent forces such as "the force of acceleration" or "the $m\vec{a}$ force," discussed in Section 4.3.

When a problem involves more than one body, you have to take the problem apart and draw a separate free-body diagram for each body. For example, Fig. 4.27c shows a separate free-body diagram for the rope in the case in which the rope is considered massless (so that no gravitational force acts on it). Figure 4.28 also shows diagrams for the block and the mason, but these are *not* complete free-body diagrams because they don't show all the forces acting on each body. (We left out the vertical forces—the weight force exerted by the earth and the upward normal force exerted by the floor.)

Figure 4.30 on page 128 presents some real-life situations and the corresponding complete free-body diagrams. Note that in each situation a person exerts a force on something in his or her surroundings, but the force that shows up in the person's free-body diagram is the surroundings pushing back *on* the person.

Test Your Understanding of Section 4.6 The buoyancy force shown in Fig. 4.30c is one half of an action–reaction pair. What force is the other half of this pair? (i) the weight of the swimmer; (ii) the forward thrust force; (iii) the backward drag force; (iv) the downward force that the swimmer exerts on the water; (v) the backward force that the swimmer exerts on the water by kicking.

4.30 Examples of free-body diagrams. In each case, the free-body diagram shows all the external forces that act on the object in question.

(a)

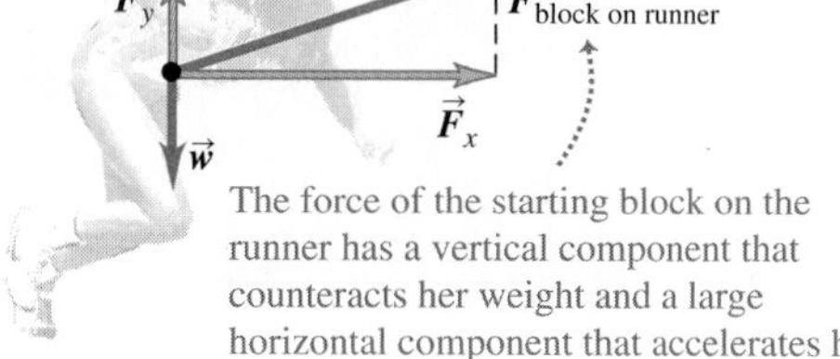
$\vec{F}_y$
$\vec{F}_{\text{block on runner}}$
$\vec{F}_x$
$\vec{w}$
The force of the starting block on the runner has a vertical component that counteracts her weight and a large horizontal component that accelerates her.

(b)

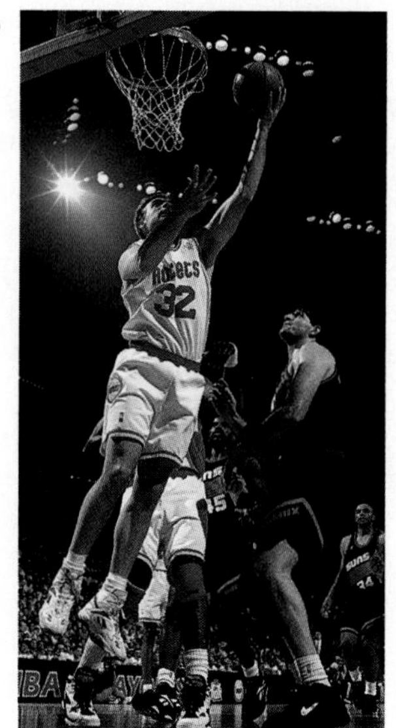

$\vec{n}$
$\vec{w}$
$\vec{w}$
This player is a freely falling object.
To jump up, this player will push down against the floor, increasing the upward reaction force $\vec{n}$ of the floor on him.

(c)

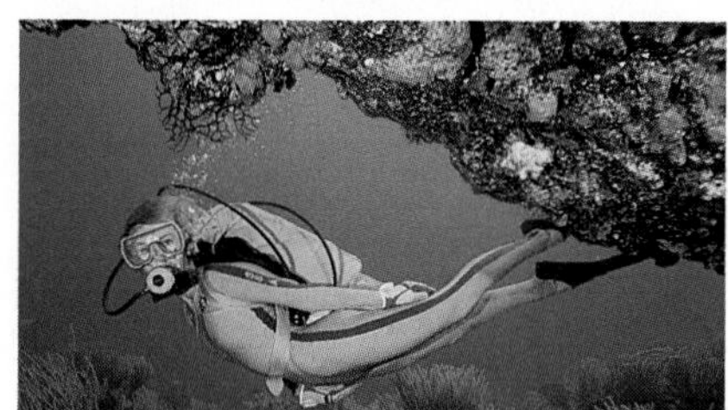

The water exerts a buoyancy force that counters the swimmer's weight.

$\vec{F}_{\text{buoyancy}}$

$\vec{F}_{\text{thrust}}$

$\vec{F}_{\text{drag}}$

$\vec{w}$

Kicking causes the water to exert a forward reaction force, or thrust, on the swimmer.

Thrust is countered by drag forces exerted by the water on the moving swimmer.

CHAPTER 4 SUMMARY

Force as a vector: Force is a quantitative measure of the interaction between two bodies. It is a vector quantity. When several forces act on a body, the effect on its motion is the same as when a single force, equal to the vector sum (resultant) of the forces, acts on the body. (See Example 4.1.)

$$\vec{R} = \vec{F}_1 + \vec{F}_2 + \vec{F}_3 + \cdots = \sum \vec{F} \quad (4.1)$$

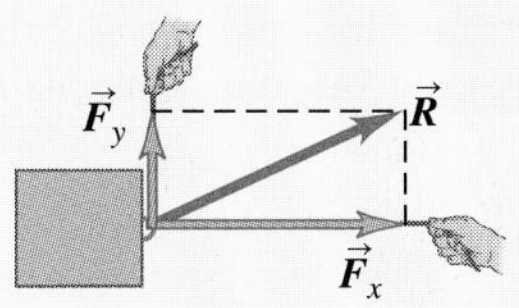

The net force on a body and Newton's first law: Newton's first law states that when the vector sum of all forces acting on a body (the *net force*) is zero, the body is in equilibrium and has zero acceleration. If the body is initially at rest, it remains at rest; if it is initially in motion, it continues to move with constant velocity. This law is valid only in inertial frames of reference. (See Examples 4.2 and 4.3.)

$$\sum \vec{F} = 0 \quad (4.3)$$

$\vec{v}$ = constant

$\vec{F}_1$ $\quad \vec{F}_2 = -\vec{F}_1$

$\Sigma \vec{F} = 0$

Mass, acceleration, and Newton's second law: The inertial properties of a body are characterized by its *mass*. The acceleration of a body under the action of a given set of forces is directly proportional to the vector sum of the forces (the *net force*) and inversely proportional to the mass of the body. This relationship is Newton's second law. Like Newton's first law, this law is valid only in inertial frames of reference. The unit of force is defined in terms of the units of mass and acceleration. In SI units, the unit of force is the newton (N), equal to $1\ \text{kg} \cdot \text{m}/\text{s}^2$. (See Examples 4.4 and 4.5.)

$$\sum \vec{F} = m\vec{a} \quad (4.7)$$

$$\sum F_x = ma_x \qquad \sum F_y = ma_y \qquad \sum F_z = ma_z \quad (4.8)$$

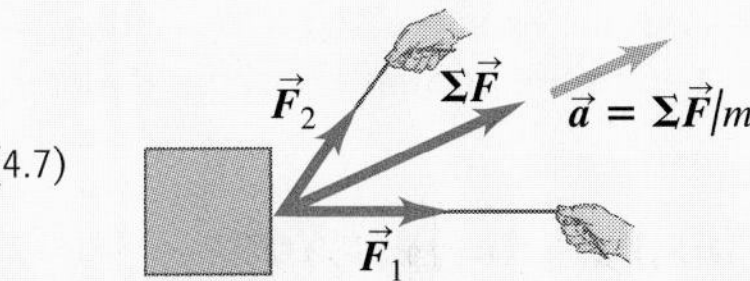

Weight: The weight $\vec{w}$ of a body is the gravitational force exerted on it by the earth. Weight is a vector quantity. The magnitude of the weight of a body at any specific location is equal to the product of its mass m and the magnitude of the acceleration due to gravity g at that location. While the weight of a body depends on its location, the mass is independent of location. (See Examples 4.6 and 4.7.)

$$w = mg \quad (4.9)$$

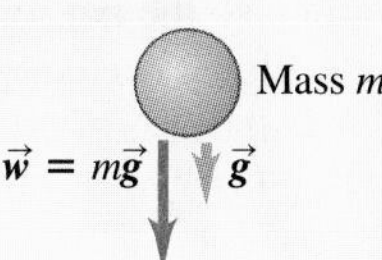

Newton's third law and action–reaction pairs: Newton's third law states that when two bodies interact, they exert forces on each other that at each instant are equal in magnitude and opposite in direction. These forces are called action and reaction forces. Each of these two forces acts on only one of the two bodies; they never act on the same body. (See Examples 4.8–4.11.)

$$\vec{F}_{A \text{ on } B} = -\vec{F}_{B \text{ on } A} \quad (4.11)$$

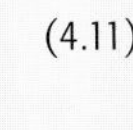

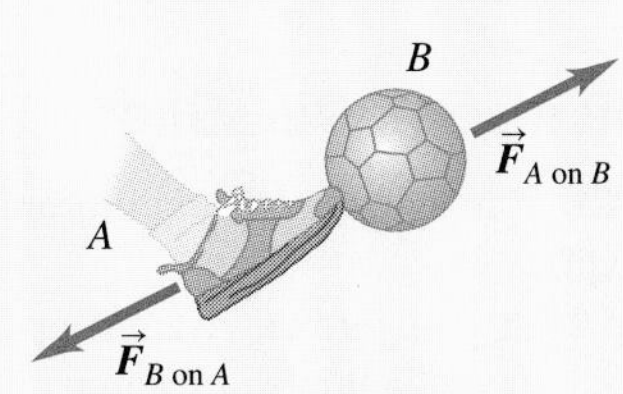

Key Terms

Answer to Chapter Opening Question ?

Newton's third law tells us that the seated child (who we'll call Ryder) pushes on the standing child (who we'll call Stan) just as hard as Stan pushes on Ryder, but in the opposite direction. This is true whether Ryder pushes on Stan "actively" (for instance, if Ryder pushed his hand against Stan's) or "passively" (if Ryder's back does the pushing, as in the photograph that opens the chapter). The force magnitudes would be greater in the "active" case than in the "passive" case, but either way Ryder's push on Stan is just as strong as Stan's push on Ryder.

Answers to Test Your Understanding Questions

4.1 **Answer: (iv)** The gravitational force on the crate points straight downward. In Fig. 4.6 the x-axis points up and to the right, and the y-axis points up and to the left. Hence the gravitational force has both an x-component and a y-component, and both are negative.

4.2 **Answer: (i), (ii), and (iv)** In (i), (ii), and (iv) the body is not accelerating, so the net force on the body is zero. [In (iv), the box remains stationary as seen in the inertial reference frame of the ground as the truck accelerates forward, like the skater in Fig. 4.11a.] In (iii), the hawk is moving in a circle; hence it is accelerating and is *not* in equilibrium.

4.3 **Answer: (iii), (i) and (iv) (tie), (ii)** The acceleration is equal to the net force divided by the mass. Hence the magnitude of the acceleration in each situation is
(i) $a = (2.0\text{ N})/(2.0\text{ kg}) = 1.0\text{ m/s}^2$;
(ii) $a = (8.0\text{ N})/(2.0\text{ N}) = 4.0\text{ m/s}^2$;
(iii) $a = (2.0\text{ N})/(8.0\text{ kg}) = 0.25\text{ m/s}^2$;
(iv) $a = (8.0\text{ N})/(8.0\text{ kg}) = 1.0\text{ m/s}^2$.

4.4 It would take twice the effort for the astronaut to walk around because her weight on the planet would be twice as much as on the earth. But it would be just as easy to catch a ball moving horizontally. The ball's *mass* is the same as on earth, so the horizontal force the astronaut would have to exert to bring it to a stop (i.e., to give it the same acceleration) would also be the same as on earth.

4.5 By Newton's third law, the two forces have equal magnitudes. Because the car has much greater mass than the mosquito, it undergoes only a tiny, imperceptible acceleration in response to the force of the impact. By contrast, the mosquito, with its minuscule mass, undergoes a catastrophically large acceleration.

4.6 **Answer: (iv)** The buoyancy force is an *upward* force that the *water* exerts on the *swimmer.* By Newton's third law, the other half of the action–reaction pair is a *downward* force that the *swimmer* exerts on the *water* and has the same magnitude as the buoyancy force. It's true that the weight of the swimmer is also downward and has the same magnitude as the buoyancy force; however, the weight acts on the same body (the swimmer) as the buoyancy force, and so these forces aren't an action–reaction pair.

PROBLEMS

For instructor-assigned homework, go to **www.masteringphysics.com** 

Discussion Questions

Q4.1. Can a body be in equilibrium when only one force acts on it? Explain.

Q4.2. A ball thrown straight up has zero velocity at its highest point. Is the ball in equilibrium at this point? Why or why not?

Q4.3. A helium balloon hovers in midair, neither ascending nor descending. Is it in equilibrium? What forces act on it?

Q4.4. When you fly in an airplane at night in smooth air, there is no sensation of motion, even though the plane may be moving at 800 km/h (500 mi/h). Why is this?

Q4.5. If the two ends of a rope in equilibrium are pulled with forces of equal magnitude and opposite direction, why is the total tension in the rope not zero?

Q4.6. You tie a brick to the end of a rope and whirl the brick around you in a horizontal circle. Describe the path of the brick after you suddenly let go of the rope.

Q4.7. When a car stops suddenly, the passengers tend to move forward relative to their seats. Why? When a car makes a sharp turn, the passengers tend to slide to one side of the car. Why?

Q4.8. Some people say that the "force of inertia" (or "force of momentum") throws the passengers forward when a car brakes sharply. What is wrong with this explanation?

Q4.9. A passenger in a moving bus with no windows notices that a ball that has been at rest in the aisle suddenly starts to move toward the rear of the bus. Think of two different possible explanations, and devise a way to decide which is correct.

Q4.10. Suppose you chose the fundamental SI units to be force, length, and time instead of mass, length, and time. What would be the units of mass in terms of those fundamental units?

Q4.11. Some of the ancient Greeks thought that the "natural state" of an object was to be at rest, so objects would seek their natural state by coming to rest if left alone. Explain why this view can actually seem quite plausible in the everyday world.

Q4.12. Why is the earth only approximately an inertial reference frame?

Q4.13. Does Newton's second law hold true for an observer in a van as it speeds up, slows down, or rounds a corner? Explain.

Q4.14. Some students refer to the quantity $m\vec{a}$ as "the force of acceleration." Is it correct to refer to this quantity as a force? If so, what exerts this force? If not, what is a better description of this quantity?

Q4.15. The acceleration of a falling body is measured in an elevator traveling upward at a constant speed of 9.8 m/s. What result is obtained?

Q4.16. You can play catch with a softball in a bus moving with constant speed on a straight road, just as though the bus were at rest. Is this still possible when the bus is making a turn at constant speed on a level road? Why or why not?

Q4.17. Students sometimes say that the force of gravity on an object is 9.8 m/s^2. What is wrong with this view?

Q4.18. The head of a hammer begins to come loose from its wooden handle. How should you strike the handle on a concrete sidewalk to reset the head? Why does this work?

Q4.19. Why can it hurt your foot more to kick a big rock than a small pebble? *Must* the big rock hurt more? Explain.

Q4.20. "It's not the fall that hurts you; it's the sudden stop at the bottom." Translate this saying into the language of Newton's laws of motion.

Q4.21. A person can dive into water from a height of 10 m without injury, but a person who jumps off the roof of a 10-m-tall building and lands on a concrete street is likely to be seriously injured. Why is there a difference?

Q4.22. Why are cars designed to crumple up in front and back for safety? Why not for side collisions and rollovers?

Q4.23. When a bullet is fired from a gun, what is the origin of the force that accelerates the bullet?

Q4.24. When a string barely strong enough lifts a heavy weight, it can lift the weight by a steady pull; but if you jerk the string, it will break. Explain in terms of Newton's laws of motion.

Q4.25. A large crate is suspended from the end of a vertical rope. Is the tension in the rope greater when the crate is at rest or when it is moving upward at constant speed? If the crate is traveling upward, is the tension in the rope greater when the crate is speeding up or when it is slowing down? In each case explain in terms of Newton's laws of motion.

Q4.26. Which feels a greater pull due to the earth's gravity, a 10-kg stone or a 20-kg stone? If you drop them, why does the 20-kg stone not fall with twice the acceleration of the 10-kg stone? Explain your reasoning.

Q4.27. Why is it incorrect to say that 1.0 kg *equals* 2.2 lb?

Q4.28. A horse is hitched to a wagon. Since the wagon pulls back on the horse just as hard as the horse pulls on the wagon, why does the wagon not remain in equilibrium, no matter how hard the horse pulls?

Q4.29. True or false? You exert a push P on an object and it pushes back on you with a force F. If the object is moving at constant velocity, then F is equal to P, but if the object is being accelerated, then P must be greater than F.

Q4.30. A large truck and a small compact car have a head-on collision. During the collision, the truck exerts a force $\vec{F}_{\text{T on C}}$ on the car, and the car exerts a force $\vec{F}_{\text{C on T}}$ on the truck. Which force has the larger magnitude, or are they the same? Does your answer depend on how fast each vehicle was moving before the collision? Why or why not?

Q4.31. When a car comes to a stop on a level highway, what force causes it to slow down? When the car increases its speed on the same highway, what force causes it to speed up? Explain.

Q4.32. A small compact car is pushing a large van that has broken down, and they travel along the road with equal velocities and accelerations. While the car is speeding up, is the force it exerts on the van larger than, smaller than, or the same magnitude as the force the van exerts on it? Which object, the car or the van, has the larger net force on it, or are the net forces the same? Explain.

Q4.33. Consider a tug-of-war between two people who pull in opposite directions on the ends of a rope. By Newton's third law, the force that A exerts on B is just as great as the force that B exerts on A. So what determines who wins? (*Hint:* Draw a free-body diagram showing all the forces that act on each person.)

Q4.34. On the moon, $g = 1.62\ \text{m/s}^2$. If a 2-kg brick drops on your foot from a height of 2 m, will this hurt more, or less, or the same if it happens on the moon instead of on the earth? Explain. If a 2-kg brick is thrown and hits you when it is moving horizontally at 6 m/s, will this hurt more, less, or the same if it happens on the moon instead of on the earth? Explain. (On the moon, assume that you are inside a pressurized structure, so you are not wearing a spacesuit.)

Q4.35. A manual for student pilots contains the following passage: "When an airplane flies at a steady altitude, neither climbing nor descending, the upward lift force from the wings equals the airplane's weight. When the airplane is climbing at a steady rate, the upward lift is greater than the weight; when the airplane is descending at a steady rate, the upward lift is less than the weight." Are these statements correct? Explain.

Q4.36. If your hands are wet and no towel is handy, you can remove some of the excess water by shaking them. Why does this get rid of the water?

Q4.37. If you are squatting down (such as when you are examining the books on the bottom shelf in a library or bookstore) and suddenly get up, you can temporarily feel light-headed. What do Newton's laws of motion have to say about why this happens?

Q4.38. When a car is hit from behind, the passengers can receive a whiplash. Use Newton's laws of motion to explain what causes this to occur.

Q4.39. In a head-on auto collision, passengers not wearing seat belts can be thrown through the windshield. Use Newton's laws of motion to explain why this happens.

Q4.40. In a head-on collision between a compact 1000-kg car and a large 2500-kg car, which one experiences the greater force? Explain. Which one experiences the greater acceleration? Explain why. Now explain why passengers in the smaller car are more likely to be injured than those in the large car, even if the bodies of both cars are equally strong.

Q4.41. Suppose you are in a rocket with no windows, traveling in deep space far from any other objects. Without looking outside the rocket or making any contact with the outside world, explain how you could determine if the rocket is (a) moving forward at a constant 80% of the speed of light and (b) accelerating in the forward direction.

Exercises

Section 4.1 Force and Interactions

4.1. Two forces have the same magnitude F. What is the angle between the two vectors if their sum has a magnitude of (a) $2F$? (b) $\sqrt{2}F$? (c) zero? Sketch the three vectors in each case.

4.2. Instead of using the x- and y-axes of Fig. 4.8 to analyze the situation of Example 4.1, use axes rotated 37.0° counterclockwise, so the y-axis is parallel to the 250-N force. (a) For these axes find the x- and y-components of the net force on the belt. (b) From the components computed in part (a) find the magnitude and direction of the net force. Compare your results to Example 4.1.

4.3. A warehouse worker pushes a crate along the floor, as shown in Fig. 4.31, with a force of 10 N that points downward at an angle of 45° below the horizontal. Find the horizontal and vertical components of the force.

Figure **4.31** Exercise 4.3.

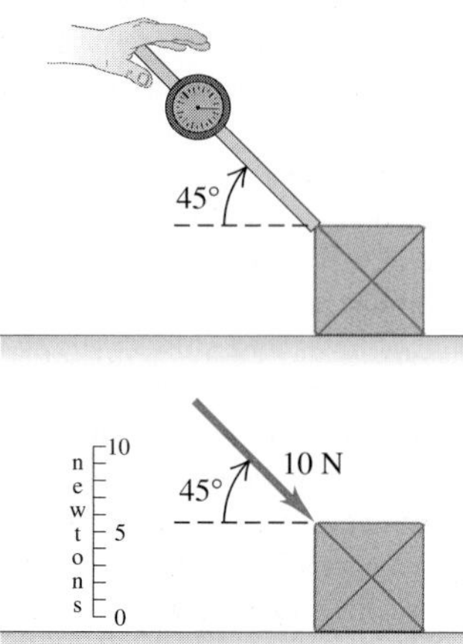

4.4. A man is dragging a trunk up the loading ramp of a mover's truck. The ramp has a slope angle of 20.0°, and the man pulls upward with a force $\vec{F}$ whose direction makes an angle of 30.0° with the ramp (Fig. 4.32). (a) How large a force $\vec{F}$ is necessary for the component F_x parallel to the ramp to be 60.0 N? (b) How large will the component F_y perpendicular to the ramp then be?

Figure **4.32** Exercise 4.4.

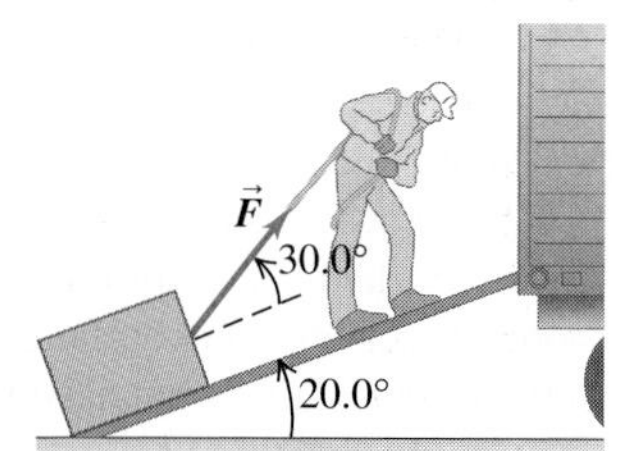

4.5. Two dogs pull horizontally on ropes attached to a post; the angle between the ropes is 60.0°. If dog *A* exerts a force of 270 N and dog *B* exerts a force of 300 N, find the magnitude of the resultant force and the angle it makes with dog *A*'s rope.

4.6. Two forces, $\vec{F}_1$ and $\vec{F}_2$, act at a point. The magnitude of $\vec{F}_1$ is 9.00 N, and its direction is 60.0° above the *x*-axis in the second quadrant. The magnitude of $\vec{F}_2$ is 6.00 N, and its direction is 53.1° below the *x*-axis in the third quadrant. (a) What are the *x*- and *y*-components of the resultant force? (b) What is the magnitude of the resultant force?

Section 4.3 Newton's Second Law

4.7. If a net horizontal force of 132 N is applied to a person with mass 60 kg who is resting on the edge of a swimming pool, what horizontal acceleration is produced?

4.8. What magnitude of net force is required to give a 135-kg refrigerator an acceleration of magnitude 1.40 m/s^2?

4.9. A box rests on a frozen pond, which serves as a frictionless horizontal surface. If a fisherman applies a horizontal force with magnitude 48.0 N to the box and produces an acceleration of magnitude 3.00 m/s^2, what is the mass of the box?

4.10. A dockworker applies a constant horizontal force of 80.0 N to a block of ice on a smooth horizontal floor. The frictional force is negligible. The block starts from rest and moves 11.0 m in 5.00 s. (a) What is the mass of the block of ice? (b) If the worker stops pushing at the end of 5.00 s, how far does the block move in the next 5.00 s?

4.11. A hockey puck with mass 0.160 kg is at rest at the origin $(x = 0)$ on the horizontal, frictionless surface of the rink. At time $t = 0$ a player applies a force of 0.250 N to the puck, parallel to the *x*-axis; he continues to apply this force until $t = 2.00$ s. (a) What are the position and speed of the puck at $t = 2.00$ s? (b) If the same force is again applied at $t = 5.00$ s, what are the position and speed of the puck at $t = 7.00$ s?

4.12. A crate with mass 32.5 kg initially at rest on a warehouse floor is acted on by a net horizontal force of 140 N. (a) What acceleration is produced? (b) How far does the crate travel in 10.0 s? (c) What is its speed at the end of 10.0 s?

4.13. A 4.50-kg toy cart undergoes an acceleration in a straight line (the *x*-axis). The graph in Fig. 4.33 shows this acceleration as a function of time. (a) Find the maximum net force on this cart. When does this maximum force occur? (b) During what times is the net force on the cart a constant? (c) When is the net force equal to zero?

Figure **4.33** Exercise 4.13.

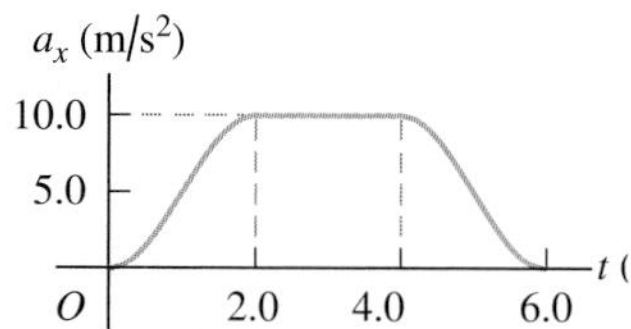

4.14. A 2.75-kg cat moves in a straight line (the *x*-axis). Figure 4.34 shows a graph of the *x*-component of this cat's velocity as a function of time. (a) Find the maximum net force on this cat. When does this force occur? (b) When is the net force on the cat equal to zero? (c) What is the net force at time 8.5 s?

Figure **4.34** Exercise 4.14.

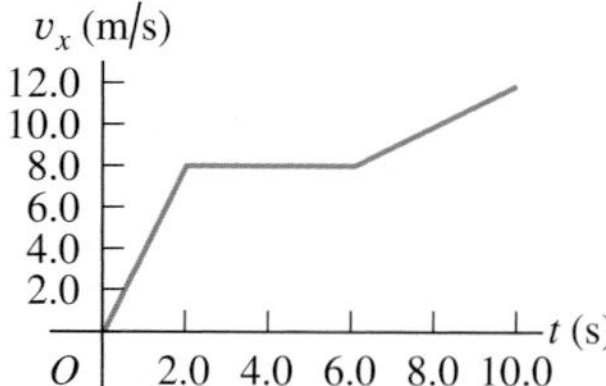

4.15. A small 8.00-kg rocket burns fuel that exerts a time-varying upward force on the rocket. This force obeys the equation $F = A + Bt^2$. Measurements show that at $t = 0$, the force is 100.0 N, and at the end of the first 2.00 s, it is 150.0 N. (a) Find the constants *A* and *B*, including their SI units. (b) Find the *net* force on this rocket and its acceleration (i) the instant after the fuel ignites and (ii) 3.00 s after fuel ignition. (c) Suppose you were using this rocket in outer space, far from all gravity. What would its acceleration be 3.00 s after fuel ignition?

4.16. An electron (mass $= 9.11 \times 10^{-31}$ kg) leaves one end of a TV picture tube with zero initial speed and travels in a straight line to the accelerating grid, which is 1.80 cm away. It reaches the grid with a speed of 3.00×10^6 m/s. If the accelerating force is constant, compute (a) the acceleration; (b) the time to reach the grid; (c) the net force, in newtons. (You can ignore the gravitational force on the electron.)

Section 4.4 Mass and Weight

4.17. Superman throws a 2400-N boulder at an adversary. What horizontal force must Superman apply to the boulder to give it a horizontal acceleration of 12.0 m/s^2?

4.18. A bowling ball weighs 71.2 N (16.0 lb). The bowler applies a horizontal force of 160 N (36.0 lb) to the ball. What is the magnitude of the horizontal acceleration of the ball?

4.19. At the surface of Jupiter's moon Io, the acceleration due to gravity is $g = 1.81\ \text{m/s}^2$. A watermelon weighs 44.0 N at the surface of the earth. (a) What is the watermelon's mass on the earth's surface? (b) What are its mass and weight on the surface of Io?

4.20. An astronaut's pack weighs 17.5 N when she is on earth but only 3.24 N when she is at the surface of an asteroid. (a) What is the acceleration due to gravity on this asteroid? (b) What is the mass of the pack on the asteroid?

Section 4.5 Newton's Third Law

4.21. World-class sprinters can accelerate out of the starting blocks with an acceleration that is nearly horizontal and has magnitude $15\ \text{m/s}^2$. How much horizontal force must a 55-kg sprinter exert on the starting blocks during a start to produce this acceleration? Which body exerts the force that propels the sprinter: the blocks or the sprinter herself?

4.22. Imagine that you are holding a book weighing 4 N at rest on the palm of your hand. Complete the following sentences: (a) A downward force of magnitude 4 N is exerted on the book by __________. (b) An upward force of magnitude __________ is exerted on __________ by your hand. (c) Is the upward force in part (b) the reaction to the downward force in part (a)? (d) The reaction to the force in part (a) is a force of magnitude __________, exerted on __________ by __________. Its direction is __________. (e) The reaction to the force in part (b) is a force of magnitude __________, exerted on __________ by __________. Its direction is __________. (f) The forces in parts (a) and (b) are equal and opposite because of Newton's __________ law. (g) The forces in parts (b) and (e) are equal and opposite because of Newton's __________ law. Now suppose that you exert an upward force of magnitude 5 N on the book. (h) Does the book remain in equilibrium? (i) Is the force exerted on the book by your hand equal and opposite to the force exerted on the book by the earth? (j) Is the force exerted on the book by the earth equal and opposite to the force exerted on the earth by the book? (k) Is the force exerted on the book by your hand equal and opposite to the force exerted on your hand by the book? Finally, suppose you snatch your hand away while the book is moving upward. (l) How many forces then act on the book? (m) Is the book in equilibrium?

4.23. A bottle is given a push along a tabletop and slides off the edge of the table. Do *not* ignore air resistance. (a) What forces are exerted on the bottle while it is falling from the table to the floor? (b) What is the reaction to each force; that is, on which body and by which body is the reaction exerted?

4.24. The upward normal force exerted by the floor is 620 N on an elevator passenger who weighs 650 N. What are the reaction forces to these two forces? Is the passenger accelerating? If so, what are the magnitude and direction of the acceleration?

4.25. A student with mass 45 kg jumps off a high diving board. Using 6.0×10^{24} kg for the mass of the earth, what is the acceleration of the earth toward her as she accelerates toward the earth with an acceleration of $9.8\ \text{m/s}^2$? Assume that the net force on the earth is the force of gravity she exerts on it.

Section 4.6 Free-Body Diagrams

4.26. An athlete throws a ball of mass m directly upward, and it feels no appreciable air resistance. Draw a free-body diagram of this ball while it is free of the athlete's hand and (a) moving upward; (b) at its highest point; (c) moving downward. (d) Repeat parts (a), (b), and (c) if the athlete throws the ball at a 60° angle above the horizontal instead of directly upward.

4.27. Two crates, A and B, sit at rest side by side on a frictionless horizontal surface. The crates have masses m_A and m_B. A horizontal force $\vec{F}$ is applied to crate A and the two crates move off to the right. (a) Draw clearly labeled free-body diagrams for crate A and for crate B. Indicate which pairs of forces, if any, are third-law action–reaction pairs. (b) If the magnitude of force $\vec{F}$ is less than the total weight of the two crates, will it cause the crates to move? Explain.

4.28. A person pulls horizontally on block B in Fig. 4.35, causing both blocks to move together as a unit. While this system is moving, make a carefully labeled free-body diagram of block A if (a) the table is frictionless and (b) there is friction between block B and the table and the pull is equal to the friction force on block B due to the table.

Figure 4.35 Exercise 4.28.

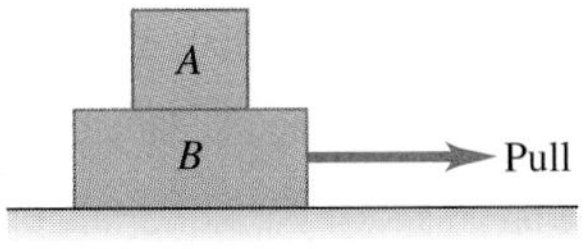

4.29. A ball is hanging from a long string that is tied to the ceiling of a train car traveling eastward on horizontal tracks. An observer inside the train car sees the ball hang motionless. Draw a clearly labeled free-body diagram for the ball if (a) the train has a uniform velocity, and (b) the train is speeding up uniformly. Is the net force on the ball zero in either case? Explain.

4.30. A large box containing your new computer sits on the bed of your pickup truck. You are stopped at a red light. The light turns green and you stomp on the gas and the truck accelerates. To your horror, the box starts to slide toward the back of the truck. Draw clearly labeled free-body diagrams for the truck and for the box. Indicate pairs of forces, if any, that are third-law action–reaction pairs. (The bed of the truck is *not* frictionless.)

4.31. A chair of mass 12.0 kg is sitting on the horizontal floor; the floor is not frictionless. You push on the chair with a force $F = 40.0$ N that is directed at an angle of 37.0° below the horizontal and the chair slides along the floor. (a) Draw a clearly labeled free-body diagram for the chair. (b) Use your diagram and Newton's laws to calculate the normal force that the floor exerts on the chair.

4.32. A skier of mass 65.0 kg is pulled up a snow-covered slope at constant speed by a tow rope that is parallel to the ground. The ground slopes upward at a constant angle of 26.0° above the horizontal, and you can ignore friction. (a) Draw a clearly labeled free-body diagram for the skier. (b) Calculate the tension in the tow rope.

4.33. A truck is pulling a car on a horizontal highway using a horizontal rope. The car is in neutral gear, so we can assume that there is no appreciable friction between its tires and the highway. As the truck is accelerating to highway speeds, draw a free-body diagram of (a) the car and (b) the truck. (c) What force accelerates this system forward? Explain how this force originates.

Problems

4.34. A .22 rifle bullet, traveling at 350 m/s, strikes a large tree, which it penetrates to a depth of 0.130 m. The mass of the bullet is 1.80 g. Assume a constant retarding force. (a) How much time is required for the bullet to stop? (b) What force, in newtons, does the tree exert on the bullet?

4.35. Two horses pull horizontally on ropes attached to a stump. The two forces $\vec{F}_1$ and $\vec{F}_2$ that they apply to the stump are such that the net (resultant) force $\vec{R}$ has a magnitude equal to that of $\vec{F}_1$ and makes an angle of 90° with $\vec{F}_1$. Let $F_1 = 1300$ N and $R = 1300$ N also. Find the magnitude of $\vec{F}_2$ and its direction (relative to $\vec{F}_1$).

4.36. You have just landed on Planet X. You take out a 100-g ball, release it from rest from a height of 10.0 m, and measure that it takes 2.2 s to reach the ground. You can ignore any force on the ball from the atmosphere of the planet. How much does the 100-g ball weigh on the surface of Planet X?

4.37. Two adults and a child want to push a wheeled cart in the direction marked x in Fig. 4.36. The two adults push with horizontal forces $\vec{F}_1$ and $\vec{F}_2$ as shown in the figure. (a) Find the magnitude and direction of the *smallest* force that the child should exert. You can ignore the effects of friction. (b) If the child exerts the minimum force found in part (a), the cart accelerates at $2.0\ \text{m/s}^2$ in the $+x$-direction. What is the weight of the cart?

Figure **4.36** Problem 4.37.

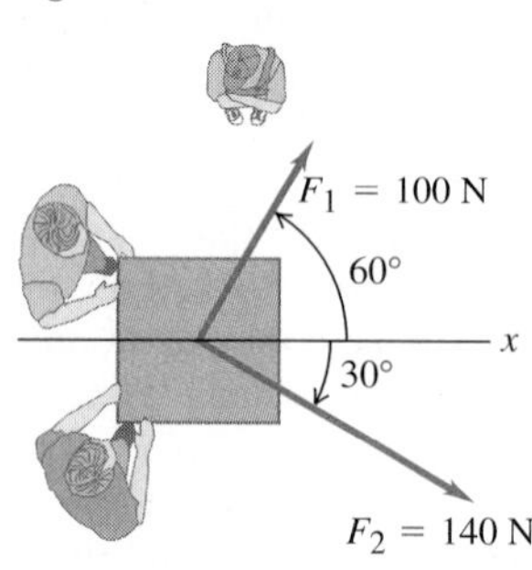

4.38. An oil tanker's engines have broken down, and the wind is blowing the tanker straight toward a reef at a constant speed of 1.5 m/s (Fig. 4.37). When the tanker is 500 m from the reef, the wind dies down just as the engineer gets the engines going again. The rudder is stuck, so the only choice is to try to accelerate straight backward away from the reef. The mass of the tanker and cargo is 3.6×10^7 kg, and the engines produce a net horizontal force of 8.0×10^4 N on the tanker. Will the ship hit the reef? If it does, will the oil be safe? The hull can withstand an impact at a speed of 0.2 m/s or less. You can ignore the retarding force of the water on the tanker's hull.

Figure **4.37** Problem 4.38.

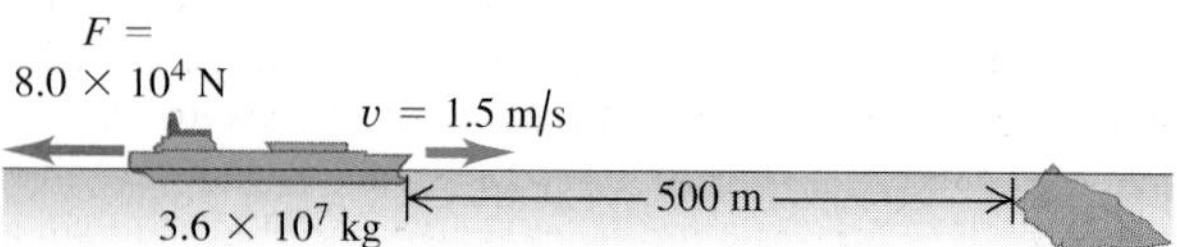

4.39. A Standing Vertical Jump. Basketball player Darrell Griffith is on record as attaining a standing vertical jump of 1.2 m (4 ft). (This means that he moved upward by 1.2 m after his feet left the floor.) Griffith weighed 890 N (200 lb). (a) What is his speed as he leaves the floor? (b) If the time of the part of the jump before his feet left the floor was 0.300 s, what was his average acceleration (magnitude and direction) while he was pushing against the floor? (c) Draw his free-body diagram (see Section 4.6). In terms of the forces on the diagram, what is the net force on him? Use Newton's laws and the results of part (b) to calculate the average force he applied to the ground.

4.40. An advertisement claims that a particular automobile can "stop on a dime." What net force would actually be necessary to stop a 850-kg automobile traveling initially at 45.0 km/h in a distance equal to the diameter of a dime, which is 1.8 cm?

4.41. A 4.80-kg bucket of water is accelerated upward by a cord of negligible mass whose breaking strength is 75.0 N. (a) Draw the free-body force diagram for the bucket. In terms of the forces on your diagram, what is the net force on the bucket? (b) Apply Newton's second law to the bucket and find the maximum upward acceleration that can be given to the bucket without breaking the cord.

4.42. A parachutist relies on air resistance (mainly on her parachute) to decrease her downward velocity. She and her parachute have a mass of 55.0 kg, and air resistance exerts a total upward force of 620 N on her and her parachute. (a) What is the weight of the parachutist? (b) Draw a free-body diagram for the parachutist (see Section 4.6). Use that diagram to calculate the net force on the parachutist. Is the net force upward or downward? (c) What is the acceleration (magnitude and direction) of the parachutist?

4.43. Two crates, one with mass 4.00 kg and the other with mass 6.00 kg, sit on the frictionless surface of a frozen pond, connected by a light rope (Fig. 4.38). A woman wearing golf shoes (so she can get traction on the ice) pulls horizontally on the 6.00-kg crate with a force F that gives the crate an acceleration of $2.50\ \text{m/s}^2$. (a) What is the acceleration of the 4.00-kg crate? (b) Draw a free-body diagram for the 4.00-kg crate. Use that diagram and Newton's second law to find the tension T in the rope that connects the two crates. (c) Draw a free-body diagram for the 6.00-kg crate. What is the direction of the net force on the 6.00-kg crate? Which is larger in magnitude, force T or force F? (d) Use part (c) and Newton's second law to calculate the magnitude of the force F.

4.44. An astronaut is tethered by a strong cable to a spacecraft. The astronaut and her spacesuit have a total mass of 105 kg, while the mass of the cable is negligible. The mass of the spacecraft is 9.05×10^4 kg. The spacecraft is far from any large astronomical

Figure **4.38** Problem 4.43.

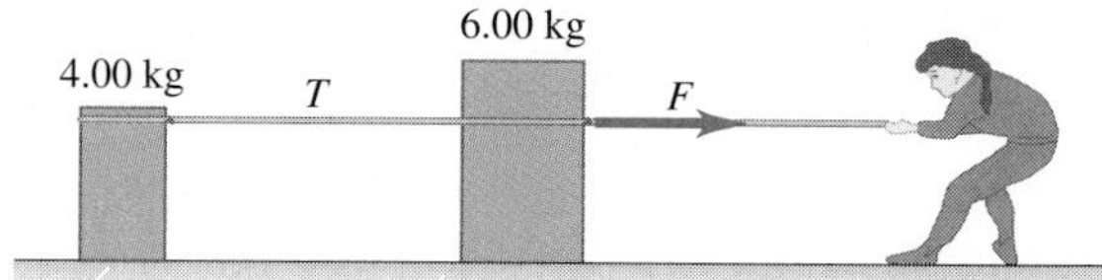

bodies, so we can ignore the gravitational forces on it and the astronaut. We also assume that both the spacecraft and the astronaut are initially at rest in an inertial reference frame. The astronaut then pulls on the cable with a force of 80.0 N. (a) What force does the cable exert on the astronaut? (b) Since $\sum \vec{F} = m\vec{a}$, how can a "massless" $(m = 0)$ cable exert a force? (c) What is the astronaut's acceleration? (d) What force does the cable exert on the spacecraft? (e) What is the acceleration of the spacecraft?

4.45. To study damage to aircraft that collide with large birds, you design a test gun that will accelerate chicken-sized objects so that their displacement along the gun barrel is given by $x = (9.0 \times 10^3\ \text{m/s}^2)t^2 - (8.0 \times 10^4\ \text{m/s}^3)t^3$. The object leaves the end of the barrel at $t = 0.025$ s. (a) How long must the gun barrel be? (b) What will be the speed of the objects as they leave the end of the barrel? (c) What net force must be exerted on a 1.50-kg object at (i) $t = 0$ and (ii) $t = 0.025$ s?

4.46. A spacecraft descends vertically near the surface of Planet X. An upward thrust of 25.0 kN from its engines slows it down at a rate of $1.20\ \text{m/s}^2$, but it speeds up at a rate of $0.80\ \text{m/s}^2$ with an upward thrust of 10.0 kN. (a) In each case, what is the direction of the acceleration of the spacecraft? (b) Draw a free-body diagram for the spacecraft. In each case, speeding up or slowing down, what is the direction of the net force on the spacecraft? (c) Apply Newton's second law to each case, slowing down or speeding up, and use this to find the spacecraft's weight near the surface of Planet X.

4.47. A 6.50-kg instrument is hanging by a vertical wire inside a space ship that is blasting off at the surface of the earth. This ship starts from rest and reaches an altitude of 276 m in 15.0 s with constant acceleration. (a) Draw a free-body diagram for the instrument during this time. Indicate which force is greater. (b) Find the force that the wire exerts on the instrument.

4.48. Suppose the rocket in Problem 4.47 is coming in for a vertical landing instead of blasting off. The captain adjusts the engine thrust so that the magnitude of the rocket's acceleration is the same as it was during blast-off. Repeat parts (a) and (b).

4.49. A gymnast of mass m climbs a vertical rope attached to the ceiling. You can ignore the weight of the rope. Draw a free-body diagram for the gymnast. Calculate the tension in the rope if the gymnast (a) climbs at a constant rate; (b) hangs motionless on the rope; (c) accelerates up the rope with an acceleration of magnitude $|\vec{a}|$; (d) slides down the rope with a downward acceleration of magnitude $|\vec{a}|$.

4.50. A loaded elevator with very worn cables has a total mass of 2200 kg, and the cables can withstand a maximum tension of 28,000 N. (a) Draw the free-body force diagram for the elevator. In terms of the forces on your diagram, what is the net force on the elevator? Apply Newton's second law to the elevator and find the maximum upward acceleration for the elevator if the cables are not to break. (b) What would be the answer to part (a) if the elevator were on the moon, where $g = 1.62 \text{ m/s}^2$?

4.51. Jumping to the Ground. A 75.0-kg man steps off a platform 3.10 m above the ground. He keeps his legs straight as he falls, but at the moment his feet touch the ground his knees begin to bend, and, treated as a particle, he moves an additional 0.60 m before coming to rest. (a) What is his speed at the instant his feet touch the ground? (b) Treating him as a particle, what is his acceleration (magnitude and direction) as he slows down, if the acceleration is assumed to be constant? (c) Draw his free-body diagram (see Section 4.6). In terms of the forces on the diagram, what is the net force on him? Use Newton's laws and the results of part (b) to calculate the average force his feet exert on the ground while he slows down. Express this force in newtons and also as a multiple of his weight.

4.52. A 4.9-N hammer head is stopped from an initial downward velocity of 3.2 m/s in a distance of 0.45 cm by a nail in a pine board. In addition to its weight, there is a 15-N downward force on the hammer head applied by the person using the hammer. Assume that the acceleration of the hammer head is constant while it is in contact with the nail and moving downward. (a) Draw a free-body diagram for the hammer head. Identify the reaction force to each action force in the diagram. (b) Calculate the downward force $\vec{F}$ exerted by the hammer head on the nail while the hammer head is in contact with the nail and moving downward. (c) Suppose the nail is in hardwood and the distance the hammer head travels in coming to rest is only 0.12 cm. The downward forces on the hammer head are the same as on part (b). What then is the force $\vec{F}$ exerted by the hammer head on the nail while the hammer head is in contact with the nail and moving downward?

4.53. A uniform cable of weight w hangs vertically downward, supported by an upward force of magnitude w at its top end. What is the tension in the cable (a) at its top end; (b) at its bottom end; (c) at its middle? Your answer to each part must include a free-body diagram. (*Hint:* For each question choose the body to analyze to be a section of the cable or a point along the cable.) (d) Graph the tension in the rope versus the distance from its top end.

4.54. The two blocks in Fig. 4.39 are connected by a heavy uniform rope with a mass of 4.00 kg. An upward force of 200 N is applied as shown. (a) Draw three free-body diagrams, one for the 6.00-kg block, one for the 4.00-kg rope, and another one for the 5.00-kg block. For each force, indicate what body exerts that force. (b) What is the acceleration of the system? (c) What is the tension at the top of the heavy rope? (d) What is the tension at the midpoint of the rope?

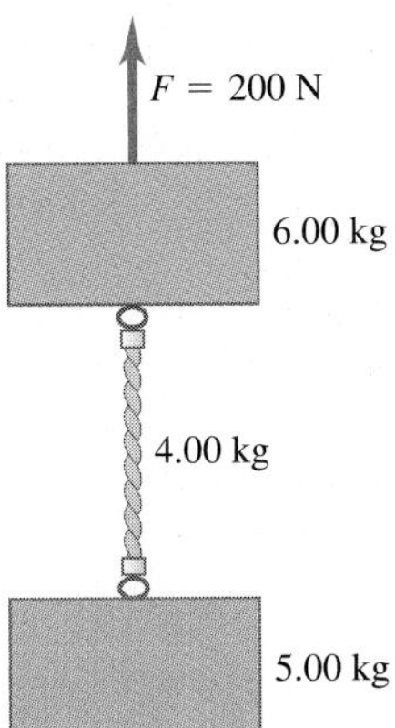

Figure **4.39** Problem 4.54.

4.55. An athlete whose mass is 90.0 kg is performing weight-lifting exercises. Starting from the rest position, he lifts, with constant acceleration, a barbell that weighs 490 N. He lifts the barbell a distance of 0.60 m in 1.6 s. (a) Draw a clearly labeled free-body force diagram for the barbell and for the athlete. (b) Use the diagrams in part (a) and Newton's laws to find the total force that his feet exert on the ground as he lifts the barbell.

4.56. A hot-air balloon consists of a basket, one passenger, and some cargo. Let the total mass be M. Even though there is an upward lift force on the balloon, the balloon is initially accelerating downward at a rate of $g/3$. (a) Draw a free-body diagram for the descending balloon. (b) Find the upward lift force in terms of the initial total weight Mg. (c) The passenger notices that he is heading straight for a waterfall and decides he needs to go up. What fraction of the total weight must he drop overboard so that the balloon accelerates *upward* at a rate of $g/2$? Assume that the upward lift force remains the same.

4.57. A student tries to raise a chain consisting of three identical links. Each link has a mass of 300 g. The three-piece chain is connected to a string and then suspended vertically, with the student holding the upper end of the string and pulling upward. Because of the student's pull, an upward force of 12 N is applied to the chain by the string. (a) Draw a free-body diagram for *each* of the links in the chain and also for the entire chain considered as a single body. (b) Use the results of part (a) and Newton's laws to find (i) the acceleration of the chain and (ii) the force exerted by the top link on the middle link.

4.58. The position of a 2.75×10^5 N training helicopter under test is given by $\vec{r} = (0.020 \text{ m/s}^3)t^3\hat{\imath} + (2.2 \text{ m/s})t\hat{\jmath} - (0.060 \text{ m/s}^2)t^2\hat{k}$. Find the net force on the helicopter at $t = 5.0$ s.

4.59. An object with mass m moves along the x-axis. Its position as a function of time is given by $x(t) = At - Bt^3$, where A and B are constants. Calculate the net force on the object as a function of time.

4.60. An object with mass m initially at rest is acted on by a force $\vec{F} = k_1\hat{\imath} + k_2t^3\hat{\jmath}$, where k_1 and k_2 are constants. Calculate the velocity $\vec{v}(t)$ of the object as a function of time.

Challenge Problems

4.61. If we know $F(t)$, the force as a function of time, for straight-line motion, Newton's second law gives us $a(t)$, the acceleration as a function of time. We can then integrate $a(t)$ to find $v(t)$ and $x(t)$. However, suppose we know $F(v)$ instead. (a) The net force on a body moving along the x-axis equals $-Cv^2$. Use Newton's second law written as $\Sigma F = m\,dv/dt$ and two integrations to show that $x - x_0 = (m/C)\ln(v_0/v)$. (b) Show that Newton's second law can be written as $\Sigma F = mv\,dv/dx$. Derive the same expression as in part (a) using this form of the second law and one integration.

4.62. An object of mass m is at rest in equilibrium at the origin. At $t = 0$ a new force $\vec{F}(t)$ is applied that has components

$$F_x(t) = k_1 + k_2y \qquad F_y(t) = k_3t$$

where k_1, k_2, and k_3 are constants. Calculate the position $\vec{r}(t)$ and velocity $\vec{v}(t)$ vectors as functions of time.

5 APPLYING NEWTON'S LAWS

LEARNING GOALS

By studying this chapter, you will learn:

- How to use Newton's first law to solve problems involving the forces that act on a body in equilibrium.
- How to use Newton's second law to solve problems involving the forces that act on an accelerating body.
- The nature of the different types of friction forces—static friction, kinetic friction, rolling friction, and fluid resistance—and how to solve problems that involve these forces.
- How to solve problems involving the forces that act on a body moving along a circular path.
- The key properties of the four fundamental forces of nature.

? Suppose a gliding bird is caught in an updraft so that it ascends at a steady rate. In this situation, which has a greater magnitude: the force of gravity or the upward force of the air on the bird?

We saw in Chapter 4 that Newton's three laws of motion, the foundation of classical mechanics, can be stated very simply. But *applying* these laws to situations such as an iceboat skating across a frozen lake, a toboggan sliding down a hill, or an airplane making a steep turn requires analytical skills and problem-solving technique. In this chapter we'll help you extend the problem-solving skills you began to develop in Chapter 4.

We begin with equilibrium problems, in which a body is at rest or moving with constant velocity. Then we generalize our problem-solving techniques to include bodies that are not in equilibrium, for which we need to deal precisely with the relationships between forces and motion. We will learn how to describe and analyze the contact force acting on a body when it rests or slides on a surface. Finally, we study the important case of uniform circular motion, in which a body moves in a circle with constant speed.

All these situations involve the concept of force, a concept we'll use throughout our study of physics. We close the chapter with a brief look at the fundamental nature of force and the classes of forces found in our physical universe.

5.1 Using Newton's First Law: Particles in Equilibrium

We learned in Chapter 4 that a body is in *equilibrium* when it is at rest or moving with constant velocity in an inertial frame of reference. A hanging lamp, a suspension bridge, an airplane flying straight and level at a constant speed—all are examples of equilibrium situations. In this section we consider only equilibrium of a body that can be modeled as a particle. (In Chapter 11, we'll consider the additional principles needed when the body can't be represented adequately as a particle.) The essential physical principle is Newton's first law: When a particle is at rest or is moving with constant velocity in an inertial frame of reference, the net force acting on it—that is, the vector sum of all the forces acting on it—must be zero:

$$\sum \vec{F} = \mathbf{0} \quad \text{(particle in equilibrium, vector form)} \tag{5.1}$$

We most often use this equation in component form:

$$\sum F_x = 0 \qquad \sum F_y = 0 \quad \text{(particle in equilibrium, component form)} \tag{5.2}$$

This section is about using Newton's first law to solve problems dealing with bodies in equilibrium. Some of these problems may seem complicated, but the important thing to remember is that *all* problems involving particles in equilibrium are done in the same way. Problem-Solving Strategy 5.1 details the steps you need to follow for any and all such problems. Study this strategy carefully, look at how it's applied in the worked-out examples, and try to apply it yourself when you solve assigned problems.

Problem-Solving Strategy 5.1 Newton's First Law: Equilibrium of a Particle

IDENTIFY *the relevant concepts:* You must use Newton's first law for any problem that involves forces acting on a body in equilibrium—that is, either at rest or moving with constant velocity. For example, a car is in equilibrium when it's parked, but also when it's traveling down a straight road at a steady speed.

If the problem involves more than one body and the bodies interact with each other, you'll also need to use Newton's *third* law. This law allows you to relate the force that one body exerts on a second body to the force that the second body exerts on the first one.

Be certain that you identify the target variable(s). Common target variables in equilibrium problems include the magnitude of one of the forces, the components of a force, or the direction (angle) of a force.

SET UP *the problem* using the following steps:

1. Draw a very simple sketch of the physical situation, showing dimensions and angles. You don't have to be an artist!
2. Draw a free-body diagram for each body that is in equilibrium. For the present, we consider the body as a particle, so you can represent it as a large dot. In your free-body diagram, *do not* include the other bodies that interact with it, such as a surface it may be resting on, or a rope pulling on it.
3. Ask yourself what is interacting with the body by touching it or in any other way. On your free-body diagram, draw a force vector for each interaction and label each force with a symbol representing the *magnitude* of the force. If you know the angle at which a force is directed, draw the angle accurately and label it. Include the body's weight, except in cases where the body has negligible mass (and hence negligible weight). If the mass is given, use $w = mg$ to find the weight. A surface in contact with the body exerts a normal force perpendicular to the surface and possibly a friction force parallel to the surface. A rope or chain exerts a pull (never a push) in a direction along its length.
4. *Do not* show in the free-body diagram any forces exerted *by* the body on any other body. The sums in Eqs. (5.1) and (5.2) include only forces that act *on* the body. For each force on the body, ask yourself "What other body causes that force?" If you can't answer that question, you may be imagining a force that isn't there.
5. Choose a set of coordinate axes and include them in your free-body diagram. (If there is more than one body in the problem, choose axes for each body separately.) Label the positive direction for each axis. If a body rests or slides on a plane surface, it usually simplifies the solution to take the axes in the directions parallel and perpendicular to this surface, even when the plane is tilted.

EXECUTE *the solution* as follows:

1. Find the components of each force along each of the body's coordinate axes. Draw a wiggly line through each force vector that has been replaced by its components, so you don't count it twice. Remember that while the *magnitude* of a force is always positive, the *component* of a force along a particular direction may be positive or negative.
2. Set the algebraic sum of all x-components of force equal to zero. In a separate equation, set the algebraic sum of all y-components equal to zero. (*Never* add x- and y-components in a single equation.)
3. If there are two or more bodies, repeat all of the above steps for each body. If the bodies interact with each other, use Newton's third law to relate the forces they exert on each other.
4. Make sure that you have as many independent equations as the number of unknown quantities. Then solve these equations to obtain the target variables.

EVALUATE *your answer:* Look at your results and ask whether they make sense. When the result is a symbolic expression or formula, try to think of special cases (particular values or extreme cases for the various quantities) for which you can guess what the results ought to be. Check to see that your formula works in these particular cases.

Example 5.1 One-dimensional equilibrium: Tension in a massless rope

A gymnast with mass $m_G = 50.0$ kg suspends herself from the lower end of a hanging rope. The upper end of the rope is attached to the gymnasium ceiling. What is the gymnast's weight? What force (magnitude and direction) does the rope exert on her? What is the tension at the top of the rope? Assume that the mass of the rope itself is negligible.

SOLUTION

IDENTIFY: The gymnast and the rope are in equilibrium, so we can apply Newton's first law to both bodies. We'll also use Newton's third law to relate the forces that the gymnast and the rope exert on each other. the target variables are the weight of the gymnast, w_G; the force that the rope exerts on the gymnast (call it $T_{\text{R on G}}$); and the tension that the ceiling exerts on the top of the rope (call it $T_{\text{C on R}}$).

SET UP: We sketch the situation (Fig. 5.1a) and draw separate free-body diagrams for the gymnast (Fig. 5.1b) and the rope (Fig. 5.1c). We take the positive y-axis to be upward, as shown. Each force acts in the vertical direction and so has only a y-component.

The two forces $T_{\text{R on G}}$ and $T_{\text{G on R}}$ are the upward force of the rope on the gymnast (in Fig. 5.1b) and the downward force of the gymnast on the rope (in Fig. 5.1c). These forces form an action–reaction pair, so they must have the same magnitude.

Note also that the gymnast's weight w_G is the attractive (downward) force exerted on the *gymnast* by the *earth*. Its reaction force is the equal to and opposite the attractive (upward) force exerted on the *earth* by the *gymnast*. This force acts on the earth, not on the gymnast, so it doesn't appear in her free-body diagram (Fig. 5.1b). Compare the discussion of the apple in Conceptual Example 4.9 (Section 4.5). Similarly, the force that the rope exerts on the ceiling doesn't appear in Fig. 5.1c.

5.1 Our sketches for this problem.

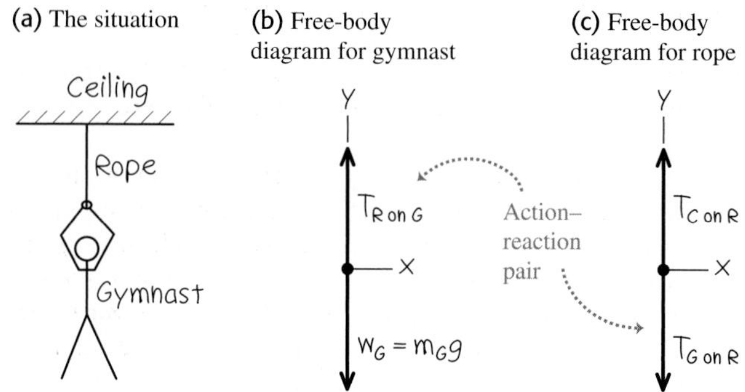

EXECUTE: The magnitude of the gymnast's weight is the product of her mass and the acceleration due to gravity, g:

$$w_G = m_G g = (50.0\text{ kg})(9.80\text{ m/s}^2) = 490\text{ N}$$

This force points in the negative y-direction, so its y-component is $-w_G$. The upward force exerted by the rope has unknown magnitude $T_{\text{R on G}}$ and positive y-component $+T_{\text{R on G}}$. Because the gymnast is in equilibrium, the sum of the y-components of force acting on her must be zero:

$$\text{Gymnast:} \quad \sum F_y = T_{\text{R on G}} + (-w_G) = 0 \quad \text{so}$$
$$T_{\text{R on G}} = w_G = 490\text{ N}$$

The rope pulls *up* on the gymnast with a force $T_{\text{R on G}}$ of magnitude 490 N. By Newton's third law, the gymnast pulls *down* on the rope with a force of the same magnitude, $T_{\text{G on R}} = 490$ N.

The rope is also in equilibrium. We have assumed that it is weightless, so the upward force of magnitude $T_{\text{C on R}}$ that the ceiling exerts on its top end must make the *net* vertical force on the rope equal to zero. Expressed as an equation, this says

$$\text{Rope:} \quad \sum F_y = T_{\text{C on R}} + (-T_{\text{G on R}}) = 0 \quad \text{so}$$
$$T_{\text{C on R}} = T_{\text{G on R}} = 490\text{ N}$$

EVALUATE: The *tension* at any point in the rope is the force that acts at that point. For this weightless rope, the tension $T_{\text{G on R}}$ at the lower end has the same value as the tension $T_{\text{C on R}}$ at the upper end. Indeed, for an ideal weightless rope, the tension has the same value at any point along the rope's length. (Compare the discussion of Conceptual Example 4.10 in Section 4.5.)

Note that we have defined tension to be the *magnitude* of a force, so it is always positive. But the y-component of force acting on the rope at its lower end is $-T_{\text{G on R}} = -490$ N.

Example 5.2 One-dimensional equilibrium: Tension in a rope with mass

Suppose that in Example 5.1, the weight of the rope is not negligible but is 120 N. Find the tension at each end of the rope.

SOLUTION

IDENTIFY: As in Example 5.1, the target variables are the magnitudes $T_{\text{G on R}}$ and $T_{\text{C on R}}$ of the forces that act at the bottom and top of the rope, respectively. Once again, we'll apply Newton's first law to the gymnast and to the rope, and use Newton's third law to relate the forces that the gymnast and rope exert on each other.

SET UP: Again we draw separate free-body diagrams for the gymnast (Fig. 5.2a) and the rope (Fig. 5.2b). The only difference from Example 5.1 is that there are now *three* forces acting on the rope: the downward force exerted by the gymnast $(T_{\text{G on R}})$, the upward force exerted by the ceiling $(T_{\text{C on R}})$, and the weight of the rope, of magnitude $w_R = 120$ N.

EXECUTE: The gymnast's free-body diagram is the same as in Example 5.1, so her equilibrium condition is also the same. From Newton's third law, $T_{\text{R on G}} = T_{\text{G on R}}$, and we have

$$\text{Gymnast:} \quad \sum F_y = T_{\text{R on G}} + (-w_G) = 0 \quad \text{so}$$
$$T_{\text{R on G}} = T_{\text{G on R}} = w_G = 490\text{ N}$$

The equilibrium condition $\sum F_y = 0$ for the rope is

$$\text{Rope:} \quad \sum F_y = T_{\text{C on R}} + (-T_{\text{G on R}}) + (-w_R) = 0$$

Note that the y-component of $T_{\text{C on R}}$ is positive because it points in the $+y$-direction, but the y-components of both $T_{\text{G on R}}$ and w_R are

5.2 Our sketches for this problem, including the weight of the rope.

(a) Free-body diagram for gymnast

(b) Free-body diagram for rope

(c) Free-body diagram for gymnast and rope as a composite body

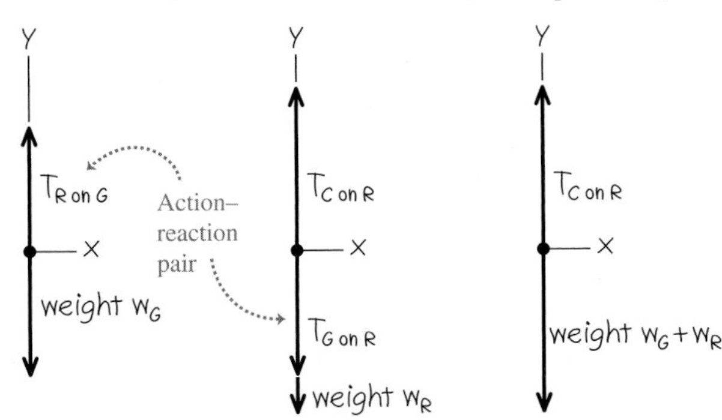

negative. When we solve for $T_{\mathrm{C\ on\ R}}$ and substitute the values $T_{\mathrm{G\ on\ R}} = T_{\mathrm{R\ on\ G}} = 490\ \mathrm{N}$ and $w_{\mathrm{R}} = 120\ \mathrm{N}$, we find

$$T_{\mathrm{C\ on\ R}} = T_{\mathrm{G\ on\ R}} + w_{\mathrm{R}} = 490\ \mathrm{N} + 120\ \mathrm{N} = 610\ \mathrm{N}$$

EVALUATE: When we include the weight of the rope, the tension is *different* at the rope's two ends. The force $T_{\mathrm{C\ on\ R}}$ exerted by the ceiling has to hold up both the 490-N weight of the gymnast and the 120-N weight of the rope, so $T_{\mathrm{C\ on\ R}} = 610\ \mathrm{N}$.

To see this more explicitly, draw a free-body diagram for a composite body consisting of the gymnast and rope considered as a unit (Fig. 5.2c). Only two external forces act on this composite body: the force $T_{\mathrm{C\ on\ R}}$ exerted by the ceiling and the total weight $w_{\mathrm{G}} + w_{\mathrm{R}} = 490\ \mathrm{N} + 120\ \mathrm{N} = 610\ \mathrm{N}$. (The forces $T_{\mathrm{G\ on\ R}}$ and $T_{\mathrm{R\ on\ G}}$ are *internal* to the composite body. Since Newton's first law involves only *external* forces, the internal forces play no role.) Hence Newton's first law applied to this composite body is

$$\text{Composite body:} \qquad \sum F_y = T_{\mathrm{C\ on\ R}} + [-(w_{\mathrm{G}} + w_{\mathrm{R}})] = 0$$

and so $T_{\mathrm{C\ on\ R}} = w_{\mathrm{G}} + w_{\mathrm{R}} = 610\ \mathrm{N}$.

This method of treating the gymnast and rope as a composite body seems a lot simpler, and you may be wondering why we didn't use it first. The answer is that we can't find the tension $T_{\mathrm{G\ on\ R}}$ at the bottom of the rope by this method. *Moral: Whenever you have more than one body in a problem involving Newton's laws, the safest approach is to treat each body separately.*

Example 5.3 Two-dimensional equilibrium

In Fig. 5.3a, a car engine with weight w hangs from a chain that is linked at ring O to two other chains, one fastened to the ceiling and the other to the wall. Find the tension in each of the three chains in terms of w. The weights of the ring and chains are negligible.

SOLUTION

IDENTIFY: The target variables are the tensions T_1, T_2, and T_3 in the three chains (Fig. 5.3a). It may seem strange that we neglect the weight of the chains and ring in this example, while in Example 5.2 we did *not* neglect the weight of a mere rope. The reason is that the weight of the chains or ring is very small compared to the weight of the massive engine. By contrast, in Example 5.2 the rope weighed a reasonable fraction of the gymnast's weight (120 N compared to 490 N).

All the bodies in the example are in equilibrium, so we'll use Newton's first law to determine T_1, T_2, and T_3. We need three simultaneous equations, one for each target variable. However, applying Newton's first law to just one body gives us just *two* equations, as in Eq. (5.2). So to solve the problem, we'll have to consider more than one body in equilibrium. We'll look at the engine (which is acted on by T_1) and the ring (which is connected to all three chains and so is acted on by all three tensions).

SET UP: Figures 5.3b and 5.3c show our free-body diagrams, including an x-y coordinate system, for the engine and the ring, respectively.

The two forces acting on the engine are its weight w and the upward force T_1 exerted by the vertical chain; the three forces acting on the ring are the tensions from the vertical chain (T_1), the horizontal chain (T_2), and the slanted chain (T_3). Because the vertical chain has negligible weight, it exerts forces of the same magnitude T_1 at both of its ends: upward on the engine in Fig. 5.3b and

5.3 (a) The situation. (b), (c) Our free-body diagrams.

(a) Engine, chains, and ring

60°
T_3
T_2
O
T_1

(b) Free-body diagram for engine

(c) Free-body diagram for ring O

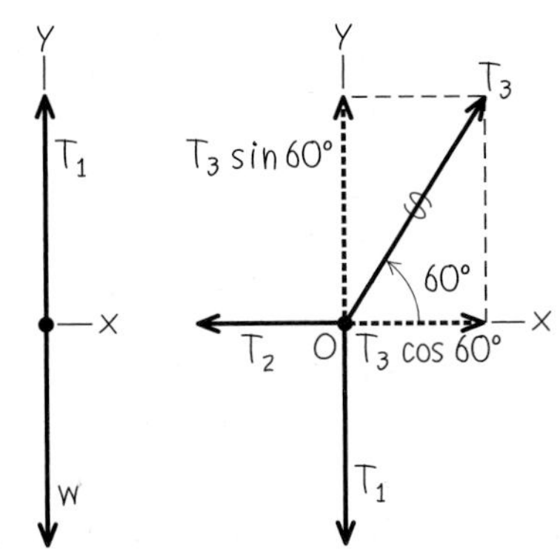

Continued

downward on the ring in Fig. 5.3c (see Example 5.1). If the weight were not negligible, these two forces would have different magnitudes, as was the case for the rope in Example 5.2. We're also neglecting the weight of the ring, which is why it isn't included in the forces in Fig. 5.3c.

EXECUTE: The forces acting on the engine are along the y-axis only, so Newton's first law says

$$\text{Engine:} \quad \sum F_y = T_1 + (-w) = 0 \qquad \text{and} \qquad T_1 = w$$

The horizontal and slanted chains do not exert forces on the engine itself because they are not attached to it. These forces appear when we apply Newton's first law to the ring, however.

In the free-body diagram for the ring (Fig. 5.3c), remember that T_1, T_2, and T_3 are the *magnitudes* of the forces. We first resolve the force with magnitude T_3 into its x- and y-components. The ring is in equilibrium, so we then write separate equations stating that the x- and y-components of the net force on the ring are zero. (Remember from Problem-Solving Strategy 5.1 that we *never* add x- and y-components together in a single equation.) We find

$$\text{Ring:} \quad \sum F_x = T_3 \cos 60° + (-T_2) = 0$$
$$\text{Ring:} \quad \sum F_y = T_3 \sin 60° + (-T_1) = 0$$

Because $T_1 = w$ (from the engine equation), we can rewrite the second ring equation as

$$T_3 = \frac{T_1}{\sin 60°} = \frac{w}{\sin 60°} = 1.155w$$

We can now use this result in the first ring equation:

$$T_2 = T_3 \cos 60° = w\frac{\cos 60°}{\sin 60°} = 0.577w$$

So we can express all three tensions as multiples of the weight w of the engine, which we assume is known. To summarize,

$$T_1 = w$$
$$T_2 = 0.577w$$
$$T_3 = 1.155w$$

EVALUATE: Our results show that the chain attached to the ceiling exerts a force on the ring of magnitude T_3, which is *greater* than the weight of the engine. If this seems strange, note that the vertical component of this force is equal to T_1, which in turn is equal to w. But since this force also has a horizontal component, its magnitude T_3 must be somewhat larger than w. Hence the chain attached to the ceiling is under the greatest tension and is the one most susceptible to breaking.

You may have thought at first that the most important body in this problem was the engine. But to get enough equations to solve the problem, we also had to consider the forces acting on a second body (the ring connecting the chains). Situations like this are fairly common in equilibrium problems, so keep this technique in mind.

Example 5.4 An inclined plane

A car of weight w rests on a slanted ramp leading to a car-transporter trailer (Fig. 5.4a). Only a cable running from the trailer to the car prevents the car from rolling backward off the ramp. (The car's brakes are off and its transmission is in neutral.) Find the tension in the cable and the force that the tracks exert on the car's tires.

SOLUTION

IDENTIFY: The car is in equilibrium, so once again we use Newton's first law. The ramp exerts a separate force on each of the car's tires, but for simplicity we lump all of these together into a single force. For a further simplification, we'll assume that there's very little friction on the car, and so we ignore the component of this force on the car that acts *parallel* to the ramp (see Fig. 4.2b).

5.4 A cable holds a car at rest on a ramp.

(a) Car on ramp

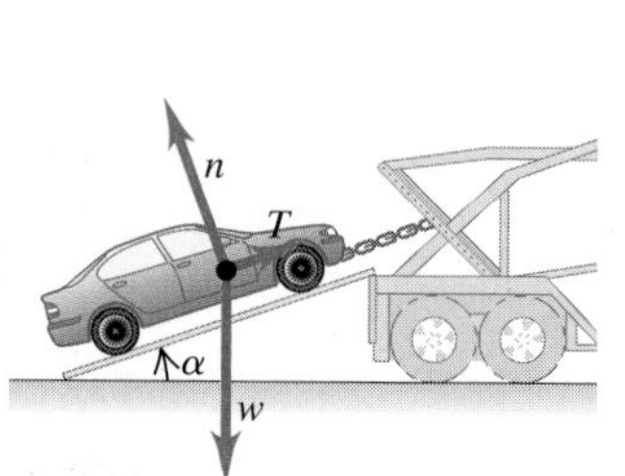

(b) Free-body diagram for car

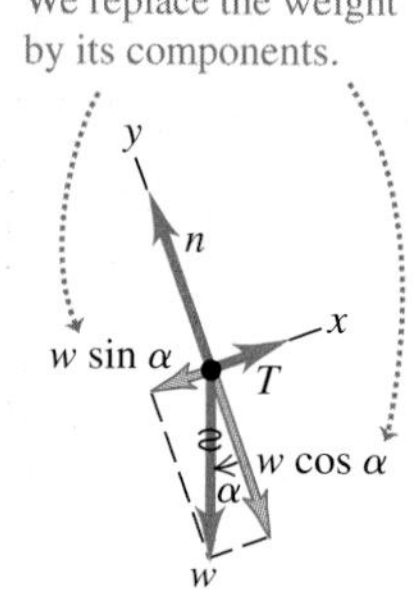

(We'll return to the friction force in Section 5.3.) Hence we can say that the ramp only exerts a force on the car that is *perpendicular* to the tracks. This force appears because the atoms on the surface of the track resist having the atoms of the tires squeezed into them. As in Section 4.1, we call this force the *normal* force (see Fig. 4.2a). The two target variables are the magnitude n of the normal force and the magnitude T of the tension in the cable.

SET UP: Figure 5.4b shows a free-body diagram for the car. The three forces acting on the car are its weight (magnitude w), the tension in the cable (magnitude T), and the normal force (magnitude n). Note that the normal force acts up and to the left because it's preventing the car from penetrating into the solid tracks.

We choose the x- and y-axes to be parallel and perpendicular to the ramp as shown. This choice makes the problem easier to analyze because only the weight force has both an x- and y-component. If we chose axes that were horizontal and vertical, our job would be harder because we'd need to find x- and y-components for *two* forces (the normal force and the tension).

Note that the angle α between the ramp and the horizontal is equal to the angle α between the weight vector $\vec{w}$ and the normal to the plane of the ramp.

EXECUTE: To write down the x- and y-components of Newton's first law, we need to find the components of the weight. One complication is that the angle α in Fig. 5.4b is *not* measured from the $+x$-axis toward the $+y$-axis. Hence we *cannot* use Eqs. (1.6) directly to find the components. (You may want to review Section 1.8 to make sure that you understand this important point.)

One approach to finding the components of $\vec{w}$ is to consider the right triangles in Fig. 5.4b. The sine of α is the magnitude of the x-component of $\vec{w}$ (that is, the side of the triangle opposite α) divided by the magnitude w (the hypotenuse of the triangle). Similarly, the cosine of α is the magnitude of the y-component (the side of the triangle adjacent to α) divided by w. Both components are negative, so $w_x = -w\sin\alpha$ and $w_y = -w\cos\alpha$.

Another approach is to recognize that one component of $\vec{w}$ must involve $\sin\alpha$ while the other component involves $\cos\alpha$. To decide which is which, draw the free-body diagram so that the angle α is noticeably smaller or larger than 45°. (You'll have to fight the natural tendency to draw such angles as being close to 45°.) We've drawn Fig. 5.4b so that α is smaller than 45°, so $\sin\alpha$ is less than $\cos\alpha$. The figure shows that the x-component of $\vec{w}$ is smaller than the y-component, so the x-component must involve $\sin\alpha$ and the y-component must involve $\cos\alpha$. We again find $w_x = -w\sin\alpha$ and $w_y = -w\cos\alpha$.

In Fig. 5.4b we draw a wiggly line through the original vector representing the weight to remind us not to count it twice. The equilibrium conditions then give us

$$\sum F_x = T + (-w\sin\alpha) = 0$$
$$\sum F_y = n + (-w\cos\alpha) = 0$$

Be sure you understand how these signs are related to our choice of coordinates. Remember that, by definition, T, w, and n are all *magnitudes* of vectors and are therefore all positive.

Solving these equations for T and n, we find

$$T = w\sin\alpha$$
$$n = w\cos\alpha$$

EVALUATE: Our answers for T and n depend on the value of α; we can check this dependence by looking at some special cases. If the angle α is zero, then $\sin\alpha = 0$ and $\cos\alpha = 1$. In this case, the ramp is horizontal; our answers tell us that no cable tension T is needed to hold the car, and the normal force n is equal in magnitude to the weight. If the angle is 90°, then $\sin\alpha = 1$ and $\cos\alpha = 0$. Then the cable tension T equals the weight w, and the normal force n is zero. Are these the results you would expect for these particular cases?

CAUTION **Normal force and weight may not be equal** It's a common error to automatically assume that the magnitude n of the normal force is equal to the weight w. But our result shows that this is *not* true in general. It's always best to treat n as a variable and solve for its value, as we have done here.

? How would the answers for T and n be affected if the car were not stationary but were being pulled up the ramp at a constant speed? This, too, is an equilibrium situation, since the car's velocity is constant. So the calculation is exactly the same, and T and n have the same values as when the car is at rest. (It's true that T must be greater than $w\sin\alpha$ to *start* the car moving up the ramp, but that's not what we asked.)

Example 5.5 Tension over a frictionless pulley

Blocks of granite are to be hauled up a 15° slope out of a quarry, and dirt is to be dumped into the quarry to fill up old holes. To simplify the process, you design a system in which a granite block on a cart with steel wheels (weight w_1, including both block and cart) is pulled uphill on steel rails by a dirt-filled bucket (weight w_2, including both dirt and bucket) dropping vertically into the quarry (Fig. 5.5a). How must the weights w_1 and w_2 be related in order for the system to move with constant speed? Ignore friction in the pulley and wheels and the weight of the cable.

SOLUTION

IDENTIFY: The cart and bucket each move with a constant velocity (that is, in a straight line at constant speed). Hence each body is in equilibrium, and we can apply Newton's first law to each.

Our two target variables are the weights w_1 and w_2. The forces that act on the bucket are its weight w_2 and an upward tension exerted by the cable. The cart has *three* forces acting on it: its weight w_1, a normal force of magnitude n exerted by the rails, and

5.5 (a) The situation. (b) Our idealized model. (c), (d) Our free-body diagrams.

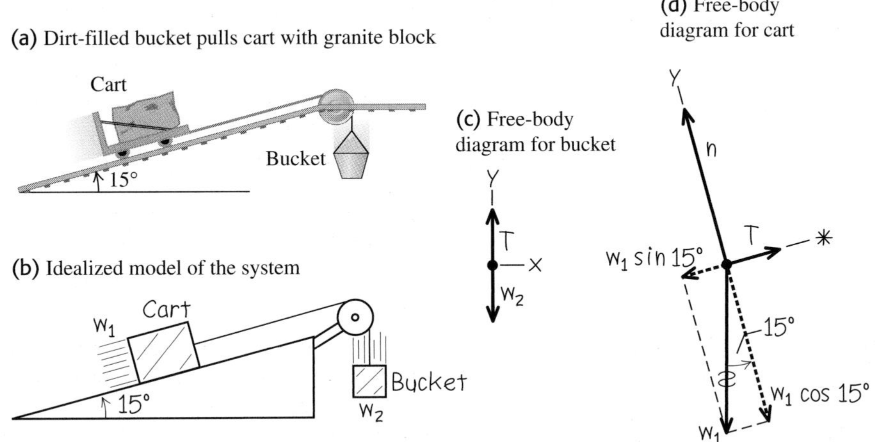

Continued

a tension force from the cable. (We're ignoring friction, so we're assuming that the rails exert no force parallel to the incline.) This is exactly like the situation for the car on the ramp in Example 5.4. As in that example, the forces on the cart are not all along the same direction, so we'll need to use both components of Newton's first law in Eq. (5.2).

We're assuming that the cable has negligible weight, so the tension forces that the rope exerts on the cart and on the bucket have the same magnitude T.

SET UP: Figure 5.5b shows our idealized model for the system, and Figs. 5.5c and 5.5d show the free-body diagrams we draw. Note that we're free to orient the axes differently for each body; the choices shown are the most convenient ones. As we did for the car in Example 5.4, we represent the weight of the granite block in terms of its x- and y-components.

EXECUTE: Applying $\sum F_y = 0$ to the dirt-filled bucket in Fig. 5.5c, we find

$$\sum F_y = T + (-w_2) = 0 \qquad \text{so} \qquad T = w_2$$

Applying $\sum F_x = 0$ to the block and cart in Fig. 5.5d, we get

$$\sum F_x = T + (-w_1 \sin 15°) = 0 \qquad \text{so} \qquad T = w_1 \sin 15°$$

Equating the two expressions for T, we find

$$w_2 = w_1 \sin 15° = 0.26 w_1$$

EVALUATE: Our analysis doesn't depend on the direction of motion, only on the velocity being constant. Hence the system can move with constant speed in *either* direction if the weight of dirt and bucket totals 26% of the weight of the granite block and cart. What would happen if w_2 were greater than $0.26w_1$? If it were less than $0.26w_1$?

Notice that we didn't need to apply the equation $\sum F_y = 0$ to the cart and block; this would be useful only if we wanted to find the value of n. Can you show that $n = w_1 \cos 15°$?

5.6 Correct and incorrect free-body diagrams for a falling body.

(a)

Only the force of gravity acts on this falling fruit.

(b) Correct free-body diagram

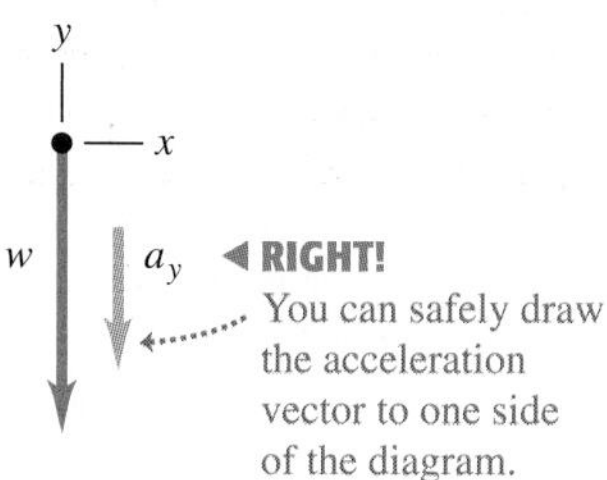
y
x
w
a_y
RIGHT!
You can safely draw the acceleration vector to one side of the diagram.

(c) Incorrect free-body diagram

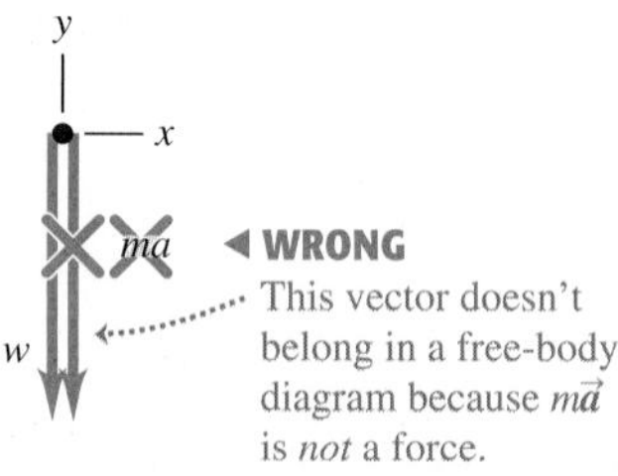
y
x
$m\vec{a}$
w
WRONG
This vector doesn't belong in a free-body diagram because $m\vec{a}$ is *not* a force.

ActivPhysics
ONLINE

2.1.5 Car Race
2.2 Lifting a Crate
2.3 Lowering a Crate
2.4 Rocket Blasts Off
2.5 Modified Atwood Machine

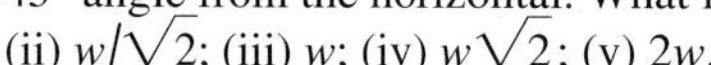

Test Your Understanding of Section 5.1 A traffic light of weight w hangs from two lightweight cables, one on each side of the light. Each cable hangs at a 45° angle from the horizontal. What is the tension in each cable? (i) $w/2$; (ii) $w/\sqrt{2}$; (iii) w; (iv) $w\sqrt{2}$; (v) $2w$.

5.2 Using Newton's Second Law: Dynamics of Particles

We are now ready to discuss *dynamics* problems. In these problems, we apply Newton's second law to bodies on which the net force is *not* zero, so the bodies are *not* in equilibrium and hence are accelerating. The net force is equal to the mass of the body times its acceleration:

$$\sum \vec{F} = m\vec{a} \qquad \text{(Newton's second law, vector form)} \qquad (5.3)$$

We most often use this relationship in component form:

$$\sum F_x = ma_x \qquad \sum F_y = ma_y \qquad \text{(Newton's second law, component form)} \qquad (5.4)$$

The following problem-solving strategy is very similar to Problem-Solving Strategy 5.1 for equilibrium problems in Section 5.1. We urge you to study it carefully, watch how we apply it in our examples, and use it when you tackle the end-of-chapter problems. Remember that you can solve *any* dynamics problem using this strategy.

CAUTION $m\vec{a}$ **doesn't belong in free-body diagrams** Remember that the quantity $m\vec{a}$ is the *result* of forces acting on a body, *not* a force itself; it's not a push or a pull exerted by anything in the body's environment. When you draw the free-body diagram for an accelerating body (like the fruit in Fig. 5.6a), make sure you *never* include the "$m\vec{a}$ force" because *there is no such force* (Fig. 5.6c). You should review Section 4.3 if you're not clear on this point. Sometimes we draw the acceleration vector $\vec{a}$ *alongside* a free-body diagram, as in Fig. 5.6b. But we *never* draw the acceleration vector with its tail touching the body (a position reserved exclusively for the forces that act on the body).

Problem-Solving Strategy 5.2 Newton's Second Law: Dynamics of Particles

IDENTIFY *the relevant concepts:* You have to use Newton's second law for *any* problem that involves forces acting on an accelerating body.

Identify the target variable—usually an acceleration or a force. If the target variable is something else, you'll need to select another concept to use. For example, suppose you want to find how fast a sled is moving when it reaches the bottom of a hill. This means your target variable is the sled's final velocity. Newton's second law will let you find the sled's acceleration; you'll then use the constant-acceleration relationships from Section 2.4 to find velocity from acceleration.

SET UP *the problem* using the following steps:

1. Draw a simple sketch of the situation. Identify one or more moving bodies to which you'll apply Newton's second law.
2. For each body you identified, draw a free-body diagram that shows all the forces acting *on* the body. Remember, the acceleration of a body is determined by the forces that act on it, *not* by the forces that it exerts on anything else. Make sure you can answer the question "What other body is applying this force?" for each force in your diagram. Never include the quantity $m\vec{a}$ in your free-body diagram; it's not a force!
3. Label each force with an algebraic symbol for the force's *magnitude.* (Remember that magnitudes are always positive. Minus signs show up later when you take components of the forces.) Usually, one of the forces will be the body's weight; it's usually best to label this as $w = mg$. If a numerical value of mass is given, you can compute the corresponding weight.
4. Choose your x- and y-coordinate axes for each body, and show them in its free-body diagram. Be sure to indicate the positive direction for each axis. If you know the direction of the acceleration, it usually simplifies things to take one positive axis along that direction. If your problem involves more than one object and the objects accelerate in different directions, you can use a different set of axes for each object.
5. In addition to Newton's second law, $\sum\vec{F} = m\vec{a}$, identify any other equations you might need. (You need as many equations as there are target variables.) For example, you might need one or more of the equations for motion with constant acceleration. If more than one body is involved, there may be relationships among their motions; for example, they may be connected by a rope. Express any such relationships as equations relating the accelerations of the various bodies.

EXECUTE *the solution* as follows:

1. For each object, determine the components of the forces along each of the object's coordinate axes. When you represent a force in terms of its components, draw a wiggly line through the original force vector to remind you not to include it twice.
2. For each object, write a separate equation for each component of Newton's second law, as in Eq. (5.4).
3. Make a list of all the known and unknown quantities. In your list, identify the target variable or variables.
4. Check that you have as many equations as there are unknowns. If you have too few equations, go back to step 5 of "Set up the problem." If you have too many equations, perhaps there is an unknown quantity that you haven't identified as such.
5. Do the easy part—the math! Solve the equations to find the target variable(s).

EVALUATE *your answer:* Does your answer have the correct units? (When appropriate, use the conversion $1\text{ N} = 1\text{ kg}\cdot\text{m/s}^2$.) Does it have the correct algebraic sign? (If the problem is about a sled sliding downhill, you probably took the positive x-axis to point down the hill. If you then find that the sled has a negative acceleration—that is, the acceleration is uphill—something went wrong in your calculations.) When possible, consider particular values or extreme cases of quantities and compare the results with your intuitive expectations. Ask, "Does this result make sense?"

Example 5.6 Straight-line motion with a constant force

An iceboat is at rest on a perfectly frictionless horizontal surface (Fig. 5.7a). A wind is blowing (along the direction of the runners) so that 4.0 s after the iceboat is released, it attains a velocity of 6.0 m/s (about 22 km/h, or 13 mi/h). What constant horizontal force F_W does the wind exert on the iceboat? The mass of iceboat and rider is 200 kg.

SOLUTION

IDENTIFY: Our target variable is one of the forces (F_W) acting on the iceboat, so we'll need to use Newton's second law. This law involves forces and acceleration, but the acceleration isn't given; we'll need to find it. Since the wind is assumed to exert a constant force, the resulting acceleration is constant and we'll be able to use one of the constant-acceleration formulas from Section 2.4.

SET UP: Figure 5.7b shows our free-body diagram for the iceboat and rider considered as a unit. The forces acting on this body are the weight w, the normal force n exerted by the surface, and the

5.7 (a) The situation. (b) Our free-body diagram.

(a) Iceboat and rider on frictionless ice

(b) Free-body diagram for iceboat and rider

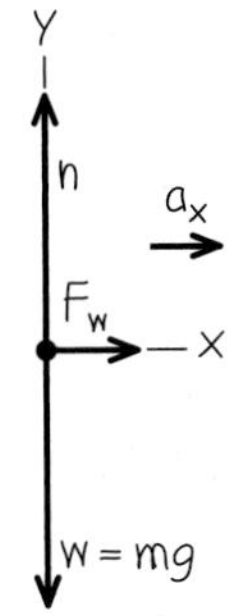

Continued

horizontal force F_W (our target variable). The net force and hence the acceleration are to the right, so we chose the positive x-axis in this direction.

To find the x-acceleration, note what we are told about the iceboat's motion: It starts at rest so that its initial x-velocity is $v_{0x} = 0$, and it attains an x-velocity $v_x = 6.0\ \text{m/s}$ after an elapsed time $t = 4.0\ \text{s}$. An equation we can use to relate the x-acceleration a_x to these quantities is Eq. (2.8), $v_x = v_{0x} + a_x t$.

EXECUTE: The *known* quantities are the mass $m = 200\ \text{kg}$, the initial and final x-velocities $v_{0x} = 0$ and $v_x = 6.0\ \text{m/s}$, and the elapsed time $t = 4.0\ \text{s}$. The three *unknown* quantities are the acceleration a_x, the normal force n, and the horizontal force F_W (the target variable). Hence we need three equations.

The first two equations are the x- and y-equations for Newton's second law. The force F_W is in the positive x-direction, while the forces n and mg are in the positive and negative y-directions, respectively. Hence we have

$$\sum F_x = F_W = ma_x$$
$$\sum F_y = n + (-mg) = 0$$

The third equation we need is the constant-acceleration relationship

$$v_x = v_{0x} + a_x t$$

To find F_W, we first solve the constant-acceleration equation for a_x and then substitute this into the $\sum F_x$ equation:

$$a_x = \frac{v_x - v_{0x}}{t} = \frac{6.0\ \text{m/s} - 0\ \text{m/s}}{4.0\ \text{s}} = 1.5\ \text{m/s}^2$$
$$F_W = ma_x = (200\ \text{kg})(1.5\ \text{m/s}^2) = 300\ \text{kg}\cdot\text{m/s}^2$$

One $\text{kg}\cdot\text{m/s}^2$ is the same as 1 newton (N), so the final answer is

$$F_W = 300\ \text{N} \qquad (\text{about } 67\ \text{lb})$$

Note that we did not need the $\sum F_y$ equation at all to find F_W. We would need this equation if we wanted to find the normal force n:

$$n - mg = 0$$
$$n = mg = (200\ \text{kg})(9.8\ \text{m/s}^2)$$
$$= 2.0 \times 10^3\ \text{N} \qquad (\text{about } 450\ \text{lb})$$

EVALUATE: Our answers for F_W and n have the correct units for a force, as they should. The magnitude n of the normal force is equal to mg, the combined weight of the iceboat and rider, because the surface is horizontal and these are the only vertical forces that act. Does it seem reasonable that the force F_W is substantially *less* than mg?

Example 5.7 Straight-line motion with friction

Suppose a constant horizontal friction force with magnitude 100 N opposes the motion of the iceboat in Example 5.6. In this case, what constant force F_W must the wind exert on the iceboat to cause the same constant x-acceleration $a_x = 1.5\ \text{m/s}^2$?

SOLUTION

IDENTIFY: Once again the target variable is F_W. We are given the x-acceleration, so to find F_W all we need is Newton's second law.

SET UP: Figure 5.8 shows our new free-body diagram. The only difference from Fig. 5.7b is the addition of the friction force $\vec{f}$, which points opposite to the motion. (Note that its *magnitude*, $f = 100\ \text{N}$, is a positive quantity but that its *component* in the x-direction is negative, equal to $-f$ or -100 N.)

5.8 Our free-body diagram for the iceboat and rider with a friction force $\vec{f}$ opposing the motion.

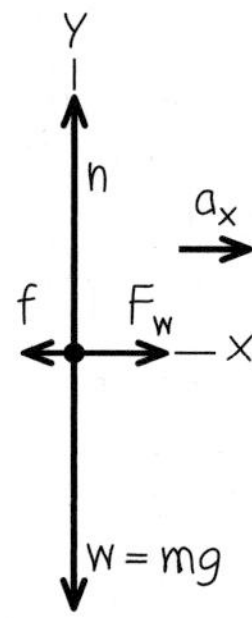

EXECUTE: Two forces now have x-components: the force of the wind and the friction force. The x-component of Newton's second law gives

$$\sum F_x = F_W + (-f) = ma_x$$
$$F_W = ma_x + f = (200\ \text{kg})(1.5\ \text{m/s}^2) + (100\ \text{N}) = 400\ \text{N}$$

EVALUATE: Because there is friction, a greater force F_W is needed than in Example 5.6. We need 100 N to overcome friction and 300 N more to give the iceboat the necessary acceleration.

Example 5.8 Tension in an elevator cable

An elevator and its load have a total mass of 800 kg (Fig. 5.9a). The elevator is originally moving downward at 10.0 m/s; it slows to a stop with constant acceleration in a distance of 25.0 m. Find the tension T in the supporting cable while the elevator is being brought to rest.

SOLUTION

IDENTIFY: The target variable is the tension T, which we will find using Newton's second law. As in Example 5.6, we'll have to determine the acceleration using the constant-acceleration formulas.

SET UP: Our free-body diagram in Fig. 5.9b shows the two forces acting on the elevator: its weight w and the tension force T of the cable. The elevator is moving downward with decreasing speed, so its acceleration is upward; we chose the positive y-axis to be in this direction.

The elevator is moving in the negative y-direction, so its initial y-velocity v_{0y} and its y-displacement $y - y_0$ are both negative: $v_{0y} = -10.0\ \text{m/s}$ and $y - y_0 = -25.0\ \text{m}$. The final y-velocity is $v_y = 0$. To find the y-acceleration a_y from this information, we'll use Eq. (2.13) in the form $v_y^2 = v_{0y}^2 + 2a_y(y - y_0)$. Once we

5.9 (a) The situation. (b) Our free-body diagram.

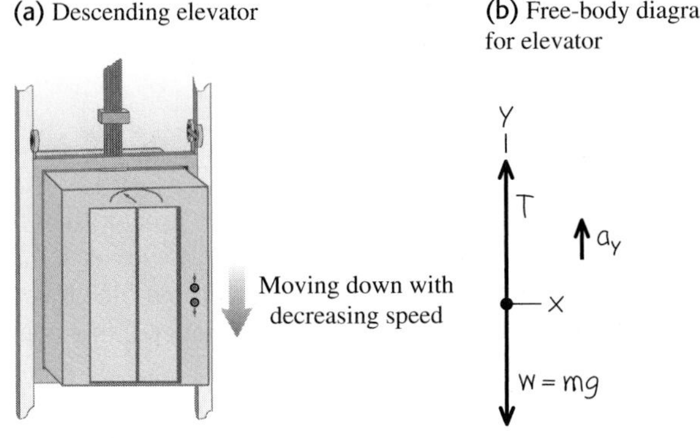

have a_y, we'll substitute it into the y-component of Newton's second law from Eq. (5.4).

EXECUTE: First let's write out Newton's second law. The tension force acts upward and the weight acts downward, so

$$\sum F_y = T + (-w) = ma_y$$

We solve for the target variable T:

$$T = w + ma_y = mg + ma_y = m(g + a_y)$$

To determine a_y, we rewrite the constant-acceleration equation $v_y^2 = v_{0y}^2 + 2a_y(y - y_0)$:

$$a_y = \frac{v_y^2 - v_{0y}^2}{2(y - y_0)} = \frac{(0)^2 - (-10.0\text{ m/s})^2}{2(-25.0\text{ m})} = +2.00\text{ m/s}^2$$

The acceleration is upward (positive), just as it should be for downward motion with decreasing speed.

Now we can substitute the acceleration into the equation for the tension:

$$T = m(g + a_y) = (800\text{ kg})(9.80\text{ m/s}^2 + 2.00\text{ m/s}^2) = 9440\text{ N}$$

EVALUATE: The tension is 1600 N *greater* than the weight. This makes sense: The net force must be upward to provide the upward acceleration that brings the elevator to a halt. Can you see that we would get the same answers for a_y and T if the elevator were moving *upward* and *gaining* speed at a rate of 2.00 m/s^2?

Example 5.9 Apparent weight in an accelerating elevator

A 50.0-kg woman stands on a bathroom scale while riding in the elevator in Example 5.8 (Fig. 5.10a). What is the reading on the scale?

SOLUTION

IDENTIFY: The scale reads the magnitude of the downward force exerted *by* the woman *on* the scale. By Newton's third law, this equals the magnitude of the upward normal force exerted *by* the scale *on* the woman. Hence our target variable is the magnitude n of the normal force.

We'll find n by applying Newton's second law to the woman. We already know her acceleration; it's the same as the acceleration of the elevator, which we calculated in Example 5.8.

SET UP: Figure 5.10b shows our free-body diagram for the woman. The forces acting on her are the normal force n exerted by the scale and her weight $w = mg = (50.0\text{ kg})(9.80\text{ m/s}^2) =$ 490 N. (The tension force, which played a major role in Example 5.8, doesn't appear here because it doesn't act directly on the woman. What pushes upward on her feet is the scale, *not* the elevator cable.) From Example 5.8, the y-acceleration of the elevator and of the woman is $a_y = +2.00\text{ m/s}^2$.

5.10 (a) The situation. (b) Our free-body diagram.

(a) Woman in a descending elevator

Moving down with decreasing speed

(b) Free-body diagram for woman

y

n

a_y

x

w = 490 N

EXECUTE: Newton's second law gives

$$\sum F_y = n + (-mg) = ma_y$$
$$n = mg + ma_y = m(g + a_y)$$
$$= (50.0\text{ kg})(9.80\text{ m/s}^2 + 2.00\text{ m/s}^2) = 590\text{ N}$$

EVALUATE: Our answer for n means that while the elevator is stopping, the scale pushes up on the woman with a force of 590 N. By Newton's third law, she pushes down on the scale with the same force; so the scale reads 590 N, which is 100 N more than her actual weight. The scale reading is called the passenger's **apparent weight.** The woman *feels* the floor pushing up harder on her feet than when the elevator is stationary or moving with constant velocity.

What would the woman feel if the elevator were accelerating *downward* so that $a_y = -2.00\text{ m/s}^2$? This would be the case if the elevator were moving upward with decreasing speed or moving downward with increasing speed. To find the answer for this situation, we just insert the new value of a_y in our equation for n:

$$n = m(g + a_y) = (50.0\text{ kg})[9.80\text{ m/s}^2 + (-2.00\text{ m/s}^2)] = 390\text{ N}$$

Now the woman feels as though she weighs only 390 N, or 100 N *less* than her actual weight.

You can feel these effects yourself; try taking a few steps in an elevator that is coming to a stop after descending (when your apparent weight is greater than your true weight w) or coming to a stop after ascending (when your apparent weight is less than w).

5.11 Astronauts in orbit feel "weightless" because they have the same acceleration as their spacecraft—*not* because they are "outside the pull of the earth's gravity." (If no gravity acted on them, the astronauts and their spacecraft wouldn't remain in orbit, but would fly off into deep space.)

Apparent Weight and Apparent Weightlessness

Let's generalize the result of Example 5.9. When a passenger with mass m rides in an elevator with y-acceleration a_y, a scale shows the passenger's apparent weight to be

$$n = m(g + a_y)$$

When the elevator is accelerating upward, a_y is positive and n is greater than the passenger's weight $w = mg$. When the elevator is accelerating downward, a_y is negative and n is less than the weight. If the passenger doesn't know the elevator is accelerating, she may feel as though her weight is changing; indeed, this is just what the scale shows.

The extreme case occurs when the elevator has a downward acceleration $a_y = -g$, that is, when it is in free fall. In that case, $n = 0$ and the passenger *seems* to be weightless. Similarly, an astronaut orbiting the earth in a spacecraft experiences *apparent weightlessness* (Fig. 5.11). In each case, the person is not truly weightless because there is still a gravitational force acting. But the person's sensations in this free-fall condition are exactly the same as though the person were in outer space with no gravitational force at all. In both cases the person and the vehicle (elevator or spacecraft) are falling together with the same acceleration g, so nothing pushes the person against the floor or walls of the vehicle.

Example 5.10 Acceleration down a hill

A toboggan loaded with vacationing students (total weight w) slides down a long, snow-covered slope. The hill slopes at a constant angle α, and the toboggan is so well waxed that there is virtually no friction. What is its acceleration?

SOLUTION

IDENTIFY: Our target variable is the acceleration, which we'll find using Newton's second law. There is no friction, so only two forces act on the toboggan: its weight w and the normal force n exerted by the hill. As in Example 5.4 (Section 5.1), the surface is inclined so the normal force is not vertical and is not opposite to the weight. Hence we must use both components of $\sum\vec{F} = m\vec{a}$ in Eq. (5.4).

SET UP: Figure 5.12 shows our sketch and free-body diagram. We take axes parallel and perpendicular to the surface of the hill, so that the acceleration (which is parallel to the hill) is along the positive x-direction.

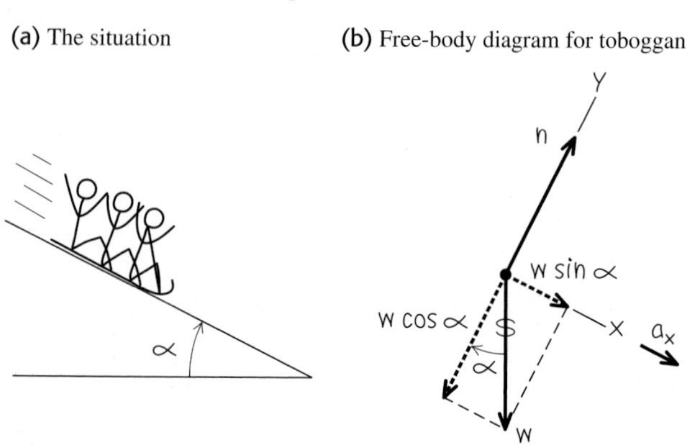

5.12 Our sketches for this problem.

EXECUTE: The normal force has only a y-component, but the weight has both x- and y-components: $w_x = w\sin\alpha$ and $w_y = -w\cos\alpha$. (Compare to Example 5.4, in which the x-component of weight was $-w\sin\alpha$. The difference is that the positive x-axis was uphill in Example 5.4, while in Fig. 5.12b it is downhill.) The wiggly line in Fig. 5.12b reminds us that we have resolved the weight into its components.

The acceleration is purely in the $+x$-direction, so $a_y = 0$. Newton's second law in component form then tells us that

$$\sum F_x = w\sin\alpha = ma_x$$
$$\sum F_y = n - w\cos\alpha = ma_y = 0$$

Since $w = mg$, the x-component equation tells us that $mg\sin\alpha = ma_x$, or

$$a_x = g\sin\alpha$$

Note that we didn't need the y-component equation to find the acceleration. That's the beauty of choosing the x-axis to lie along the acceleration direction! What the y-components tell us is the magnitude of the normal force that the hill exerts on the toboggan:

$$n = w\cos\alpha = mg\cos\alpha$$

EVALUATE: Notice that the mass does not appear in our answer for the acceleration. This means that *any* toboggan, regardless of its mass or number of passengers, slides down a frictionless hill with an acceleration of $g\sin\alpha$. In particular, if the plane is horizontal, $\alpha = 0$ and $a_x = 0$ (the toboggan does not accelerate); if the plane is vertical, $\alpha = 90°$ and $a_x = g$ (the toboggan is in free fall).

Notice also that the normal force n is not equal to the toboggan's weight (compare Example 5.4 in Section 5.1). We don't need this result here, but it will be useful in a later example.

CAUTION Common free-body diagram errors Figure 5.13 shows both the correct way (Fig. 5.13a) and a common *incorrect* way (Fig. 5.13b) to draw the free-body diagram for the toboggan. The diagram in Fig. 5.13b is wrong for two reasons: the normal force must be drawn perpendicular to the surface, and there's no such thing as the "$m\vec{a}$ force." If you remember that "normal" means "perpendicular" and that $m\vec{a}$ is not itself a force, you'll be well on your way to always drawing correct free-body diagrams.

5.13 Correct and incorrect diagrams for a toboggan on a frictionless hill.

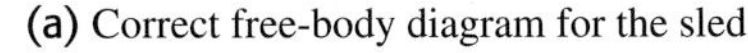

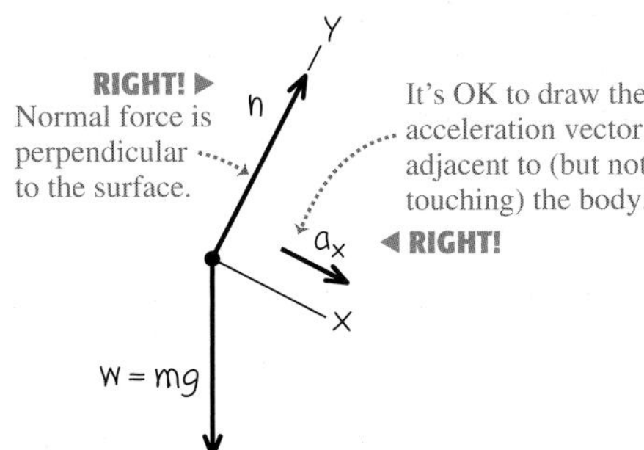

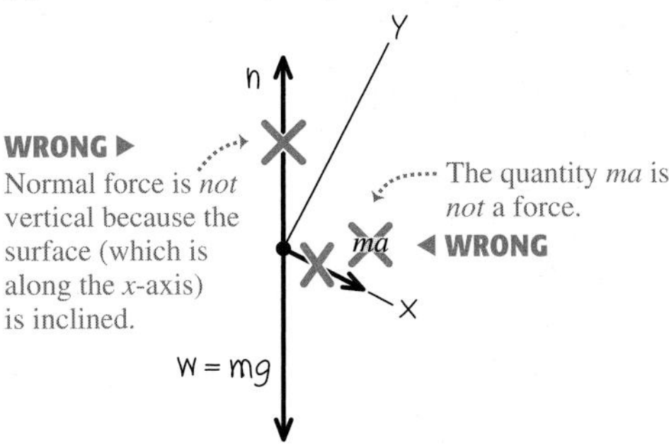

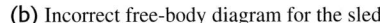

Example 5.11 Two bodies with the same acceleration

You push a 1.00-kg food tray through the cafeteria line with a constant 9.0-N force. As the tray moves, it pushes on a 0.50-kg carton of milk (Fig. 5.14a). The tray and carton slide on a horizontal surface that is so greasy that friction can be neglected. Find the acceleration of the tray and carton and the horizontal force that the tray exerts on the carton.

SOLUTION

IDENTIFY: Our *two* target variables are the acceleration of the system of tray and carton and the force of the tray on the carton. Again we will use Newton's second law, but we'll have to apply it to two different bodies to get two equations (one for each target variable).

SET UP: We can set up the problem in two ways.

Method 1: We can treat the milk carton (mass m_C) and tray (mass m_T) as separate bodies, each with its own free-body diagram (Figs. 5.14b and 5.14c). Note that the force F that you exert on the tray doesn't appear in the free-body diagram for the milk carton. Instead, what makes the carton accelerate is the force of magnitude $F_{\text{T on C}}$ exerted on it by the tray. By Newton's third law, the carton exerts a force of equal magnitude on the tray: $F_{\text{C on T}} = F_{\text{T on C}}$. We take the acceleration to be in the positive x-direction; both the tray and milk carton move with the same x-acceleration a_x.

Method 2: We can treat the tray and milk carton as a composite body of mass $m = m_T + m_C = 1.50$ kg (Fig. 5.14d). The only

5.14 Pushing a food tray and milk carton in the cafeteria line.

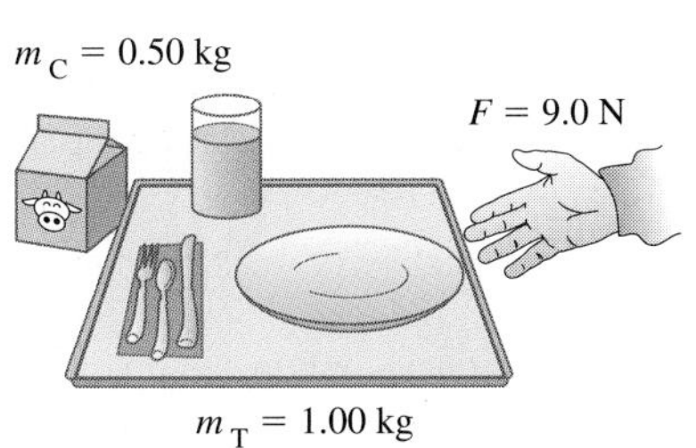

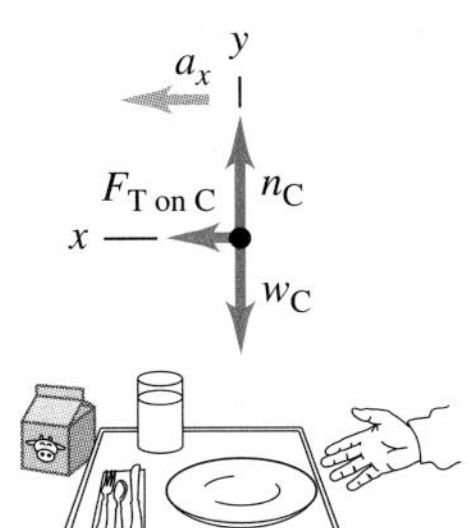

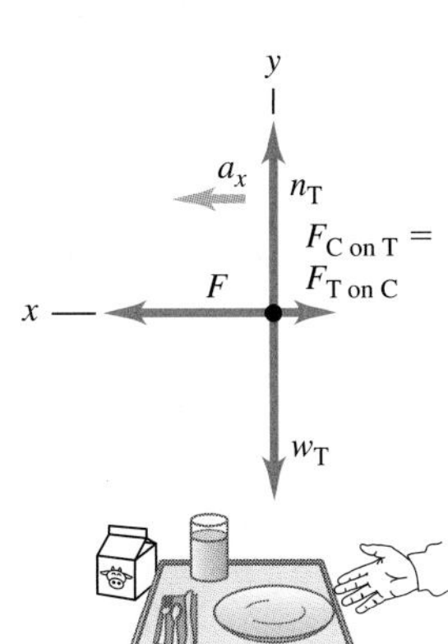

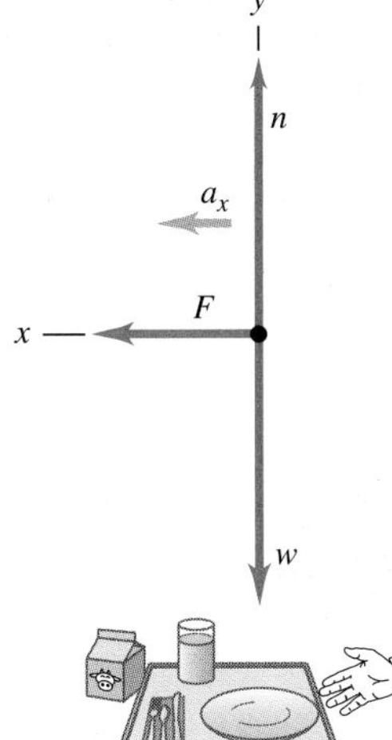

Continued

horizontal force acting on this composite body is the force F that you exert. The forces $F_{\text{T on C}}$ and $F_{\text{C on T}}$ don't come into play because they're *internal* to this composite body, and Newton's second law tells us that only *external* forces affect a body's acceleration (see Section 4.3). Hence we'll need an additional equation to find the magnitude $F_{\text{T on C}}$ using this method; we'll get this equation by also applying Newton's second law to the milk carton, as in Method 1.

EXECUTE: *Method 1:* The x-component equations of Newton's second law for the tray and for the carton are

$$\text{Tray:} \quad \sum F_x = F - F_{\text{C on T}} = F - F_{\text{T on C}} = m_{\text{T}} a_x$$
$$\text{Carton:} \quad \sum F_x = F_{\text{T on C}} = m_{\text{C}} a_x$$

These are two simultaneous equations for the two target variables a_x and $F_{\text{T on C}}$. (Two equations are all we need, which means that the y-components don't play a role in this example.) An easy way to solve the two equations for a_x is to add them; this eliminates $F_{\text{T on C}}$, giving

$$F = m_{\text{T}} a_x + m_{\text{C}} a_x = (m_{\text{T}} + m_{\text{C}}) a_x$$

and

$$a_x = \frac{F}{m_{\text{T}} + m_{\text{C}}} = \frac{9.0\text{ N}}{1.00\text{ kg} + 0.50\text{ kg}} = 6.0\text{ m/s}^2$$

Substituting this back into the equation for the carton gives

$$F_{\text{T on C}} = m_{\text{C}} a_x = (0.50\text{ kg})(6.0\text{ m/s}^2) = 3.0\text{ N}$$

Method 2: The x-component of Newton's second law for the composite body of mass m is

$$\sum F_x = F = m a_x$$

and the acceleration of this composite body is

$$a_x = \frac{F}{m} = \frac{9.0\text{ N}}{1.50\text{ kg}} = 6.0\text{ m/s}^2$$

Then, looking at the milk carton by itself, we see that to give it an acceleration of 6.0 m/s^2 requires that the tray exert a force:

$$F_{\text{T on C}} = m_{\text{C}} a_x = (0.50\text{ kg})(6.0\text{ m/s}^2) = 3.0\text{ N}$$

EVALUATE: The answers are the same with either method, as they should be. To check the answers, note that there are different forces on the two sides of the tray: $F = 9.0\text{ N}$ on the right and $F_{\text{C on T}} = 3.0\text{ N}$ on the left. Hence the net horizontal force on the tray is $F - F_{\text{C on T}} = 6.0\text{ N}$, exactly enough to accelerate a 1.00-kg tray at 6.0 m/s^2.

The method of treating the two bodies as a single composite body works *only* if the two bodies have the same magnitude *and* direction of acceleration. If the accelerations are different, we must treat the two bodies separately, as in the next example.

Example 5.12 Two bodies with the same magnitude of acceleration

Figure 5.15a shows an air-track glider with mass m_1 moving on a level, frictionless air track in the physics lab. The glider is connected to a lab weight with mass m_2 by a light, flexible, nonstretching string that passes over a small frictionless pulley. Find the acceleration of each body and the tension in the string.

SOLUTION

IDENTIFY: The glider and weight are accelerating, so again we must use Newton's second law. Our three target variables are the tension T in the string and the accelerations of the two bodies.

SET UP: The two bodies move in different directions—one horizontal, one vertical—so we can't consider them together as we did the bodies in Example 5.11. Figures 5.15b and 5.15c show our free-body diagrams and coordinate systems. It's convenient to have both bodies accelerate in the positive axis directions, so we chose the positive y-direction for the lab weight to be downward. (It's perfectly all right to use different coordinate axes for the two bodies.)

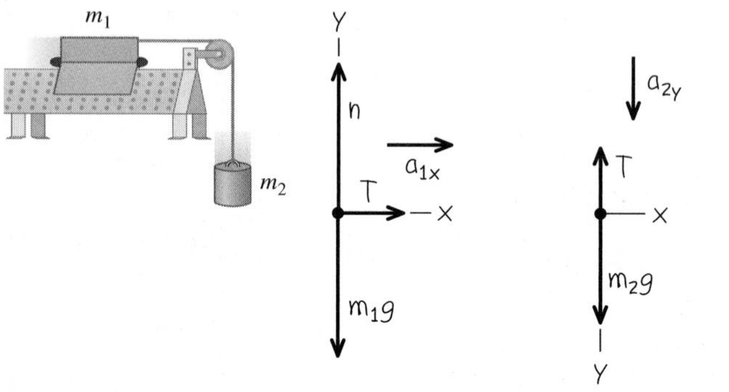

There is no friction in the pulley and we consider the string to be massless, so the tension T in the string is the same throughout; it applies a force of the same magnitude T to each body. (You may want to review Conceptual Example 4.10 in Section 4.5, where we discussed the tension force exerted by a massless string.) The weights are $m_1 g$ and $m_2 g$.

While the *directions* of the two accelerations are different, their *magnitudes* are the same. That's because the string doesn't stretch. Hence the two bodies must move equal distances in equal times, and so their speeds at any instant must be equal. When the speeds change, they change by equal amounts in a given time, so the accelerations of the two bodies must have the same magnitude a. We can express this relationship as

$$a_{1x} = a_{2y} = a$$

Thanks to this relationship, we actually have only *two* target variables: a and the tension T.

EXECUTE: For the glider on the track, Newton's second law gives

$$\text{Glider:} \quad \sum F_x = T = m_1 a_{1x} = m_1 a$$
$$\text{Glider:} \quad \sum F_y = n + (-m_1 g) = m_1 a_{1y} = 0$$

For the lab weight, the only forces are in the y-direction, and

$$\text{Lab weight:} \quad \sum F_y = m_2 g + (-T) = m_2 a_{2y} = m_2 a$$

5.15 (a) The situation. (b), (c) Our free-body diagrams.

(a) Apparatus

m_1

m_2

(b) Free-body diagram for glider

y
n
a_{1x}
T
x
$m_1 g$

(c) Free-body diagram for weight

a_{2y}
T
x
$m_2 g$
y

In these equations we've used the relationships $a_{1y} = 0$ (the glider doesn't accelerate vertically) and $a_{1x} = a_{2y} = a$ (the two objects have the same magnitude of acceleration).

The x-equation for the glider and the equation for the lab weight give us two simultaneous equations for the target variables T and a:

$$\text{Glider:} \quad T = m_1 a$$

$$\text{Lab weight:} \quad m_2 g - T = m_2 a$$

We add the two equations to eliminate T, giving

$$m_2 g = m_1 a + m_2 a = (m_1 + m_2)a$$

and so the magnitude of each body's acceleration is

$$a = \frac{m_2}{m_1 + m_2} g$$

Substituting this back into the first equation (for the glider), we get

$$T = \frac{m_1 m_2}{m_1 + m_2} g$$

EVALUATE: The acceleration is less than g, as you might expect; the lab weight accelerates more slowly because the string tension pulls it back.

The tension T is *not* equal to the weight $m_2 g$ of the lab weight, but is *less* by a factor of $m_1/(m_1 + m_2)$. If T *were* equal to $m_2 g$, then the lab weight would be in equilibrium, and it isn't.

CAUTION Tension and weight may not be equal It's a common mistake to assume that if an object is attached to a vertical string, the string tension must be equal to the object's weight. That was the case in Example 5.5, where the acceleration was zero, but it would certainly be wrong in this example! The only safe approach is to *always* treat the tension as a variable, as we have done here.

Finally, let's check some special cases. If $m_1 = 0$, then the lab weight would fall freely and there would be no tension in the string. The equations do give $T = 0$ and $a = g$ when $m_1 = 0$. Also, if $m_2 = 0$, we expect no tension and no acceleration; for this case the equations do indeed tell us that $T = 0$ and $a = 0$.

Test Your Understanding of Section 5.2 Suppose you hold the glider in Example 5.12 so that it and the weight are initially at rest. You give the glider a push to the left in Fig. 5.15a and then release it. The string remains taut as the glider moves to the left, comes instantaneously to rest, then moves to the right. At the instant the glider has zero velocity, what is the tension in the string? (i) greater than in Example 5.12; (ii) the same as in Example 5.12; (iii) less than in Example 5.12, but greater than zero; (iv) zero.

5.3 Frictional Forces

We have seen several problems where a body rests or slides on a surface that exerts forces on the body. Whenever two bodies interact by direct contact (touching) of their surfaces, we describe the interaction in terms of *contact forces*. The normal force is one example of a contact force; in this section we'll look in detail at another contact force, the force of friction.

Friction is important in many aspects of everyday life. The oil in a car engine minimizes friction between moving parts, but without friction between the tires and the road we couldn't drive or turn the car. Air drag—the frictional force exerted by the air on a body moving through it—decreases automotive fuel economy but makes parachutes work. Without friction, nails would pull out, light bulbs would unscrew effortlessly, and ice hockey would be hopeless (Fig. 5.16).

5.16 The sport of ice hockey depends on having the right amount of friction between a player's skates and the ice. If there were too much friction, the players would move too slowly; if there were too little friction, they would fall over.

Kinetic and Static Friction

When you try to slide a heavy box of books across the floor, the box doesn't move at all unless you push with a certain minimum force. Then the box starts moving, and you can usually keep it moving with less force than you needed to get it started. If you take some of the books out, you need less force than before to get it started or keep it moving. What general statements can we make about this behavior?

First, when a body rests or slides on a surface, we can think of the surface as exerting a single contact force on the body, with force components perpendicular and parallel to the surface (Fig. 5.17). The perpendicular component vector is the normal force, denoted by $\vec{n}$. The component vector parallel to the surface (and perpendicular to $\vec{n}$) is the **friction force,** denoted by $\vec{f}$. If the surface is frictionless, then $\vec{f}$ is zero but there is still a normal force. (Frictionless surfaces are an unattainable idealization, like a massless rope. But we can approximate a surface

5.17 When a block is pushed or pulled over a surface, the surface exerts a contact force on it.

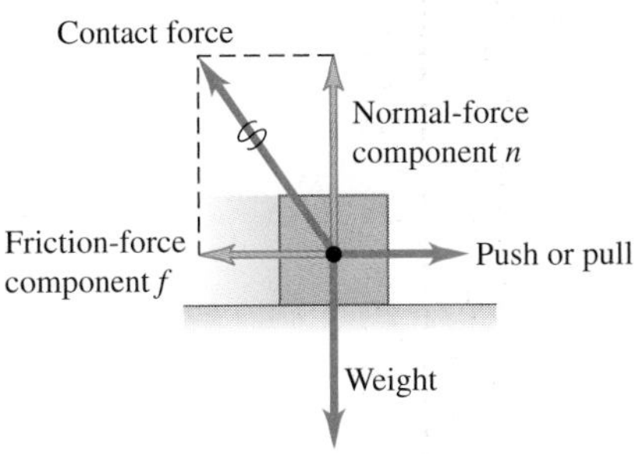

2.5 Truck Pulls Crate
2.6 Pushing a Crate Up a Wall
2.7 Skier Goes Down a Slope
2.8 Skier and Rope Tow
2.10 Truck Pulls Two Crates

as frictionless if the effects of friction are negligibly small.) The direction of the friction force is always such as to oppose relative motion of the two surfaces.

The kind of friction that acts when a body slides over a surface is called a **kinetic friction force** $\vec{f}_k$. The adjective "kinetic" and the subscript "k" remind us that the two surfaces are moving relative to each other. The *magnitude* of the kinetic friction force usually increases when the normal force increases. This is why it takes more force to slide a box full of books across the floor than to slide the same box when it is empty. This principle is also used in automotive braking systems: The harder the brake pads are squeezed against the rotating brake disks, the greater the braking effect. In many cases the magnitude of the kinetic friction force f_k is found experimentally to be approximately *proportional* to the magnitude n of the normal force. In such cases we represent the relationship by the equation

$$f_k = \mu_k n \qquad \text{(magnitude of kinetic friction force)} \qquad (5.5)$$

where μ_k (pronounced "mu-sub-k") is a constant called the **coefficient of kinetic friction.** The more slippery the surface, the smaller the coefficient of friction. Because it is a quotient of two force magnitudes, μ_k is a pure number, without units.

CAUTION Friction and normal forces are always perpendicular Remember that Eq. (5.5) is *not* a vector equation because $\vec{f}_k$ and $\vec{n}$ are always perpendicular. Rather, it is a scalar relationship between the magnitudes of the two forces.

5.18 The normal and friction forces arise from interactions between molecules at high points on the surfaces of the block and the floor.

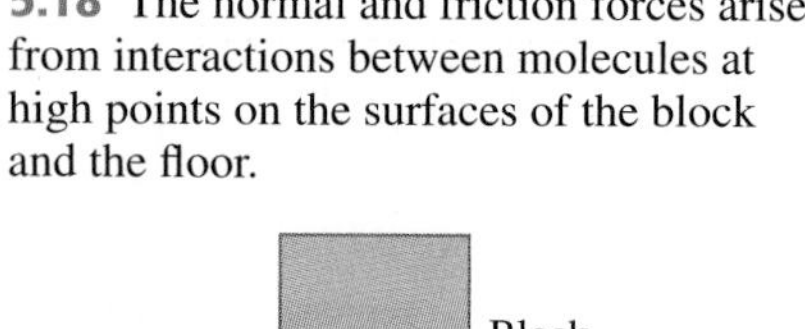

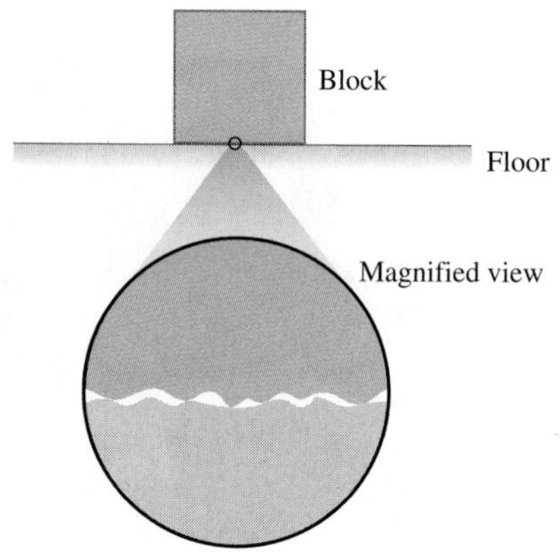

On a microscopic level, even smooth surfaces are rough; they tend to catch and cling.

Equation (5.5) is only an approximate representation of a complex phenomenon. On a microscopic level, friction and normal forces result from the intermolecular forces (fundamentally electrical in nature) between two rough surfaces at points where they come into contact (Fig. 5.18). As a box slides over the floor, bonds between the two surfaces form and break, and the total number of such bonds varies; hence the kinetic friction force is not perfectly constant. Smoothing the surfaces can actually increase friction, since more molecules are able to interact and bond; bringing two smooth surfaces of the same metal together can cause a "cold weld." Lubricating oils work because an oil film between two surfaces (such as the pistons and cylinder walls in a car engine) prevents them from coming into actual contact.

Table 5.1 lists some representative values of μ_k. Although these values are given with two significant figures, they are only approximate, since friction forces

Table 5.1 Approximate Coefficients of Friction

Materials	Coefficient of Static Friction, μ_s	Coefficient of Kinetic Friction, μ_k
Steel on steel	0.74	0.57
Aluminum on steel	0.61	0.47
Copper on steel	0.53	0.36
Brass on steel	0.51	0.44
Zinc on cast iron	0.85	0.21
Copper on cast iron	1.05	0.29
Glass on glass	0.94	0.40
Copper on glass	0.68	0.53
Teflon on Teflon	0.04	0.04
Teflon on steel	0.04	0.04
Rubber on concrete (dry)	1.0	0.8
Rubber on concrete (wet)	0.30	0.25

5.19 (a), (b), (c) When there is no relative motion, the magnitude of the static friction force f_s is less than or equal to $\mu_s n$. (d) When there is relative motion, the magnitude of the kinetic friction force f_k equals $\mu_k n$. (e) A graph of the friction force magnitude f as a function of the magnitude T of the applied force T. The kinetic friction force varies somewhat as intermolecular bonds form and break.

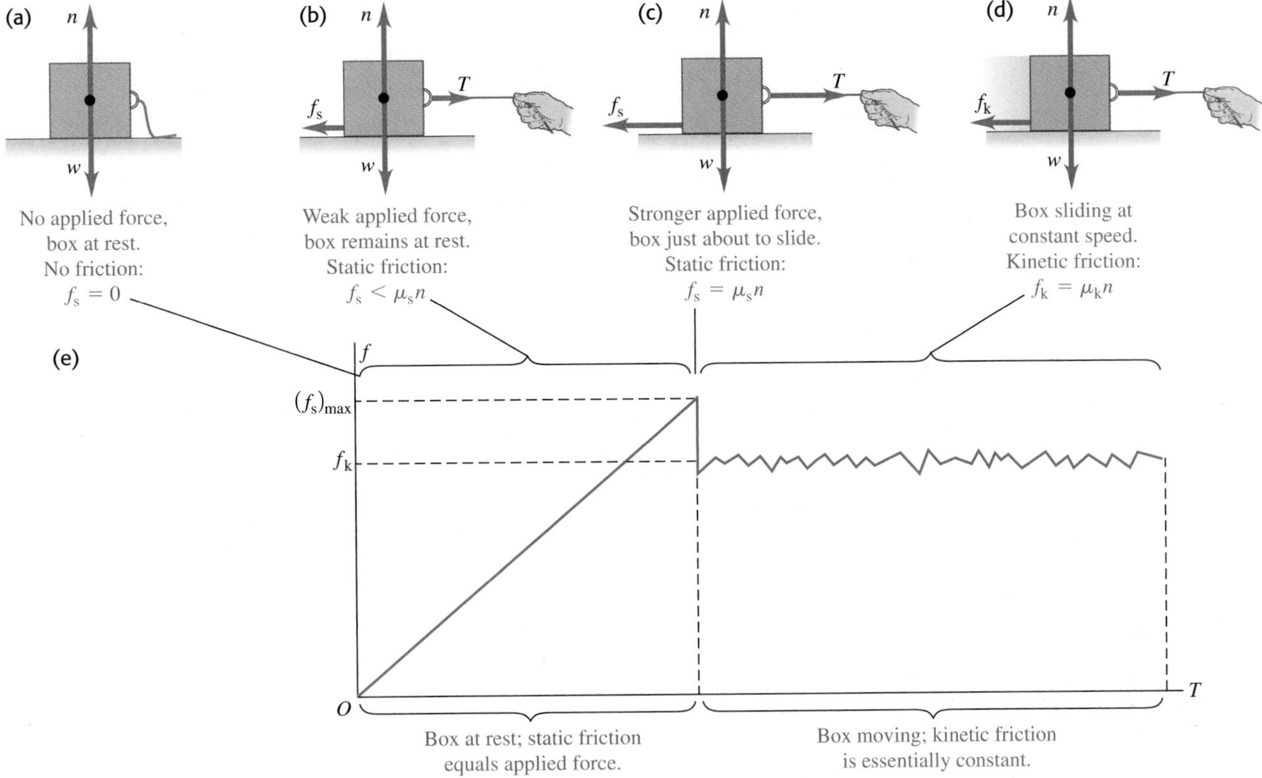

can also depend on the speed of the body relative to the surface. For now we'll ignore this effect and assume that μ_k and f_k are independent of speed, in order to concentrate on the simplest cases. Table 5.1 also lists coefficients of static friction; we'll define these shortly.

Friction forces may also act when there is *no* relative motion. If you try to slide a box across the floor, the box may not move at all because the floor exerts an equal and opposite friction force on the box. This is called a **static friction force** $\vec{f}_s$. In Fig. 5.19a, the box is at rest, in equilibrium, under the action of its weight $\vec{w}$ and the upward normal force $\vec{n}$. The normal force is equal in magnitude to the weight $(n = w)$ and is exerted on the box by the floor. Now we tie a rope to the box (Fig. 5.19b) and gradually increase the tension T in the rope. At first the box remains at rest because, as T increases, the force of static friction f_s also increases (staying equal in magnitude to T).

At some point T becomes greater than the maximum static friction force f_s the surface can exert. Then the box "breaks loose" (the tension T is able to break the bonds between molecules in the surfaces of the box and floor) and starts to slide. Figure 5.19c shows the forces when T is at this critical value. If T exceeds this value, the box is no longer in equilibrium. For a given pair of surfaces the maximum value of f_s depends on the normal force. Experiment shows that in many cases this maximum value, called $(f_s)_{max}$, is approximately *proportional* to n; we call the proportionality factor μ_s the **coefficient of static friction.** Table 5.1 lists some representative values of μ_s. In a particular situation, the actual force of static friction can have any magnitude between zero (when there is no other force parallel to the surface) and a maximum value given by $\mu_s n$. In symbols,

$$f_s \leq \mu_s n \qquad \text{(magnitude of static friction force)} \qquad (5.6)$$

Like Eq. (5.5), this is a relationship between magnitudes, *not* a vector relationship. The equality sign holds only when the applied force T has reached the critical value at which motion is about to start (Fig. 5.19c). When T is less than this value (Fig. 5.19b), the inequality sign holds. In that case we have to use the equilibrium conditions $(\sum \vec{F} = \mathbf{0})$ to find f_s. If there is no applied force $(T = 0)$ as in Fig. 5.19a, then there is no static friction force either $(f_s = 0)$.

As soon as the box starts to slide (Fig. 5.19d), the friction force usually *decreases;* it's easier to keep the box moving than to start it moving. Hence the coefficient of kinetic friction is usually *less* than the coefficient of static friction for any given pair of surfaces, as Table 5.1 shows. If we start with no applied force $(T = 0)$ and gradually increase the force, the friction force varies somewhat, as shown in Fig. 5.19e.

In some situations the surfaces will alternately stick (static friction) and slip (kinetic friction). This is what causes the horrible sound made by chalk held at the wrong angle while writing on the blackboard. Other stick-slip phenomena are the squeak of windshield wipers on dry glass and the shriek of tires sliding on asphalt pavement. A more positive example is the motion of a violin bow against the string.

When a body slides on a layer of gas, friction can be made very small. In the linear air track used in physics laboratories, the gliders are supported on a layer of air. The frictional force is velocity dependent, but at typical speeds the effective coefficient of friction is of the order of 0.001.

Example 5.13 Friction in horizontal motion

You are trying to move a 500-N crate across a level floor. To start the crate moving, you have to pull with a 230-N horizontal force. Once the crate "breaks loose" and starts to move, you can keep it moving at constant velocity with only 200 N. What are the coefficients of static and kinetic friction?

SOLUTION

IDENTIFY: The crate is in equilibrium whether it is at rest or moving with constant velocity, so we use Newton's first law as expressed by Eq. (5.2). We'll also need the relationships in Eqs. (5.5) and (5.6) to find the target variables μ_s and μ_k.

SET UP: In either situation there are four forces acting on the crate: the downward weight force (magnitude $w = 500$ N), the upward normal force (magnitude n) exerted by the ground, a tension force (magnitude T) to the right exerted by the rope, and a friction force to the left exerted by the ground. Figures 5.20a and 5.20b show our sketch and free-body diagram for the instant just before the crate starts to move, when the static friction force has its maximum possible value $(f_s)_{max} = \mu_s n$. Once the crate is moving to the right at constant velocity, the friction force changes to its kinetic form (Fig. 5.20c). Because the rope in Fig. 5.20a is in equilibrium, the tension is the same at both ends. Hence the tension force that the rope exerts on the crate has the same magnitude as the force you exert on the rope.

5.20 Our sketches for this problem.

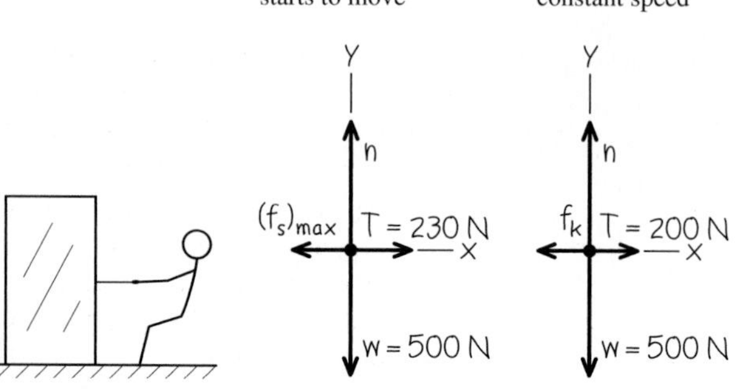

EXECUTE: Just before the crate starts to move (Fig. 5.20b), we have

$$\sum F_x = T + (-(f_s)_{max}) = 0 \quad \text{so} \quad (f_s)_{max} = T = 230\text{ N}$$
$$\sum F_y = n + (-w) = 0 \quad \text{so} \quad n = w = 500\text{ N}$$

Then we use Eq. (5.6), $(f_s)_{max} = \mu_s n$, to find the value of μ_s:

$$\mu_s = \frac{(f_s)_{max}}{n} = \frac{230\text{ N}}{500\text{ N}} = 0.46$$

After the crate starts to move, the forces are as shown in Fig. 5.20c, and we have

$$\sum F_x = T + (-f_k) = 0 \quad \text{so} \quad f_k = T = 200\text{ N}$$
$$\sum F_y = n + (-w) = 0 \quad \text{so} \quad n = w = 500\text{ N}$$

Using $f_k = \mu_k n$ from Eq. (5.5), we find

$$\mu_k = \frac{f_k}{n} = \frac{200\text{ N}}{500\text{ N}} = 0.40$$

EVALUATE: It's easier to keep the crate moving than to start it moving, and so the coefficient of kinetic friction is less than the coefficient of static friction.

Example 5.14 Static friction can be less than the maximum

In Example 5.13, what is the friction force if the crate is at rest on the surface and a horizontal force of 50 N is applied to it?

SOLUTION

IDENTIFY: The applied force is less than the maximum force of static friction, $(f_s)_{max} = 230$ N. Hence the crate remains at rest and the net force acting on it is zero. The target variable is the magnitude f_s of the friction force.

SET UP: The free-body diagram is the same as in Fig. 5.20b, but with $(f_s)_{max}$ replaced by f_s and $T = 230$ N replaced by $T = 50$ N.

EXECUTE: From the equilibrium conditions, Eq. (5.2), we have

$$\sum F_x = T + (-f_s) = 0 \qquad \text{so} \qquad f_s = T = 50\text{ N}$$

EVALUATE: In this case, f_s is less than the maximum value $(f_s)_{max} = \mu_s n$. The frictional force can prevent motion for any horizontal applied force up to 230 N.

Example 5.15 Minimizing kinetic friction

In Example 5.13, suppose you try to move the crate by tying a rope around it and pulling upward on the rope at an angle of 30° above the horizontal. How hard do you have to pull to keep the crate moving with constant velocity? Is this easier or harder than pulling horizontally? Assume $w = 500$ N and $\mu_k = 0.40$.

SOLUTION

IDENTIFY: The crate is in equilibrium because its velocity is constant, so we again apply Newton's first law. Since the crate is in motion, the ground exerts a *kinetic* friction force. The target variable is the magnitude T of the tension force.

SET UP: Figure 5.21 shows our sketch and free-body diagram. The kinetic friction force f_k is still equal to $\mu_k n$, but now the normal force n is *not* equal in magnitude to the weight of the crate. The force exerted by the rope has an additional vertical component that tends to lift the crate off the floor.

5.21 Our sketches for this problem.

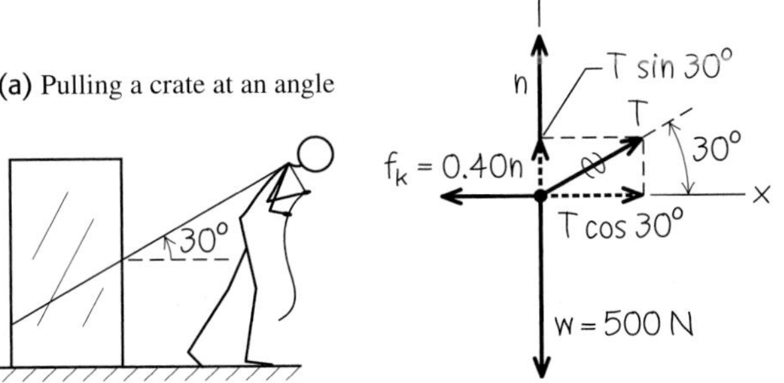

EXECUTE: From the equilibrium conditions and the equation $f_k = \mu_k n$, we have

$$\sum F_x = T\cos 30° + (-f_k) = 0 \qquad \text{so} \qquad T\cos 30° = \mu_k n$$
$$\sum F_y = T\sin 30° + n + (-w) = 0 \qquad \text{so} \qquad n = w - T\sin 30°$$

These are two equations for the two unknown quantities T and n. To solve them, we can eliminate one unknown and solve for the other. There are many ways to do this; one way is to substitute the expression for n in the second equation back into the first equation:

$$T\cos 30° = \mu_k(w - T\sin 30°)$$

Then we solve this equation for T, with the result

$$T = \frac{\mu_k w}{\cos 30° + \mu_k \sin 30°} = 188\text{ N}$$

We can substitute this result back into either of the original equations to obtain n. If we use the second equation to do this, we get

$$n = w - T\sin 30° = (500\text{ N}) - (188\text{ N})\sin 30° = 406\text{ N}$$

EVALUATE: The normal force is *less* than the weight of the box $(w = 500\text{ N})$ because the vertical component of tension pulls upward on the crate. Despite this, the tension required is a little less than the 200-N force needed when you pulled horizontally in Example 5.13. Try pulling at 22°; you'll find you need even less force (see Challenge Problem 5.123).

Example 5.16 Toboggan ride with friction I

Let's go back to the toboggan we studied in Example 5.10 (Section 5.2). The wax has worn off and there is now a nonzero coefficient of kinetic friction μ_k. The slope has just the right angle to make the toboggan slide with constant speed. Derive an expression for the slope angle in terms of w and μ_k.

SOLUTION

IDENTIFY: Our target variable is the slope angle α. The toboggan is in equilibrium because its velocity is constant, so we use Newton's first law. There are three forces acting on the toboggan: its weight, the normal force, and the kinetic friction force. Since the motion is downhill, the kinetic friction force (which opposes the motion of the toboggan over the hill) is directed uphill.

SET UP: Figure 5.22 shows our sketch and free-body diagram. We take axes perpendicular and parallel to the surface and represent the weight in terms of its components in these two directions, as shown. (Compare Fig. 5.12b in Example 5.10.) The magnitude of the friction force is given by Eq. (5.5), $f_k = \mu_k n$.

Continued

5.22 Our sketches for this problem.

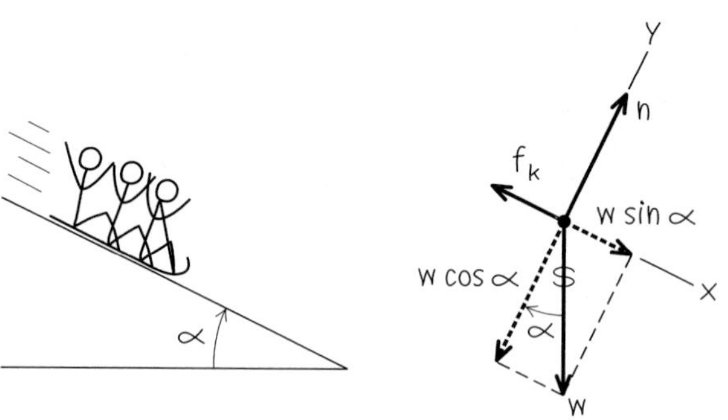

EXECUTE: The equilibrium conditions are

$$\sum F_x = w\sin\alpha + (-f_k) = w\sin\alpha - \mu_k n = 0$$
$$\sum F_y = n + (-w\cos\alpha) = 0$$

(We used the relationship $f_k = \mu_k n$ in the equation for the x-components.) Rearranging, we get

$$\mu_k n = w\sin\alpha \qquad \text{and} \qquad n = w\cos\alpha$$

Just as in Example 5.10, the normal force n is *not* equal to the weight w. When we divide the first of these equations by the second, we find

$$\mu_k = \frac{\sin\alpha}{\cos\alpha} = \tan\alpha \qquad \text{so} \qquad \alpha = \arctan\mu_k$$

EVALUATE: The weight w doesn't appear in this expression. *Any* toboggan, regardless of its weight, slides down an incline with constant speed if the coefficient of kinetic friction equals the tangent of the slope angle of the incline. The greater the coefficient of friction, the steeper the slope has to be for the toboggan to slide with constant velocity.

Example 5.17 Toboggan ride with friction II

The same toboggan with the same coefficient of friction as in Example 5.16 *accelerates* down a steeper hill. Derive an expression for the acceleration in terms of g, α, μ_k, and w.

SOLUTION

IDENTIFY: The toboggan is accelerating and hence not in equilibrium, so we must use Newton's second law, $\sum\vec{F} = m\vec{a}$, in its component form as given in Eq. (5.4). Our target variable is the downhill acceleration.

SET UP: Figure 5.23 shows our sketches. The free-body diagram (Fig. 5.23b) is almost the same as for Example 5.16. The toboggan's y-component of acceleration a_y is still zero, but the x-component a_x is not.

EXECUTE: It's convenient to express the weight as $w = mg$. Then Newton's second law in component form says

$$\sum F_x = mg\sin\alpha + (-f_k) = ma_x$$
$$\sum F_y = n + (-mg\cos\alpha) = 0$$

5.23 Our sketches for this problem.

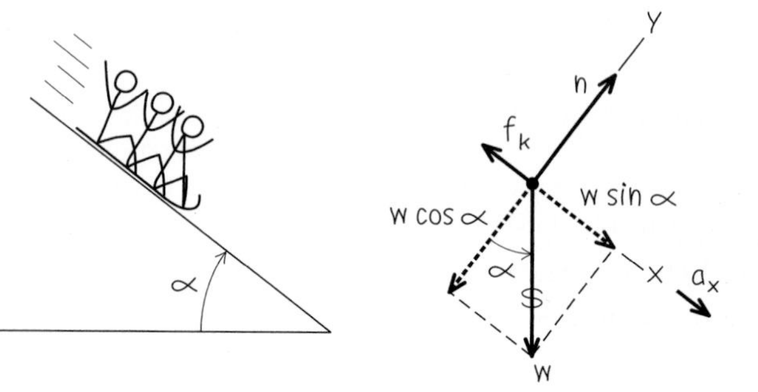

From the second equation and Eq. (5.5) we get an expression for f_k:

$$n = mg\cos\alpha$$
$$f_k = \mu_k n = \mu_k mg\cos\alpha$$

We substitute this back into the x-component equation:

$$mg\sin\alpha + (-\mu_k mg\cos\alpha) = ma_x$$
$$a_x = g(\sin\alpha - \mu_k\cos\alpha)$$

EVALUATE: Does this result make sense? Let's check some special cases. First, if the hill is vertical, $\alpha = 90°$; then $\sin\alpha = 1$, $\cos\alpha = 0$, and $a_x = g$. This is free fall, just what we would expect. Second, on a hill at angle α with no friction, $\mu_k = 0$. Then $a_x = g\sin\alpha$. The situation is the same as in Example 5.10; happily, we get the same result. Next, suppose that there is just enough friction to make the toboggan move with constant velocity. In that case $a_x = 0$, so it must be that

$$\sin\alpha = \mu_k\cos\alpha \qquad \text{and} \qquad \mu_k = \tan\alpha$$

This agrees with our result from Example 5.16. Finally, note that there may be so much friction that $\mu_k\cos\alpha$ is actually greater than $\sin\alpha$. In that case, a_x is negative; if we give the toboggan an initial downhill push to start it moving, it will slow down and eventually stop.

We have pretty much beaten the toboggan problem to death, but look what we've done: Starting with a simple problem, we extended it to more and more general situations. The general result we found in this example includes *all* the previous ones as special cases. Don't memorize this general result; it is useful only for this one set of problems. But make sure you understand how we obtained it and what it means.

One final variation that you may want to try out is the case in which we give the toboggan an initial push up the hill. The direction of the kinetic friction force is now reversed, so the acceleration is different from the downhill value. It turns out that the expression for a_x is the same as for downhill motion except that the minus sign becomes plus. Can you prove this?

Rolling Friction

It's a lot easier to move a loaded filing cabinet across a horizontal floor using a cart with wheels than to slide it. How much easier? We can define a **coefficient of rolling friction** μ_r, which is the horizontal force needed for constant speed on a flat surface divided by the upward normal force exerted by the surface. Transportation engineers call μ_r the *tractive resistance.* Typical values of μ_r are 0.002 to 0.003 for steel wheels on steel rails and 0.01 to 0.02 for rubber tires on concrete. These values show one reason railroad trains are generally much more fuel efficient than highway trucks.

Example 5.18 Motion with rolling friction

A typical car weighs about 12,000 N (about 2700 lb). If the coefficient of rolling friction is $\mu_r = 0.015$, what horizontal force is needed to make the car move with constant speed on a level road? Neglect air resistance.

SOLUTION

IDENTIFY: The car is moving with constant velocity, so this is an equilibrium problem that uses Newton's first law. The four forces on the car are the weight, the upward normal force, the backward force of rolling friction, and the unknown forward force F (our target variable).

SET UP: The free-body diagram is much like the one in Fig. 5.20c of Example 5.13, but with the kinetic friction force replaced by the rolling friction force f_r and with the tension force replaced by the unknown force F.

EXECUTE: As in Example 5.13, Newton's first law for the *vertical* components tells us that the normal force is equal in magnitude to the car's weight. Hence, from the definition of μ_r, the rolling friction force f_r is

$$f_r = \mu_r n = (0.015)(12{,}000\text{ N}) = 180\text{ N} \qquad (\text{about } 40\text{ lb})$$

Newton's first law for the *horizontal* components tells us that a forward force with this magnitude is needed to keep the car moving with constant speed.

EVALUATE: The required force is rather small, which is why it's possible to push a car by hand. (As in the case of sliding, it's easier to keep a car rolling than it is to start it rolling.) We've ignored the effects of air resistance, which is a pretty good approximation if the car is moving slowly. But at typical highway speeds, air resistance is a larger effect than rolling friction.

Try applying this analysis to the crate in Example 5.13. If the crate is on a rubber-wheeled dolly with $\mu_r = 0.02$, only a 10-N force is needed to keep it moving at constant velocity. Can you verify this?

Fluid Resistance and Terminal Speed

Activ Physics ONLINE
2.1.2 Skydiver

Sticking your hand out the window of a fast-moving car will convince you of the existence of **fluid resistance,** the force that a fluid (a gas or liquid) exerts on a body moving through it. The moving body exerts a force on the fluid to push it out of the way. By Newton's third law, the fluid pushes back on the body with an equal and opposite force.

The *direction* of the fluid resistance force acting on a body is always opposite the direction of the body's velocity relative to the fluid. The *magnitude* of the fluid resistance force usually increases with the speed of the body through the fluid. This is very different from the kinetic friction force between two surfaces in contact, which we can usually regard as independent of speed. For very low speeds, the magnitude f of the fluid resistance force is approximately proportional to the body's speed v:

$$f = kv \qquad \text{(fluid resistance at low speed)} \tag{5.7}$$

where k is a proportionality constant that depends on the shape and size of the body and the properties of the fluid. In motion through air at the speed of a tossed tennis ball or faster, the resisting force is approximately proportional to v^2 rather than to v. It is then called **air drag** or simply *drag*. Airplanes, falling raindrops, and bicyclists all experience air drag. In this case we replace Eq. (5.7) by

$$f = Dv^2 \qquad \text{(fluid resistance at high speed)} \tag{5.8}$$

Because of the v^2 dependence, air drag increases rapidly with increasing speed. The air drag on a typical car is negligible at low speeds but comparable to or greater than rolling resistance at highway speeds. The value of D depends on the shape and size of the body and on the density of the air. You should verify that the units of the constant k in Eq. (5.7) are $\text{N} \cdot \text{s/m}$ or kg/s, and that the units of the constant D in Eq. (5.8) are $\text{N} \cdot \text{s}^2/\text{m}^2$ or kg/m.

5.24 A rock falling through a fluid (water).

(a) A rock falling in water (b) Free-body diagram for rock in water

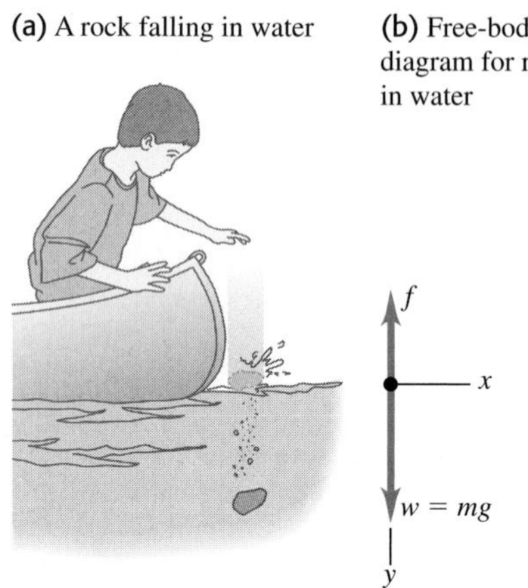

Because of the effects of fluid resistance, an object falling in a fluid does *not* have a constant acceleration. To describe its motion, we can't use the constant-acceleration relationships from Chapter 2; instead, we have to start over using Newton's second law. As an example, suppose you drop a rock at the surface of a pond and let it fall to the bottom (Fig. 5.24a). The fluid resistance force in this situation is given by Eq. (5.7). What are the acceleration, velocity, and position of the rock as functions of time?

Figure 5.24b shows the free-body diagram. We take the positive y-direction to be downward and neglect any force associated with buoyancy in the water. Since the rock is moving downward, its speed v is equal to its y-velocity v_y and the fluid resistance force is in the $-y$-direction. There are no x-components, so Newton's second law gives

$$\sum F_y = mg + (-kv_y) = ma_y$$

When the rock first starts to move, $v_y = 0$, the resisting force is zero, and the initial acceleration is $a_y = g$. As the speed increases, the resisting force also increases, until finally it is equal in magnitude to the weight. At this time $mg - kv_y = 0$, the acceleration becomes zero, and there is no further increase in speed. The final speed v_t, called the **terminal speed,** is given by $mg - kv_t = 0$, or

$$v_t = \frac{mg}{k} \qquad \text{(terminal speed, fluid resistance } f = kv\text{)} \qquad (5.9)$$

Figure 5.25 shows how the acceleration, velocity, and position vary with time. As time goes by, the acceleration approaches zero and the velocity approaches v_t (remember that we chose the positive y-direction to be down). The slope of the graph of y versus t becomes constant as the velocity becomes constant.

To see how the graphs in Fig. 5.25 are derived, we must find the relationship between speed and time during the interval before the terminal speed is reached. We go back to Newton's second law, which we rewrite using $a_y = dv_y/dt$:

$$m\frac{dv_y}{dt} = mg - kv_y$$

After rearranging terms and replacing mg/k by v_t, we integrate both sides, noting that $v_y = 0$ when $t = 0$:

$$\int_0^v \frac{dv_y}{v_y - v_t} = -\frac{k}{m}\int_0^t dt$$

5.25 Graphs of the motion of a body falling without fluid resistance and with fluid resistance proportional to the speed.

Acceleration versus time

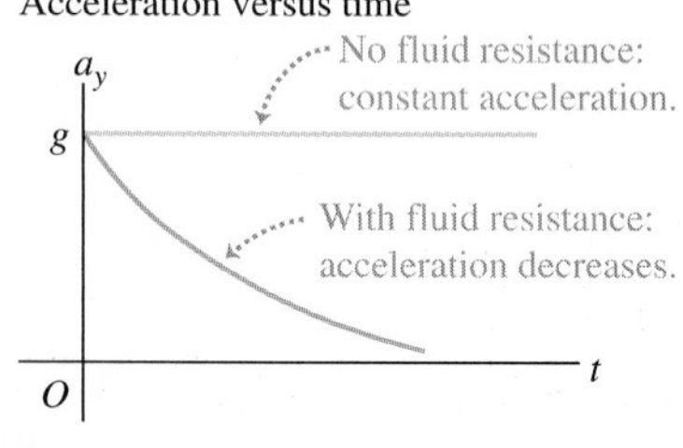

Velocity versus time

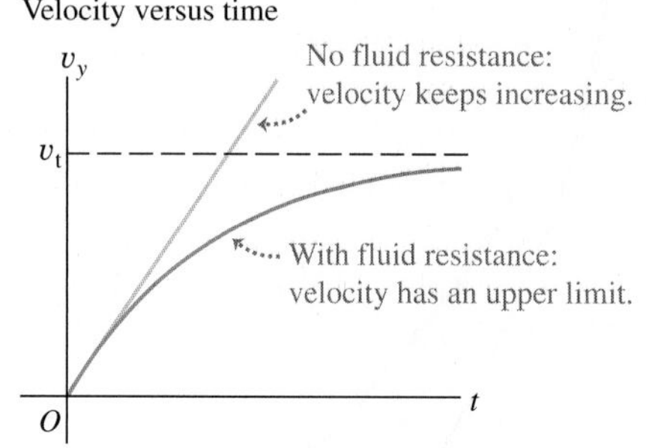

Position versus time

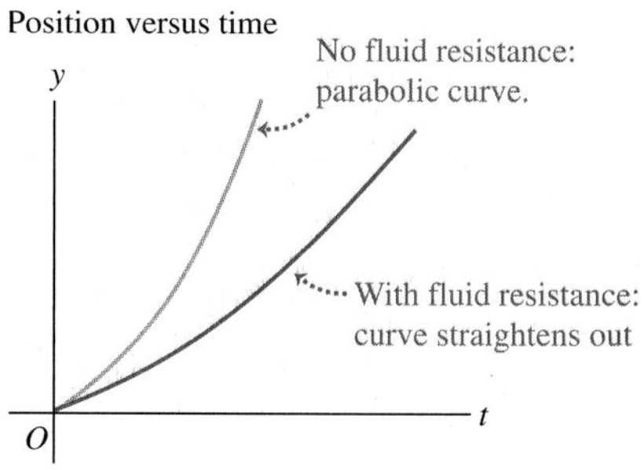

which integrates to

$$\ln\frac{v_t - v_y}{v_t} = -\frac{k}{m}t \quad \text{or} \quad 1 - \frac{v_y}{v_t} = e^{-(k/m)t}$$

and finally

$$v_y = v_t[1 - e^{-(k/m)t}] \tag{5.10}$$

Note that v_y becomes equal to the terminal speed v_t only in the limit that $t \to \infty$; the rock cannot attain terminal speed in any finite length of time.

The derivative of v_y gives a_y as a function of time, and the integral of v_y gives y as a function of time. We leave the derivations for you to complete (see Exercise 5.46); the results are

$$a_y = ge^{-(k/m)t} \tag{5.11}$$

$$y = v_t\left[t - \frac{m}{k}\left(1 - e^{-(k/m)t}\right)\right] \tag{5.12}$$

Now look again at Fig. 5.25, which shows graphs of these three relationships.

In deriving the terminal speed in Eq. (5.9), we assumed that the fluid resistance force is proportional to the speed. For an object falling through the air at high speeds, so that the fluid resistance is equal to Dv^2 as in Eq. (5.8), the terminal speed is reached when Dv^2 equals the weight mg (Fig. 5.26a). You can show that the terminal speed v_t is given by

$$v_t = \sqrt{\frac{mg}{D}} \quad \text{(terminal speed, fluid resistance } f = Dv^2\text{)} \tag{5.13}$$

This expression for terminal speed explains why heavy objects in air tend to fall faster than light objects. Two objects with the same physical size but different mass (say, a table-tennis ball and a lead ball with the same radius) have the same value of D but different values of m. The more massive object has a higher terminal speed and falls faster. The same idea explains why a sheet of paper falls faster if you first crumple it into a ball; the mass m is the same, but the smaller size makes D smaller (less air drag for a given speed) and v_t larger. Skydivers use the same principle to control their descent (Fig. 5.26b).

Figure 5.27 shows the trajectories of a baseball with and without air drag, assuming a coefficient $D = 1.3 \times 10^{-3}$ kg/m (appropriate for a batted ball at sea level). You can see that both the range of the baseball and the maximum height reached are substantially less than the zero-drag calculation would lead you to believe. Hence the baseball trajectory we calculated in Example 3.8 (Section 3.3) by ignoring air drag is quite unrealistic. Air drag is an important part of the game of baseball!

5.26 (a) Air drag and terminal speed. (b) By changing the positions of their arms and legs while falling, skydivers can change the value of the constant D in Eq. (5.8) and hence adjust the terminal speed of their fall [Eq. (5.13)].

(a) Free-body diagrams for falling with air drag

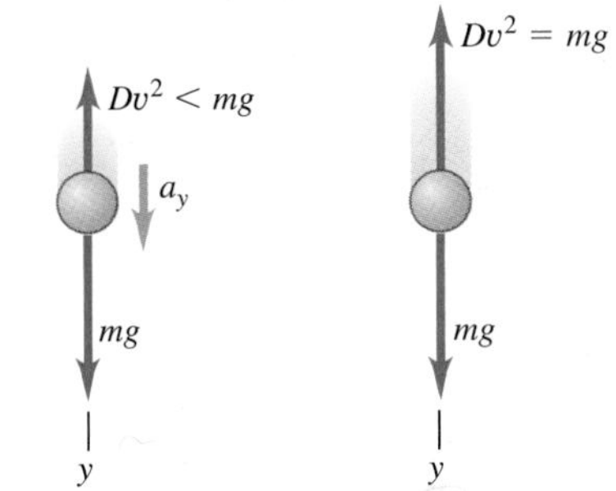
$Dv^2 < mg$
a_y
mg
y
$Dv^2 = mg$
mg
y

Before terminal speed: Object accelerating, drag force less than weight.

At terminal speed v_t: Object in equilibrium, drag force equals weight.

(b) A skydiver falling at terminal speed

5.27 Computer-generated trajectories of a baseball launched at 50 m/s at 35° above the horizontal. Note that the scales are different on the horizontal and vertical axes.

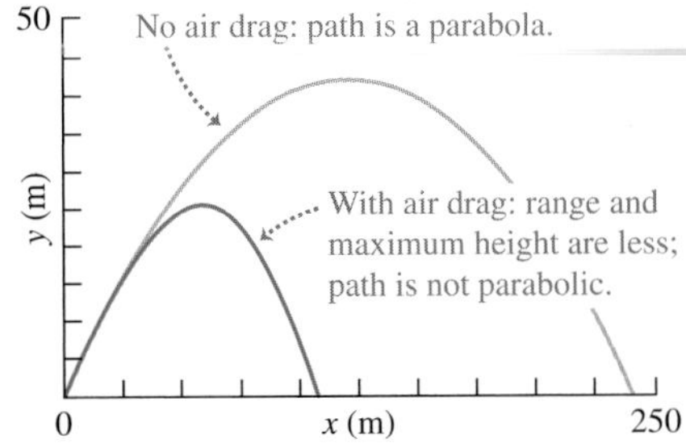
50
No air drag: path is a parabola.
With air drag: range and maximum height are less; path is not parabolic.
y (m)
0
x (m)
250

Example 5.19 Terminal speed of a skydiver

For a human body falling through air in a spread-eagle position (Fig. 5.26b), the numerical value of the constant D in Eq. (5.8) is about 0.25 kg/m. Find the terminal speed for a lightweight 50-kg skydiver.

SOLUTION

IDENTIFY: This example uses the relationship among terminal speed, mass, and drag coefficient.

SET UP: We use Eq. (5.13) to find the target variable v_t.

EXECUTE: We find for $m = 50$ kg:

$$v_t = \sqrt{\frac{mg}{D}} = \sqrt{\frac{(50\text{ kg})(9.8\text{ m/s}^2)}{0.25\text{ kg/m}}}$$
$$= 44\text{ m/s} \quad \text{(about 160 km/h, or 99 mi/h)}$$

Continued

EVALUATE: The terminal speed is proportional to the square root of the skydiver's mass, so a more robust skydiver with the same drag coefficient D but twice the mass would have a terminal speed $\sqrt{2} = 1.41$ times greater, or 63 m/s. (A skydiver with more mass would also have more frontal area and hence a larger drag coefficient, so his terminal speed would be a bit less than 63 m/s.) Even the lightweight skydiver's terminal speed is quite high, so skydives don't last very long. A drop from 2800 m (9200 ft) to the surface at the terminal speed takes only $(2800\text{ m})/(44\text{ m/s}) = 64$ s.

When the sky diver deploys the parachute, the value of D increases greatly. Hence the terminal speed of the skydiver and parachute decreases dramatically to a much slower value.

Test Your Understanding of Section 5.3 Consider a box that is placed on different surfaces. (a) In which situation(s) is there *no* friction force acting on the box? (b) In which situation(s) is there a *static* friction force acting on the box? (c) In which situation(s) is there a *kinetic* friction force on the box? (i) The box is at rest on a rough horizontal surface. (ii) The box is at rest on a rough tilted surface. (iii) The box is on the rough-surfaced flat bed of a truck—the truck is moving at a constant velocity on a straight, level road, and the box remains in the same place in the middle of the truck bed. (iv) The box is on the rough-surfaced flat bed of a truck—the truck is speeding up on a straight, level road, and the box remains in the same place in the middle of the truck bed. (v) The box is on the rough-surfaced flat bed of a truck—the truck is climbing a hill, and the box is sliding toward the back of the truck.

5.4 Dynamics of Circular Motion

We talked about uniform circular motion in Section 3.4. We showed that when a particle moves in a circular path with constant speed, the particle's acceleration is always directed toward the center of the circle (perpendicular to the instantaneous velocity). The magnitude a_{rad} of the acceleration is constant and is given in terms of the speed v and the radius R of the circle by

$$a_{\text{rad}} = \frac{v^2}{R} \quad \text{(uniform circular motion)} \tag{5.14}$$

The subscript "rad" is a reminder that at each point the acceleration is radially inward toward the center of the circle, perpendicular to the instantaneous velocity. We explained in Section 3.4 why this acceleration is often called *centripetal acceleration.*

We can also express the centripetal acceleration a_{rad} in terms of the *period T*, the time for one revolution:

$$T = \frac{2\pi R}{v} \tag{5.15}$$

In terms of the period, a_{rad} is

$$a_{\text{rad}} = \frac{4\pi^2 R}{T^2} \quad \text{(uniform circular motion)} \tag{5.16}$$

Uniform circular motion, like all other motion of a particle, is governed by Newton's second law. To make the particle accelerate toward the center of the circle, the net force $\sum\vec{F}$ on the particle must always be directed toward the center (Fig. 5.28). The magnitude of the acceleration is constant, so the magnitude F_{net} of the net force must also be constant. If the inward net force stops acting, the particle flies off in a straight line tangent to the circle (Fig. 5.29).

The magnitude of the radial acceleration is given by $a_{\text{rad}} = v^2/R$, so the magnitude F_{net} of the net force on a particle with mass m in uniform circular motion must be

$$F_{\text{net}} = ma_{\text{rad}} = m\frac{v^2}{R} \quad \text{(uniform circular motion)} \tag{5.17}$$

5.28 In uniform circular motion, both the acceleration and the net force are directed toward the center of the circle.

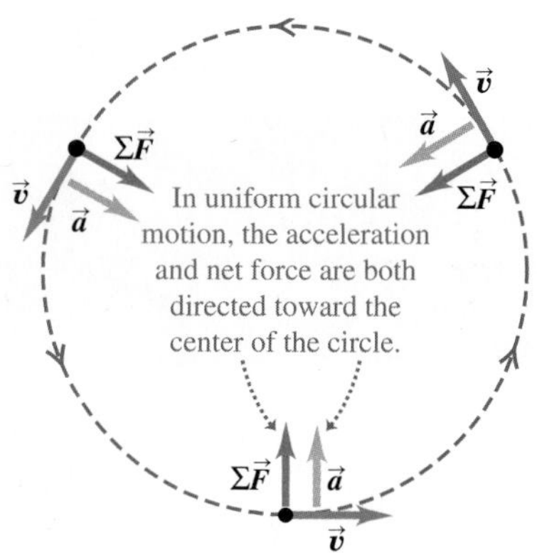
$\vec{v}$
$\vec{a}$
$\Sigma\vec{F}$
In uniform circular motion, the acceleration and net force are both directed toward the center of the circle.

5.29 What happens if the inward radial force suddenly ceases to act on a body in circular motion?

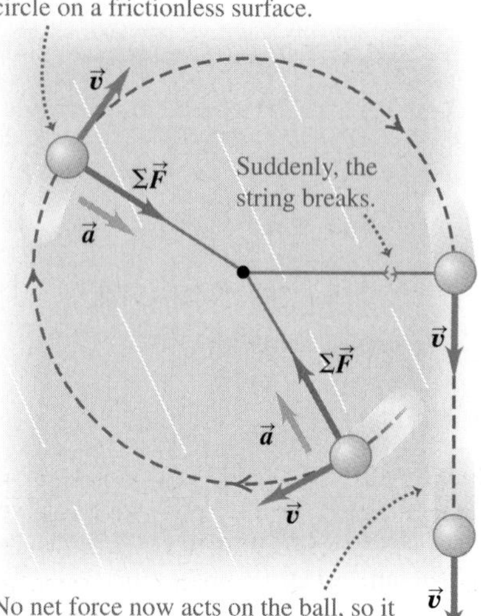
A ball attached to a string whirls in a circle on a frictionless surface.
$\vec{v}$
$\Sigma\vec{F}$
$\vec{a}$
Suddenly, the string breaks.
No net force now acts on the ball, so it obeys Newton's first law—it moves in a straight line at constant velocity.

Uniform circular motion can result from *any* combination of forces, just so the net force $\sum\vec{F}$ is always directed toward the center of the circle and has a constant magnitude. Note that the body need not move around a complete circle: Equation (5.17) is valid for *any* path that can be regarded as part of a circular arc.

CAUTION Avoid using "centrifugal force" Figure 5.30 shows both a correct free-body diagram for uniform circular motion (Fig. 5.30a) and a common *incorrect* diagram (Fig. 5.30b). Figure 5.30b is incorrect because it includes an extra outward force of magnitude $m(v^2/R)$ to "keep the body out there" or to "keep it in equilibrium." There are three reasons not to include such an outward force, usually called *centrifugal force* ("centrifugal" means "fleeing from the center") First, the body does *not* "stay out there": It is in constant motion around its circular path. Because its velocity is constantly changing in direction, the body accelerates and is *not* in equilibrium. Second, if there *were* an additional outward force that balanced the inward force, the net force would be zero and the body would move in a straight line, not a circle (Fig. 5.29). And third, the quantity $m(v^2/R)$ is *not* a force; it corresponds to the $m\vec{a}$ side of $\sum\vec{F} = m\vec{a}$ and does not appear in $\sum\vec{F}$ (Fig. 5.30a). It's true that when you ride in a car that goes around a circular path, you tend to slide to the outside of the turn as though there was a "centrifugal force." But we saw in Section 4.2 that what really happens is that you tend to keep moving in a straight line, and the outer side of the car "runs into" you as the car turns (Fig. 4.11c). *In an inertial frame of reference there is no such thing as "centrifugal force."* We won't mention this term again, and we strongly advise you to avoid using it as well.

5.30 (a) Correct and (b) incorrect free-body diagrams for a body in uniform circular motion.

(a) Correct free-body diagram

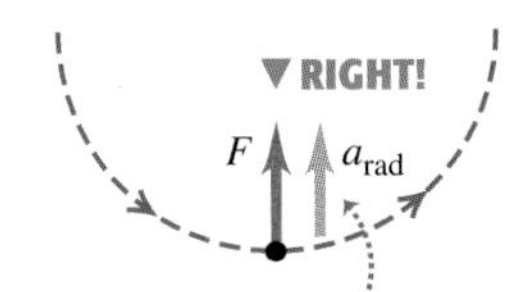

If you include the acceleration, draw it to one side of the body to show that it's not a force.

(b) Incorrect free-body diagram

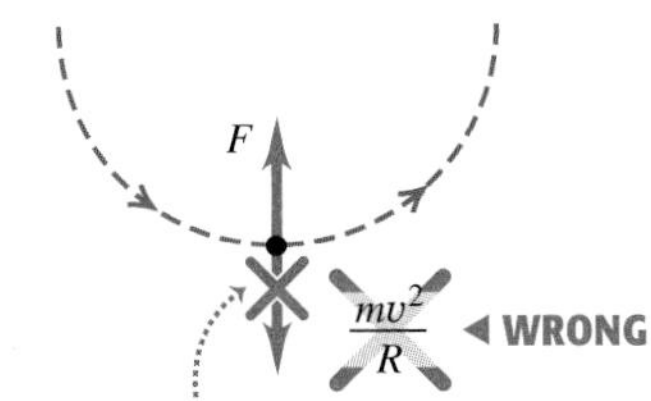

The quantity mv^2/R is *not* a force—it doesn't belong in a free-body diagram.

Example 5.20 Force in uniform circular motion

A sled with a mass of 25.0 kg rests on a horizontal sheet of essentially frictionless ice. It is attached by a 5.00-m rope to a post set in the ice. Once given a push, the sled revolves uniformly in a circle around the post (Fig. 5.31a). If the sled makes five complete revolutions every minute, find the force F exerted on it by the rope.

SOLUTION

IDENTIFY: The sled is moving in uniform circular motion, so it has a radial acceleration. We will apply Newton's second law to the sled to find the magnitude F of the force exerted by the rope (our target variable).

SET UP: Figure 5.31b shows our free-body diagram for the sled. The acceleration has only an x-component; this is toward the center of the circle, so we denote it as a_{rad}. The acceleration isn't given, so we'll need to determine its value using either Eq. (5.14) or Eq. (5.16).

5.31 (a) The situation. (b) Our free-body diagram.

(a) A sled in uniform circular motion

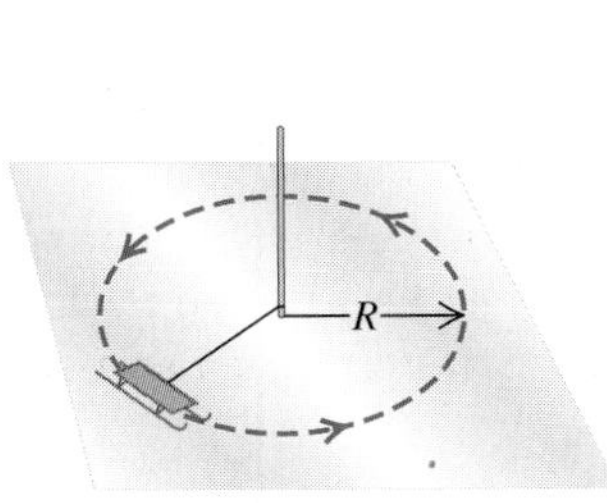

(b) Free-body diagram for the sled

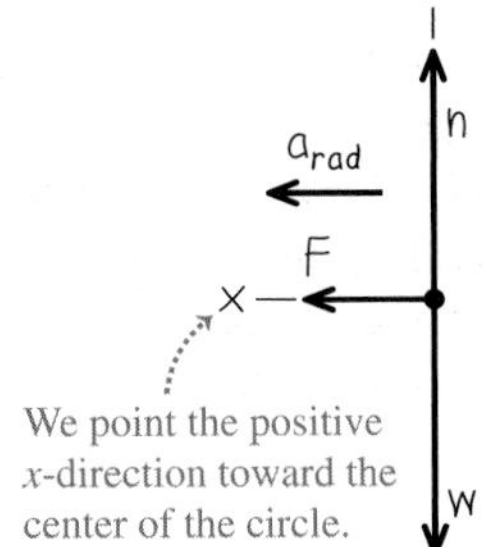

We point the positive x-direction toward the center of the circle.

EXECUTE: The acceleration in the y-direction is zero, so the net force in that direction is zero and the normal force and weight have the same magnitude. For the x-direction, Newton's second law gives

$$\sum F_x = F = ma_{rad}$$

We can find the centripetal acceleration a_{rad} using Eq. (5.16). The sled moves in a circle of radius $R = 5.00\text{ m}$ with a period $T = (60.0\text{ s})/(5\text{ rev}) = 12.0\text{ s}$, so

$$a_{rad} = \frac{4\pi^2 R}{T^2} = \frac{4\pi^2(5.00\text{ m})}{(12.0\text{ s})^2} = 1.37\text{ m/s}^2$$

Alternatively, we can first use Eq. (5.15) to find the speed v:

$$v = \frac{2\pi R}{T} = \frac{2\pi(5.00\text{ m})}{12.0\text{ s}} = 2.62\text{ m/s}$$

Then, using Eq. (5.14),

$$a_{rad} = \frac{v^2}{R} = \frac{(2.62\text{ m/s})^2}{5.00\text{ m}} = 1.37\text{ m/s}^2$$

Hence the magnitude F of the force exerted by the rope is

$$F = ma_{rad} = (25.0\text{ kg})(1.37\text{ m/s}^2)$$
$$= 34.3\text{ kg}\cdot\text{m/s}^2 = 34.3\text{ N}$$

EVALUATE: A greater force would be needed if the sled moved around the circle at a higher speed v. In fact, if v were doubled while R remained the same, F would be four times greater. Can you show this? How would F change if v remained the same but the radius R were doubled?

Example 5.21 The conical pendulum

An inventor proposes to make a pendulum clock using a pendulum bob with mass m at the end of a thin wire of length L. Instead of swinging back and forth, the bob moves in a horizontal circle with constant speed v, with the wire making a constant angle β with the vertical direction (Fig. 5.32a). This system is called a *conical pendulum* because the suspending wire traces out a cone. Find the tension F in the wire and the period T (the time for one revolution of the bob) in terms of β.

SOLUTION

IDENTIFY: To find our two target variables, the tension F and period T, we need two equations. These will be the horizontal and vertical components of Newton's second law applied to the bob. We'll find the acceleration of the bob toward the center of the circle using one of the circular motion equations.

SET UP: Figure 5.32b shows our free-body diagram for the bob as well as a coordinate system. The forces on the bob in the position shown are the weight mg and the tension F in the wire. Note that the center of the circular path is in the same horizontal plane as the bob, *not* at the top end of the wire. The horizontal component of tension is the force that produces the horizontal acceleration a_{rad} toward the center of the circle.

5.32 (a) The situation. (b) Our free-body diagram.

(a) The situation

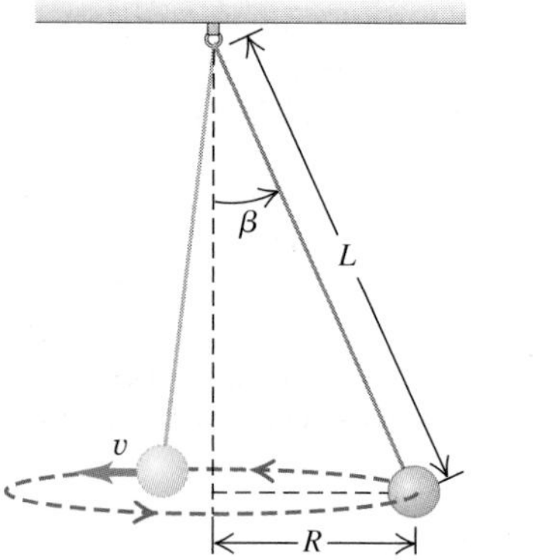

(b) Free-body diagram for the ball

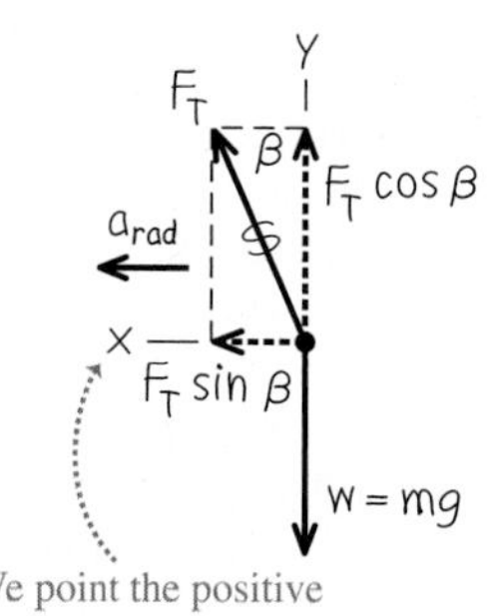

EXECUTE: The bob has zero vertical acceleration; the horizontal acceleration is toward the center of the circle, which is why we use the symbol a_{rad}. The $\sum\vec{F} = m\vec{a}$ equations are

$$\sum F_x = F\sin\beta = ma_{rad}$$
$$\sum F_y = F\cos\beta + (-mg) = 0$$

These are two equations for the two unknowns F and β. The equation for $\sum F_y$ gives $F = mg/\cos\beta$; substituting this result into the equation for $\sum F_x$ and using $\sin\beta/\cos\beta = \tan\beta$, we find

$$\tan\beta = \frac{a_{rad}}{g}$$

To relate β to the period T, we use Eq. (5.16) for a_{rad}. The radius of the circle is $R = L\sin\beta$, so

$$a_{rad} = \frac{4\pi^2 R}{T^2} = \frac{4\pi^2 L\sin\beta}{T^2}$$

Substituting this into $\tan\beta = a_{rad}/g$, we obtain

$$\tan\beta = \frac{4\pi^2 L\sin\beta}{gT^2}$$

which we can rewrite as

$$T = 2\pi\sqrt{\frac{L\cos\beta}{g}}$$

EVALUATE: For a given length L, as the angle β increases, $\cos\beta$ decreases, the period T becomes smaller, and the tension $F = mg/\cos\beta$ increases. The angle can never be 90°, however; this would require that $T = 0$, $F = \infty$, and $v = \infty$. A conical pendulum would not make a very good clock because the period depends on the angle β in such a direct way.

Example 5.22 Rounding a flat curve

The sports car in Example 3.11 (Section 3.4) is rounding a flat, unbanked curve with radius R (Fig. 5.33a). If the coefficient of static friction between tires and road is μ_s, what is the maximum speed v_{max} at which the driver can take the curve without sliding?

SOLUTION

IDENTIFY: The car's acceleration as it rounds the curve has magnitude $a_{rad} = v^2/R$. Hence the maximum speed v_{max} (our target variable) corresponds to the maximum acceleration a_{rad} and to the maximum horizontal force on the car toward the center of its circular path. The only horizontal force acting on the car is the friction force exerted by the road. So we'll need Newton's second law and our knowledge of the friction force from Section 5.3.

SET UP: The free-body diagram in Fig. 5.33b includes the car's weight $w = mg$ and the two forces exerted by the road, the normal force n and the horizontal friction force f. The friction force must

5.33 (a) The situation. (b) Our free-body diagram.

(a) Car rounding flat curve

(b) Free-body diagram for the car

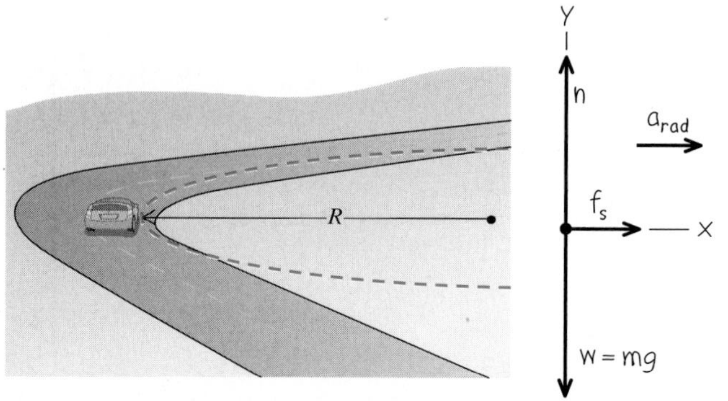

point toward the center of the circular path in order to cause the radial acceleration. Since the car doesn't move in the radial direction (it doesn't slide toward or away from the center of the circle), the friction force is *static* friction with a maximum magnitude $f_{max} = \mu_s n$ [see Eq. (5.6)].

EXECUTE: The acceleration toward the center of the circular path is $a_{rad} = v^2/R$ and there is no vertical acceleration. Thus we have

$$\sum F_x = f = ma_{rad} = m\frac{v^2}{R}$$

$$\sum F_y = n + (-mg) = 0$$

The second equation shows that $n = mg$. The first equation shows that the friction force *needed* to keep the car moving in its circular path increases with the car's speed. But the maximum friction force *available* is $f_{max} = \mu_s n = \mu_s mg$, and this determines the car's maximum speed. Substituting f_{max} for f and v_{max} for v in the $\sum F_x$ equation, we find

$$\mu_s mg = m\frac{v_{max}^2}{R}$$

so the maximum speed is

$$v_{max} = \sqrt{\mu_s gR}$$

As an example, if $\mu_s = 0.96$ and $R = 230$ m, then

$$v_{max} = \sqrt{(0.96)(9.8\ \text{m/s}^2)(230\ \text{m})} = 47\ \text{m/s}$$

or about 170 km/h (100 mi/h). This is the maximum speed for this radius.

EVALUATE: If the car's speed is slower than $\sqrt{\mu_s gR}$, the required friction force is less than the maximum possible value $f_{max} = \mu_s mg$ and the car can easily make the curve. If we try to take the curve going *faster* than the maximum speed, the car can still go in a circle without skidding, but the radius will be larger and the car will run off the road.

Note that the maximum centripetal acceleration (called the "lateral acceleration" in Example 3.11) is equal to $\mu_s g$. If the coefficient of friction is reduced, the maximum centripetal acceleration and v_{max} are also reduced. That's why it's best to take curves at a lower speed if the road is wet or icy (either of which can reduce the value of μ_s).

Example 5.23 Rounding a banked curve

For a car traveling at a certain speed, it is possible to bank a curve at just the right angle so that no friction at all is needed to maintain the car's turning radius. Then a car can safely round the curve even on wet ice. (Bobsled racing depends on this same idea.) Your engineering firm plans to rebuild the curve in Example 5.22 so that a car moving at speed v can safely make the turn even with no friction (Fig. 5.34a). At what angle β should the curve be banked?

SOLUTION

IDENTIFY: With no friction, the only two forces acting on the car are its weight and the normal force. Because the road is banked, the normal force (which acts perpendicular to the road surface) has a horizontal component. This component causes the car's horizontal acceleration toward the center of the car's circular path. Since forces and acceleration are involved, we'll use Newton's second law to find the target variable β.

SET UP: Our free-body diagram (Fig. 5.34b) is very similar to the diagram for the conical pendulum in Example 5.21 (Fig. 5.32b). The normal force acting on the car plays the role of the tension acting on the pendulum bob.

EXECUTE: The normal force $\vec{n}$ is perpendicular to the roadway at an angle β with the vertical. Thus it has a vertical component $n\cos\beta$ and a horizontal component $n\sin\beta$, as Fig. 5.34b shows. The acceleration in the x-direction is the centripetal acceleration, $a_{rad} = v^2/R$; there is no acceleration in the y-direction. Thus the equations of Newton's second law are

$$\sum F_x = n\sin\beta = ma_{rad}$$

$$\sum F_y = n\cos\beta + (-mg) = 0$$

5.34 (a) The situation. (b) Our free-body diagram.

(a) Car rounding banked curve

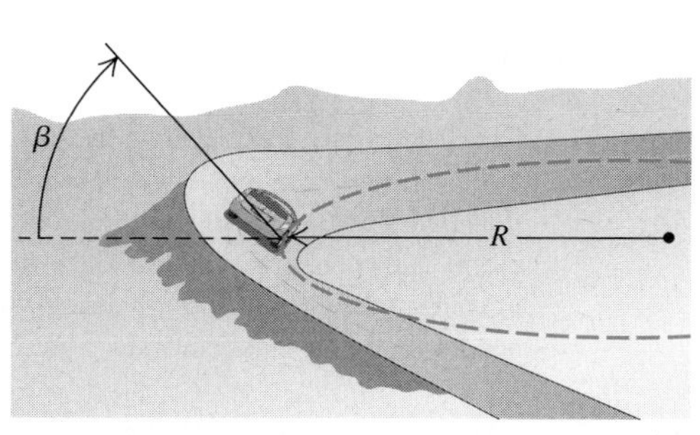

(b) Free-body diagram for the car

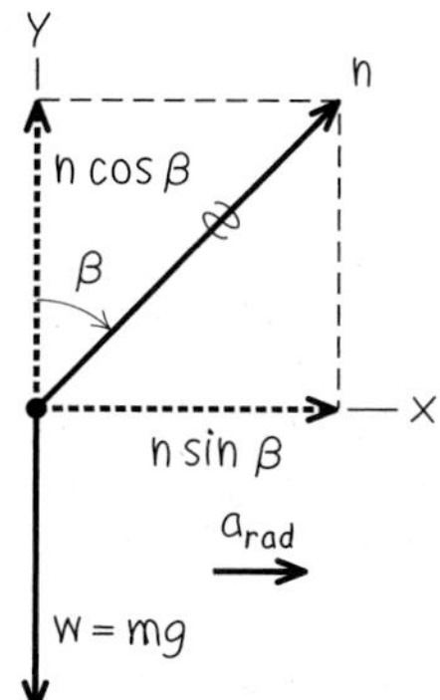

Continued

From the $\sum F_y$ equation, $n = mg/\cos\beta$. Substituting this into the $\sum F_x$ equation gives an expression for the bank angle:

$$\tan\beta = \frac{a_{\rm rad}}{g}$$

This is the same expression we found in Example 5.21. Finally, substituting the expression $a_{\rm rad} = v^2/R$, we have

$$\tan\beta = \frac{v^2}{gR}$$

EVALUATE: The bank angle depends on the speed and the radius. For a given radius, no one angle is correct for all speeds. In the design of highways and railroads, curves are often banked for the average speed of the traffic over them. If $R = 230\ \text{m}$ and $v = 25\ \text{m/s}$ (equal to a highway speed of 88 km/h, or 55 mi/h), then

$$\beta = \arctan\frac{(25\ \text{m/s})^2}{(9.8\ \text{m/s}^2)(230\ \text{m})} = 15°$$

This is within the range of banking angles actually used in highways. With the same radius and $v = 47\ \text{m/s}$, as in Example 5.22, $\beta = 44°$; such steeply banked curves are found at automobile raceways.

Banked Curves and the Flight of Airplanes

The results of Example 5.23 also apply to an airplane when it makes a turn in level flight (Fig. 5.35). When an airplane is flying in a straight line at a constant speed and at a steady altitude, the airplane's weight is exactly balanced by the lift force $\vec{L}$ exerted by the air. (The upward lift force that the air exerts on the wings is a reaction to the downward push the wings exert on the air as they move through it.) To make the airplane turn, the pilot banks the airplane to one side so that the lift force has a horizontal component as Fig. 5.35 shows. (The pilot also changes the angle at which the wings "bite" into the air so that the vertical component of lift continues to balance the weight.) The bank angle is related to the airplane's speed v and the radius R of the turn by the same expression as in Example 5.23: $\tan\beta = v^2/gR$. For an airplane to make a tight turn (small R) at high speed (large v), $\tan\beta$ must be large and the required bank angle β must approach 90°.

5.35 An airplane banks to one side in order to turn in that direction. The vertical component of the lift force $\vec{L}$ balances the force of gravity; the horizontal component of $\vec{L}$ causes the acceleration v^2/R.

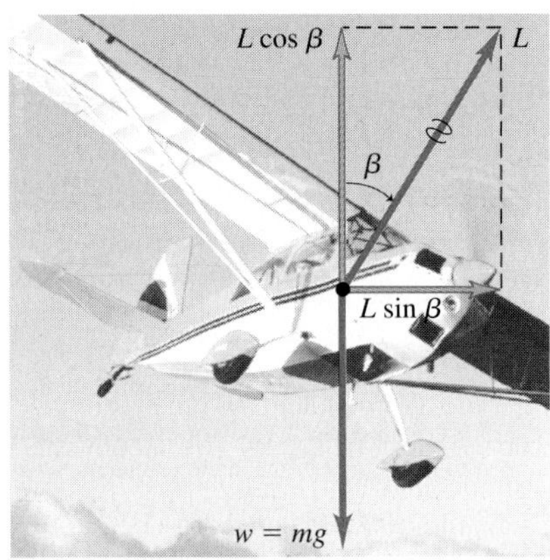

We can also apply the results of Example 5.23 to the *pilot* of an airplane. The free-body diagram for the pilot of the airplane is exactly as shown in Fig. 5.34b; the normal force $n = mg/\cos\beta$ is exerted on the pilot by the seat. As in Example 5.9, n is equal to the apparent weight of the pilot, which is greater than the pilot's true weight mg. In a tight turn with a large bank angle β, the pilot's apparent weight can be tremendous: $n = 5.8mg$ at $\beta = 80°$ and $n = 9.6mg$ at $\beta = 84°$. Pilots black out in such tight turns because the apparent weight of their blood increases by the same factor, and the human heart isn't strong enough to pump such apparently "heavy" blood to the brain.

ActivPhysics ONLINE

4.2 Circular Motion Problem Solving
4.3 Cart Goes Over Circular Path
4.4 Ball Swings on a String
4.5 Car Circles a Track

Motion in a Vertical Circle

In Examples 5.20, 5.21, 5.22, and 5.23 the body moved in a horizontal circle. Motion in a *vertical* circle is no different in principle, but the weight of the body has to be treated carefully. The following example shows what we mean.

Example 5.24 Uniform circular motion in a vertical circle

A passenger on a carnival Ferris wheel moves in a vertical circle of radius R with constant speed v. The seat remains upright during the motion. Find expressions for the force the seat exerts on the passenger at the top of the circle and at the bottom.

SOLUTION

IDENTIFY: At both the top and bottom of the circle, the target variable is the magnitude n of the normal force that the seat exerts on the passenger. We'll find this force at each position using Newton's second law and the equations of uniform circular motion.

SET UP: Figure 5.36a shows the passenger's velocity and acceleration at the two positions. Note that the acceleration points *downward* at the *top* of the circle but *upward* at the *bottom* of the circle. At each position the only forces acting are vertical: the upward normal force and the downward force of gravity. Hence we need only the vertical component of Newton's second law.

EXECUTE: Figures 5.36b and 5.36c show free-body diagrams for the two positions. We take the positive y-direction as upward in both cases. Let n_T be the upward normal force the seat applies to the passenger at the top of the circle, and let n_B be the normal force at the bottom. At the top the acceleration has magnitude v^2/R, but its vertical component is negative because its direction is downward. Hence $a_y = -v^2/R$, and Newton's second law tells us that

$$\text{Top:} \quad \sum F_y = n_T + (-mg) = -m\frac{v^2}{R} \quad \text{or}$$

$$n_T = m\left(g - \frac{v^2}{R}\right)$$

At the bottom the acceleration is upward, so $a_y = +v^2/R$ and Newton's second law is

$$\text{Bottom:} \quad \sum F_y = n_B + (-mg) = +m\frac{v^2}{R} \quad \text{or}$$

$$n_B = m\left(g + \frac{v^2}{R}\right)$$

EVALUATE: Our result for n_T tells us that at the top of the Ferris wheel, the upward force the seat applies to the passenger is *smaller* in magnitude than the passenger's weight $w = mg$. If the ride goes fast enough that $g - v^2/R$ becomes zero, the seat applies *no* force, and the passenger is about to become airborne. If v becomes still larger, n_T becomes negative; this means that a *downward* force (such as from a seat belt) is needed to keep the passenger in the seat. By contrast, the normal force n_B at the bottom is always *greater than* the passenger's weight. You feel the seat pushing up on you more firmly than when you are at rest. You can see that n_T and n_B are the values of the passenger's *apparent weight* at the top and bottom of the circle (see Section 5.2).

5.36 Our sketches for this problem.

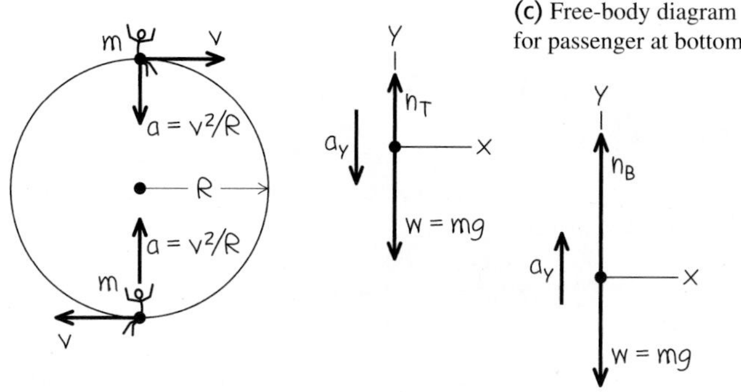
(a) Sketch of two positions
(b) Free-body diagram for passenger at top
(c) Free-body diagram for passenger at bottom
m
v
a = v²/R
R
a = v²/R
m
v
y
n_T
a_y
x
w = mg
y
n_B
a_y
x
w = mg

When we tie a string to an object and whirl it in a vertical circle, the analysis in Example 5.24 isn't directly applicable. The reason is that v is *not* constant in this case; except at the top and bottom of the circle, the net force (and hence the acceleration) does *not* point toward the center of the circle (Fig. 5.37). So both $\sum\vec{F}$ and $\vec{a}$ have a component tangent to the circle, which means that the speed changes. Hence this is a case of *nonuniform* circular motion (see Section 3.4). Even worse, we can't use the constant-acceleration formulas to relate the speeds at various points because *neither* the magnitude nor the direction of the acceleration is constant. The speed relationships we need are best obtained by using the concept of energy. We'll consider such problems in Chapter 7.

5.37 A ball moving in a vertical circle.

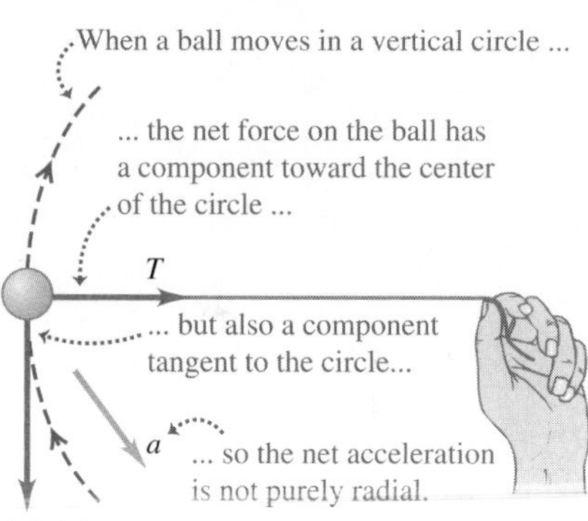
When a ball moves in a vertical circle ...
... the net force on the ball has a component toward the center of the circle ...
T
... but also a component tangent to the circle...
a
... so the net acceleration is not purely radial.
w = mg

Test Your Understanding of Section 5.4 Satellites are held in orbit by the force of our planet's gravitational attraction. A satellite in a small-radius orbit moves at a higher speed than a satellite in an orbit of large radius. Based on this information, what you can conclude about the earth's gravitational attraction for the satellite? (i) It increases with increasing distance from the earth. (ii) It is the same at all distances from the earth. (iii) It decreases with increasing distance from the earth. (iv) This information by itself isn't enough to answer the question.

*5.5 The Fundamental Forces of Nature

We have discussed several kinds of forces—including weight, tension, friction, fluid resistance, and the normal force—and we will encounter others as we continue our study of physics. But just how many kinds of forces are there? Our current understanding is that all forces are expressions of just four distinct classes of *fundamental* forces, or interactions between particles (Fig. 5.38). Two are familiar in everyday experience. The other two involve interactions between subatomic particles that we cannot observe with the unaided senses.

Gravitational interactions include the familiar force of your *weight,* which results from the earth's gravitational attraction acting on you. The mutual gravitational attraction of various parts of the earth for each other holds our planet

5.38 Examples of the fundamental interactions in nature. (a) The moon and the earth are held together and held in orbit by gravitational forces. (b) This molecule of bacterial plasmid DNA is held together by electromagnetic forces between its atoms. (c) The sun shines because in its core, strong forces between nuclear particles cause the release of energy. (d) When a massive star explodes into a supernova, a flood of energy is released by weak interactions between the star's nuclear particles.

(a) Gravitational forces hold planets together.

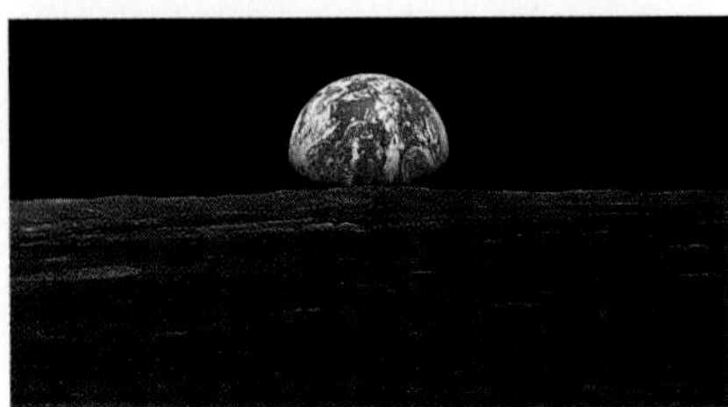

(b) Electromagnetic forces hold molecules together.

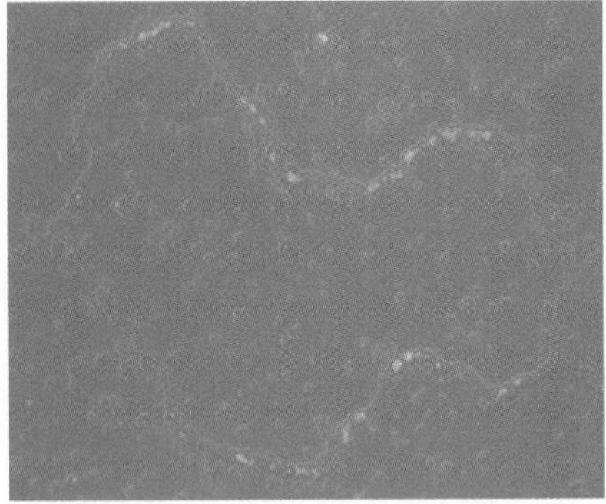

(c) Strong forces release energy to power the sun.

(d) Weak forces play a role in exploding stars.

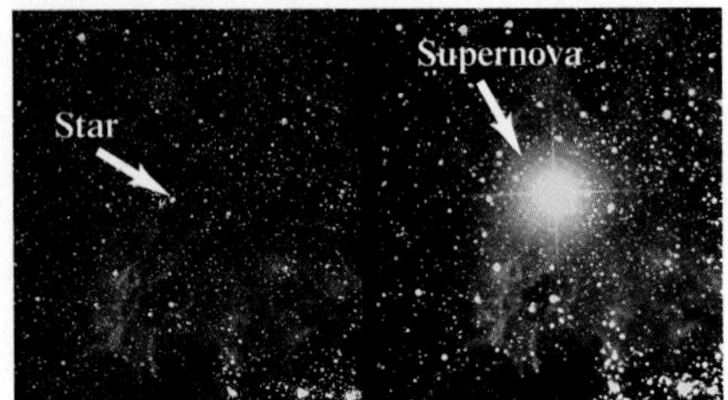

together (Fig. 5.38a). Newton recognized that the sun's gravitational attraction for the earth keeps the earth in its nearly circular orbit around the sun. In Chapter 12 we will study gravitational interactions in greater detail, and we will analyze their vital role in the motions of planets and satellites.

The second familiar class of forces, **electromagnetic interactions,** includes electric and magnetic forces. If you run a comb through your hair, the comb ends up with an electric charge; you can use the electric force exerted by this charge to pick up bits of paper. All atoms contain positive and negative electric charge, so atoms and molecules can exert electric forces on each other (Fig. 5.38b). Contact forces, including the normal force, friction, and fluid resistance, are the combination of all such forces exerted on the atoms of a body by atoms in its surroundings. *Magnetic* forces, such as those between magnets or between a magnet and a piece of iron, are actually the result of electric charges in motion. For example, an electromagnet causes magnetic interactions because electric charges move through its wires. We will study electromagnetic interactions in detail in the second half of this book.

On the atomic or molecular scale, gravitational forces play no role because electric forces are enormously stronger: The electrical repulsion between two protons is stronger than their gravitational attraction by a factor of about 10^{35}. But in bodies of astronomical size, positive and negative charges are usually present in nearly equal amounts, and the resulting electrical interactions nearly cancel out. Gravitational interactions are thus the dominant influence in the motion of planets and in the internal structure of stars.

The other two classes of interactions are less familiar. One, the **strong interaction,** is responsible for holding the nucleus of an atom together. Nuclei contain electrically neutral neutrons and positively charged protons. The electric force between charged protons tries to push them apart; the strong attractive force between nuclear particles counteracts this repulsion and makes the nucleus stable. In this context the strong interaction is also called the *strong nuclear force.* It has much shorter range than electrical interactions, but within its range it is much stronger. The strong interaction plays a key role in thermonuclear reactions that take place at the sun's core and generate the sun's heat and light (Fig. 5.38c).

Finally, there is the **weak interaction.** Its range is so short that it plays a role only on the scale of the nucleus or smaller. The weak interaction is responsible for a common form of radioactivity called beta decay, in which a neutron in a radioactive nucleus is transformed into a proton while ejecting an electron and a nearly massless particle called an antineutrino. The weak interaction between the antineutrino and ordinary matter is so feeble that an antineutrino could easily penetrate a wall of lead a million kilometers thick! Yet when a giant star undergoes a cataclysmic explosion called a supernova, most of the energy is released by way of the weak interaction (Fig. 5.38d).

In the 1960s physicists developed a theory that described the electromagnetic and weak interactions as aspects of a single *electroweak* interaction. This theory has passed every experimental test to which it has been put. Encouraged by this success, physicists have made similar attempts to describe the strong, electromagnetic, and weak interactions in terms of a single *grand unified theory* (GUT), and have taken steps toward a possible unification of all interactions into a *theory of everything* (TOE). Such theories are still speculative, and there are many unanswered questions in this very active field of current research.

CHAPTER 5 SUMMARY

Using Newton's first law: When a body is in equilibrium in an inertial frame of reference—that is, either at rest or moving with constant velocity—the vector sum of forces acting on it must be zero (Newton's first law). Free-body diagrams are essential in identifying the forces that act on the body being considered.

Newton's third law (action and reaction) is also frequently needed in equilibrium problems. The two forces in an action–reaction pair *never* act on the same body. (See Examples 5.1–5.5.)

The normal force exerted on a body by a surface is *not* always equal to the body's weight. (See Example 5.3.)

$$\sum \vec{F} = \mathbf{0} \quad \text{(vector form)} \qquad (5.1)$$

$$\sum F_x = 0 \qquad \sum F_y = 0 \quad \text{(component form)} \qquad (5.2)$$

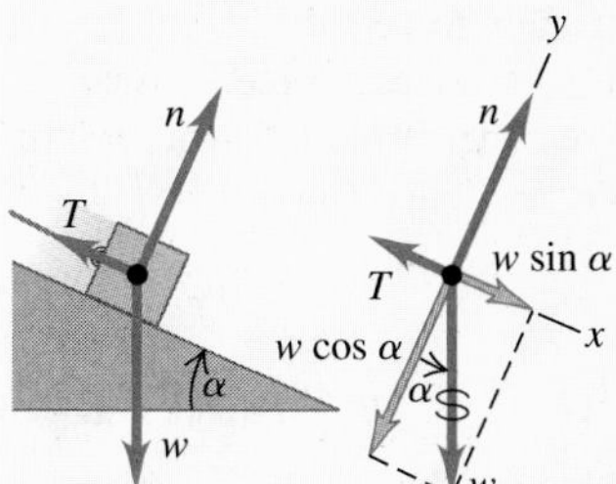

Using Newton's second law: If the vector sum of forces on a body is *not* zero, the body accelerates. The acceleration is related to the net force by Newton's second law.

Just as for equilibrium problems, free-body diagrams are essential for solving problems involving Newton's second law, and the normal force exerted on a body is not always equal to its weight. (See Examples 5.6–5.12.)

Vector form:

$$\sum \vec{F} = m\vec{a} \qquad (5.3)$$

Component form:

$$\sum F_x = ma_x \qquad \sum F_y = ma_y \qquad (5.4)$$

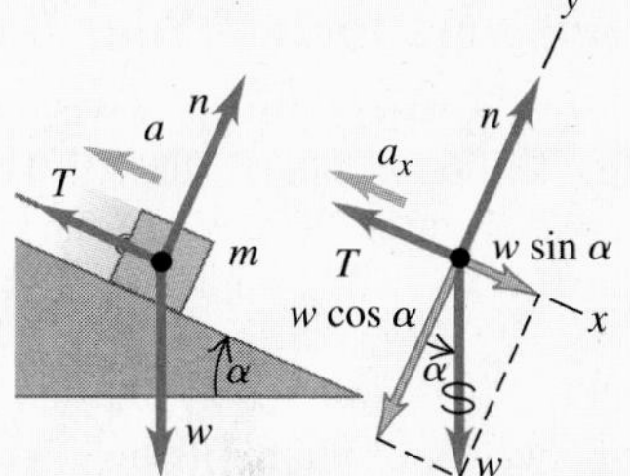

Friction and fluid resistance: The contact force between two bodies can always be represented in terms of a normal force $\vec{n}$ perpendicular to the surface of contact and a friction force $\vec{f}$ parallel to the surface.

When a body is sliding over the surface, the friction force is called *kinetic* friction. Its magnitude f_k is approximately equal to the normal force magnitude n multiplied by the coefficient of kinetic friction μ_k. When a body is *not* moving relative to a surface, the friction force is called *static* friction. The *maximum* possible static friction force is approximately equal to the magnitude n of the normal force multiplied by the coefficient of static friction μ_s. The *actual* static friction force may be anything from zero to this maximum value, depending on the situation. Usually μ_s is greater than μ_k for a given pair of surfaces in contact. (See Examples 5.13–5.17.)

Rolling friction is similar to kinetic friction, but the force of fluid resistance depends on the speed of an object through a fluid. (See Examples 5.18 and 5.19.)

Magnitude of kinetic friction force:

$$f_k = \mu_k n \qquad (5.5)$$

Magnitude of static friction force:

$$f_s \leq \mu_s n \qquad (5.6)$$

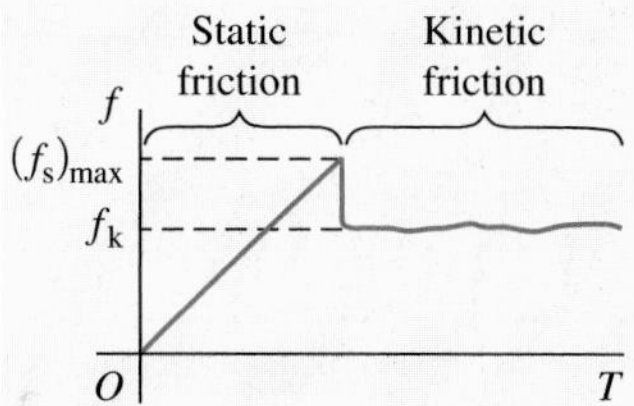

Forces in circular motion: In uniform circular motion, the acceleration vector is directed toward the center of the circle. The motion is governed by Newton's second law, $\sum \vec{F} = m\vec{a}$. (See Examples 5.20–5.24.)

Acceleration in uniform circular motion:

$$a_{rad} = \frac{v^2}{R} = \frac{4\pi^2 R}{T^2} \qquad (5.14), (5.16)$$

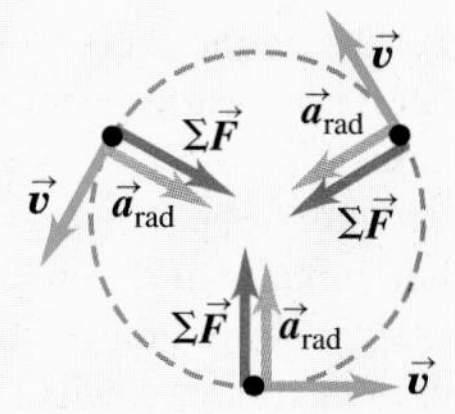

Key Terms

apparent weight, *145*
friction force, *149*
kinetic friction force, *150*
coefficient of kinetic friction, *150*
static friction force, *151*
coefficient of static friction, *151*
coefficient of rolling friction, *155*
fluid resistance, *155*
air drag, *155*
terminal speed, *156*
gravitational interaction, *163*
electromagnetic interaction, *164*
strong interaction, *164*
weak interaction, *164*

Answer to Chapter Opening Question ?

Neither; the upward force of the air has the *same* magnitude as the force of gravity. Although the bird is ascending, its vertical velocity is constant and so its vertical acceleration is zero. Hence the net vertical force on the bird must also be zero, and the individual vertical forces must balance.

Answers to Test Your Understanding Questions

5.1 **Answer: (ii)** The two cables are arranged symmetrically, so the tension in either cable has the same magnitude T. The vertical component of the tension from each cable is $T\sin 45°$ (or, equivalently, $T\cos 45°$), so Newton's first law applied to the vertical forces tells us that $2T\sin 45° - w = 0$. Hence $T = w/(2\sin 45°) = w/\sqrt{2} = 0.71w$. Each cable supports half of the weight of the traffic light, but the tension is greater than $w/2$ because only the vertical component of the tension counteracts the weight.

5.2 **Answer: (ii)** No matter what the instantaneous velocity of the glider, its acceleration is constant and has the value found in Example 5.12. In the same way, the acceleration of a body in free fall is the same whether it is ascending, descending, or at the high point of its motion (see Section 2.5).

5.3 **Answers to (a): (i), (iii); answers to (b): (ii), (iv); answer to (c): (v)** In situations (i) and (iii) the box is not accelerating (so the net force on it must be zero) and there is no other force acting parallel to the horizontal surface; hence no friction force is needed to prevent sliding. In situations (ii) and (iv) the box would start to slide over the surface if no friction were present, so a static friction force must act to prevent this. In situation (v) the box is sliding over a rough surface, so a kinetic friction force acts on it.

5.4 **Answer: (iii)** A satellite of mass m orbiting the earth at speed v in an orbit of radius r has an acceleration of magnitude v^2/r, so the net force acting on it from the earth's gravity has magnitude $F = mv^2/r$. The farther the satellite is from earth, the greater the value of r, the smaller the value of v, and hence the smaller the values of v^2/r and of F. In other words, the earth's gravitational force decreases with increasing distance.

PROBLEMS

For instructor-assigned homework, go to www.masteringphysics.com 

Discussion Questions

Q5.1. A man sits in a seat that is suspended from a rope. The rope passes over a pulley suspended from the ceiling, and the man holds the other end of the rope in his hands. What is the tension in the rope, and what force does the seat exert on the man? Draw a free-body force diagram for the man.

Q5.2. "In general, the normal force is not equal to the weight." Give an example where the two forces are equal in magnitude, and at least two examples where they are not.

Q5.3. A clothesline hangs between two poles. No matter how tightly the line is stretched, it always sags a little at the center. Explain why.

Q5.4. A car is driven up a steep hill at constant speed. Discuss all the forces acting on the car. What pushes it up the hill?

Q5.5. For medical reasons it is important for astronauts in outer space to determine their body mass at regular intervals. Devise a scheme for measuring body mass in an apparently weightless environment.

Q5.6. To push a box up a ramp, is the force required smaller if you push horizontally or if you push parallel to the ramp? Why?

Q5.7. A woman in an elevator lets go of her briefcase but it does not fall to the floor. How is the elevator moving?

Q5.8. You can classify scales for weighing objects as those that use springs and those that use standard masses to balance unknown masses. Which group would be more accurate when you use it in an accelerating spaceship? When you use it on the moon?

Q5.9. When you tighten a nut on a bolt, how are you increasing the frictional force? How does a lock washer work?

Q5.10. A block rests on an inclined plane with enough friction to prevent it from sliding down. To start the block moving, is it easier to push it up the plane or down the plane? Why?

Q5.11. A crate of books rests on a level floor. To move it along the floor at a constant velocity, why do you exert a smaller force if you pull it at an angle θ above the horizontal than if you push it at the same angle below the horizontal?

Q5.12. In a world without friction, which of the following activities could you do (or not do)? Explain your reasoning. (a) drive around an unbanked highway curve; (b) jump into the air; (c) start walking on a horizontal sidewalk; (d) climb a vertical ladder; (e) change lanes on the freeway.

Q5.13. Walking on horizontal slippery ice can be much more tiring than walking on ordinary pavement. Why?

Q5.14. When you stand with bare feet in a wet bathtub, the grip feels fairly secure, and yet a catastrophic slip is quite possible. Explain this in terms of the two coefficients of friction.

Q5.15. You are pushing a large crate from the back of a freight elevator to the front as the elevator is moving to the next floor. In which situation is the force you must apply to move the crate the smallest and in which is it the largest: when the elevator is accelerating upward, when it is accelerating downward, or when it is traveling at constant speed? Explain.

Q5.16. The moon is accelerating toward the earth. Why isn't it getting closer to us?

Q5.17. An automotive magazine calls decreasing-radius curves "the bane of the Sunday driver." Explain.

Q5.18. You often hear people say that "friction always opposes motion." Give at least one example where (a) static friction *causes* motion, and (b) kinetic friction *causes* motion.

Q5.19. If there is a net force on a particle in uniform circular motion, why doesn't the particle's speed change?

Q5.20. A curve in a road has the banking angle calculated and posted for 80 km/h. However, the road is covered with ice so you cautiously plan to drive slower than this limit. What may happen to your car? Why?

Q5.21. You swing a ball on the end of a lightweight string in a horizontal circle at constant speed. Can the string ever be truly horizontal? If not, would it slope above the horizontal or below the horizontal? Why?

Q5.22. The centrifugal force is not included in the free-body diagrams of Figs. 5.34b and 5.35. Explain why not.

Q5.23. A professor swings a rubber stopper in a horizontal circle on the end of a string in front of his class. He tells Caroline, in the first row, that he is going to let the string go when the stopper is directly in front of her face. Should Caroline worry?

Q5.24. To keep the forces on the riders within allowable limits, loop-the-loop roller coaster rides are often designed so that the loop, rather than being a perfect circle, has a larger radius of curvature at the bottom than at the top. Explain.

Q5.25. A tennis ball drops from rest at the top of a tall glass cylinder, first with the air pumped out of the cylinder so there is no air resistance, and then a second time after the air has been readmitted to the cylinder. You examine multiflash photographs of the two drops. From these photos how can you tell which one is which, or can you?

Q5.26. If you throw a baseball straight upward with speed v_0, how does its speed, when it returns to the point from where you threw it, compare to v_0 (a) in the absence of air resistance and (b) in the presence of air resistance? Explain.

Q5.27. You throw a baseball straight upward. If air resistance is *not* ignored, how does the time required for the ball to go from the height at which it was thrown up to its maximum height compare to the time required for it to fall from its maximum height back down to the height from which it was thrown? Explain your answer.

Q5.28. You take two identical tennis balls and fill one with water. You release both balls simultaneously from the top of a tall building. If air resistance is negligible, which ball strikes the ground first? Explain. What is the answer if air resistance is *not* negligible?

Q5.29. A ball is dropped from rest and feels air resistance as it falls. Which of the graphs in Fig. 5.39 best represents its acceleration as a function of time?

Q5.30. A ball is dropped from rest and feels air resistance as it falls. Which of the graphs in Fig. 5.40 best represents its vertical velocity component as a function of time?

Q5.31. When does a baseball in flight have an acceleration with a positive upward component? Explain in terms of the forces on the ball and also in terms of the velocity components compared to the terminal speed. Do *not* ignore air resistance.

Q5.32. When a batted baseball moves with air drag, does it travel a greater horizontal distance while climbing to its maximum height or while descending from its maximum height back to the ground? Or is the horizontal distance traveled the same for both? Explain in terms of the forces acting on the ball.

Figure **5.39** Question Q5.29.

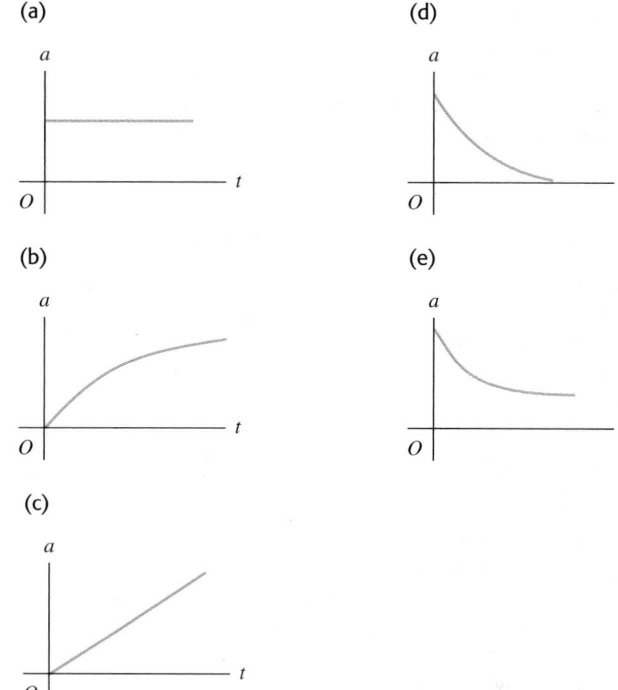

Figure **5.40** Question Q5.30.

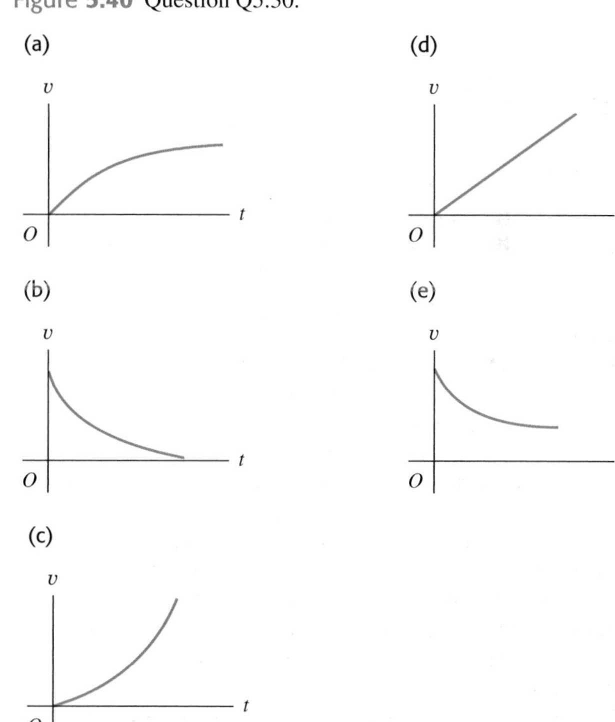

Q5.33. "A ball is thrown from the edge of a high cliff. No matter what the angle at which it is thrown, due to air resistance, the ball will eventually end up moving vertically downward." Justify this statement.

Exercises

Section 5.1 Using Newton's First Law: Particles in Equilibrium

5.1. Two 25.0-N weights are suspended at opposite ends of a rope that passes over a light, frictionless pulley. The pulley is attached to a chain that goes to the ceiling. (a) What is the tension in the rope? (b) What is the tension in the chain?

5.2. In Fig. 5.41 each of the suspended blocks has weight w. The pulleys are frictionless and the ropes have negligible weight. Calculate, in each case, the tension T in the rope in terms of the weight w. In each case, include the free-body diagram or diagrams you used to determine the answer.

Figure 5.41 Exercise 5.2.

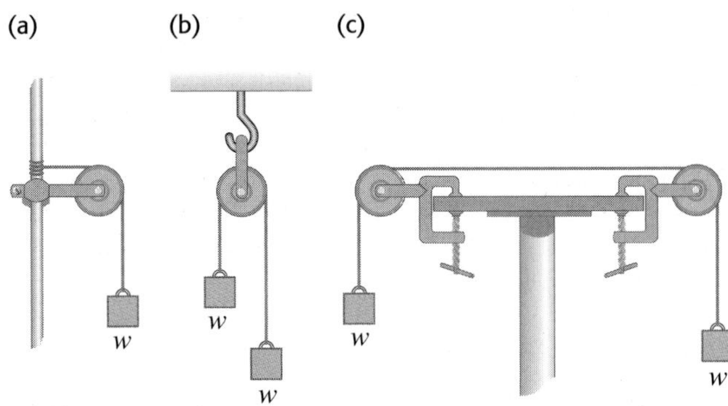

5.3. A 75.0-kg wrecking ball hangs from a uniform heavy-duty chain having a mass of 26.0 kg. (a) Find the maximum and minimum tension in the chain. (b) What is the tension at a point three-fourths of the way up from the bottom of the chain?

5.4. An adventurous archaeologist crosses between two rock cliffs by slowly going hand over hand along a rope stretched between the cliffs. He stops to rest at the middle of the rope (Fig. 5.42). The rope will break if the tension in it exceeds 2.50×10^4 N, and our hero's mass is 90.0 kg. (a) If the angle θ is 10.0°, find the tension in the rope. (b) What is the smallest value the angle θ can have if the rope is not to break?

Figure 5.42 Exercise 5.4.

5.5. A picture frame hung against a wall is suspended by two wires attached to its upper corners. If the two wires make the same angle with the vertical, what must this angle be if the tension in each wire is equal to 0.75 of the weight of the frame? (Ignore any friction between the wall and the picture frame.)

5.6. Solve the problem in Example 5.5 using coordinate axes where the y-axis is vertical and the x-axis is horizontal. Do you get the same answers using this different set of axes?

5.7. Certain streets in San Francisco make an angle of 17.5° with the horizontal. What force parallel to the street surface is required to keep a loaded 1967 Corvette of mass 1390 kg from rolling down such a street?

5.8. A large wrecking ball is held in place by two light steel cables (Fig. 5.43). If the mass m of the wrecking ball is 4090 kg, what are (a) the tension T_B in the cable that makes an angle of 40° with the vertical and (b) the tension T_A in the horizontal cable?

Figure 5.43 Exercise 5.8.

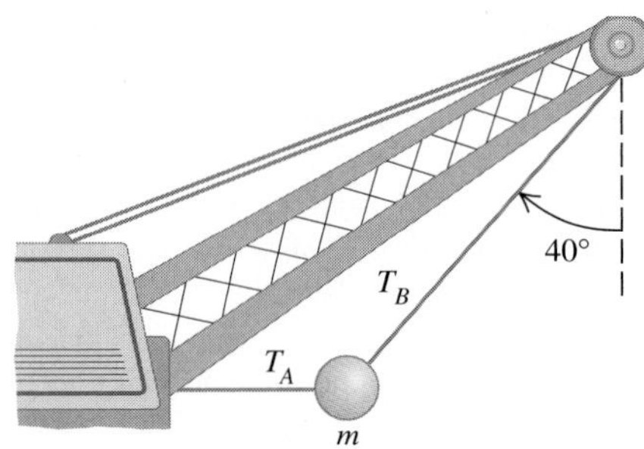

5.9. Find the tension in each cord in Fig. 5.44 if the weight of the suspended object is w.

Figure 5.44 Exercise 5.9.

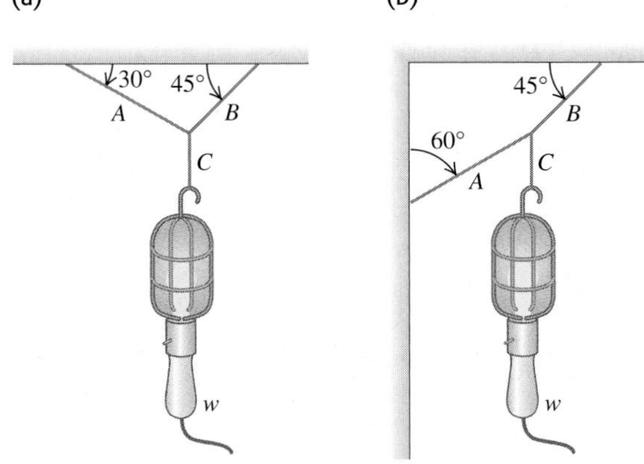

5.10. A 1130-kg car is held in place by a light cable on a very smooth (frictionless) ramp, as shown in Fig. 5.45. The cable makes an angle of 31.0° above the surface of the ramp, and the ramp itself rises at 25.0° above the horizontal. (a) Draw a free-body diagram for the car. (b) Find the tension in the cable. (c) How hard does the surface of the ramp push on the car?

Figure 5.45 Exercise 5.10.

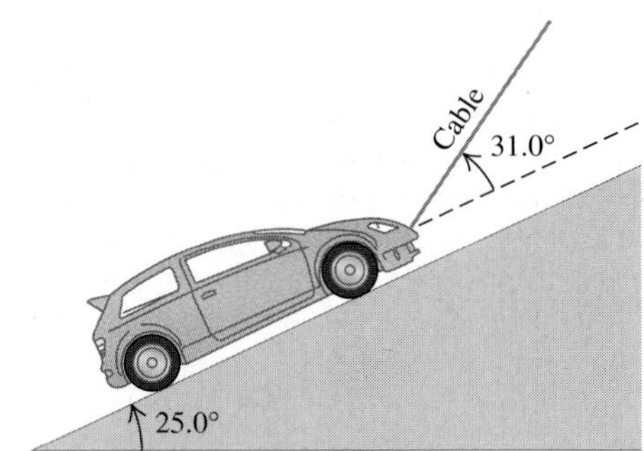

5.11. A man pushes on a piano with mass 180 kg so that it slides at constant velocity down a ramp that is inclined at 11.0° above the horizontal floor. Neglect any friction acting on the piano. Calculate the magnitude of the force applied by the man if he pushes (a) parallel to the incline and (b) parallel to the floor.

5.12. In Fig. 5.46 the weight w is 60.0 N. (a) What is the tension in the diagonal string? (b) Find the magnitudes of the horizontal forces $\vec{F}_1$ and $\vec{F}_2$ that must be applied to hold the system in the position shown.

Figure **5.46** Exercise 5.12.

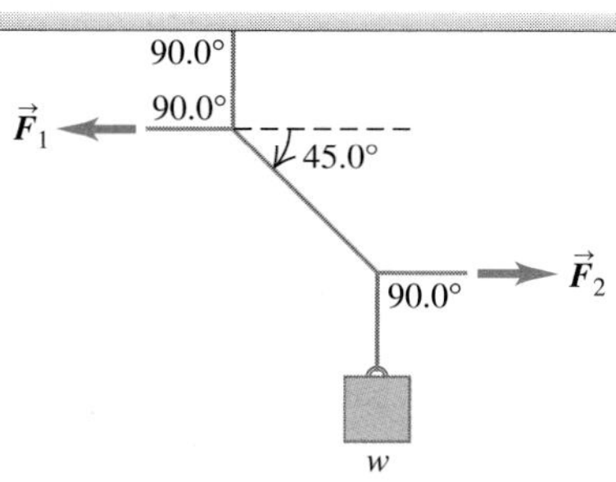

5.13. A solid uniform 45.0-kg ball of diameter 32.0 cm is supported against a vertical frictionless wall using a thin 30.0-cm wire of negligible mass, as shown in Fig. 5.47. (a) Make a free-body diagram for the ball and use it to find the tension in the wire. (b) How hard does the ball push against the wall?

Figure **5.47** Exercise 5.13.

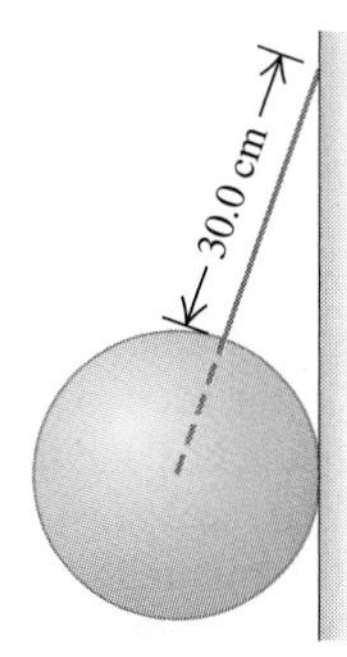

5.14. Two blocks, each with weight w, are held in place on a frictionless incline (Fig. 5.48). In terms of w and the angle α of the incline, calculate the tension in (a) the rope connecting the blocks and (b) the rope that connects block A to the wall. (c) Calculate the magnitude of the force that the incline exerts on each block. (d) Interpret your answers for the cases $\alpha = 0$ and $\alpha = 90°$.

Figure **5.48** Exercise 5.14.

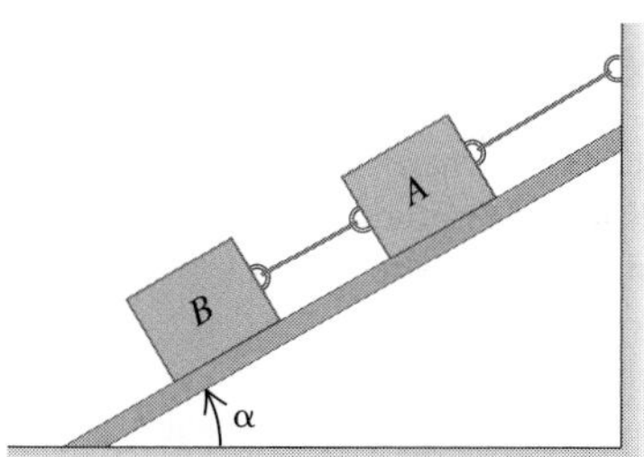

5.15. A horizontal wire holds a solid uniform ball of mass m in place on a tilted ramp that rises 35.0° above the horizontal. The surface of this ramp is perfectly smooth, and the wire is directed away from the center of the ball (Fig. 5.49). (a) Draw a free-body diagram for the ball. (b) How hard does the surface of the ramp push on the ball? (c) What is the tension in the wire?

Figure **5.49** Exercise 5.15.

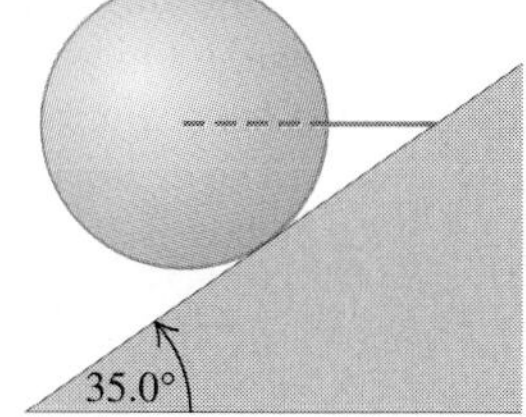

Section 5.2 Using Newton's Second Law: Dynamics of Particles

5.16. A 125-kg (including all the contents) rocket has an engine that produces a constant vertical force (the *thrust*) of 1720 N. Inside this rocket, a 15.5-N electrical power supply rests on the floor. (a) Find the acceleration of the rocket. (b) When it has reached an altitude of 120 m, how hard does the floor push on the power supply? (*Hint:* Start with a free-body diagram for the power supply.)

5.17. *Genesis* Crash. On September 8, 2004, the *Genesis* spacecraft crashed in the Utah desert because its parachute did not open. The 210-kg capsule hit the ground at 311 km/h and penetrated the soil to a depth of 81.0 cm. (a) Assuming it to be constant, what was its acceleration (in m/s^2 and in g's) during the crash? (b) What force did the ground exert on the capsule during the crash? Express the force in newtons and as a multiple of the capsule's weight. (c) For how long did this force last?

5.18. Three sleds are being pulled horizontally on frictionless horizontal ice using horizontal ropes (Fig. 5.50). The pull is horizontal and of magnitude 125 N. Find (a) the acceleration of the system and (b) the tension in ropes A and B.

Figure **5.50** Exercise 5.18.

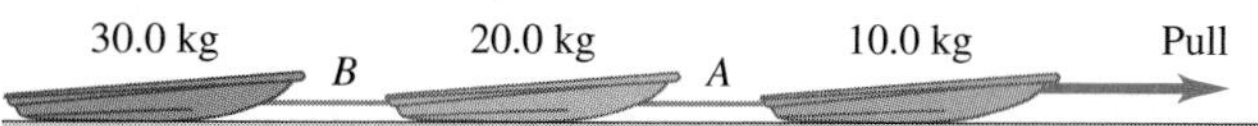

5.19. Atwood's Machine. A 15.0-kg load of bricks hangs from one end of a rope that passes over a small, frictionless pulley. A 28.0-kg counterweight is suspended from the other end of the rope, as shown in Fig. 5.51. The system is released from rest. (a) Draw two free-body diagrams, one for the load of bricks and one for the counterweight. (b) What is the magnitude of the upward acceleration of the load of bricks? (c) What is the tension in the rope while the load is moving? How does the tension compare to the weight of the load of bricks? To the weight of the counterweight?

Figure **5.51** Exercise 5.19.

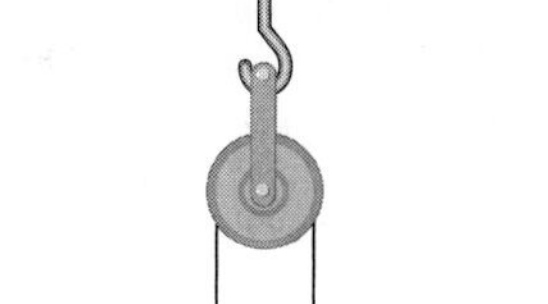

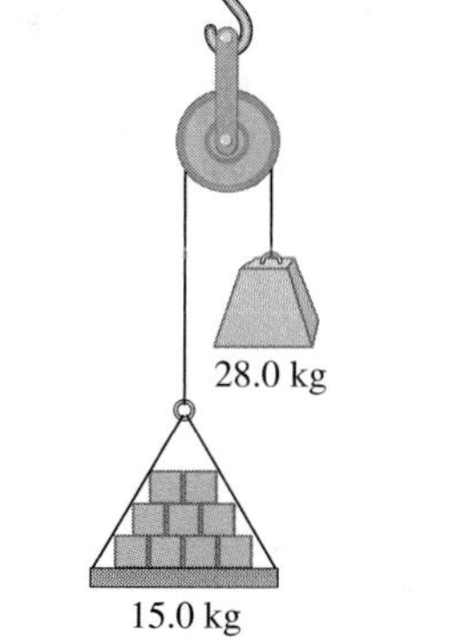

5.20. A 8.00-kg block of ice, released from rest at the top of a 1.50-m-long frictionless ramp, slides downhill, reaching a speed of 2.50 m/s at the bottom. (a) What is the angle between the ramp and the horizontal? (b) What would be the speed of the ice at the bottom if the motion were opposed by a constant friction force of 10.0 N parallel to the surface of the ramp?

5.21. A light rope is attached to a block with mass 4.00 kg that rests on a frictionless, horizontal surface. The horizontal rope passes over a frictionless, massless pulley, and a block with mass m is suspended from the other end. When the blocks are released, the tension in the rope is 10.0 N. (a) Draw two free-body diagrams, one for the 4.00-kg block and one for the block with mass m. (b) What is the acceleration of either block? (c) Find the mass m of the hanging block. (d) How does the tension compare to the weight of the hanging block?

5.22. Runway Design. A transport plane takes off from a level landing field with two gliders in tow, one behind the other. The mass of each glider is 700 kg, and the total resistance (air drag plus friction with the runway) on each may be assumed constant and equal to 2500 N. The tension in the towrope between the transport plane and the first glider is not to exceed 12,000 N. (a) If a speed of 40 m/s is required for takeoff, what minimum length of runway is needed? (b) What is the tension in the towrope between the two gliders while they are accelerating for the takeoff?

5.23. A 750.0-kg boulder is raised from a quarry 125 m deep by a long uniform chain having a mass of 575 kg. This chain is of uniform strength, but at any point it can support a maximum tension no greater than 2.50 times its weight without breaking. (a) What is the maximum acceleration the boulder can have and still get out of the quarry, and (b) how long does it take to be lifted out at maximum acceleration if it started from rest?

5.24. Apparent Weight. A 550-N physics student stands on a bathroom scale in an 850-kg (including the student) elevator that is supported by a cable. As the elevator starts moving, the scale reads 450 N. (a) Find the acceleration of the elevator (magnitude and direction). (b) What is the acceleration if the scale reads 670 N? (c) If the scale reads zero, should the student worry? Explain. (d) What is the tension in the cable in parts (a) and (c)?

5.25. A physics student playing with an air hockey table (a frictionless surface) finds that if she gives the puck a velocity of 3.80 m/s along the length (1.75 m) of the table at one end, by the time it has reached the other end the puck has drifted 2.50 cm to the right but still has a velocity component along the length of 3.80 m/s. She correctly concludes that the table is not level and correctly calculates its inclination from the given information. What is the angle of inclination?

5.26. A 2540-kg test rocket is launched vertically from the launch pad. Its fuel (of negligible mass) provides a thrust force so that its vertical velocity as a function of time is given by $v(t) = At + Bt^2$, where A and B are constants and time is measured from the instant the fuel is ignited. At the instant of ignition, the rocket has an upward acceleration of 1.50 m/s^2 and 1.00 s later an upward velocity of 2.00 m/s. (a) Determine A and B, including their SI units. (b) At 4.00 s after fuel ignition, what is the acceleration of the rocket, and (c) what thrust force does the burning fuel exert on it, assume no air resistance? Express the thrust in newtons and as a multiple of the rocket's weight. (d) What was the initial thrust due to the fuel?

Section 5.3 Frictional Forces

5.27. Free-Body Diagrams. The first two steps in the solution of Newton's second-law problems are to select an object for analysis and then to draw free-body diagrams for that object. Draw free-body diagrams for the following situations: (a) a mass M sliding down a frictionless inclined plane of angle α, and (b) a mass M sliding up a frictionless inclined plane of angle α; (c) a mass M sliding up an inclined plane of angle α with kinetic friction present.

5.28. In a laboratory experiment on friction, a 135-N block resting on a rough horizontal table is pulled by a horizontal wire. The pull gradually increases until the block begins to move and continues to increase thereafter. Figure 5.52 shows a graph of the friction force on this block as a function of the pull. (a) Identify the regions of the graph where static and kinetic friction occur. (b) Find the coefficients of static and kinetic friction between the block and the table. (c) Why does the graph slant upward in the first part but then level out? (d) What would the graph look like if a 135-N brick were placed on the box, and what would be the coefficients of friction be in that case?

Figure 5.52 Exercise 5.28.

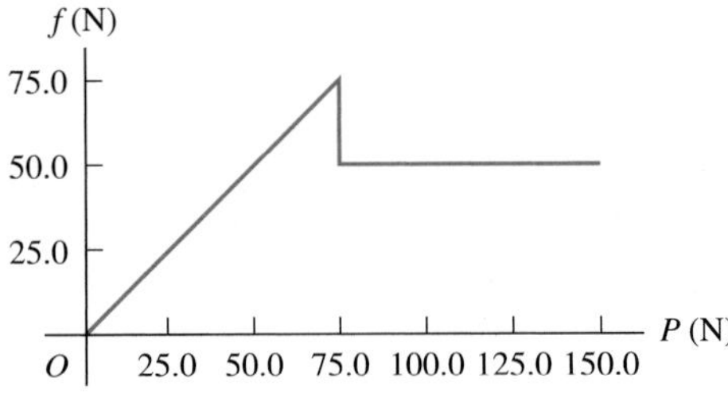

5.29. A stockroom worker pushes a box with mass 11.2 kg on a horizontal surface with a constant speed of 3.50 m/s. The coefficient of kinetic friction between the box and the surface is 0.20. (a) What horizontal force must the worker apply to maintain the motion? (b) If the force calculated in part (a) is removed, how far does the box slide before coming to rest?

5.30. A box of bananas weighing 40.0 N rests on a horizontal surface. The coefficient of static friction between the box and the surface is 0.40, and the coefficient of kinetic friction is 0.20. (a) If no horizontal force is applied to the box and the box is at rest, how large is the friction force exerted on the box? (b) What is the magnitude of the friction force if a monkey applies a horizontal force of 6.0 N to the box and the box is initially at rest? (c) What minimum horizontal force must the monkey apply to start the box in motion? (d) What minimum horizontal force must the monkey apply to keep the box moving at constant velocity once it has been started? (e) If the monkey applies a horizontal force of 18.0 N, what is the magnitude of the friction force and what is the box's acceleration?

5.31. A crate of 45.0-kg tools rests on a horizontal floor. You exert a gradually increasing horizontal push on it and observe that the crate just begins to move when your force exceeds 313 N. After that you must reduce your push to 208 N to keep it moving at a steady 25.0 cm/s. (a) What are the coefficients of static and kinetic friction between the crate and the floor? (b) What push must you exert to give it an acceleration of 1.10 m/s^2? (c) Suppose you were performing the same experiment on this crate but were doing it on the moon instead, where the acceleration due to gravity is 1.62 m/s^2. (i) What magnitude push would cause it to move? (ii) What would its acceleration be if you maintained the push in part (b)?

5.32. An 85-N box of oranges is being pushed across a horizontal floor. As it moves, it is slowing at a constant rate of 0.90 m/s each second. The push force has a horizontal component of 20 N and a vertical component of 25 N downward. Calculate the coefficient of kinetic friction between the box and floor.

5.33. You are lowering two boxes, one on top of the other, down the ramp shown in Figure 5.53 by pulling on a rope parallel to the surface of the ramp. Both boxes move together at a constant speed of 15.0 cm/s. The coefficient of kinetic friction between the ramp and the lower box is 0.444, and the coefficient of static friction between the two boxes is 0.800. (a) What force do you need to

Figure 5.53 Exercise 5.33.

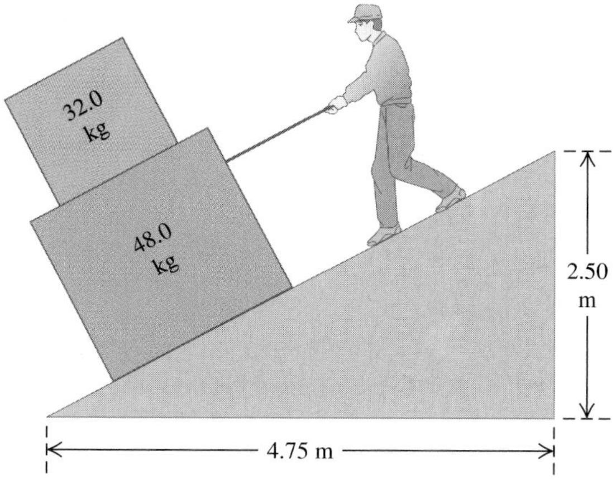

exert to accomplish this? (b) What are the magnitude and direction of the friction force on the upper box?

5.34. Stopping Distance. (a) If the coefficient of kinetic friction between tires and dry pavement is 0.80, what is the shortest distance in which you can stop an automobile by locking the brakes when traveling at 28.7 m/s (about 65 mi/h)? (b) On wet pavement the coefficient of kinetic friction may be only 0.25. How fast should you drive on wet pavement in order to be able to stop in the same distance as in part (a)? (*Note:* Locking the brakes is *not* the safest way to stop.)

5.35. Coefficient of Friction. A clean brass washer slides along a horizontal clean steel surface until it stops. Using the values from Table 5.1, how many times farther would it slide with the same initial speed if the washer were Teflon-coated?

5.36. Consider the system shown in Fig. 5.54. Block A weighs 45.0 N and block B weighs 25.0 N. Once block B is set into downward motion, it descends at a constant speed. (a) Calculate the coefficient of kinetic friction between block A and the tabletop. (b) A cat, also of weight 45.0 N, falls asleep on top of block A. If block B is now set into downward motion, what is its acceleration (magnitude and direction)?

Figure 5.54 Exercises 5.36 and 5.41; Problem 5.77.

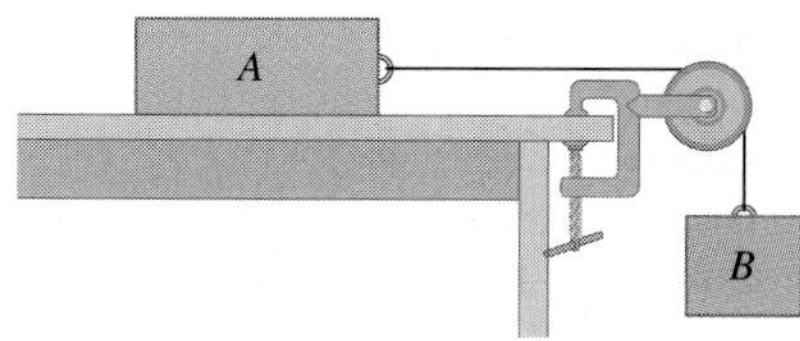

5.37. Two crates connected by a rope lie on a horizontal surface (Fig. 5.55). Crate A has mass m_A and crate B has mass m_B. The coefficient of kinetic friction between each crate and the surface is μ_k. The crates are pulled to the right at constant velocity by a horizontal force $\vec{F}$. In terms of m_A, m_B, and μ_k, calculate (a) the magnitude of the force $\vec{F}$ and (b) the tension in the rope connecting the blocks. Include the free-body diagram or diagrams you used to determine each answer.

Figure 5.55 Exercise 5.37.

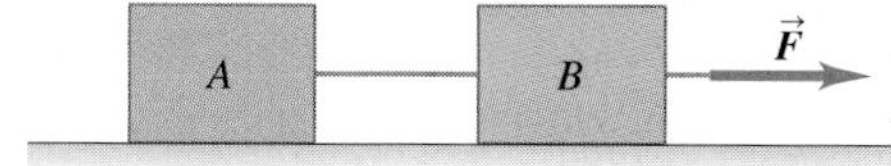

5.38. Rolling Friction. Two bicycle tires are set rolling with the same initial speed of 3.50 m/s on a long, straight road, and the distance each travels before its speed is reduced by half is measured. One tire is inflated to a pressure of 40 psi and goes 18.1 m; the other is at 105 psi and goes 92.9 m. What is the coefficient of rolling friction μ_r for each? Assume that the net horizontal force is due to rolling friction only.

5.39. Wheels. You find that it takes a horizontal force of 160 N to slide a box along the surface of a level floor at constant speed. The coefficient of static friction is 0.52, and the coefficient of kinetic friction is 0.47. If you place the box on a dolly of mass 5.3 kg and with coefficient of rolling friction 0.018, what horizontal acceleration would that 160-N force provide?

5.40. You find it takes 200 N of horizontal force to move an empty pickup truck along a level road at a speed of 2.4 m/s. You then load the pickup and pump up its tires so that its total weight increases by 42% while the coefficient of rolling friction decreases by 19%. Now what horizontal force will you need to move the pickup along the same road at the same speed? The speed is low enough that you can ignore air resistance.

5.41. As shown in Fig. 5.54, block A (mass 2.25 kg) rests on a tabletop. It is connected by a horizontal cord passing over a light, frictionless pulley to a hanging block B (mass 1.30 kg). The coefficient of kinetic friction between block A and the tabletop is 0.450. After the blocks are released from rest, find (a) the speed of each block after moving 3.00 cm and (b) the tension in the cord. Include the free-body diagram or diagrams you used to determine the answers.

5.42. A 25.0-kg box of textbooks rests on a loading ramp that makes an angle α with the horizontal. The coefficient of kinetic friction is 0.25, and the coefficient of static friction is 0.35. (a) As the angle α is increased, find the minimum angle at which the box starts to slip. (b) At this angle, find the acceleration once the box has begun to move. (c) At this angle, how fast will the box be moving after it has slid 5.0 m along the loading ramp?

5.43. A large crate with mass m rests on a horizontal floor. The coefficients of friction between the crate and the floor are μ_s and μ_k. A woman pushes downward at an angle θ below the horizontal on the crate with a force $\vec{F}$. (a) What magnitude of force $\vec{F}$ is required to keep the crate moving at constant velocity? (b) If μ_s is greater than some critical value, the woman cannot start the crate moving no matter how hard she pushes. Calculate this critical value of μ_s.

5.44. A box with mass m is dragged across a level floor having a coefficient of kinetic friction μ_k by a rope that is pulled upward at an angle θ above the horizontal with a force of magnitude F. (a) In terms of m, μ_k, θ, and g, obtain an expression for the magnitude of force required to move the box with constant speed. (b) Knowing that you are studying physics, a CPR instructor asks you how much force it would take to slide a 90-kg patient across a floor at constant speed by pulling on him at an angle of 25° above the horizontal. By dragging some weights wrapped in an old pair of pants down the hall with a spring balance, you find that $\mu_k = 0.35$. Use the result of part (a) to answer the instructor's question.

5.45. Blocks A, B, and C are placed as in Fig. 5.56 and connected by ropes of negligible mass. Both A and B weigh 25.0 N each, and the coefficient of kinetic friction between each block and the surface is 0.35. Block C descends with constant velocity. (a) Draw two separate free-body diagrams showing the forces acting on A and on B. (b) Find the tension in the rope connecting blocks A and B. (c) What is the weight of block C? (d) If the rope connecting A and B were cut, what would be the acceleration of C?

Figure 5.56 Exercise 5.45.

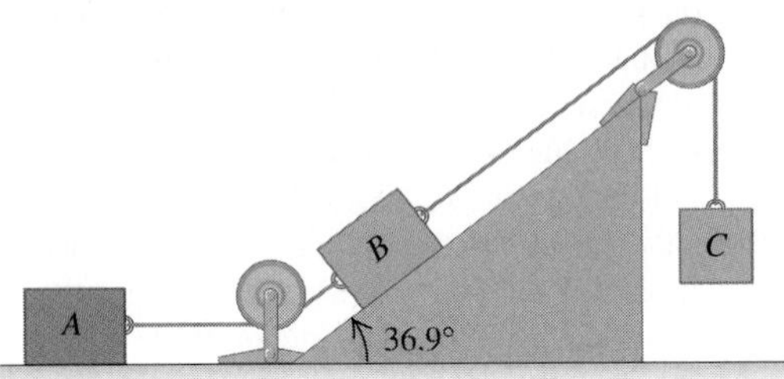

5.46. Starting from Eq. (5.10), derive Eqs. (5.11) and (5.12).

5.47. (a) In Example 5.19 (Section 5.3), what value of D is required to make $v_t = 42\ \text{m/s}$ for the skydiver? (b) If the skydiver's daughter, whose mass is 45 kg, is falling through the air and has the same D $(0.25\ \text{kg/m})$ as her father, what is the daughter's terminal speed?

5.48. You throw a baseball straight up. The drag force is proportional to v^2. In terms of g, what is the y-component of the ball's acceleration when its speed is half its terminal speed and (a) it is moving up? (b) It is moving back down?

Section 5.4 Dynamics of Circular Motion

5.49. A machine part consists of a thin 40.0-cm-long bar with small 1.15-kg masses fastened by screws to its ends. The screws can support a maximum force of 75.0 N without pulling out. This bar rotates about an axis perpendicular to it at its center. (a) As the bar is turning at a constant rate on a horizontal frictionless surface, what is the maximum speed the masses can have without pulling out the screws? (b) Suppose the machine is redesigned so that the bar turns at a constant rate in a vertical circle. Will one of the screws be more likely to pull out when the mass is at the top of the circle or at the bottom? Use a free-body diagram to see why. (c) Using the result of part (b), what is the greatest speed the masses can have without pulling a screw?

5.50. A flat (unbanked) curve on a highway has a radius of 220.0 m. A car rounds the curve at a speed of 25.0 m/s. (a) What is the minimum coefficient of friction that will prevent sliding? (b) Suppose the highway is icy and the coefficient of friction between the tires and pavement is only one-third what you found in part (a). What should be the maximum speed of the car so it can round the curve safely?

5.51. A 1125-kg car and a 2250-kg pickup truck aproach a curve on the expressway that has a radius of 225 m. (a) At what angle should the highway engineer bank this curve so that vehicles traveling at 65.0 mi/h can safely round it regardless of the condition of their tires? Should the heavy truck go slower than the lighter car? (b) As the car and truck round the curve at 65.0 mi/h, find the normal force on each one due to the highway surface.

5.52. The "Giant Swing" at a county fair consists of a vertical central shaft with a number of horizontal arms attached at its upper end (Fig. 5.57). Each arm supports a seat suspended from a cable 5.00 m long, the upper end of the cable being fastened to the arm at a point 3.00 m from the central shaft. (a) Find the time of one revolution of the swing if the cable supporting a seat makes an angle of 30.0° with the vertical. (b) Does the angle depend on the weight of the passenger for a given rate of revolution?

Figure 5.57 Exercise 5.52.

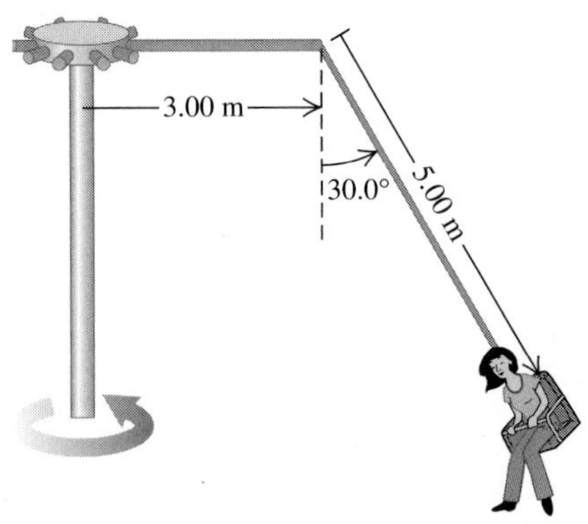

5.53. In another version of the "Giant Swing" (see Exercise 5.52), the seat is connected to two cables as shown in Fig. 5.58, one of which is horizontal. The seat swings in a horizontal circle at a rate of 32.0 rpm (rev/min). If the seat weighs 255 N and a 825-N person is sitting in it, find the tension in each cable.

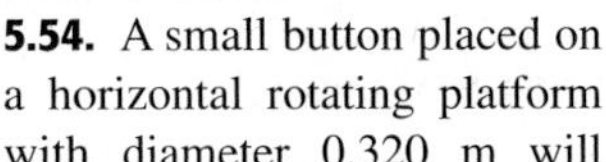

Figure 5.58 Exercise 5.53.

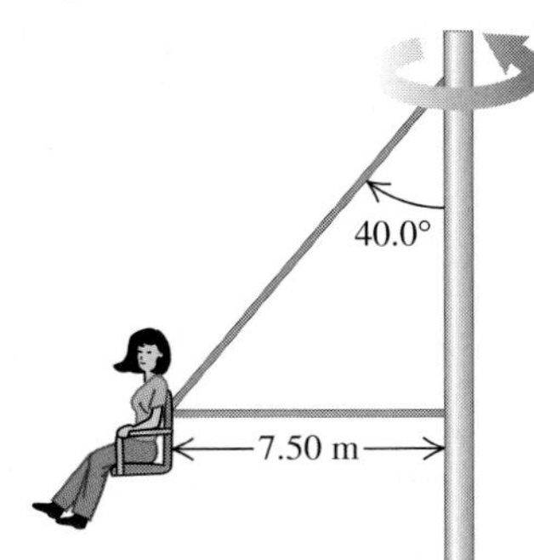

5.54. A small button placed on a horizontal rotating platform with diameter 0.320 m will revolve with the platform when it is brought up to a speed of 40.0 rev/min, provided the button is no more than 0.150 m from the axis. (a) What is the coefficient of static friction between the button and the platform? (b) How far from the axis can the button be placed, without slipping, if the platform rotates at 60.0 rev/min?

5.55. Rotating Space Stations. One problem for humans living in outer space is that they are apparently weightless. One way around this problem is to design a space station that spins about its center at a constant rate. This creates "artificial gravity" at the outside rim of the station. (a) If the diameter of the space station is 800 m, how many revolutions per minute are needed for the "artificial gravity" acceleration to be $9.80\ \text{m/s}^2$? (b) If the space station is a waiting area for travelers going to Mars, it might be desirable to simulate the acceleration due to gravity on the Martian surface $(3.70\ \text{m/s}^2)$. How many revolutions per minute are needed in this case?

5.56. The Cosmoclock 21 Ferris wheel in Yokohama City, Japan, has a diameter of 100 m. Its name comes from its 60 arms, each of which can function as a second hand (so that it makes one revolution every 60.0 s). (a) Find the speed of the passengers when the Ferris wheel is rotating at this rate. (b) A passenger weighs 882 N at the weight-guessing booth on the ground. What is his apparent weight at the highest and at the lowest point on the Ferris wheel? (c) What would be the time for one revolution if the passenger's apparent weight at the highest point were zero? (d) What then would be the passenger's apparent weight at the lowest point?

5.57. An airplane flies in a loop (a circular path in a vertical plane) of radius 150 m. The pilot's head always points toward the center of the loop. The speed of the airplane is not constant; the airplane goes slowest at the top of the loop and fastest at the bottom. (a) At the top of the loop, the pilot feels weightless. What is the speed of the airplane at this point? (b) At the bottom of the loop, the speed of the airplane is 280 km/h. What is the apparent weight of the pilot at this point? His true weight is 700 N.

5.58. A 50.0-kg stunt pilot who has been diving her airplane vertically pulls out of the dive by changing her course to a circle in a vertical plane. (a) If the plane's speed at the lowest point of the circle is 95.0 m/s, what is the minimum radius of the circle for the acceleration at this point not to exceed $4.00g$? (b) What is the apparent weight of the pilot at the lowest point of the pullout?

5.59. Stay Dry! You tie a cord to a pail of water, and you swing the pail in a vertical circle of radius 0.600 m. What minimum speed must you give the pail at the highest point of the circle if no water is to spill from it?

5.60. A bowling ball weighing 71.2 N (16.0 lb) is attached to the ceiling by a 3.80-m rope. The ball is pulled to one side and released; it then swings back and forth as a pendulum. As the rope swings through the vertical, the speed of the bowling ball is 4.20 m/s. (a) What is the acceleration of the bowling ball, in magnitude and direction, at this instant? (b) What is the tension in the rope at this instant?

Problems

5.61. Two ropes are connected to a steel cable that supports a hanging weight as shown in Fig. 5.59. (a) Draw a free-body diagram showing all of the forces acting at the knot that connects the two ropes to the steel cable. Based on your force diagram, which of the two ropes will have the greater tension? (b) If the maximum tension either rope can sustain without breaking is 5000 N, determine the maximum value of the hanging weight that these ropes can safely support. You can ignore the weight of the ropes and the steel cable.

Figure 5.59 Problem 5.61.

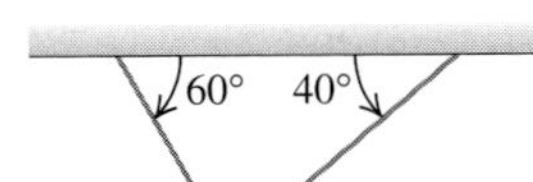

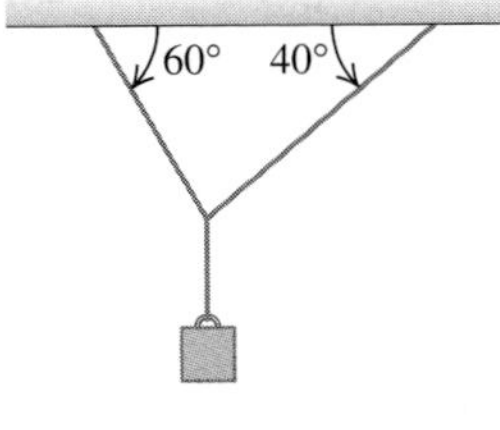

5.62. In Fig. 5.60 a worker lifts a weight w by pulling down on a rope with a force $\vec{F}$. The upper pulley is attached to the ceiling by a chain, and the lower pulley is attached to the weight by another chain. In terms of w, find the tension in each chain and the magnitude of the force $\vec{F}$ if the weight is lifted at constant speed. Include the free-body diagram or diagrams you used to determine your answers. Assume that the rope, pulleys, and chains all have negligible weights.

Figure 5.60 Problem 5.62.

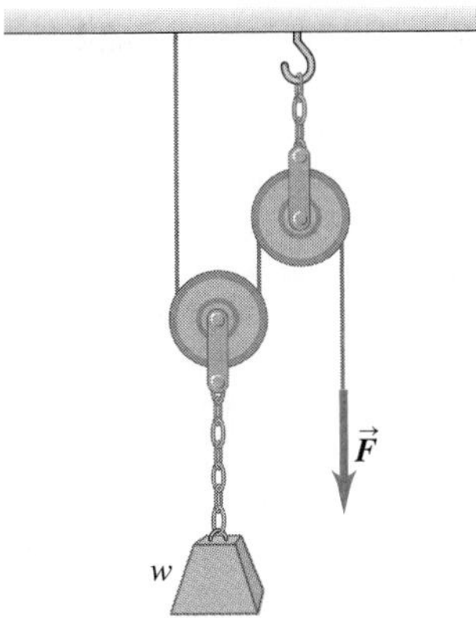

5.63. A Rope with Mass. In most problems in this book, the ropes, cords, or cables have so little mass compared to other objects in the problem that you can safely ignore their mass. But if the rope is the *only* object in the problem, then clearly you cannot ignore its mass. For example, suppose we have a clothesline attached to two poles (Fig. 5.61). The clothesline has a mass M, and each end makes an angle θ with the horizontal. What are (a) the tension at the ends of the clothesline and (b) the tension at the lowest point? (c) Why can't we have $\theta = 0$? (See Discussion Question Q5.3.) (d) Discuss your results for parts (a) and (b) in the limit that $\theta \to 90°$. The curve of the clothesline, or of any flexible cable hanging under its own weight, is called a *catenary.* [For a more advanced treatment of this curve, see K. R. Symon, *Mechanics,* 3rd ed. (Reading, MA: Addison-Wesley, 1971), pp. 237–241.]

Figure 5.61 Problem 5.63.

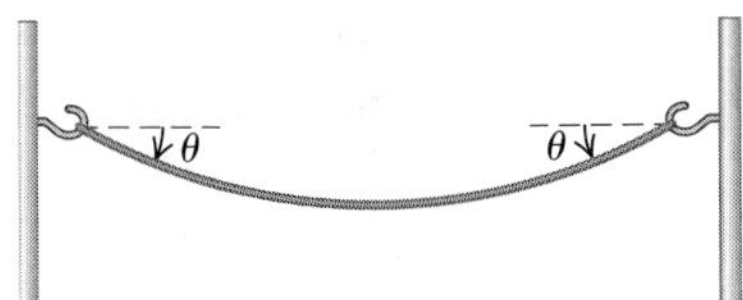

5.64. Another Rope with Mass. A block with mass M is attached to the lower end of a vertical, uniform rope with mass m and length L. A constant upward force $\vec{F}$ is applied to the top of the rope, causing the rope and block to accelerate upward. Find the tension in the rope at a distance x from the top end of the rope, where x can have any value from 0 to L.

5.65. A block with mass m_1 is placed on an inclined plane with slope angle α and is connected to a second hanging block with mass m_2 by a cord passing over a small, frictionless pulley (Fig. 5.62). The coefficient of static friction is μ_s and the coefficient of kinetic friction is μ_k. (a) Find the mass m_2 for which block m_1 moves up the plane at constant speed once it is set in motion. (b) Find the mass m_2 for which block m_1 moves down the plane at constant speed once it is set in motion. (c) For what range of values of m_2 will the blocks remain at rest if they are released from rest?

Figure 5.62 Problem 5.65.

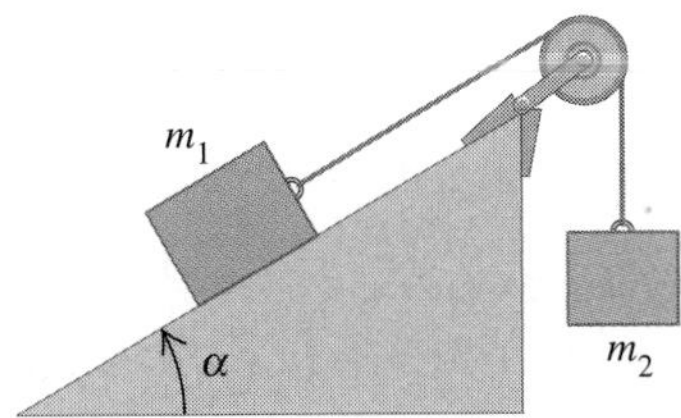

5.66. (a) Block A in Fig. 5.63 weighs 60.0 N. The coefficient of static friction between the block and the surface on which it rests is

Figure 5.63 Problem 5.66.

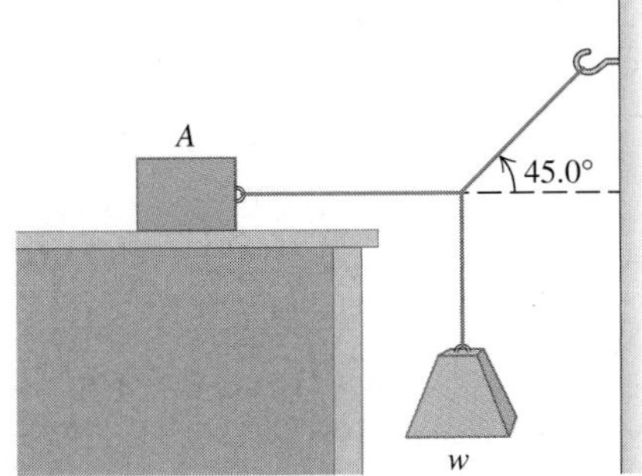

0.25. The weight w is 12.0 N and the system is in equilibrium. Find the friction force exerted on block A. (b) Find the maximum weight w for which the system will remain in equilibrium.

5.67. Block A in Fig. 5.64 weighs 1.20 N and block B weighs 3.60 N. The coefficient of kinetic friction between all surfaces is 0.300. Find the magnitude of the horizontal force $\vec{F}$ necessary to drag block B to the left at constant speed (a) if A rests on B and moves with it (Fig. 5.64a) and (b) if A is held at rest (Fig. 5.64b).

Figure **5.64** Problem 5.67.

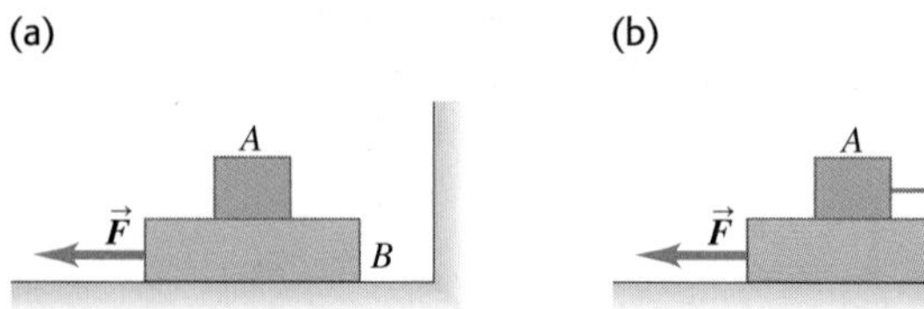

5.68. A window washer pushes his scrub brush up a vertical window at constant speed by applying a force $\vec{F}$ as shown in Fig. 5.65. The brush weighs 12.0 N and the coefficient of kinetic friction is $\mu_k = 0.150$. Calculate (a) the magnitude of the force $\vec{F}$ and (b) the normal force exerted by the window on the brush.

Figure **5.65** Problem 5.68.

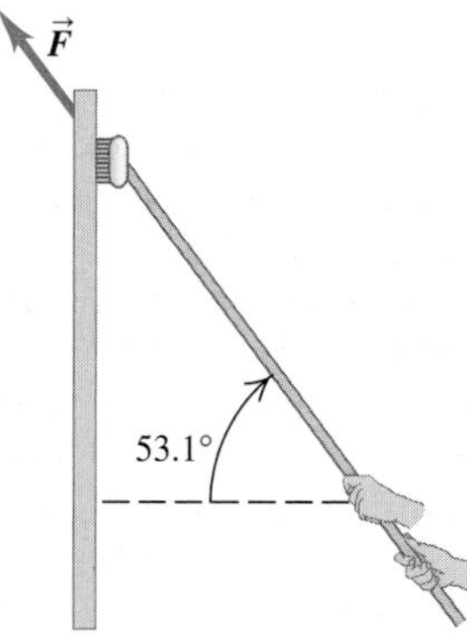

5.69. The Flying Leap of a Flea. High-speed motion pictures (3500 frames/second) of a jumping 210-μg flea yielded the data to plot the flea's acceleration as a function of time as shown in Fig. 5.66. (See "The Flying Leap of the Flea," by M. Rothschild et al. in the November 1973 *Scientific American.*) This flea was about 2 mm long and jumped at a nearly vertical takeoff angle. Use the measurements shown on the graph to answer the questions. (a) Find the *initial* net external force on the flea. How does it compare to the flea's weight? (b) Find the *maximum* net external force on this jumping flea. When does this maximum force occur? (c) Use the graph to find the flea's maximum speed.

Figure **5.66** Problem 5.69.

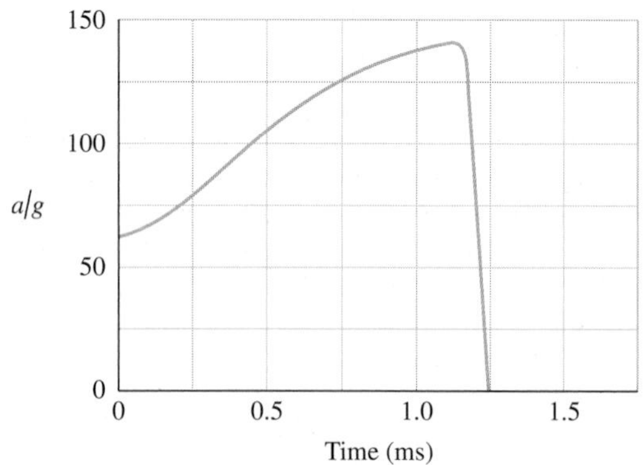

5.70. A 25,000-kg rocket blasts off vertically from the earth's surface with a constant acceleration. During the motion considered in the problem, assume that g remains constant (see Chapter 12). Inside the rocket, a 15.0-N instrument hangs from a wire that can support a maximum tension of 35.0 N. (a) Find the minimum time for this rocket to reach the sound barrier (330 m/s) without breaking the inside wire and the maximum vertical thrust of the rocket engines under these conditions. (b) How far is the rocket above the earth's surface when it breaks the sound barrier?

5.71. You are standing on a bathroom scale in an elevator in a tall building. Your mass is 72 kg. The elevator starts from rest and travels upward with a speed that varies with time according to $v(t) = (3.0 \text{ m/s}^2)t + (0.20 \text{ m/s}^3)t^2$. When $t = 4.0$ s, what is the reading of the bathroom scale?

5.72. Elevator Design. You are designing an elevator for a hospital. The force exerted on a passenger by the floor of the elevator is not to exceed 1.60 times the passenger's weight. The elevator accelerates upward with constant acceleration for a distance of 3.0 m and then starts to slow down. What is the maximum speed of the elevator?

5.73. You are working for a shipping company. Your job is to stand at the bottom of a 8.0-m-long ramp that is inclined at 37° above the horizontal. You grab packages off a conveyor belt and propel them up the ramp. The coefficient of kinetic friction between the packages and the ramp is $\mu_k = 0.30$. (a) What speed do you need to give a package at the bottom of the ramp so that it has zero speed at the top of the ramp? (b) Your coworker is supposed to grab the packages as they arrive at the top of the ramp, but she misses one and it slides back down. What is its speed when it returns to you?

5.74. A hammer is hanging by a light rope from the ceiling of a bus. The ceiling of the bus is parallel to the roadway. The bus is traveling in a straight line on a horizontal street. You observe that the hammer hangs at rest with respect to the bus when the angle between the rope and the ceiling of the bus is 74°. What is the acceleration of the bus?

5.75. A steel washer is suspended inside an empty shipping crate from a light string attached to the top of the crate. The crate slides down a long ramp that is inclined at an angle of 37° above the horizontal. The crate has mass 180 kg. You are sitting inside the crate (with a flashlight); your mass is 55 kg. As the crate is sliding down the ramp, you find the washer is at rest with respect to the crate when the string makes an angle of 68° with the top of the crate. What is the coefficient of kinetic friction between the ramp and the crate?

5.76. Lunch Time! You are riding your motorcycle one day down a wet street that slopes downward at an angle of 20° below the horizontal. As you start to ride down the hill, you notice a construction crew has dug a deep hole in the street at the bottom of the hill. A Siberian tiger, escaped from the City Zoo, has taken up residence in the hole. You apply the brakes and lock your wheels at the top of the hill, where you are moving with a speed of 20 m/s. The inclined street in front of you is 40 m long. (a) Will you plunge into the hole and become the tiger's lunch, or do you skid to a stop before you reach the hole? (The coefficients of friction between your motorcycle tires and the wet pavement are $\mu_s = 0.90$ and $\mu_k = 0.70$.) (b) What must your initial speed be if you are to stop just before reaching the hole?

5.77. In the system shown in Fig. 5.54, block A has mass m_A, block B has mass m_B, and the rope connecting them has a *nonzero* mass m_{rope}. The rope has a total length L, and the pulley has a very small radius. You can ignore any sag in the horizontal part of the rope. (a) If there is no friction between block A and the tabletop, find the acceleration of the blocks at an instant when a length d of rope hangs vertically between the pulley and block B. As block B falls, will the magnitude of the acceleration of the system increase, decrease, or remain constant? Explain. (b) Let $m_A = 2.00$ kg, $m_B = 0.400$ kg, $m_{rope} = 0.160$ kg, and $L = 1.00$ m. If there is friction between block A and the tabletop, with $\mu_k = 0.200$ and $\mu_s = 0.250$, find the minimum value of the distance d such that the blocks will start to move if they are initially at rest. (c) Repeat part (b) for the case $m_{rope} = 0.040$ kg. Will the blocks move in this case?

5.78. If the coefficient of static friction between a table and a uniform massive rope is μ_s, what fraction of the rope can hang over the edge of the table without the rope sliding?

5.79. A 30.0-kg packing case is initially at rest on the floor of a 1500-kg pickup truck. The coefficient of static friction between the case and the truck floor is 0.30, and the coefficient of kinetic friction is 0.20. Before each acceleration given below, the truck is traveling due north at constant speed. Find the magnitude and direction of the friction force acting on the case (a) when the truck accelerates at 2.20 m/s^2 northward and (b) when it accelerates at 3.40 m/s^2 southward.

5.80. Traffic Court. You are called as an expert witness in the trial of a traffic violation. The facts are these: A driver slammed on his brakes and came to a stop with constant acceleration. Measurements of his tires and the skid marks on the pavement indicate that he locked his car's wheels, the car traveled 192 ft before stopping, and the coefficient of kinetic friction between the road and his tires was 0.750. The charge is that he was speeding in a 45-mi/h zone. He pleads innocent. What is your conclusion, guilty or innocent? How fast was he going when he hit his brakes?

5.81. Two identical 15.0-kg balls, each 25.0 cm in diameter, are suspended by two 35.0-cm wires as shown in Fig. 5.67. The entire apparatus is supported by a single 18.0-cm wire, and the surfaces of the balls are perfectly smooth. (a) Find the tension in each of the three wires. (b) How hard does each ball push on the other one?

Figure **5.67** Problem 5.81.

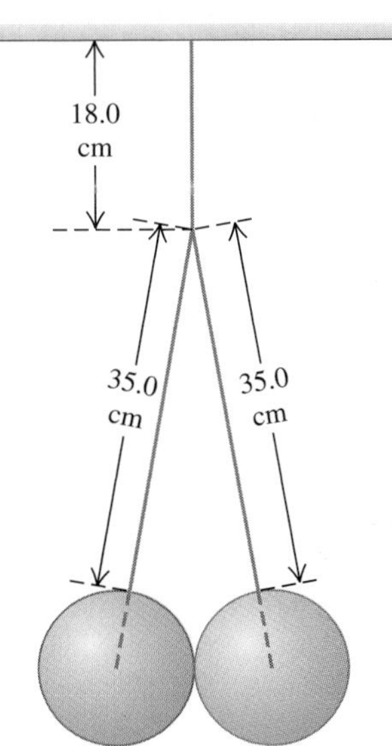

5.82. Losing Cargo. A 12.0-kg box rests on the flat floor of a truck. The coefficients of friction between the box and floor are $\mu_s = 0.19$ and $\mu_k = 0.15$. The truck stops at a stop sign and then starts to move with an acceleration of 2.20 m/s^2. If the box is 1.80 m from the rear of the truck when the truck starts, how much time elapses before the box falls off the truck? How far does the truck travel in this time?

5.83. Block A in Fig. 5.68 weighs 1.40 N, and block B weighs 4.20 N. The coefficient of kinetic friction between all surfaces is 0.30. Find the magnitude of the horizontal force $\vec{F}$ necessary to drag block B to the left at constant speed if A and B are connected by a light, flexible cord passing around a fixed, frictionless pulley.

Figure **5.68** Problem 5.83.

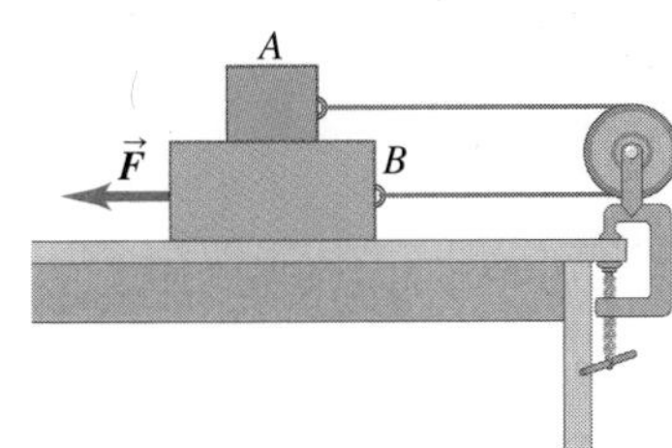

5.84. You are part of a design team for future exploration of the planet Mars, where $g = 3.7$ m/s^2. An explorer is to step out of a survey vehicle traveling horizontally at 33 m/s when it is 1200 m above the surface and then fall freely for 20 s. At that time, a portable advanced propulsion system (PAPS) is to exert a constant force that will decrease the explorer's speed to zero at the instant she touches the surface. The total mass (explorer, suit, equipment, and PAPS) is 150 kg. Assume the change in mass of the PAPS to be negligible. Find the horizontal and vertical components of the force the PAPS must exert, and for what interval of time the PAPS must exert it. You can ignore air resistance.

5.85. Block A in Fig. 5.69 has a mass of 4.00 kg, and block B has mass 12.0 kg. The coefficient of kinetic friction between block B and the horizontal surface is 0.25. (a) What is the mass of block C if block B is moving to the right and speeding up with an acceleration 2.00 m/s^2? (b) What is the tension in each cord when block B has this acceleration?

Figure **5.69** Problem 5.85.

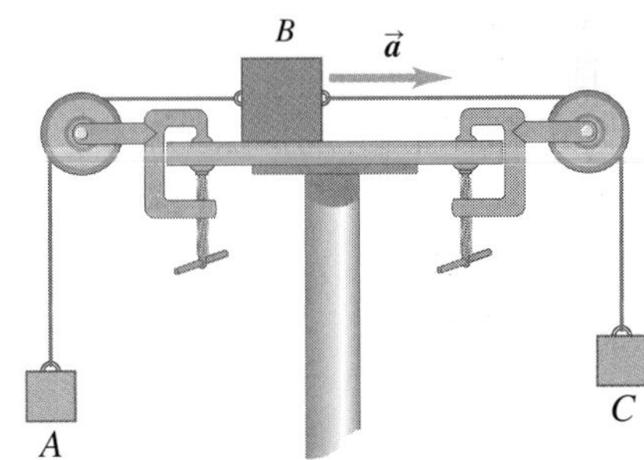

5.86. Two blocks connected by a cord passing over a small, frictionless pulley rest on frictionless planes (Fig. 5.70). (a) Which way will the system move when the blocks are released from rest? (b) What is the acceleration of the blocks? (c) What is the tension in the cord?

Figure **5.70** Problem 5.86.

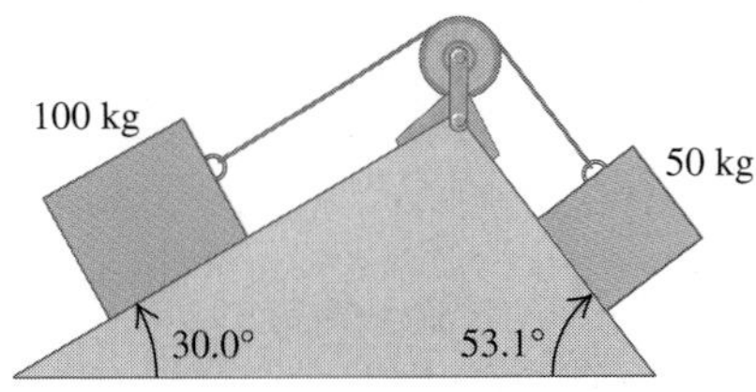

5.87. In terms of m_1, m_2, and g, find the accelerations of each block in Fig. 5.71. There is no friction anywhere in the system.

Figure **5.71** Problem 5.87.

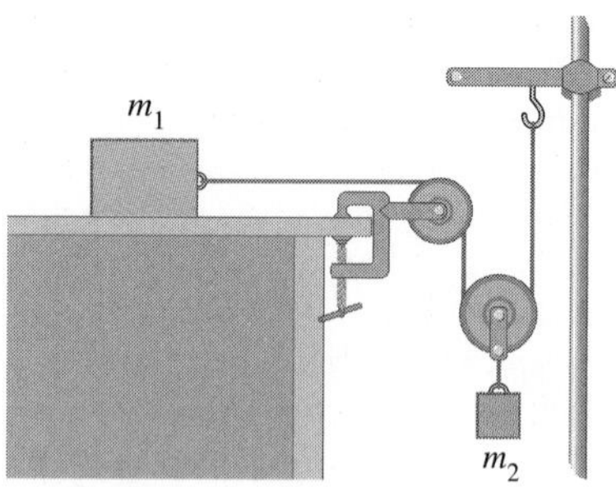

5.88. Block B, with mass 5.00 kg, rests on block A, with mass 8.00 kg, which in turn is on a horizontal tabletop (Fig. 5.72). There is no friction between block A and the tabletop, but the coefficient of static friction between block A and block B is 0.750. A light string attached to block A passes over a frictionless, massless pulley, and block C is suspended from the other end of the string. What is the largest mass that block C can have so that blocks A and B still slide together when the system is released from rest?

Figure **5.72** Problem 5.88.

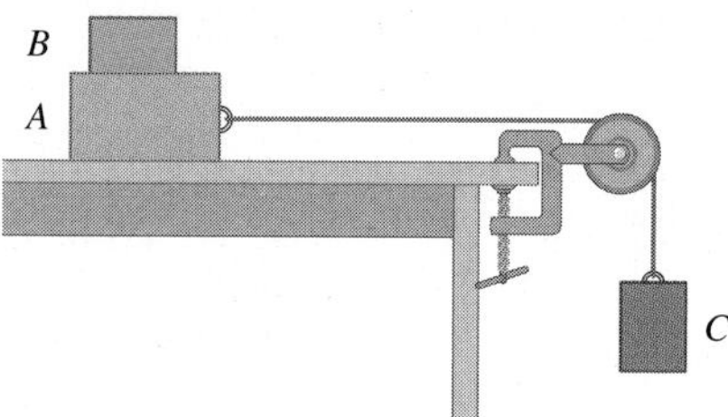

5.89. Two objects with masses 5.00 kg and 2.00 kg hang 0.600 m above the floor from the ends of a cord 6.00 m long passing over a frictionless pulley. Both objects start from rest. Find the maximum height reached by the 2.00-kg object.

5.90. Friction in an Elevator. You are riding in an elevator on the way to the 18th floor of your dormitory. The elevator is accelerating upward with $a = 1.90\ \text{m/s}^2$. Beside you is the box containing your new computer; the box and its contents have a total mass of 28.0 kg. While the elevator is accelerating upward, you push horizontally on the box to slide it at constant speed toward the elevator door. If the coefficient of kinetic friction between the box and the elevator floor is $\mu_k = 0.32$, what magnitude of force must you apply?

5.91. A block is placed against the vertical front of a cart as shown in Fig. 5.73. What acceleration must the cart have so that block A does not fall? The coefficient of static friction between the block and the cart is μ_s. How would an observer on the cart describe the behavior of the block?

Figure **5.73** Problem 5.91.

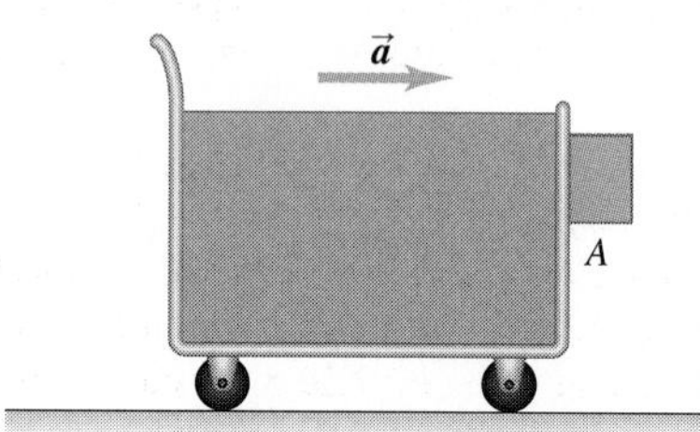

5.92. Two blocks with masses 4.00 kg and 8.00 kg are connected by a string and slide down a 30.0° inclined plane (Fig. 5.74). The coefficient of kinetic friction between the 4.00-kg block and the plane is 0.25; that between the 8.00-kg block and the plane is 0.35. (a) Calculate the acceleration of each block. (b) Calculate the tension in the string. (c) What happens if the positions of the blocks are reversed, so the 4.00-kg block is above the 8.00-kg block?

Figure **5.74** Problem 5.92.

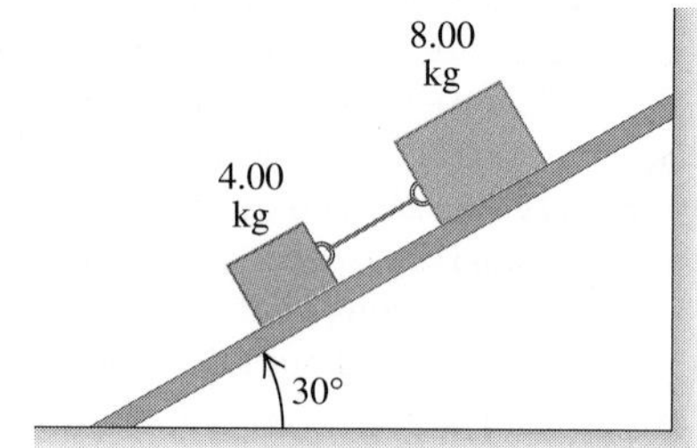

5.93. Block A, with weight $3w$, slides down an inclined plane S of slope angle 36.9° at a constant speed while plank B, with weight w, rests on top of A. The plank is attached by a cord to the wall (Fig. 5.75). (a) Draw a diagram of all the forces acting on block A. (b) If the coefficient of kinetic friction is the same between A and B and between S and A, determine its value.

Figure **5.75** Problem 5.93.

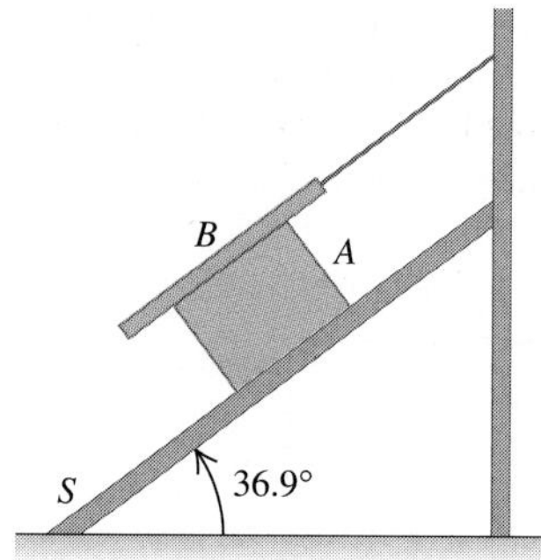

5.94. Accelerometer. The system shown in Fig. 5.76 can be used to measure the acceleration of the system. An observer riding on the platform measures the angle θ that the thread supporting the light ball makes with the vertical. There is no friction anywhere. (a) How is θ related to the acceleration of the system? (b) If $m_1 = 250$ kg and $m_2 = 1250$ kg, what is θ? (c) If you can vary m_1 and m_2, what is the largest angle θ you could achieve? Explain how you need to adjust m_1 and m_2 to do this.

Figure **5.76** Problem 5.94.

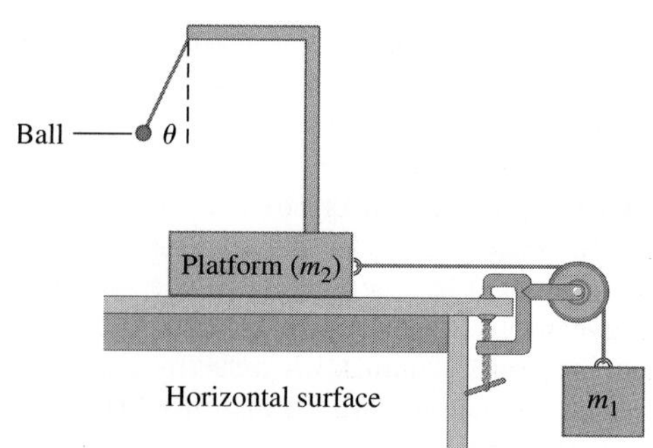

5.95. Banked Curve I. A curve with a 120-m radius on a level road is banked at the correct angle for a speed of 20 m/s. If an automobile rounds this curve at 30 m/s, what is the minimum coefficient of static friction needed between tires and road to prevent skidding?

5.96. Banked Curve II. Consider a wet roadway banked as in Example 5.23 (Section 5.4), where there is a coefficient of static friction of 0.30 and a coefficient of kinetic friction of 0.25 between the tires and the roadway. The radius of the curve is $R = 50$ m. (a) If the banking angle is $\beta = 25°$, what is the *maximum* speed the automobile can have before sliding *up* the banking? (b) What is the *minimum* speed the automobile can have before sliding *down* the banking?

5.97. Maximum Safe Speed. As you travel every day to campus, the road makes a large turn that is approximately an arc of a circle. You notice the warning sign at the start of the turn, asking for a maximum speed of 55 mi/h. You also notice that in the curved portion the road is level—that is, not banked at all. On a dry day with very little traffic, you enter the turn at a constant speed of 80 mi/h and feel that the car may skid if you do not slow down quickly. You conclude that your speed is at the limit of safety for this curve and you slow down. However, you remember reading that on dry pavement new tires have an average coefficient of static friction of about 0.76, while under the worst winter driving conditions, you may encounter wet ice for which the coefficient of static friction can be as low as 0.20. Wet ice is not unheard of on this road, so you ask yourself whether the speed limit for the turn on the roadside warning sign is for the worst-case scenario. (a) Estimate the radius of the curve from your 80-mi/h experience in the dry turn. (b) Use this estimate to find the maximum speed limit in the turn under the worst wet-ice conditions. How does this compare with the speed limit on the sign? Is the sign misleading drivers? (c) On a rainy day, the coefficient of static friction would be about 0.37. What is the maximum safe speed for the turn when the road is wet? Does your answer help you understand the maximum-speed sign?

5.98. You are riding in a school bus. As the bus rounds a flat curve at constant speed, a lunch box with mass 0.500 kg, suspended from the ceiling of the bus by a string 1.80 m long, is found to hang at rest relative to the bus when the string makes an angle of 30.0° with the vertical. In this position the lunch box is 50.0 m from the center of curvature of the curve. What is the speed v of the bus?

5.99. The Monkey and Bananas Problem. A 20-kg monkey has a firm hold on a light rope that passes over a frictionless pulley and is attached to a 20-kg bunch of bananas (Fig. 5.77). The monkey looks up, sees the bananas, and starts to climb the rope to get them. (a) As the monkey climbs, do the bananas move up, down, or remain at rest? (b) As the monkey climbs, does the distance between the monkey and the bananas decrease, increase, or remain constant? (c) The monkey releases her hold on the rope. What happens to the distance between the monkey and the bananas while she is falling?

Figure 5.77 Problem 5.99.

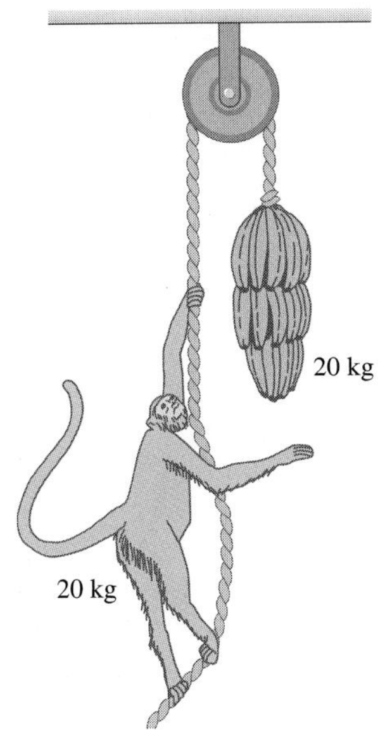

(d) Before reaching the ground, the monkey grabs the rope to stop her fall. What do the bananas do?

5.100. You throw a rock downward into water with a speed of $3mg/k$, where k is the coefficient in Eq. (5.7). Assume that the relationship between fluid resistance and speed is as given in Eq. (5.7), and calculate the speed of the rock as a function of time.

5.101. A rock with mass $m = 3.00$ kg falls from rest in a viscous medium. The rock is acted on by a net constant downward force of 18.0 N (a combination of gravity and the buoyant force exerted by the medium) and by a fluid resistance force $f = kv$, where v is the speed in m/s and $k = 2.20\ \text{N} \cdot \text{s/m}$ (see Section 5.3). (a) Find the initial acceleration a_0. (b) Find the acceleration when the speed is 3.00 m/s. (c) Find the speed when the acceleration equals $0.1a_0$. (d) Find the terminal speed v_t. (e) Find the coordinate, speed, and acceleration 2.00 s after the start of the motion. (f) Find the time required to reach a speed $0.9v_t$.

5.102. A rock with mass m slides with initial velocity v_0 on a horizontal surface. A retarding force F_R that the surface exerts on the rock is proportional to the square root of the instantaneous velocity of the rock $(F_R = -kv^{1/2})$. (a) Find expressions for the velocity and position of the rock as a function of time. (b) In terms of m, k, and v_0, at what time will the rock come to rest? (c) In terms of m, k, and v_0, what is the distance of the rock from its starting point when it comes to rest?

5.103. A fluid exerts an upward buoyancy force on an object immersed in it. In the derivation of Eq. (5.9) the buoyancy force exerted on an object by the fluid was ignored. But in some situations, where the density of the object is not much greater than the density of the fluid, you cannot ignore the buoyancy force. For a plastic sphere falling in water, you calculate the terminal speed to be 0.36 m/s when you ignore buoyancy, but you measure it to be 0.24 m/s. The buoyancy force is what fraction of the weight?

5.104. The 4.00-kg block in Fig. 5.78 is attached to a vertical rod by means of two strings. When the system rotates about the axis of the rod, the strings are extended as shown in the diagram and the tension in the upper string is 80.0 N. (a) What is the tension in the lower cord? (b) How many revolutions per minute does the system make? (c) Find the number of revolutions per minute at which the lower cord just goes slack. (d) Explain what happens if the number of revolutions per minute is less than in part (c).

Figure 5.78 Problem 5.104.

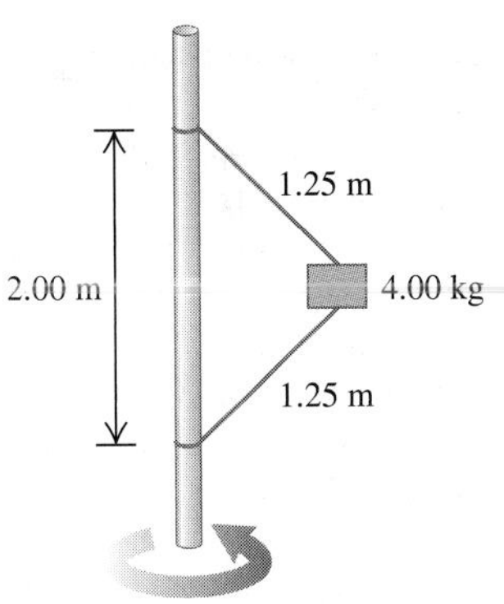

5.105. Equation (5.10) applies to the case where the initial velocity is zero. (a) Derive the corresponding equation for $v_y(t)$ when the falling object has an initial downward velocity with magnitude v_0. (b) For the case where $v_0 < v_t$, sketch a graph of v_y as a function of t and label v_t on your graph. (c) Repeat part (b) for the case where $v_0 > v_t$. (d) Discuss what your result says about $v_y(t)$ when $v_0 = v_t$.

5.106. A small rock moves in water, and the force exerted on it by the water is given by Eq. (5.7). The terminal speed of the rock is measured and found to be 2.0 m/s. The rock is projected *upward* at an initial speed of 6.0 m/s. You can ignore the buoyancy force on the rock. (a) In the absence of fluid resistance, how high will the rock rise and how long will it take to reach this maximum height?

(b) When the effects of fluid resistance are included, what are the answers to the questions in part (a)?

5.107. You observe a 1350-kg sports car rolling along flat pavement in a straight line. The only horizontal forces acting on it are a constant rolling friction and air resistance (proportional to the square of its speed). You take the following data during a time interval of 25 s: When its speed is 32 m/s, the car slows down at a rate of $-0.42\ \text{m/s}^2$, and when its speed is decreased to 24 m/s, it slows down at $-0.30\ \text{m/s}^2$. (a) Find the coefficient of rolling friction and the air drag constant D. (b) At what constant speed will this car move down an incline that makes a 2.2° angle with the horizontal? (c) How is the constant speed for an incline of angle β related to the terminal speed of this sports car if the car drops off a high cliff? Assume that in both cases the air resistance force is proportional to the square of the speed, and the air drag constant is the same.

5.108. A 70-kg person rides in a 30-kg cart moving at 12 m/s at the top of a hill that is in the shape of an arc of a circle with a radius of 40 m. (a) What is the apparent weight of the person as the cart passes over the top of the hill? (b) Determine the maximum speed that the cart may travel at the top of the hill without losing contact with the surface. Does your answer depend on the mass of the cart or the mass of the person? Explain.

5.109. Merry-Go-Round. One December identical twins Jena and Jackie are playing on a large merry-go-round (a disk mounted parallel to the ground, on a vertical axle through its center) in their school playground in northern Minnesota. Each twin has mass 30.0 kg. The icy coating on the merry-go-round surface makes it frictionless. The merry-go-round revolves at a constant rate as the twins ride on it. Jena, sitting 1.80 m from the center of the merry-go-round, must hold on to one of the metal posts attached to the merry-go-round with a horizontal force of 60.0 N to keep from sliding off. Jackie is sitting at the edge, 3.60 m from the center. (a) With what horizontal force must Jackie hold on to keep from falling off? (b) If Jackie falls off, what will be her horizontal velocity when she becomes airborne?

5.110. A passenger with mass 85 kg rides in a Ferris wheel like that in Example 5.24 (Section 5.4). The seats travel in a circle of radius 35 m. The Ferris wheel rotates at constant speed and makes one complete revolution every 25 s. Calculate the magnitude and direction of the net force exerted on the passenger by the seat when she is (a) one-quarter revolution past her lowest point and (b) one-quarter revolution past her highest point.

5.111. On the ride "Spindletop" at the amusement park Six Flags Over Texas, people stood against the inner wall of a hollow vertical cylinder with radius 2.5 m. The cylinder started to rotate, and when it reached a constant rotation rate of 0.60 rev/s, the floor on which people were standing dropped about 0.5 m. The people remained pinned against the wall. (a) Draw a force diagram for a person on this ride, after the floor has dropped. (b) What minimum coefficient of static friction is required if the person on the ride is not to slide downward to the new position of the floor? (c) Does your answer in part (b) depend on the mass of the passenger? (*Note:* When the ride is over, the cylinder is slowly brought to rest. As it slows down, people slide down the walls to the floor.)

5.112. A physics major is working to pay his college tuition by performing in a traveling carnival. He rides a motorcycle inside a hollow transparent plastic sphere. After gaining sufficient speed, he travels in a vertical circle with a radius of 13.0 m. The physics major has mass 70.0 kg, and his motorcycle has mass 40.0 kg. (a) What minimum speed must he have at the top of the circle if the tires of the motorcycle are not to lose contact with the sphere? (b) At the bottom of the circle, his speed is twice the value calculated in part (a). What is the magnitude of the normal force exerted on the motorcycle by the sphere at this point?

5.113. Ulterior Motives. You are driving a classic 1954 Nash Ambassador with a friend who is sitting to your right on the passenger side of the front seat. The Ambassador has flat bench seats. You would like to be closer to your friend and decide to use physics to achieve your romantic goal by making a quick turn. (a) Which way (to the left or to the right) should you turn the car to get your friend to slide closer to you? (b) If the coefficient of static friction between your friend and the car seat is 0.35, and you keep driving at a constant speed of 20 m/s, what is the maximum radius you could make your turn and still have your friend slide your way?

5.114. A small block with mass m rests on a frictionless horizontal tabletop a distance r from a hole in the center of the table (Fig. 5.79). A string tied to the small block passes down through the hole, and a larger block with mass M is suspended from the free end of the string. The small block is set into uniform circular motion with radius r and speed v. What must v be if the large block is to remain motionless when released?

Figure 5.79 Problem 5.114.

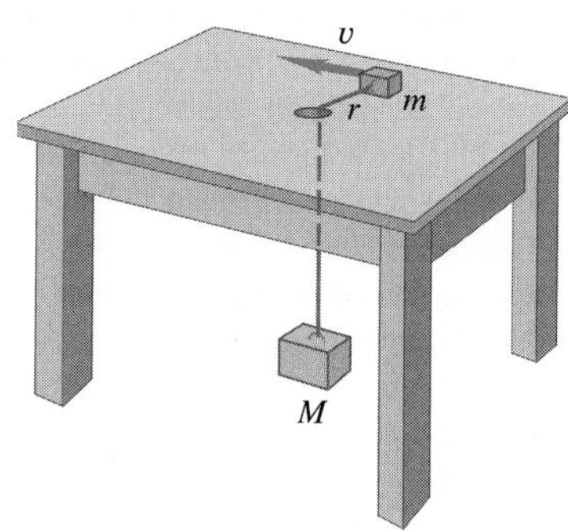

5.115. A small bead can slide without friction on a circular hoop that is in a vertical plane and has a radius of 0.100 m. The hoop rotates at a constant rate of 4.00 rev/s about a vertical diameter (Fig. 5.80). (a) Find the angle β at which the bead is in vertical equilibrium. (Of course, it has a radial acceleration toward the axis.) (b) Is it possible for the bead to "ride" at the same elevation as the center of the hoop? (c) What will happen if the hoop rotates at 1.00 rev/s?

Figure 5.80 Problem 5.115.

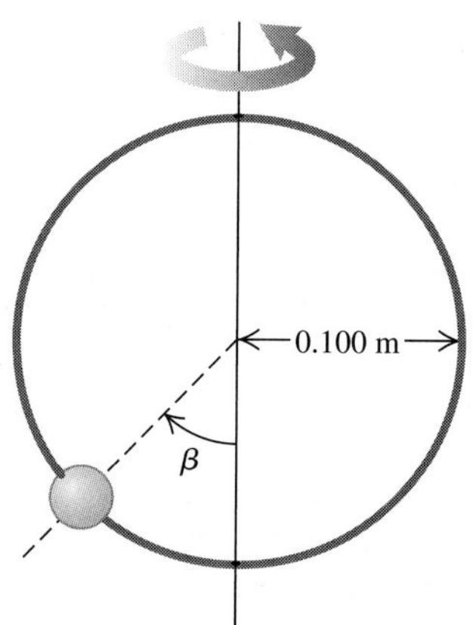

5.116. A model airplane with mass 2.20 kg moves in the xy-plane such that its x- and y-coordinates vary in time according to $x(t) = \alpha - \beta t^3$ and $y(t) = \gamma t - \delta t^2$, where $\alpha = 1.50$ m, $\beta = 0.120$ m/s^3, $\gamma = 3.00$ m/s, and $\delta = 1.00$ m/s^2. (a) Calculate the x- and y-components of the net force on the plane as functions of time. (b) Sketch the trajectory of the airplane between $t = 0$ and $t = 3.00$ s, and draw on your sketch vectors showing the net force on the airplane at $t = 0$, $t = 1.00$ s, $t = 2.00$ s, and $t = 3.00$ s. For each of these times, relate the direction of the net force to the direction that the airplane is turning, and to whether the airplane is speeding up or slowing down (or neither). (c) What are the magnitude and direction of the net force at $t = 3.00$ s?

5.117. A particle moves on a frictionless surface along a path as shown in Fig. 5.81. (The figure gives a view looking down on the surface.) The particle is initially at rest at point A and then begins to move toward B as it gains speed at a constant rate. From B to C, the particle moves along a circular path at a constant speed. The speed remains constant along the straight-line path from C to D. From D to E, the particle moves along a circular path, but now its speed is decreasing at a constant rate. The speed continues to decrease at a constant rate as the particle moves from E to F; the particle comes to a halt at F. (The time intervals between the marked points are not equal.) At each point marked with a dot, draw arrows to represent the velocity, the acceleration, and the net force acting on the particle. Draw longer or shorter arrows to represent vectors of larger or smaller magnitude.

Figure 5.81 Problem 5.117.

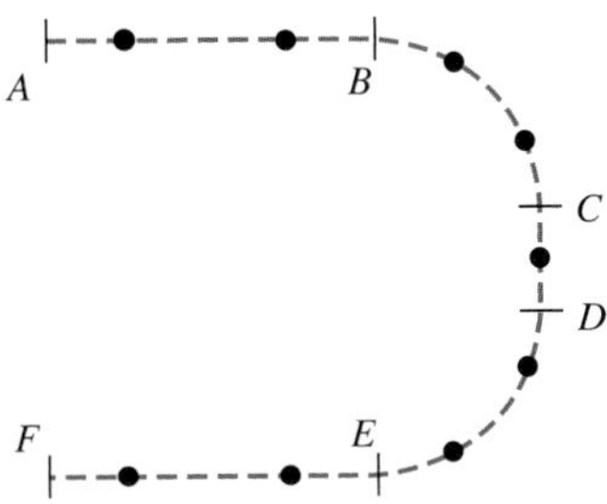

5.118. A small remote-control car with mass 1.60 kg moves at a constant speed of $v = 12.0$ m/s in a vertical circle inside a hollow metal cylinder that has a radius of 5.00 m (Fig 5.82). What is the magnitude of the normal force exerted on the car by the walls of the cylinder at (a) point A (at the bottom of the vertical circle) and (b) point B (at the top of the vertical circle)?

Figure 5.82 Problem 5.118.

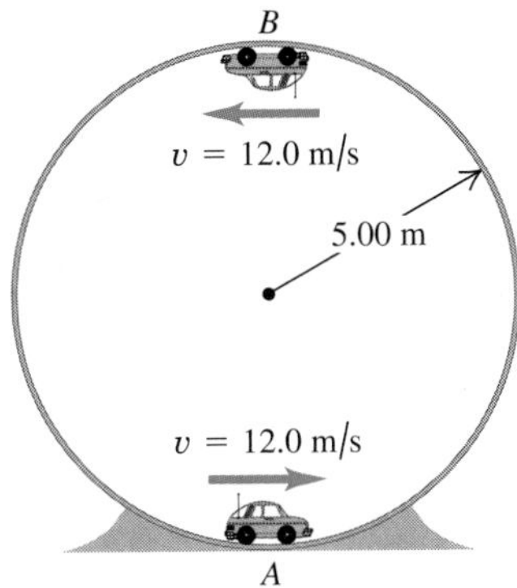

5.119. A small block with mass m is placed inside an inverted cone that is rotating about a vertical axis such that the time for one revolution of the cone is T (Fig. 5.83). The walls of the cone make an angle β with the vertical. The coefficient of static friction between the block and the cone is μ_s. If the block is to remain at a constant height h above the apex of the cone, what are the maximum and minimum values of T?

Figure 5.83 Problem 5.119.

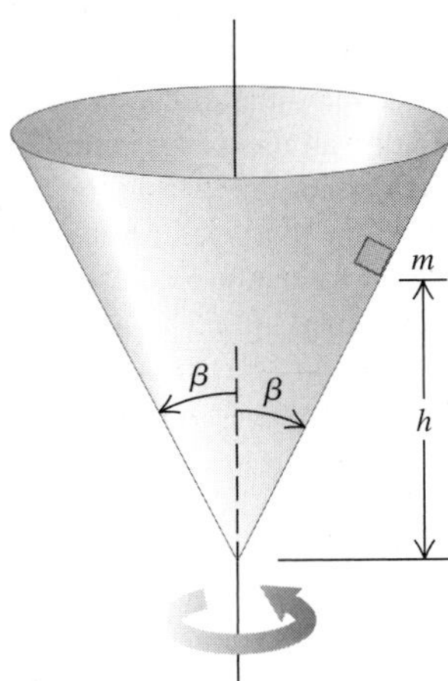

Challenge Problems

5.120. Moving Wedge. A wedge with mass M rests on a frictionless, horizontal tabletop. A block with mass m is placed on the wedge (Fig. 5.84a). There is no friction between the block and the wedge. The system is released from rest. (a) Calculate the acceleration of the wedge and the horizontal and vertical components of the acceleration of the block. (b) Do your answers to part (a) reduce to the correct results when M is very large? (c) As seen by a stationary observer, what is the shape of the trajectory of the block?

Figure 5.84 Challenge Problems 5.120 and 5.121.

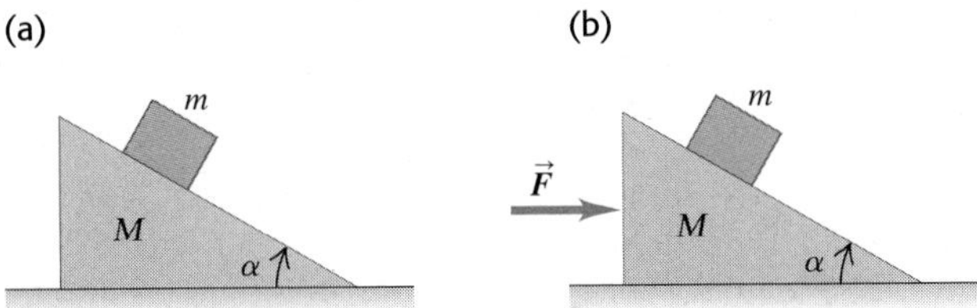

5.121. A wedge with mass M rests on a frictionless horizontal tabletop. A block with mass m is placed on the wedge and a horizontal force $\vec{F}$ is applied to the wedge (Fig. 5.84b). What must the magnitude of $\vec{F}$ be if the block is to remain at a constant height above the tabletop?

5.122. A box of weight w is accelerated up a ramp by a rope that exerts a tension T. The ramp makes an angle α with the horizontal, and the rope makes an angle θ above the ramp. The coefficient of kinetic friction between the box and the ramp is μ_k. Show that no matter what the value of α, the acceleration is maximum if $\theta = \arctan \mu_k$ (as long as the box remains in contact with the ramp).

5.123. Angle for Minimum Force. A box with weight w is pulled at constant speed along a level floor by a force $\vec{F}$ that is at an angle θ above the horizontal. The coefficient of kinetic friction between the floor and box is μ_k. (a) In terms of θ, μ_k, and w, calculate F. (b) For $w = 400$ N and $\mu_k = 0.25$, calculate F for θ ranging from 0° to 90° in increments of 10°. Graph F versus θ. (c) From the general expression in part (a), calculate the value of θ for which the value of F, required to maintain constant speed, is a minimum. (*Hint:* At a point where a function is minimum, what are the first and second derivatives of the function? Here F is a function of θ.) For the special case of $w = 400$ N and $\mu_k = 0.25$, evaluate this optimal θ and compare your result to the graph you constructed in part (b).

5.124. Falling Baseball. You drop a baseball from the roof of a tall building. As the ball falls, the air exerts a drag force proportional to the square of the ball's speed ($f = Dv^2$). (a) In a diagram, show the direction of motion and indicate, with the aid of vectors, all the forces acting on the ball. (b) Apply Newton's second law and infer from the resulting equation the general properties of the motion. (c) Show that the ball acquires a terminal speed that is as given in Eq. (5.13). (d) Derive the equation for the speed at any time. (*Note:*

$$\int \frac{dx}{a^2 - x^2} = \frac{1}{a}\operatorname{arctanh}\left(\frac{x}{a}\right)$$

where

$$\tanh(x) = \frac{e^x - e^{-x}}{e^x + e^{-x}} = \frac{e^{2x} - 1}{e^{2x} + 1}$$

defines the hyperbolic tangent.)

5.125. Double Atwood's Machine. In Fig. 5.85 masses m_1 and m_2 are connected by a light string A over a light, frictionless pulley B. The axle of pulley B is connected by a second light string C over a second light, frictionless pulley D to a mass m_3. Pulley D is suspended from the ceiling by an attachment to its axle. The system is released from rest. In terms of m_1, m_2, m_3, and g, what are (a) the acceleration of block m_3; (b) the acceleration of pulley B; (c) the acceleration of block m_1; (d) the acceleration of block m_2; (e) the tension in string A; (f) the tension in string C? (g) What do your expressions give for the special case of $m_1 = m_2$ and $m_3 = m_1 + m_2$? Is this sensible?

Figure 5.85 Challenge Problem 5.125.

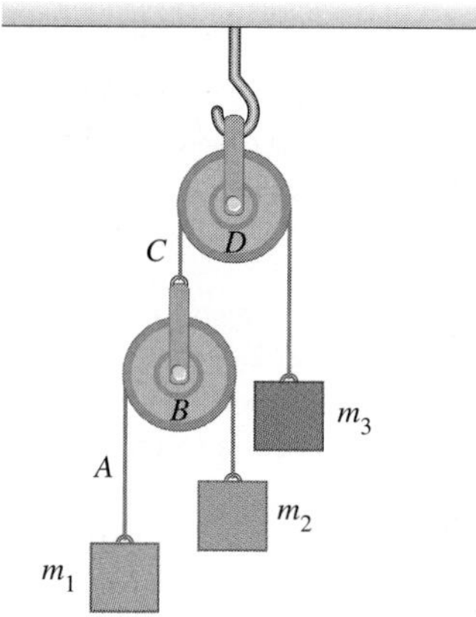

5.126. The masses of blocks A and B in Fig. 5.86 are 20.0 kg and 10.0 kg, respectively. The blocks are initially at rest on the floor and are connected by a massless string passing over a massless and frictionless pulley. An upward force $\vec{F}$ is applied to the pulley. Find the accelerations $\vec{a}_A$ of block A and $\vec{a}_B$ of block B when F is (a) 124 N; (b) 294 N; (c) 424 N.

Figure 5.86 Challenge Problem 5.126.

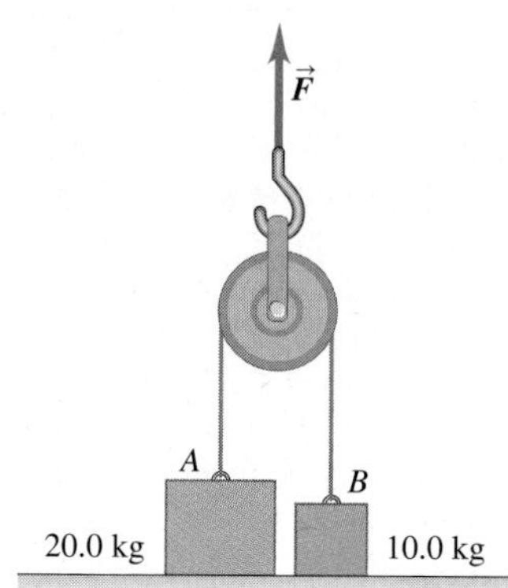

5.127. A ball is held at rest at position A in Fig. 5.87 by two light strings. The horizontal string is cut and the ball starts swinging as a pendulum. Point B is the farthest to the right the ball goes as it swings back and forth. What is the ratio of the tension in the supporting string in position B to its value at A before the horizontal string was cut?

Figure 5.87 Challenge Problem 5.127.

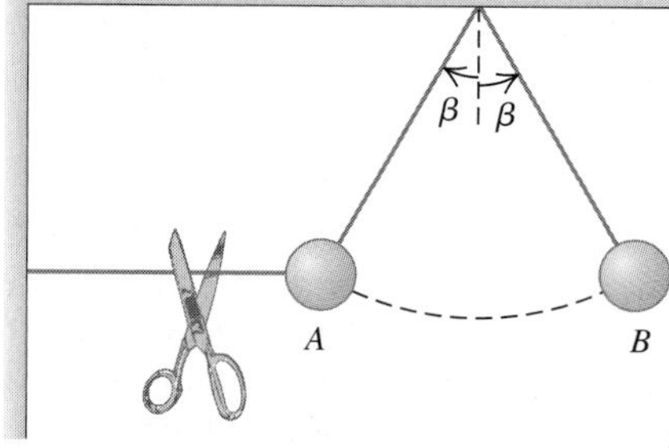

WORK AND KINETIC ENERGY

6

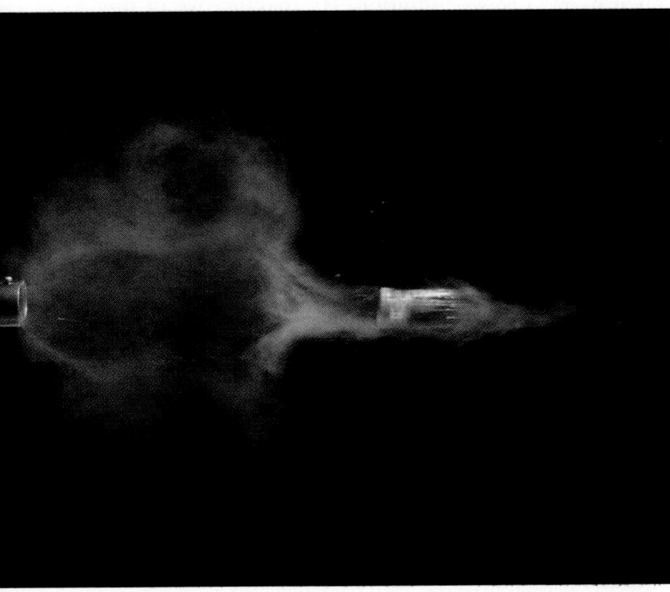

? When a shotgun fires, the expanding gases in the barrel push the shell out. According to Newton's third law, the shell exerts as much force on the gases as the gases exert on the shell. Would it be correct to say that the *shell* does work on the *gases?*

LEARNING GOALS

By studying this chapter, you will learn:

- What it means for a force to do work on a body, and how to calculate the amount of work done.
- The definition of the kinetic energy (energy of motion) of a body, and what it means physically.
- How the total work done on a body changes the body's kinetic energy, and how to use this principle to solve problems in mechanics.
- How to use the relationship between total work and change in kinetic energy when the forces are not constant, the body follows a curved path, or both.
- How to solve problems involving power (the rate of doing work).

Suppose you try to find the speed of an arrow that has been shot from a bow. You apply Newton's laws and all the problem-solving techniques that we've learned, but you run across a major stumbling block: After the archer releases the arrow, the bow string exerts a *varying* force that depends on the arrow's position. As a result, the simple methods that we've learned aren't enough to calculate the speed. Never fear; we aren't by any means finished with mechanics, and there are other methods for dealing with such problems.

The new method that we're about to introduce uses the ideas of *work* and *energy*. The importance of the energy idea stems from the *principle of conservation of energy*: Energy is a quantity that can be converted from one form to another but cannot be created or destroyed. In an automobile engine, chemical energy stored in the fuel is converted partially to the energy of the automobile's motion and partially to thermal energy. In a microwave oven, electromagnetic energy obtained from your power company is converted to thermal energy of the food being cooked. In these and all other processes, the *total* energy—the sum of all energy present in all different forms—remains the same. No exception has ever been found.

We'll use the energy idea throughout the rest of this book to study a tremendous range of physical phenomena. This idea will help you understand why a sweater keeps you warm, how a camera's flash unit can produce a short burst of light, and the meaning of Einstein's famous equation $E = mc^2$.

In this chapter, though, our concentration will be on mechanics. We'll learn about one important form of energy called *kinetic energy,* or energy of motion, and how it relates to the concept of *work*. We'll also consider *power,* which is the time rate of doing work. In Chapter 7 we'll expand the ideas of work and kinetic energy into a deeper understanding of the concepts of energy and the conservation of energy.

6.1 Work

6.1 These people are doing work as they push on the stalled car because they exert a force on the car as it moves.

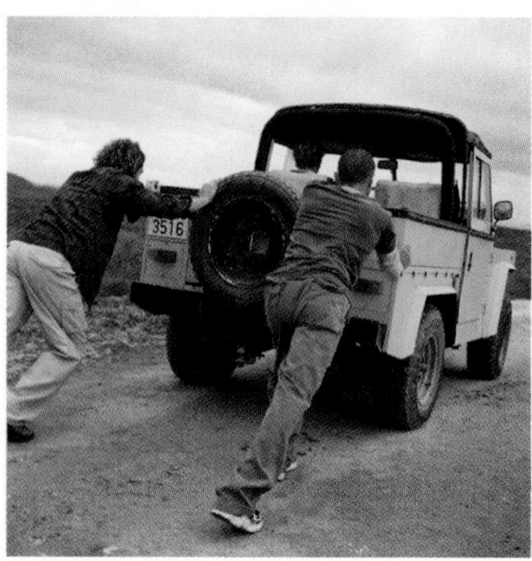

You'd probably agree that it's hard work to pull a heavy sofa across the room, to lift a stack of encyclopedias from the floor to a high shelf, or to push a stalled car off the road. Indeed, all of these examples agree with the everyday meaning of *work*—any activity that requires muscular or mental effort.

In physics, work has a much more precise definition. By making use of this definition we'll find that in any motion, no matter how complicated, the total work done on a particle by all forces that act on it equals the change in its *kinetic energy*—a quantity that's related to the particle's speed. This relationship holds even when the forces acting on the particle aren't constant, a situation that can be difficult or impossible to handle with the techniques you learned in Chapters 4 and 5. The ideas of work and kinetic energy enable us to solve problems in mechanics that we could not have attempted before.

In this section we'll see how work is defined and how to calculate work in a variety of situations involving *constant* forces. Even though we already know how to solve problems in which the forces are constant, the idea of work is still useful in such problems. Later in this chapter we'll relate work and kinetic energy, and then apply these ideas to problems in which the forces are *not* constant.

The three examples of work described above—pulling a sofa, lifting encyclopedias, and pushing a car—have something in common. In each case you do work by exerting a *force* on a body while that body *moves* from one place to another—that is, undergoes a *displacement* (Fig. 6.1). You do more work if the force is greater (you push harder on the car) or if the displacement is greater (you push the car farther down the road).

6.2 The work done by a constant force acting in the same direction as the displacement.

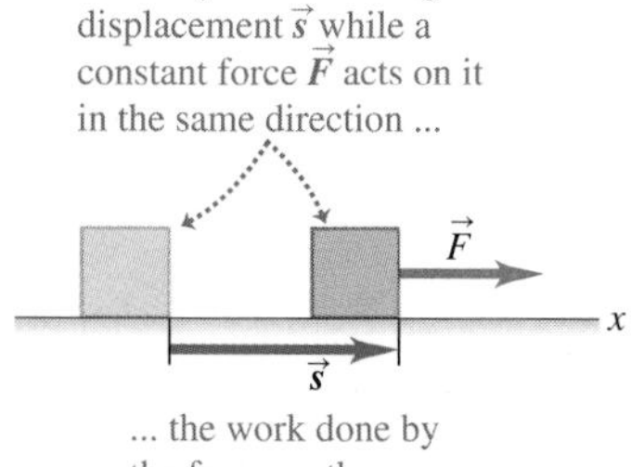
If a body moves through a displacement $\vec{s}$ while a constant force $\vec{F}$ acts on it in the same direction ...
$\vec{F}$
x
$\vec{s}$
... the work done by the force on the body is $W = Fs$.

The physicist's definition of work is based on these observations. Consider a body that undergoes a displacement of magnitude s along a straight line. (For now, we'll assume that any body we discuss can be treated as a particle so that we can ignore any rotation or changes in shape of the body.) While the body moves, a constant force $\vec{F}$ acts on it in the same direction as the displacement $\vec{s}$ (Fig. 6.2). We define the **work** W done by this constant force under these circumstances as the product of the force magnitude F and the displacement magnitude s:

$$W = Fs \qquad \text{(constant force in direction of straight-line displacement)} \tag{6.1}$$

The work done on the body is greater if either the force F or the displacement s is greater, in agreement with our observations above.

CAUTION **Work = W, weight = w** Don't confuse W (work) with w (weight). Though the symbols are similar, work and weight are different quantities.

The SI unit of work is the **joule** (abbreviated J, pronounced "jewel," and named in honor of the 19th-century English physicist James Prescott Joule). From Eq. (6.1) we see that in any system of units, the unit of work is the unit of force multiplied by the unit of distance. In SI units the unit of force is the newton and the unit of distance is the meter, so 1 joule is equivalent to 1 *newton-meter* $(\text{N} \cdot \text{m})$:

$$1 \text{ joule} = (1 \text{ newton})(1 \text{ meter}) \quad \text{or} \quad 1 \text{ J} = 1 \text{ N} \cdot \text{m}$$

In the British system the unit of force is the pound (lb), the unit of distance is the foot (ft), and the unit of work is the *foot-pound* $(\text{ft} \cdot \text{lb})$. The following conversions are useful:

$$1 \text{ J} = 0.7376 \text{ ft} \cdot \text{lb} \qquad 1 \text{ ft} \cdot \text{lb} = 1.356 \text{ J}$$

As an illustration of Eq. (6.1), think of a person pushing a stalled car. If he pushes the car through a displacement $\vec{s}$ with a constant force $\vec{F}$ in the direction of motion, the amount of work he does on the car is given by Eq. (6.1): $W = Fs$. But what if the person pushes at an angle ϕ with the car's displacement (Fig. 6.3)? Then $\vec{F}$ has a component $F_{\parallel} = F\cos\phi$ in the direction of the displacement and a component $F_{\perp} = F\sin\phi$ that acts perpendicular to the displacement. (Other

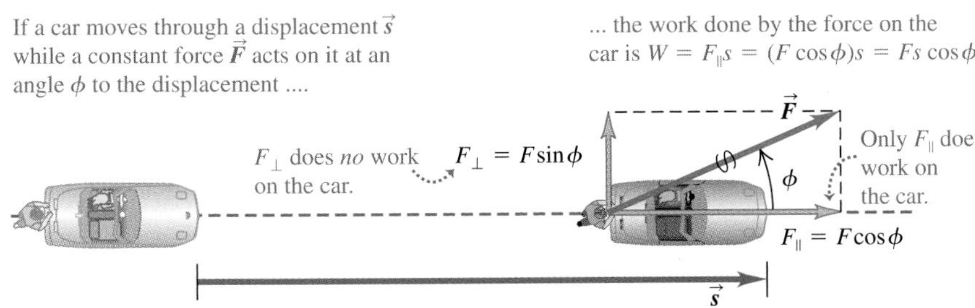
If a car moves through a displacement $\vec{s}$ while a constant force $\vec{F}$ acts on it at an angle ϕ to the displacement ....
... the work done by the force on the car is $W = F_{\parallel}s = (F\cos\phi)s = Fs\cos\phi$.
$F_{\perp}$ does *no* work on the car.
$F_{\perp} = F\sin\phi$
$\vec{F}$
ϕ
Only $F_{\parallel}$ does work on the car.
$F_{\parallel} = F\cos\phi$
$\vec{s}$

6.3 The work done by a constant force acting at an angle to the displacement.

forces must act on the car so that it moves along $\vec{s}$, not in the direction of $\vec{F}$. We're interested only in the work that the person does, however, so we'll consider only the force he exerts.) In this case only the parallel component $F_{\parallel}$ is effective in moving the car, so we define the work as the product of this force component and the magnitude of the displacement. Hence $W = F_{\parallel}s = (F\cos\phi)s$, or

ActivPhysics ONLINE

5.1 Work Calculations

$$W = Fs\cos\phi \quad \text{(constant force, straight-line displacement)} \tag{6.2}$$

We are assuming that F and ϕ are constant during the displacement. If $\phi = 0$, so that $\vec{F}$ and $\vec{s}$ are in the same direction, then $\cos\phi = 1$ and we are back to Eq. (6.1).

Equation (6.2) has the form of the *scalar product* of two vectors, which we introduced in Section 1.10: $\vec{A}\cdot\vec{B} = AB\cos\phi$. You may want to review that definition. Hence we can write Eq. (6.2) more compactly as

$$W = \vec{F}\cdot\vec{s} \quad \text{(constant force, straight-line displacement)} \tag{6.3}$$

CAUTION **Work is a scalar** Here's an essential point: Work is a *scalar* quantity, even though it's calculated by using two vector quantities (force and displacement). A 5-N force toward the east acting on a body that moves 6 m to the east does exactly the same amount of work as a 5-N force toward the north acting on a body that moves 6 m to the north.

Example 6.1 Work done by a constant force

(a) Steve exerts a steady force of magnitude 210 N (about 47 lb) on the stalled car in Fig. 6.3 as he pushes it a distance of 18 m. The car also has a flat tire, so to make the car track straight Steve must push at an angle of 30° to the direction of motion. How much work does Steve do? (b) In a helpful mood, Steve pushes a second stalled car with a steady force $\vec{F} = (160\text{ N})\hat{\imath} - (40\text{ N})\hat{\jmath}$. The displacement of the car is $\vec{s} = (14\text{ m})\hat{\imath} + (11\text{ m})\hat{\jmath}$. How much work does Steve do in this case?

SOLUTION

IDENTIFY: In both parts (a) and (b), the target variable is the work W done by Steve. In each case the force is constant and the displacement is along a straight line, so we can use Eq. (6.2) or (6.3).

SET UP: The angle between $\vec{F}$ and $\vec{s}$ is given explicitly in part (a), so we can apply Eq. (6.2) directly. In part (b) the angle isn't given, so we're better off calculating the scalar product in Eq. (6.3) from the components of $\vec{F}$ and $\vec{s}$, as in Eq. (1.21): $\vec{A}\cdot\vec{B} = A_xB_x + A_yB_y + A_zB_z$.

EXECUTE: (a) From Eq. (6.2),

$$W = Fs\cos\phi = (210\text{ N})(18\text{ m})\cos 30° = 3.3\times10^3\text{ J}$$

(b) The components of $\vec{F}$ are $F_x = 160$ N and $F_y = -40$ N, and the components of $\vec{s}$ are $x = 14$ m and $y = 11$ m. (There are no z-components for either vector.) Hence, using Eqs. (1.21) and (6.3),

$$\begin{aligned} W &= \vec{F}\cdot\vec{s} = F_xx + F_yy \\ &= (160\text{ N})(14\text{ m}) + (-40\text{ N})(11\text{ m}) \\ &= 1.8\times10^3\text{ J} \end{aligned}$$

EVALUATE: In each case the work that Steve does is more than 1000 J. This shows that 1 joule is a rather small amount of work.

Work: Positive, Negative, or Zero

In Example 6.1 the work done in pushing the cars was positive. But it's important to understand that work can also be negative or zero. This is the essential way in which work as defined in physics differs from the "everyday" definition of work. When the force has a component in the *same direction* as the displacement

6.4 A constant force $\vec{F}$ can do positive, negative, or zero work depending on the angle between $\vec{F}$ and the displacement $\vec{s}$.

(a)

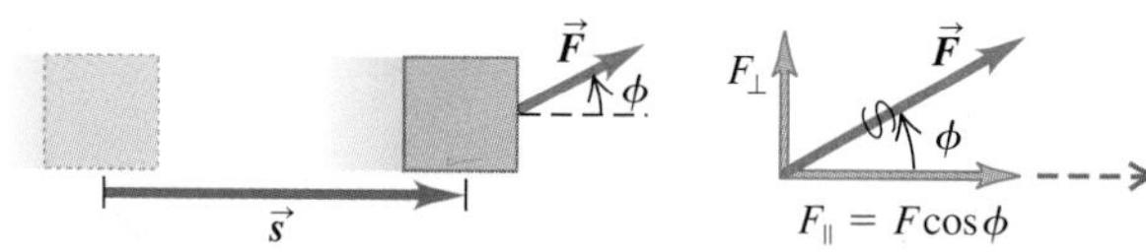

The force has a component in the direction of displacement:
- The work on the object is positive.
- $W = F_\parallel s = (F\cos\phi)s$

(b)

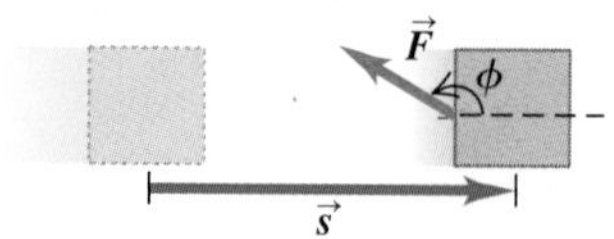

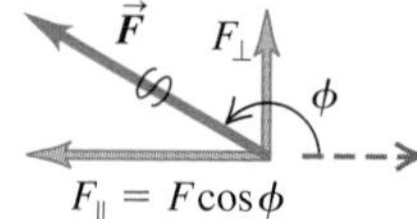

The force has a component opposite to the direction of displacement:
- The work on the object is negative.
- $W = F_\parallel s = (F\cos\phi)s$
- Mathematically, $W < 0$ because $F\cos\phi$ is negative for $90° < \phi < 270°$.

(c)

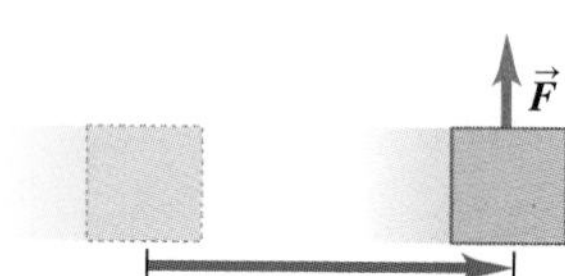

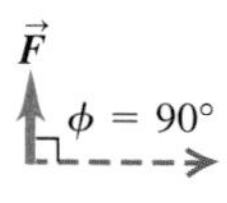

The force is perpendicular to the direction of displacement:
- The force does *no* work on the object.
- More generally, if a force acting on an object has a component $F_\perp$ perpendicular to the object's displacement, that component does no work on the object.

6.5 A weightlifter does no work on a barbell as long as he holds it stationary.

(ϕ between zero and 90°), $\cos\phi$ in Eq. (6.2) is positive and the work W is *positive* (Fig. 6.4a). When the force has a component *opposite* to the displacement (ϕ between 90° and 180°), $\cos\phi$ is negative and the work is *negative* (Fig. 6.4b). When the force is *perpendicular* to the displacement, $\phi = 90°$ and the work done by the force is *zero* (Fig. 6.4c). The cases of zero work and negative work bear closer examination, so let's look at some examples.

There are many situations in which forces act but do zero work. You might think it's "hard work" to hold a barbell motionless in the air for 5 minutes (Fig. 6.5). But in fact, you aren't doing any work at all on the barbell because there is no displacement. You get tired because the components of muscle fibers in your arm do work as they continually contract and relax. This is work done by one part of the arm exerting force on another part, however, *not* on the barbell. (We'll say more in Section 6.2 about work done by one part of a body on another part.) Even when you walk with constant velocity on a level floor while carrying a book, you still do no work on it. The book has a displacement, but the (vertical) supporting force that you exert on the book has no component in the direction of the (horizontal) motion. Then $\phi = 90°$ in Eq. (6.2), and $\cos\phi = 0$. When a body slides along a surface, the work done on the body by the normal force is zero; and when a ball on a string moves in uniform circular motion, the work done on the ball by the tension in the string is also zero. In both cases the work is zero because the force has no component in the direction of motion.

What does it really mean to do *negative* work? The answer comes from Newton's third law of motion. When a weightlifter lowers a barbell as in Fig. 6.6a, his hands and the barbell move together with the same displacement $\vec{s}$. The barbell exerts a force $\vec{F}_{\text{barbell on hands}}$ on his hands in the same direction as the hands' displacement, so the work done by the *barbell* on his *hands* is positive. (Fig. 6.6b). But by Newton's third law the weightlifter's hands exert an equal and opposite force $\vec{F}_{\text{hands on barbell}} = -\vec{F}_{\text{barbell on hands}}$ on the barbell (Fig. 6.6c). This force, which keeps the barbell from crashing to the floor, acts opposite to the barbell's displacement. Thus the work done by his *hands* on the *barbell* is negative. Because the weightlifter's hands and the barbell have the same displacement, the work that his hands do on the barbell is just the negative of the work that the barbell does on his hands. In general, when one body does negative work on a second body, the second body does an equal amount of *positive* work on the first body. ?

CAUTION **Keep track of who's doing the work** We always speak of work done *on* a particular body *by* a specific force. Always be sure to specify exactly what force is doing the

6.6 This weightlifter's hands do negative work on a barbell as the barbell does positive work on his hands.

(a) A weightlifter lowers a barbell to the floor.

$\vec{s}$

(b) The barbell does *positive* work on the weightlifter's hands.

$\vec{F}_{\text{barbell on hands}}$
$\vec{s}$
The force of the barbell on the weightlifter's hands is in the *same* direction as the hands' displacement.

(c) The weightlifter's hands do *negative* work on the barbell.

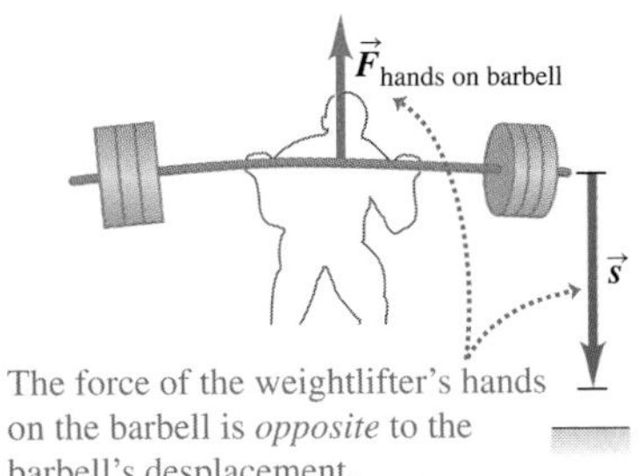
$\vec{F}_{\text{hands on barbell}}$
$\vec{s}$
The force of the weightlifter's hands on the barbell is *opposite* to the barbell's desplacement.

work you are talking about. When you lift a book, you exert an upward force on the book and the book's displacement is upward, so the work done by the lifting force on the book is positive. But the work done by the *gravitational* force (weight) on a book being lifted is *negative* because the downward gravitational force is opposite to the upward displacement.

Total Work

How do we calculate work when *several* forces act on a body? One way is to use Eq. (6.2) or (6.3) to compute the work done by each separate force. Then, because work is a scalar quantity, the *total* work W_{tot} done on the body by all the forces is the algebraic sum of the quantities of work done by the individual forces. An alternative way to find the total work W_{tot} is to compute the vector sum of the forces (that is, the net force) and then use this vector sum as $\vec{F}$ in Eq. (6.2) or (6.3). The following example illustrates both of these techniques.

Example 6.2 Work done by several forces

A farmer hitches her tractor to a sled loaded with firewood and pulls it a distance of 20 m along level ground (Fig. 6.7a). The total weight of sled and load is 14,700 N. The tractor exerts a constant 5000-N force at an angle of 36.9° above the horizontal, as shown in Fig. 6.7b. There is a 3500-N friction force opposing the sled's motion. Find the work done by each force acting on the sled and the total work done by all the forces.

SOLUTION

IDENTIFY: Each force is constant and the displacement is along a straight line, so we can calculate the work using the ideas of this section. We'll find the total work in two ways: (1) by adding together the work done on the sled by each force and (2) by finding the amount of work done by the net force on the sled.

SET UP: Since we're working with forces, we first draw a free-body diagram showing all of the forces acting on the sled and we choose a coordinate system (Fig. 6.7b). For each force—weight, normal force, force of the tractor, and friction force—we know the angle between the displacement (in the positive x-direction) and the force. Hence we can calculate the work each force does using Eq. (6.2).

As we did in Chapter 5, we'll find the net force by adding the components of the four forces. Newton's second law tells us that because the sled's motion is purely horizontal, the net force has only a horizontal component.

EXECUTE: The work W_w done by the weight is zero because its direction is perpendicular to the displacement (compare Fig. 6.4c). For the same reason, the work W_n done by the normal force is

6.7 Calculating the work done on a sled of firewood being pulled by a tractor.

(a)

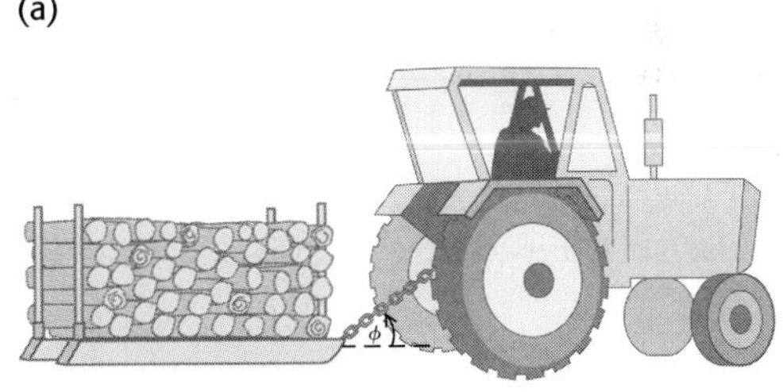

(b) Free-body diagram for sled

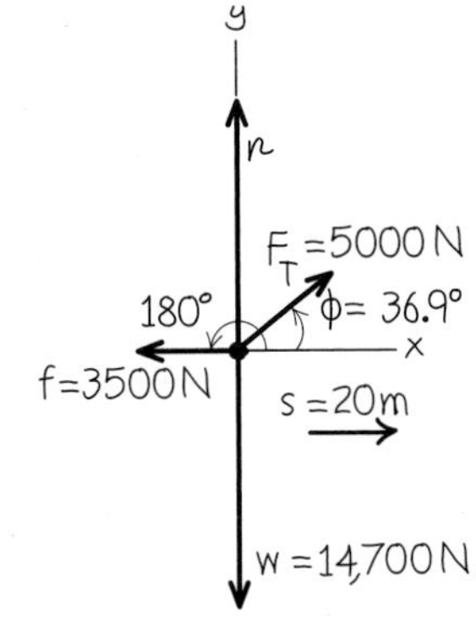
y
n
F_T=5000 N
180°
φ= 36.9°
x
f=3500N
s =20m
w =14,700N

Continued

also zero. So $W_w = W_n = 0$. (Incidentally, can you see that the magnitude of the normal force is less than the weight? Compare Example 5.15 in Section 5.3, which has a very similar free-body diagram.)

That leaves the force F_T exerted by the tractor and the friction force f. From Eq. (6.2) the work W_T done by the tractor is

$$W_T = F_T s\cos\phi = (5000\text{ N})(20\text{ m})(0.800) = 80{,}000\text{ N}\cdot\text{m}$$
$$= 80\text{ kJ}$$

The friction force $\vec{f}$ is opposite to the displacement, so for this force $\phi = 180°$ and $\cos\phi = -1$. The work W_f done by the friction force is

$$W_f = fs\cos 180° = (3500\text{ N})(20\text{ m})(-1) = -70{,}000\text{ N}\cdot\text{m}$$
$$= -70\text{ kJ}$$

The total work W_{tot} done on the sled by all forces is the *algebraic* sum of the work done by the individual forces:

$$W_{tot} = W_w + W_n + W_T + W_f = 0 + 0 + 80\text{ kJ} + (-70\text{ kJ})$$
$$= 10\text{ kJ}$$

In the alternative approach, we first find the *vector* sum of all the forces (the net force) and then use it to compute the total work. The vector sum is best found by using components. From Fig. 6.7b,

$$\sum F_x = F_T\cos\phi + (-f) = (5000\text{ N})\cos 36.9° - 3500\text{ N}$$
$$= 500\text{ N}$$
$$\sum F_y = F_T\sin\phi + n + (-w)$$
$$= (5000\text{ N})\sin 36.9° + n - 14{,}700\text{ N}$$

We don't really need the second equation; we know that the y-component of force is perpendicular to the displacement, so it does no work. Besides, there is no y-component of acceleration, so $\sum F_y$ has to be zero anyway. The total work is therefore the work done by the total x-component:

$$W_{tot} = (\sum \vec{F})\cdot\vec{s} = (\sum F_x)s = (500\text{ N})(20\text{ m}) = 10{,}000\text{ J}$$
$$= 10\text{ kJ}$$

EVALUATE: We get the same result for W_{tot} with either method, as we should.

Note that the net force in the x-direction is *not* zero, and so the sled must accelerate as it moves. In Section 6.2 we'll return to this example and see how to use the concept of work to explore the sled's motion.

Test Your Understanding of Section 6.1 An electron moves in a straight line toward the east with a constant speed of 8×10^7 m/s. It has electric, magnetic, and gravitational forces acting on it. During a 1-m displacement, the total work done on the electron is (i) positive; (ii) negative; (iii) zero; (iv) not enough information given to decide.

6.2 Kinetic Energy and the Work–Energy Theorem

The total work done on a body by external forces is related to the body's displacement—that is, to changes in its position. But the total work is also related to changes in the *speed* of the body. To see this, consider Fig. 6.8, which shows

6.8 The relationship between the total work done on a body and how the body's speed changes.

(a)

A block slides to the right on a frictionless surface.

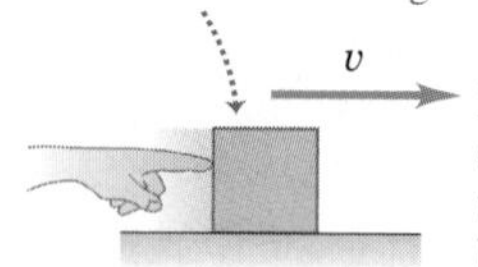

If you push to the right on the moving block, the net force on the block is to the right.

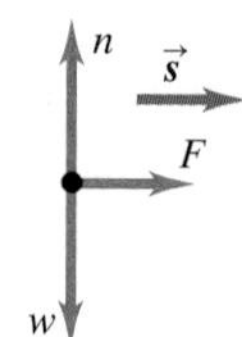

• The total work done on the block during a displacement $\vec{s}$ is positive: $W_{tot} > 0$.
• The block speeds up.

(b)

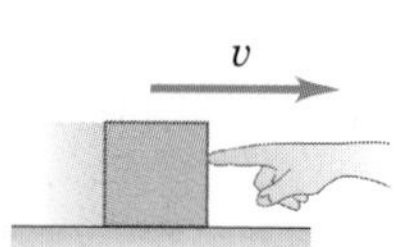

If you push to the left on the moving block, the net force on the block is to the left.

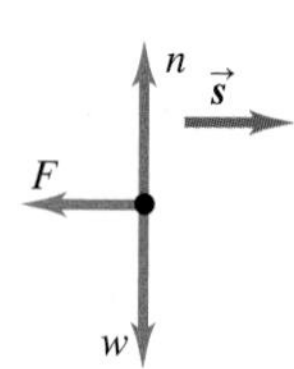

• The total work done on the block during a displacement $\vec{s}$ is negative: $W_{tot} < 0$.
• The block slows down.

(c)

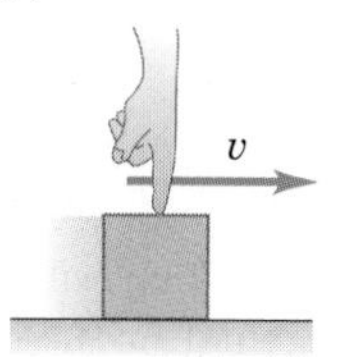

If you push straight down on the moving block, the net force on the block is zero.

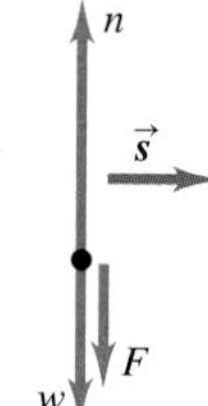

• The total work done on the block during a displacement $\vec{s}$ is zero: $W_{tot} = 0$.
• The block's speed stays the same.

three examples of a block sliding on a frictionless table. The forces acting on the block are its weight $\vec{w}$, the normal force $\vec{n}$, and the force $\vec{F}$ exerted on it by the hand.

In Fig. 6.8a the net force on the block is in the direction of its motion. From Newton's second law, this means that the block speeds up; from Eq. (6.1), this also means that the total work W_{tot} done on the block is positive. The total work is *negative* in Fig. 6.8b because the net force opposes the displacement; in this case the block slows down. The net force is zero in Fig. 6.8c, so the speed of the block stays the same and the total work done on the block is zero. We can conclude that *when a particle undergoes a displacement, it speeds up if* $W_{tot} > 0$, *slows down if* $W_{tot} < 0$, *and maintains the same speed if* $W_{tot} = 0$.

Let's make these observations more quantitative. Consider a particle with mass m moving along the x-axis under the action of a constant net force with magnitude F directed along the positive x-axis (Fig. 6.9). The particle's acceleration is constant and given by Newton's second law, $F = ma_x$. Suppose the speed changes from v_1 to v_2 while the particle undergoes a displacement $s = x_2 - x_1$ from point x_1 to x_2. Using a constant-acceleration equation, Eq. (2.13), and replacing v_{0x} by v_1, v_x by v_2, and $(x - x_0)$ by s, we have

6.9 A constant net force $\vec{F}$ does work on a moving body.

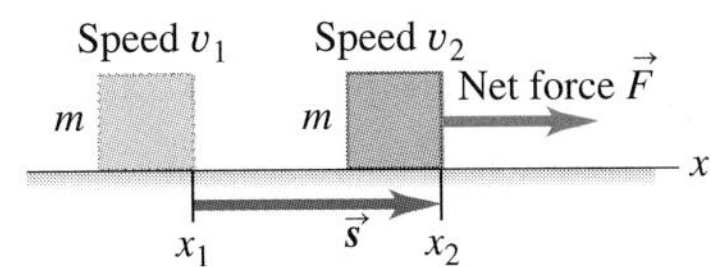

$$v_2^2 = v_1^2 + 2a_x s$$

$$a_x = \frac{v_2^2 - v_1^2}{2s}$$

When we multiply this equation by m and equate ma_x to the net force F, we find

$$F = ma_x = m\frac{v_2^2 - v_1^2}{2s} \quad \text{and}$$
$$Fs = \frac{1}{2}mv_2^2 - \frac{1}{2}mv_1^2 \qquad (6.4)$$

The product Fs is the work done by the net force F and thus is equal to the total work W_{tot} done by all the forces acting on the particle. The quantity $\frac{1}{2}mv^2$ is called the **kinetic energy** K of the particle:

$$K = \frac{1}{2}mv^2 \quad \text{(definition of kinetic energy)} \qquad (6.5)$$

Like work, the kinetic energy of a particle is a scalar quantity; it depends on only the particle's mass and speed, not its direction of motion (Fig. 6.10). A car (viewed as a particle) has the same kinetic energy when going north at 10 m/s as when going east at 10 m/s. Kinetic energy can never be negative, and it is zero only when the particle is at rest.

We can now interpret Eq. (6.4) in terms of work and kinetic energy. The first term on the right side of Eq. (6.4) is $K_2 = \frac{1}{2}mv_2^2$, the final kinetic energy of the particle (that is, after the displacement). The second term is the initial kinetic energy, $K_1 = \frac{1}{2}mv_1^2$, and the difference between these terms is the *change* in kinetic energy. So Eq. (6.4) says:

The work done by the net force on a particle equals the change in the particle's kinetic energy:

$$W_{tot} = K_2 - K_1 = \Delta K \quad \text{(work–energy theorem)} \qquad (6.6)$$

This result is the **work–energy theorem.**

6.10 Comparing the kinetic energy $K = \frac{1}{2}mv^2$ of different bodies.

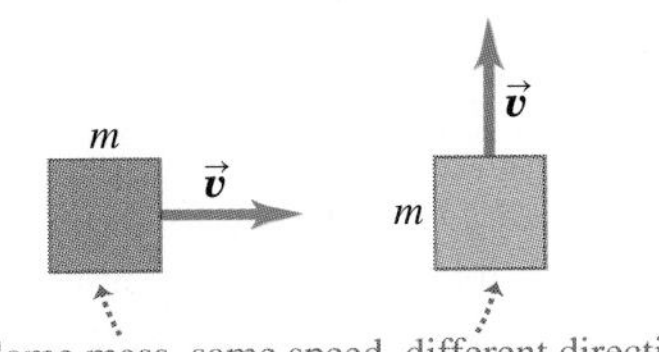

Same mass, same speed, different directions of motion: *same* kinetic energy

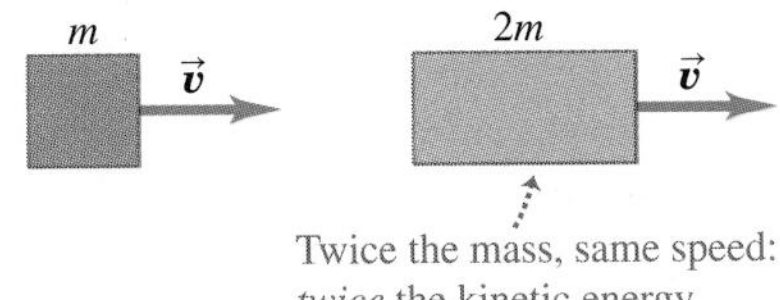

Twice the mass, same speed: *twice* the kinetic energy

m $\vec{v}$ m $2\vec{v}$

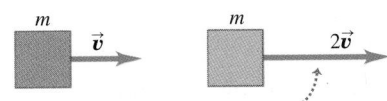

Same mass, twice the speed: *four times* the kinetic energy

The work–energy theorem agrees with our observations about the block in Fig. 6.8. When W_{tot} is *positive,* the kinetic energy *increases* (the final kinetic energy K_2 is greater than the initial kinetic energy K_1) and the particle is going faster at the end of the displacement than at the beginning. When W_{tot} is *negative,* the kinetic energy *decreases* $(K_2$ is less than $K_1)$ and the speed is less after the displacement. When $W_{tot} = 0$, the kinetic energy stays the same $(K_1 = K_2)$ and the speed is unchanged. Note that the work–energy theorem by itself tells us only about changes in *speed,* not velocity, since the kinetic energy doesn't depend on the direction of motion.

From Eq. (6.4) or (6.6), kinetic energy and work must have the same units. Hence the joule is the SI unit of both work and kinetic energy (and, as we will see later, of all kinds of energy). To verify this, note that in SI units the quantity $K = \frac{1}{2}mv^2$ has units $\text{kg} \cdot (\text{m/s})^2$ or $\text{kg} \cdot \text{m}^2/\text{s}^2$; we recall that $1\text{ N} = 1\text{ kg} \cdot \text{m/s}^2$, so

$$1\text{ J} = 1\text{ N} \cdot \text{m} = 1\ (\text{kg} \cdot \text{m/s}^2) \cdot \text{m} = 1\text{ kg} \cdot \text{m}^2/\text{s}^2$$

In the British system the unit of kinetic energy and of work is

$$1\text{ ft} \cdot \text{lb} = 1\text{ ft} \cdot \text{slug} \cdot \text{ft/s}^2 = 1\text{ slug} \cdot \text{ft}^2/\text{s}^2$$

Because we used Newton's laws in deriving the work–energy theorem, we can use this theorem only in an inertial frame of reference. Note also that the work–energy theorem is valid in *any* inertial frame, but the values of W_{tot} and $K_2 - K_1$ may differ from one inertial frame to another (because the displacement and speed of a body may be different in different frames).

We have derived the work–energy theorem for the special case of straight-line motion with constant forces, and in the following examples we'll apply it to this special case only. We'll find in the next section that the theorem is valid in general, even when the forces are not constant and the particle's trajectory is curved.

Problem-Solving Strategy 6.1 Work and Kinetic Energy

IDENTIFY *the relevant concepts:* The work–energy theorem, $W_{tot} = K_2 - K_1$, is extremely useful when you want to relate a body's speed v_1 at one point in its motion to its speed v_2 at a different point. (It's less useful for problems that involve the *time* it takes a body to go from point 1 to point 2, because the work–energy theorem doesn't involve time at all. For such problems it's usually best to use the relationships among time, position, velocity, and acceleration described in Chapters 2 and 3.)

SET UP *the problem* using the following steps:

1. Choose the initial and final positions of the body, and draw a free-body diagram showing all the forces that act on the body.
2. Choose a coordinate system. (If the motion is along a straight line, it's usually easiest to have both the initial and final positions lie along the x-axis.)
3. List the unknown and known quantities, and decide which unknowns are your target variables. The target variable may be the body's initial or final speed, the magnitude of one of the forces acting on the body, or the body's displacement.

EXECUTE *the solution:* Calculate the work W done by each force. If the force is constant and the displacement is a straight line, you can use Eq. (6.2) or (6.3). (Later in this chapter we'll see how to handle varying forces and curved trajectories.) Be sure to check signs; W must be positive if the force has a component in the direction of the displacement, negative if the force has a component opposite to the displacement, and zero if the force and displacement are perpendicular.

Add the amounts of work done by each force to find the total work W_{tot}. Sometimes it's easier to calculate the vector sum of the forces (the net force) and then find the work done by the net force; this value is also equal to W_{tot}.

Write expressions for the initial and final kinetic energies, K_1 and K_2. Note that kinetic energy involves *mass,* not *weight;* if you are given the body's weight, you'll need to use the relationship $w = mg$ to find the mass.

Finally, use $W_{tot} = K_2 - K_1$ to solve for the target variable. Remember that the right-hand side of this equation is the *final* kinetic energy minus the *initial* kinetic energy, never the other way around.

EVALUATE *your answer:* Check whether your answer makes physical sense. A key point to remember is that kinetic energy $K = \frac{1}{2}mv^2$ can never be negative. If you come up with a negative value of K, perhaps you interchanged the initial and final kinetic energies in $W_{tot} = K_2 - K_1$ or made a sign error in one of the work calculations.

Example 6.3 Using work and energy to calculate speed

Let's look again at the sled in Fig. 6.7 and the numbers at the end of Example 6.2. Suppose the initial speed v_1 is 2.0 m/s. What is the speed of the sled after it moves 20 m?

SOLUTION

IDENTIFY: We'll use the work–energy theorem, Eq. (6.6) $(W_{tot} = K_2 - K_1)$, since we are given the initial speed $v_1 = 2.0\text{ m/s}$ and want to find the final speed.

SET UP: Figure 6.11 shows our sketch of the situation. The motion is in the positive x-direction.

EXECUTE: In Example 6.2 we calculated the total work done by all the forces: $W_{tot} = 10\text{ kJ}$. Hence the kinetic energy of the sled and its load must increase by 10 kJ.

To write expressions for the initial and final kinetic energies, we need the mass of the sled and load. We are given that the *weight* is 14,700 N, so the mass is

$$m = \frac{w}{g} = \frac{14{,}700\text{ N}}{9.8\text{ m/s}^2} = 1500\text{ kg}$$

Then the initial kinetic energy K_1 is

$$K_1 = \frac{1}{2}mv_1^2 = \frac{1}{2}(1500\text{ kg})(2.0\text{ m/s})^2 = 3000\text{ kg}\cdot\text{m}^2/\text{s}^2$$
$$= 3000\text{ J}$$

The final kinetic energy K_2 is

$$K_2 = \frac{1}{2}mv_2^2 = \frac{1}{2}(1500\text{ kg})v_2^2$$

6.11 Our sketch for this problem.

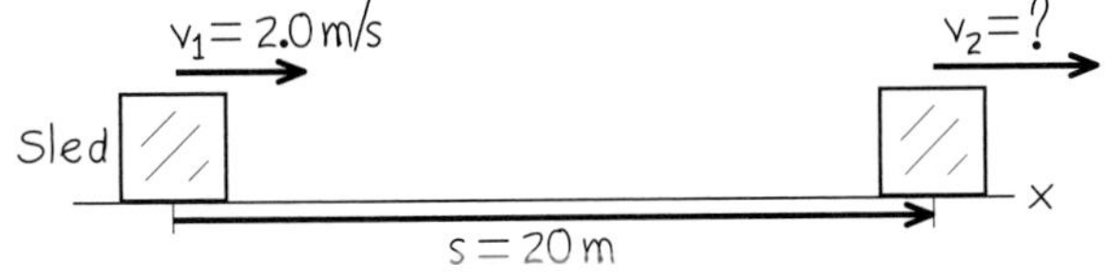

where v_2 is the unknown speed we want to find. Equation (6.6) gives

$$K_2 = K_1 + W_{tot} = 3000\text{ J} + 10{,}000\text{ J} = 13{,}000\text{ J}$$

Setting these two expressions for K_2 equal, substituting $1\text{ J} = 1\text{ kg}\cdot\text{m}^2/\text{s}^2$, and solving for v_2, we find

$$v_2 = 4.2\text{ m/s}$$

EVALUATE: The total work is positive, so the kinetic energy increases $(K_2 > K_1)$ and the speed increases $(v_2 > v_1)$.

This problem can also be done without the work–energy theorem. We can find the acceleration from $\sum\vec{F} = m\vec{a}$ and then use the equations of motion for constant acceleration to find v_2. Since the acceleration is along the x-axis,

$$a = a_x = \frac{\sum F_x}{m} = \frac{(5000\text{ N})\cos 36.9^\circ - 3500\text{ N}}{1500\text{ kg}}$$
$$= 0.333\text{ m/s}^2$$

Then, using Eq. (2.13),

$$v_2^2 = v_1^2 + 2as = (2.0\text{ m/s})^2 + 2(0.333\text{ m/s}^2)(20\text{ m})$$
$$= 17.3\text{ m}^2/\text{s}^2$$
$$v_2 = 4.2\text{ m/s}$$

This is the same result we obtained with the work–energy approach, but there we avoided the intermediate step of finding the acceleration. You will find several other examples in this chapter and the next that *can* be done without using energy considerations but that are easier when energy methods are used. When a problem can be done by two different methods, doing it by both methods (as we did in this example) is a very good way to check your work.

Example 6.4 Forces on a hammerhead

In a pile driver, a steel hammerhead with mass 200 kg is lifted 3.00 m above the top of a vertical I-beam being driven into the ground (Fig. 6.12a). The hammer is then dropped, driving the I-beam 7.4 cm farther into the ground. The vertical rails that guide the hammerhead exert a constant 60-N friction force on the hammerhead. Use the work–energy theorem to find (a) the speed of the hammerhead just as it hits the I-beam and (b) the average force the hammerhead exerts on the I-beam. Ignore the effects of the air.

SOLUTION

IDENTIFY: We'll use the work–energy theorem to relate the hammerhead's speed at different locations and the forces acting on it. There are *three* locations of interest: point 1, where the hammerhead starts from rest; point 2, where it first contacts the I-beam; and point 3, where the hammerhead comes to a halt (see Fig. 6.12a). The two unknowns are the hammerhead's speed at point 2 and the force the hammerhead exerts between points 2 and 3. Hence we'll apply the work–energy theorem twice: once for the motion from 1 to 2, and once for the motion from 2 to 3.

SET UP: Figure 6.12b shows the vertical forces on the hammerhead as it falls from point 1 to point 2. (We can ignore any horizontal forces that may be present because they do no work as the hammerhead moves vertically.) For this part of the motion, our target variable is the hammerhead's speed v_2.

Figure 6.12c shows the vertical forces on the hammerhead during the motion from point 2 to point 3. In addition to the forces shown in Fig. 6.12b, the I-beam exerts an upward normal force of magnitude n on the hammerhead. This force actually varies as the hammerhead comes to a halt, but for simplicity we'll treat n as a

Continued

constant. Hence n represents the *average* value of this upward force during the motion. Our target variable for this part of the motion is the force that the *hammerhead* exerts on the I-beam; it is the reaction force to the normal force exerted by the I-beam, so by Newton's third law its magnitude is also n.

EXECUTE: (a) From point 1 to point 2, the vertical forces are the downward weight $w = mg = (200\text{ kg})(9.8\text{ m/s}^2) = 1960\text{ N}$ and the upward friction force $f = 60\text{ N}$. Thus the net downward force is $w - f = 1900\text{ N}$. The displacement of the hammerhead from point 1 to point 2 is downward and equal to $s_{12} = 3.00\text{ m}$. The total work done on the hammerhead as it moves from point 1 to point 2 is then

$$W_{tot} = (w - f)s_{12} = (1900\text{ N})(3.00\text{ m}) = 5700\text{ J}$$

At point 1 the hammerhead is at rest, so its initial kinetic energy K_1 is zero. Hence the kinetic energy K_2 at point 2 equals the total work done on the hammerhead between points 1 and 2:

$$W_{tot} = K_2 - K_1 = K_2 - 0 = \frac{1}{2}mv_2^2 - 0$$

$$v_2 = \sqrt{\frac{2W_{tot}}{m}} = \sqrt{\frac{2(5700\text{ J})}{200\text{ kg}}} = 7.55\text{ m/s}$$

This is the hammerhead's speed at point 2, just as it hits the I-beam.

(b) As the hammerhead moves downward between points 2 and 3, the net downward force acting on it is $w - f - n$ (see Fig. 6.12c). The total work done on the hammerhead during this displacement is

$$W_{tot} = (w - f - n)s_{23}$$

The initial kinetic energy for this part of the motion is K_2, which from part (a) equals 5700 J. The final kinetic energy is $K_3 = 0$, since the hammerhead ends at rest. Then, from the work–energy theorem,

$$W_{tot} = (w - f - n)s_{23} = K_3 - K_2$$

$$n = w - f - \frac{K_3 - K_2}{s_{23}}$$

$$= 1960\text{ N} - 60\text{ N} - \frac{0\text{ J} - 5700\text{ J}}{0.074\text{ m}}$$

$$= 79{,}000\text{ N}$$

The downward force that the hammerhead exerts on the I-beam has this same magnitude, 79,000 N (about 9 tons)—more than 40 times the weight of the hammerhead.

EVALUATE: The net change in the hammerhead's kinetic energy from point 1 to point 3 is zero; a relatively small net force does positive work over a large distance, and then a much larger net force does negative work over a much smaller distance. The same thing happens if you speed up your car gradually and then drive it into a brick wall. The very large force needed to reduce the kinetic energy to zero over a short distance is what does the damage to your car—and possibly to you.

6.12 (a) A pile driver pounds an I-beam into the ground. (b), (c) Free-body diagrams. Vector lengths are not to scale.

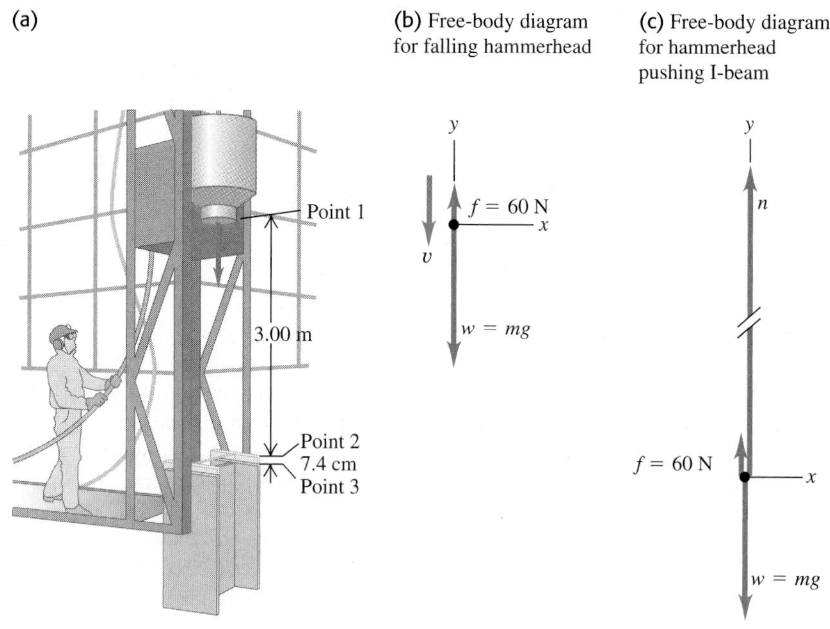

The Meaning of Kinetic Energy

Example 6.4 gives insight into the physical meaning of kinetic energy. The hammerhead is dropped from rest, and its kinetic energy when it hits the I-beam equals the total work done on it up to that point by the net force. This result is true in general: To accelerate a particle of mass m from rest (zero kinetic energy) up to a speed v, the total work done on it must equal the change in kinetic energy from zero to $K = \frac{1}{2}mv^2$:

$$W_{\text{tot}} = K - 0 = K$$

So *the kinetic energy of a particle is equal to the total work that was done to accelerate it from rest to its present speed* (Fig. 6.13). The definition $K = \frac{1}{2}mv^2$, Eq. (6.5), wasn't chosen at random; it's the *only* definition that agrees with this interpretation of kinetic energy.

In the second part of Example 6.4 the kinetic energy of the hammerhead did work on the I-beam and drove it into the ground. This gives us another interpretation of kinetic energy: *The kinetic energy of a particle is equal to the total work that particle can do in the process of being brought to rest.* This is why you pull your hand and arm backward when you catch a ball. As the ball comes to rest, it does an amount of work (force times distance) on your hand equal to the ball's initial kinetic energy. By pulling your hand back, you maximize the distance over which the force acts and so minimize the force on your hand.

6.13 When a billiards player hits a cue ball at rest, the ball's kinetic energy after being hit is equal to the work that was done on it by the cue. The greater the force exerted by the cue and the greater the distance the ball moves while in contact with it, the greater the ball's kinetic energy.

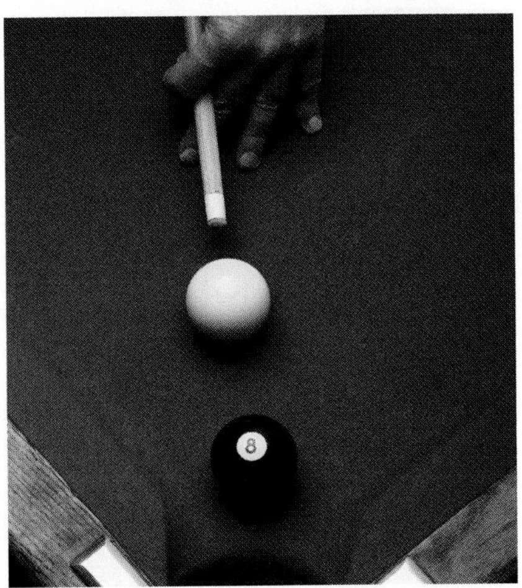

Conceptual Example 6.5 Comparing kinetic energies

Two iceboats like the one in Example 5.6 (Section 5.2) hold a race on a frictionless horizontal lake (Fig. 6.14). The two iceboats have masses m and $2m$. Each iceboat has an identical sail, so the wind exerts the same constant force $\vec{F}$ on each iceboat. The two iceboats start from rest and cross the finish line a distance s away. Which iceboat crosses the finish line with greater kinetic energy?

6.14 A race between iceboats.

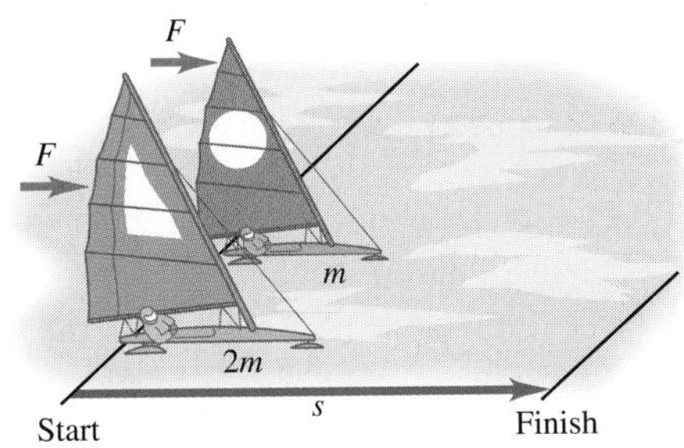

SOLUTION

If you use the mathematical definition of kinetic energy, $K = \frac{1}{2}mv^2$, Eq. (6.5), the answer to this problem isn't immediately obvious. The iceboat of mass $2m$ has greater mass, so you might guess that the larger iceboat attains a greater kinetic energy at the finish line. But the smaller iceboat, of mass m, crosses the finish line with a greater speed, and you might guess that *this* iceboat has the greater kinetic energy. How can we decide?

The correct way to approach this problem is to remember that *the kinetic energy of a particle is equal to the total work done to accelerate it from rest.* Both iceboats travel the same distance s, and only the horizontal force F in the direction of motion does work on either iceboat. Hence the total work done between the starting line and the finish line is the *same* for each iceboat, $W_{\text{tot}} = Fs$. At the finish line, each iceboat has a kinetic energy equal to the work W_{tot} done on it, because each iceboat started from rest. So both iceboats have the *same* kinetic energy at the finish line!

You might think this is a "trick" question, but it isn't. If you really understand the physical meanings of quantities such as kinetic energy, you can solve problems more easily and with better insight into the physics.

Notice that we didn't need to say anything about how much time each iceboat took to reach the finish line. This is because the work–energy theorem makes no direct reference to time, only to displacement. In fact, the iceboat of mass m takes less time to reach the finish line than does the larger iceboat of mass $2m$ because it has a greater acceleration.

Work and Kinetic Energy in Composite Systems

In this section we've been careful to apply the work–energy theorem only to bodies that we can represent as *particles*—that is, as moving point masses. New subtleties appear for more complex systems that have to be represented as many particles with different motions. We can't go into these subtleties in detail in this chapter, but here's an example.

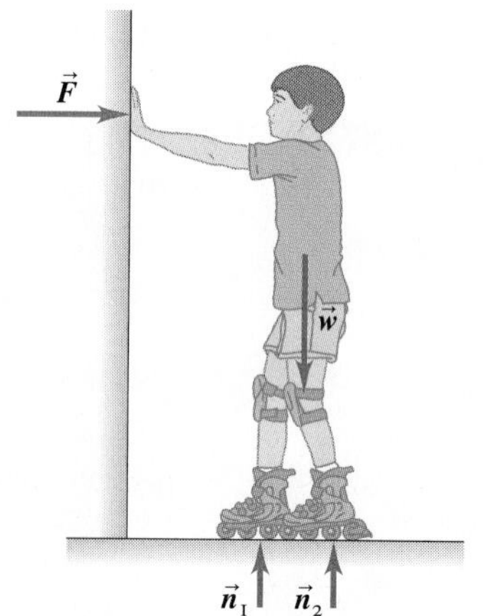

6.15 The external forces acting on a skater pushing off a wall. The work done by these forces is zero, but the skater's kinetic energy changes nonetheless.

Suppose a boy stands on frictionless roller skates on a level surface, facing a rigid wall (Fig. 6.15). He pushes against the wall, which makes him move to the right. The forces acting on him are his weight $\vec{w}$, the upward normal forces $\vec{n}_1$ and $\vec{n}_2$ exerted by the ground on his skates, and the horizontal force $\vec{F}$ exerted on him by the wall. There is no vertical displacement, so $\vec{w}, \vec{n}_1$, and $\vec{n}_2$ do no work. Force $\vec{F}$ accelerates him to the right, but the parts of his body where that force is applied (the man's hands) do not move while the force acts. Thus the force $\vec{F}$ also does no work. Where, then, does the boy's kinetic energy come from?

The explanation is that it's not adequate to represent the boy as a single point mass. Different parts of the boy's body have different motions; his hands remain stationary against the wall while his torso is moving away from the wall. The various parts of his body interact with each other, and one part can exert forces and do work on another part. Therefore the *total* kinetic energy of this *composite* system of body parts can change, even though no work is done by forces applied by bodies (such as the wall) that are outside the system. In Chapter 8 we'll consider further the motion of a collection of particles that interact with each other. We'll discover that just as for the boy in this example, the total kinetic energy of such a system can change even when no work is done on any part of the system by anything outside it.

Test Your Understanding of Section 6.2 Rank the following bodies in order of their kinetic energy, from least to greatest. (i) a 2.0-kg body moving at 5.0 m/s; (ii) a 1.0 kg body that initially was at rest and then had 30 J of work done on it; (iii) a 1.0-kg body that initially was moving at 4.0 m/s and then had 20 J of work done on it; (iv) a 2.0 kg body that initially was moving at 10 m/s and then did 80 J of work on another body.

6.16 Calculating the work done by a varying force F_x in the x-direction as a particle moves from x_1 to x_2.

(a) Particle moving from x_1 to x_2 in response to a changing force in the x-direction

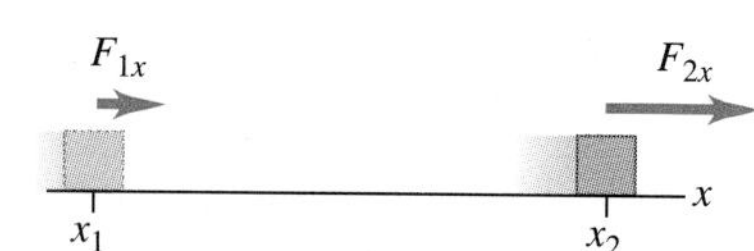

(b)

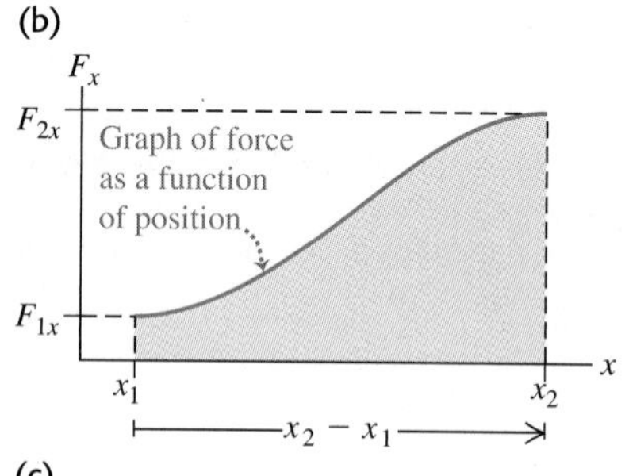

(c)

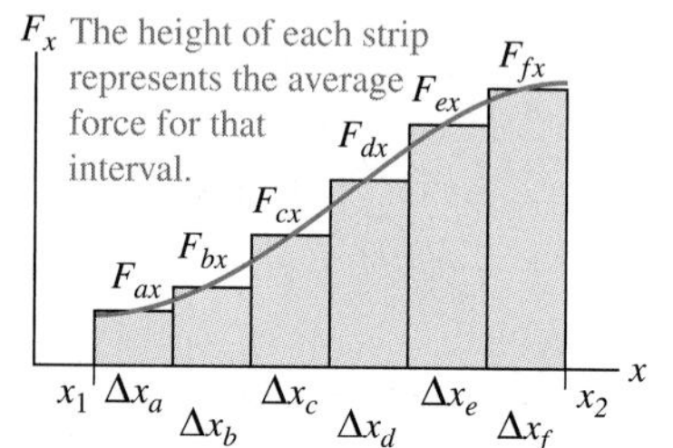

6.3 Work and Energy with Varying Forces

So far in this chapter we've considered work done by *constant forces* only. But what happens when you stretch a spring? The more you stretch it, the harder you have to pull, so the force you exert is *not* constant as the spring is stretched. We've also restricted our discussion to *straight-line* motion. There are many situations in which a body moves along a curved path and is acted on by a force that varies in magnitude, direction, or both. We need to be able to compute the work done by the force in these more general cases. Fortunately, we'll find that the work–energy theorem holds true even when varying forces are considered and when the body's path is not straight.

Work Done by a Varying Force, Straight-Line Motion

To add only one complication at a time, let's consider straight-line motion along the x-axis with a force whose x-component F_x may change as the body moves. (A real-life example is driving a car along a straight road with stop signs, so the driver has to alternately step on the gas and apply the brakes.) Suppose a particle moves along the x-axis from point x_1 to x_2 (Fig. 6.16a). Figure 6.16b is a graph of the x-component of force as a function of the particle's coordinate x. To find the work done by this force, we divide the total displacement into small segments Δx_a, Δx_b, and so on (Fig. 6.16c). We approximate the work done by the force during segment Δx_a as the average x-component of force F_{ax} in that segment multiplied by the x-displacement Δx_a. We do this for each segment and then add the results for all the segments. The work done by the force in the total displacement from x_1 to x_2 is approximately

$$W = F_{ax}\Delta x_a + F_{bx}\Delta x_b + \cdots$$

In the limit that the number of segments becomes very large and the width of each becomes very small, this sum becomes the *integral* of F_x from x_1 to x_2:

$$W = \int_{x_1}^{x_2} F_x\,dx \qquad \text{(varying } x\text{-component of force, straight-line displacement)} \tag{6.7}$$

Note that $F_{ax}\Delta x_a$ represents the *area* of the first vertical strip in Fig. 6.16c and that the integral in Eq. (6.7) represents the area under the curve of Fig. 6.16b between x_1 and x_2. *On a graph of force as a function of position, the total work done by the force is represented by the area under the curve between the initial and final positions.* An alternative interpretation of Eq. (6.7) is that the work W equals the average force that acts over the entire displacement, multiplied by the displacement.

In the special case that F_x, the x-component of the force, is constant, it may be taken outside the integral in Eq. (6.7):

$$W = \int_{x_1}^{x_2} F_x\,dx = F_x\int_{x_1}^{x_2} dx = F_x(x_2 - x_1) \qquad \text{(constant force)}$$

But $x_2 - x_1 = s$, the total displacement of the particle. So in the case of a constant force F, Eq. (6.7) says that $W = Fs$, in agreement with Eq. (6.1). The interpretation of work as the area under the curve of F_x as a function of x also holds for a constant force; $W = Fs$ is the area of a rectangle of height F and width s (Fig. 6.17).

6.17 The work done by a constant force F in the x-direction as a particle moves from x_1 to x_2.

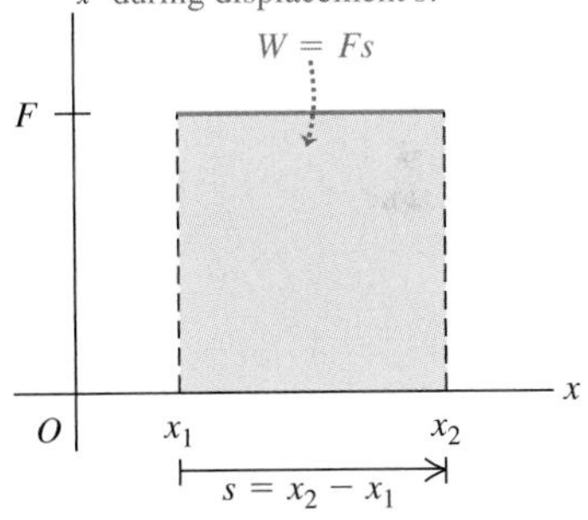
The rectangular area under the graph represents the work done by the constant force of magnitude F during displacement s:
W = Fs
Fx
F
O
x1
x2
x
s = x2 − x1

Now let's apply these ideas to the stretched spring. To keep a spring stretched beyond its unstretched length by an amount x, we have to apply a force of equal magnitude at each end (Fig. 6.18). If the elongation x is not too great, the force we apply to the right-hand end has an x-component directly proportional to x:

$$F_x = kx \qquad \text{(force required to stretch a spring)} \tag{6.8}$$

where k is a constant called the **force constant** (or spring constant) of the spring. The units of k are force divided by distance: N/m in SI units and lb/ft in British units. A floppy toy spring such as a Slinky™ has a force constant of about 1 N/m; for the much stiffer springs in an automobile's suspension, k is about 10^5 N/m. The observation that force is directly proportional to elongation for elongations that are not too great was made by Robert Hooke in 1678 and is known as **Hooke's law.** It really shouldn't be called a "law," since it's a statement about a specific device and not a fundamental law of nature. Real springs don't always obey Eq. (6.8) precisely, but it's still a useful idealized model. We'll discuss Hooke's law more fully in Chapter 11.

6.18 The force needed to stretch an ideal spring is proportional to the spring's elongation: $F_x = kx$.

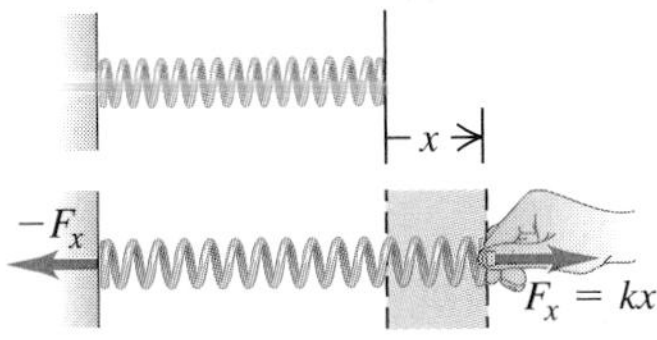
x
−Fx
Fx = kx

To stretch a spring, we must do work. We apply equal and opposite forces to the ends of the spring and gradually increase the forces. We hold the left end stationary, so the force we apply at this end does no work. The force at the moving end *does* do work. Figure 6.19 is a graph of F_x as a function of x, the elongation of the spring. The work done by this force when the elongation goes from zero to a maximum value X is

$$W = \int_0^X F_x\,dx = \int_0^X kx\,dx = \frac{1}{2}kX^2 \tag{6.9}$$

We can also obtain this result graphically. The area of the shaded triangle in Fig. 6.19, representing the total work done by the force, is equal to half the product of the base and altitude, or

$$W = \frac{1}{2}(X)(kX) = \frac{1}{2}kX^2$$

6.19 Calculating the work done to stretch a spring by a length X.

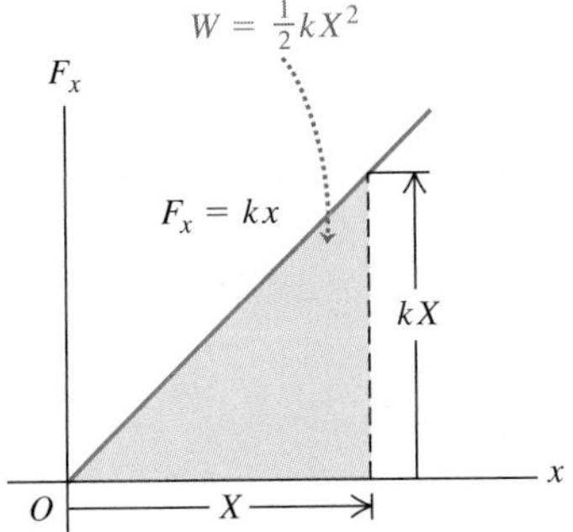
The area under the graph represents the work done on the spring as the spring is stretched from x = 0 to a maximum value X:
W = ½kX²
Fx
Fx = kx
kX
O
X
x

6.20 Calculating the work done to stretch a spring from one extension to a greater one.

(a) Stretching a spring from elongation x_1 to elongation x_2

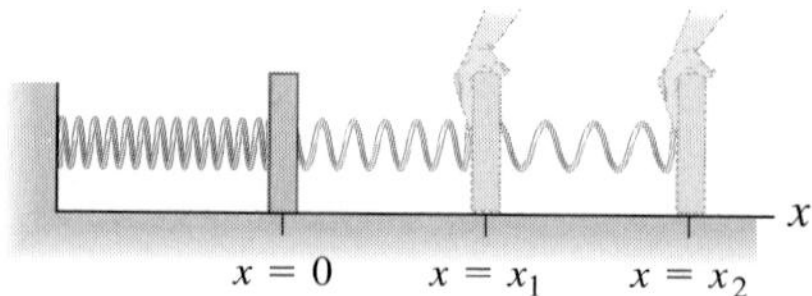

(b) Force-versus-distance graph

The trapezoidal area under the graph represents the work done on the spring to stretch it from $x = x_1$ to $x = x_2$: $W = \frac{1}{2}kx_2^2 - \frac{1}{2}kx_1^2$

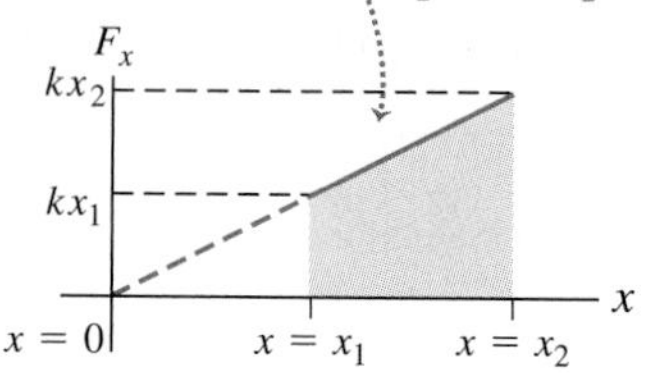

This equation also says that the work is the *average* force $kX/2$ multiplied by the total displacement X. We see that the total work is proportional to the *square* of the final elongation X. To stretch an ideal spring by 2 cm, you must do four times as much work as is needed to stretch it by 1 cm.

Equation (6.9) assumes that the spring was originally unstretched. If initially the spring is already stretched a distance x_1, the work we must do to stretch it to a greater elongation x_2 (Fig. 6.20a) is

$$W = \int_{x_1}^{x_2} F_x\,dx = \int_{x_1}^{x_2} kx\,dx = \frac{1}{2}kx_2^2 - \frac{1}{2}kx_1^2 \tag{6.10}$$

You should use your knowledge of geometry to convince yourself that the trapezoidal area under the graph in Fig. 6.20b is given by the expression in Eq. (6.10).

If the spring has spaces between the coils when it is unstretched, then it can also be compressed, and Hooke's law holds for compression as well as stretching. In this case the force and displacement are in the opposite directions from those shown in Fig. 6.18, and so F_x and x in Eq. (6.8) are both negative. Since both F_x and x are reversed, the force again is in the same direction as the displacement, and the work done by F_x is again positive. So the total work is still given by Eq. (6.9) or (6.10), even when X is negative or either or both of x_1 and x_2 are negative.

CAUTION **Work done *on* a spring vs. work done *by* a spring** Note that Eq. (6.10) gives the work that *you* must do *on* a spring to change its length. For example, if you stretch a spring that's originally relaxed, then $x_1 = 0$, $x_2 > 0$, and $W > 0$: The force you apply to one end of the spring is in the same direction as the displacement, and the work you do is positive. By contrast, the work that the *spring* does on whatever it's attached to is given by the *negative* of Eq. (6.10). Thus, as you pull on the spring, the spring does negative work on you. Paying careful attention to the sign of work will eliminate confusion later on!

Example 6.6 Work done on a spring scale

A woman weighing 600 N steps on a bathroom scale containing a stiff spring (Fig. 6.21). In equilibrium the spring is compressed 1.0 cm under her weight. Find the force constant of the spring and the total work done on it during the compression.

SOLUTION

IDENTIFY: In equilibrium the upward force exerted by the spring balances the downward force of the woman's weight. We'll use this principle and Eq. (6.8) to determine the force constant k, and we'll use Eq. (6.10) to calculate the work W that the woman does on the spring to compress it.

SET UP: We take positive values of x to correspond to elongation (upward in Fig. 6.21), so that the displacement of the spring (x) and the x-component of the force that the woman exerts on it (F_x) are both negative.

EXECUTE: The top of the spring is displaced by $x = -1.0\text{ cm} = -0.010\text{ m}$, and the woman exerts a force $F_x = -600\text{ N}$ on the spring. From Eq. (6.8) the force constant is

$$k = \frac{F_x}{x} = \frac{-600\text{ N}}{-0.010\text{ m}} = 6.0 \times 10^4\text{ N/m}$$

Then, using $x_1 = 0$ and $x_2 = -0.010\text{ m}$ in Eq. (6.10),

$$W = \frac{1}{2}kx_2^2 - \frac{1}{2}kx_1^2$$
$$= \frac{1}{2}(6.0 \times 10^4\text{ N/m})(-0.010\text{ m})^2 - 0 = 3.0\text{ J}$$

EVALUATE: The applied force and the displacement of the end of the spring were in the same direction, so the work done must have been positive—just as we found. Our arbitrary choice of the positive direction has no effect on the answer for W. (You can test this by taking the positive x-direction to be downward, corresponding to compression. You'll get the same values for k and W.)

6.21 Compressing a spring in a bathroom scale.

Because of our choice of axis, both the force component and displacement are negative. The work *on* the spring is positive.

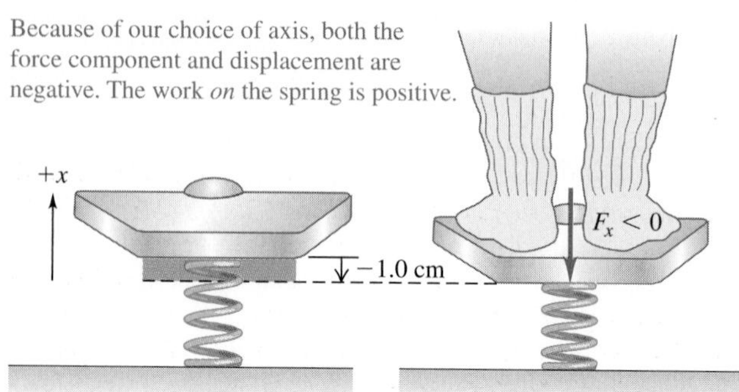

Work–Energy Theorem for Straight-Line Motion, Varying Forces

In Section 6.2 we derived the work–energy theorem, $W_{tot} = K_2 - K_1$, for the special case of straight-line motion with a constant net force. We can now prove that this theorem is true even when the force varies with position. As in Section 6.2, let's consider a particle that undergoes a displacement x while being acted on by a net force with x-component F_x, which we now allow to vary. Just as in Fig. 6.16, we divide the total displacement x into a large number of small segments Δx. We can apply the work–energy theorem, Eq. (6.6), to each segment because the value of F_x in each small segment is approximately constant. The change in kinetic energy in segment Δx_a is equal to the work $F_{ax}\Delta x_a$, and so on. The total change of kinetic energy is the sum of the changes in the individual segments, and thus is equal to the total work done on the particle during the entire displacement. So $W_{tot} = \Delta K$ holds for varying forces as well as for constant ones.

Here's an alternative derivation of the work–energy theorem for a force that may vary with position. It involves making a change of variable from x to v_x in the work integral. As a preliminary, we note that the acceleration a of the particle can be expressed in various ways, using $a_x = dv_x/dt$, $v_x = dx/dt$, and the chain rule for derivatives:

$$a_x = \frac{dv_x}{dt} = \frac{dv_x}{dx}\frac{dx}{dt} = v_x\frac{dv_x}{dx} \tag{6.11}$$

From this result, Eq. (6.7) tells us that the total work done by the *net* force F_x is

$$W_{tot} = \int_{x_1}^{x_2} F_x\,dx = \int_{x_1}^{x_2} ma_x\,dx = \int_{x_1}^{x_2} mv_x\frac{dv_x}{dx}\,dx \tag{6.12}$$

Now $(dv_x/dx)\,dx$ is the change in velocity dv_x during the displacement dx, so in Eq. (6.12) we can substitute dv_x for $(dv_x/dx)\,dx$. This changes the integration variable from x to v_x, so we change the limits from x_1 and x_2 to the corresponding x-velocities v_1 and v_2 at these points. This gives us

$$W_{tot} = \int_{v_1}^{v_2} mv_x\,dv_x$$

The integral of $v_x\,dv_x$ is just $v_x^2/2$. Substituting the upper and lower limits, we finally find

$$W_{tot} = \frac{1}{2}mv_2^2 - \frac{1}{2}mv_1^2 \tag{6.13}$$

This is the same as Eq. (6.6), so the work–energy theorem is valid even without the assumption that the net force is constant.

Example 6.7 Motion with a varying force

An air-track glider of mass 0.100 kg is attached to the end of a horizontal air track by a spring with force constant 20.0 N/m (Fig. 6.22a). Initially the spring is unstretched and the glider is moving at 1.50 m/s to the right. Find the maximum distance d that the glider moves to the right (a) if the air track is turned on so that there is no friction, and (b) if the air is turned off so that there is kinetic friction with coefficient $\mu_k = 0.47$.

SOLUTION

IDENTIFY: The force exerted by the spring is not constant, so we *cannot* use the constant-acceleration formulas of Chapter 2 to solve this problem. Instead, we'll use the work–energy theorem, which involves the distance moved (our target variable) through the formula for work.

SET UP: In Figs. 6.22b and 6.22c we chose the positive x-direction to be to the right (in the direction of the glider's motion). We take $x = 0$ at the glider's initial position (where the spring is unstretched) and $x = d$ (the target variable) at the position where the glider stops. The motion is purely horizontal, so only the horizontal forces do work. Note that Eq. (6.10) gives the work done *on* the spring as it stretches, but to use the work–energy theorem we

Continued

6.22 (a) A glider attached to an air track by a spring. (b), (c) Our free-body diagrams.

(a)

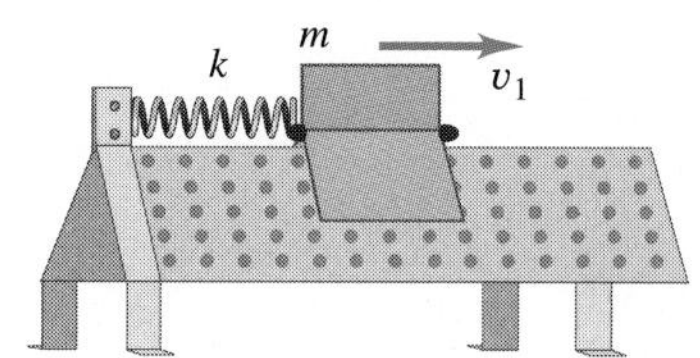

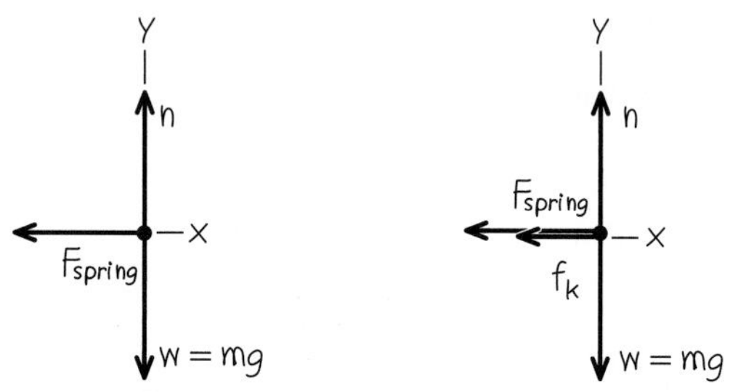

need the work done *by* the spring *on* the glider—which is the negative of Eq. (6.10).

EXECUTE: (a) As the glider moves from $x_1 = 0$ to $x_2 = d$, it does an amount of work on the spring given by Eq. (6.10): $W = \frac{1}{2}kd^2 - \frac{1}{2}k(0)^2 = \frac{1}{2}kd^2$. The amount of work that the spring does on the glider is the negative of this value, or $-\frac{1}{2}kd^2$. The spring stretches until the glider comes instantaneously to rest, so the final kinetic energy K_2 is zero. The initial kinetic energy is $\frac{1}{2}mv_1{}^2$, where $v_1 = 1.50\text{ m/s}$ is the glider's initial speed. Using the work–energy theorem, we find

$$-\frac{1}{2}kd^2 = 0 - \frac{1}{2}mv_1{}^2$$

We solve for the distance d the glider moves:

$$d = v_1\sqrt{\frac{m}{k}} = (1.50\text{ m/s})\sqrt{\frac{0.100\text{ kg}}{20.0\text{ N/m}}}$$
$$= 0.106\text{ m} = 10.6\text{ cm}$$

The stretched spring subsequently pulls the glider back to the left, so the glider is at rest only instantaneously.

(b) If the air is turned off, we must also include the work done by the constant force of kinetic friction. The normal force n is equal in magnitude to the weight of the glider, since the track is horizontal and there are no other vertical forces. Hence the magnitude of the kinetic friction force is $f_k = \mu_k n = \mu_k mg$. The friction force is directed opposite to the displacement, so the work done by friction is

$$W_{fric} = f_k d\cos 180° = -f_k d = -\mu_k mgd$$

The total work is the sum of W_{fric} and the work done by the spring, $-\frac{1}{2}kd^2$. The work–energy theorem then says that

$$-\mu_k mgd - \frac{1}{2}kd^2 = 0 - \frac{1}{2}mv_1{}^2$$

$$-(0.47)(0.100\text{ kg})(9.8\text{ m/s}^2)d - \frac{1}{2}(20.0\text{ N/m})d^2$$
$$= -\frac{1}{2}(0.100\text{ kg})(1.50\text{ m/s})^2$$
$$(10.0\text{ N/m})d^2 + (0.461\text{ N})d - (0.113\text{ N}\cdot\text{m}) = 0$$

This is a quadratic equation for d. The solutions are

$$d = \frac{-(0.461\text{ N}) \pm \sqrt{(0.461\text{ N})^2 - 4(10.0\text{ N/m})(-0.113\text{ N}\cdot\text{m})}}{2(10.0\text{ N/m})}$$
$$= 0.086\text{ m} \quad\text{or}\quad -0.132\text{ m}$$

We have used d as the symbol for a positive displacement, so only the positive value of d makes sense. Thus with friction the glider moves a distance

$$d = 0.086\text{ m} = 8.6\text{ cm}$$

EVALUATE: With friction present, the glider goes a shorter distance and the spring stretches less, as you might expect. Again the glider stops instantaneously, and again the spring force pulls the glider to the left; whether it moves or not depends on how great the *static* friction force is. How large would the coefficient of static friction μ_s have to be to keep the glider from springing back to the left?

Work–Energy Theorem for Motion Along a Curve

We can generalize our definition of work further to include a force that varies in direction as well as magnitude, and a displacement that lies along a curved path. Suppose a particle moves from point P_1 to P_2 along a curve, as shown in Fig. 6.23a. We divide the portion of the curve between these points into many infinitesimal vector displacements, and we call a typical one of these $d\vec{l}$. Each $d\vec{l}$ is tangent to the path at its position. Let $\vec{F}$ be the force at a typical point along the path, and let ϕ be the angle between $\vec{F}$ and $d\vec{l}$ at this point. Then the small element of work dW done on the particle during the displacement $d\vec{l}$ may be written as

$$dW = F\cos\phi\, dl = F_{\parallel}\, dl = \vec{F}\cdot d\vec{l}$$

where $F_{\parallel} = F\cos\phi$ is the component of $\vec{F}$ in the direction parallel to $d\vec{l}$ (Fig. 6.23b). The total work done by $\vec{F}$ on the particle as it moves from P_1 to P_2 is then

$$W = \int_{P_1}^{P_2} F\cos\phi\, dl = \int_{P_1}^{P_2} F_{\parallel}\, dl = \int_{P_1}^{P_2} \vec{F}\cdot d\vec{l} \quad \text{(work done on a curved path)} \quad (6.14)$$

We can now show that the work–energy theorem, Eq. (6.6), holds true even with varying forces and a displacement along a curved path. The force $\vec{F}$ is essentially constant over any given infinitesimal segment $d\vec{l}$ of the path, so we can apply the work–energy theorem for straight-line motion to that segment. Thus the change in the particle's kinetic energy K over that segment equals the work $dW = F_{\parallel}\, dl = \vec{F}\cdot d\vec{l}$ done on the particle. Adding up these infinitesimal quantities of work from all the segments along the whole path gives the total work done, Eq. (6.14), which equals the total change in kinetic energy over the whole path. So $W_{tot} = \Delta K = K_2 - K_1$ is true *in general,* no matter what the path and no matter what the character of the forces. This can be proved more rigorously by using steps like those in Eqs. (6.11) through (6.13) (see Challenge Problem 6.104).

Note that only the component of the net force parallel to the path, $F_{\parallel}$, does work on the particle, so only this component can change the speed and kinetic energy of the particle. The component perpendicular to the path, $F_{\perp} = F\sin\phi$, has no effect on the particle's speed; it acts only to change the particle's direction.

The integral in Eq. (6.14) is called a *line integral.* To evaluate this integral in a specific problem, we need some sort of detailed description of the path and of the way in which $\vec{F}$ varies along the path. We usually express the line integral in terms of some scalar variable, as in the following example.

6.23 A particle moves along a curved path from point P_1 to P_2, acted on by a force $\vec{F}$ that varies in magnitude and direction.

(a)

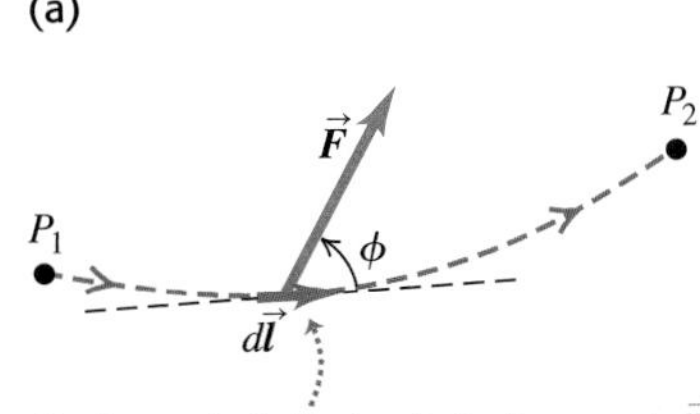

During an infinitesimal displacement $d\vec{l}$, the force $\vec{F}$ does work dW on the particle: $dW = \vec{F}\cdot d\vec{l} = F\cos\phi\, dl$

(b)

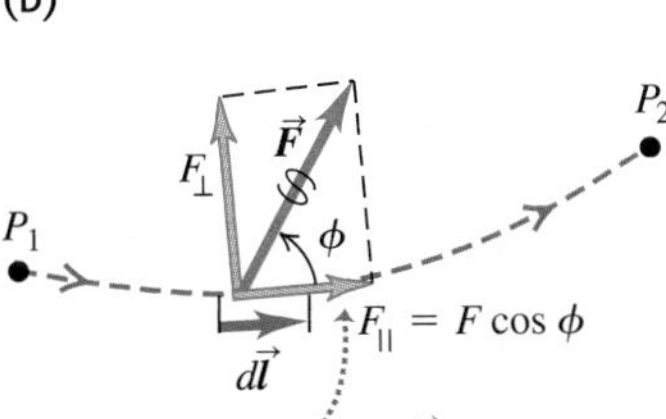

Only the component of $\vec{F}$ parallel to the displacement, $F_{\parallel} = F\cos\phi$, contributes to the work done by $\vec{F}$.

Example 6.8 Motion on a curved path I

At a family picnic you are appointed to push your obnoxious cousin Throckmorton in a swing (Fig. 6.24a). His weight is w, the length of the chains is R, and you push Throcky until the chains make an angle θ_0 with the vertical. To do this, you exert a varying horizontal force $\vec{F}$ that starts at zero and gradually increases just enough so that Throcky and the swing move very slowly and remain very nearly in equilibrium. What is the total work done on Throcky by all forces? What is the work done by the tension T in the chains? What is the work you do by exerting the force $\vec{F}$? (Neglect the weight of the chains and seat.)

SOLUTION

IDENTIFY: The motion is along a curve, so we will use Eq. (6.14) to calculate the work done by the net force, by the tension force, and by the force $\vec{F}$.

SET UP: Figure 6.24b shows our free-body diagram and coordinate system. We have replaced the tensions in the two chains with a single tension T.

EXECUTE: There are two ways to find the total work done during the motion: (1) by calculating the work done by each force and then adding the quantities of work together, and (2) by calculating the work done by the net force. The second approach is far easier in this situation because Throcky is in equilibrium at every point. Hence the net force on him is zero, the integral of the net force in Eq. (6.14) is zero, and the total work done on him by all forces is zero.

6.24 (a) Pushing cousin Throckmorton in a swing. (b) Our free-body diagram.

(a)

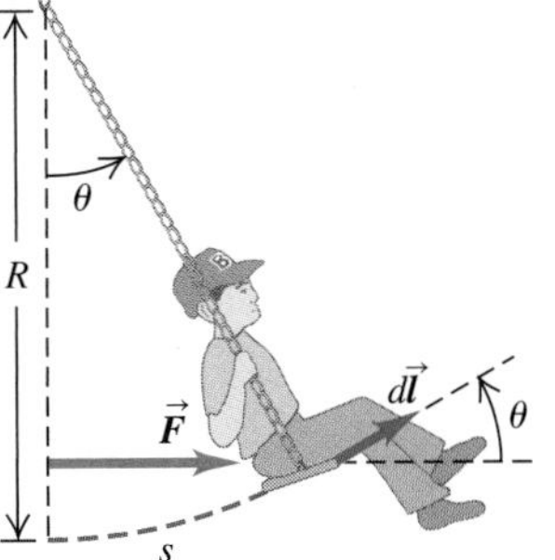

(b) Free-body diagram for Throckmorton (neglecting the weight of the chains and seat)

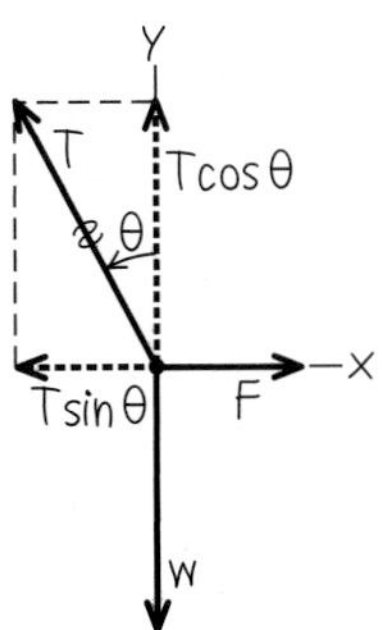

It's also easy to find the work done by the chain tension on Throcky because this force is perpendicular to the direction of motion at all points along the path. Hence at all points the angle between the chain tension and the displacement vector $d\vec{l}$ is 90° and the scalar product in Eq. (6.14) is zero. Thus the chain tension does zero work.

Continued

To compute the work done by $\vec{F}$, we need to know how this force varies with the angle θ. The net force on Throcky is zero, so $\sum F_x = 0$ and $\sum F_y = 0$. From Fig. 6.24b, we get

$$\sum F_x = F + (-T\sin\theta) = 0$$
$$\sum F_y = T\cos\theta + (-w) = 0$$

By eliminating T from these two equations, we obtain

$$F = w\tan\theta$$

The point where $\vec{F}$ is applied swings through the arc s. The arc length s equals the radius R of the circular path multiplied by the length θ (in radians), so $s = R\theta$. Therefore the displacement $d\vec{l}$ corresponding to a small change of angle $d\theta$ has a magnitude $dl = ds = R\,d\theta$. The work done by $\vec{F}$ is

$$W = \int \vec{F}\cdot d\vec{l} = \int F\cos\theta\, ds$$

Now we express everything in terms of the angle θ, whose value increases from 0 to θ_0:

$$W = \int_0^{\theta_0} (w\tan\theta)\cos\theta\,(R\,d\theta) = wR\int_0^{\theta_0}\sin\theta\,d\theta$$
$$= wR(1 - \cos\theta_0)$$

EVALUATE: If $\theta_0 = 0$, there is no displacement; then $\cos\theta_0 = 1$ and $W = 0$, as we should expect. If $\theta_0 = 90°$, then $\cos\theta_0 = 0$ and $W = wR$. In that case the work you do is the same as if you had lifted Throcky straight up a distance R with a force equal to his weight w. In fact, the quantity $R(1 - \cos\theta_0)$ is the increase in his height above the ground during the displacement, so for any value of θ_0 the work done by the force $\vec{F}$ is the change in height multiplied by the weight. This is an example of a more general result that we'll prove in Section 7.1.

Example 6.9 Motion on a curved path II

In Example 6.8 the infinitesimal displacement $d\vec{l}$ (Fig. 6.24a) has a magnitude of ds, an x-component of $ds\cos\theta$, and a y-component of $ds\sin\theta$. Hence $d\vec{l} = \hat{\imath}\,ds\cos\theta + \hat{\jmath}\,ds\sin\theta$. Use this expression and Eq. (6.14) to calculate the work done during the motion by the chain tension, by the force of gravity, and by the force $\vec{F}$.

SOLUTION

IDENTIFY: We again use Eq. (6.14), but now we'll use Eq. (1.21) to find the scalar product in terms of components.

SET UP: We use the same free-body diagram, Fig. 6.24b, as in Example 6.8.

EXECUTE: From Fig. 6.24b, we can write the three forces in terms of unit vectors:

$$\vec{T} = \hat{\imath}(-T\sin\theta) + \hat{\jmath}T\cos\theta$$
$$\vec{w} = \hat{\jmath}(-w)$$
$$\vec{F} = \hat{\imath}F$$

To use Eq. (6.14), we must calculate the scalar product of each of these forces with $d\vec{l}$. Using Eq. (1.21),

$$\vec{T}\cdot d\vec{l} = (-T\sin\theta)(ds\cos\theta) + (T\cos\theta)(ds\sin\theta) = 0$$
$$\vec{w}\cdot d\vec{l} = (-w)(ds\sin\theta) = -w\sin\theta\,ds$$
$$\vec{F}\cdot d\vec{l} = F(ds\cos\theta) = F\cos\theta\,ds$$

Since $\vec{T}\cdot d\vec{l} = 0$, the integral of this quantity is zero and the work done by the chain tension is zero (just as we found in Example 6.8). Using $ds = R\,d\theta$ as in Example 6.8, we find the work done by the force of gravity is

$$\int \vec{w}\cdot d\vec{l} = \int(-w\sin\theta)\,R\,d\theta = -wR\int_0^{\theta_0}\sin\theta\,d\theta$$
$$= -wR(1 - \cos\theta_0)$$

The work done by gravity is negative because gravity pulls down while Throcky moves upward. Finally, the work done by the force $\vec{F}$ is the integral $\int\vec{F}\cdot d\vec{l} = \int F\cos\theta\,ds$, which we calculated in Example 6.8; the answer is $+wR(1 - \cos\theta_0)$.

EVALUATE: As a check on our answers, note that the sum of all three quantities of work is zero. This is just what we concluded in Example 6.8 using the work–energy theorem.

The method of components is often the most convenient way to calculate scalar products. Use it when it makes your life easier!

Test Your Understanding of Section 6.3 In Example 5.21 (Section 5.4) we examined a conical pendulum. The speed of the pendulum bob remains constant as it travels around the circle shown in Fig. 5.32a. (a) Over one complete circle, how much work does the tension force F do on the bob? (i) a positive amount; (ii) a negative amount; (iii) zero. (b) Over one complete circle, how much work does the weight do on the bob? (i) a positive amount; (ii) a negative amount; (iii) zero. MP

6.4 Power

The definition of work makes no reference to the passage of time. If you lift a barbell weighing 100 N through a vertical distance of 1.0 m at constant velocity, you do $(100\ \text{N})(1.0\ \text{m}) = 100\ \text{J}$ of work whether it takes you 1 second, 1 hour, or 1 year to do it. But often we need to know how quickly work is done. We describe this in terms of *power*. In ordinary conversation the word "power" is often synonymous with "energy" or "force." In physics we use a much more precise definition: **Power** is the time *rate* at which work is done. Like work and energy, power is a scalar quantity.

When a quantity of work ΔW is done during a time interval Δt, the average work done per unit time or **average power** P_{av} is defined to be

$$P_{av} = \frac{\Delta W}{\Delta t} \quad \text{(average power)} \tag{6.15}$$

The rate at which work is done might not be constant. We can define **instantaneous power** P as the quotient in Eq. (6.15) as Δt approaches zero:

$$P = \lim_{\Delta t \to 0} \frac{\Delta W}{\Delta t} = \frac{dW}{dt} \quad \text{(instantaneous power)} \tag{6.16}$$

The SI unit of power is the **watt** (W), named for the English inventor James Watt. One watt equals 1 joule per second: $1\ \text{W} = 1\ \text{J/s}$ (Fig. 6.25). The kilowatt $(1\ \text{kW} = 10^3\ \text{W})$ and the megawatt $(1\ \text{MW} = 10^6\ \text{W})$ are also commonly used. In the British system, work is expressed in foot-pounds, and the unit of power is the foot-pound per second. A larger unit called the *horsepower* (hp) is also used (Fig. 6.26):

$$1\ \text{hp} = 550\ \text{ft} \cdot \text{lb/s} = 33{,}000\ \text{ft} \cdot \text{lb/min}$$

That is, a 1-hp motor running at full load does 33,000 ft · lb of work every minute. A useful conversion factor is

$$1\ \text{hp} = 746\ \text{W} = 0.746\ \text{kW}$$

The watt is a familiar unit of *electrical* power; a 100-W light bulb converts 100 J of electrical energy into light and heat each second. But there's nothing inherently electrical about a watt. A light bulb could be rated in horsepower, and an engine can be rated in kilowatts.

The *kilowatt-hour* $(\text{kW} \cdot \text{h})$ is the usual commercial unit of electrical energy. One kilowatt-hour is the total work done in 1 hour (3600 s) when the power is 1 kilowatt $(10^3\ \text{J/s})$, so

$$1\ \text{kW} \cdot \text{h} = (10^3\ \text{J/s})(3600\ \text{s}) = 3.6 \times 10^6\ \text{J} = 3.6\ \text{MJ}$$

The kilowatt-hour is a unit of *work* or *energy,* not power.

In mechanics we can also express power in terms of force and velocity. Suppose that a force $\vec{F}$ acts on a body while it undergoes a vector displacement $\Delta\vec{s}$. If $F_\parallel$ is the component of $\vec{F}$ tangent to the path (parallel to $\Delta\vec{s}$), then the work done by the force is $\Delta W = F_\parallel \Delta s$. The average power is

$$P_{av} = \frac{F_\parallel \Delta s}{\Delta t} = F_\parallel \frac{\Delta s}{\Delta t} = F_\parallel v_{av} \tag{6.17}$$

Instantaneous power P is the limit of this expression as $\Delta t \to 0$:

$$P = F_\parallel v \tag{6.18}$$

6.25 The same amount of work is done in both of these situations, but the power (the rate at which work is done) is different.

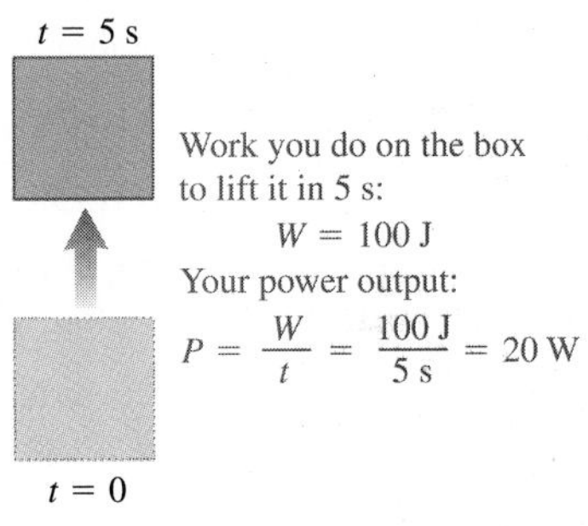

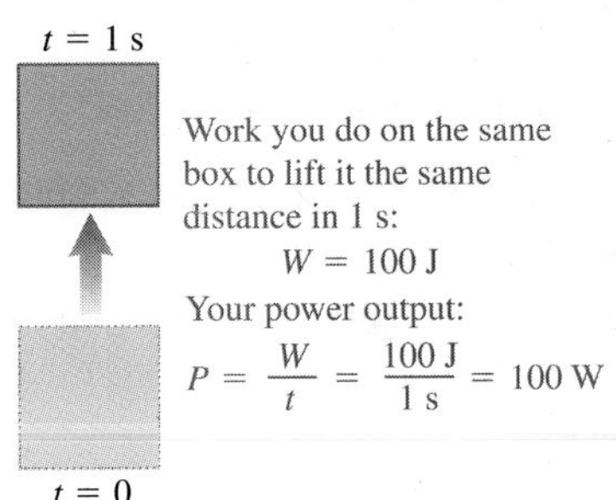

t = 1 s
Work you do on the same
box to lift it the same
distance in 1 s:
W = 100 J
Your power output:
P = W/t = 100 J / 1 s = 100 W
t = 0

6.26 The value of the horsepower derives from experiments by James Watt, who measured that a horse could do 33,000 foot-pounds of work per minute in lifting coal from a coal pit.

where v is the magnitude of the instantaneous velocity. We can also express Eq. (6.18) in terms of the scalar product:

$$P = \vec{F} \cdot \vec{v} \quad \text{(instantaneous rate at which force } \vec{F} \text{ does work on a particle)} \tag{6.19}$$

Example 6.10 Force and power

Each of the two jet engines in a Boeing 767 airliner develops a thrust (a forward force on the airplane) of 197,000 N (44,300 lb). When the airplane is flying at 250 m/s (900 km/h, or roughly 560 mi/h), what horsepower does each engine develop?

SOLUTION

IDENTIFY: Our target variable is the instantaneous power P, which is the rate at which the thrust does work.

SET UP: We use Eq. (6.18). The thrust is in the direction of motion, so $F_{\parallel}$ is just equal to the thrust.

EXECUTE: At $v = 250\text{ m/s}$, the power developed by each engine is

$$P = F_{\parallel}v = (1.97 \times 10^5\text{ N})(250\text{ m/s}) = 4.93 \times 10^7\text{ W}$$

$$= (4.93 \times 10^7\text{ W})\frac{1\text{ hp}}{746\text{ W}} = 66{,}000\text{ hp}$$

EVALUATE: The speed of modern airliners is directly related to the power of their engines (Fig. 6.27). The largest propeller-driven airliners of the 1950s had engines that developed about 3400 hp $(2.5 \times 10^6\text{ W})$, giving them maximum speeds of about 600 km/h (370 mi/h). Each engine in a Boeing 767 develops nearly 20 times more power, enabling it to fly at about 900 km/h (560 mi/h) and to carry a much heavier load.

If the engines are at maximum thrust while the airliner is at rest on the ground so that $v = 0$, the engines develop *zero* power. Force and power are not the same thing!

6.27 (a) Propeller-driven and (b) jet airliners.

(a)

(b)

Example 6.11 A "power climb"

A 50.0-kg marathon runner runs up the stairs to the top of Chicago's 443-m-tall Sears Tower, the tallest building in the United States (Fig. 6.28). To lift herself to the top in 15.0 minutes, what must be her average power output in watts? In kilowatts? In horsepower?

SOLUTION

IDENTIFY: We'll treat the runner as a particle of mass m. Her average power output P_{av} must be enough to lift her at constant speed against gravity.

SET UP: We can find P_{av} in two ways: (1) by first determining how much work she must do and then dividing it by the elapsed time, as in Eq. (6.15), or (2) by calculating the average upward force she must exert (in the direction of the climb) and then multiplying it by her upward velocity, as in Eq. (6.17).

EXECUTE: As in Example 6.8, lifting a mass m against gravity requires an amount of work equal to the weight mg multiplied by the height h it is lifted. Hence the work she must do is

$$W = mgh = (50.0\text{ kg})(9.80\text{ m/s}^2)(443\text{ m})$$
$$= 2.17 \times 10^5\text{ J}$$

6.28 How much power is required to run up the stairs of Chicago's Sears Tower in 15 minutes?

The time is 15.0 min = 900 s, so from Eq. (6.15) the average power is

$$P_{av} = \frac{2.17 \times 10^5\,\text{J}}{900\,\text{s}} = 241\,\text{W} = 0.241\,\text{kW} = 0.323\,\text{hp}$$

Let's try the calculation again using Eq. (6.17). The force exerted is vertical, and the average vertical component of velocity is $(443\,\text{m})/(900\,\text{s}) = 0.492\,\text{m/s}$, so the average power is

$$\begin{aligned} P_{av} &= F_{\parallel} v_{av} = (mg) v_{av} \\ &= (50.0\,\text{kg})(9.80\,\text{m/s}^2)(0.492\,\text{m/s}) = 241\,\text{W} \end{aligned}$$

which is the same result as before.

EVALUATE: The runner's *total* power output will be several times greater than 241 W. The reason is that the runner isn't really a particle but a collection of parts that exert forces on each other and do work, such as the work done to inhale and exhale and to make her arms and legs swing. What we've calculated is only the part of her power output that lifts her to the top of the building.

Test Your Understanding of Section 6.4 The air surrounding an airplane in flight exerts a drag force that acts opposite to the airplane's motion. When the Boeing 767 in Example 6.10 is flying in a straight line at a constant altitude at a constant 250 m/s, what is the rate at which the drag force does work on it? (i) 132,000 hp; (ii) 66,000 hp; (iii) 0; (iv) −66,000 hp; (v) −132,000 hp.

CHAPTER 6 SUMMARY

Work done by a force: When a constant force $\vec{F}$ acts on a particle that undergoes a straight-line displacement $\vec{s}$, the work done by the force on the particle is defined to be the scalar product of $\vec{F}$ and $\vec{s}$. The unit of work in SI units is 1 joule = 1 newton-meter (1 J = 1 N · m). Work is a scalar quantity; it can be positive or negative, but it has no direction in space. (See Examples 6.1 and 6.2.)

$$W = \vec{F} \cdot \vec{s} = Fs\cos\phi \quad (6.2), (6.3)$$

ϕ = angle between $\vec{F}$ and $\vec{s}$

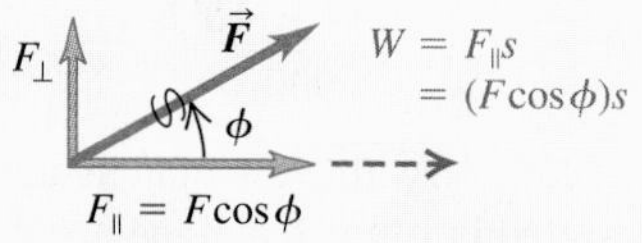

$F_\perp$, $\vec{F}$, ϕ, $W = F_\parallel s = (F\cos\phi)s$, $F_\parallel = F\cos\phi$

Kinetic energy: The kinetic energy K of a particle equals the amount of work required to accelerate the particle from rest to speed v. It is also equal to the amount of work the particle can do in the process of being brought to rest. Kinetic energy is a scalar that has no direction in space; it is always positive or zero. Its units are the same as the units of work: $1\text{ J} = 1\text{ N}\cdot\text{m} = 1\text{ kg}\cdot\text{m}^2/\text{s}^2$.

$$K = \frac{1}{2}mv^2 \quad (6.5)$$

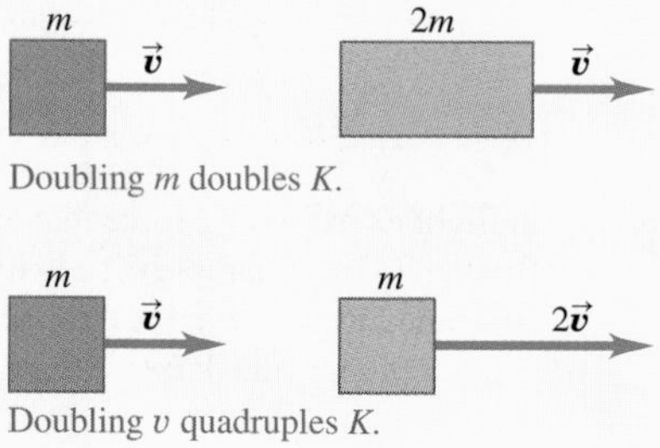

m, $\vec{v}$; $2m$, $\vec{v}$

Doubling m doubles K.

m, $\vec{v}$; m, $2\vec{v}$

Doubling v quadruples K.

The work–energy theorem: When forces act on a particle while it undergoes a displacement, the particle's kinetic energy changes by an amount equal to the total work done on the particle by all the forces. This relationship, called the work–energy theorem, is valid whether the forces are constant or varying and whether the particle moves along a straight or curved path. It is applicable only to bodies that can be treated as a particle. (See Examples 6.3–6.5)

$$W_{tot} = K_2 - K_1 = \Delta K. \quad (6.6)$$

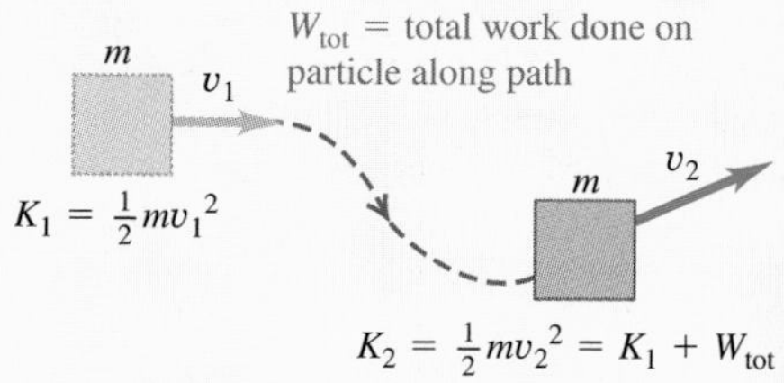

W_{tot} = total work done on particle along path

m, v_1, $K_1 = \frac{1}{2}mv_1^2$; m, v_2

$K_2 = \frac{1}{2}mv_2^2 = K_1 + W_{tot}$

Work done by a varying force or on a curved path: When a force varies during a straight-line displacement, the work done by the force is given by an integral, Eq. (6.7). (See Examples 6.6 and 6.7.) When a particle follows a curved path, the work done on it by a force $\vec{F}$ is given by an integral that involves the angle ϕ between the force and the displacement. This expression is valid even if the force magnitude and the angle ϕ vary during the displacement. (See Examples 6.8 and 6.9.)

$$W = \int_{x_1}^{x_2} F_x\,dx \quad (6.7)$$

$$W = \int_{P_1}^{P_2} F\cos\phi\,dl = \int_{P_1}^{P_2} F_\parallel\,dl = \int_{P_1}^{P_2} \vec{F}\cdot d\vec{l} \quad (6.14)$$

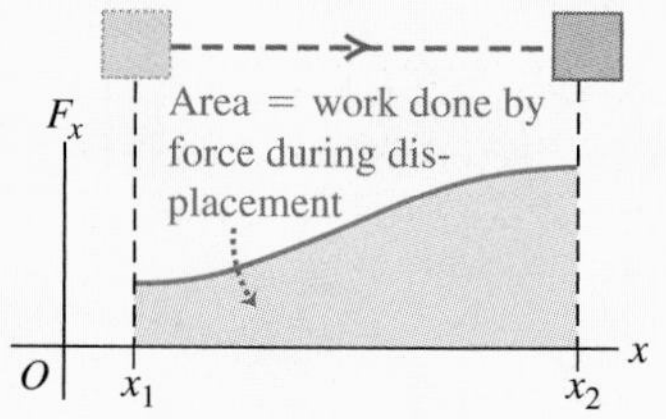

F_x; Area = work done by force during displacement; O, x_1, x_2, x

Power: Power is the time rate of doing work. The average power P_{av} is the amount of work ΔW done in time Δt divided by that time. The instantaneous power is the limit of the average power as Δt goes to zero. When a force $\vec{F}$ acts on a particle moving with velocity $\vec{v}$, the instantaneous power (the rate at which the force does work) is the scalar product of $\vec{F}$ and $\vec{v}$. Like work and kinetic energy, power is a scalar quantity. The SI unit of power is 1 watt = 1 joule/second (1 W = 1 J/s). (See Examples 6.10 and 6.11.)

$$P_{av} = \frac{\Delta W}{\Delta t} \quad (6.15)$$

$$P = \lim_{\Delta t \to 0}\frac{\Delta W}{\Delta t} = \frac{dW}{dt} \quad (6.16)$$

$$P = \vec{F}\cdot\vec{v} \quad (6.19)$$

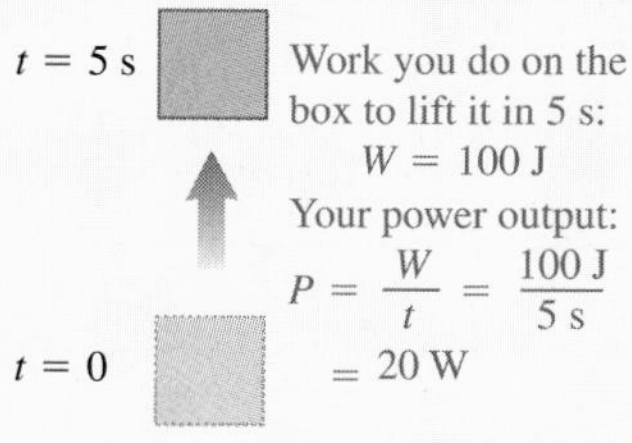

$t = 5$ s; $t = 0$

Work you do on the box to lift it in 5 s: $W = 100$ J

Your power output: $P = \frac{W}{t} = \frac{100\text{ J}}{5\text{ s}} = 20$ W

Key Terms

work, *182*
joule, *182*
kinetic energy, *187*
work–energy theorem, *187*
force constant, *193*
Hooke's law, *193*
power, *199*
average power, *199*
instantaneous power, *199*
watt, *199*

Answer to Chapter Opening Question ?

It is indeed true that the shell does work on the gases. However, because the shell exerts a backward force on the gases as the gases and shell move forward through the barrel, the work done by the shell is *negative* (see Section 6.1).

Answers to Test Your Understanding Questions

6.1 Answer: (iii) The electron has constant velocity, so its acceleration is zero and (by Newton's second law) the net force on the electron is also zero. Therefore the total work done by all the forces (equal to the work done by the net force) must be zero as well. The individual forces may do nonzero work, but that's not what the question asks.

6.2 Answer: (iv), (i), (iii), (ii) Body (i) has kinetic energy $K = \frac{1}{2}mv^2 = \frac{1}{2}(2.0\text{ kg})(5.0\text{ m/s})^2 = 25\text{ J}$. Body (ii) had zero kinetic energy initially and then had 30 J of work done it, so its final kinetic energy is $K_2 = K_1 + W = 0 + 30\text{ J} = 30\text{ J}$. Body (iii) had initial kinetic energy $K_1 = \frac{1}{2}mv_1^2 = \frac{1}{2}(1.0\text{ kg})(4.0\text{ m/s})^2 = 8.0\text{ J}$ and then had 20 J of work done on it, so its final kinetic energy is $K_2 = K_1 + W = 8.0\text{ J} + 20\text{ J} = 28\text{ J}$. Body (iv) had initial kinetic energy $K_1 = \frac{1}{2}mv_1^2 = \frac{1}{2}(2.0\text{ kg})(10\text{ m/s})^2 = 100\text{ J}$; when it did 80 J of work on another body, the other body did -80 J of work on body (iv), so the final kinetic energy of body (iv) is $K_2 = K_1 + W = 100\text{ J} + (-80\text{ J}) = 20\text{ J}$.

6.3 Answers:(a) (iii), (b) (iii) At any point during the pendulum bob's motion, the tension force and the weight both act perpendicular to the motion—that is, perpendicular to an infinitesimal displacement $d\vec{l}$ of the bob. (In Fig. 5.32b, the displacement $d\vec{l}$ would be directed outward from the plane of the free-body diagram.) Hence for either force the scalar product inside the integral in Eq. (6.14) is $\vec{F}\cdot d\vec{l} = 0$, and the work done along any part of the circular path (including a complete circle) is $W = \int\vec{F}\cdot d\vec{l} = 0$.

6.4 Answer: (v) The airliner has a constant horizontal velocity, so the net horizontal force on it must be zero. Hence the backward drag force must have the same magnitude as the forward force due to the combined thrust of the two engines. This means that the drag force must do *negative* work on the airplane at the same rate that the combined thrust force does *positive* work. The combined thrust does work at a rate of $2(66{,}000\text{ hp}) = 132{,}000\text{ hp}$, so the drag force must do work at a rate of $-132{,}000$ hp.

PROBLEMS

For instructor-assigned homework, go to www.masteringphysics.com 

Discussion Questions

Q6.1. The sign of many physical quantities depends on the choice of coordinates. For example, g can be negative or positive, depending on whether we choose upward or downward as positive. Is the same thing true of work? In other words, can we make positive work negative by a different choice of coordinates? Explain.

Q6.2. An elevator is hoisted by its cables at constant speed. Is the total work done on the elevator positive, negative, or zero? Explain.

Q6.3. A rope tied to a body is pulled, causing the body to accelerate. But according to Newton's third law, the body pulls back on the rope with an equal and opposite force. Is the total work done then zero? If so, how can the body's kinetic energy change? Explain.

Q6.4. If it takes total work W to give an object a speed v and kinetic energy K, starting from rest, what will be the object's speed (in terms of v) and kinetic energy (in terms of K) if we do twice as much work on it, again starting from rest?

Q6.5. If there is a net nonzero force on a moving object, is it possible for the total work done on the object to be zero? Explain, with an example that illustrates your answer.

Q6.6. In Example 5.5 (Section 5.1), how does the work done on the bucket by the tension in the cable compare to the work done on the cart by the tension in the cable?

Q6.7. In the conical pendulum in Example 5.21 (Section 5.4), which of the forces do work on the bob while it is swinging?

Q6.8. For the cases shown in Fig. 6.29, the object is released from rest at the top and feels no friction or air resistance. In which (if any) cases will the mass have (i) the greatest speed at the bottom and (ii) the most work done on it by the time it reaches the bottom?

Figure 6.29 Question Q6.8.

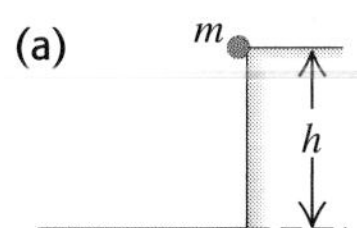

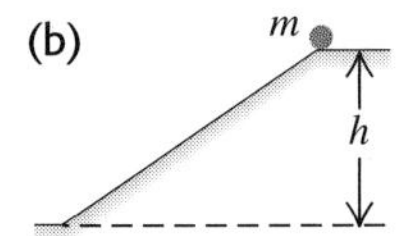

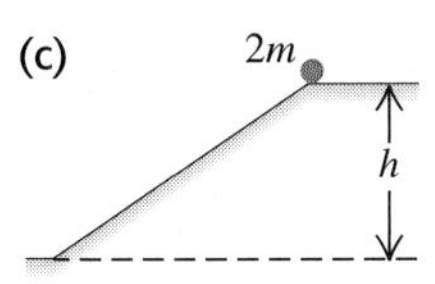

Q6.9. A force $\vec{F}$ is in the x-direction and has a magnitude that depends on x. Sketch a possible graph of F versus x such that the force does zero work on an object that moves from x_1 to x_2, even though the force magnitude is not zero at all x in this range.

Q6.10. Does the kinetic energy of a car change more when it speeds up from 10 to 15 m/s or from 15 to 20 m/s? Explain.

Q6.11. A falling brick has a mass of 1.5 kg and is moving straight downward with a speed of 5.0 m/s. A 1.5-kg physics book is sliding across the floor with a speed of 5.0 m/s. A 1.5-kg melon is traveling with a horizontal velocity component 3.0 m/s to the right and a vertical component 4.0 m/s upward. Do these objects all have the same velocity? Do these objects all have the same kinetic energy? For each question, give the reasoning behind your answer.

Q6.12. Can the *total* work done on an object during a displacement be negative? Explain. If the total work is negative, can its magnitude be larger than the initial kinetic energy of the object? Explain.

Q6.13. A net force acts on an object and accelerates it from rest to a speed v_1. In doing so, the force does an amount of work W_1. By what factor must the work done on the object be increased to produce three times the final speed, with the object again starting from rest?

Q6.14. A truck speeding down the highway has a lot of kinetic energy relative to a stopped state trooper, but no kinetic energy relative to the truck driver. In these two frames of reference, is the same amount of work required to stop the truck? Explain.

Q6.15. You are holding a briefcase by the handle, with your arm straight down by your side. Does the force your hand exerts do work on the briefcase when (a) you walk at a constant speed down a horizontal hallway and (b) you ride an escalator from the first to second floor of a building? In each case justify your answer.

Q6.16. When a book slides along a tabletop, the force of friction does negative work on it. Can friction ever do *positive* work? Explain. (*Hint:* Think of a box in the back of an accelerating truck.)

Q6.17. Time yourself while running up a flight of steps, and compute the average rate at which you do work against the force of gravity. Express your answer in watts and in horsepower.

Q6.18. Fractured Physics. Many terms from physics are badly misused in everyday language. In each case, explain the errors involved. (a) A *strong* person is called *powerful*. What is wrong with this use of *power*? (b) When a worker carries a bag of concrete along a level construction site, people say he did a lot of *work*. Did he?

Q6.19. An advertisement for a portable electrical generating unit claims that the unit's diesel engine produces 28,000 hp to drive an electrical generator that produces 30 MW of electrical power. Is this possible? Explain.

Q6.20. A car speeds up while the engine delivers constant power. Is the acceleration greater at the beginning of this process or at the end? Explain.

Q6.21. Consider a graph of instantaneous power versus time, with the vertical P axis starting at $P = 0$. What is the physical significance of the area under the P versus t curve between vertical lines at t_1 and t_2? How could you find the average power from the graph? Draw a P versus t curve that consists of two straight-line sections and for which the peak power is equal to twice the average power.

Q6.22. A nonzero net force acts on an object. Is it possible for any of the following quantities to be constant: (a) the particle's speed; (b) the particle's velocity; (c) the particle's kinetic energy.

Q6.23. When a certain force is applied to an ideal spring, the spring stretches a distance x from its unstretched length and does work W. If instead twice the force is applied, what distance (in terms of x) does the spring stretch from its unstretched length, and how much work (in terms of W) is required to stretch it this distance?

Q6.24. If work W is required to stretch a spring a distance x from its unstretched length, what work (in terms of W) is required to stretch the spring an *additional* distance x?

Exercises

Section 6.1 Work

6.1. An old oaken bucket of mass 6.75 kg hangs in a well at the end of a rope. The rope passes over a frictionless pulley at the top of the well, and you pull horizontally on the end of the rope to raise the bucket slowly a distance of 4.00 m. (a) How much work do you do on the bucket in pulling it up? (b) How much work does gravity do on the bucket? (c) What is the total work done on the bucket?

6.2. A tow truck pulls a car 5.00 km along a horizontal roadway using a cable having a tension of 850 N. (a) How much work does the cable do on the car if it pulls horizontally? If it pulls at 35.0° above the horizontal? (b) How much work does the cable do on the tow truck in both cases of part (a)? (c) How much work does gravity do on the car in part (a)?

6.3. A factory worker pushes a 30.0-kg crate a distance of 4.5 m along a level floor at constant velocity by pushing horizontally on it. The coefficient of kinetic friction between the crate and the floor is 0.25. (a) What magnitude of force must the worker apply? (b) How much work is done on the crate by this force? (c) How much work is done on the crate by friction? (d) How much work is done on the crate by the normal force? By gravity? (e) What is the total work done on the crate?

6.4. Suppose the worker in Exercise 6.3 pushes downward at an angle of 30° below the horizontal. (a) What magnitude of force must the worker apply to move the crate at constant velocity? (b) How much work is done on the crate by this force when the crate is pushed a distance of 4.5 m? (c) How much work is done on the crate by friction during this displacement? (d) How much work is done on the crate by the normal force? By gravity? (e) What is the total work done on the crate?

6.5. A 75.0-kg painter climbs a ladder that is 2.75 m long leaning against a vertical wall. The ladder makes an 30.0° angle with the wall. (a) How much work does gravity do on the painter? (b) Does the answer to part (a) depend on whether the painter climbs at constant speed or accelerates up the ladder?

6.6. Two tugboats pull a disabled supertanker. Each tug exerts a constant force of 1.80×10^6 N, one 14° west of north and the other 14° east of north, as they pull the tanker 0.75 km toward the north. What is the total work they do on the supertanker?

6.7. Two blocks are connected by a very light string passing over a massless and frictionless pulley (Figure 6.30). Traveling at constant speed, the 20.0-N block moves 75.0 cm to the right and the 12.0-N block moves 75.0 cm downward. During this process, how much work is done (a) on the 12.0-N block by (i) gravity and (ii) the tension in the string? (b) On the 20.0-N block by (i) gravity, (ii) the tension in the string, (iii) friction, and (iv) the normal force? (c) Find the total work done on each block.

Figure **6.30** Exercise 6.7.

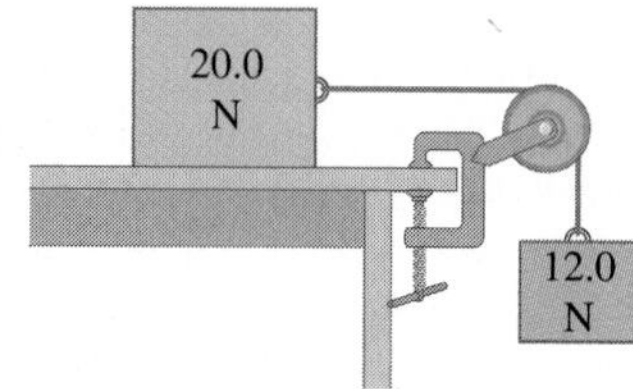

6.8. A loaded grocery cart is rolling across a parking lot in a strong wind. You apply a constant force $\vec{F} = (30\text{ N})\hat{\imath} - (40\text{ N})\hat{\jmath}$ to the cart as it undergoes a displacement $\vec{s} = (-9.0\text{ m})\hat{\imath} - (3.0\text{ m})\hat{\jmath}$. How much work does the force you apply do on the grocery cart?

6.9. A 0.800-kg ball is tied to the end of a string 1.60 m long and swung in a vertical circle. (a) During one complete circle, starting anywhere, calculate the total work done on the ball by (i) the tension in the string and (ii) gravity. (b) Repeat part (a) for motion along the semicircle from the lowest to the highest point on the path.

Section 6.2 Kinetic Energy and the Work–Energy Theorem

6.10. (a) How many joules of kinetic energy does a 750-kg automobile traveling at a typical highway speed of 65 mi/h have? (b) By what factor would its kinetic energy decrease if the car traveled half as fast? (c) How fast (in mi/h) would the car have to travel to have half as much kinetic energy as in part (a)?

6.11. Meteor Crater. About 50,000 years ago, a meteor crashed into the earth near present-day Flagstaff, Arizona. Recent (2005) measurements estimate that this meteor had a mass of about 1.4×10^8 kg (around 150,000 tons) and hit the ground at 12 km/s. (a) How much kinetic energy did this meteor deliver to the ground? (b) How does this energy compare to the energy released by a 1.0-megaton nuclear bomb? (A megaton bomb releases the same energy as a million tons of TNT, and 1.0 ton of TNT releases 4.184×10^9 J of energy.)

6.12. Some Typical Kinetic Energies. (a) How many joules of kinetic energy does a 75-kg person have when walking and when running? (b) In the Bohr model of the atom, the ground-state electron in hydrogen has an orbital speed of 2190 km/s. What is its kinetic energy? (Consult Appendix F.) (c) If you drop a 1.0-kg weight (about 2 lb) from shoulder height, how many joules of kinetic energy will it have when it reaches the ground? (d) Is it reasonable that a 30-kg child could run fast enough to have 100 J of kinetic energy?

6.13. The mass of a proton is 1836 times the mass of an electron. (a) A proton is traveling at speed V. At what speed (in terms of V) would an electron have the same kinetic energy as the proton? (b) An electron has kinetic energy K. If a proton has the same speed as the electron, what is its kinetic energy (in terms of K)?

6.14. A 4.80-kg watermelon is dropped from rest from the roof of a 25.0-m-tall building and feels no appreciable air resistance. (a) Calculate the work done by gravity on the watermelon during its displacement from the roof to the ground. (b) Just before it strikes the ground, what is the watermelon's (i) kinetic energy and (ii) speed? (c) Which of the answers in parts (a) and (b) would be *different* if there were appreciable air resistance?

6.15. Use the work–energy theorem to solve each of these problems. You can use Newton's laws to check your answers. Neglect air resistance in all cases. (a) A branch falls from the top of a 95.0-m-tall redwood tree, starting from rest. How fast is it moving when it reaches the ground? (b) A volcano ejects a boulder directly upward 525 m into the air. How fast was the boulder moving just as it left the volcano? (c) A skier moving at 5.00 m/s encounters a long, rough horizontal patch of snow having coefficient of kinetic friction 0.220 with her skis. How far does she travel on this patch before stopping? (d) Suppose the rough patch in part (c) was only 2.90 m long? How fast would the skier be moving when she reached the end of the patch? (e) At the base of a frictionless icy hill that rises at 25.0° above the horizontal, a toboggan has a speed of 12.0 m/s toward the hill. How high vertically above the base will it go before stopping?

6.16. You throw a 20-N rock vertically into the air from ground level. You observe that when it is 15.0 m above the ground, it is traveling at 25.0 m/s upward. Use the work–energy theorem to find (a) the rock's speed just as it left the ground and (b) its maximum height.

6.17. You are a member of an Alpine Rescue Team. You must project a box of supplies up an incline of constant slope angle α so that it reaches a stranded skier who is a vertical distance h above the bottom of the incline. The incline is slippery, but there is some friction present, with kinetic friction coefficient μ_k. Use the work–energy theorem to calculate the minimum speed you must give the box at the bottom of the incline so that it will reach the skier. Express your answer in terms of g, h, μ_k, and α.

6.18. A mass m slides down a smooth inclined plane from an initial vertical height h, making an angle α with the horizontal. (a) The work done by a force is the sum of the work done by the components of the force. Consider the components of gravity parallel and perpendicular to the surface of the plane. Calculate the work done on the mass by each of the components, and use these results to show that the work done by gravity is exactly the same as if the mass had fallen straight down through the air from a height h. (b) Use the work–energy theorem to prove that the speed of the mass at the bottom of the incline is the same as if it had been dropped from height h, independent of the angle α of the incline. Explain how this speed can be independent of the slope angle. (c) Use the results of part (b) to find the speed of a rock that slides down an icy frictionless hill, starting from rest 15.0 m above the bottom.

6.19. A car is stopped in a distance D by a constant friction force that is independent of the car's speed. What is the stopping distance (in terms of D) (a) if the car's initial speed is tripled, and (b) if the speed is the same as it originally was but the friction force is tripled? (Solve using the work–energy theorem.)

6.20. A moving electron has kinetic energy K_1. After a net amount of work W has been done on it, the electron is moving one-quarter as fast in the opposite direction. (a) Find W in terms of K_1. (b) Does your answer depend on the final direction of the electron's motion?

6.21. A sled with mass 8.00 kg moves in a straight line on a frictionless horizontal surface. At one point in its path, its speed is 4.00 m/s; after it has traveled 2.50 m beyond this point, its speed is 6.00 m/s. Use the work–energy theorem to find the force acting on the sled, assuming that this force is constant and that it acts in the direction of the sled's motion.

6.22. A soccer ball with mass 0.420 kg is initially moving with speed 2.00 m/s. A soccer player kicks the ball, exerting a constant force of magnitude 40.0 N in the same direction as the ball's motion. Over what distance must the player's foot be in contact with the ball to increase the ball's speed to 6.00 m/s?

6.23. A 12-pack of Omni-Cola (mass 4.30 kg) is initially at rest on a horizontal floor. It is then pushed in a straight line for 1.20 m by a trained dog that exerts a horizontal force with magnitude 36.0 N. Use the work–energy theorem to find the final speed of the 12-pack if (a) there is no friction between the 12-pack and the floor, and (b) the coefficient of kinetic friction between the 12-pack and the floor is 0.30.

6.24. A batter hits a baseball with mass 0.145 kg straight upward with an initial speed of 25.0 m/s. (a) How much work has gravity done on the baseball when it reaches a height of 20.0 m above the bat? (b) Use the work–energy theorem to calculate the speed of the baseball at a height of 20.0 m above the bat. You can ignore air resistance. (c) Does the answer to part (b) depend on whether the baseball is moving upward or downward at a height of 20.0 m? Explain.

6.25. A little red wagon with mass 7.00 kg moves in a straight line on a frictionless horizontal surface. It has an initial speed of 4.00 m/s and then is pushed 3.0 m in the direction of the initial velocity by a force with a magnitude of 10.0 N. (a) Use the work–energy theorem to calculate the wagon's final speed. (b) Calculate the acceleration produced by the force. Use this acceleration in the kinematic relationships of Chapter 2 to calculate the wagon's final speed. Compare this result to that calculated in part (a).

6.26. A block of ice with mass 2.00 kg slides 0.750 m down an inclined plane that slopes downward at an angle of 36.9° below the horizontal. If the block of ice starts from rest, what is its final speed? You can ignore friction.

6.27. Stopping Distance. A car is traveling on a level road with speed v_0 at the instant when the brakes lock, so that the tires slide rather than roll. (a) Use the work–energy theorem to calculate the minimum stopping distance of the car in terms of v_0, g, and the coefficient of kinetic friction μ_k between the tires and the road. (b) By what factor would the minimum stopping distance change if (i) the coefficient of kinetic friction were doubled, or (ii) the initial speed were doubled, or (iii) both the coefficient of kinetic friction and the initial speed were doubled?

Section 6.3 Work and Energy with Varying Forces

6.28. To stretch a spring 3.00 cm from its unstretched length, 12.0 J of work must be done. (a) What is the force constant of this spring? (b) What magnitude force is needed to stretch the spring 3.00 cm from its unstretched length? (c) How much work must be done to compress this spring 4.00 cm from its unstretched length, and what force is needed to stretch it this distance?

6.29. A force of 160 N stretches a spring 0.050 m beyond its unstretched length. (a) What magnitude of force is required to stretch the spring 0.015 m beyond its unstretched length? To compress the spring 0.020 m? (b) How much work must be done to stretch the spring 0.015 m beyond its unstretched length? To compress the spring 0.020 m from its unstretched length?

6.30. A child applies a force $\vec{F}$ parallel to the x-axis to a 10.0-kg sled moving on the frozen surface of a small pond. As the child controls the speed of the sled, the x-component of the force she applies varies with the x-coordinate of the sled as shown in Fig. 6.31. Calculate the work done by the force $\vec{F}$ when the sled moves (a) from $x = 0$ to $x = 8.0$ m; (b) from $x = 8.0$ m to $x = 12.0$ m; (c) from $x = 0$ to 12.0 m.

Figure 6.31 Exercises 6.30 and 6.31.

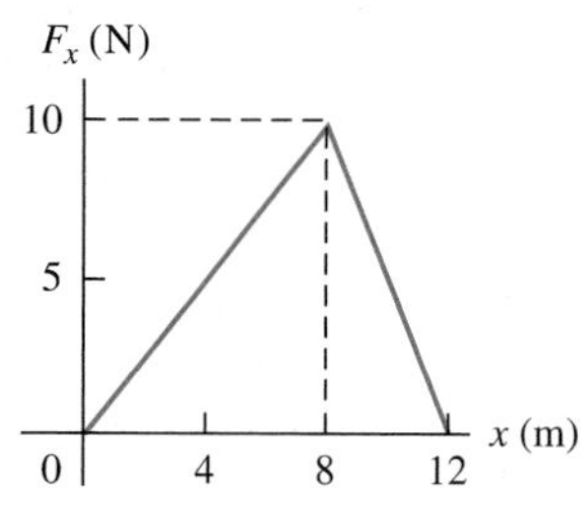

6.31. Suppose the sled in Exercise 6.30 is initially at rest at $x = 0$. Use the work–energy theorem to find the speed of the sled at (a) $x = 8.0$ m and (b) $x = 12.0$ m. You can ignore friction between the sled and the surface of the pond.

6.32. A balky cow is leaving the barn as you try harder and harder to push her back in. In coordinates with the origin at the barn door, the cow walks from $x = 0$ to $x = 6.9$ m as you apply a force with x-component $F_x = -[20.0\text{ N} + (3.0\text{ N/m})x]$. How much work does the force you apply do on the cow during this displacement?

6.33. A 6.0-kg box moving at 3.0 m/s on a horizontal, frictionless surface runs into a light spring of force constant 75 N/cm. Use the work–energy theorem to find the maximum compression of the spring.

6.34. Leg Presses. As part of your daily workout, you lie on your back and push with your feet against a platform attached to two stiff springs arranged side by side so that they are parallel to each other. When you push the platform, you compress the springs. You do 80.0 J of work when you compress the springs 0.200 m from their uncompressed length. (a) What magnitude of force must you apply to hold the platform in this position? (b) How much *additional* work must you do to move the platform 0.200 m *farther*, and what maximum force must you apply?

6.35. (a) In Example 6.7 (Section 6.3) it was calculated that with the air track turned off, the glider travels 8.6 cm before it stops instantaneously. How large would the coefficient of static friction μ_s have to be to keep the glider from springing back to the left? (b) If the coefficient of static friction between the glider and the track is $\mu_s = 0.60$, what is the maximum initial speed v_1 that the glider can be given and still remain at rest after it stops instantaneously? With the air track turned off, the coefficient of kinetic friction is $\mu_k = 0.47$.

6.36. A 4.00-kg block of ice is placed against a horizontal spring that has force constant $k = 200$ N/m and is compressed 0.025 m. The spring is released and accelerates the block along a horizontal surface. You can ignore friction and the mass of the spring. (a) Calculate the work done on the block by the spring during the motion of the block from its initial position to where the spring has returned to its uncompressed length. (b) What is the speed of the block after it leaves the spring?

6.37. A force $\vec{F}$ is applied to a 2.0-kg radio-controlled model car parallel to the x-axis as it moves along a straight track. The x-component of the force varies with the x-coordinate of the car as shown in Fig. 6.32. Calculate the work done by the force $\vec{F}$ when the car moves from (a) $x = 0$ to $x = 3.0$ m; (b) $x = 3.0$ m to $x = 4.0$ m; (c) $x = 4.0$ m to $x = 7.0$ m; (d) $x = 0$ to $x = 7.0$ m; (e) $x = 7.0$ m to $x = 2.0$ m.

Figure 6.32 Exercises 6.37 and 6.38.

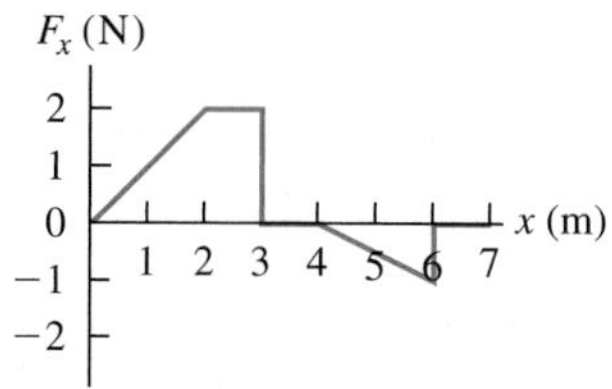

6.38. Suppose the 2.0-kg model car in Exercise 6.37 is initially at rest at $x = 0$ and $\vec{F}$ is the net force acting on it. Use the work–energy theorem to find the speed of the car at (a) $x = 3.0$ m; (b) $x = 4.0$ m; (c) $x = 7.0$ m.

6.39. At a waterpark, sleds with riders are sent along a slippery, horizontal surface by the release of a large compressed spring. The spring with force constant $k = 40.0$ N/cm and negligible mass rests on the frictionless horizontal surface. One end is in contact with a stationary wall. A sled and rider with total mass 70.0 kg are pushed against the other end, compressing the spring 0.375 m. The sled is then released with zero initial velocity. What is the sled's speed when the spring (a) returns to its uncompressed length and (b) is still compressed 0.200 m?

6.40. Half of a Spring. (a) Suppose you cut a massless ideal spring in half. If the full spring had a force constant k, what is the force constant of each half, in terms of k? (*Hint:* Think of the original spring as two equal halves, each producing the same force as the entire spring. Do you see why the forces must be equal?) (b) If you cut the spring into three equal segments instead, what is the force constant of each one, in terms of k?

6.41. A small glider is placed against a compressed spring at the bottom of an air track that slopes upward at an angle of 40.0° above the horizontal. The glider has mass 0.0900 kg. The spring has $k = 640$ N/m and negligible mass. When the spring is released, the glider travels a maximum distance of 1.80 m along the air track before sliding back down. Before reaching this maximum distance, the glider loses contact with the spring. (a) What distance was the spring originally compressed? (b) When the glider has traveled along the air track 0.80 m from its initial position against the compressed spring, is it still in contact with the spring? What is the kinetic energy of the glider at this point?

6.42. An ingenious bricklayer builds a device for shooting bricks up to the top of the wall where he is working. He places a brick on a vertical compressed spring with force constant $k = 450$ N/m and negligible mass. When the spring is released, the brick is propelled upward. If the brick has mass 1.80 kg and is to reach a maximum height of 3.6 m above its initial position on the compressed spring, what distance must the bricklayer compress the spring initially? (The brick loses contact with the spring when the spring returns to its uncompressed length. Why?)

Section 6.4 Power

6.43. How many joules of energy does a 100-watt light bulb use per hour? How fast would a 70-kg person have to run to have that amount of kinetic energy?

6.44. The total consumption of electrical energy in the United States is about 1.0×10^{19} J per year. (a) What is the average rate of electrical energy consumption in watts? (b) The population of the United States is about 300 million people. What is the average rate of electrical energy consumption per person? (c) The sun transfers energy to the earth by radiation at a rate of approximately 1.0 kW per square meter of surface. If this energy could be collected and converted to electrical energy with 40% efficiency, how great an area (in square kilometers) would be required to collect the electrical energy used in the United States?

6.45. Magnetar. On December 27, 2004, astronomers observed the greatest flash of light ever recorded from outside the solar system. It came from the highly magnetic neutron star SGR 1806-20 (a *magnetar*). During 0.20 s, this star released as much energy as our sun does in 250,000 years. If P is the average power output of our sun, what was the average power output (in terms of P) of this magnetar?

6.46. A 20.0-kg rock is sliding on a rough, horizontal surface at 8.00 m/s and eventually stops due to friction. The coefficient of kinetic friction between the rock and the surface is 0.200. What average power is produced by friction as the rock stops?

6.47. A tandem (two-person) bicycle team must overcome a force of 165 N to maintain a speed of 9.00 m/s. Find the power required per rider, assuming that each contributes equally. Express your answer in watts and in horsepower.

6.48. When its 75-kW (100-hp) engine is generating full power, a small single-engine airplane with mass 700 kg gains altitude at a rate of 2.5 m/s (150 m/min, or 500 ft/min). What fraction of the engine power is being used to make the airplane climb? (The remainder is used to overcome the effects of air resistance and of inefficiencies in the propeller and engine.)

6.49. Working Like a Horse. Your job is to lift 30-kg crates a vertical distance of 0.90 m from the ground onto the bed of a truck. (a) How many crates would you have to load onto the truck in 1 minute for the average power output you use to lift the crates to equal 0.50 hp? (b) How many crates for an average power output of 100 W?

6.50. An elevator has mass 600 kg, not including passengers. The elevator is designed to ascend, at constant speed, a vertical distance of 20.0 m (five floors) in 16.0 s, and it is driven by a motor that can provide up to 40 hp to the elevator. What is the maximum number of passengers that can ride in the elevator? Assume that an average passenger has mass 65.0 kg.

6.51. Automotive Power. It is not unusual for a 1000-kg car to get 30 mi/gal when traveling at 60 mi/h on a level road. If this car makes a 200-km trip, (a) how many joules of energy does it consume, and (b) what is the average rate of energy consumption during the trip? Note that 1.0 gal of gasoline yields 1.3×10^9 J (although this can vary). Consult Appendix E.

6.52. The aircraft carrier *John F. Kennedy* has mass 7.4×10^7 kg. When its engines are developing their full power of 280,000 hp, the *John F. Kennedy* travels at its top speed of 35 knots (65 km/h). If 70% of the power output of the engines is applied to pushing the ship through the water, what is the magnitude of the force of water resistance that opposes the carrier's motion at this speed?

6.53. A ski tow operates on a 15.0° slope of length 300 m. The rope moves at 12.0 km/h and provides power for 50 riders at one time, with an average mass per rider of 70.0 kg. Estimate the power required to operate the tow.

6.54. A typical flying insect applies an average force equal to twice its weight during each downward stroke while hovering. Take the mass of the insect to be 10 g, and assume the wings move an average downward distance of 1.0 cm during each stroke. Assuming 100 downward strokes per second, estimate the average power output of the insect.

Problems

6.55. Rotating Bar. A thin, uniform 12.0-kg bar that is 2.00 m long rotates uniformly about a pivot at one end, making 5.00 complete revolutions every 3.00 seconds. What is the kinetic energy of this bar? (*Hint*: Different points in the bar have different speeds. Break the bar up into infinitesimal segments of mass dm and integrate to add up the kinetic energy of all these segments.)

6.56. A Near-Earth Asteroid. On April 13, 2029 (Friday the 13th!), the asteroid 99942 Apophis will pass within 18,600 mi of the earth—about 1/13 the distance to the moon! It has a density of 2600 kg/m^3, can be modeled as a sphere 320 m in diameter, and will be traveling at 12.6 km/s. (a) If, due to a small disturbance in its orbit, the asteroid were to hit the earth, how much kinetic energy would it deliver? (b) The largest nuclear bomb ever tested by the United States was the "Castle/Bravo" bomb, having a yield of 15 megatons of TNT. (A megaton of TNT releases 4.184×10^{15} J of energy.) How many Castle/Bravo bombs would be equivalent to the energy of Apophis?

6.57. A luggage handler pulls a 20.0-kg suitcase up a ramp inclined at 25.0° above the horizontal by a force $\vec{F}$ of magnitude 140 N that acts parallel to the ramp. The coefficient of kinetic friction between the ramp and the incline is $\mu_k = 0.300$. If the suitcase travels 3.80 m along the ramp, calculate (a) the work done on the suitcase by the force $\vec{F}$; (b) the work done on the suitcase by the gravitational force; (c) the work done on the suitcase by the normal force; (d) the work done on the suitcase by the friction force; (e) the total work done on the suitcase. (f) If the speed of the suitcase is zero at the bottom of the ramp, what is its speed after it has traveled 3.80 m along the ramp?

6.58. Chin-Ups. While doing a chin-up, a man lifts his body 0.40 m. (a) How much work must the man do per kilogram of body mass? (b) The muscles involved in doing a chin-up can generate about 70 J of work per kilogram of muscle mass. If the man can just barely do a 0.40-m chin-up, what percentage of his body's mass do these muscles constitute? (For comparison, the *total* percentage of muscle in a typical 70-kg man with 14% body fat is about 43%.) (c) Repeat part (b) for the man's young son, who has arms half as long as his father's but whose muscles can also generate 70 J of work per kilogram of muscle mass. (d) Adults and children have about the same percentage of muscle in their bodies. Explain why children can commonly do chin-ups more easily than their fathers.

6.59. Simple Machines. Ramps for the disabled are used because a large weight w can be raised by a relatively small force equal to $w \sin \alpha$ plus the small friction force. Such inclined planes are an example of a class of devices called *simple machines.* An input force F_{in} is applied to the system and results in an output force F_{out} applied to the object that is moved. For a simple machine the ratio of these forces, F_{out}/F_{in}, is called the actual mechanical advantage (AMA). The inverse ratio of the distances that the points of application of these forces move through during the motion of the object, s_{in}/s_{out}, is called the ideal mechanical advantage (IMA). (a) Find the IMA for an inclined plane. (b) What can we say about the relationship between the work supplied to the machine, W_{in}, and the work output of the machine, W_{out}, if AMA = IMA? (c) Sketch a single pulley arranged to give IMA = 2. (d) We define the efficiency e of a simple machine to equal the ratio of the output work to the input work, $e = W_{out}/W_{in}$. Show that $e = \text{AMA}/\text{IMA}$.

6.60. Consider the blocks in Exercise 6.7 as they move 75.0 cm. Find the total work done on each one (a) if there is no friction between the table and the 20.0-N block, and (b) if $\mu_s = 0.500$ and $\mu_k = 0.325$ between the table and the 20.0-N block.

6.61. The space shuttle *Endeavour,* with mass 86,400 kg, is in a circular orbit of radius 6.66×10^6 m around the earth. It takes 90.1 min for the shuttle to complete each orbit. On a repair mission, the shuttle is cautiously moving 1.00 m closer to a disabled satellite every 3.00 s. Calculate the shuttle's kinetic energy (a) relative to the earth and (b) relative to the satellite.

6.62. A 5.00-kg package slides 1.50 m down a long ramp that is inclined at 12.0° below the horizontal. The coefficient of kinetic friction between the package and the ramp is $\mu_k = 0.310$. Calculate (a) the work done on the package by friction; (b) the work done on the package by gravity; (c) the work done on the package by the normal force; (d) the total work done on the package. (e) If the package has a speed of 2.20 m/s at the top of the ramp, what is its speed after sliding 1.50 m down the ramp?

6.63. Springs in Parallel. Two springs are in *parallel* if they are parallel to each other and are connected at their ends (Figure 6.33). We can think of this combination as being equivalent to a single spring. The force constant of the equivalent single spring is called the *effective* force constant, k_{eff}, of the combination. (a) Show that the effective force constant of this combination is $k_{eff} = k_1 + k_2$. (b) Generalize this result for N springs in parallel.

Figure 6.33 Problem 6.63.

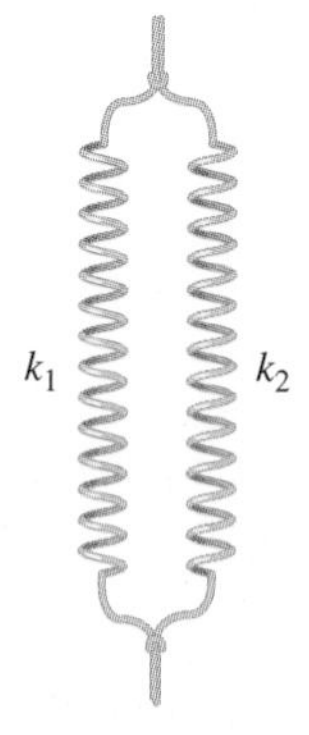

6.64. Springs in Series. Two massless springs are connected in series when they are attached one after the other, head to tail. (a) Show that the effective force constant (see Problem 6.63) of a series combination is given by $\frac{1}{k_{eff}} = \frac{1}{k_1} + \frac{1}{k_2}$. (*Hint:* For a given force, the total distance stretched by the equivalent single spring is the sum of the distances stretched by the springs in combination. Also, each spring must exert the same force. Do you see why?) (b) Generalize this result for N springs in series.

6.65. An object is attracted toward the origin with a force given by $F_x = -k/x^2$. (Gravitational and electrical forces have this distance dependence.) (a) Calculate the work done by the force F_x when the object moves in the x-direction from x_1 to x_2. If $x_2 > x_1$, is the work done by F_x positive or negative? (b) The only other force acting on the object is a force that you exert with your hand to move the object slowly from x_1 to x_2. How much work do you do? If $x_2 > x_1$, is the work you do positive or negative? (c) Explain the similarities and differences between your answers to parts (a) and (b).

6.66. The gravitational pull of the earth on an object is inversely proportional to the square of the distance of the object from the center of the earth. At the earth's surface this force is equal to the object's normal weight mg, where $g = 9.8\ \text{m/s}^2$, and at large distances, the force is zero. If a 20,000-kg asteroid falls to earth from a very great distance away, what will be its minimum speed as it strikes the earth's surface, and how much kinetic energy will it impart to our planet? You can ignore the effects of the earth's atmosphere.

6.67. Varying Coefficient of Friction. A box is sliding with a speed of 4.50 m/s on a horizontal surface when, at point P, it encounters a rough section. On the rough section, the coefficient of friction is not constant, but starts at 0.100 at P and increases linearly with distance past P, reaching a value of 0.600 at 12.5 m past point P. (a) Use the work–energy theorem to find how far this box slides before stopping. (b) What is the coefficient of friction at the stopping point? (c) How far would the box have slid if the friction coefficient didn't increase but instead had the constant value of 0.100?

6.68. Consider a spring that does not obey Hooke's law very faithfully. One end of the spring is fixed. To keep the spring stretched or compressed an amount x, a force along the x-axis with x-component $F_x = kx - bx^2 + cx^3$ must be applied to the free end. Here $k = 100\ \text{N/m}$, $b = 700\ \text{N/m}^2$, and $c = 12{,}000\ \text{N/m}^3$. Note that $x > 0$ when the spring is stretched and $x < 0$ when it is compressed. (a) How much work must be done to stretch this spring by 0.050 m from its unstretched length? (b) How much work must be done to *compress* this spring by 0.050 m from its unstretched length? (c) Is it easier to stretch or compress this spring? Explain why in terms of the dependence of F_x on x. (Many real springs behave qualitatively in the same way.)

6.69. A small block with a mass of 0.120 kg is attached to a cord passing through a hole in a frictionless, horizontal surface (Fig. 6.34). The block is originally revolving at a distance of 0.40 m from the hole with a speed of 0.70 m/s. The cord is then pulled from below, shortening the radius of the circle in which the block revolves to 0.10 m. At this new distance, the speed of the block is observed to be 2.80 m/s. (a) What is the tension in the cord in the original situation when the block has speed $v = 0.70$ m/s? (b) What is the tension in the cord in the final situation when the block has speed $v = 2.80$ m/s? (c) How much work was done by the person who pulled on the cord?

Figure 6.34 Problem 6.69.

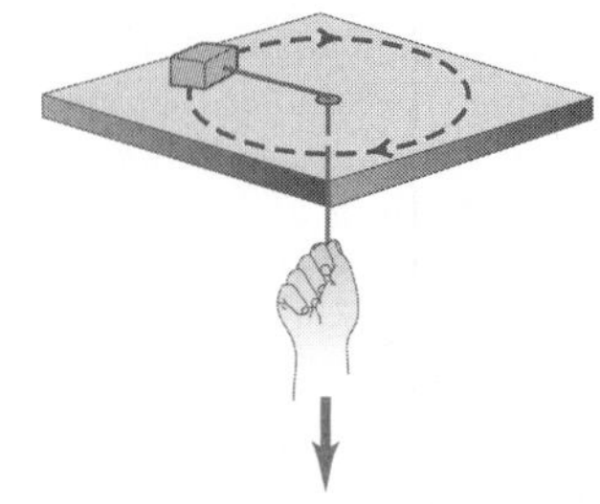

6.70. Proton Bombardment. A proton with mass 1.67×10^{-27} kg is propelled at an initial speed of 3.00×10^5 m/s directly toward a uranium nucleus 5.00 m away. The proton is repelled by the uranium nucleus with a force of magnitude $F = \alpha/x^2$, where x is the separation between the two objects and $\alpha = 2.12 \times 10^{-26}\ \text{N} \cdot \text{m}^2$. Assume that the uranium nucleus remains at rest.

(a) What is the speed of the proton when it is 8.00×10^{-10} m from the uranium nucleus? (b) As the proton approaches the uranium nucleus, the repulsive force slows down the proton until it comes momentarily to rest, after which the proton moves away from the uranium nucleus. How close to the uranium nucleus does the proton get? (c) What is the speed of the proton when it is again 5.00 m away from the uranium nucleus?

6.71. A block of ice with mass 6.00 kg is initially at rest on a frictionless, horizontal surface. A worker then applies a horizontal force $\vec{F}$ to it. As a result, the block moves along the x-axis such that its position as a function of time is given by $x(t) = \alpha t^2 + \beta t^3$, where $\alpha = 0.200\ \text{m/s}^2$ and $\beta = 0.0200\ \text{m/s}^3$. (a) Calculate the velocity of the object when $t = 4.00$ s. (b) Calculate the magnitude of $\vec{F}$ when $t = 4.00$ s. (c) Calculate the work done by the force $\vec{F}$ during the first 4.00 s of the motion.

6.72. The Genesis Crash. When the 210-kg Genesis Mission capsule crashed (see Exercise 5.17 in Chapter 5) with a speed of 311 km/h, it buried itself 81.0 cm deep in the desert floor. Assuming constant acceleration during the crash, at what average rate did the capsule do work on the desert?

6.73. You and your bicycle have combined mass 80.0 kg. When you reach the base of a bridge, you are traveling along the road at 5.00 m/s (Fig. 6.35). At the top of the bridge, you have climbed a vertical distance of 5.20 m and have slowed to 1.50 m/s. You can ignore work done by friction and any inefficiency in the bike or your legs. (a) What is the total work done on you and your bicycle when you go from the base to the top of the bridge? (b) How much work have you done with the force you apply to the pedals?

Figure 6.35 Problem 6.73.

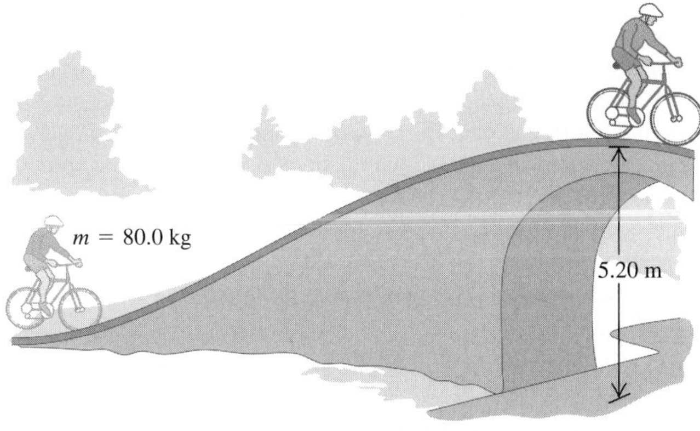

6.74. A force in the $+x$-direction has magnitude $F = b/x^n$, where b and n are constants. (a) For $n > 1$, calculate the work done on a particle by this force when the particle moves along the x-axis from $x = x_0$ to infinity. (b) Show that for $0 < n < 1$, even though F becomes zero as x becomes very large, an infinite amount of work is done by F when the particle moves from $x = x_0$ to infinity.

6.75. You are asked to design spring bumpers for the walls of a parking garage. A freely rolling 1200-kg car moving at 0.65 m/s is to compress the spring no more than 0.070 m before stopping. What should be the force constant of the spring? Assume that the spring has negligible mass.

6.76. The spring of a spring gun has force constant $k = 400$ N/m and negligible mass. The spring is compressed 6.00 cm, and a ball with mass 0.0300 kg is placed in the horizontal barrel against the compressed spring. The spring is then released, and the ball is propelled out the barrel of the gun. The barrel is 6.00 cm long, so the ball leaves the barrel at the same point that it loses contact with the spring. The gun is held so the barrel is horizontal. (a) Calculate the speed with which the ball leaves the barrel if you can ignore friction. (b) Calculate the speed of the ball as it leaves the barrel if a constant resisting force of 6.00 N acts on the ball as it moves along the barrel. (c) For the situation in part (b), at what position along the barrel does the ball have the greatest speed, and what is that speed? (In this case, the maximum speed does not occur at the end of the barrel.)

6.77. A 2.50-kg textbook is forced against a horizontal spring of negligible mass and force constant 250 N/m, compressing the spring a distance of 0.250 m. When released, the textbook slides on a horizontal tabletop with coefficient of kinetic friction $\mu_k = 0.30$. Use the work–energy theorem to find how far the textbook moves from its initial position before coming to rest.

6.78. Pushing a Cat. Your cat "Ms." (mass 7.00 kg) is trying to make it to the top of a frictionless ramp 2.00 m long and inclined upward at 30.0° above the horizontal. Since the poor cat can't get any traction on the ramp, you push her up the entire length of the ramp by exerting a constant 100-N force parallel to the ramp. If Ms. takes a running start so that she is moving at 2.40 m/s at the bottom of the ramp, what is her speed when she reaches the top of the incline? Use the work–energy theorem.

6.79. Crash Barrier. A student proposes a design for an automobile crash barrier in which a 1700-kg sport utility vehicle moving at 20.0 m/s crashes into a spring of negligible mass that slows it to a stop. So that the passengers are not injured, the acceleration of the vehicle as it slows can be no greater than 5.00g. (a) Find the required spring constant k, and find the distance the spring will compress in slowing the vehicle to a stop. In your calculation, disregard any deformation or crumpling of the vehicle and the friction between the vehicle and the ground. (b) What disadvantages are there to this design?

6.80. A physics professor is pushed up a ramp inclined upward at 30.0° above the horizontal as he sits in his desk chair that slides on frictionless rollers. The combined mass of the professor and chair is 85.0 kg. He is pushed 2.50 m along the incline by a group of students who together exert a constant horizontal force of 600 N. The professor's speed at the bottom of the ramp is 2.00 m/s. Use the work–energy theorem to find his speed at the top of the ramp.

6.81. A 5.00-kg block is moving at $v_0 = 6.00$ m/s along a frictionless, horizontal surface toward a spring with force constant $k = 500$ N/m that is attached to a wall (Fig. 6.36). The spring has negligible mass. (a) Find the maximum distance the spring will be compressed. (b) If the spring is to compress by no more than 0.150 m, what should be the maximum value of v_0?

Figure 6.36 Problem 6.81.

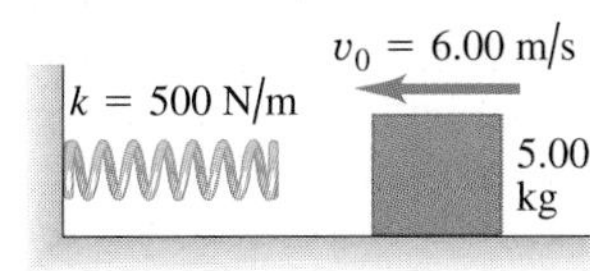

6.82. Consider the system shown in Fig. 6.37. The rope and pulley have negligible mass, and the pulley is frictionless. The coefficient of kinetic friction between the 8.00-kg block and the tabletop is $\mu_k = 0.250$. The blocks are released from rest. Use energy methods to calculate the speed of the 6.00-kg block after it has descended 1.50 m.

Figure 6.37 Problems 6.82 and 6.83.

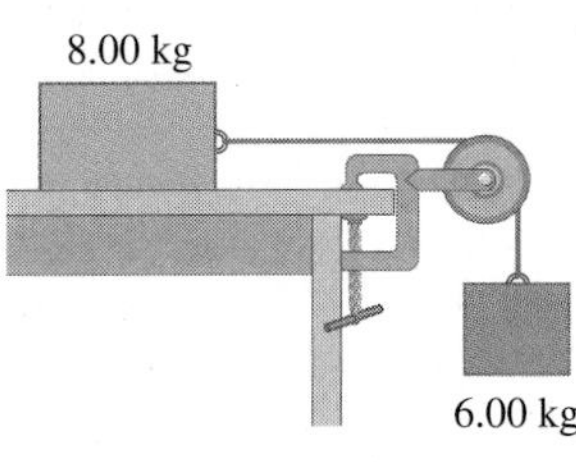

6.83. Consider the system shown in Fig. 6.37. The rope and pulley have negligible mass, and the pulley is frictionless. Initially the 6.00-kg block is moving downward and the 8.00-kg block is moving to the right, both with a speed of 0.900 m/s. The blocks come to rest after moving 2.00 m. Use the work–energy theorem to calculate the coefficient of kinetic friction between the 8.00-kg block and the tabletop.

6.84. Bow and Arrow. Figure 6.38 shows how the force exerted by the string of a compound bow on an arrow varies as a function of how far back the arrow is pulled (the draw length). Assume that the same force is exerted on the arrow as it moves forward after being released. Full draw for this bow is at a draw length of 75.0 cm. If the bow shoots a 0.0250-kg arrow from full draw, what is the speed of the arrow as it leaves the bow?

Figure 6.38 Problem 6.84.

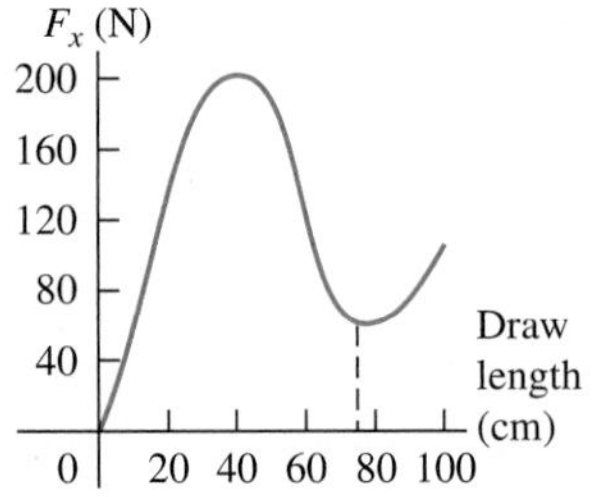

6.85. On an essentially frictionless, horizontal ice rink, a skater moving at 3.0 m/s encounters a rough patch that reduces her speed by 45% due to a friction force that is 25% of her weight. Use the work–energy theorem to find the length of this rough patch.

6.86. Rescue. Your friend (mass 65.0 kg) is standing on the ice in the middle of a frozen pond. There is very little friction between her feet and the ice, so she is unable to walk. Fortunately, a light rope is tied around her waist and you stand on the bank holding the other end. You pull on the rope for 3.00 s and accelerate your friend from rest to a speed of 6.00 m/s while you remain at rest. What is the average power supplied by the force you applied?

6.87. A pump is required to lift 800 kg of water (about 210 gallons) per minute from a well 14.0 m deep and eject it with a speed of 18.0 m/s. (a) How much work is done per minute in lifting the water? (b) How much work is done in giving the water the kinetic energy it has when ejected? (c) What must be the power output of the pump?

6.88. Find the power output of the worker in Problem 6.71 as a function of time. What is the numerical value of the power (in watts) at $t = 4.00$ s?

6.89. A physics student spends part of her day walking between classes or for recreation, during which time she expends energy at an average rate of 280 W. The remainder of the day she is sitting in class, studying, or resting; during these activities, she expends energy at an average rate of 100 W. If she expends a total of 1.1×10^7 J of energy in a 24-hour day, how much of the day did she spend walking?

6.90. All birds, independent of their size, must maintain a power output of 10–25 watts per kilogram of body mass in order to fly by flapping their wings. (a) The Andean giant hummingbird (*Patagona gigas*) has mass 70 g and flaps its wings 10 times per second while hovering. Estimate the amount of work done by such a hummingbird in each wingbeat. (b) A 70-kg athlete can maintain a power output of 1.4 kW for no more than a few seconds; the *steady* power output of a typical athlete is only 500 W or so. Is it possible for a human-powered aircraft to fly for extended periods by flapping its wings? Explain.

6.91. The Grand Coulee Dam is 1270 m long and 170 m high. The electrical power output from generators at its base is approximately 2000 MW. How many cubic meters of water must flow from the top of the dam per second to produce this amount of power if 92% of the work done on the water by gravity is converted to electrical energy? (Each cubic meter of water has a mass of 1000 kg.)

6.92. The engine of a car with mass m supplies a constant power P to the wheels to accelerate the car. You can ignore rolling friction and air resistance. The car is initially at rest. (a) Show that the speed of the car is given as a function of time by $v = (2Pt/m)^{1/2}$. (b) Show that the acceleration of the car is not constant but is given as a function of time by $a = (P/2mt)^{1/2}$. (c) Show that the displacement as a function of time is given by $x - x_0 = (8P/9m)^{1/2}\, t^{3/2}$.

6.93. Power of the Human Heart. The human heart is a powerful and extremely reliable pump. Each day it takes in and discharges about 7500 L of blood. Assume that the work done by the heart is equal to the work required to lift this amount of blood a height equal to that of the average American woman (1.63 m). The density (mass per unit volume) of blood is $1.05 \times 10^3\ \text{kg/m}^3$. (a) How much work does the heart do in a day? (b) What is the heart's power output in watts?

6.94. Six diesel units in series can provide 13.4 MW of power to the lead car of a freight train. The diesel units have total mass 1.10×10^6 kg. The average car in the train has mass 8.2×10^4 kg and requires a horizontal pull of 2.8 kN to move at a constant 27 m/s on level tracks. (a) How many cars can be in the train under these conditions? (b) This would leave no power for accelerating or climbing hills. Show that the extra force needed to accelerate the train is about the same for a 0.10-m/s^2 acceleration or a 1.0% slope (slope angle $\alpha = \arctan 0.010$). (c) With the 1.0% slope, show that an extra 2.9 MW of power is needed to maintain the 27-m/s speed of the diesel units. (d) With 2.9 MW less power available, how many cars can the six diesel units pull up a 1.0% slope at a constant 27-m/s?

6.95. It takes a force of 53 kN on the lead car of a 16-car passenger train with mass 9.1×10^5 kg to pull it at a constant 45 m/s (101 mi/h) on level tracks. (a) What power must the locomotive provide to the lead car? (b) How much more power to the lead car than calculated in part (a) would be needed to give the train an acceleration of 1.5 m/s^2, at the instant that the train has a speed of 45 m/s on level tracks? (c) How much more power to the lead car than that calculated in part (a) would be needed to move the train up a 1.5% grade (slope angle $\alpha = \arctan 0.015$) at a constant 45 m/s?

6.96. An object has several forces acting on it. One of these forces is $\vec{F} = \alpha xy\hat{\imath}$, a force in the x-direction whose magnitude depends on the position of the object, with $\alpha = 2.50\ \text{N/m}^2$. Calculate the work done on the object by this force for the following displacements of the object: (a) The object starts at the point $x = 0$, $y = 3.00$ m and moves parallel to the x-axis to the point $x = 2.00$ m, $y = 3.00$ m. (b) The object starts at the point $x = 2.00$ m, $y = 0$ and moves in the y-direction to the point $x = 2.00$ m, $y = 3.00$ m. (c) The object starts at the origin and moves on the line $y = 1.5x$ to the point $x = 2.00$ m, $y = 3.00$ m.

6.97. Cycling. For a touring bicyclist the drag coefficient $C\left(f_{\text{air}} = \frac{1}{2}CA\rho v^2\right)$ is 1.00, the frontal area A is 0.463 m^2, and the coefficient of rolling friction is 0.0045. The rider has mass 50.0 kg, and her bike has mass 12.0 kg. (a) To maintain a speed of 12.0 m/s (about 27 mi/h) on a level road, what must the rider's power output to the rear wheel be? (b) For racing, the same rider uses a different bike with coefficient of rolling friction 0.0030 and mass 9.00 kg. She also crouches down, reducing her drag coefficient to 0.88 and reducing her frontal area to 0.366 m^2. What must her power output to the rear wheel be then to maintain a speed of 12.0 m/s? (c) For the situation in part (b), what power output is required to maintain a speed of 6.0 m/s? Note the great drop in power requirement when the speed is only halved. (For more on aerodynamic speed limitations for a wide variety of human-powered vehicles, see "The Aerodynamics of Human-Powered Land Vehicles," *Scientific American,* December 1983.)

6.98. Automotive Power I. A truck engine transmits 28.0 kW (37.5 hp) to the driving wheels when the truck is traveling at a constant velocity of magnitude 60.0 km/h (37.3 mi/h) on a level road. (a) What is the resisting force acting on the truck? (b) Assume that 65% of the resisting force is due to rolling friction and the remainder is due to air resistance. If the force of rolling friction is independent of speed, and the force of air resistance is proportional to the square of the speed, what power will drive the truck at 30.0 km/h? At 120.0 km/h? Give your answers in kilowatts and in horsepower.

6.99. Automotive Power II. (a) If 8.00 hp are required to drive a 1800-kg automobile at 60.0 km/h on a level road, what is the total retarding force due to friction, air resistance, and so on? (b) What power is necessary to drive the car at 60.0 km/h up a 10.0% grade (a hill rising 10.0 m vertically in 100.0 m horizontally)? (c) What power is necessary to drive the car at 60.0 km/h *down* a 1.00% grade? (d) Down what percent grade would the car coast at 60.0 km/h?

Challenge Problems

6.100. On a winter's day in Maine, a warehouse worker is shoving boxes up a rough plank inclined at an angle α above the horizontal. The plank is partially covered with ice, with more ice near the bottom of the plank than near the top, so that the coefficient of friction increases with the distance x along the plank: $\mu = Ax$, where A is a positive constant and the bottom of the plank is at $x = 0$. (For this plank the coefficients of kinetic and static friction are equal: $\mu_k = \mu_s = \mu$.) The worker shoves a box up the plank so that it leaves the bottom of the plank moving at speed v_0. Show that when the box first comes to rest, it will remain at rest if

$$v_0^2 \geq \frac{3g\sin^2\alpha}{A\cos\alpha}$$

6.101. A Spring with Mass. We usually ignore the kinetic energy of the moving coils of a spring, but let's try to get a reasonable approximation to this. Consider a spring of mass M, equilibrium length L_0, and spring constant k. The work done to stretch or compress the spring by a distance L is $\frac{1}{2}kX^2$, where $X = L - L_0$. (a) Consider a spring, as described above, that has one end fixed and the other end moving with speed v. Assume that the speed of points along the length of the spring varies linearly with distance l from the fixed end. Assume also that the mass M of the spring is distributed uniformly along the length of the spring. Calculate the kinetic energy of the spring in terms of M and v. (*Hint:* Divide the spring into pieces of length dl; find the speed of each piece in terms of l, v, and L; find the mass of each piece in terms of dl, M, and L; and integrate from 0 to L. The result is *not* $\frac{1}{2}Mv^2$, since not all of the spring moves with the same speed.) In a spring gun, a spring of mass 0.243 kg and force constant 3200 N/m is compressed 2.50 cm from its unstretched length. When the trigger is pulled, the spring pushes horizontally on a 0.053-kg ball. The work done by friction is negligible. Calculate the ball's speed when the spring reaches its uncompressed length (b) ignoring the mass of the spring and (c) including, using the results of part (a), the mass of the spring. (d) In part (c), what is the final kinetic energy of the ball and of the spring?

6.102. An airplane in flight is subject to an air resistance force proportional to the square of its speed v. But there is an additional resistive force because the airplane has wings. Air flowing over the wings is pushed down and slightly forward, so from Newton's third law the air exerts a force on the wings and airplane that is up and slightly backward (Fig. 6.39). The upward force is the lift force that keeps the airplane aloft, and the backward force is called *induced drag.* At flying speeds, induced drag is inversely proportional to v^2, so that the total air resistance force can be expressed by $F_{air} = \alpha v^2 + \beta/v^2$, where α and β are positive constants that depend on the shape and size of the airplane and the density of the air. For a Cessna 150, a small single-engine airplane, $\alpha = 0.30\ N \cdot s^2/m^2$ and $\beta = 3.5 \times 10^5\ N \cdot m^2/s^2$. In steady flight, the engine must provide a forward force that exactly balances the air resistance force. (a) Calculate the speed (in km/h) at which this airplane will have the maximum *range* (that is, travel the greatest distance) for a given quantity of fuel. (b) Calculate the speed (in km/h) for which the airplane will have the maximum *endurance* (that is, remain in the air the longest time).

Figure 6.39 Challenge Problem 6.102.

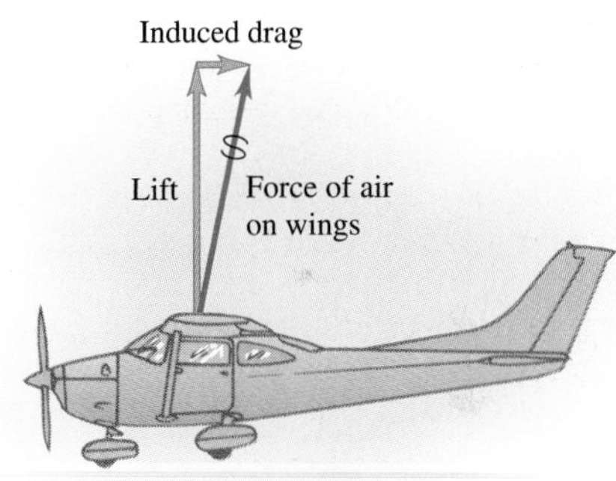

6.103. Figure 6.40 shows the oxygen consumption rate of men walking and running at different speeds. The vertical axis shows the volume of oxygen (in cm^3) that a man consumes per kilogram

Figure 6.40 Challenge Problem 6.103.

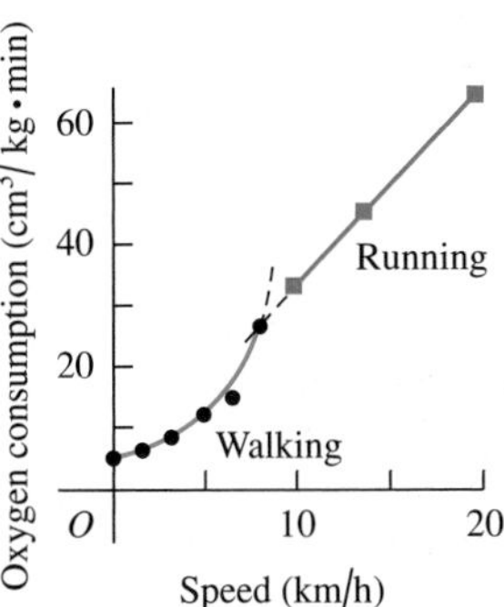

of body mass per minute. Note the transition from walking to running that occurs naturally at about 9 km/h. The metabolism of 1 cm^3 of oxygen releases about 20 J of energy. Using the data in the graph, calculate the energy required for a 70-kg man to travel 1 km on foot at (a) 5 km/h (walking); (b) 10 km/h (running); (c) 15 km/h (running). (d) Which speed is the most efficient—that is, requires the least energy to travel 1 km?

6.104. General Proof of the Work–Energy Theorem. Consider a particle that moves along a curved path in space from (x_1, y_1, z_1) to (x_2, y_2, z_2). At the initial point, the particle has velocity $\vec{v} = v_{1x}\hat{\imath} + v_{1y}\hat{\jmath} + v_{1z}\hat{k}$. The path that the particle follows may be divided into infinitesimal segments $d\vec{l} = dx\hat{\imath} + dy\hat{\jmath} + dz\hat{k}$. As the particle moves, it is acted on by a net force $\vec{F} = F_x\hat{\imath} + F_y\hat{\jmath} + F_z\hat{k}$. The force components F_x, F_y, and F_z are in general functions of position. By the same sequence of steps used in Eqs. (6.11) through (6.13), prove the work–energy theorem for this general case. That is, prove that

$$W_{\text{tot}} = K_2 - K_1$$

where

$$W_{\text{tot}} = \int_{(x_1, y_1, z_1)}^{(x_2, y_2, z_2)} \vec{F} \cdot d\vec{l} = \int_{(x_1, y_1, z_1)}^{(x_2, y_2, z_2)} (F_x\,dx + F_y\,dy + F_z\,dz)$$

POTENTIAL ENERGY AND ENERGY CONSERVATION

? As this diver enters the water, is the force of gravity doing positive or negative work on him? Is the water doing positive or negative work on him?

LEARNING GOALS

By studying this chapter, you will learn:

- How to use the concept of gravitational potential energy in problems that involve vertical motion.
- How to use the concept of elastic potential energy in problems that involve a moving body attached to a stretched or compressed spring.
- The distinction between conservative and nonconservative forces, and how to solve problems in which both kinds of forces act on a moving body.
- How to calculate the properties of a conservative force if you know the corresponding potential-energy function.
- How to use energy diagrams to understand the motion of an object moving in a straight line under the influence of a conservative force.

When a diver jumps off a high board into a swimming pool, he hits the water moving pretty fast, with a lot of kinetic energy. Where does that energy come from? The answer we learned in Chapter 6 was that the gravitational force (his weight) does work on the diver as he falls. The diver's kinetic energy—energy associated with his *motion*—increases by an amount equal to the work done.

However, there is a very useful alternative way to think about work and kinetic energy. This new approach is based on the concept of *potential energy,* which is energy associated with the *position* of a system rather than its motion. In this approach, there is *gravitational potential energy* even while the diver is standing on the high board. Energy is not added to the earth–diver system as the diver falls, but rather a storehouse of energy is *transformed* from one form (potential energy) to another (kinetic energy) as he falls. In this chapter we'll see how the work–energy theorem explains this transformation.

If the diver bounces on the end of the board before he jumps, the bent board stores a second kind of potential energy called *elastic potential energy.* We'll discuss elastic potential energy of simple systems such as a stretched or compressed spring. (An important third kind of potential energy is associated with the positions of electrically charged particles relative to each other. We'll encounter this potential energy in Chapter 23.)

We will prove that in some cases the sum of a system's kinetic and potential energy, called the *total mechanical energy* of the system, is constant during the motion of the system. This will lead us to the general statement of the *law of conservation of energy,* one of the most fundamental and far-reaching principles in all of science.

7.1 As a basketball descends, gravitational potential energy is converted to kinetic energy and the basketball's speed increases.

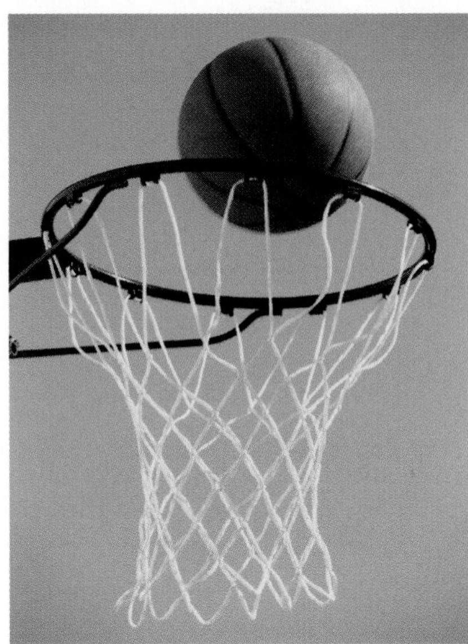

7.2 When a body moves vertically from an initial height y_1 to a final height y_2, the gravitational force $\vec{w}$ does work and the gravitational potential energy changes.

(a) A body moves downward

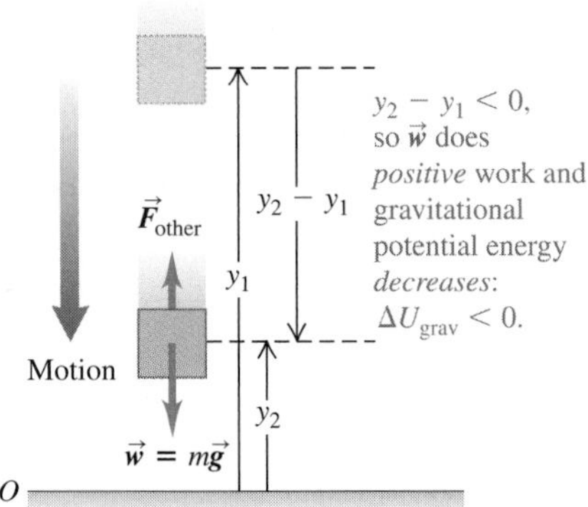
$y_2 - y_1 < 0$,
so $\vec{w}$ does
positive work and
gravitational
potential energy
decreases:
$\Delta U_{grav} < 0$.
$\vec{F}_{other}$
$y_2 - y_1$
y_1
Motion
y_2
$\vec{w} = m\vec{g}$
O

(b) A body moves upward

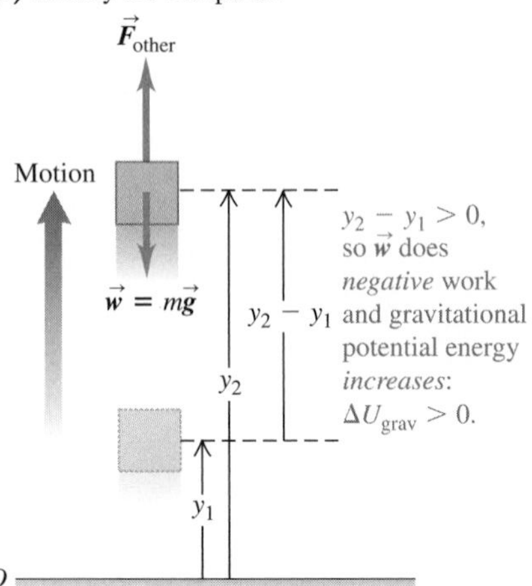
$\vec{F}_{other}$
Motion
$y_2 - y_1 > 0$,
so $\vec{w}$ does
negative work
and gravitational
potential energy
increases:
$\Delta U_{grav} > 0$.
$\vec{w} = m\vec{g}$
$y_2 - y_1$
y_2
y_1
O

7.1 Gravitational Potential Energy

We learned in Chapter 6 that a particle gains or loses kinetic energy because it interacts with other objects that exert forces on it. During any interaction, the change in a particle's kinetic energy is equal to the total work done on the particle by the forces that act on it.

In many situations it seems as though energy has been stored in a system, to be recovered later. For example, you must do work to lift a heavy stone over your head. It seems reasonable that in hoisting the stone into the air you are storing energy in the system, energy that is later converted into kinetic energy when you let the stone fall.

This example points to the idea of an energy associated with the *position* of bodies in a system. This kind of energy is a measure of the *potential* or *possibility* for work to be done; when a stone is raised into the air, there is a potential for work to be done on it by the gravitational force, but only if the stone is allowed to fall to the ground. For this reason, energy associated with position is called **potential energy.** Our discussion suggests that there is potential energy associated with a body's weight and its height above the ground. We call this *gravitational potential energy* (Fig. 7.1).

We now have *two* ways to describe what happens when a body falls without air resistance. One way is to say that gravitational potential energy decreases and the falling body's kinetic energy increases. The other way, which we learned in Chapter 6, is that a falling body's kinetic energy increases because the force of the earth's gravity (the body's weight) does work on the body. Later in this section we'll use the work–energy theorem to show that these two descriptions are equivalent.

To begin with, however, let's derive the expression for gravitational potential energy. Suppose a body with mass m moves along the (vertical) y-axis, as in Fig. 7.2. The forces acting on it are its weight, with magnitude $w = mg$, and possibly some other forces; we call the vector sum (resultant) of all the other forces $\vec{F}_{other}$. We'll assume that the body stays close enough to the earth's surface that the weight is constant. (We'll find in Chapter 12 that weight decreases with altitude.) We want to find the work done by the weight when the body moves downward from a height y_1 above the origin to a lower height y_2 (Fig. 7.2a). The weight and displacement are in the same direction, so the work W_{grav} done on the body by its weight is positive;

$$W_{grav} = Fs = w(y_1 - y_2) = mgy_1 - mgy_2 \tag{7.1}$$

This expression also gives the correct work when the body moves *upward* and y_2 is greater than y_1 (Fig. 7.2b). In that case the quantity $(y_1 - y_2)$ is negative, and W_{grav} is negative because the weight and displacement are opposite in direction.

Equation (7.1) shows that we can express W_{grav} in terms of the values of the quantity mgy at the beginning and end of the displacement. This quantity, the product of the weight mg and the height y above the origin of coordinates, is called the **gravitational potential energy,** U_{grav}:

$$U_{grav} = mgy \quad \text{(gravitational potential energy)} \tag{7.2}$$

Its initial value is $U_{grav,1} = mgy_1$ and its final value is $U_{grav,2} = mgy_2$. The change in U_{grav} is the final value minus the initial value, or $\Delta U_{grav} = U_{grav,2} - U_{grav,1}$. We can express the work W_{grav} done by the gravitational force during the displacement from y_1 to y_2 as

$$W_{grav} = U_{grav,1} - U_{grav,2} = -(U_{grav,2} - U_{grav,1}) = -\Delta U_{grav} \tag{7.3}$$

The negative sign in front of ΔU_{grav} is *essential.* When the body moves up, y increases, the work done by the gravitational force is negative, and the gravitational potential energy increases $(\Delta U_{grav} > 0)$. When the body moves down, y decreases, the gravitational force does positive work, and the gravitational potential energy decreases $(\Delta U_{grav} < 0)$. It's like drawing money out of the bank (decreasing U_{grav}) and spending it (doing positive work). As Eq. (7.3) shows, the unit of potential energy is the joule (J), the same unit as is used for work.

CAUTION **To what body does gravitational potential energy "belong"?** It is *not* correct to call $U_{grav} = mgy$ the "gravitational potential energy of the body." The reason is that gravitational potential energy U_{grav} is a *shared* property of the body and the earth. The value of U_{grav} increases if the earth stays fixed and the body moves upward, away from the earth; it also increases if the body stays fixed and the earth is moved away from it. Notice that the formula $U_{grav} = mgy$ involves characteristics of both the body (its mass m) and the earth (the value of g).

Conservation of Mechanical Energy (Gravitational Forces Only)

To see what gravitational potential energy is good for, suppose the body's weight is the *only* force acting on it, so $\vec{F}_{other} = \mathbf{0}$. The body is then falling freely with no air resistance, and can be moving either up or down. Let its speed at point y_1 be v_1 and let its speed at y_2 be v_2. The work–energy theorem, Eq. (6.6), says that the total work done on the body equals the change in the body's kinetic energy: $W_{tot} = \Delta K = K_2 - K_1$. If gravity is the only force that acts, then from Eq. (7.3), $W_{tot} = W_{grav} = -\Delta U_{grav} = U_{grav,1} - U_{grav,2}$. Putting these together, we get

$$\Delta K = -\Delta U_{grav} \quad \text{or} \quad K_2 - K_1 = U_{grav,1} - U_{grav,2}$$

which we can rewrite as

$$K_1 + U_{grav,1} = K_2 + U_{grav,2} \quad \text{(if only gravity does work)} \tag{7.4}$$

or

$$\frac{1}{2}mv_1^2 + mgy_1 = \frac{1}{2}mv_2^2 + mgy_2 \quad \text{(if only gravity does work)} \tag{7.5}$$

The sum $K + U_{grav}$ of kinetic and potential energy is called E, the **total mechanical energy of the system.** By "system" we mean the body of mass m and the earth considered together, because gravitational potential energy U is a shared property of both bodies. Then $E_1 = K_1 + U_{grav,1}$ is the total mechanical energy at y_1 and $E_2 = K_2 + U_{grav,2}$ is the total mechanical energy at y_2. Equation (7.4) says that when the body's weight is the only force doing work on it, $E_1 = E_2$. That is, E is constant; it has the same value at y_1 and y_2. But since the positions y_1 and y_2 are arbitrary points in the motion of the body, the total mechanical energy E has the same value at *all* points during the motion:

$$E = K + U_{grav} = \text{constant} \quad \text{(if only gravity does work)}$$

A quantity that always has the same value is called a *conserved* quantity. *When only the force of gravity does work, the total mechanical energy is constant—that is, is conserved* (Fig. 7.3). This is our first example of the **conservation of mechanical energy.**

When we throw a ball into the air, its speed decreases on the way up as kinetic energy is converted to potential energy; $\Delta K < 0$ and $\Delta U_{grav} > 0$. On the way back down, potential energy is converted back to kinetic energy and the ball's speed increases; $\Delta K > 0$ and $\Delta U_{grav} < 0$. But the *total* mechanical energy (kinetic plus potential) is the same at every point in the motion, provided that no force other than gravity does work on the ball (that is, air resistance must be

7.3 While this athlete is in midair, only gravity does work on him (if we neglect the minor effects of air resistance). Mechanical energy E—the sum of kinetic and gravitational potential energy—is conserved.

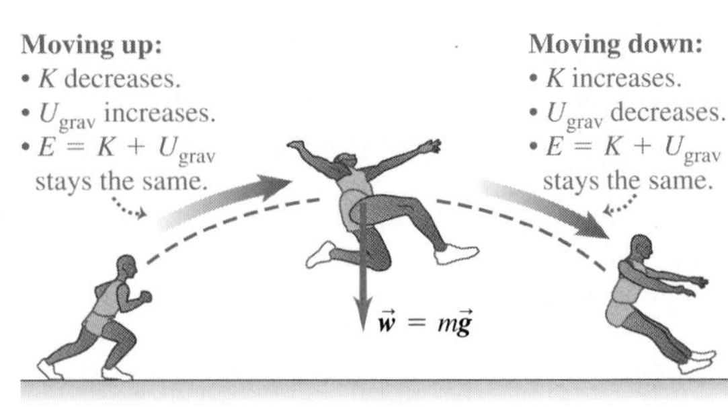
Moving up:
• K decreases.
• U_{grav} increases.
• $E = K + U_{grav}$ stays the same.
Moving down:
• K increases.
• U_{grav} decreases.
• $E = K + U_{grav}$ stays the same.
$\vec{w} = m\vec{g}$

Activ ONLINE Physics
5.2 Upward-Moving Elevator Stops
5.3 Stopping a Downward-Moving Elevator
5.6 Skier Speed

negligible). It's still true that the gravitational force does work on the body as it moves up or down, but we no longer have to calculate work directly; keeping track of changes in the value of U_{grav} takes care of this completely.

CAUTION **Choose "zero height" to be wherever you like** When working with gravitational potential energy, we may choose any height to be $y = 0$. If we shift the origin for y, the values of y_1 and y_2 change, as do the values of $U_{grav,1}$ and $U_{grav,2}$. But this shift has no effect on the *difference* in height $y_2 - y_1$ or on the *difference* in gravitational potential energy $U_{grav,2} - U_{grav,1} = mg(y_2 - y_1)$. As the following example shows, the physically significant quantity is not the value of U_{grav} at a particular point, but only the *difference* in U_{grav} between two points. So we can define U_{grav} to be zero at whatever point we choose without affecting the physics.

Example 7.1 Height of a baseball from energy conservation

You throw a 0.145-kg baseball straight up in the air, giving it an initial upward velocity of magnitude 20.0 m/s. Find how high it goes, ignoring air resistance.

SOLUTION

IDENTIFY: After the ball leaves your hand, the only force doing work on the ball is gravity. Hence we can use conservation of mechanical energy.

SET UP: We'll use Eqs. (7.4) and (7.5), taking point 1 to be where the ball leaves your hand and point 2 to be where it reaches its maximum height. As in Fig. 7.2, we take the positive y-direction to be upward. The ball's speed at point 1 is $v_1 = 20.0\text{ m/s}$; at its maximum height the ball is instantaneously at rest, so $v_2 = 0$.

We want to know how far the ball moves vertically between the two points, so our target variable is the displacement $y_2 - y_1$. If we take the origin to be where the ball leaves your hand (point 1), then $y_1 = 0$ (Fig. 7.4) and the target variable is just y_2.

EXECUTE: Since $y_1 = 0$, the potential energy at point 1 is $U_{grav,1} = mgy_1 = 0$. Furthermore, since the ball is at rest at point 2, the kinetic energy at that point is $K_2 = \frac{1}{2}mv_2^2 = 0$. Hence Eq. (7.4), which says that $K_1 + U_{grav,1} = K_2 + U_{grav,2}$, becomes

$$K_1 = U_{grav,2}$$

As the energy bar graphs in Fig. 7.4 show, the kinetic energy of the ball at point 1 is completely converted to gravitational potential energy at point 2. At point 1 the kinetic energy is

$$K_1 = \frac{1}{2}mv_1^2 = \frac{1}{2}(0.145\text{ kg})(20.0\text{ m/s})^2 = 29.0\text{ J}$$

7.4 After a baseball leaves your hand, mechanical energy $E = K + U$ is conserved.

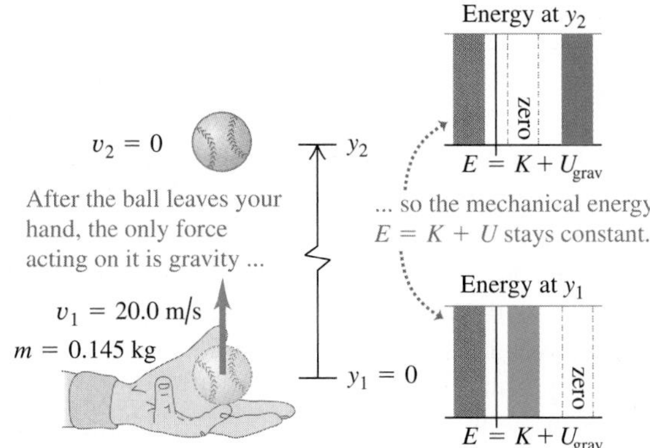
Energy at y_2
zero
$E = K + U_{grav}$
$v_2 = 0$
y_2
After the ball leaves your hand, the only force acting on it is gravity ...
... so the mechanical energy $E = K + U$ stays constant.
Energy at y_1
$v_1 = 20.0$ m/s
$m = 0.145$ kg
$y_1 = 0$
zero
$E = K + U_{grav}$

This equals the gravitational potential energy $U_{grav,2} = mgy_2$ at point 2, so

$$y_2 = \frac{U_{grav,2}}{mg} = \frac{29.0\text{ J}}{(0.145\text{ kg})(9.80\text{ m/s}^2)} = 20.4\text{ m}$$

We can also solve the equation $K_1 = U_{grav,2}$ algebraically for y_2:

$$\frac{1}{2}mv_1^2 = mgy_2$$

$$y_2 = \frac{v_1^2}{2g} = \frac{(20.0\text{ m/s})^2}{2(9.80\text{ m/s}^2)} = 20.4\text{ m}$$

EVALUATE: The mass divides out, as we should expect; we learned in Chapter 2 that the motion of a body in free fall doesn't depend on its mass. Indeed, we could have derived the result $y_2 = v_1^2/2g$ using Eq. (2.13).

In our calculation we chose the origin to be at point 1, so $y_1 = 0$ and $U_{grav,1} = 0$. What happens if we make a different choice? As an example, suppose we choose the origin to be 5.0 m below point 1, so $y_1 = 5.0$ m. Then the total mechanical energy at point 1 is part kinetic and part potential, while at point 2 it's purely potential energy. If you work through the calculation again with this choice of origin, you'll find $y_2 = 25.4$ m; this is 20.4 m above point 1, just as with the first choice of origin. In problems like this, the choice of height at which $U_{grav} = 0$ is up to you; don't agonize over the choice, though, because the physics of the answer doesn't depend on your choice.

When Forces Other Than Gravity Do Work

If other forces act on the body in addition to its weight, then $\vec{F}_{other}$ in Fig. 7.2 is *not* zero. For the pile driver described in Example 6.4 (Section 6.2), the force applied by the hoisting cable and the friction with the vertical guide rails are examples of forces that might be included in $\vec{F}_{other}$. The gravitational work W_{grav} is still given by Eq. (7.3), but the total work W_{tot} is then the sum of W_{grav} and the work done by $\vec{F}_{other}$. We will call this additional work W_{other}, so the total work done by all forces is $W_{tot} = W_{grav} + W_{other}$. Equating this to the change in kinetic energy, we have

$$W_{other} + W_{grav} = K_2 - K_1 \tag{7.6}$$

Also, from Eq. (7.3), $W_{grav} = U_{grav,1} - U_{grav,2}$, so

$$W_{other} + U_{grav,1} - U_{grav,2} = K_2 - K_1$$

which we can rearrange in the form

$$K_1 + U_{grav,1} + W_{other} = K_2 + U_{grav,2} \quad \text{(if forces other than gravity do work)} \tag{7.7}$$

Finally, using the appropriate expressions for the various energy terms, we obtain

$$\frac{1}{2}mv_1^2 + mgy_1 + W_{other} = \frac{1}{2}mv_2^2 + mgy_2 \quad \text{(if forces other than gravity do work)} \tag{7.8}$$

The meaning of Eqs. (7.7) and (7.8) is this: *The work done by all forces* other than the gravitational force *equals the change in the total mechanical energy* $E = K + U_{grav}$ *of the system, where* U_{grav} *is the gravitational potential energy.* When W_{other} is positive, E increases, and $K_2 + U_{grav,2}$ is greater than $K_1 + U_{grav,1}$. When W_{other} is negative, E decreases (Fig. 7.5). In the special case in which no forces other than the body's weight do work, $W_{other} = 0$. The total mechanical energy is then constant, and we are back to Eq. (7.4) or (7.5).

7.5 As this skydiver moves downward, the upward force of air resistance does negative work W_{other} on him. Hence the total mechanical energy $E = K + U$ decreases: The skydiver's speed and kinetic energy K stay the same, while the gravitational potential energy U goes down.

Problem-Solving Strategy 7.1 Problems Using Mechanical Energy I

MP

IDENFITY *the relevant concepts:* Decide whether the problem should be solved by energy methods, by using $\sum\vec{F} = m\vec{a}$ directly, or by a combination of these. The energy approach is best when the problem involves varying forces, motion along a curved path (discussed later in this section), or both. If the problem involves elapsed time, the energy approach is usually *not* the best choice, because it doesn't involve time directly.

SET UP *the problem* using the following steps:

1. When using the energy approach, first decide what the initial and final states (the positions and velocities) of the system are. Use the subscript 1 for the initial state and the subscript 2 for the final state. It helps to draw sketches showing the initial and final states.
2. Define your coordinate system, particularly the level at which $y = 0$. You will use it to compute gravitational potential energies. We suggest that you always choose the positive y-direction to be upward because this is what Eq. (7.2) assumes.
3. Identify all forces that do work that can't be described in terms of potential energy. (So far this means any forces other than gravity. But later in this chapter we'll see that the work done by an ideal spring can also be expressed as a change in potential energy.) A free-body diagram is always helpful.

Continued

4. List the unknown and known quantities, including the coordinates and velocities at each point. Decide which unknowns are your target variables.

EXECUTE *the solution:* Write expressions for the initial and final kinetic and potential energies—that is, K_1, K_2, $U_{grav,1}$, and $U_{grav,2}$. Then relate the kinetic and potential energies and the work done by other forces, W_{other}, using Eq. (7.7). (You will have to calculate W_{other} in terms of these forces.) If no other forces do work, this expression becomes Eq. (7.4). It's helpful to draw bar graphs showing the initial and final values of K, U_{grav}, and $E = K + U_{grav}$. Then solve to find whatever unknown quantity is required.

EVALUATE *your answer:* Check whether your answer makes physical sense. Keep in mind, here and in later sections, that the work done by each force must be represented either in $U_{grav,1} - U_{grav,2} = -\Delta U_{grav}$ or as W_{other}, but *never* in both places. The gravitational work is included in ΔU_{grav}, so make sure you did not include it again in W_{other}.

Example 7.2 Work and energy in throwing a baseball

In Example 7.1, suppose your hand moves up 0.50 m while you are throwing the ball, which leaves your hand with an upward velocity of 20.0 m/s. Again ignore air resistance. (a) Assuming that your hand exerts a constant upward force on the ball, find the magnitude of that force. (b) Find the speed of the ball at a point 15.0 m above the point where it leaves your hand.

SOLUTION

IDENTIFY: In Example 7.1 we used conservation of mechanical energy because only gravity did work. In this example, however, we must also include the nongravitational work done by your hand.

SET UP: Figure 7.6 shows a diagram of the situation, including a free-body diagram for the ball while it is being thrown. We let point 1 be where your hand first starts to move, point 2 be where the ball leaves your hand, and point 3 be where the ball is 15.0 m above point 2. The nongravitational force $\vec{F}$ of your hand acts only between points 1 and 2. Using the same coordinate system as in Example 7.1, we have $y_1 = -0.50$ m, $y_2 = 0$, and $y_3 = 15.0$ m. The ball starts at rest at point 1, so $v_1 = 0$, and we are given that the ball's speed as it leaves your hand is $v_2 = 20.0$ m/s. Our target variables are (a) the magnitude F of the force of your hand and (b) the speed v_3 at point 3.

7.6 (a) Applying energy ideas to a ball thrown vertically upward. (b) Free-body diagram for the ball as you throw it.

(a)
v_3
$y_3 = 15.0$ m
$E = K + U_{grav}$
After the ball leaves your hand, the only force acting on it is gravity ...
... so the total mechanical energy $E = K + U$ stays constant.
$v_2 = 20.0$ m/s
$y_2 = 0$
zero
$E = K + U_{grav}$
As you throw the ball, you do positive work W_{other} on it ...
0.50 m
... so the total mechanical energy E increases.
$v_1 = 0$
$y_1 = -0.50$ m
zero
$E = K + U_{grav}$
(b)
y
F
x
w

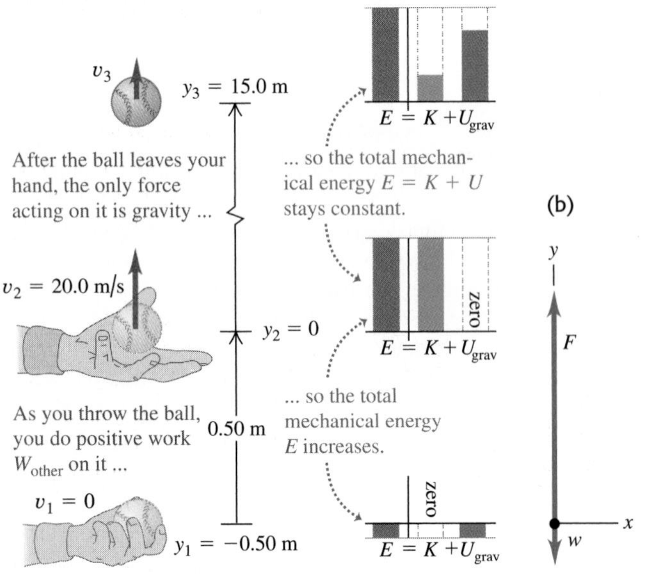

EXECUTE: (a) To determine the magnitude of $\vec{F}$, we'll first use Eq. (7.7) to calculate the work W_{other} done by this force. We have

$$K_1 = 0$$

$$U_{grav,1} = mgy_1 = (0.145\text{ kg})(9.80\text{ m/s}^2)(-0.50\text{ m}) = -0.71\text{ J}$$

$$K_2 = \frac{1}{2}mv_2^2 = \frac{1}{2}(0.145\text{ kg})(20.0\text{ m/s})^2 = 29.0\text{ J}$$

$$U_{grav,2} = mgy_2 = (0.145\text{ kg})(9.80\text{ m/s}^2)(0) = 0$$

The initial potential energy $U_{grav,1}$ is *negative* because the ball was initially below the origin. (Don't worry about having a potential energy that's less than zero. Remember, all that matters is the *difference* in potential energy from one point to another.) According to Eq. (7.7), $K_1 + U_{grav,1} + W_{other} = K_2 + U_{grav,2}$, so

$$W_{other} = (K_2 - K_1) + (U_{grav,2} - U_{grav,1})$$
$$= (29.0\text{ J} - 0) + (0 - (-0.71\text{ J})) = 29.7\text{ J}$$

The kinetic energy of the ball increases by $K_2 - K_1 = 29.0$ J, and the potential energy increases by $U_{grav,2} - U_{grav,1} = 0.71$ J; the sum is $E_2 - E_1$, the change in total mechanical energy, which is equal to W_{other}.

Assuming the upward force $\vec{F}$ that your hand applies is constant, the work W_{other} done by this force is equal to the magnitude F of the force multiplied by the upward displacement $y_2 - y_1$ over which it acts:

$$W_{other} = F(y_2 - y_1)$$

$$F = \frac{W_{other}}{y_2 - y_1} = \frac{29.7\text{ J}}{0.50\text{ m}} = 59\text{ N}$$

This is about 40 times greater than the weight of the ball.

(b) To find the speed at point 3, note that between points 2 and 3, total mechanical energy is conserved; the force of your hand no longer acts, so $W_{other} = 0$. We can then find the kinetic energy at point 3 using Eq. (7.4):

$$K_2 + U_{grav,2} = K_3 + U_{grav,3}$$

$$U_{grav,3} = mgy_3 = (0.145\text{ kg})(9.80\text{ m/s}^2)(15.0\text{ m}) = 21.3\text{ J}$$

$$K_3 = (K_2 + U_{grav,2}) - U_{grav,3}$$

$$= (29.0\text{ J} + 0\text{ J}) - 21.3\text{ J} = 7.7\text{ J}$$

Since $K_3 = \frac{1}{2}mv_{3y}^2$, where v_{3y} is the y-component of the ball's velocity at point 3, we have

$$v_{3y} = \pm\sqrt{\frac{2K_3}{m}} = \pm\sqrt{\frac{2(7.7\text{ J})}{0.145\text{ kg}}} = \pm 10\text{ m/s}$$

The significance of the plus-or-minus sign is that the ball passes point 3 *twice,* once on the way up and again on the way down. The total mechanical energy E is constant and equal to 29.0 J while the ball is in free fall, and the potential energy at point 3 is $U_{grav,3} = 21.3$ J whether the ball is moving up or down. So at point 3, the ball's kinetic energy K_3 and *speed* don't depend on the direction the ball is moving. The velocity v_{3y} is positive $(+10\text{ m/s})$ when the ball is moving up and negative (-10 m/s) when it is moving down; the speed v_3 is 10 m/s in either case.

EVALUATE: As a check on our result, recall from Example 7.1 that the ball reaches a maximum height $y = 20.4$ m. At that point all of the kinetic energy that the ball had when it left your hand at $y = 0$ has been converted to gravitational potential energy. At $y = 15.0$ m, the ball is about three-fourths of the way to its maximum height, so about three-fourths of its mechanical energy should be in the form of potential energy. (This is shown in the energy bar graphs in Fig. 7.6a.) Can you show that this is true from our results for K_3 and $U_{grav,3}$?

Gravitational Potential Energy for Motion Along a Curved Path

In our first two examples the body moved along a straight vertical line. What happens when the path is slanted or curved (Fig. 7.7a)? The body is acted on by the gravitational force $\vec{w} = m\vec{g}$ and possibly by other forces whose resultant we call $\vec{F}_{other}$. To find the work done by the gravitational force during this displacement, we divide the path into small segments $\Delta\vec{s}$; Fig. 7.7b shows a typical segment. The work done by the gravitational force over this segment is the scalar product of the force and the displacement. In terms of unit vectors, the force is $\vec{w} = m\vec{g} = -mg\hat{j}$ and the displacement is $\Delta\vec{s} = \Delta x\hat{i} + \Delta y\hat{j}$, so the work done by the gravitational force is

$$\vec{w}\cdot\Delta\vec{s} = -mg\hat{j}\cdot(\Delta x\hat{i} + \Delta y\hat{j}) = -mg\Delta y$$

The work done by gravity is the same as though the body had been displaced vertically a distance Δy, with no horizontal displacement. This is true for every segment, so the *total* work done by the gravitational force is $-mg$ multiplied by the *total* vertical displacement $(y_2 - y_1)$:

$$W_{grav} = -mg(y_2 - y_1) = mgy_1 - mgy_2 = U_{grav,1} - U_{grav,2}$$

This is the same as Eq. (7.1) or (7.3), in which we assumed a purely vertical path. So even if the path a body follows between two points is curved, the total work done by the gravitational force depends only on the difference in height between the two points of the path. This work is unaffected by any horizontal motion that may occur. So *we can use the same expression for gravitational potential energy whether the body's path is curved or straight.*

7.7 Calculating the change in gravitational potential energy for a displacement along a curved path.

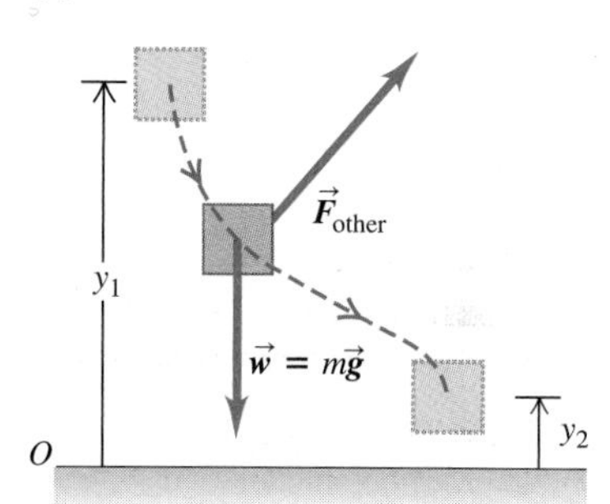

Conceptual Example 7.3 Energy in projectile motion

A batter hits two identical baseballs with the same initial speed and height but different initial angles. Prove that at a given height h, both balls have the same speed if air resistance can be neglected.

SOLUTION

If there is no air resistance, the only force acting on each ball after it is hit is its weight. Hence the total mechanical energy for each ball is constant. Figure 7.8 shows the trajectories of two balls batted at the same height with the same initial speed, and thus the same total mechanical energy, but with different initial angles. At all points at the same height the potential energy is the same. Thus the kinetic energy at this height must be the same for both balls, and the speeds are the same.

7.8 For the same initial speed and initial height, the speed of a projectile at a given elevation h is always the same, neglecting air resistance.

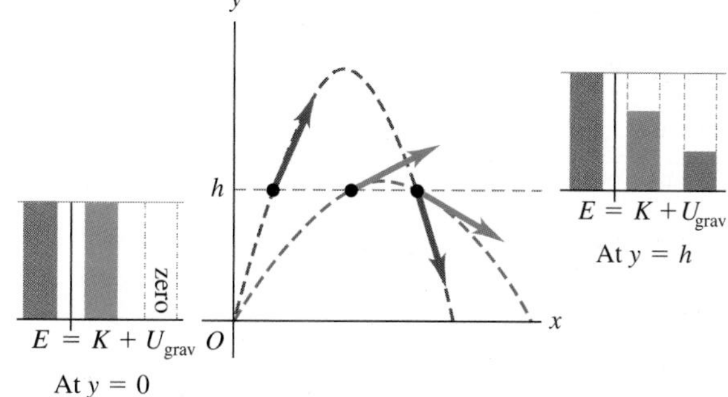

Example 7.4 Calculating speed along a vertical circle

Your cousin Throckmorton skateboards down a curved playground ramp. If we treat Throcky and his skateboard as a particle, he moves through a quarter-circle with radius $R = 3.00$ m (Fig. 7.9). The total mass of Throcky and his skateboard is 25.0 kg. He starts from rest and there is no friction. (a) Find his speed at the bottom of the ramp. (b) Find the normal force that acts on him at the bottom of the curve.

SOLUTION

IDENTIFY: We can't use the constant-acceleration equations because Throcky's acceleration isn't constant; the slope decreases as he descends. Instead, we'll use the energy approach. Since Throcky moves along a circular arc, we'll also use what we learned about circular motion in Section 5.4.

SET UP: Since there is no friction, the only force other than Throcky's weight is the normal force $\vec{n}$ exerted by the ramp (Fig. 7.9b). Although this force acts all along the path, it does *zero* work because $\vec{n}$ is perpendicular to Throcky's displacement at every point. Hence $W_{other} = 0$ and mechanical energy is conserved.

We take point 1 at the starting point and point 2 at the bottom of the curved ramp, and we let $y = 0$ be at the bottom of the ramp (Fig. 7.9a). Then $y_1 = R$ and $y_2 = 0$. (We are treating Throcky as if his entire mass were concentrated at his center.) Throcky starts at rest at the top, so $v_1 = 0$. Our target variable in part (a) is his speed at the bottom, v_2. In part (b) we want to find the magnitude n of the normal force at point 2. Because this force does no work, it doesn't appear in the energy equation, so we'll use Newton's second law instead.

EXECUTE: (a) The various energy quantities are

$$K_1 = 0 \qquad U_{grav,1} = mgR$$
$$K_2 = \frac{1}{2}mv_2^2 \qquad U_{grav,2} = 0$$

From conservation of mechanical energy,

$$\begin{aligned} K_1 + U_{grav,1} &= K_2 + U_{grav,2} \\ 0 + mgR &= \frac{1}{2}mv_2^2 + 0 \\ v_2 &= \sqrt{2gR} \\ &= \sqrt{2(9.80\ \text{m/s}^2)(3.00\ \text{m})} = 7.67\ \text{m/s} \end{aligned}$$

Notice that this answer doesn't depend on the ramp being circular; no matter what the shape of the ramp, Throcky will have the same speed $v_2 = \sqrt{2gR}$ at the bottom. This would be true even if the wheels of his skateboard lost contact with the ramp during the ride, because only the gravitational force would still do work. In fact, the speed is the same as if Throcky had fallen vertically through a height R. The answer is also independent of his mass.

(b) To find n at point 2 using Newton's second law, we need the free-body diagram at that point (Fig. 7.9b). At point 2, Throcky is moving at speed $v_2 = \sqrt{2gR}$ in a circle of radius R; his acceleration is toward the center of the circle and has magnitude

$$a_{rad} = \frac{v_2^2}{R} = \frac{2gR}{R} = 2g$$

If we take the positive y-direction to be upward, the y-component of Newton's second law is

$$\begin{aligned} \sum F_y &= n + (-w) = ma_{rad} = 2mg \\ n &= w + 2mg = 3mg \\ &= 3(25.0\ \text{kg})(9.80\ \text{m/s}^2) = 735\ \text{N} \end{aligned}$$

At point 2 the normal force is three times Throcky's weight. This result is independent of the radius of the circular ramp. We learned in Example 5.9 (Section 5.2) and Example 5.24 (Section 5.4) that the magnitude of n is the *apparent weight,* so Throcky feels as though he weighs three times his true weight mg. But as soon as he reaches the horizontal part of the ramp to the right of point 2, the normal force decreases to $w = mg$ and Throcky feels normal again. Can you see why?

EVALUATE: This example shows a general rule about the role of forces in problems in which we use energy techniques: What matters is not simply whether a force *acts,* but whether that force *does work.* If the force does no work, like the normal force $\vec{n}$ in this example, then it does not appear at all in Eq. (7.7), $K_1 + U_{grav,1} + W_{other} = K_2 + U_{grav,2}$.

Notice we had to use *both* the energy approach and Newton's second law to solve this problem; energy conservation gave us the speed and $\sum\vec{F} = m\vec{a}$ gave us the normal force. For each part of the problem we used the technique that most easily led us to the answer.

7.9 (a) Throcky skateboarding down a frictionless circular ramp. The total mechanical energy is constant. (b) Free-body diagrams for Throcky and his skateboard at various points on the ramp.

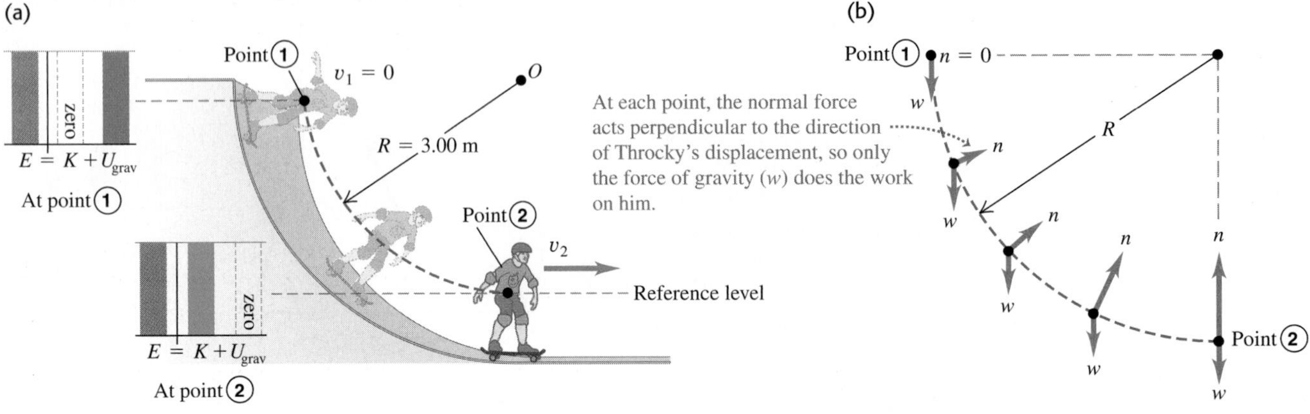

Example 7.5 A vertical circle with friction

In Example 7.4, suppose that the ramp is not frictionless and that Throcky's speed at the bottom is only 6.00 m/s. What work was done by the friction force acting on him?

SOLUTION

IDENTIFY: Figure 7.10 shows that again the normal force does no work, but now there is a friction force $\vec{f}$ that *does* do work. Hence the nongravitational work done on Throcky between points 1 and 2, W_{other}, is not zero.

SET UP: We use the same coordinate system and the same initial and final points as in Example 7.4 (see Fig. 7.10). Our target variable is the work done by friction, W_f; since friction is the only force other than gravity that does work, this is just equal to W_{other}. We'll find W_f using Eq. (7.7).

EXECUTE: The energy quantities are

$$K_1 = 0$$

$$U_{\text{grav},1} = mgR = (25.0\text{ kg})(9.80\text{ m/s}^2)(3.00\text{ m}) = 735\text{ J}$$

$$K_2 = \frac{1}{2}mv_2^2 = \frac{1}{2}(25.0\text{ kg})(6.00\text{ m/s})^2 = 450\text{ J}$$

$$U_{\text{grav},2} = 0$$

From Eq. (7.7),

$$W_f = K_2 + U_{\text{grav},2} - K_1 - U_{\text{grav},1}$$
$$= 450\text{ J} + 0 - 0 - 735\text{ J} = -285\text{ J}$$

The work done by the friction force is -285 J, and the total mechanical energy *decreases* by 285 J. Do you see why W_f has to be negative?

7.10 Free-body diagram and energy bar graphs for Throcky skateboarding down a ramp with friction.

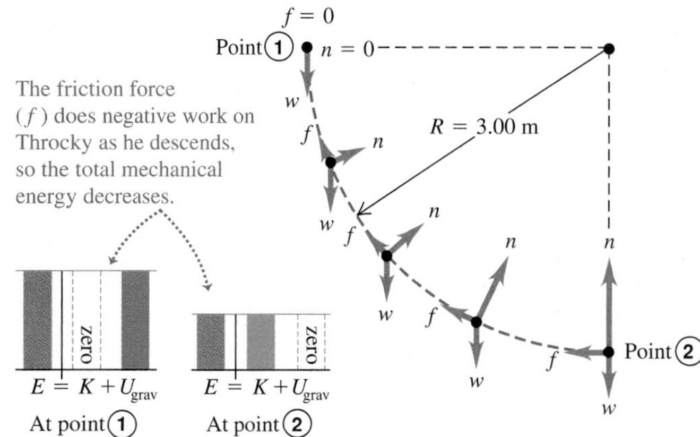

EVALUATE: Throcky's motion is determined by Newton's second law, $\Sigma\vec{F} = m\vec{a}$. But it would be very difficult to apply the second law directly to this problem because the normal and friction forces and the acceleration are continuously changing in both magnitude and direction as Throcky moves. The energy approach, by contrast, relates the motions at the top and bottom of the ramp without involving the details of what happens in between. Many problems are easy if energy considerations are used but very complex if we try to use Newton's laws directly.

Example 7.6 An inclined plane with friction

We want to load a 12-kg crate into a truck by sliding it up a ramp 2.5 m long, inclined at 30°. A worker, giving no thought to friction, calculates that he can get the crate up the ramp by giving it an initial speed of 5.0 m/s at the bottom and letting it go. But friction is *not* negligible; the crate slides 1.6 m up the ramp, stops, and slides back down (Fig. 7.11). (a) Assuming that the friction force acting on the crate is constant, find its magnitude. (b) How fast is the crate moving when it reaches the bottom of the ramp?

SOLUTION

IDENTIFY: The friction force does work on the crate as it slides. As in Example 7.2, we'll use the energy approach in part (a) to find the magnitude of the nongravitational force that does work (in this case, friction). In part (b) we'll calculate how much nongravitational work this force does as the crate slides back down and then use the energy approach to find the crate's speed at the bottom of the ramp.

SET UP: The first part of the motion is from point 1, at the bottom of the ramp, to point 2, where the crate stops instantaneously. In the second part of the motion, the crate returns to the bottom of the ramp, which we'll also call point 3 (Fig. 7.11a). We take $y = 0$ (and hence $U_{\text{grav}} = 0$) to be at ground level, so $y_1 = 0$,

7.11 (a) A crate slides partway up the ramp, stops, and slides back down. (b) Energy bar graphs for points 1, 2, and 3.

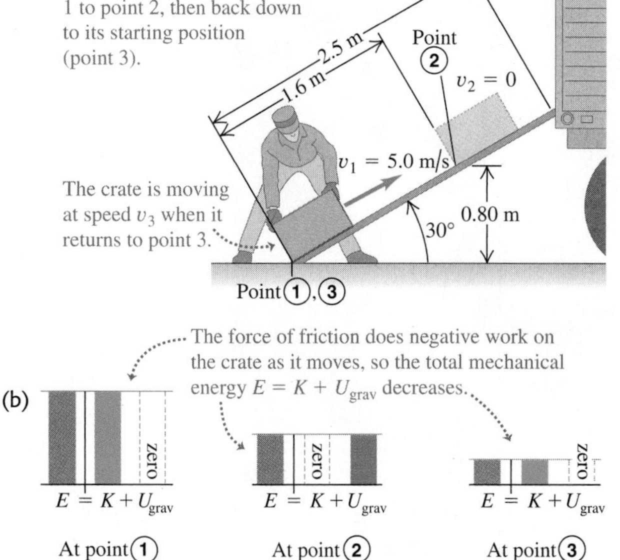

Continued

$y_2 = (1.6\text{ m})\sin 30° = 0.80\text{ m}$, and $y_3 = 0$. We are given that $v_1 = 5.0\text{ m/s}$ and $v_2 = 0$ (the crate is instantaneously at rest at point 2). Our target variable in part (a) is f, the magnitude of the friction force. In part (b) our target variable is v_3, the speed at the bottom of the ramp.

EXECUTE: (a) The energy quantities are

$$K_1 = \frac{1}{2}(12\text{ kg})(5.0\text{ m/s})^2 = 150\text{ J}$$
$$U_{\text{grav},1} = 0$$
$$K_2 = 0$$
$$U_{\text{grav},2} = (12\text{ kg})(9.8\text{ m/s}^2)(0.80\text{ m}) = 94\text{ J}$$
$$W_{\text{other}} = -fs$$

Here f is the unknown magnitude of the friction force and $s = 1.6$ m. Using Eq. (7.7), we find

$$K_1 + U_{\text{grav},1} + W_{\text{other}} = K_2 + U_{\text{grav},2}$$
$$W_{\text{other}} = -fs = (K_2 + U_{\text{grav},2}) - (K_1 + U_{\text{grav},1})$$
$$f = -\frac{(K_2 + U_{\text{grav},2}) - (K_1 + U_{\text{grav},1})}{s}$$
$$= -\frac{(0 + 94\text{ J}) - (150\text{ J} + 0)}{1.6\text{ m}} = 35\text{ N}$$

The friction force of 35 N, acting over 1.6 m, causes the mechanical energy of the crate to decrease from 150 J to 94 J (Fig. 7.11b).

(b) On the way down from point 2 to point 3 at the bottom of the ramp, the friction force and the displacement both reverse direction but have the same magnitudes, so the frictional work has the same negative value as from point 1 to point 2. The total work done by friction between points 1 and 3 is

$$W_{\text{other}} = W_{\text{fric}} = -2fs = -2(35\text{ N})(1.6\text{ m}) = -112\text{ J}$$

From part (a), $K_1 = 150$ J and $U_{\text{grav},1} = 0$. Equation (7.7) then gives

$$K_1 + U_{\text{grav},1} + W_{\text{other}} = K_3 + U_{\text{grav},3}$$
$$K_3 = K_1 + U_{\text{grav},1} - U_{\text{grav},3} + W_{\text{other}}$$
$$= 150\text{ J} + 0 - 0 + (-112\text{ J}) = 38\text{ J}$$

The crate returns to the bottom of the ramp with only 38 J of the original 150 J of mechanical energy (Fig. 7.11b). Using $K_3 = \frac{1}{2}mv_3^2$, we get

$$v_3 = \sqrt{\frac{2K_3}{m}} = \sqrt{\frac{2(38\text{ J})}{12\text{ kg}}} = 2.5\text{ m/s}$$

EVALUATE: The crate's speed when it returns to the bottom of the ramp, $v_3 = 2.5\text{ m/s}$, is less than the speed $v_1 = 5.0\text{ m/s}$ at which it left that point. That's good—energy was lost due to friction.

In part (b) we applied Eq. (7.7) to points 1 and 3, considering the entire round trip as a whole. Alternatively, we could have considered the second part of the motion by itself and applied Eq. (7.7) to points 2 and 3. Try it and see whether you get the same result for v_3.

Test Your Understanding of Section 7.1 The figure shows two different frictionless ramps. The heights y_1 and y_2 are the same for both ramps. If a block of mass m is released from rest at the left-hand end of each ramp, which block arrives at the right-hand end with the greater speed? (i) block I; (ii) block II; (iii) the speed is the same for both blocks.

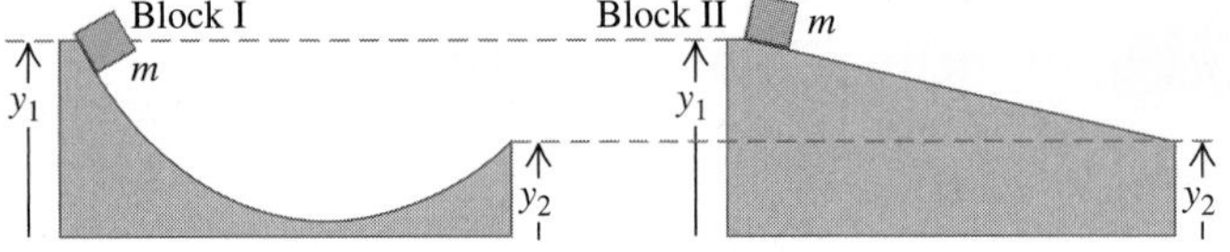

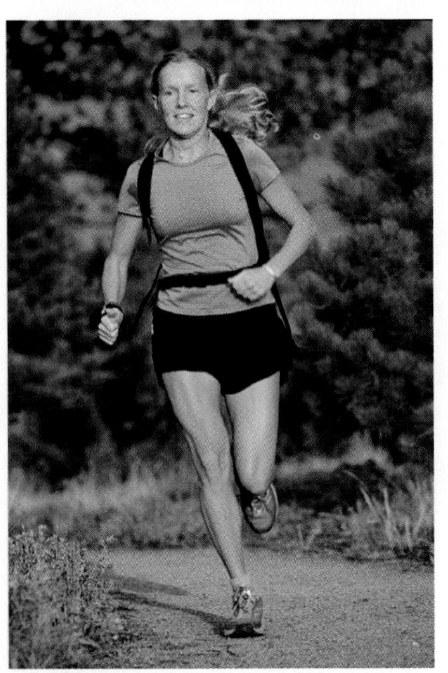

7.12 The Achilles tendon, which runs along the back of the ankle to the heel bone, acts like a natural spring. When it stretches and then relaxes, this tendon stores and then releases elastic potential energy. This spring action reduces the amount of work your leg muscles must do as you run.

7.2 Elastic Potential Energy

There are many situations in which we encounter potential energy that is not gravitational in nature. One example is a rubber-band slingshot. Work is done on the rubber band by the force that stretches it, and that work is stored in the rubber band until you let it go. Then the rubber band gives kinetic energy to the projectile.

This is the same pattern we saw with the pile driver in Section 7.1: Do work on the system to store energy, which can later be converted to kinetic energy. We'll describe the process of storing energy in a deformable body such as a spring or rubber band in terms of *elastic potential energy* (Fig. 7.12). A body is called *elastic* if it returns to its original shape and size after being deformed.

To be specific, we'll consider storing energy in an ideal spring, like the ones we discussed in Section 6.3. To keep such an ideal spring stretched by a distance x, we must exert a force $F = kx$, where k is the force constant of the spring. The ideal spring is a useful idealization because many elastic bodies show this same direct proportionality between force $\vec{F}$ and displacement x, provided that x is sufficiently small.

We proceed just as we did for gravitational potential energy. We begin with the work done by the elastic (spring) force and then combine this with the work–energy theorem. The difference is that gravitational potential energy is a shared property of a body and the earth, but elastic potential energy is stored just in the spring (or other deformable body).

Figure 7.13 shows the ideal spring from Fig. 6.18, with its left end held stationary and its right end attached to a block with mass m that can move along the x-axis. In Fig. 7.13a the body is at $x = 0$ when the spring is neither stretched nor compressed. We move the block to one side, thereby stretching or compressing the spring, and then let it go. As the block moves from one position x_1 to another position x_2, how much work does the elastic (spring) force do on the block?

We found in Section 6.3 that the work we must do *on* the spring to move one end from an elongation x_1 to a different elongation x_2 is

$$W = \frac{1}{2}kx_2^2 - \frac{1}{2}kx_1^2 \qquad \text{(work done } on \text{ a spring)}$$

where k is the force constant of the spring. If we stretch the spring farther, we do positive work on the spring; if we let the spring relax while holding one end, we do negative work on it. We also saw that this expression for work is still correct if the spring is compressed, not stretched, so that x_1 or x_2 or both are negative. Now we need to find the work done *by* the spring. From Newton's third law the two quantities of work are just negatives of each other. Changing the signs in this equation, we find that in a displacement from x_1 to x_2 the spring does an amount of work W_{el} given by

$$W_{el} = \frac{1}{2}kx_1^2 - \frac{1}{2}kx_2^2 \qquad \text{(work done } by \text{ a spring)}$$

The subscript "el" stands for *elastic.* When x_1 and x_2 are both positive and $x_2 > x_1$ (Fig. 7.13b), the spring does negative work on the block, which moves in the $+x$-direction while the spring pulls on it in the $-x$-direction. The spring stretches farther, and the block slows down. When x_1 and x_2 are both positive and $x_2 < x_1$ (Fig. 7.13c), the spring does positive work as it relaxes and the block speeds up. If the spring can be compressed as well as stretched, x_1 or x_2 or both may be negative, but the expression for W_{el} is still valid. In Fig. 7.13d, both x_1 and x_2 are negative, but x_2 is less negative than x_1; the compressed spring does positive work as it relaxes, speeding the block up.

Just as for gravitational work, we can express the work done by the spring in terms of a given quantity at the beginning and end of the displacement. This quantity is $\frac{1}{2}kx^2$, and we define it to be the **elastic potential energy:**

$$U_{el} = \frac{1}{2}kx^2 \qquad \text{(elastic potential energy)} \qquad (7.9)$$

Figure 7.14 is a graph of Eq. (7.9). The unit of U_{el} is the joule (J), the unit used for *all* energy and work quantities; to see this from Eq. (7.9), recall that the units of k are N/m and that $1\ \text{N} \cdot \text{m} = 1\ \text{J}$.

We can use Eq. (7.9) to express the work W_{el} done on the block by the elastic force in terms of the change in elastic potential energy:

$$W_{el} = \frac{1}{2}kx_1^2 - \frac{1}{2}kx_2^2 = U_{el,1} - U_{el,2} = -\Delta U_{el} \qquad (7.10)$$

When a stretched spring is stretched farther, as in Fig. 7.13b, W_{el} is negative and U_{el} *increases;* a greater amount of elastic potential energy is stored in the spring. When a stretched spring relaxes, as in Fig. 7.13c, x decreases, W_{el} is positive, and U_{el} *decreases;* the spring loses elastic potential energy. Negative values of x refer

7.13 Calculating the work done by a spring attached to a block on a horizontal surface. The quantity x is the extension or compression of the spring.

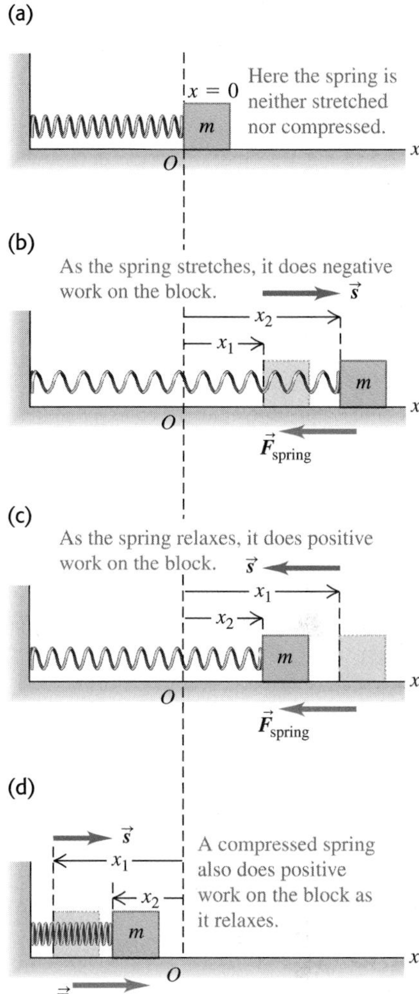
(a)
x = 0
Here the spring is neither stretched nor compressed.
m
O
x
(b)
As the spring stretches, it does negative work on the block.
s
x2
x1
m
O
x
F spring
(c)
As the spring relaxes, it does positive work on the block.
s
x1
x2
m
O
x
F spring
(d)
s
x1
x2
A compressed spring also does positive work on the block as it relaxes.
m
O
x
F spring

7.14 The graph of elastic potential energy for an ideal spring is a parabola: $U_{el} = \frac{1}{2}kx^2$, where x is the extension or compression of the spring. Elastic potential energy U_{el} is never negative.

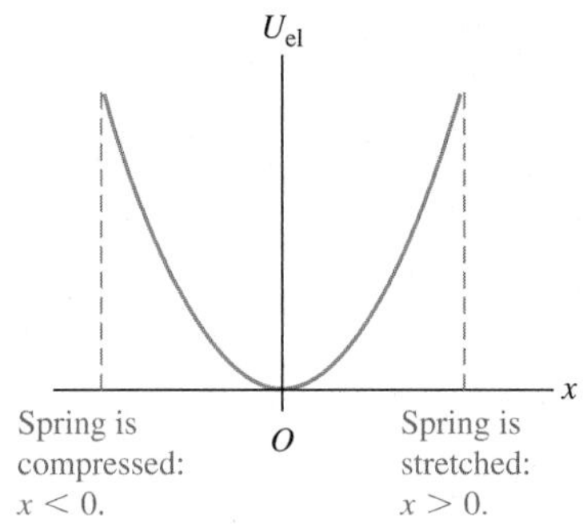
U el
x
O
Spring is compressed: x < 0.
Spring is stretched: x > 0.

to a compressed spring. But, as Fig. 7.14 shows, U_{el} is positive for both positive and negative x, and Eqs. (7.9) and (7.10) are valid for both cases. The more a spring is compressed *or* stretched, the greater its elastic potential energy.

CAUTION Gravitational potential energy vs. elastic potential energy An important difference between gravitational potential energy $U_{grav} = mgy$ and elastic potential energy $U_{el} = \frac{1}{2}kx^2$ is that we do *not* have the freedom to choose $x = 0$ to be wherever we wish. To be consistent with Eq. (7.9), $x = 0$ *must* be the position at which the spring is neither stretched nor compressed. At that position, its elastic potential energy and the force that it exerts are both zero.

The work–energy theorem says that $W_{tot} = K_2 - K_1$, no matter what kind of forces are acting on a body. If the elastic force is the *only* force that does work on the body, then

$$W_{tot} = W_{el} = U_{el,1} - U_{el,2}$$

The work–energy theorem $W_{tot} = K_2 - K_1$ then gives us

$$K_1 + U_{el,1} = K_2 + U_{el,2} \qquad \text{(if only the elastic force does work)} \tag{7.11}$$

Here U_{el} is given by Eq. (7.9), so

$$\frac{1}{2}mv_1^2 + \frac{1}{2}kx_1^2 = \frac{1}{2}mv_2^2 + \frac{1}{2}kx_2^2 \qquad \text{(if only the elastic force does work)} \tag{7.12}$$

In this case the total mechanical energy $E = K + U_{el}$—the sum of kinetic and *elastic* potential energy—is *conserved.* An example of this is the motion of the block in Fig. 7.13, provided the horizontal surface is frictionless so that no force does work other than that exerted by the spring.

For Eq. (7.12) to be strictly correct, the ideal spring that we've been discussing must also be *massless.* If the spring has a mass, it also has kinetic energy as the coils of the spring move back and forth. We can neglect the kinetic energy of the spring if its mass is much less than the mass m of the body attached to the spring. For instance, a typical automobile has a mass of 1200 kg or more. The springs in its suspension have masses of only a few kilograms, so their mass can be neglected if we want to study how a car bounces on its suspension.

Situations with Both Gravitational and Elastic Potential Energy

ActivPhysics ONLINE
5.4 Inverse Bungee Jumper
5.5 Spring-Launched Bowler

Equations (7.11) and (7.12) are valid when the only potential energy in the system is elastic potential energy. What happens when we have *both* gravitational and elastic forces, such as a block attached to the lower end of a vertically hanging spring? And what if work is also done by other forces that *cannot* be described in terms of potential energy, such as the force of air resistance on a moving block? Then the total work is the sum of the work done by the gravitational force (W_{grav}), the work done by the elastic force (W_{el}), and the work done by other forces (W_{other}): $W_{tot} = W_{grav} + W_{el} + W_{other}$. Then the work–energy theorem gives

$$W_{grav} + W_{el} + W_{other} = K_2 - K_1$$

The work done by the gravitational force is $W_{grav} = U_{grav,1} - U_{grav,2}$ and the work done by the spring is $W_{el} = U_{el,1} - U_{el,2}$. Hence we can rewrite the work–energy theorem for this most general case as

$$K_1 + U_{grav,1} + U_{el,1} + W_{other} = K_2 + U_{grav,2} + U_{el,2} \qquad \text{(valid in general)} \tag{7.13}$$

or, equivalently,

$$K_1 + U_1 + W_{\text{other}} = K_2 + U_2 \qquad \text{(valid in general)} \tag{7.14}$$

where $U = U_{\text{grav}} + U_{\text{el}} = mgy + \frac{1}{2}kx^2$ is the *sum* of gravitational potential energy and elastic potential energy. For short, we call U simply "the potential energy."

Equation (7.14) is *the most general statement* of the relationship among kinetic energy, potential energy, and work done by other forces. It says:

The work done by all forces other than the gravitational force or elastic force equals the change in the total mechanical energy $E = K + U$ of the system, where $U = U_{\text{grav}} + U_{\text{el}}$ is the sum of the gravitational potential energy and the elastic potential energy.

The "system" is made up of the body of mass m, the earth with which it interacts through the gravitational force, and the spring of force constant k.

If W_{other} is positive, $E = K + U$ increases; if W_{other} is negative, E decreases. If the gravitational and elastic forces are the *only* forces that do work on the body, then $W_{\text{other}} = 0$ and the total mechanical energy (including both gravitational and elastic potential energy) is conserved. (You should compare Eq. (7.14) to Eqs. (7.7) and (7.8), which describe situations in which there is gravitational potential energy but no elastic potential energy.)

Bungee jumping (Fig. 7.15) is an example of transformations among kinetic energy, elastic potential energy, and gravitational potential energy. As the jumper falls, gravitational potential energy decreases and is converted into the kinetic energy of the jumper and the elastic potential energy of the bungee cord. Beyond a certain point in the fall, the jumper's speed decreases so that both gravitational potential energy and kinetic energy are converted into elastic potential energy.

7.15 The fall of a bungee jumper involves an interplay among kinetic energy, gravitational potential energy, and elastic potential energy. Due to air resistance and frictional forces within the bungee cord, mechanical energy is not conserved. (If mechanical energy *were* conserved, the bungee jumper would keep bouncing up and down forever!)

Problem-Solving Strategy 7.2 Problems Using Mechanical Energy II

Problem-Solving Strategy 7.1 (Section 7.1) is equally useful in solving problems that involve elastic forces as well as gravitational forces. The only new wrinkle is that the potential energy U now includes the elastic potential energy $U_{\text{el}} = \frac{1}{2}kx^2$, where x is the displacement of the spring *from its unstretched length*. The work done by the gravitational and elastic forces is accounted for by their potential energies; the work of the other forces, W_{other}, has to be included separately.

Example 7.7 Motion with elastic potential energy

A glider with mass $m = 0.200$ kg sits on a frictionless horizontal air track, connected to a spring with force constant $k = 5.00$ N/m. You pull on the glider, stretching the spring 0.100 m, and then release it with no initial velocity. The glider begins to move back toward its equilibrium position ($x = 0$). What is its x-velocity when $x = 0.080$ m?

SOLUTION

IDENTIFY: Because the spring force varies with position, this problem can't be solved with the equations for motion with constant acceleration. Instead, we'll use the idea that as the glider starts to move, elastic potential energy is converted into kinetic energy. (The glider remains at the same height throughout the motion, so gravitational potential energy is not a factor. Hence $U = U_{\text{el}} = \frac{1}{2}kx^2$.)

7.16 Our sketches and energy bar graphs for this problem.

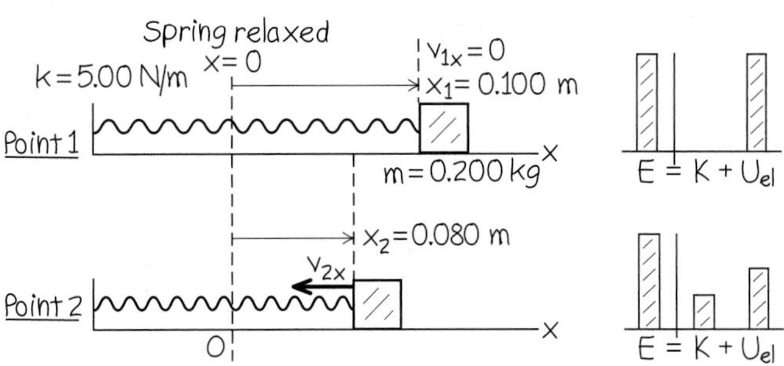

SET UP: Figure 7.16 shows our sketches. The spring force is the only force doing work on the glider, so $W_{\text{other}} = 0$ and we may use

Continued

Eq. (7.11). We designate the point where the glider is released as point 1 and $x = 0.080$ m as point 2. We know the velocity at point 1 ($v_{1x} = 0$); our target variable is the x-velocity at point 2, v_{2x}.

EXECUTE: The energy quantities are

$$K_1 = \frac{1}{2}mv_{1x}^2 = \frac{1}{2}(0.200\text{ kg})(0)^2 = 0$$

$$U_1 = \frac{1}{2}kx_1^2 = \frac{1}{2}(5.00\text{ n/m})(0.100\text{ m})^2 = 0.0250\text{ J}$$

$$K_2 = \frac{1}{2}mv_{2x}^2$$

$$U_2 = \frac{1}{2}kx_2^2 = \frac{1}{2}(5.00\text{ N/m})(0.080\text{ m})^2 = 0.0160\text{ J}$$

Then from Eq. (7.11),

$$K_2 = K_1 + U_1 - U_2 = 0 + 0.0250\text{ J} - 0.0160\text{ J} = 0.0090\text{ J}$$

$$v_{2x} = \pm\sqrt{\frac{2K_2}{m}} = \pm\sqrt{\frac{2(0.0090\text{ J})}{0.200\text{ kg}}} = \pm 0.30\text{ m/s}$$

We choose the negative root because the glider is moving in the $-x$-direction; the answer we want is $v_{2x} = -0.30$ m/s.

EVALUATE: What is the meaning of the second solution, $v_{2x} = +0.30$ m/s? Eventually the spring will compress and push the glider back to the right in the positive x-direction (see Fig. 7.13d). The second solution tells us that when the glider passes through $x = 0.080$ m while moving to the right, its speed will be 0.30 m/s—the same speed as when it passed through this point while moving to the left.

When the glider passes through the point $x = 0$, the spring is relaxed and all of the mechanical energy is in the form of kinetic energy. Can you show that the speed of the glider at this point is 0.50 m/s?

Example 7.8 Motion with elastic potential energy and work done by other forces

For the system of Example 7.7, suppose the glider is initially at rest at $x = 0$, with the spring unstretched. You then apply a constant force $\vec{F}$ in the $+x$-direction with magnitude 0.610 N to the glider. What is the glider's velocity when it has moved to $x = 0.100$ m?

SOLUTION

IDENTIFY: Although the force $\vec{F}$ you apply is constant, the spring force isn't, so the acceleration of the glider won't be constant. Total mechanical energy is not conserved because of the work done by the force $\vec{F}$, so we must use the generalized energy relationship given by Eq. (7.13). (As in Example 7.7, we ignore gravitational potential energy because the glider's height doesn't change. Hence we have only elastic potential energy, and so $U = U_{el} = \frac{1}{2}kx^2$.)

SET UP: Let point 1 be at $x = 0$, where the velocity is $v_{1x} = 0$, and let point 2 be at $x = 0.100$ m. (These points are different from the ones labeled in Fig. 7.16.) Our target variable is v_{2x}, the velocity at point 2.

EXECUTE: The energy quantities are

$$K_1 = 0$$

$$U_1 = \frac{1}{2}kx_1^2 = 0$$

$$K_2 = \frac{1}{2}mv_{2x}^2$$

$$U_2 = \frac{1}{2}kx_2^2 = \frac{1}{2}(5.00\text{ N/m})(0.100\text{ m})^2 = 0.0250\text{ J}$$

$$W_{other} = (0.610\text{ N})(0.100\text{ m}) = 0.0610\text{ J}$$

(To calculate W_{other} we multiplied the magnitude of the force by the displacement, since both are in the $+x$-direction.) Initially, the total mechanical energy is zero; the work done by the force $\vec{F}$ increases the total mechanical energy to 0.0610 J, of which 0.0250 J is elastic potential energy. The remainder is kinetic energy. From Eq. (7.13),

$$K_1 + U_1 + W_{other} = K_2 + U_2$$

$$K_2 = K_1 + U_1 + W_{other} - U_2$$

$$= 0 + 0 + 0.0610\text{ J} - 0.0250\text{ J} = 0.0360\text{ J}$$

$$v_{2x} = \sqrt{\frac{2K_2}{m}} = \sqrt{\frac{2(0.0360\text{ J})}{0.200\text{ kg}}} = 0.60\text{ m/s}$$

We choose the positive square root because the glider is moving in the $+x$-direction.

EVALUATE: To test our answer, think what would be different if we disconnected the glider from the spring. Then $\vec{F}$ would be the only force doing work, there would be zero potential energy at all times, and Eq. (7.13) would give us

$$K_2 = K_1 + W_{other} = 0 + 0.0610\text{ J}$$

$$v_{2x} = \sqrt{\frac{2K_2}{m}} = \sqrt{\frac{2(0.0610\text{ J})}{0.200\text{ kg}}} = 0.78\text{ m/s}$$

We found a lower velocity than this value because the spring does negative work on the glider as it stretches (see Fig. 7.13b).

If you stop pushing on the glider when it reaches the point $x = 0.100$ m, beyond that point the only force that does work on the glider is the spring force. Hence for $x > 0.100$ m, the total mechanical energy $E = K + U$ is conserved and maintains the same value of 0.0610 J. The glider will slow down as the spring continues to stretch, so the kinetic energy K will decrease as the potential energy increases. The glider will come to rest at a point $x = x_3$; at this point the kinetic energy is zero and the potential energy $U = U_{el} = \frac{1}{2}kx_3^2$ is equal to the total mechanical energy 0.0610 J. You should be able to show that the glider comes to rest at $x_3 = 0.156$ m, which means that it moves an additional 0.056 m after the force $\vec{F}$ is removed at $x_2 = 0.100$ m. (Since there's no friction, the glider will not remain at rest but will start moving back toward $x = 0$ due to the force of the stretched spring.)

Example 7.9 Motion with gravitational, elastic, and friction forces

In a "worst-case" design scenario, a 2000-kg elevator with broken cables is falling at 4.00 m/s when it first contacts a cushioning spring at the bottom of the shaft. The spring is supposed to stop the elevator, compressing 2.00 m as it does so (Fig. 7.17). During the motion a safety clamp applies a constant 17,000-N frictional force to the elevator. As a design consultant, you are asked to determine what the force constant of the spring should be.

SOLUTION

IDENTIFY: We'll use the energy approach to determine the force constant, which appears in the expression for elastic potential energy. Note that this problem involves *both* gravitational and elastic potential energy. Furthermore, total mechanical energy is not conserved because the friction force does negative work W_{other} on the elevator.

SET UP: Since mechanical energy isn't conserved and more than one kind of potential energy is involved, we'll use the most general form of the energy relationship, Eq. (7.13). We take point 1 as the position of the bottom of the elevator when it initially contacts the spring, and take point 2 as its position when it is at rest. We choose the origin to be at point 1, so $y_1 = 0$ and $y_2 = -2.00$ m. With this choice the coordinate of the upper end of the spring is the same as the coordinate of the elevator, so the elastic potential energy at any point between point 1 and point 2 is $U_{\text{el}} = \frac{1}{2}ky^2$. (The gravitational potential energy is $U_{\text{grav}} = mgy$ as usual.) We know the initial and final speeds of the elevator and the magnitude of the friction force, so the only unknown is the force constant k (our target variable).

EXECUTE: The elevator's initial speed is $v_1 = 4.00$ m/s, so the initial kinetic energy is

$$K_1 = \frac{1}{2}mv_1^2 = \frac{1}{2}(2000\text{ kg})(4.00\text{ m/s})^2 = 16{,}000\text{ J}$$

The elevator stops at point 2, so $K_2 = 0$. The potential energy at point 1, U_1, is zero; U_{grav} is zero because $y_1 = 0$, and $U_{\text{el}} = 0$ because the spring is not yet compressed. At point 2 there is both gravitational and elastic potential energy, so

$$U_2 = mgy_2 + \frac{1}{2}ky_2^2$$

The gravitational potential energy at point 2 is

$$mgy_2 = (2000\text{ kg})(9.80\text{ m/s}^2)(-2.00\text{ m}) = -39{,}200\text{ J}$$

The other force is the 17,000-N friction force, acting opposite to the 2.00-m displacement, so

$$W_{\text{other}} = -(17{,}000\text{ N})(2.00\text{ m}) = -34{,}000\text{ J}$$

Putting these terms into $K_1 + U_1 + W_{\text{other}} = K_2 + U_2$, we have

$$K_1 + 0 + W_{\text{other}} = 0 + \left(mgy_2 + \frac{1}{2}ky_2^2\right)$$

so the force constant of the spring is

$$\begin{aligned} k &= \frac{2(K_1 + W_{\text{other}} - mgy_2)}{y_2^2} \\ &= \frac{2[16{,}000\text{ J} + (-34{,}000\text{ J}) - (-39{,}200\text{ J})]}{(-2.00\text{ m})^2} \\ &= 1.06 \times 10^4\text{ N/m} \end{aligned}$$

This is about one-tenth the force constant of a spring in an automobile suspension.

EVALUATE: Let's note what might seem to be a paradox in this problem. The elastic potential energy in the spring at point 2 is

$$\frac{1}{2}ky_2^2 = \frac{1}{2}(1.06 \times 10^4\text{ N/m})(-2.00\text{ m})^2 = 21{,}200\text{ J}$$

This is *more* than the total mechanical energy at point 1:

$$E_1 = K_1 + U_1 = 16{,}000\text{ J} + 0 = 16{,}000\text{ J}$$

But the friction force caused the mechanical energy of the system to *decrease* by 34,000 J between point 1 and point 2. Does this mean that energy appeared from nowhere? Don't panic; there is no paradox. At point 2 there is also *negative* gravitational potential energy, $mgy_2 = -39{,}200$ J, because point 2 is below the origin. The total mechanical energy at point 2 is

$$\begin{aligned} E_2 &= K_2 + U_2 = 0 + \frac{1}{2}ky_2^2 + mgy_2 \\ &= 0 + 21{,}200\text{ J} + (-39{,}200\text{ J}) = -18{,}000\text{ J} \end{aligned}$$

This is just the initial mechanical energy of 16,000 J, minus 34,000 J lost to friction.

Will the elevator stay at the bottom of the shaft? At point 2 the compressed spring exerts an upward force of magnitude $F_{\text{spring}} = (1.06 \times 10^4\text{ N/m})(2.00\text{ m}) = 21{,}200$ N, while the downward force of gravity on the elevator is only $w = mg = (2000\text{ kg})(9.80\text{ m/s}^2) = 19{,}600$ N. So if there were no friction, there would be a net upward force of 21,200 N − 19,600 N = 1600 N and the elevator would bounce back upward. However, there *is* friction in the safety clamp, which can exert a force of as much as 17,000 N; hence the clamp can keep the elevator from rebounding.

7.17 The fall of an elevator is stopped by a spring and by a constant friction force.

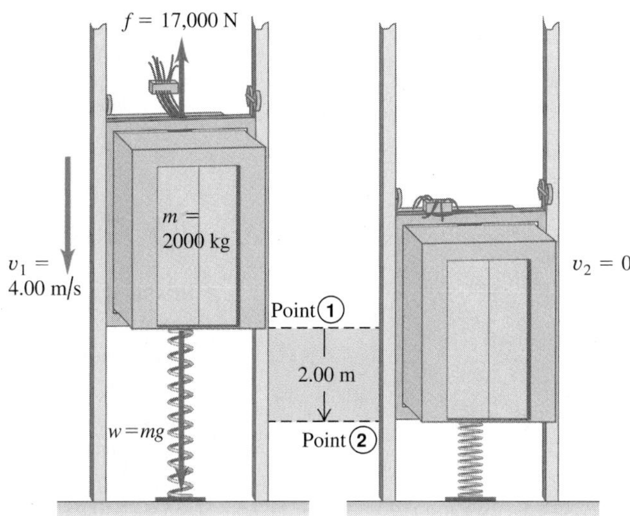

Test Your Understanding of Section 7.2 Consider the situation in Example 7.9 at the instant when the elevator is still moving downward and the spring is compressed by 1.00 m. Which of the energy bar graphs in the figure most accurately shows the kinetic energy K, gravitational potential energy U_{grav}, and elastic potential energy U_{el} at this instant?

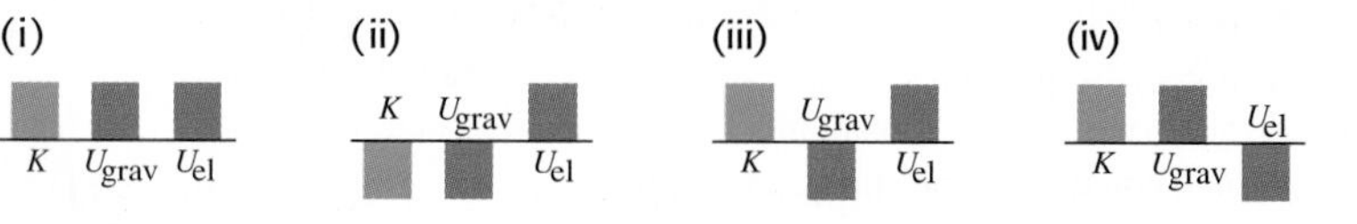

7.3 Conservative and Nonconservative Forces

In our discussions of potential energy we have talked about "storing" kinetic energy by converting it to potential energy. We always have in mind that later we may retrieve it again as kinetic energy. For example, when you throw a ball up in the air, it slows down as kinetic energy is converted into potential energy. But on the way down, the conversion is reversed, and the ball speeds up as potential energy is converted back to kinetic energy. If there is no air resistance, the ball is moving just as fast when you catch it as when you threw it.

Another example is a glider moving on a frictionless horizontal air track that runs into a spring bumper at the end of the track. The glider stops as it compresses the spring and then bounces back. If there is no friction, the glider ends up with the same speed and kinetic energy it had before the collision. Again, there is a two-way conversion from kinetic to potential energy and back. In both cases we can define a potential-energy function so that the total mechanical energy, kinetic plus potential, is constant or *conserved* during the motion.

Conservative Forces

A force that offers this opportunity of two-way conversion between kinetic and potential energies is called a **conservative force.** We have seen two examples of conservative forces: the gravitational force and the spring force. (Later in this book we will study another conservative force, the electric force between charged objects.) An essential feature of conservative forces is that their work is always *reversible.* Anything that we deposit in the energy "bank" can later be withdrawn without loss. Another important aspect of conservative forces is that a body may move from point 1 to point 2 by various paths, but the work done by a conservative force is the same for all of these paths (Fig. 7.18). Thus, if a body

7.18 The work done by a conservative force such as gravity depends only on the end points of a path, not on the specific path taken between those points.

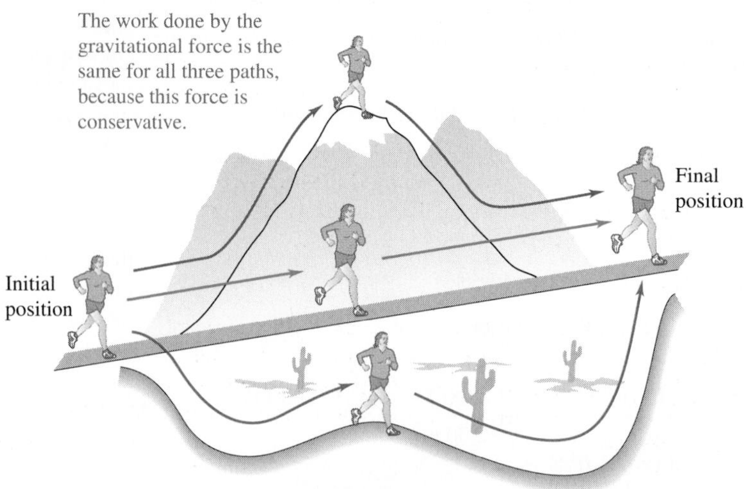

stays close to the surface of the earth, the gravitational force $m\vec{g}$ is independent of height, and the work done by this force depends only on the change in height. If the body moves around a closed path, ending at the same point where it started, the *total* work done by the gravitational force is always zero.

The work done by a conservative force *always* has four properties:

1. It can be expressed as the difference between the initial and final values of a *potential-energy* function.
2. It is reversible.
3. It is independent of the path of the body and depends only on the starting and ending points.
4. When the starting and ending points are the same, the total work is zero.

When the *only* forces that do work are conservative forces, the total mechanical energy $E = K + U$ is constant.

Nonconservative Forces

Not all forces are conservative. Consider the friction force acting on the crate sliding on a ramp in Example 7.6 (Section 7.1). When the body slides up and then back down to the starting point, the total work done on it by the friction force is *not* zero. When the direction of motion reverses, so does the friction force, and friction does *negative* work in *both* directions. When a car with its brakes locked skids across the pavement with decreasing speed (and decreasing kinetic energy), the lost kinetic energy cannot be recovered by reversing the motion or in any other way, and mechanical energy is *not* conserved. There is *no* potential-energy function for the friction force.

In the same way, the force of fluid resistance (see Section 5.3) is not conservative. If you throw a ball up in the air, air resistance does negative work on the ball while it's rising *and* while it's descending. The ball returns to your hand with less speed and less kinetic energy than when it left, and there is no way to get back the lost mechanical energy.

A force that is not conservative is called a **nonconservative force.** The work done by a nonconservative force *cannot* be represented by a potential-energy function. Some nonconservative forces, like kinetic friction or fluid resistance, cause mechanical energy to be lost or dissipated; a force of this kind is called a **dissipative force.** There are also nonconservative forces that *increase* mechanical energy. The fragments of an exploding firecracker fly off with very large kinetic energy, thanks to a chemical reaction of gunpowder with oxygen. The forces unleashed by this reaction are nonconservative because the process is not reversible. (The fragments never spontaneously reassemble themselves into a complete firecracker!)

Example 7.10 Frictional work depends on the path

You are rearranging your furniture and wish to move a 40.0-kg futon 2.50 m across the room. However, the straight-line path is blocked by a heavy coffee table that you don't want to move. Instead, you slide the futon in a dogleg path over the floor; the doglegs are 2.00 m and 1.50 m long. Compared to the straight-line path, how much more work must you do to push the futon in the dogleg path? The coefficient of kinetic friction is 0.200.

SOLUTION

IDENTIFY: Here work is done both by you and by the force of friction, so we must use the energy relationship that includes forces other than elastic or gravitational forces. We'll use this relationship to find a connection between the work that *you* do and the work done by *friction*.

7.19 Our sketch for this problem.

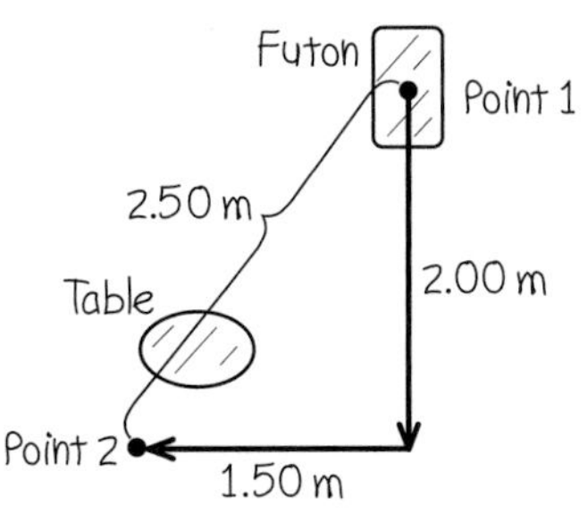

SET UP: Figure 7.19 shows our sketch. The futon is at rest at both point 1 and point 2, so $K_1 = K_2 = 0$. There is no elastic potential

Continued

energy (there are no springs), and the gravitational potential energy does not change because the futon moves only horizontally, so $U_1 = U_2$. From Eq. (7.14) it follows that $W_{other} = 0$. The other work done on the futon is the sum of the positive work you do, W_{you}, and the negative work W_{fric} done by the kinetic friction force. Since the sum of these is zero, we have

$$W_{you} = -W_{fric}$$

Thus to determine W_{you}, we'll calculate the work done by friction.

EXECUTE: Because the floor is horizontal, the normal force on the futon equals its weight mg, and the magnitude of the friction force is $f_k = \mu_k n = \mu_k mg$. The work you must do over each path is then

$$\begin{aligned} W_{you} &= -W_{fric} = -(-f_k s) = +\mu_k mgs \\ &= (0.200)(40.0\text{ kg})(9.80\text{ m/s}^2)(2.50\text{ m}) \\ &= 196\text{ J} \qquad \text{(straight-line path)} \end{aligned}$$

$$\begin{aligned} W_{you} &= -W_{fric} \\ &= (0.200)(40.0\text{ kg})(9.80\text{ m/s}^2)(2.00\text{ m} + 1.50\text{ m}) \\ &= 274\text{ J} \qquad \text{(dogleg path)} \end{aligned}$$

The extra work you must do is 274 J − 196 J = 78 J.

EVALUATE: The work done by friction is $W_{fric} = -W_{you} = -196$ J on the straight-line path and −274 J on the dogleg path. The work done by friction depends on the path taken, which illustrates that friction is a *nonconservative* force.

Example 7.11 Conservative or nonconservative?

In a certain region of space the force on an electron is $\vec{F} = Cx\hat{j}$, where C is a positive constant. The electron moves in a counterclockwise direction around a square loop in the xy-plane (Fig. 7.20). The corners of the square are at $(x, y) = (0, 0)$, $(L, 0)$, (L, L), and $(0, L)$. Calculate the work done on the electron by the force $\vec{F}$ during one complete trip around the square. Is this force conservative or nonconservative?

7.20 An electron moving around a square loop while being acted on by the force $\vec{F} = Cx\hat{j}$.

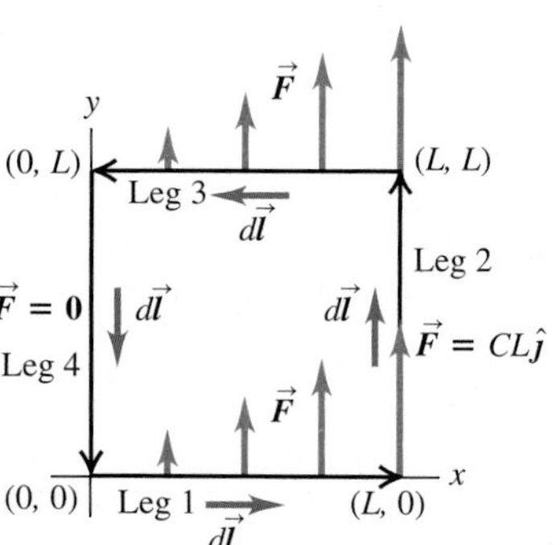

SOLUTION

IDENTIFY: In Example 7.10 the force of friction was constant in magnitude and always opposite to the displacement, so it was easy to calculate the work done. Here, however, the force $\vec{F}$ is not constant and in general is not in the same direction as the displacement.

SET UP: To calculate the work done by the force $\vec{F}$, we'll use the more general expression for work, Eq. (6.14):

$$W = \int_{P_1}^{P_2} \vec{F} \cdot d\vec{l}$$

where $d\vec{l}$ is an infinitesimal displacement. Let's calculate the work done on each leg of the square and then add the results to find the work done on the round trip.

EXECUTE: On the first leg, from $(0, 0)$ to $(L, 0)$, the force varies but is everywhere perpendicular to the displacement. So $\vec{F} \cdot d\vec{l} = 0$, and the work done on the first leg is $W_1 = 0$. The force has the same value $\vec{F} = CL\hat{j}$ everywhere on the second leg from $(L, 0)$ to (L, L). The displacement on this leg is in the $+y$-direction, so $d\vec{l} = dy\hat{j}$ and

$$\vec{F} \cdot d\vec{l} = CL\hat{j} \cdot dy\hat{j} = CL\,dy$$

The work done on the second leg is then

$$W_2 = \int_{(L,0)}^{(L,L)} \vec{F} \cdot d\vec{l} = \int_{y=0}^{y=L} CL\,dy = CL\int_0^L dy = CL^2$$

On the third leg, from (L, L) to $(0, L)$, $\vec{F}$ is again perpendicular to the displacement so $W_3 = 0$. The force is zero on the final leg, from $(0, L)$ to $(0, 0)$, so no work is done and $W_4 = 0$. The work done by the force $\vec{F}$ on the round trip is

$$W = W_1 + W_2 + W_3 + W_4 = 0 + CL^2 + 0 + 0 = CL^2$$

The starting and ending points are the same, but the total work done by $\vec{F}$ is not zero. This is a nonconservative force; it *cannot* be represented by a potential-energy function.

EVALUATE: Because W is positive, the mechanical energy *increases* as the electron goes around the loop. This is not a mathematical curiosity; it's a description of what happens in an electrical generating plant. A loop of wire is moved through a magnetic field, which gives rise to a nonconservative force similar to the one in this example. Electrons in the wire gain energy as they move around the loop, and this energy is carried via transmission lines to the consumer. (We'll discuss how this works in detail in Chapter 29.)

If the electron went around the loop clockwise instead of counterclockwise, the force $\vec{F}$ would be unaffected but the direction of each infinitesimal displacement $d\vec{l}$ would reverse. Thus the sign of work would also reverse, and the work for a clockwise round trip would be $W = -CL^2$. This is a different behavior than the nonconservative friction force. When a body slides over a stationary surface with friction, the work done by friction is always negative, no matter what the direction of motion (see Example 7.6 in Section 7.1).

The Law of Conservation of Energy

Nonconservative forces cannot be represented in terms of potential energy. But we can describe the effects of these forces in terms of kinds of energy other than kinetic and potential energy. When a car with locked brakes skids to a stop, the tires and the road surface both become hotter. The energy associated with this change in the state of the materials is called **internal energy.** Raising the temperature of a body increases its internal energy; lowering the body's temperature decreases its internal energy.

5.7 Modified Atwood Machine

To see the significance of internal energy, let's consider a block sliding on a rough surface. Friction does *negative* work on the block as it slides, and the change in internal energy of the block and surface (both of which get hotter) is *positive.* Careful experiments show that the increase in the internal energy is *exactly* equal to the absolute value of the work done by friction. In other words,

$$\Delta U_{\text{int}} = -W_{\text{other}}$$

where ΔU_{int} is the change in internal energy. If we substitute this into Eq. (7.7) or (7.14), we find

$$K_1 + U_1 - \Delta U_{\text{int}} = K_2 + U_2$$

Writing $\Delta K = K_2 - K_1$ and $\Delta U = U_2 - U_1$, we can finally express this as

$$\Delta K + \Delta U + \Delta U_{\text{int}} = 0 \qquad \text{(law of conservation of energy)} \qquad (7.15)$$

This remarkable statement is the general form of the **law of conservation of energy.** In a given process, the kinetic energy, potential energy, and internal energy of a system may all change. But the *sum* of those changes is always zero. If there is a decrease in one form of energy, it is made up for by an increase in the other forms (Fig. 7.21). When we expand our definition of energy to include internal energy, Eq. (7.15) says: *Energy is never created or destroyed; it only changes form.* No exception to this rule has ever been found.

The concept of work has been banished from Eq. (7.15); instead, it suggests that we think purely in terms of the conversion of energy from one form to another. For example, when you throw a baseball straight up, you convert a portion of the internal energy of your molecules into kinetic energy of the baseball. This is converted into gravitational potential energy as the ball climbs and back to kinetic energy as the ball falls. If there is air resistance, part of the energy is used to heat up the air and the ball and increase their internal energy. Energy is converted back into the kinetic form as the ball falls. If you catch the ball in your hand, whatever energy was not lost to the air once again becomes internal energy; the ball and your hand are now warmer than they were at the beginning. ?

In Chapters 19 and 20, we will study the relationship of internal energy to temperature changes, heat, and work. This is the heart of the area of physics called *thermodynamics.*

7.21 When 1 liter of gasoline is burned in an automotive engine, it releases 3.3×10^7 J of internal energy. Hence $\Delta U_{\text{int}} = -3.3 \times 10^7$ J, where the minus sign means that the amount of energy stored in the gasoline has decreased. This energy can be converted into kinetic energy (making the car go faster) or into potential energy (enabling the car to climb uphill).

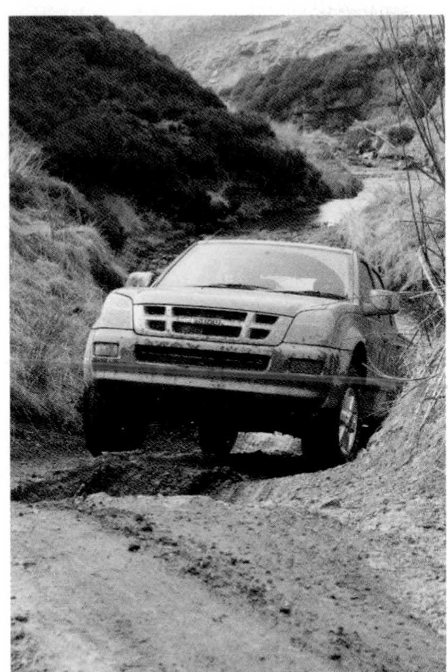

Example 7.12 Work done by friction

Let's look again at Example 7.5 (Section 7.1), in which your cousin Throcky skateboards down a curved ramp. He starts with zero kinetic energy and 735 J of potential energy, and at the bottom he has 450 J of kinetic energy and zero potential energy. So $\Delta K = +450$ J and $\Delta U = -735$ J. The work $W_{\text{other}} = W_{\text{fric}}$ done by the nonconservative friction forces is -285 J, so the change in internal energy is $\Delta U_{\text{int}} = -W_{\text{other}} = +285$ J. The wheels, the bearings, and the ramp all get a little warmer as Throcky rolls down. In accordance with Eq. (7.15), the sum of the energy changes equals zero:

$$\Delta K + \Delta U + \Delta U_{\text{int}} = +450\text{ J} + (-735\text{ J}) + 285\text{ J} = 0$$

The total energy of the system (including nonmechanical forms of energy) is conserved.

Test Your Understanding of Section 7.3 In a hydroelectric generating station, falling water is used to drive turbines ("water wheels"), which in turn run electric generators. Compared to the amount of gravitational potential energy released by the falling water, how much electrical energy is produced? (i) the same; (ii) more; (iii) less.

7.4 Force and Potential Energy

For the two kinds of conservative forces (gravitational and elastic) we have studied, we started with a description of the behavior of the *force* and derived from that an expression for the *potential energy*. For example, for a body with mass m in a uniform gravitational field, the gravitational force is $F_y = -mg$. We found that the corresponding potential energy is $U(y) = mgy$. To stretch an ideal spring by a distance x, we exert a force equal to $+kx$. By Newton's third law the force that an ideal spring exerts on a body is opposite this, or $F_x = -kx$. The corresponding potential energy function is $U(x) = \frac{1}{2}kx^2$.

In studying physics, however, you'll encounter situations in which you are given an expression for the *potential energy* as a function of position and have to find the corresponding *force*. We'll see several examples of this kind when we study electric forces later in this book: it's often far easier to calculate the electric potential energy first and then determine the corresponding electric force afterward.

Here's how we find the force that corresponds to a given potential-energy expression. First let's consider motion along a straight line, with coordinate x. We denote the x-component of force, a function of x, by $F_x(x)$, and the potential energy as $U(x)$. This notation reminds us that both F_x and U are *functions* of x. Now we recall that in any displacement, the work W done by a conservative force equals the negative of the change ΔU in potential energy:

$$W = -\Delta U$$

Let's apply this to a small displacement Δx. The work done by the force $F_x(x)$ during this displacement is approximately equal to $F_x(x)\,\Delta x$. We have to say "approximately" because $F_x(x)$ may vary a little over the interval Δx. But it is at least approximately true that

$$F_x(x)\,\Delta x = -\Delta U \qquad \text{and} \qquad F_x(x) = -\frac{\Delta U}{\Delta x}$$

You can probably see what's coming. We take the limit as $\Delta x \rightarrow 0$; in this limit, the variation of F_x becomes negligible, and we have the exact relationship

$$F_x(x) = -\frac{dU(x)}{dx} \qquad \text{(force from potential energy, one dimension)} \qquad (7.16)$$

This result makes sense; in regions where $U(x)$ changes most rapidly with x (that is, where $dU(x)/dx$ is large), the greatest amount of work is done during a given displacement, and this corresponds to a large force magnitude. Also, when $F_x(x)$ is in the positive x-direction, $U(x)$ *decreases* with increasing x. So $F_x(x)$ and $dU(x)/dx$ should indeed have opposite signs. The physical meaning of Eq. (7.16) is that *a conservative force always acts to push the system toward lower potential energy.*

As a check, let's consider the function for elastic potential energy, $U(x) = \frac{1}{2}kx^2$. Substituting this into Eq. (7.16) yields

$$F_x(x) = -\frac{d}{dx}\left(\frac{1}{2}kx^2\right) = -kx$$

7.22 A conservative force is the negative derivative of the corresponding potential energy.

(a) Spring potential energy and force as functions of x

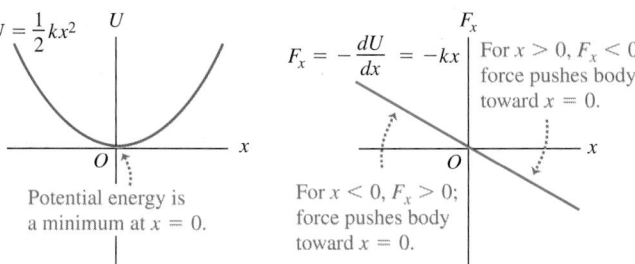

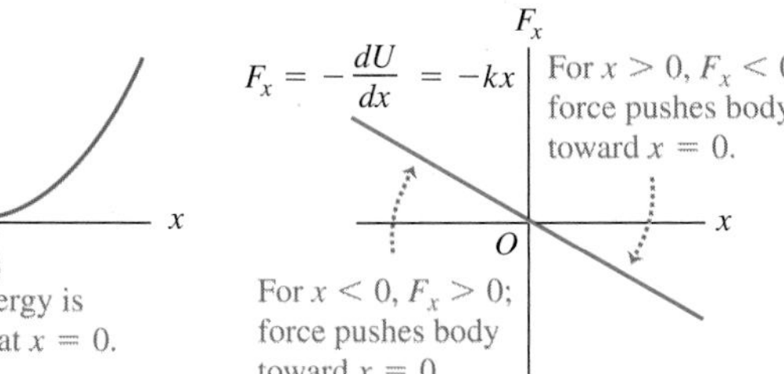

(b) Gravitational potential energy and force as function of y

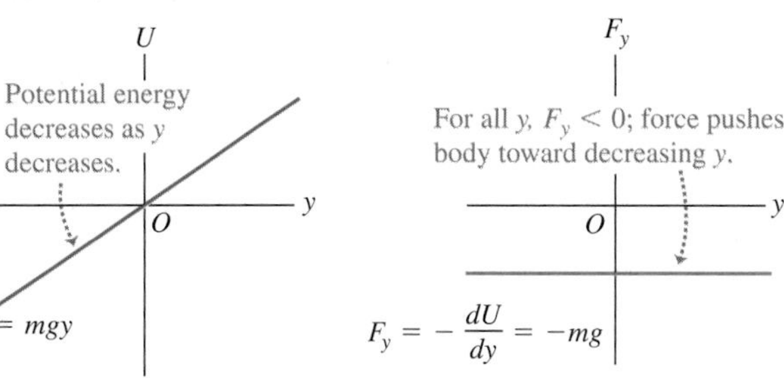

which is the correct expression for the force exerted by an ideal spring (Fig. 7.22a). Similarly, for gravitational potential energy we have $U(y) = mgy$; taking care to change x to y for the choice of axis, we get $F_y = -dU/dy = -d(mgy)/dy = -mg$, which is the correct expression for gravitational force (Fig. 7.22b).

Example 7.13 An electric force and its potential energy

An electrically charged particle is held at rest at the point $x = 0$, while a second particle with equal charge is free to move along the positive x-axis. The potential energy of the system is

$$U(x) = \frac{C}{x}$$

where C is a positive constant that depends on the magnitude of the charges. Derive an expression for the x-component of force acting on the movable charged particle, as a function of its position.

SOLUTION

IDENTIFY: We are given the potential-energy function $U(x)$, and we want to find the force function $F_x(x)$.

SET UP: We'll use Eq. (7.16), $F_x(x) = -dU(x)/dx$.

EXECUTE: The derivative with respect to x of the function $1/x$ is $-1/x^2$. So the force on the movable charged particle for $x > 0$ is

$$F_x(x) = -\frac{dU(x)}{dx} = -C\left(-\frac{1}{x^2}\right) = \frac{C}{x^2}$$

EVALUATE: The x-component of force is positive, corresponding to a repulsion between like electric charges. The potential energy is very large when the particles are close together (small x) and approaches zero as the particles move farther apart (large x); the force pushes the movable particle toward large positive values of x, for which the potential energy is less. The force $F_x(x) = C/x^2$ gets weaker as the particles move farther apart (x increases). We'll study electric forces in greater detail in Chapter 21.

Force and Potential Energy in Three Dimensions

We can extend this analysis to three dimensions, where the particle may move in the x-, y-, or z-direction, or all at once, under the action of a conservative force that has components F_x, F_y, and F_z. Each component of force may be a function of the coordinates x, y, and z. The potential-energy function U is also a function of all three space coordinates. We can now use Eq. (7.16) to find each component of force. The potential-energy change ΔU when the particle moves a small distance Δx in the x-direction is again given by $-F_x\,\Delta x$; it doesn't depend on F_y and F_z, which represent force components that are perpendicular to the displacement and do no work. So we again have the approximate relationship

$$F_x = -\frac{\Delta U}{\Delta x}$$

The y- and z-components of force are determined in exactly the same way:

$$F_y = -\frac{\Delta U}{\Delta y} \qquad F_z = -\frac{\Delta U}{\Delta z}$$

To make these relationships exact, we take the limits $\Delta x \to 0$, $\Delta y \to 0$, and $\Delta z \to 0$ so that these ratios become derivatives. Because U may be a function of all three coordinates, we need to remember that when we calculate each of these derivatives, only one coordinate changes at a time. We compute the derivative of U with respect to x by assuming that y and z are constant and only x varies, and so on. Such a derivative is called a *partial derivative.* The usual notation for a partial derivative is $\partial U/\partial x$ and so on; the symbol ∂ is a modified d. So we write

$$F_x = -\frac{\partial U}{\partial x} \quad F_y = -\frac{\partial U}{\partial y} \quad F_z = -\frac{\partial U}{\partial z} \quad \text{(force from potential energy)} \tag{7.17}$$

We can use unit vectors to write a single compact vector expression for the force $\vec{F}$:

$$\vec{F} = -\left(\frac{\partial U}{\partial x}\hat{\imath} + \frac{\partial U}{\partial y}\hat{\jmath} + \frac{\partial U}{\partial z}\hat{k}\right) \quad \text{(force from potential energy)} \tag{7.18}$$

The expression inside the parentheses represents a particular operation on the function U, in which we take the partial derivative of U with respect to each coordinate, multiply by the corresponding unit vector, and then take the vector sum. This operation is called the **gradient** of U and is often abbreviated as $\vec{\nabla}U$. Thus the force is the negative of the gradient of the potential-energy function:

$$\vec{F} = -\vec{\nabla}U \tag{7.19}$$

As a check, let's substitute into Eq. (7.19) the function $U = mgy$ for gravitational potential energy:

$$\vec{F} = -\vec{\nabla}(mgy) = -\left(\frac{\partial(mgy)}{\partial x}\hat{\imath} + \frac{\partial(mgy)}{\partial y}\hat{\jmath} + \frac{\partial(mgy)}{\partial z}\hat{k}\right) = (-mg)\hat{\jmath}$$

This is just the familiar expression for the gravitational force.

Example 7.14 Force and potential energy in two dimensions

A puck slides on a level, frictionless air-hockey table. The coordinates of the puck are x and y. It is acted on by a conservative force described by the potential-energy function

$$U(x, y) = \frac{1}{2}k(x^2 + y^2)$$

Derive an expression for the force acting on the puck, and find an expression for the magnitude of the force as a function of position.

SOLUTION

IDENTIFY: Starting with the function $U(x, y)$, we need to find the vector components and magnitude of the corresponding conservative force $\vec{F}$.

SET UP: We'll find the components of the force from $U(x, y)$ using Eq. (7.18). This function doesn't depend on z, so the partial derivative of U with respect to z is $\partial U/\partial z = 0$ and the force has no z-component. We'll then determine the magnitude of the force using the formula for the magnitude of a vector: $F = \sqrt{F_x^2 + F_y^2}$.

EXECUTE: The x- and y-components of the force are

$$F_x = -\frac{\partial U}{\partial x} = -kx \qquad F_y = -\frac{\partial U}{\partial y} = -ky$$

From Eq. (7.18) this corresponds to the vector expression

$$\vec{F} = -k(x\hat{\imath} + y\hat{\jmath})$$

Now $x\hat{\imath} + y\hat{\jmath}$ is just the position vector $\vec{r}$ of the particle, so we can rewrite this expression as $\vec{F} = -k\vec{r}$. This represents a force that at each point is opposite in direction to the position vector of the point—that is, a force that at each point is directed toward the origin. The potential energy is minimum at the origin, so again the force pushes in the direction of decreasing potential energy.

The *magnitude* of the force at any point is

$$F = \sqrt{(-kx)^2 + (-ky)^2} = k\sqrt{x^2 + y^2} = kr$$

where r is the particle's distance from the origin. This is the force that would be exerted on the puck if it were attached to one end of a spring that obeys Hooke's law and has a negligibly small length (compared to the other distances in the problem) when it is not stretched. (The other end is attached to the air-hockey table at the origin.)

EVALUATE: To check our result, note that the potential-energy function can also be expressed as $U = \frac{1}{2}kr^2$. Written this way, U is a function of a single coordinate r, so we can find the force using Eq. (7.16) with x replaced by r:

$$F_r = -\frac{dU}{dr} = -\frac{d}{dr}\left(\frac{1}{2}kr^2\right) = -kr$$

Just as we calculated above, the force has magnitude kr; the minus sign indicates that the force is radially inward (toward the origin).

Test Your Understanding of Section 7.4 A particle moving along the x-axis is acted on by a conservative force F_x. At a certain point, the force is zero. (a) Which of the following statements about the value of the potential-energy function $U(x)$ at that point is correct? (i) $U(x) = 0$; (ii) $U(x) > 0$; (iii) $U(x) < 0$; (iv) not enough information is given to decide. (b) Which of the following statements about the value of the derivative of $U(x)$ at that point is correct? (i) $dU(x)/dx = 0$; (ii) $dU(x)/dx > 0$; (iii) $dU(x)/dx < 0$; (iv) not enough information is given to decide.

7.5 Energy Diagrams

When a particle moves along a straight line under the action of a conservative force, we can get a lot of insight into its possible motions by looking at the graph of the potential-energy function $U(x)$. Figure 7.23a shows a glider with mass m that moves along the x-axis on an air track. The spring exerts on the glider a force with x-component $F_x = -kx$. Figure 7.23b is a graph of the corresponding potential-energy function $U(x) = \frac{1}{2}kx^2$. If the elastic force of the spring is the *only* horizontal force acting on the glider, the total mechanical energy $E = K + U$ is constant, independent of x. A graph of E as a function of x is thus a straight horizontal line. We use the term **energy diagram** for a graph like this, which shows both the potential-energy function $U(x)$ and the energy of the particle subjected to the force that corresponds to $U(x)$.

The vertical distance between the U and E graphs at each point represents the difference $E - U$, equal to the kinetic energy K at that point. We see that K is greatest at $x = 0$. It is zero at the values of x where the two graphs cross, labeled A and $-A$ in the diagram. Thus the speed v is greatest at $x = 0$, and it is zero at $x = \pm A$, the points of *maximum* possible displacement from $x = 0$ for a given value of the total energy E. The potential energy U can never be greater than the total energy E; if it were, K would be negative, and that's impossible. The motion is a back-and-forth oscillation between the points $x = A$ and $x = -A$.

At each point, the force F_x on the glider is equal to the negative of the slope of the $U(x)$ curve: $F_x = -dU/dx$ (see Fig. 7.22a). When the particle is at $x = 0$, the slope and the force are zero, so this is an *equilibrium* position. When x is positive, the slope of the $U(x)$ curve is positive and the force F_x is negative, directed toward the origin. When x is negative, the slope is negative and F_x is positive, again toward the origin. Such a force is called a *restoring force;* when the glider is displaced to either side of $x = 0$, the force tends to "restore" it back to $x = 0$. An analogous situation is a marble rolling around in a round-bottomed bowl. We say that $x = 0$ is a point of **stable equilibrium.** More generally, *any minimum in a potential-energy curve is a stable equilibrium position.*

Figure 7.24a shows a hypothetical but more general potential-energy function $U(x)$. Figure 7.24b shows the corresponding force $F_x = -dU/dx$. Points x_1 and x_3 are stable equilibrium points. At each of these points, F_x is zero because the slope of the $U(x)$ curve is zero. When the particle is displaced to either side, the force pushes back toward the equilibrium point. The slope of the $U(x)$ curve is also zero at points x_2 and x_4, and these are also equilibrium points. But when the particle is displaced a little to the right of either point, the slope of the $U(x)$ curve becomes negative, corresponding to a positive F_x that tends to push the particle still farther from the point. When the particle is displaced a little to the left, F_x is negative, again pushing away from equilibrium. This is analogous to a marble rolling on the top of a bowling ball. Points x_2 and x_4 are called **unstable equilibrium** points; *any maximum in a potential-energy curve is an unstable equilibrium position.*

CAUTION Potential energy and the direction of a conservative force The direction of the force on a body is *not* determined by the sign of the potential energy U. Rather, it's the sign of $F_x = -dU/dx$ that matters. As we discussed in Section 7.1, the physically significant quantity is the *difference* in the value of U between two points, which is just

7.23 (a) A glider on an air track. The spring exerts a force $F_x = -kx$. (b) The potential-energy function.

(a)

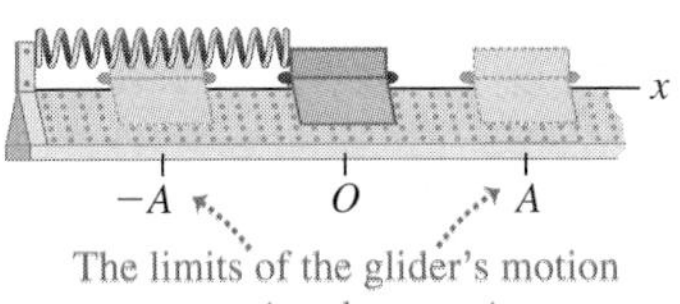

(b)

On the graph, the limits of motion are the points where the U curve intersects the horizontal line representing total mechanical energy E.

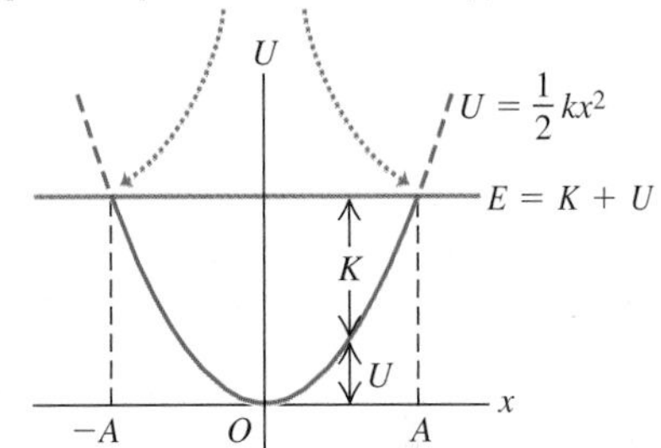

7.24 The maxima and minima of a potential-energy function $U(x)$ correspond to points where $F_x = 0$.

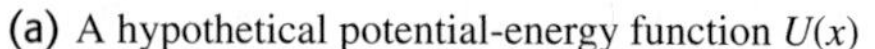

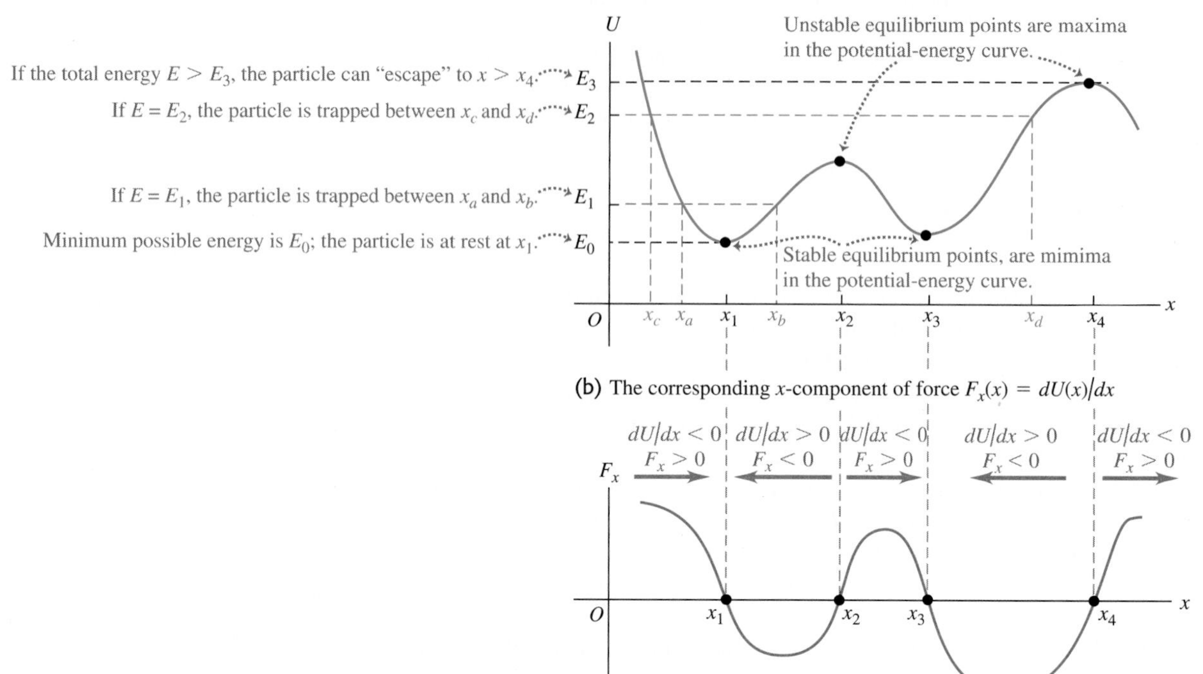

what the derivative $F_x = -dU/dx$ measures. This means that you can always add a constant to the potential-energy function without changing the physics of the situation.

(a) A hypothetical potential-energy function U(x)
U
Unstable equilibrium points are maxima in the potential-energy curve.
If the total energy E > E3, the particle can "escape" to x > x4. E3
If E = E2, the particle is trapped between xc and xd. E2
If E = E1, the particle is trapped between xa and xb. E1
Minimum possible energy is E0; the particle is at rest at x1. E0
Stable equilibrium points, are mimima in the potential-energy curve.
O xc xa x1 xb x2 x3 xd x4 x
(b) The corresponding x-component of force Fx(x) = dU(x)/dx
dU/dx < 0 Fx > 0
dU/dx > 0 Fx < 0
dU/dx < 0 Fx > 0
dU/dx > 0 Fx < 0
dU/dx < 0 Fx > 0
Fx
O x1 x2 x3 x4 x

If the total energy is E_1 and the particle is initially near x_1, it can move only in the region between x_a and x_b determined by the intersection of the E_1 and U graphs (Fig. 7.24a). Again, U cannot be greater than E_1 because K can't be negative. We speak of the particle as moving in a *potential well,* and x_a and x_b are the *turning points* of the particle's motion (since at these points, the particle stops and reverses direction). If we increase the total energy to the level E_2, the particle can move over a wider range, from x_c to x_d. If the total energy is greater than E_3, the particle can "escape" and move to indefinitely large values of x. At the other extreme, E_0 represents the least possible total energy the system can have.

Test Your Understanding of Section 7.5 The curve in Fig. 7.24b has a maximum at a point between x_2 and x_3. Which statement correctly describes what happens to the particle when it is at this point? (i) The particle's acceleration is zero. (ii) The particle accelerates in the positive x-direction; the magnitude of the acceleration is less than at any other point between x_2 and x_3. (iii) The particle accelerates in the positive x-direction; the magnitude of the acceleration is greater than at any other point between x_2 and x_3. (iv) The particle accelerates in the negative x-direction; the magnitude of the acceleration is less than at any other point between x_2 and x_3. (v) The particle accelerates in the negative x-direction; the magnitude of the acceleration is greater than at any other point between x_2 and x_3.

CHAPTER 7 SUMMARY

Gravitational potential energy and elastic potential energy: The work done on a particle by a constant gravitational force can be represented as a change in the gravitational potential energy $U_{grav} = mgy$. This energy is a shared property of the particle and the earth. A potential energy is also associated with the elastic force $F_x = -kx$ exerted by an ideal spring, where x is the amount of stretch or compression. The work done by this force can be represented as a change in the elastic potential energy of the spring, $U_{el} = \frac{1}{2}kx^2$.

$$W_{grav} = mgy_1 - mgy_2 = U_{grav,1} - U_{grav,2} = -\Delta U_{grav} \quad (7.1), (7.3)$$

$$W_{el} = \frac{1}{2}kx_1^2 - \frac{1}{2}kx_2^2 = U_{el,1} - U_{el,2} = -\Delta U_{el} \quad (7.10)$$

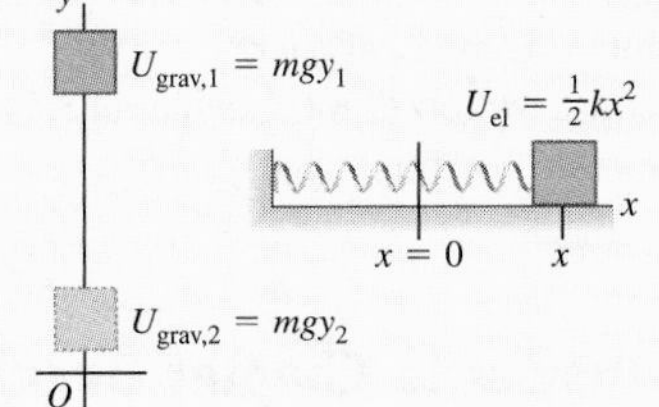

When total mechanical energy is conserved: The total potential energy U is the sum of the gravitational and elastic potential energy: $U = U_{grav} + U_{el}$. If no forces other than the gravitational and elastic forces do work on a particle, the sum of kinetic and potential energy is conserved. This sum $E = K + U$ is called the total mechanical energy. (See Examples 7.1, 7.3, 7.4, and 7.7.)

$$K_1 + U_1 = K_2 + U_2 \quad (7.4), (7.11)$$

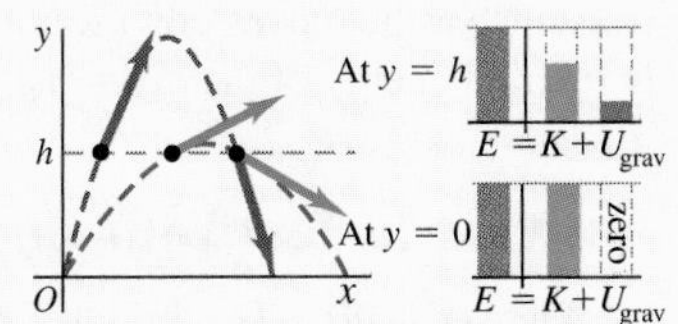

When total mechanical energy is not conserved: When forces other than the gravitational and elastic forces do work on a particle, the work W_{other} done by these other forces equals the change in total mechanical energy (kinetic energy plus total potential energy). (See Examples 7.2, 7.5, 7.6, 7.8, and 7.9.)

$$K_1 + U_1 + W_{other} = K_2 + U_2 \quad (7.14)$$

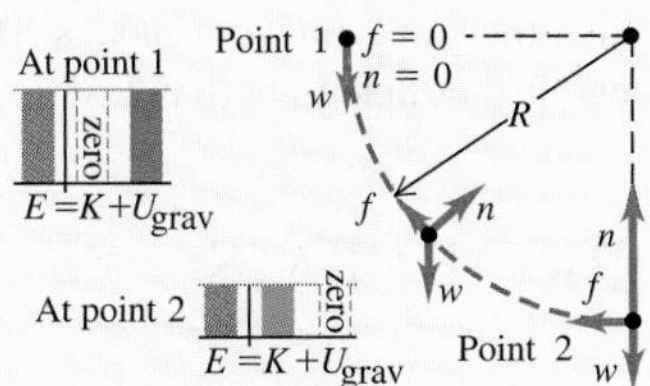

Conservative forces, nonconservative forces, and the law of conservation of energy: All forces are either conservative or nonconservative. A conservative force is one for which the work–kinetic energy relationship is completely reversible. The work of a conservative force can always be represented by a potential-energy function, but the work of a nonconservative force cannot. The work done by nonconservative forces manifests itself as changes in the internal energy of bodies. The sum of kinetic, potential, and internal energy is always conserved. (See Examples 7.10–7.12.)

$$\Delta K + \Delta U + \Delta U_{int} = 0 \quad (7.15)$$

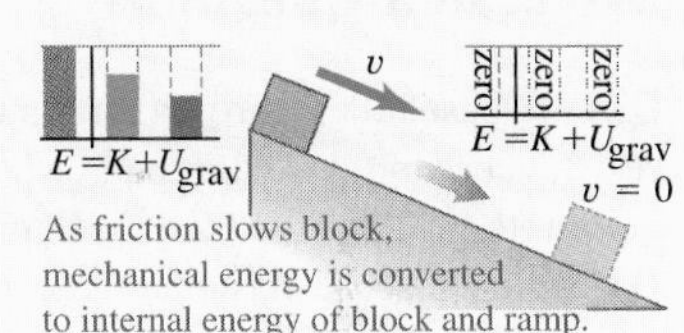

Determining force from potential energy: For motion along a straight line, a conservative force $F_x(x)$ is the negative derivative of its associated potential-energy function U. In three dimensions, the components of a conservative force are negative partial derivatives of U. (See Examples 7.13 and 7.14.)

$$F_x(x) = -\frac{dU(x)}{dx} \quad (7.16)$$

$$F_x = -\frac{\partial U}{\partial x} \quad F_y = -\frac{\partial U}{\partial y} \quad F_z = -\frac{\partial U}{\partial y} \quad (7.17)$$

$$\vec{F} = -\left(\frac{\partial U}{\partial x}\hat{\imath} + \frac{\partial U}{\partial y}\hat{\jmath} + \frac{\partial U}{\partial z}\hat{k}\right) \quad (7.18)$$

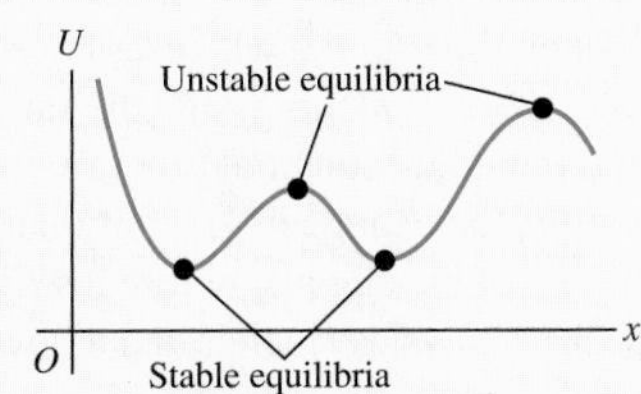

Key Terms

potential energy, *214*
gravitational potential energy, *214*
total mechanical energy, *215*
conservation of mechanical energy, *215*
elastic potential energy, *223*
conservative force, *228*
nonconservative force, *229*
dissipative force, *229*
internal energy, *231*
law of conservation of energy, *231*
gradient, *234*
energy diagram, *235*
stable equilibrium, *235*
unstable equilibrium, *236*

Answer to Chapter Opening Question ?

Gravity is doing positive work on the diver, since this force is in the same downward direction as his displacement. This corresponds to a decrease in gravitational potential energy. The water is doing negative work on the diver; it exerts an upward force of fluid resistance as he moves downward. This corresponds to an increase in internal energy of the diver and the water (see Section 7.3).

Answers to Test Your Understanding Questions

7.1 Answer: (iii) The initial kinetic energy $K_1 = 0$, the initial potential energy $U_1 = mgy_1$, and the final potential energy $U_2 = mgy_2$ are the same for both blocks. Mechanical energy is conserved in both cases, so the final kinetic energy $K = \frac{1}{2}mv_2^2$ is also the same for both blocks. Hence the speed at the right-hand end is the *same* in both cases!

7.2 Answer: (iii) The elevator is still moving downward, so the kinetic energy K is positive (remember that K can never be negative); the elevator is below point 1, so $y < 0$ and $U_{grav} < 0$; and the spring is compressed, so $U_{el} > 0$.

7.3 Answer: (iii) Because of friction in the turbines and between the water and turbines, some of the potential energy goes into raising the temperatures of the water and the mechanism.

7.4 Answers: (a) (iv), (b) (i) If $F_x = 0$ at a point, then the derivative of $U(x)$ must be zero at that point because $F_x = -dU(x)/dx$. However, this tells us absolutely nothing about the *value* of $U(x)$ at that point.

7.5 Answers: (iii) Figure 7.24b shows the x-component of force, F_x. Where this is maximum (most positive), the x-component of force and the x-acceleration have more positive values than at adjacent values of x.

PROBLEMS

For instructor-assigned homework, go to www.masteringphysics.com 

Discussion Questions

Q7.1. A baseball is thrown straight up with initial speed v_0. If air resistance cannot be ignored, when the ball returns to its initial height its speed is less than v_0. Explain why, using energy concepts.

Q7.2. A projectile has the same initial kinetic energy no matter what the angle of projection. Why doesn't it rise to the same maximum height in each case?

Q7.3. Does an object's speed at the bottom of a frictionless ramp depend on the shape of the ramp or just on its height? Explain. What if the ramp is *not* frictionless?

Q7.4. An egg is released from rest from the roof of a building and falls to the ground. Its fall is observed by a student on the roof of the building, who uses coordinates with origin at the roof, and by a student on the ground, who uses coordinates with origin at the ground. Do the two students assign the same or different values to the initial gravitational potential energy, the final gravitational potential energy, the change in gravitational potential energy, and the kinetic energy of the egg just before it strikes the ground? Explain.

Q7.5. A physics teacher had a bowling ball suspended from a very long rope attached to the high ceiling of a large lecture hall. To illustrate his faith in conservation of energy, he would back up to one side of the stage, pull the ball far to one side until the taut rope brought it just to the end of his nose, and then release it. The massive ball would swing in a mighty arc across the stage and then return to stop momentarily just in front of the nose of the stationary, unflinching teacher. However, one day after the demonstration he looked up just in time to see a student at the other side of the stage *push* the ball away from his nose as he tried to duplicate the demonstration. Tell the rest of the story and explain the reason for the potentially tragic outcome.

Q7.6. Lost Energy? The principle of the conservation of energy tells us that energy is never lost, but only changes from one form to another. Yet in many ordinary situations, energy may appear to be lost. In each case, explain what happens to the "lost" energy. (a) A box sliding on the floor comes to a halt due to friction. How did friction take away its kinetic energy, and what happened to that energy? (b) A car stops when you apply the brakes. What happened to its kinetic energy? (c) Air resistance uses up some of the original gravitational potential energy of a falling object. What type of energy did the "lost" potential energy become? (d) When a returning space shuttle touches down on the runway, it has lost almost all its kinetic energy and gravitational potential energy. Where did all that energy go?

Q7.7. Is it possible for a frictional force to *increase* the mechanical energy of a system? If so, give examples.

Q7.8. A woman bounces on a trampoline, going a little higher with each bounce. Explain how she increases the total mechanical energy.

Q7.9. Fractured Physics. People often call their electric bill a *power* bill, yet the quantity on which the bill is based is expressed in *kilowatt-hours*. What are people really being billed for?

Q7.10. A rock of mass m and a rock of mass $2m$ are both released from rest at the same height and feel no air resistance as they fall. Which statements about these rocks are true? (There may be more than one correct choice.) (a) Both have the same initial gravitational potential energy. (b) Both have the same kinetic energy when they reach the ground. (c) Both reach the ground with the same speed. (d) When it reaches the ground, the heavier rock has twice the kinetic energy of the lighter one. (e) When it reaches the ground, the heavier rock has four times the kinetic energy of the lighter one.

Q7.11. On a friction-free ice pond, a hockey puck is pressed against (but not attached to) a fixed ideal spring, compressing the spring by a distance x_0. The maximum energy stored in the spring is U_0, the maximum speed the puck gains after being released is v_0, and its maximum kinetic energy is K_0. Now the puck is pressed so it compresses the spring twice as far as before. In this case, (a) what is the maximum potential energy stored in the spring (in terms of U_0), and (b) what are the puck's maximum kinetic energy and speed (in terms of K_0 and x_0)?

Q7.12. When people are cold, they often rub their hands together to warm them up. How does doing this produce heat? Where did the heat come from?

Q7.13. You often hear it said that most of our energy ultimately comes from the sun. Trace each of the following energies back to the sun. (a) the kinetic energy of a jet plane; (b) the potential energy gained by a mountain climber; (c) the electrical energy used to run a computer; (d) the electrical energy from a hydroelectric plant.

Q7.14. A box slides down a ramp and work is done on the box by the forces of gravity and friction. Can the work of each of these forces be expressed in terms of the change in a potential-energy function? For each force explain why or why not.

Q7.15. In physical terms, explain why friction is a nonconservative force. Does it store energy for future use?

Q7.16. A compressed spring is clamped in its compressed position and then is dissolved in acid. What becomes of its potential energy?

Q7.17. Since only changes in potential energy are important in any problem, a student decides to let the elastic potential energy of a spring be zero when the spring is stretched a distance x_1. The student decides, therefore, to let $U = \frac{1}{2}k(x - x_1)^2$. Is this correct? Explain.

Q7.18. Figure 7.22a shows the potential-energy function for the force $F_x = -kx$. Sketch the potential-energy function for the force $F_x = +kx$. For this force, is $x = 0$ a point of equilibrium? Is this equilibrium stable or unstable? Explain.

Q7.19. Figure 7.22b shows the potential-energy function associated with the gravitational force between an object and the earth. Use this graph to explain why objects always fall toward the earth when they are released.

Q7.20. For a system of two particles we often let the potential energy for the force between the particles approach zero as the separation of the particles approaches infinity. If this choice is made, explain why the potential energy at noninfinite separation is positive if the particles repel one another and negative if they attract.

Q7.21. Explain why the points $x = A$ and $x = -A$ in Fig. 7.23b are called *turning points*. How are the values of E and U related at a turning point?

Q7.22. A particle is in *neutral equilibrium* if the net force on it is zero and remains zero if the particle is displaced slightly in any direction. Sketch the potential-energy function near a point of neutral equilibrium, for the case of one-dimensional motion. Give an example of an object in neutral equilibrium.

Q7.23. The net force on a particle of mass m has the potential-energy function graphed in Fig. 7.24a. If the total energy is E_1, graph the speed v of the particle versus its position x. At what value of x is the speed greatest? Sketch v versus x if the total energy is E_2.

Q7.24. The potential-energy function for a force $\vec{F}$ is $U = \alpha x^3$, where α is a positive constant. What is the direction of $\vec{F}$?

Exercises

Section 7.1 Gravitational Potential Energy

7.1. In one day, a 75-kg mountain climber ascends from the 1500-m level on a vertical cliff to the top at 2400 m. The next day, she descends from the top to the base of the cliff, which is at an elevation of 1350 m. What is her change in gravitational potential energy (a) on the first day and (b) on the second day?

7.2. A 5.00-kg sack of flour is lifted vertically at a constant speed of 3.50 m/s through a height of 15.0 m. (a) How great a force is required? (b) How much work is done on the sack by the lifting force? What becomes of this work?

7.3. A 120-kg mail bag hangs by a vertical rope 3.5 m long. A postal worker then displaces the bag to a position 2.0 m sideways from its original position, always keeping the rope taut. (a) What horizontal force is necessary to hold the bag in the new position? (b) As the bag is moved to this position, how much work is done (i) by the rope and (ii) by the worker?

7.4. A 72.0-kg swimmer jumps into the old swimming hole from a diving board 3.25 m above the water. Use energy conservation to find his speed just he hits the water (a) if he just holds his nose and drops in, (b) if he bravely jumps straight up (but just beyond the board!) at 2.50 m/s, and (c) if he manages to jump downward at 2.50 m/s.

7.5. A baseball is thrown from the roof of a 22.0-m-tall building with an initial velocity of magnitude 12.0 m/s and directed at an angle of 53.1° above the horizontal. (a) What is the speed of the ball just before it strikes the ground? Use energy methods and ignore air resistance. (b) What is the answer for part (a) if the initial velocity is at an angle of 53.1° *below* the horizontal? (c) If the effects of air resistance are included, will part (a) or (b) give the higher speed?

7.6. A crate of mass M starts from rest at the top of a frictionless ramp inclined at an angle α above the horizontal. Find its speed at the bottom of the ramp, a distance d from where it started. Do this in two ways: (a) Take the level at which the potential energy is zero to be at the bottom of the ramp with y positive upward. (b) Take the zero level for potential energy to be at the top of the ramp with y positive upward. (c) Why did the normal force not enter into your solution?

7.7. Answer part (b) of Example 7.6 (Section 7.1) by applying Eq. (7.7) to points 2 and 3, rather than to points 1 and 3 as was done in the example.

7.8. An empty crate is given an initial push down a ramp, starting it with a speed v_0, and reaches the bottom with speed v and kinetic energy K. Some books are now placed in the crate, so that the total mass is quadrupled. The coefficient of kinetic friction is constant and air resistance is negligible. Starting again with v_0 at the top of the ramp, what are the speed and kinetic energy at the bottom? Explain the reasoning behind your answers.

7.9. A small rock with mass 0.20 kg is released from rest at point A, which is at the top edge of a large, hemispherical bowl with radius $R = 0.50$ m (Fig. 7.25). Assume that the size of the rock is small compared to R, so that the rock can be treated as a particle, and assume that the rock slides rather than rolls. The work done by friction on the rock when it moves from point A to point B at the bottom of the bowl has magnitude 0.22 J. (a) Between points A and B, how much work is done on the rock by (i) the normal force and (ii) gravity? (b) What is the speed of the rock as it reaches point B? (c) Of the three forces acting on the rock as it slides down the bowl, which (if any) are constant and which are not? Explain. (d) Just as the rock reaches point B, what is the normal force on it due to the bottom of the bowl?

Figure 7.25 Exercise 7.9.

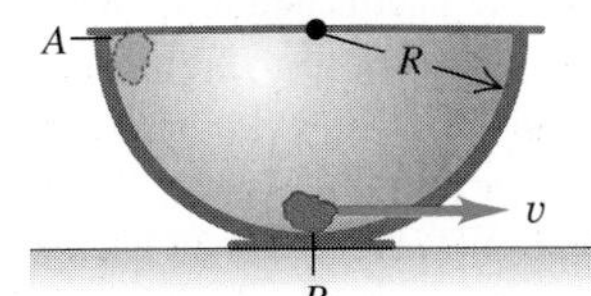

7.10. A stone of mass m is thrown upward at an angle θ above the horizontal and feels no appreciable air resistance. Use conservation of energy to show that at its highest point, it is a distance $v_0^2(\sin^2\theta)/2g$ above the point where it was launched. (*Hint:* $v_0^2 = v_{0x}^2 + v_{0y}^2$.)

7.11. You are testing a new amusement park roller coaster with an empty car with mass 120 kg. One part of the track is a vertical loop with radius 12.0 m. At the bottom of the loop (point A) the car has speed 25.0 m/s, and at the top of the loop (point B) it has speed 8.0 m/s. As the car rolls from point A to point B, how much work is done by friction?

7.12. Tarzan and Jane. Tarzan, in one tree, sights Jane in another tree. He grabs the end of a vine with length 20 m that makes an angle of 45° with the vertical, steps off his tree limb, and swings down and then up to Jane's open arms. When he arrives, his vine makes an angle of 30° with the vertical. Determine whether he gives her a tender embrace or knocks her off her limb by calculating Tarzan's speed just before he reaches Jane. You can ignore air resistance and the mass of the vine.

7.13. A 10.0-kg microwave oven is pushed 8.00 m up the sloping surface of a loading ramp inclined at an angle of 36.9° above the horizontal, by a constant force $\vec{F}$ with a magnitude 110 N and acting parallel to the ramp. The coefficient of kinetic friction between the oven and the ramp is 0.250. (a) What is the work done on the oven by the force $\vec{F}$? (b) What is the work done on the oven by the friction force? (c) Compute the increase in potential energy for the oven. (d) Use your answers to parts (a), (b), and (c) to calculate the increase in the oven's kinetic energy. (e) Use $\Sigma\vec{F} = m\vec{a}$ to calculate the acceleration of the oven. Assuming that the oven is initially at rest, use the acceleration to calculate the oven's speed after traveling 8.00 m. From this, compute the increase in the oven's kinetic energy, and compare it to the answer you got in part (d).

7.14. Pendulum. A small rock with mass 0.12 kg is fastened to a massless string with length 0.80 m to form a pendulum. The pendulum is swinging so as to make a maximum angle of 45° with the vertical. Air resistance is negligible. (a) What is the speed of the rock when the string passes through the vertical position? (b) What is the tension in the string when it makes an angle of 45° with the vertical? (c) What is the tension in the string as it passes through the vertical?

Section 7.2 Elastic Potential Energy

7.15. A force of 800 N stretches a certain spring a distance of 0.200 m. (a) What is the potential energy of the spring when it is stretched 0.200 m? (b) What is its potential energy when it is compressed 5.00 cm?

7.16. An ideal spring of negligible mass is 12.00 cm long when nothing is attached to it. When you hang a 3.15-kg weight from it, you measure its length to be 13.40 cm. If you wanted to store 10.0 J of potential energy in this spring, what would be its *total* length? Assume that it continues to obey Hooke's law.

7.17. A spring stores potential energy U_0 when it is compressed a distance x_0 from its uncompressed length. (a) In terms of U_0, how much energy does it store when it is compressed (i) twice as much and (ii) half as much? (b) In terms of x_0, how much must it be compressed from its uncompressed length to store (i) twice as much energy and (ii) half as much energy?

7.18. A slingshot will shoot a 10-g pebble 22.0 m straight up. (a) How much potential energy is stored in the slingshot's rubber band? (b) With the same potential energy stored in the rubber band, how high can the slingshot shoot a 25-g pebble? (c) What physical effects did you ignore in solving this problem?

7.19. A spring of negligible mass has force constant $k =$ 1600 N/m. (a) How far must the spring be compressed for 3.20 J of potential energy to be stored in it? (b) You place the spring vertically with one end on the floor. You then drop a 1.20-kg book onto it from a height of 0.80 m above the top of the spring. Find the maximum distance the spring will be compressed.

7.20. A 1.20-kg piece of cheese is placed on a vertical spring of negligible mass and force constant $k = 1800$ N/m that is compressed 15.0 cm. When the spring is released, how high does the cheese rise from this initial position? (The cheese and the spring are *not* attached.)

7.21. Consider the glider of Example 7.7 (Section 7.2) and Fig. 7.16. As in the example, the glider is released from rest with the spring stretched 0.100 m. What is the displacement x of the glider from its equilibrium position when its speed is 0.20 m/s? (You should get more than one answer. Explain why.)

7.22. Consider the glider of Example 7.7 (Section 7.2) and Fig. 7.16. (a) As in the example, the glider is released from rest with the spring stretched 0.100 m. What is the speed of the glider when it returns to $x = 0$? (b) What must the initial displacement of the glider be if its maximum speed in the subsequent motion is to be 2.50 m/s?

7.23. A 2.50-kg mass is pushed against a horizontal spring of force constant 25.0 N/cm on a frictionless air table. The spring is attached to the tabletop, and the mass is not attached to the spring in any way. When the spring has been compressed enough to store 11.5 J of potential energy in it, the mass is suddenly released from rest. (a) Find the greatest speed the mass reaches. When does this occur? (b) What is the greatest acceleration of the mass, and when does it occur?

7.24. (a) For the elevator of Example 7.9 (Section 7.2), what is the speed of the elevator after it has moved downward 1.00 m from point 1 in Fig. 7.17? (b) When the elevator is 1.00 m below point 1 in Fig. 7.17, what is its acceleration?

7.25. You are asked to design a spring that will give a 1160-kg satellite a speed of 2.50 m/s relative to an orbiting space shuttle. Your spring is to give the satellite a maximum acceleration of 5.00g. The spring's mass, the recoil kinetic energy of the shuttle, and changes in gravitational potential energy will all be negligible. (a) What must the force constant of the spring be? (b) What distance must the spring be compressed?

Section 7.3 Conservative and Nonconservative Forces

7.26. A 75-kg roofer climbs a vertical 7.0-m ladder to the flat roof of a house. He then walks 12 m on the roof, climbs down another vertical 7.0-m ladder, and finally walks on the ground back to his starting point. How much work is done on him by gravity (a) as he climbs up; (b) as he climbs down; (c) as he walks on the roof and on the ground? (d) What is the total work done on him by gravity during this round trip? (e) On the basis of your answer to part (d), would you say that gravity is a conservative or nonconservative force? Explain.

7.27. A 10.0-kg box is pulled by a horizontal wire in a circle on a rough horizontal surface for which the coefficient of kinetic friction is 0.250. Calculate the work done by friction during one complete circular trip if the radius is (a) 2.00 m and (b) 4.00 m. (c) On the basis of the results you just obtained, would you say that friction is a conservative or nonconservative force? Explain.

7.28. In an experiment, one of the forces exerted on a proton is $\vec{F} = -\alpha x^2\hat{\imath}$, where $\alpha = 12$ N/m^2. (a) How much work does $\vec{F}$ do when the proton moves along the straight-line path from the point

$(0.10\text{ m}, 0)$ to the point $(0.10\text{ m}, 0.40\text{ m})$? (b) Along the straight-line path from the point $(0.10\text{ m}, 0)$ to the point $(0.30\text{ m}, 0)$? (c) Along the straight-line path from the point $(0.30\text{ m}, 0)$ to the point $(0.10\text{ m}, 0)$? (d) Is the force $\vec{F}$ conservative? Explain. If $\vec{F}$ is conservative, what is the potential-energy function for it? Let $U = 0$ when $x = 0$.

7.29. A 0.60-kg book slides on a horizontal table. The kinetic friction force on the book has magnitude 1.2 N. (a) How much work is done on the book by friction during a displacement of 3.0 m to the left? (b) The book now slides 3.0 m to the right, returning to its starting point. During this second 3.0-m displacement, how much work is done on the book by friction? (c) What is the total work done on the book by friction during the complete round trip? (d) On the basis of your answer to part (c), would you say that the friction force is conservative or nonconservative? Explain.

7.30. You and three friends stand at the corners of a square whose sides are 8.0 m long in the middle of the gym floor, as shown in Fig. 7.26. You take your physics book and push it from one person to the other. The book has a mass of 1.5 kg, and the coefficient of kinetic friction between the book and the floor is $\mu_k = 0.25$. (a) The book slides from you to Beth and then from Beth to Carlos, along the lines connecting these people. What is the work done by friction during this displacement? (b) You slide the book from you to Carlos along the diagonal of the square. What is the work done by friction during this displacement? (c) You slide the book to Kim who then slides it back to you. What is the total work done by friction during this motion of the book? (d) Is the friction force on the book conservative or nonconservative? Explain.

Figure 7.26 Exercise 7.30.

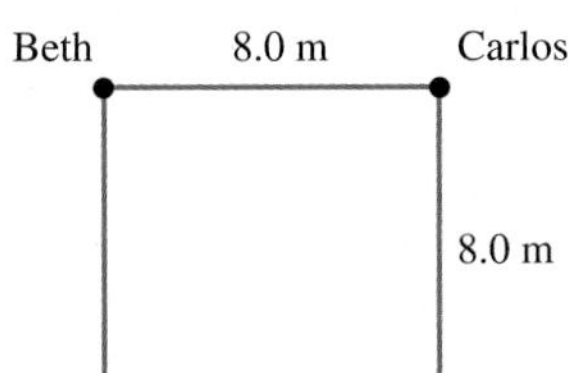

7.31. A block with mass m is attached to an ideal spring that has force constant k. (a) The block moves from x_1 to x_2, where $x_2 > x_1$. How much work does the spring force do during this displacement? (b) The block moves from x_1 to x_2 and then from x_2 to x_1. How much work does the spring force do during the displacement from x_2 to x_1? What is the total work done by the spring during the entire $x_1 \rightarrow x_2 \rightarrow x_1$ displacement? Explain why you got the answer you did. (c) The block moves from x_1 to x_3, where $x_3 > x_2$. How much work does the spring force do during this displacement? The block then moves from x_3 to x_2. How much work does the spring force do during this displacement? What is the total work done by the spring force during the $x_1 \rightarrow x_3 \rightarrow x_2$ displacement? Compare your answer to the answer in part (a), where the starting and ending points are the same but the path is different.

Section 7.4 Force and Potential Energy

7.32. The potential energy of a pair of hydrogen atoms separated by a large distance x is given by $U(x) = -C_6/x^6$, where C_6 is a positive constant. What is the force that one atom exerts on the other? Is this force attractive or repulsive?

7.33. A force parallel to the x-axis acts on a particle moving along the x-axis. This force produces potential energy $U(x)$ given by $U(x) = \alpha x^4$, where $\alpha = 1.20\text{ J/m}^4$. What is the force (magnitude and direction) when the particle is at $x = -0.800$ m?

7.34. Gravity in One Dimension. Two point masses, m_1 and m_2, lie on the x-axis, with m_1 held in place at the origin and m_2 at position x and free to move. The gravitational potential energy of these masses is found to be $U(x) = -Gm_1m_2/x$, where G is a constant (called the *gravitational constant*). You'll learn more about gravitation in Chapter 12. Find the x-component of the force acting on m_2 due to m_1. Is this force attractive or repulsive? How do you know?

7.35. Gravity in Two Dimensions. Two point masses, m_1 and m_2, lie in the xy-plane, with m_1 held in place at the origin and m_2 free to move a distance r away at a point P having coordinates x and y (Fig. 7.27). The gravitational potential energy of these masses is found to be $U(r) = -Gm_1m_2/r$, where G is the gravitational constant. (a) Show that the components of the force on m_2 due to m_1 are

Figure 7.27 Exercise 7.35.

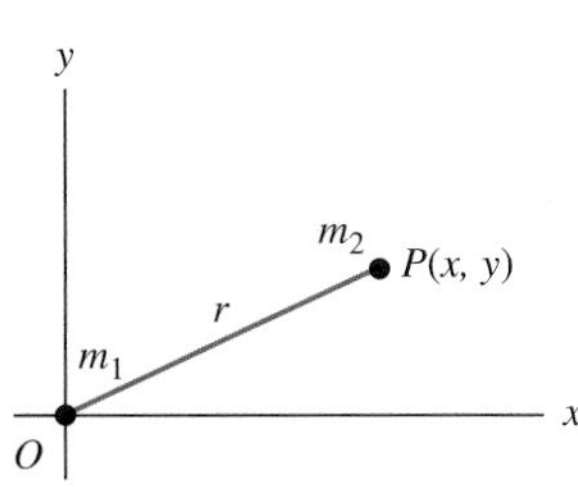

$$F_x = -\frac{Gm_1m_2x}{(x^2 + y^2)^{3/2}} \quad \text{and} \quad F_y = -\frac{Gm_1m_2y}{(x^2 + y^2)^{3/2}}$$

(*Hint:* First write r in terms of x and y.) (b) Show that the magnitude of the force on m_2 is $F = Gm_1m_2/r^2$. (c) Does m_1 attract or repel m_2? How do you know?

7.36. An object moving in the xy-plane is acted on by a conservative force described by the potential-energy function $U(x, y) = \alpha(1/x^2 + 1/y^2)$, where α is a positive constant. Derive an expression for the force expressed in terms of the unit vectors $\hat{\imath}$ and $\hat{\jmath}$.

Section 7.5 Energy Diagrams

7.37. The potential energy of two atoms in a diatomic molecule is approximated by $U(r) = a/r^{12} - b/r^6$, where r is the spacing between atoms and a and b are positive constants. (a) Find the force $F(r)$ on one atom as a function of r. Make two graphs, one of $U(r)$ versus r and one of $F(r)$ versus r. (b) Find the equilibrium distance between the two atoms. Is this equilibrium stable? (c) Suppose the distance between the two atoms is equal to the equilibrium distance found in part (b). What minimum energy must be added to the molecule to *dissociate* it—that is, to separate the two atoms to an infinite distance apart? This is called the *dissociation energy* of the molecule. (d) For the molecule CO, the equilibrium distance between the carbon and oxygen atoms is 1.13×10^{-10} m and the dissociation energy is 1.54×10^{-18} J per molecule. Find the values of the constants a and b.

7.38. A marble moves along the x-axis. The potential-energy function is shown in Fig. 7.28. (a) At which of the labeled x-coordinates is the force on the marble zero? (b) Which of the labeled x-coordinates is a position of stable equilibrium? (c) Which of the labeled x-coordinates is a position of unstable equilibrium?

Figure 7.28 Exercise 7.38.

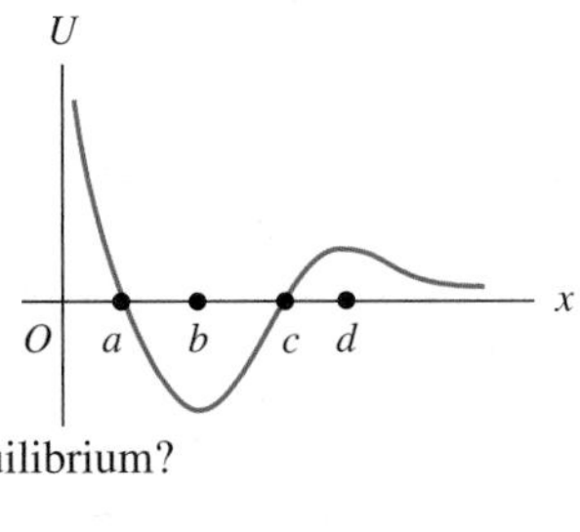

Problems

7.39. At a construction site, a 65.0-kg bucket of concrete hangs from a light (but strong) cable that passes over a light friction-free pulley and is connected to an 80.0-kg box on a horizontal roof (Fig. 7.29). The cable pulls horizontally on the box, and a 50.0-kg bag of gravel rests on top of the box. The coefficients of friction between the box and roof are shown. (a) Find the friction force on the bag of gravel and on the box. (b) Suddenly a worker picks up the bag of gravel. Use energy conservation to find the speed of the bucket after it has descended 2.00 m, from rest. (You can check your answer by solving this problem using Newton's laws.)

Figure 7.29 Problem 7.39.

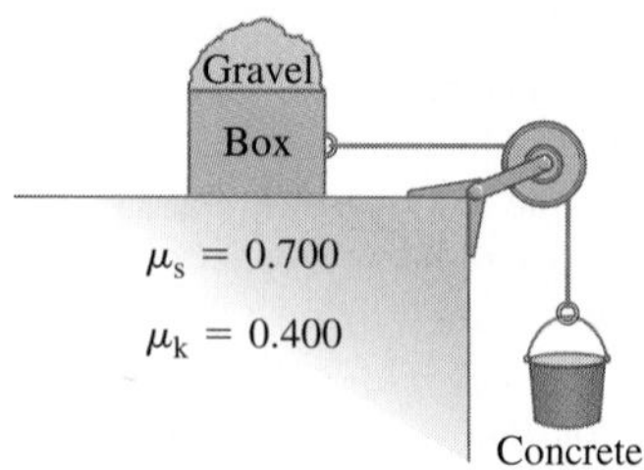

7.40. Two blocks with different mass are attached to either end of a light rope that passes over a light, frictionless pulley that is suspended from the ceiling. The masses are released from rest, and the more massive one starts to descend. After this block has descended 1.20 m, its speed is 3.00 m/s. If the total mass of the two blocks is 15.0 kg, what is the mass of each block?

7.41. Legal Physics. In an auto accident, a car hit a pedestrian and the driver then slammed on the brakes to stop the car. During the subsequent trial, the driver's lawyer claimed that he was obeying the posted 35 mi/h speed limit, but that the legal speed was too high to allow him to see and react to the pedestrian in time. You have been called in as the state's expert witness. Your investigation of the accident found that the skid marks made while the brakes were applied were 280 ft long, and the tread on the tires produced a coefficient of kinetic friction of 0.30 with the road. (a) In your testimony in court, will you say that the driver was obeying the posted speed? You must be able to back up your conclusion with clear reasoning because one of the lawyers will surely cross-examine you. (b) If the driver's speeding ticket were \$10 for each mile per hour he was driving above the posted speed limit, would he have to pay a fine? If so, how much would it be?

7.42. A 2.00-kg block is pushed against a spring with negligible mass and force constant $k = 400$ N/m, compressing it 0.220 m. When the block is released, it moves along a frictionless, horizontal surface and then up a frictionless incline with slope 37.0° (Fig. 7.30). (a) What is the speed of the block as it slides along the horizontal surface after having left the spring? (b) How far does the block travel up the incline before starting to slide back down?

Figure 7.30 Problem 7.42.

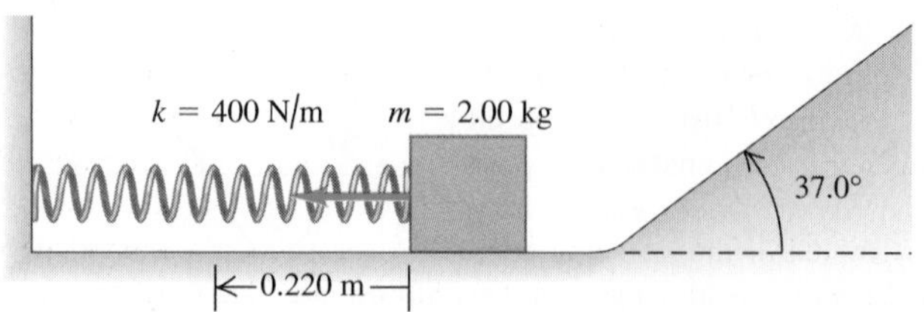

7.43. A block with mass 0.50 kg is forced against a horizontal spring of negligible mass, compressing the spring a distance of 0.20 m (Fig. 7.31). When released, the block moves on a horizontal tabletop for 1.00 m before coming to rest. The spring constant k is 100 N/m. What is the coefficient of kinetic friction μ_k between the block and the tabletop?

Figure 7.31 Problem 7.43.

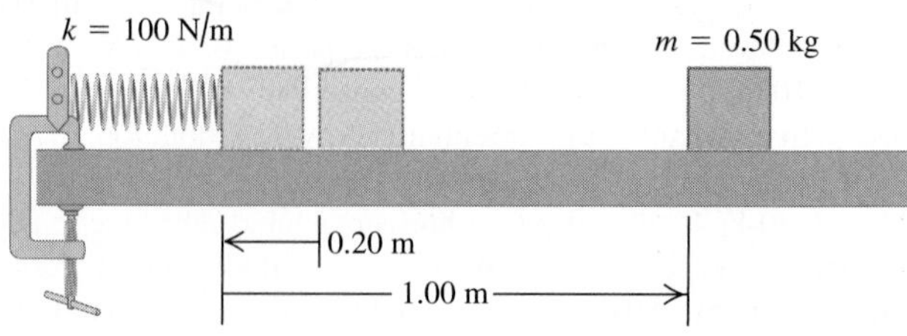

7.44. On a horizontal surface, a crate with mass 50.0 kg is placed against a spring that stores 360 J of energy. The spring is released, and the crate slides 5.60 m before coming to rest. What is the speed of the crate when it is 2.00 m from its initial position?

7.45. Bouncing Ball. A 650-gram rubber ball is dropped from an initial height of 2.50 m, and on each bounce it returns to 75% of its previous height. (a) What is the initial mechanical energy of the ball, just after it is released from its initial height? (b) How much mechanical energy does the ball lose during its first bounce? What happens to this energy? (c) How much mechanical energy is lost during the second bounce?

7.46. Riding a Loop-the-Loop. A car in an amusement park ride rolls without friction around the track shown in Fig. 7.32. It starts from rest at point A at a height h above the bottom of the loop. Treat the car as a particle. (a) What is the minimum value of h (in terms of R) such that the car moves around the loop without falling off at the top (point B)? (b) If $h = 3.50R$ and $R = 20.0$ m, compute the speed, radial acceleration, and tangential acceleration of the passengers when the car is at point C, which is at the end of a horizontal diameter. Show these acceleration components in a diagram, approximately to scale.

Figure 7.32 Problem 7.46.

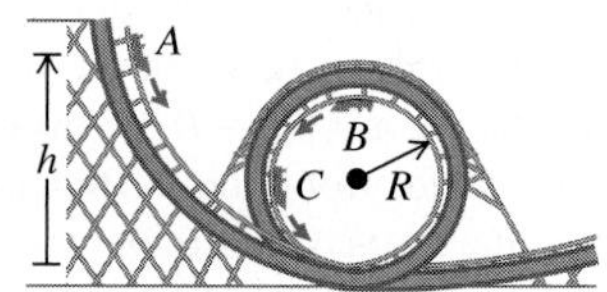

7.47. A 2.0-kg piece of wood slides on the surface shown in Fig. 7.33. The curved sides are perfectly smooth, but the rough horizontal bottom is 30 m long and has a kinetic friction coefficient of 0.20 with the wood. The piece of wood starts from rest 4.0 m above the rough bottom. (a) Where will this wood eventually come to rest? (b) For the motion from the initial release until the piece of wood comes to rest, what is the total amount of work done by friction?

Figure 7.33 Problem 7.47.

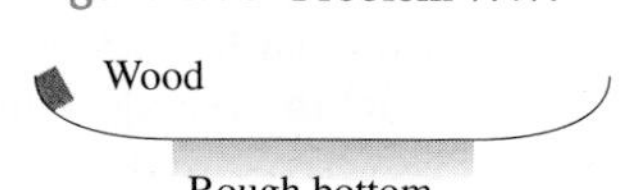

7.48. Up and Down the Hill. A 28-kg rock approaches the foot of a hill with a speed of 15 m/s. This hill slopes upward at a constant angle of 40.0° above the horizontal. The coefficients of static and kinetic friction between the hill and the rock are 0.75 and 0.20, respectively. (a) Use energy conservation to find the maximum height above the foot of the hill reached by the rock. (b) Will the rock remain at rest at its highest point, or will it slide back down the hill? (c) If the rock does slide back down, find its speed when it returns to the bottom of the hill.

7.49. A 15.0-kg stone slides down a snow-covered hill (Fig. 7.34), leaving point A with a speed of 10.0 m/s. There is no friction on the hill between points A and B, but there is friction on the level ground at the bottom of the hill, between B and the wall. After

Figure 7.34 Problem 7.49.

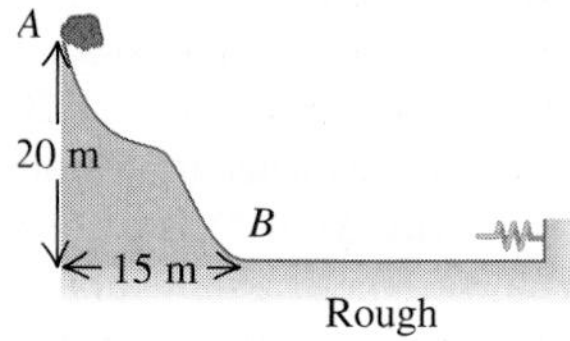

entering the rough horizontal region, the stone travels 100 m and then runs into a very long, light spring with force constant 2.00 N/m. The coefficients of kinetic and static friction between the stone and the horizontal ground are 0.20 and 0.80, respectively. (a) What is the speed of the stone when it reaches point B? (b) How far will the stone compress the spring? (c) Will the stone move again after it has been stopped by the spring?

7.50. A 2.8-kg block slides over the smooth, icy hill shown in Fig. 7.35. The top of the hill is horizontal and 70 m higher than its base. What minimum speed must the block have at the base of the hill so that it will not fall into the pit on the far side of the hill?

Figure 7.35 Problem 7.50.

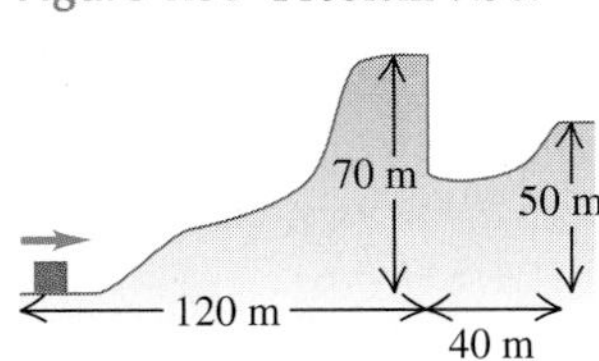

7.51. Bungee Jump. A bungee cord is 30.0 m long and, when stretched a distance x, it exerts a restoring force of magnitude kx. Your father-in-law (mass 95.0 kg) stands on a platform 45.0 m above the ground, and one end of the cord is tied securely to his ankle and the other end to the platform. You have promised him that when he steps off the platform he will fall a maximum distance of only 41.0 m before the cord stops him. You had several bungee cords to select from, and you tested them by stretching them out, tying one end to a tree, and pulling on the other end with a force of 380.0 N. When you do this, what distance will the bungee cord that you should select have stretched?

7.52. Ski Jump Ramp. You are designing a ski jump ramp for the next Winter Olympics. You need to calculate the vertical height h from the starting gate to the bottom of the ramp. The skiers push off hard with their ski poles at the start, just above the starting gate, so they typically have a speed of 2.0 m/s as they reach the gate. For safety, the skiers should have a speed of no more than 30.0 m/s when they reach the bottom of the ramp. You determine that for a 85.0-kg skier with good form, friction and air resistance will do total work of magnitude 4000 J on him during his run down the slope. What is the maximum height h for which the maximum safe speed will not be exceeded?

7.53. The Great Sandini is a 60-kg circus performer who is shot from a cannon (actually a spring gun). You don't find many men of his caliber, so you help him design a new gun. This new gun has a very large spring with a very small mass and a force constant of 1100 N/m that he will compress with a force of 4400 N. The inside of the gun barrel is coated with Teflon, so the average friction force will be only 40 N during the 4.0 m he moves in the barrel. At what speed will he emerge from the end of the barrel, 2.5 m above his initial rest position?

7.54. You are designing a delivery ramp for crates containing exercise equipment. The 1470-N crates will move at 1.8 m/s at the top of a ramp that slopes downward at 22.0°. The ramp exerts a 550-N kinetic friction force on each crate, and the maximum static friction force also has this value. Each crate will compress a spring at the bottom of the ramp and will come to rest after traveling a total distance of 8.0 m along the ramp. Once stopped, a crate must not rebound back up the ramp. Calculate the force constant of the spring that will be needed in order to meet the design criteria.

7.55. A system of two paint buckets connected by a lightweight rope is released from rest with the 12.0-kg bucket 2.00 m above the floor (Fig. 7.36). Use the principle of conservation of energy to find the speed with which this bucket strikes the floor. You can ignore friction and the mass of the pulley.

Figure 7.36 Problem 7.55.

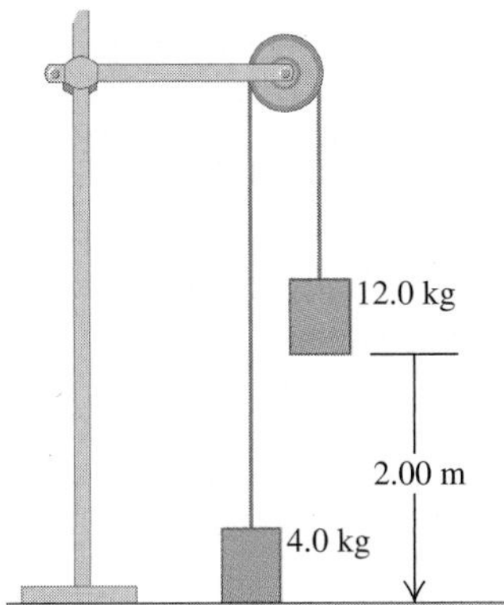

7.56. A 1500-kg rocket is to be launched with an initial upward speed of 50.0 m/s. In order to assist its engines, the engineers will start it from rest on a ramp that rises 53° above the horizontal (Fig. 7.37). At the bottom, the ramp turns upward and launches the rocket vertically. The engines provide a constant forward thrust of 2000 N, and friction with the ramp surface is a constant 500 N. How far from the base of the ramp should the rocket start, as measured along the surface of the ramp?

Figure 7.37 Problem 7.56.

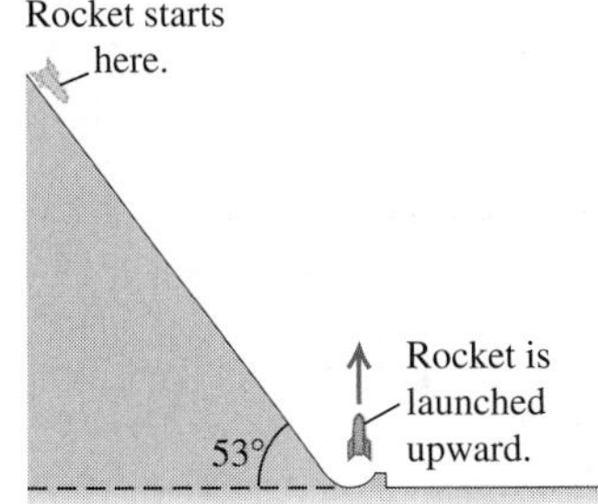

7.57. A machine part of mass m is attached to a horizontal ideal spring of force constant k that is attached to the edge of a friction-free horizontal surface. The part is pushed against the spring, compressing it a distance x_0, and then released from rest. Find the maximum (a) speed and (b) acceleration of the machine part. (c) Where in the motion do the maxima in parts (a) and (b) occur? (d) What will be the maximum extension of the spring? (e) Describe the subsequent motion of this machine part. Will it ever stop permanently?

7.58. A wooden rod of negligible mass and length 80.0 cm is pivoted about a horizontal axis through its center. A white rat with mass 0.500 kg clings to one end of the stick, and a mouse with mass 0.200 kg clings to the other end. The system is released from rest with the rod horizontal. If the animals can manage to hold on, what are their speeds as the rod swings through a vertical position?

7.59. A 0.100-kg potato is tied to a string with length 2.50 m, and the other end of the string is tied to a rigid support. The potato is held straight out horizontally from the point of support, with the string pulled taut, and is then released. (a) What is the speed of the potato at the lowest point of its motion? (b) What is the tension in the string at this point?

7.60. These data are from a computer simulation for a batted baseball with mass 0.145 kg, including air resistance:

t	x	y	v_x	v_y
0	0	0	30.0 m/s	40.0 m/s
3.05 s	70.2 m	53.6 m	18.6 m/s	0
6.59 s	124.4 m	0	11.9 m/s	−28.7 m/s

(a) How much work was done by the air on the baseball as it moved from its initial position to its maximum height? (b) How much work was done by the air on the baseball as it moved from its maximum height back to the starting elevation? (c) Explain why the magnitude of the answer in part (b) is smaller than the magnitude of the answer in part (a).

7.61. Down the Pole. A fireman of mass m slides a distance d down a pole. He starts from rest. He moves as fast at the bottom as if he had stepped off a platform a distance $h \leq d$ above the ground and descended with negligible air resistance. (a) What average friction force did the fireman exert on the pole? Does your answer make sense in the special cases of $h = d$ and $h = 0$? (b) Find a numerical value for the average friction force a 75-kg fireman exerts, for $d = 2.5$ m and $h = 1.0$ m. (c) In terms of g, h, and d, what is the speed of the fireman when he is a distance y above the bottom of the pole?

7.62. A 60.0-kg skier starts from rest at the top of a ski slope 65.0 m high. (a) If frictional forces do −10.5 kJ of work on her as she descends, how fast is she going at the bottom of the slope? (b) Now moving horizontally, the skier crosses a patch of soft snow, where $\mu_k = 0.20$. If the patch is 82.0 m wide and the average force of air resistance on the skier is 160 N, how fast is she going after crossing the patch? (c) The skier hits a snowdrift and penetrates 2.5 m into it before coming to a stop. What is the average force exerted on her by the snowdrift as it stops her?

7.63. A skier starts at the top of a very large, frictionless snowball, with a very small initial speed, and skis straight down the side (Fig. 7.38). At what point does she lose contact with the snowball and fly off at a tangent? That is, at the instant she loses contact with the snowball, what angle α does a radial line from the center of the snowball to the skier make with the vertical?

Figure 7.38 Problem 7.63.

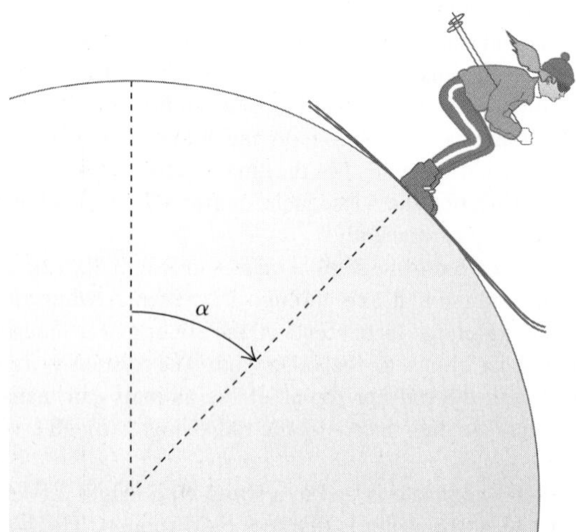

7.64. A rock is tied to a cord and the other end of the cord is held fixed. The rock is given an initial tangential velocity that causes it to rotate in a vertical circle. Prove that the tension in the cord at the lowest point exceeds the tension at the highest point by six times the weight of the rock.

7.65. In a truck-loading station at a post office, a small 0.200-kg package is released from rest at point A on a track that is one-quarter of a circle with radius 1.60 m (Fig. 7.39). The size of the package is much less than 1.60 m, so the package can be treated as a particle. It slides down the track and reaches point B with a speed of 4.80 m/s. From point B, it slides on a level surface a distance of 3.00 m to point C, where it comes to rest. (a) What is the coefficient of kinetic friction on the horizontal surface? (b) How much work is done on the package by friction as it slides down the circular arc from A to B?

Figure 7.39 Problem 7.65.

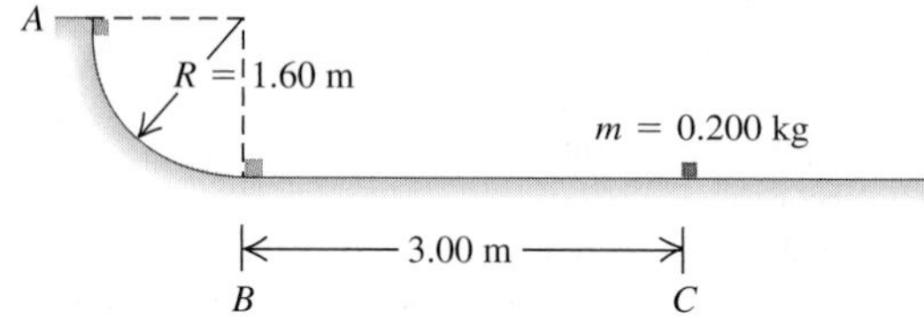

7.66. A truck with mass m has a brake failure while going down an icy mountain road of constant downward slope angle α (Fig. 7.40). Initially the truck is moving downhill at speed v_0. After careening downhill a distance L with negligible friction, the truck driver steers the runaway vehicle onto a runaway truck ramp of constant upward slope angle β. The truck ramp has a soft sand surface for which the coefficient of rolling friction is μ_r. What is the distance that the truck moves up the ramp before coming to a halt? Solve using energy methods.

Figure 7.40 Problem 7.66.

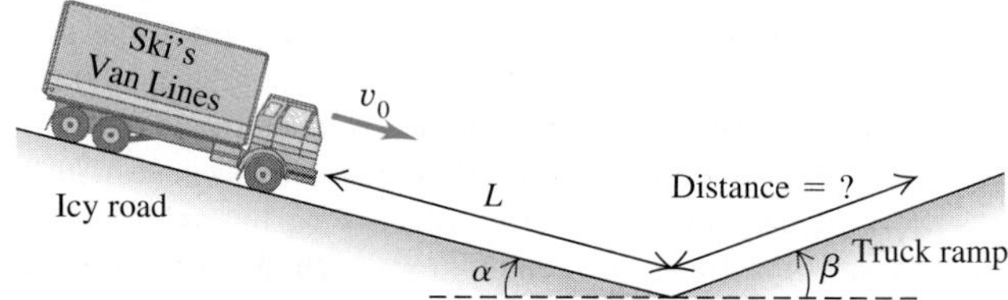

7.67. A certain spring is found *not* to obey Hooke's law; it exerts a restoring force $F_x(x) = -\alpha x - \beta x^2$ if it is stretched or compressed, where $\alpha = 60.0$ N/m and $\beta = 18.0$ N/m^2. The mass of the spring is negligible. (a) Calculate the potential-energy function $U(x)$ for this spring. Let $U = 0$ when $x = 0$. (b) An object with mass 0.900 kg on a frictionless, horizontal surface is attached to this spring, pulled a distance 1.00 m to the right (the $+x$-direction) to stretch the spring, and released. What is the speed of the object when it is 0.50 m to the right of the $x = 0$ equilibrium position?

7.68. A variable force $\vec{F}$ is maintained tangent to a frictionless, semicircular surface (Fig. 7.41). By slow variations in the force, a

Figure 7.41 Problem 7.68.

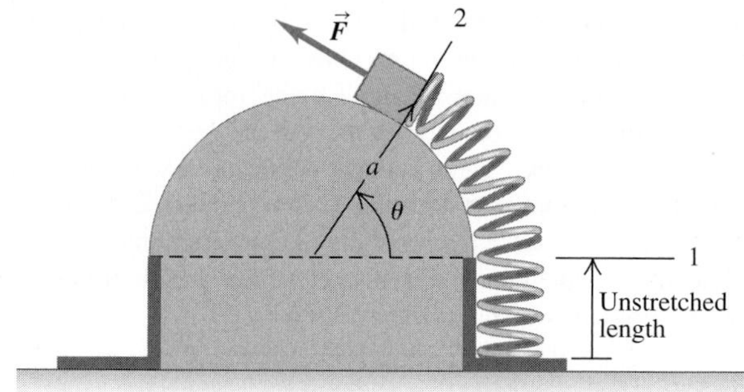

block with weight w is moved, and the spring to which it is attached is stretched from position 1 to position 2. The spring has negligible mass and force constant k. The end of the spring moves in an arc of radius a. Calculate the work done by the force $\vec{F}$.

7.69. A 0.150-kg block of ice is placed against a horizontal, compressed spring mounted on a horizontal tabletop that is 1.20 m above the floor. The spring has force constant 1900 N/m and is initially compressed 0.045 m. The mass of the spring is negligible. The spring is released, and the block slides along the table, goes off the edge, and travels to the floor. If there is negligible friction between the block of ice and the tabletop, what is the speed of the block of ice when it reaches the floor?

7.70. A 3.00-kg block is connected to two ideal horizontal springs having force constants $k_1 = 25.0$ N/cm and $k_2 = 20.0$ N/cm (Fig. 7.42). The system is initially in equilibrium on a horizontal, frictionless surface. The block is now pushed 15.0 cm to the right and released from rest. (a) What is the maximum speed of the block? Where in the motion does the maximum speed occur? (b) What is the maximum compression of spring 1?

Figure 7.42 Problem 7.70.

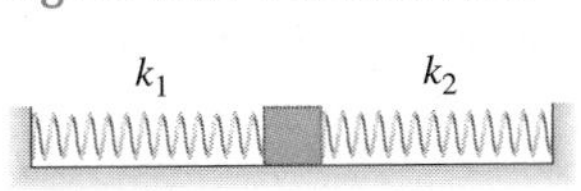

7.71. An experimental apparatus with mass m is placed on a vertical spring of negligible mass and pushed down until the spring is compressed a distance x. The apparatus is then released and reaches its maximum height at a distance h above the point where it is released. The apparatus is not attached to the spring, and at its maximum height it is no longer in contact with the spring. The maximum magnitude of acceleration the apparatus can have without being damaged is a, where $a > g$. (a) What should the force constant of the spring be? (b) What distance x must the spring be compressed initially?

7.72. If a fish is attached to a vertical spring and slowly lowered to its equilibrium position, it is found to stretch the spring by an amount d. If the same fish is attached to the end of the unstretched spring and then allowed to fall from rest, through what maximum distance does it stretch the spring? (*Hint:* Calculate the force constant of the spring in terms of the distance d and the mass m of the fish.)

7.73. A wooden block with mass 1.50 kg is placed against a compressed spring at the bottom of an incline of slope 30.0° (point A). When the spring is released, it projects the block up the incline. At point B, a distance of 6.00 m up the incline from A, the block is moving up the incline at 7.00 m/s and is no longer in contact with the spring. The coefficient of kinetic friction between the block and the incline is $\mu_k = 0.50$. The mass of the spring is negligible. Calculate the amount of potential energy that was initially stored in the spring.

7.74. A 2.00-kg package is released on a 53.1° incline, 4.00 m from a long spring with force constant 120 N/m that is attached at the bottom of the incline (Fig. 7.43). The coefficients of friction between the package and the incline are $\mu_s = 0.40$ and $\mu_k = 0.20$. The mass of the spring is negligible. (a) What is the speed of the package just before it reaches the spring? (b) What is the maximum compression of the spring? (c) The package rebounds back up the incline. How close does it get to its initial position?

Figure 7.43 Problem 7.74.

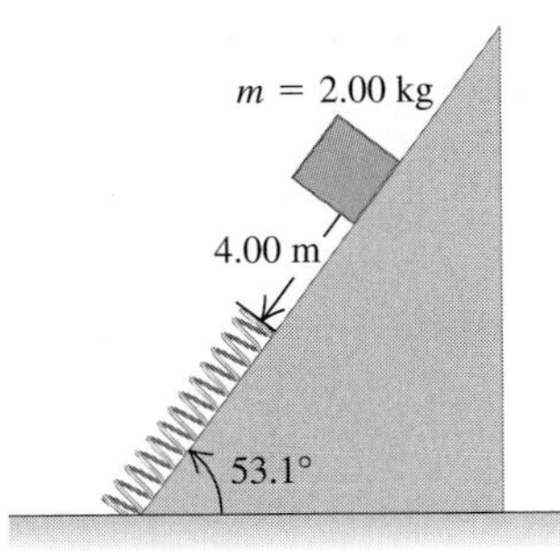

7.75. A 0.500-kg block, attached to a spring with length 0.60 m and force constant 40.0 N/m, is at rest with the back of the block at point A on a frictionless, horizontal air table (Fig. 7.44). The mass of the spring is negligible. You move the block to the right along the surface by pulling with a constant 20.0-N horizontal force. (a) What is the block's speed when the back of the block reaches point B, which is 0.25 m to the right of point A? (b) When the back of the block reaches point B, you let go of the block. In the subsequent motion, how close does the block get to the wall where the left end of the spring is attached?

Figure 7.44 Problem 7.75.

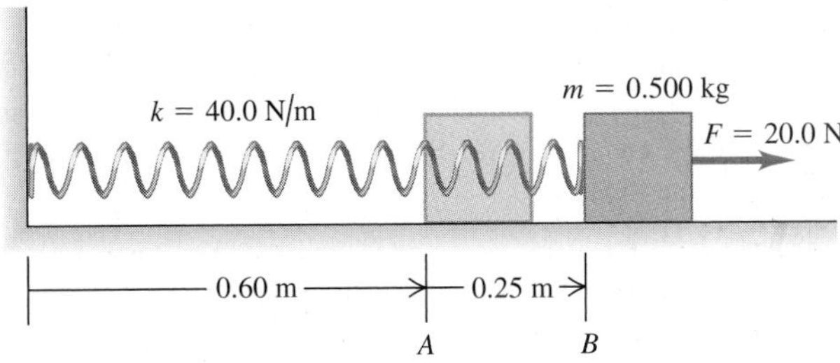

7.76. Fraternity Physics. The brothers of Iota Eta Pi fraternity build a platform, supported at all four corners by vertical springs, in the basement of their frat house. A brave fraternity brother wearing a football helmet stands in the middle of the platform; his weight compresses the springs by 0.18 m. Then four of his fraternity brothers, pushing down at the corners of the platform, compress the springs another 0.53 m until the top of the brave brother's helmet is 0.90 m below the basement ceiling. They then simultaneously release the platform. You can ignore the masses of the springs and platform. (a) When the dust clears, the fraternity asks you to calculate their fraternity brother's speed just before his helmet hit the flimsy ceiling. (b) Without the ceiling, how high would he have gone? (c) In discussing their probation, the dean of students suggests that the next time they try this, they do it outdoors on another planet. Would the answer to part (b) be the same if this stunt were performed on a planet with a different value of g? Assume that the fraternity brothers push the platform down 0.53 m as before. Explain your reasoning.

7.77. A particle with mass m is acted on by a conservative force and moves along a path given by $x = x_0 \cos \omega_0 t$ and $y = y_0 \sin \omega_0 t$, where x_0, y_0, and ω_0 are constants. (a) Find the components of the force that acts on the particle. (b) Find the potential energy of the particle as a function of x and y. Take $U = 0$ when $x = 0$ and $y = 0$. (c) Find the total energy of the particle when (i) $x = x_0$, $y = 0$ and (ii) $x = 0$, $y = y_0$.

7.78. When it is burned, 1 gallon of gasoline produces 1.3×10^8 J of energy. A 1500-kg car accelerates from rest to 37 m/s in 10 s. The engine of this car is only 15% efficient (which is typical), meaning that only 15% of the energy from the combustion of the gasoline is used to accelerate the car. The rest goes into things like the internal kinetic energy of the engine parts as well as heating of the exhaust air and engine. (a) How many gallons of gasoline does this car use during the acceleration? (b) How many such accelerations will it take to burn up 1 gallon of gas?

7.79. A hydroelectric dam holds back a lake of surface area 3.0×10^6 m^2 that has vertical sides below the water level. The water level in the lake is 150 m above the base of the dam. When the water passes through turbines at the base of the dam, its mechanical energy is converted into electrical energy with 90% efficiency. (a) If gravitational potential energy is taken to be zero at the base of the dam, how much energy is stored in the top meter of the water in the lake? The density of water is 1000 kg/m^3. (b) What volume of water must pass through the dam to produce 1000 kilowatt-hours of electrical energy? What distance does the level of water in the lake fall when this much water passes through the dam?

7.80. How much total energy is stored in the lake in Problem 7.79? As in that problem, take the gravitational potential energy to be zero at the base of the dam. Express your answer in joules and in kilowatt-hours. (*Hint:* Break the lake up into infinitesimal horizontal layers of thickness dy, and integrate to find the total potential energy.)

7.81. Gravity in Three Dimensions. A point mass m_1 is held in place at the origin, and another point mass m_2 is free to move a distance r away at a point P having coordinates x, y, and z. The gravitational potential energy of these masses is found to be $U(r) = -Gm_1m_2/r$, where G is the gravitational constant (see Exercises 7.34 and 7.35). (a) Show that the components of the force on m_2 due to m_1 are

$$F_x = -\frac{Gm_1m_2x}{(x^2+y^2+z^2)^{3/2}} \qquad F_y = -\frac{Gm_1m_2y}{(x^2+y^2+z^2)^{3/2}}$$

$$F_z = -\frac{Gm_1m_2z}{(x^2+y^2+z^2)^{3/2}}$$

(*Hint:* First write r in terms of x, y, and z.) (b) Show that the magnitude of the force on m_2 is $F = Gm_1m_2/r^2$. (c) Does m_1 attract or repel m_2? How do you know?

7.82. (a) Is the force $\vec{F} = Cy^2\hat{j}$, where C is a negative constant with units of N/m^2, conservative or nonconservative? Justify your answer. (b) Is the force $\vec{F} = Cy^2\hat{\imath}$, where C is a negative constant with units of N/m^2, conservative or nonconservative? Justify your answer.

7.83. A cutting tool under microprocessor control has several forces acting on it. One force is $\vec{F} = -\alpha xy^2\hat{j}$, a force in the negative y-direction whose magnitude depends on the position of the tool. The constant is $\alpha = 2.50$ N/m^3. Consider the displacement of the tool from the origin to the point $x = 3.00$ m, $y = 3.00$ m. (a) Calculate the work done on the tool by $\vec{F}$ if this displacement is along the straight line $y = x$ that connects these two points. (b) Calculate the work done on the tool by $\vec{F}$ if the tool is first moved out along the x-axis to the point $x = 3.00$ m, $y = 0$ and then moved parallel to the y-axis to the point $x = 3.00$ m, $y = 3.00$ m. (c) Compare the work done by $\vec{F}$ along these two paths. Is $\vec{F}$ conservative or nonconservative? Explain.

7.84. An object has several forces acting on it. One force is $\vec{F} = \alpha xy\hat{\imath}$, a force in the x-direction whose magnitude depends on the position of the object. (See Problem 6.96.) The constant is $\alpha = 2.00$ N/m^2. The object moves along the following path: (1) It starts at the origin and moves along the y-axis to the point $x = 0$, $y = 1.50$ m; (2) it moves parallel to the x-axis to the point $x = 1.50$ m, $y = 1.50$ m; (3) it moves parallel to the y-axis to the point $x = 1.50$ m, $y = 0$; (4) it moves parallel to the x-axis back to the origin. (a) Sketch this path in the xy-plane. (b) Calculate the work done on the object by $\vec{F}$ for each leg of the path and for the complete round trip. (c) Is $\vec{F}$ conservative or nonconservative? Explain.

7.85. A Hooke's law force $-kx$ and a constant conservative force F in the $+x$-direction act on an atomic ion. (a) Show that a possible potential-energy function for this combination of forces is $U(x) = \frac{1}{2}kx^2 - Fx - F^2/2k$. Is this the *only* possible function? Explain. (b) Find the stable equilibrium position. (c) Graph $U(x)$ (in units of F^2/k) versus x (in units of F/k) for values of x between $-5F/k$ and $5F/k$. (d) Are there any unstable equilibrium positions? (e) If the total energy is $E = F^2/k$, what are the maximum and minimum values of x that the ion reaches in its motion? If the ion has mass m, find its maximum speed if the total energy is $E = F^2/k$. For what value of x is the speed maximum?

7.86. A particle moves along the x-axis while acted on by a single conservative force parallel to the x-axis. The force corresponds to the potential-energy function graphed in Fig. 7.45. The particle is released from rest at point A. (a) What is the direction of the force on the particle when it is at point A? (b) At point B? (c) At what value of x is the kinetic energy of the particle a maximum? (d) What is the force on the particle when it is at point C? (e) What is the largest value of x reached by the particle during its motion? (f) What value or values of x correspond to points of stable equilibrium? (g) Of unstable equilibrium?

Figure 7.45 Problem 7.86.

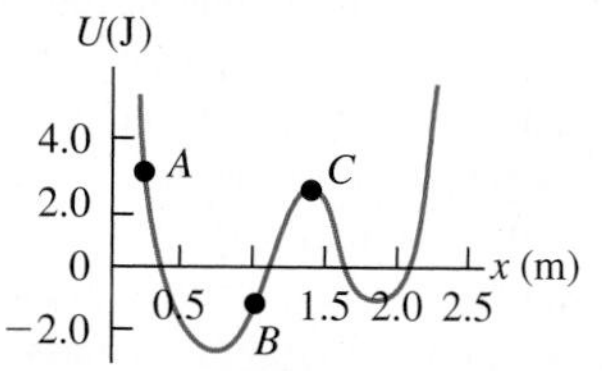

Challenge Problem

7.87. A proton with mass m moves in one dimension. The potential-energy function is $U(x) = \alpha/x^2 - \beta/x$, where α and β are positive constants. The proton is released from rest at $x_0 = \alpha/\beta$. (a) Show that $U(x)$ can be written as

$$U(x) = \frac{\alpha}{x_0^2}\left[\left(\frac{x_0}{x}\right)^2 - \frac{x_0}{x}\right]$$

Graph $U(x)$. Calculate $U(x_0)$ and thereby locate the point x_0 on the graph. (b) Calculate $v(x)$, the speed of the proton as a function of position. Graph $v(x)$ and give a qualitative description of the motion. (c) For what value of x is the speed of the proton a maximum? What is the value of that maximum speed? (d) What is the force on the proton at the point in part (c)? (e) Let the proton be released instead at $x_1 = 3\alpha/\beta$. Locate the point x_1 on the graph of $U(x)$. Calculate $v(x)$ and give a qualitative description of the motion. (f) For each release point ($x = x_0$ and $x = x_1$), what are the maximum and minimum values of x reached during the motion?

MOMENTUM, IMPULSE, AND COLLISIONS

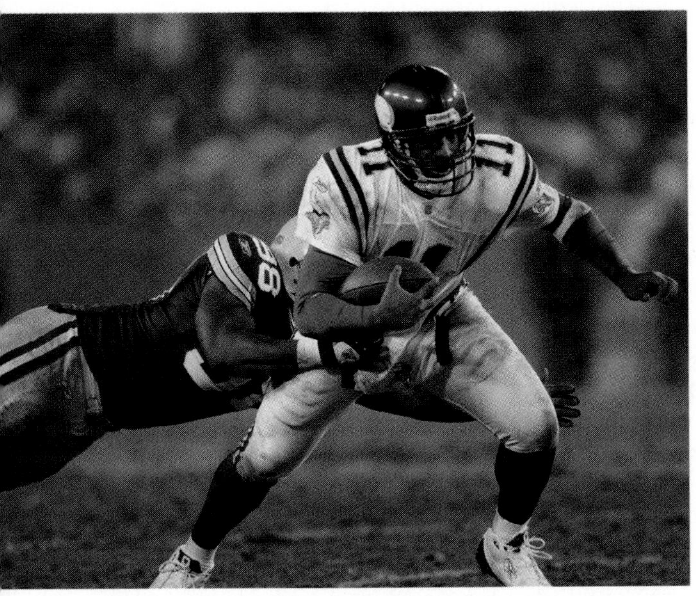

? Which could potentially cause you the greater injury: being tackled by a lightweight, fast-moving football player, or being tackled by a player with double the mass but moving at half the speed?

Learning Goals

By studying this chapter, you will learn:

- the meaning of the momentum of a particle, and how the impulse of the net force acting on a particle causes its momentum to change.
- the conditions under which the total momentum of a system of particles is constant (conserved).
- how to solve problems in which two bodies collide with each other.
- the important distinction among elastic, inelastic, and completely inelastic collisions.
- the definition of the center of mass of a system, and what determines how the center of mass moves.
- how to analyze situations such as rocket propulsion in which the mass of a body changes as it moves.

There are many questions involving forces that cannot be answered by directly applying Newton's second law, $\sum\vec{F} = m\vec{a}$. For example, when an 18-wheeler collides head-on with a compact car, what determines which way the wreckage moves after the collision? In playing pool, how do you decide how to aim the cue ball in order to knock the eight ball into the pocket? And when a meteorite collides with the earth, how much of the meteorite's kinetic energy is released in the impact?

A common theme of all these questions is that they involve forces about which we know very little: the forces between the car and the 18-wheeler, between the two pool balls, or between the meteorite and the earth. Remarkably, we will find in this chapter that we don't have to know *anything* about these forces to answer questions of this kind!

Our approach uses two new concepts, *momentum* and *impulse,* and a new conservation law, *conservation of momentum.* This conservation law is every bit as important as that of conservation of energy. The law of conservation of momentum is valid even in situations in which Newton's laws are inadequate, such as bodies moving at very high speeds (near the speed of light) or objects on a very small scale (such as the constituents of atoms). Within the domain of Newtonian mechanics, conservation of momentum enables us to analyze many situations that would be very difficult if we tried to use Newton's laws directly. Among these are *collision* problems, in which two bodies collide and can exert very large forces on each other for a short time.

8.1 Momentum and Impulse

In Chapter 6 we re-expressed Newton's second law for a particle, $\sum\vec{F} = m\vec{a}$, in terms of the work–energy theorem. This theorem helped us tackle a great number of physics problems and led us to the law of conservation of energy. Let's now return to $\sum\vec{F} = m\vec{a}$ and see yet another useful way to restate this fundamental law.

Newton's Second Law in Terms of Momentum

Consider a particle of constant mass m. (Later in this chapter we'll see how to deal with situations in which the mass of a body changes.) Because $\vec{a} = d\vec{v}/dt$, we can write Newton's second law for this particle as

$$\sum \vec{F} = m\frac{d\vec{v}}{dt} = \frac{d}{dt}(m\vec{v}) \tag{8.1}$$

We can take the mass m inside the derivative because it is constant. Thus Newton's second law says that the net force $\sum \vec{F}$ acting on a particle equals the time rate of change of the combination $m\vec{v}$, the product of the particle's mass and velocity. We'll call this combination the **momentum,** or **linear momentum,** of the particle. Using the symbol $\vec{p}$ for momentum, we have

$$\vec{p} = m\vec{v} \qquad \text{(definition of momentum)} \tag{8.2}$$

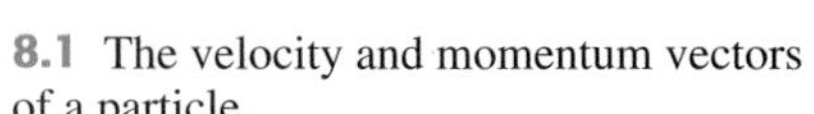

8.1 The velocity and momentum vectors of a particle.

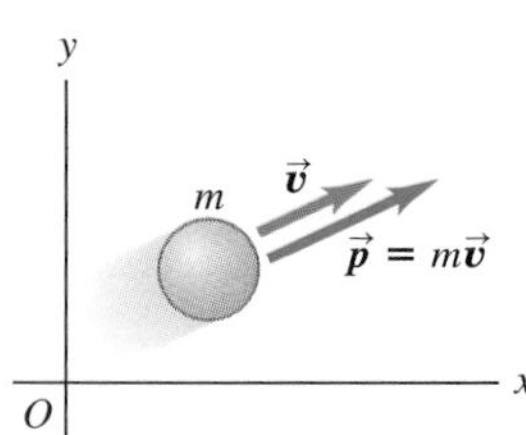

Momentum $\vec{p}$ is a vector quantity; a particle's momentum has the same direction as its velocity $\vec{v}$.

The greater the mass m and speed v of a particle, the greater is its magnitude of momentum mv. Keep in mind, however, that momentum is a *vector* quantity with the same direction as the particle's velocity (Fig. 8.1). Hence a car driving north at 20 m/s and an identical car driving east at 20 m/s have the same *magnitude* of momentum (mv) but different momentum *vectors* $(m\vec{v})$ because their directions are different.

We often express the momentum of a particle in terms of its components. If the particle has velocity components v_x, v_y, and v_z, then its momentum components p_x, p_y, and p_z (which we also call the *x-momentum, y-momentum,* and *z-momentum*) are given by

$$p_x = mv_x \qquad p_y = mv_y \qquad p_z = mv_z \tag{8.3}$$

These three component equations are equivalent to Eq. (8.2).

The units of the magnitude of momentum are units of mass times speed; the SI units of momentum are kg · m/s. The plural of momentum is "momenta."

If we now substitute the definition of momentum, Eq. (8.2), into Eq. (8.1), we get

$$\sum \vec{F} = \frac{d\vec{p}}{dt} \qquad \text{(Newton's second law in terms of momentum)} \tag{8.4}$$

The net force (vector sum of all forces) acting on a particle equals the time rate of change of momentum of the particle. This, not $\sum \vec{F} = m\vec{a}$, is the form in which Newton originally stated his second law (although he called momentum the "quantity of motion"). This law is valid only in inertial frames of reference.

According to Eq. (8.4), a rapid change in momentum requires a large net force, while a gradual change in momentum requires less net force. This principle is used in the design of automobile safety devices such as air bags (Fig. 8.2).

8.2 If a fast-moving automobile stops suddenly in a collision, the driver's momentum (mass times velocity) changes from a large value to zero in a short time. An air bag causes the driver to lose momentum more gradually than would an abrupt collision with the steering wheel, reducing the force exerted on the driver as well as the possibility of injury.

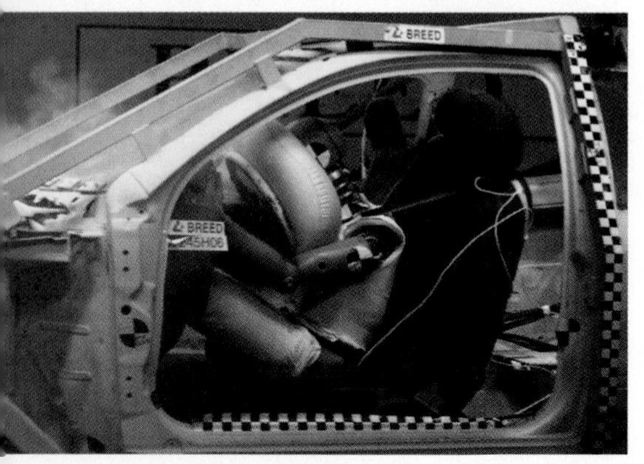

The Impulse–Momentum Theorem

A particle's momentum $\vec{p} = m\vec{v}$ and its kinetic energy $K = \frac{1}{2}mv^2$ both depend on the mass and velocity of the particle. What is the fundamental difference between these two quantities? A purely mathematical answer is that momentum is a vector whose magnitude is proportional to speed, while kinetic energy is a scalar proportional to the speed squared. But to see the *physical* difference between momentum and kinetic energy, we must first define a quantity closely related to momentum called *impulse.*

Let's first consider a particle acted on by a *constant* net force $\sum \vec{F}$ during a time interval Δt from t_1 to t_2. (We'll look at the case of varying forces shortly.)

The **impulse** of the net force, denoted by $\vec{J}$, is defined to be the product of the net force and the time interval:

$$\vec{J} = \Sigma\vec{F}(t_2 - t_1) = \Sigma\vec{F}\,\Delta t \qquad \text{(assuming constant net force)} \qquad (8.5)$$

Impulse is a vector quantity; its direction is the same as the net force $\Sigma\vec{F}$. Its magnitude is the product of the magnitude of the net force and the length of time that the net force acts. The SI unit of impulse is the newton-second $(\text{N} \cdot \text{s})$. Because $1\ \text{N} = 1\ \text{kg} \cdot \text{m/s}^2$, an alternative set of units for impulse is $\text{kg} \cdot \text{m/s}$, the same as the units of momentum.

To see what impulse is good for, let's go back to Newton's second law as restated in terms of momentum, Eq. (8.4). If the net force $\Sigma\vec{F}$ is constant, then $d\vec{p}/dt$ is also constant. In that case, $d\vec{p}/dt$ is equal to the *total* change in momentum $\vec{p}_2 - \vec{p}_1$ during the time interval $t_2 - t_1$, divided by the interval:

$$\Sigma\vec{F} = \frac{\vec{p}_2 - \vec{p}_1}{t_2 - t_1}$$

Multiplying this equation by $(t_2 - t_1)$, we have

$$\Sigma\vec{F}(t_2 - t_1) = \vec{p}_2 - \vec{p}_1$$

Comparing with Eq. (8.5), we end up with a result called the **impulse–momentum theorem:**

$$\vec{J} = \vec{p}_2 - \vec{p}_1 \qquad \text{(impulse–momentum theorem)} \qquad (8.6)$$

The change in momentum of a particle during a time interval equals the impulse of the net force that acts on the particle during that interval.

The impulse–momentum theorem also holds when forces are not constant. To see this, we integrate both sides of Newton's second law $\Sigma\vec{F} = d\vec{p}/dt$ over time between the limits t_1 and t_2:

$$\int_{t_1}^{t_2} \Sigma\vec{F}\,dt = \int_{t_1}^{t_2} \frac{d\vec{p}}{dt}\,dt = \int_{\vec{p}_1}^{\vec{p}_2} d\vec{p} = \vec{p}_2 - \vec{p}_1$$

The integral on the left is defined to be the impulse $\vec{J}$ of the net force $\Sigma\vec{F}$ during this interval:

$$\vec{J} = \int_{t_1}^{t_2} \Sigma\vec{F}\,dt \qquad \text{(general definition of impulse)} \qquad (8.7)$$

With this definition, the impulse–momentum theorem $\vec{J} = \vec{p}_2 - \vec{p}_1$, Eq. (8.6), is valid even when the net force $\Sigma\vec{F}$ varies with time.

We can define an *average* net force $\vec{F}_{\text{av}}$ such that even when $\Sigma\vec{F}$ is not constant, the impulse $\vec{J}$ is given by

$$\vec{J} = \vec{F}_{\text{av}}(t_2 - t_1) \qquad (8.8)$$

When $\Sigma\vec{F}$ is constant, $\Sigma\vec{F} = \vec{F}_{\text{av}}$ and Eq. (8.8) reduces to Eq. (8.5).

Figure 8.3a shows the x-component of net force ΣF_x as a function of time during a collision. This might represent the force on a soccer ball that is in contact with a player's foot from time t_1 to t_2. The x-component of impulse during this interval is represented by the red area under the curve between t_1 and t_2. This area is equal to the green rectangular area bounded by t_1, t_2, and $(F_{\text{av}})_x$, so $(F_{\text{av}})_x(t_2 - t_1)$ is

8.3 The meaning of the area under a graph of ΣF_x versus t.

(a)

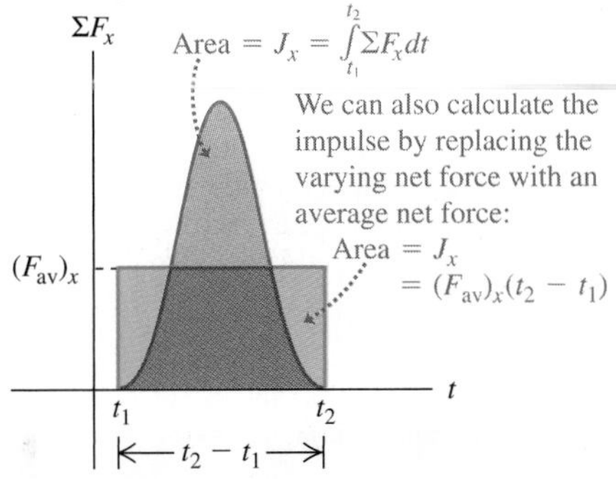
The area under the curve of net force versus time equals the impulse of the net force:
ΣF_x
Area $= J_x = \int_{t_1}^{t_2} \Sigma F_x dt$
We can also calculate the impulse by replacing the varying net force with an average net force:
Area $= J_x$
$= (F_{\text{av}})_x(t_2 - t_1)$
$(F_{\text{av}})_x$
t
t_1
t_2
$t_2 - t_1$

(b)

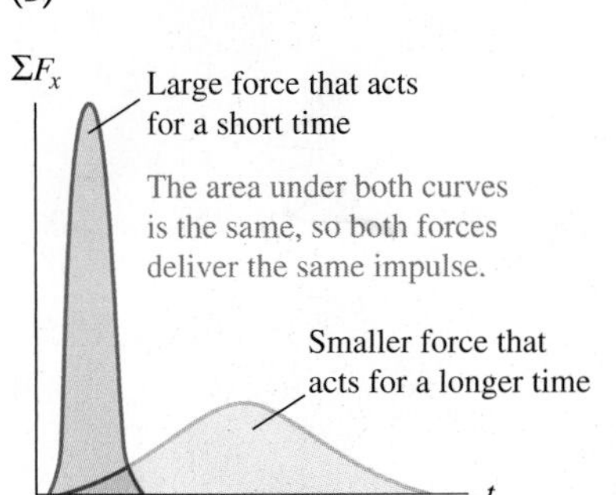
ΣF_x
Large force that acts for a short time
The area under both curves is the same, so both forces deliver the same impulse.
Smaller force that acts for a longer time
t

equal to the impulse of the actual time-varying force during the same interval. Note that a large force acting for a short time can have the same impulse as a smaller force acting for a longer time if the areas under the force–time curves are the same (Fig. 8.3b). In this language, an automobile airbag (Fig. 8.2) provides the same impulse to the driver as would the steering wheel or the dashboard by applying a weaker and less injurious force for a longer time.

Impulse and momentum are both vector quantities, and Eqs. (8.5)–(8.8) are all vector equations. In specific problems, it is often easiest to use them in component form:

$$J_x = \int_{t_1}^{t_2} \Sigma F_x \, dt = (F_{av})_x (t_2 - t_1) = p_{2x} - p_{1x} = mv_{2x} - mv_{1x}$$
$$J_y = \int_{t_1}^{t_2} \Sigma F_y \, dt = (F_{av})_y (t_2 - t_1) = p_{2y} - p_{1y} = mv_{2y} - mv_{1y} \quad (8.9)$$

and similarly for the z-component.

Momentum and Kinetic Energy Compared

ActivPhysics ONLINE
6.1 Momentum and Energy Change

We can now see the fundamental difference between momentum and kinetic energy. The impulse–momentum theorem $\vec{J} = \vec{p}_2 - \vec{p}_1$ says that changes in a particle's momentum are due to impulse, which depends on the *time* over which the net force acts. By contrast, the work–energy theorem $W_{tot} = K_2 - K_1$ tells us that kinetic energy changes when work is done on a particle; the total work depends on the *distance* over which the net force acts. Consider a particle that starts from rest at t_1 so that $\vec{v}_1 = \mathbf{0}$. Its initial momentum is $\vec{p}_1 = m\vec{v}_1 = \mathbf{0}$, and its initial kinetic energy is $K_1 = \frac{1}{2}mv_1^2 = 0$. Now let a constant net force equal to $\vec{F}$ act on that particle from time t_1 until time t_2. During this interval, the particle moves a distance s in the direction of the force. From Eq. (8.6), the particle's momentum at time t_2 is

$$\vec{p}_2 = \vec{p}_1 + \vec{J} = \vec{J}$$

where $\vec{J} = \vec{F}(t_2 - t_1)$ is the impulse that acts on the particle. So *the momentum of a particle equals the impulse that accelerated it from rest to its present speed;* impulse is the product of the net force that accelerated the particle and the *time* required for the acceleration. By comparison, the kinetic energy of the particle at t_2 is $K_2 = W_{tot} = Fs$, the total *work* done on the particle to accelerate it from rest. The total work is the product of the net force and the *distance* required to accelerate the particle (Fig. 8.4).

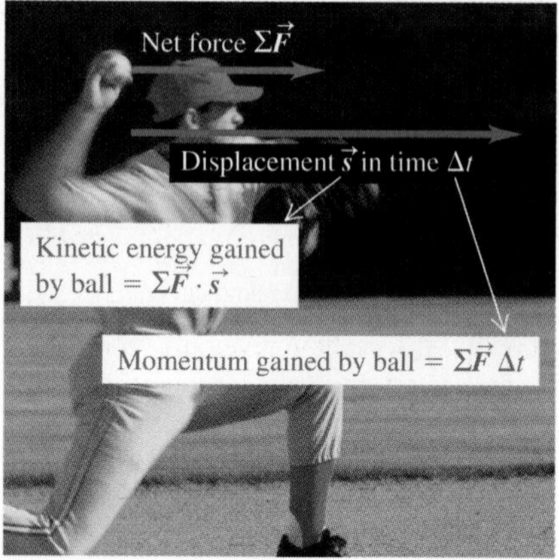

8.4 The *kinetic energy* of a pitched baseball is equal to the work the pitcher does on it (force multiplied by the distance the ball moves during the throw). The *momentum* of the ball is equal to the impulse the pitcher imparts to it (force multiplied by the time it took to bring the ball up to speed).

Here's an application of the distinction between momentum and kinetic energy. Suppose you have a choice between catching a 0.50-kg ball moving at 4.0 m/s or a 0.10-kg ball moving at 20 m/s. Which will be easier to catch? Both balls have the same magnitude of momentum, $p = mv = (0.50\text{ kg})(4.0\text{ m/s}) = (0.10\text{ kg})(20\text{ m/s}) = 2.0\text{ kg}\cdot\text{m/s}$. However, the two balls have different values of kinetic energy $K = \frac{1}{2}mv^2$; the large, slow-moving ball has $K = 4.0$ J, while the small, fast-moving ball has $K = 20$ J. Since the momentum is the same for both balls, both require the same *impulse* to be brought to rest. But stopping the 0.10-kg ball with your hand requires five times more *work* than stopping the 0.50-kg ball because the smaller ball has five times more kinetic energy. For a given force that you exert with your hand, it takes the same amount of time (the duration of the catch) to stop either ball, but your hand and arm will be pushed back five times farther if you choose to catch the small, fast-moving ball. To minimize arm strain, you should choose to catch the 0.50-kg ball with its lower kinetic energy.

Both the impulse–momentum and work–energy theorems are relationships between force and motion, and both rest on the foundation of Newton's laws. They are *integral* principles, relating the motion at two different times separated by a finite interval. By contrast, Newton's second law itself (in either of the forms $\Sigma\vec{F} = m\vec{a}$ or $\Sigma\vec{F} = d\vec{p}/dt$) is a *differential* principle, relating the forces to the rate of change of velocity or momentum at each instant.

Conceptual Example 8.1 Momentum versus kinetic energy

Consider again the race described in Conceptual Example 6.5 (Section 6.2) between two iceboats on a frictionless frozen lake. The iceboats have masses m and $2m$, and the wind exerts the same constant horizontal force $\vec{F}$ on each iceboat (see Fig. 6.14). The two iceboats start from rest and cross the finish line a distance s away. Which iceboat crosses the finish line with greater momentum?

SOLUTION

In Conceptual Example 6.5 we asked how the *kinetic energies* of the iceboats compare when they cross the finish line. The way to answer this was not to use the formula $K = \frac{1}{2}mv^2$, but to remember that a body's kinetic energy equals the total work done to accelerate it from rest. Both iceboats started from rest, and the total work done between the starting and finish lines was the same for both iceboats (because the net force and displacement were the same for both). Hence both iceboats cross the finish line with the same kinetic energy.

Similarly, the best way to compare the *momenta* of the iceboats is *not* to use the formula $\vec{p} = m\vec{v}$. By itself this formula isn't enough to determine which iceboat has greater momentum at the finish line. The iceboat of mass $2m$ has greater mass, which suggests greater momentum, but this iceboat crosses the finish line going slower than the other one, which suggests less momentum.

Instead, we use the idea that the momentum of each iceboat equals the impulse that accelerated it from rest. For each iceboat the downward force of gravity and the upward normal force add to zero, so the net force equals the constant horizontal wind force $\vec{F}$. Let Δt be the time an iceboat takes to reach the finish line, so that the impulse on the iceboat during that time is $\vec{J} = \vec{F}\,\Delta t$. Since the iceboat starts from rest, this equals the iceboat's momentum $\vec{p}$ at the finish line:

$$\vec{p} = \vec{F}\,\Delta t$$

Both iceboats are subjected to the same force $\vec{F}$, but they take different amounts of time Δt to reach the finish line. The iceboat of mass $2m$ accelerates more slowly and takes a longer time to travel the distance s; thus there is a greater impulse on this iceboat between the starting and finish lines. So the iceboat of mass $2m$ crosses the finish line with a greater magnitude of momentum than the iceboat of mass m (but with the same kinetic energy). Can you show that the iceboat of mass $2m$ has $\sqrt{2}$ times as much momentum at the finish line as the iceboat of mass m?

Example 8.2 A ball hits a wall

Suppose you throw a ball with a mass of 0.40 kg against a brick wall. It hits the wall moving horizontally to the left at 30 m/s and rebounds horizontally to the right at 20 m/s. (a) Find the impulse of the net force on the ball during its collision with the wall. (b) If the ball is in contact with the wall for 0.010 s, find the average horizontal force that the wall exerts on the ball during the impact.

SOLUTION

IDENTIFY: We're given enough information to determine the initial and final values of the ball's momentum, so we can use the impulse–momentum theorem to find the impulse. We'll then use the definition of impulse to determine the average force.

SET UP: Figure 8.5 shows our sketch. The motion is purely horizontal, so we need only a single axis. We'll take the x-axis to be horizontal and the positive direction to be to the right. Our target variable in part (a) is the x-component of impulse, J_x, which we'll find from the x-components of momentum before and after the impact, using Eqs. (8.9). In part (b), our target variable is the average x-component of force $(F_{av})_x$; once we know J_x, we can also find this force by using Eqs. (8.9).

8.5 Our sketch for this problem.

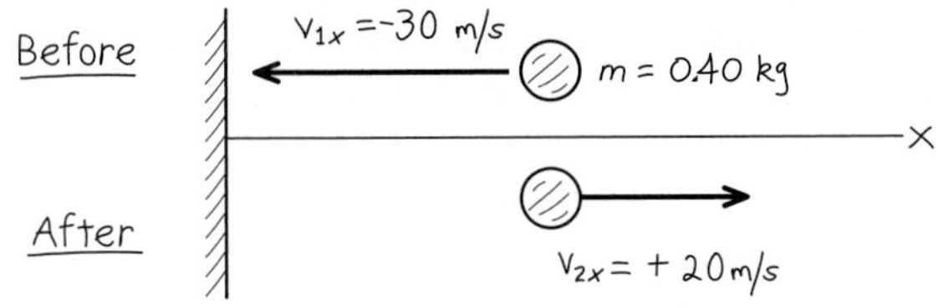

EXECUTE: (a) With our choice of x-axis, the initial and final x-components of momentum of the ball are

$$p_{1x} = mv_{1x} = (0.40\text{ kg})(-30\text{ m/s}) = -12\text{ kg}\cdot\text{m/s}$$
$$p_{2x} = mv_{2x} = (0.40\text{ kg})(+20\text{ m/s}) = +8.0\text{ kg}\cdot\text{m/s}$$

From the x-equation in Eqs. (8.9), the x-component of impulse equals the *change* in the x-momentum:

$$J_x = p_{2x} - p_{1x}$$
$$= 8.0\text{ kg}\cdot\text{m/s} - (-12\text{ kg}\cdot\text{m/s}) = 20\text{ kg}\cdot\text{m/s} = 20\text{ N}\cdot\text{s}$$

(b) The collision time is $t_2 - t_1 = \Delta t = 0.010$ s. From the x-equation in Eqs. (8.9), $J_x = (F_{av})_x(t_2 - t_1) = (F_{av})_x\,\Delta t$, so

$$(F_{av})_x = \frac{J_x}{\Delta t} = \frac{20\text{ N}\cdot\text{s}}{0.010\text{ s}} = 2000\text{ N}$$

EVALUATE: The x-component of impulse is positive—that is, to the right in Fig. 8.5. This is as it should be: The impulse represents the "kick" that the wall imparts to the ball, and this "kick" is certainly to the right.

CAUTION Momentum is a vector Because momentum is a vector, we had to include the negative sign in p_{1x}. Had we carelessly omitted it, we would have calculated the impulse to be $8.0\text{ kg}\cdot\text{m/s} - (12\text{ kg}\cdot\text{m/s}) = -4\text{ kg}\cdot\text{m/s}$. This incorrect answer would say that the wall had somehow given the ball a kick to the *left!* Make sure that you account for the *direction* of momentum in your calculations.

The force that the wall exerts on the ball has to have a large magnitude of 2000 N (equal to 450 lb, or the weight of a 200-kg

Continued

object) to change the ball's momentum in such a short time interval. Other forces that act on the ball during the collision are very weak by comparison; for instance, the gravitational force is only 3.9 N. Thus, during the brief time that the collision lasts, we can ignore all other forces on the ball to a very good approximation. Figure 8.6 is a photograph showing the impact of a tennis ball and racket.

Note that the 2000-N value we calculated is just the *average* horizontal force that the wall exerts on the ball during the impact. It corresponds to the horizontal line $(F_{av})_x$ in Fig. 8.3a. The horizontal force is zero before impact, rises to a maximum, and then decreases to zero when the ball loses contact with the wall. If the ball is relatively rigid, like a baseball or golf ball, the collision lasts a short time and the maximum force is large, as in the blue curve in Fig. 8.3b. If the ball is softer, like a tennis ball, the collision time is longer and the maximum force is less, as in the orange curve in Fig. 8.3b.

8.6 Typically, a tennis ball is in contact with the racket for approximately 0.01 s. The ball flattens noticeably due to the tremendous force exerted by the racket.

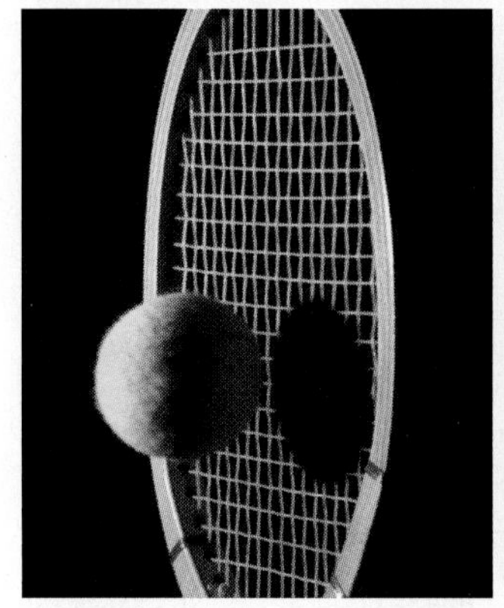
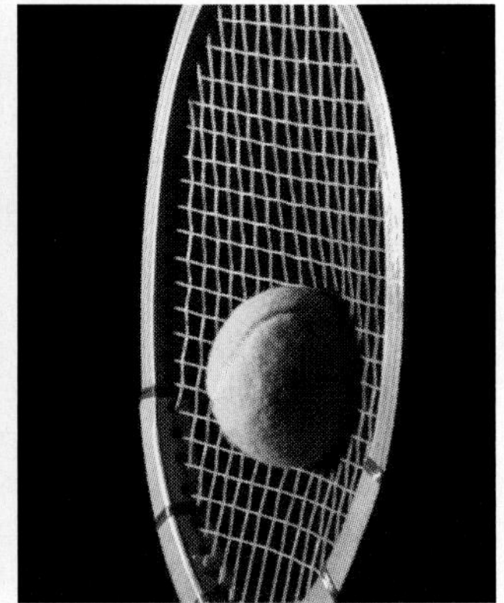

Example 8.3 Kicking a soccer ball

A soccer ball has a mass of 0.40 kg. Initially, it is moving to the left at 20 m/s, but then it is kicked and given a velocity at 45° upward and to the right, with a magnitude of 30 m/s (Fig. 8.7a). Find the impulse of the net force and the average net force, assuming a collision time $\Delta t = 0.010$ s.

SOLUTION

IDENTIFY: This example uses the same principles as Example 8.2. The key difference is that the initial and final velocities are not along the same line, so we have to be careful to treat momentum and impulse as vector quantities, using their x- and y-components.

SET UP: We take the x-axis to be horizontally to the right and the y-axis to be vertically upward. Our target variables are the components of the net impulse on the ball, J_x and J_y, and the components of the average net force on the ball, $(F_{av})_x$ and $(F_{av})_y$. We'll find them using the x- and y-components of Eqs. (8.9).

8.7 (a) Kicking a soccer ball. (b) Finding the average force on the ball from its components.

(a) Before-and-after diagram

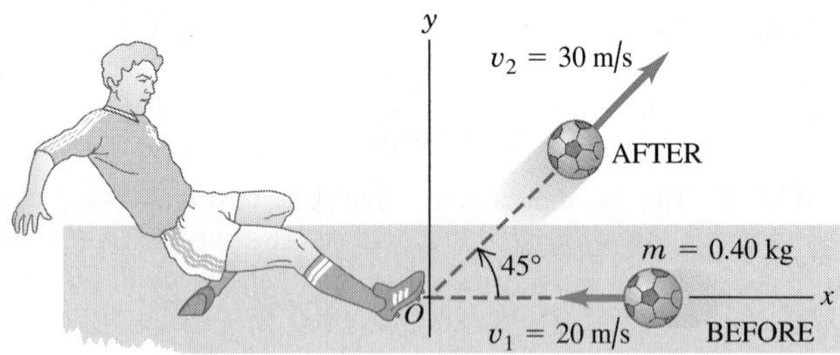

(b) Average force on the ball

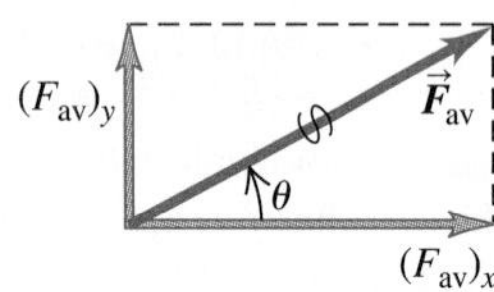

EXECUTE: With our choice of axes, we find the ball's velocity components before (subscript 1) and after (subscript 2) it is kicked:

$$v_{1x} = -20 \text{ m/s} \qquad v_{1y} = 0$$
$$v_{2x} = v_{2y} = (30 \text{ m/s})(0.707) = 21.2 \text{ m/s}$$
$$(\text{since } \cos 45° = \sin 45° = 0.707)$$

The x-component of impulse is equal to the x-component of momentum change, and the same is true for the y-components:

$$J_x = p_{2x} - p_{1x} = m(v_{2x} - v_{1x})$$
$$= (0.40 \text{ kg})[21.2 \text{ m/s} - (-20 \text{ m/s})] = 16.5 \text{ kg} \cdot \text{m/s}$$
$$J_y = p_{2y} - p_{1y} = m(v_{2y} - v_{1y})$$
$$= (0.40 \text{ kg})(21.2 \text{ m/s} - 0) = 8.5 \text{ kg} \cdot \text{m/s}$$

The components of the average net force on the ball are

$$(F_{av})_x = \frac{J_x}{\Delta t} = 1650 \text{ N} \qquad (F_{av})_y = \frac{J_y}{\Delta t} = 850 \text{ N}$$

The magnitude and direction of the average force are

$$F_{av} = \sqrt{(1650 \text{ N})^2 + (850 \text{ N})^2} = 1.9 \times 10^3 \text{ N}$$
$$\theta = \arctan\frac{850 \text{ N}}{1650 \text{ N}} = 27°$$

where θ is measured upward from the $+x$-axis (Fig. 8.7b). Note that because the ball was not initially at rest, the ball's final velocity does *not* have the same direction as the average force that acted on it.

EVALUATE: The average net force $\vec{F}_{av}$ includes the effects of the force of gravity, although these are small; the weight of the ball is only 3.9 N. As in Example 8.2, the average force acting during the collision is exerted almost entirely by the object that the ball hit (in this case, the soccer player's foot).

Test Your Understanding of Section 8.1 Rank the following situations according to the magnitude of the impulse of the net force, from largest value to smallest value. In each situation a 1000-kg automobile is moving along a straight east–west road. (i) The automobile is initially moving east at 25 m/s and comes to a stop in 10 s. (ii) The automobile is initially moving east at 25 m/s and comes to a stop in 5 s. (iii) The automobile is initially at rest, and a 2000-N net force toward the east is applied to it for 10 s. (iv) The automobile is initially moving east at 25 m/s, and a 2000-N net force toward the west is applied to it for 10 s. (v) The automobile is initially moving east at 25 m/s. Over a 30-s period, the automobile reverses direction and ends up moving west at 25 m/s.

8.2 Conservation of Momentum

The concept of momentum is particularly important in situations in which we have two or more *interacting* bodies. To see why, let's consider first an idealized system consisting of two bodies that interact with each other but not with anything else—for example, two astronauts who touch each other as they float freely in the zero-gravity environment of outer space (Fig. 8.8). Think of the astronauts as particles. Each particle exerts a force on the other; according to Newton's third law, the two forces are always equal in magnitude and opposite in direction. Hence, the *impulses* that act on the two particles are equal and opposite, and the changes in momentum of the two particles are equal and opposite.

8.8 Two astronauts push each other as they float freely in the zero-gravity environment of space.

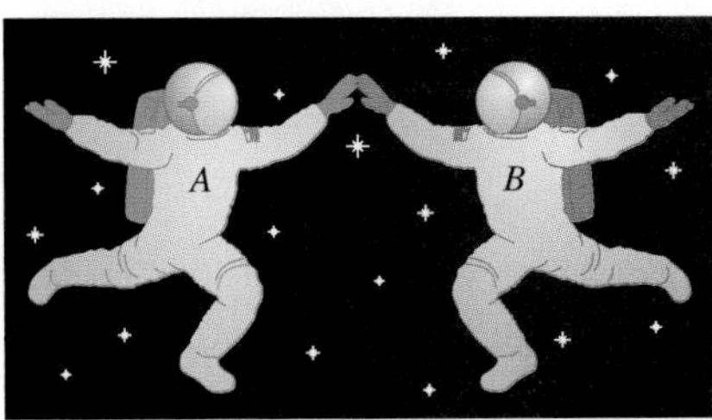

No external forces act on the two-astronaut system, so its total momentum is conserved.

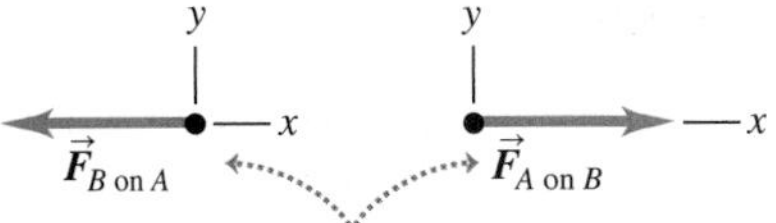

The forces the astronauts exert on each other form an action–reaction pair.

Let's go over that again with some new terminology. For any system, the forces that the particles of the system exert on each other are called **internal forces.** Forces exerted on any part of the system by some object outside it are called **external forces.** For the system shown in Fig. 8.8, the internal forces are $\vec{F}_{B \text{ on } A}$, exerted by particle B on particle A, and $\vec{F}_{A \text{ on } B}$, exerted by particle A on particle B. There are *no* external forces; when this is the case, we have an **isolated system.**

The net force on particle A is $\vec{F}_{B \text{ on } A}$ and the net force on particle B is $\vec{F}_{A \text{ on } B}$, so from Eq. (8.4) the rates of change of the momenta of the two particles are

$$\vec{F}_{B \text{ on } A} = \frac{d\vec{p}_A}{dt} \qquad \vec{F}_{A \text{ on } B} = \frac{d\vec{p}_B}{dt} \tag{8.10}$$

The momentum of each particle changes, but these changes are related to each other by Newton's third law: The two forces $\vec{F}_{B \text{ on } A}$ and $\vec{F}_{A \text{ on } B}$ are always equal in magnitude and opposite in direction. That is, $\vec{F}_{B \text{ on } A} = -\vec{F}_{A \text{ on } B}$, so $\vec{F}_{B \text{ on } A} + \vec{F}_{A \text{ on } B} = \mathbf{0}$. Adding together the two equations in Eq. (8.10), we have

$$\vec{F}_{B \text{ on } A} + \vec{F}_{A \text{ on } B} = \frac{d\vec{p}_A}{dt} + \frac{d\vec{p}_B}{dt} = \frac{d(\vec{p}_A + \vec{p}_B)}{dt} = \mathbf{0} \tag{8.11}$$

ActivPhysics ONLINE

6.3 Momentum Conservation and Collisions
6.7 Explosion Problems
6.10 Pendulum Person-Projectile Bowling

The rates of change of the two momenta are equal and opposite, so the rate of change of the vector sum $\vec{p}_A + \vec{p}_B$ is zero. We now define the **total momentum** $\vec{P}$ of the system of two particles as the vector sum of the momenta of the individual particles; that is,

$$\vec{P} = \vec{p}_A + \vec{p}_B \tag{8.12}$$

Then Eq. (8.11) becomes, finally,

$$\vec{F}_{B \text{ on } A} + \vec{F}_{A \text{ on } B} = \frac{d\vec{P}}{dt} = \mathbf{0} \tag{8.13}$$

The time rate of change of the *total* momentum $\vec{P}$ is zero. Hence the total momentum of the system is constant, even though the individual momenta of the particles that make up the system can change.

8.9 Two ice skaters push each other as they skate on a frictionless, horizontal surface. (Compare to Fig. 8.8.)

The forces the skaters exert on each other form an action–reaction pair.

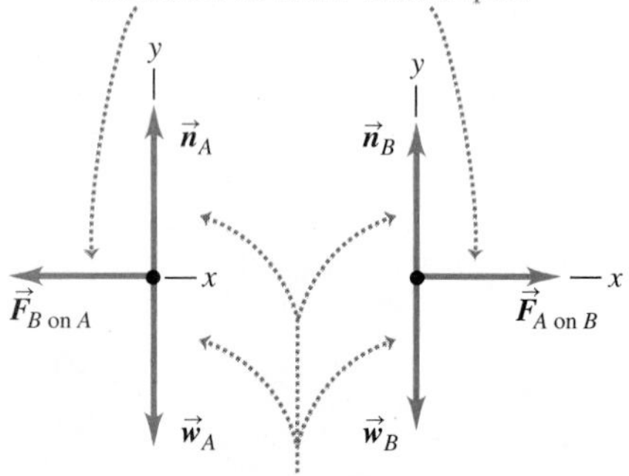

Although the normal and gravitational forces are external, their vector sum is zero, so the total momentum is conserved.

If external forces are also present, they must be included on the left side of Eq. (8.13) along with the internal forces. Then the total momentum is, in general, not constant. But if the vector sum of the external forces is zero, as in Fig. 8.9, these forces don't contribute to the sum, and $d\vec{P}/dt$ is again zero. Thus we have the following general result:

If the vector sum of the external forces on a system is zero, the total momentum of the system is constant.

This is the simplest form of the **principle of conservation of momentum.** This principle is a direct consequence of Newton's third law. What makes this principle useful is that it doesn't depend on the detailed nature of the internal forces that act between members of the system. This means that we can apply conservation of momentum even if (as is often the case) we know very little about the internal forces. We have used Newton's second law to derive this principle, so we have to be careful to use it only in inertial frames of reference.

We can generalize this principle for a system that contains any number of particles $A, B, C, \ldots$ interacting only with each other. The total momentum of such a system is

$$\vec{P} = \vec{p}_A + \vec{p}_B + \cdots = m_A\vec{v}_A + m_B\vec{v}_B + \cdots \quad \text{(total momentum of a system of particles)} \tag{8.14}$$

We make the same argument as before: The total rate of change of momentum of the system due to each action–reaction pair of internal forces is zero. Thus the total rate of change of momentum of the entire system is zero whenever the vector sum of the external forces acting on it is zero. The internal forces can change the momenta of individual particles in the system but not the *total* momentum of the system.

8.10 When applying conservation of momentum, remember that momentum is a vector quantity!

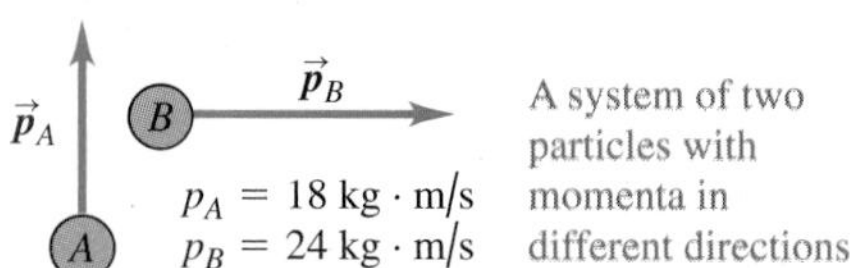

You CANNOT find the magnitude of the total momentum by adding the magnitudes of the individual momenta!

$P = p_A + p_B = 42 \text{ kg} \cdot \text{m/s}$ ◀WRONG

Instead, use vector addition:

$\vec{p}_B$

$\vec{p}_A$

$\vec{P} = \vec{p}_A + \vec{p}_B$ ◀RIGHT!

θ

$P = |\vec{p}_A + \vec{p}_B|$
$= 30 \text{ kg} \cdot \text{m/s at } \theta = 37°$

CAUTION Conservation of momentum means conservation of its components When you apply the conservation of momentum to a system, remember that momentum is a *vector* quantity. Hence you must use vector addition to compute the total momentum of a system (Fig. 8.10). Using components is usually the simplest method. If p_{Ax}, p_{Ay}, and p_{Az} are the components of momentum of particle A, and similarly for the other particles, then Eq. (8.14) is equivalent to the component equations

$$\begin{aligned} P_x &= p_{Ax} + p_{Bx} + \cdots \\ P_y &= p_{Ay} + p_{By} + \cdots \\ P_z &= p_{Az} + p_{Bz} + \cdots \end{aligned} \tag{8.15}$$

If the vector sum of the external forces on the system is zero, then P_x, P_y, and P_z are all constant.

In some ways the principle of conservation of momentum is more general than the principle of conservation of mechanical energy. For example, mechanical energy is conserved only when the internal forces are *conservative*—that is, when the forces allow two-way conversion between kinetic and potential energy—but conservation of momentum is valid even when the internal forces are *not* conservative. In this chapter we will analyze situations in which both momentum and mechanical energy are conserved, and others in which only momentum is conserved. These two principles play a fundamental role in all areas of physics, and we will encounter them throughout our study of physics.

Problem-Solving Strategy 8.1 Conservation of Momentum

IDENTIFY *the relevant concepts:* Before applying conservation of momentum to a problem, you must decide whether momentum *is* conserved! This will be true *only* if the vector sum of the external forces acting on the system of particles is zero. If this is not the case, you can't use conservation of momentum.

SET UP *the problem using the following steps:*

1. Define a coordinate system and show it in a sketch, including the positive direction for each axis. Often it is easiest to choose the x-axis in the direction of one of the initial velocities. Make sure you are using an inertial frame of reference. Most of the problems in this chapter deal with two-dimensional situations, in which the vectors have only x- and y-components, but this strategy can be generalized to include z-components when necessary.
2. Treat each body as a particle. Draw "before" and "after" sketches, and include vectors on each to represent all known velocities. Label the vectors with magnitudes, angles, components, or whatever information is given, and give each unknown magnitude, angle, or component an algebraic symbol. It's helpful to use the subscripts 1 and 2 for velocities before and after the interaction, respectively, and use letters (not numbers) to label each particle.
3. As always, identify the target variable(s) from among the unknowns.

EXECUTE *the solution as follows:*

1. Write an equation in symbols equating the total *initial* x-component of momentum (that is, before the interaction) to the total *final* x-component of momentum (that is, after the interaction), using $p_x = mv_x$ for each particle. Write another equation for the y-components, using $p_y = mv_y$ for each particle. (*Never* add the x- and y-components of velocity or momentum together in the same equation!) Even when all motions are along a line (such as the x-axis), the components of velocity along this line can be positive or negative; be careful with signs!
2. Solve these equations to determine whatever results are required. In some problems you will have to convert from the x- and y-components of a velocity to its magnitude and direction, or the reverse.
3. In some problems, energy considerations give additional relationships among the various velocities, as we will see later in this chapter.

EVALUATE *your answer:* Does your answer make physical sense? If your target variable is a certain body's momentum, check that the direction of the momentum is reasonable.

Example 8.4 Recoil of a rifle

A marksman holds a rifle of mass $m_R = 3.00$ kg loosely in his hands, so as to let it recoil freely when fired. He fires a bullet of mass $m_B = 5.00$ g horizontally with a velocity relative to the ground of $v_{Bx} = 300$ m/s. What is the recoil velocity v_{Rx} of the rifle? What are the final momentum and kinetic energy of the bullet? Of the rifle?

SOLUTION

IDENTIFY: We consider an idealized model in which the horizontal forces the marksman exerts on the rifle are negligible. Then there is no net horizontal force on the system (the bullet and rifle) during the firing of the rifle, and so the total horizontal momentum of the system is the same before and after the rifle is fired (i.e., it is conserved).

SET UP: Figure 8.11 shows our sketch. We take the positive x-axis to be the direction the rifle is aimed. Initially, both the rifle and the bullet are at rest, so the initial x-component of total momentum is zero. After the shot is fired, the bullet's x-momentum is $p_{Bx} = m_B v_{Bx}$ and the rifle's x-momentum is $p_{Rx} = m_R v_{Rx}$. Our target variables are v_{Rx}, p_{Bx}, p_{Rx}, and $K_B = \frac{1}{2}m_B v_{Bx}^2$ and $K_R = \frac{1}{2}m_R v_{Rx}^2$ (the final kinetic energies of the bullet and rifle, respectively).

EXECUTE: Conservation of the x-component of total momentum gives

$$P_x = 0 = m_B v_{Bx} + m_R v_{Rx}$$

$$v_{Rx} = -\frac{m_B}{m_R}v_{Bx} = -\left(\frac{0.00500 \text{ kg}}{3.00 \text{ kg}}\right)(300 \text{ m/s}) = -0.500 \text{ m/s}$$

8.11 Our sketch for this problem.

Before

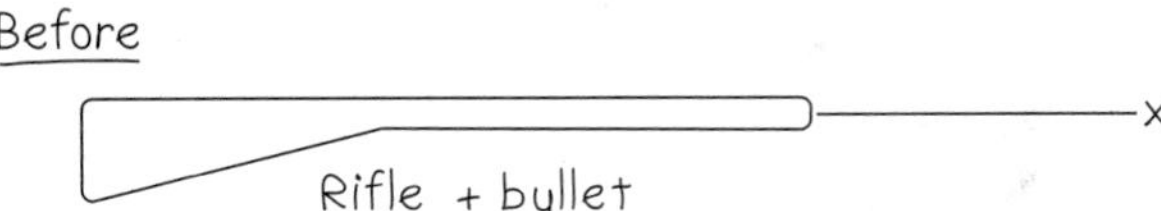

After

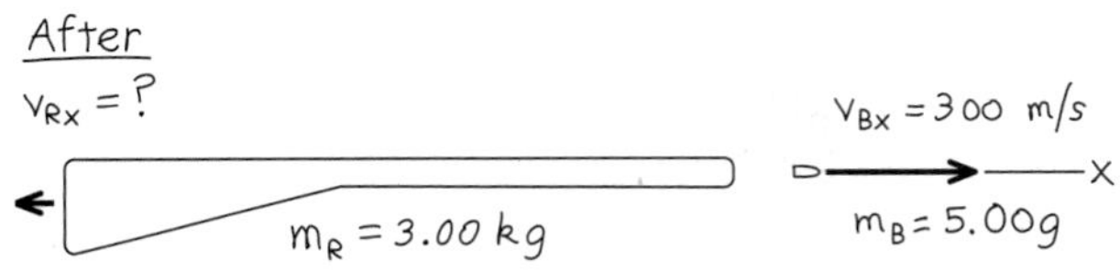

The negative sign means that the recoil is in the direction opposite to that of the bullet. If the butt of a rifle hit your shoulder at this speed, you'd feel it. It's more comfortable to hold the rifle tightly against your shoulder when you fire it; then m_R is replaced by the sum of your mass and the rifle's mass, and the recoil speed is much less.

The final momentum and kinetic energy of the bullet are

$$p_{Bx} = m_B v_{Bx} = (0.00500 \text{ kg})(300 \text{ m/s}) = 1.50 \text{ kg} \cdot \text{m/s}$$
$$K_B = \tfrac{1}{2}m_B v_{Bx}^2 = \tfrac{1}{2}(0.00500 \text{ kg})(300 \text{ m/s})^2 = 225 \text{ J}$$

For the rifle, the final momentum and kinetic energy are

$$p_{Rx} = m_R v_{Rx} = (3.00 \text{ kg})(-0.500 \text{ m/s}) = -1.50 \text{ kg} \cdot \text{m/s}$$
$$K_R = \tfrac{1}{2}m_R v_{Rx}^2 = \tfrac{1}{2}(3.00 \text{ kg})(-0.500 \text{ m/s})^2 = 0.375 \text{ J}$$

Continued

EVALUATE: The bullet and the rifle have equal and opposite *momenta* after the interaction. That's because they were subjected to equal and opposite interaction forces for the same amount of *time* (i.e., equal and opposite impulses). But the bullet acquires much greater *kinetic energy* than the rifle because the bullet travels a much greater *distance* than the rifle during the interaction. Thus the force on the bullet does more work than the force on the rifle. The ratio of the two kinetic energies, 600 : 1, is equal to the inverse ratio of the masses; in fact, it can be shown that this always happens in recoil situations. We leave the proof as a problem (see Exercise 8.22).

Our calculation doesn't depend on the details of how the rifle works. In a real rifle, the bullet is propelled forward by an explosive charge; if instead the rifle used a very stiff spring, the answers would have been exactly the same.

Example 8.5 Collision along a straight line

Two gliders move toward each other on a frictionless linear air track (Fig. 8.12a). After they collide (Fig. 8.12b), glider B moves away with a final velocity of $+2.0\text{ m/s}$ (Fig. 8.12c). What is the final velocity of glider A? How do the changes in momentum and in velocity compare for the two gliders?

SOLUTION

IDENTIFY: The total vertical force on each glider is zero; the net force on each glider is the horizontal force exerted on it by the other glider. The net *external* force on the two gliders together is zero, so the total momentum is conserved. (Compare Fig. 8.9.)

SET UP: We take the positive x-axis to be to the right, along the air track. We are given the masses and initial velocities of both gliders and the final velocity of glider B. Our target variables are v_{A2x}, the final x-component of velocity of glider A, and the changes in momentum and in velocity of the two gliders (the value after the collision minus the value before the collision).

EXECUTE: The x-component of total momentum before the collision is

$$\begin{aligned} P_x &= m_A v_{A1x} + m_B v_{B1x} \\ &= (0.50\text{ kg})(2.0\text{ m/s}) + (0.30\text{ kg})(-2.0\text{ m/s}) \\ &= 0.40\text{ kg}\cdot\text{m/s} \end{aligned}$$

8.12 Two gliders colliding on an air track.

(a) Before collision

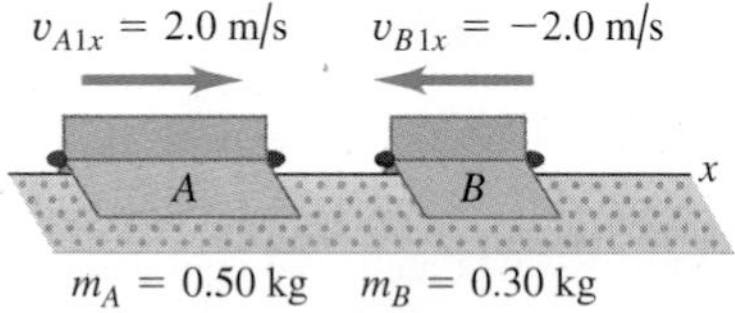

(b) Collision

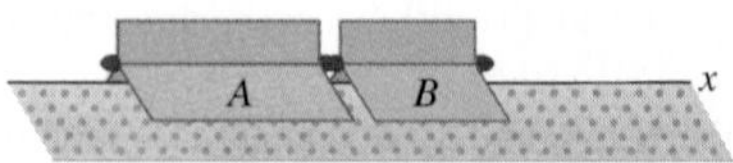

(c) After collision

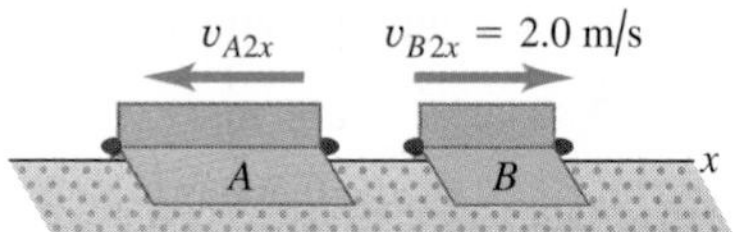

This is positive (to the right in Fig. 8.12) because glider A has a greater magnitude of momentum before the collision than does glider B. The x-component of total momentum has the same value after the collision, so

$$P_x = m_A v_{A2x} + m_B v_{B2x}$$

Solving this equation for v_{A2x}, the final x-velocity of A, we find

$$\begin{aligned} v_{A2x} &= \frac{P_x - m_B v_{B2x}}{m_A} = \frac{0.40\text{ kg}\cdot\text{m/s} - (0.30\text{ kg})(2.0\text{ m/s})}{0.50\text{ kg}} \\ &= -0.40\text{ m/s} \end{aligned}$$

The change in x-momentum of glider A is

$$\begin{aligned} m_A v_{A2x} - m_A v_{A1x} &= (0.50\text{ kg})(-0.40\text{ m/s}) \\ &\quad - (0.50\text{ kg})(2.0\text{ m/s}) = -1.2\text{ kg}\cdot\text{m/s} \end{aligned}$$

and the change in x-momentum of glider B is

$$\begin{aligned} m_B v_{B2x} - m_B v_{B1x} &= (0.30\text{ kg})(2.0\text{ m/s}) \\ &\quad - (0.30\text{ kg})(-2.0\text{ m/s}) = +1.2\text{ kg}\cdot\text{m/s} \end{aligned}$$

The two interacting gliders undergo changes in momentum that are equal in magnitude and opposite in direction. The same is *not* true of their changes in velocity, however. For A, $v_{A2x} - v_{A1x} = (-0.40\text{ m/s}) - 2.0\text{ m/s} = -2.4\text{ m/s}$; for B, $v_{B2x} - v_{B1x} = 2.0\text{ m/s} - (-2.0\text{ m/s}) = +4.0\text{ m/s}$.

EVALUATE: Why do the momentum changes have the same magnitude for the two gliders, but the velocity changes do not? By Newton's third law, both gliders were acted on for equal amounts of time by an interaction force of the same magnitude. Hence both gliders experienced impulses of the same magnitude, and therefore equal-magnitude changes in momentum. But by Newton's second law, the less massive glider (B) had a greater magnitude of acceleration and hence a greater velocity change.

Here's an application of these ideas. When a large truck collides with a car of normal size, both vehicles undergo equal changes in momentum. The occupants of the car, however, are subjected to greater acceleration (and greater chance of injury) than the occupants of the truck. An even more extreme example is what happens when a truck collides with an insect: The truck driver won't notice the resulting acceleration at all, but the insect surely will!

Example 8.6 Collision in a horizontal plane

Figure 8.13a shows two battling robots sliding on a frictionless surface. Robot A, with mass 20 kg, initially moves at 2.0 m/s parallel to the x-axis. It collides with robot B, which has mass 12 kg and is initially at rest. After the collision, robot A is moving at 1.0 m/s in a direction that makes an angle $\alpha = 30°$ with its initial direction (Fig. 8.13b). What is the final velocity of robot B?

SOLUTION

IDENTIFY: There are no horizontal (x or y) external forces, so the x-component and the y-component of the total momentum of the system are both conserved in the collision.

SET UP: Figure 8.13 shows the coordinate axes. The velocities are not all along a single line, so we have to treat momentum as a vector quantity. Momentum conservation requires that the sum of the x-components of momentum *before* the collision (subscript 1) must equal the sum *after* the collision (subscript 2), and similarly for the sums of the y-components. We write a separate momentum conservation equation for each component. Our target variable is $\vec{v}_{B2}$, the final velocity of robot B.

8.13 Views from above of the velocities (a) before and (b) after the collision.

(a) Before collision

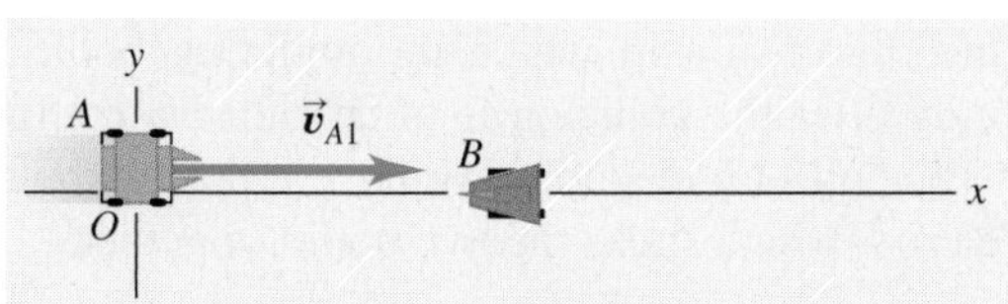

(b) After collision

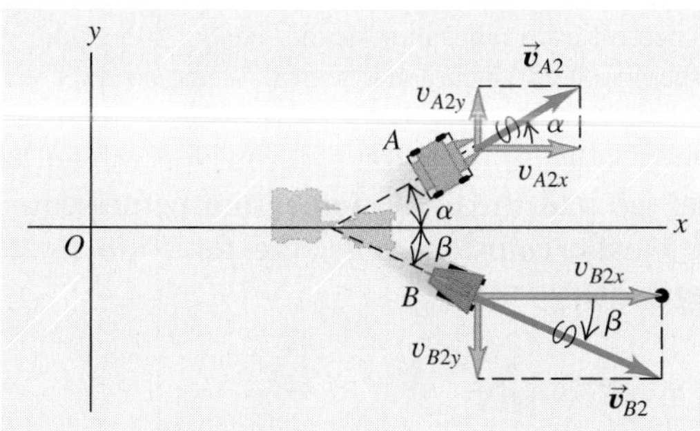

EXECUTE: Conservation of the x-component of total momentum says that

$$m_A v_{A1x} + m_B v_{B1x} = m_A v_{A2x} + m_B v_{B2x}$$

$$v_{B2x} = \frac{m_A v_{A1x} + m_B v_{B1x} - m_A v_{A2x}}{m_B}$$

$$= \frac{\begin{bmatrix}(20\text{ kg})(2.0\text{ m/s}) + (12\text{ kg})(0)\\ -(20\text{ kg})(1.0\text{ m/s})(\cos 30°)\end{bmatrix}}{12\text{ kg}}$$

$$= 1.89\text{ m/s}$$

Similarly, for the y-component of total momentum we have

$$m_A v_{A1y} + m_B v_{B1y} = m_A v_{A2y} + m_B v_{B2y}$$

$$v_{B2y} = \frac{m_A v_{A1y} + m_B v_{B1y} - m_A v_{A2y}}{m_B}$$

$$= \frac{\begin{bmatrix}(20\text{ kg})(0) + (12\text{ kg})(0)\\ -(20\text{ kg})(1.0\text{ m/s})(\sin 30°)\end{bmatrix}}{12\text{ kg}}$$

$$= -0.83\text{ m/s}$$

After the collision, robot B moves in the positive x-direction and the negative y-direction (Fig. 8.13b). The magnitude of $\vec{v}_{B2}$ is

$$v_{B2} = \sqrt{(1.89\text{ m/s})^2 + (-0.83\text{ m/s})^2} = 2.1\text{ m/s}$$

and the angle of its direction from the positive x-axis is

$$\beta = \arctan\frac{-0.83\text{ m/s}}{1.89\text{ m/s}} = -24°$$

EVALUATE: We can check our answer by looking at the values of momentum before and after the collision. Initially all of the momentum is in robot A, which has x-momentum $m_A v_{A1x} = (20\text{ kg})(2.0\text{ m/s}) = 40\text{ kg}\cdot\text{m/s}$ and zero y-momentum. After the collision, robot A has x-momentum $m_A v_{A2x} = (20\text{ kg})(1.0\text{ m/s})(\cos 30°) = 17\text{ kg}\cdot\text{m/s}$, while robot B has x-momentum $m_B v_{B2x} = (12\text{ kg})(1.89\text{ m/s}) = 23\text{ kg}\cdot\text{m/s}$; the total x-momentum is $40\text{ kg}\cdot\text{m/s}$, the same as before the collision (as it should be). In the y-direction, robot A acquires y-momentum $m_A v_{A2y} = (20\text{ kg})(1.0\text{ m/s})(\sin 30°) = 10\text{ kg}\cdot\text{m/s}$, while robot B acquires y-momentum of the same magnitude but opposite direction: $m_B v_{B2y} = (12\text{ kg})(-0.83\text{ m/s}) = -10\text{ kg}\cdot\text{m/s}$. Hence the *total* y-component of momentum after the collision has the same value (zero) as before the collision.

Test Your Understanding of Section 8.2 A spring-loaded toy sits at rest on a horizontal frictionless surface. When the spring releases, the toy breaks into three equal-mass pieces, A, B, and C, which slide along the surface. Piece A moves off in the negative x-direction, while piece B moves off in the negative y-direction. (a) What are the signs of the velocity components of piece C? (b) Which of the three pieces is moving the fastest?

MP

8.3 Momentum Conservation and Collisions

6.4 Collision Problems
6.8 Skier and Cart

To most people the term *collision* is likely to mean some sort of automotive disaster. We'll use it in that sense, but we'll also broaden the meaning to include any strong interaction between bodies that lasts a relatively short time. So we include

8.14 Two gliders undergoing an elastic collision on a frictionless surface. Each glider has a steel spring bumper that exerts a conservative force on the other glider.

(a) Before collision

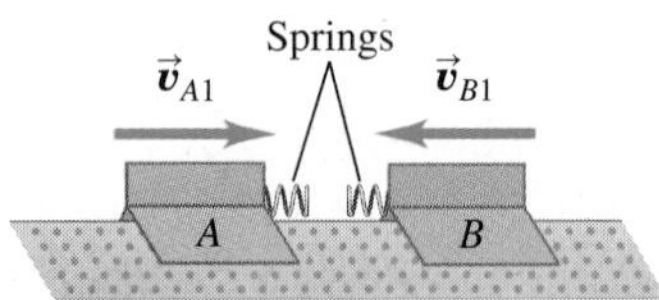

(b) Elastic collision

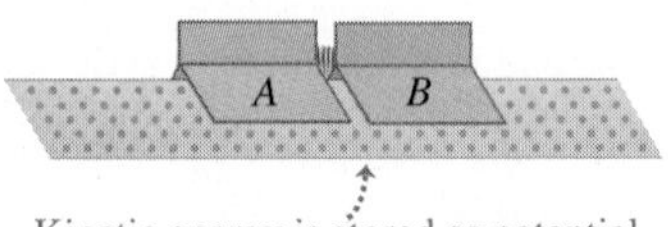

Kinetic energy is stored as potential energy in compressed springs.

(c) After collision

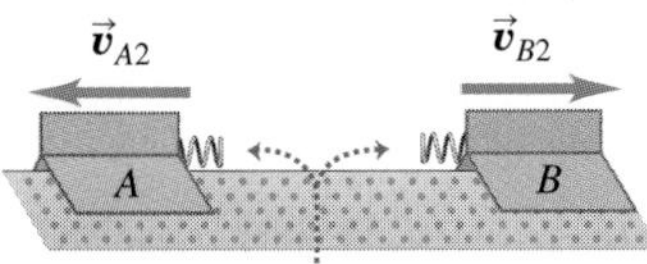

The system of the two gliders has the same kinetic energy after the collision as before it.

8.15 Two gliders undergoing a completely inelastic collision. The spring bumpers on the gliders are replaced by Velcro®, so the gliders stick together after collision.

(a) Before collision

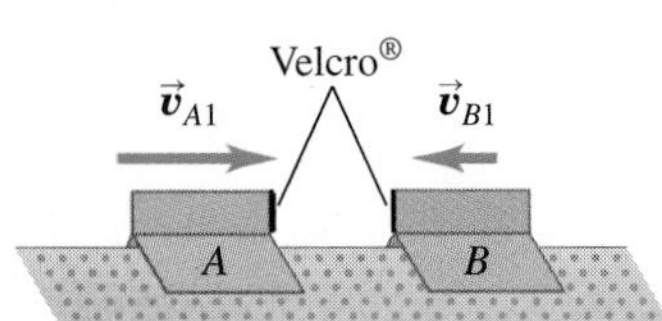

(b) Completely inelastic collision

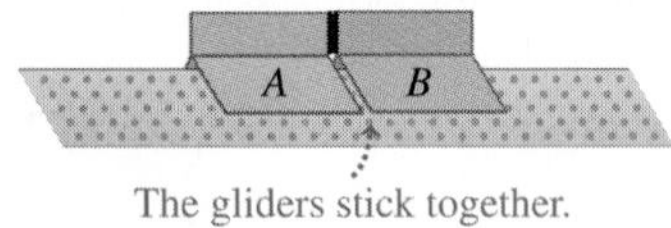

The gliders stick together.

(c) After collision

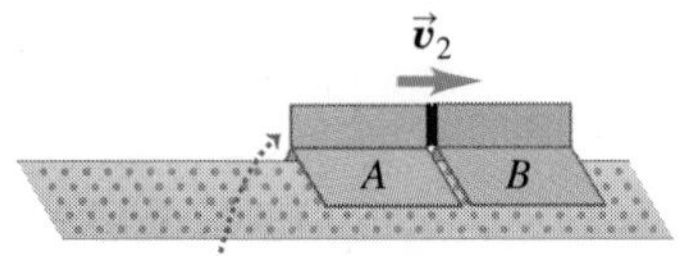

The system of the two gliders has less kinetic energy after the collision than before it.

not only car accidents but also balls colliding on a billiard table, neutrons hitting atomic nuclei in a nuclear reactor, the impact of a meteor on the Arizona desert, and a close encounter of a spacecraft with the planet Saturn.

If the forces between the bodies are much larger than any external forces, as is the case in most collisions, we can neglect the external forces entirely and treat the bodies as an *isolated* system. Then momentum is conserved and the total momentum of the system has the same value before and after the collision. Two cars colliding at an icy intersection provide a good example. Even two cars colliding on dry pavement can be treated as an isolated system during the collision if the forces between the cars are much larger than the friction forces of pavement against tires.

Elastic and Inelastic Collisions

If the forces between the bodies are also *conservative,* so that no mechanical energy is lost or gained in the collision, the total *kinetic* energy of the system is the same after the collision as before. Such a collision is called an **elastic collision.** A collision between two marbles or two billiard balls is almost completely elastic. Figure 8.14 shows a model for an elastic collision. When the gliders collide, their springs are momentarily compressed and some of the original kinetic energy is momentarily converted to elastic potential energy. Then the gliders bounce apart, the springs expand, and this potential energy is converted back to kinetic energy.

A collision in which the total kinetic energy after the collision is *less* than before the collision is called an **inelastic collision.** A meatball landing on a plate of spaghetti and a bullet embedding itself in a block of wood are examples of inelastic collisions. An inelastic collision in which the colliding bodies stick together and move as one body after the collision is often called a **completely inelastic collision.** Figure 8.15 shows an example; we have replaced the spring bumpers in Fig. 8.14 with Velcro®, which sticks the two bodies together.

CAUTION **An inelastic collision doesn't have to be *completely* inelastic** It's a common misconception that the *only* inelastic collisions are those in which the colliding bodies stick together. In fact, inelastic collisions include many situations in which the bodies do *not* stick. If two cars bounce off each other in a "fender bender," the work done to deform the fenders cannot be recovered as kinetic energy of the cars, so the collision is inelastic (Fig. 8.16).

Remember this rule: **In any collision in which external forces can be neglected, momentum is conserved and the total momentum before equals the total momentum after; in elastic collisions *only,* the total kinetic energy before equals the total kinetic energy after.**

Completely Inelastic Collisions

Let's look at what happens to momentum and kinetic energy in a *completely* inelastic collision of two bodies (*A* and *B*), as in Fig. 8.15. Because the two bodies stick together after the collision, they have the same final velocity $\vec{v}_2$:

$$\vec{v}_{A2} = \vec{v}_{B2} = \vec{v}_2$$

Conservation of momentum gives the relationship

$$m_A\vec{v}_{A1} + m_B\vec{v}_{B1} = (m_A + m_B)\vec{v}_2 \quad \text{(completely inelastic collision)} \quad (8.16)$$

If we know the masses and initial velocities, we can compute the common final velocity $\vec{v}_2$.

Suppose, for example, that a body with mass m_A and initial x-component of velocity v_{A1x} collides inelastically with a body with mass m_B that is initially at rest $(v_{B1x} = 0)$. From Eq. (8.16) the common x-component of velocity v_{2x} of both bodies after the collision is

$$v_{2x} = \frac{m_A}{m_A + m_B} v_{A1x} \quad \text{(completely inelastic collision, } B \text{ initially at rest)} \tag{8.17}$$

Let's verify that the total kinetic energy after this completely inelastic collision is less than before the collision. The motion is purely along the x-axis, so the kinetic energies K_1 and K_2 before and after the collision, respectively, are

$$K_1 = \tfrac{1}{2} m_A v_{A1x}{}^2$$

$$K_2 = \tfrac{1}{2}(m_A + m_B) v_{2x}{}^2 = \tfrac{1}{2}(m_A + m_B)\left(\frac{m_A}{m_A + m_B}\right)^2 v_{A1x}{}^2$$

The ratio of final to initial kinetic energy is

$$\frac{K_2}{K_1} = \frac{m_A}{m_A + m_B} \quad \text{(completely inelastic collision, } B \text{ initially at rest)} \tag{8.18}$$

The right side is always less than unity because the denominator is always greater than the numerator. Even when the initial velocity of m_B is not zero, it is not hard to verify that the kinetic energy after a completely inelastic collision is always less than before.

Please note: We don't recommend memorizing Eqs. (8.17) or (8.18). We derived them only to prove that kinetic energy is always lost in a completely inelastic collision.

8.16 Automobile collisions are intended to be inelastic, so that the structure of the car absorbs as much of the energy of the collision as possible. This absorbed energy cannot be recovered, since it goes into a permanent deformation of the car.

Example 8.7 A completely inelastic collision

Suppose we repeat the collision described in Example 8.5 (Section 8.2), but this time equip the gliders so that they stick together instead of bouncing apart after they collide. Their masses and initial velocities are the same as in Example 8.5. Find the common final x-velocity v_{2x}, and compare the initial and final kinetic energies.

SOLUTION

IDENTIFY: There are no external forces in the x-direction, so the x-component of momentum is conserved.

SET UP: Figure 8.17 shows our sketch. As in Example 8.5, we take the positive x-axis to point to the right. Our target variables are the final x-velocity v_{2x} and the initial and final kinetic energies of the system.

EXECUTE: From conservation of the x-component of momentum,

$$m_A v_{A1x} + m_B v_{B1x} = (m_A + m_B) v_{2x}$$

$$v_{2x} = \frac{m_A v_{A1x} + m_B v_{B1x}}{m_A + m_B} = \frac{(0.50\text{ kg})(2.0\text{ m/s}) + (0.30\text{ kg})(-2.0\text{ m/s})}{0.50\text{ kg} + 0.30\text{ kg}} = 0.50\text{ m/s}$$

Because v_{2x} is positive, the gliders move together to the right (the $+x$-direction) after the collision. Before the collision, the kinetic energies of gliders A and B are

$$K_A = \tfrac{1}{2} m_A v_{A1x}{}^2 = \tfrac{1}{2}(0.50\text{ kg})(2.0\text{ m/s})^2 = 1.0\text{ J}$$

$$K_B = \tfrac{1}{2} m_B v_{B1x}{}^2 = \tfrac{1}{2}(0.30\text{ kg})(-2.0\text{ m/s})^2 = 0.60\text{ J}$$

(Note that the kinetic energy of glider B is positive, even though the x-components of its velocity v_{B1x} and momentum $m_B v_{B1x}$ are both negative.) The *total* kinetic energy before the collision is 1.6 J. The kinetic energy after the collision is

$$\tfrac{1}{2}(m_A + m_B) v_{2x}{}^2 = \tfrac{1}{2}(0.50\text{ kg} + 0.30\text{ kg})(0.50\text{ m/s})^2 = 0.10\text{ J}$$

EVALUATE: The final kinetic energy is only $\frac{1}{16}$ of the original; $\frac{15}{16}$ is converted from mechanical energy to various other forms. If there is a ball of chewing gum between the gliders, it squashes and becomes warmer. If there is a spring between the gliders that is compressed as they lock together, then the energy is stored as potential energy of the spring. In both of these cases the *total* energy of the system is conserved, although *kinetic* energy is not. However, in an isolated system, momentum is *always* conserved, whether the collision is elastic or not.

8.17 Our sketch for this problem.

Example 8.8 The ballistic pendulum

Figure 8.18 shows a ballistic pendulum, a system for measuring the speed of a bullet. The bullet, with mass m_B, is fired into a block of wood with mass m_W, suspended like a pendulum, and makes a completely inelastic collision with it. After the impact of the bullet, the block swings up to a maximum height y. Given the values of y, m_B, and m_W, what is the initial speed v_1 of the bullet?

SOLUTION

IDENTIFY: We'll analyze this event in two stages: (1) the embedding of the bullet in the block and (2) the subsequent swinging of the block on its strings.

During the first stage, the bullet embeds itself in the block so quickly that the block has no time to move appreciably. The supporting strings remain nearly vertical, so negligible external horizontal force acts on the system of bullet plus block, and the *horizontal component of momentum* is conserved. Mechanical energy is *not* conserved in this stage because a nonconservative force does work (the force of friction between bullet and block).

In the second stage, after the collision, the block and bullet move as a unit. The only forces acting on this unit are gravity (a conservative force) and the string tensions (which do no work). Thus, as the block swings upward and to the right, *mechanical energy* is conserved. Momentum is *not* conserved during this stage because there is a net external force (the forces of gravity and string tension don't cancel when the strings are inclined).

SET UP: We take the positive x-axis to be to the right and the positive y-axis to be upward in Fig. 8.18. Our target variable is v_1. Another unknown quantity is the speed v_2 of the block and bullet as a unit just after the collision (that is, just at the end of the first stage). We'll use momentum conservation in the first stage to relate v_1 to v_2, and we'll use energy conservation in the second stage to relate v_2 to the (given) maximum height y.

EXECUTE: In the first stage, the velocities are all in the positive x-direction. Momentum conservation gives

$$m_B v_1 = (m_B + m_W) v_2 \qquad v_1 = \frac{m_B + m_W}{m_B} v_2$$

At the beginning of the second stage, the block–bullet unit has kinetic energy $K = \frac{1}{2}(m_B + m_W)v_2^2$. [As in Eq. (8.18), this is less than the kinetic energy before the collision; the collision is inelastic!] The block–bullet unit swings up and comes to rest for an instant at a height y, where its kinetic energy is zero and the potential energy is $(m_B + m_W)gy$; it then swings back down. Energy conservation gives

$$\tfrac{1}{2}(m_B + m_W)v_2^2 = (m_B + m_W)gy \qquad v_2 = \sqrt{2gy}$$

8.18 A ballistic pendulum.

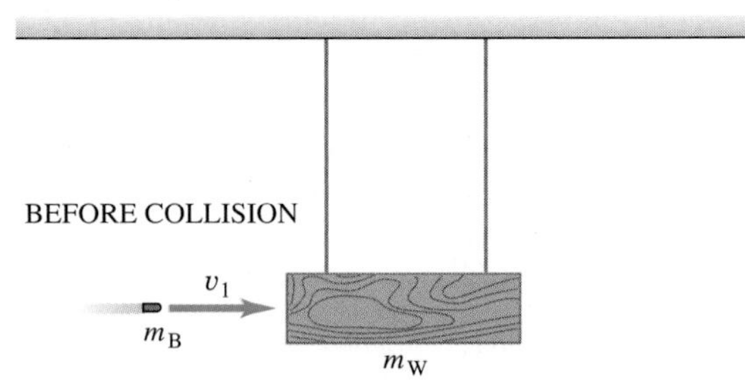

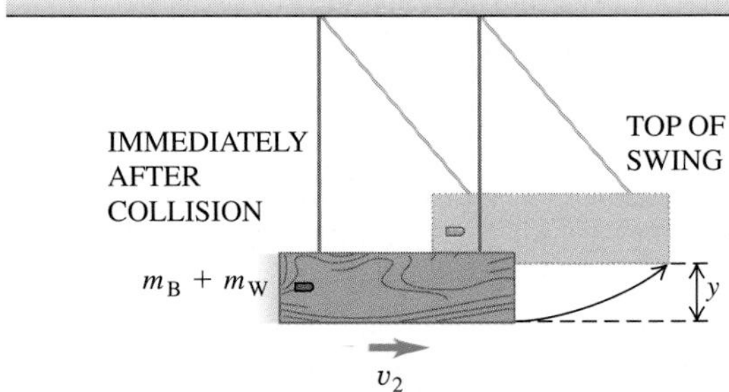

Now we substitute this expression into the momentum equation to find an expression for our target variable v_1:

$$v_1 = \frac{m_B + m_W}{m_B}\sqrt{2gy}$$

Hence measuring m_B, m_W, and y tells us the initial speed of the bullet.

EVALUATE: Let's check our answers by plugging in some realistic numbers. If $m_B = 5.00\text{ g} = 0.00500\text{ kg}$, $m_W = 2.00\text{ kg}$, and $y = 3.00\text{ cm} = 0.0300\text{ m}$, the initial speed of the bullet is

$$v_1 = \frac{0.00500\text{ kg} + 2.00\text{ kg}}{0.00500\text{ kg}}\sqrt{2(9.80\text{ m/s}^2)(0.0300\text{ m})}$$
$$= 307\text{ m/s}$$

The speed v_2 of the block just after impact is

$$v_2 = \sqrt{2gy} = \sqrt{2(9.80\text{ m/s}^2)(0.0300\text{ m})}$$
$$= 0.767\text{ m/s}$$

The kinetic energy of the bullet just before impact is $\frac{1}{2}(0.00500\text{ kg})(307\text{ m/s})^2 = 236\text{ J}$. Just after impact the kinetic energy of the bullet and block is $\frac{1}{2}(2.005\text{ kg})(0.767\text{ m/s})^2 = 0.589\text{ J}$. Nearly all the kinetic energy disappears as the wood splinters and the bullet and block become hotter.

Example 8.9 An automobile collision

A 1000-kg compact car is traveling north at 15 m/s when it collides with a 2000-kg truck traveling east at 10 m/s. All occupants are wearing seat belts and there are no injuries, but the two vehicles are thoroughly tangled and move away from the impact point as one mass. The insurance adjustor has asked you to find the velocity of the wreckage just after impact. What do you tell her?

SOLUTION

IDENTIFY: We'll assume that we can treat the cars as an isolated system during the collision. We can do so because the horizontal forces that the cars exert on each other during the collision have very large magnitudes, great enough to crumple the cars' metal skins. Compared with these forces, we can neglect any external forces such as friction. (We'll justify this assumption later.) Hence the momentum of the system of two cars has the same value just before and just after the collision.

SET UP: Figure 8.19 shows our sketch. We can find the total momentum before the collision, $\vec{P}$, using Eqs. (8.15) and the coordinate axes shown in Fig. 8.19. The momentum has the same value just after the collision; hence, once we've found $\vec{P}$, we'll be able to find the velocity $\vec{V}$ just after the collision (our second target variable) using the relationship $\vec{P} = M\vec{V}$, where M is the combined mass of the wreckage. We'll use the subscripts C and T for the car and truck, respectively.

EXECUTE: From Eqs. (8.15) the components of the total momentum $\vec{P}$ are

$$
\begin{aligned}
P_x &= p_{Cx} + p_{Tx} = m_C v_{Cx} + m_T v_{Tx} \\
&= (1000\text{ kg})(0) + (2000\text{ kg})(10\text{ m/s}) \\
&= 2.0 \times 10^4\text{ kg}\cdot\text{m/s} \\
P_y &= p_{Cy} + p_{Ty} = m_C v_{Cy} + m_T v_{Ty} \\
&= (1000\text{ kg})(15\text{ m/s}) + (2000\text{ kg})(0) \\
&= 1.5 \times 10^4\text{ kg}\cdot\text{m/s}
\end{aligned}
$$

8.19 Our sketch for this problem.

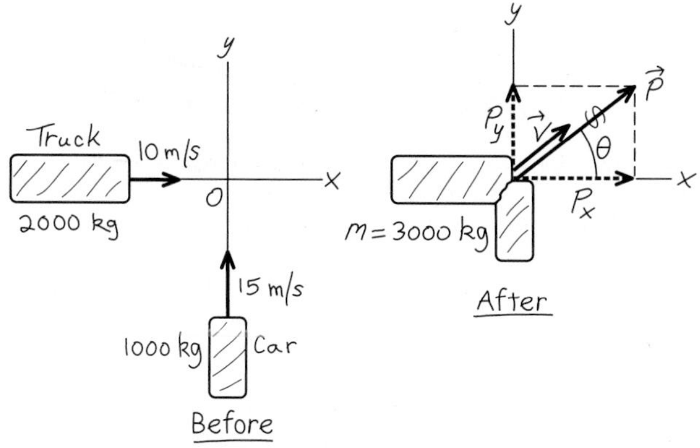

The magnitude of $\vec{P}$ is

$$
\begin{aligned}
P &= \sqrt{(2.0 \times 10^4\text{ kg}\cdot\text{m/s})^2 + (1.5 \times 10^4\text{ kg}\cdot\text{m/s})^2} \\
&= 2.5 \times 10^4\text{ kg}\cdot\text{m/s}
\end{aligned}
$$

and its direction is given by the angle θ shown in Fig. 8.19, where

$$
\tan\theta = \frac{P_y}{P_x} = \frac{1.5 \times 10^4\text{ kg}\cdot\text{m/s}}{2.0 \times 10^4\text{ kg}\cdot\text{m/s}} = 0.75 \qquad \theta = 37^\circ
$$

The total momentum just after the collision is the same as just before. Assuming that no parts fall off, the total mass of wreckage is $M = m_C + m_T = 3000$ kg. From $\vec{P} = M\vec{V}$, the direction of the velocity $\vec{V}$ just after the collision is the same as that of the momentum, and its magnitude is

$$
V = \frac{P}{M} = \frac{2.5 \times 10^4\text{ kg}\cdot\text{m/s}}{3000\text{ kg}} = 8.3\text{ m/s}
$$

EVALUATE: This is an inelastic collision, so we expect the total kinetic energy to be less after the collision than before. Carry out the calculations yourself; you will find that the initial kinetic energy is 2.1×10^5 J and the final value is 1.0×10^5 J. More than half of the initial kinetic energy is converted to other forms.

We still need to justify our assumption that we can neglect the external forces on the vehicles during the collision. To do so, note that the mass of the truck is 2000 kg, its weight is about 20,000 N, and, if the coefficient of friction is about 0.5, the friction force when it slides across the pavement is about 10,000 N. The truck's kinetic energy just before the impact is $\frac{1}{2}(2000\text{ kg})(10\text{ m/s})^2 = 1.0 \times 10^5$ J. The car may crumple 0.2 m or so; to do -1.0×10^5 J of work on the car (required to stop it) in a distance of 0.2 m would require a force of 5.0×10^5 N, which is 50 times greater than the friction force. So it's reasonable to treat the external force of friction as negligible compared with the internal forces that the vehicles exert on each other.

Classifying Collisions

It's important to remember that we can classify collisions according to energy considerations (Fig. 8.20). A collision in which kinetic energy is conserved is called *elastic.* (We'll explore these in more depth in the next section.) A collision in which the total kinetic energy decreases is called *inelastic.* When the two bodies have a common final velocity, we say that the collision is *completely inelastic.* There are also cases in which the final kinetic energy is *greater* than the initial value. Rifle recoil, discussed in Example 8.4 (Section 8.2), is an example.

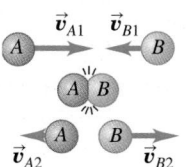

8.20 Collisions are classified according to energy considerations.

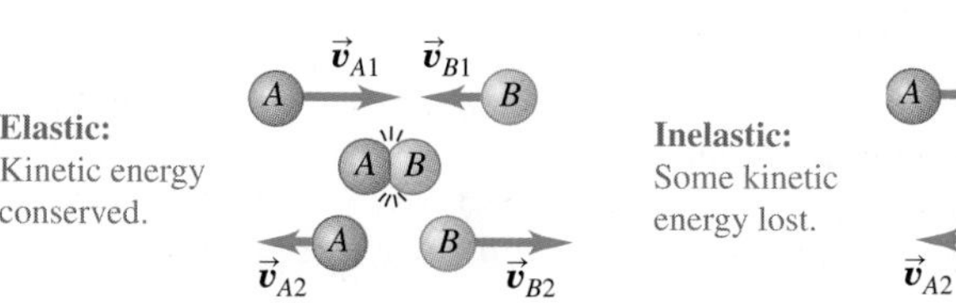

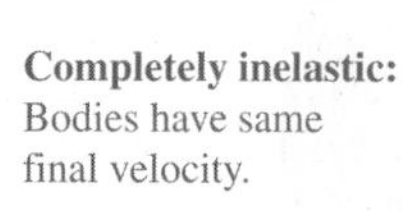

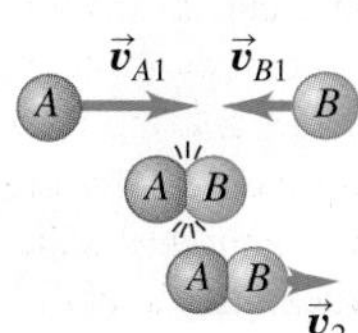

Finally, we emphasize again that we can sometimes use momentum conservation even when there are external forces acting on the system, if the net external force acting on the colliding bodies is small in comparison with the internal forces during the collision (as in Example 8.9)

Test Your Understanding of Section 8.3 For each situation, state whether the collision is elastic or inelastic. If it is inelastic, state whether it is completely inelastic. (a) You drop a ball from your hand. It collides with the floor and bounces back up so that it just reaches your hand. (b) You drop a different ball from your hand and let it collide with the ground. This ball bounces back up to half the height from which it was dropped. (c) You drop a ball of clay from your hand. When it collides with the ground, it stops.

8.4 Elastic Collisions

We saw in Section 8.3 that an *elastic collision* in an isolated system is one in which kinetic energy (as well as momentum) is conserved. Elastic collisions occur when the forces between the colliding bodies are *conservative*. When two billiard balls collide, they squash a little near the surface of contact, but then they spring back. Some of the kinetic energy is stored temporarily as elastic potential energy, but at the end it is reconverted to kinetic energy (Fig. 8.21).

ActivPhysics ONLINE
6.2 Collisions and Elasticity
6.7 Car Collisions: Two Dimensions
6.9 Pendulum Bashes Box

Let's look at an elastic collision between two bodies A and B. We start with a one-dimensional collision, in which all the velocities lie along the same line; we choose this line to be the x-axis. Each momentum and velocity then has only an x-component. We call the x-velocities before the collision v_{A1x} and v_{B1x}, and those after the collision v_{A2x} and v_{B2x}. From conservation of kinetic energy we have

$$\tfrac{1}{2}m_A v_{A1x}^2 + \tfrac{1}{2}m_B v_{B1x}^2 = \tfrac{1}{2}m_A v_{A2x}^2 + \tfrac{1}{2}m_B v_{B2x}^2$$

and conservation of momentum gives

$$m_A v_{A1x} + m_B v_{B1x} = m_A v_{A2x} + m_B v_{B2x}$$

If the masses m_A and m_B and the initial velocities v_{A1x} and v_{B1x} are known, we can solve these two equations to find the two final velocities v_{A2x} and v_{B2x}.

8.21 Billiard balls deform very little when they collide, and they quickly spring back from any deformation they do undergo. Hence the force of interaction between the balls is almost perfectly conservative, and the collision is almost perfectly elastic.

Elastic Collisions, One Body Initially at Rest

The general solution to the above equations is a little complicated, so we will concentrate on the particular case in which body B is at rest before the collision (so $v_{B1x} = 0$). Think of body B as a target for body A to hit. Then the kinetic energy and momentum conservation equations are, respectively,

$$\tfrac{1}{2}m_A v_{A1x}^2 = \tfrac{1}{2}m_A v_{A2x}^2 + \tfrac{1}{2}m_B v_{B2x}^2 \tag{8.19}$$

$$m_A v_{A1x} = m_A v_{A2x} + m_B v_{B2x} \tag{8.20}$$

We can solve for v_{A2x} and v_{B2x} in terms of the masses and the initial velocity v_{A1x}. This involves some fairly strenuous algebra, but it's worth it. No pain, no gain! The simplest approach is somewhat indirect, but along the way it uncovers an additional interesting feature of elastic collisions.

First we rearrange Eqs. (8.19) and (8.20) as follows:

$$m_B v_{B2x}^2 = m_A\left(v_{A1x}^2 - v_{A2x}^2\right) = m_A\left(v_{A1x} - v_{A2x}\right)\left(v_{A1x} + v_{A2x}\right) \tag{8.21}$$

$$m_B v_{B2x} = m_A\left(v_{A1x} - v_{A2x}\right) \tag{8.22}$$

Now we divide Eq. (8.21) by Eq. (8.22) to obtain

$$v_{B2x} = v_{A1x} + v_{A2x} \tag{8.23}$$

We substitute this expression back into Eq. (8.22) to eliminate v_{B2x} and then solve for v_{A2x}:

$$m_B(v_{A1x} + v_{A2x}) = m_A(v_{A1x} - v_{A2x})$$

$$v_{A2x} = \frac{m_A - m_B}{m_A + m_B}v_{A1x} \qquad (8.24)$$

Finally, we substitute this result back into Eq. (8.23) to obtain

$$v_{B2x} = \frac{2m_A}{m_A + m_B}v_{A1x} \qquad (8.25)$$

Now we can interpret the results. Suppose body A is a Ping-Pong ball and body B is a bowling ball. Then we expect A to bounce off after the collision with a velocity nearly equal to its original value but in the opposite direction (Fig. 8.22a), and we expect B's velocity to be much less. That's just what the equations predict. When m_A is much smaller than m_B, the fraction in Eq. (8.24) is approximately equal to (-1), so v_{A2x} is approximately equal to $-v_{A1x}$. The fraction in Eq. (8.25) is much smaller than unity, so v_{B2x} is much less than v_{A1x}. Figure 8.22b shows the opposite case, in which A is the bowling ball and B the Ping-Pong ball and m_A is much larger than m_B. What do you expect to happen then? Check your predictions against Eqs. (8.24) and (8.25).

Another interesting case occurs when the masses are equal (Fig. 8.23). If $m_A = m_B$, then Eqs. (8.24) and (8.25) give $v_{A2x} = 0$ and $v_{B2x} = v_{A1x}$. That is, the body that was moving stops dead; it gives all its momentum and kinetic energy to the body that was at rest. This behavior is familiar to all pool players.

8.22 Collisions between **(a)** a moving Ping-Pong ball and an initially stationary bowling ball, and **(b)** a moving bowling ball and an initially stationary Ping-Pong ball.

(a) Ping-Pong ball strikes bowling ball.

BEFORE

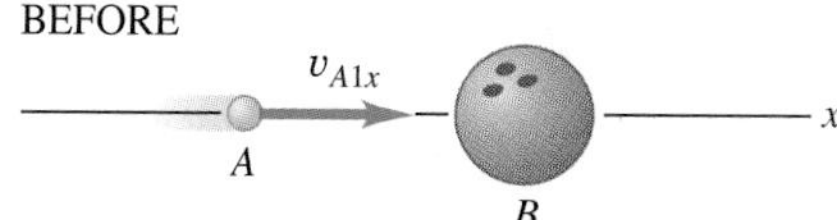

AFTER

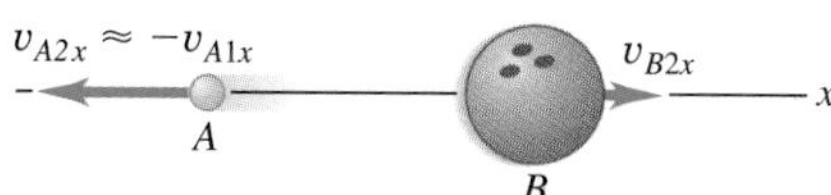

(b) Bowling ball strikes Ping-Pong ball.

BEFORE

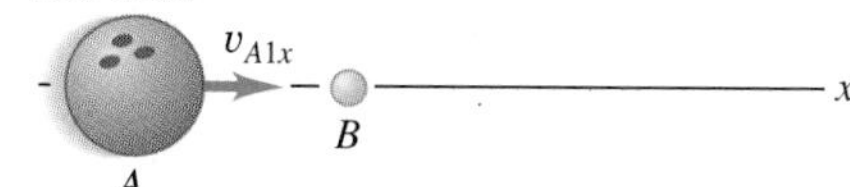

AFTER

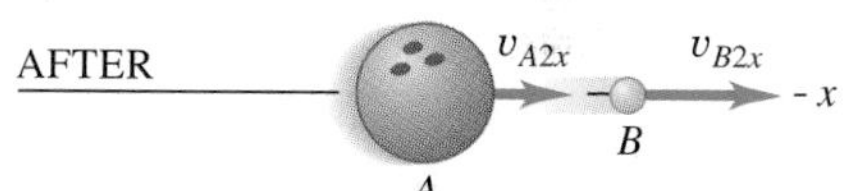

Elastic Collisions and Relative Velocity

Let's return to the more general case in which A and B have different masses. Equation (8.23) can be rewritten as

$$v_{A1x} = v_{B2x} - v_{A2x} \qquad (8.26)$$

Here $v_{B2x} - v_{A2x}$ is the velocity of B relative to A *after* the collision; from Eq. (8.26), this equals v_{A1x}, which is the *negative* of the velocity of B relative to A *before* the collision. (We discussed relative velocity in Section 3.5.) The relative velocity has the same magnitude, but opposite sign, before and after the collision. The sign changes because A and B are approaching each other before the collision but moving apart after the collision. If we view this collision from a second coordinate system moving with constant velocity relative to the first, the velocities of the bodies are different but the *relative* velocities are the same. Hence our statement about relative velocities holds for *any* straight-line elastic collision, even when neither body is at rest initially. *In a straight-line elastic collision of two bodies, the relative velocities before and after the collision have the same magnitude but opposite sign.* This means that if B is moving before the collision, Eq. (8.26) becomes

$$v_{B2x} - v_{A2x} = -(v_{B1x} - v_{A1x}) \qquad (8.27)$$

It turns out that a *vector* relationship similar to Eq. (8.27) is a general property of *all* elastic collisions, even when both bodies are moving initially and the velocities do not all lie along the same line. This result provides an alternative and equivalent definition of an elastic collision: *In an elastic collision, the relative velocity of the two bodies has the same magnitude before and after the collision.* Whenever this condition is satisfied, the total kinetic energy is also conserved.

When an elastic two-body collision isn't head-on, the velocities don't all lie along a single line. If they all lie in a plane, then each final velocity has two unknown components, and there are four unknowns in all. Conservation of energy and conservation of the x- and y-components of momentum give only three equations. To determine the final velocities uniquely, we need additional information, such as the direction or magnitude of one of the final velocities.

8.23 A one-dimensional elastic collision between bodies of equal mass.

When a moving object A has a 1-D elastic collision with an equal-mass, motionless object B...

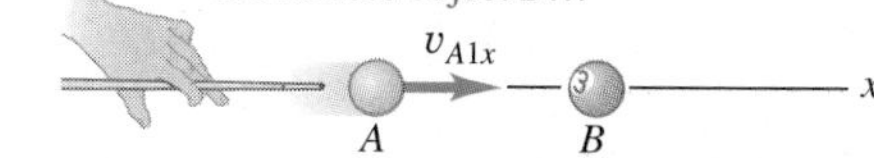

Example 8.10 An elastic straight-line collision

We repeat the air-track experiment from Example 8.5 (Section 8.2), but now we add ideal spring bumpers to the gliders so that the collision is elastic. What are the velocities of A and B after the collision?

SOLUTION

IDENTIFY: As in Example 8.5, the net external force on the system of two gliders is zero, and the momentum of the system is conserved.

SET UP: Figure 8.24 shows our sketch. We again choose the positive x-axis to point to the right. We'll find our target variables, v_{A2x} and v_{B2x}, using Eq. (8.27) and the equation of momentum conservation.

EXECUTE: From conservation of momentum,

$$m_A v_{A1x} + m_B v_{B1x} = m_A v_{A2x} + m_B v_{B2x}$$
$$(0.50\text{ kg})(2.0\text{ m/s}) + (0.30\text{ kg})(-2.0\text{ m/s}) = (0.50\text{ kg})v_{A2x} + (0.30\text{ kg})v_{B2x}$$
$$0.50v_{A2x} + 0.30v_{B2x} = 0.40\text{ m/s}$$

(In the last equation we divided through by the unit "kg.") From Eq. (8.27), the relative velocity relationship for an elastic collision, we have

$$v_{B2x} - v_{A2x} = -(v_{B1x} - v_{A1x})$$
$$= -(-2.0\text{ m/s} - 2.0\text{ m/s}) = 4.0\text{ m/s}$$

8.24 Our sketch for this problem.

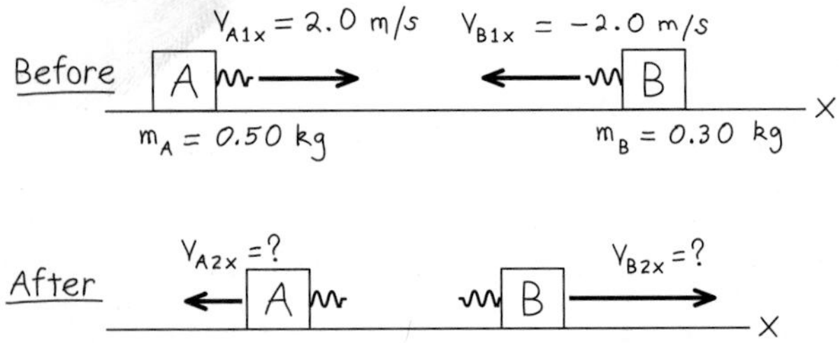

Before the collision, the velocity of B relative to A is to the left at 4.0 m/s; after the collision, the velocity of B relative to A is to the right at 4.0 m/s. Solving these equations simultaneously, we find

$$v_{A2x} = -1.0\text{ m/s} \qquad v_{B2x} = 3.0\text{ m/s}$$

EVALUATE: Both bodies reverse their directions of motion; A moves to the left at 1.0 m/s and B moves to the right at 3.0 m/s. This is different from the result of Example 8.5 because that collision was *not* elastic.

Note that unlike the situations shown in Fig. 8.22, the two gliders are *both* moving toward each other before the collision. Our results show that A (the more massive glider) moves slower after the collision than before the collision, and so loses kinetic energy. In contrast, B (the less massive glider) gains kinetic energy: It moves faster after the collision than before. The *total* kinetic energy after the elastic collision is

$$\tfrac{1}{2}(0.50\text{ kg})(-1.0\text{ m/s})^2 + \tfrac{1}{2}(0.30\text{ kg})(3.0\text{ m/s})^2 = 1.6\text{ J}$$

As expected, this equals the total kinetic energy *before* the collision (which we calculated in Example 8.7 in Section 8.3). Thus kinetic energy is transferred from A to B in the collision, with none of it lost in the process. Much the same happens when a baseball player swings a bat and hits an oncoming baseball. The collision is nearly elastic, and the more massive bat transfers kinetic energy to the less massive baseball. The baseball leaves the bat with a much greater speed—perhaps enough to make a home run.

CAUTION Be careful with the elastic collision equations You might have been tempted to solve this problem using Eqs. (8.24) and (8.25). These equations apply *only* to situations in which body B is initially at rest, which isn't the case here. When in doubt, always solve the problem at hand using equations that are applicable to a broad variety of cases.

Example 8.11 Moderator in a nuclear reactor

The fission of uranium nuclei in a nuclear reactor produces high-speed neutrons. Before a neutron can trigger additional fissions, it has to be slowed down by collisions with nuclei in the *moderator* of the reactor. The first nuclear reactor (built in 1942 at the University of Chicago) and the reactor involved in the 1986 Chernobyl accident both used carbon (graphite) as the moderator material. Suppose a neutron (mass 1.0 u) traveling at 2.6×10^7 m/s undergoes a head-on elastic collision with a carbon nucleus (mass 12 u) initially at rest. The external forces during the collision are negligible. What are the velocities after the collision? (1 u is the *atomic mass unit,* equal to 1.66×10^{-27} kg.)

SOLUTION

IDENTIFY: We are given that the external forces can be neglected (so momentum is conserved in the collision) and that the collision is elastic (so kinetic energy is also conserved).

SET UP: Figure 8.25 shows our sketch. We take the x-axis to be in the direction in which the neutron is moving initially. Because the collision is head-on, both the neutron and the carbon nucleus move along this same axis after the collision. Furthermore, because one body is initially at rest, we can use Eqs. (8.24) and (8.25) with A replaced by n (for the neutron) and B replaced by C (for the carbon nucleus). We have $m_n = 1.0$ u, $m_C = 12$ u, and $v_{n1x} = 2.6 \times 10^7$ m/s, and we need to solve for the target variables v_{n2x} and v_{C2x} (the final velocities of the neutron and the carbon nucleus, respectively).

EXECUTE: We'll let you do the arithmetic; the results are

$$v_{n2x} = -2.2 \times 10^7\text{ m/s} \qquad v_{C2x} = 0.4 \times 10^7\text{ m/s}$$

EVALUATE: The neutron ends up with $\frac{11}{13}$ of its initial speed, and the speed of the recoiling carbon nucleus is $\frac{2}{13}$ of the neutron's initial speed. [These ratios are the factors $(m_n - m_C)/(m_n + m_C)$ and $2m_n/(m_n + m_C)$ that appear in Eqs. (8.24) and (8.25), with the subscripts revised for this problem.] Kinetic energy is proportional to speed squared, so the neutron's final kinetic energy is $(\frac{11}{13})^2$, or about 0.72 of its original value. If the neutron makes a second such collision, its kinetic energy is $(0.72)^2$, or about half its original value, and so on. After several collisions, the neutron will be moving quite slowly and will be able to trigger a fission reaction in a uranium nucleus.

8.25 Our sketch for this problem.

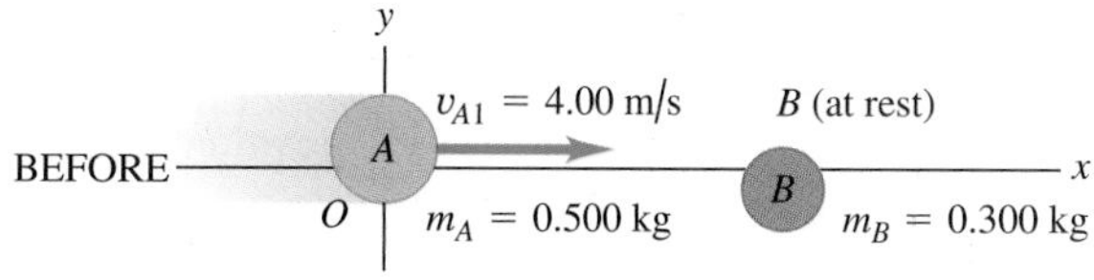

Example 8.12 A two-dimensional elastic collision

Figure 8.26 shows an elastic collision of two pucks on a frictionless air-hockey table. Puck A has mass $m_A = 0.500$ kg and puck B has mass $m_B = 0.300$ kg. Puck A has an initial velocity of 4.00 m/s in the positive x-direction and a final velocity of 2.00 m/s in an unknown direction. Puck B is initially at rest. Find the final speed v_{B2} of puck B and the angles α and β in the figure.

8.26 An elastic collision that isn't head-on.

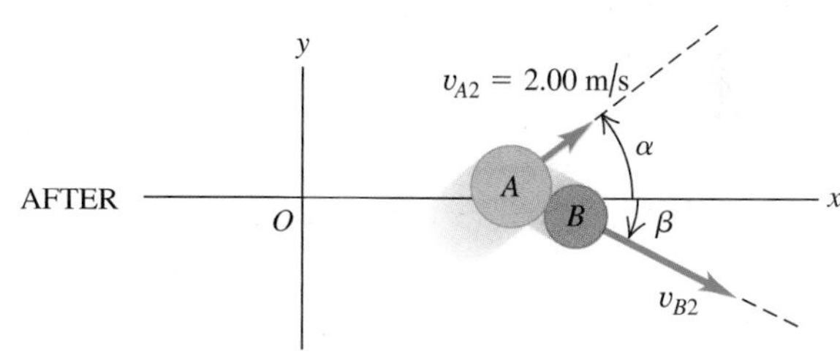

SOLUTION

IDENTIFY: Although the collision is elastic, it is *not* one-dimensional, so we can't use any of the one-dimensional formulas derived in this section. Instead, we'll use the equations for conservation of energy, conservation of x-momentum, and conservation of y-momentum.

SET UP: The target variables are given in the statement of the problem. We have three equations, which should be enough to solve for our three target variables.

EXECUTE: Because the collision is elastic, the initial and final kinetic energies are equal:

$$\tfrac{1}{2}m_A v_{A1}^2 = \tfrac{1}{2}m_A v_{A2}^2 + \tfrac{1}{2}m_B v_{B2}^2$$

$$v_{B2}^2 = \frac{m_A v_{A1}^2 - m_A v_{A2}^2}{m_B}$$

$$= \frac{(0.500\ \text{kg})(4.00\ \text{m/s})^2 - (0.500\ \text{kg})(2.00\ \text{m/s})^2}{0.300\ \text{kg}}$$

$$v_{B2} = 4.47\ \text{m/s}$$

Conservation of the x-component of total momentum gives

$$m_A v_{A1x} = m_A v_{A2x} + m_B v_{B2x}$$

$$(0.500\ \text{kg})(4.00\ \text{m/s}) = (0.500\ \text{kg})(2.00\ \text{m/s})(\cos\alpha) + (0.300\ \text{kg})(4.47\ \text{m/s})(\cos\beta)$$

and conservation of the y-component gives

$$0 = m_A v_{A2y} + m_B v_{B2y}$$

$$0 = (0.500\ \text{kg})(2.00\ \text{m/s})(\sin\alpha) - (0.300\ \text{kg})(4.47\ \text{m/s})(\sin\beta)$$

These are two simultaneous equations for α and β. The simplest solution is to eliminate β as follows: We solve the first equation for $\cos\beta$ and the second for $\sin\beta$; we then square each equation and add. Since $\sin^2\beta + \cos^2\beta = 1$, this eliminates β and leaves an equation that we can solve for $\cos\alpha$ and hence for α. We can then substitute this value back into either of the two equations and solve the result for β. We leave the details for you to work out in Exercise 8.44; the results are

$$\alpha = 36.9^\circ \qquad \beta = 26.6^\circ$$

EVALUATE: A quick way to check the answers is to make sure that the y-momentum, which was zero before the collision, is still zero after the collision. The y-momenta of the pucks are

$$p_{A2y} = (0.500\ \text{kg})(2.00\ \text{m/s})(\sin 36.9^\circ) = +0.600\ \text{kg}\cdot\text{m/s}$$

$$p_{B2y} = -(0.300\ \text{kg})(4.47\ \text{m/s})(\sin 26.6^\circ) = -0.600\ \text{kg}\cdot\text{m/s}$$

The sum of these values is zero, as it should be.

Test Your Understanding of Section 8.4 Most present-day nuclear reactors use water as a moderator (see Example 8.11). Are water molecules (mass $m_w = 18.0$ u) a better or worse moderator than carbon atoms? (One advantage of water is that it also acts as a coolant for the reactor's radioactive core.)

8.5 Center of Mass

We can restate the principle of conservation of momentum in a useful way by using the concept of **center of mass.** Suppose we have several particles with masses m_1, m_2, and so on. Let the coordinates of m_1 be (x_1, y_1), those of m_2 be (x_2, y_2), and so on. We define the center of mass of the system as the point that has coordinates (x_{cm}, y_{cm}) given by

$$x_{cm} = \frac{m_1x_1 + m_2x_2 + m_3x_3 + \cdots}{m_1 + m_2 + m_3 + \cdots} = \frac{\sum_i m_i x_i}{\sum_i m_i}$$

$$y_{cm} = \frac{m_1y_1 + m_2y_2 + m_3y_3 + \cdots}{m_1 + m_2 + m_3 + \cdots} = \frac{\sum_i m_i x_i}{\sum_i m_i} \qquad \text{(center of mass) (8.28)}$$

The position vector $\vec{r}_{cm}$ of the center of mass can be expressed in terms of the position vectors $\vec{r}_1, \vec{r}_2, \ldots$ of the particles as

$$\vec{r}_{cm} = \frac{m_1\vec{r}_1 + m_2\vec{r}_2 + m_3\vec{r}_3 + \cdots}{m_1 + m_2 + m_3 + \cdots} = \frac{\sum_i m_i \vec{r}_i}{\sum_i m_i} \qquad \text{(center of mass) (8.29)}$$

In statistical language, the center of mass is a *mass-weighted average* position of the particles.

Example 8.13 Center of mass of a water molecule

Figure 8.27 shows a simple model of the structure of a water molecule. The separation between atoms is $d = 9.57 \times 10^{-11}$ m. Each hydrogen atom has mass 1.0 u, and the oxygen atom has mass 16.0 u. Find the position of the center of mass.

SOLUTION

IDENTIFY: Nearly all the mass of each atom is concentrated in its nucleus, which is only about 10^{-5} times the overall radius of the atom. Hence we can safely represent each atom as a point particle.

SET UP: The coordinate system is shown in Fig. 8.27. We'll use Eqs. (8.28) to determine the coordinates x_{cm} and y_{cm}.

EXECUTE: The x-coordinate of each hydrogen atom is $d\cos(105°/2)$; the y-coordinates of the upper and lower hydrogen atoms are $+d\sin(105°/2)$ and $-d\sin(105°/2)$, respectively. The coordinates of the oxygen atom are $x = 0$, $y = 0$. From Eqs. (8.28) the x-coordinate of the center of mass is

$$x_{cm} = \frac{\begin{bmatrix} (1.0\text{ u})(d\cos 52.5°) + (1.0\text{ u}) \\ \times (d\cos 52.5°) + (16.0\text{ u})(0) \end{bmatrix}}{1.0\text{ u} + 1.0\text{ u} + 16.0\text{ u}} = 0.068d$$

and the y-coordinate is

$$y_{cm} = \frac{\begin{bmatrix} (1.0\text{ u})(d\sin 52.5°) + (1.0\text{ u}) \\ \times (-d\sin 52.5°) + (16.0\text{ u})(0) \end{bmatrix}}{1.0\text{ u} + 1.0\text{ u} + 16.0\text{ u}} = 0$$

Substituting the value $d = 9.57 \times 10^{-11}$ m, we find

$$x_{cm} = (0.068)(9.57 \times 10^{-11}\text{ m}) = 6.5 \times 10^{-12}\text{ m}$$

EVALUATE: The center of mass is much closer to the oxygen atom than to either hydrogen atom because the oxygen atom is much more massive. Notice that the center of mass lies along the x-axis, which is the *axis of symmetry* of this molecule. If the molecule is rotated by 180° around this axis, it looks exactly the same as before. The position of the center of mass can't be affected by this rotation, so it must lie on the axis of symmetry.

8.27 Where is the center of mass of a water molecule?

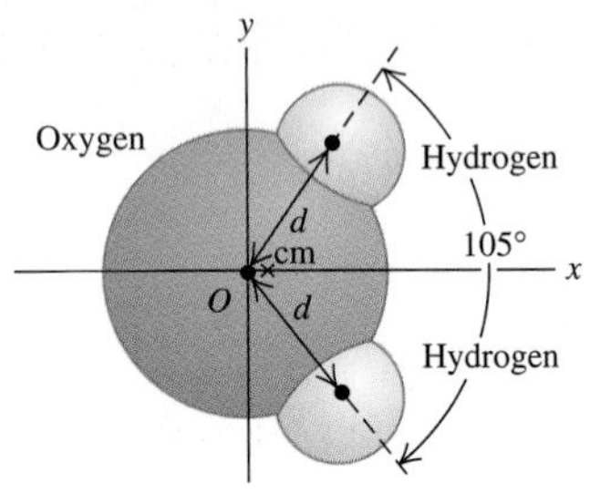

For solid bodies, in which we have (at least on a macroscopic level) a continuous distribution of matter, the sums in Eqs. (8.28) have to be replaced by integrals. The calculations can get quite involved, but we can say three general things about such problems (Fig. 8.28). First, whenever a homogeneous body has a geometric center, such as a billiard ball, a sugar cube, or a can of frozen orange juice, the center of mass is at the geometric center. Second, whenever a body has an axis of symmetry, such as a wheel or a pulley, the center of mass always lies on that axis. Third, there is no law that says the center of mass has to be within the body. For example, the center of mass of a donut is right in the middle of the hole.

We'll talk a little more about locating the center of mass in Chapter 11 in connection with the related concept of *center of gravity*.

8.28 Locating the center of mass of a symmetrical object.

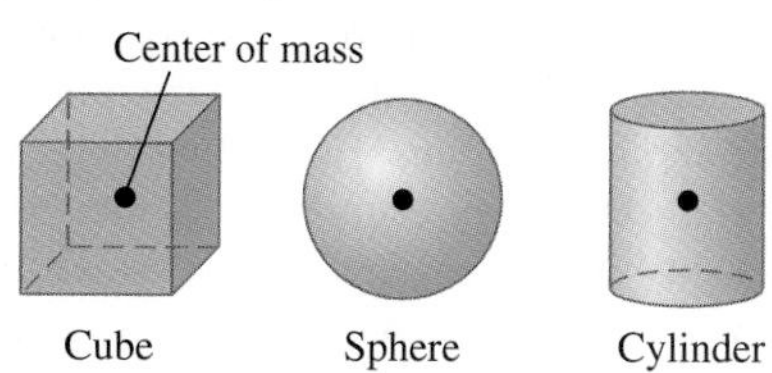

If a homogeneous object has a geometric center, that is where the center of mass is located.

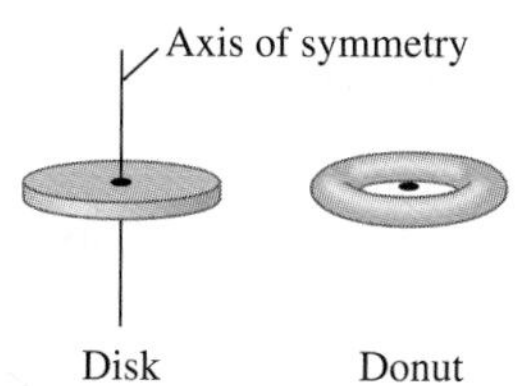

If an object has an axis of symmetry, the center of mass lies along it. As in the case of the donut, the center of mass may not be within the object.

Motion of the Center of Mass

To see the significance of the center of mass of a collection of particles, we must ask what happens to the center of mass when the particles move. The x- and y-components of velocity of the center of mass, $v_{\text{cm-}x}$ and $v_{\text{cm-}y}$, are the time derivatives of x_{cm} and y_{cm}. Also, dx_1/dt is the x-component of velocity of particle 1, and so on, so $dx_1/dt = v_{1x}$, and so on. Taking time derivatives of Eqs. (8.28), we get

$$v_{\text{cm-}x} = \frac{m_1 v_{1x} + m_2 v_{2x} + m_3 v_{3x} + \cdots}{m_1 + m_2 + m_3 + \cdots}$$
$$v_{\text{cm-}y} = \frac{m_1 v_{1y} + m_2 v_{2y} + m_3 v_{3y} + \cdots}{m_1 + m_2 + m_3 + \cdots} \tag{8.30}$$

These equations are equivalent to the single vector equation obtained by taking the time derivative of Eq. (8.29):

$$\vec{v}_{\text{cm}} = \frac{m_1 \vec{v}_1 + m_2 \vec{v}_2 + m_3 \vec{v}_3 + \cdots}{m_1 + m_2 + m_3 + \cdots} \tag{8.31}$$

We denote the *total* mass $m_1 + m_2 + \cdots$ by M. We can then rewrite Eq. (8.31) as

$$M\vec{v}_{\text{cm}} = m_1 \vec{v}_1 + m_2 \vec{v}_2 + m_3 \vec{v}_3 + \cdots = \vec{P} \tag{8.32}$$

The right side is simply the total momentum $\vec{P}$ of the system. Thus we have proved that *the total momentum is equal to the total mass times the velocity of the center of mass.* When you catch a baseball, you are really catching a collection of a very large number of molecules of masses $m_1, m_2, m_3, \ldots$. The impulse you feel is due to the total momentum of this entire collection. But this impulse is the same as if you were catching a single particle of mass $M = m_1 + m_2 + m_3 + \cdots$ moving with velocity $\vec{v}_{\text{cm}}$, the velocity of the collection's center of mass. So Eq. (8.32) helps to justify representing an extended body as a particle.

For a system of particles on which the net external force is zero, so that the total momentum $\vec{P}$ is constant, the velocity of the center of mass $\vec{v}_{\text{cm}} = \vec{P}/M$ is also constant. Suppose we mark the center of mass of a wrench and then slide the wrench with a spinning motion across a smooth, horizontal tabletop (Fig. 8.29). The overall motion appears complicated, but the center of mass follows a straight line, as though all the mass were concentrated at that point.

8.29 The center of mass of this wrench is marked with a white dot. The net external force acting on the wrench is almost zero. As the wrench spins on a smooth horizontal surface, the center of mass moves in a straight line with nearly constant velocity.

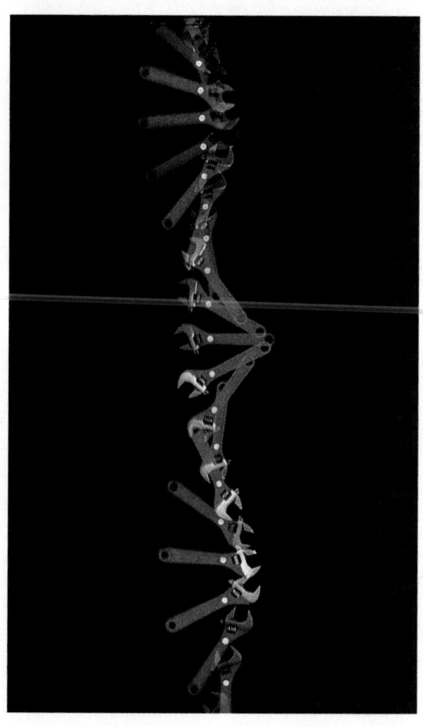

Example 8.14 A tug-of-war on the ice

James and Ramon are standing 20.0 m apart on the slippery surface of a frozen pond. Ramon has mass 60.0 kg and James has mass 90.0 kg. Midway between the two men a mug of their favorite beverage sits on the ice. They pull on the ends of a light rope that is stretched between them. When James has moved 6.0 m toward the mug, how far and in what direction has Ramon moved?

Continued

SOLUTION

IDENTIFY: The frozen surface is horizontal and essentially frictionless, so the net external force on the system of James, Ramon, and the rope is zero. Hence their total momentum is conserved. Initially there is no motion, so the total momentum is zero; thus the velocity of the center of mass is zero, and the center of mass remains at rest. We can use this to relate the positions of James and Ramon.

SET UP: Let's take the origin at the position of the mug, and let the $+x$-axis extend from the mug toward Ramon. Figure 8.30 shows our sketch. Since the rope is light, we can neglect its mass in calculating the position of the center of mass with Eq. (8.28).

8.30 Our sketch for this problem.

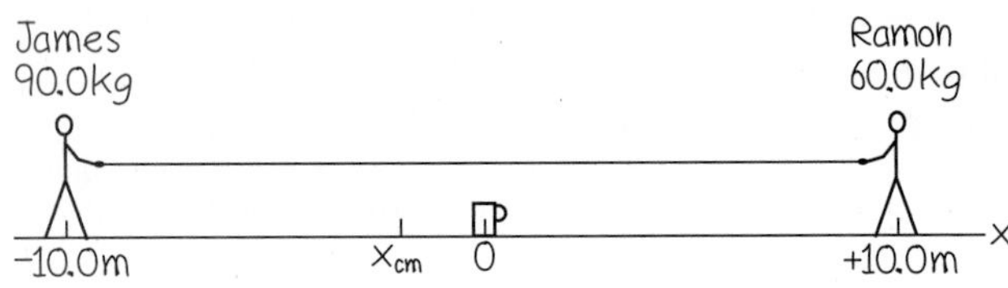

EXECUTE: The initial x-coordinates of James and Ramon are -10.0 m and $+10.0$ m, respectively, so the x-coordinate of the center of mass is

$$x_{cm} = \frac{(90.0\text{ kg})(-10.0\text{ m}) + (60.0\text{ kg})(10.0\text{ m})}{90.0\text{ kg} + 60.0\text{ kg}} = -2.0\text{ m}$$

When James moves 6.0 m toward the mug, his new x-coordinate is -4.0 m; we'll call Ramon's new x-coordinate x_2. The center of mass doesn't move, so

$$x_{cm} = \frac{(90.0\text{ kg})(-4.0\text{ m}) + (60.0\text{ kg})x_2}{90.0\text{ kg} + 60.0\text{ kg}} = -2.0\text{ m}$$

$$x_2 = 1.0\text{ m}$$

James has moved 6.0 m in the positive x-direction and is still 4.0 m from the mug, but Ramon has moved 9.0 m in the negative x-direction and is only 1.0 m from it.

EVALUATE: The ratio of how far each man moved, $(6.0\text{ m})/(9.0\text{ m}) = \frac{2}{3}$, equals the inverse ratio of their masses. Can you see why? If the two men keep moving (and if the surface is frictionless, they will!), Ramon will reach the mug first. This result is completely independent of how hard either person pulls; pulling harder just helps Ramon quench his thirst sooner.

External Forces and Center-of-Mass Motion

If the net external force on a system of particles is not zero, then total momentum is not conserved and the velocity of the center of mass changes. Let's look at the relationship between the motion of the center of mass and the forces acting on the system.

Equations (8.31) and (8.32) give the *velocity* of the center of mass in terms of the velocities of the individual particles. We take the time derivatives of these equations to show that the *accelerations* are related in the same way. Let $\vec{a}_{cm} = d\vec{v}_{cm}/dt$ be the acceleration of the center of mass; then we find

$$M\vec{a}_{cm} = m_1\vec{a}_1 + m_2\vec{a}_2 + m_3\vec{a}_3 + \cdots \quad (8.33)$$

Now $m_1\vec{a}_1$ is equal to the vector sum of forces on the first particle, and so on, so the right side of Eq. (8.33) is equal to the vector sum $\Sigma\vec{F}$ of *all* the forces on *all* the particles. Just as we did in Section 8.2, we can classify each force as *external* or *internal.* The sum of all forces on all the particles is then

$$\Sigma\vec{F} = \Sigma\vec{F}_{ext} + \Sigma\vec{F}_{int} = M\vec{a}_{cm}$$

Because of Newton's third law, the internal forces all cancel in pairs, and $\Sigma\vec{F}_{int} = \mathbf{0}$. What survives on the left side is the sum of only the *external* forces:

$$\Sigma\vec{F}_{ext} = M\vec{a}_{cm} \quad \text{(body or collection of particles)} \quad (8.34)$$

When a body or a collection of particles is acted on by external forces, the center of mass moves just as though all the mass were concentrated at that point and it were acted on by a net force equal to the sum of the external forces on the system.

This result may not sound very impressive, but in fact it is central to the whole subject of mechanics. In fact, we've been using this result all along; without it, we would not be able to represent an extended body as a point particle when we apply Newton's laws. It explains why only *external* forces can affect the motion of an extended body. If you pull upward on your belt, your belt exerts an equal downward force on your hands; these are *internal* forces that cancel and have no effect on the overall motion of your body.

8.31 (a) A shell explodes into two fragments in flight. If air resistance is ignored, the center of mass continues on the same trajectory as the shell's path before exploding. (b) The same effect occurs with exploding fireworks.

(a)

Shell explodes

After the shell explodes, the two fragments follow individual trajectories, but the center of mass continues to follow the shell's original trajectory.

cm

cm

cm

(b)

Suppose a cannon shell traveling in a parabolic trajectory (neglecting air resistance) explodes in flight, splitting into two fragments with equal mass (Fig. 8.31a). The fragments follow new parabolic paths, but the center of mass continues on the original parabolic trajectory, just as though all the mass were still concentrated at that point. A skyrocket exploding in air (Fig. 8.31b) is a spectacular example of this effect.

This property of the center of mass is important when we analyze the motion of rigid bodies. We describe the motion of an extended body as a combination of translational motion of the center of mass and rotational motion about an axis through the center of mass. We will return to this topic in Chapter 10. This property also plays an important role in the motion of astronomical objects. It's not correct to say that the moon orbits the earth; rather, the earth and moon both move in orbits around their center of mass.

There's one more useful way to describe the motion of a system of particles. Using $\vec{a}_{cm} = d\vec{v}_{cm}/dt$, we can rewrite Eq. (8.33) as

$$M\vec{a}_{cm} = M\frac{d\vec{v}_{cm}}{dt} = \frac{d(M\vec{v}_{cm})}{dt} = \frac{d\vec{P}}{dt} \tag{8.35}$$

The total system mass M is constant, so we're allowed to take it inside the derivative. Substituting Eq. (8.35) into Eq. (8.34), we find

$$\Sigma\vec{F}_{ext} = \frac{d\vec{P}}{dt} \quad \text{(extended body or system of particles)} \tag{8.36}$$

This equation looks like Eq. (8.4). The difference is that Eq. (8.36) describes a *system* of particles, such as an extended body, while Eq. (8.4) describes a single particle. The interactions between the particles that make up the system can change the individual momenta of the particles, but the *total* momentum $\vec{P}$ of the system can be changed only by external forces acting from outside the system.

Finally, we note that if the net external force is zero, Eq. (8.34) shows that the acceleration $\vec{a}_{cm}$ of the center of mass is zero. So the center-of-mass velocity $\vec{v}_{cm}$ is constant, as for the wrench in Fig. 8.29. From Eq. (8.36) the total momentum $\vec{P}$ is also constant. This reaffirms our statement in Section 8.3 of the principle of conservation of momentum.

Test Your Understanding of Section 8.5 Will the center of mass in Fig. 8.31a continue on the same parabolic trajectory even after one of the fragments hits the ground? Why or why not?

*8.6 Rocket Propulsion

ActivPhysics ONLINE
6.6 Saving an Astronaut

Momentum considerations are particularly useful for analyzing a system in which the masses of parts of the system change with time. In such cases we can't use Newton's second law $\Sigma\vec{F} = m\vec{a}$ directly because m changes. Rocket propulsion offers a typical and interesting example of this kind of analysis. A rocket is propelled forward by rearward ejection of burned fuel that initially was in the rocket (which is why rocket fuel is also called *propellant*). The forward force on the rocket is the reaction to the backward force on the ejected material. The total mass of the system is constant, but the mass of the rocket itself decreases as material is ejected.

As a simple example, consider a rocket fired in outer space, where there is no gravitational force and no air resistance. Let m denote the mass of the rocket, which will change as it expends fuel. We choose our x-axis to be along the rocket's direction of motion. Figure 8.32a shows the rocket at a time t, when its mass is m and its x-velocity relative to our coordinate system is v. (For simplicity, we will drop the subscript x in this discussion.) The x-component of total momentum at this instant is $P_1 = mv$. In a short time interval dt, the mass of the rocket changes by an amount dm. This is an inherently negative quantity because the rocket's mass m *decreases* with time. During dt, a *positive* mass $-dm$ of burned fuel is ejected from the rocket. Let v_{ex} be the exhaust *speed* of this material *relative to the rocket;* the burned fuel is ejected opposite the direction of motion, so its x-component of *velocity* relative to the rocket is $-v_{ex}$. The x-velocity v_{fuel} of the burned fuel relative to our coordinate system is then

$$v_{fuel} = v + (-v_{ex}) = v - v_{ex}$$

and the x-component of momentum of the ejected mass $(-dm)$ is

$$(-dm)v_{fuel} = (-dm)(v - v_{ex})$$

Figure 8.32b shows that at the end of the time interval dt, the x-velocity of the rocket and unburned fuel has increased to $v + dv$, and its mass has decreased to $m + dm$ (remember that dm is negative). The rocket's momentum at this time is

$$(m + dm)(v + dv)$$

Thus the *total* x-component of momentum P_2 of the rocket plus ejected fuel at time $t + dt$ is

$$P_2 = (m + dm)(v + dv) + (-dm)(v - v_{ex})$$

8.32 A rocket moving in gravity-free outer space at (a) time t and (b) time $t + dt$.

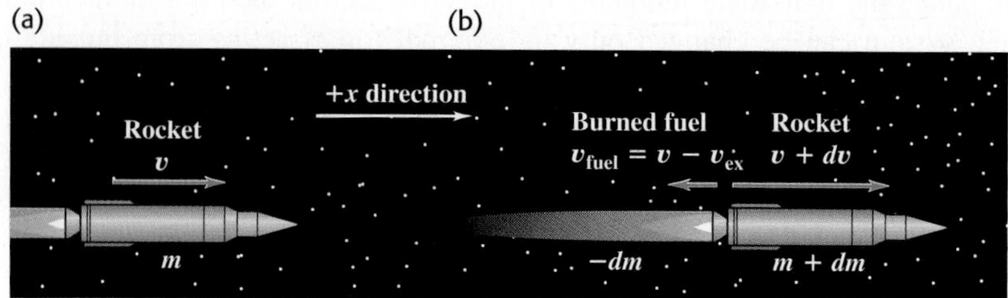

At time t, the rocket has mass m and x-component of velocity v.

At time $t + dt$, the rocket has mass $m + dm$ (where dm is inherently *negative*) and x-component of velocity $v + dv$. The burned fuel has x-component of velocity $v_{fuel} = v - v_{ex}$ and mass $-dm$. (The minus sign is needed to make $-dm$ *positive* because dm is negative.)

According to our initial assumption, the rocket and fuel are an isolated system. Thus momentum is conserved, and the total x-component of momentum of the system must be the same at time t and at time $t + dt$: $P_1 = P_2$. Hence

$$mv = (m + dm)(v + dv) + (-dm)(v - v_{ex})$$

This can be simplified to

$$m\,dv = -dm\,v_{ex} - dm\,dv$$

We can neglect the term $(-dm\,dv)$ because it is a product of two small quantities and thus is much smaller than the other terms. Dropping this term, dividing by dt, and rearranging, we find

$$m\frac{dv}{dt} = -v_{ex}\frac{dm}{dt} \qquad (8.37)$$

Now dv/dt is the acceleration of the rocket, so the left side of this equation (mass times acceleration) equals the net force F, or *thrust,* on the rocket,

$$F = -v_{ex}\frac{dm}{dt} \qquad (8.38)$$

The thrust is proportional both to the relative speed v_{ex} of the ejected fuel and to the mass of fuel ejected per unit time, $-dm/dt$. (Remember that dm/dt is negative because it is the rate of change of the rocket's mass, so F is positive.)

The x-component of acceleration of the rocket is

$$a = \frac{dv}{dt} = -\frac{v_{ex}}{m}\frac{dm}{dt} \qquad (8.39)$$

This is positive because v_{ex} is positive (remember, it's the exhaust *speed*) and dm/dt is negative. The rocket's mass m decreases continuously while the fuel is being consumed. If v_{ex} and dm/dt are constant, the acceleration increases until all the fuel is gone.

Equation (8.38) tells us that an effective rocket burns fuel at a rapid rate (large $-dm/dt$) and ejects the burned fuel at a high relative speed (large v_{ex}), as in Fig. 8.33. In the early days of rocket propulsion, people who didn't understand conservation of momentum thought that a rocket couldn't function in outer space because "it doesn't have anything to push against." On the contrary, rockets work *best* in outer space, where there is no air resistance! The launch vehicle in Fig. 8.33 is *not* "pushing against the ground" to get into the air.

If the exhaust speed v_{ex} is constant, we can integrate Eq. (8.39) to find a relationship between the velocity v at any time and the remaining mass m. At time $t = 0$, let the mass be m_0 and the velocity v_0. Then we rewrite Eq. (8.39) as

$$dv = -v_{ex}\frac{dm}{m}$$

We change the integration variables to v' and m', so we can use v and m as the upper limits (the final speed and mass). Then we integrate both sides, using limits v_0 to v and m_0 to m, and take the constant v_{ex} outside the integral:

$$\int_{v_0}^{v} dv' = -\int_{m_0}^{m} v_{ex}\frac{dm'}{m'} = -v_{ex}\int_{m_0}^{m}\frac{dm'}{m'}$$

$$v - v_0 = -v_{ex}\ln\frac{m}{m_0} = v_{ex}\ln\frac{m_0}{m} \qquad (8.40)$$

The ratio m_0/m is the original mass divided by the mass after the fuel has been exhausted. In practical spacecraft this ratio is made as large as possible to maximize the speed gain, which means that the initial mass of the rocket is almost all fuel. The final velocity of the rocket will be greater in magnitude (and is often

8.33 To provide enough thrust to lift its payload into space, this Atlas V launch vehicle exhausts more than 1000 kg of burned fuel per second at speeds of nearly 4000 m/s.

much greater) than the relative speed v_{ex} if $\ln(m_0/m) > 1$—that is, if $m_0/m > e = 2.71828\ldots$

We've assumed throughout this analysis that the rocket is in gravity-free outer space. However, gravity must be taken into account when a rocket is launched from the surface of a planet, as in Fig. 8.33 (see Problem 8.110).

Example 8.15 Acceleration of a rocket

A rocket is in outer space, far from any planet, when the rocket engine is turned on. In the first second of firing, the rocket ejects $\frac{1}{120}$ of its mass with a relative speed of 2400 m/s. What is the rocket's initial acceleration?

SOLUTION

IDENTIFY: We are given the rocket's exhaust speed v_{ex}, but not its mass m or the rate of change of its mass dm/dt. However, we are told what fraction of the initial mass is lost during a given time interval, which should be enough.

SET UP: We'll use Eq. (8.39) to find the acceleration of the rocket.

EXECUTE: The initial rate of change of mass is

$$\frac{dm}{dt} = -\frac{m_0/120}{1\text{ s}} = -\frac{m_0}{120\text{ s}}$$

where m_0 is the initial $(t = 0)$ mass of the rocket. From Eq. (8.39) the initial acceleration is

$$a = -\frac{v_{ex}}{m_0}\frac{dm}{dt} = -\frac{2400\text{ m/s}}{m_0}\left(-\frac{m_0}{120\text{ s}}\right) = 20\text{ m/s}^2$$

EVALUATE: Note that the answer didn't depend on the value of m_0. If v_{ex} is the same, the initial acceleration is the same for a 120,000-kg spacecraft that ejects 1000 kg/s as for a 60-kg astronaut equipped with a small rocket that ejects 0.5 kg/s.

Example 8.16 Speed of a rocket

Suppose that $\frac{3}{4}$ of the initial mass m_0 of the rocket in Example 8.15 is fuel, so the final mass is $m = m_0/4$, and that the fuel is completely consumed at a constant rate in a total time $t = 90$ s. If the rocket starts from rest in our coordinate system, find its speed at the end of this time.

SOLUTION

IDENTIFY: We are given the initial velocity v_0 (equal to zero), the exhaust speed v_{ex}, and the final mass m in terms of the initial mass m_0.

SET UP: We'll use Eq. (8.40) directly to find the final speed v.

EXECUTE: We have $m_0/m = 4$, so from Eq. (8.40),

$$v = v_0 + v_{ex}\ln\frac{m_0}{m} = 0 + (2400\text{ m/s})(\ln 4) = 3327\text{ m/s}$$

EVALUATE: Let's examine what happens as the rocket gains speed. At the start of the flight, when the velocity of the rocket is zero, the ejected fuel is moving to the left, relative to our coordinate system, at 2400 m/s. At the end of the first second $(t = 1\text{ s})$, the rocket is moving at 20 m/s, and the fuel's speed relative to our system is 2380 m/s. During the next second the acceleration, given by Eq. (8.39), is a little greater. At $t = 2$ s, the rocket is moving a little faster than 40 m/s, and the fuel's speed is a little less than 2360 m/s. Detailed calculation shows that at about $t = 75.6$ s, the rocket's velocity v in our coordinate system equals 2400 m/s. The burned fuel ejected after this time moves *forward,* not backward, in our system. Since the final velocity of the rocket is 3327 m/s and the relative velocity is 2400 m/s, the last portion of the ejected fuel has a forward velocity (relative to our frame of reference) of $(3327 - 2400)$ m/s $= 927$ m/s. (To illustrate our point, we are using more figures than are significant.)

Test Your Understanding of Section 8.6 (a) If a rocket in gravity-free outer space has the same thrust at all times, is its acceleration constant, increasing, or decreasing? (b) If the rocket has the same acceleration at all times, is the thrust constant, increasing, or decreasing?

CHAPTER 8 SUMMARY

Momentum of a particle: The momentum $\vec{p}$ of a particle is a vector quantity equal to the product of the particle's mass m and velocity $\vec{v}$. Newton's second law says that the net force on a particle is equal to the rate of change of the particle's momentum.

$$\vec{p} = m\vec{v} \tag{8.2}$$

$$\Sigma\vec{F} = \frac{d\vec{p}}{dt} \tag{8.4}$$

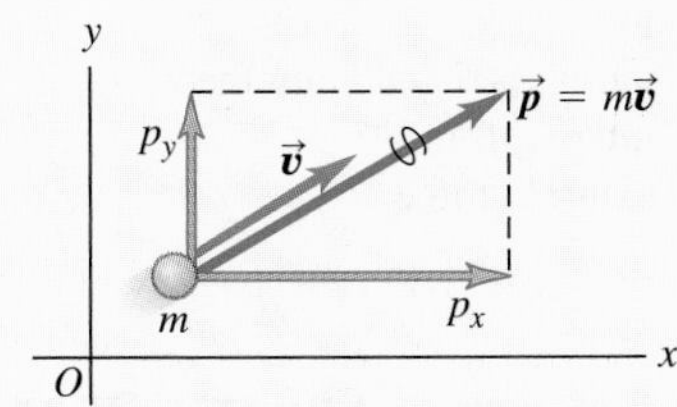

Impulse and momentum: If a constant net force $\Sigma\vec{F}$ acts on a particle for a time interval Δt from t_1 to t_2, the impulse $\vec{J}$ of the net force is the product of the net force and the time interval. If $\Sigma\vec{F}$ varies with time, $\vec{J}$ is the integral of the net force over the time interval. In any case, the change in a particle's momentum during a time interval equals the impulse of the net force that acted on the particle during that interval. The momentum of a particle equals the impulse that accelerated it from rest to its present speed. (See Examples 8.1–8.3.)

$$\vec{J} = \Sigma\vec{F}(t_2 - t_1) = \Sigma\vec{F}\,\Delta t \tag{8.5}$$

$$\vec{J} = \int_{t_1}^{t_2} \Sigma\vec{F}\,dt \tag{8.7}$$

$$\vec{J} = \vec{p}_2 - \vec{p}_1 \tag{8.6}$$

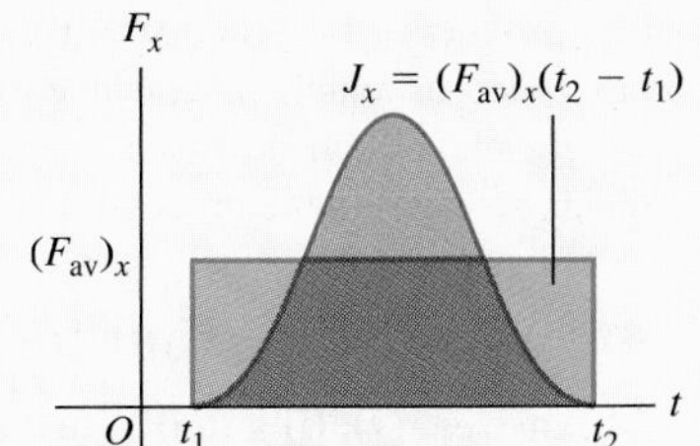

Conservation of momentum: An internal force is a force exerted by one part of a system on another. An external force is a force exerted on any part of a system by something outside the system. If the net external force on a system is zero, the total momentum of the system $\vec{P}$ (the vector sum of the momenta of the individual particles that make up the system) is constant, or conserved. Each component of total momentum is separately conserved. (See Examples 8.4–8.6)

$$\vec{P} = \vec{p}_A + \vec{p}_B + \cdots$$
$$= m_A\vec{v}_A + m_B\vec{v}_B + \cdots \tag{8.14}$$

If $\Sigma\vec{F} = \mathbf{0}$, then $\vec{P}$ = constant.

Collisions: In collisions of all kinds, the initial and final total momenta are equal. In an elastic collision between two bodies, the initial and final total kinetic energies are also equal, and the initial and final relative velocities have the same magnitude. In an inelastic two-body collision, the total kinetic energy is less after the collision than before. If the two bodies have the same final velocity, the collision is completely inelastic. (See Examples 8.7–8.12.)

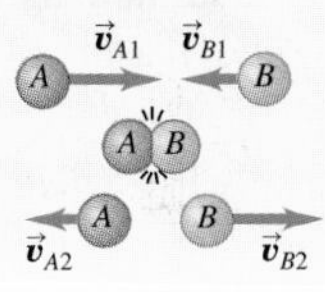

Center of mass: The position vector of the center of mass of a system of particles, $\vec{r}_{cm}$, is a weighted average of the positions $\vec{r}_1, \vec{r}_2, \ldots$ of the individual particles. The total momentum $\vec{P}$ of a system equals its total mass M multiplied by the velocity of its center of mass, $\vec{v}_{cm}$. The center of mass moves as though all the mass M were concentrated at that point. If the net external force on the system is zero, the center-of-mass velocity $\vec{v}_{cm}$ is constant. If the net external force is not zero, the center of mass accelerates as though it were a particle of mass M being acted on by the same net external force. (See Examples 8.13 and 8.14.)

$$\vec{r}_{cm} = \frac{m_1\vec{r}_1 + m_2\vec{r}_2 + m_3\vec{r}_3 + \cdots}{m_1 + m_2 + m_3 + \cdots} = \frac{\Sigma_i m_i\vec{r}_i}{\Sigma_i m_i} \tag{8.29}$$

$$\vec{P} = m_1\vec{v}_1 + m_2\vec{v}_2 + m_3\vec{v}_3 + \cdots = M\vec{v}_{cm} \tag{8.32}$$

$$\Sigma\vec{F}_{ext} = M\vec{a}_{cm} \tag{8.34}$$

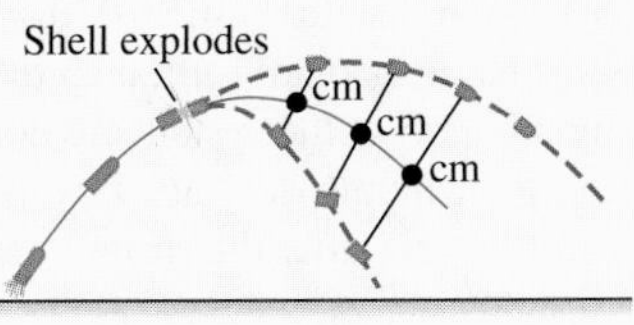

Rocket propulsion: In rocket propulsion, the mass of a rocket changes as the fuel is used up and ejected from the rocket. Analysis of the motion of the rocket must include the momentum carried away by the spent fuel as well as the momentum of the rocket itself. (See Examples 8.15 and 8.16.)

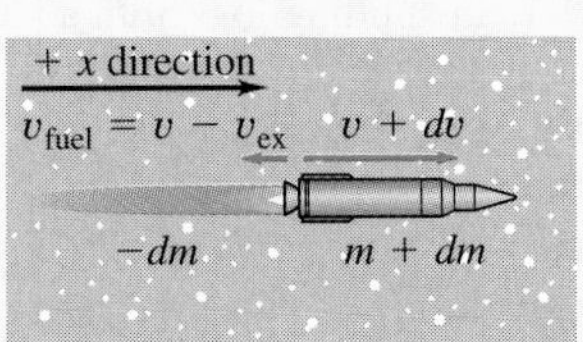

Key Terms

Answer to Chapter Opening Question ?

The two players have the same magnitude of momentum $p = mv$ (the product of mass and speed), but the faster, lightweight player has twice as much kinetic energy $K = \frac{1}{2}mv^2$. Hence, the lightweight player can do twice as much work on you (and twice as much damage) in the process of coming to a halt (see Section 8.1).

Answers to Test Your Understanding Questions

8.1 Answer: (v), (i) and (ii) (tied for second place), (iii) and (iv) (tied for third place) We use two interpretations of the impulse of the net force: (1) the net force multiplied by the time that the net force acts, and (2) the change in momentum of the particle on which the net force acts. Which interpretation we use depends on what information we are given. We take the positive x-direction to be to the east. (i) The force is not given, so we use interpretation 2: $J_x = mv_{2x} - mv_{1x} = (1000\text{ kg})(0) - (1000\text{ kg})(25\text{ m/s}) = -25{,}000\text{ kg}\cdot\text{m/s}$, so the magnitude of the impulse is $25{,}000\text{ kg}\cdot\text{m/s} = 25{,}000\text{ N}\cdot\text{s}$. (ii) For the same reason as in (i), we use interpretation 2: $J_x = mv_{2x} - mv_{1x} = (1000\text{ kg})(0) - (1000\text{ kg})(25\text{ m/s}) = -25{,}000\text{ kg}\cdot\text{m/s}$, and the magnitude of the impulse is again $25{,}000\text{ kg}\cdot\text{m/s} = 25{,}000\text{ N}\cdot\text{s}$. (iii) The final velocity is not given, so we use interpretation 1: $J_x = (\Sigma F_x)_{\text{av}}(t_2 - t_1) = (2000\text{ N})(10\text{ s}) = 20{,}000\text{ N}\cdot\text{s}$, so the magnitude of the impulse is $20{,}000\text{ N}\cdot\text{s}$. (iv) For the same reason as in (iii), we use interpretation 1: $J_x = (\Sigma F_x)_{\text{av}}(t_2 - t_1) = (-2000\text{ N})(10\text{ s}) = -20{,}000\text{ N}\cdot\text{s}$, so the magnitude of the impulse is $20{,}000\text{ N}\cdot\text{s}$. (v) The force is not given, so we use interpretation 2: $J_x = mv_{2x} - mv_{1x} = (1000\text{ kg})(-25\text{ m/s}) - (1000\text{ kg})(25\text{ m/s}) = -50{,}000\text{ kg}\cdot\text{m/s}$, so the magnitude of the impulse is $50{,}000\text{ kg}\cdot\text{m/s} = 50{,}000\text{ N}\cdot\text{s}$.

8.2 Answers: (a) $v_{C2x} > 0$, $v_{C2y} > 0$, (b) piece C There are no external horizontal forces, so the x- and y-components of the total momentum of the system are both conserved. Both components of the total momentum are zero before the spring releases, so they must be zero after the spring releases. Hence

$$P_x = 0 = m_A v_{A2x} + m_B v_{B2x} + m_C v_{C2x}$$
$$P_y = 0 = m_A v_{A2y} + m_B v_{B2y} + m_C v_{C2y}$$

We are given that $m_A = m_B = m_C$, $v_{A2x} < 0$, $v_{A2y} = 0$, $v_{B2x} = 0$, and $v_{B2y} < 0$. You can solve the above equations to show that $v_{C2x} = -v_{A2x} > 0$ and $v_{C2y} = -v_{B2y} > 0$, so the velocity components of piece C are both positive. Piece C has speed $\sqrt{v_{C2x}^2 + v_{C2y}^2} = \sqrt{v_{A2x}^2 + v_{B2y}^2}$, which is greater than the speed of either piece A or piece B.

8.3 Answers: (a) inelastic, (b) elastic, (c) completely inelastic In each case gravitational potential energy is converted to kinetic energy as the ball falls, and the collision is between the ball and the ground. In (a) all of the initial energy is converted back to gravitational potential energy, so no kinetic energy is lost in the bounce and the collision is elastic. In (b) there is less gravitational potential energy at the end than at the beginning, so some kinetic energy was lost in the bounce. Hence the collision is inelastic. In (c) the ball loses all the kinetic energy it has to give, the ball and the ground stick together, and the collision is completely inelastic.

8.4 Answer: worse After a collision with a water molecule initially at rest, the speed of the neutron is $|(m_n - m_w)/(m_n + m_w)| = |(1.0\text{ u} - 18\text{ u})/(1.0\text{ u} + 18\text{ u})| = \frac{17}{19}$ of its initial speed, and its kinetic energy is $(\frac{17}{19})^2 = 0.80$ of the initial value. Hence a water molecule is a worse moderator than a carbon atom, for which the corresponding numbers are $\frac{11}{13}$ and $(\frac{11}{13})^2 = 0.72$.

8.5 Answer: no If gravity is the only force acting on the system of two fragments, the center of mass will follow the parabolic trajectory of a freely falling object. Once a fragment lands, however, the ground exerts a normal force on that fragment. Hence the net force on the system has changed, and the trajectory of the center of mass changes in response.

8.6 Answers: (a) increasing, (b) decreasing From Eqs. (8.37) and (8.38), the thrust F is equal to $m(dv/dt)$, where m is the rocket's mass and dv/dt is its acceleration. Because m decreases with time, if the thrust F is constant, then the acceleration must increase with time (the same force acts on a smaller mass); if the acceleration dv/dt is constant, then the thrust must decrease with time (a smaller force is all that's needed to accelerate a smaller mass).

PROBLEMS

Discussion Questions

Q8.1. In splitting logs with a hammer and wedge, is a heavy hammer more effective than a lighter hammer? Why?

Q8.2. Suppose you catch a baseball and then someone invites you to catch a bowling ball with either the same momentum or the same kinetic energy as the baseball. Which would you choose? Explain.

Q8.3. When rain falls from the sky, what happens to its momentum as it hits the ground? Is your answer also valid for Newton's famous apple?

Q8.4. A car has the same kinetic energy when it is traveling south at 30 m/s as when it is traveling northwest at 30 m/s. Is the momentum of the car the same in both cases? Explain.

Q8.5. A truck is accelerating as it speeds down the highway. One inertial frame of reference is attached to the ground with its origin at a fence post. A second frame of reference is attached to a police car that is traveling down the highway at constant velocity. Is the momentum of the truck the same in these two reference frames? Explain. Is the rate of change of the truck's momentum the same in these two frames? Explain.

Q8.6. When a large, heavy truck collides with a passenger car, the occupants of the car are more likely to be hurt than the truck driver. Why?

Q8.7. A woman holding a large rock stands on a frictionless, horizontal sheet of ice. She throws the rock with speed v_0 at an angle α above the horizontal. Consider the system consisting of the woman plus the rock. Is the momentum of the system conserved? Why or why not? Is any component of the momentum of the system conserved? Again, why or why not?

Q8.8. In Example 8.7 (Section 8.3), where the two gliders in Fig. 8.15 a stick together after the collision, the collision is inelastic because $K_2 < K_1$. In Example 8.5 (Section 8.2), is the collision inelastic? Explain.

Q8.9. In a completely inelastic collision between two objects, where the objects stick together after the collision, is it possible for the final kinetic energy of the system to be zero? If so, give an example in which this would occur. If the final kinetic energy is zero, what must the initial momentum of the system be? Is the initial kinetic energy of the system zero? Explain.

Q8.10. Since for a particle the kinetic energy is given by $K = \frac{1}{2}mv^2$ and the momentum by $\vec{p} = m\vec{v}$, it is easy to show that $K = p^2/2m$. How, then, is it possible to have an event during which the total momentum of the system is constant but the total kinetic energy changes?

Q8.11. In each of Examples 8.10, 8.11, and 8.12 (Section 8.4), verify that the relative velocity vector of the two bodies has the same magnitude before and after the collision. In each case what happens to the *direction* of the relative velocity vector?

Q8.12. A glass dropped on the floor is more likely to break if the floor is concrete than if it is wood. Why? (Refer to Fig. 8.3b.)

Q8.13. In Fig. 8.22b, the kinetic energy of the Ping-Pong ball is larger after its interaction with the bowling ball than before. From where does the extra energy come? Describe the event in terms of conservation of energy.

Q8.14. A machine gun is fired at a steel plate. Is the average force on the plate from the bullet impact greater if the bullets bounce off or if they are squashed and stick to the plate? Explain.

Q8.15. A net force of 4 N acts on an object initially at rest for 0.25 s and gives it a final speed of 5 m/s. How could a net force of 2 N produce the same final speed?

Q8.16. A net force with x-component ΣF_x acts on an object from time t_1 to time t_2. The x-component of the momentum of the object is the same at t_1 as it is at t_2, but ΣF_x is not zero at all times between t_1 and t_2. What can you say about the graph of ΣF_x versus t?

Q8.17. A tennis player hits a tennis ball with a racket. Consider the system made up of the ball and the racket. Is the total momentum of the system the same just before and just after the hit? Is the total momentum just after the hit the same as 2 s later, when the ball is in midair at the high point of its trajectory? Explain any differences between the two cases.

Q8.18. In Example 8.4 (Section 8.2), consider the system consisting of the rifle plus the bullet. What is the speed of the system's center of mass after the rifle is fired? Explain.

Q8.19. An egg is released from rest from the roof of a building and falls to the ground. As the egg falls, what happens to the momentum of the system of the egg plus the earth?

Q8.20. A woman stands in the middle of a perfectly smooth, frictionless, frozen lake. She can set herself in motion by throwing things, but suppose she has nothing to throw. Can she propel herself to shore *without* throwing anything?

Q8.21. In a zero-gravity environment, can a rocket-propelled spaceship ever attain a speed greater than the relative speed with which the burnt fuel is exhausted?

Q8.22. When an object breaks into two pieces (explosion, radioactive decay, recoil, etc.), the lighter fragment gets more kinetic energy than the heavier one. This is a consequence of momentum conservation, but can you also explain it using Newton's laws of motion?

Q8.23. An apple falls from a tree and feels no air resistance. As it is falling, which of these statements about it are true? (a) Only its momentum is conserved; (b) only its mechanical energy is conserved, (c) both its momentum and its mechanical energy are conserved, (d) its kinetic energy is conserved.

Q8.24. Two pieces of clay collide and stick together. During the collision, which of these statements are true? (a) Only the momentum of the clay is conserved, (b) only the mechanical energy of the clay is conserved, (c) both the momentum and the mechanical energy of the clay are conserved, (d) the kinetic energy of the clay is conserved.

Q8.25. Two marbles are pressed together with a light ideal spring between them, but they are not attached to the spring in any way. They are then released on a frictionless horizontal table and soon move free of the spring. As the marbles are moving away from each other, which of these statements about them are true? (a) Only the momentum of the marbles is conserved, (b) only the mechanical energy of the marbles is conserved, (c) both the momentum and the mechanical energy of the marbles are conserved, (d) the kinetic energy of the marbles is conserved.

Q8.26. A very heavy SUV collides head-on with a very light compact car. Which of these statements about the collision are correct? (a) The amount of kinetic energy lost by the SUV is equal to the amount of kinetic energy gained by the compact, (b) the amount of momentum lost by the SUV is equal to the amount of momentum gained by the compact, (c) The compact feels a considerably greater force during the collision than the SUV does, (d) both cars lose the same amount of kinetic energy.

Exercises

Section 8.1 Momentum and Impulse

8.1. (a) What is the magnitude of the momentum of a 10,000-kg truck whose speed is 12.0 m/s? (b) What speed would a 2,000-kg SUV have to attain in order to have (i) the same momentum? (ii) the same kinetic energy?

8.2. In Conceptual Example 8.1 (Section 8.1), show that the iceboat with mass $2m$ has $\sqrt{2}$ times as much momentum at the finish line as does the iceboat with mass m.

8.3. (a) Show that the kinetic energy K and the momentum magnitude p of a particle with mass m are related by $K = p^2/2m$. (b) A 0.040-kg cardinal (*Richmondena cardinalis*) and a 0.145-kg baseball have the same kinetic energy. Which has the greater magnitude of momentum? What is the ratio of the cardinal's magnitude of momentum to the baseball's? (c) A 700-N man and a 450-N woman have the same momentum. Who has the greater kinetic energy? What is the ratio of the man's kinetic energy to that of the woman?

8.4. In a certain men's track and field event, the shotput has a mass of 7.30 kg and is released with a speed of 15.0 m/s at 40.0° above the horizontal over a man's straight left leg. What are the initial horizontal and vertical components of the momentum of this shotput?

8.5. One 110-kg football lineman is running to the right at 2.75 m/s while another 125-kg lineman is running directly toward him at

2.60 m/s. What are (a) the magnitude and direction of the net momentum of these two athletes, and (b) their total kinetic energy?

8.6. Two vehicles are approaching an intersection. One is a 2500-kg pickup traveling at 14.0 m/s from east to west (the $-x$-direction), and the other is a 1500-kg sedan going from south to north (the $+y$-direction at 23.0 m/s). (a) Find the x- and y-components of the net momentum of this system. (b) What are the magnitude and direction of the net momentum?

8.7. Force of a Golf Swing. A 0.0450-kg golf ball initially at rest is given a speed of 25.0 m/s when a club strikes. If the club and ball are in contact for 2.00 ms, what average force acts on the ball? Is the effect of the ball's weight during the time of contact significant? Why or why not?

8.8. Force of a Baseball Swing. A baseball has mass 0.145 kg. (a) If the velocity of a pitched ball has a magnitude of 45.0 m/s and the batted ball's velocity is 55.0 m/s in the opposite direction, find the magnitude of the change in momentum of the ball and of the impulse applied to it by the bat. (b) If the ball remains in contact with the bat for 2.00 ms, find the magnitude of the average force applied by the bat.

8.9. A 0.160-kg hockey puck is moving on an icy, frictionless, horizontal surface. At $t = 0$, the puck is moving to the right at 3.00 m/s. (a) Calculate the velocity of the puck (magnitude and direction) after a force of 25.0 N directed to the right has been applied for 0.050 s. (b) If, instead, a force of 12.0 N directed to the left is applied from $t = 0$ to $t = 0.050$ s, what is the final velocity of the puck?

8.10. An engine of the orbital maneuvering system (OMS) on a space shuttle exerts a force of $(26{,}700\text{ N})\hat{\jmath}$ for 3.90 s, exhausting a negligible mass of fuel relative to the 95,000-kg mass of the shuttle. (a) What is the impulse of the force for this 3.90 s? (b) What is the shuttle's change in momentum from this impulse? (c) What is the shuttle's change in velocity from this impulse? (d) Why can't we find the resulting change in the kinetic energy of the shuttle?

8.11. At time $t = 0$, a 2150-kg rocket in outer space fires an engine that exerts an increasing force on it in the $+x$-direction. This force obeys the equation $F_x = At^2$, where t is time, and has a magnitude of 781.25 N when $t = 1.25$ s. (a) Find the SI value of the constant A, including its units. (b) What impulse does the engine exert on the rocket during the 1.50-s interval starting 2.00 s after the engine is fired? (c) By how much does the rocket's velocity change during this interval?

8.12. A bat strikes a 0.145-kg baseball. Just before impact, the ball is traveling horizontally to the right at 50.0 m/s, and it leaves the bat traveling to the left at an angle of 30° above horizontal with a speed of 65.0 m/s. If the ball and bat are in contact for 1.75 ms, find the horizontal and vertical components of the average force on the ball.

8.13. A 2.00-kg stone is sliding to the right on a frictionless horizontal surface at 5.00 m/s when it is suddenly struck by an object that exerts a large horizontal force on it for a short period of time. The graph in Fig. 8.34 shows the magnitude of this force as a function of time. (a) What impulse does this force exert on the stone? (b) Just after the force stops acting, find the magnitude and direction of the stone's velocity if the force acts (i) to the right or (ii) to the left.

Figure 8.34 Exercise 8.13.

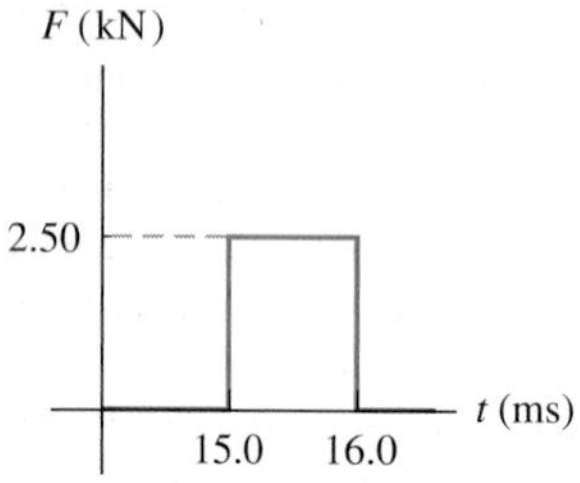

F (kN)
2.50
15.0 16.0
t (ms)

Section 8.2 Conservation of Momentum

8.14. A 68.5-kg astronaut is doing a repair in space on the orbiting space station. She throws a 2.25-kg tool away from her at 3.20 m/s relative to the space station. With what speed and in what direction will she begin to move?

8.15. Animal Propulsion. Squids and octopuses propel themselves by expelling water. They do this by keeping water in a cavity and then suddenly contracting the cavity to force out the water through an opening. A 6.50-kg squid (including the water in the cavity) at rest suddenly sees a dangerous predator. (a) If the squid has 1.75 kg of water in its cavity, at what speed must it expel this water to suddenly achieve a speed of 2.50 m/s to escape the predator? Neglect any drag effects of the surrounding water. (b) How much kinetic energy does the squid create by this maneuver?

8.16. You are standing on a sheet of ice that covers the football stadium parking lot in Buffalo; there is negligible friction between your feet and the ice. A friend throws you a 0.400-kg ball that is traveling horizontally at 10.0 m/s. Your mass is 70.0 kg. (a) If you catch the ball, with what speed do you and the ball move afterward? (b) If the ball hits you and bounces off your chest, so afterward it is moving horizontally at 8.0 m/s in the opposite direction, what is your speed after the collision?

8.17. On a frictionless, horizontal air table, puck A (with mass 0.250 kg) is moving toward puck B (with mass 0.350 kg), which is initially at rest. After the collision, puck A has a velocity of 0.120 m/s to the left, and puck B has a velocity of 0.650 m/s to the right. (a) What was the speed of puck A before the collision? (b) Calculate the change in the total kinetic energy of the system that occurs during the collision.

8.18. When cars are equipped with flexible bumpers, they will bounce off each other during low-speed collisions, thus causing less damage. In one such accident, a 1750-kg car traveling to the right at 1.50 m/s collides with a 1450-kg car going to the left at 1.10 m/s. Measurements show that the heavier car's speed just after the collision was 0.250 m/s in its original direction. You can ignore any road friction during the collision. (a) What was the speed of the lighter car just after the collision? (b) Calculate the change in the combined kinetic energy of the two-car system during this collision.

8.19. The expanding gases that leave the muzzle of a rifle also contribute to the recoil. A .30-caliber bullet has mass 0.00720 kg and a speed of 601 m/s relative to the muzzle when fired from a rifle that has mass 2.80 kg. The loosely held rifle recoils at a speed of 1.85 m/s relative to the earth. Find the momentum of the propellant gases in a coordinate system attached to the earth as they leave the muzzle of the rifle.

8.20. Block A in Fig. 8.35 has mass 1.00 kg, and block B has mass 3.00 kg. The blocks are forced together, compressing a spring S between them; then the system is released from rest on a level, frictionless surface. The spring, which has negligible mass, is not fastened to either block and drops to the surface after it has expanded. Block B acquires a speed of 1.20 m/s. (a) What is the final speed of block A? (b) How much potential energy was stored in the compressed spring?

Figure 8.35 Exercise 8.20.

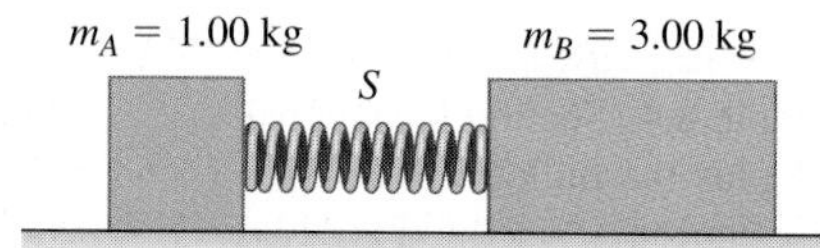

8.21. A hunter on a frozen, essentially frictionless pond uses a rifle that shoots 4.20-g bullets at 965 m/s. The mass of the hunter (including his gun) is 72.5 kg, and the hunter holds tight to the gun after firing it. Find the recoil velocity of the hunter if he fires the rifle (a) horizontally and (b) at 56.0° above the horizontal.

8.22. An atomic nucleus suddenly bursts apart (fissions) into two pieces. Piece A, of mass m_A, travels off to the left with speed v_A. Piece B, of mass m_B, travels off to the right with speed v_B. (a) Use conservation of momentum to solve for v_B in terms of m_A, m_B, and v_A. (b) Use the results of part (a) to show that $K_A/K_B = m_B/m_A$, where K_A and K_B are the kinetic energies of the two pieces.

8.23. The nucleus of ^{214}Po decays radioactively by emitting an alpha particle (mass 6.65×10^{-27} kg) with kinetic energy 1.23×10^{-12} J, as measured in the laboratory reference frame. Assuming that the Po was initially at rest in this frame, find the recoil velocity of the nucleus that remains after the decay.

8.24. You are standing on a large sheet of frictionless ice and holding a large rock. In order to get off the ice, you throw the rock so it has velocity 12.0 m/s relative to the earth at an angle of 35.0° above the horizontal. If your mass is 70.0 kg and the rock's mass is 15.0 kg, what is your speed after you throw the rock (see Discussion Question Q8.7)?

8.25. Two ice skaters, Daniel (mass 65.0 kg) and Rebecca (mass 45.0 kg), are practicing. Daniel stops to tie his shoelace and, while at rest, is struck by Rebecca, who is moving at 13.0 m/s before she collides with him. After the collision, Rebecca has a velocity of magnitude 8.00 m/s at an angle of 53.1° from her initial direction. Both skaters move on the frictionless, horizontal surface of the rink. (a) What are the magnitude and direction of Daniel's velocity after the collision? (b) What is the change in total kinetic energy of the two skaters as a result of the collision?

8.26. An astronaut in space cannot use a scale or balance to weigh objects because there is no gravity. But she does have devices to measure distance and time accurately. She knows her own mass is 78.4 kg, but she is unsure of the mass of a large gas canister in the airless rocket. When this canister is approaching her at 3.50 m/s, she pushes against it, which slows it down to 1.20 m/s (but does not reverse it) and gives her a speed of 2.40 m/s. What is the mass of this canister?

8.27. Changing Mass. An open-topped freight car with mass 24,000 kg is coasting without friction along a level track. It is raining very hard, and the rain is falling vertically downward. Originally, the car is empty and moving with a speed of 4.00 m/s. What is the speed of the car after it has collected 3000 kg of rainwater?

8.28. Asteroid Collision. Two asteroids of equal mass in the asteroid belt between Mars and Jupiter collide with a glancing blow. Asteroid A, which was initially traveling at 40.0 m/s, is deflected 30.0° from its original direction, while asteroid B travels at 45.0° to the original direction of A (Fig. 8.36). (a) Find the speed of each asteroid after the collision. (b) What fraction of the original kinetic energy of asteroid A dissipates during this collision?

Figure 8.36 Exercise 8.28.

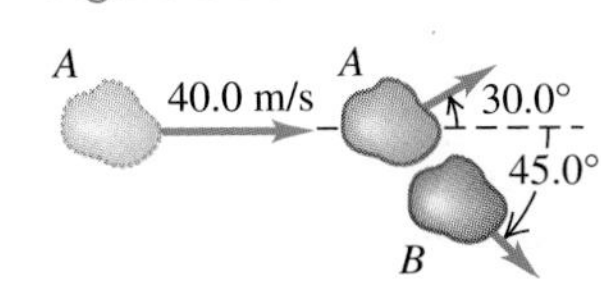

Section 8.3 Momentum Conservation and Collisions

8.29. A 15.0-kg fish swimming at 1.10 m/s suddenly gobbles up a 4.50-kg fish that is initially stationary. Neglect any drag effects of the water. (a) Find the speed of the large fish just after it eats the small one. (b) How much mechanical energy was dissipated during this meal?

8.30. Two fun-loving otters are sliding toward each other on a muddy (and hence frictionless) horizontal surface. One of them, of mass 7.50 kg, is sliding to the left at 5.00 m/s, while the other, of mass 5.75 kg, is slipping to the right at 6.00 m/s. They hold fast to each other after they collide. (a) Find the magnitude and direction of the velocity of these free-spirited otters right after they collide. (b) How much mechanical energy dissipates during this play?

8.31. Deep Impact Mission. In July 2005, NASA's "Deep Impact" mission crashed a 372-kg probe directly onto the surface of the comet Tempel 1, hitting the surface at 37,000 km/h. The original speed of the comet at that time was about 40,000 km/h, and its mass was estimated to be in the range $(0.10\text{–}2.5) \times 10^{14}$ kg. Use the smallest value of the estimated mass. (a) What change in the comet's velocity did this collision produce? Would this change be noticeable? (b) Suppose this comet were to hit the earth and fuse with it. By how much would it change our planet's velocity? Would this change be noticeable? (The mass of the earth is 5.97×10^{24} kg.)

8.32. A 1050-kg sports car is moving westbound at 15.0 m/s on a level road when it collides with a 6320-kg truck driving east on the same road at 10.0 m/s. The two vehicles remain locked together after the collision. (a) What is the velocity (magnitude and direction) of the two vehicles just after the collision? (b) At what speed should the truck have been moving so that it and car are both stopped in the collision? (c) Find the change in kinetic energy of the system of two vehicles for the situations of part (a) and part (b). For which situation is the change in kinetic energy greater in magnitude?

8.33. On a very muddy football field, a 110-kg linebacker tackles an 85-kg halfback. Immediately before the collision, the linebacker is slipping with a velocity of 8.8 m/s north and the halfback is sliding with a velocity of 7.2 m/s east. What is the velocity (magnitude and direction) at which the two players move together immediately after the collision?

8.34. Two skaters collide and grab on to each other on frictionless ice. One of them, of mass 70.0 kg, is moving to the right at 2.00 m/s, while the other, of mass 65.0 kg, is moving to the left at 2.50 m/s. What are the magnitude and direction of the velocity of these skaters just after they collide?

8.35. Two cars, one a compact with mass 1200 kg and the other a large gas-guzzler with mass 3000 kg, collide head-on at typical freeway speeds. (a) Which car has a greater magnitude of momentum change? Which car has a greater velocity change? (b) If the larger car changes its velocity by Δv, calculate the change in the velocity of the small car in terms of Δv. (c) Which car's occupants would you expect to sustain greater injuries? Explain.

8.36. Bird Defense. To protect their young in the nest, peregrine falcons will fly into birds of prey (such as ravens) at high speed. In one such episode, a 600-g falcon flying at 20.0 m/s hit a 1.50-kg raven flying at 9.0 m/s. The falcon hit the raven at right angles to its original path and bounced back at 5.0 m/s. (These figures were estimated by the author as he watched this attack occur in northern New Mexico.) (a) By what angle did the falcon change the raven's direction of motion? (b) What was the raven's speed right after the collision?

8.37. At the intersection of Texas Avenue and University Drive, a yellow subcompact car with mass 950 kg traveling east on University collides with a red pickup truck with mass 1900 kg that is traveling north on Texas and ran a red light (Fig. 8.37). The two vehicles stick together as a result of the collision, and the wreckage slides at 16.0 m/s in the direction 24.0° east of north. Calculate the

Figure 8.37 Exercise 8.37.

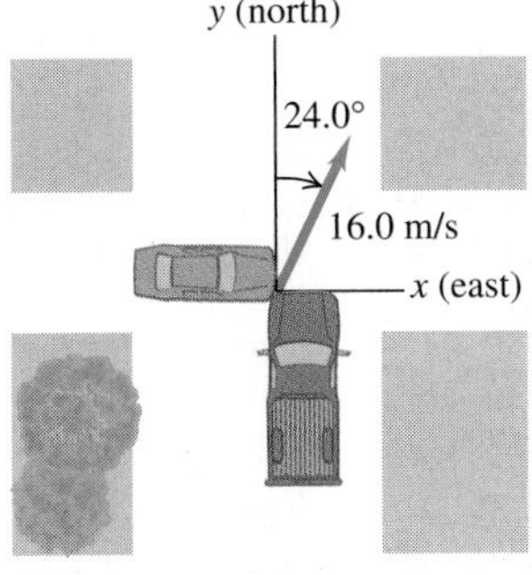

speed of each vehicle before the collision. The collision occurs during a heavy rainstorm; you can ignore friction forces between the vehicles and the wet road.

8.38. A 5.00-g bullet is fired horizontally into a 1.20-kg wooden block resting on a horizontal surface. The coefficient of kinetic friction between block and surface is 0.20. The bullet remains embedded in the block, which is observed to slide 0.230 m along the surface before stopping. What was the initial speed of the bullet?

8.39. A Ballistic Pendulum. A 12.0-g rifle bullet is fired with a speed of 380 m/s into a ballistic pendulum with mass 6.00 kg, suspended from a cord 70.0 cm long (see Example 8.8 in Section 8.3). Compute (a) the vertical height through which the pendulum rises, (b) the initial kinetic energy of the bullet, and (c) the kinetic energy of the bullet and pendulum immediately after the bullet becomes embedded in the pendulum.

8.40. You and your friends are doing physics experiments on a frozen pond that serves as a frictionless, horizontal surface. Sam, with mass 80.0 kg, is given a push and slides eastward. Abigail, with mass 50.0 kg, is sent sliding northward. They collide, and after the collision Sam is moving at 37.0° north of east with a speed of 6.00 m/s and Abigail is moving at 23.0° south of east with a speed of 9.00 m/s. (a) What was the speed of each person before the collision? (b) By how much did the total kinetic energy of the two people decrease during the collision?

Section 8.4 Elastic Collisions

8.41. Blocks A (mass 2.00 kg) and B (mass 10.00 kg) move on a frictionless, horizontal surface. Initially, block B is at rest and block A is moving toward it at 2.00 m/s. The blocks are equipped with ideal spring bumpers, as in Example 8.10. The collision is head-on, so all motion before and after the collision is along a straight line. (a) Find the maximum energy stored in the spring bumpers and the velocity of each block at that time. (b) Find the velocity of each block after they have moved apart.

8.42. A 0.150-kg glider is moving to the right on a frictionless, horizontal air track with a speed of 0.80 m/s. It has a head-on collision with a 0.300-kg glider that is moving to the left with a speed of 2.20 m/s. Find the final velocity (magnitude and direction) of each glider if the collision is elastic.

8.43. A 10.0-g marble slides to the left with a velocity of magnitude 0.400 m/s on the frictionless, horizontal surface of an icy New York sidewalk and has a head-on, elastic collision with a larger 30.0-g marble sliding to the right with a velocity of magnitude 0.200 m/s (Fig. 8.38). (a) Find the velocity of each marble (magnitude and direction) after the collision. (Since the collision is head-on, all the motion is along a line.) (b) Calculate the *change in momentum* (that is, the momentum after the collision minus the momentum before the collision) for each marble. Compare the values you get for each marble. (c) Calculate the *change in kinetic energy* (that is, the kinetic energy after the collision minus the kinetic energy before the collision) for each marble. Compare the values you get for each marble.

Figure 8.38 Exercise 8.43.

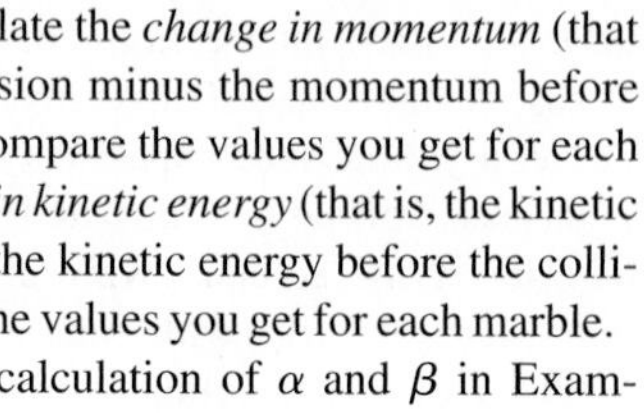

8.44. Supply the details of the calculation of α and β in Example 8.12 (Section 8.4).

8.45. Moderators. Canadian nuclear reactors use *heavy water* moderators in which elastic collisions occur between the neutrons and deuterons of mass 2.0 u (see Example 8.11 in Section 8.4). (a) What is the speed of a neutron, expressed as a fraction of its original speed, after a head-on, elastic collision with a deuteron that is initially at rest? (b) What is its kinetic energy, expressed as a fraction of its original kinetic energy? (c) How many such successive collisions will reduce the speed of a neutron to 1/59,000 of its original value?

8.46. You are at the controls of a particle accelerator, sending a beam of 1.50×10^7 m/s protons (mass m) at a gas target of an unknown element. Your detector tells you that some protons bounce straight back after a collision with one of the nuclei of the unknown element. All such protons rebound with a speed of 1.20×10^7 m/s. Assume that the initial speed of the target nucleus is negligible and the collision is elastic. (a) Find the mass of one nucleus of the unknown element. Express your answer in terms of the proton mass m. (b) What is the speed of the unknown nucleus immediately after such a collision?

Section 8.5 Center of Mass

8.47. Three odd-shaped blocks of chocolate have the following masses and center-of-mass coordinates: (1) 0.300 kg, (0.200 m, 0.300 m); (2) 0.400 kg, (0.100 m, −0.400 m); (3) 0.200 kg, (−0.300 m, 0.600 m). Find the coordinates of the center of mass of the system of three chocolate blocks.

8.48. Find the position of the center of mass of the system of the sun and Jupiter. (Since Jupiter is more massive than the rest of the planets combined, this is essentially the position of the center of mass of the solar system.) Does the center of mass lie inside or outside the sun? Use the data in Appendix F.

8.49. Pluto and Charon. Pluto's diameter is approximately 2370 km, and the diameter of its satellite Charon is 1250 km. Although the distance varies, they are often about 19,700 km apart, center-to-center. Assuming that both Pluto and Charon have the same composition and hence the same average density, find the location of the center of mass of this system relative to the center of Pluto.

8.50. A 1200-kg station wagon is moving along a straight highway at 12.0 m/s. Another car, with mass 1800 kg and speed 20.0 m/s, has its center of mass 40.0 m ahead of the center of mass of the station wagon (Fig. 8.39). (a) Find the position of the center of mass of the system consisting of the two automobiles. (b) Find the magnitude of the total momentum of the system from the given data. (c) Find the speed of the center of mass of the system. (d) Find the total momentum of the system, using the speed of the center of mass. Compare your result with that of part (b).

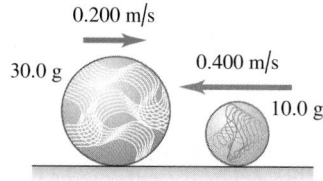

Figure 8.39 Exercise 8.50.

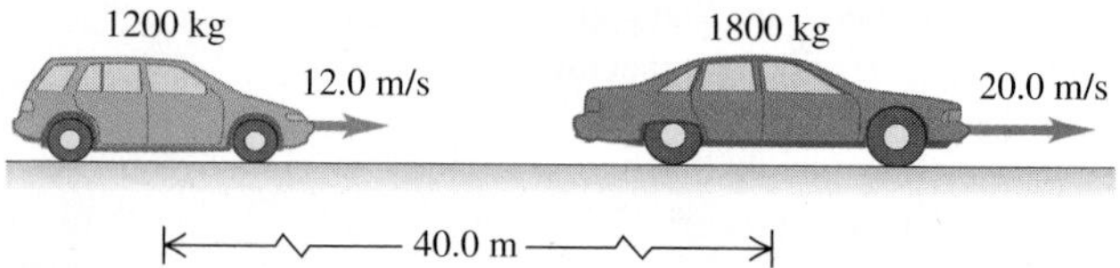

8.51. A machine part consists of a thin, uniform 4.00-kg bar that is 1.50 m long, hinged perpendicular to a similar vertical bar of mass 3.00 kg and length 1.80 m. The longer bar has a small but dense 2.00-kg ball at one end (Fig. 8.40). By what distance will the center of mass of this part move horizontally and vertically if the vertical bar is pivoted counterclockwise through 90° to make the entire part horizontal?

Figure 8.40 Exercise 8.51.

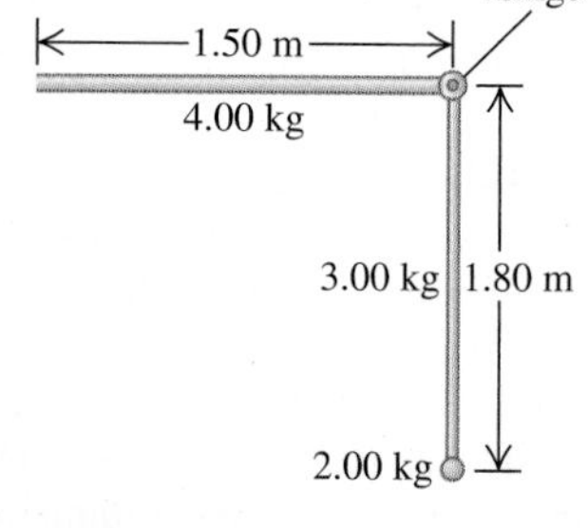

8.52. At one instant, the center of mass of a system of two particles is located on the x-axis at $x = 2.0$ m and has a velocity of $(5.0 \text{ m/s})\hat{\imath}$. One of the particles is at the origin. The other particle has a mass of 0.10 kg and is at rest on the x-axis at $x = 8.0$ m. (a) What is the mass of the particle at the origin? (b) Calculate the total momentum of this system. (c) What is the velocity of the particle at the origin?

8.53. In Example 8.14 (Section 8.5), Ramon pulls on the rope to give himself a speed of 0.70 m/s. What is James's speed?

8.54. A system consists of two particles. At $t = 0$ one particle is at the origin; the other, which has a mass of 0.50 kg, is on the y-axis at $y = 6.0$ m. At $t = 0$ the center of mass of the system is on the y-axis at $y = 2.4$ m. The velocity of the center of mass is given by $(0.75 \text{ m/s}^3)t^2\hat{\imath}$. (a) Find the total mass of the system. (b) Find the acceleration of the center of mass at any time t. (c) Find the net external force acting on the system at $t = 3.0$ s.

8.55. A radio-controlled model airplane has a momentum given by $[(-0.75 \text{ kg} \cdot \text{m/s}^3)t^2 + (3.0 \text{ kg} \cdot \text{m/s})]\hat{\imath} + (0.25 \text{ kg} \cdot \text{m/s}^2)t\hat{\jmath}$. What are the x-, y-, and z-components of the net force on the airplane?

*Section 8.6 Rocket Propulsion

***8.56.** A small rocket burns 0.0500 kg of fuel per second, ejecting it as a gas with a velocity relative to the rocket of magnitude 1600 m/s. (a) What is the thrust of the rocket? (b) Would the rocket operate in outer space where there is no atmosphere? If so, how would you steer it? Could you brake it?

***8.57.** A 70-kg astronaut floating in space in a 110-kg MMU (manned maneuvering unit) experiences an acceleration of 0.029 m/s^2 when he fires one of the MMU's thrusters. (a) If the speed of the escaping N_2 gas relative to the astronaut is 490 m/s, how much gas is used by the thruster in 5.0 s? (b) What is the thrust of the thruster?

***8.58.** A rocket is fired in deep space, where gravity is negligible. If the rocket has an initial mass of 6000 kg and ejects gas at a relative velocity of magnitude 2000 m/s, how much gas must it eject in the first second to have an initial acceleration of 25.0 m/s^2?

***8.59.** A rocket is fired in deep space, where gravity is negligible. In the first second it ejects $\frac{1}{160}$ of its mass as exhaust gas and has an acceleration of 15.0 m/s^2. What is the speed of the exhaust gas relative to the rocket?

***8.60.** A C6-5 model rocket engine has an impulse of 10.0 N · s for 1.70 s, while burning 0.0125 kg of propellant. It has a maximum thrust of 13.3 N. The initial mass of the engine plus propellant is 0.0258 kg. (a) What fraction of the maximum thrust is the average thrust? (b) Calculate the relative speed of the exhaust gases, assuming it is constant. (c) Assuming that the relative speed of the exhaust gases is constant, find the final speed of the engine if it was attached to a very light frame and fired from rest in gravity-free outer space.

***8.61.** A single-stage rocket is fired from rest from a deep-space platform, where gravity is negligible. If the rocket burns its fuel in 50.0 s and the relative speed of the exhaust gas is $v_{ex} = 2100$ m/s, what must the mass ratio m_0/m be for a final speed v of 8.00 km/s (about equal to the orbital speed of an earth satellite)?

***8.62.** Obviously, we can make rockets to go very fast, but what is a reasonable top speed? Assume that a rocket is fired from rest at a space station in deep space, where gravity is negligible. (a) If the rocket ejects gas at a relative speed of 2000 m/s and you want the rocket's speed eventually to be $1.00 \times 10^{-3}c$, where c is the speed of light, what fraction of the initial mass of the rocket and fuel is *not* fuel? (b) What is this fraction if the final speed is to be 3000 m/s?

Problems

8.63. A steel ball with mass 40.0 g is dropped from a height of 2.00 m onto a horizontal steel slab. The ball rebounds to a height of 1.60 m. (a) Calculate the impulse delivered to the ball during impact. (b) If the ball is in contact with the slab for 2.00 ms, find the average force on the ball during impact.

8.64. In a volcanic eruption, a 2400-kg boulder is thrown vertically upward into the air. At its highest point, it suddenly explodes (due to trapped gases) into two fragments, one being three times the mass of the other. The lighter fragment starts out with only horizontal velocity and lands 274 m directly north of the point of the explosion. Where will the other fragment land? Neglect any air resistance.

8.65. Just before it is struck by a racket, a tennis ball weighing 0.560 N has a velocity of $(20.0 \text{ m/s})\hat{\imath} - (4.0 \text{ m/s})\hat{\jmath}$. During the 3.00 ms that the racket and ball are in contact, the net force on the ball is constant and equal to $-(380 \text{ N})\hat{\imath} + (110 \text{ N})\hat{\jmath}$. (a) What are the x- and y-components of the impulse of the net force applied to the ball? (b) What are the x- and y-components of the final velocity of the ball?

8.66. Three coupled railroad cars roll along and couple with a fourth car, which is initially at rest. These four cars roll along and couple with a fifth car initially at rest. This process continues until the speed of the final collection of railroad cars is one-fifth the speed of the initial three railroad cars. All the cars are identical. Ignoring friction, how many cars are in the final collection?

8.67. A 1500-kg blue convertible is traveling south, and a 2000-kg red SUV is traveling west. If the total momentum of the system consisting of the two cars is 8000 kg · m/s directed at 60.0° west of south, what is the speed of each vehicle?

8.68. Three identical pucks on a horizontal air table have repelling magnets. They are held together and then released simultaneously. Each has the same speed at any instant. One puck moves due west. What is the direction of the velocity of each of the other two pucks?

8.69. Spheres A (mass 0.020 kg), B (mass 0.030 kg), and C (mass 0.050 kg) are approaching the origin as they slide on a frictionless air table (Fig. 8.41). The initial velocities of A and B are given in the figure. All three spheres arrive at the origin at the same time and stick together. (a) What must the x- and y-components of the initial velocity of C be if all three objects are to end up moving at 0.50 m/s in the $+x$-direction after the collision? (b) If C has the velocity found in part (a), what is the change in the kinetic energy of the system of three spheres as a result of the collision?

Figure **8.41** Problem 8.69.

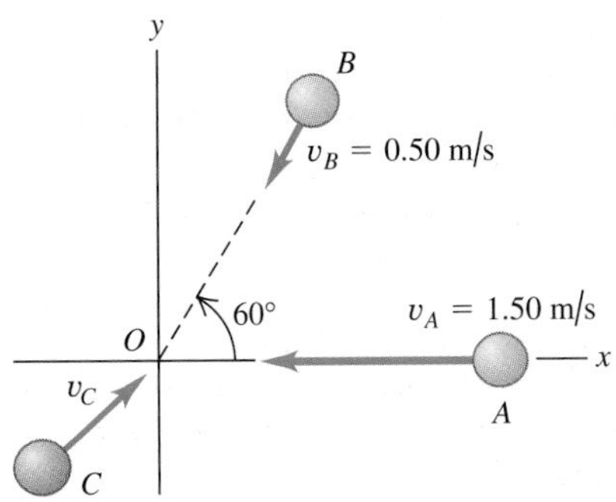

8.70. A railroad handcar is moving along straight, frictionless tracks with negligible air resistance. In the following cases, the car initially has a total mass (car and contents) of 200 kg and is traveling east with a velocity of magnitude 5.00 m/s. Find the *final*

velocity of the car in each case, assuming that the handcar does not leave the tracks. (a) A 25.0-kg mass is thrown sideways out of the car with a velocity of magnitude 2.00 m/s relative to the car's initial velocity. (b) A 25.0-kg mass is thrown backward out of the car with a velocity of 5.00 m/s relative to the initial motion of the car. (c) A 25.0-kg mass is thrown into the car with a velocity of 6.00 m/s relative to the ground and opposite in direction to the initial velocity of the car.

8.71. Changing Mass. A railroad hopper car filled with sand is rolling with an initial speed of 15.0 m/s on straight, horizontal tracks. You can ignore frictional forces on the railroad car. The total mass of the car plus sand is 85,000 kg. The hopper door is not fully closed so sand leaks out the bottom. After 20 min, 13,000 kg of sand has leaked out. Then what is the speed of the railroad car? (Compare your analysis with that used to solve Exercise 8.27.)

8.72. At a classic auto show, a 840-kg 1955 Nash Metropolitan motors by at 9.0 m/s, followed by a 1620-kg 1957 Packard Clipper purring past at 5.0 m/s. (a) Which car has the greater kinetic energy? What is the ratio of the kinetic energy of the Nash to that of the Packard? (b) Which car has the greater magnitude of momentum? What is the ratio of the magnitude of momentum of the Nash to that of the Packard? (c) Let F_N be the net force required to stop the Nash in time t, and let F_P be the net force required to stop the Packard in the same time. Which is larger: F_N or F_P? What is the ratio F_N/F_P of these two forces? (d) Now let F_N be the net force required to stop the Nash in a distance d, and let F_P be the net force required to stop the Packard in the same distance. Which is larger: F_N or F_P? What is the ratio F_N/F_P?

8.73. A soldier on a firing range fires an eight-shot burst from an assault weapon at a full automatic rate of 1000 rounds per minute. Each bullet has a mass of 7.45 g and a speed of 293 m/s relative to the ground as it leaves the barrel of the weapon. Calculate the average recoil force exerted on the weapon during that burst.

8.74. A 0.150-kg frame, when suspended from a coil spring, stretches the spring 0.050 m. A 0.200-kg lump of putty is dropped from rest onto the frame from a height of 30.0 cm (Fig. 8.42). Find the maximum distance the frame moves downward from its initial position.

Figure 8.42 Problem 8.74.

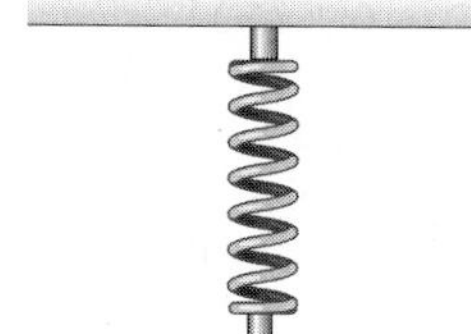

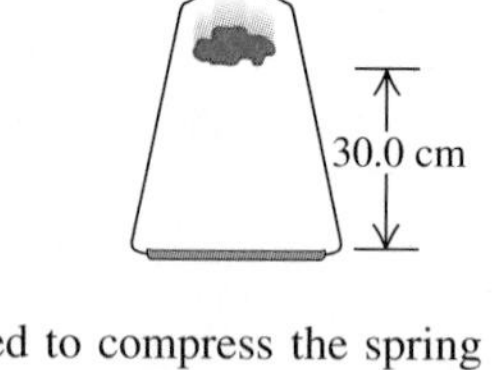

8.75. A rifle bullet with mass 8.00 g strikes and embeds itself in a block with mass 0.992 kg that rests on a frictionless, horizontal surface and is attached to a coil spring (Fig. 8.43). The impact compresses the spring 15.0 cm. Calibration of the spring shows that a force of 0.750 N is required to compress the spring 0.250 cm. (a) Find the magnitude of the block's velocity just after impact. (b) What was the initial speed of the bullet?

Figure 8.43 Problem 8.75.

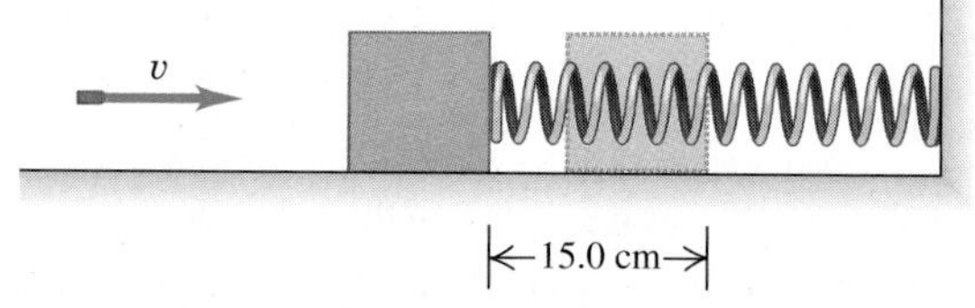

8.76. A Ricocheting Bullet. 0.100-kg stone rests on a frictionless, horizontal surface. A bullet of mass 6.00 g, traveling horizontally at 350 m/s, strikes the stone and rebounds horizontally at right angles to its original direction with a speed of 250 m/s. (a) Compute the magnitude and direction of the velocity of the stone after it is struck. (b) Is the collision perfectly elastic?

8.77. A movie stuntman (mass 80.0 kg) stands on a window ledge 5.0 m above the floor (Fig. 8.44). Grabbing a rope attached to a chandelier, he swings down to grapple with the movie's villain (mass 70.0 kg), who is standing directly under the chandelier. (Assume that the stuntman's center of mass moves downward 5.0 m. He releases the rope just as he reaches the villain.) (a) With what speed do the entwined foes start to slide across the floor? (b) If the coefficient of kinetic friction of their bodies with the floor is $\mu_k = 0.250$, how far do they slide?

Figure 8.44 Problem 8.77.

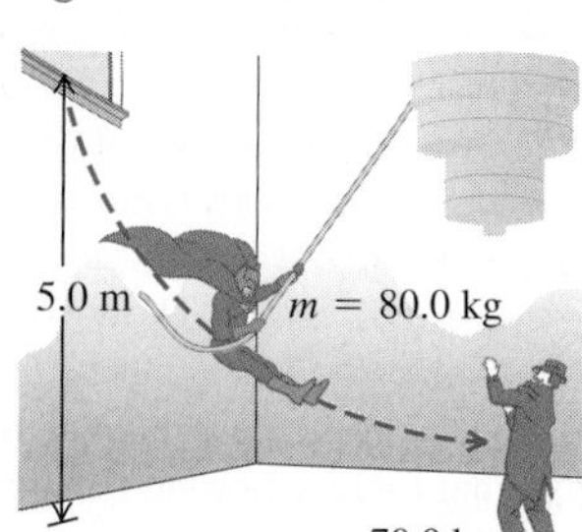

8.78. Two identical masses are released from rest in a smooth hemispherical bowl of radius R, from the positions shown in Fig. 8.45. You can ignore friction between the masses and the surface of the bowl. If they stick together when they collide, how high above the bottom of the bowl will the masses go after colliding?

Figure 8.45 Problem 8.78.

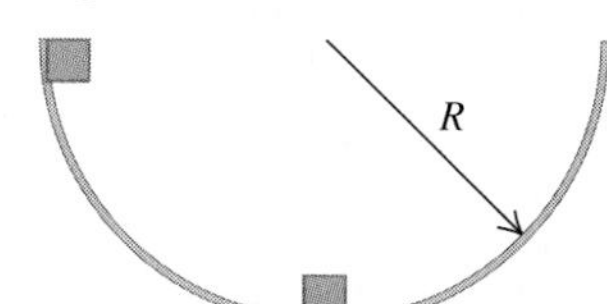

8.79. A ball with mass M, moving horizontally at 5.00 m/s, collides elastically with a block with mass $3M$ that is initially hanging at rest from the ceiling on the end of a 50.0-cm wire. Find the maximum angle through which the block swings after it is hit.

8.80. A 20.00-kg lead sphere is hanging from a hook by a thin wire 3.50 m long, and is free to swing in a complete circle. Suddenly it is struck horizontally by a 5.00-kg steel dart that embeds itself in the lead sphere. What must be the minimum initial speed of the dart so that the combination makes a complete circular loop after the collision?

8.81. An 8.00-kg ball, hanging from the ceiling by a light wire 135 cm long, is struck in an elastic collision by a 2.00-kg ball moving horizontally at 5.00 m/s just before the collision. Find the tension in the wire just after the collision.

8.82. A rubber ball of mass m is released from rest at height h above the floor. After its first bounce, it rises to 90% of its original height. What impulse (magnitude and direction) does the floor exert on this ball during its first bounce? Express your answer in terms of the variables m and h.

8.83. A 4.00-g bullet, traveling horizontally with a velocity of magnitude 400 m/s, is fired into a wooden block with mass 0.800 kg, initially at rest on a level surface. The bullet passes through the block and emerges with its speed reduced to 120 m/s. The block slides a distance of 45.0 cm along the surface from its initial position. (a) What is the coefficient of kinetic friction between block and surface? (b) What is the decrease in kinetic energy of the bullet? (c) What is the kinetic energy of the block at the instant after the bullet passes through it?

8.84. A 5.00-g bullet is shot *through* a 1.00-kg wood block suspended on a string 2.00 m long. The center of mass of the block rises a distance of 0.45 cm. Find the speed of the bullet as it emerges from the block if its initial speed is 450 m/s.

8.85. A neutron with mass m makes a head-on, elastic collision with a nucleus of mass M, which is initially at rest. (a) Show that if the neutron's initial kinetic energy is K_0, the kinetic energy that it loses during the collision is $4mMK_0/(M + m)^2$. (b) For what value of M does the incident neutron lose the most energy? (c) When M has the value calculated in part (b), what is the speed of the neutron after the collision?

8.86. Energy Sharing in Elastic Collisions. A stationary object with mass m_B is struck head-on by an object with mass m_A that is moving initially at speed v_0. (a) If the collision is elastic, what percentage of the original energy does each object have after the collision? (b) What does your answer in part (a) give for the special cases (i) $m_A = m_B$ and (ii) $m_A = 5m_B$? (c) For what values, if any, of the mass ratio m_A/m_B is the original kinetic energy shared equally by the two objects after the collision?

8.87. In a shipping company distribution center, an open cart of mass 50.0 kg is rolling to the left at a speed of 5.00 m/s (Fig. 8.46). You can ignore friction between the cart and the floor. A 15.0-kg package slides down a chute that is inclined at 37° from the horizontal and leaves the end of the chute with a speed of 3.00 m/s. The package lands in the cart and they roll off together. If the lower end of the chute is a vertical distance of 4.00 m above the bottom of the cart, what are (a) the speed of the package just before it lands in the cart and (b) the final speed of the cart?

Figure 8.46 Problem 8.87.

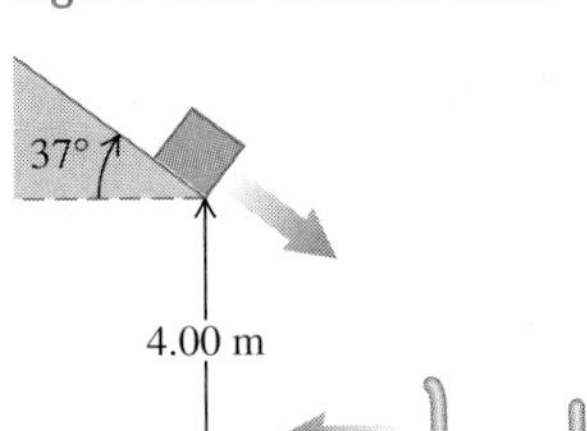

8.88. A blue puck with mass 0.0400 kg, sliding with a velocity of magnitude 0.200 m/s on a frictionless, horizontal air table, makes a perfectly elastic, head-on collision with a red puck with mass m, initially at rest. After the collision, the velocity of the blue puck is 0.050 m/s in the same direction as its initial velocity. Find (a) the velocity (magnitude and direction) of the red puck after the collision; and (b) the mass m of the red puck.

8.89. Two asteroids with masses m_A and m_B are moving with velocities $\vec{v}_A$ and $\vec{v}_B$ with respect to an astronomer in a space vehicle. (a) Show that the total kinetic energy as measured by the astronomer is

$$K = \tfrac{1}{2}Mv_{cm}^2 + \tfrac{1}{2}(m_A v_A'^2 + m_B v_B'^2)$$

with $\vec{v}_{cm}$ and M defined as in Section 8.5, $\vec{v}_A' = \vec{v}_A - \vec{v}_{cm}$, and $\vec{v}_B' = \vec{v}_B - \vec{v}_{cm}$. In this expression the total kinetic energy of the two asteroids is the energy associated with their center of mass plus the energy associated with the internal motion relative to the center of mass. (b) If the asteroids collide, what is the *minimum* possible kinetic energy they can have after the collision, as measured by the astronomer? Explain.

8.90. Suppose you hold a small ball in contact with, and directly over, the center of a large ball. If you then drop the small ball a short time after dropping the large ball, the small ball rebounds with surprising speed. To show the extreme case, ignore air resistance and suppose the large ball makes an elastic collision with the floor and then rebounds to make an elastic collision with the still-descending small ball. Just before the collision between the two balls, the large ball is moving upward with velocity $\vec{v}$ and the small ball has velocity $-\vec{v}$. (Do you see why?) Assume the large ball has a much greater mass than the small ball. (a) What is the velocity of the small ball immediately after its collision with the large ball? (b) From the answer to part (a), what is the ratio of the small ball's rebound distance to the distance it fell before the collision?

8.91. Jack and Jill are standing on a crate at rest on the frictionless, horizontal surface of a frozen pond. Jack has mass 75.0 kg, Jill has mass 45.0 kg, and the crate has mass 15.0 kg. They remember that they must fetch a pail of water, so each jumps horizontally from the top of the crate. Just after each jumps, that person is moving away from the crate with a speed of 4.00 m/s relative to the crate. (a) What is the final speed of the crate if both Jack and Jill jump simultaneously and in the same direction? (*Hint:* Use an inertial coordinate system attached to the ground.) (b) What is the final speed of the crate if Jack jumps first and then a few seconds later Jill jumps in the same direction? (c) What is the final speed of the crate if Jill jumps first and then Jack, again in the same direction?

8.92. Energy Sharing. An object with mass m, initially at rest, explodes into two fragments, one with mass m_A and the other with mass m_B, where $m_A + m_B = m$. (a) If energy Q is released in the explosion, how much kinetic energy does each fragment have immediately after the collision? (b) What percentage of the total energy released does each fragment get when one fragment has four times the mass of the other?

8.93. Neutron Decay. A neutron at rest decays (breaks up) to a proton and an electron. Energy is released in the decay and appears as kinetic energy of the proton and electron. The mass of a proton is 1836 times the mass of an electron. What fraction of the total energy released goes into the kinetic energy of the proton?

8.94. A ^{232}Th (thorium) nucleus at rest decays to a ^{228}Ra (radium) nucleus with the emission of an alpha particle. The total kinetic energy of the decay fragments is 6.54×10^{-13} J. An alpha particle has 1.76% of the mass of a ^{228}Ra nucleus. Calculate the kinetic energy of (a) the recoiling ^{228}Ra nucleus and (b) the alpha particle.

8.95. Antineutrino. In beta decay, a nucleus emits an electron. A ^{210}Bi (bismuth) nucleus at rest undergoes beta decay to ^{210}Po (polonium). Suppose the emitted electron moves to the right with a momentum of 5.60×10^{-22} kg · m/s. The ^{210}Po nucleus, with mass 3.50×10^{-25} kg, recoils to the left at a speed of 1.14×10^{-3} m/s. Momentum conservation requires that a second particle, called an antineutrino, must also be emitted. Calculate the magnitude and direction of the momentum of the antineutrino that is emitted in this decay.

8.96. A proton moving with speed v_{A1} in the $+x$-direction makes an elastic, off-center collision with an identical proton originally at rest. After impact, the first proton moves with speed v_{A2} in the first quadrant at an angle α with the x-axis, and the second moves with speed v_{B2} in the fourth quadrant at an angle β with the x-axis (Fig. 8.13). (a) Write the equations expressing conservation of linear momentum in the x- and y-directions. (b) Square the equations from part (a) and add them. (c) Now introduce the fact that the collision is elastic. (d) Prove that $\alpha + \beta = \pi/2$. (You have shown that this equation is obeyed in any elastic, off-center collision between objects of equal mass when one object is initially at rest.)

8.97. Hockey puck B rests on a smooth ice surface and is struck by a second puck A, which has the same mass. Puck A is initially traveling at 15.0 m/s and is deflected 25.0° from its initial direction. Assume that the collision is perfectly elastic. Find the final speed of each puck and the direction of B's velocity after the collision. [*Hint:* Use the relationship derived in part (d) of Problem 8.96.]

8.98. Jonathan and Jane are sitting in a sleigh that is at rest on frictionless ice. Jonathan's weight is 800 N, Jane's weight is 600 N, and that of the sleigh is 1000 N. They see a poisonous spider on the floor of the sleigh and immediately jump off. Jonathan jumps to the left with a velocity of 5.00 m/s at 30.0° above the horizontal (relative to the ice), and Jane jumps to the right at 7.00 m/s at 36.9° above the horizontal (relative to the ice). Calculate the sleigh's horizontal velocity (magnitude and direction) after they jump out.

8.99. The objects in Fig. 8.47 are constructed of uniform wire bent into the shapes shown. Find the position of the center of mass of each.

Figure **8.47** Problem 8.99.

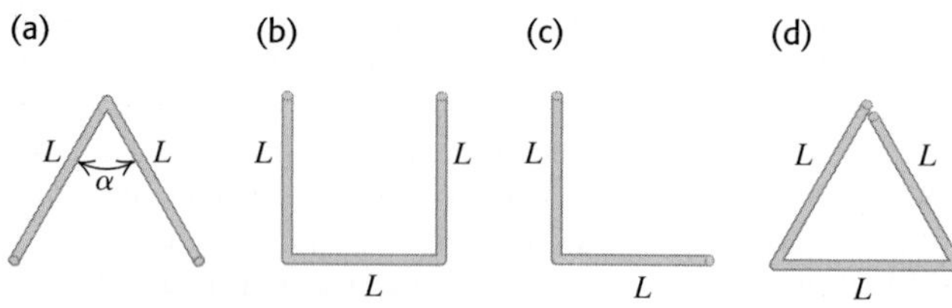

8.100. A 45.0-kg woman stands up in a 60.0-kg canoe 5.00 m long. She walks from a point 1.00 m from one end to a point 1.00 m from the other end (Fig. 8.48). If you ignore resistance to motion of the canoe in the water, how far does the canoe move during this process?

Figure **8.48** Problem 8.100.

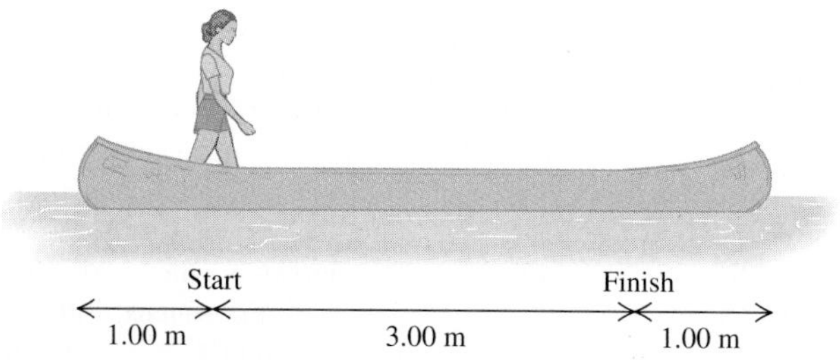

8.101. You are standing on a concrete slab that in turn is resting on a frozen lake. Assume there is no friction between the slab and the ice. The slab has a weight five times your weight. If you begin walking forward at 2.00 m/s relative to the ice, with what speed, relative to the ice, does the slab move?

8.102. A 20.0-kg projectile is fired at an angle of 60.0° above the horizontal with a speed of 80.0 m/s. At the highest point of its trajectory, the projectile explodes into two fragments with equal mass, one of which falls vertically with zero initial speed. You can ignore air resistance. (a) How far from the point of firing does the other fragment strike if the terrain is level? (b) How much energy is released during the explosion?

8.103. A fireworks rocket is fired vertically upward. At its maximum height of 80.0 m, it explodes and breaks into two pieces, one with mass 1.40 kg and the other with mass 0.28 kg. In the explosion, 860 J of chemical energy is converted to kinetic energy of the two fragments. (a) What is the speed of each fragment just after the explosion? (b) It is observed that the two fragments hit the ground at the same time. What is the distance between the points on the ground where they land? Assume that the ground is level and air resistance can be ignored.

8.104. A 12.0-kg shell is launched at an angle of 55.0° above the horizontal with an initial speed of 150 m/s. When it is at its highest point, the shell exploded into two fragments, one three times heavier than the other. The two fragments reach the ground at the same time. Assume that air resistance can be ignored. If the heavier fragment lands back at the same point from which the shell was launched, where will the lighter fragment land and how much energy was released in the explosion?

8.105. A Nuclear Reaction. Fission, the process that supplies energy in nuclear power plants, occurs when a heavy nucleus is split into two medium-sized nuclei. One such reaction occurs when a neutron colliding with a ^{235}U (uranium) nucleus splits that nucleus into a ^{141}Ba (barium) nucleus and a ^{92}Kr (krypton) nucleus. In this reaction, two neutrons also are split off from the original ^{235}U. Before the collision, the arrangement is as shown in Fig. 8.49a. After the collision, the ^{141}Ba nucleus is moving in the $+z$-direction and the ^{92}Kr nucleus in the $-z$-direction. The three neutrons are moving in the xy-plane, as shown in Fig. 8.49b. If the incoming neutron has an initial velocity of magnitude 3.0×10^3 m/s and a final velocity of magnitude 2.0×10^3 m/s in the directions shown, what are the speeds of the other two neutrons, and what can you say about the speeds of the ^{141}Ba and ^{92}Kr nuclei? (The mass of the ^{141}Ba nucleus is approximately 2.3×10^{-25} kg, and the mass of ^{92}Kr is about 1.5×10^{-25} kg.)

Figure **8.49** Problem 8.105.

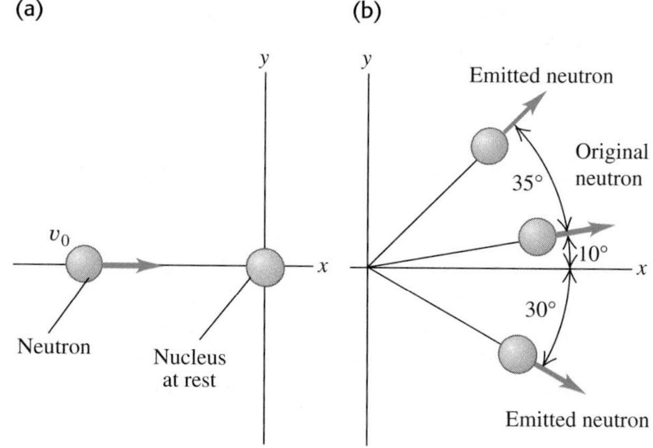

8.106. Center-of-Mass Coordinate System. Puck A (mass m_A) is moving on a frictionless, horizontal air table in the $+x$-direction with velocity $\vec{v}_{A1}$ and makes an elastic, head-on collision with puck B (mass m_B), which is initially at rest. After the collision, both pucks are moving along the x-axis. (a) Calculate the velocity of the center of mass of the two-puck system before the collision. (b) Consider a coordinate system whose origin is at the center of mass and moves with it. Is this an inertial reference frame? (c) What are the initial velocities $\vec{u}_{A1}$ and $\vec{u}_{B1}$ of the two pucks in this center-of-mass reference frame? What is the total momentum in this frame? (d) Use conservation of momentum and energy, applied in the center-of-mass reference frame, to relate the final momentum of each puck to its initial momentum and thus the final velocity of each puck to its initial velocity. Your results should show that a one-dimensional, elastic collision has a very simple description in center-of-mass coordinates. (e) Let $m_A = 0.400$ kg, $m_B = 0.200$ kg, and $v_{A1} = 6.00$ m/s. Find the center-of-mass velocities $\vec{u}_{A1}$ and $\vec{u}_{B1}$, apply the simple result found in part (d), and transform back to velocities in a stationary frame to find the final velocities of the pucks. Does your result agree with Eqs. (8.24) and (8.25)?

8.107. The *coefficient of restitution* ϵ for a head-on collision is defined as the ratio of the relative speed after the collision to the relative speed before. (a) What is ϵ for a completely inelastic collision? (b) What is ϵ for an elastic collision? (c) A ball is dropped from a height h onto a stationary surface and rebounds back to a height H_1. Show that $\epsilon = \sqrt{H_1/h}$. (d) A properly inflated basketball should have a coefficient of restitution of 0.85. When dropped from a height of 1.2 m above a solid wood floor, to what height should a properly inflated basketball bounce? (e) The height of the first bounce is H_1. If ϵ is constant, show that the height of the nth bounce is $H_n = \epsilon^{2n}h$. (f) If ϵ is constant, what is the height of the eighth bounce of a properly inflated basketball dropped from 1.2 m?

8.108. Binding Energy of the Hydrogen Molecule. When two hydrogen atoms of mass m combine to form a diatomic hydrogen molecule (H_2), the potential energy of the system after they combine is $-\Delta$, where Δ is a positive quantity called the *binding energy* of the molecule. (a) Show that in a collision that involves only two hydrogen atoms, it is *impossible* to form an H_2 molecule because momentum and energy cannot simultaneously be conserved. (*Hint:* If you can show this to be true in one frame of reference, then it is true in all frames of reference. Can you see why?) (b) An H_2 molecule can be formed in a collision that involves *three* hydrogen atoms. Suppose that before such a collision, each of the three atoms has speed 1.00×10^3 m/s, and they are approaching at 120° angles so that at any instant, the atoms lie at the corners of an equilateral triangle. Find the speeds of the H_2 molecule and of the single hydrogen atom that remains after the collision. The binding energy of H_2 is $\Delta = 7.23 \times 10^{-19}$ J, and the mass of the hydrogen atom is 1.67×10^{-27} kg.

8.109. A wagon with two boxes of gold, having total mass 300 kg, is cut loose from the horses by an outlaw when the wagon is at rest 50 m up a 6.0° slope (Fig. 8.50). The outlaw plans to have the wagon roll down the slope and across the level ground, and then fall into a canyon where his confederates wait. But in a tree 40 m from the canyon edge wait the Lone Ranger (mass 75.0 kg) and Tonto (mass 60.0 kg). They drop vertically into the wagon as it passes beneath them. (a) If they require 5.0 s to grab the gold and jump out, will they make it before the wagon goes over the edge? The wagon rolls with negligible friction. (b) When the two heroes drop into the wagon, is the kinetic energy of the system of the heroes plus the wagon conserved? If not, does it increase or decrease, and by how much?

Figure 8.50 Problem 8.109.

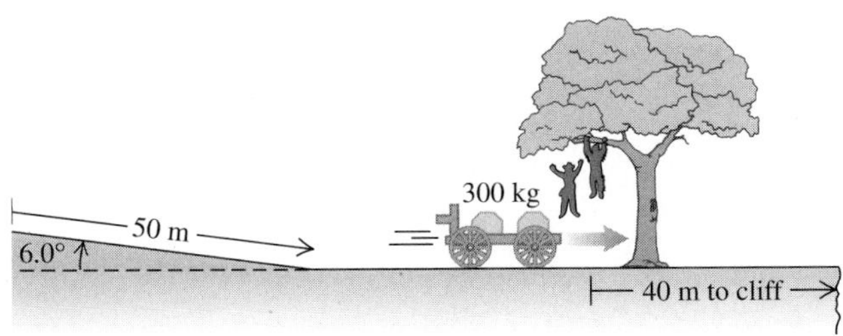

***8.110.** In Section 8.6, we considered a rocket fired in outer space where there is no air resistance and where gravity is negligible. Suppose instead that the rocket is accelerating vertically upward from rest on the earth's surface. Continue to ignore air resistance and consider only that part of the motion where the altitude of the rocket is small so that g may be assumed to be constant. (a) How is Eq. (8.37) modified by the presence of the gravity force? (b) Derive an expression for the acceleration a of the rocket, analogous to Eq. (8.39). (c) What is the acceleration of the rocket in Example 8.15 (Section 8.6) if it is near the earth's surface rather than in outer space? You can ignore air resistance. (d) Find the speed of the rocket in Example 8.16 (Section 8.6) after 90 s if the rocket is fired from the earth's surface rather than in outer space. You can ignore air resistance. How does your answer compare with the rocket speed calculated in Example 8.16?

***8.111. A Multistage Rocket.** Suppose the first stage of a two-stage rocket has total mass 12,000 kg, of which 9000 kg is fuel. The total mass of the second stage is 1000 kg, of which 700 kg is fuel. Assume that the relative speed v_{ex} of ejected material is constant, and ignore any effect of gravity. (The effect of gravity is small during the firing period if the rate of fuel consumption is large.) (a) Suppose the entire fuel supply carried by the two-stage rocket is utilized in a single-stage rocket with the same total mass of 13,000 kg. In terms of v_{ex}, what is the speed of the rocket, starting from rest, when its fuel is exhausted? (b) For the two-stage rocket, what is the speed when the fuel of the first stage is exhausted if the first stage carries the second stage with it to this point? This speed then becomes the initial speed of the second stage. At this point, the second stage separates from the first stage. (c) What is the final speed of the second stage? (d) What value of v_{ex} is required to give the second stage of the rocket a speed of 7.00 km/s?

***8.112.** For the rocket described in Examples 8.15 and 8.16 (Section 8.6), the mass of the rocket as a function of time is

$$m(t) = \begin{cases} m_0 & \text{for } t < 0 \\ m_0\left(1 - \dfrac{t}{120\text{ s}}\right) & \text{for } 0 \le t \le 90\text{ s} \\ m_0/4 & \text{for } t \ge 90\text{ s} \end{cases}$$

(a) Calculate and graph the velocity of the rocket as a function of time from $t = 0$ to $t = 100$ s. (b) Calculate and graph the acceleration of the rocket as a function of time from $t = 0$ to $t = 100$ s. (c) A 75-kg astronaut lies on a reclined chair during the firing of the rocket. What is the maximum net force exerted by the chair on the astronaut during the firing? How does your answer compare with her weight on earth?

Challenge Problems

8.113. In Section 8.5 we calculated the center of mass by considering objects composed of a *finite* number of point masses or objects that, by symmetry, could be represented by a finite number of point masses. For a solid object whose mass distribution does not allow for a simple determination of the center of mass by symmetry, the sums of Eqs. (8.28) must be generalized to integrals

$$x_{cm} = \frac{1}{M}\int x\,dm \qquad y_{cm} = \frac{1}{M}\int y\,dm$$

where x and y are the coordinates of the small piece of the object that has mass dm. The integration is over the whole of the object. Consider a thin rod of length L, mass M, and cross-sectional area A. Let the origin of the coordinates be at the left end of the rod and the positive x-axis lie along the rod. (a) If the density $\rho = M/V$ of the object is uniform, perform the integration described above to show that the x-coordinate of the center of mass of the rod is at its geometrical center. (b) If the density of the object varies linearly with x—that is, $\rho = \alpha x$, where α is a positive constant—calculate the x-coordinate of the rod's center of mass.

8.114. Use the methods of Challenge Problem 8.113 to calculate the x- and y-coordinates of the center of mass of a semicircular metal plate with uniform density ρ and thickness t. Let the radius of the plate be a. The mass of the plate is thus $M = \frac{1}{2}\rho\pi a^2 t$. Use the coordinate system indicated in Fig. 8.51.

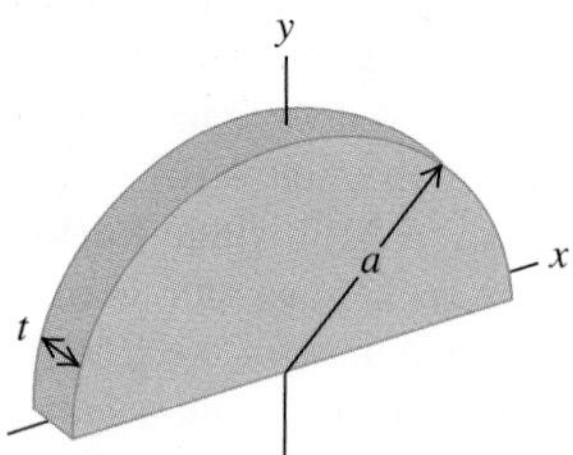

Figure 8.51 Challenge Problem 8.114.

8.115. One-fourth of a rope of length l is hanging down over the edge of a frictionless table. The rope has a uniform, linear density (mass per unit length) λ (Greek lambda), and the end already on the table is held by a person. How much work does the person do when she pulls on the rope to raise the rest of the rope slowly onto the table? Do the problem in two ways as follows. (a) Find the force that the person must exert to raise the rope and from this the work done. Note that this force is variable because at different times, different amounts of rope are hanging over the edge. (b) Suppose the segment of the rope initially hanging over the edge of the table has all of its mass concentrated at its center of mass. Find the work necessary to raise this to table height. You will probably find this approach simpler than that of part (a). How do the answers compare, and why is this so?

***8.116 A Variable-Mass Raindrop.** In a rocket-propulsion problem the mass is variable. Another such problem is a raindrop falling through a cloud of small water droplets. Some of these small droplets adhere to the raindrop, thereby *increasing* its mass as it falls. The force on the raindrop is

$$F_{\text{ext}} = \frac{dp}{dt} = m\frac{dv}{dt} + v\frac{dm}{dt}$$

Suppose the mass of the raindrop depends on the distance x that it has fallen. Then $m = kx$, where k is a constant, and $dm/dt = kv$. This gives, since $F_{\text{ext}} = mg$,

$$mg = m\frac{dv}{dt} + v(kv)$$

Or, dividing by k,

$$xg = x\frac{dv}{dt} + v^2$$

This is a differential equation that has a solution of the form $v = at$, where a is the acceleration and is constant. Take the initial velocity of the raindrop to be zero. (a) Using the proposed solution for v, find the acceleration a. (b) Find the distance the raindrop has fallen in $t = 3.00$ s. (c) Given that $k = 2.00$ g/m, find the mass of the raindrop at $t = 3.00$ s. For many more intriguing aspects of this problem, see K. S. Krane, *Amer. Jour. Phys.*, Vol. 49 (1981), pp. 113–117.

9 ROTATION OF RIGID BODIES

N57MD
MARYLAND STATE POLICE

? All segments of a rotating helicopter blade have the same angular velocity and angular acceleration. Compared to a given blade segment, how many times greater is the linear speed of a second segment twice as far from the axis of rotation? How many times greater is the linear acceleration?

LEARNING GOALS

By studying this chapter, you will learn:

- How to describe the rotation of a rigid body in terms of angular coordinate, angular velocity, and angular acceleration.
- How to analyze rigid-body rotation when the angular acceleration is constant.
- How to relate the rotation of a rigid body to the linear velocity and linear acceleration of a point on the body.
- The meaning of a body's moment of inertia about a rotation axis, and how it relates to rotational kinetic energy.
- How to calculate the moment of inertia of various bodies.

What do the motions of a compact disc, a Ferris wheel, a circular saw blade, and a ceiling fan have in common? None of these can be represented adequately as a moving *point;* each involves a body that *rotates* about an axis that is stationary in some inertial frame of reference.

Rotation occurs at all scales, from the motion of electrons in atoms to the motions of entire galaxies. We need to develop some general methods for analyzing the motion of a rotating body. In this chapter and the next we consider bodies that have definite size and definite shape, and that in general can have rotational as well as translational motion.

Real-world bodies can be very complicated; the forces that act on them can deform them—stretching, twisting, and squeezing them. We'll neglect these deformations for now and assume that the body has a perfectly definite and unchanging shape and size. We call this idealized model a **rigid body.** This chapter and the next are mostly about rotational motion of a rigid body.

We begin with kinematic language for *describing* rotational motion. Next we look at the kinetic energy of rotation, the key to using energy methods for rotational motion. Then in Chapter 10 we'll develop dynamic principles that relate the forces on a body to its rotational motion.

9.1 Angular Velocity and Acceleration

In analyzing rotational motion, let's think first about a rigid body that rotates about a *fixed axis*—an axis that is at rest in some inertial frame of reference and does not change direction relative to that frame. The rotating rigid body might be a motor shaft, a chunk of beef on a barbecue skewer, or a merry-go-round.

Figure 9.1 shows a rigid body (in this case, the indicator needle of a speedometer) rotating about a fixed axis. The axis passes through point O and is

9.1 A speedometer needle (an example of a rigid body) rotating counterclockwise about a fixed axis.

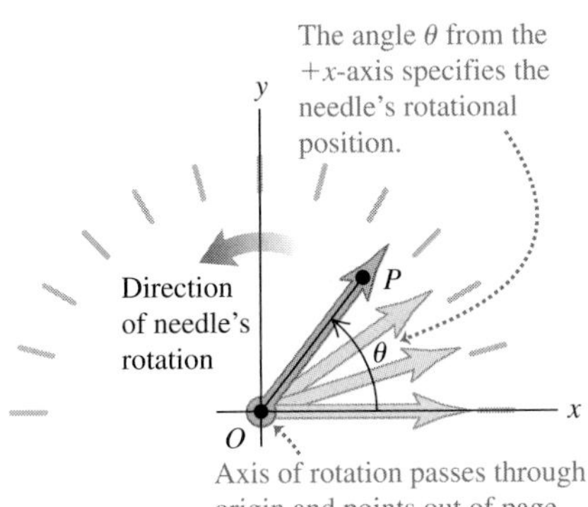

The angle θ from the +x-axis specifies the needle's rotational position.
y
x
P
θ
O
Direction of needle's rotation
Axis of rotation passes through origin and points out of page.

perpendicular to the plane of the diagram, which we choose to call the xy-plane. One way to describe the rotation of this body would be to choose a particular point P on the body and to keep track of the x- and y-coordinates of this point. This isn't a terribly convenient method, since it takes two numbers (the two coordinates x and y) to specify the rotational position of the body. Instead, we notice that the line OP is fixed in the body and rotates with it. The angle θ that this line makes with the $+x$-axis describes the rotational position of the body; we will use this single quantity θ as a *coordinate* for rotation.

The angular coordinate θ of a rigid body rotating around a fixed axis can be positive or negative. If we choose positive angles to be measured counterclockwise from the positive x-axis, then the angle θ in Fig. 9.1 is positive. If we instead choose the positive rotation direction to be clockwise, then θ in Fig. 9.1 is negative. When we considered the motion of a particle along a straight line, it was essential to specify the direction of positive displacement along that line; when we discuss rotation around a fixed axis, it's just as essential to specify the direction of positive rotation.

9.2 Measuring angles in radians.

(a)

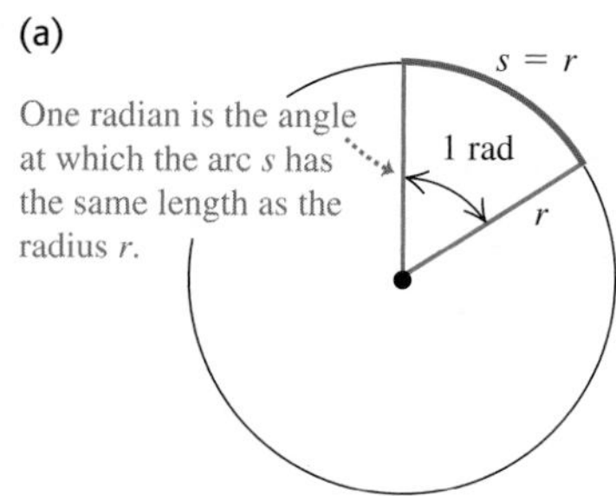
$s = r$
One radian is the angle at which the arc s has the same length as the radius r.
1 rad
r

(b)

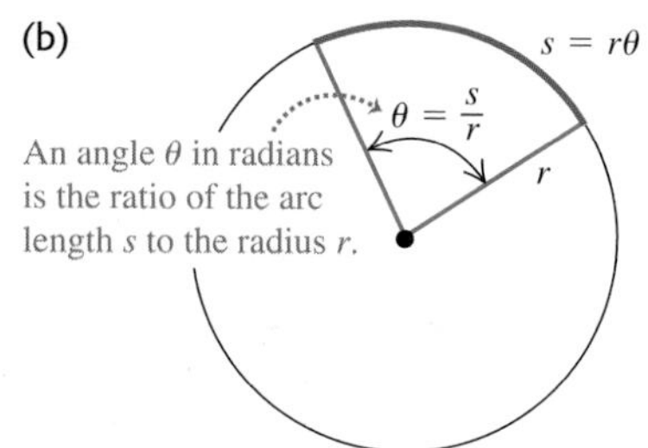
$s = r\theta$
$\theta = \frac{s}{r}$
An angle θ in radians is the ratio of the arc length s to the radius r.
r

To describe rotational motion, the most natural way to measure the angle θ is not in degrees, but in **radians.** As shown in Fig. 9.2a, one radian (1 rad) is the angle subtended at the center of a circle by an arc with a length equal to the radius of the circle. In Fig. 9.2b an angle θ is subtended by an arc of length s on a circle of radius r. The value of θ (in radians) is equal to s divided by r:

$$\theta = \frac{s}{r} \quad \text{or} \quad s = r\theta \tag{9.1}$$

An angle in radians is the ratio of two lengths, so it is a pure number, without dimensions. If $s = 3.0$ m and $r = 2.0$ m, then $\theta = 1.5$, but we will often write this as 1.5 rad to distinguish it from an angle measured in degrees or revolutions.

The circumference of a circle (that is, the arc length all the way around the circle) is 2π times the radius, so there are 2π (about 6.283) radians in one complete revolution $(360°)$. Therefore

$$1 \text{ rad} = \frac{360°}{2\pi} = 57.3°$$

Similarly, $180° = \pi$ rad, $90° = \pi/2$ rad, and so on. If we had insisted on measuring the angle θ in degrees, we would have needed to include an extra factor of $(2\pi/360)$ on the right-hand side of $s = r\theta$ in Eq. (9.1). By measuring angles in radians, we keep the relationship between angle and distance along an arc as simple as possible.

Angular Velocity

The coordinate θ shown in Fig. 9.1 specifies the rotational position of a rigid body at a given instant. We can describe the rotational *motion* of such a rigid body in terms of the rate of change of θ. We'll do this in an analogous way to our description of straight-line motion in Chapter 2. In Fig. 9.3a, a reference line OP in a rotating body makes an angle θ_1 with the $+x$-axis at time t_1. At a later time t_2 the angle has changed to θ_2. We define the **average angular velocity** $\omega_{\text{av-}z}$ (the Greek letter omega) of the body in the time interval $\Delta t = t_2 - t_1$ as the ratio of the **angular displacement** $\Delta\theta = \theta_2 - \theta_1$ to Δt:

$$\omega_{\text{av-}z} = \frac{\theta_2 - \theta_1}{t_2 - t_1} = \frac{\Delta\theta}{\Delta t} \tag{9.2}$$

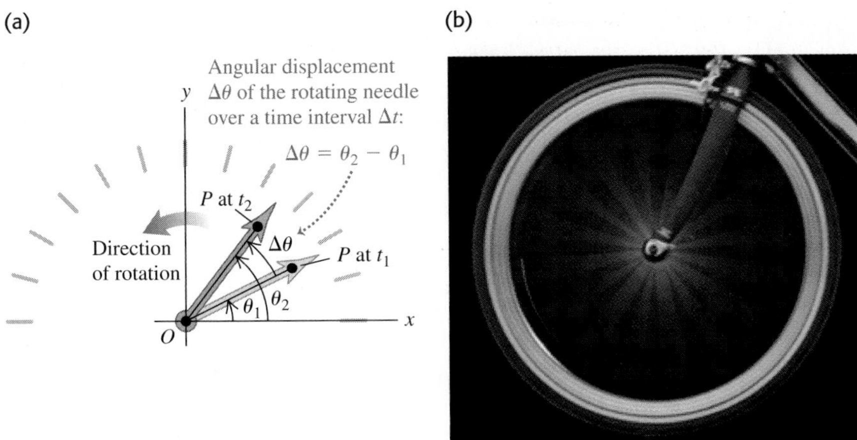
(a)
(b)
Angular displacement
$\Delta\theta$ of the rotating needle
over a time interval Δt:
$\Delta\theta = \theta_2 - \theta_1$
y
P at t_2
$\Delta\theta$
P at t_1
Direction
of rotation
θ_1
θ_2
O
x

9.3 (a) Angular displacement $\Delta\theta$ of a rotating body. (b) Every part of a rotating rigid body has the same angular velocity $\Delta\theta/\Delta t$.

The subscript z indicates that the body in Fig. 9.3a is rotating about the z-axis, which is perpendicular to the plane of the diagram. The **instantaneous angular velocity** ω_z is the limit of $\omega_{\text{av-}z}$ as Δt approaches zero—that is, the derivative of θ with respect to t:

$$\omega_z = \lim_{\Delta t \to 0} \frac{\Delta\theta}{\Delta t} = \frac{d\theta}{dt} \qquad \text{(definition of angular velocity)} \qquad (9.3)$$

When we refer simply to "angular velocity," we mean the instantaneous angular velocity, not the average angular velocity.

The angular velocity ω_z can be positive or negative, depending on the direction in which the rigid body is rotating (Fig. 9.4). The angular *speed* ω, which we will use extensively in Sections 9.3 and 9.4, is the magnitude of angular velocity. Like ordinary (linear) speed v, the angular speed is never negative.

CAUTION **Angular velocity vs. linear velocity** Keep in mind the distinction between angular velocity ω_z and ordinary velocity, or *linear velocity*, v_x (see Section 2.2). If an object has a velocity v_x, the object as a whole is *moving* along the x-axis. By contrast, if an object has an angular velocity ω_z, then it is *rotating* around the z-axis. We do *not* mean that the object is moving along the z-axis.

9.4 A rigid body's average angular velocity (shown here) and instantaneous angular velocity can be positive or negative.

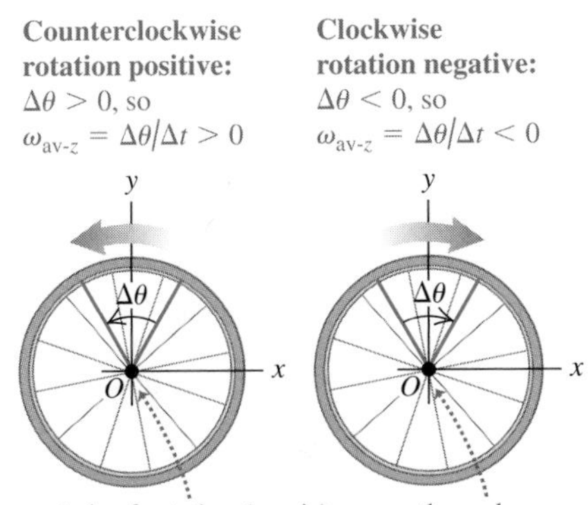
Counterclockwise
rotation positive:
$\Delta\theta > 0$, so
$\omega_{\text{av-}z} = \Delta\theta/\Delta t > 0$
Clockwise
rotation negative:
$\Delta\theta < 0$, so
$\omega_{\text{av-}z} = \Delta\theta/\Delta t < 0$
y
y
$\Delta\theta$
$\Delta\theta$
x
x
O
O
Axis of rotation (z-axis) passes through
origin and points out of page.

Different points on a rotating rigid body move different distances in a given time interval, depending on how far the point lies from the rotation axis. But because the body is rigid, *all* points rotate through the same angle in the same time (Fig. 9.3b). Hence *at any instant, every part of a rotating rigid body has the same angular velocity.* The angular velocity is positive if the body is rotating in the direction of increasing θ and negative if it is rotating in the direction of decreasing θ.

If the angle θ is in radians, the unit of angular velocity is the radian per second (rad/s). Other units, such as the revolution per minute (rev/min or rpm), are often used. Since 1 rev $= 2\pi$ rad, two useful conversions are

$$1 \text{ rev/s} = 2\pi \text{ rad/s} \qquad \text{and} \qquad 1 \text{ rev/min} = 1 \text{ rpm} = \frac{2\pi}{60} \text{ rad/s}$$

That is, 1 rad/s is about 10 rpm.

Example 9.1 Calculating angular velocity

The flywheel of a prototype car engine is under test. The angular position θ of the flywheel is given by

$$\theta = (2.0\ \text{rad/s}^3)t^3$$

The diameter of the flywheel is 0.36 m. (a) Find the angle θ, in radians and in degrees, at times $t_1 = 2.0$ s and $t_2 = 5.0$ s. (b) Find the distance that a particle on the rim moves during that time interval. (c) Find the average angular velocity, in rad/s and in rev/min (rpm), between $t_1 = 2.0$ s and $t_2 = 5.0$ s. (d) Find the instantaneous angular velocity at time $t = t_2 = 5.0$ s.

SOLUTION

IDENTIFY: We need to find the values θ_1 and θ_2 of the angular position at times t_1 and t_2, the angular displacement $\Delta\theta$ between t_1 and t_2, the distance traveled and the average angular velocity between t_1 and t_2, and the instantaneous angular velocity at t_2.

SET UP: We're given the angular position θ as a function of time, so we can easily find our first two target variables θ_1 and θ_2; the angular displacement $\Delta\theta$ is the difference between θ_1 and θ_2. Given $\Delta\theta$ we'll find the distance and the average angular velocity using Eqs. (9.1) and (9.2), respectively. To find the instantaneous angular velocity, we'll take the derivative of θ with respect to time, as in Eq. (9.3).

EXECUTE: (a) We substitute the values of t into the given equation:

$$\theta_1 = (2.0\ \text{rad/s}^3)(2.0\ \text{s})^3 = 16\ \text{rad}$$
$$= (16\ \text{rad})\frac{360°}{2\pi\ \text{rad}} = 920°$$
$$\theta_2 = (2.0\ \text{rad/s}^3)(5.0\ \text{s})^3 = 250\ \text{rad}$$
$$= (250\ \text{rad})\frac{360°}{2\pi\ \text{rad}} = 14{,}000°$$

(b) The flywheel turns through an angular displacement of $\Delta\theta = \theta_2 - \theta_1 = 250\ \text{rad} - 16\ \text{rad} = 234\ \text{rad}$. The radius r is half the diameter, or 0.18 m. Equation (9.1) gives

$$s = r\theta = (0.18\ \text{m})(234\ \text{rad}) = 42\ \text{m}$$

To use Eq. (9.1), the angle *must* be expressed in radians. We drop "radians" from the unit for s because θ is really a dimensionless pure number; s is a distance and is measured in meters, the same unit as r.

(c) In Eq. (9.2) we have

$$\omega_{\text{av-}z} = \frac{\theta_2 - \theta_1}{t_2 - t_1} = \frac{250\ \text{rad} - 16\ \text{rad}}{5.0\ \text{s} - 2.0\ \text{s}} = 78\ \text{rad/s}$$
$$= \left(78\frac{\text{rad}}{\text{s}}\right)\left(\frac{1\ \text{rev}}{2\pi\ \text{rad}}\right)\left(\frac{60\ \text{s}}{1\ \text{min}}\right) = 740\ \text{rev/min}$$

(d) We use Eq. (9.3):

$$\omega_z = \frac{d\theta}{dt} = \frac{d}{dt}[(2.0\ \text{rad/s}^3)t^3] = (2.0\ \text{rad/s}^3)(3t^2)$$
$$= (6.0\ \text{rad/s}^3)t^2$$

At time $t = 5.0$ s,

$$\omega_z = (6.0\ \text{rad/s}^3)(5.0\ \text{s})^2 = 150\ \text{rad/s}$$

EVALUATE: Our result in part (d) shows that ω_z is proportional to t^2 and hence increases with time. Our numerical results are consistent with this result: The 150-rad/s instantaneous angular velocity at $t = 5.0$ s is greater than the 78-rad/s average angular velocity for the 3.0-s interval leading up to that time (from $t_1 = 2.0$ s to $t_2 = 5.0$ s).

Angular Velocity As a Vector

As we have seen, our notation for the angular velocity ω_z about the z-axis is reminiscent of the notation v_x for the ordinary velocity along the x-axis (see Section 2.2). Just as v_x is the x-component of the velocity vector $\vec{v}$, ω_z is the z-component of an angular velocity *vector* $\vec{\omega}$ directed along the axis of rotation. As Fig. 9.5a

(a)

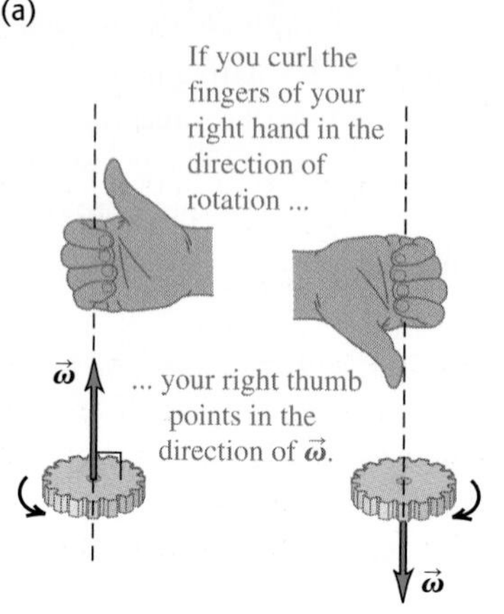
If you curl the fingers of your right hand in the direction of rotation ...
... your right thumb points in the direction of $\vec{\omega}$.
$\vec{\omega}$
$\vec{\omega}$

(b)

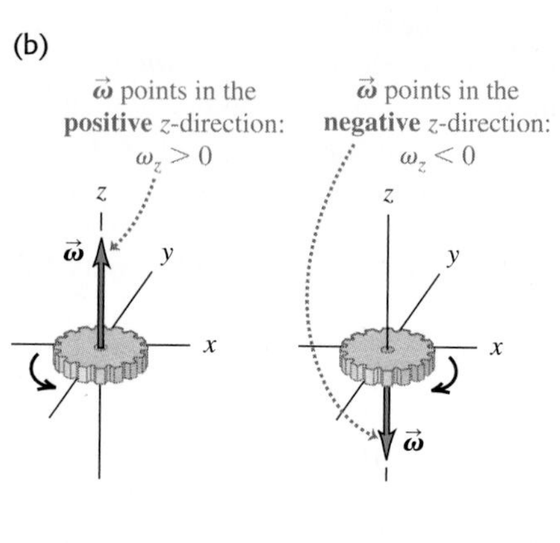
$\vec{\omega}$ points in the **positive** z-direction: $\omega_z > 0$
$\vec{\omega}$ points in the **negative** z-direction: $\omega_z < 0$
z
y
x
z
y
x
$\vec{\omega}$
$\vec{\omega}$

9.5 (a) The right-hand rule for the direction of the angular velocity vector $\vec{\omega}$. Reversing the direction of rotation reverses the direction of $\vec{\omega}$. (b) The sign of ω_z for rotation along the z-axis.

shows, the direction of $\vec{\omega}$ is given by the right-hand rule that we used to define the vector product in Section 1.10. If the rotation is about the z-axis, then $\vec{\omega}$ has only a z-component; this component is positive if $\vec{\omega}$ is along the positive z-axis and negative if $\vec{\omega}$ is along the negative z-axis (Fig. 9.5b).

The vector formulation is especially useful in situations in which the direction of the rotation axis *changes.* We'll examine such situations briefly at the end of Chapter 10. In this chapter, however, we'll consider only situations in which the rotation axis is fixed. Hence throughout this chapter we'll use "angular velocity" to refer to ω_z, the component of the angular velocity vector $\vec{\omega}$ along the axis.

Angular Acceleration

When the angular velocity of a rigid body changes, it has an *angular acceleration.* When you pedal your bicycle harder to make the wheels turn faster or apply the brakes to bring the wheels to a stop, you're giving the wheels an angular acceleration. You also impart an angular acceleration whenever you change the rotation speed of a piece of spinning machinery such as an automobile engine's crankshaft.

If ω_{1z} and ω_{2z} are the instantaneous angular velocities at times t_1 and t_2, we define the **average angular acceleration** $\alpha_{\text{av-}z}$ over the interval $\Delta t = t_2 - t_1$ as the change in angular velocity divided by Δt (Fig. 9.6):

$$\alpha_{\text{av-}z} = \frac{\omega_{2z} - \omega_{1z}}{t_2 - t_1} = \frac{\Delta\omega_z}{\Delta t} \tag{9.4}$$

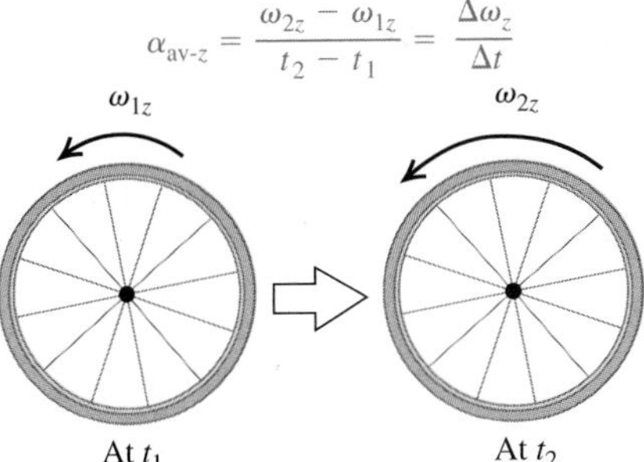
The average angular acceleration is the change in angular velocity divided by the time interval:
$\alpha_{\text{av-}z} = \frac{\omega_{2z} - \omega_{1z}}{t_2 - t_1} = \frac{\Delta\omega_z}{\Delta t}$
ω_{1z}
ω_{2z}
At t_1
At t_2

9.6 Calculating the average angular acceleration of a rotating rigid body.

The **instantaneous angular acceleration** α_z is the limit of $\alpha_{\text{av-}z}$ as $\Delta t \to 0$:

$$\alpha_z = \lim_{\Delta t \to 0} \frac{\Delta\omega_z}{\Delta t} = \frac{d\omega_z}{dt} \quad \text{(definition of angular acceleration)} \tag{9.5}$$

The usual unit of angular acceleration is the radian per second per second, or rad/s^2. From now on we will use the term "angular acceleration" to mean the instantaneous angular acceleration rather than the average angular acceleration.

Because $\omega_z = d\theta/dt$, we can also express angular acceleration as the second derivative of the angular coordinate:

$$\alpha_z = \frac{d}{dt}\frac{d\theta}{dt} = \frac{d^2\theta}{dt^2} \tag{9.6}$$

You have probably noticed that we are using Greek letters for angular kinematic quantities: θ for angular position, ω_z for angular velocity, and α_z for angular acceleration. These are analogous to x for position, v_x for velocity, and a_x for acceleration, respectively, in straight-line motion. In each case, velocity is the rate of change of position with respect to time and acceleration is the rate of change of velocity with respect to time. We will sometimes use the terms "*linear* velocity" and "*linear* acceleration" for the familiar quantities we defined in Chapters 2 and 3 to distinguish clearly between these and the *angular* quantities introduced in this chapter.

In rotational motion, if the angular acceleration α_z is positive, then the angular velocity ω_z is increasing; if α_z is negative, then ω_z is decreasing. The rotation is speeding up if α_z and ω_z have the same sign and slowing down if α_z and ω_z have opposite signs. (These are exactly the same relationships as those between *linear* acceleration a_x and *linear* velocity v_x for straight-line motion; see Section 2.3.)

Example 9.2 Calculating angular acceleration

In Example 9.1 we found that the instantaneous angular velocity ω_z of the flywheel at any time t is given by

$$\omega_z = (6.0 \text{ rad/s}^3)t^2$$

(a) Find the average angular acceleration between $t_1 = 2.0$ s and $t_2 = 5.0$ s. (b) Find the instantaneous angular acceleration at time $t_2 = 5.0$ s.

SOLUTION

IDENTIFY: This example uses the definitions of average angular acceleration $\alpha_{\text{av-}z}$ and instantaneous angular acceleration α_z.

SET UP: We'll use Eqs. (9.4) and (9.5) to find the value of $\alpha_{\text{av-}z}$ between t_1 and t_2 and the value of α_z at $t = t_2$.

EXECUTE: (a) The values of ω_z at the two times are

$$\omega_{1z} = (6.0 \text{ rad/s}^3)(2.0 \text{ s})^2 = 24 \text{ rad/s}$$
$$\omega_{2z} = (6.0 \text{ rad/s}^3)(5.0 \text{ s})^2 = 150 \text{ rad/s}$$

From Eq. (9.4) the average angular acceleration is

$$\alpha_{\text{av-}z} = \frac{150 \text{ rad/s} - 24 \text{ rad/s}}{5.0 \text{ s} - 2.0 \text{ s}} = 42 \text{ rad/s}^2$$

(b) From Eq. (9.5) the instantaneous angular acceleration at any time t is

$$\alpha_z = \frac{d\omega_z}{dt} = \frac{d}{dt}[(6.0 \text{ rad/s}^3)(t^2)] = (6.0 \text{ rad/s}^3)(2t) = (12 \text{ rad/s}^3)t$$

At time $t = 5.0$ s,

$$\alpha_z = (12 \text{ rad/s}^3)(5.0 \text{ s}) = 60 \text{ rad/s}^2$$

EVALUATE: Note that the angular acceleration is *not* constant in this situation. The angular velocity ω_z is always increasing because α_z is always positive. Furthermore, the rate at which the angular velocity increases is itself increasing, since α_z increases with time.

9.7 When the rotation axis is fixed, the angular acceleration and angular velocity vectors both lie along that axis.

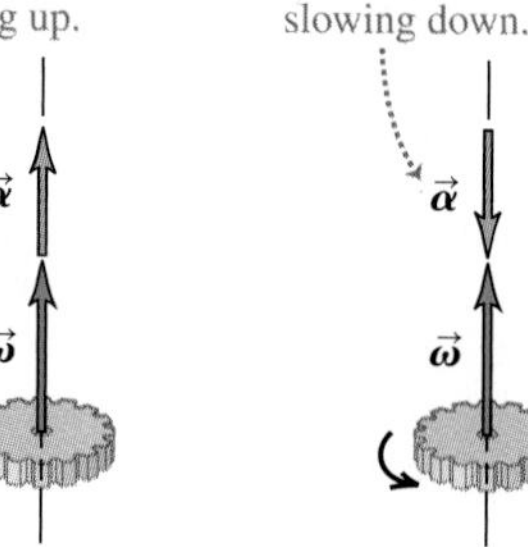

Angular Acceleration As a Vector

Just as we did for angular velocity, it's useful to define an angular acceleration *vector* $\vec{\alpha}$. Mathematically, $\vec{\alpha}$ is the time derivative of the angular velocity vector $\vec{\omega}$. If the object rotates around the fixed z-axis, then $\vec{\alpha}$ has only a z-component; the quantity α_z is just that component. In this case, $\vec{\alpha}$ is in the same direction as $\vec{\omega}$ if the rotation is speeding up and opposite to $\vec{\omega}$ if the rotation is slowing down (Fig. 9.7).

The angular acceleration vector will be particularly useful in Chapter 10 when we discuss what happens when the rotation axis can change direction. In this chapter, however, the rotation axis will always be fixed and we need use only the z-component α_z.

Test Your Understanding of Section 9.1 The figure shows a graph of ω_z and α_z versus time for a particular rotating body. (a) During which time intervals is the rotation speeding up? (i) $0 < t < 2$ s; (ii) $2 \text{ s} < t < 4$ s; (iii) $4 \text{ s} < t < 6$ s. (b) During which time intervals is the rotation slowing down? (i) $0 < t < 2$ s; (ii) $2 \text{ s} < t < 4$ s; (iii) $4 \text{ s} < 5 < 6$ s.

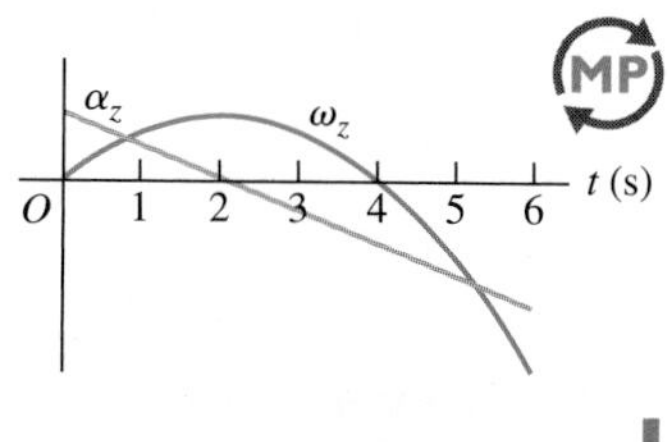

9.2 Rotation with Constant Angular Acceleration

In Chapter 2 we found that straight-line motion is particularly simple when the acceleration is constant. This is also true of rotational motion about a fixed axis. When the angular acceleration is constant, we can derive equations for angular velocity and angular position using exactly the same procedure that we used for straight-line motion in Section 2.4. In fact, the equations we are about to derive are identical to Eqs. (2.8), (2.12), (2.13), and (2.14) if we replace x with θ, v_x with ω_z, and a_x with α_z. We suggest that you review Section 2.4 before continuing.

Let ω_{0z} be the angular velocity of a rigid body at time $t = 0$, and let ω_z be its angular velocity at any later time t. The angular acceleration α_z is constant and equal to the average value for any interval. Using Eq. (9.4) with the interval from 0 to t, we find

$$\alpha_z = \frac{\omega_z - \omega_{0z}}{t - 0} \quad \text{or}$$

$$\omega_z = \omega_{0z} + \alpha_z t \qquad \text{(constant angular acceleration only)} \qquad (9.7)$$

The product $\alpha_z t$ is the total change in ω_z between $t = 0$ and the later time t; the angular velocity ω_z at time t is the sum of the initial value ω_{0z} and this total change.

With constant angular acceleration, the angular velocity changes at a uniform rate, so its average value between 0 and t is the average of the initial and final values:

$$\omega_{\text{av-}z} = \frac{\omega_{0z} + \omega_z}{2} \qquad (9.8)$$

We also know that $\omega_{\text{av-}z}$ is the total angular displacement $(\theta - \theta_0)$ divided by the time interval $(t - 0)$:

$$\omega_{\text{av-}z} = \frac{\theta - \theta_0}{t - 0} \qquad (9.9)$$

When we equate Eqs. (9.8) and (9.9) and multiply the result by t, we get

$$\theta - \theta_0 = \frac{1}{2}(\omega_{0z} + \omega_z)t \qquad \text{(constant angular acceleration only)} \qquad (9.10)$$

To obtain a relationship between θ and t that doesn't contain ω_z, we substitute Eq. (9.7) into Eq. (9.10):

$$\theta - \theta_0 = \frac{1}{2}[\omega_{0z} + (\omega_{0z} + \alpha_z t)]t \quad \text{or}$$

$$\theta = \theta_0 + \omega_{0z}t + \frac{1}{2}\alpha_z t^2 \qquad \text{(constant angular acceleration only)} \qquad (9.11)$$

That is, if at the initial time $t = 0$ the body is at angular position θ_0 and has angular velocity ω_{0z}, then its angular position θ at any later time t is the sum of three terms: its initial angular position θ_0, plus the rotation $\omega_{0z}t$ it would have if the angular velocity were constant, plus an additional rotation $\frac{1}{2}\alpha_z t^2$ caused by the changing angular velocity.

Following the same procedure as for straight-line motion in Section 2.4, we can combine Eqs. (9.7) and (9.11) to obtain a relationship between θ and ω_z that does not contain t. We invite you to work out the details, following the same procedure we used to get Eq. (2.13). (See Exercise 9.12.) In fact, because of the perfect analogy between straight-line and rotational quantities, we can simply take Eq. (2.13) and replace each straight-line quantity by its rotational analog. We get

$$\omega_z^2 = \omega_{0z}^2 + 2\alpha_z(\theta - \theta_0) \qquad \text{(constant angular acceleration only)} \qquad (9.12)$$

CAUTION **Constant angular acceleration** Keep in mind that all of these results are valid *only* when the angular acceleration α_z is *constant;* be careful not to try to apply them to problems in which α_z is *not* constant. Table 9.1 shows the analogy between Eqs. (9.7), (9.10), (9.11), and (9.12) for fixed-axis rotation with constant angular acceleration and the corresponding equations for straight-line motion with constant linear acceleration.

7.7 Rotational Kinematics

Table 9.1 Comparison of Linear and Angular Motion with Constant Acceleration

Straight-Line Motion with Constant Linear Acceleration	Fixed-Axis Rotation with Constant Angular Acceleration
$a_x = \text{constant}$	$\alpha_z = \text{constant}$
$v_x = v_{0x} + a_x t$	$\omega_z = \omega_{0z} + \alpha_z t$
$x = x_0 + v_{0x}t + \frac{1}{2}a_x t^2$	$\theta = \theta_0 + \omega_{0z}t + \frac{1}{2}\alpha_z t^2$
$v_x^2 = v_{0x}^2 + 2a_x(x - x_0)$	$\omega_z^2 = \omega_{0z}^2 + 2\alpha_z(\theta - \theta_0)$
$x - x_0 = \frac{1}{2}(v_x + v_{0x})t$	$\theta - \theta_0 = \frac{1}{2}(\omega_z + \omega_{0z})t$

Example 9.3 Rotation with constant angular acceleration

You have just finished watching a movie on DVD and the disc is slowing to a stop. The angular velocity of the disc at $t = 0$ is 27.5 rad/s and its angular acceleration is a constant -10.0 rad/s^2. A line PQ on the surface of the disc lies along the $+x$-axis at $t = 0$ (Fig. 9.8). (a) What is the disc's angular velocity at $t = 0.300$ s? (b) What angle does the line PQ make with the $+x$-axis at this time?

SOLUTION

IDENTIFY: The angular acceleration of the disc is constant, so we can use any of the equations derived in this section. Our target variables are the angular velocity and the angular displacement at $t = 0.300$ s.

SET UP: We are given the initial angular velocity $\omega_{0z} = 27.5$ rad/s, the initial angle $\theta_0 = 0$ between the line PQ and the $+x$-axis, the angular acceleration $\alpha_z = -10.0 \text{ rad/s}^2$, and the time $t = 0.300$ s.

9.8 A line PQ on a rotating DVD at $t = 0$.

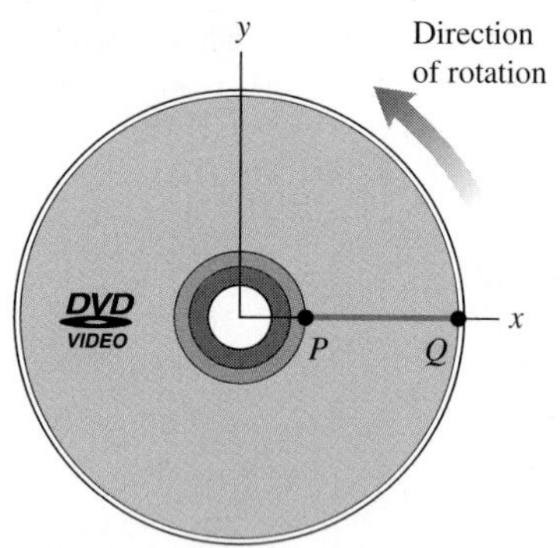

With this information it's easiest to use Eqs. (9.7) and (9.11) to find the target variables ω_z and θ, respectively.

EXECUTE: (a) From Eq. (9.7), at $t = 0.300$ s we have

$$\omega_z = \omega_{0z} + \alpha_z t = 27.5 \text{ rad/s} + (-10.0 \text{ rad/s}^2)(0.300 \text{ s}) = 24.5 \text{ rad/s}$$

(b) From Eq. (9.11),

$$\theta = \theta_0 + \omega_{0z}t + \frac{1}{2}\alpha_z t^2$$
$$= 0 + (27.5 \text{ rad/s})(0.300 \text{ s}) + \frac{1}{2}(-10.0 \text{ rad/s}^2)(0.300 \text{ s})^2$$
$$= 7.80 \text{ rad} = 7.80 \text{ rad}\left(\frac{1 \text{ rev}}{2\pi \text{ rad}}\right) = 1.24 \text{ rev}$$

The DVD has turned through one complete revolution plus an additional 0.24 revolution—that is, through an additional angle of $(0.24 \text{ rev})(360°/\text{rev}) = 87°$. Hence the line PQ is at an angle of 87° with the $+x$-axis.

EVALUATE: Our answer to part (a) tells us that the angular velocity has decreased. This is as it should be, since α_z is negative. We can also use our answer for ω_z in part (a) to check our result for θ in part (b). To do so, we solve Eq. (9.12), $\omega_z^2 = \omega_{0z}^2 + 2\alpha_z(\theta - \theta_0)$, for the angle θ:

$$\theta = \theta_0 + \left(\frac{\omega_z^2 - \omega_{0z}^2}{2\alpha_z}\right)$$
$$= 0 + \frac{(24.5 \text{ rad/s})^2 - (27.5 \text{ rad/s})^2}{2(-10.0 \text{ rad/s}^2)} = 7.80 \text{ rad}$$

which agrees with the result we found earlier.

Test Your Understanding of Section 9.2 Suppose the DVD in Example 9.3 was initially spinning at twice the rate (55.0 rad/s rather than 27.5 rad/s) and slowed down at twice the rate (-20.0 rad/s^2 rather than -10.0 rad/s^2). (a) Compared to the situation in Example 9.3, how long would it take the DVD to come to a stop? (i) the same amount of time; (ii) twice as much time; (iii) 4 times as much time; (iv) $\frac{1}{2}$ as much time; (v) $\frac{1}{4}$ as much time. (b) Compared to the situation in Example 9.3, through how many revolutions would the DVD rotate before coming to a stop? (i) the same number of revolutions; (ii) twice as many revolutions; (iii) 4 times as many revolutions; (iv) $\frac{1}{2}$ as many revolutions; (v) $\frac{1}{4}$ as many revolutions.

9.3 Relating Linear and Angular Kinematics

How do we find the linear speed and acceleration of a particular point in a rotating rigid body? We need to answer this question to proceed with our study of rotation. For example, to find the kinetic energy of a rotating body, we have to start from $K = \frac{1}{2}mv^2$ for a particle, and this requires knowing the speed v for each particle in the body. So it's worthwhile to develop general relationships between the *angular* speed and acceleration of a rigid body rotating about a fixed axis and the *linear* speed and acceleration of a specific point or particle in the body.

Linear Speed in Rigid-Body Rotation

When a rigid body rotates about a fixed axis, every particle in the body moves in a circular path. The circle lies in a plane perpendicular to the axis and is centered on the axis. The speed of a particle is directly proportional to the body's angular velocity; the faster the body rotates, the greater the speed of each particle. In Fig. 9.9, point P is a constant distance r from the axis of rotation, so it moves in a circle of radius r. At any time, the angle θ (in radians) and the arc length s are related by

$$s = r\theta$$

We take the time derivative of this, noting that r is constant for any specific particle, and take the absolute value of both sides:

$$\left|\frac{ds}{dt}\right| = r\left|\frac{d\theta}{dt}\right|$$

Now $|ds/dt|$ is the absolute value of the rate of change of arc length, which is equal to the instantaneous *linear* speed v of the particle. Analogously, $|d\theta/dt|$, the absolute value of the rate of change of the angle, is the instantaneous **angular speed** ω—that is, the magnitude of the instantaneous angular velocity in rad/s. Thus

$$v = r\omega \quad \text{(relationship between linear and angular speeds)} \quad (9.13)$$

The farther a point is from the axis, the greater its linear speed. The *direction* of the linear velocity *vector* is tangent to its circular path at each point (Fig. 9.9).

CAUTION **Speed vs. velocity** Keep in mind the distinction between the linear and angular *speeds* v and ω, which appear in Eq. (9.13), and the linear and angular *velocities* v_x and ω_z. The quantities without subscripts, v and ω, are never negative; they are the magnitudes of the vectors $\vec{v}$ and $\vec{\omega}$, respectively, and their values tell you only how fast a particle is moving (v) or how fast a body is rotating (ω). The corresponding quantities with subscripts, v_x and ω_z, can be either positive or negative; their signs tell you the direction of the motion.

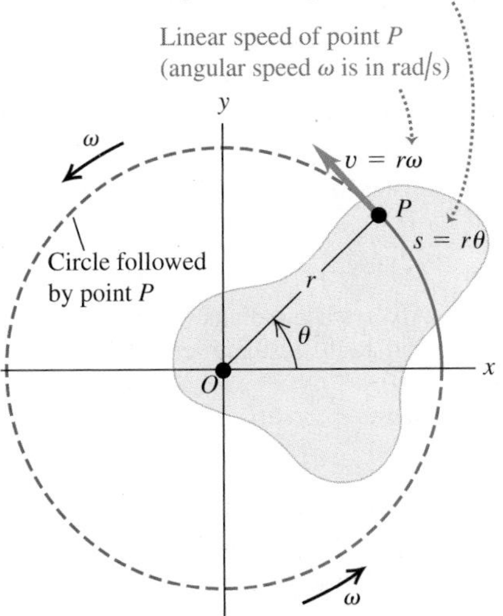

9.9 A rigid body rotating about a fixed axis through point O.

Linear Acceleration in Rigid-Body Rotation

We can represent the acceleration of a particle moving in a circle in terms of its centripetal and tangential components, a_{rad} and a_{tan} (Fig. 9.10), as we did in Section 3.4. It would be a good idea to review that section now. We found that the **tangential component of acceleration** a_{tan}, the component parallel to the instantaneous velocity, acts to change the *magnitude* of the particle's velocity (i.e., the speed) and is equal to the rate of change of speed. Taking the derivative of Eq. (9.13), we find

$$a_{tan} = \frac{dv}{dt} = r\frac{d\omega}{dt} = r\alpha \quad \text{(tangential acceleration of a point on a rotating body)} \quad (9.14)$$

9.10 A rigid body whose rotation is speeding up. The acceleration of point P has a component a_{rad} toward the rotation axis (perpendicular to $\vec{v}$) and a component a_{tan} along the circle that point P follows (parallel to $\vec{v}$).

Radial and tangential acceleration components:
- $a_{rad} = \omega^2 r$ is point P's centripetal acceleration.
- $a_{tan} = r\alpha$ means that P's rotation is speeding up (the body has angular acceleration).

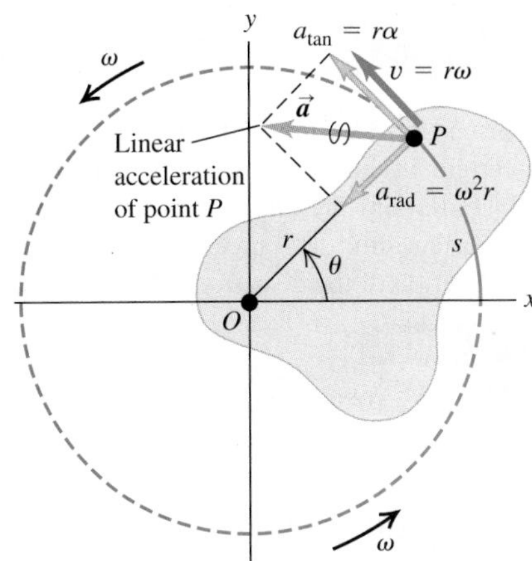

This component of a particle's acceleration is always tangent to the circular path of the particle.

The quantity $\alpha = d\omega/dt$ in Eq. (9.14) is the rate of change of the angular *speed.* It is not quite the same as $\alpha_z = d\omega_z/dt$, which is the rate of change of the angular *velocity.* For example, consider a body rotating so that its angular velocity vector points in the $-z$-direction (Fig. 9.5b). If the body is gaining angular speed at a rate of 10 rad/s per second, then $\alpha = 10\ \text{rad/s}^2$. But ω_z is negative and becoming more negative as the rotation gains speed, so $\alpha_z = -10\ \text{rad/s}^2$. The rule for rotation about a fixed axis is that α is equal to α_z if ω_z is positive but equal to $-\alpha_z$ if ω_z is negative.

The component of the particle's acceleration directed toward the rotation axis, the **centripetal component of acceleration** a_{rad}, is associated with the change of *direction* of the particle's velocity. In Section 3.4 we worked out the relationship $a_{rad} = v^2/r$. We can express this in terms of ω by using Eq. (9.13):

$$a_{rad} = \frac{v^2}{r} = \omega^2 r \quad \text{(centripetal acceleration of a point on a rotating body)} \qquad (9.15)$$

This is true at each instant, *even when ω and v are not constant.* The centripetal component always points toward the axis of rotation.

The vector sum of the centripetal and tangential components of acceleration of a particle in a rotating body is the linear acceleration $\vec{a}$ (Fig. 9.10).

CAUTION **Use angles in radians in all equations** It's important to remember that Eq. (9.1), $s = r\theta$, is valid *only* when θ is measured in radians. The same is true of any equation derived from this, including Eqs. (9.13), (9.14), and (9.15). When you use these equations, you *must* express the angular quantities in radians, not revolutions or degrees (Fig. 9.11).

9.11 Always use radians when relating linear and angular quantities.

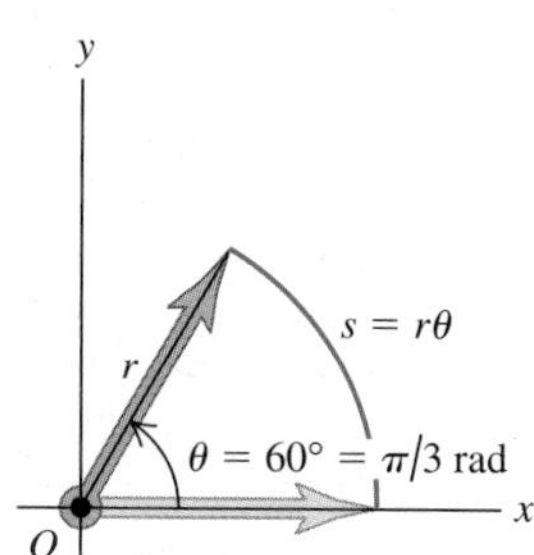

In any equation that relates linear quantities to angular quantities, the angles MUST be expressed in radians ...

RIGHT! ▶ $s = (\pi/3)r$

... never in degrees or revolutions.

WRONG ▶ $s = 60r$

Equations (9.1), (9.13), and (9.14) also apply to any particle that has the same tangential velocity as a point in a rotating rigid body. For example, when a rope wound around a circular cylinder unwraps without stretching or slipping, its speed and acceleration at any instant are equal to the speed and tangential acceleration of the point at which it is tangent to the cylinder. The same principle holds for situations such as bicycle chains and sprockets, belts and pulleys that turn without slipping, and so on. We will have several opportunities to use these relationships later in this chapter and in Chapter 10. Note that Eq. (9.15) for the centripetal component a_{rad} is applicable to the rope or chain *only* at points that are in contact with the cylinder or sprocket. Other points do not have the same acceleration toward the center of the circle that points on the cylinder or sprocket have.

Example 9.4 Throwing a discus

A discus thrower moves the discus in a circle of radius 80.0 cm. At a certain instant, the thrower is spinning at an angular speed of 10.0 rad/s and the angular speed is increasing at 50.0 rad/s². At this instant, find the tangential and centripetal components of the acceleration of the discus and the magnitude of the acceleration.

SOLUTION

IDENTIFY: We model the discus as a particle traveling on a circular path (Fig. 9.12a), so we can use the ideas developed in this section.

SET UP: We are given the radius $r = 0.800$ m, the angular speed $\omega = 10.0$ rad/s, and the rate of change of angular speed $\alpha = 50.0\ \text{rad/s}^2$. (Fig. 9.12b).The first two target variables are the acceleration components a_{tan} and a_{rad}, which we'll find with Eqs. (9.14) and (9.15), respectively. Given these components of the acceleration vector, we'll find its magnitude a (the third target variable) using the Pythagorean theorem.

EXECUTE: From Eqs. (9.14) and (9.15),

$$a_{tan} = r\alpha = (0.800\ \text{m})(50.0\ \text{rad/s}^2) = 40.0\ \text{m/s}^2$$

$$a_{rad} = \omega^2 r = (10.0\ \text{rad/s})^2(0.800\ \text{m}) = 80.0\ \text{m/s}^2$$

The magnitude of the acceleration vector is

$$a = \sqrt{a_{tan}{}^2 + a_{rad}{}^2} = 89.4\ \text{m/s}^2$$

9.12 (a) Whirling a discus in a circle. (b) Our sketch showing the acceleration components for the discus.

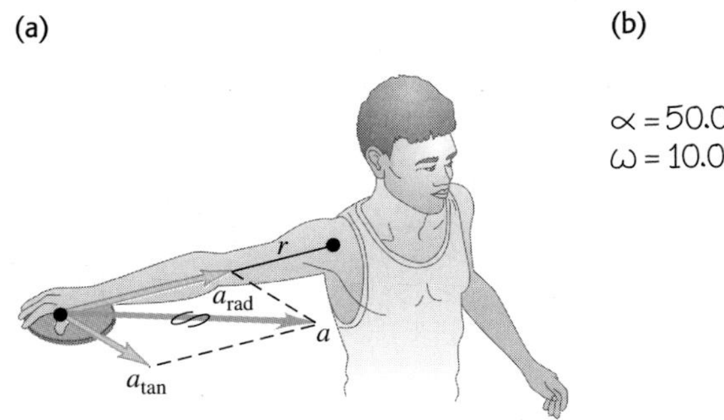

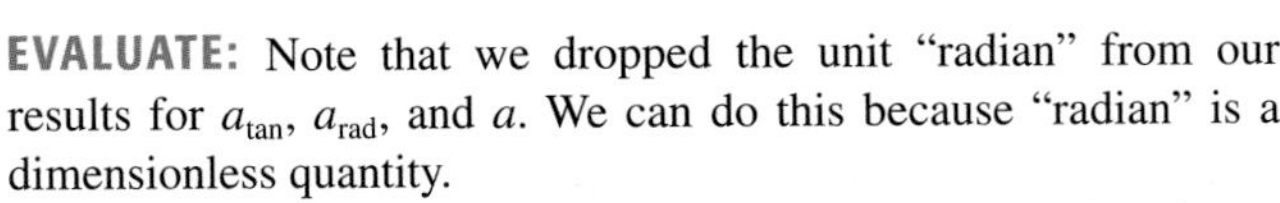

EVALUATE: Note that we dropped the unit "radian" from our results for a_{tan}, a_{rad}, and a. We can do this because "radian" is a dimensionless quantity.

The magnitude a is about nine times g, the acceleration due to gravity. Can you show that if the angular speed doubles to 20.0 rad/s while α remains the same, the acceleration magnitude a increases to 322 m/s², or almost $33g$?

Example 9.5 Designing a propeller

You are asked to design an airplane propeller to turn at 2400 rpm. The forward airspeed of the plane is to be 75.0 m/s (270 km/h, or about 168 mi/h), and the speed of the tips of the propeller blades through the air must not exceed 270 m/s (Fig. 9.13a). (This is about 0.80 times the speed of sound in air. If the propeller tips were to move too close to the speed of sound, they would produce a tremendous amount of noise.) (a) What is the maximum radius the propeller can have? (b) With this radius, what is the acceleration of the propeller tip?

SOLUTION

IDENTIFY: The object of interest in this example is a particle at the tip of the propeller; our target variables are the particle's distance from the axis and its acceleration. Note that the speed of this particle through the air (which cannot exceed 270 m/s) is due to both the propeller's rotation *and* the forward motion of the airplane.

SET UP: As Fig. 9.13b shows, the velocity $\vec{v}_{tip}$ of a particle at the propeller tip is the vector sum of its tangential velocity due to the propeller's rotation (magnitude v_{tan}, given by Eq. (9.13)) and the forward velocity of the airplane (magnitude $v_{plane} = 75.0\ \text{m/s}$). The rotation plane of the propeller is perpendicular to the direction of flight, so these two vectors are perpendicular and we can use the Pythagorean theorem to relate v_{tan} and v_{plane} to v_{tip}. We will then set $v_{tip} = 270\ \text{m/s}$ and solve for the radius r. Note that the angular speed of the propeller is constant, so the acceleration of the propeller tip has only a radial component; we'll find it using Eq. (9.15).

EXECUTE: We first convert ω to rad/s (see Fig. 9.11):

$$\omega = 2400\ \text{rpm} = \left(2400\,\frac{\text{rev}}{\text{min}}\right)\left(\frac{2\pi\ \text{rad}}{1\ \text{rev}}\right)\left(\frac{1\ \text{min}}{60\ \text{s}}\right)$$

$$= 251\ \text{rad/s}$$

9.13 (a) A propeller-driven airplane in flight. (b) Our sketch showing the velocity components for the propeller tip.

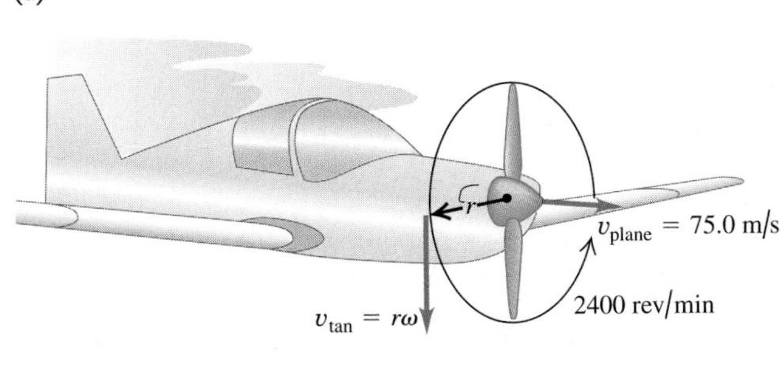

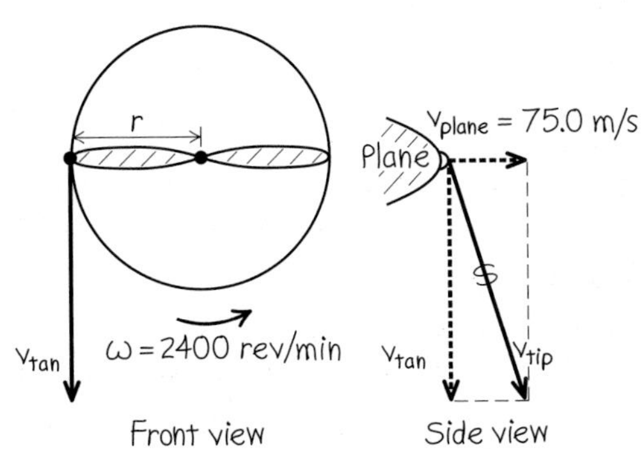

Continued

(a) From Fig. 9.13b and Eq. (9.13), the velocity magnitude v_{total} is given by

$$v_{tip}^2 = v_{plane}^2 + v_{tan}^2 = v_{plane}^2 + r^2\omega^2 \quad \text{so}$$

$$r^2 = \frac{v_{tip}^2 - v_{plane}^2}{\omega^2} \quad \text{and} \quad r = \frac{\sqrt{v_{tip}^2 - v_{plane}^2}}{\omega}$$

If $v_{tip} = 270$ m/s, the propeller radius is

$$r = \frac{\sqrt{(270\text{ m/s})^2 - (75.0\text{ m/s})^2}}{251\text{ rad/s}} = 1.03\text{ m}$$

(b) The centripetal acceleration is

$$a_{rad} = \omega^2 r$$
$$= (251\text{ rad/s})^2(1.03\text{ m}) = 6.5 \times 10^4\text{ m/s}^2$$

The *tangential* acceleration is zero because the angular speed is constant.

EVALUATE: From $\Sigma\vec{F} = m\vec{a}$, the propeller must exert a force of 6.5×10^4 N on each kilogram of material at its tip! This is why propellers are made out of tough material, usually aluminum alloy.

Conceptual Example 9.6 Bicycle gears

How are the angular speeds of the two bicycle sprockets in Fig. 9.14 related to the number of teeth on each sprocket?

SOLUTION

The chain does not slip or stretch, so it moves at the same tangential speed v on both sprockets. From Eq. (9.13),

$$v = r_{front}\omega_{front} = r_{rear}\omega_{rear} \quad \text{so} \quad \frac{\omega_{rear}}{\omega_{front}} = \frac{r_{front}}{r_{rear}}$$

The angular speed is inversely proportional to the radius. This relationship also holds for pulleys connected by a belt, provided the belt doesn't slip. For chain sprockets the teeth must be equally spaced on the circumferences of both sprockets for the chain to mesh properly with both. Let N_{front} and N_{rear} be the numbers of teeth; the condition that the tooth spacing is the same on both sprockets is

$$\frac{2\pi r_{front}}{N_{front}} = \frac{2\pi r_{rear}}{N_{rear}} \quad \text{or} \quad \frac{r_{front}}{r_{rear}} = \frac{N_{front}}{N_{rear}}$$

Combining this with the other equation, we get

$$\frac{\omega_{rear}}{\omega_{front}} = \frac{N_{front}}{N_{rear}}$$

9.14 The sprockets and chain of a bicycle.

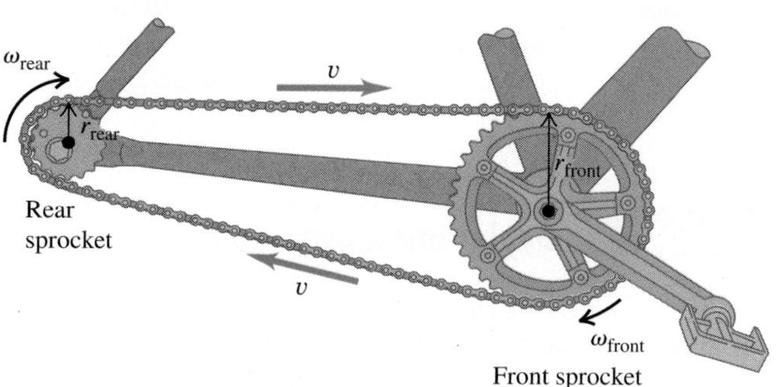

The angular speed of each sprocket is inversely proportional to the number of teeth. On a multispeed bike, you get the highest angular speed ω_{rear} of the rear wheel for a given pedaling rate ω_{front} when the ratio N_{front}/N_{rear} is maximum; this means using the largest-radius front sprocket (largest N_{front}) and the smallest-radius rear sprocket (smallest N_{rear}).

Test Your Understanding of Section 9.3 Information is stored on a CD or DVD (see Fig. 9.8) in a coded pattern of tiny pits. The pits are arranged in a track that spirals outward toward the rim of the disc. As the disc spins inside a player, the track is scanned at a constant *linear* speed. How must the rotation speed of the disc change as the player's scanning head moves over the track? (i) The rotation speed must increase. (ii) The rotation speed must decrease. (iii) The rotation speed must stay the same.

MP

9.4 Energy in Rotational Motion

ActivPhysics ONLINE

7.7 Rotational Inertia

A rotating rigid body consists of mass in motion, so it has kinetic energy. As we will see, we can express this kinetic energy in terms of the body's angular speed and a new quantity, called *moment of inertia,* that depends on the body's mass and how the mass is distributed.

To begin, we think of a body as being made up of a large number of particles, with masses $m_1, m_2, \ldots$ at distances $r_1, r_2, \ldots$ from the axis of rotation. We label the particles with the index i: The mass of the ith particle is m_i and its distance from the axis of rotation is r_i. The particles don't necessarily all lie in the same plane, so we specify that r_i is the *perpendicular* distance from the axis to the ith particle.

When a rigid body rotates about a fixed axis, the speed v_i of the ith particle is given by Eq. (9.13), $v_i = r_i\omega$, where ω is the body's angular speed. Different particles have different values of r, but ω is the same for all (otherwise, the body wouldn't be rigid). The kinetic energy of the ith particle can be expressed as

$$\frac{1}{2}m_i v_i^2 = \frac{1}{2}m_i r_i^2\omega^2$$

The *total* kinetic energy of the body is the sum of the kinetic energies of all its particles:

$$K = \frac{1}{2}m_1 r_1^2\omega^2 + \frac{1}{2}m_2 r_2^2\omega^2 + \cdots = \sum_i \frac{1}{2}m_i r_i^2\omega^2$$

Taking the common factor $\omega^2/2$ out of this expression, we get

$$K = \frac{1}{2}(m_1 r_1^2 + m_2 r_2^2 + \cdots)\omega^2 = \frac{1}{2}\left(\sum_i m_i r_i^2\right)\omega^2$$

The quantity in parentheses, obtained by multiplying the mass of each particle by the square of its distance from the axis of rotation and adding these products, is denoted by I and is called the **moment of inertia** of the body for this rotation axis:

$$I = m_1 r_1^2 + m_2 r_2^2 + \cdots = \sum_i m_i r_i^2 \quad \text{(definition of moment of inertia)} \qquad (9.16)$$

The word "moment" means that I depends on how the body's mass is distributed in space; it has nothing to do with a "moment" of time. For a body with a given rotation axis and a given total mass, the greater the distance from the axis to the particles that make up the body, the greater the moment of inertia. In a rigid body, the distances r_i are all constant and I is independent of how the body rotates around the given axis. The SI unit of moment of inertia is the kilogram-meter^2 $(\text{kg} \cdot \text{m}^2)$.

In terms of moment of inertia I, the **rotational kinetic energy** K of a rigid body is

$$K = \frac{1}{2}I\omega^2 \quad \text{(rotational kinetic energy of a rigid body)} \qquad (9.17)$$

The kinetic energy given by Eq. (9.17) is *not* a new form of energy; it's simply the sum of the kinetic energies of the individual particles that make up the rotating rigid body. To use Eq. (9.17), ω *must* be measured in radians per second, not revolutions or degrees per second, to give K in joules. That's because we used $v_i = r_i\omega$ in our derivation.

Equation (9.17) gives a simple physical interpretation of moment of inertia: *The greater the moment of inertia, the greater the kinetic energy of a rigid body rotating with a given angular speed* ω. We learned in Chapter 6 that the kinetic energy of a body equals the amount of work done to accelerate that body from rest. So the greater a body's moment of inertia, the harder it is to start the body rotating if it's at rest and the harder it is to stop its rotation if it's already rotating (Fig. 9.15). For this reason, I is also called the *rotational inertia.*

The next example shows how *changing* the rotation axis can affect the value of I.

9.15 An apparatus free to rotate around a vertical axis. To vary the moment of inertia, the two equal-mass cylinders can be locked into different positions on the horizontal shaft.

• Mass close to axis
• Small moment of inertia
• Easy to start apparatus rotating

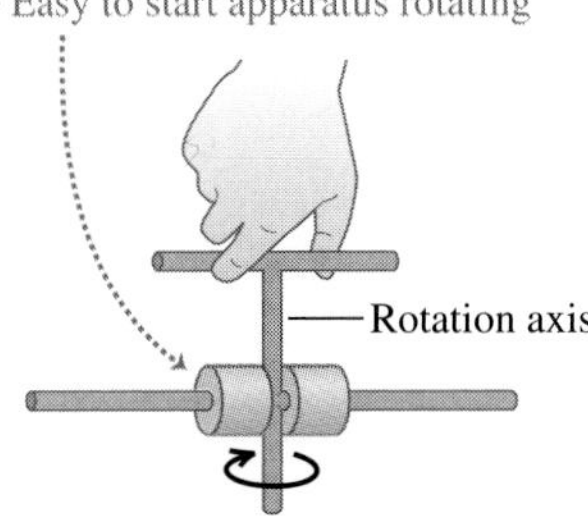

• Mass farther from axis
• Greater moment of inertia
• Harder to start apparatus rotating

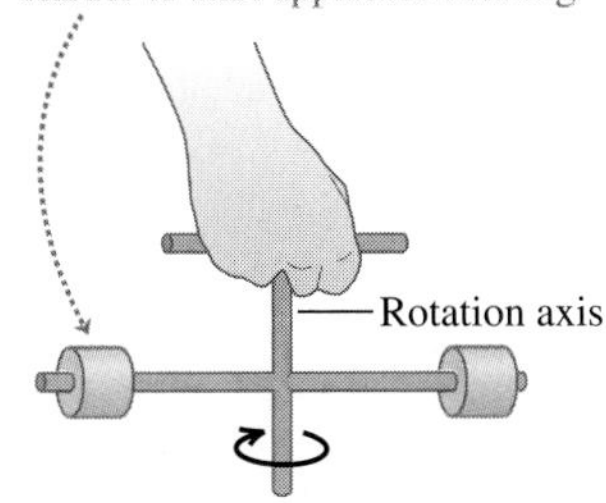

Example 9.7 Moments of inertia for different rotation axes

An engineer is designing a machine part consisting of three heavy disks linked by lightweight struts (Fig. 9.16). (a) What is the moment of inertia of this body about an axis through the center of disk A, perpendicular to the plane of the diagram? (b) What is the moment of inertia about an axis through the centers of disks B and C? (c) If the body rotates about an axis through A perpendicular to the plane of the diagram, with angular speed $\omega = 4.0$ rad/s, what is its kinetic energy?

SOLUTION

IDENTIFY: We'll consider the disks as massive particles and the lightweight struts as massless rods. Then we can use the ideas of this section to calculate the moment of inertia of this collection of three particles.

SET UP: In parts (a) and (b), we'll use Eq. (9.16) to find the moments of inertia for each of the two axes. Given the moment of inertia for axis A, we'll use Eq. (9.17) in part (c) to find the rotational kinetic energy.

EXECUTE: (a) The particle at point A lies *on* the axis. Its distance r from the axis is zero, so it contributes nothing to the moment of inertia. Equation (9.16) gives

$$I = \sum m_i r_i^2 = (0.10\text{ kg})(0.50\text{ m})^2 + (0.20\text{ kg})(0.40\text{ m})^2 = 0.057\text{ kg}\cdot\text{m}^2$$

(b) The particles at B and C both lie *on* the axis, so for them $r = 0$ and neither contributes to the moment of inertia. Only A contributes, and we have

$$I = \sum m_i r_i^2 = (0.30\text{ kg})(0.40\text{ m})^2 = 0.048\text{ kg}\cdot\text{m}^2$$

(c) From Eq. (9.17),

$$K = \frac{1}{2}I\omega^2 = \frac{1}{2}(0.057\text{ kg}\cdot\text{m}^2)(4.0\text{ rad/s})^2 = 0.46\text{ J}$$

EVALUATE: Our results show that the moment of inertia for the axis through A is greater than that for the axis through B and C. Hence, of the two axes, it's easier to make the machine part rotate about the axis through B and C.

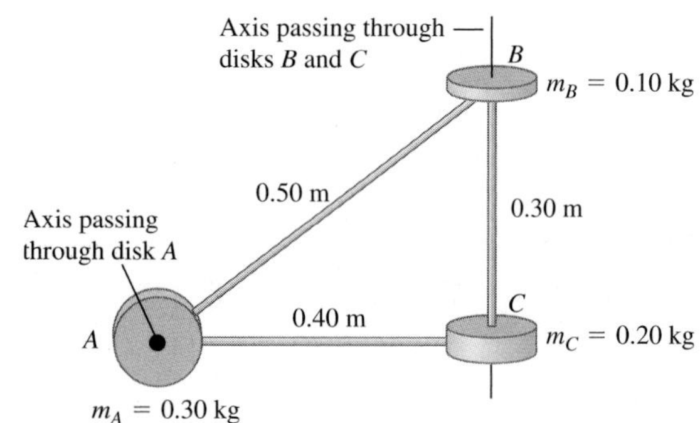

9.16 An oddly shaped machine part.

CAUTION Moment of inertia depends on the choice of axis The results of parts (a) and (b) of Example 9.7 show that the moment of inertia of a body depends on the location and orientation of the axis. It's not enough to just say, "The moment of inertia of this body is 0.048 kg · m²." We have to be specific and say, "The moment of inertia of this body *about the axis through B and C* is 0.048 kg · m²."

In Example 9.7 we represented the body as several point masses, and we evaluated the sum in Eq. (9.16) directly. When the body is a *continuous* distribution of matter, such as a solid cylinder or plate, the sum becomes an integral, and we need to use calculus to calculate the moment of inertia. We will give several examples of such calculations in Section 9.6; meanwhile, Table 9.2 gives moments of inertia for several familiar shapes in terms of their masses and dimensions. Each body shown in Table 9.2 is *uniform;* that is, the density has the same value at all points within the solid parts of the body.

CAUTION Computing the moment of inertia You may be tempted to try to compute the moment of inertia of a body by assuming that all the mass is concentrated at the center of mass and multiplying the total mass by the square of the distance from the center of mass to the axis. Resist that temptation; it doesn't work! For example, when a uniform thin rod of length L and mass M is pivoted about an axis through one end, perpendicular to the rod, the moment of inertia is $I = ML^2/3$ [case (b) in Table 9.2]. If we took the mass as concentrated at the center, a distance $L/2$ from the axis, we would obtain the *incorrect* result $I = M(L/2)^2 = ML^2/4$.

Now that we know how to calculate the kinetic energy of a rotating rigid body, we can apply the energy principles of Chapter 7 to rotational motion. Here are some points of strategy and some examples.

Table 9.2 Moments of Inertia of Various Bodies

(a) Slender rod, axis through center

$I = \frac{1}{12}ML^2$

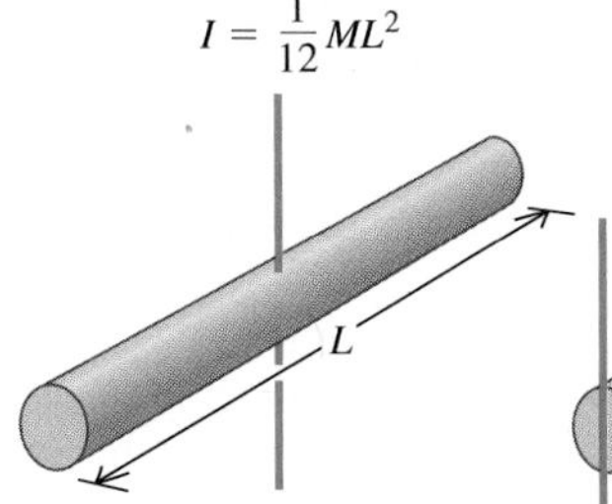

(b) Slender rod, axis through one end

$I = \frac{1}{3}ML^2$

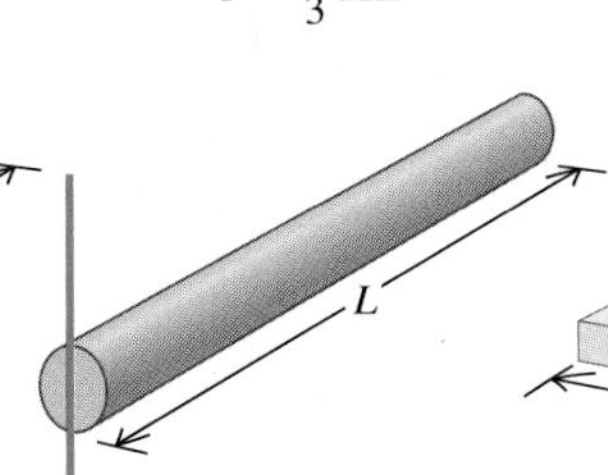

(c) Rectangular plate, axis through center

$I = \frac{1}{12}M(a^2 + b^2)$

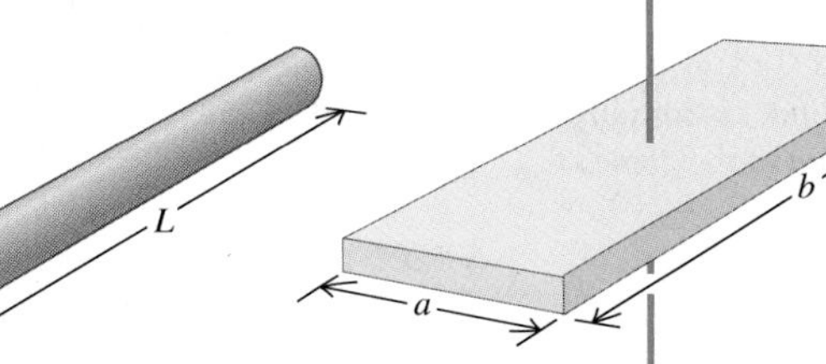

(d) Thin rectangular plate, axis along edge

$I = \frac{1}{3}Ma^2$

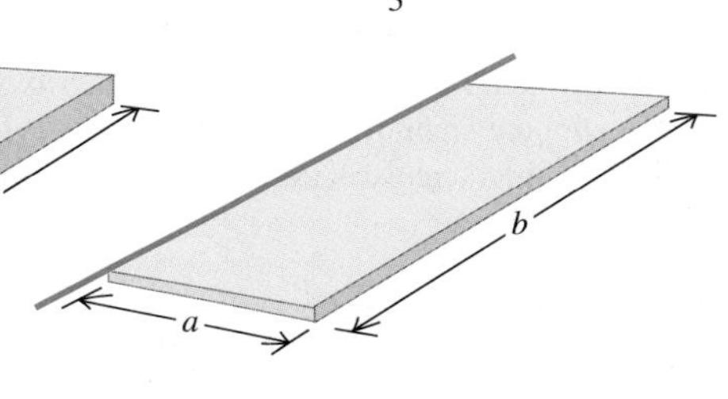

(e) Hollow cylinder

$I = \frac{1}{2}M(R_1^{\,2} + R_2^{\,2})$

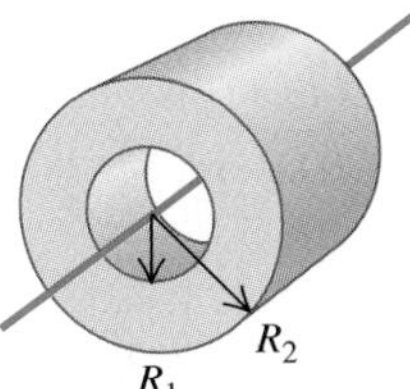

(f) Solid cylinder

$I = \frac{1}{2}MR^2$

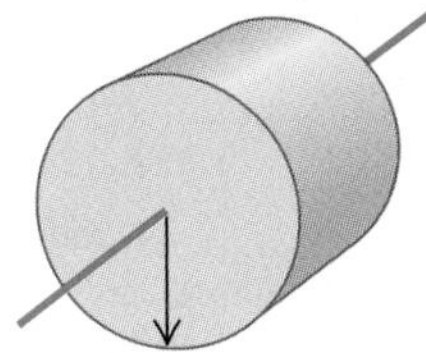

(g) Thin-walled hollow cylinder

$I = MR^2$

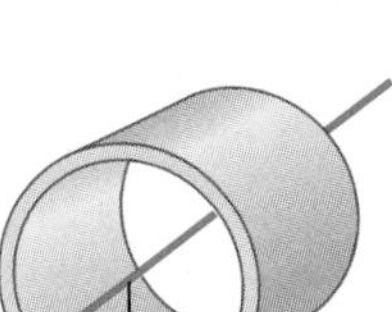
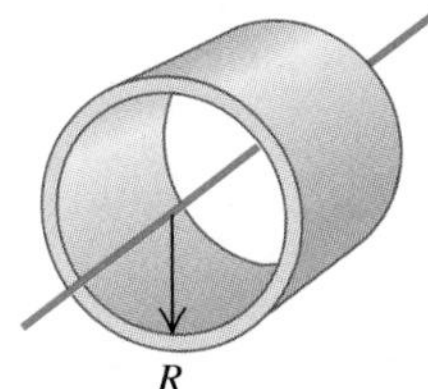

(h) Solid sphere

$I = \frac{2}{5}MR^2$

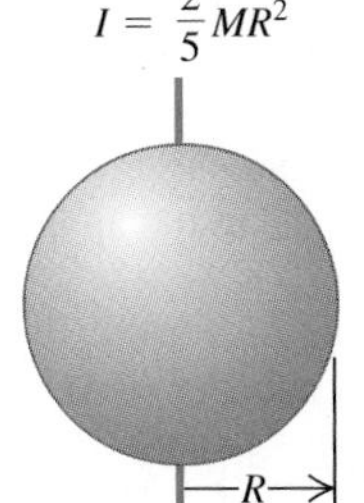
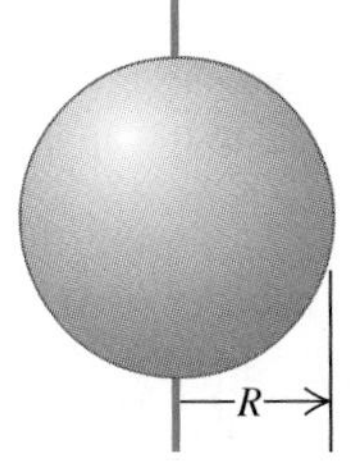

(i) Thin-walled hollow sphere

$I = \frac{2}{3}MR^2$

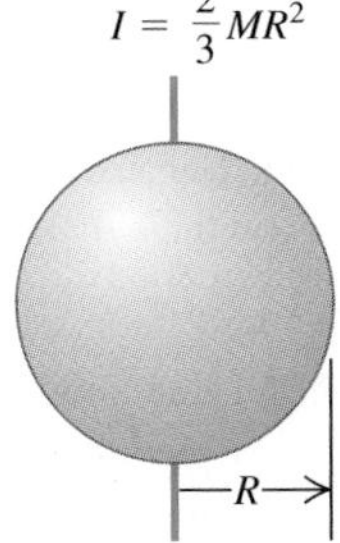

Problem-Solving Strategy 9.1 Rotational Energy

IDENTIFY *the relevant concepts:* You can use work–energy relationships and conservation of energy to find relationships involving position and motion of a rigid body rotating around a fixed axis. As we saw in Chapter 7, the energy method is usually not helpful for problems that involve elapsed time. In Chapter 10 we'll see how to approach rotational problems of this kind.

SET UP *the problem* using the same steps as in Problem-Solving Strategy 7.1 (Section 7.1), with the following addition:

5. Many problems involve a rope or cable wrapped around a rotating rigid body, which functions as a pulley. In these situations, remember that the point on the pulley that contacts the rope has the same linear speed as the rope, provided the rope doesn't slip on the pulley. You can then take advantage of Eqs. (9.13) and (9.14), which relate the linear speed and tangential acceleration of a point on a rigid body to the angular velocity and angular acceleration of the body. Examples 9.8 and 9.9 illustrate this point.

EXECUTE *the solution:* As in Chapter 7, write expressions for the initial and final kinetic and potential energies $(K_1, K_2, U_1, \text{and } U_2)$ and the nonconservative work W_{other} (if any). The new feature is rotational kinetic energy, which is expressed in terms of the body's moment of inertia I for the given axis and its angular speed ω $\left(K = \frac{1}{2}I\omega^2\right)$ instead of its mass m and speed v. Substitute these expressions into $K_1 + U_1 + W_{\text{other}} = K_2 + U_2$ (if nonconservative work is done) or $K_1 + U_1 = K_2 + U_2$ (if only conservative work is done) and solve for the target variable(s). As in Chapter 7, it's helpful to draw bar graphs showing the initial and final values of K, U, and $E = K + U$.

EVALUATE *your answer:* As always, check whether your answer makes physical sense.

Example 9.8 An unwinding cable I

A light, flexible, nonstretching cable is wrapped several times around a winch drum, a solid cylinder of mass 50 kg and diameter 0.120 m, which rotates about a stationary horizontal axis held by frictionless bearings (Fig. 9.17). The free end of the cable is pulled with a constant 9.0-N force for a distance of 2.0 m. It unwinds without slipping and turns the cylinder. If the cylinder is initially at rest, find its final angular speed and the final speed of the cable.

SOLUTION

IDENTIFY: We will solve this problem using energy methods. Point 1 is when the cylinder first begins to move, and point 2 is when the cable has moved 2.0 m. We'll assume that the light cable is massless, so that only the cylinder has kinetic energy. The cylinder doesn't move vertically, so there are no changes in gravitational potential energy. There is friction between the cable and the cylinder, which is what makes the cylinder rotate when the cable is pulled. But because the cable doesn't slip, there is no sliding of the cable relative to the cylinder and no mechanical energy is lost in friction. Because the cable is massless, the force that the cable exerts on the cylinder rim is equal to the applied force F.

9.17 A cable unwinds from a cylinder (side view).

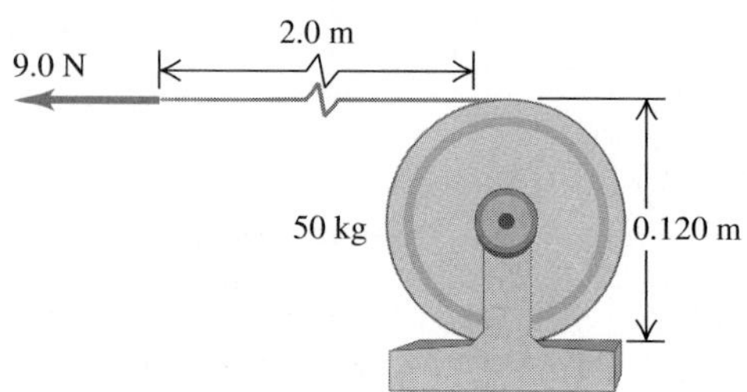

SET UP: The cylinder starts at rest, so the initial kinetic energy is $K_1 = 0$. Between points 1 and 2 the force F does work on the cylinder over a distance $s = 2.0$ m. As a result, the kinetic energy at point 2 is $K_2 = \frac{1}{2}I\omega^2$. One of our target variables is ω; the other is the speed of the cable at point 2, which is equal to the tangential speed v of the cylinder at that point. We'll find v from ω by using Eq. (9.13).

EXECUTE: The work done on the cylinder is $W_{\text{other}} = Fs = (9.0\text{ N})(2.0\text{ m}) = 18$ J. From Table 9.2 the moment of inertia is

$$I = \frac{1}{2}mR^2 = \frac{1}{2}(50\text{ kg})(0.060\text{ m})^2 = 0.090\text{ kg}\cdot\text{m}^2$$

(The radius R is half the diameter of the cylinder.) The relationship $K_1 + U_1 + W_{\text{other}} = K_2 + U_2$ then gives

$$0 + 0 + W_{\text{other}} = \frac{1}{2}I\omega^2 + 0$$

$$\omega = \sqrt{\frac{2W_{\text{other}}}{I}} = \sqrt{\frac{2(18\text{ J})}{0.090\text{ kg}\cdot\text{m}^2}}$$

$$= 20\text{ rad/s}$$

The final tangential speed of the cylinder, and hence the final speed of the cable, is

$$v = R\omega = (0.060\text{ m})(20\text{ rad/s}) = 1.2\text{ m/s}$$

EVALUATE: If the mass of the cable can't be neglected, then some of the work done would go into the kinetic energy of the cable. Hence the cylinder would end up with less kinetic energy and a smaller angular speed than we calculated here.

Example 9.9 An unwinding cable II

We wrap a light, flexible cable around a solid cylinder with mass M and radius R. The cylinder rotates with negligible friction about a stationary horizontal axis. We tie the free end of the cable to a block of mass m and release the object with no initial velocity at a distance h above the floor. As the block falls, the cable unwinds without stretching or slipping, turning the cylinder. Find the speed of the falling block and the angular speed of the cylinder just as the block strikes the floor.

SOLUTION

IDENTIFY: As in Example 9.8, the cable doesn't slip and friction does no work. The cable does no *net* work; at its upper end the force and displacement are in the same direction, and at its lower end they are in opposite directions. Thus the total work done by the two ends of the cable is zero. Hence only gravity does work, and so mechanical energy is conserved.

SET UP: Figure 9.18a shows the situation just before the block begins to fall. At this point the system has no kinetic energy, so

9.18 Our sketches for this problem.

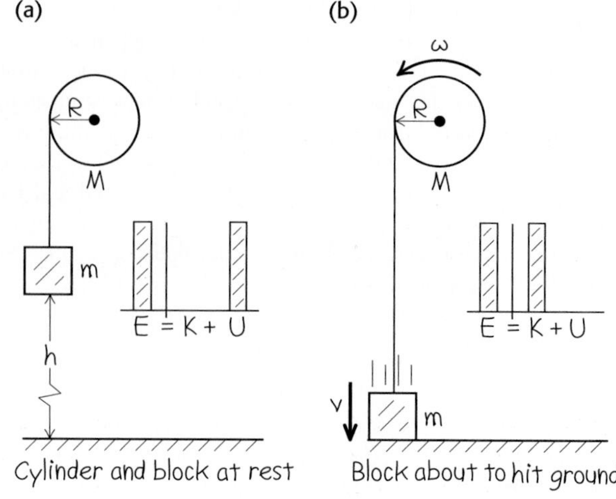

$K_1 = 0$. We take the potential energy to be zero when the block is at floor level; then $U_1 = mgh$ and $U_2 = 0$. (We can ignore the gravitational potential energy for the rotating cylinder, since its height doesn't change.) Just before the block hits the floor (Fig. 9.18b), both the block and the cylinder have kinetic energy. The total kinetic energy K_2 at that instant is

$$K_2 = \frac{1}{2}mv^2 + \frac{1}{2}I\omega^2$$

From Table 9.2 the moment of inertia of the cylinder is $I = \frac{1}{2}MR^2$. Also, v and ω are related by $v = R\omega$, since the speed of the falling block must be equal to the tangential speed at the outer surface of the cylinder. We'll use these relationships to solve for the target variables v and ω shown in Fig. 9.18b.

EXECUTE: We use our expressions for K_1, U_1, K_2, and U_2 and the relationship $\omega = v/R$ in the energy-conservation equation $K_1 + U_1 = K_2 + U_2$. We then solve for v:

$$0 + mgh = \frac{1}{2}mv^2 + \frac{1}{2}\left(\frac{1}{2}MR^2\right)\left(\frac{v}{R}\right)^2 + 0 = \frac{1}{2}\left(m + \frac{1}{2}M\right)v^2$$

$$v = \sqrt{\frac{2gh}{1 + M/2m}}$$

The final angular speed of the cylinder is $\omega = v/R$.

EVALUATE: Let's check some particular cases. When M is much larger than m, v is very small, as we would expect. When M is much smaller than m, v is nearly equal to $\sqrt{2gh}$, which is the speed of a body that falls freely from an initial height h. Does it surprise you that v doesn't depend on the radius of the cylinder?

Gravitational Potential Energy for an Extended Body

ActivPhysics ONLINE

7.12 Woman and Flywheel Elevator—Energy Approach

7.13 Rotoride—Energy Approach

In Example 9.9 the cable was of negligible mass, so we could ignore its kinetic energy as well as the gravitational potential energy associated with it. If the mass is *not* negligible, we need to know how to calculate the *gravitational potential energy* associated with such an extended body. If the acceleration of gravity g is the same at all points on the body, the gravitational potential energy is the same as though all the mass were concentrated at the center of mass of the body. Suppose we take the y-axis vertically upward. Then for a body with total mass M, the gravitational potential energy U is simply

$$U = Mgy_{cm} \quad \text{(gravitational potential energy for an extended body)} \quad (9.18)$$

where y_{cm} is the y-coordinate of the center of mass. This expression applies to any extended body, whether it is rigid or not (Fig. 9.19).

To prove Eq. (9.18), we again represent the body as a collection of mass elements m_i. The potential energy for element m_i is $m_i g y_i$, so the total potential energy is

$$U = m_1gy_1 + m_2gy_2 + \cdots = (m_1y_1 + m_2y_2 + \cdots)g$$

But from Eq. (8.28), which defines the coordinates of the center of mass,

$$m_1y_1 + m_2y_2 + \cdots = (m_1 + m_2 + \cdots)y_{cm} = My_{cm}$$

where $M = m_1 + m_2 + \cdots$ is the total mass. Combining this with the above expression for U, we find $U = Mgy_{cm}$ in agreement with Eq. (9.18).

We leave the application of Eq. (9.18) to the problems. We'll make use of this relationship in Chapter 10 in the analysis of rigid-body problems in which the axis of rotation moves.

9.19 In a technique called the "Fosbury flop" after its innovator, this athlete arches his body as he passes over the bar in the high jump. As a result, his center of mass actually passes *under* the bar. This technique requires a smaller increase in gravitational potential energy [Eq. (9.18)] than the older method of straddling the bar.

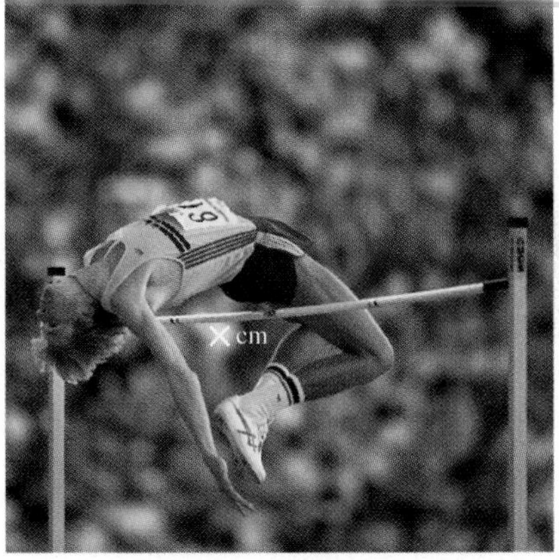

Test Your Understanding of Section 9.4 Suppose the cylinder and block in Example 9.9 have the same mass, so $m = M$. Just before the block strikes the floor, which statement is correct about the relationship between the kinetic energy of the falling block and the rotational kinetic energy of the cylinder? (i) The block has more kinetic energy than the cylinder. (ii) The block has less kinetic energy than the cylinder. (iii) The block and the cylinder have equal amounts of kinetic energy.

MP

9.5 Parallel-Axis Theorem

We pointed out in Section 9.4 that a body doesn't have just one moment of inertia. In fact, it has infinitely many, because there are infinitely many axes about which it might rotate. But there is a simple relationship between the moment of inertia I_{cm} of a body of mass M about an axis through its center of

9.20 The mass element m_i has coordinates (x_i, y_i) with respect to an axis of rotation through the center of mass (cm) and coordinates $(x_i - a, y_i - b)$ with respect to the parallel axis through point P.

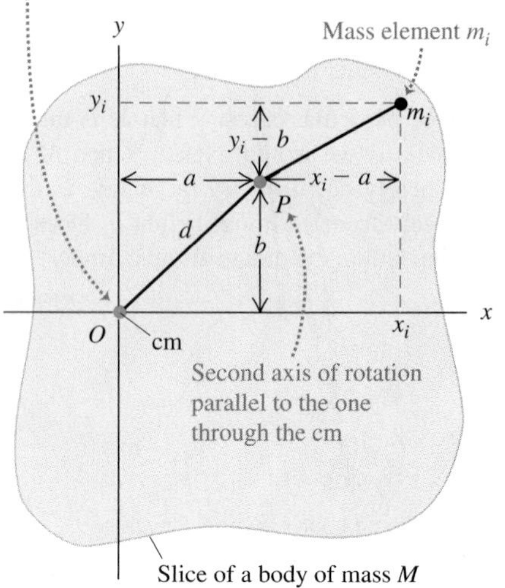

mass and the moment of inertia I_P about any other axis parallel to the original one but displaced from it by a distance d. This relationship, called the **parallel-axis theorem,** states that

$$I_P = I_{cm} + Md^2 \qquad \text{(parallel-axis theorem)} \tag{9.19}$$

To prove this theorem, we consider two axes, both parallel to the z-axis, one through the center of mass and the other through a point P (Fig. 9.20). First we take a very thin slice of the body, parallel to the xy-plane and perpendicular to the z-axis. We take the origin of our coordinate system to be at the center of mass of the body; the coordinates of the center of mass are then $x_{cm} = y_{cm} = z_{cm} = 0$. The axis through the center of mass passes through this thin slice at point O, and the parallel axis passes through point P, whose x- and y-coordinates are (a, b). The distance of this axis from the axis through the center of mass is d, where $d^2 = a^2 + b^2$.

We can write an expression for the moment of inertia I_P about the axis through point P. Let m_i be a mass element in our slice, with coordinates (x_i, y_i, z_i). Then the moment of inertia I_{cm} of the slice about the axis through the center of mass (at O) is

$$I_{cm} = \sum_i m_i(x_i^2 + y_i^2)$$

The moment of inertia of the slice about the axis through P is

$$I_P = \sum_i m_i[(x_i - a)^2 + (y_i - b)^2]$$

These expressions don't involve the coordinates z_i measured perpendicular to the slices, so we can extend the sums to include *all* particles in *all* slices. Then I_P becomes the moment of inertia of the *entire* body for an axis through P. We then expand the squared terms and regroup, and obtain

$$I_P = \sum_i m_i(x_i^2 + y_i^2) - 2a\sum_i m_i x_i - 2b\sum_i m_i y_i + (a^2 + b^2)\sum_i m_i$$

The first sum is I_{cm}. From Eq. (8.28), the definition of the center of mass, the second and third sums are proportional to x_{cm} and y_{cm}; these are zero because we have taken our origin to be the center of mass. The final term is d^2 multiplied by the total mass, or Md^2. This completes our proof that $I_P = I_{cm} + Md^2$.

As Eq. (9.19) shows, a rigid body has a lower moment of inertia about an axis through its center of mass than about any other parallel axis. Thus it's easier to start a body rotating if the rotation axis passes through the center of mass. This suggests that it's somehow most natural for a rotating body to rotate about an axis through its center of mass; we'll make this idea more quantitative in Chapter 10.

Example 9.10 Using the parallel-axis theorem

A part of a mechanical linkage (Fig. 9.21) has a mass of 3.6 kg. We measure its moment of inertia about an axis 0.15 m from its center of mass to be $I_P = 0.132\ \text{kg} \cdot \text{m}^2$. What is the moment of inertia I_{cm} about a parallel axis through the center of mass?

9.21 Calculating I_{cm} from a measurement of I_P.

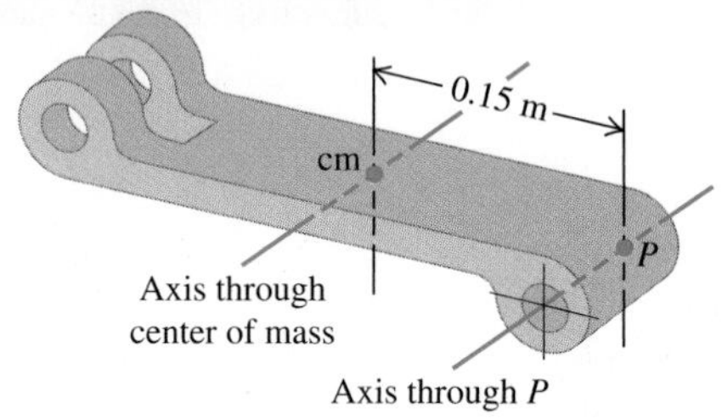

SOLUTION

IDENTIFY: The parallel-axis theorem allows us to relate the moments of inertia I_{cm} and I_P through the two parallel axes.

SET UP: We'll use Eq. (9.19) to determine the target variable I_{cm}.

EXECUTE: Rearranging the equation and substituting the values,

$$I_{cm} = I_P - Md^2 = 0.132\ \text{kg} \cdot \text{m}^2 - (3.6\ \text{kg})(0.15\ \text{m})^2$$
$$= 0.051\ \text{kg} \cdot \text{m}^2$$

EVALUATE: Our result shows that I_{cm} is less than I_P. This is as it should be: As we saw earlier, the moment of inertia for an axis through the center of mass is lower than for any other parallel axis.

Test Your Understanding of Section 9.5 A pool cue is a wooden rod with a uniform composition and tapered with a larger diameter at one end than at the other end. Use the parallel-axis theorem to decide whether a pool cue has a larger moment of inertia (i) for an axis through the thicker end of the rod and perpendicular to the length of the rod, or (ii) for an axis through the thinner end of the rod and perpendicular to the length of the rod.

*9.6 Moment-of-Inertia Calculations

NOTE: This optional section is for students who are familiar with integral calculus.

If a rigid body is a continuous distribution of mass—like a solid cylinder or a solid sphere—it cannot be represented by a few point masses. In this case the sum of masses and distances that defines the moment of inertia [Eq. (9.16)] becomes an integral. Imagine dividing the body into elements of mass dm that are very small, so that all points in a particular element are at essentially the same perpendicular distance from the axis of rotation. We call this distance r, as before. Then the moment of inertia is

$$I = \int r^2 \, dm \tag{9.20}$$

To evaluate the integral, we have to represent r and dm in terms of the same integration variable. When the object is effectively one-dimensional, such as the slender rods (a) and (b) in Table 9.2, we can use a coordinate x along the length and relate dm to an increment dx. For a three-dimensional object it is usually easiest to express dm in terms of an element of volume dV and the *density* ρ of the body. Density is mass per unit volume, $\rho = dm/dV$, so we may also write Eq. (9.20) as

$$I = \int r^2 \rho \, dV$$

This expression tells us that a body's moment of inertia depends on how its density varies within its volume (Fig. 9.22). If the body is uniform in density, then we may take ρ outside the integral:

$$I = \rho \int r^2 \, dV \tag{9.21}$$

To use this equation, we have to express the volume element dV in terms of the differentials of the integration variables, such as $dV = dx\,dy\,dz$. The element dV must always be chosen so that all points within it are at very nearly the same distance from the axis of rotation. The limits on the integral are determined by the shape and dimensions of the body. For regularly shaped bodies, this integration is often easy to do.

9.22 By measuring small variations in the orbits of satellites, geophysicists can measure the earth's moment of inertia. This tells us how our planet's mass is distributed within its interior. The data show that the earth is far denser at the core than in its outer layers.

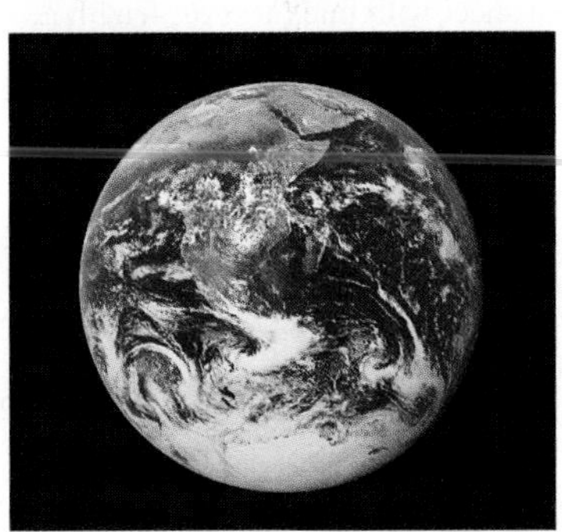

Example 9.11 Uniform thin rod, axis perpendicular to length

Figure 9.23 shows a slender uniform rod with mass M and length L. It might be a baton held by a twirler in a marching band (less the rubber end caps). Compute its moment of inertia about an axis through O, at an arbitrary distance h from one end.

SOLUTION

IDENTIFY: The rod is a continuous distribution of mass, so we must use integration to find the moment of inertia. We choose as an element of mass a short section of rod with length dx at a distance x from point O.

9.23 Finding the moment of inertia of a thin rod about an axis through O.

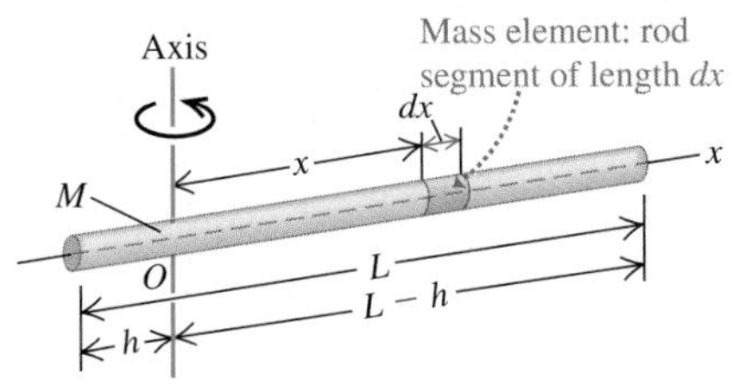

SET UP: The ratio of the mass dm of an element to the total mass M is equal to the ratio of its length dx to the total length L:

$$\frac{dm}{M} = \frac{dx}{L} \quad \text{so} \quad dm = \frac{M}{L}dx$$

We'll determine I from Eq. (9.20) with r replaced by x (see Fig. 9.23).

EXECUTE: Figure 9.23 shows that the integration limits on x are from $-h$ to $(L - h)$. Hence we obtain

$$I = \int x^2\,dm = \frac{M}{L}\int_{-h}^{L-h} x^2\,dx$$

$$= \left[\frac{M}{L}\left(\frac{x^3}{3}\right)\right]_{-h}^{L-h} = \frac{1}{3}M(L^2 - 3Lh + 3h^2)$$

EVALUATE: From this general expression we can find the moment of inertia about an axis through any point on the rod. For example, if the axis is at the left end, $h = 0$ and

$$I = \frac{1}{3}ML^2$$

If the axis is at the right end, we should get the same result. Putting $h = L$, we again get

$$I = \frac{1}{3}ML^2$$

If the axis passes through the center, the usual place for a twirled baton, then $h = L/2$ and

$$I = \frac{1}{12}ML^2$$

These results agree with the expressions in Table 9.2.

Example 9.12 Hollow or solid cylinder, rotating about axis of symmetry

Figure 9.24 shows a hollow, uniform cylinder with length L, inner radius R_1, and outer radius R_2. It might be a steel cylinder in a printing press or a sheet-steel rolling mill. Find the moment of inertia about the axis of symmetry of the cylinder.

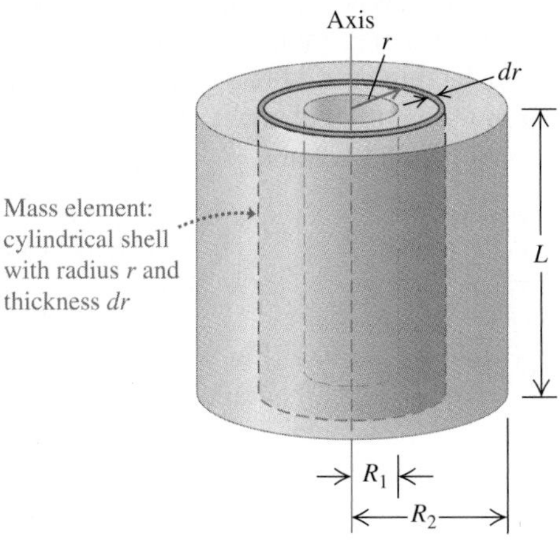

9.24 Finding the moment of inertia of a hollow cylinder about its symmetry axis.

SOLUTION

IDENTIFY: Again we must use integration to find the moment of inertia, but now we choose as a volume element a thin cylindrical shell of radius r, thickness dr, and length L. All parts of this element are at very nearly the same distance from the axis.

SET UP: The volume of the element is very nearly equal to that of a flat sheet with thickness dr, length L, and width $2\pi r$ (the circumference of the shell). Then

$$dm = \rho\,dV = \rho(2\pi r L\,dr)$$

We will use this expression in Eq. (9.20) and integrate from $r = R_1$ to $r = R_2$.

EXECUTE: The moment of inertia is given by

$$I = \int r^2\,dm = \int_{R_1}^{R_2} r^2\rho(2\pi r L\,dr)$$

$$= 2\pi\rho L\int_{R_1}^{R_2} r^3\,dr$$

$$= \frac{2\pi\rho L}{4}(R_2^4 - R_1^4)$$

$$= \frac{\pi\rho L}{2}(R_2^2 - R_1^2)(R_2^2 + R_1^2)$$

It is usually more convenient to express the moment of inertia in terms of the total mass M of the body, which is its density ρ multiplied by the total volume V. The volume is

$$V = \pi L(R_2^2 - R_1^2)$$

so the total mass M is

$$M = \rho V = \pi L\rho(R_2^2 - R_1^2)$$

Hence the moment of inertia is

$$I = \frac{1}{2}M(R_1^2 + R_2^2)$$

EVALUATE: This agrees with Table 9.2, case (e). If the cylinder is solid, such as a lawn roller, $R_1 = 0$. Calling the outer radius R_2 simply R, we find that the moment of inertia of a solid cylinder of radius R is

$$I = \frac{1}{2}MR^2$$

If the cylinder has a very thin wall (like a pipe), R_1 and R_2 are very nearly equal; if R represents this common radius,

$$I = MR^2$$

We could have predicted this last result; in a thin-walled cylinder, all the mass is the same distance $r = R$ from the axis, so $I = \int r^2\,dm = R^2\int dm = MR^2$.

Example 9.13 Uniform sphere with radius R, axis through center

Find the moment of inertia of a solid, uniform sphere (like a billiard ball or ball bearing) about an axis through its center.

SOLUTION

IDENTIFY: To calculate the moment of inertia we divide the sphere into thin disks of thickness dx (Fig. 9.25), whose moment of inertia we know from Example 9.12. We'll integrate over these to find the total moment of inertia. The only tricky point is that the radius and mass of a disk depend on its distance x from the center of the sphere.

SET UP: The radius r of the disk shown in Fig. 9.25 is

$$r = \sqrt{R^2 - x^2}$$

Its volume is

$$dV = \pi r^2\, dx = \pi(R^2 - x^2)\, dx$$

9.25 Finding the moment of inertia of a sphere about an axis through its center.

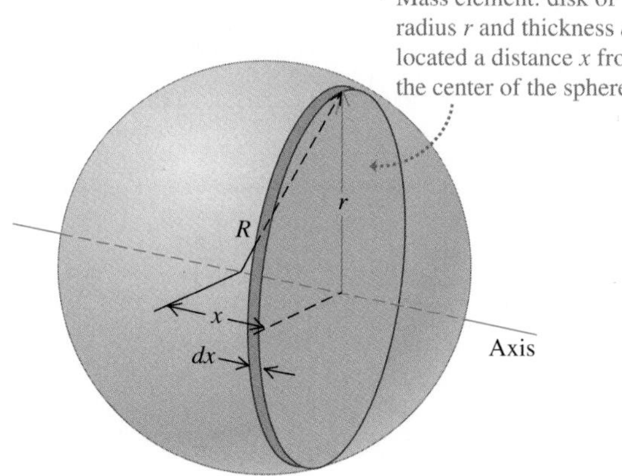

and its mass is

$$dm = \rho\, dV = \pi\rho(R^2 - x^2)\, dx$$

EXECUTE: From Example 9.12, the moment of inertia of a disk of radius r and mass dm is

$$dI = \frac{1}{2}r^2\, dm = \frac{1}{2}(\sqrt{R^2 - x^2})^2[\pi\rho(R^2 - x^2)\, dx]$$
$$= \frac{\pi\rho}{2}(R^2 - x^2)^2\, dx$$

Integrating this expression from $x = 0$ to $x = R$ gives the moment of inertia of the right hemisphere. The total I for the entire sphere, including both hemispheres, is just twice this:

$$I = (2)\frac{\pi\rho}{2}\int_0^R (R^2 - x^2)^2\, dx$$

Carrying out the integration, we obtain

$$I = \frac{8\pi\rho}{15}R^5$$

The mass M of the sphere of volume $V = 4\pi R^3/3$ is

$$M = \rho V = \frac{4\pi\rho R^3}{3}$$

By comparing the expressions for I and M, we find

$$I = \frac{2}{5}MR^2$$

EVALUATE: This result agrees with the expression in Table 9.2, case (h). Note that the moment of inertia of a solid sphere of mass M and radius R is less than the moment of inertia of a solid *cylinder* of the same mass and radius, $I = \frac{1}{2}MR^2$. The reason is that more of the sphere's mass is located close to the axis.

Test Your Understanding of Section 9.6 Two hollow cylinders have the same inner and outer radii and the same mass, but they have different lengths. One is made of low-density wood and the other of high-density lead. Which cylinder has the greater moment of inertia around its axis of symmetry? (i) the wood cylinder; (ii) the lead cylinder; (iii) the two moments of inertia are equal.

CHAPTER 9 SUMMARY

Rotational kinematics: When a rigid body rotates about a stationary axis (usually called the z-axis), its position is described by an angular coordinate θ. The angular velocity ω_z is the time derivative of θ, and the angular acceleration α_z is the time derivative of ω_z or the second derivative of θ. (See Examples 9.1 and 9.2.) If the angular acceleration is constant, then θ, ω_z, and α_z are related by simple kinematic equations analogous to those for straight-line motion with constant linear acceleration. (See Example 9.3.)

$$\omega_z = \lim_{\Delta t \to 0} \frac{\Delta\theta}{\Delta t} = \frac{d\theta}{dt} \quad (9.3)$$

$$\alpha_z = \lim_{\Delta t \to 0} \frac{\Delta\omega_z}{\Delta t} = \frac{d\omega_z}{dt} = \frac{d^2\theta}{dt^2} \quad (9.5)$$

$$\theta = \theta_0 + \omega_{0z}t + \frac{1}{2}\alpha_z t^2 \quad (9.11)$$
(constant α_z only)

$$\theta - \theta_0 = \frac{1}{2}(\omega_z + \omega_{0z})t \quad (9.10)$$
(constant α_z only)

$$\omega_z = \omega_{0z} + \alpha_z t \quad (9.7)$$
(constant α_z only)

$$\omega_z^2 = \omega_{0z}^2 + 2\alpha_z(\theta - \theta_0) \quad (9.12)$$
(constant α_z only)

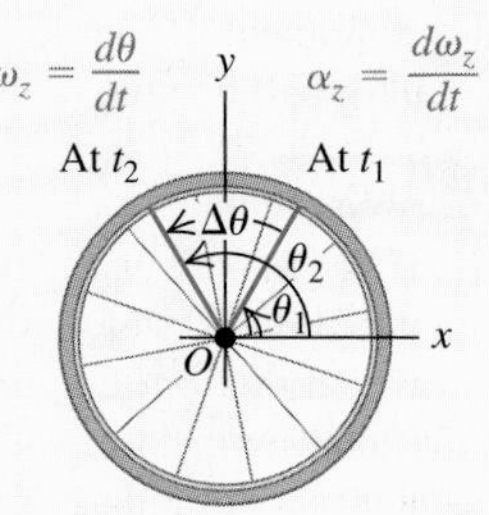

Relating linear and angular kinematics: The angular speed ω of a rigid body is the magnitude of its angular velocity. The rate of change of ω is $\alpha = d\omega/dt$. For a particle in the body a distance r from the rotation axis, the speed v and the components of the acceleration $\vec{a}$ are related to ω and α. (See Examples 9.4–9.6.)

$$v = r\omega \quad (9.13)$$

$$a_{tan} = \frac{dv}{dt} = r\frac{d\omega}{dt} = r\alpha \quad (9.14)$$

$$a_{rad} = \frac{v^2}{r} = \omega^2 r \quad (9.15)$$

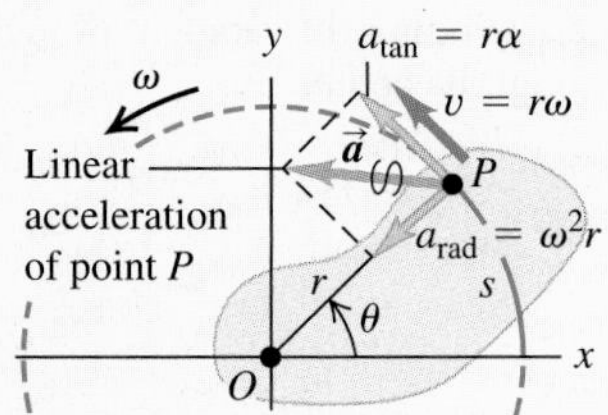

Moment of inertia and rotational kinetic energy: The moment of inertia I of a body about a given axis is a measure of its rotational inertia: The greater the value of I, the more difficult it is to change the state of the body's rotation. The moment of inertia can be expressed as a sum over the particles m_i that make up the body, each of which is at its own perpendicular distance r_i from the axis. The rotational kinetic energy of a rigid body rotating about a fixed axis depends on the angular speed ω and the moment of inertia I for that rotation axis. (See Examples 9.7–9.9.)

$$I = m_1r_1^2 + m_2r_2^2 + \cdots = \sum_i m_ir_i^2 \quad (9.16)$$

$$K = \frac{1}{2}I\omega^2 \quad (9.17)$$

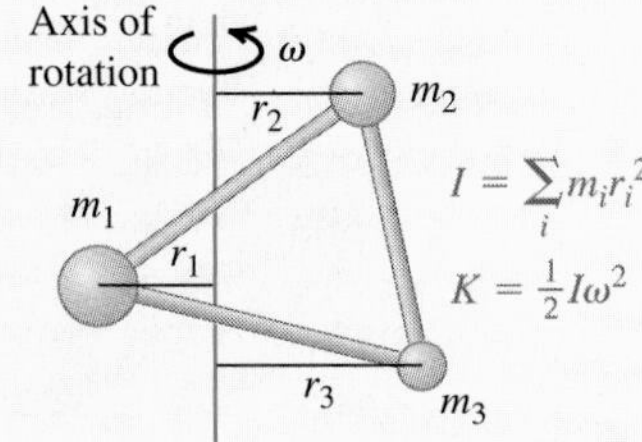

Calculating the moment of inertia: The parallel-axis theorem relates the moments of inertia of a rigid body of mass M about two parallel axes: an axis through the center of mass (moment of inertia I_{cm}) and a parallel axis a distance d from the first axis (moment of inertia I_P). (See Example 9.10.) If the body has a continuous mass distribution, the moment of inertia can be calculated by integration. (See Examples 9.11–9.13.)

$$I_P = I_{cm} + Md^2 \quad (9.19)$$

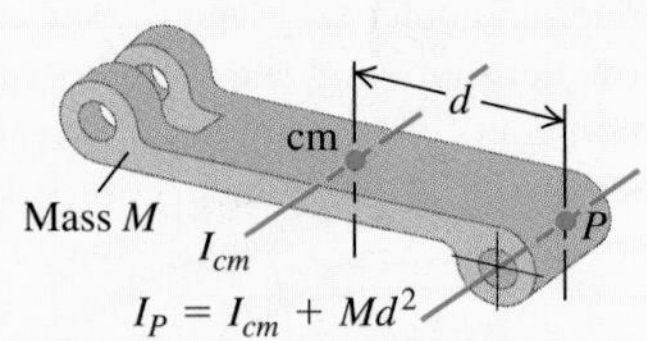

Key Terms

rigid body, *285*
radian, *286*
average angular velocity, *286*
angular displacement, *286*
instantaneous angular velocity, *287*
average angular acceleration, *289*
instantaneous angular acceleration, *289*
angular speed, *293*
tangential component of acceleration, *293*
centripetal component of acceleration, *294*
moment of inertia, *297*
rotational kinetic energy, *297*
parallel-axis theorem, *302*

Answer to Chapter Opening Question ?

Both segments of the rigid blade have the same angular speed ω. From Eqs. (9.13) and (9.15), doubling the distance r for the same ω doubles the linear speed $v = r\omega$ and doubles the radial acceleration $a_{rad} = \omega^2 r$.

Answers to Test Your Understanding Questions

9.1 Answers: (a) (i) and (iii), (b) (ii) The rotation is speeding up when the angular velocity and angular acceleration have the same sign, and slowing down when they have opposite signs. Hence it is speeding up for $0 < t < 2$ s (ω_z and α_z are both positive) and for $4 \text{ s} < t < 6$ s (ω_z and α_z are both negative), but is slowing down for $2 \text{ s} < t < 4$ s (ω_z is positive and α_z is negative). Note that the body is rotating in one direction for $t < 4$ s (ω_z is positive) and in the opposite direction for $t > 4$ s (ω_z is negative).

9.2 Answers: (a) (i), (b) (ii) When the DVD comes to rest, $\omega_z = 0$. From Eq. (9.7), the *time* when this occurs is $t = (\omega_z - \omega_{0z})/\alpha_z = -\omega_{0z}/\alpha_z$ (this is a positive time because α_z is negative). If we double the initial angular velocity ω_{0z} and also double the angular acceleration α_z, their ratio is unchanged and the rotation stops in the same amount of time. The *angle* through which the DVD rotates is given by Eq. (9.10): $\theta - \theta_0 = \frac{1}{2}(\omega_{0z} + \omega_z)t = \frac{1}{2}\omega_{0z}t$ (since the final angular velocity is $\omega_z = 0$). The initial angular velocity ω_{0z} has been doubled but the time t is the same, so the angular displacement $\theta - \theta_0$ (and hence the number of revolutions) has doubled. You can also come to the same conclusion using Eq. (9.12).

9.3 Answer: (ii) From Eq. (9.13), $v = r\omega$. To maintain a constant linear speed v, the angular speed ω must decrease as the scanning head moves outward (greater r).

9.4 Answer: (i) The kinetic energy in the falling block is $\frac{1}{2}mv^2$, and the kinetic energy in the rotating cylinder is $\frac{1}{2}I\omega^2 = \frac{1}{2}(\frac{1}{2}mR^2)(\frac{v}{R})^2 = \frac{1}{4}mv^2$. Hence the total kinetic energy of the system is $\frac{3}{4}mv^2$, of which two-thirds is in the block and one-third is in the cylinder.

9.5 Answer: (ii) More of the mass of the pool cue is concentrated at the thicker end, so the center of mass is closer to that end. The moment of inertia through a point P at either end is $I_P = I_{cm} + Md^2$; the thinner end is farther from the center of mass, so the distance d and the moment of inertia I_P are greater for the thinner end.

9.6 Answer: (iii) Our result from Example 9.12 does *not* depend on the cylinder length L. The moment of inertia depends only on the *radial* distribution of mass, not on its distribution along the axis.

PROBLEMS

For instructor-assigned homework, go to www.masteringphysics.com 

Discussion Questions

Q9.1. Which of the following formulas is valid if the angular acceleration of an object is *not* constant? Explain your reasoning in each case. (a) $v = r\omega$; (b) $a_{tan} = r\alpha$; (c) $\omega = \omega_0 + \alpha t$; (d) $a_{tan} = r\omega^2$; (e) $K = \frac{1}{2}I\omega^2$.

Q9.2. A diatomic molecule can be modeled as two point masses, m_1 and m_2, slightly separated (Fig. 9.26). If the molecule is oriented along the y-axis, it has kinetic energy K when it spins about the x-axis. What will its kinetic energy (in terms of K) be if it spins at the same angular speed about (a) the z-axis and (b) the y-axis?

Figure 9.26 Question Q9.2.

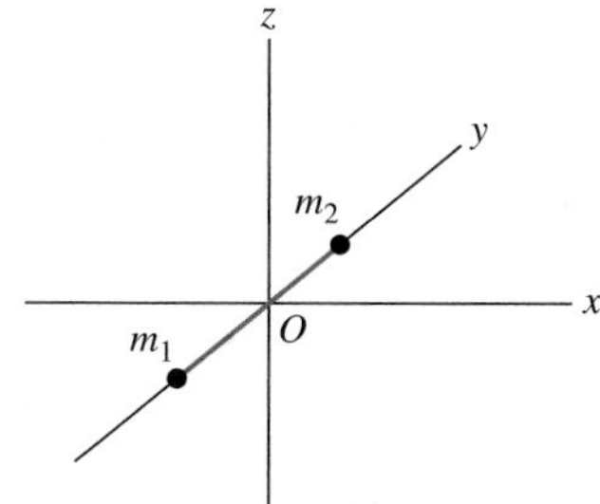

Q9.3. What is the difference between tangential and radial acceleration for a point on a rotating body?

Q9.4. In Fig. 9.14, all points on the chain have the same linear speed. Is the magnitude of the linear acceleration also the same for all points on the chain? How are the angular accelerations of the two sprockets related? Explain.

Q9.5. In Fig. 9.14, how are the radial accelerations of points at the teeth of the two sprockets related? Explain the reasoning behind your answer.

Q9.6. A flywheel rotates with constant angular velocity. Does a point on its rim have a tangential acceleration? A radial acceleration? Are these accelerations constant in magnitude? In direction? In each case give the reasoning behind your answer.

Q9.7. What is the purpose of the spin cycle of a washing machine? Explain in terms of acceleration components.

Q9.8. Although angular velocity and angular acceleration can be treated as vectors, the angular displacement θ, despite having a magnitude and a direction, cannot. This is because θ does not follow the commutative law of vector addition (Eq. 1.3). Prove this to yourself in the following way: Lay your physics textbook flat on the desk in front of you with the cover side up so you can read the writing on it. Rotate it through 90° about a horizontal axis so that the farthest edge comes toward you. Call this angular displacement θ_1. Then rotate it by 90° about a vertical axis so that the left edge comes toward you. Call this angular displacement θ_2. The spine of the book should now face you, with the writing on it oriented so that you can read it. Now start over again but carry out the two rotations in the reverse order. Do you get a different result? That is, does $\theta_1 + \theta_2$ equal $\theta_2 + \theta_1$? Now repeat this experiment but this time with an angle of 1° rather than 90°. Do you think that the infinitesimal displacement $d\vec{\theta}$ obeys the commutative law of addition and hence qualifies as a vector? If so, how is the direction of $d\vec{\theta}$ related to the direction of $\vec{\omega}$?

Q9.9. Can you think of a body that has the same moment of inertia for all possible axes? If so, give an example, and if not, explain why this is not possible. Can you think of a body that has the same moment of inertia for all axes passing through a certain point? If so, give an example and indicate where the point is located.

Q9.10. To maximize the moment of inertia of a flywheel while minimizing its weight, what shape and distribution of mass should it have? Explain.

Q9.11. How might you determine experimentally the moment of inertia of an irregularly shaped body about a given axis?

Q9.12. A cylindrical body has mass M and radius R. Can the mass be distributed within the body in such a way that its moment of inertia about its axis of symmetry is greater than MR^2? Explain.

Q9.13. Describe how you could use part (b) of Table 9.2 to derive the result in part (d).

Q9.14. A hollow spherical shell of radius R that is rotating about an axis through its center has rotational kinetic energy K. If you want to modify this sphere so that it has three times as much kinetic energy at the same angular speed while keeping the same mass, what should be its radius in terms of R?

Q9.15. For the equations for I given in parts (a) and (b) of Table 9.2 to be valid, must the rod have a circular cross section? Is there any restriction on the size of the cross section for these equations to apply? Explain.

Q9.16. In part (d) of Table 9.2, the thickness of the plate must be much less than a for the expression given for I to apply. But in part (c), the expression given for I applies no matter how thick the plate is. Explain.

Q9.17. Two identical balls, A and B, are each attached to very light string, and each string is wrapped around the rim of a frictionless pulley of mass M. The only difference is that the pulley for ball A is a solid disk, while the one for ball B is a hollow disk, like part (e) in Table 9.2. If both balls are released from rest and fall the same distance, which one will have more kinetic energy, or will they have the same kinetic energy? Explain your reasoning.

Q9.18. An elaborate pulley consists of four identical balls at the ends of spokes extending out from a rotating drum (Fig. 9.27). A box is connected to a light thin rope wound around the rim of the drum. When it is released from rest, the box acquires a speed V after having fallen a distance d. Now the four balls are moved inward closer to the drum, and the box is again released from rest. After it has fallen a distance d, will its speed be equal to V, greater than V, or less than V? Show or explain why.

Figure 9.27 Question 9.18.

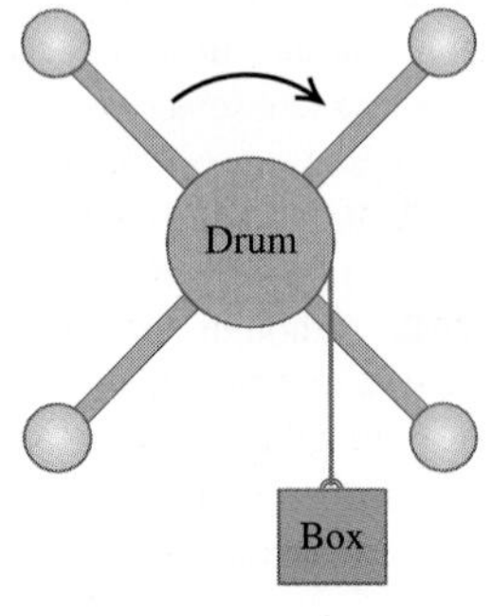

Q9.19. You can use any angular measure—radians, degrees, or revolutions—in some of the equations in Chapter 9, but you can use only radian measure in others. Identify those for which using radians is necessary and those for which it is not, and in each case give the reasoning behind your answer.

Q9.20. When calculating the moment of inertia of an object, can we treat all its mass as if it were concentrated at the center of mass of the object? Justify your answer.

Q9.21. A wheel is rotating about an axis perpendicular to the plane of the wheel and passing through the center of the wheel. The angular speed of the wheel is increasing at a constant rate. Point A is on the rim of the wheel and point B is midway between the rim and center of the wheel. For each of the following quantities, is its magnitude larger at point A, at point B, or is it the same at both points? (a) angular speed; (b) tangential speed; (c) angular acceleration; (d) tangential acceleration; (e) radial acceleration. Justify each of your answers.

Exercises

Section 9.1 Angular Velocity and Acceleration

9.1. (a) What angle in radians is subtended by an arc 1.50 m long on the circumference of a circle of radius 2.50 m? What is this angle in degrees? (b) An arc 14.0 cm long on the circumference of a circle subtends an angle of 128°. What is the radius of the circle? (c) The angle between two radii of a circle with radius 1.50 m is 0.700 rad. What length of arc is intercepted on the circumference of the circle by the two radii?

9.2. An airplane propeller is rotating at 1900 rpm (rev/min). (a) Compute the propeller's angular velocity in rad/s. (b) How many seconds does it take for the propeller to turn through 35°?

9.3. The angular velocity of a flywheel obeys the equation $\omega_z(t) = A + Bt^2$, where t is in seconds and A and B are constants having numerical values 2.75 (for A) and 1.50 (for B). (a) What are the units of A and B if ω is in rad/s? (b) What is the angular acceleration of the wheel at (i) $t = 0.00$ and (ii) $t = 5.00$ s? (c) Through what angle does the flywheel turn during the first 2.00 s? (*Hint:* See Section 2.6.)

9.4. A fan blade rotates with angular velocity given by $\omega_z(t) = \gamma - \beta t^2$, where $\gamma = 5.00$ rad/s and $\beta = 0.800$ rad/s^3. (a) Calculate the angular acceleration as a function of time. (b) Calculate the instantaneous angular acceleration α_z at $t = 3.00$ s and the average angular acceleration $\alpha_{\text{av-}z}$ for the time interval $t = 0$ to $t = 3.00$ s. How do these two quantities compare? If they are different, why are they different?

9.5. A child is pushing a merry-go-round. The angle through which the merry-go-round has turned varies with time according to $\theta(t) = \gamma t + \beta t^3$, where $\gamma = 0.400$ rad/s and $\beta = 0.0120$ rad/s^3. (a) Calculate the angular velocity of the merry-go-round as a function of time. (b) What is the initial value of the angular velocity? (c) Calculate the instantaneous value of the angular velocity ω_z at $t = 5.00$ s and the average angular velocity $\omega_{\text{av-}z}$ for the time interval $t = 0$ to $t = 5.00$ s. Show that $\omega_{\text{av-}z}$ is *not* equal to the average of the instantaneous angular velocities at $t = 0$ and $t = 5.00$ s, and explain why it is not.

9.6. At $t = 0$ the current to a dc electric motor is reversed, resulting in an angular displacement of the motor shaft given by $\theta(t) = (250\ \text{rad/s})t - (20.0\ \text{rad/s}^2)t^2 - (1.50\ \text{rad/s}^3)t^3$. (a) At what time is the angular velocity of the motor shaft zero? (b) Calculate the angular acceleration at the instant that the motor shaft has zero angular velocity. (c) How many revolutions does the motor shaft turn through between the time when the current is reversed and the instant when the angular velocity is zero? (d) How fast was the motor shaft rotating at $t = 0$, when the current was reversed? (e) Calculate the average angular velocity for the time period from $t = 0$ to the time calculated in part (a).

9.7. The angle θ through which a disk drive turns is given by $\theta(t) = a + bt - ct^3$, where a, b, and c are constants, t is in seconds, and θ is in radians. When $t = 0$, $\theta = \pi/4$ rad and the angular velocity is 2.00 rad/s, and when $t = 1.50$ s, the angular acceleration is 1.25 rad/s^2. (a) Find a, b, and c, including their units. (b) What is the angular acceleration when $\theta = \pi/4$ rad? (c) What are θ and the angular velocity when the angular acceleration is 3.50 rad/s^2?

9.8. A wheel is rotating about an axis that is in the z-direction. The angular velocity ω_z is -6.00 rad/s at $t = 0$, increases linearly with time, and is $+8.00$ m/s at $t = 7.00$ s. We have taken counterclockwise rotation to be positive. (a) Is the angular acceleration during this time interval positive or negative? (b) During what time interval is the speed of the wheel increasing? Decreasing? (c) What is the angular displacement of the wheel at $t = 7.00$ s?

Section 9.2 Rotation with Constant Angular Acceleration

9.9. A bicycle wheel has an initial angular velocity of 1.50 rad/s. (a) If its angular acceleration is constant and equal to 0.300 rad/s^2, what is its angular velocity at $t = 2.50$ s? (b) Through what angle has the wheel turned between $t = 0$ and $t = 2.50$ s?

9.10. An electric fan is turned off, and its angular velocity decreases uniformly from 500 rev/min to 200 rev/min in 4.00 s. (a) Find the angular acceleration in rev/s^2 and the number of revolutions made by the motor in the 4.00-s interval. (b) How many more seconds are required for the fan to come to rest if the angular acceleration remains constant at the value calculated in part (a)?

9.11. The rotating blade of a blender turns with constant angular acceleration 1.50 rad/s^2. (a) How much time does it take to reach an angular velocity of 36.0 rad/s, starting from rest? (b) Through how many revolutions does the blade turn in this time interval?

9.12. (a) Derive Eq. (9.12) by combining Eqs. (9.7) and (9.11) to eliminate t. (b) The angular velocity of an airplane propeller increases from 12.0 rad/s to 16.0 rad/s while turning through 7.00 rad. What is the angular acceleration in rad/s^2?

9.13. A turntable rotates with a constant 2.25 rad/s^2 angular acceleration. After 4.00 s it has rotated through an angle of 60.0 rad. What was the angular velocity of the wheel at the beginning of the 4.00-s interval?

9.14. A circular saw blade 0.200 m in diameter starts from rest. In 6.00 s it accelerates with constant angular acceleration to an angular velocity of 140 rad/s. Find the angular acceleration and the angle through which the blade has turned.

9.15. A high-speed flywheel in a motor is spinning at 500 rpm when a power failure suddenly occurs. The flywheel has mass 40.0 kg and diameter 75.0 cm. The power is off for 30.0 s, and during this time the flywheel slows due to friction in its axle bearings. During the time the power is off, the flywheel makes 200 complete revolutions. (a) At what rate is the flywheel spinning when the power comes back on? (b) How long after the beginning of the power failure would it have taken the flywheel to stop if the power had not come back on, and how many revolutions would the wheel have made during this time?

9.16. A computer disk drive is turned on starting from rest and has constant angular acceleration. If it took 0.750 s for the drive to make its *second* complete revolution, (a) how long did it take to make the first complete revolution, and (b) what is its angular acceleration, in rad/s^2?

9.17. A safety device brings the blade of a power mower from an initial angular speed of ω_1 to rest in 1.00 revolution. At the same constant acceleration, how many revolutions would it take the blade to come to rest from an initial angular speed ω_3 that was three times as great, $\omega_3 = 3\omega_1$?

9.18. A straight piece of reflecting tape extends from the center of a wheel to its rim. You darken the room and use a camera and strobe unit that flashes once every 0.050 s to take pictures of the wheel as it rotates counterclockwise. You trigger the strobe so that the first flash ($t = 0$) occurs when the tape is horizontal to the right at an angular displacement of zero. For the following situations draw a sketch of the photo you will get for the time exposure over five flashes (at $t = 0$, 0.050 s, 0.100 s, 0.150 s, and 0.200 s), and graph θ versus t and ω versus t for $t = 0$ to $t = 0.200$ s. (a) The angular velocity is constant at 10.0 rev/s. (b) The wheel starts from rest with a constant angular acceleration of 25.0 rev/s^2. (c) The wheel is rotating at 10.0 rev/s at $t = 0$ and changes angular velocity at a constant rate of -50.0 rev/s^2.

9.19. At $t = 0$ a grinding wheel has an angular velocity of 24.0 rad/s. It has a constant angular acceleration of 30.0 rad/s^2 until a circuit breaker trips at $t = 2.00$ s. From then on, it turns through 432 rad as it coasts to a stop at constant angular acceleration. (a) Through what total angle did the wheel turn between $t = 0$ and the time it stopped? (b) At what time did it stop? (c) What was its acceleration as it slowed down?

Section 9.3 Relating Linear and Angular Kinematics

9.20. In a charming 19th-century hotel, an old-style elevator is connected to a counterweight by a cable that passes over a rotating disk 2.50 m in diameter (Fig. 9.28). The elevator is raised and lowered by turning the disk, and the cable does not slip on the rim of the disk but turns with it. (a) At how many rpm must the disk turn to raise the elevator at 25.0 cm/s? (b) To start the elevator moving, it must be accelerated at $\frac{1}{8}g$. What must be the angular acceleration of the disk, in rad/s^2? (c) Through what angle (in radians and degrees) has the disk turned when it has raised the elevator 3.25 m between floors?

Figure **9.28** Exercise 9.20.

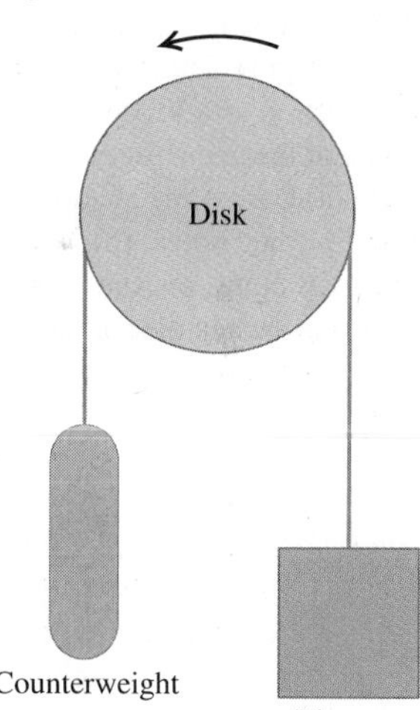

9.21. Using astronomical data from Appendix F, along with the fact that the earth spins on its axis once per day, calculate (a) the earth's orbital angular speed (in rad/s) due to its motion around the sun, (b) its angular speed (in rad/s) due to its axial spin, (c) the tangential speed of the earth around the sun (assuming a circular orbit), (d) the tangential speed of a point on the earth's equator due to the planet's axial spin, and (e) the radial and tangential acceleration components of the point in part (d).

9.22. Compact Disc. A compact disc (CD) stores music in a coded pattern of tiny pits 10^{-7} m deep. The pits are arranged in a track that spirals outward toward the rim of the disc; the inner and outer radii of this spiral are 25.0 mm and 58.0 mm, respectively. As the disc spins inside a CD player, the track is scanned at a constant *linear* speed of 1.25 m/s. (a) What is the angular speed of the CD when the innermost part of the track is scanned? The outermost part of the track? (b) The maximum playing time of a CD is 74.0 min. What would be the length of the track on such a maximum-duration CD if it were stretched out in a straight line? (c) What is the average angular acceleration of a maximum-duration CD during its 74.0-min playing time? Take the direction of rotation of the disc to be positive.

9.23. A wheel of diameter 40.0 cm starts from rest and rotates with a constant angular acceleration of 3.00 $\mathrm{rad/s^2}$. At the instant the wheel has computed its second revolution, compute the radial acceleration of a point on the rim in two ways: (a) using the relationship $a_{\mathrm{rad}} = \omega^2 r$ and (b) from the relationship $a_{\mathrm{rad}} = v^2/r$.

9.24. Ultracentrifuge. Find the required angular speed (in rev/min) of an ultracentrifuge for the radial acceleration of a point 2.50 cm from the axis to equal 400,000g (that is, 400,000 times the acceleration due to gravity).

9.25. A flywheel with a radius of 0.300 m starts from rest and accelerates with a constant angular acceleration of 0.600 $\mathrm{rad/s^2}$. Compute the magnitude of the tangential acceleration, the radial acceleration, and the resultant acceleration of a point on its rim (a) at the start; (b) after it has turned through 60.0°; (c) after it has turned through 120.0°.

9.26. An electric turntable 0.750 m in diameter is rotating about a fixed axis with an initial angular velocity of 0.250 rev/s and a constant angular acceleration of 0.900 $\mathrm{rev/s^2}$. (a) Compute the angular velocity of the turntable after 0.200 s. (b) Through how many revolutions has the turntable spun in this time interval? (c) What is the tangential speed of a point on the rim of the turntable at $t = 0.200$ s? (d) What is the magnitude of the *resultant* acceleration of a point on the rim at $t = 0.200$ s?

9.27. Centrifuge. An advertisement claims that a centrifuge takes up only 0.127 m of bench space but can produce a radial acceleration of 3000g at 5000 rev/min. Calculate the required radius of the centrifuge. Is the claim realistic?

9.28. (a) Derive an equation for the radial acceleration that includes v and ω, but not r. (b) You are designing a merry-go-round for which a point on the rim will have a radial acceleration of 0.500 $\mathrm{m/s^2}$ when the tangential velocity of that point has magnitude 2.00 m/s. What angular velocity is required to achieve these values?

9.29. Electric Drill. According to the shop manual, when drilling a 12.7-mm-diameter hole in wood, plastic, or aluminum, a drill should have a speed of 1250 rev/min. For a 12.7-mm-diameter drill bit turning at a constant 1250 rev/min, find (a) the maximum linear speed of any part of the bit and (b) the maximum radial acceleration of any part of the bit.

9.30. At $t = 3.00$ s a point on the rim of a 0.200-m-radius wheel has a tangential speed of 50.0 m/s as the wheel slows down with a tangential acceleration of constant magnitude 10.0 $\mathrm{m/s^2}$. (a) Calculate the wheel's constant angular acceleration. (b) Calculate the angular velocities at $t = 3.00$ s and $t = 0$. (c) Through what angle did the wheel turn between $t = 0$ and $t = 3.00$ s? (d) At what time will the radial acceleration equal g?

9.31. The spin cycles of a washing machine have two angular speeds, 423 rev/min and 640 rev/min. The internal diameter of the drum is 0.470 m. (a) What is the ratio of the maximum radial force on the laundry for the higher angular speed to that for the lower speed? (b) What is the ratio of the maximum tangential speed of the laundry for the higher angular speed to that for the lower speed? (c) Find the laundry's maximum tangential speed and the maximum radial acceleration, in terms of g.

9.32. You are to design a rotating cylindrical axle to lift 800-N buckets of cement from the ground to a rooftop 78.0 m above the ground. The buckets will be attached to a hook on the free end of a cable that wraps around the rim of the axle; as the axle turns, the buckets will rise. (a) What should the diameter of the axle be in order to raise the buckets at a steady 2.00 cm/s when it is turning at 7.5 rpm? (b) If instead the axle must give the buckets an upward acceleration of 0.400 $\mathrm{m/s^2}$, what should the angular acceleration of the axle be?

9.33. While riding a multispeed bicycle, the rider can select the radius of the rear sprocket that is fixed to the rear axle. The front sprocket of a bicycle has radius 12.0 cm. If the angular speed of the front sprocket is 0.600 rev/s, what is the radius of the rear sprocket for which the tangential speed of a point on the rim of the rear wheel will be 5.00 m/s? The rear wheel has radius 0.330 m.

Section 9.4 Energy in Rotational Motion

9.34. Four small spheres, each of which you can regard as a point of mass 0.200 kg, are arranged in a square 0.400 m on a side and connected by extremely light rods (Fig. 9.29). Find the moment of inertia of the system about an axis (a) through the center of the square, perpendicular to its plane (an axis through point O in the figure); (b) bisecting two opposite sides of the square (an axis along the line AB in the figure); (c) that passes through the centers of the upper left and lower right spheres and through point O.

Figure 9.29 Exercise 9.34.

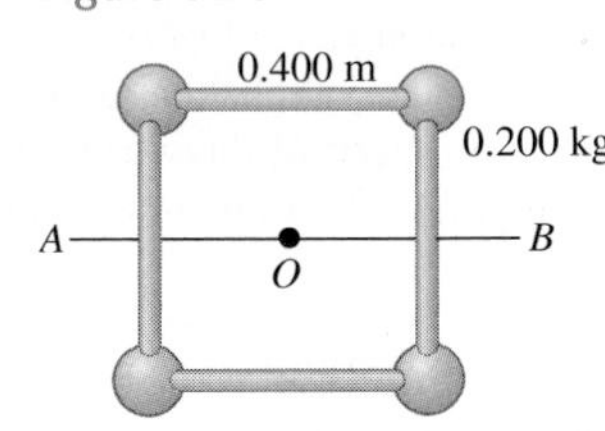

9.35. Calculate the moment of inertia of each of the following uniform objects about the axes indicated. Consult Table 9.2 as needed. (a) A thin 2.50-kg rod of length 75.0 cm, about an axis perpendicular to it and passing through (i) one end and (ii) its center, and (iii) about an axis parallel to the rod and passing through it. (b) A 3.00-kg sphere 38.0 cm in diameter, about an axis through its center, if the sphere is (i) solid and (ii) a thin-walled hollow shell. (c) An 8.00-kg cylinder, of length 19.5 cm and diameter 12.0 cm, about the central axis of the cylinder, if the cylinder is (i) thin-walled and hollow, and (ii) solid.

9.36. Small blocks, each with mass m, are clamped at the ends and at the center of a rod of length L and negligible mass. Compute the moment of inertia of the system about an axis perpendicular to the rod and passing through (a) the center of the rod and (b) a point one-fourth of the length from one end.

9.37. A uniform bar has two small balls glued to its ends. The bar is 2.00 m long and has mass 4.00 kg, while the balls each have mass 0.500 kg and can be treated as point masses. Find the moment of inertia of this combination about each of the following axes: (a) an axis perpendicular to the bar through its center; (b) an axis perpendicular to the bar through one of the balls; (c) an axis parallel to the bar through both balls; (d) an axis parallel to the bar and 0.500 m from it.

9.38. A twirler's baton is made of a slender metal cylinder of mass M and length L. Each end has a rubber cap of mass m, and you can accurately treat each cap as a particle in this problem. Find the total moment of inertia of the baton about the usual twirling axis (perpendicular to the baton through its center).

9.39. A wagon wheel is constructed as shown in Fig. 9.30. The radius of the wheel is 0.300 m, and the rim has mass 1.40 kg. Each of the eight spokes that lie along a diameter and

Figure 9.30 Exercise 9.39.

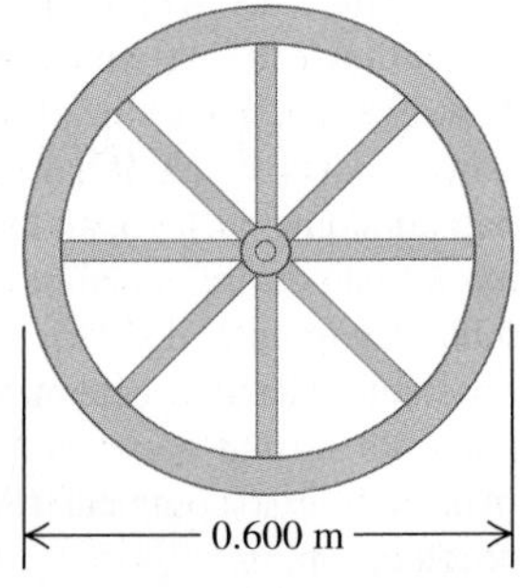

are 0.300 m long has mass 0.280 kg. What is the moment of inertia of the wheel about an axis through its center and perpendicular to the plane of the wheel? (Use the formulas given in Table 9.2.)

9.40. A uniform disk of radius R is cut in half so that the remaining half has mass M (Fig. 9.31a). (a) What is the moment of inertia of this half about an axis perpendicular to its plane through point A? (b) Why did your answer in part (a) come out the same as if this were a complete disk of mass M? (c) What would be the moment of inertia of a quarter disk of mass M and radius R about an axis perpendicular to its plane passing through point B (Fig. 9.31b)?

Figure 9.31 Exercise 9.40.

(a)

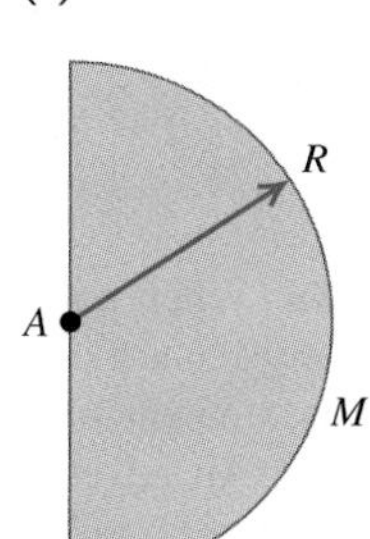

(b)

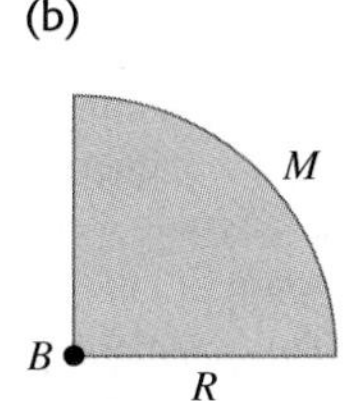

9.41. A compound disk of outside diameter 140.0 cm is made up of a uniform solid disk of radius 50.0 cm and area density 3.00 g/cm^2 surrounded by a concentric ring of inner radius 50.0 cm, outer radius 70.0 cm, and area density 2.00 g/cm^2. Find the moment of inertia of this object about an axis perpendicular to the plane of the object and passing through its center.

9.42. An airplane propeller is 2.08 m in length (from tip to tip) with mass 117 kg and is rotating at 2400 rpm (rev/min) about an axis through its center. You can model the propeller as a slender rod. (a) What is its rotational kinetic energy? (b) Suppose that, due to weight constraints, you had to reduce the propeller's mass to 75.0% of its original mass, but you still needed to keep the same size and kinetic energy. What would its angular speed have to be, in rpm?

9.43. Energy from the Moon? Suppose that some time in the future we decide to tap the moon's rotational energy for use on earth. In additional to the astronomical data in Appendix F, you may need to know that the moon spins on its axis once every 27.3 days. Assume that the moon is uniform throughout. (a) How much total energy could we get from the moon's rotation? (b) The world presently uses about 4.0×10^{20} J of energy per year. If in the future the world uses five times as much energy yearly, for how many years would the moon's rotation provide us energy? In light of your answer, does this seem like a cost-effective energy source in which to invest?

9.44. You need to design an industrial turntable that is 60.0 cm in diameter and has a kinetic energy of 0.250 J when turning at 45.0 rpm (rev/min). (a) What must be the moment of inertia of the turntable about the rotation axis? (b) If your workshop makes this turntable in the shape of a uniform solid disk, what must be its mass?

9.45. The flywheel of a gasoline engine is required to give up 500 J of kinetic energy while its angular velocity decreases from 650 rev/min to 520 rev/min. What moment of inertia is required?

9.46. A light, flexible rope is wrapped several times around a *hollow* cylinder, with a weight of 40.0 N and a radius of 0.25 m, that rotates without friction about a fixed horizontal axis. The cylinder is attached to the axle by spokes of a negligible moment of inertia. The cylinder is initially at rest. The free end of the rope is pulled with a constant force P for a distance of 5.00 m, at which point the end of the rope is moving at 6.00 m/s. If the rope does not slip on the cylinder, what is the value of P?

9.47. Energy is to be stored in a 70.0-kg flywheel in the shape of a uniform solid disk with radius $R = 1.20$ m. To prevent structural failure of the flywheel, the maximum allowed radial acceleration of a point on its rim is 3500 m/s^2. What is the maximum kinetic energy that can be stored in the flywheel?

9.48. Suppose the solid cylinder in the apparatus described in Example 9.9 (Section 9.4) is replaced by a thin-walled, hollow cylinder with the same mass M and radius R. The cylinder is attached to the axle by spokes of a negligible moment of inertia. (a) Find the speed of the hanging mass m just as it strikes the floor. (b) Use energy concepts to explain why the answer to part (a) is different from the speed found in Example 9.9.

9.49. A frictionless pulley has the shape of a uniform solid disk of mass 2.50 kg and radius 20.0 cm. A 1.50-kg stone is attached to a very light wire that is wrapped around the rim of the pulley (Fig. 9.32), and the system is released from rest. (a) How far must the stone fall so that the pulley has 4.50 J of kinetic energy? (b) What percent of the total kinetic energy does the pulley have?

Figure 9.32 Exercise 9.49.

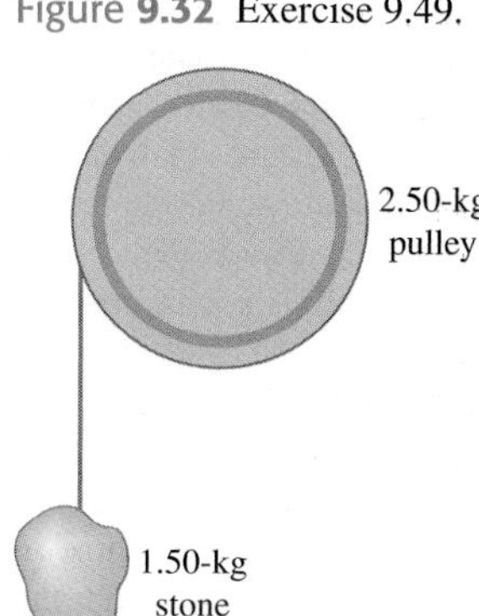

9.50. A bucket of mass m is tied to a massless cable that is wrapped around the outer rim of a frictionless uniform pulley of radius R, similar to the system shown in Fig. 9.32. In terms of the stated variables, what must be the moment of inertia of the pulley so that it always has half as much kinetic energy as the bucket?

9.51. How *I* Scales. If we multiply all the design dimensions of an object by a scaling factor f, its volume and mass will be multiplied by f^3. (a) By what factor will its moment of inertia be multiplied? (b) If a $\frac{1}{48}$-scale model has a rotational kinetic energy of 2.5 J, what will be the kinetic energy for the full-scale object of the same material rotating at the same angular velocity?

9.52. A uniform 2.00-m ladder of mass 9.00 kg is leaning against a vertical wall while making an angle of 53.0° with the floor. A worker pushes the ladder up against the wall until it is vertical. How much work did this person do against gravity?

9.53. A uniform 3.00-kg rope 24.0 m long lies on the ground at the top of a vertical cliff. A mountain climber at the top lets down half of it to help his partner climb up the cliff. What was the change in potential energy of the rope during this maneuver?

Section 9.5 Parallel-Axis Theorem

9.54. Find the moment of inertia of a hoop (a thin-walled, hollow ring) with mass M and radius R about an axis perpendicular to the hoop's plane at an edge.

9.55. About what axis will a uniform, balsa-wood sphere have the same moment of inertia as does a thin-walled, hollow, lead sphere of the same mass and radius, with the axis along a diameter?

9.56. Use the parallel-axis theorem to show that the moments of inertia given in parts (a) and (b) of Table 9.2 are consistent.

9.57. A thin, rectangular sheet of metal has mass M and sides of length a and b. Use the parallel-axis theorem to calculate the moment of inertia of the sheet for an axis that is perpendicular to the plane of the sheet and that passes through one corner of the sheet.

9.58. (a) For the thin rectangular plate shown in part (d) of Table 9.2, find the moment of inertia about an axis that lies in the plane of the plate, passes through the center of the plate, and is parallel to the axis shown in the figure. (b) Find the moment of inertia of the plate for an axis that lies in the plane of the plate, passes through the center of the plate, and is perpendicular to the axis in part (a).

9.59. A thin uniform rod of mass M and length L is bent at its center so that the two segments are now perpendicular to each other. Find its moment of inertia about an axis perpendicular to its plane and passing through (a) the point where the two segments meet and (b) the midpoint of the line connecting its two ends.

*Section 9.6 Moment-of-Inertia Calculations

***9.60.** Using the information in Table 9.2 and the parallel-axis theorem, find the moment of inertia of the slender rod with mass M and length L shown in Fig. 9.23 about an axis through O, at an arbitrary distance h from one end. Compare your result to that found by integration in Example 9.11 (Section 9.6).

***9.61.** Use Eq. (9.20) to calculate the moment of inertia of a uniform, solid disk with mass M and radius R for an axis perpendicular to the plane of the disk and passing through its center.

***9.62.** Use Eq. (9.20) to calculate the moment of inertia of a slender, uniform rod with mass M and length L about an axis at one end, perpendicular to the rod.

***9.63.** A slender rod with length L has a mass per unit length that varies with distance from the left end, where $x = 0$, according to $dm/dx = \gamma x$, where γ has units of kg/m^2. (a) Calculate the total mass of the rod in terms of γ and L. (b) Use Eq. (9.20) to calculate the moment of inertia of the rod for an axis at the left end, perpendicular to the rod. Use the expression you derived in part (a) to express I in terms of M and L. How does your result compare to that for a uniform rod? Explain this comparison. (c) Repeat part (b) for an axis at the right end of the rod. How do the results for parts (b) and (c) compare? Explain this result.

Problems

9.64. Sketch a wheel lying in the plane of your paper and rotating counterclockwise. Choose a point on the rim and draw a vector $\vec{r}$ from the center of the wheel to that point. (a) What is the direction of $\vec{\omega}$? (b) Show that the velocity of the point is $\vec{v} = \vec{\omega} \times \vec{r}$. (c) Show that the radial acceleration of the point is $\vec{a}_{rad} = \vec{\omega} \times \vec{v} = \vec{\omega} \times (\vec{\omega} \times \vec{r})$ (see Exercise 9.28).

9.65. Trip to Mars. You are working on a project with NASA to launch a rocket to Mars, with the rocket blasting off from earth when earth and Mars are aligned along a straight line from the sun. If Mars is now 60° ahead of earth in its orbit around the sun, when should you launch the rocket? (*Note:* All the planets orbit the sun in the same direction, 1 year on Mars is 1.9 earth-years, and assume circular orbits for both planets.)

9.66. A roller in a printing press turns through an angle $\theta(t)$ given by $\theta(t) = \gamma t^2 - \beta t^3$, where $\gamma = 3.20\ \text{rad/s}^2$ and $\beta = 0.500\ \text{rad/s}^3$. (a) Calculate the angular velocity of the roller as a function of time. (b) Calculate the angular acceleration of the roller as a function of time. (c) What is the maximum positive angular velocity, and at what value of t does it occur?

***9.67.** A disk of radius 25.0 cm is free to turn about an axle perpendicular to it through its center. It has very thin but strong string wrapped around its rim, and the string is attached to a ball that is pulled tangentially away from the rim of the disk (Fig. 9.33). The pull increases in magnitude and produces an acceleration of the ball that obeys the equation $a(t) = At$, where t is in seconds and A is a constant. The cylinder starts from rest, and at the end of the third second, the ball's acceleration is 1.80 m/s^2. (a) Find A. (b) Express the angular acceleration of the disk as a function of time. (c) How much time after the disk has begun to turn does it reach an angular speed of 15.0 rad/s? (d) Through what angle has the disk turned just as it reaches 15.0 rad/s? (*Hint:* See Section 2.6.)

Figure 9.33 Problem 9.67.

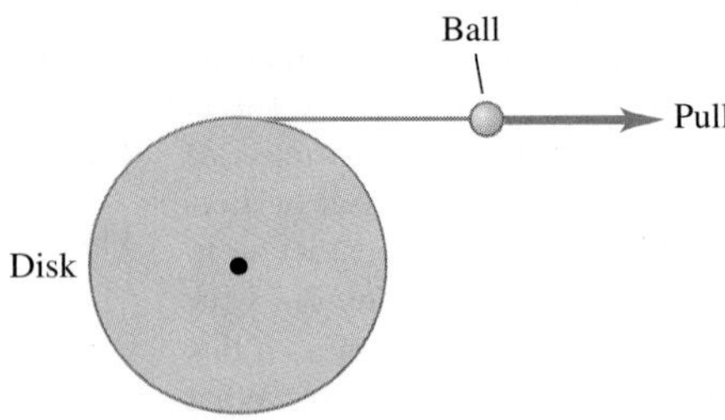

9.68. When a toy car is rapidly scooted across the floor, it stores energy in a flywheel. The car has mass 0.180 kg, and its flywheel has moment of inertia $4.00 \times 10^{-5}\ \text{kg} \cdot \text{m}^2$. The car is 15.0 cm long. An advertisement claims that the car can travel at a scale speed of up to 700 km/h (440 mi/h). The scale speed is the speed of the toy car multiplied by the ratio of the length of an actual car to the length of the toy. Assume a length of 3.0 m for a real car. (a) For a scale speed of 700 km/h, what is the actual translational speed of the car? (b) If all the kinetic energy that is initially in the flywheel is converted to the translational kinetic energy of the toy, how much energy is originally stored in the flywheel? (c) What initial angular velocity of the flywheel was needed to store the amount of energy calculated in part (b)?

9.69. A classic 1957 Chevrolet Corvette of mass 1240 kg starts from rest and speeds up with a constant tangential acceleration of 3.00 m/s^2 on a circular test track of radius 60.0 m. Treat the car as a particle. (a) What is its angular acceleration? (b) What is its angular speed 6.00 s after it starts? (c) What is its radial acceleration at this time? (d) Sketch a view from above showing the circular track, the car, the velocity vector, and the acceleration component vectors 6.00 s after the car starts. (e) What are the magnitudes of the total acceleration and net force for the car at this time? (f) What angle do the total acceleration and net force make with the car's velocity at this time?

9.70. Engineers are designing a system by which a falling mass m imparts kinetic energy to a rotating uniform drum to which it is attached by thin, very light wire wrapped around the rim of the drum (Fig. 9.34). There is no appreciable friction in the axle of the drum, and everything starts from rest. This system is being tested on earth, but it is to be used on Mars, where the acceleration due to gravity is 3.71 m/s^2. In the earth tests, when m is set to 15.0 kg and allowed to fall through 5.00 m, it gives 250.0 J of kinetic energy to the drum. (a) If the system is operated on Mars, through what distance would the 15.0-0 mass have to fall to give the same amount of kinetic energy to the drum? (b) How fast would the 15.0-kg mass be moving on Mars just as the drum gained 250.0 J of kinetic energy?

Figure 9.34 Problem 9.70.

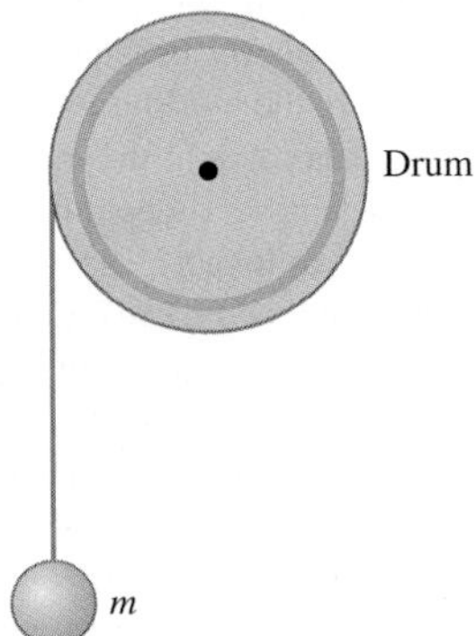

9.71. A vacuum cleaner belt is looped over a shaft of radius 0.45 cm and a wheel of radius 2.00 cm. The arrangement of the belt, shaft, and wheel is similar to that of the chain and sprockets in Fig. 9.14. The motor turns the shaft at 60.0 rev/s and the moving belt turns the wheel, which in turn is connected by another shaft to the roller that beats the dirt out of the rug being vacuumed. Assume that the belt doesn't slip on either the shaft or the wheel. (a) What is the speed of a point on the belt? (b) What is the angular velocity of the wheel, in rad/s?

9.72. The motor of a table saw is rotating at 3450 rev/min. A pulley attached to the motor shaft drives a second pulley of half the diameter by means of a V-belt. A circular saw blade of diameter 0.208 m is mounted on the same rotating shaft as the second pulley. (a) The operator is careless and the blade catches and throws back a small piece of wood. This piece of wood moves with linear speed equal to the tangential speed of the rim of the blade. What is this speed? (b) Calculate the radial acceleration of points on the outer edge of the blade to see why sawdust doesn't stick to its teeth.

9.73. A wheel changes its angular velocity with a constant angular acceleration while rotating about a fixed axis through its center. (a) Show that the change in the magnitude of the radial acceleration during any time interval of a point on the wheel is twice the product of the angular acceleration, the angular displacement, and the perpendicular distance of the point from the axis. (b) The radial acceleration of a point on the wheel that is 0.250 m from the axis changes from 25.0 m/s^2 to 85.0 m/s^2 as the wheel rotates through 15.0 rad. Calculate the tangential acceleration of this point. (c) Show that the change in the wheel's kinetic energy during any time interval is the product of the moment of inertia about the axis, the angular acceleration, and the angular displacement. (d) During the 15.0-rad angular displacement of part (b), the kinetic energy of the wheel increases from 20.0 J to 45.0 J. What is the moment of inertia of the wheel about the rotation axis?

9.74. A sphere consists of a solid wooden ball of uniform density 800 kg/m^3 and radius 0.20 m and is covered with a thin coating of lead foil with area density 20 kg/m^2. Calculate the moment of inertia of this sphere about an axis passing through its center.

9.75. Estimate your own moment of inertia about a vertical axis through the center of the top of your head when you are standing up straight with your arms outstretched. Make reasonable approximations and measure or estimate necessary quantities.

9.76. A thin uniform rod 50.0 cm long with mass 0.320 kg is bent at its center into a V shape, with a 70.0° angle at its vertex. Find the moment of inertia of this V-shaped object about an axis perpendicular to the plane of the V at its vertex.

9.77. It has been argued that power plants should make use of off-peak hours (such as late at night) to generate mechanical energy and store it until it is needed during peak load times, such as the middle of the day. One suggestion has been to store the energy in large flywheels spinning on nearly frictionless ball bearings. Consider a flywheel made of iron (density 7800 kg/m^3) in the shape of a 10.0-cm-thick uniform disk. (a) What would the diameter of such a disk need to be if it is to store 10.0 megajoules of kinetic energy when spinning at 90.0 rpm about an axis perpendicular to the disk at its center? (b) What would be the centripetal acceleration of a point on its rim when spinning at this rate?

9.78. While redesigning a rocket engine, you want to reduce its weight by replacing a solid spherical part with a hollow spherical shell of the same size. The parts rotate about an axis through their center. You need to make sure that the new part always has the same rotational kinetic energy as the original part had at any given rate of rotation. If the original part had mass M, what must be the mass of the new part?

9.79. The earth, which is not a uniform sphere, has a moment of inertia of $0.3308MR^2$ about an axis through its north and south poles. It takes the earth 86,164 s to spin once about this axis. Use Appendix F to calculate (a) the earth's kinetic energy due to its rotation about this axis and (b) the earth's kinetic energy due to its orbital motion around the sun. (c) Explain how the value of the earth's moment of inertia tells us that the mass of the earth is concentrated toward the planet's center.

9.80. A uniform, solid disk with mass m and radius R is pivoted about a horizontal axis through its center. A small object of the same mass m is glued to the rim of the disk. If the disk is released from rest with the small object at the end of a horizontal radius, find the angular speed when the small object is directly below the axis.

9.81. A metal sign for a car dealership is a thin, uniform right triangle with base length b and height h. The sign has mass M. (a) What is the moment of inertia of the sign for rotation about the side of length h? (b) If $M = 5.40$ kg, $b = 1.60$ m, and $h = 1.20$ m, what is the kinetic energy of the sign when it is rotating about an axis along the 1.20-m side at 2.00 rev/s?

9.82. Measuring *I*. As an intern with an engineering firm, you are asked to measure the moment of inertia of a large wheel, for rotation about an axis through its center. Since you were a good physics student, you know what to do. You measure the diameter of the wheel to be 0.740 m and find that it weighs 280 N. You mount the wheel, using frictionless bearings, on a horizontal axis through the wheel's center. You wrap a light rope around the wheel and hang a 8.00-kg mass from the free end of the rope, as shown in Fig. 9.18. You release the mass from rest; the mass descends and the wheel turns as the rope unwinds. You find that the mass has speed 5.00 m/s after it has descended 2.00 m. (a) What is the moment of inertia of the wheel for an axis perpendicular to the wheel at its center? (b) Your boss tells you that a larger I is needed. He asks you to design a wheel of the same mass and radius that has $I = 19.0\ kg \cdot m^2$. How do you reply?

9.83. A meter stick with a mass of 0.160 kg is pivoted about one end so it can rotate without friction about a horizontal axis. The meter stick is held in a horizontal position and released. As it swings through the vertical, calculate (a) the change in gravitational potential energy that has occurred; (b) the angular speed of the stick; (c) the linear speed of the end of the stick opposite the axis. (d) Compare the answer in part (c) to the speed of a particle that has fallen 1.00 m, starting from rest.

9.84. Exactly one turn of a flexible rope with mass m is wrapped around a uniform cylinder with mass M and radius R. The cylinder rotates without friction about a horizontal axle along the cylinder axis. One end of the rope is attached to the cylinder. The cylinder starts with angular speed ω_0. After one revolution of the cylinder the rope has unwrapped and, at this instant, hangs vertically down, tangent to the cylinder. Find the angular speed of the cylinder and the linear speed of the lower end of the rope at this time. You can ignore the thickness of the rope. [*Hint:* Use Eq. (9.18).]

9.85. The pulley in Fig. 9.35 has radius R and a moment of inertia I. The rope does not slip over the pulley, and the pulley spins on a frictionless axle. The coefficient of kinetic friction between block A and the tabletop is μ_k. The system is released from rest, and block B descends. Block A has mass m_A and block B has mass m_B. Use energy methods to calculate the speed of block B as a function of the distance d that it has descended.

Figure 9.35 Problem 9.85.

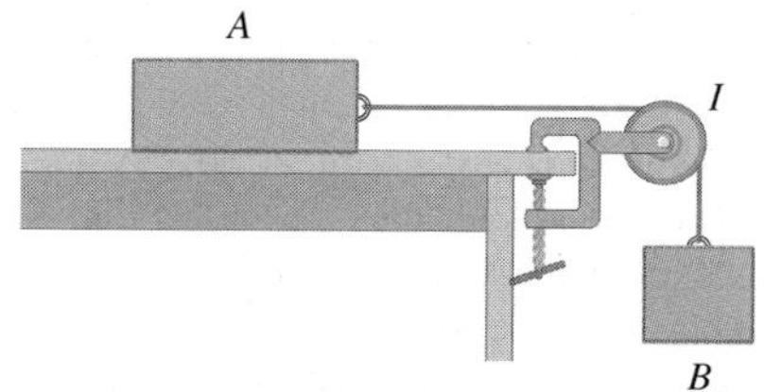

9.86. The pulley in Fig. 9.36 has radius 0.160 m and moment of inertia $0.480\ \text{kg}\cdot\text{m}^2$. The rope does not slip on the pulley rim. Use energy methods to calculate the speed of the 4.00-kg block just before it strikes the floor.

Figure 9.36 Problem 9.86.

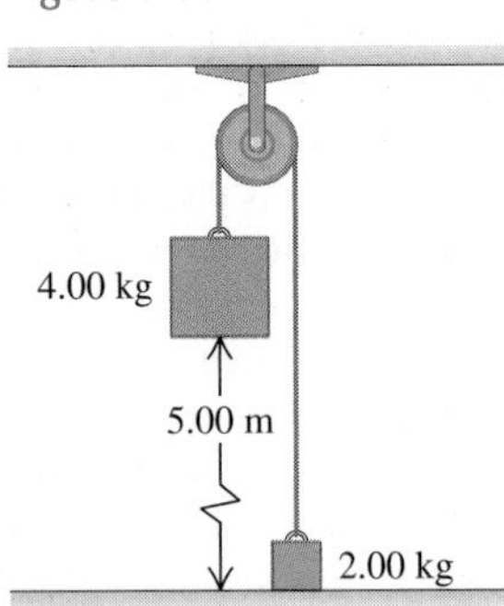

9.87. You hang a thin hoop with radius R over a nail at the rim of the hoop. You displace it to the side (within the plane of the hoop) through an angle β from its equilibrium position and let it go. What is its angular speed when it returns to its equilibrium position? [*Hint:* Use Eq. (9.18).]

9.88. A passenger bus in Zurich, Switzerland, derived its motive power from the energy stored in a large flywheel. The wheel was brought up to speed periodically, when the bus stopped at a station, by an electric motor, which could then be attached to the electric power lines. The flywheel was a solid cylinder with mass 1000 kg and diameter 1.80 m; its top angular speed was 3000 rev/min. (a) At this angular speed, what is the kinetic energy of the flywheel? (b) If the average power required to operate the bus is 1.86×10^4 W, how long could it operate between stops?

9.89. Two metal disks, one with radius $R_1 = 2.50$ cm and mass $M_1 = 0.80$ kg and the other with radius $R_2 = 5.00$ cm and mass $M_2 = 1.60$ kg, are welded together and mounted on a frictionless axis through their common center (Fig. 9.37). (a) What is the total moment of inertia of the two disks? (b) A light string is wrapped around the edge of the smaller disk, and a 1.50-kg block is suspended from the free end of the string. If the block is released from rest at a distance of 2.00 m above the floor, what is its speed just before it strikes the floor? (c) Repeat the calculation of part (b), this time with the string wrapped around the edge of the larger disk. In which case is the final speed of the block the greatest? Explain why this is so.

Figure 9.37 Problem 9.89.

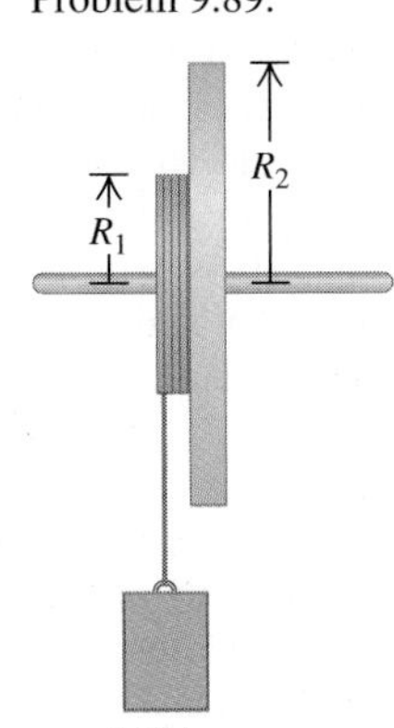

9.90. In the cylinder and mass combination described in Example 9.9 (Section 9.4), suppose the falling mass m is made of ideal rubber, so that no mechanical energy is lost when the mass hits the ground. (a) If the cylinder is originally not rotating and the mass m is released from rest at a height h above the ground, to what height will this mass rebound if it bounces straight back up from the floor? (b) Explain, in terms of energy, why the answer to part (a) is *less* than h.

9.91. In the system shown in Fig. 9.18, a 12.0-kg mass is released from rest and falls, causing the uniform 10.0-kg cylinder of diameter 30.0 cm to turn about a frictionless axle through its center. How far will the mass have to descend to give the cylinder 250 J of kinetic energy?

9.92. In Fig. 9.38, the cylinder and pulley turn without friction about stationary horizontal axles that pass through their centers. A light rope is wrapped around the cylinder, passes over the pulley, and has a 3.00-kg box suspended from its free end. There is no slipping between the rope and the pulley surface. The uniform cylinder has mass 5.00 kg and radius 40.0 cm. The pulley is a uniform disk with mass 2.00 kg and radius 20.0 cm. The box is released from rest and descends as the rope unwraps from the cylinder. Find the speed of the box when it has fallen 1.50 m.

Figure 9.38 Problem 9.92.

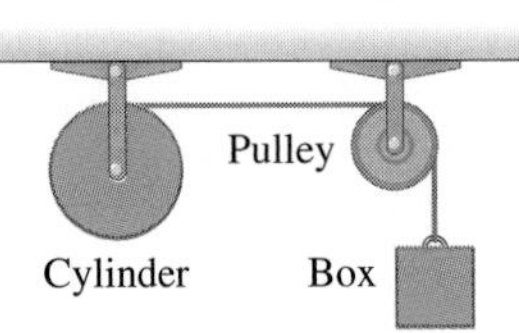

9.93. A thin, flat, uniform disk has mass M and radius R. A circular hole of radius $R/4$, centered at a point $R/2$ from the disk's center, is then punched in the disk. (a) Find the moment of inertia of the disk with the hole about an axis through the original center of the disk, perpendicular to the plane of the disk. (*Hint:* Find the moment of inertia of the piece punched from the disk.) (b) Find the moment of inertia of the disk with the hole about an axis through the center of the hole, perpendicular to the plane of the disk.

9.94. A pendulum is made of a uniform solid sphere with mass M and radius R suspended from the end of a light rod. The distance from the pivot at the upper end of the rod to the center of the sphere is L. The pendulum's moment of inertia I_P for rotation about the pivot is usually approximated as ML^2. (a) Use the parallel-axis theorem to show that if R is 5% of L and the mass of the rod is ignored, I_P is only 0.1% greater than ML^2. (b) If the mass of the rod is 1% of M and R is much less than L, what is the ratio of I_{rod} for an axis at the pivot to ML^2?

9.95. Perpendicular-Axis Theorem. Consider a rigid body that is a thin, plane sheet of arbitrary shape. Take the body to lie in the xy-plane and let the origin O of coordinates be located at any point within or outside the body. Let I_x and I_y be the moments of inertia about the x- and y-axes, and let I_O be the moment of inertia about an axis through O perpendicular to the plane. (a) By considering mass elements m_i with coordinates (x_i, y_i), show that $I_x + I_y = I_O$. This is called the perpendicular-axis theorem. Note that point O does not have to be the center of mass. (b) For a thin washer with mass M and with inner and outer radii R_1 and R_2, use the perpendicular-axis theorem to find the moment of inertia about an axis that is in the plane of the washer and that passes through its center. You may use the information in Table 9.2. (c) Use the perpendicular-axis theorem to show that for a thin, square sheet with mass M and side L, the moment of inertia about *any* axis in the plane of the sheet that passes through the center of the sheet is $\frac{1}{12}ML^2$. You may use the information in Table 9.2.

9.96. A thin, uniform rod is bent into a square of side length a. If the total mass is M, find the moment of inertia about an axis through the center and perpendicular to the plane of the square. (*Hint:* Use the parallel-axis theorem.)

***9.97.** A cylinder with radius R and mass M has density that increases linearly with distance r from the cylinder axis, $\rho = \alpha r$, where α is a positive constant. (a) Calculate the moment of inertia of the cylinder about a longitudinal axis through its center in terms of M and R. (b) Is your answer greater or smaller than the moment of inertia of a cylinder of the same mass and radius but of uniform density? Explain why this result makes qualitative sense.

Figure 9.39 Problem 9.98.

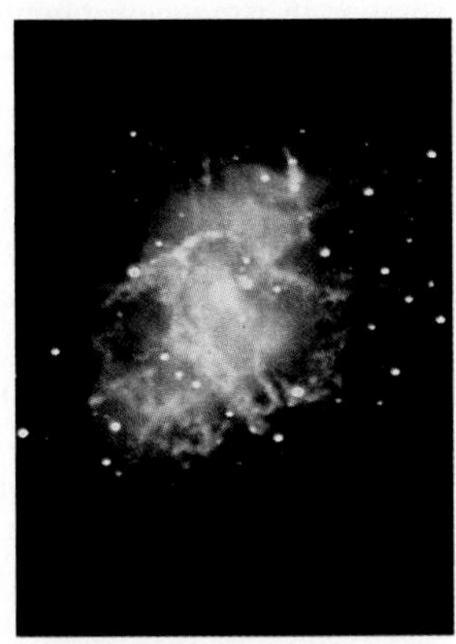

9.98. Neutron Stars and Supernova Remnants. The Crab Nebula is a cloud of glowing gas about 10 light-years across, located about 6500 light years from the earth (Fig. 9.39). It is the remnant of a star that underwent a *supernova explosion,* seen on earth in 1054 A.D. Energy is released by the

Crab Nebula at a rate of about 5×10^{31} W, about 10^5 times the rate at which the sun radiates energy. The Crab Nebula obtains its energy from the rotational kinetic energy of a rapidly spinning *neutron star* at its center. This object rotates once every 0.0331 s, and this period is increasing by 4.22×10^{-13} s for each second of time that elapses. (a) If the rate at which energy is lost by the neutron star is equal to the rate at which energy is released by the nebula, find the moment of inertia of the neutron star. (b) Theories of supernovae predict that the neutron star in the Crab Nebula has a mass about 1.4 times that of the sun. Modeling the neutron star as a solid uniform sphere, calculate its radius in kilometers. (c) What is the linear speed of a point on the equator of the neutron star? Compare to the speed of light. (d) Assume that the neutron star is uniform and calculate its density. Compare to the density of ordinary rock (3000 kg/m^3) and to the density of an atomic nucleus (about 10^{17} kg/m^3). Justify the statement that a neutron star is essentially a large atomic nucleus.

Challenge Problems

9.99. The moment of inertia of a sphere with uniform density about an axis through its center is $\frac{2}{5}MR^2 = 0.400MR^2$. Satellite observations show that the earth's moment of inertia is $0.3308MR^2$. Geophysical data suggest the earth consists of five main regions: the inner core $(r = 0 \text{ to } r = 1220 \text{ km})$ of average density $12{,}900 \text{ kg/m}^3$, the outer core $(r = 1220 \text{ km to } r = 3480 \text{ km})$ of average density $10{,}900 \text{ kg/m}^3$, the lower mantle $(r = 3480 \text{ km to } r = 5700 \text{ km})$ of average density 4900 kg/m^3, the upper mantle $(r = 5700 \text{ km to } r = 6350 \text{ km})$ of average density 3600 kg/m^3, and the outer crust and oceans $(r = 6350 \text{ km to } r = 6370 \text{ km})$ of average density 2400 kg/m^3. (a) Show that the moment of inertia about a diameter of a uniform spherical shell of inner radius R_1, outer radius R_2, and density ρ is $I = \rho(8\pi/15)(R_2^5 - R_1^5)$. (*Hint:* Form the shell by superposition of a sphere of density ρ and a smaller sphere of density $-\rho$.) (b) Check the given data by using them to calculate the mass of the earth. (c) Use the given data to calculate the earth's moment of inertia in terms of MR^2.

***9.100.** Calculate the moment of inertia of a uniform solid cone about an axis through its center (Fig. 9.40). The cone has mass M and altitude h. The radius of its circular base is R.

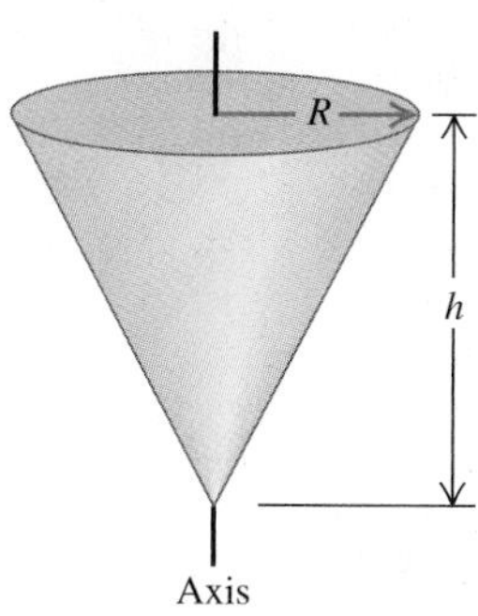

Figure 9.40 Challenge Problem 9.100.

9.101. On a compact disc (CD), music is coded in a pattern of tiny pits arranged in a track that spirals outward toward the rim of the disc. As the disc spins inside a CD player, the track is scanned at a constant *linear* speed of $v = 1.25 \text{ m/s}$. Because the radius of the track varies as it spirals outward, the *angular* speed of the disc must change as the CD is played. (See Exercise 9.22.) Let's see what angular acceleration is required to keep v constant. The equation of a spiral is $r(\theta) = r_0 + \beta\theta$, where r_0 is the radius of the spiral at $\theta = 0$ and β is a constant. On a CD, r_0 is the inner radius of the spiral track. If we take the rotation direction of the CD to be positive, β must be positive so that r increases as the disc turns and θ increases. (a) When the disc rotates through a small angle $d\theta$, the distance scanned along the track is $ds = r\,d\theta$. Using the above expression for $r(\theta)$, integrate ds to find the total distance s scanned along the track as a function of the total angle θ through which the disc has rotated. (b) Since the track is scanned at a constant linear speed v, the distance s found in part (a) is equal to vt. Use this to find θ as a function of time. There will be two solutions for θ; choose the positive one, and explain why this is the solution to choose. (c) Use your expression for $\theta(t)$ to find the angular velocity ω_z and the angular acceleration α_z as functions of time. Is α_z constant? (d) On a CD, the inner radius of the track is 25.0 mm, the track radius increases by 1.55 μm per revolution, and the playing time is 74.0 min. Find the values of r_0 and β, and find the total number of revolutions made during the playing time. (e) Using your results from parts (c) and (d), make graphs of ω_z (in rad/s) versus t and α_z (in rad/s^2) versus t between $t = 0$ and $t = 74.0$ min.

10 DYNAMICS OF ROTATIONAL MOTION

LEARNING GOALS

By studying this chapter, you will learn:

- What is meant by the torque produced by a force.
- How the net torque on a body affects the rotational motion of the body.
- How to analyze the motion of a body that both rotates and moves as a whole through space.
- How to solve problems that involve work and power for rotating bodies.
- What is meant by the angular momentum of a particle or of a rigid body.
- How the angular momentum of a system changes with time.
- Why a spinning gyroscope goes through the curious motion called precession.

? If this skydiver isn't touching the ground, how can he change his rotation speed? What physical principle is at work here?

We learned in Chapters 4 and 5 that a net force applied to a body gives that body an acceleration. But what does it take to give a body an *angular* acceleration? That is, what does it take to start a stationary body rotating or to bring a spinning body to a halt? A force is required, but it must be applied in a way that gives a twisting or turning action.

In this chapter we will define a new physical quantity, *torque,* that describes the twisting or turning effort of a force. We'll find that the net torque acting on a rigid body determines its angular acceleration, in the same way that the net force on a body determines its linear acceleration. We'll also look at work and power in rotational motion so as to understand such problems as how energy is transmitted by the rotating drive shaft in a car. Finally, we will develop a new conservation principle, *conservation of angular momentum,* that is tremendously useful for understanding the rotational motion of both rigid and nonrigid bodies. We'll finish this chapter by studying *gyroscopes,* rotating devices that seemingly defy common sense and don't fall over when you might think they should—but that actually behave in perfect accordance with the dynamics of rotational motion.

10.1 Which of these three equal-magnitude forces is most likely to loosen the tight bolt?

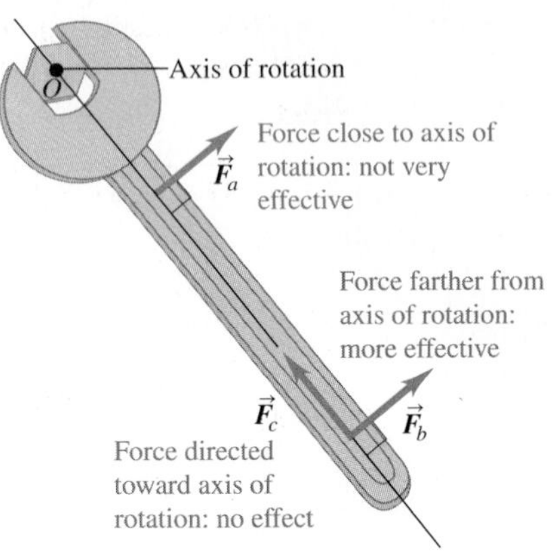

10.1 Torque

We know that forces acting on a body can affect its **translational motion**—that is, the motion of the body as a whole through space. Now we want to learn which aspects of a force determine how effective it is in causing or changing *rotational* motion. The magnitude and direction of the force are important, but so is the point on the body where the force is applied. In Fig. 10.1 a wrench is being used to loosen a tight bolt. Force $\vec{F}_b$, applied near the end of the handle, is more effective than an equal force $\vec{F}_a$ applied near the bolt. Force $\vec{F}_c$ doesn't do any good at all; it's applied at the same point and has the same magnitude as $\vec{F}_b$, but it's directed along the length of the handle. The quantitative measure of the tendency of a force to cause or change a body's rotational motion is called *torque;* we say that $\vec{F}_a$ applies a torque about point O to the wrench in Fig. 10.1, $\vec{F}_b$ applies a greater torque about O, and $\vec{F}_c$ applies zero torque about O.

Figure 10.2 shows three examples of how to calculate torque. The body in the figure can rotate about an axis that is perpendicular to the plane of the figure and passes through point O. Three forces, $\vec{F}_1$,$\vec{F}_2$, and $\vec{F}_3$, act on the body in the plane of the figure. The tendency of the first of these forces, $\vec{F}_1$, to cause a rotation about O depends on its magnitude F_1. It also depends on the *perpendicular* distance l_1 between point O and the **line of action** of the force (that is, the line along which the force vector lies). We call the distance l_1 the **lever arm** (or **moment arm**) of force $\vec{F}_1$ about O. The twisting effort is directly proportional to both F_1 and l_1, so we define the **torque** (or *moment*) of the force $\vec{F}_1$ with respect to O as the product $F_1 l_1$. We use the Greek letter τ (tau) for torque. In general, for a force of magnitude F whose line of action is a perpendicular distance l from O, the torque is

$$\tau = Fl \tag{10.1}$$

10.2 The torque of a force about a point is the product of the force magnitude and the lever arm of the force.

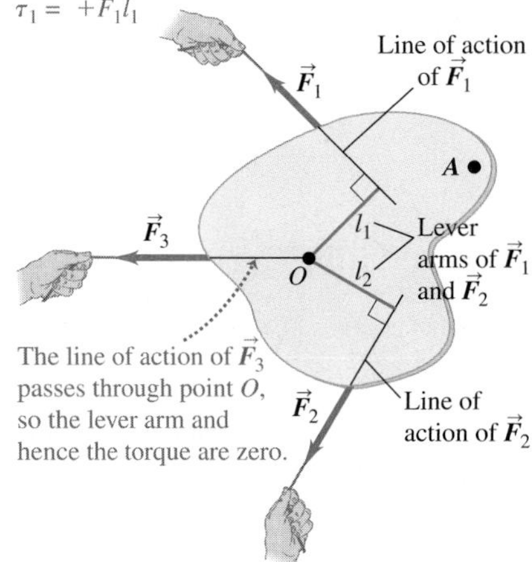

$\vec{F}_1$ tends to cause *counterclockwise* rotation about point O, so its torque is *positive*: $\tau_1 = +F_1 l_1$
Line of action of $\vec{F}_1$
$\vec{F}_1$
A
$\vec{F}_3$
l_1
Lever arms of $\vec{F}_1$ and $\vec{F}_2$
O
l_2
The line of action of $\vec{F}_3$ passes through point O, so the lever arm and hence the torque are zero.
$\vec{F}_2$
Line of action of $\vec{F}_2$
$\vec{F}_2$ tends to cause *clockwise* rotation about point O, so its torque is *negative*: $\tau_2 = -F_2 l_2$

Physicists usually use the term "torque," while engineers usually use "moment" (unless they are talking about a rotating shaft). Both groups use the term "lever arm" or "moment arm" for the distance l.

The lever arm of $\vec{F}_1$ in Fig. 10.2 is the perpendicular distance l_1, and the lever arm of $\vec{F}_2$ is the perpendicular distance l_2. The line of action of $\vec{F}_3$ passes through point O, so the lever arm for $\vec{F}_3$ is zero and its torque with respect to O is zero. In the same way, force $\vec{F}_c$ in Fig. 10.1 has zero torque with respect to point O; $\vec{F}_b$ has a greater torque than $\vec{F}_a$ because its lever arm is greater.

CAUTION **Torque is always measured about a point** Note that torque is *always* defined with reference to a specific point. If we shift the position of this point, the torque of each force may also change. For example, the torque of force $\vec{F}_3$ in Fig. 10.2 is zero with respect to point O, but the torque of $\vec{F}_3$ is *not* zero about point A. It's not enough to refer to "the torque of $\vec{F}$"; you must say "the torque of $\vec{F}$ with respect to point X" or "the torque of $\vec{F}$ about point X."

ActivPhysics ONLINE
7.1 Calculating Torques

Force $\vec{F}_1$ in Fig. 10.2 tends to cause *counterclockwise* rotation about O, while $\vec{F}_2$ tends to cause *clockwise* rotation. To distinguish between these two possibilities, we need to choose a positive sense of rotation. With the choice that *counterclockwise torques are positive and clockwise torques are negative,* the torques of $\vec{F}_1$ and $\vec{F}_2$ about O are

$$\tau_1 = +F_1 l_1 \qquad \tau_2 = -F_2 l_2$$

Figure 10.2 shows this choice for the sign of torque. We will often use the symbol $\circlearrowleft\!+$ to indicate our choice of the positive sense of rotation.

The SI unit of torque is the newton-meter. In our discussion of work and energy we called this combination the joule. But torque is *not* work or energy, and torque should be expressed in newton-meters, *not* joules.

Figure 10.3 shows a force $\vec{F}$ applied at a point P described by a position vector $\vec{r}$ with respect to the chosen point O. There are three ways to calculate the torque of this force:

1. Find the lever arm l and use $\tau = Fl$.
2. Determine the angle ϕ between the vectors $\vec{r}$ and $\vec{F}$; the lever arm is $r\sin\phi$, so $\tau = rF\sin\phi$.
3. Represent $\vec{F}$ in terms of a radial component F_{rad} along the direction of $\vec{r}$ and a tangential component F_{tan} at right angles, perpendicular to $\vec{r}$. (We call this a tangential component because if the body rotates, the point where the force acts moves in a circle, and this component is tangent to that circle.)

10.3 Three ways to calculate the torque of the force $\vec{F}$ about the point O. In this figure, $\vec{r}$ and $\vec{F}$ are in the plane of the page and the torque vector $\vec{\tau}$ points out of the page toward you.

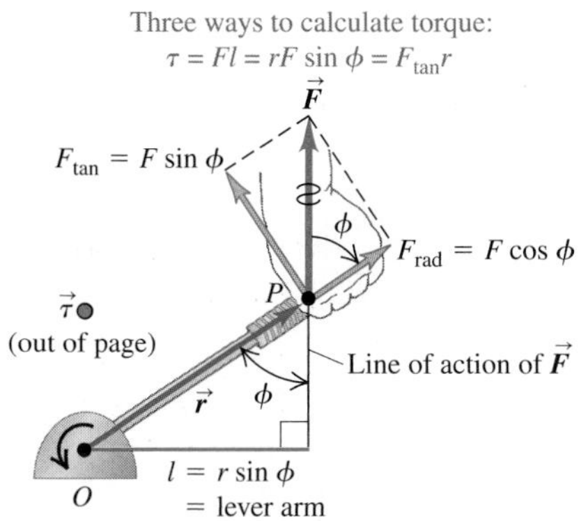

Three ways to calculate torque: $\tau = Fl = rF\sin\phi = F_{tan}r$
$\vec{F}$
$F_{tan} = F\sin\phi$
ϕ
$F_{rad} = F\cos\phi$
P
$\vec{\tau}$ (out of page)
Line of action of $\vec{F}$
$\vec{r}$
ϕ
O
$l = r\sin\phi$ = lever arm

10.4 The torque vector $\vec{\tau} = \vec{r} \times \vec{F}$ is directed along the axis of the bolt, perpendicular to both $\vec{r}$ and $\vec{F}$. The fingers of the right hand curl in the direction of the rotation that the torque tends to cause.

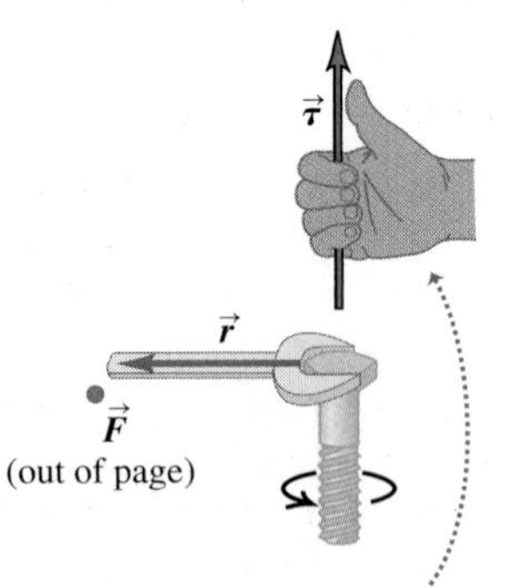

If you point the fingers of your right hand in the direction of $\vec{r}$ and then curl them in the direction of $\vec{F}$, your outstretched thumb points in the direction of $\vec{\tau}$

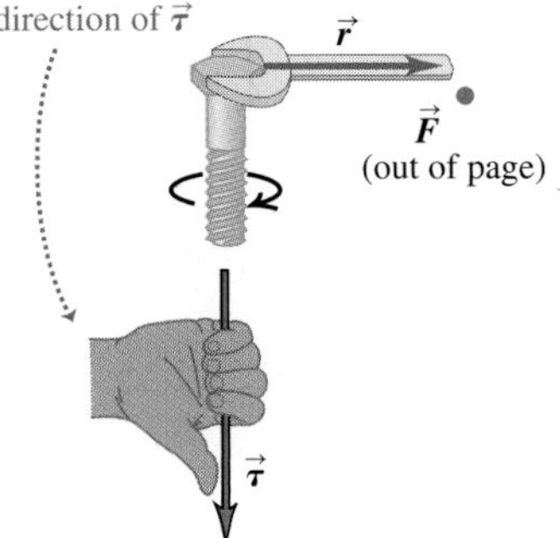

Then $F_{tan} = F\sin\phi$ and $\tau = r(F\sin\phi) = F_{tan}r$. The component F_{rad} produces *no* torque with respect to O because its lever arm with respect to that point is zero (compare to forces $\vec{F}_c$ in Fig. 10.1 and $\vec{F}_3$ in Fig. 10.2).

Summarizing these three expressions for torque, we have

$$\tau = Fl = rF\sin\phi = F_{tan}r \qquad \text{(magnitude of torque)} \tag{10.2}$$

Torque as a Vector

We saw in Section 9.1 that angular velocity and angular acceleration can be represented as vectors; the same is true for torque. To see how to do this, note that the quantity $rF\sin\phi$ in Eq. (10.2) is the magnitude of the *vector product* $\vec{r} \times \vec{F}$ that we defined in Section 1.10. (You should go back and review that definition.) We now generalize the definition of torque as follows: When a force $\vec{F}$ acts at a point having a position vector $\vec{r}$ with respect to an origin O, as in Fig. 10.3, the torque $\vec{\tau}$ of the force with respect to O is the *vector* quantity

$$\vec{\tau} = \vec{r} \times \vec{F} \qquad \text{(definition of torque vector)} \tag{10.3}$$

The torque as defined in Eq. (10.2) is just the magnitude of the torque vector $\vec{r} \times \vec{F}$. The direction of $\vec{\tau}$ is perpendicular to both $\vec{r}$ and $\vec{F}$. In particular, if both $\vec{r}$ and $\vec{F}$ lie in a plane perpendicular to the axis of rotation, as in Fig. 10.3, then the torque vector $\vec{\tau} = \vec{r} \times \vec{F}$ is directed along the axis of rotation, with a sense given by the right-hand rule (Fig. 1.29). Figure 10.4 shows the direction relationships.

In diagrams that involve $\vec{r}$, $\vec{F}$, and $\vec{\tau}$, it's common to have one of the vectors oriented perpendicular to the page. (Indeed, by the very nature of the cross product, $\vec{\tau} = \vec{r} \times \vec{F}$ *must* be perpendicular to the plane of the vectors $\vec{r}$ and $\vec{F}$.) We use a dot (•) to represent a vector that points out of the page (see Fig. 10.3) and a cross (×) to represent a vector that points into the page.

In the following sections we will usually be concerned with rotation of a body about an axis oriented in a specified constant direction. In that case, only the component of torque along that axis is of interest, and we often call that component the torque with respect to the specified *axis*.

Example 10.1 Applying a torque

A weekend plumber, unable to loosen a pipe fitting, slips a piece of scrap pipe (a "cheater") over his wrench handle. He then applies his full weight of 900 N to the end of the cheater by standing on it. The distance from the center of the fitting to the point where the weight acts is 0.80 m, and the wrench handle and cheater make an angle of 19° with the horizontal (Fig. 10.5a). Find the magnitude and direction of the torque he applies about the center of the pipe fitting.

10.5 (a) A weekend plumber tries to loosen a pipe fitting by standing on a "cheater." (b) Our vector diagram to find the torque about O.

(a) Diagram of situation

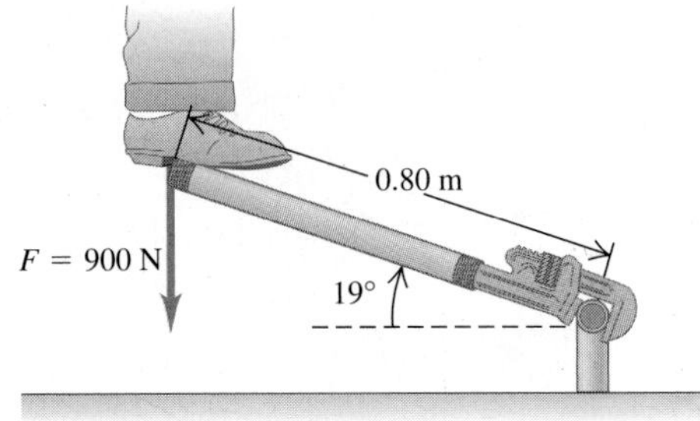

(b) Free-body diagram

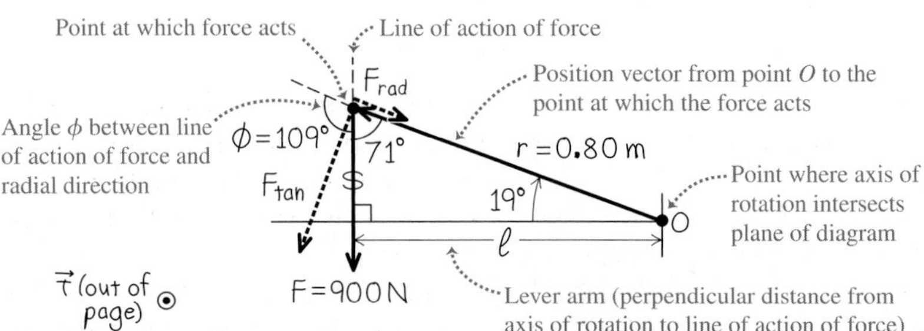

SOLUTION

IDENTIFY: Figure 10.5b shows the vectors $\vec{r}$ and $\vec{F}$ and the angle between them ($\phi = 109°$). We'll use our knowledge of these vectors to calculate the torque vector $\vec{\tau} = \vec{r} \times \vec{F}$.

SET UP: Equation (10.1) or (10.2) will tell us the magnitude of the torque, and the right-hand rule with Eq. (10.3) will tell us the torque direction.

EXECUTE: To use Eq. (10.1), we first calculate the lever arm l. As Fig. 10.5b shows,

$$l = (0.80\text{ m})\sin 109° = (0.80\text{ m})\sin 71° = 0.76\text{ m}$$

Then Eq. (10.1) tells us that the magnitude of the torque is

$$\tau = Fl = (900\text{ N})(0.76\text{ m}) = 680\text{ N}\cdot\text{m}$$

Or, from Eq. (10.2),

$$\tau = rF\sin\phi = (0.80\text{ m})(900\text{ N})(\sin 109°) = 680\text{ N}\cdot\text{m}$$

Alternatively, we can find F_{tan}, the tangential component of $\vec{F}$. This is the component that acts perpendicular to $\vec{r}$ (that is, perpendicular to the "cheater"). The vector $\vec{r}$ is oriented 19° from the horizontal, so the perpendicular to $\vec{r}$ is oriented 19° from the vertical. Since $\vec{F}$ is vertical, this means $F_{tan} = F(\cos 19°) = (900\text{ N})(\cos 19°) = 851$ N. Then the torque is

$$\tau = F_{tan}r = (851\text{ N})(0.80\text{ m}) = 680\text{ N}\cdot\text{m}$$

If you curl the fingers of your right hand from the direction of $\vec{r}$ (in the plane of Fig. 10.5b, to the left and up) into the direction of $\vec{F}$ (straight down), your right thumb points out of the plane of the figure. This is the direction of the torque $\vec{\tau}$.

EVALUATE: We've already checked our answer for the magnitude τ by calculating it in three different ways. To check our result for the direction of the torque, note that the force in Fig. 10.5 tends to produce a counterclockwise rotation about O. If you curl the fingers of your right hand in a counterclockwise direction, the thumb points out of the plane of Fig. 10.5, which is indeed the direction of the torque.

Test Your Understanding of Section 10.1 The figure shows a force P being applied to one end of a lever of length L. What is the magnitude of the torque of this force about point A? (i) $PL\sin\theta$; (ii) $PL\cos\theta$; (iii) $PL\tan\theta$.

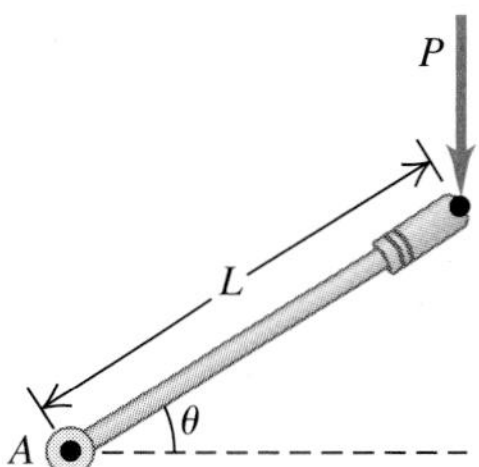

10.2 Torque and Angular Acceleration for a Rigid Body

We are now ready to develop the fundamental relationship for the rotational dynamics of a rigid body. We will show that the angular acceleration of a rotating rigid body is directly proportional to the sum of the torque components along the axis of rotation. The proportionality factor is the moment of inertia.

To develop this relationship, we again imagine the body as being made up of a large number of particles. We choose the axis of rotation to be the z-axis; the first particle has mass m_1 and distance r_1 from this axis (Fig. 10.6). The *net force* $\vec{F}_1$ acting on this particle has a component $F_{1,rad}$ along the radial direction, a component $F_{1,tan}$ that is tangent to the circle of radius r_1 in which the particle moves as the body rotates, and a component F_{1z} along the axis of rotation. Newton's second law for the tangential component is

$$F_{1,tan} = m_1 a_{1,tan} \tag{10.4}$$

We can express the tangential acceleration of the first particle in terms of the angular acceleration α_z of the body using Eq. (9.14): $a_{1,tan} = r_1\alpha_z$. Using this relationship and multiplying both sides of Eq. (10.4) by r_1, we obtain

$$F_{1,tan}r_1 = m_1 r_1^2 \alpha_z \tag{10.5}$$

From Eq. (10.2), $F_{1,tan}r_1$ is just the *torque* of the net force with respect to the rotation axis, equal to the component τ_{1z} of the torque vector along the rotation axis. The subscript z is a reminder that the torque affects rotation around the z-axis, in the same way that the subscript on F_{1z} is a reminder that this force affects the motion of particle 1 along the z-axis.

Neither of the components $F_{1,rad}$ or F_{1z} contributes to the torque about the z-axis, since neither tends to change the particle's rotation about that axis. So

ActivPhysics ONLINE

7.8 Rotoride–Dynamics Approach
7.9 Falling Ladder
7.10 Woman and Flywheel Elevator–Dynamics Approach

10.6 As a rigid body rotates around the z-axis, a net force $\vec{F}_1$ acts on one particle of the body. Only the force component $F_{1,tan}$ can affect the rotation, because only $F_{1,tan}$ exerts a torque about O with a z-component (along the rotation axis).

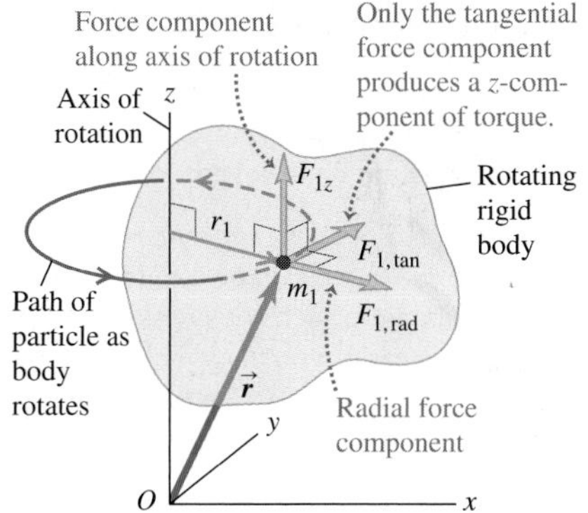

10.7 Loosening or tightening a screw requires giving it an angular acceleration and hence applying a torque. This is made easier by using a screwdriver with a large-radius handle, which provides a large lever arm for the force you apply with your hand.

$\tau_{1z} = F_{1,\tan} r_1$ is the total torque acting on the particle with respect to the rotation axis. Also, $m_1 r_1^2$ is I_1, the moment of inertia of the particle about the rotation axis. Hence we can rewrite Eq. (10.5) as

$$\tau_{1z} = I_1 \alpha_z = m_1 r_1^2 \alpha_z$$

We write an equation like this for every particle in the body and then add all these equations:

$$\tau_{1z} + \tau_{2z} + \cdots = I_1 \alpha_z + I_2 \alpha_z + \cdots = m_1 r_1^2 \alpha_z + m_2 r_2^2 \alpha_z + \cdots$$

or

$$\sum \tau_{iz} = \left(\sum m_i r_i^2\right) \alpha_z \qquad (10.6)$$

The left side of Eq. (10.6) is the sum of all the torques about the rotation axis that act on all the particles. The right side is $I = \sum m_i r_i^2$, the total moment of inertia about the rotation axis, multiplied by the angular acceleration α_z. Note that α_z is the same for every particle because this is a *rigid* body. Thus for the rigid body as a whole, Eq. (10.6) is the *rotational analog of Newton's second law:*

$$\sum \tau_z = I \alpha_z \qquad (10.7)$$

(rotational analog of Newton's second law for a rigid body)

Just as Newton's second law says that the net force on a particle equals the particle's mass times its acceleration, Eq. (10.7) says that the net torque on a rigid body equals the body's moment of inertia about the rotation axis times its angular acceleration (Fig. 10.7).

Note that because our derivation assumed that the angular acceleration α_z is the same for all particles in the body, Eq. (10.7) is valid *only* for *rigid* bodies. Hence this equation doesn't apply to a rotating tank of water or a swirling tornado of air, different parts of which have different angular accelerations. Also note that since our derivation used Eq. (9.14), $a_{\tan} = r\alpha_z$, α_z must be measured in rad/s^2.

The torque on each particle is due to the net force on that particle, which is the vector sum of external and internal forces (see Section 8.2). According to Newton's third law, the *internal* forces that any pair of particles in the rigid body exert on each other are equal and opposite (Fig. 10.8). If these forces act along the line joining the two particles, their lever arms with respect to any axis are also equal. So the torques for each such pair are equal and opposite, and add to zero. Hence *all* the internal torques add to zero, so the sum $\sum \tau_z$ in Eq. (10.7) includes only the torques of the *external* forces.

Often, an important external force acting on a body is its *weight.* This force is not concentrated at a single point; it acts on every particle in the entire body. Nevertheless, it turns out that if $\vec{g}$ has the same value at all points, we always get the correct torque (about any specified axis) if we assume that all the weight is concentrated at the *center of mass* of the body. We will prove this statement in Chapter 11, but meanwhile we will use it for some of the problems in this chapter.

10.8 Two particles in a rigid body exert equal and opposite forces on each other. If the forces act along the line joining the particles, the lever arms of the forces are the same and the torques due to the two forces are equal and opposite. Only *external* torques affect the body's rotation.

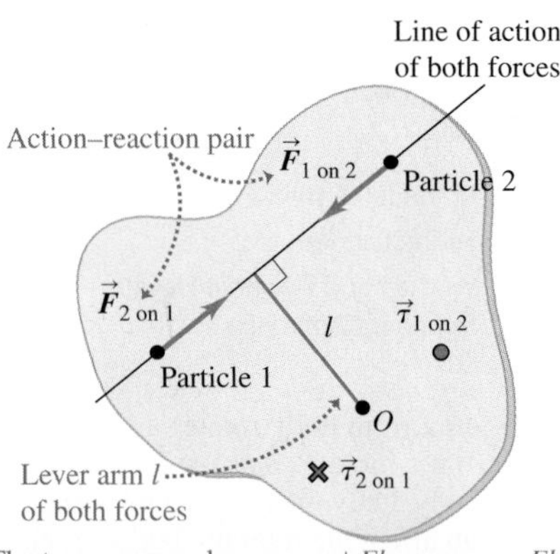

The torques cancel: $\tau_{1 \text{ on } 2} = +Fl$; $\tau_{2 \text{ on } 1} = -Fl$

Problem-Solving Strategy 10.1 Rotational Dynamics for Rigid Bodies

Our strategy for solving problems in rotational dynamics is very similar to Problem-Solving Strategy 5.2 (Section 5.2) for solving problems that involve Newton's second law.

IDENTIFY *the relevant concepts:* The equation $\sum \tau_z = I\alpha_z$ is useful whenever torques act on a rigid body—that is, whenever forces act on the body in such a way as to change its rotation.

In some cases you may be able to use an energy approach instead, as we did in Section 9.4. However, if the target variable is a force, a torque, an acceleration, an angular acceleration, or an elapsed time, using $\sum \tau_z = I\alpha_z$ is almost always the best approach.

SET UP *the problem* using the following steps:

1. Draw a sketch of the situation and select the body or bodies to be analyzed.
2. For each body, draw a free-body diagram and label unknown quantities with algebraic symbols. A new consideration is that

Continued

you must show the *shape* of the body accurately, including all dimensions and angles you will need for torque calculations.

3. Choose coordinate axes for each body and indicate a positive sense of rotation for each rotating body. If there is a linear acceleration, it's usually simplest to pick a positive axis in its direction. If you know the sense of α_z in advance, picking it as the positive sense of rotation simplifies the calculations.

EXECUTE *the solution* as follows:

1. For each body in the problem, decide whether it undergoes translational motion, rotational motion, or both. Then apply $\sum\vec{F} = m\vec{a}$ (as in Section 5.2), $\sum\tau_z = I\alpha_z$, or both to the body. Be careful to write separate equations of motion for each body.
2. There may be *geometrical* relationships between the motions of two or more bodies, as with a string that unwinds from a pulley while turning it or a wheel that rolls without slipping (to be discussed in Section 10.3). Express these relationships in algebraic form, usually as relationships between two linear accelerations or between a linear acceleration and an angular acceleration.
3. Check that the number of equations matches the number of unknown quantities. Then solve the equations to find the target variable(s).

EVALUATE *your answer:* Check that the algebraic signs of your results make sense. As an example, suppose the problem is about a spool of thread. If you are pulling thread off the spool, your answers should *not* tell you that the spool is turning in the direction that rolls the thread back on the spool! Whenever possible, check the results for special cases or extreme values of quantities. Ask yourself: "Does this result make sense?"

Example 10.2 An unwinding cable I

Figure 10.9a shows the same situation that we analyzed in Example 9.8 (Section 9.4) using energy methods. A cable is wrapped several times around a uniform solid cylinder that can rotate about its axis. The cylinder has diameter 0.120 m and mass 50 kg. The cable is pulled with a force of 9.0 N. Assuming that the cable unwinds without stretching or slipping, what is its acceleration?

SOLUTION

IDENTIFY: Our target variable is the acceleration of the cable, which we cannot find directly using the energy method of Section 9.4 (which does not involve acceleration). Instead, we'll apply rotational dynamics to the cylinder. To obtain the acceleration of the cable, we'll find a relationship between the motion of the cable and the motion of the rim of the cylinder.

SET UP: The cylinder rotates counterclockwise when the cable is pulled, so we take counterclockwise rotation to be positive. The net force on the cylinder must be zero because its center of mass remains at rest (Fig. 10.9b). The weight (magnitude Mg) and the normal force (magnitude n) exerted by the cylinder's bearings act along lines through the rotation axis. Hence these forces produce no torque with respect to that axis. The only torque about the rotation axis is due to the force F.

EXECUTE: The force F has a lever arm equal to the radius R of the cylinder: $l = R = 0.060$ m, so the torque due to F is $\tau_z = FR$. (This torque is positive as it tends to cause a counterclockwise rotation.) From Example 9.8, the moment of inertia of the cylinder about the rotation axis is $I = \frac{1}{2}MR^2$. Hence Eq. (10.7) gives us the *angular* acceleration of the cylinder:

$$\alpha_z = \frac{\tau_z}{I} = \frac{FR}{MR^2/2} = \frac{2F}{MR} = \frac{2(9.0\ \text{N})}{(50\ \text{kg})(0.060\ \text{m})} = 6.0\ \text{rad/s}^2$$

(Be certain to check that these units are correct. We can add the "rad" to our result because a radian is a dimensionless quantity.)

To get the *linear* acceleration of the cable, we need a kinematic relationship. We remarked in Section 9.3 that the acceleration of a cable unwinding from a cylinder is the same as the tangential component of acceleration of a point on the surface of the cylinder where the cable is tangent to it. This tangential acceleration is given by Eq. (9.14):

$$a_x = R\alpha = (0.060\ \text{m})(6.0\ \text{rad/s}^2) = 0.36\ \text{m/s}^2$$

EVALUATE: Can you use this result, together with an equation from Chapter 2, to determine the speed of the cable after it has been pulled 2.0 m? Try it, and compare your result with Example 9.8, in which we found this speed using work and energy considerations.

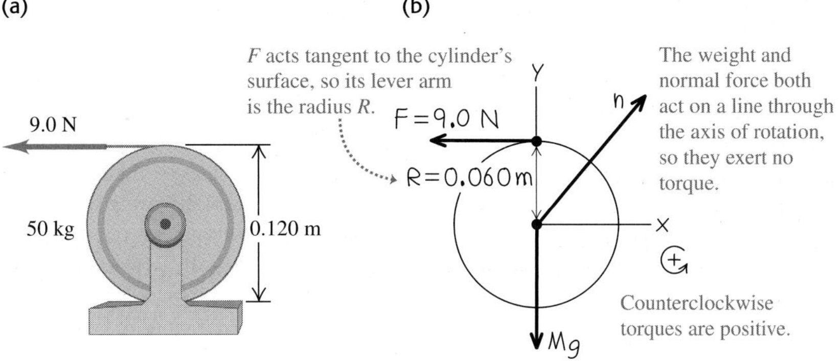

10.9 (a) Cylinder and cable. (b) Our free-body diagram for the cylinder.

Example 10.3 An unwinding cable II

Let us revisit the situation that we analyzed in Example 9.9 (Section 9.4) using energy methods. This time, find the acceleration of the block of mass m.

SOLUTION

IDENTIFY: We'll apply translational dynamics to the hanging block and rotational dynamics to the cylinder. Because the cable doesn't slip on the cylinder, there is a relationship between the linear acceleration of the block (our target variable) and the angular acceleration of the cylinder.

SET UP: In Fig. 10.10, we sketch the situation and draw a free-body diagram for each body. We take the positive sense of rotation for the cylinder to be counterclockwise and the positive direction of the y-coordinate for the object to be downward.

EXECUTE: For the object, Newton's second law gives

$$\sum F_y = mg + (-T) = ma_y$$

For the cylinder, the weight Mg and the normal force n (exerted by the bearing) have no torques with respect to the rotation axis because they act along lines through that axis, just as in Example 10.2. The only torque is that due to the cable tension T. Applying Eq. (10.7) to the cylinder gives

$$\sum \tau_z = RT = I\alpha_z = \frac{1}{2}MR^2\alpha_z$$

As in Example 10.2, the acceleration of the cable is the same as the tangential acceleration of a point on the cylinder rim. According to Eq. (9.14), this acceleration is given by $a_y = a_{tan} = R\alpha_z$. We use this to replace $R\alpha_z$ with a_y in the cylinder equation above, and then divide by R; the result is

$$T = \frac{1}{2}Ma_y$$

Now we substitute this expression for T into Newton's second law for the object and solve for the acceleration a_y:

$$mg - \frac{1}{2}Ma_y = ma_y$$

$$a_y = \frac{g}{1 + M/2m}$$

EVALUATE: The acceleration is positive (in the downward direction) and less than g, as it should be, since the cable is holding the object back. To see how much force the cable exerts, substitute our expression for a_y back into Newton's second law for the object to find T:

$$T = mg - ma_y = mg - m\left(\frac{g}{1 + M/2m}\right) = \frac{mg}{1 + 2m/M}$$

The tension in the cable is *not* equal to the weight mg of the object; if it were, the object could not accelerate.

Let's check some particular cases. When M is much larger than m, the tension is nearly equal to mg, and the acceleration is correspondingly much less than g. When M is zero, $T = 0$ and $a_y = g$; the object then falls freely. If the object starts from rest $(v_{0y} = 0)$ a height h above the floor, its y-velocity when it strikes the ground is given by $v_y^2 = v_{0y}^2 + 2a_yh = 2a_yh$, so $v_0 = 0$

$$v_y = \sqrt{2a_yh} = \sqrt{\frac{2gh}{1 + M/2m}}$$

This is the same result we obtained from energy considerations in Example 9.9.

10.10 (a) Our diagram of the situation. (b) Our free-body diagrams for the cylinder and the block. We assume the cable has negligible mass.

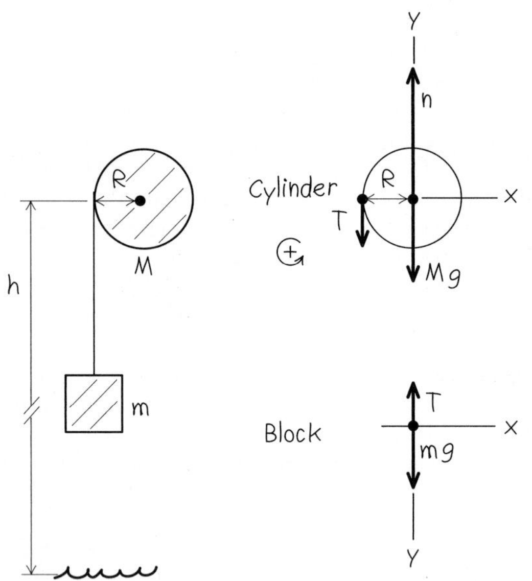

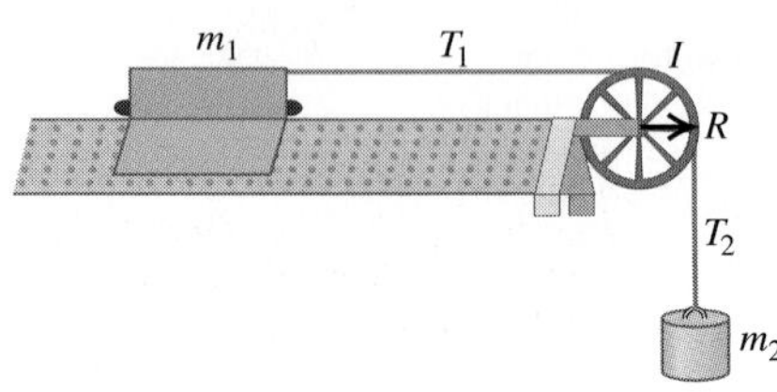

Test Your Understanding of Section 10.2 The figure shows a glider of mass m_1 that can slide without friction on a horizontal air track. It is attached to an object of mass m_2 by a massless string. The pulley has radius R and moment of inertia I about its axis of rotation. When released, the hanging object accelerates downward, the glider accelerates to the right, and the string turns the pulley without slipping or stretching. Rank the magnitudes of the following forces that act during the motion, in order from largest to smallest magnitude. (i) the tension force (magnitude T_1) in the horizontal part of the string; (ii) the tension force (magnitude T_2) in the vertical part of the string; (iii) the weight m_2g of the hanging object.

10.3 Rigid-Body Rotation About a Moving Axis

We can extend our analysis of the dynamics of rotational motion to some cases in which the axis of rotation moves. When that happens, the motion of the body is **combined translation and rotation.** The key to understanding such situations is this: Every possible motion of a rigid body can be represented as a combination of *translational motion of the center of mass* and *rotation about an axis through the center of mass.* This is true even when the center of mass accelerates, so that it is not at rest in any inertial frame. Figure 10.11 illustrates this for the motion of a tossed baton: The center of mass of the baton follows a parabolic curve, as though the baton were a particle located at the center of mass. Other examples of combined translational and rotational motions include a ball rolling down a hill and a yo-yo unwinding at the end of a string.

10.11 The motion of a rigid body is a combination of translational motion of the center of mass and rotation around the center of mass.

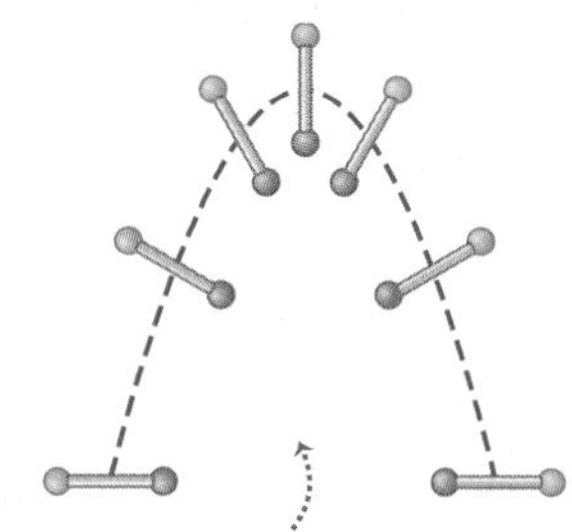

This baton toss can be represented as a combination of ...

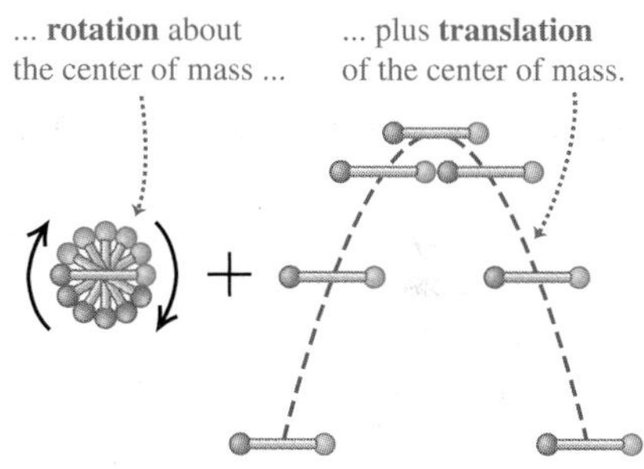
... **rotation** about the center of mass ...
... plus **translation** of the center of mass.
+

Combined Translation and Rotation: Energy Relationships

It's beyond the scope of this book to prove that the motion of a rigid body can always be divided into translation of the center of mass and rotation about the center of mass. But we can show that this is true for the *kinetic energy* of a rigid body that has both translational and rotational motions. In this case, the body's kinetic energy is the sum of a part $\frac{1}{2}Mv_{\text{cm}}{}^2$ associated with motion of the center of mass and a part $\frac{1}{2}I_{\text{cm}}\omega^2$ associated with rotation about an axis through the center of mass:

$$K = \frac{1}{2}Mv_{\text{cm}}{}^2 + \frac{1}{2}I_{\text{cm}}\omega^2 \qquad (10.8)$$

(rigid body with both translation and rotation)

To prove this relationship, we again imagine the rigid body to be made up of particles. Consider a typical particle with mass m_i as shown in Fig. 10.12. The velocity $\vec{v}_i$ of this particle relative to an inertial frame is the vector sum of the velocity $\vec{v}_{\text{cm}}$ of the center of mass and the velocity $\vec{v}_i'$ of the particle *relative to* the center of mass:

$$\vec{v}_i = \vec{v}_{\text{cm}} + \vec{v}_i' \qquad (10.9)$$

The kinetic energy K_i of this particle in the inertial frame is $\frac{1}{2}m_iv_i^2$, which we can also express as $\frac{1}{2}m_i(\vec{v}_i \cdot \vec{v}_i)$. Substituting Eq. (10.9) into this, we get

$$\begin{aligned} K_i &= \frac{1}{2}m_i(\vec{v}_{\text{cm}} + \vec{v}_i') \cdot (\vec{v}_{\text{cm}} + \vec{v}_i') \\ &= \frac{1}{2}m_i(\vec{v}_{\text{cm}} \cdot \vec{v}_{\text{cm}} + 2\vec{v}_{\text{cm}} \cdot \vec{v}_i' + \vec{v}_i' \cdot \vec{v}_i') \\ &= \frac{1}{2}m_i(v_{\text{cm}}{}^2 + 2\vec{v}_{\text{cm}} \cdot \vec{v}_i' + v_i'^2) \end{aligned}$$

The total kinetic energy is the sum $\sum K_i$ for all the particles making up the body. Expressing the three terms in this equation as separate sums, we get

$$K = \sum K_i = \sum\left(\frac{1}{2}m_iv_{\text{cm}}{}^2\right) + \sum(m_i\vec{v}_{\text{cm}} \cdot \vec{v}_i') + \sum\left(\frac{1}{2}m_iv_i'^2\right)$$

The first and second terms have common factors that can be taken outside the sum:

$$K = \frac{1}{2}\left(\sum m_i\right)v_{\text{cm}}{}^2 + \vec{v}_{\text{cm}} \cdot \left(\sum m_i\vec{v}_i'\right) + \sum\left(\frac{1}{2}m_iv_i'^2\right) \qquad (10.10)$$

10.12 A rigid body with both translation and rotation.

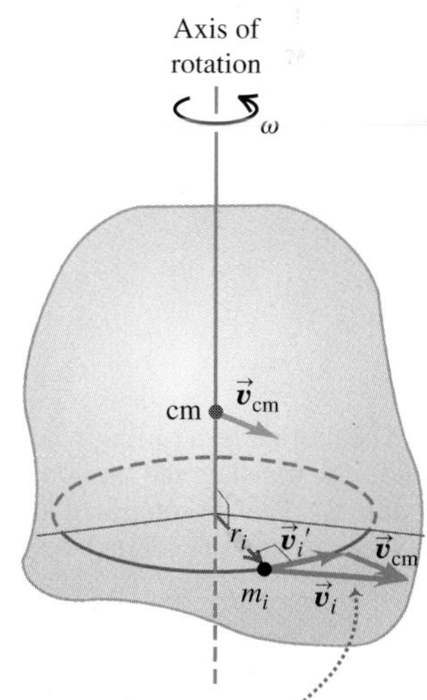
Axis of rotation
ω
cm
$\vec{v}_{\text{cm}}$
r_i
$\vec{v}_i'$
$\vec{v}_{\text{cm}}$
m_i
$\vec{v}_i$

Velocity $\vec{v}_i$ of particle in rotating, translating rigid body = (velocity $\vec{v}_{\text{cm}}$ of center of mass) plus (particle's velocity $\vec{v}_i'$ relative to center of mass)

Now comes the reward for our effort. In the first term, $\sum m_i$ is the total mass M. The second term is zero because $\sum m_i \vec{v}_i'$ is M times the velocity of the center of mass *relative to the center of mass,* and this is zero by definition. The last term is the sum of the kinetic energies of the particles computed by using their speeds with respect to the center of mass; this is just the kinetic energy of rotation around the center of mass. Using the same steps that led to Eq. (9.17) for the rotational kinetic energy of a rigid body, we can write this last term as $\frac{1}{2}I_{cm}\omega^2$, where I_{cm} is the moment of inertia with respect to the axis through the center of mass and ω is the angular speed. So Eq. (10.10) becomes Eq. (10.8):

$$K = \frac{1}{2}Mv_{cm}^2 + \frac{1}{2}I_{cm}\omega^2$$

Rolling Without Slipping

7.11 Race Between a Block and a Disk

An important case of combined translation and rotation is **rolling without slipping,** such as the motion of the wheel shown in Fig. 10.13. The wheel is symmetrical, so its center of mass is at its geometric center. We view the motion in an inertial frame of reference in which the surface on which the wheel rolls is at rest. In this frame, the point on the wheel that contacts the surface must be instantaneously *at rest* so that it does not slip. Hence the velocity $\vec{v}_1'$ of the point of contact relative to the center of mass must have the same magnitude but opposite direction as the center-of-mass velocity $\vec{v}_{cm}$. If the radius of the wheel is R and its angular speed about the center of mass is ω, then the magnitude of $\vec{v}_1'$ is $R\omega$; hence we must have

$$v_{cm} = R\omega \qquad \text{(condition for rolling without slipping)} \qquad (10.11)$$

As Fig. 10.13 shows, the velocity of a point on the wheel is the vector sum of the velocity of the center of mass and the velocity of the point relative to the center of mass. Thus while point 1, the point of contact, is instantaneously at rest, point 3 at the top of the wheel is moving forward *twice as fast* as the center of mass, and points 2 and 4 at the sides have velocities at 45° to the horizontal.

At any instant we can think of the wheel as rotating about an "instantaneous axis" of rotation that passes through the point of contact with the ground. The angular velocity ω is the same for this axis as for an axis through the center of mass; an observer at the center of mass sees the rim make the same number of revolutions per second as does an observer at the rim watching the center of mass spin around him. If we think of the motion of the rolling wheel in Fig. 10.13 in this way, the kinetic energy of the wheel is $K = \frac{1}{2}I_1\omega^2$, where I_1 is the moment of

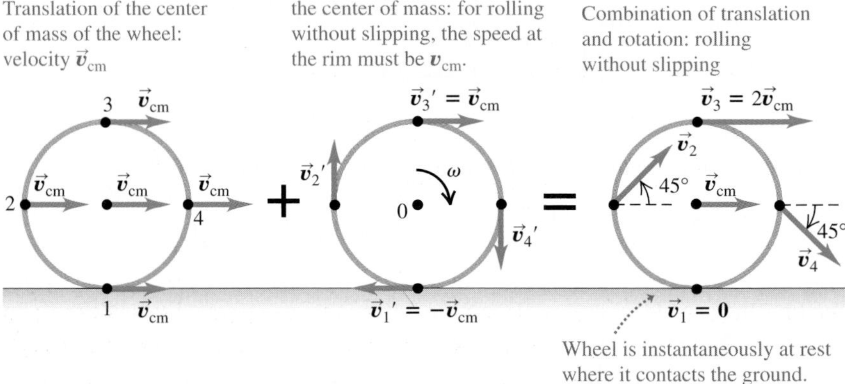

10.13 The motion of a rolling wheel is the sum of the translational motion of the center of mass plus the rotational motion of the wheel around the center of mass.

inertia of the wheel about an axis through point 1. But by the parallel-axis theorem, Eq. (9.19), $I_1 = I_{cm} + MR^2$, where M is the total mass of the wheel and I_{cm} is the moment of inertia with respect to an axis through the center of mass. Using Eq. (10.11), the kinetic energy of the wheel is

$$K = \frac{1}{2}I_1\omega^2 = \frac{1}{2}I_{cm}\omega^2 + \frac{1}{2}MR^2\omega^2 = \frac{1}{2}I_{cm}\omega^2 + \frac{1}{2}Mv_{cm}^2$$

which is the same as Eq. (10.8).

CAUTION **Rolling without slipping** Note that the relationship $v_{cm} = R\omega$ holds *only* if there is rolling without slipping. When a drag racer first starts to move, the rear tires are spinning very fast even though the racer is hardly moving, so $R\omega$ is greater than v_{cm} (Fig. 10.14). If a driver applies the brakes too heavily so that the car skids, the tires will spin hardly at all and $R\omega$ is less than v_{cm}.

10.14 The smoke rising from this drag racer's rear tires shows that the tires are slipping on the road, so v_{cm} is *not* equal to $R\omega$.

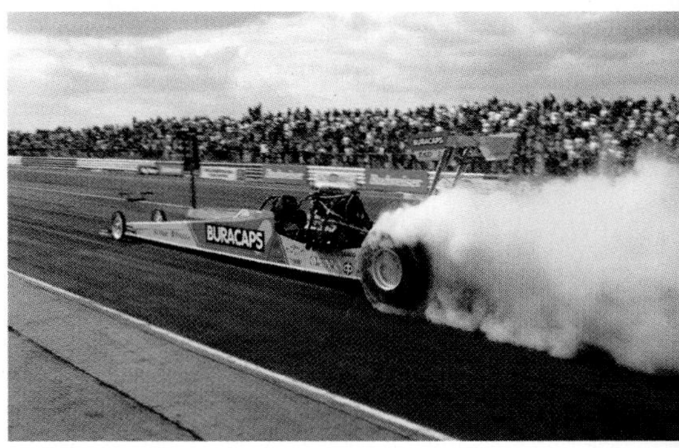

If a rigid body changes height as it moves, we must also consider gravitational potential energy. As we discussed in Section 9.4, the gravitational potential energy associated with any extended body of mass M, rigid or not, is the same as if we replace the body by a particle of mass M located at the body's center of mass. That is,

$$U = Mgy_{cm}$$

Example 10.4 Speed of a primitive yo-yo

A primitive yo-yo is made by wrapping a string several times around a solid cylinder with mass M and radius R (Fig. 10.15). You hold the end of the string stationary while releasing the cylinder with no initial motion. The string unwinds but does not slip or stretch as the cylinder drops and rotates. Use energy considerations to find the speed v_{cm} of the center of mass of the solid cylinder after it has dropped a distance h.

10.15 Calculating the speed of a primitive yo-yo.

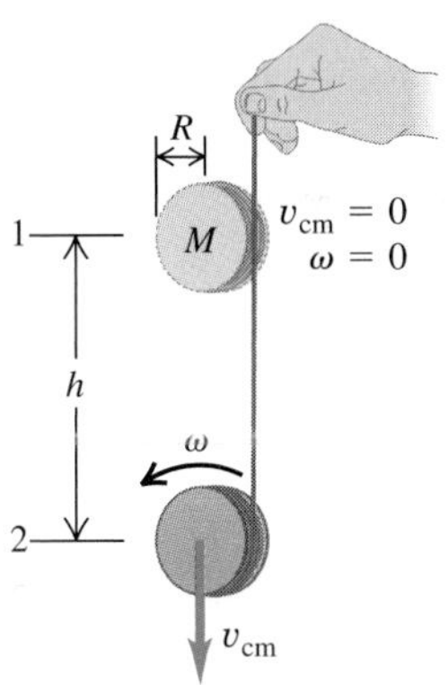

SOLUTION

IDENTIFY: The upper end of the string is held fixed, not pulled upward, so the hand in Fig. 10.15 does no work on the system of string and cylinder. As in Example 9.8 (Section 9.4), there is friction between the string and the cylinder, but because the string never slips on the surface of the cylinder, no mechanical energy is lost. Thus we can use conservation of mechanical energy.

SET UP: The potential energies are $U_1 = Mgh$ and $U_2 = 0$. The string has no kinetic energy because it's massless. The initial kinetic energy of the cylinder is $K_1 = 0$, and its final kinetic energy K_2 is given by Eq. (10.8). The moment of inertia is $I = \frac{1}{2}MR^2$, and $\omega = v_{cm}/R$ because the cylinder does not slip on the string.

EXECUTE: From Eq. (10.8), the kinetic energy at point 2 is

$$K_2 = \frac{1}{2}Mv_{cm}^2 + \frac{1}{2}\left(\frac{1}{2}MR^2\right)\left(\frac{v_{cm}}{R}\right)^2$$
$$= \frac{3}{4}Mv_{cm}^2$$

The kinetic energy is $1\frac{1}{2}$ times as great as it would be if the yo-yo were falling at speed v_{cm} without rotating. Two-thirds of the total kinetic energy $(\frac{1}{2}Mv_{cm}^2)$ is translational and one-third $(\frac{1}{4}Mv_{cm}^2)$ is rotational. Then, conservation of energy gives

$$K_1 + U_1 = K_2 + U_2$$
$$0 + Mgh = \frac{3}{4}Mv_{cm}^2 + 0$$

and

$$v_{cm} = \sqrt{\frac{4}{3}gh}$$

EVALUATE: This is less than the speed $\sqrt{2gh}$ that a dropped object would have, because one-third of the potential energy released as the cylinder falls appears as rotational kinetic energy.

Example 10.5 Race of the rolling bodies

In a physics lecture demonstration, an instructor "races" various round rigid bodies by releasing them from rest at the top of an inclined plane (Fig. 10.16). What shape should a body have to reach the bottom of the incline first?

SOLUTION

IDENTIFY: We can again use conservation of energy because there is no sliding of the rigid bodies over the inclined plane. Kinetic friction does no work if the bodies roll without slipping. We can also ignore the effects of *rolling friction,* introduced in Section 5.3, provided the bodies and the surface on which they roll are perfectly rigid. (Later in this section we'll explain why this is so.)

SET UP: Each body starts from rest at the top of an incline with height h, so $K_1 = 0$, $U_1 = Mgh$, and $U_2 = 0$. The kinetic energy at the bottom of the incline is given by Eq. (10.8). If the bodies roll without slipping, $\omega = v_{cm}/R$. We can express the moments of inertia of all the round bodies in Table 9.2 (about axes through their centers of mass) as $I_{cm} = cMR^2$, where c is a pure number less than or equal to 1 that depends on the shape of the body. Our goal is to find the value of c that gives the body the greatest speed at the bottom of the incline.

10.16 Which body rolls down the incline fastest, and why?

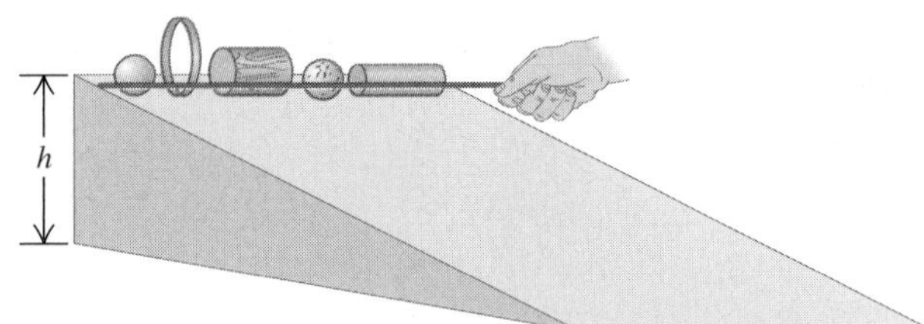

EXECUTE: From conservation of energy,

$$K_1 + U_1 = K_2 + U_2$$

$$0 + Mgh = \frac{1}{2}Mv_{cm}^2 + \frac{1}{2}cMR^2\left(\frac{v_{cm}}{R}\right)^2 + 0$$

$$= \frac{1}{2}(1 + c)Mv_{cm}^2$$

Hence the speed at the bottom of the incline is

$$v_{cm} = \sqrt{\frac{2gh}{1 + c}}$$

EVALUATE: This is a fairly amazing result; the speed doesn't depend on either the mass M of the body or its radius R. All uniform solid cylinders have the same speed at the bottom, even if their masses and radii are different, because they have the same c. All solid spheres have the same speed, and so on. The smaller the value of c, the faster the body is moving at the bottom (and at any point on the way down). Small-c bodies always beat large-c bodies because they have less of their kinetic energy tied up in rotation and have more available for translation. Reading the values of c from Table 9.2, we see that the order of finish is as follows: any solid sphere, any solid cylinder, any thin-walled hollow sphere, and any thin-walled hollow cylinder.

Combined Translation and Rotation: Dynamics

We can also analyze the combined translational and rotational motions of a rigid body from the standpoint of dynamics. We showed in Section 8.5 that for a body with total mass M, the acceleration $\vec{a}_{cm}$ of the center of mass is the same as that of a point mass M acted on by all the external forces on the actual body:

$$\sum \vec{F}_{ext} = M\vec{a}_{cm} \qquad (10.12)$$

The rotational motion about the center of mass is described by the rotational analog of Newton's second law, Eq. (10.7):

$$\sum \tau_z = I_{cm}\alpha_z \qquad (10.13)$$

where I_{cm} is the moment of inertia with respect to an axis through the center of mass and the sum $\sum \tau_z$ includes all external torques with respect to this axis. It's not immediately obvious that Eq. (10.13) should apply to the motion of a translating rigid body; after all, our derivation of $\sum \tau_z = I\alpha_z$ in Section 10.2 assumed that the axis of rotation was stationary. But in fact, Eq. (10.13) is valid *even when the axis of rotation moves,* provided the following two conditions are met:

1. The axis through the center of mass must be an axis of symmetry.
2. The axis must not change direction.

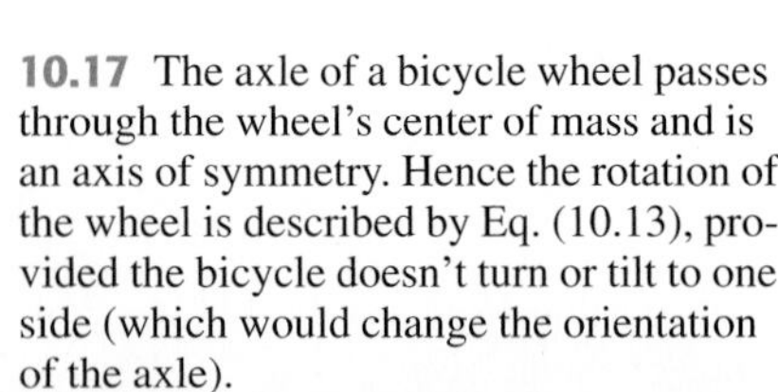

10.17 The axle of a bicycle wheel passes through the wheel's center of mass and is an axis of symmetry. Hence the rotation of the wheel is described by Eq. (10.13), provided the bicycle doesn't turn or tilt to one side (which would change the orientation of the axle).

These conditions are satisfied for many types of rotation (Fig. 10.17). Note that in general this moving axis of rotation is *not* at rest in an inertial frame of reference.

We can now solve dynamics problems involving a rigid body that undergoes translational and rotational motions at the same time, provided that the rotation axis satisfies the two conditions just mentioned. Problem-Solving Strategy 10.1

(Section 10.2) is equally useful here, and you should review it now. Keep in mind that when a body undergoes translational and rotational motions at the same time, we need two separate equations of motion *for the same body.* One of these, Eq. (10.12), describes the translational motion of the center of mass. The other equation of motion, Eq. (10.13), describes the rotational motion about the axis through the center of mass.

Example 10.6 Acceleration of a primitive yo-yo

For the primitive yo-yo in Example 10.4 (Fig. 10.18a), find the downward acceleration of the cylinder and the tension in the string.

SOLUTION

IDENTIFY: Figure 10.18b shows our free-body diagram for the yo-yo, including the choice of positive coordinate directions. With these coordinates, our target variables are $a_{\text{cm-}y}$ and T.

SET UP: We'll use Eqs. (10.12) and (10.13), along with the condition that the string does not slip on the cylinder.

EXECUTE: The equation for the translational motion of the center of mass is

$$\sum F_y = Mg + (-T) = Ma_{\text{cm-}y} \tag{10.14}$$

10.18 Dynamics of a primitive yo-yo (see Fig. 10.15).

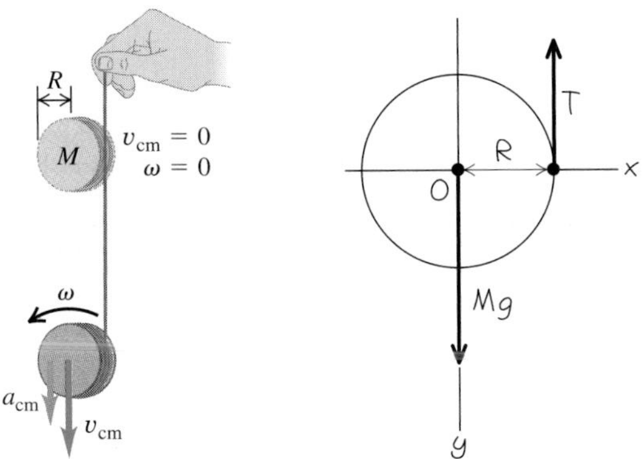

The moment of inertia for an axis through the center of mass is $I_{\text{cm}} = \frac{1}{2}MR^2$. Only the tension force has a torque with respect to the axis through the center of mass, so the equation for rotational motion about this axis is

$$\sum \tau_z = TR = I_{\text{cm}}\alpha_z = \frac{1}{2}MR^2\alpha_z \tag{10.15}$$

The string unwinds without slipping, so $v_{\text{cm-}z} = R\omega_z$ from Eq. (10.11); the derivative of this relationship with respect to time is

$$a_{\text{cm-}y} = R\alpha_z \tag{10.16}$$

We now use Eq. (10.16) to eliminate α_z from Eq. (10.15) and then solve Eqs. (10.14) and (10.15) simultaneously for T and $a_{\text{cm-}y}$. The results are amazingly simple:

$$a_{\text{cm-}y} = \frac{2}{3}g \qquad T = \frac{1}{3}Mg$$

Using the constant-acceleration formula $v_{\text{cm-}y}^2 = v_{\text{cm-}0y}^2 + 2a_{\text{cm-}y}h$, you can show that the speed of the yo-yo after it has fallen a distance h is $v_{\text{cm}} = \sqrt{\frac{4}{3}gh}$, just as we found in Example 10.4.

EVALUATE: From the standpoint of dynamics, the tension force is essential; it causes the yo-yo's acceleration to be less than g, and its torque is what causes the yo-yo to turn. Yet when we analyzed this situation using energy methods in Example 10.4, we didn't have to consider the tension force at all! Because no mechanical energy was lost or gained, from the energy standpoint the string is merely a way to convert some of the gravitational potential energy into rotational kinetic energy.

Example 10.7 Acceleration of a rolling sphere

A solid bowling ball rolls without slipping down the return ramp at the side of the alley (Fig. 10.19a). The ramp is inclined at an angle β to the horizontal. What are the ball's acceleration and the magnitude of the friction force on the ball? Treat the ball as a uniform solid sphere, ignoring the finger holes.

SOLUTION

IDENTIFY: Our target variables are the acceleration of the ball's center of mass and the magnitude of the friction force. The free-body diagram in Fig. 10.19b shows that only the friction force exerts a torque about the center of mass.

SET UP: As in Example 10.6, we use Eq. (10.12) to describe the translational motion and Eq. (10.13) to describe the rotational motion.

10.19 A bowling ball rolling down a ramp.

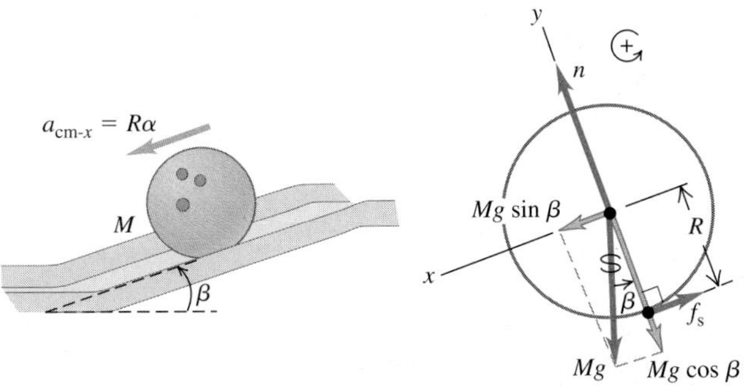

Continued

EXECUTE: From Table 9.2 the moment of inertia of a solid sphere is $I_{cm} = \frac{2}{5}MR^2$. The equations of motion for translation and for rotation about the axis through the center of mass, respectively, are

$$\sum F_x = Mg\sin\beta + (-f) = Ma_{cm\text{-}x} \quad (10.17)$$

$$\sum \tau_z = fR = I_{cm}\alpha_z = \left(\frac{2}{5}MR^2\right)\alpha_z \quad (10.18)$$

If the ball rolls without slipping, we have the same kinematic relationship $a_{cm\text{-}x} = R\alpha_z$ as in Example 10.6. We use this to eliminate α_z from Eq. (10.18):

$$fR = \frac{2}{5}MRa_{cm\text{-}x}$$

This equation and Eq. (10.17) are two equations for two unknowns, $a_{cm\text{-}x}$ and f. We solve Eq. (10.17) for f, substitute the expression into the above equation to eliminate f, and then solve for $a_{cm\text{-}x}$ to obtain

$$a_{cm\text{-}x} = \frac{5}{7}g\sin\beta$$

The acceleration is just $\frac{5}{7}$ as large as it would be if the ball could *slide* without friction down the slope, like the toboggan in Example 5.10 (Section 5.2). Finally, we substitute this back into Eq. (10.17) and solve for f:

$$f = \frac{2}{7}Mg\sin\beta$$

EVALUATE: Because the ball does not slip at the instantaneous point of contact with the ramp, the friction force f is a *static* friction force; it prevents slipping and gives the ball its angular acceleration. We can derive an expression for the minimum coefficient of static friction μ_s needed to prevent slipping. The normal force is $n = Mg\cos\beta$. The maximum force of static friction equals $\mu_s n$, so the coefficient of friction must be at least as great as

$$\mu_s = \frac{f}{n} = \frac{\frac{2}{7}Mg\sin\beta}{Mg\cos\beta} = \frac{2}{7}\tan\beta$$

If the plane is tilted only a little, β is small, and only a small value of μ_s is needed to prevent slipping. But as the angle increases, the required value of μ_s increases, as we might expect intuitively. If the ball begins to slip, Eqs. (10.17) and (10.18) are both still valid, but it's no longer true that $v_{cm\text{-}x} = R\omega_z$ or $a_{cm\text{-}x} = R\alpha_z$; we have only two equations for three unknowns ($a_{cm\text{-}x}$, α_z, and f). To solve the problem of rolling *with* slipping requires taking *kinetic* friction into account (see Challenge Problem 10.101).

If the bowling ball descends a vertical distance h as it moves down the ramp, the displacement along the ramp is $h/\sin\beta$. You should be able to show that the speed of the ball at the bottom of the ramp would be $v_{cm} = \sqrt{\frac{10}{7}gh}$, which is just the result you found in Example 10.5 with $c = \frac{2}{5}$.

If the ball were rolling *uphill*, the force of friction would still be directed uphill as in Fig. 10.19b. Can you see why?

Rolling Friction

In Example 10.5 we said that we can ignore rolling friction if both the rolling body and the surface over which it rolls are perfectly rigid. In Fig. 10.20a a perfectly rigid sphere is rolling down a perfectly rigid incline. The line of action of the normal force passes through the center of the sphere, so its torque is zero; there is no sliding at the point of contact, so the friction force does no work. Figure 10.20b shows a more realistic situation, in which the surface "piles up" in front of the sphere and the sphere rides in a shallow trench. Because of these deformations, the contact forces on the sphere no longer act along a single point, but over an area; the forces are concentrated on the front of the sphere as shown. As a result, the normal force now exerts a torque that opposes the rotation. In addition, there is some sliding of the sphere over the surface due to the deformation, causing mechanical energy to be lost. The combination of these two effects is the phenomenon of *rolling friction.* Rolling friction also occurs if the rolling body is deformable, such as an automobile tire. Often the rolling body and the surface are rigid enough that rolling friction can be ignored, as we have assumed in all the examples in this section.

10.20 Rolling down **(a)** a perfectly rigid surface and **(b)** a deformable surface. The deformation in part **(b)** is greatly exaggerated.

(a) Perfectly rigid sphere rolling on a perfectly rigid surface

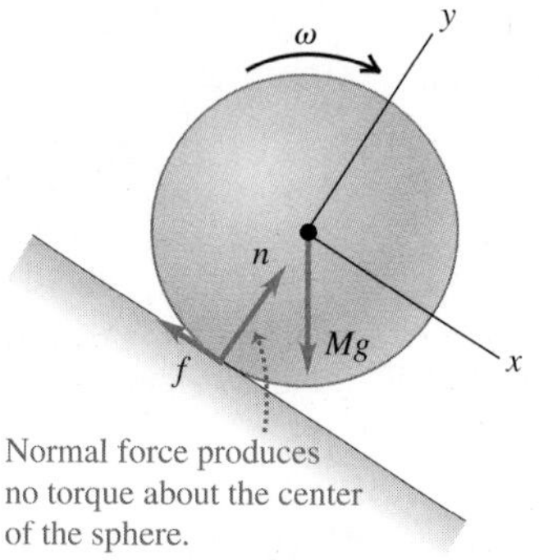
ω
y
n
Mg
f
x
Normal force produces no torque about the center of the sphere.

(b) Rigid sphere rolling on a deformable surface

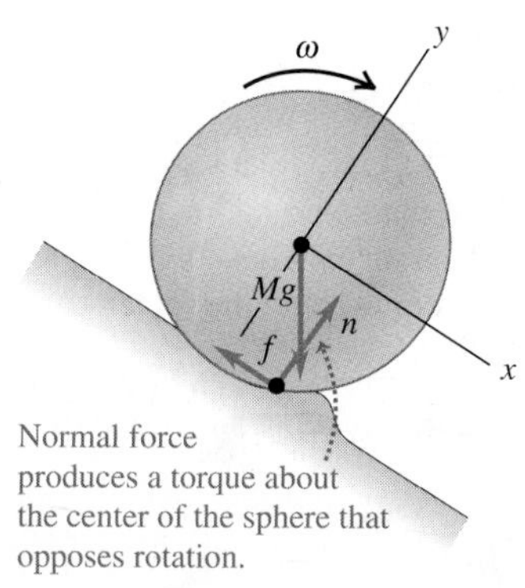
ω
y
Mg
n
f
x
Normal force produces a torque about the center of the sphere that opposes rotation.

Test Your Understanding of Section 10.3 Suppose the solid cylinder used as a yo-yo in Example 10.6 is replaced by a hollow cylinder of the same mass and radius. (a) Will the acceleration of the yo-yo (i) increase, (ii) decrease, or (iii) remain the same? (b) Will the string tension (i) increase, (ii) decrease, or (iii) remain the same?

10.4 Work and Power in Rotational Motion

When you pedal a bicycle, you apply forces to a rotating body and do work on it. Similar things happen in many other real-life situations, such as a rotating motor shaft driving a power tool or a car engine propelling the vehicle. We can express this work in terms of torque and angular displacement.

Suppose a tangential force $\vec{F}_{tan}$ acts at the rim of a pivoted disk—for example, a child running while pushing on a playground merry-go-round (Fig. 10.21a). The disk rotates through an infinitesimal angle $d\theta$ about a fixed axis during an infinitesimal time interval dt (Fig. 10.21b). The work dW done by the force $\vec{F}_{tan}$ while a point on the rim moves a distance ds is $dW = F_{tan}\,ds$. If $d\theta$ is measured in radians, then $ds = R\,d\theta$ and

$$dW = F_{tan}R\,d\theta$$

Now $F_{tan}R$ is the *torque* τ_z due to the force $\vec{F}_{tan}$, so

$$dW = \tau_z\,d\theta \tag{10.19}$$

The total work W done by the torque during an angular displacement from θ_1 to θ_2 is

$$W = \int_{\theta_1}^{\theta_2} \tau_z\,d\theta \qquad \text{(work done by a torque)} \tag{10.20}$$

If the torque remains *constant* while the angle changes by a finite amount $\Delta\theta = \theta_2 - \theta_1$, then

$$W = \tau_z(\theta_2 - \theta_1) = \tau_z\Delta\theta \qquad \text{(work done by a constant torque)} \tag{10.21}$$

10.21 A tangential force applied to a rotating body does work.

(a)

(b) Overhead view of merry-go-round

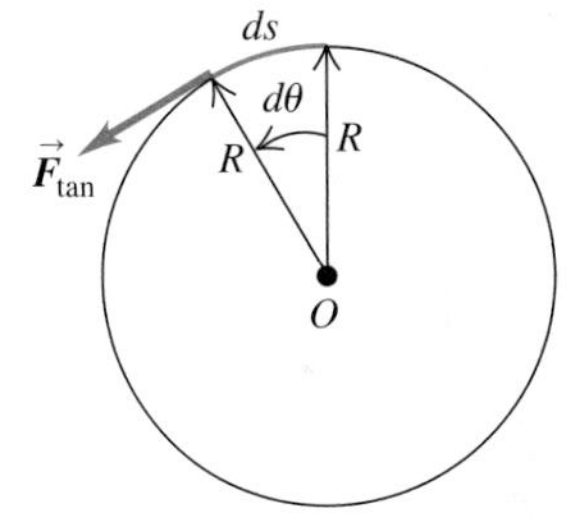

The work done by a *constant* torque is the product of torque and the angular displacement. If torque is expressed in newton-meters $(\mathrm{N \cdot m})$ and angular displacement in radians, the work is in joules. Equation (10.21) is the rotational analog of Eq. (6.1), $W = Fs$, and Eq. (10.20) is the analog of Eq. (6.7), $W = \int F_x\,dx$, for the work done by a force in a straight-line displacement.

If the force in Fig. 10.21 had an axial component (parallel to the rotation axis) or a radial component (directed toward or away from the axis), that component would do no work because the displacement of the point of application has only a tangential component. An axial or radial component of force would also make no contribution to the torque about the axis of rotation. So Eqs. (10.20) and (10.21) are correct for *any* force, no matter what its components.

When a torque does work on a rotating rigid body, the kinetic energy changes by an amount equal to the work done. We can prove this by using exactly the same procedure that we used in Eqs. (6.11) through (6.13) for the translational kinetic energy of a particle. Let τ_z represent the *net* torque on the body so that $\tau_z = I\alpha_z$ from Eq. (10.7), and assume that the body is rigid so that the moment of inertia I is constant. We then transform the integrand in Eq. (10.20) into an integrand with respect to ω_z as follows:

$$\tau_z\,d\theta = (I\alpha_z)\,d\theta = I\frac{d\omega_z}{dt}\,d\theta = I\frac{d\theta}{dt}\,d\omega_z = I\omega_z\,d\omega_z$$

10.22 The rotational kinetic energy of a wind turbine is equal to the total work done to set it spinning.

Since τ_z is the net torque, the integral in Eq. (10.20) is the *total* work done on the rotating rigid body. This equation then becomes

$$W_{tot} = \int_{\omega_1}^{\omega_2} I\omega_z \, d\omega_z = \frac{1}{2}I\omega_2^2 - \frac{1}{2}I\omega_1^2 \qquad (10.22)$$

The change in the rotational kinetic energy of a *rigid* body equals the work done by forces exerted from outside the body (Fig. 10.22). This equation is analogous to Eq. (6.13), the work–energy theorem for a particle.

What about the *power* associated with work done by a torque acting on a rotating body? When we divide both sides of Eq. (10.19) by the time interval dt during which the angular displacement occurs, we find

$$\frac{dW}{dt} = \tau_z \frac{d\theta}{dt}$$

But dW/dt is the rate of doing work, or *power P*, and $d\theta/dt$ is angular velocity ω_z, so

$$P = \tau_z \omega_z \qquad (10.23)$$

When a torque τ_z (with respect to the axis of rotation) acts on a body that rotates with angular velocity ω_z, its power (rate of doing work) is the product of τ_z and ω_z. This is the analog of the relationship $P = \vec{F} \cdot \vec{v}$ that we developed in Section 6.4 for particle motion.

Example 10.8 Engine power and torque

The power output of an automobile engine is advertised to be 200 hp at 6000 rpm. What is the corresponding torque?

SOLUTION

IDENTIFY: This example uses the relationship among power, angular velocity, and torque (the target variable).

SET UP: We are given the power output P and the angular velocity ω_z, so we can find the torque using Eq. (10.23).

EXECUTE: First we have to convert the power to watts and the angular velocity to rad/s:

$$P = 200 \text{ hp} = 200 \text{ hp}\left(\frac{746 \text{ W}}{1 \text{ hp}}\right) = 1.49 \times 10^5 \text{ W}$$

$$\omega_z = 6000 \text{ rev/min} = \left(\frac{6000 \text{ rev}}{1 \text{ min}}\right)\left(\frac{2\pi \text{ rad}}{1 \text{ rev}}\right)\left(\frac{1 \text{ min}}{60 \text{ s}}\right) = 628 \text{ rad/s}$$

From Eq. (10.23),

$$\tau_z = \frac{P}{\omega_z} = \frac{1.49 \times 10^5 \text{ N} \cdot \text{m/s}}{628 \text{ rad/s}} = 237 \text{ N} \cdot \text{m}$$

EVALUATE: You could apply this much torque by using a wrench 0.25 m long and applying a force of 948 N (213 lb) to the end of its handle. Could you do it?

Example 10.9 Calculating power from torque

An electric motor exerts a constant torque of 10 N · m on a grindstone mounted on its shaft. The moment of inertia of the grindstone about the shaft is 2.0 kg · m^2. If the system starts from rest, find the work done by the motor in 8.0 seconds and the kinetic energy at the end of this time. What was the average power delivered by the motor?

SOLUTION

IDENTIFY: Since the torque is constant, the grindstone has a constant angular acceleration α_z. If we can find the value of α_z, we can find the angle $\Delta\theta$ through which the grindstone turns in 8.0 s [which, through Eq. (10.21), tells us the work done W] and the angular velocity ω_z at that time (which tells us the kinetic energy K). We can find the average power P_{av} by dividing the work done by the time interval.

SET UP: We use the rotational version of Newton's second law, $\sum\tau_z = I\alpha_z$, to find the angular acceleration α_z. Given this we use the kinematics equations from Section 9.2 to calculate $\Delta\theta$ and ω_z and from these calculate W, K, and P_{av}.

EXECUTE: We have $\sum\tau_z = 10$ N · m (the only torque acting is that due to the motor) and $I = 2.0$ kg · m^2, so from $\sum\tau_z = I\alpha_z$ the angular acceleration is 5.0 rad/s^2. From Eq. (9.11) the total angle through which the system turns in 8.0 s is

$$\Delta\theta = \frac{1}{2}\alpha_z t^2 = \frac{1}{2}(5.0 \text{ rad/s}^2)(8.0 \text{ s})^2 = 160 \text{ rad}$$

and the total work done by the torque is

$$W = \tau_z \Delta\theta = (10\ \text{N}\cdot\text{m})(160\ \text{rad}) = 1600\ \text{J}$$

From Eqs. (9.7) and (9.17), the angular velocity and kinetic energy at $t = 8.0$ s are

$$\omega_z = \alpha_z t = (5.0\ \text{rad/s}^2)(8.0\ \text{s}) = 40\ \text{rad/s}$$

$$K = \frac{1}{2}I\omega_z^2 = \frac{1}{2}(2.0\ \text{kg}\cdot\text{m}^2)(40\ \text{rad/s})^2 = 1600\ \text{J}$$

The initial kinetic energy was zero, so the work done equals the increase in kinetic energy [see Eq. (10.22)].

The average power is

$$P_{\text{av}} = \frac{1600\ \text{J}}{8.0\ \text{s}} = 200\ \text{J/s} = 200\ \text{W}$$

EVALUATE: We can check our answer for *average* power by considering the *instantaneous* power $P = \tau_z\omega_z$. Because ω_z increases continuously, P increases continuously as well; its value is zero at $t = 0$ and increases to $(10\ \text{N}\cdot\text{m})(40\ \text{rad/s}) = 400$ W at $t = 8.0$ s. The angular velocity and the power increase uniformly with time, so the *average* power is just half this maximum value, or 200 W.

Test Your Understanding of Section 10.4 You apply equal torques to two different cylinders, one of which has a moment of inertia twice as large as the other cylinder. Each cylinder is initially at rest. After one complete rotation, which cylinder has the greater kinetic energy? (i) the cylinder with the larger moment of inertia; (ii) the cylinder with the smaller moment of inertia; (iii) both cylinders have the same kinetic energy.

10.5 Angular Momentum

Every rotational quantity that we have encountered in Chapters 9 and 10 is the analog of some quantity in the translational motion of a particle. The analog of *momentum* of a particle is **angular momentum,** a vector quantity denoted as $\vec{L}$. Its relationship to momentum $\vec{p}$ (which we will often call *linear momentum* for clarity) is exactly the same as the relationship of torque to force, $\vec{\tau} = \vec{r} \times \vec{F}$. For a particle with constant mass m, velocity $\vec{v}$, momentum $\vec{p} = m\vec{v}$, and position vector $\vec{r}$ relative to the origin O of an inertial frame, we define angular momentum $\vec{L}$ as

$$\vec{L} = \vec{r} \times \vec{p} = \vec{r} \times m\vec{v} \quad \text{(angular momentum of a particle)} \quad (10.24)$$

The value of $\vec{L}$ depends on the choice of origin O, since it involves the particle's position vector relative to O. The units of angular momentum are $\text{kg}\cdot\text{m}^2/\text{s}$.

In Fig. 10.23 a particle moves in the xy-plane; its position vector $\vec{r}$ and momentum $\vec{p} = m\vec{v}$ are shown. The angular momentum vector $\vec{L}$ is perpendicular to the xy-plane. The right-hand rule for vector products shows that its direction is along the $+z$-axis, and its magnitude is

$$L = mvr\sin\phi = mvl \quad (10.25)$$

where l is the perpendicular distance from the line of $\vec{v}$ to O. This distance plays the role of "lever arm" for the momentum vector.

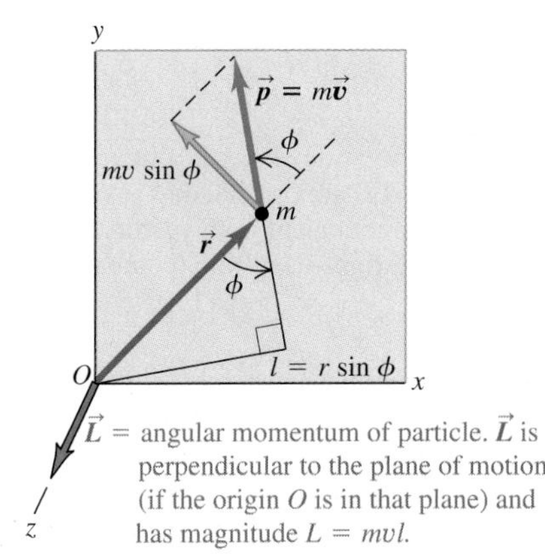
y
$\vec{p} = m\vec{v}$
ϕ
$mv \sin\phi$
m
$\vec{r}$
ϕ
O
$l = r\sin\phi$
x
z
$\vec{L}$ = angular momentum of particle. $\vec{L}$ is perpendicular to the plane of motion (if the origin O is in that plane) and has magnitude $L = mvl$.

10.23 Calculating the angular momentum $\vec{L} = \vec{r} \times m\vec{v} = \vec{r} \times \vec{p}$ of a particle with mass m moving in the xy-plane.

When a net force $\vec{F}$ acts on a particle, its velocity and momentum change, so its angular momentum may also change. We can show that the *rate of change* of angular momentum is equal to the torque of the net force. We take the time derivative of Eq. (10.24), using the rule for the derivative of a product:

$$\frac{d\vec{L}}{dt} = \left(\frac{d\vec{r}}{dt} \times m\vec{v}\right) + \left(\vec{r} \times m\frac{d\vec{v}}{dt}\right) = (\vec{v} \times m\vec{v}) + (\vec{r} \times m\vec{a})$$

The first term is zero because it contains the vector product of the vector $\vec{v} = d\vec{r}/dt$ with itself. In the second term we replace $m\vec{a}$ with the net force $\vec{F}$, obtaining

$$\frac{d\vec{L}}{dt} = \vec{r} \times \vec{F} = \vec{\tau} \quad \text{(for a particle acted on by net force } \vec{F}\text{)} \quad (10.26)$$

The rate of change of angular momentum of a particle equals the torque of the net force acting on it. Compare this result to Eq. (8.3), which states that the rate of change $d\vec{p}/dt$ of the *linear* momentum of a particle equals the net force that acts on it.

Angular Momentum of a Rigid Body

We can use Eq. (10.25) to find the total angular momentum of a *rigid body* rotating about the z-axis with angular speed ω. First consider a thin slice of the body lying in the xy-plane (Fig. 10.24). Each particle in the slice moves in a circle centered at the origin, and at each instant its velocity $\vec{v}_i$ is perpendicular to its position vector $\vec{r}_i$, as shown. Hence in Eq. (10.25), $\phi = 90°$ for every particle. A particle with mass m_i at a distance r_i from O has a speed v_i equal to $r_i\omega$. From Eq. (10.25) the magnitude L_i of its angular momentum is

$$L_i = m_i(r_i\omega)\,r_i = m_i r_i^2\omega \tag{10.27}$$

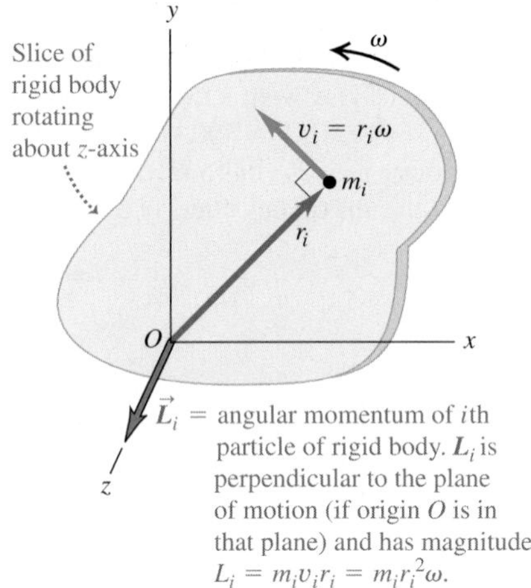

10.24 Calculating the angular momentum of a particle of mass m_i in a rigid body rotating at angular speed ω. (Compare Fig. 10.23.)

The direction of each particle's angular momentum, as given by the right-hand rule for the vector product, is along the $+z$-axis.

The *total* angular momentum of the slice of the body lying in the xy-plane is the sum $\sum L_i$ of the angular momenta L_i of the particles. Summing Eq. (10.27), we have

$$L = \sum L_i = \left(\sum m_i r_i^2\right)\omega = I\omega$$

where I is the moment of inertia of the slice about the z-axis.

We can do this same calculation for the other slices of the body, all parallel to the xy-plane. For points that do not lie in the xy-plane, a complication arises because the $\vec{r}$ vectors have components in the z-direction as well as the x- and y-directions; this gives the angular momentum of each particle a component perpendicular to the z-axis. But *if the z-axis is an axis of symmetry,* the perpendicular components for particles on opposite sides of this axis add up to zero (Fig. 10.25). So when a body rotates about an axis of symmetry, its angular momentum vector $\vec{L}$ lies along the symmetry axis, and its magnitude is $L = I\omega$.

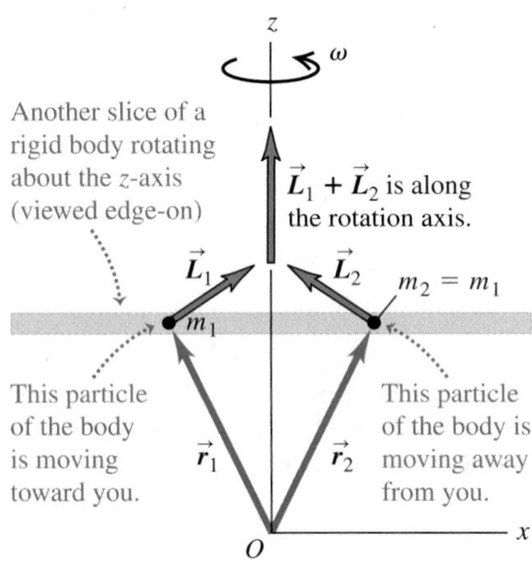

10.25 Two particles of the same mass located symmetrically on either side of the rotation axis of a rigid body. While the angular momentum vectors $\vec{L}_1$ and $\vec{L}_2$ of the two particles do not lie along the rotation axis, their vector sum $\vec{L}_1 + \vec{L}_2$ does.

The angular velocity vector $\vec{\omega}$ also lies along the rotation axis, as we discussed at the end of Section 9.1. Hence for a rigid body rotating around an axis of symmetry, $\vec{L}$ and $\vec{\omega}$ are in the same direction (Fig. 10.26). So we have the *vector* relationship

$$\vec{L} = I\vec{\omega} \quad \text{(for a rigid body rotating around a symmetry axis)} \tag{10.28}$$

From Eq. (10.26) the rate of change of angular momentum of a particle equals the torque of the net force acting on the particle. For any system of particles (including both rigid and nonrigid bodies), the rate of change of the *total* angular momentum equals the sum of the torques of all forces acting on all the particles. The torques of the *internal* forces add to zero if these forces act along the line from one particle to another, as in Fig. 10.8, and so the sum of the torques includes only the torques of the *external* forces. (A similar cancellation occurred in our discussion of center-of-mass motion in Section 8.5.) If the total angular momentum of the system of particles is $\vec{L}$ and the sum of the external torques is $\sum\vec{\tau}$, then

$$\sum\vec{\tau} = \frac{d\vec{L}}{dt} \quad \text{(for any system of particles)} \tag{10.29}$$

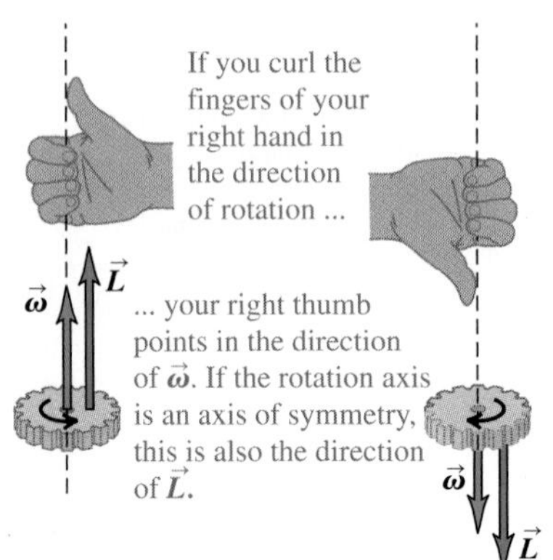

If you curl the fingers of your right hand in the direction of rotation ...
$\vec{\omega}$
$\vec{L}$
... your right thumb points in the direction of $\vec{\omega}$. If the rotation axis is an axis of symmetry, this is also the direction of $\vec{L}$.
$\vec{\omega}$
$\vec{L}$

10.26 For rotation about an axis of symmetry, $\vec{\omega}$ and $\vec{L}$ are parallel and along the axis. The directions of both vectors are given by the right-hand rule (compare Fig. 9.5).

Finally, if the system of particles is a rigid body rotating about a symmetry axis (the z-axis), then $L_z = I\omega_z$ and I is constant. If this axis has a fixed direction in space, then the vectors $\vec{L}$ and $\vec{\omega}$ change only in magnitude, not in direction. In that case, $dL_z/dt = I\,d\omega_z/dt = I\alpha_z$, or

$$\sum\tau_z = I\alpha_z$$

which is again our basic relationship for the dynamics of rigid-body rotation. If the body is *not* rigid, I may change, and in that case, L changes even when ω is constant. For a nonrigid body, Eq. (10.29) is still valid, even though Eq. (10.7) is not.

When the axis of rotation is *not* a symmetry axis, the angular momentum is in general *not* parallel to the axis (Fig. 10.27). As the body turns, the angular momentum vector $\vec{L}$ traces out a cone around the rotation axis. Because $\vec{L}$ changes, there must be a net external torque acting on the body even though the angular velocity magnitude ω may be constant. If the body is an unbalanced wheel on a car, this torque is provided by friction in the bearings, which causes the bearings to wear out. "Balancing" a wheel means distributing the mass so that the rotation axis is an axis of symmetry; then $\vec{L}$ points along the rotation axis, and no net torque is required to keep the wheel turning.

In fixed-axis rotation we often use the term "angular momentum of the body" to refer to only the *component* of $\vec{L}$ along the rotation axis of the body (the z-axis in Fig. 10.27), with a positive or negative sign to indicate the sense of rotation just as with angular velocity.

10.27 If the rotation axis of a rigid body is not a symmetry axis, $\vec{L}$ does not in general lie along the rotation axis. Even if $\vec{\omega}$ is constant, the direction of $\vec{L}$ changes and a net torque is required to maintain rotation.

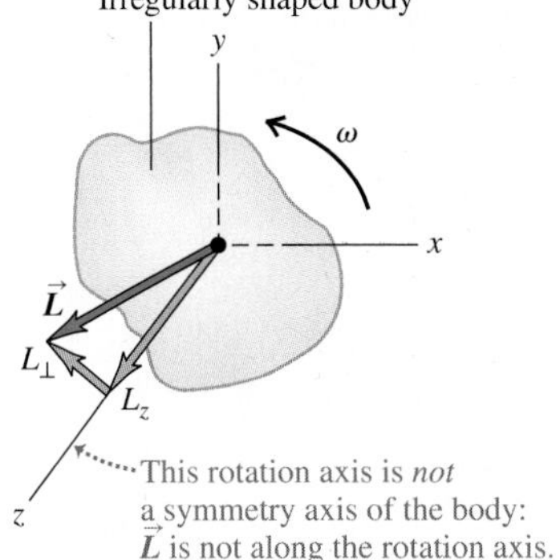
Irregularly shaped body
y
ω
x
L
L⊥
Lz
z
This rotation axis is not a symmetry axis of the body: L is not along the rotation axis.

Example 10.10 Angular momentum and torque

A turbine fan in a jet engine has a moment of inertia of $2.5\ \text{kg}\cdot\text{m}^2$ about its axis of rotation. As the turbine is starting up, its angular velocity as a function of time is

$$\omega_z = (40\ \text{rad/s}^3)t^2$$

(a) Find the fan's angular momentum as a function of time, and find its value at time $t = 3.0\ \text{s}$. (b) Find the net torque acting on the fan as a function of time, and find the torque at time $t = 3.0\ \text{s}$.

SOLUTION

IDENTIFY: Just like an electric fan, the turbine fan rotates about an axis of symmetry (the z-axis). Hence the angular momentum vector has only a z-component L_z, which we can determine from the angular velocity ω_z. Since the direction of angular momentum is constant, the net torque likewise has only a component τ_z along the rotation axis; this is equal to the time derivative of L_z.

SET UP: We use Eq. (10.28) to find L_z from ω_z and Eq. (10.29) to find τ_z from the time derivative of L_z.

EXECUTE: (a) The component of angular momentum along the rotation (z) axis is

$$L_z = I\omega_z = (2.5\ \text{kg}\cdot\text{m}^2)(40\ \text{rad/s}^3)t^2 = (100\ \text{kg}\cdot\text{m}^2/\text{s}^3)t^2$$

(We dropped "rad" from the answer because a radian is a dimensionless quantity.) At time $t = 3.0\ \text{s}$, $L_z = 900\ \text{kg}\cdot\text{m}^2/\text{s}$.

(b) From Eq. (10.29), the net torque component along the rotation axis is

$$\tau_z = \frac{dL_z}{dt} = (100\ \text{kg}\cdot\text{m}^2/\text{s}^3)(2t) = (200\ \text{kg}\cdot\text{m}^2/\text{s}^3)t$$

At time $t = 3.0\ \text{s}$,

$$\tau_z = (200\ \text{kg}\cdot\text{m}^2/\text{s}^3)(3.0\ \text{s}) = 600\ \text{kg}\cdot\text{m}^2/\text{s}^2 = 600\ \text{N}\cdot\text{m}$$

EVALUATE: As a check on our result, note that the angular acceleration of the turbine fan is $\alpha_z = d\omega_z/dt = (40\ \text{rad/s}^2)(2t) = (80\ \text{rad/s}^2)t$. From the rotational equivalent of Newton's second law, the torque on the fan is $\tau_z = I\alpha_z = (2.5\ \text{kg}\cdot\text{m}^2)(80\ \text{rad/s}^2)t = (200\ \text{kg}\cdot\text{m}^2/\text{s}^3)t$, just as we calculated above.

Test Your Understanding of Section 10.5 A ball is attached to one end of a piece of string. You hold the other end of the string and whirl the ball in a circle around your hand. (a) If the ball moves at a constant speed, is its linear momentum $\vec{p}$ constant? Why or why not? (b) Is its angular momentum $\vec{L}$ constant? Why or why not?

10.6 Conservation of Angular Momentum

We have just seen that angular momentum can be used for an alternative statement of the basic dynamic principle for rotational motion. It also forms the basis for the **principle of conservation of angular momentum.** Like conservation of energy and of linear momentum, this principle is a universal conservation law, valid at all scales from atomic and nuclear systems to the motions of galaxies. This principle follows directly from Eq. (10.29): $\sum\vec{\tau} = d\vec{L}/dt$. If $\sum\vec{\tau} = \mathbf{0}$, then $d\vec{L}/dt = \mathbf{0}$, and $\vec{L}$ is constant.

ActivPhysics ONLINE
7.14 Ball Hits Bat

When the net external torque acting on a system is zero, the total angular momentum of the system is constant (conserved).

10.28 A falling cat twists different parts of its body in different directions so that it lands feet first. At all times during this process the angular momentum of the cat as a whole remains zero.

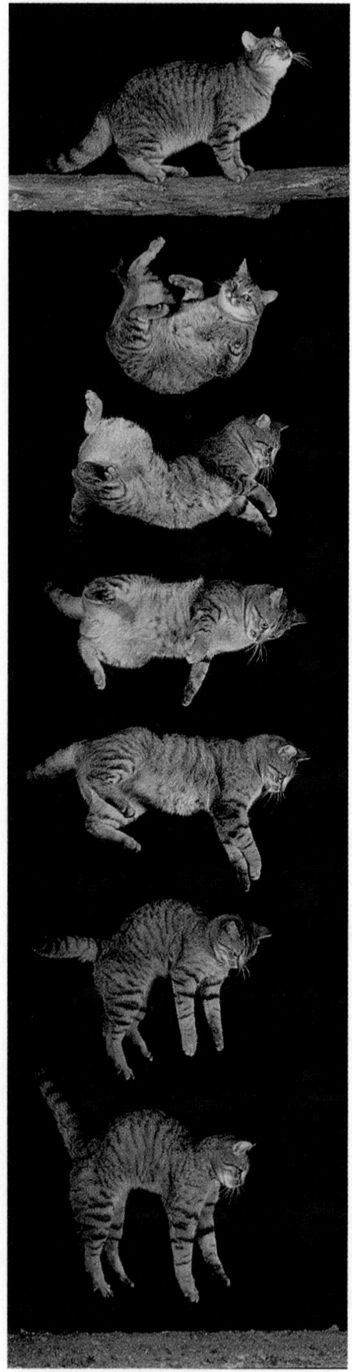

A circus acrobat, a diver, and an ice skater pirouetting on the toe of one skate all take advantage of this principle. Suppose an acrobat has just left a swing with arms and legs extended and rotating counterclockwise about her center of mass. When she pulls her arms and legs in, her moment of inertia I_{cm} with respect to her center of mass changes from a large value I_1 to a much smaller value I_2. The only external force acting on her is her weight, which has no torque with respect to an axis through her center of mass. So her angular momentum $L_z = I_{cm}\omega_z$ remains constant, and her angular velocity ω_z increases as I_{cm} decreases. That is,

$$I_1\omega_{1z} = I_2\omega_{2z} \qquad \text{(zero net external torque)} \tag{10.30}$$

When a skater or ballerina spins with arms outstretched and then pulls her arms in, her angular velocity increases as her moment of inertia decreases. In each case there is conservation of angular momentum in a system in which the net external torque is zero.

When a system has several parts, the internal forces that the parts exert on each other cause changes in the angular momenta of the parts, but the *total* angular momentum doesn't change. Here's an example. Consider two bodies A and B that interact with each other but not with anything else, such as the astronauts we discussed in Section 8.2 (Fig. 8.8). Suppose body A exerts a force $\vec{F}_{A \text{ on } B}$ on body B; the corresponding torque (with respect to whatever point we choose) is $\vec{\tau}_{A \text{ on } B}$. According to Eq. (10.29), this torque is equal to the rate of change of angular momentum of B:

$$\vec{\tau}_{A \text{ on } B} = \frac{d\vec{L}_B}{dt}$$

At the same time, body B exerts a force $\vec{F}_{B \text{ on } A}$ on body A, with a corresponding torque $\vec{\tau}_{B \text{ on } A}$, and

$$\vec{\tau}_{B \text{ on } A} = \frac{d\vec{L}_A}{dt}$$

From Newton's third law, $\vec{F}_{B \text{ on } A} = -\vec{F}_{A \text{ on } B}$. Furthermore, if the forces act along the same line, as in Fig. 10.8, their lever arms with respect to the chosen axis are equal. Thus the *torques* of these two forces are equal and opposite, and $\vec{\tau}_{B \text{ on } A} = -\vec{\tau}_{A \text{ on } B}$. So if we add the two preceding equations, we find

$$\frac{d\vec{L}_A}{dt} + \frac{d\vec{L}_B}{dt} = \mathbf{0}$$

or, because $\vec{L}_A + \vec{L}_B$ is the *total* angular momentum $\vec{L}$ of the system,

$$\frac{d\vec{L}}{dt} = \mathbf{0} \qquad \text{(zero net external torque)} \tag{10.31}$$

That is, the total angular momentum of the system is constant. The torques of the internal forces can transfer angular momentum from one body to the other, but they can't change the *total* angular momentum of the system (Fig. 10.28).

Example 10.11 Anyone can be a ballerina

An acrobatic physics professor stands at the center of a turntable, holding his arms extended horizontally with a 5.0-kg dumbbell in each hand (Fig. 10.29). He is set rotating about a vertical axis, making one revolution in 2.0 s. Find the prof's new angular velocity if he pulls the dumbbells in to his stomach. His moment of inertia (without the dumbbells) is 3.0 kg · m² when his arms are outstretched, dropping to 2.2 kg · m² when his hands are at his stomach. The dumbbells are 1.0 m from the axis initially and 0.20 m from it at the end. Treat the dumbbells as particles.

SOLUTION

IDENTIFY: If we neglect friction in the turntable, no external torques act about the vertical (z) axis. Hence the angular momentum about this axis is constant.

SET UP: We'll use Eq. (10.30) to find our target variable, the final angular velocity ω_{2z}.

EXECUTE: The moment of inertia of the system is $I = I_{prof} + I_{dumbbells}$. Each dumbbell of mass m contributes mr^2 to $I_{dumbbells}$, where r is the perpendicular distance from the rotation axis to the dumbbell. Initially we have

$$I_1 = 3.0 \text{ kg} \cdot \text{m}^2 + 2(5.0 \text{ kg})(1.0 \text{ m})^2 = 13 \text{ kg} \cdot \text{m}^2$$

$$\omega_{1z} = \frac{1 \text{ rev}}{2.0 \text{ s}} = 0.50 \text{ rev/s}$$

10.29 Fun with conservation of angular momentum.

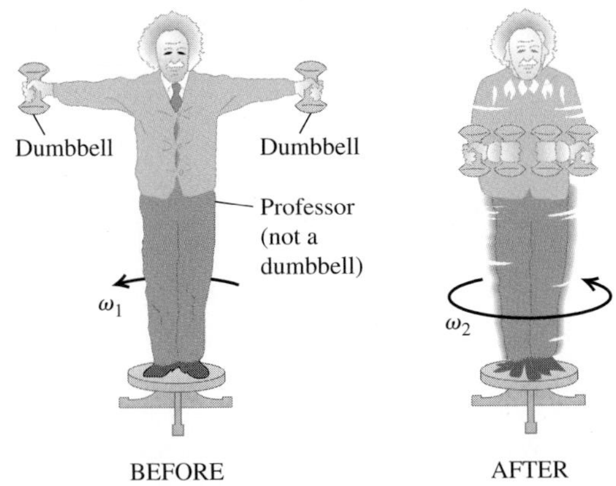

The final moment of inertia is

$$I_2 = 2.2 \text{ kg} \cdot \text{m}^2 + 2(5.0 \text{ kg})(0.20 \text{ m})^2 = 2.6 \text{ kg} \cdot \text{m}^2$$

From Eq. (10.30), the final angular velocity is

$$\omega_{2z} = \frac{I_1}{I_2}\omega_{1z} = \frac{13 \text{ kg} \cdot \text{m}^2}{2.6 \text{ kg} \cdot \text{m}^2}(0.50 \text{ rev/s}) = 2.5 \text{ rev/s}$$

That is, the angular velocity increases by a factor of 5 while the angular momentum remains constant. Note that we didn't have to change "revolutions" to "radians" in this calculation. Why not?

EVALUATE: It's useful to examine how the kinetic energy changes in this process. To calculate the kinetic energy, we must express ω_1 and ω_2 in rad/s. (Why?) We have $\omega_{1z} = (0.50 \text{ rev/s})(2\pi \text{ rad/rev}) = 3.14 \text{ rad/s}$ and $\omega_{2z} = (2.5 \text{ rev/s})(2\pi \text{ rad/rev}) = 15.7 \text{ rad/s}$. The initial kinetic energy is

$$K_1 = \frac{1}{2}I_1\omega_{1z}^2 = \frac{1}{2}(13 \text{ kg} \cdot \text{m}^2)(3.14 \text{ rad/s})^2 = 64 \text{ J}$$

and the final kinetic energy is

$$K_2 = \frac{1}{2}I_2\omega_{2z}^2 = \frac{1}{2}(2.6 \text{ kg} \cdot \text{m}^2)(15.7 \text{ rad/s})^2 = 320 \text{ J}$$

The extra kinetic energy came from the work that the prof did to pull his arms and the dumbbells inward.

Example 10.12 A rotational "collision" I

Figure 10.30 shows two disks: one (A) an engine flywheel, and the other (B) a clutch plate attached to a transmission shaft. Their moments of inertia are I_A and I_B; initially, they are rotating with constant angular speeds ω_A and ω_B, respectively. We then push the disks together with forces acting along the axis, so as not to apply any torque on either disk. The disks rub against each other and eventually reach a common final angular speed ω. Derive an expression for ω.

SOLUTION

IDENTIFY: The only torque acting on either disk is the torque applied by the other disk; there are no external torques. Thus the total angular momentum of the system of two disks is the same before and after they are pushed together. At the end they rotate together as one body with total moment of inertia $I = I_A + I_B$ and angular speed ω, which is our target variable.

SET UP: Figure 10.30 shows that all of the angular velocities are in the same direction, so we can regard ω_A, ω_B, and ω as the components of angular velocity along the rotation axis.

EXECUTE: Conservation of angular momentum gives

$$I_A\omega_A + I_B\omega_B = (I_A + I_B)\omega$$

$$\omega = \frac{I_A\omega_A + I_B\omega_B}{I_A + I_B}$$

10.30 When the net external torque is zero, angular momentum is conserved.

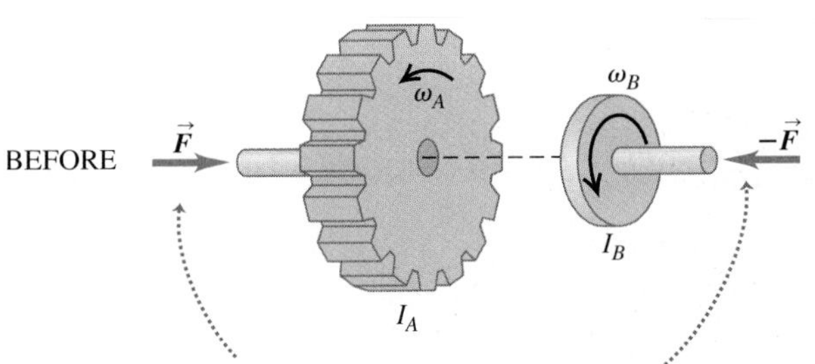

Forces $\vec{F}$ and $-\vec{F}$ are along the axis of rotation, and thus exert no torque about this axis on either disk.

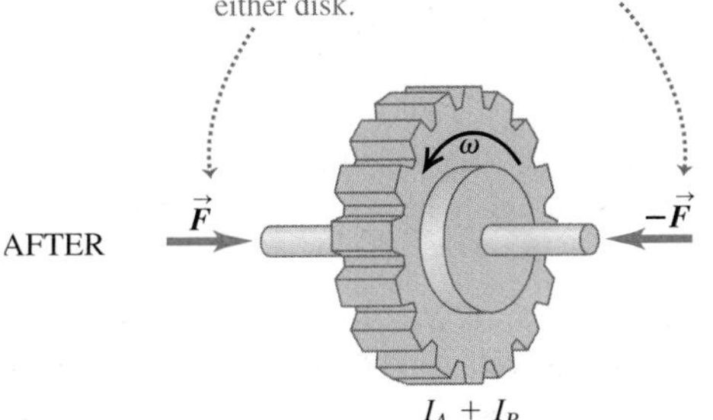

Continued

EVALUATE: This "collision" between two disks is analogous to a completely inelastic collision (see Section 8.3). When two objects in translational motion along the same axis come together and stick, the linear momentum of the system is conserved. In the situation shown in Fig. 10.30, two objects in *rotational* motion along the same axis come together and stick, and the *angular* momentum is conserved. The kinetic energy of the system decreases in a completely inelastic collision; in the next example we'll see what becomes of the kinetic energy in the "collision" of two rotating disks.

Example 10.13 A rotational "collision" II

In Example 10.12, suppose flywheel A has a mass of 2.0 kg, a radius of 0.20 m, and an initial angular speed of 50 rad/s (about 500 rpm) and that clutch plate B has a mass of 4.0 kg, a radius of 0.10 m, and an initial angular speed of 200 rad/s. Find the common final angular speed ω after the disks are pushed into contact. What happens to the kinetic energy during this process?

SOLUTION

IDENTIFY: We need to calculate the rotational kinetic energy of each disk before the collision and their combined kinetic energy after the collision.

SET UP: We'll use the result of Example 10.12 and the expression $K = \frac{1}{2}I\omega^2$ for rotational kinetic energy.

EXECUTE: The moments of inertia of the two disks are

$$I_A = \frac{1}{2}m_A r_A^2 = \frac{1}{2}(2.0\text{ kg})(0.20\text{ m})^2 = 0.040\text{ kg}\cdot\text{m}^2$$

$$I_B = \frac{1}{2}m_B r_B^2 = \frac{1}{2}(4.0\text{ kg})(0.10\text{ m})^2 = 0.020\text{ kg}\cdot\text{m}^2$$

From Example 10.12 the final angular speed is

$$\begin{aligned}\omega &= \frac{I_A\omega_A + I_B\omega_B}{I_A + I_B} \\ &= \frac{(0.040\text{ kg}\cdot\text{m}^2)(50\text{ rad/s}) + (0.020\text{ kg}\cdot\text{m}^2)(200\text{ rad/s})}{0.040\text{ kg}\cdot\text{m}^2 + 0.020\text{ kg}\cdot\text{m}^2} \\ &= 100\text{ rad/s}\end{aligned}$$

The kinetic energy before the collision is

$$\begin{aligned}K_1 &= \frac{1}{2}I_A\omega_A^2 + \frac{1}{2}I_B\omega_B^2 \\ &= \frac{1}{2}(0.040\text{ kg}\cdot\text{m}^2)(50\text{ rad/s})^2 \\ &\quad + \frac{1}{2}(0.020\text{ kg}\cdot\text{m}^2)(200\text{ rad/s})^2 \\ &= 450\text{ J}\end{aligned}$$

The kinetic energy after the collision is

$$\begin{aligned}K_2 &= \frac{1}{2}(I_A + I_B)\omega^2 \\ &= \frac{1}{2}(0.040\text{ kg}\cdot\text{m}^2 + 0.020\text{ kg}\cdot\text{m}^2)(100\text{ rad/s})^2 = 300\text{ J}\end{aligned}$$

EVALUATE: One-third of the initial kinetic energy was lost during this "angular collision," the rotational analog of a completely inelastic collision. We shouldn't expect kinetic energy to be conserved, even though the net external force and torque are zero, because nonconservative (frictional) internal forces act while the two disks rub together and gradually approach a common angular velocity.

Example 10.14 Angular momentum in a crime bust

A door 1.00 m wide, of mass 15 kg, is hinged at one side so that it can rotate without friction about a vertical axis. It is unlatched. A police officer fires a bullet with a mass of 10 g and a speed of 400 m/s into the exact center of the door, in a direction perpendicular to the plane of the door. Find the angular speed of the door just after the bullet embeds itself in the door. Is kinetic energy conserved?

SOLUTION

IDENTIFY: We consider the door and bullet together as a system. There is no external torque about the axis defined by the hinges, so angular momentum about this axis is conserved.

SET UP: Figure 10.31 shows our sketch. The initial angular momentum is wholly in the bullet and is given by Eq. (10.25). The final angular momentum is that of a rigid body composed of the door and the embedded bullet. We'll set these two equal to each

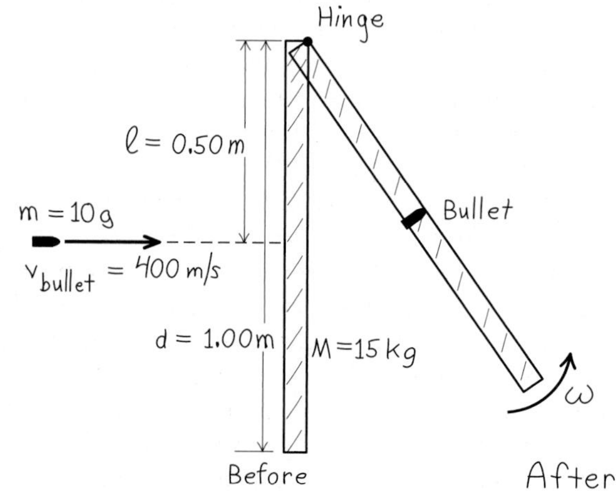

10.31 Our sketch for this problem.

other and solve for the angular speed ω of the door and bullet just after the collision.

EXECUTE: The initial angular momentum of the bullet is:

$$L = mvl = (0.010\ \text{kg})(400\ \text{m/s})(0.50\ \text{m}) = 2.0\ \text{kg}\cdot\text{m}^2/\text{s}$$

The final angular momentum is $I\omega$, where $I = I_{door} + I_{bullet}$. From Table 9.2, for a door of width d,

$$I_{door} = \frac{Md^2}{3} = \frac{(15\ \text{kg})(1.0\ \text{m})^2}{3} = 5.0\ \text{kg}\cdot\text{m}^2$$

The moment of inertia of the bullet (with respect to the axis along the hinges) is

$$I_{bullet} = ml^2 = (0.010\ \text{kg})(0.50\ \text{m})^2 = 0.0025\ \text{kg}\cdot\text{m}^2$$

Conservation of angular momentum requires that $mvl = I\omega$, or

$$\omega = \frac{mvl}{I} = \frac{2.0\ \text{kg}\cdot\text{m}^2/\text{s}}{5.0\ \text{kg}\cdot\text{m}^2 + 0.0025\ \text{kg}\cdot\text{m}^2} = 0.40\ \text{rad/s}$$

The collision of bullet and door is inelastic because nonconservative friction forces act during the impact. Thus we do not expect kinetic energy to be conserved. To check, we calculate the initial and final kinetic energies:

$$K_1 = \frac{1}{2}mv^2 = \frac{1}{2}(0.010\ \text{kg})(400\ \text{m/s})^2 = 800\ \text{J}$$

$$K_2 = \frac{1}{2}I\omega^2 = \frac{1}{2}(5.0025\ \text{kg}\cdot\text{m}^2)(0.40\ \text{rad/s})^2 = 0.40\ \text{J}$$

The final kinetic energy is only 1/2000 of the initial value!

EVALUATE: The final angular speed of the door is quite slow: At 0.40 rad/s, the door takes 3.9 s to swing through 90° ($\pi/2$ radians). Can you see that the speed would double if the bullet were shot into the edge of the door near the doorknob?

Test Your Understanding of Section 10.6 If the polar ice caps were to completely melt due to global warming, the melted ice would redistribute itself over the earth. This change would cause the length of the day (the time needed for the earth to rotate once on its axis) to (i) increase; (ii) decrease; (iii) remain the same. (*Hint:* Use angular momentum ideas. Assume that the sun, moon, and planets exert negligibly small torques on the earth.)

10.7 Gyroscopes and Precession

In all the situations we've looked at so far in this chapter, the axis of rotation either has stayed fixed or has moved and kept the same direction (such as rolling without slipping). But a variety of new physical phenomena, some quite unexpected, can occur when the axis of rotation can change direction. For example, consider a toy gyroscope that's supported at one end (Fig. 10.32). If we hold it with the flywheel axis horizontal and let go, the free end of the axis simply drops owing to gravity—*if* the flywheel isn't spinning. But if the flywheel *is* spinning, what happens is quite different. One possible motion is a steady circular motion of the axis in a horizontal plane, combined with the spin motion of the flywheel about the axis. This surprising, nonintuitive motion of the axis is called **precession.** Precession is found in nature as well as in rotating machines such as gyroscopes. As you read these words, the earth itself is precessing; its spin axis (through the north and south poles) slowly changes direction, going through a complete cycle of precession every 26,000 years.

10.32 A gyroscope supported at one end. The horizontal circular motion of the flywheel and axis is called precession. The angular speed of precession is Ω.

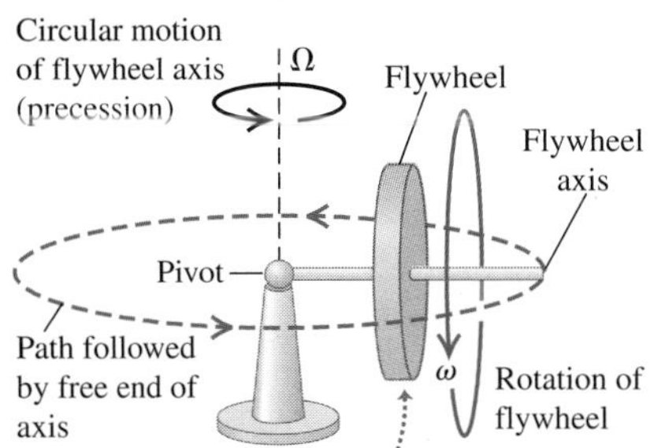

When the flywheel and its axis are stationary, they will fall to the table surface. When the flywheel spins, it and its axis "float" in the air while moving in a circle about the pivot.

To study this strange phenomenon of precession, we must remember that angular velocity, angular momentum, and torque are all *vector* quantities. In particular, we need the general relationship between the net torque $\sum\vec{\tau}$ that acts on a body and the rate of change of the body's angular momentum $\vec{L}$, given by Eq. (10.29), $\sum\vec{\tau} = d\vec{L}/dt$. Let's first apply this equation to the case in which the flywheel is *not* spinning (Fig. 10.33a). We take the origin O at the pivot and assume that the flywheel is symmetrical, with mass M and moment of inertia I about the flywheel axis. The flywheel axis is initially along the x-axis. The only external forces on the gyroscope are the normal force $\vec{n}$ acting at the pivot (assumed to be frictionless) and the weight $\vec{w}$ of the flywheel that acts at its center of mass, a distance r from the pivot. The normal force has zero torque with respect to the pivot, and the weight has a torque $\vec{\tau}$ in the y-direction, as shown in Fig. 10.33a. Initially, there is no rotation, and the initial angular momentum $\vec{L}_i$ is

10.33 (a) If the flywheel in Fig. 10.32 is initially not spinning, its initial angular momentum is zero (b) In each successive time interval dt, the torque produces a change $d\vec{L} = \vec{\tau}\,dt$ in the angular momentum. The flywheel acquires an angular momentum $\vec{L}$ in the same direction as $\vec{\tau}$, and the flywheel axis falls.

(a) Nonrotating flywheel falls

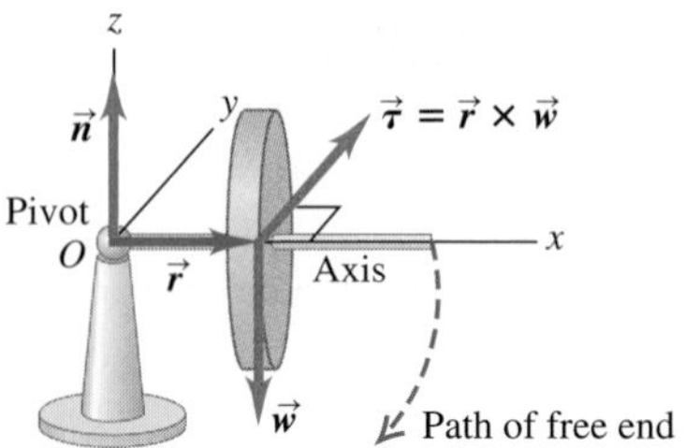

When the flywheel is not rotating, its weight creates a torque around the pivot, causing it to fall along a circular path until its axis rests on the table surface.

(b) View from above as flywheel falls

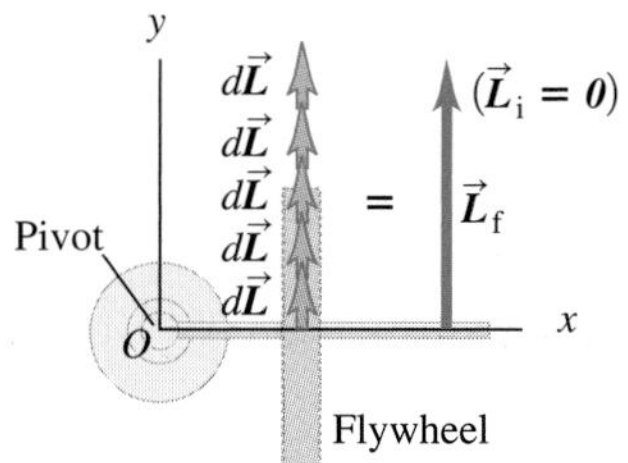

In falling, the flywheel rotates about the pivot and thus acquires an angular momentum $\vec{L}$. The *direction* of $\vec{L}$ stays constant.

zero. From Eq. (10.29) the *change* $d\vec{L}$ in angular momentum in a short time interval dt following this is

$$d\vec{L} = \vec{\tau}\,dt \tag{10.32}$$

This change is in the y-direction because $\vec{\tau}$ is. As each additional time interval dt elapses, the angular momentum changes by additional increments $d\vec{L}$ in the y-direction because the direction of the torque is constant (Fig. 10.33b). The steadily increasing horizontal angular momentum means that the gyroscope rotates downward faster and faster around the y-axis until it hits either the stand or the table on which it sits.

Now let's see what happens if the flywheel *is* spinning initially, so the initial angular momentum $\vec{L}_i$ is not zero (Fig. 10.34a). Since the flywheel rotates around its symmetry axis, $\vec{L}_i$ lies along the axis. But each change in angular momentum $d\vec{L}$ is perpendicular to the axis because the torque $\vec{\tau} = \vec{r} \times \vec{w}$ is perpendicular to the axis (Fig. 10.34b). This causes the *direction* of $\vec{L}$ to change, but not its magnitude. The changes $d\vec{L}$ are always in the horizontal xy-plane, so the angular momentum vector and the flywheel axis with which it moves are always horizontal. In other words, the axis doesn't fall—it just precesses.

If this still seems mystifying to you, think about a ball attached to a string. If the ball is initially at rest and you pull the string toward you, the ball moves toward you also. But if the ball is initially moving and you continuously pull the string in a direction perpendicular to the ball's motion, the ball moves in a circle around your hand; it does not approach your hand at all. In the first case the ball has zero linear momentum $\vec{p}$ to start with; when you apply a force $\vec{F}$ toward you for a time dt, the ball acquires a momentum $d\vec{p} = \vec{F}\,dt$, which is also toward you. But if the ball already has linear momentum $\vec{p}$, a change in momentum $d\vec{p}$ that's perpendicular to $\vec{p}$ changes the direction of motion, not the speed. Replace $\vec{p}$ with $\vec{L}$ and $\vec{F}$ with $\vec{\tau}$ in this argument, and you'll see that precession is simply the rotational analog of uniform circular motion.

At the instant shown in Fig. 10.34a, the gyroscope has angular momentum $\vec{L}$. A short time interval dt later, the angular momentum is $\vec{L} + d\vec{L}$; the infinitesimal change in angular momentum is $d\vec{L} = \vec{\tau}dt$, which is perpendicular to $\vec{L}$. As the vector diagram in Fig. 10.35 shows, this means that the flywheel axis of the gyroscope has turned through a small angle $d\phi$ given by $d\phi = |d\vec{L}|/|\vec{L}|$. The rate at which the axis moves, $d\phi/dt$, is called the **precession angular speed;** denoting this quantity by Ω, we find

$$\Omega = \frac{d\phi}{dt} = \frac{|d\vec{L}|/|\vec{L}|}{dt} = \frac{\tau_z}{L_z} = \frac{wr}{I\omega} \tag{10.33}$$

Thus the precession angular speed is *inversely* proportional to the angular speed of spin about the axis. A rapidly spinning gyroscope precesses slowly; if friction

10.34 (a) The flywheel is spinning initially with angular momentum $\vec{L}_i$. The forces (not shown) are the same as those in Fig. 10.33a. (b) Because the initial angular momentum is not zero, each change $d\vec{L} = \vec{\tau}\,dt$ in angular momentum is perpendicular to $\vec{L}$. As a result, the magnitude of $\vec{L}$ remains the same but its direction changes continuously.

(a) Rotating flywheel

When the flywheel is rotating, the system starts with an angular momentum $\vec{L}_i$ parallel to the flywheel's axis of rotation.

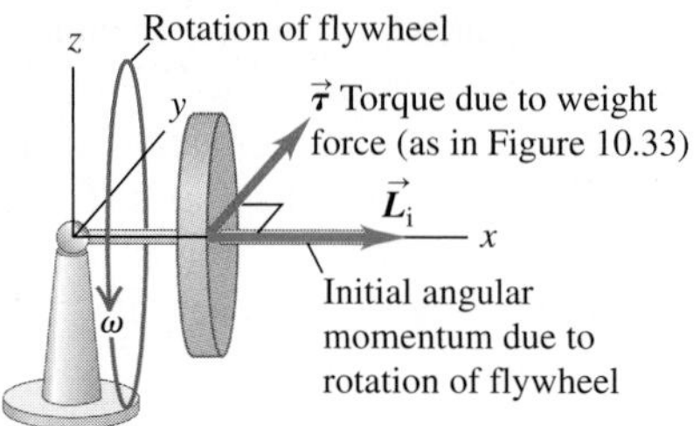

(b) View from above

Now the effect of the torque is to cause the angular momentum to precess around the pivot. The gyroscope circles around its pivot without falling.

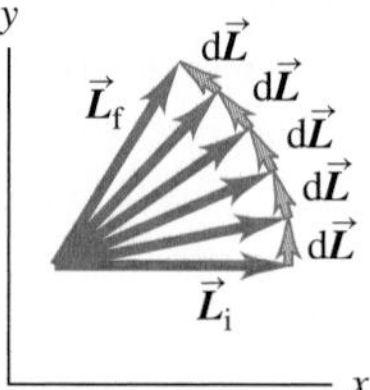

in its bearings causes the flywheel to slow down, the precession angular speed *increases!* The precession angular speed of the earth is very slow $(1 \text{ rev}/26{,}000 \text{ yr})$ because its spin angular momentum L_z is large and the torque τ_z, due to the gravitational influences of the moon and sun, is relatively small.

As a gyroscope precesses, its center of mass moves in a circle with radius r in a horizontal plane. Its vertical component of acceleration is zero, so the upward normal force $\vec{n}$ exerted by the pivot must be just equal in magnitude to the weight. The circular motion of the center of mass with angular speed Ω requires a force $\vec{F}$ directed toward the center of the circle, with magnitude $F = M\Omega^2 r$. This force must also be supplied by the pivot.

One key assumption that we made in our analysis of the gyroscope was that the angular momentum vector $\vec{L}$ is associated only with the spin of the flywheel and is purely horizontal. But there will also be a vertical component of angular momentum associated with the precessional motion of the gyroscope. By ignoring this, we've tacitly assumed that the precession is *slow*—that is, that the precession angular speed Ω is very much less than the spin angular speed ω. As Eq. (10.33) shows, a large value of ω automatically gives a small value of Ω, so this approximation is reasonable. When the precession is not slow, additional effects show up, including an up-and-down wobble or *nutation* of the flywheel axis that's superimposed on the precessional motion. You can see nutation occurring in a gyroscope as its spin slows down, so that Ω increases and the vertical component of $\vec{L}$ can no longer be ignored.

10.35 Detailed view of part of Fig. 10.34b.

In a time dt, the angular momentum vector and the flywheel axis (to which it is parallel) precess together through an angle $d\phi$.

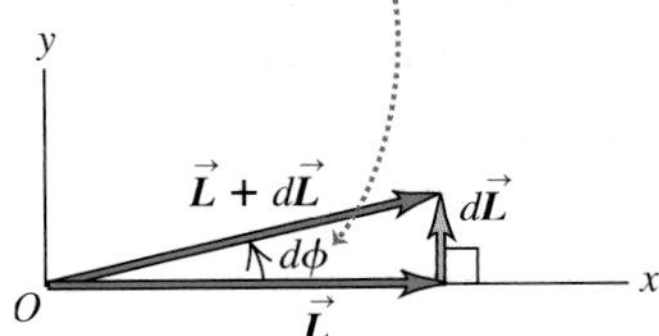

Example 10.15 A precessing gyroscope

Figure 10.36a shows a top view of a cylindrical gyroscope wheel that has been set spinning by an electric motor. The pivot is at O, and the mass of the axle is negligible. (a) As seen from above, is the precession clockwise or counterclockwise? (b) If the gyro takes 4.0 s for one revolution of precession, at what angular speed does the wheel spin?

SOLUTION

IDENTIFY: This situation is similar to the precessing flywheel shown in Fig. 10.34.

SET UP: We'll determine the direction of precession using the right-hand rule as in Fig. 10.34, which shows the same kind of gyroscope as Fig. 10.36. We'll use the relationship between precession angular speed Ω and spin angular speed ω, Eq. (10.33), to find the value of ω.

EXECUTE: (a) The right-hand rule shows that $\vec{\omega}$ and $\vec{L}$ are to the left (Fig. 10.36b). The weight $\vec{w}$ points into the page in this top view and acts at the center of mass (denoted by an $\times$); the torque $\vec{\tau} = \vec{r} \times \vec{w}$ is toward the top of the page; and $d\vec{L}/dt$ is also toward the top of the page. Adding a small $d\vec{L}$ to the $\vec{L}$ that we have initially changes the direction of $\vec{L}$ as shown, so the precession is clockwise as seen from above.

(b) Be careful not to confuse ω and Ω! We are given $\Omega = (1 \text{ rev})/(4.0 \text{ s}) = (2\pi \text{ rad})/(4.0 \text{ s}) = 1.57 \text{ rad/s}$. The weight is equal to mg, and the moment of inertia about its symmetry axis of a solid

10.36 In which direction and at what speed does this gyroscope precess?

(a) Top view of spinning cylindrical gyroscope wheel

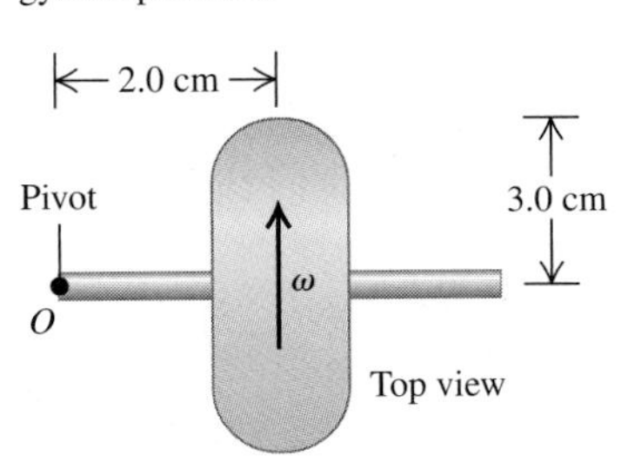

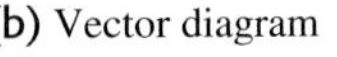

(b) Vector diagram

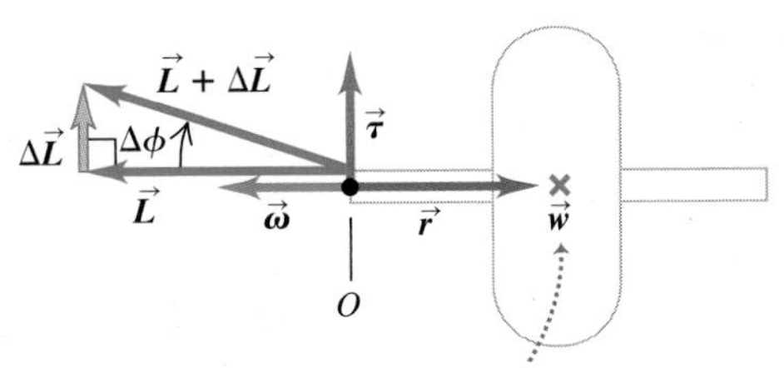

This symbol represents the weight force pointing into the page.

Continued

cylinder with radius R is $I = \frac{1}{2}mR^2$. Solving Eq. (10.33) for ω, we find

$$\omega = \frac{wr}{I\Omega} = \frac{mgr}{(mR^2/2)\Omega} = \frac{2gr}{R^2\Omega}$$

$$= \frac{2(9.8\ \text{m/s}^2)(2.0 \times 10^{-2}\ \text{m})}{(3.0 \times 10^{-2}\ \text{m})^2(1.57\ \text{rad/s})} = 280\ \text{rad/s} = 2600\ \text{rev/min}$$

EVALUATE: The precession angular speed Ω is very much less than the spin angular speed ω, so this is an example of slow precession.

Test Your Understanding of Section 10.7 Suppose the mass of the flywheel in Fig. 10.34 were doubled but all other dimensions and the spin angular speed remained the same. What effect would this change have on the precession angular speed Ω? (i) Ω would increase by a factor of 4; (ii) Ω would double; (iii) Ω would be unaffected; (iv) Ω would be one-half as much; (v) Ω would be one-quarter as much.

CHAPTER 10 SUMMARY

Torque: When a force $\vec{F}$ acts on a body, the torque of that force with respect to a point O has a magnitude given by the product of the force magnitude F and the lever arm l. More generally, torque is a vector $\vec{\tau}$ equal to the vector product of $\vec{r}$ (the position vector of the point at which the force acts) and $\vec{F}$. (See Example 10.1.)

$$\tau = Fl \quad (10.2)$$

$$\vec{\tau} = \vec{r} \times \vec{F} \quad (10.3)$$

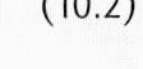

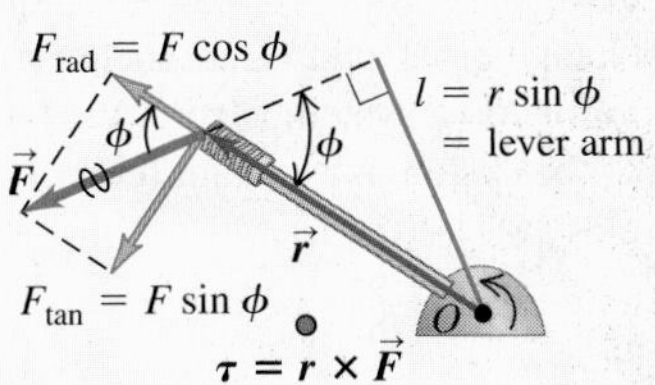

Rotational dynamics: The rotational analog of Newton's second law says that the net torque acting on a body equals the product of the body's moment of inertia and its angular acceleration. (See Examples 10.2 and 10.3.)

$$\sum \tau_z = I\alpha_z \quad (10.7)$$

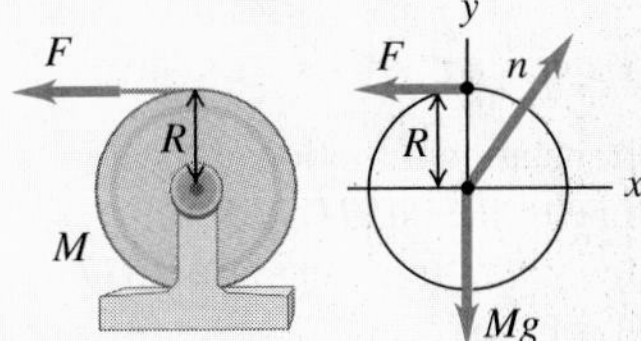

Combined translation and rotation: If a rigid body is both moving through space and rotating, its motion can be regarded as translational motion of the center of mass plus rotational motion about an axis through the center of mass. Thus the kinetic energy is a sum of translational and rotational kinetic energies. For dynamics, Newton's second law describes the motion of the center of mass, and the rotational equivalent of Newton's second law describes rotation about the center of mass. In the case of rolling without slipping, there is a special relationship between the motion of the center of mass and the rotational motion. (See Examples 10.4–10.7.)

$$K = \frac{1}{2}Mv_{cm}^2 + \frac{1}{2}I_{cm}\omega^2 \quad (10.8)$$

$$\sum \vec{F}_{ext} = M\vec{a}_{cm} \quad (10.12)$$

$$\sum \tau_z = I_{cm}\alpha_z \quad (10.13)$$

$$v_{cm} = R\omega \quad (10.11)$$

(rolling without slipping)

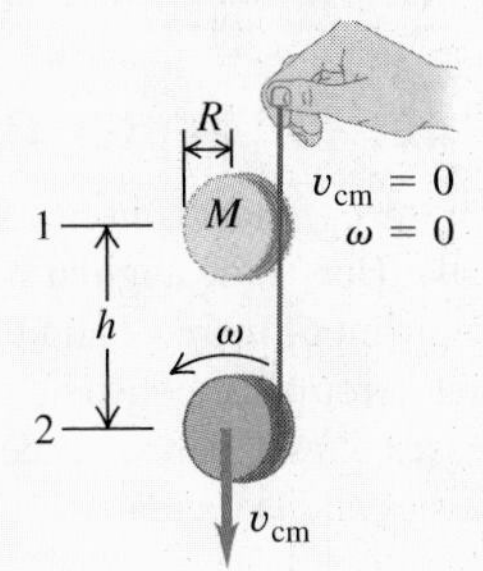

Work done by a torque: A torque that acts on a rigid body as it rotates does work on that body. The work can be expressed as an integral of the torque. The work–energy theorem says that the total rotational work done on a rigid body is equal to the change in rotational kinetic energy. The power, or rate at which the torque does work, is the product of the torque and the angular velocity (See Examples 10.8 and 10.9.)

$$W = \int_{\theta_1}^{\theta_2} \tau_z \, d\theta \quad (10.20)$$

$$W = \tau_z(\theta_2 - \theta_1) = \tau_z \Delta\theta \quad (10.21)$$

(constant torque only)

$$W_{tot} = \frac{1}{2}I\omega_2^2 - \frac{1}{2}I\omega_1^2 \quad (10.22)$$

$$P = \tau_z \omega_z \quad (10.23)$$

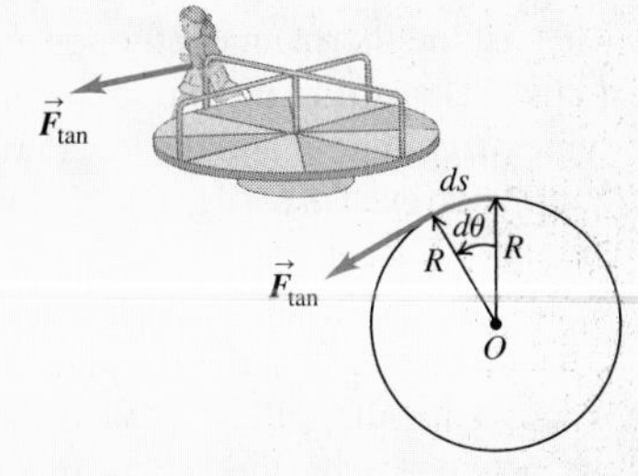

Angular momentum: The angular momentum of a particle with respect to point O is the vector product of the particle's position vector $\vec{r}$ relative to O and its momentum $\vec{p} = m\vec{v}$. When a symmetrical body rotates about a stationary axis of symmetry, its angular momentum is the product of its moment of inertia and its angular velocity vector $\vec{\omega}$. If the body is not symmetrical or the rotation (z) axis is not an axis of symmetry, the component of angular momentum along the rotation axis is $I\omega_z$. (See Example 10.10.)

$$\vec{L} = \vec{r} \times \vec{p} = \vec{r} \times m\vec{v} \quad (10.24)$$

(particle)

$$\vec{L} = I\vec{\omega} \quad (10.28)$$

(rigid body rotating about axis of symmetry)

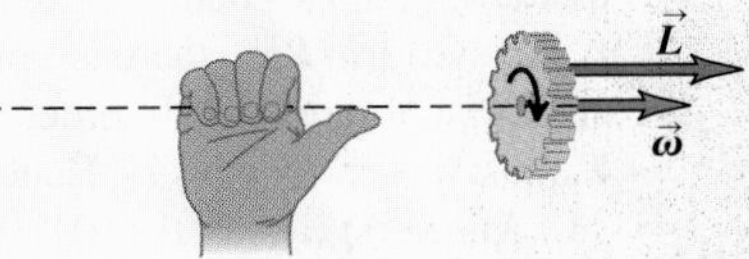

Rotational dynamics and angular momentum: The net external torque on a system is equal to the rate of change of its angular momentum. If the net external torque on a system is zero, the total angular momentum of the system is constant (conserved). (See Examples 10.11–10.15.)

$$\sum \vec{\tau} = \frac{d\vec{L}}{dt} \quad (10.29)$$

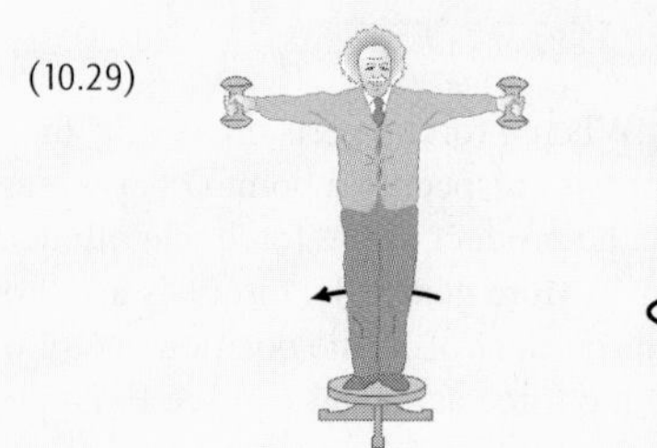

Key Terms

translational motion, *316*
line of action, *317*
lever arm (moment arm), *317*
torque, *317*
combined translation and rotation, *323*
rolling without slipping, *324*
angular momentum, *331*
principle of conservation of angular momentum, *333*
precession, *337*
precession angular speed, *338*

Answer to Chapter Opening Question ?

When the gymnast is in midair, no net torque acts about his center of mass. Hence the angular momentum of his body (the product of the moment of inertia I and the angular speed ω) around the center of mass remains constant. By moving his limbs outward, he increases I and hence ω decreases; if he pulls his limbs in, I decreases and ω increases.

Answers to Test Your Understanding Questions

10.1 Answer: (ii) The force P acts along a vertical line, so the lever arm is the horizontal distance from A to the line of action. This is the horizontal component of the distance L, which is $L\cos\theta$. Hence the magnitude of the torque is the product of the force magnitude P and the lever arm $L\cos\theta$, or $\tau = PL\cos\theta$.

10.2 Answer: (iii), (ii), (i) In order for the hanging object of mass m_2 to accelerate downward, the net force on it must be downward. Hence the magnitude m_2g of the downward weight force must be greater than the magnitude T_2 of the upward tension force. In order for the pulley to have a clockwise angular acceleration, the net torque on the pulley must be clockwise. The tension T_2 tends to rotate the pulley clockwise, while the tension T_1 tends to rotate the pulley counterclockwise. Both tension forces have the same lever arm R, so there is a clockwise torque T_2R and a counterclockwise torque T_1R. In order for the net torque to be clockwise, T_2 must be greater than T_1. Hence $m_2g > T_2 > T_1$.

10.3 Answers: (a) (ii), (b) (i) If you redo the calculation of Example 10.6 with a hollow cylinder (moment of inertia $I_{cm} = MR^2$ instead of a solid cylinder (moment of inertia $I_{cm} = \frac{1}{2}MR^2$), you will find $a_{cm\text{-}y} = \frac{1}{2}g$ and $T = \frac{1}{2}Mg$ (instead of $a_{cm\text{-}y} = \frac{2}{3}g$ and $T = \frac{1}{3}Mg$ for a solid cylinder). Hence the acceleration is less but the tension is greater. You can come to the same conclusion without doing the calculation. The greater moment of inertia means that the hollow cylinder will rotate more slowly and hence will roll downward more slowly. In order to slow the downward motion, a greater upward tension force is needed to oppose the downward force of gravity.

10.4 Answer: (iii) You apply the same torque over the same angular displacement to both cylinders. Hence, by Eq. (10.21), you do the same amount of work to both cylinders and impart the same kinetic energy to both. (The one with the smaller moment of inertia ends up with a greater angular speed, but that isn't what we are asked. Compare Conceptual Example 6.5 in Section 6.2.)

10.5 Answers: (a) no, (b) yes As the ball goes around the circle, the magnitude of $\vec{p} = m\vec{v}$ remains the same (the speed is constant) but its direction changes, so the linear momentum vector isn't constant. But $\vec{L} = \vec{r} \times \vec{p}$ *is* constant: The ball maintains a constant magnitude (the speed and the perpendicular distance from your hand to the ball are both constant) and a constant direction (along the rotation axis, perpendicular to the plane of the ball's motion). The linear momentum changes because there is a net *force* $\vec{F}$ on the ball (toward the center of the circle). The angular momentum remains constant because there is no net *torque;* the vector $\vec{r}$ points from your hand to the ball and the force $\vec{F}$ on the ball is directed toward your hand, so the vector product $\vec{\tau} = \vec{r} \times \vec{F}$ is zero.

10.6 Answer: (i) In the absence of any external torques, the earth's angular momentum $L_z = I\omega_z$ would remain constant. The melted ice would move from the poles toward the equator—that is, away from our planet's rotation axis—and the earth's moment of inertia I would increase slightly. Hence the angular velocity ω_z would decrease slightly and the day would be slightly longer.

10.7 Answer: (iii) Doubling the flywheel mass would double both its moment of inertia I and its weight w, so the ratio I/w would be unchanged. Equation (10.33) shows that the precession angular speed depends on this ratio, so there would be *no* effect on the value of Ω.

PROBLEMS

For instructor-assigned homework, go to www.masteringphysics.com 

Discussion Questions

Q10.1. When cylinder-head bolts in an automobile engine are tightened, the critical quantity is the *torque* applied to the bolts. Why is the torque more important than the actual *force* applied to the wrench handle?

Q10.2. Can a single force applied to a body change both its translational and rotational motion? Explain.

Q10.3. Suppose you could use wheels of any type in the design of a soapbox-derby racer (an unpowered, four-wheel vehicle that coasts from rest down a hill). To conform to the rules on the total weight of the vehicle and rider, should you design with large massive wheels or small light wheels? Should you use solid wheels or wheels with most of the mass at the rim? Explain.

Q10.4. A four-wheel-drive car is accelerating forward from rest. Show the direction the car's wheels turn and how this causes a friction force due to the pavement that accelerates the car forward.

Q10.5. Serious bicyclists say that if you reduce the weight of a bike, it is more effective if you do so in the wheels rather than in the frame. Why would reducing weight in the wheels make it easier on the bicyclist than reducing the same amount in the frame?

Q10.6. The harder you hit the brakes while driving forward, the more the front end of your car will move down (and the rear end move up). Why? What happens when cars accelerate forward? Why do drag racers not use front-wheel drive only?

Q10.7. When an acrobat walks on a tightrope, she extends her arms straight out from her sides. She does this to make it easier for her to catch herself if she should tip to one side or the other. Explain how this works. [*Hint:* Think about Eq. (10.7).]

Q10.8. When you turn on an electric motor, it takes longer to come up to final speed if a grinding wheel is attached to the shaft. Why?

Q10.9. Experienced cooks can tell whether an egg is raw or hard-boiled by rolling it down a slope (taking care to catch it at the bottom). How is this possible? What are they looking for?

Q10.10. The work done by a force is the product of force and distance. The torque due to a force is the product of force and distance. Does this mean that torque and work are equivalent? Explain.

Q10.11. A valued client brings a treasured ball to your engineering firm, wanting to know whether the ball is solid or hollow. He has tried tapping on it, but that has given insufficient information. Design a simple, inexpensive experiment that you could perform quickly, without injuring the precious ball, to find out whether it is solid or hollow.

Q10.12. You make two versions of the same object out of the same material having uniform density. For one version, all the dimensions are exactly twice as great as for the other one. If the same torque acts on both versions, giving the smaller version angular acceleration α, what will be the angular acceleration of the larger version in terms of α?

Q10.13. Two identical masses are attached to frictionless pulleys by very light strings wrapped around the rim of the pulley and are released from rest. Both pulleys have the same mass and same diameter, but one is solid and the other is a hoop. As the masses fall, in which case is the tension in the string greater, or is it the same in both cases? Justify your answer.

Q10.14. The force of gravity acts on the baton in Fig. 10.11, and forces produce torques that cause a body's angular velocity to change. Why, then, is the angular velocity of the baton in the figure constant?

Q10.15. A certain solid uniform ball reaches a maximum height h_0 when it rolls up a hill without slipping. What maximum height (in terms of h_0) will it reach if you (a) double its diameter, (b) double its mass, (c) double both its diameter and mass, (d) double its angular speed at the bottom of the hill?

Q10.16. A wheel is rolling without slipping on a horizontal surface. In an inertial frame of reference in which the surface is at rest, is there any point on the wheel that has a velocity that is purely vertical? Is there any point that has a horizontal velocity component opposite to the velocity of the center of mass? Explain. Do your answers change if the wheel is slipping as it rolls? Why or why not?

Q10.17. Part of the kinetic energy of a moving automobile is in the rotational motion of its wheels. When the brakes are applied hard on an icy street, the wheels "lock" and the car starts to slide. What becomes of the rotational kinetic energy?

Q10.18. A hoop, a uniform solid cylinder, a spherical shell, and a uniform solid sphere are released from rest at the top of an incline. What is the order in which they arrive at the bottom of the incline? Does it matter whether or not the masses and radii of the objects are all the same? Explain.

Q10.19. A ball is rolling along at speed v without slipping on a horizontal surface when it comes to a hill that rises at a constant angle above the horizontal. In which case will it go higher up the hill: if the hill has enough friction to prevent slipping or if the hill is perfectly smooth? Justify your answers in both cases in terms of energy conservation and in terms of Newton's second law.

Q10.20. You are standing at the center of a large horizontal turntable in a carnival funhouse. The turntable is set rotating on frictionless bearings, and it rotates freely (that is, there is no motor driving the turntable). As you walk toward the edge of the turntable, what happens to the combined angular momentum of you and the turntable? What happens to the rotation speed of the turntable? Explain your answer.

Q10.21. Global Warming. As the earth's climate continues to warm, ice near the poles will melt and be added to the oceans. What effect will this have on the length of the day? (*Hint:* Consult a map to see where the oceans lie.)

Q10.22. A point particle travels in a straight line at constant speed, and the closest distance it comes to the origin of coordinates is a distance l. With respect to this origin, does the particle have nonzero angular momentum? As the particle moves along its straight-line path, does its angular momentum with respect to the origin change?

Q10.23. In Example 10.11 (Section 10.6) the angular speed ω changes, and this must mean that there is nonzero angular acceleration. But there is no torque about the rotation axis if the forces the professor applies to the weights are directly, radially inward. Then, by Eq. (10.7), α_z must be zero. Explain what is wrong with this reasoning that leads to this apparent contradiction.

Q10.24. In Example 10.11 (Section 10.6) the rotational kinetic energy of the professor and dumbbells increases. But since there are no external torques, no work is being done to change the rotational kinetic energy. Then, by Eq. (10.22), the kinetic energy must remain the same! Explain what is wrong with this reasoning that leads to this apparent contradiction. Where *does* the extra kinetic energy come from?

Q10.25. As discussed in Section 10.6, the angular momentum of a circus acrobat is conserved as she tumbles through the air. Is her *linear* momentum conserved? Why or why not?

Q10.26. If you stop a spinning raw egg for the shortest possible instant and then release it, the egg will start spinning again. If you do the same to a hard-boiled egg, it will remain stopped. Try it. Explain it.

Q10.27. A helicopter has a large main rotor that rotates in a horizontal plane and provides lift. There is also a small rotor on the tail that rotates in a vertical plane. What is the purpose of the tail rotor? (*Hint:* If there were no tail rotor, what would happen when the pilot changed the angular speed of the main rotor?) Some helicopters have no tail rotor, but instead have two large main rotors that rotate in a horizontal plane. Why is it important that the two main rotors rotate in opposite directions?

Q10.28. In a common design for a gyroscope, the flywheel and flywheel axis are enclosed in a light, spherical frame with the flywheel at the center of the frame. The gyroscope is then balanced on top of a pivot so that the flywheel is directly above the pivot. Does the gyroscope precess if it is released while the flywheel is spinning? Explain.

Q10.29. A gyroscope takes 3.8 s to precess 1.0 revolution about a vertical axis. Two minutes later, it takes only 1.9 s to precess 1.0 revolution. No one has touched the gyroscope. Explain.

Q10.30. A gyroscope is precessing as in Fig. 10.32. What happens if you gently add some weight to the end of the flywheel axis farthest from the pivot?

Q10.31. A bullet emerges from a rifle spinning on its axis. Explain how this prevents the bullet from tumbling and keeps the streamlined end pointed forward.

Q10.32. A certain uniform turntable of diameter D_0 has an angular momentum L_0. If you want to redesign it so it retains the same mass but has twice as much angular momentum at the same angular velocity as before, what should be its diameter in terms of D_0?

Exercises

Section 10.1 Torque

10.1. Calculate the torque (magnitude and direction) about point O due to the force $\vec{F}$ in each of the cases sketched in Fig. 10.37. In each case, the force $\vec{F}$ and the rod both lie in the plane of the page, the rod has length 4.00 m, and the force has magnitude $F = 10.0$ N.

Figure **10.37** Exercise 10.1.

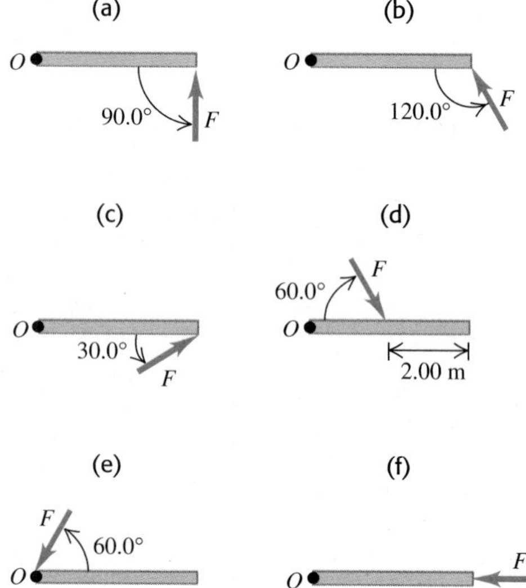

10.2. Calculate the net torque about point O for the two forces applied as in Fig. 10.38. The rod and both forces are in the plane of the page.

Figure **10.38** Exercise 10.2.

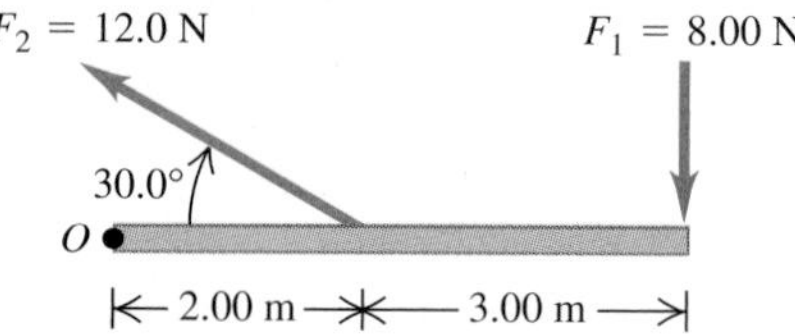

10.3. A square metal plate 0.180 m on each side is pivoted about an axis through point O at its center and perpendicular to the plate (Fig. 10.39). Calculate the net torque about this axis due to the three forces shown in the figure if the magnitudes of the forces are $F_1 = 18.0$ N, $F_2 = 26.0$ N, and $F_3 = 14.0$ N. The plate and all forces are in the plane of the page.

Figure **10.39** Exercise 10.3.

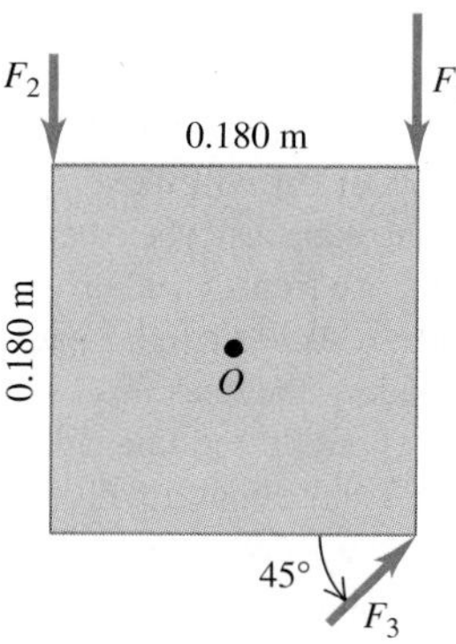

10.4. Three forces are applied to a wheel of radius 0.350 m, as shown in Fig. 10.40. One force is perpendicular to the rim, one is tangent to it, and the other one makes a 40.0° angle with the radius. What is the net torque on the wheel due to these three forces for an axis perpendicular to the wheel and passing through its center?

Figure **10.40** Exercise 10.4.

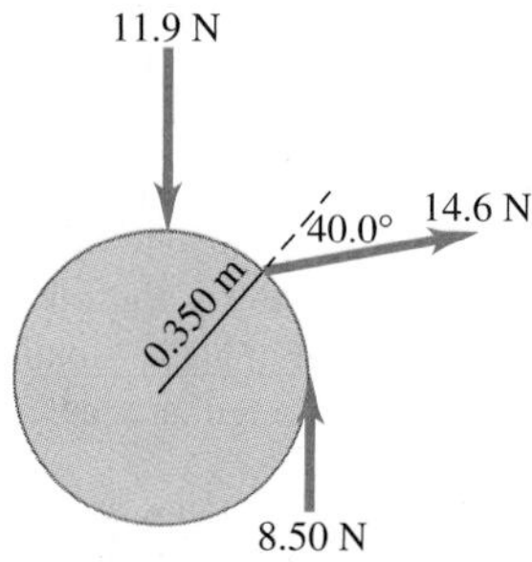

10.5. One force acting on a machine part is $\vec{F} = (-5.00\text{ N})\hat{\imath} + (4.00\text{ N})\hat{\jmath}$. The vector from the origin to the point where the force is applied is $\vec{r} = (-0.450\text{ m})\hat{\imath} + (0.150\text{ m})\hat{\jmath}$. (a) In a sketch, show $\vec{r}$, $\vec{F}$, and the origin. (b) Use the right-hand rule to determine the direction of the torque. (c) Calculate the vector torque produced by this force. Verify that the direction of the torque is the same as you obtained in part (b).

10.6. A machinist is using a wrench to loosen a nut. The wrench is 25.0 cm long, and he exerts a 17.0-N force at the end of the handle at 37° with the handle (Fig. 10.41). (a) What torque does the machinist exert about the center of the nut? (b) What is the maximum torque he could exert with this force, and how should the force be oriented?

Figure **10.41** Exercise 10.6.

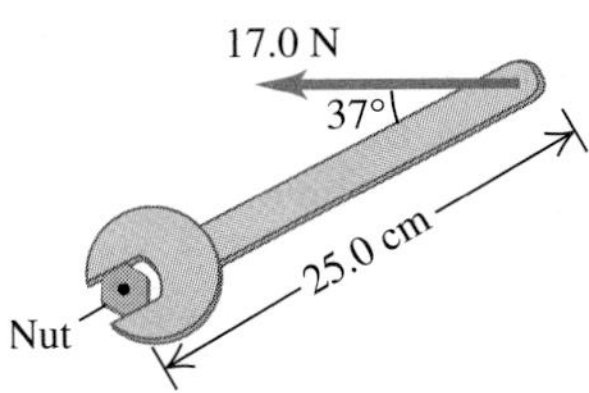

Section 10.2 Torque and Angular Acceleration for a Rigid Body

10.7. The flywheel of an engine has moment of inertia 2.50 kg · m^2 about its rotation axis. What constant torque is required to bring it up to an angular speed of 400 rev/min in 8.00 s, starting from rest?

10.8. A uniform, 8.40-kg, spherical shell 50.0 cm in diameter has four small 2.00-kg masses attached to its outer surface and equally spaced around it. This combination is spinning about an axis running through the center of the sphere and two of the small masses (Fig. 10.42). What friction torque is needed to reduce its angular speed from 75.0 rpm to 50.0 rpm in 30.0 s?

Figure **10.42** Exercise 10.8.

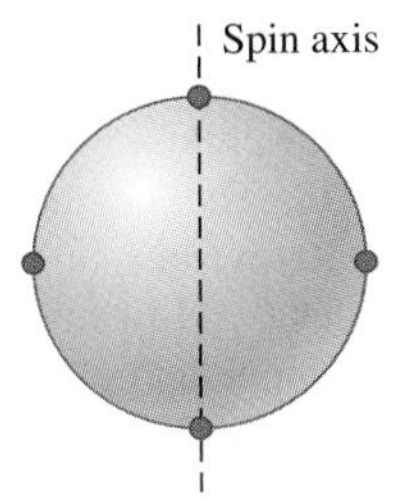

Spin axis

10.9. A machine part has the shape of a solid uniform sphere of mass 225 g and diameter 3.00 cm. It is spinning about a frictionless axle through its center, but at one point on its equator it is scraping against metal, resulting in a friction force of 0.0200 N at that point. (a) Find its angular acceleration. (b) How long will it take to decrease its rotational speed by 22.5 rad/s?

10.10. A cord is wrapped around the rim of a solid uniform wheel 0.250 m in radius and of mass 9.20 kg. A steady horizontal pull of 40.0 N to the right is exerted on the cord, pulling it off tangentially from the wheel. The wheel is mounted on frictionless bearings on a horizontal axle through its center. (a) Compute the angular acceleration of the wheel and the acceleration of the part of the cord that has already been pulled off the wheel. (b) Find the magnitude and direction of the force that the axle exerts on the wheel. (c) Which of the answers in parts (a) and (b) would change if the pull were upward instead of horizontal?

10.11. A solid, uniform cylinder with mass 8.25 kg and diameter 15.0 cm is spinning at 220 rpm on a thin, frictionless axle that passes along the cylinder axis. You design a simple friction brake to stop the cylinder by pressing the brake against the outer rim with a normal force. The coefficient of kinetic friction between the brake and rim is 0.333. What must the applied normal force be to bring the cylinder to rest after it has turned through 5.25 revolutions?

10.12. A stone is suspended from the free end of a wire that is wrapped around the outer rim of a pulley, similar to what is shown in Fig. 10.10. The pulley is a uniform disk with mass 10.0 kg and radius 50.0 cm and turns on frictionless bearings. You measure that the stone travels 12.6 m in the first 3.00 s starting from rest. Find (a) the mass of the stone and (b) the tension in the wire.

10.13. A grindstone in the shape of a solid disk with diameter 0.520 m, and a mass of 50.0 kg is rotating at 850 rev/min. You press an ax against the rim with a normal force of 160 N (Fig. 10.43), and the grindstone comes to rest in 7.50 s. Find the coefficient of friction between the ax and the grindstone. You can ignore friction in the bearings.

Figure **10.43** Exercise 10.13 and Problem 10.53.

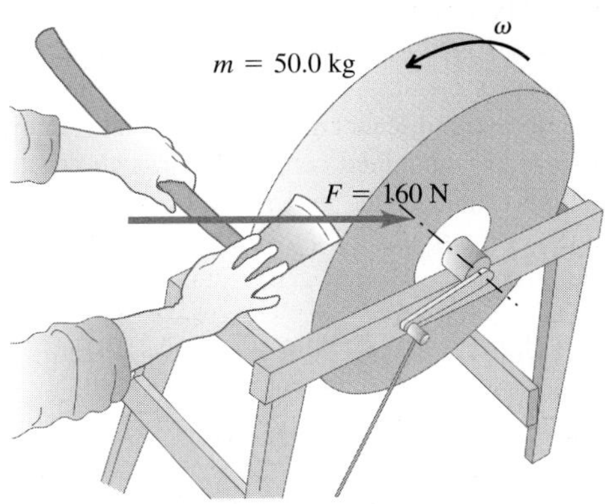

10.14. A 15.0-kg bucket of water is suspended by a very light rope wrapped around a solid uniform cylinder 0.300 m in diameter with mass 12.0 kg. The cylinder pivots on a frictionless axle through its center. The bucket is released from rest at the top of a well and falls 10.0 m to the water. (a) What is the tension in the rope while the bucket is falling? (b) With what speed does the bucket strike the water? (c) What is the time of fall? (d) While the bucket is falling, what is the force exerted on the cylinder by the axle?

10.15. A 2.00-kg textbook rests on a frictionless, horizontal surface. A cord attached to the book passes over a pulley whose diameter is 0.150 m, to a hanging book with mass 3.00 kg. The system is released from rest, and the books are observed to move 1.20 m in 0.800 s. (a) What is the tension in each part of the cord? (b) What is the moment of inertia of the pulley about its rotation axis?

10.16. A 12.0-kg box resting on a horizontal, frictionless surface is attached to a 5.00-kg weight by a thin, light wire that passes over a frictionless pulley (Fig. 10.44). The pulley has the shape of a uniform solid disk of mass 2.00 kg and diameter 0.500 m. After the system is released, find (a) the tension in the wire on both sides of the pulley, (b) the acceleration of the box, and (c) the horizontal and vertical components of the force that the axle exerts on the pulley.

Figure **10.44** Exercise 10.16.

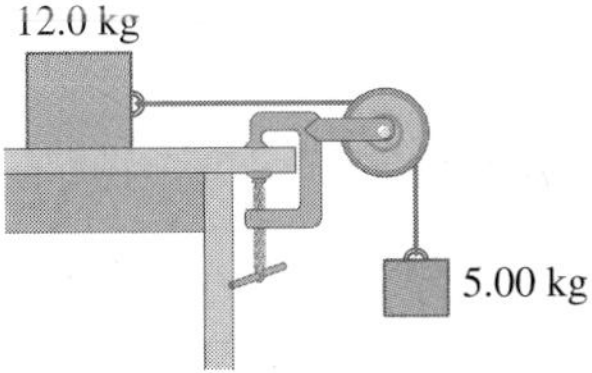

10.17. A thin, uniform, 15.0-kg post, 1.75 m long, is held vertically using a cable and is attached to a 5.00-kg mass and a pivot at its bottom end (Fig. 10.45). The string attached to the 5.00-kg mass passes over a massless, frictionless pulley and pulls perpendicular to the post. Suddenly the cable breaks. (a) Find the angular acceleration of the post about the pivot just after the cable breaks. (b) Will the angular acceleration in part (a) remain constant as the post falls (before it hits the pulley)? Why? (c) What is the acceleration of the

Figure **10.45** Exercise 10.17.

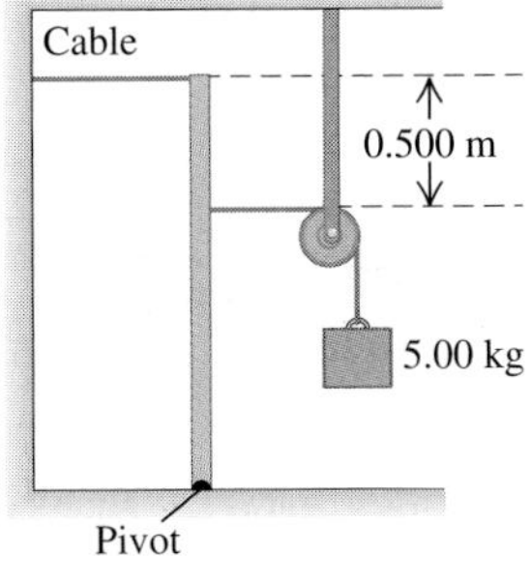

5.00-kg mass the instant after the cable breaks? Does this acceleration remain constant? Why?

10.18. A thin, horizontal rod with length l and mass M pivots about a vertical axis at one end. A force with constant magnitude F is applied to the other end, causing the rod to rotate in a horizontal plane. The force is maintained perpendicular to the rod and to the axis of rotation. Calculate the magnitude of the angular acceleration of the rod.

Section 10.3 Rigid-Body Rotation About a Moving Axis

10.19. A 2.20-kg hoop 1.20 m in diameter is rolling to the right without slipping on a horizontal floor at a steady 3.00 rad/s. (a) How fast is its center moving? (b) What is the total kinetic energy of the hoop? (c) Find the velocity vector of each of the following points, as viewed by a person at rest on the ground: (i) the highest point on the hoop; (ii) the lowest point on the hoop, (iii) a point on the right side of the hoop, midway between the top and the bottom. (d) Find the velocity vector for each of the points in part (c), except as viewed by someone moving along with same velocity as the hoop.

10.20. A string is wrapped several times around the rim of a small hoop with radius 8.00 cm and mass 0.180 kg. The free end of the string is held in place and the hoop is released from rest (Fig. 10.46). After the hoop has descended 75.0 cm, calculate (a) the angular speed of the rotating hoop and (b) the speed of its center.

Figure **10.46** Exercise 10.20 and Problem 10.72.

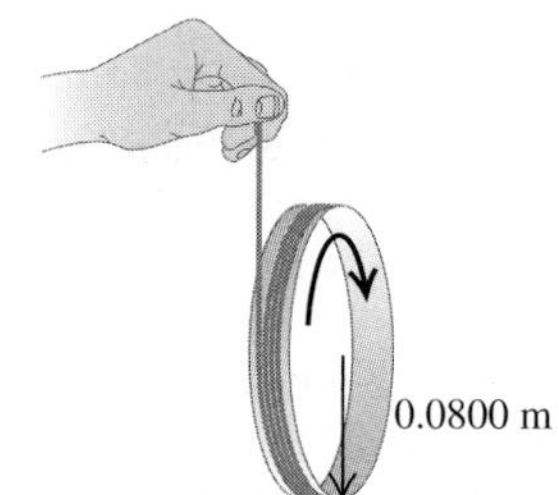

10.21. What fraction of the total kinetic energy is rotational for the following objects rolling without slipping on a horizontal surface? (a) a uniform solid cylinder; (b) a uniform sphere; (c) a thin-walled, hollow sphere; (d) a hollow cylinder with outer radius R and inner radius $R/2$.

10.22. A hollow, spherical shell with mass 2.00 kg rolls without slipping down a 38.0° slope. (a) Find the acceleration, the friction force, and the minimum coefficient of friction needed to prevent slipping. (b) How would your answers to part (a) change if the mass were doubled to 4.00 kg?

10.23. A solid ball is released from rest and slides down a hillside that slopes downward at 65.0° from the horizontal. (a) What minimum value must the coefficient of static friction between the hill and ball surfaces have for no slipping to occur? (b) Would the coefficient of friction calculated in part (a) be sufficient to prevent a hollow ball (such as a soccer ball) from slipping? Justify your answer. (c) In part (a), why did we use the coefficient of static friction and not the coefficient of kinetic friction?

10.24. A uniform marble rolls down a symmetric bowl, starting from rest at the top of the left side. The top of each side is a distance h above the bottom of the bowl. The left half of the bowl is rough enough to cause the marble to roll without slipping, but the right half has no friction because it is coated with oil. (a) How far up the smooth side will the marble go, measured vertically from the bottom? (b) How high would the marble go if both sides were as rough as the left side? (c) How do you account for the fact that the marble goes *higher* with friction on the right side than without friction?

10.25. A 392-N wheel comes off a moving truck and rolls without slipping along a highway. At the bottom of a hill it is rotating at 25.0 rad/s. The radius of the wheel is 0.600 m, and its moment of inertia about its rotation axis is $0.800MR^2$. Friction does work on the wheel as it rolls up the hill to a stop, a height h above the bottom of the hill; this work has absolute value 3500 J. Calculate h.

10.26. A Ball Rolling Uphill. A bowling ball rolls without slipping up a ramp that slopes upward at an angle β to the horizontal (see Example 10.7 in Section 10.3). Treat the ball as a uniform, solid sphere, ignoring the finger holes. (a) Draw the free-body diagram for the ball. Explain why the friction force must be directed *uphill.* (b) What is the acceleration of the center of mass of the ball? (c) What minimum coefficient of static friction is needed to prevent slipping?

Section 10.4 Work and Power in Rotational Motion

10.27. A playground merry-go-round has radius 2.40 m and moment of inertia 2100 kg · m^2 about a vertical axle through its center, and it turns with negligible friction. (a) A child applies an 18.0-N force tangentially to the edge of the merry-go-round for 15.0 s. If the merry-go-round is initially at rest, what is its angular speed after this 15.0-s interval? (b) How much work did the child do on the merry-go-round? (c) What is the average power supplied by the child?

10.28. The engine delivers 175 hp to an aircraft propeller at 2400 rev/min. (a) How much torque does the aircraft engine provide? (b) How much work does the engine do in one revolution of the propeller?

10.29. A 1.50-kg grinding wheel is in the form of a solid cylinder of radius 0.100 m. (a) What constant torque will bring it from rest to an angular speed of 1200 rev/min in 2.5 s? (b) Through what angle has it turned during that time? (c) Use Eq. (10.21) to calculate the work done by the torque. (d) What is the grinding wheel's kinetic energy when it is rotating at 1200 rev/min? Compare your answer to the result in part (c).

10.30. An electric motor consumes 9.00 kJ of electrical energy in 1.00 min. If one-third of this energy goes into heat and other forms of internal energy of the motor, with the rest going to the motor output, how much torque will this engine develop if you run it at 2500 rpm?

10.31. The carbide tips of the cutting teeth of a circular saw are 8.6 cm from the axis of rotation. (a) The no-load speed of the saw, when it is not cutting anything, is 4800 rev/min. Why is its no-load power output negligible? (b) While the saw is cutting lumber, its angular speed slows to 2400 rev/min and the power output is 1.9 hp. What is the tangential force that the wood exerts on the carbide tips?

10.32. An airplane propeller is 2.08 m in length (from tip to tip) and has a mass of 117 kg. When the airplane's engine is first started, it applies a constant torque of 1950 N · m to the propeller, which starts from rest. (a) What is the angular acceleration of the propeller? Model the propeller as a slender rod and see Table 9.2. (b) What is the propeller's angular speed after making 5.00 revolutions? (c) How much work is done by the engine during the first 5.00 revolutions? (d) What is the average power output of the engine during the first 5.00 revolutions? (e) What is the instantaneous power output of the motor at the instant that the propeller has turned through 5.00 revolutions?

10.33. (a) Compute the torque developed by an industrial motor whose output is 150 kW at an angular speed of 4000 rev/min. (b) A drum with negligible mass, 0.400 m in diameter, is attached to the motor shaft, and the power output of the motor is used to raise a weight hanging from a rope wrapped around the drum. How heavy a weight can the motor lift at constant speed? (c) At what constant speed will the weight rise?

Section 10.5 Angular Momentum

10.34. A woman with mass 50 kg is standing on the rim of a large disk that is rotating at 0.50 rev/s about an axis through its center. The disk has mass 110 kg and radius 4.0 m. Calculate the magnitude of the total angular momentum of the woman-plus-disk system. (Assume that you can treat the woman as a point.)

10.35. A 2.00-kg rock has a horizontal velocity of magnitude 12.0 m/s when it is at point P in Fig. 10.47. (a) At this instant, what are the magnitude and direction of its angular momentum relative to point O? (b) If the only force acting on the rock is its weight, what is the rate of change (magnitude and direction) of its angular momentum at this instant?

Figure 10.47 Exercise 10.35.

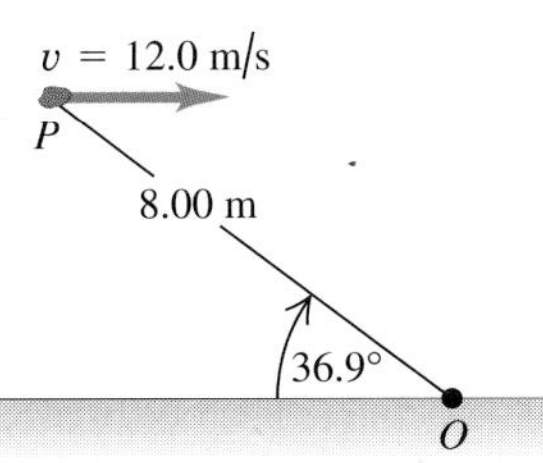

10.36. (a) Calculate the magnitude of the angular momentum of the earth in a circular orbit around the sun. Is it reasonable to model it as a particle? (b) Calculate the magnitude of the angular momentum of the earth due to its rotation around an axis through the north and south poles, modeling it as a uniform sphere. Consult Appendix E and the astronomical data in Appendix F.

10.37. Find the magnitude of the angular momentum of the second hand on a clock about an axis through the center of the clock face. The clock hand has a length of 15.0 cm and a mass of 6.00 g. Take the second hand to be a slender rod rotating with constant angular velocity about one end.

10.38. A hollow, thin-walled sphere of mass 12.0 kg and diameter 48.0 cm is rotating about an axle through its center. The angle (in radians) through which it turns as a function of time (in seconds) is given by $\theta(t) = At^2 + Bt^4$, where A has numerical value 1.50 and B has numerical value 1.10. (a) What are the units of the constants A and B? (b) At the time 3.00 s, find (i) the angular momentum of the sphere and (ii) the net torque on the sphere.

Section 10.6 Conservation of Angular Momentum

10.39. Under some circumstances, a star can collapse into an extremely dense object made mostly of neutrons and called a *neutron star.* The density of a neutron star is roughly 10^{14} times as great as that of ordinary solid matter. Suppose we represent the star as a uniform, solid, rigid sphere, both before and after the collapse. The star's initial radius was 7.0×10^5 km (comparable to our sun); its final radius is 16 km. If the original star rotated once in 30 days, find the angular speed of the neutron star.

10.40. A small block on a frictionless, horizontal surface has a mass of 0.0250 kg. It is attached to a massless cord passing through a hole in the surface (Fig. 10.48). The block is originally revolving at a distance of 0.300 m from the hole with an angular speed of 1.75 rad/s. The cord is then pulled from below, shortening the radius of the circle in which the block revolves to 0.150 m. Model the block as a particle. (a) Is angular momentum of the block conserved? Why or why not? (b) What is the new angular speed? (c) Find the change in kinetic energy of the block. (d) How much work was done in pulling the cord?

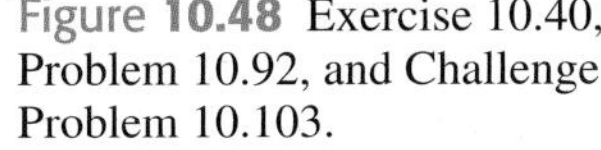
Figure 10.48 Exercise 10.40, Problem 10.92, and Challenge Problem 10.103.

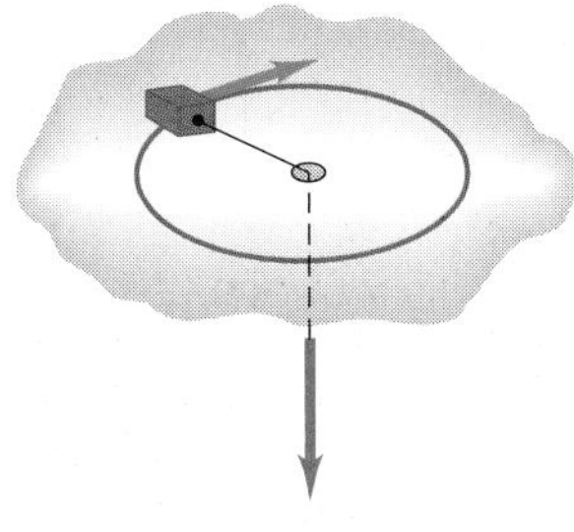

10.41. The Spinning Figure Skater. The outstretched hands and arms of a figure skater preparing for a spin can be considered a slender rod pivoting about an axis through its center (Fig. 10.49). When the skater's hands and arms are brought in and wrapped around his body to execute the spin, the hands and arms can be considered a thin-walled, hollow cylinder. His hands and arms have a combined mass 8.0 kg. When outstretched, they span 1.8 m; when wrapped, they form a cylinder of radius 25 cm. The moment of inertia about the rotation axis of the remainder of his body is constant and equal to $0.40 \text{ kg} \cdot \text{m}^2$. If his original angular speed is 0.40 rev/s, what is his final angular speed?

Figure 10.49 Exercise 10.41.

10.42. A diver comes off a board with arms straight up and legs straight down, giving her a moment of inertia about her rotation axis of $18 \text{ kg} \cdot \text{m}^2$. She then tucks into a small ball, decreasing this moment of inertia to $3.6 \text{ kg} \cdot \text{m}^2$. While tucked, she makes two complete revolutions in 1.0 s. If she hadn't tucked at all, how many revolutions would she have made in the 1.5 s from board to water?

10.43. A large wooden turntable in the shape of a flat uniform disk has a radius of 2.00 m and a total mass of 120 kg. The turntable is initially rotating at 3.00 rad/s about a vertical axis through its center. Suddenly, a 70.0-kg parachutist makes a soft landing on the turntable at a point near the outer edge. (a) Find the angular speed of the turntable after the parachutist lands. (Assume that you can treat the parachutist as a particle.) (b) Compute the kinetic energy of the system before and after the parachutist lands. Why are these kinetic energies not equal?

10.44. A solid wood door 1.00 m wide and 2.00 m high is hinged along one side and has a total mass of 40.0 kg. Initially open and at rest, the door is struck at its center by a handful of sticky mud with mass 0.500 kg, traveling perpendicular to the door at 12.0 m/s just before impact. Find the final angular speed of the door. Does the mud make a significant contribution to the moment of inertia?

10.45. A small 10.0-g bug stands at one end of a thin uniform bar that is initially at rest on a smooth horizontal table. The other end of the bar pivots about a nail driven into the table and can rotate freely, without friction. The bar has mass 50.0 g and is 100 cm in length. The bug jumps off in the horizontal direction, perpendicular to the bar, with a speed of 20.0 cm/s relative to the table. (a) What is the angular speed of the bar just after the frisky insect leaps? (b) What is the total kinetic energy of the system just after the bug leaps? (c) Where does this energy come from?

10.46. Asteroid Collision! Suppose that an asteroid traveling straight toward the center of the earth were to collide with our planet at the equator and bury itself just below the surface. What would have to be the mass of this asteroid, in terms of the earth's mass M, for the day to become 25.0% longer than it presently is as a result of the collision? Assume that the asteroid is very small compared to the earth and that the earth is uniform throughout.

10.47. A thin, uniform metal bar, 2.00 m long and weighing 90.0 N, is hanging vertically from the ceiling by a frictionless pivot. Suddenly it is struck 1.50 m below the ceiling by a small 3.00-kg ball, initially traveling horizontally at 10.0 m/s. The ball rebounds in the opposite direction with a speed of 6.00 m/s. (a) Find the angular speed of the bar just after the collision. (b) During the collision, why is the angular momentum conserved but not the linear momentum?

Section 10.7 Gyroscopes and Precession

10.48. Draw a top view of the gyroscope shown in Fig. 10.32. (a) Draw labeled arrows on your sketch for $\vec{\omega}$, $\vec{L}$, and $\vec{\tau}$. Draw $d\vec{L}$ produced by $\vec{\tau}$. Draw $\vec{L} + d\vec{L}$. Determine the sense of the precession by examining the directions of $\vec{L}$ and $\vec{L} + d\vec{L}$. (b) Reverse the direction of the spin angular velocity of the rotor and repeat all the steps in part (a). (c) Move the pivot to the other end of the shaft, with the same direction of spin angular velocity as in part (b), and repeat all the steps. (d) Keeping the pivot as in part (c), reverse the spin angular velocity of the rotor and repeat all the steps.

10.49. The rotor (flywheel) of a toy gyroscope has mass 0.140 kg. Its moment of inertia about its axis is $1.20 \times 10^{-4}\ \text{kg} \cdot \text{m}^2$. The mass of the frame is 0.0250 kg. The gyroscope is supported on a single pivot (Fig. 10.50) with its center of mass a horizontal distance of 4.00 cm from the pivot. The gyroscope is precessing in a horizontal plane at the rate of one revolution in 2.20 s. (a) Find the upward force exerted by the pivot. (b) Find the angular speed with which the rotor is spinning about its axis, expressed in rev/min. (c) Copy the diagram and draw vectors to show the angular momentum of the rotor and the torque acting on it.

Figure 10.50 Exercise 10.49.

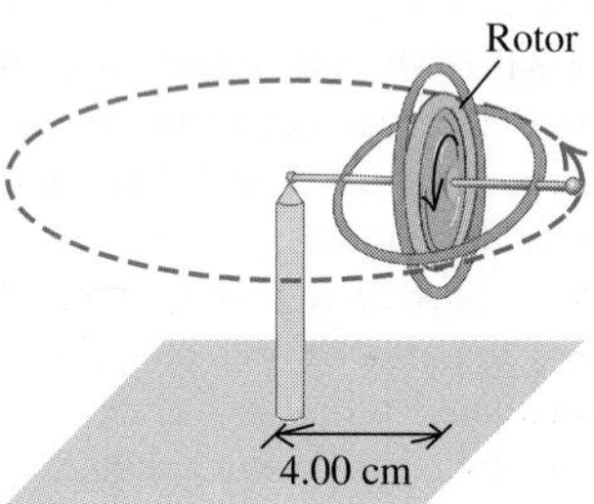

10.50. A Gyroscope on the Moon. A certain gyroscope precesses at a rate of 0.50 rad/s when used on earth. If it were taken to a lunar base, where the acceleration due to gravity is $0.165g$, what would be its precession rate?

10.51. A gyroscope is precessing about a vertical axis. Describe what happens to the precession angular speed if the following changes in the variables are made, with all other variables remaining the same: (a) the angular speed of the spinning flywheel is doubled; (b) the total weight is doubled; (c) the moment of inertia about the axis of the spinning flywheel is doubled; (d) the distance from the pivot to the center of gravity is doubled. (e) What happens if all four of the variables in parts (a) through (d) are doubled?

10.52. The earth precesses once every 26,000 years and spins on its axis once a day. Estimate the magnitude of the torque that causes the precession of the earth. You may need some data from Appendix F. Make the estimate by assuming (i) the earth is a uniform sphere and (ii) the precession of the earth is like that of the gyroscope shown in Fig. 10.34. In this model, the precession axis and rotation axis are perpendicular. Actually, the angle between these two axes for the earth is only $23\frac{1}{2}°$; this affects the calculated torque by about a factor of 2.

Problems

10.53. A 50.0-kg grindstone is a solid disk 0.520 m in diameter. You press an ax down on the rim with a normal force of 160 N (Fig. 10.43). The coefficient of kinetic friction between the blade and the stone is 0.60, and there is a constant friction torque of $6.50\ \text{N} \cdot \text{m}$ between the axle of the stone and its bearings. (a) How much force must be applied tangentially at the end of a crank handle 0.500 m long to bring the stone from rest to 120 rev/min in 9.00 s? (b) After the grindstone attains an angular speed of 120 rev/min, what tangential force at the end of the handle is needed to maintain a constant angular speed of 120 rev/min? (c) How much time does it take the grindstone to come from 120 rev/min to rest if it is acted on by the axle friction alone?

10.54. An experimental bicycle wheel is placed on a test stand so that it is free to turn on its axle. If a constant net torque of $5.00\ \text{N} \cdot \text{m}$ is applied to the tire for 2.00 s, the angular speed of the tire increases from 0 to 100 rev/min. The external torque is then removed, and the wheel is brought to rest by friction in its bearings in 125 s. Compute (a) the moment of inertia of the wheel about the rotation axis; (b) the friction torque; (c) the total number of revolutions made by the wheel in the 125-s time interval.

10.55. Speedometer. Your car's speedometer converts the angular speed of the wheels to the linear speed of the car, assuming standard-size tires and no slipping on the pavement. (a) If your car's standard tires are 24 inches in diameter, at what rate (in rpm) are your wheels rotating when you are driving at a freeway speed of 60 mi/h? (b) Suppose you put oversize, 30-inch-diameter tires on your car. How fast are you really going when your speedometer reads 60 mi/h? (c) If you now put on undersize, 20-inch-diameter tires, what will the speedometer read when you are actually traveling at 50 mi/h?

10.56. A uniform hollow disk has two pieces of thin light wire wrapped around its outer rim and is supported from the ceiling (Fig. 10.51). Suddenly one of the wires breaks, and the remaining wire does not slip as the disk rolls down. Use energy conservation to find the speed of the center of this disk after it has fallen a distance of 1.20 m.

Figure 10.51 Problem 10.56.

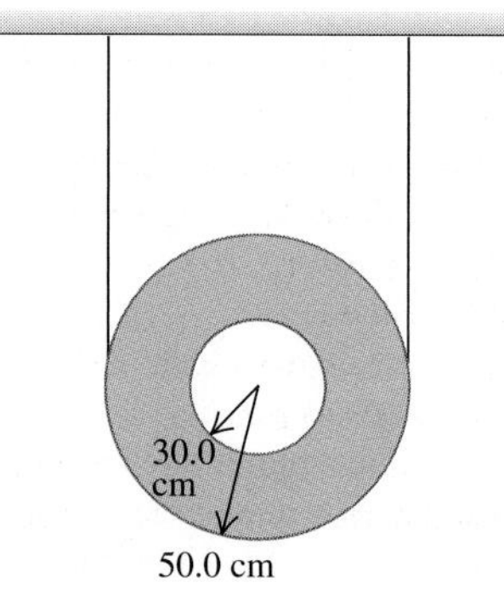

10.57. A thin, uniform 3.80-kg bar, 80.0 cm long, has very small 2.50-kg balls glued on at either end (Fig. 10.52). It is supported horizontally by a thin, horizontal, frictionless axle passing through its center and perpendicular to the bar. Suddenly the right-hand ball becomes detached and falls off, but the other ball remains glued to the bar. (a) Find the angular acceleration of the bar just after the ball falls off. (b) Will the angular acceleration remain constant as the bar continues to swing? If not, will it increase or decrease? (c) Find the angular velocity of the bar just as it swings through its vertical position.

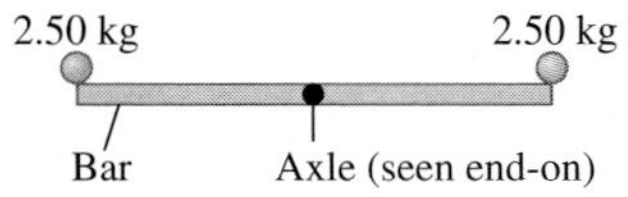

Figure 10.52 Problem 10.57.

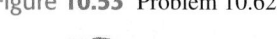

2.50 kg 2.50 kg

Bar Axle (seen end-on)

10.58. While exploring a castle, Exena the Exterminator is spotted by a dragon who chases her down a hallway. Exena runs into a room and attempts to swing the heavy door shut before the dragon gets her. The door is initially perpendicular to the wall, so it must be turned through 90° to close. The door is 3.00 m tall and 1.25 m wide, and it weighs 750 N. You can ignore the friction at the hinges. If Exena applies a force of 220 N at the edge of the door and perpendicular to it, how much time does it take her to close the door?

10.59. A thin rod of length l lies on the $+x$-axis with its left end at the origin. A string pulls on the rod with a force $\vec{F}$ directed toward a point P a distance h above the rod. Where along the rod should you attach the string to get the greatest torque about the origin if point P is (a) above the right end of the rod? (b) Above the left end of the rod? (c) Above the center of the rod?

10.60. Balancing Act. Attached to one end of a long, thin, uniform rod of length L and mass M is a small blob of clay of the same mass M. (a) Locate the position of the center of mass of the system of rod and clay. Note this position on a drawing of the rod. (b) You carefully balance the rod on a frictionless tabletop so that it is standing vertically, with the end without the clay touching the table. If the rod is now tipped so that it is a small angle θ away from the vertical, determine its angular acceleration at this instant. Assume that the end without the clay remains in contact with the tabletop. (*Hint:* See Table 9.2.) (c) You again balance the rod on the frictionless tabletop so that it is standing vertically, but now the end of the rod *with* the clay is touching the table. If the rod is again tipped so that it is a small angle θ away from the vertical, determine its angular acceleration at this instant. Assume that the end with the clay remains in contact with the tabletop. How does this compare to the angular acceleration in part (b)? (d) A pool cue is a tapered wooden rod that is thick at one end and thin at the other. You can easily balance a pool cue vertically on one finger if the thin end is in contact with your finger; this is quite a bit harder to do if the thick end is in contact with your finger. Explain why there is a difference.

10.61. You connect a light string to a point on the edge of a uniform vertical disk with radius R and mass M. The disk is free to rotate without friction about a stationary horizontal axis through its center. Initially, the disk is at rest with the string connection at the highest point on the disk. You pull the string with a constant horizontal force $\vec{F}$ until the wheel has made exactly one-quarter revolution about a horizontal axis through its center, and then you let go. (a) Use Eq. (10.20) to find the work done by the string. (b) Use Eq. (6.14) to find the work done by the string. Do you obtain the same result as in part (a)? (c) Find the final angular speed of the disk. (d) Find the maximum tangential acceleration of a point on the disk. (e) Find the maximum radial (centripetal) acceleration of a point on the disk.

10.62. The mechanism shown in Fig. 10.53 is used to raise a crate of supplies from a ship's hold. The crate has total mass 50 kg. A rope is wrapped around a wooden cylinder that turns on a metal axle. The cylinder has radius 0.25 m and moment of inertia $I = 2.9\ \text{kg} \cdot \text{m}^2$ about the axle. The crate is suspended from the free end of the rope. One end of the axle pivots on frictionless bearings; a crank handle is attached to the other end. When the crank is turned, the end of the handle rotates about the axle in a vertical circle of radius 0.12 m, the cylinder turns, and the crate is raised. What magnitude of the force $\vec{F}$ applied tangentially to the rotating crank is required to raise the crate with an acceleration of $0.80\ \text{m/s}^2$? (You can ignore the mass of the rope as well as the moments of inertia of the axle and the crank.)

Figure 10.53 Problem 10.62.

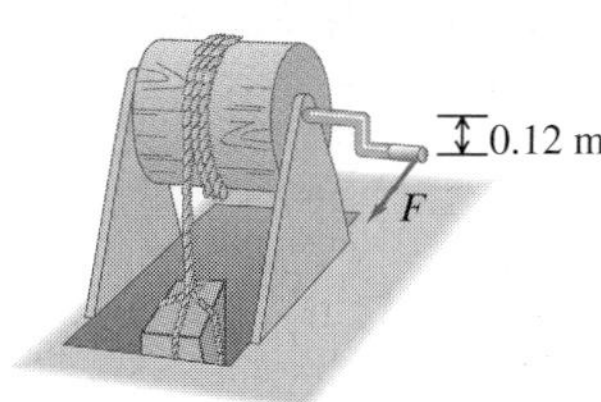

10.63. A large 16.0-kg roll of paper with radius $R = 18.0$ cm rests against the wall and is held in place by a bracket attached to a rod through the center of the roll (Fig. 10.54). The rod turns without friction in the bracket, and the moment of inertia of the paper and rod about the axis is $0.260\ \text{kg} \cdot \text{m}^2$. The other end of the bracket is attached by a frictionless hinge to the wall such that the bracket makes an angle of 30.0° with the wall. The weight of the bracket is negligible. The coefficient of kinetic friction between the paper and the wall is $\mu_k = 0.25$. A constant vertical force $F = 40.0$ N is applied to the paper, and the paper unrolls. (a) What is the magnitude of the force that the rod exerts on the paper as it unrolls? (b) What is the magnitude of the angular acceleration of the roll?

Figure 10.54 Problem 10.63.

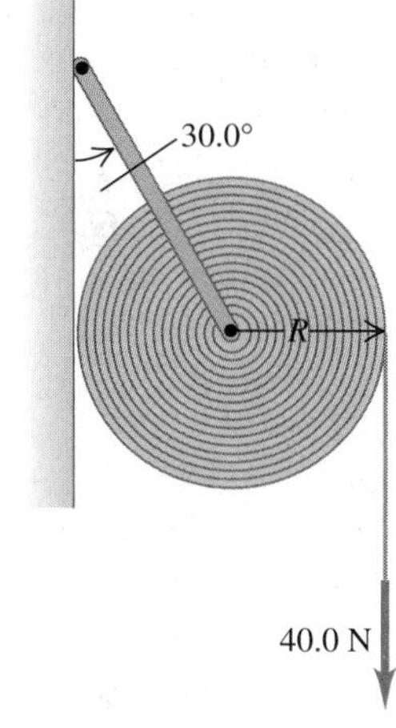

10.64. A block with mass $m = 5.00$ kg slides down a surface inclined 36.9° to the horizontal (Fig. 10.55). The coefficient of kinetic friction is 0.25. A string attached to the block is wrapped around a flywheel on a fixed axis at O. The flywheel has mass 25.0 kg and moment of inertia $0.500\ \text{kg} \cdot \text{m}^2$ with respect to the axis of rotation. The string pulls without slipping at a perpendicular distance of 0.200 m from that axis. (a) What is the acceleration of the block down the plane? (b) What is the tension in the string?

Figure 10.55 Problem 10.64.

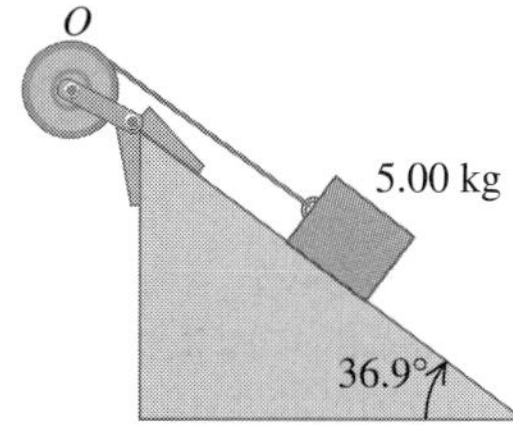

10.65. Two metal disks, one with radius $R_1 = 2.50$ cm and mass $M_1 = 0.80$ kg and the other with radius $R_2 = 5.00$ cm and mass $M_2 = 1.60$ kg, are welded together and mounted on a frictionless axis through their common center, as in Problem 9.89. (a) A light string is wrapped around the edge of the smaller disk, and a 1.50 kg block is suspended from the free end of the string. What is the magnitude of the downward acceleration of the block after it is released? (b) Repeat the calculation of part (a), this time with the string wrapped around the edge of the larger disk. In which case is the acceleration of the block greater? Does your answer make sense?

10.66. A lawn roller in the form of a thin-walled, hollow cylinder with mass M is pulled horizontally with a constant horizontal force F applied by a handle attached to the axle. If it rolls without slipping, find the acceleration and the friction force.

10.67. Two weights are connected by a very light flexible cord that passes over a 50.0-N frictionless pulley of radius 0.300 m. The pulley is a solid uniform disk and is supported by a hook connected to the ceiling (Fig. 10.56). What force does the ceiling exert on the hook?

Figure 10.56 Problem 10.67.

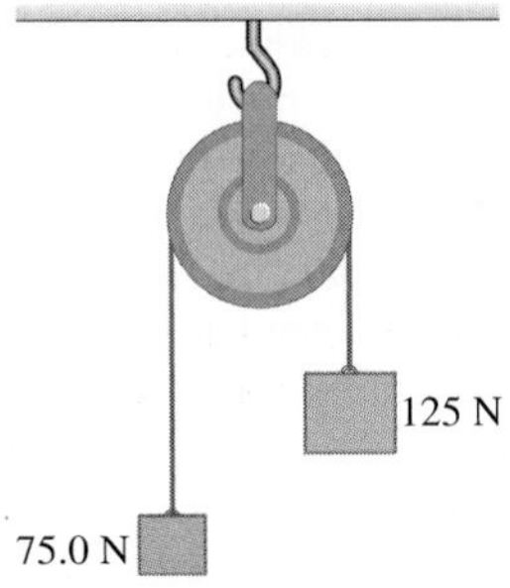

10.68. A solid disk is rolling without slipping on a level surface at a constant speed of 2.50 m/s. (a) If the disk rolls up a 30.0° ramp, how far along the ramp will it move before it stops? (b) Explain why your answer in part (a) does not depend on either the mass or the radius of the disk.

10.69. The Yo-yo. A yo-yo is made from two uniform disks, each with mass m and radius R, connected by a light axle of radius b. A light, thin string is wound several times around the axle and then held stationary while the yo-yo is released from rest, dropping as the string unwinds. Find the linear acceleration and angular acceleration of the yo-yo and the tension in the string.

10.70. A thin-walled, hollow spherical shell of mass m and radius r starts from rest and rolls without slipping down the track shown in Fig. 10.57. Points A and B are on a circular part of the track having radius R. The diameter of the shell is very small compared to h_0 and R, and rolling friction is negligible. (a) What is the minimum height h_0 for which this shell will make a complete loop-the-loop on the circular part of the track? (b) How hard does the track push on the shell at point B, which is at the same level as the center of the circle? (c) Suppose that the track had no friction and the shell was released from the same height h_0 you found in part (a). Would it make a complete loop-the-loop? How do you know? (d) In part (c), how hard does the track push on the shell at point A, the top of the circle? How hard did it push on the shell in part (a)?

Figure 10.57 Problem 10.70.

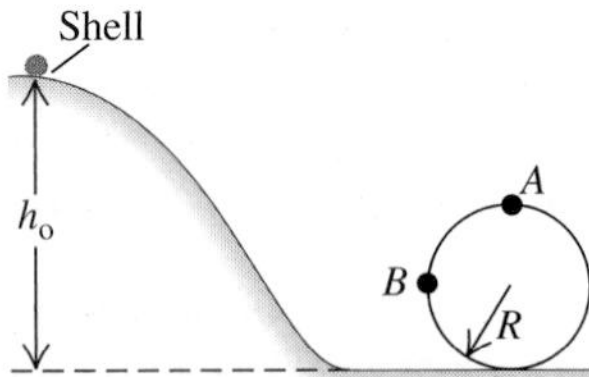

10.71. Figure 10.58 shows three identical yo-yos initially at rest on a horizontal surface. For each yo-yo, the string is pulled in the direction shown. In each case, there is sufficient friction for the yo-yo to roll without slipping. Draw the free-body diagram for each yo-yo. In what direction will each yo-yo rotate? (Try it!) Explain your answers.

Figure 10.58 Problem 10.71.

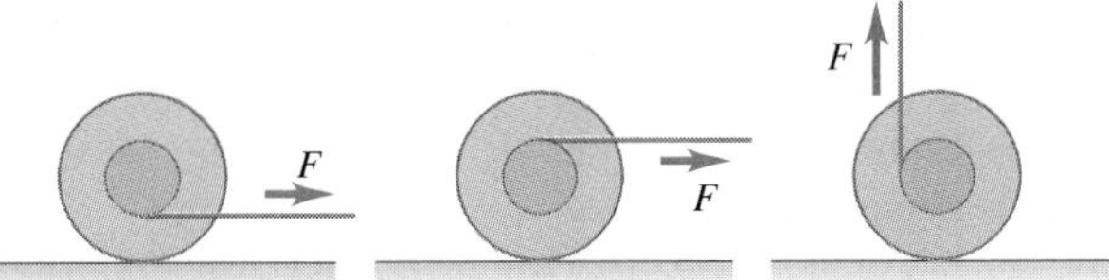

10.72. As shown in Fig. 10.46, a string is wrapped several times around the rim of a small hoop with radius 0.0800 m and mass 0.180 kg. The free end of the string is pulled upward in just the right way so that the hoop does not move vertically as the string unwinds. (a) Find the tension in the string as the string unwinds. (b) Find the angular acceleration of the hoop as the string unwinds. (c) Find the upward acceleration of the hand that pulls on the free end of the string. (d) How would your answers be different if the hoop were replaced by a solid disk of the same mass and radius?

10.73. Starting from rest, a constant force $F = 100$ N is applied to the free end of a 50-m cable wrapped around the outer rim of a uniform solid cylinder, similar to the situation shown in Fig. 10.9(a). The cylinder has mass 4.00 kg and diameter 30.0 cm and is free to turn about a fixed, frictionless axle through its center. (a) How long does it take to unwrap all the cable, and how fast is the cable moving just as the last bit comes off? (b) Now suppose that the cylinder is replaced by a uniform hoop, with all other quantities remaining unchanged. In this case, would the answers in part (a) be larger or smaller? Explain.

10.74. A uniform marble rolls without slipping down the path shown in Fig. 10.59, starting from rest. (a) Find the minimum height h required for the marble not to fall into the pit. (b) The moment of inertia of the marble depends on its radius. Explain why the answer to part (a) does not depend on the radius of the marble. (c) Solve part (a) for a block that slides without friction instead of the rolling marble. How does the minimum h in this case compare to the answer in part (a)?

Figure 10.59 Problem 10.74

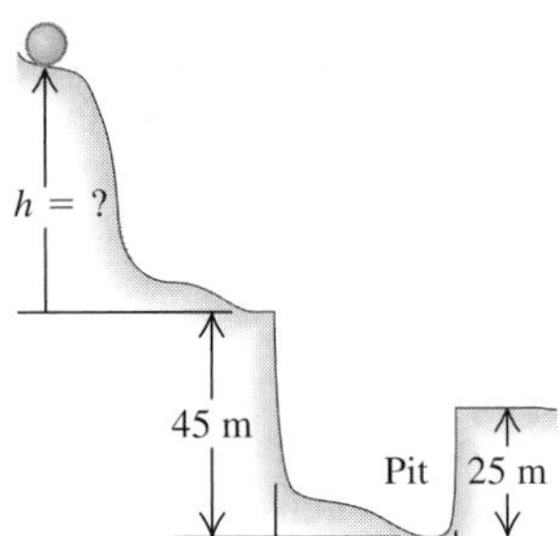

10.75. Rolling Stones. A solid, uniform, spherical boulder starts from rest and rolls down a 50.0-m-high hill, as shown in Fig. 10.60. The top half of the hill is rough enough to cause the boulder to roll without slipping, but the lower half is covered with ice and there is no friction. What is the translational speed of the boulder when it reaches the bottom of the hill?

Figure 10.60 Problem 10.75.

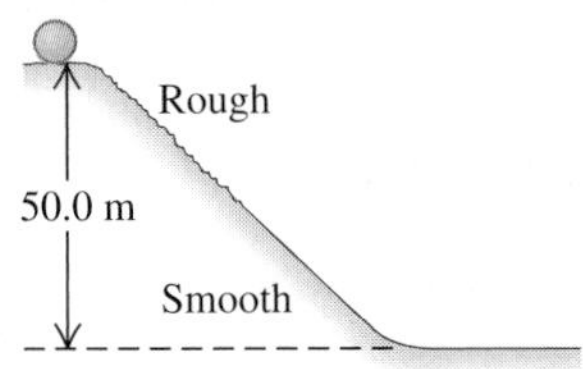

10.76. A solid, uniform ball rolls without slipping up a hill, as shown in Fig. 10.61. At the top of the hill, it is moving horizontally, and then it goes over the vertical cliff. (a) How far from the foot of the cliff does the ball land, and how fast is it

Figure 10.61 Problem 10.76.

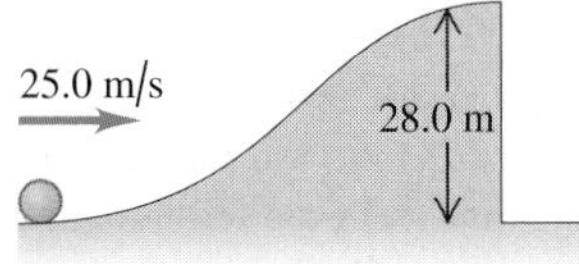

moving just before it lands? (b) Notice that when the balls lands, it has a greater translational speed than when it was at the bottom of the hill. Does this mean that the ball somehow gained energy? Explain!

10.77. A 42.0-cm-diameter wheel, consisting of a rim and six spokes, is constructed from a thin, rigid plastic material having a linear mass density of 25.0 g/cm. This wheel is released from rest at the top of a hill 58.0 m high. (a) How fast is it rolling when it reaches the bottom of the hill? (b) How would your answer change if the linear mass density and the diameter of the wheel were each doubled?

10.78. A high-wheel antique bicycle has a large front wheel with the foot-powered crank mounted on its axle and a small rear wheel turning independently of the front wheel; there is no chain connecting the wheels. The radius of the front wheel is 65.5 cm, and the radius of the rear wheel is 22.0 cm. Your modern bike has a wheel diameter of 66.0 cm (26 inches) and front and rear sprockets with radii of 11.0 cm and 5.5 cm, respectively. The rear sprocket is rigidly attached to the axle of the rear wheel. You ride your modern bike and turn the front sprocket at 1.00 rev/s. The wheels of both bikes roll along the ground without slipping. (a) What is your linear speed when you ride your modern bike? (b) At what rate must you turn the crank of the antique bike in order to travel at the same speed as in part (a)? (c) What then is the angular speed (in rev/s) of the small rear wheel of the antique bike?

10.79. In a lab experiment you let a uniform ball roll down a curved track. The ball starts from rest and rolls without slipping. While on the track, the ball descends a vertical distance h. The lower end of the track is horizontal and extends over the edge of the lab table; the ball leaves the track traveling horizontally. While free falling after leaving the track, the ball moves a horizontal distance x and a vertical distance y. (a) Calculate x in terms of h and y, ignoring the work done by friction. (b) Would the answer to part (a) be any different on the moon? (c) Although you do the experiment very carefully, your measured value of x is consistently a bit smaller than the value calculated in part (a). Why? (d) What would x be for the same h and y as in part (a) if you let a silver dollar roll down the track? You can ignore the work done by friction.

10.80. In a spring gun, a spring of force constant 400 N/m is compressed 0.15 m. When fired, 80.0% of the elastic potential energy stored in the spring is eventually converted into the kinetic energy of a 0.0590-kg uniform ball that is rolling without slipping at the base of a ramp. The ball continues to roll without slipping up the ramp with 90.0% of the kinetic energy at the bottom converted into an increase in gravitational potential energy at the instant it stops. (a) What is the speed of the ball's center of mass at the base of the ramp? (b) At this position, what is the speed of a point at the top of the ball? (c) At this position, what is the speed of a point at the bottom of the ball? (d) What maximum vertical height up the ramp does the ball move?

10.81. If a wheel rolls along a horizontal surface at constant speed, the coordinates of a certain point on the rim of the wheel are $x(t) = R[(2\pi t/T) - \sin(2\pi t/T)]$ and $y(t) = R[1 - \cos(2\pi t/T)]$, where R and T are constants. (a) Sketch the trajectory of the point from $t = 0$ to $t = 2T$. A curve with this shape is called a *cycloid.* (b) What are the meanings of the constants R and T? (c) Find the x- and y-components of the velocity and of the acceleration of the point at any time t. (d) Find the times at which the point is instantaneously at rest. What are the x- and y-components of the acceleration at these times? (e) Find the magnitude of the acceleration of the point. Does it depend on time? Compare to the magnitude of the acceleration of a particle in uniform circular motion, $a_{rad} = 4\pi^2R/T^2$. Explain your result for the magnitude of the acceleration of the point on the rolling wheel, using the idea that rolling is a combination of rotational and translational motion.

10.82. A child rolls a 0.600-kg basketball up a long ramp. The basketball can be considered a thin-walled, hollow sphere. When the child releases the basketball at the bottom of the ramp, it has a speed of 8.0 m/s. When the ball returns to her after rolling up the ramp and then rolling back down, it has a speed of 4.0 m/s. Assume the work done by friction on the basketball is the same when the ball moves up or down the ramp and that the basketball rolls without slipping. Find the maximum vertical height increase of the ball as it rolls up the ramp.

10.83. A uniform, solid cylinder with mass M and radius $2R$ rests on a horizontal tabletop. A string is attached by a yoke to a frictionless axle through the center of the cylinder so that the cylinder can rotate about the axle. The string runs over a disk-shaped pulley with mass M and radius R that is mounted on a frictionless axle through its center. A block of mass M is suspended from the free end of the string (Fig. 10.62). The string doesn't slip over the pulley surface, and the cylinder rolls without slipping on the tabletop. Find the magnitude of the acceleration of the block after the system is released from rest.

Figure **10.62** Problem 10.83.

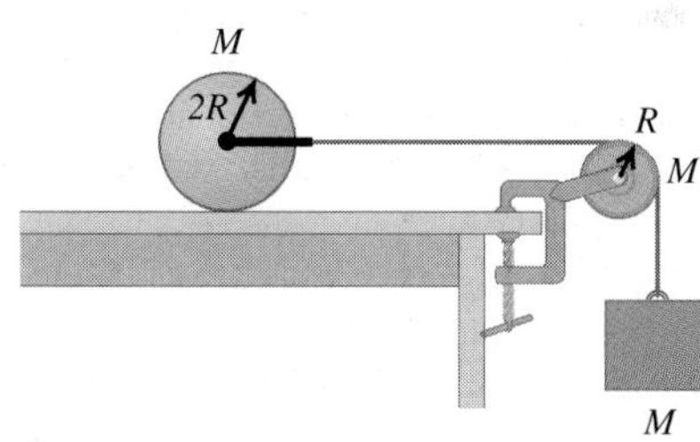

10.84. A uniform drawbridge 8.00 m long is attached to the roadway by a frictionless hinge at one end, and it can be raised by a cable attached to the other end. The bridge is at rest, suspended at 60.0° above the horizontal, when the cable suddenly breaks. (a) Find the angular acceleration of the drawbridge just after the cable breaks. (Gravity behaves as though it all acts at the center of mass.) (b) Could you use the equation $\omega = \omega_0 + \alpha t$ to calculate the angular speed of the drawbridge at a later time? Explain why. (c) What is the angular speed of the drawbridge as it becomes horizontal?

10.85. A 5.00-kg ball is dropped from a height of 12.0 m above one end of a uniform bar that pivots at its center. The bar has mass 8.00 kg and is 4.00 m in length. At the other end of the bar sits another 5.00-kg ball, unattached to the bar. The dropped ball sticks to the bar after the collision. How high will the other ball go after the collision?

10.86. A uniform, 0.0300-kg rod of length 0.400 m rotates in a horizontal plane about a fixed axis through its center and perpendicular to the rod. Two small rings, each with mass 0.0200 kg, are mounted so that they can slide along the rod. They are initially held by catches at positions 0.0500 m on each side of the center of the rod, and the system is rotating at 30.0 rev/min. With no other changes in the system, the catches are released, and the rings slide outward along the rod and fly off at the ends. (a) What is the angular speed of the system at the instant when the rings reach the ends of the rod? (b) What is the angular speed of the rod after the rings leave it?

10.87. A uniform rod of length L rests on a frictionless horizontal surface. The rod pivots about a fixed frictionless axis at one end. The rod is initially at rest. A bullet traveling parallel to the horizontal surface and perpendicular to the rod with speed v strikes the rod at its center and becomes embedded in it. The mass of the bullet is one-fourth the mass of the rod. (a) What is the final angular speed of the rod? (b) What is the ratio of the kinetic energy of the system after the collision to the kinetic energy of the bullet before the collision?

10.88. The solid wood door of a gymnasium is 1.00 m wide and 2.00 m high, has total mass 35.0 kg, and is hinged along one side. The door is open and at rest when a stray basketball hits the center of the door head-on, applying an average force of 1500 N to the door for 8.00 ms. Find the angular speed of the door after the impact. [*Hint:* Integrating Eq. (10.29) yields $\Delta L_z = \int_{t_1}^{t_2}(\sum\tau_z)\,dt = (\sum\tau_z)_{av}\Delta t$. The quantity $\int_{t_1}^{t_2}(\sum\tau_z)\,dt$ is called the angular impulse.]

10.89. A target in a shooting gallery consists of a vertical square wooden board, 0.250 m on a side and with mass 0.750 kg, that pivots on a horizontal axis along its top edge. The board is struck face-on at its center by a bullet with mass 1.90 g that is traveling at 360 m/s and that remains embedded in the board. (a) What is the angular speed of the board just after the bullet's impact? (b) What maximum height above the equilibrium position does the center of the board reach before starting to swing down again? (c) What minimum bullet speed would be required for the board to swing all the way over after impact?

10.90. Neutron Star Glitches. Occasionally, a rotating neutron star (see Exercise 10.39) undergoes a sudden and unexpected speedup called a *glitch*. One explanation is that a glitch occurs when the crust of the neutron star settles slightly, decreasing the moment of inertia about the rotation axis. A neutron star with angular speed $\omega_0 = 70.4$ rad/s underwent such a glitch in October 1975 that increased its angular speed to $\omega = \omega_0 + \Delta\omega$, where $\Delta\omega/\omega_0 = 2.01 \times 10^{-6}$. If the radius of the neutron star before the glitch was 11 km, by how much did its radius decrease in the starquake? Assume that the neutron star is a uniform sphere.

10.91. A 500.0-g bird is flying horizontally at 2.25 m/s, not paying much attention, when it suddenly flies into a stationary vertical bar, hitting it 25.0 cm below the top (Fig. 10.63). The bar is uniform, 0.750 m long, has a mass of 1.50 kg, and is hinged at its base. The collision stuns the bird so that it just drops to the ground afterward (but soon recovers to fly happily away). What is the angular velocity of the bar (a) just after it is hit by the bird, and (b) just as it reaches the ground?

Figure 10.63 Problem 10.91.

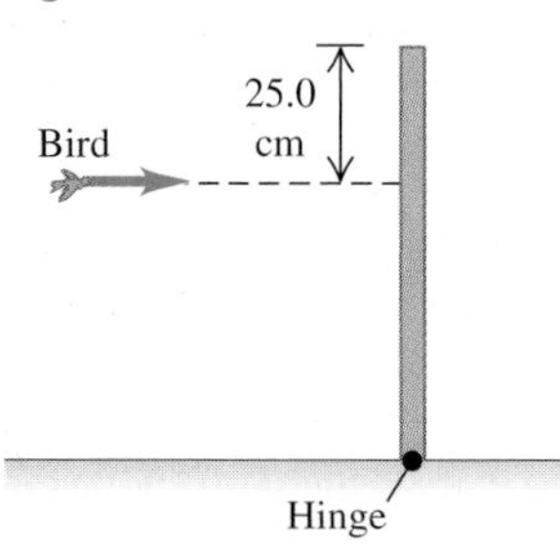

10.92. A small block with mass 0.250 kg is attached to a string passing through a hole in a frictionless, horizontal surface (see Fig. 10.48). The block is originally revolving in a circle with a radius of 0.800 m about the hole with a tangential speed of 4.00 m/s. The string is then pulled slowly from below, shortening the radius of the circle in which the block revolves. The breaking strength of the string is 30.0 N. What is the radius of the circle when the string breaks?

10.93. A horizontal plywood disk with mass 7.00 kg and diameter 1.00 m pivots on frictionless bearings about a vertical axis through its center. You attach a circular model-railroad track of negligible mass and average diameter 0.95 m to the disk. A 1.20-kg, battery-driven model train rests on the tracks. To demonstrate conservation of angular momentum, you switch on the train's engine. The train moves counterclockwise, soon attaining a constant speed of 0.600 m/s relative to the tracks. Find the magnitude and direction of the angular velocity of the disk relative to the earth.

10.94. A stiff uniform wire of mass M_0 and length L_0 is cut, bent, and the parts soldered together so that it forms a circular wheel having four identical spokes coming out from the center. None of the wire is wasted, and you can neglect the mass of the solder. (a) What is the moment of inertia of this wheel about an axle through its center perpendicular to the plane of the wheel? (b) If the wheel is given an initial spin with angular velocity ω_0. and stops uniformly in time T, what is the frictional torque at its axle?

10.95. In a physics laboratory you do the following ballistic pendulum experiment: You shoot a ball of mass m horizontally from a spring gun with a speed v. The ball is immediately caught a distance r below a frictionless pivot by a pivoted catcher assembly of mass M. The moment of inertia of this assembly about its rotation axis through the pivot is I. The distance r is much greater than the radius of the ball. (a) Use conservation of angular momentum to show that the angular speed of the ball and catcher just after the ball is caught is $\omega = mvr/(mr^2 + I)$. (b) After the ball is caught, the center of mass of the ball-catcher assembly system swings up with a maximum height increase h. Use conservation of energy to show that $\omega = \sqrt{2(M + m)gh/(mr^2 + I)}$. (c) Your lab partner says that linear momentum is conserved in the collision and derives the expression $mv = (m + M)V$, where V is the speed of the ball immediately after the collision. She then uses conservation of energy to derive that $V = \sqrt{2gh}$, so that $mv = (m + M)\sqrt{2gh}$. Use the results of parts (a) and (b) to show that this equation is satisfied only for the special case when r is given by $I = Mr^2$.

10.96. A 55-kg runner runs around the edge of a horizontal turntable mounted on a vertical, frictionless axis through its center. The runner's velocity relative to the earth has magnitude 2.8 m/s. The turntable is rotating in the opposite direction with an angular velocity of magnitude 0.20 rad/s relative to the earth. The radius of the turntable is 3.0 m, and its moment of inertia about the axis of rotation is 80 kg · m². Find the final angular velocity of the system if the runner comes to rest relative to the turntable. (You can model the runner as a particle.)

10.97. Recession of the Moon. Careful measurements of the earth–moon separation indicate that our satellite is presently moving away from us at approximately 3.0 cm per year. Neglect any angular momentum that the moon might be transferred from the earth to the moon. Calculate the rate of change (in rad/s per year) of the moon's angular velocity around the earth (consult Appendix E and the astronomical data in Appendix F). Is its angular velocity increasing or decreasing? (*Hint:* If L = constant, then $dL/dt = 0$.)

10.98. Center of Percussion. A baseball bat rests on a frictionless, horizontal surface. The bat has a length of 0.900 m, a mass of 0.800 kg, and its center of mass is 0.600 m from the handle end of the bat (Fig. 10.64). The moment of inertia of the bat about its center of mass is 0.0530 kg · m². The bat is struck by a baseball traveling perpendicular to the bat. The impact applies an impulse $J = \int_{t_1}^{t_2} F\,dt$ at a point a distance x from the handle end of the bat. What must x be so that the handle end of the bat remains at rest as the bat begins to move? [*Hint:* Consider the motion of the center of mass and the rotation about the center of mass. Find x so that these two motions combine to give $v = 0$ for the end of the bat just after the collision. Also, note that integration of Eq. (10.29) gives

$\Delta L = \int_{t_1}^{t_2}(\Sigma\tau)\,dt$ (see Problem 10.88).] The point on the bat you have located is called the *center of percussion.* Hitting a pitched ball at the center of percussion of the bat minimizes the "sting" the batter experiences on the hands.

Figure 10.64 Problem 10.98.

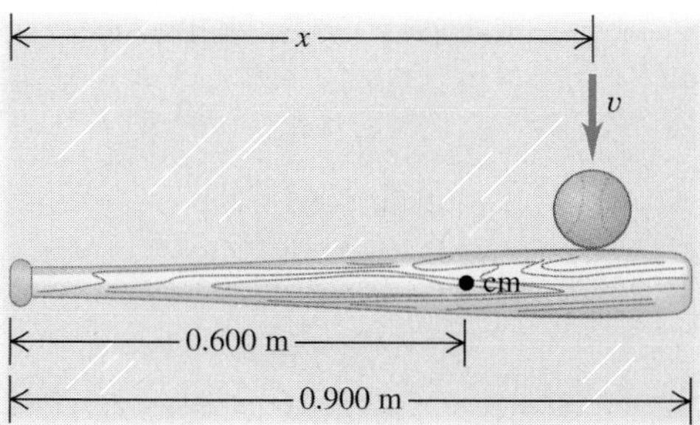

10.99. Consider a gyroscope with an axis that is not horizontal but is inclined from the horizontal by an angle β. Show that the precession angular frequency does not depend on the value of β but is given by Eq. (10.33).

Challenge Problems

10.100. A uniform ball of radius R rolls without slipping between two rails such that the horizontal distance is d between the two contact points of the rails to the ball. (a) In a sketch, show that at any instant $v_{cm} = \omega\sqrt{R^2 - d^2/4}$. Discuss this expression in the limits $d = 0$ and $d = 2R$. (b) For a uniform ball starting from rest and descending a vertical distance h while rolling without slipping down a ramp, $v_{cm} = \sqrt{10gh/7}$. Replacing the ramp with the two rails, show that

$$v_{cm} = \sqrt{\frac{10gh}{5 + 2/(1 - d^2/4R^2)}}$$

In each case, the work done by friction has been ignored. (c) Which speed in part (b) is smaller? Why? Answer in terms of how the loss of potential energy is shared between the gain in translational and rotational kinetic energies. (d) For which value of the ratio d/R do the two expressions for the speed in part (b) differ by 5.0%? By 0.50%?

10.101. When an object is rolling without slipping, the rolling friction force is much less than the friction force when the object is sliding; a silver dollar will roll on its edge much farther than it will slide on its flat side (see Section 5.3). When an object is rolling without slipping on a horizontal surface, we can approximate the friction force to be zero, so that a_x and α_z are approximately zero and v_x and ω_z are approximately constant. Rolling without slipping means $v_x = r\omega_z$ and $a_x = r\alpha_z$. If an object is set in motion on a surface *without* these equalities, sliding (kinetic) friction will act on the object as it slips until rolling without slipping is established. A solid cylinder with mass M and radius R, rotating with angular speed ω_0 about an axis through its center, is set on a horizontal surface for which the kinetic friction coefficient is μ_k. (a) Draw a free-body diagram for the cylinder on the surface. Think carefully about the direction of the kinetic friction force on the cylinder. Calculate the accelerations a_x of the center of mass and α_z of rotation about the center of mass. (b) The cylinder is initially slipping completely, so initially $\omega_z = \omega_0$ but $v_x = 0$. Rolling without slipping sets in when $v_x = R\omega_z$. Calculate the *distance* the cylinder rolls before slipping stops. (c) Calculate the work done by the friction force on the cylinder as it moves from where it was set down to where it begins to roll without slipping.

10.102. A demonstration gyroscope wheel is constructed by removing the tire from a bicycle wheel 0.650 m in diameter, wrapping lead wire around the rim, and taping it in place. The shaft projects 0.200 m at each side of the wheel, and a woman holds the ends of the shaft in her hands. The mass of the system is 8.00 kg; its entire mass may be assumed to be located at its rim. The shaft is horizontal, and the wheel is spinning about the shaft at 5.00 rev/s. Find the magnitude and direction of the force each hand exerts on the shaft (a) when the shaft is at rest; (b) when the shaft is rotating in a horizontal plane about its center at 0.050 rev/s; (c) when the shaft is rotating in a horizontal plane about its center at 0.300 rev/s. (d) At what rate must the shaft rotate in order that it may be supported at one end only?

10.103. A block with mass m is revolving with linear speed v_1 in a circle of radius r_1 on a frictionless horizontal surface (see Fig. 10.48). The string is slowly pulled from below until the radius of the circle in which the block is revolving is reduced to r_2. (a) Calculate the tension T in the string as a function of r, the distance of the block from the hole. Your answer will be in terms of the initial velocity v_1 and the radius r_1. (b) Use $W = \int_{r_1}^{r_2}\vec{T}(r)\cdot d\vec{r}$ to calculate the work done by $\vec{T}$ when r changes from r_1 to r_2. (c) Compare the results of part (b) to the change in the kinetic energy of the block.

11 EQUILIBRIUM AND ELASTICITY

LEARNING GOALS

By studying this chapter, you will learn:

- The conditions that must be satisfied for a body or structure to be in equilibrium.
- What is meant by the center of gravity of a body, and how it relates to the body's stability.
- How to solve problems that involve rigid bodies in equilibrium.
- How to analyze situations in which a body is deformed by tension, compression, pressure, or shear.
- What happens when a body is stretched so much that it deforms or breaks.

? This Roman aqueduct uses the principle of the arch to sustain the weight of the structure and the water it carries. Are the blocks that make up the arch being compressed, stretched, or a combination?

We've devoted a good deal of effort to understanding why and how bodies accelerate in response to the forces that act on them. But very often we're interested in making sure that bodies *don't* accelerate. Any building, from a multistory skyscraper to the humblest shed, must be designed so that it won't topple over. Similar concerns arise with a suspension bridge, a ladder leaning against a wall, or a crane hoisting a bucket full of concrete.

A body that can be modeled as a *particle* is in equilibrium whenever the vector sum of the forces acting on it is zero. But for the situations we've just described, that condition isn't enough. If forces act at different points on an extended body, an additional requirement must be satisfied to ensure that the body has no tendency to *rotate:* The sum of the *torques* about any point must be zero. This requirement is based on the principles of rotational dynamics developed in Chapter 10. We can compute the torque due to the weight of a body using the concept of center of gravity, which we introduce in this chapter.

Rigid bodies don't bend, stretch, or squash when forces act on them. But the rigid body is an idealization; all real materials are *elastic* and do deform to some extent. Elastic properties of materials are tremendously important. You want the wings of an airplane to be able to bend a little, but you'd rather not have them break off. The steel frame of an earthquake-resistant building has to be able to flex, but not too much. Many of the necessities of everyday life, from rubber bands to suspension bridges, depend on the elastic properties of materials. In this chapter we'll introduce the concepts of *stress, strain,* and *elastic modulus* and a simple principle called *Hooke's law* that helps us predict what deformations will occur when forces are applied to a real (not perfectly rigid) body.

11.1 Conditions for Equilibrium

We learned in Sections 4.2 and 5.1 that a particle is in *equilibrium*—that is, the particle does not accelerate—in an inertial frame of reference if the vector sum of all the forces acting on the particle is zero, $\sum \vec{F} = \mathbf{0}$. For an *extended* body, the equivalent statement is that the center of mass of the body has zero acceleration if the vector sum of all external forces acting on the body is zero, as discussed in Section 8.5. This is often called the **first condition for equilibrium.** In vector and component forms,

$$\sum \vec{F} = \mathbf{0}$$

$$\sum F_x = 0 \qquad \sum F_y = 0 \qquad \sum F_z = 0 \qquad \text{(first condition for equilibrium)} \qquad (11.1)$$

where the sum includes *external* forces only.

A second condition for an extended body to be in equilibrium is that the body must have no tendency to *rotate.* This condition is based on the dynamics of rotational motion in exactly the same way that the first condition is based on Newton's first law. A rigid body that, in an inertial frame, is not rotating about a certain point has zero angular momentum about that point. If it is not to start rotating about that point, the rate of change of angular momentum must *also* be zero. From the discussion in Section 10.5, particularly Eq. (10.29), this means that the sum of torques due to all the external forces acting on the body must be zero. A rigid body in equilibrium can't have any tendency to start rotating about *any* point, so the sum of external torques must be zero about any point. This is the **second condition for equilibrium:**

$$\sum \vec{\tau} = \mathbf{0} \quad \text{about any point} \qquad \text{(second condition for equilibrium)} \qquad (11.2)$$

The sum of the torques due to all external forces acting on the body, with respect to any specified point, must be zero.

In this chapter we will apply the first and second conditions for equilibrium to situations in which a rigid body is at rest (no translation or rotation). Such a body is said to be in **static equilibrium** (Fig. 11.1). But the same conditions apply to a rigid body in uniform *translational* motion (without rotation), such as an airplane in flight with constant speed, direction, and altitude. Such a body is in equilibrium but is not static.

11.1 To be in static equilibrium, a body at rest must satisfy *both* conditions for equilibrium: It can have no tendency to accelerate as a whole or to start rotating.

(a) This body is in static equilibrium.

Equilibrium conditions:

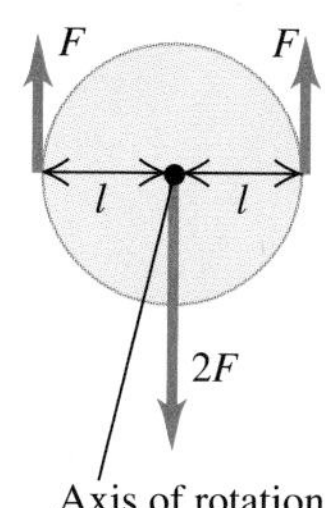

First condition satisfied: Net force = 0, so body at rest has no tendency to start moving as a whole.

Second condition satisfied: Net torque about the axis = 0, so body at rest has no tendency to start rotating.

(b) This body has no tendency to accelerate as a whole, but it has a tendency to start rotating.

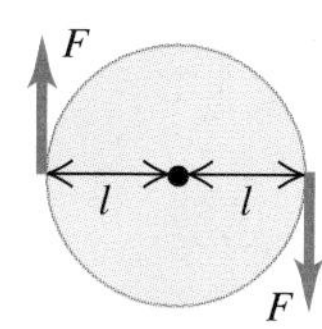

First condition satisfied: Net force = 0, so body at rest has no tendency to start moving as a whole.

Second condition NOT satisfied: There is a net clockwise torque about the axis, so body at rest will start rotating clockwise.

(c) This body has a tendency to accelerate as a whole but no tendency to start rotating.

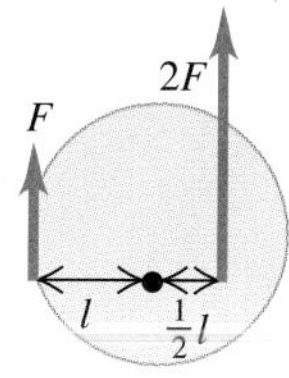

First condition NOT satisfied: There is a net upward force, so body at rest will start moving upward.

Second condition satisfied: Net torque about the axis = 0 so body at rest has no tendency to start rotating.

Test Your Understanding of Section 11.1 Which situation satisfies both the first and second conditions for equilibrium? (i) a seagull gliding at a constant angle below the horizontal and at a constant speed; (ii) an automobile crankshaft turning at an increasing angular speed in the engine of a parked car; (iii) a thrown baseball that does not rotate as it sails through the air.

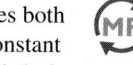

11.2 Center of Gravity

In most equilibrium problems, one of the forces acting on the body is its weight. We need to be able to calculate the *torque* of this force. The weight doesn't act at a single point; it is distributed over the entire body. But we can always calculate the torque due to the body's weight by assuming that the entire force of gravity (weight) is concentrated at a point called the **center of gravity** (abbreviated "cg"). The acceleration due to gravity decreases with altitude; but if we can ignore this variation over the vertical dimension of the body, then the body's center of gravity is identical to its *center of mass* (abbreviated "cm"), which we defined in Section 8.5. We stated this result without proof in Section 10.2, and now we'll prove it.

7.2 A Tilted Beam: Torques and Equilibrium

7.3 Arm Levers

First let's review the definition of the center of mass. For a collection of particles with masses $m_1, m_2, \ldots$ and coordinates $(x_1, y_1, z_1), (x_2, y_2, z_2), \ldots$, the coordinates x_{cm}, y_{cm}, and z_{cm} of the center of mass are given by

$$x_{cm} = \frac{m_1x_1 + m_2x_2 + m_3x_3 + \cdots}{m_1 + m_2 + m_3 + \cdots} = \frac{\sum_i m_ix_i}{\sum_i m_i}$$

$$y_{cm} = \frac{m_1y_1 + m_2y_2 + m_3y_3 + \cdots}{m_1 + m_2 + m_3 + \cdots} = \frac{\sum_i m_iy_i}{\sum_i m_i} \quad \text{(center of mass)} \quad (11.3)$$

$$z_{cm} = \frac{m_1z_1 + m_2z_2 + m_3z_3 + \cdots}{m_1 + m_2 + m_3 + \cdots} = \frac{\sum_i m_iz_i}{\sum_i m_i}$$

Also, x_{cm}, y_{cm}, and z_{cm} are the components of the position vector $\vec{r}_{cm}$ of the center of mass, so Eqs. (11.3) are equivalent to the vector equation

$$\vec{r}_{cm} = \frac{m_1\vec{r}_1 + m_2\vec{r}_2 + m_3\vec{r}_3 + \cdots}{m_1 + m_2 + m_3 + \cdots} = \frac{\sum_i m_i\vec{r}_i}{\sum_i m_i} \quad (11.4)$$

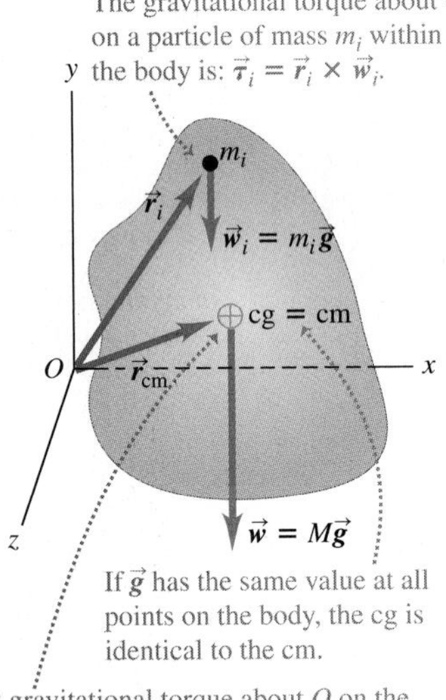
The gravitational torque about O on a particle of mass m_i within the body is: $\vec{\tau}_i = \vec{r}_i \times \vec{w}_i$.
y
m_i
$\vec{r}_i$
$\vec{w}_i = m_i\vec{g}$
cg = cm
O
$\vec{r}_{cm}$
x
z
$\vec{w} = M\vec{g}$
If $\vec{g}$ has the same value at all points on the body, the cg is identical to the cm.
The net gravitational torque about O on the entire body can be found by assuming that all the weight acts at the cg: $\vec{\tau} = \vec{r}_{cm} \times \vec{w}$.

11.2 The center of gravity (cg) and center of mass (cm) of an extended body.

Now let's consider the gravitational torque on a body of arbitrary shape (Fig. 11.2). We assume that the acceleration due to gravity $\vec{g}$ has the same magnitude and direction at every point in the body. Every particle in the body experiences a gravitational force, and the total weight of the body is the vector sum of a large number of parallel forces. A typical particle has mass m_i and weight $\vec{w}_i = m_i\vec{g}$. If $\vec{r}_i$ is the position vector of this particle with respect to an arbitrary origin O, then the torque vector $\vec{\tau}_i$ of the weight $\vec{w}_i$ with respect to O is, from Eq. (10.3),

$$\vec{\tau}_i = \vec{r}_i \times \vec{w}_i = \vec{r}_i \times m_i\vec{g}$$

The *total* torque due to the gravitational forces on all the particles is

$$\begin{aligned}\vec{\tau} &= \sum_i \vec{\tau}_i = \vec{r}_1 \times m_1\vec{g} + \vec{r}_2 \times m_2\vec{g} + \cdots \\ &= (m_1\vec{r}_1 + m_2\vec{r}_2 + \cdots) \times \vec{g} \\ &= \left(\sum_i m_i\vec{r}_i\right) \times \vec{g}\end{aligned}$$

When we multiply and divide this by the total mass of the body,

$$M = m_1 + m_2 + \cdots = \sum_i m_i$$

we get

$$\vec{\tau} = \frac{m_1\vec{r}_1 + m_2\vec{r}_2 + \cdots}{m_1 + m_2 + \cdots} \times M\vec{g} = \frac{\sum_i m_i\vec{r}_i}{\sum_i m_i} \times M\vec{g}$$

The fraction in this equation is just the position vector $\vec{r}_{cm}$ of the center of mass, with components x_{cm}, y_{cm}, and z_{cm}, as given by Eq. (11.4), and $M\vec{g}$ is equal to the total weight $\vec{w}$ of the body. Thus

$$\vec{\tau} = \vec{r}_{cm} \times M\vec{g} = \vec{r}_{cm} \times \vec{w} \quad (11.5)$$

The total gravitational torque, given by Eq. (11.5), is the same as though the total weight $\vec{w}$ were acting on the position $\vec{r}_{cm}$ of the center of mass, which we also call the *center of gravity.* **If $\vec{g}$ has the same value at all points on a body, its center of gravity is identical to its center of mass.** Note, however, that the center of mass is defined independently of any gravitational effect.

While the value of $\vec{g}$ does vary somewhat with elevation, the variation is extremely slight (Fig. 11.3). Hence we will assume throughout this chapter that the center of gravity and center of mass are identical unless explicitly stated otherwise.

11.3 The acceleration due to gravity at the bottom of the 452-m-tall Petronas Towers in Malaysia is only 0.014% greater than at the top. The center of gravity of the towers is only about 2 cm below the center of mass.

Finding and Using the Center of Gravity

We can often use symmetry considerations to locate the center of gravity of a body, just as we did for the center of mass. The center of gravity of a homogeneous sphere, cube, circular sheet, or rectangular plate is at its geometric center. The center of gravity of a right circular cylinder or cone is on its axis of symmetry.

For a body with a more complex shape, we can sometimes locate the center of gravity by thinking of the body as being made of symmetrical pieces. For example, we could approximate the human body as a collection of solid cylinders, with a sphere for the head. Then we can compute the coordinates of the center of gravity of the combination from Eqs. (11.3), letting $m_1, m_2, \ldots$ be the masses of the individual pieces and $(x_1, y_1, z_1), (x_2, y_2, z_2), \ldots$ be the coordinates of their centers of gravity.

When a body acted on by gravity is supported or suspended at a single point, the center of gravity is always at or directly above or below the point of suspension. If it were anywhere else, the weight would have a torque with respect to the point of suspension, and the body could not be in rotational equilibrium. Figure 11.4 shows how to use this fact to determine experimentally the location of the center of gravity of an irregular body.

Using the same reasoning, we can see that a body supported at several points must have its center of gravity somewhere within the area bounded by the supports. This explains why a car can drive on a straight but slanted road if the slant angle is relatively small (Fig. 11.5a) but will tip over if the angle is too steep (Fig. 11.5b). The truck in Fig. 11.5c has a higher center of gravity than the car and will tip over on a shallower incline. When a truck overturns on a highway and blocks traffic for hours, it's the high center of gravity that's to blame.

The lower the center of gravity and the larger the area of support, the more difficult it is to overturn a body. Four-legged animals such as deer and horses have a large area of support bounded by their legs; hence they are naturally stable and need only small feet or hooves. Animals that walk erect on two legs, such as

11.4 Finding the center of gravity of an irregularly shaped body—in this case, a coffee mug.

What is the center of gravity of this mug?
① Suspend the mug from any point. A vertical line extending down from the point of suspension passes through the center of gravity.
② Now suspend the mug from a different point. A vertical line extending down from this point intersects the first line at the center of gravity (which is inside the mug).
Center of gravity

11.5 In (a) the center of gravity is within the area bounded by the supports, and the car is in equilibrium. The car in (b) and the truck in (c) will tip over because their centers of gravity lie outside the area of support.

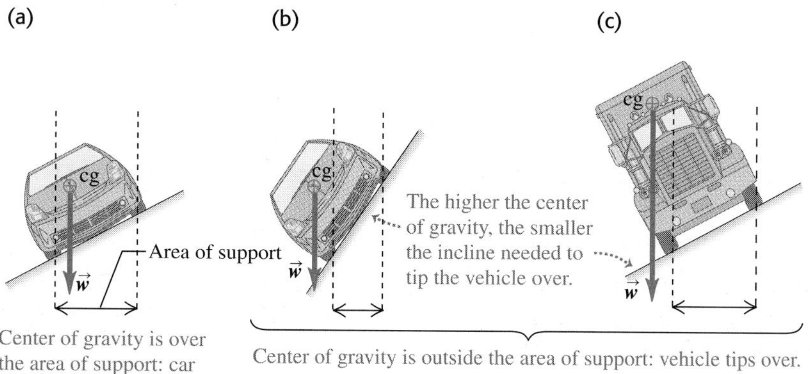

humans and birds, need relatively large feet to give them a reasonable area of support. If a two-legged animal holds its body approximately horizontal, like a chicken or the dinosaur *Tyrannosaurus rex,* it must perform a delicate balancing act as it walks to keep its center of gravity over the foot that is on the ground. A chicken does this by moving its head; *T. rex* probably did it by moving its massive tail.

Example 11.1 Walking the plank

A uniform wooden plank of length $L = 6.0$ m and mass $M = 90$ kg rests on top of two sawhorses separated by $D = 1.5$ m, located equal distances from the center of the plank. Your cousin Throckmorton tries to stand on the right-hand end of the plank. If the plank is to remain at rest, how massive can Throckmorton be?

SOLUTION

IDENTIFY: If the system of plank and Throckmorton is just in balance, the center of gravity of this system will be directly over the right-hand sawhorse (just barely within the area bounded by the two supports). The target variable is Throcky's mass.

SET UP: Figure 11.6 shows our sketch. We take the origin at C, the geometric center and center of gravity of the uniform plank, and take the positive x-axis to point horizontally to the right. Then the x-coordinates of the centers of gravity of the plank (mass M) and Throcky (unknown mass m) are $x_P = 0$ and $x_T = L/2 = 3.0$ m, respectively. We will use Eqs. (11.3) to locate the center of gravity of the system of plank and Throcky.

11.6 Our sketch for this problem.

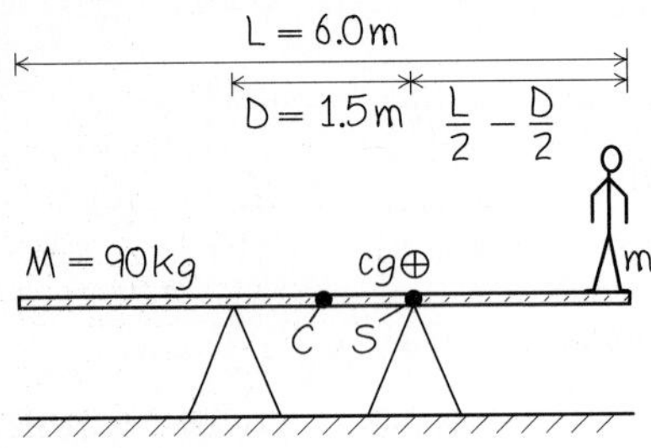

EXECUTE: From the first of Eqs. (11.3),

$$x_{cg} = \frac{M(0) + m(L/2)}{M + m} = \frac{m}{M + m}\frac{L}{2}$$

Setting this equal to $D/2$, the x-coordinate of the right-hand sawhorse, we have

$$\frac{m}{M + m}\frac{L}{2} = \frac{D}{2}$$

$$mL = (M + m)D$$

$$m = M\frac{D}{L - D} = (90\text{ kg})\frac{1.5\text{ m}}{6.0\text{ m} - 1.5\text{ m}}$$

$$= 30\text{ kg}$$

EVALUATE: To check our result, let's repeat the calculation with a different choice of origin. Now we take the origin to be at S, the position of the right-hand sawhorse, so that $x_{cg} = 0$. The centers of gravity of the plank and Throcky are now at $x_P = -D/2$ and $x_T = (L/2) - (D/2)$, respectively, so

$$x_{cg} = \frac{M(-D/2) + m[(L/2) - (D/2)]}{M + m} = 0$$

$$m = \frac{MD/2}{(L/2) - (D/2)} = M\frac{D}{L - D} = 30\text{ kg}$$

The mass doesn't depend on our arbitrary choice of origin.

A 60-kg child could stand only halfway between the right-hand sawhorse and the end of the plank. Can you see why?

11.7 At what point will the meter stick with rock attached be in balance?

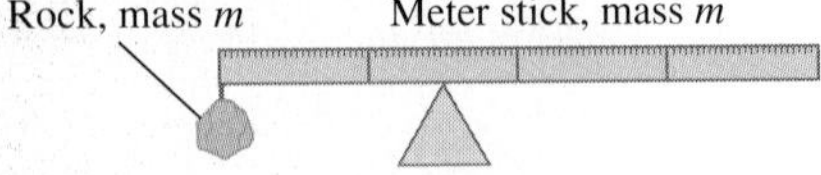

Test Your Understanding of Section 11.2 A rock is attached to the left end of a uniform meter stick that has the same mass as the rock. In order for the combination of rock and meter stick to balance atop the triangular object in Fig. 11.7, how far from the left end of the stick should the triangular object be placed? (i) less than 0.25 m; (ii) 0.25 m; (iii) between 0.25 m and 0.50 m; (iv) 0.50 m; (v) more than 0.50 m.

ActivPhysics ONLINE

7.4 Two Painters on a Beam

7.5 Lecturing from a Beam

11.3 Solving Rigid-Body Equilibrium Problems

There are just two key conditions for rigid-body equilibrium: The vector sum of the forces on the body must be zero, and the sum of the torques about any point must be zero. To keep things simple, we'll restrict our attention to situations in which we can treat all forces as acting in a single plane, which we'll call the xy-plane. Then we can ignore the condition $\sum F_z = 0$ in Eqs. (11.1), and in Eq. (11.2) we need consider only the z-components of torque (perpendicular to the plane). The first and second conditions for equilibrium are then

$$\sum F_x = 0 \quad \text{and} \quad \sum F_y = 0 \quad \text{(first condition for equilibrium, forces in } xy\text{-plane)}$$
$$\sum \tau_z = 0 \quad \text{(second condition for equilibrium, forces in } xy\text{-plane)} \tag{11.6}$$

CAUTION **Choosing the reference point for calculating torques** In equilibrium problems, the choice of reference point for calculating torques in $\sum \tau_z$ is completely arbitrary. But once you make your choice, you must use the *same* point to calculate *all* the torques on a body. It helps to pick the point so as to simplify the calculations as much as possible.

The challenge is to apply these simple conditions to specific problems. Problem-Solving Strategy 11.1 is very similar to the suggestions given in Section 5.2 for the equilibrium of a particle. You should compare it with Problem-Solving Strategy 10.1 (Section 10.2) for rotational dynamics problems.

Problem-Solving Strategy 11.1 Equilibrium of a Rigid Body

IDENTIFY *the relevant concepts:* The first and second conditions for equilibrium are useful whenever there is a rigid body that is not rotating and not accelerating in space.

SET UP *the problem* using the following steps:

1. Draw a sketch of the physical situation, including dimensions, and select the body in equilibrium to be analyzed.
2. Draw a free-body diagram showing the forces acting *on* the selected body and no others. *Do not* include forces exerted *by* this body on other bodies. Be careful to show correctly the point at which each force acts; this is crucial for correct torque calculations. You can't represent a rigid body as a point.
3. Choose coordinate axes and specify a positive direction of rotation for torques. Represent forces in terms of their components with respect to the axes you have chosen; when you do this, cross out the original force so that you don't include it twice.
4. In choosing a point about which to compute torques, note that if a force has a line of action that goes *through* a particular point, the torque of the force with respect to that point is zero. You can often eliminate unknown forces or components from the torque equation by a clever choice of point for your calculation. The body doesn't actually have to be pivoted about an axis through the chosen point.

EXECUTE *the solution* as follows:

1. Write equations expressing the equilibrium conditions. Remember that $\sum F_x = 0$, $\sum F_y = 0$, and $\sum \tau_z = 0$ are always separate equations; *never* add x- and y-components in a single equation. Also remember that when a force is represented in terms of its components, you can compute the torque of that force by finding the torque of each component separately, each with its appropriate lever arm and sign, and adding the results. This is often easier than determining the lever arm of the original force.
2. You always need as many equations as you have unknowns. Depending on the number of unknowns, you may need to compute torques with respect to two or more axes to obtain enough equations. Often, there are several equally good sets of force and torque equations for a particular problem; there is usually no single "right" combination of equations.

EVALUATE *your answer:* A useful way to check your results is to rewrite the second condition for equilibrium, $\sum \tau_z = 0$, using a different choice of origin. If you've done everything correctly, you'll get the same answers using this new choice of origin as you did with your original choice.

Example 11.2 Weight distribution for a car

An auto magazine reports that a certain sports car has 53% of its weight on the front wheels and 47% on its rear wheels, with a 2.46-m wheelbase. This means that the total normal force on the front wheels is $0.53w$ and that on the rear wheels is $0.47w$, where w is the total weight. The wheelbase is the distance between the front and rear axles. How far in front of the rear axle is the car's center of gravity?

SOLUTION

IDENTIFY: We can use the two conditions for equilibrium, since the car is assumed to be at rest. The conditions also apply when the car is traveling in a straight line at constant speed, since the net force and net torque on the car are also zero in that situation. The target variable is the coordinate of the car's center of gravity.

Continued

SET UP: Figure 11.8 shows our sketch and a free-body diagram for the car, including x- and y-axes and our convention that counterclockwise torques are positive. The weight w acts at the center of gravity. The distance we want is L_{cg}; this is the lever arm of the weight with respect to the rear axle R, so it is reasonable to take torques with respect to R. The torque due to the weight is negative because it tends to cause a clockwise rotation about R. The torque due to the upward normal force at the front axle F is positive because it tends to cause a counterclockwise rotation about R.

11.8 Our sketches for this problem.

(a)

(b)

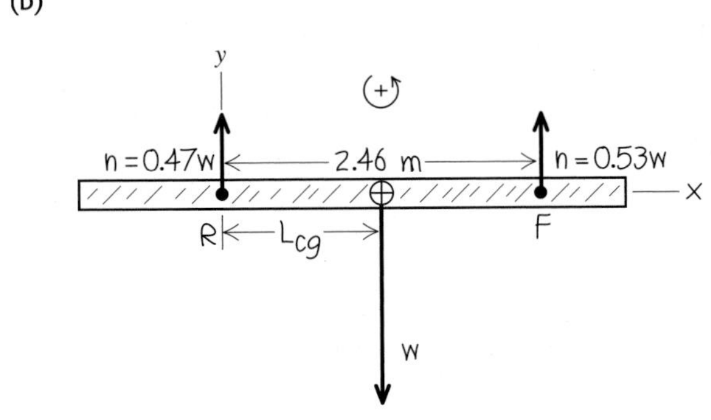

EXECUTE: You can see from Fig. 11.8b that the first condition for equilibrium is satisfied: $\sum F_x = 0$ because there aren't any x-components of force and $\sum F_y = 0$ because $0.47w + 0.53w + (-w) = 0$. The force equation doesn't involve the target variable L_{cg}, so we must solve for it using the torque equation for point R:

$$\sum \tau_R = 0.47w(0) - wL_{cg} + 0.53w(2.46\ \text{m}) = 0$$
$$L_{cg} = 1.30\ \text{m}$$

EVALUATE: Note that the cg is between the two supports, as it must be (see Section 11.2). You can check the numerical result for the cg position by writing the torque equation about the front axle F. You'll find that the cg is 1.16 m behind the front axle, or $(2.46\ \text{m}) - (1.16\ \text{m}) = 1.30\ \text{m}$ in front of the rear axle.

You can show that if f is the fraction of the weight on the front wheels and d is the wheelbase, the center of gravity is a distance fd in front of the rear wheels. The farther back the center of gravity, the smaller the value of fd and the smaller the fraction of weight on the front wheels. That's why owners of rear-wheel-drive vehicles put bags of sand in their trunks to improve traction on snow and ice. Would this strategy help with a front-wheel-drive car?

Example 11.3 A heroic rescue

Sir Lancelot is trying to rescue the Lady Elayne from Castle Von Doom by climbing a uniform ladder that is 5.0 m long and weighs 180 N. Lancelot, who weighs 800 N, stops a third of the way up the ladder (Fig. 11.9a). The bottom of the ladder rests on a horizontal stone ledge and leans across the moat in equilibrium against a vertical wall that is frictionless because of a thick layer of moss. The ladder makes an angle of 53.1° with the horizontal, conveniently forming a 3-4-5 right triangle. (a) Find the normal and friction forces on the ladder at its base. (b) Find the minimum coefficient of static friction needed to prevent slipping at the base. (c) Find the magnitude and direction of the contact force on the ladder at the base.

SOLUTION

IDENTIFY: The system of ladder and Lancelot is stationary, so we can use the two conditions for equilibrium to solve part (a). In part (b), we also need the relationship given in Section 5.3 among the static friction force, the coefficient of static friction, and the normal force. The contact force asked for in part (c) is the vector sum of the normal and friction forces acting at the base of the ladder, which we find in part (a).

SET UP: Figure 11.9b shows the free-body diagram for the system of the ladder and Lancelot. We choose the x- and y-directions as shown and take counterclockwise torques to be positive. The ladder is uniform, so its center of gravity is at its geometric center. Lancelot's 800-N weight acts at a point on the ladder one-third of the way from the base toward the wall.

The frictionless wall exerts only a normal force n_1 at the top of the ladder. The forces at the base are the upward normal force n_2 and the static friction force f_s, which must point to the right to prevent slipping; the magnitudes n_2 and f_s are the target variables in part (a). From Eq. (5.6), these magnitudes are related by $f_s \le \mu_s n_2$, where μ_s is the coefficient of static friction, the target variable in part (b).

EXECUTE: (a) From Eqs. (11.6), the first condition for equilibrium gives

$$\sum F_x = f_s + (-n_1) = 0$$
$$\sum F_y = n_2 + (-800\ \text{N}) + (-180\ \text{N}) = 0$$

These are two equations for the three unknowns n_1, n_2, and f_s. The first equation tells us that the two horizontal forces must be equal and opposite, and the second equation gives

$$n_2 = 980\ \text{N}$$

The ground pushes up with a force of 980 N to balance the total (downward) weight $(800\ \text{N} + 180\ \text{N})$.

We don't yet have enough equations, but now we can use the second condition for equilibrium. We can take torques about any point we choose. The smart choice is point B, which gives us the fewest terms and fewest unknowns in the torque equation. That's because the two forces n_2 and f_s have no torque about that point. From Fig. 11.9b we see that the lever arm for the ladder's weight is 1.5 m, the lever arm for Lancelot's weight is 1.0 m, and the lever arm for n_1 is 4.0 m. The torque equation for point B is

$$\sum \tau_B = n_1(4.0\ \text{m}) - (180\ \text{N})(1.5\ \text{m}) - (800\ \text{N})(1.0\ \text{m}) + n_2(0) + f_s(0) = 0$$

Solving for n_1, we get $n_1 = 268\ \text{N}$. We now substitute this back into the $\sum F_x = 0$ equation to get

$$f_s = 268\ \text{N}$$

(b) The static friction force f_s cannot exceed $\mu_s n_2$, so the *minimum* coefficient of static friction to prevent slipping is

$$(\mu_s)_{min} = \frac{f_s}{n_2} = \frac{268\text{ N}}{980\text{ N}} = 0.27$$

(c) The components of the contact force $\vec{F}_B$ at the base are the static friction force f_s and the normal force n_2, so

$$\vec{F}_B = f_s\hat{\imath} + n_2\hat{\jmath} = (268\text{ N})\hat{\imath} + (980\text{ N})\hat{\jmath}$$

The magnitude and direction of $\vec{F}_B$ (Fig. 11.9c) are then

$$F_B = \sqrt{(268\text{ N})^2 + (980\text{ N})^2} = 1020\text{ N}$$

$$\theta = \arctan\frac{980\text{ N}}{268\text{ N}} = 75°$$

EVALUATE: As Fig. 11.9c shows, the contact force $\vec{F}_B$ is *not* directed along the length of the ladder. You may be surprised by this, but there's really no good reason the two directions should be the same. Can you show that if $\vec{F}_B$ were directed along the ladder, there would be a net counterclockwise torque with respect to the top of the ladder, and equilibrium would be impossible?

Here are a few final comments. First, as Lancelot climbs higher on the ladder, the lever arm and torque of his weight about B increase; this increases the values of n_1, f_s, and $(\mu_s)_{min}$. At the top, his lever arm would be nearly 3 m, giving a minimum coefficient of static friction of nearly 0.7. The value of μ_s would not be this large for Lancelot's medieval ladder, so his ladder is likely to slip as he climbs. To prevent this, present-day ladders are usually equipped with nonslip rubber pads.

Second, a larger ladder angle would decrease the lever arms with respect to B of the weights of the ladder and Lancelot and increase the lever arm of n_1, all of which would decrease the required friction force. The R. D. Werner Ladder Co. recommends that its ladders be used at an angle of 75°. (Why not 90°?)

Finally, if we had assumed friction on the wall as well as on the floor, the problem would be impossible to solve by using the equilibrium conditions alone. (Try it!) Such a problem is said to be *statically indeterminate*. The difficulty is that it's no longer adequate to treat the body as being perfectly rigid. Another simple example of such a problem is a four-legged table; there is no way to use the equilibrium conditions alone to find the force on each separate leg.

11.9 (a) Sir Lancelot pauses a third of the way up the ladder, fearing it will slip. (b) Free-body diagram for the system of Sir Lancelot and the ladder. (c) The contact force at B is the superposition of the normal force and the static friction force.

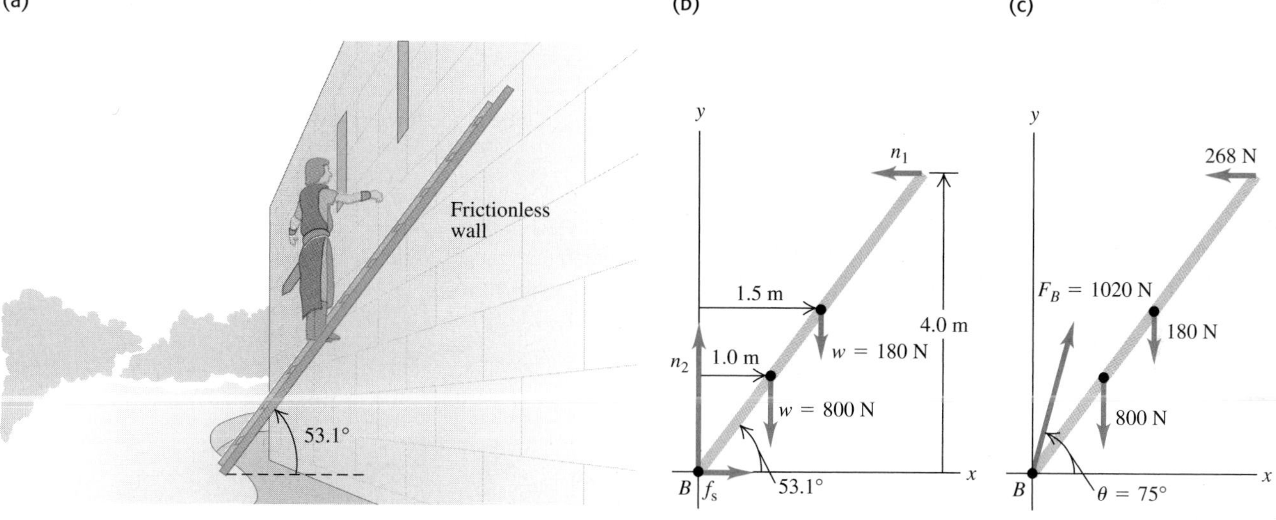

Example 11.4 Equilibrium and pumping iron

Figure 11.10a shows a horizontal human arm lifting a dumbbell. The forearm is in equilibrium under the action of the weight w of the dumbbell, the tension T in the tendon connected to the biceps muscle, and the force E exerted on the forearm by the upper arm at the elbow joint. For clarity the point A where the tendon is attached is drawn farther away from the elbow than its actual position. The weight w and the angle θ between the tension force and the horizontal are given; we want to find the tendon tension and the two components of force at the elbow (three unknown scalar quantities in all). We neglect the weight of the forearm itself.

SOLUTION

IDENTIFY: The system is at rest, so once again we use the conditions for equilibrium.

SET UP: As Fig. 11.10b shows, we represent the tendon force in terms of its components T_x and T_y, using the given angle θ and the unknown magnitude T:

$$T_x = T\cos\theta \qquad T_y = T\sin\theta$$

We also represent the force at the elbow in terms of its components E_x and E_y. We'll guess that the directions of these components are

Continued

as shown in Fig. 11.10b; there's no need to agonize over this guess, since the results for E_x and E_y will tell us the actual directions. Our target variables are the magnitude T of the tendon tension and the components E_x and E_y of the force at the elbow.

EXECUTE: The simplest way to find the tension T is to take torques about the elbow joint. The resulting torque equation does not contain E_x, E_y, or T_x because the lines of action of all these forces pass through this point. The torque equation is then simply

$$\sum \tau_E = Lw - DT_y = 0$$

From this we find

$$T_y = \frac{Lw}{D} \quad \text{and} \quad T = \frac{Lw}{D\sin\theta}$$

To find E_x and E_y, we use the first conditions for equilibrium, $\sum F_x = 0$ and $\sum F_y = 0$:

$$\sum F_x = T_x + (-E_x) = 0$$

$$E_x = T_x = T\cos\theta = \frac{Lw}{D\sin\theta}\cos\theta = \frac{Lw}{D}\cot\theta$$

$$= \frac{Lw}{D}\frac{D}{h} = \frac{Lw}{h}$$

$$\sum F_y = T_y + E_y + (-w) = 0$$

$$E_y = w - \frac{Lw}{D} = -\frac{(L-D)w}{D}$$

The negative sign shows that our guess for the direction of E_y, shown in Fig. 11.10b, was wrong; it is actually vertically *downward*.

EVALUATE: We can check our results by finding E_x and E_y in a different way that uses two more torque equations. We take torques about the tendon attach point, A:

$$\sum \tau_A = (L-D)w + DE_y = 0 \quad \text{and} \quad E_y = -\frac{(L-D)w}{D}$$

Finally, we take torques about point B in the figure:

$$\sum \tau_B = Lw - hE_x = 0 \quad \text{and} \quad E_x = \frac{Lw}{h}$$

We chose points A and B because the tendon tension T has zero torque about either of these points. (Can you see why from Fig. 11.10b?) Notice how much we have simplified these calculations by choosing the point for calculating torques so as to eliminate one or more of the unknown quantities.

In our alternative determination of E_x and E_y, we didn't explicitly use the first condition for equilibrium (that the vector sum of the forces is zero). As a consistency check, you should compute $\sum F_x$ and $\sum F_y$ to verify that they really *are* zero!

As a specific example, suppose $w = 200$ N, $D = 0.050$ m, $L = 0.30$ m, and $\theta = 80°$. Then from $\tan\theta = h/D$, we find

$$h = D\tan\theta = (0.050\text{ m})(5.67) = 0.28\text{ m}$$

From the previous general results we find

$$T = \frac{Lw}{D\sin\theta} = \frac{(0.30\text{ m})(200\text{ N})}{(0.050\text{ m})(0.98)} = 1220\text{ N}$$

$$E_y = -\frac{(L-D)w}{D} = -\frac{(0.30\text{ m} - 0.050\text{ m})(200\text{ N})}{0.050\text{ m}}$$

$$= -1000\text{ N}$$

$$E_x = \frac{Lw}{h} = \frac{(0.30\text{ m})(200\text{ N})}{0.28\text{ m}} = 210\text{ N}$$

The magnitude of the force at the elbow is

$$E = \sqrt{E_x^2 + E_y^2} = 1020\text{ N}$$

In view of the magnitudes of our results, neglecting the weight of the forearm itself, which may be 20 N or so, will cause only relatively small errors in our results.

11.10 (a) The situation. (b) Our free-body diagram for the forearm. The weight of the forearm is neglected, and the distance D is greatly exaggerated for clarity.

(a)

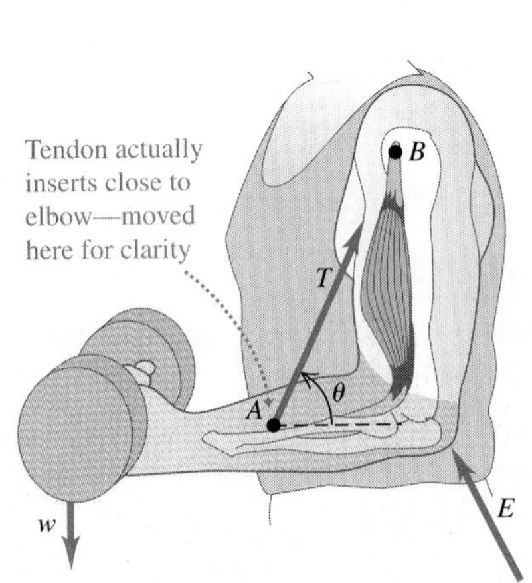

(b)

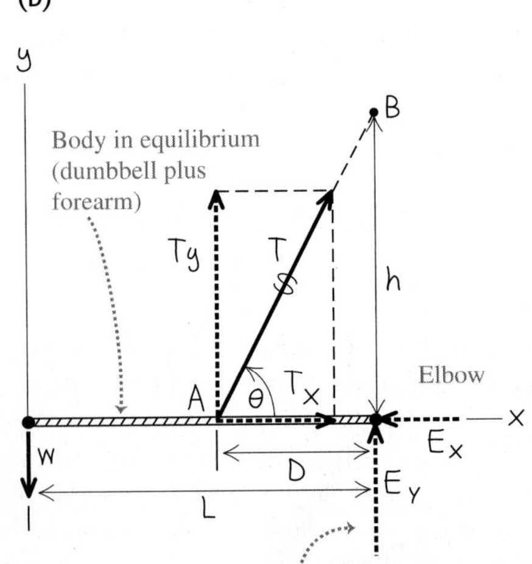

Test Your Understanding of Section 11.3 A metal advertising sign (weight w) for a specialty shop is suspended from the end of a horizontal rod of length L and negligible mass (Fig. 11.11). The rod is supported by a cable at an angle θ from the horizontal and by a hinge at point P. Rank the following force magnitudes in order from greatest to smallest: (i) the weight w of the sign; (ii) the tension in the cable; (iii) the vertical component of force exerted on the rod by the hinge at P.

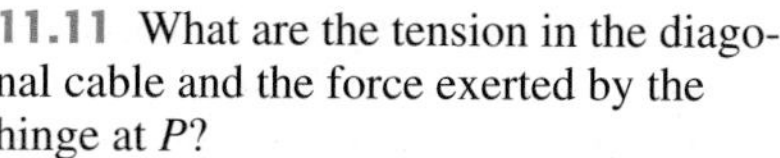

11.11 What are the tension in the diagonal cable and the force exerted by the hinge at P?

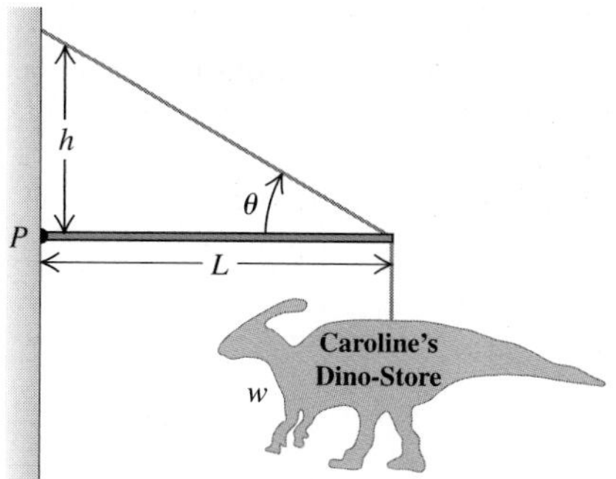

11.4 Stress, Strain, and Elastic Moduli

The rigid body is a useful idealized model, but the stretching, squeezing, and twisting of real bodies when forces are applied are often too important to ignore. Figure 11.12 shows three examples. We want to study the relationship between the forces and deformations for each case.

For each kind of deformation we will introduce a quantity called **stress** that characterizes the strength of the forces causing the deformation, on a "force per unit area" basis. Another quantity, **strain,** describes the resulting deformation. When the stress and strain are small enough, we often find that the two are directly proportional, and we call the proportionality constant an **elastic modulus.** The harder you pull on something, the more it stretches; the more you squeeze it, the more it compresses. We can express this relationship as an equation:

$$\frac{\text{Stress}}{\text{Strain}} = \text{Elastic modulus} \qquad \text{(Hooke's law)} \tag{11.7}$$

The proportionality of stress and strain (under certain conditions) is called **Hooke's law,** after Robert Hooke (1635–1703), a contemporary of Newton. We used one form of Hooke's law in Sections 6.3 and 7.2: The elongation of an ideal spring is proportional to the stretching force. Remember that Hooke's law is not really a general law but an experimental finding that is valid over only a limited range. The last section of this chapter discusses what this limited range is.

11.12 Three types of stress. (a) Bridge cables under *tensile stress,* being stretched by forces acting at their ends. (b) A diver under *bulk stress,* being squeezed from all sides by forces due to water pressure. (c) A ribbon under *shear stress,* being deformed and eventually cut by forces exerted by the scissors.

11.13 An object in tension. The net force on the object is zero, but the object deforms. The tensile stress (the ratio of the force to the cross-sectional area) produces a tensile strain (the elongation divided by the initial length). The elongation Δl is exaggerated for clarity.

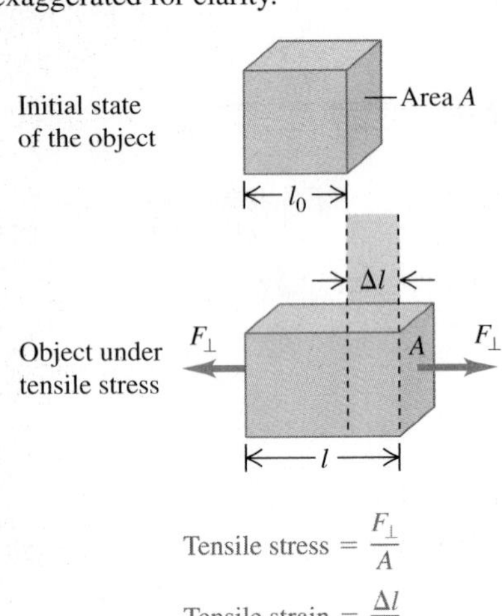

Tensile and Compressive Stress and Strain

The simplest elastic behavior to understand is the stretching of a bar, rod, or wire when its ends are pulled (Fig. 11.12a). Figure 11.13 shows an object that initially has uniform cross-sectional area A and length l_0. We then apply forces of equal magnitude $F_\perp$ but opposite directions at the ends (this ensures that the object has no tendency to move left or right). We say that the object is in **tension.** We've already talked a lot about tension in ropes and strings; it's the same concept here. The subscript $\perp$ is a reminder that the forces act perpendicular to the cross section.

We define the **tensile stress** at the cross section as the ratio of the force $F_\perp$ to the cross-sectional area A:

$$\text{Tensile stress} = \frac{F_\perp}{A} \tag{11.8}$$

This is a *scalar* quantity because $F_\perp$ is the *magnitude* of the force. The SI unit of stress is the **pascal** (abbreviated Pa and named for the 17th-century French scientist and philosopher Blaise Pascal). Equation (11.8) shows that 1 pascal equals 1 newton per square meter (N/m^2):

$$1 \text{ pascal} = 1 \text{ Pa} = 1 \text{ N/m}^2$$

In the British system the logical unit of stress would be the pound per square foot, but the pound per square inch (lb/in.^{2} or psi) is more commonly used. The conversion factors are

$$1 \text{ psi} = 6895 \text{ Pa} \qquad \text{and} \qquad 1 \text{ Pa} = 1.450 \times 10^{-4} \text{ psi}$$

The units of stress are the same as those of *pressure,* which we will encounter often in later chapters. Air pressure in automobile tires is typically around 3×10^5 Pa = 300 kPa, and steel cables are commonly required to withstand tensile stresses of the order of 10^8 Pa.

The object shown in Fig. 11.13 stretches to a length $l = l_0 + \Delta l$ when under tension. The elongation Δl does not occur only at the ends; every part of the bar stretches in the same proportion. The **tensile strain** of the object is equal to the fractional change in length, which is the ratio of the elongation Δl to the original length l_0:

$$\text{Tensile strain} = \frac{l - l_0}{l_0} = \frac{\Delta l}{l_0} \tag{11.9}$$

Tensile strain is stretch per unit length. It is a ratio of two lengths, always measured in the same units, and so is a pure (dimensionless) number with no units.

Experiment shows that for a sufficiently small tensile stress, stress and strain are proportional, as in Eq. (11.7). The corresponding elastic modulus is called **Young's modulus,** denoted by Y:

$$Y = \frac{\text{Tensile stress}}{\text{Tensile strain}} = \frac{F_\perp/A}{\Delta l/l_0} = \frac{F_\perp}{A}\frac{l_0}{\Delta l} \quad \text{(Young's modulus)} \tag{11.10}$$

Since strain is a pure number, the units of Young's modulus are the same as those of stress: force per unit area. Some typical values are listed in Table 11.1. (This table also gives values of two other elastic moduli that we will discuss later in this chapter.) A material with a large value of Y is relatively unstretchable; a large stress is required for a given strain. For example, the value of Y for cast steel $(2 \times 10^{11} \text{ Pa})$ is much larger than that for rubber $(5 \times 10^8 \text{ Pa})$.

11.14 An object in compression. The compressive stress and compressive strain are defined in the same way as tensile stress and strain (see Fig. 11.13), except that Δl now denotes the distance that the object contracts.

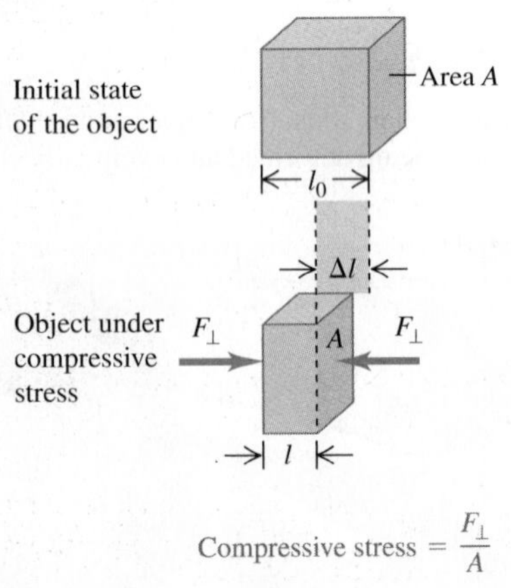

When the forces on the ends of a bar are pushes rather than pulls (Fig. 11.14), the bar is in **compression** and the stress is a **compressive stress.** The **compressive strain** of an object in compression is defined in the same way as the tensile strain, but Δl has the opposite direction. Hooke's law and Eq. (11.10) are valid for compression as well as tension if the compressive stress is not too great. For many materials, Young's modulus has the same value for both tensile and compressive stresses. Composite materials such as concrete and

Table 11.1 Approximate Elastic Moduli

Material	Young's Modulus, Y (Pa)	Bulk Modulus, B (Pa)	Shear Modulus, S (Pa)
Aluminum	7.0×10^{10}	7.5×10^{10}	2.5×10^{10}
Brass	9.0×10^{10}	6.0×10^{10}	3.5×10^{10}
Copper	11×10^{10}	14×10^{10}	4.4×10^{10}
Crown glass	6.0×10^{10}	5.0×10^{10}	2.5×10^{10}
Iron	21×10^{10}	16×10^{10}	7.7×10^{10}
Lead	1.6×10^{10}	4.1×10^{10}	0.6×10^{10}
Nickel	21×10^{10}	17×10^{10}	7.8×10^{10}
Steel	20×10^{10}	16×10^{10}	7.5×10^{10}

stone are an exception; they can withstand compressive stresses but fail under comparable tensile stresses. Stone was the primary building material used in ancient civilizations such as the Babylonians, Assyrians, and Romans, so their structures had to be designed to avoid tensile stresses. This explains why they made extensive use of arches in doorways and bridges, where the weight of the overlying material compresses the stones of the arch together and does not place them under tension.

In many situations, bodies can experience both tensile and compressive stresses at the same time. As an example, a horizontal beam supported at each end sags under its own weight. As a result, the top of the beam is under compression, while the bottom of the beam is under tension (Fig. 11.15a). To minimize the stress and hence the bending strain, the top and bottom of the beam are given a large cross-sectional area. There is neither compression nor tension along the centerline of the beam, so this part can have a small cross section; this helps to keep the weight of the bar to a minimum and further helps to reduce the stress. The result is an I-beam of the familiar shape used in building construction (Fig. 11.15b).

(a)

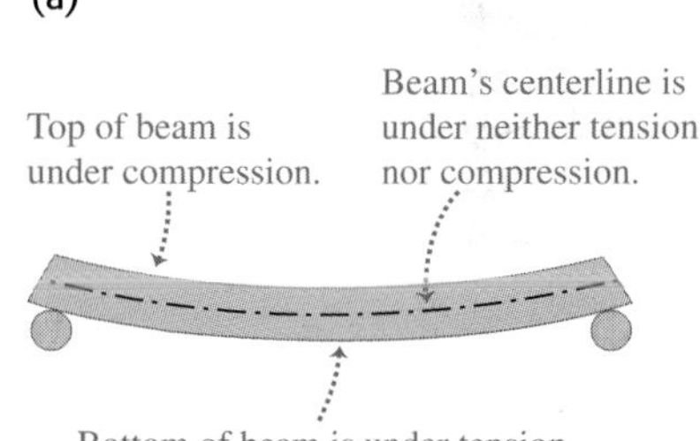
Top of beam is under compression.
Beam's centerline is under neither tension nor compression.
Bottom of beam is under tension.

(b)

The top and bottom of an I-beam are broad to minimize the compressive and tensile stresses.
The beam can be narrow near its centerline, which is under neither compression nor tension.

11.15 (a) A beam supported at both ends is under both compression and tension. (b) The cross-sectional shape of an I-beam minimizes both stress and weight.

Example 11.5 Tensile stress and strain

A steel rod 2.0 m long has a cross-sectional area of $0.30\ \text{cm}^2$. The rod is now hung by one end from a support structure, and a 550-kg milling machine is hung from the rod's lower end. Determine the stress, the strain, and the elongation of the rod.

SOLUTION

IDENTIFY: This example uses the definitions of stress, strain, and Young's modulus, which is the appropriate elastic modulus for an object under tension.

SET UP: We use Eqs. (11.8), (11.9), and (11.10) to find the tensile stress, the tensile strain, and the elongation Δl. We also use the value of Y for steel from Table 11.1.

EXECUTE: We find

$$\text{Stress} = \frac{F_\perp}{A} = \frac{(550\ \text{kg})(9.8\ \text{m/s}^2)}{3.0 \times 10^{-5}\ \text{m}^2} = 1.8 \times 10^8\ \text{Pa}$$

$$\text{Strain} = \frac{\Delta l}{l_0} = \frac{\text{Stress}}{Y} = \frac{1.8 \times 10^8\ \text{Pa}}{20 \times 10^{10}\ \text{Pa}} = 9.0 \times 10^{-4}$$

$$\begin{aligned}\text{Elongation} &= \Delta l = (\text{Strain}) \times l_0 = (9.0 \times 10^{-4})(2.0\ \text{m}) \\ &= 0.0018\ \text{m} = 1.8\ \text{mm}\end{aligned}$$

EVALUATE: The small size of this elongation, which results from a load of more than half a ton, is a testament to the stiffness of steel.

Bulk Stress and Strain

When a scuba diver plunges deep into the ocean, the water exerts nearly uniform pressure everywhere on his surface and squeezes him to a slightly smaller volume (Fig. 11.12b). This is a different situation from the tensile and compressive stresses and strains we have discussed. The stress is now a uniform pressure on all sides, and the resulting deformation is a volume change. We use the terms **bulk stress (or volume stress)** and **bulk strain** (or **volume strain**) to describe these quantities.

If an object is immersed in a fluid (liquid or gas) at rest, the fluid exerts a force on any part of the object's surface; this force is *perpendicular* to the surface. (If we tried to make the fluid exert a force parallel to the surface, the fluid would slip sideways to counteract the effort.) The force $F_\perp$ per unit area that the fluid exerts on the surface of an immersed object is called the **pressure** p in the fluid:

$$p = \frac{F_\perp}{A} \quad \text{(pressure in a fluid)} \tag{11.11}$$

The pressure in a fluid increases with depth. For example, the pressure of the air is about 21% greater at sea level than in Denver (at an elevation of 1.6 km, or 1.0 mi). If an immersed object is relatively small, however, we can ignore pressure differences due to depth for the purpose of calculating bulk stress. Hence we will treat the pressure as having the same value at all points on an immersed object's surface.

Pressure has the same units as stress; commonly used units include 1 Pa $(=1\ \text{N/m}^2)$ and 1 lb/in.^2 (1 psi). Also in common use is the **atmosphere,** abbreviated atm. One atmosphere is the approximate average pressure of the earth's atmosphere at sea level:

$$1\ \text{atmosphere} = 1\ \text{atm} = 1.013 \times 10^5\ \text{Pa} = 14.7\ \text{lb/in.}^2$$

CAUTION **Pressure vs. force** Unlike force, pressure has no intrinsic direction: The pressure on the surface of an immersed object is the same no matter how the surface is oriented. Hence pressure is a *scalar* quantity, not a vector quantity.

Pressure plays the role of stress in a volume deformation. The corresponding strain is the fractional change in volume (Fig. 11.16)—that is, the ratio of the volume change ΔV to the original volume V_0:

$$\text{Bulk (volume) strain} = \frac{\Delta V}{V_0} \tag{11.12}$$

Volume strain is the change in volume per unit volume. Like tensile or compressive strain, it is a pure number, without units.

When Hooke's law is obeyed, an increase in pressure (bulk stress) produces a *proportional* bulk strain (fractional change in volume). The corresponding elastic modulus (ratio of stress to strain) is called the **bulk modulus,** denoted by B. When the pressure on a body changes by a small amount Δp, from p_0 to $p_0 + \Delta p$, and the resulting bulk strain is $\Delta V/V_0$, Hooke's law takes the form

$$B = \frac{\text{Bulk stress}}{\text{Bulk strain}} = -\frac{\Delta p}{\Delta V/V_0} \quad \text{(bulk modulus)} \tag{11.13}$$

We include a minus sign in this equation because an *increase* of pressure always causes a *decrease* in volume. In other words, if Δp is positive, ΔV is negative. The bulk modulus B itself is a positive quantity.

For small pressure changes in a solid or a liquid, we consider B to be constant. The bulk modulus of a *gas,* however, depends on the initial pressure p_0. Table 11.1 includes values of the bulk modulus for several solid materials. Its units, force per unit area, are the same as those of pressure (and of tensile or compressive stress).

11.16 An object under bulk stress. Without the stress, the cube has volume V_0; when the stress is applied, the cube has a smaller volume V. The volume change ΔV is exaggerated for clarity.

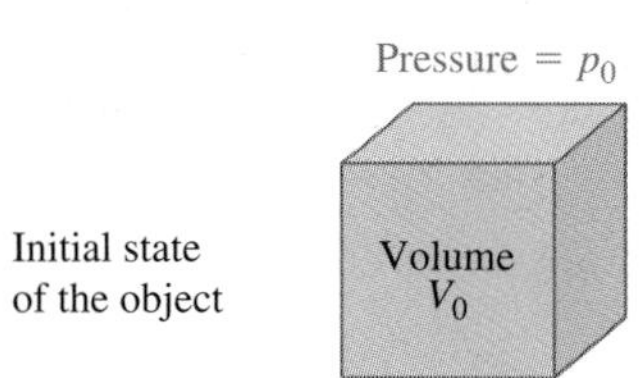

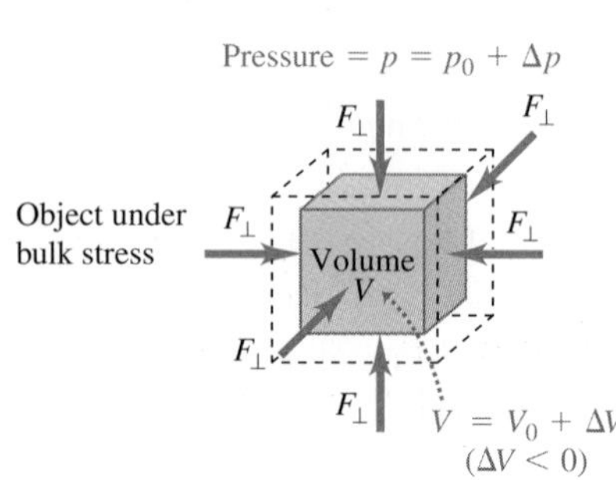

The reciprocal of the bulk modulus is called the **compressibility** and is denoted by k. From Eq. (11.13),

$$k = \frac{1}{B} = -\frac{\Delta V/V_0}{\Delta p} = -\frac{1}{V_0}\frac{\Delta V}{\Delta p} \quad \text{(compressibility)} \qquad (11.14)$$

Compressibility is the fractional decrease in volume, $-\Delta V/V_0$, per unit increase Δp in pressure. The units of compressibility are those of *reciprocal pressure,* Pa^{-1} or atm^{-1}.

Table 11.2 lists the values of compressibility k for several liquids. For example, the compressibility of water is $46.4 \times 10^{-6}\ \text{atm}^{-1}$, which means that the volume of water decreases by 46.4 parts per million for each 1-atmosphere increase in pressure. Materials with small bulk modulus and large compressibility are easier to compress.

Table 11.2 Compressibilities of Liquids

	Compressibility, k	
Liquid	Pa^{-1}	atm^{-1}
Carbon disulfide	93×10^{-11}	94×10^{-6}
Ethyl alcohol	110×10^{-11}	111×10^{-6}
Glycerine	21×10^{-11}	21×10^{-6}
Mercury	3.7×10^{-11}	3.8×10^{-6}
Water	45.8×10^{-11}	46.4×10^{-6}

Example 11.6 Bulk stress and strain

A hydraulic press contains $0.25\ \text{m}^3$ (250 L) of oil. Find the decrease in the volume of the oil when it is subjected to a pressure increase $\Delta p = 1.6 \times 10^7$ Pa (about 160 atm or 2300 psi). The bulk modulus of the oil is $B = 5.0 \times 10^9$ Pa (about 5.0×10^4 atm), and its compressibility is $k = 1/B = 20 \times 10^{-6}\ \text{atm}^{-1}$.

SOLUTION

IDENTIFY: This example uses the ideas of bulk stress and strain. Our target variable is the volume change ΔV.

SET UP: We are given both the bulk modulus and the compressibility, so we can use either Eq. (11.13) or Eq. (11.14) to find ΔV.

EXECUTE: Solving Eq. (11.13) for ΔV, we find

$$\Delta V = -\frac{V_0\,\Delta p}{B} = -\frac{(0.25\ \text{m}^3)(1.6 \times 10^7\ \text{Pa})}{5.0 \times 10^9\ \text{Pa}}$$
$$= -8.0 \times 10^{-4}\ \text{m}^3 = -0.80\ \text{L}$$

Alternatively, we can use Eq. (11.14). Solving for ΔV and using the approximate unit conversions given above, we get

$$\Delta V = -kV_0\,\Delta p = -(20 \times 10^{-6}\ \text{atm}^{-1})(0.25\ \text{m}^3)(160\ \text{atm})$$
$$= -8.0 \times 10^{-4}\ \text{m}^3$$

EVALUATE: We get the same result for ΔV with either approach, as we should. Note that ΔV is negative, indicating that the volume decreases when the pressure increases. Even though the pressure increase is very large, the *fractional* change in volume is very small:

$$\frac{\Delta V}{V_0} = \frac{-8.0 \times 10^{-4}\ \text{m}^3}{0.25\ \text{m}^3} = -0.0032, \quad \text{or} \quad -0.32\%$$

Shear Stress and Strain

The third kind of stress-strain situation is called *shear.* The ribbon in Fig. 11.12c is under **shear stress:** One part of the ribbon is being pushed up while an adjacent part is being pushed down, producing a deformation of the ribbon. Figure 11.17 shows a body being deformed by a shear stress. In the figure, forces of equal magnitude but opposite direction act *tangent* to the surfaces of opposite ends of the object. We define the shear stress as the force $F_\parallel$ acting tangent to the surface, divided by the area A on which it acts:

$$\text{Shear stress} = \frac{F_\parallel}{A} \qquad (11.15)$$

Shear stress, like the other two types of stress, is a force per unit area.

Figure 11.17 shows that one face of the object under shear stress is displaced by a distance x relative to the opposite face. We define **shear strain** as the ratio of the displacement x to the transverse dimension h:

$$\text{Shear strain} = \frac{x}{h} \qquad (11.16)$$

In real-life situations, x is nearly always much smaller than h. Like all strains, shear strain is a dimensionless number; it is a ratio of two lengths.

11.17 An object under shear stress. Forces are applied tangent to opposite surfaces of the object (in contrast to the situation in Fig. 11.13, in which the forces act perpendicular to the surfaces). The deformation x is exaggerated for clarity.

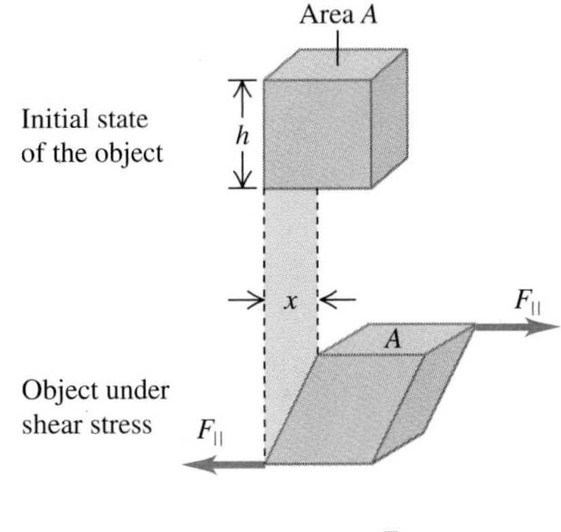

Shear stress $= \frac{F_\parallel}{A}$

Shear strain $= \frac{x}{h}$

If the forces are small enough that Hooke's law is obeyed, the shear strain is *proportional* to the shear stress. The corresponding elastic modulus (ratio of shear stress to shear strain) is called the **shear modulus,** denoted by S:

$$S = \frac{\text{Shear stress}}{\text{Shear strain}} = \frac{F_{\parallel}/A}{x/h} = \frac{F_{\parallel}}{A}\frac{h}{x} \quad \text{(shear modulus)} \tag{11.17}$$

with x and h defined as in Fig. 11.17.

Table 11.1 gives several values of shear modulus. For a given material, S is usually one-third to one-half as large as Young's modulus Y for tensile stress. Keep in mind that the concepts of shear stress, shear strain, and shear modulus apply to *solid* materials only. The reason is that the shear forces in Fig. 11.17 are required to deform the solid block, and the block tends to return to its original shape if the shear forces are removed. By contrast, gases and liquids do not have definite shapes.

Example 11.7 Shear stress and strain

Suppose the object in Fig. 11.17 is the brass base plate of an outdoor sculpture; it experiences shear forces as a result of an earthquake. The frame is 0.80 m square and 0.50 cm thick. How large a force must be exerted on each of its edges if the displacement x (see Fig. 11.17) is 0.16 mm?

SOLUTION

IDENTIFY: This example uses the relationship among shear stress, shear strain, and shear modulus. Our target variable is the force $F_{\parallel}$ exerted parallel to each edge, as shown in Fig. 11.17.

SET UP: We first find the shear strain using Eq. (11.16), and then determine the shear stress using Eq. (11.17). We can then solve for the target variable $F_{\parallel}$ using Eq. (11.15). The values of all the other quantities are given, including the shear modulus of brass (from Table 11.1, $S = 3.5 \times 10^{10}$ Pa). Note that h in Fig. 11.17 represents the 0.80-m length of each side of the square plate, and the area A is the product of the 0.80-m length and the 0.50-cm thickness.

EXECUTE: The shear strain is

$$\text{Shear strain} = \frac{x}{h} = \frac{1.6 \times 10^{-4}\ \text{m}}{0.80\ \text{m}} = 2.0 \times 10^{-4}$$

From Eq. (11.17) the shear stress equals the shear strain multiplied by the shear modulus S:

$$\begin{aligned}\text{Stress} &= (\text{Shear strain}) \times S \\ &= (2.0 \times 10^{-4})(3.5 \times 10^{10}\ \text{Pa}) = 7.0 \times 10^{6}\ \text{Pa}\end{aligned}$$

From Eq. (11.15), the force at each edge is the shear stress multiplied by the area of the edge:

$$\begin{aligned}F_{\parallel} &= (\text{Shear stress}) \times A \\ &= (7.0 \times 10^{6}\ \text{Pa})(0.80\ \text{m})(0.0050\ \text{m}) = 2.8 \times 10^{4}\ \text{N}\end{aligned}$$

EVALUATE: The required force is more than 3 tons! Brass has a large shear modulus, which means that it's intrinsically difficult to deform. Furthermore, the plate is relatively thick (0.50 cm), so the area A is relatively large and a large force $F_{\parallel}$ is needed to provide the necessary stress $F_{\parallel}/A$.

Test Your Understanding of Section 11.4 A copper rod of cross-sectional area 0.500 cm^2 and length 1.00 m is elongated by 2.00×10^{-2} mm, and a steel rod of the same cross-sectional area but 0.100 m in length is elongated by 2.00×10^{-3} mm. (a) Which rod has greater tensile *strain?* (i) the copper rod; (ii) the steel rod; (iii) the strain is the same for both. (b) Which rod is under greater tensile *stress?* (i) the copper rod; (ii) the steel rod; (iii) the stress is the same for both. MP

11.5 Elasticity and Plasticity

Hooke's law—the proportionality of stress and strain in elastic deformations—has a limited range of validity. In the preceding section we used phrases such as "provided that the forces are small enough that Hooke's law is obeyed." Just what *are* the limitations of Hooke's law? We know that if you pull, squeeze, or twist *anything* hard enough, it will bend or break. Can we be more precise than that?

Let's look at tensile stress and strain again. Suppose we plot a graph of stress as a function of strain. If Hooke's law is obeyed, the graph is a straight line with a slope equal to Young's modulus. Figure 11.18 shows a typical stress-strain graph for a metal such as copper or soft iron. The strain is shown as the *percent* elongation; the horizontal scale is not uniform beyond the first portion of the curve, up to a strain of less than 1%. The first portion is a straight line, indicating Hooke's law behavior with stress directly proportional to strain. This straight-line portion ends at point a; the stress at this point is called the *proportional limit.*

From a to b, stress and strain are no longer proportional, and Hooke's law is *not* obeyed. If the load is gradually removed, starting at any point between O and b, the curve is retraced until the material returns to its original length. The deformation is *reversible,* and the forces are conservative; the energy put into the material to cause the deformation is recovered when the stress is removed. In region Ob we say that the material shows *elastic behavior.* Point b, the end of this region, is called the *yield point;* the stress at the yield point is called the *elastic limit.*

When we increase the stress beyond point b, the strain continues to increase. But now when we remove the load at some point beyond b, say c, the material does not come back to its original length. Instead, it follows the red line in Fig. 11.18. The length at zero stress is now greater than the original length; the material has undergone an irreversible deformation and has acquired what we call a *permanent set.* Further increase of load beyond c produces a large increase in strain for a relatively small increase in stress, until a point d is reached at which *fracture* takes place. The behavior of the material from b to d is called *plastic flow* or *plastic deformation.* A plastic deformation is irreversible; when the stress is removed, the material does not return to its original state.

For some materials, such as the one whose properties are graphed in Fig. 11.18, a large amount of plastic deformation takes place between the elastic limit and the fracture point. Such a material is said to be *ductile.* But if fracture occurs soon after the elastic limit is passed, the material is said to be *brittle.* A soft iron wire that can have considerable permanent stretch without breaking is ductile, while a steel piano string that breaks soon after its elastic limit is reached is brittle.

Something very curious can happen when an object is stretched and then allowed to relax. An example is shown in Fig. 11.19, which is a stress-strain curve for vulcanized rubber that has been stretched by more than seven times its original length. The stress is not proportional to the strain, but the behavior is elastic because when the load is removed, the material returns to its original length. However, the material follows *different* curves for increasing and decreasing stress. This is called *elastic hysteresis.* The work done by the material when it returns to its original shape is less than the work required to deform it; there are nonconservative forces associated with internal friction. Rubber with large elastic hysteresis is very useful for absorbing vibrations, such as in engine mounts and shock-absorber bushings for cars.

The stress required to cause actual fracture of a material is called the *breaking stress,* the *ultimate strength,* or (for tensile stress) the *tensile strength.* Two materials, such as two types of steel, may have very similar elastic constants but vastly different breaking stresses. Table 11.3 gives typical values of breaking stress for several materials in tension. The conversion factor 6.9×10^8 Pa = 100,000 psi may help put these numbers in perspective. For example, if the breaking stress of a particular steel is 6.9×10^8 Pa, then a bar with a 1-in.^{2} cross section has a breaking strength of 100,000 lb.

11.18 Typical stress-strain diagram for a ductile metal under tension.

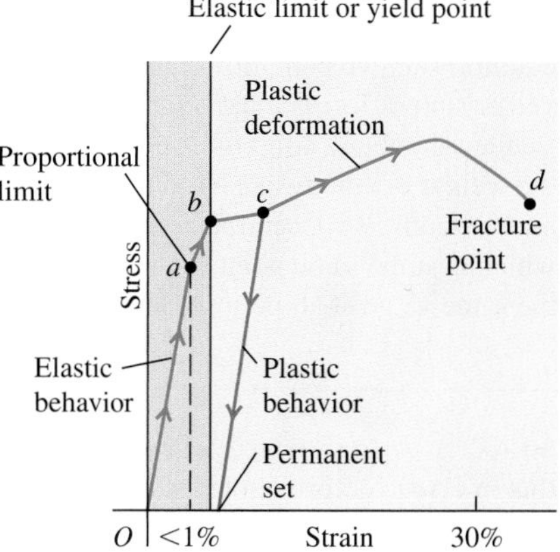

11.19 Typical stress-strain diagram for vulcanized rubber. The curves are different for increasing and decreasing stress, a phenomenon called elastic hysteresis.

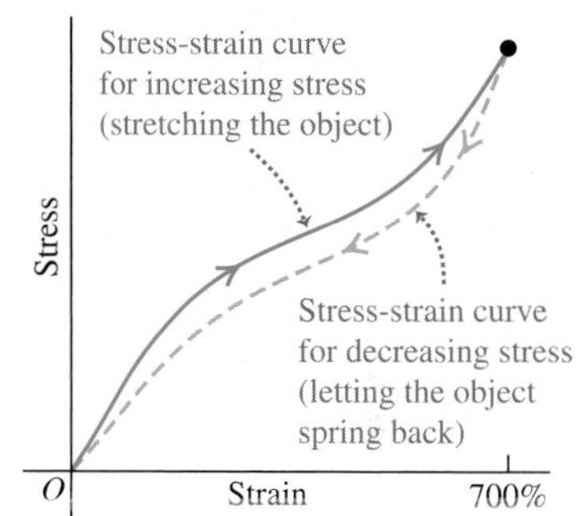

Table 11.3 Approximate Breaking Stresses

Material	Breaking Stress (Pa or N/m^2)
Aluminum	2.2×10^8
Brass	4.7×10^8
Glass	10×10^8
Iron	3.0×10^8
Phosphor bronze	5.6×10^8
Steel	$5 - 20 \times 10^8$

Test Your Understanding of Section 11.5 While parking your car on a crowded street, you accidentally back into a steel post. You pull forward until the car no longer touches the post and then get out to inspect the damage. What does your rear bumper look like if the strain in the impact was (a) less than at the proportional limit; (b) greater than at the proportional limit, but less than at the yield point; (c) greater than at the yield point, but less than at the fracture point; and (d) greater than at the fracture point?

CHAPTER 11 SUMMARY

Conditions for equilibrium: For a rigid body to be in equilibrium, two conditions must be satisfied. First, the vector sum of forces must be zero. Second, the sum of torques about any point must be zero. The torque due to the weight of a body can be found by assuming the entire weight is concentrated at the center of gravity, which is at the same point as the center of mass if $\vec{g}$ has the same value at all points. (See Examples 11.1–11.4.)

$$\sum F_x = 0 \qquad \sum F_y = 0 \qquad \sum F_z = 0 \tag{11.1}$$

$$\sum \vec{\tau} = 0 \quad \text{about } any \text{ point} \tag{11.2}$$

$$\vec{r}_{\text{cm}} = \frac{m_1\vec{r}_1 + m_2\vec{r}_2 + m_3\vec{r}_3 + \cdots}{m_1 + m_2 + m_3 + \cdots} \tag{11.4}$$

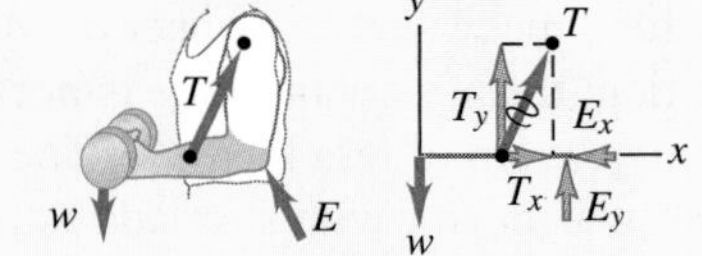

Stress, strain, and Hooke's law: Hooke's law states that in elastic deformations, stress (force per unit area) is proportional to strain (fractional deformation). The proportionality constant is called the elastic modulus.

$$\frac{\text{Stress}}{\text{Strain}} = \text{Elastic modulus} \tag{11.7}$$

Tensile and compressive stress: Tensile stress is tensile force per unit area, $F_\perp/A$. Tensile strain is fractional change in length, $\Delta l/l_0$. The elastic modulus is called Young's modulus Y. Compressive stress and strain are defined in the same way. (See Example 11.5.)

$$Y = \frac{\text{Tensile stress}}{\text{Tensile strain}} = \frac{F_\perp/A}{\Delta l/l_0} = \frac{F_\perp}{A}\frac{l_0}{\Delta l} \tag{11.10}$$

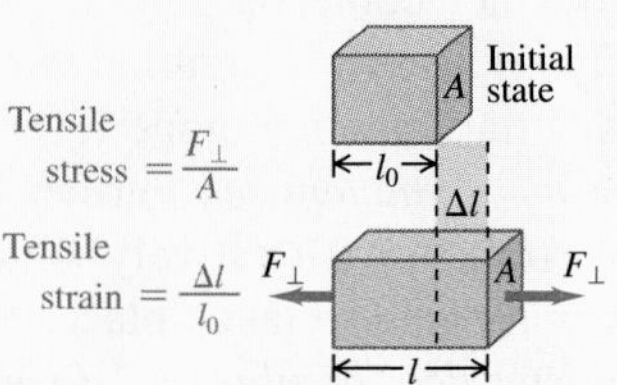

Bulk stress: Pressure in a fluid is force per unit area. Bulk stress is pressure change, Δp, and bulk strain is fractional volume change, $\Delta V/V_0$. The elastic modulus is called the bulk modulus, B. Compressibility, k, is the reciprocal of bulk modulus: $k = 1/B$. (See Example 11.6.)

$$p = \frac{F_\perp}{A} \tag{11.11}$$

$$B = \frac{\text{Bulk stress}}{\text{Bulk strain}} = -\frac{\Delta p}{\Delta V/V_0} \tag{11.13}$$

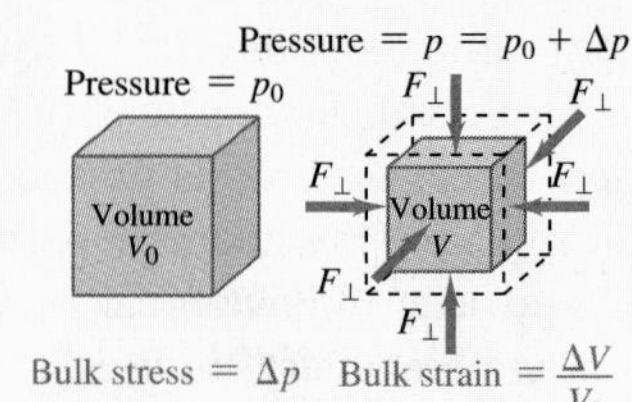

Shear stress: Shear stress is force per unit area, $F_\parallel/A$, for a force applied tangent to a surface. Shear strain is the displacement x of one side divided by the transverse dimension h. The elastic modulus is called the shear modulus, S. (See Example 11.7.)

$$S = \frac{\text{Shear stress}}{\text{Shear strain}} = \frac{F_\parallel/A}{x/h} = \frac{F_\parallel}{A}\frac{h}{x} \tag{11.17}$$

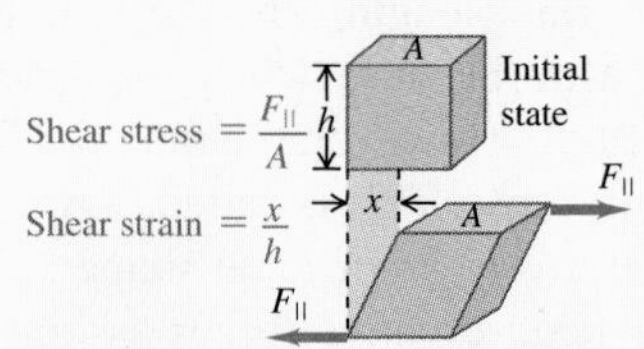

The limits of Hooke's law: The proportional limit is the maximum stress for which stress and strain are proportional. Beyond the proportional limit, Hooke's law is not valid. The elastic limit is the stress beyond which irreversible deformation occurs. The breaking stress, or ultimate strength, is the stress at which the material breaks.

Key Terms

first condition for equilibrium, *355*
second condition for equilibrium, *355*
static equilibrium, *355*
center of gravity, *355*
stress, *363*
strain, *363*
elastic modulus, *363*
Hooke's law, *363*
tension, *364*
tensile stress, *364*
pascal, *364*
tensile strain, *364*
Young's modulus, *364*
compression, *364*
compressive stress, *364*
compressive strain, *364*
bulk stress (volume stress), *366*
bulk strain (volume strain), *366*
pressure, *366*
atmosphere, *366*
bulk modulus, *366*
compressibility, *367*
shear stress, *367*
shear strain, *367*
shear modulus, *368*

Answer to Chapter Opening Question ?

Each stone in the arch is under compression, not tension. This is because the forces on the stones tend to push them inward toward the center of the arch and thus squeeze them together. Compared to a solid supporting wall, a wall with arches is just as strong yet much more economical to build.

Answers to Test Your Understanding Questions

11.1 Answer: (i) Situation (i) satisfies both equilibrium conditions because the seagull has zero acceleration (so $\sum\vec{F} = \mathbf{0}$) and no tendency to start rotating (so $\sum\vec{\tau} = \mathbf{0}$). Situation (ii) satisfies the first condition because the crankshaft as a whole does not accelerate through space, but it does not satisfy the second condition; the crankshaft has an angular acceleration, so $\sum\vec{\tau}$ is not zero. Situation (iii) satisfies the second condition (there is no tendency to rotate) but not the first one; the baseball accelerates in its flight (due to gravity), so $\sum\vec{F}$ is not zero.

11.2 Answer: (ii) In equilibrium, the center of gravity must be at the point of support. Since the rock and meter stick have the same mass and hence the same weight, the center of gravity of the system is midway between their respective centers. The cg of the meter stick alone is 0.50 m from the left end (that is, at the middle of the meter stick), so the cg of the combination of rock and meter stick is 0.25 m from the left end.

11.3 Answer: (ii), (i), (iii) This is the same situation described in Example 11.4, with the rod replacing the forearm, the hinge replacing the elbow, and the cable replacing the tendon. The only difference is that the cable attachment point is at the end of the rod, so the distances D and L are identical. From Example 11.4, the tension is

$$T = \frac{Lw}{L\sin\theta} = \frac{w}{\sin\theta}$$

Since $\sin\theta$ is less than 1, the tension T is greater than the weight w. The vertical component of the force exerted by the hinge is

$$E_y = -\frac{(L - L)w}{L} = 0$$

In this situation, the hinge exerts *no* vertical force. You can see this easily if you calculate torques around the right end of the horizontal rod: The only force that exerts a torque around this point is the vertical component of the hinge force, so this force component must be zero.

11.4 Answers: (a) (iii), (b) (ii) In (a), the copper rod has 10 times the elongation Δl of the steel rod, but it also has 10 times the original length l_0. Hence the tensile strain $\Delta l/l_0$ is the same for both rods. In (b), the stress is equal to Young's modulus Y multiplied by the strain. From Table 11.1, steel has a larger value of Y, so a greater stress is required to produce the same strain.

11.5 In (a) and (b), the bumper will have sprung back to its original shape (although the paint may be scratched). In (c), the bumper will have a permanent dent or deformation. In (d), the bumper will be torn or broken.

PROBLEMS

For instructor-assigned homework, go to **www.masteringphysics.com**

Discussion Questions

Q11.1. Does a rigid object in uniform rotation about a fixed axis satisfy the first and second conditions for equilibrium? Why? Does it then follow that every particle in this object is in equilibrium? Explain.

Q11.2. (a) Is it possible for an object to be in translational equilibrium (the first condition) but *not* in rotational equilibrium (the second condition)? Illustrate your answer with a simple example. (b) Can an object be in rotational equilibrium yet *not* in translational equilibrium? Justify your answer with a simple example.

Q11.3. Car tires are sometimes "balanced" on a machine that pivots the tire and wheel about the center. Weights are placed around the wheel rim until it does not tip from the horizontal plane. Discuss this procedure in terms of the center of gravity.

Q11.4. Does the center of gravity of a solid body always lie within the material of the body? If not, give a counterexample.

Q11.5. In Section 11.2 we always assumed that the value of g was the same at all points on the body. This is *not* a good approximation if the dimensions of the body are great enough, because the value of g decreases with altitude. If this is taken into account, will the center of gravity of a long, vertical rod be above, below, or at its center of mass? Explain how this can be used to keep the long axis of an orbiting spacecraft pointed toward the earth. (This would be useful for a weather satellite that must always keep its camera lens trained on the earth.) The moon is not exactly spherical but is somewhat elongated. Explain why this same effect is responsible for keeping the same face of the moon pointed toward the earth at all times.

Q11.6. You are balancing a wrench by suspending it at a single point. Is the equilibrium stable, unstable, or neutral if the point is above, at, or below the wrench's center of gravity? In each case give the reasoning behind your answer. (For rotation, a rigid body is in *stable* equilibrium if a small rotation of the body produces a torque that tends to return the body to equilibrium; it is in *unstable* equilibrium if a small rotation produces a torque that tends to take the body farther from equilibrium; and it is in *neutral* equilibrium if a small rotation produces no torque.)

Q11.7. You can probably stand flatfooted on the floor and then rise up and balance on your tiptoes. Why are you unable do it if your toes are touching the wall of your room? (Try it!)

Q11.8. You freely pivot a horseshoe from a horizontal nail through one of its nail holes. You then hang a long string with a weight at its bottom from the same nail, so that the string hangs vertically in front of the horseshoe without touching it. How do you know that the horseshoe's center of gravity is along the line behind the string? How can you locate the center of gravity by repeating the process at another nail hole? Will the center of gravity be within the solid material of the horseshoe?

Q11.9. An object consists of a ball of weight W glued to the end of a uniform bar also of weight W. If you release it from rest, with the bar horizontal, what will be its behavior be as it falls if air resistance is negligible? Will it (a) remain horizontal; (b) rotate about its center of gravity; (c) rotate about the ball; or (d) rotate so that the ball swings downward? Explain your reasoning.

Q11.10. Suppose that the object in Question 11.9 is released from rest with the bar tilted at 60° above the horizontal with the ball at the upper end. As it is falling, will it (a) rotate about its center of gravity until it is horizontal; (b) rotate about its center of gravity until it is vertical with the ball at the bottom; (c) rotate about the ball until it is vertical with the ball at the bottom; or (d) remain at 60° above the horizontal?

Q11.11. Why must a water skier moving with constant velocity lean backward? What determines how far back she must lean? Draw a free-body diagram for the water skier to justify your answers.

Q11.12. In pioneer days, when a Conestoga wagon was stuck in the mud, people would grasp the wheel spokes and try to turn the wheels, rather than simply pushing the wagon. Why?

Q11.13. The mighty Zimbo claims to have leg muscles so strong that he can stand flat on his feet and lean forward to pick up an apple on the floor with his teeth. Should you pay to see him perform, or do you have any suspicions about his claim? Why?

Q11.14. Why is it easier to hold a 10-kg dumbbell in your hand at your side than it is to hold it with your arm extended horizontally?

Q11.15. Certain features of a person, such as height and mass, are fixed (at least over relatively long periods of time). Are the following features also fixed? (a) location of the center of gravity of the body; (b) moment of inertia of the body about an axis through the person's center of mass. Explain your reasoning.

Q11.16. During pregnancy, women often develop back pains from leaning backward while walking. Why do they have to walk this way?

Q11.17. Why is a tapered water glass with a narrow base easier to tip over than a glass with straight sides? Does it matter whether the glass is full or empty?

Q11.18. When a tall, heavy refrigerator is pushed across a rough floor, what factors determine whether it slides or tips?

Q11.19. If a metal wire has its length doubled and its diameter tripled, by what factor does its Young's modulus change?

Q11.20. Why is concrete with steel reinforcing rods embedded in it stronger than plain concrete?

Q11.21. A metal wire of diameter D stretches by 0.100 mm when supporting a weight W. If the same length wire is used to support a weight three times as heavy, what would its diameter have to be (in terms of D) so it still stretched only 0.100 mm?

Q11.22. Compare the mechanical properties of a steel cable, made by twisting many thin wires together, with the properties of a solid steel rod of the same diameter. What advantages does each have?

Q11.23. The material in human bones and elephant bones is essentially the same, but an elephant has much thicker legs. Explain why, in terms of breaking stress.

Q11.24. There is a small but appreciable amount of elastic hysteresis in the large tendon at the back of a horse's leg. Explain how this can cause damage to the tendon if a horse runs too hard for too long a time.

Q11.25. When rubber mounting blocks are used to absorb machine vibrations through elastic hysteresis, as mentioned in Section 11.5, what becomes of the energy associated with the vibrations?

Exercises

Section 11.2 Center of Gravity

11.1. A 2.40-kg, 50.0-cm-long uniform bar has a small 1.10-kg mass glued to its left end and a small 2.20-kg mass glued to the other end. You want to balance this system horizontally on a fulcrum placed just under its center of gravity. How far from the left end should the fulcrum be placed?

11.2. The center of gravity of an irregular object is shown in Fig. 11.20. You need to move the center of gravity 2.20 cm to the left by gluing on a tiny 1.50-kg mass, which will then be considered as part of the object. Where should you attach this additional mass?

Figure **11.20** Exercise 11.2.

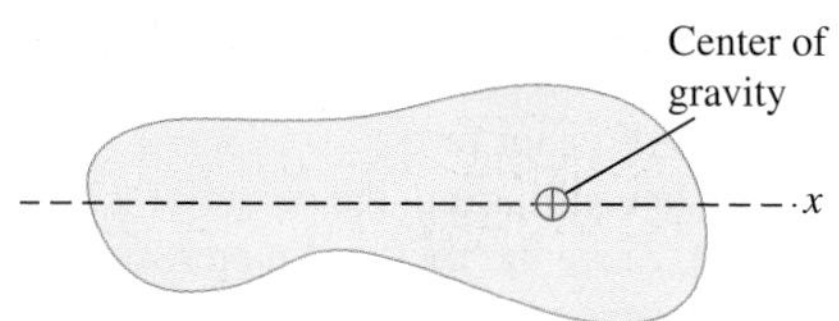

11.3. A box of negligible mass rests at the left end of a 2.00-m, 25.0-kg plank (Fig. 11.21). The width of the box is 75.0 cm, and sand is to be distributed uniformly throughout it. The center of gravity of the nonuniform plank is 50.0 cm from the right end. What mass of sand should be put into the box so that the plank balances horizontally on a fulcrum placed just below its midpoint?

Figure **11.21** Exercise 11.3.

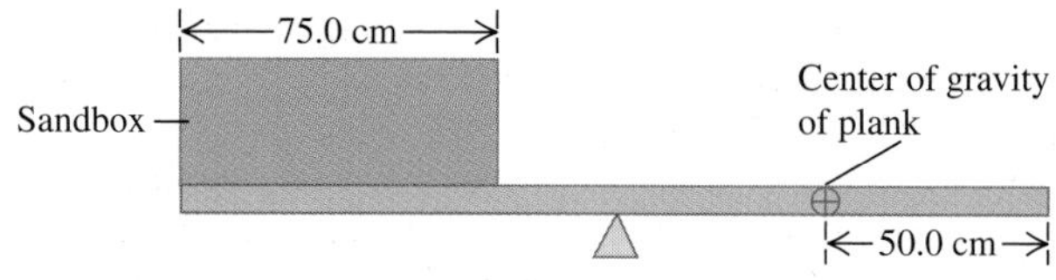

Section 11.3 Solving Rigid-Body Equilibrium Problems

11.4. A uniform 300-N trapdoor in a floor is hinged at one side. Find the net upward force needed to begin to open it and the total force exerted on the door by the hinges (a) if the upward force is applied at the center and (b) if the upward force is applied at the center of the edge opposite the hinges.

11.5. Raising a Ladder. A ladder carried by a fire truck is 20.0 m long. The ladder weighs 2800 N and its center of gravity is at its center. The ladder is pivoted at one end (A) about a pin (Fig. 11.22); you can ignore the friction torque at the pin. The ladder is raised into position by a force applied by a hydraulic piston at C. Point C is 8.0 m from A, and the force $\vec{F}$ exerted by the piston makes an angle of 40° with the ladder. What magnitude must $\vec{F}$ have to just lift the ladder off the support bracket at B? Start with a free-body diagram of the ladder.

Figure 11.22 Exercise 11.5.

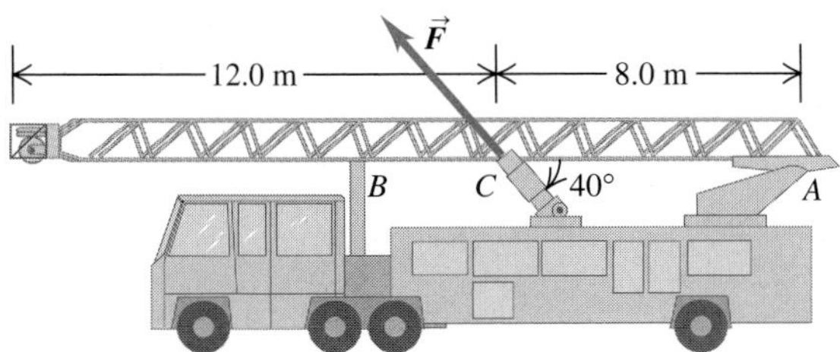

11.6. Two people are carrying a uniform wooden board that is 3.00 m long and weighs 160 N. If one person applies an upward force equal to 60 N at one end, at what point does the other person lift? Begin with a free-body diagram of the board.

11.7. Two people carry a heavy electric motor by placing it on a light board 2.00 m long. One person lifts at one end with a force of 400 N, and the other lifts the opposite end with a force of 600 N. (a) What is the weight of the motor, and where along the board is its center of gravity located? (b) Suppose the board is not light but weighs 200 N, with its center of gravity at its center, and the two people each exert the same forces as before. What is the weight of the motor in this case, and where is its center of gravity located?

11.8. A 60.0-cm, uniform, 50.0-N shelf is supported horizontally by two vertical wires attached to the sloping ceiling (Fig. 11.23). A very small 25.0-N tool is placed on the shelf midway between the points where the wires are attached to it. Find the tension in each wire. Begin by making a free-body diagram of the shelf.

Figure 11.23 Exercise 11.8.

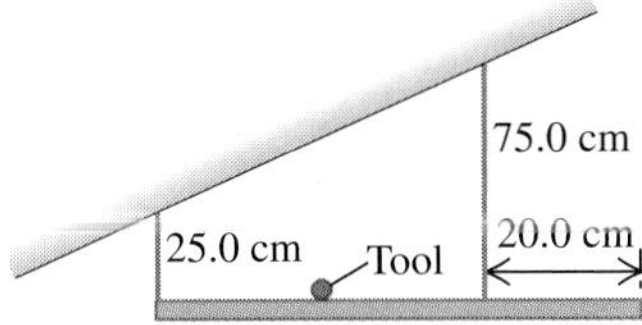

11.9. A 350-N, uniform, 1.50-m bar is suspended horizontally by two vertical cables at each end. Cable A can support a maximum tension of 500.0 N without breaking, and cable B can support up to 400.0 N. You want to place a small weight on this bar. (a) What is the heaviest weight you can put on without breaking either cable, and (b) where should you put this weight?

11.10. A uniform ladder 5.0 m long rests against a frictionless, vertical wall with its lower end 3.0 m from the wall. The ladder weighs 160 N. The coefficient of static friction between the foot of the ladder and the ground is 0.40. A man weighing 740 N climbs slowly up the ladder. Start by drawing a free-body diagram of the ladder. (a) What is the maximum frictional force that the ground can exert on the ladder at its lower end? (b) What is the actual frictional force when the man has climbed 1.0 m along the ladder? (c) How far along the ladder can the man climb before the ladder starts to slip?

11.11. A diving board 3.00 m long is supported at a point 1.00 m from the end, and a diver weighing 500 N stands at the free end (Fig. 11.24). The diving board is of uniform cross section and weighs 280 N. Find (a) the force at the support point and (b) the force at the left-hand end.

Figure 11.24 Exercise 11.11.

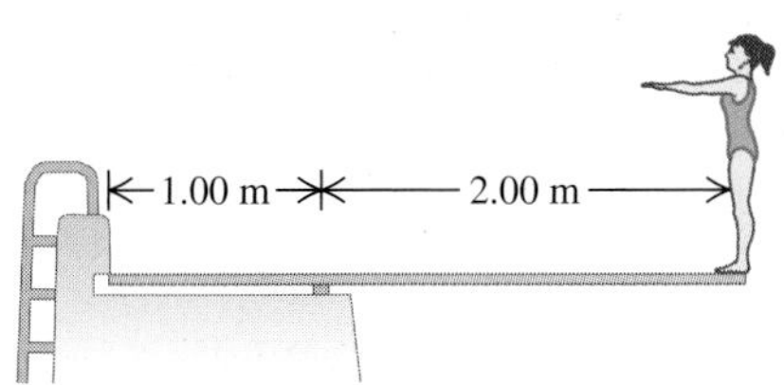

11.12. A uniform aluminum beam 9.00 m long, weighing 300 N, rests symmetrically on two supports 5.00 m apart (Fig. 11.25). A boy weighing 600 N starts at point A and walks toward the right. (a) In the same diagram construct two graphs showing the upward forces F_A and F_B exerted on the beam at points A and B, as functions of the coordinate x of the boy. Let 1 cm = 100 N vertically, and 1 cm = 1.00 m horizontally. (b) From your diagram, how far beyond point B can the boy walk before the beam tips? (c) How far from the right end of the beam should support B be placed so that the boy can walk just to the end of the beam without causing it to tip?

Figure 11.25 Exercise 11.12.

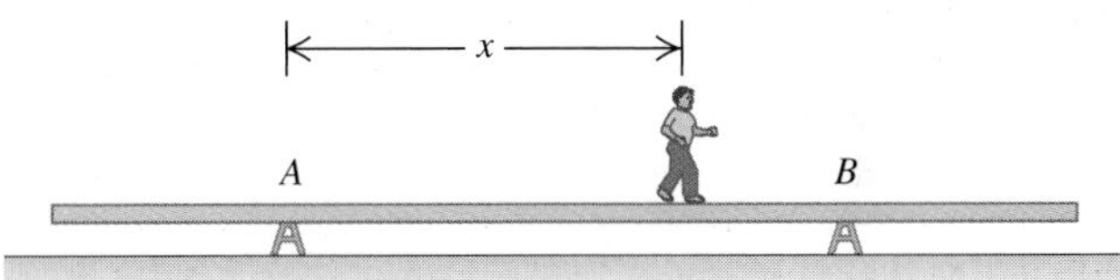

11.13. Find the tension T in each cable and the magnitude and direction of the force exerted on the strut by the pivot in each of the arrangements in Fig. 11.26. In each case let w be the weight of the suspended crate full of priceless art objects. The strut is uniform and also has weight w. Start each case with a free-body diagram of the strut.

Figure 11.26 Exercise 11.13.

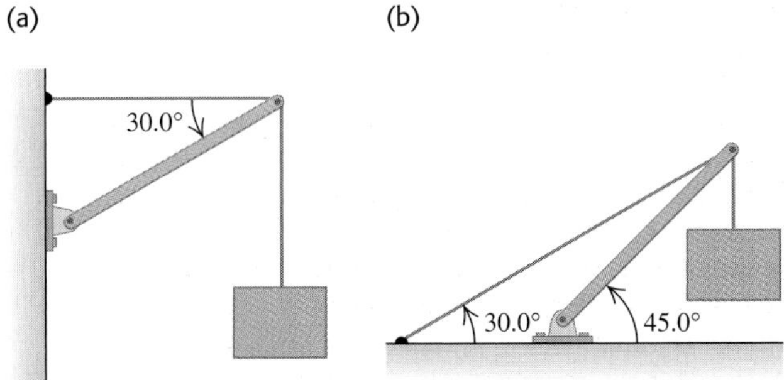

11.14. The horizontal beam in Fig. 11.27 weighs 150 N, and its center of gravity is at its center. Find (a) the tension in the cable and (b) the horizontal and vertical components of the force exerted on the beam at the wall.

11.15. A door 1.00 m wide and 2.00 m high weighs 280 N and is supported by two hinges, one 0.50 m from the top and the other 0.50 m from the bottom.

Figure 11.27 Exercise 11.14.

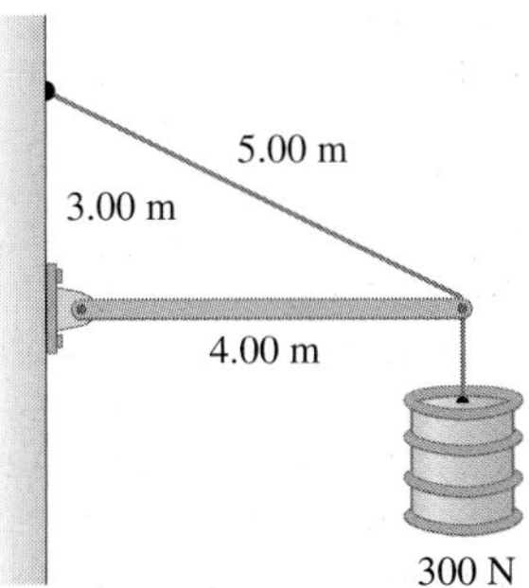

Each hinge supports half the total weight of the door. Assuming that the door's center of gravity is at its center, find the horizontal components of force exerted on the door by each hinge.

11.16. Suppose that you can lift no more than 650 N (around 150 lb) unaided. (a) How much can you lift using a 1.4-m-long wheelbarrow that weighs 80.0 N and whose center of gravity is 0.50 m from the center of the wheel (Fig. 11.28)? The center of gravity of the load carried in the wheelbarrow is also 0.50 m from the center of the wheel. (b) Where does the force come from to enable you to lift more than 650 N using the wheelbarrow?

Figure 11.28 Exercise 11.16.

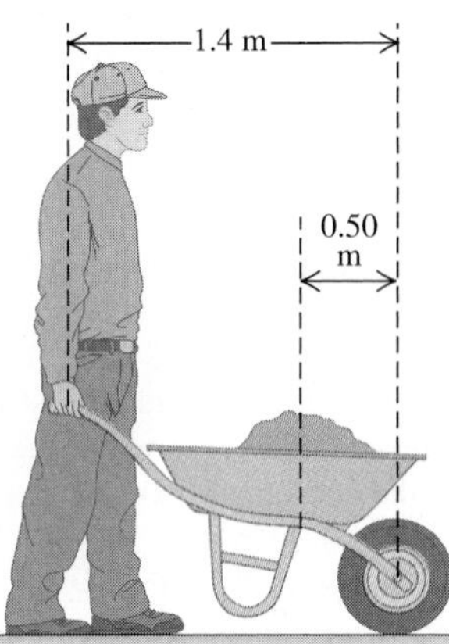

11.17. You take your dog Clea to the vet, and the doctor decides he must locate the little beast's center of gravity. It would be awkward to hang the pooch from the ceiling, so the vet must devise another method. He places Clea's front feet on one scale and her hind feet on another. The front scale reads 157 N, while the rear scale reads 89 N. The vet next measures Clea and finds that her rear feet are 0.95 m behind her front feet. How much does Clea weigh, and where is her center of gravity?

11.18. A 15,000-N crane pivots around a friction-free axle at its base and is supported by a cable making a 25° angle with the crane (Fig. 11.29). The crane is 16 m long and is not uniform, its center of gravity being 7.0 m from the axle as measured along the crane. The cable is attached 3.0 m from the upper end of the crane. When the crane is raised to 55° above the horizontal holding an 11,000-N pallet of bricks by a 2.2-m very light cord, find (a) the tension in the cable, and (b) the horizontal and vertical components of the force that the axle exerts on the crane. Start with a free-body diagram of the crane.

Figure 11.29 Exercise 11.18.

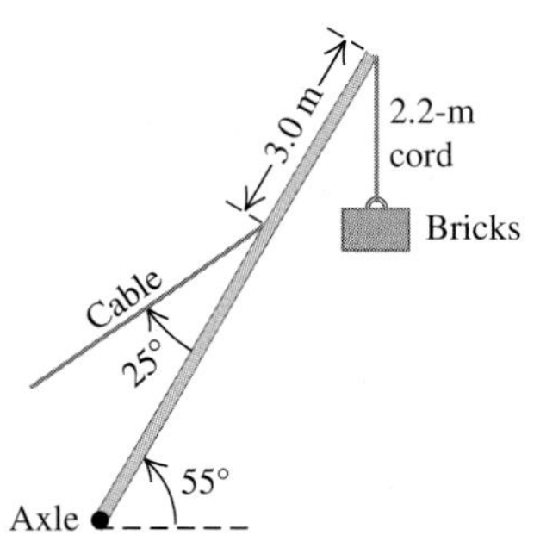

11.19. A 3.00-m-long, 240-N, uniform rod at the zoo is held in a horizontal position by two ropes at its ends (Fig. 11.30). The left rope makes an angle of 150° with the rod and the right rope makes an angle θ with the horizontal. A 90-N howler monkey (*Alouatta seniculus*) hangs motionless 0.50 m from the right end of the rod as he carefully studies you. Calculate the tensions in the two ropes and the angle θ. First make a free-body diagram of the rod.

Figure 11.30 Exercise 11.19.

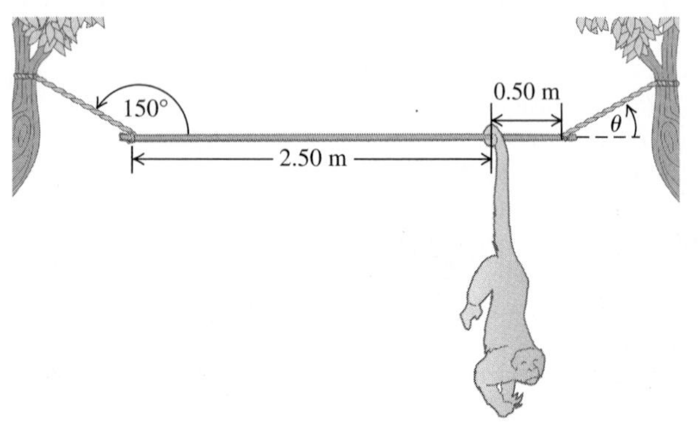

11.20. A nonuniform beam 4.50 m long and weighing 1.00 kN makes an angle of 25.0° below the horizontal. It is held in position by a frictionless pivot at its upper right end and by a cable 3.00 m farther down the beam and perpendicular to it (Fig. 11.31). The center of gravity of the beam is 2.00 m down the beam from the pivot. Lighting equipment exerts a 5.00-kN downward force on the lower left end of the beam. Find the tension T in the cable and the horizontal and vertical components of the force exerted on the beam by the pivot. Start by sketching a free-body diagram of the beam.

Figure 11.31 Exercise 11.20.

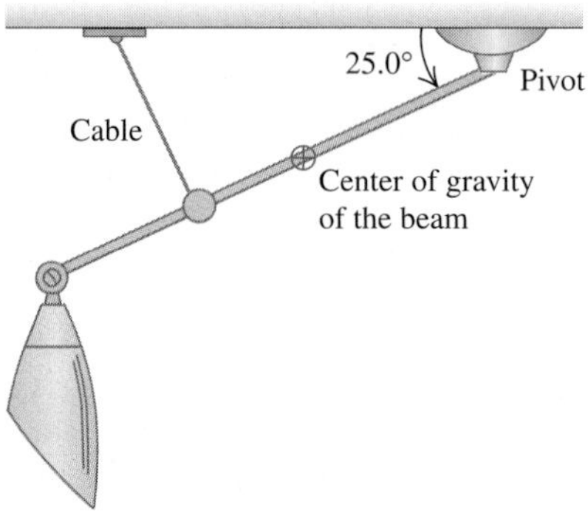

11.21. A Couple. Two forces equal in magnitude and opposite in direction, acting on an object at two different points, form what is called a *couple.* Two antiparallel forces with equal magnitudes $F_1 = F_2 = 8.00\ N$ are applied to a rod as shown in Fig. 11.32. (a) What should the distance l between the forces be if they are to provide a net torque of $6.40\ \text{N} \cdot \text{m}$ about the left end of the rod? (b) Is the sense of this torque clockwise or counterclockwise? (c) Repeat parts (a) and (b) for a pivot at the point on the rod where $\vec{F}_2$ is applied.

Figure 11.32 Exercise 11.21.

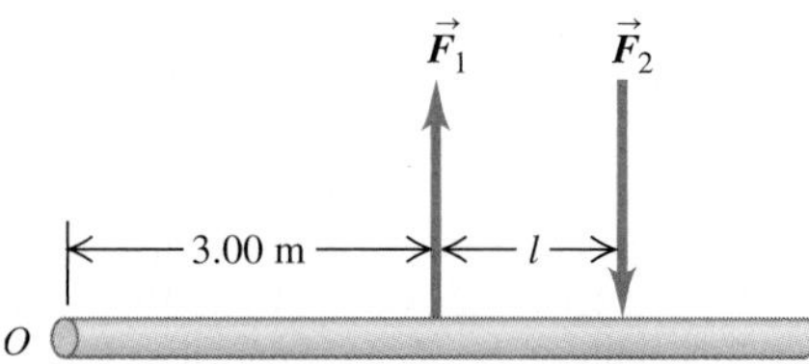

Section 11.4 Stress, Strain, and Elastic Moduli

11.22. Biceps Muscle. A relaxed biceps muscle requires a force of 25.0 N for an elongation of 3.0 cm; the same muscle under maximum tension requires a force of 500 N for the same elongation. Find Young's modulus for the muscle tissue under each of these conditions if the muscle is assumed to be a uniform cylinder with length 0.200 m and cross-sectional area 50.0 cm^2.

11.23. A circular steel wire 2.00 m long must stretch no more than 0.25 cm when a tensile force of 400 N is applied to each end of the wire. What minimum diameter is required for the wire?

11.24. Two circular rods, one steel and the other copper, are joined end to end. Each rod is 0.750 m long and 1.50 cm in diameter. The combination is subjected to a tensile force with magnitude 4000 N. For each rod, what are (a) the strain and (b) the elongation?

11.25. A metal rod that is 4.00 m long and 0.50 cm^2 in cross-sectional area is found to stretch 0.20 cm under a tension of 5000 N. What is Young's modulus for this metal?

11.26. Stress on a Mountaineer's Rope. A nylon rope used by mountaineers elongates 1.10 m under the weight of a 65.0-kg climber. If the rope is 45.0 m in length and 7.0 mm in diameter, what is Young's modulus for nylon?

11.27. In constructing a large mobile, an artist hangs an aluminum sphere of mass 6.0 kg from a vertical steel wire 0.50 m long and 2.5×10^{-3} cm^2 in cross-sectional area. On the bottom of the sphere he attaches a similar steel wire, from which he hangs a brass cube of mass 10.0 kg. For each wire, compute (a) the tensile strain and (b) the elongation.

11.28. A vertical, solid steel post 25 cm in diameter and 2.50 m long is required to support a load of 8000 kg. You can ignore the weight of the post. What are (a) the stress in the post; (b) the strain in the post; and (c) the change in the post's length when the load is applied?

11.29. Outside a house 1.0 km from ground zero of a 100-kiloton nuclear bomb explosion, the pressure will rapidly rise to as high as 2.8 atm while the pressure inside the house remains 1.0 atm. If the front of the house measures 3.33 m high by 15.0 m wide, what is the resulting net force exerted by the air on the front of the house?

11.30. A solid gold bar is pulled up from the hold of the sunken RMS *Titanic.* (a) What happens to its volume as it goes from the pressure at the ship to the lower pressure at the ocean's surface? (b) The pressure difference is proportional to the depth. How many times greater would the volume change have been had the ship been twice as deep? (c) The bulk modulus of lead is one-fourth that of gold. Find the ratio of the volume change of a solid lead bar to that of a gold bar of equal volume for the same pressure change.

11.31. A petite young woman distributes her 500 N weight equally over the heels of her high-heeled shoes. Each heel has an area of 0.750 cm^2. (a) What pressure is exerted on the floor by each heel? (b) With the same pressure, how much weight could be supported by two flat-bottomed sandals, each of area 200 cm^2?

11.32. In the Challenger Deep of the Marianas Trench, the depth of seawater is 10.9 km and the pressure is 1.16×10^8 Pa (about 1.15×10^3 atm). (a) If a cubic meter of water is taken from the surface to this depth, what is the change in its volume? (Normal atmospheric pressure is about 1.0×10^5 Pa. Assume that k for seawater is the same as the freshwater value given in Table 11.2.) (b) What is the density of seawater at this depth? (At the surface, seawater has a density of 1.03×10^3 kg/m^3.)

11.33. A specimen of oil having an initial volume of 600 cm^3 is subjected to a pressure increase of 3.6×10^6 Pa, and the volume is found to decrease by 0.45 cm^3. What is the bulk modulus of the material? The compressibility?

11.34. A square steel plate is 10.0 cm on a side and 0.500 cm thick. (a) Find the shear strain that results if a force of magnitude 9.0×10^5 N is applied to each of the four sides, parallel to the side. (b) Find the displacement x in centimeters.

11.35. A copper cube measures 6.00 cm on each side. The bottom face is held in place by very strong glue to a flat horizontal surface, while a horizontal force F is applied to the upper face parallel to one of the edges. (Consult Table 11.1.) (a) Show that the glue exerts a force F on the bottom face that is equal but opposite to the force on the top face. (b) How large must F be to cause the cube to deform by 0.250 mm? (c) If the same experiment were performed on a lead cube of the same size as the copper one, by what distance would it deform for the same force as in part (b)?

11.36. Shear forces are applied to a rectangular solid. The same forces are applied to another rectangular solid of the same material, but with three times each edge length. In each case the forces are small enough that Hooke's law is obeyed. What is the ratio of the shear strain for the larger object to that of the smaller object?

Section 11.5 Elasticity and Plasticity

11.37. In a materials testing laboratory, a metal wire made from a new alloy is found to break when a tensile force of 90.8 N is applied perpendicular to each end. If the diameter of the wire is 1.84 mm, what is the breaking stress of the alloy?

11.38. A 4.0-m-long steel wire has a cross-sectional area of 0.050 cm^2. Its proportional limit has a value of 0.0016 times its Young's modulus (see Table 11.1). Its breaking stress has a value of 0.0065 times its Young's modulus. The wire is fastened at its upper end and hangs vertically. (a) How great a weight can be hung from the wire without exceeding the proportional limit? (b) How much will the wire stretch under this load? (c) What is the maximum weight that the wire can support?

11.39. A steel cable with cross-sectional area 3.00 cm^2 has an elastic limit of 2.40×10^8 Pa. Find the maximum upward acceleration that can be given a 1200-kg elevator supported by the cable if the stress is not to exceed one-third of the elastic limit.

11.40. A brass wire is to withstand a tensile force of 350 N without breaking. What minimum diameter must the wire have?

Problems

11.41. Mountain Climbing. Mountaineers often use a rope to lower themselves down the face of a cliff (this is called *rappelling*). They do this with their body nearly horizontal and their feet pushing against the cliff (Fig. 11.33). Suppose that an 82.0-kg climber, who is 1.90 m tall and has a center of gravity 1.1 m from his feet, rappels down a vertical cliff with his body raised 35.0° above the horizontal. He holds the rope 1.40 m from his feet, and it makes a 25.0° angle with the cliff face. (a) What tension does his rope need to support? (b) Find the horizontal and vertical components of the force that the cliff face exerts on the climber's feet. (c) What minimum coefficient of static friction is needed to prevent the climber's feet from slipping on the cliff face if he has one foot at a time against the cliff?

Figure 11.33 Problem 11.41.

11.42. Sir Lancelot rides slowly out of the castle at Camelot and onto the 12.0-m-long drawbridge that passes over the moat (Fig. 11.34). Unbeknownst to him, his enemies have partially

Figure 11.34 Problem 11.42.

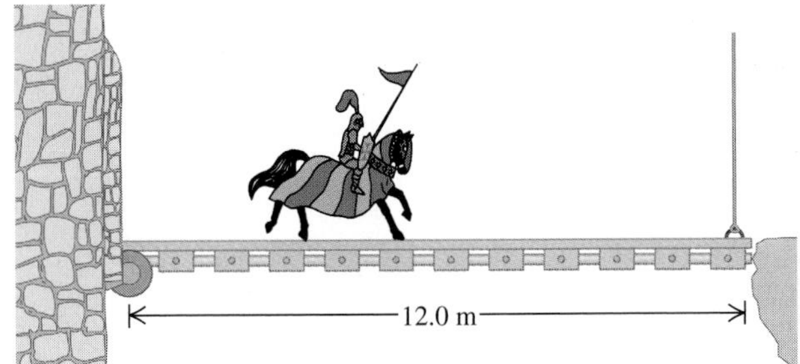

severed the vertical cable holding up the front end of the bridge so that it will break under a tension of 5.80×10^3 N. The bridge has mass 200 kg and its center of gravity is at its center. Lancelot, his lance, his armor, and his horse together have a combined mass of 600 kg. Will the cable break before Lancelot reaches the end of the drawbridge? If so, how far from the castle end of the bridge will the center of gravity of the horse plus rider be when the cable breaks?

11.43. Three vertical forces act on an airplane when it is flying at a constant altitude and with a constant velocity. These are the weight of the airplane, an aerodynamic force on the wing of the airplane, and an aerodynamic force on the airplane's horizontal tail. (The aerodynamic forces are exerted by the surrounding air, and are reactions to the forces that the wing and tail exert on the air as the airplane flies through it.) For a particular light airplane with a weight of 6700 N, the center of gravity is 0.30 m in front of the point where the wing's vertical aerodynamic force acts and 3.66 m in front of the point where the tail's vertical aerodynamic force acts. Determine the magnitude and direction (upward or downward) of each of the two vertical aerodynamic forces.

11.44. A pickup truck has a wheelbase of 3.00 m. Ordinarily, 10,780 N rests on the front wheels and 8820 N on the rear wheels when the truck is parked on a level road. (a) A box weighing 3600 N is now placed on the tailgate, 1.00 m behind the rear axle. How much total weight now rests on the front wheels? On the rear wheels? (b) How much weight would need to be placed on the tailgate to make the front wheels come off the ground?

11.45. A uniform, 255-N rod that is 2.00 m long carries a 225-N weight at its right end and an unknown weight W toward the left end (Fig. 11.35). When W is placed 50.0 cm from the left end of the rod, the system just balances horizontally when the fulcrum is located 75.0 cm from the right end. (a) Find W. (b) If W is now moved 25.0 cm to the right, how far and in what direction must the fulcrum be moved to restore balance?

Figure 11.35 Problem 11.45.

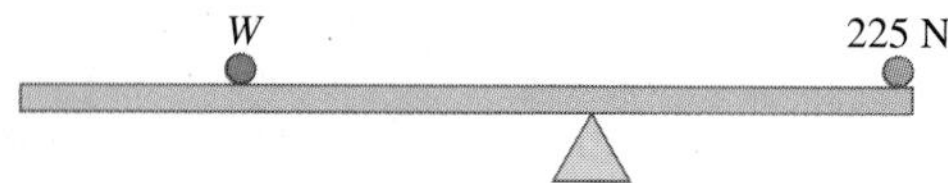

11.46. A thin uniform metal rod is bent into three perpendicular segments, two of which have length L. You want to determine what the length of the third segment should be so that the unit will hang with two segments horizontal when it is supported by a hook as shown in Fig. 11.36. Find x in terms of L.

Figure 11.36 Problem 11.46.

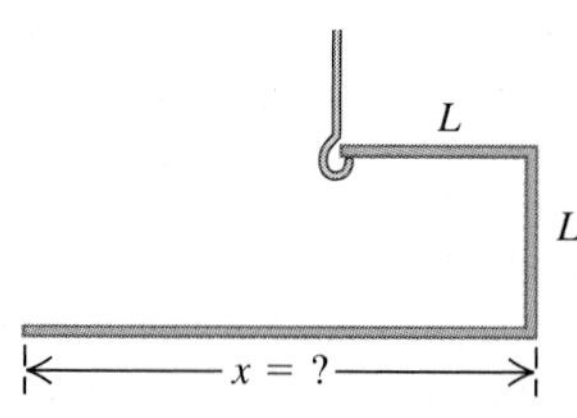

11.47. You open a restaurant and hope to entice customers by hanging out a sign (Fig. 11.37). The uniform horizontal beam supporting the sign is 1.50 m long, has a mass of 18.0 kg, and is hinged to the wall. The sign itself is uniform with a mass of 28.0 kg and overall length of 1.20 m. The two wires supporting the sign are each 32.0 cm long, are 90.0 cm apart, and are equally spaced from the middle of the sign. The cable supporting the beam is 2.00 m long. (a) What minimum tension must your cable be able to support without having your sign come crashing down? (b) What minimum vertical force must the hinge be able to support without pulling out of the wall?

Figure 11.37 Problem 11.47.

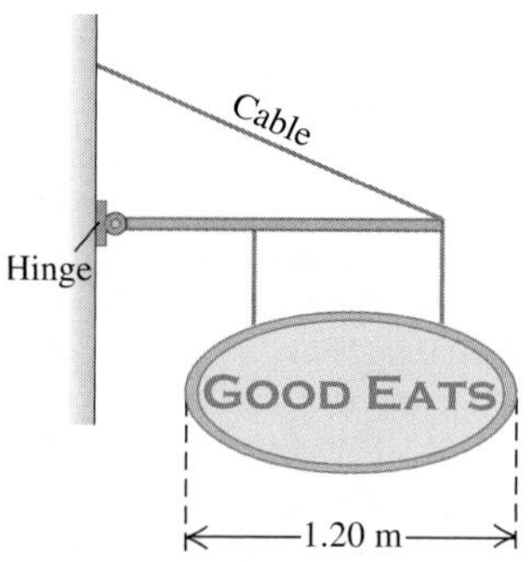

11.48. A claw hammer is used to pull a nail out of a board (Fig. 11.38). The nail is at an angle of 60° to the board, and a force $\vec{F}_1$ of magnitude 500 N applied to the nail is required to pull it from the board. The hammer head contacts the board at point A, which is 0.080 m from where the nail enters the board. A horizontal force $\vec{F}_2$ is applied to the hammer handle at a distance of 0.300 m above the board. What magnitude of force $\vec{F}_2$ is required to apply the required 500-N force (F_1) to the nail? (You can ignore the weight of the hammer.)

Figure 11.38 Problem 11.48.

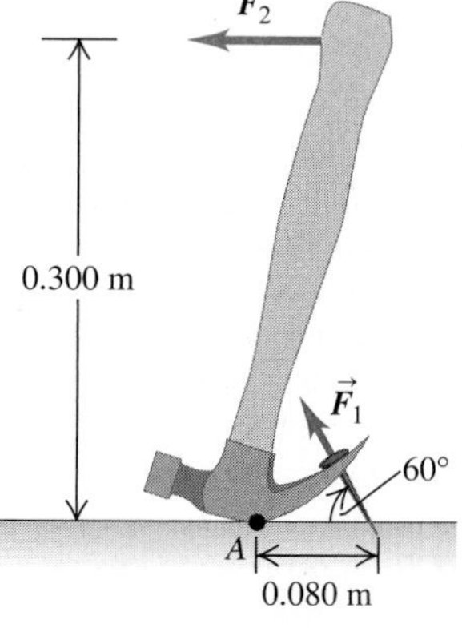

11.49. End A of the bar AB in Fig. 11.39 rests on a frictionless horizontal surface, and end B is hinged. A horizontal force $\vec{F}$ of magnitude 120 N is exerted on end A. You can ignore the weight of the bar. What are the horizontal and vertical components of the force exerted by the bar on the hinge at B?

Figure 11.39 Problem 11.49.

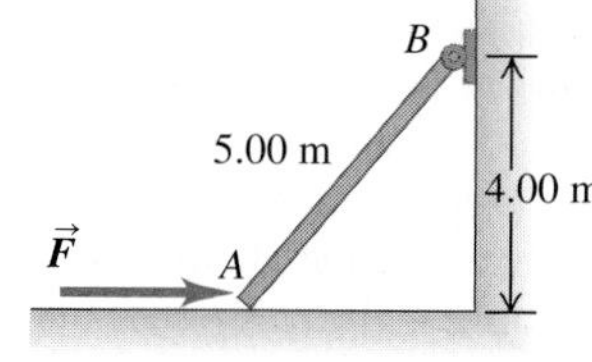

11.50. A museum of modern art is displaying an irregular 358-N sculpture by hanging it from two thin vertical wires, A and B, that are 1.25 m apart (Fig. 11.40). The center of gravity of this piece of art is located 48.0 cm from its extreme right tip. Find the tension in each wire.

Figure 11.40 Problem 11.50.

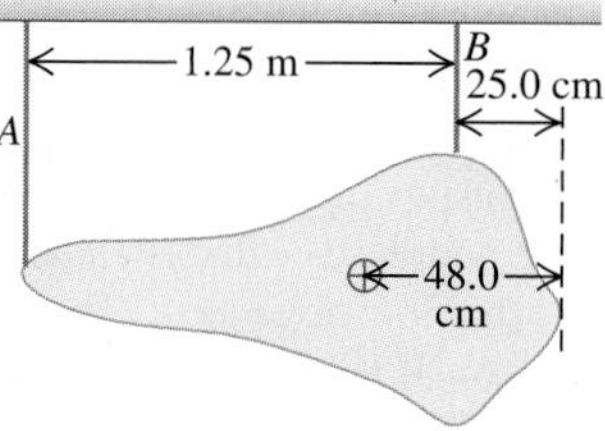

11.51. A beam of mass M and length L is supported horizontally at its ends by two cables making angles θ and ϕ with the horizontal ceiling (Fig. 11.41). (a) Show that if the beam is uniform, these two angles must be equal and the tensions in the cables must also be equal. (b) Suppose now that the center of gravity is $3L/4$ from the left end of the beam. Show that the angles are not completely independent but must obey the equation $\tan\theta = 3\tan\phi$.

Figure 11.41 Problem 11.51.

11.52. A Truck on a Drawbridge. A loaded cement mixer drives onto an old drawbridge, where it stalls with its center of gravity three-quarters of the way across the span. The truck driver radios for help, sets the handbrake, and waits. Meanwhile, a boat approaches, so the drawbridge is raised by means of a cable attached to the end opposite the hinge (Fig. 11.42). The drawbridge is 40.0 m long and has a mass of 12,000 kg; its center of gravity is at its midpoint. The cement mixer, with driver, has mass 30,000 kg. When the drawbridge has been raised to an angle of 30° above the horizontal, the cable makes an angle of 70° with the surface of the bridge. (a) What is the tension T in the cable when the drawbridge is held in this position? (b) What are the horizontal and vertical components of the force the hinge exerts on the span?

Figure 11.42 Problem 11.52.

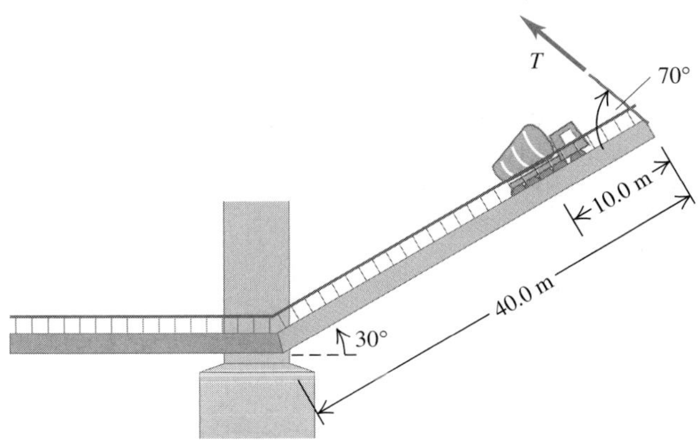

11.53. A uniform solid cylinder of mass M is supported on a ramp that rises at an angle θ above the horizontal by a wire that is wrapped around its rim and pulls on it tangentially parallel to the ramp (Fig. 11.43). (a) Show that there *must* be friction on the surface for the cylinder to balance this way. (b) Show that the tension in the wire must be equal to the friction force, and find this tension.

Figure 11.43 Problem 11.53.

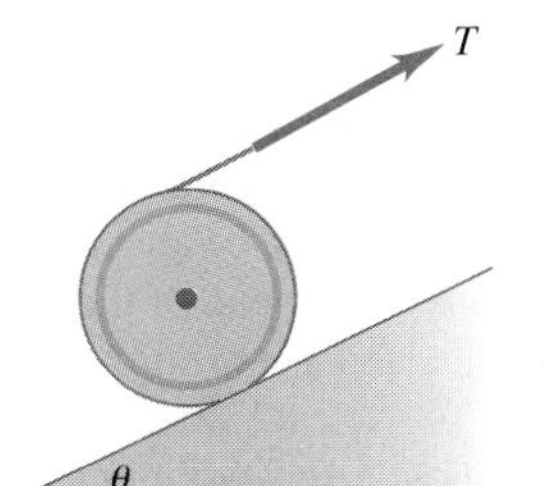

11.54. A nonuniform fire escape ladder is 6.0 m long when extended to the icy alley below. It is held at the top by a frictionless pivot, and there is negligible frictional force from the icy surface at the bottom. The ladder weighs 250 N, and its center of gravity is 2.0 m along the ladder from its bottom. A mother and child of total weight 750 N are on the ladder 1.5 m from the pivot. The ladder makes an angle θ with the horizontal. Find the magnitude and direction of (a) the force exerted by the icy alley on the ladder and (b) the force exerted by the ladder on the pivot. (c) Do your answers in parts (a) and (b) depend on the angle θ?

11.55. A uniform strut of mass m makes an angle θ with the horizontal. It is supported by a frictionless pivot located at one-third its length from its lower left end and a horizontal rope at its upper right end. A cable and package of total weight w hang from its upper right end. (a) Find the vertical and horizontal components V and H of the pivot's force on the strut as well as the tension T in the rope. (b) If the maximum safe tension in the rope is 700 N and the mass of the strut is 20.0 kg, find the maximum safe weight of the cable and package when the strut makes an angle of 55.0° with the horizontal. (c) For what angle θ can no weight be safely suspended from the right end of the strut?

11.56. You are asked to design the decorative mobile shown in Fig. 11.44. The strings and rods have negligible weight, and the rods are to hang horizontally. (a) Draw a free-body diagram for each rod. (b) Find the weights of the balls A, B, and C. Find the tensions in the strings S_1, S_2, and S_3. (c) What can you say about the horizontal location of the mobile's center of gravity? Explain.

Figure 11.44 Problem 11.56.

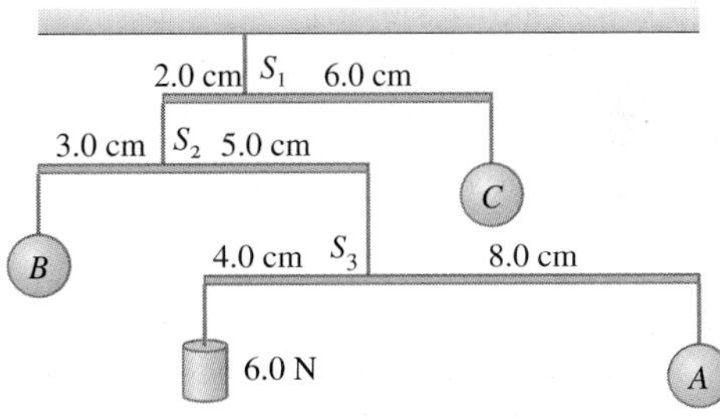

11.57. A uniform, 7.5-m-long beam weighing 9000 N is hinged to a wall and supported by a thin cable attached 1.5 m from the free end of the beam. The cable runs between the beam and the wall and makes a 40° angle with the beam. What is the tension in the cable when the beam is at an angle of 30° above the horizontal?

11.58. A uniform drawbridge must be held at a 37° angle above the horizontal to allow ships to pass underneath. The drawbridge weighs 45,000 N and is 14.0 m long. A cable is connected 3.5 m from the hinge where the bridge pivots (measured along the bridge) and pulls horizontally on the bridge to hold it in place. (a) What is the tension in the cable? (b) Find the magnitude and direction of the force the hinge exerts on the bridge.

11.59. A uniform, 250-kg beam is supported by a cable connected to the ceiling, as shown in Fig. 11.45. The lower end of the beam rests on the floor. (a) What is the tension in the cable? (b) What is the minimum coefficient of static friction between the beam and the floor required for the beam to remain in this position?

Figure 11.45 Problem 11.59.

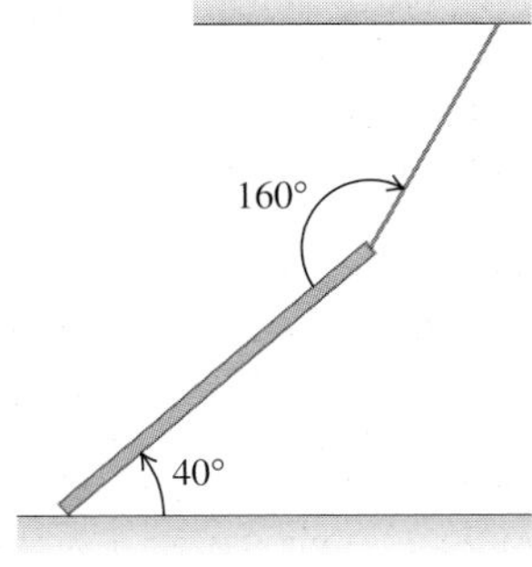

11.60. (a) In Fig. 11.46 a 6.00-m-long, uniform beam is hanging from a point 1.00 m to the right of its center. The beam weighs 140 N and makes an angle of 30.0° with the vertical. At the right-hand end of the beam a 100-N weight is hung; an unknown weight w hangs at the left end. If the system is in equilibrium, what is w? You can ignore the thickness of the beam. (b) If the beam makes, instead, an angle of 45.0° with the vertical, what is w?

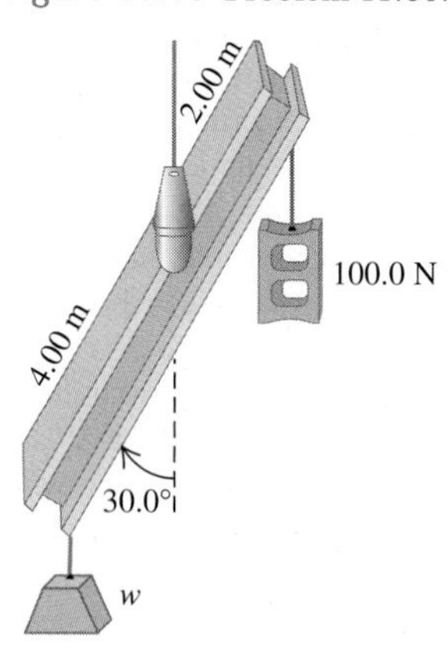

Figure 11.46 Problem 11.60.

11.61. A uniform, horizontal flagpole 5.00 m long with a weight of 200 N is hinged to a vertical wall at one end. A 600-N stuntwoman hangs from its other end. The flagpole is supported by a guy wire running from its outer end to a point on the wall directly above the pole. (a) If the tension in this wire is not to exceed 1000 N, what is the minimum height above the pole at which it may be fastened to the wall? (b) If the flagpole remains horizontal, by how many newtons would the tension be increased if the wire were fastened 0.50 m below this point?

11.62. A holiday decoration consists of two shiny glass spheres with masses 0.0240 kg and 0.0360 kg suspended, as shown in Fig. 11.47, from a uniform rod with mass 0.120 kg and length 1.00 m. The rod is suspended from the ceiling by a vertical cord at each end, so that it is horizontal. Calculate the tension in each of the cords A through F.

Figure 11.47 Problem 11.62.

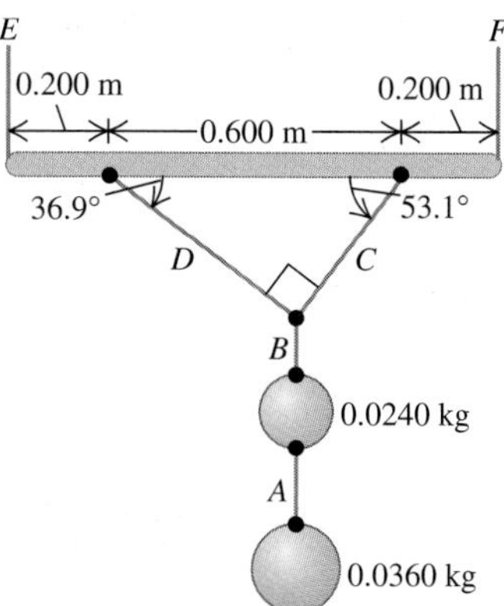

11.63. A uniform rectangular plate of width d, height h, and weight W is supported with its top and bottom edges horizontal (Fig. 11.48). At the lower left corner there is a hinge, and at the upper right corner there is a cable. (a) For what angle θ with the vertical will the tension in the cable be the least, and what is that tension? (b) Under the conditions of part (a), find the horizontal and vertical components of the force that the hinge exerts on the plate.

Figure 11.48 Problem 11.63.

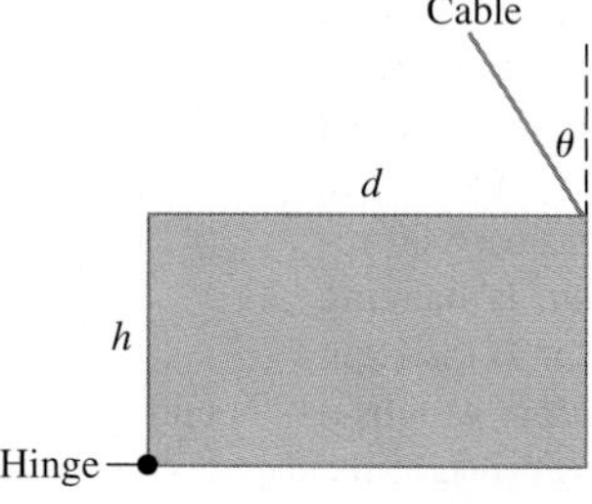

11.64. When you stretch a wire, rope, or rubber band, it gets thinner as well as longer. When Hooke's law holds, the fractional decrease in width is proportional to the tensile strain. If w_0 is the original width and Δw is the change in width, then $\Delta w/w_0 = -\sigma\Delta l/l_0$, where the minus sign reminds us that width decreases when length increases. The dimensionless constant σ, different for different materials, is called *Poisson's ratio.* (a) If the steel rod of Example 11.5 (Section 11.4) has a circular cross section and a Poisson's ratio of 0.23, what is its change in diameter when the milling machine is hung from it? (b) A cylinder made of nickel (Poisson's ratio $= 0.42$) has radius 2.0 cm. What tensile force $F_\perp$ must be applied perpendicular to each end of the cylinder to cause its radius to decrease by 0.10 mm? Assume that the breaking stress and proportional limit for the metal are extremely large and are not exceeded.

11.65. A worker wants to turn over a uniform 1250-N rectangular crate by pulling at 53.0° on one of its vertical sides (Fig. 11.49). The floor is rough enough to prevent the crate from slipping. (a) What pull is needed to just start the crate to tip? (b) How hard does the floor push on the crate? (c) Find the friction force on the crate. (d) What is the minimum coefficient of static friction needed to prevent the crate from slipping on the floor?

Figure 11.49 Problem 11.65.

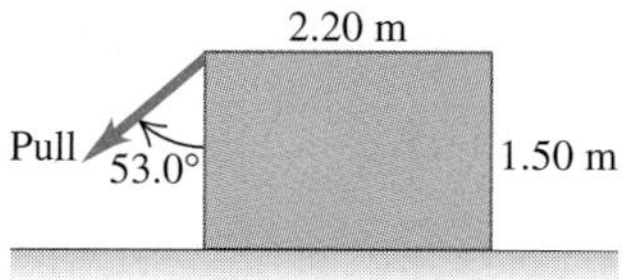

11.66. One end of a uniform meter stick is placed against a vertical wall (Fig. 11.50). The other end is held by a lightweight cord that makes an angle θ with the stick. The coefficient of static friction between the end of the meter stick and the wall is 0.40. (a) What is the maximum value the angle θ can have if the stick is to remain in equilibrium? (b) Let the angle θ be 15°. A block of the same weight as the meter stick is suspended from the stick, as shown, at a distance x from the wall. What is the minimum value of x for which the stick will remain in equilibrium? (c) When $\theta = 15°$, how large must the coefficient of static friction be so that the block can be attached 10 cm from the left end of the stick without causing it to slip?

Figure 11.50 Problem 11.66.

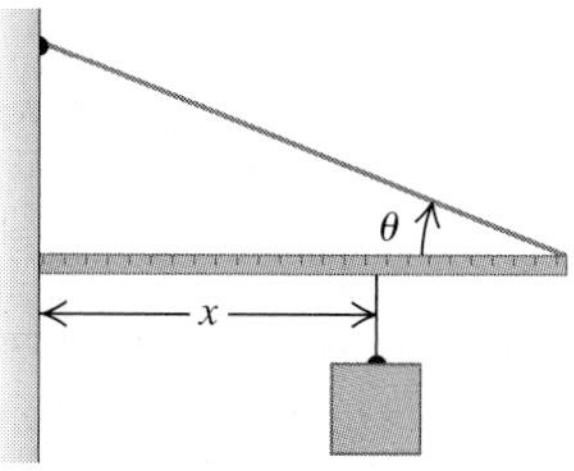

11.67. Two friends are carrying a 200-kg crate up a flight of stairs. The crate is 1.25 m long and 0.500 m high, and its center of gravity is at its center. The stairs make a 45.0° angle with respect to the floor. The crate also is carried at a 45.0° angle, so that its bottom side is parallel to the slope of the stairs (Fig. 11.51). If the force each person applies is

Figure 11.51 Problem 11.67.

vertical, what is the magnitude of each of these forces? Is it better to be the person above or below on the stairs?

11.68. Forearm. In the human arm, the forearm and hand pivot about the elbow joint. Consider a simplified model in which the biceps muscle is attached to the forearm 3.80 cm from the elbow joint. Assume that the person's hand and forearm together weigh 15.0 N and that their center of gravity is 15.0 cm from the elbow (not quite halfway to the hand). The forearm is held horizontally at a right angle to the upper arm, with the biceps muscle exerting its force perpendicular to the forearm. (a) Draw a free-body diagram for the forearm, and find the force exerted by the biceps when the hand is empty. (b) Now the person holds a 80.0-N weight in his hand, with the forearm still horizontal. Assume that the center of gravity of this weight is 33.0 cm from the elbow. Construct a free-body diagram for the forearm, and find the force now exerted by the biceps. Explain why the biceps muscle needs to be very strong. (c) Under the conditions of part (b), find the magnitude and direction of the force that the elbow joint exerts on the forearm. (d) While holding the 80.0-N weight, the person raises his forearm until it is at an angle of 53.0° above the horizontal. If the biceps muscle continues to exert its force perpendicular to the forearm, what is this force when the forearm is in this position? Has the force increased or decreased from its value in part (b)? Explain why this is so, and test your answer by actually doing this with your own arm.

11.69. Refer to the discussion of holding a dumbbell in Example 11.4 (Section 11.3). The maximum weight that can be held in this way is limited by the maximum allowable tendon tension T (determined by the strength of the tendons) and by the distance D from the elbow to where the tendon attaches to the forearm. (a) Let T_{max} represent the maximum value of the tendon tension. Use the results of Example 11.4 to express w_{max} (the maximum weight that can be held) in terms of T_{max}, L, D, and h. Your expression should *not* include the angle θ. (b) The tendons of different primates are attached to the forearm at different values of D. Calculate the derivative of w_{max} with respect to D, and determine whether the derivative is positive or negative. (c) A chimpanzee tendon is attached to the forearm at a point farther from the elbow than for humans. Use this to explain why chimpanzees have stronger arms than humans. (The disadvantage is that chimpanzees have less flexible arms than do humans.)

11.70. A uniform, 90.0-N table is 3.6 m long, 1.0 m high, and 1.2 m wide. A 1500-N weight is placed 0.50 m from one end of the table, a distance of 0.60 m from each of the two legs at that end. Draw a free-body diagram for the table and find the force that each of the four legs exerts on the floor.

11.71. Flying Buttress. (a) A symmetric building has a roof sloping upward at 35.0° above the horizontal on each side. If each side of the uniform roof weighs 10,000 N, find the horizontal force that this roof exerts at the top of the wall, which tends to push out the walls. Which type of building would be more in danger of collapsing: one with tall walls or one with short walls? Explain. (b) As you saw in part (a), tall walls are in danger of collapsing from the weight of the roof. This problem plagued the ancient builders of large structures. A solution used in the great Gothic cathedrals during the 1200s was the flying buttress, a stone support running between the walls and the ground that helped to hold in the walls. A Gothic church has a uniform roof weighing a total of 20,000 N and rising at 40° above the horizontal at each wall. The walls are 40 m tall, and a flying buttress meets each wall 10 m below the base of the roof. What horizontal force must this flying buttress apply to the wall?

11.72. You are trying to raise a bicycle wheel of mass m and radius R up over a curb of height h. To do this, you apply a horizontal force $\vec{F}$ (Fig. 11.52). What is the smallest magnitude of the force $\vec{F}$ that will succeed in raising the wheel onto the curb when the force is applied (a) at the center of the wheel, and (b) at the top of the wheel? (c) In which case is less force required?

Figure **11.52** Problem 11.72.

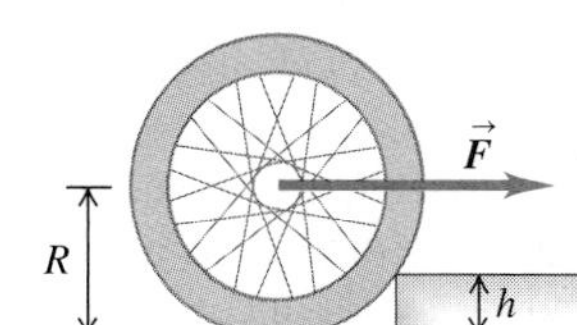

11.73. The Farmyard Gate. A gate 4.00 m wide and 2.00 m high weighs 500 N. Its center of gravity is at its center, and it is hinged at A and B. To relieve the strain on the top hinge, a wire CD is connected as shown in Fig. 11.53. The tension in CD is increased until the horizontal force at hinge A is zero. (a) What is the tension in the wire CD? (b) What is the magnitude of the horizontal component of the force at hinge B? (c) What is the combined vertical force exerted by hinges A and B?

Figure **11.53** Problem 11.73.

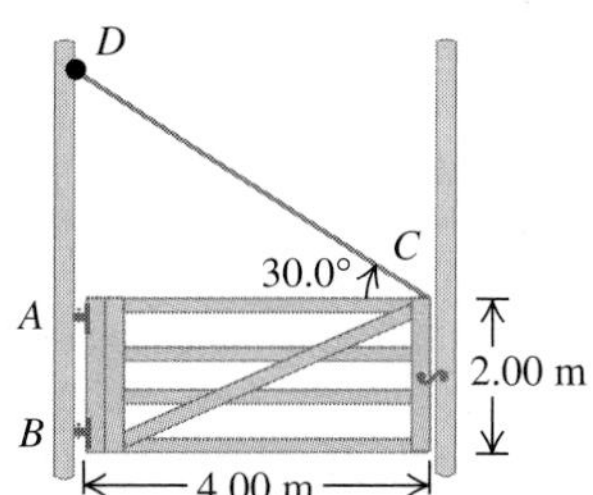

11.74. If you put a uniform block at the edge of a table, the center of the block must be over the table for the block not to fall off. (a) If you stack two identical blocks at the table edge, the center of the top block must be over the bottom block, and the center of gravity of the two blocks together must be over the table. In terms of the length L of each block, what is the maximum overhang possible (Fig. 11.54)? (b) Repeat part (a) for three identical blocks and for four identical blocks. (c) Is it possible to make a stack of blocks such that the uppermost block is not directly over the table at all? How many blocks would it take to do this? (Try this with your friends using copies of this book.)

Figure **11.54** Problem 11.74.

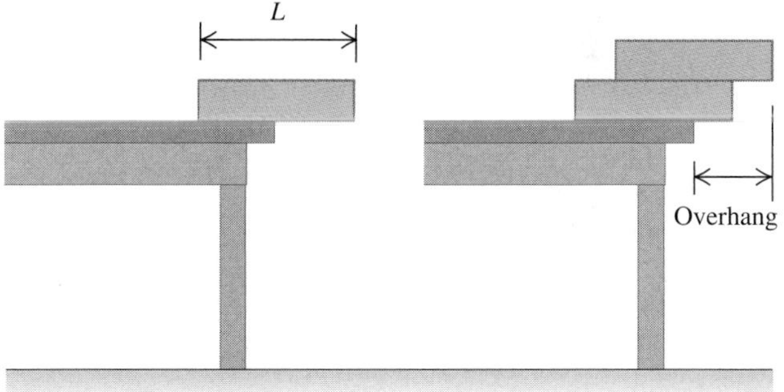

11.75. Two uniform 75.0-g marbles 2.00 cm in diameter are stacked as shown in Fig. 11.55 in a container that is 3.00 cm wide. (a) Find the force that the container exerts on the marbles at the points of contact A, B, and C. (b) What force does each marble exert on the other?

Figure **11.55** Problem 11.75.

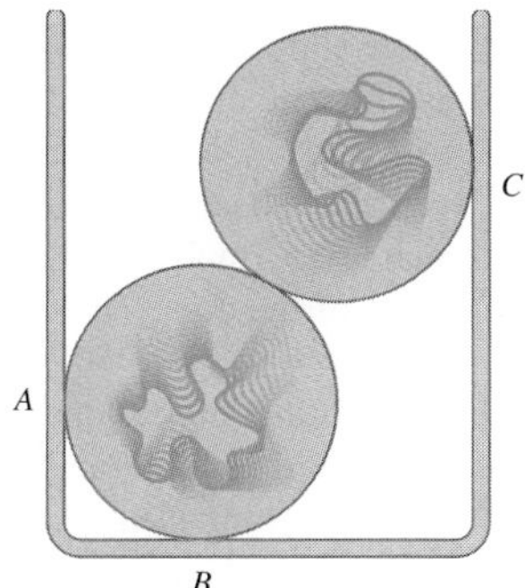

11.76. Two identical, uniform beams weighing 260 N each are connected at one end by a frictionless hinge. A light horizontal crossbar attached at the midpoints of the beams maintains an angle of 53.0° between the beams. The beams are suspended from the ceiling by vertical wires such that they form a "V," as shown in Fig. 11.56. (a) What force does the crossbar exert on each beam? (b) Is the crossbar under tension or compression? (c) What force (magnitude and direction) does the hinge at point A exert on each beam?

Figure **11.56** Problem 11.76.

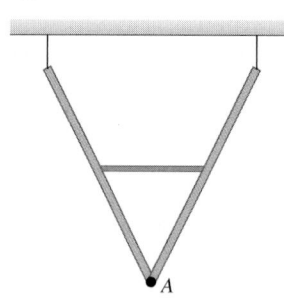

11.77. An engineer is designing a conveyor system for loading hay bales into a wagon (Fig. 11.57). Each bale is 0.25 m wide, 0.50 m high, and 0.80 m long (the dimension perpendicular to the plane of the figure), with mass 30.0 kg. The center of gravity of each bale is at its geometrical center. The coefficient of static friction between a bale and the conveyor belt is 0.60, and the belt moves with constant speed. (a) The angle β of the conveyor is slowly increased. At some critical angle a bale will tip (if it doesn't slip first), and at some different critical angle it will slip (if it doesn't tip first). Find the two critical angles and determine which happens at the smaller angle. (b) Would the outcome of part (a) be different if the coefficient of friction were 0.40?

Figure **11.57** Problem 11.77.

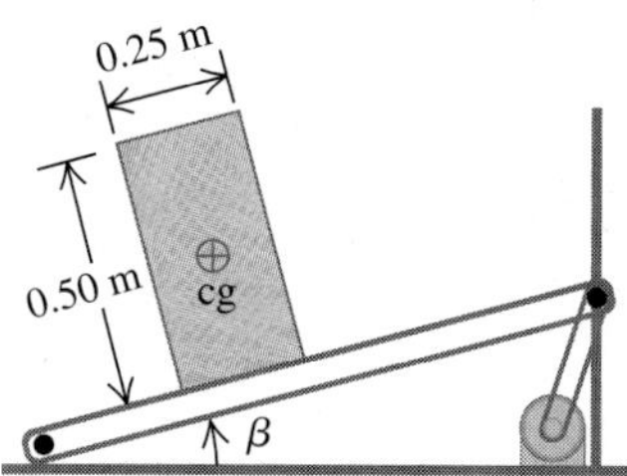

11.78. The hay bale of Problem 11.77 is dragged along a horizontal surface with constant speed by a force $\vec{F}$ (Fig. 11.58). The coefficient of kinetic friction is 0.35. (a) Find the magnitude of the force $\vec{F}$. (b) Find the value of h at which the bale just begins to tip.

Figure **11.58** Problem 11.78.

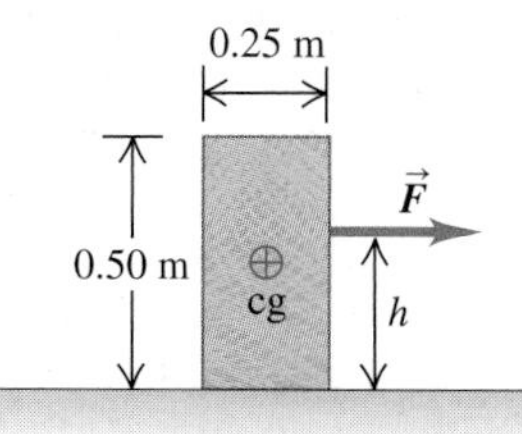

11.79. A garage door is mounted on an overhead rail (Fig. 11.59). The wheels at A and B have rusted so that they do not roll, but rather slide along the track. The coefficient of kinetic friction is 0.52. The distance between the wheels is 2.00 m, and each is 0.50 m from the vertical sides of the door. The door is uniform and weighs 950 N. It is pushed to the left at constant speed by a horizontal force $\vec{F}$. (a) If the distance h is 1.60 m, what is the vertical component of the force exerted on each wheel by the track? (b) Find the maximum value h can have without causing one wheel to leave the track.

Figure **11.59** Problem 11.79.

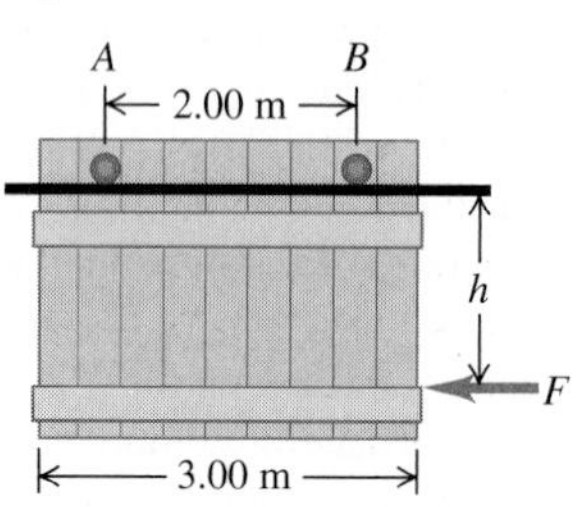

11.80. A horizontal boom is supported at its left end by a frictionless pivot. It is held in place by a cable attached to the right-hand end of the boom. A chain and crate of total weight w hang from somewhere along the boom. The boom's weight w_b cannot be ignored and the boom may or may not be uniform. (a) Show that the tension in the cable is the same whether the cable makes an angle θ or an angle $180° - \theta$ with the horizontal, and that the horizontal force component exerted on the boom by the pivot has equal magnitude but opposite direction for the two angles. (b) Show that the cable cannot be horizontal. (c) Show that the tension in the cable is a minimum when the cable is vertical, pulling upward on the right end of the boom. (d) Show that when the cable is vertical, the force exerted by the pivot on the boom is vertical.

11.81. Prior to being placed in its hole, a 5700-N, 9.0-m-long, uniform utility pole makes some nonzero angle with the vertical. A vertical cable attached 2.0 m below its upper end holds it in place while its lower end rests on the ground. (a) Find the tension in the cable and the magnitude and direction of the force exerted by the ground on the pole. (b) Why don't we need to know the angle the pole makes with the vertical, as long as it is not zero?

11.82. A weight W is supported by attaching it to a vertical uniform metal pole by a thin cord passing over a pulley having negligible mass and friction. The cord is attached to the pole 40.0 cm below the top and pulls horizontally on it (Fig. 11.60). The pole is pivoted about a hinge at its base, is 1.75 m tall, and weighs 55.0 N. A thin wire connects the top of the pole to a vertical wall. The nail that holds this wire to the wall will pull out if an *outward* force greater than 22.0 N acts on it. (a) What is the greatest weight W that can be supported this way without pulling out the nail? (b) What is the *magnitude* of the force that the hinge exerts on the pole?

Figure **11.60** Problem 11.82.

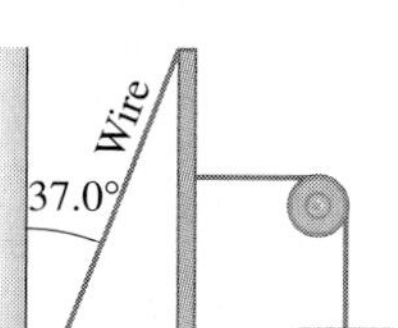
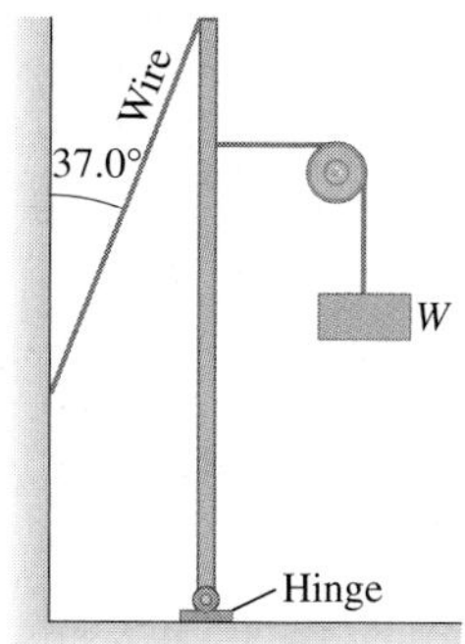

11.83. Pyramid Builders. Ancient pyramid builders are balancing a uniform rectangular slab of stone tipped at an angle θ above the horizontal using a rope (Fig. 11.61). The rope is held by five workers who share the force equally. (a) If $\theta = 20.0°$, what force does each worker exert on the rope? (b) As θ increases, does each worker have to exert more or less force than in part (a), assuming they do not change the angle of the rope? Why? (c) At what angle do the workers need to exert *no force* to balance the slab? What happens if θ exceeds this value?

Figure **11.61** Problem 11.83.

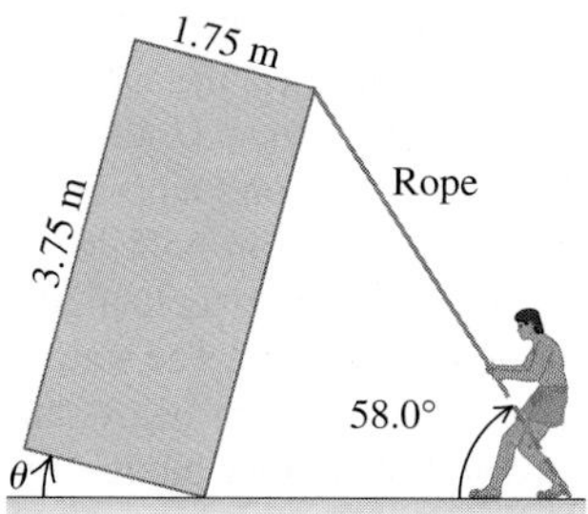

11.84. Hooke's Law for a Wire. A wire of length l_0 and cross-sectional area A supports a hanging weight W. (a) Show that if the wire obeys Equation (11.7), it behaves like a spring of force constant AY/l_0, where Y is Young's modulus for the material of which the wire is made. (b) What would the force constant be for a 75.0-cm length of 16-gauge $(\text{diameter} = 1.291\text{ mm})$ copper wire? See Table 11.1. (c) What would W have to be to stretch the wire in part (b) by 1.25 mm?

11.85. A 12.0-kg mass, fastened to the end of an aluminum wire with an unstretched length of 0.50 m, is whirled in a vertical circle with a constant angular speed of 120 rev/min. The cross-sectional area of the wire is 0.014 cm^2. Calculate the elongation of the wire when the mass is (a) at the lowest point of the path and (b) at the highest point of its path.

11.86. A metal wire 3.50 m long and 0.70 mm in diameter was given the following test. A load weighing 20 N was originally hung from the wire to keep it taut. The position of the lower end of the wire was read on a scale as load was added.

Added Load (N)	Scale Reading (cm)
0	3.02
10	3.07
20	3.12
30	3.17
40	3.22
50	3.27
60	3.32
70	4.27

(a) Graph these values, plotting the increase in length horizontally and the added load vertically. (b) Calculate the value of Young's modulus. (c) The proportional limit occurred at a scale reading of 3.34 cm. What was the stress at this point?

11.87. A 1.05-m-long rod of negligible weight is supported at its ends by wires A and B of equal length (Fig. 11.62). The cross-sectional area of A is 2.00 mm^2 and that of B is 4.00 mm^2. Young's modulus for wire A is 1.80×10^{11} Pa; that for B is 1.20×10^{11} Pa. At what point along the rod should a weight w be suspended to produce (a) equal stresses in A and B, and (b) equal strains in A and B?

Figure 11.62 Problem 11.87.

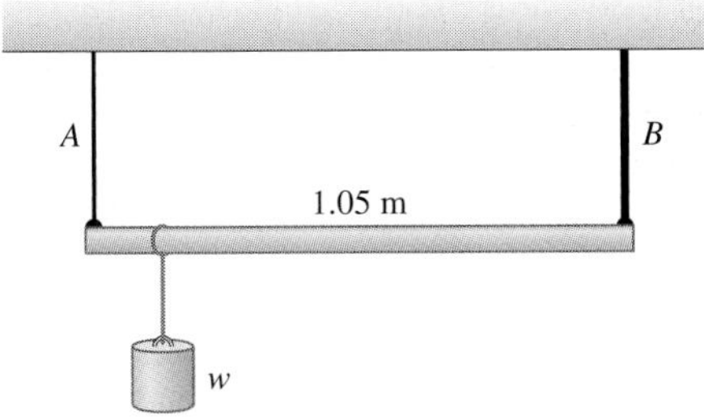

11.88. An amusement park ride consists of airplane-shaped cars attached to steel rods (Fig. 11.63). Each rod has a length of 15.0 m and a cross-sectional area of 8.00 cm^2. (a) How much is the rod stretched when the ride is at rest? (Assume that each car plus two people seated in it has a total weight of 1900 N.) (b) When operating, the ride has a maximum angular speed of 8.0 rev/min. How much is the rod stretched then?

Figure 11.63 Problem 11.88.

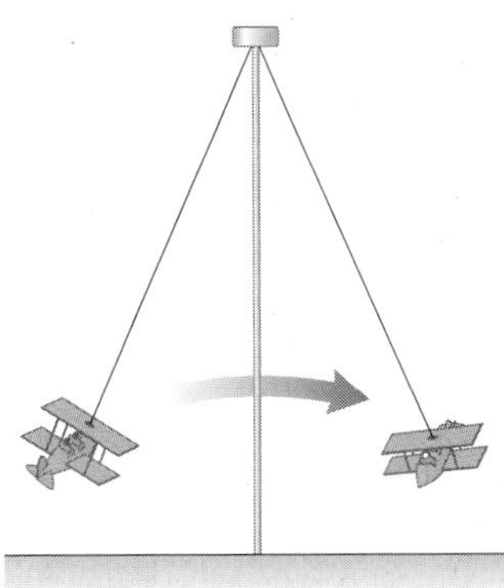

11.89. A brass rod with a length of 1.40 m and a cross-sectional area of 2.00 cm^2 is fastened end to end to a nickel rod with length L and cross-sectional area 1.00 cm^2. The compound rod is subjected to equal and opposite pulls of magnitude 4.00×10^4 N at its ends. (a) Find the length L of the nickel rod if the elongations of the two rods are equal. (b) What is the stress in each rod? (c) What is the strain in each rod?

11.90. Stress on the Shin Bone. Compressive strength of our bones is important in everyday life. Young's modulus for bone is about 1.4×10^{10} Pa. Bone can take only about a 1.0% change in its length before fracturing. (a) What is the maximum force that can be applied to a bone whose minimum cross-sectional area is 3.0 cm^2? (This is approximately the cross-sectional area of a tibia, or shin bone, at its narrowest point.) (b) Estimate the maximum height from which a 70-kg man could jump and not fracture the tibia. Take the time between when he first touches the floor and when he has stopped to be 0.030 s, and assume that the stress is distributed equally between his legs.

11.91. You hang a floodlamp from the end of a vertical steel wire. The floodlamp stretches the wire 0.18 mm and the stress is proportional to the strain. How much would it have stretched (a) if the wire were twice as long? (b) If the wire had the same length but twice the diameter? (c) For a copper wire of the original length and diameter?

11.92. A moonshiner produces pure ethanol (ethyl alcohol) late at night and stores it in a stainless steel tank in the form of a cylinder 0.300 m in diameter with a tight-fitting piston at the top. The total volume of the tank is 250 L (0.250 m^3). In an attempt to squeeze a little more into the tank, the moonshiner piles 1420 kg of lead bricks on top of the piston. What additional volume of ethanol can the moonshiner squeeze into the tank? (Assume that the wall of the tank is perfectly rigid.)

11.93. A bar with cross-sectional area A is subjected to equal and opposite tensile forces $\vec{F}$ at its ends. Consider a plane through the bar making an angle θ with a plane at right angles to the bar (Fig. 11.64). (a) What is the tensile (normal) stress at this plane in terms of F, A, and θ? (b) What is the shear (tangential) stress at the plane in terms of F, A, and θ? (c) For what value of θ is the tensile stress a maximum? (d) For what value of θ is the shear stress a maximum?

Figure 11.64 Problem 11.93.

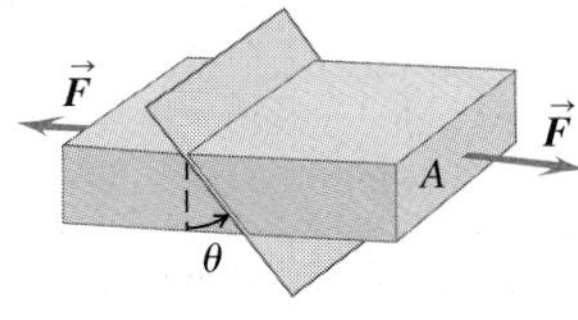

11.94. A horizontal, uniform, copper rod has an original length l_0, cross-sectional area A, Young's modulus Y, and mass m. It is supported by a frictionless pivot at its right end and by a cable at its left end. Both pivot and cable are attached so that they exert their forces uniformly over the rod's cross section. The cable makes an angle θ with the rod and compresses it. (a) Find the stress exerted by the cable and pivot on the rod. (b) Find the change in length of the rod due to this stress. (c) The mass of the rod equals $\rho A l_0$, where ρ is the density. Show that the answers to parts (a) and (b) are independent of the cross-sectional area of the rod. (d) The density of copper is 8900 kg/m^3. Take Y for compression as given for copper in Table 11.1. Find the stress and change in length for an original length of 1.8 m and an angle of 30°. (e) By how much would you multiply the answers of part (d) if the rod were twice as long?

Challenge Problems

11.95. A bookcase weighing 1500 N rests on a horizontal surface for which the coefficient of static friction is $\mu_s = 0.40$. The bookcase is 1.80 m tall and 2.00 m wide; its center of gravity is at its geometrical center. The bookcase rests on four short legs that are each 0.10 m from the edge of the bookcase. A person pulls on a rope attached to an upper corner of the bookcase with a force $\vec{F}$ that makes an angle θ with the bookcase (Fig. 11.65). (a) If $\theta = 90°$, so $\vec{F}$ is horizontal, show that as F is increased from zero, the bookcase will start to slide before it tips, and calculate the magnitude of $\vec{F}$ that will start the bookcase sliding. (b) If $\theta = 0°$, so $\vec{F}$ is vertical, show that the bookcase will tip over rather than slide, and calculate the magnitude of $\vec{F}$ that will cause the bookcase to start to tip. (c) Calculate as a function of θ the magnitude of $\vec{F}$ that will cause the bookcase to start to slide and the magnitude that will cause it to start to tip. What is the smallest value that θ can have so that the bookcase will still start to slide before it starts to tip?

Figure 11.65 Challenge Problem 11.95.

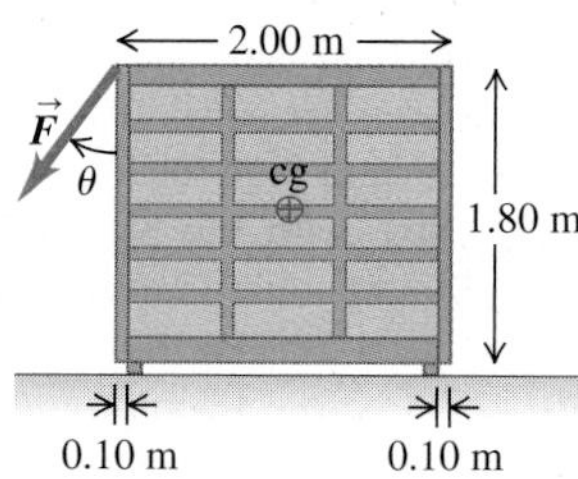

11.96. Knocking Over a Post. One end of a post weighing 400 N and with height h rests on a rough horizontal surface with $\mu_s = 0.30$. The upper end is held by a rope fastened to the surface and making an angle of 36.9° with the post (Fig. 11.66). A horizontal force $\vec{F}$ is exerted on the post as shown. (a) If the force $\vec{F}$ is applied at the midpoint of the post, what is the largest value it can have without causing the post to slip? (b) How large can the force be without causing the post to slip if its point of application is $\frac{6}{10}$ of the way from the ground to the top of the post? (c) Show that if the point of application of the force is too high, the post cannot be made to slip, no matter how great the force. Find the critical height for the point of application.

Figure 11.66 Challenge Problem 11.96.

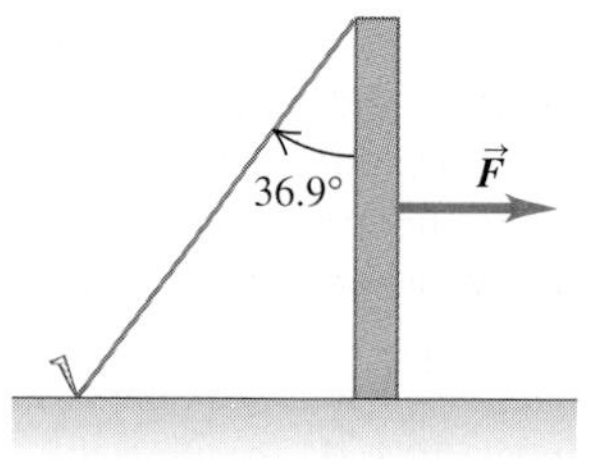

11.97. Minimizing the Tension. A heavy horizontal girder of length L has several objects suspended from it. It is supported by a frictionless pivot at its left end and a cable of negligible weight that is attached to an I-beam at a point a distance h directly above the girder's center. Where should the other end of the cable be attached to the girder so that the cable's tension is a minimum? (*Hint:* In evaluating and presenting your answer, don't forget that the maximum distance of the point of attachment from the pivot is the length L of the beam.)

11.98. Two ladders, 4.00 m and 3.00 m long, are hinged at point A and tied together by a horizontal rope 0.90 m above the floor (Fig. 11.67). The ladders weigh 480 N and 360 N, respectively, and the center of gravity of each is at its center. Assume that the floor is freshly waxed and frictionless. (a) Find the upward force at the bottom of each ladder. (b) Find the tension in the rope. (c) Find the magnitude of the force one ladder exerts on the other at point A. (d) If an 800-N painter stands at point A, find the tension in the horizontal rope.

Figure 11.67 Challenge Problem 11.98.

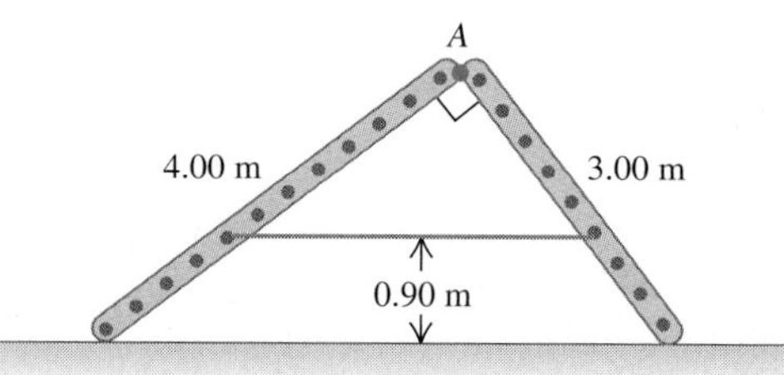

11.99. A device for measuring compressibility consists of a cylinder filled with oil and fitted with a piston at one end. A block of sodium is immersed in the oil, and a force is applied to the piston. Assume that the piston and walls of the cylinder are perfectly rigid and that there are no friction and no oil leak. Compute the compressibility of the sodium in terms of the applied force F, the piston displacement x, the piston area A, the initial volume of the oil V_O, the initial volume of the sodium V_S, and the compressibility of the oil k_O.

11.100. Bulk Modulus of an Ideal Gas. The equation of state (the equation relating pressure, volume, and temperature) for an ideal gas is $pV = nRT$, where n and R are constants. (a) Show that if the gas is compressed while the temperature T is held constant, the bulk modulus is equal to the pressure. (b) When an ideal gas is compressed without the transfer of any heat into or out of it, the pressure and volume are related by $pV^\gamma =$ constant, where γ is a constant having different values for different gases. Show that, in this case, the bulk modulus is given by $B = \gamma p$.

11.101. An angler hangs a 4.50-kg fish from a vertical steel wire 1.50 m long and 5.00×10^{-3} cm^2 in cross-sectional area. The upper end of the wire is securely fastened to a support. (a) Calculate the amount the wire is stretched by the hanging fish. The angler now applies a force $\vec{F}$ to the fish, pulling it very slowly downward by 0.500 mm from its equilibrium position. For this downward motion, calculate (b) the work done by gravity; (c) the work done by the force $\vec{F}$; (d) the work done by the force the wire exerts on the fish; and (e) the change in the elastic potential energy (the potential energy associated with the tensile stress in the wire). Compare the answers in parts (d) and (e).

GRAVITATION

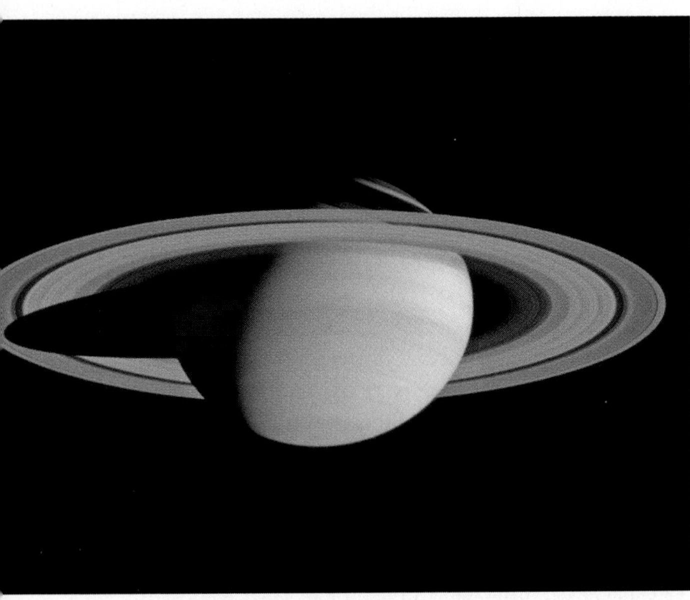

?The rings of Saturn are made of countless individual orbiting particles. Do all the ring particles orbit at the same speed, or do the inner particles orbit faster or slower than the outer ones?

LEARNING GOALS

By studying this chapter, you will learn:

- How to calculate the gravitational forces that any two bodies exert on each other.
- How to relate the weight of an object to the general expression for gravitational force.
- How to use and interpret the generalized expression for gravitational potential energy.
- How to relate the speed, orbital period, and mechanical energy of a satellite in a circular orbit.
- The laws that describe the motions of planets, and how to work with these laws.
- What black holes are, how to calculate their properties, and how they are discovered.

Some of the earliest investigations in physical science started with questions that people asked about the night sky. Why doesn't the moon fall to earth? Why do the planets move across the sky? Why doesn't the earth fly off into space rather than remaining in orbit around the sun? The study of gravitation provides the answers to these and many related questions.

As we remarked in Chapter 5, gravitation is one of the four classes of interactions found in nature, and it was the earliest of the four to be studied extensively. Newton discovered in the 17th century that the same interaction that makes an apple fall out of a tree also keeps the planets in their orbits around the sun. This was the beginning of *celestial mechanics,* the study of the dynamics of objects in space. Today, our knowledge of celestial mechanics allows us to determine how to put a satellite into any desired orbit around the earth or to choose just the right trajectory to send a spacecraft to another planet.

In this chapter you will learn the basic law that governs gravitational interactions. This law is *universal:* Gravity acts in the same fundamental way between the earth and your body, between the sun and a planet, and between a planet and one of its moons. We'll apply the law of gravitation to phenomena such as the variation of weight with altitude, the orbits of satellites around the earth, and the orbits of planets around the sun.

12.1 Newton's Law of Gravitation

The example of gravitational attraction that's probably most familiar to you is your *weight,* the force that attracts you toward the earth. During his study of the motions of the planets and of the moon, Newton discovered the fundamental character of the gravitational attraction between *any* two bodies. Along with his three laws of motion, Newton published the **law of gravitation** in 1687. It may be stated as follows:

Every particle of matter in the universe attracts every other particle with a force that is directly proportional to the product of the masses of the particles and inversely proportional to the square of the distance between them.

Translating this into an equation, we have

$$F_g = \frac{Gm_1m_2}{r^2} \quad \text{(law of gravitation)} \tag{12.1}$$

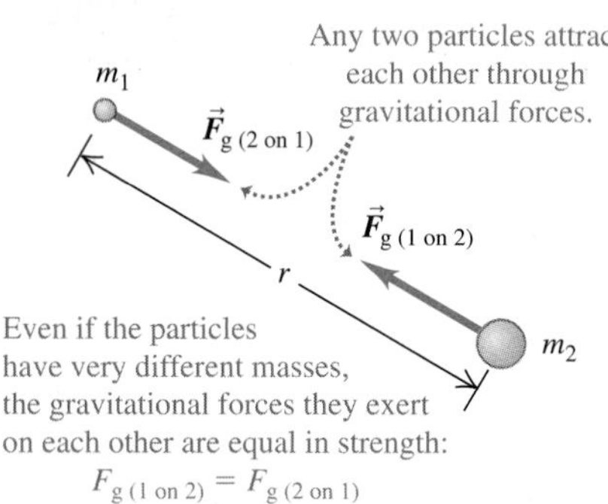

m_1
$\vec{F}_{g\,(2\text{ on }1)}$
Any two particles attract each other through gravitational forces.
$\vec{F}_{g\,(1\text{ on }2)}$
r
m_2
Even if the particles have very different masses, the gravitational forces they exert on each other are equal in strength:
$F_{g\,(1\text{ on }2)} = F_{g\,(2\text{ on }1)}$

12.1 The gravitational forces between two particles of masses m_1 and m_2.

where F_g is the magnitude of the gravitational force on either particle, m_1 and m_2 are their masses, r is the distance between them (Fig. 12.1), and G is a fundamental physical constant called the **gravitational constant.** The numerical value of G depends on the system of units used.

Equation (12.1) tells us that the gravitational force between two particles decreases with increasing distance r: If the distance is doubled, the force is only one-fourth as great, and so on. Although many of the stars in the night sky are far more massive than the sun, they are so far away that their gravitational force on the earth is negligibly small.

CAUTION Don't confuse g and G Because the symbols g and G are so similar, it's common to confuse the two very different gravitational quantities that these symbols represent. Lowercase g is the acceleration due to gravity, which relates the weight w of a body to its mass m: $w = mg$. The value of g is different at different locations on the earth's surface and on the surfaces of different planets. By contrast, capital G relates the gravitational force between any two bodies to their masses and the distance between them. We call G a *universal* constant because it has the same value for any two bodies, no matter where in space they are located. In the next section we'll see how the values of g and G are related.

Gravitational forces always act along the line joining the two particles, and they form an action–reaction pair. Even when the masses of the particles are different, the two interaction forces have equal magnitude (Fig. 12.1). The attractive force that your body exerts on the earth has the same magnitude as the force that the earth exerts on you. When you fall from a diving board into a swimming pool, the entire earth rises up to meet you! (You don't notice this because the earth's mass is greater than yours by a factor of about 10^{23}. Hence the earth's acceleration is only 10^{-23} as great as yours.)

12.2 The gravitational effect *outside* any spherically symmetric mass distribution is the same as though all of the mass were concentrated at its center.

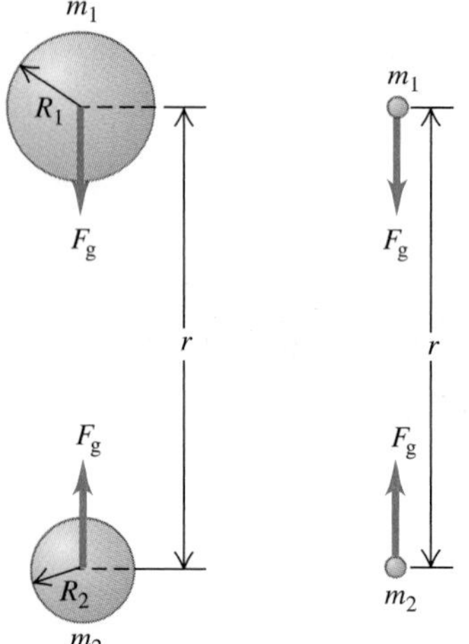

(a) The gravitational force between two spherically symmetric masses m_1 and m_2 ...
(b) ... is the same as if we concentrated all the mass of each sphere at the sphere's center.
m_1
R_1
F_g
r
F_g
R_2
m_2
m_1
F_g
r
F_g
m_2

Gravitation and Spherically Symmetric Bodies

We have stated the law of gravitation in terms of the interaction between two *particles.* It turns out that the gravitational interaction of any two bodies having *spherically symmetric* mass distributions (such as solid spheres or spherical shells) is the same as though we concentrated all the mass of each at its center, as in Fig. 12.2. Thus, if we model the earth as a spherically symmetric body with mass m_E, the force it exerts on a particle or a spherically symmetric body with mass m, at a distance r between centers, is

$$F_g = \frac{Gm_Em}{r^2} \tag{12.2}$$

provided that the body lies outside the earth. A force of the same magnitude is exerted *on* the earth by the body. (We will prove these statements in Section 12.6.)

At points *inside* the earth the situation is different. If we could drill a hole to the center of the earth and measure the gravitational force on a body at various depths, we would find that toward the center of the earth the force *decreases,* rather than increasing as $1/r^2$. As the body enters the interior of the earth (or other spherical body), some of the earth's mass is on the side of the body opposite from the center and pulls in the opposite direction. Exactly at the center, the earth's gravitational force on the body is zero.

Spherically symmetric bodies are an important case because moons, planets, and stars all tend to be spherical. Since all particles in a body gravitationally attract each other, the particles tend to move to minimize the distance between them. As a result, the body naturally tends to assume a spherical shape, just as a lump of clay forms into a sphere if you squeeze it with equal forces on all sides. This effect is greatly reduced in celestial bodies of low mass, since the gravitational attraction is less, and these bodies tend *not* to be spherical (Fig. 12.3).

12.3 Spherical and nonspherical bodies: the planet Jupiter and one of Jupiter's small moons, Amalthea.

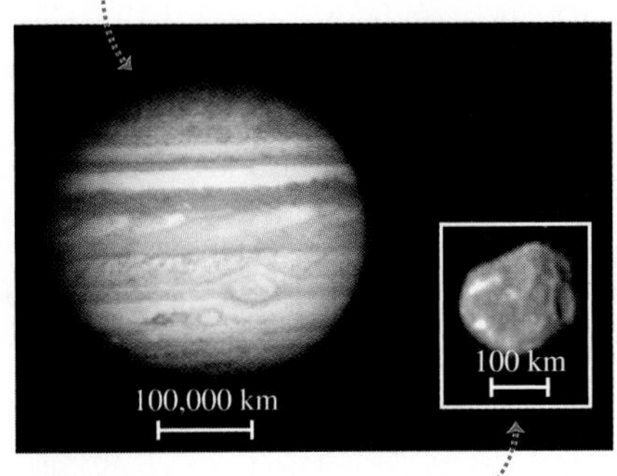

Determining the Value of G

To determine the value of the gravitational constant G, we have to *measure* the gravitational force between two bodies of known masses m_1 and m_2 at a known distance r. The force is extremely small for bodies that are small enough to be brought into the laboratory, but it can be measured with an instrument called a *torsion balance,* which Sir Henry Cavendish used in 1798 to determine G.

A modern version of the Cavendish torsion balance is shown in Fig. 12.4. A light, rigid rod shaped like an inverted T is supported by a very thin, vertical quartz fiber. Two small spheres, each of mass m_1, are mounted at the ends of the horizontal arms of the T. When we bring two large spheres, each of mass m_2, to the positions shown, the attractive gravitational forces twist the T through a small angle. To measure this angle, we shine a beam of light on a mirror fastened to the T. The reflected beam strikes a scale, and as the T twists, the reflected beam moves along the scale.

After calibrating the Cavendish balance, we can measure gravitational forces and thus determine G. The presently accepted value (in SI units) is

$$G = 6.6742(10) \times 10^{-11}\ \text{N} \cdot \text{m}^2/\text{kg}^2$$

To three significant figures, $G = 6.67 \times 10^{-11}\ \text{N} \cdot \text{m}^2/\text{kg}^2$. Because $1\ \text{N} = 1\ \text{kg} \cdot \text{m}/\text{s}^2$, the units of G can also be expressed (in fundamental SI units) as $\text{m}^3/(\text{kg} \cdot \text{s}^2)$.

Gravitational forces combine vectorially. If each of two masses exerts a force on a third, the *total* force on the third mass is the vector sum of the individual forces of the first two. Example 12.3 makes use of this property, which is often called *superposition of forces*.

12.4 The principle of the Cavendish balance, used for determining the value of G. The angle of deflection has been exaggerated here for clarity.

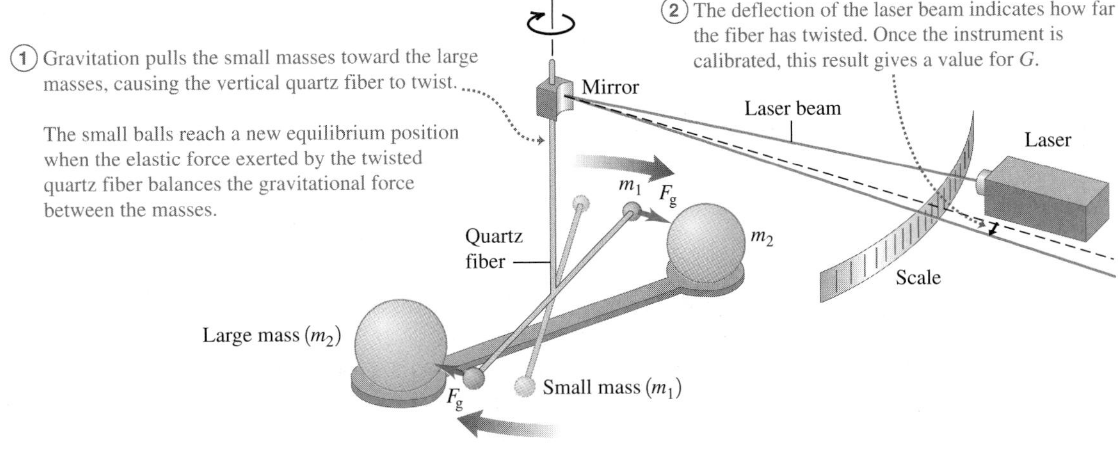

① Gravitation pulls the small masses toward the large masses, causing the vertical quartz fiber to twist.
The small balls reach a new equilibrium position when the elastic force exerted by the twisted quartz fiber balances the gravitational force between the masses.
② The deflection of the laser beam indicates how far the fiber has twisted. Once the instrument is calibrated, this result gives a value for G.
Mirror
Laser beam
Laser
m_1
F_g
m_2
Quartz fiber
Scale
Large mass (m_2)
F_g
Small mass (m_1)

Example 12.1 Calculating gravitational force

The mass m_1 of one of the small spheres of a Cavendish balance is 0.0100 kg, the mass m_2 of one of the large spheres is 0.500 kg, and the center-to-center distance between each large sphere and the nearer small one is 0.0500 m. Find the gravitational force F_g on each sphere due to the nearest other sphere.

SOLUTION

IDENTIFY: Because the 0.0100-kg and 0.500-kg objects are spherically symmetric, we can calculate the gravitational force of one on the other by assuming that they are particles separated by 0.0500 m. Each sphere experiences the *same* magnitude of force from the other sphere, even though their masses are very different.

SET UP: We use the law of gravitation, Eq. (12.1), to determine F_g.

EXECUTE: The magnitude of the force that one sphere exerts on the other is

$$F_g = \frac{(6.67 \times 10^{-11}\ \text{N}\cdot\text{m}^2/\text{kg}^2)(0.0100\ \text{kg})(0.500\ \text{kg})}{(0.0500\ \text{m})^2}$$

$$= 1.33 \times 10^{-10}\ \text{N}$$

EVALUATE: This is a very small force, which is what we expect: We don't experience noticeable gravitational pulls from ordinary low-mass objects in our environment. It takes a truly massive object such as the earth to exert a substantial gravitational force.

Example 12.2 Acceleration due to gravitational attraction

Suppose one large sphere and one small sphere are detached from the apparatus in Example 12.1 and placed 0.0500 m (between centers) from each other at a point in space far removed from all other bodies. What is the magnitude of the acceleration of each, relative to an inertial system?

SOLUTION

IDENTIFY: The gravitational forces that the two spheres exert on each other have the same magnitude. (The system of two spheres is so distant from other bodies that we can neglect any other forces.) But the *accelerations* of the two spheres are different because their masses are different.

SET UP: We found the magnitude of the force on each sphere in Example 12.1. To determine the magnitude of each sphere's acceleration, we'll use Newton's second law.

EXECUTE: The acceleration of the smaller sphere has magnitude

$$a_1 = \frac{F_g}{m_1} = \frac{1.33 \times 10^{-10}\ \text{N}}{0.0100\ \text{kg}} = 1.33 \times 10^{-8}\ \text{m/s}^2$$

The acceleration of the larger sphere has magnitude

$$a_2 = \frac{F_g}{m_2} = \frac{1.33 \times 10^{-10}\ \text{N}}{0.500\ \text{kg}} = 2.66 \times 10^{-10}\ \text{m/s}^2$$

EVALUATE: The larger sphere has 50 times the mass of the smaller one and hence has 1/50 the acceleration. Note that the accelerations are *not* constant; the gravitational forces increase as the spheres move toward each other.

Example 12.3 Superposition of gravitational forces

Many stars in the sky are actually systems of two or more stars held together by their mutual gravitational attraction. Figure 12.5 shows a three-star system at an instant when the stars are at the vertices of a 45° right triangle. Find the magnitude and direction of the total gravitational force exerted on the small star by the two large ones.

SOLUTION

IDENTIFY: We use the principle of superposition: The total force on the small star is the vector sum of the forces due to each large star.

SET UP: We assume that the stars are spheres so that we can use the law of gravitation for each force, as in Fig. 12.2. We first calculate the magnitude of each force using Eq. (12.1) and then compute the vector sum using components along the axes shown in Fig. 12.5.

12.5 The total gravitational force on the small star (at O) is the vector sum of the forces exerted on it by the two larger stars. (For comparison, the mass of the sun—a rather ordinary star—is 1.99×10^{30} kg and the earth–sun distance is 1.50×10^{11} m.)

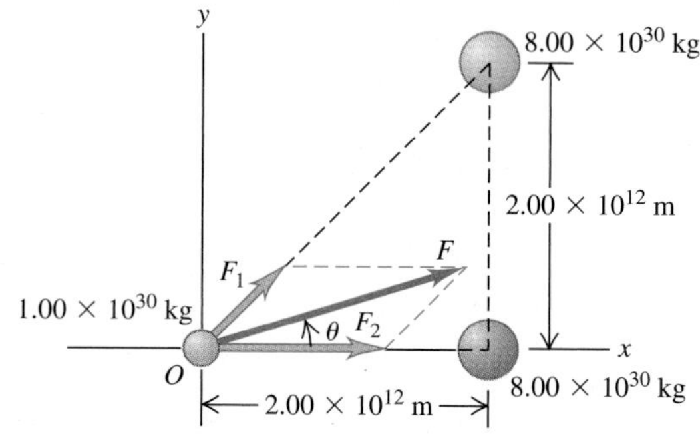

EXECUTE: The magnitude F_1 of the force on the small star due to the upper large one is

$$F_1 = \frac{\begin{bmatrix}(6.67 \times 10^{-11}\ \text{N}\cdot\text{m}^2/\text{kg}^2) \\ \times(8.00 \times 10^{30}\ \text{kg})(1.00 \times 10^{30}\ \text{kg})\end{bmatrix}}{(2.00 \times 10^{12}\ \text{m})^2 + (2.00 \times 10^{12}\ \text{m})^2}$$
$$= 6.67 \times 10^{25}\ \text{N}$$

The magnitude F_2 of the force due to the lower large star is

$$F_2 = \frac{\begin{bmatrix}(6.67 \times 10^{-11}\ \text{N}\cdot\text{m}^2/\text{kg}^2) \\ \times(8.00 \times 10^{30}\ \text{kg})(1.00 \times 10^{30}\ \text{kg})\end{bmatrix}}{(2.00 \times 10^{12}\ \text{m})^2}$$
$$= 1.33 \times 10^{26}\ \text{N}$$

The x- and y-components of these forces are

$$F_{1x} = (6.67 \times 10^{25}\ \text{N})(\cos 45°) = 4.72 \times 10^{25}\ \text{N}$$
$$F_{1y} = (6.67 \times 10^{25}\ \text{N})(\sin 45°) = 4.72 \times 10^{25}\ \text{N}$$
$$F_{2x} = 1.33 \times 10^{26}\ \text{N}$$
$$F_{2y} = 0$$

The components of the total force on the small star are

$$F_x = F_{1x} + F_{2x} = 1.81 \times 10^{26}\ \text{N}$$
$$F_y = F_{1y} + F_{2y} = 4.72 \times 10^{25}\ \text{N}$$

The magnitude of this force is

$$F = \sqrt{F_x^2 + F_y^2} = \sqrt{(1.81 \times 10^{26}\ \text{N})^2 + (4.72 \times 10^{25}\ \text{N})^2}$$
$$= 1.87 \times 10^{26}\ \text{N}$$

and its direction relative to the x-axis is

$$\theta = \arctan\frac{F_y}{F_x} = \arctan\frac{4.72 \times 10^{25}\ \text{N}}{1.81 \times 10^{26}\ \text{N}} = 14.6°$$

EVALUATE: While the total force on the small star is tremendous, the magnitude of the resulting acceleration is not: $a = F/m = (1.87 \times 10^{26}\ \text{N})/(1.00 \times 10^{30}\ \text{kg}) = 1.87 \times 10^{-4}\ \text{m/s}^2$.

Can you show that the total force on the small star is *not* directed toward the center of mass of the two large stars? (See Problem 12.51.)

Why Gravitational Forces Are Important

Comparing Examples 12.1 and 12.3 shows that gravitational forces are negligible between ordinary household-sized objects, but very substantial between objects that are the size of stars. Indeed, gravitation is *the* most important force on the scale of planets, stars, and galaxies (Fig. 12.6). It is responsible for holding our earth together and for keeping the planets in orbit about the sun. The mutual gravitational attraction between different parts of the sun compresses material at the sun's core to very high densities and temperatures, making it possible for nuclear reactions to take place there. These reactions generate the sun's energy output, which makes it possible for life to exist on earth and for you to read these words.

The gravitational force is so important on the cosmic scale because it acts *at a distance,* without any direct contact between bodies. Electric and magnetic forces have this same remarkable property, but they are less important on astronomical scales because large accumulations of matter are electrically neutral; that is, they contain equal amounts of positive and negative charge. As a result, the electric and magnetic forces between stars or planets are very small or zero. The strong and weak interactions that we discussed in Section 5.5 also act at a distance, but their influence is negligible at distances much greater than the diameter of an atomic nucleus (about 10^{-14} m).

A useful way to describe forces that act at a distance is in terms of a *field.* One body sets up a disturbance or field at all points in space, and the force that acts on a second body at a particular point is its response to the first body's field at that point. There is a field associated with each force that acts at a distance, and so we refer to gravitational fields, electric fields, magnetic fields, and so on. We won't need the field concept for our study of gravitation in this chapter, so we won't discuss it further here. But in later chapters we'll find that the field concept is an extraordinarily powerful tool for describing electric and magnetic interactions.

12.6 Our solar system is part of a spiral galaxy like this one, which contains roughly 10^{11} stars as well as gas, dust, and other matter. The entire assemblage is held together by the mutual gravitational attraction of all the matter in the galaxy.

Test Your Understanding of Section 12.1 The planet Saturn has about 100 times the mass of the earth and is about 10 times farther from the sun than the earth is. Compared to the acceleration of the earth caused by the sun's gravitational pull, how great is the acceleration of Saturn due to the sun's gravitation? (i) 100 times greater; (ii) 10 times greater; (iii) the same; (iv) $1/10$ as great; (v) $1/100$ as great.

12.2 Weight

We defined the *weight* of a body in Section 4.4 as the attractive gravitational force exerted on it by the earth. We can now broaden our definition:

The weight of a body is the total gravitational force exerted on the body by all other bodies in the universe.

When the body is near the surface of the earth, we can neglect all other gravitational forces and consider the weight as just the earth's gravitational attraction. At the surface of the *moon* we consider a body's weight to be the gravitational attraction of the moon, and so on.

If we again model the earth as a spherically symmetric body with radius R_E and mass m_E, the weight w of a small body of mass m at the earth's surface (a distance R_E from its center) is

$$w = F_g = \frac{Gm_E m}{R_E^2} \quad \text{(weight of a body of mass } m \text{ at the earth's surface)} \tag{12.3}$$

But we also know from Section 4.4 that the weight w of a body is the force that causes the acceleration g of free fall, so by Newton's second law, $w = mg$. Equating this with Eq. (12.3) and dividing by m, we find

$$g = \frac{Gm_E}{R_E^2} \quad \text{(acceleration due to gravity at the earth's surface)} \tag{12.4}$$

The acceleration due to gravity g is independent of the mass m of the body because m doesn't appear in this equation. We already knew that, but we can now see how it follows from the law of gravitation.

We can *measure* all the quantities in Eq. (12.4) except for m_E, so this relationship allows us to compute the mass of the earth. Solving Eq. (12.4) for m_E and using $R_E = 6380\ \text{km} = 6.38 \times 10^6\ \text{m}$ and $g = 9.80\ \text{m/s}^2$, we find

$$m_E = \frac{gR_E^2}{G} = 5.98 \times 10^{24}\ \text{kg}$$

This is very close to the currently accepted value of 5.974×10^{24} kg. Once Cavendish had measured G, he computed the mass of the earth in just this way.

At a point above the earth's surface a distance r from the center of the earth (a distance $r - R_E$ above the surface), the weight of a body is given by Eq. (12.3) with R_E replaced by r:

$$w = F_g = \frac{Gm_E m}{r^2} \tag{12.5}$$

The weight of a body decreases inversely with the square of its distance from the earth's center (Fig. 12.7). Figure 12.8 shows how the weight varies with height above the earth for an astronaut who weighs 700 N at the earth's surface.

The *apparent* weight of a body on earth differs slightly from the earth's gravitational force because the earth rotates and is therefore not precisely an inertial frame of reference. We have ignored this effect in our earlier discussion and have assumed that the earth *is* an inertial system. We will return to the effect of the earth's rotation in Section 12.7.

In our discussion of weight, we've used the fact that the earth is an approximately spherically symmetric distribution of mass. But this does *not* mean that the earth is uniform. To demonstrate that it cannot be uniform, let's first calculate

12.7 In an airliner at high altitude, you are farther from the center of the earth than when on the ground and hence weigh slightly less. Can you show that at an altitude of 10 km above the surface, you weigh 0.3% less than you do on the ground?

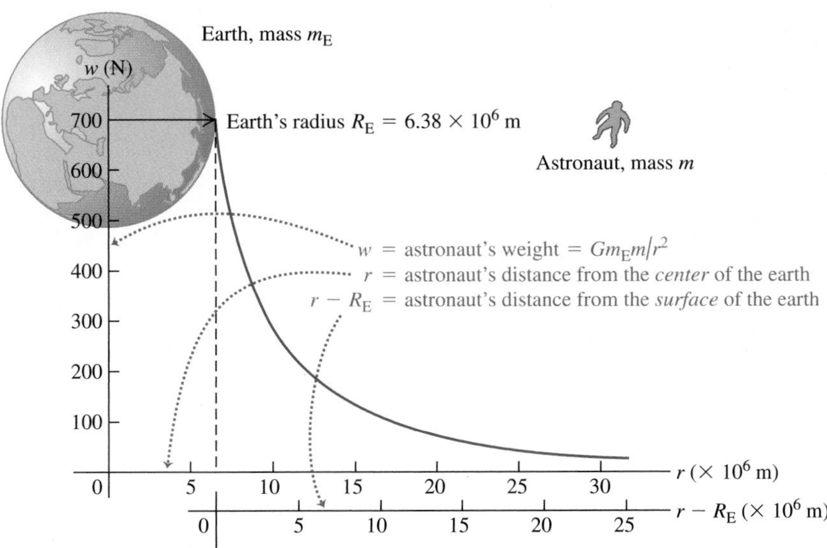

12.8 An astronaut who weighs 700 N at the earth's surface experiences less gravitational attraction when above the surface. The relevant distance r is from the astronaut to the *center* of the earth (*not* from the astronaut to the earth's surface).

the average *density,* or mass per unit volume, of the earth. If we assume a spherical earth, the volume is

$$V_E = \frac{4}{3}\pi R_E^3 = \frac{4}{3}\pi(6.38 \times 10^6\ \text{m})^3 = 1.09 \times 10^{21}\ \text{m}^3$$

The average density ρ (the Greek letter rho) of the earth is the total mass divided by the total volume:

$$\rho = \frac{m_E}{V_E} = \frac{5.97 \times 10^{24}\ \text{kg}}{1.09 \times 10^{21}\ \text{m}^3}$$
$$= 5500\ \text{kg/m}^3 = 5.5\ \text{g/cm}^3$$

(For comparison, the density of water is $1000\ \text{kg/m}^3 = 1.00\ \text{g/cm}^3$.) If the earth were uniform, we would expect the density of individual rocks near the earth's surface to have this same value. In fact, the density of surface rocks is substantially lower, ranging from about $2000\ \text{kg/m}^3 = 2\ \text{g/cm}^3$ for sedimentary rocks to about $3300\ \text{kg/m}^3 = 3.3\ \text{g/cm}^3$ for basalt. So the earth *cannot* be uniform, and the interior of the earth must be much more dense than the surface in order that the *average* density be $5500\ \text{kg/m}^3 = 5.5\ \text{g/cm}^3$. According to geophysical models of the earth's interior, the maximum density at the center is about $13{,}000\ \text{kg/m}^3 = 13\ \text{g/cm}^3$. Figure 12.9 is a graph of density as a function of distance from the center.

12.9 The density of the earth decreases with increasing distance from its center.

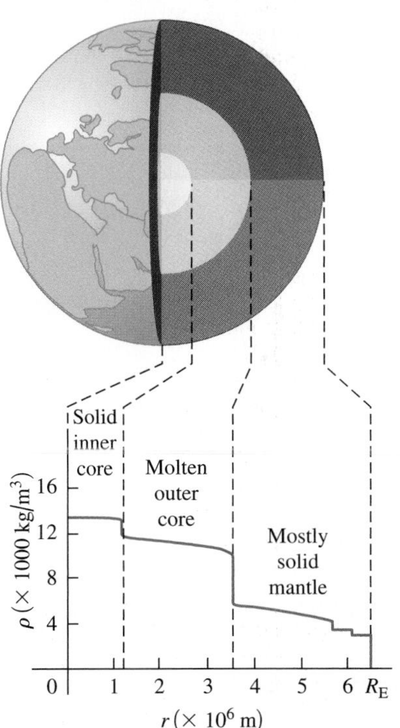

Example 12.4 Gravity on Mars

An unmanned lander is sent to the surface of the planet Mars, which has radius $R_M = 3.40 \times 10^6$ m and mass $m_M = 6.42 \times 10^{23}$ kg. The earth weight of the Mars lander is 3920 N. Calculate its weight F_g and the acceleration g_M due to the gravity of Mars: (a) 6.0×10^6 m above the surface of Mars (the distance at which the moon Phobos orbits Mars); and (b) at the surface of Mars. Neglect the gravitational effects of the (very small) moons of Mars.

SOLUTION

IDENTIFY: We need to find the lander weight F_g and the gravitational acceleration g_M at two different distances from the center of Mars.

SET UP: We find the weight F_g using Eq. (12.5) with m_E (the mass of the earth) replaced with m_M (the mass of Mars). Note that the

Continued

value of G is the same everywhere in the universe; it is a fundamental physical constant. We then find the acceleration g_M using $F_g = mg_M$, where m is the mass of the lander. We're not given the value of this mass, but we can determine it from the lander's weight on earth.

EXECUTE: (a) The distance r from the *center* of Mars is

$$r = (6.0 \times 10^6\ \text{m}) + (3.40 \times 10^6\ \text{m}) = 9.4 \times 10^6\ \text{m}$$

The mass m of the lander is its earth weight w divided by the acceleration of gravity g on earth:

$$m = \frac{w}{g} = \frac{3920\ \text{N}}{9.8\ \text{m/s}^2} = 400\ \text{kg}$$

The mass is the same whether the lander is on the earth, on Mars, or in between. From Eq. (12.5),

$$\begin{aligned} F_g &= \frac{Gm_M m}{r^2} \\ &= \frac{(6.67 \times 10^{-11}\ \text{N}\cdot\text{m}^2/\text{kg}^2)(6.42 \times 10^{23}\ \text{kg})(400\ \text{kg})}{(9.4 \times 10^6\ \text{m})^2} \\ &= 194\ \text{N} \end{aligned}$$

The acceleration due to the gravity of Mars at this point is

$$g_M = \frac{F_g}{m} = \frac{194\ \text{N}}{400\ \text{kg}} = 0.48\ \text{m/s}^2$$

This is also the acceleration experienced by Phobos in its orbit, 6.0×10^6 m above the surface of Mars. (b) To find F_g and g_M at the surface, we repeat the calculations in part (a), replacing $r = 9.4 \times 10^6$ m with $R_M = 3.40 \times 10^6$ m. Alternatively, because F_g and g_M are inversely proportional to $1/r^2$ (at any point outside the planet), we can multiply the results of part (a) by the factor

$$\left(\frac{9.4 \times 10^6\ \text{m}}{3.40 \times 10^6\ \text{m}}\right)^2$$

You should use both methods to show that at the surface $F_g = 1500$ N and $g_M = 3.7\ \text{m/s}^2$.

EVALUATE: The results for part (b) show that an object's weight and the acceleration due to gravity are roughly 40% as large on the surface of Mars as they are on the earth's surface. Science-fiction films and stories set on Mars commonly describe the planet's lower temperatures and thinner atmosphere, but they seldom focus on the experience of being in a low-gravity environment.

Test Your Understanding of Section 12.2 Rank the following hypothetical planets in order from highest to lowest surface gravity: (i) mass = 2 times the mass of the earth, radius = 2 times the radius of the earth; (ii) mass = 4 times the mass of the earth, radius = 4 times the radius of the earth; (iii) mass = 4 times the mass of the earth, radius = 2 times the radius of the earth; (iv) mass = 2 times the mass of the earth, radius = 4 times the radius of the earth.

12.3 Gravitational Potential Energy

When we first developed the concept of gravitational potential energy in Section 7.1, we assumed that the gravitational force on a body is constant in magnitude and direction. This led to the expression $U = mgy$. But we now know that the earth's gravitational force on a body of mass m at any point outside the earth is given more generally by Eq. (12.2), $F_g = Gm_E m/r^2$, where m_E is the mass of the earth and r is the distance of the body from the earth's center. For problems in which r changes enough that the gravitational force can't be considered constant, we need a more general expression for gravitational potential energy.

To find this expression, we follow the same basic sequence of steps as in Section 7.1. We consider a body of mass m outside the earth, and first compute the work W_{grav} done by the gravitational force when the body moves directly away from or toward the center of the earth from $r = r_1$ to $r = r_2$, as in Fig. 12.10. This work is given by

$$W_{grav} = \int_{r_1}^{r_2} F_r\, dr \tag{12.6}$$

where F_r is the radial component of the gravitational force $\vec{F}$—that is, the component in the direction *outward* from the center of the earth. Because $\vec{F}$ points

12.10 Calculating the work done on a body by the gravitational force as the body moves from radial coordinate r_1 to r_2.

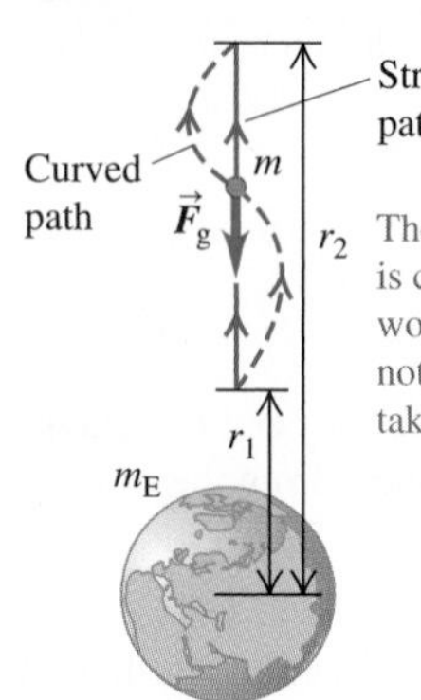
Straight path
Curved path
m
$\vec{F}_g$
r_2
r_1
m_E
The gravitational force is conservative: The work done by $\vec{F}_g$ does not depend on the path taken from r_1 to r_2.

directly *inward* toward the center of the earth, F_r is negative. It differs from Eq. (12.2), the magnitude of the gravitational force, by a minus sign:

$$F_r = -\frac{Gm_Em}{r^2} \qquad (12.7)$$

Substituting Eq. (12.7) into Eq. (12.6), we see that W_{grav} is given by

$$W_{grav} = -Gm_Em\int_{r_1}^{r_2}\frac{dr}{r^2} = \frac{Gm_Em}{r_2} - \frac{Gm_Em}{r_1} \qquad (12.8)$$

The path doesn't have to be a straight line; it could also be a curve like the one in Fig. 12.10. By an argument similar to that in Section 7.1, this work depends only on the initial and final values of r, not on the path taken. This also proves that the gravitational force is always *conservative.*

We now define the corresponding potential energy U so that $W_{grav} = U_1 - U_2$, as in Eq. (7.3). Comparing this with Eq. (12.8), we see that the appropriate definition for **gravitational potential energy** is

$$U = -\frac{Gm_Em}{r} \quad \text{(gravitational potential energy)} \qquad (12.9)$$

Figure 12.11 shows how the gravitational potential energy depends on the distance r between the body of mass m and the center of the earth. When the body moves away from the earth, r increases, the gravitational force does negative work, and U increases (i.e., becomes less negative). When the body "falls" toward earth, r decreases, the gravitational work is positive, and the potential energy decreases (i.e., becomes more negative).

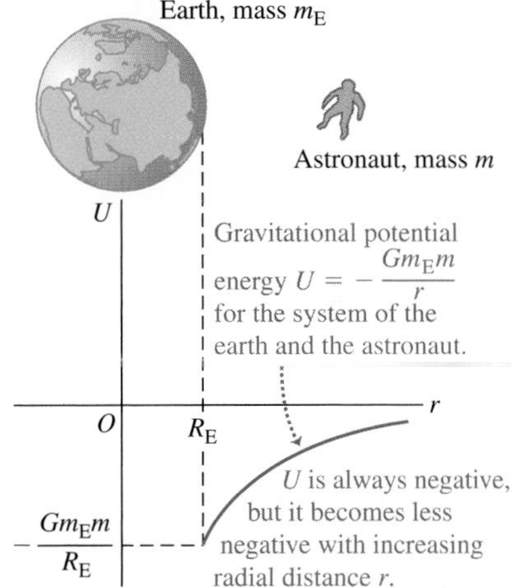

12.11 A graph of the gravitational potential energy U for the system of the earth (mass m_E) and an astronaut (mass m) versus the astronaut's distance r from the center of the earth.

You may be troubled by Eq. (12.9) because it states that gravitational potential energy is always negative. But in fact you've seen negative values of U before. In using the formula $U = mgy$ in Section 7.1, we found that U was negative whenever the body of mass m was at a value of y below the arbitrary height we chose to be $y = 0$—that is, whenever the body and the earth were closer together than some certain arbitrary distance. (See, for instance, Example 7.2 in Section 7.1.) In defining U by Eq. (12.9), we have chosen U to be zero when the body of mass m is infinitely far from the earth $(r = \infty)$. As the body moves toward the earth, gravitational potential energy decreases and so becomes negative.

If we wanted, we could make $U = 0$ at the surface of the earth, where $r = R_E$, by simply adding the quantity Gm_Em/R_E to Eq. (12.9). This would make U positive when $r > R_E$. We won't do this for two reasons: One, it would make the expression for U more complicated; and two, the added term would not affect the *difference* in potential energy between any two points, which is the only physically significant quantity.

CAUTION Gravitational force vs. gravitational potential energy Be careful not to confuse the expressions for gravitational force, Eq. (12.7), and gravitational potential energy, Eq. (12.9). The force F_r is proportional to $1/r^2$, while potential energy U is proportional to $1/r$.

Armed with Eq. (12.9), we can now use general energy relationships for problems in which the $1/r^2$ behavior of the earth's gravitational force has to be included. If the gravitational force on the body is the only force that does work, the total mechanical energy of the system is constant, or *conserved.* In the following example we'll use this principle to calculate **escape speed,** the speed required for a body to escape completely from a planet.

Example 12.5 "From the earth to the moon"

In Jules Verne's 1865 story with this title, three men were sent to the moon in a shell fired from a giant cannon sunk in the earth in Florida. (a) Find the muzzle speed needed to shoot the shell straight up to a height above the earth equal to the earth's radius. (b) Find the *escape speed*—that is, the muzzle speed that would allow the shell to escape from the earth completely. Neglect air resistance, the earth's rotation, and the gravitational pull of the moon. The earth's radius is $R_E = 6380 \text{ km} = 6.38 \times 10^6 \text{ m}$, and its mass is $m_E = 5.97 \times 10^{24} \text{ kg}$ (see Appendix F).

SOLUTION

IDENTIFY: Once the shell leaves the muzzle of the cannon, only the (conservative) gravitational force does work and mechanical energy is conserved. We use this fact to find the speed at which the shell must leave the muzzle into order to (a) come to a halt at a distance of two earth radii from the planet's center and (b) come to a halt at an infinite distance from earth.

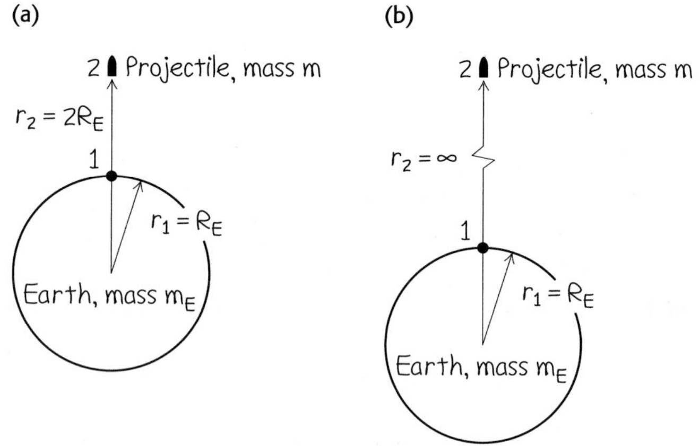

12.12 Our sketches for this problem.

SET UP: In both parts (a) and (b) we use the equation for energy conservation, $K_1 + U_1 = K_2 + U_2$, where the potential energy U is given by Eq. (12.9). Figure 12.12 shows our sketches. Point 1 is where the shell leaves the cannon with speed v_1 (the target variable). At this point the distance from the center of the earth is $r_1 = R_E$, the earth's radius. Point 2 is where the shell reaches its maximum height; in part (a) it is at $r_2 = 2R_E$ (Fig. 12.12a), and in part (b) it is infinitely far from the earth at $r_2 = \infty$ (Fig 12.12b). In either case the shell is at rest at point 2, so $v_2 = 0$ and $K_2 = 0$. Let m be the mass of the shell (with passengers).

EXECUTE: (a) We can determine v_1 from the energy-conservation equation

$$K_1 + U_1 = K_2 + U_2$$

$$\frac{1}{2}mv_1^2 + \left(-\frac{Gm_Em}{R_E}\right) = 0 + \left(-\frac{Gm_Em}{2R_E}\right)$$

Rearranging this, we find that

$$v_1 = \sqrt{\frac{Gm_E}{R_E}}$$

$$= \sqrt{\frac{(6.67 \times 10^{-11} \text{ N} \cdot \text{m}^2/\text{kg}^2)(5.97 \times 10^{24} \text{ kg})}{6.38 \times 10^6 \text{ m}}}$$

$$= 7900 \text{ m/s} (= 28{,}400 \text{ km/h} = 17{,}700 \text{ mi/h})$$

(b) We want the shell barely to be able to "reach" point 2 at $r_2 = \infty$, with no kinetic energy left over. Hence $K_2 = 0$ and $U_2 = 0$ (the potential energy goes to zero at infinity; see Fig. 12.11). The total energy is therefore zero, and when the shell is fired its positive kinetic energy K_1 and negative potential energy U_1 must also add to zero:

$$\frac{1}{2}mv_1^2 + \left(-\frac{Gm_Em}{R_E}\right) = 0 + 0$$

$$v_1 = \sqrt{\frac{2Gm_E}{R_E}}$$

$$= \sqrt{\frac{2(6.67 \times 10^{-11} \text{ N} \cdot \text{m}^2/\text{kg}^2)(5.97 \times 10^{24} \text{ kg})}{6.38 \times 10^6 \text{ m}}}$$

$$= 1.12 \times 10^4 \text{ m/s} (= 40{,}200 \text{ km/h} = 25{,}000 \text{ mi/h})$$

EVALUATE: This result does not depend on the mass of the shell, nor does it depend on the direction in which the shell is launched. Modern spacecraft launched from Florida must attain essentially the speed found in part (b) to escape the earth. A spacecraft on the ground at Cape Canaveral is already moving at 410 m/s to the east because of the earth's rotation; by launching to the east, the spacecraft takes advantage of this "free" contribution toward escape speed.

To generalize our result, the initial speed v_1 needed for a body to escape from the surface of a spherical mass M with radius R (ignoring air resistance) is

$$v_1 = \sqrt{\frac{2GM}{R}} \quad \text{(escape speed)}$$

You can use this result to compute the escape speed for other bodies. You will find 5.02×10^3 m/s for Mars, 5.95×10^4 m/s for Jupiter, and 6.18×10^5 m/s for the sun.

More on Gravitational Potential Energy

As a final note, let's show that when we are close to the earth's surface, Eq. (12.9) reduces to the familiar $U = mgy$ from Chapter 7. We first rewrite Eq. (12.8) as

$$W_{grav} = Gm_Em\frac{r_1 - r_2}{r_1r_2}$$

If the body stays close to the earth, then in the denominator we may replace r_1 and r_2 by R_E, the earth's radius, so

$$W_{\text{grav}} = Gm_E m \frac{r_1 - r_2}{R_E^2}$$

According to Eq. (12.4), $g = Gm_E/R_E^2$, so

$$W_{\text{grav}} = mg(r_1 - r_2)$$

If we replace the r's by y's, this is just Eq. (7.1) for the work done by a constant gravitational force. In Section 7.1 we used this equation to derive Eq. (7.2), $U = mgy$, so we may consider this expression for gravitational potential energy to be a special case of the more general Eq. (12.9).

Test Your Understanding of Section 12.3 Is it possible for a planet to have the same surface gravity as the earth (that is, the same value of g at the surface) and yet have a greater escape speed?

12.4 The Motion of Satellites

Artificial satellites orbiting the earth are a familiar part of modern technology (Fig. 12.13). But how do they stay in orbit, and what determines the properties of their orbits? We can use Newton's laws and the law of gravitation to provide the answers. We'll see in the next section that the motion of planets can be analyzed in the same way.

To begin, think back to the discussion of projectile motion in Section 3.3. In Example 3.6 a motorcycle rider rides horizontally off the edge of a cliff, launching himself into a parabolic path that ends on the flat ground at the base of the cliff. If he survives and repeats the experiment with increased launch speed, he will land farther from the starting point. We can imagine him launching himself with great enough speed that the earth's curvature becomes significant. As he falls, the earth curves away beneath him. If he is going fast enough, and if his launch point is high enough that he clears the mountaintops, he may be able to go right on around the earth without ever landing.

Figure 12.14 shows a variation on this theme. We launch a projectile from point A in the direction AB, tangent to the earth's surface. Trajectories 1 through 7 show the effect of increasing the initial speed. In trajectories 3 through 5 the

12.13 With a length of 13.2 m and a mass of 11,000 kg, the Hubble Space Telescope is among the largest satellites placed in orbit.

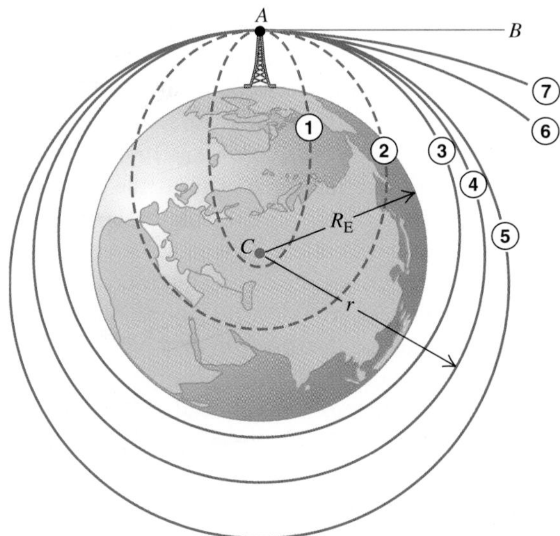
A
B
1
2
3
4
5
6
7
R_E
C
r
A projectile is launched from A toward B. Trajectories 1 through 7 show the effect of increasing initial speed.

12.14 Trajectories of a projectile launched from a great height (ignoring air resistance). Orbits 1 and 2 would be completed as shown if the earth were a point mass at C. (This illustration is based on one in Isaac Newton's *Principia*.)

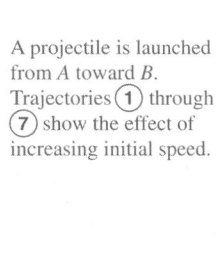

ActivPhysics ONLINE

4.6 Satellites Orbit

projectile misses the earth and becomes a satellite. If there is no retarding force, the projectile's speed when it returns to point A is the same as its initial speed and it repeats its motion indefinitely.

Trajectories 1 through 5 close on themselves and are called **closed orbits.** All closed orbits are ellipses or segments of ellipses; trajectory 4 is a circle, a special case of an ellipse. (We'll discuss the properties of an ellipse in Section 12.5.) Trajectories 6 and 7 are **open orbits.** For these paths the projectile never returns to its starting point but travels ever farther away from the earth.

Satellites: Circular Orbits

12.15 The force $\vec{F}_g$ due to the earth's gravitational attraction provides the centripetal acceleration that keeps a satellite in orbit. Compare to Fig. 5.28.

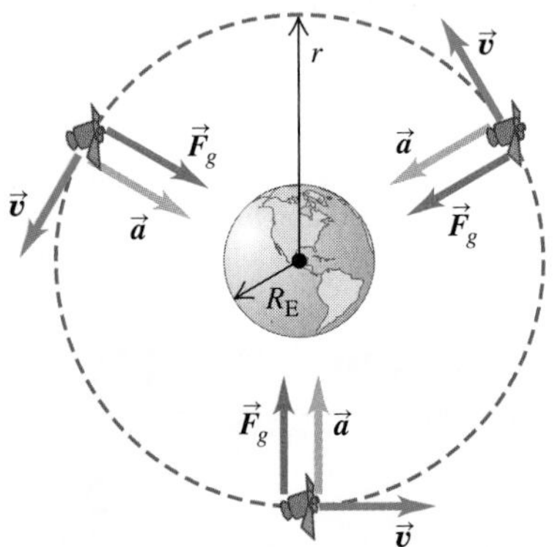

The satellite is in a circular orbit: Its acceleration $\vec{a}$ is always perpendicular to its velocity $\vec{v}$, so its speed v is constant.

A *circular* orbit, like trajectory 4 in Fig. 12.14, is the simplest case. It is also an important case, since many artificial satellites have nearly circular orbits and the orbits of the planets around the sun are also fairly circular. The only force acting on a satellite in circular orbit around the earth is the earth's gravitational attraction, which is directed toward the center of the earth and hence toward the center of the orbit (Fig. 12.15). As we discussed in Section 5.4, this means that the satellite is in *uniform* circular motion and its speed is constant. The satellite isn't falling *toward* the earth; rather, it's constantly falling *around* the earth. In a circular orbit the speed is just right to keep the distance from the satellite to the center of the earth constant.

Let's see how to find the constant speed v of a satellite in a circular orbit. **?** The radius of the orbit is r, measured from the *center* of the earth; the acceleration of the satellite has magnitude $a_{rad} = v^2/r$ and is always directed toward the center of the circle. By the law of gravitation, the net force (gravitational force) on the satellite of mass m has magnitude $F_g = Gm_E m/r^2$ and is in the same direction as the acceleration. Newton's second law $(\sum\vec{F} = m\vec{a})$ then tells us that

$$\frac{Gm_E m}{r^2} = \frac{mv^2}{r}$$

Solving this for v, we find

$$v = \sqrt{\frac{Gm_E}{r}} \quad \text{(circular orbit)} \quad (12.10)$$

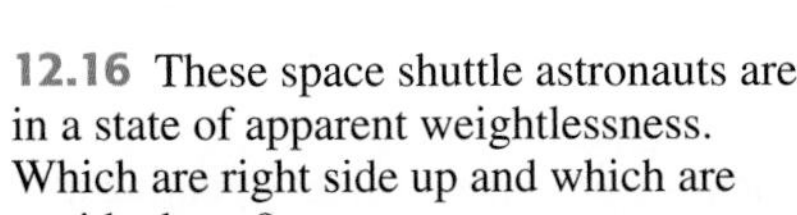

12.16 These space shuttle astronauts are in a state of apparent weightlessness. Which are right side up and which are upside down?

This relationship shows that we can't choose the orbit radius r and the speed v independently; for a given radius r, the speed v for a circular orbit is determined.

The satellite's mass m doesn't appear in Eq. (12.10), which shows that the motion of a satellite does not depend on its mass. If we could cut a satellite in half without changing its speed, each half would continue on with the original motion. An astronaut on board a space shuttle is herself a satellite of the earth, held by the earth's gravitational attraction in the same orbit as the shuttle. The astronaut has the same velocity and acceleration as the shuttle, so nothing is pushing her against the floor or walls of the shuttle. She is in a state of *apparent weightlessness,* as in a freely falling elevator; see the discussion following Example 5.9 in Section 5.2. (*True* weightlessness would occur only if the astronaut were infinitely far from any other masses, so that the gravitational force on her would be zero.) Indeed, every part of her body is apparently weightless; she feels nothing pushing her stomach against her intestines or her head against her shoulders (Fig. 12.16).

Apparent weightlessness is not just a feature of circular orbits; it occurs whenever gravity is the only force acting on a spacecraft. Hence it occurs for orbits of any shape, including open orbits such as trajectories (6) and (7) in Fig. 12.14.

12.17 Both the International Space Station and the moon are satellites of the earth. The moon orbits much farther from the center of the earth than does the Space Station, so it has a slower orbital speed and a longer orbital period.

International Space Station
Distance from center of earth = 6800 km (400 km above the surface)
Orbital speed = 7.7 km/s
Orbital period = 93 min

Moon
Distance from center of earth = 384,000 km
Orbital speed = 1.0 km/s
Orbital period = 27.3 days

We can derive a relationship between the radius r of a circular orbit and the period T, the time for one revolution. The speed v is the distance $2\pi r$ traveled in one revolution, divided by the period:

$$v = \frac{2\pi r}{T} \tag{12.11}$$

To get an expression for T, we solve Eq. (12.11) for T and substitute v from Eq. (12.10):

$$T = \frac{2\pi r}{v} = 2\pi r\sqrt{\frac{r}{Gm_E}} = \frac{2\pi r^{3/2}}{\sqrt{Gm_E}} \quad \text{(circular orbit)} \tag{12.12}$$

Equations (12.10) and (12.12) show that larger orbits correspond to slower speeds and longer periods (Fig. 12.17).

It's interesting to compare Eq. (12.10) to the calculation of escape speed in Example 12.5. We see that the escape speed from a spherical body with radius R is $\sqrt{2}$ times greater than the speed of a satellite in a circular orbit at that radius. If our spacecraft is in circular orbit around *any* planet, we have to multiply our speed by a factor of $\sqrt{2}$ to escape to infinity, regardless of the planet's mass.

Since the speed v in a circular orbit is determined by Eq. (12.10) for a given orbit radius r, the total mechanical energy $E = K + U$ is determined as well. Using Eqs. (12.9) and (12.10), we have

$$E = K + U = \frac{1}{2}mv^2 + \left(-\frac{Gm_E m}{r}\right) = \frac{1}{2}m\left(\frac{Gm_E}{r}\right) - \frac{Gm_E m}{r}$$
$$E = -\frac{Gm_E m}{2r} \quad \text{(circular orbit)} \tag{12.13}$$

The total mechanical energy in a circular orbit is negative and equal to one-half the potential energy. Increasing the orbit radius r means increasing the mechanical energy (that is, making E less negative). If the satellite is in a relatively low orbit that encounters the outer fringes of earth's atmosphere, mechanical energy decreases due to negative work done by the force of air resistance; as a result, the orbit radius decreases until the satellite hits the ground or burns up in the atmosphere.

We have talked mostly about earth satellites, but we can apply the same analysis to the circular motion of *any* body under its gravitational attraction to a stationary body. Other examples include the earth's moon and the moons of other worlds (Fig. 12.18).

12.18 The two small satellites of Pluto were discovered in 2005. In accordance with Eq. (12.12), the larger the satellite's orbit, the longer it takes to complete one orbit around Pluto.

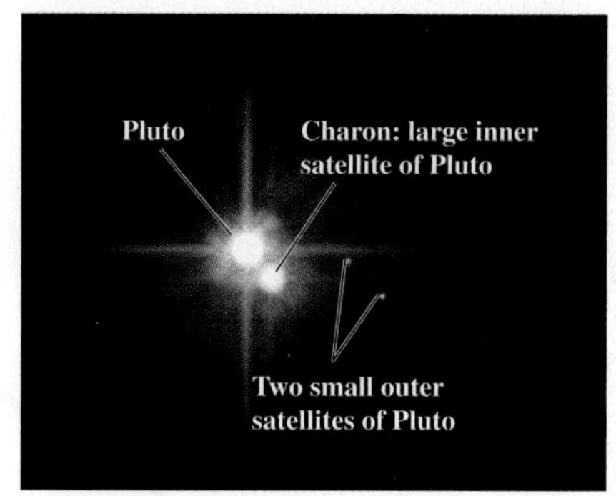

Example 12.6 A satellite orbit

Suppose you want to place a 1000-kg weather satellite into a circular orbit 300 km above the earth's surface. (a) What speed, period, and radial acceleration must it have? (b) How much work has to be done to place this satellite in orbit? (c) How much additional work would have to be done to make this satellite escape the earth? The earth's radius is $R_E = 6380$ km and its mass is $m_E = 5.97 \times 10^{24}$ kg.

SOLUTION

IDENTIFY: The satellite is in a circular orbit, so we can use the equations derived in this section.

SET UP: In part (a), we first find the radius r of the satellite's orbit from its altitude. We then calculate the speed v and period T using Eqs. (12.10) and (12.12). The acceleration in a circular orbit is given by the familiar formula from Chapter 3, $a_{rad} = v^2/r$. In parts (b) and (c), the work required is the difference between the initial and final mechanical energy, which for a circular orbit is given by Eq. (12.13).

EXECUTE: (a) The radius of the satellite's orbit is

$$r = 6380 \text{ km} + 300 \text{ km} = 6680 \text{ km} = 6.68 \times 10^6 \text{ m}$$

From Eq. (12.10), the orbital speed is

$$v = \sqrt{\frac{Gm_E}{r}} = \sqrt{\frac{(6.67 \times 10^{-11} \text{ N}\cdot\text{m}^2/\text{kg}^2)(5.97 \times 10^{24} \text{ kg})}{6.68 \times 10^6 \text{ m}}}$$
$$= 7720 \text{ m/s}$$

We find the orbital period from Eq. (12.12):

$$T = \frac{2\pi r}{v} = \frac{2\pi(6.68 \times 10^6 \text{ m})}{7720 \text{ m/s}}$$
$$= 5440 \text{ s} = 90.6 \text{ min}$$

The radial acceleration is

$$a_{rad} = \frac{v^2}{r} = \frac{(7720 \text{ m/s})^2}{6.68 \times 10^6 \text{ m}}$$
$$= 8.92 \text{ m/s}^2$$

This is the value of g at a height of 300 km above the earth's surface; it is somewhat less than the value of g at the surface.

(b) The work required is the difference between E_2, the total mechanical energy when the satellite is in orbit, and E_1, the original mechanical energy when the satellite was at rest on the launch pad back on earth. From Eq. (12.13), the energy in orbit is

$$E_2 = -\frac{Gm_E m}{2r}$$
$$= -\frac{(6.67 \times 10^{-11} \text{ N}\cdot\text{m}^2/\text{kg}^2)(5.97 \times 10^{24} \text{ kg})(1000 \text{ kg})}{2(6.38 \times 10^6 \text{ m})}$$
$$= -2.99 \times 10^{10} \text{ J}$$

At rest on the earth's surface $(r = R_E)$, the kinetic energy is zero:

$$E_1 = K_1 + U_1 = 0 + \left(-\frac{Gm_E m}{R_E}\right)$$
$$= -\frac{(6.67 \times 10^{-11} \text{ N}\cdot\text{m}^2/\text{kg}^2)(5.97 \times 10^{24} \text{ kg})(1000 \text{ kg})}{6.38 \times 10^6 \text{ m}}$$
$$= -6.25 \times 10^{10} \text{ J}$$

and so

$$W_{required} = E_2 - E_1 = -2.99 \times 10^{10} \text{ J} - (-6.25 \times 10^{10} \text{ J})$$
$$= 3.26 \times 10^{10} \text{ J}$$

(c) We saw in part (b) of Example 12.5 that for a satellite to escape to infinity, the total mechanical energy must be zero. The total mechanical energy in the circular orbit is $E_2 = -2.99 \times 10^{10}$ J; to increase this to zero, an amount of work equal to 2.99×10^{10} J would have to be done. This extra energy could be supplied by rocket engines attached to the satellite.

EVALUATE: In part (b) we ignored the satellite's initial kinetic energy (while it was still on the launch pad) due to the rotation of the earth. You should check to see how much difference this makes (see Example 12.5 for useful data).

Test Your Understanding of Section 12.4 Your personal spacecraft is in a low-altitude circular orbit around the earth. Air resistance from the outer regions of the atmosphere does negative work on the spacecraft, causing the orbital radius to decrease slightly. Does the speed of the spacecraft (i) remain the same, (ii) increase, or (iii) decrease?

12.5 Kepler's Laws and the Motion of Planets

The name *planet* comes from a Greek word meaning "wanderer," and indeed the planets continuously change their positions in the sky relative to the background of stars. One of the great intellectual accomplishments of the 16th and 17th centuries was the threefold realization that the earth is also a planet, that all planets orbit the sun, and that the apparent motions of the planets as seen from the earth can be used to precisely determine their orbits.

The first and second of these ideas were published by Nicolaus Copernicus in Poland in 1543. The nature of planetary orbits was deduced between 1601 and

1619 by the German astronomer and mathematician Johannes Kepler, using a voluminous set of precise data on apparent planetary motions compiled by his mentor, the Danish astronomer Tycho Brahe. By trial and error, Kepler discovered three empirical laws that accurately described the motions of the planets:

1. **Each planet moves in an elliptical orbit, with the sun at one focus of the ellipse.**
2. **A line from the sun to a given planet sweeps out equal areas in equal times.**
3. **The periods of the planets are proportional to the $\frac{3}{2}$ powers of the major axis lengths of their orbits.**

Kepler did not know *why* the planets moved in this way. Three generations later, when Newton turned his attention to the motion of the planets, he discovered that each of Kepler's laws can be *derived;* they are consequences of Newton's laws of motion and the law of gravitation. Let's see how each of Kepler's laws arises.

12.19 Geometry of an ellipse. The sum of the distances SP and $S'P$ is the same for every point on the curve. The sizes of the sun (S) and planet (P) are exaggerated for clarity.

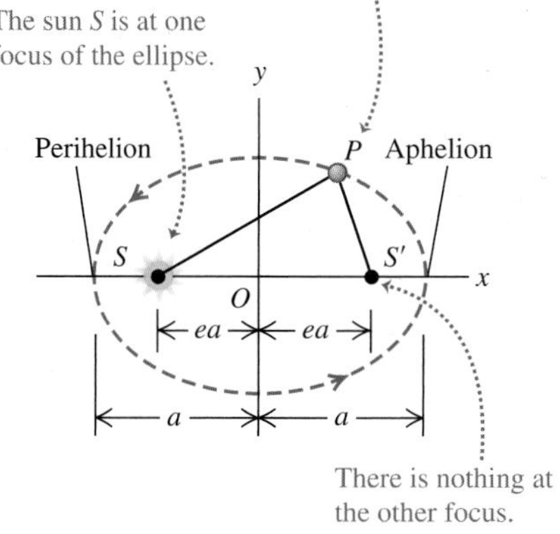

A planet P follows an elliptical orbit.
The sun S is at one focus of the ellipse.
y
Perihelion
P Aphelion
S
S′
x
O
ea
ea
a
a
There is nothing at the other focus.

Kepler's First Law

First consider the elliptical orbits described in Kepler's first law. Figure 12.19 shows the geometry of an ellipse. The longest dimension is the *major axis,* with half-length a; this half-length is called the **semi-major axis.** The sum of the distances from S to P and from S' to P is the same for all points on the curve. S and S' are the *foci* (plural of *focus*). The sun is at S, and the planet is at P; we think of them both as points because the size of each is very small in comparison to the distance between them. There is nothing at the other focus S'.

The distance of each focus from the center of the ellipse is ea, where e is a dimensionless number between 0 and 1 called the **eccentricity.** If $e = 0$, the ellipse is a circle. The actual orbits of the planets are fairly circular; their eccentricities range from 0.007 for Venus to 0.206 for Mercury. (The earth's orbit has $e = 0.017$.) The point in the planet's orbit closest to the sun is the *perihelion,* and the point most distant from the sun is the *aphelion.*

Newton was able to show that for a body acted on by an attractive force proportional to $1/r^2$, the only possible closed orbits are a circle or an ellipse; he also showed that open orbits (trajectories 6 and 7 in Fig. 12.14) must be parabolas or hyperbolas. These results can be derived by a straightforward application of Newton's laws and the law of gravitation, together with a lot more differential equations than we're ready for.

12.20 (a) The planet (P) moves about the sun (S) in an elliptical orbit. (b) In a time dt the line SP sweeps out an area $dA = \frac{1}{2}(r\,d\theta)r = \frac{1}{2}r^2\,d\theta$. (c) The planet's speed varies so that the line SP sweeps out the same area A in a given time t regardless of the planet's position in its orbit.

(a)

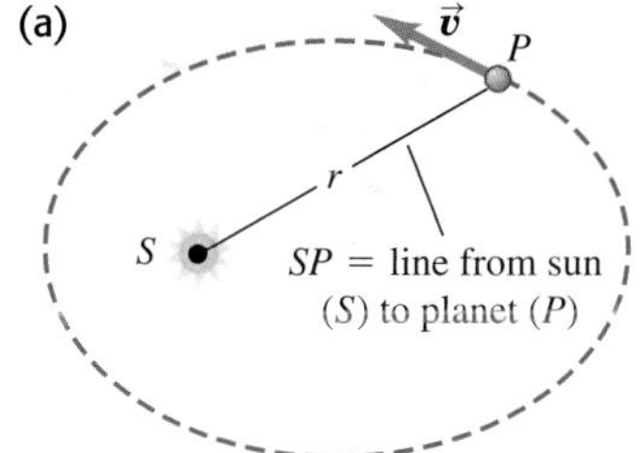

v⃗
P
r
S
SP = line from sun (S) to planet (P)

(b)

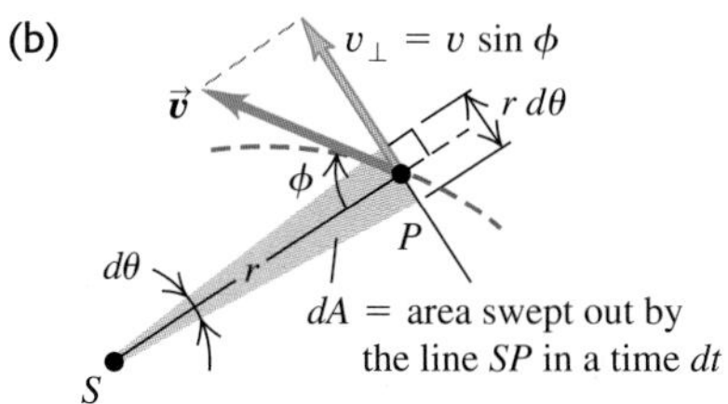

v⊥ = v sin φ
v⃗
r dθ
φ
P
dθ
r
dA = area swept out by the line SP in a time dt
S

(c)

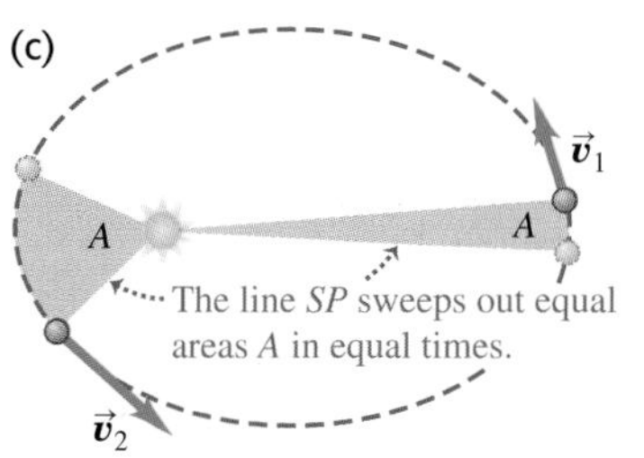

v⃗1
A
A
The line SP sweeps out equal areas A in equal times.
v⃗2

Kepler's Second Law

Figure 12.20 shows Kepler's second law. In a small time interval dt, the line from the sun S to the planet P turns through an angle $d\theta$. The area swept out is the colored triangle with height r, base length $r\,d\theta$, and area $dA = \frac{1}{2}r^2\,d\theta$ (Fig. 12.20b). The rate at which area is swept out, dA/dt, is called the *sector velocity:*

$$\frac{dA}{dt} = \frac{1}{2}r^2\frac{d\theta}{dt} \tag{12.14}$$

The essence of Kepler's second law is that the sector velocity has the same value at all points in the orbit. When the planet is close to the sun, r is small and $d\theta/dt$ is large; when the planet is far from the sun, r is large and $d\theta/dt$ is small.

To see how Kepler's second law follows from Newton's laws, we express dA/dt in terms of the velocity vector $\vec{v}$ of the planet P. The component of $\vec{v}$ perpendicular to the radial line is $v_\perp = v\sin\phi$. From Fig. 12.20b the displacement along the direction of $v_\perp$ during time dt is $r\,d\theta$, so we also have $v_\perp = r\,d\theta/dt$. Using this relationship in Eq. (12.14), we find

$$\frac{dA}{dt} = \frac{1}{2}rv\sin\phi \qquad \text{(sector velocity)} \tag{12.15}$$

Now $rv\sin\phi$ is the magnitude of the vector product $\vec{r} \times \vec{v}$, which in turn is $1/m$ times the angular momentum $\vec{L} = \vec{r} \times m\vec{v}$ of the planet with respect to the sun. So we have

$$\frac{dA}{dt} = \frac{1}{2m}\left|\vec{r} \times m\vec{v}\right| = \frac{L}{2m} \tag{12.16}$$

Thus Kepler's second law—that sector velocity is constant—means that angular momentum is constant!

It is easy to see why the angular momentum of the planet *must* be constant. According to Eq. (10.26), the rate of change of $\vec{L}$ equals the torque of the gravitational force $\vec{F}$ acting on the planet:

$$\frac{d\vec{L}}{dt} = \vec{\tau} = \vec{r} \times \vec{F}$$

In our situation, $\vec{r}$ is the vector from the sun to the planet, and the force $\vec{F}$ is directed from the planet to the sun. So these vectors always lie along the same line, and their vector product $\vec{r} \times \vec{F}$ is zero. Hence $d\vec{L}/dt = \mathbf{0}$. This conclusion does not depend on the $1/r^2$ behavior of the force; angular momentum is conserved for *any* force that acts always along the line joining the particle to a fixed point. Such a force is called a *central force.* (Kepler's first and third laws are valid *only* for a $1/r^2$ force.)

Conservation of angular momentum also explains why the orbit lies in a plane. The vector $\vec{L} = \vec{r} \times m\vec{v}$ is always perpendicular to the plane of the vectors $\vec{r}$ and $\vec{v}$; since $\vec{L}$ is constant in magnitude *and* direction, $\vec{r}$ and $\vec{v}$ always lie in the same plane, which is just the plane of the planet's orbit.

Kepler's Third Law

We have already derived Kepler's third law for the particular case of circular orbits. Equation (12.12) shows that the period of a satellite or planet in a circular orbit is proportional to the $\frac{3}{2}$ power of the orbit radius. Newton was able to show that this same relationship holds for an *elliptical* orbit, with the orbit radius r replaced by the semi-major axis a:

$$T = \frac{2\pi a^{3/2}}{\sqrt{Gm_S}} \quad \text{(elliptical orbit around the sun)} \tag{12.17}$$

Since the planet orbits the sun, not the earth, we have replaced the earth's mass m_E in Eq. (12.12) with the sun's mass m_S. Note that the period does not depend on the eccentricity e. An asteroid in an elongated elliptical orbit with semi-major axis a will have the same orbital period as a planet in a circular orbit of radius a. The key difference is that the asteroid moves at different speeds at different points in its elliptical orbit (Fig. 12.20c), while the planet's speed is constant around its circular orbit.

Conceptual Example 12.7 Orbital speeds

At what point in an elliptical orbit (Fig. 12.19) does a planet have the greatest speed?

SOLUTION

Mechanical energy is conserved as the planet moves around its orbit. The planet's kinetic energy $K = \frac{1}{2}mv^2$ is maximum when the potential energy $U = -Gm_Sm/r$ is minimum (that is, most negative; see Fig. 12.11), which occurs when r is a minimum. Hence the speed v is maximum at perihelion.

Your intuition about falling bodies is helpful here. As the planet falls inward toward the sun, it picks up speed, and its speed is maximum when closest to the sun. By the same reasoning, the planet slows down as it moves away from the sun, and its speed is minimum at aphelion.

Example 12.8 Kepler's third law

The asteroid Pallas has an orbital period of 4.62 years and an orbital eccentricity of 0.233. Find the semi-major axis of its orbit.

SOLUTION

IDENTIFY: This example uses Kepler's third law, which relates the period T and the semi-major axis a for an object (like an asteroid) that orbits.

SET UP: We use Eq. (12.17) to determine a from the given value of T. Note that we don't need the value of the eccentricity.

EXECUTE: From Eq. (12.17), $a^{3/2} = (\sqrt{Gm_S}\,T)/2\pi$. To solve for a, we raise this expression to the $\frac{2}{3}$ power:

$$a = \left(\frac{Gm_S T^2}{4\pi^2}\right)^{1/3}$$

Since $G = 6.67 \times 10^{-11}\ \mathrm{N \cdot m^2/kg^2}$ and $m_S = 1.99 \times 10^{30}$ kg (the mass of the sun from Appendix F) are given in SI units, we must express the period T in seconds rather than years using a conversion factor from Appendix E: $T = (4.62\ \mathrm{yr})(3.156 \times 10^7\ \mathrm{s/yr}) = 1.46 \times 10^8$ s. Using this value, we find $a = 4.15 \times 10^{11}$ m. (Plug in the numbers yourself to check.)

EVALUATE: Our result is intermediate between the semi-major axes of Mars and Jupiter (see Appendix F). Indeed, most known asteroids orbit in an "asteroid belt" between the orbits of these two planets.

As a historical note, Pallas wasn't discovered until 1802, almost two centuries after the publication of Kepler's third law. While Kepler deduced his three laws from the motions of the five planets (other than the earth) known in his time, these laws have proven to apply equally well to all of the planets, asteroids, and comets subsequently discovered to be orbiting the sun.

Example 12.9 Comet Halley

Comet Halley moves in an elongated elliptical orbit around the sun (Fig. 12.21). At perihelion, the comet is 8.75×10^7 km from the sun; at aphelion, it is 5.26×10^9 km from the sun. Find the semi-major axis, eccentricity, and period of the orbit.

SOLUTION

IDENTIFY: We are given the perihelion and aphelion distances, and we are to find the semi-major axis a, eccentricity e, and orbital period T (which is related to the semi-major axis by Kepler's third law).

SET UP: Figure 12.19 shows us how to find a and e from the perihelion and aphelion distances. Once we know the value of a, we can find the orbital period from Eq. (12.17).

EXECUTE: From Fig. 12.19 the length of the major axis equals the sum of the comet–sun distance at perihelion and the comet–sun distance at aphelion. The length of the major axis is $2a$, so

$$a = \frac{8.75 \times 10^7\ \mathrm{km} + 5.26 \times 10^9\ \mathrm{km}}{2} = 2.67 \times 10^9\ \mathrm{km}$$

(a)

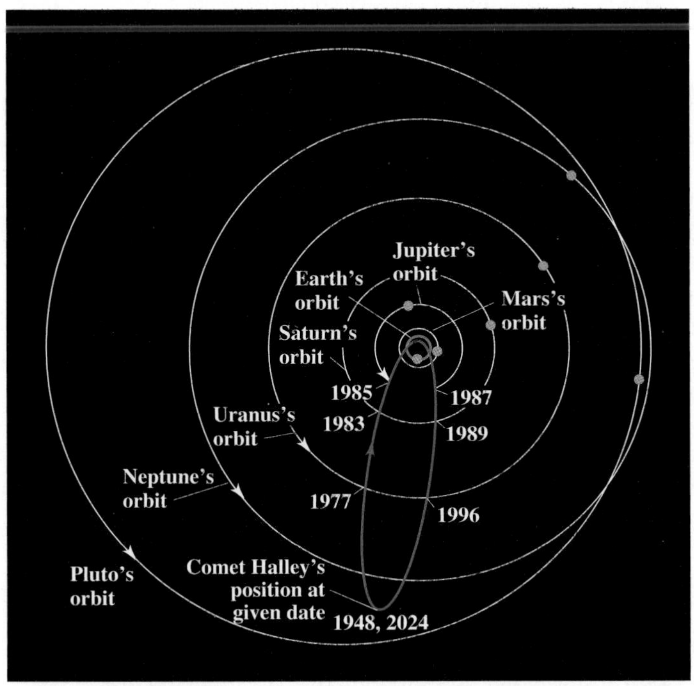

(b)

12.21 (a) The orbit of Comet Halley. (b) Comet Halley as it appeared in 1986. At the heart of the comet is an icy body, called the nucleus, that is about 10 km across. When the comet's orbit carries it close to the sun, the heat of sunlight causes the nucleus to partially evaporate. The evaporated material forms the tail, which can be tens of millions of kilometers long.

Continued

Further inspection of Fig. 12.19 shows that the comet–sun distance at perihelion is

$$a - ea = a(1 - e)$$

Since we are given that this distance is 8.75×10^7 km, the eccentricity is

$$e = 1 - \frac{8.75 \times 10^7 \text{ km}}{a} = 1 - \frac{8.75 \times 10^7 \text{ km}}{2.67 \times 10^9 \text{ km}} = 0.967$$

The period is given by Eq. (12.17):

$$T = \frac{2\pi a^{3/2}}{\sqrt{Gm_S}} = \frac{2\pi(2.67 \times 10^{12} \text{ m})^{3/2}}{\sqrt{(6.67 \times 10^{-11} \text{ N} \cdot \text{m}^2/\text{kg}^2)(1.99 \times 10^{30} \text{ kg})}}$$
$$= 2.38 \times 10^9 \text{ s} = 75.5 \text{ years}$$

EVALUATE: The eccentricity is very close to 1, so the comet has a very elongated orbit (see Fig. 12.21a). Comet Halley was at perihelion in early 1986; it will next reach perihelion one period later, in 2061.

Planetary Motions and the Center of Mass

We have assumed that as a planet or comet orbits the sun, the sun remains absolutely stationary. Of course, this can't be correct; because the sun exerts a gravitational force on the planet, the planet exerts a gravitational force on the sun of the same magnitude but opposite direction. In fact, *both* the sun and the planet orbit around their common center of mass (Fig. 12.22). We've made only a small error by ignoring this effect, however; the sun's mass is about 750 times the total mass of all the planets combined, so the center of mass of the solar system is not far from the center of the sun. Remarkably, astronomers have used this effect to detect the presence of planets orbiting other stars. Sensitive telescopes are able to detect the apparent "wobble" of a star as it orbits the common center of mass of the star and an unseen companion planet. (The planets are too faint to observe directly.) By analyzing these "wobbles," astronomers have discovered planets in orbit around more than a hundred other stars.

12.22 A star and its planet both orbit about their common center of mass.

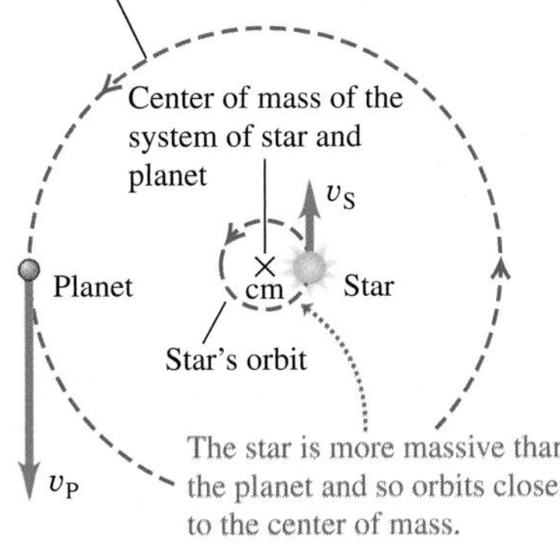
Planet's orbit around the center of mass
Center of mass of the system of star and planet
v_S
Planet
cm
Star
Star's orbit
The star is more massive than the planet and so orbits closer to the center of mass.
v_P
The planet and star are always on opposite sides of the center of mass.

Newton's analysis of planetary motions is used on a daily basis by modern-day astronomers. But the most remarkable result of Newton's work is that the motions of bodies in the heavens obey the *same* laws of motion as do bodies on the earth. This *Newtonian synthesis,* as it has come to be called, is one of the great unifying principles of science. It has had profound effects on the way that humanity looks at the universe—not as a realm of impenetrable mystery, but as a direct extension of our everyday world, subject to scientific study and calculation.

Test Your Understanding of Section 12.5 The orbit of Comet X has a semi-major axis that is four times larger than the semi-major axis of Comet Y. What is the ratio of the orbital period of X to the orbital period of Y? (i) 2; (ii) 4; (iii) 8; (iv) 16; (v) 32; (vi) 64.

*12.6 Spherical Mass Distributions

We have stated without proof that the gravitational interaction between two spherically symmetric mass distributions is the same as though all the mass of each were concentrated at its center. Now we're ready to prove this statement. Newton searched for a proof for several years, and he delayed publication of the law of gravitation until he found one.

Here's our program. Rather than starting with two spherically symmetric masses, we'll tackle the simpler problem of a point mass m interacting with a thin spherical shell with total mass M. We will show that when m is outside the sphere, the *potential energy* associated with this gravitational interaction is the same as though M were all concentrated at the center of the sphere. We learned in Section 7.4 that the force is the negative derivative of the potential energy, so the *force* on m is also the same as for a point mass M. Any spherically symmetric mass distribution can be thought of as being made up of many concentric spherical shells, so our result will also hold for *any* spherically symmetric M.

A Point Mass Outside a Spherical Shell

We start by considering a ring on the surface of the shell (Fig. 12.23a), centered on the line from the center of the shell to m. We do this because all of the particles that make up the ring are the same distance s from the point mass m. From Eq. (12.9) the potential energy of interaction between the earth (mass m_E) and a point mass m, separated by a distance r, is $U = -Gm_E m/r$. By changing notation in this expression, we see that in the situation shown in Fig. 12.23a, the potential energy of interaction between the point mass m and a particle of mass m_i within the ring is given by

$$U_i = -\frac{Gmm_i}{s}$$

To find the potential energy of interaction between m and the entire ring of mass $dM = \sum_i m_i$, we sum this expression for U_i over all particles in the ring. Calling this potential energy dU, we find

$$dU = \sum_i U_i = \sum_i \left(-\frac{Gmm_i}{s}\right) = -\frac{Gm}{s}\sum_i m_i = -\frac{Gm\,dM}{s} \qquad (12.18)$$

To proceed, we need to know the mass dM of the ring. We can find this with the aid of a little geometry. The radius of the shell is R, so in terms of the angle ϕ shown in the figure, the radius of the ring is $R\sin\phi$, and its circumference is $2\pi R\sin\phi$. The width of the ring is $R\,d\phi$, and its area dA is approximately equal to its width times its circumference:

$$dA = 2\pi R^2 \sin\phi\,d\phi$$

The ratio of the ring mass dM to the total mass M of the shell is equal to the ratio of the area dA of the ring to the total area $A = 4\pi R^2$ of the shell:

$$\frac{dM}{M} = \frac{2\pi R^2 \sin\phi\,d\phi}{4\pi R^2} = \frac{1}{2}\sin\phi\,d\phi \qquad (12.19)$$

Now we solve Eq. (12.19) for dM and substitute the result into Eq. (12.18) to find the potential energy of interaction between the point mass m and the ring:

$$dU = -\frac{GMm\sin\phi\,d\phi}{2s} \qquad (12.20)$$

The total potential energy of interaction between the point mass and the *shell* is the integral of Eq. (12.20) over the whole sphere as ϕ varies from 0 to π (*not* 2π!) and s varies from $r - R$ to $r + R$. To carry out the integration, we have to express the integrand in terms of a single variable; we choose s. To express ϕ and $d\phi$ in terms of s, we have to do a little more geometry. Figure 12.23b shows that s is the hypotenuse of a right triangle with sides $(r - R\cos\phi)$ and $R\sin\phi$, so the Pythagorean theorem gives

$$\begin{aligned} s^2 &= (r - R\cos\phi)^2 + (R\sin\phi)^2 \\ &= r^2 - 2rR\cos\phi + R^2 \end{aligned} \qquad (12.21)$$

We take differentials of both sides:

$$2s\,ds = 2rR\sin\phi\,d\phi$$

Next we divide this by $2rR$ and substitute the result into Eq. (12.20):

$$dU = -\frac{GMm}{2s}\frac{s\,ds}{rR} = -\frac{GMm}{2rR}ds \qquad (12.22)$$

We can now integrate Eq. (12.22), recalling that s varies from $r - R$ to $r + R$:

$$U = -\frac{GMm}{2rR}\int_{r-R}^{r+R} ds = -\frac{GMm}{2rR}[(r + R) - (r - R)] \qquad (12.23)$$

12.23 Calculating the gravitational potential energy of interaction between a point mass m outside a spherical shell and a ring on the surface of the shell.

(a) Geometry of the situation

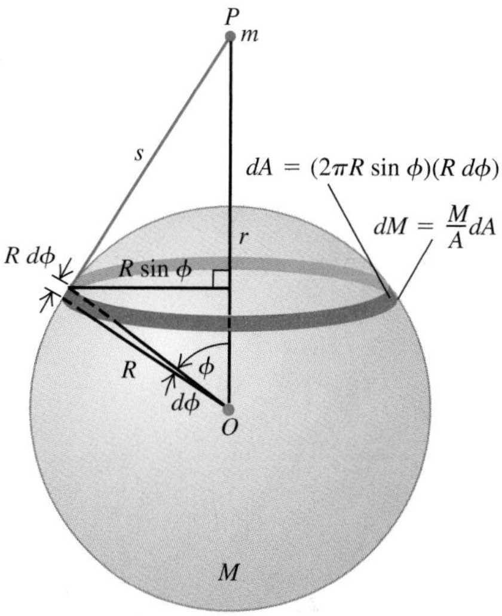

(b) The distance s is the hypotenuse of a right triangle with sides $(r - R\cos\phi)$ and $R\sin\phi$.

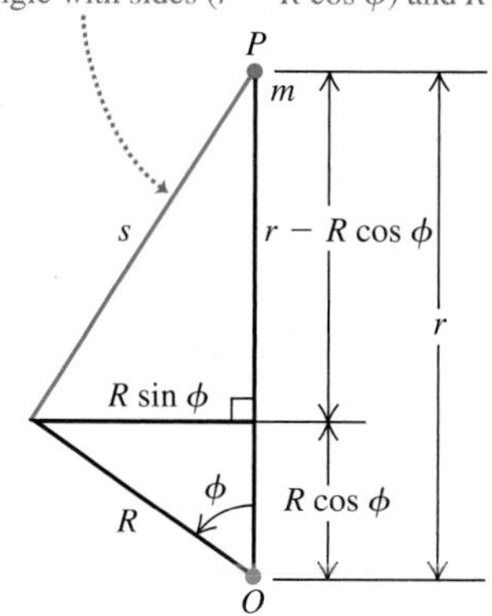

Finally, we have

$$U = -\frac{GMm}{r} \quad \text{(point mass } m \text{ outside spherical shell } M) \tag{12.24}$$

This is equal to the potential energy of two point masses m and M at a distance r. So we have proved that the gravitational potential energy of the spherical shell M and the point mass m at any distance r is the same as though they were point masses. Because the force is given by $F_r = -dU/dr$, the force is also the same.

The Gravitational Force Between Spherical Mass Distributions

Any spherically symmetric mass distribution can be thought of as a combination of concentric spherical shells. Because of the principle of superposition of forces, what is true of one shell is also true of the combination. So we have proved half of what we set out to prove: that the gravitational interaction between any spherically symmetric mass distribution and a point mass is the same as though all the mass of the spherically symmetric distribution were concentrated at its center.

The other half is to prove that *two* spherically symmetric mass distributions interact as though they were both points. That's easier. In Fig. 12.23a the forces the two bodies exert on each other are an action–reaction pair, and they obey Newton's third law. So we have also proved that the force that m exerts *on* the sphere M is the same as though M were a point. But now if we replace m with a spherically symmetric mass distribution centered at m's location, the resulting gravitational force on any part of M is the same as before, and so is the total force. This completes our proof.

A Point Mass Inside a Spherical Shell

We assumed at the beginning that the point mass m was outside the spherical shell, so our proof is valid only when m is outside a spherically symmetric mass distribution. When m is *inside* a spherical shell, the geometry is as shown in Fig. 12.24. The entire analysis goes just as before; Eqs. (12.18) through (12.22) are still valid. But when we get to Eq. (12.23), the limits of integration have to be changed to $R - r$ and $R + r$. We then have

12.24 When a point mass m is *inside* a uniform spherical shell of mass M, the potential energy is the same no matter where inside the shell the point mass is located. The force from the masses' mutual gravitational interaction is zero.

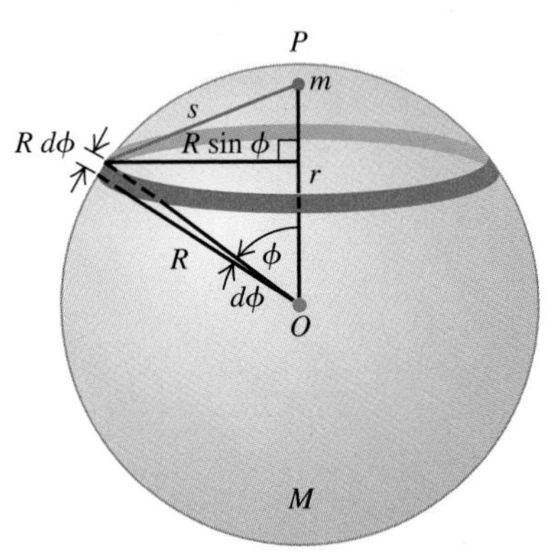

$$U = -\frac{GMm}{2rR}\int_{R-r}^{R+r} ds = -\frac{GMm}{2rR}[(R + r) - (R - r)] \tag{12.25}$$

and the final result is

$$U = -\frac{GMm}{R} \quad \text{(point mass } m \text{ inside spherical shell } M) \tag{12.26}$$

Compare this result to Eq. (12.24): Instead of having r, the distance between m and the center of M, in the denominator, we have R, the radius of the shell. This means that U in Eq. (12.26) doesn't depend on r and thus has the same value everywhere inside the shell. When m moves around inside the shell, no work is done on it, so the force on m at any point inside the shell must be zero.

More generally, at any point in the interior of any spherically symmetric mass distribution (not necessarily a shell), at a distance r from its center, the gravitational force on a point mass m is the same as though we removed all the mass at points farther than r from the center and concentrated all the remaining mass at the center.

Example 12.10 "Journey to the center of the earth"

Suppose we drill a hole through the earth (radius R_E, mass m_E) along a diameter and drop a mail pouch (mass m) down the hole. Derive an expression for the gravitational force on the pouch as a function of its distance r from the center. Assume that the density of the earth is uniform (not a very realistic model; see Fig. 12.9).

SOLUTION

IDENTIFY: According to the statements above, the gravitational force at a distance r from the center is determined only by the mass M within a spherical region of radius r (Fig. 12.25). The mass outside this radius has no effect on the mail pouch.

SET UP: The gravitational force on the mail pouch is the same as if all the mass M within radius r were concentrated at the center of the earth. The mass of a uniform sphere is proportional to the volume of the sphere, which is $\frac{4}{3}\pi r^3$ for the sphere of radius r and $\frac{4}{3}\pi R_E^3$ for the entire earth.

EXECUTE: The ratio of the mass M of the sphere of radius r to the mass of the earth, m_E, is

$$\frac{M}{m_E} = \frac{\frac{4}{3}\pi r^3}{\frac{4}{3}\pi R_E^3} = \frac{r^3}{R_E^3}, \quad \text{so} \quad M = m_E \frac{r^3}{R_E^3}$$

The magnitude of the gravitational force on m is given by

$$F_g = \frac{GMm}{r^2} = \frac{Gm}{r^2}\left(m_E \frac{r^3}{R_E^3}\right) = \frac{Gm_E m}{R_E^3} r$$

EVALUATE: At points inside this uniform-density sphere, F_g is *directly proportional* to the distance r from the center, rather than proportional to $1/r^2$ as it is outside the sphere. Right at the surface, where $r = R_E$, the above expression gives $F_g = Gm_E m/R_E^2$, as we should expect. In the next chapter we'll learn how to compute the time it would take for the mail pouch to emerge on the other side of the earth under the assumption of uniform density.

12.25 A hole through the center of the earth (assumed to be uniform). When an object is a distance r from the center, only the mass inside a sphere of radius r exerts a net gravitational force on it.

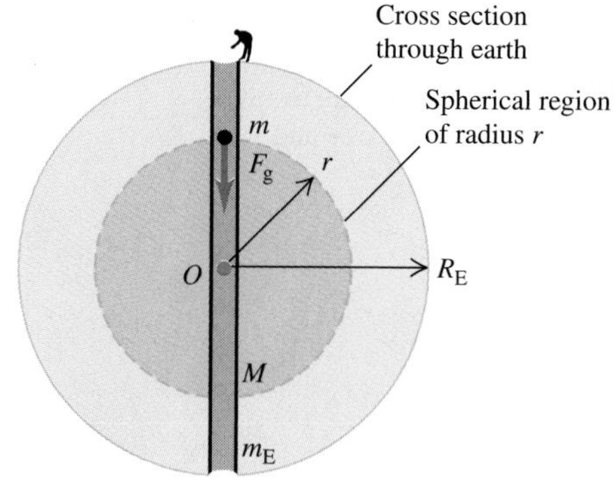

Test Your Understanding of Section 12.6 In the classic 1913 science-fiction novel *At the Earth's Core* by Edgar Rice Burroughs, explorers discover that the earth is a hollow sphere and that an entire civilization lives on the inside of the sphere. Would it be possible to stand and walk on the inner surface of a hollow, nonrotating planet?

*12.7 Apparent Weight and the Earth's Rotation

Because the earth rotates on its axis, it is not precisely an inertial frame of reference. For this reason the apparent weight of a body on earth is not precisely equal to the earth's gravitational attraction, which we will call the **true weight** $\vec{w}_0$ of the body. Figure 12.26 is a cutaway view of the earth, showing three observers. Each one holds a spring scale with a body of mass m hanging from it. Each scale applies a tension force $\vec{F}$ to the body hanging from it, and the reading on each scale is the magnitude F of this force. If the observers are unaware of the earth's rotation, each one *thinks* that the scale reading equals the weight of the body because he thinks the body on his spring scale is in equilibrium. So each observer thinks that the tension $\vec{F}$ must be opposed by an equal and opposite force $\vec{w}$, which we call the **apparent weight.** But if the bodies are rotating with the earth, they are *not* precisely in equilibrium. Our problem is to find the relationship between the apparent weight $\vec{w}$ and the true weight $\vec{w}_0$.

If we assume that the earth is spherically symmetric, then the true weight $\vec{w}_0$ has magnitude $Gm_E m/R_E^2$, where m_E and R_E are the mass and radius of the earth. This value is the same for all points on the earth's surface. If the center of the earth can be taken as the origin of an inertial coordinate system, then the body at the north pole really *is* in equilibrium in an inertial system, and the reading on that observer's spring scale is equal to w_0. But the body at the equator is moving in a circle of radius R_E with speed v, and there must be a net inward force equal to the mass times the centripetal acceleration:

$$w_0 - F = \frac{mv^2}{R_E}$$

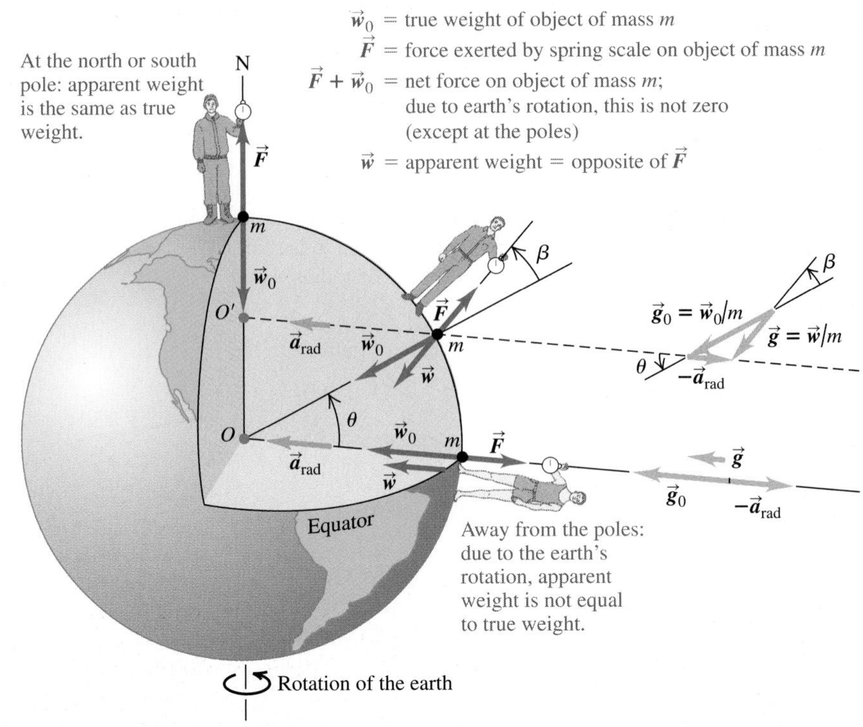

$\vec{w}_0$ = true weight of object of mass m
$\vec{F}$ = force exerted by spring scale on object of mass m
$\vec{F} + \vec{w}_0$ = net force on object of mass m; due to earth's rotation, this is not zero (except at the poles)
$\vec{w}$ = apparent weight = opposite of $\vec{F}$
At the north or south pole: apparent weight is the same as true weight.
N
$\vec{F}$
m
$\vec{w}_0$
O'
$\vec{a}_{rad}$
$\vec{w}_0$
$\vec{F}$
m
$\vec{w}$
β
$\vec{g}_0 = \vec{w}_0/m$
$\vec{g} = \vec{w}/m$
θ
$-\vec{a}_{rad}$
O
θ
$\vec{w}_0$
m
$\vec{F}$
$\vec{a}_{rad}$
$\vec{w}$
$\vec{g}$
$\vec{g}_0$
$-\vec{a}_{rad}$
Equator
Away from the poles: due to the earth's rotation, apparent weight is not equal to true weight.
Rotation of the earth

12.26 Except at the poles, the reading for an object being weighed on a scale (the *apparent weight*) is less than the gravitational force of attraction on the object (the *true weight*). The reason is that a net force is needed to provide a centripetal acceleration as the object rotates with the earth. For clarity, the illustration greatly exaggerates the angle β between the true and apparent weight vectors.

So the magnitude of the apparent weight (equal to the magnitude of F) is

$$w = w_0 - \frac{mv^2}{R_E} \quad \text{(at the equator)} \tag{12.27}$$

If the earth were not rotating, the body when released would have a free-fall acceleration $g_0 = w_0/m$. Since the earth *is* rotating, the falling body's actual acceleration relative to the observer at the equator is $g = w/m$. Dividing Eq. (12.27) by m and using these relationships, we find

$$g = g_0 - \frac{v^2}{R_E} \quad \text{(at the equator)}$$

To evaluate v^2/R_E, we note that in 86,164 s a point on the equator moves a distance equal to the earth's circumference, $2\pi R_E = 2\pi(6.38 \times 10^6\ \text{m})$. (The solar day, 86,400 s, is $\frac{1}{365}$ longer than this because in one day the earth also completes $\frac{1}{365}$ of its orbit around the sun.) Thus we find

$$v = \frac{2\pi(6.38 \times 10^6\ \text{m})}{86{,}164\ \text{s}} = 465\ \text{m/s}$$

$$\frac{v^2}{R_E} = \frac{(465\ \text{m/s})^2}{6.38 \times 10^6\ \text{m}} = 0.0339\ \text{m/s}^2$$

So for a spherically symmetric earth the acceleration due to gravity should be about $0.03\ \text{m/s}^2$ less at the equator than at the poles.

At locations intermediate between the equator and the poles, the true weight $\vec{w}_0$ and the centripetal acceleration are not along the same line, and we need to write a vector equation corresponding to Eq. (12.27). From Fig. 12.26 we see that the appropriate equation is

$$\vec{w} = \vec{w}_0 - m\vec{a}_{rad} = m\vec{g}_0 - m\vec{a}_{rad} \tag{12.28}$$

The difference in the magnitudes of g and g_0 lies between zero and $0.0339\ \text{m/s}^2$. As shown in Fig. 12.26, the *direction* of the apparent weight differs from the

Table 12.1 Variations of g with Latitude and Elevation

Station	North Latitude	Elevation (m)	$g\,(\text{m/s}^2)$
Canal Zone	09°	0	9.78243
Jamaica	18°	0	9.78591
Bermuda	32°	0	9.79806
Denver, Co	40°	1638	9.79609
Pittsburgh, PA	40.5°	235	9.80118
Cambridge, MA	42°	0	9.80398
Greenland	70°	0	9.82534

direction toward the center of the earth by a small angle β, which is 0.1° or less.

Table 12.1 gives the values of g at several locations, showing variations with latitude. There are also small additional variations due to the lack of perfect spherical symmetry of the earth, local variations in density, and differences in elevation.

Apparent Weight and Apparent Weightlessness

Our discussion of apparent weight can also be applied to the phenomenon of apparent weightlessness in orbiting spacecraft, which we described in Section 12.4. Bodies in an orbiting spacecraft are *not* weightless; the earth's gravitational attraction continues to act on them just as though they were at rest relative to the earth. The apparent weight of a body in a spacecraft is again given by Eq. (12.28):

$$\vec{w} = \vec{w}_0 - m\vec{a}_{\text{rad}} = m\vec{g}_0 - m\vec{a}_{\text{rad}}$$

But for a spacecraft in orbit, as well as any body inside the spacecraft, the acceleration $\vec{a}_{\text{rad}}$ toward the earth's center is equal to the value of the acceleration of gravity $\vec{g}_0$ at the position of the spacecraft. Hence

$$\vec{g}_0 = \vec{a}_{\text{rad}}$$

and the apparent weight is

$$\vec{w} = \mathbf{0}$$

This is what we mean when we say that an astronaut or other body in the spacecraft is apparently weightless. Note that we didn't make any assumptions about the shape of the orbit. As we mentioned in Section 12.4, an astronaut will be apparently weightless no matter what the orbit (Fig. 12.27).

12.27 This orbiting astronaut is acted on by the earth's gravity, but he *feels* weightless because his acceleration is equal to $\vec{g}$.

Test Your Understanding of Section 12.7 Imagine a planet that has the same mass and radius as the earth, but that makes 10 rotations during the time the earth makes one rotation. What would be the difference between the acceleration due to gravity at the planet's equator and the acceleration due to gravity at its poles? (i) 0.00339 m/s²; (ii) 0.0339 m/s²; (iii) 0.339 m/s²; (iv) 3.39 m/s².

12.8 Black Holes

The concept of a black hole is one of the most interesting and startling products of modern gravitational theory, yet the basic idea can be understood on the basis of Newtonian principles.

The Escape Speed from a Star

Think first about the properties of our own sun. Its mass $M = 1.99 \times 10^{30}$ kg and radius $R = 6.96 \times 10^{8}$ m are much larger than those of any planet, but compared to other stars, our sun is not exceptionally massive. You can find the sun's average density ρ in the same way we found the average density of the earth in Section 12.2:

$$\rho = \frac{M}{V} = \frac{M}{\frac{4}{3}\pi R^3} = \frac{1.99 \times 10^{30}\ \text{kg}}{\frac{4}{3}\pi(6.96 \times 10^8\ \text{m})^3}$$
$$= 1410\ \text{kg/m}^3$$

The sun's temperatures range from 5800 K (about 5500°C, or 10,000°F) at the surface up to 1.5×10^7 K (about 2.7×10^7°F) in the interior, so it surely contains no solids or liquids. Yet gravitational attraction pulls the sun's gas atoms together until the sun is, on average, 41% denser than water and about 1200 times as dense as the air we breathe.

Now think about the escape speed for a body at the surface of the sun. In Example 12.5 (Section 12.3) we found that the escape speed from the surface of a spherical mass M with radius R is $v = \sqrt{2GM/R}$. We can relate this to the average density. Substituting $M = \rho V = \rho(\frac{4}{3}\pi R^3)$ into the expression for escape speed gives

$$v = \sqrt{\frac{2GM}{R}} = \sqrt{\frac{8\pi G\rho}{3}}R \qquad (12.29)$$

Using either form of this equation, you can show that the escape speed for a body at the surface of our sun is $v = 6.18 \times 10^5$ m/s (about 2.2 million km/h, or 1.4 million mi/h). This value, roughly 1/500 the speed of light, is independent of the mass of the escaping body; it depends on only the mass and radius (or average density and radius) of the sun.

Now consider various stars with the same average density ρ and different radii R. Equation (12.29) shows that for a given value of density ρ, the escape speed v is directly proportional to R. In 1783 the Rev. John Mitchell, an amateur astronomer, noted that if a body with the same average density as the sun had about 500 times the radius of the sun, its escape speed would be greater than the speed of light c. With his statement that "all light emitted from such a body would be made to return toward it," Mitchell became the first person to suggest the existence of what we now call a **black hole**—an object that exerts a gravitational force on other bodies, but cannot emit any light of its own.

Black Holes, the Schwarzschild Radius, and the Event Horizon

The first expression for escape speed in Eq. (12.29) suggests that a body of mass M will act as a black hole if its radius R is less than or equal to a certain critical radius. How can we determine this critical radius? You might think that you can find the answer by simply setting $v = c$ in Eq. (12.29). As a matter of fact, this does give the correct result, but only because of two compensating errors. The kinetic energy of light is *not* $mc^2/2$, and the gravitational potential energy near a black hole is *not* given by Eq. (12.9). In 1916, Karl Schwarzschild used Einstein's general theory of relativity (in part a generalization and extension of Newtonian gravitation theory) to derive an expression for the critical radius R_S, now called the **Schwarzschild radius.** The result turns out to be the same as though we had set $v = c$ in Eq. (12.29), so

$$c = \sqrt{\frac{2GM}{R_S}}$$

Solving for the Schwarzschild radius R_S, we find

$$R_S = \frac{2GM}{c^2} \quad \text{(Schwarzschild radius)} \qquad (12.30)$$

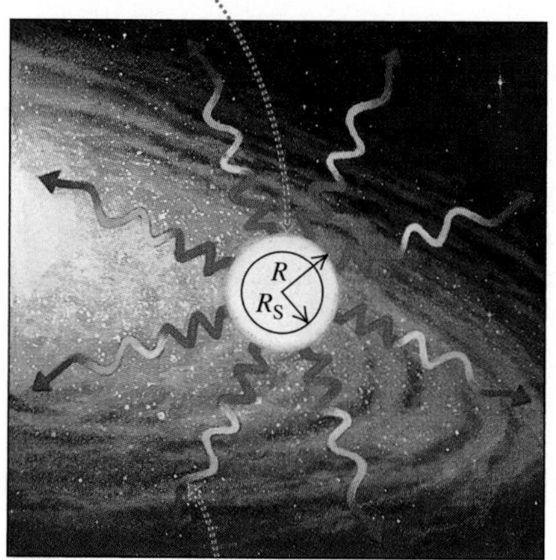

(a) When the radius R of a body is greater than the Schwarzschild radius R_S, light can escape from the surface of the body.

Gravity acting on the escaping light "red shifts" it to longer wavelengths.

(b) If all of the mass of the body lies inside radius R_S, the body is a black hole: No light can escape from it.

12.28 (a) A body with a radius R greater than the Schwarzschild radius R_S. (b) If the body collapses to a radius smaller than R_S, it is a black hole with an escape speed greater than the speed of light. The surface of the sphere of radius R_S is called the event horizon of the black hole.

If a spherical, nonrotating body with mass M has a radius less than R_S, then *nothing* (not even light) can escape from the surface of the body, and the body is a black hole (Fig. 12.28). In this case, any other body within a distance R_S of the center of the black hole is trapped by the gravitational attraction of the black hole and cannot escape from it.

The surface of the sphere with radius R_S surrounding a black hole is called the **event horizon:** Since light can't escape from within that sphere, we can't see events occurring inside. All that an observer outside the event horizon can know about a black hole is its mass (from its gravitational effects on other bodies), its electric charge (from the electric forces it exerts on other charged bodies), and its angular momentum (because a rotating black hole tends to drag space—and everything in that space—around with it). All other information about the body is irretrievably lost when it collapses inside its event horizon.

Example 12.11 Black hole calculations

Astrophysical theory suggests that a burned-out star will collapse under its own gravity to form a black hole when its mass is at least three solar masses. If it does, what is the radius of its event horizon?

SOLUTION

IDENTIFY: The radius in question is the Schwarzschild radius.

SET UP: We use Eq. (12.30) with a value of M equal to three solar masses, or $M = 3(1.99 \times 10^{30}\text{ kg}) = 6.0 \times 10^{30}\text{ kg}$.

EXECUTE: From Eq. (12.30),

$$R_S = \frac{2GM}{c^2} = \frac{2(6.67 \times 10^{-11}\text{ N}\cdot\text{m}^2/\text{kg}^2)(6.0 \times 10^{30}\text{ kg})}{(3.00 \times 10^8\text{ m/s})^2}$$
$$= 8.9 \times 10^3\text{ m} = 8.9\text{ km}$$

or less than 6 miles.

EVALUATE: If the radius of such an object is just equal to the Schwarzschild radius, the average density has the incredibly large value

$$\rho = \frac{M}{\frac{4}{3}\pi R^3} = \frac{6.0 \times 10^{30}\text{ kg}}{\frac{4}{3}\pi(8.9 \times 10^3\text{ m})^3}$$
$$= 2.0 \times 10^{18}\text{ kg/m}^3$$

This is about 10^{15} times as great as the density of familiar matter on earth and is comparable to the densities of atomic nuclei. In fact, once the body collapses to a radius of R_S, nothing can prevent it from collapsing further. All of the mass ends up being crushed down to a single point called a *singularity* at the center of the event horizon. This point has zero volume and so has *infinite* density.

A Visit to a Black Hole

At points far from a black hole, its gravitational effects are the same as those of any normal body with the same mass. If the sun collapsed to form a black hole, the orbits of the planets would be unaffected. But things get dramatically different close to the black hole. If you decided to become a martyr for science and jump into a black hole, the friends you left behind would notice several odd effects as you moved toward the event horizon, most of them associated with effects of general relativity.

If you carried a radio transmitter to send back your comments on what was happening, your friends would have to retune their receiver continuously to lower and lower frequencies, an effect called the *gravitational red shift.* Consistent with this shift, they would observe that your clocks (electronic or biological) would appear to run more and more slowly, an effect called *time dilation.* In fact, during their lifetimes they would never see you make it to the event horizon.

In your frame of reference, you would make it to the event horizon in a rather short time but in a rather disquieting way. As you fell feet first into the black hole, the gravitational pull on your feet would be greater than that on your head, which would be slightly farther away from the black hole. The *differences* in gravitational force on different parts of your body would be great enough to stretch you along the direction toward the black hole and compress you perpendicular to it. These effects (called *tidal forces*) would rip you to atoms, and then rip your atoms apart, before you reached the event horizon.

Detecting Black Holes

If light cannot escape from a black hole and if black holes are as small as Example 12.11 suggests, how can we know that such things exist? The answer is that any gas or dust near the black hole tends to be pulled into an *accretion disk* that swirls around and into the black hole, rather like a whirlpool (Fig. 12.29). Friction within the accretion disk's material causes it to lose mechanical energy and spiral into the black hole; as it moves inward, it is compressed together. This causes heating of the material, just as air compressed in a bicycle pump gets hotter. Temperatures in excess of 10^6 K can occur in the accretion disk, so hot that the disk emits not just visible light (as do bodies that are "red-hot" or "white-hot") but x rays. Astronomers look for these x rays (emitted by the material *before* it crosses the event horizon) to signal the presence of a black hole. Several promising candidates have been found, and astronomers now express considerable confidence in the existence of black holes.

Black holes in binary star systems like the one depicted in Fig. 12.29 have masses a few times greater than the sun's mass. There is also mounting evidence for the existence of much larger *supermassive black holes.* One example is thought to lie at the center of our Milky Way galaxy, some 26,000 light-years from earth in the direction of the constellation Sagittarius. High-resolution images of the galactic center reveal stars moving at speeds greater than 1500 km/s about an unseen object that lies at the position of a source of radio

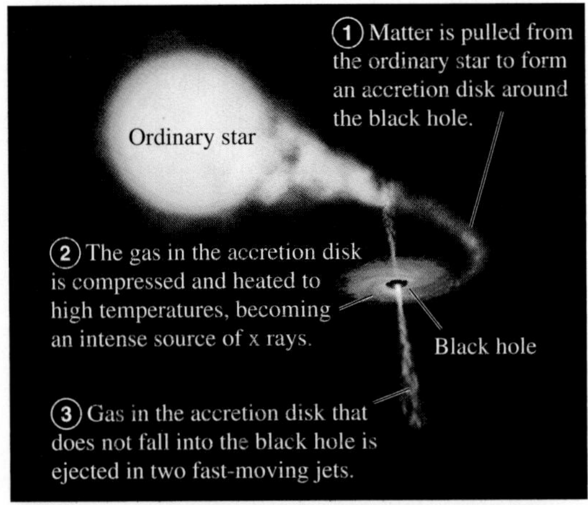

① Matter is pulled from the ordinary star to form an accretion disk around the black hole.
Ordinary star
② The gas in the accretion disk is compressed and heated to high temperatures, becoming an intense source of x rays.
Black hole
③ Gas in the accretion disk that does not fall into the black hole is ejected in two fast-moving jets.

12.29 A binary star system in which an ordinary star and a black hole orbit each other. The black hole itself cannot be seen, but the x rays from its accretion disk can be detected.

waves called Sgr A* (Fig. 12.30). By analyzing these motions, astronomers can infer the period T and semi-major axis a of each star's orbit. The mass m_X of the unseen object can then be calculated using Kepler's third law in the form given in Eq. (12.17), with the mass of the sun m_S replaced by m_X:

$$T = \frac{2\pi a^{3/2}}{\sqrt{Gm_X}} \quad \text{so} \quad m_X = \frac{4\pi^2 a^3}{GT^2}$$

The conclusion is that the mysterious dark object at the galactic center has a mass of 7.3×10^{36} kg, or 3.7 *million* times the mass of the sun. Yet observations with radio telescopes show that it has a radius no more than about 10^{11} m, comparable to the distance from the earth to the sun. These observations suggest that this massive, compact object is a black hole with a Schwarzschild radius of 1.1×10^{10} m. Astronomers hope to improve the resolution of their observations so that they can actually see the event horizon of this black hole.

Other lines of research suggest that even larger black holes, in excess of 10^9 times the mass of the sun, lie at the centers of other galaxies. Observational and theoretical studies of black holes of all sizes continue to be an exciting area of research in both physics and astronomy.

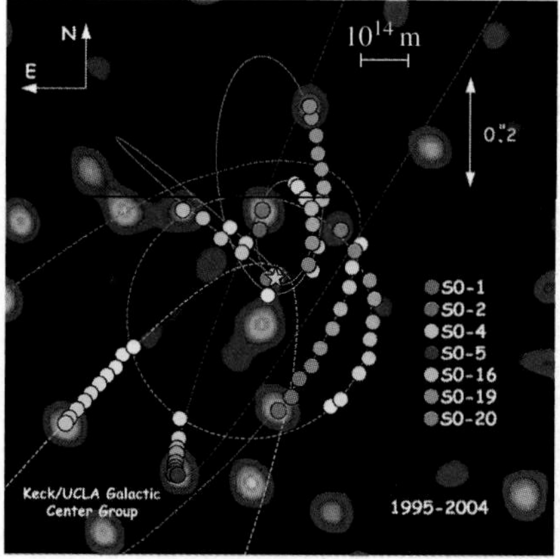

12.30 This false-color image shows the motions of stars at the center of our galaxy over a nine-year period. Analyzing these orbits using Kepler's third law indicates that the stars are moving about an unseen object that is some 3.7×10^6 times the mass of the sun. The scale bar indicates a length of 10^{14} m (670 times the distance from the earth to the sun) at the distance of the galactic center.

Test Your Understanding of Section 12.8 If the sun somehow collapsed to form a black hole, what effect would this event have on the orbit of the earth? (i) The orbit would shrink; (ii) the orbit would expand; (iii) the orbit would remain the same size.

CHAPTER 12 SUMMARY

Newton's law of gravitation: *Any* two bodies with masses m_1 and m_2, a distance r apart, attract each other with forces inversely proportional to r^2. These forces form an action–reaction pair and obey Newton's third law. When two or more bodies exert gravitational forces on a particular body, the total gravitational force on that individual body is the vector sum of the forces exerted by the other bodies. The gravitational interaction between spherical mass distributions, such as planets or stars, is the same as if all the mass of each distribution were concentrated at the center. (See Examples 12.1–12.3 and 12.10.)

$$F_g = \frac{Gm_1m_2}{r^2} \qquad (12.1)$$

m_1 $\vec{F}_{g\,(2\text{ on }1)}$ $\vec{F}_{g\,(1\text{ on }2)}$ r m_2

$F_{g\,(1\text{ on }2)} = F_{g\,(2\text{ on }1)}$

Gravitational force, weight, and gravitational potential energy: The weight w of a body is the total gravitational force exerted on it by all other bodies in the universe. Near the surface of the earth (mass m_E and radius R_E), the weight is essentially equal to the gravitational force of the earth alone. The gravitational potential energy U of two masses m and m_E separated by a distance r is inversely proportional to r. The potential energy is never positive; it is zero only when the two bodies are infinitely far apart. (See Examples 12.4 and 12.5.)

$$w = F_g = \frac{Gm_Em}{R_E^2} \qquad (12.3)$$

(weight at earth's surface)

$$g = \frac{Gm_E}{R_E^2} \qquad (12.4)$$

(acceleration due to gravity at earth's surface)

$$U = -\frac{Gm_Em}{r} \qquad (12.9)$$

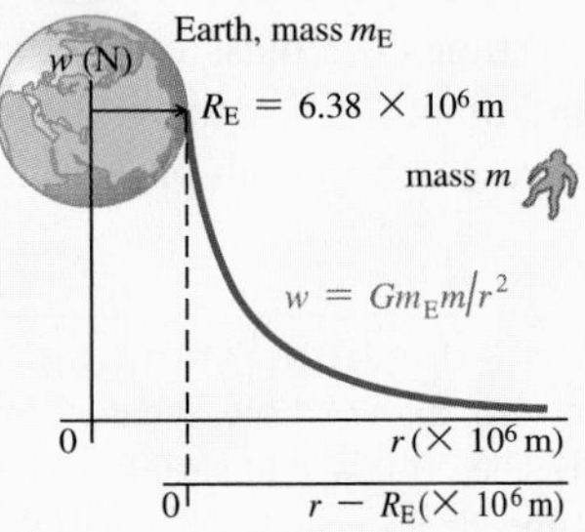

Orbits: When a satellite moves in a circular orbit, the centripetal acceleration is provided by the gravitational attraction of the earth. Kepler's three laws describe the more general case: an elliptical orbit of a planet around the sun or a satellite around a planet. (See Examples 12.6–12.9.)

$$v = \sqrt{\frac{Gm_E}{r}}$$

(speed in circular orbit) (12.10)

$$T = \frac{2\pi r}{v} = 2\pi r\sqrt{\frac{r}{Gm_E}} = \frac{2\pi r^{3/2}}{\sqrt{Gm_E}}$$

(period in circular orbit) (12.12)

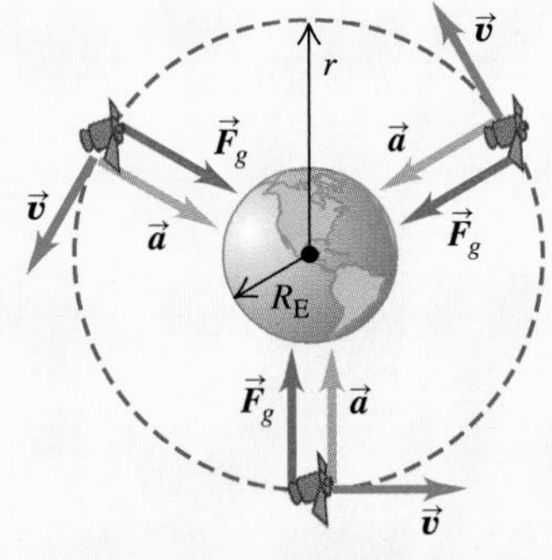

Black holes: If a nonrotating spherical mass distribution with total mass M has a radius less than its Schwarzschild radius R_S, it is called a black hole. The gravitational interaction prevents anything, including light, from escaping from within a sphere with radius R_S. (See Example 12.11.)

$$R_S = \frac{2GM}{c^2}$$

(Schwarzschild radius) (12.30)

If all of the body is inside its Schwarzschild radius $R_S = 2GM/c^2$, the body is a black hole.

Key Terms

law of gravitation, *384*
gravitational constant, *384*
gravitational potential energy, *391*
escape speed, *391*
closed orbit, *394*
open orbit, *394*
semi-major axis, *397*
eccentricity, *397*
true weight, *403*
apparent weight, *403*
black hole, *406*
Schwarzschild radius, *406*
event horizon, *407*

Answer to Chapter Opening Question ?

The smaller the orbital radius r of a satellite, the faster its orbital speed v see [Eq. (12.10)]. Hence a particle near the inner edge of Saturn's rings has a faster speed than a particle near the outer edge of the rings.

Answers to Test Your Understanding Questions

12.1 Answer: (v) From Eq. (12.1), the gravitational force of the sun (mass m_1) on a planet (mass m_2) a distance r away has magnitude $F_g = Gm_1m_2/r^2$. Compared to the earth, Saturn has a value of r^2 that is $10^2 = 100$ times greater and a value of m_2 that is also 100 times greater. Hence the *force* that the sun exerts on Saturn has the same magnitude as the force that the sun exerts on earth. The *acceleration* of a planet equals the net force divided by the planet's mass: Since Saturn has 100 times more mass than the earth, its acceleration is $1/100$ as great as that of the earth.
12.2 Answer: (iii), (i), (ii), (iv) From Eq. (12.4), the acceleration due to gravity at the surface of a planet of mass m_P and radius R_P is $g_P = Gm_P/R_P^2$. That is, g_P is directly proportional to the planet's mass and inversely proportional to the square of its radius. It follows that compared to the value of g at the earth's surface, the value of g_P on each planet is (i) $2/2^2 = 1/2$ as great; (ii) $4/4^2 = 1/4$ as great; (iii) $4/2^2 = 1$ time as great—that is, the same as on earth; and (iv) $2/4^2 = 1/8$ as great.
12.3 Answer: yes This is possible because surface gravity and escape speed depend in different ways on the planet's mass m_P and radius R_P: The value of g at the surface is Gm_P/R_P^2, while the escape speed is $\sqrt{2Gm_P/R_P}$. For the planet Saturn, for example, m_P is about 100 times the earth's mass and R_P is about 10 times the earth's radius. The value of g is different than on earth by a factor $(100)/(10)^2 = 1$ (i.e., it is the same as on earth), while the escape speed is greater by a factor $\sqrt{100/10} = 3.2$. It may help to remember that the surface gravity tells you about conditions right next to the planet's surface, while the escape speed (which tells you how fast you must travel to escape to infinity) depends on conditions at *all* points between the planet's surface and infinity. Because Saturn has so much more mass than the earth, its gravitational effects are appreciable at much greater distances and its escape speed is higher.
12.4 Answer: (ii) Equation (12.10) shows that in a smaller-radius orbit, the spacecraft has a faster speed. The negative work done by air resistance decreases the *total* mechanical energy $E = K + U$; the kinetic energy K increases (becomes more positive), but the gravitational potential energy U decreases (becomes more negative) by a greater amount.
12.5 Answer: (iii) Equation (12.17) shows that the orbital period T is proportional to the $\frac{3}{2}$ power of the semi-major axis a. Hence the orbital period of Comet X is longer than that of Comet Y by a factor of $4^{3/2} = 8$.
12.6 Answer: no Our analysis shows that there is *zero* gravitational force inside a hollow spherical shell. Hence visitors to the interior of a hollow planet would find themselves weightless, and they could not stand or walk on the planet's inner surface.
12.7 Answer: (iv) The discussion following Eq. (12.27) shows that the difference between the acceleration due to gravity at the equator and at the poles is v^2/R_E. Since this planet has the same radius and hence the same circumference as the earth, the speed v at its equator must be 10 times the speed of the earth's equator. Hence v^2/R_E is $10^2 = 100$ times greater than for the earth, or $100(0.0339\ \text{m/s}^2) = 3.39\ \text{m/s}^2$. The acceleration due to gravity at the poles is $9.80\ \text{m/s}^2$, while at the equator it is dramatically less, $9.80\ \text{m/s}^2 - 3.39\ \text{m/s}^2 = 6.41\ \text{m/s}^2$. You can show that if this planet were to rotate 17.0 times faster than the earth, the acceleration due to gravity at the equator would be *zero* and loose objects would fly off the equator's surface!
12.8 Answer: (iii) If the sun collapsed into a black hole (which, according to our understanding of stars, it cannot do), it would have the same mass but a much smaller radius. Because the gravitational attraction of the sun on the earth does not depend on the sun's radius, the earth's orbit would be unaffected.

PROBLEMS

For instructor-assigned homework, go to www.masteringphysics.com

Discussion Questions

Q12.1. A student wrote: "The only reason an apple falls downward to meet the earth instead of the earth rising upward to meet the apple is that the earth is much more massive and so exerts a much greater pull." Please comment.
Q12.2. A planet makes a circular orbit with period T around a star. If it were to orbit, at the same distance, a star with three times the mass of the original star, would the new period (in terms of T) would be (a) $3T$, (b) $T\sqrt{3}$, (c) T, (d) $T/\sqrt{3}$, or (e) $T/3$?
Q12.3. If all planets had the same average density, how would the acceleration due to gravity at the surface of a planet depend on its radius?
Q12.4. Is a pound of butter on the earth the same amount as a pound of butter on Mars? What about a kilogram of butter? Explain.
Q12.5. Example 12.2 (Section 12.1) shows that the acceleration of each sphere caused by the gravitational force is inversely proportional to the mass of that sphere. So why does the force of gravity give all masses the same acceleration when they are dropped near the surface of the earth?
Q12.6. When will you attract the sun more: today at noon, or tonight at midnight? Explain.
Q12.7. Since the moon is constantly attracted toward the earth by the gravitational interaction, why doesn't it crash into the earth?

Q12.8. A planet makes a circular orbit with period T around a star. If the planet were to orbit at the same distance around this star, but had three times as much mass, what would the new period (in terms of T) would be: (a) $3T$, (b) $T\sqrt{3}$, (c) T, (d) $T/\sqrt{3}$, or (e) $T/3$?

Q12.9. The sun pulls on the moon with a force that is more than twice the magnitude of the force with which the earth attracts the moon. Why, then, doesn't the sun take the moon away from the earth?

Q12.10. As defined in Chapter 7, gravitational potential energy is $U = mgy$ and is positive for a body of mass m above the earth's surface (which is at $y = 0$). But in this chapter, gravitational potential energy is $U = -Gm_E m/r$, which is *negative* for a body of mass m above the earth's surface (which is at $r = R_E$). How can you reconcile these seemingly incompatible descriptions of gravitational potential energy?

Q12.11. A planet is moving at constant speed in a circular orbit around a star. In one complete orbit, what is the net amount of work done on the planet by the star's gravitational force: positive, negative, or zero? What if the planet's orbit is an ellipse, so that the speed is not constant? Explain your answers.

Q12.12. Does the escape speed for an object at the earth's surface depend on the direction in which it is launched? Explain. Does your answer depend on whether or not you include the effects of air resistance?

Q12.13. If a projectile is fired straight up from the earth's surface, what would happen if the total mechanical energy (kinetic plus potential) is (a) less than zero, and (b) greater than zero? In each case, ignore air resistance and the gravitational effects of the sun, the moon, and the other planets.

Q12.14. Discuss whether this statement is correct: "In the absence of air resistance, the trajectory of a projectile thrown near the earth's surface is an *ellipse,* not a parabola."

Q12.15. The earth is closer to the sun in November than in May. In which of these months does it move faster in its orbit? Explain why.

Q12.16. A communications firm wants to place a satellite in orbit so that it is always directly above the earth's 45th parallel (latitude 45° north). This means that the plane of the orbit will not pass through the center of the earth. Is such an orbit possible? Why or why not?

Q12.17. At what point in an elliptical orbit is the acceleration maximum? At what point is it minimum? Justify your answers.

Q12.18. Which takes more fuel: a voyage from the earth to the moon or from the moon to the earth? Explain.

Q12.19. What would Kepler's third law be for circular orbits if an amendment to Newton's law of gravitation made the gravitational force inversely proportional to r^3? Would this change affect Kepler's other two laws? Explain.

Q12.20. In the elliptical orbit of Comet Halley shown in Fig. 12.21a, the sun's gravity is responsible for making the comet fall inward from aphelion to perihelion. But what is responsible for making the comet move from perihelion back outward to aphelion?

Q12.21. Many people believe that orbiting astronauts feel weightless because they are "beyond the pull of the earth's gravity." How far from the earth would a spacecraft have to travel to be truly beyond the earth's gravitational influence? If a spacecraft were really unaffected by the earth's gravity, would it remain in orbit? Explain. What is the real reason astronauts in orbit feel weightless?

Q12.22. As part of their training before going into orbit, astronauts ride in an airliner that is flown along the same parabolic trajectory as a freely falling projectile. Explain why this gives the same experience of apparent weightlessness as being in orbit.

Exercises

Section 12.1 Newton's Law of Gravitation

12.1. What is the ratio of the gravitational pull of the sun on the moon to that of the earth on the moon? (Assume the distance of the moon from the sun can be approximated by the distance of the earth from the sun.) Use the data in Appendix F. Is it more accurate to say that the moon orbits the earth, or that the moon orbits the sun?

12.2. Cavendish Experiment. In the Cavendish balance apparatus shown in Fig. 12.4, suppose that $m_1 = 1.10$ kg, $m_2 = 25.0$ kg, and the rod connecting the m_1 pairs is 30.0 cm long. If, in each pair, m_1 and m_2 are 12.0 cm apart center-to-center, find (a) the net force and (b) the net torque (about the rotation axis) on the rotating part of the apparatus. (c) Does it seem that the torque in part (b) would be enough to easily rotate the rod? Suggest some ways to improve the sensitivity of this experiment.

12.3. How far from a very small 100-kg ball would a particle have to be placed so that the ball pulled on the particle just as hard as the earth does? Is it reasonable that you could actually set up this as an experiment? Why?

12.4. Two uniform spheres, each with mass M and radius R, touch each other. What is the magnitude of their gravitational force of attraction?

12.5. An interplanetary spaceship passes through the point in space where the gravitational forces from the sun and the earth on the ship exactly cancel. (a) How far from the center of the earth is it? Use the data in Appendix F. (b) Once it reached the point found in part (a), could the spaceship turn off its engines and just hover there indefinitely? Explain.

12.6. (a) In Fig. 12.31 what are the magnitude and direction of the net gravitational force exerted on the 0.100-kg uniform sphere by the other two uniform spheres? The centers of all three spheres are on the same line. (b) According to Newton's third law, does the 0.100-kg sphere exert forces of the same magnitude as your answer to part (a), but in the opposite direction, on *each* of the other two spheres?

Figure **12.31** Exercise 12.6.

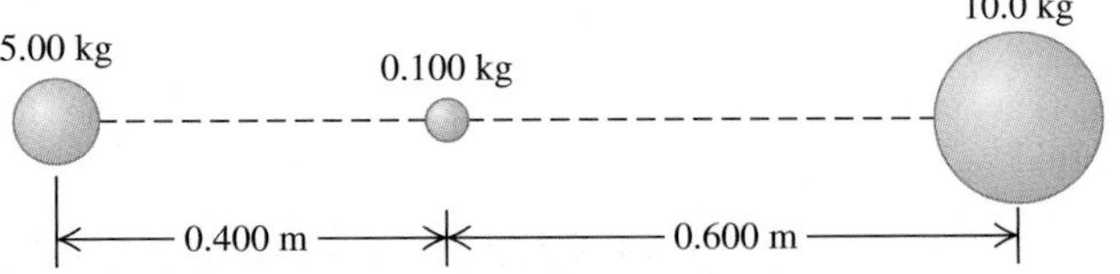

12.7. A typical adult human has a mass of about 70 kg. (a) What force does a full moon exert on such a human when it is directly overhead with its center 378,000 km away? (b) Compare this force with the force exerted on the human by the earth.

12.8. An 8.00-kg point mass and a 15.0-kg point mass are held in place 50.0 cm apart. A particle of mass m is released from a point between the two masses 20.0 cm from the 8.00-kg mass along the line connecting the two fixed masses. Find the magnitude and direction of the acceleration of the particle.

12.9. Calculate the magnitude and direction of the net gravitational force on the moon due to the earth and the sun when the moon is in each of the positions shown in Fig. 12.32. (Note that the figure is *not* drawn to scale. Assume that the sun is in the plane of the earth-moon orbit, even though this is not actually the case.) Use the data in Appendix F.

12.10. Four identical masses of 800 kg each are placed at the corners of a square whose side length is 10.0 cm. What is the net gravitational force (magnitude and direction) on one of the masses, due to the other three?

Figure 12.32 Exercise 12.9.

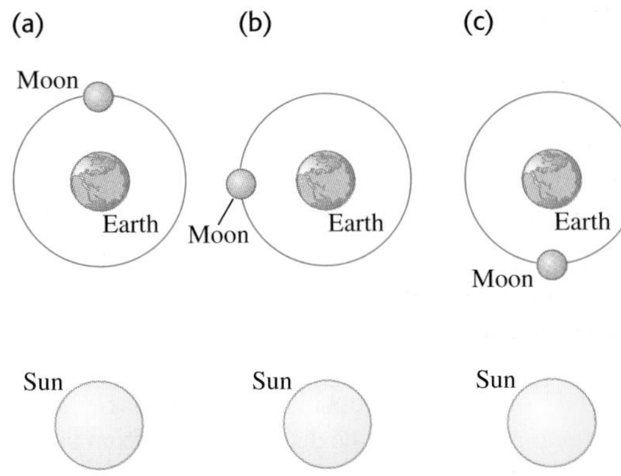

12.11. A particle of mass $3m$ is located 1.00 m from a particle of mass m. (a) Where should you put a third mass M so that the net gravitational force on M due to the two masses is exactly zero? (b) Is the equilibrium of M at this point stable or unstable (i) for points along the line connecting m and $3m$, and (ii) for points along the line passing through M and perpendicular to the line connecting m and $3m$?

12.12. The point masses m and $2m$ lie along the x-axis, with m at the origin and $2m$ at $x = L$. A third point mass M is moved along the x-axis. (a) At what point is the net gravitational force on M due to the other two masses equal to zero? (b) Sketch the x-component of the net force on M due to m and $2m$, taking quantities to the right as positive. Include the regions $x < 0$, $0 < x < L$, and $x > L$. Be especially careful to show the behavior of the graph on either side of $x = 0$ and $x = L$.

12.13. Two uniform spheres, each of mass 0.260 kg, are fixed at points A and B (Fig. 12.32). Find the magnitude and direction of the initial acceleration of a uniform sphere with mass 0.010 kg if released from rest at point P and acted on only by forces of gravitational attraction of the spheres at A and B.

Figure 12.33 Exercise 12.13.

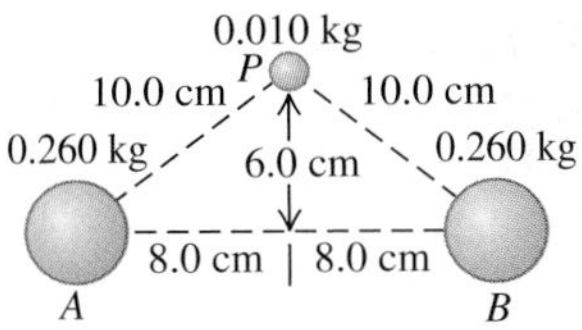

0.010 kg, P, 10.0 cm, 10.0 cm, 0.260 kg, 6.0 cm, 0.260 kg, 8.0 cm, 8.0 cm, A, B

Section 12.2 Weight

12.14. Use the mass and radius of the dwarf planet Pluto given in Appendix F to calculate the acceleration due to gravity at the surface of Pluto.

12.15. At what distance above the surface of the earth is the acceleration due to the earth's gravity 0.980 m/s^2 if the acceleration due to gravity at the surface has magnitude 9.80 m/s^2?

12.16. The mass of Venus is 81.5% that of the earth, and its radius is 94.9% that of the earth. (a) Compute the acceleration due to gravity on the surface of Venus from these data. (b) If a rock weighs 75.0 N on earth, what would it weigh at the surface of Venus?

12.17. Titania, the largest moon of the planet Uranus, has $\frac{1}{8}$ the radius of the earth and $\frac{1}{1700}$ the mass of the earth. (a) What is the acceleration due to gravity at the surface of Titania? (b) What is the average density of Titania? (This is less than the density of rock, which is one piece of evidence that Titania is made primarily of ice.)

12.18. Rhea, one of Saturn's moons, has a radius of 765 km and an acceleration due to gravity of 0.278 m/s^2 at its surface. Calculate its mass and average density.

12.19. Calculate the earth's gravity force on a 75-kg astronaut who is repairing the Hubble Space Telescope 600 km above the earth's surface, and then compare this value with his weight at the earth's surface. In view of your result, explain why we say astronauts are weightless when they orbit the earth in a satellite such as a space shuttle. Is it because the gravitational pull of the earth is negligibly small?

12.20. Neutron stars, such as the one at the center of the Crab Nebula, have about the same mass as our sun but have a *much* smaller diameter. If you weigh 675 N on the earth, what would you weigh at the surface of a neutron star that has the same mass as our sun and a diameter of 20 km?

12.21. An experiment using the Cavendish balance to measure the gravitational constant G found that a uniform 0.400-kg sphere attracts another uniform 0.00300-kg sphere with a force of 8.00×10^{-10} N, when the distance between the centers of the spheres is 0.0100 m. The acceleration due to gravity at the earth's surface is 9.80 m/s^2, and the radius of the earth is 6380 km. Compute the mass of the earth from these data.

12.22. Exploring Europa. There is strong evidence that Europa, a satellite of Jupiter, has a liquid ocean beneath its icy surface. Many scientists think we should land a vehicle there to search for life. Before launching it, we would want to test such a lander under the gravity conditions at the surface of Europa. One way to do this is to put the lander at the end of a rotating arm in an orbiting earth satellite. If the arm is 4.25 m long and pivots about one end, at what angular speed (in rpm) should it spin so that the acceleration of the lander is the same as the acceleration due to gravity at the surface of Europa? The mass of Europa is 4.8×10^{22} kg and its diameter is 3138 km.

Section 12.3 Gravitational Potential Energy

12.23. The asteroid Dactyl, discovered in 1993, has a radius of only about 700 m and a mass of about 3.6×10^{12} kg. Use the results of Example 12.5 (Section 12.3) to calculate the escape speed for an object at the surface of Dactyl. Could a person reach this speed just by walking?

12.24. Mass of a Comet. On July 4, 2005, the NASA spacecraft Deep Impact fired a projectile onto the surface of Comet Tempel 1. This comet is about 9.0 km across. Observations of surface debris released by the impact showed that dust with a speed as low as 1.0 m/s was able to escape the comet. (a) Assuming a spherical shape, what is the mass of this comet? (*Hint:* See Example 12.5 in Section 12.3.) (b) How far from the comet's center will this debris be when it has lost (i) 90.0% of its initial kinetic energy at the surface; and (ii) all of its kinetic energy at the surface?

12.25. Use the results of Example 12.5 (Section 12.3) to calculate the escape speed for a spacecraft (a) from the surface of Mars; and (b) from the surface of Jupiter. Use the data in Appendix F. (c) Why is the escape speed for a spacecraft independent of the spacecraft's mass?

12.26. Ten days after it was launched toward Mars in December 1998, the *Mars Climate Orbiter* spacecraft (mass 629 kg) was 2.87×10^6 km from the earth and traveling at 1.20×10^4 km/h relative to the earth. At this time, what were (a) the spacecraft's kinetic energy relative to the earth and (b) the potential energy of the earth-spacecraft system?

Section 12.4 The Motion of Satellites

12.27. For a satellite to be in a circular orbit 780 km above the surface of the earth, (a) what orbital speed must it be given, and (b) what is the period of the orbit (in hours)?

12.28. Aura Mission. On July 15, 2004, NASA launched the Aura spacecraft to study the earth's climate and atmosphere. This satellite was injected into an orbit 705 km above the earth's surface, and we shall assume a circular orbit. (a) How many hours does it take this satellite to make one orbit? (b) How fast (in km/s) is the Aura spacecraft moving?

12.29. Assume that the earth's orbit around the sun is circular. Use the earth's orbital radius and orbital period given in Appendix F to calculate the mass of the sun.

12.30. International Space Station. The International Space Station makes 15.65 revolutions per day in its orbit around the earth. Assuming a circular orbit, how high is this satellite above the surface of the earth?

12.31. Deimos, a moon of Mars, is about 12 km in diameter with mass 2.0×10^{15} kg. Suppose you are stranded alone on Deimos and want to play a one-person game of baseball. You would be the pitcher, and you would be the batter! (a) With what speed would you have to throw a baseball so that it would go into a circular orbit just above the surface and return to you so you could hit it? Do you think you could actually throw it at this speed? (b) How long (in hours) after throwing the ball should you be ready to hit it? Would this be an action-packed baseball game?

Section 12.5 Kepler's Laws and the Motion of Planets

12.32. Planet Vulcan. Suppose that a planet were discovered between the sun and Mercury, with a circular orbit of radius equal to $\frac{2}{3}$ of the average orbit radius of Mercury. What would be the orbital period of such a planet? (Such a planet was once postulated, in part to explain the precession of Mercury's orbit. It was even given the name Vulcan, although we now have no evidence that it actually exists. Mercury's precession has been explained by general relativity.)

12.33. The star Rho^1 Cancri is 57 light-years from the earth and has a mass 0.85 times that of our sun. A planet has been detected in a circular orbit around Rho^1 Cancri with an orbital radius equal to 0.11 times the radius of the earth's orbit around the sun. What are (a) the orbital speed and (b) the orbital period of the planet of Rho^1 Cancri?

12.34. In March 2006, two small satellites were discovered orbiting Pluto, one at a distance of 48,000 km and the other at 64,000 km. Pluto already was known to have a large satellite Charon, orbiting at 19,600 km with an orbital period of 6.39 days. Assuming that the satellites do not affect each other, find the orbital periods of the two small satellites *without* using the mass of Pluto.

12.35. (a) Use Fig. 12.19 to show that the sun-planet distance at perihelion is $(1 - e)a$, the sun-planet distance at aphelion is $(1 + e)a$, and therefore the sum of these two distances is $2a$. (b) When the dwarf planet Pluto was at perihelion in 1989, it was almost 100 million km closer to the sun than Neptune. The semi-major axes of the orbits of Pluto and Neptune are 5.92×10^{12} m and 4.50×10^{12} m, respectively, and the eccentricities are 0.248 and 0.010. Find Pluto's closest distance and Neptune's farthest distance from the sun. (c) How many years after being at perihelion in 1989 will Pluto again be at perihelion?

12.36. Hot Jupiters. In 2004 astronomers reported the discovery of a large Jupiter-sized planet orbiting very close to the star HD 179949 (hence the term "hot Jupiter"). The orbit was just $\frac{1}{9}$ the distance of Mercury from our sun, and it takes the planet only 3.09 days to make one orbit (assumed to be circular). (a) What is the mass of the star? Express your answer in kilograms and as a multiple of our sun's mass. (b) How fast (in km/s) is this planet moving?

12.37. The *Helios B* spacecraft had a speed of 71 km/s when it was 4.3×10^7 km from the sun. (a) Prove that it was not in a circular orbit about the sun. (b) Prove that its orbit about the sun was closed and therefore elliptical.

*Section 12.6 Spherical Mass Distributions

12.38. A uniform, spherical, 1000.0-kg shell has a radius of 5.00 m. (a) Find the gravitational force this shell exerts on a 2.00-kg point mass placed at the following distances from the center of the shell: (i) 5.01 m, (ii) 4.99 m, (iii) 2.72 m. (b) Sketch a qualitative graph of the magnitude of the gravitational force this sphere exerts on a point mass m as a function of the distance r of m from the center of the sphere. Include the region from $r = 0$ to $r \rightarrow \infty$.

12.39. A uniform, solid, 1000.0-kg sphere has a radius of 5.00 m. (a) Find the gravitational force this sphere exerts on a 2.00-kg point mass placed at the following distances from the center of the sphere: (i) 5.01 m, and (ii) 2.50 m. (b) Sketch a qualitative graph of the magnitude of the gravitational force this sphere exerts on a point mass m as a function of the distance r of m from the center of the sphere. Include the region from $r = 0$ to $r \rightarrow \infty$.

12.40. A thin, uniform rod has length L and mass M. A small uniform sphere of mass m is placed a distance x from one end of the rod, along the axis of the rod (Fig. 12.34). (a) Calculate the gravitational potential energy of the rod–sphere system. Take the potential energy to be zero when the rod and sphere are infinitely far apart. Show that your answer reduces to the expected result when x is much larger than L. (*Hint:* Use the power series expansion for $\ln(1 + x)$ given in Appendix B.) (b) Use $F_x = -dU/dx$ to find the magnitude and direction of the gravitational force exerted on the sphere by the rod (see Section 7.4). Show that your answer reduces to the expected result when x is much larger than L.

Figure 12.34 Exercise 12.40 and Problem 12.84.

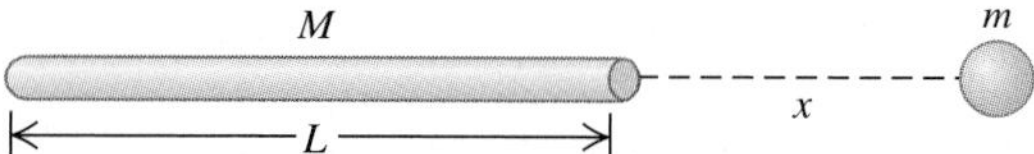

12.41. Consider the ring-shaped body of Fig. 12.35. A particle with mass m is placed a distance x from the center of the ring, along the line through the center of the ring and perpendicular to its plane. (a) Calculate the gravitational potential energy U of this system. Take the potential energy to be zero when the two objects are far apart. (b) Show that your answer to part (a) reduces to the expected result when x is much larger than the radius a of the ring. (c) Use $F_x = -dU/dx$ to find the magnitude and direction of the force on the particle (see Section 7.4). (d) Show that your answer to part (c) reduces to the expected result when x is much larger than a. (e) What are the values of U and F_x when $x = 0$? Explain why these results make sense.

Figure 12.35 Exercise 12.41 and Problem 12.83.

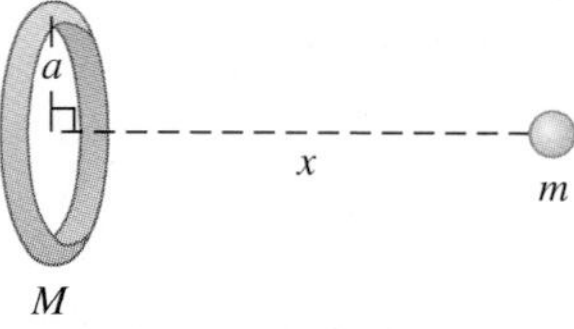

*Section 12.7 Apparent Weight and the Earth's Rotation

12.42. The weight of Santa Claus at the North Pole, as determined by a spring balance, is 875 N. What would this spring balance read for his weight at the equator, assuming that the earth is spherically symmetric?

12.43. The acceleration due to gravity at the north pole of Neptune is approximately 10.7 m/s². Neptune has mass 1.0×10^{26} kg and radius 2.5×10^4 km and rotates once around its axis in about 16 h.

(a) What is the gravitational force on a 5.0-kg object at the north pole of Neptune? (b) What is the apparent weight of this same object at Neptune's equator? (Note that Neptune's "surface" is gaseous, not solid, so it is impossible to stand on it.)

*Section 12.8 Black Holes

12.44. Mini Black Holes. Cosmologists have speculated that black holes the size of a proton could have formed during the early days of the Big Bang when the universe began. If we take the diameter of a proton to be 1.0×10^{-15} m, what would be the mass of a mini black hole?

12.45. To what fraction of its current radius would the earth have to be compressed to become a black hole?

12.46. (a) Show that a black hole attracts an object of mass m with a force of $mc^2R_S/(2r^2)$, where r is the distance between the object and the center of the black hole. (b) Calculate the magnitude of the gravitational force exerted by a black hole of Schwarzschild radius 14.0 mm on a 5.00-kg mass 3000 km from it. (c) What is the mass of this black hole?

12.47. At the Galaxy's Core. Astronomers have observed a small, massive object at the center of our Milky Way galaxy (see Section 12.8). A ring of material orbits this massive object; the ring has a diameter of about 15 light-years and an orbital speed of about 200 km/s. (a) Determine the mass of the object at the center of the Milky Way galaxy. Give your answer both in kilograms and in solar masses (one solar mass is the mass of the sun). (b) Observations of stars, as well as theories of the structure of stars, suggest that it is impossible for a single star to have a mass of more than about 50 solar masses. Can this massive object be a single, ordinary star? (c) Many astronomers believe that the massive object at the center of the Milky Way galaxy is a black hole. If so, what must the Schwarzschild radius of this black hole be? Would a black hole of this size fit inside the earth's orbit around the sun?

12.48. In 2005 astronomers announced the discovery of a large black hole in the galaxy Markarian 766 having clumps of matter orbiting around once every 27 hours and moving at 30,000 km/s. (a) How far are these clumps from the center of the black hole? (b) What is the mass of this black hole, assuming circular orbits? Express your answer in kilograms and as a multiple of our sun's mass. (c) What is the radius of its event horizon?

Problems

12.49. Three uniform spheres are fixed at the positions shown in Fig. 12.36. (a) What are the magnitude and direction of the force on a 0.0150-kg particle placed at P? (b) If the spheres are in deep outer space and a 0.0150-kg particle is released from rest 300 m from the origin along a line 45° below the $-x$-axis, what will the particle's speed be when it reaches the origin?

Figure 12.36 Problem 12.49.

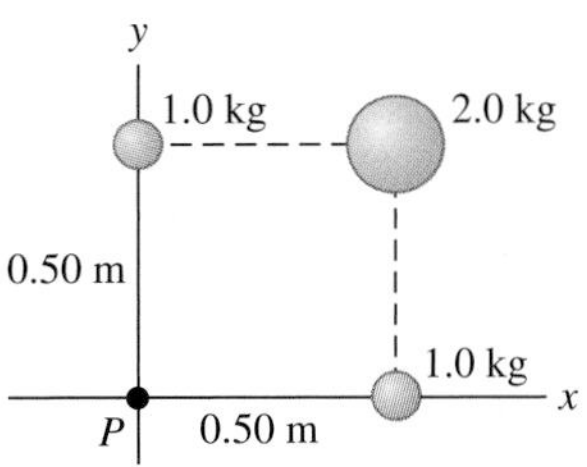

12.50. A uniform sphere with mass 60.0 kg is held with its center at the origin, and a second uniform sphere with mass 80.0 kg is held with its center at the point $x = 0$, $y = 3.00$ m. (a) What are the magnitude and direction of the net gravitational force due to these objects on a third uniform sphere with mass 0.500 kg placed at the point $x = 4.00$ m, $y = 0$? (b) Where, other than infinitely far away, could the third sphere be placed such that the net gravitational force acting on it from the other two spheres is equal to zero?

12.51. (a) Show that the gravitational force on the small star due to the two large stars in Example 12.3 (Section 12.1) is *not* directed toward the point midway between the two large masses. (b) Consider the two large stars as making up a single, rigid body, as if they were joined by a rod of negligible mass. Calculate the torque exerted by the small star on the rigid body for a pivot at its center of mass. (c) Explain how the result in part (b) shows that the center of mass does not coincide with the center of gravity. Why is this the case in this situation?

12.52. At a certain instant, the earth, the moon, and a stationary 1250-kg spacecraft lie at the vertices of an equilateral triangle whose sides are 3.84×10^5 km in length. (a) Find the magnitude and direction of the net gravitational force exerted on the spacecraft by the earth and moon. State the direction as an angle measured from a line connecting the earth and the spacecraft. In a sketch, show the earth, the moon, the spacecraft, and the force vector. (b) What is the minimum amount of work that you would have to do to move the spacecraft to a point far from the earth and moon? You can ignore any gravitational effects due to the other planets or the sun.

12.53. An experiment is performed in deep space with two uniform spheres, one with mass 25.0 kg and the other with mass 100.0 kg. They have equal radii, $r = 0.20$ m. The spheres are released from rest with their centers 40.0 m apart. They accelerate toward each other because of their mutual gravitational attraction. You can ignore all gravitational forces other than that between the two spheres. (a) Explain why linear momentum is conserved. (b) When their centers are 20.0 m apart, find (i) the speed of each sphere and (ii) the magnitude of the relative velocity with which one sphere is approaching the other. (c) How far from the initial position of the center of the 25.0-kg sphere do the surfaces of the two spheres collide?

12.54. Assume that the moon orbits the earth in a circular orbit. From the observed orbital period of 27.3 days, calculate the distance of the moon from the center of the earth. Assume that the moon's motion is determined solely by the gravitational force exerted on it by the earth, and use the mass of the earth given in Appendix F.

12.55. Geosynchronous Satellites. Many satellites are moving in a circle in the earth's equatorial plane. They are at such a height above the earth's surface that they always remain above the same point. (a) Find the altitude of these satellites above the earth's surface. (Such an orbit is said to be *geosynchronous*.) (b) Explain, with a sketch, why the radio signals from these satellites cannot directly reach receivers on earth that are north of 81.3° N latitude.

12.56. A landing craft with mass 12,500 kg is in a circular orbit 5.75×10^5 m above the surface of a planet. The period of the orbit is 5800 s. The astronauts in the lander measure the diameter of the planet to be 9.60×10^6 m. The lander sets down at the north pole of the planet. What is the weight of a 85.6-kg astronaut as he steps out onto the planet's surface?

12.57. What is the escape speed from a 300-km-diameter asteroid with a density of 2500 kg/m^3?

12.58. (a) Asteroids have average densities of about 2500 kg/m^3 and radii from 470 km down to less than a kilometer. Assuming that the asteroid has a spherically symmetric mass distribution, estimate the radius of the largest asteroid from which you could escape simply by jumping off. (*Hint:* You can estimate your jump speed by relating it to the maximum height that you can jump on earth.) (b) Europa, one of Jupiter's four large moons, has a radius of 1570 km. The acceleration due to gravity at its surface is 1.33 m/s^2. Calculate its average density.

12.59. (a) Suppose you are at the earth's equator and observe a satellite passing directly overhead and moving from west to east in the sky. Exactly 12.0 hours later, you again observe this satellite to be directly overhead. How far above the earth's surface is the satellite's orbit? (b) You observe another satellite directly overhead and traveling east to west. This satellite is again overhead in 12.0 hours. How far is this satellite's orbit above the surface of the earth?

12.60. Planet X rotates in the same manner as the earth, around an axis through its north and south poles, and is perfectly spherical. An astronaut who weighs 943.0 N on the earth weighs 915.0 N at the north pole of Planet X and only 850.0 N at its equator. The distance from the north pole to the equator is 18,850 km, measured along the surface of Planet X. (a) How long is the day on Planet X? (b) If a 45,000-kg satellite is placed in a circular orbit 2000 km above the surface of Planet X, what will be its orbital period?

12.61. There are two equations from which a change in the gravitational potential energy U of the system of a mass m and the earth can be calculated. One is $U = mgy$ (Eq. 7.2). The other is $U = -Gm_E m/r$ (Eq. 12.9). As shown in Section 12.3, the first equation is correct only if the gravitational force is a constant over the change in height Δy. The second is always correct. Actually, the gravitational force is never exactly constant over any change in height, but if the variation is small, we can ignore it. Consider the difference in U between a mass at the earth's surface and a distance h above it using both equations, and find the value of h for which Eq. (7.2) is in error by 1%. Express this value of h as a fraction of the earth's radius, and also obtain a numerical value for it.

12.62. Your starship, the *Aimless Wanderer,* lands on the mysterious planet Mongo. As chief scientist-engineer, you make the following measurements: A 2.50-kg stone thrown upward from the ground at 12.0 m/s returns to the ground in 8.00 s; the circumference of Mongo at the equator is 2.00×10^5 km; and there is no appreciable atmosphere on Mongo. The starship commander, Captain Confusion, asks for the following information: (a) What is the mass of Mongo? (b) If the *Aimless Wanderer* goes into a circular orbit 30,000 km above the surface of Mongo, how many hours will it take the ship to complete one orbit?

12.63. Calculate the percent difference between your weight in Sacramento, near sea level, and at the top of Mount Everest, which is 8800 m above sea level.

12.64. In Example 12.5 (Section 12.3) we ignored the gravitational effects of the moon on a spacecraft en route from the earth to the moon. In fact, we must include the gravitational potential energy due to the moon as well. For this problem, you can ignore the motion of the earth and moon. (a) If the moon has radius R_M and the distance between the centers of the earth and the moon is R_{EM}, find the total gravitational potential energy of the particle-earth and particle-moon systems when a particle with mass m is between the earth and the moon, and a distance r from the center of the earth. Take the gravitational potential energy to be zero when the objects are far from each other. (b) There is a point along a line between the earth and the moon where the net gravitational force is zero. Use the expression derived in part (a) and numerical values from Appendix F to find the distance of this point from the center of the earth. With what speed must a spacecraft be launched from the surface of the earth just barely to reach this point? (c) If a spacecraft were launched from the earth's surface toward the moon with an initial speed of 11.2 km/s, with what speed would it impact the moon?

12.65. An unmanned spacecraft is in a circular orbit around the moon, observing the lunar surface from an altitude of 50.0 km (see Appendix F). To the dismay of scientists on earth, an electrical fault causes an on-board thruster to fire, decreasing the speed of the spacecraft by 20.0 m/s. If nothing is done to correct its orbit, with what speed (in km/h) will the spacecraft crash into the lunar surface?

***12.66.** What would be the length of a day (that is, the time required for one rotation of the earth on its axis) if the rate of rotation of the earth were such that $g = 0$ at the equator?

12.67. Falling Hammer. A hammer with mass m is dropped from rest from a height h above the earth's surface. This height is not necessarily small compared with the radius R_E of the earth. If you ignore air resistance, derive an expression for the speed v of the hammer when it reaches the surface of the earth. Your expression should involve h, R_E, and m_E, the mass of the earth.

12.68. (a) Calculate how much work is required to launch a spacecraft of mass m from the surface of the earth (mass m_E, radius R_E) and place it in a circular *low earth orbit*—that is, an orbit whose altitude above the earth's surface is much less than R_E. (As an example, the International Space Station is in low earth orbit at an altitude of about 400 km, much less than $R_E = 6380$ km.) You can ignore the kinetic energy that the spacecraft has on the ground due to the earth's rotation. (b) Calculate the minimum amount of additional work required to move the spacecraft from low earth orbit to a very great distance from the earth. You can ignore the gravitational effects of the sun, the moon, and the other planets. (c) Justify the statement: "In terms of energy, low earth orbit is halfway to the edge of the universe."

12.69. A spacecraft is to be launched from the surface of the earth so that it will escape from the solar system altogether. (a) Find the speed relative to the center of the earth with which the spacecraft must be launched. Take into consideration the gravitational effects of both the earth and the sun, and include the effects of the earth's orbital speed, but ignore air resistance. (b) The rotation of the earth can help this spacecraft achieve escape speed. Find the speed that the spacecraft must have relative to the earth's *surface* if the spacecraft is launched from Florida at the point shown in Fig. 12.37. The rotation and orbital motions of the earth are in the same direction. The launch facilities in Florida are 28.5° north of the equator. (c) The European Space Agency (ESA) uses launch facilities in French Guiana (immediately north of Brazil), 5.15° north of the equator. What speed relative to the earth's surface would a spacecraft need to escape the solar system if launched from French Guiana?

Figure 12.37 Problem 12.69.

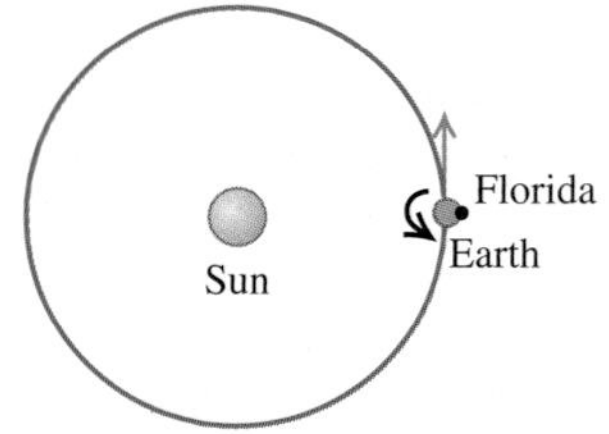

***12.70. Gravity Inside the Earth.** Find the gravitational force that the earth exerts on a 10.0-kg mass if it is placed at the following locations. Consult Fig. 12.9, and assume a constant density through each of the interior regions (mantle, outer core, inner core), but *not* the same density in each of these regions. Use the graph to estimate the average density for each region. (a) at the surface of the earth; (b) at the outer surface of the molten outer core; (c) at the surface of the solid inner core; (d) at the center of the earth.

12.71. Kirkwood Gaps. Hundreds of thousands of asteroids orbit the sun within the *asteroid belt,* which extends from about 3×10^8 km to about 5×10^8 km from the sun. (a) Find the orbital period (in years) of (i) an asteroid at the inside of the belt and (ii) an asteroid at the outside of the belt. Assume circular orbits. (b) In 1867 the American astronomer Daniel Kirkwood pointed out that several gaps exist in the asteroid belt where relatively few asteroids are found. It is now understood that these *Kirkwood gaps* are caused by the gravitational attraction of Jupiter, the largest planet, which orbits the sun once every 11.86 years. As an example, if an asteroid has an orbital period half that of Jupiter, or 5.93 years, on every other orbit this asteroid would be at its closest to Jupiter and feel a strong attraction toward the planet. This attraction, acting over and over on successive orbits, could sweep asteroids out of the Kirkwood gap. Use this hypothesis to determine the orbital radius for this Kirkwood gap. (c) One of several other Kirkwood gaps appears at a distance from the sun where the orbital period is 0.400 that of Jupiter. Explain why this happens, and find the orbital radius for this Kirkwood gap.

12.72. If a satellite is in a sufficiently low orbit, it will encounter air drag from the earth's atmosphere. Since air drag does negative work (the force of air drag is directed opposite the motion), the mechanical energy will decrease. According to Eq. (12.13), if E decreases (becomes more negative), the radius r of the orbit will decrease. If air drag is relatively small, the satellite can be considered to be in a circular orbit of continually decreasing radius. (a) According to Eq. (12.10), if the radius of a satellite's circular orbit decreases, the satellite's orbital speed v *increases.* How can you reconcile this with the statement that the mechanical energy *decreases?* (*Hint:* Is air drag the only force that does work on the satellite as the orbital radius decreases?) (b) Due to air drag, the radius of a satellite's circular orbit decreases from r to $r - \Delta r$, where the positive quantity Δr is much less than r. The mass of the satellite is m. Show that the increase in orbital speed is $\Delta v = +(\Delta r/2)\sqrt{Gm_E/r^3}$; that the change in kinetic energy is $\Delta K = +(Gm_E m/2r^2)\,\Delta r$; that the change in gravitational potential energy is $\Delta U = -2\,\Delta K = -(Gm_E m/r^2)\,\Delta r$; and that the amount of work done by the force of air drag is $W = -(Gm_E m/2r^2)\,\Delta r$. Interpret these results in light of your comments in part (a). (c) A satellite with mass 3000 kg is initially in a circular orbit 300 km above the earth's surface. Due to air drag, the satellite's altitude decreases to 250 km. Calculate the initial orbital speed; the increase in orbital speed; the initial mechanical energy; the change in kinetic energy; the change in gravitational potential energy; the change in mechanical energy; and the work done by the force of air drag. (d) Eventually a satellite will descend to a low enough altitude in the atmosphere that the satellite burns up and the debris falls to the earth. What becomes of the initial mechanical energy?

12.73. Binary Star—Equal Masses. Two identical stars with mass M orbit around their center of mass. Each orbit is circular and has radius R, so that the two stars are always on opposite sides of the circle. (a) Find the gravitational force of one star on the other. (b) Find the orbital speed of each star and the period of the orbit. (c) How much energy would be required to separate the two stars to infinity?

12.74. Binary Star—Different Masses. Two stars, with masses M_1 and M_2, are in circular orbits around their center of mass. The star with mass M_1 has an orbit of radius R_1; the star with mass M_2 has an orbit of radius R_2. (a) Show that the ratio of the orbital radii of the two stars equals the reciprocal of the ratio of their masses, that is, $R_1/R_2 = M_2/M_1$. (b) Explain why the two stars have the same orbital period, and show that the period T is given by $T = 2\pi(R_1 + R_2)^{3/2}/\sqrt{G(M_1 + M_2)}$. (c) The two stars in a certain binary star system move in circular orbits. The first star, Alpha, has an orbital speed of 36.0 km/s. The second star, Beta, has an orbital speed of 12.0 km/s. The orbital period is 137 d. What are the masses of each of the two stars? (d) One of the best candidates for a black hole is found in the binary system called A0620-0090. The two objects in the binary system are an orange star, V616 Monocerotis, and a compact object believed to be a black hole (Fig. 12.22). The orbital period of A0620-0090 is 7.75 hours, the mass of V616 Monocerotis is estimated to be 0.67 times the mass of the sun, and the mass of the black hole is estimated to be 3.8 times the mass of the sun. Assuming that the orbits are circular, find the radius of each object's orbit and the orbital speed of each object. Compare these answers to the orbital radius and orbital speed of the earth in its orbit around the sun.

12.75. Comets travel around the sun in elliptical orbits with large eccentricities. If a comet has speed 2.0×10^4 m/s when at a distance of 2.5×10^{11} m from the center of the sun, what is its speed when at a distance of 5.0×10^{10} m?

12.76. As Mars orbits the sun in its elliptical orbit, its distance of closest approach to the center of the sun (at perihelion) is 2.067×10^{11} m, and its maximum distance from the center of the sun (at aphelion) is 2.492×10^{11} m. If the orbital speed of Mars at aphelion is 2.198×10^4 m/s, what is its orbital speed at perihelion? (You can ignore the influence of the other planets.)

12.77. Consider a spacecraft in an elliptical orbit around the earth. At the low point, or perigee, of its orbit, it is 400 km above the earth's surface; at the high point, or apogee, it is 4000 km above the earth's surface. (a) What is the period of the spacecraft's orbit? (b) Using conservation of angular momentum, find the ratio of the spacecraft's speed at perigee to its speed at apogee. (c) Using conservation of energy, find the speed at perigee and the speed at apogee. (d) It is necessary to have the spacecraft escape from the earth completely. If the spacecraft's rockets are fired at perigee, by how much would the speed have to be increased to achieve this? What if the rockets were fired at apogee? Which point in the orbit is more efficient to use?

12.78. The planet Uranus has a radius of 25,560 km and a surface acceleration due to gravity of 11.1 m/s^2 at its poles. Its moon Miranda (discovered by Kuiper in 1948) is in a circular orbit about Uranus at an altitude of 104,000 km above the planet's surface. Miranda has a mass of 6.6×10^{19} kg and a radius of 235 km. (a) Calculate the mass of Uranus from the given data. (b) Calculate the magnitude of Miranda's acceleration due to its orbital motion about Uranus. (c) Calculate the acceleration due to Miranda's gravity at the surface of Miranda. (d) Do the answers to parts (b) and (c) mean that an object released 1 m above Miranda's surface on the side toward Uranus will fall *up* relative to Miranda? Explain.

12.79. A 3000-kg spacecraft is in a circular orbit 2000 km above the surface of Mars. How much work must the spacecraft engines perform to move the spacecraft to a circular orbit that is 4000 km above the surface?

12.80. One of the brightest comets of the 20th century was Comet Hyakutake, which passed close to the sun in early 1996. The orbital period of this comet is estimated to be about 30,000 years. Find the semi-major axis of this comet's orbit. Compare it to the average sun-Pluto distance and to the distance to Alpha Centauri, the nearest star to the sun, which is 4.3 light-years distant.

12.81. Planets are not uniform inside. Normally, they are densest at the center and have decreasing density outward toward the surface. Model a spherically symmetric planet, with the same radius as the earth, as having a density that decreases linearly with distance from the center. Let the density be 15.0×10^3 kg/m^3 at the center and 2.0×10^3 kg/m^3 at the surface. What is the acceleration due to gravity at the surface of this planet?

12.82. A uniform wire with mass M and length L is bent into a semicircle. Find the magnitude and direction of the gravitational force this wire exerts on a point with mass m placed at the center of curvature of the semicircle.

***12.83.** An object in the shape of a thin ring has radius a and mass M. A uniform sphere with mass m and radius R is placed with its center at a distance x to the right of the center of the ring, along a line through the center of the ring, and perpendicular to its plane (Fig. 12.35). What is the gravitational force that the sphere exerts on the ring-shaped object? Show that your result reduces to the expected result when x is much larger than a.

***12.84.** A thin, uniform rod has length L and mass M. Calculate the magnitude of the gravitational force the rod exerts on a particle with mass m that is at a point along the axis of the rod a distance x from one end (Fig. 12.34). Show that your result reduces to the expected result when x is much larger than L.

***12.85.** A shaft is drilled from the surface to the center of the earth (Fig. 12.25). As in Example 12.10 (Section 12.6), make the unrealistic assumption that the density of the earth is uniform. With this approximation, the gravitational force on an object with mass m, that is inside the earth at a distance r from the center, has magnitude $F_g = Gm_Emr/R_E^3$ (as shown in Example 12.10) and points toward the center of the earth. (a) Derive an expression for the gravitational potential energy $U(r)$ of the object–earth system as a function of the object's distance from the center of the earth. Take the potential energy to be zero when the object is at the center of the earth. (b) If an object is released in the shaft at the earth's surface, what speed will it have when it reaches the center of the earth?

Challenge Problems

12.86. (a) When an object is in a circular orbit of radius r around the earth (mass m_E), the period of the orbit is T, given by Eq. (12.12), and the orbital speed is v, given by Eq. (12.10). Show that when the object is moved into a circular orbit of slightly larger radius $r + \Delta r$, where $\Delta r \ll r$, its new period is $T + \Delta T$ and its new orbital speed is $v - \Delta v$, where Δr, ΔT, and Δv are all positive quantities and

$$\Delta T = \frac{3\pi \Delta r}{v} \qquad \text{and} \qquad \Delta v = \frac{\pi\, \Delta r}{T}$$

(*Hint:* Use the expression $(1 + x)^n \approx 1 + nx$, valid for $|x| \ll 1$.) (b) The International Space Station (ISS) is in a nearly circular orbit at an altitude of 398.00 km above the surface of the earth. A maintenance crew is about to arrive on the space shuttle that is also in a circular orbit in the same orbital plane as the ISS, but with an altitude of 398.10 km. The crew has come to remove a faulty 125-m electrical cable, one end of which is attached to the ISS and the other end of which is floating free in space. The plan is for the shuttle to snag the free end just at the moment that the shuttle, the ISS, and the center of the earth all lie along the same line. The cable will then break free from the ISS when it becomes taut. How long after the free end is caught by the space shuttle will it detach from the ISS? Give your answer in minutes. (c) If the shuttle misses catching the cable, show that the crew must wait a time $t \approx T^2/\Delta T$ before they have a second chance. Find the numerical value of t and explain whether it would be worth the wait.

12.87. Interplanetary Navigation. The most efficient way to send a spacecraft from the earth to another planet is by using a *Hohmann transfer orbit* (Fig. 12.38). If the orbits of the departure and destination planets are circular, the Hohmann transfer orbit is an elliptical orbit whose perihelion and aphelion are tangent to the orbits of the two planets. The rockets are fired briefly at the departure planet to put the spacecraft into the transfer orbit; the spacecraft then coasts until it reaches the destination planet. The rockets are then fired again to put the spacecraft into the same orbit about the sun as the destination planet. (a) For a flight from earth to Mars, in what direction must the rockets be fired at the earth and at Mars: in the direction of motion, or opposite the direction of motion? What about from a flight from Mars to the earth? (b) How long does a one-way trip from the the earth to Mars take, between the firings of the rockets? (c) To reach Mars from the earth, the launch must be timed so that Mars will be at the right spot when the spacecraft reaches Mars's orbit around the sun. At launch, what must the angle between a sun-Mars line and a sun-earth line be? Use data from Appendix F.

Figure 12.38 Challenge Problem 12.87.

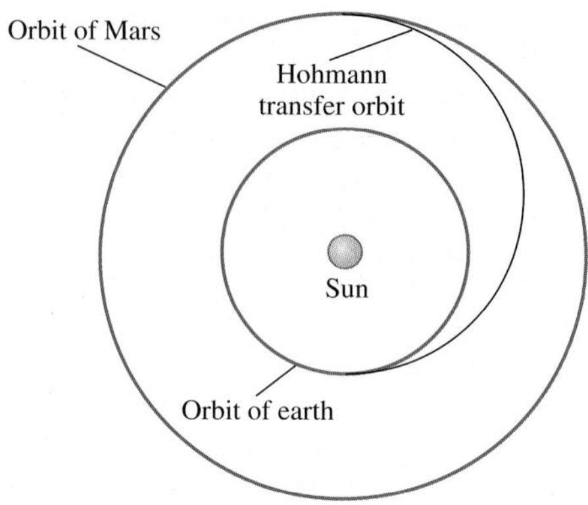

12.88. Tidal Forces near a Black Hole. An astronaut inside a spacecraft, which protects her from harmful radiation, is orbiting a black hole at a distance of 120 km from its center. The black hole is 5.00 times the mass of the sun and has a Schwarzschild radius of 15.0 km. The astronaut is positioned inside the spaceship such that one of her 0.030-kg ears is 6.0 cm farther from the black hole than the center of mass of the spacecraft and the other ear is 6.0 cm closer. (a) What is the tension between her ears? Would the astronaut find it difficult to keep from being torn apart by the gravitational forces? (Since her whole body orbits with the same angular velocity, one ear is moving too slowly for the radius of its orbit and the other is moving too fast. Hence her head must exert forces on her ears to keep them in their orbits.) (b) Is the center of gravity of her head at the same point as the center of mass? Explain.

***12.89.** Mass M is distributed uniformly over a disk of radius a. Find the gravitational force (magnitude and direction) between this disk-shaped mass and a particle with mass m located a distance x above the center of the disk (Fig. 12.39). Does your result reduce to the correct expression as x becomes very large? (*Hint:* Divide the disk into infinitesimally thin concentric rings, use the expression derived in Exercise 12.41 for the gravitational force due to each ring, and integrate to find the total force.)

Figure 12.39 Challenge Problem 12.89.

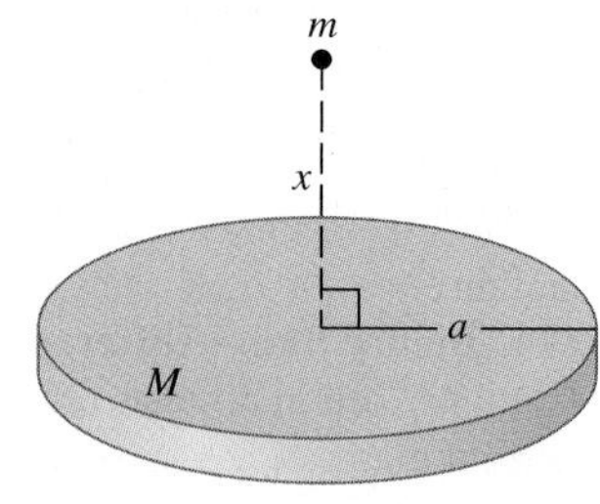

***12.90.** Mass M is distributed uniformly along a line of length $2L$. A particle with mass m is at a point that is a distance a above the center of the line on its perpendicular bisector (point P in Fig. 12.40). For the gravitational force that the line exerts on the particle, calculate the components perpendicular and parallel to the line. Does your result reduce to the correct expression as a becomes very large?

Figure 12.40 Challenge Problem 12.90.

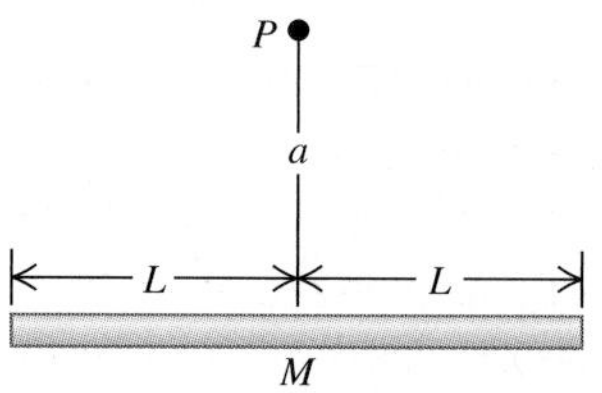

PERIODIC MOTION

13

?Suppose you doubled the mass of a clock's pendulum (including the rod and the weight at the end) while keeping its dimensions the same. Would the clock run fast or slow?

LEARNING GOALS

By studying this chapter, you will learn:

- How to describe oscillations in terms of amplitude, period, frequency, and angular frequency.
- How to do calculations with simple harmonic motion, an important type of oscillation.
- How to use energy concepts to analyze simple harmonic motion.
- How to apply the ideas of simple harmonic motion to different physical situations.
- How to analyze the motions of a simple pendulum.
- What a physical pendulum is, and how to calculate the properties of its motion.
- What determines how rapidly an oscillation dies out.
- How a driving force applied to an oscillator at the right frequency can cause a very large response, or resonance.

Many kinds of motion repeat themselves over and over: the vibration of a quartz crystal in a watch, the swinging pendulum of a grandfather clock, the sound vibrations produced by a clarinet or an organ pipe, and the back-and-forth motion of the pistons in a car engine. This kind of motion, called **periodic motion** or **oscillation,** is the subject of this chapter. Understanding periodic motion will be essential for our later study of waves, sound, alternating electric currents, and light.

A body that undergoes periodic motion always has a stable equilibrium position. When it is moved away from this position and released, a force or torque comes into play to pull it back toward equilibrium. But by the time it gets there, it has picked up some kinetic energy, so it overshoots, stopping somewhere on the other side, and is again pulled back toward equilibrium. Picture a ball rolling back and forth in a round bowl or a pendulum that swings back and forth past its straight-down position.

In this chapter we will concentrate on two simple examples of systems that can undergo periodic motions: spring-mass systems and pendulums. We will also study why oscillations often tend to die out with time and why some oscillations can build up to greater and greater displacements from equilibrium when periodically varying forces act.

13.1 Describing Oscillation

Figure 13.1 shows one of the simplest systems that can have periodic motion. A body with mass m rests on a frictionless horizontal guide system, such as a linear air track, so it can move only along the x-axis. The body is attached to a spring of negligible mass that can be either stretched or compressed. The left end of the spring is held fixed and the right end is attached to the body. The spring force is the only horizontal force acting on the body; the vertical normal and gravitational forces always add to zero.

13.1 A system that can have periodic motion.

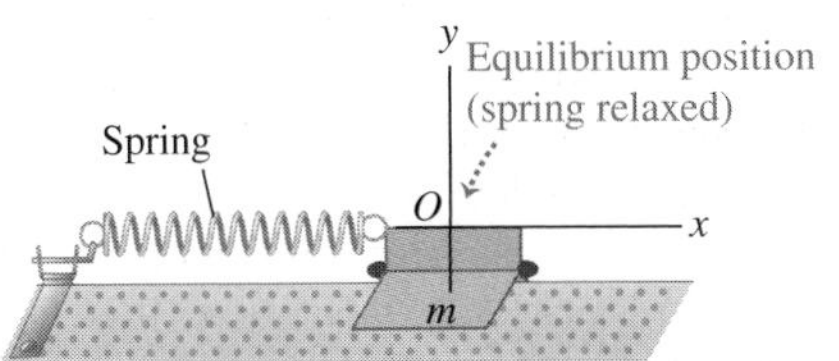

13.2 Model for periodic motion. When the body is displaced from its equilibrium position at $x = 0$, the spring exerts a restoring force back toward the equilibrium position.

(a)

$x > 0$: glider displaced to the right from the equilibrium position.

$F_x < 0$, so $a_x < 0$: stretched spring pulls glider toward equilibrium position.

(b)

$x = 0$: The relaxed spring exerts no force on the glider, so the glider has zero acceleration.

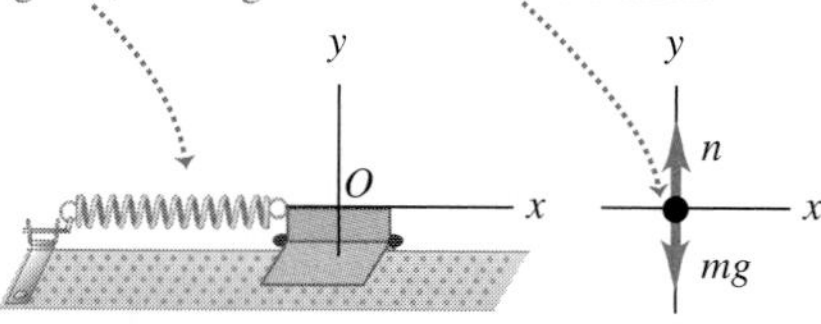

(c)

$x < 0$: glider displaced to the left from the equilibrium position.

$F_x > 0$, so $a_x > 0$: compressed spring pushes glider toward equilibrium position.

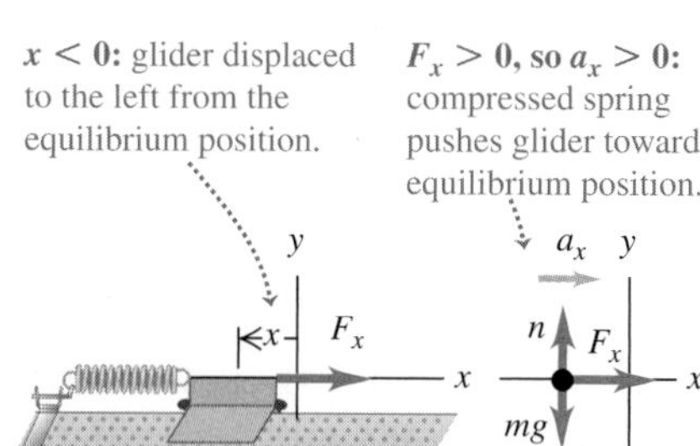

It's simplest to define our coordinate system so that the origin O is at the equilibrium position, where the spring is neither stretched nor compressed. Then x is the x-component of the **displacement** of the body from equilibrium and is also the change in the length of the spring. The x-component of the force that the spring exerts on the body is F_x, and the x-component of acceleration a_x is given by $a_x = F_x/m$.

Figure 13.2 shows the body for three different displacements of the spring. Whenever the body is displaced from its equilibrium position, the spring force tends to restore it to the equilibrium position. We call a force with this character a **restoring force.** Oscillation can occur only when there is a restoring force tending to return the system to equilibrium.

Let's analyze how oscillation occurs in this system. If we displace the body to the right to $x = A$ and then let go, the net force and the acceleration are to the left (Fig. 13.2a). The speed increases as the body approaches the equilibrium position O. When the body is at O, the net force acting on it is zero (Fig. 13.2b), but because of its motion it *overshoots* the equilibrium position. On the other side of the equilibrium position the body is still moving to the left, but the net force and the acceleration are to the right (Fig. 13.2c); hence the speed decreases until the body comes to a stop. We will show later that with an ideal spring, the stopping point is at $x = -A$. The body then accelerates to the right, overshoots equilibrium again, and stops at the starting point $x = A$, ready to repeat the whole process. The body is oscillating! If there is no friction or other force to remove mechanical energy from the system, this motion repeats forever; the restoring force perpetually draws the body back toward the equilibrium position, only to have the body overshoot time after time.

In different situations the force may depend on the displacement x from equilibrium in different ways. But oscillation *always* occurs if the force is a *restoring* force that tends to return the system to equilibrium.

Amplitude, Period, Frequency, and Angular Frequency

Here are some terms that we'll use in discussing periodic motions of all kinds:

The **amplitude** of the motion, denoted by A, is the maximum magnitude of displacement from equilibrium—that is, the maximum value of $|x|$. It is always positive. If the spring in Fig. 13.2 is an ideal one, the total overall range of the motion is $2A$. The SI unit of A is the meter. A complete vibration, or **cycle,** is one complete round trip—say, from A to $-A$ and back to A, or from O to A, back through O to $-A$, and back to O. Note that motion from one side to the other (say, $-A$ to A) is a half-cycle, not a whole cycle.

The **period,** T, is the time for one cycle. It is always positive. The SI unit is the second, but it is sometimes expressed as "seconds per cycle."

The **frequency,** f, is the number of cycles in a unit of time. It is always positive. The SI unit of frequency is the hertz:

$$1 \text{ hertz} = 1 \text{ Hz} = 1 \text{ cycle/s} = 1 \text{ s}^{-1}$$

This unit is named in honor of the German physicist Heinrich Hertz (1857–1894), a pioneer in investigating electromagnetic waves.

The **angular frequency,** ω, is 2π times the frequency:

$$\omega = 2\pi f$$

We'll learn shortly why ω is a useful quantity. It represents the rate of change of an angular quantity (not necessarily related to a rotational motion) that is always measured in radians, so its units are rad/s. Since f is in cycle/s, we may regard the number 2π as having units rad/cycle.

From the definitions of period T and frequency f we see that each is the reciprocal of the other:

$$f = \frac{1}{T} \qquad T = \frac{1}{f} \qquad \text{(relationships between frequency and period)} \qquad (13.1)$$

Also, from the definition of ω,

$$\omega = 2\pi f = \frac{2\pi}{T} \quad \text{(angular frequency)} \tag{13.2}$$

Example 13.1 Period, frequency, and angular frequency

An ultrasonic transducer (a kind of loudspeaker) used for medical diagnosis oscillates at a frequency of 6.7 MHz = 6.7×10^6 Hz. How much time does each oscillation take, and what is the angular frequency?

SOLUTION

IDENTIFY: Our target variables are the period T and the angular frequency ω.

SET UP: We are given the frequency f, so we can find these variables using Eqs. (13.1) and (13.2).

EXECUTE: From Eqs. (13.1) and (13.2),

$$T = \frac{1}{f} = \frac{1}{6.7 \times 10^6\ \text{Hz}} = 1.5 \times 10^{-7}\ \text{s} = 0.15\ \mu\text{s}$$

$$\begin{aligned}\omega &= 2\pi f = 2\pi(6.7 \times 10^6\ \text{Hz}) \\ &= (2\pi\ \text{rad/cycle})(6.7 \times 10^6\ \text{cycle/s}) \\ &= 4.2 \times 10^7\ \text{rad/s}\end{aligned}$$

EVALUATE: This is a very rapid vibration, with large f and ω and small T. A slow vibration has small f and ω and large T.

Test Your Understanding of Section 13.1 A body like that shown in Fig. 13.2 oscillates back and forth. For each of the following values of the body's x-velocity v_x and x-acceleration a_x, state whether its displacement x is positive, negative, or zero. (a) $v_x > 0$ and $a_x > 0$; (b) $v_x > 0$ and $a_x < 0$; (c) $v_x < 0$ and $a_x > 0$; (d) $v_x < 0$ and $a_x < 0$; (e) $v_x = 0$ and $a_x < 0$; (f) $v_x > 0$ and $a_x = 0$.

13.2 Simple Harmonic Motion

The simplest kind of oscillation occurs when the restoring force F_x is *directly proportional* to the displacement from equilibrium x. This happens if the spring in Figs. 13.1 and 13.2 is an ideal one that obeys Hooke's law. The constant of proportionality between F_x and x is the force constant k. (You may want to review Hooke's law and the definition of the force constant in Section 6.3.) On either side of the equilibrium position, F_x and x always have opposite signs. In Section 6.3 we represented the force acting *on* a stretched ideal spring as $F_x = kx$. The x-component of force the spring exerts *on the body* is the negative of this, so the x-component of force F_x on the body is

$$F_x = -kx \quad \text{(restoring force exerted by an ideal spring)} \tag{13.3}$$

This equation gives the correct magnitude and sign of the force, whether x is positive, negative, or zero (Fig. 13.3). The force constant k is always positive and has units of N/m (a useful alternative set of units is kg/s^2). We are assuming that there is no friction, so Eq. (13.3) gives the *net* force on the body.

When the restoring force is directly proportional to the displacement from equilibrium, as given by Eq. (13.3), the oscillation is called **simple harmonic motion,** *abbreviated* **SHM.** The acceleration $a_x = d^2x/dt^2 = F_x/m$ of a body in SHM is given by

$$a_x = \frac{d^2x}{dt^2} = -\frac{k}{m}x \quad \text{(simple harmonic motion)} \tag{13.4}$$

The minus sign means the acceleration and displacement always have opposite signs. This acceleration is *not* constant, so don't even think of using the constant-acceleration equations from Chapter 2. We'll see shortly how to solve this

13.3 An idealized spring exerts a restoring force that obeys Hooke's law, $F_x = -kx$. Oscillation with such a restoring force is called simple harmonic motion.

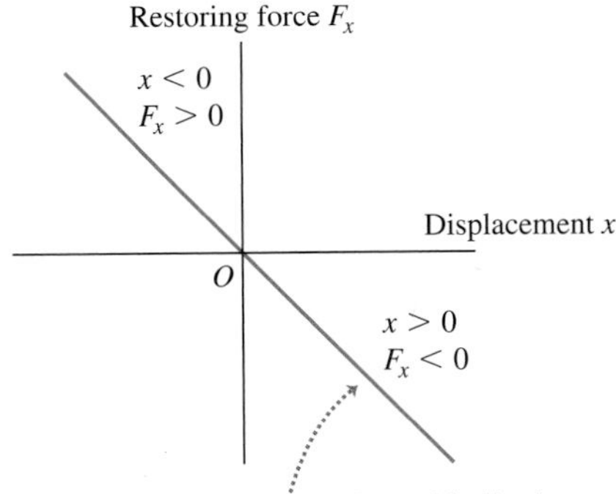
Restoring force F_x
$x < 0$
$F_x > 0$
Displacement x
O
$x > 0$
$F_x < 0$
The restoring force exerted by an idealized spring is directly proportional to the displacement (Hooke's law, $F_x = -kx$): the graph of F_x versus x is a straight line.

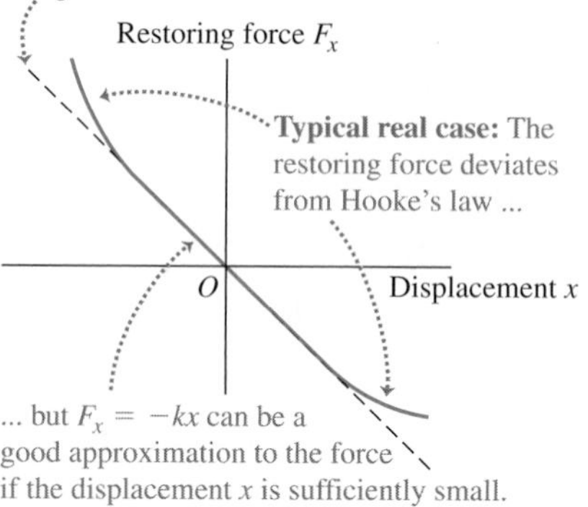
Ideal case: The restoring force obeys Hooke's law ($F_x = -kx$), so the graph of F_x versus x is a straight line.
Restoring force F_x
Typical real case: The restoring force deviates from Hooke's law ...
O
Displacement x
... but $F_x = -kx$ can be a good approximation to the force if the displacement x is sufficiently small.

13.4 In most real oscillations Hooke's law applies provided the body doesn't move too far from equilibrium. In such a case small-amplitude oscillations are approximately simple harmonic.

equation to find the displacement x as a function of time. A body that undergoes simple harmonic motion is called a **harmonic oscillator.**

Why is simple harmonic motion important? Keep in mind that not all periodic motions are simple harmonic; in periodic motion in general, the restoring force depends on displacement in a more complicated way than in Eq. (13.3). But in many systems the restoring force is *approximately* proportional to displacement if the displacement is sufficiently small (Fig. 13.4). That is, if the amplitude is small enough, the oscillations of such systems are approximately simple harmonic and therefore approximately described by Eq. (13.4). Thus we can use SHM as an approximate model for many different periodic motions, such as the vibration of the quartz crystal in a watch, the motion of a tuning fork, the electric current in an alternating-current circuit, and the oscillations of atoms in molecules and solids.

Circular Motion and the Equations of SHM

To explore the properties of simple harmonic motion, we must express the displacement x of the oscillating body as a function of time, $x(t)$. The second derivative of this function, d^2x/dt^2, must be equal to $(-k/m)$ times the function itself, as required by Eq. (13.4). As we mentioned, the formulas for constant acceleration from Section 2.4 are no help because the acceleration changes constantly as the displacement x changes. Instead, we'll find $x(t)$ by noticing a striking similarity between SHM and another form of motion that we've already studied in detail.

Figure 13.5a shows a top view of a horizontal disk of radius A with a ball attached to its rim at point Q. The disk rotates with constant angular speed ω (measured in rad/s), so the ball moves in uniform circular motion. A horizontal light beam shines on the rotating disk and casts a shadow of the ball on a screen. The shadow at point P oscillates back and forth as the ball moves in a circle. We then arrange a body attached to an ideal spring, like the combination shown in Figs. 13.1 and 13.2, so that the body oscillates parallel to the shadow. We will prove that the motion of the body and the motion of the ball's shadow are *identical* if the amplitude of the body's oscillation is equal to the disk radius A, and if the angular frequency $2\pi f$ of the oscillating body is equal to the angular speed ω of the rotating disk. That is, *simple harmonic motion is the projection of uniform circular motion onto a diameter.*

We can verify this remarkable statement by finding the acceleration of the shadow at P and comparing it to the acceleration of a body undergoing SHM, given

13.5 (a) Relating uniform circular motion and simple harmonic motion. (b) The ball's shadow moves exactly like a body oscillating on an ideal spring.

(a) Apparatus for creating the reference circle

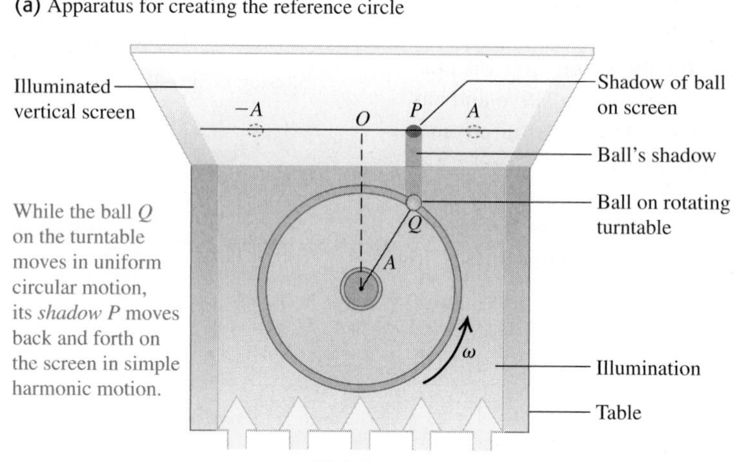
Illuminated vertical screen
$-A$
O
P
A
Shadow of ball on screen
Ball's shadow
Ball on rotating turntable
Q
A
While the ball Q on the turntable moves in uniform circular motion, its *shadow P* moves back and forth on the screen in simple harmonic motion.
ω
Illumination
Table
Light beam

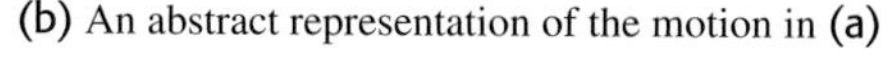
(b) An abstract representation of the motion in (a)

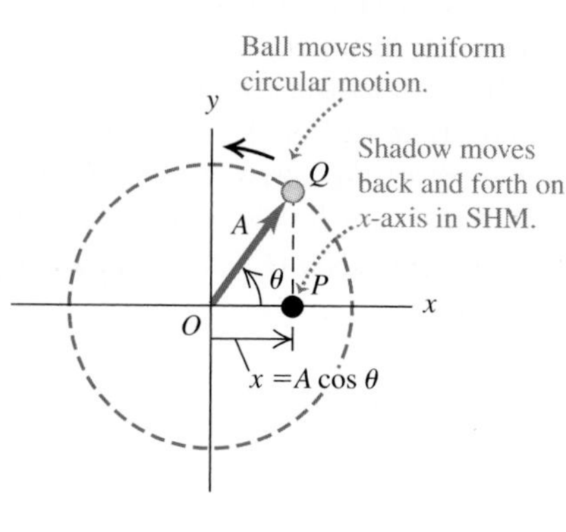
Ball moves in uniform circular motion.
y
Shadow moves back and forth on x-axis in SHM.
Q
A
θ
P
x
O
$x = A\cos\theta$

by Eq. (13.4). The circle in which the ball moves so that its projection matches the motion of the oscillating body is called the **reference circle;** we will call the point Q the *reference point.* We take the reference circle to lie in the xy-plane, with the origin O at the center of the circle (Fig. 13.5b). At time t the vector OQ from the origin to the reference point Q makes an angle θ with the positive x-axis. As the point Q moves around the reference circle with constant angular speed ω, the vector OQ rotates with the same angular speed. Such a rotating vector is called a **phasor.** (This term was in use long before the invention of the Star Trek stun gun with a similar name. The phasor method for analyzing oscillations is useful in many areas of physics. We'll use phasors when we study alternating-current circuits in Chapter 31 and the interference of light in Chapters 35 and 36.)

The x-component of the phasor at time t is just the x-coordinate of the point Q:

$$x = A\cos\theta \tag{13.5}$$

This is also the x-coordinate of the shadow P, which is the *projection* of Q onto the x-axis. Hence the x-velocity of the shadow P along the x-axis is equal to the x-component of the velocity vector of the reference point Q (Fig. 13.6a), and the x-acceleration of P is equal to the x-component of the acceleration vector of Q (Fig. 13.6b). Since point Q is in uniform circular motion, its acceleration vector $\vec{a}_Q$ is always directed toward O. Furthermore, the magnitude of $\vec{a}_Q$ is constant and given by the angular speed squared times the radius of the circle (see Section 9.3):

$$a_Q = \omega^2 A \tag{13.6}$$

Figure 13.6b shows that the x-component of $\vec{a}_Q$ is $a_x = -a_Q\cos\theta$. Combining this with Eqs. (13.5) and (13.6), we get that the acceleration of point P is

$$a_x = -a_Q\cos\theta = -\omega^2 A\cos\theta \quad \text{or} \tag{13.7}$$

$$a_x = -\omega^2 x \tag{13.8}$$

The acceleration of the point P is directly proportional to the displacement x and always has the opposite sign. These are precisely the hallmarks of simple harmonic motion.

Equation (13.8) is *exactly* the same as Eq. (13.4) for the acceleration of a harmonic oscillator, provided that the angular speed ω of the reference point Q is related to the force constant k and mass m of the oscillating body by

$$\omega^2 = \frac{k}{m} \quad \text{or} \quad \omega = \sqrt{\frac{k}{m}} \tag{13.9}$$

We have been using the same symbol ω for the angular *speed* of the reference point Q and the angular *frequency* of the oscillating point P. The reason is that these quantities are equal! If point Q makes one complete revolution in time T, then point P goes through one complete cycle of oscillation in the same time; hence T is the period of the oscillation. During time T the point Q moves through 2π radians, so its angular speed is $\omega = 2\pi/T$. But this is just the same as Eq. (13.2) for the angular frequency of the point P, which verifies our statement about the two interpretations of ω. This is why we introduced angular frequency in Section 13.1; this quantity makes the connection between oscillation and circular motion. So we reinterpret Eq. (13.9) as an expression for the angular frequency of simple harmonic motion for a body of mass m, acted on by a restoring force with force constant k:

$$\omega = \sqrt{\frac{k}{m}} \quad \text{(simple harmonic motion)} \tag{13.10}$$

When you start a body oscillating in SHM, the value of ω is not yours to choose; it is predetermined by the values of k and m. The units of k are N/m or kg/s^2, so

13.6 The (a) x-velocity and (b) x-acceleration of the ball's shadow P (See Fig. 13.5) are the x-components of the velocity and acceleration vectors, respectively, of the ball Q.

(a) Using the reference circle to determine the x-velocity of point P

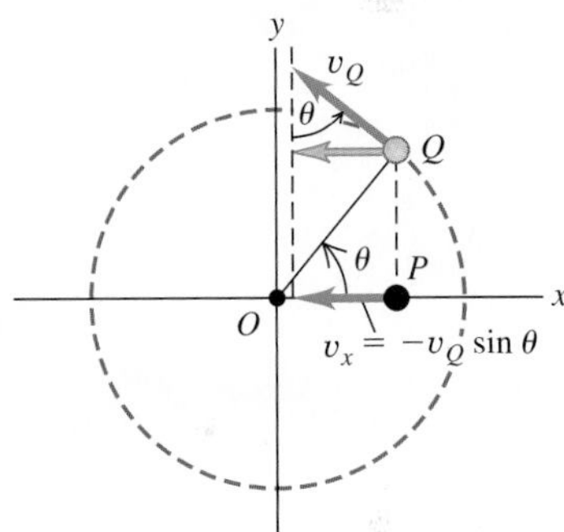

(b) Using the reference circle to determine the x-acceleration of point P

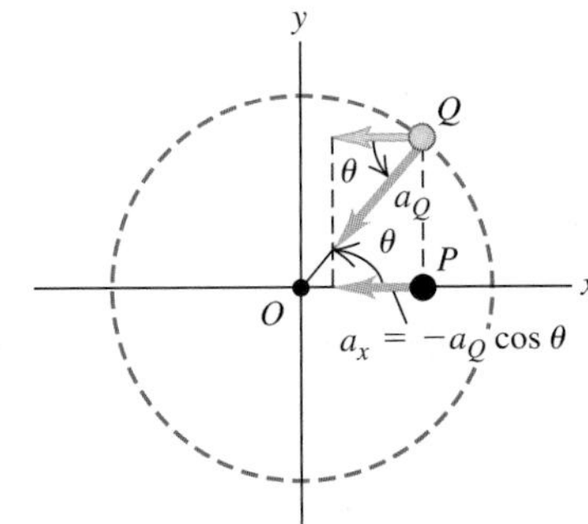

k/m is in $(\text{kg/s}^2)/\text{kg} = \text{s}^{-2}$. When we take the square root in Eq. (13.10), we get s^{-1}, or more properly rad/s because this is an *angular* frequency (recall that a radian is not a true unit).

According to Eqs. (13.1) and (13.2), the frequency f and period T are

$$f = \frac{\omega}{2\pi} = \frac{1}{2\pi}\sqrt{\frac{k}{m}} \quad \text{(simple harmonic motion)} \tag{13.11}$$

$$T = \frac{1}{f} = \frac{2\pi}{\omega} = 2\pi\sqrt{\frac{m}{k}} \quad \text{(simple harmonic motion)} \tag{13.12}$$

We see from Eq. (13.12) that a larger mass m, with its greater inertia, will have less acceleration, move more slowly, and take a longer time for a complete cycle (Fig. 13.7). In contrast, a stiffer spring (one with a larger force constant k) exerts a greater force at a given deformation x, causing greater acceleration, higher speeds, and a shorter time T per cycle.

13.7 The greater the mass m in a tuning fork's tines, the lower the frequency of oscillation $f = (1/2\pi)\sqrt{k/m}$ and the lower the pitch of the sound that the tuning fork produces.

Tines with large mass m: low frequency $f = 128$ Hz

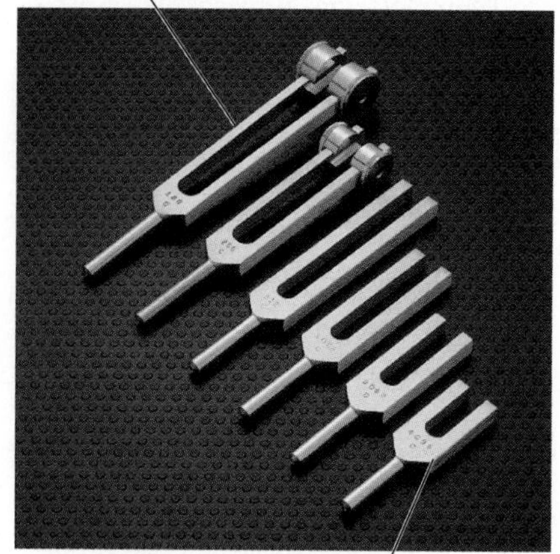

Tines with small mass m: high frequency $f = 4096$ Hz

CAUTION Don't confuse frequency and angular frequency You can run into trouble if you don't make the distinction between frequency f and angular frequency $\omega = 2\pi f$. Frequency tells you how many cycles of oscillation occur per second, while angular frequency tells you how many radians per second this corresponds to on the reference circle. In solving problems, pay careful attention to whether the goal is to find f or ω.

Period and Amplitude in SHM

Equations (13.11) and (13.12) show that the period and frequency of simple harmonic motion are completely determined by the mass m and the force constant k. *In simple harmonic motion the period and frequency do not depend on the amplitude A.* For given values of m and k, the time of one complete oscillation is the same whether the amplitude is large or small. Equation (13.3) shows why we should expect this. Larger A means that the body reaches larger values of $|x|$ and is subjected to larger restoring forces. This increases the average speed of the body over a complete cycle; this exactly compensates for having to travel a larger distance, so the same total time is involved.

The oscillations of a tuning fork are essentially simple harmonic motion, which means that it always vibrates with the same frequency, independent of amplitude. This is why a tuning fork can be used as a standard for musical pitch. If it were not for this characteristic of simple harmonic motion, it would be impossible to make familiar types of mechanical and electronic clocks run accurately or to play most musical instruments in tune. If you encounter an oscillating body with a period that *does* depend on the amplitude, the oscillation is *not* simple harmonic motion.

Example 13.2 Angular frequency, frequency, and period in SHM

A spring is mounted horizontally, with its left end held stationary. By attaching a spring balance to the free end and pulling toward the right (Fig. 13.8a), we determine that the stretching force is proportional to the displacement and that a force of 6.0 N causes a displacement of 0.030 m. We remove the spring balance and attach a 0.50-kg glider to the end, pull it a distance of 0.020 m along a frictionless air track, release it, and watch it oscillate (Fig. 13.8b). (a) Find the force constant of the spring. (b) Find the angular frequency, frequency, and period of the oscillation.

SOLUTION

IDENTIFY: Because the spring force (equal in magnitude to the stretching force) is proportional to the displacement, the motion is simple harmonic.

SET UP: We find the value of the force constant k using Hooke's law, Eq. (13.3), and the values of ω, f, and T using Eqs. (13.10), (13.11), and (13.12), respectively.

EXECUTE: (a) When $x = 0.030$ m, the force the spring exerts on the spring balance is $F_x = -6.0$ N. From Eq. (13.3),

$$k = -\frac{F_x}{x} = -\frac{-6.0\text{ N}}{0.030\text{ m}} = 200\text{ N/m} = 200\text{ kg/s}^2$$

13.8 (a) The force exerted *on* the spring (shown by the vector F) has x-component $F_x = +6.0$ N. The force exerted *by* the spring has x-component $F_x = -6.0$ N. (b) A glider is attached to the same spring and allowed to oscillate.

(a)

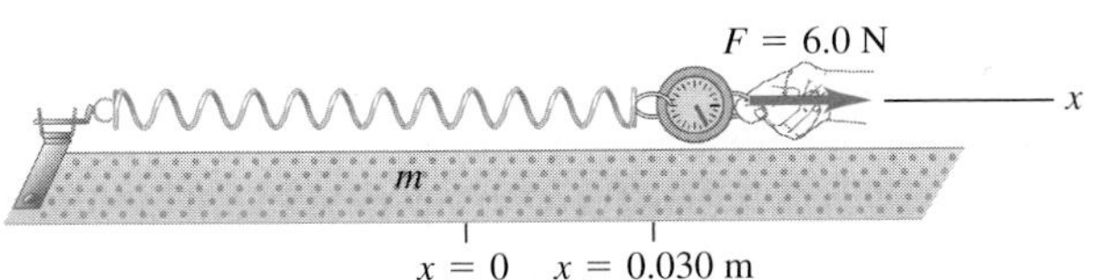

(b)

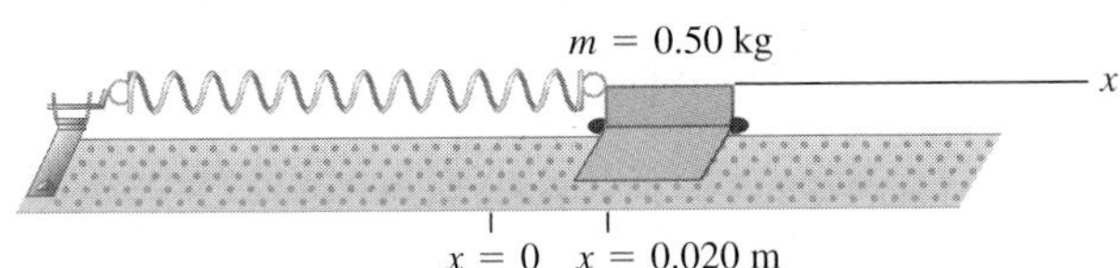

(b) Using $m = 0.50$ kg in Eq. (13.10), we find

$$\omega = \sqrt{\frac{k}{m}} = \sqrt{\frac{200\text{ kg/s}^2}{0.50\text{ kg}}} = 20\text{ rad/s}$$

The frequency f is

$$f = \frac{\omega}{2\pi} = \frac{20\text{ rad/s}}{2\pi\text{ rad/cycle}} = 3.2\text{ cycle/s} = 3.2\text{ Hz}$$

The period T is the reciprocal of the frequency f:

$$T = \frac{1}{f} = \frac{1}{3.2\text{ cycle/s}} = 0.31\text{ s}$$

A period is usually stated in "seconds" rather than "seconds per cycle."

EVALUATE: The amplitude of the oscillation is 0.020 m, the distance to the right that we pulled the glider attached to the spring before releasing it. We didn't need to use this information to find the angular frequency, frequency, or period, because in SHM none of these quantities depend on the amplitude.

Displacement, Velocity, and Acceleration in SHM

ActivPhysics ONLINE

9.1 Position Graphs and Equations
9.2 Describing Vibrational Motion
9.5 Ape Drops Tarzan

We still need to find the displacement x as a function of time for a harmonic oscillator. Equation (13.4) for a body in simple harmonic motion along the x-axis is identical to Eq. (13.8) for the x-coordinate of the reference point in uniform circular motion with constant angular speed $\omega = \sqrt{k/m}$. It follows that Eq. (13.5), $x = A\cos\theta$, describes the coordinate x for both of these situations. If at $t = 0$ the phasor OQ makes an angle ϕ (the Greck letter phi) with the positive x-axis, then at any later time t this angle is $\theta = \omega t + \phi$. We substitute this into Eq. (13.5) to obtain

$$x = A\cos(\omega t + \phi) \quad \text{(displacement in SHM)} \tag{13.13}$$

where $\omega = \sqrt{k/m}$. Figure 13.9 shows a graph of Eq. (13.13) for the particular case $\phi = 0$. The displacement x is a periodic function of time, as expected for SHM. We could also have written Eq. (13.13) in terms of a sine function rather than a cosine by using the identity $\cos\alpha = \sin(\alpha + \pi/2)$. *In simple harmonic motion the position is a periodic, sinusoidal function of time.* There are many other periodic functions, but none so smooth and simple as a sine or cosine function.

13.9 Graph of x versus t [See Eq. (13.13)] for simple harmonic motion. The case shown has $\phi = 0$.

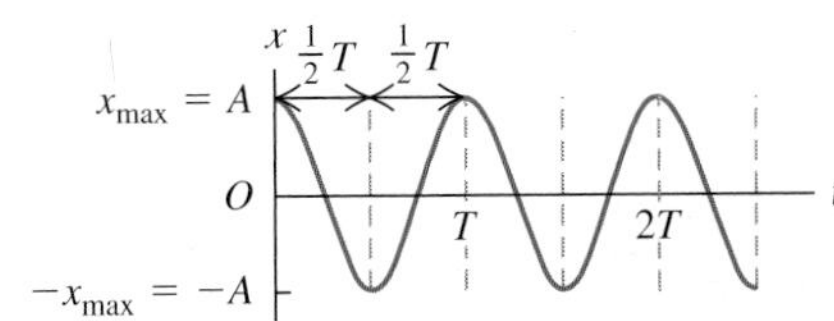

The value of the cosine function is always between -1 and 1, so in Eq. (13.13), x is always between $-A$ and A. This confirms that A is the amplitude of the motion.

The period T is the time for one complete cycle of oscillation, as Fig. 13.9 shows. The cosine function repeats itself whenever the quantity in parentheses in Eq. (13.13) increases by 2π radians. Thus, if we start at time $t = 0$, the time T to complete one cycle is given by

$$\omega T = \sqrt{\frac{k}{m}}T = 2\pi \quad \text{or} \quad T = 2\pi\sqrt{\frac{m}{k}}$$

13.10 Variations of simple harmonic motion. All cases shown have $\phi = 0$ [see Eq. (13.13)].

MP

(a) Increasing m; same A and k

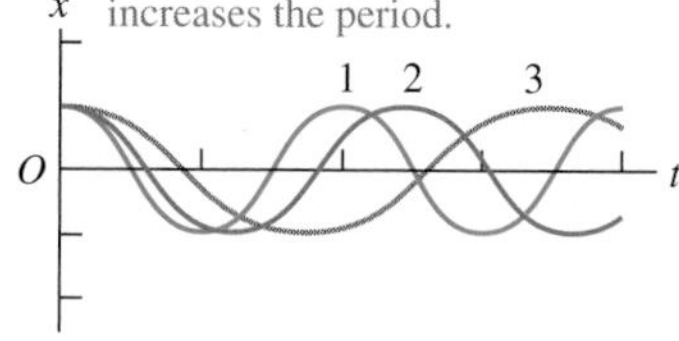
Mass m increases from curve
1 to 2 to 3. Increasing m alone
increases the period.
x
1 2 3
O
t

(b) Increasing k; same A and m

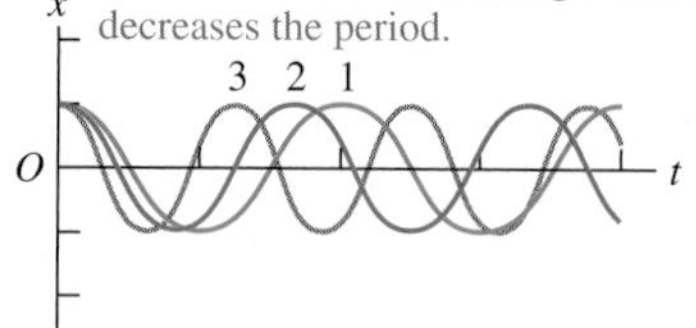
Force constant k increases from
curve 1 to 2 to 3. Increasing k alone
decreases the period.
x
3 2 1
O
t

(c) Increasing A; same k and m

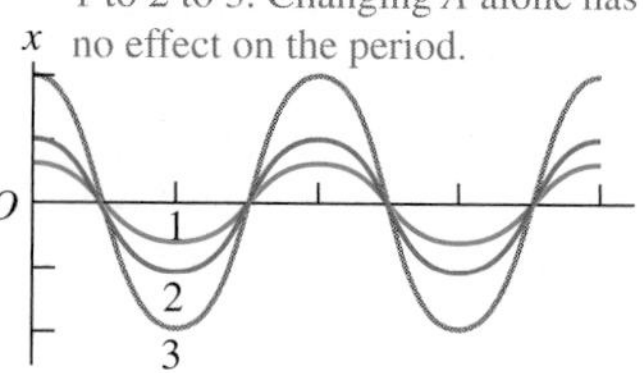
Amplitude A increases from curve
1 to 2 to 3. Changing A alone has
no effect on the period.
x
O
t
1
2
3

13.11 Variations of SHM: displacement versus time for the same harmonic oscillator with different phase angles ϕ.

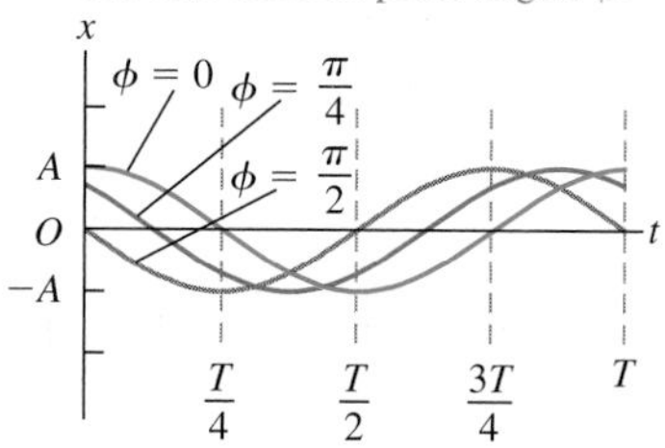
These three curves show SHM with
the same period T and amplitude A
but with different phase angles φ.
x
φ = 0
φ = π/4
φ = π/2
A
O
−A
t
T/4
T/2
3T/4
T

which is just Eq. (13.12). Changing either m or k changes the period of oscillation, as shown in Figs 13.10a and 13.10b. The period does not depend on the amplitude A (Fig. 13.10c).

The constant ϕ in Eq. (13.13) is called the **phase angle.** It tells us at what point in the cycle the motion was at $t = 0$ (equivalent to where around the circle the point Q was at $t = 0$). We denote the position at $t = 0$ by x_0. Putting $t = 0$ and $x = x_0$ in Eq. (13.13), we get

$$x_0 = A\cos\phi \tag{13.14}$$

If $\phi = 0$, then $x_0 = A\cos 0 = A$, and the body starts at its maximum positive displacement. If $\phi = \pi$, then $x_0 = A\cos\pi = -A$, and the particle starts at its maximum *negative* displacement. If $\phi = \pi/2$, then $x_0 = A\cos(\pi/2) = 0$, and the particle is initially at the origin. Figure 13.11 shows the displacement x versus time for three different phase angles.

We find the velocity v_x and acceleration a_x as functions of time for a harmonic oscillator by taking derivatives of Eq. (13.13) with respect to time:

$$v_x = \frac{dx}{dt} = -\omega A\sin(\omega t + \phi) \qquad \text{(velocity in SHM)} \tag{13.15}$$

$$a_x = \frac{dv_x}{dt} = \frac{d^2x}{dt^2} = -\omega^2 A\cos(\omega t + \phi) \qquad \text{(acceleration in SHM)} \tag{13.16}$$

The velocity v_x oscillates between $v_{max} = +\omega A$ and $-v_{max} = -\omega A$, and the acceleration a_x oscillates between $a_{max} = +\omega^2 A$ and $-a_{max} = -\omega^2 A$ (Fig. 13.12). Comparing Eq. (13.16) with Eq. (13.13) and recalling that $\omega^2 = k/m$ from Eq. (13.9), we see that

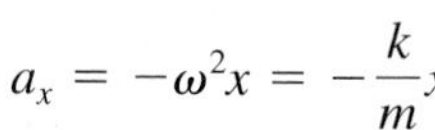

$$a_x = -\omega^2 x = -\frac{k}{m}x$$

which is just Eq. (13.4) for simple harmonic motion. This confirms that Eq. (13.13) for x as a function of time is correct.

We actually derived Eq. (13.16) earlier in a geometrical way by taking the x-component of the acceleration vector of the reference point Q. This was done in Fig. 13.6b and Eq. (13.7) (recall that $\theta = \omega t + \phi$). In the same way, we could have derived Eq. (13.15) by taking the x-component of the velocity vector of Q, as shown in Fig. 13.6b. We'll leave the details for you to work out (see Problem 13.85).

Note that the sinusoidal graph of displacement versus time (Fig. 13.12a) is shifted by one-quarter period from the graph of velocity versus time (Fig. 13.12b) and by one-half period from the graph of acceleration versus time (Fig. 13.12c). Figure 13.13 shows why this is so. When the body is passing through the equilibrium position so that the displacement is zero, the velocity equals either v_{max} or $-v_{max}$ (depending on which way the body is moving) and

13.12 Graphs of (a) x versus t, (b) v_x versus t, and (c) a_x versus t for a body in SHM. For the motion depicted in these graphs, $\phi = \pi/3$.

(a) Displacement x as a function of time t

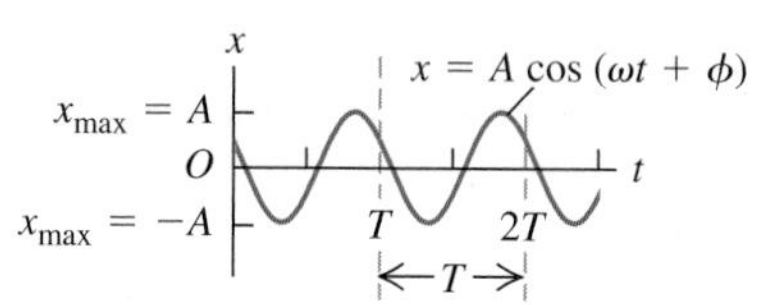
x
x = A cos (ωt + φ)
x_max = A
O
−x_max = −A
t
T
2T
T

(b) Velocity v_x as a function of time t

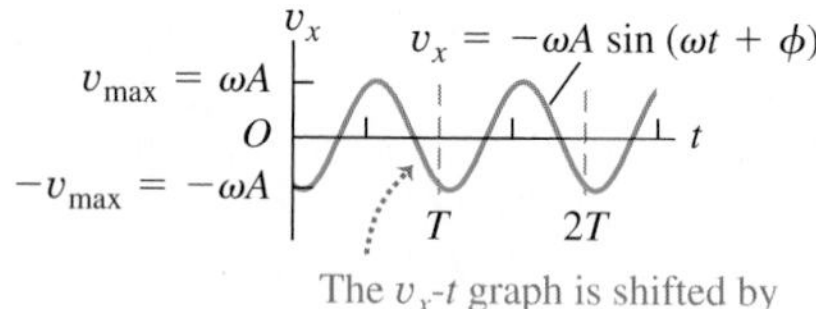
v_x
v_x = −ωA sin (ωt + φ)
v_max = ωA
O
−v_max = −ωA
t
T
2T
The v_x-t graph is shifted by
1/4 cycle from the x-t graph.

(c) Acceleration a_x as a function of time t

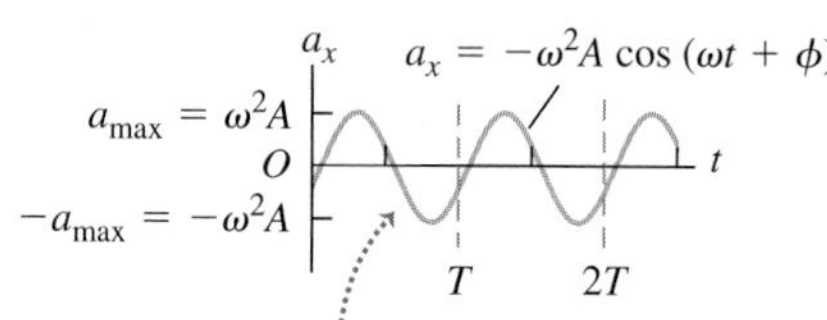
a_x
a_x = −ω²A cos (ωt + φ)
a_max = ω²A
O
−a_max = −ω²A
t
T
2T

The a_x-t graph is shifted by $\frac{1}{4}$ cycle from the v_x-t graph and by $\frac{1}{2}$ cycle from the x-t graph.

the acceleration is zero. When the body is at either its maximum positive displacement, $x = +A$, or its maximum negative displacement, $x = -A$, the velocity is zero and the body is instantaneously at rest. At these points, the restoring force $F_x = -kx$ and the acceleration of the body have their maximum magnitudes. At $x = +A$ the acceleration is negative and equal to $-a_{max}$. At $x = -A$ the acceleration is positive: $a_x = +a_{max}$.

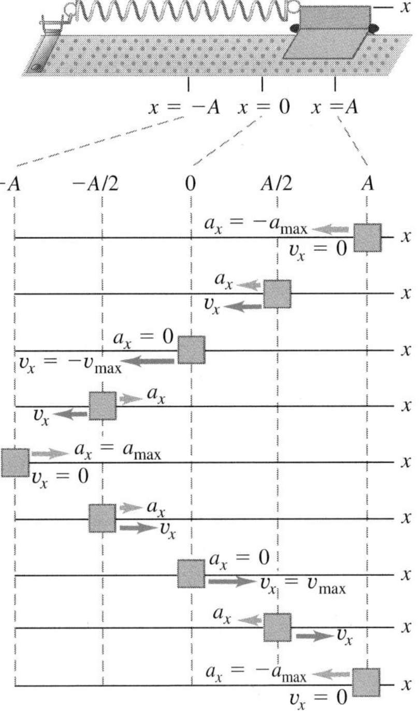

13.13 How x-velocity v_x and x-acceleration a_x vary during one cycle of SHM.

If we are given the initial position x_0 and initial velocity v_{0x} for the oscillating body, we can determine the amplitude A and the phase angle ϕ. Here's how to do it. The initial velocity v_{0x} is the velocity at time $t = 0$; putting $v_x = v_{0x}$ and $t = 0$ in Eq. (13.15), we find

$$v_{0x} = -\omega A \sin\phi \tag{13.17}$$

To find ϕ, we divide Eq. (13.17) by Eq. (13.14). This eliminates A and gives an equation that we can solve for ϕ:

$$\frac{v_{0x}}{x_0} = \frac{-\omega A \sin\phi}{A\cos\phi} = -\omega\tan\phi$$

$$\phi = \arctan\left(-\frac{v_{0x}}{\omega x_0}\right) \quad \text{(phase angle in SHM)} \tag{13.18}$$

It is also easy to find the amplitude A if we are given x_0 and v_{0x}. We'll sketch the derivation, and you can fill in the details. Square Eq. (13.14); then divide Eq. (13.17) by ω, square it, and add to the square of Eq. (13.14). The right side will be $A^2(\sin^2\phi + \cos^2\phi)$, which is equal to A^2. The final result is

$$A = \sqrt{x_0^2 + \frac{v_{0x}^2}{\omega^2}} \quad \text{(amplitude in SHM)} \tag{13.19}$$

Note that when the body has both an initial displacement x_0 and a nonzero initial velocity v_{0x}, the amplitude A is *not* equal to the initial displacement. That's reasonable; if you start the body at a positive x_0 but give it a positive velocity v_{0x}, it will go *farther* than x_0 before it turns and comes back.

Problem-Solving Strategy 13.1 Simple Harmonic Motion I: Describing Motion

MP

IDENTIFY *the relevant concepts:* An oscillating system undergoes simple harmonic motion (SHM) *only* if the restoring force is directly proportional to the displacement. Be certain that this is the case for the problem at hand before attempting to use any of the results of this section. As always, identify the target variables.

SET UP *the problem* using the following steps:

1. Identify the known and unknown quantities, and determine which are the target variables.
2. It's useful to distinguish between two kinds of quantities. *Basic properties* of the system include the mass m and the force constant k as well as quantities derived from m and k, such as the period T, frequency f, and angular frequency ω. *Properties of the motion* describe how the system behaves when it is set into motion in a particular way. They include the amplitude A, maximum velocity v_{max}, and phase angle ϕ as well as the values of x, v_x, and a_x at a particular time.
3. If necessary, define an x-axis as in Fig. 13.13, with the equilibrium position at $x = 0$.

EXECUTE *the solution* as follows:

1. Use the equations given in Sections 13.1 and 13.2 to solve for the target variables.
2. If you need to calculate the phase angle, be certain to express it in radians. The quantity ωt in Eq. (13.13) is naturally in radians, so ϕ must be as well.
3. If you need to find the values of x, v_x, and a_x at various times, use Eqs. (13.13), (13.15), and (13.16), respectively. If the initial position x_0 and initial velocity v_{0x} are both given, you can determine the phase angle and amplitude from Eqs. (13.18) and (13.19). If the body is given an initial positive displacement x_0 but zero initial velocity $(v_{0x} = 0)$, then the amplitude is $A = x_0$ and the phase angle is $\phi = 0$. If it has an initial positive velocity v_{0x} but no initial displacement $(x_0 = 0)$, the amplitude is $A = v_{0x}/\omega$ and the phase angle is $\phi = -\pi/2$.

EVALUATE *your answer:* Check your results to make sure they're consistent. As an example, suppose you've used the initial position and velocity to find general expressions for x and v_x at time t. If you substitute $t = 0$ into these expressions, you should get back the correct values of x_0 and v_{0x}.

Example 13.3 Describing SHM

Let's return to the system of mass and horizontal spring we considered in Example 13.2, with $k = 200\ \text{N/m}$ and $m = 0.50\ \text{kg}$. This time we give the body an initial displacement of $+0.015\ \text{m}$ and an initial velocity of $+0.40\ \text{m/s}$. (a) Find the period, amplitude, and phase angle of the motion. (b) Write equations for the displacement, velocity, and acceleration as functions of time.

SOLUTION

IDENTIFY: As in Example 13.2, the oscillations are SHM and we may use the expressions developed in this section.

SET UP: We are given the values of k, m, x_0, and v_{0x}. From them, we calculate the target variables T, A, and ϕ and the expressions for x, v_x, and a_x as functions of time.

EXECUTE: (a) The period is the same as in Example 13.2, $T = 0.31\ \text{s}$. In simple harmonic motion the period does not depend on the amplitude, only on the values of k and m. In Example 13.2 we found that $\omega = 20\ \text{rad/s}$. So from Eq. (13.19),

$$\begin{aligned} A &= \sqrt{x_0^2 + \frac{v_{0x}^2}{\omega^2}} \\ &= \sqrt{(0.015\ \text{m})^2 + \frac{(0.40\ \text{m/s})^2}{(20\ \text{rad/s})^2}} \\ &= 0.025\ \text{m} \end{aligned}$$

To find the phase angle ϕ, we use Eq. (13.18):

$$\begin{aligned} \phi &= \arctan\left(-\frac{v_{0x}}{\omega x_0}\right) \\ &= \arctan\left(-\frac{0.40\ \text{m/s}}{(20\ \text{rad/s})(0.015\ \text{m})}\right) = -53^\circ = -0.93\ \text{rad} \end{aligned}$$

(b) The displacement, velocity, and acceleration at any time are given by Eqs. (13.13), (13.15), and (13.16), respectively. Substituting the values, we get

$$\begin{aligned} x &= (0.025\ \text{m})\cos[(20\ \text{rad/s})t - 0.93\ \text{rad}] \\ v_x &= -(0.50\ \text{m/s})\sin[(20\ \text{rad/s})t - 0.93\ \text{rad}] \\ a_x &= -(10\ \text{m/s}^2)\cos[(20\ \text{rad/s})t - 0.93\ \text{rad}] \end{aligned}$$

The velocity varies sinusoidally between $-0.50\ \text{m/s}$ and $+0.50\ \text{m/s}$, and the acceleration varies sinusoidally between $-10\ \text{m/s}^2$ and $+10\ \text{m/s}^2$.

EVALUATE: You can check the results for x and v_x as functions of time by substituting $t = 0$ and evaluating the result. You should get $x = x_0 = 0.015\ \text{m}$ and $v_x = v_{0x} = 0.40\ \text{m/s}$. Do you?

Test Your Understanding of Section 13.2 A glider is attached to a spring as shown in Fig. 13.13. If the glider is moved to $x = 0.10\ \text{m}$ and released from rest at time $t = 0$, it will oscillate with amplitude $A = 0.10\ \text{m}$ and phase angle $\phi = 0$. (a) Suppose instead that at $t = 0$ the glider is at $x = 0.10\ \text{m}$ and is moving to the right in Fig. 13.13. In this situation is the amplitude greater than, less than, or equal to 0.10 m? Is the phase angle greater than, less than, or equal to zero? (b) Suppose instead that at $t = 0$ the glider is at $x = 0.10\ \text{m}$ and is moving to the left in Fig. 13.13. In this situation is the amplitude greater than, less than, or equal to 0.10 m? Is the phase angle greater than, less than, or equal to zero?

ActivPhysics ONLINE

9.3 Vibrational Energy
9.4 Two Ways to Weigh Young Tarzan
9.6 Releasing a Vibrating Skier I
9.7 Releasing a Vibrating Skier II
9.8 One- and Two-Spring Vibrating Systems
9.9 Vibro-Ride

13.3 Energy in Simple Harmonic Motion

We can learn even more about simple harmonic motion by using energy considerations. Take another look at the body oscillating on the end of a spring in Figs. 13.2 and 13.13. We've already noted that the spring force is the only horizontal force on the body. The force exerted by an ideal spring is a conservative force, and the vertical forces do no work, so the total mechanical energy of the system is *conserved*. We also assume that the mass of the spring itself is negligible.

The kinetic energy of the body is $K = \frac{1}{2}mv^2$ and the potential energy of the spring is $U = \frac{1}{2}kx^2$, just as in Section 7.2. (You'll find it helpful to review that section.) There are no nonconservative forces that do work, so the total mechanical energy $E = K + U$ is conserved:

$$E = \frac{1}{2}mv_x^2 + \frac{1}{2}kx^2 = \text{constant} \tag{13.20}$$

(Since the motion is one-dimensional, $v^2 = v_x^2$.)

The total mechanical energy E is also directly related to the amplitude A of the motion. When the body reaches the point $x = A$, its maximum displacement from equilibrium, it momentarily stops as it turns back toward the equilibrium position. That is, when $x = A$ (or $-A$), $v_x = 0$. At this point the energy is entirely potential, and $E = \frac{1}{2}kA^2$. Because E is constant, it is equal to $\frac{1}{2}kA^2$ at any other point. Combining this expression with Eq. (13.20), we get

$$E = \frac{1}{2}mv_x^2 + \frac{1}{2}kx^2 = \frac{1}{2}kA^2 = \text{constant} \quad \text{(total mechanical energy in SHM)} \tag{13.21}$$

We can verify this equation by substituting x and v_x from Eqs. (13.13) and (13.15) and using $\omega^2 = k/m$ from Eq. (13.9):

$$\begin{aligned} E &= \frac{1}{2}mv_x^2 + \frac{1}{2}kx^2 = \frac{1}{2}m[-\omega A\sin(\omega t + \phi)]^2 + \frac{1}{2}k[A\cos(\omega t + \phi)]^2 \\ &= \frac{1}{2}kA^2\sin^2(\omega t + \phi) + \frac{1}{2}kA^2\cos^2(\omega t + \phi) \\ &= \frac{1}{2}kA^2 \end{aligned}$$

(Recall that $\sin^2\alpha + \cos^2\alpha = 1$.) Hence our expressions for displacement and velocity in SHM are consistent with energy conservation, as they must be.

We can use Eq. (13.21) to solve for the velocity v_x of the body at a given displacement x:

$$v_x = \pm\sqrt{\frac{k}{m}}\sqrt{A^2 - x^2} \tag{13.22}$$

The $\pm$ sign means that at a given value of x the body can be moving in either direction. For example, when $x = \pm A/2$,

$$v_x = \pm\sqrt{\frac{k}{m}}\sqrt{A^2 - \left(\pm\frac{A}{2}\right)^2} = \pm\sqrt{\frac{3}{4}}\sqrt{\frac{k}{m}}A$$

Equation (13.22) also shows that the *maximum* speed v_{max} occurs at $x = 0$. Using Eq. (13.10), $\omega = \sqrt{k/m}$, we find that

$$v_{max} = \sqrt{\frac{k}{m}}A = \omega A \tag{13.23}$$

This agrees with Eq. (13.15), which showed that v_x oscillates between $-\omega A$ and $+\omega A$.

Interpreting E, K, and U in SHM

Figure 13.14 shows the energy quantities E, K, and U at $x = 0$, $x = \pm A/2$, and $x = \pm A$. Figure 13.15 is a graphical display of Eq. (13.21); energy (kinetic, potential, and total) is plotted vertically and the coordinate x is plotted horizontally. The

13.14 Graphs of E, K, and U versus displacement in SHM. The velocity of the body is *not* constant, so these images of the body at equally spaced positions are *not* equally spaced in time.

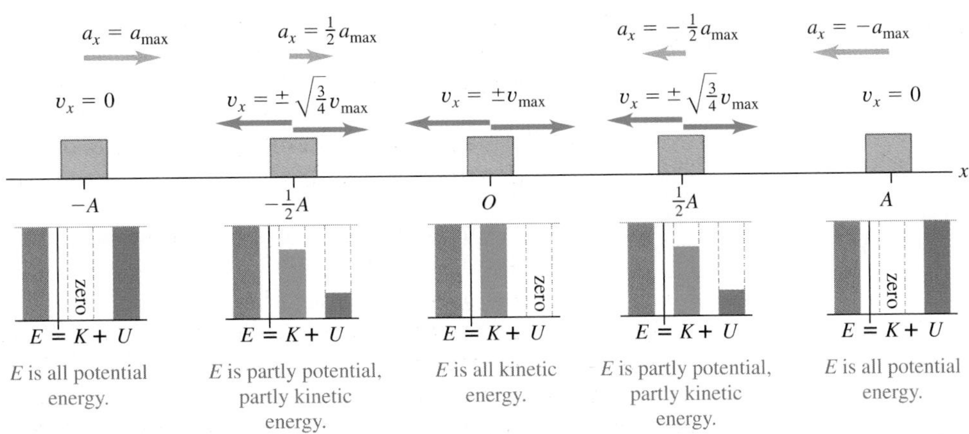

13.15 Kinetic energy K, potential energy U, and total mechanical energy E as functions of position for SHM. At each value of x the sum of the values of K and U equals the constant value of E. Can you show that the energy is half kinetic and half potential at $x = \pm\sqrt{\frac{1}{2}}A$?

(a) The potential energy U and total mechanical energy E for a body in SHM as a function of displacement x

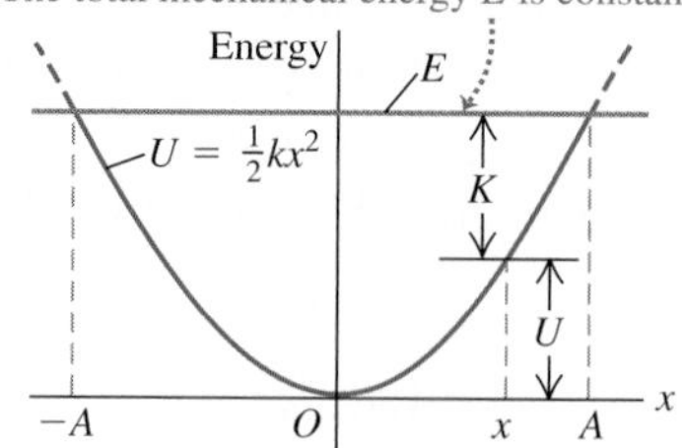
The total mechanical energy E is constant.
Energy
E
U = ½kx²
K
U
x
−A
O
x
A

(b) The same graph as in (a), showing kinetic energy K as well

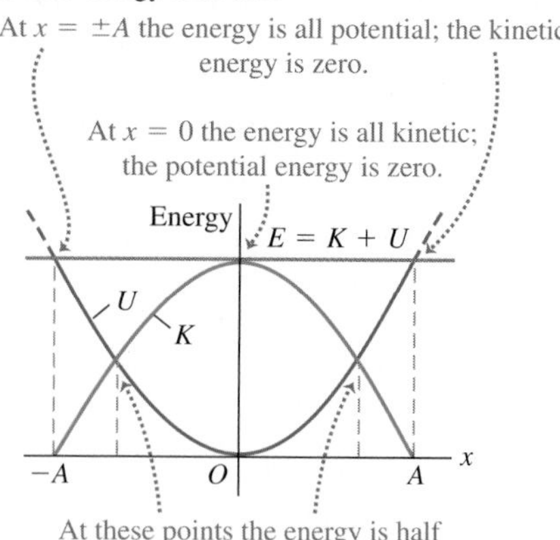
At x = ±A the energy is all potential; the kinetic energy is zero.
At x = 0 the energy is all kinetic; the potential energy is zero.
Energy
E = K + U
U
K
x
−A
O
A
At these points the energy is half kinetic and half potential.

parabolic curve in Fig. 13.15a represents the potential energy $U = \frac{1}{2}kx^2$. The horizontal line represents the total mechanical energy E, which is constant and does not vary with x. At any value of x between $-A$ and A, the vertical distance from the x-axis to the parabola is U; since $E = K + U$, the remaining vertical distance up to the horizontal line is K. Figure 13.15b shows both K and U as functions of x. The horizontal line for E intersects the potential-energy curve at $x = -A$ and $x = A$, so at these points the energy is entirely potential, the kinetic energy is zero, and the body comes momentarily to rest before reversing direction. As the body oscillates between $-A$ and A, the energy is continuously transformed from potential to kinetic and back again.

Figure 13.15a shows the connection between the amplitude A and the corresponding total mechanical energy $E = \frac{1}{2}kA^2$. If we tried to make x greater than A (or less than $-A$), U would be greater than E, and K would have to be negative. But K can never be negative, so x can't be greater than A or less than $-A$.

Problem-Solving Strategy 13.2 Simple Harmonic Motion II: Energy

MP

The energy equation, Eq. (13.21), is a useful alternative relationship between velocity and position, especially when energy quantities are also required. If the problem involves a relationship among position, velocity, and acceleration without reference to time, it is usually easier to use Eq. (13.4) (from Newton's second law) or Eq. (13.21) (from energy conservation) than to use the general expressions for x, v_x, and a_x as functions of time [Eqs. (13.13), (13.15), and (13.16), respectively]. Because the energy equation involves x^2 and v_x^2, it cannot tell you the sign of x or of v_x; you have to infer the sign from the situation. For instance, if the body is moving from the equilibrium position toward the point of greatest positive displacement, then x is positive and v_x is positive.

Example 13.4 Velocity, acceleration, and energy in SHM

In the oscillation described in Example 13.2, $k = 200$ N/m, $m = 0.50$ kg, and the oscillating mass is released from rest at $x = 0.020$ m. (a) Find the maximum and minimum velocities attained by the oscillating body. (b) Compute the maximum acceleration. (c) Determine the velocity and acceleration when the body has moved halfway to the center from its original position. (d) Find the total energy, potential energy, and kinetic energy at this position.

SOLUTION

IDENTIFY: The problem refers to the motion at various *positions* in the motion, not at specified *times*. This is a hint that we can use the energy relationships found in this section to solve for the target variables.

SET UP: Figure 13.13 shows the choice of x-axis. The maximum displacement from equilibrium is $A = 0.020$ m. For any position x we use Eqs. (13.22) and (13.4) to find the velocity v_x and acceleration a_x, respectively. Given the velocity and position, we use Eq. (13.21) to find the energy quantities K, U, and E.

EXECUTE: (a) The velocity v_x at any displacement x is given by Eq. (13.22):

$$v_x = \pm\sqrt{\frac{k}{m}}\sqrt{A^2 - x^2}$$

The maximum velocity occurs when the body is moving to the right through the equilibrium position, where $x = 0$:

$$v_x = v_{max} = \sqrt{\frac{k}{m}}A = \sqrt{\frac{200\ \text{N/m}}{0.50\ \text{kg}}}(0.020\ \text{m}) = 0.40\ \text{m/s}$$

The minimum (i.e., most negative) velocity occurs when the body is moving to the left through $x = 0$; its value is $-v_{max} = -0.40$ m/s.

(b) From Eq. (13.4),

$$a_x = -\frac{k}{m}x$$

The maximum (most positive) acceleration occurs at the most negative value of x, $x = -A$; therefore

$$a_{max} = -\frac{k}{m}(-A) = -\frac{200\ \text{N/m}}{0.50\ \text{kg}}(-0.020\ \text{m}) = 8.0\ \text{m/s}^2$$

The minimum (most negative) acceleration is $-8.0\ \text{m/s}^2$, occurring at $x = +A = +0.020$ m.

(c) At a point halfway to the center from the initial position, $x = A/2 = 0.010$ m. From Eq. (13.22),

$$v_x = -\sqrt{\frac{200\ \text{N/m}}{0.50\ \text{kg}}}\sqrt{(0.020\ \text{m})^2 - (0.010\ \text{m})^2} = -0.35\ \text{m/s}$$

We choose the negative square root because the body is moving from $x = A$ toward $x = 0$. From Eq. (13.4),

$$a_x = -\frac{200\ \text{N/m}}{0.50\ \text{kg}}(0.010\ \text{m}) = -4.0\ \text{m/s}^2$$

At this point the velocity and the acceleration have the same sign, so the speed is increasing. The conditions at $x = 0$, $\pm A/2$, and $\pm A$ are shown in Fig. 13.14.

(d) The total energy has the same value at all points during the motion:

$$E = \frac{1}{2}kA^2 = \frac{1}{2}(200\ \text{N/m})(0.020\ \text{m})^2 = 0.040\ \text{J}$$

The potential energy is

$$U = \frac{1}{2}kx^2 = \frac{1}{2}(200\ \text{N/m})(0.010\ \text{m})^2 = 0.010\ \text{J}$$

and the kinetic energy is

$$K = \frac{1}{2}mv_x^2 = \frac{1}{2}(0.50\ \text{kg})(-0.35\ \text{m/s})^2 = 0.030\ \text{J}$$

EVALUATE: At the point $x = A/2$, the energy is one-fourth potential energy and three-fourths kinetic energy. You can check this result by inspecting Fig. 13.15b.

Example 13.5 Energy and momentum in SHM

A block with mass M attached to a horizontal spring with force constant k is moving with simple harmonic motion having amplitude A_1. At the instant when the block passes through its equilibrium position, a lump of putty with mass m is dropped vertically onto the block from a very small height and sticks to it. (a) Find the new amplitude and period. (b) Repeat part (a) for the case in which the putty is dropped on the block when it is at one end of its path.

SOLUTION

IDENTIFY: The problem involves the motion at a given position, not a given time, so we can use energy methods. Before the putty lands on the block, the mechanical energy of the oscillating block and spring is constant. When the putty lands on the block, it's a completely inelastic collision (see Section 8.3); the horizontal component of momentum is conserved, but kinetic energy decreases. Once the collision ends, the mechanical energy remains constant at its new value.

SET UP: Figure 13.16 shows our sketches. In each part we consider what happens before, during, and after the collision. We find the amplitude A_2 after the collision from the final energy of the system, and we find the period T_2 after the collision using the relationship between period and mass.

EXECUTE: (a) Before the collision the total mechanical energy of the block and spring is $E_1 = \frac{1}{2}kA_1^2$. Since the block is at the equilibrium position, $U = 0$, and the energy is purely kinetic (Fig. 13.16a). If we let v_1 be the speed of the block at the equilibrium position, we have

$$E_1 = \frac{1}{2}Mv_1^2 = \frac{1}{2}kA_1^2 \qquad \text{so} \qquad v_1 = \sqrt{\frac{k}{M}}A_1$$

During the collision the x-component of momentum of the system of block and putty is conserved. (Why?) Just before the collision this component is the sum of Mv_1 (for the block) and zero (for the putty). Just after the collision the block and putty move together with speed v_2, and their combined x-component of momentum is $(M + m)v_2$. From conservation of momentum,

$$Mv_1 + 0 = (M + m)v_2 \qquad \text{so} \qquad v_2 = \frac{M}{M + m}v_1$$

13.16 Our sketches for this problem.

(a)

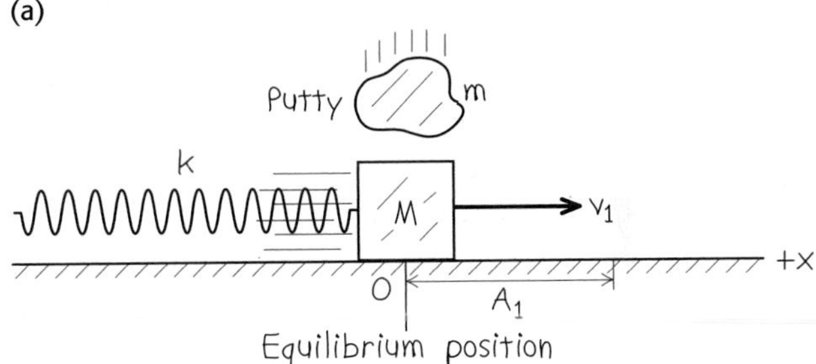

(b)

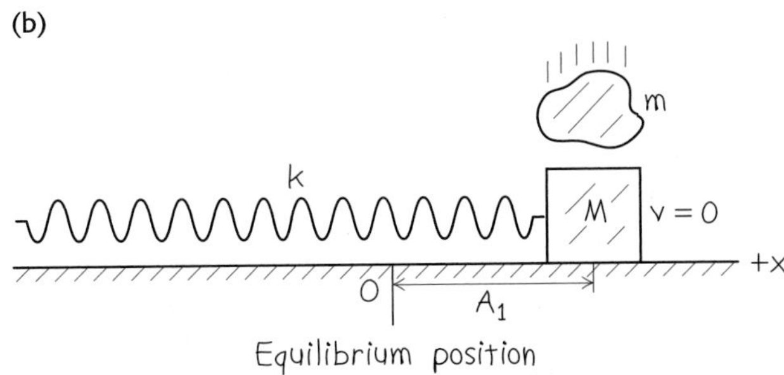

Continued

The collision lasts a very short time, so just after the collision the block and putty are still at the equilibrium position. The energy is still purely kinetic but is *less* than before the collision:

$$E_2 = \frac{1}{2}(M + m)v_2^2 = \frac{1}{2}\frac{M^2}{M + m}v_1^2 = \frac{M}{M + m}\left(\frac{1}{2}Mv_1^2\right)$$
$$= \left(\frac{M}{M + m}\right)E_1$$

Since E_2 equals $\frac{1}{2}kA_2^2$, where A_2 is the amplitude after the collision, we have

$$\frac{1}{2}kA_2^2 = \left(\frac{M}{M + m}\right)\frac{1}{2}kA_1^2$$
$$A_2 = A_1\sqrt{\frac{M}{M + m}}$$

The larger the putty mass m, the smaller the final amplitude.

Finding the period of oscillation after the collision is the easy part. Using Eq. (13.12), we have

$$T_2 = 2\pi\sqrt{\frac{M + m}{k}}$$

(b) When the putty drops, the block is instantaneously at rest (Fig. 13.16b). The x-component of momentum is zero both before and after the collision: The block has zero kinetic energy just before the collision, and the block and putty have zero kinetic energy just after the collision. The energy is all potential energy stored in the spring, so adding the extra mass of the putty has *no effect* on the mechanical energy. That is,

$$E_2 = E_1 = \frac{1}{2}kA_1^2$$

and the amplitude after the collision is unchanged $(A_2 = A_1)$. The period still changes when the putty is added, though; its value doesn't depend on how the mass is added, only on what the total mass is. So T_2 is the same as we found in part (a), $T_2 = 2\pi\sqrt{(M + m)/k}$.

EVALUATE: Why is energy lost in part (a) but not in part (b)? The difference is that in part (a) the putty slides against the moving block during the collision, and energy is dissipated by kinetic friction.

Test Your Understanding of Section 13.3 (a) To double the total energy for a mass-spring system oscillating in SHM, by what factor must the amplitude increase? (i) 4; (ii) 2; (iii) $\sqrt{2} = 1.414$; (iv) $\sqrt[4]{2} = 1.189$. (b) By what factor will the frequency change due to this amplitude increase? (i) 4; (ii) 2; (iii) $\sqrt{2} = 1.414$; (iv) $\sqrt[4]{2} = 1.189$; (v) it does not change.

13.4 Applications of Simple Harmonic Motion

So far, we've looked at a grand total of *one* situation in which simple harmonic motion (SHM) occurs: a body attached to an ideal horizontal spring. But SHM can occur in any system in which there is a restoring force that is directly proportional to the displacement from equilibrium, as given by Eq. (13.3), $F_x = -kx$. The restoring force will originate in different ways in different situations, so the force constant k has to be found for each case by examining the net force on the system. Once this is done, it's straightforward to find the angular frequency ω, frequency f, and period T; we just substitute the value of k into Eqs. (13.10), (13.11), and (13.12), respectively. Let's use these ideas to examine several examples of simple harmonic motion.

Vertical SHM

Suppose we hang a spring with force constant k (Fig. 13.17a) and suspend from it a body with mass m. Oscillations will now be vertical; will they still be SHM? In Fig. 13.17b the body hangs at rest, in equilibrium. In this position the spring is stretched an amount Δl just great enough that the spring's upward vertical force $k\,\Delta l$ on the body balances its weight mg:

$$k\,\Delta l = mg$$

Take $x = 0$ to be this equilibrium position and take the positive x-direction to be upward. When the body is a distance x *above* its equilibrium position (Fig. 13.17c), the extension of the spring is $\Delta l - x$. The upward force it exerts on the body is then $k(\Delta l - x)$, and the net x-component of force on the body is

$$F_{net} = k(\Delta l - x) + (-mg) = -kx$$

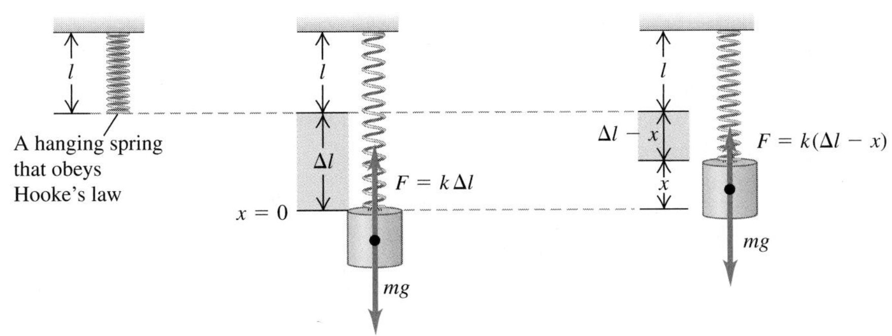
(a)
(b) A body is suspended from the spring. It is in equilibrium when the upward force exerted by the stretched spring equals the body's weight.
(c) If the body is displaced from equilibrium, the net force on the body is proportional to its displacement. The oscillations are SHM.
l
A hanging spring that obeys Hooke's law
Δl
$x = 0$
$F = k\Delta l$
mg
$\Delta l - x$
x
$F = k(\Delta l - x)$

13.17 A body attached to a hanging spring.

that is, a net downward force of magnitude kx. Similarly, when the body is *below* the equilibrium position, there is a net upward force with magnitude kx. In either case there is a restoring force with magnitude kx. If the body is set in vertical motion, it oscillates in SHM with the same angular frequency as though it were horizontal, $\omega = \sqrt{k/m}$. So vertical SHM doesn't differ in any essential way from horizontal SHM. The only real change is that the equilibrium position $x = 0$ no longer corresponds to the point at which the spring is unstretched. The same ideas hold if a body with weight mg is placed atop a compressible spring (Fig. 13.18) and compresses it a distance Δl.

13.18 If the weight mg compresses the spring a distance Δl, the force constant is $k = mg/\Delta l$ and the angular frequency for vertical SHM is $\omega = \sqrt{k/m}$—the same as if the body were suspended from the spring (See Fig. 13.17).

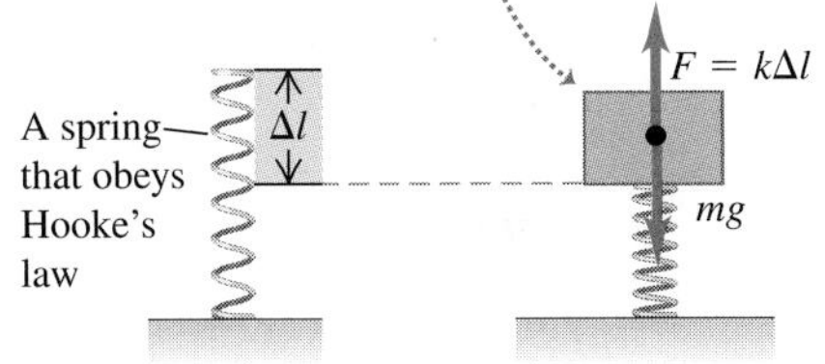
A body is placed atop the spring. It is in equilibrium when the upward force exerted by the compressed spring equals the body's weight.
A spring that obeys Hooke's law
Δl
$F = k\Delta l$
mg

Example 13.6 Vertical SHM in an old car

The shock absorbers in an old car with mass 1000 kg are completely worn out. When a 980-N person climbs slowly into the car to its center of gravity, the car sinks 2.8 cm. When the car, with the person aboard, hits a bump, the car starts oscillating up and down in SHM. Model the car and person as a single body on a single spring, and find the period and frequency of the oscillation.

SOLUTION

IDENTIFY: The situation is like that shown in Fig. 13.18.

SET UP: The compression of the spring when the extra weight is added tells us the force constant, which we can use to find the period and frequency (the target variables).

EXECUTE: When the force increases by 980 N, the spring compresses an additional 0.028 m, and the coordinate x of the car changes by -0.028 m. Hence the effective force constant (including the effect of the entire suspension) is

$$k = -\frac{F_x}{x} = -\frac{980\ \text{N}}{-0.028\ \text{m}} = 3.5 \times 10^4\ \text{kg/s}^2$$

The person's mass is $w/g = (980\ \text{N})/(9.8\ \text{m/s}^2) = 100$ kg. The *total* oscillating mass is $m = 1000\ \text{kg} + 100\ \text{kg} = 1100$ kg. The period T is

$$T = 2\pi\sqrt{\frac{m}{k}} = 2\pi\sqrt{\frac{1100\ \text{kg}}{3.5 \times 10^4\ \text{kg/s}^2}} = 1.11\ \text{s}$$

and the frequency is

$$f = \frac{1}{T} = \frac{1}{1.11\ \text{s}} = 0.90\ \text{Hz}$$

EVALUATE: A persistent oscillation with a period of about 1 second makes for a very unpleasant ride. The purpose of shock absorbers is to make such oscillations die out (see Section 13.7).

Angular SHM

A mechanical watch keeps time based on the oscillations of a balance wheel (Fig. 13.19). The wheel has a moment of inertia I about its axis. A coil spring exerts a restoring torque τ_z that is proportional to the angular displacement θ from the equilibrium position. We write $\tau_z = -\kappa\theta$, where κ (the Greek letter kappa) is a constant called the *torsion constant.* Using the rotational analog of

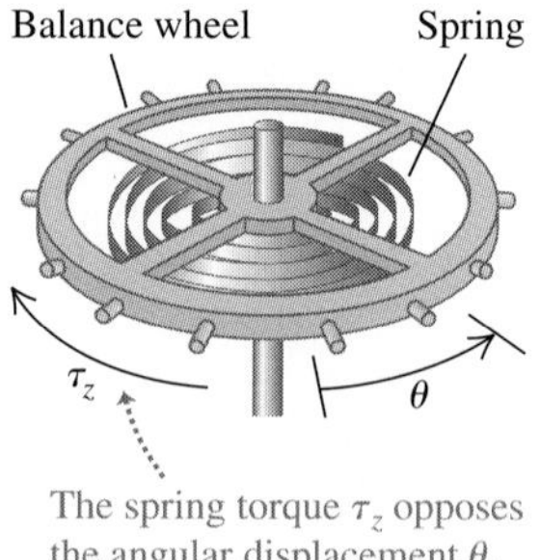

Balance wheel
Spring
τ_z
θ
The spring torque τ_z opposes the angular displacement θ.

13.19 The balance wheel of a mechanical watch. The spring exerts a restoring torque that is proportional to the angular displacement θ, so the motion is angular SHM.

Newton's second law for a rigid body, $\Sigma\tau_z = I\alpha_z = I\,d^2\theta/dt^2$, we can find the equation of motion:

$$-\kappa\theta = I\alpha \qquad \text{or} \qquad \frac{d^2\theta}{dt^2} = -\frac{\kappa}{I}\theta$$

The form of this equation is exactly the same as Eq. (13.4) for the acceleration in simple harmonic motion, with x replaced by θ and k/m replaced by κ/I. So we are dealing with a form of *angular* simple harmonic motion. The angular frequency ω and frequency f are given by Eqs. (13.10) and (13.11), respectively, with the same replacement:

$$\omega = \sqrt{\frac{\kappa}{I}} \quad \text{and} \quad f = \frac{1}{2\pi}\sqrt{\frac{\kappa}{I}} \quad \text{(angular SHM)} \tag{13.24}$$

The motion is described by the function

$$\theta = \Theta\cos(\omega t + \phi)$$

where Θ (the Greek letter theta) plays the role of an angular amplitude.

It's a good thing that the motion of a balance wheel *is* simple harmonic. If it weren't, the frequency might depend on the amplitude, and the watch would run too fast or too slow as the spring ran down.

*Vibrations of Molecules

The following discussion of the vibrations of molecules uses the binomial theorem. If you aren't familiar with this theorem, you should read about it in the appropriate section of a math textbook.

When two atoms are separated from each other by a few atomic diameters, they can exert attractive forces on each other. But if the atoms are so close to each other that their electron shells overlap, the forces between the atoms are repulsive. Between these limits, there can be an equilibrium separation distance at which two atoms form a *molecule.* If these atoms are displaced slightly from equilibrium, they will oscillate.

As an example, we'll consider one type of interaction between atoms called the *van der Waals interaction.* Our immediate task here is to study oscillations, so we won't go into the details of how this interaction arises. Let the center of one atom be at the origin and let the center of the other atom be a distance r away (Fig. 13.20a); the equilibrium distance between centers is $r = R_0$. Experiment shows that the van der Waals interaction can be described by the potential-energy function

$$U = U_0\left[\left(\frac{R_0}{r}\right)^{12} - 2\left(\frac{R_0}{r}\right)^{6}\right] \tag{13.25}$$

13.20 (a) Two atoms with centers separated by r. (b) Potential energy U in the van der Waals interaction as a function of r. (c) Force F_r on the right-hand atom as a function of r.

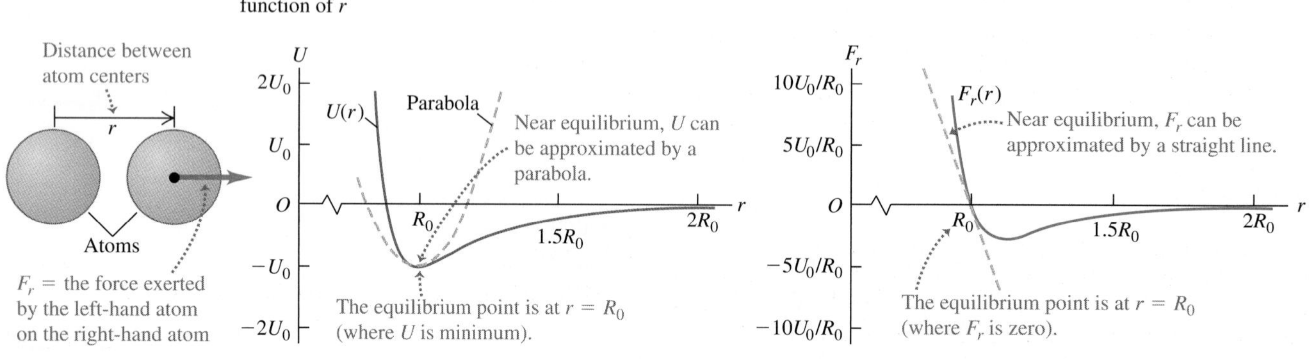

(a) Two-atom system
Distance between atom centers
r
Atoms
F_r = the force exerted by the left-hand atom on the right-hand atom
(b) Potential energy U of the two-atom system as a function of r
U
$2U_0$
U_0
O
$-U_0$
$-2U_0$
$U(r)$
Parabola
Near equilibrium, U can be approximated by a parabola.
R_0
$1.5R_0$
$2R_0$
r
The equilibrium point is at $r = R_0$ (where U is minimum).
(c) The force F_r as a function of r
F_r
$10U_0/R_0$
$5U_0/R_0$
O
$-5U_0/R_0$
$-10U_0/R_0$
$F_r(r)$
Near equilibrium, F_r can be approximated by a straight line.
R_0
$1.5R_0$
$2R_0$
r
The equilibrium point is at $r = R_0$ (where F_r is zero).

where U_0 is a positive constant with units of joules. When the two atoms are very far apart, $U = 0$; when they are separated by the equilibrium distance $r = R_0$, $U = -U_0$. The force on the second atom is the negative derivative of Eq. (13.25):

$$F_r = -\frac{dU}{dr} = U_0\left[\frac{12R_0^{12}}{r^{13}} - 2\frac{6R_0^6}{r^7}\right] = 12\frac{U_0}{R_0}\left[\left(\frac{R_0}{r}\right)^{13} - \left(\frac{R_0}{r}\right)^7\right] \quad (13.26)$$

The potential energy and force are plotted in Figs. 13.20b and 13.20c, respectively. The force is positive for $r < R_0$ and negative for $r > R_0$, so it is a *restoring* force.

Let's examine the restoring force F_r in Eq. (13.26). We let x represent the displacement from equilibrium:

$$x = r - R_0 \qquad \text{so} \qquad r = R_0 + x$$

In terms of x, the force F_r in Eq. (13.26) becomes

$$\begin{aligned} F_r &= 12\frac{U_0}{R_0}\left[\left(\frac{R_0}{R_0+x}\right)^{13} - \left(\frac{R_0}{R_0+x}\right)^7\right] \\ &= 12\frac{U_0}{R_0}\left[\frac{1}{(1+x/R_0)^{13}} - \frac{1}{(1+x/R_0)^7}\right] \end{aligned} \quad (13.27)$$

This looks nothing like Hooke's law, $F_x = -kx$, so we might be tempted to conclude that molecular oscillations cannot be SHM. But let us restrict ourselves to *small-amplitude* oscillations so that the absolute value of the displacement x is small in comparison to R_0 and the absolute value of the ratio x/R_0 is much less than 1. We can then simplify Eq. (13.27) by using the *binomial theorem:*

$$(1+u)^n = 1 + nu + \frac{n(n-1)}{2!}u^2 + \frac{n(n-1)(n-2)}{3!}u^3 + \cdots \quad (13.28)$$

If $|u|$ is much less than 1, each successive term in Eq. (13.28) is much smaller than the one it follows, and we can safely approximate $(1+u)^n$ by just the first two terms. In Eq. (13.27), u is replaced by x/R_0 and n equals -13 or -7, so

$$\frac{1}{(1+x/R_0)^{13}} = (1+x/R_0)^{-13} \approx 1 + (-13)\frac{x}{R_0}$$

$$\frac{1}{(1+x/R_0)^{7}} = (1+x/R_0)^{-7} \approx 1 + (-7)\frac{x}{R_0}$$

$$F_r \approx 12\frac{U_0}{R_0}\left[\left(1 + (-13)\frac{x}{R_0}\right) - \left(1 + (-7)\frac{x}{R_0}\right)\right] = -\left(\frac{72U_0}{R_0^2}\right)x \quad (13.29)$$

This is just Hooke's law, with force constant $k = 72U_0/R_0^2$. (Note that k has the correct units, J/m^2 or N/m.) So oscillations of molecules bound by the van der Waals interaction can be simple harmonic motion, provided that the amplitude is small in comparison to R_0 so that the approximation $|x/R_0| \ll 1$ used in the derivation of Eq. (13.29) is valid.

You can also show that the potential energy U in Eq. (13.25) can be written as $U \approx \frac{1}{2}kx^2 + C$, where $C = -U_0$ and k is again equal to $72U_0/R_0^2$. Adding a constant to the potential energy has no effect on the physics, so the system of two atoms is fundamentally no different from a mass attached to a horizontal spring for which $U = \frac{1}{2}kx^2$. The proof is left to you (see Exercise 13.39).

Example 13.7 Molecular vibration

Two argon atoms can form a weakly bound molecule, Ar_2, held together by a van der Waals interaction with $U_0 = 1.68 \times 10^{-21}$ J and $R_0 = 3.82 \times 10^{-10}$ m. Find the frequency for small oscillations of one of the atoms about its equilibrium position.

SOLUTION

IDENTIFY: This is just the situation shown in Fig. 13.20.

Continued

SET UP: Because the oscillations are small, we can use Eq. (13.11) to obtain the frequency of simple harmonic motion. The force constant is given by Eq. (13.29).

EXECUTE: The force constant is

$$k = \frac{72U_0}{R_0^2} = \frac{72(1.68 \times 10^{-21}\ \text{J})}{(3.82 \times 10^{-10}\ \text{m})^2} = 0.829\ \text{J/m}^2 = 0.829\ \text{N/m}$$

This is comparable to the force constant of a loose, floppy toy spring like a Slinky™.

From the periodic table of the elements (see Appendix D), the average atomic mass of argon is

$$(39.948\ \text{u})(1.66 \times 10^{-27}\ \text{kg/1 u}) = 6.63 \times 10^{-26}\ \text{kg.}$$

If one of the argon atoms is fixed and the other atom oscillates, the frequency of oscillation is

$$f = \frac{1}{2\pi}\sqrt{\frac{k}{m}} = \frac{1}{2\pi}\sqrt{\frac{0.829\ \text{N/m}}{6.63 \times 10^{-26}\ \text{kg}}} = 5.63 \times 10^{11}\ \text{Hz}$$

The oscillating mass is very small, so even a floppy spring causes very rapid oscillations.

EVALUATE: Our answer for f isn't quite right. If there is no net external force acting on the molecule, the center of mass of the molecule (located halfway between the two atoms) doesn't accelerate. To ensure this, both atoms must oscillate with the same amplitude in opposite directions. It turns out that we can account for this by replacing m with $m/2$ in the expression for f. (See Problem 13.86.) This makes f larger by a factor of $\sqrt{2}$, so $f = \sqrt{2}(5.63 \times 10^{11}\ \text{Hz}) = 7.96 \times 10^{11}$ Hz. An additional complication is that on the atomic scale we must use quantum mechanics, not Newtonian mechanics, to describe motion; happily, the frequency has the same value in quantum mechanics.

Test Your Understanding of Section 13.4 A block attached to a hanging ideal spring oscillates up and down with a period of 10 s on earth. If you take the block and spring to Mars, where the acceleration due to gravity is only about 40% as large as on earth, what will be the new period of oscillation? (i) 10 s; (ii) more than 10 s; (iii) less than 10 s.

13.21 The dynamics of a simple pendulum.

(a) A real pendulum

(b) An idealized simple pendulum

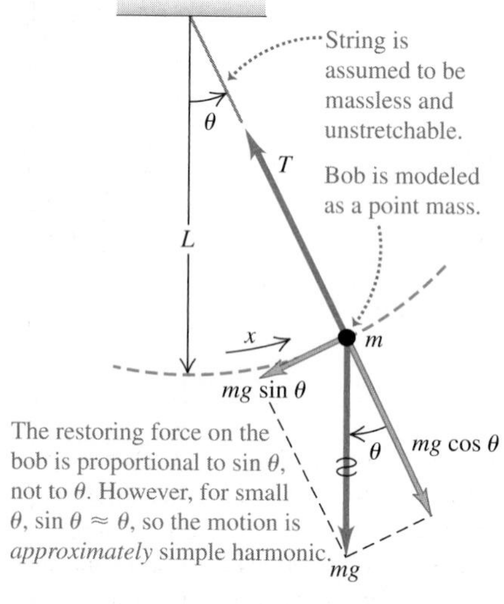

String is assumed to be massless and unstretchable.
Bob is modeled as a point mass.
θ
T
L
x
m
mg sin θ
θ
mg cos θ
mg
The restoring force on the bob is proportional to sin θ, not to θ. However, for small θ, sin θ ≈ θ, so the motion is approximately simple harmonic.

13.5 The Simple Pendulum

A **simple pendulum** is an idealized model consisting of a point mass suspended by a massless, unstretchable string. When the point mass is pulled to one side of its straight-down equilibrium position and released, it oscillates about the equilibrium position. Familiar situations such as a wrecking ball on a crane's cable or a person on a swing (Fig. 13.21a) can be modeled as simple pendulums.

The path of the point mass (sometimes called a pendulum bob) is not a straight line but the arc of a circle with radius L equal to the length of the string (Fig. 13.21b). We use as our coordinate the distance x measured along the arc. If the motion is simple harmonic, the restoring force must be directly proportional to x or (because $x = L\theta$) to θ. Is it?

In Fig. 13.21b we represent the forces on the mass in terms of tangential and radial components. The restoring force F_θ is the tangential component of the net force:

$$F_\theta = -mg\sin\theta \qquad (13.30)$$

The restoring force is provided by gravity; the tension T merely acts to make the point mass move in an arc. The restoring force is proportional *not* to θ but to $\sin\theta$, so the motion is *not* simple harmonic. However, if the angle θ is *small*, $\sin\theta$ is very nearly equal to θ in radians (Fig. 13.22). For example, when $\theta = 0.1$ rad (about 6°), $\sin\theta = 0.0998$, a difference of only 0.2%. With this approximation, Eq. (13.30) becomes

$$F_\theta = -mg\theta = -mg\frac{x}{L} \quad \text{or}$$

$$F_\theta = -\frac{mg}{L}x \qquad (13.31)$$

The restoring force is then proportional to the coordinate for small displacements, and the force constant is $k = mg/L$. From Eq. (13.10) the angular frequency ω of a simple pendulum with small amplitude is

$$\omega = \sqrt{\frac{k}{m}} = \sqrt{\frac{mg/L}{m}} = \sqrt{\frac{g}{L}} \quad \text{(simple pendulum, small amplitude)} \tag{13.32}$$

The corresponding frequency and period relationships are

$$f = \frac{\omega}{2\pi} = \frac{1}{2\pi}\sqrt{\frac{g}{L}} \quad \text{(simple pendulum, small amplitude)} \tag{13.33}$$

$$T = \frac{2\pi}{\omega} = \frac{1}{f} = 2\pi\sqrt{\frac{L}{g}} \quad \text{(simple pendulum, small amplitude)} \tag{13.34}$$

13.22 For small angular displacements θ, the restoring force $F_\theta = -mg\sin\theta$ on a simple pendulum is approximately equal to $-mg\theta$; that is, it is approximately proportional to the displacement θ. Hence for small angles the oscillations are simple harmonic.

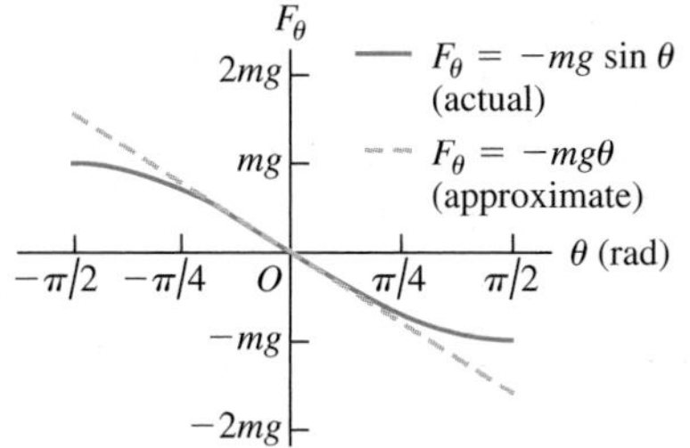

? Note that these expressions do not involve the *mass* of the particle. This is because the restoring force, a component of the particle's weight, is proportional to m. Thus the mass appears on *both* sides of $\Sigma\vec{F} = m\vec{a}$ and cancels out. (This is the same physics that explains why bodies of different masses fall with the same acceleration in a vacuum.) For small oscillations, the period of a pendulum for a given value of g is determined entirely by its length.

ActivPhysics ONLINE
9.10 Pendulum Frequency
9.11 Risky Pendulum Walk
9.12 Physical Pendulum

The dependence on L and g in Eqs. (13.32) through (13.34) is just what we should expect. A long pendulum has a longer period than a shorter one. Increasing g increases the restoring force, causing the frequency to increase and the period to decrease.

We emphasize again that the motion of a pendulum is only *approximately* simple harmonic. When the amplitude is not small, the departures from simple harmonic motion can be substantial. But how small is "small"? The period can be expressed by an infinite series; when the maximum angular displacement is Θ, the period T is given by

$$T = 2\pi\sqrt{\frac{L}{g}}\left(1 + \frac{1^2}{2^2}\sin^2\frac{\Theta}{2} + \frac{1^2\cdot 3^2}{2^2\cdot 4^2}\sin^4\frac{\Theta}{2} + \cdots\right) \tag{13.35}$$

We can compute the period to any desired degree of precision by taking enough terms in the series. We invite you to check that when $\Theta = 15°$ (on either side of the central position), the true period is longer than that given by the approximate Eq. (13.34) by less than 0.5%.

The usefulness of the pendulum as a timekeeper depends on the period being *very nearly* independent of amplitude, provided that the amplitude is small. Thus, as a pendulum clock runs down and the amplitude of the swings decreases a little, the clock still keeps very nearly correct time.

Example 13.8 A simple pendulum

Find the period and frequency of a simple pendulum 1.000 m long at a location where $g = 9.800\ \text{m/s}^2$.

SOLUTION

IDENTIFY: Since this is a simple pendulum, we can use the ideas of this section.

SET UP: We use Eq. (13.34) to determine the period T of the pendulum from its length, and Eq. (13.1) to find the frequency f from T.

EXECUTE: From Eqs. (13.34) and (13.1),

$$T = 2\pi\sqrt{\frac{L}{g}} = 2\pi\sqrt{\frac{1.000\ \text{m}}{9.800\ \text{m/s}^2}} = 2.007\ \text{s}$$

$$f = \frac{1}{T} = \frac{1}{2.007\text{s}} = 0.4983\ \text{Hz}$$

EVALUATE: The period is almost exactly 2 s. In fact, when the metric system was first established, the second was defined as half the period of a 1-meter pendulum. This wasn't a very good standard for time, however, because the value of g varies from place to place. We discussed more modern time standards in Section 1.3.

Test Your Understanding of Section 13.5 When a body oscillating on a horizontal spring passes through its equilibrium position, its acceleration is zero (see Fig. 13.2b). When the bob of an oscillating simple pendulum passes through its equilibrium position, is its acceleration zero?

13.23 Dynamics of a physical pendulum.

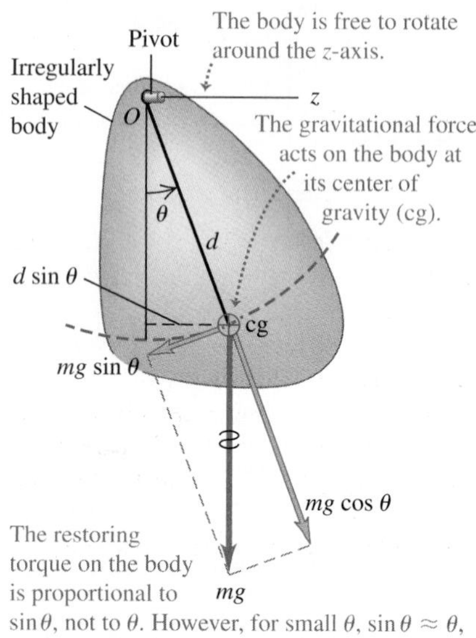
Pivot
The body is free to rotate around the z-axis.
Irregularly shaped body
O
z
The gravitational force acts on the body at its center of gravity (cg).
θ
d
d sin θ
cg
mg sin θ
mg
mg cos θ

The restoring torque on the body is proportional to $mg \sin\theta$, not to θ. However, for small θ, $\sin\theta \approx \theta$, so the motion is *approximately* simple harmonic.

13.6 The Physical Pendulum

A **physical pendulum** is any *real* pendulum that uses an extended body, as contrasted to the idealized model of the *simple* pendulum with all the mass concentrated at a single point. For small oscillations, analyzing the motion of a real, physical pendulum is almost as easy as for a simple pendulum. Figure 13.23 shows a body of irregular shape pivoted so that it can turn without friction about an axis through point O. In the equilibrium position the center of gravity is directly below the pivot; in the position shown in the figure, the body is displaced from equilibrium by an angle θ, which we use as a coordinate for the system. The distance from O to the center of gravity is d, the moment of inertia of the body about the axis of rotation through O is I, and the total mass is m. When the body is displaced as shown, the weight mg causes a restoring torque

$$\tau_z = -(mg)(d\sin\theta) \tag{13.36}$$

The negative sign shows that the restoring torque is clockwise when the displacement is counterclockwise, and vice versa.

When the body is released, it oscillates about its equilibrium position. The motion is not simple harmonic because the torque τ_z is proportional to $\sin\theta$ rather than to θ itself. However, if θ is small, we can approximate $\sin\theta$ by θ in radians, just as we did in analyzing the simple pendulum. Then the motion is *approximately* simple harmonic. With this approximation,

$$\tau_z = -(mgd)\theta$$

The equation of motion is $\sum\tau_z = I\alpha_z$, so

$$-(mgd)\theta = I\alpha_z = I\frac{d^2\theta}{dt^2}$$

$$\frac{d^2\theta}{dt^2} = -\frac{mgd}{I}\theta \tag{13.37}$$

Comparing this with Eq. (13.4), we see that the role of (k/m) for the spring-mass system is played here by the quantity (mgd/I). Thus the angular frequency is

$$\omega = \sqrt{\frac{mgd}{I}} \quad \text{(physical pendulum, small amplitude)} \tag{13.38}$$

The frequency f is $1/2\pi$ times this, and the period T is

$$T = 2\pi\sqrt{\frac{I}{mgd}} \quad \text{(physical pendulum, small amplitude)} \tag{13.39}$$

Equation (13.39) is the basis of a common method for experimentally determining the moment of inertia of a body with a complicated shape. First locate the center of gravity of the body by balancing. Then suspend the body so that it is free to oscillate about an axis, and measure the period T of small-amplitude oscillations. Finally, use Eq. (13.39) to calculate the moment of inertia I of the body about this axis from T, the body's mass m, and the distance d from the axis to the center of gravity (see Exercise 13.49). Biomechanics researchers use this method to find the moments of inertia of an animal's limbs. This information is important for analyzing how an animal walks, as we'll see in the second of the two following examples.

Example 13.9 Physical pendulum versus simple pendulum

Suppose the body in Fig. 13.23 is a uniform rod with length L, pivoted at one end. Find the period of its motion.

SOLUTION

IDENTIFY: Our target variable is the oscillation period of a rod, which acts as a physical pendulum. We need to know the rod's moment of inertia to do this.

SET UP: We use Table 9.2 (Section 9.4) to find the moment of inertia of the rod, and then substitute this value into Eq. (13.39) to determine the period of oscillation.

EXECUTE: From Table 9.2, the moment of inertia of a uniform rod about an axis through one end is $I = \frac{1}{3}ML^2$. The distance from the pivot to the center of gravity is $d = L/2$. From Eq. (13.39),

$$T = 2\pi\sqrt{\frac{\frac{1}{3}ML^2}{MgL/2}} = 2\pi\sqrt{\frac{2L}{3g}}$$

EVALUATE: If the rod is a meter stick $(L = 1.00\text{ m})$ and $g = 9.80\text{ m/s}^2$, then

$$T = 2\pi\sqrt{\frac{2(1.00\text{ m})}{3(9.80\text{ m/s}^2)}} = 1.64\text{ s}$$

The period is smaller by a factor of $\sqrt{2/3} = 0.816$ than the period of a simple pendulum with the same length, calculated in Example 13.8. The cg of the rod is half as far from the pivot as the cg of the simple pendulum, which means the torque is half as great. By itself that would give the rod a period $\sqrt{2}$ times greater than the simple pendulum. But the rod's moment of inertia around one end, $I = \frac{1}{3}ML^2$, is one-third that of the simple pendulum, which by itself would make the rod's period $\sqrt{1/3}$ that of the simple pendulum. The moment of inertia factor is more important in this case, which is why the rod has a shorter period than the simple pendulum.

Example 13.10 *Tyrannosaurus rex* and the physical pendulum

All walking animals, including humans, have a natural walking pace—that is, a number of steps per minute that is more comfortable than a faster or slower pace. Suppose this natural pace corresponds to the oscillation of the leg as a physical pendulum. (a) How does the natural walking pace depend on the length L of the leg, measured from hip to foot? Treat the leg as a uniform rod pivoted at the hip joint. (b) Fossil evidence shows that *Tyrannosaurus rex,* a two-legged dinosaur that lived about 65 million years ago at the end of the Cretaceous period, had a leg length $L = 3.1$ m and a stride length $S = 4.0$ m (the distance from one footprint to the next print of the same foot; Fig. 13.24). Estimate the walking speed of *T. rex.*

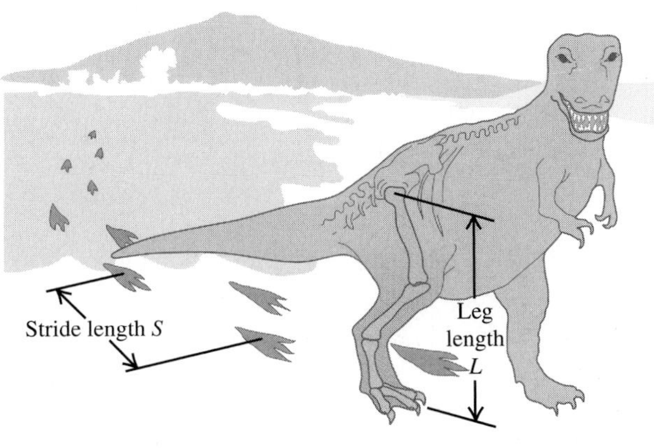

13.24 The walking speed of *Tyrannosaurus rex* can be estimated from leg length L and stride length S.

SOLUTION

IDENTIFY: Our target variables are (a) the relationship between the walking pace and the leg length and (b) the walking speed of *T. rex.*

SET UP: We treat the leg as a physical pendulum, with a period of oscillation as found in Example 13.9. The shorter the period, the faster the walking pace. We can find the walking speed from the period and the stride length.

EXECUTE: (a) From Example 13.9 the period of oscillation of the leg is $T = 2\pi\sqrt{2L/3g}$, which is proportional to $\sqrt{L}$. Each period (a complete back-and-forth swing of the leg) corresponds to *two* steps, so the walking pace in steps per unit time is just twice the oscillation frequency $f = 1/T$. Hence the walking pace is proportional to $1/\sqrt{L}$. Animals with short legs (small values of L), such as mice or Chihuahuas, have rapid walking paces; humans, giraffes, and other animals with long legs (large values of L) walk at slower paces.

(b) According to our model for the natural walking pace, the elapsed time for one stride of a walking *Tyrannosaurus rex* is

$$T = 2\pi\sqrt{\frac{2L}{3g}} = 2\pi\sqrt{\frac{2(3.1\text{ m})}{3(9.8\text{ m/s}^2)}} = 2.9\text{ s}$$

The distance moved during this time is the stride length S, so the walking speed is

$$v = \frac{S}{T} = \frac{4.0\text{ m}}{2.9\text{ s}} = 1.4\text{ m/s} = 5.0\text{ km/h} = 3.1\text{ mi/h}$$

This is about the same as a typical human walking speed!

Continued

EVALUATE: Our estimate must be somewhat in error because a uniform rod isn't a very good model for a leg. The legs of many animals, including *T. rex* as well as humans, are tapered; there is a lot more mass between the knee and the hip than between the knee and the foot. Thus the center of mass is less than $L/2$ from the hip; a reasonable guess would be about $L/4$. The moment of inertia is therefore *considerably* less than $ML^2/3$, probably somewhere around $ML^2/15$. Try these numbers out with the analysis of Example 13.9; you'll get a shorter oscillation period and an even faster walking speed for *T. rex*.

Test Your Understanding of Section 13.6 The center of gravity of a simple pendulum of mass m and length L is located at the position of the pendulum bob, a distance L from the pivot point. The center of gravity of a uniform rod of the same mass m and length $2L$ pivoted at one end is also a distance L from the pivot point. How does the period of this uniform rod compare to the period of the simple pendulum? (i) The rod has a longer period; (ii) the rod has a shorter period; (iii) the rod has the same period.

13.7 Damped Oscillations

The idealized oscillating systems we have discussed so far are frictionless. There are no nonconservative forces, the total mechanical energy is constant, and a system set into motion continues oscillating forever with no decrease in amplitude.

Real-world systems always have some dissipative forces, however, and oscillations die out with time unless we replace the dissipated mechanical energy (Fig. 13.25). A mechanical pendulum clock continues to run because potential energy stored in the spring or a hanging weight system replaces the mechanical energy lost due to friction in the pivot and the gears. But eventually the spring runs down or the weights reach the bottom of their travel. Then no more energy is available, and the pendulum swings decrease in amplitude and stop.

13.25 A swinging bell left to itself will eventually stop oscillating due to damping forces (air resistance and friction at the point of suspension).

The decrease in amplitude caused by dissipative forces is called **damping,** and the corresponding motion is called **damped oscillation.** The simplest case to analyze in detail is a simple harmonic oscillator with a frictional damping force that is directly proportional to the *velocity* of the oscillating body. This behavior occurs in friction involving viscous fluid flow, such as in shock absorbers or sliding between oil-lubricated surfaces. We then have an additional force on the body due to friction, $F_x = -bv_x$, where $v_x = dx/dt$ is the velocity and b is a constant that describes the strength of the damping force. The negative sign shows that the force is always opposite in direction to the velocity. The *net* force on the body is then

$$\sum F_x = -kx - bv_x \tag{13.40}$$

and Newton's second law for the system is

$$-kx - bv_x = ma_x \quad \text{or} \quad -kx - b\frac{dx}{dt} = m\frac{d^2x}{dt^2} \tag{13.41}$$

Equation (13.41) is a differential equation for x; it would be the same as Eq. (13.4), the equation for the acceleration in SHM, except for the added term $-bdx/dt$. Solving this equation is a straightforward problem in differential equations, but we won't go into the details here. If the damping force is relatively small, the motion is described by

$$x = Ae^{-(b/2m)t}\cos(\omega' t + \phi) \quad \text{(oscillator with little damping)} \tag{13.42}$$

The angular frequency of oscillation ω' is given by

$$\omega' = \sqrt{\frac{k}{m} - \frac{b^2}{4m^2}} \quad \text{(oscillator with little damping)} \tag{13.43}$$

You can verify that Eq. (13.42) is a solution of Eq. (13.41) by calculating the first and second derivatives of x, substituting them into Eq. (13.41), and checking whether the left and right sides are equal. This is a straightforward but slightly tedious procedure.

The motion described by Eq. (13.42) differs from the undamped case in two ways. First, the amplitude $Ae^{-(b/2m)t}$ is not constant but decreases with time because of the decreasing exponential factor $e^{-(b/2m)t}$. Figure 13.26 is a graph of Eq. (13.42) for the case $\phi = 0$; it shows that the larger the value of b, the more quickly the amplitude decreases.

Second, the angular frequency ω', given by Eq. (13.43), is no longer equal to $\omega = \sqrt{k/m}$ but is somewhat smaller. It becomes zero when b becomes so large that

$$\frac{k}{m} - \frac{b^2}{4m^2} = 0 \quad \text{or} \quad b = 2\sqrt{km} \qquad (13.44)$$

When Eq. (13.44) is satisfied, the condition is called **critical damping.** The system no longer oscillates but returns to its equilibrium position without oscillation when it is displaced and released.

If b is greater than $2\sqrt{km}$, the condition is called **overdamping.** Again there is no oscillation, but the system returns to equilibrium more slowly than with critical damping. For the overdamped case the solutions of Eq. (13.41) have the form

$$x = C_1 e^{-a_1 t} + C_2 e^{-a_2 t}$$

where C_1 and C_2 are constants that depend on the initial conditions and a_1 and a_2 are constants determined by m, k, and b.

When b is less than the critical value, as in Eq. (13.42), the condition is called **underdamping.** The system oscillates with steadily decreasing amplitude.

In a vibrating tuning fork or guitar string, it is usually desirable to have as little damping as possible. By contrast, damping plays a beneficial role in the oscillations of an automobile's suspension system. The shock absorbers provide a velocity-dependent damping force so that when the car goes over a bump, it doesn't continue bouncing forever (Fig. 13.27). For optimal passenger comfort, the system should be critically damped or slightly underdamped. Too much damping would be counterproductive; if the suspension is overdamped and the car hits a second bump just after the first one, the springs in the suspension will still be compressed somewhat from the first bump and will not be able to fully absorb the impact.

Energy in Damped Oscillations

In damped oscillations the damping force is nonconservative; the mechanical energy of the system is not constant but decreases continuously, approaching zero after a long time. To derive an expression for the rate of change of energy, we first write an expression for the total mechanical energy E at any instant:

$$E = \frac{1}{2}mv_x^2 + \frac{1}{2}kx^2$$

To find the rate of change of this quantity, we take its time derivative:

$$\frac{dE}{dt} = mv_x\frac{dv_x}{dt} + kx\frac{dx}{dt}$$

But $dv_x/dt = a_x$ and $dx/dt = v_x$, so

$$\frac{dE}{dt} = v_x(ma_x + kx)$$

From Eq. (13.41), $ma_x + kx = -bdx/dt = -bv_x$, so

$$\frac{dE}{dt} = v_x(-bv_x) = -bv_x^2 \quad \text{(damped oscillations)} \qquad (13.45)$$

13.26 Graph of displacement versus time for an oscillator with little damping [see Eq. (13.42)] and with phase angle $\phi = 0$. The curves are for two values of the damping constant b.

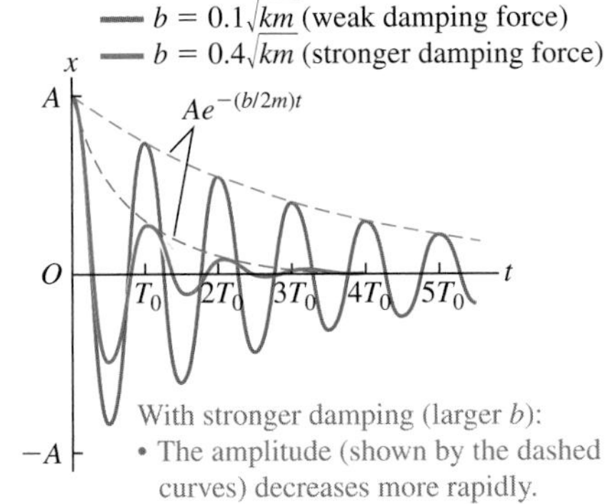

b = 0.1√km (weak damping force)
b = 0.4√km (stronger damping force)
x
A
Ae^−(b/2m)t
O
T0 2T0 3T0 4T0 5T0
t
−A
With stronger damping (larger b):
• The amplitude (shown by the dashed curves) decreases more rapidly.
• The period T increases (T0 = period with zero damping).

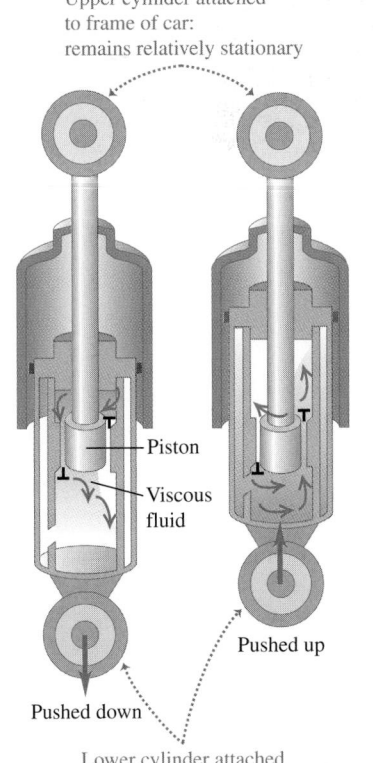

13.27 An automobile shock absorber. The viscous fluid causes a damping force that depends on the relative velocity of the two ends of the unit.

Upper cylinder attached to frame of car: remains relatively stationary

Piston

Viscous fluid

Pushed up

Pushed down

Lower cylinder attached to axle and wheel: moves up and down

The right side of Eq. (13.45) is **negative** whenever the oscillating body is in motion, whether the x-velocity v_x is positive or negative. This shows that as the body moves, the energy decreases, though not at a uniform rate. The term $-bv_x^2 = (-bv_x)v_x$ (force times velocity) is the rate at which the damping force does (negative) work on the system (that is, the damping *power*). This equals the rate of change of the total mechanical energy of the system.

Similar behavior occurs in electric circuits containing inductance, capacitance, and resistance. There is a natural frequency of oscillation, and the resistance plays the role of the damping constant b. We will study these circuits in detail in Chapters 30 and 31.

Test Your Understanding of Section 13.7 An airplane is flying in a straight line at a constant altitude. If a wind gust strikes and raises the nose of the airplane, the nose will bob up and down until the airplane eventually returns to its original attitude. Are these oscillations (i) undamped, (ii) underdamped, (iii) critically damped, or (iv) overdamped?

13.8 Forced Oscillations and Resonance

A damped oscillator left to itself will eventually stop moving altogether. But we can maintain a constant-amplitude oscillation by applying a force that varies with time in a periodic or cyclic way, with a definite period and frequency. As an example, consider your cousin Throckmorton on a playground swing. You can keep him swinging with constant amplitude by giving him a little push once each cycle. We call this additional force a **driving force.**

Damped Oscillation with a Periodic Driving Force

If we apply a periodically varying driving force with angular frequency ω_d to a damped harmonic oscillator, the motion that results is called a **forced oscillation** or a *driven oscillation.* It is different from the motion that occurs when the system is simply displaced from equilibrium and then left alone, in which case the system oscillates with a **natural angular frequency** ω' determined by m, k, and b, as in Eq. (13.43). In a forced oscillation, however, the angular frequency with which the mass oscillates is equal to the driving angular frequency ω_d. This does *not* have to be equal to the angular frequency ω' with which the system would oscillate without a driving force. If you grab the ropes of Throckmorton's swing, you can force the swing to oscillate with any frequency you like.

Suppose we force the oscillator to vibrate with an angular frequency ω_d that is nearly *equal* to the angular frequency ω' it would have with no driving force. What happens? The oscillator is naturally disposed to oscillate at $\omega = \omega'$, so we expect the amplitude of the resulting oscillation to be larger than when the two frequencies are very different. Detailed analysis and experiment shows that this is just what happens. The easiest case to analyze is a *sinusoidally* varying force—say, $F(t) = F_{max} \cos \omega_d t$. If we vary the frequency ω_d of the driving force, the amplitude of the resulting forced oscillation varies in an interesting way (Fig. 13.28). When there is very little damping (small b), the amplitude goes through a sharp peak as the driving angular frequency ω_d nears the natural oscillation angular frequency ω'. When the damping is increased (larger b), the peak becomes broader and smaller in height and shifts toward lower frequencies.

We could work out an expression that shows how the amplitude A of the forced oscillation depends on the frequency of a sinusoidal driving force, with

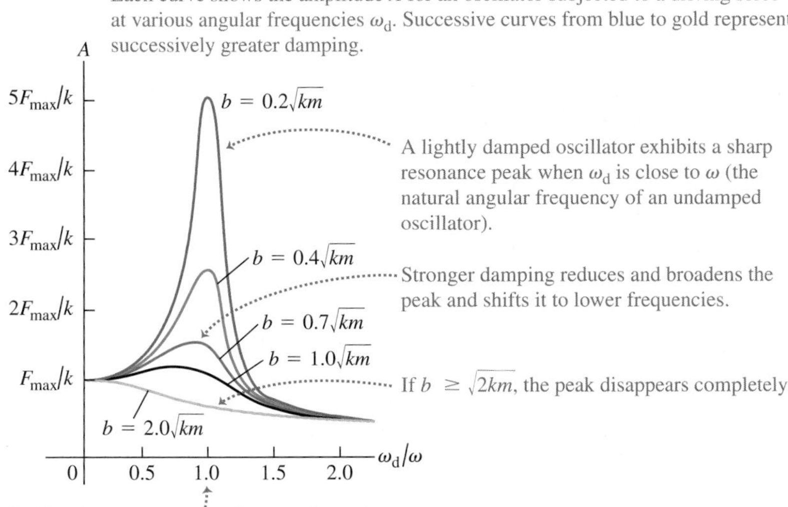

Each curve shows the amplitude A for an oscillator subjected to a driving force at various angular frequencies ω_d. Successive curves from blue to gold represent successively greater damping.
A
$5F_{max}/k$
$4F_{max}/k$
$3F_{max}/k$
$2F_{max}/k$
F_{max}/k
$b = 0.2\sqrt{km}$
A lightly damped oscillator exhibits a sharp resonance peak when ω_d is close to ω (the natural angular frequency of an undamped oscillator).
$b = 0.4\sqrt{km}$
Stronger damping reduces and broadens the peak and shifts it to lower frequencies.
$b = 0.7\sqrt{km}$
$b = 1.0\sqrt{km}$
If $b \geq \sqrt{2km}$, the peak disappears completely.
$b = 2.0\sqrt{km}$
0
0.5
1.0
1.5
2.0
ω_d/ω
Driving frequency ω_d equals natural angular frequency ω of an undamped oscillator.

13.28 Graph of the amplitude A of forced oscillation as a function of the angular frequency ω_d of the driving force. The horizontal axis shows the ratio of ω_d to the angular frequency $\omega = \sqrt{k/m}$ of an undamped oscillator. Each curve has a different value of the damping constant b.

maximum value F_{max}. That would involve more differential equations than we're ready for, but here is the result:

$$A = \frac{F_{max}}{\sqrt{(k - m\omega_d^2)^2 + b^2\omega_d^2}} \quad \text{(amplitude of a driven oscillator)} \quad (13.46)$$

When $k - m\omega_d^2 = 0$, the first term under the radical is zero, so A has a maximum near $\omega_d = \sqrt{k/m}$. The height of the curve at this point is proportional to $1/b$; the less damping, the higher the peak. At the low-frequency extreme, when $\omega_d = 0$, we get $A = F_{max}/k$. This corresponds to a *constant* force F_{max} and a constant displacement $A = F_{max}/k$ from equilibrium, as we might expect.

Resonance and Its Consequences

The fact that there is an amplitude peak at driving frequencies close to the natural frequency of the system is called **resonance.** Physics is full of examples of resonance; building up the oscillations of a child on a swing by pushing with a frequency equal to the swing's natural frequency is one. A vibrating rattle in a car that occurs only at a certain engine speed or wheel-rotation speed is an all-too-familiar example. Inexpensive loudspeakers often have an annoying boom or buzz when a musical note happens to coincide with the resonant frequency of the speaker cone or the speaker housing. In Chapter 16 we will study other examples of resonance that involve sound. Resonance also occurs in electric circuits, as we will see in Chapter 31; a tuned circuit in a radio or television receiver responds strongly to waves having frequencies near its resonant frequency, and this fact is used to select a particular station and reject the others.

Resonance in mechanical systems can be destructive. A company of soldiers once destroyed a bridge by marching across it in step; the frequency of their steps was close to a natural vibration frequency of the bridge, and the resulting oscillation had large enough amplitude to tear the bridge apart. Ever since, marching soldiers have been ordered to break step before crossing a bridge. Some years ago, vibrations of the engines of a particular airplane had just the right frequency to resonate with the natural frequencies of its wings. Large oscillations built up, and occasionally the wings fell off.

Nearly everyone has seen the film of the collapse of the Tacoma Narrows suspension bridge in 1940 (Fig. 13.29). This is usually cited as an example of resonance driven by the wind, but there's some doubt whether it should be called that.

13.29 The Tacoma Narrows Bridge collapsed four months and six days after it was opened for traffic. The main span was 2800 ft long and 39 ft wide, with 8-ft-high steel stiffening girders on both sides. The maximum amplitude of the torsional vibrations was 35°; the frequency was about 0.2 Hz.

The wind didn't have to vary *periodically* with a frequency close to a natural frequency of the bridge. The airflow past the bridge was turbulent, and vortices were formed in the air with a regular frequency that depended on the flow speed. It is conceivable that this frequency may have coincided with a natural frequency of the bridge. But the cause may well have been something more subtle called a *self-excited oscillation,* in which the aerodynamic forces caused by a *steady* wind blowing on the bridge tended to displace it farther from equilibrium at times when it was already moving away from equilibrium. It is as though we had a damping force such as the $-bv_x$ term in Eq. (13.40) but with the sign reversed. Instead of draining mechanical energy away from the system, this anti-damping force pumps energy into the system, building up the oscillations to destructive amplitudes. The approximate differential equation is Eq. (13.41) with the sign of the b term reversed, and the oscillating solution is Eq. (13.42) with a *positive* sign in the exponent. You can see that we're headed for trouble. Engineers have learned how to stabilize suspension bridges, both structurally and aerodynamically, to prevent such disasters.

Test Your Understanding of Section 13.8 When driven at a frequency near its natural frequency, an oscillator with very little damping has a much greater response than the same oscillator with more damping. When driven at a frequency that is much higher or lower than the natural frequency, which oscillator will have the greater response: (i) the one with very little damping or (ii) the one with more damping? MP

CHAPTER 13 SUMMARY

Periodic motion: Periodic motion is motion that repeats itself in a definite cycle. It occurs whenever a body has a stable equilibrium position and a restoring force that acts when it is displaced from equilibrium. Period T is the time for one cycle. Frequency f is the number of cycles per unit time. Angular frequency ω is 2π times the frequency. (See Example 13.1.)

$$f = \frac{1}{T} \qquad T = \frac{1}{f} \tag{13.1}$$

$$\omega = 2\pi f = \frac{2\pi}{T} \tag{13.2}$$

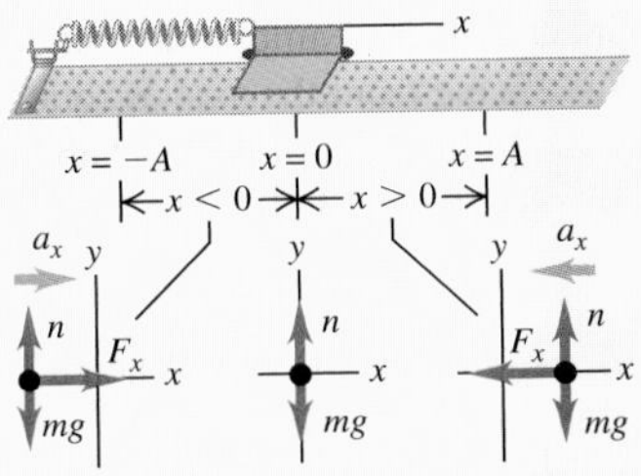

Simple harmonic motion: If the restoring force F_x in periodic motion is directly proportional to the displacement x, the motion is called simple harmonic motion (SHM). In many cases this condition is satisfied if the displacement from equilibrium is small. The angular frequency, frequency, and period in SHM do not depend on the amplitude, but only on the mass m and force constant k. The displacement, velocity, and acceleration in SHM are sinusoidal functions of time; the amplitude A and phase angle ϕ of the oscillation are determined by the initial position and velocity of the body. (See Examples 13.2, 13.3, 13.6, and 13.7.)

$$F_x = -kx \tag{13.3}$$

$$a_x = \frac{F_x}{m} = -\frac{k}{m}x \tag{13.4}$$

$$\omega = \sqrt{\frac{k}{m}} \tag{13.10}$$

$$f = \frac{\omega}{2\pi} = \frac{1}{2\pi}\sqrt{\frac{k}{m}} \tag{13.11}$$

$$T = \frac{1}{f} = 2\pi\sqrt{\frac{m}{k}} \tag{13.12}$$

$$x = A\cos(\omega t + \phi) \tag{13.13}$$

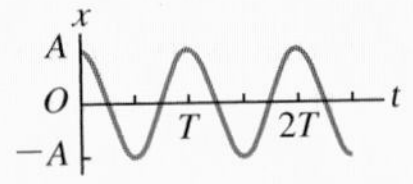

Energy in simple harmonic motion: Energy is conserved in SHM. The total energy can be expressed in terms of the force constant k and amplitude A. (See Examples 13.4 and 13.5.)

$$E = \frac{1}{2}mv_x^2 + \frac{1}{2}kx^2 = \frac{1}{2}kA^2 = \text{constant} \tag{13.21}$$

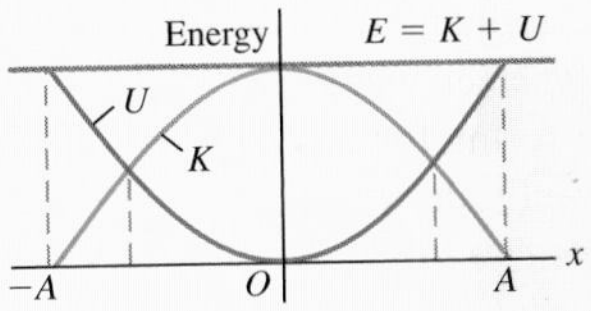

Angular simple harmonic motion: In angular SHM, the frequency and angular frequency are related to the moment of inertia I and the torsion constant κ.

$$\omega = \sqrt{\frac{\kappa}{I}} \quad \text{and} \quad f = \frac{1}{2\pi}\sqrt{\frac{\kappa}{I}} \tag{13.24}$$

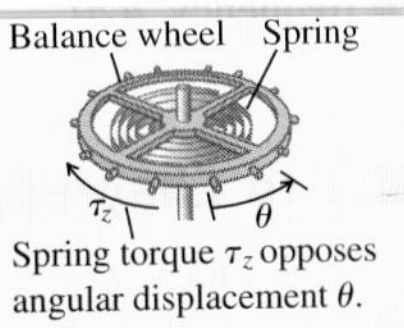

Simple pendulum: A simple pendulum consists of a point mass m at the end of a massless string of length L. Its motion is approximately simple harmonic for sufficiently small amplitude; the angular frequency, frequency, and period then depend only on g and L, not on the mass or amplitude. (See Example 13.8.)

$$\omega = \sqrt{\frac{g}{L}} \tag{13.32}$$

$$f = \frac{\omega}{2\pi} = \frac{1}{2\pi}\sqrt{\frac{g}{L}} \tag{13.33}$$

$$T = \frac{2\pi}{\omega} = \frac{1}{f} = 2\pi\sqrt{\frac{L}{g}} \tag{13.34}$$

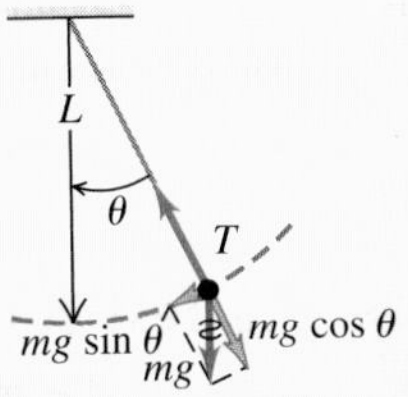

horizo
taken
that in
Mars t
13.5 A
the equ
taneou
derivat
changi
Hence
lar to t
To cau
string i
greater
on the
circula
13.6 A
by Eq.
pivot t

PRC

Discu

Q13.1.
of a spr
distance
period?
cuss ho
Q13.2.
are, at le
each dif
Q13.3. I
SHM? V
Q13.4.
spring a
has reac
pebble i
Will the
or remai
each ans
mum kir
Q13.5. I
of each
SHM us
mass anc
Q13.6. T
the sprin
of the m
Q13.7. T
ideal spr
would th
spring w
Explain.
Q13.8. Y
to sleep.
small roc
your dig
necklace.
earth or h

14.4 Fluid Flow

We are now ready to consider *motion* of a fluid. Fluid flow can be extremely complex, as shown by the currents in river rapids or the swirling flames of a campfire. But some situations can be represented by relatively simple idealized models. An **ideal fluid** is a fluid that is *incompressible* (that is, its density cannot change) and has no internal friction (called **viscosity**). Liquids are approximately incompressible in most situations, and we may also treat a gas as incompressible if the pressure differences from one region to another are not too great. Internal friction in a fluid causes shear stresses when two adjacent layers of fluid move relative to each other, as when fluid flows inside a tube or around an obstacle. In some cases we can neglect these shear forces in comparison with forces arising from gravitation and pressure differences.

The path of an individual particle in a moving fluid is called a **flow line.** If the overall flow pattern does not change with time, the flow is called **steady flow.** In steady flow, every element passing through a given point follows the same flow line. In this case the "map" of the fluid velocities at various points in space remains constant, although the velocity of a particular particle may change in both magnitude and direction during its motion. A **streamline** is a curve whose tangent at any point is in the direction of the fluid velocity at that point. When the flow pattern changes with time, the streamlines do not coincide with the flow lines. We will consider only steady-flow situations, for which flow lines and streamlines are identical.

14.19 A flow tube bounded by flow lines. In steady flow, fluid cannot cross the walls of a flow tube.

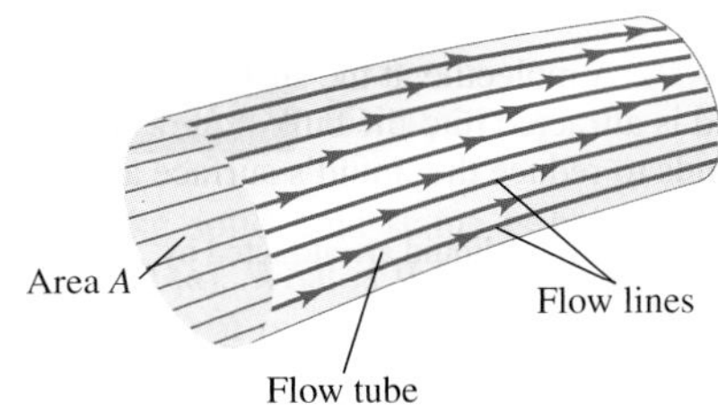

The flow lines passing through the edge of an imaginary element of area, such as the area A in Fig. 14.19, form a tube called a **flow tube.** From the definition of a flow line, in steady flow no fluid can cross the side walls of a flow tube; the fluids in different flow tubes cannot mix.

Figure 14.20 shows patterns of fluid flow from left to right around a number of obstacles. The photographs were made by injecting dye into water flowing between two closely spaced glass plates. These patterns are typical of **laminar flow,** in which adjacent layers of fluid slide smoothly past each other and the flow is steady. (A *lamina* is a thin sheet.) At sufficiently high flow rates, or when boundary surfaces cause abrupt changes in velocity, the flow can become irregular and chaotic. This is called **turbulent flow** (Fig. 14.21). In turbulent flow there is no steady-state pattern; the flow pattern changes continuously.

The Continuity Equation

The mass of a moving fluid doesn't change as it flows. This leads to an important quantitative relationship called the **continuity equation.** Consider a portion of a flow tube between two stationary cross sections with areas A_1 and A_2

14.20 Laminar flow around obstacles of different shapes.

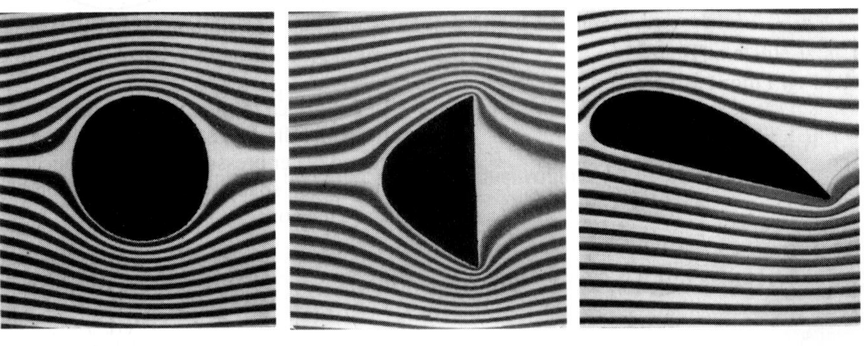

14.21 The flow of smoke rising from these incense sticks is laminar up to a certain point, and then becomes turbulent.

(b) The density of air is about 1.2 kg/m³, so the buoyant force of air on the statue is

$$B = \rho_{\text{air}} V g = (1.2\ \text{kg/m}^3)(7.77 \times 10^{-4}\ \text{m}^3)(9.80\ \text{m/s}^2)$$
$$= 9.1 \times 10^{-3}\ \text{N}$$

This is only 62 parts per million of the statue's actual weight. This effect is not within the precision of our data, and we ignore it. Thus the tension in the cable with the statue in air is equal to the statue's weight, 147 N.

EVALUATE: Note that the buoyant force is proportional to the density of the *fluid,* not the density of the statue. The denser the fluid, the greater the buoyant force and the smaller the cable tension. If the fluid had the same density as the statue, the buoyant force would be equal to the statue's weight and the tension would be zero (the cable would go slack). If the fluid were denser than the statue, the tension would be *negative:* the buoyant force would be greater than the statue's weight, and a downward force would be required to keep the statue from rising upward.

Surface Tension

An object less dense than water, such as an air-filled beach ball, floats with part of its volume below the surface. Conversely, a paper clip can rest *atop* a water surface even though its density is several times that of water. This is an example of **surface tension:** The surface of the liquid behaves like a membrane under tension (Fig. 14.15). Surface tension arises because the molecules of the liquid exert attractive forces on each other. There is zero net force on a molecule inside the volume of the liquid, but a surface molecule is drawn into the volume (Fig. 14.16). Thus the liquid tends to minimize its surface area, just as a stretched membrane does.

Surface tension explains why freely falling raindrops are spherical (*not* teardrop-shaped): A sphere has a smaller surface area for its volume than any other shape. It also explains why hot, soapy water is used for washing. To wash clothing thoroughly, water must be forced through the tiny spaces between the fibers (Fig. 14.17). To do so requires increasing the surface area of the water, which is difficult to achieve because of surface tension. The job is made easier by increasing the temperature of the water and adding soap, both of which decrease the surface tension.

Surface tension is important for a millimeter-sized water drop, which has a relatively large surface area for its volume. (A sphere of radius r has surface area $4\pi r^2$ and volume $(4\pi/3)r^3$. The ratio of surface area to volume is $3/r$, which increases with decreasing radius.) For large quantities of liquid, however, the ratio of surface area to volume is relatively small, and surface tension is negligible compared to pressure forces. For the remainder of this chapter, we will consider only fluids in bulk and hence will ignore the effects of surface tension.

14.15 The surface of the water acts like a membrane under tension, allowing this water strider to literally "walk on water."

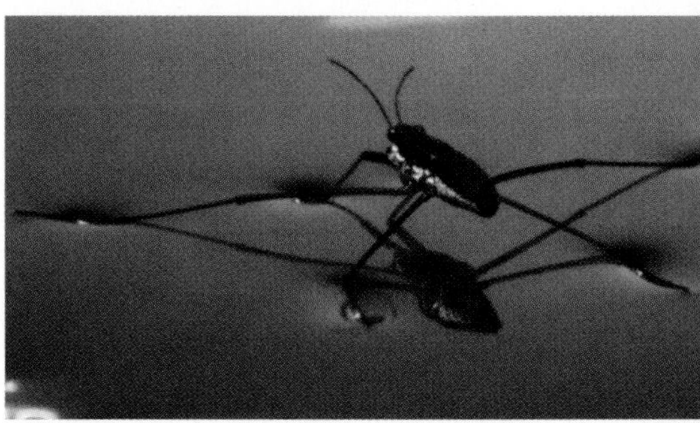

14.16 A molecule at the surface of a liquid is attracted into the bulk liquid, which tends to reduce the liquid's surface area.

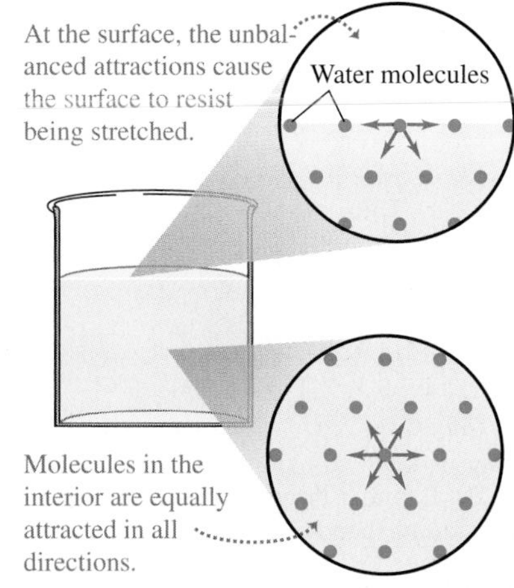
Molecules in a liquid are attracted by neighboring molecules.
At the surface, the unbalanced attractions cause the surface to resist being stretched.
Water molecules
Molecules in the interior are equally attracted in all directions.

Test Your Understanding of Section 14.3 You place a container of seawater on a scale and note the reading on the scale. You now suspend the statue of Example 14.5 in the water (Fig. 14.18). How does the scale reading change? (i) It increases by 7.84 N; (ii) it decreases by 7.84 N; (iii) it remains the same; (iv) none of these.

14.18 How does the scale reading change when the statue is immersed in water?

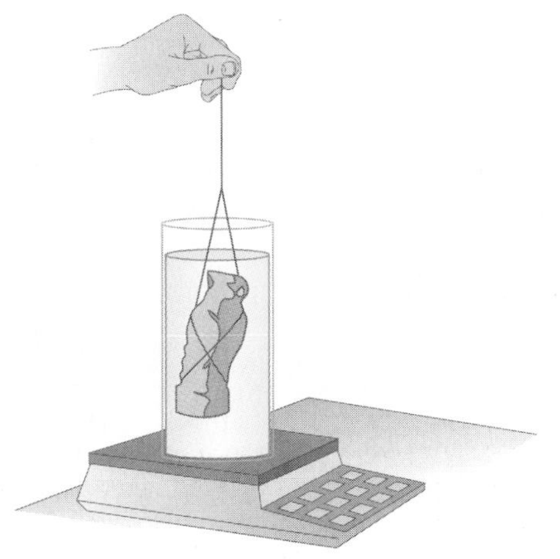

14.17 Surface tension makes it difficult to force water through small crevices. The required water pressure p can be reduced by using hot, soapy water, which has less surface tension.

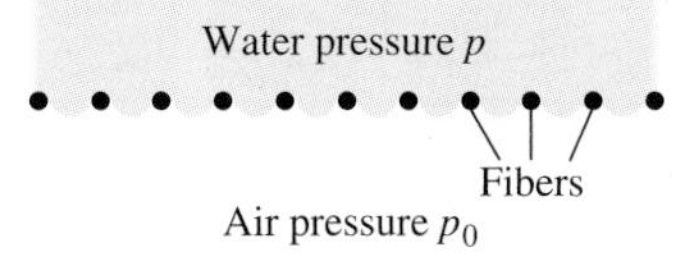
Water pressure p
Fibers
Air pressure p_0

14.4 Fluid Flow

We are now ready to consider *motion* of a fluid. Fluid flow can be extremely complex, as shown by the currents in river rapids or the swirling flames of a campfire. But some situations can be represented by relatively simple idealized models. An **ideal fluid** is a fluid that is *incompressible* (that is, its density cannot change) and has no internal friction (called **viscosity**). Liquids are approximately incompressible in most situations, and we may also treat a gas as incompressible if the pressure differences from one region to another are not too great. Internal friction in a fluid causes shear stresses when two adjacent layers of fluid move relative to each other, as when fluid flows inside a tube or around an obstacle. In some cases we can neglect these shear forces in comparison with forces arising from gravitation and pressure differences.

The path of an individual particle in a moving fluid is called a **flow line.** If the overall flow pattern does not change with time, the flow is called **steady flow.** In steady flow, every element passing through a given point follows the same flow line. In this case the "map" of the fluid velocities at various points in space remains constant, although the velocity of a particular particle may change in both magnitude and direction during its motion. A **streamline** is a curve whose tangent at any point is in the direction of the fluid velocity at that point. When the flow pattern changes with time, the streamlines do not coincide with the flow lines. We will consider only steady-flow situations, for which flow lines and streamlines are identical.

14.19 A flow tube bounded by flow lines. In steady flow, fluid cannot cross the walls of a flow tube.

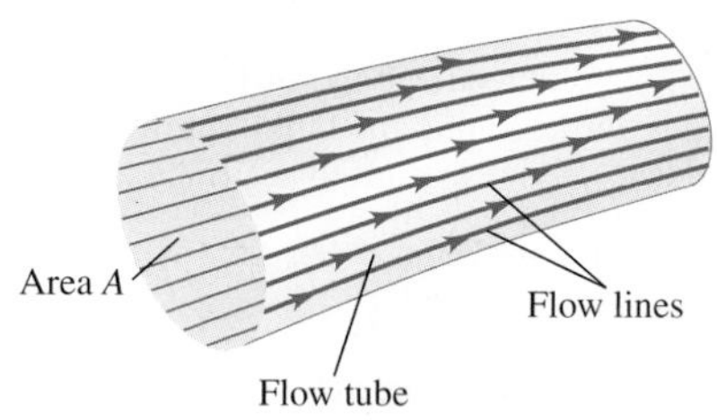

The flow lines passing through the edge of an imaginary element of area, such as the area A in Fig. 14.19, form a tube called a **flow tube.** From the definition of a flow line, in steady flow no fluid can cross the side walls of a flow tube; the fluids in different flow tubes cannot mix.

Figure 14.20 shows patterns of fluid flow from left to right around a number of obstacles. The photographs were made by injecting dye into water flowing between two closely spaced glass plates. These patterns are typical of **laminar flow,** in which adjacent layers of fluid slide smoothly past each other and the flow is steady. (A *lamina* is a thin sheet.) At sufficiently high flow rates, or when boundary surfaces cause abrupt changes in velocity, the flow can become irregular and chaotic. This is called **turbulent flow** (Fig. 14.21). In turbulent flow there is no steady-state pattern; the flow pattern changes continuously.

The Continuity Equation

The mass of a moving fluid doesn't change as it flows. This leads to an important quantitative relationship called the **continuity equation.** Consider a portion of a flow tube between two stationary cross sections with areas A_1 and A_2

14.20 Laminar flow around obstacles of different shapes.

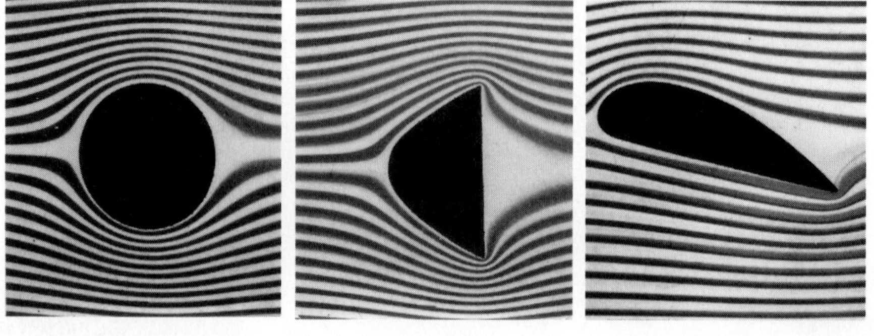

14.21 The flow of smoke rising from these incense sticks is laminar up to a certain point, and then becomes turbulent.

EXECUTE: For the two fluids, Eq. (14.6) becomes

$$p = p_0 + \rho_{\text{water}} g h_{\text{water}}$$
$$p = p_0 + \rho_{\text{oil}} g h_{\text{oil}}$$

14.11 Our sketch for this problem.

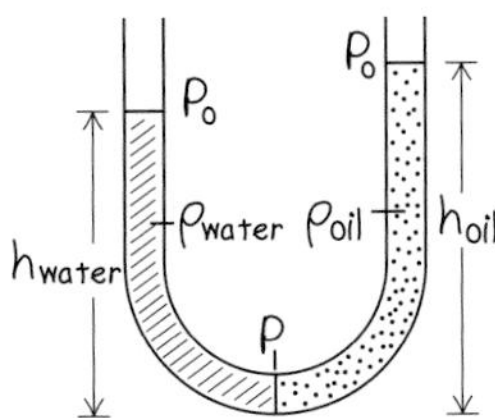

p_0
p_0
ρ_{water}
ρ_{oil}
h_{oil}
h_{water}
p

Since the pressure p at the bottom of the tube is the same for both fluids, we set these two expressions equal to each other and solve for h_{oil} in terms of h_{water}. You can show that the result is

$$h_{\text{oil}} = \frac{\rho_{\text{water}}}{\rho_{\text{oil}}} h_{\text{water}}$$

EVALUATE: Since oil is less dense than water, the ratio $\rho_{\text{water}}/\rho_{\text{oil}}$ is greater than unity and h_{oil} is greater than h_{water} (as shown in Fig. 14.11). That is, a greater height of low-density oil is needed to produce the same pressure p at the bottom of the tube.

Test Your Understanding of Section 14.2 Mercury is less dense at high temperatures than at low temperatures. Suppose you move a mercury barometer from the cold interior of a tightly sealed refrigerator to outdoors on a hot summer day. You find that the column of mercury remains at the same height in the tube. Compared to the air pressure inside the refrigerator, is the air pressure outdoors (i) higher, (ii) lower, or (iii) the same? (Ignore the very small change in the dimensions of the glass tube due to the temperature change.)

14.3 Buoyancy

Buoyancy is a familiar phenomenon: A body immersed in water seems to weigh less than when it is in air. When the body is less dense than the fluid, it floats. The human body usually floats in water, and a helium-filled balloon floats in air.

Archimedes's principle states: When a body is completely or partially immersed in a fluid, the fluid exerts an upward force on the body equal to the weight of the fluid displaced by the body.

To prove this principle, we consider an arbitrary element of fluid at rest. In Fig. 14.12a the irregular outline is the surface boundary of this element of fluid. The arrows represent the forces exerted on the boundary surface by the surrounding fluid.

The entire fluid is in equilibrium, so the sum of all the y-components of force on this element of fluid is zero. Hence the sum of the y-components of the *surface* forces must be an upward force equal in magnitude to the weight mg of the fluid inside the surface. Also, the sum of the torques on the element of fluid must be zero, so the line of action of the resultant y-component of surface force must pass through the center of gravity of this element of fluid.

(a) Arbitrary element of fluid in equilibrium

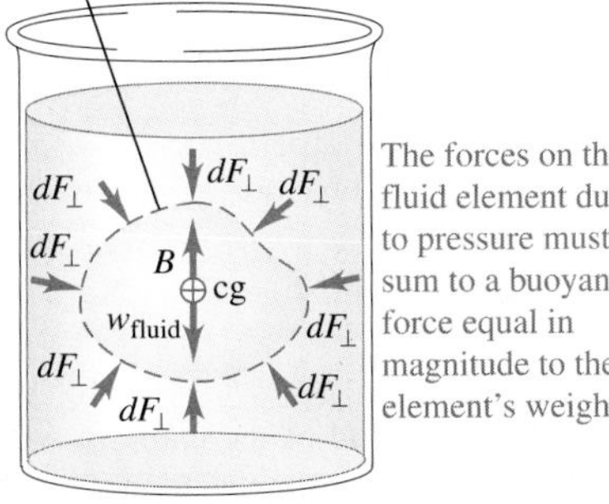

$dF_\perp$
B
cg
w_{fluid}
The forces on the fluid element due to pressure must sum to a buoyant force equal in magnitude to the element's weight.

(b) Fluid element replaced with solid body of the same size and shape

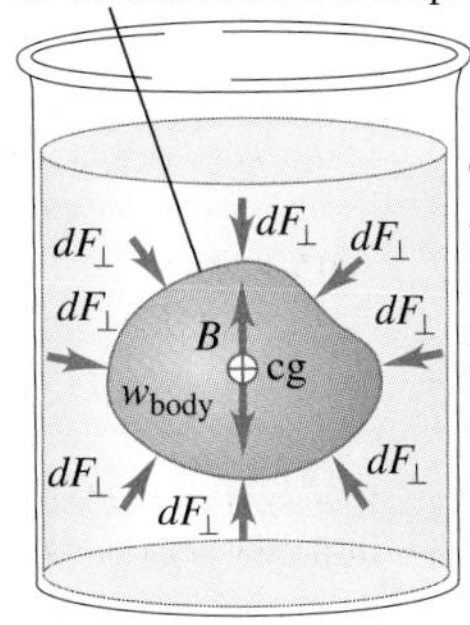

$dF_\perp$
B
cg
w_{body}
The forces due to pressure are the same, so the body must be acted upon by the same buoyant force as the fluid element, *regardless of the body's weight.*

14.12 Archimedes's principle.

14.13 Measuring the density of a fluid.

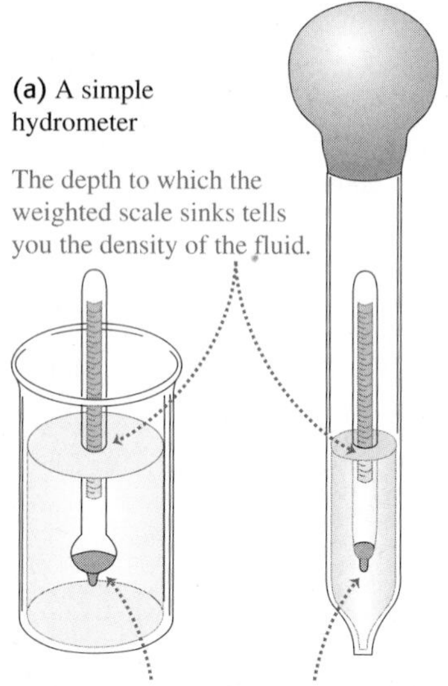
(b) Using a hydrometer to measure the density of battery acid or antifreeze
(a) A simple hydrometer
The depth to which the weighted scale sinks tells you the density of the fluid.
The weight at the bottom makes the scale float upright

Now we remove the fluid inside the surface and replace it with a solid body having exactly the same shape (Fig. 14.12b). The pressure at every point is exactly the same as before. So the total upward force exerted on the body by the fluid is also the same, again equal in magnitude to the weight mg of the fluid displaced to make way for the body. We call this upward force the **buoyant force** on the solid body. The line of action of the buoyant force again passes through the center of gravity of the displaced fluid (which doesn't necessarily coincide with the center of gravity of the body).

When a balloon floats in equilibrium in air, its weight (including the gas inside it) must be the same as the weight of the air displaced by the balloon. ? A fish's flesh is denser than water, yet a fish can float while submerged because it has a gas-filled cavity within its body. This makes the fish's *average* density the same as water, so its net weight is the same as the weight of the water it displaces. A body whose average density is *less* than that of a liquid can float partially submerged at the free upper surface of the liquid. The greater the density of the liquid, the less of the body is submerged. When you swim in seawater (density 1030 kg/m^3), your body floats higher than in fresh water (1000 kg/m^3).

A practical example of buoyancy is the hydrometer, used to measure the density of liquids (Fig. 14.13a). The calibrated float sinks into the fluid until the weight of the fluid it displaces is exactly equal to its own weight. The hydrometer floats *higher* in denser liquids than in less dense liquids, and a scale in the top stem permits direct density readings. Figure 14.13b shows a type of hydrometer that is commonly used to measure the density of battery acid or antifreeze. The bottom of the large tube is immersed in the liquid; the bulb is squeezed to expel air and is then released, like a giant medicine dropper. The liquid rises into the outer tube, and the hydrometer floats in this sample of the liquid.

Example 14.5 Buoyancy

A 15.0-kg solid gold statue is being raised from a sunken ship (Fig. 14.14a). What is the tension in the hoisting cable when the statue is (a) at rest and completely immersed; and (b) at rest and out of the water?

SOLUTION

IDENTIFY: When the statue is immersed, it experiences an upward buoyant force equal in magnitude to the weight of fluid displaced. To find the tension, we note that the statue is in equilibrium (it is at rest) and consider the three forces acting on it: weight, the buoyant force, and the tension in the cable.

SET UP: Figure 14.14b shows the free-body diagram for the statue in equilibrium. Our target variable is the tension T. We are given the weight mg, and we can calculate the buoyant force B by using Archimedes's principle. We do this for two cases: (a) when the statue is immersed in water and (b) when it is out of the water and immersed in air.

EXECUTE: (a) To find the buoyant force, we first find the volume of the statue, using the density of gold from Table 14.1:

$$V = \frac{m}{\rho_{\text{gold}}} = \frac{15.0 \text{ kg}}{19.3 \times 10^3 \text{ kg/m}^3} = 7.77 \times 10^{-4} \text{ m}^3$$

Using Table 14.1 again, we find the weight of this volume of seawater:

$$\begin{aligned} w_{\text{sw}} &= m_{\text{sw}} g = \rho_{\text{sw}} V g \\ &= (1.03 \times 10^3 \text{ kg/m}^3)(7.77 \times 10^{-4} \text{ m}^3)(9.80 \text{ m/s}^2) \\ &= 7.84 \text{ N} \end{aligned}$$

This equals the buoyant force B.

14.14 What is the tension in the cable hoisting the statue?

(a) Immersed statue in equilibrium

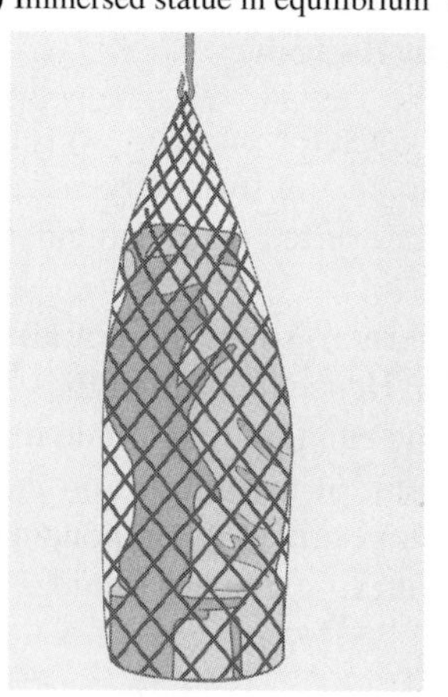

(b) Free-body diagram of statue

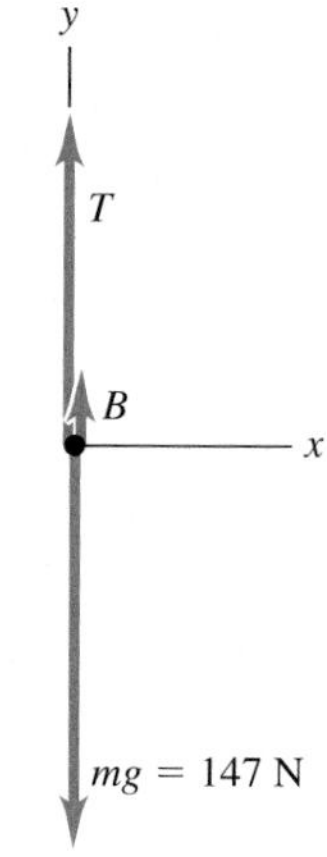
y
T
B
x
mg = 147 N

The statue is at rest, so the net external force acting on it is zero. From Fig. 14.14b,

$$\begin{aligned} \sum F_y &= B + T + (-mg) = 0 \\ T &= mg - B = (15.0 \text{ kg})(9.80 \text{ m/s}^2) - 7.84 \text{ N} \\ &= 147 \text{ N} - 7.84 \text{ N} = 139 \text{ N} \end{aligned}$$

If a spring scale is attached to the upper end of the cable, it will indicate 7.84 N less than if the statue were not immersed in seawater. Hence the submerged statue seems to weigh 139 N, about 5% less than its actual weight of 147 N.

(Fig. 14.22). The fluid speeds at these sections are v_1 and v_2, respectively. No fluid flows in or out across the sides of the tube because the fluid velocity is tangent to the wall at every point on the wall. During a small time interval dt, the fluid at A_1 moves a distance $v_1\,dt$, so a cylinder of fluid with height $v_1\,dt$ and volume $dV_1 = A_1 v_1\,dt$ flows into the tube across A_1. During this same interval, a cylinder of volume $dV_2 = A_2 v_2\,dt$ flows out of the tube across A_2.

Let's first consider the case of an incompressible fluid so that the density ρ has the same value at all points. The mass dm_1 flowing into the tube across A_1 in time dt is $dm_1 = \rho A_1 v_1\,dt$. Similarly, the mass dm_2 that flows out across A_2 in the same time is $dm_2 = \rho A_2 v_2\,dt$. In steady flow the total mass in the tube is constant, so $dm_1 = dm_2$ and

$$\rho A_1 v_1\,dt = \rho A_2 v_2\,dt \qquad \text{or}$$

$$A_1 v_1 = A_2 v_2 \qquad \text{(continuity equation, incompressible fluid)} \qquad (14.10)$$

The product Av is the *volume flow rate* dV/dt, the rate at which volume crosses a section of the tube:

$$\frac{dV}{dt} = Av \qquad \text{(volume flow rate)} \qquad (14.11)$$

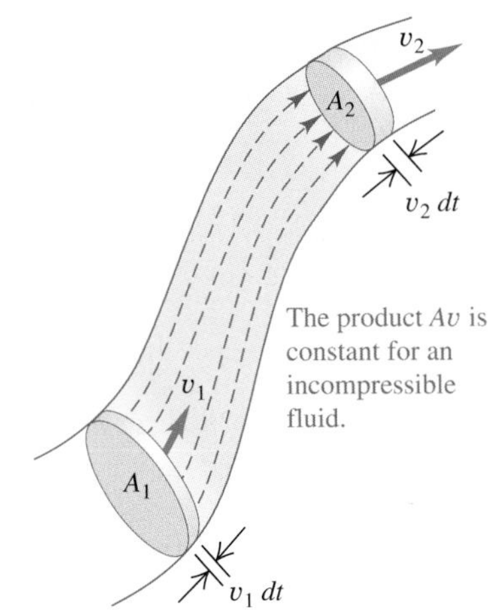

v_2
A_2
$v_2\,dt$
The product Av is constant for an incompressible fluid.
v_1
A_1
$v_1\,dt$

14.22 A flow tube with changing cross-sectional area. If the fluid is incompressible, the product Av has the same value at all points along the tube.

The *mass* flow rate is the mass flow per unit time through a cross section. This is equal to the density ρ times the volume flow rate dV/dt.

Equation (14.10) shows that the volume flow rate has the same value at all points along any flow tube. When the cross section of a flow tube decreases, the speed increases, and vice versa. The deep part of a river has larger cross section and slower current than the shallow part, but the volume flow rates are the same in both. This is the essence of the familiar maxim, "Still waters run deep." The stream of water from a faucet narrows as it gains speed during its fall, but dV/dt is the same everywhere along the stream. If a water pipe with 2-cm diameter is connected to a pipe with 1-cm diameter, the flow speed is four times as great in the 1-cm part as in the 2-cm part.

We can generalize Eq. (14.10) for the case in which the fluid is *not* incompressible. If ρ_1 and ρ_2 are the densities at sections 1 and 2, then

$$\rho_1 A_1 v_1 = \rho_2 A_2 v_2 \qquad \text{(continuity equation, compressible fluid)} \qquad (14.12)$$

If the fluid is denser at point 2 than at point 1 $(\rho_2 > \rho_1)$, the volume flow rate at point 2 will be less than at point 1 $(A_2 v_2 < A_1 v_1)$. We leave the details to you (see Exercise 14.38). If the fluid is incompressible so that ρ_1 and ρ_2 are always equal, Eq. (14.12) reduces to Eq. (14.10).

Example 14.6 Incompressible fluid flow

As part of a lubricating system for heavy machinery, oil of density $850\ \text{kg/m}^3$ is pumped through a cylindrical pipe of diameter 8.0 cm at a rate of 9.5 liters per second. (a) What is the speed of the oil? What is the mass flow rate? (b) If the pipe diameter is reduced to 4.0 cm, what are the new values of the speed and volume flow rate? Assume that the oil is incompressible.

SOLUTION

IDENTIFY: The key point is that the fluid is incompressible, so we can use the idea of the continuity equation to relate mass flow rate, volume flow rate, flow tube area, and flow speed.

SET UP: We use the definition of volume flow rate, Eq. (14.11), to determine the speed v_1 in the 8.0-cm-diameter section. The mass flow rate is the product of the density and the volume flow rate. The continuity equation for incompressible flow, Eq. (14.10), allows us to find the speed v_2 in the 4.0-cm-diameter section.

EXECUTE: (a) The volume flow rate dV/dt equals the product $A_1 v_1$, where A_1 is the cross-sectional area of the pipe of diameter 8.0 cm and radius 4.0 cm. Hence

$$v_1 = \frac{dV/dt}{A_1} = \frac{(9.5\ \text{L/s})(10^{-3}\ \text{m}^3/\text{L})}{\pi(4.0 \times 10^{-2}\ \text{m})^2} = 1.9\ \text{m/s}$$

Continued

The mass flow rate is $\rho\, dV/dt = (850\ \text{kg/m}^3)(9.5 \times 10^{-3}\ \text{m}^3/\text{s}) = 8.1\ \text{kg/s}$.

(b) Since the oil is incompressible, the volume flow rate has the *same* value (9.5 L/s) in both sections of pipe. From Eq. (14.10),

$$v_2 = \frac{A_1}{A_2}v_1 = \frac{\pi(4.0 \times 10^{-2}\ \text{m})^2}{\pi(2.0 \times 10^{-2}\ \text{m})^2}(1.9\ \text{m/s}) = 7.6\ \text{m/s}$$

EVALUATE: The second section of pipe has one-half the diameter and one-fourth the cross-sectional area of the first section. Hence the speed must be four times greater in the second section, which is just what our result shows ($v_2 = 4v_1$).

Test Your Understanding of Section 14.4 A maintenance crew is working on a section of a three-lane highway, leaving only one lane open to traffic. The result is much slower traffic flow (a traffic jam). Do cars on a highway behave like (i) the molecules of an incompressible fluid or (ii) the molecules of a compressible fluid?

14.5 Bernoulli's Equation

According to the continuity equation, the speed of fluid flow can vary along the paths of the fluid. The pressure can also vary; it depends on height as in the static situation (see Section 14.2), and it also depends on the speed of flow. We can derive an important relationship called *Bernoulli's equation* that relates the pressure, flow speed, and height for flow of an ideal, incompressible fluid. Bernoulli's equation is an essential tool in analyzing plumbing systems, hydroelectric generating stations, and the flight of airplanes.

The dependence of pressure on speed follows from the continuity equation, Eq. (14.10). When an incompressible fluid flows along a flow tube with varying cross section, its speed *must* change, and so an element of fluid must have an acceleration. If the tube is horizontal, the force that causes this acceleration has to be applied by the surrounding fluid. This means that the pressure *must* be different in regions of different cross section; if it were the same everywhere, the net force on every fluid element would be zero. When a horizontal flow tube narrows and a fluid element speeds up, it must be moving toward a region of lower pressure in order to have a net forward force to accelerate it. If the elevation also changes, this causes an additional pressure difference.

14.23 Deriving Bernoulli's equation. The net work done on a fluid element by the pressure of the surrounding fluid equals the change in the kinetic energy plus the change in the gravitational potential energy.

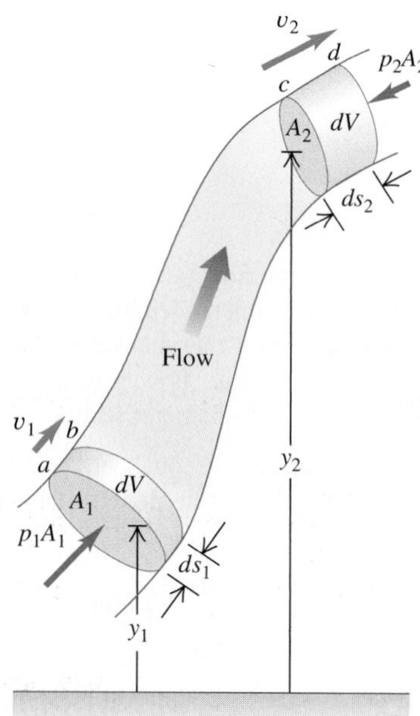

Deriving Bernoulli's Equation

To derive Bernoulli's equation, we apply the work-energy theorem to the fluid in a section of a flow tube. In Fig. 14.23 we consider the element of fluid that at some initial time lies between the two cross sections a and c. The speeds at the lower and upper ends are v_1 and v_2. In a small time interval dt, the fluid that is initially at a moves to b, a distance $ds_1 = v_1\, dt$, and the fluid that is initially at c moves to d, a distance $ds_2 = v_2\, dt$. The cross-sectional areas at the two ends are A_1 and A_2, as shown. The fluid is incompressible; hence by the continuity equation, Eq. (14.10), the volume of fluid dV passing *any* cross section during time dt is the same. That is, $dV = A_1\, ds_1 = A_2\, ds_2$.

Let's compute the *work* done on this fluid element during dt. We assume that there is negligible internal friction in the fluid (i.e., no viscosity), so the only nongravitational forces that do work on the fluid element are due to the pressure of the surrounding fluid. The pressures at the two ends are p_1 and p_2; the force on the cross section at a is p_1A_1, and the force at c is p_2A_2. The net work dW done on the element by the surrounding fluid during this displacement is therefore

$$dW = p_1A_1\, ds_1 - p_2A_2\, ds_2 = (p_1 - p_2)\, dV \tag{14.13}$$

The second term has a negative sign because the force at c opposes the displacement of the fluid.

The work dW is due to forces other than the conservative force of gravity, so it equals the change in the total mechanical energy (kinetic energy plus gravitational potential energy) associated with the fluid element. The mechanical energy for the fluid between sections b and c does not change. At the beginning of dt the fluid between a and b has volume $A_1\,ds_1$, mass $\rho A_1\,ds_1$, and kinetic energy $\frac{1}{2}\rho(A_1\,ds_1)v_1^2$. At the end of dt the fluid between c and d has kinetic energy $\frac{1}{2}\rho(A_2\,ds_2)v_2^2$. The net change in kinetic energy dK during time dt is

$$dK = \frac{1}{2}\rho\,dV(v_2^2 - v_1^2) \tag{14.14}$$

What about the change in gravitational potential energy? At the beginning of dt, the potential energy for the mass between a and b is $dm\,gy_1 = \rho\,dV\,gy_1$. At the end of dt, the potential energy for the mass between c and d is $dm\,gy_2 = \rho\,dV\,gy_2$. The net change in potential energy dU during dt is

$$dU = \rho\,dV\,g(y_2 - y_1) \tag{14.15}$$

Combining Eqs. (14.13), (14.14), and (14.15) in the energy equation $dW = dK + dU$, we obtain

$$\begin{aligned}(p_1 - p_2)\,dV &= \frac{1}{2}\rho\,dV(v_2^2 - v_1^2) + \rho\,dV\,g(y_2 - y_1)\\ p_1 - p_2 &= \frac{1}{2}\rho(v_2^2 - v_1^2) + \rho g(y_2 - y_1)\end{aligned} \tag{14.16}$$

This is **Bernoulli's equation.** It states that the work done on a unit volume of fluid by the surrounding fluid is equal to the sum of the changes in kinetic and potential energies per unit volume that occur during the flow. We may also interpret Eq. (14.16) in terms of pressures. The first term on the right is the pressure difference associated with the change of speed of the fluid. The second term on the right is the additional pressure difference caused by the weight of the fluid and the difference in elevation of the two ends.

We can also express Eq. (14.16) in a more convenient form as

$$p_1 + \rho g y_1 + \frac{1}{2}\rho v_1^2 = p_2 + \rho g y_2 + \frac{1}{2}\rho v_2^2 \quad \text{(Bernoulli's equation)} \tag{14.17}$$

The subscripts 1 and 2 refer to *any* two points along the flow tube, so we can also write

$$p + \rho g y + \frac{1}{2}\rho v^2 = \text{constant} \tag{14.18}$$

Note that when the fluid is *not* moving (so $v_1 = v_2 = 0$), Eq. (14.17) reduces to the pressure relationship we derived for a fluid at rest, Eq. (14.5).

CAUTION **Bernoulli's principle applies only in certain situations** We stress again that Bernoulli's equation is valid for only incompressible, steady flow of a fluid with no internal friction (no viscosity). It's a simple equation that's easy to use; don't let this tempt you to use it in situations in which it doesn't apply!

Problem-Solving Strategy 14.1 Bernoulli's Equation

Bernoulli's equation is derived from the work–energy theorem, so it isn't surprising that much of Problem-Solving Strategy 7.1 (Section 7.1) is applicable here.

IDENTIFY *the relevant concepts:* First ensure that the fluid flow is steady and that the fluid is incompressible and has no internal friction. This case is an idealization, but it holds up surprisingly well for fluids flowing through sufficiently large pipes and for flows within bulk fluids (e.g., air flowing around an airplane or water flowing around a fish).

SET UP *the problem* using the following steps:

1. Always begin by identifying clearly the points 1 and 2 referred to in Bernoulli's equation.
2. Define your coordinate system, particularly the level at which $y = 0$.

Continued

3. Make lists of the unknown and known quantities in Eq. (14.17). The variables are p_1, p_2, v_1, v_2, y_1, and y_2, and the constants are ρ and g. Decide which unknowns are your target variables.

EXECUTE *the solution* as follows: Write Bernoulli's equation and solve for the unknowns. In some problems you will need to use the continuity equation, Eq. (14.10), to get a relationship between the two speeds in terms of cross-sectional areas of pipes or containers. Or perhaps you will know both speeds and need to determine one of the areas. You may also need to use Eq. (14.11) to find the volume flow rate.

EVALUATE *your answer:* As always, verify that the results make physical sense. Double check that you have used consistent units. In SI units, pressure is in pascals, density in kilograms per cubic meter, and speed in meters per second. Also note that the pressures must be either all absolute pressures or all gauge pressures.

Example 14.7 Water pressure in the home

Water enters a house through a pipe with an inside diameter of 2.0 cm at an absolute pressure of 4.0×10^5 Pa (about 4 atm). A 1.0-cm-diameter pipe leads to the second-floor bathroom 5.0 m above (Fig. 14.24). When the flow speed at the inlet pipe is 1.5 m/s, find the flow speed, pressure, and volume flow rate in the bathroom.

SOLUTION

IDENTIFY: We assume that the water flows at a steady rate. The pipe has a relatively large diameter, so it's reasonable to ignore internal friction. Water is rather incompressible, so it's a good approximation to use Bernoulli's equation.

SET UP: Let points 1 and 2 be at the inlet pipe and at the bathroom, respectively. We are given the speed v_1 and pressure p_1 at the inlet pipe, and the pipe diameters at points 1 and 2 (from which we calculate the areas A_1 and A_2). We take $y_1 = 0$ (at the inlet) and $y_2 = 5.0$ m (at the bathroom). Our first two target variables are the speed v_2 and pressure p_2. Since we have more than one unknown, we use both Bernoulli's equation and the continuity equation for an incompressible fluid. Once we find v_2, we can calculate the volume flow rate $v_2 A_2$ at point 2.

EXECUTE: We find the speed v_2 at the bathroom using the continuity equation, Eq. (14.10):

$$v_2 = \frac{A_1}{A_2}v_1 = \frac{\pi(1.0\text{ cm})^2}{\pi(0.50\text{ cm})^2}(1.5\text{ m/s}) = 6.0\text{ m/s}$$

We are given p_1 and v_1, and we can find p_2 from Bernoulli's equation, Eq. (14.16):

$$\begin{aligned} p_2 &= p_1 - \frac{1}{2}\rho(v_2^2 - v_1^2) - \rho g(y_2 - y_1) = 4.0 \times 10^5\text{ Pa} \\ &\quad -\frac{1}{2}(1.0 \times 10^3\text{ kg/m}^3)(36\text{ m}^2/\text{s}^2 - 2.25\text{ m}^2/\text{s}^2) \\ &\quad -(1.0 \times 10^3\text{ kg/m}^3)(9.8\text{ m/s}^2)(5.0\text{ m}) \\ &= 4.0 \times 10^5\text{ Pa} - 0.17 \times 10^5\text{ Pa} - 0.49 \times 10^5\text{ Pa} \\ &= 3.3 \times 10^5\text{ Pa} = 3.3\text{ atm} = 48\text{ lb/in.}^2 \end{aligned}$$

14.24 What is the water pressure in the second-story bathroom of this house?

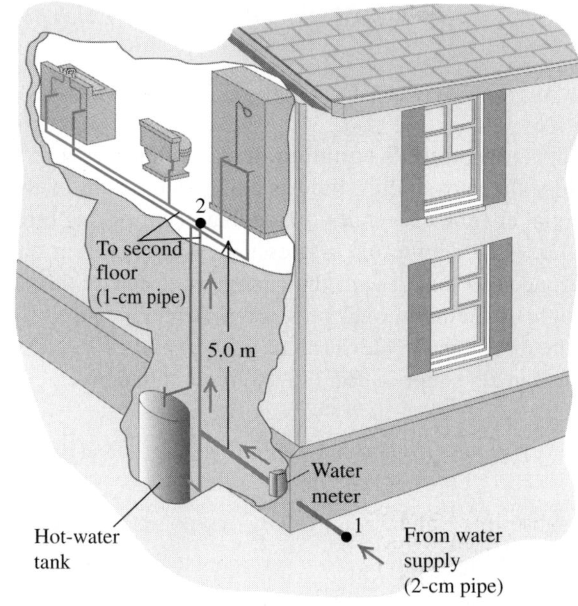

The volume flow rate is

$$\begin{aligned} \frac{dV}{dt} &= A_2 v_2 = \pi(0.50 \times 10^{-2}\text{ m})^2(6.0\text{ m/s}) \\ &= 4.7 \times 10^{-4}\text{ m}^3/\text{s} = 0.47\text{ L/s} \end{aligned}$$

EVALUATE: This is a reasonable flow rate for a bathroom faucet or shower. Note that after the water is turned off, v_1 and v_2 are both zero, the term $\frac{1}{2}\rho(v_2^2 - v_1^2)$ in the equation for pressure vanishes, and the pressure p_2 rises to 3.5×10^5 Pa.

Example 14.8 Speed of efflux

Figure 14.25 shows a gasoline storage tank with cross-sectional area A_1, filled to a depth h. The space above the gasoline contains air at pressure p_0, and the gasoline flows out through a short pipe with area A_2. Derive expressions for the flow speed in the pipe and the volume flow rate.

SOLUTION

IDENTIFY: We consider the entire volume of moving liquid as a single flow tube of an incompressible fluid with negligible internal friction. Hence, we can use Bernoulli's principle.

SET UP: Points 1 and 2 in Fig. 14.25 are at the surface of the gasoline and at the short exit pipe, respectively. At point 1 the pressure is p_0 and at point 2 it is atmospheric pressure p_{atm}. We take $y = 0$ at the exit pipe, so $y_1 = h$ and $y_2 = 0$. Because A_1 is very much larger than A_2, the upper surface of the gasoline will drop very slowly and we can regard v_1 as essentially equal to zero. We find the target variable v_2 from Eq. (14.17) and the volume flow rate from Eq. (14.11).

EXECUTE: We apply Bernoulli's equation to points 1 and 2

$$p_0 + \frac{1}{2}\rho v_1^2 + \rho g h = p_{atm} + \frac{1}{2}\rho v_2^2 + \rho g(0)$$

$$v_2^2 = v_1^2 + 2\left(\frac{p_0 - p_{atm}}{\rho}\right) + 2gh$$

Using $v_1 = 0$, we find

$$v_2^2 = 2\left(\frac{p_0 - p_{atm}}{\rho}\right) + 2gh$$

From Eq. (14.11), the volume flow rate is $dV/dt = v_2 A_2$.

EVALUATE: The speed v_2, sometimes called the *speed of efflux,* depends on both the pressure difference $(p_0 - p_{atm})$ and the height h of the liquid level in the tank. If the top of the tank is vented to the atmosphere, $p_0 = p_{atm}$ and there is zero pressure difference: $p_0 - p_{atm} = 0$. In that case,

$$v_2 = \sqrt{2gh}$$

14.25 Calculating the speed of efflux for gasoline flowing out the bottom of a storage tank.

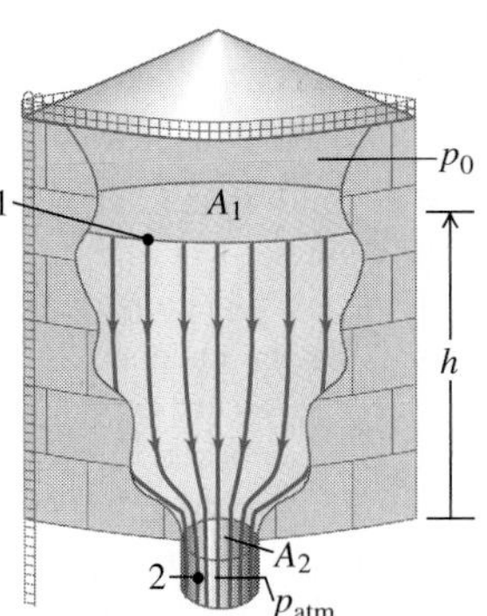

That is, the speed of efflux from an opening at a distance h below the top surface of the liquid is the *same* as the speed a body would acquire in falling freely through a height h. This result is called *Torricelli's theorem.* It is valid not only for an opening in the bottom of a container, but also for a hole in a side wall at a depth h below the surface. In this case the volume flow rate is

$$\frac{dV}{dt} = A_2\sqrt{2gh}$$

Example 14.9 The Venturi meter

Figure 14.26 shows a *Venturi meter,* used to measure flow speed in a pipe. The narrow part of the pipe is called the *throat.* Derive an expression for the flow speed v_1 in terms of the cross-sectional areas A_1 and A_2 and the difference in height h of the liquid levels in the two vertical tubes.

14.26 The Venturi meter.

Difference in height results from reduced pressure in throat (point 2).

SOLUTION

IDENTIFY: The flow is steady, and we assume the fluid is incompressible and has negligible internal friction. Hence we can use Bernoulli's equation.

SET UP: We apply Bernoulli's equation to the wide (point 1) and narrow (point 2) parts of the pipe. The difference in height between the two vertical tubes tells us the pressure difference between points 1 and 2.

EXECUTE: The two points are at the same vertical coordinate $(y_1 = y_2)$, so Eq. (14.17) says

$$p_1 + \frac{1}{2}\rho v_1^2 = p_2 + \frac{1}{2}\rho v_2^2$$

From the continuity equation, $v_2 = (A_1/A_2)v_1$. Substituting this and rearranging, we get

$$p_1 - p_2 = \frac{1}{2}\rho v_1^2\left(\frac{A_1^2}{A_2^2} - 1\right)$$

From Section 14.2, the pressure difference $p_1 - p_2$ is also equal to $\rho g h$, where h is the difference in the liquid levels in the two tubes. Combining this with the above result and solving for v_1, we get

$$v_1 = \sqrt{\frac{2gh}{(A_1/A_2)^2 - 1}}$$

EVALUATE: Because A_1 is greater than A_2, v_2 is greater than v_1 and the pressure p_2 in the throat is *less* than p_1. A net force to the right accelerates the fluid as it enters the throat, and a net force to the left slows it as it leaves.

Conceptual Example 14.10 Lift on an airplane wing

Figure 14.27a shows flow lines around a cross section of an airplane wing. The flow lines crowd together above the wing, corresponding to increased flow speed and reduced pressure in this region, just as in the Venturi throat. The upward force on the underside of the wing is greater than the downward force on the top side; there is a net upward force, or *lift.* Lift is not simply due to the impulse of air striking the underside of the wing; in fact, it turns out that the reduced pressure on the upper wing surface makes the greatest contribution to the lift. (This highly simplified discussion ignores the formation of vortices; a more complete discussion would take these into account.)

We can also understand the lift force on the basis of momentum changes. Figure 14.27a shows that there is a net *downward* change in the vertical component of momentum of the air flowing past the wing, corresponding to the downward force the wing exerts on the air. The reaction force *on* the wing is *upward,* as we concluded above.

A similar flow pattern and lift force are found in the vicinity of any humped object in a wind. In a sufficiently strong wind, the lift force on the top of an open umbrella can collapse the umbrella upward. A lift force also acts on a car driving at high speed due to air moving over the car's curved upper surface. Such lift can reduce traction on the car's tires, which is why many cars are equipped with an aerodynamic "spoiler" at the car's tail. The spoiler is shaped like an upside-down wing and provides a downward force on the rear wheels.

CAUTION **A misconception about wings** Simplified discussions of wings often claim that air travels faster over the top of a wing because "it has farther to travel." This picture assumes that two adjacent air molecules that part company at the front of the wing, one traveling over the upper surface of the wing and one under the lower surface, must meet again at the wing's trailing edge. Not so! Figure 14.27b shows a computer simulation of parcels of air flowing around an airplane wing. Parcels that are adjacent at the front of the wing do *not* meet at the trailing edge, because the flow over the top of the wing is actually faster than in the simplified (but incorrect) picture. In accordance with Bernoulli's equation, this faster speed means that there is even lower pressure above the wing (and hence greater lift) than the simplified description would suggest.

14.27 (a) Flow lines around an airplane wing. The momentum of a parcel of air (relative to the wing) is $\vec{p}_i$ before encountering the wing and $\vec{p}_f$ afterward. (b) Computer simulation of parcels of air flowing around a wing.

(a) Flow lines around an airplane wing

The flowlines of air moving over the top of the wing are crowded together, so the flow speed is higher and the pressure consequently lower.

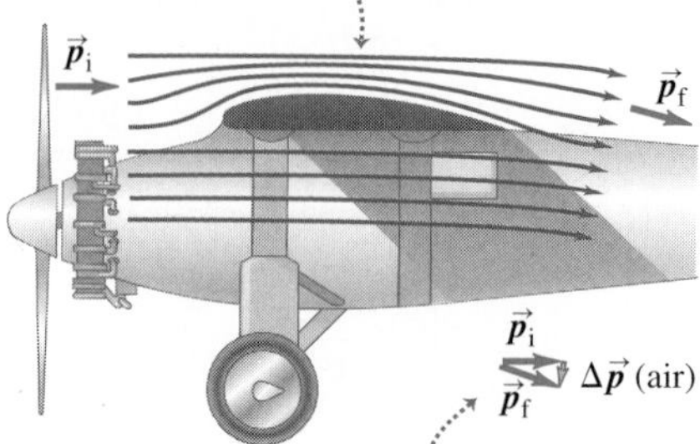

An equivalent explanation: The wing's shape imparts a net downward momentum to the air, so the reaction force on the airplane is upward.

(b) Computer simulation of airflow around an airplane wing

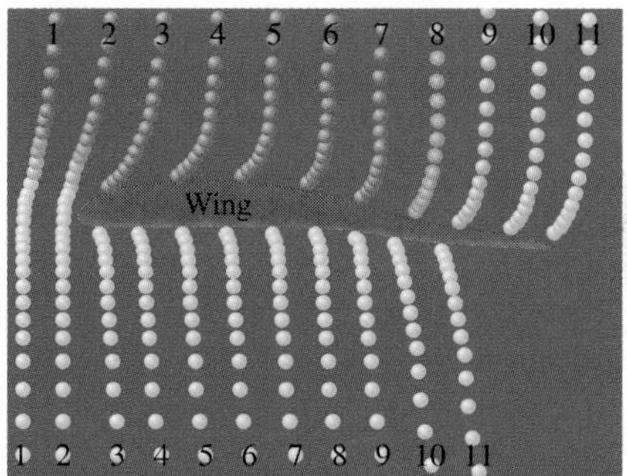

Image of air parcels flowing around a wing, showing that the air goes much faster over the top than over the bottom (and that air parcels which are together at the leading edge of the wing do *not* meet up at the trailing edge!)

Test Your Understanding of Section 14.5 Which is the most accurate statement of Bernoulli's principle? (i) Fast-moving air causes lower pressure; (ii) lower pressure causes fast-moving air; (iii) both (i) and (ii) are equally accurate.

*14.6 Viscosity and Turbulence

In our discussion of fluid flow we assumed that the fluid had no internal friction and that the flow was laminar. While these assumptions are often quite valid, in many important physical situations the effects of viscosity (internal friction) and turbulence (nonlaminar flow) are extremely important. Let's take a brief look at some of these situations.

Viscosity

Viscosity is internal friction in a fluid. Viscous forces oppose the motion of one portion of a fluid relative to another. Viscosity is the reason it takes effort to paddle a canoe through calm water, but it is also the reason the paddle works. Viscous effects are important in the flow of fluids in pipes, the flow of blood, the lubrication of engine parts, and many other situations.

Fluids that flow readily, such as water or gasoline, have smaller viscosities than do "thick" liquids such as honey or motor oil. Viscosities of all fluids are strongly temperature dependent, increasing for gases and decreasing for liquids as the temperature increases (Fig. 14.28). An important goal in the design of oils for engine lubrication is to *reduce* the temperature variation of viscosity as much as possible.

A viscous fluid always tends to cling to a solid surface in contact with it. There is always a thin *boundary layer* of fluid near the surface, in which the fluid is nearly at rest with respect to the surface. That's why dust particles can cling to a fan blade even when it is rotating rapidly, and why you can't get all the dirt off your car by just squirting a hose at it.

Viscosity has important effects on the flow of liquids through pipes, including the flow of blood in the circulatory system. First think about a fluid with zero viscosity so that we can apply Bernoulli's equation, Eq. (14.17). If the two ends of a long cylindrical pipe are at the same height $(y_1 = y_2)$ and the flow speed is the same at both ends (so $v_1 = v_2$), Bernoulli's equation tells us that the pressure is the same at both ends of the pipe. But this result simply isn't true if we take viscosity into account. To see why, consider Fig. 14.29, which shows the flow-speed profile for laminar flow of a viscous fluid in a long cylindrical pipe. Due to viscosity, the speed is *zero* at the pipe walls (to which the fluid clings) and is greatest at the center of the pipe. The motion is like a lot of concentric tubes sliding relative to one another, with the central tube moving fastest and the outermost tube at rest. Viscous forces between the tubes oppose this sliding, so to keep the flow going we must apply a greater pressure at the back of the flow than at the front. That's why you have to keep squeezing a tube of toothpaste or a packet of ketchup (both viscous fluids) to keep the fluid coming out of its container. Your fingers provide a pressure at the back of the flow that is far greater than the atmospheric pressure at the front of the flow.

The pressure difference required to sustain a given volume flow rate through a cylindrical pipe of length L and radius R turns out to be proportional to L/R^4. If we decrease R by one-half, the required pressure increases by $2^4 = 16$; decreasing R by a factor of 0.90 (a 10% reduction) increases the required pressure difference by a factor of $(1/0.90)^4 = 1.52$ (a 52% increase). This simple relationship explains the connection between a high-cholesterol diet (which tends to narrow the arteries) and high blood pressure. Due to the R^4 dependence, even a small narrowing of the arteries can result in substantially elevated blood pressure and added strain on the heart muscle.

14.28 Lava is an example of a viscous fluid. The viscosity decreases with increasing temperature: The hotter the lava, the more easily it can flow.

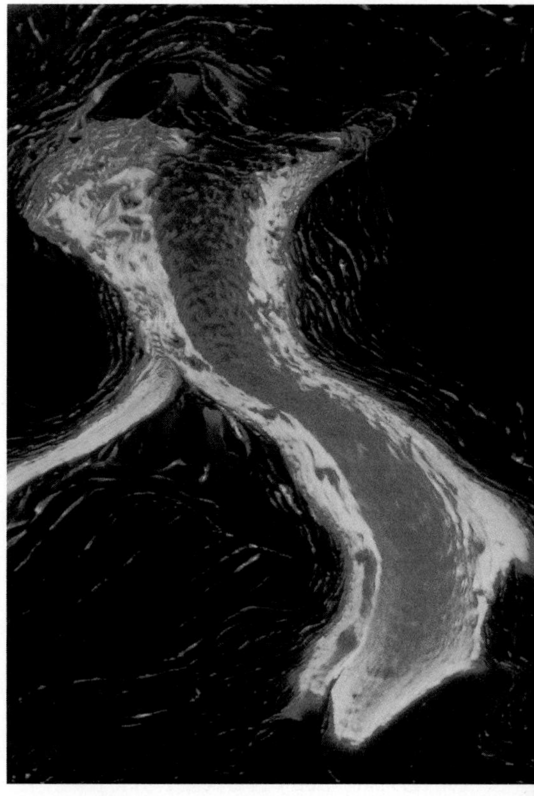

14.29 Velocity profile for a viscous fluid in a cylindrical pipe.

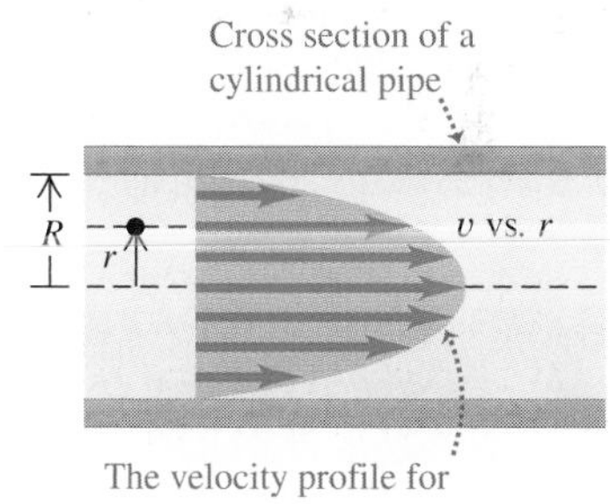
Cross section of a cylindrical pipe
R
r
v vs. r
The velocity profile for viscous fluid flowing in the pipe has a parabolic shape.

Turbulence

When the speed of a flowing fluid exceeds a certain critical value, the flow is no longer laminar. Instead, the flow pattern becomes extremely irregular and complex, and it changes continuously with time; there is no steady-state pattern. This irregular, chaotic flow is called **turbulence.** Figure 14.21 shows the contrast between laminar and turbulent flow for smoke rising in air. Bernoulli's equation is *not* applicable to regions where there is turbulence because the flow is not steady.

Whether a flow is laminar or turbulent depends in part on the fluid's viscosity. The greater the viscosity, the greater the tendency for the fluid to flow in sheets or lamina and the more likely the flow is to be laminar. (When we discussed

Bernoulli's equation in Section 14.5, we assumed that the flow was laminar and that the fluid had zero viscosity. In fact, a *little* viscosity is needed to ensure that the flow is laminar.)

For a fluid of a given viscosity, flow speed is a determining factor for the onset of turbulence. A flow pattern that is stable at low speeds suddenly becomes unstable when a critical speed is reached. Irregularities in the flow pattern can be caused by roughness in the pipe wall, variations in the density of the fluid, and many other factors. At low flow speeds, these disturbances damp out; the flow pattern is *stable* and tends to maintain its laminar nature (Fig. 14.30a). When the critical speed is reached, however, the flow pattern becomes unstable. The disturbances no longer damp out but grow until they destroy the entire laminar-flow pattern (Fig. 14.30b).

Normal blood flow in the human aorta is laminar, but a small disturbance such as a heart pathology can cause the flow to become turbulent. Turbulence makes noise, which is why listening to blood flow with a stethoscope is a useful diagnostic technique.

14.30 The flow of water from a faucet is (a) laminar at low speeds but (b) turbulent at sufficiently high speeds.

Conceptual Example 14.11 The curve ball

Does a curve ball *really* curve? Yes, it certainly does, and the reason is turbulence. Fig. 14.31a shows a ball moving through the air from left to right. To an observer moving with the center of the ball, the air stream appears to move from right to left, as shown by the flow lines in the figure. Because of the high speeds that are ordinarily involved (near 160 km/h, or 100 mi/h), there is a region of *turbulent* flow behind the ball.

Figure 14.31b shows a *spinning* ball with "top spin." Layers of air near the ball's surface are pulled around in the direction of the spin by friction between the ball and air and by the air's internal friction (viscosity). The speed of air relative to the ball's surface becomes slower at the top of the ball than at the bottom, and turbulence occurs farther forward on the top side than on the bottom. This asymmetry causes a pressure difference; the average pressure at the top of the ball is now greater than that at the bottom. The net force deflects the ball downward, as shown in Fig. 14.31c. This is why "top spin" is used in tennis to keep a very fast serve in the court (Fig. 14.31d). In a baseball curve pitch, the ball spins about a nearly vertical axis, and the actual deflection is sideways. In that case, Fig. 14.31c is a *top* view of the situation. A curve ball thrown by a left-handed pitcher curves *toward* a right-handed batter, making it harder to hit (Fig. 14.31e).

A similar effect occurs with golf balls, which always have "back spin" from impact with the slanted face of the golf club. The resulting pressure difference between the top and bottom of the ball causes a lift force that keeps the ball in the air considerably longer than would be possible without spin. A well-hit drive appears from the tee to "float" or even curve *upward* during the initial portion of its flight. This is a real effect, not an illusion. The dimples on the ball play an essential role; the viscosity of air gives an undimpled ball a much shorter trajectory than a dimpled one with the same initial velocity and spin. Figure 14.31f shows the backspin of a golf ball just after it is struck by a club.

14.31 (a)–(e) Analyzing the motion of a spinning ball through the air. (f) Stroboscopic photograph of a golf ball being struck by a club. The picture was taken at 1000 flashes per second. The ball rotates about once in eight pictures, corresponding to an angular speed of 125 rev/s, or 7500 rpm.

(a) Motion of air relative to a nonspinning ball

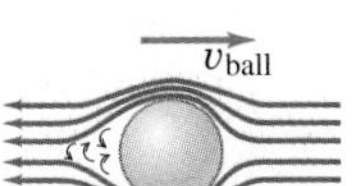

(b) Motion of a spinning ball

This side of the ball moves opposite to the airflow.

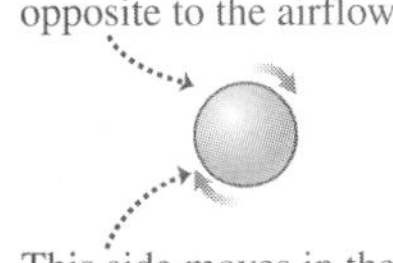

This side moves in the direction of the airflow.

(c) Force generated when a spinning ball moves through air

A moving ball drags the adjacent air with it. So, when air moves past a spinning ball:

On one side, the ball **slows the air**, creating a region of **high pressure**.

On the other side, the ball **speeds the air**, creating a region of **low pressure**.

The resultant force points in the direction of the low-pressure side.

(d) Spin pushing a tennis ball downward

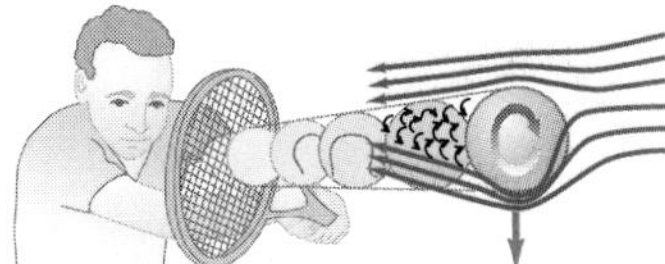

(e) Spin causing a curve ball to be deflected sideways

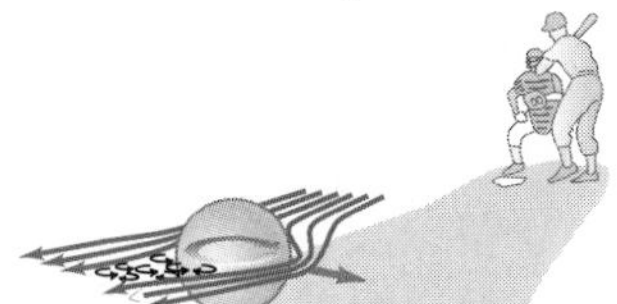

(f) Backspin of a golf ball

Test Your Understanding of Section 14.6 How much more thumb pressure must a nurse use to administer an injection with a hypodermic needle of inside diameter 0.30 mm compared to one with inside diameter 0.60 mm? Assume that the two needles have the same length and that the volume flow rate is the same in both cases. (i) twice as much; (ii) 4 times as much; (iii) 8 times as much; (iv) 16 times as much; (v) 32 times as much.

CHAPTER 14 SUMMARY

Density and pressure: Density is mass per unit volume. If a mass m of homogeneous material has volume V, its density ρ is the ratio m/V. Specific gravity is the ratio of the density of a material to the density of water. (See Example 14.1.)

Pressure is normal force per unit area. Pascal's law states that pressure applied to an enclosed fluid is transmitted undiminished to every portion of the fluid. Absolute pressure is the total pressure in a fluid; gauge pressure is the difference between absolute pressure and atmospheric pressure. The SI unit of pressure is the pascal (Pa): 1 Pa = 1 N/m^2. (See Example 14.2.)

$$\rho = \frac{m}{V} \qquad (14.1)$$

$$p = \frac{dF_\perp}{dA} \qquad (14.2)$$

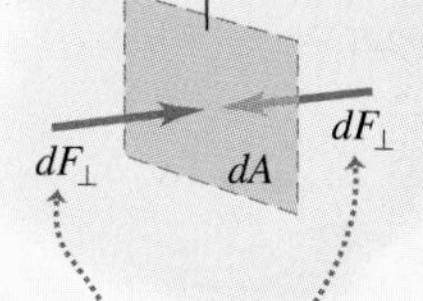

Pressures in a fluid at rest: The pressure difference between points 1 and 2 in a static fluid of uniform density ρ (an incompressible fluid) is proportional to the difference between the elevations y_1 and y_2. If the pressure at the surface of an incompressible liquid at rest is p_0, then the pressure at a depth h is greater by an amount ρgh. (See Examples 14.3 and 14.4.)

$$p_2 - p_1 = -\rho g(y_2 - y_1) \qquad (14.5)$$
(pressure in a fluid of uniform density)

$$p = p_0 + \rho gh \qquad (14.6)$$
(pressure in a fluid of uniform density)

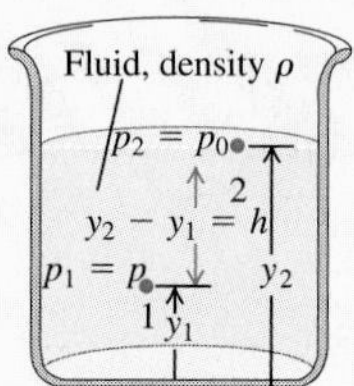

Buoyancy: Archimedes's principle states that when a body is immersed in a fluid, the fluid exerts an upward buoyant force on the body equal to the weight of the fluid that the body displaces. (See Example 14.5.)

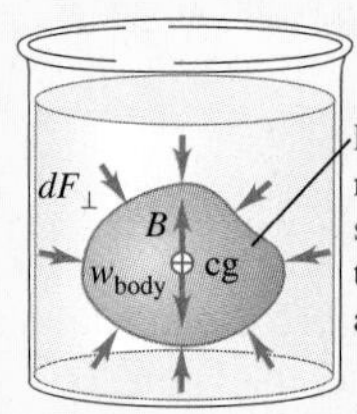

Fluid flow: An ideal fluid is incompressible and has no viscosity (no internal friction). A flow line is the path of a fluid particle; a streamline is a curve tangent at each point to the velocity vector at that point. A flow tube is a tube bounded at its sides by flow lines. In laminar flow, layers of fluid slide smoothly past each other. In turbulent flow, there is great disorder and a constantly changing flow pattern.

Conservation of mass in an incompressible fluid is expressed by the continuity equation, which relates the flow speeds v_1 and v_2 for two cross sections A_1 and A_2 in a flow tube. The product Av equals the volume flow rate, dV/dt, the rate at which volume crosses a section of the tube. (See Example 14.6.)

Bernoulli's equation relates the pressure p, flow speed v, and elevation y for any two points, assuming steady flow in an ideal fluid. (See Examples 14.7–14.10.)

$$A_1v_1 = A_2v_2 \qquad (14.10)$$
(continuity equation, incompressible fluid)

$$\frac{dV}{dt} = Av \qquad (14.11)$$
(volume flow rate)

$$p_1 + \rho g y_1 + \frac{1}{2}\rho v_1^2 = p_2 + \rho g y_2 + \frac{1}{2}\rho v_2^2 \qquad (14.17)$$
(Bernoulli's equation)

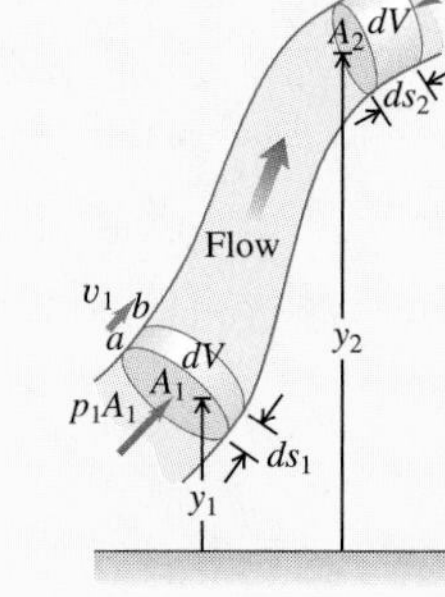

Key Terms

fluid statics, *456*
fluid dynamics, *456*
density, *456*
specific gravity, *457*
average density, *457*
pressure, *458*
pascal, *458*
atmospheric pressure, *458*
Pascal's law, *460*
gauge pressure, *461*
absolute pressure, *461*
mercury barometer, *462*
buoyancy, *463*
Archimedes's principle, *463*
buoyant force, *464*
surface tension, *465*
ideal fluid, *466*
viscosity, *466*
flow line, *466*
steady flow, *466*
streamline, *466*
flow tube, *466*
laminar flow, *466*
turbulent flow, *466*
continuity equation, *466*
Bernoulli's equation, *469*
viscosity, *473*
turbulence, *473*

Answer to Chapter Opening Question ?

The flesh of both the shark and the tropical fish is denser than seawater, so left to themselves they would sink. However, a tropical fish has a gas-filled body cavity called a swimbladder, so that the *average* density of the fish's body is the same as seawater and the fish neither sinks nor rises. Sharks have no such cavity. Hence they must swim constantly to keep from sinking, using their pectoral fins to provide lift much like the wings of an airplane (see Section 14.5).

Answers to Test Your Understanding Questions

14.1 Answer: (ii), (iv), (i) and (iii) (tie) (v) In each case the average density equals the mass divided by the volume. Hence we have (i) $\rho = (4.00\text{ kg})/(1.60 \times 10^{-3}\text{ m}^3) = 2.50 \times 10^3\text{ kg/m}^3$; (ii) $\rho = (8.00\text{ kg})/(1.60 \times 10^{-3}\text{ m}^3) = 5.00 \times 10^3\text{ kg/m}^3$; (iii) $\rho = (8.00\text{ kg})/(3.20 \times 10^{-3}\text{ m}^3) = 2.50 \times 10^3\text{ kg/m}^3$; (iv) $\rho = (2560\text{ kg})/(0.640\text{ m}^3) = 4.00 \times 10^3\text{ kg/m}^3$; (v) $\rho = (2560\text{ kg})/(1.28\text{ m}^3) = 2.00 \times 10^3\text{ kg/m}^3$. Note that compared to object (i), object (ii) has double the mass but the same volume and so has double the average density. Object (iii) has double the mass and double the volume of object (i), so (i) and (iii) have the same average density. Finally, object (v) has the same mass as object (iv) but double the volume, so (v) has half the average density of (iv).

14.2 Answer: (ii) From Eq. (14.9), the pressure outside the barometer is equal to the product ρgh. When the barometer is taken out of the refrigerator, the density ρ decreases while the height h of the mercury column remains the same. Hence the air pressure must be lower outdoors than inside the refrigerator.

14.3 Answer: (i) Consider the water, the statue, and the container together as a system; the total weight of the system does not depend on whether the statue is immersed. The total supporting force, including the tension T and the upward force F of the scale on the container (equal to the scale reading), is the same in both cases. But we saw in Example 14.5 that T decreases by 7.84 N when the statue is immersed, so the scale reading F must *increase* by 7.84 N. An alternative viewpoint is that the water exerts an upward buoyant force of 7.84 N on the statue, so the statue must exert an equal downward force on the water, making the scale reading 7.84 N greater than the weight of water and container.

14.4 Answer: (ii) A highway that narrows from three lanes to one is like a pipe whose cross-sectional area narrows to one-third of its value. If cars behaved like the molecules of an incompressible fluid, then as the cars encountered the one-lane section, the spacing between cars (the "density") would stay the same but the cars would triple their speed. This would keep the "volume flow rate" (number of cars per second passing a point on the highway) the same. In real life cars behave like the molecules of a *compressible* fluid: They end up packed closer (the "density" increases) and fewer cars per second pass a point on the highway (the "volume flow rate" decreases).

14.5 Answer: (ii) Newton's second law tells us that a body accelerates (its velocity changes) in response to a net force. In fluid flow, a pressure difference between two points means that fluid particles moving between those two points experience a force, and this force causes the fluid particles to accelerate and change speed.

14.6 Answer: (iv) The required pressure is proportional to $1/R^4$, where R is the inside radius of the needle (half the inside diameter). With the smaller-diameter needle, the pressure is greater by a factor of $[(0.60\text{ mm})/(0.30\text{ mm})]^4 = 2^4 = 16$.

PROBLEMS

For instructor-assigned homework, go to www.masteringphysics.com 

Discussion Questions

Q14.1. A cube of oak wood with very smooth faces normally floats in water. Suppose you submerge it completely and press one face flat against the bottom of a tank so that no water is under that face. Will the block float to the surface? Is there a buoyant force on it? Explain.

Q14.2. A rubber hose is attached to a funnel, and the free end is bent around to point upward. When water is poured into the funnel, it rises in the hose to the same level as in the funnel, even though the funnel has a lot more water in it than the hose does. Why? What supports the extra weight of the water in the funnel?

Q14.3. Comparing Example 14.1 (Section 14.1) and Example 14.2 (Section 14.2), it seems that 700 N of air is exerting a downward force of 2.0×10^6 N on the floor. How is this possible?

Q14.4. Equation (14.7) shows that an area ratio of 100 to 1 can give 100 times more output force than input force. Doesn't this violate conservation of energy? Explain.

Q14.5. You have probably noticed that the lower the tire pressure, the larger the contact area between the tire and the road. Why?

Q14.6. In hot-air ballooning, a large balloon is filled with air heated by a gas burner at the bottom. Why must the air be heated? How does the balloonist control ascent and descent?

Q14.7. In describing the size of a large ship, one uses such expressions as "it displaces 20,000 tons." What does this mean? Can the weight of the ship be obtained from this information?

Q14.8. You drop a solid sphere of aluminum in a bucket of water that sits on the ground. The buoyant force equals the weight of water displaced; this is less than the weight of the sphere, so the sphere sinks to the bottom. If you take the bucket with you on an elevator that accelerates upward, the apparent weight of the water increases and the buoyant force on the sphere increases. Could the acceleration of the elevator be great enough to make the sphere pop up out of the water? Explain.

Q14.9. A rigid, lighter-than-air dirigible filled with helium cannot continue to rise indefinitely. Why? What determines the maximum height it can attain?

Q14.10. Air pressure decreases with increasing altitude. So why is air near the surface not continuously drawn upward toward the lower-pressure regions above?

Q14.11. The purity of gold can be tested by weighing it in air and in water. How? Do you think you could get away with making a fake gold brick by gold-plating some cheaper material?

Q14.12. During the Great Mississippi Flood of 1993, the levees in St. Louis tended to rupture first at the bottom. Why?

Q14.13. A cargo ship travels from the Atlantic Ocean (salt water) to Lake Ontario (freshwater) via the St. Lawrence River. The ship rides several centimeters lower in the water in Lake Ontario than it did in the ocean. Explain why.

Q14.14. You push a piece of wood under the surface of a swimming pool. After it is completely submerged, you keep pushing it deeper and deeper. As you do this, what will happen to the buoyant force on it? Will the force keep increasing, stay the same, or decrease? Why?

Q14.15. An old question is "Which weighs more, a pound of feathers or a pound of lead?" If the weight in pounds is the gravitational force, will a pound of feathers balance a pound of lead on opposite pans of an equal-arm balance? Explain, taking into account buoyant forces.

Q14.16. Suppose the door of a room makes an airtight but frictionless fit in its frame. Do you think you could open the door if the air pressure on one side were standard atmospheric pressure and the air pressure on the other side differed from standard by 1%? Explain.

Q14.17. At a certain depth in an incompressible liquid, the absolute pressure is p. At twice this depth, will the absolute pressure be equal to $2p$, greater than $2p$, or less than $2p$? Justify your answer.

Q14.18. A piece of iron is glued to the top of a block of wood. When the block is placed in a bucket of water with the iron on top, the block floats. The block is now turned over so that the iron is submerged beneath the wood. Does the block float or sink? Does the water level in the bucket rise, drop, or stay the same? Explain your answers.

Q14.19. You take an empty glass jar and push it into a tank of water with the open mouth of the jar downward, so that the air inside the jar is trapped and cannot get out. If you push the jar deeper into the water, does the buoyant force on the jar stay the same? If not, does it increase or decrease? Explain your answer.

Q14.20. You are floating in a canoe in the middle of a swimming pool. Your friend is at the edge of the pool, carefully noting the level of the water on the side of the pool. You have a bowling ball with you in the canoe. If you carefully drop the bowling ball over the side of the canoe and it sinks to the bottom of the pool, does the water level in the pool rise or fall?

Q14.21. You are floating in a canoe in the middle of a swimming pool. A large bird flies up and lights on your shoulder. Does the water level in the pool rise or fall?

Q14.22. At a certain depth in the incompressible ocean the gauge pressure is p_g. At three times this depth, will the gauge pressure be greater than $3p_g$, equal to $3p_g$, or less than $3p_g$? Justify your answer.

Q14.23. An ice cube floats in a glass of water. When the ice melts, will the water level in the glass rise, fall, or remain unchanged? Explain.

Q14.24. You are told, "Bernoulli's equation tells us that where there is higher fluid speed, there is lower fluid pressure, and vice versa." Is this statement always true, even for an idealized fluid? Explain.

Q14.25. If the velocity at each point in space in steady-state fluid flow is constant, how can a fluid particle accelerate?

Q14.26. In a store-window vacuum cleaner display, a table-tennis ball is suspended in midair in a jet of air blown from the outlet hose of a tank-type vacuum cleaner. The ball bounces around a little but always moves back toward the center of the jet, even if the jet is tilted from the vertical. How does this behavior illustrate Bernoulli's equation?

Q14.27. A tornado consists of a rapidly whirling air vortex. Why is the pressure always much lower in the center than at the outside? How does this condition account for the destructive power of a tornado?

Q14.28. Airports at high elevations have longer runways for takeoffs and landings than do airports at sea level. One reason is that aircraft engines develop less power in the thin air well above sea level. What is another reason?

Q14.29. When a smooth-flowing stream of water comes out of a faucet, it narrows as it falls. Explain why this happens.

Q14.30. Identical-size lead and aluminum cubes are suspended at different depths by two wires in a large vat of water (Fig. 14.32). (a) Which cube experiences a greater buoyant force? (b) For which cube is the tension in the wire greater? (c) Which cube experiences a greater force on its lower face? (d) For which cube is the difference in pressure between the upper and lower faces greater?

Figure **14.32** Question Q14.30.

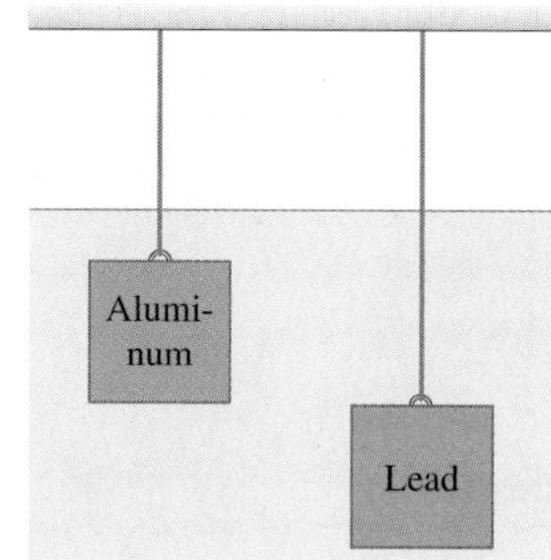

Exercises

Section 14.1 Density

14.1. On a part-time job, you are asked to bring a cylindrical iron rod of length 85.8 cm and diameter 2.85 cm from a storage room to a machinist. Will you need a cart? (To answer, calculate the weight of the rod.)

14.2. Miles per Kilogram. The density of gasoline is 737 kg/m^3. If your new hybrid car gets 45.0 miles per gallon of gasoline, what is its mileage in miles per kilogram of gasoline? (See Appendix E.)

14.3. You purchase a rectangular piece of metal that has dimensions $5.0 \times 15.0 \times 30.0$ mm and mass 0.0158 kg. The seller tells you that the metal is gold. To check this, you compute the average density of the piece. What value do you get? Were you cheated?

14.4. Gold Brick. You win the lottery and decide to impress your friends by exhibiting a million-dollar cube of gold. At the time, gold is selling for \$426.60 per troy ounce, and 1.0000 troy ounce equals 31.1035 g. How tall would your million-dollar cube be?

14.5. A uniform lead sphere and a uniform aluminum sphere have the same mass. What is the ratio of the radius of the aluminum sphere to the radius of the lead sphere?

14.6. (a) What is the average density of the sun? (b) What is the average density of a neutron star that has the same mass as the sun but a radius of only 20.0 km?

14.7. A hollow cylindrical copper pipe is 1.50 m long and has an outside diameter of 3.50 cm and an inside diameter of 2.50 cm. How much does it weigh?

Section 14.2 Pressure in a Fluid

14.8. Black Smokers. Black smokers are hot volcanic vents that emit smoke deep in the ocean floor. Many of them teem with exotic creatures, and some biologists think that life on earth may have begun around such vents. The vents range in depth from about 1500 m to 3200 m below the surface. What is the gauge pressure at a 3200-m deep vent, assuming that the density of water does not vary? Express your answer in pascals and atmospheres.

14.9. Oceans on Mars. Scientists have found evidence that Mars may once have had an ocean 0.500 km deep. The acceleration due to gravity on Mars is 3.71 m/s^2. (a) What would be the gauge pressure at the bottom of such an ocean, assuming it was freshwater? (b) To what depth would you need to go in the earth's ocean to experience the same gauge pressure?

14.10. (a) Calculate the difference in blood pressure between the feet and top of the head for a person who is 1.65 m tall. (b) Consider a cylindrical segment of a blood vessel 2.00 cm long and 1.50 mm in diameter. What *additional* outward force would such a vessel need to withstand in the person's feet compared to a similar vessel in her head?

14.11. In intravenous feeding, a needle is inserted in a vein in the patient's arm and a tube leads from the needle to a reservoir of fluid (density 1050 kg/m^3) located at height h above the arm. The top of the reservoir is open to the air. If the gauge pressure inside the vein is 5980 Pa, what is the minimum value of h that allows fluid to enter the vein? Assume the needle diameter is large enough that you can ignore the viscosity (see Section 14.6) of the fluid.

14.12. A barrel contains a 0.120-m layer of oil floating on water that is 0.250 m deep. The density of the oil is 600 kg/m^3. (a) What is the gauge pressure at the oil–water interface? (b) What is the gauge pressure at the bottom of the barrel?

14.13. A 975-kg car has its tires each inflated to "32.0 pounds." (a) What are the absolute and gauge pressures in these tires in lb/in.^2, Pa, and atm? (b) If the tires were perfectly round, could the tire pressure exert any force on the pavement? (Assume that the tire walls are flexible so that the pressure exerted by the tire on the pavement equals the air pressure inside the tire.) (c) If you examine a car's tires, it is obvious that there is some flattening at the bottom. What is the total contact area for all four tires of the flattened part of the tires at the pavement?

14.14. You are designing a diving bell to withstand the pressure of seawater at a depth of 250 m. (a) What is the gauge pressure at this depth? (You can ignore changes in the density of the water with depth.) (b) At this depth, what is the net force due to the water outside and the air inside the bell on a circular glass window 30.0 cm in diameter if the pressure inside the diving bell equals the pressure at the surface of the water? (You can ignore the small variation of pressure over the surface of the window.)

14.15. What gauge pressure must a pump produce to pump water from the bottom of the Grand Canyon (elevation 730 m) to Indian Gardens (elevation 1370 m)? Express your results in pascals and in atmospheres.

14.16. The liquid in the open-tube manometer in Fig. 14.9a is mercury, $y_1 = 3.00$ cm, and $y_2 = 7.00$ cm. Atmospheric pressure is 980 millibars. (a) What is the absolute pressure at the bottom of the U-shaped tube? (b) What is the absolute pressure in the open tube at a depth of 4.00 cm below the free surface? (c) What is the absolute pressure of the gas in the tank? (d) What is the gauge pressure of the gas in pascals?

14.17. There is a maximum depth at which a diver can breathe through a snorkel tube (Fig. 14.33) because as the depth increases, so does the pressure difference, which tends to collapse the diver's lungs. Since the snorkel connects the air in the lungs to the atmosphere at the surface, the pressure inside the lungs is atmospheric pressure. What is the external–internal pressure difference when the diver's lungs are at a depth of 6.1 m (about 20 ft)? Assume that the diver is in freshwater. (A scuba diver breathing from compressed air tanks can operate at greater depths than can a snorkeler, since the pressure of the air inside the scuba diver's lungs increases to match the external pressure of the water.)

Figure 14.33 Exercise 14.17.

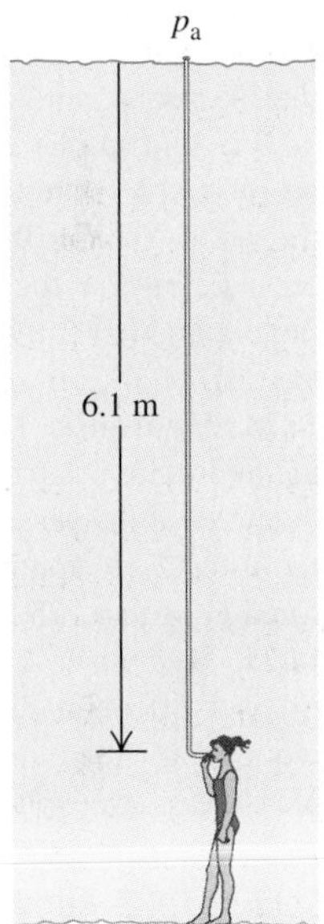

14.18. A tall cylinder with a cross-sectional area 12.0 cm^2 is partially filled with mercury; the surface of the mercury is 5.00 cm above the bottom of the cylinder. Water is slowly poured in on top of the mercury, and the two fluids don't mix. What volume of water must be added to double the gauge pressure at the bottom of the cylinder?

14.19. A lake in the far north of the Yukon is covered with a 1.75-m-thick layer of ice. Find the absolute pressure and the gauge pressure at a depth of 2.50 m in the lake.

14.20. A closed container is partially filled with water. Initially, the air above the water is at atmospheric pressure $(1.01 \times 10^5\ \text{Pa})$ and the gauge pressure at the bottom of the water is 2500 Pa. Then additional air is pumped in, increasing the pressure of the air above the water by 1500 Pa. (a) What is the gauge pressure at the bottom of the water? (b) By how much must the water level in the container be reduced, by drawing some water out through a valve at the bottom of the container, to return the gauge pressure at the bottom of the water to its original value of 2500 Pa? The pressure of the air above the water is maintained at 1500 Pa above atmospheric pressure.

14.21. An electrical short cuts off all power to a submersible diving vehicle when it is 30 m below the surface of the ocean. The crew must push out a hatch of area 0.75 m^2 and weight 300 N on the bottom to escape. If the pressure inside is 1.0 atm, what downward force must the crew exert on the hatch to open it?

14.22. Exploring Venus. The surface pressure on Venus is 92 atm, and the acceleration due to gravity there is 0.894*g*. In a future exploratory mission, an upright cylindrical tank of benzene is sealed at the top but still pressurized at 92 atm just above the benzene. The tank has a diameter of 1.72 m, and the benzene column is 11.50 m tall. Ignore any effects due to the very high temperature on Venus. (a) What total force is exerted on the inside surface of the bottom of the tank? (b) What force does the Venusian atmosphere exert on the outside surface of the bottom of the tank? (c) What total inward force does the atmosphere exert on the vertical walls of the tank?

14.23. A cylindrical disk of wood weighing 45.0 N and having a diameter of 30.0 cm floats on a cylinder of oil of density 0.850 g/cm^3 (Fig. 14.34). The cylinder of oil is 75.0 cm deep and has a diameter the same as that of the wood. (a) What is the gauge pressure at the top of the oil column? (b) Suppose now that someone puts a weight of 83.0 N on top of the wood, but no oil seeps around the edge of the wood. What is the *change* in pressure at (i) the bottom of the oil, and (ii) halfway down in the oil?

Figure 14.34 Exercise 14.23.

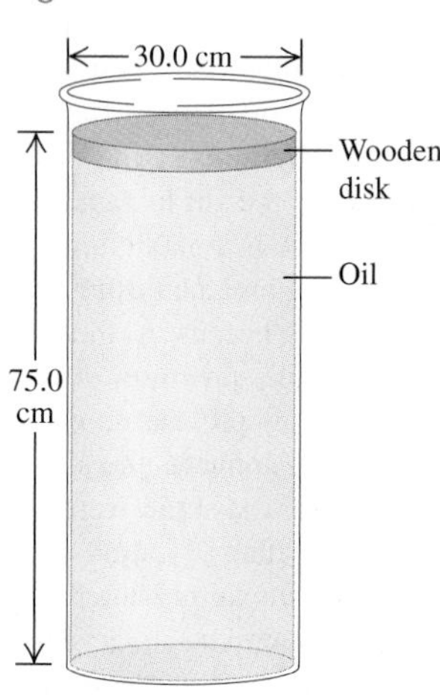

14.24. Hydraulic Lift I. For the hydraulic lift shown in Fig. 14.8, what must be the ratio of the diameter of the vessel at the car to the diameter of the vessel where the force F_1 is applied so that a 1520-kg car can be lifted with a force F_1 of just 125 N?

14.25. Hydraulic Lift II. The piston of a hydraulic automobile lift is 0.30 m in diameter. What gauge pressure, in pascals, is required to lift a car with a mass of 1200 kg? Also express this pressure in atmospheres.

Section 14.3 Buoyancy

14.26. A slab of ice floats on a freshwater lake. What minimum volume must the slab have for a 45.0-kg woman to be able to stand on it without getting her feet wet?

14.27. An ore sample weighs 17.50 N in air. When the sample is suspended by a light cord and totally immersed in water, the tension in the cord is 11.20 N. Find the total volume and the density of the sample.

14.28. You are preparing some apparatus for a visit to a newly discovered planet Caasi having oceans of glycerine and a surface acceleration due to gravity of 4.15 m/s^2. If your apparatus floats in the oceans on earth with 25.0% of its volume submerged, what percentage will be submerged in the glycerine oceans of Caasi?

14.29. An object of average density ρ floats at the surface of a fluid of density ρ_{fluid}. (a) How must the two densities be related? (b) In view of the answer to part (a), how can steel ships float in water? (c) In terms of ρ and ρ_{fluid}, what fraction of the object is submerged and what fraction is above the fluid? Check that your answers give the correct limiting behavior as $\rho \rightarrow \rho_{fluid}$ and as $\rho \rightarrow 0$. (d) While on board your yacht, your cousin Throckmorton cuts a rectangular piece (dimensions $5.0 \times 4.0 \times 3.0$ cm) out of a life preserver and throws it into the ocean. The piece has a mass of 42 g. As it floats in the ocean, what percentage of its volume is above the surface?

14.30. A hollow plastic sphere is held below the surface of a freshwater lake by a cord anchored to the bottom of the lake. The sphere has a volume of 0.650 m^3 and the tension in the cord is 900 N. (a) Calculate the buoyant force exerted by the water on the sphere. (b) What is the mass of the sphere? (c) The cord breaks and the sphere rises to the surface. When the sphere comes to rest, what fraction of its volume will be submerged?

14.31. A cubical block of wood, 10.0 cm on a side, floats at the interface between oil and water with its lower surface 1.50 cm below the interface (Fig. 14.35). The density of the oil is 790 kg/m^3. (a) What is the gauge pressure at the upper face of the block? (b) What is the gauge pressure at the lower face of the block? (c) What are the mass and density of the block?

Figure 14.35 Exercise 14.31.

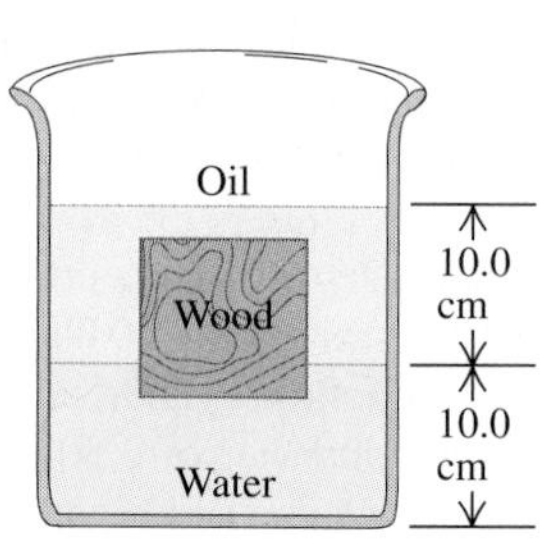

14.32. A solid aluminum ingot weighs 89 N in air. (a) What is its volume? (b) The ingot is suspended from a rope and totally immersed in water. What is the tension in the rope (the *apparent* weight of the ingot in water)?

14.33. A rock is suspended by a light string. When the rock is in air, the tension in the string is 39.2 N. When the rock is totally immersed in water, the tension is 28.4 N. When the rock is totally immersed in an unknown liquid, the tension is 18.6 N. What is the density of the unknown liquid?

Section 14.4 Fluid Flow

14.34. Water runs into a fountain, filling all the pipes, at a steady rate of 0.750 m/s^3. (a) How fast will it shoot out of a hole 4.50 cm in diameter? (b) At what speed will it shoot out if the diameter of the hole is three times as large?

14.35. A shower head has 20 circular openings, each with radius 1.0 mm. The shower head is connected to a pipe with radius 0.80 cm. If the speed of water in the pipe is 3.0 m/s, what is its speed as it exits the shower-head openings?

14.36. Water is flowing in a pipe with a varying cross-sectional area, and at all points the water completely fills the pipe. At point 1 the cross-sectional area of the pipe is 0.070 m^2, and the magnitude of the fluid velocity is 3.50 m/s. (a) What is the fluid speed at points in the pipe where the cross-sectional area is (a) 0.105 m^2 and (b) 0.047 m^2? (c) Calculate the volume of water discharged from the open end of the pipe in 1.00 hour.

14.37. Water is flowing in a pipe with a circular cross section but with varying cross-sectional area, and at all points the water completely fills the pipe. (a) At one point in the pipe the radius is 0.150 m. What is the speed of the water at this point if water is flowing into this pipe at a steady rate of 1.20 m^3/s? (b) At a second point in the pipe the water speed is 3.80 m/s. What is the radius of the pipe at this point?

14.38. (a) Derive Eq. (14.12). (b) If the density increases by 1.50% from point 1 to point 2, what happens to the volume flow rate?

Section 14.5 Bernoulli's Equation

14.39. A sealed tank containing seawater to a height of 11.0 m also contains air above the water at a gauge pressure of 3.00 atm. Water flows out from the bottom through a small hole. How fast is this water moving?

14.40. A small circular hole 6.00 mm in diameter is cut in the side of a large water tank, 14.0 m below the water level in the tank. The top of the tank is open to the air. Find (a) the speed of efflux of the water, and (b) the volume discharged per second.

14.41. What gauge pressure is required in the city water mains for a stream from a fire hose connected to the mains to reach a vertical height of 15.0 m? (Assume that the mains have a much larger diameter than the fire hose.)

14.42. At one point in a pipeline the water's speed is 3.00 m/s and the gauge pressure is 5.00×10^4 Pa. Find the gauge pressure at a second point in the line, 11.0 m lower than the first, if the pipe diameter at the second point is twice that at the first.

14.43. Lift on an Airplane. Air streams horizontally past a small airplane's wings such that the speed is 70.0 m/s over the top surface and 60.0 m/s past the bottom surface. If the plane has a wing area of 16.2 m^2 on the top and on the bottom, what is the net vertical force that the air exerts on the airplane? The density of the air is 1.20 kg/m^3.

14.44. A soft drink (mostly water) flows in a pipe at a beverage plant with a mass flow rate that would fill 220 0.355-L cans per minute. At point 2 in the pipe, the gauge pressure is 152 kPa and the cross-sectional area is 8.00 cm^2. At point 1, 1.35 m above point 2, the cross-sectional area is 2.00 cm^2. Find the (a) mass flow rate; (b) volume flow rate; (c) flow speeds at points 1 and 2; (d) gauge pressure at point 1.

14.45. At a certain point in a horizontal pipeline, the water's speed is 2.50 m/s and the gauge pressure is 1.80×10^4 Pa. Find the gauge pressure at a second point in the line if the cross-sectional area at the second point is twice that at the first.

14.46. A golf course sprinkler system discharges water from a horizontal pipe at the rate of 7200 cm^3/s. At one point in the pipe, where the radius is 4.00 cm, the water's absolute pressure is 2.40×10^5 Pa. At a second point in the pipe, the water passes through a constriction where the radius is 2.00 cm. What is the water's absolute pressure as it flows through this constriction?

Problems

14.47. In a lecture demonstration, a professor pulls apart two hemispherical steel shells (diameter D) with ease using their attached handles. She then places them together, pumps out the air to an absolute pressure of p, and hands them to a bodybuilder in the back row to pull apart. (a) If atmospheric pressure is p_0, how much force must the bodybuilder exert on each shell? (b) Evaluate your answer for the case $p = 0.025$ atm, $D = 10.0$ cm.

14.48. The deepest point known in any of the earth's oceans is in the Marianas Trench, 10.92 km deep. (a) Assuming water is incompressible, what is the pressure at this depth? Use the density of seawater. (b) The actual pressure is 1.16×10^8 Pa; your calculated value will be less because the density actually varies with depth. Using the compressibility of water and the actual pressure, find the density of the water at the bottom of the Marianas Trench. What is the percent change in the density of the water?

14.49. A swimming pool is 5.0 m long, 4.0 m wide, and 3.0 m deep. Compute the force exerted by the water against (a) the bottom; and (b) either end. (*Hint:* Calculate the force on a thin, horizontal strip at a depth h, and integrate this over the end of the pool.) Do not include the force due to air pressure.

14.50. The upper edge of a gate in a dam runs along the water surface. The gate is 2.00 m high and 4.00 m wide and is hinged along a horizontal line through its center (Fig. 14.36). Calculate the torque about the hinge arising from the force due to the water. (*Hint:* Use a procedure similar to that used in Problem 14.49; calculate the torque on a thin, horizontal strip at a depth h and integrate this over the gate.)

Figure 14.36 Problem 14.50.

14.51. Force and Torque on a Dam. A dam has the shape of a rectangular solid. The side facing the lake has area A and height H. The surface of the freshwater lake behind the dam is at the top of the dam. (a) Show that the net horizontal force exerted by the water on the dam equals $\frac{1}{2}\rho g H A$—that is, the average gauge pressure across the face of the dam times the area (see Problem 14.49). (b) Show that the torque exerted by the water about an axis along the bottom of the dam is $\rho g H^2 A/6$. (c) How do the force and torque depend on the size of the lake?

14.52. Submarines on Europa. Some scientists are eager to send a remote-controlled submarine to Jupiter's moon Europa to search for life in its oceans below an icy crust. Europa's mass has been measured to be 4.78×10^{22} kg, its diameter is 3130 km, and it has no appreciable atmosphere. Assume that the layer of ice at the surface is not thick enough to exert substantial force on the water. If the windows of the submarine you are designing are 25.0 cm square and can stand a maximum inward force of 9750 N per window, what is the greatest depth to which this submarine can safely dive?

14.53. An astronaut is standing at the north pole of a newly discovered, spherically symmetric planet of radius R. In his hands he holds a container full of a liquid with mass m and volume V. At the surface of the liquid, the pressure is p_0; at a depth d below the surface, the pressure has a greater value p. From this information, determine the mass of the planet.

14.54. Ballooning on Mars. It has been proposed that we could explore Mars using inflated balloons to hover just above the surface. The buoyancy of the atmosphere would keep the balloon aloft. The density of the Martian atmosphere is 0.0154 kg/m^3 (although this varies with temperature). Suppose we construct these balloons of a thin but tough plastic having a density such that each square meter has a mass of 5.00 g. We inflate them with a very light gas whose mass we can neglect. (a) What should be the radius and mass of these balloons so they just hover above the surface of Mars? (b) If we released one of the balloons from part (a) on earth, where the atmospheric density is 1.20 kg/m^3, what would be its initial acceleration assuming it was the same size as on Mars? Would it go up or down? (c) If on Mars these balloons have five times the radius found in part (a), how heavy an instrument package could they carry?

14.55. The earth does not have a uniform density; it is most dense at its center and least dense at its surface. An approximation of its density is $\rho(r) = A - Br$, where $A = 12{,}700$ kg/m^3 and $B = 1.50 \times 10^{-3}$ kg/m^4. Use $R = 6.37 \times 10^6$ m for the radius of the earth approximated as a sphere. (a) Geological evidence indicates that the densities are 13,100 kg/m^3 and 2,400 kg/m^3 at the earth's center and surface, respectively. What values does the linear approximation model give for the densities at these two locations? (b) Imagine dividing the earth into concentric, spherical shells. Each shell has radius r, thickness dr, volume $dV = 4\pi r^2\,dr$, and mass $dm = \rho(r)dV$. By integrating from $r = 0$ to $r = R$, show that the mass of the earth in this model is $M = \frac{4}{3}\pi R^3(A - \frac{3}{4}BR)$. (c) Show that the given values of A and B give the correct mass of the earth to within 0.4%. (d) We saw in Section 12.6 that a uniform spherical shell gives no contribution to g inside it. Show that

$g(r) = \frac{4}{3}\pi Gr(A - \frac{3}{4}Br)$ inside the earth in this model. (e) Verify that the expression of part (d) gives $g = 0$ at the center of the earth and $g = 9.85 \text{ m/s}^2$ at the surface. (f) Show that in this model g does *not* decrease uniformly with depth but rather has a maximum of $4\pi GA^2/9B = 10.01 \text{ m/s}^2$ at $r = 2A/3B = 5640$ km.

14.56. In Example 12.10 (Section 12.6) we saw that inside a planet of uniform density (not a realistic assumption for the earth) the acceleration due to gravity increases uniformly with distance from the center of the planet. That is, $g(r) = g_s r/R$, where g_s is the acceleration due to gravity at the surface, r is the distance from the center of the planet, and R is the radius of the planet. The interior of the planet can be treated approximately as an incompressible fluid of density ρ. (a) Replace the height y in Eq. (14.4) with the radial coordinate r and integrate to find the pressure inside a uniform planet as a function of r. Let the pressure at the surface be zero. (This means ignoring the pressure of the planet's atmosphere.) (b) Using this model, calculate the pressure at the center of the earth. (Use a value of ρ equal to the average density of the earth, calculated from the mass and radius given in Appendix F.) (c) Geologists estimate the pressure at the center of the earth to be approximately 4×10^{11} Pa. Does this agree with your calculation for the pressure at $r = 0$? What might account for any differences?

14.57. A U-shaped tube open to the air at both ends contains some mercury. A quantity of water is carefully poured into the left arm of the U-shaped tube until the vertical height of the water column is 15.0 cm (Fig. 14.37). (a) What is the gauge pressure at the water–mercury interface? (b) Calculate the vertical distance h from the top of the mercury in the right-hand arm of the tube to the top of the water in the left-hand arm.

Figure **14.37** Problem 14.57.

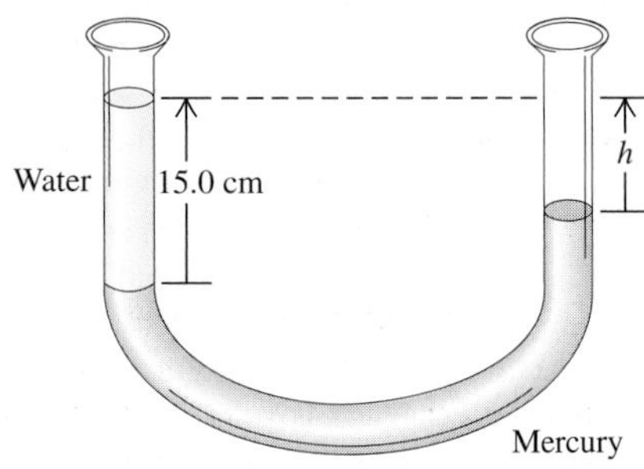

14.58. The Great Molasses Flood. On the afternoon of January 15, 1919, an unusually warm day in Boston, a 27.4-m-high, 27.4-m-diameter cylindrical metal tank used for storing molasses ruptured. Molasses flooded into the streets in a 9-m-deep stream, killing pedestrians and horses, and knocking down buildings. The molasses had a density of 1600 kg/m^3. If the tank was full before the accident, what was the total outward force the molasses exerted on its sides? (*Hint:* Consider the outward force on a circular ring of the tank wall of width dy and at a depth y below the surface. Integrate to find the total outward force. Assume that before the tank ruptured, the pressure at the surface of the molasses was equal to the air pressure outside the tank.)

14.59. An open barge has the dimensions shown in Fig. 14.38. If the barge is made out of 4.0-cm-thick steel plate on each of its four sides and its bottom, what mass of coal can the barge carry in freshwater without sinking? Is there enough room in the barge to hold this amount of coal? (The density of coal is about 1500 kg/m^3.)

Figure **14.38** Problem 14.59.

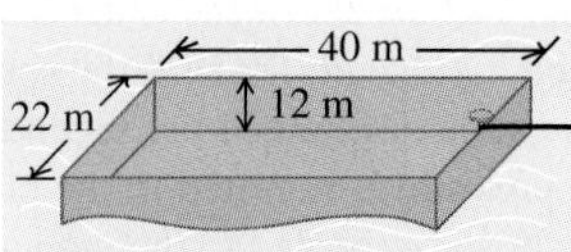

14.60. A hot-air balloon has a volume of 2200 m^3. The balloon fabric (the envelope) weighs 900 N. The basket with gear and full propane tanks weighs 1700 N. If the balloon can barely lift an additional 3200 N of passengers, breakfast, and champagne when the outside air density is 1.23 kg/m^3, what is the average density of the heated gases in the envelope?

14.61. Advertisements for a certain small car claim that it floats in water. (a) If the car's mass is 900 kg and its interior volume is 3.0 m^3, what fraction of the car is immersed when it floats? You can ignore the volume of steel and other materials. (b) Water gradually leaks in and displaces the air in the car. What fraction of the interior volume is filled with water when the car sinks?

14.62. A single ice cube with mass 9.70 g floats in a glass completely full of 420 cm^3 of water. You can ignore the water's surface tension and its variation in density with temperature (as long as it remains a liquid). (a) What volume of water does the ice cube displace? (b) When the ice cube has completely melted, has any water overflowed? If so, how much? If not, explain why this is so. (c) Suppose the water in the glass had been very salty water of density 1050 kg/m^3. What volume of salt water would the 9.70-g ice cube displace? (d) Redo part (b) for the freshwater ice cube in the salty water.

14.63. A piece of wood is 0.600 m long, 0.250 m wide, and 0.080 m thick. Its density is 600 kg/m^3. What volume of lead must be fastened underneath it to sink the wood in calm water so that its top is just even with the water level? What is the mass of this volume of lead?

14.64. A hydrometer consists of a spherical bulb and a cylindrical stem with a cross-sectional area of 0.400 cm^2 (see Fig. 14.13a). The total volume of bulb and stem is 13.2 cm^3. When immersed in water, the hydrometer floats with 8.00 cm of the stem above the water surface. When the hydrometer is immersed in an organic fluid, 3.20 cm of the stem is above the surface. Find the density of the organic fluid. (*Note:* This illustrates the precision of such a hydrometer. Relatively small density differences give rise to relatively large differences in hydrometer readings.)

14.65. The densities of air, helium, and hydrogen (at $p = 1.0$ atm and $T = 20°\text{C}$) are 1.20 kg/m^3, 0.166 kg/m^3, and 0.0899 kg/m^3, respectively. (a) What is the volume in cubic meters displaced by a hydrogen-filled airship that has a total "lift" of 120 kN? (The "lift" is the amount by which the buoyant force exceeds the weight of the gas that fills the airship.) (b) What would be the "lift" if helium were used instead of hydrogen? In view of your answer, why is helium used in modern airships like advertising blimps?

14.66. SHM of a Floating Object. An object with height h, mass M, and a uniform cross-sectional area A floats upright in a liquid with density ρ. (a) Calculate the vertical distance from the surface of the liquid to the bottom of the floating object at equilibrium. (b) A downward force with magnitude F is applied to the top of the object. At the new equilibrium position, how much farther below the surface of the liquid is the bottom of the object than it was in part (a)? (Assume that some of the object remains above the surface of the liquid.) (c) Your result in part (b) shows that if the force is suddenly removed, the object will oscillate up and down in SHM. Calculate the period of this motion in terms of the density ρ of the liquid, the mass M, and cross-sectional area A of the object. You can ignore the damping due to fluid friction (see Section 13.7).

14.67. A 950-kg cylindrical can buoy floats vertically in salt water. The diameter of the buoy is 0.900 m. (a) Calculate the additional distance the buoy will sink when a 70.0-kg man stands on top. (Use the expression derived in part (b) of Problem 14.66.) (b) Calculate the period of the resulting vertical SHM when the man dives off. (Use the expression derived in part (c) of Problem 14.66, and as in that problem, you can ignore the damping due to fluid friction.)

14.68. A firehose must be able to shoot water to the top of a building 35.0 m tall when aimed straight up. Water enters this hose at a steady rate of 0.500 m^3/s and shoots out of a round nozzle. (a) What is the maximum diameter this nozzle can have? (b) If the only nozzle available has a diameter twice as great, what is the highest point the water can reach?

14.69. You drill a small hole in the side of a vertical cylindrical water tank that is standing on the ground with its top open to the air. (a) If the water level has a height H, at what height above the base should you drill the hole for the water to reach its greatest distance from the base of the cylinder when it hits the ground? (b) What is the greatest distance the water will reach?

14.70. A vertical cylindrical tank of cross-sectional area A_1 is open to the air at the top and contains water to a depth h_0. A worker accidentally pokes a hole of area A_2 in the bottom of the tank. (a) Derive an equation for the depth h of the water as a function of time t after the hole is poked. (b) How long after the hole is made does it take for the tank to empty out?

14.71. A block of balsa wood placed in one scale pan of an equal-arm balance is exactly balanced by a 0.0950-kg brass mass in the other scale pan. Find the true mass of the balsa wood if its density is 150 kg/m^3. Explain why it is accurate to ignore the buoyancy in air of the brass but *not* the buoyancy in air of the balsa wood.

14.72. Block A in Fig. 14.39 hangs by a cord from spring balance D and is submerged in a liquid C contained in beaker B. The mass of the beaker is 1.00 kg; the mass of the liquid is 1.80 kg. Balance D reads 3.50 kg, and balance E reads 7.50 kg. The volume of block A is 3.80×10^{-3} m^3. (a) What is the density of the liquid? (b) What will each balance read if block A is pulled up out of the liquid?

Figure 14.39 Problem 14.72.

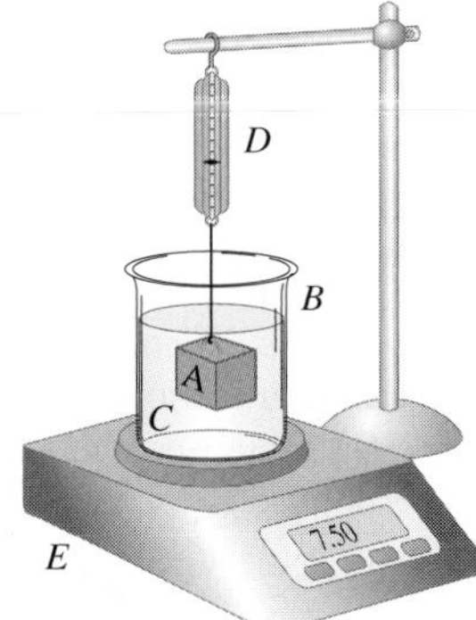

14.73. A hunk of aluminum is completely covered with a gold shell to form an ingot of weight 45.0 N. When you suspend the ingot from a spring balance and submerge the ingot in water, the balance reads 39.0 N. What is the weight of the gold in the shell?

14.74. A plastic ball has radius 12.0 cm and floats in water with 16.0% of its volume submerged. (a) What force must you apply to the ball to hold it at rest totally below the surface of the water? (b) If you let go of the ball, what is its acceleration the instant you release it?

14.75. The weight of a king's solid crown is w. When the crown is suspended by a light rope and completely immersed in water, the tension in the rope (the crown's apparent weight) is fw. (a) Prove that the crown's relative density (specific gravity) is $1/(1-f)$. Discuss the meaning of the limits as f approaches 0 and 1. (b) If the crown is solid gold and weighs 12.9 N in air, what is its apparent weight when completely immersed in water? (c) Repeat part (b) if the crown is solid lead with a very thin gold plating, but still has a weight in air of 12.9 N.

14.76. A piece of steel has a weight w, an apparent weight (see Problem 14.75) w_{water} when completely immersed in water, and an apparent weight w_{fluid} when completely immersed in an unknown fluid. (a) Prove that the fluid's density relative to water (specific gravity) is $(w - w_{fluid})/(w - w_{water})$. (b) Is this result reasonable for the three cases of w_{fluid} greater than, equal to, or less than w_{water}? (c) The apparent weight of the piece of steel in water of density 1000 kg/m^3 is 87.2% of its weight. What percentage of its weight will its apparent weight be in formic acid (density 1220 kg/m^3)?

14.77. You cast some metal of density ρ_m in a mold, but you are worried that there might be cavities within the casting. You measure the weight of the casting to be w, and the buoyant force when it is completely surrounded by water to be B. (a) Show that $V_0 = B/(\rho_{water}g) - w/(\rho_m g)$ is the total volume of any enclosed cavities. (b) If your metal is copper, the casting's weight is 156 N, and the buoyant force is 20 N, what is the total volume of any enclosed cavities in your casting? What fraction is this of the total volume of the casting?

14.78. A cubical block of wood 0.100 m on a side and with a density of 550 kg/m^3 floats in a jar of water. Oil with a density of 750 kg/m^3 is poured on the water until the top of the oil layer is 0.035 m below the top of the block. (a) How deep is the oil layer? (b) What is the gauge pressure at the block's lower face?

14.79. Dropping Anchor. An iron anchor with mass 35.0 kg and density 7860 kg/m^3 lies on the deck of a small barge that has vertical sides and floats in a freshwater river. The area of the bottom of the barge is 8.00 m^2. The anchor is thrown overboard but is suspended above the bottom of the river by a rope; the mass and volume of the rope are small enough to ignore. After the anchor is overboard and the barge has finally stopped bobbing up and down, has the barge risen or sunk down in the water? By what vertical distance?

14.80. Assume that crude oil from a supertanker has density 750 kg/m^3. The tanker runs aground on a sandbar. To refloat the tanker, its oil cargo is pumped out into steel barrels, each of which has a mass of 15.0 kg when empty and holds 0.120 m^3 of oil. You can ignore the volume occupied by the steel from which the barrel is made. (a) If a salvage worker accidentally drops a filled, sealed barrel overboard, will it float or sink in the seawater? (b) If the barrel floats, what fraction of its volume will be above the water surface? If it sinks, what minimum tension would have to be exerted by a rope to haul the barrel up from the ocean floor? (c) Repeat parts (a) and (b) if the density of the oil is 910 kg/m^3 and the mass of each empty barrel is 32.0 kg.

14.81. A cubical block of density ρ_B and with sides of length L floats in a liquid of greater density ρ_L. (a) What fraction of the block's volume is above the surface of the liquid? (b) The liquid is denser than water (density ρ_W) and does not mix with it. If water is poured on the surface of the liquid, how deep must the water layer be so that the water surface just rises to the top of the block? Express your answer in terms of L, ρ_B, ρ_L, and ρ_W. (c) Find the depth of the water layer in part (b) if the liquid is mercury, the block is made of iron, and the side length is 10.0 cm.

14.82. A barge is in a rectangular lock on a freshwater river. The lock is 60.0 m long and 20.0 m wide, and the steel doors on each end are closed. With the barge floating in the lock, a 2.50×10^6 N load of scrap metal is put onto the barge. The metal has density 9000 kg/m^3. (a) When the load of scrap metal, initially on the bank, is placed onto the barge, what vertical distance does the water in the lock rise? (b) The scrap metal is now pushed overboard into the water. Does the water level in the lock rise, fall, or remain the same? If it rises or falls, by what vertical distance does it change?

14.83. A U-shaped tube with a horizontal portion of length l (Fig. 14.40) contains a liquid. What is the difference in height between the liquid columns in the vertical arms (a) if the tube has an acceleration a toward the right? and (b) if the tube is mounted on a horizontal turntable rotating with an angular speed ω with one of the vertical arms on the axis of rotation? (c) Explain why the difference in height does not depend on the density of the liquid or on the cross-sectional area of the tube. Would it be the same if the vertical tubes did not have equal cross-sectional areas? Would it be the same if the horizontal portion were tapered from one end to the other? Explain.

Figure 14.40 Problem 14.83.

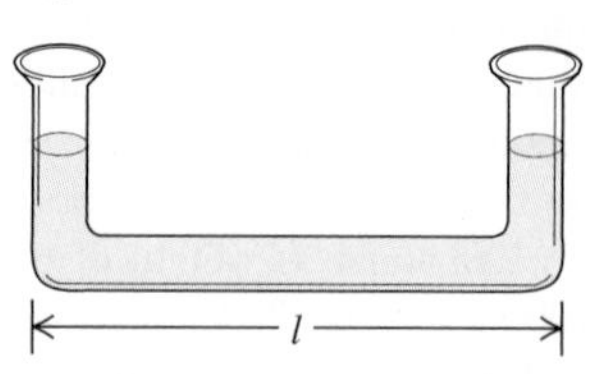

14.84. A cylindrical container of an incompressible liquid with density ρ rotates with constant angular speed ω about its axis of symmetry, which we take to be the y-axis (Fig. 14.41). (a) Show that the pressure at a given height within the fluid increases in the radial direction (outward from the axis of rotation) according to $\partial p/\partial r = \rho\omega^2 r$. (b) Integrate this partial differential equation to find the pressure as a function of distance from the axis of rotation along a horizontal line at $y = 0$. (c) Combine the result of part (b) with Eq. (14.5) to show that the surface of the rotating liquid has a *parabolic* shape, that is, the height of the liquid is given by $h(r) = \omega^2 r^2/2g$. (This technique is used for making parabolic telescope mirrors; liquid glass is rotated and allowed to solidify while rotating.)

Figure 14.41 Problem 14.84.

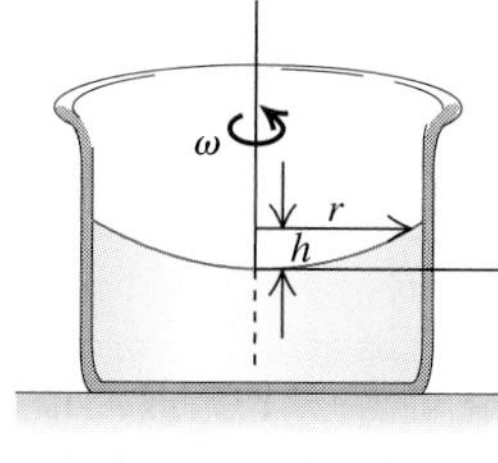

14.85. An incompressible fluid with density ρ is in a horizontal test tube of inner cross-sectional area A. The test tube spins in a horizontal circle in an ultracentrifuge at an angular speed ω. Gravitational forces are negligible. Consider a volume element of the fluid of area A and thickness dr' a distance r' from the rotation axis. The pressure on its inner surface is p and on its outer surface is $p + dp$. (a) Apply Newton's second law to the volume element to show that $dp = \rho\omega^2 r' dr'$. (b) If the surface of the fluid is at a radius r_0 where the pressure is p_0, show that the pressure p at a distance $r \geq r_0$ is $p = p_0 + \rho\omega^2(r^2 - r_0^2)/2$. (c) An object of volume V and density ρ_{ob} has its center of mass at a distance R_{cmob} from the axis. Show that the net horizontal force on the object is $\rho V\omega^2 R_{cm}$, where R_{cm} is the distance from the axis to the center of mass of the displaced fluid. (d) Explain why the object will move inward if $\rho R_{cm} > \rho_{ob}R_{cmob}$ and outward if $\rho R_{cm} < \rho_{ob}R_{cmob}$. (e) For small objects of uniform density, $R_{cm} = R_{cmob}$. What happens to a mixture of small objects of this kind with different densities in an ultracentrifuge?

14.86. Untethered helium balloons, floating in a car that has all the windows rolled up and outside air vents closed, move in the direction of the car's acceleration, but loose balloons filled with air move in the opposite direction. To show why, consider only the horizontal forces acting on the balloons. Let a be the magnitude of the car's forward acceleration. Consider a horizontal tube of air with a cross-sectional area A that extends from the windshield, where $x = 0$ and $p = p_0$, back along the x-axis. Now consider a volume element of thickness dx in this tube. The pressure on its front surface is p and the pressure on its rear surface is $p + dp$. Assume the air has a constant density ρ. (a) Apply Newton's second law to the volume element to show that $dp = \rho a\, dx$. (b) Integrate the result of part (a) to find the pressure at the front surface in terms of a and x. (c) To show that considering ρ constant is reasonable, calculate the pressure difference in atm for a distance as long as 2.5 m and a large acceleration of 5.0 m/s^2. (d) Show that the net horizontal force on a balloon of volume V is $\rho V a$. (e) For negligible friction forces, show that the acceleration of the balloon (average density ρ_{bal}) is $(\rho/\rho_{bal})a$, so that the acceleration relative to the car is $a_{rel} = [(\rho/\rho_{bal}) - 1]a$. (f) Use the expression for a_{rel} in part (e) to explain the movement of the balloons.

14.87. Water stands at a depth H in a large, open tank whose side walls are vertical (Fig. 14.42). A hole is made in one of the walls at a depth h below the water surface. (a) At what distance R from the foot of the wall does the emerging stream strike the floor? (b) How far above the bottom of the tank could a second hole be cut so that the stream emerging from it could have the same range as for the first hole?

Figure 14.42 Problem 14.87.

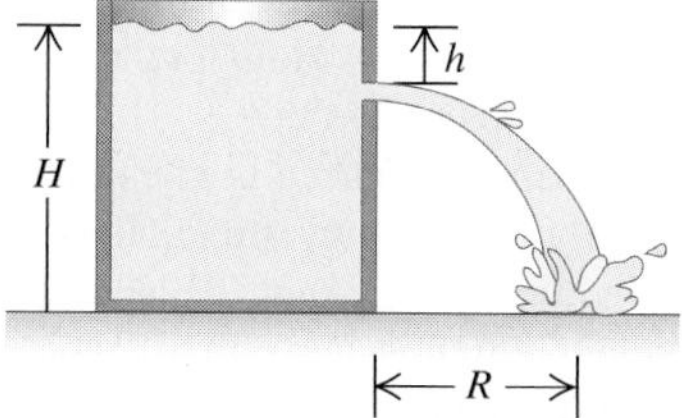

14.88. A cylindrical bucket, open at the top, is 25.0 cm high and 10.0 cm in diameter. A circular hole with a cross-sectional area 1.50 cm^2 is cut in the center of the bottom of the bucket. Water flows into the bucket from a tube above it at the rate of $2.40 \times 10^{-4} \text{m}^3/\text{s}$. How high will the water in the bucket rise?

14.89. Water flows steadily from an open tank as in Fig. 14.43. The elevation of point 1 is 10.0 m, and the elevation of points 2 and 3 is 2.00 m. The cross-sectional area at point 2 is 0.0480 m^2; at point 3 it is 0.0160 m^2. The area of the tank is very large compared with the cross-sectional area of the pipe. Assuming that Bernoulli's equation applies, compute (a) the discharge rate in cubic meters per second; and (b) the gauge pressure at point 2.

Figure 14.43 Problem 14.89.

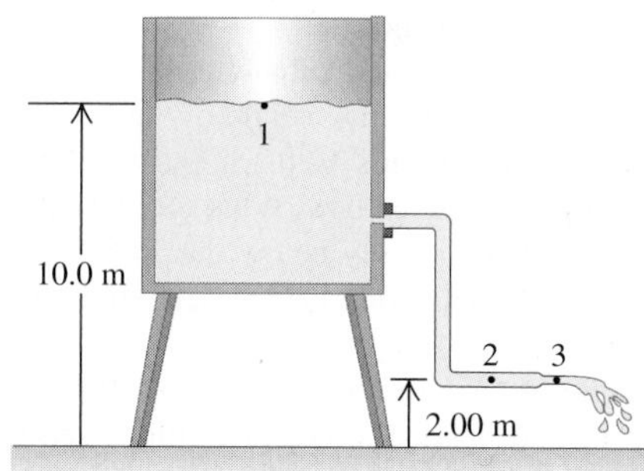

14.90. In 1993 the radius of Hurricane Emily was about 350 km. The wind speed near the center ("eye") of the hurricane, whose radius was about 30 km, reached about 200 km/h. As air swirled in from the rim of the hurricane toward the eye, its angular momentum remained roughly constant. (a) Estimate the wind speed at the rim of the hurricane. (b) Estimate the pressure difference at the earth's surface between the eye and the rim. (*Hint:* See Table 14.1.). Where is the pressure greater? (c) If the kinetic energy of the swirling air in the eye could be converted completely to gravitational potential energy, how high would the air go? (d) In fact, the air in the eye is lifted to heights of several kilometers. How can you reconcile this with your answer to part (c)?

14.91. Two very large open tanks A and F (Fig. 14.44) contain the same liquid. A horizontal pipe BCD, having a constriction at C and open to the air at D, leads out of the bottom of tank A, and a vertical pipe E opens into the constriction at C and dips into the liquid in tank F. Assume streamline flow and no viscosity. If the cross-sectional area at C is one-half the area at D and if D is a distance h_1 below the level of the liquid in A, to what height h_2 will liquid rise in pipe E? Express your answer in terms of h_1.

Figure **14.44** Problem 14.91.

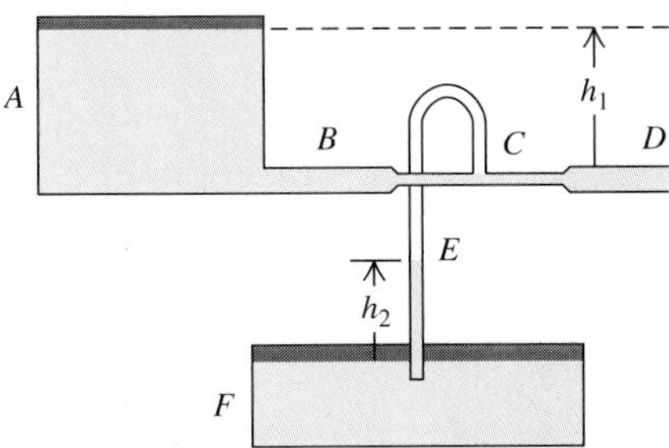

14.92. The horizontal pipe shown in Fig. 14.45 has a cross-sectional area of 40.0 cm^2 at the wider portions and 10.0 cm^2 at the constriction. Water is flowing in the pipe, and the discharge from the pipe is 6.00×10^{-3} m^3/s(6.00 L/s). Find (a) the flow speeds at the wide and the narrow portions; (b) the pressure difference between these portions; (c) the difference in height between the mercury columns in the U-shaped tube.

Figure **14.45** Problem 14.92.

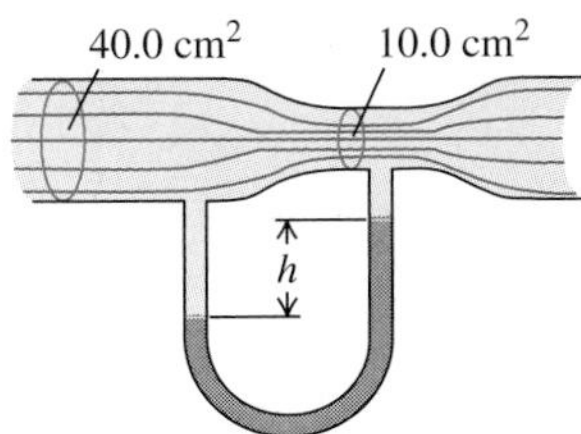

14.93. A liquid flowing from a vertical pipe has a definite shape as it flows from the pipe. To get the equation for this shape, assume that the liquid is in free fall once it leaves the pipe. Just as it leaves the pipe, the liquid has speed v_0 and the radius of the stream of liquid is r_0. (a) Find an equation for the speed of the liquid as a function of the distance y it has fallen. Combining this with the equation of continuity, find an expression for the radius of the stream as a function of y. (b) If water flows out of a vertical pipe at a speed of 1.20 m/s, how far below the outlet will the radius be one-half the original radius of the stream?

Challenge Problems

14.94. A rock with mass $m = 3.00$ kg is suspended from the roof of an elevator by a light cord. The rock is totally immersed in a bucket of water that sits on the floor of the elevator, but the rock doesn't touch the bottom or sides of the bucket. (a) When the elevator is at rest, the tension in the cord is 21.0 N. Calculate the volume of the rock. (b) Derive an expression for the tension in the cord when the elevator is accelerating *upward* with an acceleration of magnitude a. Calculate the tension when $a = 2.50$ m/s^2 upward. (c) Derive an expression for the tension in the cord when the elevator is accelerating *downward* with an acceleration of magnitude a. Calculate the tension when $a = 2.50$ m/s^2 downward. (d) What is the tension when the elevator is in free fall with a downward acceleration equal to g?

14.95. Suppose a piece of styrofoam, $\rho = 180$ kg/m^3, is held completely submerged in water (Fig. 14.46). (a) What is the tension in the cord? Find this using Archimedes's principle. (b) Use $p = p_0 + \rho g h$ to calculate directly the force exerted by the water on the two sloped sides and the bottom of the styrofoam; then show that the vector sum of these forces is the buoyant force.

Figure **14.46** Challenge Problem 14.95.

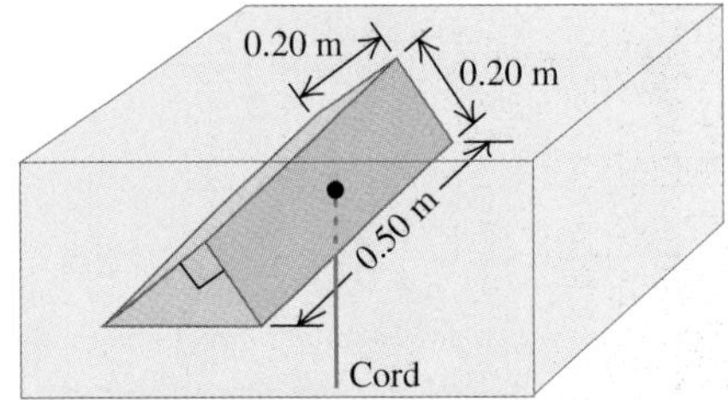

14.96. A large tank with diameter D, open to the air, contains water to a height H. A small hole with diameter d $(d \ll D)$ is made at the base of the tank. Ignoring any effects of viscosity, calculate the time it takes for the tank to drain completely.

14.97. A *siphon,* as shown in Fig. 14.47, is a convenient device for removing liquids from containers. To establish the flow, the tube must be initially filled with fluid. Let the fluid have density ρ, and let the atmospheric pressure be p_a. Assume that the cross-sectional area of the tube is the same at all points along it. (a) If the lower end of the siphon is at a distance h below the surface of the liquid in the container, what is the speed of the fluid as it flows out the lower end of the siphon? (Assume that the container has a very large diameter, and ignore any effects of viscosity.) (b) A curious

Figure **14.47** Challenge Problem 14.97.

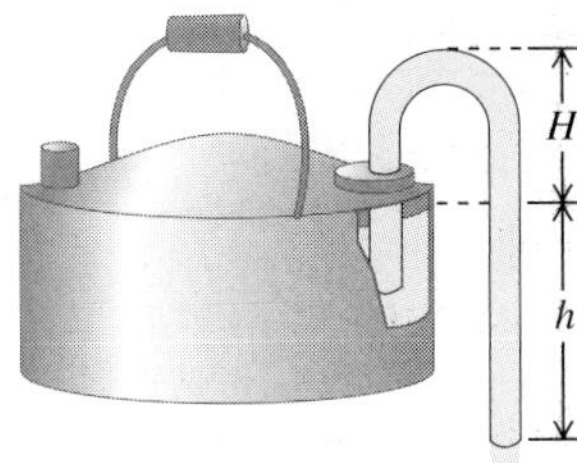

feature of a siphon is that the fluid initially flows "uphill." What is the greatest height H that the high point of the tube can have if flow is still to occur?

14.98. The following passage is quoted from a letter. *It is the practice of carpenters hereabouts, when laying out and leveling up the foundations of relatively long buildings, to use a garden hose filled with water, with glass tubes 10 to 12 inches long thrust into the ends of the hose. The theory is that water, seeking a common level, will be the same height in both the tubes and thus effect a level. Now the question rises as to what happens if a bubble of air is left in the hose. Our greybeards contend the air will not affect the reading from one end to the other. Others say that it will cause important inaccuracies.* Can you give a relatively simple solution to this problem, together with an explanation? Figure 14.48 gives a rough sketch of the situation that caused the dispute.

Figure **14.48** Challenge Problem 14.98.

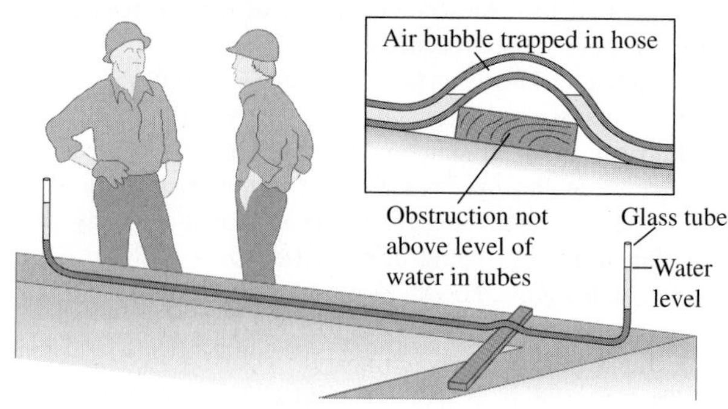

MECHANICAL WAVES

15

?When an earthquake strikes, the news of the event travels through the body of the earth in the form of seismic waves. Which aspects of a seismic wave determine how much power is carried by the wave?

LEARNING GOALS

By studying this chapter, you will learn:

- What is meant by a mechanical wave, and the different varieties of mechanical waves.
- How to use the relationship among speed, frequency, and wavelength for a periodic wave.
- How to interpret and use the mathematical expression for a sinusoidal periodic wave.
- How to calculate the speed of waves on a rope or string.
- How to calculate the rate at which a mechanical wave transports energy.
- What happens when mechanical waves overlap and interfere.
- The properties of standing waves on a string, and how to analyze these waves.
- How stringed instruments produce sounds of specific frequencies.

Ripples on a pond, musical sounds, seismic tremors triggered by an earthquake—all these are *wave* phenomena. Waves can occur whenever a system is disturbed from equilibrium and when the disturbance can travel, or *propagate,* from one region of the system to another. As a wave propagates, it carries energy. The energy in light waves from the sun warms the surface of our planet; the energy in seismic waves can crack our planet's crust.

This chapter and the next are about mechanical waves—waves that travel within some material called a *medium.* (Chapter 16 is concerned with sound, an important type of mechanical wave.) We'll begin this chapter by deriving the basic equations for describing waves, including the important special case of *sinusoidal* waves in which the wave pattern is a repeating sine or cosine function. To help us understand waves in general, we'll look at the simple case of waves that travel on a stretched string or rope.

Waves on a string play an important role in music. When a musician strums a guitar or bows a violin, she makes waves that travel in opposite directions along the instrument's strings. What happens when these oppositely directed waves overlap is called *interference.* We'll discover that sinusoidal waves can occur on a guitar or violin string only for certain special frequencies, called *normal-mode frequencies,* determined by the properties of the string. The normal-mode frequencies of a stringed instrument determine the pitch of the musical sounds that the instrument produces. (In the next chapter we'll find that interference also helps explain the pitches of *wind* instruments such as flutes and pipe organs.)

Not all waves are mechanical in nature. *Electromagnetic* waves—including light, radio waves, infrared and ultraviolet radiation, and x rays—can propagate even in empty space, where there is *no* medium. We'll explore these and other nonmechanical waves in later chapters.

ActivPhysics ONLINE
10.1 Properties of Mechanical Waves

15.1 Types of Mechanical Waves

A **mechanical wave** is a disturbance that travels through some material or substance called the **medium** for the wave. As the wave travels through the medium, the particles that make up the medium undergo displacements of various kinds, depending on the nature of the wave.

Figure 15.1 shows three varieties of mechanical waves. In Fig. 15.1a the medium is a string or rope under tension. If we give the left end a small upward shake or wiggle, the wiggle travels along the length of the string. Successive sections of string go through the same motion that we gave to the end, but at successively later times. Because the displacements of the medium are perpendicular or *transverse* to the direction of travel of the wave along the medium, this is called a **transverse wave.**

In Fig. 15.1b the medium is a liquid or gas in a tube with a rigid wall at the right end and a movable piston at the left end. If we give the piston a single back-and-forth motion, displacement and pressure fluctuations travel down the length of the medium. This time the motions of the particles of the medium are back and forth along the *same* direction that the wave travels. We call this a **longitudinal wave.**

In Fig. 15.1c the medium is a liquid in a channel, such as water in an irrigation ditch or canal. When we move the flat board at the left end forward and back once, a wave disturbance travels down the length of the channel. In this case the displacements of the water have *both* longitudinal and transverse components.

Each of these systems has an equilibrium state. For the stretched string it is the state in which the system is at rest, stretched out along a straight line. For the fluid in a tube it is a state in which the fluid is at rest with uniform pressure. And for the liquid in a trough it is a smooth, level water surface. In each case the wave motion is a disturbance from the equilibrium state that travels from one region of the medium to another. And in each case there are forces that tend to restore the system to its equilibrium position when it is displaced, just as the force of gravity tends to pull a pendulum toward its straight-down equilibrium position when it is displaced.

15.1 Three ways to make a wave that moves to the right. (a) The hand moves the string up and then returns, producing a transverse wave. (b) The piston moves to the right, compressing the gas or liquid, and then returns, producing a longitudinal wave. (c) The board moves to the right and then returns, producing a combination of longitudinal and transverse waves.

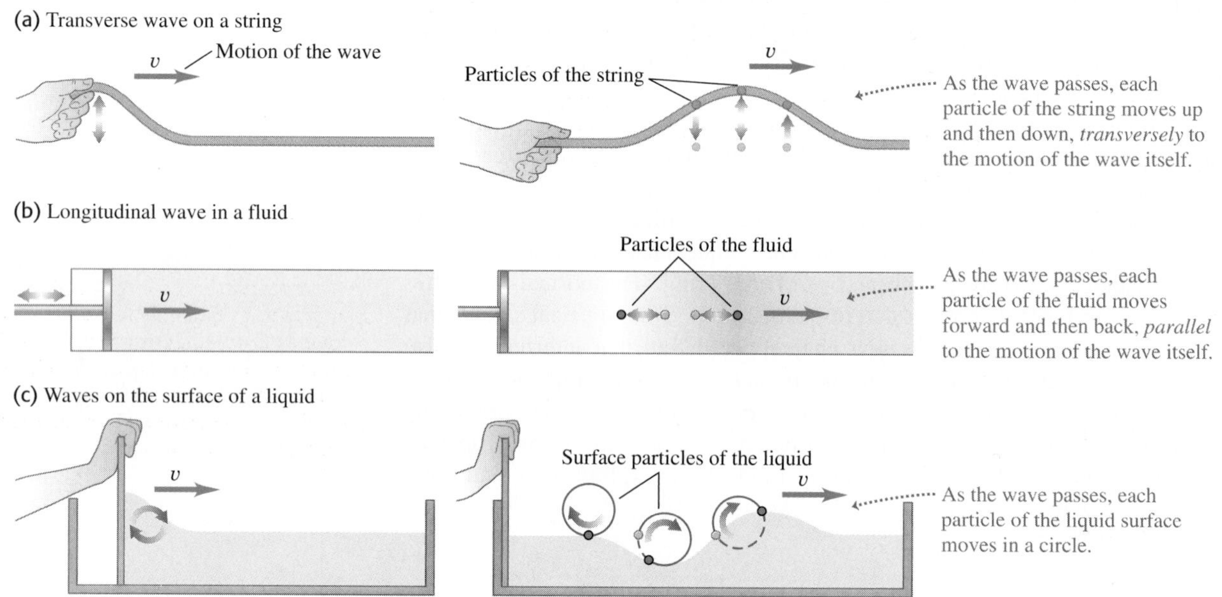
(a) Transverse wave on a string
v
Motion of the wave
Particles of the string
v
As the wave passes, each particle of the string moves up and then down, *transversely* to the motion of the wave itself.
(b) Longitudinal wave in a fluid
v
Particles of the fluid
v
As the wave passes, each particle of the fluid moves forward and then back, *parallel* to the motion of the wave itself.
(c) Waves on the surface of a liquid
v
Surface particles of the liquid
v
As the wave passes, each particle of the liquid surface moves in a circle.

These examples have three things in common. First, in each case the disturbance travels or *propagates* with a definite speed through the medium. This speed is called the speed of propagation, or simply the **wave speed.** Its value is determined in each case by the mechanical properties of the medium. We will use the symbol v for wave speed. (The wave speed is *not* the same as the speed with which particles move when they are disturbed by the wave. We'll return to this point in Section 15.3.) Second, the medium itself does not travel through space; its individual particles undergo back-and-forth or up-and-down motions around their equilibrium positions. The overall pattern of the wave disturbance is what travels. Third, to set any of these systems into motion, we have to put in energy by doing mechanical work on the system. The wave motion transports this energy from one region of the medium to another. *Waves transport energy, but not matter, from one region to another* (Fig. 15.2).

15.2 "Doing the wave" at a sports stadium is an example of a mechanical wave: The disturbance propagates through the crowd, but there is no transport of matter (none of the spectators moves from one seat to another).

Test Your Understanding of Section 15.1 What type of wave is "the wave" shown in Fig. 15.2? (i) transverse; (ii) longitudinal; (iii) a combination of transverse and longitudinal.

15.2 Periodic Waves

The transverse wave on a stretched string in Fig. 15.1a is an example of a *wave pulse.* The hand shakes the string up and down just once, exerting a transverse force on it as it does so. The result is a single "wiggle," or pulse, that travels along the length of the string. The tension in the string restores its straight-line shape once the pulse has passed.

A more interesting situation develops when we give the free end of the string a repetitive, or *periodic,* motion. (You may want to review the discussion of periodic motion in Chapter 13 before going ahead.) Then each particle in the string also undergoes periodic motion as the wave propagates, and we have a **periodic wave.**

Periodic Transverse Waves

In particular, suppose we move the string up and down with *simple harmonic motion* (SHM) with amplitude A, frequency f, angular frequency $\omega = 2\pi f$, and period $T = 1/f = 2\pi/\omega$. Figure 15.3 shows one way to do this. The wave that results is a symmetrical sequence of *crests* and *troughs.* As we will see, periodic waves with simple harmonic motion are particularly easy to analyze; we call them **sinusoidal waves.** It also turns out that *any* periodic wave can be represented as a combination of sinusoidal waves. So this particular kind of wave motion is worth special attention.

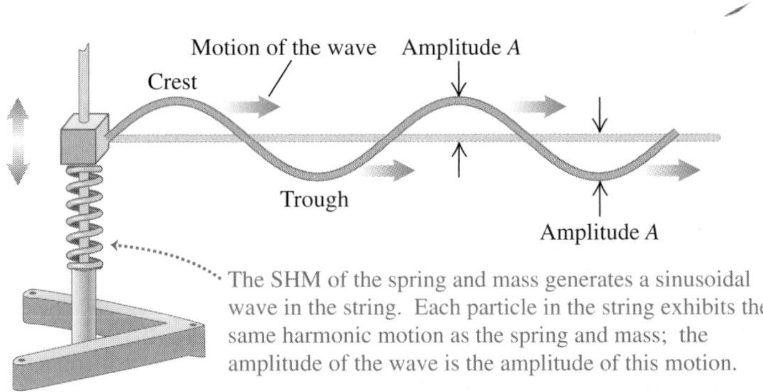
Motion of the wave
Amplitude A
Crest
Trough
Amplitude A
The SHM of the spring and mass generates a sinusoidal wave in the string. Each particle in the string exhibits the same harmonic motion as the spring and mass; the amplitude of the wave is the amplitude of this motion.

15.3 A block of mass m attached to a spring undergoes simple harmonic motion, producing a sinusoidal wave that travels to the right on the string. (In a real-life system a driving force would have to be applied to the block to replace the energy carried away by the wave.)

15.4 A sinusoidal transverse wave traveling to the right along a string. The vertical scale is exaggerated.

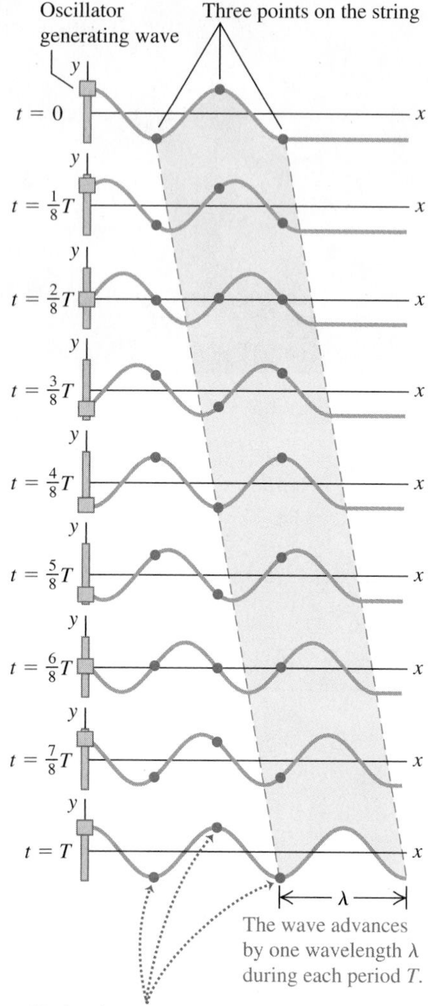

The string is shown at time intervals of $\frac{1}{8}$ period for a total of one period T. The highlighting shows the motion of one wavelength of the wave.
Oscillator generating wave
Three points on the string
$t = 0$
$t = \frac{1}{8}T$
$t = \frac{2}{8}T$
$t = \frac{3}{8}T$
$t = \frac{4}{8}T$
$t = \frac{5}{8}T$
$t = \frac{6}{8}T$
$t = \frac{7}{8}T$
$t = T$
y
x
λ
The wave advances by one wavelength λ during each period T.
Each point moves up and down in place. Particles one wavelength apart move in phase with each other.

15.5 A series of drops falling into water produces a periodic wave that spreads radially outward. The wave crests and troughs are concentric circles. The wavelength λ is the radial distance between adjacent crests or adjacent troughs.

λ

In Fig. 15.3 the wave that advances along the string is a *continuous succession* of transverse sinusoidal disturbances. Figure 15.4 shows the shape of a part of the string near the left end at time intervals of $\frac{1}{8}$ of a period, for a total time of one period. The wave shape advances steadily toward the right, as indicated by the highlighted area. As the wave moves, any point on the string (any of the red dots, for example) oscillates up and down about its equilibrium position with simple harmonic motion. *When a sinusoidal wave passes through a medium, every particle in the medium undergoes simple harmonic motion with the same frequency.*

CAUTION **Wave motion vs. particle motion** Be very careful to distinguish between the motion of the *transverse wave* along the string and the motion of a *particle* of the string. The wave moves with constant speed v *along* the length of the string, while the motion of the particle is simple harmonic and *transverse* (perpendicular) to the length of the string.

For a periodic wave, the shape of the string at any instant is a repeating pattern. The length of one complete wave pattern is the distance from one crest to the next, or from one trough to the next, or from any point to the corresponding point on the next repetition of the wave shape. We call this distance the **wavelength** of the wave, denoted by λ (the Greek letter lambda). The wave pattern travels with constant speed v and advances a distance of one wavelength λ in a time interval of one period T. So the wave speed v is given by $v = \lambda/T$ or, because $f = 1/T$,

$$v = \lambda f \qquad \text{(periodic wave)} \qquad (15.1)$$

The speed of propagation equals the product of wavelength and frequency. The frequency is a property of the *entire* periodic wave because all points on the string oscillate with the same frequency f.

Waves on a string propagate in just one dimension (in Fig. 15.4, along the x-axis). But the ideas of frequency, wavelength, and amplitude apply equally well to waves that propagate in two or three dimensions. Figure 15.5 shows a wave propagating in two dimensions on the surface of a tank of water. As with waves on a string, the wavelength is the distance from one crest to the next, and the amplitude is the height of a crest above the equilibrium level.

In many important situations including waves on a string, the wave speed v is determined entirely by the mechanical properties of the medium. In this case, increasing f causes λ to decrease so that the product $v = \lambda f$ remains the same, and waves of *all* frequencies propagate with the same wave speed. In this chapter we will consider *only* waves of this kind. (In later chapters we will study the propagation of light waves in matter for which the wave speed depends on frequency; this turns out to be the reason prisms break white light into a spectrum and raindrops create a rainbow.)

Periodic Longitudinal Waves

To understand the mechanics of a periodic *longitudinal* wave, we consider a long tube filled with a fluid, with a piston at the left end as in Fig. 15.1b. If we push the piston in, we compress the fluid near the piston, increasing the pressure in this region. This region then pushes against the neighboring region of fluid, and so on, and a wave pulse moves along the tube.

Now suppose we move the piston back and forth with simple harmonic motion, along a line parallel to the axis of the tube (Fig. 15.6). This motion forms regions in the fluid where the pressure and density are greater or less than the equilibrium values. We call a region of increased density a *compression;* a region of reduced density is a *rarefaction.* Figure 15.6 shows compressions as darkly shaded areas and rarefactions as lightly shaded areas. The wavelength is the distance from one compression to the next or from one rarefaction to the next.

15.6 Using an oscillating piston to make a sinusoidal longitudinal wave in a fluid.

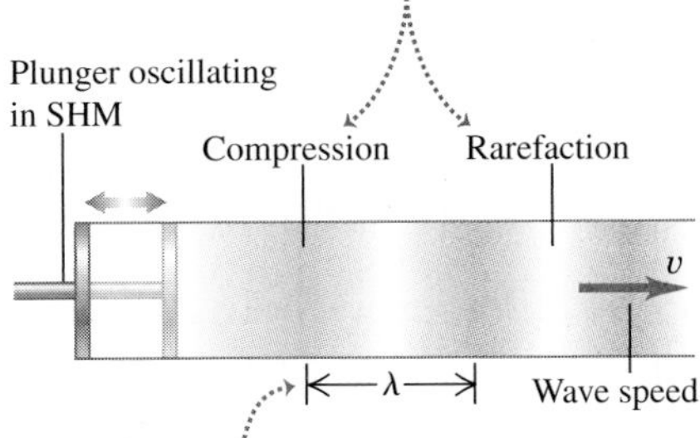
Forward motion of the plunger creates a compression (a zone of high density); backward motion creates a rarefaction (a zone of low density).
Plunger oscillating in SHM
Compression
Rarefaction
v
λ
Wave speed
The wavelength λ is the distance between corresponding points on successive cycles.

15.7 A sinusoidal longitudinal wave traveling to the right in a fluid. The wave has the same amplitude A and period T as the oscillation of the piston.

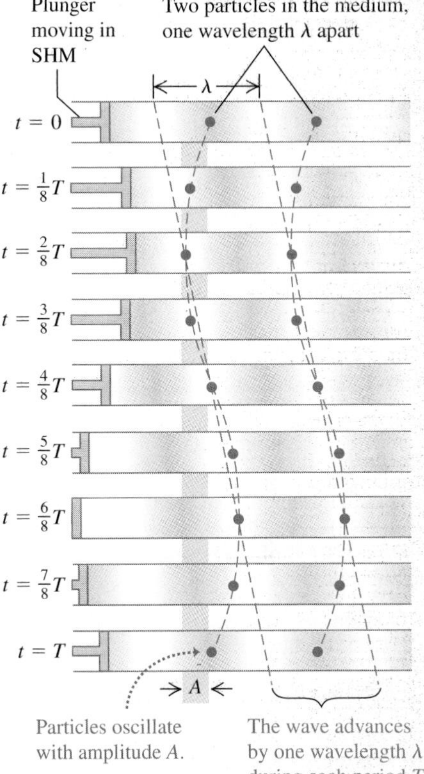
Longitudinal waves are shown at intervals of $\frac{1}{8}T$ for one period T.
Plunger moving in SHM
Two particles in the medium, one wavelength λ apart
λ
$t = 0$
$t = \frac{1}{8}T$
$t = \frac{2}{8}T$
$t = \frac{3}{8}T$
$t = \frac{4}{8}T$
$t = \frac{5}{8}T$
$t = \frac{6}{8}T$
$t = \frac{7}{8}T$
$t = T$
A
Particles oscillate with amplitude A.
The wave advances by one wavelength λ during each period T.

Figure 15.7 shows the wave propagating in the fluid-filled tube at time intervals of $\frac{1}{8}$ of a period, for a total time of one period. The pattern of compressions and rarefactions moves steadily to the right, just like the pattern of crests and troughs in a sinusoidal transverse wave (compare Fig. 15.4). Each particle in the fluid oscillates in SHM parallel to the direction of wave propagation (that is, left and right) with the same amplitude A and period T as the piston. The particles shown by the two red dots in Fig. 15.7 are one wavelength apart, and so oscillate in phase with each other.

Just like the sinusoidal transverse wave shown in Fig. 15.4, in one period T the longitudinal wave in Fig. 15.7 travels one wavelength λ to the right. Hence the fundamental equation $v = \lambda f$ holds for longitudinal waves as well as for transverse waves, and indeed for *all* types of periodic waves. Just as for transverse waves, in this chapter and the next we will consider only situations in which the speed of longitudinal waves does not depend on the frequency.

Example 15.1 Wavelength of a musical sound

Sound waves are longitudinal waves in air. The speed of sound depends on temperature; at 20°C it is 344 m/s (1130 ft/s). What is the wavelength of a sound wave in air at 20°C if the frequency is 262 Hz (the approximate frequency of middle C on a piano)?

SOLUTION

IDENTIFY: This problem involves the relationship among wave speed, wavelength, and frequency for a periodic wave. The target variable is the wavelength λ.

SET UP: The wave speed $v = 344$ m/s and the frequency $f = 262$ Hz are given, so we can use the relationship in Eq. (15.1) among v, λ, and f.

EXECUTE: We solve Eq. (15.1) for the target variable λ:

$$\lambda = \frac{v}{f} = \frac{344 \text{ m/s}}{262 \text{ Hz}} = \frac{344 \text{ m/s}}{262 \text{ s}^{-1}} = 1.31 \text{ m}$$

Note that the units of frequency are either hertz (Hz) or inverse seconds (s^{-1}).

EVALUATE: What happens to the wavelength if the frequency changes? The speed of sound waves is unaffected by changes in frequency, so the relationship $\lambda = v/f$ tells us that wavelength will change in inverse proportion to the frequency. As an example, the high C sung by coloratura sopranos is two octaves above middle C. Each octave corresponds to a factor of 2 in frequency, so the frequency of high C is four times that of middle C: $f = 4(262 \text{ Hz}) = 1048$ Hz. Hence the *wavelength* of high C is *one-fourth* as large: $\lambda = (1.31 \text{ m})/4 = 0.328$ m.

Test Your Understanding of Section 15.2 If you double the wavelength of a wave on a particular string, what happens to the wave speed v and the frequency f? (i) v doubles and f is unchanged; (ii) v is unchanged and f doubles; (iii) v becomes one-half as great and f is unchanged; (iv) v is unchanged and f becomes one-half as great; (v) none of these.

15.3 Mathematical Description of a Wave

Many characteristics of periodic waves can be described by using the concepts of wave speed, amplitude, period, frequency, and wavelength. Often, though, we need a more detailed description of the positions and motions of individual particles of the medium at particular times during wave propagation. For this description we need the concept of a *wave function,* a function that describes the position of any particle in the medium at any time. We will concentrate on *sinusoidal* waves, in which each particle undergoes simple harmonic motion about its equilibrium position.

As a specific example, let's look at waves on a stretched string. If we ignore the sag of the string due to gravity, the equilibrium position of the string is along a straight line. We take this to be the x-axis of a coordinate system. Waves on a string are *transverse;* during wave motion a particle with equilibrium position x is displaced some distance y in the direction perpendicular to the x-axis. The value of y depends on which particle we are talking about (that is, y depends on x) and also on the time t when we look at it. Thus y is a *function* of both x and t; $y = y(x, t)$. We call $y(x, t)$ the **wave function** that describes the wave. If we know this function for a particular wave motion, we can use it to find the displacement (from equilibrium) of any particle at any time. From this we can find the velocity and acceleration of any particle, the shape of the string, and anything else we want to know about the behavior of the string at any time.

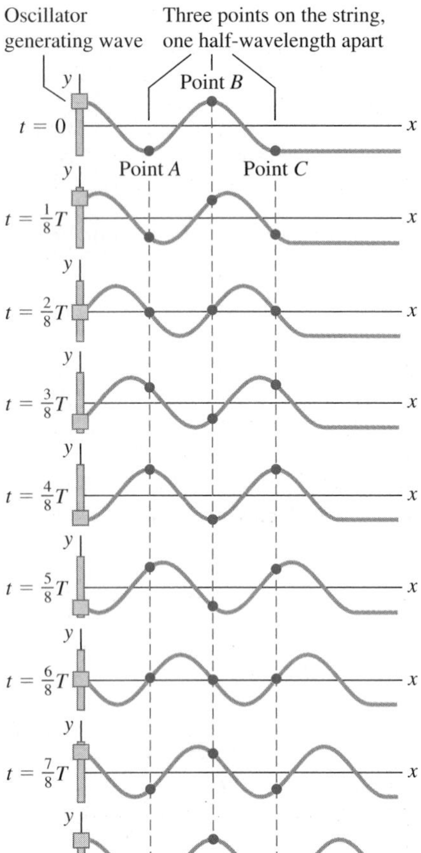

15.8 Tracking the oscillations of three points on a string as a sinusoidal wave propagates along it.

Wave Function for a Sinusoidal Wave

Let's see how to determine the form of the wave function for a sinusoidal wave. Suppose a sinusoidal wave travels from left to right (the direction of increasing x) along the string, as in Fig. 15.8. Every particle of the string oscillates with simple harmonic motion with the same amplitude and frequency. But the oscillations of particles at different points on the string are *not* all in step with each other. The particle at point B in Fig. 15.8 is at its maximum positive value of y at $t = 0$ and returns to $y = 0$ at $t = \frac{2}{8}T$; these same events occur for a particle at point A or point C at $t = \frac{4}{8}T$ and $t = \frac{6}{8}T$, exactly one half-period later. For any two particles of the string, the motion of the particle on the right (in terms of the wave, the "downstream" particle) lags behind the motion of the particle on the left by an amount proportional to the distance between the particles.

Hence the cyclic motions of various points on the string are out of step with each other by various fractions of a cycle. We call these differences *phase differences,* and we say that the *phase* of the motion is different for different points. For example, if one point has its maximum positive displacement at the same time that another has its maximum negative displacement, the two are a half-cycle out of phase. (This is the case for points A and B, or points B and C.)

Suppose that the displacement of a particle at the left end of the string $(x = 0)$, where the wave originates, is given by

$$y(x = 0, t) = A\cos\omega t = A\cos 2\pi f t \tag{15.2}$$

That is, the particle oscillates in simple harmonic motion with amplitude A, frequency f, and angular frequency $\omega = 2\pi f$. The notation $y(x = 0, t)$ reminds us that the motion of this particle is a special case of the wave function $y(x, t)$ that describes the entire wave. At $t = 0$ the particle at $x = 0$ is at its maximum positive displacement $(y = A)$ and is instantaneously at rest (because the value of y is a maximum).

The wave disturbance travels from $x = 0$ to some point x to the right of the origin in an amount of time given by x/v, where v is the wave speed. So the motion of point x at time t is the same as the motion of point $x = 0$ at the earlier time $t - x/v$. Hence we can find the displacement of point x at time t by simply replacing t in Eq. (15.2) by $(t - x/v)$. When we do that, we find the following expression for the wave function:

$$y(x,t) = A\cos\left[\omega\left(t - \frac{x}{v}\right)\right]$$

Because $\cos(-\theta) = \cos\theta$, we can rewrite the wave function as

$$y(x,t) = A\cos\left[\omega\left(\frac{x}{v} - t\right)\right] = A\cos 2\pi f\left(\frac{x}{v} - t\right) \quad \text{(sinusoidal wave moving in } +x\text{-direction)} \tag{15.3}$$

The displacement $y(x,t)$ is a function of both the location x of the point and the time t. We could make Eq. (15.3) more general by allowing for different values of the phase angle, as we did for simple harmonic motion in Section 13.2, but for now we omit this.

We can rewrite the wave function given by Eq. (15.3) in several different but useful forms. We can express it in terms of the period $T = 1/f$ and the wavelength $\lambda = v/f$:

$$y(x,t) = A\cos 2\pi\left(\frac{x}{\lambda} - \frac{t}{T}\right) \quad \text{(sinusoidal wave moving in } +x\text{-direction)} \tag{15.4}$$

We get another convenient form of the wave function if we define a quantity k, called the **wave number:**

$$k = \frac{2\pi}{\lambda} \quad \text{(wave number)} \tag{15.5}$$

Substituting $\lambda = 2\pi/k$ and $f = \omega/2\pi$ into the wavelength-frequency relationship $v = \lambda f$ gives

$$\omega = vk \quad \text{(periodic wave)} \tag{15.6}$$

We can then rewrite Eq. (15.4) as

$$y(x,t) = A\cos(kx - \omega t) \quad \text{(sinusoidal wave moving in } +x\text{-direction)} \tag{15.7}$$

Which of these various forms for the wave function $y(x,t)$ we use in any specific problem is a matter of convenience. Note that ω has units rad/s, so for unit consistency in Eqs. (15.6) and (15.7) the wave number k must have the units rad/m. (Some physicists define the wave number as $1/\lambda$ rather than $2\pi/\lambda$. When reading other texts, be sure to determine how this term is defined.)

Graphing the Wave Function

The wave function $y(x,t)$ is graphed as a function of x for a specific time t in Fig. 15.9a. This graph gives the displacement y of a particle from its equilibrium position as a function of the coordinate x of the particle. If the wave is a transverse wave on a string, the graph in Fig. 15.9a represents the shape of the string at that instant, like a flash photograph of the string. In particular, at time $t = 0$,

$$y(x, t = 0) = A\cos kx = A\cos 2\pi\frac{x}{\lambda}$$

Figure 15.9b is a graph of the wave function versus time t for a specific coordinate x. This graph gives the displacement y of the particle at that coordinate as a

15.9 Two graphs of the wave function $y(x,t)$ in Eq. (15.7). **(a)** Graph of displacement y versus coordinate x at time $t = 0$. **(b)** Graph of displacement y versus time t at coordinate $x = 0$. The vertical scale is exaggerated in both (a) and (b).

(a) If we use Eq. (15.7) to plot y as a function of x for time $t = 0$, the curve shows the *shape* of the string at $t = 0$.

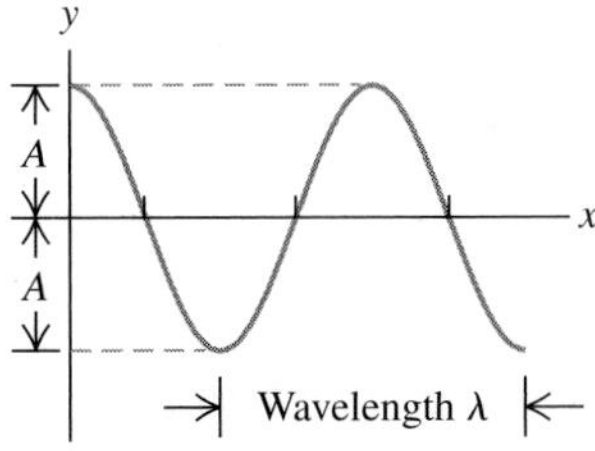

(b) If we use Eq. (15.7) to plot y as a function of t for position $x = 0$, the curve shows the *displacement* y of the particle at $x = 0$ as a function of time.

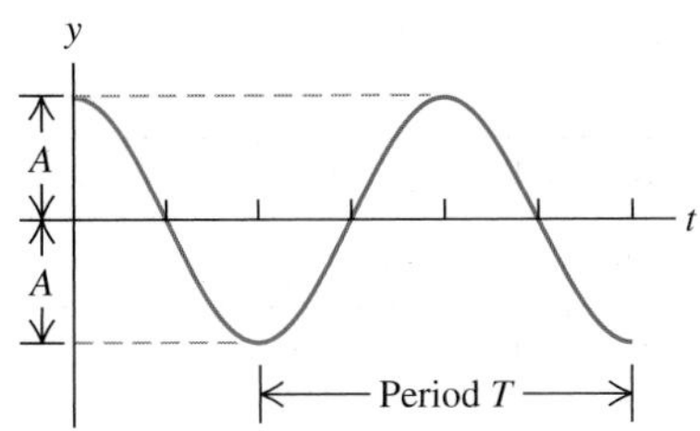

function of time; that is, it describes the motion of that particle. In particular, at the position $x = 0$,

$$y(x = 0, t) = A\cos(-\omega t) = A\cos\omega t = A\cos 2\pi\frac{t}{T}$$

This is consistent with our original statement about the motion at $x = 0$, Eq. (15.2).

CAUTION Wave graphs Although they may look the same at first glance, Figs. 15.9a and 15.9b are *not* identical. Figure 15.9a is a picture of the shape of the string at $t = 0$, while Fig. 15.9b is a graph of the displacement y of a particle at $x = 0$ as a function of time.

More on the Wave Function

We can modify Eqs. (15.3) through (15.7) to represent a wave traveling in the *negative* x-direction. In this case the displacement of point x at time t is the same as the motion of point $x = 0$ at the *later* time $(t + x/v)$, so in Eq. (15.2) we replace t by $(t + x/v)$. For a wave traveling in the negative x-direction,

$$y(x, t) = A\cos 2\pi f\left(\frac{x}{v} + t\right) = A\cos 2\pi\left(\frac{x}{\lambda} + \frac{t}{T}\right) = A\cos(kx + \omega t) \quad (15.8)$$

(sinusoidal wave moving in $-x$-direction)

In the expression $y(x, t) = A\cos(kx \pm \omega t)$ for a wave traveling in the $-x$ or $+x$-direction, the quantity $(kx \pm \omega t)$ is called the **phase.** It plays the role of an angular quantity (always measured in radians) in Eq. (15.7) or (15.8), and its value for any values of x and t determines what part of the sinusoidal cycle is occurring at a particular point and time. For a crest (where $y = A$ and the cosine function has the value 1), the phase could be 0, 2π, 4π, and so on; for a trough (where $y = -A$ and the cosine has the value -1), it could be π, 3π, 5π, and so on.

The wave speed is the speed with which we have to move along with the wave to keep alongside a point of a given phase, such as a particular crest of a wave on a string. For a wave traveling in the $+x$-direction, that means $kx - \omega t =$ constant. Taking the derivative with respect to t, we find $k\,dx/dt = \omega$, or

$$\frac{dx}{dt} = \frac{\omega}{k}$$

Comparing this with Eq. (15.6), we see that dx/dt is equal to the speed v of the wave. Because of this relationship, v is sometimes called the *phase velocity* of the wave. (*Phase speed* would be a better term.)

Problem-Solving Strategy 15.1 Mechanical Waves

IDENTIFY *the relevant concepts:* Wave problems fall into two broad categories. *Kinematics* problems are concerned with describing wave motion; they involve wave speed v, wavelength λ (or wave number k), frequency f (or angular frequency ω), and amplitude A. They may also involve the position, velocity, and acceleration of individual particles in the medium. *Dynamics* problems also use concepts from Newton's laws such as force and mass. As an example, later in this chapter we'll encounter problems that involve the relationship of wave speed to the mechanical properties of the wave medium.

As always, make sure that you identify the target variable(s) for the problem. In some cases you'll be asked to find an expression for the wave function.

SET UP *the problem* using the following steps:

1. Make a list of the quantities whose values are given. To help you visualize the situation, you'll find it useful to sketch graphs of y versus x (like Fig. 15.9a) and of y versus t (like Fig. 15.9b). Label your graphs with the values of the known quantities.

2. Decide which equations you'll need to use. If any two of v, f, and λ are given, use Eq. (15.1) ($v = \lambda f$) to find the third quantity (see Example 15.1). If the problem involves the angular frequency ω and/or the wave number k, use the definitions of those quantities and Eq. (15.6) ($\omega = vk$). You may also need the various forms of the wave function given in Eqs. (15.3), (15.4), and (15.7).
3. If the wave speed isn't given and you don't have enough information to determine it using $v = \lambda f$, you may be able to use the relationship between v and the mechanical properties of the system. (In the next section we'll develop this relationship for waves on a string.)

EXECUTE *the solution* as follows: Solve for the unknown quantities using the equations you've selected. In some problems all you need to do is find the value of one of the wave variables.

If you're asked to determine the wave function, you need to know A and any two of v, λ, and f (or v, k, and ω). Once you have this information, you can use it in Eq. (15.3), (15.4), or (15.7) to get the specific wave function for the problem at hand. Once you have that, you can find the value of y at any point (value of x) and at any time by substituting into the wave function.

EVALUATE *your answer:* Look at your results with a critical eye. Check to see whether the values of v, f, and λ (or v, ω, and k) agree with the relationships given in Eq. (15.1) or (15.6). If you've calculated the wave function, check one or more special cases for which you can guess what the results ought to be

Example 15.2 Wave on a clothesline

Your cousin Throckmorton is playing with the clothesline. He unties one end, holds it taut, and wiggles the end up and down sinusoidally with frequency 2.00 Hz and amplitude 0.075 m. The wave speed is $v = 12.0\ \text{m/s}$. At time $t = 0$ the end has maximum positive displacement and is instantaneously at rest. Assume no wave bounces back from the far end to muddle up the pattern. (a) Find the amplitude, angular frequency, period, wavelength, and wave number of the wave. (b) Write a wave function describing the wave. (c) Write equations for the displacement as a function of time of Throckmorton's end of the clothesline and of a point 3.00 m from his end.

SOLUTION

IDENTIFY: This is a kinematics problem about the motion of the clothesline. Since Throcky moves his hand in a sinusoidal way, he produces a sinusoidal wave that propagates down the clothesline. Hence we can use all of the expressions we've developed in this section. Our target variables in part (a) are amplitude A, angular frequency ω, period T, wavelength λ, and wave number k, so we need to use the equations that relate these quantities. In parts (b) and (c) our target "variables" are actually expressions for displacement; to find these, we use the general equations for the wave function of a sinusoidal wave.

SET UP: A photograph of the clothesline at time $t = 0$ would look just like Fig. 15.9a, with the maximum displacement at $x = 0$ (the end that Throcky has in his hand). We take the positive x-direction to be the direction in which the wave propagates, so we can use Eqs. (15.4) and (15.7) to describe the displacement of the clothesline as a function of position x and time t. We also use the relationships $f = 1/T$, $\omega = 2\pi f$, $k = 2\pi/\lambda$, $v = \lambda f$, and $\omega = vk$.

EXECUTE: (a) The amplitude A of the wave is just the amplitude of the motion of the end of the clothesline, $A = 0.075\ \text{m}$. Similarly, the wave frequency is $f = 2.00\ \text{Hz}$, the same as the frequency of the end of the clothesline. The angular frequency is

$$\omega = 2\pi f = (2\pi\ \text{rad/cycle})(2.00\ \text{cycles/s}) = 4.00\pi\ \text{rad/s}$$
$$= 12.6\ \text{rad/s}$$

The period is $T = 1/f = 0.500\ \text{s}$. We get the wavelength from Eq. (15.1):

$$\lambda = \frac{v}{f} = \frac{12.0\ \text{m/s}}{2.00\ \text{s}^{-1}} = 6.00\ \text{m}$$

We find the wave number from Eq. (15.5) or (15.6):

$$k = \frac{2\pi}{\lambda} = \frac{2\pi\ \text{rad}}{6.00\ \text{m}} = 1.05\ \text{rad/m} \quad \text{or}$$

$$k = \frac{\omega}{v} = \frac{4.00\pi\ \text{rad/s}}{12.0\ \text{m/s}} = 1.05\ \text{rad/m}$$

(b) Since we found the values of A, T, and λ in part (a), we can write the wave function using Eq. (15.4):

$$y(x, t) = A\cos 2\pi\left(\frac{x}{\lambda} - \frac{t}{T}\right)$$
$$= (0.075\ \text{m})\cos 2\pi\left(\frac{x}{6.00\ \text{m}} - \frac{t}{0.500\ \text{s}}\right)$$
$$= (0.075\ \text{m})\cos[(1.05\ \text{rad/m})x - (12.6\ \text{rad/s})t]$$

We can also get this same equation from Eq. (15.7) by using the values of ω and k we obtained in part (a).

(c) With our choice of the positive x-direction, the two points in question are at $x = 0$ and $x = +3.00\ \text{m}$. For each point, we can find the displacement as a function of time by substituting these values of x into the wave function we found in part (b):

$$y(x = 0, t) = (0.075\ \text{m})\cos 2\pi\left(\frac{0}{6.00\ \text{m}} - \frac{t}{0.500\ \text{s}}\right)$$
$$= (0.075\ \text{m})\cos(12.6\ \text{rad/s})t$$

$$y(x = +3.00\ \text{m}, t) = (0.075\ \text{m})\cos 2\pi\left(\frac{3.00\ \text{m}}{6.00\ \text{m}} - \frac{t}{0.500\ \text{s}}\right)$$
$$= (0.075\ \text{m})\cos[\pi - (12.6\ \text{rad/s})t]$$
$$= -(0.075\ \text{m})\cos(12.6\ \text{rad/s})t$$

Continued

EVALUATE: In part (b), the quantity $(1.05 \text{ rad/m})x - (12.6 \text{ rad/s})t$ is the *phase* of a point x on the string at time t. The phases of the two points in part (c) differ by π because these points are separated by one half-wavelength $(\lambda/2 = (6.00 \text{ m})/2 = 3.00 \text{ m})$. Both points oscillate in SHM with the same frequency and amplitude, but their oscillations are one half-cycle out of phase. Thus, while a graph of y versus t for the point at $x = 0$ is a cosine curve (like Fig. 15.9b), a graph of y versus t for the point $x = 3.00$ m is a *negative* cosine (the same as a cosine curve shifted by one half-cycle).

Using the expression for $y(x = 0, t)$ in part (c), can you show that the end of the string at $x = 0$ is instantaneously at rest at $t = 0$, just as we stated at the beginning of this example? (*Hint:* Calculate the y-velocity at this point by taking the derivative of y with respect to t.)

Particle Velocity and Acceleration in a Sinusoidal Wave

From the wave function we can get an expression for the transverse velocity of any *particle* in a transverse wave. We call this v_y to distinguish it from the wave propagation speed v. To find the transverse velocity v_y at a particular point x, we take the derivative of the wave function $y(x, t)$ with respect to t, keeping x constant. If the wave function is

$$y(x, t) = A\cos(kx - \omega t)$$

then

$$v_y(x, t) = \frac{\partial y(x, t)}{\partial t} = \omega A\sin(kx - \omega t) \tag{15.9}$$

The ∂ in this expression is a modified d, used to remind us that $y(x, t)$ is a function of *two* variables and that we are allowing only one (t) to vary. The other (x) is constant because we are looking at a particular point on the string. This derivative is called a *partial derivative*. If you haven't reached this point yet in your study of calculus, don't fret; it's a simple idea.

Equation (15.9) shows that the transverse velocity of a particle varies with time, as we expect for simple harmonic motion. The maximum particle speed is ωA; this can be greater than, less than, or equal to the wave speed v, depending on the amplitude and frequency of the wave.

The *acceleration* of any particle is the *second* partial derivative of $y(x, t)$ with respect to t:

$$a_y(x, t) = \frac{\partial^2 y(x, t)}{\partial t^2} = -\omega^2 A\cos(kx - \omega t) = -\omega^2 y(x, t) \tag{15.10}$$

The acceleration of a particle equals $-\omega^2$ times its displacement, which is the result we obtained in Section 13.2 for simple harmonic motion.

We can also compute partial derivatives of $y(x, t)$ with respect to x, holding t constant. This corresponds to studying the shape of the string at one instant of time, like a flash photo. The first derivative $\partial y(x, t)/\partial x$ is the *slope* of the string at any point. The second partial derivative with respect to x is the *curvature* of the string:

$$\frac{\partial^2 y(x, t)}{\partial x^2} = -k^2 A\cos(kx - \omega t) = -k^2 y(x, t) \tag{15.11}$$

From Eqs. (15.10) and (15.11) and the relationship $\omega = vk$ we see that

$$\frac{\partial^2 y(x, t)/\partial t^2}{\partial^2 y(x, t)/\partial x^2} = \frac{\omega^2}{k^2} = v^2 \quad \text{and}$$

$$\frac{\partial^2 y(x, t)}{\partial x^2} = \frac{1}{v^2}\frac{\partial^2 y(x, t)}{\partial t^2} \quad \text{(wave equation)} \tag{15.12}$$

We've derived Eq. (15.12) for a wave traveling in the positive x-direction. You can use the same steps to show that the wave function for a sinusoidal wave propagating in the *negative* x-direction, $y(x, t) = A\cos(kx + \omega t)$, also satisfies this equation.

Equation (15.12), called the **wave equation,** is one of the most important equations in all of physics. Whenever it occurs, we know that a disturbance can propagate as a wave along the x-axis with wave speed v. The disturbance need not be a sinusoidal wave; we'll see in the next section that *any* wave on a string obeys Eq. (15.12), whether the wave is periodic or not (see also Problem 15.61). In Chapter 32 we will find that electric and magnetic fields satisfy the wave equation; the wave speed will turn out to be the speed of light, which will lead us to the conclusion that light is an electromagnetic wave.

Figure 15.10a shows the transverse velocity v_y and transverse acceleration a_y, given by Eqs. (15.9) and (15.10), for several points on a string as a sinusoidal wave passes along it. Note that at points where the string has an upward curvature $(\partial^2 y/\partial x^2 > 0)$, the acceleration of that point is positive $(a_y = \partial^2 y/\partial t^2 > 0)$; this follows from the wave equation, Eq. (15.12). For the same reason the acceleration is negative $(a_y = \partial^2 y/\partial t^2 < 0)$ at points where the string has a downward curvature $(\partial^2 y/\partial x^2 < 0)$, and the acceleration is zero $(a_y = \partial^2 y/\partial t^2 = 0)$ at points of inflection where the curvature is zero $(\partial^2 y/\partial x^2 = 0)$. We emphasize again that v_y and a_y are the *transverse* velocity and acceleration of points on the string; these points move along the y-direction, not along the propagation direction of the wave. Figure 15.10b shows the transverse motions of several points on the string.

The concept of wave function is equally useful with *longitudinal* waves, and everything we have said about wave functions can be adapted to this case. The quantity y still measures the displacement of a particle of the medium from its equilibrium position; the difference is that for a longitudinal wave, this displacement is *parallel* to the x-axis instead of perpendicular to it. We'll discuss longitudinal waves in detail in Chapter 16.

Test Your Understanding of Section 15.3 Figure 15.8 shows a sinusoidal wave of period T on a string at times $0, \frac{1}{8}T, \frac{2}{8}T, \frac{3}{8}T, \frac{4}{8}T, \frac{5}{8}T, \frac{6}{8}T, \frac{7}{8}T$, and T. (a) At which time is point A on the string moving upward with maximum speed? (b) At which time does point B on the string have the greatest upward acceleration? (c) At which time does point C on the string have a downward acceleration but an upward velocity? MP

15.10 (a) Another view of the wave at $t = 0$ in Fig. 15.9a. The vectors show the transverse velocity v_y and transverse acceleration a_y at several points on the string. (b) From $t = 0$ to $t = 0.05\,T$, a particle at point 1 is displaced to point 1′, a particle at point 2 is displaced to point 2′, and so on.

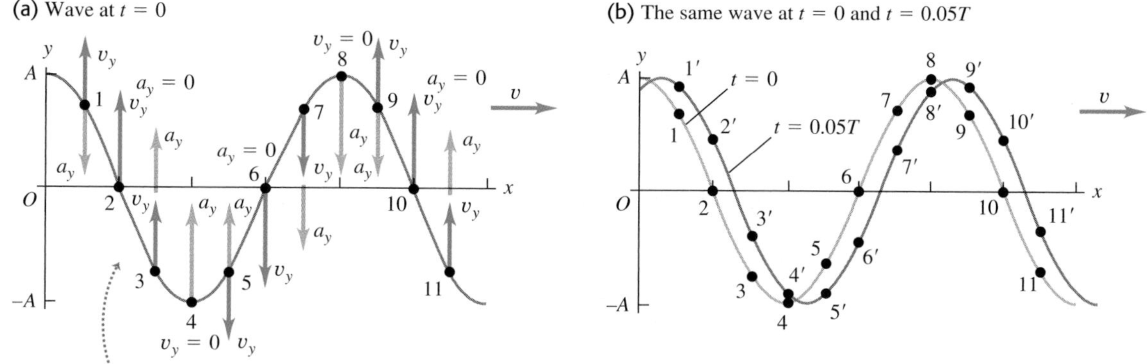

- Acceleration a_y at each point on the string is proportional to displacement y at that point.
- Acceleration is upward where string curves upward, downward where string curves downward.

ActivPhysics ONLINE
10.2 Speed of Waves on a String

15.4 Speed of a Transverse Wave

One of the key properties of any wave is the wave *speed.* Light waves in air have a much greater speed of propagation than do sound waves in air (3.00×10^8 m/s versus 344 m/s); that's why you see the flash from a bolt of lightning before you hear the clap of thunder. In this section we'll see what determines the speed of propagation of one particular kind of wave: transverse waves on a string. The speed of these waves is important to understand in its own right because it is an essential part of analyzing stringed musical instruments, as we'll discuss later in this chapter. Furthermore, the speeds of many kinds of mechanical waves turn out to have the same basic mathematical expression as does the speed of waves on a string.

The physical quantities that determine the speed of transverse waves on a string are the *tension* in the string and its *mass per unit length* (also called *linear mass density*). We might guess that increasing the tension should increase the restoring forces that tend to straighten the string when it is disturbed, thus increasing the wave speed. We might also guess that increasing the mass should make the motion more sluggish and decrease the speed. Both these guesses turn out to be right. We'll develop the exact relationship among wave speed, tension, and mass per unit length by two different methods. The first is simple in concept and considers a specific wave shape; the second is more general but also more formal. Choose whichever you like better.

Wave Speed on a String: First Method

We consider a perfectly flexible string (Fig. 15.11). In the equilibrium position the tension is F, and the linear mass density (mass per unit length) is μ. (When portions of the string are displaced from equilibrium, the mass per unit length decreases a little, and the tension increases a little.) We ignore the weight of the string so that when the string is at rest in the equilibrium position, the string forms a perfectly straight line as in Fig. 15.11a.

Starting at time $t = 0$, we apply a constant upward force F_y at the left end of the string. We might expect that the end would move with constant acceleration; that would happen if the force were applied to a *point* mass. But here the effect of the force F_y is to set successively more and more mass in motion. The wave travels with constant speed v, so the division point P between moving and nonmoving portions moves with the same constant speed v (Fig. 15.11b).

15.11 Propagation of a transverse wave on a string.

(a) String in equilibrium

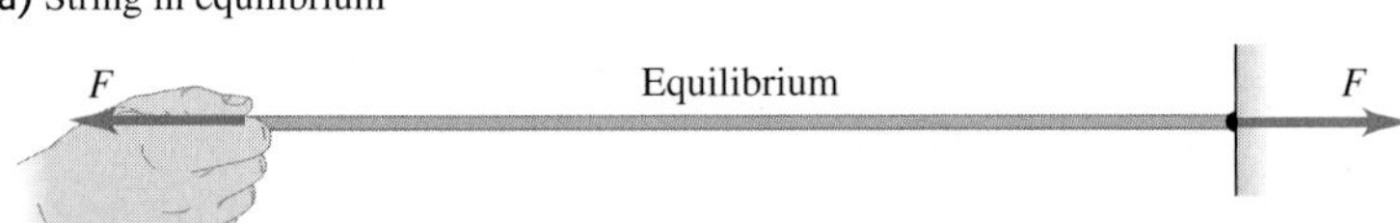
F
Equilibrium
F

(b) Part of the string in motion

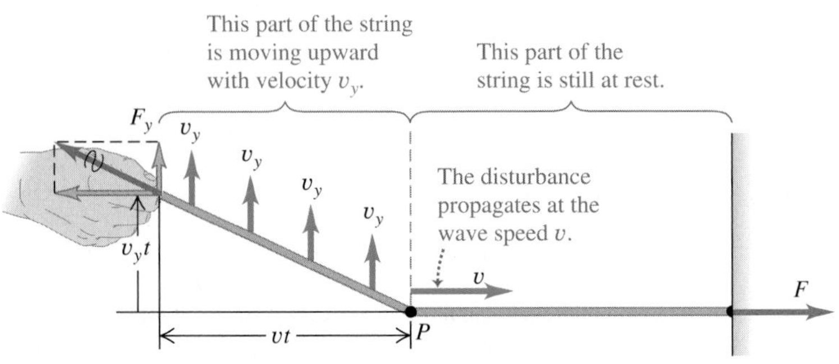
This part of the string is moving upward with velocity v_y.
This part of the string is still at rest.
F_y
v_y
v_y
v_y
v_y
The disturbance propagates at the wave speed v.
v
$v_y t$
vt
P
F

Figure 15.11b shows that all particles in the moving portion of the string move upward with constant *velocity* v_y, not constant acceleration. To see why this is so, we note that the *impulse* of the force F_y up to time t is $F_y t$. According to the impulse–momentum theorem (see Section 8.1), the impulse is equal to the change in the total transverse component of momentum $(mv_y - 0)$ of the moving part of the string. Because the system started with *no* transverse momentum, this is equal to the total momentum at time t:

$$F_y t = mv_y$$

The total momentum thus must increase proportionately with time. But since the division point P moves with constant speed, the length of string that is in motion and hence the total mass m in motion are also proportional to the time t that the force has been acting. So the *change* of momentum must be associated entirely with the increasing amount of mass in motion, not with an increasing velocity of an individual mass element. That is, mv_y changes because m, not v_y, changes.

At time t, the left end of the string has moved up a distance $v_y t$, and the boundary point P has advanced a distance vt. The total force at the left end of the string has components F and F_y. Why F? There is no motion in the direction along the length of the string, so there is no unbalanced horizontal force. Therefore F, the magnitude of the horizontal component, does not change when the string is displaced. In the displaced position the tension is $(F^2 + F_y^2)^{1/2}$ (greater than F), and the string stretches somewhat.

To derive an expression for the wave speed v, we again apply the impulse–momentum theorem to the portion of the string in motion at time t—that is, the portion to the left of P in Fig. 15.11b. The transverse *impulse* (transverse force times time) is equal to the change of transverse *momentum* of the moving portion (mass times transverse component of velocity). The impulse of the transverse force F_y in time t is $F_y t$. In Fig. 15.11b the right triangle whose vertex is at P, with sides $v_y t$ and vt, is similar to the right triangle whose vertex is at the position of the hand, with sides F_y and F. Hence

$$\frac{F_y}{F} = \frac{v_y t}{vt} \qquad F_y = F\frac{v_y}{v}$$

and

$$\text{Transverse impulse} = F_y t = F\frac{v_y}{v}t$$

The mass of the moving portion of the string is the product of the mass per unit length μ and the length vt, or μvt. The transverse momentum is the product of this mass and the transverse velocity v_y:

$$\text{Transverse momentum} = (\mu vt)v_y$$

We note again that the momentum increases with time *not* because mass is moving faster, as was usually the case in Chapter 8, but because *more mass* is brought into motion. But the impulse of the force F_y is still equal to the total change in momentum of the system. Applying this relationship, we obtain

$$F\frac{v_y}{v}t = \mu vtv_y$$

Solving this for v, we find

$$v = \sqrt{\frac{F}{\mu}} \qquad \text{(speed of a transverse wave on a string)} \qquad (15.13)$$

15.12 These cables have a relatively large amount of mass per unit length (μ) and a low tension (F). If the cables are disturbed—say, by a bird landing on them—transverse waves will travel along them at a slow speed $v = \sqrt{F/\mu}$.

15.13 Free-body diagram for a segment of string. The force at each end of the string is tangent to the string at the point of application.

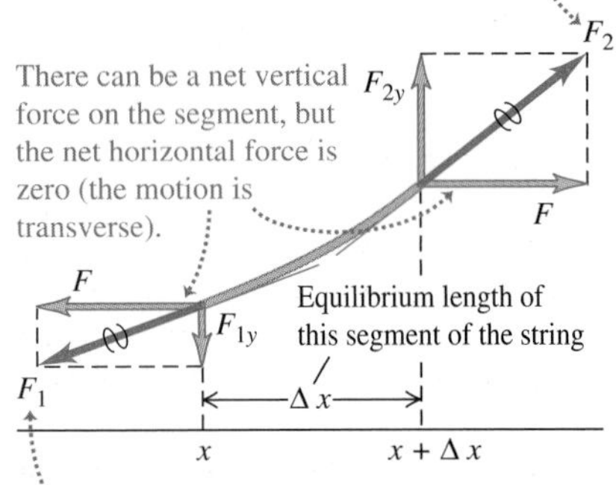
The string to the right of the segment (not shown) exerts a force $\vec{F}_2$ on the segment.
F_2
There can be a net vertical force on the segment, but the net horizontal force is zero (the motion is transverse).
F_{2y}
F
F
F_{1y}
Equilibrium length of this segment of the string
F_1
Δx
x
$x + \Delta x$
The string to the left of the segment (not shown) exerts a force $\vec{F}_1$ on the segment.

Equation (15.13) confirms our prediction that the wave speed v should increase when the tension F increases but decrease when the mass per unit length μ increases (Fig. 15.12).

Note that v_y does not appear in Eq. (15.13); thus the wave speed doesn't depend on v_y. Our calculation considered only a very special kind of pulse, but we can consider *any* shape of wave disturbance as a series of pulses with different values of v_y. So even though we derived Eq. (15.13) for a special case, it is valid for *any* transverse wave motion on a string, including the sinusoidal and other periodic waves we discussed in Section 15.3. Note also that the wave speed doesn't depend on the amplitude or frequency of the wave, in accordance with our assumptions in Section 15.3.

Wave Speed on a String: Second Method

Here is an alternative derivation of Eq. (15.13). If you aren't comfortable with partial derivatives, it can be omitted. We apply Newton's second law, $\sum\vec{F} = m\vec{a}$, to a small segment of string whose length in the equilibrium position is Δx (Fig. 15.13). The mass of the segment is $m = \mu\,\Delta x$; the forces at the ends are represented in terms of their x- and y-components. The x-components have equal magnitude F and add to zero because the motion is transverse and there is no component of acceleration in the x-direction. To obtain F_{1y} and F_{2y}, we note that the ratio F_{1y}/F is equal in magnitude to the *slope* of the string at point x and that F_{2y}/F is equal to the slope at point $x + \Delta x$. Taking proper account of signs, we find

$$\frac{F_{1y}}{F} = -\left(\frac{\partial y}{\partial x}\right)_x \qquad \frac{F_{2y}}{F} = \left(\frac{\partial y}{\partial x}\right)_{x+\Delta x} \tag{15.14}$$

The notation reminds us that the derivatives are evaluated at points x and $x + \Delta x$, respectively. From Eq. (15.14) we find that the net y-component of force is

$$F_y = F_{1y} + F_{2y} = F\left[\left(\frac{\partial y}{\partial x}\right)_{x+\Delta x} - \left(\frac{\partial y}{\partial x}\right)_x\right] \tag{15.15}$$

We now equate F_y from Eq. (15.15) to the mass $\mu\,\Delta x$ times the y-component of acceleration $\partial^2 y/\partial t^2$. We obtain

$$F\left[\left(\frac{\partial y}{\partial x}\right)_{x+\Delta x} - \left(\frac{\partial y}{\partial x}\right)_x\right] = \mu\,\Delta x\frac{\partial^2 y}{\partial t^2} \tag{15.16}$$

or, dividing by $F\,\Delta x$,

$$\frac{\left(\frac{\partial y}{\partial x}\right)_{x+\Delta x} - \left(\frac{\partial y}{\partial x}\right)_x}{\Delta x} = \frac{\mu}{F}\frac{\partial^2 y}{\partial t^2} \tag{15.17}$$

We now take the limit as $\Delta x \rightarrow 0$. In this limit, the left side of Eq. (15.17) becomes the derivative of $\partial y/\partial x$ with respect to x (at constant t)—that is, the *second* (partial) derivative of y with respect to x:

$$\frac{\partial^2 y}{\partial x^2} = \frac{\mu}{F}\frac{\partial^2 y}{\partial t^2} \tag{15.18}$$

Now, finally, comes the punch line of our story. Equation (15.18) has exactly the same form as the *wave equation,* Eq. (15.12), that we derived at the end of Section 15.3. That equation and Eq. (15.18) describe the very same wave motion, so they must be identical. Comparing the two equations, we see that for this to be so, we must have

$$v = \sqrt{\frac{F}{\mu}} \tag{15.19}$$

which is the same expression as Eq. (15.13).

In going through this derivation, we didn't make any special assumptions about the shape of the wave. Since our derivation led us to rediscover Eq. (15.12), the wave equation, we conclude that the wave equation is valid for waves on a string that have *any* shape.

The Speed of Mechanical Waves

Equation (15.13) or (15.19) gives the wave speed for only the special case of mechanical waves on a stretched string or rope. Remarkably, it turns out that for many types of mechanical waves, including waves on a string, the expression for wave speed has the same general form:

$$v = \sqrt{\frac{\text{Restoring force returning the system to equilibrium}}{\text{Inertia resisting the return to equilibrium}}}$$

To interpret this expression, let's look at the now-familiar case of waves on a string. The tension F in the string plays the role of the restoring force; it tends to bring the string back to its undisturbed, equilibrium configuration. The mass of the string—or, more properly, the linear mass density μ—provides the inertia that prevents the string from returning instantaneously to equilibrium. Hence we have $v = \sqrt{F/\mu}$ for the speed of waves on a string.

In Chapter 16 we'll see a similar expression for the speed of sound waves in a gas. Roughly speaking, the gas pressure provides the force that tends to return the gas to its undisturbed state when a sound wave passes through. The inertia is provided by the density, or mass per unit volume, of the gas.

Example 15.3 Calculating wave speed

One end of a nylon rope is tied to a stationary support at the top of a vertical mine shaft 80.0 m deep (Fig. 15.14). The rope is stretched taut by a box of mineral samples with mass 20.0 kg attached at the lower end. The mass of the rope is 2.00 kg. The geologist at the bottom of the mine signals to his colleague at the top by jerking the rope sideways. (a) What is the speed of a transverse wave on the rope? (b) If a point on the rope is given a transverse simple harmonic motion with a frequency of 2.00 Hz, how many cycles of the wave are there in the rope's length?

15.14 Sending signals along a vertical rope using transverse waves.

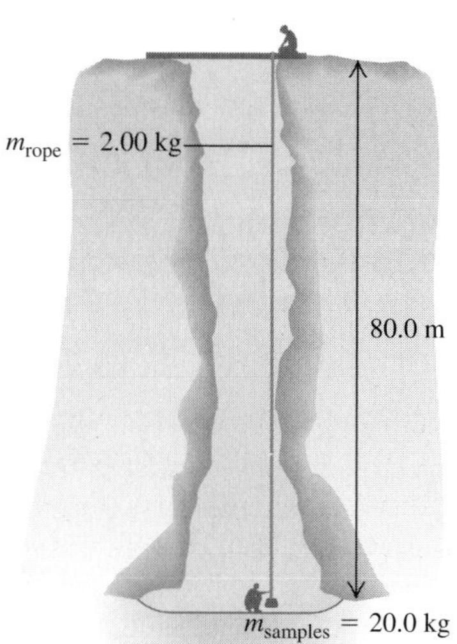

SOLUTION

IDENTIFY: In part (a) the target variable is the wave speed. This part involves *dynamics*—that is, the relationship between the wave speed and the properties of the rope (tension and liner mass density). Part (b) involves *kinematics*, since we need to know how wave speed, frequency, and wavelength are related. (The target variable is actually the number of wavelengths that fit into the length of the rope.)

We'll assume that the tension in the rope is provided by the weight of the box of samples. In fact, the weight of the rope itself contributes to the tension, which means that the tension is different at the top and bottom of the rope. We'll ignore this effect here, since the weight of the rope is small compared to the weight of the samples.

SET UP: We use the relationship $v = \sqrt{F/\mu}$ in part (a). If we neglect the weight of the rope itself, the tension F is just equal to the weight of the box. In part (b) we use the equation $v = f\lambda$ to find the wavelength, which we then compare to the 80.0-m length of the rope.

EXECUTE: (a) The tension in the rope (due to the sample box) is

$$F = m_{samples}g = (20.0\text{ kg})(9.80\text{ m/s}^2) = 196\text{ N}$$

Continued

and the mass per unit length of the rope is

$$\mu = \frac{m_{\text{rope}}}{L} = \frac{2.00\text{ kg}}{80.0\text{ m}} = 0.0250\text{ kg/m}$$

Hence, from Eq. (15.13), the wave speed is

$$v = \sqrt{\frac{F}{\mu}} = \sqrt{\frac{196\text{ N}}{0.0250\text{ kg/m}}} = 88.5\text{ m/s}$$

(b) From Eq. (15.1),

$$\lambda = \frac{v}{f} = \frac{88.5\text{ m/s}}{2.00\text{ s}^{-1}} = 44.3\text{ m}$$

The length of the rope is 80.0 m, so the number of wave cycles in the rope is

$$\frac{80.0\text{ m/s}}{44.3\text{ m/cycle}} = 1.81\text{ cycles}$$

EVALUATE: If we do account for the weight of the rope, the tension is greater at the top of the rope than at the bottom. Hence the wave speed increases and the wavelength increases as the wave travels up the rope. Can you verify that the wave speed at the top of the rope is 92.9 m/s?

Test Your Understanding of Section 15.4 The six strings of a guitar are the same length and under nearly the same tension, but they have different thicknesses. On which string do waves travel the fastest? (i) the thickest string; (ii) the thinnest string; (iii) the wave speed is the same on all strings.

15.5 Energy in Wave Motion

Every wave motion has *energy* associated with it. The energy we receive from sunlight and the destructive effects of ocean surf and earthquakes bear this out. To produce any of the wave motions we have discussed in this chapter, we have to apply a force to a portion of the wave medium; the point where the force is applied moves, so we do *work* on the system. As the wave propagates, each portion of the medium exerts a force and does work on the adjoining portion. In this way a wave can transport energy from one region of space to another.

15.15 (a) Point a on a string carrying a wave from left to right. (b) The components of the force exerted on the part of the string to the right of point a by the part of the string to the left of point a.

(a) Slope $= \frac{\Delta y}{\Delta x}$, a, Δy, Δx

(b) y, F, a, x, F_y

As an example of energy considerations in wave motion, let's look again at transverse waves on a string. How is energy transferred from one portion of string to another? Picture a wave traveling from left to right (the positive x-direction) on the string, and consider a particular point a on the string (Fig. 15.15a). The string to the left of point a exerts a force on the string to the right of it, and vice versa. In Fig. 15.15b the string to the left of a has been removed, and the force it exerts at a is represented by the components F and F_y, as we did in Figs. 15.11 and 15.13. We note again that F_y/F is equal to the negative of the *slope* of the string at a, which is also given by $\partial y/\partial x$. Putting these together, we have

$$F_y(x,t) = -F\frac{\partial y(x,t)}{\partial x} \tag{15.20}$$

We need the negative sign because F_y is negative when the slope is positive. We write the vertical force as $F_y(x,t)$ as a reminder that its value may be different at different points along the string and at different times.

When point a moves in the y-direction, the force F_y does *work* on this point and therefore transfers energy into the part of the string to the right of a. The corresponding power P (rate of doing work) at the point a is the transverse force $F_y(x,t)$ at a times the transverse velocity $v_y(x,t) = \partial y(x,t)/\partial t$ of that point:

$$P(x,t) = F_y(x,t)v_y(x,t) = -F\frac{\partial y(x,t)}{\partial x}\frac{\partial y(x,t)}{\partial t} \tag{15.21}$$

This power is the *instantaneous* rate at which energy is transferred along the string. Its value depends on the position x on the string and on the time t. Note that energy is being transferred only at points where the string has a nonzero slope ($\partial y/\partial x$ is nonzero), so that there is a transverse component of the tension force, and where the string has a nonzero transverse velocity ($\partial y/\partial t$ is nonzero) so that the transverse force can do work.

Equation (15.21) is valid for *any* wave on a string, sinusoidal or not. For a sinusoidal wave with wave function given by Eq. (15.7), we have

$$
\begin{aligned}
y(x,t) &= A\cos(kx - \omega t)\\
\frac{\partial y(x,t)}{\partial x} &= -kA\sin(kx - \omega t)\\
\frac{\partial y(x,t)}{\partial t} &= \omega A\sin(kx - \omega t)\\
P(x,t) &= Fk\omega A^2\sin^2(kx - \omega t)
\end{aligned}
\qquad (15.22)
$$

By using the relationships $\omega = vk$ and $v^2 = F/\mu$, we can also express Eq. (15.22) in the alternative form

$$P(x,t) = \sqrt{\mu F}\,\omega^2 A^2\sin^2(kx - \omega t) \qquad (15.23)$$

The $\sin^2$ function is never negative, so the instantaneous power in a sinusoidal wave is either positive (so that energy flows in the positive x-direction) or zero (at points where there is no energy transfer). Energy is never transferred in the direction opposite to the direction of wave propagation (Fig. 15.16).

The maximum value of the instantaneous power $P(x,t)$ occurs when the $\sin^2$ function has the value unity:

$$P_{\text{max}} = \sqrt{\mu F}\,\omega^2 A^2 \qquad (15.24)$$

To obtain the *average* power from Eq. (15.23), we note that the *average* value of the $\sin^2$ function, averaged over any whole number of cycles, is $\frac{1}{2}$. Hence the average power is

$$P_{\text{av}} = \frac{1}{2}\sqrt{\mu F}\,\omega^2 A^2 \quad \text{(average power, sinusoidal wave on a string)} \qquad (15.25)$$

15.16 The instantaneous power $P(x,t)$ in a sinusoidal wave as given by Eq. (15.23), shown as a function of time at coordinate $x = 0$. The power is never negative, which means that energy never flows opposite to the direction of wave propagation.

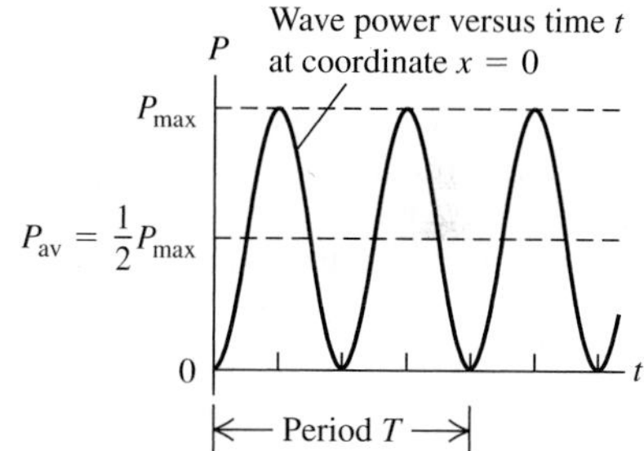

The average power is just one-half of the maximum instantaneous power (see Fig. 15.16).

The average rate of energy transfer is proportional to the square of the amplitude and to the square of the frequency. This proportionality is a general result for mechanical waves of all types, including seismic waves (see the photo that opens this chapter). For a mechanical wave, the rate of energy transfer quadruples if the frequency is doubled (for the same amplitude) or if the amplitude is doubled (for the same frequency). ?

Electromagnetic waves turn out to be a bit different. While the average rate of energy transfer in an electromagnetic wave is proportional to the square of the amplitude, just as for mechanical waves, it is independent of the value of ω.

Example 15.4 Power in a wave

(a) In Example 15.2, at what maximum rate does Throcky put energy into the clothesline? That is, what is his maximum instantaneous power? Assume that the linear mass density of the clothesline is $\mu = 0.250$ kg/m and that Throcky applies tension $F = 36.0$ N. (b) What is his average power? (c) As Throcky tires, the amplitude decreases. What is the average power when the amplitude has dropped to 7.50 mm?

SOLUTION

IDENTIFY: Our target variable in part (a) is the *maximum instantaneous* power, while the target variable in parts (b) and (c) is the *average* power. As we've seen, these two quantities have different values for a sinusoidal wave. We'll be able to calculate the values of both quantities because we know all the other properties of the wave from Example 15.2.

SET UP: For part (a) we use Eq. (15.24), and for parts (b) and (c) we use Eq. (15.25).

EXECUTE: (a) The maximum instantaneous power is

$$
\begin{aligned}
P_{\text{max}} &= \sqrt{\mu F}\,\omega^2 A^2\\
&= \sqrt{(0.250\text{ kg/m})(36.0\text{ N})}\,(4.00\pi\text{ rad/s})^2(0.075\text{ m})^2\\
&= 2.66\text{ W}
\end{aligned}
$$

Continued

(b) From Eqs. (15.24) and (15.25), the average power is one-half of the maximum instantaneous power, so

$$P_{av} = \frac{1}{2}(2.66\ \text{W}) = 1.33\ \text{W}$$

(c) The new amplitude is $\frac{1}{10}$ of the value we used in parts (a) and (b). The average power is proportional to the *square* of the amplitude, so now the average power is

$$P_{av} = \left(\frac{1}{10}\right)^2 (1.33\ \text{W}) = 0.0133\ \text{W} = 13.3\ \text{mW}$$

EVALUATE: The *maximum* instantaneous power in part (a) occurs when the quantity $\sin^2(kx - \omega t)$ in Eq. (15.23) is equal to 1. At any given value of x, this happens twice per period of the wave—once when the sine function is equal to $+1$, and once when it's equal to -1. The *minimum* instantaneous power is zero; this occurs when $\sin(kx - \omega t) = 0$, which also happens twice per period.

Can you confirm that the given values of μ and F give the wave speed mentioned in Example 15.2?

Wave Intensity

Waves on a string carry energy in just one dimension of space (along the direction of the string). But other types of waves, including sound waves in air and seismic waves in the body of the earth, carry energy across all three dimensions of space. For waves that travel in three dimensions, we define the **intensity** (denoted by I) to be *the time average rate at which energy is transported by the wave, per unit area,* across a surface perpendicular to the direction of propagation. That is, intensity I is average power per unit area. It is usually measured in watts per square meter (W/m^2).

If waves spread out equally in all directions from a source, the intensity at a distance r from the source is inversely proportional to r^2 (Fig. 15.17). This follows directly from energy conservation. If the power output of the source is P, then the average intensity I_1 through a sphere with radius r_1 and surface area $4\pi r_1^2$ is

$$I_1 = \frac{P}{4\pi r_1^2}$$

The average intensity I_2 through a sphere with a different radius r_2 is given by a similar expression. If no energy is absorbed between the two spheres, the power P must be the same for both, and

$$4\pi r_1^2 I_1 = 4\pi r_2^2 I_2$$

$$\frac{I_1}{I_2} = \frac{r_2^2}{r_1^2} \quad \text{(inverse-square law for intensity)} \qquad (15.26)$$

The intensity I at any distance r is therefore inversely proportional to r^2. This relationship is called the *inverse-square law* for intensity.

15.17 The greater the distance from a wave source, the greater the area over which the wave power is distributed and the smaller the wave intensity.

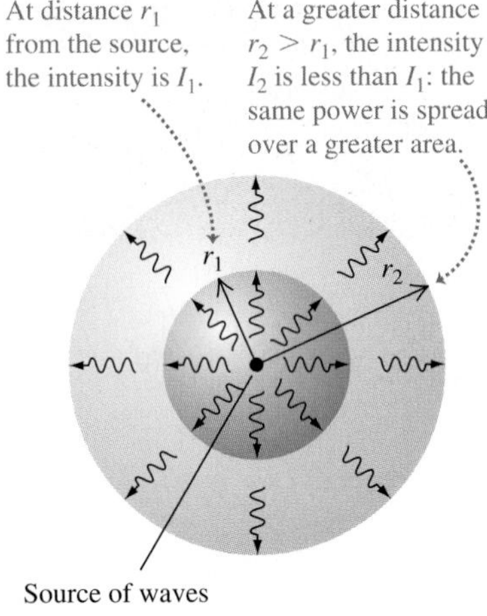
At distance r_1 from the source, the intensity is I_1.
At a greater distance $r_2 > r_1$, the intensity I_2 is less than I_1: the same power is spread over a greater area.
r_1
r_2
Source of waves

Example 15.5 The inverse-square law

A tornado warning siren on top of a tall pole radiates sound waves uniformly in all directions. At a distance of 15.0 m the intensity of the sound is $0.250\ \text{W/m}^2$. At what distance from the siren is the intensity $0.010\ \text{W/m}^2$?

SOLUTION

IDENTIFY: Because waves spread out equally in all directions, we can use the inverse-square law. Our target variable is a distance from the wave source.

SET UP: The relationship to use is Eq. (15.26). We are given the distance $r_1 = 15.0$ m at which the intensity is $I_1 = 0.250\ \text{W/m}^2$, and we want to find the distance r_2 at which the intensity is $I_2 = 0.010\ \text{W/m}^2$.

EXECUTE: We solve Eq. (15.26) for r_2:

$$r_2 = r_1\sqrt{\frac{I_1}{I_2}} = (15.0\ \text{m})\sqrt{\frac{0.250\ \text{W/m}^2}{0.010\ \text{W/m}^2}} = 75.0\ \text{m}$$

EVALUATE: As a check on our answer, note that r_2 is five times greater than r_1. By the inverse-square law, the intensity I_2 should be $1/5^2 = 1/25$ as great as I_1, and indeed it is.

By using the inverse-square law we've assumed that the sound waves travel in straight lines away from the siren. A more realistic solution of this problem would account for the reflection of sound waves from the ground. Such a solution is beyond our scope, however.

Test Your Understanding of Section 15.5 Four identical strings each carry a sinusoidal wave of frequency 10 Hz. The string tension and wave amplitude are different for different strings. Rank the following strings in order from highest to lowest value of the average wave power: (i) tension 10 N, amplitude 1.0 mm; (ii) tension 40 N, amplitude 1.0 mm; (iii) tension 10 N, amplitude 4.0 mm; (iv) tension 20 N, amplitude 2.0 mm.

15.6 Wave Interference, Boundary Conditions, and Superposition

Up to this point we've been discussing waves that propagate continuously in the same direction. But when a wave strikes the boundaries of its medium, all or part of the wave is *reflected.* When you yell at a building wall or a cliff face some distance away, the sound wave is reflected from the rigid surface and you hear an echo. When you flip the end of a rope whose far end is tied to a rigid support, a pulse travels the length of the rope and is reflected back to you. In both cases, the initial and reflected waves overlap in the same region of the medium. This overlapping of waves is called **interference.** (In general, the term "interference" refers to what happens when two or more waves pass through the same region at the same time.)

As a simple example of wave reflections and the role of the boundary of a wave medium, let's look again at transverse waves on a stretched string. What happens when a wave pulse or a sinusoidal wave arrives at the *end* of the string?

If the end is fastened to a rigid support, it is a *fixed* end that cannot move. The arriving wave exerts a force on the support; the reaction to this force, exerted *by* the support *on* the string, "kicks back" on the string and sets up a *reflected* pulse or wave traveling in the reverse direction. Figure 15.18 is a series of photographs showing the reflection of a pulse at the fixed end of a long coiled spring. The reflected pulse moves in the opposite direction from the initial, or *incident,* pulse, and its displacement is also opposite. Figure 15.19a illustrates this situation for a wave pulse on a string.

15.18 A series of images of a wave pulse, equally spaced in time from top to bottom. The pulse starts at the left in the top image, travels to the right, and is reflected from the fixed end at the right.

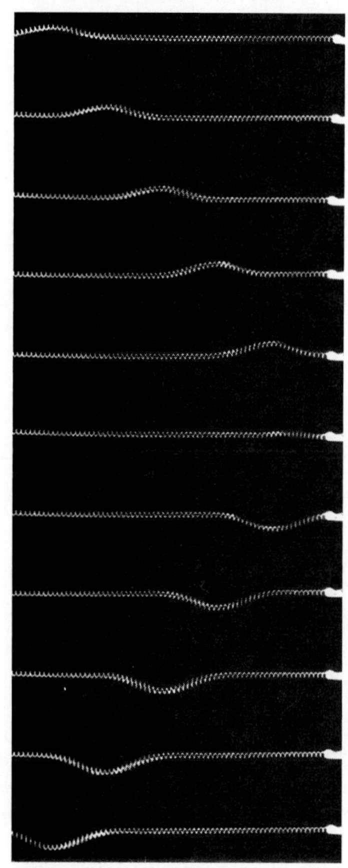

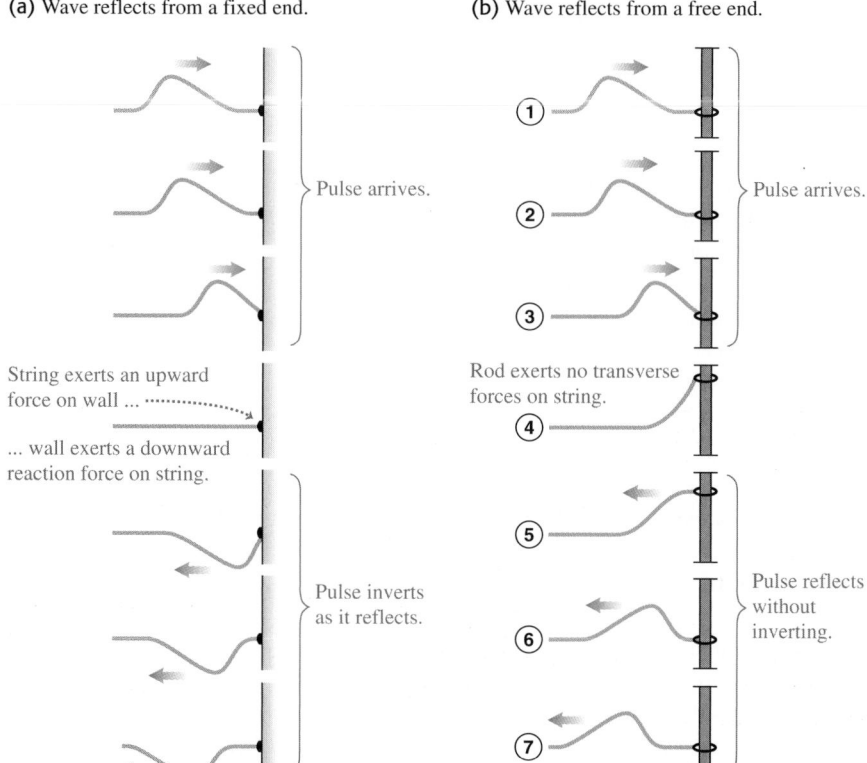

(a) Wave reflects from a fixed end.

Pulse arrives.

String exerts an upward force on wall ...

... wall exerts a downward reaction force on string.

Pulse inverts as it reflects.

(b) Wave reflects from a free end.

1 2 3 Pulse arrives.

Rod exerts no transverse forces on string.

4

5 6 7 Pulse reflects without inverting.

15.19 Reflection of a wave pulse (a) at a fixed end of a string and (b) at a free end. Time increases from top to bottom in each figure.

15.20 Overlap of two wave pulses—one right side up, one inverted—traveling in opposite directions. Time increases from top to bottom.

As the pulses overlap, the displacement of the string at any point is the algebraic sum of the displacements due to the individual pulses.

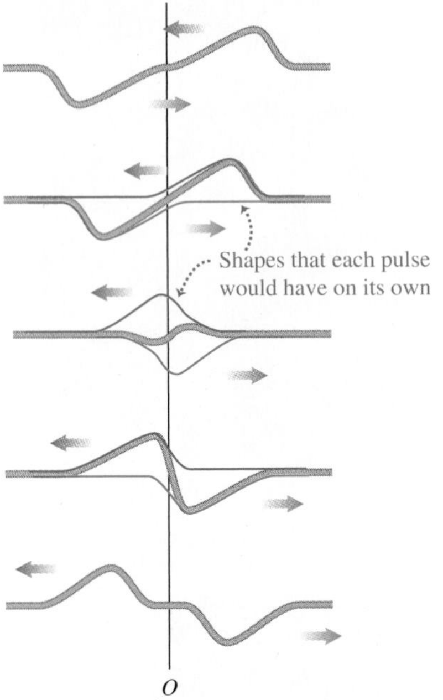

15.21 Overlap of two wave pulses—both right side up—traveling in opposite directions. Time increases from top to bottom. Compare to Fig. 15.20.

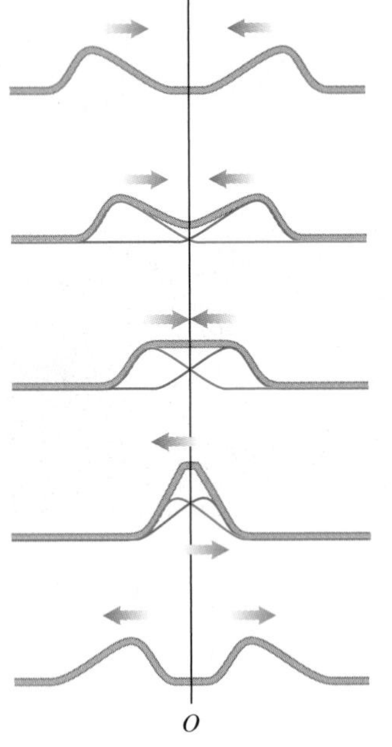

The opposite situation from an end that is held stationary is a *free* end, one that is perfectly free to move in the direction perpendicular to the length of the string. For example, the string might be tied to a light ring that slides on a frictionless rod perpendicular to the string, as in Fig. 15.19b. The ring and rod maintain the tension but exert no transverse force. When a wave arrives at this free end, the ring slides along the rod. The ring reaches a maximum displacement, and both it and the string come momentarily to rest, as in drawing 4 in Fig. 15.19b. But the string is now stretched, giving increased tension, so the free end of the string is pulled back down, and again a reflected pulse is produced (drawing 7). As for a fixed end, the reflected pulse moves in the opposite direction from the initial pulse, but now the direction of the displacement is the same as for the initial pulse. The conditions at the end of the string, such as a rigid support or the complete absence of transverse force, are called **boundary conditions.**

The formation of the reflected pulse is similar to the overlap of two pulses traveling in opposite directions. Figure 15.20 shows two pulses with the same shape, one inverted with respect to the other, traveling in opposite directions. As the pulses overlap and pass each other, the total displacement of the string is the *algebraic sum* of the displacements at that point in the individual pulses. Because these two pulses have the same shape, the total displacement at point O in the middle of the figure is zero at all times. Thus the motion of the left half of the string would be the same if we cut the string at point O, threw away the right side, and held the end at O fixed. The two pulses on the left side then correspond to the incident and reflected pulses, combining so that the total displacement at O is *always* zero. For this to occur, the reflected pulse must be inverted relative to the incident pulse.

Figure 15.21 shows two pulses with the same shape, traveling in opposite directions but *not* inverted relative to each other. The displacement at point O in the middle of the figure is not zero, but the slope of the string at this point is always zero. According to Eq. (15.20), this corresponds to the absence of any transverse force at this point. In this case the motion of the left half of the string would be the same as if we cut the string at point O and attached the end to a frictionless sliding ring (Fig. 15.19b) that maintains tension without exerting any transverse force. In other words, this situation corresponds to reflection of a pulse at a free end of a string at point O. In this case the reflected pulse is *not* inverted.

The Principle of Superposition

Combining the displacements of the separate pulses at each point to obtain the actual displacement is an example of the **principle of superposition:** When two waves overlap, the actual displacement of any point on the string at any time is obtained by adding the displacement the point would have if only the first wave were present and the displacement it would have if only the second wave were present. In other words, the wave function $y(x, t)$ that describes the resulting motion in this situation is obtained by *adding* the two wave functions for the two separate waves:

$$y(x, t) = y_1(x, t) + y_2(x, t) \qquad \text{(principle of superposition)} \qquad (15.27)$$

Mathematically, this additive property of wave functions follows from the form of the wave equation, Eq. (15.12) or (15.18), which every physically possible wave function must satisfy. Specifically, the wave equation is *linear;* that is, it contains the function $y(x, t)$ only to the first power (there are no terms involving $y(x, t)^2$, $y(x, t)^{1/2}$, etc.). As a result, if any two functions $y_1(x, t)$ and $y_2(x, t)$ satisfy the wave equation separately, their sum $y_1(x, t) + y_2(x, t)$ also satisfies it and is therefore a physically possible motion. Because this principle depends on the linearity of the wave equation and the corresponding linear-combination property of its solutions, it is also called the *principle of linear superposition.* For some physical systems, such as a medium that does not obey Hooke's law, the wave equation is *not* linear; this principle does not hold for such systems.

The principle of superposition is of central importance in all types of waves. When a friend talks to you while you are listening to music, you can distinguish the sound of speech and the sound of music from each other. This is precisely because the total sound wave reaching your ears is the algebraic sum of the wave produced by your friend's voice and the wave produced by the speakers of your stereo. If two sound waves did *not* combine in this simple linear way, the sound you would hear in this situation would be a hopeless jumble. Superposition also applies to electromagnetic waves (such as light) and many other types of waves.

Test Your Understanding of Section 15.6 Figure 15.22 shows two wave pulses with different shapes traveling in different directions along a string. Make a series of sketches like Fig. 15.21 showing the shape of the string as the two pulses approach, overlap, and then pass each other.

15.22 Two wave pulses with different shapes.

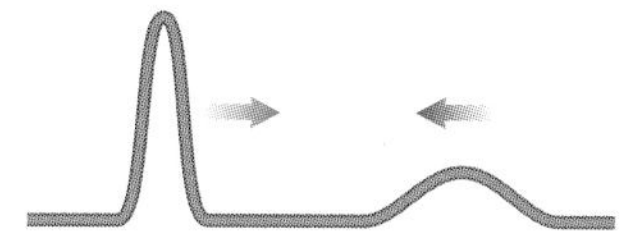

15.7 Standing Waves on a String

We have talked about the reflection of a wave *pulse* on a string when it arrives at a boundary point (either a fixed end or a free end). Now let's look at what happens when a *sinusoidal* wave is reflected by a fixed end of a string. We'll again approach the problem by considering the superposition of two waves propagating through the string, one representing the original or incident wave and the other representing the wave reflected at the fixed end.

Figure 15.23 shows a string that is fixed at its left end. Its right end is moved up and down in simple harmonic motion to produce a wave that travels to the left; the wave reflected from the fixed end travels to the right. The resulting motion when the two waves combine no longer looks like two waves traveling in opposite directions. The string appears to be subdivided into a number of segments, as in

15.23 (a)–(d) Time exposures of standing waves in a stretched string. From (a) to (d), the frequency of oscillation of the right-hand end increases and the wavelength of the standing wave decreases. (e) The extremes of the motion of the standing wave in part (b), with nodes at the center and at the ends. The right-hand end of the string moves very little compared to the antinodes and so is essentially a node.

(a) String is one-half wavelength long.

(b) String is one wavelength long.

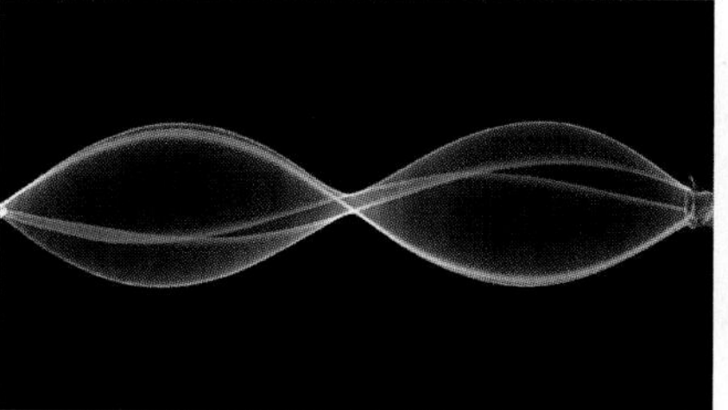

(c) String is one and a half wavelengths long.

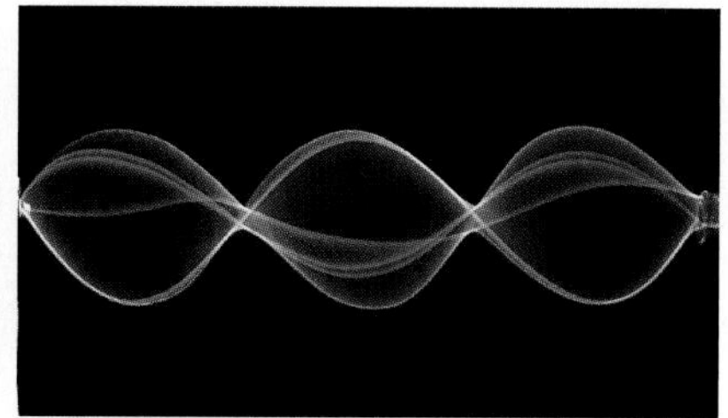

(d) String is two wavelengths long.

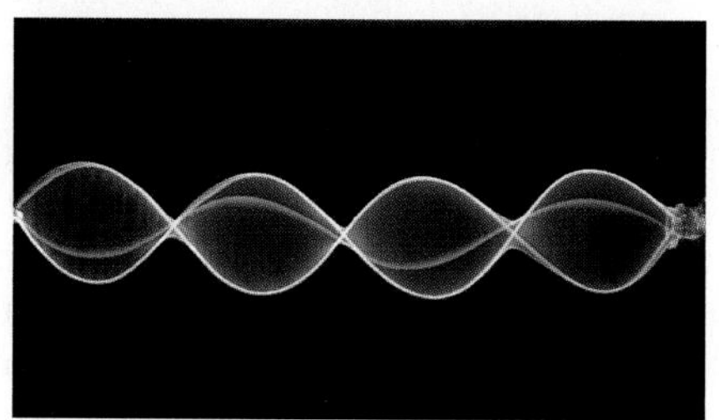

(e) The shape of the string in (b) at two different instants

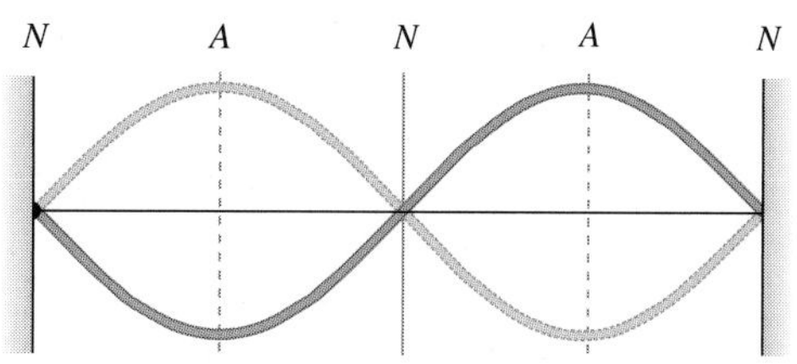

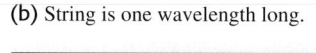

N = **nodes:** points at which the string never moves

A = **antinodes:** points at which the amplitude of string motion is greatest

the time-exposure photographs of Figs. 15.23a, 15.23b, 15.23c, and 15.23d. Figure 15.23e shows two instantaneous shapes of the string in Fig. 15.23b. Let's compare this behavior with the waves we studied in Sections 15.1 through 15.5. In a wave that travels along the string, the amplitude is constant and the wave pattern moves with a speed equal to the wave speed. Here, instead, the wave pattern remains in the same position along the string and its amplitude fluctuates. There are particular points called **nodes** (labeled N in Fig. 15.23e) that never move at all. Midway between the nodes are points called **antinodes** (labeled A in Fig. 15.23e) where the amplitude of motion is greatest. Because the wave pattern doesn't appear to be moving in either direction along the string, it is called a **standing wave.** (To emphasize the difference, a wave that *does* move along the string is called a **traveling wave.**)

The principle of superposition explains how the incident and reflected waves combine to form a standing wave. In Fig. 15.24 the red curves show a wave traveling to the left. The blue curves show a wave traveling to the right with the same propagation speed, wavelength, and amplitude. The waves are shown at nine instants, $\frac{1}{16}$ of a period apart. At each point along the string, we add the displacements (the values of y) for the two separate waves; the result is the total wave on the string, shown in brown.

15.24 Formation of a standing wave. A wave traveling to the left (red curves) combines with a wave traveling to the right (blue curves) to form a standing wave (brown curves).

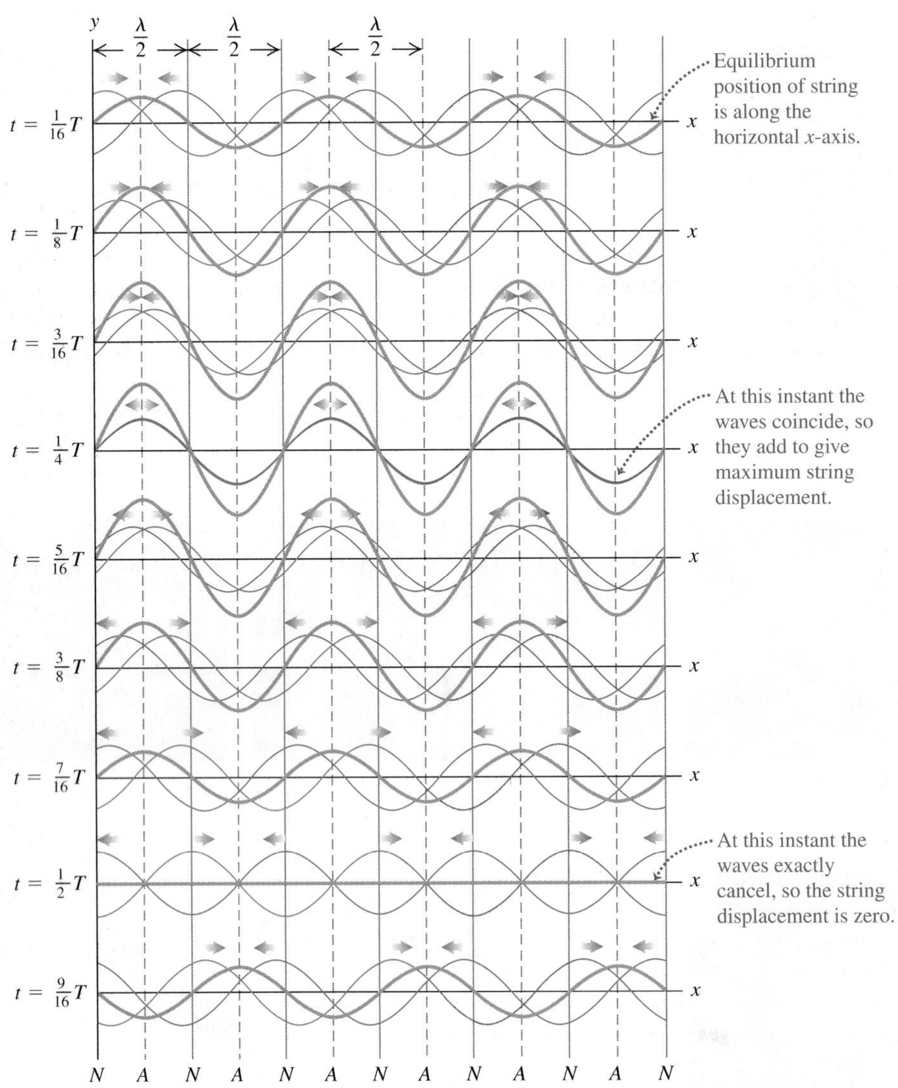

At certain instants, such as $t = \frac{1}{4}T$, the two wave patterns are exactly in phase with each other, and the shape of the string is a sine curve with twice the amplitude of either individual wave. At other instants, such as $t = \frac{1}{2}T$, the two waves are exactly out of phase with each other, and the total wave at that instant is zero. The resultant displacement is *always* zero at those places marked N at the bottom of Fig. 15.24. These are the *nodes.* At a node the displacements of the two waves in red and blue are always equal and opposite and cancel each other out. This cancellation is called **destructive interference.** Midway between the nodes are the points of *greatest* amplitude, or the *antinodes,* marked A. At the antinodes the displacements of the two waves in red and blue are always identical, giving a large resultant displacement; this phenomenon is called **constructive interference.** We can see from the figure that the distance between successive nodes or between successive antinodes is one half-wavelength, or $\lambda/2$.

We can derive a wave function for the standing wave of Fig. 15.24 by adding the wave functions $y_1(x, t)$ and $y_2(x, t)$ for two waves with equal amplitude, period, and wavelength traveling in opposite directions. Here $y_1(x, t)$ (the red curves in Fig. 15.24) represents an incoming, or *incident,* wave traveling to the left along the $+x$-axis, arriving at the point $x = 0$ and being reflected; $y_2(x, t)$ (the blue curves in Fig. 15.24) represents the *reflected* wave traveling to the right from $x = 0$. We noted in Section 15.6 that the wave reflected from a fixed end of a string is inverted, so we give a negative sign to one of the waves:

$$y_1(x, t) = -A\cos(kx + \omega t) \qquad \text{(incident wave traveling to the left)}$$
$$y_2(x, t) = A\cos(kx - \omega t) \qquad \text{(reflected wave traveling to the right)}$$

Note also that the change in sign corresponds to a shift in *phase* of 180° or π radians. At $x = 0$ the motion from the reflected wave is $A\cos\omega t$ and the motion from the incident wave is $-A\cos\omega t$, which we can also write as $A\cos(\omega t + \pi)$. From Eq. (15.27), the wave function for the standing wave is the sum of the individual wave functions:

$$y(x, t) = y_1(x, t) + y_2(x, t) = A[-\cos(kx + \omega t) + \cos(kx - \omega t)]$$

We can rewrite each of the cosine terms by using the identities for the cosine of the sum and difference of two angles: $\cos(a \pm b) = \cos a\cos b \mp \sin a\sin b$. Applying these and combining terms, we obtain the wave function for the standing wave:

$$y(x, t) = y_1(x, t) + y_2(x, t) = (2A\sin kx)\sin\omega t \qquad \text{or}$$

$$y(x, t) = (A_{SW}\sin kx)\sin\omega t \qquad \text{(standing wave on a string, fixed end at } x = 0\text{)} \qquad (15.28)$$

The standing wave amplitude A_{SW} is twice the amplitude A of either of the original traveling waves:

$$A_{SW} = 2A$$

Equation (15.28) has two factors: a function of x and a function of t. The factor $A_{SW}\sin kx$ shows that at each instant the shape of the string is a sine curve. But unlike a wave traveling along a string, the wave shape stays in the same position, oscillating up and down as described by the $\sin\omega t$ factor. This behavior is shown graphically by the brown curves in Fig. 15.24. Each point in the string still undergoes simple harmonic motion, but all the points between any successive pair of nodes oscillate *in phase.* This is in contrast to the phase differences between oscillations of adjacent points that we see with a wave traveling in one direction.

We can use Eq. (15.28) to find the positions of the nodes; these are the points for which $\sin kx = 0$, so the displacement is *always* zero. This occurs when $kx = 0, \pi, 2\pi, 3\pi, \ldots$, or, using $k = 2\pi/\lambda$,

$$\begin{aligned} x &= 0, \frac{\pi}{k}, \frac{2\pi}{k}, \frac{3\pi}{k}, \ldots \\ &= 0, \frac{\lambda}{2}, \frac{2\lambda}{2}, \frac{3\lambda}{2}, \ldots \end{aligned} \quad \text{(nodes of a standing wave on a string, fixed end at } x = 0) \qquad (15.29)$$

In particular, there is a node at $x = 0$, as there should be, since this point is a fixed end of the string.

A standing wave, unlike a traveling wave, *does not* transfer energy from one end to the other. The two waves that form it would individually carry equal amounts of power in opposite directions. There is a local flow of energy from each node to the adjacent antinodes and back, but the *average* rate of energy transfer is zero at every point. If you evaluate the wave power given by Eq. (15.21) using the wave function of Eq. (15.28), you will find that the average power is zero (see Challenge Problem 15.84).

Problem-Solving Strategy 15.2 Standing Waves

MP

IDENTIFY *the relevant concepts:* As with traveling waves, it's useful to distinguish between the purely kinematic quantities, such as wave speed v, wavelength λ, and frequency f, and the dynamic quantities involving the properties of the medium, such as F and μ for transverse waves on a string. Once you decide what the target variable is, try to determine whether the problem is only kinematic in nature or whether the properties of the medium are also involved.

SET UP *the problem* using the following steps:

1. To visualize nodes and antinodes in standing waves, it is always helpful to draw diagrams. For a string you can draw the shape at one instant and label the nodes N and antinodes A. The distance between two adjacent nodes or two adjacent antinodes is always $\lambda/2$, and the distance between a node and the adjacent antinode is always $\lambda/4$.
2. Decide which equations you'll need to use. The wave function for the standing wave, like Eq. (15.28), is almost always useful.
3. You can compute the wave speed if you know either λ and f (or, equivalently, $k = 2\pi/\lambda$ and $\omega = 2\pi f$) or the properties of the medium (for a string, F and μ).

EXECUTE *the solution* as follows: Solve for the unknown quantities using the equations you've selected. Once you have the wave function, you can find the value of the displacement y at any point in the wave medium (value of x) and at any time. You can find the velocity of a particle in the wave medium by taking the partial derivative of y with respect to time. To find the acceleration of such a particle, take the second partial derivative of y with respect to time.

EVALUATE *your answer:* Compare your numerical answers with your diagram. Check that the wave function is compatible with the boundary conditions (for example, the displacement should be zero at a fixed end).

Example 15.6 Standing waves on a guitar string

One of the strings of a guitar lies along the x-axis when in equilibrium. The end of the string at $x = 0$ (the bridge of the guitar) is tied down. An incident sinusoidal wave, corresponding to the red curves in Fig. 15.24, travels along the string in the $-x$-direction at 143 m/s with an amplitude of 0.750 mm and a frequency of 440 Hz. This wave is reflected from the fixed end at $x = 0$, and the superposition of the incident traveling wave and the reflected traveling wave forms a standing wave. (a) Find the equation giving the displacement of a point on the string as a function of position and time. (b) Locate the points on the string that don't move at all. (c) Find the amplitude, maximum transverse velocity, and maximum transverse acceleration at the points of maximum oscillation.

SOLUTION

IDENTIFY: This is a *kinematics* problem in which we are asked to describe the motion of the string (see Problem-Solving Strategy 15.1 in Section 15.3). The target variables are the wave function of the standing wave in part (a), the locations of the points that don't move, or the *nodes* in part (b), and the maximum values of displacement y, transverse velocity v_y, and transverse acceleration a_y. in part (c). (Waves on a string are transverse waves, so *transverse* means "in the direction of the displacement"—that is, in the y-direction.) To find these quantities we use the expression that we derived in this section for a standing wave on a string with a fixed end, as well as other relationships from Sections 15.2 and 15.3.

SET UP: Since there is a fixed end at $x = 0$, we may use Eqs. (15.28) and (15.29) to describe this standing wave. We also use the relationships among ω, k, f, λ, and the wave speed v.

EXECUTE: (a) To use Eq. (15.28) we need the values of A_{SW}, ω, and k. The amplitude of the incident wave is $A = 0.750\text{ mm} =$

7.50×10^{-4} m; the reflected wave has the same amplitude, and the standing wave amplitude is $A_{SW} = 2A = 1.50 \times 10^{-3}$ m. The angular frequency ω and wave number k are

$$\omega = 2\pi f = (2\pi \text{ rad})(440 \text{ s}^{-1}) = 2760 \text{ rad/s}$$

$$k = \frac{\omega}{v} = \frac{2760 \text{ rad/s}}{143 \text{ m/s}} = 19.3 \text{ rad/m}$$

Then Eq. (15.28) gives

$$\begin{aligned} y(x,t) &= (A_{SW}\sin kx)\sin\omega t \\ &= [(1.50 \times 10^{-3} \text{ m})\sin(19.3 \text{ rad/m})x]\sin(2760 \text{ rad/s})t \end{aligned}$$

(b) The positions of the nodes are given by Eq. (15.29): $x = 0$, $\lambda/2$, λ, $3\lambda/2$, ... The wavelength is

$$\lambda = \frac{v}{f} = \frac{143 \text{ m/s}}{440 \text{ Hz}} = 0.325 \text{ m}$$

so the nodes are at the following distances from the fixed end:

$$x = 0, 0.163 \text{ m}, 0.325 \text{ m}, 0.488 \text{ m}, \ldots$$

(c) From the expression in part (a) for $y(x, t)$, we see that the maximum displacement from equilibrium is 1.50×10^{-3} m $=$ 1.50 mm, which is just twice the amplitude of the incident wave. This maximum occurs at the *antinodes*, which are midway between adjacent nodes (that is, at $x = 0.081$ m, 0.244 m, 0.406 m, . . .).

For a particle on the string at any point x, the transverse (y-) velocity is

$$\begin{aligned} v_y(x,t) &= \frac{\partial y(x,t)}{\partial t} \\ &= [(1.50 \times 10^{-3} \text{ m})\sin(19.3 \text{ rad/m})x] \\ &\quad \times [(2760 \text{ rad/s})\cos(2760 \text{ rad/s})t] \\ &= [(4.15 \text{ m/s})\sin(19.3 \text{ rad/m})x]\cos(2760 \text{ rad/s})t \end{aligned}$$

At an antinode, $\sin(19.3 \text{ rad/m})x = \pm 1$ and the transverse velocity varies in value between 4.15 m/s and -4.15 m/s. As is always the case in simple harmonic motion, the maximum velocity occurs when the particle is passing through the equilibrium position ($y = 0$).

The transverse acceleration $a_y(x, t)$ is the first partial derivative of $v_y(x, t)$ with respect to time (that is, the *second* partial derivative of $y(x, t)$ with respect to time). We leave the calculation to you; the result is

$$\begin{aligned} a_y(x,t) &= \frac{\partial v_y(x,t)}{\partial t} = \frac{\partial^2 y(x,t)}{\partial t^2} \\ &= [(-1.15 \times 10^4 \text{ m/s}^2)\sin(19.3 \text{ rad/m})x] \\ &\quad \times \sin(2760 \text{ rad/s})t \end{aligned}$$

At the antinodes, the transverse acceleration varies in value between $+1.15 \times 10^4$ m/s^2 and -1.15×10^4 m/s^2.

EVALUATE: The maximum transverse velocity at an antinode is quite respectable (about 15 km/h, or 9.3 mi/h). But the maximum transverse acceleration is tremendous, 1170 times the acceleration due to gravity! Guitar strings are made of sturdy stuff to be able to withstand such acceleration.

Guitar strings are actually tied down at *both* ends. We'll see the consequences of this in the next section.

Test Your Understanding of Section 15.7 Suppose the frequency of the standing wave in Example 15.6 were doubled from 440 Hz to 880 Hz. Would all of the nodes for $f = 440$ Hz also be nodes for $f = 880$ Hz? If so, would there be additional nodes for $f = 880$ Hz? If not, which nodes are absent for $f = 880$ Hz?

15.8 Normal Modes of a String

ActivPhysics ONLINE

10.4 Standing Waves on Strings
10.5 Tuning a Stringed Instrument: Standing Waves
10.6 String Mass and Standing Waves

When we described standing waves on a string rigidly held at one end, as in Fig. 15.23, we made no assumptions about the length of the string or about what was happening at the other end. Let's now consider a string of a definite length L, rigidly held at *both* ends. Such strings are found in many musical instruments, including pianos, violins, and guitars. When a guitar string is plucked, a wave is produced in the string; this wave is reflected and re-reflected from the ends of the string, making a standing wave. This standing wave on the string in turn produces a sound wave in the air, with a frequency determined by the properties of the string. This is what makes stringed instruments so useful in making music.

To understand these properties of standing waves on a string fixed at both ends, let's first examine what happens when we set up a sinusoidal wave on such a string. The standing wave that results must have a node at *both* ends of the string. We saw in the preceding section that adjacent nodes are one half-wavelength ($\lambda/2$) apart, so the length of the string must be $\lambda/2$, or $2(\lambda/2)$, or $3(\lambda/2)$, or in general some integer number of half-wavelengths:

$$L = n\frac{\lambda}{2} \quad (n = 1, 2, 3, \ldots) \quad \text{(string fixed at both ends)} \quad (15.30)$$

15.25 Each string of a violin naturally oscillates at one or more of its harmonic frequencies, producing sound waves in the air with the same frequencies.

That is, if a string with length L is fixed at both ends, a standing wave can exist only if its wavelength satisfies Eq. (15.30).

Solving this equation for λ and labeling the possible values of λ as λ_n, we find

$$\lambda_n = \frac{2L}{n} \quad (n = 1, 2, 3, \ldots) \quad \text{(string fixed at both ends)} \tag{15.31}$$

Waves can exist on the string if the wavelength is *not* equal to one of these values, but there cannot be a steady wave pattern with nodes and antinodes, and the total wave cannot be a standing wave. Equation (15.31) is illustrated by the standing waves shown in Figs. 15.23a, 15.23b, 15.23c, and 15.23d; these represent $n = 1, 2, 3$, and 4, respectively.

Corresponding to the series of possible standing-wave wavelengths λ_n is a series of possible standing-wave frequencies f_n, each related to its corresponding wavelength by $f_n = v/\lambda_n$. The smallest frequency f_1 corresponds to the largest wavelength (the $n = 1$ case), $\lambda_1 = 2L$:

$$f_1 = \frac{v}{2L} \quad \text{(string fixed at both ends)} \tag{15.32}$$

This is called the **fundamental frequency.** The other standing-wave frequencies are $f_2 = 2v/2L$, $f_3 = 3v/2L$, and so on. These are all integer multiples of the fundamental frequency f_1, such as $2f_1$, $3f_1$, $4f_1$, and so on, and we can express *all* the frequencies as

$$f_n = n\frac{v}{2L} = nf_1 \quad (n = 1, 2, 3, \ldots) \quad \text{(string fixed at both ends)} \tag{15.33}$$

These frequencies are called **harmonics,** and the series is called a **harmonic series.** Musicians sometimes call f_2, f_3, and so on **overtones;** f_2 is the second harmonic or the first overtone, f_3 is the third harmonic or the second overtone, and so on. The first harmonic is the same as the fundamental frequency (Fig. 15.25).

For a string with fixed ends at $x = 0$ and $x = L$, the wave function $y(x, t)$ of the nth standing wave is given by Eq. (15.28) (which satisfies the condition that there is a node at $x = 0$), with $\omega = \omega_n = 2\pi f_n$ and $k = k_n = 2\pi/\lambda_n$:

$$y_n(x, t) = A_{SW} \sin k_n x \sin \omega_n t \tag{15.34}$$

You can easily show that this wave function has nodes at both $x = 0$ and $x = L$, as it must.

A **normal mode** of an oscillating system is a motion in which all particles of the system move sinusoidally with the same frequency. For a system made up of a string of length L fixed at both ends, each of the wavelengths given by Eq. (15.31) corresponds to a possible normal-mode pattern and frequency. There are infinitely many normal modes, each with its characteristic frequency and vibration pattern. Figure 15.26 shows the first four normal-mode patterns and their associ-

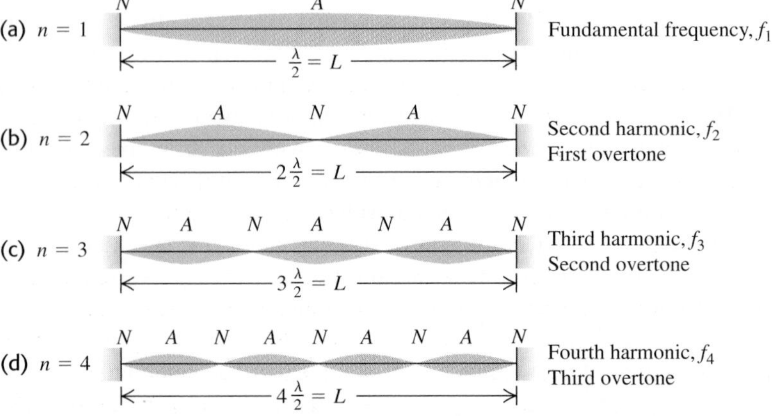

15.26 The first four normal modes of a string fixed at both ends. (Compare these to the photographs in Fig. 15.23.)

ated frequencies and wavelengths; these correspond to Eq. (15.34) with $n = 1, 2, 3$, and 4. By contrast, a harmonic oscillator, which has only one oscillating particle, has only one normal mode and one characteristic frequency. The string fixed at both ends has infinitely many normal modes because it is made up of a very large (effectively infinite) number of particles. More complicated oscillating systems also have infinite numbers of normal modes, though with more complex normal-mode patterns than a string (Fig. 15.27).

15.27 Astronomers have discovered that the sun oscillates in several different normal modes. This computer simulation shows one such mode.

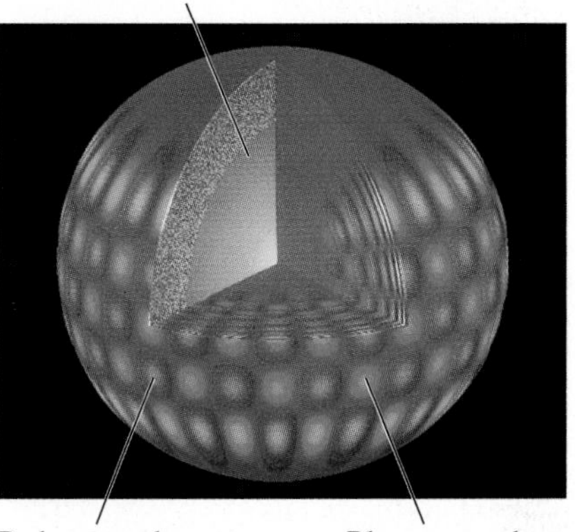

Complex Standing Waves

If we could displace a string so that its shape is the same as one of the normal-mode patterns and then release it, it would vibrate with the frequency of that mode. Such a vibrating string would displace the surrounding air with the same frequency, producing a traveling sinusoidal sound wave that your ears would perceive as a pure tone. But when a string is struck (as in a piano) or plucked (as is done to guitar strings), the shape of the displaced string is *not* as simple as one of the patterns in Fig. 15.26. The fundamental as well as many overtones are present in the resulting vibration. This motion is therefore a combination or *superposition* of many normal modes. Several simple-harmonic motions of different frequencies are present simultaneously, and the displacement of any point on the string is the sum (or superposition) of displacements associated with the individual modes. The sound produced by the vibrating string is likewise a superposition of traveling sinusoidal sound waves, which you perceive as a rich, complex tone with the fundamental frequency f_1. The standing wave on the string and the traveling sound wave in the air have similar **harmonic content** (the extent to which frequencies higher than the fundamental are present). The harmonic content depends on how the string is initially set into motion. If you pluck the strings of an acoustic guitar in the normal location over the sound hole, the sound that you hear has a different harmonic content than if you pluck the strings next to the fixed end on the guitar body.

ActivPhysics Online
10.10 Complex Waves: Fourier Analysis

It is possible to represent every possible motion of the string as some superposition of normal-mode motions. Finding this representation for a given vibration pattern is called *harmonic analysis.* The sum of sinusoidal functions that represents a complex wave is called a *Fourier series.* Figure 15.28 shows how a standing wave that is produced by plucking a guitar string of length L at a point $L/4$ from one end can be represented as a combination of sinusoidal functions.

15.28 When a guitar string is plucked (pulled into a triangular shape) and released, a standing wave results. The standing wave is well represented (except at the sharp maximum point) by the sum of just three sinusoidal functions. Including additional sinusoidal functions further improves the representation.

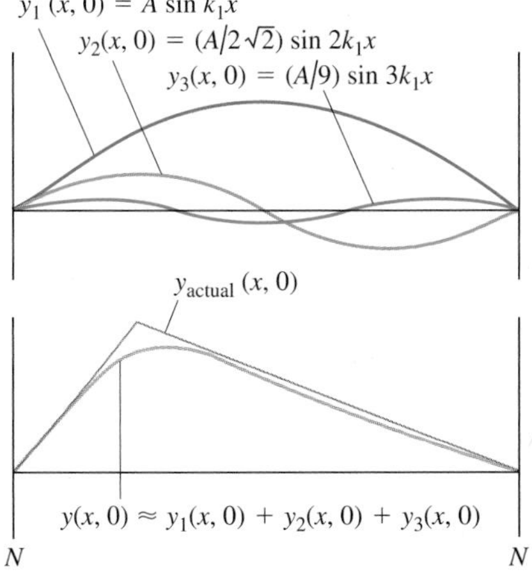

Standing Waves and String Instruments

As we have seen, the fundamental frequency of a vibrating string is $f_1 = v/2L$. The speed v of waves on the string is determined by Eq. (15.13), $v = \sqrt{F/\mu}$. Combining these equations, we find

$$f_1 = \frac{1}{2L}\sqrt{\frac{F}{\mu}} \quad \text{(string fixed at both ends)} \qquad (15.35)$$

This is also the fundamental frequency of the sound wave created in the surrounding air by the vibrating string. Familiar musical instruments show how f_1 depends on the properties of the string. The inverse dependence of frequency on length L is illustrated by the long strings of the bass (low-frequency) section of the piano or the bass viol compared with the shorter strings on the treble section of the piano or the violin (Fig. 15.29). The pitch of a violin or guitar is usually varied by pressing a string against the fingerboard with the fingers to change the length L of the vibrating portion of the string. Increasing the tension F increases the wave speed v and thus increases the frequency (and the pitch). All string instruments are "tuned" to the correct frequencies by varying the tension; you tighten the string to raise the pitch. Finally, increasing the mass per unit length μ decreases the wave

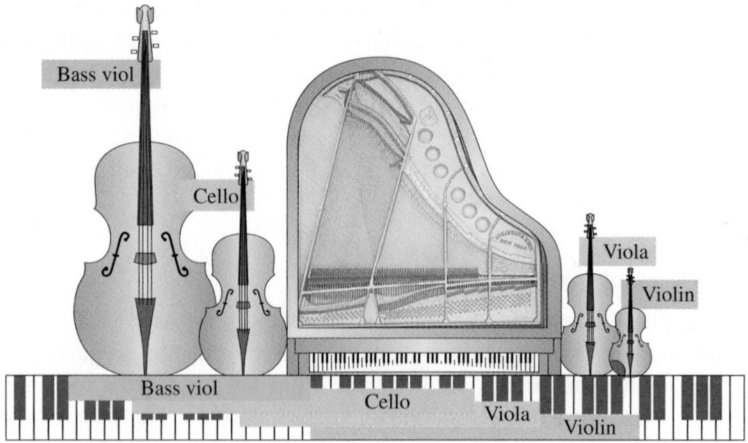

15.29 Comparing the range of a concert grand piano to the ranges of a bass viol, a cello, a viola, and a violin. In all cases, longer strings produce bass notes and shorter strings produce treble notes.

speed and thus the frequency. The lower notes on a steel guitar are produced by thicker strings, and one reason for winding the bass strings of a piano with wire is to obtain the desired low frequency from a relatively short string.

Wind instruments such as saxophones and trombones also have normal modes. As for stringed instruments, the frequencies of these normal modes determine the pitch of the musical tones that these instruments produce. We'll discuss these instruments and many other aspects of sound in Chapter 16.

Example 15.7 A giant bass viol

In an effort to get your name in the *Guinness Book of World Records,* you set out to build a bass viol with strings that have a length of 5.00 m between fixed points. One string has a linear mass density of 40.0 g/m and a fundamental frequency of 20.0 Hz (the lowest frequency that the human ear can hear). Calculate (a) the tension of this string, (b) the frequency and wavelength on the string of the second harmonic, and (c) the frequency and wavelength on the string of the second overtone.

SOLUTION

IDENTIFY: The target variable in part (a) is the string tension; we find this from the expression for the fundamental frequency of the string, which involves the tension. In parts (b) and (c) the target variables are the frequency and wavelength of different harmonics. We determine these from the given length of the string and the fundamental frequency.

SET UP: For part (a), the equation to use is Eq. (15.35); it involves the known values of f_1, L, and μ as well as the target variable F. We solve parts (b) and (c) using Eqs. (15.31) and (15.33).

EXECUTE: (a) We solve Eq. (15.35) for the string tension F:

$$F = 4\mu L^2 f_1^2 = 4(40.0 \times 10^{-3}\ \text{kg/m})(5.00\ \text{m})^2(20.0\ \text{s}^{-1})^2$$
$$= 1600\ \text{N} = 360\ \text{lb}$$

(b) The second harmonic is denoted by $n = 2$. From Eq. (15.33), the second harmonic frequency is

$$f_2 = 2f_1 = 2(20.0\ \text{Hz}) = 40.0\ \text{Hz}$$

From Eq. (15.31), the wavelength on the string of the second harmonic is

$$\lambda_2 = \frac{2L}{2} = 5.00\ \text{m}$$

(c) The second overtone is the "second tone over" (above) the fundamental—that is, $n = 3$. Its frequency and wavelength are

$$f_3 = 3f_1 = 3(20.0\ \text{Hz}) = 60.0\ \text{Hz}$$
$$\lambda_3 = \frac{2L}{3} = 3.33\ \text{m}$$

EVALUATE: The tension in part (a) is a bit larger than in a real bass viol, for which the string tension is typically a few hundred newtons. The wavelengths in parts (b) and (c) are equal to the length of the string and two-thirds the length of the string, respectively; these results agree with the drawings of standing waves in Fig. 15.26.

Example 15.8 From waves on a string to sound waves in air

What are the frequency and wavelength of the sound waves produced in the air when the string in Example 15.7 is vibrating at its fundamental frequency? The speed of sound in air at 20°C is 344 m/s.

SOLUTION

IDENTIFY: Our target variables are f and λ for the sound wave produced by the bass viol, *not* for the standing wave on the string.

However, when the string vibrates at a particular frequency, the surrounding air is forced to vibrate at the same frequency. So the frequency of the sound wave is the same as that of the standing wave on the string. The relationship $\lambda = v/f$ shows that the *wavelength* of the sound wave is typically different from the wavelength of the standing wave on the string, because the two waves have different speeds.

SET UP: The only equation we need is $v = \lambda f$. We apply this to both the standing wave on the string (speed v_{string}) and the traveling sound wave (speed v_{sound}).

EXECUTE: The sound wave frequency is the same as the standing-wave fundamental frequency: $f = f_1 = 20.0\text{ Hz}$. The wavelength of the sound wave is

$$\lambda_{1(\text{sound})} = \frac{v_{\text{sound}}}{f_1} = \frac{344\text{ m/s}}{20.0\text{ Hz}} = 17.2\text{ m}$$

EVALUATE: Note that $\lambda_{1(\text{sound})}$ is greater than the wavelength of the standing wave on the string, $\lambda_{1(\text{string})} = 2L = 2(5.00\text{ m}) = 10.0\text{ m}$. This is because the speed of sound is greater than the speed of waves on the string, $v_{\text{string}} = \lambda_{1(\text{string})} f_1 = (10.0\text{ m})(20.0\text{ Hz}) = 200\text{ m/s}$. Hence, for *any* normal mode on this string, the sound wave that is produced has the same frequency as the wave on the string but a wavelength that is greater by a factor of $v_{\text{sound}}/v_{\text{string}} = (344\text{ m/s})/(200\text{ m/s}) = 1.72$.

Test Your Understanding of Section 15.8 While a guitar string is vibrating, you gently touch the midpoint of the string to ensure that the string does not vibrate at that point. Which normal modes *cannot* be present on the string while you are touching it in this way?

CHAPTER 15 SUMMARY

Waves and their properties: A wave is any disturbance from an equilibrium condition that propagates from one region to another. A mechanical wave always travels within some material called the medium. The wave disturbance propagates at the wave speed v, which depends on the type of wave and the properties of the medium.

In a periodic wave, the motion of each point of the medium is periodic. A sinusoidal wave is a special periodic wave in which each point moves in simple harmonic motion. For any periodic wave, the frequency f is the number of cycles per unit time, the period T is the time for one cycle, the wavelength λ is the distance over which the wave pattern repeats, and the amplitude A is the maximum displacement of a particle in the medium. The product of λ and f equals the wave speed. (See Example 15.1.)

$$v = \lambda f \qquad (15.1)$$

Wave functions and wave dynamics: The wave function $y(x, t)$ describes the displacements of individual particles in the medium. Equations (15.3), (15.4), and (15.7) give the wave equation for a sinusoidal wave traveling in the $+x$-direction. If the wave is moving in the $-x$-direction, the minus signs in the cosine functions are replaced by plus signs. (See Example 15.2.)

The wave function obeys a partial differential equation called the wave equation, Eq. (15.12).

The speed of transverse waves on a string depends on the tension F and mass per unit length μ. (See Example 15.3.)

$$y(x,t) = A\cos\left[\omega\left(\frac{x}{v} - t\right)\right] = A\cos 2\pi f\left(\frac{x}{v} - t\right) \qquad (15.3)$$

$$y(x,t) = A\cos 2\pi\left(\frac{x}{\lambda} - \frac{t}{T}\right) \qquad (15.4)$$

$$y(x,t) = A\cos(kx - \omega t) \qquad (15.7)$$

where $k = 2\pi/\lambda$ and $\omega = 2\pi f = vk$

$$\frac{\partial^2 y(x,t)}{\partial x^2} = \frac{1}{v^2}\frac{\partial^2 y(x,t)}{\partial t^2} \qquad (15.12)$$

$$v = \sqrt{\frac{F}{\mu}} \quad \text{(waves on a string)} \qquad (15.13)$$

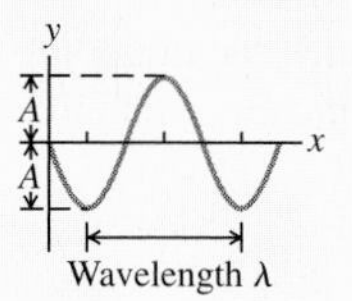

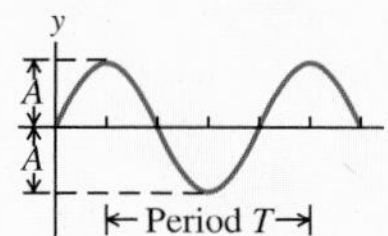

Wave power: Wave motion conveys energy from one region to another. For a sinusoidal mechanical wave, the average power P_{av} is proportional to the square of the wave amplitude and the square of the frequency. For waves that spread out in three dimensions, the wave intensity I is inversely proportional to the distance from the source. (See Examples 15.4 and 15.5.)

$$P_{av} = \frac{1}{2}\sqrt{\mu F}\,\omega^2 A^2 \qquad (15.25)$$

(average power, sinusoidal wave)

$$\frac{I_1}{I_2} = \frac{r_2^2}{r_1^2} \qquad (15.26)$$

(inverse-square law for intensity)

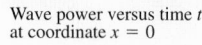

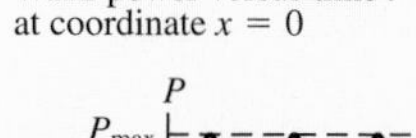
Wave power versus time t at coordinate $x = 0$

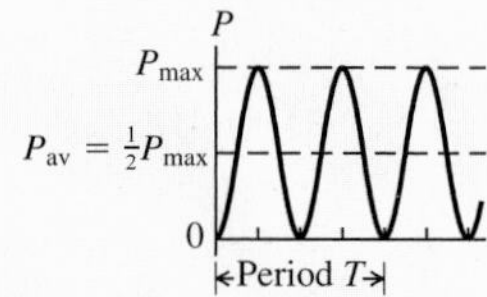

Wave superposition: A wave that reaches a boundary of the medium in which it propagates is reflected. The principle of superposition states that the total wave displacement at any point where two or more waves overlap is the sum of the displacements of the individual waves.

$$y(x,t) = y_1(x,t) + y_2(x,t) \qquad (15.27)$$

(principle of superposition)

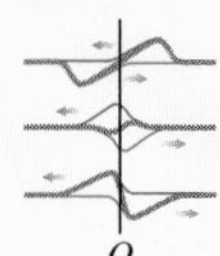

Standing waves on a string: When a sinusoidal wave is reflected from a fixed or free end of a stretched string, the incident and reflected waves combine to form a standing sinusoidal wave with nodes and antinodes. Adjacent nodes are spaced a distance $\lambda/2$ apart, as are adjacent antinodes. (See Example 15.6.)

When both ends of a string with length L are held fixed, standing waves can occur only when L is an integer multiple of $\lambda/2$. Each frequency with its associated vibration pattern is called a normal mode. The lowest frequency f_1 is called the fundamental frequency. (See Examples 15.7 and 15.8.)

$$y(x, t) = (A_{SW} \sin kx) \sin \omega t \quad (15.28)$$
(standing on a wave on a string, fixed end at $x = 0$)

$$f_n = n\frac{v}{2L} = nf_1 \ (n = 1, 2, 3, \ldots) \quad (15.33)$$

$$f_1 = \frac{1}{2L}\sqrt{\frac{F}{\mu}} \quad (15.35)$$
(string fixed at both ends)

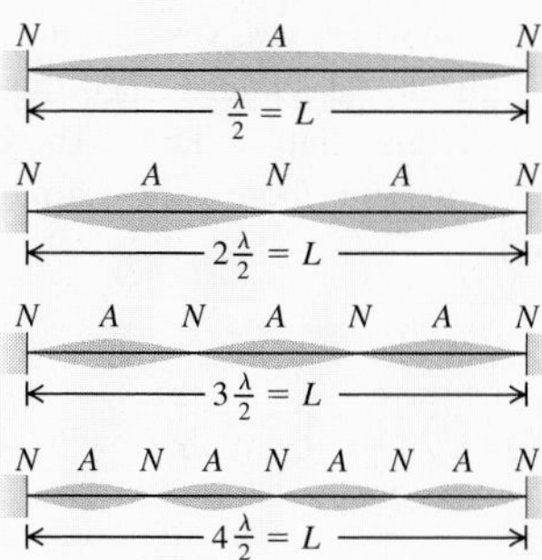

Key Terms

mechanical wave, *488*
medium, *488*
transverse wave, *488*
longitudinal wave, *488*
wave speed, *489*
periodic wave, *489*
sinusoidal wave, *489*
wavelength, *490*
wave function, *492*
wave number, *493*
phase, *494*
wave equation, *497*
intensity, *504*
interference, *505*
boundary condition, *506*
principle of superposition, *506*
node, *508*
antinode, *508*
standing wave, *508*
traveling wave, *508*
destructive interference, *509*
constructive interference, *509*
fundamental frequency, *512*
harmonics, *512*
harmonic series, *512*
overtone, *512*
normal mode, *512*
harmonic content, *513*

Answer to Chapter Opening Question ?

The power of a mechanical wave depends on its frequency and amplitude [see Eq. (15.25)].

Answers to Test Your Understanding Questions

15.1 Answer: (i) The "wave" travels horizontally from one spectator to the next along each row of the stadium, but the displacement of each spectator is vertically upward. Since the displacement is perpendicular to the direction in which the wave travels, the wave is transverse.

15.2 Answer: (iv) The speed of waves on a string, v, does not depend on the wavelength. We can rewrite the relationship $v = \lambda f$ as $f = v/\lambda$, which tells us that if the wavelength λ doubles, the frequency f becomes one-half as great.

15.3 Answers: (a) $\frac{2}{8}T$, (b) $\frac{4}{8}T$, (c) $\frac{5}{8}T$ Since the wave is sinusoidal, each point on the string oscillates in simple harmonic motion (SHM). Hence we can apply all of the ideas from Chapter 13 about SHM to the wave depicted in Fig. 15.8. (a) A particle in SHM has its maximum speed when it is passing through the equilibrium position ($y = 0$ in Fig. 15.8). The particle at point A is moving upward through this position at $t = \frac{2}{8}T$. (b) In vertical SHM the greatest *upward* acceleration occurs when a particle is at its maximum *downward* displacement. This occurs for the particle at point B at $t = \frac{4}{8}T$. (c) A particle in vertical SHM has a *downward* acceleration when its displacement is *upward*. The particle at C has an upward displacement and is moving downward at $t = \frac{5}{8}T$.

15.4 Answer: (ii) The relationship $v = \sqrt{F/\mu}$ [Eq. (15.13)] says that the wave speed is greatest on the string with the smallest linear mass density. This is the thinnest string, which has the smallest amount of mass m and hence the smallest linear mass density $\mu = m/L$ (all strings are the same length).

15.5 Answer: (iii), (iv), (ii), (i) Equation (15.25) says that the average power in a sinusoidal wave on a string is $P_{av} = \frac{1}{2}\sqrt{\mu F}\omega^2 A^2$. All four strings are identical, so all have the same mass, the same length, and the same linear mass density μ. The frequency f is the same for each wave, as is the angular frequency $\omega = 2\pi f$. Hence the average wave power for each string is proportional to the square root of the string tension F and the square of the amplitude A. Compared to string (i), the average power in each string is (ii) $\sqrt{4} = 2$ times greater; (ii) $4^2 = 16$ times greater; and (iv) $\sqrt{2}(2)^2 = 4\sqrt{2}$ times greater.

15.6 Answer:

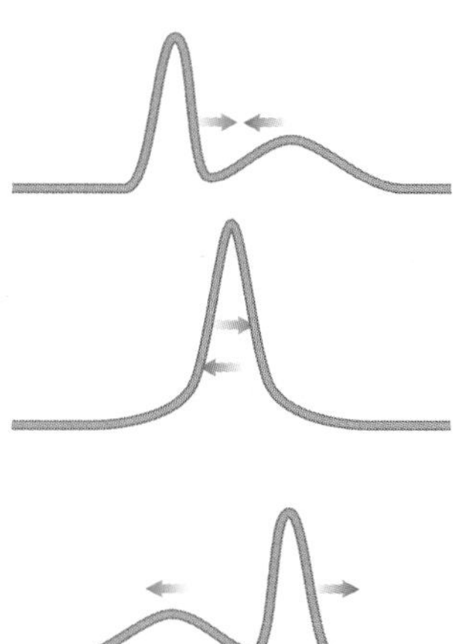

15.7 Answers: yes, yes Doubling the frequency makes the wavelength half as large. Hence the spacing between nodes (equal to $\lambda/2$) is also half as large. There are nodes at all of the previous positions, but there is also a new node between every pair of old nodes.

15.8 Answers: $n = 1, 3, 5, \ldots$ When you touch the string at its center, you are demanding that there be a node at the center. Hence only standing waves with a node at $x = L/2$ are allowed. From Figure 15.26 you can see that the normal modes $n = 1, 3, 5, \ldots$ cannot be present.

PROBLEMS

 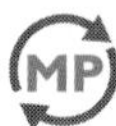

Discussion Questions

Q15.1. Two waves travel on the same string. Is it possible for them to have (a) different frequencies; (b) different wavelengths; (c) different speeds; (d) different amplitudes; (e) the same frequency but different wavelengths? Explain your reasoning.

Q15.2. Under a tension F, it takes 2.00 s for a pulse to travel the length of a taut wire. What tension is required (in terms of F) for the pulse to take 6.00 s instead?

Q15.3. What kinds of energy are associated with waves on a stretched string? How could you detect such energy experimentally?

Q15.4. The amplitude of a wave decreases gradually as the wave travels down a long, stretched string. What happens to the energy of the wave when this happens?

Q15.5. For the wave motions discussed in this chapter, does the speed of propagation depend on the amplitude? What makes you say this?

Q15.6. The speed of ocean waves depends on the depth of the water; the deeper the water, the faster the wave travels. Use this to explain why ocean waves crest and "break" as they near the shore.

Q15.7. Is it possible to have a longitudinal wave on a stretched string? Why or why not? Is it possible to have a transverse wave on a steel rod? Again, why or why not? If your answer is yes in either case, explain how you would create such a wave.

Q15.8. An echo is sound reflected from a distant object, such as a wall or a cliff. Explain how you can determine how far away the object is by timing the echo.

Q15.9. Why do you see lightning before you hear the thunder? A familiar rule of thumb is to start counting slowly, once per second, when you see the lightning; when you hear the thunder, divide the number you have reached by 3 to obtain your distance from the lightning in kilometers (or divide by 5 to obtain your distance in miles). Why does this work, or does it?

Q15.10. For transverse waves on a string, is the wave speed the same as the speed of any part of the string? Explain the difference between these two speeds. Which one is constant?

Q15.11. Children make toy telephones by sticking each end of a long string through a hole in the bottom of a paper cup and knotting it so it will not pull out. When the spring is pulled taut, sound can be transmitted from one cup to the other. How does this work? Why is the transmitted sound louder than the sound traveling through air for the same distance?

Q15.12. The four strings on a violin have different thicknesses, but are all under approximately the same tension. Do waves travel faster on the thick strings or the thin strings? Why? How does the fundamental vibration frequency compare for the thick versus the thin strings?

Q15.13. A sinusoidal wave can be described by a cosine function, which is negative just as often as positive. So why isn't the average power delivered by this wave zero?

Q15.14. Two strings of different mass per unit length μ_1 and μ_2 are tied together and stretched with a tension F. A wave travels along the string and passes the discontinuity in μ. Which of the following wave properties will be the same on both sides of the discontinuity, and which ones will change? speed of the wave; frequency; wavelength. Explain the physical reasoning behind each of your answers.

Q15.15. A long rope with mass m is suspended from the ceiling and hangs vertically. A wave pulse is produced at the lower end of the rope, and the pulse travels up the rope. Does the speed of the wave pulse change as it moves up the rope, and if so, does it increase or decrease?

Q15.16. In a transverse wave on a string, the motion of the string is perpendicular to the length of the string. How, then, is it possible for energy to move along the length of the string?

Q15.17. Both wave intensity and gravitation obey inverse-square laws. Do they do so for the same reason? Discuss the reason for each of these inverse-square laws as well as you can.

Q15.18. Energy can be transferred along a string by wave motion. However, in a standing wave on a string, no energy can ever be transferred past a node. Why not?

Q15.19. Can a standing wave be produced on a string by superposing two waves traveling in opposite directions with the same frequency but different amplitudes? Why or why not? Can a standing wave be produced by superposing two waves traveling in opposite directions with different frequencies but the same amplitude? Why or why not?

Q15.20. If you stretch a rubber band and pluck it, you hear a (somewhat) musical tone. How does the frequency of this tone change as you stretch the rubber band further? (Try it!) Does this agree with Eq. (15.35) for a string fixed at both ends? Explain.

Q15.21. A musical interval of an *octave* corresponds to a factor of 2 in frequency. By what factor must the tension in a guitar or violin string be increased to raise its pitch one octave? To raise it two octaves? Explain your reasoning. Is there any danger in attempting these changes in pitch?

Q15.22. By touching a string lightly at its center while bowing, a violinist can produce a note exactly one octave above the note to which the string is tuned—that is, a note with exactly twice the frequency. Why is this possible?

Q15.23. As we discussed in Section 15.1, water waves are a combination of longitudinal and transverse waves. Defend the following statement: "When water waves hit a vertical wall, the wall is a node of the longitudinal displacement but an antinode of the transverse displacement."

Q15.24. Violins are short instruments, while cellos and basses are long. In terms of the frequency of the waves they produce, explain why this is so.

Q15.25. What is the purpose of the frets on a guitar? In terms of the frequency of the vibration of the strings, explain their use.

Exercises

Section 15.2 Periodic Waves

15.1. The speed of sound in air at 20°C is 344 m/s. (a) What is the wavelength of a sound wave with a frequency of 784 Hz, corresponding to the note G_5 on a piano, and how many milliseconds does each vibration take? (b) What is the wavelength of a sound wave one octave higher than the note in part (a)?

15.2. Audible Sound. Provided the amplitude is sufficiently great, the human ear can respond to longitudinal waves over a range of frequencies from about 20.0 Hz to about 20.0 kHz. (a) If you were to mark the beginning of each complete wave pattern with a red dot for the long-wavelength sound and a blue dot for the short-wavelength sound, how far apart would the red dots be, and how far apart would the blue dots be? (b) In reality would adjacent dots in each set be far enough apart for you to easily measure their separation with a meterstick? (c) Suppose you repeated part (a) in water, where sound travels at 1480 m/s. How far apart would the dots be in each set? Could you readily measure their separation with a meterstick?

15.3. Tsunami! On December 26, 2004, a great earthquake occurred off the coast of Sumatra and triggered immense waves (tsunami) that killed some 200,000 people. Satellites observing these waves from space measured 800 km from one wave crest to the next and a period between waves of 1.0 hour. What was the speed of these waves in m/s and km/h? Does your answer help you understand why the waves caused such devastation?

15.4. Ultrasound Imaging. Sound having frequencies above the range of human hearing (about 20,000 Hz) is called *ultrasound.* Waves above this frequency can be used to penetrate the body and to produce images by reflecting from surfaces. In a typical ultrasound scan, the waves travel through body tissue with a speed of 1500 m/s. For a good, detailed image, the wavelength should be no more than 1.0 mm. What frequency sound is required for a good scan?

15.5. Visible Light. Light is a wave, but not a mechanical wave. The quantities that oscillate are electric and magnetic fields. Light visible to humans has wavelengths between 400 nm (violet) and 700 nm (red), and all light travels through vacuum at speed $c = 3.00 \times 10^8$ m/s. (a) What are the limits of the frequency and period of visible light? (b) Could you time a single light vibration with a stopwatch?

Section 15.3 Mathematical Description of a Wave

15.6. A certain transverse wave is described by

$$y(x,t) = (6.50\text{ mm})\cos 2\pi\left(\frac{x}{28.0\text{ cm}} - \frac{t}{0.0360\text{ s}}\right)$$

Determine the wave's (a) amplitude; (b) wavelength; (c) frequency; (d) speed of propagation; (e) direction of propagation.

15.7. Transverse waves on a string have wave speed 8.00 m/s, amplitude 0.0700 m, and wavelength 0.320 m. The waves travel in the $-x$-direction, and at $t = 0$ the $x = 0$ end of the string has its maximum upward displacement. (a) Find the frequency, period, and wave number of these waves. (b) Write a wave function describing the wave. (c) Find the transverse displacement of a particle at $x = 0.360$ m at time $t = 0.150$ s. (d) How much time must elapse from the instant in part (c) until the particle at $x = 0.360$ m next has maximum upward displacement?

15.8. A water wave traveling in a straight line on a lake is described by the equation

$$y(x,t) = (3.75\text{ cm})\cos(0.450\text{ cm}^{-1}x + 5.40\text{ s}^{-1}t)$$

where y is the displacement perpendicular to the undisturbed surface of the lake. (a) How much time does it take for one complete wave pattern to go past a fisherman in a boat at anchor, and what horizontal distance does the wave crest travel in that time? (b) What are the wave number and the number of waves per second that pass the fisherman? (c) How fast does a wave crest travel past the fisherman, and what is the maximum speed of his cork floater as the wave causes it to bob up and down?

15.9. Which of the following wave functions satisfies the wave equation, Eq. (15.12)? (a) $y(x,t) = A\cos(kx + \omega t)$; (b) $y(x,t) = A\sin(kx + \omega t)$; (c) $y(x,t) = A(\cos kx + \cos \omega t)$. (d) For the wave of part (b), write the equations for the transverse velocity and transverse acceleration of a particle at point x.

15.10. A wave on a string is described by $y(x,t) = A\cos(kx - \omega t)$. (a) Graph y, v_y, and a_y as functions of x for time $t = 0$. (b) Consider the following points on the string: (i) $x = 0$; (ii) $x = \pi/4k$; (iii) $x = \pi/2k$; (iv) $x = 3\pi/4k$; (v) $x = \pi/k$; (vi) $x = 5\pi/4k$; (vii) $x = 3\pi/2k$; (viii) $x = 7\pi/4k$. For a particle at each of these points at $t = 0$, describe in words whether the particle is moving and in what direction, and whether the particle is speeding up, slowing down, or instantaneously not accelerating.

15.11. A sinusoidal wave is propagating along a stretched string that lies along the x-axis. The displacement of the string as a function of time is graphed in Fig.15.30 for particles at $x = 0$ and at $x = 0.0900$ m. (a) What is the amplitude of the wave? (b) What is the period of the wave? (c) You are told that the two points $x = 0$ and $x = 0.0900$ m are within one wavelength of each other. If the wave is moving in the $+x$-direction, determine the wavelength and the wave speed. (d) If instead the wave is moving in the $-x$-direction, determine the wavelength and the wave speed. (e) Would it be possible to determine definitively the wavelength in parts (c) and (d) if you were not told that the two points were within one wavelength of each other? Why or why not?

Figure 15.30 Exercise 15.11.

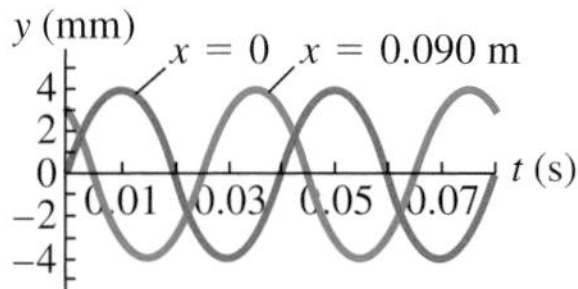

15.12. Speed of Propagation vs. Particle Speed. (a) Show that Eq. (15.3) may be written as

$$y(x,t) = A\cos\left[\frac{2\pi}{\lambda}(x - vt)\right]$$

(b) Use $y(x,t)$ to find an expression for the transverse velocity v_y of a particle in the string on which the wave travels. (c) Find the maximum speed of a particle of the string. Under what circumstances is this equal to the propagation speed v? Less than v? Greater than v?

15.13. A transverse wave on a string has amplitude 0.300 cm, wavelength 12.0 cm, and speed 6.00 cm/s. It is represented by $y(x,t)$ as given in Exercise 15.12. (a) At time $t = 0$, compute y at

1.5-cm intervals of x (that is, at $x = 0$, $x = 1.5$ cm, $x = 3.0$ cm, and so on) from $x = 0$ to $x = 12.0$ cm. Graph the results. This is the shape of the string at time $t = 0$. (b) Repeat the calculations for the same values of x at times $t = 0.400$ s and $t = 0.800$ s. Graph the shape of the string at these instants. In what direction is the wave traveling?

Section 15.4 Speed of a Transverse Wave

15.14. With what tension must a rope with length 2.50 m and mass 0.120 kg be stretched for transverse waves of frequency 40.0 Hz to have a wavelength of 0.750 m?

15.15. One end of a horizontal rope is attached to a prong of an electrically driven tuning fork that vibrates the rope transversely at 120 Hz. The other end passes over a pulley and supports a 1.50-kg mass. The linear mass density of the rope is 0.0550 kg/m. (a) What is the speed of a transverse wave on the rope? (b) What is the wavelength? (c) How would your answers to parts (a) and (b) change if the mass were increased to 3.00 kg?

15.16. A 1.50-m string of weight 1.25 N is tied to the ceiling at its upper end, and the lower end supports a weight W. When you pluck the string slightly, the waves traveling up the string obey the equation

$$y(x, t) = (8.50 \text{ mm})\cos(172 \text{ m}^{-1} x - 2730 \text{ s}^{-1} t)$$

(a) How much time does it take a pulse to travel the full length of the string? (b) What is the weight W? (c) How many wavelengths are on the string at any instant of time? (d) What is the equation for waves traveling *down* the string?

15.17. A thin, 75.0-cm wire has a mass of 16.5 g. One end is tied to a nail, and the other end is attached to a screw that can be adjusted to vary the tension in the wire. (a) To what tension (in newtons) must you adjust the screw so that a transverse wave of wavelength 3.33 cm makes 875 vibrations per second? (b) How fast would this wave travel?

15.18. Weighty Rope. If in Example 15.3 (Section 15.4) we do *not* neglect the weight of the rope, what is the wave speed (a) at the bottom of the rope; (b) at the middle of the rope; (c) at the top of the rope?

15.19. A simple harmonic oscillator at the point $x = 0$ generates a wave on a rope. The oscillator operates at a frequency of 40.0 Hz and with an amplitude of 3.00 cm. The rope has a linear mass density of 50.0 g/m and is stretched with a tension of 5.00 N. (a) Determine the speed of the wave. (b) Find the wavelength. (c) Write the wave function $y(x, t)$ for the wave. Assume that the oscillator has its maximum upward displacement at time $t = 0$. (d) Find the maximum transverse acceleration of points on the rope. (e) In the discussion of transverse waves in this chapter, the force of gravity was ignored. Is that a reasonable approximation for this wave? Explain.

Section 15.5 Energy in Wave Motion

15.20. A piano wire with mass 3.00 g and length 80.0 cm is stretched with a tension of 25.0 N. A wave with frequency 120.0 Hz and amplitude 1.6 mm travels along the wire. (a) Calculate the average power carried by the wave. (b) What happens to the average power if the wave amplitude is halved?

15.21. A jet plane at take-off can produce sound of intensity 10.0 W/m^2 at 30.0 m away. But you prefer the tranquil sound of normal conversation, which is 1.0 μW/m^2. Assume that the plane behaves like a point source of sound. (a) What is the closest distance you should live from the airport runway to preserve your peace of mind? (b) What intensity from the jet does your friend experience if she lives twice as far from the runway as you do? (c) What power of sound does the jet produce at take-off?

15.22. Threshold of Pain. You are investigating the report of a UFO landing in an isolated portion of New Mexico, and you encounter a strange object that is radiating sound waves uniformly in all directions. Assume that the sound comes from a point source and that you can ignore reflections. You are slowly walking toward the source. When you are 7.5 m from it, you measure its intensity to be 0.11 W/m^2. An intensity of 1.0 W/m^2 is often used as the "threshold of pain." How much closer to the source can you move before the sound intensity reaches this threshold?

15.23. Energy Output. By measurement you determine that sound waves are spreading out equally in all directions from a point source and that the intensity is 0.026 W/m^2 at a distance of 4.3 m from the source. (a) What is the intensity at a distance of 3.1 m from the source? (b) How much sound energy does the source emit in one hour if its power output remains constant?

15.24. A fellow student with a mathematical bent tells you that the wave function of a traveling wave on a thin rope is $y(x, t) = 2.30 \text{ mm} \cos[(6.98 \text{ rad/m})x + (742 \text{ rad/s})t]$. Being more practical, you measure the rope to have a length of 1.35 m and a mass of 0.00338 kg. You are then asked to determine the following: (a) amplitude; (b) frequency; (c) wavelength; (d) wave speed; (e) direction the wave is traveling; (f) tension in the rope; (g) average power transmitted by the wave.

15.25. What is the total power output of the siren in Example 15.5?

Section 15.6 Wave Interference, Boundary Conditions, and Superposition

15.26. Reflection. A wave pulse on a string has the dimensions shown in Fig. 15.31 at $t = 0$. The wave speed is 40 cm/s. (a) If point O is a fixed end, draw the total wave on the string at $t = 15$ ms, 20 ms, 25 ms, 30 ms, 35 ms, 40 ms, and 45 ms. (b) Repeat part (a) for the case in which point O is a free end.

Figure 15.31 Exercise 15.26.

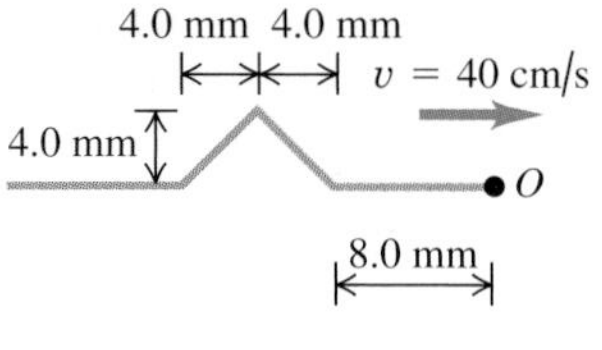

15.27. Reflection. A wave pulse on a string has the dimensions shown in Fig. 15.32 at $t = 0$. The wave speed is 5.0 m/s. (a) If point O is a fixed end, draw the total wave on the string at $t = 1.0$ ms, 2.0 ms, 3.0 ms, 4.0 ms, 5.0 ms, 6.0 ms, and 7.0 ms. (b) Repeat part (a) for the case in which point O is a free end.

Figure 15.32 Exercise 15.27.

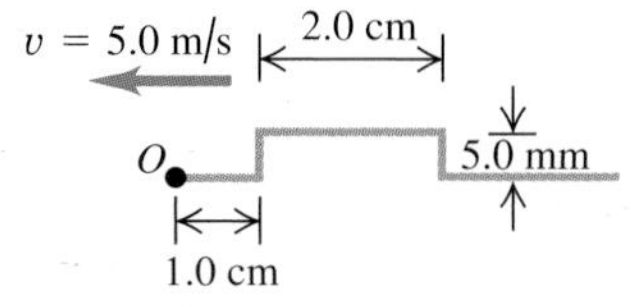

15.28. Interference of Triangular Pulses. Two triangular wave pulses are traveling toward each other on a stretched string as shown in Fig.15.33. Each pulse is identical to the other and travels at 2.00 cm/s. The leading edges of the pulses are 1.00 cm apart at $t = 0$. Sketch the shape of the string at $t = 0.250$ s, $t = 0.500$ s, $t = 0.750$ s, $t = 1.000$ s, and $t = 1.250$ s.

Figure 15.33 Exercise 15.28.

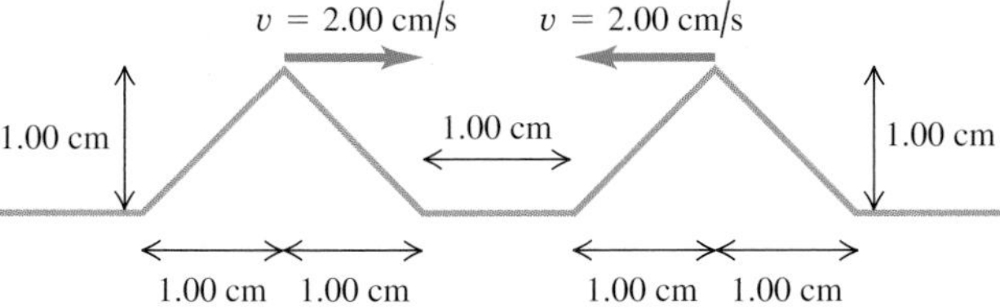

15.29. Suppose that the left-traveling pulse in Exercise 15.28 is *below* the level of the unstretched string instead of above it. Make the same sketches that you did in that exercise.

15.30. Two pulses are moving in opposite directions at 1.0 cm/s on a taut string, as shown in Fig. 15.34. Each square is 1.0 cm. Sketch the shape of the string at the end of (a) 6.0 s; (b) 7.0 s; (c) 8.0 s.

Figure 15.34 Exercise 15.30.

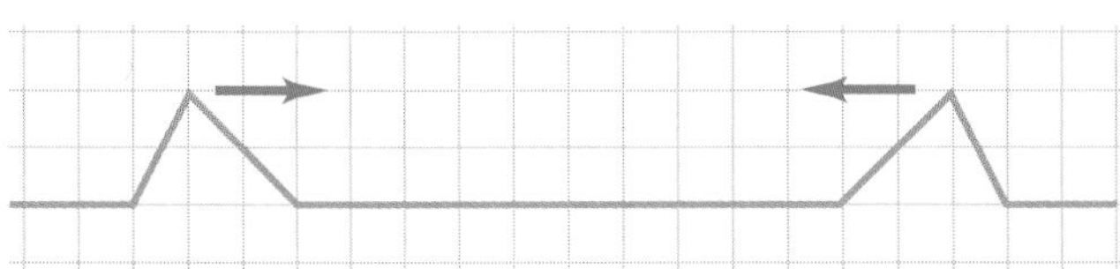

15.31. Interference of Rectangular Pulses. Figure 15.35 shows two rectangular wave pulses on a stretched string traveling toward each other. Each pulse is traveling with a speed of 1.00 mm/s and has the height and width shown in the figure. If the leading edges of the pulses are 8.00 mm apart at $t = 0$, sketch the shape of the string at $t = 4.00$ s, $t = 6.00$ s, and $t = 10.0$ s.

Figure 15.35 Exercise 15.31.

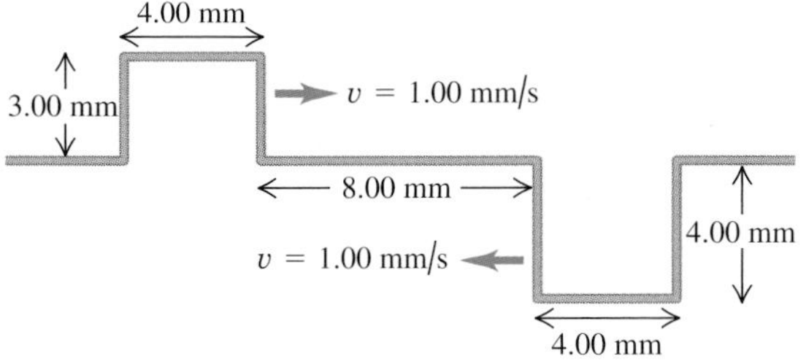

15.32. Two traveling waves moving on a string are identical except for opposite velocities. They obey the equation $y(x, t) = A\sin(kx \pm \omega t)$, where the plus-or-minus sign in the argument depends on the direction the wave is traveling. (a) Show that the vibrating string is described by the equation $y_{\text{net}}(x, t) = 2A\sin kx\cos\omega t$. (*Hint:* Use the trigonometric formulas for $\sin(a \pm b)$.) (b) Show that the string never moves at the places along it for which $x = n\lambda/2$, where n is a nonnegative integer.

Section 15.7 Standing Waves on a String

15.33. Standing waves on a wire are described by Eq. (15.28), with $A_{\text{SW}} = 2.50$ mm, $\omega = 942$ rad/s, and $k = 0.750\pi$ rad/m. The left end of the wire is at $x = 0$. At what distances from the left end are (a) the nodes of the standing wave and (b) the antinodes of the standing wave?

15.34. Adjacent antinodes of a standing wave on a string are 15.0 cm apart. A particle at an antinode oscillates in simple harmonic motion with amplitude 0.850 cm and period 0.0750 s. The string lies along the $+x$-axis and is fixed at $x = 0$. (a) How far apart are the adjacent nodes? (b) What are the wavelength, amplitude, and speed of the two traveling waves that form this pattern? (c) Find the maximum and minimum transverse speeds of a point at an antinode. (d) What is the shortest distance along the string between a node and an antinode?

15.35. Wave Equation and Standing Waves. (a) Prove by direct substitution that $y(x, t) = (A_{\text{SW}}\sin kx)\sin\omega t$ is a solution of the wave equation, Eq. (15.12), for $v = \omega/k$. (b) Explain why the relationship $v = \omega/k$ for *traveling* waves also applies to *standing* waves.

15.36. Give the details of the derivation of Eq. (15.28) from $y_1(x, t) + y_2(x, t) = A[-\cos(kx + \omega t) + \cos(kx - \omega t)]$.

15.37. Let $y_1(x, t) = A\cos(k_1x - \omega_1t)$ and $y_2(x, t) = A\cos(k_2x - \omega_2t)$ be two solutions to the wave equation, Eq. (15.12), for the same v. Show that $y(x, t) = y_1(x, t) + y_2(x, t)$ is also a solution to the wave equation.

Section 15.8 Normal Modes of a String

15.38. A 1.50-m-long rope is stretched between two supports with a tension that makes the speed of transverse waves 48.0 m/s. What are the wavelength and frequency of (a) the fundamental; (b) the second overtone; (c) the fourth harmonic?

15.39. A wire with mass 40.0 g is stretched so that its ends are tied down at points 80.0 cm apart. The wire vibrates in its fundamental mode with frequency 60.0 Hz and with an amplitude at the antinodes of 0.300 cm. (a) What is the speed of propagation of transverse waves in the wire? (b) Compute the tension in the wire. (c) Find the maximum transverse velocity and acceleration of particles in the wire.

15.40. A piano tuner stretches a steel piano wire with a tension of 800 N. The steel wire is 0.400 m long and has a mass of 3.00 g. (a) What is the frequency of its fundamental mode of vibration? (b) What is the number of the highest harmonic that could be heard by a person who is capable of hearing frequencies up to 10,000 Hz?

15.41. A thin, taut string tied at both ends and oscillating in its third harmonic has its shape described by the equation $y(x, t) = (5.60\text{ cm})\sin[(0.0340\text{ rad/cm})x]\sin[(50.0\text{ rad/s})t]$, where the origin is at the left end of the string, the x-axis is along the string and the y-axis is perpendicular to the string. (a) Draw a sketch that shows the standing wave pattern. (b) Find the amplitude of the two traveling waves that make up this standing wave. (c) What is the length of the string? (d) Find the wavelength, frequency, period, and speed of the traveling waves. (e) Find the maximum transverse speed of a point on the string. (f) What would be the equation $y(x, t)$ for this string if it were vibrating in its eighth harmonic?

15.42. The wave function of a standing wave is $y(x, t) = 4.44\text{ mm}\sin[(32.5\text{ rad/m})x]\sin[(754\text{ rad/s})t]$. For the two traveling waves that make up this standing wave, find the (a) amplitude; (b) wavelength; (c) frequency; (d) wave speed; (e) wave functions.

(f) From the information given, can you determine which harmonic this is? Explain.

15.43. Consider again the rope and traveling wave of Exercise 15.24. Assume that the ends of the rope are held fixed and that this traveling wave and the reflected wave are traveling in the opposite direction. (a) What is the wave function $y(x, t)$ for the standing wave that is produced? (b) In which harmonic is the standing wave oscillating? (c) What is the frequency of the fundamental oscillation?

15.44. One string of a certain musical instrument is 75.0 cm long and has a mass of 8.75 g. It is being played in a room where the speed of sound is 344 m/s. (a) To what tension must you adjust the string so that, when vibrating in its second overtone, it produces sound of wavelength 3.35 cm? (b) What frequency sound does this string produce in its fundamental mode of vibration?

15.45. The portion of the string of a certain musical instrument between the bridge and upper end of the finger board (that part of the string that is free to vibrate) is 60.0 cm long, and this length of the string has mass 2.00 g. The string sounds an A_4 note (440 Hz) when played. (a) Where must the player put a finger (what distance x from bridge) to play a D_5 note (587 Hz)? (See Fig. 15.36.) For both the A_4 and D_5 notes, the string vibrates in its fundamental mode. (b) Without retuning, is it possible to play a G_4 note (392 Hz) on this string? Why or why not?

Figure 15.36 Exercise 15.45.

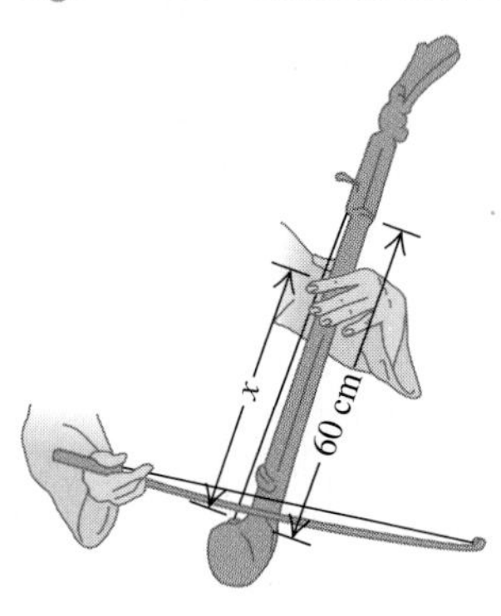

15.46. (a) A horizontal string tied at both ends is vibrating in its fundamental mode. The traveling waves have speed v, frequency f, amplitude A, and wavelength λ. Calculate the maximum transverse velocity and maximum transverse acceleration of points located at (i) $x = \lambda/2$, (ii) $x = \lambda/4$, and (iii) $x = \lambda/8$ from the left-hand end of the string. (b) At each of the points in part (a), what is the amplitude of the motion? (c) At each of the points in part (a), how much time does it take the string to go from its largest upward displacement to its largest downward displacement?

15.47. Guitar String. One of the 63.5-cm-long strings of an ordinary guitar is tuned to produce the note B_3 (frequency 245 Hz) when vibrating in its fundamental mode. (a) Find the speed of transverse waves on this string. (b) If the tension in this string is increased by 1.0%, what will be the new fundamental frequency of the string? (c) If the speed of sound in the surrounding air is 344 m/s, find the frequency and wavelength of the sound wave produced in the air by the vibration of the B_3 string. How do these compare to the frequency and wavelength of the standing wave on the string?

15.48. Waves on a Stick. A flexible stick 2.0 m long is not fixed in any way and is free to vibrate. Make clear drawings of this stick vibrating in its first three harmonics, and then use your drawings to find the wavelengths of each of these harmonics. (*Hint:* Should the ends be nodes or antinodes?)

Problems

15.49. A transverse sine wave with an amplitude of 2.50 mm and a wavelength of 1.80 m travels from left to right along a long, horizontal, stretched string with a speed of 36.0 m/s. Take the origin at the left end of the undisturbed string. At time $t = 0$ the left end of the string has its maximum upward displacement. (a) What are the frequency, angular frequency, and wave number of the wave? (b) What is the function $y(x, t)$ that describes the wave? (c) What is $y(t)$ for a particle at the left end of the string? (d) What is $y(t)$ for a particle 1.35 m to the right of the origin? (e) What is the maximum magnitude of transverse velocity of any particle of the string? (f) Find the transverse displacement and the transverse velocity of a particle 1.35 m to the right of the origin at time $t = 0.0625$ s.

15.50. A transverse wave on a rope is given by

$$y(x, t) = (0.750 \text{ cm})\cos\pi[(0.400 \text{ cm}^{-1})x + (250 \text{ s}^{-1})t]$$

(a) Find the amplitude, period, frequency, wavelength, and speed of propagation. (b) Sketch the shape of the rope at these values of t: 0, 0.0005 s, 0.0010 s. (c) Is the wave traveling in the $+x$- or $-x$-direction? (d) The mass per unit length of the rope is 0.0500 kg/m. Find the tension. (e) Find the average power of this wave.

15.51. Three pieces of string, each of length L, are joined together end to end, to make a combined string of length $3L$. The first piece of string has mass per unit length μ_1, the second piece has mass per unit length $\mu_2 = 4\mu_1$, and the third piece has mass per unit length $\mu_3 = \mu_1/4$. (a) If the combined string is under tension F, how much time does it take a transverse wave to travel the entire length $3L$? Give your answer in terms of L, F, and μ_1. (b) Does your answer to part (a) depend on the order in which the three pieces are joined together? Explain.

15.52. A 1750-N irregular beam is hanging horizontally by its ends from the ceiling by two vertical wires (A and B), each 1.25 m long and weighing 2.50 N. The center of gravity of this beam is one-third of the way along the beam from the end where wire A is attached. If you pluck both strings at the same time at the beam, what is the time delay between the arrival of the two pulses at the ceiling? Which pulse arrives first?

15.53. Ant Joy Ride. You place your pet ant Klyde (mass m) on top of a horizontal, stretched rope, where he holds on tightly. The rope has mass M and length L and is under tension F. You start a sinusoidal transverse wave of wavelength λ and amplitude A propagating along the rope. The motion of the rope is in a vertical plane. Klyde's mass is so small that his presence has no effect on the propagation of the wave. (a) What is Klyde's top speed as he oscillates up and down? (b) Klyde enjoys the ride and begs for more. You decide to double his top speed by changing the tension while keeping the wavelength and amplitude the same. Should the tension be increased or decreased, and by what factor?

15.54. Weightless Ant. An ant with mass m is standing peacefully on top of a horizontal, stretched rope. The rope has mass per unit length μ and is under tension F. Without warning, Cousin Throckmorton starts a sinusoidal transverse wave of wavelength λ propagating along the rope. The motion of the rope is in a vertical plane. What minimum wave amplitude will make the ant become momentarily weightless? Assume that m is so small that the presence of the ant has no effect on the propagation of the wave.

15.55. When a transverse sinusoidal wave is present on a string, the particles of the string undergo SHM. This is the same motion as that of a mass m attached to an ideal spring of force constant k', for which the angular frequency of oscillation was found in Chapter 13 to be $\omega = \sqrt{k'/m}$. Consider a string with tension F and mass per unit length μ, along which is propagating a sinusoidal wave with amplitude A and wavelength λ. (a) Find the "force constant" k' of the restoring force that acts on a short segment of the string of length Δx (where $\Delta x \ll \lambda$). (b) How does the "force constant" calculated in part (b) depend on F, μ, A, and λ? Explain the physical reasons this should be so.

15.56. A 5.00-m, 0.732-kg wire is used to support two uniform 235-N posts of equal length (Fig. 15.37). Assume that the wire is essentially horizontal and that the speed of sound is 344 m/s. A strong wind is blowing, causing the wire to vibrate in its 7th overtone. What are the frequency and wavelength of the sound this wire produces?

Figure **15.37** Problem 15.56.

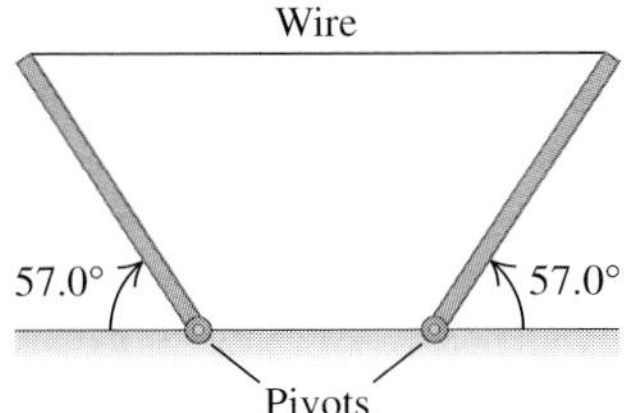

15.57. A Nonsinusoidal Wave. The shape of a wave on a string at a specific instant is shown in Fig. 15.38. The wave is propagating to the right, in the $+x$-direction. (a) Determine the direction of the transverse *velocity* of each of the six labeled points on the string. If the velocity is zero, state it as such. Explain your reasoning. (b) Determine the direction of the transverse *acceleration* of each of the six labeled points on the string. Explain your reasoning. (c) How would your answers be affected if the wave were propagating to the left, in the $-x$-direction?

Figure **15.38** Problem 15.57.

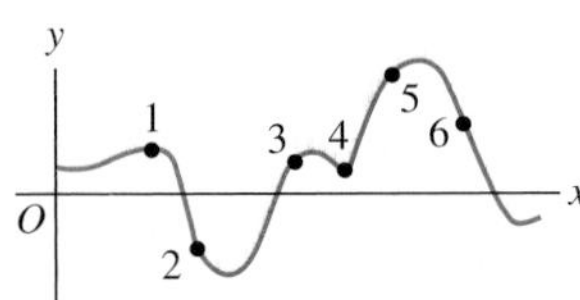

15.58. A continuous succession of sinusoidal wave pulses are produced at one end of a very long string and travel along the length of the string. The wave has frequency 40.0 Hz, amplitude 5.00 mm, and wavelength 0.600 m. (a) How long does it take the wave to travel a distance of 8.00 m along the length of the string? (b) How long does it take a point on the string to travel a distance of 8.00 m, once the wave train has reached the point and set it into motion? (c) In parts (a) and (b), how does the time change if the amplitude is doubled?

15.59. Two-Dimensional Waves. A stretched string lies along the x-axis. The string is displaced along both the y- and z-directions, so that the transverse displacement of the string is given by

$$y(x,t) = A\cos(kx - \omega t) \qquad z(x,t) = A\sin(kx - \omega t)$$

(a) Draw a graph of z versus y for a particle on the string at $x = 0$. This shows the trajectory of the particle as seen by an observer on the $+x$-axis looking back toward $x = 0$. Indicate the position of the particle at $t = 0$, $t = \pi/2\omega$, $t = \pi/\omega$, and $t = 3\pi/2\omega$. (b) Find the velocity vector of a particle at an *arbitrary* position x on the string. Show that this represents the tangential velocity of a particle moving in a circle of radius A with angular velocity ω, and show that the speed of the particle is constant (i.e., the particle is in uniform circular motion). (See Problem 3.75.) (c) Find the acceleration vector of the particle in part (b). Show that the acceleration is always directed toward the center of the circle and that its magnitude is $a = \omega^2 A$. Explain these results in terms of uniform circular motion. Suppose that the displacement of the string was instead given by

$$y(x,t) = A\cos(kx - \omega t) \qquad z(x,t) = -A\sin(kx - \omega t)$$

Describe how the motion of a particle at x would be different from the motion described in part (a).

15.60. A vertical, 1.20-m length of 18-gauge (diameter of 1.024 mm) copper wire has a 100.0-N ball hanging from it. (a) What is the wavelength of the third harmonic for this wire? (b) A 500.0-N ball now *replaces* the original ball. What is the change in the wavelength of the third harmonic caused by replacing the light ball with the heavy one? (*Hint:* See Table 11.1 for Young's modulus.)

15.61. Waves of Arbitrary Shape. (a) Explain why *any* wave described by a function of the form $y(x,t) = f(x - vt)$ moves in the $+x$-direction with speed v. (b) Show that $y(x,t) = f(x - vt)$ satisfies the wave equation, no matter what the functional form of f. To do this, write $y(x,t) = f(u)$, where $u = x - vt$. Then, to take partial derivatives of $y(x,t)$, use the chain rule:

$$\frac{\partial y(x,t)}{\partial t} = \frac{df(u)}{du}\frac{\partial u}{\partial t} = \frac{df(u)}{du}(-v)$$
$$\frac{\partial y(x,t)}{\partial x} = \frac{df(u)}{du}\frac{\partial u}{\partial x} = \frac{df(u)}{du}$$

(c) A wave pulse is described by the function $y(x,t) = De^{-(Bx-Ct)^2}$, where B, C, and D are all positive constants. What is the speed of this wave?

15.62. Equation (15.7) for a sinusoidal wave can be made more general by including a phase angle ϕ, where $0 \le \phi \le 2\pi$ (in radians). Then the wave function $y(x,t)$ becomes

$$y(x,t) = A\cos(kx - \omega t + \phi)$$

(a) Sketch the wave as a function of x at $t = 0$ for $\phi = 0$, $\phi = \pi/4$, $\phi = \pi/2$, $\phi = 3\pi/4$, and $\phi = 3\pi/2$. (b) Calculate the transverse velocity $v_y = \partial y/\partial t$. (c) At $t = 0$, a particle on the string at $x = 0$ has displacement $y = A/\sqrt{2}$. Is this enough information to determine the value of ϕ? In addition, if you are told that a particle at $x = 0$ is moving toward $y = 0$ at $t = 0$, what is the value of ϕ? (d) Explain in general what you must know about the wave's behavior at a given instant to determine the value of ϕ.

15.63. (a) Show that Eq. (15.25) can also be written as $P_{av} = \frac{1}{2}Fk\omega A^2$, where k is the wave number of the wave. (b) If the tension F in the string is quadrupled while the amplitude A is kept the same, how must k and ω each change to keep the average power constant? [*Hint:* Recall Eq. (15.6).]

15.64. Energy in a Triangular Pulse. A triangular wave pulse on a taut string travels in the positive x-direction with speed v. The tension in the string is F, and the linear mass density of the string is μ. At $t = 0$, the shape of the pulse is given by

$$y(x,0) = \begin{cases} 0 & \text{if } x < -L \\ h(L+x)/L & \text{for } -L < x < 0 \\ h(L-x)/L & \text{for } 0 < x < L \\ 0 & \text{for } x > L \end{cases}$$

(a) Draw the pulse at $t = 0$. (b) Determine the wave function $y(x,t)$ at all times t. (c) Find the instantaneous power in the wave. Show that the power is zero except for $-L < (x - vt) < L$ and that in this interval the power is constant. Find the value of this constant power.

15.65. A sinusoidal transverse wave travels on a string. The string has length 8.00 m and mass 6.00 g. The wave speed is 30.0 m/s, and the wavelength is 0.200 m. (a) If the wave is to have an average power of 50.0 W, what must be the amplitude of the wave? (b) For this same string, if the amplitude and wavelength are the same as in part (a), what is the average power for the wave if the tension is increased such that the wave speed is doubled?

15.66. Instantaneous Power in a Wave. (a) Graph $y(x, t)$ as given by Eq. (15.7) as a function of x for a given time t (say, $t = 0$). On the same axes, make a graph of the instantaneous power $P(x, t)$ as given by Eq. (15.23). (b) Explain the connection between the slope of the graph of $y(x, t)$ versus x and the value of $P(x, t)$. In particular, explain what is happening at points where $P = 0$, where there is no instantaneous energy transfer. (c) The quantity $P(x, t)$ always has the same sign. What does this imply about the direction of energy flow? (d) Consider a wave moving in the $-x$-direction, for which $y(x, t) = A\cos(kx + \omega t)$. Calculate $P(x, t)$ for this wave, and make a graph of $y(x, t)$ and $P(x, t)$ as functions of x for a given time t (say, $t = 0$). What differences arise from reversing the direction of the wave?

15.67. A metal wire, with density ρ and Young's modulus Y, is stretched between rigid supports. At temperature T, the speed of a transverse wave is found to be v_1. When the temperature is increased to $T + \Delta T$, the speed decreases to $v_2 < v_1$. Determine the coefficient of linear expansion of the wire.

15.68. A vibrating string 50.0 cm long is under a tension of 1.00 N. The results from five successive stroboscopic pictures are shown in Fig. 15.39. The strobe rate is set at 5000 flashes per minute, and observations reveal that the maximum displacement occurred at flashes 1 and 5 with no other maxima in between. (a) Find the period, frequency, and wavelength for the traveling waves on this string. (b) In what normal mode (harmonic) is the string vibrating? (c) What is the speed of the traveling waves on the string? (d) How fast is point P moving when the string is in (i) position 1 and (ii) position 3? (e) What is the mass of this string? (Section 15.3).

Figure 15.39 Problem 15.68.

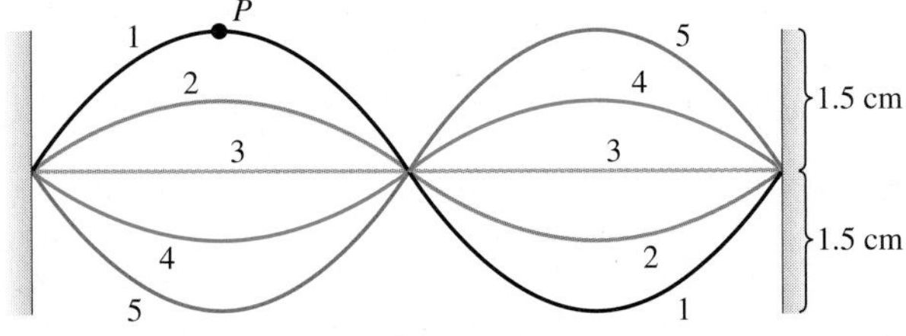

15.69. Clothesline Nodes. Cousin Throckmorton is once again playing with the clothesline in Example 15.2 (Section 15.3). One end of the clothesline is attached to a vertical post. Throcky holds the other end loosely in his hand, so that the speed of waves on the clothesline is a relatively slow 0.720 m/s. He finds several frequencies at which he can oscillate his end of the clothesline so that a light clothespin 45.0 cm from the post doesn't move. What are these frequencies?

15.70. A guitar string is vibrating in its fundamental mode, with nodes at each end. The length of the segment of the string that is free to vibrate is 0.386 m. The maximum transverse acceleration of a point at the middle of the segment is 8.40×10^3 m/s^2 and the maximum transverse velocity is 3.80 m/s. (a) What is the amplitude of this standing wave? (b) What is the wave speed for the transverse traveling waves on this string?

15.71. As shown in Exercise 15.35, a standing wave given by Eq. (15.28) satisfies the wave equation Eq. (15.12). (a) Show that a standing wave given by Eq. (15.28) also satisfies the equation

$$\frac{\partial^2 y(x, t)}{\partial t^2} = -\omega^2 y(x, t)$$

Interpret this equation in terms of what you know about simple harmonic motion. (b) Does a traveling wave given by $y(x, t) = A\cos(kx - \omega t)$ also satisfy the equation in part (a)? Interpret this result.

15.72. (a) The red and blue waves in Fig. 15.20 combine so that the displacement of the string at O is always zero. To show this mathematically for a wave of arbitrary shape, consider a wave moving to the right along the string in Fig. 15.20 (shown in blue) that, at time T, is given by $y_1(x, T) = f(x)$, where f is some function of x. (The form of $f(x)$ determines the shape of the wave.) If the point O corresponds to $x = 0$, explain why, at time T, the wave moving to the left in Fig. 15.20 (shown in red) is given by the function $y_2(x, T) = -f(-x)$. (b) Show that the total wave function $y(x, T) = y_1(x, T) + y_2(x, T)$ is zero at O, independent of the form of the function $f(x)$. (c) The red and blue waves in Fig. 15.21 combine so that the slope of the string at O is always zero. To show this mathematically for a wave of arbitrary shape, again let the wave moving to the right in Fig. 15.21 (shown in blue) be given by $y_1(x, T) = f(x)$ at time T. Explain why the wave moving to the left (shown in red) at this same time T is given by $y_2(x, T) = f(-x)$. (d) Show that the total wave function $y(x, T) = y_1(x, T) + y_2(x, T)$ has zero slope at O, independent of the form of the function $f(x)$, as long as $f(x)$ has a finite first derivative.

15.73. A string that lies along the $+x$-axis has a free end at $x = 0$. (a) By using steps similar to those used to derive Eq. (15.28), show that an incident traveling wave $y_1(x, t) = A\cos(kx + \omega t)$ gives rise to a standing wave $y(x, t) = 2A\cos\omega t\cos kx$. (b) Show that the standing wave has an antinode at its free end $(x = 0)$. (c) Find the maximum displacement, maximum speed, and maximum acceleration of the free end of the string.

15.74. A string with both ends held fixed is vibrating in its third harmonic. The waves have a speed of 192 m/s and a frequency of 240 Hz. The amplitude of the standing wave at an antinode is 0.400 cm. (a) Calculate the amplitude at points on the string a distance of (i) 40.0 cm; (ii) 20.0 cm; and (iii) 10.0 cm from the left end of the string. (b) At each point in part (a), how much time does it take the string to go from its largest upward displacement to its largest downward displacement? (c) Calculate the maximum transverse velocity and the maximum transverse acceleration of the string at each of the points in part (a).

15.75. A uniform cylindrical steel wire, 55.0 cm long and 1.14 mm in diameter, is fixed at both ends. To what tension must it be adjusted so that, when vibrating in its first overtone, it produces the note D# of frequency 311 Hz? Assume that it stretches an insignificant amount. (*Hint:* See Table 14.1.)

15.76. Holding Up Under Stress. A string or rope will break apart if it is placed under too much tensile stress [Eq. (11.8)]. Thicker ropes can withstand more tension without breaking because the thicker the rope, the greater the cross-sectional area and the smaller the stress. One type of steel has density 7800 kg/m^3 and will break if the tensile stress exceeds 7.0×10^8 N/m^2. You want to make a guitar string from 4.0 g of this type of steel. In use, the guitar string must be able to withstand a tension of 900 N without breaking. Your job is the following: (a) Determine the maximum length and minimum radius the string can have. (b) Determine the highest possible fundamental frequency of standing waves on this string, if the entire length of the string is free to vibrate.

15.77. Combining Standing Waves. A guitar string of length L is plucked in such a way that the total wave produced is the sum of the fundamental and the second harmonic. That is, the standing wave is given by

$$y(x, t) = y_1(x, t) + y_2(x, t)$$

where

$$y_1(x, t) = C\sin\omega_1 t\sin k_1 x$$
$$y_2(x, t) = C\sin\omega_2 t\sin k_2 x$$

with $\omega_1 = vk_1$ and $\omega_2 = vk_2$. (a) At what values of x are the nodes of y_1? (b) At what values of x are the nodes of y_2? (c) Graph the total wave at $t = 0, t = \frac{1}{8}f_1, t = \frac{1}{4}f_1, t = \frac{3}{8}f_1$, and $t = \frac{1}{2}f_1$. (d) Does the sum of the two standing waves y_1 and y_2 produce a standing wave? Explain.

15.78. When a massive aluminum sculpture is hung from a steel wire, the fundamental frequency for transverse standing waves on the wire is 250.0 Hz. The sculpture (but not the wire) is then completely submerged in water. (a) What is the new fundamental frequency? (*Hint:* See Table 14.1.) (b) Why is it a good approximation to treat the wire as being fixed at both ends?

15.79. Tuning an Instrument. A musician tunes the C-string of her instrument to a fundamental frequency of 65.4 Hz. The vibrating portion of the string is 0.600 m long and has a mass of 14.4 g. (a) With what tension must the musician stretch it? (b) What percent increase in tension is needed to increase the frequency from 65.4 Hz to 73.4 Hz, corresponding to a rise in pitch from C to D?

Challenge Problems

15.80. Longitudinal Waves on a Spring. A long spring such as a Slinky™ is often used to demonstrate longitudinal waves. (a) Show that if a spring that obeys Hooke's law has mass m, length L, and force constant k', the speed of longitudinal waves on the spring is $v = L\sqrt{k'/m}$. (b) Evaluate v for a spring with $m = 0.250$ kg, $L = 2.00$ m, and $k' = 1.50$ N/m.

15.81. (a) Show that for a wave on a string, the kinetic energy *per unit length of string* is

$$u_k(x, t) = \frac{1}{2}\mu v_y^2(x, t) = \frac{1}{2}\mu\left(\frac{\partial y(x, t)}{\partial t}\right)^2$$

where μ is the mass per unit length. (b) Calculate $u_k(x, t)$ for a sinusoidal wave given by Eq. (15.7). (c) There is also elastic potential energy in the string, associated with the work required to deform and stretch the string. Consider a short segment of string at position x that has unstretched length Δx, as in Fig. 15.13. Ignoring the (small) curvature of the segment, its slope is $\partial y(x, t)/\partial x$. Assume that the displacement of the string from equilibrium is small, so that $\partial y/\partial x$ has a magnitude much less than unity. Show that the stretched length of the segment is approximately

$$\Delta x\left[1 + \frac{1}{2}\left(\frac{\partial y(x, t)}{\partial x}\right)^2\right]$$

(*Hint:* Use the relationship $\sqrt{1 + u} \approx 1 + \frac{1}{2}u$, valid for $|u| \ll 1$.) (d) The potential energy stored in the segment equals the work done by the string tension F (which acts along the string) to stretch the segment from its unstretched length Δx to the length calculated in part (c). Calculate this work and show that the potential energy *per unit length of string* is

$$u_p(x, t) = \frac{1}{2}F\left(\frac{\partial y(x, t)}{\partial x}\right)^2$$

(e) Calculate $u_p(x, t)$ for a sinusoidal wave given by Eq. (15.7). (f) Show that $u_k(x, t) = u_p(x, t)$ for all x and t. (g) Show $y(x, t)$, $u_k(x, t)$, and $u_p(x, t)$ as functions of x for $t = 0$ in one graph with all three functions on the same axes. Explain why u_k and u_p are maximum where y is zero, and vice versa. (h) Show that the instantaneous power in the wave, given by Eq. (15.22), is equal to the total energy per unit length multiplied by the wave speed v. Explain why this result is reasonable.

15.82. A deep-sea diver is suspended beneath the surface of Loch Ness by a 100-m-long cable that is attached to a boat on the surface (Fig. 15.40). The diver and his suit have a total mass of 120 kg and a volume of 0.0800 m^3. The cable has a diameter of 2.00 cm and a linear mass density of $\mu = 1.10$ kg/m. The diver thinks he sees something moving in the murky depths and jerks the end of the cable back and forth to send transverse waves up the cable as a signal to his companions in the boat. (a) What is the tension in the cable at its lower end, where it is attached to the diver? Do not forget to include the buoyant force that the water (density 1000 kg/m^3) exerts on him. (b) Calculate the tension in the cable a distance x above the diver. The buoyant force on the cable must be included in your calculation. (c) The speed of transverse waves on the cable is given by $v = \sqrt{F/\mu}$ (Eq. 15.13). The speed therefore varies along the cable, since the tension is not constant. (This expression neglects the damping force that the water exerts on the moving cable.) Integrate to find the time required for the first signal to reach the surface.

Figure 15.40 Challenge Problem 15.82.

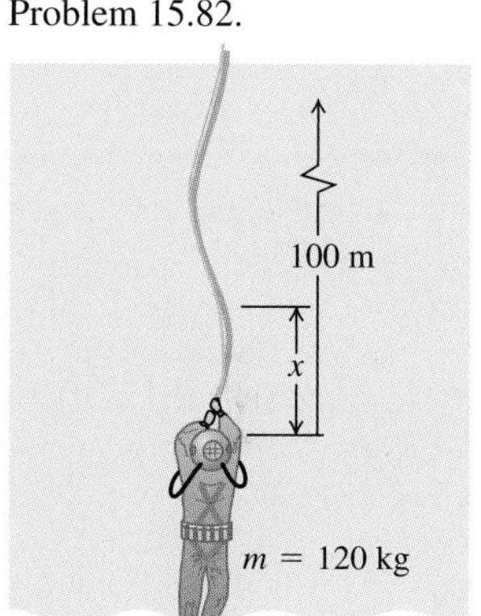

15.83. A uniform rope with length L and mass m is held at one end and whirled in a horizontal circle with angular velocity ω. You can ignore the force of gravity on the rope. Find the time required for a transverse wave to travel from one end of the rope to the other.

15.84. Instantaneous Power in a Standing Wave. From Eq. (15.21), the instantaneous rate at which a wave transmits energy along a string (instantaneous power) is

$$P(x, t) = -F\frac{\partial y(x, t)}{\partial x}\frac{\partial y(x, t)}{\partial t}$$

where F is the tension. (a) Evaluate $P(x, t)$ for a standing wave of the form given by Eq. (15.28). (b) Show that for all values of x, the *average* power P_{av} carried by the standing wave is zero. (Equation (15.25) does not apply here. Can you see why?) (c) For a standing wave given by Eq. (15.28), graph $P(x, t)$ and the displacement $y(x, t)$ as functions of x for $t = 0, t = \pi/4\omega$, $t = \pi/2\omega$, and $t = 3\pi/4\omega$. (Positive $P(x, t)$ means energy is flowing in the $+x$-direction; negative $P(x, t)$ means the flow is in the

$-x$-direction.) (d) The *kinetic* energy per unit length of string is greatest where the string has the greatest transverse speed, and the *potential* energy per unit length of string is greatest where the string has the steepest slope (because there the string is stretched the most). (See Challenge Problem 15.81.) Using these ideas, discuss the flow of energy along the string.

15.85. Out of Tune. The B-string of a guitar is made of steel (density 7800 kg/m^3), is 63.5 cm long, and has diameter 0.406 mm. The fundamental frequency is $f = 247.0$ Hz. (a) Find the string tension. (b) If the tension F is changed by a small amount ΔF, the frequency f changes by a small amount Δf. Show that

$$\frac{\Delta f}{f} = \frac{1}{2}\frac{\Delta f}{f}$$

(c) The string is tuned as in part (a) when its temperature is 18.5°C. Strenuous playing can make the temperature of the string rise, changing its vibration frequency. Find Δf if the temperature of the string rises to 29.5°C. The steel string has a Young's modulus of 2.00×10^{11} Pa and a coefficient of linear expansion of $1.20 \times 10^{-5}\ (\mathrm{C}°)^{-1}$. Assume that the temperature of the body of the guitar remains constant. Will the vibration frequency rise or fall?

SOUND AND HEARING

16

? Most people like to listen to music, but hardly anyone likes to listen to noise. What is the physical difference between musical sound and noise?

LEARNING GOALS

By studying this chapter, you will learn:

- How to describe a sound wave in terms of either particle displacements or pressure fluctuations.
- How to calculate the speed of sound waves in different materials.
- How to calculate the intensity of a sound wave.
- What determines the particular frequencies of sound produced by an organ or a flute.
- How resonance occurs in musical instruments.
- What happens when sound waves from different sources overlap.
- How to describe what happens when two sound waves of slightly different frequencies are combined.
- Why the pitch of a siren changes as it moves past you.

Of all the mechanical waves that occur in nature, the most important in our everyday lives are longitudinal waves in a medium—usually air—called *sound* waves. The reason is that the human ear is tremendously sensitive and can detect sound waves even of very low intensity. Besides their use in spoken communication, our ears allow us to pick up a myriad of cues about our environment, from the welcome sound of a meal being prepared to the warning sound of an approaching car. The ability to hear an unseen nocturnal predator was essential to the survival of our ancestors, so it is no exaggeration to say that we humans owe our existence to our highly evolved sense of hearing.

Up to this point we have described mechanical waves primarily in terms of displacement; however, a description of sound waves in terms of *pressure* fluctuations is often more appropriate, largely because the ear is primarily sensitive to changes in pressure. We'll study the relationships among displacement, pressure fluctuation, and intensity and the connections between these quantities and human sound perception.

When a source of sound or a listener moves through the air, the listener may hear a different frequency from the one emitted by the source. This is the Doppler effect, which has important applications in medicine and technology.

16.1 Sound Waves

The most general definition of **sound** is a longitudinal wave in a medium. Our main concern in this chapter is with sound waves in air, but sound can travel through any gas, liquid, or solid. You may be all too familiar with the propagation of sound through a solid if your neighbor's stereo speakers are right next to your wall.

The simplest sound waves are sinusoidal waves, which have definite frequency, amplitude, and wavelength. The human ear is sensitive to waves in the frequency range from about 20 to 20,000 Hz, called the **audible range,** but we also use the

16.1 A sinusoidal longitudinal wave traveling to the right in a fluid. (Compare to Fig. 15.7.)

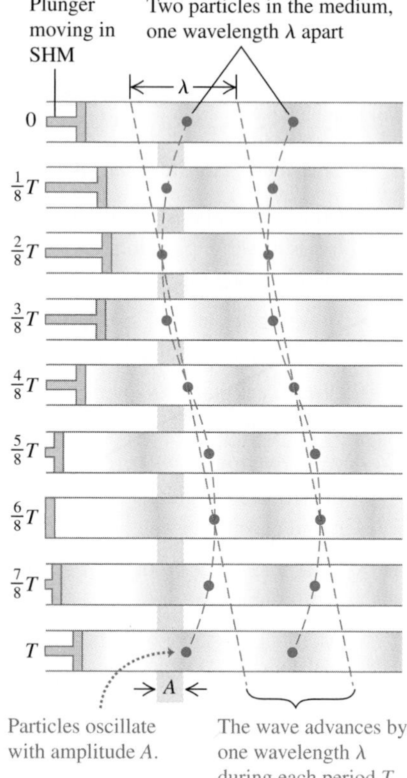
Longitudinal waves are shown at intervals of $\frac{1}{8}T$ for one period T
Plunger moving in SHM
Two particles in the medium, one wavelength λ apart
λ
0
$\frac{1}{8}T$
$\frac{2}{8}T$
$\frac{3}{8}T$
$\frac{4}{8}T$
$\frac{5}{8}T$
$\frac{6}{8}T$
$\frac{7}{8}T$
T
A
Particles oscillate with amplitude A.
The wave advances by one wavelength λ during each period T.

term "sound" for similar waves with frequencies above **(ultrasonic)** and below **(infrasonic)** the range of human hearing.

Sound waves usually travel out in all directions from the source of sound, with an amplitude that depends on the direction and distance from the source. We'll return to this point in the next section. For now, we concentrate on the idealized case of a sound wave that propagates in the positive x-direction only. As we discussed in Section 15.3, such a wave is described by a wave function $y(x, t)$, which gives the instantaneous displacement y of a particle in the medium at position x at time t. If the wave is sinusoidal, we can express it using Eq. (15.7):

$$y(x, t) = A\cos(kx - \omega t) \quad \text{(sound wave propagating in the } +x\text{-direction)} \tag{16.1}$$

Remember that in a longitudinal wave the displacements are *parallel* to the direction of travel of the wave, so distances x and y are measured parallel to each other, not perpendicular as in a transverse wave. The amplitude A is the maximum displacement of a particle in the medium from its equilibrium position (Fig. 16.1). Hence A is also called the **displacement amplitude.**

Sound Waves As Pressure Fluctuations

Sound waves may also be described in terms of variations of *pressure* at various points. In a sinusoidal sound wave in air, the pressure fluctuates above and below atmospheric pressure p_a in a sinusoidal variation with the same frequency as the motions of the air particles. The human ear operates by sensing such pressure variations. A sound wave entering the ear canal exerts a fluctuating pressure on one side of the eardrum; the air on the other side of the eardrum, vented to the outside by the Eustachian tube, is at atmospheric pressure. The pressure difference on the two sides of the eardrum sets it into motion. Microphones and similar devices also usually sense pressure differences, not displacements, so it is very useful to develop a relationship between these two descriptions.

Let $p(x, t)$ be the instantaneous pressure fluctuation in a sound wave at any point x at time t. That is, $p(x, t)$ is the amount by which the pressure *differs* from normal atmospheric pressure p_a. Think of $p(x, t)$ as the *gauge pressure* defined in Section 14.2; it can be either positive or negative. The *absolute* pressure at a point is then $p_a + p(x, t)$.

To see the connection between the pressure fluctuation $p(x, t)$ and the displacement $y(x, t)$ in a sound wave propagating in the $+x$-direction, consider an imaginary cylinder of a wave medium (gas, liquid, or solid) with cross-sectional area S and axis along the direction of propagation (Fig. 16.2). When no sound wave is present, the cylinder has length Δx and volume $V = S\Delta x$, as shown by the shaded volume in Fig. 16.2. When a wave is present, at time t the end of the cylinder that is initially at x is displaced by $y_1 = y(x, t)$, and the end that is initially at $x + \Delta x$ is displaced by $y_2 = y(x + \Delta x, t)$; this is shown by the red lines. If $y_2 > y_1$, as shown in Fig. 16.2, the cylinder's volume has increased, which causes a decrease in pressure. If $y_2 < y_1$, the cylinder's volume has decreased and the pressure has increased. If $y_2 = y_1$, the cylinder is simply shifted to the left or right; there is no volume change and no pressure fluctuation. The pressure fluctuation depends on the *difference* between the displacement at neighboring points in the medium.

16.2 As a sound wave propagates along the x-axis, the left and right ends undergo different displacements y_1 and y_2.

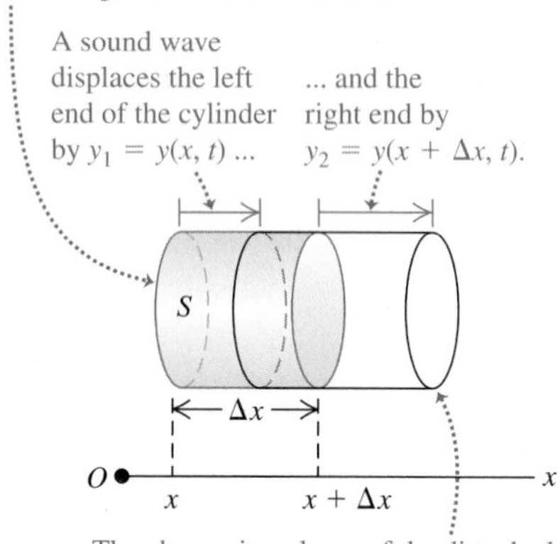
Undisturbed cylinder of fluid has cross-sectional area S, length Δx, and volume $S\Delta x$.
A sound wave displaces the left end of the cylinder by $y_1 = y(x, t)$ ...
... and the right end by $y_2 = y(x + \Delta x, t)$.
S
Δx
O
x
$x + \Delta x$
x
The change in volume of the disturbed cylinder of fluid is $S(y_2 - y_1)$.

Quantitatively, the change in volume ΔV of the cylinder is

$$\Delta V = S(y_2 - y_1) = S[y(x + \Delta x, t) - y(x, t)]$$

In the limit as $\Delta x \to 0$, the fractional change in volume dV/V (volume change divided by original volume) is

$$\frac{dV}{V} = \lim_{\Delta x \to 0} \frac{S[y(x + \Delta x, t) - y(x, t)]}{S\Delta x} = \frac{\partial y(x, t)}{\partial x} \tag{16.2}$$

The fractional volume change is related to the pressure fluctuation by the bulk modulus B, which by definition [Eq. (11.13)] is $B = -p(x, t)/(dV/V)$ (see Section 11.4). Solving for $p(x, t)$, we have

$$p(x, t) = -B\frac{\partial y(x, t)}{\partial x} \tag{16.3}$$

The negative sign arises because when $\partial y(x, t)/\partial x$ is positive, the displacement is greater at $x + \Delta x$ than at x, corresponding to an increase in volume and a *decrease* in pressure.

When we evaluate $\partial y(x, t)/\partial x$ for the sinusoidal wave of Eq. (16.1), we find

$$p(x, t) = BkA\sin(kx - \omega t) \tag{16.4}$$

Figure 16.3 shows $y(x, t)$ and $p(x, t)$ for a sinusoidal sound wave at $t = 0$. It also shows how individual particles of the wave are displaced at this time. While $y(x, t)$ and $p(x, t)$ describe the same wave, these two functions are one-quarter cycle out of phase: At any time, the displacement is greatest where the pressure fluctuation is zero, and vice versa. In particular, note that the compressions (points of greatest pressure and density) and rarefactions (points of lowest pressure and density) are points of *zero* displacement.

CAUTION **Graphs of a sound wave** Keep in mind that the graphs in Fig. 16.3 show the wave at only *one* instant of time. Because the wave is propagating in the $+x$-direction, as time goes by the wave patterns in the functions $y(x, t)$ and $p(x, t)$ move to the right at the wave speed $v = \omega/k$. Hence the positions of the compressions and rarefactions also move to the right at this same speed. The particles, by contrast, simply oscillate back and forth in simple harmonic motion as shown in Fig. 16.1.

Equation (16.4) shows that the quantity BkA represents the maximum pressure fluctuation. We call this the **pressure amplitude,** denoted by p_{max}:

$$p_{max} = BkA \quad \text{(sinusoidal sound wave)} \tag{16.5}$$

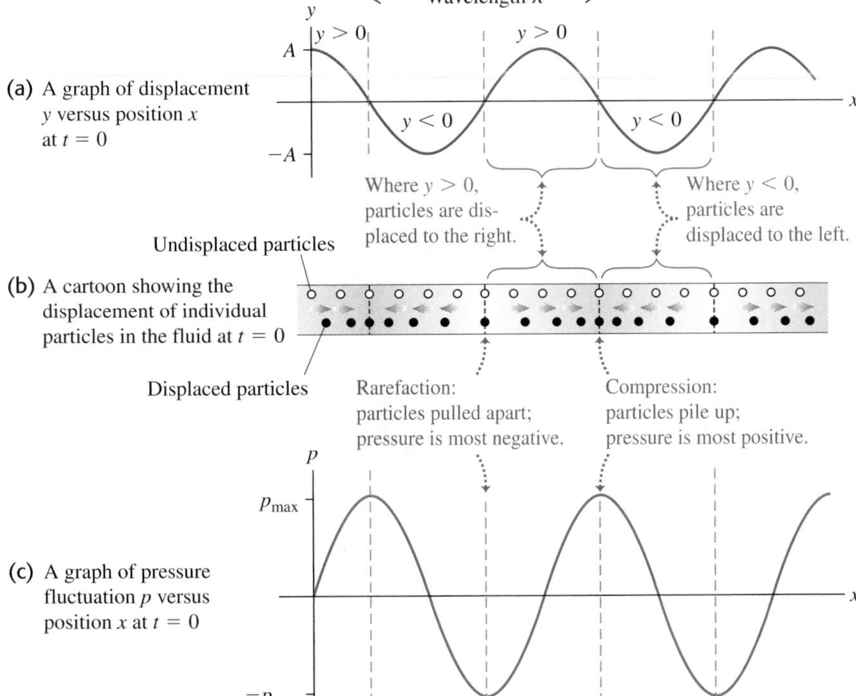

16.3 Three ways to describe a sound wave.

The pressure amplitude is directly proportional to the displacement amplitude A, as we might expect, and it also depends on wavelength. Waves of shorter wavelength λ (larger wave number $k = 2\pi/\lambda$) have greater pressure variations for a given amplitude because the maxima and minima are squeezed closer together. A medium with a large value of bulk modulus B requires a relatively large pressure amplitude for a given displacement amplitude because large B means a less compressible medium; that is, greater pressure change is required for a given volume change.

Example 16.1 Amplitude of a sound wave in air

In a sinusoidal sound wave of moderate loudness the maximum pressure variations are of the order of 3.0×10^{-2} Pa above and below atmospheric pressure p_a (nominally 1.013×10^5 Pa at sea level). Find the corresponding maximum displacement if the frequency is 1000 Hz. In air at normal atmospheric pressure and density, the speed of sound is 344 m/s and the bulk modulus is 1.42×10^5 Pa.

SOLUTION

IDENTIFY: This problem involves the relationship between two different ways of describing a sound wave: in terms of displacement and in terms of pressure. The target variable is the displacement amplitude A.

SET UP: We are given the pressure amplitude p_{max}, wave speed v, frequency f, and bulk modulus B. Our target variable A is related to p_{max} by Eq. (16.5). We also use the relationship $\omega = vk$ [Eq. (15.6)] to determine the wave number k from v and the angular frequency $\omega = 2\pi f$.

EXECUTE: From Eq. (16.5), the maximum displacement is $A = p_{max}/Bk$. From Eq. (15.6), the wave number is

$$k = \frac{\omega}{v} = \frac{2\pi f}{v} = \frac{(2\pi \text{ rad})(1000 \text{ Hz})}{344 \text{ m/s}} = 18.3 \text{ rad/m}$$

Then

$$A = \frac{p_{max}}{Bk} = \frac{3.0 \times 10^{-2} \text{ Pa}}{(1.42 \times 10^5 \text{ Pa})(18.3 \text{ rad/m})} = 1.2 \times 10^{-8} \text{ m}$$

EVALUATE: This displacement amplitude is only about $\frac{1}{100}$ the size of a human cell. Remember that the ear actually senses pressure fluctuations; it detects these minuscule displacements only indirectly.

Example 16.2 Amplitude of a sound wave in the inner ear

When a sound wave enters the ear, it sets the eardrum into oscillation, which in turn causes oscillation of the three tiny bones in the middle ear called the *ossicles* (Fig. 16.4). This oscillation is finally transmitted to the fluid-filled inner ear; the motion of the fluid disturbs hair cells within the inner ear, which transmit nerve impulses to the brain with the information that a sound is present. The moving part of the eardrum has an area of about 43 mm^2, and the area of the stapes (the smallest of the ossicles) where it connects to the inner ear is about 3.2 mm^2. For the sound in Example 16.1, determine (a) the pressure amplitude and (b) the displacement amplitude of the wave in the fluid of the inner ear. The speed of sound in this fluid is about 1500 m/s.

SOLUTION

IDENTIFY: Although the sound wave is now traveling in liquid (mostly water) rather than gas, the same principles and relationships among the properties of the wave apply.

SET UP: We can safely neglect the mass of the ossicles (about 58 mg $= 5.8 \times 10^{-5}$ kg), so the force exerted by the ossicles on the fluid in the inner ear is the same as the force exerted on the eardrum and ossicles by the sound wave in air. (We used this same idea in Chapters 4 and 5 when we said that the tension is the same at either end of a massless rope.) Hence the pressure amplitude p_{max} is greater in the inner ear than in the outside air because the same force is exerted on a smaller area (the area of the stapes versus the area of the eardrum).

Given the pressure amplitude in the inner ear, we find the displacement amplitude using Eq. (16.5). The values of B and k are different than in the air. To determine k, note that the wave in the inner ear has the same angular frequency ω as the wave in the air

16.4 The anatomy of the human ear. The middle ear is the size of a small marble; the ossicles (incus, malleus, and stapes) are the smallest bones in the human body.

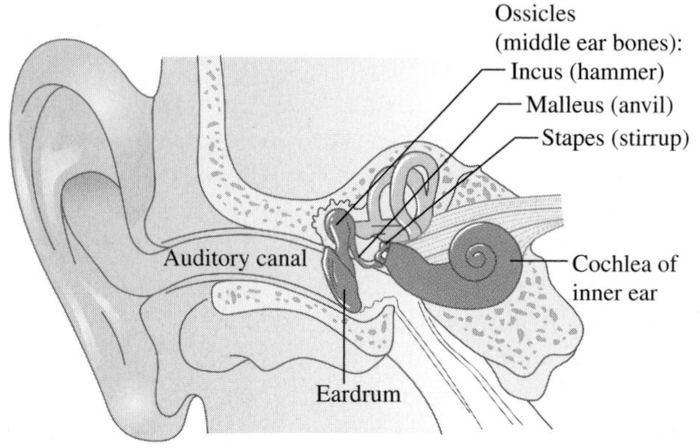

because the air, eardrum, ossicles, and inner-ear fluid all oscillate together. But because the wave speed v is greater in the inner ear than in the air $(1500 \text{ m/s}$ versus $344 \text{ m/s})$, the wave number $k = \omega/v$ is smaller.

EXECUTE: (a) Using the area of the eardrum and pressure amplitude found in Example 16.1, the maximum force exerted by the sound wave in air on the eardrum is $F_{max} = p_{max(air)}S_{eardrum}$. Hence the pressure amplitude in the inner ear fluid is

$$p_{max(inner\ ear)} = \frac{F_{max}}{S_{stapes}} = \frac{p_{max(air)}S_{eardrum}}{S_{stapes}} = \frac{(3.0 \times 10^{-2}\ \text{Pa})(43\ \text{mm}^2)}{3.2\ \text{mm}^2} = 0.40\ \text{Pa}$$

(b) To find the maximum displacement, we again use the relationship $A = p_{max}/Bk$ as in Example 16.1. The fluid in the inner ear is mostly water, which has a much greater bulk modulus than air because water is much more difficult to compress. From Table 11.2 the compressibility of water (unfortunately also called k) equals $45.8 \times 10^{-11}\ \text{Pa}^{-1}$, so $B_{fluid} = 1/(45.8 \times 10^{-11}\ \text{Pa}^{-1}) = 2.18 \times 10^9\ \text{Pa}$.

We determine the value of the wave number k using the value of ω from Example 16.1 and $v = 1500\ \text{m/s}$ for the inner-ear fluid. Hence

$$k_{inner\ ear} = \frac{\omega}{v_{inner\ ear}} = \frac{(2\pi\ \text{rad})(1000\ \text{Hz})}{1500\ \text{m/s}} = 4.2\ \text{rad/m}$$

When we put everything together, the maximum displacement of the fluid in the inner ear is

$$A_{inner\ ear} = \frac{p_{max(inner\ ear)}}{B_{fluid}k_{inner\ ear}} = \frac{0.40\ \text{Pa}}{(2.18 \times 10^9\ \text{Pa})(4.2\ \text{rad/m})} = 4.4 \times 10^{-11}\ \text{m}$$

EVALUATE: The result in part (a) shows that the effect of the ossicles is to increase the pressure amplitude in the inner ear by a factor of $(43\ \text{mm}^2)/(3.2\ \text{mm}^2) = 13$. This amplification factor helps give the human ear its great sensitivity.

The displacement amplitude in the inner ear is even smaller than in the air. What really matters in the inner ear, however, is the *pressure* amplitude, since the pressure variations within the fluid cause the forces that set the hair cells into motion.

Perception of Sound Waves

The physical characteristics of a sound wave are directly related to the perception of that sound by a listener. For a given frequency, the greater the pressure amplitude of a sinusoidal sound wave, the greater the perceived **loudness.** The relationship between pressure amplitude and loudness is not a simple one, and it varies from one person to another. One important factor is that the ear is not equally sensitive to all frequencies in the audible range. A sound at one frequency may seem louder than one of equal pressure amplitude at a different frequency. At 1000 Hz the minimum pressure amplitude that can be perceived with normal hearing is about 3×10^{-5} Pa; to produce the same loudness at 200 Hz or 15,000 Hz requires about 3×10^{-4} Pa. Perceived loudness also depends on the health of the ear. A loss of sensitivity at the high-frequency end usually happens naturally with age but can be further aggravated by excessive noise levels. Studies have shown that many young rock musicians have suffered permanent ear damage and have hearing that is typical of persons 65 years of age. Headphones for personal music players used at high volume pose similar threats to hearing. Be careful!

The frequency of a sound wave is the primary factor in determining the **pitch** of a sound, the quality that lets us classify the sound as "high" or "low." The higher the frequency of a sound (within the audible range), the higher the pitch that a listener will perceive. Pressure amplitude also plays a role in determining pitch. When a listener compares two sinusoidal sound waves with the same frequency but different pressure amplitudes, the one with the greater pressure amplitude is usually perceived as louder but also as slightly lower in pitch.

Musical sounds have wave functions that are more complicated than a simple sine function. The pressure fluctuation in the sound wave produced by a clarinet is shown in Fig. 16.5a. The pattern is so complex because the column of air in a wind instrument like a clarinet vibrates at a fundamental frequency and at many harmonics at the same time. (In Section 15.8, we described this same behavior for a string that has been plucked, bowed, or struck. We'll examine the physics of wind instruments in Section 16.5.) The sound wave produced in the surrounding air has a similar amount of each harmonic—that is, a similar *harmonic content.* Figure 16.5b shows the harmonic content of the sound of a clarinet. The mathematical process of translating a pressure–time graph like Fig. 16.5a into a graph of harmonic content like Fig. 16.5b is called *Fourier analysis.*

10.10 Complex Waves: Fourier Analysis

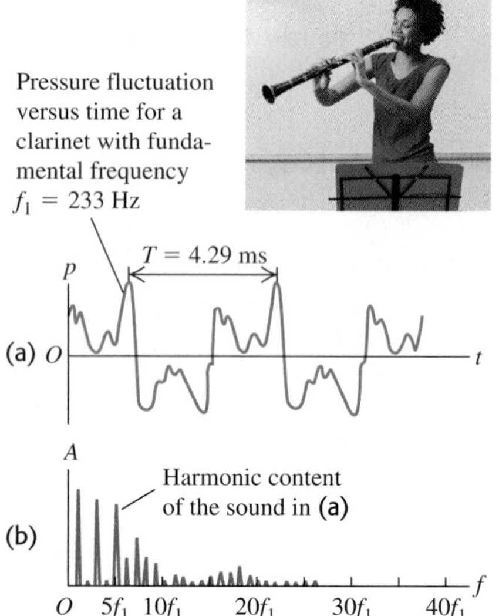

16.5 Different representations of the sound of (a), (b) a clarinet and (c), (d) an alto recorder. (Graphs adapted from R.E. Berg and D.G. Stork, *The Physics of Sound,* Prentice-Hall, 1982.)

Pressure fluctuation versus time for an alto recorder with fundamental frequency $f_1 = 523$ Hz

$T = 1.91$ ms

p

(c) O t

A

Harmonic content of the sound in (c)

(d)

O $5f_1$ $10f_1$ $20f_1$ $30f_1$ $40f_1$ f

Two tones produced by different instruments might have the same fundamental frequency (and thus the same pitch) but sound different because of different harmonic content. The difference in sound is called *tone color, quality,* or **timbre** and is often described in subjective terms such as reedy, golden, round, mellow, and tinny. A tone that is rich in harmonics, like the clarinet tone in Figs. 16.5a and 16.5b, usually sounds thin and "stringy" or "reedy," while a tone containing mostly a fundamental, like the alto recorder tone in Figs. 16.5c and 16.5d, is more mellow and flutelike. The same principle applies to the human voice, which is another example of a wind instrument; the vowels "a" and "e" sound different because of differences in harmonic content.

Another factor in determining tone quality is the behavior at the beginning (*attack*) and end (*decay*) of a tone. A piano tone begins with a thump and then dies away gradually. A harpsichord tone, in addition to having different harmonic content, begins much more quickly with a click, and the higher harmonics begin before the lower ones. When the key is released, the sound also dies away much more rapidly with a harpsichord than with a piano. Similar effects are present in other musical instruments. With wind and string instruments the player has considerable control over the attack and decay of the tone, and these characteristics help to define the unique characteristics of each instrument.

Unlike the tones made by musical instruments or the vowels in human speech, **noise** is a combination of *all* frequencies, not just frequencies that are integer multiples of a fundamental frequency. (An extreme case is "white noise," which contains equal amounts of all frequencies across the audible range.) Examples include the sound of the wind and the hissing sound you make in saying the consonant "s." ?

Test Your Understanding of Section 16.1 You use an electronic signal generator to produce a sinusoidal sound wave in air. You then increase the frequency of the wave from 100 Hz to 400 Hz while keeping the pressure amplitude constant. What effect does this have on the displacement amplitude of the sound wave? (i) It becomes four times greater; (ii) it becomes twice as great; (iii) it is unchanged; (iv) it becomes $\frac{1}{2}$ as great; (v) it becomes $\frac{1}{4}$ as great.

16.2 Speed of Sound Waves

We found in Section 15.4 that the speed v of a transverse wave on a string depends on the string tension F and the linear mass density μ: $v = \sqrt{F/\mu}$. What, we may ask, is the corresponding expression for the speed of sound waves in a gas or liquid? On what properties of the medium does the speed depend?

We can make an educated guess about these questions by remembering a claim that we made in Section 15.4: For mechanical waves in general, the expression for the wave speed is of the form

$$v = \sqrt{\frac{\text{Restoring force returning the system to equilibrium}}{\text{Inertia resisting the return to equilibrium}}}$$

A sound wave in a bulk fluid causes compressions and rarefactions of the fluid, so the restoring-force term in the above expression must be related to how easy or difficult it is to compress the fluid. This is precisely what the bulk modulus B of the medium tells us. According to Newton's second law, inertia is related to mass. The "massiveness" of a bulk fluid is described by its density, or mass per unit volume, ρ. (The corresponding quantity for a string is the mass per unit length, μ.) Hence we expect that the speed of sound waves should be of the form $v = \sqrt{B/\rho}$.

To check our guess, we'll derive the speed of sound waves in a fluid in a pipe. This is a situation of some importance, since all musical wind instruments are fundamentally pipes in which a longitudinal wave (sound) propagates in a fluid (air)

(Fig. 16.6). Human speech works on the same principle; sound waves propagate in your vocal tract, which is basically an air-filled pipe connected to the lungs at one end (your larynx) and to the outside air at the other end (your mouth). The steps in our derivation are completely parallel to those we used in Section 15.4 to find the speed of transverse waves, so you'll find it useful to review that section.

16.6 When a wind instrument like this French horn is played, sound waves propagate through the air within the instrument's pipes. The properties of the sound that emerges from the large bell depend on the speed of these waves.

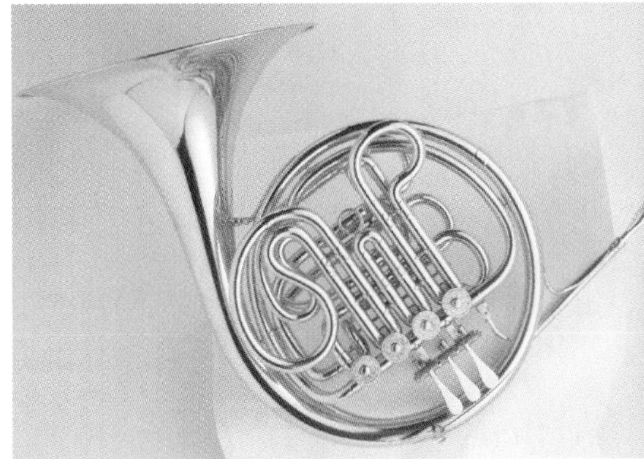

Speed of Sound in a Fluid

Figure 16.7 shows a fluid (either liquid or gas) with density ρ in a pipe with cross-sectional area A. In the equilibrium state, the fluid is under a uniform pressure p. In Fig. 16.7a the fluid is at rest. We take the x-axis along the length of the pipe. This is also the direction in which we make a longitudinal wave propagate, so the displacement y is also measured along the pipe, just as in Section 16.1 (see Fig. 16.2).

At time $t = 0$ we start the piston at the left end moving toward the right with constant speed v_y. This initiates a wave motion that travels to the right along the length of the pipe, in which successive sections of fluid begin to move and become compressed at successively later times.

Figure 16.7b shows the fluid at time t. All portions of fluid to the left of point P are moving to the right with speed v_y, and all portions to the right of P are still at rest. The boundary between the moving and stationary portions travels to the right with a speed equal to the speed of propagation or wave speed v. At time t the piston has moved a distance $v_y t$, and the boundary has advanced a distance vt. As with a transverse disturbance in a string, we can compute the speed of propagation from the impulse–momentum theorem.

16.7 A sound wave propagating in a fluid confined to a tube. **(a)** Fluid in equilibrium. **(b)** A time t after the piston begins moving to the right at speed v_y, the fluid between the piston and point P is in motion. The speed of sound waves is v.

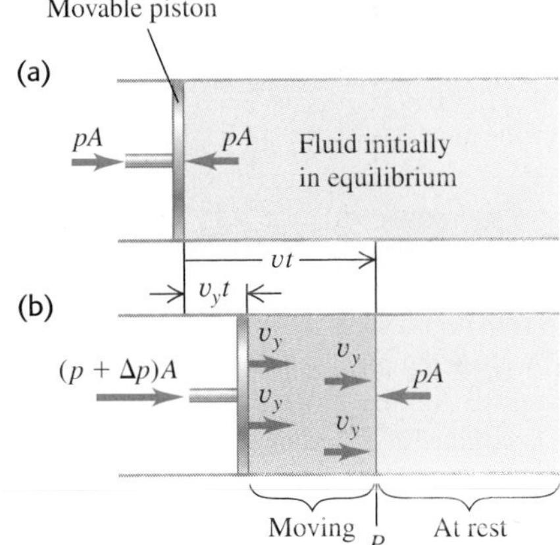

The quantity of fluid set in motion in time t is the amount that originally occupied a section of the cylinder with length vt, cross-sectional area A, and volume vtA. The mass of this fluid is ρvtA, and its longitudinal momentum (that is, momentum along the length of the pipe) is

$$\text{Longitudinal momentum} = (\rho vtA)v_y$$

Next we compute the increase of pressure, Δp, in the moving fluid. The original volume of the moving fluid, Avt, has decreased by an amount $Av_y t$. From the definition of the bulk modulus B, Eq. (11.13) in Section 11.5,

$$B = \frac{-\text{Pressure change}}{\text{Fractional volume change}} = \frac{-\Delta p}{-Av_y t/Avt}$$

$$\Delta p = B\frac{v_y}{v}$$

The pressure in the moving fluid is $p + \Delta p$ and the force exerted on it by the piston is $(p + \Delta p)A$. The net force on the moving fluid (see Fig. 16.7b) is ΔpA, and the longitudinal impulse is

$$\text{Longitudinal impulse} = \Delta pAt = B\frac{v_y}{v}At$$

Because the fluid was at rest at time $t = 0$, the change in momentum up to time t is equal to the momentum at that time. Applying the impulse–momentum theorem (Section 8.1), we find

$$B\frac{v_y}{v}At = \rho vtAv_y \tag{16.6}$$

When we solve this expression for v, we get

$$v = \sqrt{\frac{B}{\rho}} \quad \text{(speed of a longitudinal wave in a fluid)} \tag{16.7}$$

which agrees with our educated guess. Thus the speed of propagation of a longitudinal pulse in a fluid depends only on the bulk modulus B and the density ρ of the medium.

While we derived Eq. (16.7) for waves in a pipe, it also applies to longitudinal waves in a bulk fluid. Thus the speed of sound waves traveling in air or water is determined by this equation.

Speed of Sound in a Solid

When a longitudinal wave propagates in a *solid* rod or bar, the situation is somewhat different. The rod expands sideways slightly when it is compressed longitudinally, while a fluid in a pipe with constant cross section cannot move sideways. Using the same kind of reasoning that led us to Eq. (16.7), we can show that the speed of a longitudinal pulse in the rod is given by

$$v = \sqrt{\frac{Y}{\rho}} \quad \text{(speed of a longitudinal wave in a solid rod)} \tag{16.8}$$

where Y is Young's modulus, defined in Section 11.4.

CAUTION **Solid rods vs. bulk solids** Equation (16.8) applies only to a rod or bar whose sides are free to bulge and shrink a little as the wave travels. It does not apply to longitudinal waves in a *bulk* solid, since in these materials, sideways motion in any element of material is prevented by the surrounding material. The speed of longitudinal waves in a bulk solid depends on the density, the bulk modulus, and the *shear* modulus; a full discussion is beyond the scope of this book.

Table 16.1 Speed of Sound in Various Bulk Materials

Material	Speed of Sound (m/s)
Gases	
Air (20°C)	344
Helium (20°C)	999
Hydrogen (20°C)	1330
Liquids	
Liquid helium (4 K)	211
Mercury (20°C)	1451
Water (0°C)	1402
Water (20°C)	1482
Water (100°C)	1543
Solids	
Aluminum	6420
Lead	1960
Steel	5941

As with the derivation for a transverse wave on a string, Eqs. (16.7) and (16.8) are valid for sinusoidal and other periodic waves, not just for the special case discussed here.

Table 16.1 lists the speed of sound in several bulk materials. Sound waves travel more slowly in lead than in aluminum or steel because lead has a lower bulk modulus and shear modulus and a higher density.

Example 16.3 Wavelength of sonar waves

A ship uses a sonar system to detect underwater objects (Fig. 16.8). The system emits underwater sound waves and measures the time interval for the reflected wave (echo) to return to the detector. Determine the speed of sound waves in water using Eq. (16.7) and find the wavelength of a 262-Hz wave.

SOLUTION

IDENTIFY: Our target variables are the speed and wavelength of a sound wave in a fluid.

16.8 A sonar system uses underwater sound waves to detect and locate submerged objects.

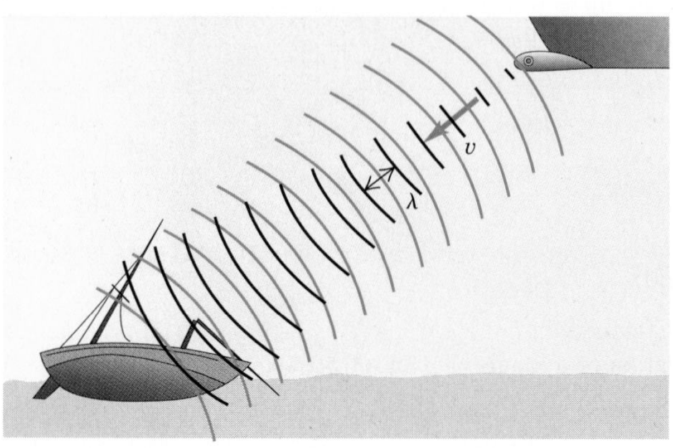

SET UP: To use Eq. (16.7) for the wave speed, we find the bulk modulus of water from the compressibility (Table 11.2) and the density ($\rho = 1.00 \times 10^3\ \text{kg/m}^3$). Given the speed and the frequency $f = 262$ Hz, we find the wavelength from the relationship $v = f\lambda$.

EXECUTE: From Table 11.2 we find that the compressibility of water, which is the reciprocal of the bulk modulus, is $k = 45.8 \times 10^{-11}\ \text{Pa}^{-1}$. Thus $B = (1/45.8) \times 10^{11}$ Pa. We obtain

$$v = \sqrt{\frac{B}{\rho}} = \sqrt{\frac{(1/45.8) \times 10^{11}\ \text{Pa}}{1.00 \times 10^3\ \text{kg/m}^3}}$$
$$= 1480\ \text{m/s}$$

The wavelength is given by

$$\lambda = \frac{v}{f} = \frac{1480\ \text{m/s}}{262\ \text{s}^{-1}} = 5.65\ \text{m}$$

EVALUATE: The calculated value of v agrees well with the experimental value in Table 16.1. Though water is far denser than air (ρ is larger), it is also far more incompressible (B is larger) and the speed $v = \sqrt{B/\rho}$ turns out to be more than four times the speed of sound in air at ordinary temperatures.

We found in Example 15.1 (Section 15.2) that a wave of this frequency in air has a wavelength of 1.31 m. The speed of sound in water is greater than in air, so the wavelength $\lambda = v/f$ must be greater as well; this is just as we calculated.

Dolphins emit high-frequency sound waves (typically 100,000 Hz) and use the echoes for guidance and for hunting. The corresponding wavelength in water is 1.48 cm. With this high-frequency "sonar" system they can sense objects that are roughly as small as the wavelength (but not much smaller). *Ultrasonic imaging* is a medical technique that uses exactly the same physical principle; sound waves of very high frequency and very short wavelength, called *ultrasound,* are scanned over the human body, and the "echoes" from interior organs are used to create an image. With ultrasound of frequency 5 MHz $= 5 \times 10^6$ Hz, the wavelength in water (the primary constituent of the body) is 0.3 mm, and features as small as this can be discerned in the image. Ultrasound is used for the study of heart-valve action, detection of tumors, and prenatal examinations (Fig. 16.9). Ultrasound is more sensitive than x rays in distinguishing various kinds of tissues and does not have the radiation hazards associated with x rays.

Example 16.4 Speed of a longitudinal wave

What is the speed of longitudinal waves in a lead rod?

SOLUTION

IDENTIFY: Waves of this kind are made by clamping the rod in place and striking one end face-on with a hammer. The amplitude of the resulting waves is so small as to be nearly invisible to the naked eye. But the question is about the *speed* of the waves, which does not depend on the amplitude. Note that we cannot simply use the value for lead from Table 16.1, as that value refers to the speed of sound in a *bulk* material, not a rod.

SET UP: Equation (16.8) applies to this situation. We find the values of Young's modulus Y and the density ρ from Tables 11.1 and 14.1, respectively.

EXECUTE: We find $Y = 1.6 \times 10^{10}$ Pa and $\rho = 11.3 \times 10^3\ \text{kg/m}^3$ (that is, 11.3 times the density of water), so

$$v = \sqrt{\frac{Y}{\rho}} = \sqrt{\frac{1.6 \times 10^{10}\ \text{Pa}}{11.3 \times 10^3\ \text{kg/m}^3}} = 1.2 \times 10^3\ \text{m/s}$$

EVALUATE: This is more than three times the speed of sound in air, but slower than the speed of sound in *bulk* lead (see Table 16.1). The reason is that for lead the bulk modulus is greater than Young's modulus.

Speed of Sound in a Gas

Most of the sound waves that we encounter on a daily basis propagate in air. To use Eq. (16.7) to find the speed of sound waves in air, we must keep in mind that the bulk modulus of a gas depends on the pressure of the gas: The greater the pressure applied to a gas to compress it, the more it resists further compression and hence the greater the bulk modulus. (That's why specific values of the bulk modulus for gases are not given in Table 11.1.) The expression for the bulk modulus of a gas for use in Eq. (16.7) is

$$B = \gamma p_0 \tag{16.9}$$

where p_0 is the equilibrium pressure of the gas. The quantity γ (the Greek letter gamma) is called the *ratio of heat capacities.* It is a dimensionless number that characterizes the thermal properties of the gas. (We'll learn more about this quantity in Chapter 19.) As an example, the ratio of heat capacities for air is $\gamma = 1.40$. At normal atmospheric pressure $p_0 = 1.01 \times 10^5$ Pa, so $B = (1.40)(1.013 \times 10^5\ \text{Pa}) = 1.42 \times 10^5$ Pa. This value is minuscule compared to the bulk modulus of a typical solid (see Table 11.1), which is approximately 10^{10} to 10^{11} Pa. This shouldn't be surprising: It's simply a statement that air is far easier to compress than steel.

The density ρ of a gas also depends on the pressure, which in turn depends on the temperature. It turns out that the ratio B/ρ for a given type of ideal gas does *not* depend on the pressure at all, only the temperature. From Eq. (16.7), this means that the speed of sound in a gas is fundamentally a function of temperature T:

$$v = \sqrt{\frac{\gamma RT}{M}} \quad \text{(speed of sound in an ideal gas)} \tag{16.10}$$

16.9 This three-dimensional image of a fetus in the womb was made using a sequence of ultrasound scans. Each individual scan reveals a two-dimensional "slice" through the fetus; a large number of these slices were then combined digitally to yield this remarkable view.

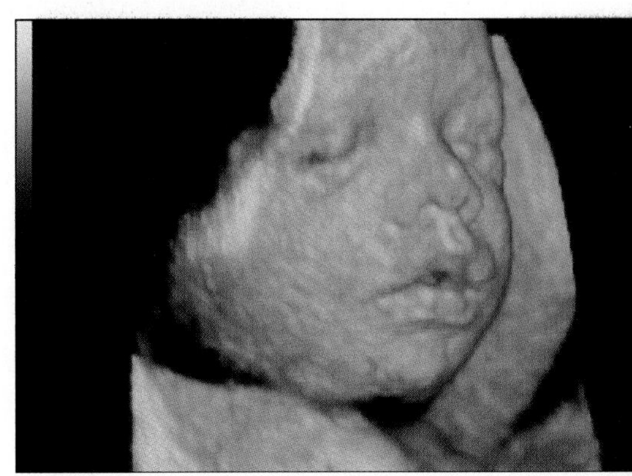

ActivPhysics ONLINE
10.3 Speed of Sound in a Gas

This expression incorporates several quantities that you may recognize from your study of ideal gases in chemistry and which we will study in Chapters 17, 18, and 19. The temperature T is the *absolute* temperature in kelvins (K), equal to the Celsius temperature plus 273.15; thus 20.00°C corresponds to $T = 293.15$ K. The quantity M is the *molar mass,* or mass per mole of the substance of which the gas is composed. The *gas constant* R has the same value for all gases. The current best numerical value of R is

$$R = 8.314472(15)\ \text{J/mol} \cdot \text{K}$$

which for practical calculations we can write as 8.314 J/mol · K.

For any particular gas, γ, R, and M are constants, and the wave speed is proportional to the square root of the absolute temperature. We will see in Chapter 18 that Eq. (16.10) is almost identical to the expression for the average speed of molecules in an ideal gas. This shows that sound speeds and molecular speeds are closely related; exploring that relationship in detail would be beyond our scope.

Example 16.5 Speed of sound in air

Compute the speed of sound waves in air at room temperature ($T = 20°\text{C}$) and find the range of wavelengths in air to which the human ear (which can hear frequencies in the range of 20–20,000 Hz) is sensitive. The mean molar mass for air (a mixture of principally nitrogen and oxygen) is 28.8×10^{-3} kg/mol and the ratio of heat capacities is $\gamma = 1.40$.

SOLUTION

IDENTIFY: This problem uses the relationship between the properties of a gas and the speed of sound in that gas.

SET UP: We use Eq. (16.10) to find the sound speed and the relationship $v = f\lambda$ to determine the wavelength that corresponds to each frequency.

EXECUTE: At $T = 20°\text{C} = 293$ K we find

$$v = \sqrt{\frac{\gamma RT}{M}}$$

$$= \sqrt{\frac{(1.40)(8.314\ \text{J/mol} \cdot \text{K})(293\ \text{K})}{28.8 \times 10^{-3}\ \text{kg/mol}}} = 344\ \text{m/s}$$

Using this value of v and the expression $\lambda = v/f$, we find that at 20°C a 20-Hz note corresponds to a wavelength of 17 m and a 20,000-Hz note corresponds to a wavelength of 1.7 cm.

EVALUATE: Our calculated value of v agrees with the measured speed of sound at this temperature to within 0.3%.

It's interesting to note that bats can hear much higher frequencies. Like dolphins, bats use high-frequency sound waves for navigation. A typical frequency is 100 kHz; the corresponding wavelength in air at 20°C is about 3.4 mm. It turns out that sound waves with such short wavelengths are more easily reflected from small objects than are long-wavelength waves. This is important for certain species of bats that track the reflected sound from the small flying insects that they eat.

In this discussion we have ignored the *molecular* nature of a gas and have treated it as a continuous medium. A gas is actually composed of molecules in random motion, separated by distances that are large in comparison with their diameters. The vibrations that constitute a wave in a gas are superposed on the random thermal motion. At atmospheric pressure, a molecule travels an average distance of about 10^{-7} m between collisions, while the displacement amplitude of a faint sound may be only 10^{-9} m. We can think of a gas with a sound wave passing through as being comparable to a swarm of bees; the swarm as a whole oscillates slightly while individual insects move about through the swarm, apparently at random.

Test Your Understanding of Section 16.2 Mercury is 13.6 times denser than water. Based on Table 16.1, at 20°C which of these liquids has the greater bulk modulus? (i) mercury; (ii) water; (iii) both are about the same; (iv) not enough information is given to decide.

16.3 Sound Intensity

Traveling sound waves, like all other traveling waves, transfer energy from one region of space to another. We saw in Section 15.5 that a useful way to describe the energy carried by a sound wave is through the *wave intensity* I, equal to the time average rate at which energy is transported per unit area across a surface perpendicular to the direction of propagation. Let's see how to express the intensity of a sound wave in terms of the displacement amplitude A or pressure amplitude p_{max}.

Intensity and Displacement Amplitude

For simplicity, let us consider a sound wave propagating in the $+x$-direction so that we can use our expressions from Section 16.1 for the displacement $y(x, t)$ and pressure fluctuation $p(x, t)$—Eqs. (16.1) and (16.4), respectively. In Section 6.4 we saw that power equals the product of force and velocity [see Eq. (6.18)]. So the power per unit area in this sound wave equals the product of $p(x, t)$ (force per unit area) and the *particle* velocity $v_y(x, t)$. The particle velocity $v_y(x, t)$ is the velocity at time t of that portion of the wave medium at coordinate x. Using Eqs. (16.1) and (16.4), we find

$$
\begin{aligned}
v_y(x, t) &= \frac{\partial y(x, t)}{\partial t} = \omega A \sin(kx - \omega t) \\
p(x, t) v_y(x, t) &= [BkA \sin(kx - \omega t)][\omega A \sin(kx - \omega t)] \\
&= B\omega k A^2 \sin^2(kx - \omega t)
\end{aligned}
$$

CAUTION Wave velocity vs. particle velocity Remember that the velocity of the wave as a whole is *not* the same as the particle velocity. While the wave continues to move in the direction of propagation, individual particles in the wave medium merely slosh back and forth, as shown in Fig. (16.1). Furthermore, the maximum speed of a particle of the medium can be very different from the wave speed.

The intensity is, by definition, the time average value of $p(x, t) v_y(x, t)$. For any value of x the average value of the function $\sin^2(kx - \omega t)$ over one period $T = 2\pi/\omega$ is $\frac{1}{2}$, so

$$I = \frac{1}{2} B\omega k A^2 \tag{16.11}$$

By using the relationships $\omega = vk$ and $v^2 = B/\rho$, we can transform Eq. (16.11) into the form

$$I = \frac{1}{2}\sqrt{\rho B}\,\omega^2 A^2 \quad \text{(intensity of a sinusoidal sound wave)} \tag{16.12}$$

This equation shows why in a stereo system, a low-frequency woofer has to vibrate with much larger amplitude than a high-frequency tweeter to produce the same sound intensity.

Intensity and Pressure Amplitude

It is usually more useful to express I in terms of the pressure amplitude p_{max}. Using Eq. (16.5) and the relationship $\omega = vk$, we find

$$I = \frac{\omega p_{max}^2}{2Bk} = \frac{v p_{max}^2}{2B} \tag{16.13}$$

By using the wave speed relationship $v^2 = B/\rho$, we can also write Eq. (16.13) in the alternative forms

$$I = \frac{p_{max}^2}{2\rho v} = \frac{p_{max}^2}{2\sqrt{\rho B}} \quad \text{(intensity of a sinusoidal sound wave)} \tag{16.14}$$

16.10 By cupping your hands like this, you direct the sound waves emerging from your mouth so that they don't propagate to the sides. Hence the intensity decreases with distance more slowly than the inverse-square law would predict, and you can be heard at greater distances.

You should verify these expressions (see Exercise 16.16). Comparison of Eqs. (16.12) and (16.14) shows that sinusoidal sound waves of the same intensity but different frequency have different displacement amplitudes A but the *same* pressure amplitude p_{max}. This is another reason it is usually more convenient to describe a sound wave in terms of pressure fluctuations, not displacement.

The *total* average power carried across a surface by a sound wave equals the product of the intensity at the surface and the surface area if the intensity over the surface is uniform. The average total sound power emitted by a person speaking in an ordinary conversational tone is about 10^{-5} W, while a loud shout corresponds to about 3×10^{-2} W. If all the residents of New York City were to talk at the same time, the total sound power would be about 100 W, equivalent to the electric power requirement of a medium-sized light bulb. On the other hand, the power required to fill a large auditorium or stadium with loud sound is considerable (see Example 16.8.)

If the sound source emits waves in all directions equally, the intensity decreases with increasing distance r from the source according to the inverse-square law: The intensity is proportional to $1/r^2$. We discussed this law and its consequences in Section 15.5. If the sound goes predominantly in one direction, the inverse-square law does not apply and the intensity decreases with distance more slowly than $1/r^2$ (Fig. 16.10).

The inverse-square relationship also does not apply indoors because sound energy can reach a listener by reflection from the walls and ceiling. Indeed, part of the architect's job in designing an auditorium is to tailor these reflections so that the intensity is as nearly uniform as possible over the entire auditorium.

Problem-Solving Strategy 16.1 Sound Intensity

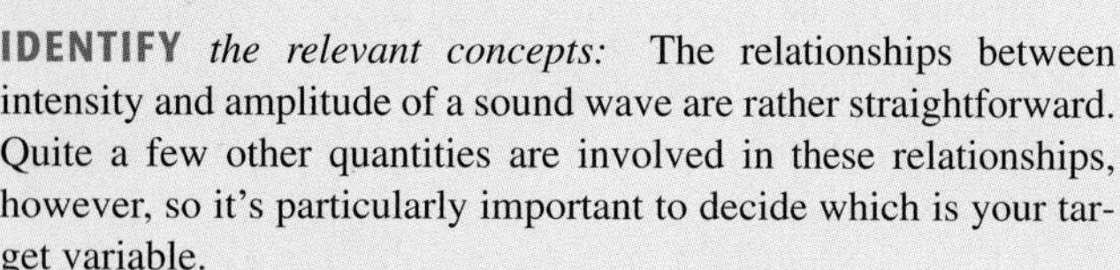

IDENTIFY *the relevant concepts:* The relationships between intensity and amplitude of a sound wave are rather straightforward. Quite a few other quantities are involved in these relationships, however, so it's particularly important to decide which is your target variable.

SET UP *the problem* using the following steps:

1. Sort the various physical quantities into categories. The amplitude is described by A or p_{max}, and the frequency f can be determined from ω, k, or λ. These quantities are related through the wave speed v, which in turn is determined by the properties of the medium: B and ρ for a liquid; γ, T, and M for a gas.
2. Determine which quantities are given and which are the unknown target variables. Then start looking for relationships that take you where you want to go.

EXECUTE *the solution* as follows: Use the equations you've selected to solve for the target variables. Be certain that all of the quantities are expressed in the correct units. In particular, if temperature is used to calculate the speed of sound in a gas, make sure that it is expressed in kelvins (Celsius temperature plus 273.15).

EVALUATE *your answer:* There are multiple relationships among the quantities that describe a wave. Try using an alternative one to check your results.

Example 16.6 Intensity of a sound wave in air

Find the intensity of the sound wave in Example 16.1, with $p_{max} = 3.0 \times 10^{-2}$ Pa. Assume the temperature is 20°C so that the density of air is $\rho = 1.20\ \text{kg/m}^3$ and the speed of sound is $v = 344$ m/s.

SOLUTION

IDENTIFY: Our target variable is the intensity I of the sound wave. We are given the pressure amplitude p_{max} of the wave as well as the density ρ and wave speed v for the medium.

SET UP: We can determine I from p_{max}, ρ, and v using Eq. (16.14).

EXECUTE: From Eq. (16.14),

$$I = \frac{{p_{max}}^2}{2\rho v} = \frac{(3.0 \times 10^{-2}\ \text{Pa})^2}{2(1.20\ \text{kg/m}^3)(344\ \text{m/s})}$$
$$= 1.1 \times 10^{-6}\ \text{J/(s} \cdot \text{m}^2) = 1.1 \times 10^{-6}\ \text{W/m}^2$$

EVALUATE: This seems like a very low intensity, but in fact it is well within the range of sound intensities encountered on a daily basis. A very loud sound wave at the threshold of pain has a pressure amplitude of about 30 Pa and an intensity of about 1 W/m^2. The pressure amplitude of the faintest sound wave that can be heard is about 3×10^{-5} Pa, and the corresponding intensity is about 10^{-12} W/m^2. (Try these values of p_{max} in Eq. (16.14) to check that the corresponding intensities are as we have stated.)

Example 16.7 Same intensity, different frequencies

A 20-Hz sound wave has the same intensity as the 1000-Hz sound wave in Examples 16.1 and 16.6. What are the displacement amplitude and pressure amplitude of the 20-Hz sound wave?

SOLUTION

IDENTIFY: We are given the intensity and frequency of the sound wave. Our target variables are the displacement amplitude A and pressure amplitude p_{max}.

SET UP: Given the intensity, we can use Eq. (16.12) to determine the displacement amplitude A. Note that we are not given the value of B. However, ρ and B depend on only the properties of the medium, not the amplitude or frequency, so their values will cancel out if we equate the intensities at 20 Hz and at 1000 Hz. We can also use Eq. (16.14) to find the pressure amplitude at 20 Hz.

EXECUTE: Inspection of Eq. (16.12) shows that if a wave in a given medium (same ρ and B) has the same intensity I at two different frequencies, then the product ωA must have the same value for both frequencies. From Example 16.1, $A = 1.2 \times 10^{-8}$ m at 1000 Hz, so

$$(20 \text{ Hz})A_{20} = (1000 \text{ Hz})(1.2 \times 10^{-8} \text{ m})$$
$$A_{20} = 6.0 \times 10^{-7} \text{ m} = 0.60\ \mu\text{m}$$

Do you understand why we didn't have to convert the frequencies to angular frequencies?

Since the intensity is the same for both frequencies, Eq. (16.14) shows that the *pressure* amplitude p_{max} must also be the same for both. Hence $p_{max} = 3.0 \times 10^{-2}$ Pa for $f = 20$ Hz.

EVALUATE: Our result reinforces the idea that pressure amplitude offers a more convenient description of a sound wave than displacement amplitude. Note also that using Eq. (16.5) and $k = \omega/v$, we get $p_{max} = BkA = (B/v)\omega A$; the bulk modulus B and wave speed v depend on only the medium, so we again conclude that the product ωA must have the same value for both frequencies.

Example 16.8 "Play it loud!"

For an outdoor concert we want the sound intensity at a distance of 20 m from the speaker array to be 1 W/m^2. Assuming that the sound waves have the same intensity in all directions, what acoustic power output is needed from the speaker array?

SOLUTION

IDENTIFY: This example uses the definition of intensity as power per unit area. Here the total power is the target variable, and the area in question is a hemisphere centered on the speaker array.

SET UP: We make the assumptions that the speakers are near ground level and that the acoustic power is spread uniformly over a hemisphere 20 m in radius (that is, we assume that none of the acoustic power is directed into the ground). The surface area of this hemisphere is equal to $(\frac{1}{2})(4\pi)(20 \text{ m})^2$, or about 2500 m^2. The required power is the product of this area and the intensity.

EXECUTE: The speaker array power is

$$(1 \text{ W/m}^2)(2500 \text{ m}^2) = 2500 \text{ W} = 2.5 \text{ kW}$$

EVALUATE: The electrical power input to the speaker would need to be considerably larger because the efficiency of such devices is not very high (typically a few percent for ordinary speakers, and up to 25% for horn-type speakers).

The Decibel Scale

Because the ear is sensitive over a broad range of intensities, a *logarithmic* intensity scale is usually used. The **sound intensity level** β of a sound wave is defined by the equation

$$\beta = (10 \text{ dB}) \log \frac{I}{I_0} \quad \text{(definition of sound intensity level)} \quad (16.15)$$

In this equation, I_0 is a reference intensity, chosen to be 10^{-12} W/m^2, approximately the threshold of human hearing at 1000 Hz. Recall that "log" means the logarithm to base 10. Sound intensity levels are expressed in **decibels,** abbreviated dB. A decibel is $\frac{1}{10}$ of a *bel,* a unit named for Alexander Graham Bell (the inventor of the telephone). The bel is inconveniently large for most purposes, and the decibel is the usual unit of sound intensity level.

If the intensity of a sound wave equals I_0 or 10^{-12} W/m^2, its sound intensity level is 0 dB. An intensity of 1 W/m^2 corresponds to 120 dB. Table 16.2 gives the sound intensity levels in decibels of several familiar sounds. You can use Eq. (16.15) to check the value of sound intensity level β given for each intensity in the table.

Table 16.2 Sound Intensity Levels from Various Sources (Representative Values)

Source or Description of Sound	Sound Intensity Level, β (dB)	Intensity, I (W/m^2)
Military jet aircraft 30 m away	140	10^2
Threshold of pain	120	1
Riveter	95	3.2×10^{-3}
Elevated train	90	10^{-3}
Busy street traffic	70	10^{-5}
Ordinary conversation	65	3.2×10^{-6}
Quiet automobile	50	10^{-7}
Quiet radio in home	40	10^{-8}
Average whisper	20	10^{-10}
Rustle of leaves	10	10^{-11}
Threshold of hearing at 1000 Hz	0	10^{-12}

Because the ear is not equally sensitive to all frequencies in the audible range, some sound-level meters weight the various frequencies unequally. One such scheme leads to the so-called dBA scale; this scale deemphasizes the low and very high frequencies, where the ear is less sensitive than at midrange frequencies.

Example 16.9 Temporary deafness

A 10-minute exposure to 120-dB sound will typically shift your threshold of hearing at 1000 Hz from 0 dB up to 28 dB for a while. Ten years of exposure to 92-dB sound will cause a *permanent* shift up to 28 dB. What intensities correspond to 28 dB and 92 dB?

SOLUTION

IDENTIFY: We are given two different sound intensity levels in dB, and we want to find the corresponding intensities in W/m^2.

SET UP: We can solve Eq. (16.15) to find the intensity I that corresponds to each value of the sound intensity level β.

EXECUTE: We rearrange Eq. (16.15) by dividing both sides by 10 dB and then using the relationship $10^{\log x} = x$:

$$I = I_0 10^{\beta/(10\text{ dB})}$$

When $\beta = 28$ dB,

$$I = (10^{-12}\text{ W/m}^2)10^{(28\text{ dB}/10\text{ dB})}$$
$$= (10^{-12}\text{ W/m}^2)10^{2.8} = 6.3 \times 10^{-10}\text{ W/m}^2$$

Similarly, for $\beta = 92$ dB,

$$I = (10^{-12}\text{ W/m}^2)10^{(92\text{ dB}/10\text{ dB})} = 1.6 \times 10^{-3}\text{ W/m}^2$$

EVALUATE: If your answers are a factor of 10 too large, you may have entered 10×10^{-12} in your calculator instead of 1×10^{-12}. Be careful!

Example 16.10 A bird sings in a meadow

Consider an idealized model with a bird (treated as a point source) emitting constant sound power, with intensity inversely proportional to the square of the distance from the bird. By how many decibels does the sound intensity level drop when you move twice as far away from the bird?

SOLUTION

IDENTIFY: Because the decibel scale is logarithmic, the *difference* between two sound intensity levels (the target variable) corresponds to the *ratio* of the corresponding intensities. The ratio of the intensities comes from the inverse-square law.

SET UP: We label the two points P_1 and P_2 (Fig. 16.11). We use Eq. (16.15), the definition of sound intensity level, twice (once at each point). We use Eq. (15.26), the statement of the inverse-square law, to relate the intensities at the two points.

16.11 When you double your distance from a point source of sound, by how much does the sound intensity level decrease?

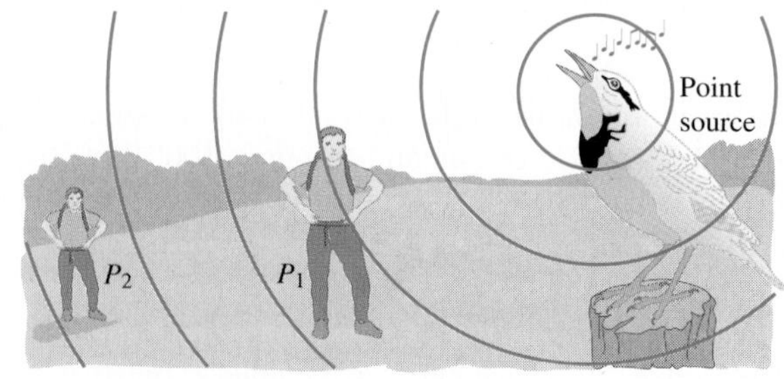

EXECUTE: The difference in sound intensity level, $\beta_2 - \beta_1$, is given by

$$\beta_2 - \beta_1 = (10\text{ dB})\left(\log\frac{I_2}{I_0} - \log\frac{I_1}{I_0}\right)$$
$$= (10\text{ dB})[(\log I_2 - \log I_0) - (\log I_1 - \log I_0)]$$
$$= (10\text{ dB})\log\frac{I_2}{I_1}$$

Now we use the reciprocal of Eq. (15.26); $I_2/I_1 = r_1^2/r_2^2$, so

$$\beta_2 - \beta_1 = (10\text{ dB})\log\frac{r_1^2}{r_2^2} = (10\text{ dB})\log\frac{r_1^2}{(2r_1)^2}$$
$$= (10\text{ dB})\log\frac{1}{4} = -6.0\text{ dB}$$

A decrease in intensity of a factor of 4 corresponds to a 6-dB decrease in sound intensity level.

EVALUATE: Our result is negative, which tells us (correctly) that the sound intensity level is less at P_2 than at P_1. The 6-dB difference doesn't depend on the value of the sound intensity level at P_1. If P_1 is relatively close to the bird so that $\beta_1 = 56$ dB, then at a point P_2 twice as far away, $\beta_2 = 50$ dB; if point P_1 is more distant from the bird so that $\beta_1 = 28$ dB, then at a point P_2 twice as far away, $\beta_2 = 22$ dB.

It's interesting to note that the perceived *loudness* of a sound is not directly proportional to its intensity. As an example, most people usually interpret an increase of 8 to 10 dB in sound intensity level (corresponding to an intensity that increases by a factor of 6 to 10) as a doubling of loudness.

Test Your Understanding of Section 16.3 You double the intensity of a sound wave in air while leaving the frequency unchanged. (The pressure, density, and temperature of the air remain unchanged as well.) What effect does this have on the displacement amplitude, pressure amplitude, bulk modulus, sound speed, and sound intensity level?

16.4 Standing Sound Waves and Normal Modes

When longitudinal (sound) waves propagate in a fluid in a pipe with finite length, the waves are reflected from the ends in the same way that transverse waves on a string are reflected at its ends. The superposition of the waves traveling in opposite directions again forms a standing wave. Just as for transverse standing waves on a string (see Section 15.7), standing sound waves (normal modes) in a pipe can be used to create sound waves in the surrounding air. This is the operating principle of the human voice as well as many musical instruments, including woodwinds, brasses, and pipe organs.

Transverse waves on a string, including standing waves, are usually described only in terms of the displacement of the string. But, as we have seen, sound waves in a fluid may be described either in terms of the displacement of the fluid or in terms of the pressure variation in the fluid. To avoid confusion, we'll use the terms **displacement node** and **displacement antinode** to refer to points where particles of the fluid have zero displacement and maximum displacement, respectively.

We can demonstrate standing sound waves in a column of gas using an apparatus called Kundt's tube (Fig. 16.12). A horizontal glass tube a meter or so long

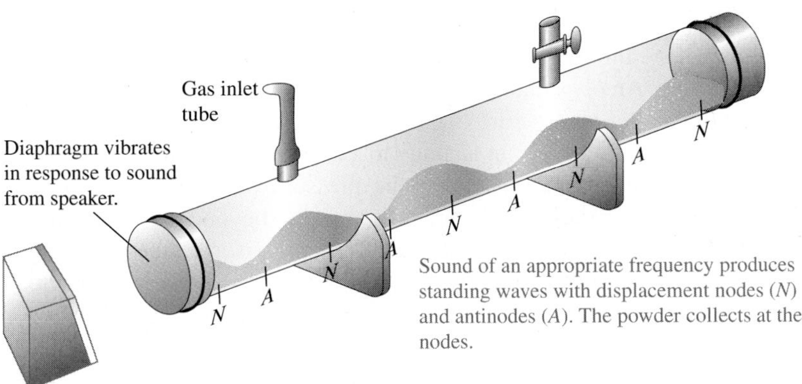
Gas inlet tube
Diaphragm vibrates in response to sound from speaker.
Speaker
N
A
N
A
N
A
N
A
N
Sound of an appropriate frequency produces standing waves with displacement nodes (N) and antinodes (A). The powder collects at the nodes.

16.12 Demonstrating standing sound waves using a Kundt's tube. The blue shading represents the density of the gas at an instant when the gas pressure at the displacement nodes is a maximum or a minimum.

16.13 In a standing sound wave, a displacement node N is a pressure antinode (a point where the pressure fluctuates the most) and a displacement antinode A is a pressure node (a point where the pressure does not fluctuate at all).

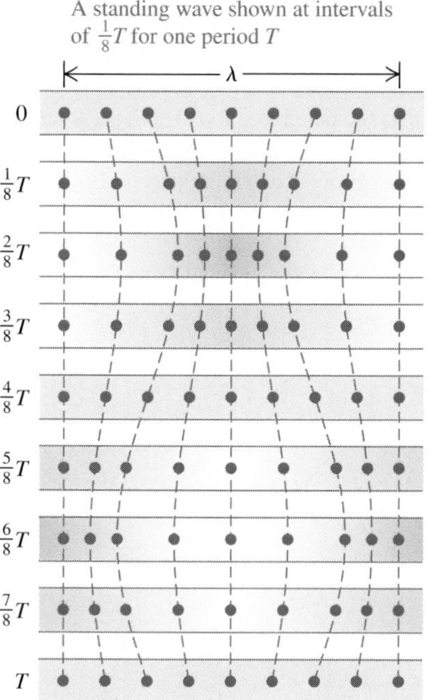

is closed at one end and has a flexible diaphragm at the other end that can transmit vibrations. A nearby loudspeaker is driven by an audio oscillator and amplifier; this produces sound waves that force the diaphragm to vibrate sinusoidally with a frequency that we can vary. The sound waves within the tube are reflected at the other, closed end of the tube. We spread a small amount of light powder uniformly along the bottom of the tube. As we vary the frequency of the sound, we pass through frequencies at which the amplitude of the standing waves becomes large enough for the powder to be swept along the tube at those points where the gas is in motion. The powder therefore collects at the displacement nodes (where the gas is not moving). Adjacent nodes are separated by a distance equal to $\lambda/2$, and we can measure this distance. Given the wavelength, we can use this experiment to determine the wave speed: We read the frequency f from the oscillator dial, and we can then calculate the speed v of the waves from the relationship $v = \lambda f$.

Figure 16.13 shows the motions of nine different particles within a gas-filled tube in which there is a standing sound wave. A particle at a displacement node (N) does not move, while a particle at a displacement antinode (A) oscillates with maximum amplitude. Note that particles on opposite sides of a displacement node vibrate in opposite phase. When these particles approach each other, the gas between them is compressed and the pressure rises; when they recede from each other, there is an expansion and the pressure drops. Hence at a displacement *node* the gas undergoes the maximum amount of compression and expansion, and the variations in pressure and density above and below the average have their maximum value. By contrast, particles on opposite sides of a displacement *antinode* vibrate *in phase;* the distance between the particles is nearly constant, and there is *no* variation in pressure or density at a displacement antinode.

We use the term **pressure node** to describe a point in a standing sound wave at which the pressure and density do not vary and the term **pressure antinode** to describe a point at which the variations in pressure and density are greatest. Using these terms, we can summarize our observations about standing sound waves as follows:

A pressure node is always a displacement antinode, and a pressure antinode is always a displacement node.

Figure 16.12 depicts a standing sound wave at an instant at which the pressure variations are greatest; the blue shading shows that the density and pressure of the gas have their maximum and minimum values at the displacement nodes (labeled N).

When reflection takes place at a *closed* end of a pipe (an end with a rigid barrier or plug), the displacement of the particles at this end must always be zero, analogous to a fixed end of a string. Thus a closed end of a pipe is a displacement node and a pressure antinode; the particles do not move, but the pressure variations are maximum. An *open* end of a pipe is a pressure node because it is open to the atmosphere, where the pressure is constant. Because of this, an open end is always a displacement *antinode,* in analogy to a free end of a string; the particles oscillate with maximum amplitude, but the pressure does not vary. (Strictly speaking, the pressure node actually occurs somewhat beyond an open end of a pipe. But if the diameter of the pipe is small in comparison to the wavelength, which is true for most musical instruments, this effect can safely be neglected.) Thus longitudinal waves in a column of fluid are reflected at the closed and open ends of a pipe in the same way that transverse waves in a string are reflected at fixed and free ends, respectively.

Conceptual Example 16.11 The sound of silence

A directional loudspeaker aims a sound wave of wavelength λ at a wall (Fig. 16.14). At what distances from the wall could you stand and hear no sound at all?

SOLUTION

Your ear detects pressure variations in the air; increases or decreases in the pressure outside your eardrum cause it to move slightly in or out, a motion that generates an electrical signal that is sent to the brain. (If you've ever had trouble getting your ears to "pop" on a drive up into the mountains or on an airline flight, you're familiar with just how sensitive your ears are to pressure changes.) Hence you will hear no sound if your ear is at a pressure node, which is a displacement antinode. The wall is a displacement node; the distance from a node to an adjacent antinode is $\lambda/4$, and the distance from one antinode to the next is $\lambda/2$ (Fig. 16.14). Hence the distances d from the wall at which no sound will be heard are

$$d = \lambda/4$$
(first displacement antinode and pressure node)

$$d = \lambda/4 + \lambda/2 = 3\lambda/4$$
(second displacement antinode and pressure node)

$$d = 3\lambda/4 + \lambda/2 = 5\lambda/4$$
(third displacement antinode and pressure node)

and so on. If the loudspeaker is not highly directional, this effect is hard to notice because of multiple reflections of sound waves from the floor, ceiling, and other points on the walls.

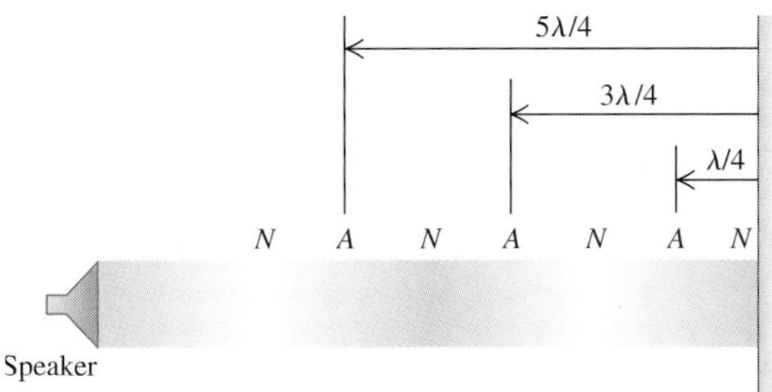

16.14 When a sound wave is directed at a wall, it interferes with the reflected wave to create a standing wave. The N's and A's are *displacement* nodes and antinodes.

Organ Pipes and Wind Instruments

The most important application of standing sound waves is the production of musical tones by wind instruments. Organ pipes are one of the simplest examples (Fig. 16.15). Air is supplied by a blower, at a gauge pressure typically of the order of 10^3 Pa $(10^{-2}$ atm$)$, to the bottom end of the pipe (Fig. 16.16). A stream of air emerges from the narrow opening at the edge of the horizontal surface and is directed against the top edge of the opening, which is called the *mouth* of the pipe. The column of air in the pipe is set into vibration, and there is a series of possible normal modes, just as with the stretched string. The mouth always acts as an open end; thus it is a pressure node and a displacement antinode. The other end of the pipe (at the top in Fig. 16.16) may be either open or closed.

16.15 Organ pipes of different sizes produce tones with different frequencies.

In Fig. 16.17, both ends of the pipe are open, so both ends are pressure nodes and displacement antinodes. An organ pipe that is open at both ends is called an *open pipe*. The fundamental frequency f_1 corresponds to a standing-wave pattern with a displacement antinode at each end and a displacement node in the middle (Fig. 16.17a). The distance between adjacent antinodes is always equal to one half-wavelength, and in this case that is equal to the length L of the pipe; $\lambda/2 = L$. The corresponding frequency, obtained from the relationship $f = v/\lambda$, is

$$f_1 = \frac{v}{2L} \quad \text{(open pipe)} \tag{16.16}$$

Figures 16.17b and 16.17c show the second and third harmonics (first and second overtones); their vibration patterns have two and three displacement nodes, respectively. For these, a half-wavelength is equal to $L/2$ and $L/3$, respectively, and the frequencies are twice and three times the fundamental, respectively. That is, $f_2 = 2f_1$ and $f_3 = 3f_1$. For *every* normal mode of an open pipe the length L must be an integer number of half-wavelengths, and the possible wavelengths λ_n are given by

$$L = n\frac{\lambda_n}{2} \quad \text{or} \quad \lambda_n = \frac{2L}{n} \quad (n = 1, 2, 3, \ldots) \quad \text{(open pipe)} \tag{16.17}$$

16.16 Cross sections of an organ pipe at two instants one half-period apart. The N's and A's are *displacement* nodes and antinodes; as the blue shading shows, these are points of maximum pressure variation and zero pressure variation, respectively.

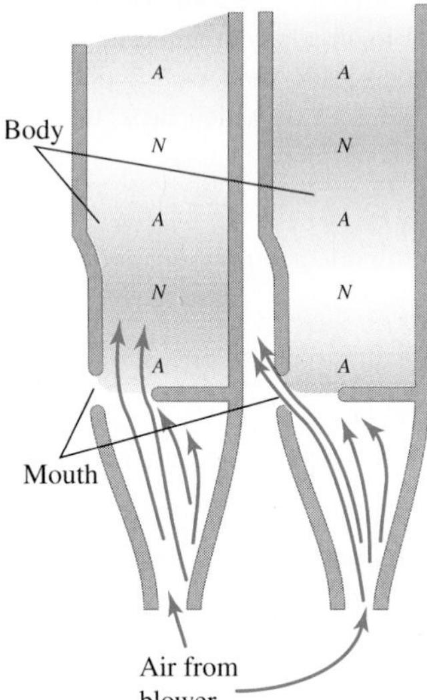

The corresponding frequencies f_n are given by $f_n = v/\lambda_n$, so all the normal-mode frequencies for a pipe that is open at both ends are given by

$$f_n = \frac{nv}{2L} \qquad (n = 1, 2, 3, \ldots) \qquad \text{(open pipe)} \tag{16.18}$$

The value $n = 1$ corresponds to the fundamental frequency, $n = 2$ to the second harmonic (or first overtone), and so on. Alternatively, we can say

$$f_n = nf_1 \qquad (n = 1, 2, 3, \ldots) \qquad \text{(open pipe)} \tag{16.19}$$

with f_1 given by Eq. (16.16).

Figure 16.18 shows a pipe that is open at the left end but closed at the right end. This is called a *stopped pipe*. The left (open) end is a displacement antinode

16.17 A cross section of an open pipe showing the first three normal modes. The shading indicates the pressure variations. The red curves are graphs of the displacement along the pipe axis at two instants separated in time by one half-period. The N's and A's are the *displacement* nodes and antinodes; interchange these to show the *pressure* nodes and antinodes.

(a)
Fundamental: $f_1 = \dfrac{v}{2L}$

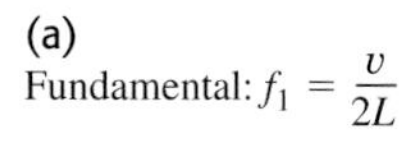

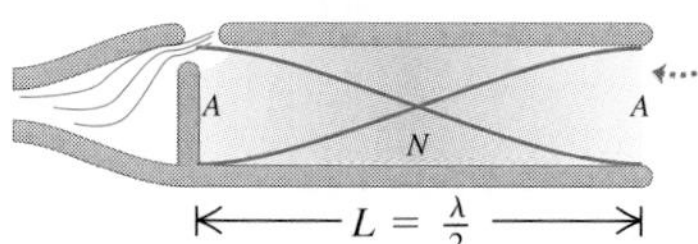

(b)
Second harmonic: $f_2 = 2\dfrac{v}{2L} = 2f_1$

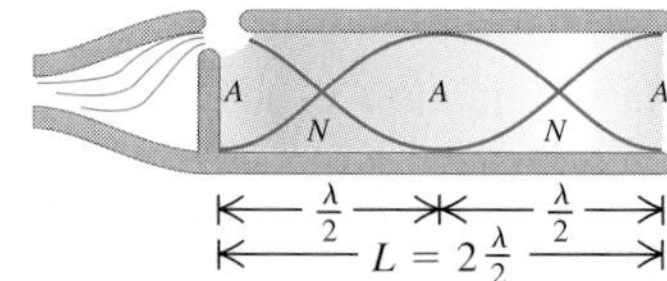

(c)
Third harmonic: $f_3 = 3\dfrac{v}{2L} = 3f_1$

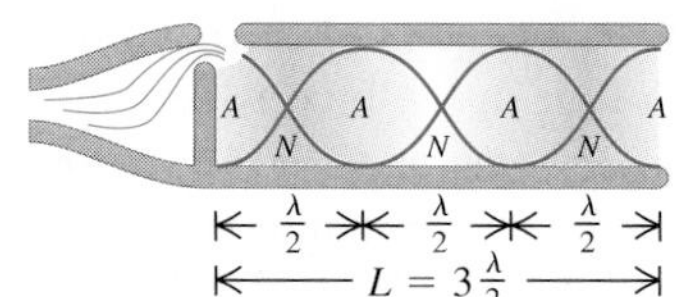

16.18 A cross section of a stopped pipe showing the first three normal modes as well as the *displacement* nodes and antinodes. Only odd harmonics are possible.

(a)
Fundamental: $f_1 = \dfrac{v}{4L}$

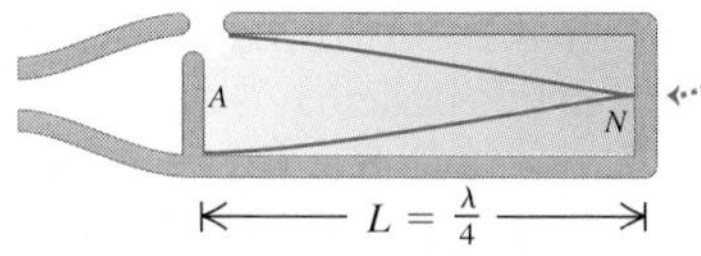

(b)
Third harmonic: $f_3 = 3\dfrac{v}{4L} = 3f_1$

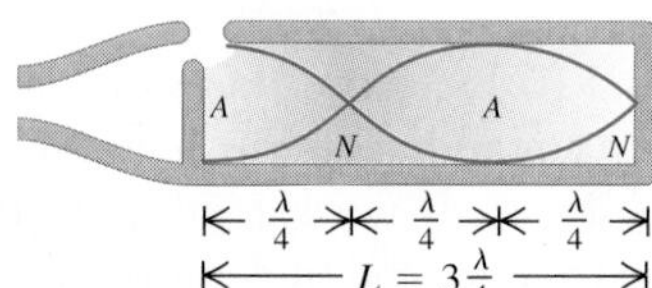

(c)
Fifth harmonic: $f_5 = 5\dfrac{v}{4L} = 5f_1$

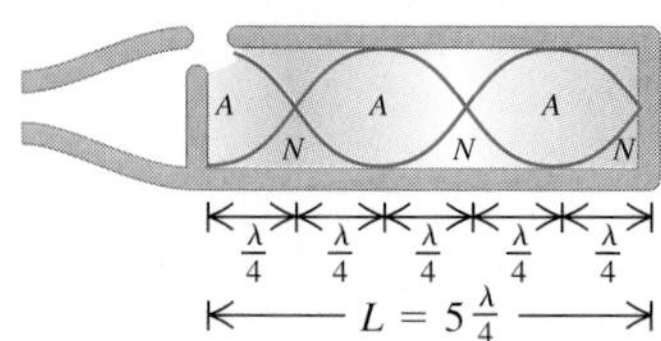

(pressure node), but the right (closed) end is a displacement node (pressure antinode). The distance between a node and the adjacent antinode is always one quarter-wavelength. Figure 16.18a shows the lowest-frequency mode; the length of the pipe is a quarter-wavelength $(L = \lambda_1/4)$. The fundamental frequency is $f_1 = v/\lambda_1$, or

$$f_1 = \frac{v}{4L} \quad \text{(stopped pipe)} \tag{16.20}$$

This is one-half the fundamental frequency for an *open* pipe of the same length. In musical language, the *pitch* of a closed pipe is one octave lower (a factor of 2 in frequency) than that of an open pipe of the same length. Figure 16.18b shows the next mode, for which the length of the pipe is *three-quarters* of a wavelength, corresponding to a frequency $3f_1$. For Fig. 16.18c, $L = 5\lambda/4$ and the frequency is $5f_1$. The possible wavelengths are given by

$$L = n\frac{\lambda_n}{4} \quad \text{or} \quad \lambda_n = \frac{4L}{n} \quad (n = 1, 3, 5, \dots) \quad \text{(stopped pipe)} \tag{16.21}$$

The normal-mode frequencies are given by $f_n = v/\lambda_n$, or

$$f_n = \frac{nv}{4L} \quad (n = 1, 3, 5, \dots) \quad \text{(stopped pipe)} \tag{16.22}$$

or

$$f_n = nf_1 \quad (n = 1, 3, 5, \dots) \quad \text{(stopped pipe)} \tag{16.23}$$

with f_1 given by Eq. (16.20). We see that the second, fourth, and all *even* harmonics are missing. In a pipe that is closed at one end, the fundamental frequency is $f_1 = v/4L$, and only the odd harmonics in the series $(3f_1, 5f_1, \dots)$ are possible.

A final possibility is a pipe that is closed at *both* ends, with displacement nodes and pressure antinodes at both ends. This wouldn't be of much use as a musical instrument because there would be no way for the vibrations to get out of the pipe.

Example 16.12 A tale of two pipes

On a day when the speed of sound is 345 m/s, the fundamental frequency of a stopped organ pipe is 220 Hz. (a) How long is this stopped pipe? (b) The second *overtone* of this pipe has the same wavelength as the third *harmonic* of an open pipe. How long is the open pipe?

SOLUTION

IDENTIFY: This problem uses the relationship between the length and normal-mode frequencies of an open pipe (Fig. 16.17) and a stopped pipe (Fig. 16.18).

SET UP: Since this is a stopped pipe (open at one end and closed at the other), the normal-mode frequencies are given by Eq. (16.22). We use this to determine the length L from the frequency in part (a). In part (b), we must make a comparison to an open pipe, for which the frequencies are given by Eq. (16.18).

EXECUTE: (a) For a stopped pipe, $f_1 = v/4L$, so the length of the stopped pipe is

$$L_{\text{stopped}} = \frac{v}{4f_1} = \frac{345\ \text{m/s}}{4(220\ \text{s}^{-1})} = 0.392\ \text{m}$$

(b) The frequency of the first overtone of a stopped pipe is $f_3 = 3f_1$, and the frequency of the second overtone is $f_5 = 5f_1$:

$$f_5 = 5f_1 = 5(220\ \text{Hz}) = 1100\ \text{Hz}$$

If the wavelengths are the same, the frequencies are the same, so the frequency of the third harmonic of the open pipe is also 1100 Hz. The third harmonic of an open pipe is at $3f_1 = 3(v/2L)$. If this equals 1100 Hz, then

$$1100\ \text{Hz} = 3\left(\frac{345\ \text{m/s}}{2L_{\text{open}}}\right) \quad \text{and} \quad L_{\text{open}} = 0.470\ \text{m}$$

EVALUATE: The stopped pipe is 0.392 m long and has a fundamental frequency of 220 Hz; the open pipe is longer, 0.470 m, but has a higher fundamental frequency of $(1100\ \text{Hz})/3 = 367$ Hz. If this seems like a contradiction, you should again compare Figs. 16.17a and 16.18a.

In an organ pipe in actual use, several modes are always present at once; the motion of the air is a superposition of these modes. This situation is analogous to a string that is struck or plucked, as in Fig. 15.28. Just as for a vibrating string, a complex standing wave in the pipe produces a traveling sound wave in the surrounding air with a harmonic content similar to that of the standing wave. A very narrow pipe produces a sound wave rich in higher harmonics, which we hear as a thin and "stringy" tone; a fatter pipe produces mostly the fundamental mode, heard as a softer, more flutelike tone. The harmonic content also depends on the shape of the pipe's mouth.

We have talked about organ pipes, but this discussion is also applicable to other wind instruments. The flute and the recorder are directly analogous. The most significant difference is that those instruments have holes along the pipe. Opening and closing the holes with the fingers changes the effective length L of the air column and thus changes the pitch. Any individual organ pipe, by comparison, can play only a single note. The flute and recorder behave as *open* pipes, while the clarinet acts as a *stopped* pipe (closed at the reed end, open at the bell).

Equations (16.18) and (16.22) show that the frequencies of any wind instrument are proportional to the speed of sound v in the air column inside the instrument. As Eq. (16.10) shows, v depends on temperature; it increases when temperature increases. Thus the pitch of all wind instruments rises with increasing temperature. An organ that has some of its pipes at one temperature and others at a different temperature is bound to sound out of tune.

Test Your Understanding of Section 16.4 If you connect a hose to one end of a metal pipe and blow compressed air into it, the pipe produces a musical tone. If instead you blow compressed helium into the pipe at the same pressure and temperature, will the pipe produce (i) the same tone, (ii) a higher-pitch tone, or (iii) a lower-pitch tone?

16.19 (a) The air in an open pipe is forced to oscillate at the same frequency as the sinusoidal sound waves coming from the loudspeaker. (b) The resonance curve of the open pipe graphs the amplitude of the standing sound wave in the pipe as a function of the driving frequency.

(a)

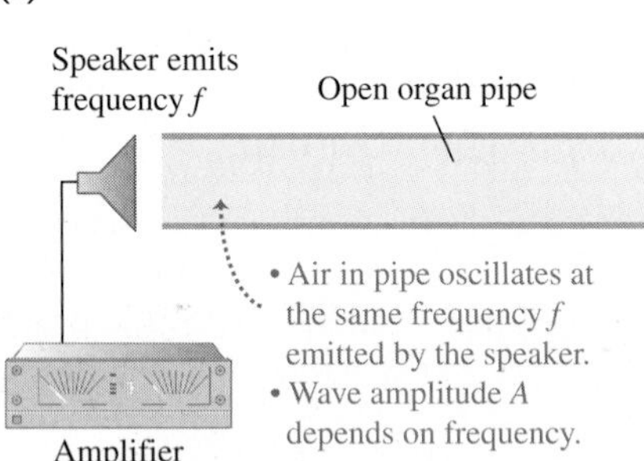
Speaker emits frequency f
Open organ pipe
• Air in pipe oscillates at the same frequency f emitted by the speaker.
• Wave amplitude A depends on frequency.
Amplifier

(b) Resonance curve: graph of amplitude A versus driving frequency f. Peaks occur at normal-mode frequencies of the pipe: $f_1, f_2 = 2f_1, f_3 = 3f_1, \ldots$

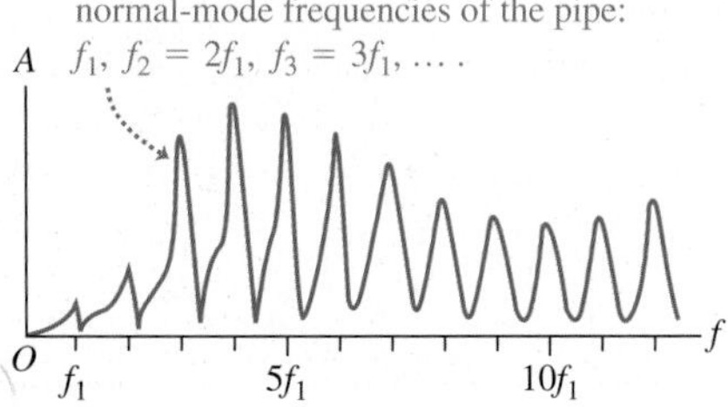
A
O
f
f_1
$5f_1$
$10f_1$

16.5 Resonance and Sound

Many mechanical systems have normal modes of oscillation. As we have seen, these include columns of air (as in an organ pipe) and stretched strings (as in a guitar; see Section 15.8). In each mode, every particle of the system oscillates with simple harmonic motion at the same frequency as the mode. Air columns and stretched strings have an infinite series of normal modes, but the basic concept is closely related to the simple harmonic oscillator, discussed in Chapter 13, which has only a single normal mode (that is, only one frequency at which it oscillates after being disturbed).

Suppose we apply a periodically varying force to a system that can oscillate. The system is then forced to oscillate with a frequency equal to the frequency of the applied force (called the *driving frequency*). This motion is called a *forced oscillation.* We talked about forced oscillations of the harmonic oscillator in Section 13.8, and we suggest that you review that discussion. In particular, we described the phenomenon of mechanical **resonance.** A simple example of resonance is pushing Cousin Throckmorton on a swing. The swing is a pendulum; it has only a single normal mode, with a frequency determined by its length. If we push the swing periodically with this frequency, we can build up the amplitude of the motion. But if we push with a very different frequency, the swing hardly moves at all.

Resonance also occurs when a periodically varying force is applied to a system with many normal modes. An example is shown in Fig. 16.19a. An open organ pipe is placed next to a loudspeaker that is driven by an amplifier and emits pure sinusoidal sound waves of frequency f, which can be varied by adjusting the amplifier. The air in the pipe is forced to vibrate with the same frequency f as the *driving force* provided by the loudspeaker. In general the amplitude of this motion is relatively small, and the air inside the pipe will not move in any of the normal-mode patterns shown in Fig. 16.17. But if the frequency f of the force is close to one of the normal-mode frequencies, the air in the pipe moves in the normal-mode pattern for that frequency, and the amplitude can become quite large. Figure 16.19b shows the amplitude of oscillation of the air in the pipe as a function of the driving frequency f. The shape of this graph is called the **resonance curve** of the pipe; it has peaks where f equals the normal-mode frequencies of the pipe. The detailed shape of the resonance curve depends on the geometry of the pipe.

If the frequency of the force is precisely *equal* to a normal-mode frequency, the system is in resonance, and the amplitude of the forced oscillation is maximum. If there were no friction or other energy-dissipating mechanism, a driving force at a normal-mode frequency would continue to add energy to the system, and the amplitude would increase indefinitely. In such an idealized case the peaks in the resonance curve of Fig. 16.19b would be infinitely high. But in any real system there is always some dissipation of energy, or damping, as we discussed in Section 13.8; the amplitude of oscillation in resonance may be large, but it cannot be infinite.

The "sound of the ocean" you hear when you put your ear next to a large seashell is due to resonance. The noise of the outside air moving past the seashell is a mixture of sound waves of almost all audible frequencies, which forces the air inside the seashell to oscillate. The seashell behaves like an organ pipe, with a set of normal-mode frequencies; hence the inside air oscillates most strongly at those frequencies, producing the seashell's characteristic sound. To hear a similar phenomenon, uncap a full bottle of your favorite beverage and blow across the open top. The noise is provided by your breath blowing across the top, and the "organ pipe" is the column of air inside the bottle above the surface of the liquid. If you take a drink and repeat the experiment, you will hear a lower tone because the "pipe" is longer and the normal-mode frequencies are lower.

Resonance also occurs when a stretched string is forced to oscillate (see Section 15.8). Suppose that one end of a stretched string is held fixed while the other is given a transverse sinusoidal motion with small amplitude, setting up standing waves. If the frequency of the driving mechanism is *not* equal to one of the normal-mode frequencies of the string, the amplitude at the antinodes is fairly small. However, if the frequency is equal to any one of the normal-mode frequencies, the string is in resonance, and the amplitude at the antinodes is very much larger than that at the driven end. The driven end is not precisely a node, but it lies much closer to a node than to an antinode when the string is in resonance. The photographs in Fig. 15.23 were made this way, with the left end of the string fixed and the right end oscillating vertically with small amplitude; large-amplitude standing waves resulted when the frequency of oscillation of the right end was equal to the fundamental frequency or to one of the first three overtones.

It is easy to demonstrate resonance with a piano. Push down the damper pedal (the right-hand pedal) so that the dampers are lifted and the strings are free to vibrate, and then sing a steady tone into the piano. When you stop singing, the piano seems to continue to sing the same note. The sound waves from your voice excite vibrations in the strings that have natural frequencies close to the frequencies (fundamental and harmonics) present in the note you sang.

A more spectacular example is a singer breaking a wine glass with her amplified voice. A good-quality wine glass has normal-mode frequencies that you can hear by tapping it. If the singer emits a loud note with a frequency corresponding exactly to one of these normal-mode frequencies, large-amplitude oscillations can build up and break the glass (Fig. 16.20).

Resonance is a very important concept, not only in mechanical systems but in all areas of physics. In Chapter 31 we will see examples of resonance in electric circuits.

16.20 The frequency of the sound from this trumpet exactly matches one of the normal-mode frequencies of the goblet. The resonant vibrations of the goblet have such large amplitude that the goblet tears itself apart.

Example 16.13 An organ–guitar duet

A stopped organ pipe is sounded near a guitar, causing one of the strings to vibrate with large amplitude. We vary the tension of the string until we find the maximum amplitude. The string is 80% as long as the stopped pipe. If both the pipe and the string vibrate at their fundamental frequency, calculate the ratio of the wave speed on the string to the speed of sound in air.

SOLUTION

IDENTIFY: The large response of the string is an example of resonance. It occurs because the organ pipe and the guitar string have the same fundamental frequency.

SET UP: Letting the subscripts a and s stand for the air in the pipe and the string, respectively, the condition for resonance is $f_{1a} = f_{1s}$. Equation (16.20) gives the fundamental frequency for a stopped pipe, while the fundamental frequency for a guitar string held at both ends is given by Eq. (15.32). These expressions involve the wave speed in air (v_a) and on the string (v_s) and the lengths of the pipe and string; we are given that $L_s = 0.80L_a$, and our target variable is the ratio v_s/v_a.

EXECUTE: From Eqs. (16.20) and (15.32), $f_{1a} = v_a/4L_a$ and $f_{1s} = v_s/2L_s$. Setting these equal to each other, we find

$$\frac{v_a}{4L_a} = \frac{v_s}{2L_s}$$

Substituting $L_s = 0.80L_a$ and rearranging, we get

$$\frac{v_s}{v_a} = 0.40$$

EVALUATE: As an example, if the speed of sound in air is 345 m/s, the wave speed on the string is $(0.40)(345\text{ m/s}) = 138\text{ m/s}$. Note that while the standing waves in the pipe and on the string have the same frequency, they have different *wavelengths* $\lambda = v/f$ because the two media have different wave speeds v. Which standing wave has the greater wavelength?

Test Your Understanding of Section 16.5 A stopped organ pipe of length L has a fundamental frequency of 220 Hz. For which of the following organ pipes will there be a resonance if a tuning fork of frequency 660 Hz is sounded next to the pipe? (There may be more than one correct answer.) (i) a stopped organ pipe of length L; (ii) a stopped organ pipe of length $2L$; (iii) an open organ pipe of length L; (iii) an open organ pipe of length $2L$.

16.6 Interference of Waves

Wave phenomena that occur when two or more waves overlap in the same region of space are grouped under the heading *interference.* As we have seen, standing waves are a simple example of an interference effect: Two waves traveling in opposite directions in a medium combine to produce a standing wave pattern with nodes and antinodes that do not move.

16.21 Two speakers driven by the same amplifier. Constructive interference occurs at point P, and destructive interference occurs at point Q.

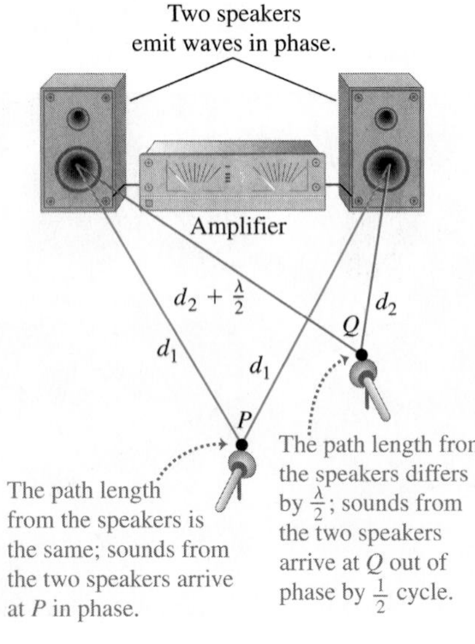
Two speakers
emit waves in phase.
Amplifier
$d_2 + \frac{\lambda}{2}$
d_2
Q
d_1
d_1
P
The path length from the speakers is the same; sounds from the two speakers arrive at P in phase.
The path length from the speakers differs by $\frac{\lambda}{2}$; sounds from the two speakers arrive at Q out of phase by $\frac{1}{2}$ cycle.

Figure 16.21 shows an example of another type of interference that involves waves that spread out in space. Two speakers, driven in phase by the same amplifier, emit identical sinusoidal sound waves with the same constant frequency. We place a microphone at point P in the figure, equidistant from the speakers. Wave crests emitted from the two speakers at the same time travel equal distances and arrive at point P at the same time; hence the waves arrive in phase, and there is constructive interference. The total wave amplitude at P is twice the amplitude from each individual wave, and we can measure this combined amplitude with the microphone.

Now let's move the microphone to point Q, where the distances from the two speakers to the microphone differ by a half-wavelength. Then the two waves arrive a half-cycle out of step, or *out of phase;* a positive crest from one speaker arrives at the same time as a negative crest from the other. Destructive interference takes place, and the amplitude measured by the microphone is much *smaller* than when only one speaker is present. If the amplitudes from the two speakers are equal, the two waves cancel each other out completely at point Q, and the total amplitude there is zero.

CAUTION Interference and traveling waves Although this situation bears some resemblance to standing waves in a pipe, the total wave in Fig. 16.21 is a *traveling* wave, not a standing wave. To see why, recall that in a standing wave there is no net flow of energy in any direction. By contrast, in Fig. 16.21 there is an overall flow of energy from the speakers into the surrounding air; this is characteristic of a traveling wave. The interference between the waves from the two speakers simply causes the energy flow to be *channeled* into certain directions (for example, toward P) and away from other directions (for example, away from Q). You can see another difference between Fig. 16.21 and a standing wave by considering a point, such as Q, where destructive interference occurs. Such a point is *both* a displacement node *and* a pressure node because there is no wave at all at this point. Compare this to a standing wave, in which a pressure node is a displacement antinode and vice versa.

Constructive interference occurs wherever the distances traveled by the two waves differ by a whole number of wavelengths, $0, \lambda, 2\lambda, 3\lambda, \ldots$; in all these cases the waves arrive at the microphone in phase (Fig. 16.22a). If the distances from the two speakers to the microphone differ by any half-integer number of wavelengths, $\lambda/2, 3\lambda/2, 5\lambda/2, \ldots$, the waves arrive at the microphone out of phase and there will be destructive interference (Fig. 16.22b). In this case, little or no sound energy flows toward the microphone directly in front of the speakers. The energy is instead directed to the sides, where constructive interference occurs.

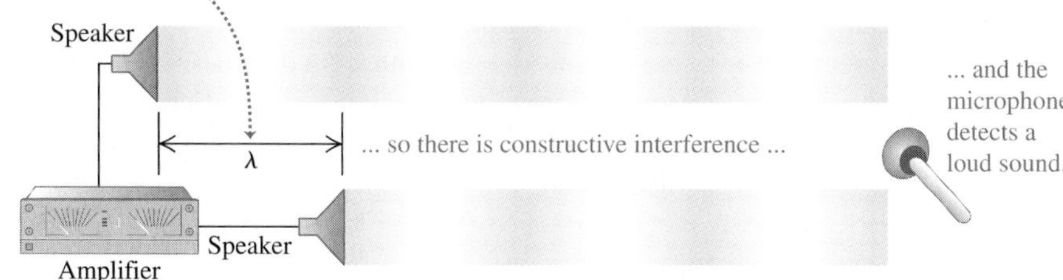
(a) The path lengths from the speakers to the microphone differ by λ ...
Speaker
λ
... so there is constructive interference ...
... and the microphone detects a loud sound.
Speaker
Amplifier

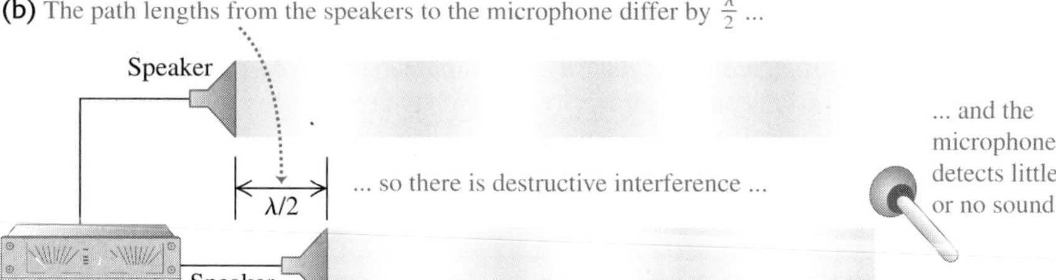
(b) The path lengths from the speakers to the microphone differ by λ/2 ...
Speaker
λ/2
... so there is destructive interference ...
... and the microphone detects little or no sound.
Speaker
Amplifier

16.22 Two speakers driven by the same amplifier, emitting waves in phase. Only the waves directed toward the microphone are shown, and they are separated for clarity. **(a)** Constructive interference occurs when the path difference is $0, \lambda, 2\lambda, 3\lambda, \ldots$. **(b)** Destructive interference occurs when the path difference is $\lambda/2, 3\lambda/2, 5\lambda/2, \ldots$.

Example 16.14 Loudspeaker interference

Two small loudspeakers, A and B (Fig. 16.23), are driven by the same amplifier and emit pure sinusoidal waves in phase. If the speed of sound is 350 m/s, (a) for what frequencies does constructive interference occur at point P? (b) For what frequencies does destructive interference occur at point P?

SOLUTION

IDENTIFY: The nature of the interference at P depends on the difference in path lengths from points A and B to P and how this difference compares to the wavelength.

SET UP: We calculate the path lengths from A to P and from B to P using the Pythagorean theorem. Constructive interference occurs

16.23 What sort of interference occurs at P?

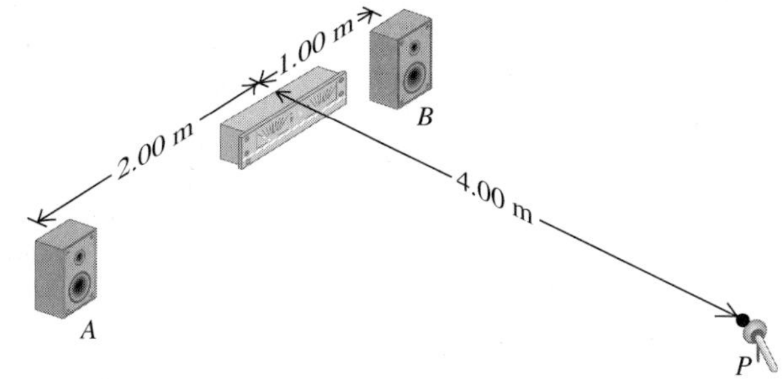
1.00 m
B
2.00 m
4.00 m
A
P

Continued

when the difference in path lengths equals a whole number of wavelengths, while destructive interference occurs when the path length difference is a half-integer number of wavelengths. To find the corresponding frequencies, we use the relationship $v = f\lambda$.

EXECUTE: The distance from speaker A to point P is $[(2.00\text{ m})^2 + (4.00\text{ m})^2]^{1/2} = 4.47$ m, and the distance from speaker B to point P is $[(1.00\text{ m})^2 + (4.00\text{ m})^2]^{1/2} = 4.12$ m. The path difference is $d = 4.47\text{ m} - 4.12\text{ m} = 0.35$ m.

(a) Constructive interference occurs when the path difference is $d = 0, \lambda, 2\lambda, \ldots$ or $d = 0, v/f, 2v/f, \ldots = nv/f$. So the possible frequencies are

$$f_n = \frac{nv}{d} = n\frac{350\text{ m/s}}{0.35\text{ m}} \qquad (n = 1, 2, 3, \ldots)$$
$$= 1000\text{ Hz}, 2000\text{ Hz}, 3000\text{ Hz}, \ldots$$

(b) Destructive interference occurs when the path difference is $d = \lambda/2, 3\lambda/2, 5\lambda/2, \ldots$ or $d = v/2f, 3v/2f, 5v/2f, \ldots$. The possible frequencies are

$$f_n = \frac{nv}{2d} = n\frac{350\text{ m/s}}{2(0.35\text{ m})} \qquad (n = 1, 2, 3, \ldots)$$
$$= 500\text{ Hz}, 1500\text{ Hz}, 2500\text{ Hz}, \ldots$$

EVALUATE: As we increase the frequency, the sound at point P alternates between large and small amplitudes; the maxima and minima occur at the frequencies we have found. It can be hard to notice this effect in an ordinary room because of multiple reflections from the walls, floor, and ceiling. Such an experiment is best done either outdoors or in an anechoic chamber, which has walls that absorb almost all sound and thereby eliminate reflections.

Experiments closely analogous to the one in Example 16.14, but using light, have provided both strong evidence for the wave nature of light and a means of measuring its wavelengths. We will discuss these experiments in detail in Chapter 35.

Interference effects are used to control noise from very loud sound sources such as gas-turbine power plants or jet engine test cells. The idea is to use additional sound sources that in some regions of space interfere destructively with the unwanted sound and cancel it out. Microphones in the controlled area feed signals back to the sound sources, which are continuously adjusted for optimum cancellation of noise in the controlled area.

Test Your Understanding of Section 16.6 Suppose that speaker A in Fig. 16.23 emits a sinusoidal sound wave of frequency 500 Hz and speaker B emits a sinusoidal sound wave of frequency 1000 Hz. What sort of interference will there be between these two waves? (i) constructive interference at various points, including point P, and destructive interference at various other points; (ii) destructive interference at various points, including point P, and constructive interference at various points; (iii) neither (i) nor (ii).

16.7 Beats

10.7 Beats and Beat Frequency

In Section 16.6 we talked about *interference* effects that occur when two different waves with the same frequency overlap in the same region of space. Now let's look at what happens when we have two waves with equal amplitude but slightly different frequencies. This occurs, for example, when two tuning forks with slightly different frequencies are sounded together, or when two organ pipes that are supposed to have exactly the same frequency are slightly "out of tune."

Consider a particular point in space where the two waves overlap. The displacements of the individual waves at this point are plotted as functions of time in Fig. 16.24a. The total length of the time axis represents 1 second, and the frequencies are 16 Hz (blue graph) and 18 Hz (red graph). Applying the principle of superposition, we add the two displacements at each instant of time to find the total displacement at that time. The result is the graph of Fig. 16.24b. At certain times the two waves are in phase; their maxima coincide and their amplitudes add. But because of their slightly different frequencies, the two waves cannot be in phase at all times. Indeed, at certain times (like $t = 0.50$ s in Fig. 16.24) the two waves are exactly *out* of phase. The two waves then cancel each other, and the total amplitude is zero.

The resultant wave in Fig. 16.24b looks like a single sinusoidal wave with a varying amplitude that goes from a maximum to zero and back. In this example

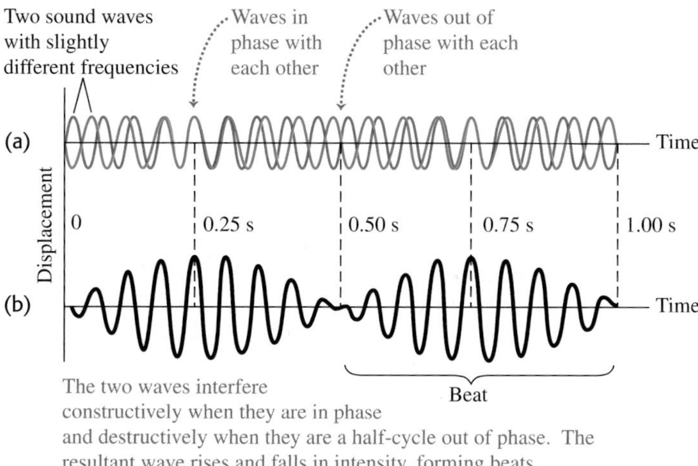
Two sound waves
with slightly
different frequencies
Waves in
phase with
each other
Waves out of
phase with each
other
(a)
Time
Displacement
0
0.25 s
0.50 s
0.75 s
1.00 s
(b)
Time
The two waves interfere
constructively when they are in phase
and destructively when they are a half-cycle out of phase. The
resultant wave rises and falls in intensity, forming beats.
Beat

16.24 Beats are fluctuations in amplitude produced by two sound waves of slightly different frequency, here 16 Hz and 18 Hz. (a) Individual waves. (b) Resultant wave formed by superposition of the two waves. The beat frequency is 18 Hz − 16 Hz = 2 Hz.

the amplitude goes through two maxima and two minima in 1 second, so the frequency of this amplitude variation is 2 Hz. The amplitude variation causes variations of loudness called **beats,** and the frequency with which the loudness varies is called the **beat frequency.** In this example the beat frequency is the *difference* of the two frequencies. If the beat frequency is a few hertz, we hear it as a waver or pulsation in the tone.

We can prove that the beat frequency is *always* the difference of the two frequencies f_a and f_b. Suppose f_a is larger than f_b; the corresponding periods are T_a and T_b, with $T_a < T_b$. If the two waves start out in phase at time $t = 0$, they are again in phase when the first wave has gone through exactly one more cycle than the second. This happens at a value of t equal to T_{beat}, the *period* of the beat. Let n be the number of cycles of the first wave in time T_{beat}; then the number of cycles of the second wave in the same time is $(n - 1)$, and we have the relationships

$$T_{\text{beat}} = nT_a \qquad \text{and} \qquad T_{\text{beat}} = (n-1)T_b$$

Eliminating n between these two equations, we find

$$T_{\text{beat}} = \frac{T_a T_b}{T_b - T_a}$$

The reciprocal of the beat period is the beat *frequency,* $f_{\text{beat}} = 1/T_{\text{beat}}$, so

$$f_{\text{beat}} = \frac{T_b - T_a}{T_a T_b} = \frac{1}{T_a} - \frac{1}{T_b}$$

and finally

$$f_{\text{beat}} = f_a - f_b \qquad \text{(beat frequency)} \tag{16.24}$$

As claimed, the beat frequency is the difference of the two frequencies. In using Eq. (16.24), remember that f_a is the higher frequency.

An alternative way to derive Eq. (16.24) is to write functions to describe the curves in Fig. 16.24a and then add them. Suppose that at a certain position the two waves are given by $y_a(t) = A\sin 2\pi f_a t$ and $y_b(t) = -A\sin 2\pi f_b t$. We use the trigonometric identity

$$\sin a - \sin b = 2\sin\frac{1}{2}(a-b)\cos\frac{1}{2}(a+b)$$

We can then express the total wave $y(t) = y_a(t) + y_b(t)$ as

$$y_a(t) + y_b(t) = \left[2A\sin\frac{1}{2}(2\pi)(f_a - f_b)t\right]\cos\frac{1}{2}(2\pi)(f_a + f_b)t$$

The amplitude factor (the quantity in brackets) varies slowly with frequency $\frac{1}{2}(f_a - f_b)$. The cosine factor varies with a frequency equal to the *average* frequency $\frac{1}{2}(f_a + f_b)$. The *square* of the amplitude factor, which is proportional to the intensity that the ear hears, goes through two maxima and two minima per cycle. So the beat frequency f_{beat} that is heard is twice the quantity $\frac{1}{2}(f_a - f_b)$, or just $f_a - f_b$, in agreement with Eq. (16.24).

Beats between two tones can be heard up to a beat frequency of about 6 or 7 Hz. Two piano strings or two organ pipes differing in frequency by 2 or 3 Hz sound wavery and "out of tune," although some organ stops contain two sets of pipes deliberately tuned to beat frequencies of about 1 to 2 Hz for a gently undulating effect. Listening for beats is an important technique in tuning all musical instruments.

At frequency differences greater than about 6 or 7 Hz, we no longer hear individual beats, and the sensation merges into one of *consonance* or *dissonance,* depending on the frequency ratio of the two tones. In some cases the ear perceives a tone called a *difference tone,* with a pitch equal to the beat frequency of the two tones. For example, if you listen to a whistle that produces sounds at 1800 Hz and 1900 Hz when blown, you will hear not only these tones but also a much lower 100-Hz tone.

The engines on multiengine propeller aircraft have to be synchronized so that the propeller sounds don't cause annoying beats, which are heard as loud throbbing sounds (Fig. 16.25). On some planes this is done electronically; on others the pilot does it by ear, just like tuning a piano.

16.25 If the two propellers on this airplane are not precisely synchronized, the pilots, passengers, and listeners on the ground will hear beats.

Test Your Understanding of Section 16.7 One tuning fork vibrates at 440 Hz, while a second tuning fork vibrates at an unknown frequency. When both tuning forks are sounded simultaneously, you hear a tone that rises and falls in intensity three times per second. What is the frequency of the second tuning fork? (i) 434 Hz; (ii) 437 Hz; (iii) 443 Hz; (iv) 446 Hz; (v) either 434 Hz or 446 Hz; (vi) either 437 Hz or 443 Hz.

16.8 The Doppler Effect

ActivPhysics Online

10.8 Doppler Effect: Conceptual Introduction

10.9 Doppler Effect: Problems

You've probably noticed that when a car approaches you with its horn sounding, the pitch seems to drop as the car passes. This phenomenon, first described by the 19th-century Austrian scientist Christian Doppler, is called the **Doppler effect.** When a source of sound and a listener are in motion relative to each other, the frequency of the sound heard by the listener is not the same as the source frequency. A similar effect occurs for light and radio waves; we'll return to this later in this section.

To analyze the Doppler effect for sound, we'll work out a relationship between the frequency shift and the velocities of source and listener relative to the medium (usually air) through which the sound waves propagate. To keep things simple, we consider only the special case in which the velocities of both source and listener lie along the line joining them. Let v_S and v_L be the velocity components along this line for the source and the listener, respectively, relative to the medium. We choose the positive direction for both v_S and v_L to be the direction from the listener L to the source S. The speed of sound relative to the medium, v, is always considered positive.

Moving Listener

Let's think first about a listener L moving with velocity v_L toward a stationary source S (Fig. 16.26). The source emits a sound wave with frequency f_S and wavelength $\lambda = v/f_S$. The figure shows four wave crests, separated by equal dis-

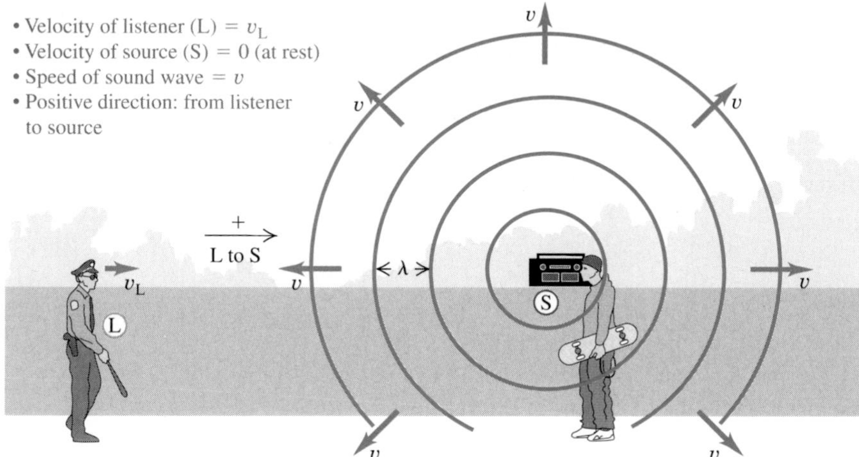

16.26 A listener moving toward a stationary source hears a frequency that is higher than the source frequency. This is because the relative speed of listener and wave is greater than the wave speed v.

tances λ. The wave crests approaching the moving listener have a speed of propagation *relative to the listener* of $(v + v_L)$. So the frequency f_L with which the crests arrive at the listener's position (that is, the frequency the listener hears) is

$$f_L = \frac{v + v_L}{\lambda} = \frac{v + v_L}{v/f_S} \tag{16.25}$$

or

$$f_L = \left(\frac{v + v_L}{v}\right)f_S = \left(1 + \frac{v_L}{v}\right)f_S \quad \text{(moving listener, stationary source)} \tag{16.26}$$

So a listener moving toward a source $(v_L > 0)$, as in Fig. 16.26, hears a higher frequency (higher pitch) than does a stationary listener. A listener moving away from the source $(v_L < 0)$ hears a lower frequency (lower pitch).

Moving Source and Moving Listener

Now suppose the source is also moving, with velocity v_S (Fig. 16.27). The wave speed relative to the wave medium (air) is still v; it is determined by the properties of the medium and is not changed by the motion of the source. But the wavelength is no longer equal to v/f_S. Here's why. The time for emission of one cycle of the wave is the period $T = 1/f_S$. During this time, the wave travels a distance $vT = v/f_S$ and the source moves a distance $v_S T = v_S/f_S$. The wavelength is the distance between successive wave crests, and this is determined by the *relative* displacement of source and wave. As Fig. 16.27 shows, this is different in front of

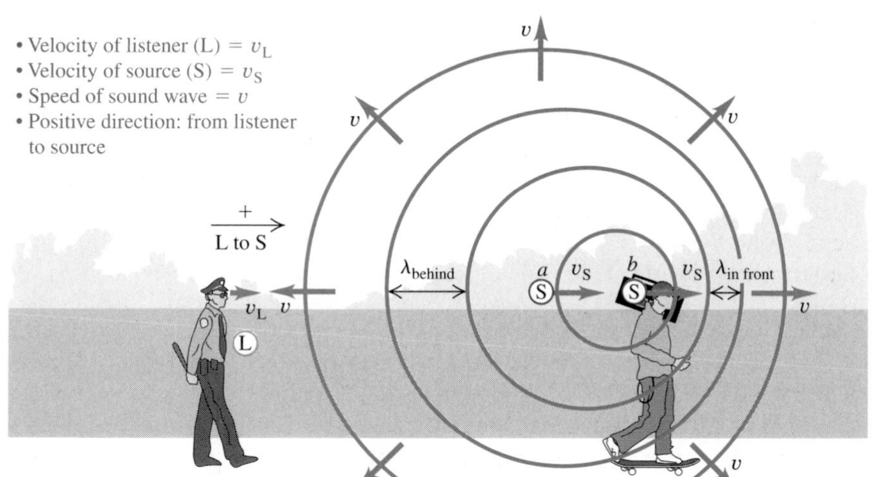

16.27 Wave crests emitted by a moving source are crowded together in front of the source (to the right of this source) and stretched out behind it (to the left of this source).

and behind the source. In the region to the right of the source in Fig. 16.27 (that is, in front of the source), the wavelength is

$$\lambda_{\text{in front}} = \frac{v}{f_S} - \frac{v_S}{f_S} = \frac{v - v_S}{f_S} \quad \text{(wavelength in front of a moving source)} \tag{16.27}$$

In the region to the left of the source (that is, behind the source), it is

$$\lambda_{\text{behind}} = \frac{v + v_S}{f_S} \quad \text{(wavelength behind a moving source)} \tag{16.28}$$

The waves in front of and behind the source are compressed and stretched out, respectively, by the motion of the source.

To find the frequency heard by the listener behind the source, we substitute Eq.(16.28) into the first form of Eq. (16.25):

$$f_L = \frac{v + v_L}{\lambda_{\text{behind}}} = \frac{v + v_L}{(v + v_S)/f_S}$$

$$f_L = \frac{v + v_L}{v + v_S} f_S \quad \text{(Doppler effect, moving source and moving listener)} \tag{16.29}$$

This expresses the frequency f_L heard by the listener in terms of the frequency f_S of the source.

Although we derived it for the particular situation shown in Fig. 16.27, Eq. (16.29) includes *all* possibilities for motion of source and listener (relative to the medium) along the line joining them. If the listener happens to be at rest in the medium, v_L is zero. When both source and listener are at rest or have the same velocity relative to the medium, $v_L = v_S$ and $f_L = f_S$. Whenever the direction of the source or listener velocity is opposite to the direction from the listener toward the source (which we have defined as positive), the corresponding velocity to be used in Eq. (16.29) is negative.

As an example, the frequency heard by a listener at rest $(v_L = 0)$ is $f_L = [v/(v + v_S)]f_S$. If the source is moving toward the listener (in the negative direction), then $v_S < 0, f_L > f_S$, and the listener hears a higher frequency than that emitted by the source. If instead the source is moving away from the listener (in the positive direction), then $v_S > 0, f_L < f_S$, and the listener hears a lower frequency. This explains the change in pitch that you hear from the siren of an ambulance as it passes you (Fig. 16.28).

16.28 The Doppler effect explains why the siren on a fire engine or ambulance has a high pitch $(f_L > f_S)$ when it is approaching you $(v_S < 0)$ and a low pitch $(f_L < f_S)$ when it is moving away $(v_S > 0)$.

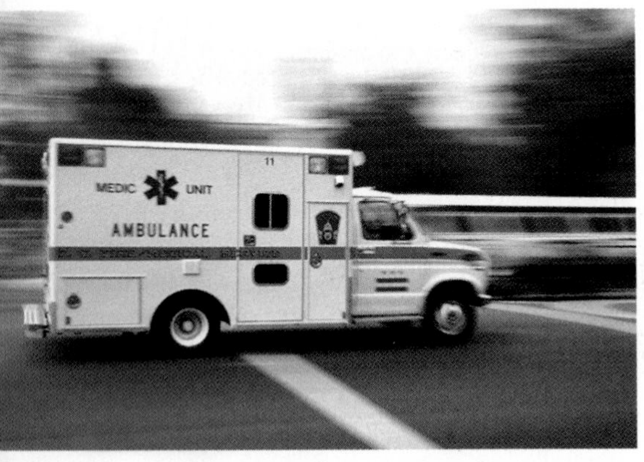

Problem-Solving Strategy 16.2 Doppler Effect

IDENTIFY *the relevant concepts:* The Doppler effect is relevant whenever the source of waves, the wave detector (listener), or both are in motion.

SET UP *the problem* using the following steps:

1. Establish a coordinate system. Define the positive direction to be the direction from the listener to the source, and make sure you know the signs of all relevant velocities. A velocity in the direction from the listener toward the source is positive; a velocity in the opposite direction is negative. Also, the velocities must all be measured relative to the air in which the sound is traveling.
2. Use consistent notation to identify the various quantities: subscript S for source, L for listener.
3. Determine which unknown quantities are your target variables.

EXECUTE *the solution* as follows:

1. Use Eq. (16.29) to relate the frequencies at the source and the listener, the sound speed, and the velocities of the source and the listener. If the source is moving, you can find the wavelength measured by the listener using Eq.(16.27) or (16.28).
2. When a wave is reflected from a surface, either stationary or moving, the analysis can be carried out in two steps. In the first, the surface plays the role of listener; the frequency with which the wave crests arrive at the surface is f_L. Then think of the surface as a new source, emitting waves with this same frequency f_L. Finally, determine what frequency is heard by a listener detecting this new wave.

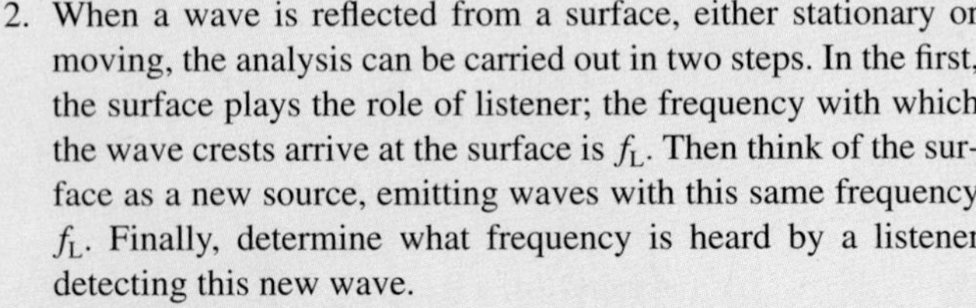

EVALUATE *your answer:* Ask whether your final result makes sense. If the source and the listener are moving toward each other, $f_L > f_S$; if they are moving apart, $f_L < f_S$. If the source and the listener have no relative motion, $f_L = f_S$.

Example 16.15 Doppler effect I: Wavelengths

A police siren emits a sinusoidal wave with frequency $f_S = 300$ Hz. The speed of sound is 340 m/s. (a) Find the wavelength of the waves if the siren is at rest in the air. (b) If the siren is moving at 30 m/s (108 km/h, or 67 mi/h), find the wavelengths of the waves in front of and behind the source.

SOLUTION

IDENTIFY: The Doppler effect is not involved in part (a), since neither the source nor the listener is moving. In part (b), the source is in motion and we must invoke the Doppler effect.

SET UP: Figure 16.29 shows the situation. We use the relationship $v = \lambda f$ to determine the wavelength when the police siren is at rest. When it is in motion, we find the wavelength on either side of the siren using Eqs. (16.27) and (16.28).

EXECUTE: (a) When the source is at rest,

$$\lambda = \frac{v}{f_S} = \frac{340 \text{ m/s}}{300 \text{ Hz}} = 1.13 \text{ m}$$

16.29 Our sketch for this problem.

(b) The situation is shown in Fig. 16.29. From Eq. (16.27), in front of the siren,

$$\lambda_{\text{in front}} = \frac{v - v_S}{f_S} = \frac{340 \text{ m/s} - 30 \text{ m/s}}{300 \text{ Hz}} = 1.03 \text{ m}$$

From Eq. (16.28), behind the siren,

$$\lambda_{\text{behind}} = \frac{v + v_S}{f_S} = \frac{340 \text{ m/s} + 30 \text{ m/s}}{300 \text{ Hz}} = 1.23 \text{ m}$$

EVALUATE: The wavelength is less in front of the siren and greater behind the siren, as it should be.

Example 16.16 Doppler effect II: Frequencies

If a listener L is at rest and the siren in Example 16.15 is moving away from L at 30 m/s, what frequency does the listener hear?

SOLUTION

IDENTIFY: Our target variable is the frequency f_L heard by the listener, who is behind the moving source.

SET UP: Figure 16.30 shows the situation. We know $f_S = 300$ Hz from Example 16.15, and we have $v_L = 0$ and $v_S = 30$ m/s. (The source velocity v_S is positive because the siren is moving in the same direction as the direction from listener to source.)

16.30 Our sketch for this problem.

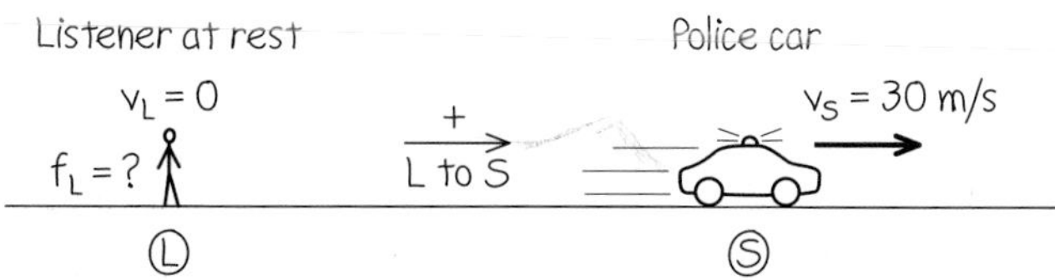

EXECUTE: From Eq. (16.29),

$$f_L = \frac{v}{v + v_S} f_S = \frac{340 \text{ m/s}}{340 \text{ m/s} + 30 \text{ m/s}} (300 \text{ Hz}) = 276 \text{ Hz}$$

EVALUATE: The source and listener are moving apart, so the frequency f_L heard by the listener is less than the frequency f_S emitted by the source.

Here's an alternative approach we can use to check our result. From Example 16.15, the wavelength behind the source (which is where the listener in Fig. 16.30 is located) is 1.23 m, so

$$f_L = \frac{v}{\lambda} = \frac{340 \text{ m/s}}{1.23 \text{ m}} = 276 \text{ Hz}$$

Even though the source is moving, the wave speed v relative to the stationary listener is unchanged.

Example 16.17 Doppler effect III: A moving listener

If the siren is at rest and the listener is moving away from the siren at 30 m/s, what frequency does the listener hear?

SOLUTION

IDENTIFY: Again our target variable is the frequency f_L heard by the listener, but now the listener is in motion and the source is at rest.

SET UP: Figure 16.31 shows the situation. The positive direction (from listener to source) is still from left to right, so $v_L = -30$ m/s.

EXECUTE: From Eq. (16.29),

$$f_L = \frac{v + v_L}{v} f_S = \frac{340 \text{ m/s} + (-30 \text{ m/s})}{340 \text{ m/s}} (300 \text{ Hz}) = 274 \text{ Hz}$$

16.31 Our sketch for this problem.

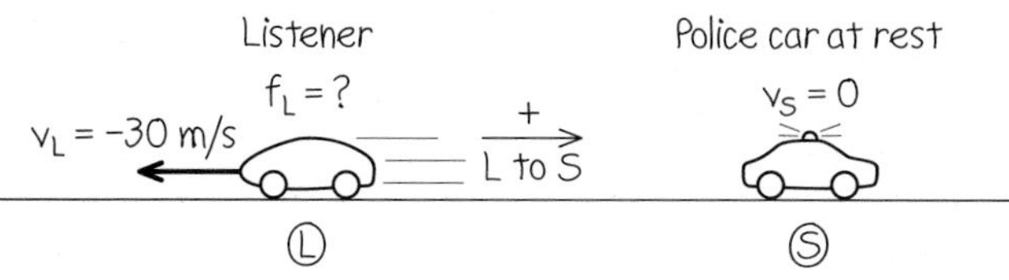

EVALUATE: Again the frequency heard by the listener is less than the source frequency. Note that the *relative velocity* of source and listener is the same as in Example 16.16, but the Doppler shift is different because the velocities relative to the *air* are different.

Example 16.18 Doppler effect IV: Moving source, moving listener

If the siren is moving away from the listener with a speed of 45 m/s relative to the air and the listener is moving toward the siren with a speed of 15 m/s relative to the air, what frequency does the listener hear?

SOLUTION

IDENTIFY: Now *both* the listener and the source are in motion. Once again our target variable is the frequency f_L heard by the listener.

SET UP: Figure 16.32 shows the situation. Both the source velocity $v_S = 45\text{ m/s}$ and the listener's velocity $v_L = 15\text{ m/s}$ are positive because both velocity vectors point in the direction from listener to source.

16.32 Our sketch for this problem.

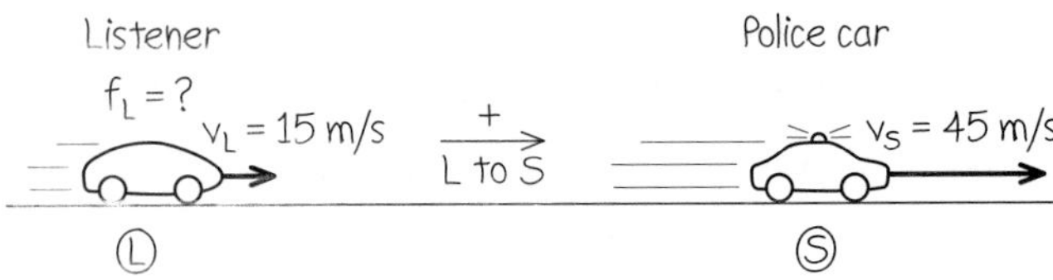

EXECUTE: Once again using Eq. (16.29), we find

$$f_L = \frac{v + v_L}{v + v_S}f_S = \frac{340\text{ m/s} + 15\text{ m/s}}{340\text{ m/s} + 45\text{ m/s}}(300\text{ Hz})$$
$$= 277\text{ Hz}$$

EVALUATE: The frequency heard by the listener is again less than the source frequency, but the value is different than in the preceding two examples, even though the source and listener move away from each other at 30 m/s in all three cases. The *sign* of the Doppler shift of frequency (that is, whether f_L is less than or greater than f_S) depends on how the source and the listener are moving relative to each other; to determine the *value* of the Doppler shift of frequency, you must know the velocities of source and listener relative to the air.

Example 16.19 Doppler effect V: A double Doppler shift

The police car with its 300-Hz siren is moving toward a warehouse at 30 m/s, intending to crash through the door. What frequency does the driver of the police car hear reflected from the warehouse?

SOLUTION

IDENTIFY: In this situation there are *two* Doppler shifts, as shown in Fig. 16.33. In the first shift, the warehouse is the stationary "listener." The frequency of sound reaching the warehouse, which we call f_W, is greater than 300 Hz because the source is approaching. In the second shift, the warehouse acts as a source of sound with frequency f_W, and the listener is the driver of the police car; she hears a frequency greater than f_W because she is approaching the source.

16.33 Two stages of the sound wave's motion from the police car to the warehouse and back to the police car.

(a) Sound travels from police car's siren (source S) to warehouse ("listener" L).

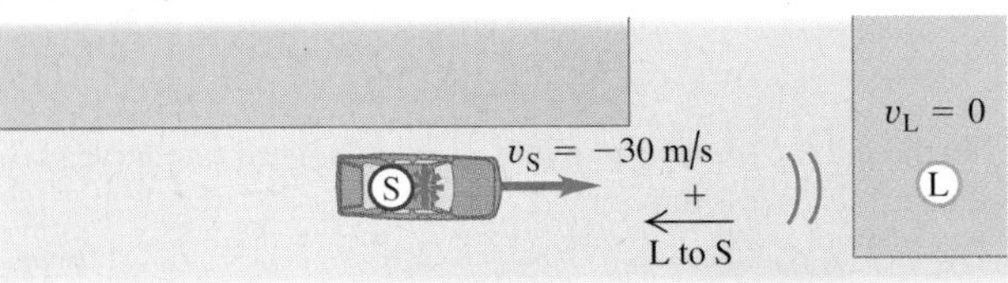

(b) Reflected sound travels from warehouse (source S) to police car (listener L).

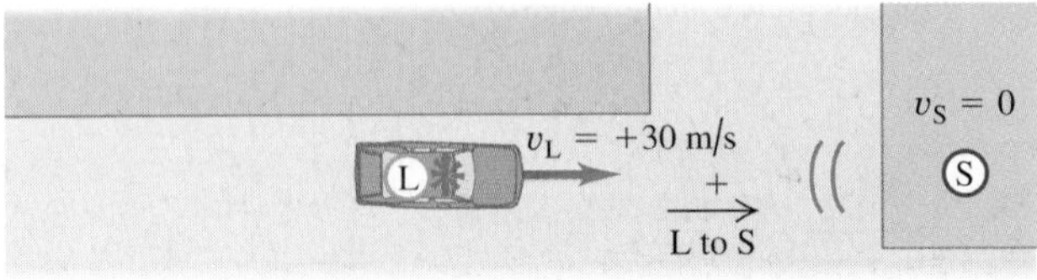

SET UP: To determine f_W, we use Eq. (16.29) with f_L replaced by f_W. For this part of the problem, $v_L = v_W = 0$ (the warehouse is at rest) and $v_S = -30\text{ m/s}$ (the siren is moving in the negative direction from source to listener).

To determine the frequency heard by the driver, which is our target variable, we again use Eq. (16.29) but now with f_S replaced by f_W. For this second part of the problem, $v_S = 0$ because the stationary warehouse is the source and the velocity of the listener (the driver) is $v_L = +30\text{ m/s}$. (The listener's velocity is positive because it is in the direction from listener to source.)

EXECUTE: The frequency reaching the warehouse is

$$f_W = \frac{v}{v + v_S}f_S = \frac{340\text{ m/s}}{340\text{ m/s} + (-30\text{ m/s})}(300\text{ Hz}) = 329\text{ Hz}$$

Then the frequency heard by the driver is

$$f_L = \frac{v + v_L}{v}f_W = \frac{340\text{ m/s} + 30\text{ m/s}}{340\text{ m/s}}(329\text{ Hz}) = 358\text{ Hz}$$

EVALUATE: Because there are two Doppler shifts, the reflected sound heard by the driver has an even higher frequency than the sound heard by a stationary listener in the warehouse.

Doppler Effect for Electromagnetic Waves

In the Doppler effect for sound, the velocities v_L and v_S are always measured relative to the *air* or whatever medium we are considering. There is also a Doppler effect for *electromagnetic* waves in empty space, such as light waves or radio waves. In this case there is no medium that we can use as a reference to measure velocities, and all that matters is the *relative* velocity of source and receiver. (By contrast, the Doppler effect for sound does not depend simply on this relative velocity, as discussed in Example 16.18.)

To derive the expression for the Doppler frequency shift for light, we have to use the special theory of relativity. We will discuss this in Chapter 37, but for now we quote the result without derivation. The wave speed is the speed of light, usually denoted by c, and it is the same for both source and receiver. In the frame of reference in which the receiver is at rest, the source is moving away from the receiver with velocity v. (If the source is *approaching* the receiver, v is negative.) The source frequency is again f_S. The frequency f_R measured by the receiver R (the frequency of arrival of the waves at the receiver) is then given by

$$f_R = \sqrt{\frac{c - v}{c + v}} f_S \quad \text{(Doppler effect for light)} \qquad (16.30)$$

When v is positive, the source is moving directly *away* from the receiver and f_R is always *less* than f_S; when v is negative, the source is moving directly *toward* the receiver and f_R is *greater* than f_S. The qualitative effect is the same as for sound, but the quantitative relationship is different.

A familiar application of the Doppler effect for radio waves is the radar device mounted on the side window of a police car to check other cars' speeds. The electromagnetic wave emitted by the device is reflected from a moving car, which acts as a moving source, and the wave reflected back to the device is Doppler-shifted in frequency. The transmitted and reflected signals are combined to produce beats, and the speed can be computed from the frequency of the beats. Similar techniques ("Doppler radar") are used to measure wind velocities in the atmosphere.

The Doppler effect is also used to track satellites and other space vehicles. In Fig. 16.34 a satellite emits a radio signal with constant frequency f_S. As the satellite orbits past, it first approaches and then moves away from the receiver; the frequency f_R of the signal received on earth changes from a value greater than f_S to a value less than f_S as the satellite passes overhead.

16.34 Change of velocity component along the line of sight of a satellite passing a tracking station. The frequency received at the tracking station changes from high to low as the satellite passes overhead.

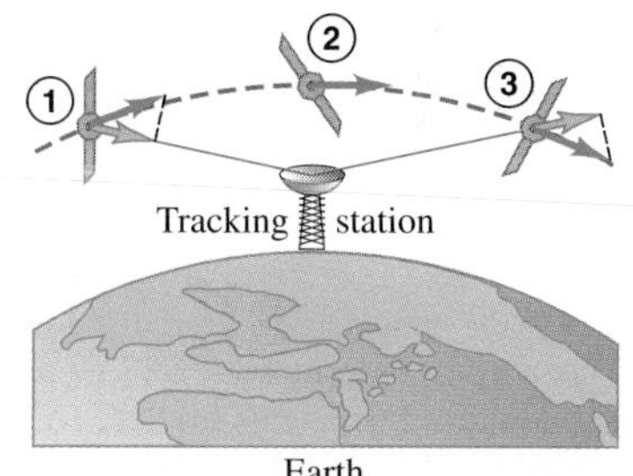

The Doppler effect for electromagnetic waves, including visible light, is important in astronomy. Astronomers compare wavelengths of light from distant stars to those emitted by the same elements on earth. For example, in a binary star system, in which two stars orbit about their common center of mass, one star's light is Doppler-shifted to higher frequencies when that star is moving toward an observer on earth and to lower frequencies when it is moving away. Measurements of the frequency shifts reveal information about the orbits and masses of the stars that make up the binary system.

Light from most galaxies is shifted toward the longer-wavelength or red end of the visible spectrum, an effect called the *red shift.* This is often described as a Doppler shift resulting from motion of these galaxies away from us. However, from the point of view of the general theory of relativity, it is something much more fundamental: It is associated with the expansion of space itself. Distant galaxies have large red shifts because their light has been in transit for a long time and the wavelength of that light has shared in the expansion of all the space through which it moved. Extrapolating this expansion backward to 13.7 billion years ago leads to the "Big Bang" picture. The Big Bang was not an explosion in space but the initial rapid expansion of space itself.

Test Your Understanding of Section 16.8 You are at an outdoor concert with a wind blowing at 10 m/s from the performers toward you. Is the sound you hear Doppler-shifted? If so, is it shifted to lower or higher frequencies?

*16.9 Shock Waves

You may have experienced "sonic booms" caused by an airplane flying overhead faster than the speed of sound. We can see qualitatively why this happens from Fig. 16.35. Let v_S denote the *speed* of the airplane relative to the air, so that it is always positive. The motion of the airplane through the air produces sound; if v_S is less than the speed of sound v, the waves in front of the airplane are crowded together with a wavelength given by Eq. (16.27):

$$\lambda_{\text{in front}} = \frac{v - v_S}{f_S}$$

As the speed v_S of the airplane approaches the speed of sound v, the wavelength approaches zero and the wave crests pile up on each other (Fig. 16.35a). The airplane must exert a large force to compress the air in front of it; by Newton's third law, the air exerts an equally large force back on the airplane. Hence there is a large increase in aerodynamic drag (air resistance) as the airplane approaches the speed of sound, a phenomenon known as the "sound barrier."

When v_S is greater in magnitude than v, the source of sound is **supersonic,** and Eqs. (16.27) and (16.29) for the Doppler effect no longer describe the sound wave in front of the source. Figure 16.35b shows a cross section of what happens. As the airplane moves, it displaces the surrounding air and produces sound. A series of wave crests is emitted from the nose of the airplane; each spreads out in a circle centered at the position of the airplane when it emitted the crest. After a time t the crest emitted from point S_1 has spread to a circle with radius vt, and the airplane has moved a greater distance $v_S t$ to position S_2. You can see that the circular crests interfere constructively at points along the blue line that makes an angle α with the direction of the airplane velocity, leading to a very-large-amplitude wave crest along this line. This large-amplitude crest is called a **shock wave** (Fig. 16.35c).

From the right triangle in Fig. 16.35b we can see that the angle α is given by

$$\sin\alpha = \frac{vt}{v_S t} = \frac{v}{v_S} \quad \text{(shock wave)} \tag{16.31}$$

In this relationship, v_S is the *speed* of the source (the magnitude of its velocity) relative to the air and is always positive. The ratio v_S/v is called the **Mach number.** It is greater than unity for all supersonic speeds, and sin α in Eq. (16.31) is the reciprocal of the Mach number. The first person to break the sound barrier

16.35 Wave crests around a sound source S moving (a) slightly slower than the speed of sound v and (b) faster than the sound speed v. (c) This photograph shows a T-38 jet airplane moving at 1.1 times the speed of sound. Separate shock waves are produced by the nose, wings, and tail. The angles of these waves vary because the air speeds up and slows down as it moves around the airplane, so the relative speed v_S of the airplane and air is different for shock waves produced at different points.

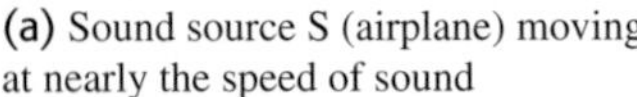
(a) Sound source S (airplane) moving at nearly the speed of sound

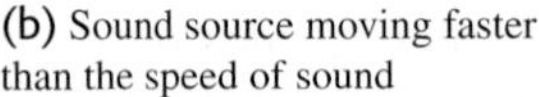
(b) Sound source moving faster than the speed of sound

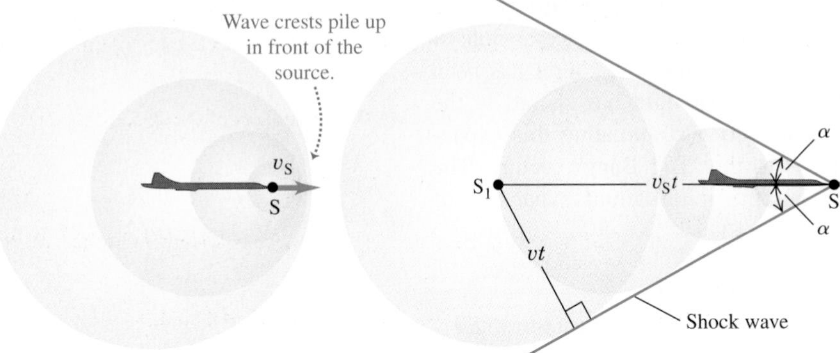

(c) Shock waves around a supersonic airplane

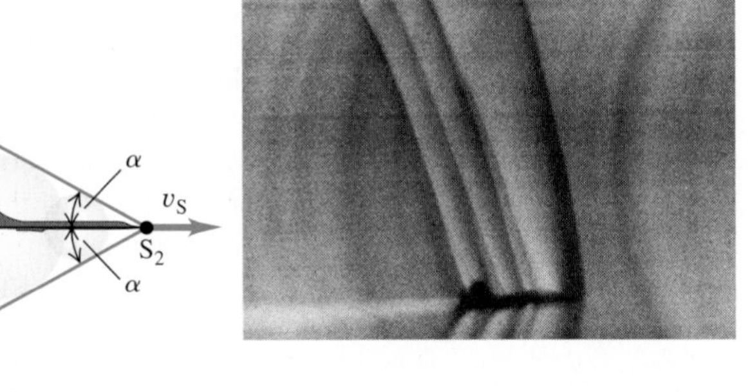

16.36 The first supersonic airplane, the Bell X-1, was shaped much like a 50-caliber bullet—which was known to be able to travel faster than sound.

was Capt. Chuck Yeager of the U.S. Air Force, flying the Bell X-1 at Mach 1.06 on October 14, 1947 (Fig. 16.36).

Shock waves are actually three-dimensional; a shock wave forms a *cone* around the direction of motion of the source. If the source (possibly a supersonic jet airplane or a rifle bullet) moves with constant velocity, the angle α is constant, and the shock-wave cone moves along with the source. It's the arrival of this shock wave that causes the sonic boom you hear after a supersonic airplane has passed by. The larger the airplane, the stronger the sonic boom; the shock wave produced at ground level by the (now retired) Concorde supersonic airliner flying at 12,000 m (40,000 ft) caused a sudden jump in air pressure of about 20 Pa. In front of the shock-wave cone, there is no sound. Inside the cone a stationary listener hears the Doppler-shifted sound of the airplane moving away.

CAUTION **Shock waves** We emphasize that a shock wave is produced *continuously* by any object that moves through the air at supersonic speed, not only at the instant that it "breaks the sound barrier." The sound waves that combine to form the shock wave, as in Fig. 16.35b, are created by the motion of the object itself, not by any sound source that the object may carry. The cracking noises of a bullet and of the tip of a circus whip are due to their supersonic motion. A supersonic jet airplane may have very loud engines, but these do not cause the shock wave. Indeed, a space shuttle makes a very loud sonic boom when coming in for a landing; its engines are out of fuel at this point, so it is a supersonic glider.

Shock waves have applications outside of aviation. They are used to break up kidney stones and gallstones without invasive surgery, using a technique with the impressive name *extracorporeal shock-wave lithotripsy.* A shock wave produced outside the body is focused by a reflector or acoustic lens so that as much of it as possible converges on the stone. When the resulting stresses in the stone exceed its tensile strength, it breaks into small pieces and can be eliminated. This technique requires accurate determination of the location of the stone, which may be done using ultrasonic imaging techniques (see the discussion of ultrasonic imaging on page 535).

Example 16.20 Sonic boom from a supersonic airplane

An airplane is flying at Mach 1.75 at an altitude of 8000 m, where the speed of sound is 320 m/s. How long after the plane passes directly overhead will you hear the sonic boom?

SOLUTION

IDENTIFY: The shock wave forms a cone trailing backward from the airplane, so the problem is really asking for how much time elapses from when the airplane flies overhead to when the shock wave reaches you.

SET UP: Figure 16.37 shows the situation just as the shock wave reaches you at point L. A time t (our target variable) has elapsed since the airplane passed overhead, during which the airliner flying at speed v_S has traveled a distance $v_S t$. We use trigonometry to solve for t.

EXECUTE: From Eq. (16.31) the angle α of the shock cone is

$$\alpha = \arcsin \frac{1}{1.75} = 34.8°$$

The speed of the plane is the speed of sound multiplied by the Mach number:

$$v_S = (1.75)(320 \text{ m/s}) = 560 \text{ m/s}$$

Continued

16.37 You hear a sonic boom when the shock wave reaches you at L (*not* just when the plane breaks the sound barrier). A listener to the right of L has not yet heard the sonic boom but will shortly; a listener to the left of L has already heard the sonic boom.

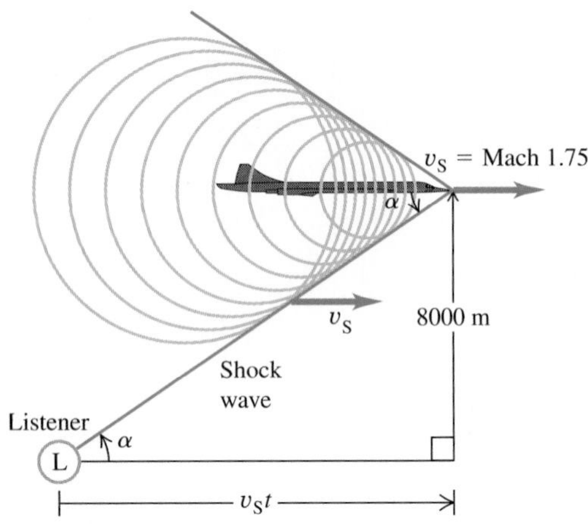

From Fig. 16.37 we have

$$\tan \alpha = \frac{8000\text{ m}}{v_S t}$$

$$t = \frac{8000\text{ m}}{(560\text{ m/s})(\tan 34.8°)} = 20.5\text{ s}$$

EVALUATE: You hear the boom 20.5 s after the airplane passes overhead, and at that time it has traveled $(560\text{ m/s})(20.5\text{ s}) =$ 11.5 km past the straight-overhead point.

In this calculation we assumed that the speed of sound is the same at all altitudes, so $\alpha = \arcsin v/v_S$ is a constant and the shock wave forms a perfect cone. In fact, the speed of sound decreases with increasing altitude. How would this affect the result?

Test Your Understanding of Section 16.9 What would you hear if you were directly behind (to the left of) the supersonic airplane in Fig. 16.37? (i) a sonic boom; (ii) the sound of the airplane, Doppler-shifted to higher frequencies; (iii) the sound of the airplane, Doppler-shifted to lower frequencies; (iv) nothing.

CHAPTER 16 SUMMARY

Sound waves: Sound consists of longitudinal waves in a medium. A sinusoidal sound wave is characterized by its frequency f and wavelength λ (or angular frequency ω and wave number k) and by its displacement amplitude A. The pressure amplitude p_{max} is directly proportional to the displacement amplitude, the wave number, and the bulk modulus B of the wave medium. (See Examples 16.1 and 16.2.)

The speed of a sound wave in a fluid depends on the bulk modulus B and density ρ. If the fluid is an ideal gas, the speed can be expressed in terms of the temperature T, molar mass M, and ratio of heat capacities γ of the gas. The speed of longitudinal waves in a solid rod depends on the density and Young's modulus Y. (See Examples 16.3–16.5.)

$$p_{max} = BkA \quad (16.5)$$
(sinusoidal sound wave)

$$v = \sqrt{\frac{B}{\rho}} \quad (16.7)$$
(longitudinal wave in a fluid)

$$v = \sqrt{\frac{\gamma RT}{M}} \quad (16.10)$$
(sound wave in a ideal gas)

$$v = \sqrt{\frac{Y}{\rho}} \quad (16.8)$$
(longitudinal wave in a solid rod)

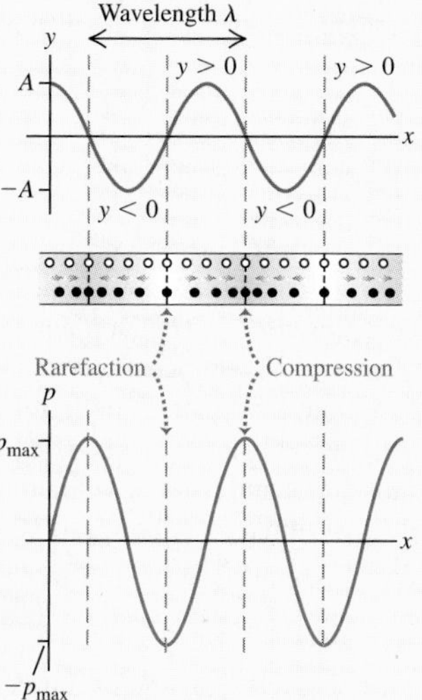

Intensity and sound intensity level: The intensity I of a sound wave is the time average rate at which energy is transported by the wave, per unit area. For a sinusoidal wave, the intensity can be expressed in terms of the displacement amplitude A or the pressure amplitude p_{max}. (See Examples 16.6–16.8.)

The sound intensity level β of a sound wave is a logarithmic measure of its intensity. It is measured relative to I_0, an arbitrary intensity defined to be $10^{-12}\ \text{W/m}^2$. Sound intensity levels are expressed in decibels (dB). (See Examples 16.9 and 16.10.)

$$I = \frac{1}{2}\sqrt{\rho B}\,\omega^2 A^2 = \frac{p_{max}{}^2}{2\rho v} = \frac{p_{max}{}^2}{2\sqrt{\rho B}} \quad (16.12), (16.14)$$
(intensity of a sinusoidal sound wave)

$$\beta = (10\ \text{dB}) \log \frac{I}{I_0} \quad (16.15)$$
(definition of sound intensity level)

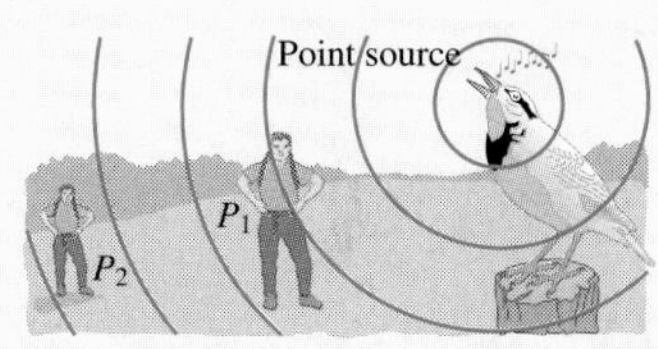

Standing sound waves: Standing sound waves can be set up in a pipe or tube. A closed end is a displacement node and a pressure antinode; an open end is a displacement antinode and a pressure node. For a pipe of length L open at both ends, the normal-mode frequencies are integer multiples of the sound speed divided by $2L$. For a stopped pipe (one that is open at only one end), the normal-mode frequencies are the odd multiples of the sound speed divided by $4L$. (See Examples 16.11 and 16.12.)

A pipe or other system with normal-mode frequencies can be driven to oscillate at any frequency. A maximum response, or resonance, occurs if the driving frequency is close to one of the normal-mode frequencies of the system. (See Example 16.13.)

$$f_n = \frac{nv}{2L} \quad (n = 1, 2, 3, \ldots) \quad (16.18)$$
(open pipe)

$$f_n = \frac{nv}{4L} \quad (n = 1, 3, 5, \ldots) \quad (16.22)$$
(stopped pipe)

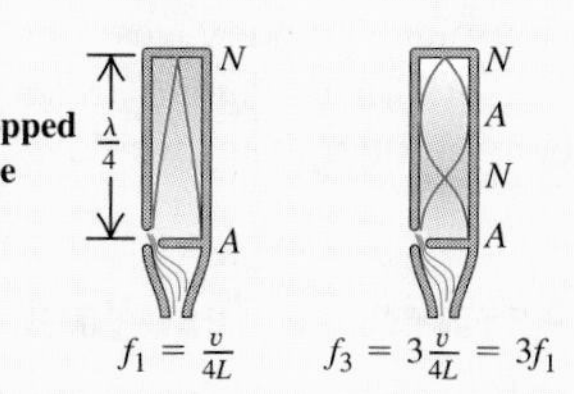

Interference: When two or more waves overlap in the same region of space, the resulting effects are called interference. The resulting amplitude can be either larger or smaller than the amplitude of each individual wave, depending on whether the waves are in phase (constructive interference) or out of phase (destructive interference). (See Example 16.14.)

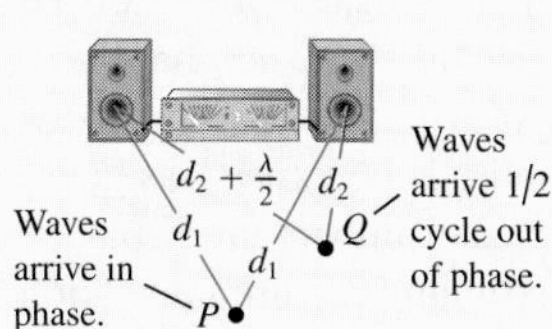

Beats: Beats are heard when two tones with slightly different frequencies f_a and f_b are sounded together. The beat frequency f_{beat} is the difference between f_a and f_b.

$$f_{beat} = f_a - f_b \quad (16.24)$$
(beat frequency)

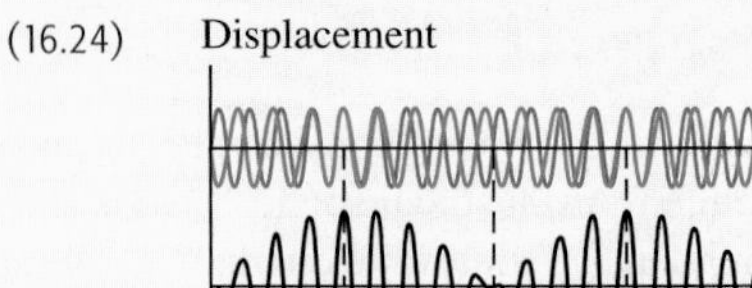

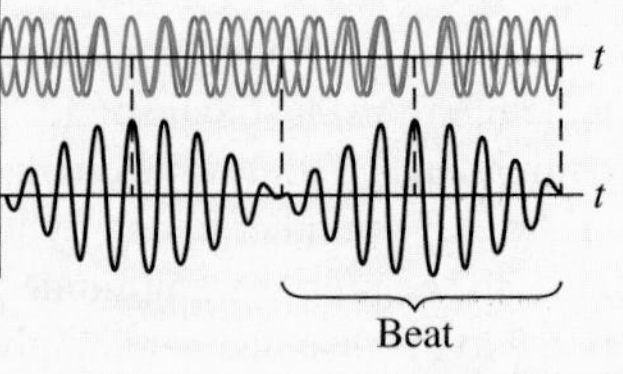

Doppler effect: The Doppler effect for sound is the frequency shift that occurs when there is motion of a source of sound, a listener, or both, relative to the medium. The source and listener frequencies f_S and f_L are related by the source and listener velocities v_S and v_L relative to the medium and to the speed of sound v. (See Examples 16.15–16.19)

$$f_L = \frac{v + v_L}{v + v_S} f_S \quad (16.29)$$
(Doppler effect, moving source and moving listener)

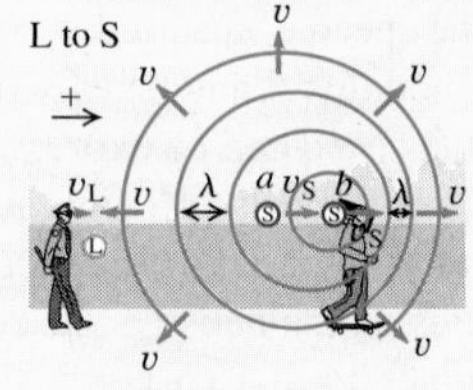

***Shock waves:** A sound source moving with a speed v_S greater than the speed of sound v creates a shock wave. The wave front is a cone with angle α. (See Example 16.20.)

$$\sin\alpha = \frac{v}{v_S} \quad (16.31)$$

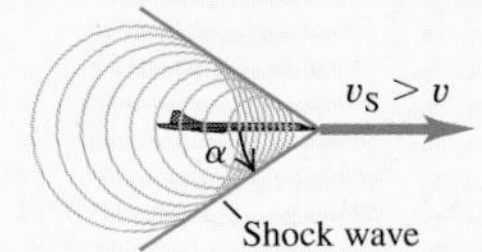

Key Terms

sound, *527*
audible range, *527*
ultrasonic, *528*
infrasonic, *528*
displacement amplitude, *528*
pressure amplitude, *529*
loudness, *531*
pitch, *531*
timbre, *532*
noise, *532*
sound intensity level, *539*
decibel, *539*
displacement node, *541*
displacement antinode, *541*
pressure node, *542*
pressure antinode, *542*
resonance, *546*
resonance curve, *547*
beats, *551*
beat frequency, *551*
Doppler effect, *552*
*supersonic, *558*
*shock wave, *558*
*Mach number, *558*

Answer to Chapter Opening Question ?

Both musical sounds and noise are made up of a combination of sinusoidal sound waves. The difference is that the frequencies of the sine waves in musical sound are all integer multiples of a fundamental frequency, while *all* frequencies are present in noise.

Answers to Test Your Understanding Questions

16.1 Answer: (v) From Eq. (16.5), the displacement amplitude is $A = p_{max}/Bk$. The pressure amplitude p_{max} and bulk modulus B remain the same, but the frequency f increases by a factor of 4. Hence the wave number $k = \omega/v = 2\pi f/v$ also increases by a factor of 4. Since A is inversely proportional to k, the displacement amplitude becomes $\frac{1}{4}$ as great. In other words, at higher frequency a smaller maximum displacement is required to produce the same maximum pressure fluctuation.

16.2 Answer: (i) From Eq. (16.7), the speed of longitudinal waves (sound) in a fluid is $v = \sqrt{B/\rho}$. We can rewrite this to give an expression for the bulk modulus B in terms of the fluid density ρ and the sound speed v: $B = \rho v^2$. At 20°C the speed of sound in mercury is slightly less than in water (1451 m/s versus 1482 m/s), but the density of mercury is greater than that of water by a large factor (13.6). Hence the bulk modulus of mercury is greater than that of water by a factor of $(13.6)(1451/1482)^2 = 13.0$.

16.3 Answer: A and p_{max} increase by a factor of $\sqrt{2}$, B and v are unchanged, β increases by 3.0 dB Equations (16.9) and (16.10) show that the bulk modulus B and sound speed v remain the same because the physical properties of the air are unchanged. From Eqs. (16.12) and (16.14), the intensity is proportional to the square of the displacement amplitude or the square of the pressure amplitude. Hence doubling the intensity means that A and p_{max} both increase by a factor of $\sqrt{2}$. Example 16.10 shows that *multiplying* the intensity by a factor of $2(I_2/I_1 = 2)$ corresponds to *adding* to the sound intensity level by $(10\text{ dB})\log(I_2/I_1) = (10\text{ dB})\log 2 = 3.0\text{ dB}$.

16.4 Answer: (ii) Helium is less dense and has a lower molar mass than air, so sound travels faster in helium than in air. The normal-mode frequencies for a pipe are proportional to the sound speed v, so the frequency and hence the pitch increase when the air in the pipe is replaced with helium.

16.5 Answer: (i) and (iv) There will be a resonance if 660 Hz is one of the pipe's normal-mode frequencies. A stopped organ pipe has normal-mode frequencies that are odd multiples of its fundamental frequency [see Eq. (16.22) and Fig. 16.18]. Hence pipe (i), which has fundamental frequency 220 Hz, also has a normal-mode frequency of $3(220\text{ Hz}) = 660\text{ Hz}$. Pipe (ii) has twice the length of pipe (i); from Eq. (16.20), the fundamental frequency of a stopped pipe is inversely proportional to the length, so pipe (ii) has a fundamental frequency of $(\frac{1}{2})(220\text{ Hz}) = 110\text{ Hz}$. Its other normal-mode frequencies are 330 Hz, 550 Hz, 770 Hz, . . . , so a 660-Hz tuning fork will not cause resonance. Pipe (iii) is an open pipe of the same length as pipe (i), so its fundamental frequency is twice as great as for pipe (i) [compare Eqs. (16.16) and (16.20)], or $2(220\text{ Hz}) = 440\text{ Hz}$. Its other normal-mode frequencies are integer multiples of the fundamental frequency [see Eq. (16.19)], or 880 Hz, 1320 Hz, . . . , none of which match the 660-Hz frequency of the tuning fork. Pipe (iv) is also an open pipe but with twice the length of pipe (iii) [see Eq. (16.18)], so its normal-mode frequencies are one-half those of pipe (iii): 220 Hz, 440 Hz, 660 Hz, . . . , so the third harmonic will resonate with the tuning fork.

16.6 **Answer: (iii)** Constructive and destructive interference between two waves can occur only if the two waves have the same frequency. In this case the frequencies are different, so there are no points where the two waves always reinforce each other (constructive interference) or always cancel each other (destructive interference).

16.7 **Answer: (vi)** The beat frequency is 3 Hz, so the difference between the two tuning fork frequencies is also 3 Hz. Hence the second tuning fork vibrates at a frequency of either 443 Hz or 437 Hz. You can distinguish between the two possibilities by comparing the pitches of the two tuning forks sounded one at a time: the frequency is 437 Hz if the second tuning fork has a lower pitch and 443 Hz if it has a higher pitch.

16.8 **Answer: no** The air (the medium for sound waves) is moving from the source toward the listener. Hence, relative to the air, both the source and the listener are moving in the direction from listener to source. So both velocities are positive and $v_S = v_L = +10\text{ m/s}$. The equality of these two velocities means that the numerator and the denominator in Eq. (16.29) are the same, so $f_L = f_S$ and there is *no* Doppler shift.

16.9 **Answer: (iii)** Figure 16.37 shows that there are sound waves inside the cone of the shock wave. Behind the airplane the wave crests are spread apart, just as they are behind the moving source in Fig. 16.27. Hence the waves that reach you have an increased wavelength and a lower frequency.

PROBLEMS

For instructor-assigned homework, go to www.masteringphysics.com 

Discussion Questions

Q16.1. When sound travels from air into water, does the frequency of the wave change? The speed? The wavelength? Explain your reasoning.

Q16.2. The hero of a western movie listens for an oncoming train by putting his ear to the track. Why does this method give an earlier warning of the approach of a train than just listening in the usual way?

Q16.3. Would you expect the pitch (or frequency) of an organ pipe to increase or decrease with increasing temperature? Explain.

Q16.4. In most modern wind instruments the pitch is changed by using keys or valves to change the length of the vibrating air column. The bugle, however, has no valves or keys, yet it can play many notes. How might this be possible? Are there restrictions on what notes a bugle can play?

Q16.5. Symphonic musicians always "warm up" their wind instruments by blowing into them before a performance. What purpose does this serve?

Q16.6. In a popular and amusing science demonstration, a person inhales helium and then his voice becomes high and squeaky. Why does this happen? (*Warning:* Inhaling too much helium can cause unconsciousness or death.)

Q16.7. Lane dividers on highways sometimes have regularly spaced ridges or ripples. When the tires of a moving car roll along such a divider, a musical note is produced. Why? Explain how this phenomenon could be used to measure the car's speed.

Q16.8. The tone quality of an acoustic guitar is different when the strings are plucked near the bridge (the lower end of the strings) than when they are plucked near the sound hole (close to the center of the strings). Why?

Q16.9. Which has a more direct influence on the loudness of a sound wave: the *displacement* amplitude or the *pressure* amplitude? Explain your reasoning.

Q16.10. If the pressure amplitude of a sound wave is halved, by what factor does the intensity of the wave decrease? By what factor must the pressure amplitude of a sound wave be increased in order to increase the intensity by a factor of 16? Explain.

Q16.11. Does the sound intensity level β obey the inverse-square law? Why?

Q16.12. A small fraction of the energy in a sound wave is absorbed by the air through which the sound passes. How does this modify the inverse-square relationship between intensity and distance from the source? Explain your reasoning.

Q16.13. A wire under tension and vibrating in its first overtone produces sound of wavelength λ. What is the new wavelength of the sound (in terms of λ) if the tension is doubled?

Q16.14. A small metal band is slipped onto one of the tines of a tuning fork. As this band is moved closer and closer to the end of the tine, what effect does this have on the wavelength and frequency of the sound the tine produces? Why?

Q16.15. An organist in a cathedral plays a loud chord and then releases the keys. The sound persists for a few seconds and gradually dies away. Why does it persist? What happens to the sound energy when the sound dies away?

Q16.16. Two vibrating tuning forks have identical frequencies, but one is stationary and the other is mounted at the rim of a rotating platform. What does a listener hear? Explain.

Q16.17. A large church has part of the organ in the front of the church and part in the back. A person walking rapidly down the aisle while both segments are playing at once reports that the two segments sound out of tune. Why?

Q16.18. A sound source and a listener are both at rest on the earth, but a strong wind is blowing from the source toward the listener. Is there a Doppler effect? Why or why not?

Q16.19. Can you think of circumstances in which a Doppler effect would be observed for surface waves in water? For elastic waves propagating in a body of water deep below the surface? If so, describe the circumstances and explain your reasoning. If not, explain why not.

Q16.20. Stars other than our sun normally appear featureless when viewed through telescopes. Yet astronomers can readily use the light from these stars to determine that they are rotating and even measure the speed of their surface. How do you think they can do this?

Q16.21. If you wait at a railroad crossing as a train approaches and passes, you hear a Doppler shift in its sound. But if you listen closely, you hear that the change in frequency is continuous; it does not suddenly go from one high frequency to another low frequency. Instead the frequency *smoothly* (but rather quickly) changes from high to low as the train passes. Why does this smooth change occur?

Q16.22. In case 1, a source of sound approaches a stationary observer at speed v. In case 2, the observer moves toward the stationary source at the same speed v. If the source is always producing the same frequency sound, will the observer hear the same frequency in both cases, since the relative speed is the same each time? Why not?

***Q16.23.** Does an aircraft make a sonic boom only at the instant its speed exceeds Mach 1? Explain your reasoning.

***Q16.24.** If you are riding in a supersonic aircraft, what do you hear? Explain your reasoning. In particular, do you hear a continuous sonic boom? Why or why not?

***Q16.25.** A jet airplane is flying at a constant altitude at a steady speed v_S greater than the speed of sound. Describe what observers at points A, B, and C hear at the instant shown in Fig. 16.38, when the shock wave has just reached point B. Explain your reasoning.

Figure **16.38** Question Q16.25.

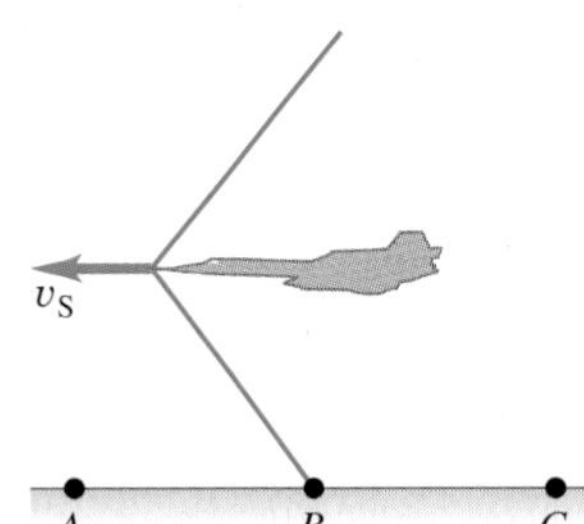

Exercises

Unless indicated otherwise, assume the speed of sound in air to be $v = 344 \text{m/s}$.

Section 16.1 Sound Waves

16.1. Example 16.1 (Section 16.1) showed that for sound waves in air with frequency 1000 Hz, a displacement amplitude of 1.2×10^{-8} m produces a pressure amplitude of 3.0×10^{-2} Pa. (a) What is the wavelength of these waves? (b) For 1000-Hz waves in air, what displacement amplitude would be needed for the pressure amplitude to be at the pain threshold, which is 30 Pa? (c) For what wavelength and frequency will waves with a displacement amplitude of 1.2×10^{-8} m produce a pressure amplitude of 1.5×10^{-3} Pa?

16.2. Example 16.1 (Section 16.1) showed that for sound waves in air with frequency 1000 Hz, a displacement amplitude of 1.2×10^{-8} m produces a pressure amplitude of 3.0×10^{-2} Pa. Water at 20°C has a bulk modulus of 2.2×10^{9} Pa, and the speed of sound in water at this temperature is 1480 m/s. For 1000-Hz sound waves in 20°C water, what displacement amplitude is produced if the pressure amplitude is 3.0×10^{-2} Pa? Explain why your answer is much less than 1.2×10^{-8} Pa.

16.3. Consider a sound wave in air that has displacement amplitude 0.0200 mm. Calculate the pressure amplitude for frequencies of (a) 150 Hz; (b) 1500 Hz; (c) 15,000 Hz. In each case compare the result to the pain threshold, which is 30 Pa.

16.4. A loud factory machine produces sound having a displacement amplitude of 1.00 μm, but the frequency of this sound can be adjusted. In order to prevent ear damage to the workers, the maximum pressure amplitude of the sound waves is limited to 10.0 Pa. Under the conditions of this factory, the bulk modulus of air is 1.42×10^{5} Pa. What is the highest-frequency sound to which this machine can be adjusted without exceeding the prescribed limit? Is this frequency audible to the workers?

Section 16.2 Speed of Sound Waves

16.5. (a) In a liquid with density 1300 kg/m^3, longitudinal waves with frequency 400 Hz are found to have wavelength 8.00 m. Calculate the bulk modulus of the liquid. (b) A metal bar with a length of 1.50 m has density 6400 kg/m^3. Longitudinal sound waves take 3.90×10^{-4} s to travel from one end of the bar to the other. What is Young's modulus for this metal?

16.6. A major earthquake centered on Loma Prieta, California, near San Francisco, occurred at 5:04 P.M. local time on October 17, 1989 (in UTC, Coordinated Universal Time, 0h 4m 15s on October 18, 1989). The primary seismic waves (P waves) from such an earthquake are longitudinal waves that travel through the earth's crust. P waves were detected at Caracas, Venezuela, at 0h 13m 54s UTC; at Kevo, Finland, at 0h 15m 35s UTC; and at Vienna, Austria, at 0h 17m 02s UTC. The distances the P waves traveled from Loma Prieta were 6280 km to Caracas, 8690 km to Kevo, and 9650 km to Vienna. a) Use the arrival times to calculate the average speed of the P waves that traveled to these three cities. How can you account for any differences between the average speeds? (b) The average density of the earth's crust is about 3.3 g/cm^3. Use this value to calculate the bulk modulus of the earth's crust along the path traveled by the P waves to each of the three cities. How do your answers compare to the bulk moduli in Table 11.1?

16.7. A submerged scuba diver hears the sound of a boat horn directly above her on the surface of the lake. At the same time, a friend on dry land 22.0 m from the boat also hears the horn (Fig. 16.39). The horn is 1.2 m above the surface of the water. What is the distance (labeled by "?" in Fig. 16.39) from the horn to the diver? Both air and water are at 20°C.

Figure **16.39** Exercise 16.7.

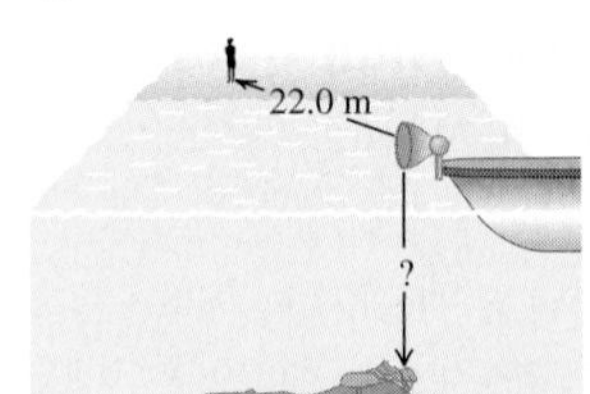

16.8. At a temperature of 27.0°C, what is the speed of longitudinal waves in (a) hydrogen (molar mass 2.02 g/mol)? (b) helium (molar mass 4.00 g/mol); (c) argon (molar mass 39.9 g/mol)? See Table 19.1 for values of γ. (d) Compare your answers for parts (a), (b), and (c) with the speed in air at the same temperature.

16.9. An oscillator vibrating at 1250 Hz produces a sound wave that travels through an ideal gas at 325 m/s when the gas temperature is 22.0°C. For a certain experiment, you need to have the same oscillator produce sound of wavelength 28.5 cm in this gas. What should the gas temperature be to achieve this wavelength?

16.10. (a) Show that the fractional change in the speed of sound (dv/v) due to a very small temperature change dT is given by $dv/v = \frac{1}{2}\, dT/T$. (*Hint:* Start with Eq. 16.10.) (b) The speed of sound in air at 20°C is found to be 344 m/s. Use the result in part (a) to find the change in the speed of sound for a 1.0°C change in air temperature.

16.11. An 80.0-m-long brass rod is struck at one end. A person at the other end hears two sounds as a result of two longitudinal waves, one traveling in the metal rod and the other traveling in the air. What is the time interval between the two sounds? The speed of sound in air is 344 m/s; relevant information about brass can be found in Table 11.1 and Table 14.1.

16.12. What is the difference between the speed of longitudinal waves in air at 27.0°C and their speed at −13.0°C?

16.13. What must be the stress (F/A) in a stretched wire of a material whose Young's modulus is Y for the speed of longitudinal waves to equal 30 times the speed of transverse waves?

Section 16.3 Sound Intensity

16.14. Use information from Table 16.2 to answer the following questions about sound in air. At 20°C the bulk modulus for air is 1.42×10^5 Pa and its density is 1.20 kg/m^3. At this temperature, what are the pressure amplitude (in Pa and atm) and the displacement amplitude (in m and nm) (a) for the softest sound a person can normally hear at 1000 Hz and (b) for the sound from a riveter at the same frequency? (c) How much energy per second does each wave deliver to a square 5.00 mm on a side?

16.15. Longitudinal Waves in Different Fluids. (a) A longitudinal wave propagating in a water-filled pipe has intensity 3.00×10^{-6} W/m^2 and frequency 3400 Hz. Find the amplitude A and wavelength λ of the wave. Water has density 1000 kg/m^3 and bulk modulus 2.18×10^9 Pa. (b) If the pipe is filled with air at pressure 1.00×10^5 Pa and density 1.20 kg/m^3, what will be the amplitude A and wavelength λ of a longitudinal wave with the same intensity and frequency as in part (a)? (c) In which fluid is the amplitude larger, water or air? What is the ratio of the two amplitudes? Why is this ratio so different from 1.00?

16.16. Derive Eq. (16.14) from the equations that precede it.

16.17. A sound wave in air at 20°C has a frequency of 150 Hz and a displacement amplitude of 5.00×10^{-3} mm. For this sound wave calculate the (a) pressure amplitude (in Pa); (b) intensity (in W/m^2); (c) sound intensity level (in decibels).

16.18. (a) What is the sound intensity level in a car when the sound intensity is 0.500 μW/m^2? (b) What is the sound intensity level in the air near a jackhammer when the pressure amplitude of the sound is 0.150 Pa and the temperature is 20.0°C?

16.19. For a person with normal hearing, the faintest sound that can be heard at a frequency of 400 Hz has a pressure amplitude of about 6.0×10^{-5} Pa. Calculate the (a) intensity; (b) sound intensity level; (c) displacement amplitude of this sound wave at 20°C.

16.20. The intensity due to a number of independent sound sources is the sum of the individual intensities. (a) When four quadruplets cry simultaneously, how many decibels greater is the sound intensity level than when a single one cries? (b) To increase the sound intensity level again by the same number of decibels as in part (a), how many more crying babies are required?

16.21. A baby's mouth is 30 cm from her father's ear and 1.50 m from her mother's ear. What is the difference between the sound intensity levels heard by the father and by the mother?

16.22. The Sacramento City Council recently adopted a law to reduce the allowed sound intensity level of the much despised leaf blowers from their current level of about 95 dB to 70 dB. With the new law, what is the ratio of the new allowed intensity to the previously allowed intensity?

16.23. (a) By what factor must the sound intensity be increased to raise the sound intensity level by 13.0 dB? (b) Explain why you don't need to know the original sound intensity.

Section 16.4 Standing Sound Waves and Normal Modes

16.24. The fundamental frequency of a pipe that is open at both ends is 594 Hz. (a) How long is this pipe? If one end is now closed, find (b) the wavelength and (c) the frequency of the new fundamental.

16.25. Standing sound waves are produced in a pipe that is 1.20 m long. For the fundamental and first two overtones, determine the locations along the pipe (measured from the left end) of the displacement nodes and the pressure nodes if (a) the pipe is open at both ends and (b) the pipe is closed at the left end and open at the right end.

16.26. Find the fundamental frequency and the frequency of the first three overtones of a pipe 45.0 cm long (a) if the pipe is open at both ends and (b) if the pipe is closed at one end. Use v = 344 m/s. (c) For each of these cases, what is the number of the highest harmonic that may be heard by a person who can hear frequencies from 20 Hz to 20,000 Hz?

16.27. The Human Voice. The human vocal tract is a pipe that extends about 17 cm from the lips to the vocal folds (also called "vocal cords") near the middle of your throat. The vocal folds behave rather like the reed of a clarinet, and the vocal tract acts like a stopped pipe. Estimate the first three standing-wave frequencies of the vocal tract. Use v = 344 m/s. (The answers are only an estimate, since the position of lips and tongue affects the motion of air in the vocal tract.)

16.28. Human Ear. The auditory canal of the ear (see Fig. 16.4) is filled with air. One end is open, and the other end is closed by the eardrum. A particular person's auditory canal is 2.40 cm long and can be modeled as a pipe. (a) What are the fundamental frequency and wavelength of this person's auditory canal? Is this sound audible? (b) Find the frequency of the highest *audible* harmonic of this person's canal. Which harmonic is this?

16.29. A certain pipe produces a fundamental frequency of 262 Hz in air. (a) If the pipe is filled with helium at the same temperature, what fundamental frequency does it produce? (The molar mass of air is 28.8 g/mol, and the molar mass of helium is 4.00 g/mol.) (b) Does your answer to part (a) depend on whether the pipe is open or stopped? Why or why not?

16.30. Singing in the Shower. A pipe closed at both ends can have standing waves inside of it, but you normally don't hear them because little of the sound can get out. But you *can* hear them if you are *inside* the pipe, such as someone singing in the shower. (a) Show that the wavelengths of standing waves in a pipe of length L that is closed at both ends are $\lambda_n = 2L/n$ and the frequencies are given by $f_n = nv/2L = nf_1$, where $n = 1, 2, 3, \ldots$. (b) Modeling it as a pipe, find the frequency of the fundamental and the first two overtones for a shower 2.50 m tall. Are these frequencies audible?

Section 16.5 Resonance and Sound

16.31. You blow across the open mouth of an empty test tube and produce the fundamental standing wave of the air column inside the test tube. The speed of sound in air is 344 m/s and the test tube acts as a stopped pipe. (a) If the length of the air column in the test tube is 14.0 cm, what is the frequency of this standing wave? (b) What is the frequency of the fundamental standing wave in the air column if the test tube is half filled with water?

16.32. You have a stopped pipe of adjustable length close to a taut 85.0-cm, 7.25-g wire under a tension of 4110 N. You want to adjust the length of the pipe so that, when it produces sound at its fundamental frequency, this sound causes the wire to vibrate in its second *overtone* with very large amplitude. How long should the pipe be?

Section 16.6 Interference of Waves

16.33. Two loudspeakers, A and B (Fig. 16.40), are driven by the same amplifier and emit sinusoidal waves in phase. Speaker B is 2.00 m to the right of speaker A. Consider point Q along the extension of the line connecting the speakers, 1.00 m to the right of speaker B. Both speakers emit sound waves that travel directly from the speaker to point Q. (a) What is the lowest frequency for which *constructive* interference occurs at point Q? (b) What is the lowest frequency for which *destructive* interference occurs at point Q?

Figure **16.40** Exercises 16.33 and 16.34.

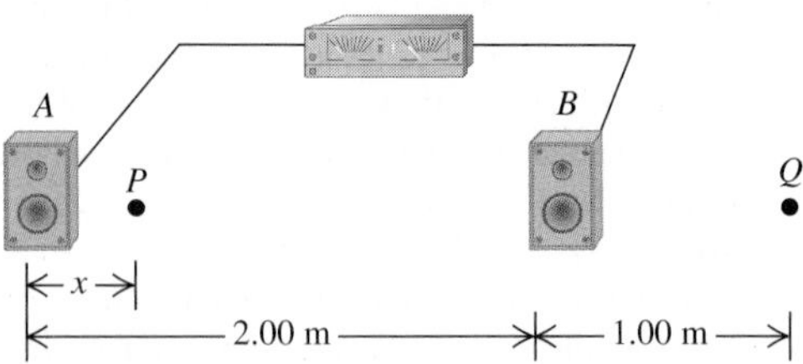

16.34. Two loudspeakers, A and B (Fig. 16.40), are driven by the same amplifier and emit sinusoidal waves in phase. Speaker B is 2.00 m to the right of speaker A. The frequency of the sound waves produced by the loudspeakers is 206 Hz. Consider point P between the speakers and along the line connecting them, a distance x to the right of speaker A. Both speakers emit sound waves that travel directly from the speaker to point P. (a) For what values of x will *destructive* interference occur at point P? (b) For what values of x will *constructive* interference occur at point P? (c) Interference effects like those in parts (a) and (b) are almost never a factor in listening to home stereo equipment. Why not?

16.35. Two loudspeakers, A and B, are driven by the same amplifier and emit sinusoidal waves in phase. Speaker B is 12.0 m to the right of speaker A. The frequency of the waves emitted by each speaker is 688 Hz. You are standing between the speakers, along the line connecting them, and are at a point of constructive interference. How far must you walk toward speaker B to move to a point of destructive interference?

16.36. Two loudspeakers, A and B, are driven by the same amplifier and emit sinusoidal waves in phase. The frequency of the waves emitted by each speaker is 172 Hz. You are 8.00 m from A. What is the closest you can be to B and be at a point of destructive interference?

16.37. Two loudspeakers, A and B, are driven by the same amplifier and emit sinusoidal waves in phase. The frequency of the waves emitted by each speaker is 860 Hz. Point P is 12.0 m from A and 13.4 m from B. Is the interference at P constructive or destructive? Give the reasoning behind your answer.

Section 16.7 Beats

16.38. Two guitarists attempt to play the same note of wavelength 6.50 cm at the same time, but one of the instruments is slightly out of tune and plays a note of wavelength 6.52 cm instead. What is the frequency of the beat these musicians hear when they play together?

16.39. Two organ pipes, open at one end but closed at the other, are each 1.14 m long. One is now lengthened by 2.00 cm. Find the frequency of the beat they produce when playing together in their fundamental.

16.40. Two identical taut strings under the same tension F produce a note of the same fundamental frequency f_0. The tension in one of them is now increased by a very small amount ΔF. (a) If they are played together in their fundamental, show that the frequency of the beat produced is $f_{\text{beat}} = f_0(\Delta F/2F)$. (b) Two identical violin strings, when in tune and stretched with the same tension, have a fundamental frequency of 440.0 Hz. One of the strings is retuned by increasing its tension. When this is done, 1.5 beats per second are heard when both strings are plucked simultaneously at their centers. By what percentage was the string tension changed?

Section 16.8 The Doppler Effect

16.41. On the planet Arrakis a male ornithoid is flying toward his mate at 25.0 m/s while singing at a frequency of 1200 Hz. If the stationary female hears a tone of 1240 Hz, what is the speed of sound in the atmosphere of Arrakis?

16.42. In Example 16.19 (Section 16.8), suppose the police car is moving away from the warehouse at 20 m/s. What frequency does the driver of the police car hear reflected from the warehouse?

16.43. Two train whistles, A and B, each have a frequency of 392 Hz. A is stationary and B is moving toward the right (away from A) at a speed of 35.0 m/s. A listener is between the two whistles and is moving toward the right with a speed of 15.0 m/s (Fig. 16.41). No wind is blowing. (a) What is the frequency from A as heard by the listener? (b) What is the frequency from B as heard by the listener? (c) What is the beat frequency detected by the listener?

Figure **16.41** Exercise 16.43.

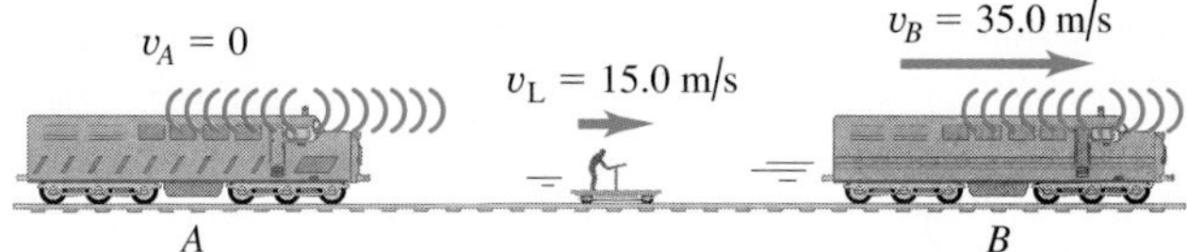

16.44. A railroad train is traveling at 25.0 m/s in still air. The frequency of the note emitted by the locomotive whistle is 400 Hz. What is the wavelength of the sound waves a) in front of the locomotive and (b) behind the locomotive? What is the frequency of the sound heard by a stationary listener c) in front of the locomotive and (d) behind the locomotive?

16.45. A swimming duck paddles the water with its feet once every 1.6 s, producing surface waves with this period. The duck is moving at constant speed in a pond where the speed of surface waves is 0.32 m/s, and the crests of the waves ahead of the duck are spaced 0.12 m apart. (a) What is the duck's speed? (b) How far apart are the crests behind the duck?

16.46. Moving Source vs. Moving Listener. (a) A sound source producing 1.00-kHz waves moves toward a stationary listener at one-half the speed of sound. What frequency will the listener hear? (b) Suppose instead that the source is stationary and the listener moves toward the source at one-half the speed of sound. What frequency does the listener hear? How does your answer compare to that in part (a)? Explain on physical grounds why the two answers differ.

16.47. A car alarm is emitting sound waves of frequency 520 Hz. You are on a motorcycle, traveling directly away from the car. How fast must you be traveling if you detect a frequency of 490 Hz?

16.48. A railroad train is traveling at 30.0 m/s in still air. The frequency of the note emitted by the train whistle is 262 Hz. What frequency is heard by a passenger on a train moving in the opposite direction to the first at 18.0 m/s and (a) approaching the first; and (b) receding from the first?

16.49. Doppler Radar. A giant thunderstorm is moving toward a weather station at 45.0 mi/h (20.1 m/s). If the station sends a radar beam of frequency 200.0 MHz toward the storm, what is the difference in frequency between the emitted beam and the beam reflected back from the storm? Be careful to carry plenty of significant figures! (*Hint:* The storm reflects the same frequency that it receives.)

16.50. Extrasolar Planets. In the not-too-distant future, it should be possible to detect the presence of planets moving around other stars by measuring the Doppler shift in the infrared light they emit. If a planet is going around its star at 50.00 km/s while emitting infrared light of frequency 3.330×10^{14} Hz, what frequency light will be received from this planet when it is moving directly away from us? (*Note:* Infrared light is light having wavelengths longer than those of visible light.)

16.51. How fast (as a percentage of light speed) would a star have to be moving so that the frequency of the light we receive from it is 10.0% higher than the frequency of the light it is emitting? Would it be moving away from us or toward us? (Assume it is moving either directly away from us or directly toward us.)

*Section 16.9 Shock Waves

***16.52.** The shock-wave cone created by the space shuttle at one instant during its reentry into the atmosphere makes an angle of 58.0° with its direction of motion. The speed of sound at this altitude is 331 m/s. (a) What is the Mach number of the shuttle at this instant, and (b) how fast (in m/s and mi/h) is it traveling relative to the atmosphere? (c) What would be its Mach number and the angle of its shock-wave cone if it flew at the same speed but at low altitude where the speed of sound is 344 m/s?

***16.53.** A jet plane flies overhead at Mach 1.70 and at a constant altitude of 950 m. (a) What is the angle α of the shock-wave cone? (b) How much time after the plane passes directly overhead do you hear the sonic boom? Neglect the variation of the speed of sound with altitude.

Problems

16.54. (a) Defend the following statement: "In a sinusoidal sound wave, the pressure variation given by Eq. (16.4) is greatest where the displacement given by Eq. (16.1) is zero." (b) For a sinusoidal sound wave given by Eq. (16.1) with amplitude $A = 10.0 \mu$m and wavelength $\lambda = 0.250$ m, graph the displacement y and pressure fluctuation p as functions of x at time $t = 0$. Show at least two wavelengths of the wave on your graphs. (c) The displacement y in a *non*sinusoidal sound wave is shown in Fig. 16.42 as a function of x for $t = 0$. Draw a graph showing the pressure fluctuation p in this wave as a function of x at $t = 0$. This sound wave has the same 10.0-μm amplitude as the wave in part (b). Does it have the same pressure amplitude? Why or why not? (d) Is the statement in part (a) necessarily true if the sound wave is *not* sinusoidal? Explain your reasoning.

Figure 16.42 Problem 16.54.

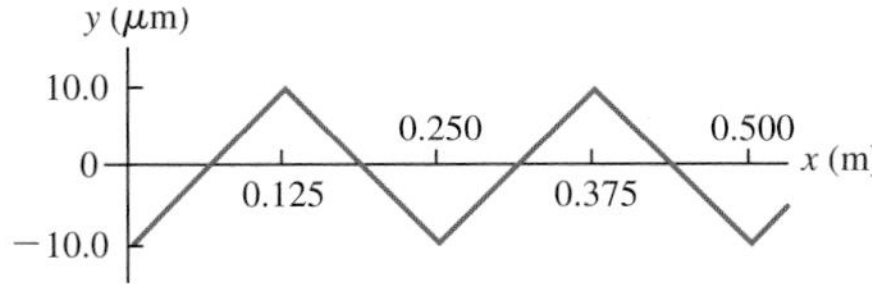

16.55. A soprano and a bass are singing a duet. While the soprano sings an $A^{\#}$ at 932 Hz, the bass sings an $A^{\#}$ but three octaves lower. In this concert hall, the density of air is 1.20 kg/m^3 and its bulk modulus is 1.42×10^5 Pa. In order for their notes to have the same sound intensity level, what must be (a) the ratio of the pressure amplitude of the bass to that of the soprano, and (b) the ratio of the displacement amplitude of the bass to that of the soprano? (c) What displacement amplitude (in m and nm) does the soprano produce to sing her $A^{\#}$ at 72.0 dB?

16.56. The sound from a trumpet radiates uniformly in all directions in 20°C air. At a distance of 5.00 m from the trumpet the sound intensity level is 52.0 dB. The frequency is 587 Hz. (a) What is the pressure amplitude at this distance? (b) What is the displacement amplitude? (c) At what distance is the sound intensity level 30.0 dB?

16.57. A Thermometer. Suppose you have a tube of length L containing a gas whose temperature you want to take, but you cannot get inside the tube. One end is closed, and the other end is open but a small speaker producing sound of variable frequency is at that end. You gradually increase the frequency of the speaker until the sound from the tube first becomes very loud. With further increase of the frequency, the loudness decreases but then gets very loud again at still higher frequencies. Call f_0 the lowest frequency at which the sound is very loud. (a) Show that the absolute temperature of this gas is given by $T = 16ML^2f_0^2/\gamma R$, where M is the molar mass of the gas, γ is the ratio of its heat capacities, and R is the ideal gas constant. (b) At what frequency above f_0 will the sound from the tube next reach a maximum in loudness? (c) How could you determine the speed of sound in this tube at temperature T?

16.58. A uniform 165-N bar is supported horizontally by two identical wires A and B (Fig. 16.43). A small 185-N cube of lead is placed $\frac{3}{4}$ of the way from A to B. The wires are each 75.0 cm long and have a mass of 5.50 g. If both of them are simultaneously plucked at the center, what is the frequency of the beats that they will produce when vibrating in their fundamental?

Figure 16.43 Problem 16.58.

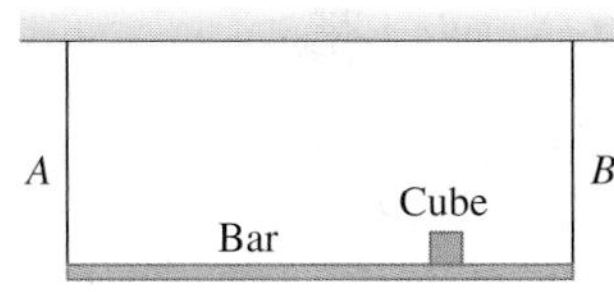

16.59. A person is playing a small flute 10.75 cm long, open at one end and closed at the other, near a taut string having a fundamental frequency of 600.0 Hz. If the speed of sound is 344.0 m/s, for which harmonics of the flute will the string resonate? In each case, which harmonic of the string is in resonance?

16.60. A New Musical Instrument. You have designed a new musical instrument of very simple construction. Your design consists of a metal tube with length L and diameter $L/10$. You have stretched a string of mass per unit length μ across the open end of the tube. The other end of the tube is closed. To produce the musical effect you're looking for, you want the frequency of the third-harmonic standing wave on the string to be the same as the fundamental frequency for sound waves in the air column in the tube. The speed of sound waves in this air column is v_s. (a) What must be the tension of the string to produce the desired effect? (b) What happens to the sound produced by the instrument if the tension is changed to twice the value calculated in part (a)? (c) For the tension calculated in part (a), what other harmonics of the string, if any, are in resonance with standing waves in the air column?

16.61. An organ pipe has two successive harmonics with frequencies 1372 and 1764 Hz. (a) Is this an open or a stopped pipe? Explain. (b) What two harmonics are these? (c) What is the length of the pipe?

16.62. Longitudinal Standing Waves in a Solid. Longitudinal standing waves can be produced in a solid rod by holding it at some point between the fingers of one hand and stroking it with the other hand. The rod oscillates with antinodes at both ends. (a) Why are the ends antinodes and not nodes? (b) The fundamental frequency can be obtained by stroking the rod while it is held at its center. Explain why this is the *only* place to hold the rod to obtain the fundamental. (c) Calculate the fundamental frequency of a steel rod of length 1.50 m (see Table 16.1). (d) What is the next possible standing-wave frequency of this rod? Where should the rod be held to excite a standing wave of this frequency?

16.63. (a) Determine the first three normal-mode frequencies for a pipe of length L that is closed at *both* ends. Explain your reasoning. (b) Use the results of part (a) to estimate the normal-mode frequencies of a shower stall. Explain the connection between these frequencies and the observation that your singing voice probably sounds better in the shower, especially when you sing at certain frequencies.

16.64. One type of steel has a density of $7.8 \times 10^3\ \text{kg/m}^3$ and a breaking stress of $7.0 \times 10^8\ \text{N/m}^2$. A cylindrical guitar string is to be made of 4.00 g of this steel. (a) What are the length and radius of the longest and thinnest string that can be placed under a tension of 900 N without breaking? (b) What is the highest fundamental frequency that this string could have?

16.65. A long tube contains air at a pressure of 1.00 atm and a temperature of 77.0°C. The tube is open at one end and closed at the other by a movable piston. A tuning fork near the open end is vibrating with a frequency of 500 Hz. Resonance is produced when the piston is at distances 18.0, 55.5, and 93.0 cm from the open end. (a) From these measurements, what is the speed of sound in air at 77.0°C? (b) From the result of part (a), what is the value of γ? (c) These data show that a displacement antinode is slightly outside of the open end of the tube. How far outside is it?

16.66. Human Hearing. The auditory canal of the human ear (see Fig. 16.4) extends about 2.5 cm from the outside ear to the eardrum. (a) Explain why the human ear is especially sensitive to sounds at frequencies around 3500 Hz. Use $v = 344\ \text{m/s}$. (b) Would you expect the ear to be especially sensitive to frequencies around 7000 Hz? Around 10,500 Hz? Why or why not?

16.67. A platinum wire (density $21.4\ \text{g/cm}^3$) is 225 μm in diameter and 0.450 m long. One end of the wire is attached to the ceiling, while a 420-g mass is attached to the other end so that the wire hangs vertically under tension. If a vibrating tuning fork of just the right frequency is held next to the wire, the wire begins to vibrate as well. (a) What tuning-fork frequencies will cause this to happen? You may assume that the bottom end of the wire (to which the mass is attached) is essentially stationary, and that the tension in the wire is essentially constant along its length. (b) Justify the assumptions made in part (a).

16.68. The frequency of the note F_4 is 349 Hz. (a) If an organ pipe is open at one end and closed at the other, what length must it have for its fundamental mode to produce this note at 20.0°C? (b) At what air temperature will the frequency be 370 Hz, corresponding to a rise in pitch from F to $F^{\#}$? (Ignore the change in length of the pipe due to the temperature change.)

16.69. A standing wave with a frequency of 1100 Hz in a column of methane (CH_4) at 20.0°C produces nodes that are 0.200 m apart. What is the value of γ for methane? (The molar mass of methane is 16.0 g/mol.)

16.70. Two identical loudspeakers are located at points A and B, 2.00 m apart. The loudspeakers are driven by the same amplifier and produce sound waves with a frequency of 784 Hz. Take the speed of sound in air to be 344 m/s. A small microphone is moved out from point B along a line perpendicular to the line connecting A and B (line BC in Fig. 16.44). (a) At what distances from B will there be *destructive* interference? (b) At what distances from B will there be *constructive* interference? (c) If the frequency is made low enough, there will be no positions along the line BC at which destructive interference occurs. How low must the frequency be for this to be the case?

Figure **16.44** Problem 16.70.

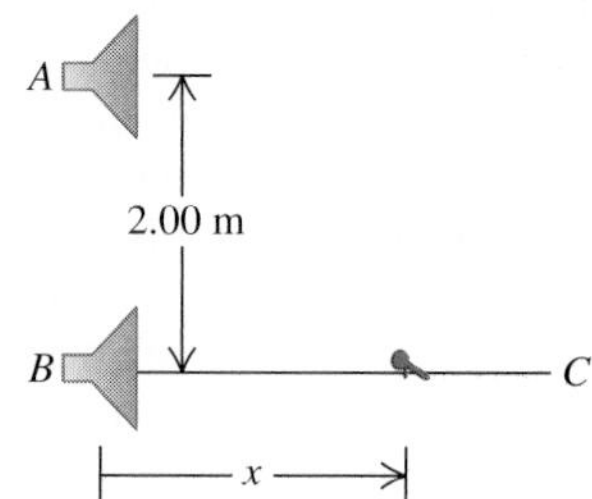

16.71. Wagnerian Opera. A man marries a great Wagnerian soprano but, alas, he discovers he cannot stand Wagnerian opera. In order to save his eardrums, the unhappy man decides he must silence his larklike wife for good. His plan is to tie her to the front of his car and send car and soprano speeding toward a brick wall. This soprano is quite shrewd, however, having studied physics in her student days at the music conservatory. She realizes that this wall has a resonant frequency of 600 Hz, which means that if a continuous sound wave of this frequency hits the wall, it will fall down, and she will be saved to sing more Isoldes. The car is heading toward the wall at a high speed of 30 m/s. (a) At what frequency must the soprano sing so that the wall will crumble? (b) What frequency will the soprano hear reflected from the wall just before it crumbles?

16.72. A bat flies toward a wall, emitting a steady sound of frequency 2.00 kHz. This bat hears its own sound plus the sound reflected by the wall. How fast should the bat fly in order to hear a beat frequency of 10.0 Hz?

16.73. A small sphere of radius R is arranged to pulsate so that its radius varies in simple harmonic motion between a minimum of $R - \Delta R$ and a maximum of $R + \Delta R$ with frequency f. This produces sound waves in the surrounding air of density ρ and bulk modulus B. (a) Find the intensity of sound waves at the surface of the sphere. (The amplitude of oscillation of the sphere is the same as that of the air at the surface of the sphere.) (b) Find the total acoustic power radiated by the sphere. (c) At a distance $d \gg R$ from the center of the sphere, find the amplitude, pressure amplitude, and intensity of the sound wave.

16.74. Ultrasound in Medicine. A 2.00-MHz sound wave travels through a pregnant woman's abdomen and is reflected from the fetal heart wall of her unborn baby. The heart wall is moving toward the sound receiver as the heart beats. The reflected sound is then mixed with the transmitted sound, and 85 beats per second are detected. The speed of sound in body tissue is 1500 m/s. Calculate the speed of the fetal heart wall at the instant this measurement is made.

16.75. The sound source of a ship's sonar system operates at a frequency of 22.0 kHz. The speed of sound in water (assumed to be at a uniform 20°C) is 1482 m/s. (a) What is the wavelength of the waves emitted by the source? (b) What is the difference in frequency between the directly radiated waves and the waves reflected from a whale traveling directly toward the ship at 4.95 m/s? The ship is at rest in the water.

16.76. A police siren of frequency f_{siren} is attached to a vibrating platform. The platform and siren oscillate up and down in simple harmonic motion with amplitude A_p and frequency f_p. (a) Find the maximum and minimum sound frequencies that you would hear at a position directly above the siren. (b) At what point in the motion of the platform is the maximum frequency heard? The minimum frequency? Explain.

16.77. Horseshoe bats (genus *Rhinolophus*) emit sounds from their nostrils and then listen to the frequency of the sound reflected from their prey to determine the prey's speed. (The "horseshoe" that gives the bat its name is a depression around the nostrils that acts like a focusing mirror, so that the bat emits sound in a narrow beam like a flashlight.) A *Rhinolophus* flying at speed v_{bat} emits sound of frequency f_{bat}; the sound it hears reflected from an insect flying toward it has a higher frequency f_{refl}. (a) Show that the speed of the insect is

$$v_{\text{insect}} = v\left[\frac{f_{\text{refl}}(v - v_{\text{bat}}) - f_{\text{bat}}(v + v_{\text{bat}})}{f_{\text{refl}}(v - v_{\text{bat}}) + f_{\text{bat}}(v + v_{\text{bat}})}\right]$$

where v is the speed of sound. (b) If $f_{\text{bat}} = 80.7\text{kHz}$, $f_{\text{refl}} = 83.5\text{kHz}$, and $v_{\text{bat}} = 3.9\text{ m/s}$, calculate the speed of the insect.

16.78. (a) Show that Eq. (16.30) can be written as

$$f_R = f_S\left(1 - \frac{v}{c}\right)^{1/2}\left(1 + \frac{v}{c}\right)^{-1/2}$$

(b) Use the binomial theorem to show that if $v \ll c$, this is approximately equal to

$$f_R = f_S\left(1 - \frac{v}{c}\right)$$

(c) A pilotless reconnaissance aircraft emits a radio signal with a frequency of 243 MHz. It is flying directly toward a test engineer on the ground. The engineer detects beats between the received signal and a local signal also of frequency 243 MHz. The beat frequency is 46.0 Hz. What is the speed of the aircraft? (Radio waves travel at the speed of light, $c = 3.00 \times 10^8\text{ m/s}$.)

16.79. Supernova! The gas cloud known as the Crab Nebula can be seen with even a small telescope. It is the remnant of a *supernova,* a cataclysmic explosion of a star. The explosion was seen on the earth on July 4, 1054 C.E. The streamers glow with the characteristic red color of heated hydrogen gas. In a laboratory on the earth, heated hydrogen produces red light with frequency 4.568×10^{14} Hz; the red light received from streamers in the Crab Nebula pointed toward the earth has frequency 4.586×10^{14} Hz. (a) Estimate the speed with which the outer edges of the Crab Nebula are expanding. Assume that the speed of the center of the nebula relative to the earth is negligible. (You may use the formulas derived in Problem 16.78. The speed of light is $3.00 \times 10^8\text{ m/s}$.) (b) Assuming that the expansion speed has been constant since the supernova explosion, estimate the diameter of the Crab Nebula. Give your answer in meters and in light-years. (c) The angular diameter of the Crab Nebula as seen from earth is about 5 arc minutes $\left(1\text{ arc minute} = \frac{1}{60}\text{ degree}\right)$. Estimate the distance (in light-years) to the Crab Nebula, and estimate the year in which the supernova explosion actually took place.

16.80. Weather Forecasting. A radar installation used for monitoring thunderstorms emits radio waves at a frequency of 2800 MHz. A line of thunderstorms is approaching the installation at 42.0 km/h. (a) In the frame of reference of the thunderstorms, is the frequency of the radio waves greater than or less than 2800 MHz? Why? By what amount does the frequency differ from 2800 MHz? (You may use the formulas derived in Problem 16.78. Radio waves travel at the speed of light, $c = 3.00 \times 10^8\text{ m/s}$.) (b) Radio waves are reflected from the water drops in the thunderstorms, and the reflected waves are detected back at the installation. As measured by the receiver at the installation, is the frequency of these reflected waves greater or less than 2800 MHz? Why? By what amount does the frequency of the reflected waves differ from 2800 MHz?

16.81. A woman stands at rest in front of a large, smooth wall. She holds a vibrating tuning fork of frequency f_0 directly in front of her (between her and the wall). (a) The woman now runs toward the wall with speed v_W. She detects beats due to the interference between the sound waves reaching her directly from the fork and those reaching her after being reflected from the wall. How many beats per second will she detect? (*Note:* If the beat frequency is too large, the woman may have to use some instrumentation other than her ears to detect and count the beats.) (b) If the woman instead runs away from the wall, holding the tuning fork at her back so it is between her and the wall, how many beats per second will she detect?

***16.82.** On a clear day you see a jet plane flying overhead. From the apparent size of the plane, you determine that it is flying at a constant altitude h. You hear the sonic boom at time T after the plane passes directly overhead. Show that if the speed of sound v is the same at all altitudes, the speed of the plane is

$$v_S = \frac{hv}{\sqrt{h^2 - v^2T^2}}$$

(*Hint:* Trigonometric identities will be useful.)

Challenge Problems

16.83. Figure 16.45 shows the pressure fluctuation p of a nonsinusoidal sound wave as a function of x for $t = 0$. The wave is traveling in the $+x$-direction. (a) Graph the pressure fluctuation p as a function of t for $x = 0$. Show at least two cycles of oscillation. (b) Graph the displacement y in this sound wave as a function of x at $t = 0$. At $x = 0$, the displacement at $t = 0$ is zero. Show at least two wavelengths of the wave. (c) Graph the displacement y as a function of t for $x = 0$. Show at least two cycles of oscillation. (d) Calculate the maximum velocity and the maximum acceleration of an element of the air through which this sound wave is traveling. (e) Describe how the cone of a loudspeaker must move as a function of time to produce the sound wave in this problem.

Figure **16.45** Challenge Problem 16.83.

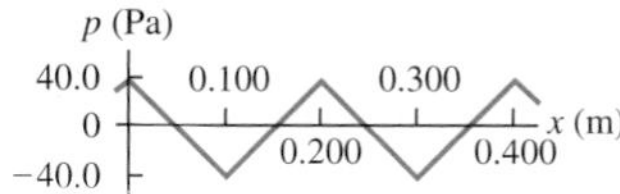

16.84. Two loudspeakers, A and B, radiate sound uniformly in all directions in air at 20°C. The acoustic power output from A is 8.00×10^{-4} W, and from B it is 6.00×10^{-5} W. Both loudspeakers are vibrating in phase at a frequency of 172 Hz. (a) Determine the difference in phase of the two signals at a point C along the line joining A and B, 3.00 m from B and 4.00 m from A (Fig. 16.46). (b) Determine the intensity and sound intensity level at C from speaker A if speaker B is turned off and the intensity and sound intensity level at point C from speaker B if speaker A is turned off. (c) With both speakers on, what are the intensity and sound intensity level at C?

Figure **16.46** Challenge Problem 16.84.

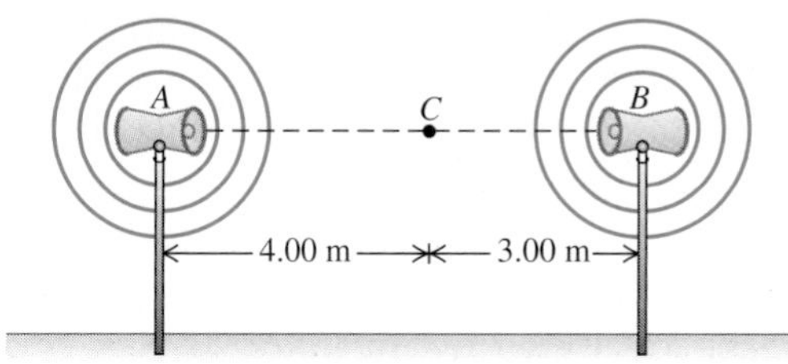

17 TEMPERATURE AND HEAT

LEARNING GOALS

By studying this chapter, you will learn:

- The meaning of thermal equilibrium, and what thermometers really measure.
- How different types of thermometers function.
- The physics behind the absolute, or Kelvin, temperature scale.
- How the dimensions of an object change as a result of a temperature change.
- The meaning of heat, and how it differs from temperature.
- How to do calculations that involve heat flow, temperature changes, and changes of phase.
- How heat is transferred by conduction, convection, and radiation.

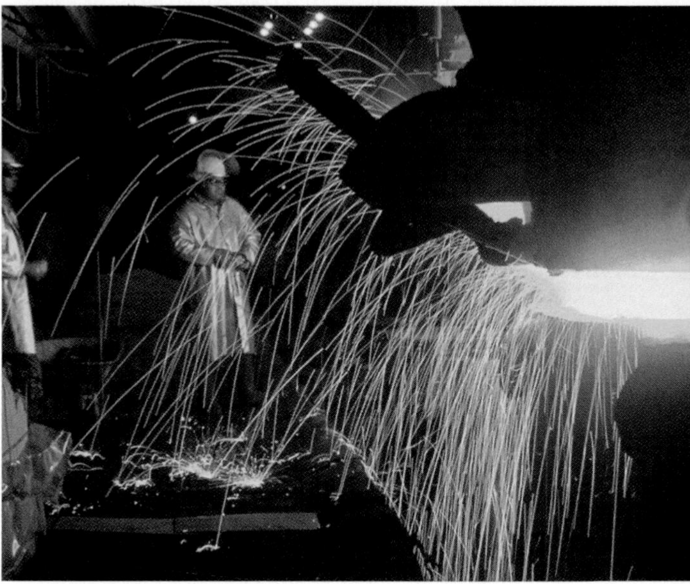

? At a steelworks, molten iron is heated to 1500° Celsius to remove impurities. Is it accurate to say that the molten iron contains heat?

Whether it's a sweltering summer day or a frozen midwinter night, your body needs to be kept at a nearly constant temperature. It has effective temperature-control mechanisms, but sometimes it needs help. On a hot day you wear less clothing to improve heat transfer from your body to the air and for better cooling by evaporation of perspiration. You drink cold beverages and may sit near a fan or in an air-conditioned room. On a cold day you wear more clothes or stay indoors where it's warm. When you're outside, you keep active and drink hot liquids to stay warm. The concepts in this chapter will help you understand the basic physics of keeping warm or cool.

The terms "temperature" and "heat" are often used interchangeably in everyday language. In physics, however, these two terms have very different meanings. In this chapter we'll define temperature in terms of how it's measured and see how temperature changes affect the dimensions of objects. We'll see that heat refers to energy transfer caused by temperature differences and learn how to calculate and control such energy transfers.

Our emphasis in this chapter is on the concepts of temperature and heat as they relate to *macroscopic* objects such as cylinders of gas, ice cubes, and the human body. In Chapter 18 we'll look at these same concepts from a *microscopic* viewpoint in terms of the behavior of individual atoms and molecules. These two chapters lay the groundwork for the subject of **thermodynamics,** the study of energy transformations involving heat, mechanical work, and other aspects of energy and how these transformations relate to the properties of matter. Thermodynamics forms an indispensable part of the foundation of physics, chemistry, and the life sciences, and its applications turn up in such places as car engines, refrigerators, biochemical processes, and the structure of stars. We'll explore the key ideas of thermodynamics in Chapters 19 and 20.

17.1 Temperature and Thermal Equilibrium

The concept of **temperature** is rooted in qualitative ideas of "hot" and "cold" based on our sense of touch. A body that feels hot usually has a higher temperature than a similar body that feels cold. That's pretty vague, and the senses can be deceived. But many properties of matter that we can *measure* depend on temperature. The length of a metal rod, steam pressure in a boiler, the ability of a wire to conduct an electric current, and the color of a very hot glowing object—all these depend on temperature.

Temperature is also related to the kinetic energies of the molecules of a material. In general this relationship is fairly complex, so it's not a good place to start in *defining* temperature. In Chapter 18 we will look at the relationship between temperature and the energy of molecular motion for an ideal gas. It is important to understand, however, that temperature and heat can be defined independently of any detailed molecular picture. In this section we'll develop a *macroscopic* definition of temperature.

To use temperature as a measure of hotness or coldness, we need to construct a temperature scale. To do this, we can use any measurable property of a system that varies with its "hotness" or "coldness." Figure 17.1a shows a familiar system that is used to measure temperature. When the system becomes hotter, the colored liquid (usually mercury or ethanol) expands and rises in the tube, and the value of L increases. Another simple system is a quantity of gas in a constant-volume container (Fig. 17.1b). The pressure p, measured by the gauge, increases or decreases as the gas becomes hotter or colder. A third example is the electrical resistance R of a conducting wire, which also varies when the wire becomes hotter or colder. Each of these properties gives us a number (L, p, or R) that varies with hotness and coldness, so each property can be used to make a **thermometer.**

17.1 Two devices for measuring temperature.

(a) Changes in temperature cause the liquid's volume to change.

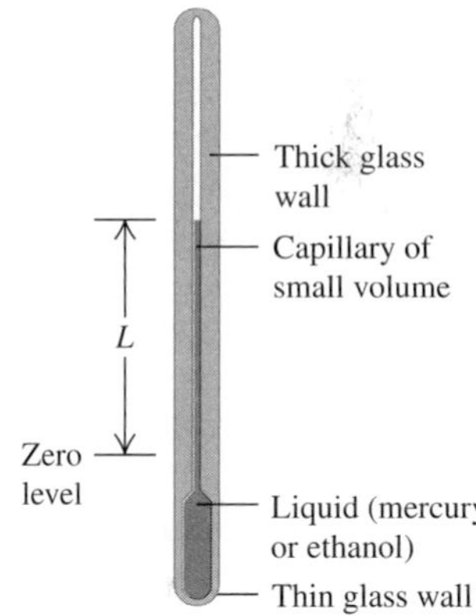

(b) Changes in temperature cause the pressure of the gas to change.

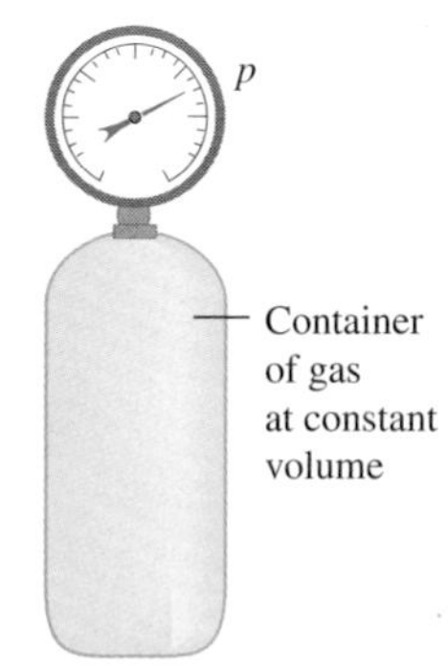

To measure the temperature of a body, you place the thermometer in contact with the body. If you want to know the temperature of a cup of hot coffee, you stick the thermometer in the coffee; as the two interact, the thermometer becomes hotter and the coffee cools off a little. After the thermometer settles down to a steady value, you read the temperature. The system has reached an *equilibrium* condition, in which the interaction between the thermometer and the coffee causes no further change in the system. We call this a state of **thermal equilibrium.**

If two systems are separated by an insulating material or **insulator** such as wood, plastic foam, or fiberglass, they influence each other more slowly. Camping coolers are made with insulating materials to delay the ice and cold food inside from warming up and attaining thermal equilibrium with the hot summer air outside. An *ideal insulator* is a material that permits no interaction at all between the two systems. It prevents the systems from attaining thermal equilibrium if they aren't in thermal equilibrium at the start. An ideal insulator is just that, an idealization; real insulators, like those in camping coolers, aren't ideal, so the contents of the cooler will warm up eventually.

The Zeroth Law of Thermodynamics

We can discover an important property of thermal equilibrium by considering three systems, A, B, and C, that initially are not in thermal equilibrium (Fig. 17.2). We surround them with an ideal insulating box so that they cannot interact with anything except each other. We separate systems A and B with an ideal insulating wall (the green slab in Fig. 17.2a), but we let system C interact with both systems A and B. This interaction is shown in the figure by a yellow slab representing a thermal **conductor,** a material that *permits* thermal interactions through it. We wait until thermal equilibrium is attained; then A and B are each in thermal equilibrium with C. But are they in thermal equilibrium *with each other?*

To find out, we separate system C from systems A and B with an ideal insulating wall (Fig. 17.2b), and then we replace the insulating wall between A and B with a

17.2 The zeroth law of thermodynamics.

(a) If systems A and B are each in thermal equilibrium with system C ...

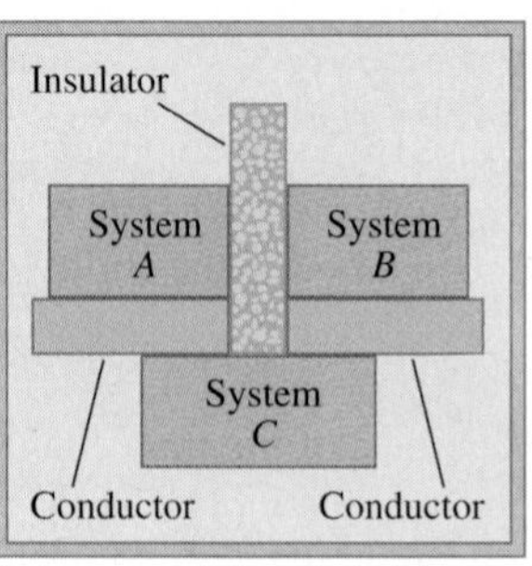

(b) ... then systems A and B are in thermal equilibrium with each other.

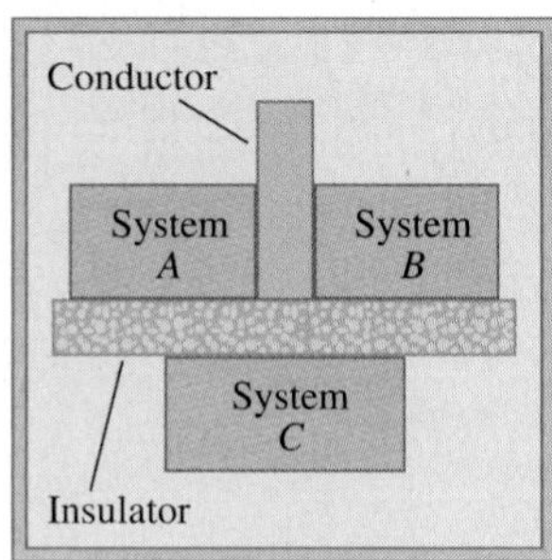

conducting wall that lets A and B interact. What happens? Experiment shows that *nothing* happens; there are no additional changes to A or B. We conclude

If C is initially in thermal equilibrium with both A and B, then A and B are also in thermal equilibrium with each other. This result is called the zeroth law of thermodynamics.

(The importance of this law was recognized only after the first, second, and third laws of thermodynamics had been named. Since it is fundamental to all of them, the name "zeroth" seemed appropriate.)

Now suppose system C is a thermometer, such as the tube-and-liquid system of Fig. 17.1a. In Fig. 17.2a the thermometer C is in contact with both A and B. In thermal equilibrium, when the thermometer reading reaches a stable value, the thermometer measures the temperature of both A and B; hence A and B both have the *same* temperature. Experiment shows that thermal equilibrium isn't affected by adding or removing insulators, so the reading of thermometer C wouldn't change if it were in contact only with A or only with B. We conclude

Two systems are in thermal equilibrium if and only if they have the same temperature.

This is what makes a thermometer useful; a thermometer actually measures *its own* temperature, but when a thermometer is in thermal equilibrium with another body, the temperatures must be equal. When the temperatures of two systems are different, they *cannot* be in thermal equilibrium.

Test Your Understanding of Section 17.1 You put a thermometer in a pot of hot water and record the reading. What temperature have you recorded? (i) the temperature of the water; (ii) the temperature of the thermometer; (iii) an equal average of the temperatures of the water and thermometer; (iv) a weighted average of the temperatures of the water and thermometer, with more emphasis on the temperature of the water; (v) a weighted average of the water and thermometer, with more emphasis on the temperature of the thermometer.

17.2 Thermometers and Temperature Scales

To make the liquid-in-tube device shown in Fig. 17.1a into a useful thermometer, we need to mark a scale on the tube wall with numbers on it. These numbers are arbitrary, and historically many different schemes have been used. Suppose we label the thermometer's liquid level at the freezing temperature of pure water "zero" and the level at the boiling temperature "100," and divide the distance between these two points into 100 equal intervals called *degrees*. The result is the **Celsius temperature scale** (formerly called the *centigrade* scale in English-speaking countries). The Celsius temperature for a state colder than freezing water is a negative number. The Celsius scale is used, both in everyday life and in science and industry, almost everywhere in the world.

Another common type of thermometer uses a *bimetallic strip,* made by bonding strips of two different metals together (Fig. 17.3a). When the temperature of the composite strip increases, one metal expands more than the other and the strip bends (Fig. 17.3b). This strip is usually formed into a spiral, with the outer end anchored to the thermometer case and the inner end attached to a pointer (Fig. 17.3c). The pointer rotates in response to temperature changes.

In a *resistance thermometer* the changing electrical resistance of a coil of fine wire, a carbon cylinder, or a germanium crystal is measured. Because resistance can be measured very precisely, resistance thermometers are usually more precise than most other types.

Some thermometers work by detecting the amount of infrared radiation emitted by an object. (We'll see in Section 17.7 that *all* objects emit electromagnetic radiation, including infrared, as a consequence of their temperature.) A modern example is a *temporal artery thermometer* (Fig. 17.4). A nurse runs this over a patient's forehead in the vicinity of the temporal artery, and an infrared sensor in the thermometer measures the radiation from the skin. Tests show that this device gives more accurate values of body temperature than do oral or ear thermometers.

In the **Fahrenheit temperature scale,** still used in everyday life in the United States, the freezing temperature of water is 32°F (thirty-two degrees Fahrenheit) and the boiling temperature is 212°F, both at standard atmospheric pressure. There are 180 degrees between freezing and boiling, compared to 100 on the Celsius scale, so one Fahrenheit degree represents only $\frac{100}{180}$, or $\frac{5}{9}$, as great a temperature change as one Celsius degree.

To convert temperatures from Celsius to Fahrenheit, note that a Celsius temperature T_C is the number of Celsius degrees above freezing; the number of Fahrenheit degrees above freezing is $\frac{9}{5}$ of this. But freezing on the Fahrenheit scale is at 32°F, so to obtain the actual Fahrenheit temperature T_F, multiply the Celsius value by $\frac{9}{5}$ and then add 32°. Symbolically,

$$T_F = \frac{9}{5}T_C + 32° \qquad (17.1)$$

To convert Fahrenheit to Celsius, solve this equation for T_C:

$$T_C = \frac{5}{9}(T_F - 32°) \qquad (17.2)$$

In words, subtract 32° to get the number of Fahrenheit degrees above freezing, and then multiply by $\frac{5}{9}$ to obtain the number of Celsius degrees above freezing—that is, the Celsius temperature.

We don't recommend memorizing Eqs. (17.1) and (17.2). Instead, try to understand the reasoning that led to them so that you can derive them on the spot when you need them, checking your reasoning with the relationship 100°C = 212°F.

It is useful to distinguish between an actual temperature and a temperature *interval* (a difference or change in temperature). An actual temperature of 20° is stated as 20°C (twenty degrees Celsius), and a temperature *interval* of 10° is 10 C° (ten Celsius degrees). A beaker of water heated from 20°C to 30°C undergoes a temperature change of 10 C°.

Test Your Understanding of Section 17.2 Which of the following types of thermometers have to be in thermal equilibrium with the object being measured in order to give accurate readings? (i) a bimetallic strip; (ii) a resistance thermometer; (iii) a temporal artery thermometer; (iv) both (i) and (ii); (v) all of (i), (ii), and (iii).

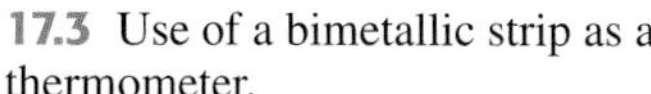

17.3 Use of a bimetallic strip as a thermometer.

(a) A bimetallic strip

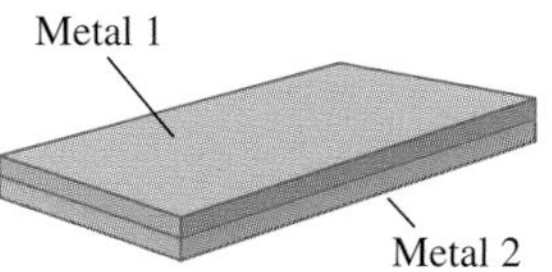

(b) The strip bends when its temperature is raised.

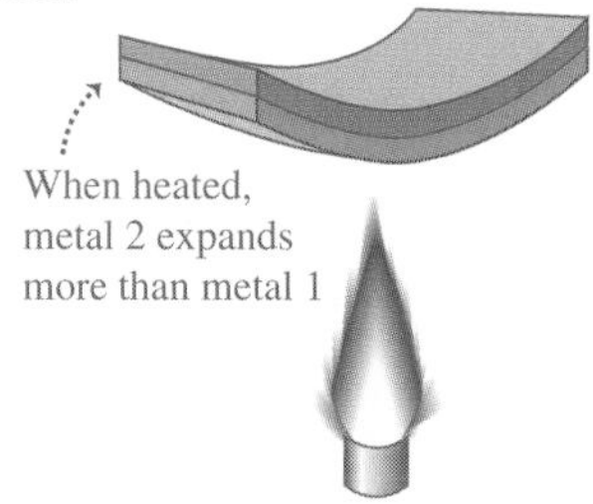

(c) A bimetallic strip used in a thermometer

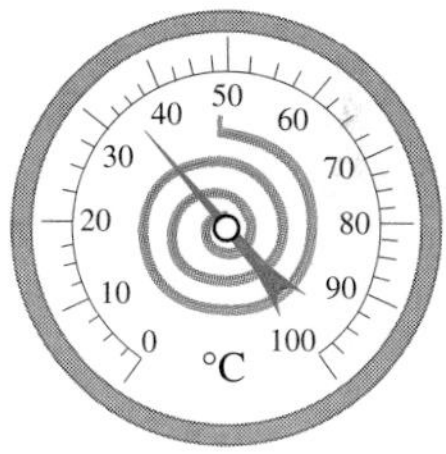

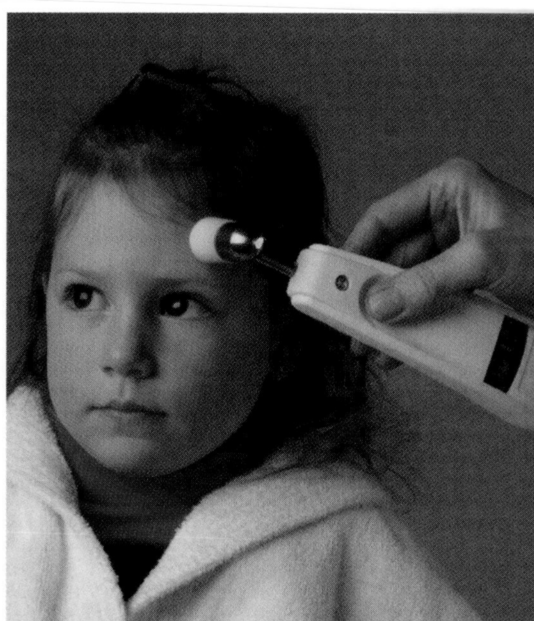

17.4 A temporal artery thermometer measures infrared radiation from the skin that overlies one of the important arteries in the head. Although the thermometer cover touches the skin, the infrared detector inside the cover does not.

17.3 Gas Thermometers and the Kelvin Scale

When we calibrate two thermometers, such as a liquid-in-tube system and a resistance thermometer, so that they agree at 0°C and 100°C, they may not agree exactly at intermediate temperatures. Any temperature scale defined in this way always depends somewhat on the specific properties of the material used. Ideally, we would like to define a temperature scale that *doesn't* depend on the properties of a particular material. To establish a truly material-independent scale, we first need to develop some principles of thermodynamics. We'll return to this fundamental problem in Chapter 20. Here we'll discuss a thermometer that comes close to the ideal, the *gas thermometer.*

The principle of a gas thermometer is that the pressure of a gas at constant volume increases with temperature. A quantity of gas is placed in a constant-volume container (Fig. 17.5a), and its pressure is measured by one of the devices described in Section 14.2. To calibrate a constant-volume gas thermometer, we measure the pressure at two temperatures, say 0°C and 100°C, plot these points on a graph, and draw a straight line between them. Then we can read from the graph the temperature corresponding to any other pressure. Figure 17.5b shows the results of three such experiments, each using a different type and quantity of gas.

By extrapolating this graph, we see that there is a hypothetical temperature, −273.15°C, at which the absolute pressure of the gas would become zero. We might expect that this temperature would be different for different gases, but it turns out to be the *same* for many different gases (at least in the limit of very low gas density). We can't actually observe this zero-pressure condition. Gases liquefy and solidify at very low temperatures, and the proportionality of pressure to temperature no longer holds.

We use this extrapolated zero-pressure temperature as the basis for a temperature scale with its zero at this temperature. This is the **Kelvin temperature scale,** named for the British physicist Lord Kelvin (1824–1907). The units are the same size as those on the Celsius scale, but the zero is shifted so that 0 K = −273.15°C and 273.15 K = 0°C; that is,

$$T_K = T_C + 273.15 \tag{17.3}$$

This scale is shown in Fig. 17.5b. A common room temperature, 20°C (= 68°F), is 20 + 273.15, or about 293 K.

17.5 (a) Using a constant-volume gas thermometer to measure temperature. (b) The greater the amount of gas in the thermometer, the higher the graph of pressure p versus temperature T.

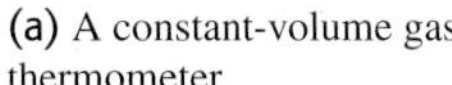

(a) A constant-volume gas thermometer

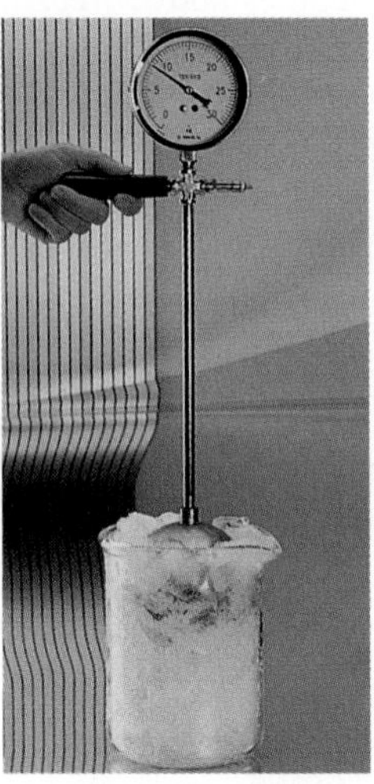

(b) Graphs of pressure versus temperature at constant volume for three different types and quantities of gas

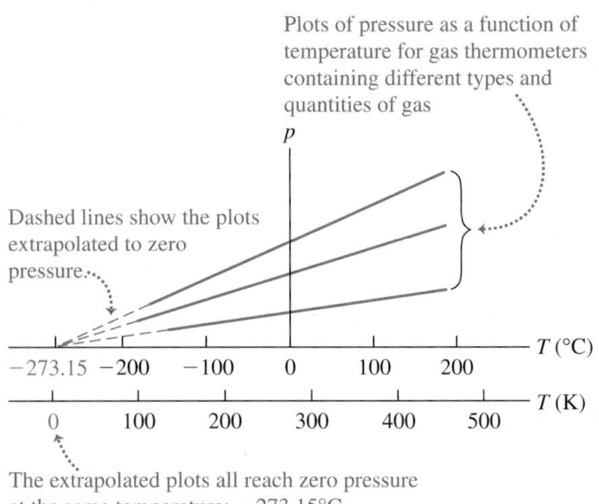
Plots of pressure as a function of temperature for gas thermometers containing different types and quantities of gas
p
Dashed lines show the plots extrapolated to zero pressure.
T (°C)
−273.15 −200 −100 0 100 200
T (K)
0 100 200 300 400 500
The extrapolated plots all reach zero pressure at the same temperature: −273.15°C.

CAUTION Never say "degrees kelvin" In SI nomenclature, "degree" is not used with the Kelvin scale; the temperature mentioned above is read "293 kelvins," not "degrees kelvin" (Fig. 17.6). We capitalize Kelvin when it refers to the temperature scale; however, the *unit* of temperature is the *kelvin,* which is not capitalized (but is nonetheless abbreviated as a capital K).

17.6 Correct and incorrect uses of the Kelvin scale.

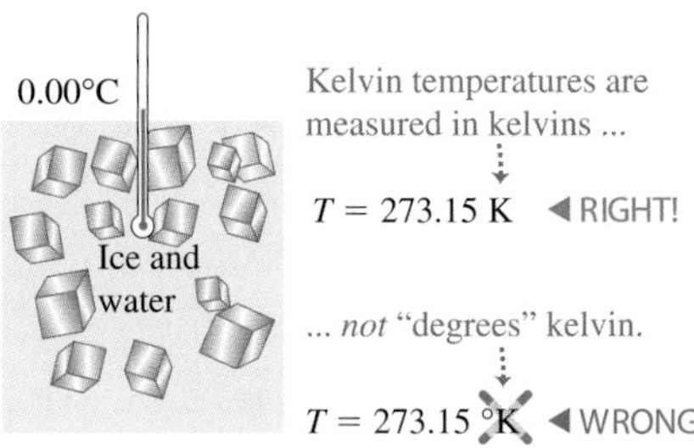

Example 17.1 Body temperature

You place a small piece of melting ice in your mouth. Eventually, the water all converts from ice at $T_1 = 32.00°\text{F}$ to body temperature, $T_2 = 98.60°\text{F}$. Express these temperatures as °C and K, and find $\Delta T = T_2 - T_1$ in both cases.

SOLUTION

IDENTIFY: Our target variables are temperatures T_1 and T_2 expressed in Celsius degrees and in kelvins, as well as the difference between these two temperatures.

SET UP: We convert Fahrenheit to Celsius temperatures using Eq. (17.2), and Celsius to Kelvin temperatures using Eq. (17.3).

EXECUTE: First we find the Celsius temperatures. We know that $T_1 = 32.00°\text{F} = 0.00°\text{C}$, and 98.60°F is $98.60 - 32.00 =$ 66.60 F° above freezing; we multiply this by $(5\ \text{C}°/9\ \text{F}°)$ to find 37.00 C° above freezing, or $T_2 = 37.00°\text{C}$.

To get the Kelvin temperatures, we just add 273.15 to each Celsius temperature: $T_1 = 273.15\ \text{K}$ and $T_2 = 310.15\ \text{K}$. "Normal" body temperature is 37.0°C, but if your doctor says that your temperature is 310 K, don't be alarmed.

The temperature *difference* $\Delta T = T_2 - T_1$ is $37.00\ \text{C}° = 37.00\ \text{K}$.

EVALUATE: The Celsius and Kelvin scales have different zero points but the same size degrees. Therefore any temperature difference is the *same* on the Celsius and Kelvin scales but not the same on the Fahrenheit scale.

The Kelvin Scale and Absolute Temperature

The Celsius scale has two fixed points, the normal freezing and boiling temperatures of water. But we can define the Kelvin scale using a gas thermometer with only a single reference temperature. We define the ratio of any two temperatures T_1 and T_2 on the Kelvin scale as the ratio of the corresponding gas-thermometer pressures p_1 and p_2:

$$\frac{T_2}{T_1} = \frac{p_2}{p_1} \quad \text{(constant-volume gas thermometer, } T \text{ in kelvins)} \tag{17.4}$$

The pressure p is directly proportional to the Kelvin temperature, as shown in Fig. 17.5b. To complete the definition of T, we need only specify the Kelvin temperature of a single specific state. For reasons of precision and reproducibility, the state chosen is the *triple point* of water. This is the unique combination of temperature and pressure at which solid water (ice), liquid water, and water vapor can all coexist. It occurs at a temperature of 0.01°C and a water-vapor pressure of 610 Pa (about 0.006 atm). (This is the pressure of the *water;* it has nothing to do directly with the gas pressure in the *thermometer.*) The triple-point temperature T_{triple} of water is *defined* to have the value $T_{\text{triple}} = 273.16\ \text{K}$, corresponding to 0.01°C. From Eq. (17.4), if p_{triple} is the pressure in a gas thermometer at temperature T_{triple} and p is the pressure at some other temperature T, then T is given on the Kelvin scale by

$$T = T_{\text{triple}}\frac{p}{p_{\text{triple}}} = (273.16\ \text{K})\frac{p}{p_{\text{triple}}} \tag{17.5}$$

17.7 Relationships among Kelvin (K), Celsius (C), and Fahrenheit (F) temperature scales. Temperatures have been rounded off to the nearest degree.

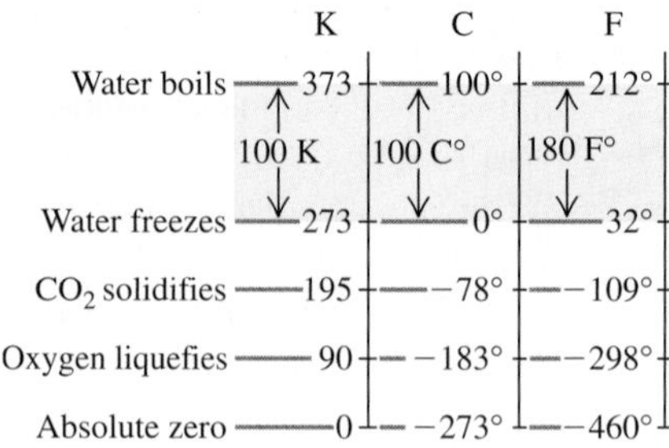

Low-pressure gas thermometers using various gases are found to agree very closely, but they are large, bulky, and very slow to come to thermal equilibrium. They are used principally to establish high-precision standards and to calibrate other thermometers.

Figure 17.7 shows the relationships among the three temperature scales we have discussed. The Kelvin scale is called an **absolute temperature scale,** and its zero point ($T = 0\text{ K} = -273.15°\text{C}$, the temperature at which $p = 0$ in Eq. (17.5)) is called **absolute zero.** At absolute zero a system of molecules (such as a quantity of a gas, a liquid, or a solid) has its *minimum* possible total energy (kinetic plus potential); because of quantum effects, however, it is *not* correct to say that all molecular motion ceases at absolute zero. To define more completely what we mean by absolute zero, we need to use the thermodynamic principles developed in the next several chapters. We will return to this concept in Chapter 20.

Test Your Understanding of Section 17.3 Rank the following temperatures from highest to lowest: (i) 0.00°C; (ii) 0.00°F (iii) 260.00 K; (iv) 77.00 K; (v) −180.00°C.

17.4 Thermal Expansion

Most materials expand when their temperatures increase. Rising temperatures make the liquid expand in a liquid-in-tube thermometer (Fig. 17.1a) and bend bimetallic strips (Fig. 17.3b). The decks of bridges need special joints and supports to allow for expansion. A completely filled and tightly capped bottle of water cracks when it is heated, but you can loosen a metal jar lid by running hot water over it. These are all examples of *thermal expansion.*

Linear Expansion

Suppose a rod of material has a length L_0 at some initial temperature T_0. When the temperature changes by ΔT, the length changes by ΔL. Experiments show that if ΔT is not too large (say, less than 100 C° or so), ΔL is *directly proportional* to ΔT (Fig. 17.8a). If two rods made of the same material have the same temperature change, but one is twice as long as the other, then the *change* in its length is also twice as great. Therefore ΔL must also be proportional to L_0 (Fig. 17.8b). Introducing a proportionality constant α (which is different for different materials), we may express these relationships in an equation:

$$\Delta L = \alpha L_0 \Delta T \quad \text{(linear thermal expansion)} \tag{17.6}$$

If a body has length L_0 at temperature T_0, then its length L at a temperature $T = T_0 + \Delta T$ is

$$L = L_0 + \Delta L = L_0 + \alpha L_0 \Delta T = L_0(1 + \alpha \Delta T) \tag{17.7}$$

The constant α, which describes the thermal expansion properties of a particular material, is called the **coefficient of linear expansion.** The units of α are K^{-1} or $(\text{C}°)^{-1}$. (Remember that a temperature *interval* is the same in the Kelvin and Celsius scales.) For many materials, every linear dimension changes according to Eq. (17.6) or (17.7). Thus L could be the thickness of a rod, the side length of a square sheet, or the diameter of a hole. Some materials, such as wood or single crystals, expand differently in different directions. We won't consider this complication.

17.8 How the length of a rod changes with a change in temperature. (Length changes are exaggerated for clarity.)

(a) For moderate temperature changes, ΔL is directly proportional to ΔT.

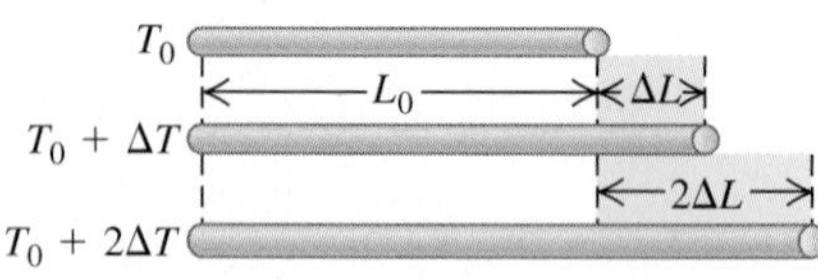

(b) ΔL is also directly proportional to L_0.

T_0 — L_0 — ΔL — $T_0 + \Delta T$

T_0 — $2L_0$ — $2\Delta L$ — $T_0 + \Delta T$

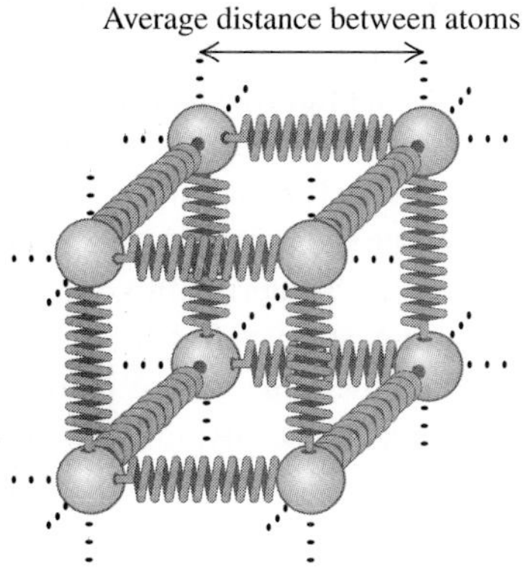

(a) A model of the forces between neighboring atoms in a solid
Average distance between atoms

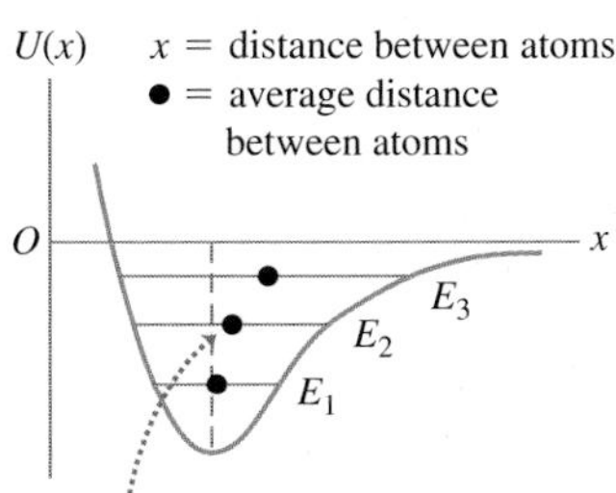

17.9 (a) We can model atoms in a solid as being held together by "springs" that are easier to stretch than to compress. (b) A graph of the "spring" potential energy $U(x)$ versus distance x between neighboring atoms is *not* symmetrical (compare Fig. 13.20b). As the energy increases and the atoms oscillate with greater amplitude, the *average* distance increases.

We can understand thermal expansion qualitatively on a molecular basis. Picture the interatomic forces in a solid as springs, as in Fig. 17.9. (We explored the analogy between spring forces and interatomic forces in Section 13.4.) Each atom vibrates about its equilibrium position. When the temperature increases, the energy and amplitude of the vibration also increase. The interatomic spring forces are not symmetrical about the equilibrium position; they usually behave like a spring that is easier to stretch than to compress. As a result, when the amplitude of vibration increases, the *average* distance between atoms also increases. As the atoms get farther apart, every dimension increases.

CAUTION **Heating an object with a hole** If a solid object has a hole in it, what happens to the size of the hole when the temperature of the object increases? A common misconception is that if the object expands, the hole will shrink because material expands into the hole. But the truth of the matter is that if the object expands, the hole will expand too (Fig. 17.10); as we stated above, *every* linear dimension of an object changes in the same way when the temperature changes. If you're not convinced, think of the atoms in Fig. 17.9a as outlining a cubical hole. When the object expands, the atoms move apart and the hole increases in size. The only situation in which a "hole" will fill in due to thermal expansion is when two separate objects expand and close the gap between them (Fig. 17.11).

17.10 When an object undergoes thermal expansion, any holes in the object expand as well. (The expansion is exaggerated.)

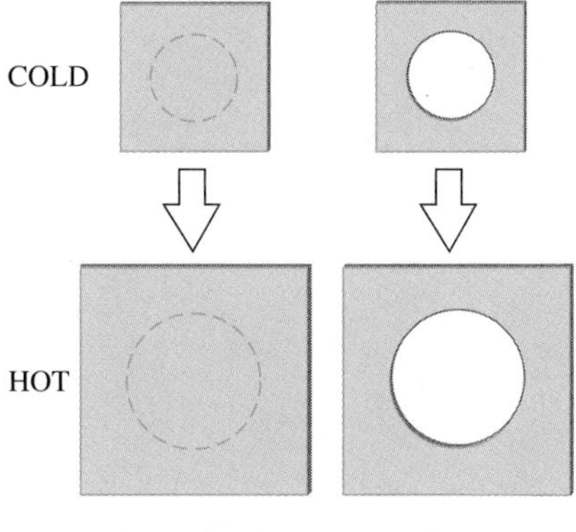

...so a hole cut out of the plate must expand, too.

The direct proportionality expressed by Eq. (17.6) is not exact; it is *approximately* correct only for sufficiently small temperature changes. For a given material, α varies somewhat with the initial temperature T_0 and the size of the temperature interval. We'll ignore this complication here, however. Average values of α for several materials are listed in Table 17.1 on page 578. Within the precision of these values we don't need to worry whether T_0 is 0°C or 20°C or some other temperature. Note that typical values of α are very small; even for a temperature change of 100 C°, the fractional length change $\Delta L/L_0$ is only of the order of $1/1000$ for the metals in the table.

17.11 When this SR-71 aircraft is sitting on the ground, its wing panels fit together so loosely that fuel leaks out of the wings onto the ground. But once it is in flight at over three times the speed of sound, air friction heats the panels so much that they expand to make a perfect fit. (In-flight refueling makes up for the lost fuel.)

Volume Expansion

Increasing temperature usually causes increases in *volume* for both solid and liquid materials. Just as with linear expansion, experiments show that if the temperature change ΔT is not too great (less than 100 C° or so), the increase in volume ΔV is approximately proportional to both the temperature change ΔT and the initial volume V_0:

$$\Delta V = \beta V_0 \Delta T \quad \text{(volume thermal expansion)} \quad (17.8)$$

Table 17.1 Coefficients of Linear Expansion

Material	α [K^{-1} or $(C°)^{-1}$]
Aluminum	2.4×10^{-5}
Brass	2.0×10^{-5}
Copper	1.7×10^{-5}
Glass	$0.4–0.9 \times 10^{-5}$
Invar (nickel–iron alloy)	0.09×10^{-5}
Quartz (fused)	0.04×10^{-5}
Steel	1.2×10^{-5}

The constant β characterizes the volume expansion properties of a particular material; it is called the **coefficient of volume expansion.** The units of β are K^{-1} or $(C°)^{-1}$. As with linear expansion, β varies somewhat with temperature, and Eq. (17.8) is an approximate relationship that is valid only for small temperature changes. For many substances, β decreases at low temperatures. Several values of β in the neighborhood of room temperature are listed in Table 17.2. Note that the values for liquids are generally much larger than those for solids.

For solid materials there is a simple relationship between the volume expansion coefficient β and the linear expansion coefficient α. To derive this relationship, we consider a cube of material with side length L and volume $V = L^3$. At the initial temperature the values are L_0 and V_0. When the temperature increases by dT, the side length increases by dL and the volume increases by an amount dV given by

$$dV = \frac{dV}{dL}\,dL = 3L^2\,dL$$

Now we replace L and V by the initial values L_0 and V_0. From Eq. (17.6), dL is

$$dL = \alpha L_0\,dT$$

Since $V_0 = L_0^3$, this means that dV can also be expressed as

$$dV = 3L_0^2\alpha L_0\,dT = 3\alpha V_0\,dT$$

This is consistent with the infinitesimal form of Eq. (17.8), $dV = \beta V_0\,dT$, only if

$$\beta = 3\alpha \tag{17.9}$$

You should check this relationship for some of the materials listed in Tables 17.1 and 17.2.

Table 17.2 Coefficients of Volume Expansion

Solids	β [K^{-1} or $(C°)^{-1}$]	Liquids	β [K^{-1} or $(C°)^{-1}$]
Aluminum	7.2×10^{-5}	Ethanol	75×10^{-5}
Brass	6.0×10^{-5}	Carbon disulfide	115×10^{-5}
Copper	5.1×10^{-5}	Glycerin	49×10^{-5}
Glass	$1.2–2.7 \times 10^{-5}$	Mercury	18×10^{-5}
Invar	0.27×10^{-5}		
Quartz (fused)	0.12×10^{-5}		
Steel	3.6×10^{-5}		

Problem-Solving Strategy 17.1 Thermal Expansion

IDENTIFY *the relevant concepts:* Decide whether the problem involves changes in length (linear thermal expansion) or in volume (volume thermal expansion).

SET UP *the problem* using the following steps:

1. Choose Eq. (17.6) for linear expansion and Eq. (17.8) for volume expansion.
2. Identify which quantities in Eq. (17.6) or (17.8) are known and which are the unknown target variables.

EXECUTE *the solution* as follows:

1. Solve for the target variables. Often you will be given two temperatures and asked to compute ΔT. Or you may be given an initial temperature T_0 and asked to find a final temperature corresponding to a given length or volume change. In this case, plan to find ΔT first; then the final temperature is $T_0 + \Delta T$.
2. Unit consistency is crucial, as always. L_0 and ΔL (or V_0 and ΔV) must have the same units, and if you use a value of α or β in K^{-1} or $(C°)^{-1}$, then ΔT must be in kelvins or Celsius degrees $(C°)$. But you can use K and C° interchangeably.

EVALUATE *your answer:* Check whether your results make sense. Remember that the sizes of holes in a material expand with temperature just the same way as any other linear dimension, and the volume of a hole (such as the volume of a container) expands the same way as the corresponding solid shape.

Example 17.2 Length change due to temperature change I

A surveyor uses a steel measuring tape that is exactly 50.000 m long at a temperature of 20°C. What is its length on a hot summer day when the temperature is 35°C?

SOLUTION

IDENTIFY: This problem concerns linear expansion. We are given the initial length and initial temperature of the tape, and our target variable is the tape's length at the final temperature.

SET UP: We use Eq. (17.6) to find the change ΔL in the tape's length. We are given $L = 50.000$ m, $T_0 = 20°\text{C}$, and $T = 35°\text{C}$, and the value of α is found from Table 17.1. The target variable is the new length $L = L_0 + \Delta L$.

EXECUTE: The temperature change is $\Delta T = T - T_0 = 15\ \text{C}°$, so from Eq. (17.6) the change in length ΔL and the final length $L = L_0 + \Delta L$ are

$$\Delta L = \alpha L_0 \Delta T = (1.2 \times 10^{-5}\ \text{K}^{-1})(50\ \text{m})(15\ \text{K})$$
$$= 9.0 \times 10^{-3}\ \text{m} = 9.0\ \text{mm}$$
$$L = L_0 + \Delta L = 50.000\ \text{m} + 0.009\ \text{m} = 50.009\ \text{m}$$

Thus the length at 35°C is 50.009 m.

EVALUATE: Note that L_0 is given to five significant figures but that we need only two of them to compute ΔL. Note also that ΔL is proportional to the initial length L_0: A 5.0-m tape would expand by 0.90 mm, and a 0.50-m (50-cm) tape would expand by a mere 0.090 mm.

This example shows that metals expand very little under moderate temperature changes. Even a metal baking pan in a 200°C (392°F) oven is only slightly larger than it is at room temperature.

Example 17.3 Length change due to temperature change II

In Example 17.2 the surveyor uses the measuring tape to measure a distance when the temperature is 35°C; the value that she reads off the tape is 35.794 m. What is the actual distance? Assume that the tape is calibrated for use at 20°C.

SOLUTION

IDENTIFY: As we saw in Example 17.2, at 35°C the tape has expanded slightly. The distance between two successive meter marks is slightly more than 1 meter, so the scale underestimates the actual distance.

SET UP: The actual distance (our target variable) is *larger* than the distance read off the tape by a factor equal to the ratio of the tape's length L at 35°C to its length L_0 at 20°C.

EXECUTE: The ratio L/L_0 is $(50.009\ \text{m})/(50.000\ \text{m})$, so the true distance is

$$\frac{50.009\ \text{m}}{50.000\ \text{m}}(35.794\ \text{m}) = 35.800\ \text{m}$$

EVALUATE: Although the difference of $0.008\ \text{m} = 8\ \text{mm}$ between the scale reading and the actual distance seems small, it can be important in precision work.

Example 17.4 Volume change due to temperature change

A glass flask with volume 200 cm^3 is filled to the brim with mercury at 20°C. How much mercury overflows when the temperature of the system is raised to 100°C? The coefficient of linear expansion of the glass is $0.40 \times 10^{-5}\ \text{K}^{-1}$.

SOLUTION

IDENTIFY: This problem involves the volume expansion of the glass and of the mercury. The amount of overflow depends on the *difference* between the volume changes for these two materials.

SET UP: The amount of overflow is equal to the difference between the values of ΔV for mercury and for glass, both given by Eq. (17.8). For the mercury to overflow, its coefficient of volume expansion β must be larger than that for glass. The value for mercury is $\beta_{\text{mercury}} = 18 \times 10^{-5}\ \text{K}^{-1}$ from Table 17.2, and we find the value of β for this type of glass from Eq. (17.9), $\beta = 3\alpha$.

EXECUTE: The coefficient of volume expansion for the glass is

$$\beta_{\text{glass}} = 3\alpha_{\text{glass}} = 3(0.40 \times 10^{-5}\ \text{K}^{-1}) = 1.2 \times 10^{-5}\ \text{K}^{-1}$$

Continued

The increase in volume of the glass flask is

$$\begin{aligned}\Delta V_{\text{glass}} &= \beta_{\text{glass}} V_0 \Delta T \\ &= (1.2 \times 10^{-5}\ \text{K}^{-1})(200\ \text{cm}^3)(100°\text{C} - 20°\text{C}) \\ &= 0.19\ \text{cm}^3\end{aligned}$$

The increase in volume of the mercury is

$$\begin{aligned}\Delta V_{\text{mercury}} &= \beta_{\text{mercury}} V_0 \Delta T \\ &= (18 \times 10^{-5}\ \text{K}^{-1})(200\ \text{cm}^3)(100°\text{C} - 20°\text{C}) \\ &= 2.9\ \text{cm}^3\end{aligned}$$

The volume of mercury that overflows is

$$\Delta V_{\text{mercury}} - \Delta V_{\text{glass}} = 2.9\ \text{cm}^3 - 0.19\ \text{cm}^3 = 2.7\ \text{cm}^3$$

EVALUATE: This is basically how a mercury-in-glass thermometer works, except that instead of letting the mercury overflow and run all over the place, the thermometer has it rise inside a sealed tube as T increases.

As Tables 17.1 and 17.2 show, glass has smaller coefficients of expansion α and β than do most metals. This is why you can use hot water to loosen a metal lid on a glass jar; the metal expands more than the glass does.

17.12 The volume of 1 gram of water in the temperature range from 0°C to 10°C. By 100°C the volume has increased to 1.034 cm³. If the coefficient of volume expansion were constant, the curve would be a straight line.

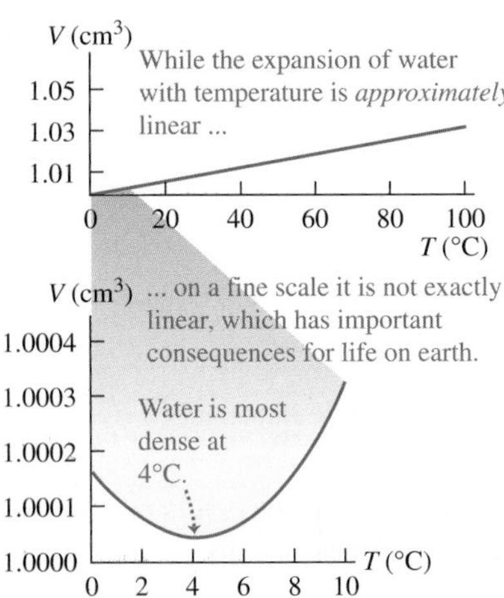

17.13 The interlocking teeth of an expansion joint on a bridge. These joints are needed to accommodate changes in length that result from thermal expansion.

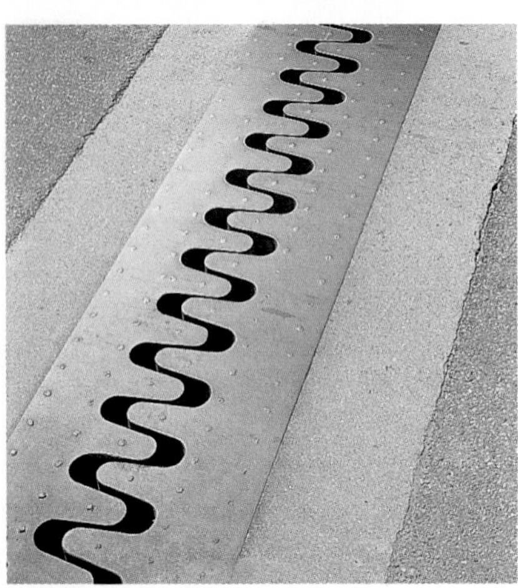

Thermal Expansion of Water

Water, in the temperature range from 0°C to 4°C, *decreases* in volume with increasing temperature. In this range its coefficient of volume expansion is *negative.* Above 4°C, water expands when heated (Fig. 17.12). Hence water has its greatest density at 4°C. Water also expands when it freezes, which is why ice humps up in the middle of the compartments in an ice cube tray. By contrast, most materials contract when they freeze.

This anomalous behavior of water has an important effect on plant and animal life in lakes. A lake cools from the surface down; above 4°C, the cooled water at the surface flows to the bottom because of its greater density. But when the surface temperature drops below 4°C, the water near the surface is less dense than the warmer water below. Hence the downward flow ceases, and the water near the surface remains colder than that at the bottom. As the surface freezes, the ice floats because it is less dense than water. The water at the bottom remains at 4°C until nearly the entire lake is frozen. If water behaved like most substances, contracting continuously on cooling and freezing, lakes would freeze from the bottom up. Circulation due to density differences would continuously carry warmer water to the surface for efficient cooling, and lakes would freeze solid much more easily. This would destroy all plant and animal life that cannot withstand freezing. If water did not have this special property, the evolution of life would have taken a very different course.

Thermal Stress

If we clamp the ends of a rod rigidly to prevent expansion or contraction and then change the temperature, tensile or compressive stresses called **thermal stresses** develop. The rod would like to expand or contract, but the clamps won't let it. The resulting stresses may become large enough to strain the rod irreversibly or even break it. (You may want to review the discussion of stress and strain in Section 11.4).

Engineers must account for thermal stress when designing structures. Concrete highways and bridge decks usually have gaps between sections, filled with a flexible material or bridged by interlocking teeth (Fig. 17.13), to permit expansion and contraction of the concrete. Long steam pipes have expansion joints or U-shaped sections to prevent buckling or stretching with temperature changes. If one end of a steel bridge is rigidly fastened to its abutment, the other end usually rests on rollers.

To calculate the thermal stress in a clamped rod, we compute the amount the rod *would* expand (or contract) if not held and then find the stress needed to compress (or stretch) it back to its original length. Suppose that a rod with length L_0 and cross-sectional area A is held at constant length while the temperature is reduced (negative ΔT), causing a tensile stress. The fractional change in length if the rod were free to contract would be

$$\left(\frac{\Delta L}{L_0}\right)_{\text{thermal}} = \alpha \Delta T \tag{17.10}$$

Both ΔL and ΔT are negative. The tension must increase by an amount F that is just enough to produce an equal and opposite fractional change in length $(\Delta L/L_0)_{\text{tension}}$. From the definition of Young's modulus, Eq. (11.10),

$$Y = \frac{F/A}{\Delta L/L_0} \quad \text{so} \quad \left(\frac{\Delta L}{L_0}\right)_{\text{tension}} = \frac{F}{AY} \tag{17.11}$$

If the length is to be constant, the *total* fractional change in length must be zero. From Eqs. (17.10) and (17.11), this means that

$$\left(\frac{\Delta L}{L_0}\right)_{\text{thermal}} + \left(\frac{\Delta L}{L_0}\right)_{\text{tension}} = \alpha \Delta T + \frac{F}{AY} = 0$$

Solving for the tensile stress F/A required to keep the rod's length constant, we find

$$\frac{F}{A} = -Y\alpha\,\Delta T \qquad \text{(thermal stress)} \tag{17.12}$$

For a decrease in temperature, ΔT is negative, so F and F/A are positive; this means that a *tensile* force and stress are needed to maintain the length. If ΔT is positive, F and F/A are negative, and the required force and stress are *compressive.*

If there are temperature differences within a body, nonuniform expansion or contraction will result and thermal stresses can be induced. You can break a glass bowl by pouring very hot water into it; the thermal stress between the hot and cold parts of the bowl exceeds the breaking stress of the glass, causing cracks. The same phenomenon makes ice cubes crack when dropped into warm water. Heat-resistant glasses such as Pyrex™ have exceptionally low expansion coefficients and high strength.

Example 17.5 Thermal stress

An aluminum cylinder 10 cm long, with a cross-sectional area of 20 cm^2, is to be used as a spacer between two steel walls. At 17.2°C it just slips in between the walls. When it warms to 22.3°C, calculate the stress in the cylinder and the total force it exerts on each wall, assuming that the walls are perfectly rigid and a constant distance apart.

SOLUTION

IDENTIFY: Our target variables are the thermal stress in the cylinder and the associated force it exerts on each of the walls that holds it in place.

SET UP: Figure 17.14 shows our sketch of the situation. We use Eq. (17.12) to relate the stress to the temperature change. The relevant values of Young's modulus Y and the coefficient of linear expansion α are those for aluminum, the material of which the cylinder is made; we find these values from Tables 11.1 and 17.1, respectively.

17.14 Our sketch for this problem.

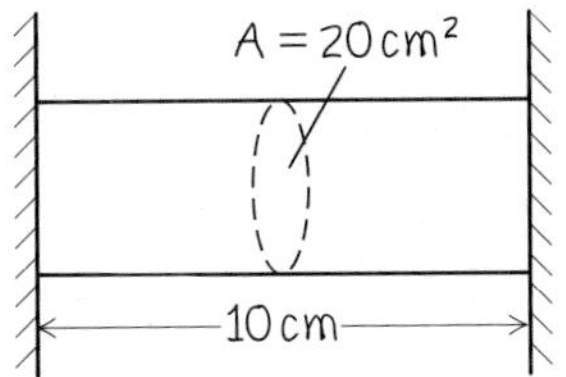

Continued

EXECUTE: For aluminum, $Y = 7.0 \times 10^{10}$ Pa and $\alpha = 2.4 \times 10^{-5}\ \mathrm{K}^{-1}$. The temperature change is $\Delta T = 22.3°\mathrm{C} - 17.2°\mathrm{C} = 5.1\ \mathrm{C}° = 5.1$ K. The stress is F/A; from Eq. (17.12),

$$\frac{F}{A} = -Y\alpha\Delta T = -(0.70 \times 10^{11}\ \mathrm{Pa})(2.4 \times 10^{-5}\ \mathrm{K}^{-1})(5.1\ \mathrm{K})$$

$$= -8.6 \times 10^{6}\ \mathrm{Pa}\ (\text{or } -1200\ \mathrm{lb/in.}^2)$$

The negative sign indicates that compressive rather than tensile stress is needed to keep the cylinder's length constant. This stress is independent of the length and cross-sectional area of the cylinder. The total force F is the cross-sectional area times the stress:

$$F = A\left(\frac{F}{A}\right) = (20 \times 10^{-4}\ \mathrm{m}^2)(-8.6 \times 10^{6}\ \mathrm{Pa})$$

$$= -1.7 \times 10^{4}\ \mathrm{N}$$

or nearly 2 tons. The negative sign indicates compression.

EVALUATE: The stress on the cylinder and the force it exerts on each wall are immense.This points out the importance of accounting for such thermal stresses in engineering.

Test Your Understanding of Section 17.4 In the bimetallic strip shown in Fig. 17.3a, metal 1 is copper. Which of the following materials could be used for metal 2? (There may be more than one correct answer). (i) steel; (ii) brass; (iii) aluminum.

17.5 Quantity of Heat

When you put a cold spoon into a cup of hot coffee, the spoon warms up and the coffee cools down as they approach thermal equilibrium. The interaction that causes these temperature changes is fundamentally a transfer of *energy* from one substance to another. Energy transfer that takes place solely because of a temperature difference is called *heat flow* or *heat transfer,* and energy transferred in this way is called **heat.**

An understanding of the relationship between heat and other forms of energy emerged gradually during the 18th and 19th centuries. Sir James Joule (1818–1889) studied how water can be warmed by vigorous stirring with a paddle wheel (Fig. 17.15a). The paddle wheel adds energy to the water by doing *work* on it, and Joule found that *the temperature rise is directly proportional to the amount of work done.* The same temperature change can also be caused by putting the water in contact with some hotter body (Fig. 17.15b); hence this interaction must also involve an energy exchange. We will explore the relationship between heat and mechanical energy in greater detail in Chapters 19 and 20.

17.15 The same temperature change of the same system may be accomplished by (a) doing work on it or (b) adding heat to it.

(a) Raising the temperature of water by doing work on it

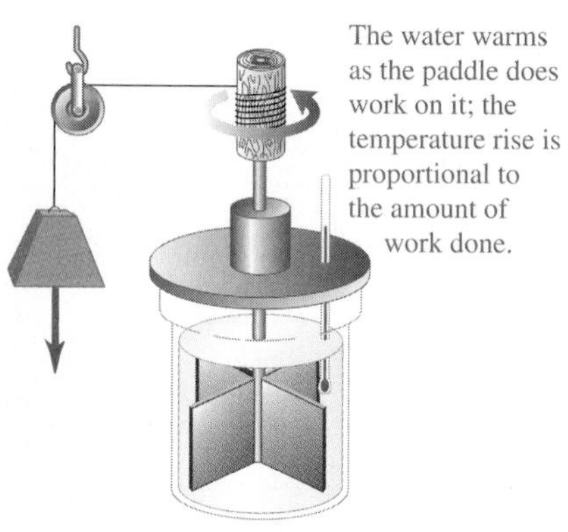

The water warms as the paddle does work on it; the temperature rise is proportional to the amount of work done.

(b) Raising the temperature of water by direct heating

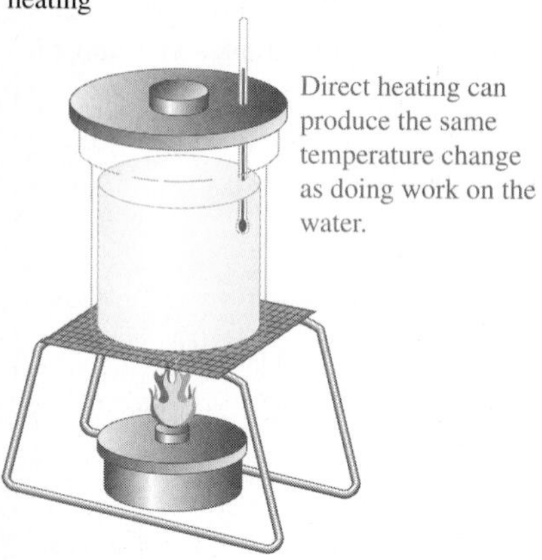

Direct heating can produce the same temperature change as doing work on the water.

CAUTION Temperature vs. heat It is absolutely essential for you to keep clearly in mind the distinction between *temperature* and *heat.* Temperature depends on the physical state of a material and is a quantitative description of its hotness or coldness. In physics the term "heat" always refers to energy in transit from one body or system to another because of a temperature difference, never to the amount of energy contained within a particular system. We can change the temperature of a body by adding heat to it or taking heat away, or by adding or subtracting energy in other ways, such as mechanical work (Fig. 17.15a). If we cut a body in half, each half has the same temperature as the whole; but to raise the temperature of each half by a given interval, we add *half* as much heat as for the whole.

We can define a *unit* of quantity of heat based on temperature changes of some specific material. The **calorie** (abbreviated cal) is defined as *the amount of heat required to raise the temperature of 1 gram of water from 14.5°C to 15.5°C.* The kilocalorie (kcal), equal to 1000 cal, is also used; a food-value calorie is actually a kilocalorie (Fig. 17.16 on the next page). A corresponding unit of heat using Fahrenheit degrees and British units is the **British thermal unit,** or Btu. One Btu is the quantity of heat required to raise the temperature of 1 pound (weight) of water 1 F° from 63°F to 64°F.

Because heat is energy in transit, there must be a definite relationship between these units and the familiar mechanical energy units such as the joule. Experiments similar in concept to Joule's have shown that

$$1 \text{ cal} = 4.186 \text{ J}$$
$$1 \text{ kcal} = 1000 \text{ cal} = 4186 \text{ J}$$
$$1 \text{ Btu} = 778 \text{ ft} \cdot \text{lb} = 252 \text{ cal} = 1055 \text{ J}$$

The calorie is not a fundamental SI unit. The International Committee on Weights and Measures recommends using the joule as the basic unit of energy in all forms, including heat. We will follow that recommendation in this book.

17.16 The motto "Komm in Schwung mit Zucker" on these German sugar packets can be translated as "Sugar gives you momentum." In fact, sugar gives you *energy:* According to the label, each packet has an energy content of 22 kilocalories (22 food-value calories) or 92 kilojoules. (We discussed the difference between energy and momentum in Section 8.1.)

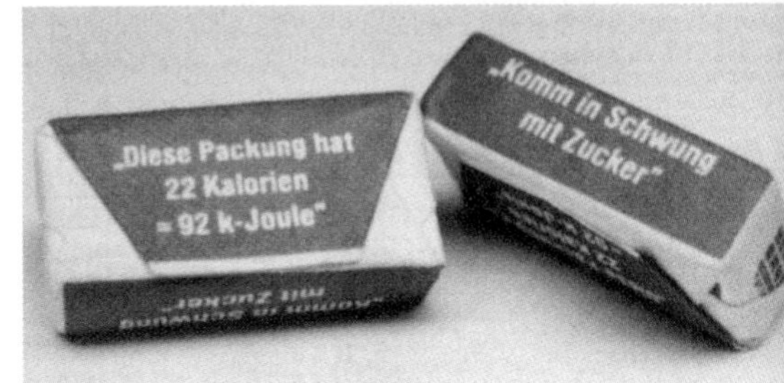

Specific Heat

We use the symbol Q for quantity of heat. When it is associated with an infinitesimal temperature change dT, we call it dQ. The quantity of heat Q required to increase the temperature of a mass m of a certain material from T_1 to T_2 is found to be approximately proportional to the temperature change $\Delta T = T_2 - T_1$. It is also proportional to the mass m of material. When you're heating water to make tea, you need twice as much heat for two cups as for one if the temperature change is the same. The quantity of heat needed also depends on the nature of the material; raising the temperature of 1 kilogram of water by 1 C° requires 4190 J of heat, but only 910 J is needed to raise the temperature of 1 kilogram of aluminum by 1 C°.

Putting all these relationships together, we have

$$Q = mc\,\Delta T \qquad \text{(heat required for temperature change } \Delta T \text{ of mass } m) \qquad (17.13)$$

where c is a quantity, different for different materials, called the **specific heat** of the material. For an infinitesimal temperature change dT and corresponding quantity of heat dQ,

$$dQ = mc\,dT \qquad (17.14)$$

$$c = \frac{1}{m}\frac{dQ}{dT} \qquad \text{(specific heat)} \qquad (17.15)$$

In Eqs. (17.13), (17.14), and (17.15), Q (or dQ) and ΔT (or dT) can be either positive or negative. When they are positive, heat enters the body and its temperature increases; when they are negative, heat leaves the body and its temperature decreases.

CAUTION **The definition of heat** Remember that dQ does not represent a change in the amount of heat *contained* in a body; this is a meaningless concept. Heat is always energy *in transit* as a result of a temperature difference. There is no such thing as "the amount of heat in a body."

The specific heat of water is approximately

$$4190 \text{ J/kg} \cdot \text{K} \qquad 1 \text{ cal/g} \cdot \text{C°} \qquad \text{or} \qquad 1 \text{ Btu/lb} \cdot \text{F°}$$

The specific heat of a material always depends somewhat on the initial temperature and the temperature interval. Figure 17.17 shows this dependence for water. In the problems and examples in this chapter we will usually ignore this small variation.

17.17 Specific heat of water as a function of temperature. The value of c varies by less than 1% between 0°C and 100°C.

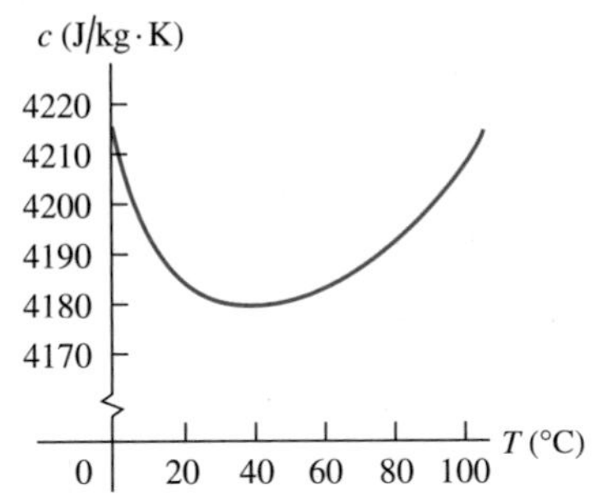

Example 17.6 Feed a cold, starve a fever

During a bout with the flu an 80-kg man ran a fever of 39.0°C (102.2°F) instead of the normal body temperature of 37.0°C (98.6°F). Assuming that the human body is mostly water, how much heat is required to raise his temperature by that amount?

SOLUTION

IDENTIFY: This problem uses the relationship among heat (the target variable), mass, specific heat, and temperature change.

SET UP: We are given the values of $m = 80$ kg, $c = 4190$ J/kg · K (for water), and $\Delta T = 39.0°\text{C} - 37.0°\text{C} = 2.0\ \text{C}° = 2.0$ K. We use Eq. (17.13) to determine the required heat.

EXECUTE: From Eq. (17.13),

$$Q = mc\,\Delta T = (80\ \text{kg})(4190\ \text{J/kg}\cdot\text{K})(2.0\ \text{K}) = 6.7 \times 10^5\ \text{J}$$

EVALUATE: This corresponds to 160 kcal, or 160 food-value calories. In fact, the specific heat of the human body is more nearly equal to 3480 J/kg · K, about 83% that of water. The difference is due to the presence of protein, fat, and minerals, which have lower specific heats. With this value of c, the required heat is 5.6×10^5 J = 133 kcal. Either result shows us that were it not for the body's temperature-regulating systems, taking in energy in the form of food would produce measurable changes in body temperature. (In the case of a person with the flu, the elevated temperature results from the body's extra activity in fighting infection.)

Example 17.7 Overheating electronics

You are designing an electronic circuit element made of 23 mg of silicon. The electric current through it adds energy at the rate of 7.4 mW = 7.4×10^{-3} J/s. If your design doesn't allow any heat transfer out of the element, at what rate does its temperature increase? The specific heat of silicon is 705 J/kg · K.

SOLUTION

IDENTIFY: The energy added to the circuit element gives rise to a temperature increase, just as if heat were flowing into the element at a rate of 7.4×10^{-3} J/s. Our target variable is the *rate* of temperature change.

SET UP: From Eq. (17.13), the temperature change ΔT in kelvins is proportional to the heat transferred in joules, so the rate of temperature change in K/s is proportional to the rate of heat transfer in J/s.

EXECUTE: In 1 second, $Q = (7.4 \times 10^{-3}\ \text{J/s})(1\ \text{s}) = 7.4 \times 10^{-3}$ J. From Eq. (17.13), $Q = mc\,\Delta T$, the temperature change in 1 second is

$$\Delta T = \frac{Q}{mc} = \frac{7.4 \times 10^{-3}\ \text{J}}{(23 \times 10^{-6}\ \text{kg})(705\ \text{J/kg}\cdot\text{K})} = 0.46\ \text{K}$$

Alternatively, we can divide both sides of Eq. (17.14) by dt and rearrange:

$$\frac{dT}{dt} = \frac{dQ/dt}{mc}$$

$$= \frac{7.4 \times 10^{-3}\ \text{J/s}}{(23 \times 10^{-6}\ \text{kg})(705\ \text{J/kg}\cdot\text{K})} = 0.46\ \text{K/s}$$

EVALUATE: At this rate of temperature rise (27 K every minute), the circuit element would soon self-destruct. Heat transfer is an important design consideration in electronic circuit elements.

Molar Heat Capacity

Sometimes it's more convenient to describe a quantity of substance in terms of the number of *moles n* rather than the *mass m* of material. Recall from your study of chemistry that a mole of any pure substance always contains the same number of molecules. (We will discuss this point in more detail in Chapter 18.) The *molar mass* of any substance, denoted by M, is the mass per mole. (The quantity M is sometimes called *molecular weight,* but *molar mass* is preferable; the quantity depends on the mass of a molecule, not its weight.) For example, the molar mass of water is 18.0 g/mol = 18.0×10^{-3} kg/mol; 1 mole of water has a mass of 18.0 g = 0.0180 kg. The total mass m of material is equal to the mass per mole M times the number of moles n:

$$m = nM \tag{17.16}$$

Replacing the mass m in Eq. (17.13) by the product nM, we find

$$Q = nMc\,\Delta T \tag{17.17}$$

The product Mc is called the **molar heat capacity** (or *molar specific heat*) and is denoted by C (capitalized). With this notation we rewrite Eq. (17.17) as

$$Q = nC\,\Delta T \quad \text{(heat required for temperature change of } n \text{ moles)} \tag{17.18}$$

Comparing to Eq. (17.15), we can express the molar heat capacity C (heat per mole per temperature change) in terms of the specific heat c (heat per mass per temperature change) and the molar mass M (mass per mole):

$$C = \frac{1}{n}\frac{dQ}{dT} = Mc \qquad \text{(molar heat capacity)} \qquad (17.19)$$

For example, the molar heat capacity of water is

$$C = Mc = (0.0180\ \text{kg/mol})(4190\ \text{J/kg}\cdot\text{K}) = 75.4\ \text{J/mol}\cdot\text{K}$$

Values of specific heat and molar heat capacity for several substances are given in Table 17.3. Note the remarkably large specific heat for water (Fig. 17.18).

CAUTION **The meaning of "heat capacity"** The term "heat capacity" is unfortunate because it gives the erroneous impression that a body *contains* a certain amount of heat. Remember, heat is energy in transit to or from a body, not the energy residing in the body.

17.18 Water has a much higher specific heat than the glass or metals used to make cookware. This helps explain why it takes several minutes to boil water on a stove, even though the pot or kettle reaches a high temperature very quickly.

Precise measurements of specific heats and molar heat capacities require great experimental skill. Usually, a measured quantity of energy is supplied by an electric current in a heater wire wound around the specimen. The temperature change ΔT is measured with a resistance thermometer or thermocouple embedded in the specimen. This sounds simple, but great care is needed to avoid or compensate for unwanted heat transfer between the sample and its surroundings. Measurements for solid materials are usually made at constant atmospheric pressure; the corresponding values are called the *specific heat* and *molar heat capacity at constant pressure,* denoted by c_p and C_p. For a gas it is usually easier to keep the substance in a container with constant *volume;* the corresponding values are called the *specific heat* and *molar heat capacity at constant volume,* denoted by c_V and C_V. For a given substance, C_V and C_p are different. If the system can expand while heat is added, there is additional energy exchange through the performance of *work* by the system on its surroundings. If the volume is constant, the system does no work. For gases the difference between C_p and C_V is substantial. We will study heat capacities of gases in detail in Section 19.7.

The last column of Table 17.3 shows something interesting. The molar heat capacities for most elemental solids are about the same: about 25 J/mol · K. This correlation, named the *rule of Dulong and Petit* (for its discoverers), forms the basis for a very important idea. The number of atoms in 1 mole is the same for all

Table 17.3 Approximate Specific Heats and Molar Heat Capacities (Constant Pressure)

Substance	Specific Heat, c (J/kg · K)	Molar Mass, M (kg/mol)	Molar Heat Capacity, C (J/mol · K)
Aluminum	910	0.0270	24.6
Beryllium	1970	0.00901	17.7
Copper	390	0.0635	24.8
Ethanol	2428	0.0461	111.9
Ethylene glycol	2386	0.0620	148.0
Ice (near 0°C)	2100	0.0180	37.8
Iron	470	0.0559	26.3
Lead	130	0.207	26.9
Marble ($CaCO_3$)	879	0.100	87.9
Mercury	138	0.201	27.7
Salt (NaCl)	879	0.0585	51.4
Silver	234	0.108	25.3
Water (liquid)	4190	0.0180	75.4

elemental substances. This means that on a *per atom* basis, about the same amount of heat is required to raise the temperature of each of these elements by a given amount, even though the *masses* of the atoms are very different. The heat required for a given temperature increase depends only on *how many* atoms the sample contains, not on the mass of an individual atom. We will see the reason the rule of Dulong and Petit works so well when we study the molecular basis of heat capacities in greater detail in Chapter 18.

Test Your Understanding of Section 17.5 You wish to raise the temperature of each the following samples from 20°C to 21°C. Rank these in order of the amount of heat needed to do this, from highest to lowest. (i) 1 kilogram of mercury; (ii) 1 kilogram of ethanol; (iii) 1 mole of mercury; (iv) 1 mole of ethanol.

17.6 Calorimetry and Phase Changes

Calorimetry means "measuring heat." We have discussed the energy transfer (heat) involved in temperature changes. Heat is also involved in *phase changes,* such as the melting of ice or boiling of water. Once we understand these additional heat relationships, we can analyze a variety of problems involving quantity of heat.

Phase Changes

We use the term **phase** to describe a specific state of matter, such as a solid, liquid, or gas. The compound H_2O exists in the *solid phase* as ice, in the *liquid phase* as water, and in the *gaseous phase* as steam. (These are also referred to as **states of matter:** the solid state, the liquid state, and the gaseous state.) A transition from one phase to another is called a **phase change** or *phase transition.* For any given pressure a phase change takes place at a definite temperature, usually accompanied by absorption or emission of heat and a change of volume and density.

A familiar example of a phase change is the melting of ice. When we add heat to ice at 0°C and normal atmospheric pressure, the temperature of the ice *does not* increase. Instead, some of it melts to form liquid water. If we add the heat slowly, to maintain the system very close to thermal equilibrium, the temperature remains at 0°C until all the ice is melted (Fig. 17.19). The effect of adding heat to this system is not to raise its temperature but to change its *phase* from solid to liquid.

17.19 The surrounding air is at room temperature, but this ice–water mixture remains at 0°C until all of the ice has melted and the phase change is complete.

To change 1 kg of ice at 0°C to 1 kg of liquid water at 0°C and normal atmospheric pressure requires 3.34×10^5 J of heat. The heat required per unit mass is called the **heat of fusion** (or sometimes *latent heat of fusion*), denoted by L_f. For water at normal atmospheric pressure the heat of fusion is

$$L_f = 3.34 \times 10^5 \text{ J/kg} = 79.6 \text{ cal/g} = 143 \text{ Btu/lb}$$

More generally, to melt a mass m of material that has a heat of fusion L_f requires a quantity of heat Q given by

$$Q = mL_f$$

This process is *reversible.* To freeze liquid water to ice at 0°C, we have to *remove* heat; the magnitude is the same, but in this case, Q is negative because heat is removed rather than added. To cover both possibilities and to include other kinds of phase changes, we write

$$Q = \pm mL \qquad \text{(heat transfer in a phase change)} \qquad (17.20)$$

The plus sign (heat entering) is used when the material melts; the minus sign (heat leaving) is used when it freezes. The heat of fusion is different for different materials, and it also varies somewhat with pressure.

For any given material at any given pressure, the freezing temperature is the same as the melting temperature. At this unique temperature the liquid and solid phases (liquid water and ice, for example) can coexist in a condition called **phase equilibrium.**

We can go through this whole story again for *boiling* or *evaporation,* a phase transition between liquid and gaseous phases. The corresponding heat (per unit mass) is called the **heat of vaporization** L_v. At normal atmospheric pressure the heat of vaporization L_v for water is

$$L_v = 2.256 \times 10^6 \text{ J/kg} = 539 \text{ cal/g} = 970 \text{ Btu/lb}$$

That is, it takes 2.256×10^6 J to change 1 kg of liquid water at 100°C to 1 kg of water vapor at 100°C. By comparison, to raise the temperature of 1 kg of water from 0°C to 100°C requires $Q = mc\,\Delta T = (1.00 \text{ kg})(4190 \text{ J/kg} \cdot \text{C}°) \times (100 \text{ C}°) = 4.19 \times 10^5$ J, less than one-fifth as much heat as is required for vaporization at 100°C. This agrees with everyday kitchen experience; a pot of water may reach boiling temperature in a few minutes, but it takes a much longer time to completely evaporate all the water away.

Like melting, boiling is a reversible transition. When heat is removed from a gas at the boiling temperature, the gas returns to the liquid phase, or *condenses,* giving up to its surroundings the same quantity of heat (heat of vaporization) that was needed to vaporize it. At a given pressure the boiling and condensation temperatures are always the same; at this temperature the liquid and gaseous phases can coexist in phase equilibrium.

Both L_v and the boiling temperature of a material depend on pressure. Water boils at a lower temperature (about 95°C) in Denver than in Pittsburgh because Denver is at higher elevation and the average atmospheric pressure is lower. The heat of vaporization is somewhat greater at this lower pressure, about 2.27×10^6 J/kg.

Table 17.4 lists heats of fusion and vaporization for several materials and their melting and boiling temperatures at normal atmospheric pressure. Very few *elements* have melting temperatures in the vicinity of ordinary room temperatures; one of the few is the metal gallium, shown in Fig. 17.20.

17.20 The metal gallium, shown here melting in a person's hand, is one of the few elements that melt in the vicinity of room temperature. Its melting temperature is 29.8°C, and its heat of fusion is 8.04×10^4 J/kg.

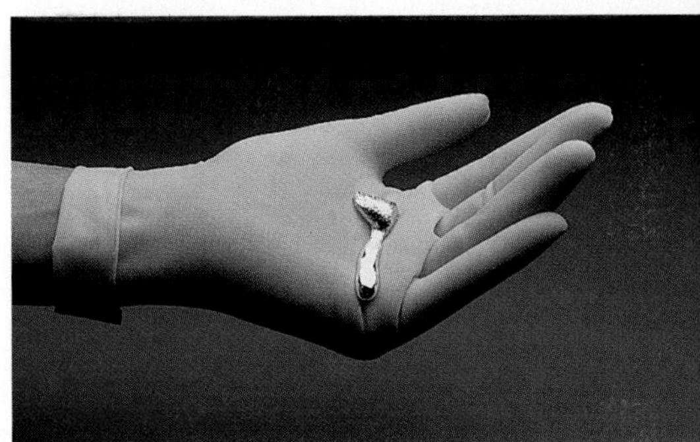

Table 17.4 Heats of Fusion and Vaporization

Substance	Normal Melting Point K	Normal Melting Point °C	Heat of Fusion, L_f (J/kg)	Normal Boiling Point K	Normal Boiling Point °C	Heat of Vaporization, L_v (J/kg)
Helium	*	*	*	4.216	−268.93	20.9×10^3
Hydrogen	13.84	−259.31	58.6×10^3	20.26	−252.89	452×10^3
Nitrogen	63.18	−209.97	25.5×10^3	77.34	−195.8	201×10^3
Oxygen	54.36	−218.79	13.8×10^3	90.18	−183.0	213×10^3
Ethanol	159	−114	104.2×10^3	351	78	854×10^3
Mercury	234	−39	11.8×10^3	630	357	272×10^3
Water	273.15	0.00	334×10^3	373.15	100.00	2256×10^3
Sulfur	392	119	38.1×10^3	717.75	444.60	326×10^3
Lead	600.5	327.3	24.5×10^3	2023	1750	871×10^3
Antimony	903.65	630.50	165×10^3	1713	1440	561×10^3
Silver	1233.95	960.80	88.3×10^3	2466	2193	2336×10^3
Gold	1336.15	1063.00	64.5×10^3	2933	2660	1578×10^3
Copper	1356	1083	134×10^3	1460	1187	5069×10^3

*A pressure in excess of 25 atmospheres is required to make helium solidify. At 1 atmosphere pressure, helium remains a liquid down to absolute zero.

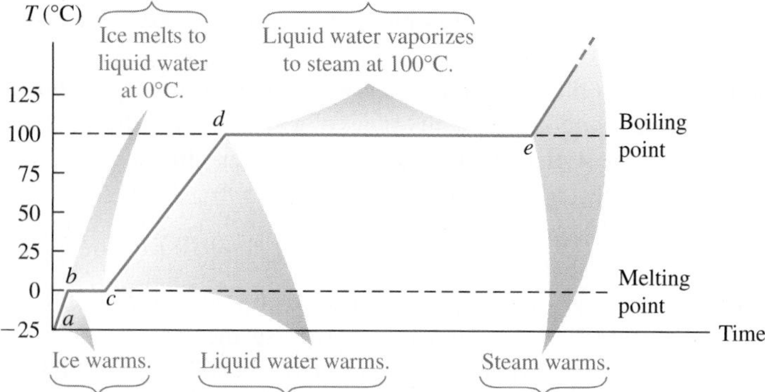

Phase of water changes. During these periods, temperature stays constant and the phase change proceeds as heat is added: $Q = +mL$.
T (°C)
Ice melts to liquid water at 0°C.
Liquid water vaporizes to steam at 100°C.
125
100
75
50
25
0
−25
a
b
c
d
e
Boiling point
Melting point
Time
Ice warms.
Liquid water warms.
Steam warms.
Temperature of water changes. During these periods, temperature rises as heat is added: $Q = mc\Delta T$.

17.21 Graph of temperature versus time for a specimen of water initially in the solid phase (ice). Heat is added to the specimen at a constant rate. The temperature remains constant during each change of phase, provided that the pressure remains constant.

Figure 17.21 shows how the temperature varies when we add heat continuously to a specimen of ice with an initial temperature below 0°C (point *a*). The temperature rises until we reach the melting point (point *b*). As more heat is added, the temperature remains constant until all the ice has melted (point *c*). Then the temperature rises again until the boiling temperature is reached (point *d*). At that point the temperature again is constant until all the water is transformed into the vapor phase (point *e*). If the rate of heat input is constant, the line for the solid phase (ice) has a steeper slope than does the line for the liquid phase (water). Do you see why? (See Table 17.3.)

A substance can sometimes change directly from the solid to the gaseous phase. This process is called *sublimation,* and the solid is said to *sublime.* The corresponding heat is called the *heat of sublimation,* L_s. Liquid carbon dioxide cannot exist at a pressure lower than about 5×10^5 Pa (about 5 atm), and "dry ice" (solid carbon dioxide) sublimes at atmospheric pressure. Sublimation of water from frozen food causes freezer burn. The reverse process, a phase change from gas to solid, occurs when frost forms on cold bodies such as refrigerator cooling coils.

Very pure water can be cooled several degrees below the freezing temperature without freezing; the resulting unstable state is described as *supercooled.* When a small ice crystal is dropped in or the water is agitated, it crystallizes within a second or less. Supercooled water *vapor* condenses quickly into fog droplets when a disturbance, such as dust particles or ionizing radiation, is introduced. This principle is used in "seeding" clouds, which often contain supercooled water vapor, to cause condensation and rain.

A liquid can sometimes be *superheated* above its normal boiling temperature. Any small disturbance such as agitation causes local boiling with bubble formation.

Steam heating systems for buildings use a boiling–condensing process to transfer heat from the furnace to the radiators. Each kilogram of water that is turned to steam in the boiler absorbs over 2×10^6 J (the heat of vaporization L_v of water) from the boiler and gives it up when it condenses in the radiators. Boiling–condensing processes are also used in refrigerators, air conditioners, and heat pumps. We will discuss these systems in Chapter 20.

The temperature-control mechanisms of many warm-blooded animals make use of heat of vaporization, removing heat from the body by using it to evaporate water from the tongue (panting) or from the skin (sweating). Evaporative cooling enables humans to maintain normal body temperature in hot, dry desert climates where the air temperature may reach 55°C (about 130°F). The skin temperature may be as much as 30°C cooler than the surrounding air. Under these conditions a normal person may perspire several liters per day, and this lost water must be replaced. Old-time desert rats (such as one of the authors) state that in the desert, any canteen that holds less than a gallon should be viewed as a toy! Evaporative cooling also explains why you feel cold when you first step out of a swimming pool (Fig. 17.22).

Evaporative cooling is also used to cool buildings in hot, dry climates and to condense and recirculate "used" steam in coal-fired or nuclear-powered electric-generating plants. That's what goes on in the large, tapered concrete towers that you see at such plants.

Chemical reactions such as combustion are analogous to phase changes in that they involve definite quantities of heat. Complete combustion of 1 gram of gasoline produces about 46,000 J or about 11,000 cal, so the **heat of combustion** L_c of gasoline is

$$L_c = 46{,}000 \text{ J/g} = 4.6 \times 10^7 \text{ J/kg}$$

Energy values of foods are defined similarly. When we say that a gram of peanut butter "contains 6 calories," we mean that 6 kcal of heat (6,000 cal or 25,000 J) is released when the carbon and hydrogen atoms in the peanut butter react with oxygen (with the help of enzymes) and are completely converted to CO_2 and H_2O. Not all of this energy is directly useful for mechanical work. We will study the *efficiency* of energy utilization in Chapter 20.

17.22 The water may be warm and it may be a hot day, but these children will feel cold when they first step out of the swimming pool. That's because as water evaporates from their skin, it removes the heat of vaporization from their bodies. To stay warm, they will need to dry off immediately.

Heat Calculations

Let's look at some examples of calorimetry calculations (calculations with heat). The basic principle is very simple: When heat flow occurs between two bodies that are isolated from their surroundings, the amount of heat lost by one body must equal the amount gained by the other. Heat is energy in transit, so this principle is really just conservation of energy. Calorimetry, dealing entirely with one conserved quantity, is in many ways the simplest of all physical theories!

Problem-Solving Strategy 17.2 Calorimetry Problems

IDENTIFY *the relevant concepts:* When heat flow occurs between two bodies that are isolated from their surroundings, the amount of heat lost by one body must equal the amount gained by the other body.

SET UP *the problem* using the following steps:

1. Identify which objects exchange heat. To avoid confusion with algebraic signs, take each quantity of heat *added* to a body as *positive* and each quantity *leaving* a body as *negative.* When two or more bodies interact, the *algebraic sum* of the quantities of heat transferred to all the bodies must be zero.
2. Each object will undergo a temperature change with no phase change, a phase change at constant temperature, or both. Use Eq. (17.13) to describe temperature changes and Eq. (17.20) to describe phase changes.
3. Consult Table 17.3 for values of the specific heat or molar heat capacity and Table 17.4 for heats of fusion or vaporization.
4. Be certain to identify which quantities are known and which are the unknown target variables.

EXECUTE *the solution* as follows:

1. Solve Eq. (17.13) and/or Eq. (17.20) for the target variables. Often you will need to find an unknown temperature. Represent it by an algebraic symbol such as T. Then if a body has an initial temperature of 20°C and an unknown final temperature T, the temperature change for the body is $\Delta T = T_{\text{final}} - T_{\text{initial}} = T - 20°\text{C}$ (*not* $20°\text{C} - T$).
2. In problems where a phase change takes place, as when ice melts, you may not know in advance whether *all* the material undergoes a phase change or only part of it. You can always assume one or the other, and if the resulting calculation gives an absurd result (such as a final temperature higher or lower than *any* of the initial temperatures), you know the initial assumption was wrong. Back up and try again!

EVALUATE *your answer:* A common error is to use the wrong algebraic sign for either a Q or ΔT term. Double check your calculations, and make sure that the final results are physically sensible.

Example 17.8 A temperature change with no phase change

A geologist working in the field drinks her morning coffee out of an aluminum cup. The cup has a mass of 0.120 kg and is initially at 20.0°C when she pours in 0.300 kg of coffee initially at 70.0°C. What is the final temperature after the coffee and the cup attain thermal equilibrium? (Assume that coffee has the same specific heat as water and that there is no heat exchange with the surroundings.)

SOLUTION

IDENTIFY: The two objects we must consider are the cup and the coffee, and the target variable is their common final temperature.

SET UP: No phase changes occur in this situation, so the only equation we need is Eq. (17.13).

Continued

EXECUTE: By using Table 17.3, the (negative) heat gained by the coffee is

$$Q_{\text{coffee}} = m_{\text{coffee}}c_{\text{water}}\,\Delta T_{\text{coffee}}$$
$$= (0.300\text{ kg})(4190\text{ J/kg}\cdot\text{K})(T - 70.0°\text{C})$$

The (positive) heat gained by the aluminum cup is

$$Q_{\text{aluminum}} = m_{\text{aluminum}}\,c_{\text{aluminum}}\,\Delta T_{\text{aluminum}}$$
$$= (0.120\text{ kg})(910\text{ J/kg}\cdot\text{K})(T - 20.0°\text{C})$$

We equate the sum of these two quantities of heat to zero, obtaining an algebraic equation for T:

$$Q_{\text{coffee}} + Q_{\text{aluminum}} = 0 \quad \text{or}$$
$$(0.300\text{ kg})(4190\text{ J/kg}\cdot\text{K})(T - 70.0°\text{C}) + (0.120\text{ kg})(910\text{ J/kg}\cdot\text{K})(T - 20.0°\text{C}) = 0$$

Solution of this equation gives $T = 66.0°\text{C}$.

EVALUATE: The final temperature is much closer to the initial temperature of the coffee than to that of the cup; water has a much higher specific heat than aluminum, and we have more than twice as much mass of water. We can also find the quantities of heat by substituting the value $T = 66.0°\text{C}$ back into the original equations. We find that $Q_{\text{coffee}} = -5.0 \times 10^3$ J and $Q_{\text{aluminum}} = +5.0 \times 10^3$ J; Q_{coffee} is negative, which means that the coffee loses heat.

Example 17.9 Changes in both temperature and phase

A physics student wants to cool 0.25 kg of Diet Omni-Cola (mostly water), initially at 25°C, by adding ice initially at −20°C. How much ice should she add so that the final temperature will be 0°C with all the ice melted if the heat capacity of the container may be neglected?

SOLUTION

IDENTIFY: The ice and the Omni-Cola are the objects that exchange heat. The Omni-Cola undergoes a temperature change only, while the ice undergoes both a temperature change and a phase change from solid to liquid. The target variable is the mass of ice, m_{ice}.

SET UP: We use Eq. (17.13) to find the amount of heat involved in warming the ice to 0°C and cooling the Omni-Cola to 0°C. In addition, we'll need Eq. (17.20) to calculate the heat required to melt the ice at 0°C.

EXECUTE: The Omni-Cola loses heat, so the heat added to it is negative:

$$Q_{\text{Omni}} = m_{\text{Omni}}c_{\text{water}}\,\Delta T_{\text{Omni}}$$
$$= (0.25\text{ kg})(4190\text{ J/kg}\cdot\text{K})(0°\text{C} - 25°\text{C})$$
$$= -26{,}000\text{ J}$$

From Table 17.3, the specific heat of ice (not the same as for liquid water) is 2.1×10^3 J/kg · K. Let the mass of ice be m_{ice}; then the heat Q_1 needed to warm it from −20°C to 0°C is

$$Q_1 = m_{\text{ice}}\,c_{\text{ice}}\,\Delta T_{\text{ice}}$$
$$= m_{\text{ice}}(2.1 \times 10^3\text{ J/kg}\cdot\text{K})[0°\text{C} - (-20°\text{C})]$$
$$= m_{\text{ice}}(4.2 \times 10^4\text{ J/kg})$$

From Eq. (17.20) the additional heat Q_2 needed to melt this mass of ice is the mass times the heat of fusion. Using Table 17.4, we find

$$Q_2 = m_{\text{ice}}\,L_f$$
$$= m_{\text{ice}}(3.34 \times 10^5\text{ J/kg})$$

The sum of these three quantities must equal zero:

$$Q_{\text{Omni}} + Q_1 + Q_2 = -26{,}000\text{ J} + m_{\text{ice}}(42{,}000\text{ J/kg}) + m_{\text{ice}}(334{,}000\text{ J/kg}) = 0$$

Solving this for m_{ice}, we get $m_{\text{ice}} = 0.069\text{ kg} = 69\text{ g}$.

EVALUATE: This mass of ice corresponds to three or four medium-size ice cubes, which seems reasonable for the quantity of Omni-Cola in this problem.

Example 17.10 What's cooking?

A heavy copper pot of mass 2.0 kg (including the copper lid) is at a temperature of 150°C. You pour 0.10 kg of water at 25°C into the pot, then quickly close the lid of the pot so that no steam can escape. Find the final temperature of the pot and its contents, and determine the phase (liquid or gas) of the water. Assume that no heat is lost to the surroundings.

SOLUTION

IDENTIFY: The two objects that exchange heat are the water and the pot. Note that there are three conceivable outcomes in this situation. One, none of the water boils, and the final temperature is less than 100°C; two, a portion of the water boils, giving a mixture of water and steam at 100°C; or three, all the water boils, giving 0.10 kg of steam at a temperature of 100°C or greater.

SET UP: We again use Eq. (17.13) for the heat transferred in a temperature change and Eq. (17.20) for the heat transferred in a phase change.

EXECUTE: The simplest case to calculate is the first possibility. Let the common final temperature of the liquid water and the copper pot be T. Since we are assuming that no phase changes take place, the sum of the quantities of heat added to the two materials is

$$Q_{\text{water}} + Q_{\text{copper}} = m_{\text{water}}c_{\text{water}}(T - 25°\text{C}) + m_{\text{copper}}c_{\text{copper}}(T - 150°\text{C})$$
$$= (0.10\text{ kg})(4190\text{ J/kg}\cdot\text{K})(T - 25°\text{C}) + (2.0\text{ kg})(390\text{ J/kg}\cdot\text{K})(T - 150°\text{C})$$
$$= 0$$

Solving this for T, we find $T = 106°\text{C}$. But this is above the boiling point of water, which contradicts our assumption that none of the water boils! So this assumption can't be correct; at least some of the water undergoes a phase change.

If we try the second possibility, in which the final temperature is 100°C, we have to find the fraction of water that changes to the gaseous phase. Let this fraction be x; the (positive) amount of heat needed to vaporize this water is $(xm_{\text{water}})L_v$. Setting the final temperature T equal to 100°C, we have

$$\begin{aligned}Q_{\text{water}} &= m_{\text{water}}c_{\text{water}}(100°\text{C} - 25°\text{C}) + xm_{\text{water}}L_v \\ &= (0.10\text{ kg})(4190\text{ J/kg}\cdot\text{K})(75\text{ K}) \\ &\quad + x(0.10\text{ kg})(2.256 \times 10^6\text{ J/kg}) \\ &= 3.14 \times 10^4\text{ J} + x(2.256 \times 10^5\text{ J}) \\ Q_{\text{copper}} &= m_{\text{copper}}c_{\text{copper}}(100°\text{C} - 150°\text{C}) \\ &= (2.0\text{ kg})(390\text{ J/kg}\cdot\text{K})(-50\text{ K}) = -3.90 \times 10^4\text{ J}\end{aligned}$$

Now require that the sum of all the quantities of heat be zero:

$$\begin{aligned}Q_{\text{water}} + Q_{\text{copper}} &= 3.14 \times 10^4\text{ J} + x(2.256 \times 10^5\text{ J}) \\ &\quad -3.90 \times 10^4\text{ J} = 0 \\ x &= \frac{3.90 \times 10^4\text{ J} - 3.14 \times 10^4\text{ J}}{2.256 \times 10^5\text{ J}} = 0.034\end{aligned}$$

This makes sense, and we conclude that the final temperature of the water and copper is 100°C. Of the original 0.10 kg of water, $0.034(0.10\text{ kg}) = 0.0034\text{ kg} = 3.4\text{ g}$ has been converted to steam at 100°C.

EVALUATE: Had x turned out to be greater than 1, we would have again had a contradiction (the fraction of water that vaporized can't be greater than 1). In this case the third possibility would have been the correct description, all the water would have vaporized, and the final temperature would have been greater than 100°C. Can you show that this would have been the case if we had originally poured less than 15 g of 25°C water into the pot?

Example 17.11 Combustion, temperature change, and phase change

In a particular gasoline camp stove, 30% of the energy released in burning the fuel actually goes to heating the water in the pot on the stove. If we heat 1.00 L (1.00 kg) of water from 20°C to 100°C and boil 0.25 kg of it away, how much gasoline do we burn in the process?

SOLUTION

IDENTIFY: In this problem all of the water undergoes a temperature change and part of the water also undergoes a phase change from liquid to gas. This requires a certain amount of heat, which we use to determine the amount of gasoline that must be burned (the target variable).

SET UP: We use Eqs. (17.13) and (17.20) as well as the idea of heat of combustion.

EXECUTE: The heat required to raise the temperature of the water from 20°C to 100°C is

$$\begin{aligned}Q_1 &= mc\,\Delta T = (1.00\text{ kg})(4190\text{ J/kg}\cdot\text{K})(80\text{ K}) \\ &= 3.35 \times 10^5\text{ J}\end{aligned}$$

To boil 0.25 kg of water at 100°C requires

$$Q_2 = mL_v = (0.25\text{ kg})(2.256 \times 10^6\text{ J/kg}) = 5.64 \times 10^5\text{ J}$$

The total energy needed is the sum of these, or 8.99×10^5 J This is only 0.30 of the total heat of combustion, so that energy is $(8.99 \times 10^5\text{ J})/0.30 = 3.00 \times 10^6$ J. As we mentioned earlier, 1 gram of gasoline releases 46,000 J, so the mass of gasoline required is

$$\frac{3.00 \times 10^6\text{ J}}{46{,}000\text{ J/g}} = 65\text{ g}$$

or a volume of about 0.09 L of gasoline.

EVALUATE: This result is a testament to the tremendous amount of energy that can be released by burning even a small quantity of gasoline. Note that most of the heat delivered was used to boil away 0.25 L of water. Can you show that another 123 g of gasoline would be required to boil away the remaining water?

Test Your Understanding of Section 17.6 You take a block of ice at 0°C and add heat to it at a steady rate. It takes a time t to completely convert the block of ice to steam at 100°C. What do you have at time $t/2$? (i) all ice at 0°C; (ii) a mixture of ice and water at 0°C; (iii) water at a temperature between 0°C and 100°C; (iv) a mixture of water and steam at 100°C.

17.7 Mechanisms of Heat Transfer

We have talked about *conductors* and *insulators,* materials that permit or prevent heat transfer between bodies. Now let's look in more detail at *rates* of energy transfer. In the kitchen you use a metal or glass pot for good heat transfer from the stove to whatever you're cooking, but your refrigerator is insulated with a material that *prevents* heat from flowing into the food inside the refrigerator. How do we describe the difference between these two materials?

17.23 Steady-state heat flow due to conduction in a uniform rod.

(a) Heat current H

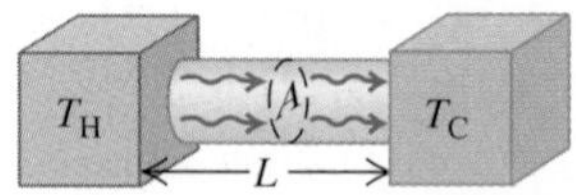

(b) Doubling the cross-sectional area of the conductor doubles the heat current (H is proportional to A).

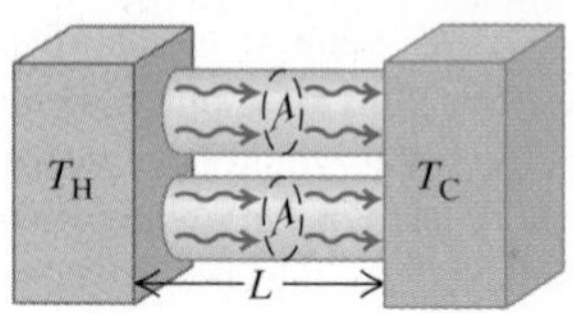

(c) Doubling the length of the conductor halves the heat current (H is inversely proportional to L).

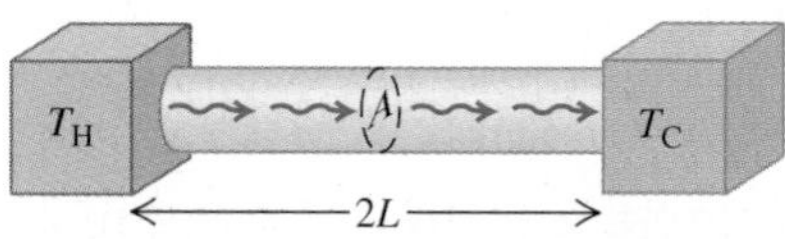

Table 17.5 Thermal Conductivities

Substance	$k\,(\text{W/m}\cdot\text{K})$
Metals	
Aluminum	205.0
Brass	109.0
Copper	385.0
Lead	34.7
Mercury	8.3
Silver	406.0
Steel	50.2
Solids (representative values)	
Brick, insulating	0.15
Brick, red	0.6
Concrete	0.8
Cork	0.04
Felt	0.04
Fiberglass	0.04
Glass	0.8
Ice	1.6
Rock wool	0.04
Styrofoam	0.01
Wood	0.12–0.04
Gases	
Air	0.024
Argon	0.016
Helium	0.14
Hydrogen	0.14
Oxygen	0.023

The three mechanisms of heat transfer are conduction, convection, and radiation. *Conduction* occurs within a body or between two bodies in contact. *Convection* depends on motion of mass from one region of space to another. *Radiation* is heat transfer by electromagnetic radiation, such as sunshine, with no need for matter to be present in the space between bodies.

Conduction

If you hold one end of a copper rod and place the other end in a flame, the end you are holding gets hotter and hotter, even though it is not in direct contact with the flame. Heat reaches the cooler end by **conduction** through the material. On the atomic level, the atoms in the hotter regions have more kinetic energy, on the average, than their cooler neighbors. They jostle their neighbors, giving them some of their energy. The neighbors jostle *their* neighbors, and so on through the material. The atoms themselves do not move from one region of material to another, but their energy does.

Most metals also use another, more effective mechanism to conduct heat. Within the metal, some electrons can leave their parent atoms and wander through the crystal lattice. These "free" electrons can rapidly carry energy from the hotter to the cooler regions of the metal, so metals are generally good conductors of heat. A metal rod at 20°C feels colder than a piece of wood at 20°C because heat can flow more easily from your hand into the metal. The presence of "free" electrons also causes most metals to be good electrical conductors.

Heat transfer occurs only between regions that are at different temperatures, and the direction of heat flow is always from higher to lower temperature. Figure 17.23a shows a rod of conducting material with cross-sectional area A and length L. The left end of the rod is kept at a temperature T_H and the right end at a lower temperature T_C, so heat flows from left to right. The sides of the rod are covered by an ideal insulator, so no heat transfer occurs at the sides.

When a quantity of heat dQ is transferred through the rod in a time dt, the rate of heat flow is dQ/dt. We call this rate the **heat current,** denoted by H. That is, $H = dQ/dt$. Experiments show that the heat current is proportional to the cross-sectional area A of the rod (Fig. 17.23b) and to the temperature difference $(T_H - T_C)$ and is inversely proportional to the rod length L (Fig. 17.23c). Introducing a proportionality constant k called the **thermal conductivity** of the material, we have

$$H = \frac{dQ}{dt} = kA\frac{T_H - T_C}{L} \quad \text{(heat current in conduction)} \qquad (17.21)$$

The quantity $(T_H - T_C)/L$ is the temperature difference *per unit length;* it is called the magnitude of the **temperature gradient.** The numerical value of k depends on the material of the rod. Materials with large k are good conductors of heat; materials with small k are poor conductors or insulators. Equation (17.21) also gives the heat current through a slab or through *any* homogeneous body with uniform cross section A perpendicular to the direction of flow; L is the length of the heat-flow path.

The units of heat current H are units of energy per time, or power; the SI unit of heat current is the watt $(1\text{ W} = 1\text{ J/s})$. We can find the units of k by solving Eq. (17.21) for k; you can show that the SI units are $\text{W/m}\cdot\text{K}$. Some numerical values of k are given in Table 17.5.

The thermal conductivity of "dead" (that is, nonmoving) air is very small. A wool sweater keeps you warm because it traps air between the fibers. In fact, many insulating materials such as Styrofoam and fiberglass are mostly dead air. Figure 17.24 shows a ceramic material with very unusual thermal properties, including very small conductivity.

If the temperature varies in a nonuniform way along the length of the conducting rod, we introduce a coordinate x along the length and generalize the temperature gradient to be dT/dx. The corresponding generalization of Eq. (17.21) is

$$H = \frac{dQ}{dt} = -kA\frac{dT}{dx} \qquad (17.22)$$

The negative sign shows that heat always flows in the direction of *decreasing* temperature.

For thermal insulation in buildings, engineers use the concept of **thermal resistance,** denoted by R. The thermal resistance R of a slab of material with area A is defined so that the heat current H through the slab is

$$H = \frac{A(T_H - T_C)}{R} \qquad (17.23)$$

where T_H and T_C are the temperatures on the two sides of the slab. Comparing this with Eq. (17.21), we see that R is given by

$$R = \frac{L}{k} \qquad (17.24)$$

where L is the thickness of the slab. The SI unit of R is $1\ \text{m}^2 \cdot \text{K/W}$. In the units used for commercial insulating materials in the United States, H is expressed in Btu/h, A is in ft^2, and $T_H - T_C$ in F°. $(1\ \text{Btu/h} = 0.293\ \text{W.})$ The units of R are then $\text{ft}^2 \cdot \text{F}° \cdot \text{h/Btu}$, though values of R are usually quoted without units; a 6-inch-thick layer of fiberglass has an R value of 19 (that is, $R = 19\ \text{ft}^2 \cdot \text{F}° \cdot \text{h/Btu}$), a 2-inch-thick slab of polyurethane foam has an R value of 12, and so on. Doubling the thickness doubles the R value. Common practice in new construction in severe northern climates is to specify R values of around 30 for exterior walls and ceilings. When the insulating material is in layers, such as a plastered wall, fiberglass insulation, and wood exterior siding, the R values are additive. Do you see why? (See Problem 17.110.)

17.24 This protective tile, developed for use in the space shuttle, has extraordinary thermal properties. The extremely small thermal conductivity and small heat capacity of the material make it possible to hold the tile by its edges, even though its temperature is high enough to emit the light for this photograph.

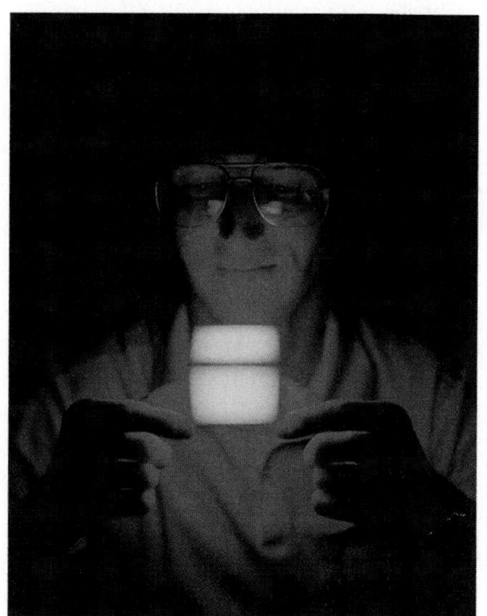

Problem-Solving Strategy 17.3 Heat Conduction

IDENTIFY *the relevant concepts:* The concept of heat conduction comes into play whenever two objects at different temperature are placed in contact.

SET UP *the problem* using the following steps:

1. Identify the direction of heat flow in the problem (from hot to cold). In Eq. (17.21), L is always measured along this direction, and A is always an area perpendicular to this direction. Often when a box or other container has an irregular shape but uniform wall thickness, you can approximate it as a flat slab with the same thickness and total wall area.
2. Identify the target variable.

EXECUTE *the solution* as follows:

1. If heat flows through a single object, use Eq. (17.21) to solve for the target variable.
2. In some problems the heat flows through two different materials in succession. The temperature at the interface between the two materials is then intermediate between T_H and T_C; represent it by a symbol such as T. The temperature differences for the two materials are then $(T_H - T)$ and $(T - T_C)$. In steady-state heat flow, the same heat has to pass through both materials in succession, so the heat current H must be *the same* in both materials.
3. If there are two *parallel* heat-flow paths, so that some heat flows through each, then the total H is the sum of the quantities H_1 and H_2 for the separate paths. An example is heat flow from inside to outside a house, both through the glass in a window and through the surrounding frame. In this case the temperature difference is the same for the two paths, but L, A, and k may be different for the two paths.
4. As always, it is essential to use a consistent set of units. If you use a value of k expressed in $\text{W/m} \cdot \text{K}$, don't use distances in centimeters, heat in calories, or T in degrees Fahrenheit!

EVALUATE *your answer:* As always, ask yourself whether the results are physically reasonable.

Example 17.12 Conduction through a picnic cooler

A Styrofoam box used to keep drinks cold at a picnic (Fig. 17.25a) has total wall area (including the lid) of 0.80 m^2 and wall thickness 2.0 cm. It is filled with ice, water, and cans of Omni-Cola at 0°C. What is the rate of heat flow into the box if the temperature of the outside wall is 30°C? How much ice melts in one day?

SOLUTION

IDENTIFY: The first target variable is the heat current H. The second is the amount of ice melted, which depends on the heat current (heat per unit time), the elapsed time, and the heat of fusion.

SET UP: We use Eq. (17.21) to describe the heat current and Eq. (17.20), $Q = mL_f$, to determine the mass m of ice that melts due to the heat flow.

EXECUTE: We assume that the total heat flow is approximately the same as it would be through a flat slab of area 0.80 m^2 and thickness 2.0 cm = 0.020 m (Fig. 17.25b). We find k from Table 17.5. From Eq. (17.21) the heat current (rate of heat flow) is

$$H = kA\frac{T_H - T_C}{L} = (0.010\ \text{W/m}\cdot\text{K})(0.80\ \text{m}^2)\frac{30°\text{C} - 0°\text{C}}{0.020\ \text{m}}$$
$$= 12\ \text{W} = 12\ \text{J/s}$$

The total heat flow Q in one day (86,400 s) is

$$Q = Ht = (12\ \text{J/s})(86{,}400\ \text{s}) = 1.04 \times 10^6\ \text{J}$$

The heat of fusion of ice is 3.34×10^5 J/kg, so the quantity of ice melted by this quantity of heat is

$$m = \frac{Q}{L_f} = \frac{1.04 \times 10^6\ \text{J}}{3.34 \times 10^5\ \text{J/kg}} = 3.1\ \text{kg}$$

EVALUATE: The low heat current is a result of the low thermal conductivity of Styrofoam. A substantial amount of heat flows in 24 hours, but a relatively small amount of ice melts because the heat of fusion is high.

17.25 Conduction of heat across the walls of a Styrofoam cooler.

(a) A cooler at the beach

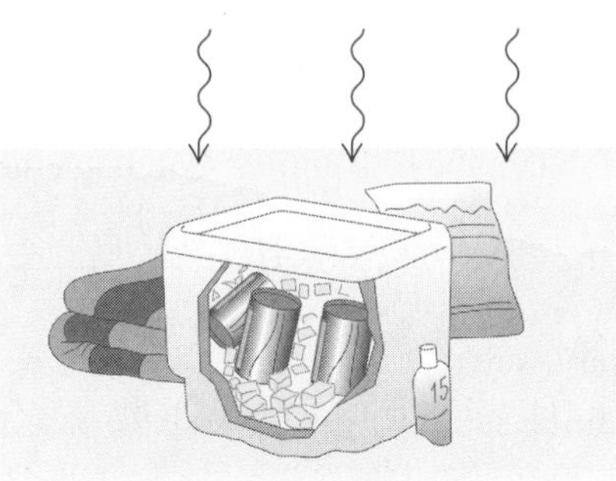

(b) Our sketch for this problem

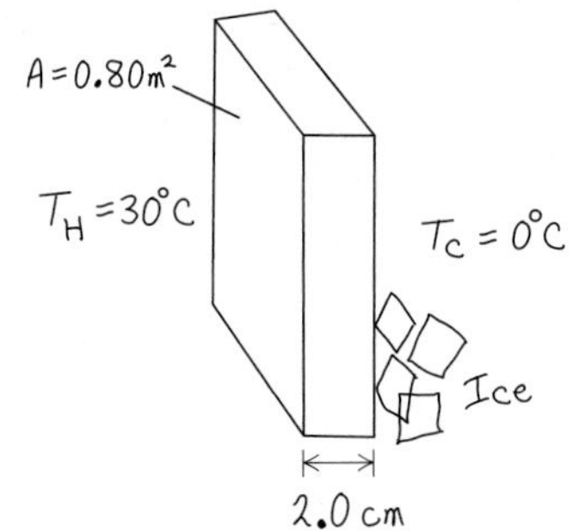

Example 17.13 Conduction through two bars I

A steel bar 10.0 cm long is welded end to end to a copper bar 20.0 cm long. Both bars are insulated perfectly on their sides. Each bar has a square cross section, 2.00 cm on a side. The free end of the steel bar is maintained at 100°C by placing it in contact with steam, and the free end of the copper bar is maintained at 0°C by placing it in contact with ice. Find the temperature at the junction of the two bars and the total rate of heat flow.

SOLUTION

IDENTIFY: In this problem there is heat flow through two bars of different composition. As we discussed in Problem-Solving Strategy 17.3, the heat currents in the two end-to-end bars must be the same.

SET UP: Figure 17.26 shows the situation. We write Eq. (17.21) twice, once for each bar, and set the heat currents H_{steel} and H_{copper} equal to each other. Both expressions for the heat current involve the temperature T at the junction, which is one of our target variables.

EXECUTE: Setting the two heat currents equal, we have

$$H_{steel} = \frac{k_{steel}A(100°\text{C} - T)}{L_{steel}} = H_{copper} = \frac{k_{copper}A(T - 0°\text{C})}{L_{copper}}$$

The areas A are equal and may be divided out. Substituting $L_{steel} = 0.100$ m, $L_{copper} = 0.200$ m, and numerical values of k from Table 17.5, we find

$$\frac{(50.2\ \text{W/m}\cdot\text{K})(100°\text{C} - T)}{0.100\ \text{m}} = \frac{(385\ \text{W/m}\cdot\text{K})\ (T - 0°\text{C})}{0.200\ \text{m}}$$

17.26 Our sketch for this problem.

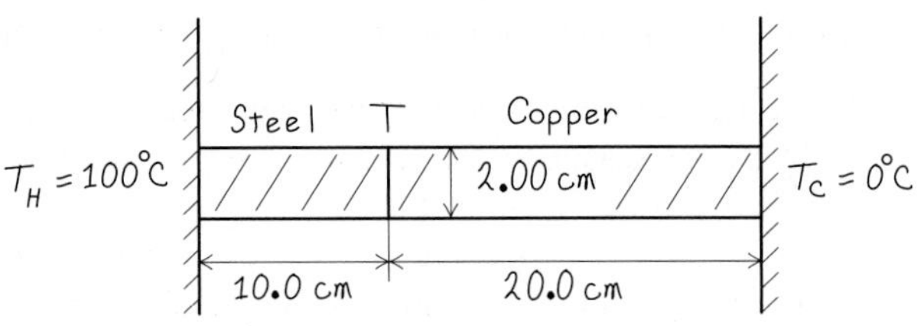

Rearranging and solving for T, we find

$$T = 20.7°\text{C}$$

We can find the total heat current by substituting this value for T back into either of the above expressions:

$$H_{\text{steel}} = \frac{(50.2\ \text{W/m}\cdot\text{K})(0.0200\ \text{m})^2(100°\text{C} - 20.7°\text{C})}{0.100\ \text{m}}$$

$$= 15.9\ \text{W}$$

or

$$H_{\text{copper}} = \frac{(385\ \text{W/m}\cdot\text{K})(0.0200\ \text{m})^2(20.7°\text{C})}{0.200\ \text{m}} = 15.9\ \text{W}$$

EVALUATE: Even though the steel bar is shorter, the temperature drop across it is much greater than across the copper bar (from 100°C to 20.7°C in the steel versus from 20.7°C to 0°C in the copper). This difference arises because steel is a much poorer conductor than copper.

Example 17.14 Conduction through two bars II

In Example 17.13, suppose the two bars are separated. One end of each bar is maintained at 100°C and the other end of each bar is maintained at 0°C. What is the *total* rate of heat flow in the two bars?

SOLUTION

IDENTIFY: In this case the bars are side by side rather than end to end. The total heat current is now the *sum* of the currents in the two bars.

SET UP: Figure 17.27 shows the situation. For each bar, $T_H - T_C = 100°\text{C} - 0°\text{C} = 100\ \text{K}$.

EXECUTE: We write the heat currents for the two rods individually, and then add them to get the total heat current:

$$H = H_{\text{steel}} + H_{\text{copper}} = \frac{k_{\text{steel}}A(T_H - T_C)}{L_{\text{steel}}} + \frac{k_{\text{copper}}A(T_H - T_C)}{L_{\text{copper}}}$$

$$= \frac{(50.2\ \text{W/m}\cdot\text{K})(0.0200\ \text{m})^2(100\ \text{K})}{0.100\ \text{m}}$$

$$+ \frac{(385\ \text{W/m}\cdot\text{K})(0.0200\ \text{m})^2(100\ \text{K})}{0.200\ \text{m}}$$

$$= 20.1\ \text{W} + 77.0\ \text{W} = 97.1\ \text{W}$$

EVALUATE: The heat flow in the copper bar is much greater than that in the steel bar, even though it is longer, because the thermal conductivity of copper is much larger. The total heat flow is much greater than in Example 17.13, partly because the total cross section for heat flow is greater and partly because the full 100-K temperature difference appears across each bar.

17.27 Our sketch for this problem.

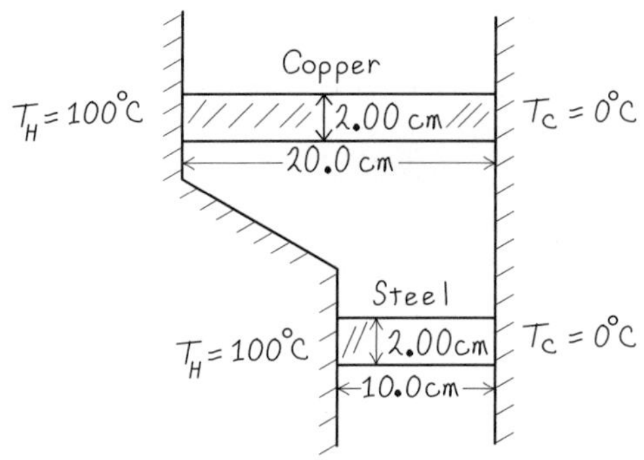

Convection

Convection is the transfer of heat by mass motion of a fluid from one region of space to another. Familiar examples include hot-air and hot-water home heating systems, the cooling system of an automobile engine, and the flow of blood in the body. If the fluid is circulated by a blower or pump, the process is called *forced convection;* if the flow is caused by differences in density due to thermal expansion, such as hot air rising, the process is called *natural convection* or *free convection* (Fig. 17.28).

Free convection in the atmosphere plays a dominant role in determining the daily weather, and convection in the oceans is an important global heat-transfer mechanism. On a smaller scale, soaring hawks and glider pilots make use of thermal updrafts from the warm earth. The most important mechanism for heat transfer within the human body (needed to maintain nearly constant temperature in various environments) is *forced* convection of blood, with the heart serving as the pump.

Convective heat transfer is a very complex process, and there is no simple equation to describe it. Here are a few experimental facts:

1. The heat current due to convection is directly proportional to the surface area. This is the reason for the large surface areas of radiators and cooling fins.
2. The viscosity of fluids slows natural convection near a stationary surface, giving a surface film that on a vertical surface typically has about the same insulating value as 1.3 cm of plywood (R value $= 0.7$). Forced convection

17.28 A heating element in the tip of this submerged tube warms the surrounding water, producing a complex pattern of free convection.

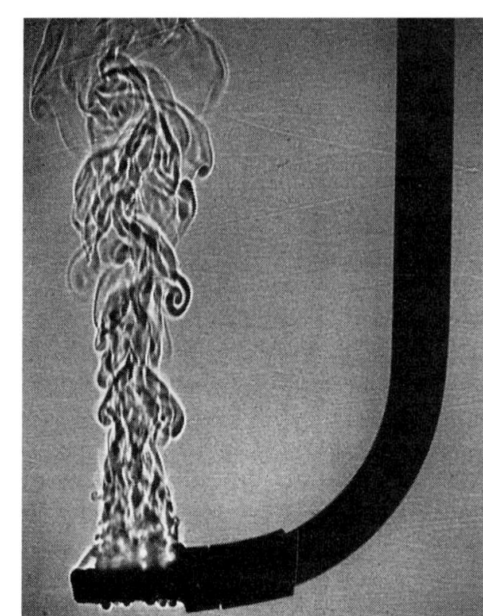

Example 18.2 Compressing gas in an automobile engine

In an automobile engine, a mixture of air and gasoline is compressed in the cylinders before being ignited. A typical engine has a compression ratio of 9.00 to 1; this means that the gas in the cylinders is compressed to $1/(9.00)$ of its original volume (Fig. 18.3). The initial pressure is 1.00 atm and the initial temperature is 27°C. If the pressure after compression is 21.7 atm, find the temperature of the compressed gas.

18.3 Cutaway of an automobile engine. While the air–gasoline mixture is being compressed prior to ignition, the intake and exhaust valves are both in the closed (up) position.

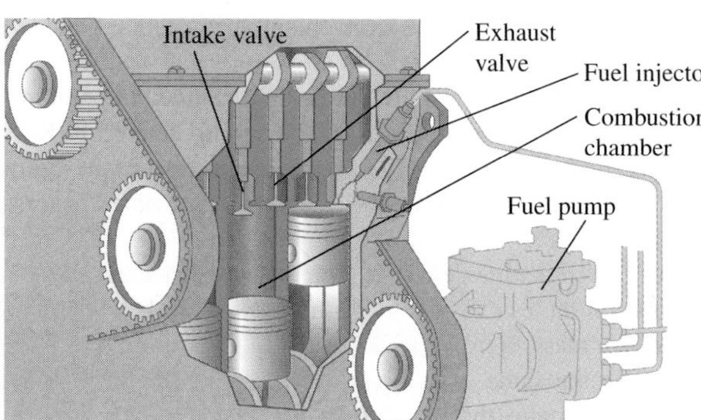

SOLUTION

IDENTIFY: In this problem we are asked to compare two states of the same quantity of ideal gas. The target variable is the temperature in the compressed state. The intake and exhaust valves at the top of the cylinder in Fig. 18.3 stay closed during the compression, so the quantity of gas is constant.

SET UP: Let state 1 be the uncompressed gas, and let state 2 be the fully compressed gas. Then $p_1 = 1.00$ atm, $p_2 = 21.7$ atm, and $V_1 = 9.00\ V_2$. Converting temperature to the Kelvin scale by adding 273, we get $T_1 = 300$ K; the final temperature T_2 is the target variable. The number of moles of gas n is constant, so we can use Eq. (18.6).

EXECUTE: Solving Eq. (18.6) for the temperature T_2 of the compressed gas, we get

$$T_2 = T_1 \frac{p_2 V_2}{p_1 V_1} = (300\ \text{K}) \frac{(21.7\ \text{atm})\ V_2}{(1.00\ \text{atm})(9.00\ V_2)}$$

$$= 723\ \text{K} = 450°\text{C}$$

We didn't need to know the values of V_1 and V_2, only their ratio.

EVALUATE: Note that T_2 is the temperature of the air–gasoline mixture *before* the mixture is ignited; when burning starts, the temperature becomes higher still.

Example 18.3 Mass of air in a scuba tank

A typical tank used for scuba diving has a volume of 11.0 L (about 0.4 ft^3) and a gauge pressure, when full, of 2.10×10^7 Pa (about 3000 psig). The "empty" tank contains 11.0 L of air at 21°C and 1 atm $(1.013 \times 10^5\ \text{Pa})$. When the tank is filled with hot air from a compressor, the temperature is 42°C and the gauge pressure is 2.11×10^7 Pa. What mass of air was added? (Air is a mixture of gases, about 78% nitrogen, 21% oxygen, and 1% miscellaneous; its average molar mass is 28.8 g/mol $= 28.8 \times 10^{-3}$ kg/mol.)

SOLUTION

IDENTIFY: Our target variable is the *difference* between the mass present at the beginning (state 1) and at the end (state 2).

SET UP: We are given the molar mass of air, so we can use Eq. (18.2) to find the target variable if we know the number of moles present in states 1 and 2. We determine n_1 and n_2 by applying Eq. (18.3) to each state individually.

EXECUTE: We must remember to convert the temperatures to the Kelvin scale by adding 273 and to convert the pressure to absolute by adding 1.013×10^5 Pa. From Eq. (18.3), the number of moles n_1 in the "empty" tank is

$$n_1 = \frac{p_1 V_1}{R T_1} = \frac{(1.013 \times 10^5\ \text{Pa})(11.0 \times 10^{-3}\ \text{m}^3)}{(8.314\ \text{J/mol} \cdot \text{K})(294\ \text{K})} = 0.46\ \text{mol}$$

The volume of the metal tank is hardly affected by the increased pressure, so $V_1 = V_2$. The number of moles in the full tank is

$$n_2 = \frac{p_2 V_2}{R T_2} = \frac{(2.11 \times 10^7\ \text{Pa})(11.0 \times 10^{-3}\ \text{m}^3)}{(8.314\ \text{J/mol} \cdot \text{K})(315\ \text{K})} = 88.6\ \text{mol}$$

We added $n_2 - n_1 = 88.6\ \text{mol} - 0.46\ \text{mol} = 88.1$ mol to the tank. From Eq. (18.2), the added mass is $M(n_2 - n_1) = (28.8 \times 10^{-3}\ \text{kg/mol})(88.1\ \text{mol}) = 2.54$ kg.

EVALUATE: The added mass is not insubstantial: You could certainly use a scale to determine whether the tank was empty or full.

Could this problem have been solved in the same way as Example 18.2? The volume is constant, so $p/nT = R/V$ is constant and $p_1/n_1 T_1 = p_2/n_2 T_2$; this can be solved for n_2/n_1, the ratio of the final and initial numbers of moles. But we need the *difference* of these two numbers, not the ratio, so this equation by itself isn't enough to solve the problem.

The proportionality of pressure to absolute temperature is familiar; in fact, in Chapter 17 we *defined* a temperature scale in terms of pressure in a constant-volume gas thermometer. That may make it seem that the pressure–temperature relationship in the ideal-gas equation, Eq. (18.3), is just a result of the way we define temperature. But the equation also tells us what happens when we change the volume or the amount of substance. Also, the gas-thermometer scale turns out to correspond closely to a temperature scale that does *not* depend on the properties of any particular material. We'll define this scale in Chapter 20. For now, consider this equation as being based on this genuinely material-independent temperature scale.

Problem-Solving Strategy 18.1 Ideal Gases

MP

IDENTIFY *the relevant concepts:* Unless the problem explicitly states otherwise, you can use the ideal-gas equation for any situation in which you need to find the state (pressure, volume, temperature, and/or number of moles) of a gas.

SET UP *the problem* using the following steps:

1. Identify the target variables.
2. In some problems you will be concerned with only one state of the system, in which case Eq. (18.3) is the relationship to use. Some of the quantities in this equation will be known; others will be unknown. Make a list of what you know and what you have to find.
3. In other problems you will compare two different states of the same amount of gas. Decide which is state 1 and which is state 2, and make a list of the quantities for each: p_1, p_2, V_1, V_2, T_1, T_2. If all but one of these quantities are known, you can use Eq. (18.6). Otherwise, use Eq. (18.3). For example, if p_1, V_1, and n are given, you can't use Eq. (18.6) because you don't know T_1.
4. Some problems involve the density ρ (mass per volume) rather than the number of moles n and the volume V. In this case it's most convenient to use Eq. (18.5), $\rho = pM/RT$.

EXECUTE *the solution* as follows:

1. Use a consistent set of units. You may have to convert atmospheres to pascals or liters to cubic meters ($1\ \text{m}^3 = 10^3\ \text{L} = 10^6\ \text{cm}^3$). Sometimes the problem statement will make one system of units clearly more convenient than others. Decide on your system and stick to it.

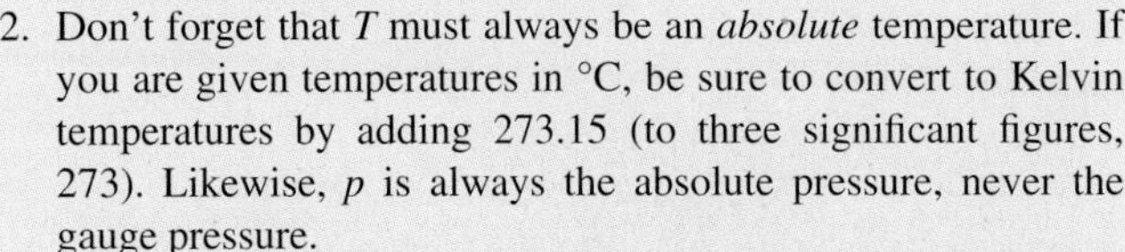

2. Don't forget that T must always be an *absolute* temperature. If you are given temperatures in °C, be sure to convert to Kelvin temperatures by adding 273.15 (to three significant figures, 273). Likewise, p is always the absolute pressure, never the gauge pressure.
3. You may sometimes have to convert between mass m_{total} and number of moles n. The relationship is $m_{\text{total}} = Mn$, where M is the molar mass. Here's a tricky point: If you use Eq. (18.4), you *must* use the same mass units for m_{total} and M. So if M is in grams per mole (the usual units for molar mass), then m_{total} must also be in grams. If you want to use m_{total} in kilograms, then you must convert M to kg/mol. For example, the molar mass of oxygen is 32 g/mol or 32×10^{-3} kg/mol. Be careful!
4. Once you have taken care of steps 1–3, solve for the target variables.

EVALUATE *your answer:* Look carefully at your results and see whether they make physical sense. For example, we'll find in Example 18.1 that a mole of gas at 1 atmosphere pressure and 0°C occupies a volume of 22.4 liters. If you do a calculation of the amount of air inside a 1-liter volume and get a fantastically large answer like $n = 5000$ moles, you probably converted units incorrectly or made an algebraic error.

Example 18.1 Volume of a gas at STP

The condition called **standard temperature and pressure** (STP) for a gas is defined to be a temperature of $0°\text{C} = 273.15\ \text{K}$ and a pressure of $1\ \text{atm} = 1.013 \times 10^5\ \text{Pa}$. If you want to keep a mole of an ideal gas in your room at STP, how big a container do you need?

SOLUTION

IDENTIFY: This problem involves the properties of an ideal gas. We are given the pressure and temperature, and our target variable is the volume.

SET UP: We are asked about the properties of a single state of the system, so we use Eq. (18.3).

EXECUTE: From Eq. (18.3), using R in J/mol · K,

$$V = \frac{nRT}{p} = \frac{(1\ \text{mol})(8.314\ \text{J/mol}\cdot\text{K})(273.15\ \text{K})}{1.013 \times 10^5\ \text{Pa}}$$

$$= 0.0224\ \text{m}^3 = 22.4\ \text{L}$$

EVALUATE: You may be familiar with this result from your study of chemistry. Note that 22.4 L is almost exactly the volume of three basketballs. A cube 0.282 m on a side would also do the job.

Example 18.2 Compressing gas in an automobile engine

In an automobile engine, a mixture of air and gasoline is compressed in the cylinders before being ignited. A typical engine has a compression ratio of 9.00 to 1; this means that the gas in the cylinders is compressed to $1/(9.00)$ of its original volume (Fig. 18.3). The initial pressure is 1.00 atm and the initial temperature is 27°C. If the pressure after compression is 21.7 atm, find the temperature of the compressed gas.

18.3 Cutaway of an automobile engine. While the air–gasoline mixture is being compressed prior to ignition, the intake and exhaust valves are both in the closed (up) position.

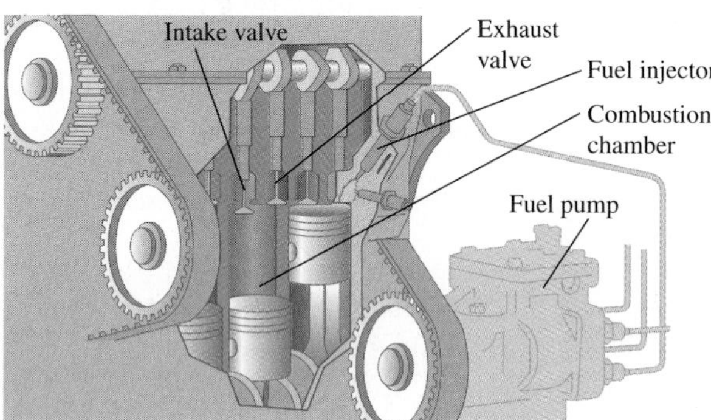

SOLUTION

IDENTIFY: In this problem we are asked to compare two states of the same quantity of ideal gas. The target variable is the temperature in the compressed state. The intake and exhaust valves at the top of the cylinder in Fig. 18.3 stay closed during the compression, so the quantity of gas is constant.

SET UP: Let state 1 be the uncompressed gas, and let state 2 be the fully compressed gas. Then $p_1 = 1.00$ atm, $p_2 = 21.7$ atm, and $V_1 = 9.00\ V_2$. Converting temperature to the Kelvin scale by adding 273, we get $T_1 = 300$ K; the final temperature T_2 is the target variable. The number of moles of gas n is constant, so we can use Eq. (18.6).

EXECUTE: Solving Eq. (18.6) for the temperature T_2 of the compressed gas, we get

$$T_2 = T_1 \frac{p_2 V_2}{p_1 V_1} = (300\ \text{K}) \frac{(21.7\ \text{atm})\ V_2}{(1.00\ \text{atm})(9.00\ V_2)}$$
$$= 723\ \text{K} = 450°\text{C}$$

We didn't need to know the values of V_1 and V_2, only their ratio.

EVALUATE: Note that T_2 is the temperature of the air–gasoline mixture *before* the mixture is ignited; when burning starts, the temperature becomes higher still.

Example 18.3 Mass of air in a scuba tank

A typical tank used for scuba diving has a volume of 11.0 L (about 0.4 ft^3) and a gauge pressure, when full, of 2.10×10^7 Pa (about 3000 psig). The "empty" tank contains 11.0 L of air at 21°C and 1 atm $(1.013 \times 10^5\ \text{Pa})$. When the tank is filled with hot air from a compressor, the temperature is 42°C and the gauge pressure is 2.11×10^7 Pa. What mass of air was added? (Air is a mixture of gases, about 78% nitrogen, 21% oxygen, and 1% miscellaneous; its average molar mass is 28.8 g/mol $= 28.8 \times 10^{-3}$ kg/mol.)

SOLUTION

IDENTIFY: Our target variable is the *difference* between the mass present at the beginning (state 1) and at the end (state 2).

SET UP: We are given the molar mass of air, so we can use Eq. (18.2) to find the target variable if we know the number of moles present in states 1 and 2. We determine n_1 and n_2 by applying Eq. (18.3) to each state individually.

EXECUTE: We must remember to convert the temperatures to the Kelvin scale by adding 273 and to convert the pressure to absolute by adding 1.013×10^5 Pa. From Eq. (18.3), the number of moles n_1 in the "empty" tank is

$$n_1 = \frac{p_1 V_1}{RT_1} = \frac{(1.013 \times 10^5\ \text{Pa})(11.0 \times 10^{-3}\ \text{m}^3)}{(8.314\ \text{J/mol} \cdot \text{K})(294\ \text{K})} = 0.46\ \text{mol}$$

The volume of the metal tank is hardly affected by the increased pressure, so $V_1 = V_2$. The number of moles in the full tank is

$$n_2 = \frac{p_2 V_2}{RT_2} = \frac{(2.11 \times 10^7\ \text{Pa})(11.0 \times 10^{-3}\ \text{m}^3)}{(8.314\ \text{J/mol} \cdot \text{K})(315\ \text{K})} = 88.6\ \text{mol}$$

We added $n_2 - n_1 = 88.6\ \text{mol} - 0.46\ \text{mol} = 88.1$ mol to the tank. From Eq. (18.2), the added mass is $M(n_2 - n_1) = (28.8 \times 10^{-3}\ \text{kg/mol})(88.1\ \text{mol}) = 2.54$ kg.

EVALUATE: The added mass is not insubstantial: You could certainly use a scale to determine whether the tank was empty or full.

Could this problem have been solved in the same way as Example 18.2? The volume is constant, so $p/nT = R/V$ is constant and $p_1/n_1 T_1 = p_2/n_2 T_2$; this can be solved for n_2/n_1, the ratio of the final and initial numbers of moles. But we need the *difference* of these two numbers, not the ratio, so this equation by itself isn't enough to solve the problem.

18.1 Equations of State

The conditions in which a particular material exists are described by physical quantities such as pressure, volume, temperature, and amount of substance. For example, a tank of oxygen in a welding outfit has a pressure gauge and a label stating its volume. We could add a thermometer and place the tank on a scale to determine its mass. These variables describe the *state* of the material and are called **state variables.**

8.4 State Variables and Ideal Gas Law

The volume V of a substance is usually determined by its pressure p, temperature T, and amount of substance, described by the mass m_{total} or number of moles n. (We are calling the total mass of a substance m_{total} because later in the chapter we will use m for the mass of one molecule.) Ordinarily, we can't change one of these variables without causing a change in another. When the tank of oxygen gets hotter, the pressure increases. If the tank gets too hot, it explodes; this happens occasionally with overheated steam boilers.

In a few cases the relationship among p, V, T, and m (or n) is simple enough that we can express it as an equation called the **equation of state.** When it's too complicated for that, we can use graphs or numerical tables. Even then, the relationship among the variables still exists; we call it an equation of state even when we don't know the actual equation.

Here's a simple (though approximate) equation of state for a solid material. The temperature coefficient of volume expansion β (see Section 17.4) is the fractional volume change $\Delta V/V_0$ per unit temperature change, and the compressibility k (see Section 11.4) is the negative of the fractional volume change $\Delta V/V_0$ per unit pressure change. If a certain amount of material has volume V_0 when the pressure is p_0 and the temperature is T_0, the volume V at slightly differing pressure p and temperature T is approximately

$$V = V_0[1 + \beta(T - T_0) - k(p - p_0)] \qquad (18.1)$$

(There is a negative sign in front of the term $k(p - p_0)$ because an *increase* in pressure causes a *decrease* in the volume.) Equation (18.1) is called an *equation of state* for the material.

The Ideal-Gas Equation

Another simple equation of state is the one for an *ideal gas.* Figure 18.1 shows an experimental setup to study the behavior of a gas. The cylinder has a movable piston to vary the volume, the temperature can be varied by heating, and we can pump any desired amount of any gas into the cylinder. We then measure the pressure, volume, temperature, and amount of gas. Note that *pressure* refers both to the force per unit area exerted by the cylinder on the gas and to the force per unit area exerted by the gas on the cylinder; by Newton's third law, these must be equal.

It is usually easiest to describe the amount of gas in terms of the number of moles n, rather than the mass. We did this when we defined molar heat capacity in Section 17.5; you may want to review that section. The **molar mass** M of a compound (sometimes called *molecular weight*) is the mass per mole, and the total mass m_{total} of a given quantity of that compound is the number of moles n times the mass per mole M:

$$m_{total} = nM \qquad \text{(total mass, number of moles, and molar mass)} \qquad (18.2)$$

Hence if we know the number of moles of gas in the cylinder, we can determine the mass of gas using Eq. (18.2).

18.1 A hypothetical setup for studying the behavior of gases. By heating the gas, varying the volume with a movable piston, and adding more gas, we can control the gas pressure p, volume V, temperature T, and number of moles n.

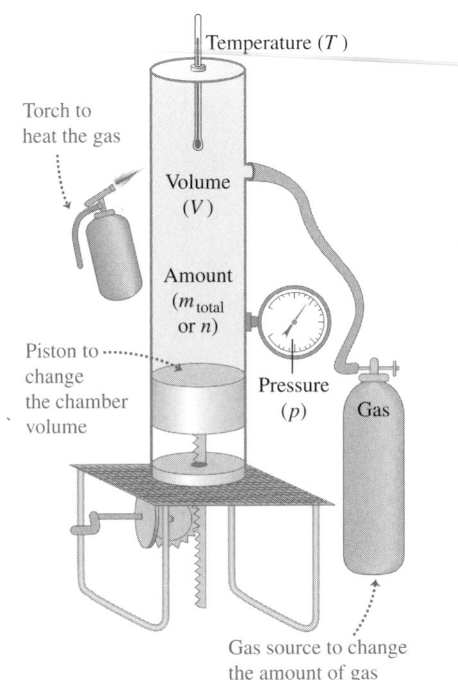

Measurements of the behavior of various gases lead to three conclusions:

1. The volume V is proportional to the number of moles n. If we double the number of moles, keeping pressure and temperature constant, the volume doubles.
2. The volume varies *inversely* with the absolute pressure p. If we double the pressure while holding the temperature T and number of moles n constant, the gas compresses to one-half of its initial volume. In other words, $pV = \text{constant}$ when n and T are constant.
3. The pressure is proportional to the *absolute* temperature. If we double the absolute temperature, keeping the volume and number of moles constant, the pressure doubles. In other words, $p = (\text{constant})T$ when n and V are constant.

18.2 The ideal-gas equation $pV = nRT$ gives a good description of the air inside an inflated vehicle tire, where the pressure is about 3 atmospheres and the temperature is much too high for nitrogen or oxygen to liquefy. As the tire warms (T increases), the volume V changes only slightly but the pressure p increases.

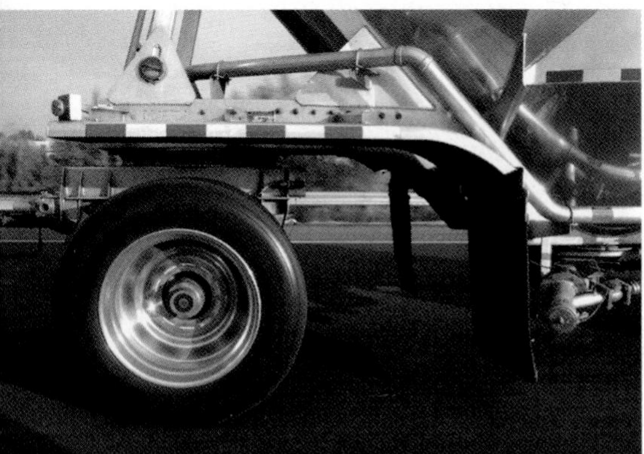

These three relationships can be combined neatly into a single equation, called the **ideal-gas equation:**

$$pV = nRT \qquad \text{(ideal-gas equation)} \tag{18.3}$$

where R is a proportionality constant. An **ideal gas** is one for which Eq. (18.3) holds precisely for *all* pressures and temperatures. This is an idealized model; it works best at very low pressures and high temperatures, when the gas molecules are far apart and in rapid motion. It is reasonably good (within a few percent) at moderate pressures (such as a few atmospheres) and at temperatures well above those at which the gas liquefies (Fig. 18.2).

We might expect that the constant R in the ideal-gas equation would have different values for different gases, but it turns out to have the same value for *all* gases, at least at sufficiently high temperature and low pressure. It is called the **gas constant** (or *ideal-gas constant*). The numerical value of R depends on the units of p, V, and T. In SI units, in which the unit of p is Pa $(1\text{ Pa} = 1\text{N/m}^2)$ and the unit of V is m^3, the current best numerical value of R is

$$R = 8.314472(15)\ \text{J/mol}\cdot\text{K}$$

or $R = 8.314\ \text{J/mol}\cdot\text{K}$ to four significant figures. Note that the units of pressure times volume are the same as the units of work or energy (for example, N/m^2 times m^3); that's why R has units of energy per mole per unit of absolute temperature. In chemical calculations, volumes are often expressed in liters (L) and pressures in atmospheres (atm). In this system, to four significant figures,

$$R = 0.08206\,\frac{\text{L}\cdot\text{atm}}{\text{mol}\cdot\text{K}}$$

We can express the ideal-gas equation, Eq. (18.3), in terms of the mass m_{total} of gas, using $m_{\text{total}} = nM$ from Eq. (18.2):

$$pV = \frac{m_{\text{total}}}{M}RT \tag{18.4}$$

From this we can get an expression for the density $\rho = m_{\text{total}}/V$ of the gas:

$$\rho = \frac{pM}{RT} \tag{18.5}$$

CAUTION **Density vs. pressure** When using Eq. (18.5), be certain that you distinguish between the Greek letter ρ (rho) for density and the letter p for pressure.

For a *constant mass* (or constant number of moles) of an ideal gas the product nR is constant, so the quantity pV/T is also constant. If the subscripts 1 and 2 refer to any two states of the same mass of a gas, then

$$\frac{p_1V_1}{T_1} = \frac{p_2V_2}{T_2} = \text{constant} \qquad \text{(ideal gas, constant mass)} \tag{18.6}$$

Notice that you don't need the value of R to use this equation.

Example 18.4 Variation of atmospheric pressure with elevation

Find the variation of atmospheric pressure with elevation in the earth's atmosphere, assuming that the temperature is 0°C at all elevations. Ignore the variation of g with elevation.

SOLUTION

IDENTIFY: As the elevation increases, both the atmospheric pressure and the density decrease. Hence we have *two* unknown functions of elevation; to solve for them, we need two separate relationships. One of these is the ideal-gas equation, which we can write in terms of pressure and density; the other is the relationship between pressure and density in a fluid in equilibrium, discussed in Section 14.2.

SET UP: In Section 14.2, we found the general equation $dp/dy = -\rho g$, [Eq. (14.4)], for the variation of pressure p with elevation y as a function of density ρ. Equation (18.5), $\rho = pM/RT$, states the ideal-gas equation in terms of density. We are told to assume that g and T are the same at all elevations; we also assume that the atmosphere has the same chemical composition, and hence the same molar mass M, at all heights. We then combine the two expressions and solve for $p(y)$.

EXECUTE: We substitute $\rho = pM/RT$ into $dp/dy = -\rho g$, separate variables, and integrate, letting p_1 be the pressure at elevation y_1 and p_2 be the pressure at y_2:

$$\frac{dp}{dy} = -\frac{pM}{RT}g$$

$$\int_{p_1}^{p_2} \frac{dp}{p} = -\frac{Mg}{RT}\int_{y_1}^{y_2} dy$$

$$\ln\frac{p_2}{p_1} = -\frac{Mg}{RT}(y_2 - y_1)$$

$$\frac{p_2}{p_1} = e^{-Mg(y_2-y_1)/RT}$$

Now let $y_1 = 0$ be at sea level and let the pressure at that point be $p_0 = 1.013 \times 10^5$ Pa. Then our final expression for the pressure p at any height y is

$$p = p_0 e^{-Mgy/RT}$$

EVALUATE: According to our calculation, the pressure decreases exponentially with elevation. The graph in Fig. 18.4 shows that the slope dp/dy becomes less negative with greater elevation. That result makes sense, since $dp/dy = -\rho g$ and the density also decreases with elevation. At the summit of Mount Everest, where $y = 8863$ m,

$$\frac{Mgy}{RT} = \frac{(28.8 \times 10^{-3}\ \text{kg/mol})(9.80\ \text{m/s}^2)(8863\ \text{m})}{(8.314\ \text{J/mol}\cdot\text{K})(273\ \text{K})} = 1.10$$

$$p = (1.013 \times 10^5\ \text{Pa})e^{-1.10} = 0.337 \times 10^5\ \text{Pa}$$
$$= 0.33\ \text{atm}$$

The assumption of constant temperature isn't realistic, and g decreases a little with increasing elevation (see Challenge Problem 18.92). Even so, this example shows why mountaineers need to carry oxygen on Mount Everest. It also shows why jet airliners, which typically fly at altitudes of 8000 to 12,000 m, *must* have pressurized cabins for passenger comfort and health.

18.4 The variation of atmospheric pressure p with elevation y, assuming a constant temperature T.

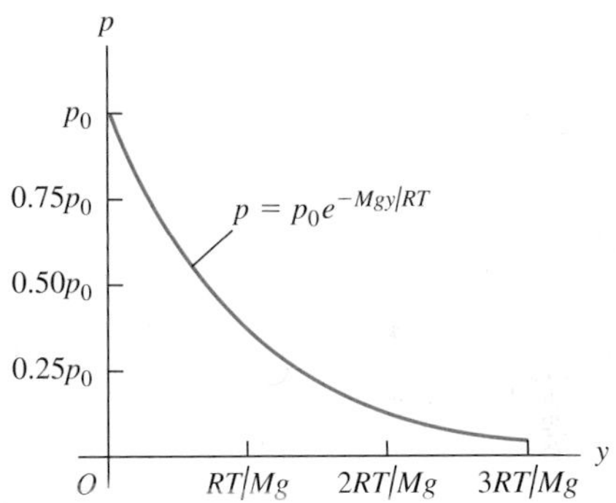

The van der Waals Equation

The ideal-gas equation, Eq. (18.3), can be obtained from a simple molecular model that ignores the volumes of the molecules themselves and the attractive forces between them (Fig. 18.5a). We'll examine that model in Section 18.3.

(a) An idealized model of a gas

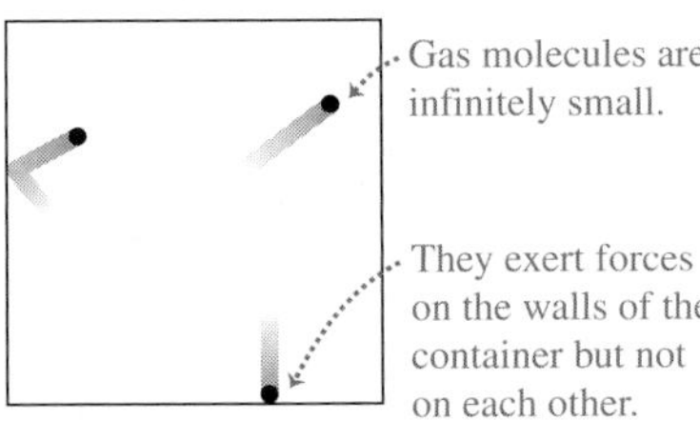

Gas molecules are infinitely small.
They exert forces on the walls of the container but not on each other.

(b) A more realistic model of a gas

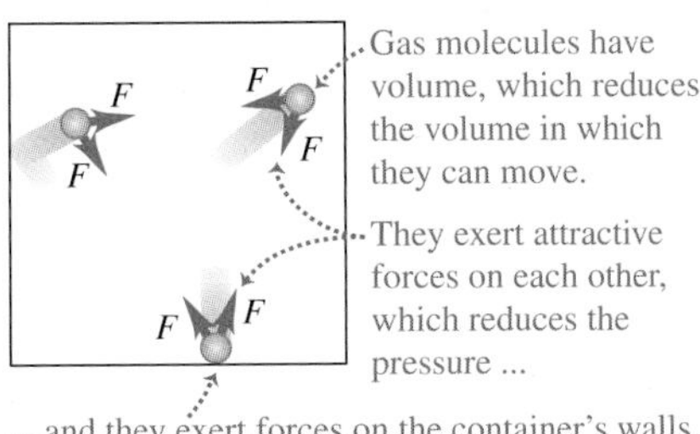

F
Gas molecules have volume, which reduces the volume in which they can move.
They exert attractive forces on each other, which reduces the pressure ...
... and they exert forces on the container's walls.

18.5 A gas as modeled by (a) the ideal-gas equation and (b) the van der Waals equation.

Meanwhile, we mention another equation of state, the **van der Waals equation,** that makes approximate corrections for these two omissions (Fig. 18.5b). This equation was developed by the 19th-century Dutch physicist J. D. van der Waals; the interaction between atoms that we discussed in Section 13.4 was named the *van der Waals interaction* after him. The van der Waals equation is

$$\left(p + \frac{an^2}{V^2}\right)(V - nb) = nRT \qquad (18.7)$$

The constants a and b are empirical constants, different for different gases. Roughly speaking, b represents the volume of a mole of molecules; the total volume of the molecules is then nb, and the net volume available for the molecules to move around in is $V - nb$. The constant a depends on the attractive intermolecular forces, which reduce the pressure of the gas for given values of n, V, and T by *pulling* the molecules together as they *push* on the walls of the container. The decrease in pressure is proportional to the number of molecules per unit volume in a layer near the wall (which are exerting the pressure on the wall) and is also proportional to the number per unit volume in the next layer beyond the wall (which are doing the attracting). Hence the decrease in pressure due to intermolecular forces is proportional to n^2/V^2.

When n/V is small (that is, when the gas is *dilute*), the average distance between molecules is large, the corrections in the van der Waals equation become insignificant, and Eq. (18.7) reduces to the ideal-gas equation. As an example, for carbon dioxide gas (CO_2) the constants in the van der Waals equation are $a = 0.364\ \text{J} \cdot \text{m}^3/\text{mol}^2$ and $b = 4.27 \times 10^{-5}\ \text{m}^3/\text{mol}$. We found in Example 18.1 that 1 mole of an ideal gas at $T = 0°\text{C} = 273.15\ \text{K}$ and $p = 1\ \text{atm} = 1.013 \times 10^5\ \text{Pa}$ occupies a volume $V = 0.0224\ \text{m}^3$; according to Eq. (18.7), 1 mole of CO_2 occupying this volume at this temperature would be at a pressure 532 Pa less than 1 atm, a difference of only 0.5% from the ideal-gas value.

18.6 Isotherms, or constant-temperature curves, for a constant amount of an ideal gas.

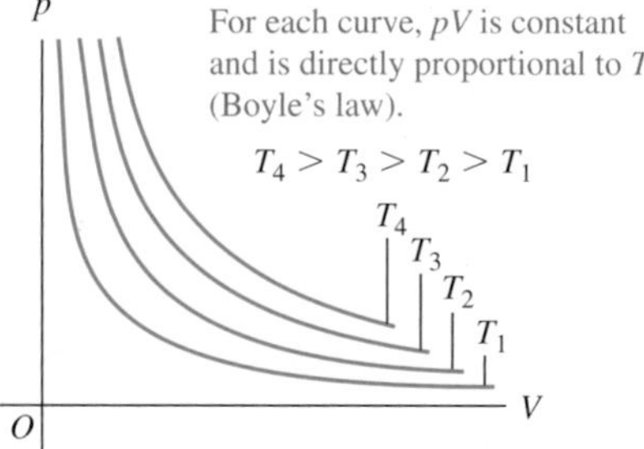
Each curve represents pressure as a function of volume for an ideal gas at a single temperature.
p
For each curve, pV is constant and is directly proportional to T (Boyle's law).
T4 > T3 > T2 > T1
T4
T3
T2
T1
O
V

pV-Diagrams

We could in principle represent the p-V-T relationship graphically as a *surface* in a three-dimensional space with coordinates p, V, and T. This representation sometimes helps us grasp the overall behavior of the substance, but ordinary two-dimensional graphs are usually more convenient. One of the most useful of these is a set of graphs of pressure as a function of volume, each for a particular constant temperature. Such a diagram is called a ***pV*-diagram.** Each curve, representing behavior at a specific temperature, is called an **isotherm,** or a *pV-isotherm.*

Figure 18.6 shows pV-isotherms for a constant amount of an ideal gas. The highest temperature is T_4; the lowest is T_1. This is a graphical representation of the ideal-gas equation of state. We can read off the volume V corresponding to any given pressure p and temperature T in the range shown.

Figure 18.7 shows a pV-diagram for a material that *does not* obey the ideal-gas equation. At temperatures below T_c the isotherms develop flat regions in which we can compress the material without an increase in pressure. Observation of the gas shows that it is *condensing* from the vapor (gas) to the liquid phase. The flat parts of the isotherms in the shaded area of Fig. 18.7 represent conditions of liquid-vapor *phase equilibrium.* As the volume decreases, more and more material goes from vapor to liquid, but the pressure does not change. (To keep the temperature constant during condensation, we have to remove the heat of vaporization, discussed in Section 17.6.)

When we compress such a gas at a constant temperature T_2 in Fig. 18.7, it is vapor until point a is reached. Then it begins to liquefy; as the volume decreases further, more material liquefies, and *both* the pressure and the temperature remain constant. At point b, all the material is in the liquid state. After this, any further compression results in a very rapid rise of pressure, because liquids are in general much less compressible than gases. At a lower constant temperature T_1, similar behavior occurs, but the condensation begins at lower pressure and greater volume

18.7 A pV-diagram for a nonideal gas, showing isotherms for temperatures above and below the critical temperature T_c. The liquid–vapor equilibrium region is shown as a green shaded area. At still lower temperatures the material might undergo phase transitions from liquid to solid or from gas to solid; these are not shown in this diagram.

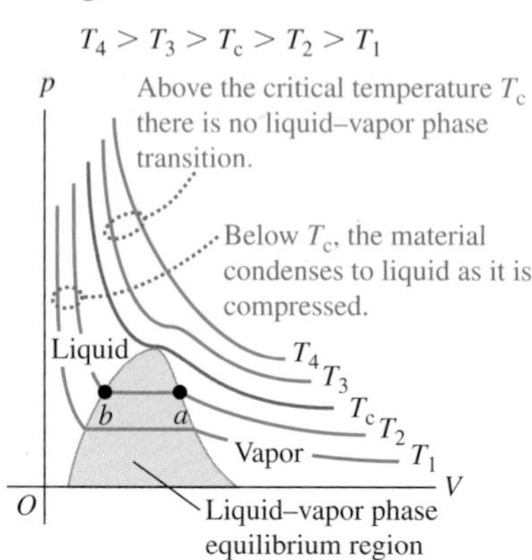
T4 > T3 > Tc > T2 > T1
p
Above the critical temperature Tc there is no liquid–vapor phase transition.
Below Tc, the material condenses to liquid as it is compressed.
Liquid
b
a
T4
T3
Tc
T2
T1
Vapor
V
O
Liquid–vapor phase equilibrium region

than at the constant temperature T_2. At temperatures greater than T_c, *no* phase transition occurs as the material is compressed; at the highest temperatures, such as T_4, the curves resemble the ideal-gas curves of Fig. 18.6. We call T_c the *critical temperature* for this material. In Section 18.6 we'll discuss what happens to the phase of the gas above the critical temperature.

We will use pV-diagrams often in the next two chapters. We will show that the *area* under a pV-curve (whether or not it is an isotherm) represents the *work* done by the system during a volume change. This work, in turn, is directly related to heat transfer and changes in the *internal energy* of the system, which we'll get to in Chapter 19.

Test Your Understanding of Section 18.1 Rank the following ideal gases in order from highest to lowest number of moles: (i) pressure 1 atm, volume 1 L, and temperature 300 K; (ii) pressure 2 atm, volume 1 L, and temperature 300 K; (iii) pressure 1 atm, volume 2 L, and temperature 300 K; (iv) pressure 1 atm, volume 1 L, and temperature 600 K; (v) pressure 2 atm, volume 1 L, and temperature 600 K.

18.2 Molecular Properties of Matter

We have studied several properties of matter in bulk, including elasticity, density, surface tension, heat capacities, and equations of state, with only passing references to molecular structure. Now we want to look in more detail at the relationship of bulk behavior to microscopic structure. We begin with a general discussion of the molecular structure of matter. Then in the next two sections we develop the kinetic-molecular model of an ideal gas, obtaining from this molecular model the equation of state and an expression for heat capacity.

Molecules and Intermolecular Forces

All familiar matter is made up of **molecules.** For any specific chemical compound, all the molecules are identical. The smallest molecules contain one atom each and are of the order of 10^{-10} m in size; the largest contain many atoms and are at least 10,000 times larger. In gases the molecules move nearly independently; in liquids and solids they are held together by intermolecular forces that are electrical in nature, arising from interactions of the electrically charged particles that make up the molecules. Gravitational forces between molecules are negligible in comparison with electrical forces.

18.8 How the force between molecules and their potential energy of interaction depend on their separation r.

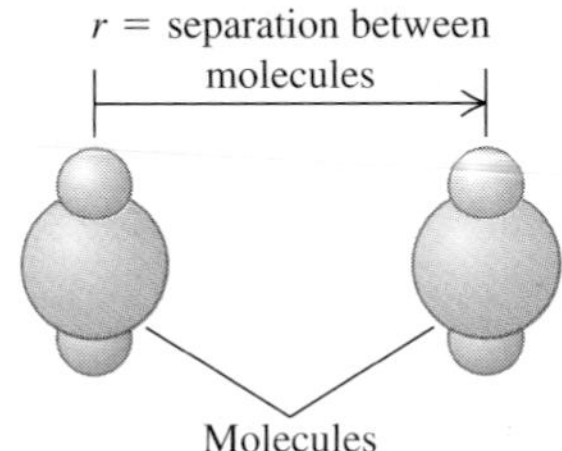

r = separation between molecules
Molecules

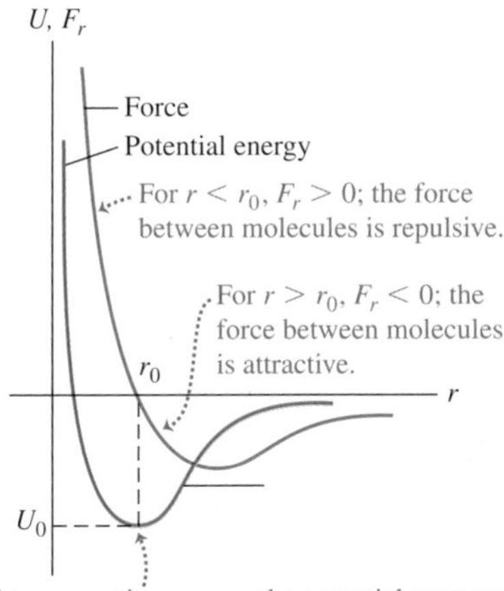

U, F_r
Force
Potential energy
For r < r_0, F_r > 0; the force between molecules is repulsive.
For r > r_0, F_r < 0; the force between molecules is attractive.
r_0
r
U_0

At a separation $r = r_0$, the potential energy of the two molecules is minimum and the force between the molecules is zero.

The interaction of two *point* electric charges is described by a force (repulsive for like charges, attractive for unlike charges) with a magnitude proportional to $1/r^2$, where r is the distance between the points. We will study this relationship, called *Coulomb's law,* in Chapter 21. Molecules are *not* point charges but complex structures containing both positive and negative charge, and their interactions are more complex. The force between molecules in a gas varies with the distance r between molecules somewhat as shown in Fig. 18.8, where a positive F_r corresponds to a repulsive force and a negative F_r to an attractive force. When molecules are far apart, the intermolecular forces are very small and usually attractive. As a gas is compressed and its molecules are brought closer together, the attractive forces increase. The intermolecular force becomes zero at an equilibrium spacing r_0, corresponding roughly to the spacing between molecules in the liquid and solid states. In liquids and solids, relatively large pressures are needed to compress the substance appreciably. This shows that at molecular distances slightly *less* than the equilibrium spacing, the forces become *repulsive* and relatively large.

Figure 18.8 also shows the potential energy as a function of r. This function has a *minimum* at r_0, where the force is zero. The two curves are related by $F_r(r) = -dU/dr$, as we showed in Section 7.4. Such a potential energy function is often called a **potential well.** A molecule at rest at a distance r_0 from a second molecule would need an additional energy $|U_0|$, the "depth" of the potential well, to "escape" to an indefinitely large value of r.

18.9 Schematic representation of the cubic crystal structure of sodium chloride.

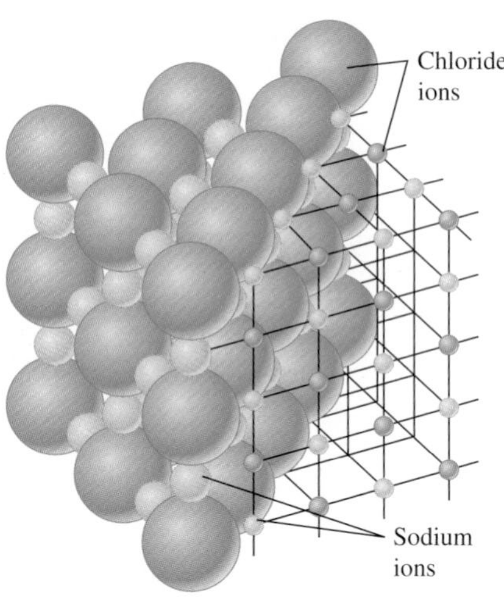

18.10 A scanning tunneling microscope image of the surface of a silicon crystal. The area shown is only 9.0 nm (9.0×10^{-9} m) across. Each blue "bead" is an individual silicon atom; you can clearly see how these atoms are arranged in a (nearly) perfect array of hexagons.

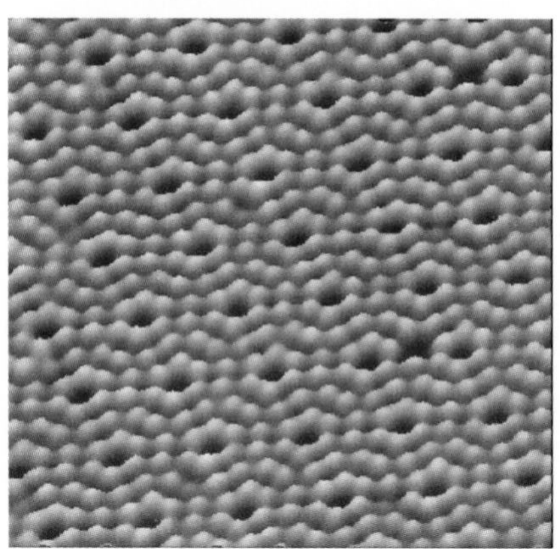

Molecules are always in motion; their kinetic energies usually increase with temperature. At very low temperatures the average kinetic energy of a molecule may be much *less* than the depth of the potential well. The molecules then condense into the liquid or solid phase with average intermolecular spacings of about r_0. But at higher temperatures the average kinetic energy becomes larger than the depth $|U_0|$ of the potential well. Molecules can then escape the intermolecular force and become free to move independently, as in the gaseous phase of matter.

In *solids,* molecules vibrate about more or less fixed points. In a crystalline solid these points are arranged in a recurring *crystal lattice.* Figure 18.9 shows the cubic crystal structure of sodium chloride (ordinary salt). A scanning tunneling microscope image of individual silicon atoms on the surface of a crystal is shown in Fig. 18.10.

The vibration of molecules in a solid about their equilibrium positions may be nearly simple harmonic if the potential well is approximately parabolic in shape at distances close to r_0. (We discussed this kind of simple harmonic motion in Section 13.4.) But if the potential-energy curve rises more gradually for $r > r_0$ than for $r < r_0$, as in Fig. 18.8, the average position shifts to larger r with increasing amplitude. As we pointed out in Section 17.4, this is the basis of thermal expansion.

In a *liquid,* the intermolecular distances are usually only slightly greater than in the solid phase of the same substance, but the molecules have much greater freedom of movement. Liquids show regularity of structure only in the immediate neighborhood of a few molecules. This is called *short-range order,* in contrast with the *long-range order* of a solid crystal.

The molecules of a *gas* are usually widely separated and so have only very small attractive forces. A gas molecule moves in a straight line until it collides with another molecule or with a wall of the container. In molecular terms, an *ideal gas* is a gas whose molecules exert *no* attractive forces on each other (Fig. 18.5a) and therefore have no *potential* energy.

At low temperatures, most common substances are in the solid phase. As the temperature rises, a substance melts and then vaporizes. From a molecular point of view, these transitions are in the direction of increasing molecular kinetic energy. Thus temperature and molecular kinetic energy are closely related.

Moles and Avogadro's Number

We have used the mole as a measure of quantity of substance. One **mole** of any pure chemical element or compound contains a definite number of molecules, the same number for all elements and compounds. The official SI definition is

One mole is the amount of substance that contains as many elementary entities as there are atoms in 0.012 kilogram of carbon-12.

In our discussion, the "elementary entities" are molecules. (In a monatomic substance such as carbon or helium, each molecule is a single atom, but we'll still call it a molecule here.) Note that atoms of a given element may occur in any of several isotopes, which are chemically identical but have different atomic masses; "carbon-12" refers to a specific isotope of carbon.

The number of molecules in a mole is called **Avogadro's number,** denoted by N_A. The current best numerical value of N_A is

$$N_A = 6.02214199(47) \times 10^{23} \text{ molecules/mol} \qquad \text{(Avogadro's number)}$$

The *molar mass* M of a compound is the mass of 1 mole. It is equal to the mass m of a single molecule multiplied by Avogadro's number:

$$M = N_A m \qquad \text{(molar mass, Avogadro's number, and mass of a molecule)} \tag{18.8}$$

When the molecule consists of a single atom, the term *atomic mass* is often used instead of molar mass or molecular weight.

Example 18.5 Atomic and molecular mass

Find the mass of a single hydrogen atom and the mass of an oxygen molecule.

SOLUTION

IDENTIFY: This problem involves the relationship between the mass of a molecule or atom (our target variable) and the corresponding molar mass.

SET UP: We use Eq. (18.8) in the form $m = M/N_A$ and the values of the molar masses from the periodic table of the elements (See Appendix D).

EXECUTE: The mass per mole of atomic hydrogen (that is, the atomic mass) is 1.008 g/mol. Therefore the mass m_H of a single hydrogen atom is

$$m_H = \frac{1.008 \text{ g/mol}}{6.022 \times 10^{23} \text{ atoms/mol}} = 1.674 \times 10^{-24} \text{ g/atom}$$

From Appendix D, the atomic mass of oxygen is 16.0 g/mol, so the molar mass of oxygen, which has diatomic (two-atom) molecules, is 32.0 g/mol. The mass of a single molecule of O_2 is

$$m_{O_2} = \frac{32.0 \text{ g/mol}}{6.022 \times 10^{23} \text{ molecules/mol}} = 53.1 \times 10^{-24} \text{ g/molecule}$$

EVALUATE: We note that the values in Appendix D are for the *average* atomic masses of a natural sample of each element. Such a sample may contain several different isotopes of the element, each with a different atomic mass. Natural samples of hydrogen and oxygen are almost entirely made up of just one isotope; this is not the case for all elements, however.

Test Your Understanding of Section 18.2 Suppose you could adjust the value of r_0 for the molecules of a certain chemical compound (Fig. 18.8) by turning a dial. If you doubled the value of r_0, the density of the solid form of this compound would become (i) twice as great; (ii) four times as great; (iii) eight times as great; (iv) $\frac{1}{2}$ as great; (v) $\frac{1}{4}$ as great; (vi) $\frac{1}{8}$ as great.

18.3 Kinetic-Molecular Model of an Ideal Gas

ActivPhysics Online 8.1 Characteristics of a Gas

The goal of any molecular theory of matter is to understand the *macroscopic* properties of matter in terms of its atomic or molecular structure and behavior. Such theories are of tremendous practical importance; once we have this understanding, we can design materials to have specific desired properties. Such analysis has led to the development of high-strength steels, glasses with special optical properties, semiconductor materials for electronic devices, and countless other materials essential to contemporary technology.

In this and the following sections we will consider a simple molecular model of an ideal gas. This *kinetic-molecular model* represents the gas as a large number of particles bouncing around in a closed container. In this section we use the kinetic-molecular model to understand how the ideal-gas equation of state, Eq. (18.3), is related to Newton's laws. In the following section we use the kinetic-molecular model to predict the molar heat capacity of an ideal gas. We'll go on to elaborate the model to include "particles" that are not points but have a finite size. We will be able to see why polyatomic gases have larger molar heat capacities than monatomic gases.

The following discussion of the kinetic-molecular model has several steps, and you may need to go over them several times to grasp how they all go together. Don't get discouraged!

Here are the assumptions of our model:

1. A container with volume V contains a very large number N of identical molecules, each with mass m.
2. The molecules behave as point particles; their size is small in comparison to the average distance between particles and to the dimensions of the container.
3. The molecules are in constant motion; they obey Newton's laws of motion. Each molecule collides occasionally with a wall of the container. These collisions are perfectly elastic.
4. The container walls are perfectly rigid and infinitely massive and do not move.

CAUTION **Molecules vs. moles** Make sure you don't confuse N, the number of *molecules* in the gas, with n, the number of *moles*. The number of molecules is equal to the number of moles multiplied by Avogadro's number: $N = nN_A$.

Collisions and Gas Pressure

18.11 Elastic collision of a molecule with an idealized container wall.

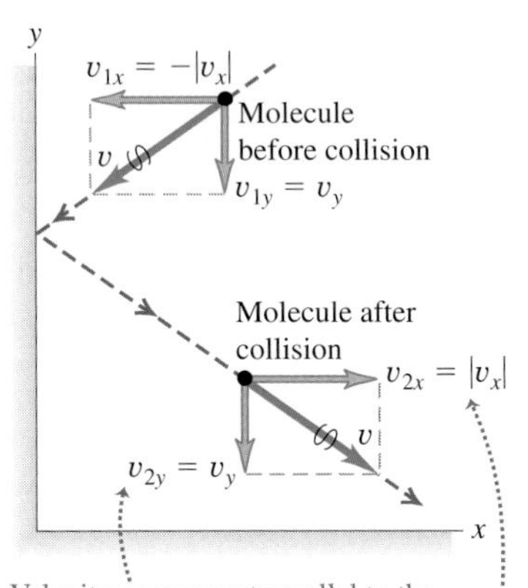

$v_{1x} = -|v_x|$
Molecule before collision
$v_{1y} = v_y$
Molecule after collision
$v_{2x} = |v_x|$
$v_{2y} = v_y$
• Velocity component parallel to the wall (y-component) does not change.
• Velocity component perpendicular to the wall (x-component) reverses direction.
• Speed v does not change.

During collisions the molecules exert *forces* on the walls of the container; this is the origin of the *pressure* that the gas exerts. In a typical collision (Fig. 18.11) the velocity component parallel to the wall is unchanged, and the component perpendicular to the wall reverses direction but does not change in magnitude.

Our program is first to determine the *number* of collisions that occur per unit time for a certain area A of wall. Then we find the total momentum change associated with these collisions and the force needed to cause this momentum change. From this we can determine the pressure, which is force per unit area, and compare the result to the ideal-gas equation. We'll find a direct connection between the temperature of the gas and the kinetic energy of the gas molecules.

To begin, we will assume that all molecules in the gas have the same *magnitude* of x-velocity, $|v_x|$. This isn't right, but making this temporary assumption helps to clarify the basic ideas. We will show later that this assumption isn't really necessary.

As shown in Fig. 18.11, for each collision the x-component of velocity changes from $-|v_x|$ to $+|v_x|$. So the x-component of momentum changes from $-m|v_x|$ to $+m|v_x|$, and the *change* in the x-component of momentum is $m|v_x| - (-m|v_x|) = 2m|v_x|$.

18.12 For a molecule to strike the wall in area A during a time interval dt, the molecule must be headed for the wall and be within the shaded cylinder of length $|v_x|\,dt$ at the beginning of the interval.

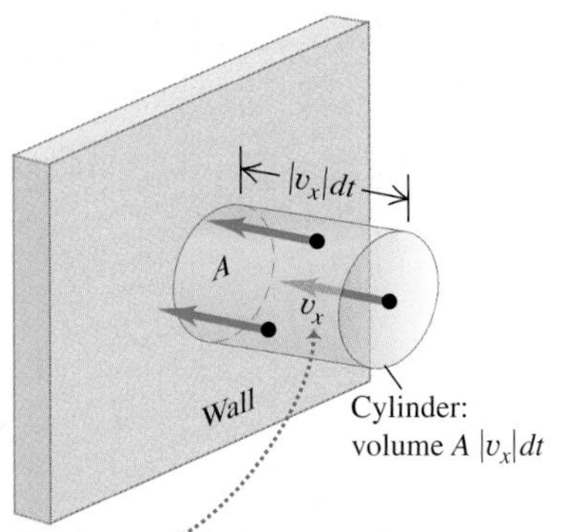

$|v_x|dt$
A
v_x
Wall
Cylinder: volume $A\,|v_x|dt$
All molecules are assumed to have the same magnitude $|v_x|$ of x-velocity.

If a molecule is going to collide with a given wall area A during a small time interval dt, then at the beginning of dt it must be within a distance $|v_x|\,dt$ from the wall (Fig. 18.12) and it must be headed toward the wall. So the number of molecules that collide with A during dt is equal to the number of molecules within a cylinder with base area A and length $|v_x|\,dt$ that have their x-velocity aimed toward the wall. The volume of such a cylinder is $A|v_x|\,dt$. Assuming that the number of molecules per unit volume (N/V) is uniform, the *number* of molecules in this cylinder is $(N/V)(A|v_x|\,dt)$. On the average, half of these molecules are moving toward the wall and half are moving away from it. So the number of collisions with A during dt is

$$\frac{1}{2}\left(\frac{N}{V}\right)(A|v_x|\,dt)$$

For the system of all molecules in the gas, the total momentum change dP_x during dt is the *number* of collisions multiplied by $2m|v_x|$:

$$dP_x = \frac{1}{2}\left(\frac{N}{V}\right)(A|v_x|\,dt)(2m|v_x|) = \frac{NAmv_x^2\,dt}{V} \tag{18.9}$$

(We are using capital P for total momentum and small p for pressure. Be careful!) We wrote v_x^2 rather than $|v_x|^2$ in the final expression because the square of the absolute value of a number is equal to the square of that number. The *rate* of change of momentum component P_x is

$$\frac{dP_x}{dt} = \frac{NAmv_x^2}{V} \tag{18.10}$$

According to Newton's second law, this rate of change of momentum equals the force exerted by the wall area A on the gas molecules. From Newton's *third* law this is equal and opposite to the force exerted *on* the wall *by* the molecules. Pressure p is the magnitude of the force exerted on the wall per unit area, and we obtain

$$p = \frac{F}{A} = \frac{Nmv_x^2}{V} \tag{18.11}$$

The pressure exerted by the gas depends on the number of molecules per volume (N/V), the mass m per molecule, and the speed of the molecules.

Pressure and Molecular Kinetic Energies

We mentioned that $|v_x|$ is really *not* the same for all the molecules. But we could have sorted the molecules into groups having the same $|v_x|$ within each group, then added up the resulting contributions to the pressure. The net effect of all this is just to replace v_x^2 in Eq. (18.11) by the *average* value of v_x^2, which we denote by $(v_x^2)_{av}$. Furthermore, $(v_x^2)_{av}$ is related simply to the *speeds* of the molecules. The speed v of any molecule is related to the velocity components v_x, v_y, and v_z by

$$v^2 = v_x^2 + v_y^2 + v_z^2$$

We can average this relation over all molecules:

$$(v^2)_{av} = (v_x^2)_{av} + (v_y^2)_{av} + (v_z^2)_{av}$$

But there is no real difference in our model between the x-, y-, and z-directions. (Molecular speeds are very fast in a typical gas, so the effects of gravity are negligibly small.) It follows that $(v_x^2)_{av}$, $(v_y^2)_{av}$, and $(v_z^2)_{av}$ must all be *equal.* Hence $(v^2)_{av}$ is equal to $3(v_x^2)_{av}$ and

$$(v_x^2)_{av} = \frac{1}{3}(v^2)_{av}$$

so Eq. (18.11) becomes

$$pV = \frac{1}{3}Nm(v^2)_{av} = \frac{2}{3}N\left[\frac{1}{2}m(v^2)_{av}\right] \tag{18.12}$$

We notice that $\frac{1}{2}m(v^2)_{av}$ is the average translational kinetic energy of a single molecule. The product of this and the total number of molecules N equals the total random kinetic energy K_{tr} of translational motion of all the molecules. (The notation K_{tr} reminds us that this energy is associated with *translational* motion. There may be additional energies associated with rotational and vibrational motion of molecules.) The product pV equals two-thirds of the total translational kinetic energy:

$$pV = \frac{2}{3}K_{tr} \tag{18.13}$$

Now we compare this with the ideal-gas equation,

$$pV = nRT$$

which is based on experimental studies of gas behavior. For the two equations to agree, we must have

$$K_{tr} = \frac{3}{2}nRT \quad \text{(average translational kinetic energy of } n \text{ moles of ideal gas)} \tag{18.14}$$

This remarkably simple result shows that K_{tr} is *directly proportional* to the absolute temperature T (Fig. 18.13). We will use this important result several times in the following discussion.

The average translational kinetic energy of a single molecule is the total translational kinetic energy K_{tr} of all molecules divided by the number of molecules, N:

$$\frac{K_{tr}}{N} = \frac{1}{2}m(v^2)_{av} = \frac{3nRT}{2N}$$

Also, the total number of molecules N is the number of moles n multiplied by Avogadro's number N_A, so

$$N = nN_A \qquad \frac{n}{N} = \frac{1}{N_A}$$

and

$$\frac{K_{tr}}{N} = \frac{1}{2}m(v^2)_{av} = \frac{3}{2}\left(\frac{R}{N_A}\right)T \tag{18.15}$$

18.13 Summer air (top) is warmer than winter air (bottom); that is, the average translational kinetic energy of air molecules is greater in summer.

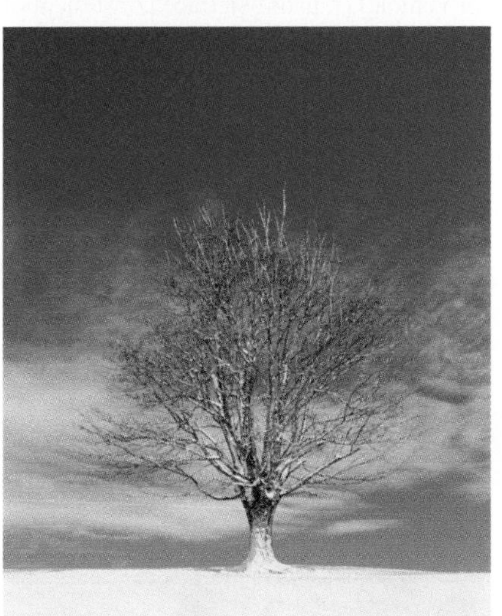

The ratio R/N_A occurs frequently in molecular theory. It is called the **Boltzmann constant,** k:

$$k = \frac{R}{N_A} = \frac{8.314 \text{ J/mol} \cdot \text{K}}{6.022 \times 10^{23} \text{ molecules/mol}}$$
$$= 1.381 \times 10^{-23} \text{ J/molecule} \cdot \text{K}$$

(The current best numerical value of k is $1.3806503(24) \times 10^{-23}$ J/molecule · K) In terms of k we can rewrite Eq. (18.15) as

$$\frac{1}{2}m(v^2)_{av} = \frac{3}{2}kT \quad \text{(average translational kinetic energy of a gas molecule)} \tag{18.16}$$

This shows that the average translational kinetic energy *per molecule* depends only on the temperature, not on the pressure, volume, or kind of molecule. We can obtain the average translational kinetic energy *per mole* by multiplying Eq. (18.16) by Avogadro's number and using the relation $M = N_A m$:

$$N_A\frac{1}{2}m(v^2)_{av} = \frac{1}{2}M(v^2)_{av} = \frac{3}{2}RT \quad \text{(average translational kinetic energy per mole of gas)} \tag{18.17}$$

The translational kinetic energy of a mole of ideal-gas molecules depends only on T.

Finally, it is sometimes convenient to rewrite the ideal-gas equation on a molecular basis. We use $N = N_A n$ and $R = N_A k$ to obtain the alternative form of the ideal-gas equation:

$$pV = NkT \tag{18.18}$$

This shows that we can think of the Boltzmann constant k as a gas constant on a "per-molecule" basis instead of the usual "per-mole" basis for R.

Molecular Speeds

From Eqs. (18.16) and (18.17) we can obtain expressions for the square root of $(v^2)_{av}$, called the **root-mean-square speed** (or **rms speed**) v_{rms}:

$$v_{rms} = \sqrt{(v^2)_{av}} = \sqrt{\frac{3kT}{m}} = \sqrt{\frac{3RT}{M}} \quad \text{(root-mean-square speed of a gas molecule)} \tag{18.19}$$

It might seem more natural to characterize molecular speeds by their *average* value rather than by v_{rms}, but we see that v_{rms} follows more directly from Eqs. (18.16) and (18.17). To compute the rms speed, we square each molecular speed, add, divide by the number of molecules, and take the square root; v_{rms} is the *root* of the *mean* of the *squares*. Example 18.7 illustrates this procedure.

Equations (18.16) and (18.19) show that at a given temperature T, gas molecules of different mass m have the same average kinetic energy but different root-mean-square speeds. On average, the nitrogen molecules $(M = 28 \text{ g/mol})$ in the air around you are moving faster than are the oxygen molecules $(M = 32 \text{ g/mol})$. Hydrogen molecules $(M = 2 \text{ g/mol})$ are fastest of all; this is why there is hardly any hydrogen in the earth's atmosphere, despite its being the most common element in the universe (Fig. 18.14). A sizable fraction of any H_2 molecules in the atmosphere would have speeds greater than the earth's escape speed of 1.12×10^4 m/s (calculated in Example 12.5 in Section 12.3) and would escape into space. The heavier, slower-moving gases cannot escape so easily, which is why they predominate in our atmosphere.

18.14 While hydrogen is a desirable fuel for vehicles, it is only a trace constituent of our atmosphere (0.00005% by volume). Hence hydrogen fuel has to be generated by electrolysis of water, which is itself an energy-intensive process.

The assumption that individual molecules undergo perfectly elastic collisions with the container wall is actually a little too simple. More detailed investigation has shown that in most cases, molecules actually adhere to the wall for a short time and then leave again with speeds that are characteristic of the temperature *of the wall.* However, the gas and the wall are ordinarily in thermal equilibrium and have the same temperature. So there is no net energy transfer between gas and wall, and this discovery does not alter the validity of our conclusions.

Problem-Solving Strategy 18.2 Kinetic-Molecular Theory

IDENTIFY *the relevant concepts:* Use the results of the kinetic-molecular model whenever you are asked to relate macroscopic properties of a gas, such as temperature and pressure, to microscopic properties, such as molecular speeds.

SET UP *the problem* using the following steps:

1. Identify which variables are known and which are the unknown target variables.
2. Choose the equation(s) to be used from among Eqs. (18.14), (18.16), and (18.19).

EXECUTE *the solution* as follows: As you solve for the target variable, be on your guard for inconsistency in units. Special caution is needed in the following places:

1. The usual units for molar mass M are grams per mole; the molar mass of oxygen (O_2) is 32 g/mol, for example. These units are often omitted in tables. In equations such as Eq. (18.19), when you use SI units you *must* express M in kilograms per mole by multiplying the table value by $(1\ \text{kg}/10^3\ \text{g})$. Thus in SI units, M for oxygen is 32×10^{-3} kg/mol.
2. Are you working on a "per-molecule" basis or a "per-mole" basis? Remember that m is the mass of a single molecule and M is the mass of a mole of molecules; N is the number of molecules and n is the number of moles; k is the gas constant per molecule and R is the gas constant per mole. You can do a complete unit check if you think of N as having units of "molecules"; then m has units of "mass per molecule," and k has units of "joules per molecule per kelvin."
3. Remember that T is always *absolute* (Kelvin) temperature.

EVALUATE *your answer:* Are your answers reasonable? Keep in mind that typical molecular speeds at room temperature are several hundred meters per second. If your answer seems dramatically different, recheck your calculations.

Example 18.6 Calculating molecular kinetic energy and v_{rms}

(a) What is the average translational kinetic energy of a molecule of an ideal gas at a temperature of 27°C? (b) What is the total random translational kinetic energy of the molecules in 1 mole of this gas? (c) What is the root-mean-square speed of oxygen molecules at this temperature?

SOLUTION

IDENTIFY: This problem involves the translational kinetic energy of an ideal gas on a per-molecule basis and a per-mole basis, as well as the rms speed of molecules in the gas.

SET UP: We are given temperature $T = 27°\text{C}$ and number of moles $n = 1$ mol, and the molecular mass m is that for oxygen. We use Eq. (18.16) to determine the average kinetic energy of a molecule, Eq. (18.14) to find the total molecular kinetic energy, and Eq. (18.19) to find the rms speed of a molecule.

EXECUTE: (a) To use Eq. (18.16), we first convert the temperature to the Kelvin scale: $27°\text{C} = 300$ K. Then

$$\frac{1}{2}m(v^2)_{\text{av}} = \frac{3}{2}kT = \frac{3}{2}(1.38 \times 10^{-23}\ \text{J/K})(300\ \text{K})$$
$$= 6.21 \times 10^{-21}\ \text{J}$$

This answer does not depend on the mass of the molecule.

(b) From Eq. (18.14), the total translational kinetic energy of a mole of molecules is

$$K_{\text{tr}} = \frac{3}{2}nRT = \frac{3}{2}(1\ \text{mol})(8.314\ \text{J/mol}\cdot\text{K})(300\ \text{K})$$
$$= 3740\ \text{J}$$

This is about the same kinetic energy as that of a sprinter in a 100-m dash.

(c) From Example 18.5 (Section 18.2), the mass of an oxygen molecule is

$$m_{O_2} = (53.1 \times 10^{-24}\ \text{g})(1\ \text{kg}/10^3\ \text{g}) = 5.31 \times 10^{-26}\ \text{kg}$$

From Eq. (18.19),

$$v_{\text{rms}} = \sqrt{\frac{3kT}{m}} = \sqrt{\frac{3(1.38 \times 10^{-23}\ \text{J/K})(300\ \text{K})}{5.31 \times 10^{-26}\ \text{kg}}}$$
$$= 484\ \text{m/s}$$

This is 1740 km/h, or 1080 mi/h! Alternatively,

$$v_{\text{rms}} = \sqrt{\frac{3RT}{M}} = \sqrt{\frac{3(8.314\ \text{J/mol}\cdot\text{K})(300\ \text{K})}{32.0 \times 10^{-3}\ \text{kg/mol}}}$$
$$= 484\ \text{m/s}$$

EVALUATE: We can check our result in part (b) by noting that the translational kinetic energy per mole must be equal to the average translational kinetic energy per molecule from part (a) multiplied by Avogadro's number N_A: $K_{\text{tr}} = (6.022 \times 10^{23}\ \text{molecules})(6.21 \times 10^{-21}\ \text{J/molecule}) = 3740$ J.

In part (c), note that when we use Eq. (18.19) with R in SI units, we must express M in *kilograms* per mole, not grams per mole. In this example we use $M = 32.0 \times 10^{-3}$ kg/mol, *not* 32.0 g/mol.

Example 18.7 rms and average speeds

Five gas molecules chosen at random are found to have speeds of 500, 600, 700, 800, and 900 m/s. Find the rms speed. Is it the same as the *average* speed?

SOLUTION

IDENTIFY: To solve this problem, we must use the definitions of the root mean square and the average of a collection of numbers.

SET UP: To find the *root-mean-square* value, we square each speed, find the average (mean) of the squares, and then take the square root of the result.

EXECUTE: The average value of v^2 for the five molecules is

$$(v^2)_{av} = \frac{\begin{bmatrix}(500\text{ m/s})^2 + (600\text{ m/s})^2 + (700\text{ m/s})^2 \\ + (800\text{ m/s})^2 + (900\text{ m/s})^2\end{bmatrix}}{5}$$

$$= 5.10 \times 10^5 \text{ m}^2/\text{s}^2$$

The square root of this is v_{rms}:

$$v_{rms} = 714 \text{ m/s}$$

The *average* speed v_{av} is given by

$$v_{av} = \frac{500\text{ m/s} + 600\text{ m/s} + 700\text{ m/s} + 800\text{ m/s} + 900\text{ m/s}}{5}$$

$$= 700 \text{ m/s}$$

EVALUATE: We see that in general, v_{rms} and v_{av} are *not* the same. Roughly speaking, v_{rms} gives greater weight to the higher speeds than does v_{av}.

Collisions Between Molecules

We have ignored the possibility that two gas molecules might collide. If they are really points, they *never* collide. But consider a more realistic model in which the molecules are rigid spheres with radius r. How often do they collide with other molecules? How far do they travel, on average, between collisions? We can get approximate answers from the following rather primitive model.

Consider N spherical molecules with radius r in a volume V. Suppose only one molecule is moving. When it collides with another molecule, the distance between centers is $2r$. Suppose we draw a cylinder with radius $2r$, with its axis parallel to the velocity of the molecule (Fig. 18.15). The moving molecule collides with any other molecule whose center is inside this cylinder. In a short time dt a molecule with speed v travels a distance $v\,dt$; during this time it collides with any molecule that is in the cylindrical volume of radius $2r$ and length $v\,dt$. The volume of the cylinder is $4\pi r^2 v\,dt$. There are N/V molecules per unit volume, so the number dN with centers in this cylinder is

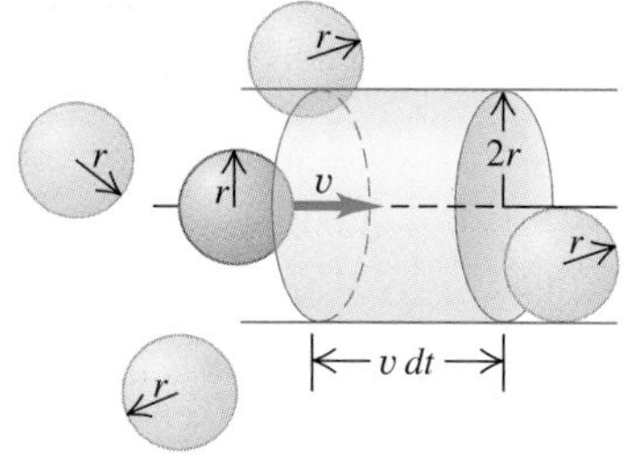

18.15 In a time dt a molecule with radius r will collide with any other molecule within a cylindrical volume of radius $2r$ and length $v\,dt$.

$$dN = 4\pi r^2 v\,dt\,N/V$$

Thus the number of collisions *per unit time* is

$$\frac{dN}{dt} = \frac{4\pi r^2 v N}{V}$$

This result assumes that only one molecule is moving. The analysis is quite a bit more involved when all the molecules move at once. It turns out that in this case the collisions are more frequent, and the above equation has to be multiplied by a factor of $\sqrt{2}$:

$$\frac{dN}{dt} = \frac{4\pi\sqrt{2}r^2 v N}{V}$$

The average time t_{mean} between collisions, called the *mean free time,* is the reciprocal of this expression:

$$t_{mean} = \frac{V}{4\pi\sqrt{2}r^2 v N} \tag{18.20}$$

The average distance traveled between collisions is called the **mean free path,** denoted by λ (the Greek letter lambda). In our simple model, this is just the molecule's speed v multiplied by t_{mean}:

$$\lambda = vt_{\text{mean}} = \frac{V}{4\pi\sqrt{2}r^2N} \quad \text{(mean free path of a gas molecule)} \quad (18.21)$$

The mean free path is inversely proportional to the number of molecules per unit volume (N/V) and inversely proportional to the cross-sectional area πr^2 of a molecule; the more molecules there are and the larger the molecule, the shorter the mean distance between collisions (Fig. 18.16). Note that the mean free path *does not* depend on the speed of the molecule.

We can express Eq. (18.21) in terms of macroscopic properties of the gas, using the ideal-gas equation in the form of Eq. (18.18), $pV = NkT$. We find

$$\lambda = \frac{kT}{4\pi\sqrt{2}r^2p} \quad (18.22)$$

If the temperature is increased at constant pressure, the gas expands, the average distance between molecules increases, and λ increases. If the pressure is increased at constant temperature, the gas compresses and λ decreases.

18.16 If you try to walk through a crowd, your mean free path—the distance you can travel on average without running into another person—depends on how large the people are and how closely they are spaced.

Example 18.8 Calculating mean free path

(a) Estimate the mean free path of a molecule of air at 27°C and 1 atm. Model the molecules as spheres with radius $r = 2.0 \times 10^{-10}$ m. (b) Estimate the mean free time of an oxygen molecule with $v = v_{\text{rms}}$.

SOLUTION

IDENTIFY: This problem uses the concepts of mean free path and mean free time (which are our target variables).

SET UP: We use Eq. (18.21) to determine the mean free path λ. To find the mean free time t_{mean} we could use Eq. (18.20), but it's more convenient to use the basic relationship $\lambda = vt_{\text{mean}}$ in Eq. (18.21). For the speed v we use the root-mean-square speed for oxygen calculated in Example 18.6.

EXECUTE: (a) From Eq. (18.22),

$$\begin{aligned}\lambda &= \frac{kT}{4\pi\sqrt{2}r^2p} \\ &= \frac{(1.38 \times 10^{-23}\ \text{J/K})(300\ \text{K})}{4\pi\sqrt{2}(2.0 \times 10^{-10}\ \text{m})^2(1.01 \times 10^5\ \text{Pa})} \\ &= 5.8 \times 10^{-8}\ \text{m}\end{aligned}$$

The molecule doesn't get very far between collisions, but the distance is still several hundred times the radius of the molecule. To get a mean free path of 1 meter, the pressure must be about 5.8×10^{-8} atm. Pressures this low are found 100 km or so above the earth's surface, at the outer fringe of our atmosphere.

(b) From Example 18.6, for oxygen at 27°C the root-mean-square speed is $v_{\text{rms}} = 484$ m/s, so the mean free time for a molecule with this speed is

$$t_{\text{mean}} = \frac{\lambda}{v} = \frac{5.8 \times 10^{-8}\ \text{m}}{484\ \text{m/s}} = 1.2 \times 10^{-10}\ \text{s}$$

This molecule undergoes about 10^{10} collisions per second!

EVALUATE: Note that the mean free *path* calculated in part (a) doesn't depend on the molecule's speed, but the mean free *time* does. Slower molecules have a longer average time interval t_{mean} between collisions than do fast ones, but the average *distance* λ between collisions is the same no matter what the molecule's speed.

Test Your Understanding of Section 18.3 Rank the following gases in order from (a) highest to lowest rms speed of molecules and (b) highest to lowest average translational kinetic energy of a molecule: (i) oxygen ($M = 32.0$ g/mol) at 300 K; (ii) nitrogen ($M = 28.0$ g/mol) at 300 K; (iii) oxygen at 330 K; (iv) nitrogen at 330 K.

18.4 Heat Capacities

When we introduced the concept of heat capacity in Section 17.5, we talked about ways to *measure* the specific heat or molar heat capacity of a particular material. Now we'll see how these numbers can be *predicted* on theoretical grounds. That's a significant step forward.

Heat Capacities of Gases

The basis of our analysis is that heat is *energy* in transit. When we add heat to a substance, we are increasing its molecular energy. In this discussion we will keep the volume of the gas constant so that we don't have to worry about energy transfer through mechanical work. If we were to let the gas expand, it would do work by pushing on moving walls of its container, and this additional energy transfer would have to be included in our calculations. We'll return to this more general case in Chapter 19. For now, with the volume held constant, we are concerned with C_V, the molar heat capacity *at constant volume.*

18.17 (a) A fixed volume V of a monatomic ideal gas. (b) When an amount of heat dQ is added to the gas, the total translational kinetic energy increases by $dK_{tr} = dQ$ and the temperature increases by $dT = dQ/nC_V$.

(a)

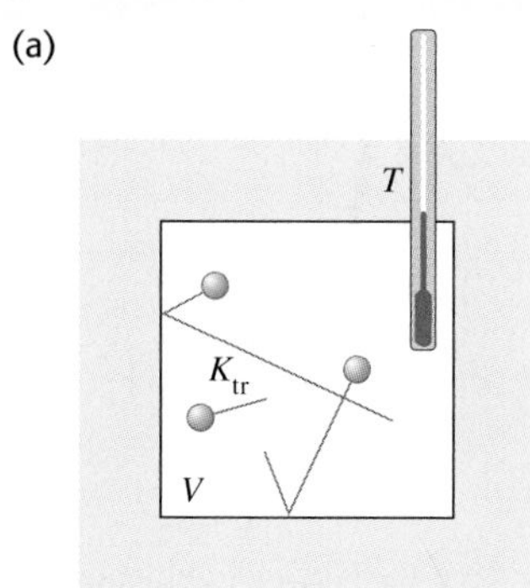

(b)

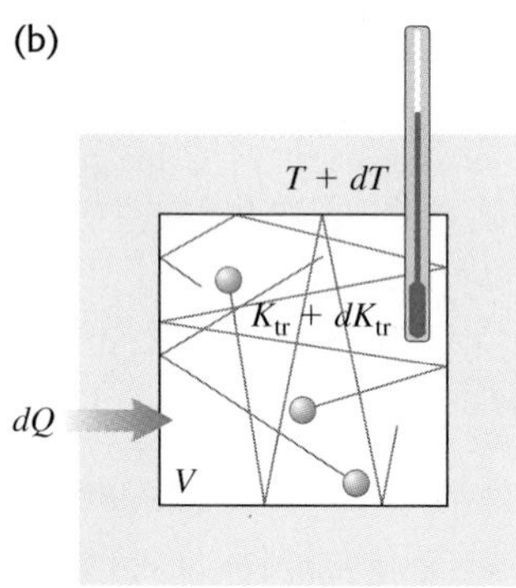

In the simple kinetic-molecular model of Section 18.3 the molecular energy consists only of the translational kinetic energy K_{tr} of the pointlike molecules. This energy is directly proportional to the absolute temperature T, as shown by Eq. (18.14), $K_{tr} = \frac{3}{2}nRT$. When the temperature changes by a small amount dT, the corresponding change in kinetic energy is

$$dK_{tr} = \frac{3}{2}nR\,dT \qquad (18.23)$$

From the definition of molar heat capacity at constant volume, C_V (see Section 17.5), we also have

$$dQ = nC_V\,dT \qquad (18.24)$$

where dQ is the heat input needed for a temperature change dT. Now if K_{tr} represents the total molecular energy, as we have assumed, then dQ and dK_{tr} must be *equal* (Fig. 18.17). Equating the expressions given by Eqs. (18.23) and (18.24), we get

$$nC_V\,dT = \frac{3}{2}nR\,dT$$

$$C_V = \frac{3}{2}R \quad \text{(ideal gas of point particles)} \qquad (18.25)$$

This surprisingly simple result says that the molar heat capacity (at constant volume) of *every* gas whose molecules can be represented as points is equal to $3R/2$.

To see whether this makes sense, let's first check the units. The gas constant *does* have units of energy per mole per kelvin, the correct units for a molar heat capacity. But more important is whether Eq. (18.25) agrees with *measured* values of molar heat capacities. In SI units, Eq. (18.25) gives

$$C_V = \frac{3}{2}(8.314\ \text{J/mol}\cdot\text{K}) = 12.47\ \text{J/mol}\cdot\text{K}$$

Table 18.1 Molar Heat Capacities of Gases

Type of Gas	Gas	C_V (J/mol · K)
Monatomic	He	12.47
	Ar	12.47
Diatomic	H_2	20.42
	N_2	20.76
	O_2	21.10
	CO	20.85
Polyatomic	CO_2	28.46
	SO_2	31.39
	H_2S	25.95

For comparison, Table 18.1 gives measured values of C_V for several gases. We see that for *monatomic* gases our prediction is right on the money, but that it is way off for diatomic and polyatomic gases.

This comparison tells us that our point-molecule model is good enough for monatomic gases but that for diatomic and polyatomic molecules we need something more sophisticated. For example, we can picture a diatomic molecule as *two* point masses, like a little elastic dumbbell, with an interaction force between the atoms of the kind shown in Fig. 18.8. Such a molecule can have additional kinetic energy associated with *rotation* about axes through its center of mass. The atoms may also have *vibrating* motion along the line joining them, with additional kinetic and potential energies. Figure 18.18 shows these possibilities.

When heat flows into a *monatomic* gas at constant volume, *all* of the added energy goes into an increase in random *translational* molecular kinetic energy. Equation (18.23) shows that this gives rise to an increase in temperature. But when the temperature is increased by the same amount in a *diatomic* or *polyatomic* gas, additional heat is needed to supply the increased rotational and vibrational energies. Thus polyatomic gases have *larger* molar heat capacities than monatomic gases, as Table 18.1 shows.

But how do we know how much energy is associated with each additional kind of motion of a complex molecule, compared to the translational kinetic energy? The new principle that we need is called the principle of **equipartition of energy.** It can be derived from sophisticated statistical-mechanics considerations; that derivation is beyond our scope, and we will treat the principle as an axiom.

The principle of equipartition of energy states that each velocity component (either linear or angular) has, on average, an associated kinetic energy per molecule of $\frac{1}{2}kT$, or one-half the product of the Boltzmann constant and the absolute temperature. The number of velocity components needed to describe the motion of a molecule completely is called the number of **degrees of freedom.** For a monatomic gas, there are three degrees of freedom (for the velocity components v_x, v_y, and v_z); this gives a total average kinetic energy per molecule of $3\left(\frac{1}{2}kT\right)$, consistent with Eq. (18.16).

For a *diatomic* molecule there are two possible axes of rotation, perpendicular to each other and to the molecule's axis. (We don't include rotation about the molecule's own axis because in ordinary collisions there is no way for this rotational motion to change.) If we assign five degrees of freedom to a diatomic molecule, the average total kinetic energy per molecule is $\frac{5}{2}kT$ instead of $\frac{3}{2}kT$. The total kinetic energy of n moles is $K_{\text{total}} = nN_A\left(\frac{5}{2}kT\right) = \frac{5}{2}n(kN_A)T = \frac{5}{2}nRT$, and the molar heat capacity (at constant volume) is

$$C_V = \frac{5}{2}R \qquad \text{(diatomic gas, including rotation)} \qquad (18.26)$$

In SI units,

$$C_V = \frac{5}{2}(8.314\ \text{J/mol}\cdot\text{K}) = 20.79\ \text{J/mol}\cdot\text{K}$$

This agrees within a few percent with the measured values for diatomic gases given in Table 18.1.

Vibrational motion can also contribute to the heat capacities of gases. Molecular bonds are not rigid; they can stretch and bend, and the resulting vibrations lead to additional degrees of freedom and additional energies. For most diatomic gases, however, vibrational motion does *not* contribute appreciably to heat capacity. The reason for this is a little subtle and involves some concepts of quantum mechanics. Briefly, vibrational energy can change only in finite steps. If the energy change of the first step is much larger than the energy possessed by most molecules, then nearly all the molecules remain in the minimum-energy state of motion. In that case, changing the temperature does not change their average vibrational energy appreciably, and the vibrational degrees of freedom are said to be "frozen out." In more complex molecules the gaps between permitted energy levels are sometimes much smaller, and then vibration *does* contribute to heat capacity. The rotational energy of a molecule also changes by finite steps, but they are usually much smaller; the "freezing out" of rotational degrees of freedom occurs only in rare instances, such as for the hydrogen molecule below about 100 K.

18.18 Motions of a diatomic molecule.

(a) **Translational motion.** The molecule moves as a whole; its velocity may be described as the x-, y-, and z-velocity components of its center of mass.

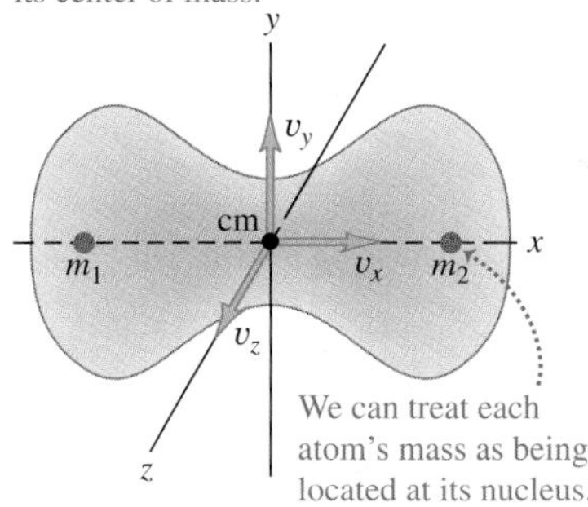

(b) **Rotational motion.** The molecule rotates about its center of mass. This molecule has two independent axes of rotation.

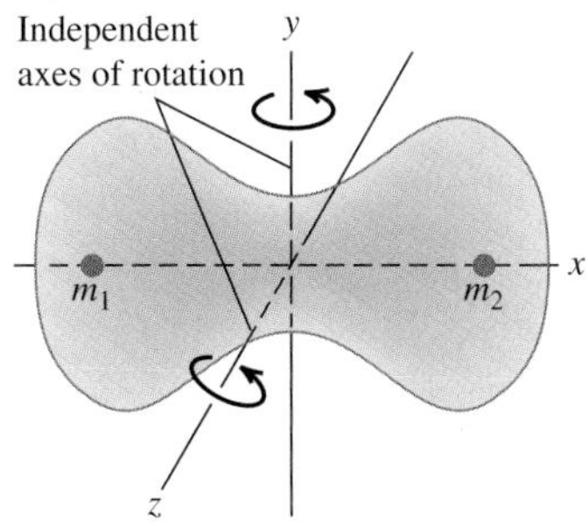

(c) **Vibrational motion.** The molecule oscillates as though the nuclei were connected by a spring.

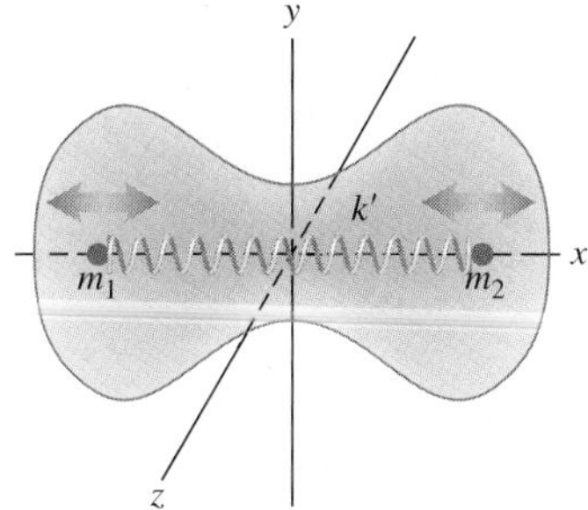

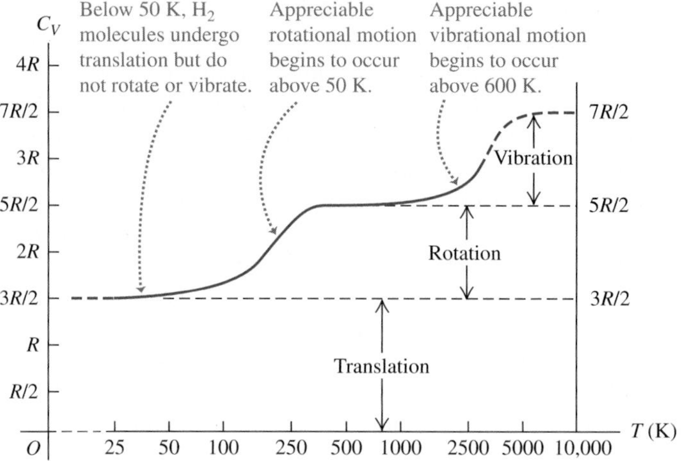

18.19 Experimental values of C_V, the molar heat capacity at constant volume, for hydrogen gas (H_2). The temperature is plotted on a logarithmic scale.

In Table 18.1 the large values of C_V for some polyatomic molecules show the contributions of vibrational energy. In addition, a molecule with three or more atoms that are not in a straight line has three, not two, rotational degrees of freedom.

From this discussion we expect heat capacities to be temperature-dependent, generally increasing with increasing temperature. Figure 18.19 is a graph of the temperature dependence of C_V for hydrogen gas (H_2), showing the temperatures at which the rotational and vibrational energies begin to contribute to the heat capacity.

Heat Capacities of Solids

We can carry out a similar heat-capacity analysis for a crystalline solid. Consider a crystal consisting of N identical atoms (a *monatomic solid*). Each atom is bound to an equilibrium position by interatomic forces. The elasticity of solid materials shows us that these forces must permit stretching and bending of the bonds. We can think of a crystal as an array of atoms connected by little springs (Fig. 18.20). Each atom can *vibrate* about its equilibrium position.

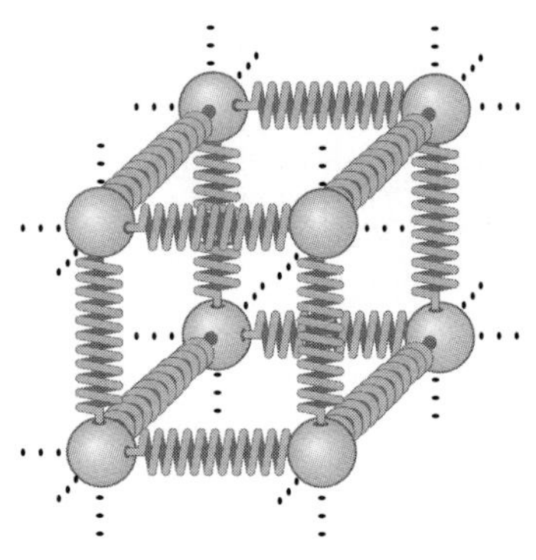

18.20 To visualize the forces between neighboring atoms in a crystal, envision every atom as being attached to its neighbors by springs.

Each atom has three degrees of freedom, corresponding to its three components of velocity. According to the equipartition principle, each atom has an average kinetic energy of $\frac{1}{2}kT$ for each degree of freedom. In addition, each atom has *potential* energy associated with the elastic deformation. For a simple harmonic oscillator (discussed in Chapter 13) it is not hard to show that the average kinetic energy of an atom is *equal* to its average potential energy. In our model of a crystal, each atom is essentially a three-dimensional harmonic oscillator; it can be shown that the equality of average kinetic and potential energies also holds here, provided that the "spring" forces obey Hooke's law.

Thus we expect each atom to have an average kinetic energy $\frac{3}{2}kT$ and an average potential energy $\frac{3}{2}kT$, or an average total energy $3kT$ per atom. If the crystal contains N atoms or n moles, its total energy is

$$E_{\text{total}} = 3NkT = 3nRT \tag{18.27}$$

From this we conclude that the molar heat capacity of a crystal should be

$$C_V = 3R \qquad \text{(ideal monatomic solid)} \tag{18.28}$$

In SI units,

$$C_V = (3)(8.314\ \text{J/mol} \cdot \text{K}) = 24.9\ \text{J/mol} \cdot \text{K}$$

This is the **rule of Dulong and Petit,** which we encountered as an *empirical* finding in Section 17.5: Elemental solids all have molar heat capacities of about 25 J/mol · K. Now we have *derived* this rule from kinetic theory. The agreement is only approximate, to be sure, but considering the very simple nature of our model, it is quite significant.

At low temperatures, the heat capacities of most solids *decrease* with decreasing temperature (Fig. 18.21) for the same reason that vibrational degrees of freedom of molecules are frozen out at low temperatures. At very low temperatures the quantity kT is much *smaller* than the smallest energy step the vibrating atoms can take. Hence most of the atoms remain in their lowest energy states because the next higher energy level is out of reach. The average vibrational energy per atom is then *less* than $3kT$, and the heat capacity per molecule is *less* than $3k$. At higher temperatures when kT is *large* in comparison to the minimum energy step, the equipartition principle holds, and the total heat capacity is $3k$ per molecule or $3R$ per mole as the Dulong and Petit rule predicts. Quantitative understanding of the temperature variation of heat capacities was one of the triumphs of quantum mechanics during its initial development in the 1920s.

18.21 Experimental values of C_V for lead, aluminum, silicon, and diamond. At high temperatures, C_V for each solid approaches about $3R$, in agreement with the rule of Dulong and Petit. At low temperatures, C_V is much less than $3R$.

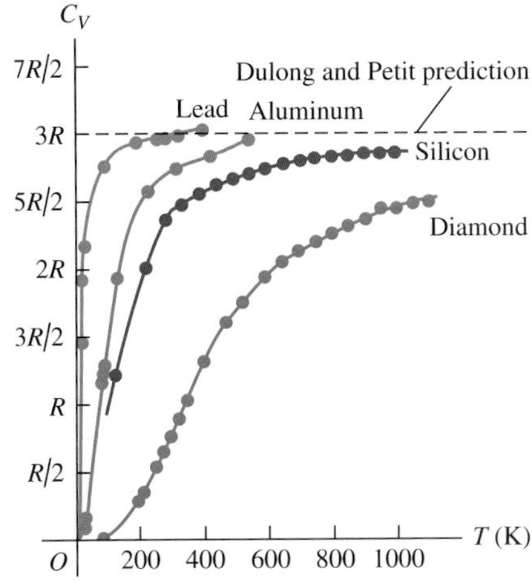

Test Your Understanding of Section 18.4 A cylinder with a fixed volume contains hydrogen gas (H_2) at 25 K. You then add heat to the gas at a constant rate until its temperature reaches 500 K. Does the temperature of the gas increase at a constant rate? Why or why not? If not, does the temperature increase most rapidly near the beginning or near the end of this process?

*18.5 Molecular Speeds

As we mentioned in Section 18.3, the molecules in a gas don't all have the same speed. Figure 18.22 shows one experimental scheme for measuring the distribution of molecular speeds. A substance is vaporized in a hot oven; molecules of the vapor escape through an aperture in the oven wall and into a vacuum chamber. A series of slits blocks all molecules except those in a narrow beam, which is aimed at a pair of rotating disks. A molecule passing through the slit in the first disk is blocked by the second disk unless it arrives just as the slit in the second disk is lined up with the beam. The disks function as a speed selector that passes only molecules within a certain narrow speed range. This range can be varied by changing the disk rotation speed, and we can measure how many molecules lie within each of various speed ranges.

To describe the results of such measurements, we define a function $f(v)$ called a *distribution function.* If we observe a total of N molecules, the number dN having speeds in the range between v and $v + dv$ is given by

$$dN = Nf(v)\,dv \qquad (18.29)$$

18.22 A molecule with a speed v passes through the slit in the first rotating disk. When the molecule reaches the second rotating disk, the disks have rotated through the offset angle θ. If $v = \omega x/\theta$, the molecule passes through the slit in the second rotating disk and reaches the detector.

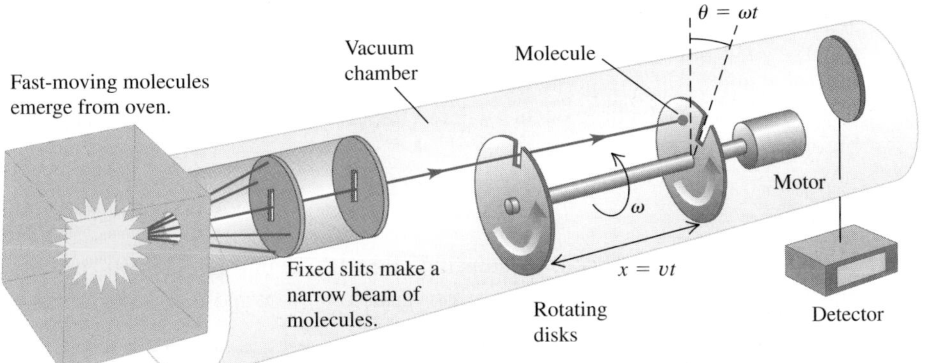

We can also say that the *probability* that a randomly chosen molecule will have a speed in the interval v to $v + dv$ is $f(v)\,dv$. Hence $f(v)$ is the probability per unit speed *interval;* it is *not* equal to the probability that a molecule has speed exactly equal to v. Since a probability is a pure number, $f(v)$ has units of reciprocal speed (s/m).

18.23 (a) Curves of the Maxwell–Boltzmann distribution function $f(v)$ for three temperatures. (b) The shaded areas under the curve represent the fractions of molecules within certain speed ranges. The most probable speed v_{mp} for a given temperature is at the peak of the curve.

(a)

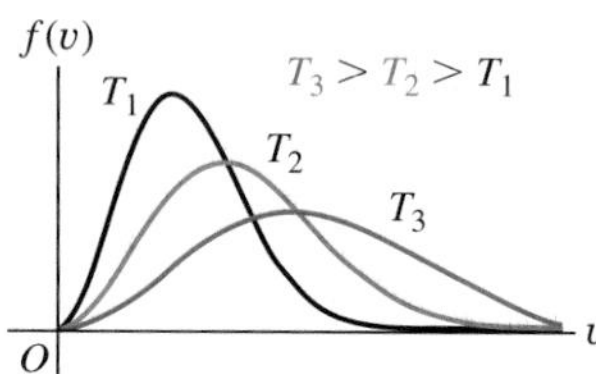

As temperature increases:
• the curve flattens.
• the maximum shifts to higher speeds.

(b)

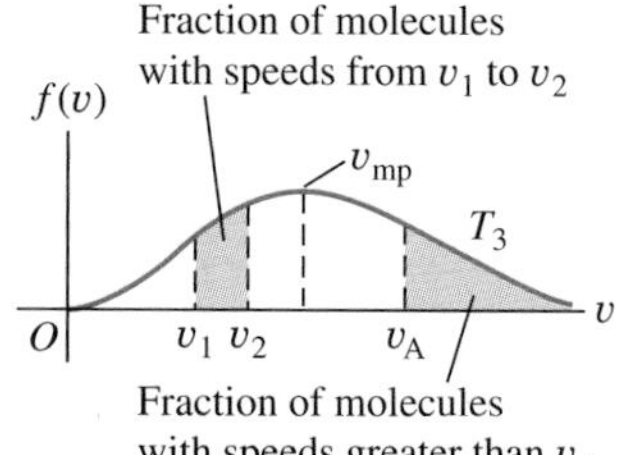

Figure 18.23a shows distribution functions for three different temperatures. At each temperature the height of the curve for any value of v is proportional to the number of molecules with speeds near v. The peak of the curve represents the *most probable speed* v_{mp} for the corresponding temperature. As the temperature increases, the average molecular kinetic energy increases, and so the peak of $f(v)$ shifts to higher and higher speeds.

Figure 18.23b shows that the area under a curve between any two values of v represents the fraction of all the molecules having speeds in that range. Every molecule must have *some* value of v, so the integral of $f(v)$ over all v must be unity for any T.

If we know $f(v)$, we can calculate the most probable speed v_{mp}, the average speed v_{av}, and the rms speed v_{rms}. To find v_{mp}, we simply find the point where $df/dv = 0$; this gives the value of the speed where the curve has its peak. To find v_{av}, we take the number $Nf(v)\,dv$ having speeds in each interval dv, multiply each number by the corresponding speed v, add all these products (by integrating over all v from zero to infinity), and finally divide by N. That is,

$$v_{av} = \int_0^\infty v f(v)\,dv \qquad (18.30)$$

The rms speed is obtained similarly; the average of v^2 is given by

$$(v^2)_{av} = \int_0^\infty v^2 f(v)\,dv \qquad (18.31)$$

and v_{rms} is the square root of this.

The Maxwell–Boltzmann Distribution

The function $f(v)$ describing the actual distribution of molecular speeds is called the **Maxwell–Boltzmann distribution.** It can be derived from statistical-mechanics considerations, but that derivation is beyond our scope. Here is the result:

$$f(v) = 4\pi\left(\frac{m}{2\pi kT}\right)^{3/2} v^2 e^{-mv^2/2kT} \quad \text{(Maxwell–Boltzmann distribution)} \qquad (18.32)$$

8.2 Maxwell-Boltzmann Distribution—Conceptual Analysis

8.3 Maxwell-Boltzmann Distribution—Quantitative Analysis

We can also express this function in terms of the translational kinetic energy of a molecule, which we denote by ϵ; that is, $\epsilon = \frac{1}{2}mv^2$. We invite you (see Exercise 18.47) to verify that when this is substituted into Eq. (18.32), the result is

$$f(v) = \frac{8\pi}{m}\left(\frac{m}{2\pi kT}\right)^{3/2} \epsilon e^{-\epsilon/kT} \qquad (18.33)$$

This form shows that the exponent in the Maxwell–Boltzmann distribution function is $-\epsilon/kT$ and that the shape of the curve is determined by the relative magnitude of ϵ and kT at any point. We leave it to you (see Exercise 18.48) to prove that the *peak* of each curve occurs where $\epsilon = kT$, corresponding to a most probable speed v_{mp} given by

$$v_{mp} = \sqrt{\frac{2kT}{m}} \qquad (18.34)$$

To find the average speed, we substitute Eq. (18.32) into Eq. (18.30) and carry out the integration, making a change of variable $v^2 = x$ and then integrating by parts. The result is

$$v_{av} = \sqrt{\frac{8kT}{\pi m}} \qquad (18.35)$$

Finally, to find the rms speed, we substitute Eq. (18.32) into Eq. (18.31). Evaluating the resulting integral takes some mathematical acrobatics, but we can find it in a table of integrals. The result is

$$v_{\text{rms}} = \sqrt{\frac{3kT}{m}} \tag{18.36}$$

This result agrees with Eq. (18.19); it *must* agree if the Maxwell–Boltzmann distribution is to be consistent with the equipartition theorem and our other kinetic-theory calculations.

Table 18.2 shows the fraction of all the molecules in an ideal gas that have speeds *less than* various multiples of v_{rms}. These numbers were obtained by numerical integration; they are the same for all ideal gases.

The distribution of molecular speeds in liquids is similar, although not identical, to that for gases. We can understand the vapor pressure of a liquid and the phenomenon of boiling on this basis. Suppose a molecule must have a speed at least as great as v_A in Fig. 18.23b to escape from the surface of a liquid into the adjacent vapor. The number of such molecules, represented by the area under the "tail" of each curve (to the right of v_A), increases rapidly with temperature. Thus the rate at which molecules can escape is strongly temperature-dependent. This process is balanced by another one in which molecules in the vapor phase collide inelastically with the surface and are trapped back into the liquid phase. The number of molecules suffering this fate per unit time is proportional to the pressure in the vapor phase. Phase equilibrium between liquid and vapor occurs when these two competing processes proceed at exactly the same rate. So if the molecular speed distributions are known for various temperatures, we can make a theoretical prediction of vapor pressure as a function of temperature. When liquid evaporates, it's the high-speed molecules that escape from the surface. The ones that are left have less energy on average; this gives us a molecular view of evaporative cooling.

Table 18.2 Fractions of Molecules in an Ideal Gas with Speeds Less than Various Multiples of v/v_{rms}

v/v_{rms}	Fraction
0.20	0.011
0.40	0.077
0.60	0.218
0.80	0.411
1.00	0.608
1.20	0.771
1.40	0.882
1.60	0.947
1.80	0.979
2.00	0.993

Rates of chemical reactions are often strongly temperature dependent, and the reason is contained in the Maxwell–Boltzmann distribution. When two reacting molecules collide, the reaction can occur only when the molecules are close enough for the electric-charge distributions of their electrons to interact strongly. This requires a minimum energy, called the *activation energy,* and thus a certain minimum molecular speed. Figure 18.23a shows that the number of molecules in the high-speed tail of the curve increases rapidly with temperature. Thus we expect the rate of any reaction that depends on an activation energy to increase rapidly with temperature. Similarly, many plant growth processes have strongly temperature-dependent rates, as can be seen by the rapid and diverse growth in tropical rain forests.

Test Your Understanding of Section 18.5 A quantity of gas containing N molecules has a speed distribution function $f(v)$. How many molecules have speeds between v_1 and $v_2 > v_1$? (i) $\int_0^{v_2} f(v)\,dv - \int_0^{v_1} f(v)\,dv$; (ii) $N[\int_0^{v_2} f(v)\,dv - \int_0^{v_1} f(v)\,dv]$; (iii) $\int_0^{v_1} f(v)\,dv - \int_0^{v_2} f(v)\,dv$; (iv) $N[\int_0^{v_1} f(v)\,dv - \int_0^{v_2} f(v)\,dv]$; (v) none of these.

18.6 Phases of Matter

We've talked a lot about ideal gases in the last few sections. An ideal gas is the simplest system to analyze from a molecular viewpoint because we ignore the interactions between molecules. But those interactions are the very thing that makes matter condense into the liquid and solid phases under some conditions. So it's not surprising that theoretical analysis of liquid and solid structure and behavior is a lot more complicated than that for gases. We won't try to go far here with a microscopic picture, but we can talk in general about phases of matter, phase equilibrium, and phase transitions.

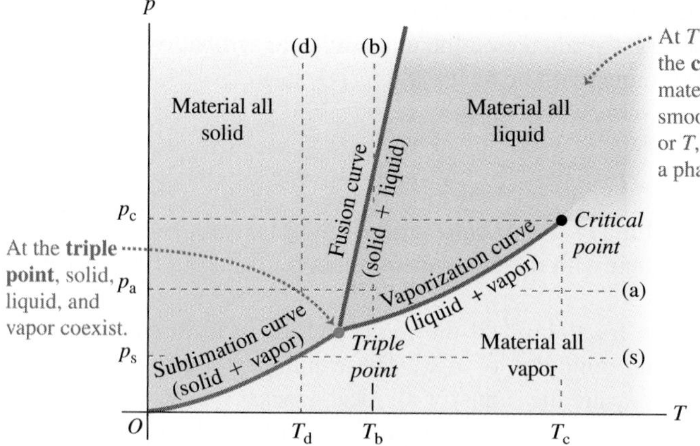

18.24 A typical pT phase diagram, showing regions of temperature and pressure at which the various phases exist and where phase changes occur.

In Section 17.6 we learned that each phase is stable only in certain ranges of temperature and pressure. A transition from one phase to another ordinarily takes place under conditions of **phase equilibrium** between the two phases, and for a given pressure this occurs at only one specific temperature. We can represent these conditions on a graph with axes p and T, called a **phase diagram;** Fig. 18.24 shows an example. Each point on the diagram represents a pair of values of p and T. Only a single phase can exist at each point, except for points on the solid lines, where two phases can coexist in phase equilibrium.

These lines separate the diagram into solid, liquid, and vapor regions. For example, the fusion curve separates the solid and liquid areas and represents possible conditions of solid-liquid phase equilibrium. Similarly, the vaporization curve separates the liquid and vapor areas, and the sublimation curve separates the solid and vapor areas. The three curves meet at the **triple point,** the only condition under which all three phases can coexist (Fig. 18.25). In Section 17.3 we used the triple-point temperature of water to define the Kelvin temperature scale. Triple-point data for several substances are given in Table 18.3.

18.25 Atmospheric pressure on earth is higher than the triple-point pressure of water (see line (a) in Fig. 18.24). Depending on the temperature, water can exist as a vapor (in the atmosphere), as a liquid (in the ocean), or as a solid (like the iceberg shown here).

Table 18.3 Triple-Point Data

Substance	Temperature (K)	Pressure (Pa)
Hydrogen	13.80	0.0704×10^5
Deuterium	18.63	0.171×10^5
Neon	24.56	0.432×10^5
Nitrogen	63.18	0.125×10^5
Oxygen	54.36	0.00152×10^5
Ammonia	195.40	0.0607×10^5
Carbon dioxide	216.55	5.17×10^5
Sulfur dioxide	197.68	0.00167×10^5
Water	273.16	0.00610×10^5

If we add heat to a substance at a constant pressure p_a, it goes through a series of states represented by the horizontal line (a) in Figure 18.24. The melting and boiling temperatures at this pressure are the temperatures at which the line intersects the fusion and vaporization curves, respectively. When the pressure is p_s, constant-pressure heating transforms a substance from solid directly to vapor. This process is called *sublimation;* the intersection of line (s) with the sublimation curve gives the temperature T_s at which it occurs for a pressure p_s. At any pressure less than the triple-point pressure, no liquid phase is possible. The triple-point pressure for carbon dioxide is 5.1 atm. At normal atmospheric pressure, solid carbon dioxide ("dry ice") undergoes sublimation; there is no liquid phase at this pressure.

Line (b) in Fig. 18.24 represents compression at a constant temperature T_b. The material passes from vapor to liquid and then to solid at the points where line (b) crosses the vaporization curve and fusion curve, respectively. Line (d) shows constant-temperature compression at a lower temperature T_d; the material passes from vapor to solid at the point where line (d) crosses the sublimation curve.

We saw in the pV-diagram of Fig. 18.7 that a liquid-vapor phase transition occurs only when the temperature and pressure are less than those at the point lying at the top of the green shaded area labeled "Liquid-vapor phase equilibrium region." This point corresponds to the endpoint at the top of the vaporization curve in Fig. 18.24. It is called the **critical point,** and the corresponding values of p and T are called the critical pressure and temperature, p_c and T_c. A gas at a pressure *above* the critical pressure does not separate into two phases when it is cooled at constant pressure (along a horizontal line above the critical point in Fig. 18.24). Instead, its properties change gradually and continuously from those we ordinarily associate with a gas (low density, large compressibility) to those of a liquid (high density, small compressibility) *without a phase transition.*

If this stretches credibility, think about liquid-phase transitions at successively higher points on the vaporization curve. As we approach the critical point, the *differences* in physical properties (such as density, bulk modulus, and viscosity) between the liquid and vapor phases become smaller and smaller. Exactly *at* the critical point they all become zero, and at this point the distinction between liquid and vapor disappears. The heat of vaporization also grows smaller and smaller as we approach the critical point, and it too becomes zero at the critical point.

For nearly all familiar materials the critical pressures are much greater than atmospheric pressure, so we don't observe this behavior in everyday life. For example, the critical point for water is at 647.4 K and 221.2×10^5 Pa (about 218 atm or 3210 psi). But high-pressure steam boilers in electric generating plants regularly run at pressures and temperatures well above the critical point.

Many substances can exist in more than one solid phase. A familiar example is carbon, which exists as noncrystalline soot and crystalline graphite and diamond. Water is another example; at least eight types of ice, differing in crystal structure and physical properties, have been observed at very high pressures.

pVT-Surfaces

We remarked in Section 18.1 that the equation of state of any material can be represented graphically as a surface in a three-dimensional space with coordinates p, V, and T. Such a surface is seldom useful in representing detailed quantitative information, but it can add to our general understanding of the behavior of materials at various temperatures and pressure. Figure 18.26 shows a typical pVT-surface. The light lines represent pV-isotherms; projecting them onto the pV-plane would give a diagram similar to Fig. 18.7. The pV-isotherms represent contour lines on the pVT-surface, just as contour lines on a topographic map represent the elevation (the third dimension) at each point. The projections of the edges of the surface onto the pT-plane give the pT phase diagram of Fig. 18.24.

Line *abcdef* in Fig. 18.26 represents constant-pressure heating, with melting along *bc* and vaporization along *de*. Note the volume changes that occur as T increases along this line. Line *ghjklm* corresponds to an isothermal (constant temperature) compression, with liquefaction along *hj* and solidification along *kl*. Between these, segments *gh* and *jk* represent isothermal compression with increase in pressure; the pressure increases are much greater in the liquid region *jk* and the solid region *lm* than in the vapor region *gh*. Finally, line *nopq* represents isothermal solidification directly from the vapor phase; this is the process involved in growth of crystals directly from vapor, as in the formation of snowflakes or frost and in the fabrication of some solid-state electronic devices. These three lines on the pVT-surface are worth careful study.

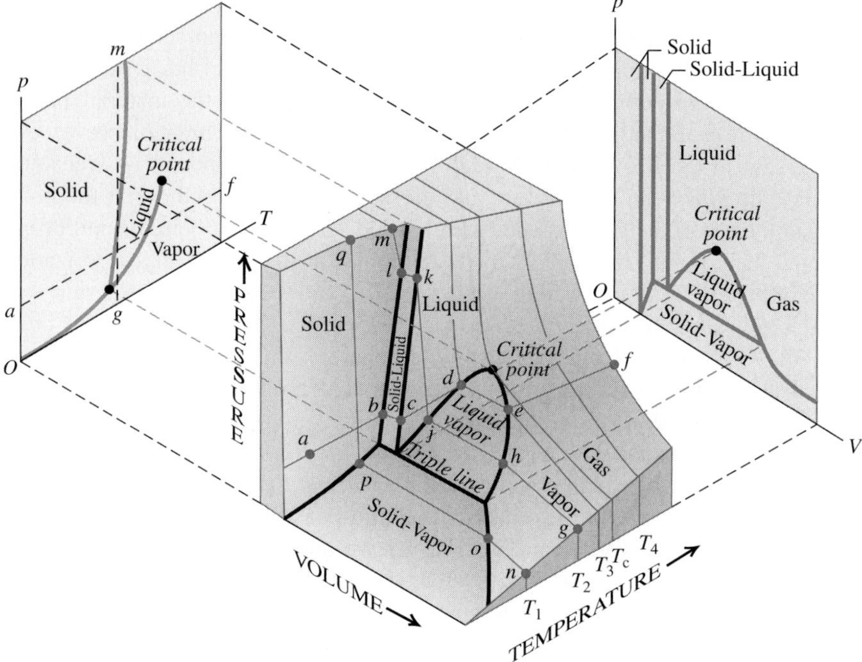

18.26 A pVT-surface for a substance that expands on melting. Projections of the boundaries on the surface on the pT- and pV-planes are also shown.

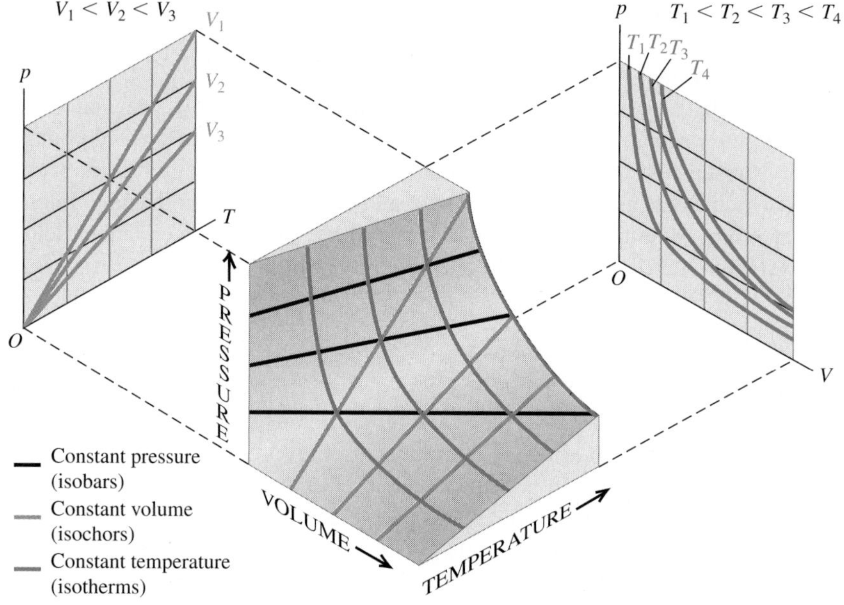

18.27 A pVT-surface for an ideal gas. At the left, each red line corresponds to a certain constant volume; at the right, each green line corresponds to a certain constant temperature.

For contrast, Fig. 18.27 shows the much simpler pVT-surface for a substance that obeys the ideal-gas equation of state under all conditions. The projections of the constant-temperature curves onto the pV-plane correspond to the curves of Fig. 18.6, and the projections of the constant-volume curves onto the pT-plane show the direct proportionality of pressure to absolute temperature.

Test Your Understanding of Section 18.6 The average atmospheric pressure on Mars is 6.0×10^2 Pa. Could there be lakes or rivers on Mars today? What about in the past, when the atmospheric pressure is thought to have been substantially greater than today?

CHAPTER 18 SUMMARY

Equations of state: The pressure p, volume V, and absolute temperature T of a given quantity of a substance are called state variables. They are related by an equation of state. This relationship pertains only to equilibrium states, in which p and T are uniform throughout the system. The ideal-gas equation of state relates p, V, T, and the number of moles n through a constant R that is the same for all gases. (See Examples 18.1–18.4.)

A pV-diagram is a set of graphs, called isotherms, each showing pressure as a function of volume for a constant temperature.

$$pV = nRT \quad (18.3)$$

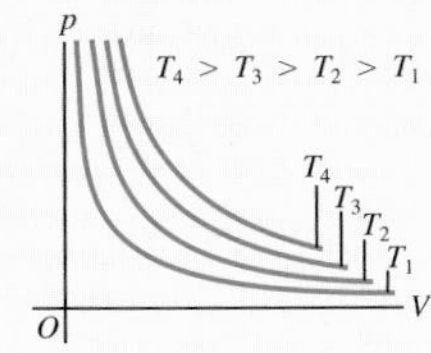

Molecular properties of matter: The molar mass M of a pure substance is the mass per mole. The mass m_{total} of a quantity of substance equals M multiplied by the number of moles n. Avogadro's number N_A is the number of molecules in a mole. The mass m of an individual molecule is M divided by N_A. (See Example 18.5.)

$$m_{total} = nM \quad (18.2)$$

$$M = N_A m \quad (18.8)$$

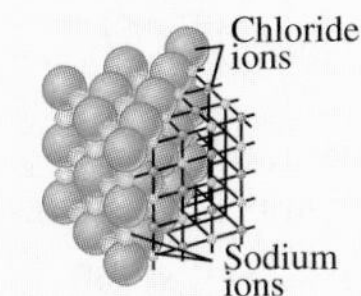

Kinetic-molecular model of an ideal gas: In an ideal gas, the total translational kinetic energy of the gas as a whole (K_{tr}) and the average translational kinetic energy per molecule $[\frac{1}{2}m(v^2)_{av}]$ are proportional to the absolute temperature T. The root-mean-square speed of molecules in an ideal gas is proportional to the square root of T. These expressions involve the Boltzmann constant $k = R/N_A$. (See Examples 18.6 and 18.7.)

The mean free path λ of molecules in an ideal gas depends on the number of molecules per volume (N/V) and the molecular radius r. (See Example 18.8.)

$$K_{tr} = \frac{3}{2}nRT \quad (18.14)$$

$$\frac{1}{2}m(v^2)_{av} = \frac{3}{2}kT \quad (18.16)$$

$$v_{rms} = \sqrt{(v^2)_{av}} = \sqrt{\frac{3kT}{m}} = \sqrt{\frac{3RT}{M}} \quad (18.19)$$

$$\lambda = vt_{mean} = \frac{V}{4\pi\sqrt{2}r^2N} \quad (18.21)$$

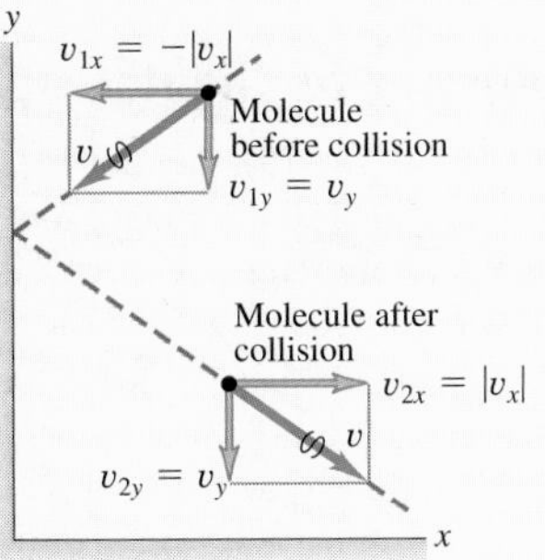

Heat capacities: The molar heat capacity at constant volume C_V can be expressed as a simple multiple of the gas constant R for certain idealized cases: an ideal monatomic gas [Eq. (18.25)]; an ideal diatomic gas including rotation energy [Eq. (18.26)]; and an ideal monatomic solid [Eq. (18.28)]. Many real systems are approximated well by these idealizations.

$$C_V = \frac{3}{2}R \quad \text{(monatomic gas)} \quad (18.25)$$

$$C_V = \frac{5}{2}R \quad \text{(diatomic gas)} \quad (18.26)$$

$$C_V = 3R \quad \text{(monatomic solid)} \quad (18.28)$$

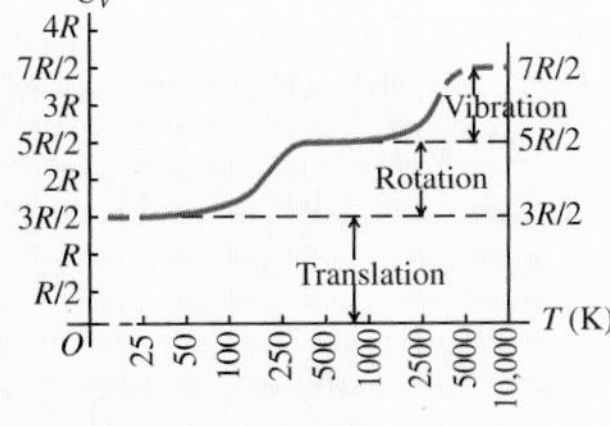

Molecular speeds: The speeds of molecules in an ideal gas are distributed according to the Maxwell–Boltzmann distribution $f(v)$. The quantity $f(v)\,dv$ describes what fraction of the molecules have speeds between v and $v + dv$.

$$f(v) = 4\pi\left(\frac{m}{2\pi kT}\right)^{3/2} v^2 e^{-mv^2/2kT} \quad (18.32)$$

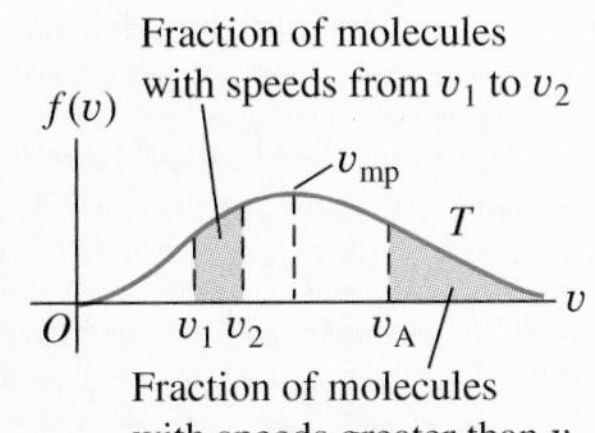

Phases of matter: Ordinary matter exists in the solid, liquid, and gas phases. A phase diagram shows conditions under which two phases can coexist in phase equilibrium. All three phases can coexist at the triple point. The vaporization curve ends at the critical point, above which the distinction between the liquid and gas phases disappears.

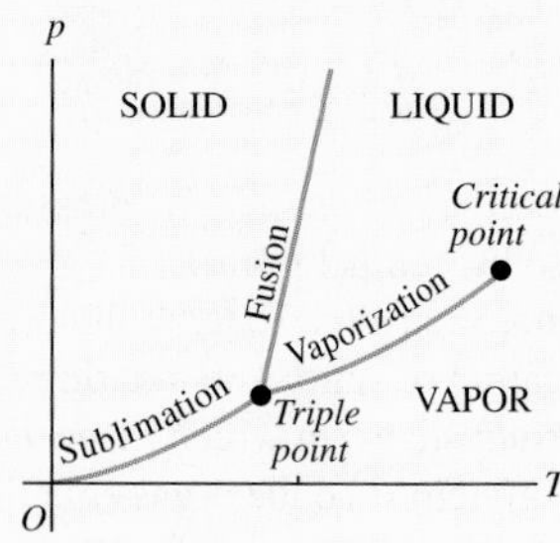

Key Terms

state variables, *611*
equation of state, *611*
molar mass, *611*
ideal-gas equation, *612*
ideal gas, *612*
gas constant, *612*
standard temperature and pressure, *613*
van der Waals equation, *616*
pV-diagram, *616*
isotherm, *616*
molecule, *617*
potential well, *617*
mole, *618*
Avogadro's number, *618*
Boltzmann constant, *622*
root-mean-square speed (rms speed), *622*
mean free path, *625*
equipartition of energy, *627*
degrees of freedom, *627*
rule of Dulong and Petit, *628*
Maxwell–Boltzmann distribution, *630*
phase equilibrium, *632*
phase diagram, *632*
triple point, *632*
critical point, *633*

Answer to Chapter Opening Question ?

From Eq. (18.19), the root-mean-square speed of a gas molecule is proportional to the square root of the absolute temperature T. The temperature range we're considering is from $(25 + 273.15)$ K $=$ 298 K to $(100 + 273.15)$ K $=$ 373 K. Hence the speeds increase by a factor of $\sqrt{(373\text{ K})/(298\text{ K})} = 1.12$; that is, there is a 12% increase. While 100°C feels far warmer than 25°C, the difference in molecular speeds is relatively small.

Answers to Test Your Understanding Questions

18.1 Answer: (ii) and (iii) (tie), (i) and (v) (tie), (iv) We can rewrite the ideal-gas equation, Eq. (18.3), as $n = pV/RT$. This tells us that the number of moles n is proportional to the pressure and volume and inversely proportional to the absolute temperature. Hence, compared to (i), the number of moles in each case is (ii) $(2)(1)/(1) = 2$ times as much, (iii) $(1)(2)/(1) = 2$ times as much, (iv) $(1)(1)/(2) = \frac{1}{2}$ as much, and (v) $(2)(1)/(2) =$ 1 times as much (that is, equal).

18.2 Answer: (vi) The value of r_0 determines the equilibrium separation of the molecules in the solid phase, so doubling r_0 means that the separation doubles as well. Hence a solid cube of this compound might grow from 1 cm on a side to 2 cm on a side. The volume would then be $2^3 = 8$ times larger, and the density (mass divided by volume) would be $\frac{1}{8}$ as great.

18.3 Answers: (a) (iv), (ii), (iii), (i); (b) (iii) and (iv) (tie), (i) and (ii) (tie) (a) Equation (18.19) tells us that $v_{rms} = \sqrt{3RT/M}$, so the rms speed is proportional to the square root of the ratio of absolute temperature T to molar mass M. Compared to (i) oxygen at 300 K, v_{rms} in the other cases is (ii) $\sqrt{(32.0\text{ g/mol})/(28.0\text{ g/mol})} =$ 1.07 times faster, (iii) $\sqrt{(330\text{ K})/(300\text{ K})} = 1.05$ times faster, and (iv) $\sqrt{(330\text{ K})(32.0\text{ g/mol})/(300\text{ K})(28.0\text{ g/mol})} = 1.12$ times faster. (b) From Eq. (18.16), the average translational kinetic energy per molecule is $\frac{1}{2}m(v^2)_{av} = \frac{3}{2}kT$, which is directly proportional to T and independent of M. We have $T = 300$ K for cases (i) and (ii) and $T = 330$ K for cases (iii) and (iv), so $\frac{1}{2}m(v^2)_{av}$ has equal values for cases (iii) and (iv) and equal (but smaller) values for cases (i) and (ii).

18.4 Answers: no, near the beginning Adding a small amount of heat dQ to the gas changes the temperature by dT, where $dQ = nC_V\,dT$ from Eq. (18.24). Figure 18.19 shows that C_V for H_2 varies with temperature between 25 K and 500 K, so a given amount of heat gives rise to different amounts of temperature change during the process. Hence the temperature will *not* increase at a constant rate. The temperature change $dT = dQ/nC_V$ is inversely proportional to C_V, so the temperature increases most rapidly at the beginning of the process when the temperature is lowest and C_V is smallest (see Fig. 18.19).

18.5 Answer: (ii) Figure 18.23b shows that the *fraction* of molecules with speeds between v_1 and v_2 equals the area under the curve of $f(v)$ versus v from $v = v_1$ to $v = v_2$. This is equal to the integral $\int_{v_1}^{v_2} f(v)\,dv$, which in turn is equal to the difference between the integrals $\int_0^{v_2} f(v)\,dv$ (the fraction of molecules with speeds from 0 to v_2 and $\int_0^{v_1} f(v)\,dv$ (the fraction of molecules with speeds from 0 to the slower speed v_1). The *number* of molecules with speeds from v_1 to v_2 equals the fraction of molecules in this speed range multiplied by N, the total number of molecules.

18.6 Answers: no, yes The triple-point pressure of water from Table 18.3 is 6.10×10^2 Pa. The present-day pressure on Mars is just less than this value, corresponding to the line labeled p_s in Fig. 18.24. Hence liquid water cannot exist on the present-day Martian surface, and there are no rivers or lakes. Planetary scientists conclude that liquid water could have and almost certainly did exist on Mars in the past, when the atmosphere was thicker.

PROBLEMS

For instructor-assigned homework, go to www.masteringphysics.com

Discussion Questions

Q18.1. Section 18.1 states that ordinarily, pressure, volume, and temperature cannot change individually without one affecting the others. Yet when a liquid evaporates, its volume changes, even though its pressure and temperature are constant. Is this inconsistent? Why or why not?

Q18.2. In the ideal-gas equation, could an equivalent Celsius temperature be used instead of the Kelvin one if an appropriate numerical value of the constant R is used? Why or why not?

Q18.3. On a chilly morning you can "see your breath." Can you really? What are you actually seeing? Does this phenomenon depend on the temperature of the air, the humidity, or both? Explain.

Q18.4. When a car is driven some distance, the air pressure in the tires increases. Why? Should you let out some air to reduce the pressure? Why or why not?

Q18.5. The coolant in an automobile radiator is kept at a pressure higher than atmospheric pressure. Why is this desirable? The radiator cap will release coolant when the gauge pressure of the coolant reaches a certain value, typically 15 lb/in.^2 or so. Why not just seal the system completely?

Q18.6. Unwrapped food placed in a freezer experiences dehydration, known as "freezer burn." Why?

Q18.7. "Freeze-drying" food involves the same process as "freezer burn," referred to Question 18.6. For freeze-drying, the food is usually frozen first, and then placed in a vacuum chamber and irradiated with infrared radiation. What is the purpose of the vacuum? The radiation? What advantages might freeze-drying have in comparison to ordinary drying?

Q18.8. A group of students drove from their university (near sea level) up into the mountains for a skiing weekend. Upon arriving at the slopes, they discovered that the bags of potato chips they had brought for snacks had all burst open. What caused this to happen?

Q18.9. How does evaporation of perspiration from your skin cool your body?

Q18.10. A rigid, perfectly insulated container has a membrane dividing its volume in half. One side contains a gas at an absolute temperature T_0 and pressure p_0, while the other half is completely empty. Suddenly a small hole develops in the membrane, allowing the gas to leak out into the other half until it eventually occupies twice its original volume. In terms of T_0 and p_0, what will be the new temperature and pressure of the gas when it is distributed equally in both halves of the container? Explain your reasoning.

Q18.11. (a) Which has more atoms: a kilogram of hydrogen or a kilogram of lead? Which has more mass? (b) Which has more atoms: a mole of hydrogen or a mole of lead? Which has more mass? Explain your reasoning.

Q18.12. Use the concepts of the kinetic-molecular model to explain: (a) why the pressure of a gas in a rigid container increases as heat is added to the gas and; (b) why the pressure of a gas increases as we compress it, even if we do not change its temperature.

Q18.13. The proportion of various gases in the earth's atmosphere changes somewhat with altitude. Would you expect the proportion of oxygen at high altitude to be greater or less than at sea level compared to the proportion of nitrogen? Why?

Q18.14. Comment on the following statement: *When two gases are mixed, if they are to be in thermal equilibrium, they must have the same average molecular speed.* Is the statement correct? Why or why not?

Q18.15. The kinetic-molecular model contains a hidden assumption about the temperature of the container walls. What is this assumption? What would happen if this assumption were not valid?

Q18.16. The temperature of an ideal gas is directly proportional to the average kinetic energy of its molecules. If a container of ideal gas is moving past you at 2000 m/s, is the temperature of the gas higher than if the container was at rest? Explain your reasoning.

Q18.17. If the pressure of an ideal monatomic gas is increased while the number of moles is kept constant, what happens to the average translational kinetic energy of one atom of the gas? Is it possible to change *both* the volume and the pressure of an ideal gas and keep the average translational kinetic energy of the atoms constant? Explain.

Q18.18. In deriving the ideal-gas equation from the kinetic-molecular model, we ignored potential energy due to the earth's gravity. Is this omission justified? Why or why not?

Q18.19. The derivation of the ideal-gas equation included the assumption that the number of molecules is very large, so that we could compute the average force due to many collisions. However, the ideal-gas equation holds accurately only at low pressures, where the molecules are few and far between. Is this inconsistent? Why or why not?

Q18.20. A gas storage tank has a small leak. The pressure in the tank drops more quickly if the gas is hydrogen or helium than if it is oxygen. Why?

Q18.21. Consider two specimens of ideal gas at the same temperature. Specimen A has the same total mass as specimen B, but the molecules in specimen A have greater molar mass than they do in specimen B. In which specimen is the total kinetic energy of the gas greater? Does your answer depend on the molecular structure of the gases? Why or why not?

Q18.22. The temperature of an ideal monatomic gas is increased from 25°C to 50°C. Does the average translational kinetic energy of each gas atom double? Explain. If your answer is no, what would the final temperature be if the average translational kinetic energy was doubled?

Q18.23. If the root-mean-square speed of the atoms of an ideal gas is to be doubled, by what factor must the Kelvin temperature of the gas be increased? Explain.

Q18.24. (a) If you apply the same amount of heat to 1.00 mol of an ideal monatomic gas and 1.00 mol of an ideal diatomic gas, which one (if any) will increase more in temperature? (b) Physically, *why* do diatomic gases have a greater molar heat capacity than monatomic gases?

Q18.25. The discussion in Section 18.4 concluded that all ideal diatomic gases have the same heat capacity C_V. Does this mean that it takes the same amount of heat to raise the temperature of 1.0 g of each one by 1.0 K? Explain your reasoning.

***Q18.26.** In a gas that contains N molecules, is it accurate to say that the number of molecules with speed v is equal to $f(v)$? Is it accurate to say that this number is given by $Nf(v)$? Explain your answers.

***Q18.27.** Imagine a special air filter placed in a window of a house. The tiny holes in the filter allow only air molecules moving faster than a certain speed to exit the house, and allow only air molecules moving slower than that speed to enter the house from outside. What effect would this filter have on the temperature inside the house? (It turns out that the second law of thermodynamics—which we will discuss in Chapter 20—tells us that such a wonderful air filter would be impossible to make.)

Q18.28. A beaker of water at room temperature is placed in an enclosure, and the air pressure in the enclosure is slowly reduced. When the air pressure is reduced sufficiently, the water begins to boil. The temperature of the water does not rise when it boils; in fact, the temperature *drops* slightly. Explain these phenomena.

Q18.29. Ice is slippery to walk on, and especially slippery if you wear ice skates. What does this tell you about how the melting temperature of ice depends on pressure? Explain.

Q18.30. Hydrothermal vents are openings in the ocean floor that discharge very hot water. The water emerging from one such vent off the Oregon coast, 2400 m below the surface, has a temperature of 279°C. Despite its high temperature, the water doesn't boil. Why not?

Q18.31. The dark areas on the moon's surface are called *maria,* Latin for "seas," and were once thought to be bodies of water. In fact, the maria are not "seas" at all, but plains of solidified lava. Given that there is no atmosphere on the moon, how can you explain the absence of liquid water on the moon's surface?

Q18.32. In addition to the normal cooking directions printed on the back of a box of rice, there are also "high-altitude directions." The only difference is that the "high-altitude directions" suggest increasing the cooking time and using a greater volume of boiling water in which to cook the rice. Why should the directions depend on the altitude in this way?

Exercises

Section 18.1 Equations of State

18.1. A 20.0-L tank contains 0.225 kg of helium at 18.0°C. The molar mass of helium is 4.00 g/mol. (a) How many moles of helium are in the tank? (b) What is the pressure in the tank, in pascals and in atmospheres?

18.2. Helium gas with a volume of 2.60 L, under a pressure of 1.30 atm and at a temperature of 41.0°C, is warmed until both pressure and volume are doubled. (a) What is the final temperature? (b) How many grams of helium are there? The molar mass of helium is 4.00 g/mol.

18.3. A cylindrical tank has a tight-fitting piston that allows the volume of the tank to be changed. The tank originally contains 0.110 m^3 of air at a pressure of 3.40 atm. The piston is slowly pulled out until the volume of the gas is increased to 0.390 m^3. If the temperature remains constant, what is the final value of the pressure?

18.4. A 3.00-L tank contains air at 3.00 atm and 20.0°C. The tank is sealed and cooled until the pressure is 1.00 atm. (a) What is the temperature then in degrees Celsius? Assume that the volume of the tank is constant. (b) If the temperature is kept at the value found in part (a) and the gas is compressed, what is the volume when the pressure again becomes 3.00 atm?

18.5. (a) Use the ideal-gas law to estimate the number of air molecules in your physics lab room, assuming all the air is N_2. (b) Calculate the particle density in the lab (that is, the number of molecules per cubic centimeter).

18.6. You have several identical balloons. You experimentally determine that a balloon will break if its volume exceeds 0.900 L. The pressure of the gas inside the balloon equals air pressure (1.00 atm. (a) If the air inside the balloon is at a constant temperature of 22.0°C and behaves as an ideal gas, what mass of air can you blow into one of the balloons before it bursts? (b) Repeat part (a) if the gas is helium rather than air.

18.7. A Jaguar XK8 convertible has an eight-cylinder engine. At the beginning of its compression stroke, one of the cylinders contains 499 cm^3 of air at atmospheric pressure $(1.01 \times 10^5$ Pa$)$ and a temperature of 27.0°C. At the end of the stroke, the air has been compressed to a volume of 46.2 cm^3 and the gauge pressure has increased to 2.72×10^6 Pa. Compute the final temperature.

18.8. A welder using a tank of volume 0.0750 m^3 fills it with oxygen (molar mass 32.0 g/mol) at a gauge pressure of 3.00×10^5 Pa and temperature of 37.0°C. The tank has a small leak, and in time some of the oxygen leaks out. On a day when the temperature is 22.0°C, the gauge pressure of the oxygen in the tank is 1.80×10^5 Pa. Find (a) the initial mass of oxygen and (b) the mass of oxygen that has leaked out.

18.9. A large cylindrical tank contains 0.750 m^3 of nitrogen gas at 27°C and 1.50×10^5 Pa (absolute pressure). The tank has a tight-fitting piston that allows the volume to be changed. What will be the pressure if the volume is decreased to 0.480 m^3 and the temperature is increased to 157°C?

18.10. An empty cylindrical canister 1.50 m long and 90.0 cm in diameter is to be filled with pure oxygen at 22.0°C to store in a space station. To hold as much gas as possible, the absolute pressure of the oxygen will be 21.0 atm. The molar mass of oxygen is 32.0 g/mol. (a) How many moles of oxygen does this canister hold? (b) For someone lifting this canister, by how many kilograms does this gas increase the mass to be lifted?

18.11. The gas inside a balloon will always have a pressure nearly equal to atmospheric pressure, since that is the pressure applied to the outside of the balloon. You fill a balloon with helium (a nearly ideal gas) to a volume of 0.600 L at a temperature of 19.0°C. What is the volume of the balloon if you cool it to the boiling point of liquid nitrogen (77.3 K)?

18.12. Deviations from the Ideal-Gas Equation. For carbon dioxide gas (CO_2), the constants in the van der Waals equation are $a = 0.364\ \text{J} \cdot \text{m}^3/\text{mol}^2$ and $b = 4.27 \times 10^{-5}\ \text{m}^3/\text{mol}$. (a) If 1.00 mol of CO_2 gas at 350 K is confined to a volume of 400 cm^3, find the pressure of the gas using the ideal-gas equation and the van der Waals equation. (b) Which equation gives a lower pressure? Why? What is the percentage difference of the van der Waals equation result from the ideal-gas equation result? (c) The gas is kept at the same temperature as it expands to a volume of 4000 cm^3. Repeat the calculations of parts (a) and (b). (d) Explain how your calculations show that the van der Waals equation is equivalent to the ideal-gas equation if n/V is small.

18.13. The total lung volume for a typical physics student is 6.00 L. A physics student fills her lungs with air at an absolute pressure of 1.00 atm. Then, holding her breath, she compresses her chest cavity, decreasing her lung volume to 5.70 L. What is the pressure of the air in her lungs then? Assume that the temperature of the air remains constant.

18.14. A diver observes a bubble of air rising from the bottom of a lake (where the absolute pressure is 3.50 atm) to the surface (where the pressure is 1.00 atm). The temperature at the bottom is

4.0°C, and the temperature at the surface is 23.0°C. (a) What is the ratio of the volume of the bubble as it reaches the surface to its volume at the bottom? (b) Would it be safe for the diver to hold his breath while ascending from the bottom of the lake to the surface? Why or why not?

18.15. A metal tank with volume 3.10 L will burst if the absolute pressure of the gas it contains exceeds 100 atm. (a) If 11.0 mol of an ideal gas is put into the tank at a temperature of 23.0°C, to what temperature can the gas be warmed before the tank ruptures? You can ignore the thermal expansion of the tank. (b) Based on your answer to part (a), is it reasonable to ignore the thermal expansion of the tank? Explain.

18.16. Three moles of an ideal gas are in a rigid cubical box with sides of length 0.200 m. (a) What is the force that the gas exerts on each of the six sides of the box when the gas temperature is 20.0°C? (b) What is the force when the temperature of the gas is increased to 100.0°C?

18.17. With the assumptions of Example 18.4 (Section 18.1), at what altitude above sea level is air pressure 90% of the pressure at sea level?

18.18. Make the same assumptions as in Example 18.4 (Section 18.1). How does the percentage decrease in air pressure in going from sea level to an altitude of 100 m compare to that when going from sea level to an altitude of 1000 m? If your second answer is not 10 times your first answer, explain why.

18.19. With the assumptions of Example 18.4 (Section 18.1), how does the density of air at sea level compare to the density at an altitude of 100 m above sea level?

18.20. With the assumption that the air temperature is a uniform 0.0°C (as in Example 18.4), what is the density of the air at an altitude of 1.00 km as a percentage of the density at the surface?

18.21. At an altitude of 11,000 m (a typical cruising altitude for a jet airliner), the air temperature is -56.5°C and the air density is 0.364 kg/m^3. What is the pressure of the atmosphere at that altitude? (*Note:* The temperature at this altitude is not the same as at the surface of the earth, so the calculation of Example 18.4 in Section 18.1 doesn't apply.)

Section 18.2 Molecular Properties of Matter

18.22. A large organic molecule has a mass of 1.41×10^{-21} kg. What is the molar mass of this compound?

18.23. Suppose you inherit 3.00 mol of gold from your uncle (an eccentric chemist) at a time when this metal is selling for $14.75 per gram. Consult the periodic table in Appendix D and Table 14.1. (a) To the nearest dollar, what is this gold worth? (b) If you have your gold formed into a spherical nugget, what is its diameter?

18.24. Modern vacuum pumps make it easy to attain pressures of the order of 10^{-13} atm in the laboratory. (a) At a pressure of 9.00×10^{-14} atm and an ordinary temperature of 300.0 K, how many molecules are present in a volume of 1.00 cm^3 ? (b) How many molecules would be present at the same temperature but at 1.00 atm instead?

18.25. The Lagoon Nebula (Fig. 18.28) is a cloud of hydrogen gas located 3900 light-years from the earth. The cloud is about 45 light-years in diameter and glows because of its high temperature of 7500 K. (The gas is raised to this temperature by the stars that lie within the nebula.) The cloud is also very thin; there are only 80 molecules per cubic centimeter. (a) Find the gas pressure (in atmospheres) in the Lagoon Nebula. Compare it to the laboratory pressure referred to in Exercise 18.24. (b) Science fiction films sometimes show starships being buffeted by turbulence as they fly through gas clouds such as the Lagoon Nebula. Does this seem realistic? Why or why not?

Figure **18.28** Exercise 18.25.

18.26. In a gas at standard conditions, what is the length of the side of a cube that contains a number of molecules equal to the population of the earth (about 6×10^9 people)?

18.27. How many moles are in a 1.00-kg bottle of water? How many molecules? The molar mass of water is 18.0 g/mol.

18.28. How Close Together Are Gas Molecules? Consider an ideal gas at 27°C and 1.00 atm pressure. To get some idea how close these molecules are to each other, on the average, imagine them to be uniformly spaced, with each molecule at the center of a small cube. (a) What is the length of an edge of each cube if adjacent cubes touch but do not overlap? (b) How does this distance compare with the diameter of a typical molecule? (c) How does their separation compare with the spacing of atoms in solids, which typically are about 0.3 nm apart?

18.29. Consider 5.00 mol of liquid water. (a) What volume is occupied by this amount of water? The molar mass of water is 18.0 g/mol. (b) Imagine the molecules to be, on average, uniformly spaced, with each molecule at the center of a small cube. What is the length of an edge of each small cube if adjacent cubes touch but don't overlap? (c) How does this distance compare with the diameter of a molecule?

Section 18.3 Kinetic-Molecular Model of an Ideal Gas

18.30. A flask contains a mixture of neon (Ne), krypton (Kr), and radon (Rn) gases. Compare (a) the average kinetic energies of the three types of atoms and; (b) the root-mean-square speeds. (*Hint:* The periodic table in Appendix D shows the molar mass (in g/mol) of each element under the chemical symbol for that element.)

18.31. Gaseous Diffusion of Uranium. (a) A process called *gaseous diffusion* is often used to separate isotopes of uranium—that is, atoms of the elements that have different masses, such as ^{235}U and ^{238}U. The only gaseous compound of uranium at ordinary temperatures is uranium hexafluoride, UF_6. Speculate on how $^{235}UF_6$ and $^{238}UF_6$ molecules might be separated by diffusion. (b) The molar masses for $^{235}UF_6$ and $^{238}UF_6$ molecules are 0.349 kg/mol and 0.352 kg/mol, respectively. If uranium hexafluoride acts as an ideal gas, what is the ratio of the root-mean-square speed of $^{235}UF_6$ molecules to that of $^{238}UF_6$ molecules if the temperature is uniform?

18.32. The ideas of average and root-mean-square value can be applied to any distribution. A class of 150 students had the following scores on a 100-point quiz:

Score	Number of Students
10	11
20	12
30	24
40	15
50	19
60	10
70	12
80	20
90	17
100	10

(a) Find the average score for the class. (b) Find the root-mean-square score for the class.

18.33. We have two equal-size boxes, A and B. Each box contains gas that behaves as an ideal gas. We insert a thermometer into each box and find that the gas in box A is at a temperature of 50°C while the gas in box B is at 10°C. This is all we know about the gas in the boxes. Which of the following statements *must* be true? Which *could* be true? (a) The pressure in A is higher than in B. (b) There are more molecules in A than in B. (c) A and B cannot contain the same type of gas. (d) The molecules in A have more average kinetic energy per molecule than those in B. (e) The molecules in A are moving faster than those in B. Explain the reasoning behind your answers.

18.34. STP. The conditions of standard temperature and pressure (STP) are a temperature of 0.00°C and a pressure of 1.00 atm. (a) How many liters does 1.00 mol of any ideal gas occupy at STP? (b) For a scientist on Venus, an absolute pressure of 1 Venusian-atmosphere is 92 Earth-atmospheres. Of course she would use the Venusian-atmosphere to define STP. Assuming she kept the same temperature, how many liters would 1 mole of ideal gas occupy on Venus?

18.35. (a) A deuteron, ${}^2_1H$, is the nucleus of a hydrogen isotope and consists of one proton and one neutron. The plasma of deuterons in a nuclear fusion reactor must be heated to about 300 million K. What is the rms speed of the deuterons? Is this a significant fraction of the speed of light $(c = 3.0 \times 10^8 \text{ m/s})$? (b) What would the temperature of the plasma be if the deuterons had an rms speed equal to $0.10c$?

18.36. Martian Climate. The atmosphere of Mars is mostly CO_2 (molar mass 44.0 g/mol) under a pressure of 650 Pa, which we shall assume remains constant. In many places the temperature varies from 0.0°C in summer to −100°C in winter. Over the course of a martian year, what are the ranges of (a) the rms speeds of the CO_2 molecules, and (b) the density (in mol/m^3) of the atmosphere?

18.37. (a) Oxygen (O_2) has a molar mass of 32.0 g/mol. What is the average translational kinetic energy of an oxygen molecule at a temperature of 300 K? (b) What is the average value of the square of its speed? (c) What is the root-mean-square speed? (d) What is the momentum of an oxygen molecule traveling at this speed? (e) Suppose an oxygen molecule traveling at this speed bounces back and forth between opposite sides of a cubical vessel 0.10 m on a side. What is the average force the molecule exerts on one of the walls of the container? (Assume that the molecule's velocity is perpendicular to the two sides that it strikes.) (f) What is the average force per unit area? (g) How many oxygen molecules traveling at this speed are necessary to produce an average pressure of 1 atm? (h) Compute the number of oxygen molecules that are actually contained in a vessel of this size at 300 K and atmospheric pressure. (i) Your answer for part (h) should be three times as large as the answer for part (g). Where does this discrepancy arise?

18.38. Calculate the mean free path of air molecules at a pressure of 3.50×10^{-13} atm and a temperature of 300 K. (This pressure is readily attainable in the laboratory; see Exercise 18.24.) As in Example 18.8, model the air molecules as spheres of radius 2.0×10^{-10} m.

18.39. At what temperature is the root-mean-square speed of nitrogen molecules equal to the root-mean-square speed of hydrogen molecules at 20.0°C? (*Hint:* The periodic table in Appendix D shows the molar mass (in g/mol) of each element under the chemical symbol for that element. The molar mass of H_2 is twice the molar mass of hydrogen atoms, and similarly for N_2.)

18.40. Smoke particles in the air typically have masses of the order of 10^{-16} kg. The Brownian motion (rapid, irregular movement) of these particles, resulting from collisions with air molecules, can be observed with a microscope. (a) Find the root-mean-square speed of Brownian motion for a particle with a mass of 3.00×10^{-16} kg in air at 300 K. (b) Would the root-mean-square speed be different if the particle were in hydrogen gas at the same temperature? Explain.

Section 18.4 Heat Capacities

18.41. (a) How much heat does it take to increase the temperature of 2.50 mol of a diatomic ideal gas by 30.0 K near room temperature if the gas is held at constant volume? (b) What is the answer to the question in part (a) if the gas is monatomic rather than diatomic?

18.42. Perfectly rigid containers each hold n moles of ideal gas, one being hydrogen (H_2) and other being neon (Ne). If it takes 100 J of heat to increase the temperature of the hydrogen by 2.50°C, by how many degrees will the same amount of heat raise the temperature of the neon?

18.43. (a) Compute the specific heat capacity at constant volume of nitrogen (N_2) gas, and compare with the specific heat capacity of liquid water. The molar mass of N_2 is 28.0 g/mol. (b) You warm 1.00 kg of water at a constant volume of 1.00 L from 20.0°C to 30.0°C in a kettle. For the same amount of heat, how many kilograms of 20.0°C air would you be able to warm to 30.0°C? What volume (in liters) would this air occupy at 20.0°C and a pressure of 1.00 atm? Make the simplifying assumption that air is 100% N_2.

18.44. (a) Calculate the specific heat capacity at constant volume of water vapor, assuming the nonlinear triatomic molecule has three translational and three rotational degrees of freedom and that vibrational motion does not contribute. The molar mass of water is 18.0 g/mol. (b) The actual specific heat capacity of water vapor at low pressures is about 2000 J/kg · K. Compare this with your calculation and comment on the actual role of vibrational motion.

18.45. (a) Use Eq. 18.28 to calculate the heat capacity at constant volume of aluminum in units of J/kg · K. Consult the periodic table in Appendix D. (b) Compare the answer in part (a) with the value given in Table 17.3. Try to explain any disagreement between these two values.

*Section 18.5 Molecular Speeds

***18.46.** For a gas of nitrogen molecules (N_2), what must the temperature be if 94.7% of all the molecules have speeds less than (a) 1500 m/s; (b) 1000 m/s; (c) 500 m/s? Use Table 18.2. The molar mass of N_2 is 28.0 g/mol.

***18.47.** Derive Eq. (18.33) from Eq. (18.32).

***18.48.** Prove that $f(v)$ as given by Eq. (18.33) is maximum for $\epsilon = kT$. Use this result to obtain Eq. (18.34).

***18.49.** For diatomic carbon dioxide gas (CO_2, molar mass 44.0 g/mol) at $T = 300$ K, calculate (a) the most probable speed v_{mp}; (b) the average speed v_{av}; (c) the root-mean-square speed v_{rms}.

Section 18.6 Phases of Matter

18.50. Puffy cumulus clouds, which are made of water droplets, occur at lower altitudes in the atmosphere. Wispy cirrus clouds, which are made of ice crystals, occur only at higher altitudes. Find the altitude y (measured from sea level) above which only cirrus clouds can occur. On a typical day and at altitudes less than 11 km, the temperature at an altitude y is given by $T = T_0 - \alpha y$, where $T_0 = 15.0°C$ and $\alpha = 6.0$ C°/1000 m.

18.51. Solid water (ice) is slowly warmed from a very low temperature. (a) What minimum external pressure p_1 must be applied to the solid if a melting phase transition is to be observed? Describe the sequence of phase transitions that occur if the applied pressure p is such that $p < p_1$. (b) Above a certain maximum pressure p_2, no boiling transition is observed. What is this pressure? Describe the sequence of phase transitions that occur if $p_1 < p < p_2$.

18.52. A physicist places a piece of ice at 0.00°C and a beaker of water at 0.00°C inside a glass box and closes the lid of the box. All the air is then removed from the box. If the ice, water, and beaker are all maintained at a temperature of 0.00°C, describe the final equilibrium state inside the box.

18.53. The atmosphere of the planet Mars is 95.3% carbon dioxide (CO_2) and about 0.03% water vapor. The atmospheric pressure is only about 600 Pa, and the surface temperature varies from −30°C to −100°C. The polar ice caps contain both CO_2 ice and water ice. Could there be *liquid* CO_2 on the surface of Mars? Could there be liquid water? Why or why not?

Problems

18.54. (a) Use Eq. (18.1) to estimate the change in the volume of a solid steel sphere of volume 11 L when the temperature and pressure increase from 21°C and 1.013×10^5 Pa to 42°C and 2.10×10^7 Pa. (*Hint:* Consult Chapters 11 and 17 to determine the values of β and k.) (b) In Example 18.3 the change in volume of an 11-L steel scuba tank was ignored. Was this a good approximation? Explain.

18.55. A cylinder 1.00 m tall with inside diameter 0.120 m is used to hold propane gas (molar mass 44.1 g/mol) for use in a barbecue. It is initially filled with gas until the gauge pressure is 1.30×10^6 Pa and the temperature is 22.0°C. The temperature of the gas remains constant as it is partially emptied out of the tank, until the gauge pressure is 2.50×10^5 Pa. Calculate the mass of propane that has been used.

18.56. During a test dive in 1939, prior to being accepted by the U.S. Navy, the submarine *Squalus* sank at a point where the depth of water was 73.0 m. The temperature at the surface was 27.0°C, and at the bottom it was 7.0°C. The density of seawater is 1030 kg/m^3. (a) A diving bell was used to rescue 33 trapped crewmen from the *Squalus*. The diving bell was in the form of a circular cylinder 2.30 m high, open at the bottom and closed at the top. When the diving bell was lowered to the bottom of the sea, to what height did water rise within the diving bell? (*Hint:* You may ignore the relatively small variation in water pressure between the bottom of the bell and the surface of the water within the bell.) (b) At what gauge pressure must compressed air have been supplied to the bell while on the bottom to expel all the water from it?

18.57. Atmosphere of Titan. Titan, the largest satellite of Saturn, has a thick nitrogen atmosphere. At its surface, the pressure is 1.5 Earth-atmospheres and the temperature is 94 K. (a) What is the surface temperature in °C? (b) Calculate the surface density in Titan's atmosphere in molecules per cubic meter. (c) Compare the density of Titan's surface atmosphere to the density of Earth's atmosphere at 22°C. Which body has denser atmosphere?

18.58. Pressure on Venus. At the surface of Venus the average temperature is a balmy 460°C due to the greenhouse effect (global warming!), the pressure is 92 Earth-atmospheres, and the acceleration due to gravity is $0.894g_{\text{Earth}}$. The atmosphere is nearly all CO_2 (molar mass 44.0 g/mol) and the temperature remains remarkably constant. We shall assume that the temperature does not change at all with altitude. (a) What is the atmospheric pressure 1.00 km above the surface of Venus? Express your answer in Venus-atmospheres and Earth-atmospheres. (b) What is the root-mean-square speed of the CO_2 molecules at the surface of Venus and at an altitude of 1.00 km?

18.59. An automobile tire has a volume of 0.0150 m^3 on a cold day when the temperature of the air in the tire is 5.0°C and atmospheric pressure is 1.02 atm. Under these conditions the gauge pressure is measured to be 1.70 atm (about 25 lb/in.^{2}). After the car is driven on the highway for 30 min, the temperature of the air in the tires has risen to 45.0°C and the volume has risen to 0.0159 m^3. What then is the gauge pressure?

18.60. A flask with a volume of 1.50 L, provided with a stopcock, contains ethane gas (C_2H_6) at 300 K and atmospheric pressure (1.013×10^5 Pa). The molar mass of ethane is 30.1 g/mol. The system is warmed to a temperature of 380 K, with the stopcock open to the atmosphere. The stopcock is then closed, and the flask is cooled to its original temperature. (a) What is the final pressure of the ethane in the flask? (b) How many grams of ethane remain in the flask?

18.61. A balloon whose volume is 750 m^3 is to be filled with hydrogen at atmospheric pressure (1.01×10^5 Pa). (a) If the hydrogen is stored in cylinders with volumes of 1.90 m^3 at a gauge pressure of 1.20×10^6 Pa, how many cylinders are required? Assume that the temperature of the hydrogen remains constant. (b) What is the total weight (in addition to the weight of the gas) that can be supported by the balloon if the gas in the balloon and the surrounding air are both at 15.0°C? The molar mass of hydrogen (H_2) is 2.02 g/mol. The density of air at 15.0°C and atmospheric pressure is 1.23 kg/m^3. See Chapter 14 for a discussion of buoyancy. (c) What weight could be supported if the balloon were filled with helium (molar mass 4.00 g/mol) instead of hydrogen, again at 15.0°C?

18.62. A vertical cylindrical tank contains 1.80 mol of an ideal gas under a pressure of 1.00 atm at 20.0°C. The round part of the tank has a radius of 10.0 cm, and the gas is supporting a piston that can move up and down in the cylinder without friction. (a) What is the mass of this piston? (b) How tall is the column of gas that is supporting the piston?

18.63. A large tank of water has a hose connected to it, as shown in Fig. 18.29. The tank is sealed at the top and has compressed air between the water surface and the top. When the water height h has the value 3.50 m, the absolute pressure p of the compressed air

Figure 18.29 Problem 18.63.

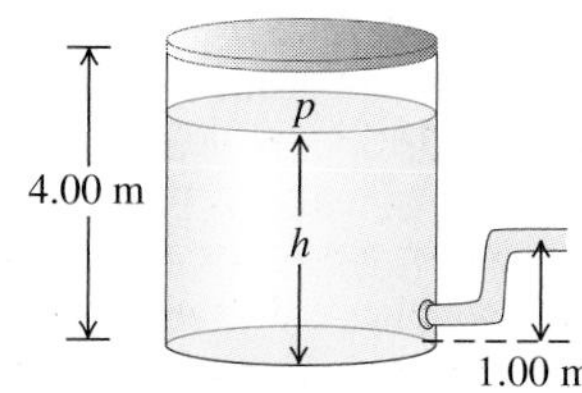

is 4.20×10^5 Pa. Assume that the air above the water expands at constant temperature, and take the atmospheric pressure to be 1.00×10^5 Pa. (a) What is the speed with which water flows out of the hose when $h = 3.50$ m? (b) As water flows out of the tank, h decreases. Calculate the speed of flow for $h = 3.00$ m and for $h = 2.00$ m. (c) At what value of h does the flow stop?

18.64. A person at rest inhales 0.50 L of air with each breath at a pressure of 1.00 atm and a temperature of 20.0°C. The inhaled air is 21.0% oxygen. (a) How many oxygen molecules does this person inhale with each breath? (b) Suppose this person is now resting at an elevation of 2,000 m but the temperature is still 20.0°C. Assuming that the oxygen percentage and volume per inhalation are the same as stated above, how many oxygen molecules does this person now inhale with each breath? (c) Given that the body still requires the same number of oxygen molecules per second as at sea level to maintain its functions, explain why some people report "shortness of breath" at high elevations.

18.65. How Many Atoms Are You? Estimate the number of atoms in the body of a 50-kg physics student. Note that the human body is mostly water, which has molar mass 18.0 g/mol, and that each water molecule contains three atoms.

18.66. The size of an oxygen molecule is about 2.0×10^{-10} m. Make a rough estimate of the pressure at which the finite volume of the molecules should cause noticeable deviations from ideal-gas behavior at ordinary temperatures $(T = 300 \text{ K})$.

18.67. You have two identical containers, one containing gas A and the other gas B. The masses of these molecules are $m_A = 3.34 \times 10^{-27}$ kg and $m_B = 5.34 \times 10^{-26}$ kg. Both gases are under the same pressure and are at 10.0°C. (a) Which molecules (A or B) have greater translational kinetic energy per molecule and rms speeds? Now you want to raise the temperature of only one of these containers so that both gases will have the same rms speed. (b) For which gas should you raise the temperature? (c) At what temperature will you accomplish your goal? (d) Once you have accomplished your goal, which molecules (A or B) now have greater average translational kinetic energy per molecule?

18.68. Insect Collisions. A cubical cage 1.25 m on each side contains 2500 angry bees, each flying randomly at 1.10 m/s. We can model these insects as spheres 1.50 cm in diameter. On the average, (a) how far does a typical bee travel between collisions, (b) what is the average time between collisions, and (c) how many collisions per second does a bee make?

18.69. Successive Approximations and the van der Waals Equation. In the ideal-gas equation, the number of moles per volume n/V is simply equal to p/RT. In the van der Waals equation, solving for n/V in terms of the pressure p and temperature T is somewhat more involved. (a) Show that the van der Waals equation can be written as

$$\frac{n}{V} = \left(\frac{p + an^2/V^2}{RT}\right)\left(1 - \frac{bn}{V}\right)$$

(b) The van der Waals parameters for hydrogen sulfide gas (H_2S) are $a = 0.448 \text{ J} \cdot \text{m}^3/\text{mol}^2$ and $b = 4.29 \times 10^{-5} \text{ m}^3/\text{mol}$. Determine the number of moles per volume of H_2S gas at 127°C and an absolute pressure of 9.80×10^5 Pa as follows: (i) Calculate a first approximation using the ideal-gas equation, $n/V = p/RT$. (ii) Substitute this approximation for n/V into the right-hand side of the equation in part (a). The result is a new, improved approximation for n/V. (iii) Substitute the new approximation for n/V into the right-hand side of the equation in (a). The result is a further improved approximation for n/V. (iv) Repeat step (iii) until successive approximations agree to the desired level of accuracy (in this case, to three significant figures). (c) Compare your final result in part (b) to the result p/RT obtained using the ideal-gas equation. Which result gives a larger value of n/V? Why?

18.70. Gas on Europa. A canister of 1.20 mol of nitrogen gas (28.0 g/mol) at 25.0°C is left on Jupiter's satellite after completion of a future space mission. Europa has no appreciable atmosphere, and the acceleration due to gravity at its surface is 1.30 m/s^2. After some time, the canister springs a small leak, allowing molecules to escape through a small hole. What is the maximum height (in km) above Europa's surface that a N_2 molecule having speed equal to the rms speed will reach if it is shot straight up out of the hole in the canister? Ignore the variation in g with altitude,

18.71. You blow up a spherical balloon to a diameter of 50.0 cm until the absolute pressure inside is 1.25 atm and the temperature is 22.0°C. Assume that all the gas in N_2 is of molar mass 28.0 g/mol. (a) Find the mass of a single N_2 molecule. (b) How much translational kinetic energy does an average N_2 molecule have? (c) How many N_2 molecules are in this balloon? (d) What is the *total* translational kinetic energy of all the molecules in the balloon?

18.72. (a) Compute the increase in gravitational potential energy for a nitrogen molecule (molar mass 28.0 g/mol) for an increase in elevation of 400 m near the earth's surface. (b) At what temperature is this equal to the average kinetic energy of a nitrogen molecule? (c) Is it possible that a nitrogen molecule near sea level where $T = 15.0$°C could rise to an altitude of 400 m? Is it likely that it could do so without hitting any other molecules along the way? Explain.

18.73. The Lennard-Jones Potential. A commonly used potential-energy function for the interaction of two molecules (see Fig. 18.8) is the Lennard-Jones 6-12 potential

$$U(r) = U_0\left[\left(\frac{R_0}{r}\right)^{12} - 2\left(\frac{R_0}{r}\right)^6\right]$$

where r is the distance between the centers of the molecules and U_0 and R_0 are positive constants. The corresponding force $F(r)$ is given in Eq. (13.26). (a) Graph $U(r)$ and $F(r)$ versus r. (b) Let r_1 be the value of r at which $U(r) = 0$, and let r_2 be the value of r at which $F(r) = 0$. Show the locations of r_1 and r_2 on your graphs of $U(r)$ and $F(r)$. Which of these values represents the equilibrium separation between the molecules? (c) Find the values of r_1 and r_2 in terms of R_0, and find the ratio r_1/r_2. (d) If the molecules are located a distance r_2 apart [as calculated in part (c)], how much work must be done to pull them apart so that $r \to \infty$?

18.74. (a) What is the total random translational kinetic energy of 5.00 L of hydrogen gas (molar mass 2.016 g/mol) with pressure 1.01×10^5 Pa and temperature 300 K? (*Hint:* Use the procedure of Problem 18.71 as a guide.) (b) If the tank containing the gas is placed on a swift jet moving at 300.0 m/s, by what percentage is the *total* kinetic energy of the gas increased? (c) Since the kinetic energy of the gas molecules is greater when it is on the jet, does this mean that its temperature has gone up? Explain.

18.75. The speed of propagation of a sound wave in air at 27°C is about 350 m/s. Calculate, for comparison, (a) v_{rms} for nitrogen molecules and (b) the rms value of v_x at this temperature. The molar mass of nitrogen (N_2) is 28.0 g/mol.

18.76. Hydrogen on the Sun. The surface of the sun has a temperature of about 5800 K and consists largely of hydrogen atoms. (a) Find the rms speed of a hydrogen atom at this temperature. (The mass of a single hydrogen atom is 1.67×10^{-27} kg.) (b) The escape speed for a particle to leave the gravitational influence of the sun is given by $(2GM/R)^{1/2}$, where M is the sun's mass, R its radius, and G the gravitational constant (see Example 12.5 of Section 12.3). Use the data in Appendix F to calculate this escape speed. (c) Can appreciable quantities of hydrogen escape from the sun? Can *any* hydrogen escape? Explain.

18.77. (a) Show that a projectile with mass m can "escape" from the surface of a planet if it is launched vertically upward with a kinetic energy greater than mgR_p, where g is the acceleration due to gravity at the planet's surface and R_p is the planet's radius. Ignore air resistance. (See Problem 18.76.) (b) If the planet in question is the earth, at what temperature does the average translational kinetic energy of a nitrogen molecule (molar mass 28.0 g/mol) equal that required to escape? What about a hydrogen molecule (molar mass 2.02 g/mol)? (c) Repeat part (b) for the moon, for which $g = 1.63 \text{ m/s}^2$ and $R_p = 1740$ km. (d) While the earth and the moon have similar average surface temperatures, the moon has essentially no atmosphere. Use your results from parts (b) and (c) to explain why.

18.78. Planetary Atmospheres. (a) The temperature near the top of Jupiter's multicolored cloud layer is about 140 K. The temperature at the top of the earth's troposphere, at an altitude of about 20 km, is about 220 K. Calculate the rms speed of hydrogen molecules in both these environments. Give your answers in m/s and as a fraction of the escape speed from the respective planet (see Problem 18.76). (b) Hydrogen gas (H_2) is a rare element in the earth's atmosphere. In the atmosphere of Jupiter, by contrast, 89% of all molecules are H_2. Explain why, using your results from part (a). (c) Suppose an astronomer claims to have discovered an oxygen (O_2) atmosphere on the asteroid Ceres. How likely is this? Ceres has a mass equal to 0.014 times the mass of the moon, a density of 2400 kg/m^3, and a surface temperature of about 200 K.

18.79. (a) For what mass of molecule or particle is v_{rms} equal to 1.00 mm/s at 300 K? (b) If the particle is an ice crystal, how many molecules does it contain? The molar mass of water is 18.0 g/mol. (c) Calculate the diameter of the particle if it is a spherical piece of ice. Would it be visible to the naked eye?

18.80. In describing the heat capacities of solids in Section 18.4, we stated that the potential energy $U = \frac{1}{2}kx^2$ of a harmonic oscillator averaged over one period of the motion is equal to the kinetic energy $K = \frac{1}{2}mv^2$ averaged over one period. Prove this result using Eqs. (13.13) and (13.15) for the position and velocity of a simple harmonic oscillator. For simplicity, assume that the initial position and velocity make the phase angle ϕ equal to zero. (*Hint:* Use the trigonometric identities $\cos^2(\theta) = [1 + \cos(2\theta)]/2$ and $\sin^2(\theta) = [1 - \cos(2\theta)]/2$. What is the average value of $\cos(2\omega t)$ over one period?)

18.81. It is possible to make crystalline solids that are only one layer of atoms thick. Such "two-dimensional" crystals can be created by depositing atoms on a very flat surface. (a) If the atoms in such a two-dimensional crystal can move only within the plane of the crystal, what will be its molar heat capacity near room temperature? Give your answer as a multiple of R and in J/mol · K. (b) At very low temperatures, will the molar heat capacity of a two-dimensional crystal be greater than, less than, or equal to the result you found in part (a)? Explain why.

18.82. (a) Calculate the total *rotational* kinetic energy of the molecules in 1.00 mol of a diatomic gas at 300 K. (b) Calculate the moment of inertia of an oxygen molecule (O_2) for rotation about either the y- or z-axis shown in Fig. 18.18. Treat the molecule as two massive points (representing the oxygen atoms) separated by a distance of 1.21×10^{-10} m. The molar mass of oxygen *atoms* is 16.0 g/mol. (c) Find the rms angular velocity of rotation of an oxygen molecule about either the y- or z-axis shown in Fig. 18.15. How does your answer compare to the angular velocity of a typical piece of rapidly rotating machinery (10,000 rev/min)?

18.83. For each polyatomic gas in Table 18.1, compute the value of the molar heat capacity at constant volume, C_V, on the assumption that there is no vibrational energy. Compare with the measured values in the table, and compute the fraction of the total heat capacity that is due to vibration for each of the three gases. (*Note:* CO_2 is linear; SO_2 and H_2S are not. Recall that a linear polyatomic molecule has two rotational degrees of freedom, and a nonlinear molecule has three.)

***18.84.** (a) Show that $\int_0^\infty f(v)\,dv = 1$, where $f(v)$ is the Maxwell–Boltzmann distribution of Eq. (18.32). (b) In terms of the physical definition of $f(v)$, explain why the integral in part (a) *must* have this value.

***18.85.** Calculate the integral in Eq. (18.31), $\int_0^\infty v^2 f(v)\,dv$, and compare this result to $(v^2)_{av}$ as given by Eq. (18.16). (*Hint:* You may use the tabulated integral

$$\int_0^\infty x^{2n} e^{-\alpha x^2}\,dx = \frac{1 \cdot 3 \cdot 5 \cdots (2n-1)}{2^{n+1}\alpha^n}\sqrt{\frac{\pi}{\alpha}}$$

where n is a positive integer and α is a positive constant.)

***18.86.** Calculate the integral in Eq. (18.30), $\int_0^\infty v f(v)\,dv$, and compare this result to v_{av} as given by Eq. (18.35). (*Hint:* Make the change of variable $v^2 = x$ and use the tabulated integral

$$\int_0^\infty x^n e^{-\alpha x}\,dx = \frac{n!}{\alpha^{n+1}}$$

where n is a positive integer and α is a positive constant.)

***18.87.** (a) Explain why in a gas of N molecules, the number of molecules having speeds in the *finite* interval v to $v + \Delta v$ is $\Delta N = N\int_v^{v+\Delta v} f(v)\,dv$. (b) If Δv is small, then $f(v)$ is approximately constant over the interval and $\Delta N \approx Nf(v)\,\Delta v$. For oxygen gas ($O_2$, molar mass 32.0 g/mol) at $T = 300$ K, use this approximation to calculate the number of molecules with speeds within $\Delta v = 20$ m/s of v_{mp}. Express your answer as a multiple of N. (c) Repeat part (b) for speeds within $\Delta v = 20$ m/s of $7v_{mp}$. (d) Repeat parts (b) and (c) for a temperature of 600 K. (e) Repeat parts (b) and (c) for a temperature of 150 K. (f) What do your results tell you about the shape of the distribution as a function of temperature? Do your conclusions agree with what is shown in Fig. 18.26?

18.88. Meteorology. The *vapor pressure* is the pressure of the vapor phase of a substance when it is in equilibrium with the solid or liquid phase of the substance. The *relative humidity* is the partial pressure of water vapor in the air divided by the vapor pressure of water at that same temperature, expressed as a percentage. The air is saturated when the humidity is 100%. (a) The vapor pressure of water at 20.0°C is 2.34×10^3 Pa. If the air temperature is 20.0°C and the relative humidity is 60%, what is the partial pressure of water vapor in the atmosphere (that is, the pressure due to water vapor alone)? (b) Under the conditions of part (a), what is the mass of water in 1.00 m^3 of air? (The molar mass of water is 18.0 g/mol. Assume that water vapor can be treated as an ideal gas.)

18.89. The Dew Point. The vapor pressure of water (see Problem 18.88) decreases as the temperature decreases. If the amount of water vapor in the air is kept constant as the air is cooled, a temperature is reached, called the *dew point,* at which the partial pressure and vapor pressure coincide and the vapor is saturated. If the air is cooled further, vapor condenses to liquid until the partial pressure again equals the vapor pressure at that temperature. The temperature in a room is 30.0°C. A meteorologist cools a metal can by gradually adding cold water. When the can temperature reaches 16.0°C, water droplets form on its outside surface. What is the relative humidity of the 30.0°C air in the room? The table lists the vapor pressure of water at various temperatures:

Temperature (°C)	Vapor Pressure (Pa)
10.0	1.23×10^3
12.0	1.40×10^3
14.0	1.60×10^3
16.0	1.81×10^3
18.0	2.06×10^3
20.0	2.34×10^3
22.0	2.65×10^3
24.0	2.99×10^3
26.0	3.36×10^3
28.0	3.78×10^3
30.0	4.25×10^3

18.90. Altitude at Which Clouds Form. On a spring day in the midwestern United States, the air temperature at the surface is 28.0°C. Puffy cumulus clouds form at an altitude where the air temperature equals the dew point (see Problem 18.89). If the air temperature decreases with altitude at a rate of 0.6 C°/100 m, at approximately what height above the ground will clouds form if the relative humidity at the surface is 35% and 80%? (*Hint:* Use the table in Problem 18.89.)

Challenge Problems

18.91. Dark Nebulae and the Interstellar Medium. The dark area in Fig. 18.30 that appears devoid of stars is a *dark nebula,* a cold gas cloud in interstellar space that contains enough material to block out light from the stars behind it. A typical dark nebula is about 20 light-years in diameter and contains about 50 hydrogen atoms per cubic centimeter (monatomic hydrogen, *not* H_2) at a temperature of about 20 K. (A light-year is the distance light travels in vacuum in one year and is equal to 9.46×10^{15} m.) (a) Estimate the mean free path for a hydrogen atom in a dark nebula. The radius of a hydrogen atom is 5.0×10^{-11} m. (b) Estimate the rms speed of a hydrogen atom and the mean free time (the average time between collisions for a given atom). Based on this result, do you think that atomic collisions, such as those leading to H_2 molecule formation, are very important in determining the composition of the nebula? (c) Estimate the pressure inside a dark nebula. (d) Compare the rms speed of a hydrogen atom to the escape speed at the surface of the nebula (assumed spherical). If the space around the nebula were a vacuum, would such a cloud be stable or would it tend to evaporate? (e) The stability of dark nebulae is explained by the presence of the *interstellar medium* (ISM), an even thinner gas that permeates space and in which the dark nebulae are embedded. Show that for dark nebulae to be in equilibrium with the ISM, the numbers of atoms per volume (N/V) and the temperatures (T) of dark nebulae and the ISM must be related by

$$\frac{(N/V)_{\text{nebula}}}{(N/V)_{\text{ISM}}} = \frac{T_{\text{ISM}}}{T_{\text{nebula}}}$$

(f) In the vicinity of the sun, the ISM contains about 1 hydrogen atom per 200 cm^3. Estimate the temperature of the ISM in the vicinity of the sun. Compare to the temperature of the sun's surface, about 5800 K. Would a spacecraft coasting through interstellar space burn up? Why or why not?

Figure **18.30** Challenge Problem 18.91.

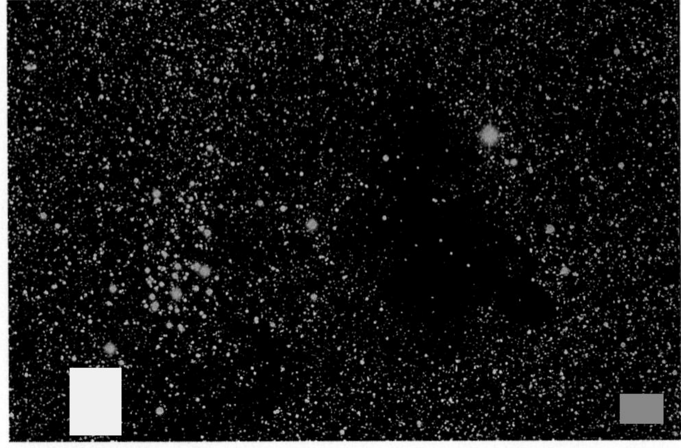

18.92. Earth's Atmosphere. In the *troposphere,* the part of the atmosphere that extends from earth's surface to an altitude of about 11 km, the temperature is not uniform but decreases with increasing elevation. (a) Show that if the temperature variation is approximated by the linear relationship

$$T = T_0 - \alpha y$$

where T_0 is the temperature at the earth's surface and T is the temperature at height y, the pressure p at height y is given by

$$\ln\left(\frac{p}{p_0}\right) = \frac{Mg}{R\alpha}\ln\left(\frac{T_0 - \alpha y}{T_0}\right)$$

where p_0 is the pressure at the earth's surface and M is the molar mass for air. The coefficient α is called the lapse rate of temperature. It varies with atmospheric conditions, but an average value is about 0.6 C°/100 m. (b) Show that the above result reduces to the result of Example 18.4 (Section 18.1) in the limit that $\alpha \to 0$. (c) With $\alpha = 0.6$ C°/100 m, calculate p for $y = 8863$ m and compare your answer to the result of Example 18.4. Take $T_0 = 288$ K and $p_0 = 1.00$ atm.

18.93. Van der Waals Equation and Critical Points. (a) In pV-diagrams the slope $\partial p/\partial V$ along an isotherm is never positive. Explain why. (b) Regions where $\partial p/\partial V = 0$ represent equilibrium between two phases; volume can change with no change in pressure, as when water boils at atmospheric pressure. We can use this to determine the temperature, pressure, and volume per mole at the critical point using the equation of state $p = p(V, T, n)$. If $T > T_c$, then $p(V)$ has no maximum along an isotherm, but if $T < T_c$, then $p(V)$ has a maximum. Explain how this leads to the following condition for determining the critical point:

$$\frac{\partial p}{\partial V} = 0 \quad \text{and} \quad \frac{\partial^2 p}{\partial V^2} = 0 \quad \text{at the critical point}$$

(c) Solve the van der Waals equation (Eq. 18.7) for p; that is, find $p(V, T, n)$. Find $\partial p/\partial V$ and $\partial^2 p/\partial V^2$. Set these equal to zero to obtain two equations for V, T, and n. (d) Simultaneous solution of the two equations obtained in part (c) gives the temperature and volume per mole at the critical point, T_c and $(V/n)_c$. Find these constants in terms of a and b. (*Hint:* Divide one equation by the other to eliminate T.) (e) Substitute these values into the equation of state to find p_c, the pressure at the critical point. (f) Use the results from parts (d) and (e) to find the ratio $RT_c/p_c(V/n)_c$. This should not contain either a or b and so should have the same value for all gases. (g) Compute the ratio $RT_c/p_c(V/n)_c$ for the gases H_2, N_2, and H_2O using the critical point data given in the table.

Gas	T_c (K)	p_c (Pa)	$(V/n)_c$ (m^3/mol)
H_2	33.3	13.0×10^5	65.0×10^{-6}
N_2	126.2	33.9×10^5	90.1×10^{-6}
H_2O	647.4	221.2×10^5	56.0×10^{-6}

(h) Discuss how well the results of part (g) compare to the prediction of part (f) based on the van der Waals equation. What do you conclude about the accuracy of the van der Waals equation as a description of the behavior of gases near the critical point?

18.94. *In Example 18.7 (Section 18.3) we saw that $v_{rms} > v_{av}$. It is not difficult to show that this is *always* the case. (The only exception is when the particles have the same speed, in which case $v_{rms} = v_{av}$.) (a) For two particles with speeds v_1 and v_2, show that $v_{rms} \geq v_{av}$, regardless of the numerical values of v_1 and v_2. Then show that $v_{rms} > v_{av}$ if $v_1 \neq v_2$. (b) Suppose that for a collection of N particles you know that $v_{rms} > v_{av}$. Another particle, with speed u, is added to the collection of particles. If the new rms and average speeds are denoted as v'_{rms} and v'_{av}, show that

$$v'_{rms} = \sqrt{\frac{Nv_{rms}^2 + u^2}{N+1}} \quad \text{and} \quad v'_{av} = \frac{Nv_{av} + u}{N+1}$$

(c) Use the expressions in part (b) to show that $v'_{rms} > v'_{av}$ regardless of the numerical value of u. (d) Explain why your results for (a) and (c) together show that $v_{rms} > v_{av}$ for any collection of particles if the particles do not all have the same speed.

19 THE FIRST LAW OF THERMODYNAMICS

LEARNING GOALS

By studying this chapter, you will learn:

- How to represent heat transfer and work done in a thermodynamic process.
- How to calculate the work done by a thermodynamic system when its volume changes.
- What is meant by a path between thermodynamic states.
- How to use the first law of thermodynamics to relate heat transfer, work done, and internal energy change.
- How to distinguish among adiabatic, isochoric, isobaric, and isothermal processes.
- How we know that the internal energy of an ideal gas depends only on its temperature.
- The difference between molar heat capacities at constant volume and at constant pressure, and how to use these quantities in calculations.
- How to analyze adiabatic processes in an ideal gas.

? A steam locomotive operates using the first law of thermodynamics: Water is heated and boils, and the expanding steam does work to propel the locomotive. Would it be possible for the steam to propel the locomotive by doing work as it *condenses?*

Every time you drive a car, turn on an air conditioner, or cook a meal, you reap the practical benefits of *thermodynamics,* the study of relationships involving heat, mechanical work, and other aspects of energy and energy transfer. For example, in a car engine heat is generated by the chemical reaction of oxygen and vaporized gasoline in the engine's cylinders. The heated gas pushes on the pistons within the cylinders, doing mechanical work that is used to propel the car. This is an example of a *thermodynamic process.*

The first law of thermodynamics, central to the understanding of such processes, is an extension of the principle of conservation of energy. It broadens this principle to include energy exchange by both heat transfer and mechanical work and introduces the concept of the *internal energy* of a system. Conservation of energy plays a vital role in every area of physical science, and the first law has extremely broad usefulness. To state energy relationships precisely, we need the concept of a *thermodynamic system.* We'll discuss *heat* and *work* as two means of transferring energy into or out of such a system.

19.1 The popcorn in the pot is a thermodynamic system. In the thermodynamic process shown here, heat is added to the system, and the system does work on its surroundings to lift the lid of the pot.

19.1 Thermodynamic Systems

We have studied energy transfer through mechanical work (Chapter 6) and through heat transfer (Chapters 17 and 18). Now we are ready to combine and generalize these principles.

We always talk about energy transfer to or from some specific *system.* The system might be a mechanical device, a biological organism, or a specified quantity of material, such as the refrigerant in an air conditioner or steam expanding in a turbine. In general, a **thermodynamic system** is any collection of objects that is convenient to regard as a unit, and that may have the potential to exchange energy with its surroundings. A familiar example is a quantity of popcorn kernels in a pot with a lid. When the pot is placed on a stove, energy is added to the popcorn by conduction of heat. As the popcorn pops and expands, it does work as it exerts an upward force on the lid and moves it through a displacement (Fig. 19.1). The *state* of the popcorn changes in this process, since the volume, temperature, and pressure of the popcorn all change as it pops. A process such as this one, in which there are changes in the state of a thermodynamic system, is called a **thermodynamic process.**

In mechanics we used the concept of *system* on a regular basis in connection with free-body diagrams and conservation of energy and momentum. With *thermodynamic* systems, as with all others, it is essential to define clearly at the start exactly what is and is not included in the system. Only then can we describe unambiguously the energy transfers into and out of that system. For instance, in our popcorn example we defined the system to include the popcorn but not the pot, lid, or stove.

Thermodynamics has its roots in many practical problems other than popping popcorn (Fig. 19.2). The gasoline engine in an automobile, the jet engines in an airplane, and the rocket engines in a launch vehicle use the heat of combustion of their fuel to perform mechanical work in propelling the vehicle. Muscle tissue in living organisms metabolizes chemical energy in food and performs mechanical work on the organism's surroundings. A steam engine or steam turbine uses the heat of combustion of coal or other fuel to perform mechanical work such as driving an electric generator or pulling a train.

19.2 (a) A rocket engine uses the heat of combustion of its fuel to do work propelling the launch vehicle. (b) Humans and other biological organisms are more complicated systems than we can analyze fully in this book, but the same basic principles of thermodynamics apply to them.

(a)

(b)

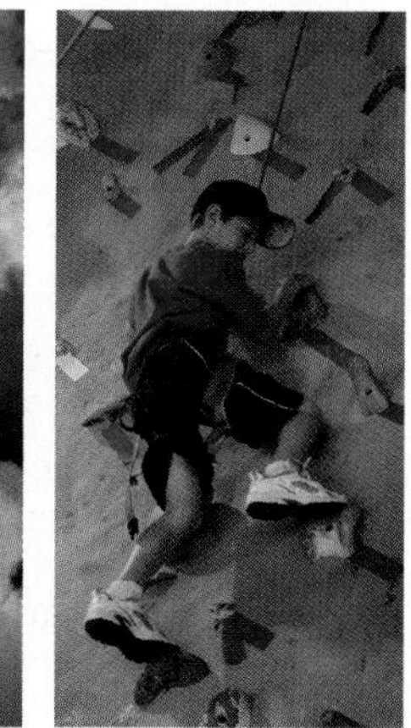

Signs for Heat and Work in Thermodynamics

We describe the energy relationships in any thermodynamic process in terms of the quantity of heat Q added *to* the system and the work W done *by* the system. Both Q and W may be positive, negative, or zero (Fig. 19.3). A positive value of Q represents heat flow *into* the system, with a corresponding input of energy to it; negative Q represents heat flow *out of* the system. A positive value of W represents work done *by* the system against its surroundings, such as work done by an expanding gas, and hence corresponds to energy *leaving* the system. Negative W, such as work done during compression of a gas in which work is done *on the gas* by its surroundings, represents energy *entering* the system. We will use these conventions consistently in the examples in this chapter and the next.

CAUTION **Be careful with the sign of work W** Note that our sign rule for work is *opposite* to the one we used in mechanics, in which we always spoke of the work done by the forces acting *on* a body. In thermodynamics it is usually more convenient to call W the work done *by* the system so that when a system expands, the pressure, volume change, and work are all positive. Take care to use the sign rules for work and heat consistently!

19.3 A thermodynamic system may exchange energy with its surroundings (environment) by means of heat, work, or both. Note the sign conventions for Q and W.

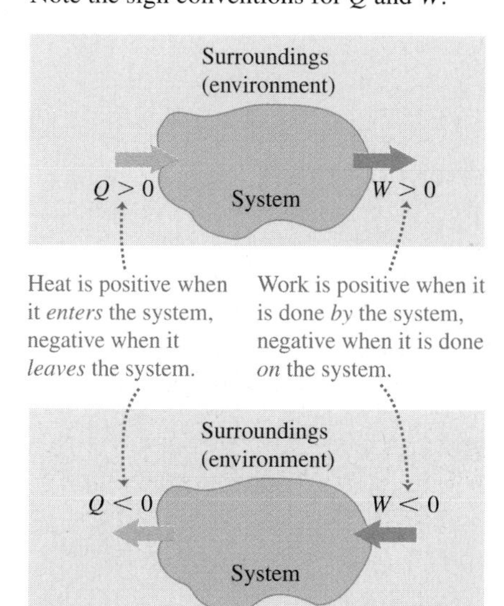
Surroundings
(environment)
Q > 0
System
W > 0
Heat is positive when it enters the system, negative when it leaves the system.
Work is positive when it is done by the system, negative when it is done on the system.
Surroundings
(environment)
Q < 0
W < 0
System

Test Your Understanding of Section 19.1 In Example 17.8 (Section 17.6), what is the sign of Q for the coffee? For the aluminum cup? If a block slides along a horizontal surface with friction, what is the sign of W for the block?

19.2 Work Done During Volume Changes

A simple but common example of a thermodynamic system is a quantity of gas enclosed in a cylinder with a movable piston. Internal-combustion engines, steam engines, and compressors in refrigerators and air conditioners all use some version of such a system. In the next several sections we will use the gas-in-cylinder system to explore several kinds of processes involving energy transformations.

We'll use a microscopic viewpoint, based on the kinetic and potential energies of individual molecules in a material, to develop intuition about thermodynamic quantities. But it is important to understand that the central principles of thermodynamics can be treated in a completely *macroscopic* way, without reference to microscopic models. Indeed, part of the great power and generality of thermodynamics is that it does *not* depend on details of the structure of matter.

19.4 A molecule striking a piston **(a)** does positive work if the piston is moving away from the molecule and **(b)** does negative work if the piston is moving toward the molecule. Hence a gas does positive work when it expands as in **(a)** but does negative work when it compresses as in **(b)**.

(a)

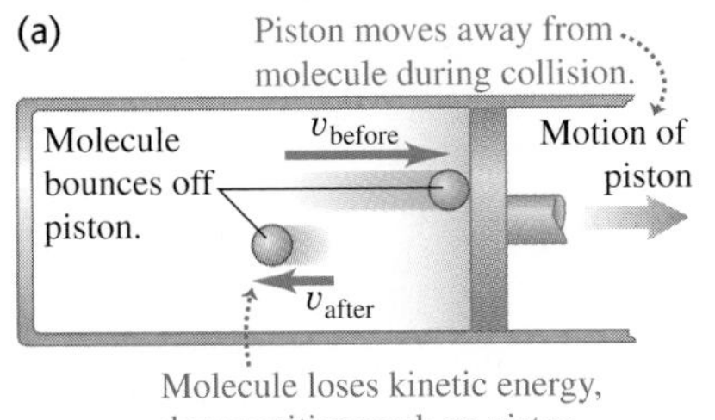

(b)

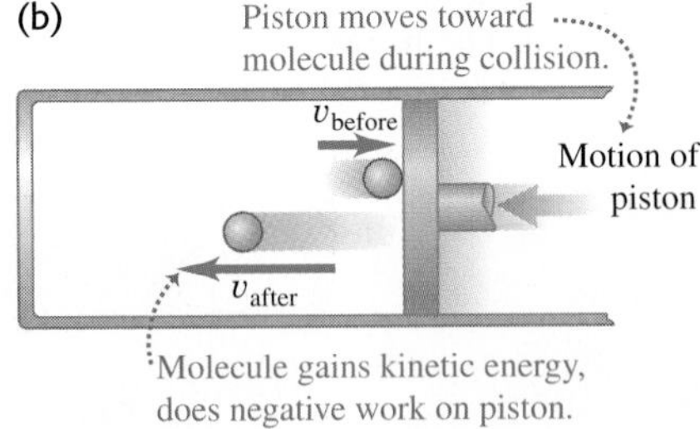

First we consider the *work* done by the system during a volume change. When a gas expands, it pushes outward on its boundary surfaces as they move outward. Hence an expanding gas always does positive work. The same thing is true of any solid or fluid material that expands under pressure, such as the popcorn in Fig. 19.1.

We can understand the work done by a gas in a volume change by considering the molecules that make up the gas. When one such molecule collides with a stationary surface, it exerts a momentary force on the wall but does no work because the wall does not move. But if the surface is moving, like a piston in a gasoline engine, the molecule *does* do work on the surface during the collision. If the piston in Fig. 19.4a moves to the right, so that the volume of the gas increases, the molecules that strike the piston exert a force through a distance and do *positive* work on the piston. If the piston moves toward the left as in Fig. 19.4b, so the volume of the gas decreases, then positive work is done *on* the molecule during the collision. Hence the gas molecules do *negative* work on the piston. ?

Figure 19.5 shows a system whose volume can change (a gas, liquid, or solid) in a cylinder with a movable piston. Suppose that the cylinder has cross-sectional area A and that the pressure exerted by the system at the piston face is p. The total force F exerted by the system on the piston is $F = pA$. When the piston moves out an infinitesimal distance dx, the work dW done by this force is

$$dW = F\,dx = pA\,dx$$

But

$$A\,dx = dV$$

where dV is the infinitesimal change of volume of the system. Thus we can express the work done by the system in this infinitesimal volume change as

$$dW = p\,dV \tag{19.1}$$

In a finite change of volume from V_1 to V_2,

$$W = \int_{V_1}^{V_2} p\,dV \quad \text{(work done in a volume change)} \tag{19.2}$$

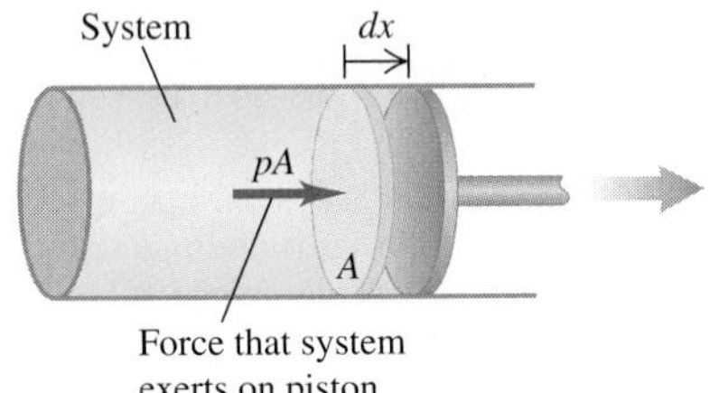

19.5 The infinitesimal work done by the system during the small expansion dx is $dW = pA\,dx$.

In general, the pressure of the system may vary during the volume change. For example, this is the case in the cylinders of an automobile engine as the pistons move back and forth. To evaluate the integral in Eq. (19.2), we have to know how the pressure varies as a function of volume. We can represent this relationship as a graph of p as a function of V (a pV-diagram, described at the end of Section 18.1). Figure 19.6 a shows a simple example. In this figure, Eq. (19.2) is repre-

19.6 The work done equals the area under the curve on a pV-diagram.

(a) pV-diagram for a system undergoing an expansion with varying pressure

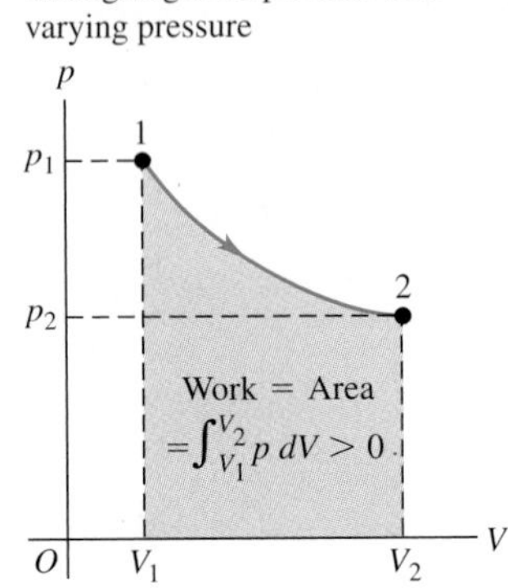

(b) pV-diagram for a system undergoing a compression with varying pressure

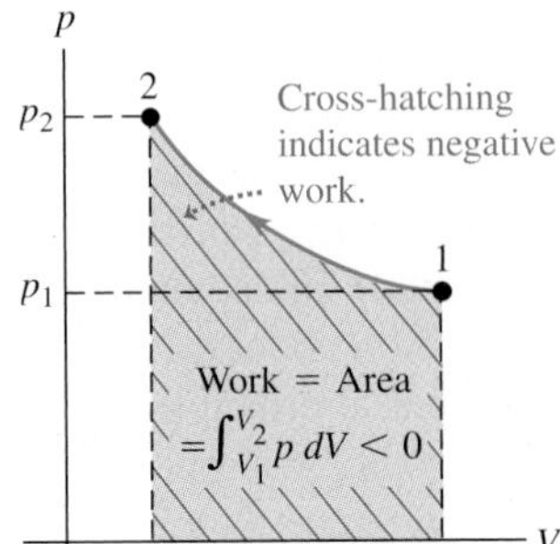

(c) pV-diagram for a system undergoing an expansion with constant pressure

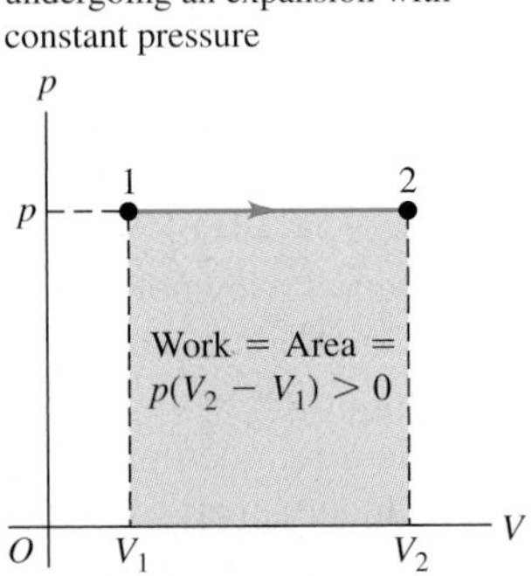

sented graphically as the *area* under the curve of p versus V between the limits V_1 and V_2. (In Section 6.3 we used a similar interpretation of the work done by a force F as the area under the curve of F versus x between the limits x_1 and x_2.)

According to the rule we stated in Section 19.1, work is *positive* when a system *expands.* In an expansion from state 1 to state 2 in Fig. 19.6a the area under the curve and the work are positive. A *compression* from 1 to 2 in Fig. 19.6b gives a *negative* area; when a system is compressed, its volume decreases and it does *negative* work on its surroundings (see also Fig. 19.4b).

CAUTION **Be careful with subscripts 1 and 2** When using Eq. (19.2), always remember that V_1 is the *initial* volume and V_2 is the *final* volume. That's why the labels 1 and 2 are reversed in Fig. 19.6b compared to Fig. 19.6a, even though both processes move between the same two thermodynamic states.

If the pressure p remains constant while the volume changes from V_1 to V_2 (Fig. 19.6c), the work done by the system is

$$W = p(V_2 - V_1) \quad \text{(work done in a volume change at constant pressure)} \tag{19.3}$$

ActivPhysics ONLINE
8.5 Work Done By a Gas

In any process in which the volume is *constant,* the system does no work because there is no displacement.

Example 19.1 Isothermal expansion of an ideal gas

An ideal gas undergoes an *isothermal* (constant-temperature) *expansion* at temperature T, during which its volume changes from V_1 to V_2. How much work does the gas do?

SOLUTION

IDENTIFY: The ideal-gas law tells us that if the temperature of an ideal gas remains constant, the quantity $pV = nRT$ also remains constant. If the volume V changes, the pressure p must change as well. Hence this problem asks for the work done by a gas that changes volume with varying pressure.

SET UP: Although it may be tempting to do so, we *cannot* use Eq. (19.3) to calculate the work done because the temperature, not the pressure, is constant. Instead we must use Eq. (19.2). To evaluate the integral in this equation we need to know the pressure as a function of volume; for this we use the ideal-gas law, Eq. (18.3).

EXECUTE: From Eq. (19.2),

$$W = \int_{V_1}^{V_2} p\, dV$$

From Eq. (18.3) the pressure p of n moles of ideal gas occupying volume V at absolute temperature T is

$$p = \frac{nRT}{V}$$

where R is the gas constant. We substitute this into the integral, take the constants n, R, and T outside, and evaluate the integral:

$$W = nRT\int_{V_1}^{V_2} \frac{dV}{V} = nRT \ln\frac{V_2}{V_1} \quad \text{(ideal gas, isothermal process)}$$

Also, when T is constant,

$$p_1V_1 = p_2V_2 \quad \text{or} \quad \frac{V_2}{V_1} = \frac{p_1}{p_2}$$

so the isothermal work may also be expressed as

$$W = nRT \ln\frac{p_1}{p_2} \quad \text{(ideal gas, isothermal process)}$$

EVALUATE: We check our result by noting that in an expansion $V_2 > V_1$ and the ratio V_2/V_1 is greater than 1. The logarithm of a number greater than 1 is positive, so $W > 0$, as it should be. As an additional check, look at our second expression for W: In an isothermal expansion the volume increases and the pressure drops, so $p_2 < p_1$, the ratio $p_1/p_2 > 1$, and $W = nRT\ln(p_1/p_2)$ is again positive.

These results also apply to an isothermal *compression* of a gas, for which $V_2 < V_1$ and $p_2 > p_1$.

Test Your Understanding of Section 19.2 A quantity of ideal gas undergoes an expansion that increases its volume from V_1 to $V_2 = 2V_1$. The final pressure of the gas is p_2. Does the gas do more work on its surroundings if the expansion is at constant *pressure* or at constant *temperature?* (i) constant pressure; (ii) constant temperature; (iii) the same amount of work is done in both cases; (iv) not enough information is given to decide.

19.3 Paths Between Thermodynamic States

We've seen that if a thermodynamic process involves a change in volume, the system undergoing the process does work (either positive or negative) on its surroundings. Heat also flows into or out of the system during the process if there is a temperature difference between the system and its surroundings. Let's now examine how the work done by and the heat added to the system during a thermodynamic process depend on the details of how the process takes place.

Work Done in a Thermodynamic Process

When a thermodynamic system changes from an initial state to a final state, it passes through a series of intermediate states. We call this series of states a **path.** There are always infinitely many different possibilities for these intermediate states. When they are all equilibrium states, the path can be plotted on a pV-diagram (Fig. 19.7a). Point 1 represents an initial state with pressure p_1 and volume V_1, and point 2 represents a final state with pressure p_2 and volume V_2. To pass from state 1 to state 2, we could keep the pressure constant at p_1 while the system expands to volume V_2 (point 3 in Fig. 19.7b), then reduce the pressure to p_2 (probably by decreasing the temperature) while keeping the volume constant at V_2 (to point 2 on the diagram). The work done by the system during this process is the area under the line $1 \rightarrow 3$; no work is done during the constant-volume process $3 \rightarrow 2$. Or the system might traverse the path $1 \rightarrow 4 \rightarrow 2$ (Fig. 19.7c); in that case the work is the area under the line $4 \rightarrow 2$, since no work is done during the constant-volume process $1 \rightarrow 4$. The smooth curve from 1 to 2 is another possibility (Fig. 19.7d), and the work for this path is different from that for either of the other paths.

We conclude that *the work done by the system depends not only on the initial and final states, but also on the intermediate states—that is, on the path.* Furthermore, we can take the system through a series of states forming a closed loop, such as $1 \rightarrow 3 \rightarrow 2 \rightarrow 4 \rightarrow 1$. In this case the final state is the same as the initial state, but the total work done by the system is *not* zero. (In fact, it is represented on the graph by the area enclosed by the loop; can you prove that? See Exercise 19.7.) It follows that it doesn't make sense to talk about the amount of work *contained in* a system. In a particular state, a system may have definite values of the state coordinates p, V, and T, but it wouldn't make sense to say that it has a definite value of W.

19.7 The work done by a system during a transition between two states depends on the path chosen.

(a)

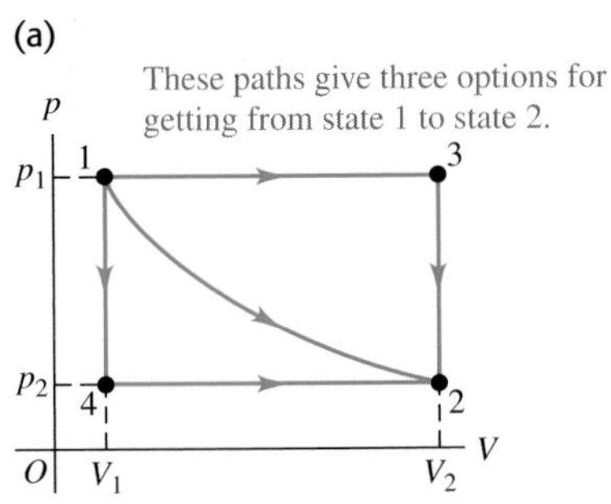
These paths give three options for getting from state 1 to state 2.
p
p_1
p_2
1
2
3
4
O
V_1
V_2
V

(b)

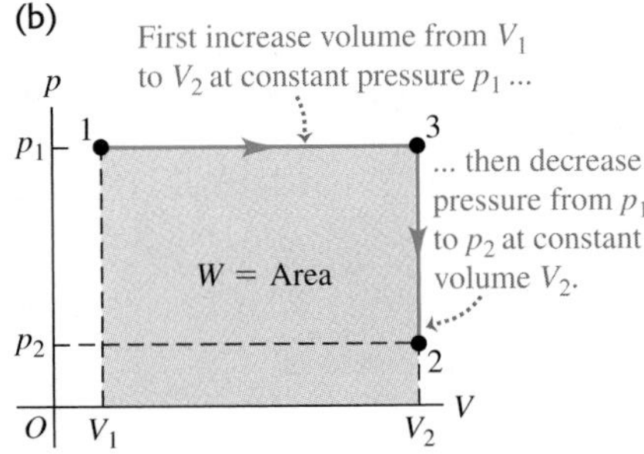
First increase volume from V_1 to V_2 at constant pressure p_1 ...
... then decrease pressure from p_1 to p_2 at constant volume V_2.
W = Area
p
p_1
p_2
1
2
3
O
V_1
V_2
V

(c)

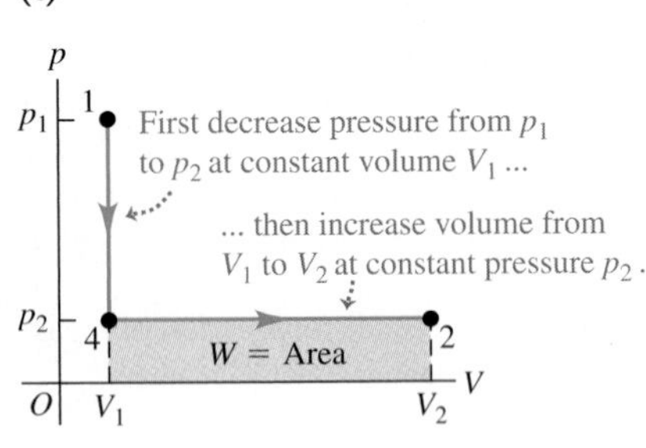
First decrease pressure from p_1 to p_2 at constant volume V_1 ...
... then increase volume from V_1 to V_2 at constant pressure p_2.
W = Area
p
p_1
p_2
1
2
4
O
V_1
V_2
V

(d)

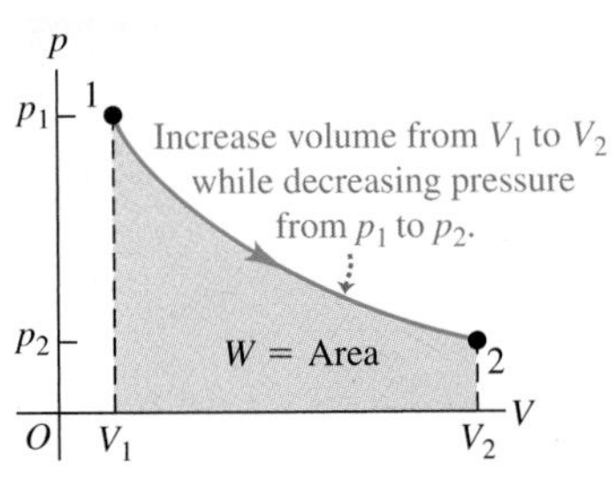
Increase volume from V_1 to V_2 while decreasing pressure from p_1 to p_2.
W = Area
p
p_1
p_2
1
2
O
V_1
V_2
V

Heat Added in a Thermodynamic Process

Like work, the *heat* added to a thermodynamic system when it undergoes a change of state depends on the path from the initial state to the final state. Here's an example. Suppose we want to change the volume of a certain quantity of an ideal gas from 2.0 L to 5.0 L while keeping the temperature constant at $T = 300$ K. Figure 19.8 shows two different ways in which we can do this. In Fig. 19.8a the gas is contained in a cylinder with a piston, with an initial volume of 2.0 L. We let the gas expand slowly, supplying heat from the electric heater to keep the temperature at 300 K. After expanding in this slow, controlled, isothermal manner, the gas reaches its final volume of 5.0 L; it absorbs a definite amount of heat in the process.

Figure 19.8b shows a different process leading to the same final state. The container is surrounded by insulating walls and is divided by a thin, breakable partition into two compartments. The lower part has volume 2.0 L and the upper part has volume 3.0 L. In the lower compartment we place the same amount of the same gas as in Fig. 19.8a, again at $T = 300$ K. The initial state is the same as before. Now we break the partition; the gas undergoes a rapid, uncontrolled expansion, with no heat passing through the insulating walls. The final volume is

5.0 L, the same as in Fig. 19.8a. The gas does no work during this expansion because it doesn't push against anything that moves. This uncontrolled expansion of a gas into vacuum is called a **free expansion;** we will discuss it further in Section 19.6.

Experiments have shown that when an ideal gas undergoes a free expansion, there is no temperature change. Therefore the final state of the gas is the same as in Fig. 19.8a. The intermediate states (pressures and volumes) during the transition from state 1 to state 2 are entirely different in the two cases; Figs. 19.8a and 19.8b represent *two different paths* connecting the *same states* 1 and 2. For the path in Fig. 19.8b, *no* heat is transferred into the system, and the system does no work. Like work, *heat depends not only on the initial and final states but also on the path.*

Because of this path dependence, it would not make sense to say that a system "contains" a certain quantity of heat. To see this, suppose we assign an arbitrary value to the "heat in a body" in some reference state. Then presumably the "heat in the body" in some other state would equal the heat in the reference state plus the heat added when the body goes to the second state. But that's ambiguous, as we have just seen; the heat added depends on the *path* we take from the reference state to the second state. We are forced to conclude that there is *no* consistent way to define "heat in a body"; it is not a useful concept.

While it doesn't make sense to talk about "work in a body" or "heat in a body," it *does* make sense to speak of the amount of *internal energy* in a body. This important concept is our next topic.

19.8 (a) Slow, controlled isothermal expansion of a gas from an initial state 1 to a final state 2 with the same temperature but lower pressure. (b) Rapid, uncontrolled expansion of the same gas starting at the same state 1 and ending at the same state 2.

(a) System does work on piston; hot plate adds heat to system ($W > 0$ and $Q > 0$).

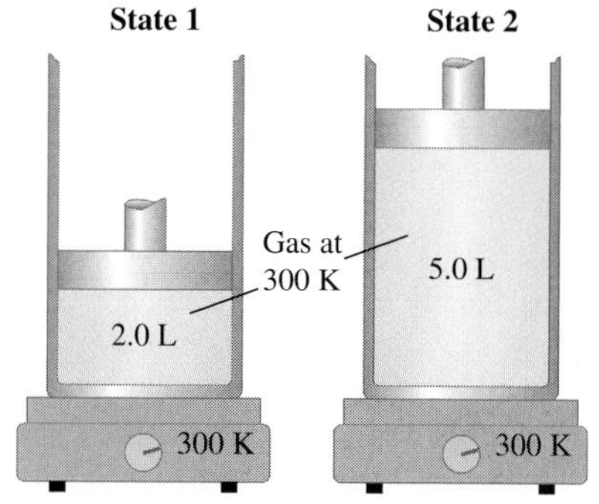

(b) System does no work; no heat enters or leaves system ($W = 0$ and $Q = 0$).

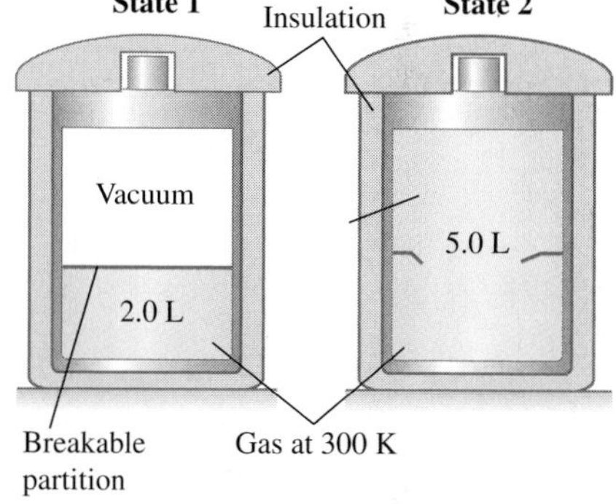

Test Your Understanding of Section 19.3 The system described in Fig. 19.7a undergoes four different thermodynamic processes. Each process is represented in a pV-diagram as a straight line from the initial state to the final state. (These processes are different from those shown in the pV-diagrams of Fig. 19.7.) Rank the processes in order of the amount of work done by the system, from the most positive to the most negative. (i) $1 \rightarrow 2$; (ii) $2 \rightarrow 1$; (iii) $3 \rightarrow 4$; (iv) $4 \rightarrow 3$.

19.4 Internal Energy and the First Law of Thermodynamics

Internal energy is one of the most important concepts in thermodynamics. In Section 7.3, when we discussed energy changes for a body sliding with friction, we stated that warming a body increased its internal energy and that cooling the body decreased its internal energy. But what *is* internal energy? We can look at it in various ways; let's start with one based on the ideas of mechanics. Matter consists of atoms and molecules, and these are made up of particles having kinetic and potential energies. We *tentatively* define the **internal energy** of a system as the sum of the kinetic energies of all of its constituent particles, plus the sum of all the potential energies of interaction among these particles.

ActivPhysics ONLINE
8.6 Heat, Internal Energy, and First Law of Thermodynamics

CAUTION **Is it internal?** Note that internal energy does *not* include potential energy arising from the interaction between the system and its surroundings. If the system is a glass of water, placing it on a high shelf increases the gravitational potential energy arising from the interaction between the glass and the earth. But this has no effect on the interaction between the molecules of the water, and so the internal energy of the water does not change.

We use the symbol U for internal energy. (We used this same symbol in our study of mechanics to represent potential energy. You may have to remind yourself occasionally that U has a different meaning in thermodynamics.) During a change of state of the system the internal energy may change from an initial value U_1 to a final value U_2. We denote the change in internal energy as $\Delta U = U_2 - U_1$.

We know that heat transfer is energy transfer. When we add a quantity of heat Q to a system and the system does no work during the process, the internal energy increases by an amount equal to Q; that is, $\Delta U = Q$. When a system does work W by expanding against its surroundings and no heat is added during the process, energy leaves the system and the internal energy decreases. That is, when W is positive, ΔU is negative, and vice versa. So $\Delta U = -W$. When *both* heat transfer and work occur, the *total* change in internal energy is

$$U_2 - U_1 = \Delta U = Q - W \quad \text{(first law of thermodynamics)} \tag{19.4}$$

We can rearrange this to the form

$$Q = \Delta U + W \tag{19.5}$$

19.9 In a thermodynamic process, the internal energy U of a system may (a) increase $(\Delta U > 0)$, (b) decrease $(\Delta U < 0)$, or (c) remain the same $(\Delta U = 0)$.

(a) More heat is added to system than system does work: Internal energy of system increases.

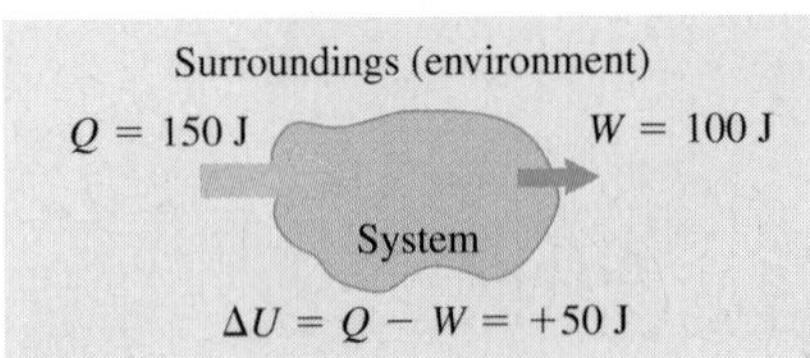

(b) More heat flows out of system than work is done: Internal energy of system decreases.

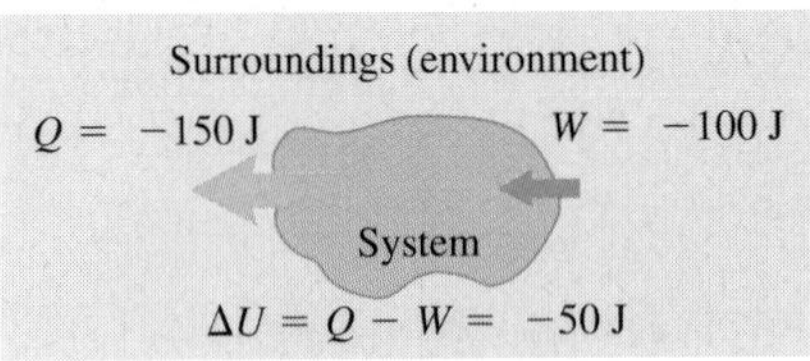

(c) Heat added to system equals work done by system: Internal energy of system unchanged.

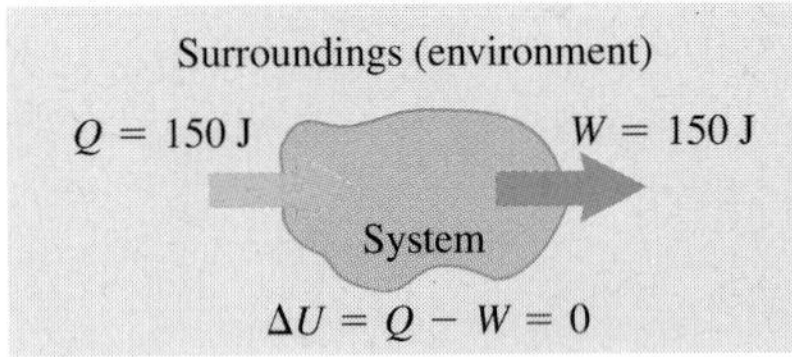

The message of Eq. (19.5) is that in general, when heat Q is added to a system, some of this added energy remains within the system, changing its internal energy by an amount ΔU; the remainder leaves the system again as the system does work W against its surroundings. Because W and Q may be positive, negative, or zero, ΔU can be positive, negative, or zero for different processes (Fig. 19.9).

Equation (19.4) or (19.5) is the **first law of thermodynamics.** It is a generalization of the principle of conservation of energy to include energy transfer through heat as well as mechanical work. As you will see in later chapters, this principle can be extended to ever-broader classes of phenomena by identifying additional forms of energy and energy transfer. In every situation in which it seems that the total energy in all known forms is not conserved, it has been possible to identify a new form of energy such that the total energy, including the new form, *is* conserved. There is energy associated with electric fields, with magnetic fields, and, according to the theory of relativity, even with mass itself.

Understanding the First Law of Thermodynamics

At the beginning of this discussion we tentatively defined internal energy in terms of microscopic kinetic and potential energies. This has drawbacks, however. Actually *calculating* internal energy in this way for any real system would be hopelessly complicated. Furthermore, this definition isn't an *operational* one because it doesn't describe how to determine internal energy from physical quantities that we can measure directly.

So let's look at internal energy in another way. Starting over, we define the *change* in internal energy ΔU during any change of a system as the quantity given by Eq. (19.4), $\Delta U = Q - W$. This *is* an operational definition because we can measure Q and W. It does not define U itself, only ΔU. This is not a shortcoming because we can *define* the internal energy of a system to have a specified value in some reference state, and then use Eq. (19.4) to define the internal energy in any other state. This is analogous to our treatment of potential energy in Chapter 7, in which we arbitrarily defined the potential energy of a mechanical system to be zero at a certain position.

This new definition trades one difficulty for another. If we define ΔU by Eq. (19.4), then when the system goes from state 1 to state 2 by two different paths, how do we know that ΔU is the same for the two paths? We have already seen that Q and W are, in general, *not* the same for different paths. If ΔU, which equals $Q - W$, is also path dependent, then ΔU is ambiguous. If so, the concept of internal energy of a system is subject to the same criticism as the erroneous concept of quantity of heat in a system, as we discussed at the end of Section 19.3.

The only way to answer this question is through *experiment.* For various materials we measure Q and W for various changes of state and various paths to learn whether ΔU is or is not path dependent. The results of many such investigations are clear and unambiguous: While Q and W depend on the path, $\Delta U = Q - W$ *is independent of path. The change in internal energy of a system during any thermodynamic process depends only on the initial and final states, not on the path leading from one to the other.*

Experiment, then, is the ultimate justification for believing that a thermodynamic system in a specific state has a unique internal energy that depends only on that state. An equivalent statement is that the internal energy U of a system is a function of the state coordinates p, V, and T (actually, any two of these, since the three variables are related by the equation of state).

To say that the first law of thermodynamics, given by Eq. (19.4) or (19.5), represents conservation of energy for thermodynamic processes is correct, as far as it goes. But an important *additional* aspect of the first law is the fact that internal energy depends only on the state of a system (Fig. 19.10). In changes of state, the change in internal energy is independent of the path.

All this may seem a little abstract if you are satisfied to think of internal energy as microscopic mechanical energy. There's nothing wrong with that view, and we will make use of it at various times during our discussion. But in the interest of precise *operational* definitions, internal energy, like heat, can and must be defined in a way that is independent of the detailed microscopic structure of the material.

19.10 The internal energy of a cup of coffee depends on just its thermodynamic state—how much water and ground coffee it contains, and what its temperature is. It does not depend on the history of how the coffee was prepared—that is, the thermodynamic path that led to its current state.

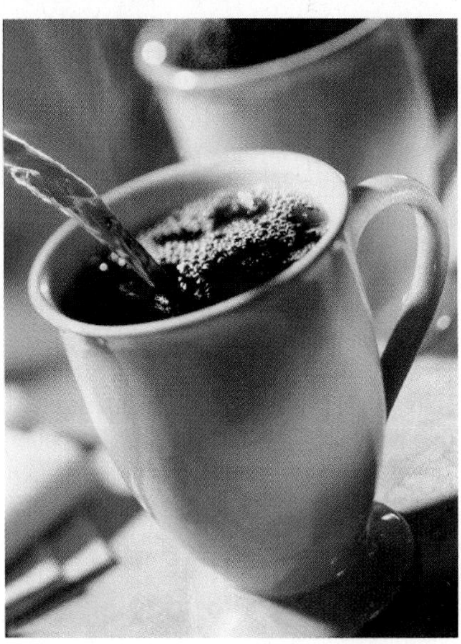

Cyclic Processes and Isolated Systems

Two special cases of the first law of thermodynamics are worth mentioning. A process that eventually returns a system to its initial state is called a *cyclic process.* For such a process, the final state is the same as the initial state, and so the *total* internal energy change must be zero. Then

$$U_2 = U_1 \quad \text{and} \quad Q = W$$

If a net quantity of work W is done by the system during this process, an equal amount of energy must have flowed into the system as heat Q. But there is no reason either Q or W individually has to be zero (Fig. 19.11).

Another special case occurs in an *isolated system,* one that does no work on its surroundings and has no heat flow to or from its surroundings. For any process taking place in an isolated system,

$$W = Q = 0$$

and therefore

$$U_2 = U_1 = \Delta U = 0$$

In other words, *the internal energy of an isolated system is constant.*

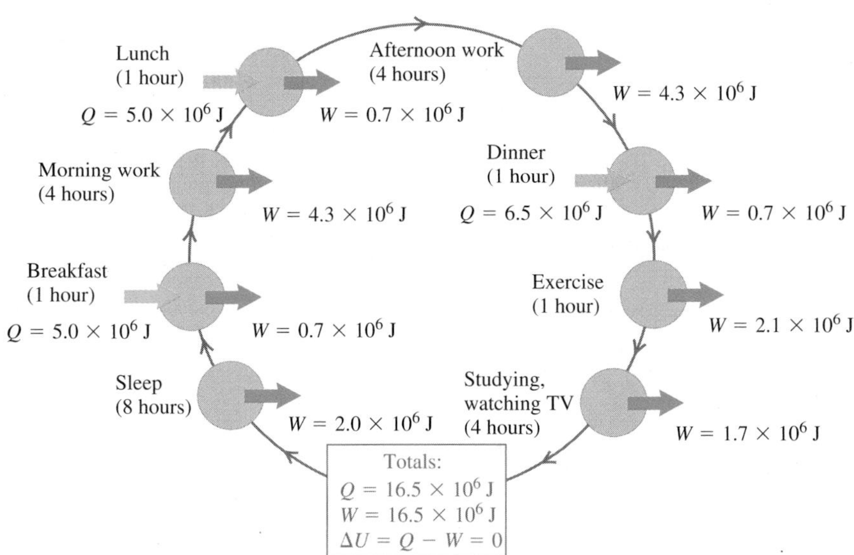

19.11 Every day, your body (a thermodynamic system) goes through a cyclic thermodynamic process like this one. Heat Q is added by metabolizing food, and your body does work W in breathing, walking, and other activities. If you return to the same state at the end of the day, $Q = W$ and the net change in your internal energy is zero.

Problem-Solving Strategy 19.1 The First Law of Thermodynamics

IDENTIFY *the relevant concepts:* The first law of thermodynamics is the statement of the law of conservation of energy in its most general form. You can apply it to *any* situation in which you are concerned with changes in the internal energy of a system, with heat flow into or out of a system, and/or with work done by or on a system.

SET UP *the problem* using the following steps:

1. Carefully define what the thermodynamic system is.
2. The first law of thermodynamics focuses on systems that go through thermodynamic processes. Some problems involve processes with more than one step, so make sure that you identify the initial and final states for each step.
3. Identify the known quantities and the target variables.
4. Check whether you have enough equations. The first law, $\Delta U = Q - W$, can be applied just once to each step in a thermodynamic process, so you will often need additional equations. These often include Eq. (19.2) for the work done in a volume change and the equation of state of the material that makes up the thermodynamic system (for an ideal gas, $pV = nRT$).

EXECUTE *the solution* as follows:

1. You shouldn't be surprised to be told that consistent units are essential. If p is in Pa and V in m^3, then W is in joules. Otherwise, you may want to convert the pressure and volume units into units of Pa and m^3. If a heat capacity is given in terms of calories, usually the simplest procedure is to convert it to joules. Be especially careful with moles. When you use $n = m_{total}/M$ to convert between total mass and number of moles, remember that if m_{total} is in kilograms, M must be in *kilograms* per mole. The usual units for M are *grams* per mole; be careful!
2. The internal energy change ΔU in any thermodynamic process or series of processes is independent of the path, whether the substance is an ideal gas or not. This point is of the utmost importance in the problems in this chapter and the next. Sometimes you will be given enough information about one path between the given initial and final states to calculate ΔU for that path. Since ΔU is the same for every possible path between the same two states, you can then relate the various energy quantities for other paths.
3. When a process consists of several distinct steps, it often helps to make a table showing Q, W, and ΔU for each step. Put these quantities for each step on a different line, and arrange them so the Q's, W's, and ΔU's form columns. Then you can apply the first law to each line; in addition, you can add each column and apply the first law to the sums. Do you see why?
4. Using steps 1–3, solve for the target variables.

EVALUATE *your answer:* Check your results for reasonableness. In particular, make sure that each of your answers has the correct algebraic sign. Remember that a positive Q means that heat flows *into* the system, and a negative Q means that heat flows *out of* the system. A positive W means that work is done *by* the system on its environment, while a negative W means that work is done *on* the system by its environment.

Example 19.2 Working off your dessert

You propose to eat a 900-calorie hot fudge sundae (with whipped cream) and then run up several flights of stairs to work off the energy you have taken in. How high do you have to climb? Assume that your mass is 60.0 kg.

SOLUTION

IDENTIFY: Eating the hot fudge sundae corresponds to a heat flow into your body, and running up stairs means that you do work. We can relate these quantities using the first law of thermodynamics.

SET UP: The system consists of your body. We are given that 900 food calories of heat flow into your body. The purpose of running up the stairs is to make sure that the final state of the system is the same as the initial state (no fatter, no leaner), so there is no net change in internal energy: $\Delta U = 0$. The work you must do to raise your mass m a height h is $W = mgh$; our target variable is h.

EXECUTE: Using the first law of thermodynamics, $\Delta U = 0 = Q - W$, so $W = Q$: The work that you do running up the stairs must just equal the heat input from the sundae. From $W = mgh$, the height that you climb is $h = Q/mg$. Before substituting values into this equation, we first convert units: One food-value calorie is 1 kcal = 1000 cal = 4190 J (to three significant figures), so

$$Q = 900\ \text{kcal}\,(4190\ \text{J}/1\ \text{kcal}) = 3.77 \times 10^6\ \text{J}$$

Then

$$h = \frac{Q}{mg} = \frac{3.77 \times 10^6\ \text{J}}{(60.0\ \text{kg})(9.80\ \text{m/s}^2)}$$
$$= 6410\ \text{m} \qquad (\text{about } 21{,}000\ \text{ft})$$

EVALUATE: Good luck! We have assumed 100% efficiency in the conversion of food energy into mechanical work; this isn't very realistic. As a result, the actual distance you would have to climb is quite a bit less than we have calculated. We'll talk more about efficiency later.

Example 19.3 A cyclic process

Figure 19.12 shows a pV-diagram for a *cyclic* process, one in which the initial and final states are the same. It starts at point a and proceeds counterclockwise in the pV-diagram to point b, then back to a, and the total work is $W = -500$ J. (a) Why is the work negative? (b) Find the change in internal energy and the heat added during this process.

SOLUTION

IDENTIFY: This problem asks us to relate the change in internal energy, the heat added, and the work done in a thermodynamic process. Hence we can apply the first law of thermodynamics.

19.12 The net work done by the system in the process *aba* is -500 J. What would it have been if the process had proceeded clockwise in this pV-diagram?

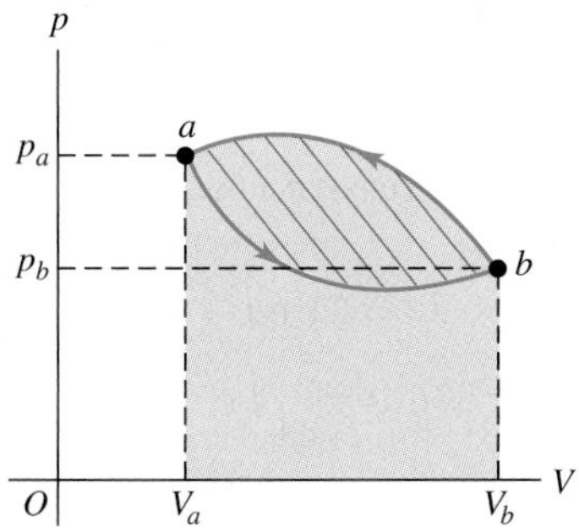

SET UP: The thermodynamic process here has two steps: $a \to b$ via the lower curve in Fig. 19.12 and $b \to a$ via the upper curve. But note that the questions in (a) and (b) are about the *entire* cyclic process $a \to b \to a$ (around the loop in Fig. 19.12).

EXECUTE: (a) The work done equals the area under the curve, with the area taken as positive for increasing volume and negative for decreasing volume. The area under the lower curve from *a* to *b* is positive, but it is smaller than the absolute value of the negative area under the upper curve from *b* back to *a*. Therefore the net area (the area enclosed by the path, shown with red stripes) and the work are negative. In other words, 500 more joules of work is done *on* the system than *by* the system.

(b) For this and any other cyclic process (in which the beginning and end points are the same), $\Delta U = 0$, so $Q = W = -500$ J. That is, 500 joules of heat must come *out of* the system.

EVALUATE: This example illustrates a general principle about pV-diagrams of cyclic processes: The total work is positive if the process goes around the cycle in a clockwise direction, and the total work is negative if the process goes around the cycle in a counterclockwise direction (as in Fig. 19.12).

Example 19.4 Comparing thermodynamic processes

A series of thermodynamic processes is shown in the pV-diagram of Fig. 19.13. In process *ab*, 150 J of heat is added to the system, and in process *bd*, 600 J of heat is added. Find (a) the internal energy change in process *ab*; (b) the internal energy change in process *abd* (shown in light blue); and (c) the total heat added in process *acd* (shown in dark blue).

SOLUTION

IDENTIFY: In each process we use $\Delta U = Q - W$ to determine the desired quantity.

SET UP: We are given $Q_{ab} = +150$ J and $Q_{bd} = +600$ J (both values are positive because heat is *added* to the system). Our target variables are (a) ΔU_{ab}, (b) ΔU_{abd}, and (c) Q_{acd}.

EXECUTE: (a) No volume change occurs during process *ab*, so $W_{ab} = 0$ and $\Delta U_{ab} = Q_{ab} = 150$ J.

(b) Process *bd* occurs at constant pressure, so the work done by the system during this expansion is

$$\begin{aligned} W_{bd} &= p(V_2 - V_1) \\ &= (8.0 \times 10^4 \text{ Pa})(5.0 \times 10^{-3} \text{ m}^3 - 2.0 \times 10^{-3} \text{ m}^3) \\ &= 240 \text{ J} \end{aligned}$$

19.13 A pV-diagram showing the various thermodynamic processes.

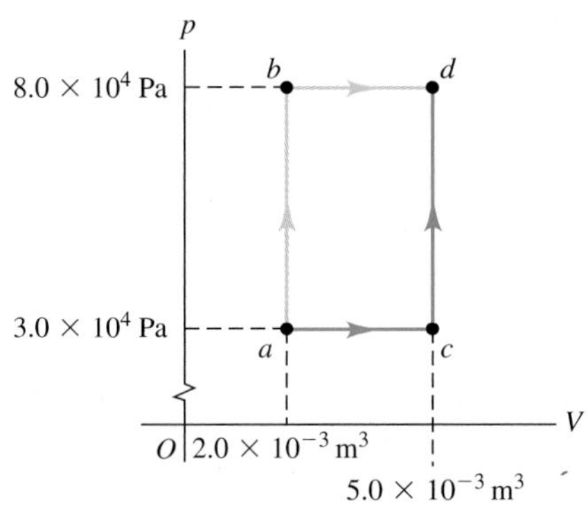

The total work for process *abd* is

$$W_{abd} = W_{ab} + W_{bd} = 0 + 240 \text{ J} = 240 \text{ J}$$

and the total heat is

$$Q_{abd} = Q_{ab} + Q_{bd} = 150 \text{ J} + 600 \text{ J} = 750 \text{ J}$$

Applying Eq. (19.4) to *abd*, we find

$$\Delta U_{abd} = Q_{abd} - W_{abd} = 750 \text{ J} - 240 \text{ J} = 510 \text{ J}$$

(c) Because ΔU is independent of path, the internal energy change is the same for path *acd* as for path *abd*; that is,

$$\Delta U_{acd} = \Delta U_{abd} = 510 \text{ J}$$

The total work for the path *acd* is

$$\begin{aligned} W_{acd} &= W_{ac} + W_{cd} = p(V_2 - V_1) + 0 \\ &= (3.0 \times 10^4 \text{ Pa})(5.0 \times 10^{-3} \text{ m}^3 - 2.0 \times 10^{-3} \text{ m}^3) \\ &= 90 \text{ J} \end{aligned}$$

Now we apply Eq. (19.5) to process *acd*:

$$Q_{acd} = \Delta U_{acd} + W_{acd} = 510 \text{ J} + 90 \text{ J} = 600 \text{ J}$$

Here is a tabulation of the various quantities:

Step	Q	W	$\Delta U = Q - W$	Step	Q	W	$\Delta U = Q - W$
ab	150 J	0 J	150 J	*ac*	?	90 J	?
bd	600 J	240 J	360 J	*cd*	?	0 J	?
abd	750 J	240 J	510 J	*acd*	600 J	90 J	510 J

EVALUATE: We see that although ΔU is the same (510 J) for *abd* and *acd*, W (240 J versus 90 J) and Q (750 J versus 600 J) are quite different for the two processes.

Notice that we don't have enough information to find Q or ΔU for the processes *ac* and *cd*. We were nonetheless able to analyze the composite process *acd* by comparing it to the process *abd*, which has the same initial and final states and for which we have more complete information.

Example 19.5 Thermodynamics of boiling water

One gram of water $(1\ \text{cm}^3)$ becomes $1671\ \text{cm}^3$ of steam when boiled at a constant pressure of 1 atm $(1.013 \times 10^5\ \text{Pa})$. The heat of vaporization at this pressure is $L_v = 2.256 \times 10^6\ \text{J/kg}$. Compute (a) the work done by the water when it vaporizes and (b) its increase in internal energy.

SOLUTION

IDENTIFY: The new feature of this problem is that the heat added causes the system (water) to change phase from liquid to vapor. We can nonetheless apply the first law of thermodynamics, which is true for thermodynamic processes of all kinds.

SET UP: The water is boiled at a constant pressure, so we can calculate the work W done by the water using Eq. (19.3). We can calculate the heat Q added to the water from the mass and the heat of vaporization, and we can then find the internal energy change using $\Delta U = Q - W$.

EXECUTE: (a) From Eq. (19.3), the work done by the vaporizing water is

$$\begin{aligned} W &= p(V_2 - V_1) \\ &= (1.013 \times 10^5\ \text{Pa})(1671 \times 10^{-6}\ \text{m}^3 - 1 \times 10^{-6}\ \text{m}^3) \\ &= 169\ \text{J} \end{aligned}$$

(b) From Eq. (17.20), the heat added to the water to vaporize it is

$$Q = mL_v = (10^{-3}\ \text{kg})(2.256 \times 10^6\ \text{J/kg}) = 2256\ \text{J}$$

From the first law of thermodynamics, Eq. (19.4), the change in internal energy is

$$\Delta U = Q - W = 2256\ \text{J} - 169\ \text{J} = 2087\ \text{J}$$

EVALUATE: To vaporize 1 gram of water, we have to add 2256 J of heat. Most (2087 J) of this added energy remains in the system as an increase in internal energy. The remaining 169 J leaves the system again as it does work against the surroundings while expanding from liquid to vapor. The increase in internal energy is associated mostly with the intermolecular forces that hold the molecules together in the liquid state. These forces are attractive, so the associated potential energies are greater after work has been done to pull the molecules apart, forming the vapor state. It's like increasing gravitational potential energy by pulling an elevator farther from the center of the earth.

Infinitesimal Changes of State

In the preceding examples the initial and final states differ by a finite amount. Later we will consider *infinitesimal* changes of state in which a small amount of heat dQ is added to the system, the system does a small amount of work dW, and its internal energy changes by an amount dU. For such a process we state the first law in differential form as

$$dU = dQ - dW \quad \text{(first law of thermodynamics, infinitesimal process)} \tag{19.6}$$

For the systems we will discuss, the work dW is given by $dW = p\,dV$, so we can also state the first law as

$$dU = dQ - p\,dV \tag{19.7}$$

Test Your Understanding of Section 19.4 Rank the following thermodynamic processes according to the change in internal energy in each process, from most positive to most negative. (i) As you do 250 J of work on a system, it transfers 250 J of heat to its surroundings; (ii) as you do 250 J of work on a system, it absorbs 250 J of heat from its surroundings; (iii) as a system does 250 J of work on you, it transfers 250 J of heat to its surroundings; (iv) as a system does 250 J of work on you, it absorbs 250 J of heat from its surroundings.

19.5 Kinds of Thermodynamic Processes

8.4 State Variables and Ideal Gas Law

In this section we describe four specific kinds of thermodynamic processes that occur often in practical situations. These can be summarized briefly as "no heat transfer" or *adiabatic,* "constant volume" or *isochoric,* "constant pressure" or *isobaric,* and "constant temperature" or *isothermal.* For some of these processes we can use a simplified form of the first law of thermodynamics.

Adiabatic Process

An **adiabatic process** (pronounced "ay-dee-ah-*bat*-ic") is defined as one with no heat transfer into or out of a system; $Q = 0$. We can prevent heat flow either by surrounding the system with thermally insulating material or by carrying out the process so quickly that there is not enough time for appreciable heat flow. From the first law we find that for every adiabatic process,

$$U_2 - U_1 = \Delta U = -W \qquad \text{(adiabatic process)} \qquad (19.8)$$

When a system expands adiabatically, W is positive (the system does work on its surroundings), so ΔU is negative and the internal energy decreases. When a system is *compressed* adiabatically, W is negative (work is done on the system by its surroundings) and U increases. In many (but not all) systems an increase of internal energy is accompanied by a rise in temperature, and a decrease in internal energy with a drop in temperature (Fig. 19.14).

The compression stroke in an internal-combustion engine is an approximately adiabatic process. The temperature rises as the air–fuel mixture in the cylinder is compressed. The expansion of the burned fuel during the power stroke is also an approximately adiabatic expansion with a drop in temperature. In Section 19.8 we'll consider adiabatic processes in an ideal gas.

19.14 When the cork is popped on a bottle of champagne, the pressurized gases inside the bottle expand into the outside air so rapidly that there is no time for them to exchange heat with their surroundings. Hence the expansion is adiabatic. As the expanding gases do work on their surroundings, their internal energy and temperature both drop; the lowered temperature makes water vapor condense and form a miniature cloud.

Isochoric Process

An **isochoric process** (pronounced "eye-so-*kor*-ic") is a *constant-volume* process. When the volume of a thermodynamic system is constant, it does no work on its surroundings. Then $W = 0$ and

$$U_2 - U_1 = \Delta U = Q \qquad \text{(isochoric process)} \qquad (19.9)$$

In an isochoric process, all the energy added as heat remains in the system as an increase in internal energy. Heating a gas in a closed constant-volume container is an example of an isochoric process. The processes *ab* and *cd* in Example 19.4 are also examples of isochoric processes. (Note that there are types of work that do not involve a volume change. For example, we can do work on a fluid by stirring it. In some literature, "isochoric" is used to mean that no work of any kind is done.)

Isobaric Process

An **isobaric process** (pronounced "eye-so-*bear*-ic") is a *constant-pressure* process. In general, none of the three quantities ΔU, Q, and W is zero in an isobaric process, but calculating W is easy nonetheless. From Eq. (19.3),

$$W = p(V_2 - V_1) \qquad \text{(isobaric process)} \qquad (19.10)$$

Example 19.5 concerns an isobaric process, boiling water at constant pressure (Fig. 19.15).

19.15 Most cooking involves isobaric processes. That's because the air pressure above a saucepan or frying pan, or inside a microwave oven, remains essentially constant while the food is being heated.

Isothermal Process

An **isothermal process** is a *constant-temperature* process. For a process to be isothermal, any heat flow into or out of the system must occur slowly enough that thermal equilibrium is maintained. In general, none of the quantities ΔU, Q, or W is zero in an isothermal process.

In some special cases the internal energy of a system depends *only* on its temperature, not on its pressure or volume. The most familiar system having this special property is an ideal gas, as we'll discuss in the next section. For such systems, if the temperature is constant, the internal energy is also constant; $\Delta U = 0$ and $Q = W$. That is, any energy entering the system as heat Q must leave it again as work W done by the system. Example 19.1, involving an ideal gas, is an example of an isothermal process in which U is also constant. For most systems other than

19.16 Four different processes for a constant amount of an ideal gas, all starting at state a. For the adiabatic process, $Q = 0$; for the isochoric process, $W = 0$; and for the isothermal process, $\Delta U = 0$. The temperature increases only during the isobaric expansion.

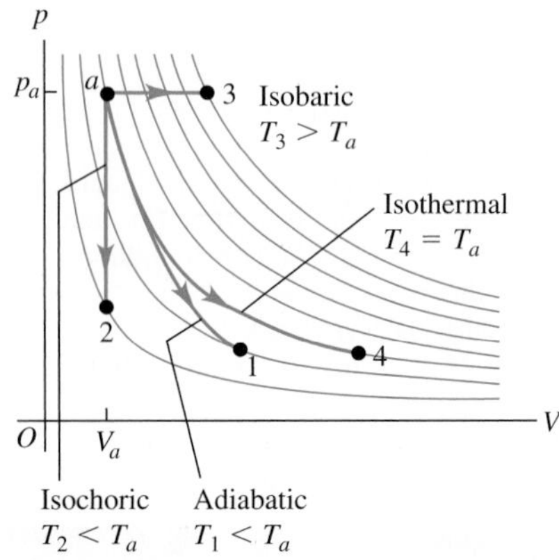

19.17 The partition is broken (or removed) to start the free expansion of gas into the vacuum region.

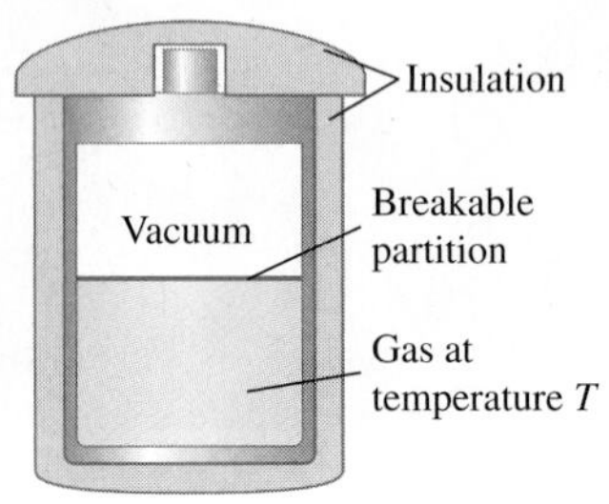

ideal gases, the internal energy depends on pressure as well as temperature, so U may vary even when T is constant.

Figure 19.16 shows a pV-diagram for these four processes for a constant amount of an ideal gas. The path followed in an adiabatic process (a to 1) is called an **adiabat.** A vertical line (constant volume) is an **isochor,** a horizontal line (constant pressure) is an **isobar,** and a curve of constant temperature (shown as light blue lines in Fig. 19.16) is an **isotherm.**

Test Your Understanding of Section 19.5 Which of the processes in Fig. 19.7 are isochoric? Which are isobaric? Is it possible to tell if any of the processes are isothermal or adiabatic?

19.6 Internal Energy of an Ideal Gas

We now show that for an ideal gas, the internal energy U depends only on temperature, not on pressure or volume. Let's think again about the free-expansion experiment described in Section 19.3. A thermally insulated container with rigid walls is divided into two compartments by a partition (Fig. 19.17). One compartment has a quantity of an ideal gas and the other is evacuated.

When the partition is removed or broken, the gas expands to fill both parts of the container. The gas does no work on its surroundings because the walls of the container don't move, and there is no heat flow through the insulation. So both Q and W are zero and the internal energy U is constant. This is true of any substance, whether it is an ideal gas or not.

Does the *temperature* change during a free expansion? Suppose it *does* change, while the internal energy stays the same. In that case we have to conclude that the internal energy depends on both the temperature and the volume or on both the temperature and the pressure, but certainly not on the temperature alone. But if T is constant during a free expansion, for which we know that U is constant even though both p and V change, then we have to conclude that U depends only on T, not on p or V.

Many experiments have shown that when a low-density gas undergoes a free expansion, its temperature *does not* change. Such a gas is essentially an ideal gas. The conclusion is:

The internal energy of an ideal gas depends only on its temperature, not on its pressure or volume.

This property, in addition to the ideal-gas equation of state, is part of the ideal-gas model. Make sure you understand that U depends only on T for an ideal gas, for we will make frequent use of this fact.

For nonideal gases, some temperature change occurs during free expansions, even though the internal energy is constant. This shows that the internal energy cannot depend *only* on temperature; it must depend on pressure as well. From the microscopic viewpoint, in which internal energy U is the sum of the kinetic and potential energies for all the particles that make up the system, this is not surprising. Nonideal gases usually have attractive intermolecular forces, and when molecules move farther apart, the associated potential energies increase. If the total internal energy is constant, the kinetic energies must decrease. Temperature is directly related to molecular *kinetic* energy, and for such a gas a free expansion is usually accompanied by a *drop* in temperature.

Test Your Understanding of Section 19.6 Is the internal energy of a solid likely to be independent of its volume, as is the case for an ideal gas? Explain your reasoning. (*Hint:* See Fig. 18.20.)

19.7 Heat Capacities of an Ideal Gas

We defined specific heat and molar heat capacity in Section 17.5. We also remarked at the end of that section that the specific heat or molar heat capacity of a substance depends on the conditions under which the heat is added. It is usually easiest to measure the heat capacity of a gas in a closed container under constant-volume conditions. The corresponding heat capacity is the **molar heat capacity at constant volume,** denoted by C_V. Heat capacity measurements for solids and liquids are usually carried out in the atmosphere under constant atmospheric pressure, and we call the corresponding heat capacity the **molar heat capacity at constant pressure,** C_p. If neither p nor V is constant, we have an infinite number of possible heat capacities.

Let's consider C_V and C_p for an ideal gas. To measure C_V, we raise the temperature of an ideal gas in a rigid container with constant volume, neglecting its thermal expansion (Fig. 19.18a). To measure C_p, we let the gas expand just enough to keep the pressure constant as the temperature rises (Fig. 19.18b).

Why should these two molar heat capacities be different? The answer lies in the first law of thermodynamics. In a constant-volume temperature increase, the system does no work, and the change in internal energy ΔU equals the heat added Q. In a constant-pressure temperature increase, on the other hand, the volume *must* increase; otherwise, the pressure (given by the ideal-gas equation of state $p = nRT/V$) could not remain constant. As the material expands, it does an amount of work W. According to the first law,

$$Q = \Delta U + W \tag{19.11}$$

For a given temperature increase, the internal energy change ΔU of an ideal gas has the same value no matter what the process (remember that the internal energy of an ideal gas depends only on temperature, not on pressure or volume). Equation (19.11) then shows that the heat input for a constant-pressure process must be *greater* than that for a constant-volume process because additional energy must be supplied to account for the work W done during the expansion. So C_p is greater than C_V for an ideal gas. The pV-diagram in Fig. 19.19 shows this relationship. For air, C_p is 40% greater than C_V.

For a very few substances (one of which is water between 0°C and 4°C) the volume *decreases* during heating. In this case, W is negative, the heat input is *less* than in the constant-volume case, and C_p is *less* than C_V.

19.18 Measuring the molar heat capacity of an ideal gas (a) at constant volume and (b) at constant pressure.

(a) Constant volume: $dQ = nC_V\,dT$

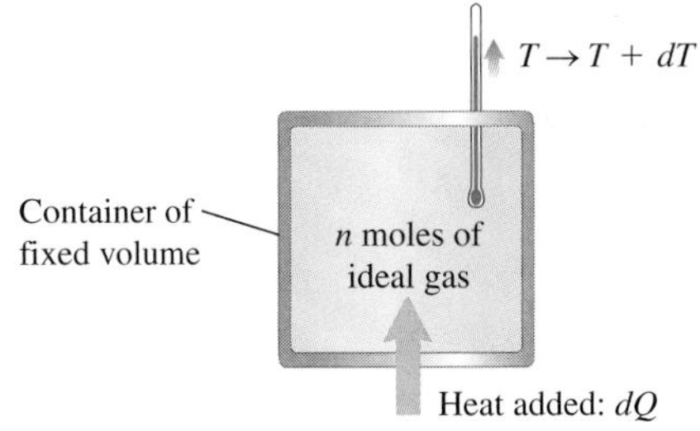

(b) Constant pressure: $dQ = nC_p\,dT$

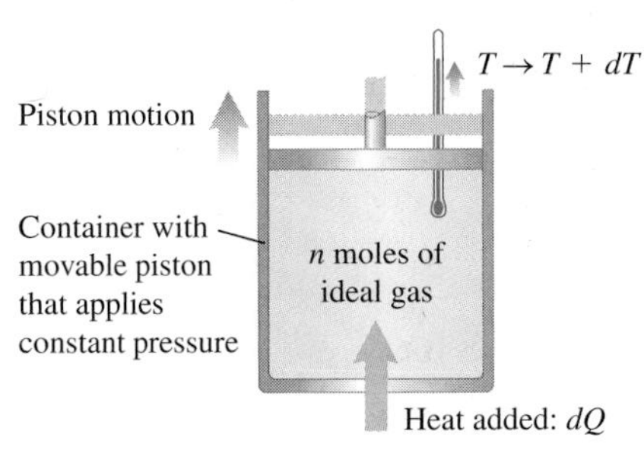

Relating C_p and C_V for an Ideal Gas

We can derive a simple relationship between C_p and C_V for an ideal gas. First consider the constant-*volume* process. We place n moles of an ideal gas at temperature T in a constant-volume container. We place it in thermal contact with a hotter body; an infinitesimal quantity of heat dQ flows into the gas, and its temperature increases by an infinitesimal amount dT. By the definition of C_V, the molar heat capacity at constant volume,

$$dQ = nC_V\,dT \tag{19.12}$$

The pressure increases during this process, but the gas does no work $(dW = 0)$ because the volume is constant. The first law in differential form, Eq. (19.6), is $dQ = dU + dW$. Since $dW = 0$, $dQ = dU$ and Eq. (19.12) can also be written as

$$dU = nC_V\,dT \tag{19.13}$$

Now consider a constant-*pressure* process with the same temperature change dT. We place the same gas in a cylinder with a piston that we can allow to move just enough to maintain constant pressure, as shown in Fig. 19.18b. Again we bring the system into contact with a hotter body. As heat flows into the gas, it

19.19 Raising the temperature of an ideal gas from T_1 to T_2 by a constant-volume or a constant-pressure process. For an ideal gas, U depends only on T, so ΔU is the same for both processes. But for the constant-pressure process, more heat Q must be added to both increase U and do work W. Hence $C_p > C_V$.

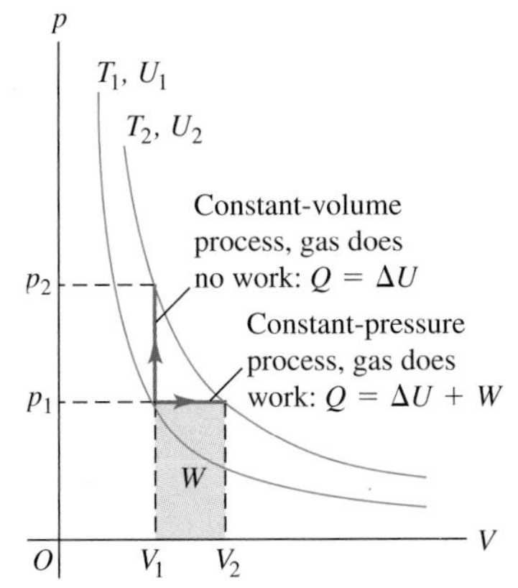

ActivPhysics ONLINE

8.7 Heat Capacity
8.8 Isochoric Process
8.9 Isobaric Process
8.10 Isothermmal Process

expands at constant pressure and does work. By the definition of C_p, the molar heat capacity at constant pressure, the amount of heat dQ entering the gas is

$$dQ = nC_p\,dT \tag{19.14}$$

The work dW done by the gas in this constant-pressure process is

$$dW = p\,dV$$

We can also express dW in terms of the temperature change dT by using the ideal-gas equation of state, $pV = nRT$. Because p is constant, the change in V is proportional to the change in T:

$$dW = p\,dV = nR\,dT \tag{19.15}$$

Now we substitute Eqs. (19.14) and (19.15) into the first law, $dQ = dU + dW$. We obtain

$$nC_p\,dT = dU + nR\,dT \tag{19.16}$$

Now here comes the crux of the calculation. The internal energy change dU for the constant-pressure process is again given by Eq. (19.13), $dU = nC_V\,dT$, *even though now the volume is not constant.* Why is this so? Recall the discussion of Section 19.6; one of the special properties of an ideal gas is that its internal energy depends *only* on temperature. Thus the *change* in internal energy during any process must be determined only by the temperature change. If Eq. (19.13) is valid for an ideal gas for one particular kind of process, it must be valid for an ideal gas for *every* kind of process with the same dT. So we may replace dU in Eq. (19.16) by $nC_V\,dT$:

$$nC_p\,dT = nC_V\,dT + nR\,dT$$

When we divide each term by the common factor $n\,dT$, we get

$$C_p = C_V + R \quad \text{(molar heat capacities of an ideal gas)} \tag{19.17}$$

As we predicted, the molar heat capacity of an ideal gas at constant pressure is *greater* than the molar heat capacity at constant volume; the difference is the gas constant R. (Of course, R must be expressed in the same units as C_p and C_V, such as $\text{J/mol} \cdot \text{K}$.)

We have used the ideal-gas model to derive Eq. (19.17), but it turns out to be obeyed to within a few percent by many real gases at moderate pressures. Measured values of C_p and C_V are given in Table 19.1 for several real gases at low pressures; the difference in most cases is approximately $R = 8.314\ \text{J/mol} \cdot \text{K}$.

The table also shows that the molar heat capacity of a gas is related to its molecular structure, as we discussed in Section 18.4. In fact, the first two columns of Table 19.1 are the same as Table 18.1.

Table 19.1 Molar Heat Capacities of Gases at Low Pressure

Type of Gas	Gas	C_V (J/mol · K)	C_p (J/mol · K)	$C_p - C_V$ (J/mol · K)	$\gamma = C_p/C_V$
Monatomic	He	12.47	20.78	8.31	1.67
	Ar	12.47	20.78	8.31	1.67
Diatomic	H_2	20.42	28.74	8.32	1.41
	N_2	20.76	29.07	8.31	1.40
	O_2	20.85	29.17	8.31	1.40
	CO	20.85	29.16	8.31	1.40
Polyatomic	CO_2	28.46	36.94	8.48	1.30
	SO_2	31.39	40.37	8.98	1.29
	H_2S	25.95	34.60	8.65	1.33

The Ratio of Heat Capacities

The last column of Table 19.1 lists the values of the dimensionless **ratio of heat capacities, C_p/C_V,** denoted by γ (the Greek letter gamma):

$$\gamma = \frac{C_p}{C_V} \quad \text{(ratio of heat capacities)} \tag{19.18}$$

(This is sometimes called the "ratio of specific heats.") For gases, C_p is always greater than C_V and γ is always greater than unity. This quantity plays an important role in *adiabatic* processes for an ideal gas, which we will study in the next section.

We can use our kinetic-theory discussion of the molar heat capacity of an ideal gas (see Section 18.4) to predict values of γ. As an example, an ideal monatomic gas has $C_V = \frac{3}{2}R$. From Eq. (19.17),

$$C_p = C_V + R = \frac{3}{2}R + R = \frac{5}{2}R$$

so

$$\gamma = \frac{C_p}{C_V} = \frac{\frac{5}{2}R}{\frac{3}{2}R} = \frac{5}{3} = 1.67$$

As Table 19.1 shows, this agrees well with values of γ computed from measured heat capacities. For most diatomic gases near room temperature, $C_V = \frac{5}{2}R$, $C_p = C_V + R = \frac{7}{2}R$, and

$$\gamma = \frac{C_p}{C_V} = \frac{\frac{7}{2}R}{\frac{5}{2}R} = \frac{7}{5} = 1.40$$

also in good agreement with measured values.

Here's a final reminder: For an ideal gas the internal energy change in *any* process is given by $\Delta U = nC_V\,\Delta T$, *whether the volume is constant or not.* This relationship, which comes in handy in the following example, holds for other substances *only* when the volume is constant.

Example 19.6 Cooling your room

A typical dorm room or bedroom contains about 2500 moles of air. Find the change in the internal energy of this much air when it is cooled from 23.9°C to 11.6°C at a constant pressure of 1.00 atm. Treat the air as an ideal gas with $\gamma = 1.400$.

SOLUTION

IDENTIFY: Our target variable is the change in the internal energy ΔU of an ideal gas in a constant-pressure process. We are given the number of moles and the temperature change.

SET UP: Your first impulse may be to find C_p and then calculate Q from $Q = nC_p\,\Delta T$; find the volume change and find the work done by the gas from $W = p\,\Delta V$; then finally use the first law to find ΔU. This would be perfectly correct, but there's a much easier way. For an ideal gas the internal energy change is $\Delta U = nC_V\,\Delta T$ for *every* process, *whether the volume is constant or not.* So all we have to do is find C_V and use this expression for ΔU.

EXECUTE: We are given the value of γ for air, so we use Eqs. (19.17) and (19.18) to determine C_V:

$$\gamma = \frac{C_p}{C_V} = \frac{C_V + R}{C_V} = 1 + \frac{R}{C_V}$$

$$C_V = \frac{R}{\gamma - 1} = \frac{8.314\ \text{J/mol}\cdot\text{K}}{1.400 - 1} = 20.79\ \text{J/mol}\cdot\text{K}$$

Then

$$\begin{aligned}\Delta U &= nC_V\,\Delta T \\ &= (2500\ \text{mol})(20.79\ \text{J/mol}\cdot\text{K})(11.6°\text{C} - 23.9°\text{C}) \\ &= -6.39 \times 10^5\ \text{J}\end{aligned}$$

EVALUATE: A room air conditioner must extract this much internal energy from the air in your room and transfer it to the air outside. We'll discuss how this is done in Chapter 20.

Test Your Understanding of Section 19.7 You want to cool a storage cylinder containing 10 moles of compressed gas from 30°C to 20°C. For which kind of gas would this be easiest? (i) a monatomic gas; (ii) a diatomic gas; (iii) a polyatomic gas; (iv) it would be equally easy for all of these.

19.8 Adiabatic Processes for an Ideal Gas

An adiabatic process, defined in Section 19.5, is a process in which no heat transfer takes place between a system and its surroundings. Zero heat transfer is an idealization, but a process is approximately adiabatic if the system is well insulated or if the process takes place so quickly that there is not enough time for appreciable heat flow to occur.

In an adiabatic process, $Q = 0$, so from the first law, $\Delta U = -W$. An adiabatic process for an ideal gas is shown in the pV-diagram of Fig. 19.20. As the gas expands from volume V_a to V_b, it does positive work, so its internal energy decreases and its temperature drops. If point a, representing the initial state, lies on an isotherm at temperature $T + dT$, then point b for the final state is on a different isotherm at a lower temperature T. For an ideal gas an adiabatic curve (adiabat) at any point is always *steeper* than the isotherm passing through the same point. For an adiabatic *compression* from V_b to V_a the situation is reversed and the temperature rises.

19.20 A pV-diagram of an adiabatic ($Q = 0$) process for an ideal gas. As the gas expands from V_a to V_b, it does positive work W on its environment, its internal energy decreases ($\Delta U = -W < 0$), and its temperature drops from $T + dT$ to T. (An adiabatic process is also shown in Fig. 19.16.)

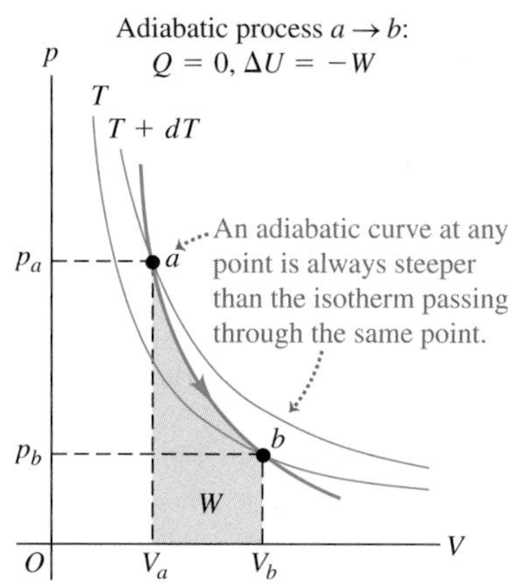
Adiabatic process $a \rightarrow b$:
$Q = 0, \Delta U = -W$
p
T
$T + dT$
An adiabatic curve at any point is always steeper than the isotherm passing through the same point.
p_a
a
p_b
b
W
O
V_a
V_b
V

The air in the output hoses of air compressors used in gasoline stations, in paint-spraying equipment, and to fill scuba tanks is always warmer than the air entering the compressor; this is because the compression is rapid and hence approximately adiabatic. Adiabatic *cooling* occurs when you open a bottle of your favorite carbonated beverage. The gas just above the beverage surface expands rapidly in a nearly adiabatic process; the temperature of the gas drops so much that water vapor in the gas condenses, forming a miniature cloud (see Fig. 19.14).

CAUTION **"Heating" and "cooling" without heat** Keep in mind that when we talk about "adiabatic heating" and "adiabatic cooling," we really mean "raising the temperature" and "lowering the temperature," respectively. In an adiabatic process, the temperature change is due to work done by or on the system; there is *no* heat flow at all.

Adiabatic Ideal Gas: Relating V, T, and p

ActivPhysics ONLINE
8.11 Adiabatic Process

We can derive a relationship between volume and temperature changes for an infinitesimal adiabatic process in an ideal gas. Equation (19.13) gives the internal energy change dU for *any* process for an ideal gas, adiabatic or not, so we have $dU = nC_V\,dT$. Also, the work done by the gas during the process is given by $dW = p\,dV$. Then, since $dU = -dW$ for an adiabatic process, we have

$$nC_V\,dT = -p\,dV \tag{19.19}$$

To obtain a relationship containing only the volume V and temperature T, we eliminate p using the ideal-gas equation in the form $p = nRT/V$. Substituting this into Eq.(19.19) and rearranging, we get

$$nC_V\,dT = -\frac{nRT}{V}\,dV$$

$$\frac{dT}{T} + \frac{R}{C_V}\frac{dV}{V} = 0$$

The coefficient R/C_V can be expressed in terms of $\gamma = C_p/C_V$. We have

$$\frac{R}{C_V} = \frac{C_p - C_V}{C_V} = \frac{C_p}{C_V} - 1 = \gamma - 1$$

$$\frac{dT}{T} + (\gamma - 1)\frac{dV}{V} = 0 \tag{19.20}$$

Because γ is always greater than unity for a gas, $(\gamma - 1)$ is always positive. This means that in Eq. (19.20), dV and dT always have opposite signs. An adiabatic *expansion* of an ideal gas $(dV > 0)$ always occurs with a *drop* in temperature $(dT < 0)$, and an adiabatic *compression* $(dV < 0)$ always occurs with a *rise* in temperature $(dT > 0)$; this confirms our earlier prediction.

For finite changes in temperature and volume we integrate Eq. (19.20), obtaining

$$\begin{aligned} \ln T + (\gamma - 1)\ln V &= \text{constant} \\ \ln T + \ln V^{\gamma-1} &= \text{constant} \\ \ln\left(TV^{\gamma-1}\right) &= \text{constant} \end{aligned}$$

and finally,

$$TV^{\gamma-1} = \text{constant} \tag{19.21}$$

Thus for an initial state (T_1, V_1) and a final state (T_2, V_2),

$$T_1V_1^{\gamma-1} = T_2V_2^{\gamma-1} \quad \text{(adiabatic process, ideal gas)} \tag{19.22}$$

Because we have used the ideal-gas equation in our derivation of Eqs. (19.21) and (19.22), the T's must always be *absolute* (Kelvin) temperatures.

We can also convert Eq. (19.21) into a relationship between pressure and volume by eliminating T, using the ideal-gas equation in the form $T = pV/nR$. Substituting this into Eq. (19.21), we find

$$\frac{pV}{nR}V^{\gamma-1} = \text{constant}$$

or, because n and R are constant,

$$pV^{\gamma} = \text{constant} \tag{19.23}$$

For an initial state (p_1, V_1) and a final state (p_2, V_2), Eq. (19.23) becomes

$$p_1V_1^{\gamma} = p_2V_2^{\gamma} \quad \text{(adiabatic process, ideal gas)} \tag{19.24}$$

We can also calculate the *work* done by an ideal gas during an adiabatic process. We know that $Q = 0$ and $W = -\Delta U$ for *any* adiabatic process. For an ideal gas, $\Delta U = nC_V(T_2 - T_1)$. If the number of moles n and the initial and final temperatures T_1 and T_2 are known, we have simply

$$W = nC_V(T_1 - T_2) \quad \text{(adiabatic process, ideal gas)} \tag{19.25}$$

We may also use $pV = nRT$ in this equation to obtain

$$W = \frac{C_V}{R}(p_1V_1 - p_2V_2) = \frac{1}{\gamma - 1}(p_1V_1 - p_2V_2) \quad \text{(adiabatic process, ideal gas)} \tag{19.26}$$

(We used the result $C_V = R/(\gamma - 1)$ from Example 19.6.) If the process is an expansion, the temperature drops, T_1 is greater than T_2, p_1V_1 is greater than p_2V_2, and the work is *positive,* as we should expect. If the process is a compression, the work is negative.

Throughout this analysis of adiabatic processes we have used the ideal-gas equation of state, which is valid only for *equilibrium* states. Strictly speaking, our results are valid only for a process that is fast enough to prevent appreciable heat exchange with the surroundings (so that $Q = 0$ and the process is adiabatic), yet slow enough that the system does not depart very much from thermal and mechanical equilibrium. Even when these conditions are not strictly satisfied, though, Eqs. (19.22), (19.24), and (19.26) give useful approximate results.

Example 19.7 Adiabatic compression in a diesel engine

The compression ratio of a diesel engine is 15 to 1; this means that air in the cylinders is compressed to $\frac{1}{15}$ of its initial volume (Fig. 19.21). If the initial pressure is 1.01×10^5 Pa and the initial temperature is 27°C (300 K), find the final pressure and the temperature after compression. Air is mostly a mixture of diatomic oxygen and nitrogen; treat it as an ideal gas with $\gamma = 1.40$.

SOLUTION

IDENTIFY: Since this problem involves the adiabatic compression of an ideal gas, we can use the ideas of this section.

19.21 Adiabatic compression of air in a cylinder of a diesel engine.

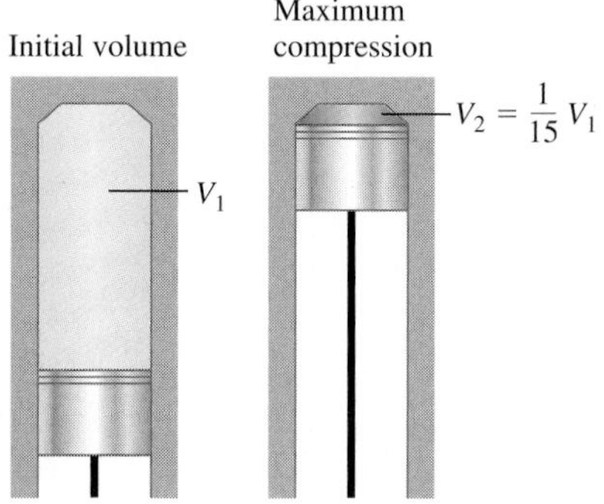

SET UP: We are given the initial pressure $p_1 = 1.01 \times 10^5$ Pa and the initial temperature $T_1 = 300$ K, and we are told that the ratio of initial and final volumes is $V_1/V_2 = 15$. We can find the final temperature T_2 using Eq. (19.22) and the final pressure p_2 using Eq. (19.24).

EXECUTE: From Eq. (19.22),

$$T_2 = T_1\left(\frac{V_1}{V_2}\right)^{\gamma-1} = (300\text{ K})(15)^{0.40} = 886\text{ K} = 613°\text{C}$$

From Eq. (19.24),

$$p_2 = p_1\left(\frac{V_1}{V_2}\right)^{\gamma} = (1.01 \times 10^5\text{ Pa})(15)^{1.40}$$
$$= 44.8 \times 10^5\text{ Pa} = 44\text{ atm}$$

EVALUATE: If the compression had been isothermal, the final pressure would have been 15 atm, but because the temperature also increases during an adiabatic compression, the final pressure is much greater. When fuel is injected into the cylinders near the end of the compression stroke, the high temperature of the air attained during compression causes the fuel to ignite spontaneously without the need for spark plugs.

Example 19.8 Work done in an adiabatic process

In Example 19.7, how much work does the gas do during the compression if the initial volume of the cylinder is $1.00\text{ L} = 1.00 \times 10^{-3}\text{ m}^3$? Assume that C_V for air is 20.8 J/mol · K and $\gamma = 1.40$.

SOLUTION

IDENTIFY: Our target variable is the work done *by* the gas during the adiabatic compression. We are given the initial volume of the gas, and we know (from Example 19.7) the initial and final values of temperature and pressure.

SET UP: We use Eq. (19.25) to determine the work done. We are not given the number of moles n, but we can calculate it from the given information using the ideal-gas law $pV = nRT$.

EXECUTE: The number of moles is

$$n = \frac{p_1V_1}{RT_1} = \frac{(1.01 \times 10^5\text{ Pa})(1.00 \times 10^{-3}\text{ m}^3)}{(8.314\text{ J/mol}\cdot\text{K})(300\text{ K})}$$
$$= 0.0405\text{ mol}$$

and Eq. (19.25) gives

$$W = nC_V(T_1 - T_2)$$
$$= (0.0405\text{ mol})(20.8\text{ J/mol}\cdot\text{K})(300\text{ K} - 886\text{ K})$$
$$= -494\text{ J}$$

EVALUATE: We can check our result using Eq. (19.26), the alternative expression for work done by an ideal gas in an adiabatic process:

$$W = \frac{1}{\gamma - 1}(p_1V_1 - p_2V_2)$$
$$= \frac{1}{1.40 - 1}\left[\begin{array}{l}(1.01 \times 10^5\text{ Pa})(1.00 \times 10^{-3}\text{ m}^3)\\ -(44.8 \times 10^5\text{ Pa})\left(\dfrac{1.00 \times 10^{-3}\text{ m}^3}{15}\right)\end{array}\right]$$
$$= -494\text{ J}$$

The work is negative because the gas is compressed.

Test Your Understanding of Section 19.8 You have four samples of ideal gas, each of which contains the same number of moles of gas and has the same initial temperature, volume, and pressure. You compress each sample to one-half of its initial volume. Rank the four samples in order from highest to lowest value of the final pressure. (i) a monatomic gas compressed isothermally; (ii) a monatomic gas compressed adiabatically; (iii) a diatomic gas compressed isothermally; (iv) a diatomic gas compressed adiabatically.

CHAPTER 19 SUMMARY

Heat and work in thermodynamic processes: A thermodynamic system has the potential to exchange energy with its surroundings by heat transfer or by mechanical work. When a system at pressure p changes volume from V_1 to V_2, it does an amount of work W given by the integral of p with respect to volume. If the pressure is constant, the work done is equal to p times the change in volume. A negative value of W means that work is done on the system. (See Example 19.1.)

In any thermodynamic process, the heat added to the system and the work done by the system depend not only on the initial and final states, but also on the path (the series of intermediate states through which the system passes).

$$W = \int_{V_1}^{V_2} p\,dV \qquad (19.2)$$

$$W = p(V_2 - V_1) \qquad (19.3)$$
(constant pressure only)

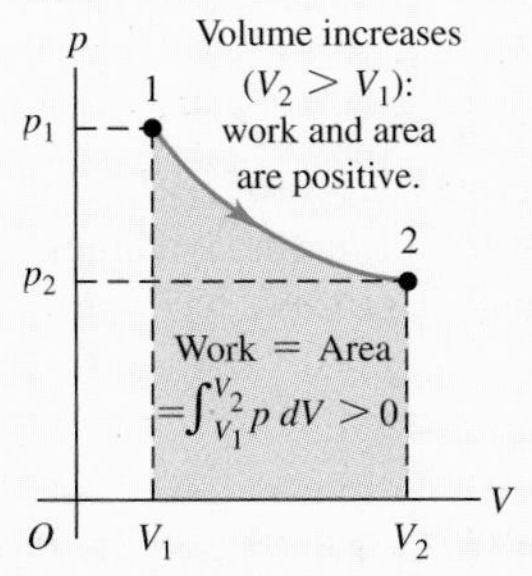

The first law of thermodynamics: The first law of thermodynamics states that when heat Q is added to a system while the system does work W, the internal energy U changes by an amount equal to $Q - W$. This law can also be expressed for an infinitesimal process. (See Examples 19.2, 19.3, and 19.5.)

The internal energy of any thermodynamic system depends only on its state. The change in internal energy in any process depends only on the initial and final states, not on the path. The internal energy of an isolated system is constant. (See Example 19.4.)

$$\Delta U = Q - W \qquad (19.4)$$

$$dU = dQ - dW \qquad (19.6)$$
(infinitesimal process)

Surroundings
(environment)
$Q = 150\text{ J}$
$W = 100\text{ J}$
System
$\Delta U = Q - W = +50\text{ J}$

Important types of thermodynamic processes:

- Adiabatic process: No heat transfer into or out of a system; $Q = 0$.
- Isochoric process: Constant volume; $W = 0$.
- Isobaric process: Constant pressure; $W = p(V_2 - V_1)$.
- Isothermal process: Constant temperature.

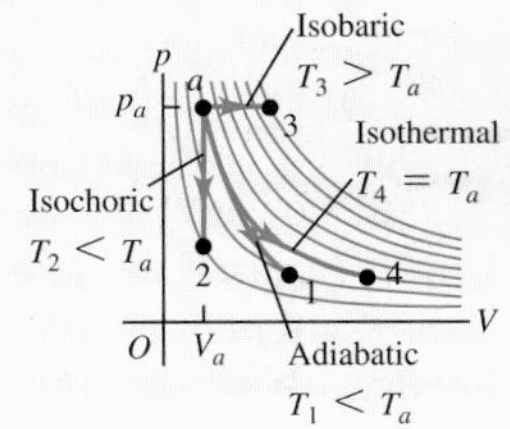

Thermodynamics of ideal gases: The internal energy of an ideal gas depends only on its temperature, not its pressure or volume. For other substances the internal energy generally depends on both pressure and temperature.

The molar heat capacities C_V and C_p of an ideal gas differ by R, the ideal gas constant. The dimensionless ratio of heat capacities, C_p/C_V, is denoted by γ. (See Example 19.6.)

$$C_p = C_V + R \qquad (19.17)$$

$$\gamma = \frac{C_p}{C_V} \qquad (19.18)$$

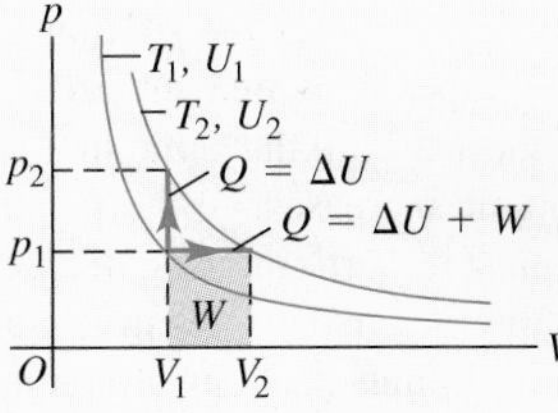

Adiabatic processes in ideal gases: For an adiabatic process for an ideal gas, the quantities $TV^{\gamma-1}$ and pV^{γ} are constant. The work done by an ideal gas during an adiabatic expansion can be expressed in terms of the initial and final values of temperature, or in terms of the initial and final values of pressure and volume. (See Examples 19.7 and 19.8.)

$$W = nC_V(T_1 - T_2)$$
$$= \frac{C_V}{R}(p_1V_1 - p_2V_2) \qquad (19.25)$$
$$= \frac{1}{\gamma - 1}(p_1V_1 - p_2V_2) \qquad (19.26)$$

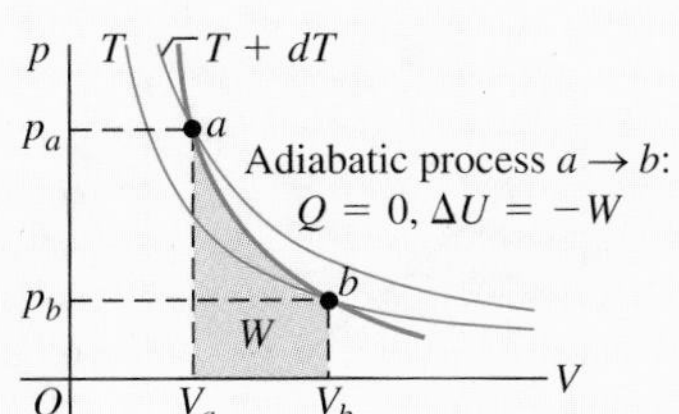

Key Terms

thermodynamic system, *646*
thermodynamic process, *647*
path, *650*
free expansion, *651*
internal energy, *651*
first law of thermodynamics, *652*
adiabatic process, *657*
isochoric process, *657*
isobaric process, *657*
isothermal process, *657*
adiabat, *658*
isochor, *658*
isobar, *658*
isotherm, *658*
molar heat capacity at constant volume, *659*
molar heat capacity at constant pressure, *659*
ratio of heat capacities, *661*

Answer to Chapter Opening Question ?

No. The work done by a gas as its volume changes from V_1 to V_2 is equal to the integral $\int p\, dV$ between those two volume limits. If the volume of the gas contracts, the final volume V_2 is less than the initial volume V_1 and the gas does negative work. Propelling the locomotive requires that the gas do positive work, so the gas doesn't contribute to propulsion while contracting.

Answers to Test Your Understanding Questions

19.1 Answers: negative, positive, positive Heat flows out of the coffee, so $Q_{\text{coffee}} < 0$; heat flows into the aluminum cup, so $Q_{\text{aluminum}} > 0$. In mechanics, we would say that negative work is done *on* the block, since the surface exerts a force on the block that opposes the block's motion. But in thermodynamics we use the opposite convention and say that $W > 0$, which means that positive work is done *by* the block on the surface.

19.2 Answer: (ii) The work done in an expansion is represented by the area under the curve of pressure p versus volume V. In an isothermal expansion the pressure decreases as the volume increases, so the pV-diagram looks like Fig. 19.6a and the work done equals the shaded area under the blue curve from point 1 to point 2. If, however, the expansion is at constant pressure, the curve of p versus V would be the same as the dashed horizontal line at pressure p_2 in Fig. 19.6a. The area under this dashed line is smaller than the area under the blue curve for an isothermal expansion, so less work is done in the constant-pressure expansion than in the isothermal expansion.

19.3 Answer: (i) and (iv) (tie), (ii) and (iii) (tie) The accompanying figure shows the pV-diagrams for each of the four processes. The trapezoidal area under the curve, and hence the absolute value of the work, is the same in all four cases. In cases (i) and (iv) the volume increases, so the system does positive work as it expands against its surroundings. In cases (ii) and (iii) the volume decreases, so the system does negative work (shown by cross-hatching) as the surroundings push inward on it.

19.4 Answer: (ii), (i) and (iv) (tie), (iii) In the expression $\Delta U = Q - W$, Q is the heat *added* to the system and W is the work done *by* the system. If heat is transferred from the system to its surroundings, Q is negative; if work is done on the system, W is negative. Hence we have (i) $Q = -250\text{ J}$, $W = -250\text{ J}$, $\Delta U = -250\text{ J} - (-250\text{ J}) = 0$; (ii) $Q = 250\text{ J}$, $W = -250\text{ J}$, $\Delta U = 250\ J - (-250\text{ J}) = 500\text{ J}$; (iii) $Q = -250\text{ J}$, $W = 250\text{ J}$, $\Delta U = -250\text{ J} - 250\text{ J} = -500\text{ J}$; and (iv) $Q = 250\text{ J}$, $W = 250\text{ J}$, $\Delta U = 250\text{ J} - 250\text{ J} = 0$.

19.5 Answers: $1 \rightarrow 4$ and $3 \rightarrow 2$ are isochoric; $1 \rightarrow 3$ and $4 \rightarrow 2$ are isobaric; no In a pV-diagram like those shown in Fig. 19.7, isochoric processes are represented by vertical lines (lines of constant volume) and isobaric processes are represented by horizontal lines (lines of constant pressure). The process $1 \rightarrow 2$ in Fig. 19.7 is shown as a curved line, which superficially resembles the adiabatic and isothermal processes for an ideal gas in Fig. 19.16. Without more information we can't tell whether process $1 \rightarrow 2$ is isothermal, adiabatic, or neither.

19.6 Answer: no Using the model of a solid in Fig. 18.20, we can see that the internal energy of a solid *does* depend on its volume. Compressing the solid means compressing the "springs" between the atoms, thereby increasing their stored potential energy and hence the internal energy of the solid.

19.7 Answer: (i) For a given number of moles n and a given temperature change ΔT, the amount of heat that must be transferred out of a fixed volume of air is $Q = nC_V\Delta T$. Hence the amount of heat transfer required is least for the gas with the smallest value of C_V. From Table 19.1, the value of C_V is smallest for monatomic gases.

19.8 Answer: (ii), (iv), (i) and (iii) (tie) Samples (i) and (iii) are compressed isothermally, so $pV = \text{constant}$. The volume of each sample decreases to one-half of its initial value, so the final pressure is twice the initial pressure. By contrast, samples (ii) and (iv) are compressed adiabatically, so $pV^{\gamma} = \text{constant}$ and the pressure increases by a factor of 2^{γ}. Sample (ii) is a monatomic gas for which $\gamma = \frac{5}{3}$, so its final pressure is $2^{\frac{5}{3}} = 3.17$ times greater than the initial pressure. Sample (iv) is a diatomic gas for which $\gamma = \frac{7}{5}$, so its final pressure is greater than the initial pressure by a factor of $2^{\frac{7}{5}} = 2.64$.

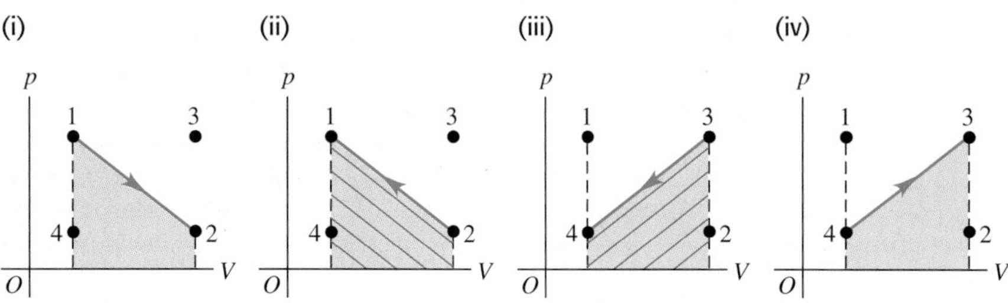

PROBLEMS

For instructor-assigned homework, go to www.masteringphysics.com 

Discussion Questions

Q19.1. For the following processes, is the work done by the system (defined as the expanding or contracting gas) on the environment positive or negative? (a) expansion of the burned gasoline–air mixture in the cylinder of an automobile engine; (b) opening a bottle of champagne; (c) filling a scuba tank with compressed air; (d) partial crumpling of a sealed, empty water bottle, as you drive from the mountains down to sea level.

Q19.2. It is not correct to say that a body contains a certain amount of heat, yet a body can transfer heat to another body. How can a body give away something it does not have in the first place?

Q19.3. In which situation must you do more work: inflating a balloon at sea level or inflating the same balloon to the same volume at the summit of Mt. McKinley? Explain in terms of pressure and volume change.

Q19.4. If you are told the initial and final states of a system and the associated change in internal energy, can you determine whether the internal energy change was due to work or to heat transfer? Explain.

Q19.5. Discuss the application of the first law of thermodynamics to a mountaineer who eats food, gets warm and perspires a lot during a climb, and does a lot of mechanical work in raising herself to the summit. The mountaineer also gets warm during the descent. Is the source of this energy the same as the source during the ascent?

Q19.6. When ice melts at 0°C, its volume decreases. Is the internal energy change greater than, less than, or equal to the heat added? How can you tell?

Q19.7. You hold an inflated balloon over a hot air vent in your house and watch it slowly expand. You then remove it and let it cool back to room temperature. During the expansion, which was larger: the heat added to the balloon or the work done by the air inside it? Explain. (Assume that air is an ideal gas.) Once the balloon has returned to room temperature, how does the net heat gained or lost by the air inside it compare to the net work done on or by the surrounding air?

Q19.8. You bake chocolate chip cookies and put them, still warm, in a container with a loose (not airtight) lid. What kind of process does the air inside the container undergo as the cookies gradually cool to room temperature (isothermal, isochoric, adiabatic, isobaric, or some combination)? Explain your answer.

Q19.9. Imagine a gas made up entirely of negatively charged electrons. Like charges repel, so the electrons exert repulsive forces on each other. Would you expect that the temperature of such a gas would rise, fall, or stay the same in a free expansion? Why?

Q19.10. There are a few materials that contract when their temperature is increased, such as water between 0°C and 4°C. Would you expect C_p for such materials to be greater or less than C_V? Explain?

Q19.11. When you blow on the back of your hand with your mouth wide open, your breath feels warm. But if you partially close your mouth to form an "o" and then blow on your hand, your breath feels cool. Why?

Q19.12. In hot-air balloons, the air in the balloon envelope is heated through a hole in the bottom by a propane burner. The hot air inside the envelope stays at atmospheric pressure because of the hole in the bottom, and the volume of the envelope is essentially constant. Thus, when the pilot fires up the burner to heat the air, the volume of the envelope and the pressure inside it are constant, but the temperature rises. The ideal-gas law seems to forbid this. What's going on?

Q19.13. On a warm summer day, a large cylinder of compressed gas (propane or butane) is used to supply several large gas burners at a cookout. After a while, frost forms on the outside of the tank. Why?

Q19.14. When you use a hand pump to inflate the tires of your bicycle, the pump gets warm after a while. Why? What happens to the temperature of the air in the pump as you compress it? Why does this happen? When you raise the pump handle to draw outside air into the pump, what happens to the temperature of the air taken in? Again, why does this happen?

Q19.15. In the carburetor of an aircraft or automobile engine, air flows through a relatively small aperture and then expands. In cool, foggy weather, ice sometimes forms in this aperture even though the outside air temperature is above freezing. Why?

Q19.16. On a sunny day, large "bubbles" of air form on the sun-warmed earth, gradually expand, and finally break free to rise through the atmosphere. Soaring birds and glider pilots are fond of using these "thermals" to gain altitude easily. This expansion is essentially an adiabatic process. Why?

Q19.17. The prevailing winds on the Hawaiian island of Kauai blow from the northeast. The winds cool as they go up the slope of Mt. Waialeale (elevation 1523 m), causing water vapor to condense and rain to fall. There is much more precipitation at the summit than at the base of the mountain. In fact, Mt. Waialeale is the rainiest spot on earth, averaging 11.7 m of rainfall a year. But what makes the winds cool?

Q19.18. Applying the same considerations as in Question 19.17, explain why the island of Niihau, a few kilometers to the southwest of Kauai, is almost a desert and farms there need to be irrigated.

Q19.19. In a constant-volume process, $dU = nC_V dT$. But in a constant-pressure process, it is *not* true that $dU = nC_p dT$. Why not?

Q19.20. When a gas surrounded by air is compressed adiabatically, its temperature rises even though there is no heat input to the gas. Where does the energy come from to raise the temperature?

Q19.21. When a gas expands adiabatically, it does work on its surroundings. But if there is no heat input to the gas, where does the energy come from to do the work?

Q19.22. The gas used in separating the two uranium isotopes ^{235}U and ^{238}U has the formula UF_6. If you added heat at equal rates to a mole of UF_6 gas and a mole of H_2 gas, which one's temperature would you expect to rise faster? Explain.

Exercises

Section 19.2 Work Done During Volume Changes and Section 19.3 Paths Between Thermodynamic States

19.1. Two moles of an ideal gas are heated at constant pressure from $T = 27°C$ to $T = 107°C$. (a) Draw a pV-diagram for this process. (b) Calculate the work done by the gas.

19.2. Six moles of an ideal gas are in a cylinder fitted at one end with a movable piston. The initial temperature of the gas is 27.0°C and the pressure is constant. As part of a machine design project, calculate the final temperature of the gas after it has done 1.75×10^3 J of work.

19.3. Two moles of an ideal gas are compressed in a cylinder at a constant temperature of 85.0°C until the original pressure has tripled. (a) Sketch a pV-diagram for this process. (b) Calculate the amount of work done.

19.4. A metal cylinder with rigid walls contains 2.50 mol of oxygen gas. The gas is cooled until the pressure decreases to 30.0% of its original value. You can ignore the thermal contraction of the cylinder. (a) Draw a pV-diagram for this process. (b) Calculate the work done by the gas.

19.5. During the time 0.305 mol of an ideal gas undergoes an isothermal compression at 22.0°C, 518 J of work is done on it by the surroundings. (a) If the final pressure is 1.76 atm, what was the initial pressure? (b) Sketch a pV-diagram for the process.

19.6. A gas undergoes two processes. In the first, the volume remains constant at 0.200 m^3 and the pressure increases from 2.00×10^5 Pa to 5.00×10^5 Pa. The second process is a compression to a volume of 0.120 m^3 at a constant pressure of 5.00×10^5 Pa. (a) In a pV-diagram, show both processes. (b) Find the total work done by the gas during both processes.

19.7. Work Done in a Cyclic Process. (a) In Fig. 19.7a, consider the closed loop $1 \rightarrow 3 \rightarrow 2 \rightarrow 4 \rightarrow 1$. This is a *cyclic* process in which the initial and final states are the same. Find the total work done by the system in this cyclic process, and show that it is equal to the area enclosed by the loop. (b) How is the work done for the process in part (a) related to the work done if the loop is traversed in the opposite direction, $1 \rightarrow 4 \rightarrow 2 \rightarrow 3 \rightarrow 1$? Explain.

Section 19.4 Internal Energy and the First Law of Thermodynamics

19.8. You close off the nozzle of a bicycle tire pump and very slowly depress the plunger so that the air inside is compressed to half its original volume. Assume the air behaves like an ideal gas. If you do this so slowly that the temperature of the air inside the pump never changes: (a) Is the work done by the air in the pump positive or negative? (b) Is the heat flow to the air positive or negative? (c) What can you say about the relative *magnitudes* of the heat flow and the work? Explain.

19.9. A gas in a cylinder expands from a volume of 0.110 m^3 to 0.320 m^3. Heat flows into the gas just rapidly enough to keep the pressure constant at 1.80×10^5 Pa during the expansion. The total heat added is 1.15×10^5 J. (a) Find the work done by the gas. (b) Find the change in internal energy of the gas. (c) Does it matter whether the gas is ideal? Why or why not?

19.10. Five moles of an ideal monatomic gas with an initial temperature of 127°C expand and, in the process, absorb 1200 J of heat and do 2100 J of work. What is the final temperature of the gas?

19.11. You kick a soccer ball, compressing it suddenly to $\frac{2}{3}$ of its original volume. In the process, you do 410 J of work on the air (assumed to be an ideal gas) inside the ball. (a) What is the change in internal energy of the air inside the ball due to being compressed? (b) Does the temperature of the air inside the ball rise or fall due to being compressed? Explain.

19.12. A gas in a cylinder is held at a constant pressure of 2.30×10^5 Pa and is cooled and compressed from 1.70 m^3 to 1.20 m^3. The internal energy of the gas decreases by 1.40×10^5 J. (a) Find the work done by the gas. (b) Find the absolute value $|Q|$ of the heat flow into or out of the gas, and state the direction of the heat flow. (c) Does it matter whether the gas is ideal? Why or why not?

19.13. Doughnuts: Breakfast of Champions! A typical doughnut contains 2.0 g of protein, 17.0 g of carbohydrates, and 7.0 g of fat. The average food energy values of these substances are 4.0 kcal/g for protein and carbohydrates and 9.0 kcal/g for fat. (a) During heavy exercise, an average person uses energy at a rate of 510 kcal/h. How long would you have to exercise to "work off" one doughnut? (b) If the energy in the doughnut could somehow be converted into the kinetic energy of your body as a whole, how fast could you move after eating the doughnut? Take your mass to be 60 kg, and express your answer in m/s and km/h.

19.14. A liquid is irregularly stirred in a well-insulated container and thereby undergoes a rise in temperature. Regard the liquid as the system. (a) Has heat been transferred? How can you tell? (b) Has work been done? How can you tell? Why is it important that the stirring is irregular? (c) What is the sign of ΔU? How can you tell?

19.15. An ideal gas is taken from a to b on the pV-diagram shown in Fig. 19.22. During this process, 400 J of heat is added and the pressure doubles. (a) How much work is done by or on the gas? Explain. (b) How does the temperature of the gas at a compare to its temperature at b? Be specific. (c) How does the internal energy of the gas at a compare to the internal energy at b? Again, be specific and explain.

Figure 19.22 Exercise 19.15.

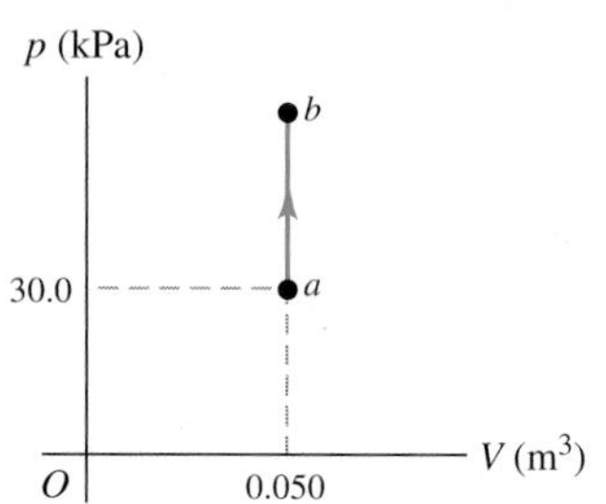

19.16. A system is taken from state a to state b along the three paths shown in Fig. 19.23. (a) Along which path is the work done by the system the greatest? The least? (b) If $U_b > U_a$, along which path is the absolute value $|Q|$ of the heat transfer the greatest? For this path, is heat absorbed or liberated by the system?

Figure 19.23 Exercise 19.16.

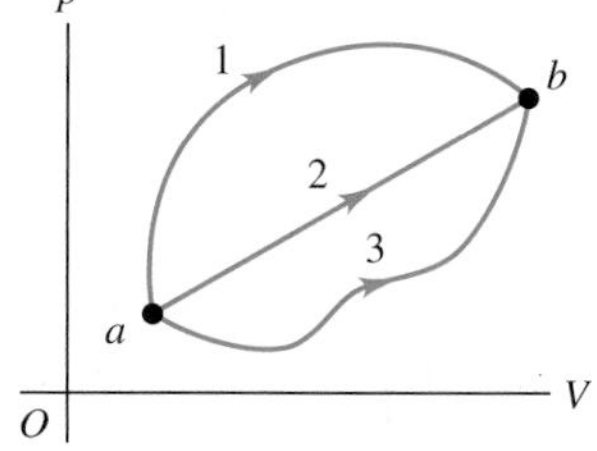

19.17. A thermodynamic system undergoes a cyclic process as shown in Fig. 19.24. The cycle consists of two closed loops: I and II. (a) Over one complete cycle, does the system do positive or negative work? (b) In each of loops I and II, is the net work done by the system positive or negative? (c) Over one complete cycle, does heat flow into or out of the system? (d) In each of loops I and II, does heat flow into or out of the system?

Figure 19.24 Exercise 19.17.

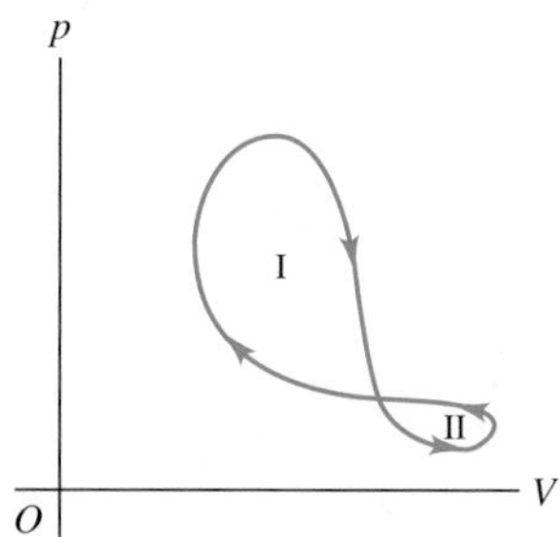

19.18. A student performs a combustion experiment by burning a mixture of fuel and oxygen in a constant-volume metal can surrounded by a water bath. During the experiment the temperature of the water is observed to rise. Regard the mixture of fuel and oxygen as the system. (a) Has heat been transferred? How can you tell? (b) Has work been done? How can you tell? (c) What is the sign of ΔU? How can you tell?

19.19. Boiling Water at High Pressure. When water is boiled at a pressure of 2.00 atm, the heat of vaporization is 2.20×10^6 J/kg and the boiling point is 120°C. At this pressure, 1.00 kg of water has a volume of 1.00×10^{-3} m^3, and 1.00 kg of steam has a volume of 0.824 m^3. (a) Compute the work done when 1.00 kg of steam is formed at this temperature. (b) Compute the increase in internal energy of the water.

Section 19.5 Kinds of Thermodynamic Processes, Section 19.6 Internal Energy of an Ideal Gas, and Section 19.7 Heat Capacities of an Ideal Gas

19.20. During an isothermal compression of an ideal gas, 335 J of heat must be removed from the gas to maintain constant temperature. How much work is done by the gas during the process?

19.21. A cylinder contains 0.250 mol of carbon dioxide (CO_2) gas at a temperature of 27.0°C. The cylinder is provided with a frictionless piston, which maintains a constant pressure of 1.00 atm on the gas. The gas is heated until its temperature increases to 127.0°C. Assume that the CO_2 may be treated as an ideal gas. (a) Draw a pV-diagram for this process. (b) How much work is done by the gas in this process? (c) On what is this work done? (d) What is the change in internal energy of the gas? (e) How much heat was supplied to the gas? (f) How much work would have been done if the pressure had been 0.50 atm?

19.22. A cylinder contains 0.0100 mol of helium at $T = 27.0°\text{C}$. (a) How much heat is needed to raise the temperature to 67.0°C while keeping the volume constant? Draw a pV-diagram for this process. (b) If instead the pressure of the helium is kept constant, how much heat is needed to raise the temperature from 27.0°C to 67.0°C? Draw a pV-diagram for this process. (c) What accounts for the difference between your answers to parts (a) and (b)? In which case is more heat required? What becomes of the additional heat? d) If the gas is ideal, what is the change in its internal energy in part (a)? In part (b)? How do the two answers compare? Why?

19.23. In an experiment to simulate conditions inside an automobile engine, 0.185 mol of air at a temperature of 780 K and a pressure of 3.00×10^6 Pa is contained in a cylinder of volume 40.0 cm^3. Then 645 J of heat is transferred to the cylinder. (a) If the volume of the cylinder is constant while the heat is added, what is the final temperature of the air? Assume that the air is essentially nitrogen gas, and use the data in Table 19.1 even though the pressure is not low. Draw a pV-diagram for this process. (b) If instead the volume of the cylinder is allowed to increase while the pressure remains constant, find the final temperature of the air. Draw a pV-diagram for this process.

19.24. An ideal gas expands while the pressure is kept constant. During this process, does heat flow into the gas or out of the gas? Justify your answer.

19.25. Heat Q flows into a monatomic ideal gas, and the volume increases while the pressure is kept constant. What fraction of the heat energy is used to do the expansion work of the gas?

19.26. When a quantity of monatomic ideal gas expands at a constant pressure of 4.00×10^4 Pa, the volume of the gas increases from $2.00 \times 10^{-3}\ \text{m}^3$ to $8.00 \times 10^{-3}\ \text{m}^3$. What is the change in the internal energy of the gas?

19.27. A cylinder with a movable piston contains 3.00 mol of N_2 gas (assumed to behave like an ideal gas). (a) The N_2 is heated at constant volume until 1557 J of heat have been added. Calculate the change in temperature. (b) Suppose the same amount of heat is added to the N_2, but this time the gas is allowed to expand while remaining at constant pressure. Calculate the temperature change. (c) In which case, (a) or (b), is the final internal energy of the N_2 higher? How do you know? What accounts for the difference between the two cases?

19.28. Three moles of an ideal monatomic gas expands at a constant pressure of 2.50 atm; the volume of the gas changes from $3.20 \times 10^{-2}\ \text{m}^3$ to $4.50 \times 10^{-2}\ \text{m}^3$. (a) Calculate the initial and final temperatures of the gas. (b) Calculate the amount of work the gas does in expanding. (c) Calculate the amount of heat added to the gas. (d) Calculate the change in internal energy of the gas.

19.29. The temperature of 0.150 mol of an ideal gas is held constant at 77.0°C while its volume is reduced to 25.0% of its initial volume. The initial pressure of the gas is 1.25 atm. (a) Determine the work done by the gas. (b) What is the change in its internal energy? (c) Does the gas exchange heat with its surroundings? If so, how much? Does the gas absorb or liberate heat?

19.30. Propane gas (C_3H_8) behaves like an ideal gas with $\gamma = 1.127$. Determine the molar heat capacity at constant volume and the molar heat capacity at constant pressure.

19.31. An experimenter adds 970 J of heat to 1.75 mol of an ideal gas to heat it from 10.0°C to 25.0°C at constant pressure. The gas does +223 J of work during the expansion. (a) Calculate the change in internal energy of the gas. (b) Calculate γ for the gas.

Section 19.8 Adiabatic Processes for an Ideal Gas

19.32. In an adiabatic process for an ideal gas, the pressure decreases. In this process does the internal energy of the gas increase or decrease? Explain your reasoning.

19.33. A monatomic ideal gas that is initially at a pressure of 1.50×10^5 Pa and has a volume of 0.0800 m^3 is compressed adiabatically to a volume of 0.0400 m^3. (a) What is the final pressure? (b) How much work is done by the gas? (c) What is the ratio of the final temperature of the gas to its initial temperature? Is the gas heated or cooled by this compression?

19.34. The engine of a Ferrari F355 F1 sports car takes in air at 20.0°C and 1.00 atm and compresses it adiabatically to 0.0900 times the original volume. The air may be treated as an ideal gas with $\gamma = 1.40$. (a) Draw a pV-diagram for this process. (b) Find the final temperature and pressure.

19.35. Two moles of carbon monoxide (CO) start at a pressure of 1.2 atm and a volume of 30 liters. The gas is then compressed adiabatically to $\frac{1}{3}$ this volume. Assume that the gas may be treated as ideal. What is the change in the internal energy of the gas? Does the internal energy increase or decrease? Does the temperature of the gas increase or decrease during this process? Explain.

19.36. A player bounces a basketball on the floor, compressing it to 80.0% of its original volume. The air (assume it is essentially N_2 gas) inside the ball is originally at a temperature of 20.0°C and a pressure of 2.00 atm. The ball's diameter is 23.9 cm. (a) What temperature does the air in the ball reach at its maximum compression? (b) By how much does the internal energy of the air change between the ball's original state and its maximum compression?

19.37. During an adiabatic expansion the temperature of 0.450 mol of argon (Ar) drops from 50.0°C to 10.0°C. The argon may be treated as an ideal gas. (a) Draw a pV-diagram for this process. (b) How much work does the gas do? (c) What is the change in internal energy of the gas?

19.38. A cylinder contains 0.100 mol of an ideal monatomic gas. Initially the gas is at a pressure of 1.00×10^5 Pa and occupies a volume of $2.50 \times 10^{-3}\ \text{m}^3$. (a) Find the initial temperature of the gas in kelvins. (b) If the gas is allowed to expand to twice the initial volume, find the final temperature (in kelvins) and pressure of the gas if the expansion is (i) isothermal; (ii) isobaric; (iii) adiabatic.

19.39. On a warm summer day, a large mass of air (atmospheric pressure 1.01×10^5 Pa) is heated by the ground to a temperature of 26.0°C and then begins to rise through the cooler surrounding air. (This can be treated approximately as an adiabatic process; why?) Calculate the temperature of the air mass when it has risen to a level at which atmospheric pressure is only 0.850×10^5 Pa. Assume that air is an ideal gas, with $\gamma = 1.40$. (This rate of cooling for dry, rising air, corresponding to roughly 1°C per 100 m of altitude, is called the *dry adiabatic lapse rate*.)

Problems

19.40. Figure 19.25 shows the pV-diagram for an isothermal expansion of 1.50 mol of an ideal gas, at a temperature of 15.0°C. (a) What is the change in internal energy of the gas? Explain. (b) Calculate the work done by (or on) the gas and the heat absorbed (or released) by the gas during the expansion.

Figure **19.25** Problem 19.40.

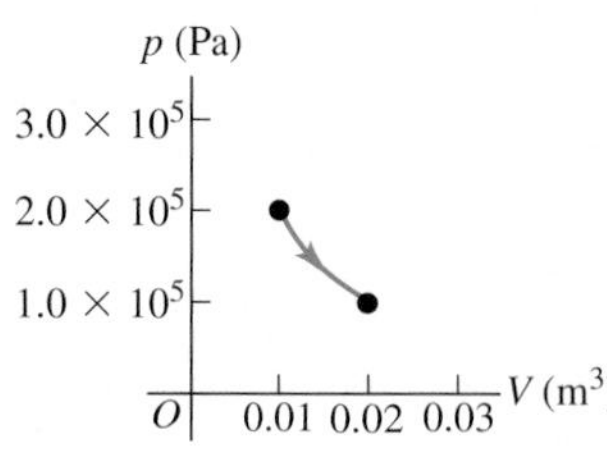

19.41. A quantity of air is taken from state a to state b along a path that is a straight line in the pV-diagram (Fig. 19.26). (a) In this process, does the temperature of the gas increase, decrease, or stay the same? Explain. (b) If $V_a = 0.0700\ \text{m}^3$, $V_b = 0.1100\ \text{m}^3$, $p_a = 1.00 \times 10^5$ Pa, and $p_b = 1.40 \times 10^5$ Pa, what is the work W done by the gas in this process? Assume that the gas may be treated as ideal.

Figure **19.26** Problem 19.41.

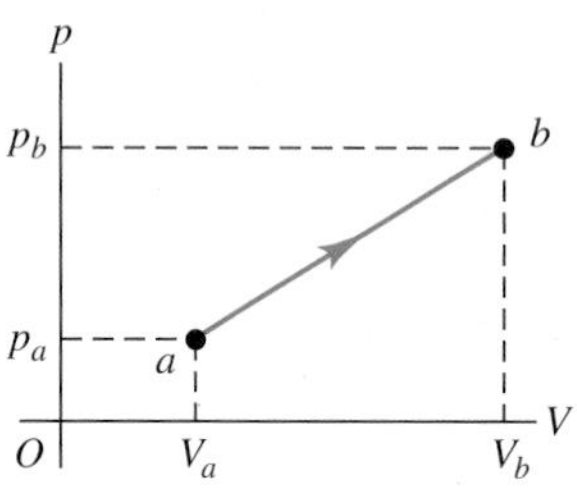

19.42. One-half mole of an ideal gas is taken from state a to state c, as shown in Fig. 19.27. (a) Calculate the final temperature of the gas. (b) Calculate the work done on (or by) the gas as it moves from state a to state c. (c) Does heat leave the system or enter the system during this process? How much heat? Explain.

Figure **19.27** Problem 19.42.

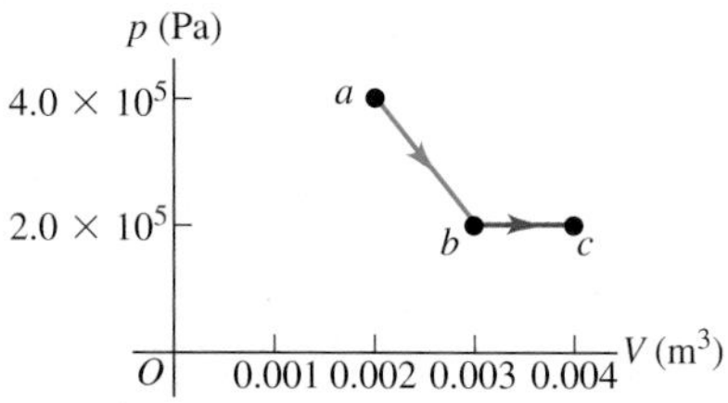

19.43. When a system is taken from state a to state b in Fig. 19.28 along the path acb, 90.0 J of heat flows into the system and 60.0 J of work is done by the system. (a) How much heat flows into the system along path adb if the work done by the system is 15.0 J? (b) When the system is returned from b to a along the curved path, the absolute value of the work done by the system is 35.0 J. Does the system absorb or liberate heat? How much heat? (c) If $U_a = 0$ and $U_d = 8.0$ J, find the heat absorbed in the processes ad and db.

Figure **19.28** Problem 19.43.

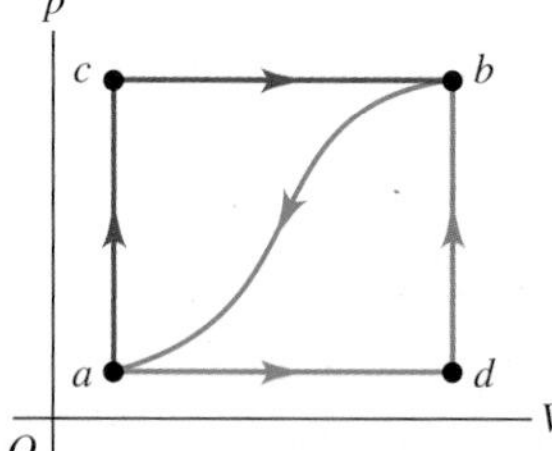

19.44. A thermodynamic system is taken from state a to state c in Fig. 19.29 along either path abc or path adc. Along path abc, the work W done by the system is 450 J. Along path adc, W is 120 J. The internal energies of each of the four states shown in the figure are $U_a = 150$ J, $U_b = 240$ J, $U_c = 680$ J, and $U_d = 330$ J. Calculate the heat flow Q for each of the four processes ab, bc, ad, and dc. In each process, does the system absorb or liberate heat?

Figure **19.29** Problem 19.44.

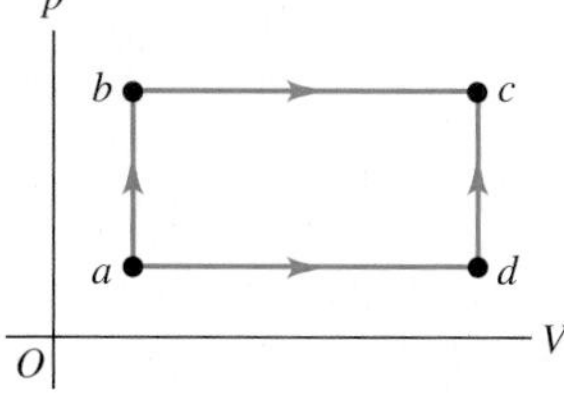

19.45. A volume of air (assumed to be an ideal gas) is first cooled without changing its volume and then expanded without changing its pressure, as shown by the path abc in Fig. 19.30. (a) How does the final temperature of the gas compare with its initial temperature? (b) How much heat does the air exchange with its surroundings during the process abc? Does the air absorb heat or release heat during this process? Explain. (c) If the air instead expands from state a to state c by the straight-line path shown, how much heat does it exchange with its surroundings?

Figure **19.30** Problem 19.45.

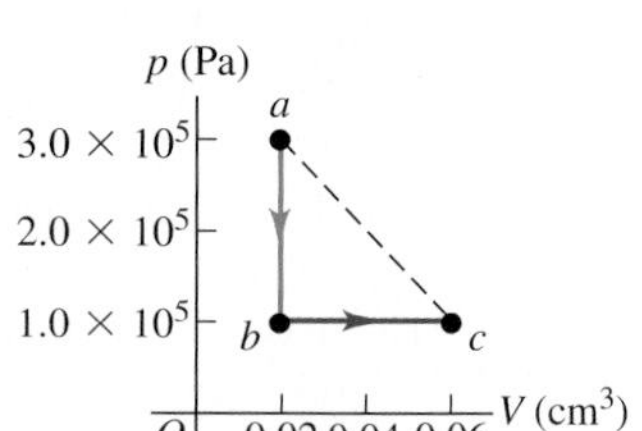

19.46. Three moles of argon gas (assumed to be an ideal gas) originally at a pressure of 1.50×10^4 Pa and a volume of $0.0280\ \text{m}^3$ are first heated and expanded at constant pressure to a volume of $0.0435\ \text{m}^3$, then heated at constant volume until the pressure reaches 3.50×10^4 Pa, then cooled and compressed at constant pressure until the volume is again $0.0280\ \text{m}^3$, and finally cooled at constant volume until the pressure drops to its original value of 1.50×10^4 Pa. (a) Draw the pV-diagram for this cycle. (b) Calculate the total work done by (or on) the gas during the cycle. (c) Calculate the net heat exchanged with the surroundings. Does the gas gain or lose heat overall?

19.47. Two moles of an ideal monatomic gas go through the cycle abc. For the complete cycle, 800 J of heat flows out of the gas. Process ab is at constant pressure, and process bc is at constant volume. States a and b have temperatures $T_a = 200$ K and $T_b = 300$ K. (a) Sketch the pV-diagram for the cycle. (b) What is the work W for the process ca?

19.48. Three moles of an ideal gas are taken around the cycle abc shown in Fig. 19.31. For this gas, $C_p = 29.1\ \text{J/mol} \cdot \text{K}$. Process ac is at constant pressure, process ba is at constant volume, and process cb is adiabatic. The temperatures of the gas in states a, c, and b are $T_a = 300$ K, $T_c = 492$ K, and $T_b = 600$ K. Calculate the total work W for the cycle.

Figure **19.31** Problem 19.48.

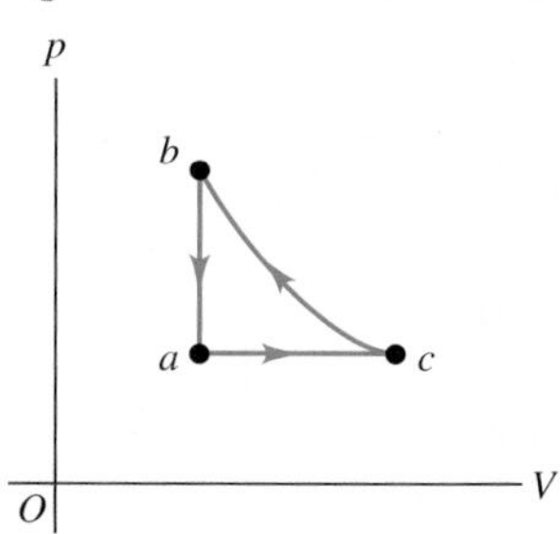

19.49. Starting with 2.50 mol of N_2 gas (assumed to be ideal) in a cylinder at 1.00 atm and 20.0°C, a chemist first heats the gas at constant volume, adding 1.52×10^4 J of heat, then continues heating and allows the gas to expand at constant pressure to twice its original volume. (a) Calculate the final temperature of the gas. (b) Calculate the amount of work done by the gas. (c) Calculate the amount of heat added to the gas while it was expanding. (d) Calculate the change in internal energy of the gas for the whole process.

19.50. Nitrogen gas in an expandable container is cooled from 50.0°C to 10.0°C with the pressure held constant at 3.00×10^5 Pa. The total heat liberated by the gas is 2.50×10^4 J. Assume that the gas may be treated as ideal. (a) Find the number of moles of gas. (b) Find the change in internal energy of the gas. (c) Find the work done by the gas. (d) How much heat would be liberated by the gas for the same temperature change if the volume were constant?

19.51. In a certain process, 2.15×10^5 J of heat is liberated by a system, and at the same time the system contracts under a constant external pressure of 9.50×10^5 Pa. The internal energy of the system is the same at the beginning and end of the process. Find the change in volume of the system. (The system is *not* an ideal gas.)

19.52. A cylinder with a frictionless, movable piston like that shown in Fig. 19.5 contains a quantity of helium gas. Initially the gas is at a pressure of 1.00×10^5 Pa, has a temperature of 300 K, and occupies a volume of 1.50 L. The gas then undergoes two processes. In the first, the gas is heated and the piston is allowed to move to keep the temperature equal to 300 K. This continues until the pressure reaches 2.50×10^4 Pa. In the second process, the gas is compressed at constant pressure until it returns to its original volume of 1.50 L. Assume that the gas may be treated as ideal. (a) In a pV-diagram, show both processes. (b) Find the volume of the gas at the end of the first process, and find the pressure and temperature at the end of the second process. (c) Find the total work done by the gas during both processes. (d) What would you have to do to the gas to return it to its original pressure and temperature?

19.53. A Thermodynamic Process in a Liquid. A chemical engineer is studying the properties of liquid methanol (CH_3OH). She uses a steel cylinder with a cross-sectional area of $0.0200\ m^2$ and containing $1.20 \times 10^{-2}\ m^3$ of methanol. The cylinder is equipped with a tightly fitting piston that supports a load of 3.00×10^4 N. The temperature of the system is increased from 20.0°C to 50.0°C. For methanol, the coefficient of volume expansion is $1.20 \times 10^{-3}\ K^{-1}$, the density is $791\ kg/m^3$, and the specific heat capacity at constant pressure is $c_p = 2.51 \times 10^3\ J/kg \cdot K$. You can ignore the expansion of the steel cylinder. Find (a) the increase in volume of the methanol; (b) the mechanical work done by the methanol against the 3.00×10^4 N force; (c) the amount of heat added to the methanol; (d) the change in internal energy of the methanol. (e) Based on your results, explain whether there is any substantial difference between the specific heat capacities c_p (at constant pressure) and c_V (at constant volume) for methanol under these conditions.

19.54. A Thermodynamic Process in a Solid. A cube of copper 2.00 cm on a side is suspended by a string. (The physical properties of copper are given in Tables 14.1, 17.2, and 17.3.) The cube is heated with a burner from 20.0°C to 90.0°C. The air surrounding the cube is at atmospheric pressure (1.01×10^5 Pa). Find (a) the increase in volume of the cube; (b) the mechanical work done by the cube to expand against the pressure of the surrounding air; (c) the amount of heat added to the cube; (d) the change in internal energy of the cube. (e) Based on your results, explain whether there is any substantial difference between the specific heat capacities c_p (at constant pressure) and c_V (at constant volume) for copper under these conditions.

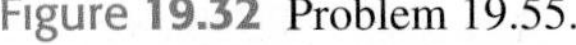

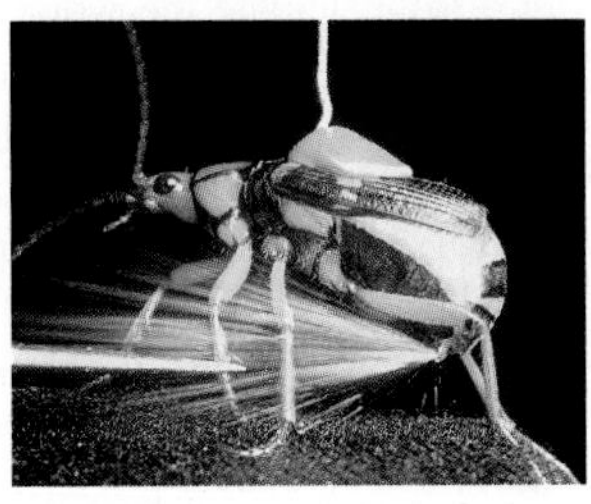

Figure 19.32 Problem 19.55.

19.55. A Thermodynamic Process in an Insect. The African bombardier beetle *Stenaptinus insignis* can emit a jet of defensive spray from the movable tip of its abdomen (Fig. 19.32). The beetle's body has reservoirs of two different chemicals; when the beetle is disturbed, these chemicals are combined in a reaction chamber, producing a compound that is warmed from 20°C to 100°C by the heat of reaction. The high pressure produced allows the compound to be sprayed out at speeds up to 19 m/s (68 km/h), scaring away predators of all kinds. (The beetle shown in the figure is 2 cm long.) Calculate the heat of reaction of the two chemicals (in J/kg). Assume that the specific heat capacity of the two chemicals and the spray is the same as that of water, $4.19 \times 10^3\ J/kg \cdot K$, and that the initial temperature of the chemicals is 20°C.

Figure 19.33 Problem 19.56.

19.56. High-Altitude Research. A large research balloon containing $2.00 \times 10^3\ m^3$ of helium gas at 1.00 atm and a temperature of 15.0°C rises rapidly from ground level to an altitude at which the atmospheric pressure is only 0.900 atm (Fig. 19.33). Assume the helium behaves like an ideal gas and the balloon's ascent is too rapid to permit much heat exchange with the surrounding air. (a) Calculate the volume of the gas at the higher altitude. (b) calculate the temperature of the gas at the higher altitude. (c) What is the change in internal energy of the helium as the balloon rises to the higher altitude?

19.57. Chinook. During certain seasons strong winds called chinooks blow from the west across the eastern slopes of the Rockies and downhill into Denver and nearby areas. Although the mountains are cool, the wind in Denver is very hot; within a few minutes after the chinook wind arrives, the temperature can climb 20 C° ("chinook" is a Native American word meaning "snow eater"). Similar winds occur in the Alps (called foehns) and in southern California (called Santa Anas). (a) Explain why the temperature of the chinook wind rises as it descends the slopes. Why is it important that the wind be fast moving? (b) Suppose a strong wind is blowing toward Denver (elevation 1630 m) from Grays Peak (80 km west of Denver, at an elevation of 4350 m), where the air pressure is 5.60×10^4 Pa and the air temperature is −15.0°C. The temperature and pressure in Denver before the wind arrives are 2.0°C and 8.12×10^4 Pa. By how many Celsius degrees will the temperature in Denver rise when the chinook arrives?

19.58. A certain ideal gas has molar heat capacity at constant volume C_V. A sample of this gas initially occupies a volume V_0 at pressure p_0 and absolute temperature T_0. The gas expands isobarically to a volume $2V_0$ and then expands further adiabatically to a final volume of $4V_0$. (a) Draw a pV-diagram for this sequence of processes. (b) Compute the total work done by the gas for this sequence of processes. (c) Find the final temperature of the gas. (d) Find the absolute value $|Q|$ of the total heat flow into or out of the gas for this sequence of processes, and state the direction of heat flow.

19.59. An air pump has a cylinder 0.250 m long with a movable piston. The pump is used to compress air from the atmosphere (at absolute pressure 1.01×10^5 Pa) into a very large tank at 4.20×10^5 Pa gauge pressure. (For air, $C_V = 20.8\ J/mol \cdot K$.) (a) The piston begins the compression stroke at the open end of the cylinder. How far down the length of the cylinder has the piston moved when air first begins to flow from the cylinder into the tank? Assume that the compression is adiabatic. (b) If the air is taken into the pump at 27.0°C, what is the temperature of the compressed air? (c) How much work does the pump do in putting 20.0 mol of air into the tank?

19.60. Engine Turbochargers and Intercoolers. The power output of an automobile engine is directly proportional to the mass of air that can be forced into the volume of the engine's cylinders to react chemically with gasoline. Many cars have a *turbocharger,* which compresses the air before it enters the engine, giving a greater mass of air per volume. This rapid, essentially adiabatic compression also heats the air. To compress it further, the air then passes through an *intercooler* in which the air exchanges heat with its surroundings at essentially constant pressure. The air is then drawn into the cylinders. In a typical installation, air is taken into the turbocharger at atmospheric pressure $(1.01 \times 10^5\ \text{Pa})$, density $\rho = 1.23\ \text{kg/m}^3$, and temperature 15.0°C. It is compressed adiabatically to 1.45×10^5 Pa. In the intercooler, the air is cooled to the original temperature of 15.0°C at a constant pressure of 1.45×10^5 Pa. (a) Draw a pV-diagram for this sequence of processes. b) If the volume of one of the engine's cylinders is 575 cm^3, what mass of air exiting from the intercooler will fill the cylinder at 1.45×10^5 Pa? Compared to the power output of an engine that takes in air at 1.01×10^5 Pa at 15.0°C, what percentage increase in power is obtained by using the turbocharger and intercooler? (c) If the intercooler is not used, what mass of air exiting from the turbocharger will fill the cylinder at 1.45×10^5 Pa? Compared to the power output of an engine that takes in air at 1.01×10^5 Pa at 15.0°C, what percentage increase in power is obtained by using the turbocharger alone?

19.61. A monatomic ideal gas expands slowly to twice its original volume, doing 300 J of work in the process. Find the heat added to the gas and the change in internal energy of the gas if the process is (a) isothermal; (b) adiabatic; (c) isobaric.

19.62. A cylinder with a piston contains 0.250 mol of oxygen at 2.40×10^5 Pa and 355 K. The oxygen may be treated as an ideal gas. The gas first expands isobarically to twice its original volume. It is then compressed isothermally back to its original volume, and finally it is cooled isochorically to its original pressure. (a) Show the series of processes on a pV-diagram. (b) Compute the temperature during the isothermal compression. (c) Compute the maximum pressure. (d) Compute the total work done by the piston on the gas during the series of processes.

19.63. Use the conditions and processes of Problem 19.62 to compute (a) the work done by the gas, the heat added to it, and its internal-energy change during the initial expansion; (b) the work done, the heat added, and the internal-energy change during the final cooling; (c) the internal-energy change during the isothermal compression.

19.64. A cylinder with a piston contains 0.150 mol of nitrogen at 1.80×10^5 Pa and 300 K. The nitrogen may be treated as an ideal gas. The gas is first compressed isobarically to half its original volume. It then expands adiabatically back to its original volume, and finally it is heated isochorically to its original pressure. (a) Show the series of processes in a pV-diagram. (b) Compute the temperatures at the beginning and end of the adiabatic expansion. (c) Compute the minimum pressure.

19.65. Use the conditions and processes of Problem 19.64 to compute (a) the work done by the gas, the heat added to it, and its internal-energy change during the initial compression; (b) the work done by the gas, the heat added to it, and its internal-energy change during the adiabatic expansion; (c) the work done, the heat added, and the internal-energy change during the final heating.

19.66. Comparing Thermodynamic Processes. In a cylinder, 1.20 mol of an ideal monatomic gas, initially at 3.60×10^5 Pa and 300 K, expands until its volume triples. Compute the work done by the gas if the expansion is (a) isothermal; (b) adiabatic; (c) isobaric. (d) Show each process in a pV-diagram. In which case is the absolute value of the work done by the gas greatest? Least? (e) In which case is the absolute value of the heat transfer greatest? Least? (f) In which case is the absolute value of the change in internal energy of the gas greatest? Least?

19.67. In a cylinder sealed with a piston, you rapidly compress 3.00 L of N_2 gas initially at 1.00 atm pressure and 0.00°C to half its original volume. Assume the N_2 behaves like an ideal gas. (a) Calculate the final temperature and pressure of the gas. (b) If you now cool the gas back to 0.00°C without changing the pressure, what is its final volume?

Challenge Problems

19.68. Oscillations of a Piston. A vertical cylinder of radius r contains a quantity of ideal gas and is fitted with a piston with mass m that is free to move (Fig. 19.34). The piston and the walls of the cylinder are frictionless and the entire cylinder is placed in a constant-temperature bath. The outside air pressure is p_0. In equilibrium, the piston sits at a height h above the bottom of the cylinder. (a) Find the absolute pressure of the gas trapped below the piston when in equilibrium. (b) The piston is pulled up by a small distance and released. Find the net force acting on the piston when its base is a distance $h + y$ above the bottom of the cylinder, where y is much less than h. (c) After the piston is displaced from equilibrium and released, it oscillates up and down. Find the frequency of these small oscillations. If the displacement is not small, are the oscillations simple harmonic? How can you tell?

Figure **19.34** Challenge Problem 19.68.

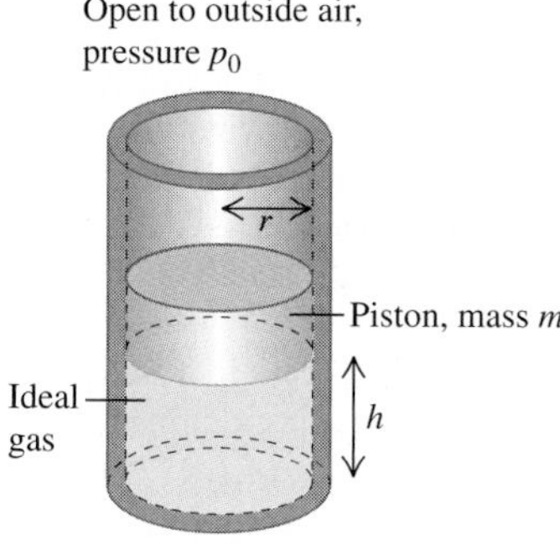

19.69. The van der Waals equation of state, an approximate representation of the behavior of gases at high pressure, is given by Eq. (18.7):

$$\left(p + \frac{an^2}{V^2}\right)(V - nb) = nRT$$

where a and b are constants having different values for different gases. (In the special case of $a = b = 0$, this is the ideal-gas equation.) (a) Calculate the work done by a gas with this equation of state in an isothermal expansion from V_1 to V_2. Show that your answer agrees with the ideal-gas result found in Example 19.1 (Section 19.2) when you set $a = b = 0$. (b) For ethane gas (C_2H_6), $a = 0.554\ \text{J} \cdot \text{m}^3/\text{mol}^2$ and $b = 6.38 \times 10^{-5}\ \text{m}^3/\text{mol}$. Calculate the work W done by 1.80 mol of ethane when it expands from $2.00 \times 10^{-3}\ \text{m}^3$ to $4.00 \times 10^{-3}\ \text{m}^3$ at a constant temperature of 300 K. Do the calculation using (i) the van der Waals equation of state and (ii) the ideal-gas equation of state. (c) How large is the difference between the two results for W in part (b)? For which equation of state is W larger? Use the interpretation of the terms a and b given in Section 18.1 to explain why this should be so. Are the differences between the two equations of state important in this case?

THE SECOND LAW OF THERMODYNAMICS

20

? The second law of thermodynamics tells us that heat naturally flows from a hot body (such as a freshly cooked ear of corn) to a cold one (such as a pat of butter). Is it *ever* possible for heat to flow from a cold body to a hot one?

LEARNING GOALS

By studying this chapter, you will learn:

- What determines whether a thermodynamic process is reversible or irreversible.
- What a heat engine is, and how to calculate its efficiency.
- The physics of internal-combustion engines.
- How refrigerators and heat engines are related, and how to analyze the performance of a refrigerator.
- How the second law of thermodynamics sets limits on the efficiency of engines and the performance of refrigerators.
- How to do calculations involving the idealized Carnot cycle for engines and refrigerators.
- What is meant by entropy, and how to use this concept to analyze thermodynamic processes.

Many thermodynamic processes proceed naturally in one direction but not the opposite. For example, heat by itself always flows from a hot body to a cooler body, never the reverse. Heat flow from a cool body to a hot body would not violate the first law of thermodynamics; energy would be conserved. But it doesn't happen in nature. Why not? As another example, note that it is easy to convert mechanical energy completely into heat; this happens every time we use a car's brakes to stop it. In the reverse direction, there are plenty of devices that convert heat *partially* into mechanical energy. (An automobile engine is an example.) But even the cleverest would-be inventors have never succeeded in building a machine that converts heat *completely* into mechanical energy. Again, why not?

The answer to both of these questions has to do with the *directions* of thermodynamic processes and is called the *second law of thermodynamics.* This law places fundamental limitations on the efficiency of an engine or a power plant. It also places limitations on the minimum energy input needed to operate a refrigerator. So the second law is directly relevant for many important practical problems.

We can also state the second law in terms of the concept of *entropy,* a quantitative measure of the degree of disorder or randomness of a system. The idea of entropy helps explain why ink mixed with water never spontaneously unmixes and why we never observe a host of other seemingly possible processes.

20.1 Directions of Thermodynamic Processes

Thermodynamic processes that occur in nature are all **irreversible processes.** These are processes that proceed spontaneously in one direction but not the other (Fig. 20.1a). The flow of heat from a hot body to a cooler body is irreversible, as is the free expansion of a gas discussed in Sections 19.3 and 19.6. Sliding a book across a table converts mechanical energy into heat by friction; this process is

20.1 Reversible and irreversible processes.

(a) A block of ice melts *irreversibly* when we place it in a hot (70°C) metal box.

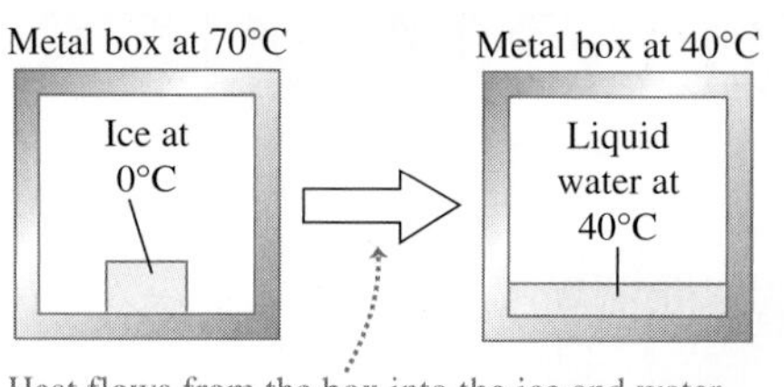

Heat flows from the box into the ice and water, never the reverse.

(b) A block of ice at 0°C can be melted *reversibly* if we put it in a 0°C metal box.

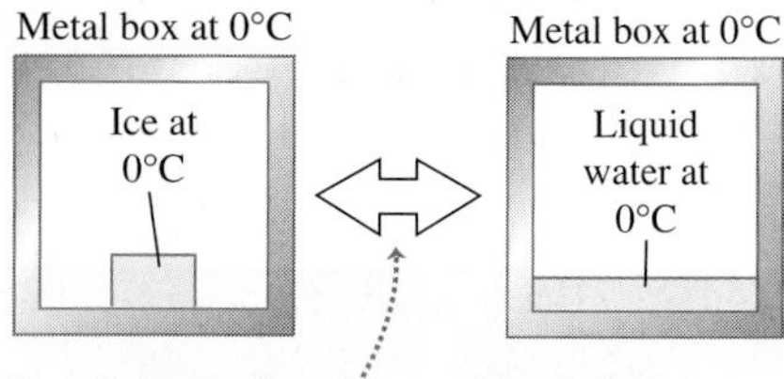

By infinitesimally raising or lowering the temperature of the box, we can make heat flow into the ice to melt it or make heat flow out of the water to refreeze it.

irreversible, for no one has ever observed the reverse process (in which a book initially at rest on the table would spontaneously start moving and the table and book would cool down). Our main topic for this chapter is the *second law of thermodynamics,* which determines the preferred direction for such processes.

Despite this preferred direction for every natural process, we can think of a class of idealized processes that *would* be reversible. A system that undergoes such an idealized **reversible process** is always very close to being in thermodynamic equilibrium within itself and with its surroundings. Any change of state that takes place can then be reversed (made to go the other way) by making only an infinitesimal change in the conditions of the system. For example, we can reverse heat flow between two bodies whose temperatures differ only infinitesimally by making only a very small change in one temperature or the other (Fig. 20.1b).

Reversible processes are thus **equilibrium processes,** with the system always in thermodynamic equilibrium. Of course, if a system were *truly* in thermodynamic equilibrium, no change of state would take place. Heat would not flow into or out of a system with truly uniform temperature throughout, and a system that is truly in mechanical equilibrium would not expand and do work against its surroundings. A reversible process is an idealization that can never be precisely attained in the real world. But by making the temperature gradients and the pressure differences in the substance very small, we can keep the system very close to equilibrium states and make the process nearly reversible. That's why we call a reversible process a *quasi-equilibrium process.*

By contrast, heat flow with finite temperature difference, free expansion of a gas, and conversion of work to heat by friction are all *irreversible* processes; no small change in conditions could make any of them go the other way. They are also all *nonequilibrium* processes, in that the system is not in thermodynamic equilibrium at any point until the end of the process.

Disorder and Thermodynamic Processes

There is a relationship between the direction of a process and the *disorder* or *randomness* of the resulting state. For example, imagine a tedious sorting job, such as alphabetizing a thousand book titles written on file cards. Throw the alphabetized stack of cards into the air. Do they come down in alphabetical order? Alas, no: their tendency is to come down in a random or disordered state. In the free expansion of a gas discussed in Sections 19.3 and 19.6, the air is more disordered after it has expanded into the entire box than when it was confined in one side, just as your clothes are more disordered when scattered all over your floor than when confined to your closet.

Similarly, macroscopic kinetic energy is energy associated with organized, coordinated motions of many molecules, but heat transfer involves changes in energy of random, disordered molecular motion. Therefore conversion of mechanical energy into heat involves an increase of randomness or disorder.

In the following sections we will introduce the second law of thermodynamics by considering two broad classes of devices: *heat engines,* which are partly successful in converting heat into work, and *refrigerators,* which are partly successful in transporting heat from cooler to hotter bodies.

Test Your Understanding of Section 20.1 Your left and right hands are normally at the same temperature, just like the metal box and ice in Fig. 20.1b. Is rubbing your hands together to warm them (i) a reversible process or (ii) an irreversible process?

20.2 Heat Engines

ActivPhysics ONLINE
8.12 Cyclic Process–Strategies
8.13 Cyclic Process–Problems

The essence of our technological society is the ability to use sources of energy other than muscle power. Sometimes, mechanical energy is directly available; water power and wind power are examples. But most of our energy comes from the burning of fossil fuels (coal, oil, and gas) and from nuclear reactions. They supply energy that is transferred as *heat.* This is directly useful for heating buildings, for cooking, and for chemical processing, but to operate a machine or propel a vehicle, we need *mechanical* energy.

Thus it's important to know how to take heat from a source and convert as much of it as possible into mechanical energy or work. This is what happens in gasoline engines in automobiles, jet engines in airplanes, steam turbines in electric power plants, and many other systems. Closely related processes occur in the animal kingdom; food energy is "burned" (that is, carbohydrates combine with oxygen to yield water, carbon dioxide, and energy) and partly converted to mechanical energy as an animal's muscles do work on its surroundings.

Any device that transforms heat partly into work or mechanical energy is called a **heat engine** (Fig. 20.2). Usually, a quantity of matter inside the engine undergoes inflow and outflow of heat, expansion and compression, and sometimes change of phase. We call this matter the **working substance** of the engine. In internal-combustion engines, such as those used in automobiles, the working substance is a mixture of air and fuel; in a steam turbine it is water.

20.2 All motorized vehicles other than purely electric vehicles use heat engines for propulsion. (Hybrid vehicles use their internal-combustion engine to help charge the batteries for the electric motor.)

The simplest kind of engine to analyze is one in which the working substance undergoes a **cyclic process,** a sequence of processes that eventually leaves the substance in the same state in which it started. In a steam turbine the water is recycled and used over and over. Internal-combustion engines do not use the same air over and over, but we can still analyze them in terms of cyclic processes that approximate their actual operation.

Hot and Cold Reservoirs

All heat engines *absorb* heat from a source at a relatively high temperature, perform some mechanical work, and *discard* or *reject* some heat at a lower temperature. As far as the engine is concerned, the discarded heat is wasted. In internal-combustion engines the waste heat is that discarded in the hot exhaust gases and the cooling system; in a steam turbine it is the heat that must flow out of the used steam to condense and recycle the water.

When a system is carried through a cyclic process, its initial and final internal energies are equal. For any cyclic process, the first law of thermodynamics requires that

$$U_2 - U_1 = 0 = Q - W \qquad \text{so} \qquad Q = W$$

That is, the net heat flowing into the engine in a cyclic process equals the net work done by the engine.

When we analyze heat engines, it helps to think of two bodies with which the working substance of the engine can interact. One of these, called the *hot reservoir,* represents the heat source; it can give the working substance large amounts of heat at a constant temperature T_H without appreciably changing its own temperature. The other body, called the *cold reservoir,* can absorb large amounts of discarded heat from the engine at a constant lower temperature T_C. In a steam-turbine system the flames and hot gases in the boiler are the hot reservoir, and the cold water and air used to condense and cool the used steam are the cold reservoir.

We denote the quantities of heat transferred from the hot and cold reservoirs as Q_H and Q_C, respectively. A quantity of heat Q is positive when heat is transferred *into* the working substance and is negative when heat leaves the working substance. Thus in a heat engine, Q_H is positive but Q_C is negative, representing heat *leaving* the working substance. This sign convention is consistent with the rules we stated in Section 19.1; we will continue to use those rules here. Frequently, it clarifies the relationships to state them in terms of the absolute values of the Q's and W's because absolute values are always positive. When we do this, our notation will show it explicitly.

Energy-Flow Diagrams and Efficiency

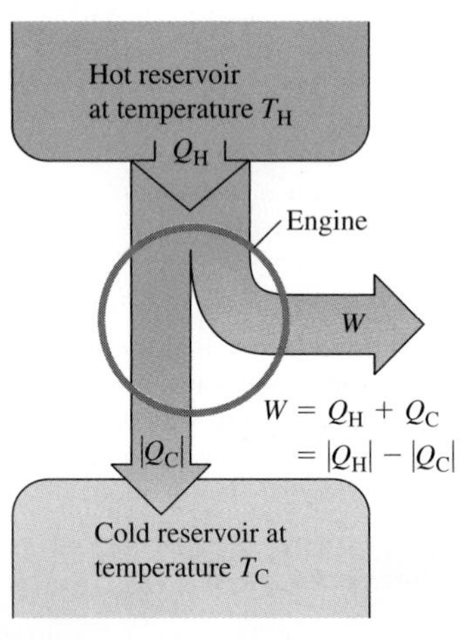

20.3 Schematic energy-flow diagram for a heat engine.

We can represent the energy transformations in a heat engine by the *energy-flow diagram* of Fig. 20.3. The engine itself is represented by the circle. The amount of heat Q_H supplied to the engine by the hot reservoir is proportional to the width of the incoming "pipeline" at the top of the diagram. The width of the outgoing pipeline at the bottom is proportional to the magnitude $|Q_C|$ of the heat rejected in the exhaust. The branch line to the right represents the portion of the heat supplied that the engine converts to mechanical work, W.

When an engine repeats the same cycle over and over, Q_H and Q_C represent the quantities of heat absorbed and rejected by the engine *during one cycle;* Q_H is positive, and Q_C is negative. The *net* heat Q absorbed per cycle is

$$Q = Q_H + Q_C = |Q_H| - |Q_C| \tag{20.1}$$

The useful output of the engine is the net work W done by the working substance. From the first law,

$$W = Q = Q_H + Q_C = |Q_H| - |Q_C| \tag{20.2}$$

Ideally, we would like to convert *all* the heat Q_H into work; in that case we would have $Q_H = W$ and $Q_C = 0$. Experience shows that this is impossible; there is always some heat wasted, and Q_C *is never zero.* We define the **thermal efficiency** of an engine, denoted by e, as the quotient

$$e = \frac{W}{Q_H} \tag{20.3}$$

The thermal efficiency e represents the fraction of Q_H that *is* converted to work. To put it another way, e is what you get divided by what you pay for. This is always less than unity, an all-too-familiar experience! In terms of the flow diagram of Fig. 20.3, the most efficient engine is one for which the branch pipeline representing the work output is as wide as possible and the exhaust pipeline representing the heat thrown away is as narrow as possible.

When we substitute the two expressions for W given by Eq. (20.2) into Eq. (20.3), we get the following equivalent expressions for e:

$$e = \frac{W}{Q_H} = 1 + \frac{Q_C}{Q_H} = 1 - \left|\frac{Q_C}{Q_H}\right| \quad \text{(thermal efficiency of an engine)} \tag{20.4}$$

Note that e is a quotient of two energy quantities and thus is a pure number, without units. Of course, we must always express W, Q_H, and Q_C in the same units.

Problem-Solving Strategy 20.1 Heat Engines

Problems involving heat engines are, first and foremost, problems in the first law of thermodynamics. Hence Problem-Solving Strategy 19.1 (Section 19.4) is equally useful throughout the present chapter, and we suggest that you reread it.

IDENTIFY *the relevant concepts:* A heat engine is any device that converts heat partially to work, as shown schematically in Fig. 20.3. We will see in Section 20.4 that a refrigerator is essentially a heat engine running in reverse, so many of the same concepts apply.

SET UP *the problem* as suggested in Problem-Solving Strategy 19.1. Equation (20.4) is useful in situations for which the thermal efficiency of the engine is relevant. It's helpful to sketch an energy-flow diagram like Fig. 20.3.

EXECUTE *the solution* as follows:

1. Be very careful with the sign conventions for W and the various Q's. W is positive when the system expands and does work; W is negative when the system is compressed. Each Q is positive if it represents heat entering the system and is negative if it represents heat leaving the system. When you know that a quantity is negative, such as Q_C in the above discussion, it sometimes helps to write it as $Q_C = -|Q_C|$.
2. Some problems deal with power rather than energy quantities. Power is work per unit time $(P = W/t)$, and rate of heat transfer (heat current) H is heat transfer per unit time $(H = Q/t)$. In such problems it helps to ask, "What is W or Q in one second (or one hour)?"
3. Keeping steps 1 and 2 in mind, solve for the target variables.

EVALUATE *your answer:* Use the first law of thermodynamics to check your results, paying particular attention to algebraic signs.

Example 20.1 Analyzing a heat engine

A gasoline engine in a large truck takes in 10,000 J of heat and delivers 2000 J of mechanical work per cycle. The heat is obtained by burning gasoline with heat of combustion $L_c = 5.0 \times 10^4$ J/g. (a) What is the thermal efficiency of this engine? (b) How much heat is discarded in each cycle? (c) How much gasoline is burned in each cycle? (d) If the engine goes through 25 cycles per second, what is its power output in watts? In horsepower? (e) How much gasoline is burned per second? Per hour?

SOLUTION

IDENTIFY: This problem is about a heat engine, so we can use the ideas of this section.

SET UP: Figure 20.4 is our sketch of the energy-flow diagram for one engine cycle. We are given the amount of work done by the engine per cycle $(W = 2000 \text{ J})$ and the amount of heat taken in by the engine per cycle $(Q_H = 10{,}000 \text{ J})$.

Hence we use the first form of Eq. (20.4) to find the thermal efficiency. The first law of thermodynamics tells us the amount of heat rejected per cycle, and the heat of combustion tells us how much gasoline must be burned per cycle and hence per unit time.

20.4 Our sketch for this problem.

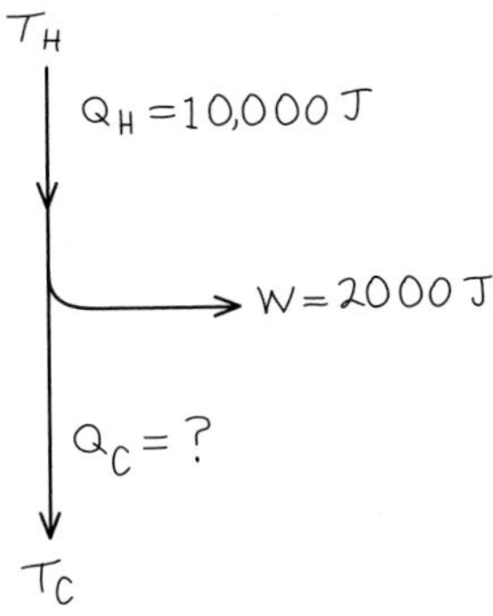

EXECUTE: (a) From the first expression in Eq. (20.4), the thermal efficiency is

$$e = \frac{W}{Q_H} = \frac{2000 \text{ J}}{10{,}000 \text{ J}} = 0.20 = 20\%$$

This is a fairly typical figure for cars and trucks if W includes only the work actually delivered to the wheels.

(b) From Eq. (20.2), $W = Q_H + Q_C$ so

$$Q_C = W - Q_H = 2000 \text{ J} - 10{,}000 \text{ J}$$
$$= -8000 \text{ J}$$

That is, 8000 J of heat leaves the engine during each cycle.

(c) Let m be the mass of gasoline burned during each cycle. Then

$$Q_H = mL_c$$
$$m = \frac{Q_H}{L_c} = \frac{10{,}000 \text{ J}}{5.0 \times 10^4 \text{ J/g}} = 0.20 \text{ g}$$

(d) The power P (rate of doing work) is the work per cycle multiplied by the number of cycles per second:

$$P = (2000 \text{ J/cycle})(25 \text{ cycles/s}) = 50{,}000 \text{ W} = 50 \text{ kW}$$
$$= (50{,}000 \text{ W})\frac{1 \text{ hp}}{746 \text{ W}} = 67 \text{ hp}$$

(e) The mass of gasoline burned per second is the mass per cycle multiplied by the number of cycles per second:

$$(0.20 \text{ g/cycle})(25 \text{ cycles/s}) = 5.0 \text{ g/s}$$

The mass burned per hour is

$$(5.0 \text{ g/s})\frac{3600 \text{ s}}{1 \text{ h}} = 18{,}000 \text{ g/h} = 18 \text{ kg/h}$$

EVALUATE: We can check our result in part (e) by converting it to a more familiar quantity, the amount of fuel consumed per unit distance. The density of gasoline is about 0.70 g/cm^3, so this is about 25,700 cm^3, 25.7 L, or 6.8 gallons of gasoline per hour. If the truck is traveling at 55 mi/h (88 km/h), this represents fuel consumption of 8.1 miles/gallon (3.4 km/L). This is substantially greater fuel consumption than a passenger car, but fairly typical of large trucks.

Test Your Understanding of Section 20.2 Rank the following heat engines in order from highest to lowest thermal efficiency. (i) an engine that in one cycle absorbs 5000 J of heat and rejects 4500 J of heat; (ii) an engine that in one cycle absorbs 25,000 J of heat and does 2000 J of work; (iii) an engine that in one cycle does 400 J of work and rejects 2800 J of heat.

20.3 Internal-Combustion Engines

The gasoline engine, used in automobiles and many other types of machinery, is a familiar example of a heat engine. Let's look at its thermal efficiency. Figure 20.5 shows the operation of one type of gasoline engine. First a mixture of air and gasoline vapor flows into a cylinder through an open intake valve while the piston descends, increasing the volume of the cylinder from a minimum of V (when the piston is all the way up) to a maximum of rV (when it is all the way down). The quantity r is called the **compression ratio;** for present-day automobile engines its value is typically 8 to 10. At the end of this *intake stroke,* the intake valve closes and the mixture is compressed, approximately adiabatically, to volume V during the *compression stroke.* The mixture is then ignited by the spark plug, and the heated gas expands, approximately adiabatically, back to volume rV, pushing on the piston and doing work; this is the *power stroke.* Finally, the exhaust valve opens, and the combustion products are pushed out (during the *exhaust stroke*), leaving the cylinder ready for the next intake stroke.

The Otto Cycle

Figure 20.6 is a pV-diagram for an idealized model of the thermodynamic processes in a gasoline engine. This model is called the **Otto cycle.** At point a the gasoline–air mixture has entered the cylinder. The mixture is compressed adiabatically to point b and is then ignited. Heat Q_H is added to the system by the burning gasoline along line bc, and the power stroke is the adiabatic expansion to d. The gas is cooled to the temperature of the outside air along line da; during this process, heat $|Q_C|$ is rejected. In practice, this gas leaves the engine as exhaust and does not enter the engine again. But since an equivalent amount of gasoline and air enters, we may consider the process to be cyclic.

20.5 Cycle of a four-stroke internal-combustion engine.

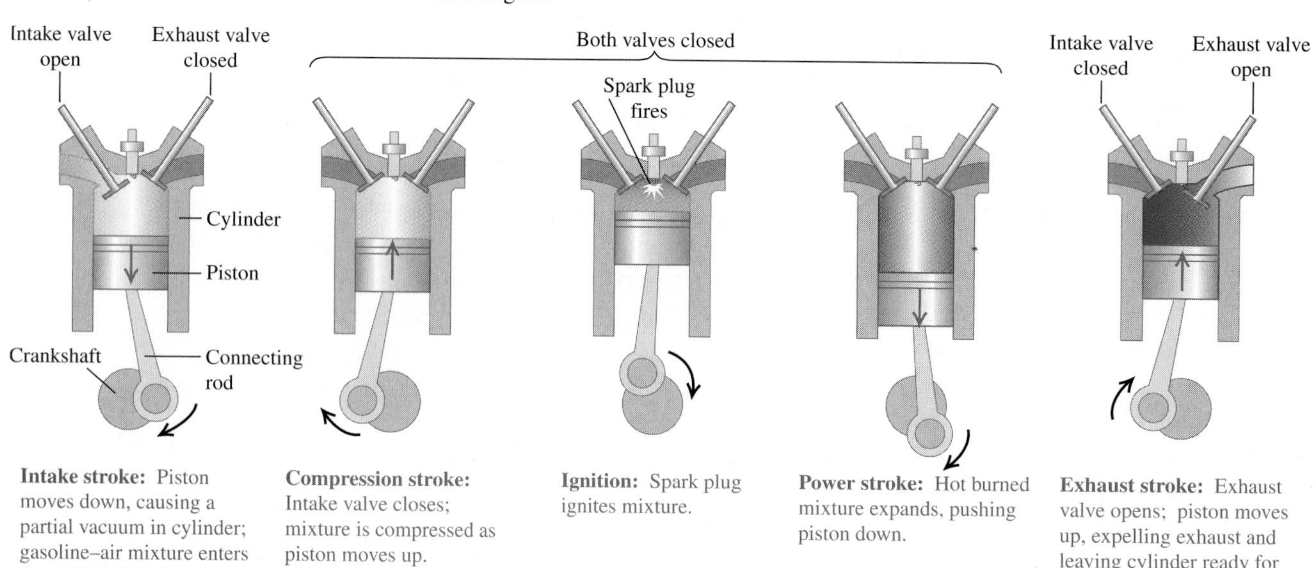
Intake valve open
Exhaust valve closed
Both valves closed
Spark plug fires
Intake valve closed
Exhaust valve open
Cylinder
Piston
Crankshaft
Connecting rod
Intake stroke: Piston moves down, causing a partial vacuum in cylinder; gasoline–air mixture enters through intake valve.
Compression stroke: Intake valve closes; mixture is compressed as piston moves up.
Ignition: Spark plug ignites mixture.
Power stroke: Hot burned mixture expands, pushing piston down.
Exhaust stroke: Exhaust valve opens; piston moves up, expelling exhaust and leaving cylinder ready for next intake stroke.

We can calculate the efficiency of this idealized cycle. Processes bc and da are constant-volume, so the heats Q_H and Q_C are related simply to the temperatures:

$$Q_H = nC_V(T_c - T_b) > 0$$
$$Q_C = nC_V(T_a - T_d) < 0$$

The thermal efficiency is given by Eq. (20.4). Inserting the above expressions and cancelling out the common factor nC_V, we find

$$e = \frac{Q_H + Q_C}{Q_H} = \frac{T_c - T_b + T_a - T_d}{T_c - T_b} \tag{20.5}$$

To simplify this further, we use the temperature–volume relationship for adiabatic processes for an ideal gas, Eq. (19.22). For the two adiabatic processes ab and cd,

$$T_a(rV)^{\gamma-1} = T_b V^{\gamma-1} \quad \text{and} \quad T_d(rV)^{\gamma-1} = T_c V^{\gamma-1}$$

We divide each of these equations by the common factor $V^{\gamma-1}$ and substitute the resulting expressions for T_b and T_c back into Eq. (20.5). The result is

$$e = \frac{T_d r^{\gamma-1} - T_a r^{\gamma-1} + T_a - T_d}{T_d r^{\gamma-1} - T_a r^{\gamma-1}} = \frac{(T_d - T_a)(r^{\gamma-1} - 1)}{(T_d - T_a) r^{\gamma-1}}$$

Dividing out the common factor $(T_d - T_a)$, we get

$$e = 1 - \frac{1}{r^{\gamma-1}} \quad \text{(thermal efficiency in Otto cycle)} \tag{20.6}$$

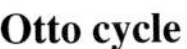

20.6 The pV-diagram for the Otto cycle, an idealized model of the thermodynamic processes in a gasoline engine.

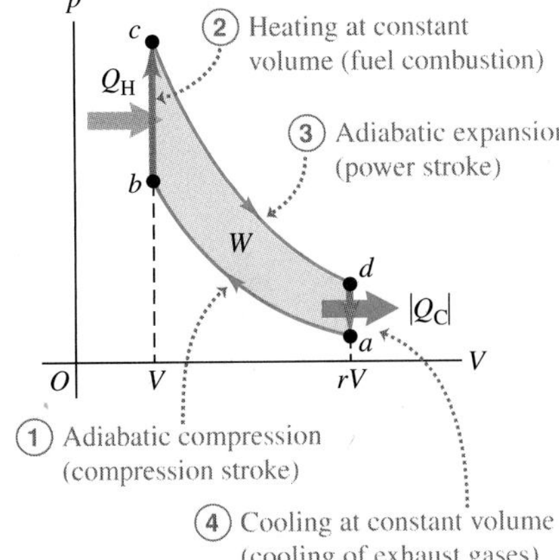

The thermal efficiency given by Eq. (20.6) is always less than unity, even for this idealized model. With $r = 8$ and $\gamma = 1.4$ (the value for air) the theoretical efficiency is $e = 0.56$, or 56%. The efficiency can be increased by increasing r. However, this also increases the temperature at the end of the adiabatic compression of the air–fuel mixture. If the temperature is too high, the mixture explodes spontaneously during compression instead of burning evenly after the spark plug ignites it. This is called *pre-ignition* or *detonation;* it causes a knocking sound and can damage the engine. The octane rating of a gasoline is a measure of its antiknock qualities. The maximum practical compression ratio for high-octane, or "premium," gasoline is about 10 to 13. Higher ratios can be used with more exotic fuels.

The Otto cycle, which we have just described, is a highly idealized model. It assumes that the mixture behaves as an ideal gas; it neglects friction, turbulence, loss of heat to cylinder walls, and many other effects that combine to reduce the efficiency of a real engine. Another source of inefficiency is incomplete combustion. A mixture of gasoline vapor with just enough air for complete combustion of the hydrocarbons to H_2O and CO_2 does not ignite readily. Reliable ignition requires a mixture that is "richer" in gasoline. The resulting incomplete combustion leads to CO and unburned hydrocarbons in the exhaust. The heat obtained from the gasoline is then less than the total heat of combustion; the difference is wasted, and the exhaust products contribute to air pollution. Efficiencies of real gasoline engines are typically around 35%.

The Diesel Cycle

The Diesel engine is similar in operation to the gasoline engine. The most important difference is that there is no fuel in the cylinder at the beginning of the compression stroke. A little before the beginning of the power stroke, the injectors start to inject fuel directly into the cylinder, just fast enough to keep the pressure approximately constant during the first part of the power stroke. Because of the

20.7 The pV-diagram for the idealized Diesel cycle.

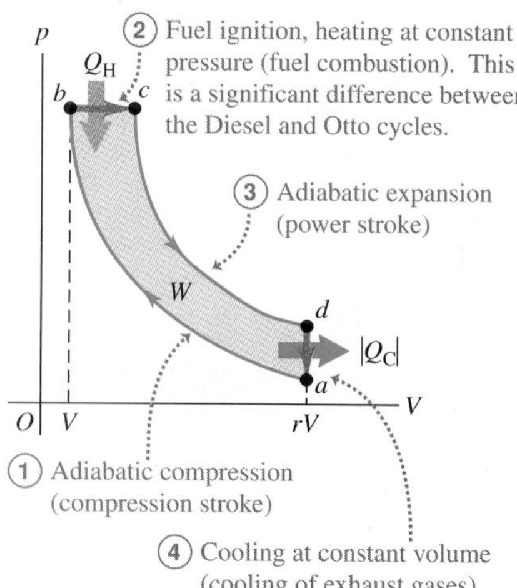

high temperature developed during the adiabatic compression, the fuel ignites spontaneously as it is injected; no spark plugs are needed.

Fig. 20.7 shows the idealized **Diesel cycle.** Starting at point a, air is compressed adiabatically to point b, heated at constant pressure to point c, expanded adiabatically to point d, and cooled at constant volume to point a. Because there is no fuel in the cylinder during most of the compression stroke, pre-ignition cannot occur, and the compression ratio r can be much higher than for a gasoline engine. This improves efficiency and ensures reliable ignition when the fuel is injected (because of the high temperature reached during the adiabatic compression). Values of r of 15 to 20 are typical; with these values and $\gamma = 1.4$, the theoretical efficiency of the idealized Diesel cycle is about 0.65 to 0.70. As with the Otto cycle, the efficiency of any actual engine is substantially less than this. While Diesel engines are very efficient, they must be built to much tighter tolerances than gasoline engines and the fuel-injection system requires careful maintenance.

Test Your Understanding of Section 20.3 For an Otto-cycle engine with cylinders of a fixed size and a fixed compression ratio, which of the following aspects of the pV-diagram in Fig. 20.6 would change if you doubled the amount of fuel burned per cycle? (There may be more than one correct answer.) (i) the vertical distance between points b and c; (ii) the vertical distance between points a and d; (iii) the horizontal distance between points b and a.

20.4 Refrigerators

We can think of a **refrigerator** as a heat engine operating in reverse. A heat engine takes heat from a hot place and gives off heat to a colder place. A refrigerator does the opposite; it takes heat from a cold place (the inside of the refrigerator) and gives it off to a warmer place (usually the air in the room where the refrigerator is located). A heat engine has a net *output* of mechanical work; the refrigerator requires a net *input* of mechanical work. Using the sign conventions from Section 20.2, for a refrigerator Q_C is positive but both W and Q_H are negative; hence $|W| = -W$ and $|Q_H| = -Q_H$.

20.8 Schematic energy-flow diagram of a refrigerator.

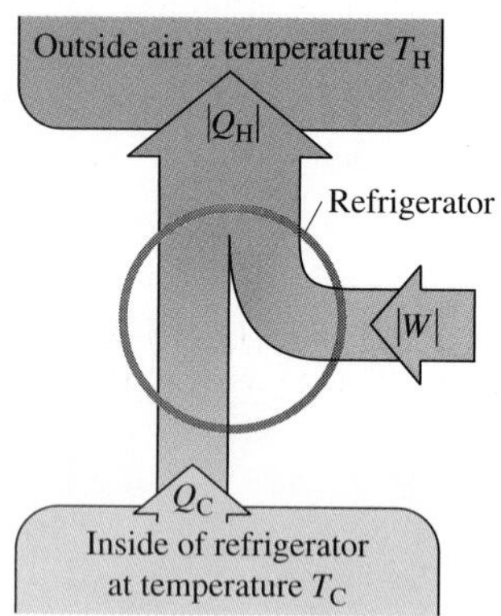

Fig. 20.8 shows an energy-flow diagram for a refrigerator. From the first law for a cyclic process,

$$Q_H + Q_C - W = 0 \qquad \text{or} \qquad -Q_H = Q_C - W$$

or, because both Q_H and W are negative,

$$|Q_H| = Q_C + |W| \tag{20.7}$$

Thus, as the diagram shows, the heat $|Q_H|$ leaving the working substance and given to the hot reservoir is always *greater* than the heat Q_C taken from the cold reservoir. Note that the absolute-value relationship

$$|Q_H| = |Q_C| + |W| \tag{20.8}$$

is valid for both heat engines and refrigerators.

From an economic point of view, the best refrigeration cycle is one that removes the greatest amount of heat $|Q_C|$ from the inside of the refrigerator for the least expenditure of mechanical work, $|W|$. The relevant ratio is therefore $|Q_C|/|W|$; the larger this ratio, the better the refrigerator. We call this ratio the **coefficient of performance,** denoted by K. From Eq. (20.8), $|W| = |Q_H| - |Q_C|$, so

$$K = \frac{|Q_C|}{|W|} = \frac{|Q_C|}{|Q_H| - |Q_C|} \quad \text{(coefficient of performance of a refrigerator)} \tag{20.9}$$

As always, we measure Q_H, Q_C, and W all in the same energy units; K is then a dimensionless number.

20.9 (a) Principle of the mechanical refrigeration cycle. (b) How the key elements are arranged in a practical refrigerator.

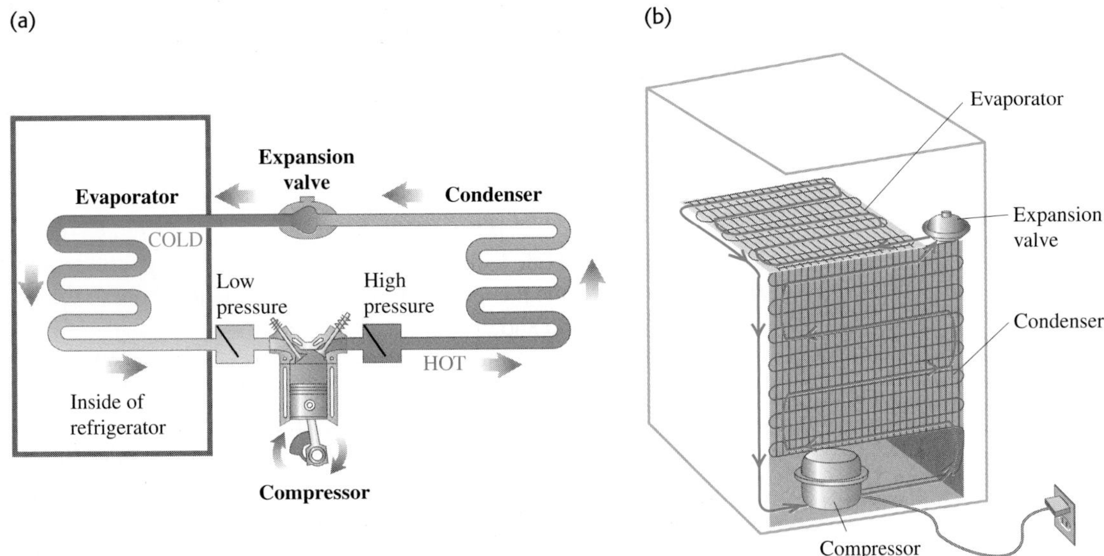

Practical Refrigerators

The principles of the common refrigeration cycle are shown schematically in Fig. 20.9a. The fluid "circuit" contains a refrigerant fluid (the working substance). The left side of the circuit (including the cooling coils inside the refrigerator) is at low temperature and low pressure; the right side (including the condenser coils outside the refrigerator) is at high temperature and high pressure. Ordinarily, both sides contain liquid and vapor in phase equilibrium.

The compressor takes in fluid, compresses it adiabatically, and delivers it to the condenser coil at high pressure. The fluid temperature is then higher than that of the air surrounding the condenser, so the refrigerant gives off heat $|Q_H|$ and partially condenses to liquid. The fluid then expands adiabatically into the evaporator at a rate controlled by the expansion valve. As the fluid expands, it cools considerably, enough that the fluid in the evaporator coil is colder than its surroundings. It absorbs heat $|Q_C|$ from its surroundings, cooling them and partially vaporizing. The fluid then enters the compressor to begin another cycle. The compressor, usually driven by an electric motor (Fig. 20.9b), requires energy input and does work $|W|$ *on* the working substance during each cycle.

An air conditioner operates on exactly the same principle. In this case the refrigerator box becomes a room or an entire building. The evaporator coils are inside, the condenser is outside, and fans circulate air through these (Fig. 20.10).

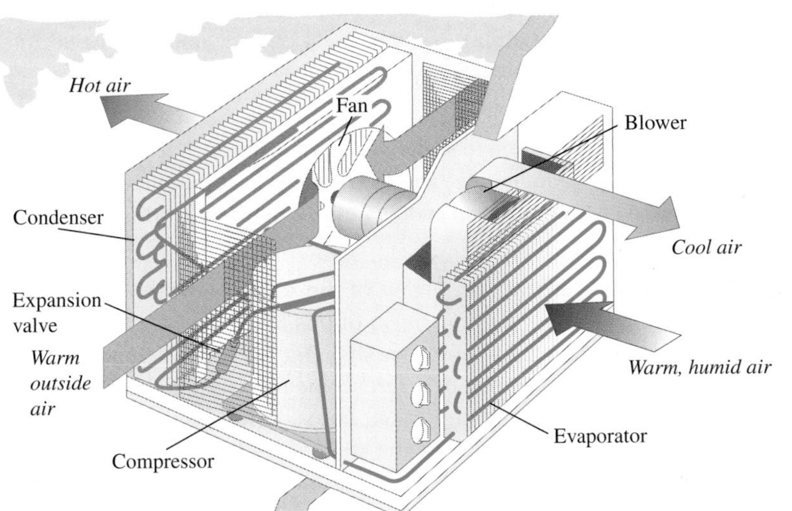

20.10 An air conditioner works on the same principle as a refrigerator.

In large installations the condenser coils are often cooled by water. For air conditioners the quantities of greatest practical importance are the *rate* of heat removal (the heat current H from the region being cooled) and the *power* input $P = W/t$ to the compressor. If heat $|Q_C|$ is removed in time t, then $H = |Q_C|/t$. Then we can express the coefficient of performance as

$$K = \frac{|Q_C|}{|W|} = \frac{Ht}{Pt} = \frac{H}{P}$$

Typical room air conditioners have heat removal rates H of 5000 to 10,000 Btu/h, or about 1500–3000 W, and require electric power input of about 600 to 1200 W. Typical coefficients of performance are about 3; the actual values depend on the inside and outside temperatures.

Unfortunately, K is often expressed commercially in mixed units, with H in Btu per hour and P in watts. In these units, H/P is called the **energy efficiency rating** (EER); the units, customarily omitted, are (Btu/h)/W. Because 1 W = 3.413 Btu/h, the EER is numerically 3.413 times as large as the dimensionless K. Room air conditioners typically have an EER of about 10.

A variation on this theme is the **heat pump,** used to heat buildings by cooling the outside air. It functions like a refrigerator turned inside out. The evaporator coils are outside, where they take heat from cold air, and the condenser coils are inside, where they give off heat to the warmer air. With proper design, the heat $|Q_H|$ delivered to the inside per cycle can be considerably greater than the work $|W|$ required to get it there.

Work is *always* needed to transfer heat from a colder to a hotter body. Heat flows spontaneously from hotter to colder, and to reverse this flow requires the addition of work from the outside. Experience shows that it is impossible to make a refrigerator that transports heat from a colder body to a hotter body without the addition of work. If no work were needed, the coefficient of performance would be infinite. We call such a device a *workless refrigerator;* it is a mythical beast, like the unicorn and the free lunch. ?

Test Your Understanding of Section 20.4 Can you cool your house by leaving the refrigerator door open?

20.5 The Second Law of Thermodynamics

Experimental evidence suggests strongly that it is *impossible* to build a heat engine that converts heat completely to work—that is, an engine with 100% thermal efficiency. This impossibility is the basis of one statement of the **second law of thermodynamics,** as follows:

It is impossible for any system to undergo a process in which it absorbs heat from a reservoir at a single temperature and converts the heat completely into mechanical work, with the system ending in the same state in which it began.

We will call this the "engine" statement of the second law. (It is also known to physicists as the *Kelvin–Planck statement* of this law.)

The basis of the second law of thermodynamics is the difference between the nature of internal energy and that of macroscopic mechanical energy. In a moving body the molecules have random motion, but superimposed on this is a coordinated motion of every molecule in the direction of the body's velocity. The kinetic energy associated with this *coordinated* macroscopic motion is what we call the kinetic energy of the moving body. The kinetic and potential energies associated with the *random* motion constitute the internal energy.

When a body sliding on a surface comes to rest as a result of friction, the organized motion of the body is converted to random motion of molecules in the body and in the surface. Since we cannot control the motions of individual molecules, we cannot convert this random motion completely back to organized motion. We can convert *part* of it, and this is what a heat engine does.

If the second law were *not* true, we could power an automobile or run a power plant by cooling the surrounding air. Neither of these impossibilities violates the *first* law of thermodynamics. The second law, therefore, is not a deduction from the first but stands by itself as a separate law of nature. The first law denies the possibility of creating or destroying energy; the second law limits the *availability* of energy and the ways in which it can be used and converted.

Restating the Second Law

Our analysis of refrigerators in Section 20.4 forms the basis for an alternative statement of the second law of thermodynamics. Heat flows spontaneously from hotter to colder bodies, never the reverse. A refrigerator does take heat from a colder to a hotter body, but its operation requires an input of mechanical energy or work. Generalizing this observation, we state:

It is impossible for any process to have as its sole result the transfer of heat from a cooler to a hotter body.

We'll call this the "refrigerator" statement of the second law. (It is also known as the *Clausius statement.*) It may not seem to be very closely related to the "engine" statement. In fact, though, the two statements are completely equivalent. For example, if we could build a workless refrigerator, violating the second or "refrigerator" statement of the second law, we could use it in conjunction with a heat engine, pumping the heat rejected by the engine back to the hot reservoir to be reused. This composite machine (Fig. 20.11a) would violate the "engine" statement of the second law because its net effect would be to take a net quantity of heat $Q_H - |Q_C|$ from the hot reservoir and convert it completely to work W.

Alternatively, if we could make an engine with 100% thermal efficiency, in violation of the first statement, we could run it using heat from the hot reservoir and use the work output to drive a refrigerator that pumps heat from the cold reservoir to the hot (Fig. 20.11b). This composite device would violate the "refrigerator" statement because its net effect would be to take heat Q_C from the cold reservoir and deliver it to the hot reservoir without requiring any input of work. Thus any device that violates one form of the second law can be used to make a device that violates the other form. If violations of the first form are impossible, so are violations of the second!

The conversion of work to heat, as in friction or viscous fluid flow, and heat flow from hot to cold across a finite temperature gradient, are *irreversible* processes. The "engine" and "refrigerator" statements of the second law state that these processes can be only partially reversed. We could cite other examples. Gases always seep spontaneously through an opening from a region of high pressure to a region of low pressure; gases and miscible liquids left by themselves always tend to mix, not to unmix. The second law of thermodynamics is an expression of the inherent one-way aspect of these and many other irreversible processes. Energy conversion is an essential aspect of all plant and animal life and of human technology, so the second law of thermodynamics is of the utmost fundamental importance in the world we live in.

20.11 Energy-flow diagrams showing that the two forms of the second law are equivalent.

(a) The "engine" statement of the second law of thermodynamics

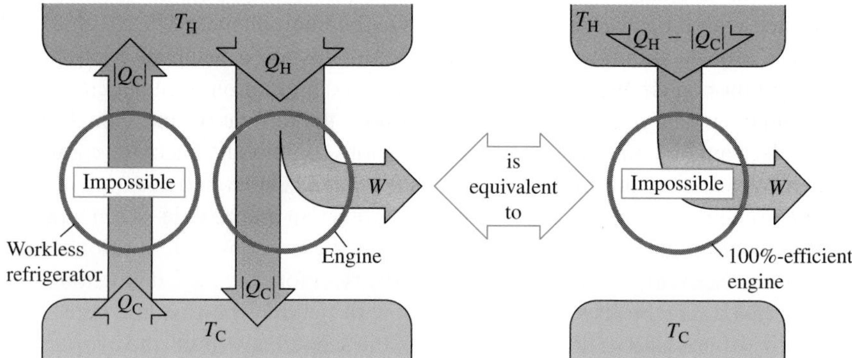

If a workless refrigerator were possible, it could be used in conjunction with an ordinary heat engine to form a 100%-efficient engine, converting heat $Q_H - |Q_C|$ completely to work.

(b) The "refrigerator" statement of the second law of thermodynamics

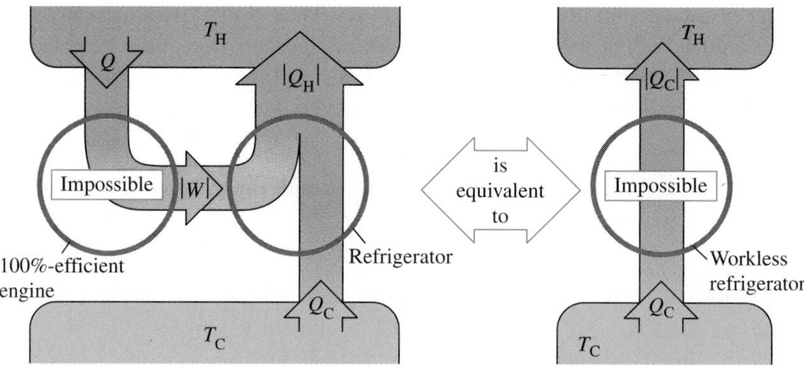

If a 100%-efficient engine were possible, it could be used in conjunction with an ordinary refrigerator to form a workless refrigerator, transferring heat Q_C from the cold to the hot reservoir with no input of work.

Test Your Understanding of Section 20.5 Would a 100%-efficient engine (Fig. 20.11a) violate the *first* law of thermodynamics? What about a workless refrigerator (Fig. 20.11b)?

20.12 The temperature of the firebox of a steam engine is much higher than the temperature of water in the boiler, so heat flows irreversibly from firebox to water. Carnot's quest to understand the efficiency of steam engines led him to the idea that an ideal engine would involve only *reversible* processes.

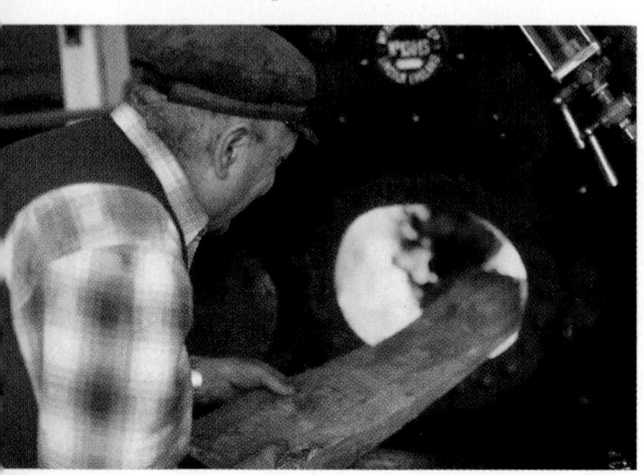

20.6 The Carnot Cycle

According to the second law, no heat engine can have 100% efficiency. How great an efficiency *can* an engine have, given two heat reservoirs at temperatures T_H and T_C? This question was answered in 1824 by the French engineer Sadi Carnot (1796–1832), who developed a hypothetical, idealized heat engine that has the maximum possible efficiency consistent with the second law. The cycle of this engine is called the **Carnot cycle.**

To understand the rationale of the Carnot cycle, we return to a recurrent theme in this chapter: *reversibility* and its relationship to directions of thermodynamic processes. Conversion of work to heat is an irreversible process; the purpose of a heat engine is a *partial* reversal of this process, the conversion of heat to work with as great an efficiency as possible. For maximum heat-engine efficiency, therefore, *we must avoid all irreversible processes* (Fig. 20.12). This requirement turns out to be enough to determine the basic sequence of steps in the Carnot cycle, as we will show next.

Heat flow through a finite temperature drop is an irreversible process. Therefore, during heat transfer in the Carnot cycle there must be *no* finite temperature difference. When the engine takes heat from the hot reservoir at temperature T_H, the working substance of the engine must also be at T_H; otherwise, irreversible heat flow would occur. Similarly, when the engine discards heat to the cold reservoir at T_C, the engine itself must be at T_C. That is, every process that involves heat transfer must be *isothermal* at either T_H or T_C.

Conversely, in any process in which the temperature of the working substance of the engine is intermediate between T_H and T_C, there must be *no* heat transfer between the engine and either reservoir because such heat transfer could not be reversible. Therefore any process in which the temperature T of the working substance changes must be *adiabatic.*

The bottom line is that every process in our idealized cycle must be either isothermal or adiabatic. In addition, thermal and mechanical equilibrium must be maintained at all times so that each process is completely reversible.

Steps of the Carnot Cycle

The Carnot cycle consists of two reversible isothermal and two reversible adiabatic processes. Fig. 20.13 shows a Carnot cycle using as its working substance an ideal gas in a cylinder with a piston. It consists of the following steps:

8.14 Carnot Cycle

1. The gas expands isothermally at temperature T_H, absorbing heat Q_H (ab).
2. It expands adiabatically until its temperature drops to T_C (bc).
3. It is compressed isothermally at T_C, rejecting heat $|Q_C|$ (cd).
4. It is compressed adiabatically back to its initial state at temperature T_H (da).

We can calculate the thermal efficiency e of a Carnot engine in the special case shown in Fig.20.13 in which the working substance is an *ideal gas.* To carry out this calculation, we will first find the ratio Q_C/Q_H of the quantities of heat transferred in the two isothermal processes and then use Eq. (20.4) to find e.

For an ideal gas the internal energy U depends only on temperature and is thus constant in any isothermal process. For the isothermal expansion ab, $\Delta U_{ab} = 0$ and Q_H is equal to the work W_{ab} done by the gas during its isothermal expansion at temperature T_H. We calculated this work in Example 19.1 (Section 19.2); using that result, we have

$$Q_H = W_{ab} = nRT_H \ln \frac{V_b}{V_a} \tag{20.10}$$

20.13 The Carnot cycle for an ideal gas. The light blue lines in the pV-diagram are isotherms (curves of constant temperature) and the dark blue lines are adiabats (curves of zero heat flow).

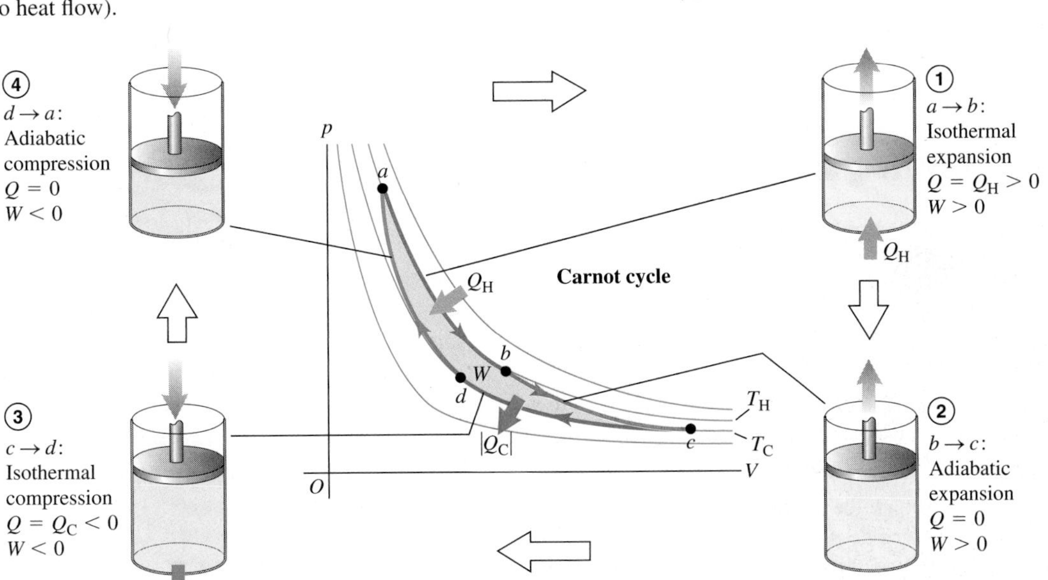

Similarly,

$$Q_C = W_{cd} = nRT_C \ln \frac{V_d}{V_c} = -nRT_C \ln \frac{V_c}{V_d} \tag{20.11}$$

Because V_d is less than V_c, Q_C is negative ($Q_C = -|Q_C|$); heat flows out of the gas during the isothermal compression at temperature T_C.

The ratio of the two quantities of heat is thus

$$\frac{Q_C}{Q_H} = -\left(\frac{T_C}{T_H}\right)\frac{\ln(V_c/V_d)}{\ln(V_b/V_a)} \tag{20.12}$$

This can be simplified further by use of the temperature–volume relationship for an adiabatic process, Eq. (19.22). We find for the two adiabatic processes:

$$T_H V_b^{\gamma-1} = T_C V_c^{\gamma-1} \quad \text{and} \quad T_H V_a^{\gamma-1} = T_C V_d^{\gamma-1}$$

Dividing the first of these by the second, we find

$$\frac{V_b^{\gamma-1}}{V_a^{\gamma-1}} = \frac{V_c^{\gamma-1}}{V_d^{\gamma-1}} \quad \text{and} \quad \frac{V_b}{V_a} = \frac{V_c}{V_d}$$

Thus the two logarithms in Eq. (20.12) are equal, and that equation reduces to

$$\frac{Q_C}{Q_H} = -\frac{T_C}{T_H} \quad \text{or} \quad \frac{|Q_C|}{|Q_H|} = \frac{T_C}{T_H} \quad \text{(heat transfer in a Carnot engine)} \tag{20.13}$$

The ratio of the heat rejected at T_C to the heat absorbed at T_H is just equal to the ratio T_C/T_H. Then from Eq. (20.4) the efficiency of the Carnot engine is

$$e_{\text{Carnot}} = 1 - \frac{T_C}{T_H} = \frac{T_H - T_C}{T_H} \quad \text{(efficiency of a Carnot engine)} \tag{20.14}$$

This simple result says that the efficiency of a Carnot engine depends only on the temperatures of the two heat reservoirs. The efficiency is large when the temperature *difference* is large, and it is very small when the temperatures are nearly equal. The efficiency can never be exactly unity unless $T_C = 0$; we'll see later that this, too, is impossible.

CAUTION **Use Kelvin temperature in Carnot calculations** In all calculations involving the Carnot cycle, you must make sure that you use *absolute* (Kelvin) temperatures only. That's because Eqs. (20.10) through (20.14) come from the ideal-gas equation $pV = nRT$, in which T is absolute temperature.

Example 20.2 Analyzing a Carnot engine I

A Carnot engine takes 2000 J of heat from a reservoir at 500 K, does some work, and discards some heat to a reservoir at 350 K. How much work does it do, how much heat is discarded, and what is the efficiency?

SOLUTION

IDENTIFY: This problem involves a Carnot engine, so we can use the ideas of this section as well as the concepts from Section 20.2 (which apply to heat engines of all kinds).

SET UP: Figure 20.14 shows the energy-flow diagram for this problem. For this Carnot engine we are given $Q_H = 2000$ J, the amount of heat absorbed, and the temperatures $T_H = 500$ K and $T_C = 350$ K of the hot and cold reservoirs, respectively. We find

20.14 Our sketch for this problem.

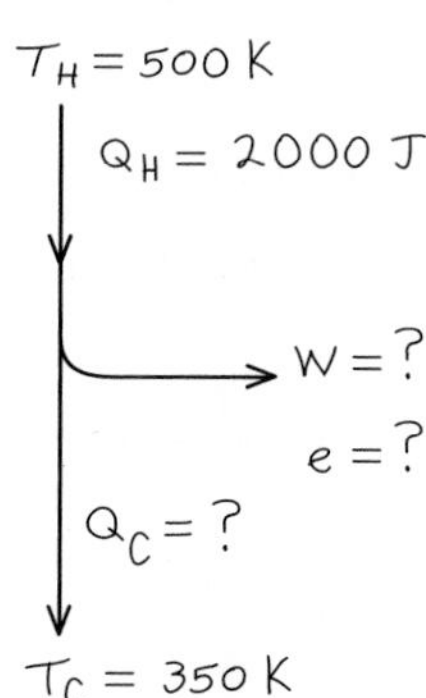

the amount of heat discarded using Eq. (20.13), and then calculate the amount of work done using the first law of thermodynamics: The work done in a complete cycle is the sum of the heat absorbed and the (negative) heat discarded [see Eq. (20.2)]. We find the efficiency from the two temperatures using Eq. (20.14).

EXECUTE: From Eq. (20.13) the heat Q_C discarded by the engine is

$$Q_C = -Q_H \frac{T_C}{T_H} = -(2000\ \text{J})\frac{350\ \text{K}}{500\ \text{K}}$$
$$= -1400\ \text{J}$$

Then from the first law, the work W done by the engine is

$$W = Q_H + Q_C = 2000\ \text{J} + (-1400\ \text{J})$$
$$= 600\ \text{J}$$

From Eq. (20.14) the thermal efficiency is

$$e = 1 - \frac{T_C}{T_H} = 1 - \frac{350\ \text{K}}{500\ \text{K}} = 0.30 = 30\%$$

EVALUATE: The negative sign of Q_C is correct: it shows that heat flows *out* of the engine and into the cold reservoir. Note that we can check our result for e by using the basic definition of thermal efficiency:

$$e = \frac{W}{Q_H} = \frac{600\ \text{J}}{2000\ \text{J}} = 0.30 = 30\%$$

Example 20.3 Analyzing a Carnot engine II

Suppose 0.200 mol of an ideal diatomic gas $(\gamma = 1.40)$ undergoes a Carnot cycle with temperatures 227°C and 27°C. The initial pressure is $p_a = 10.0 \times 10^5$ Pa, and during the isothermal expansion at the higher temperature the volume doubles. (a) Find the pressure and volume at each of points a, b, c, and d in the pV-diagram of Fig.20.13. (b) Find Q, W, and ΔU for each step and for the entire cycle. (c) Determine the efficiency directly from the results of part (b), and compare it with the result from Eq. (20.14).

SOLUTION

IDENTIFY: This problem involves the properties of the Carnot cycle as well as those of an ideal gas.

SET UP: We are given the number of moles and the pressure and temperature at point a (which is at the higher of the two reservoir temperatures), so we can find the volume at a using the ideal-gas equation. We then find the pressure and volume at the other points from the equations given in this section in combination with the ideal-gas equation. Next, for each step in the cycle, we use Eqs. (20.10) and (20.11) to find the heat flow and work done, and we use Eq. (19.13) to calculate the internal energy change. As in Example 20.2, we find the efficiency using Eq. (20.14).

EXECUTE: (a) We first remember to convert the Celsius temperatures to absolute temperatures: The higher temperature is $T_H = (227 + 273.15)\ \text{K} = 500\ \text{K}$ and the lower temperature is $T_C = (27 + 273.15)\ \text{K} = 300\ \text{K}$. We then use the ideal-gas equation to find V_a:

$$V_a = \frac{nRT_H}{p_a} = \frac{(0.200\ \text{mol})(8.314\ \text{J/mol}\cdot\text{K})(500\ \text{K})}{10.0 \times 10^5\ \text{Pa}}$$
$$= 8.31 \times 10^{-4}\ \text{m}^3$$

The volume doubles during the isothermal expansion $a \rightarrow b$, so

$$V_b = 2V_a = 2(8.31 \times 10^{-4}\ \text{m}^3)$$
$$= 16.6 \times 10^{-4}\ \text{m}^3$$

Also, during the isothermal expansion $a \rightarrow b$, $p_aV_a = p_bV_b$, so

$$p_b = \frac{p_aV_a}{V_b} = 5.00 \times 10^5\ \text{Pa}$$

For the adiabatic expansion $b \rightarrow c$, $T_HV_b^{\gamma-1} = T_CV_c^{\gamma-1}$, so

$$V_c = V_b\left(\frac{T_H}{T_C}\right)^{1/(\gamma-1)} = (16.6 \times 10^{-4}\ \text{m}^3)\left(\frac{500\ \text{K}}{300\ \text{K}}\right)^{2.5}$$
$$= 59.6 \times 10^{-4}\ \text{m}^3$$

Using the ideal-gas equation again for point c, we find

$$p_c = \frac{nRT_C}{V_c} = \frac{(0.200\ \text{mol})(8.314\ \text{J/mol}\cdot\text{K})(300\ \text{K})}{59.6 \times 10^{-4}\ \text{m}^3}$$
$$= 0.837 \times 10^5\ \text{Pa}$$

For the adiabatic compression $d \rightarrow a$, $T_CV_d^{\gamma-1} = T_HV_a^{\gamma-1}$, and

$$V_d = V_a\left(\frac{T_H}{T_C}\right)^{1/(\gamma-1)} = (8.31 \times 10^{-4}\ \text{m}^3)\left(\frac{500\ \text{K}}{300\ \text{K}}\right)^{2.5}$$
$$= 29.8 \times 10^{-4}\ \text{m}^3$$

$$p_d = \frac{nRT_C}{V_d} = \frac{(0.200\ \text{mol})(8.314\ \text{J/mol}\cdot\text{K})(300\ \text{K})}{29.8 \times 10^{-4}\ \text{m}^3}$$
$$= 1.67 \times 10^5\ \text{Pa}$$

(b) For the isothermal expansion $a \rightarrow b$, $\Delta U_{ab} = 0$. To find $W_{ab}\ (=Q_H)$, we use Eq. (20.10):

$$W_{ab} = Q_H = nRT_H \ln\frac{V_b}{V_a}$$
$$= (0.200\ \text{mol})(8.314\ \text{J/mol}\cdot\text{K})(500\ \text{K})(\ln 2)$$
$$= 576\ \text{J}$$

For the adiabatic expansion $b \rightarrow c$, $Q_{bc} = 0$. From the first law of thermodynamics, $\Delta U_{bc} = Q_{bc} - W_{bc} = -W_{bc}$; hence the work W_{bc} done by the gas in this process equals the negative of the change in internal energy of the gas. From Eq. (19.13) we have $\Delta U = nC_V\Delta T$, where $\Delta T = T_C - T_H$ (final temperature minus initial temperature). Using $C_V = 20.8\ \text{J/mol}\cdot\text{K}$ for an ideal diatomic gas, we find

$$W_{bc} = -\Delta U_{bc} = -nC_V(T_C - T_H) = nC_V(T_H - T_C)$$
$$= (0.200\ \text{mol})(20.8\ \text{J/mol}\cdot\text{K})(500\ \text{K} - 300\ \text{K})$$
$$= 832\ \text{J}$$

Continued

For the isothermal compression $c \rightarrow d$, $\Delta U_{cd} = 0$; Eq. (20.11) gives

$$W_{cd} = Q_C = nRT_C \ln\frac{V_d}{V_c}$$
$$= (0.200\,\text{mol})(8.314\,\text{J/mol}\cdot\text{K})(300\,\text{K})\left(\ln\frac{29.8\times10^{-4}\,\text{m}^3}{59.6\times10^{-4}\,\text{m}^3}\right)$$
$$= -346\ \text{J}$$

For the adiabatic compression $d \rightarrow a$, $Q_{da} = 0$, and

$$W_{da} = -\Delta U_{da} = -nC_V(T_H - T_C) = nC_V(T_C - T_H)$$
$$= (0.200\ \text{mol})(20.8\ \text{J/mol}\cdot\text{K})(300\ \text{K} - 500\ \text{K})$$
$$= -832\ \text{J}$$

We can tabulate the results as follows:

Process	Q	W	ΔU
$a \rightarrow b$	576 J	576 J	0
$b \rightarrow c$	0	832 J	−832 J
$c \rightarrow d$	−346 J	−346 J	0
$d \rightarrow a$	0	−832 J	832 J
Total	230 J	230 J	0

(c) From the table, $Q_H = 576$ J and the total work is 230 J. Thus

$$e = \frac{W}{Q_H} = \frac{230\ \text{J}}{576\ \text{J}} = 0.40 = 40\%$$

We can compare this with the result from Eq. (20.14):

$$e = \frac{T_H - T_C}{T_H} = \frac{500\ \text{K} - 300\ \text{K}}{500\ \text{K}} = 0.40 = 40\%$$

EVALUATE: In the table of results in part (b), note that for the entire cycle $Q = W$ and $\Delta U = 0$. These results are just what we would expect: In a complete cycle, the net heat input is used to do work with zero net change in the internal energy of the system. Note also that the quantities of work in the two adiabatic processes are negatives of each other. Can you show from the analysis leading to Eq. (20.13) that this must *always* be the case in a Carnot cycle?

Note that the efficiency in this example is greater than that obtained in Example 20.2. That's because the ratio of the high and low temperatures is higher, $(500\ \text{K})/(300\ \text{K})$ as compared to $(500\text{K})/(350\ \text{K})$.

The Carnot Refrigerator

Because each step in the Carnot cycle is reversible, the *entire cycle* may be reversed, converting the engine into a refrigerator. The coefficient of performance of the Carnot refrigerator is obtained by combining the general definition of K, Eq. (20.9), with Eq. (20.13) for the Carnot cycle. We first rewrite Eq. (20.9) as

$$K = \frac{|Q_C|}{|Q_H| - |Q_C|} = \frac{|Q_C|/|Q_H|}{1 - |Q_C|/|Q_H|}$$

Then we substitute Eq. (20.13), $|Q_C|/|Q_H| = T_C/T_H$, into this expression. The result is

$$K_{\text{Carnot}} = \frac{T_C}{T_H - T_C} \quad \text{(coefficient of performance of a Carnot refrigerator)} \tag{20.15}$$

When the temperature difference $T_H - T_C$ is small, K is much larger than unity; in this case a lot of heat can be "pumped" from the lower to the higher temperature with only a little expenditure of work. But the greater the temperature difference, the smaller the value of K and the more work is required to transfer a given quantity of heat.

Example 20.4 Analyzing a Carnot refrigerator

If the cycle described in Example 20.3 is run backward as a refrigerator, what is its coefficient of performance?

SOLUTION

IDENTIFY: This problem uses the ideas of Section 20.3 (for refrigerators in general) as well as the above discussion of Carnot refrigerators.

SET UP: Equation (20.9) gives the coefficient of performance of *any* refrigerator in terms of the heat extracted from the cold reservoir per cycle and the work that must be done per cycle.

EXECUTE: In Example 20.3 we found that in one cycle the Carnot engine rejects heat $Q_C = -346$ J to the cold reservoir and does work $W = 230$ J. Hence, when run in reverse as a refrigerator, the system extracts heat $Q_C = +346$ J from the cold reservoir while requiring a work input of $W = -230$ J. From Eq. (20.9),

$$K = \frac{|Q_C|}{|W|} = \frac{346\ \text{J}}{230\ \text{J}} = 1.50$$

Because the cycle is a Carnot cycle, we may also use Eq. (20.15):

$$K = \frac{T_C}{T_H - T_C} = \frac{300\ \text{K}}{500\ \text{K} - 300\ \text{K}} = 1.50$$

EVALUATE: For a Carnot cycle, e and K depend only on the temperatures, as shown by Eqs. (20.14) and (20.15), and we don't need to calculate Q and W. For cycles containing irreversible processes, however, these two equations are not valid, and more detailed calculations are necessary.

20.15 Proving that the Carnot engine has the highest possible efficiency. A "superefficient" engine (more efficient than a Carnot engine) combined with a Carnot refrigerator could convert heat completely into work with no net heat transfer to the cold reservoir. This would violate the second law of thermodynamics.

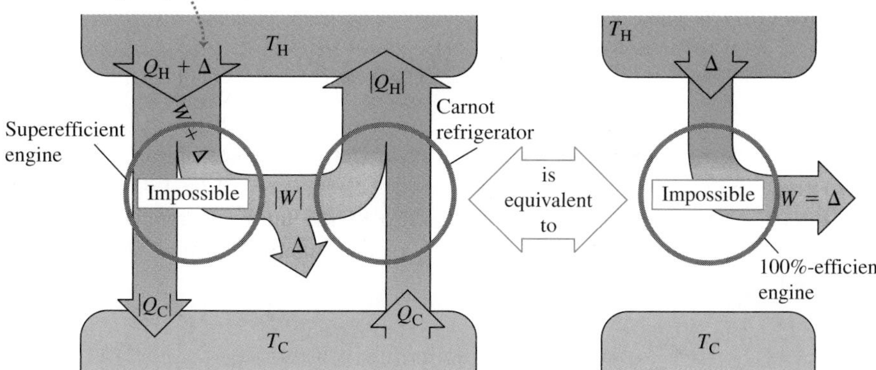
If a superefficient engine were possible, it could be used in conjunction with a Carnot refrigerator to convert the heat Δ completely to work, with no net transfer to the cold reservoir.
T_H
$Q_H + \Delta$
$|Q_H|$
Carnot refrigerator
Superefficient engine
$W + \Delta$
Impossible
$|W|$
Δ
is equivalent to
T_H
Δ
Impossible
$W = \Delta$
100%-efficient engine
$|Q_C|$
Q_C
T_C
T_C

The Carnot Cycle and the Second Law

We can prove that **no engine can be more efficient than a Carnot engine operating between the same two temperatures.** The key to the proof is the above observation that since each step in the Carnot cycle is reversible, the *entire cycle* may be reversed. Run backward, the engine becomes a refrigerator. Suppose we have an engine that is more efficient than a Carnot engine (Fig. 20.15). Let the Carnot engine, run backward as a refrigerator by negative work $-|W|$, take in heat Q_C from the cold reservoir and expel heat $|Q_H|$ to the hot reservoir. The superefficient engine expels heat $|Q_C|$, but to do this, it takes in a greater amount of heat $Q_H + \Delta$. Its work output is then $W + \Delta$, and the net effect of the two machines together is to take a quantity of heat Δ and convert it completely into work. This violates the engine statement of the second law. We could construct a similar argument that a superefficient engine could be used to violate the refrigerator statement of the second law. Note that we don't have to assume that the superefficient engine is reversible. In a similar way we can show that *no refrigerator can have a greater coefficient of performance than a Carnot refrigerator operating between the same two temperatures.*

Thus the statement that no engine can be more efficient than a Carnot engine is yet another equivalent statement of the second law of thermodynamics. It also follows directly that **all Carnot engines operating between the same two temperatures have the same efficiency, irrespective of the nature of the working substance.** Although we derived Eq. (20.14) for a Carnot engine using an ideal gas as its working substance, it is in fact valid for *any* Carnot engine, no matter what its working substance.

Equation (20.14), the expression for the efficiency of a Carnot engine, sets an upper limit to the efficiency of a real engine such as a steam turbine. To maximize this upper limit and the actual efficiency of the real engine, the designer must make the intake temperature T_H as high as possible and the exhaust temperature T_C as low as possible (Fig. 20.16).

The exhaust temperature cannot be lower than the lowest temperature available for cooling the exhaust. For a steam turbine at an electric power plant, T_C may be the temperature of river or lake water; then we want the boiler temperature T_H to be as high as possible. The vapor pressures of all liquids increase rapidly with temperature, so we are limited by the mechanical strength of the boiler. At 500°C the vapor pressure of water is about 240×10^5 Pa (235 atm); this is about the maximum practical pressure in large present-day steam boilers.

20.16 To maximize efficiency, the temperatures inside a jet engine are made as high as possible. Exotic ceramic materials are used that can withstand temperatures in excess of 1000°C without melting or becoming soft.

*The Kelvin Temperature Scale

In Chapter 17 we expressed the need for a temperature scale that doesn't depend on the properties of any particular material. We can now use the Carnot cycle to define such a scale. The thermal efficiency of a Carnot engine operating between two heat reservoirs at temperatures T_H and T_C is independent of the nature of the working substance and depends only on the temperatures. From Eq. (20.4), this thermal efficiency is

$$e = \frac{Q_H + Q_C}{Q_H} = 1 + \frac{Q_C}{Q_H}$$

Therefore the ratio Q_C/Q_H is the same for *all* Carnot engines operating between two given temperatures T_H and T_C.

Kelvin proposed that we *define* the ratio of the temperatures, T_C/T_H, to be equal to the magnitude of the ratio Q_C/Q_H of the quantities of heat absorbed and rejected:

$$\frac{T_C}{T_H} = \frac{|Q_C|}{|Q_H|} = -\frac{Q_C}{Q_H} \quad \text{(definition of Kelvin temperature)} \quad (20.16)$$

Equation (20.16) looks identical to Eq. (20.13), but there is a subtle and crucial difference. The temperatures in Eq. (20.13) are based on an ideal-gas thermometer, as defined in Section 17.3, while Eq. (20.16) *defines* a temperature scale based on the Carnot cycle and the second law of thermodynamics and is independent of the behavior of any particular substance. Thus the **Kelvin temperature scale** is truly *absolute*. To complete the definition of the Kelvin scale, we assign, as in Section 17.3, the arbitrary value of 273.16 K to the temperature of the triple point of water. When a substance is taken around a Carnot cycle, the ratio of the heats absorbed and rejected, $|Q_H|/|Q_C|$, is equal to the ratio of the temperatures of the reservoirs *as expressed on the gas-thermometer scale* defined in Section 17.3. Since the triple point of water is chosen to be 273.16 K in both scales, it follows that *the Kelvin and ideal-gas scales are identical.*

The zero point on the Kelvin scale is called **absolute zero.** Absolute zero can be interpreted on a molecular level; at absolute zero the system has its *minimum* possible total internal energy (kinetic plus potential). Because of quantum effects, however, it is *not* true that at $T = 0$, all molecular motion ceases. There are theoretical reasons for believing that absolute zero cannot be attained experimentally, although temperatures below 10^{-7} K have been achieved. The more closely we approach absolute zero, the more difficult it is to get closer. One statement of the *third law of thermodynamics* is that it is impossible to reach absolute zero in a finite number of thermodynamic steps.

Test Your Understanding of Section 20.6 An inventor looking for financial support comes to you with an idea for a gasoline engine that runs on a novel type of thermodynamic cycle. His design is made entirely of copper and is air-cooled. He claims that the engine will be 85% efficient. Should you invest in this marvelous new engine? (*Hint:* See Table 17.4.)

20.7 Entropy

The second law of thermodynamics, as we have stated it, is rather different in form from many familiar physical laws. It is not an equation or a quantitative relationship but rather a statement of *impossibility.* However, the second law *can* be stated as a quantitative relationship with the concept of *entropy,* the subject of this section.

We have talked about several processes that proceed naturally in the direction of increasing disorder. Irreversible heat flow increases disorder because the molecules are initially sorted into hotter and cooler regions; this sorting is lost when the system comes to thermal equilibrium. Adding heat to a body increases its disorder because it increases average molecular speeds and therefore the randomness of molecular motion. Free expansion of a gas increases its disorder because the molecules have greater randomness of position after the expansion than before. Figure 20.17 shows another process in which disorder increases.

20.17 When firecrackers explode, disorder increases: The neatly packaged chemicals within each firecracker are dispersed in all directions, and the stored chemical energy is converted to random kinetic energy of the fragments.

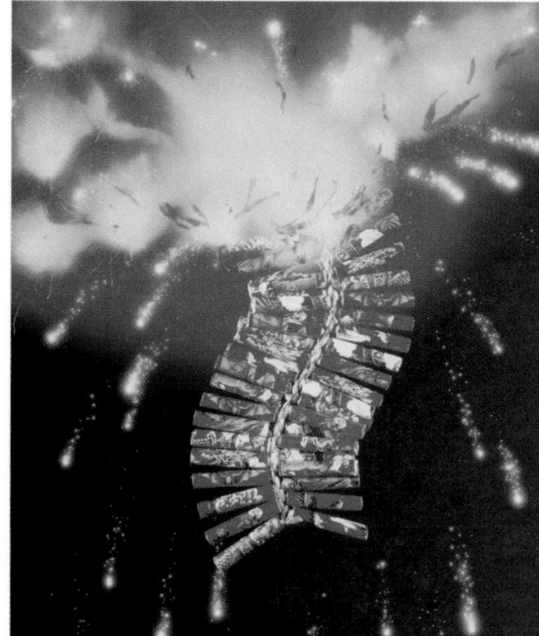

Entropy and Disorder

Entropy provides a *quantitative* measure of disorder. To introduce this concept, let's consider an infinitesimal isothermal expansion of an ideal gas. We add heat dQ and let the gas expand just enough to keep the temperature constant. Because the internal energy of an ideal gas depends only on its temperature, the internal energy is also constant; thus from the first law, the work dW done by the gas is equal to the heat dQ added. That is,

$$dQ = dW = p\,dV = \frac{nRT}{V}dV \qquad \text{so} \qquad \frac{dV}{V} = \frac{dQ}{nRT}$$

The gas is in a more disordered state after the expansion than before because the molecules are moving in a larger volume and have more randomness of position. Thus the fractional volume change dV/V is a measure of the increase in disorder, and the above equation shows that it is proportional to the quantity dQ/T. We introduce the symbol S for the entropy of the system, and we define the infinitesimal entropy change dS during an infinitesimal reversible process at absolute temperature T as

$$dS = \frac{dQ}{T} \qquad \text{(infinitesimal reversible process)} \qquad (20.17)$$

If a total amount of heat Q is added during a reversible isothermal process at absolute temperature T, the total entropy change $\Delta S = S_2 - S_1$ is given by

$$\Delta S = S_2 - S_1 = \frac{Q}{T} \qquad \text{(reversible isothermal process)} \qquad (20.18)$$

Entropy has units of energy divided by temperature; the SI unit of entropy is 1 J/K.

We can see how the quotient Q/T is related to the increase in disorder. Higher temperature means greater randomness of motion. If the substance is initially cold, with little molecular motion, adding heat Q causes a substantial fractional increase in molecular motion and randomness. But if the substance is already hot, the same quantity of heat adds relatively little to the greater molecular motion already present. So the quotient Q/T is an appropriate characterization of the increase in randomness or disorder when heat flows into a system.

Example 20.5 Entropy change in melting

One kilogram of ice at 0°C is melted and converted to water at 0°C. Compute its change in entropy, assuming that the melting is done reversibly. The heat of fusion of water is $L_f = 3.34 \times 10^5$ J/kg.

SOLUTION

IDENTIFY: The melting occurs at a constant temperature of 0°C, so this is a reversible isothermal process.

SET UP: We are given the amount of heat added (in terms of the heat of fusion) and the temperature $T = 273$ K. (Note that in entropy calculations we must always use absolute, or Kelvin, temperatures.) We can then calculate the entropy change using Eq. (20.18).

Continued

EXECUTE: The heat needed to melt the ice is $Q = mL_f = 3.34 \times 10^5$ J. From Eq. (20.18) the increase in entropy of the system is

$$\Delta S = S_2 - S_1 = \frac{Q}{T} = \frac{3.34 \times 10^5 \text{ J}}{273 \text{ K}} = 1.22 \times 10^3 \text{ J/K}$$

EVALUATE: This increase corresponds to the increase in disorder when the water molecules go from the highly ordered state of a crystalline solid to the much more disordered state of a liquid (Fig. 20.18).

In any *isothermal* reversible process, the entropy change equals the heat transferred divided by the absolute temperature. When we refreeze the water, Q has the opposite sign, and the entropy change of the water is $\Delta S = -1.22 \times 10^3$ J/K. The water molecules rearrange themselves into a crystal to form ice, so disorder and entropy both decrease.

20.18 Water molecules are arranged in a regular, ordered way in an ice crystal. When the ice melts, the hydrogen bonds between molecules are broken, increasing the water's disorder and its entropy.

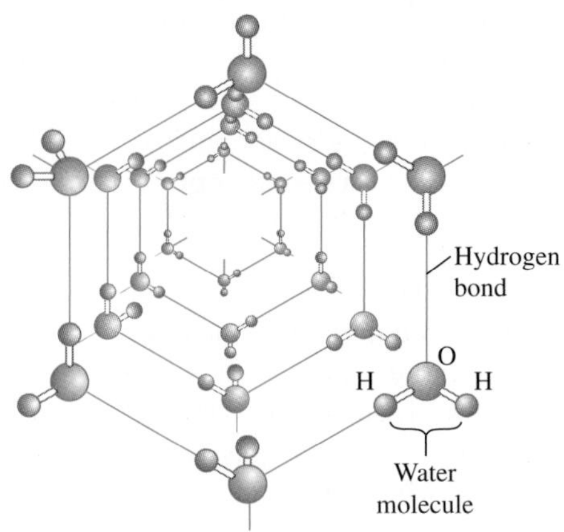

Entropy in Reversible Processes

We can generalize the definition of entropy change to include *any* reversible process leading from one state to another, whether it is isothermal or not. We represent the process as a series of infinitesimal reversible steps. During a typical step, an infinitesimal quantity of heat dQ is added to the system at absolute temperature T. Then we sum (integrate) the quotients dQ/T for the entire process; that is,

$$\Delta S = \int_1^2 \frac{dQ}{T} \quad \text{(entropy change in a reversible process)} \tag{20.19}$$

The limits 1 and 2 refer to the initial and final states.

Because entropy is a measure of the disorder of a system in any specific state, it must depend only on the current state of the system, not on its past history. We will show later that this is indeed the case. When a system proceeds from an initial state with entropy S_1 to a final state with entropy S_2, the change in entropy $\Delta S = S_2 - S_1$ defined by Eq. (20.19) does not depend on the path leading from the initial to the final state but is the same for *all possible* processes leading from state 1 to state 2. Thus the entropy of a system must also have a definite value for any given state of the system. We recall that *internal energy,* introduced in Chapter 19, also has this property, although entropy and internal energy are very different quantities.

Since entropy is a function only of the state of a system, we can also compute entropy changes in *irreversible* (nonequilibrium) processes for which Eqs. (20.17) and (20.19) are not applicable. We simply invent a path connecting the given initial and final states that *does* consist entirely of reversible equilibrium processes and compute the total entropy change for that path. It is not the actual path, but the entropy change must be the same as for the actual path.

As with internal energy, the above discussion does not tell us how to calculate entropy itself, but only the change in entropy in any given process. Just as with internal energy, we may arbitrarily assign a value to the entropy of a system in a specified reference state and then calculate the entropy of any other state with reference to this.

Example 20.6 Entropy change in a temperature change

One kilogram of water at 0°C is heated to 100°C. Compute its change in entropy.

SOLUTION

IDENTIFY: In practice, the process described would be done irreversibly, perhaps by setting a pan of water on an electric range whose cooking surface is maintained at 100°C. But the entropy change of the water depends only on the initial and final states of the system, and is the same whether the process is reversible or irreversible.

SET UP: We can imagine that the temperature of the water is increased reversibly in a series of infinitesimal steps, in each of which the temperature is raised by an infinitesimal amount dT. We then use Eq. (20.19) to integrate over all these steps and calculate the entropy change for the total process.

EXECUTE: From Eq. (17.14) the heat required to carry out each such infinitesimal step is $dQ = mc\,dT$. Substituting this into Eq. (20.19) and integrating, we find

$$\Delta S = S_2 - S_1 = \int_1^2 \frac{dQ}{T} = \int_{T_1}^{T_2} mc\frac{dT}{T} = mc\ln\frac{T_2}{T_1}$$

$$= (1.00\text{ kg})(4190\text{ J/kg}\cdot\text{K})\left(\ln\frac{373\text{ K}}{273\text{ K}}\right)$$

$$= 1.31 \times 10^3\text{ J/K}$$

EVALUATE: The entropy change is positive, as it must be for a process in which the system absorbs heat.

In this calculation we assumed that the specific heat c doesn't depend on temperature. That's a pretty good approximation, since c for water increases by only 1% between 0°C and 100°C.

CAUTION **When $\Delta S = Q/T$ can (and cannot) be used** In solving this problem you might be tempted to avoid doing an integral by using the simpler expression in Eq. (20.18), $\Delta S = Q/T$. This would be incorrect, however, because Eq. (20.18) is applicable only to *isothermal* processes, and the initial and final temperatures in our example are *not* the same. The *only* correct way to find the entropy change in a process with different initial and final temperatures is to use Eq. (20.19).

Conceptual Example 20.7 A reversible adiabatic process

A gas expands adiabatically and reversibly. What is its change in entropy?

SOLUTION

In an adiabatic process, no heat enters or leaves the system. Hence $dQ = 0$ and there is *no* change in entropy in this reversible process: $\Delta S = 0$. Every *reversible* adiabatic process is a constant-entropy process. (For this reason, reversible adiabatic processes are also called *isentropic* processes.) The increase in disorder resulting from the gas occupying a greater volume is exactly balanced by the decrease in disorder associated with the lowered temperature and reduced molecular speeds.

Example 20.8 Entropy change in a free expansion

A thermally insulated box is divided by a partition into two compartments, each having volume V (Fig. 20.19). Initially, one compartment contains n moles of an ideal gas at temperature T, and the other compartment is evacuated. We then break the partition, and the gas expands to fill both compartments. What is the entropy change in this free-expansion process?

SOLUTION

IDENTIFY: For this process, $Q = 0$, $W = 0$, $\Delta U = 0$, and therefore (because the system is an ideal gas) $\Delta T = 0$. We might think that the entropy change is zero because there is no heat exchange. But Eq. (20.19) can be used to calculate entropy changes for *reversible* processes only; this free expansion is *not* reversible, and there *is* an entropy change. The process is adiabatic because $Q = 0$, but it is not isentropic because $\Delta S \neq 0$. As we mentioned

20.19 (a,b) Free expansion of an insulated ideal gas. (c) The free-expansion process doesn't pass through equilibrium states from a to b. However, the entropy change $S_b - S_a$ can be calculated by using the isothermal path shown or *any* reversible path from a to b.

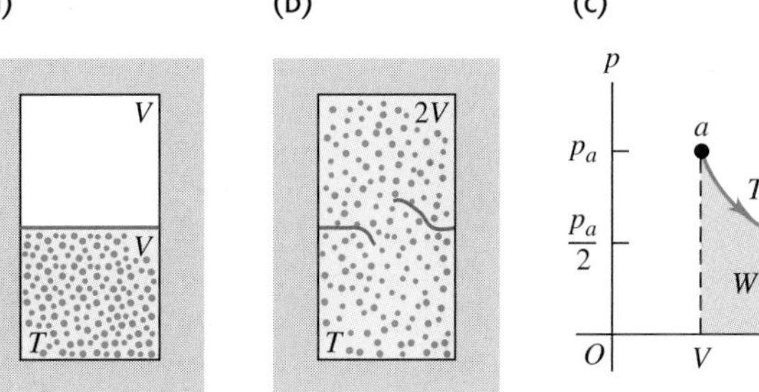

Continued

at the beginning of this section, entropy increases in a free expansion because the positions of the molecules are more random than before the expansion.

SET UP: To calculate ΔS, we recall that the entropy change depends only on the initial and final states. We can devise a *reversible* process having the same endpoints, use Eq. (20.19) to calculate its entropy change, and thus determine the entropy change in the original process. An appropriate reversible process in this case is an isothermal expansion from V to $2V$ at temperature T. The gas does work W during this substitute expansion, so an equal amount of heat Q must be supplied to keep the internal energy constant. We find the entropy change for this reversible isothermal process using Eq. (20.18); the entropy change for the free expansion will be the same.

EXECUTE: We found in Example 19.1 (Section 19.2) that the work done by n moles of ideal gas in an isothermal expansion from V_1 to V_2 is $W = nRT\ln(V_2/V_1)$. Using $V_1 = V$ and $V_2 = 2V$, we have

$$Q = W = nRT\ln\frac{2V}{V} = nRT\ln 2$$

Thus the entropy change is

$$\Delta S = \frac{Q}{T} = nR\ln 2$$

which is also the entropy change for the free expansion with the same initial and final states. For 1 mole,

$$\Delta S = (1\text{ mol})(8.314\text{ J/mol}\cdot\text{K})(\ln 2) = 5.76\text{ J/K}$$

EVALUATE: The entropy change is positive, as we predicted. The factor $(\ln 2)$ in our answer is a result of the volume having increased by a factor of 2. Can you show that if the volume had increased in the free expansion from V to xV, where x is an arbitrary number, the entropy change would have been $\Delta S = nR\ln x$?

Example 20.9 Entropy and the Carnot cycle

For the Carnot engine in Example 20.2 (Section 20.6), find the total entropy change in the engine during one cycle.

SOLUTION

IDENTIFY: All four steps in the Carnot cycle are reversible (see Fig. 20.13), so we can use the expression for the change in entropy in a reversible process.

SET UP: We find the entropy change ΔS for each step and then add the entropy changes to get the total ΔS for the cycle as a whole.

EXECUTE: There is no entropy change during the adiabatic expansion or adiabatic compression. During the isothermal expansion at $T_H = 500$ K the engine takes in 2000 J of heat, and its entropy change, from Eq. (20.18), is

$$\Delta S_H = \frac{Q_H}{T_H} = \frac{2000\text{ J}}{500\text{ K}} = 4.0\text{ J/K}$$

During the isothermal compression at $T_C = 350$ K the engine gives off 1400 J of heat, and its entropy change is

$$\Delta S_C = \frac{Q_C}{T_C} = \frac{-1400\text{ J}}{350\text{ K}} = -4.0\text{ J/K}$$

The total entropy change in the engine during one cycle is $\Delta S_{total} = \Delta S_H + \Delta S_C = 4.0\text{ J/K} + (-4.0\text{ J/K}) = 0$.

EVALUATE: The result $\Delta S_{total} = 0$ tells us that when the Carnot engine completes a cycle, it has the same entropy as it did at the beginning of the cycle. We'll explore this result in the following subsection.

What is the total entropy change of the engine's *environment* during this cycle? The hot (500 K) reservoir gives off 2000 J of heat during the reversible isothermal expansion, so its entropy change is $(-2000\text{ J})/(500\text{ K}) = -4.0\text{ J/K}$; the cold (350 K) reservoir absorbs 1400 J of heat during the reversible isothermal compression, so its entropy change is $(+1400\text{ J})/(350\text{ K}) = +4.0\text{ J/K}$. Thus each individual reservoir has an entropy change; however, the sum of these changes—that is, the total entropy change of the system's environment—is zero.

These results apply to the special case of the Carnot cycle, for which *all* of the processes are reversible. In this case we find that the total entropy change of the system and the environment together is zero. We will see that if the cycle includes irreversible processes (as is the case for the Otto cycle or Diesel cycle of Section 20.3), the total entropy change of the system and the environment *cannot* be zero, but rather must be positive.

Entropy in Cyclic Processes

Example 20.9 showed that the total entropy change for a cycle of a particular Carnot engine, which uses an ideal gas as its working substance, is zero. This result follows directly from Eq. (20.13), which we can rewrite as

$$\frac{Q_H}{T_H} + \frac{Q_C}{T_C} = 0 \qquad (20.20)$$

The quotient Q_H/T_H equals ΔS_H, the entropy change of the engine that occurs at $T = T_H$. Likewise, Q_C/T_C equals ΔS_C, the (negative) entropy change of the engine that occurs at $T = T_C$. Hence Eq. (20.20) says that $\Delta S_H + \Delta S_C = 0$; that is, there is zero net entropy change in one cycle.

What about Carnot engines that use a different working substance? According to the second law, *any* Carnot engine operating between given temperatures T_H and T_C has the same efficiency $e = 1 - T_C/T_H$ [Eq. (20.14)]. Combining this expression for e with Eq. (20.4), $e = 1 + Q_C/Q_H$, just reproduces Eq. (20.20). So Eq. (20.20) is valid for any Carnot engine working between these temperatures, whether its working substance is an ideal gas or not. We conclude that *the total entropy change in one cycle of any Carnot engine is zero.*

This result can be generalized to show that the total entropy change during *any* reversible cyclic process is zero. A reversible cyclic process appears on a pV-diagram as a closed path (Fig. 20.20a). We can approximate such as path as closely as we like by a sequence of isothermal and adiabatic processes forming parts of many long, thin Carnot cycles (Fig. 20.20b). The total entropy change for the full cycle is the sum of the entropy changes for each small Carnot cycle, each of which is zero. So **the total entropy change during *any* reversible cycle is zero:**

$$\int \frac{dQ}{T} = 0 \qquad \text{(reversible cyclic process)} \tag{20.21}$$

It follows that when a system undergoes a reversible process leading from any state a to any other state b, *the entropy change of the system is independent of the path* (Fig. 20.20c). If the entropy change for path 1 were different from the change for path 2, the system could be taken along path 1 and then backward along path 2 to the starting point, with a nonzero net change in entropy. This would violate the conclusion that the total entropy change in such a cyclic process must be zero. Because the entropy change in such processes is independent of path, we conclude that in any given state, the system has a definite value of entropy that depends only on the state, not on the processes that led to that state.

Entropy in Irreversible Processes

In an idealized, reversible process involving only equilibrium states, the total entropy change of the system and its surroundings is zero. But all *irreversible* processes involve an increase in entropy. Unlike energy, *entropy is not a conserved quantity.* The entropy of an isolated system *can* change, but as we shall see, it can never decrease. The free expansion of a gas, described in Example 20.8, is an irreversible process in an isolated system in which there is an entropy increase.

20.20 (a) A reversible cyclic process for an ideal gas is shown as a red closed path on a pV-diagram. Several ideal-gas isotherms are shown in blue. (b) We can approximate the path in (a) by a series of long, thin Carnot cycles; one of these is highlighted in gold. The total entropy change is zero for each Carnot cycle and for the actual cyclic process. (c) The entropy change between points a and b is independent of the path.

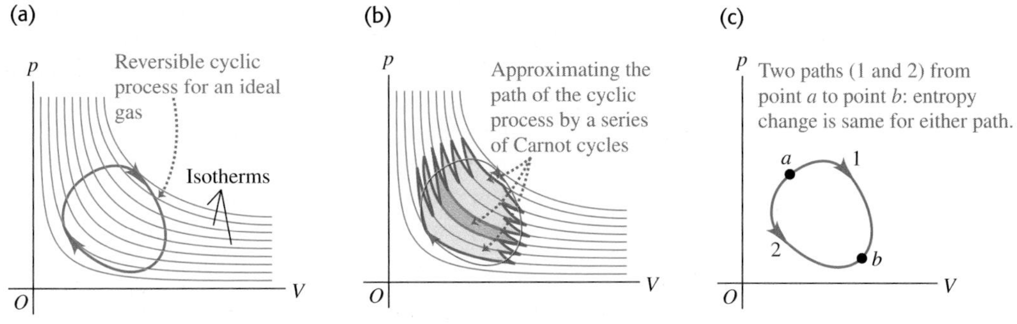

Example 20.10 An irreversible process

Suppose 1.00 kg of water at 100°C is placed in thermal contact with 1.00 kg of water at 0°C. What is the total change in entropy? Assume that the specific heat of water is constant at 4190 J/kg · K over this temperature range.

SOLUTION

IDENTIFY: This process involves irreversible heat flow because of the temperature differences.

SET UP: Since there are equal masses of 0°C water and 100°C water, the final temperature is the average of these two temperatures, or 50°C. Although the processes are irreversible, we can calculate the entropy changes for the (initially) hot water and the (initially) cold water in the same way as in Example 20.6 by assuming that the process occurs reversibly. We must use Eq. (20.19) to calculate ΔS for each substance because the temperatures change in the process.

EXECUTE: The final temperature is 50°C = 323 K. The entropy change of the hot water is

$$\Delta S_{\text{hot}} = mc\int_{T_1}^{T_2}\frac{dT}{T} = (1.00\text{ kg})(4190\text{ J/kg}\cdot\text{K})\int_{373\text{K}}^{323\text{K}}\frac{dT}{T}$$

$$= (4190\text{ J/K})\left(\ln\frac{323\text{ K}}{373\text{ K}}\right) = -603\text{ J/K}$$

The entropy change of the cold water is

$$\Delta S_{\text{cold}} = (4190\text{ J/K})\left(\ln\frac{323\text{ K}}{273\text{ K}}\right) = +705\text{ J/K}$$

The *total* entropy change of the system is

$$\Delta S_{\text{total}} = \Delta S_{\text{hot}} + \Delta S_{\text{cold}} = (-603\text{ J/K}) + 705\text{ J/K} = +102\text{ J/K}$$

EVALUATE: An irreversible heat flow in an isolated system is accompanied by an increase in entropy. We could have reached the same end state by simply mixing the two quantities of water. This, too, is an irreversible process; because the entropy depends only on the state of the system, the total entropy change would be the same, 102 J/K.

It's worth noting that the entropy of the system increases *continuously* as the two quantities of water come to equilibrium. For example, the first 4190 J of heat transferred cools the hot water to 99°C and warms the cold water to 1°C. The net change in entropy for this step is approximately

$$\Delta S = \frac{-4190\text{ J}}{373\text{ K}} + \frac{4190\text{ J}}{273\text{ K}} = +4.1\text{ J/K}$$

Can you show in a similar way that the net entropy change is positive for *any* one-degree temperature change leading to the equilibrium condition?

Entropy and the Second Law

The results of Example 20.10 about the flow of heat from a higher to a lower temperature, or the mixing of substances at different temperatures, are characteristic of *all* natural (that is, irreversible) processes. When we include the entropy changes of all the systems taking part in the process, the increases in entropy are always greater than the decreases. In the special case of a *reversible* process, the increases and decreases are equal. Hence we can state the general principle: **When all systems taking part in a process are included, the entropy either remains constant or increases.** In other words: **No process is possible in which the total entropy decreases, when all systems taking part in the process are included.** This is an alternative statement of the second law of thermodynamics in terms of entropy. Thus it is equivalent to the "engine" and "refrigerator" statements discussed earlier. Fig. 20.21 shows a specific example of this general principle.

The increase of entropy in every natural, irreversible process measures the increase of disorder or randomness in the universe associated with that process. Consider again the example of mixing hot and cold water (Example 20.10). We *might* have used the hot and cold water as the high- and low-temperature reservoirs of a heat engine. While removing heat from the hot water and giving heat to the cold water, we could have obtained some mechanical work. But once the hot and cold water have been mixed and have come to a uniform temperature, this opportunity to convert heat to mechanical work is lost irretrievably. The lukewarm water will never *unmix* itself and separate into hotter and colder portions. No decrease in *energy* occurs when the hot and cold water are mixed. What has been lost is not *energy,* but *opportunity,* the opportunity to convert part of the heat from the hot water into mechanical work. Hence when entropy increases, energy becomes less *available,* and the universe becomes more random or "run down."

20.21 The mixing of colored ink and water starts from a state of relative order (low entropy) in which each fluid is separate and distinct from the other. The final state after mixing is more disordered (has greater entropy). Spontaneous unmixing of the ink and water, a process in which there would be a net decrease in entropy, is never observed.

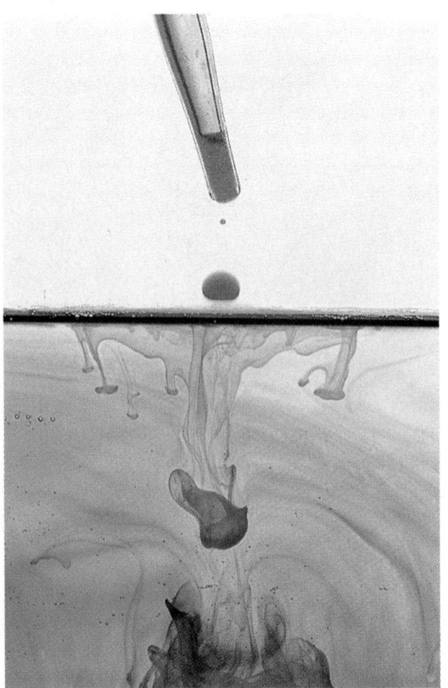

Test Your Understanding of Section 20.7 Suppose 2.00 kg of water at 50°C spontaneously changes temperature, so that half of the water cools to 0°C while the other half spontaneously warms to 100°C. (All of the water remains liquid, so it doesn't freeze or boil.) What would be the entropy change of the water? Is this process possible? (Hint: See Example 20.10.)

*20.8 Microscopic Interpretation of Entropy

We described in Section 19.4 how the internal energy of a system could be calculated, at least in principle, by adding up all the kinetic energies of its constituent particles and all the potential energies of interaction among the particles. This is called a *microscopic* calculation of the internal energy. We can also make a microscopic calculation of the entropy S of a system. Unlike energy, however, entropy is not something that belongs to each individual particle or pair of particles in the system. Rather, entropy is a measure of the disorder of the system as a whole. To see how to calculate entropy microscopically, we first have to introduce the idea of *macroscopic* and *microscopic states.*

Suppose you toss N identical coins on the floor, and half of them show heads and half show tails. This is a description of the large-scale or **macroscopic state** of the system of N coins. A description of the **microscopic state** of the system includes information about each individual coin: Coin 1 was heads, coin 2 was tails, coin 3 was tails, and so on. There can be many microscopic states that correspond to the same macroscopic description. For instance, with $N = 4$ coins there are six possible states in which half are heads and half are tails (Fig. 20.22). The number of microscopic states grows rapidly with increasing N; for $N = 100$ there are $2^{100} = 1.27 \times 10^{30}$ microscopic states, of which 1.01×10^{29} are half heads and half tails.

The least probable outcomes of the coin toss are the states that are either all heads or all tails. It is certainly possible that you could throw 100 heads in a row, but don't bet on it; the probability of doing this is only 1 in 1.27×10^{30}. The most probable outcome of tossing N coins is that half are heads and half are tails. The reason is that this *macroscopic* state has the greatest number of corresponding *microscopic* states, as shown in Fig. 20.22.

To make the connection to the concept of entropy, note that N coins that are all heads constitute a completely ordered macroscopic state; the description "all heads" completely specifies the state of each one of the N coins. The same is true if the coins are all tails. But the macroscopic description "half heads, half tails" by itself tells you very little about the state (heads or tails) of each individual coin. We say that the system is *disordered* because we know so little about its microscopic state. Compared to the state "all heads" or "all tails," the state "half heads, half tails" has a much greater number of possible microscopic states, much greater disorder, and hence much greater entropy (which is a quantitative measure of disorder).

Now instead of N coins, consider a mole of an ideal gas containing Avogadro's number of molecules. The macroscopic state of this gas is given by its pressure p, volume V, and temperature T; a description of the microscopic state involves stating the position and velocity for each molecule in the gas. At a given pressure, volume, and temperature, the gas may be in any one of an astronomically large number of microscopic states, depending on the positions and velocities of its 6.02×10^{23} molecules. If the gas undergoes a free expansion into a greater volume, the range of possible positions increases, as does the number of possible microscopic states. The system becomes more disordered, and the entropy increases as calculated in Example 20.8 (Section 20.7).

We can draw the following general conclusion: **For any system, the most probable macroscopic state is the one with the greatest number of corresponding microscopic states, which is also the macroscopic state with the greatest disorder and the greatest entropy.**

20.22 All possible microscopic states of four coins. There can be several possible microscopic states for each macroscopic state.

Macroscopic state
Corresponding microscopic states
Four heads
Three heads, one tails
Two heads, two tails
One head, three tails
Four tails

Calculating Entropy: Microscopic States

Let w represent the number of possible microscopic states for a given macroscopic state. (For the four coins shown in Fig. 20.22 the state of four heads has $w = 1$, the state of three heads and one tails has $w = 4$, and so on.) Then the entropy S of a macroscopic state can be shown to be given by

$$S = k \ln w \qquad \text{(microscopic expression for entropy)} \qquad (20.22)$$

where $k = R/N_A$ is the Boltzmann constant (gas constant per molecule) introduced in Section 18.3. As Eq. (20.22) shows, increasing the number of possible microscopic states w increases the entropy S.

What matters in a thermodynamic process is not the absolute entropy S but the *difference* in entropy between the initial and final states. Hence an equally valid and useful definition would be $S = k \ln w + C$, where C is a constant, since C cancels in any calculation of an entropy difference between two states. But it's convenient to set this constant equal to zero and use Eq. (20.22). With this choice, since the smallest possible value of w is unity, the smallest possible value of S for any system is $k \ln 1 = 0$. Entropy can *never* be negative.

In practice, calculating w is a difficult task, so Eq. (20.22) is typically used only to calculate the absolute entropy S of certain special systems. But we can use this relationship to calculate *differences* in entropy between one state and another. Consider a system that undergoes a thermodynamic process that takes it from macroscopic state 1, for which there are w_1 possible microscopic states, to macroscopic state 2, with w_2 associated microscopic states. The change in entropy in this process is

$$\Delta S = S_2 - S_1 = k \ln w_2 - k \ln w_1 = k \ln \frac{w_2}{w_1} \qquad (20.23)$$

The *difference* in entropy between the two macroscopic states depends on the *ratio* of the numbers of possible microscopic states.

As the following example shows, using Eq. (20.23) to calculate a change in entropy from one macroscopic state to another gives the same results as considering a reversible process connecting those two states and using Eq. (20.19).

Example 20.11 A microscopic calculation of entropy change

Use Eq. (20.23) to calculate the entropy change in the free expansion of n moles of gas at temperature T described in Example 20.8 (Fig. 20.23).

SOLUTION

IDENTIFY: We are asked to calculate the entropy change using the number of microstates in the initial macroscopic state (Fig. 20.23a) and in the final macroscopic state (Fig. 20.23b).

SET UP: When the partition is broken, the velocities of the molecules are unaffected, since no work is done. But each molecule now has twice as much volume in which it can move and hence has twice the number of possible positions. This is all we need to calculate the entropy change using Eq. (20.23).

EXECUTE: Let w_1 be the number of microscopic states of the system as a whole when the gas occupies volume V (Fig. 20.23a). The

20.23 In a free expansion of N molecules in which the volume doubles, the number of possible microscopic states increases by 2^N.

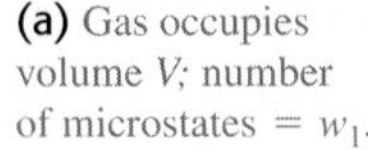

(a) Gas occupies volume V; number of microstates $= w_1$.

(b) Gas occupies volume $2V$; number of microstates $= w_2 = 2^N w_1$.

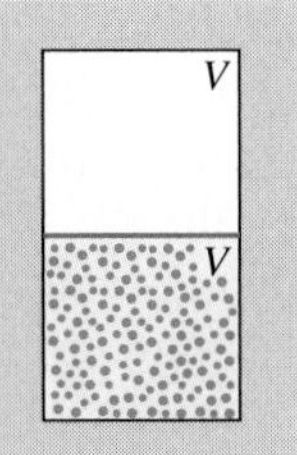

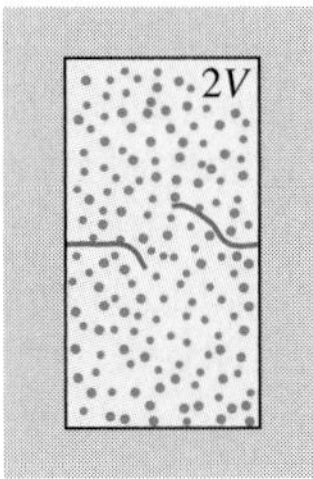

number of molecules is $N = nN_A$, and each molecule has twice as many possible states after the partition is broken. Hence the number w_2 of microscopic states when the gas occupies volume $2V$ (Fig. 20.23b) is greater by a factor of 2^N; that is, $w_2 = 2^N w_1$.

The change in entropy in this process is

$$\Delta S = k\ln\frac{w_2}{w_1} = k\ln\frac{2^N w_1}{w_1} = k\ln 2^N$$
$$= Nk\ln 2$$

Since $N = nN_A$ and $k = R/N_A$, this becomes

$$\Delta S = (nN_A)(R/N_A)\ln 2 = nR\ln 2$$

EVALUATE: We have found the same result as in Example 20.8, but without any reference to the thermodynamic path taken.

Microscopic States and the Second Law

The relationship between entropy and the number of microscopic states gives us new insight into the entropy statement of the second law of thermodynamics, that the entropy of a closed system can never decrease. From Eq. (20.22) this means that a closed system can never spontaneously undergo a process that decreases the number of possible microscopic states.

An example of such a forbidden process would be if all of the air in your room spontaneously moved to one half of the room, leaving a vacuum in the other half. Such a "free compression" would be the reverse of the free expansion of Examples 20.8 and 20.11. This would decrease the number of possible microscopic states by a factor of 2^N. Strictly speaking, this process is not impossible! The probability of finding a given molecule in one half of the room is $\frac{1}{2}$, so the probability of finding all of the molecules in one half of the room at once is $(\frac{1}{2})^N$. (This is exactly the same as the probability of having a tossed coin come up heads N times in a row.) This probability is *not* zero. But lest you worry about suddenly finding yourself gasping for breath in the evacuated half of your room, consider that a typical room might hold 1000 moles of air, and so $N = 1000N_A = 6.02 \times 10^{26}$ molecules. The probability of all the molecules being in the same half of the room is therefore $(\frac{1}{2})^{6.02\times 10^{26}}$. Expressed as a decimal, this number has more than 10^{26} zeros to the right of the decimal point!

Because the probability of such a "free compression" taking place is so vanishingly small, it has almost certainly never occurred anywhere in the universe since the beginning of time. We conclude that for all practical purposes the second law of thermodynamics is never violated.

Test Your Understanding of Section 20.8 A quantity of N molecules of an ideal gas initially occupies volume V. The gas then expands to volume $2V$. The number of microscopic states of the gas increases in this expansion. Under which of the following circumstances will this number increase the most? (i) if the expansion is reversible and isothermal; (ii) if the expansion is reversible and adiabatic; (iii) the number will change by the same amount for both circumstances.

CHAPTER 20 SUMMARY

Reversible and irreversible processes: A reversible process is one whose direction can be reversed by an infinitesimal change in the conditions of the process, and in which the system is always in or very close to thermal equilibrium. All other thermodynamic processes are irreversible.

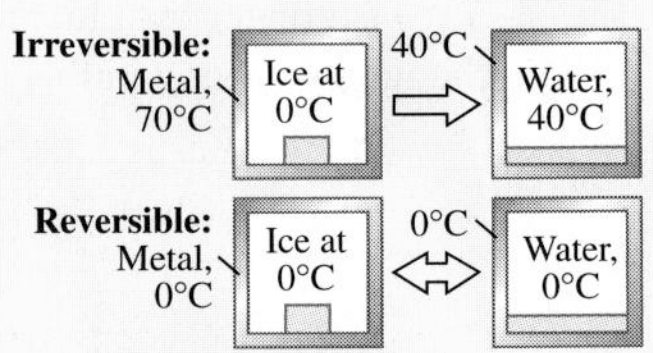

Heat engines: A heat engine takes heat Q_H from a source, converts part of it to work W, and discards the remainder $|Q_C|$ at a lower temperature. The thermal efficiency e of a heat engine measures how much of the absorbed heat is converted to work. (See Example 20.1)

$$e = \frac{W}{Q_H} = 1 + \frac{Q_C}{Q_H} = 1 - \left|\frac{Q_C}{Q_H}\right| \quad (20.4)$$

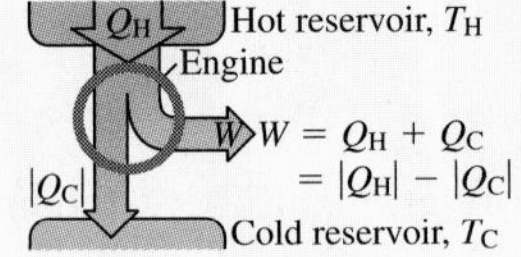

The Otto cycle: A gasoline engine operating on the Otto cycle has a theoretical maximum thermal efficiency e that depends on the compression ratio r and the ratio of heat capacities γ of the working substance.

$$e = 1 - \frac{1}{r^{\gamma-1}} \quad (20.6)$$

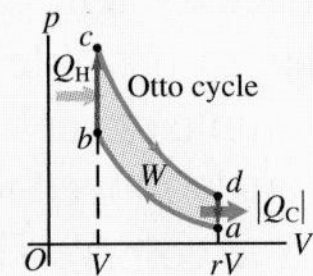

Refrigerators: A refrigerator takes heat Q_C from a colder place, has a work input $|W|$, and discards heat $|Q_H|$ at a warmer place. The effectiveness of the refrigerator is given by its coefficient of performance K.

$$K = \frac{|Q_C|}{|W|} = \frac{|Q_C|}{|Q_H| - |Q_C|} \quad (20.9)$$

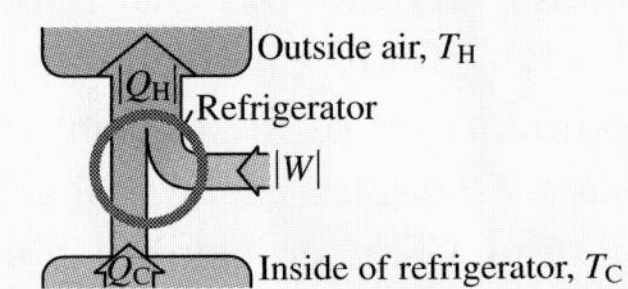

The second law of thermodynamics: The second law of thermodynamics describes the directionality of natural thermodynamic processes. It can be stated in several equivalent forms. The *engine* statement is that no cyclic process can convert heat completely into work. The *refrigerator* statement is that no cyclic process can transfer heat from a colder place to a hotter place with no input of mechanical work.

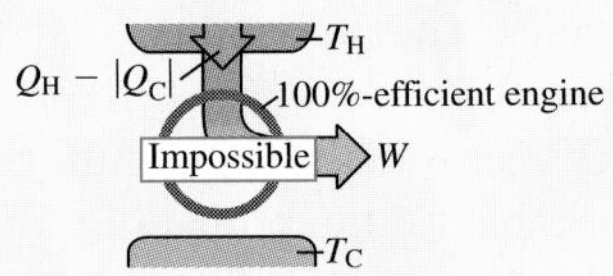

The Carnot cycle: The Carnot cycle operates between two heat reservoirs at temperatures T_H and T_C and uses only reversible processes. Its thermal efficiency depends only on T_H and T_C. An additional equivalent statement of the second law is that no engine operating between the same two temperatures can be more efficient than a Carnot engine. (See Examples 20.2 and 20.3.)

A Carnot engine run backward is a Carnot refrigerator. Its coefficient of performance depends only on T_H and T_C. Another form of the second law states that no refrigerator operating between the same two temperatures can have a larger coefficient of performance than a Carnot refrigerator. (See Example 20.4.)

$$e_{Carnot} = 1 - \frac{T_C}{T_H} = \frac{T_H - T_C}{T_H} \quad (20.14)$$

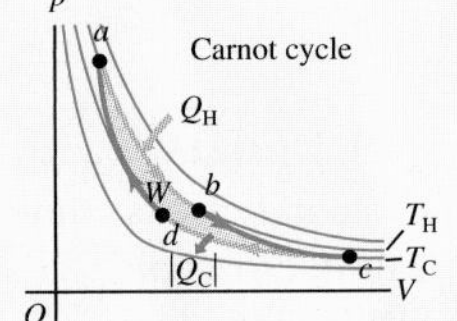

$$K_{Carnot} = \frac{T_C}{T_H - T_C} \quad (20.15)$$

Entropy: Entropy is a quantitative measure of the disorder of a system. The entropy change in any reversible process depends on the amount of heat flow and the absolute temperature T. Entropy depends only on the state of the system, and the change in entropy between given initial and final states is the same for all processes leading from one state to the other. This fact can be used to find the entropy change in an irreversible process. (See Examples 20.5–20.10)

An important statement of the second law of thermodynamics is that the entropy of an isolated system may increase but can never decrease. When a system interacts with its surroundings, the total entropy change of system and surroundings can never decrease. When the interaction involves only reversible processes, the total entropy is constant and $\Delta S = 0$; when there is any irreversible process, the total entropy increases and $\Delta S > 0$.

$$\Delta S = \int_1^2 \frac{dQ}{T} \qquad (20.19)$$

(reversible process)

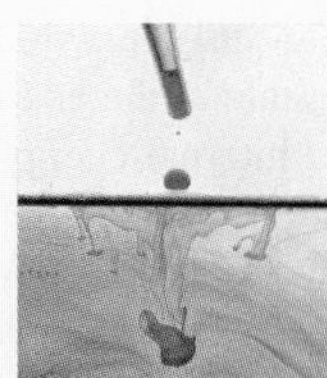

Entropy and microscopic states: When a system is in a particular macroscopic state, the particles that make up the system may be in any of w possible microscopic states. The greater the number w, the greater the entropy. (See Example 20.11.)

$$S = k \ln w \qquad (20.22)$$

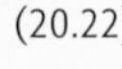
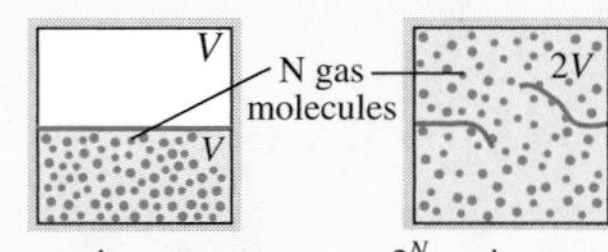

Key Terms

irreversible process, *673*
reversible process, *674*
equilibrium process, *674*
heat engine, *675*
working substance, *675*
cyclic process, *675*
thermal efficiency, *676*
compression ratio, *678*
Otto cycle, *678*
Diesel cycle, *680*
refrigerator, *680*
coefficient of performance, *680*
energy efficiency rating, *681–682*
heat pump, *682*
second law of thermodynamics, *682*
Carnot cycle, *684*
Kelvin temperature scale, *690*
absolute zero, *690*
entropy, *691*
macroscopic state, *697*
microscopic state, *697*

Answer to Chapter Opening Question ?

Yes. That's what a refrigerator does: It makes heat flow from the cold interior of the refrigerator to the warm outside. The second law of thermodynamics says that heat cannot *spontaneously* flow from a cold body to a hot one. A refrigerator has a motor that does work on the system to *force* the heat to flow in that way.

Answers to Test Your Understanding Questions

20.1 Answer: (ii) Like sliding a book across a table, rubbing your hands together uses friction to convert mechanical energy into heat. The (impossible) reverse process would involve your hands spontaneously getting colder, with the released energy forcing your hands to move rhythmically back and forth!

20.2 Answer: (iii), (i), (ii) From Eq. (20.4) the efficiency is $e = W/Q_H$, and from Eq. (20.2) $W = Q_H + Q_C = |Q_H| - |Q_C|$. For engine (i) $Q_H = 5000\text{ J}$ and $Q_C = -4500\text{ J}$, so $W = 5000\text{ J} + (-4500\text{ J}) = 500\text{ J}$ and $e = (500\text{ J})/(5000\text{ H}) = 0.100$. For engine (ii) $Q_H = 25{,}000\text{ J}$ and $W = 2000\text{ J}$, so $e = (2000\text{ J})/(25{,}000\text{ J}) = 0.080$. For engine (iii) $W = 400\text{ J}$ and $Q_C = -2800\text{ J}$, so $Q_H = W - Q_C = 400\text{ J} - (-2800\text{ J}) = 3200\text{ J}$ and $e = (400\text{ J})/(3200\text{ J}) = 0.125$.

20.3 Answers: (i), (ii) Doubling the amount of fuel burned per cycle means that Q_H is doubled, so the resulting pressure increase from b to c in Fig. 20.6 is greater. The compression ratio and hence the efficiency remain the same, so $|Q_C|$ (the amount of heat rejected to the environment) must increase by the same factor as Q_H. Hence the pressure drop from d to a in Fig. 20.6 is also greater. The volume V and the compression ratio r don't change, so the horizontal dimensions of the pV-diagram don't change.

20.4 Answer: no A refrigerator uses an input of work to transfer heat from one system (the refrigerator's interior) to another system (its exterior, which includes the house in which the refrigerator is installed). If the door is open, these two systems are really the *same* system and will eventually come to the same temperature. By the first law of thermodynamics, all of the work input to the refrigerator motor will be converted into heat and the temperature in your house will actually *increase*. To cool the house you need a system that will transfer heat from it to the outside world, such as an air conditioner or heat pump.

20.5 Answers: no, no Both the 100%-efficient engine of Fig. 20.11a and the workless refrigerator of Fig. 20.11b return to the same state at the end of a cycle as at the beginning, so the net change in internal energy of each system is zero $(\Delta U = 0)$. For the 100%-efficient engine, the net heat flow into the engine equals the net work done, so $Q = W$, $Q - W = 0$, and the first law $(\Delta U = Q - W)$ is obeyed. For the workless refrigerator, no net work is done (so $W = 0$) and as much heat flows into it as out (so $Q = 0$), so again $Q - W = 0$ and $\Delta U = Q - W$ in accordance with the first law. It is the second law of thermodynamics that tells us that both the 100%-efficient engine and the workless refrigerator are impossible.

20.6 Answer: no The efficiency can be no better than that of a Carnot engine running between the same two temperature limits, $e_{\text{Carnot}} = 1 - (T_C/T_H)$ [Eq. (20.14)]. The temperature T_C of the cold reservoir for this air-cooled engine is about 300 K (ambient temperature), and the temperature T_H of the hot reservoir cannot exceed the melting point of copper, 1356 K (see Table 17.4). Hence the maximum possible Carnot efficiency is $e = 1 - (300\text{ K})/(1356\text{ K}) = 0.78$, or 78%. The temperature of any real engine would be less than this, so it would be impossible for the inventor's engine to attain 85% efficiency. You should invest your money elsewhere.

20.7 Answers: −102 J/K, no The process described is exactly the opposite of the process used in Example 20.10. The result violates the second law of thermodynamics, which states that the entropy of an isolated system cannot decrease.

20.8 Answer: (i) For case (i), we saw in Example 20.8 (Section 20.7) that for an ideal gas, the entropy change in a free expansion is the same as in an isothermal expansion. From Eq. (20.23), this implies that the ratio of the number of microscopic states after and before the expansion, w_2/w_1, is also the same for these two cases. From Example 20.11, $w_2/w_1 = 2^N$, so the number of microscopic states increases by a factor 2^N. For case (ii), in a reversible expansion the entropy change is $\Delta S = \int dQ/T = 0$; if the expansion is adiabatic there is no heat flow, so $\Delta S = 0$. From Eq. (20.23), $w_2/w_1 = 1$ and there is *no* change in the number of microscopic states. The difference is that in an adiabatic expansion the temperature drops and the molecules move more slowly, so they have fewer microscopic states available to them than in an isothermal expansion.

PROBLEMS

Discussion Questions

Q20.1. A pot is half-filled with water, and a lid is placed on it, forming a tight seal so that no water vapor can escape. The pot is heated on a stove, forming water vapor inside the pot. The heat is then turned off and the water vapor condenses back to liquid. Is this cycle reversible or irreversible? Why?

Q20.2. Give two examples of reversible processes and two examples of irreversible processes in purely mechanical systems, such as blocks sliding on planes, springs, pulleys, and strings. Explain what makes each process reversible or irreversible.

Q20.3. What irreversible processes occur in a gasoline engine? Why are they irreversible?

Q20.4. Suppose you try to cool the kitchen of your house by leaving the refrigerator door open. What happens? Why? Would the result be the same if you left open a picnic cooler full of ice? Explain the reason for any differences.

Q20.5. A member of the U.S. Congress proposed a scheme to produce energy as follows. Water molecules (H_2O) are to be broken apart to produce hydrogen and oxygen. The hydrogen is then burned (that is, combined with oxygen), releasing energy in the process. The only product of this combustion is water, so there is no pollution. In light of the second law of thermodynamics, what do you think of this energy-producing scheme?

Q20.6. Is it a violation of the second law of thermodynamics to convert mechanical energy completely into heat? To convert heat completely into work? Explain your answers.

Q20.7. Imagine a special air filter placed in a window of a house. The tiny holes in the filter allow only air molecules moving faster than a certain speed to exit the house, and allow only air molecules moving slower than that speed to enter the house from outside. Explain why such an air filter would cool the house, and why the second law of thermodynamics makes building such a filter an impossible task.

Q20.8. An electric motor has its shaft coupled to that of an electric generator. The motor drives the generator, and some current from the generator is used to run the motor. The excess current is used to light a home. What is wrong with this scheme?

Q20.9. When a wet cloth is hung up in a hot wind in the desert, it is cooled by evaporation to a temperature that may be 20 C° or so below that of the air. Discuss this process in light of the second law of thermodynamics.

Q20.10. Compare the pV-diagram for the Otto cycle in Fig. 20.6 with the diagram for the Carnot heat engine in Fig. 20.13. Explain some of the important differences between the two cycles.

Q20.11. If no real engine can be as efficient as a Carnot engine operating between the same two temperatures, what is the point of developing and using Eq. (20.14)?

Q20.12. The efficiency of heat engines is high when the temperature difference between the hot and cold reservoirs is large. Refrigerators, on the other hand, work better when the temperature difference is small. Thinking of the mechanical refrigerator cycle shown in Fig. 20.9, explain in physical terms why it takes less work to remove heat from the working substance if the two reservoirs (the inside of the refrigerator and the outside air) are at nearly the same temperature, than if the outside air is much warmer than the interior of the refrigerator.

Q20.13. What would be the efficiency of a Carnot engine operating with $T_H = T_C$? What would be the efficiency if $T_C = 0$ K and T_H were any temperature above 0 K? Interpret your answers.

Q20.14. Real heat engines, like the gasoline engine in a car, always have some friction between their moving parts, although lubricants keep the friction to a minimum. Would a heat engine with completely frictionless parts be 100% efficient? Why or why not? Does the answer depend on whether or not the engine runs on the Carnot cycle? Again, why or why not?

Q20.15. Does a refrigerator full of food consume more power if the room temperature is 20°C than if it is 15°C? Or is the power consumption the same? Explain your reasoning.

Q20.16. In Example 20.4, a Carnot refrigerator requires a work input of only 230 J to extract 346 J of heat from the cold reservoir.

Doesn't this discrepancy imply a violation of the law of conservation of energy? Explain why or why not.

Q20.17. Explain why each of the following processes is an example of increasing disorder or randomness: mixing hot and cold water; free expansion of a gas; irreversible heat flow; developing heat by mechanical friction. Are entropy increases involved in all of these? Why or why not?

Q20.18. The free expansion of a gas is an adiabatic process and so no heat is transferred. No work is done, so the internal energy does not change. Thus, $Q/T = 0$, yet the disorder of the system and thus its entropy have increased after the expansion. Why does Eq. 20.19 not apply to this situation?

Q20.19. Are the earth and sun in thermal equilibrium? Are there entropy changes associated with the transmission of energy from the sun to the earth? Does radiation differ from other modes of heat transfer with respect to entropy changes? Explain your reasoning.

Q20.20. Discuss the entropy changes involved in the preparation and consumption of a hot fudge sundae.

Q20.21. If you run a movie film backwards, it is as if the direction of time were reversed. In the time-reversed movie, would you see processes that violate conservation of energy? Conservation of linear momentum? Would you see processes that violate the second law of thermodynamics? In each case, if law-breaking processes could occur, give some examples.

Q20.22. Some critics of biological evolution claim that it violates the second law of thermodynamics, since evolution involves simple life forms developing into more complex and more highly ordered organisms. Explain why this is not a valid argument against evolution.

Q20.23. A growing plant creates a highly complex and organized structure out of simple materials such as air, water, and trace minerals. Does this violate the second law of thermodynamics? Why or why not? What is the plant's ultimate source of energy? Explain your reasoning.

Exercises

Section 20.2 Heat Engines

20.1. A diesel engine performs 2200 J of mechanical work and discards 4300 J of heat each cycle. (a) How much heat must be supplied to the engine in each cycle? (b) What is the thermal efficiency of the engine?

20.2. An aircraft engine takes in 9000 J of heat and discards 6400 J each cycle. (a) What is the mechanical work output of the engine during one cycle? (b) What is the thermal efficiency of the engine?

20.3. A Gasoline Engine. A gasoline engine takes in 1.61×10^4 J of heat and delivers 3700 J of work per cycle. The heat is obtained by burning gasoline with a heat of combustion of 4.60×10^4 J/g. (a) What is the thermal efficiency? (b) How much heat is discarded in each cycle? (c) What mass of fuel is burned in each cycle? (d) If the engine goes through 60.0 cycles per second, what is its power output in kilowatts? In horsepower?

20.4. A gasoline engine has a power output of 180 kW (about 241 hp). Its thermal efficiency is 28.0%. (a) How much heat must be supplied to the engine per second? (b) How much heat is discarded by the engine per second?

20.5. A certain nuclear-power plant has a mechanical-power output (used to drive an electric generator) of 330 MW. Its rate of heat input from the nuclear reactor is 1300 MW. (a) What is the thermal efficiency of the system? (b) At what rate is heat discarded by the system?

Section 20.3 Internal-Combustion Engines

20.6. (a) Calculate the theoretical efficiency for an Otto cycle engine with $\gamma = 1.40$ and $r = 9.50$. (b) If this engine takes in 10,000 J of heat from burning its fuel, how much heat does it discard to the outside air?

20.7. What compression ratio r must an Otto cycle have to achieve an ideal efficiency of 65.0% if $\gamma = 1.40$?

20.8. The Otto-cycle engine in a Mercedes-Benz SLK230 has a compression ratio of 8.8. (a) What is the ideal efficiency of the engine? Use $\gamma = 1.40$. (b) The engine in a Dodge Viper GT2 has a slightly higher compression ratio of 9.6. How much increase in the ideal efficiency results from this increase in the compression ratio?

Section 20.4 Refrigerators

20.9. A refrigerator has a coefficient of performance of 2.10. In each cycle it absorbs 3.40×10^4 J of heat from the cold reservoir. (a) How much mechanical energy is required each cycle to operate the refrigerator? (b) During each cycle, how much heat is discarded to the high-temperature reservoir?

20.10. A room air conditioner has a coefficient of performance of 2.9 on a hot day, and uses 850 W of electrical power. (a) How many joules of heat does the air conditioner remove from the room in one minute? (b) How many joules of heat does the air conditioner deliver to the hot outside air in one minute? (c) Explain why your answers to parts (a) and (b) are not the same.

20.11. A window air-conditioner unit absorbs 9.80×10^4 J of heat per minute from the room being cooled and in the same time period deposits 1.44×10^5 J of heat into the outside air. (a) What is the power consumption of the unit in watts? (b) What is the energy efficiency rating of the unit?

20.12. A freezer has a coefficient of performance of 2.40. The freezer is to convert 1.80 kg of water at 25.0°C to 1.80 kg of ice at −5.0°C in hour. (a) What amount of heat must be removed from the water at 25.0°C to convert it to ice at −5.0°C? (b) How much electrical energy is consumed by the freezer during this hour? (c) How much wasted heat is delivered to the room in which the freezer sits?

Section 20.6 The Carnot Cycle

20.13. A Carnot engine whose high-temperature reservoir is at 620 K takes in 550 J of heat at this temperature in each cycle and gives up 335 J to the low-temperature reservoir. (a) How much mechanical work does the engine perform during each cycle? (b) What is the temperature of the low-temperature reservoir? (c) What is the thermal efficiency of the cycle?

20.14. A Carnot engine is operated between two heat reservoirs at temperatures of 520 K and 300 K. (a) If the engine receives 6.45 kJ of heat energy from the reservoir at 520 K in each cycle, how many joules per cycle does it discard to the reservoir at 300 K? (b) How much mechanical work is performed by the engine during each cycle? (c) What is the thermal efficiency of the engine?

20.15. A Carnot engine has an efficiency of 59% and performs 2.5×10^4 J of work in each cycle. (a) How much heat does the engine extract from its heat source in each cycle? (b) Suppose the engine exhausts heat at room temperature (20.0°C). What is the temperature of its heat source?

20.16. An ice-making machine operates in a Carnot cycle. It takes heat from water at 0.0°C and rejects heat to a room at 24.0°C. Suppose that 85.0 kg of water at 0.0°C are converted to ice at 0.0°C. (a) How much heat is discharged into the room? (b) How much energy must be supplied to the device?

20.17. A Carnot refrigerator is operated between two heat reservoirs at temperatures of 320 K and 270 K. (a) If in each cycle the refrigerator receives 415 J of heat energy from the reservoir at 270 K, how many joules of heat energy does it deliver to the reservoir at 320 K? (b) If the refrigerator completes 165 cycles each minute, what power input is required to operate it? (c) What is the coefficient of performance of the refrigerator?

20.18. A Carnot device extracts 5.00 kJ of heat from a body at $-10.0°C$. How much work is done if the device exhausts heat into the environment at (a) 25.0°C; (b) 0.0°C; (c) $-25.0°C$; In each case, is the device acting as an engine or as a refrigerator?

20.19. A certain brand of freezer is advertised to use 730 kW · h of energy per year. (a) Assuming the freezer operates for 5 hours each day, how much power does it require while operating? (b) If the freezer keeps its interior at a temperature of $-5.0°C$ in a 20.0°C room, what is its theoretical maximum performance coefficient? (c) What is the theoretical maximum amount of ice this freezer could make in an hour, starting with water at 20.0°C?

20.20. An ideal Carnot engine operates between 500°C and 100°C with a heat input of 250 J per cycle. (a) How much heat is delivered to the cold reservoir in each cycle? (b) What minimum number of cycles is necessary for the engine to lift a 500-kg rock through a height of 100 m?

20.21. A Carnot heat engine has a thermal efficiency of 0.600, and the temperature of its hot reservoir is 800 K. If 3000 J of heat is rejected to the cold reservoir in one cycle, what is the work output of the engine during one cycle?

20.22. A Carnot heat engine uses a hot reservoir consisting of a large amount of boiling water and a cold reservoir consisting of a large tub of ice and water. In 5 minutes of operation, the heat rejected by the engine melts 0.0400 kg of ice. During this time, how much work W is performed by the engine?

20.23. You design an engine that takes in 1.50×10^4 J of heat at 650 K in each cycle and rejects heat at a temperature of 350 K. The engine completes 240 cycles in 1 minute. What is the theoretical maximum power output of your engine, in horsepower?

20.24. (a) Show that the efficiency e of a Carnot engine and the coefficient of performance K of a Carnot refrigerator are related by $K = (1 - e)/e$. The engine and refrigerator operate between the same hot and cold reservoirs. (b) What is K for the limiting values $e \to 1$ and $e \to 0$? Explain.

Section 20.7 Entropy

20.25. A sophomore with nothing better to do adds heat to 0.350 kg of ice at 0.0°C until it is all melted. (a) What is the change in entropy of the water? (b) The source of heat is a very massive body at a temperature of 25.0°C. What is the change in entropy of this body? (c) What is the total change in entropy of the water and the heat source?

20.26. You decide to take a nice hot bath but discover that your thoughtless roommate has used up most of the hot water. You fill the tub with 270 kg of 30.0°C water and attempt to warm it further by pouring in 5.00 kg of boiling water from the stove. (a) Is this a reversible or an irreversible process? Use physical reasoning to explain. (b) Calculate the final temperature of the bath water. (c) Calculate the net change in entropy of the system (bath water + boiling water), assuming no heat exchange with the air or the tub itself.

20.27. A 15.0-kg block of ice at 0.0°C melts to liquid water at 0.0°C inside a large room that has a temperature of 20.0°C. Treat the ice and the room as an isolated system, and assume that the room is large enough for its temperature change to be ignored. (a) Is the melting of the ice reversible or irreversible? Explain, using simple physical reasoning without resorting to any equations. (b) Calculate the net entropy change of the system during this process. Explain whether or not this result is consistent with your answer to part (a).

20.28. You make tea with 0.250 kg of 85.0°C water and let it cool to room temperature (20.0°C) before drinking it. (a) Calculate the entropy change of the water while it cools. (b) The cooling process is essentially isothermal for the air in your kitchen. Calculate the change in entropy of the air while the tea cools, assuming that all the heat lost by the water goes into the air. What is the total entropy change of the system tea + air?

20.29. Three moles of an ideal gas undergo a reversible isothermal compression at 20.0°C. During this compression, 1850 J of work is done on the gas. What is the change of entropy of the gas?

20.30. What is the change in entropy of 0.130 kg of helium gas at the normal boiling point of helium when it all condenses isothermally to 1.00 L of liquid helium? (*Hint:* See Table 17.4 in Section 17.6.)

20.31. (a) Calculate the change in entropy when 1.00 kg of water at 100°C is vaporized and converted to steam at 100°C (see Table 17.4). (b) Compare your answer to the change in entropy when 1.00 kg of ice is melted at 0°C, calculated in Example 20.5 (Section 20.7). Is the change in entropy greater for melting or for vaporization? Interpret your answer using the idea that entropy is a measure of the randomness of a system.

20.32. (a) Calculate the change in entropy when 1.00 mol of water (molecular mass 18.0 g/mol) at 100°C evaporates to form water vapor at 100°C. (b) Repeat the calculation of part (a) for 1.00 mol of liquid nitrogen, 1.00 mol of silver, and 1.00 mol of mercury when each is vaporized at its normal boiling point. (See Table 17.4 for the heats of vaporization, and Appendix D for the molar masses. Note that the nitrogen molecule is N_2.) (c) Your results in parts (a) and (b) should be in relatively close agreement. (This is called the *rule of Drepez and Trouton.*) Explain why this should be so, using the idea that entropy is a measure of the randomness of a system.

20.33. If 25.0 g of the metal gallium melts in your hand (see Fig. 17.20), what is the change in entropy of the gallium in this process? What about the change in entropy of your hand? Is it positive or negative? Is its magnitude greater or less than that of the change in entropy of the gallium?

*Section 20.8 Microscopic Interpretation of Entropy

***20.34.** A box is separated by a partition into two parts of equal volume. The left side of the box contains 500 molecules of nitrogen gas; the right side contains 100 molecules of oxygen gas. The two gases are at the same temperature. The partition is punctured, and equilibrium is eventually attained. Assume that the volume of the box is large enough for each gas to undergo a free expansion and not change temperature. (a) On average, how many molecules of each type will there be in either half of the box? (b) What is the change in entropy of the system when the partition is punctured? (c) What is the probability that the molecules will be found in the same distribution as they were before the partition was punctured—that is, 500 nitrogen molecules in the left half and 100 oxygen molecules in the right half?

***20.35.** Two moles of an ideal gas occupy a volume V. The gas expands isothermally and reversibly to a volume $3V$. (a) Is the velocity distribution changed by the isothermal expansion?

Explain. (b) Use Eq. (20.23) to calculate the change in entropy of the gas. (c) Use Eq. (20.18) to calculate the change in entropy of the gas. Compare this result to that obtained in part (b).

***20.36.** A lonely party balloon with a volume of 2.40 L and containing 0.100 mol of air is left behind to drift in the temporarily uninhabited and depressurized International Space Station. Sunlight coming through a porthole heats and explodes the balloon, causing the air in it to undergo a free expansion into the empty station, whose total volume is 425 m^3. Calculate the entropy change of the air during the expansion.

Problems

20.37. You design a Carnot engine that operates between temperatures of 500 K and 400 K and produces 2000 J of work in each cycle. (a) Calculate your engine's efficiency. (b) Calculate the amount of heat discarded during the isothermal compression at 400 K. (c) *Sketch* the 500 K and 400 K isotherms on a pV-diagram (no calculations); then sketch the Carnot cycle followed by your engine. (d) On the same diagram, *sketch* the 300 K isotherm; then sketch, in a different color if possible, the Carnot cycle starting at the same point on the 500 K isotherm but operating in a cycle between the 500 K and 300 K isotherms. (e) Compare the areas inside the loops (the net work done) for the two cycles. Notice that the same amount of heat is extracted from the hot reservoir in both cases. Can you explain why less heat is "wasted" during the 300 K isothermal compression than during the 400 K compression?

20.38. You are designing a Carnot engine that has 2 mol of CO_2 as its working substance; the gas may be treated as ideal. The gas is to have a maximum temperature of 527°C and a maximum pressure of 5.00 atm. With a heat input of 400 J per cycle, you want 300 J of useful work. (a) Find the temperature of the cold reservoir. (b) For how many cycles must this engine run to melt completely a 10.0-kg block of ice originally at 0.0°C, using only the heat rejected by the engine?

20.39. A Carnot engine whose low-temperature reservoir is at −90.0°C has an efficiency of 40.0%. An engineer is assigned the problem of increasing this to 45.0%. (a) By how many Celsius degrees must the temperature of the high-temperature reservoir be increased if the temperature of the low-temperature reservoir remains constant? (b) By how many Celsius degrees must the temperature of the low-temperature reservoir be decreased if the temperature of the high-temperature reservoir remains constant?

20.40. A heat engine takes 0.350 mol of a diatomic ideal gas around the cycle shown in the pV-diagram of Fig. 20.24. Process $1 \rightarrow 2$ is at constant volume, process $2 \rightarrow 3$ is adiabatic, and process $3 \rightarrow 1$ is at a constant pressure of 1.00 atm. The value of γ for this gas is 1.40. (a) Find the pressure and volume at points 1, 2, and 3. (b) Calculate Q, W, and ΔU for each of the three processes. (c) Find the net work done by the gas in the cycle. (d) Find the net heat flow into the engine in one cycle. (e) What is the thermal efficiency of the engine? How does this compare to the efficiency of a Carnot-cycle engine operating between the same minimum and maximum temperatures T_1 and T_2?

Figure 20.24 Problem 20.40.

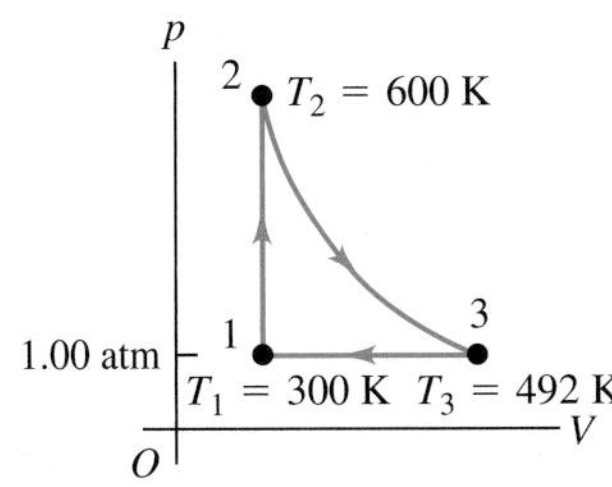

20.41. You build a heat engine that takes 1.00 mol of an ideal diatomic gas through the cycle shown in Fig. 20.25. (a) Show that segment ab is an isothermal compression. (b) During which segment(s) of the cycle is heat absorbed by the gas? During which segment(s) is heat rejected? How do you know? (c) Calculate the temperature at points a, b, and c. (d) Calculate the net heat exchanged with the surroundings and the net work done by the engine in one cycle. (e) Calculate the thermal efficiency of the engine.

Figure 20.25 Problem 20.41.

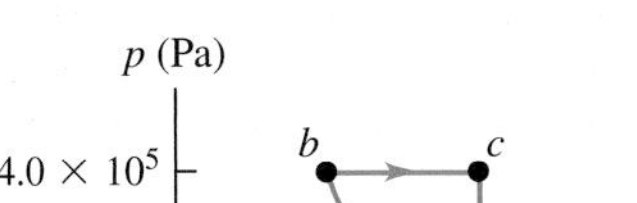
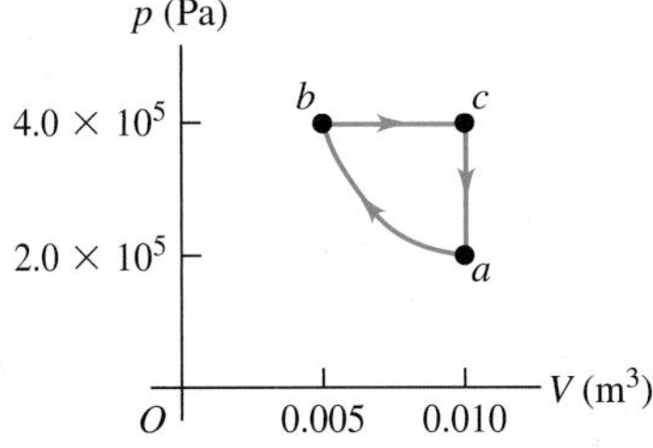

20.42. Heat Pump. A heat pump is a heat engine run in reverse. In winter it pumps heat from the cold air outside into the warmer air inside the building, maintaining the building at a comfortable temperature. In summer it pumps heat from the cooler air inside the building to the warmer air outside, acting as an air conditioner. (a) If the outside temperature in winter is −5.0°C and the inside temperature is 17.0°C, how many joules of heat will the heat pump deliver to the inside for each joule of electrical energy used to run the unit, assuming an ideal Carnot cycle? (b) Suppose you have the option of using electrical resistance heating rather than a heat pump. How much electrical energy would you need in order to deliver the same amount of heat to the inside of the house as in part (a)? Consider a Carnot heat pump delivering heat to the inside of a house to maintain it at 68°F. Show that the heat pump delivers less heat for each joule of electrical energy used to operate the unit as the outside temperature decreases. Notice that this behavior is opposite to the dependence of the efficiency of a Carnot heat engine on the difference in the reservoir temperatures. Explain why this is so.

20.43. A heat engine operates using the cycle shown in Fig. 20.26. The working substance is 2.00 mol of helium gas, which reaches a maximum temperature of 327°C. Assume the helium can be treated as an ideal gas. Process bc is isothermal. The pressure in states a and c is 1.00×10^5 Pa, and the pressure in state b is 3.00×10^5 Pa. (a) How much heat enters the gas and how much leaves the gas each cycle? (b) How much work does the engine do each cycle, and what is its efficiency? (c) Compare this engine's efficiency with the maximum possible efficiency attainable with the hot and cold reservoirs used by this cycle.

Figure 20.26 Problem 20.43.

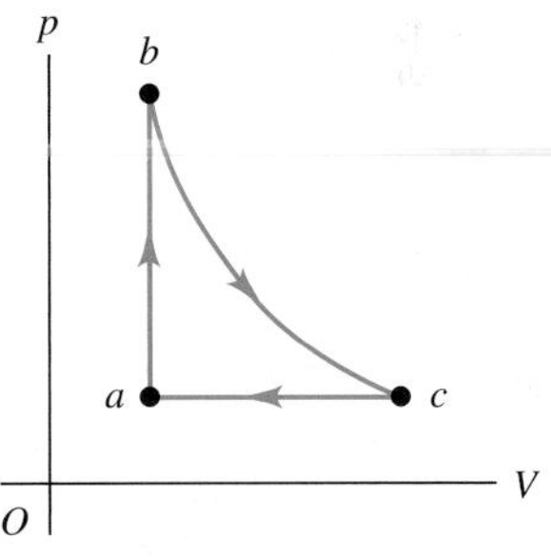

20.44. As a budding mechanical engineer, you are called upon to design a Carnot engine that has 2.00 mol of a monatomic ideal gas as its working substance and operates from a high-temperature reservoir at 500°C. The engine is to lift a 15.0-kg weight 2.00 m per cycle, using 500 J of heat input. The gas in the engine chamber can have a minimum volume of 5.00 L during the cycle. (a) Draw a pV-diagram for this cycle. Show in your diagram where heat enters and leaves the gas. (b) What must be the temperature of the cold reservoir? (c) What is the thermal efficiency of the engine? (d) How much heat energy does this engine waste per cycle? (e) What is the maximum pressure that the gas chamber will have to withstand?

20.45. An experimental power plant at the Natural Energy Laboratory of Hawaii generates electricity from the temperature gradient of the ocean. The surface and deep-water temperatures are 27°C and 6°C, respectively. (a) What is the maximum theoretical efficiency of this power plant? (b) If the power plant is to produce 210 kW of power, at what rate must heat be extracted from the warm water? At what rate must heat be absorbed by the cold water? Assume the maximum theoretical efficiency. (c) The cold water that enters the plant leaves it at a temperature of 10°C. What must be the flow rate of cold water through the system? Give your answer in kg/h and L/h.

20.46. What is the thermal efficiency of an engine that operates by taking n moles of diatomic ideal gas through the cycle $1 \rightarrow 2 \rightarrow 3 \rightarrow 4 \rightarrow 1$ shown in Fig. 20.27?

Figure 20.27 Problem 20.46.

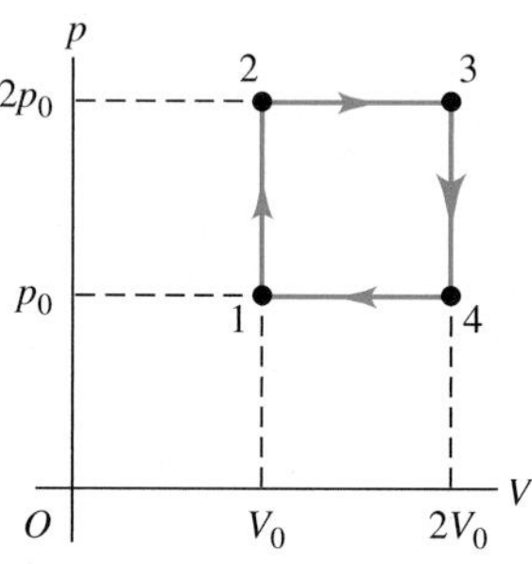

20.47. A cylinder contains oxygen at a pressure of 2.00 atm. The volume is 4.00 L, and the temperature is 300 K. Assume that the oxygen may be treated as an ideal gas. The oxygen is carried through the following processes:

(i) Heated at constant pressure from the initial state (state 1) to state 2, which has $T = 450$ K.
(ii) Cooled at constant volume to 250 K (state 3).
(iii) Compressed at constant temperature to a volume of 4.00 L (state 4).
(iv) Heated at constant volume to 300 K, which takes the system back to state 1.

(a) Show these four processes in a pV-diagram, giving the numerical values of p and V in each of the four states. (b) Calculate Q and W for each of the four processes. (c) Calculate the net work done by the oxygen. (d) What is the efficiency of this device as a heat engine? How does this compare to the efficiency of a Carnot-cycle engine operating between the same minimum and maximum temperatures of 250 K and 450 K?

20.48. Thermodynamic Processes for a Refrigerator. A refrigerator operates on the cycle shown in Fig. 20.28. The compression $(d \rightarrow a)$ and expansion $(b \rightarrow c)$ steps are adiabatic. The temperature, pressure, and volume of the coolant in each of the four states a, b, c, and d are given in the table.

State	T (°C)	P (kPa)	V (m^3)	U (kJ)	Percentage That Is Liquid
a	80	2305	0.0682	1969	0
b	80	2305	0.00946	1171	100
c	5	363	0.2202	1005	54
d	5	363	0.4513	1657	5

(a) In each cycle, how much heat is taken from inside the refrigerator into the coolant while the coolant is in the evaporator? (b) In each cycle, how much heat is exhausted from the coolant into the air outside the refrigerator while the coolant is in the condenser? (c) In each cycle, how much work is done by the motor that operates the compressor? (d) Calculate the coefficient of performance of the refrigerator.

Figure 20.28 Problem 20.48.

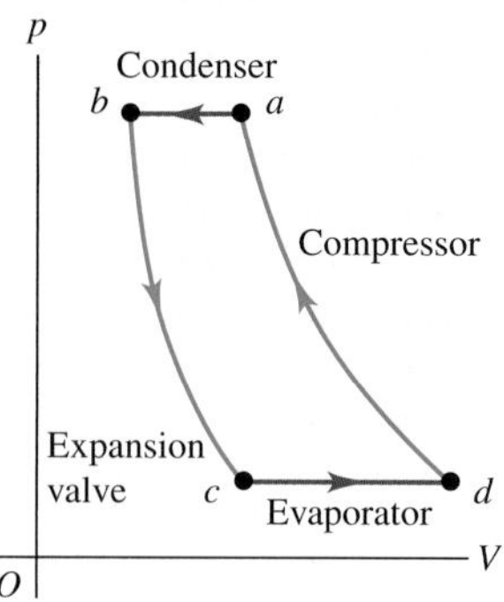

20.49. A monatomic ideal gas is taken around the cycle shown in Fig. 20.29 in the direction shown in the figure. The path for process $c \rightarrow a$ is a straight line in the pV-diagram. (a) Calculate Q, W, and ΔU for each process $a \rightarrow b$, $b \rightarrow c$, and $c \rightarrow a$. (b) What are Q, W, and ΔU for one complete cycle? (c) What is the efficiency of the cycle?

Figure 20.29 Problem 20.49.

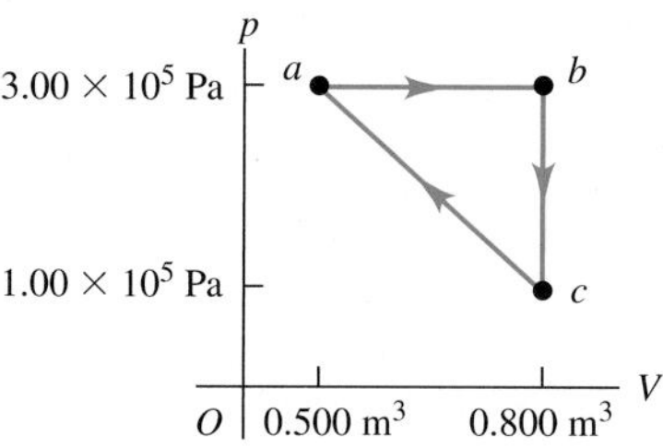

20.50. A Stirling-Cycle Engine. The *Stirling cycle* is similar to the Otto cycle, except that the compression and expansion of the gas are done at constant temperature, not adiabatically as in the Otto cycle. The Stirling cycle is used in *external* combustion engines (in fact, burning fuel is not necessary; *any* way of producing a temperature difference will do—solar, geothermal, ocean temperature gradient, etc.), which means that the gas inside the cylinder is not used in the combustion process. Heat is supplied by burning fuel steadily outside the cylinder, instead of explosively inside the cylinder as in the Otto cycle. For this reason Stirling-cycle engines are quieter than Otto-cycle engines, since there are no intake and exhaust valves (a major source of engine noise). While small Stirling engines are used for a variety of purposes, Stirling engines for automobiles have not been successful because they are larger, heavier, and more expensive than conventional automobile engines. In the cycle, the working fluid goes through the following sequence of steps (Fig. 20.30):

Figure 20.30 Problem 20.50.

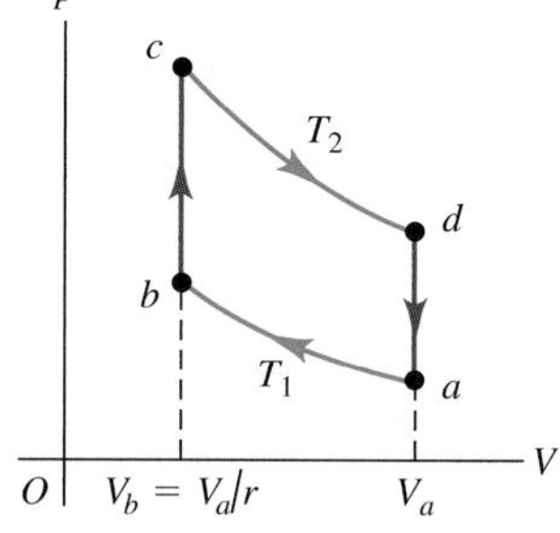

(i) Compressed isothermally at temperature T_1 from the initial state a to state b, with a compression ratio r.
(ii) Heated at constant volume to state c at temperature T_2.
(iii) Expanded isothermally at T_2 to state d.
(iv) Cooled at constant volume back to the initial state a.

Assume that the working fluid is n moles of an ideal gas (for which C_V is independent of temperature). (a) Calculate Q, W, and ΔU for each of the processes $a \rightarrow b$, $b \rightarrow c$, $c \rightarrow d$, and $d \rightarrow a$. (b) In the Stirling cycle, the heat transfers in the processes $b \rightarrow c$ and $d \rightarrow a$ do not involve external heat sources but rather use *regeneration:* The same substance that transfers heat to the gas inside the cylinder in the process $b \rightarrow c$ also absorbs heat back from the gas in the process $d \rightarrow a$. Hence the heat transfers $Q_{b \rightarrow c}$ and $Q_{d \rightarrow a}$ do not play a role in determining the efficiency of the engine. Explain this last statement by comparing the expressions for $Q_{b \rightarrow c}$ and $Q_{d \rightarrow a}$ calculated in part (a). (c) Calculate the efficiency of a Stirling-cycle engine in terms of the temperatures T_1 and T_2. How does this compare to the efficiency of a Carnot-cycle engine operating between these same two temperatures? (Historically, the Stirling cycle was devised before the Carnot cycle.) Does this result violate the second law of thermodynamics? Explain. Unfortunately, actual Stirling-cycle engines cannot achieve this efficiency due to problems with the heat-transfer processes and pressure losses in the engine.

20.51. A Carnot engine operates between two heat reservoirs at temperatures T_H and T_C. An inventor proposes to increase the efficiency by running one engine between T_H and an intermediate temperature T' and a second engine between T' and T_C, using as input the heat expelled by the first engine. Compute the efficiency of this composite system, and compare it to that of the original engine.

20.52. A typical coal-fired power plant generates 1000 MW of usable power at an overall thermal efficiency of 40%. (a) What is the rate of heat input to the plant? (b) The plant burns anthracite coal, which has a heat of combustion of 2.65×10^7 J/kg. How much coal does the plant use per day, if it operates continuously? (c) At what rate is heat ejected into the cool reservoir, which is the nearby river? (d) The river's temperature is 18.0°C before it reaches the power plant and 18.5°C after it has received the plant's waste heat. Calculate the river's flow rate, in cubic meters per second. (e) By how much does the river's entropy increase each second?

20.53. Automotive Thermodynamics. A Volkswagen Passat has a six-cylinder Otto-cycle engine with compression ratio $r = 10.6$. The diameter of each cylinder, called the *bore* of the engine, is 82.5 mm. The distance that the piston moves during the compression in Fig. 20.5, called the *stroke* of the engine, is 86.4 mm. The initial pressure of the air–fuel mixture (at point a in Fig. 20.6) is 8.50×10^4 Pa, and the initial temperature is 300 K (the same as the outside air). Assume that 200 J of heat is added to each cylinder in each cycle by the burning gasoline, and that the gas has $C_V = 20.5$ J/mol · K and $\gamma = 1.40$. (a) Calculate the total work done in one cycle in each cylinder of the engine, and the heat released when the gas is cooled to the temperature of the outside air. (b) Calculate the volume of the air–fuel mixture at point a in the cycle. (c) Calculate the pressure, volume, and temperature of the gas at points b, c, and d in the cycle. In a pV-diagram, show the numerical values of p, V, and T for each of the four states. (d) Compare the efficiency of this engine with the efficiency of a Carnot-cycle engine operating between the same maximum and minimum temperatures.

20.54. An air conditioner operates on 800 W of power and has a performance coefficient of 2.80 with a room temperature of 21.0°C and an outside temperature of 35.0°C. (a) Calculate the rate of heat removal for this unit. (b) Calculate the rate at which heat is discharged to the outside air. (c) Calculate the total entropy change in the room if the air conditioner runs for 1 hour. Calculate the total entropy change in the outside air for the same time period. (d) What is the net change in entropy for the system (room + outside air)?

20.55. Unavailable Energy. The discussion of entropy and the second law that follows Example 20.10 (Section 20.7) says that the increase in entropy in an irreversible process is associated with energy becoming less available. Consider a Carnot cycle that uses a low-temperature reservoir with Kelvin temperature T_c. This is a true reservoir—that is, large enough not to change temperature when it accepts heat from the engine. Let the engine accept heat from an object of temperature T', where $T' > T_c$. The object is of finite size, so it cools as heat is extracted from it. The engine continues to operate until $T' = T_c$. (a) Show that the total magnitude of heat rejected to the low-temperature reservoir is $T_c|\Delta S_h|$, where ΔS_h is the change in entropy of the high-temperature reservoir. (b) Apply the result of part (a) to 1.00 kg of water initially at a temperature of 373 K as the heat source for the engine and $T_c = 273$ K. How much total mechanical work can be performed by the engine until it stops? (c) Repeat part (b) for 2.00 kg of water at 323 K. (d) Compare the amount of work that can be obtained from the energy in the water of Example 20.10 before and after it is mixed. Discuss whether your result shows that energy has become less available.

20.56. The maximum power that can be extracted by a wind turbine from an air stream is approximately

$$P = kd^2v^3$$

where d is the blade diameter, v is the wind speed, and the constant $k = 0.5$ W · s³/m⁵. (a) Explain the dependence of P on d and on v by considering a cylinder of air that passes over the turbine blades in time t (Fig. 20.31). This cylinder has diameter d, length $L = vt$, and density ρ. (b) The Mod-5B wind turbine at Kahaku on the Hawaiian island of Oahu has a blade diameter of 97 m (slightly longer than a football field) and sits atop a 58-m tower. It can produce 3.2 MW of electric power. Assuming 25% efficiency, what wind speed is required to produce this amount of power? Give your answer in m/s and in km/h. (c) Commercial wind turbines are commonly located in or downwind of mountain passes. Why?

Figure 20.31 Problem 20.56.

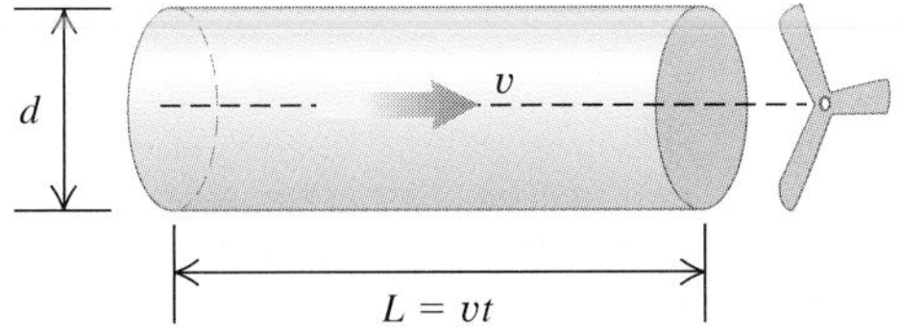

20.57. (a) How much work must a Carnot refrigerator do on a hot day to transfer 1000 J of heat from its interior at 10°C to the outside air at 35.0°C? (b) How much work must the same refrigerator do to transfer the same amount of heat if the interior temperature is the same, but the outside air is at only 15.0°C? (c) Sketch pV-diagrams for these two situations. Can you explain in physical terms why more work must be done when the temperature difference between the two isothermal stages is greater?

20.58. A 0.0500-kg cube of ice at an initial temperature of −15.0°C is placed in 0.600 kg of water at $T = 45.0$°C in an insulated container of negligible mass. (a) Calculate the final temperature of the water once the ice has melted. (b) Calculate the change in entropy of the system.

20.59. (a) For the Otto cycle shown in Fig. 20.6, calculate the changes in entropy of the gas in each of the constant-volume processes $b \rightarrow c$ and $d \rightarrow a$ in terms of the temperatures T_a, T_b, T_c, and T_d and the number of moles n and the heat capacity C_V of the gas. (b) What is the total entropy change in the engine during one cycle? (*Hint:* Use the relationships between T_a and T_b and between T_d and T_c.) (c) The processes $b \rightarrow c$ and $d \rightarrow a$ occur irreversibly in a real Otto engine. Explain how can this be reconciled with your result in part (b).

20.60. A *TS*-Diagram. (a) Graph a Carnot cycle, plotting Kelvin temperature vertically and entropy horizontally. This is called a temperature–entropy diagram, or *TS*-diagram. (b) Show that the area under any curve representing a reversible path in a temperature–entropy diagram represents the heat absorbed by the system. (c) Derive from your diagram the expression for the thermal efficiency of a Carnot cycle. (d) Draw a temperature–entropy diagram for the Stirling cycle, described in Problem 20.50. Use this diagram to relate the efficiency of the Carnot and Stirling cycles.

20.61. A physics student immerses one end of a copper rod in boiling water at 100°C and the other end in an ice–water mixture at 0°C. The sides of the rod are insulated. After steady-state conditions have been achieved in the rod, 0.160 kg of ice melts in a certain time interval. For this time interval, find (a) the entropy change of the boiling water; (b) the entropy change of the ice–water mixture; (c) the entropy change of the copper rod; (d) the total entropy change of the entire system.

20.62. To heat 1 cup of water $(250\ \text{cm}^3)$ to make coffee, you place an electric heating element in the cup. As the water temperature increases from 20°C to 65°C, the temperature of the heating element remains at a constant 120°C. Calculate the change in entropy of (a) the water; (b) the heating element; (c) the system of water and heating element. (Make the same assumption about the specific heat of water as in Example 20.10 in Section 20.7, and ignore the heat that flows into the ceramic coffee cup itself.) (d) Is this process reversible or irreversible? Explain.

20.63. An object of mass m_1, specific heat capacity c_1, and temperature T_1 is placed in contact with a second object of mass m_2, specific heat capacity c_2, and temperature $T_2 > T_1$. As a result, the temperature of the first object increases to T and the temperature of the second object decreases to T'. (a) Show that the entropy increase of the system is

$$\Delta S = m_1 c_1 \ln \frac{T}{T_1} + m_2 c_2 \ln \frac{T'}{T_2}$$

and show that energy conservation requires that

$$m_1 c_1 (T - T_1) = m_2 c_2 (T_2 - T')$$

(b) Show that the entropy change ΔS, considered as a function of T, is a *maximum* if $T = T'$, which is just the condition of thermodynamic equilibrium. (c) Discuss the result of part (b) in terms of the idea of entropy as a measure of disorder.

Challenge Problem

20.64. Consider a Diesel cycle that starts (at point a in Fig. 20.7) with air at temperature T_a. The air may be treated as an ideal gas. (a) If the temperature at point c is T_c, derive an expression for the efficiency of the cycle in terms of the compression ratio r. (b) What is the efficiency if $T_a = 300\ \text{K}$, $T_c = 950\ \text{K}$, $\gamma = 1.40$, and $r = 21.0$?

ELECTRIC CHARGE AND ELECTRIC FIELD

21

?Water makes life possible: The cells of your body could not function without water in which to dissolve essential biological molecules. What electrical properties of water make it such a good solvent?

LEARNING GOALS

By studying this chapter, you will learn:

- The nature of electric charge, and how we know that electric charge is conserved.
- How objects become electrically charged.
- How to use Coulomb's law to calculate the electric force between charges.
- The distinction between electric force and electric field.
- How to calculate the electric field due to a collection of charges.
- How to use the idea of electric field lines to visualize and interpret electric fields.
- How to calculate the properties of electric dipoles.

Back in Chapter 5, we briefly mentioned the four kinds of fundamental forces. To this point the only one of these forces that we have examined in any detail is gravity. Now we are ready to examine the force of *electromagnetism,* which encompasses both electricity and magnetism. Our exploration of electromagnetic phenomena will occupy our attention for most of the remainder of this book.

Electromagnetic interactions involve particles that have a property called *electric charge,* an attribute that is as fundamental as mass. Just as objects with mass are accelerated by gravitational forces, so electrically charged objects are accelerated by electric forces. The annoying electric spark you feel when you scuff your shoes across a carpet and then reach for a metal doorknob is due to charged particles leaping between your finger and the doorknob. Electric currents, such as those in a flashlight or a television, are simply streams of charged particles flowing within wires in response to electric forces. Even the forces that hold atoms together to form solid matter, and that keep the atoms of solid objects from passing through each other, are fundamentally due to electric interactions between the charged particles within atoms.

We begin our study of electromagnetism in this chapter by examining the nature of electric charge. We'll find that electric charge is quantized and that it obeys a conservation principle. We then turn to a discussion of the interactions of electric charges that are at rest in our frame of reference, called *electrostatic* interactions. Such interactions are of tremendous importance in chemistry and biology and have many technological applications. Electrostatic interactions are governed by a simple relationship known as *Coulomb's law* and are most conveniently described by using the concept of *electric field.* In later chapters we'll expand our discussion to include electric charges in motion. This will lead us to an understanding of magnetism and, remarkably, of the nature of light.

While the key ideas of electromagnetism are conceptually simple, applying them to practical problems will make use of many of your mathematical skills, especially your knowledge of geometry and integral calculus. For this reason you may find this chapter and those that follow to be more mathematically demanding than earlier chapters. The reward for your extra effort will be a deeper understanding of principles that are at the heart of modern physics and technology.

21.1 Electric Charge

The ancient Greeks discovered as early as 600 B.C. that after they rubbed amber with wool, the amber could attract other objects. Today we say that the amber has acquired a net **electric charge,** or has become *charged.* The word "electric" is derived from the Greek word *elektron,* meaning amber. When you scuff your shoes across a nylon carpet, you become electrically charged, and you can charge a comb by passing it through dry hair.

Plastic rods and fur (real or fake) are particularly good for demonstrating **electrostatics,** the interactions between electric charges that are at rest (or nearly so). Figure 21.1a shows two plastic rods and a piece of fur. After we charge each rod by rubbing it with the piece of fur, we find that the rods repel each other.

When we rub glass rods with silk, the glass rods also become charged and repel each other (Fig. 21.1b). But a charged plastic rod *attracts* a charged glass rod; furthermore, the plastic rod and the fur attract each other, and the glass rod and the silk attract each other (Fig. 21.1c).

These experiments and many others like them have shown that there are exactly two kinds of electric charge: the kind on the plastic rod rubbed with fur and the kind on the glass rod rubbed with silk. Benjamin Franklin (1706–1790) suggested calling these two kinds of charge *negative* and *positive,* respectively, and these names are still used. The plastic rod and the silk have negative charge; the glass rod and the fur have positive charge.

Two positive charges or two negative charges repel each other. A positive charge and a negative charge attract each other.

21.1 Experiments in electrostatics. (a) Negatively charged objects repel each other. (b) Positively charged objects repel each other. (c) Positvely charged objects and negatively charged objects attract each other.

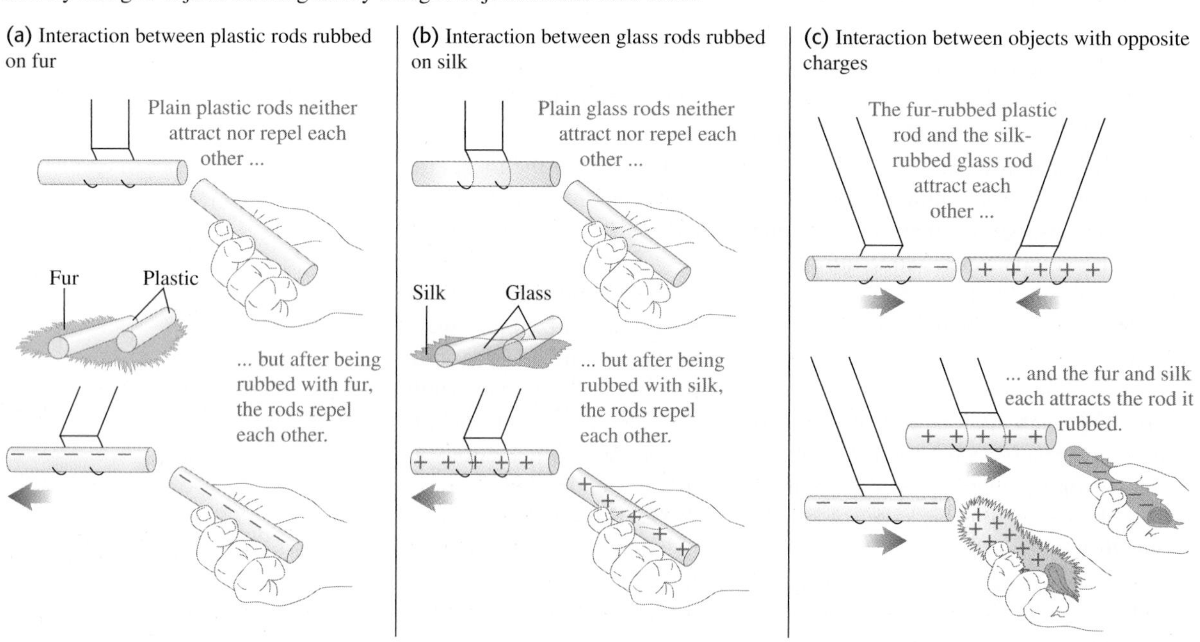
(a) Interaction between plastic rods rubbed on fur
Plain plastic rods neither attract nor repel each other ...
Fur
Plastic
... but after being rubbed with fur, the rods repel each other.
(b) Interaction between glass rods rubbed on silk
Plain glass rods neither attract nor repel each other ...
Silk
Glass
... but after being rubbed with silk, the rods repel each other.
(c) Interaction between objects with opposite charges
The fur-rubbed plastic rod and the silk-rubbed glass rod attract each other ...
... and the fur and silk each attracts the rod it rubbed.

21.2 Schematic diagram of the operation of a laser printer.

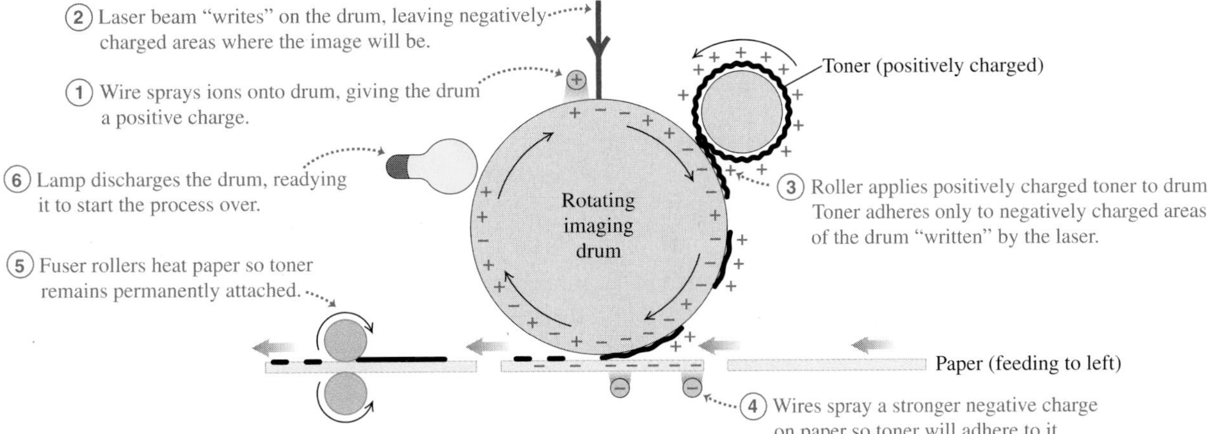

(2) Laser beam "writes" on the drum, leaving negatively charged areas where the image will be.
(1) Wire sprays ions onto drum, giving the drum a positive charge.
(6) Lamp discharges the drum, readying it to start the process over.
(5) Fuser rollers heat paper so toner remains permanently attached.
Rotating imaging drum
Toner (positively charged)
(3) Roller applies positively charged toner to drum. Toner adheres only to negatively charged areas of the drum "written" by the laser.
Paper (feeding to left)
(4) Wires spray a stronger negative charge on paper so toner will adhere to it.

CAUTION **Electric attraction and repulsion** The attraction and repulsion of two charged objects are sometimes summarized as "Like charges repel, and opposite charges attract." But keep in mind that the phrase "like charges" does *not* mean that the two charges are exactly identical, only that both charges have the same algebraic *sign* (both positive or both negative). "Opposite charges" means that both objects have an electric charge, and those charges have different signs (one positive and the other negative).

One technological application of forces between charged bodies is in a laser printer (Fig. 21.2). Initially the printer's light-sensitive imaging drum is given a positive charge. As the drum rotates, a laser beam shines on selected areas of the drum, leaving those areas with a *negative* charge. Positively charged particles of toner adhere only to the areas of the drum "written" by the laser. When a piece of paper is placed in contact with the drum, the toner particles stick to the paper and form an image.

Electric Charge and the Structure of Matter

When you charge a rod by rubbing it with fur or silk as in Fig. 21.1, there is no visible change in the appearance of the rod. What, then, actually happens to the rod when you charge it? To answer this question, we must look more closely at the structure and electric properties of atoms, the building blocks of ordinary matter of all kinds.

The structure of atoms can be described in terms of three particles: the negatively charged **electron**, the positively charged **proton,** and the uncharged **neutron** (Fig. 21.3). The proton and neutron are combinations of other entities called *quarks,* which have charges of $\pm\frac{1}{3}$ and $\pm\frac{2}{3}$ times the electron charge. Isolated quarks have not been observed, and there are theoretical reasons to believe that it is impossible in principle to observe a quark in isolation.

The protons and neutrons in an atom make up a small, very dense core called the **nucleus,** with dimensions of the order of 10^{-15} m. Surrounding the nucleus are the electrons, extending out to distances of the order of 10^{-10} m from the nucleus. If an atom were a few kilometers across, its nucleus would be the size of a tennis ball. The negatively charged electrons are held within the atom by the attractive electric forces exerted on them by the positively charged nucleus. (The protons and neutrons are held within the stable atomic nuclei by an attractive interaction, called the *strong nuclear force,* that overcomes the electric repulsion of the protons. The strong nuclear force has a short range, and its effects do not extend far beyond the nucleus.)

21.3 The structure of an atom. The particular atom depicted here is lithium (see Fig. 21.4a).

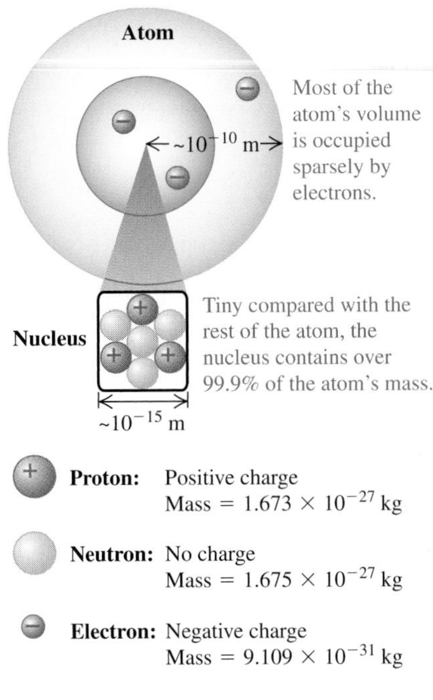

Atom
$\sim 10^{-10}$ m
Most of the atom's volume is occupied sparsely by electrons.
Nucleus
Tiny compared with the rest of the atom, the nucleus contains over 99.9% of the atom's mass.
$\sim 10^{-15}$ m
Proton: Positive charge Mass = 1.673×10^{-27} kg
Neutron: No charge Mass = 1.675×10^{-27} kg
Electron: Negative charge Mass = 9.109×10^{-31} kg
The charges of the electron and proton are equal in magnitude.

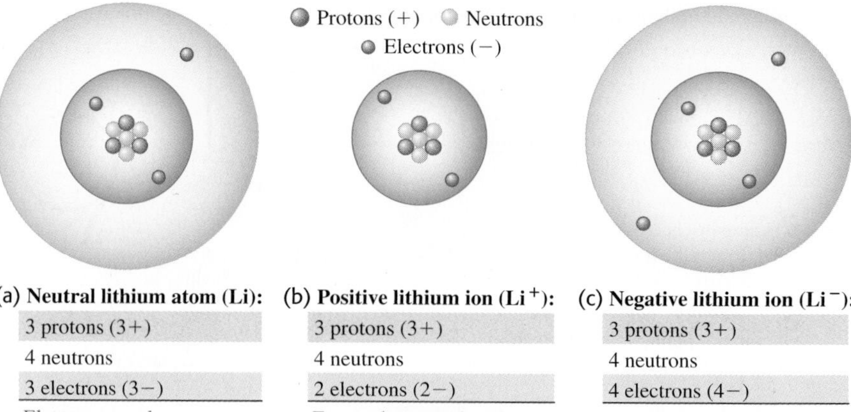

21.4 (a) A neutral atom has as many electrons as it does protons. (b) A positive ion has a deficit of electrons. (c) A negative ion has an excess of electrons. (The electron "shells" are a schematic representation of the actual electron distribution, a diffuse cloud many times larger than the nucleus.)

The masses of the individual particles, to the precision that they are presently known, are

$$\begin{aligned} \text{Mass of electron} &= m_e = 9.1093826(16) \times 10^{-31}\ \text{kg} \\ \text{Mass of proton} &= m_p = 1.67262171(29) \times 10^{-27}\ \text{kg} \\ \text{Mass of neutron} &= m_n = 1.67492728(29) \times 10^{-27}\ \text{kg} \end{aligned}$$

The numbers in parentheses are the uncertainties in the last two digits. Note that the masses of the proton and neutron are nearly equal and are roughly 2000 times the mass of the electron. Over 99.9% of the mass of any atom is concentrated in its nucleus.

The negative charge of the electron has (within experimental error) *exactly* the same magnitude as the positive charge of the proton. In a neutral atom the number of electrons equals the number of protons in the nucleus, and the net electric charge (the algebraic sum of all the charges) is exactly zero (Fig. 21.4a). The number of protons or electrons in a neutral atom of an element is called the **atomic number** of the element. If one or more electrons are removed, the remaining positively charged structure is called a **positive ion** (Fig. 21.4b). A **negative ion** is an atom that has *gained* one or more electrons (Fig. 21.4c). This gaining or losing of electrons is called **ionization.**

When the total number of protons in a macroscopic body equals the total number of electrons, the total charge is zero and the body as a whole is electrically neutral. To give a body an excess negative charge, we may either *add negative* charges to a neutral body or *remove positive* charges from that body. Similarly, we can create an excess positive charge by either *adding positive* charge or *removing negative* charge. In most cases, negatively charged (and highly mobile) electrons are added or removed, and a "positively charged body" is one that has lost some of its normal complement of electrons. When we speak of the charge of a body, we always mean its *net* charge. The net charge is always a very small fraction (typically no more than 10^{-12}) of the total positive charge or negative charge in the body.

Electric Charge Is Conserved

Implicit in the foregoing discussion are two very important principles. First is the **principle of conservation of charge:**

The algebraic sum of all the electric charges in any closed system is constant.

If we rub together a plastic rod and a piece of fur, both initially uncharged, the rod acquires a negative charge (since it takes electrons from the fur) and the fur acquires a positive charge of the *same* magnitude (since it has lost as many electrons as the rod has gained). Hence the total electric charge on the two bodies together does not change. In any charging process, charge is not created or destroyed; it is merely *transferred* from one body to another.

Conservation of charge is thought to be a *universal* conservation law. No experimental evidence for any violation of this principle has ever been observed. Even in high-energy interactions in which particles are created and destroyed, such as the creation of electron–positron pairs, the total charge of any closed system is exactly constant.

The second important principle is:

The magnitude of charge of the electron or proton is a natural unit of charge.

Every observable amount of electric charge is always an integer multiple of this basic unit. We say that charge is *quantized.* A familiar example of quantization is money. When you pay cash for an item in a store, you have to do it in one-cent increments. Cash can't be divided into amounts smaller than one cent, and electric charge can't be divided into amounts smaller than the charge of one electron or proton. (The quark charges, $\pm\frac{1}{3}$ and $\pm\frac{2}{3}$ of the electron charge, are probably not observable as isolated charges.) Thus the charge on any macroscopic body is always either zero or an integer multiple (negative or positive) of the electron charge.

Understanding the electric nature of matter gives us insight into many aspects of the physical world (Fig. 21.5). The chemical bonds that hold atoms together to form molecules are due to electric interactions between the atoms. They include the strong ionic bonds that hold sodium and chlorine atoms together to make table salt and the relatively weak bonds between the strands of DNA that record your body's genetic code. The normal force exerted on you by the chair in which you're sitting arises from electric forces between charged particles in the atoms of your seat and in the atoms of your chair. The tension force in a stretched string and the adhesive force of glue are likewise due to the electric interactions of atoms.

21.5 Most of the forces on this water skier are electric. Electric interactions between adjacent molecules give rise to the force of the water on the ski, the tension in the tow rope, and the resistance of the air on the skier's body. Electric interactions also hold the atoms of the skier's body together. Only one wholly nonelectric force acts on the skier: the force of gravity.

Test Your Understanding of Section 21.1 (a) Strictly speaking, does the plastic rod in Fig. 21.1 weigh more, less, or the same after rubbing it with fur? (b) What about the glass rod after rubbing it with silk? What about (c) the fur and (d) the silk?

21.2 Conductors, Insulators, and Induced Charges

Some materials permit electric charge to move easily from one region of the material to another, while others do not. For example, Fig. 21.6a shows a copper wire supported by a nylon thread. Suppose you touch one end of the wire to a charged plastic rod and attach the other end to a metal ball that is initially uncharged; you then remove the charged rod and the wire. When you bring another charged body up close to the ball (Figs. 21.6b and 21.6c), the ball is attracted or repelled, showing that the ball has become electrically charged. Electric charge has been transferred through the copper wire between the ball and the surface of the plastic rod.

The copper wire is called a **conductor** of electricity. If you repeat the experiment using a rubber band or nylon thread in place of the wire, you find that *no* charge is transferred to the ball. These materials are called **insulators.** Conductors permit the easy movement of charge through them, while insulators do not. (The supporting nylon threads shown in Fig. 21.6 are insulators, which prevents charge from leaving the metal ball and copper wire.)

As an example, carpet fibers on a dry day are good insulators. As you walk across a carpet, the rubbing of your shoes against the fibers causes charge to build

21.6 Copper is a good conductor of electricity; nylon is a good insulator. (a) The copper wire conducts charge between the metal ball and the charged plastic rod to charge the ball negatively. Afterward, the metal ball is (b) repelled by a negatively charged plastic rod and (c) attracted to a positively charged glass rod.

(a)

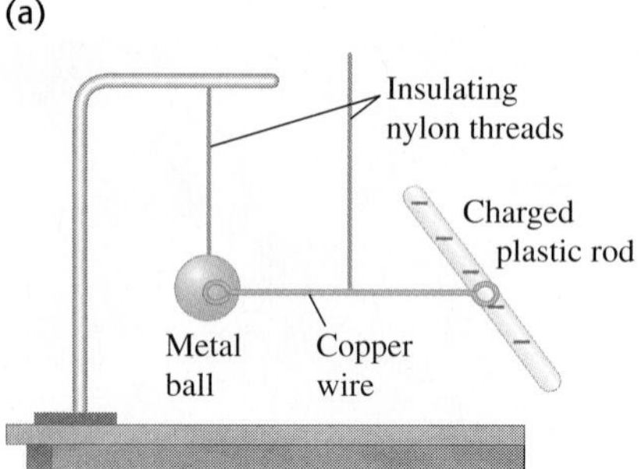

The wire conducts charge from the negatively charged plastic rod to the metal ball.

(b)

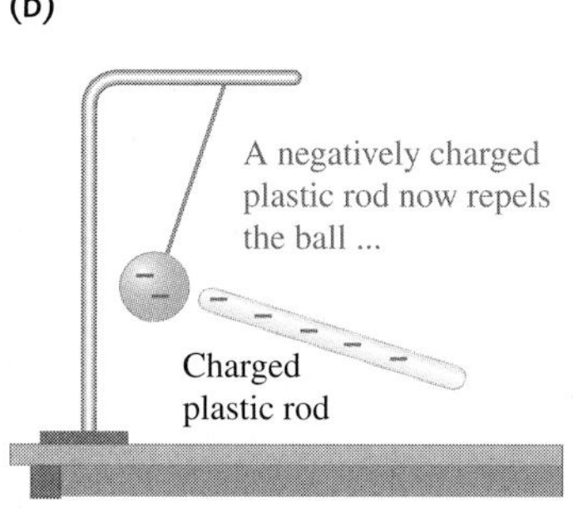

(c)

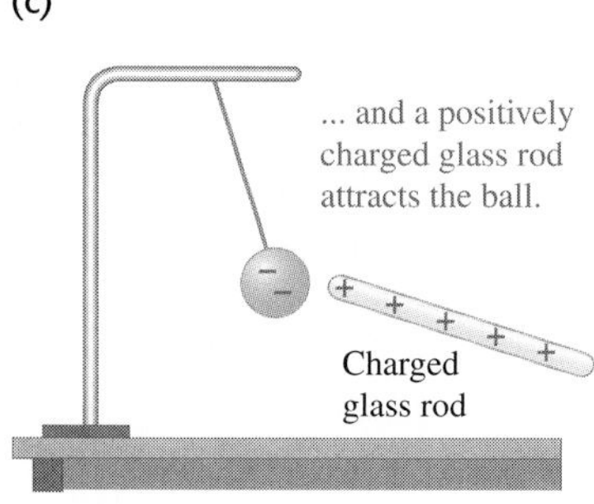

up on you, and this charge remains on you because it can't flow through the insulating fibers. If you then touch a conducting object such as a doorknob, a rapid charge transfer takes place between your finger and the doorknob, and you feel a shock. One way to prevent this is to wind some of the carpet fibers around conducting cores so that any charge that builds up on you can be transferred harmlessly to the carpet. Another solution is to coat the carpet fibers with an antistatic layer that does not easily transfer electrons to or from your shoes; this prevents any charge from building up on you in the first place.

Most metals are good conductors, while most nonmetals are insulators. Within a solid metal such as copper, one or more outer electrons in each atom become detached and can move freely throughout the material, just as the molecules of a gas can move through the spaces between the grains in a bucket of sand. The motion of these negatively charged electrons carries charge through the metal. The other electrons remain bound to the positively charged nuclei, which themselves are bound in nearly fixed positions within the material. In an insulator there are no, or very few, free electrons, and electric charge cannot move freely through the material. Some materials called *semiconductors* are intermediate in their properties between good conductors and good insulators.

Charging by Induction

We can charge a metal ball using a copper wire and an electrically charged plastic rod, as in Fig. 21.6a. In this process, some of the excess electrons on the rod are transferred from it to the ball, leaving the rod with a smaller negative charge. There is a different technique in which the plastic rod can give another body a charge of *opposite* sign without losing any of its own charge. This process is called charging by **induction.**

Figure 21.7 shows an example of charging by induction. An uncharged metal ball is supported on an insulating stand (Fig. 21.7a). When you bring a negatively charged rod near it, without actually touching it (Fig. 21.7b), the free electrons in the metal ball are repelled by the excess electrons on the rod, and they shift toward the right, away from the rod. They cannot escape from the ball because the supporting stand and the surrounding air are insulators. So we get excess negative charge at the right surface of the ball and a deficiency of negative charge (that is, a net positive charge) at the left surface. These excess charges are called **induced charges.**

Not all of the free electrons move to the right surface of the ball. As soon as any induced charge develops, it exerts forces toward the *left* on the other free electrons. These electrons are repelled by the negative induced charge on the right and attracted toward the positive induced charge on the left. The system reaches an equilibrium state in which the force toward the right on an electron, due to the charged rod, is just balanced by the force toward the left due to the induced charge. If we remove the charged rod, the free electrons shift back to the left, and the original neutral condition is restored.

21.7 Charging a metal ball by induction.

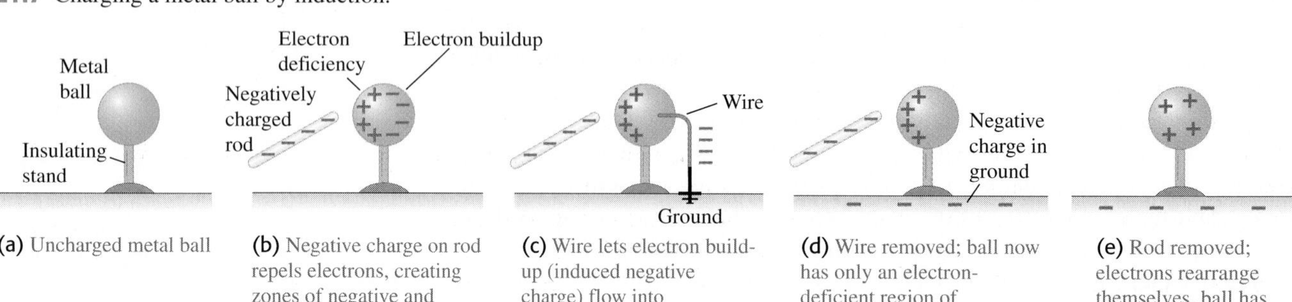

(a) Uncharged metal ball

(b) Negative charge on rod repels electrons, creating zones of negative and positive **induced charge**.

(c) Wire lets electron buildup (induced negative charge) flow into ground.

(d) Wire removed; ball now has only an electron-deficient region of positive charge.

(e) Rod removed; electrons rearrange themselves, ball has overall electron deficiency (net positive charge).

21.8 The charges within the molecules of an insulating material can shift slightly. As a result, a comb with either sign of charge attracts a neutral insulator. By Newton's third law the neutral insulator exerts an equal-magnitude attractive force on the comb.

(a) A charged comb picking up uncharged pieces of plastic

(b) How a negatively charged comb attracts an insulator

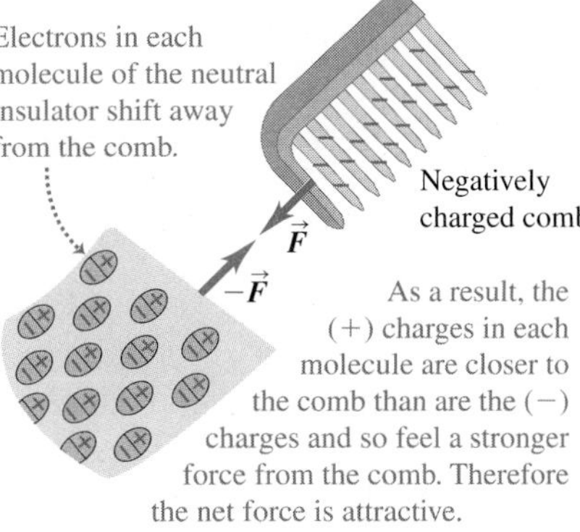

Electrons in each molecule of the neutral insulator shift away from the comb.
Negatively charged comb
$\vec{F}$
$-\vec{F}$
As a result, the (+) charges in each molecule are closer to the comb than are the (−) charges and so feel a stronger force from the comb. Therefore the net force is attractive.

(c) How a positively charged comb attracts an insulator

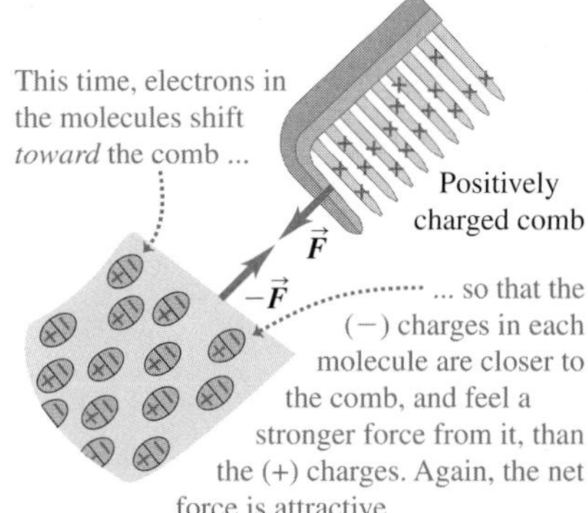

What happens if, while the plastic rod is nearby, you touch one end of a conducting wire to the right surface of the ball and the other end to the earth (Fig. 21.7c)? The earth is a conductor, and it is so large that it can act as a practically infinite source of extra electrons or sink of unwanted electrons. Some of the negative charge flows through the wire to the earth. Now suppose you disconnect the wire (Fig. 21.7d) and then remove the rod (Fig. 21.7e); a net positive charge is left on the ball. The charge on the negatively charged rod has not changed during this process. The earth acquires a negative charge that is equal in magnitude to the induced positive charge remaining on the ball.

Charging by induction would work just as well if the mobile charges in the ball were positive charges instead of negatively charged electrons, or even if both positive and negative mobile charges were present. In a metallic conductor the mobile charges are always negative electrons, but it is often convenient to describe a process *as though* the moving charges were positive. In ionic solutions and ionized gases, both positive and negative charges are mobile.

Electric Forces on Uncharged Objects

Finally, we note that a charged body can exert forces even on objects that are *not* charged themselves. If you rub a balloon on the rug and then hold the balloon against the ceiling, it sticks, even though the ceiling has no net electric charge. After you electrify a comb by running it through your hair, you can pick up uncharged bits of paper or plastic with the comb (Fig. 21.8a). How is this possible?

This interaction is an induced-charge effect. Even in an insulator, electric charges can shift back and forth a little when there is charge nearby. This is shown in Fig. 21.8b; the negatively charged plastic comb causes a slight shifting of charge within the molecules of the neutral insulator, an effect called *polarization*. The positive and negative charges in the material are present in equal amounts, but the positive charges are closer to the plastic comb and so feel an attraction that is stronger than the repulsion felt by the negative charges, giving a net attractive force. (In Section 21.3 we will study how electric forces depend on distance.) Note that a neutral insulator is also attracted to a *positively* charged comb (Fig. 21.8c). Now the charges in the insulator shift in the opposite direction; the negative charges in the insulator are closer to the comb and feel an attractive force that is stronger than the repulsion felt by the positive charges in the insulator. Hence a charged object of *either* sign exerts an attractive force on an uncharged insulator.

The attraction between a charged object and an uncharged one has many important practical applications, including the electrostatic painting process used in the automobile industry (Fig. 21.9). A metal object to be painted is connected to the earth ("ground" in Fig. 21.9), and the paint droplets are given an electric charge as they exit the sprayer nozzle. Induced charges of the opposite sign

21.9 The electrostatic painting process (compare Figs. 21.7b and 21.7c).

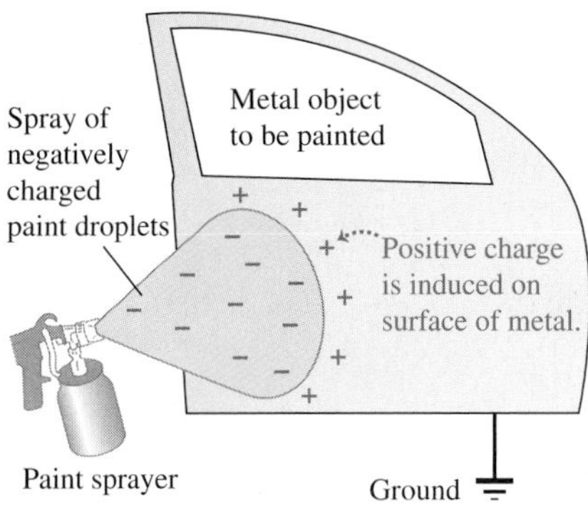

appear in the object as the droplets approach, just as in Fig. 21.7b, and they attract the droplets to the surface. This process minimizes overspray from clouds of stray paint particles and gives a particularly smooth finish.

Test Your Understanding of Section 21.2 You have two lightweight metal spheres, each hanging from an insulating nylon thread. One of the spheres has a net negative charge, while the other sphere has no net charge. (a) If the spheres are close together but do not touch, will they (i) attract each other, (ii) repel each other, or (iii) exert no force on each other? (b) You now allow the two spheres to touch. Once they have touched, will the two spheres (i) attract each other, (ii) repel each other, or (iii) exert no force on each other?

21.3 Coulomb's Law

ActivPhysics ONLINE

11.1 Electric Force: Coulomb's Law
11.2 Electric Force: Superposition Principle
11.3 Electric Force: Superposition (Quantitative)

Charles Augustin de Coulomb (1736–1806) studied the interaction forces of charged particles in detail in 1784. He used a torsion balance (Fig. 21.10a) similar to the one used 13 years later by Cavendish to study the much weaker gravitational interaction, as we discussed in Section 12.1. For **point charges,** charged bodies that are very small in comparison with the distance r between them, Coulomb found that the electric force is proportional to $1/r^2$. That is, when the distance r doubles, the force decreases to $\frac{1}{4}$ of its initial value; when the distance is halved, the force increases to four times its initial value.

The electric force between two point charges also depends on the quantity of charge on each body, which we will denote by q or Q. To explore this dependence, Coulomb divided a charge into two equal parts by placing a small charged spherical conductor into contact with an identical but uncharged sphere; by symmetry, the charge is shared equally between the two spheres. (Note the essential role of the principle of conservation of charge in this procedure.) Thus he could obtain one-half, one-quarter, and so on, of any initial charge. He found that the forces that two point charges q_1 and q_2 exert on each other are proportional to each charge and therefore are proportional to the *product* q_1q_2 of the two charges.

Thus Coulomb established what we now call **Coulomb's law:**

The magnitude of the electric force between two point charges is directly proportional to the product of the charges and inversely proportional to the square of the distance between them.

21.10 (a) Measuring the electric force between point charges. (b) The electric forces between point charges obey Newton's third law: $\vec{F}_{1\text{ on }2} = -\vec{F}_{2\text{ on }1}$.

(a) A torsion balance of the type used by Coulomb to measure the electric force

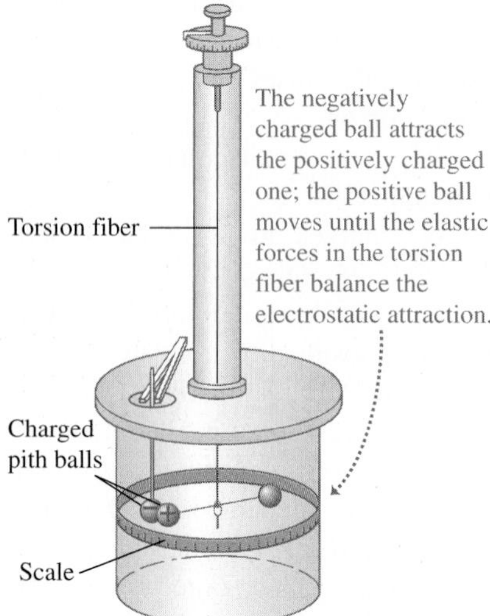
The negatively charged ball attracts the positively charged one; the positive ball moves until the elastic forces in the torsion fiber balance the electrostatic attraction.
Torsion fiber
Charged pith balls
Scale

(b) Interactions between point charges

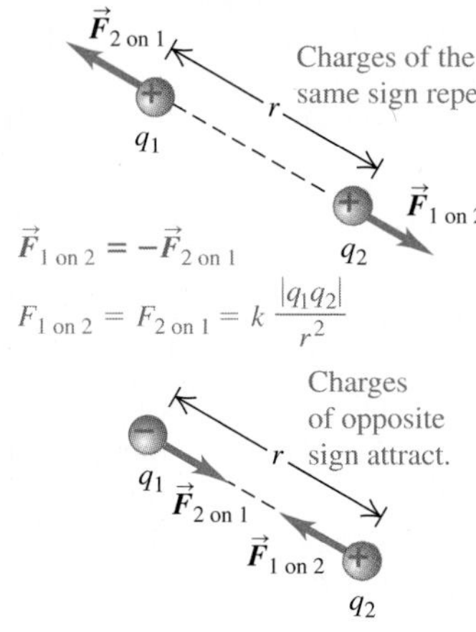
$\vec{F}_{2\text{ on }1}$
Charges of the same sign repel.
r
q_1
$\vec{F}_{1\text{ on }2}$
q_2
$\vec{F}_{1\text{ on }2} = -\vec{F}_{2\text{ on }1}$
$F_{1\text{ on }2} = F_{2\text{ on }1} = k\frac{|q_1q_2|}{r^2}$
Charges of opposite sign attract.
r
q_1
$\vec{F}_{2\text{ on }1}$
$\vec{F}_{1\text{ on }2}$
q_2

In mathematical terms, the magnitude F of the force that each of two point charges q_1 and q_2 a distance r apart exerts on the other can be expressed as

$$F = k\frac{|q_1 q_2|}{r^2} \tag{21.1}$$

where k is a proportionality constant whose numerical value depends on the system of units used. The absolute value bars are used in Eq. (21.1) because the charges q_1 and q_2 can be either positive or negative, while the force magnitude F is always positive.

The directions of the forces the two charges exert on each other are always along the line joining them. When the charges q_1 and q_2 have the same sign, either both positive or both negative, the forces are repulsive; when the charges have opposite signs, the forces are attractive (Fig. 21.10b). The two forces obey Newton's third law; they are always equal in magnitude and opposite in direction, even when the charges are not equal in magnitude.

The proportionality of the electric force to $1/r^2$ has been verified with great precision. There is no reason to suspect that the exponent is different from precisely 2. Thus the form of Eq. (21.1) is the same as that of the law of gravitation. But electric and gravitational interactions are two distinct classes of phenomena. Electric interactions depend on electric charges and can be either attractive or repulsive, while gravitational interactions depend on mass and are always attractive (because there is no such thing as negative mass).

Fundamental Electric Constants

The value of the proportionality constant k in Coulomb's law depends on the system of units used. In our study of electricity and magnetism we will use SI units exclusively. The SI electric units include most of the familiar units such as the volt, the ampere, the ohm, and the watt. (There is *no* British system of electric units.) The SI unit of electric charge is called one **coulomb** (1 C). In SI units the constant k in Eq. (21.1) is

$$k = 8.987551787 \times 10^9 \text{ N} \cdot \text{m}^2/\text{C}^2 \cong 8.988 \times 10^9 \text{ N} \cdot \text{m}^2/\text{C}^2$$

The value of k is known to such a large number of significant figures because this value is closely related to the speed of light in vacuum. (We will show this in Chapter 32 when we study electromagnetic radiation.) As we discussed in Section 1.3, this speed is *defined* to be exactly $c = 2.99792458 \times 10^8$ m/s. The numerical value of k is defined in terms of c to be precisely

$$k = (10^{-7} \text{ N} \cdot \text{s}^2/\text{C}^2)c^2$$

You should check this expression to confirm that k has the right units.

In principle we can measure the electric force F between two equal charges q at a measured distance r and use Coulomb's law to determine the charge. Thus we could regard the value of k as an operational definition of the coulomb. For reasons of experimental precision it is better to define the coulomb instead in terms of a unit of electric *current* (charge per unit time), the *ampere,* equal to 1 coulomb per second. We will return to this definition in Chapter 28.

In SI units we usually write the constant k in Eq. (21.1) as $1/4\pi\epsilon_0$, where ϵ_0 ("epsilon-nought" or "epsilon-zero") is another constant. This appears to complicate matters, but it actually simplifies many formulas that we will encounter in later chapters. From now on, we will usually write Coulomb's law as

$$F = \frac{1}{4\pi\epsilon_0}\frac{|q_1 q_2|}{r^2} \quad \text{(Coulomb's law: force between two point charges)} \tag{21.2}$$

The constants in Eq. (21.2) are approximately

$$\epsilon_0 = 8.854 \times 10^{-12}\ \mathrm{C^2/N \cdot m^2} \quad \text{and} \quad \frac{1}{4\pi\epsilon_0} = k = 8.988 \times 10^9\ \mathrm{N \cdot m^2/C^2}$$

In examples and problems we will often use the approximate value

$$\frac{1}{4\pi\epsilon_0} = 9.0 \times 10^9\ \mathrm{N \cdot m^2/C^2}$$

which is within about 0.1% of the correct value.

As we mentioned in Section 21.1, the most fundamental unit of charge is the magnitude of the charge of an electron or a proton, which is denoted by e. The most precise value available as of the writing of this book is

$$e = 1.60217653(14) \times 10^{-19}\ \mathrm{C}$$

One coulomb represents the negative of the total charge of about 6×10^{18} electrons. For comparison, a copper cube 1 cm on a side contains about 2.4×10^{24} electrons. About 10^{19} electrons pass through the glowing filament of a flashlight bulb every second.

In electrostatics problems (that is, problems that involve charges at rest), it's very unusual to encounter charges as large as 1 coulomb. Two 1-C charges separated by 1 m would exert forces on each other of magnitude 9×10^9 N (about 1 million tons)! The total charge of all the electrons in a copper one-cent coin is even greater, about 1.4×10^5 C, which shows that we can't disturb electric neutrality very much without using enormous forces. More typical values of charge range from about 10^{-9} to about 10^{-6} C. The microcoulomb $(1\ \mu\mathrm{C} = 10^{-6}\ \mathrm{C})$ and the nanocoulomb $(1\ \mathrm{nC} = 10^{-9}\ \mathrm{C})$ are often used as practical units of charge.

Example 21.1 Electric force versus gravitational force

An α particle ("alpha") is the nucleus of a helium atom. It has mass $m = 6.64 \times 10^{-27}$ kg and charge $q = +2e = 3.2 \times 10^{-19}$ C. Compare the force of the electric repulsion between two α particles with the force of gravitational attraction between them.

SOLUTION

IDENTIFY: This problem involves Newton's law for the gravitational force F_g between particles (see Section 12.1) and Coulomb's law for the electric force F_e between point charges. We are asked to compare these forces, so our target variable is the *ratio* of these two forces, F_e/F_g.

SET UP: Figure 21.11 shows our sketch. The magnitude of the repulsive electric force is given by Eq. (21.2):

$$F_e = \frac{1}{4\pi\epsilon_0}\frac{q^2}{r^2}$$

The magnitude F_g of the attractive gravitational force is given by Eq. (12.1):

$$F_g = G\frac{m^2}{r^2}$$

EXECUTE: The ratio of the electric force to the gravitational force is

$$\frac{F_e}{F_g} = \frac{1}{4\pi\epsilon_0 G}\frac{q^2}{m^2} = \frac{9.0 \times 10^9\ \mathrm{N \cdot m^2/C^2}}{6.67 \times 10^{-11}\ \mathrm{N \cdot m^2/kg^2}}\frac{(3.2 \times 10^{-19}\ \mathrm{C})^2}{(6.64 \times 10^{-27}\ \mathrm{kg})^2}$$
$$= 3.1 \times 10^{35}$$

EVALUATE: This astonishingly large number shows that the gravitational force in this situation is completely negligible in comparison to the electric force. This is always true for interactions of atomic and subatomic particles. (Notice that this result doesn't depend on the distance r between the two α particles.) But within objects the size of a person or a planet, the positive and negative charges are nearly equal in magnitude, and the net electric force is usually much *smaller* than the gravitational force.

21.11 Our sketch for this problem.

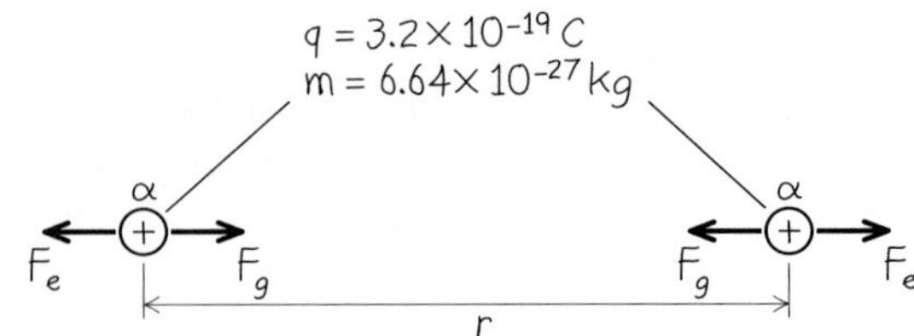

Superposition of Forces

Coulomb's law as we have stated it describes only the interaction of two *point* charges. Experiments show that when two charges exert forces simultaneously on a third charge, the total force acting on that charge is the *vector sum* of the forces that the two charges would exert individually. This important property, called the **principle of superposition of forces,** holds for any number of charges. By using this principle, we can apply Coulomb's law to *any* collection of charges. Several of the examples at the end of this section show applications of the superposition principle.

Strictly speaking, Coulomb's law as we have stated it should be used only for point charges *in a vacuum.* If matter is present in the space between the charges, the net force acting on each charge is altered because charges are induced in the molecules of the intervening material. We will describe this effect later. As a practical matter, though, we can use Coulomb's law unaltered for point charges in air. At normal atmospheric pressure, the presence of air changes the electric force from its vacuum value by only about one part in 2000.

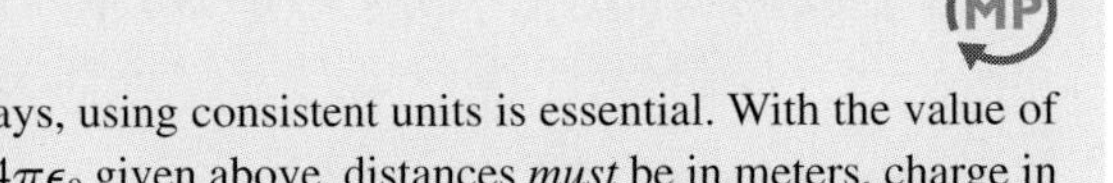

Problem-Solving Strategy 21.1 Coulomb's Law

IDENTIFY *the relevant concepts:* Coulomb's law comes into play whenever you need to know the electric force acting between charged particles.

SET UP *the problem* using the following steps:

1. Make a drawing showing the locations of the charged particles, and label each particle with its charge. This step is particularly important if more than two charged particles are present.
2. If three or more charges are present and they do not all lie on the same line, set up an *xy*-coordinate system.
3. Often you will need to find the electric force on just one particle. If so, identify that particle.

EXECUTE *the solution* as follows:

1. For each particle that exerts a force on the particle of interest, calculate the magnitude of that force using Eq.(21.2).
2. Sketch the electric force vectors acting on the particle(s) of interest due to each of the other particles (that is, make a free-body diagram). Remember that the force exerted by particle 1 on particle 2 points from particle 2 toward particle 1 if the two charges have opposite signs, but points from particle 2 directly away from particle 1 if the charges have the same sign.
3. Calculate the total electric force on the particle(s) of interest. Remember that the electric force, like any force, is a *vector.* When the forces acting on a charge are caused by two or more other charges, the total force on the charge is the *vector sum* of the individual forces. You may want to go back and review the vector algebra in Sections 1.7 through 1.9. It's often helpful to use components in an *xy*-coordinate system. Be sure to use correct vector notation; if a symbol represents a vector quantity, put an arrow over it. If you get sloppy with your notation, you will also get sloppy with your thinking.
4. As always, using consistent units is essential. With the value of $k = 1/4\pi\epsilon_0$ given above, distances *must* be in meters, charge in coulombs, and force in newtons. If you are given distances in centimeters, inches, or furlongs, don't forget to convert! When a charge is given in microcoulombs (μC) or nanocoulombs (nC), remember that 1 μC $= 10^{-6}$ C and 1 nC $= 10^{-9}$ C.
5. Some examples and problems in this and later chapters involve a continuous distribution of charge along a line or over a surface. In these cases the vector sum described in step 3 becomes a vector integral, usually carried out by use of components. We divide the total charge distribution into infinitesimal pieces, use Coulomb's law for each piece, and then integrate to find the vector sum. Sometimes this process can be done without explicit use of integration.
6. In many situations the charge distribution will be *symmetrical.* For example, you might be asked to find the force on a charge Q in the presence of two other identical charges q, one above and to the left of Q and the other below and to the left of Q. If the distances from Q to each of the other charges are the same, the force on Q from each charge has the same magnitude; if each force vector makes the same angle with the horizontal axis, adding these vectors to find the net force is particularly easy. Whenever possible, exploit any symmetries to simplify the problem-solving process.

EVALUATE *your answer:* Check whether your numerical results are reasonable, and confirm that the direction of the net electric force agrees with the principle that like charges repel and opposite charges attract.

Example 21.2 Force between two point charges

Two point charges, $q_1 = +25$ nC and $q_2 = -75$ nC, are separated by a distance of 3.0 cm (Fig. 21.12a). Find the magnitude and direction of (a) the electric force that q_1 exerts on q_2; and (b) the electric force that q_2 exerts on q_1.

SOLUTION

IDENTIFY: This problem asks for the electric forces that two charges exert on each other, so we will need to use Coulomb's law.

SET UP: We use Eq. (21.2) to calculate the magnitude of the force that each particle exerts on the other. We use Newton's third law to relate the forces that the two particles exert on each other.

EXECUTE: (a) After we convert charge to coulombs and distance to meters, the magnitude of the force that q_1 exerts on q_2 is

$$F_{1\text{ on }2} = \frac{1}{4\pi\epsilon_0}\frac{|q_1 q_2|}{r^2}$$

$$= (9.0 \times 10^9\ \text{N}\cdot\text{m}^2/\text{C}^2)\frac{|(+25 \times 10^{-9}\ \text{C})(-75 \times 10^{-9}\ \text{C})|}{(0.030\ \text{m})^2}$$

$$= 0.019\ \text{N}$$

Since the two charges have opposite signs, the force is attractive; that is, the force that acts on q_2 is directed toward q_1 along the line joining the two charges, as shown in Fig. 21.12b.

21.12 What force does q_1 exert on q_2, and what force does q_2 exert on q_1? Gravitational forces are negligible.

(a) The two charges

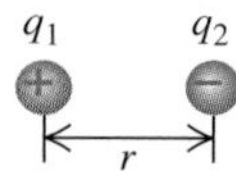

(b) Free-body diagram for charge q_2

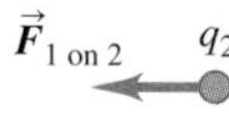

(c) Free-body diagram for charge q_1

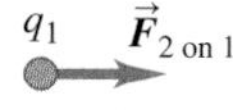

(b) Newton's third law applies to the electric force. Even though the charges have different magnitudes, the magnitude of the force that q_2 exerts on q_1 is the *same* as the magnitude of the force that q_1 exerts on q_2:

$$F_{2\text{ on }1} = 0.019\ \text{N}$$

Newton's third law also states that the direction of the force that q_2 exerts on q_1 is exactly opposite the direction of the force that q_1 exerts on q_2; this is shown in Fig. 21.12c.

EVALUATE: Note that the force on q_1 is directed toward q_2, as it must be, since charges of opposite sign attract each other.

Example 21.3 Vector addition of electric forces on a line

Two point charges are located on the positive x-axis of a coordinate system. Charge $q_1 = 1.0$ nC is 2.0 cm from the origin, and charge $q_2 = -3.0$ nC is 4.0 cm from the origin. What is the total force exerted by these two charges on a charge $q_3 = 5.0$ nC located at the origin? Gravitational forces are negligible.

SOLUTION

IDENTIFY: Here there are *two* electric forces acting on the charge q_3, and we must add these forces to find the total force.

SET UP: Figure 21.13a shows the coordinate system. Our target variable is the net electric force exerted *on* charge q_3 by the other two charges. This is the vector sum of the forces due to q_1 and q_2 individually.

EXECUTE: Figure 21.13b is a free-body diagram for charge q_3. Note that q_3 is repelled by q_1 (which has the same sign) and attracted to q_2 (which has the opposite sign). Converting charge to coulombs and distance to meters, we use Eq. (21.2) to find the magnitude $F_{1\text{ on }3}$ of the force of q_1 on q_3:

$$F_{1\text{ on }3} = \frac{1}{4\pi\epsilon_0}\frac{|q_1 q_3|}{r^2}$$

$$= (9.0 \times 10^9\ \text{N}\cdot\text{m}^2/\text{C}^2)\frac{(1.0 \times 10^{-9}\ \text{C})(5.0 \times 10^{-9}\ \text{C})}{(0.020\ \text{m})^2}$$

$$= 1.12 \times 10^{-4}\ \text{N} = 112\ \mu\text{N}$$

This force has a negative x-component because q_3 is repelled (that is, pushed in the negative x-direction) by q_1.

The magnitude $F_{2\text{ on }3}$ of the force of q_2 on q_3 is

$$F_{2\text{ on }3} = \frac{1}{4\pi\epsilon_0}\frac{|q_2 q_3|}{r^2}$$

$$= (9.0 \times 10^9\ \text{N}\cdot\text{m}^2/\text{C}^2)\frac{(3.0 \times 10^{-9}\ \text{C})(5.0 \times 10^{-9}\ \text{C})}{(0.040\ \text{m})^2}$$

$$= 8.4 \times 10^{-5}\ \text{N} = 84\ \mu\text{N}$$

This force has a positive x-component because q_3 is attracted (that is, pulled in the positive x-direction) by q_2. The sum of the x-components is

$$F_x = -112\ \mu\text{N} + 84\ \mu\text{N} = -28\ \mu\text{N}$$

There are no y- or z-components. Thus the total force on q_3 is directed to the left, with magnitude $28\ \mu\text{N} = 2.8 \times 10^{-5}$ N.

EVALUATE: To check the magnitudes of the individual forces, note that q_2 has three times as much charge (in magnitude) as q_1 but is twice as far from q_3. From Eq. (21.2) this means that $F_{2\text{ on }3}$ must be $3/2^2 = \frac{3}{4}$ as large as $F_{1\text{ on }3}$. Indeed, our results show that this ratio is $(84\ \mu\text{N})/(112\ \mu\text{N}) = 0.75$. The direction of the net force also makes sense: $\vec{F}_{1\text{ on }3}$ is opposite to and has a larger magnitude than $\vec{F}_{2\text{ on }3}$, so the net force is in the direction of $\vec{F}_{1\text{ on }3}$.

21.13 Our sketches for this problem.

(a) Our diagram of the situation (b) Free-body diagram for q_3

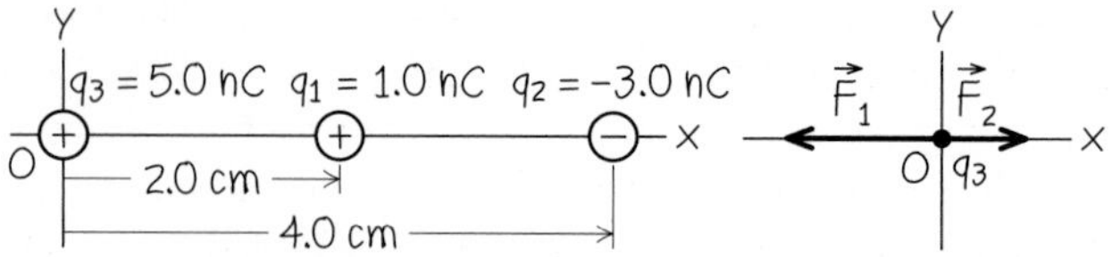

Example 21.4 Vector addition of electric forces in a plane

Two equal positive point charges $q_1 = q_2 = 2.0\ \mu\text{C}$ are located at $x = 0$, $y = 0.30$ m and $x = 0$, $y = -0.30$ m, respectively. What are the magnitude and direction of the total (net) electric force that these charges exert on a third point charge $Q = 4.0\ \mu\text{C}$ at $x = 0.40$ m, $y = 0$?

SOLUTION

IDENTIFY: As in Example 21.3, we have to compute the force that each charge exerts on Q and then find the vector sum of the forces.

SET UP: Figure 21.14 shows the situation. Since the three charges do not all lie on a line, the best way to calculate the forces that q_1 and q_2 exert on Q is to use components.

21.14 Our sketch for this problem.

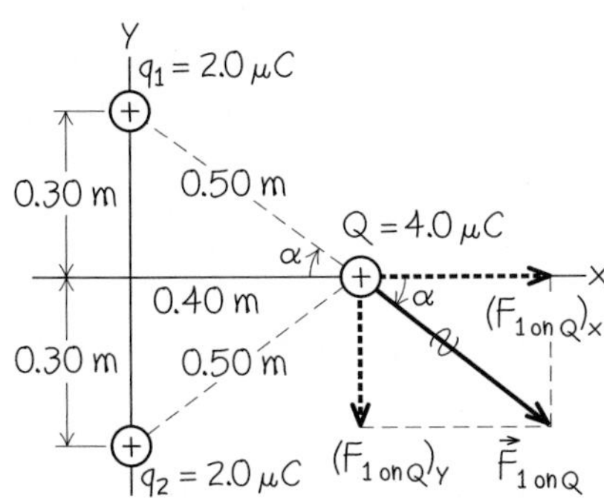

EXECUTE: Figure 21.14 shows the force on Q due to the upper charge q_1. From Coulomb's law the magnitude F of this force is

$$F_{1\text{ on }Q} = (9.0 \times 10^9\ \text{N}\cdot\text{m}^2/\text{C}^2)\frac{(4.0 \times 10^{-6}\ \text{C})(2.0 \times 10^{-6}\ \text{C})}{(0.50\ \text{m})^2}$$

$$= 0.29\ \text{N}$$

The angle α is below the x-axis, so the components of this force are given by

$$(F_{1\text{ on }Q})_x = (F_{1\text{ on }Q})\cos\alpha = (0.29\ \text{N})\frac{0.40\ \text{m}}{0.50\ \text{m}} = 0.23\ \text{N}$$

$$(F_{1\text{ on }Q})_y = -(F_{1\text{ on }Q})\sin\alpha = -(0.29\ \text{N})\frac{0.30\ \text{m}}{0.50\ \text{m}} = -0.17\ \text{N}$$

The lower charge q_2 exerts a force with the same magnitude but at an angle α *above* the x-axis. From symmetry we see that its x-component is the same as that due to the upper charge, but its y-component has the opposite sign. So the components of the total force $\vec{F}$ on Q are

$$F_x = 0.23\ \text{N} + 0.23\ \text{N} = 0.46\ \text{N}$$
$$F_y = -0.17\ \text{N} + 0.17\ \text{N} = 0$$

The total force on Q is in the $+x$-direction, with magnitude 0.46 N.

EVALUATE: The total force on Q is in a direction that points neither directly away from q_1 nor directly away from q_2. Rather, this direction is a compromise that points away from the *system* of charges q_1 and q_2. Can you see that the total force would *not* be in the $+x$-direction if q_1 and q_2 were not equal or if the geometrical arrangement of the changes were not so symmetrical?

Test Your Understanding of Section 21.3 Suppose that charge q_2 in Example 21.4 were $-2.0\ \mu\text{C}$. In this case, the total electric force on Q would be (i) in the positive x-direction; (ii) in the negative x-direction; (iii) in the positive y-direction; (iv) in the negative y-direction; (v) zero; (vi) none of these.

21.4 Electric Field and Electric Forces

When two electrically charged particles in empty space interact, how does each one know the other is there? What goes on in the space between them to communicate the effect of each one to the other? We can begin to answer these questions, and at the same time reformulate Coulomb's law in a very useful way, by using the concept of *electric field*.

Electric Field

To introduce this concept, let's look at the mutual repulsion of two positively charged bodies A and B (Fig. 21.15a). Suppose B has charge q_0, and let $\vec{F}_0$ be the electric force of A on B. One way to think about this force is as an "action-at-a-distance" force—that is, as a force that acts across empty space without needing any matter (such as a push rod or a rope) to transmit it through the intervening space. (Gravity can also be thought of as an "action-at-a-distance" force.) But a more fruitful way to visualize the repulsion between A and B is as a two-stage process. We first envision that body A, as a result of the charge that it carries, somehow *modifies the properties of the space around it.* Then body B, as

21.15 A charged body creates an electric field in the space around it.

(a) A and B exert electric forces on each other.

(b) Remove body B ...

... and label its former position as P.

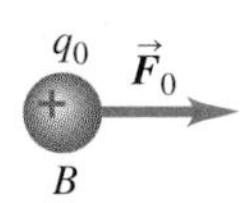

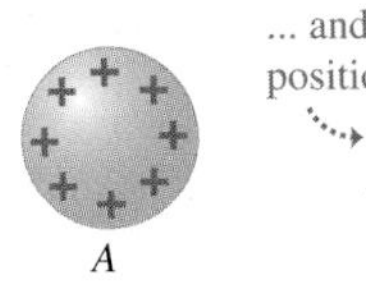

(c) Body A sets up an electric field $\vec{E}$ at point P.

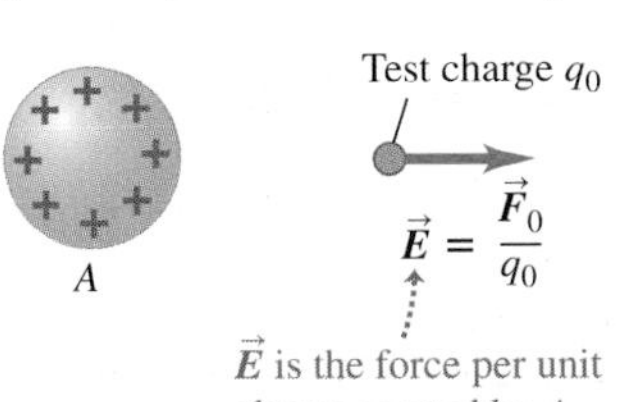

$\vec{E}$ is the force per unit charge exerted by A on a test charge at P.

ActivPhysics ONLINE

11.4 Electric Field: Point Change
11.9 Motion of a Charge in an Electric Field: Introduction
11.10 Motion in an Electric Field: Problems

a result of the charge that *it* carries, senses how space has been modified at its position. The response of body B is to experience the force $\vec{F}_0$.

To elaborate how this two-stage process occurs, we first consider body A by itself: We remove body B and label its former position as point P (Fig. 21.15b). We say that the charged body A produces or causes an **electric field** at point P (and at all other points in the neighborhood). This electric field is present at P even if there is no charge at P; it is a consequence of the charge on body A only. If a point charge q_0 is then placed at point P, it experiences the force $\vec{F}_0$. We take the point of view that this force is exerted on q_0 *by the field* at P (Fig. 21.15c). Thus the electric field is the intermediary through which A communicates its presence to q_0. Because the point charge q_0 would experience a force at *any* point in the neighborhood of A, the electric field that A produces exists at all points in the region around A.

We can likewise say that the point charge q_0 produces an electric field in the space around it and that this electric field exerts the force $-\vec{F}_0$ on body A. For each force (the force of A on q_0 and the force of q_0 on A), one charge sets up an electric field that exerts a force on the second charge. We emphasize that this is an *interaction* between *two* charged bodies. A single charge produces an electric field in the surrounding space, but this electric field cannot exert a net force on the charge that created it; this is an example of the general principle that a body cannot exert a net force on itself, as discussed in Section 4.3. (If this principle wasn't valid, you would be able to lift yourself to the ceiling by pulling up on your belt!)

The electric force on a charged body is exerted by the electric field created by *other* charged bodies.

To find out experimentally whether there is an electric field at a particular point, we place a small charged body, which we call a **test charge,** at the point (Fig. 21.15c). If the test charge experiences an electric force, then there is an electric field at that point. This field is produced by charges other than q_0.

Force is a vector quantity, so electric field is also a vector quantity. (Note the use of vector signs as well as boldface letters and plus, minus, and equals signs in the following discussion.) We define the *electric field* $\vec{E}$ at a point as the electric force $\vec{F}_0$ experienced by a test charge q_0 at the point, divided by the charge q_0. That is, the electric field at a certain point is equal to the *electric force per unit charge* experienced by a charge at that point:

$$\vec{E} = \frac{\vec{F}_0}{q_0} \quad \text{(definition of electric field as electric force per unit charge)} \tag{21.3}$$

In SI units, in which the unit of force is 1 N and the unit of charge is 1 C, the unit of electric field magnitude is 1 newton per coulomb (1 N/C).

If the field $\vec{E}$ at a certain point is known, rearranging Eq. (21.3) gives the force $\vec{F}_0$ experienced by a point charge q_0 placed at that point. This force is just equal to the electric field $\vec{E}$ produced at that point by charges other than q_0, multiplied by the charge q_0:

$$\vec{F}_0 = q_0\vec{E} \quad \text{(force exerted on a point charge } q_0 \text{ by an electric field } \vec{E}\text{)} \tag{21.4}$$

21.16 The force $\vec{F}_0 = q_0\vec{E}$ exerted on a point charge q_0 placed in an electric field $\vec{E}$.

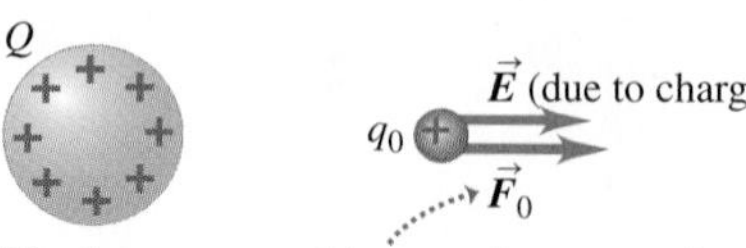

The force on a positive test charge q_0 points in the direction of the electric field.

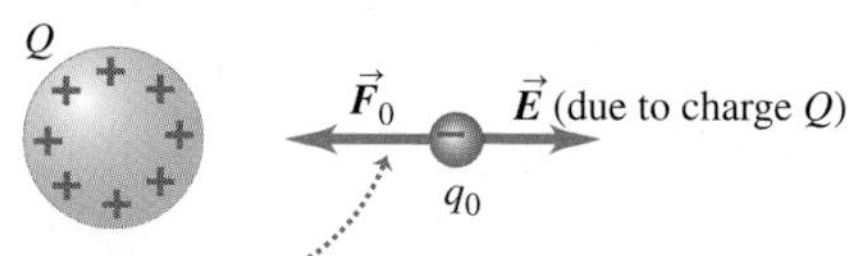

The force on a negative test charge q_0 points opposite to the electric field.

The charge q_0 can be either positive or negative. If q_0 is *positive,* the force $\vec{F}_0$ experienced by the charge is the same direction as $\vec{E}$; if q_0 is *negative,* $\vec{F}_0$ and $\vec{E}$ are in opposite directions (Fig. 21.16).

While the electric field concept may be new to you, the basic idea—that one body sets up a field in the space around it and a second body responds to that field—is one that you've actually used before. Compare Eq. (21.4) to the familiar expression for the gravitational force $\vec{F}_g$ that the earth exerts on a mass m_0:

$$\vec{F}_g = m_0\vec{g} \qquad (21.5)$$

In this expression, $\vec{g}$ is the acceleration due to gravity. If we divide both sides of Eq. (21.5) by the mass m_0, we obtain

$$\vec{g} = \frac{\vec{F}_g}{m_0}$$

Thus $\vec{g}$ can be regarded as the gravitational force per unit mass. By analogy to Eq. (21.3), we can interpret $\vec{g}$ as the *gravitational field.* Thus we treat the gravitational interaction between the earth and the mass m_0 as a two-stage process: The earth sets up a gravitational field $\vec{g}$ in the space around it, and this gravitational field exerts a force given by Eq. (21.5) on the mass m_0 (which we can regard as a *test mass*). In this sense, you've made use of the field concept every time you've used Eq. (21.5) for the force of gravity. The gravitational field $\vec{g}$, or gravitational force per unit mass, is a useful concept because it does not depend on the mass of the body on which the gravitational force is exerted; likewise, the electric field $\vec{E}$, or electric force per unit charge, is useful because it does not depend on the charge of the body on which the electric force is exerted.

CAUTION **$\vec{F}_0 = q_0\vec{E}_0$ is for *point* test charges only** The electric force experienced by a test charge q_0 can vary from point to point, so the electric field can also be different at different points. For this reason, Eq. (21.4) can be used only to find the electric force on a *point* charge. If a charged body is large enough in size, the electric field $\vec{E}$ may be noticeably different in magnitude and direction at different points on the body, and calculating the net electric force on the body can become rather complicated.

We have so far ignored a subtle but important difficulty with our definition of electric field: In Fig. 21.15 the force exerted by the test charge q_0 on the charge distribution on body A may cause this distribution to shift around. This is especially true if body A is a conductor, on which charge is free to move. So the electric field around A when q_0 is present may not be the same as when q_0 is absent. But if q_0 is very small, the redistribution of charge on body A is also very small. So to make a completely correct definition of electric field, we take the *limit* of Eq. (21.3) as the test charge q_0 approaches zero and as the disturbing effect of q_0 on the charge distribution becomes negligible:

$$\vec{E} = \lim_{q_0 \to 0} \frac{\vec{F}_0}{q_0}$$

In practical calculations of the electric field $\vec{E}$ produced by a charge distribution, we will consider the charge distribution to be fixed, and so we will not need this limiting process.

21.17 The electric field $\vec{E}$ produced at point P by an isolated point charge q at S. Note that in both (b) and (c), $\vec{E}$ is *produced* by q [see Eq. (21.7)] but *acts* on the charge q_0 at point P [see Eq. (21.4)].

(a)

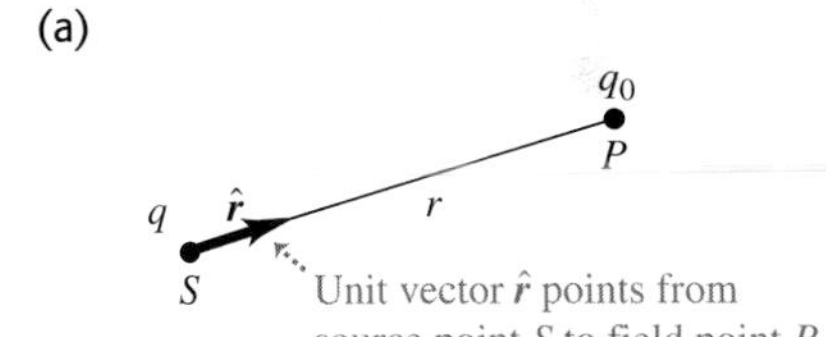
q_0
P
q
$\hat{r}$
r
S
Unit vector $\hat{r}$ points from source point S to field point P.

(b)

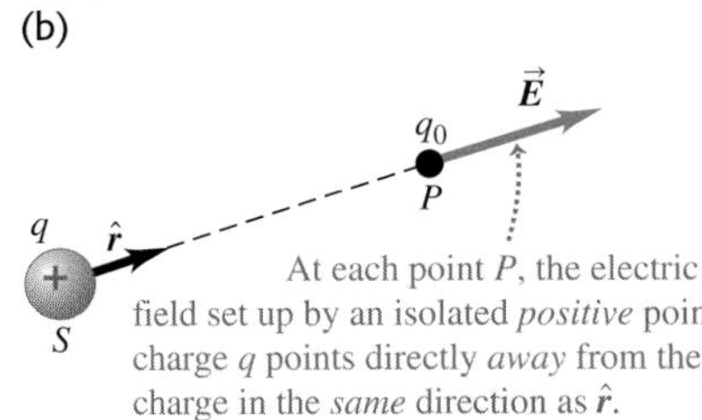
$\vec{E}$
q_0
P
q
$\hat{r}$
+
S
At each point P, the electric field set up by an isolated *positive* point charge q points directly *away* from the charge in the *same* direction as $\hat{r}$.

(c)

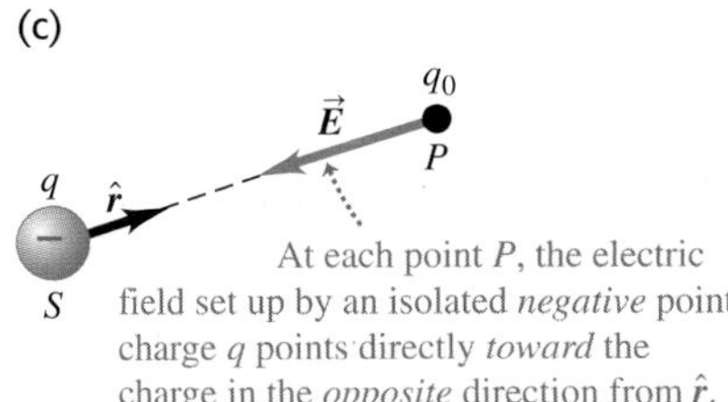
q_0
$\vec{E}$
P
q
$\hat{r}$
–
S
At each point P, the electric field set up by an isolated *negative* point charge q points directly *toward* the charge in the *opposite* direction from $\hat{r}$.

Electric Field of a Point Charge

If the source distribution is a point charge q, it is easy to find the electric field that it produces. We call the location of the charge the **source point,** and we call the point P where we are determining the field the **field point.** It is also useful to introduce a *unit vector* $\hat{r}$ that points along the line from source point to field point (Fig. 21.17a). This unit vector is equal to the displacement vector $\vec{r}$ from the source point to the field point, divided by the distance $\hat{r} = |\vec{r}|$ between these two points; that is, $\hat{r} = \vec{r}/r$. If we place a small test charge q_0 at the field point P, at a distance r from the source point, the magnitude F_0 of the force is given by Coulomb's law, Eq. (21.2):

$$F_0 = \frac{1}{4\pi\epsilon_0}\frac{|qq_0|}{r^2}$$

21.18 A point charge q produces an electric field $\vec{E}$ at *all* points in space. The field strength decreases with increasing distance.

(a) The field produced by a positive point charge points *away from* the charge.

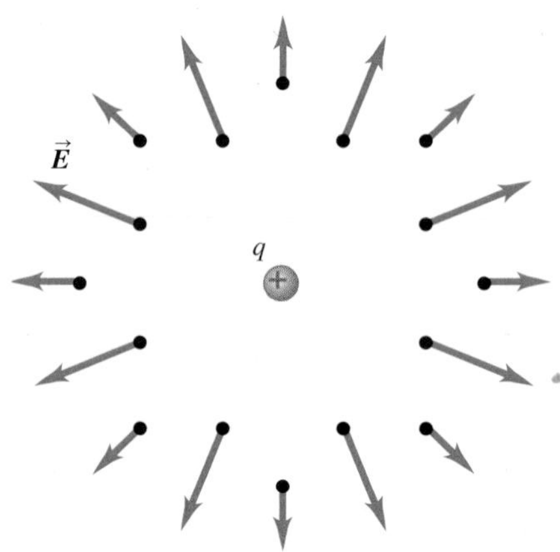

(b) The field produced by a negative point charge points *toward* the charge.

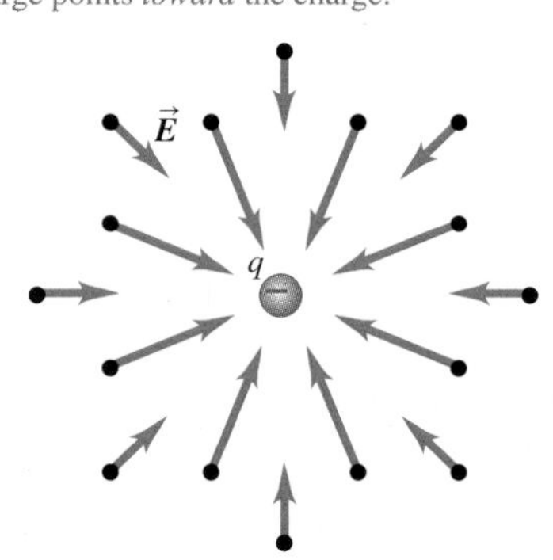

From Eq. (21.3) the magnitude E of the electric field at P is

$$E = \frac{1}{4\pi\epsilon_0}\frac{|q|}{r^2} \quad \text{(magnitude of electric field of a point charge)} \quad (21.6)$$

Using the unit vector $\hat{r}$, we can write a *vector* equation that gives both the magnitude and direction of the electric field $\vec{E}$:

$$\vec{E} = \frac{1}{4\pi\epsilon_0}\frac{q}{r^2}\hat{r} \quad \text{(electric field of a point charge)} \quad (21.7)$$

By definition, the electric field of a point charge always points *away from* a positive charge (that is, in the same direction as $\hat{r}$; see Fig. 21.17b) but *toward* a negative charge (that is, in the direction opposite $\hat{r}$; see Fig. 21.17c).

We have emphasized calculating the electric field $\vec{E}$ at a certain point. But since $\vec{E}$ can vary from point to point, it is not a single vector quantity but rather an *infinite* set of vector quantities, one associated with each point in space. This is an example of a **vector field.** Figure 21.18 shows a number of the field vectors produced by a positive or negative point charge. If we use a rectangular (x, y, z) coordinate system, each component of $\vec{E}$ at any point is in general a function of the coordinates (x, y, z) of the point. We can represent the functions as $E_x(x, y, z)$, $E_y(x, y, z)$, and $E_z(x, y, z)$. Vector fields are an important part of the language of physics, not just in electricity and magnetism. One everyday example of a vector field is the velocity $\vec{v}$ of wind currents; the magnitude and direction of $\vec{v}$, and hence its vector components, vary from point to point in the atmosphere.

In some situations the magnitude and direction of the field (and hence its vector components) have the same values everywhere throughout a certain region; we then say that the field is *uniform* in this region. An important example of this is the electric field inside a *conductor.* If there is an electric field within a conductor, the field exerts a force on every charge in the conductor, giving the free charges a net motion. By definition an electrostatic situation is one in which the charges have *no* net motion. We conclude that *in electrostatics the electric field at every point within the material of a conductor must be zero.* (Note that we are not saying that the field is necessarily zero in a *hole* inside a conductor.)

With the concept of electric field, our description of electric interactions has two parts. First, a given charge distribution acts as a source of electric field. Second, the electric field exerts a force on any charge that is present in the field. Our analysis often has two corresponding steps: first, calculating the field caused by a source charge distribution; second, looking at the effect of the field in terms of force and motion. The second step often involves Newton's laws as well as the principles of electric interactions. In the next section we show how to calculate fields caused by various source distributions, but first here are some examples of calculating the field due to a point charge and of finding the force on a charge due to a given field $\vec{E}$.

Example 21.5 Electric-field magnitude for a point charge

What is the magnitude of the electric field at a field point 2.0 m from a point charge $q = 4.0$ nC? (The point charge could represent any small charged object with this value of q, provided the dimensions of the object are much less than the distance from the object to the field point.)

SOLUTION

IDENTIFY: This problem uses the expression for the electric field due to a point charge.

SET UP: We are given the magnitude of the charge and the distance from the object to the field point, so we use Eq. (21.6) to calculate the field magnitude E.

EXECUTE: From Eq. (21.6),

$$E = \frac{1}{4\pi\epsilon_0}\frac{|q|}{r^2} = (9.0 \times 10^9\ \text{N}\cdot\text{m}^2/\text{C}^2)\frac{4.0 \times 10^{-9}\ \text{C}}{(2.0\ \text{m})^2}$$
$$= 9.0\ \text{N/C}$$

EVALUATE: To check our result, we use the definition of electric field as the electric force per unit charge. We can first use Coulomb's law, Eq. (21.2), to find the magnitude F_0 of the force on a test charge q_0 placed 2.0 m from q:

$$F_0 = \frac{1}{4\pi\epsilon_0}\frac{|qq_0|}{r^2} = (9.0 \times 10^9\ \text{N}\cdot\text{m}^2/\text{C}^2)\frac{4.0 \times 10^{-9}\ \text{C}|q_0|}{(2.0\ \text{m})^2}$$
$$= (9.0\ \text{N/C})|q_0|$$

Then, from Eq. (21.3), the magnitude of $\vec{E}$ is

$$E = \frac{F_0}{|q_0|} = 9.0\ \text{N/C}$$

Because q is positive, the *direction* of $\vec{E}$ at this point is along the line from q toward q_0, as shown in Fig. 21.17b. However, the magnitude and direction of $\vec{E}$ do not depend on the sign of q_0. Do you see why not?

Example 21.6 Electric-field vector for a point charge

A point charge $q = -8.0$ nC is located at the origin. Find the electric-field vector at the field point $x = 1.2$ m, $y = -1.6$ m.

SOLUTION

IDENTIFY: In this problem we are asked to find the electric-field *vector* $\vec{E}$ due to a point charge. Hence we need to find either the components of $\vec{E}$ or its magnitude and direction.

SET UP: Figure 21.19 shows the situation. The electric field is given in vector form by Eq. (21.7). To use this equation, we first find the distance r from the source point S (the position of the charge q) to the field point P, as well as the unit vector $\hat{r}$ that points in the direction from S to P.

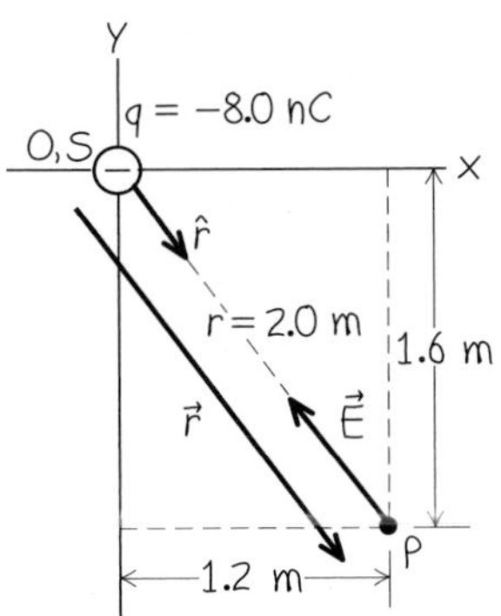

21.19 Our sketch for this problem.

EXECUTE: The distance from the charge at the source point S (which in this example is at the origin O) to the field point P is

$$r = \sqrt{x^2 + y^2} = \sqrt{(1.2\ \text{m})^2 + (-1.6\ \text{m})^2} = 2.0\ \text{m}$$

The unit vector $\hat{r}$ is directed from the source point to the field point. This is equal to the displacement vector $\vec{r}$ from the source point to the field point (shown shifted to one side in Fig. 21.19 so as not to obscure the other vectors), divided by its magnitude r:

$$\hat{r} = \frac{\vec{r}}{r} = \frac{x\hat{\imath} + y\hat{\jmath}}{r}$$
$$= \frac{(1.2\ \text{m})\hat{\imath} + (-1.6\ \text{m})\hat{\imath}}{2.0\ \text{m}} = 0.60\hat{\imath} - 0.80\hat{\jmath}$$

Hence the electric-field vector is

$$\vec{E} = \frac{1}{4\pi\epsilon_0}\frac{q}{r^2}\hat{r}$$
$$= (9.0 \times 10^9\ \text{N}\cdot\text{m}^2/\text{C}^2)\frac{(-8.0 \times 10^{-9}\ \text{C})}{(2.0\ \text{m})^2}(0.60\hat{\imath} - 0.80\hat{\jmath})$$
$$= (-11\ \text{N/C})\hat{\imath} + (14\ \text{N/C})\hat{\jmath}$$

EVALUATE: Since q is negative, $\vec{E}$ points from the field point to the charge (the source point), in the direction opposite to $\hat{r}$ (compare Fig. 21.17c). We leave the calculation of the magnitude and direction of $\vec{E}$ to you (see Exercise 21.36).

Example 21.7 Electron in a uniform field

When the terminals of a battery are connected to two large parallel conducting plates, the resulting charges on the plates cause an electric field $\vec{E}$ in the region between the plates that is very nearly uniform. (We will see the reason for this uniformity in the next section. Charged plates of this kind are used in common electrical devices called *capacitors,* to be discussed in Chapter 24.) If the plates are horizontal and separated by 1.0 cm and the plates are connected to a 100-volt battery, the magnitude of the field is $E = 1.00 \times 10^4$ N/C. Suppose the direction of $\vec{E}$ is vertically upward, as shown by the vectors in Fig. 21.20. (a) If an electron is released from rest at the upper plate, what is its acceleration? (b) What speed and kinetic energy does the electron acquire while traveling 1.0 cm to the lower plate? (c) How much time is

21.20 A uniform electric field between two parallel conducting plates connected to a 100-volt battery. (The separation of the plates is exaggerated in this figure relative to the dimensions of the plates.)

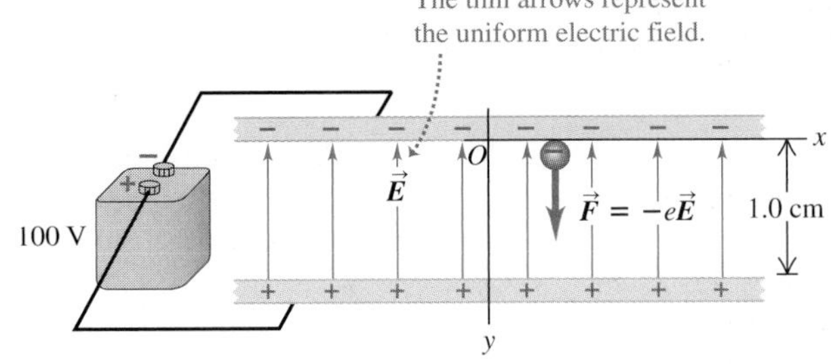

Continued

required for it to travel this distance? An electron has charge $-e = -1.60 \times 10^{-19}$ C and mass $m = 9.11 \times 10^{-31}$ kg.

SOLUTION

IDENTIFY: This example involves several concepts: the relationship between electric field and electric force, the relationship between force and acceleration, the definition of kinetic energy, and the kinematic relationships among acceleration, distance, velocity, and time.

SET UP: Figure 21.20 shows our coordinate system. We are given the electric field, so we use Eq. (21.4) to find the force on the electron and Newton's second law to find its acceleration. Because the field is uniform between the plates, the force and acceleration are constant and we can use the constant-acceleration formulas from Chapter 3 to find the electron's velocity and travel time. We find the kinetic energy using the definition $K = \frac{1}{2}mv^2$.

EXECUTE: (a) Note that $\vec{E}$ is upward (in the $+y$-direction) but $\vec{F}$ is downward because the charge of the electron is negative. Thus F_y is negative. Because F_y is constant, the electron moves with constant acceleration a_y given by

$$a_y = \frac{F_y}{m} = \frac{-eE}{m} = \frac{(-1.60 \times 10^{-19}\ \text{C})(1.00 \times 10^4\ \text{N/C})}{9.11 \times 10^{-31}\ \text{kg}}$$
$$= -1.76 \times 10^{15}\ \text{m/s}^2$$

This is an enormous acceleration! To give a 1000-kg car this acceleration, we would need a force of about 2×10^{18} N (about 2×10^{14} tons). The gravitational force on the electron is completely negligible compared to the electric force.

(b) The electron starts from rest, so its motion is in the y-direction only (the direction of the acceleration). We can find the electron's speed at any position using the constant-acceleration formula $v_y^2 = v_{0y}^2 + 2a_y(y - y_0)$. We have $v_{0y} = 0$ and $y_0 = 0$, so the speed $|v_y|$ when $y = -1.0$ cm $= -1.0 \times 10^{-2}$ m is

$$|v_y| = \sqrt{2a_y y} = \sqrt{2(-1.76 \times 10^{15}\ \text{m/s}^2)(-1.0 \times 10^{-2}\ \text{m})}$$
$$= 5.9 \times 10^6\ \text{m/s}$$

The velocity is downward, so its y-component is $v_y = -5.9 \times 10^6$ m/s. The electron's kinetic energy is

$$K = \frac{1}{2}mv^2 = \frac{1}{2}(9.11 \times 10^{-31}\ \text{kg})(5.9 \times 10^6\ \text{m/s})^2$$
$$= 1.6 \times 10^{-17}\ \text{J}$$

(c) From the constant-acceleration formula $v_y = v_{0y} + a_y t$, we find that the time required is very brief:

$$t = \frac{v_y - v_{0y}}{a_y} = \frac{(-5.9 \times 10^6\ \text{m/s}) - (0\ \text{m/s})}{-1.76 \times 10^{15}\ \text{m/s}^2}$$
$$= 3.4 \times 10^{-9}\ \text{s}$$

(We could also have found the time by solving the equation $y = y_0 + v_{0y}t + \frac{1}{2}a_y t^2$ for t.)

EVALUATE: This example shows that in problems about subatomic particles such as electrons, many quantities—including acceleration, speed, kinetic energy, and time—will have *very* different values from what we have seen for ordinary objects such as baseballs and automobiles.

Example 21.8 An electron trajectory

If we launch an electron into the electric field of Example 21.7 with an initial horizontal velocity v_0 (Fig. 21.21), what is the equation of its trajectory?

SOLUTION

IDENTIFY: We found the electron's acceleration in Example 21.7. Our goal is to find the trajectory that corresponds to that acceleration.

SET UP: The acceleration is constant and in the negative y-direction (there is no acceleration in the x-direction). Hence we can use the kinematic equations from Chapter 3 for two-dimensional motion with constant acceleration.

EXECUTE: We have $a_x = 0$ and $a_y = (-e)E/m$. At $t = 0$, $x_0 = y_0 = 0$, $v_{0x} = v_0$, and $v_{0y} = 0$; hence at time t,

$$x = v_0 t \quad \text{and} \quad y = \frac{1}{2}a_y t^2 = -\frac{1}{2}\frac{eE}{m}t^2$$

Eliminating t between these equations, we get

$$y = -\frac{1}{2}\frac{eE}{mv_0^2}x^2$$

EVALUATE: This is the equation of a parabola, just like the trajectory of a projectile launched horizontally in the earth's gravitational field (discussed in Section 3.3). For a given initial velocity of the electron, the curvature of the trajectory depends on the field magnitude E. If we reverse the signs of the charges on the two plates in Fig. 21.21, the direction of $\vec{E}$ reverses, and the electron trajectory will curve up, not down. Hence we can "steer" the electron by varying the charges on the plates. The electric field between charged conducting plates can be used in this way to control the trajectory of electron beams in oscilloscopes.

21.21 The parabolic trajectory of an electron in a uniform electric field.

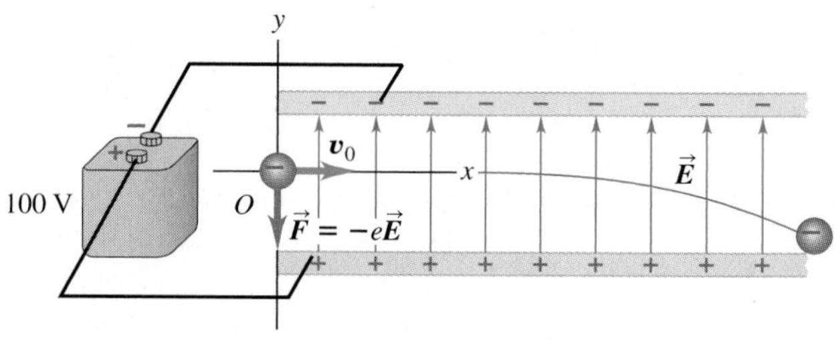

Test Your Understanding of Section 21.4 (a) A negative point charge moves along a straight-line path directly toward a stationary positive point charge. Which aspect(s) of the electric force on the negative point charge will remain constant as it moves? (i) magnitude; (ii) direction; (iii) both magnitude and direction; (iv) neither magnitude nor direction. (b) A negative point charge moves along a circular orbit around a positive point charge. Which aspect(s) of the electric force on the negative point charge will remain constant as it moves? (i) magnitude; (ii) direction; (iii) both magnitude and direction; (iv) neither magnitude nor direction.

21.5 Electric-Field Calculations

ActivPhysics ONLINE
11.5 Electric Field Due to a Dipole
11.6 Electric Field: Problems

Equation (21.7) gives the electric field caused by a single point charge. But in most realistic situations that involve electric fields and forces, we encounter charge that is *distributed* over space. The charged plastic and glass rods in Fig. 21.1 have electric charge distributed over their surfaces, as does the imaging drum of a laser printer (Fig. 21.2). In this section we'll learn to calculate electric fields caused by various distributions of electric charge. Calculations of this kind are of tremendous importance for technological applications of electric forces. To determine the trajectories of electrons in a TV tube, of atomic nuclei in an accelerator for cancer radiotherapy, or of charged particles in a semiconductor electronic device, you have to know the detailed nature of the electric field acting on the charges.

The Superposition of Electric Fields

To find the field caused by a charge distribution, we imagine the distribution to be made up of many point charges $q_1, q_2, q_3, \ldots$. (This is actually quite a realistic description, since we have seen that charge is carried by electrons and protons that are so small as to be almost pointlike.) At any given point P, each point charge produces its own electric field $\vec{E}_1, \vec{E}_2, \vec{E}_3, \ldots$, so a test charge q_0 placed at P experiences a force $\vec{F}_1 = q_0\vec{E}_1$ from charge q_1, a force $\vec{F}_2 = q_0\vec{E}_2$ from charge q_2, and so on. From the principle of superposition of forces discussed in Section 21.3, the *total* force $\vec{F}_0$ that the charge distribution exerts on q_0 is the vector sum of these individual forces:

$$\vec{F}_0 = \vec{F}_1 + \vec{F}_2 + \vec{F}_3 + \cdots = q_0\vec{E}_1 + q_0\vec{E}_2 + q_0\vec{E}_3 + \cdots$$

The combined effect of all the charges in the distribution is described by the *total* electric field $\vec{E}$ at point P. From the definition of electric field, Eq. (21.3), this is

$$\vec{E} = \frac{\vec{F}_0}{q_0} = \vec{E}_1 + \vec{E}_2 + \vec{E}_3 + \cdots$$

The total electric field at P is the vector sum of the fields at P due to each point charge in the charge distribution (Fig. 21.22). This is the **principle of superposition of electric fields.**

21.22 Illustrating the principle of superposition of electric fields.

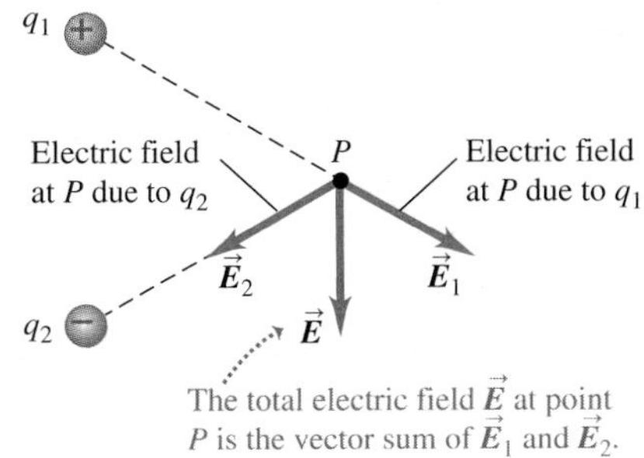
q_1
Electric field at P due to q_2
P
Electric field at P due to q_1
$\vec{E}_2$
$\vec{E}_1$
q_2
$\vec{E}$
The total electric field $\vec{E}$ at point P is the vector sum of $\vec{E}_1$ and $\vec{E}_2$.

When charge is distributed along a line, over a surface, or through a volume, a few additional terms are useful. For a line charge distribution (such as a long, thin, charged plastic rod), we use λ (the Greek letter lambda) to represent the **linear charge density** (charge per unit length, measured in C/m). When charge is distributed over a surface (such as the surface of the imaging drum of a laser printer), we use σ (sigma) to represent the **surface charge density** (charge per unit area, measured in C/m^2). And when charge is distributed through a volume, we use ρ (rho) to represent the **volume charge density** (charge per unit volume, C/m^3).

Some of the calculations in the following examples may look fairly intricate; in electric-field calculations a certain amount of mathematical complexity is in the nature of things. After you've worked through the examples one step at a time, the process will seem less formidable. We will use many of the calculational techniques in these examples in Chapter 28 to calculate the *magnetic* fields caused by charges in motion.

Problem-Solving Strategy 21.2 Electric-Field Calculations

IDENTIFY *the relevant concepts:* Use the principle of superposition whenever you need to calculate the electric field due to a charge distribution (two or more point charges, a distribution over a line, surface, or volume, or a combination of these).

SET UP *the problem* using the following steps:

1. Make a drawing that clearly shows the locations of the charges and your choice of coordinate axes.
2. On your drawing, indicate the position of the *field point* (the point at which you want to calculate the electric field $\vec{E}$). Sometimes the field point will be at some arbitrary position along a line. For example, you may be asked to find $\vec{E}$ at any point on the x-axis.

EXECUTE *the solution* as follows:

1. Be sure to use a consistent set of units. Distances must be in meters and charge must be in coulombs. If you are given centimeters or nanocoulombs, don't forget to convert.
2. When adding up the electric fields caused by different parts of the charge distribution, remember that electric field is a vector, so you *must* use vector addition. Don't simply add together the magnitudes of the individual fields; the directions are important, too.
3. Take advantage of any symmetries in the charge distribution. For example, if a positive charge and a negative charge of equal magnitude are placed symmetrically with respect to the field point, they produce electric fields of the same magnitude but with mirror-image directions. Exploiting these symmetries will simplify your calculations.
4. Most often you will use components to compute vector sums. Use the methods you learned in Chapter 1; review them if necessary. Use proper vector notation; distinguish carefully between scalars, vectors, and components of vectors. Be certain the components are consistent with your choice of coordinate axes.
5. In working out the directions of $\vec{E}$ vectors, be careful to distinguish between the *source point* and the *field point.* The field produced by a point charge always points from source point to field point if the charge is positive; it points in the opposite direction if the charge is negative.
6. In some situations you will have a continuous distribution of charge along a line, over a surface, or through a volume. Then you must define a small element of charge that can be considered as a point, find its electric field at point P, and find a way to add the fields of all the charge elements. Usually it is easiest to do this for each component of $\vec{E}$ separately, and often you will need to evaluate one or more integrals. Make certain the limits on your integrals are correct; especially when the situation has symmetry, make sure you don't count the charge twice.

EVALUATE *your answer:* Check that the direction of $\vec{E}$ is reasonable. If your result for the electric-field magnitude E is a function of position (say, the coordinate x), check your result in any limits for which you know what the magnitude should be. When possible, check your answer by calculating it in a different way.

Example 21.9 Field of an electric dipole

Point charges q_1 and q_2 of $+12$ nC and -12 nC, respectively, are placed 0.10 m apart (Fig. 21.23). This combination of two charges with equal magnitude and opposite sign is called an *electric dipole.* (Such combinations occur frequently in nature. For example, in Figs. 21.8b and 21.8c, each molecule in the neutral insulator is an electric dipole. We'll study dipoles in more detail in Section 21.7.) Compute the electric field caused by q_1, the field caused by q_2, and the total field (a) at point a; (b) at point b; and (c) at point c.

SOLUTION

IDENTIFY: We need to find the total electric field at three different points due to two point charges. We will use the principle of superposition: $\vec{E} = \vec{E}_1 + \vec{E}_2$.

SET UP: Figure 21.23 shows the coordinate system and the locations of the three field points a, b, and c.

21.23 Electric field at three points, a, b, and c, set up by charges q_1 and q_2, which form an electric dipole.

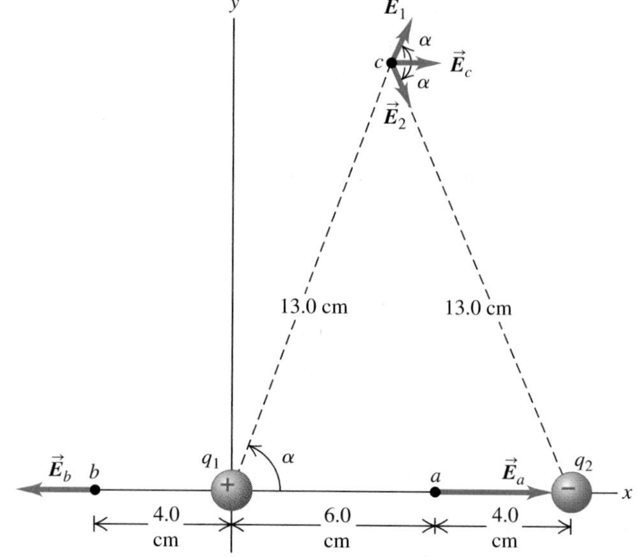

EXECUTE: (a) At point a the field $\vec{E}_1$ caused by the positive charge q_1 and the field $\vec{E}_2$ caused by the negative charge q_2 are both directed toward the right. The magnitudes of $\vec{E}_1$ and $\vec{E}_2$ are

$$E_1 = \frac{1}{4\pi\epsilon_0}\frac{|q_1|}{r^2} = (9.0 \times 10^9\ \text{N}\cdot\text{m}^2/\text{C}^2)\frac{12 \times 10^{-9}\ \text{C}}{(0.060\ \text{m})^2}$$
$$= 3.0 \times 10^4\ \text{N/C}$$
$$E_2 = \frac{1}{4\pi\epsilon_0}\frac{|q_2|}{r^2} = (9.0 \times 10^9\ \text{N}\cdot\text{m}^2/\text{C}^2)\frac{12 \times 10^{-9}\ \text{C}}{(0.040\ \text{m})^2}$$
$$= 6.8 \times 10^4\ \text{N/C}$$

The components of $\vec{E}_1$ and $\vec{E}_2$ are

$$E_{1x} = 3.0 \times 10^4\ \text{N/C} \qquad E_{1y} = 0$$
$$E_{2x} = 6.8 \times 10^4\ \text{N/C} \qquad E_{2y} = 0$$

Hence at point a the total electric field $\vec{E}_a = \vec{E}_1 + \vec{E}_2$ has components

$$(E_a)_x = E_{1x} + E_{2x} = (3.0 + 6.8) \times 10^4\ \text{N/C}$$
$$(E_a)_y = E_{1y} + E_{2y} = 0$$

At point a the total field has magnitude 9.8×10^4 N/C and is directed toward the right, so

$$\vec{E}_a = (9.8 \times 10^4\ \text{N/C})\hat{\imath}$$

(b) At point b the field $\vec{E}_1$ due to q_1 is directed toward the left, while the field $\vec{E}_2$ due to q_2 is directed toward the right. The magnitudes of $\vec{E}_1$ and $\vec{E}_2$ are

$$E_1 = \frac{1}{4\pi\epsilon_0}\frac{|q_1|}{r^2} = (9.0 \times 10^9\ \text{N}\cdot\text{m}^2/\text{C}^2)\frac{12 \times 10^{-9}\ \text{C}}{(0.040\ \text{m})^2}$$
$$= 6.8 \times 10^4\ \text{N/C}$$
$$E_2 = \frac{1}{4\pi\epsilon_0}\frac{|q_2|}{r^2} = (9.0 \times 10^9\ \text{N}\cdot\text{m}^2/\text{C}^2)\frac{12 \times 10^{-9}\ \text{C}}{(0.140\ \text{m})^2}$$
$$= 0.55 \times 10^4\ \text{N/C}$$

The components of $\vec{E}_1$, $\vec{E}_2$, and the total field $\vec{E}_b$ at point b are

$$E_{1x} = -6.8 \times 10^4\ \text{N/C} \qquad E_{1y} = 0$$
$$E_{2x} = 0.55 \times 10^4\ \text{N/C} \qquad E_{2y} = 0$$
$$(E_b)_x = E_{1x} + E_{2x} = (-6.8 + 0.55) \times 10^4\ \text{N/C}$$
$$(E_b)_y = E_{1y} + E_{2y} = 0$$

That is, the electric field at b has magnitude 6.2×10^4 N/C and is directed toward the left, so

$$\vec{E}_b = (-6.2 \times 10^4\ \text{N/C})\hat{\imath}$$

(c) At point c, both $\vec{E}_1$ and $\vec{E}_2$ have the same magnitude, since this point is equidistant from both charges and the charge magnitudes are the same:

$$E_1 = E_2 = \frac{1}{4\pi\epsilon_0}\frac{|q|}{r^2} = (9.0 \times 10^9\ \text{N}\cdot\text{m}^2/\text{C}^2)\frac{12 \times 10^{-9}\ \text{C}}{(0.130\ \text{m})^2}$$
$$= 6.39 \times 10^3\ \text{N/C}$$

The directions of $\vec{E}_1$ and $\vec{E}_2$ are shown in Fig 21.23. The x-components of both vectors are the same:

$$E_{1x} = E_{2x} = E_1\cos\alpha = (6.39 \times 10^3\ \text{N/C})\left(\frac{5}{13}\right)$$
$$= 2.46 \times 10^3\ \text{N/C}$$

From symmetry the y-components E_{1y} and E_{2y} are equal and opposite and so add to zero. Hence the components of the total field $\vec{E}_c$ are

$$(E_c)_x = E_{1x} + E_{2x} = 2(2.46 \times 10^3\ \text{N/C}) = 4.9 \times 10^3\ \text{N/C}$$
$$(E_c)_y = E_{1y} + E_{2y} = 0$$

So at point c the total electric field has magnitude 4.9×10^3 N/C and is directed toward the right, so

$$\vec{E}_c = (4.9 \times 10^3\ \text{N/C})\hat{\imath}$$

Does it surprise you that the field at point c is parallel to the line between the two charges?

EVALUATE: An alternative way to find the electric field at c is to use the vector expression for the field of a point charge, Eq. (21.7). The displacement vector $\vec{r}_1$ from q_1 to point c, a distance $r = 13.0$ cm away, is

$$\vec{r}_1 = r\cos\alpha\hat{\imath} + r\sin\alpha\hat{\jmath}$$

Hence the unit vector that points from q_1 to c is

$$\hat{r}_1 = \frac{\vec{r}_1}{r} = \cos\alpha\hat{\imath} + \sin\alpha\hat{\jmath}$$

and the field due to q_1 at point c is

$$\vec{E}_1 = \frac{1}{4\pi\epsilon_0}\frac{q_1}{r^2}\hat{r}_1 = \frac{1}{4\pi\epsilon_0}\frac{q_1}{r^2}(\cos\alpha\hat{\imath} + \sin\alpha\hat{\jmath})$$

By symmetry the unit vector $\hat{r}_2$ that points from q_2 to point c has the opposite x-component but the same y-component, so the field at c due to q_2 is

$$\vec{E}_2 = \frac{1}{4\pi\epsilon_0}\frac{q_2}{r^2}\hat{r}_2 = \frac{1}{4\pi\epsilon_0}\frac{q_2}{r^2}(-\cos\alpha\hat{\imath} + \sin\alpha\hat{\jmath})$$

Since $q_2 = -q_1$, the total field at c is

$$\vec{E}_c = \vec{E}_1 + \vec{E}_2$$
$$= \frac{1}{4\pi\epsilon_0}\frac{q_1}{r^2}(\cos\alpha\hat{\imath} + \text{in}\alpha\hat{\jmath}) + \frac{1}{4\pi\epsilon_0}\frac{(-q_1)}{r^2}(-\cos\alpha\hat{\imath} + \sin\alpha\hat{\jmath})$$
$$= \frac{1}{4\pi\epsilon_0}\frac{q_1}{r^2}(2\cos\alpha\,\hat{\imath})$$
$$= (9.0 \times 10^9\ \text{N}\cdot\text{m}^2/\text{C}^2)\frac{12 \times 10^{-9}\ \text{C}}{(0.13\ \text{m})^2}\left[2\left(\frac{5}{13}\right)\right]\hat{\imath}$$
$$= (4.9 \times 10^3\ \text{N/C})\hat{\imath}$$

as before.

Example 21.10 Field of a ring of charge

A ring-shaped conductor with radius a carries a total charge Q uniformly distributed around it (Fig. 21.24). Find the electric field at a point P that lies on the axis of the ring at a distance x from its center.

SOLUTION

IDENTIFY: This is a problem in the superposition of electric fields. The new wrinkle is that the charge is distributed continuously around the ring rather than in a number of point charges.

SET UP: The field point is an arbitrary point on the x-axis in Fig. 21.24. Our target variable is the electric field at such a point as a function of the coordinate x.

EXECUTE: As shown in Fig. 21.24, we imagine the ring divided into infinitesimal segments of length ds. Each segment has charge dQ and acts as a point-charge source of electric field. Let $d\vec{E}$ be the electric field from one such segment; the net electric field at P is then the sum of all contributions $d\vec{E}$ from all the segments that make up the ring. (This same technique works for any situation in which charge is distributed along a line or a curve.)

The calculation of $\vec{E}$ is greatly simplified because the field point P is on the symmetry axis of the ring. Consider two segments at the top and bottom of the ring: The contributions $d\vec{E}$ to the field at P from these segments have the same x-component but opposite y-components. Hence the total y-component of field due to this pair of segments is zero. When we add up the contributions from all such pairs of segments, the total field $\vec{E}$ will have only a component along the ring's symmetry axis (the x-axis), with no component perpendicular to that axis (that is, no y-component or z-component). So the field at P is described completely by its x-component E_x.

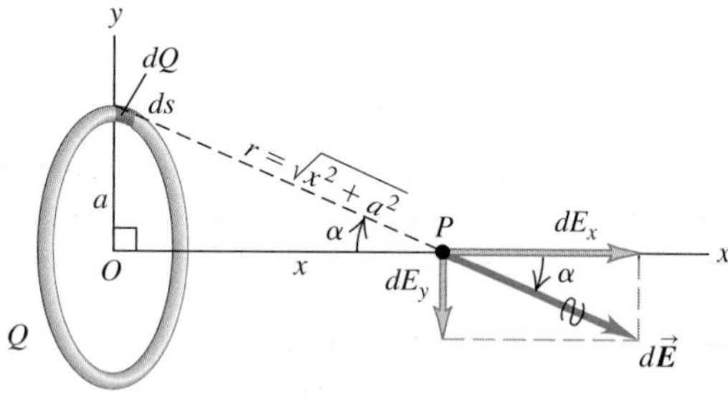

21.24 Calculating the electric field on the axis of a ring of charge. In this figure, the charge is assumed to be positive.

To calculate E_x, note that the square of the distance r from a ring segment to the point P is $r^2 = x^2 + a^2$. Hence the magnitude of this segment's contribution $d\vec{E}$ to the electric field at P is

$$dE = \frac{1}{4\pi\epsilon_0}\frac{dQ}{x^2 + a^2}$$

Using $\cos\alpha = x/r = x/(x^2 + a^2)^{1/2}$, the x-component dE_x of this field is

$$dE_x = dE\cos\alpha = \frac{1}{4\pi\epsilon_0}\frac{dQ}{x^2 + a^2}\frac{x}{\sqrt{x^2 + a^2}} = \frac{1}{4\pi\epsilon_0}\frac{x\,dQ}{(x^2 + a^2)^{3/2}}$$

To find the *total* x-component E_x of the field at P, we integrate this expression over all segments of the ring:

$$E_x = \int \frac{1}{4\pi\epsilon_0}\frac{x\,dQ}{(x^2 + a^2)^{3/2}}$$

Since x does not vary as we move from point to point around the ring, all the factors on the right side except dQ are constant and can be taken outside the integral. The integral of dQ is just the total charge Q, and we finally get

$$\vec{E} = E_x\hat{\imath} = \frac{1}{4\pi\epsilon_0}\frac{Qx}{(x^2 + a^2)^{3/2}}\hat{\imath} \qquad (21.8)$$

EVALUATE: Our result for $\vec{E}$ shows that at the center of the ring ($x = 0$) the field is zero. We should expect this; charges on opposite sides of the ring would push in opposite directions on a test charge at the center, and the forces would add to zero. When the field point P is much farther from the ring than its size (that is, $x \gg a$), the denominator in Eq. (21.8) becomes approximately equal to x^3, and the expression becomes approximately

$$\vec{E} = \frac{1}{4\pi\epsilon_0}\frac{Q}{x^2}\hat{\imath}$$

In other words, when we are so far from the ring that its size a is negligible in comparison to the distance x, its field is the same as that of a point charge. To an observer far from the ring, the ring would appear like a point, and the electric field reflects this.

In this example we used a *symmetry argument* to conclude that $\vec{E}$ had only an x-component at a point on the ring's axis of symmetry. We'll use symmetry arguments many times in this and subsequent chapters. Keep in mind, however, that such arguments can be used only in special cases. At a point in the xy-plane that is not on the x-axis in Fig. 21.24, the symmetry argument doesn't apply, and the field has in general both x- and y-components.

Example 21.11 Field of a line of charge

Positive electric charge Q is distributed uniformly along a line with length $2a$, lying along the y-axis between $y = -a$ and $y = +a$. (This might represent one of the charged rods in Fig. 21.1.) Find the electric field at point P on the x-axis at a distance x from the origin.

SOLUTION

IDENTIFY: As in Example 21.10, our target variable is the electric field due to a continuous distribution of charge.

SET UP: Figure 21.25 shows the situation. We need to find the electric field at P as a function of the coordinate x. The x-axis is the perpendicular bisector of the charged line, so as in Example 21.10 we will be able to make use of a symmetry argument.

EXECUTE: We divide the line charge into infinitesimal segments, each of which acts as a point charge; let the length of a typical segment at height y be dy. If the charge is distributed uniformly, the linear charge density λ at any point on the line is equal to $Q/2a$ (the total charge divided by the total length). Hence the charge dQ in a segment of length dy is

$$dQ = \lambda dy = \frac{Q dy}{2a}$$

The distance r from this segment to P is $(x^2 + y^2)^{1/2}$, so the magnitude of field dE at P due to this segment is

$$dE = \frac{1}{4\pi\epsilon_0}\frac{dQ}{r^2} = \frac{Q}{4\pi\epsilon_0}\frac{dy}{2a(x^2 + y^2)}$$

We represent this field in terms of its x- and y-components:

$$dE_x = dE \cos\alpha \qquad dE_y = -dE \sin\alpha$$

We note that $\sin\alpha = y/(x^2 + y^2)^{1/2}$ and $\cos\alpha = x/(x^2 + y^2)^{1/2}$; combining these with the expression for dE, we find

$$dE_x = \frac{Q}{4\pi\epsilon_0}\frac{x\,dy}{2a(x^2 + y^2)^{3/2}}$$

$$dE_y = -\frac{Q}{4\pi\epsilon_0}\frac{y\,dy}{2a(x^2 + y^2)^{3/2}}$$

To find the total field components E_x and E_y, we integrate these expressions, noting that to include all of Q, we must integrate from $y = -a$ to $y = +a$. We invite you to work out the details of the integration; an integral table is helpful. The final results are

$$E_x = \frac{1}{4\pi\epsilon_0}\frac{Qx}{2a}\int_{-a}^{a}\frac{dy}{(x^2 + y^2)^{3/2}} = \frac{Q}{4\pi\epsilon_0}\frac{1}{x\sqrt{x^2 + a^2}}$$

$$E_y = -\frac{1}{4\pi\epsilon_0}\frac{Q}{2a}\int_{-a}^{a}\frac{y\,dy}{(x^2 + y^2)^{3/2}} = 0$$

or, in vector form,

$$\vec{E} = \frac{1}{4\pi\epsilon_0}\frac{Q}{x\sqrt{x^2 + a^2}}\hat{\imath} \qquad (21.9)$$

EVALUATE: Using a symmetry argument as in Example 21.10, we could have guessed that E_y would be zero; if we place a positive test charge at P, the upper half of the line of charge pushes downward on it, and the lower half pushes up with equal magnitude.

21.25 Our sketch for this problem.

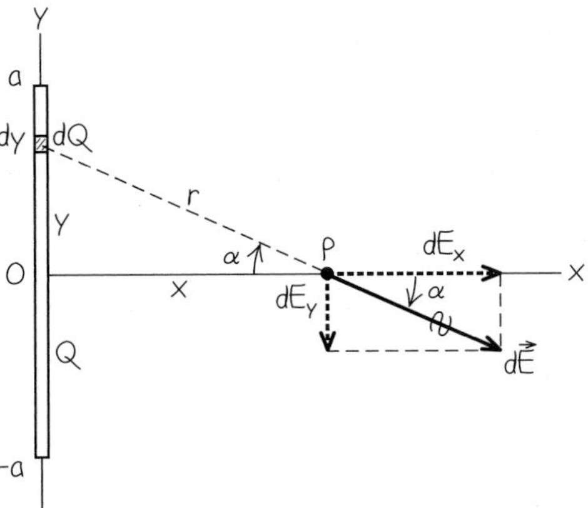

To explore our result, let's first see what happens in the limit that x is much larger than a. Then we can neglect a in the denominator of Eq. (21.9), and our result becomes

$$\vec{E} = \frac{1}{4\pi\epsilon_0}\frac{Q}{x^2}\hat{\imath}$$

This means that if point P is very far from the line charge in comparison to the length of the line, the field at P is the same as that of a point charge. We found a similar result for the charged ring in Example 21.10.

To further explore our exact result for $\vec{E}$, Eq. (21.9), let's express it in terms of the linear charge density $\lambda = Q/2a$. Substituting $Q = 2a\lambda$ into Eq. (21.9) and simplifying, we get

$$\vec{E} = \frac{1}{2\pi\epsilon_0}\frac{\lambda}{x\sqrt{(x^2/a^2) + 1}}\hat{\imath} \qquad (21.10)$$

Now we can answer the question: What is $\vec{E}$ at a distance x from a *very* long line of charge? To find the answer we take the *limit* of Eq. (21.10) as a becomes very large. In this limit, the term x^2/a^2 in the denominator becomes much smaller than unity and can be thrown away. We are left with

$$\vec{E} = \frac{\lambda}{2\pi\epsilon_0 x}\hat{\imath}$$

The field magnitude depends only on the distance of point P from the line of charge. So at any point P at a perpendicular distance r from the line in any direction, $\vec{E}$ has magnitude

$$E = \frac{\lambda}{2\pi\epsilon_0 r} \qquad \text{(infinite line of charge)}$$

Thus the electric field due to an infinitely long line of charge is proportional to $1/r$ rather than to $1/r^2$ as for a point charge. The direction of $\vec{E}$ is radially outward from the line if λ is positive and radially inward if λ is negative.

There's really no such thing in nature as an infinite line of charge. But when the field point is close enough to the line, there's very little difference between the result for an infinite line and the real-life finite case. For example, if the distance r of the field point from the center of the line is 1% of the length of the line, the value of E differs from the infinite-length value by less than 0.02%.

Example 21.12 Field of a uniformly charged disk

Find the electric field caused by a disk of radius R with a uniform positive surface charge density (charge per unit area) σ, at a point along the axis of the disk a distance x from its center. Assume that x is positive.

SOLUTION

IDENTIFY: This example is similar to Examples 21.10 and 21.11 in that our target variable is the electric field along a symmetry axis of a continuous charge distribution.

SET UP: Figure 21.26 shows the situation. We can represent the charge distribution as a collection of concentric rings of charge dQ, as shown in Fig. 21.26. From Example 21.10 we know the field of a single ring on its axis of symmetry, so all we have to do is add the contributions of the rings.

EXECUTE: A typical ring has charge dQ, inner radius r, and outer radius $r + dr$ (Fig. 21.26). Its area dA is approximately equal to its width dr times its circumference $2\pi r$, or $dA = 2\pi r\,dr$. The charge per unit area is $\sigma = dQ/dA$, so the charge of the ring is $dQ = \sigma\,dA = \sigma\,(2\pi r\,dr)$, or

$$dQ = 2\pi\sigma r\,dr$$

We use this in place of Q in the expression for the field due to a ring found in Example 21.10, Eq. (21.8), and also replace the ring radius a with r. The field component dE_x at point P due to charge dQ is

$$dE_x = \frac{1}{4\pi\epsilon_0}\frac{dQ}{r^2} = \frac{1}{4\pi\epsilon_0}\frac{(2\pi\sigma r\,dr)x}{(x^2 + r^2)^{3/2}}$$

21.26 Our sketch for this problem.

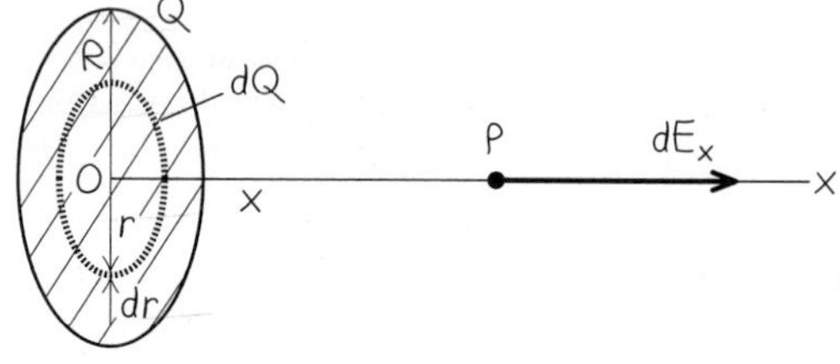

To find the total field due to all the rings, we integrate dE_x over r from $r = 0$ to $r = R$ (*not* from $-R$ to R):

$$E_x = \int_0^R \frac{1}{4\pi\epsilon_0}\frac{(2\pi\sigma r\,dr)x}{(x^2 + r^2)^{3/2}} = \frac{\sigma x}{2\epsilon_0}\int_0^R \frac{r\,dr}{(x^2 + r^2)^{3/2}}$$

Remember that x is a constant during the integration and that the integration variable is r. The integral can be evaluated by use of the substitution $z = x^2 + r^2$. We'll let you work out the details; the result is

$$E_x = \frac{\sigma x}{2\epsilon_0}\left[-\frac{1}{\sqrt{x^2 + R^2}} + \frac{1}{x}\right] = \frac{\sigma}{2\epsilon_0}\left[1 - \frac{1}{\sqrt{(R^2/x^2) + 1}}\right] \qquad (21.11)$$

The electric field due to the ring has no components perpendicular to the axis. Hence at point P in Fig. 21.26, $dE_y = dE_z = 0$ for each ring, and the total field has $E_y = E_z = 0$.

EVALUATE Suppose we keep increasing the radius R of the disk, simultaneously adding charge so that the surface charge density σ (charge per unit area) is constant. In the limit that R is much larger than the distance x of the field point from the disk, the term $1/\sqrt{(R^2/x^2) + 1}$ in Eq. (21.11) becomes negligibly small, and we get

$$E = \frac{\sigma}{2\epsilon_0} \qquad (21.12)$$

Our final result does not contain the distance x from the plane. Hence the electric field produced by an *infinite* plane sheet of charge is *independent of the distance from the sheet.* The field direction is everywhere perpendicular to the sheet, away from it. There is no such thing as an infinite sheet of charge, but if the dimensions of the sheet are much larger than the distance x of the field point P from the sheet, the field is very nearly given by Eq. (21.11).

If P is to the *left* of the plane $(x < 0)$, the result is the same except that the direction of $\vec{E}$ is to the left instead of the right. If the surface charge density is negative, the directions of the fields on both sides of the plane are toward it rather than away from it.

Example 21.13 Field of two oppositely charged infinite sheets

Two infinite plane sheets are placed parallel to each other, separated by a distance d (Fig. 21.27). The lower sheet has a uniform positive surface charge density σ, and the upper sheet has a uniform negative surface charge density $-\sigma$ with the same magnitude. Find the electric field between the two sheets, above the upper sheet, and below the lower sheet.

SOLUTION

IDENTIFY: From Example 21.12 we know the electric field due to a single infinite plane sheet of charge. Our goal is to find the electric field due to *two* such sheets.

SET UP: We use the principle of superposition to combine the electric fields produced by the two sheets, as shown in Fig. 21.27.

21.27 Finding the electric field due to two oppositely charged infinite sheets. The sheets are seen edge-on; only a portion of the infinite sheets can be shown!

y

$\vec{E}_1$ $\vec{E}_2$ $\vec{E} = \vec{E}_1 + \vec{E}_2 = \mathbf{0}$

Sheet 2 $-\sigma$ x

d $\vec{E}_1$ $\vec{E}_2$ $\vec{E} = \vec{E}_1 + \vec{E}_2$

Sheet 1 $+\sigma$

$\vec{E}_1$ $\vec{E}_2$ $\vec{E} = \vec{E}_1 + \vec{E}_2 = \mathbf{0}$

EXECUTE: Let sheet 1 be the lower sheet of positive charge, and let sheet 2 be the upper sheet of negative charge; the fields due to each sheet are $\vec{E}_1$ and $\vec{E}_2$, respectively. From Eq. (21.12) of Example 21.12, both $\vec{E}_1$ and $\vec{E}_2$ have the same magnitude at all points, no matter how far from either sheet:

$$E_1 = E_2 = \frac{\sigma}{2\epsilon_0}$$

At all points, the direction of $\vec{E}_1$ is away from the positive charge of sheet 1, and the direction of $\vec{E}_2$ is toward the negative charge of sheet 2. These fields and the x- and y-axes are shown in Fig. 21.27.

CAUTION Electric fields are not "flows" You may be surprised that $\vec{E}_1$ is unaffected by the presence of sheet 2 and that $\vec{E}_2$ is unaffected by the presence of sheet 1. Indeed, you may have thought that the field of one sheet would be unable to "penetrate" the other sheet. You might conclude this if you think of the electric field as some kind of physical substance that "flows" into or out of charges. But in fact there is no such substance, and the electric fields $\vec{E}_1$ and $\vec{E}_2$ depend only on the individual charge distributions that create them. The *total* field is just the vector sum of $\vec{E}_1$ and $\vec{E}_2$.

At points between the sheets, $\vec{E}_1$ and $\vec{E}_2$ reinforce each other; at points above the upper sheet or below the lower sheet, $\vec{E}_1$ and $\vec{E}_2$ cancel each other. Thus the total field is

$$\vec{E} = \vec{E}_1 + \vec{E}_2 = \begin{cases} \mathbf{0} & \text{above the upper sheet} \\ \dfrac{\sigma}{\epsilon_0}\hat{\jmath} & \text{between the sheets} \\ \mathbf{0} & \text{below the lower sheet} \end{cases}$$

Because we considered the sheets to be infinite, our result does not depend on the separation d.

EVALUATE: Note that the field between the oppositely charged sheets is uniform. We used this in Examples 21.7 and 21.8, in which two large parallel conducting plates were connected to the terminals of a battery. The battery causes the two plates to become oppositely charged, giving a field between the plates that is essentially uniform if the plate separation is much smaller than the dimensions of the plates. In Chapter 23 we will examine how a battery can produce such separation of positive and negative charge. An arrangement of two oppositely charged conducting plates is called a *capacitor;* these devices prove to be of tremendous practical utility and are the principal subject of Chapter 24.

Test Your Understanding of Section 21.5 Suppose that the line of charge in Fig. 21.25 (Example 21.11) had charge $+Q$ distributed uniformly between $y = 0$ and $y = +a$ and had charge $-Q$ distributed uniformly between $y = 0$ and $y = -a$. In this situation, the electric field at P would be (i) in the positive x-direction; (ii) in the negative x-direction; (iii) in the positive y-direction; (iv) in the negative y-direction; (v) zero; (vi) none of these.

21.6 Electric Field Lines

The concept of an electric field can be a little elusive because you can't see an electric field directly. Electric field *lines* can be a big help for visualizing electric fields and making them seem more real. An **electric field line** is an imaginary line or curve drawn through a region of space so that its tangent at any point is in the direction of the electric-field vector at that point. Figure 21.28 shows the basic idea. (We used a similar concept in our discussion of fluid flow in Section 14.5. A *streamline* is a line or curve whose tangent at any point is in the direction of the velocity of the fluid at that point. However, the similarity between electric field lines and fluid streamlines is a mathematical one only; there is nothing "flowing" in an electric field.) The English scientist Michael Faraday (1791–1867) first introduced the concept of field lines. He called them "lines of force," but the term "field lines" is preferable.

21.28 The direction of the electric field at any point is tangent to the field line through that point.

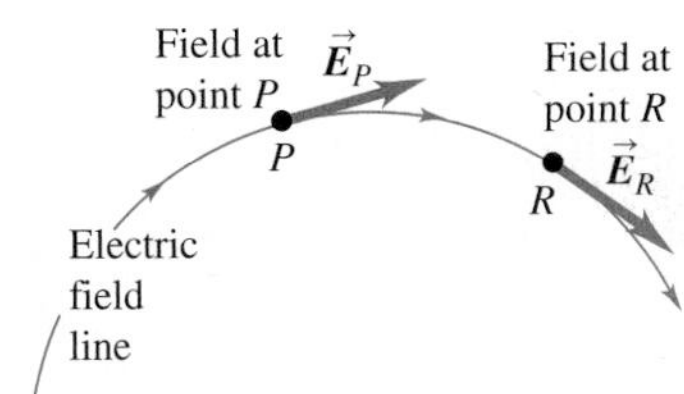

Electric field lines show the direction of $\vec{E}$ at each point, and their spacing gives a general idea of the *magnitude* of $\vec{E}$ at each point. Where $\vec{E}$ is strong, we draw lines bunched closely together; where $\vec{E}$ is weaker, they are farther apart. At any particular point, the electric field has a unique direction, so only one field line can pass through each point of the field. In other words, *field lines never intersect.*

Figure 21.29 shows some of the electric field lines in a plane containing (a) a single positive charge; (b) two equal-magnitude charges, one positive and one negative (a dipole); and (c) two equal positive charges. Diagrams such as these are sometimes called *field maps;* they are cross sections of the actual three-dimensional patterns. The direction of the total electric field at every point in each diagram is along the tangent to the electric field line passing through the point. Arrowheads indicate the direction of the $\vec{E}$-field vector along each field

21.29 Electric field lines for three different charge distributions. In general, the magnitude of $\vec{E}$ is different at different points along a given field line.

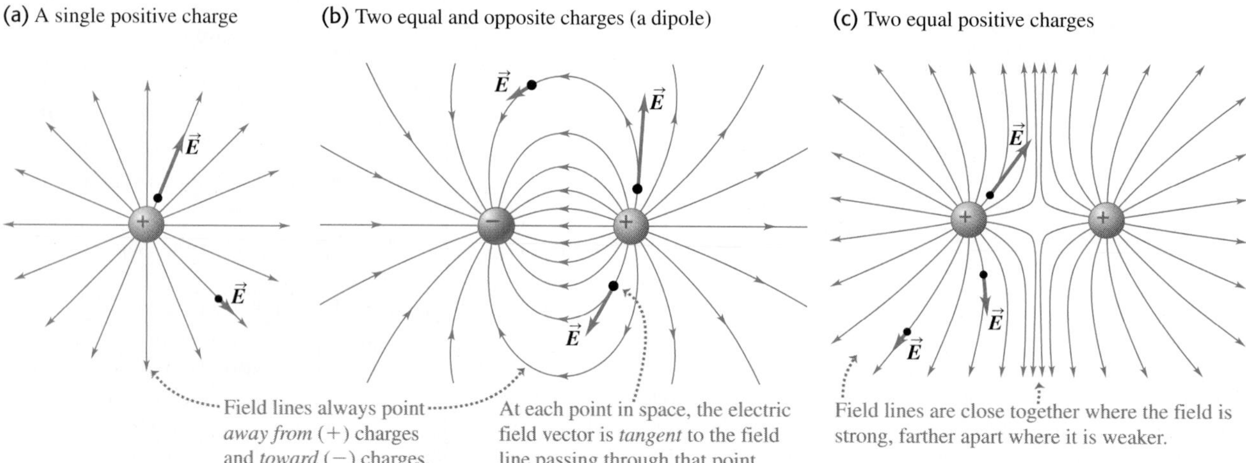

line. The actual field vectors have been drawn at several points in each pattern. Notice that in general, the magnitude of the electric field is different at different points on a given field line; a field line is *not* a curve of constant electric-field magnitude!

(a) A single positive charge
(b) Two equal and opposite charges (a dipole)
(c) Two equal positive charges
Field lines always point *away from* (+) charges and *toward* (−) charges.
At each point in space, the electric field vector is *tangent* to the field line passing through that point.
Field lines are close together where the field is strong, farther apart where it is weaker.

Figure 21.29 shows that field lines are directed *away* from positive charges (since close to a positive point charge, $\vec{E}$ points away from the charge) and *toward* negative charges (since close to a negative point charge, $\vec{E}$ points toward the charge). In regions where the field magnitude is large, such as between the positive and negative charges in Fig. 21.29b, the field lines are drawn close together. In regions where the field magnitude is small, such as between the two positive charges in Fig. 21.29c, the lines are widely separated. In a *uniform* field, the field lines are straight, parallel, and uniformly spaced, as in Fig. 21.20.

Figure 21.30 is a view from above of a demonstration setup for visualizing electric field lines. In the arrangement shown here, the tips of two positively charged wires are inserted in a container of insulating liquid, and some grass seeds are floated on the liquid. The grass seeds are electrically neutral insulators, but the electric field of the two charged wires causes *polarization* of the grass seeds; there is a slight shifting of the positive and negative charges within the molecules of each seed, like that shown in Fig. 21.8. The positively charged end of each grass seed is pulled in the direction of $\vec{E}$ and the negatively charged end is pulled opposite $\vec{E}$. Hence the long axis of each grass seed tends to orient parallel to the electric field, in the direction of the field line that passes through the position of the seed (Fig. 21.30b).

21.30 (a) Electric field lines produced by two equal point charges. The pattern is formed by grass seeds floating on a liquid above two charged wires. Compare this pattern with Fig. 21.29c. (b) The electric field causes polarization of the grass seeds, which in turn causes the seeds to align with the field.

(a)

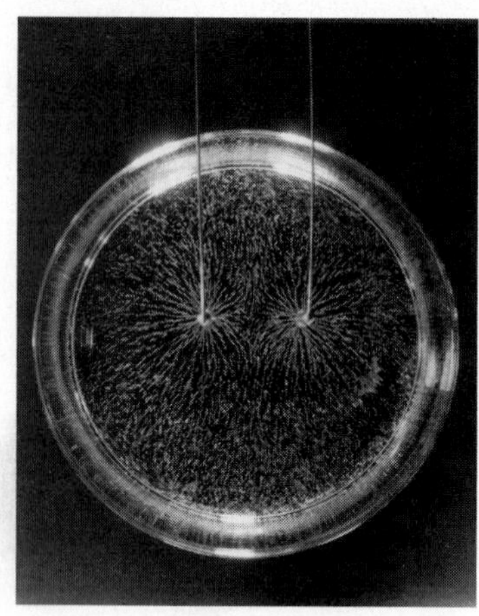

(b)

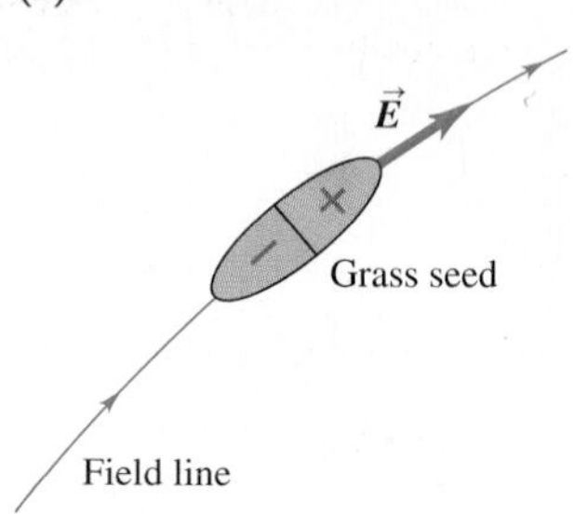

CAUTION Electric field lines are not the same as trajectories It's a common misconception that if a charged particle of charge q is in motion where there is an electric field, the particle must move along an electric field line. Because $\vec{E}$ at any point is tangent to the field line that passes through that point, it is indeed true that the *force* $\vec{F} = q\vec{E}$ on the particle, and hence the particle's acceleration, are tangent to the field line. But we learned in Chapter 3 that when a particle moves on a curved path, its acceleration *cannot* be tangent to the path. So in general, the trajectory of a charged particle is *not* the same as a field line.

Test Your Understanding of Section 21.6 Suppose the electric field lines in a region of space are straight lines. If a charged particle is released from rest in that region, will the trajectory of the particle be along a field line?

21.7 Electric Dipoles

An **electric dipole** is a pair of point charges with equal magnitude and opposite sign (a positive charge q and a negative charge $-q$) separated by a distance d. We introduced electric dipoles in Example 21.9 (Section 21.5); the concept is worth exploring further because many physical systems, from molecules to TV antennas, can be described as electric dipoles. We will also use this concept extensively in our discussion of dielectrics in Chapter 24.

Figure 21.31 a shows a molecule of water (H_2O), which in many ways behaves like an electric dipole. The water molecule as a whole is electrically neutral, but the chemical bonds within the molecule cause a displacement of charge; the result is a net negative charge on the oxygen end of the molecule and a net positive charge on the hydrogen end, forming an electric dipole. The effect is equivalent to shifting one electron only about 4×10^{-11} m (about the radius of a hydrogen atom), but the consequences of this shift are profound. Water is an excellent solvent for ionic substances such as table salt (sodium chloride, NaCl) precisely because the water molecule is an electric dipole (Fig. 21.31b). When dissolved in water, salt dissociates into a positive sodium ion (Na^+) and a negative chlorine ion (Cl^-), which tend to be attracted to the negative and positive ends, respectively, of water molecules; this holds the ions in solution. If water molecules were not electric dipoles, water would be a poor solvent, and almost all of the chemistry that occurs in aqueous solutions would be impossible. This includes all of the biochemical reactions that occur in all of the life on earth. In a very real sense, your existence as a living being depends on electric dipoles!

21.31 (a) A water molecule is an example of an electric dipole. (b) Each test tube contains a solution of a different substance in water. The large electric dipole moment of water makes it an excellent solvent.

(a) A water molecule, showing positive charge as red and negative charge as blue

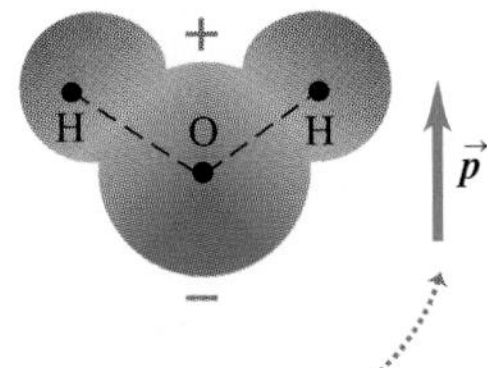

The electric dipole moment $\vec{p}$ is directed from the negative end to the positive end of the molecule.

(b) Various substances dissolved in water

We examine two questions about electric dipoles. First, what forces and torques does an electric dipole experience when placed in an external electric field (that is, a field set up by charges outside the dipole)? Second, what electric field does an electric dipole itself produce?

Force and Torque on an Electric Dipole

To start with the first question, let's place an electric dipole in a *uniform* external electric field $\vec{E}$, as shown in Fig. 21.32. The forces $\vec{F}_+$ and $\vec{F}_-$ on the two charges both have magnitude qE, but their directions are opposite, and they add to zero. *The net force on an electric dipole in a uniform external electric field is zero.*

However, the two forces don't act along the same line, so their *torques* don't add to zero. We calculate torques with respect to the center of the dipole. Let the angle between the electric field $\vec{E}$ and the dipole axis be ϕ; then the lever arm for both $\vec{F}_+$ and $\vec{F}_-$ is $(d/2)\sin\phi$. The torque of $\vec{F}_+$ and the torque of $\vec{F}_-$ both have the same magnitude of $(qE)(d/2)\sin\phi$, and both torques tend to rotate the dipole clockwise (that is, $\vec{\tau}$ is directed into the page in Fig. 21.32). Hence the magnitude of the net torque is twice the magnitude of either individual torque:

$$\tau = (qE)(d\sin\phi) \qquad (21.13)$$

where $d \sin \phi$ is the perpendicular distance between the lines of action of the two forces.

The product of the charge q and the separation d is the magnitude of a quantity called the **electric dipole moment,** denoted by p:

$$p = qd \qquad \text{(magnitude of electric dipole moment)} \qquad (21.14)$$

The units of p are charge times distance $(\mathrm{C \cdot m})$. For example, the magnitude of the electric dipole moment of a water molecule is $p = 6.13 \times 10^{-30}\ \mathrm{C \cdot m}$.

21.32 The net force on this electric dipole is zero, but there is a torque directed into the page that tends to rotate the dipole clockwise.

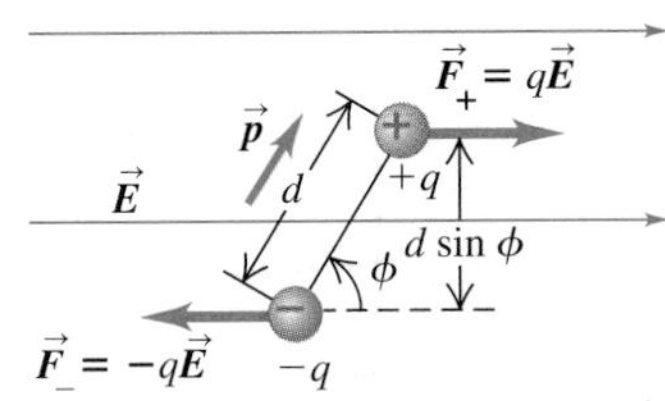

CAUTION **The symbol p has multiple meanings** Be careful not to confuse dipole moment with momentum or pressure. There aren't as many letters in the alphabet as there are physical quantities, so some letters are used several times. The context usually makes it clear what we mean, but be careful.

We further define the electric dipole moment to be a *vector* quantity $\vec{p}$. The magnitude of $\vec{p}$ is given by Eq. (21.14), and its direction is along the dipole axis from the negative charge to the positive charge as shown in Fig. 21.32.

In terms of p, Eq. (21.13) for the magnitude τ of the torque exerted by the field becomes

$$\tau = pE \sin\phi \qquad \text{(magnitude of the torque on an electric dipole)} \quad (21.15)$$

Since the angle ϕ in Fig. 21.32 is the angle between the directions of the vectors $\vec{p}$ and $\vec{E}$, this is reminiscent of the expression for the magnitude of the *vector product* discussed in Section 1.10. (You may want to review that discussion.) Hence we can write the torque on the dipole in vector form as

$$\vec{\tau} = \vec{p} \times \vec{E} \qquad \text{(torque on an electric dipole, in vector form)} \quad (21.16)$$

You can use the right-hand rule for the vector product to verify that in the situation shown in Fig. 21.32, $\vec{\tau}$ is directed into the page. The torque is greatest when $\vec{p}$ and $\vec{E}$ are perpendicular and is zero when they are parallel or antiparallel. The torque always tends to turn $\vec{p}$ to line it up with $\vec{E}$. The position $\phi = 0$, with $\vec{p}$ parallel to $\vec{E}$, is a position of stable equilibrium, and the position $\phi = \pi$, with $\vec{p}$ and $\vec{E}$ antiparallel, is a position of unstable equilibrium. The polarization of a grass seed in the apparatus of Fig. 21.30b gives it an electric dipole moment; the torque exerted by $\vec{E}$ then causes the seed to align with $\vec{E}$ and hence with the field lines.

Potential Energy of an Electric Dipole

When a dipole changes direction in an electric field, the electric-field torque does *work* on it, with a corresponding change in potential energy. The work dW done by a torque τ during an infinitesimal displacement $d\phi$ is given by Eq. (10.19): $dW = \tau\, d\phi$. Because the torque is in the direction of decreasing ϕ, we must write the torque as $\tau = -pE \sin\phi$, and

$$dW = \tau\, d\phi = -pE \sin\phi\, d\phi$$

In a finite displacement from ϕ_1 to ϕ_2 the total work done on the dipole is

$$\begin{aligned} W &= \int_{\phi_1}^{\phi_2} (-pE \sin\phi)\, d\phi \\ &= pE \cos\phi_2 - pE \cos\phi_1 \end{aligned}$$

The work is the negative of the change of potential energy, just as in Chapter 7: $W = U_1 - U_2$. So we see that a suitable definition of potential energy U for this system is

$$U(\phi) = -pE \cos\phi \quad (21.17)$$

In this expression we recognize the *scalar product* $\vec{p} \cdot \vec{E} = pE\cos\phi$, so we can also write

$$U = -\vec{p} \cdot \vec{E} \qquad \text{(potential energy for a dipole in an electric field)} \quad (21.18)$$

The potential energy has its minimum value $U = -pE$ (i.e., its most negative value) at the stable equilibrium position, where $\phi = 0$ and $\vec{p}$ is parallel to $\vec{E}$. The potential energy is maximum when $\phi = \pi$ and $\vec{p}$ is antiparallel to $\vec{E}$; then $U = +pE$. At $\phi = \pi/2$, where $\vec{p}$ is perpendicular to $\vec{E}$, U is zero. We could of course define U differently so that it is zero at some other orientation of $\vec{p}$, but our definition is simplest.

Equation (21.18) gives us another way to look at the effect shown in Fig. 21.30. The electric field $\vec{E}$ gives each grass seed an electric dipole moment, and the grass seed then aligns itself with $\vec{E}$ to minimize the potential energy.

Example 21.14 Force and torque on an electric dipole

Figure 21.33a shows an electric dipole in a uniform electric field with magnitude 5.0×10^5 N/C directed parallel to the plane of the figure. The charges are $\pm 1.6 \times 10^{-19}$ C; both lie in the plane and are separated by 0.125 nm $= 0.125 \times 10^{-9}$ m. (Both the charge magnitude and the distance are typical of molecular quantities.) Find (a) the net force exerted by the field on the dipole; (b) the magnitude and direction of the electric dipole moment; (c) the magnitude and direction of the torque; (d) the potential energy of the system in the position shown.

SOLUTION

IDENTIFY: This problem uses the ideas of this section about an electric dipole placed in an electric field.

SET UP: We use the relationship $\vec{F} = q\vec{E}$ for each point charge to find the force on the dipole as a whole. Equation (21.14) tells us the dipole moment, Eq. (21.16) tells us the torque on the dipole, and Eq. (21.18) tells us the potential energy of the system.

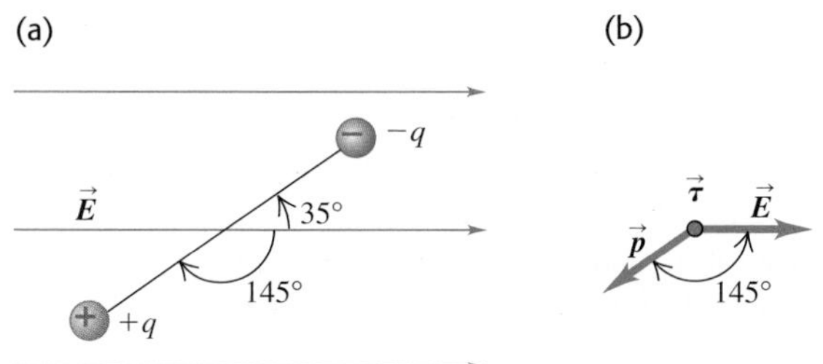

21.33 (a) An electric dipole. (b) Directions of the electric dipole moment, electric field, and torque.

EXECUTE: (a) Since the field is uniform, the forces on the two charges are equal and opposite, and the total force is zero.

(b) The magnitude p of the electric dipole moment $\vec{p}$ is

$$p = qd = (1.6 \times 10^{-19}\,\text{C})(0.125 \times 10^{-9}\,\text{m})$$
$$= 2.0 \times 10^{-29}\,\text{C} \cdot \text{m}$$

The direction of $\vec{p}$ is from the negative to the positive charge, 145° clockwise from the electric-field direction (Fig. 21.33b).

(c) The magnitude of the torque is

$$\tau = pE \sin\phi = (2.0 \times 10^{-29}\,\text{C})(5.0 \times 10^5\,\text{N/C})(\sin 145°)$$
$$= 5.7 \times 10^{-24}\,\text{N} \cdot \text{m}$$

From the right-hand rule for vector products (see Section 1.10), the direction of the torque $\vec{\tau} = \vec{p} \times \vec{E}$ is out of the page. This corresponds to a counterclockwise torque that tends to align $\vec{p}$ with $\vec{E}$.

(d) The potential energy is

$$U = -pE\cos\phi$$
$$= -(2.0 \times 10^{-29}\,\text{C} \cdot \text{m})(5.0 \times 10^5\,\text{N/C})(\cos 145°)$$
$$= 8.2 \times 10^{-24}\,\text{J}$$

EVALUATE: The dipole moment, torque, and potential energy are all exceedingly small. Don't be surprised by this result: Remember that we are looking at a single molecule, which is a very small object indeed!

In this discussion we have assumed that $\vec{E}$ is uniform, so there is no net force on the dipole. If $\vec{E}$ is not uniform, the forces at the ends may not cancel completely, and the net force may not be zero. Thus a body with zero net charge but an electric dipole moment can experience a net force in a nonuniform electric field. As we mentioned in Section 21.1, an uncharged body can be polarized by an electric field, giving rise to a separation of charge and an electric dipole moment. This is how uncharged bodies can experience electrostatic forces (see Fig. 21.8).

Field of an Electric Dipole

Now let's think of an electric dipole as a *source* of electric field. What does the field look like? The general shape of things is shown by the field map of Fig. 21.29b. At each point in the pattern the total $\vec{E}$ field is the vector sum of the fields from the two individual charges, as in Example 21.9 (Section 21.5). Try drawing diagrams showing this vector sum for several points.

To get quantitative information about the field of an electric dipole, we have to do some calculating, as illustrated in the next example. Notice the use of the principle of superposition of electric fields to add up the contributions to the field of the individual charges. Also notice that we need to use approximation techniques even for the relatively simple case of a field due to two charges. Field calculations often become very complicated, and computer analysis is typically used to determine the field due to an arbitrary charge distribution.

Example 21.15 Field of an electric dipole, revisited

In Fig. 21.34 an electric dipole is centered at the origin, with $\vec{p}$ in the direction of the $+y$-axis. Derive an approximate expression for the electric field at a point on the y-axis for which y is much larger than d. Use the binomial expansion of $(1 + x)^n$—that is, $(1 + x)^n \cong 1 + nx + n(n - 1)x^2/2 + \cdots$ —for the case $|x| < 1$. (This problem illustrates a useful calculational technique.)

SOLUTION

IDENTIFY: We use the principle of superposition: The total electric field is the vector sum of the field produced by the positive charge and the field produced by the negative charge.

SET UP: At the field point shown in Fig. 21.34, the field of the positive charge has a positive (upward) y-component and the field of the negative charge has a negative (downward) y-component. We add these components to find the total field and then apply the approximation that y is much greater than d.

21.34 Finding the electric field of an electric dipole at a point on its axis.

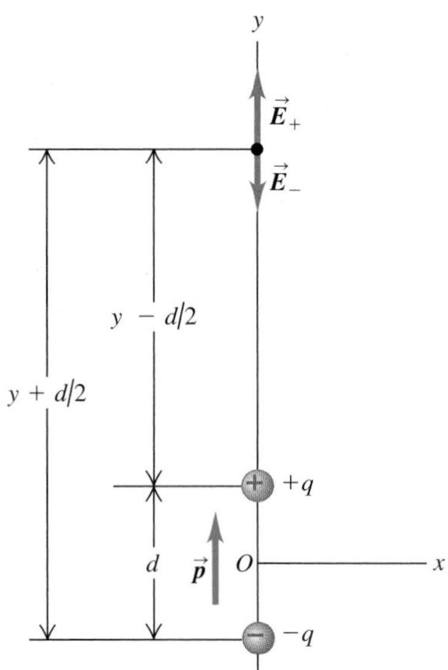

EXECUTE: The total y-component E_y of electric field from the two charges is

$$E_y = \frac{q}{4\pi\epsilon_0}\left[\frac{1}{(y - d/2)^2} - \frac{1}{(y + d/2)^2}\right]$$
$$= \frac{q}{4\pi\epsilon_0 y^2}\left[\left(1 - \frac{d}{2y}\right)^{-2} - \left(1 + \frac{d}{2y}\right)^{-2}\right]$$

We used this same approach in Example 21.9 (Section 21.5). Now comes the approximation. When y is much greater than d—that is, when we are far away from the dipole compared to its size—the quantity $d/2y$ is much smaller than 1. With $n = -2$ and $d/2y$ playing the role of x in the binomial expansion, we keep only the first two terms. The terms we discard are much smaller than those we keep, and we have

$$\left(1 - \frac{d}{2y}\right)^{-2} \cong 1 + \frac{d}{y} \quad \text{and} \quad \left(1 + \frac{d}{2y}\right)^{-2} \cong 1 - \frac{d}{y}$$

Hence E_y is given approximately by

$$E \cong \frac{q}{4\pi\epsilon_0 y^2}\left[1 + \frac{d}{y} - \left(1 - \frac{d}{y}\right)\right]$$
$$= \frac{qd}{2\pi\epsilon_0 y^3}$$
$$= \frac{p}{2\pi\epsilon_0 y^3}$$

EVALUATE: An alternative route to this expression is to put the fractions in the E_y expression over a common denominator and combine, then approximate the denominator $(y - d/2)^2(y + d/2)^2$ as y^4. We leave the details to you (see Exercise 21.65).

For points P off the coordinate axes, the expressions are more complicated, but at *all* points far away from the dipole (in any direction) the field drops off as $1/r^3$. We can compare this with the $1/r^2$ behavior of a point charge, the $1/r$ behavior of a long line charge, and the independence of r for a large sheet of charge. There are charge distributions for which the field drops off even more quickly. An *electric quadrupole* consists of two equal dipoles with opposite orientation, separated by a small distance. The field of a quadrupole at large distances drops off as $1/r^4$.

Test Your Understanding of Section 21.7 An electric dipole is placed in a region of uniform electric field $\vec{E}$, with the electric dipole moment $\vec{p}$, pointing in the direction opposite to $\vec{E}$. Is the dipole (i) in stable equilibrium, (ii) in unstable equilibrium, or (iii) neither? (*Hint:* You many want to review Section 7.5.)

CHAPTER 21 SUMMARY

Electric charge, conductors, and insulators: The fundamental quantity in electrostatics is electric charge. There are two kinds of charge, positive and negative. Charges of the same sign repel each other; charges of opposite sign attract. Charge is conserved; the total charge in an isolated system is constant.

All ordinary matter is made of protons, neutrons, and electrons. The positive protons and electrically neutral neutrons in the nucleus of an atom are bound together by the nuclear force; the negative electrons surround the nucleus at distances much greater than the nuclear size. Electric interactions are chiefly responsible for the structure of atoms, molecules, and solids.

Conductors are materials that permit electric charge to move easily within them. Insulators permit charge to move much less readily. Most metals are good conductors; most nonmetals are insulators.

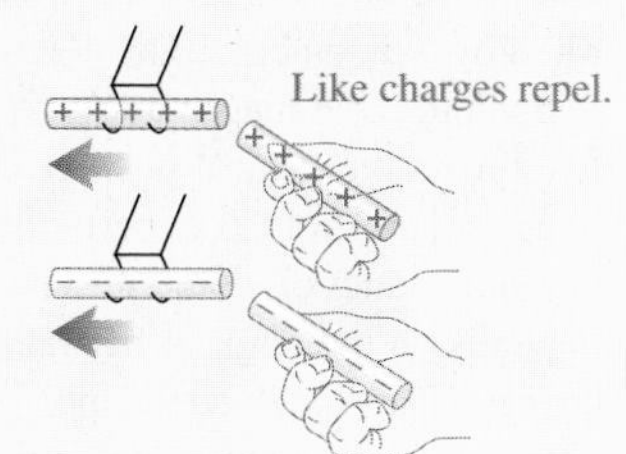

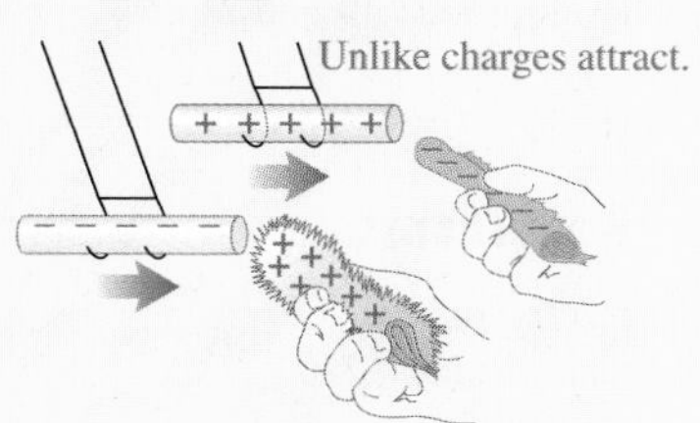

Coulomb's law: Coulomb's law is the basic law of interaction for point electric charges. For charges q_1 and q_2 separated by a distance r, the magnitude of the force on either charge is proportional to the product $q_1 q_2$ and inversely proportional to r^2. The force on each charge is along the line joining the two charges—repulsive if q_1 and q_2 have the same sign, attractive if they have opposite signs. The forces form an action–reaction pair and obey Newton's third law. In SI units the unit of electric charge is the coulomb, abbreviated C. (See Examples 21.1 and 21.2.)

The principle of superposition of forces states that when two or more charges each exert a force on a charge, the total force on that charge is the vector sum of the forces exerted by the individual charges. (See Examples 21.3 and 21.4.)

$$F = \frac{1}{4\pi\epsilon_0}\frac{|q_1 q_2|}{r^2} \qquad (21.2)$$

$$\frac{1}{4\pi\epsilon_0} = 8.988 \times 10^9\ \mathrm{N\cdot m^2/C^2}$$

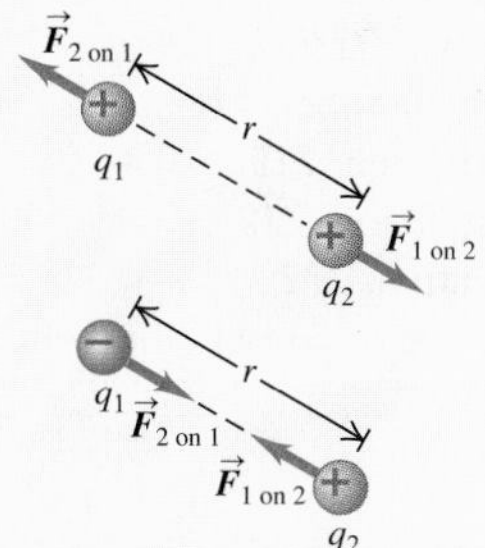

Electric field: Electric field $\vec{E}$, a vector quantity, is the force per unit charge exerted on a test charge at any point, provided the test charge is small enough that it does not disturb the charges that cause the field. The electric field produced by a point charge is directed radially away from or toward the charge. (See Examples 21.5–21.8.)

$$\vec{E} = \frac{\vec{F}_0}{q_0} \qquad (21.3)$$

$$\vec{E} = \frac{1}{4\pi\epsilon_0}\frac{q}{r^2}\hat{r} \qquad (21.7)$$

Superposition of electric fields: The principle of superposition of electric fields states that the electric field $\vec{E}$ of any combination of charges is the vector sum of the fields caused by the individual charges. To calculate the electric field caused by a continuous distribution of charge, divide the distribution into small elements, calculate the field caused by each element, and then carry out the vector sum or each component sum, usually by integrating. Charge distributions are described by linear charge density λ, surface charge density σ, and volume charge density ρ. (See Examples 21.9–21.13.)

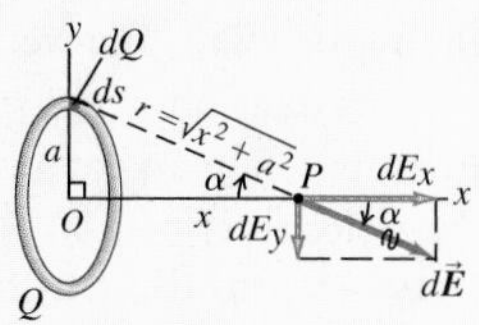

Electric field lines: Field lines provide a graphical representation of electric fields. At any point on a field line, the tangent to the line is in the direction of $\vec{E}$ at that point. The number of lines per unit area (perpendicular to their direction) is proportional to the magnitude of $\vec{E}$ at the point.

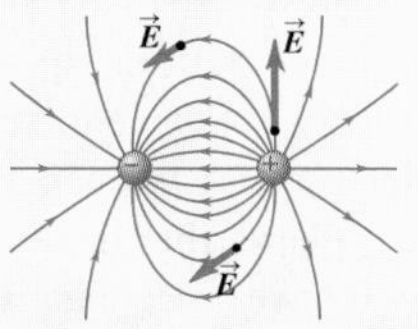

Electric dipoles: An electric dipole is a pair of electric charges of equal magnitude q but opposite sign, separated by a distance d. The electric dipole moment $\vec{p}$ is defined to have magnitude $p = qd$. The direction of $\vec{p}$ is from negative toward positive charge. An electric dipole in an electric field $\vec{E}$ experiences a torque $\vec{\tau}$ equal to the vector product of $\vec{p}$ and $\vec{E}$. The magnitude of the torque depends on the angle ϕ between $\vec{p}$ and $\vec{E}$. The potential energy U for an electric dipole in an electric field also depends on the relative orientation of $\vec{p}$ and $\vec{E}$. (See Examples 21.14 and 21.15.)

$$\tau = pE\sin\phi \quad (21.15)$$

$$\vec{\tau} = \vec{p} \times \vec{E} \quad (21.16)$$

$$U = -\vec{p}\cdot\vec{E} \quad (21.18)$$

Key Terms

Answer to Chapter Opening Question ?

Water molecules have a permanent electric dipole moment: One end of the molecule has a positive charge and the other end has a negative charge. These ends attract negative and positive ions, respectively, holding the ions apart in solution. Water is less effective as a solvent for materials whose molecules do not ionize (called *nonionic* substances), such as oils.

Answers to Test Your Understanding Questions

21.1 Answers: (a) the plastic rod weighs more, (b) the glass rod weighs less, (c) the fur weighs a little less, (d) the silk weighs a little less The plastic rod gets a negative charge by taking electrons from the fur, so the rod weighs a little more and the fur weighs a little less after the rubbing. By contrast, the glass rod gets a positive charge by giving electrons to the silk. Hence, after they are rubbed together, the glass rod weighs a little less and the silk weighs a little more. The weight change is *very* small: The number of electrons transferred is a small fraction of a mole, and a mole of electrons has a mass of only $(6.02 \times 10^{23}\ \text{electrons})(9.11 \times 10^{-31}\ \text{kg/electron}) = 5.48 \times 10^{-7}\ \text{kg} = 0.548$ milligram!

21.2 Answers: (a) (i), (b) (ii) Before the two spheres touch, the negatively charged sphere exerts a repulsive force on the electrons in the other sphere, causing zones of positive and negative induced charge (see Fig. 21.7b). The positive zone is closer to the negatively charged sphere than the negative zone, so there is a net force of attraction that pulls the spheres together, like the comb and insulator in Fig. 21.8b. Once the two metal spheres touch, some of the excess electrons on the negatively charged sphere will flow onto the other sphere (because metals are conductors). Then both spheres will have a net negative charge and will repel each other.

21.3 Answer: (iv) The force exerted by q_1 on Q is still as in Example 21.4. The magnitude of the force exerted by q_2 on Q is still equal to $F_{1\text{ on }Q}$, but the direction of the force is now *toward* q_2 at an angle α below the x-axis. Hence the x-components of the two forces cancel while the (negative) y-components add together, and the total electric force is in the negative y-direction.

21.4 Answers: (a) (ii), (b) (i) The electric field $\vec{E}$ produced by a positive point charge points directly away from the charge (see Fig. 21.18a) and has a magnitude that depends on the distance r from the charge to the field point. Hence a second, negative point charge $q < 0$ will feel a force $\vec{F} = q\vec{E}$ that points directly toward the positive charge and has a magnitude that depends on the distance r between the two charges. If the negative charge moves directly toward the positive charge, the direction of the force remains the same (along the line of the negative charge's motion) but the force magnitude increases as the distance r decreases. If the negative charge moves in a circle around the positive charge, the force magnitude stays the same (because the distance r is constant) but the force direction changes (when the negative charge is on the right side of the positive charge, the force is to the left; when the negative charge is on the left side of the positive charge, the force is to the right).

21.5 Answer: (iv) Think of a pair of segments of length dy, one at coordinate $y > 0$ and the other at coordinate $-y < 0$. The upper segment has a positive charge and produces an electric field $d\vec{E}$ at P that points away from the segment, so this $d\vec{E}$ has a positive x-component and a negative y-component, like the vector $d\vec{E}$ in Fig. 21.25. The lower segment has the same amount of negative charge. It produces a $d\vec{E}$ that has the same magnitude but points *toward* the lower segment, so it has a negative x-component and a negative y-component. By symmetry, the two x-components are equal but opposite, so they cancel. Thus the total electric field has only a negative y-component.

21.6 Answer: yes If the field lines are straight, $\vec{E}$ must point in the same direction throughout the region. Hence the force $\vec{F} = q\vec{E}$ on a particle of charge q is always in the same direction. A particle released from rest accelerates in a straight line the direction of $\vec{F}$, and so its trajectory is a straight line that will be along a field line.
21.7 Answer: (ii) Equations (21.17) and (21.18) tell is that the potential energy for a dipole in an electric field is $U = -\vec{p}\cdot\vec{E} = -pE\cos\phi$, where ϕ is the angle between the directions of $\vec{p}$ and $\vec{E}$. If $\vec{p}$ and $\vec{E}$ point in opposite directions, so that $\phi = 180°$, we have $\cos\phi = -1$ and $U = +pE$. This is the maximum value that U can have. From our discussion of energy diagrams in Section 7.5, it follows that this is a situation of unstable equilibrium.

Another way to see this is from Eq. (21.15), which tells us that the magnitude of the torque on an electric dipole is $\tau = pE\sin\phi$. This is zero if $\phi = 180°$, so there is no torque, and if left undisturbed the dipole will not rotate. However, if the dipole is disturbed slightly so that ϕ is a little less than 180°, there will be a nonzero torque that tries to rotate the dipole toward $\phi = 0$ so that $\vec{p}$ and $\vec{E}$ point in the same direction. Hence if the dipole is disturbed from the equilibrium orientation at $\phi = 180°$, it moves farther away from that orientation—which is the hallmark of unstable equilbrium.

You can show that the situation in which $\vec{p}$ and $\vec{E}$ point in the same direction ($\phi = 0$) is a case of *stable* equilibrium: The potential energy is minimum, and if the dipole is displaced slightly there is a torque that tries to return it to the original orientation (a *restoring* torque).

PROBLEMS

For instructor-assigned homework, go to **www.masteringphysics.com** 

Discussion Questions

Q21.1. If you peel two strips of transparent tape off the same roll and immediately let them hang near each other, they will repel each other. If you then stick the sticky side of one to the shiny side of the other and rip them apart, they will attract each other. Give a plausible explanation, involving transfer of electrons between the strips of tape, for this sequence of events.
Q21.2. Two metal spheres are hanging from nylon threads. When you bring the spheres close to each other, they tend to attract. Based on this information alone, discuss all the possible ways that the spheres could be charged. Is it possible that after the spheres touch, they will cling together? Explain.
Q21.3. The electric force between two charged particles becomes weaker with increasing distance. Suppose instead that the electric force were *independent* of distance. In this case, would a charged comb still cause a neutral insulator to become polarized as in Fig. 21.8? Why or why not? Would the neutral insulator still be attracted to the comb? Again, why or why not?
Q21.4. Your clothing tends to cling together after going through the dryer. Why? Would you expect more or less clinging if all your clothing were made of the same material (say, cotton) than if you dried different kinds of clothing together? Again, why? (You may want to experiment with your next load of laundry.)
Q21.5. An uncharged metal sphere hangs from a nylon thread. When a positively charged glass rod is brought close to the metal sphere, the sphere is drawn toward the rod. But if the sphere touches the rod, it suddenly flies away from the rod. Explain why the sphere is first attracted and then repelled.
Q21.6. The free electrons in a metal are gravitationally attracted toward the earth. Why, then, don't they all settle to the bottom of the conductor, like sediment settling to the bottom of a river?
Q21.7. Some of the free electrons in a good conductor (such as a piece of copper) move at speeds of 10^6 m/s or faster. Why don't these electrons fly out of the conductor completely?
Q21.8. Good electrical conductors, such as metals, are typically good conductors of heat; electrical insulators, such as wood, are typically poor conductors of heat. Explain why there should be a relationship between electrical conduction and heat conduction in these materials.
Q21.9. Defend this statement: "If there were only one electrically charged particle in the entire universe, the concept of electric charge would be meaningless."
Q21.10. Two identical metal objects are mounted on insulating stands. Describe how you could place charges of opposite sign but exactly equal magnitude on the two objects.
Q21.11. You can use plastic food wrap to cover a container by stretching the material across the top and pressing the overhanging material against the sides. What makes it stick? (*Hint:* The answer involves the electric force.) Does the food wrap stick to itself with equal tenacity? Why or why not? Does it work with metallic containers? Again, why or why not?
Q21.12. If you walk across a nylon rug and then touch a large metal object such as a doorknob, you may get a spark and a shock. Why does this tend to happen more on dry days than on humid days? (*Hint:* See Fig. 21.31.) Why are you less likely to get a shock if you touch a *small* metal object, such as a paper clip?
Q21.13. You have a negatively charged object. How can you use it to place a net negative charge on an insulated metal sphere? To place a net positive charge on the sphere?
Q21.14. When two point charges of equal mass and charge are released on a frictionless table, each has an initial acceleration a_0. If instead you keep one fixed and release the other one, what will be its initial acceleration: a_0, $2a_0$, or $a_0/2$? Explain.
Q21.15. A point charge of mass m and charge Q and another point charge of mass m but charge $2Q$ are released on a frictionless table. If the charge Q has an initial acceleration a_0, what will be the acceleration of $2Q$: a_0, $2a_0$, $4a_0$, $a_0/2$, or $a_0/4$? Explain.
Q21.16. A proton is placed in a uniform electric field and then released. Then an electron is placed at this same point and released. Do these two particles experience the same force? The same acceleration? Do they move in the same direction when released?
Q21.17. In Example 21.1 (Section 21.3) we saw that the electric force between two α particles is of the order of 10^{35} times as strong as the gravitational force. So why do we readily feel the gravity of the earth but no electrical force from it?
Q21.18. What similarities do electrical forces have with gravitational forces? What are the most significant differences?
Q21.19. At a distance R from a point charge its electric field is E_0. At what distance (in terms of R) from the point charge would the electric field be $\frac{1}{3}E_0$
Q21.20. Atomic nuclei are made of protons and neutrons. This shows that there must be another kind of interaction in addition to gravitational and electric forces. Explain.

Q21.21. Sufficiently strong electric fields can cause atoms to become positively ionized—that is, to lose one or more electrons. Explain how this can happen. What determines how strong the field must be to make this happen?

Q21.22. The electric fields at point P due to the positive charges q_1 and q_2 are shown in Fig. 21.35. Does the fact that they cross each other violate the statement in Section 21.6 that electric field lines never cross? Explain.

Figure **21.35** Question Q21.22.

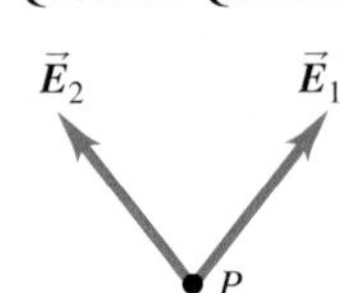

Q21.23. The air temperature and the velocity of the air have different values at different places in the earth's atmosphere. Is the air velocity a vector field? Why or why not? Is the air temperature a vector field? Again, why or why not?

Exercises

Section 21.3 Coulomb's Law

21.1. Excess electrons are placed on a small lead sphere with mass 8.00 g so that its net charge is -3.20×10^{-9} C. (a) Find the number of excess electrons on the sphere. (b) How many excess electrons are there per lead atom? The atomic number of lead is 82, and its atomic mass is 207 g/mol.

21.2. Lightning occurs when there is a flow of electric charge (principally electrons) between the ground and a thundercloud. The maximum rate of charge flow in a lightning bolt is about 20,000 C/s; this lasts for 100 μs or less. How much charge flows between the ground and the cloud in this time? How many electrons flow during this time?

21.3. Estimate how many electrons there are in your body. Make any assumptions you feel are necessary, but clearly state what they are. (*Hint:* Most of the atoms in your body have equal numbers of electrons, protons, and neutrons.) What is the combined charge of all these electrons?

21.4. Particles in a Gold Ring. You have a pure (24-karat) gold ring with mass 17.7 g. Gold has an atomic mass of 197 g/mol and an atomic number of 79. (a) How many protons are in the ring, and what is their total positive charge? (b) If the ring carries no net charge, how many electrons are in it?

21.5. An average human weighs about 650 N. If two such generic humans each carried 1.0 coulomb of excess charge, one positive and one negative, how far apart would they have to be for the electric attraction between them to equal their 650-N weight?

21.6. Two small spheres spaced 20.0 cm apart have equal charge. How many excess electrons must be present on each sphere if the magnitude of the force of repulsion between them is 4.57×10^{-21} N?

21.7. Two small plastic spheres are given positive electrical charges. When they are 15.0 cm apart, the repulsive force between them has magnitude 0.220 N. What is the charge on each sphere (a) if the two charges are equal and (b) if one sphere has four times the charge of the other?

21.8. Two small aluminum spheres, each having mass 0.0250 kg, are separated by 80.0 cm. (a) How many electrons does each sphere contain? (The atomic mass of aluminum is 26.982 g/mol, and its atomic number is 13.) (b) How many electrons would have to be removed from one sphere and added to the other to cause an attractive force between the spheres of magnitude 1.00×10^4 N (roughly 1 ton)? Assume that the spheres may be treated as point charges. (c) What fraction of all the electrons in each sphere does this represent?

21.9. Two very small 8.55-g spheres, 15.0 cm apart from center to center, are charged by adding equal numbers of electrons to each of them. Disregarding all other forces, how many electrons would you have to add to each sphere so that the two spheres will accelerate at 25.0g when released? Which way will they accelerate?

21.10. (a) Assuming that only gravity is acting on it, how far does an electron have to be from a proton so that its acceleration is the same as that of a freely falling object at the earth's surface? (b) Suppose the earth were made only of protons but had the same size and mass it presently has. What would be the acceleration of an electron released at the surface? Is it necessary to consider the gravitational attraction as well as the electrical force? Why or why not?

21.11. In an experiment in space, one proton is held fixed and another proton is released from rest a distance of 2.50 mm away. (a) What is the initial acceleration of the proton after it is released? (b) Sketch qualitative (no numbers!) acceleration–time and velocity–time graphs of the released proton's motion.

21.12. A negative charge $-0.550\ \mu$C exerts an upward 0.200-N force on an unknown charge 0.300 m directly below it. (a) What is the unknown charge (magnitude and sign)? (b) What are the magnitude and direction of the force that the unknown charge exerts on the -0.550-μC charge?

21.13. Three point charges are arranged on a line. Charge $q_3 = +5.00$ nC and is at the origin. Charge $q_2 = -3.00$ nC and is at $x = +4.00$ cm. Charge q_1 is at $x = +2.00$ cm. What is q_1 (magnitude and sign) if the net force on q_3 is zero?

21.14. In Example 21.4, suppose the point charge on the y-axis at $y = -0.30$ m has negative charge $-2.0\ \mu$C, and the other charges remain the same. Find the magnitude and direction of the net force on Q. How does your answer differ from that in Example 21.3? Explain the differences.

21.15. In Example 21.3, calculate the net force on charge q_1.

21.16. In Example 21.4, what is the net force (magnitude and direction) on charge q_1 exerted by the other two charges?

21.17. Three point charges are arranged along the x-axis. Charge $q_1 = +3.00\ \mu$C is at the origin, and charge $q_2 = -5.00\ \mu$C is at $x = 0.200$ m. Charge $q_3 = -8.00\ \mu$C. Where is q_3 located if the net force on q_1 is 7.00 N in the $-x$-direction?

21.18. Repeat Exercise 21.17, for $q_3 = +8.00\ \mu$C.

21.19. Two point charges are located on the y-axis as follows: charge $q_1 = -1.50$ nC at $y = -0.600$ m, and charge $q_2 = +3.20$ nC at the origin $(y = 0)$. What is the total force (magnitude and direction) exerted by these two charges on a third charge $q_3 = +5.00$ nC located at $y = -0.400$ m?

21.20. Two point charges are placed on the x-axis as follows: Charge $q_1 = +4.00$ nC is located at $x = 0.200$ m, and charge $q_2 = +5.00$ nC is at $x = -0.300$ m. What are the magnitude and direction of the total force exerted by these two charges on a negative point charge $q_3 = -6.00$ nC that is placed at the origin?

21.21. A positive point charge q is placed on the $+y$-axis at $y = a$, and a negative point charge $-q$ is placed on the $-y$-axis at $y = -a$. A negative point charge $-Q$ is located at some point on the $+x$-axis. (a) In a free-body diagram, show the forces that act on the charge $-Q$. (b) Find the x- and y-components of the net force that the two charges q and $-q$ exert on $-Q$. (Your answer should involve only k, q, Q, a and the coordinate x of the third charge.) (c) What is the net force on the charge $-Q$ when it is at the origin $(x = 0)$? (d) Graph the y-component of the net force on the charge $-Q$ as a function of x for values of x between $-4a$ and $+4a$.

21.22. Two positive point charges q are placed on the y-axis at $y = a$ and $y = -a$. A negative point charge $-Q$ is located at some point on the $+x$-axis. (a) In a free-body diagram, show the forces that act on the charge $-Q$. (b) Find the x- and y-components of the net force that the two positive charges exert on $-Q$. (Your answer should involve only k, q, Q, a and the coordinate x of the third charge.) (c) What is the net force on the charge $-Q$ when it is at the origin $(x = 0)$? (d) Graph the x-component of the net force on the charge $-Q$ as a function of x for values of x between $-4a$ and $+4a$.

21.23. Four identical charges Q are placed at the corners of a square of side L. (a) In a free-body diagram, show all of the forces that act on one of the charges. (b) Find the magnitude and direction of the total force exerted on one charge by the other three charges.

21.24. Two charges, one of 2.50 μC and the other of -3.50 μC, are placed on the x-axis, one at the origin and the other at $x = 0.600$ m, as shown in Fig. 21.36. Find the position on the x-axis where the net force on a small charge $+q$ would be zero.

Figure 21.36 Exercise 21.24.

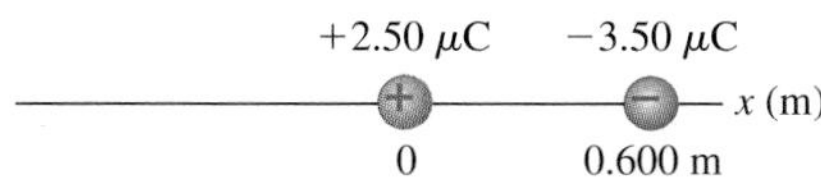

Section 21.4 Electric Field and Electric Forces

21.25. A proton is placed in a uniform electric field of 2.75×10^3 N/C. Calculate: (a) the magnitude of the electric force felt by the proton; (b) the proton's acceleration; (c) the proton's speed after 1.00 μs in the field, assuming it starts from rest.

21.26. A particle has charge -3.00 nC. (a) Find the magnitude and direction of the electric field due to this particle at a point 0.250 m directly above it. (b) At what distance from this particle does its electric field have a magnitude of 12.0 N/C?

21.27. A proton is traveling horizontally to the right at 4.50×10^6 m/s. (a) Find the magnitude and direction of the weakest electric field that can bring the proton uniformly to rest over a distance of 3.20 cm. (b) How much time does it take the proton to stop after entering the field? (c) What minimum field (magnitude and direction) would be needed to stop an electron under the conditions of part (a)?

21.28. An electron is released from rest in a uniform electric field. The electron accelerates vertically upward, traveling 4.50 m in the first 3.00 μs after it is released. (a) What are the magnitude and direction of the electric field? (b) Are we justified in ignoring the effects of gravity? Justify your answer quantitatively.

21.29. (a) What must the charge (sign and magnitude) of a 1.45-g particle be for it to remain stationary when placed in a downward-directed electric field of magnitude 650 N/C? (b) What is the magnitude of an electric field in which the electric force on a proton is equal in magnitude to its weight?

21.30. (a) What is the electric field of an iron nucleus at a distance of 6.00×10^{-10} m from the nucleus? The atomic number of iron is 26. Assume that the nucleus may be treated as a point charge. (b) What is the electric field of a proton at a distance of 5.29×10^{-11} m from the proton? (This is the radius of the electron orbit in the Bohr model for the ground state of the hydrogen atom.)

21.31. Two point charges are separated by 25.0 cm (Fig. 21.37). Find the net electric field these charges produce at (a) point A and (b) point B. (c) What would be the manitude and direction of the electric force this combination of charges would produce on a proton at A?

Figure 21.37 Exercise 21.31.

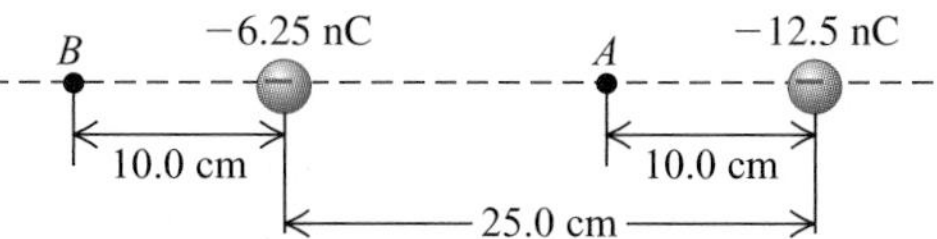

21.32. Electric Field of the Earth. The earth has a net electric charge that causes a field at points near its surface equal to 150 N/C and directed in toward the center of the earth. (a) What magnitude and sign of charge would a 60-kg human have to acquire to overcome his or her weight by the force exerted by the earth's electric field? (b) What would be the force of repulsion between two people each with the charge calculated in part (a) and separated by a distance of 100 m? Is use of the earth's electric field a feasible means of flight? Why or why not?

21.33. An electron is projected with an initial speed $v_0 = 1.60 \times 10^6$ m/s into the uniform field between the parallel plates in Fig. 21.38. Assume that the field between the plates is uniform and directed vertically downward, and that the field outside the plates is zero. The electron enters the field at a point midway between the plates. (a) If the electron just misses the upper plate as it emerges from the field, find the magnitude of the electric field. (b) Suppose that in Fig. 21.38 the electron is replaced by a proton with the same initial speed v_0. Would the proton hit one of the plates? If the proton would not hit one of the plates, what would be the magnitude and direction of its vertical displacement as it exits the region between the plates? (c) Compare the paths traveled by the electron and the proton and explain the differences. (d) Discuss whether it is reasonable to ignore the effects of gravity for each particle.

Figure 21.38 Exercise 21.33.

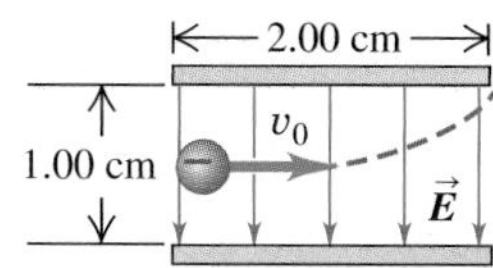

21.34. Point charge $q_1 = -5.00$ nC is at the origin and point charge $q_2 = +3.00$ nC is on the x-axis at $x = 3.00$ cm. Point P is on the y-axis at $y = 4.00$ cm. (a) Calculate the electric fields $\vec{E}_1$ and $\vec{E}_2$ at point P due to the charges q_1 and q_2. Express your results in terms of unit vectors (see Example 21.6). (b) Use the results of part (a) to obtain the resultant field at P, expressed in unit vector form.

21.35. In Exercise 21.33, what is the speed of the electron as it emerges from the field?

21.36. (a) Calculate the magnitude and direction (relative to the $+x$-axis) of the electric field in Example 21.6. (b) A -2.5-nC point charge is placed at the point P in Fig. 21.19. Find the magnitude and direction of (i) the force that the -8.0-nC charge at the origin exerts on this charge and (ii) the force that this charge exerts on the -8.0-nC charge at the origin.

21.37. (a) For the electron in Examples 21.7 and 21.8, compare the weight of the electron to the magnitude of the electric force on the electron. Is it appropriate to ignore the gravitational force on the electron in these examples? Explain. (b) A particle with charge $+e$ is placed at rest between the charged plates in Fig. 21.20. What must the mass of this object be if it is to remain at rest? Give your answer in kilograms and in multiples of the electron mass. (c) Does the answer to part (b) depend on where between the plates the object is placed? Why or why not?

21.38. A uniform electric field exists in the region between two oppositely charged plane parallel plates. A proton is released from rest at the surface of the positively charged plate and strikes the surface of the opposite plate, 1.60 cm distant from the first, in a time interval of 1.50×10^{-6} s. (a) Find the magnitude of the electric field. (b) Find the speed of the proton when it strikes the negatively charged plate.

21.39. A point charge is at the origin. With this point charge as the source point, what is the unit vector $\hat{r}$ in the direction of (a) the field point at $x = 0$, $y = -1.35$ m; (b) the field point at $x = 12.0$ cm, $y = 12.0$ cm; (c) the field point at $x = -1.10$ m, $y = 2.60$ m? Express your results in terms of the unit vectors $\hat{\imath}$ and $\hat{\jmath}$.

21.40. A $+8.75$-μC point charge is glued down on a horizontal frictionless table. It is tied to a -6.50-μC point charge by a light, nonconducting 2.50-cm wire. A uniform electric field of magnitude 1.85×10^8 N/C is directed parallel to the wire, as shown in Fig. 21.39. (a) Find the tension in the wire. (b) What would the tension be if both charges were negative?

Figure 21.39 Exercise 21.40.

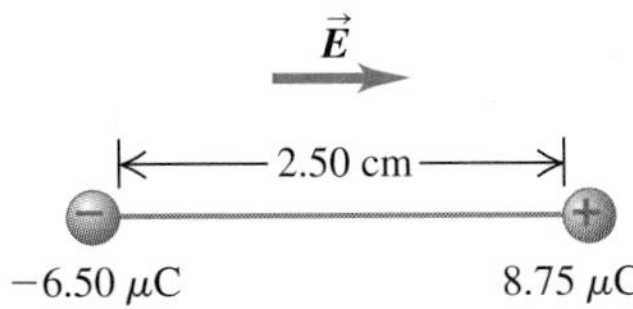

21.41. (a) An electron is moving east in a uniform electric field of 1.50 N/C directed to the west. At point A, the velocity of the electron is 4.50×10^5 m/s toward the east. What is the speed of the electron when it reaches point B, 0.375 m east of point A? (b) A proton is moving in the uniform electric field of part (a). At point A, the velocity of the proton is 1.90×10^4 m/s, east. What is the speed of the proton at point B?

21.42. Electric Field in the Nucleus. Protons in the nucleus are of the order of 10^{-15} m (1 fm) apart. (a) What is the magnitude of the electric field produced by a proton at a distance of 1.50 fm from it? (b) How does this field compare in magnitude to the field in Example 21.7?

Section 21.5 Electric-Field Calculations

21.43. Two positive point charges q are placed on the x-axis, one at $x = a$ and one at $x = -a$. (a) Find the magnitude and direction of the electric field at $x = 0$. (b) Derive an expression for the electric field at points on the x-axis. Use your result to graph the x-component of the electric field as a function of x, for values of x between $-4a$ and $+4a$.

21.44. Two particles having charges $q_1 = 0.500$ nC and $q_2 = 8.00$ nC are separated by a distance of 1.20 m. At what point along the line connecting the two charges is the total electric field due to the two charges equal to zero?

21.45. A $+2.00$-nC point charge is at the origin, and a second -5.00-nC point charge is on the x-axis at $x = 0.800$ m. (a) Find the electric field (magnitude and direction) at each of the following points on the x-axis: (i) $x = 0.200$ m; (ii) $x = 1.20$ m; (iii) $x = -0.200$ m. (b) Find the net electric force that the two charges would exert on an electron placed at each point in part (a).

21.46. Repeat Exercise 21.44, but now let $q_1 = -4.00$ nC.

21.47. Three negative point charges lie along a line as shown in Fig. 21.40. Find the magnitude and direction of the electric field this combination of charges produces at point P, which lies 6.00 cm. from the -2.00-μC charge measured perpendiular to the line connecting the three charges.

Figure 21.40 Exercise 21.47.

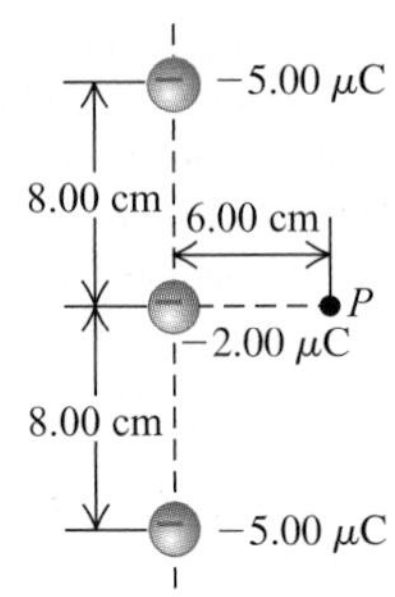

21.48. A positive point charge q is placed at $x = a$, and a negative point charge $-q$ is placed at $x = -a$. (a) Find the magnitude and direction of the electric field at $x = 0$. (b) Derive an expression for the electric field at points on the x-axis. Use your result to graph the x-component of the electric field as a function of x, for values of x between $-4a$ and $+4a$.

21.49. In a rectangular coordinate system a positive point charge $q = 6.00 \times 10^{-9}$ C is placed at the point $x = +0.150$ m, $y = 0$, and an identical point charge is placed at $x = -0.150$ m, $y = 0$. Find the x- and y-components, the magnitude, and the direction of the electric field at the following points: (a) the origin; (b) $x = 0.300$ m, $y = 0$; (c) $x = 0.150$ m, $y = -0.400$ m; (d) $x = 0$, $y = 0.200$ m.

21.50. A point charge $q_1 = -4.00$ nC is at the point $x = 0.600$ m, $y = 0.800$ m, and a second point charge $q_2 = +6.00$ nC is at the point $x = 0.600$ m, $y = 0$. Calculate the magnitude and direction of the net electric field at the origin due to these two point charges.

21.51. Repeat Exercise 21.49 for the case where the point charge at $x = +0.150$ m, $y = 0$ is positive and the other is negative, each with magnitude 6.00×10^{-9} C.

21.52. A very long, straight wire has charge per unit length 1.50×10^{-10} C/m. At what distance from the wire is the electric-field magnitude equal to 2.50 N/C?

21.53. Positive electric charge is distributed along the y-axis with charge per unit length λ. (a) Consider the case where charge is distributed only between the points $y = a$ and $y = -a$. For points on the $+x$-axis, graph the x-component of the electric field as a function of x for values of x between $x = a/2$ and $x = 4a$. (b) Consider instead the case where charge is distributed along the entire y-axis with the same charge per unit length λ. Using the same graph as in part (a), plot the x-component of the electric field as a function of x for values of x between $x = a/2$ and $x = 4a$. Label which graph refers to which situation.

21.54. A straight, nonconducting plastic wire 8.50 cm long carries a charge density of $+175$ nC/m distributed uniformly along its length. It is lying on a horizontal tabletop. (a) Find the magnitude and direction of the electric field this wire produces at a point 6.00 cm directly above its midpoint. (b) If the wire is now bent into a circle lying flat on the table, find the magnitude and direction of the electric field it produces at a point 6.00 cm directly above its center.

21.55. A ring-shaped conductor with radius $a = 2.50$ cm has a total positive charge $Q = +0.125$ nC uniformly distributed around it, as shown in Fig. 21.24. The center of the ring is at the origin of coordinates O. (a) What is the electric field (magnitude and direction) at point P, which is on the x-axis at $x = 40.0$ cm? (b) A point charge $q = -2.50$ μC is placed at the point P described in part (a). What are the magnitude and direction of the force exerted *by* the charge q *on* the ring?

21.56. A charge of -6.50 nC is spread uniformly over the surface of one face of a nonconducting disk of radius 1.25 cm. (a) Find the magnitude and direction of the electric field this disk produces at a point P on the axis of the disk a distance of 2.00 cm from its center. (b) Suppose that the charge were all pushed away from the center and distributed uniformly on the outer rim of the disk. Find the magnitude and direction of the electric field at point P. (c) If the charge is all brought to the center of the disk, find the magnitude and direction of the electric field at point P. (d) Why is the field in part (a) stronger than the field in part (b)? Why is the field in part (c) the strongest of the three fields?

21.57. Two horizontal, infinite, plane sheets of charge are separated by a distance d. The lower sheet has negative charge with uniform surface charge density $-\sigma < 0$. The upper sheet has positive charge with uniform surface charge density $\sigma > 0$. What is the electric field (magnitude, and direction if the field is nonzero) (a) above the upper sheet, (b) below the lower sheet, (c) between the sheets?

Section 21.6 Electric Field Lines

21.58. Infinite sheet A carries a positive uniform charge density σ, and sheet B, which is to the right of A and parallel to it, carries a uniform negative charge density -2σ. (a) Sketch the electric field lines for this pair of sheets. Include the region between the sheets as well as the regions to the left of A and to the right of B. (b) Repeat part (a) for the case in which sheet B carries a charge density of $+2\sigma$.

21.59. Suppose the charge shown in Fig. 21.29a is fixed in position. A small, positively charged particle is then placed at some point in the figure and released. Will the trajectory of the particle follow an electric field line? Why or why not? Suppose instead that the particle is placed at some point in Fig. 21.29b and released (the positive and negative charges shown in the figure are fixed in position). Will its trajectory follow an electric field line? Again, why or why not? Explain any differences between your answers for the two different situations.

21.60. Sketch the electric field lines for a disk of radius R with a positive uniform surface charge density σ. Use what you know about the electric field very close to the disk and very far from the disk to make your sketch.

21.61. (a) Sketch the electric field lines for an infinite line of charge. You may find it helpful to show the field lines in a plane containing the line of charge in one sketch and the field lines in a plane perpendicular to the line of charge in a second sketch. (b) Explain how your sketches show (i) that the magnitude E of the electric field depends only on the distance r from the line of charge and (ii) that E decreases like $1/r$.

21.62. Figure 21.41 shows some of the electric field lines due to three point charges arranged along the vertical axis. All three charges have the same magnitude. (a) What are the signs of the three charges? Explain your reasoning. (b) At what point(s) is the magnitude of the electric field the smallest? Explain your reasoning. Explain how the fields produced by each individual point charge combine to give a small net field at this point or points.

Figure **21.41** Exercise 21.62.

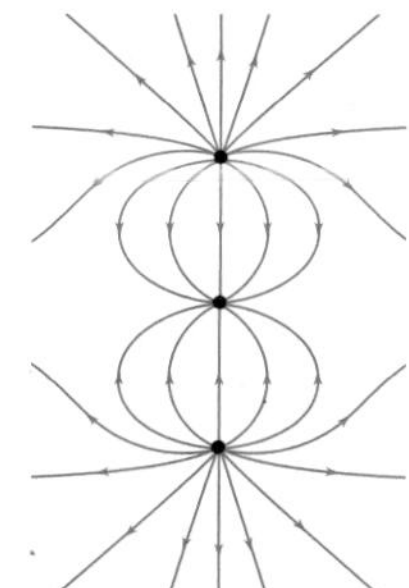

Section 21.7 Electric Dipoles

21.63. Point charges $q_1 = -4.5$ nC and $q_2 = +4.5$ nC are separated by 3.1 mm, forming an electric dipole. (a) Find the electric dipole moment (magnitude and direction). (b) The charges are in a uniform electric field whose direction makes an angle of 36.9° with the line connecting the charges. What is the magnitude of this field if the torque exerted on the dipole has magnitude 7.2×10^{-9} N · m?

21.64. The ammonia molecule (NH_3) has a dipole moment of 5.0×10^{-30} C · m. Ammonia molecules in the gas phase are placed in a uniform electric field $\vec{E}$ with magnitude 1.6×10^6 N/C. (a) What is the change in electric potential energy when the dipole moment of a molecule changes its orientation with respect to $\vec{E}$ from parallel to perpendicular? (b) At what absolute temperature T is the average translational kinetic energy $\frac{3}{2}kT$ of a molecule equal to the change in potential energy calculated in part (a)? (*Note:* Above this temperature, thermal agitation prevents the dipoles from aligning with the electric field.)

21.65. In Example 21.15, the approximate result $E \cong p/2\pi\epsilon_0 y^3$ was derived for the electric field of a dipole at points on the dipole axis. (a) Rederive this result by putting the fractions in the expression for E_y over a common denominator, as described in Example 21.15. (b) Explain why the approximate result also gives the correct approximate expression for E_y for $y < 0$.

21.66. The dipole moment of the water molecule (H_2O) is 6.17×10^{-30} C · m. Consider a water molecule located at the origin whose dipole moment $\vec{p}$ points in the $+x$-direction. A chlorine ion (Cl^-), of charge -1.60×10^{-19} C, is located at $x = 3.00 \times 10^{-9}$ m. Find the magnitude and direction of the electric force that the water molecule exerts on the chlorine ion. Is this force attractive or repulsive? Assume that x is much larger than the separation d between the charges in the dipole, so that the approximate expression for the electric field along the dipole axis derived in Example 21.15 can be used.

21.67. Surface Tension. The surface of a polar liquid, such as water, can be viewed as a series of dipoles strung together in the stable arrangement in which the dipole moment vectors are parallel to the surface and all point in the same direction. Suppose now that something presses inward on the surface, distorting the dipoles as shown in Fig. 21.42. (a) Show that the two slanted dipoles exert a net upward force on the dipole between them, and hence oppose the downward external force. (b) Show that the dipoles attract each other and hence resist being separated. The force between dipoles opposes penetration of the liquid's surface and is a simple model for surface tension (see Section 14.3 and Fig. 14.15).

Figure **21.42** Exercise 21.67.

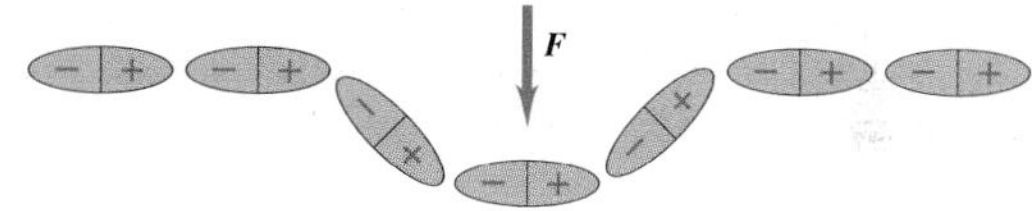

21.68. Consider the electric dipole of Example 21.15. (a) Derive an expression for the magnitude of the electric field produced by the dipole at a point on the x-axis in Fig. 21.34. What is the direction of this electric field? (b) How does the electric field at points on the x-axis depend on x when x is very large?

21.69. Torque on a Dipole. An electric dipole with dipole moment $\vec{p}$ is in a uniform electric field $\vec{E}$. (a) Find the orientations of the dipole for which the torque on the dipole is zero. (b) Which of the orientations in part (a) is stable, and which is unstable? (*Hint:* Consider a small displacement away from the equilibrium position and see what happens.) (c) Show that for the stable orientation in part (b), the dipole's own electric field tends to oppose the external field.

21.70. A dipole consisting of charges $\pm e$, 220 nm apart, is placed between two very large (essentially infinite) sheets carrying equal but opposite charge densities of 125 μC/m^2. (a) What is the maximum potential energy this dipole can have due to the sheets, and how should it be oriented relative to the sheets to attain this value? (b) What is the maximum torque the sheets can exert on the dipole, and how should it be oriented relative to the sheets to attain this value? (c) What net force do the two sheets exert on the dipole?

21.71. Three charges are at the corners of an isosceles triangle as shown in Fig. 21.43. The $\pm 5.00\text{-}\mu\text{C}$ charges form a dipole. (a) Find the force (magnitude and direction) the $-10.00\text{-}\mu\text{C}$ charge exerts on the dipole. (b) For an axis perpendicular to the line connecting the $\pm 5.00\text{-}\mu\text{C}$ charges at the midpoint of this line, find the torque (magnitude and direction) exerted on the dipole by the $-10.00\text{-}\mu\text{C}$ charge.

Figure **21.43** Exercise 21.71.

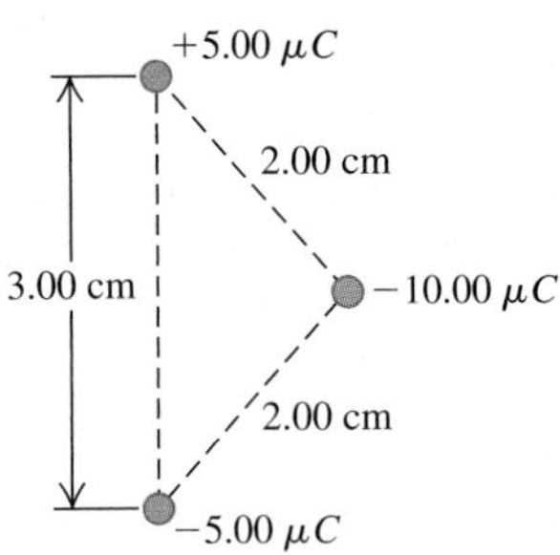

Problems

21.72. A charge $q_1 = +5.00$ nC is placed at the origin of an xy-coordinate system, and a charge $q_2 = -2.00$ nC is placed on the positive x-axis at $x = 4.00$ cm. (a) If a third charge $q_3 = +6.00$ nC is now placed at the point $x = 4.00$ cm, $y = 3.00$ cm, find the x- and y-components of the total force exerted on this charge by the other two. (b) Find the magnitude and direction of this force.

21.73. Two positive point charges Q are held fixed on the x-axis at $x = a$ and $x = -a$. A third positive point charge q, with mass m, is placed on the x-axis away from the origin at a coordinate x such that $|x| \ll a$. The charge q, which is free to move along the x-axis, is then released. (a) Find the frequency of oscillation of the charge q. (*Hint:* Review the definition of simple harmonic motion in Section 13.2. Use the binomial expansion $(1 + z)^n = 1 + nz + n(n-1)z^2/2 + \cdots$, valid for the case $|z| < 1$.) (b) Suppose instead that the charge q were placed on the y-axis at a coordinate y such that $|y| \ll a$, and then released. If this charge is free to move anywhere in the xy-plane, what will happen to it? Explain your answer.

21.74. Two identical spheres with mass m are hung from silk threads of length L, as shown in Fig. 21.44. Each sphere has the same charge, so $q_1 = q_2 = q$. The radius of each sphere is very small compared to the distance between the spheres, so they may be treated as point charges. Show that if the angle θ is small, the equilibrium separation d between the spheres is $d = (q^2L/2\pi\epsilon_0 mg)^{1/3}$. (*Hint:* If θ is small, then $\tan\theta \cong \sin\theta$.)

Figure **21.44** Problems 21.74, 21.75, and 21.76.

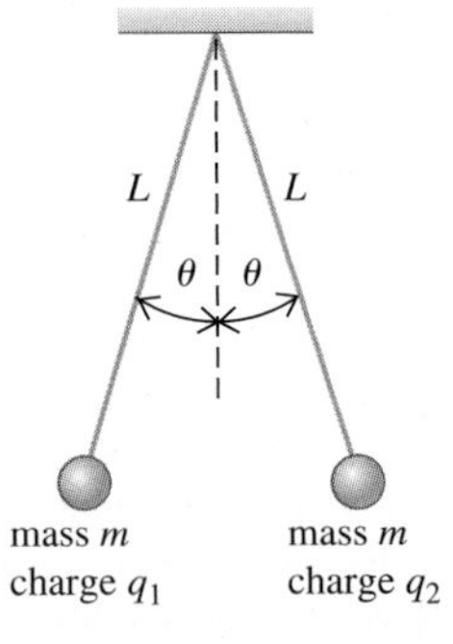

21.75. Two small spheres with mass $m = 15.0$ g are hung by silk threads of length $L = 1.20$ m from a common point (Fig. 21.44). When the spheres are given equal quantities of negative charge, so that $q_1 = q_2 = q$, each thread hangs at $\theta = 25.0°$ from the vertical. (a) Draw a diagram showing the forces on each sphere. Treat the spheres as point charges. (b) Find the magnitude of q. (c) Both threads are now shortened to length $L = 0.600$ m, while the charges q_1 and q_2 remain unchanged. What new angle will each thread make with the vertical? (*Hint:* This part of the problem can be solved numerically by using trial values for θ and adjusting the values of θ until a self-consistent answer is obtained.)

21.76. Two identical spheres are each attached to silk threads of length $L = 0.500$ m and hung from a common point (Fig. 21.44). Each sphere has mass $m = 8.00$ g. The radius of each sphere is very small compared to the distance between the spheres, so they may be treated as point charges. One sphere is given positive charge q_1, and the other a different positive charge q_2; this causes the spheres to separate so that when the spheres are in equilibrium, each thread makes an angle $\theta = 20.0°$ with the vertical. (a) Draw a free-body diagram for each sphere when in equilibrium, and label all the forces that act on each sphere. (b) Determine the magnitude of the electrostatic force that acts on each sphere, and determine the tension in each thread. (c) Based on the information you have been given, what can you say about the magnitudes of q_1 and q_2? Explain your answers. (d) A small wire is now connected between the spheres, allowing charge to be transferred from one sphere to the other until the two spheres have equal charges; the wire is then removed. Each thread now makes an angle of 30.0° with the vertical. Determine the original charges. (*Hint:* The total charge on the pair of spheres is conserved.)

21.77. Sodium chloride (NaCl, ordinary table salt) is made up of positive sodium ions (Na^+) and negative chloride ions (Cl^-). (a) If a point charge with the same charge and mass as all the Na^+ ions in 0.100 mol of NaCl is 2.00 cm from a point charge with the same charge and mass as all the Cl^- ions, what is the magnitude of the attractive force between these two point charges? (b) If the positive point charge in part (a) is held in place and the negative point charge is released from rest, what is its initial acceleration? (See Appendix D for atomic masses.) (c) Does it seem reasonable that the ions in NaCl could be separated in this way? Why or why not? (In fact, when sodium chloride dissolves in water, it breaks up into Na^+ and Cl^- ions. However, in this situation there are additional electric forces exerted by the water molecules on the ions.)

21.78. Two point charges q_1 and q_2 are held in place 4.50 cm apart. Another point charge $Q = -1.75\ \mu\text{C}$ of mass 5.00 g is initially located 3.00 cm from each of these charges (Fig. 21.45) and released from rest. You observe that the initial acceleration of Q is 324 m/s² upward, parallel to the line connecting the two point charges. Find q_1 and q_2.

Figure **21.45** Problem 21.78.

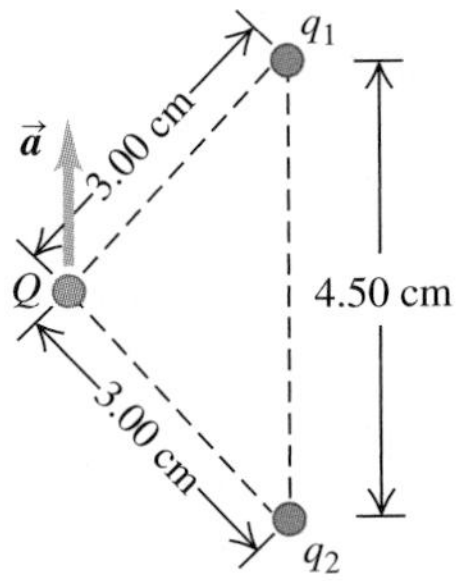

21.79. Three identical point charges q are placed at each of three corners of a square of side L. Find the magnitude and direction of the net force on a point charge $-3q$ placed (a) at the center of the square and (b) at the vacant corner of the square. In each case, draw a free-body diagram showing the forces exerted on the $-3q$ charge by each of the other three charges.

21.80. Three point charges are placed on the y-axis: a charge q at $y = a$, a charge $-2q$ at the origin, and a charge q at $y = -a$. Such an arrangement is called an electric quadrupole. (a) Find the magnitude and direction of the electric field at points on the positive x-axis. (b) Use the binomial expansion to find an approximate expression for the electric field valid for $x \gg a$. Contrast this behavior to that of the electric field of a point charge and that of the electric field of a dipole.

21.81. Strength of the Electric Force. Imagine two 1.0-g bags of protons, one at the earth's north pole and the other at the south pole. (a) How many protons are in each bag? (b) Calculate the gravitational attraction and the electrical repulsion that each bag exerts on the other. (c) Are the forces in part (b) large enough for you to feel if you were holding one of the bags?

21.82. Electric Force Within the Nucleus. Typical dimensions of atomic nuclei are of the order of 10^{-15} m (1 fm). (a) If two protons in a nucleus are 2.0 fm apart, find the magnitude of the electric force each one exerts on the other. Express the answer in newtons and in pounds. Would this force be large enough for a person to feel? (b) Since the protons repel each other so strongly, why don't they shoot out of the nucleus?

21.83. If Atoms Were Not Neutral . . . Because the charges on the electron and proton have the same absolute value, atoms are electrically neutral. Suppose this were not precisely true, and the absolute value of the charge of the electron were less than the charge of the proton by 0.00100%. (a) Estimate what the net charge of this textbook would be under these circumstances. Make any assumptions you feel are justified, but state clearly what they are. (*Hint:* Most of the atoms in this textbook have equal numbers of electrons, protons, and neutrons.) (b) What would be the magnitude of the electric force between two textbooks placed 5.0 m apart? Would this force be attractive or repulsive? Estimate what the acceleration of each book would be if the books were 5.0 m apart and there were no nonelectrical forces on them. (c) Discuss how the fact that ordinary matter is stable shows that the absolute values of the charges on the electron and proton must be identical to a *very* high level of accuracy.

21.84. Two tiny balls of mass m carry equal but opposite charges of magnitude q. They are tied to the same ceiling hook by light strings of length L. When a horizontal uniform electric field E is turned on, the balls hang with an angle θ between the strings (Fig. 21.46). (a) Which ball (the right or the left) is positive, and which is negative? (b) Find the angle θ between the strings in terms of E, q, m, and g. (c) As the electric field is gradually increased in strength, what does your result from part (b) give for the largest possible angle θ?

Figure 21.46 Problem 21.84.

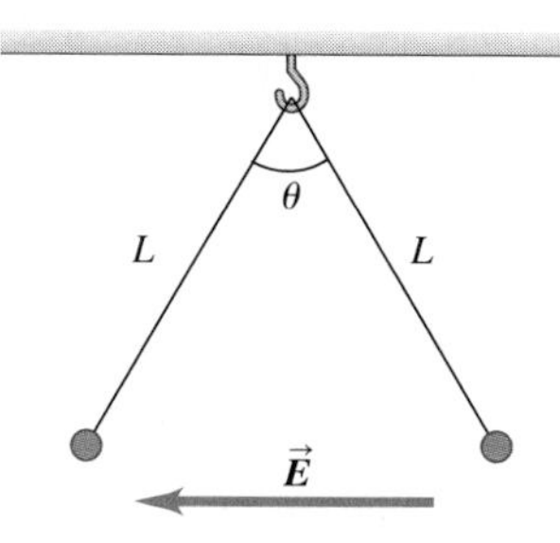

21.85. Two small, copper spheres each have radius 1.00 mm. (a) How many atoms does each sphere contain? (b) Assume that each copper atom contains 29 protons and 29 electrons. We know that electrons and protons have charges of exactly the same magnitude, but let's explore the effect of small differences (see also Problem 21.83). If the charge of a proton is $+e$ and the magnitude of the charge of an electron is 0.100% smaller, what is the net charge of each sphere and what force would one sphere exert on the other if they were separated by 1.00 m?

21.86. Operation of an Inkjet Printer. In an inkjet printer, letters are built up by squirting drops of ink at the paper from a rapidly moving nozzle. The ink drops, which have a mass of 1.4×10^{-8} g each, leave the nozzle and travel toward the paper at 20 m/s, passing through a charging unit that gives each drop a positive charge q by removing some electrons from it. The drops then pass between parallel deflecting plates 2.0 cm long where there is a uniform vertical electric field with magnitude 8.0×10^4 N/C. If a drop is to be deflected 0.30 mm by the time it reaches the end of the deflection plates, what magnitude of charge must be given to the drop?

21.87. A proton is projected into a uniform electric field that points vertically upward and has magnitude E. The initial velocity of the proton has a magnitude v_0 and is directed at an angle α below the horizontal. (a) Find the maximum distance h_{max} that the proton descends vertically below its initial elevation. You can ignore gravitational forces. (b) After what horizontal distance d does the proton return to its original elevation? (c) Sketch the trajectory of the proton. (d) Find the numerical values of h_{max} and d if $E = 500$ N/C, $v_0 = 4.00 \times 10^5$ m/s, and $\alpha = 30.0°$.

21.88. A negative point charge $q_1 = -4.00$ nC is on the x-axis at $x = 0.60$ m. A second point charge q_2 is on the x-axis at $x = -1.20$ m. What must the sign and magnitude of q_2 be for the net electric field at the origin to be (a) 50.0 N/C in the $+x$-direction and (b) 50.0 N/C in the $-x$-direction?

21.89. Positive charge Q is distributed uniformly along the x-axis from $x = 0$ to $x = a$. A positive point charge q is located on the positive x-axis at $x = a + r$, a distance r to the right of the end of Q (Fig. 21.47). (a) Calculate the x- and y-components of the electric field produced by the charge distribution Q at points on the positive x-axis where $x > a$. (b) Calculate the force (magnitude and direction) that the charge distribution Q exerts on q. (c) Show that if $r \gg a$, the magnitude of the force in part (b) is approximately $Qq/4\pi\epsilon_0 r^2$. Explain why this result is obtained.

Figure 21.47 Problem 21.89.

21.90. Positive charge Q is distributed uniformly along the positive y-axis between $y = 0$ and $y = a$. A negative point charge $-q$ lies on the positive x-axis, a distance x from the origin (Fig. 21.48). (a) Calculate the x- and y-components of the electric field produced by the charge distribution Q at points on the positive x-axis. (b) Calculate the x- and y-components of the force that the charge distribution Q exerts on q. (c) Show that if $x \gg a$, $F_x \cong -Qq/4\pi\epsilon_0 x^2$ and $F_y \cong +Qqa/8\pi\epsilon_0 x^3$. Explain why this result is obtained.

Figure 21.48 Problem 21.90.

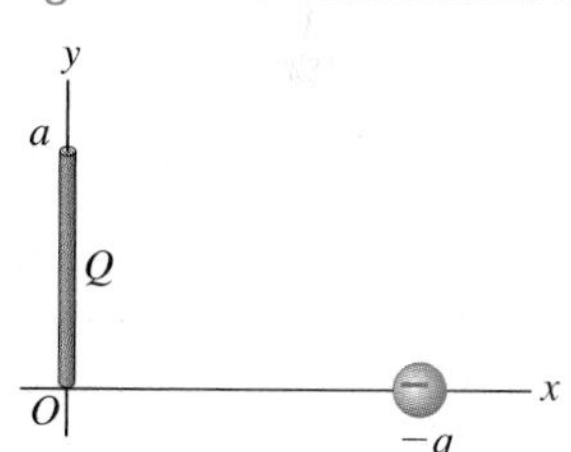

21.91. A charged line like that shown in Fig. 21.25 extends from $y = 2.50$ cm to $y = -2.50$ cm. The total charge distributed uniformly along the line is -9.00 nC. (a) Find the electric field (magnitude and direction) on the x-axis at $x = 10.0$ cm. (b) Is the magnitude of the electric field you calculated in part (a) larger or smaller than the electric field 10.0 cm from a point charge that has the same total charge as this finite line of charge? In terms of the approximation used to derive $E = Q/4\pi\epsilon_0 x^2$ for a point charge from Eq. (21.9), explain why this is so. (c) At what distance x does the result for the finite line of charge differ by 1.0% from that for the point charge?

21.92. A Parallel Universe. Imagine a parallel universe in which the electric force has the same properties as in our universe but there is no gravity. In this parallel universe, the sun carries charge Q, the earth carries charge $-Q$, and the electric attraction between them keeps the earth in orbit. The earth in the parallel universe has the same mass, the same orbital radius, and the same orbital period as in our universe. Calculate the value of Q. (Consult Appendix F as needed.)

21.93. A uniformly charged disk like the disk in Fig. 21.26 has radius 2.50 cm and carries a total charge of 4.0×10^{-12} C. (a) Find the electric field (magnitude and direction) on the x-axis at $x = 20.0$ cm. (b) Show that for $x \gg R$, Eq. (21.11) becomes $E = Q/4\pi\epsilon_0 x^2$, where Q is the total charge on the disk. (c) Is the magnitude of the electric field you calculated in part (a) larger or smaller than the electric field 20.0 cm from a point charge that has the same total charge as this disk? In terms of the approximation used in part (b) to derive $E = Q/4\pi\epsilon_0 x^2$ for a point charge from Eq. (21.11), explain why this is so. (d) What is the percent difference between the electric fields produced by the finite disk and by a point charge with the same charge at $x = 20.0$ cm and at $x = 10.0$ cm?

21.94. (a) Let $f(x)$ be an even function of x so that $f(x) = f(-x)$. Show that $\int_{-a}^{a} f(x)dx = 2\int_0^a f(x)dx$. (*Hint:* Write the integral from $-a$ to a as the sum of the integral from $-a$ to 0 and the integral from 0 to a. In the first integral, make the change of variable $x' = -x$.) (b) Let $g(x)$ be an odd function of x so that $g(x) = -g(-x)$. Use the method given in the hint for part (a) to show that $\int_{-a}^{a} g(x)dx = 0$. (c) Use the result of part (b) to show why E_y in Example 21.11 (Section 21.5) is zero.

21.95. Positive charge $+Q$ is distributed uniformly along the $+x$-axis from $x = 0$ to $x = a$. Negative charge $-Q$ is distributed uniformly along the $-x$-axis from $x = 0$ to $x = -a$. (a) A positive point charge q lies on the positive y-axis, a distance y from the origin. Find the force (magnitude and direction) that the positive and negative charge distributions together exert on q. Show that this force is proportional to y^{-3} for $y \gg a$. (b) Suppose instead that the positive point charge q lies on the positive x-axis, a distance $x > a$ from the origin. Find the force (magnitude and direction) that the charge distribution exerts on q. Show that this force is proportional to x^{-3} for $x \gg a$.

21.96. Positive charge Q is uniformly distributed around a semicircle of radius a (Fig. 21.49). Find the electric field (magnitude and direction) at the center of curvature P.

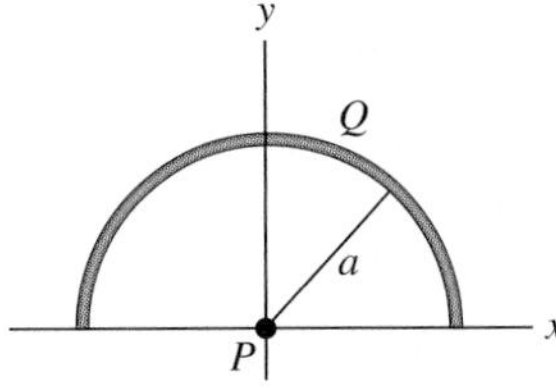

Figure **21.49** Problem 21.96.

21.97. Negative charge $-Q$ is distributed uniformly around a quarter-circle of radius a that lies in the first quadrant, with the center of curvature at the origin. Find the x- and y-components of the net electric field at the origin.

21.98. A small sphere with mass m carries a positive charge q and is attached to one end of a silk fiber of length L. The other end of the fiber is attached to a large vertical insulating sheet that has a positive surface charge density σ. Show that when the sphere is in equilibrium, the fiber makes an angle equal to arctan $(q\sigma/2mg\epsilon_0)$ with the vertical sheet.

21.99. Two 1.20-m nonconducting wires meet at a right angle. One segment carries $+2.50\ \mu$C of charge distributed uniformly along its length, and the other carries $-2.50\ \mu$C distributed uniformly along it, as shown in Fig. 21.50. (a) Find the magnitude and direction of the electric field these wires produce at point P, which is 60.0 cm from each wire. (b) If an electron is released at P, what are the magnitude and direction of the net force that these wires exert on it?

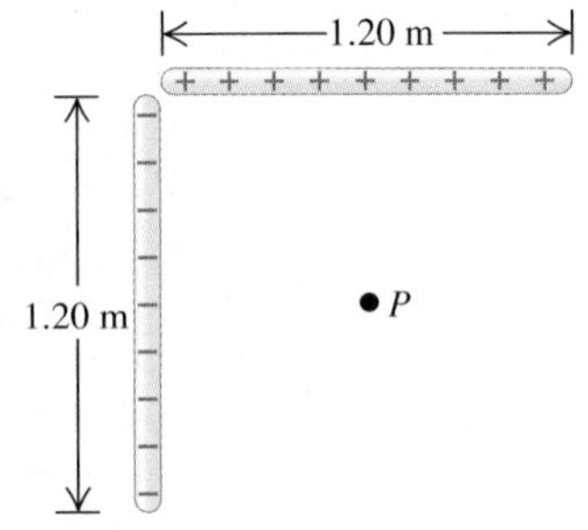

Figure **21.50** Problem 21.99.

21.100. Two very large parallel sheets are 5.00 cm apart. Sheet A carries a uniform surface charge density of $-9.50 \mu\text{C/m}^2$, and sheet B, which is to the right of A, carries a uniform charge of $-11.6\ \mu\text{C/m}^2$. Assume the sheets are large enough to be treated as infinite. Find the magnitude and direction of the net electric field these sheets produce at a point (a) 4.00 cm to the right of sheet A; (b) 4.00 cm to the left of sheet A; (c) 4.00 cm to the right of sheet B.

21.101. Repeat Problem 21.100 for the case where sheet B is positive.

21.102. Two very large horizontal sheets are 4.25 cm apart and carry equal but opposite uniform surface charge densities of magnitude σ. You want to use these sheets to hold stationary in the region between them an oil droplet of mass 324 μg that carries an excess of five electrons. Assuming that the drop is in vacuum, (a) which way should the electric field between the plates point, and (b) what should σ be?

21.103. An infinite sheet with positive charge per unit area σ lies in the xy-plane. A second infinite sheet with negative charge per unit area $-\sigma$ lies in the yz-plane. Find the net electric field at all points that do not lie in either of these planes. Express your answer in terms of the unit vectors $\hat{\imath}$, $\hat{\jmath}$, and $\hat{k}$.

21.104. A thin disk with a circular hole at its center, called an *annulus,* has inner radius R_1 and outer radius R_2 (Fig. 21.51). The disk has a uniform positive surface charge density σ on its surface. (a) Determine the total electric charge on the annulus. (b) The annulus lies in the yz-plane, with its center at the origin. For an arbitrary point on the x-axis (the axis of the annulus), find the magnitude and direction of the electric field $\vec{E}$. Consider points both above and below the annulus in Fig. 21.51. (c) Show that at points on the x-axis that are sufficiently close to the origin, the magnitude of the electric field is approximately proportional to the distance between the center of the annulus and the point. How close is "sufficiently close"? (d) A point particle with mass m and negative charge $-q$ is free to move along the x-axis (but cannot move off the axis). The particle is originally placed at rest at $x = 0.01R_1$ and released. Find the frequency of oscillation of the particle. (*Hint:* Review Section 13.2. The annulus is held stationary.)

Figure **21.51** Problem 21.104.

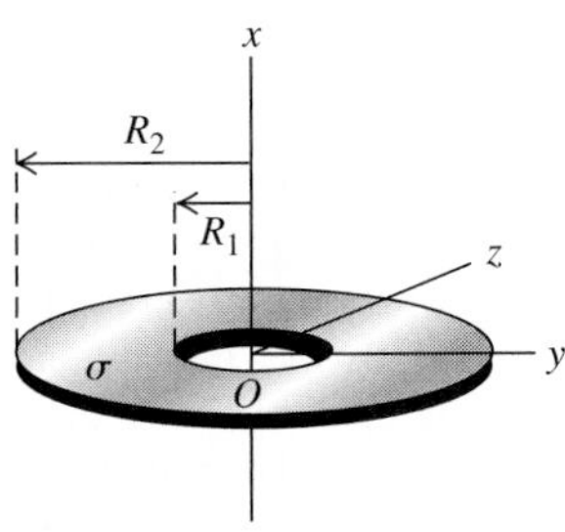

Challenge Problems

21.105. Three charges are placed as shown in Fig. 21.52. The magnitude of q_1 is 2.00 μC, but its sign and the value of the charge q_2 are not known. Charge q_3 is $+4.00\ \mu$C, and the net force $\vec{F}$ on q_3 is entirely in the negative x-direction. (a) Considering the different possible signs of q_1 and there are four possible force diagrams representing the forces $\vec{F}_1$ and $\vec{F}_2$ that q_1 and q_2 exert on q_3. Sketch these four possible force configurations. (b) Using the sketches from part (a) and the direction of $\vec{F}$, deduce the signs of the charges q_1 and q_2. (c) Calculate the magnitude of q_2. (d) Determine F, the magnitude of the net force on q_3.

Figure **21.52** Challenge Problem 21.105.

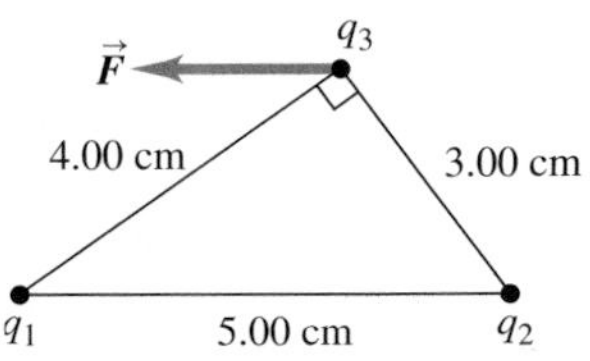

21.106. Two charges are placed as shown in Fig. 21.53. The magnitude of q_1 is 3.00 μC, but its sign and the value of the charge q_2 are not known. The direction of the net electric field $\vec{E}$ at point P is entirely in the negative y-direction. (a) Considering the different possible signs of q_1 and q_2, there are four possible diagrams that could represent the electric fields $\vec{E}_1$ and $\vec{E}_2$ produced by q_1 and q_2. Sketch the four possible electric field configurations. (b) Using the sketches from part (a) and the direction of $\vec{E}$, deduce the signs of q_1 and q_2. (c) Determine the magnitude of $\vec{E}$.

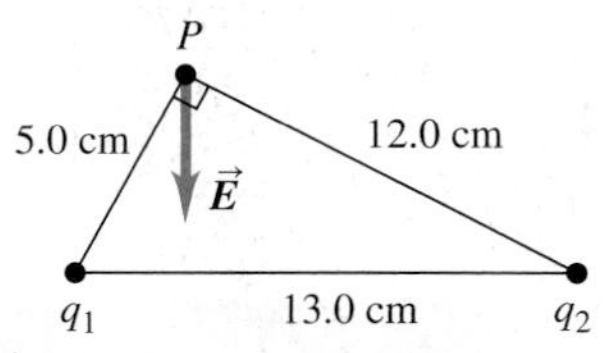

Figure 21.53 Challenge Problem 21.106.

21.107. Two thin rods of length L lie along the x-axis, one between $x = a/2$ and $x = a/2 + L$ and the other between $x = -a/2$ and $x = -a/2 - L$. Each rod has positive charge Q distributed uniformly along its length. (a) Calculate the electric field produced by the second rod at points along the positive x-axis. (b) Show that the magnitude of the force that one rod exerts on the other is

$$F = \frac{Q^2}{4\pi\epsilon_0 L^2}\ln\left[\frac{(a + L)^2}{a(a + 2L)}\right]$$

(c) Show that if $a \gg L$, the magnitude of this force reduces to $F = Q^2/4\pi\epsilon_0 a^2$. (*Hint:* Use the expansion $\ln(1 + z) = z - z^2/2 + z^3/3 - \cdots$, valid for $|z| \ll 1$. Carry *all* expansions to at least order L^2/a^2.) Interpret this result.

22 GAUSS'S LAW

LEARNING GOALS

By studying this chapter, you will learn:

- How you can determine the amount of charge within a closed surface by examining the electric field on the surface.
- What is meant by electric flux, and how to calculate it.
- How Gauss's law relates the electric flux through a closed surface to the charge enclosed by the surface.
- How to use Gauss's law to calculate the electric field due to a symmetrical charge distribution.
- Where the charge is located on a charged conductor.

? This child acquires an electric charge by touching the charged metal sphere. The charged hairs on the child's head repel and stand out. If the child stands *inside* a large, charged metal sphere, will her hair stand on end?

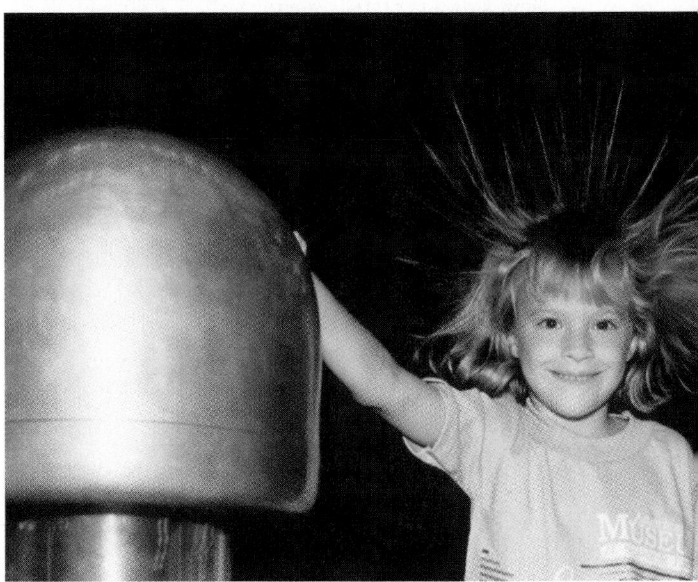

Often, there are both an easy way and a hard way to do a job; the easy way may involve nothing more than using the right tools. In physics, an important tool for simplifying problems is the *symmetry properties* of systems. Many physical systems have symmetry; for example, a cylindrical body doesn't look any different after you've rotated it around its axis, and a charged metal sphere looks just the same after you've turned it about any axis through its center.

Gauss's law is part of the key to using symmetry considerations to simplify electric-field calculations. For example, the field of a straight-line or plane-sheet charge distribution, which we derived in Section 21.5 using some fairly strenuous integrations, can be obtained in a few lines with the help of Gauss's law. But Gauss's law is more than just a way to make certain calculations easier. Indeed, it is a fundamental statement about the relationship between electric charges and electric fields. Among other things, Gauss's law can help us understand how electric charge distributes itself over conducting bodies.

Here's what Gauss's law is all about. Given any general distribution of charge, we surround it with an imaginary surface that encloses the charge. Then we look at the electric field at various points on this imaginary surface. Gauss's law is a relationship between the field at *all* the points on the surface and the total charge enclosed within the surface. This may sound like a rather indirect way of expressing things, but it turns out to be a tremendously useful relationship. Above and beyond its use as a calculational tool, Gauss's law can help us gain deeper insights into electric fields. We will make use of these insights repeatedly in the next several chapters as we pursue our study of electromagnetism.

22.1 Charge and Electric Flux

The discussion of Gauss's law in this section is based on and inspired by the innovative ideas of Ruth W. Chabay and Bruce A. Sherwood in *Electric and Magnetic Interactions* (John Wiley & Sons, 1994).

In Chapter 21 we asked the question, "Given a charge distribution, what is the electric field produced by that distribution at a point *P*?" We saw that the answer could be found by representing the distribution as an assembly of point charges, each of which produces an electric field $\vec{E}$ given by Eq. (21.7). The total field at P is then the vector sum of the fields due to all the point charges.

But there is an alternative relationship between charge distributions and electric fields. To discover this relationship, let's stand the question of Chapter 21 on its head and ask, "If the electric field pattern is known in a given region, what can we determine about the charge distribution in that region?"

Here's an example. Consider the box shown in Fig. 22.1a, which may or may not contain electric charge. We'll imagine that the box is made of a material that has no effect on any electric fields; it's of the same breed as the massless rope and the frictionless incline. Better still, let the box represent an *imaginary* surface that may or may not enclose some charge. We'll refer to the box as a **closed surface** because it completely encloses a volume. How can you determine how much (if any) electric charge lies within the box?

Knowing that a charge distribution produces an electric field and that an electric field exerts a force on a test charge, you move a test charge q_0 around the vicinity of the box. By measuring the force $\vec{F}$ experienced by the test charge at different positions, you make a three-dimensional map of the electric field $\vec{E} = \vec{F}/q_0$ outside the box. In the case shown in Fig. 22.1b, the map turns out to be the same as that of the electric field produced by a positive point charge (Fig. 21.29a). From the details of the map, you can find the exact value of the point charge inside the box.

To determine the contents of the box, we actually need to measure $\vec{E}$ only on the *surface* of the box. In Fig. 22.2a there is a single positive point charge inside the box, and in Fig. 22.2b there are two such charges. The field patterns on the surfaces of the boxes are different in detail, but in both cases the electric field points out of the box. Figures 22.2c and 22.2d show cases with one and two negative point charges, respectively, inside the box. Again, the details of $\vec{E}$ on the surface of the box are different, but in both cases the field points into the box.

11.7 Electric Flux

22.1 How can you measure the charge inside a box without opening it?

(a) A box containing an unknown amount of charge

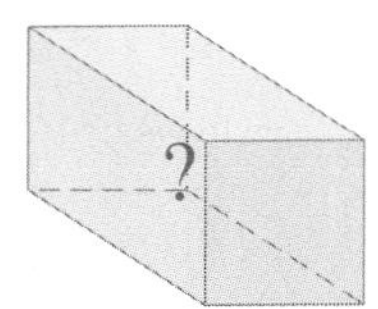

(b) Using a test charge outside the box to probe the amount of charge inside the box

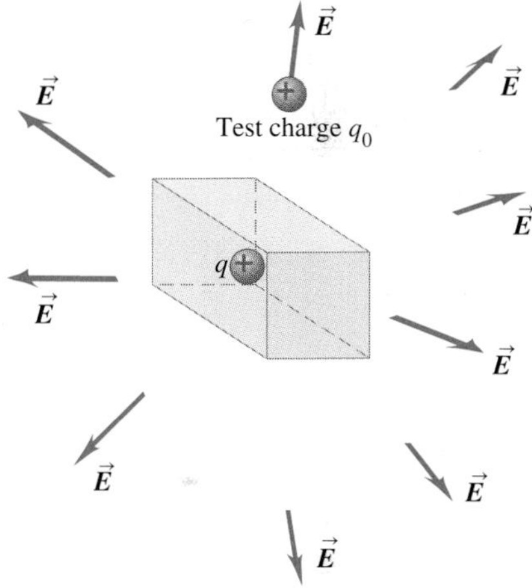

22.2 The electric field on the surface of boxes containing (a) a single positive point charge, (b) two positive point charges, (c) a single negative point charge, or (d) two negative point charges.

(a) Positive charge inside box, outward flux

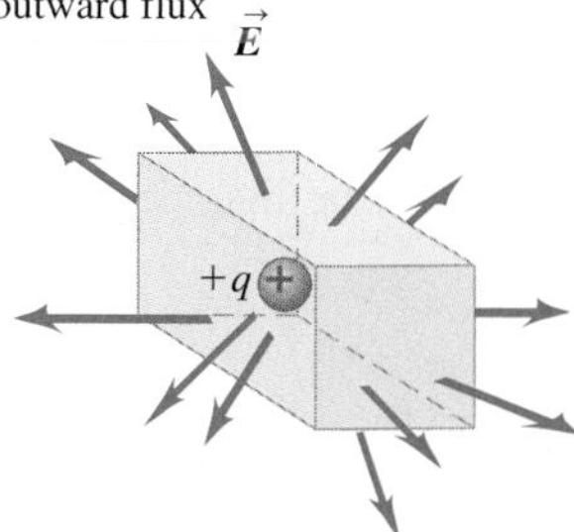

(b) Positive charges inside box, outward flux

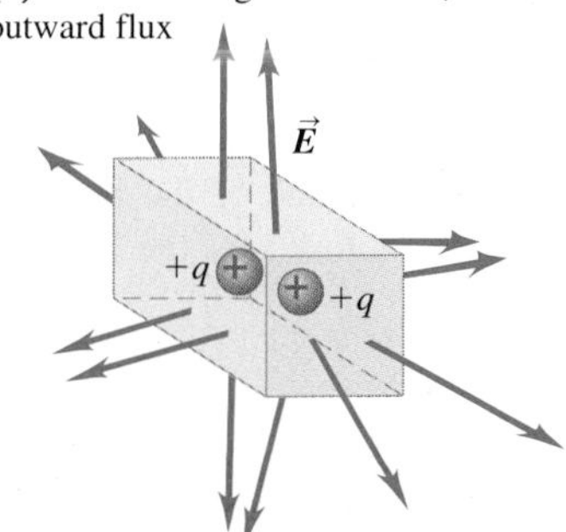

(c) Negative charge inside box, inward flux

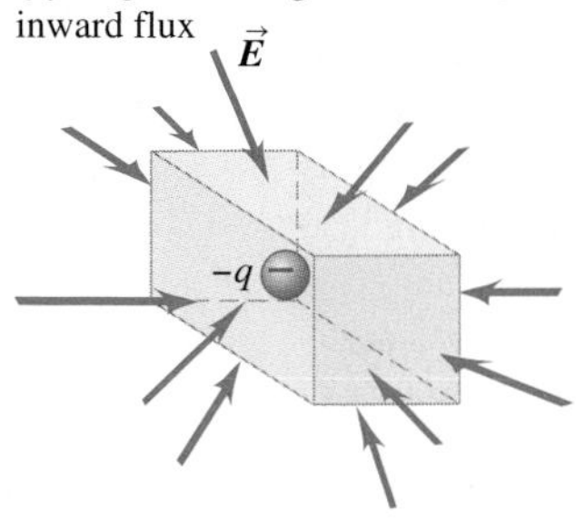

(d) Negative charges inside box, inward flux

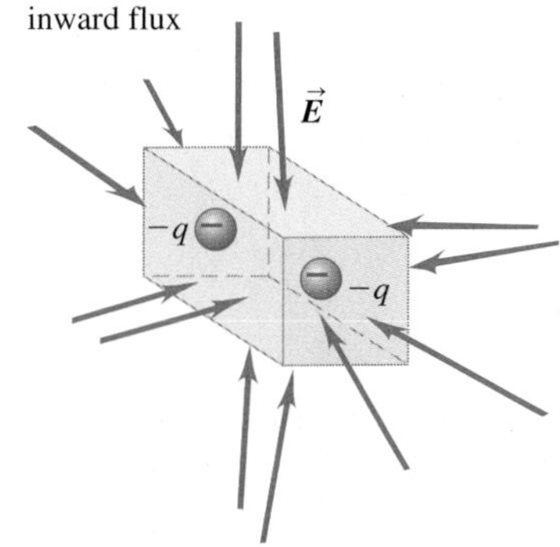

Electric Flux and Enclosed Charge

In Section 21.4 we mentioned the analogy between electric-field vectors and the velocity vectors of a fluid in motion. This analogy can be helpful, even though an electric field does not actually "flow." Using this analogy, in Figs. 22.2a and 22.2b, in which the electric field vectors point out of the surface, we say that there is an outward **electric flux.** (The word "flux" comes from a Latin word meaning "flow.") In Figs. 22.2c and 22.2d the $\vec{E}$ vectors point into the surface, and the electric flux is *inward.*

Figure 22.2 suggests a simple relationship: Positive charge inside the box goes with an outward electric flux through the box's surface, and negative charge inside goes with an inward electric flux. What happens if there is *zero* charge inside the box? In Fig. 22.3a the box is empty and $\vec{E} = \mathbf{0}$ everywhere, so there is no electric flux into or out of the box. In Fig. 22.3b, one positive and one negative point charge of equal magnitude are enclosed within the box, so the *net* charge inside the box is zero. There is an electric field, but it "flows into" the box on half of its surface and "flows out of" the box on the other half. Hence there is no *net* electric flux into or out of the box.

The box is again empty in Fig. 22.3c. However, there is charge present *outside* the box; the box has been placed with one end parallel to a uniformly charged infinite sheet, which produces a uniform electric field perpendicular to the sheet (as we learned in Example 21.12 of Section 21.5). On one end of the box, $\vec{E}$ points into the box; on the opposite end, $\vec{E}$ points out of the box; and on the sides, $\vec{E}$ is parallel to the surface and so points neither into nor out of the box. As in Fig. 22.3b, the inward electric flux on one part of the box exactly compensates for the outward electric flux on the other part. So in all of the cases shown in Fig. 22.3, there is no *net* electric flux through the surface of the box, and no *net* charge is enclosed in the box.

Figures 22.2 and 22.3 demonstrate a connection between the *sign* (positive, negative, or zero) of the *net* charge enclosed by a closed surface and the sense (outward, inward, or none) of the net electric flux through the surface. There is also a connection between the *magnitude* of the net charge inside the closed surface and the *strength* of the net "flow" of $\vec{E}$ over the surface. In both Figs. 22.4a and 22.4b there is a single point charge inside the box, but in Fig. 22.4b the magnitude of the charge is twice as great, and so $\vec{E}$ is everywhere twice as great in magnitude as in Fig. 22.4a. If we keep in mind the fluid-flow analogy, this means that the net outward electric flux is also twice as great in Fig. 22.4b as in Fig. 22.4a. This suggests that the net electric flux through the surface of the box is *directly proportional* to the magnitude of the net charge enclosed by the box.

22.3 Three cases in which there is zero *net* charge inside a box and no net electric flux through the surface of the box. (a) An empty box with $\vec{E} = \mathbf{0}$. (b) A box containing one positive and one equal-magnitude negative point charge. (c) An empty box immersed in a uniform electric field.

(a) No charge inside box, zero flux

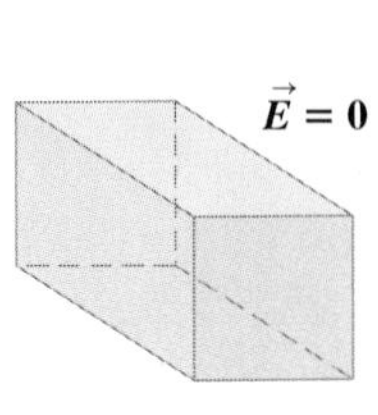

(b) Zero *net* charge inside box, inward flux cancels outward flux.

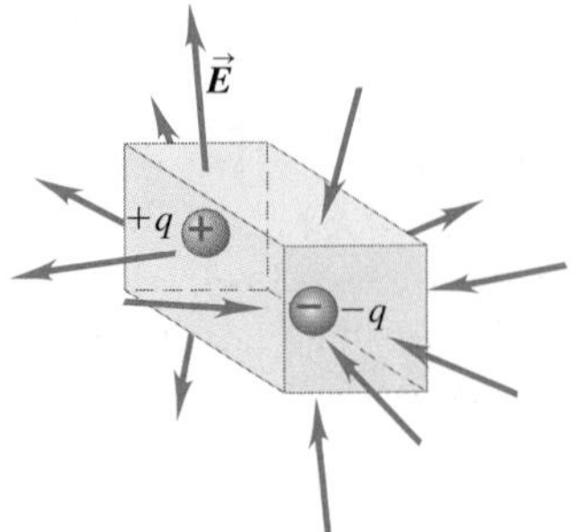

(c) No charge inside box, inward flux cancels outward flux.

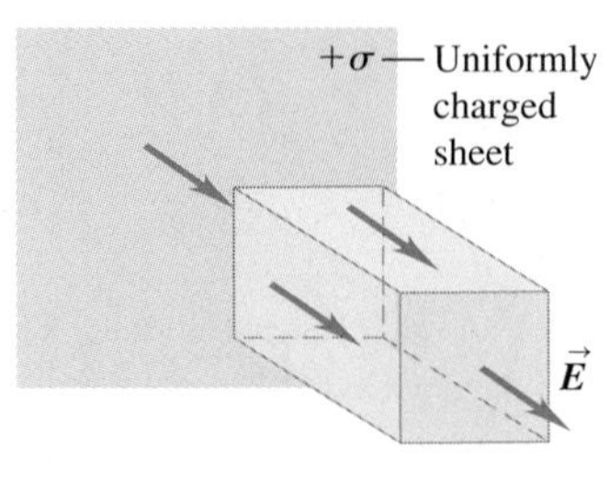

This conclusion is independent of the size of the box. In Fig. 22.4c the point charge $+q$ is enclosed by a box with twice the linear dimensions of the box in Fig.22.4a. The magnitude of the electric field of a point charge decreases with distance according to $1/r^2$, so the average magnitude of $\vec{E}$ on each face of the large box in Fig. 22.4c is just $\frac{1}{4}$ of the average magnitude on the corresponding face in Fig. 22.4a. But each face of the large box has exactly four times the area of the corresponding face of the small box. Hence the outward electric flux is the *same* for the two boxes if we *define* electric flux as follows: For each face of the box, take the product of the average perpendicular component of $\vec{E}$ and the area of that face; then add up the results from all faces of the box. With this definition the net electric flux due to a single point charge inside the box is independent of the size of the box and depends only on the net charge inside the box.

We have seen that there is a relationship between the net amount of charge inside a closed surface and the electric flux through that surface. For the special cases of a closed surface in the shape of a rectangular box and charge distributions made up of point charges or infinite charged sheets, we have found:

1. Whether there is a net outward or inward electric flux through a closed surface depends on the sign of the enclosed charge.
2. Charges *outside* the surface do not give a net electric flux through the surface.
3. The net electric flux is directly proportional to the net amount of charge enclosed within the surface but is otherwise independent of the size of the closed surface.

These observations are a qualitative statement of *Gauss's law.*

Do these observations hold true for other kinds of charge distributions and for closed surfaces of arbitrary shape? The answer to these questions will prove to be yes. But to explain why this is so, we need a precise mathematical statement of what we mean by electric flux. This is developed in the next section.

22.4 (a) A box enclosing a positive point charge $+q$. (b) Doubling the charge causes the magnitude of $\vec{E}$ to double, and it doubles the electric flux through the surface. (c) If the charge stays the same but the dimensions of the box are doubled, the flux stays the same. The magnitude of $\vec{E}$ on the surface decreases by a factor of $\frac{1}{4}$, but the area through which $\vec{E}$ "flows" increases by a factor of 4.

(a) A box containing a charge

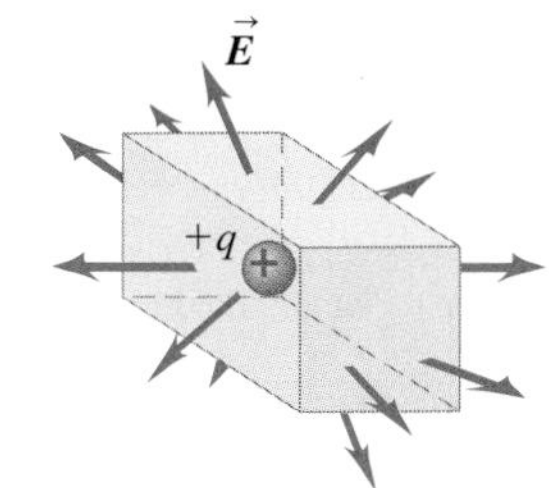

(b) Doubling the enclosed charge doubles the flux.

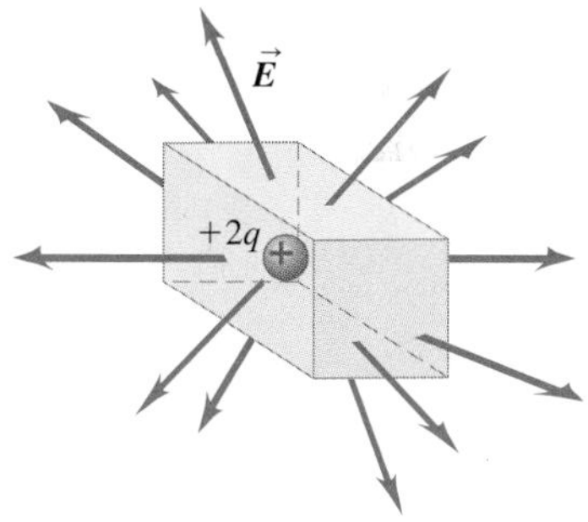

(c) Doubling the box dimensions *does not change* the flux.

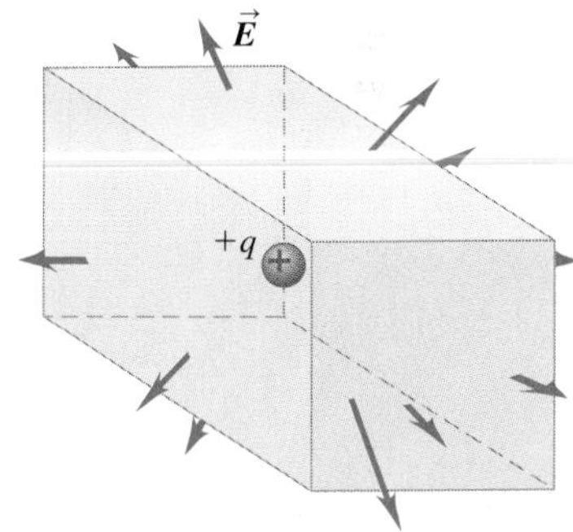

Test Your Understanding of Section 22.1 If all of the dimensions of the box in Fig. 22.2a are increased by a factor of 3, what effect will this change have on the electric flux through the box? (i) The flux will be $3^2 = 9$ times greater; (ii) the flux will be 3 times greater; (iii) the flux will be unchanged; (iv) the flux will be $(\frac{1}{3})$ as great; (v) the flux will be $(\frac{1}{3})^2 = \frac{1}{9}$ as great; (vi) not enough information is given to decide.

22.2 Calculating Electric Flux

In the preceding section we introduced the concept of *electric flux*. Qualitatively, the electric flux through a surface is a description of whether the electric field $\vec{E}$ points into or out of the surface. We used this to give a rough qualitative statement of Gauss's law: The net electric flux through a closed surface is directly proportional to the net charge inside that surface. To be able to make full use of this law, we need to know how to *calculate* electric flux. To do this, let's again make use of the analogy between an electric field $\vec{E}$ and the field of velocity vectors $\vec{v}$ in a flowing fluid. (Again, keep in mind that this is only an analogy; an electric field is *not* a flow.)

Flux: Fluid-Flow Analogy

Figure 22.5 shows a fluid flowing steadily from left to right. Let's examine the volume flow rate dV/dt (in, say, cubic meters per second) through the wire rectangle with area A. When the area is perpendicular to the flow velocity $\vec{v}$ (Fig. 22.5a) and the flow velocity is the same at all points in the fluid, the volume flow rate dV/dt is the area A multiplied by the flow speed v:

$$\frac{dV}{dt} = vA$$

22.5 The volume flow rate of fluid through the wire rectangle (a) is vA when the area of the rectangle is perpendicular to $\vec{v}$ and (b) is $vA\cos\phi$ when the rectangle is tilted at an angle ϕ.

(a) A wire rectangle in a fluid

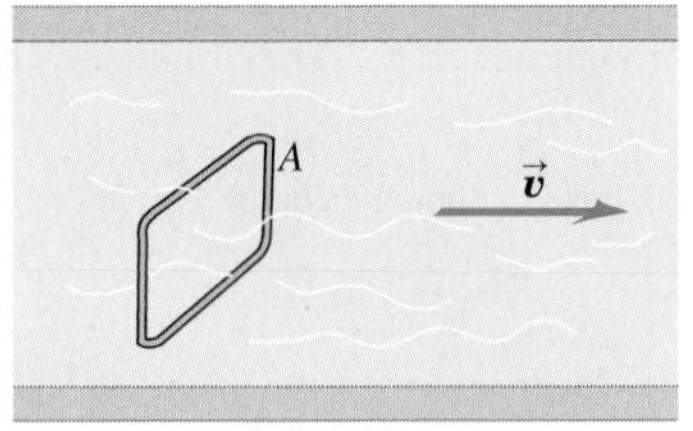

(b) The wire rectangle tilted by an angle ϕ

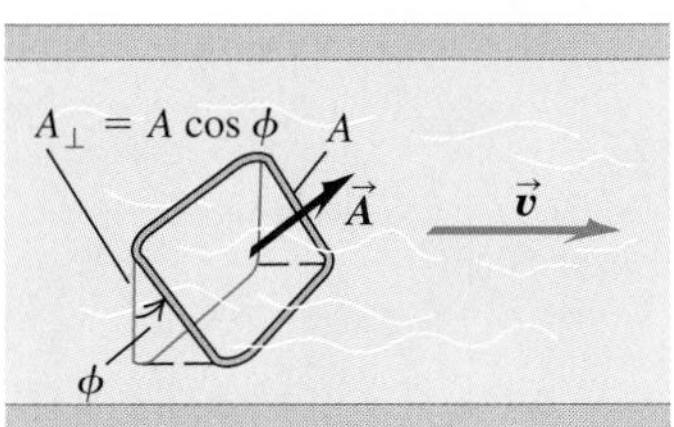

When the rectangle is tilted at an angle ϕ (Fig. 22.5b) so that its face is not perpendicular to $\vec{v}$, the area that counts is the silhouette area that we see when we look in the direction of $\vec{v}$. This area, which is outlined in red and labeled $A_\perp$ in Fig. 22.5b, is the *projection* of the area A onto a surface perpendicular to $\vec{v}$. Two sides of the projected rectangle have the same length as the original one, but the other two are foreshortened by a factor of $\cos\phi$, so the projected area $A_\perp$ is equal to $A\cos\phi$. Then the volume flow rate through A is

$$\frac{dV}{dt} = vA\cos\phi$$

If $\phi = 90°$, $dV/dt = 0$; the wire rectangle is edge-on to the flow, and no fluid passes through the rectangle.

Also, $v\cos\phi$ is the component of the vector $\vec{v}$ perpendicular to the plane of the area A. Calling this component $v_\perp$, we can rewrite the volume flow rate as

$$\frac{dV}{dt} = v_\perp A$$

We can express the volume flow rate more compactly by using the concept of *vector area* $\vec{A}$, a vector quantity with magnitude A and a direction perpendicular to the plane of the area we are describing. The vector area $\vec{A}$ describes both the size of an area and its orientation in space. In terms of $\vec{A}$, we can write the volume flow rate of fluid through the rectangle in Fig. 22.5b as a scalar (dot) product:

$$\frac{dV}{dt} = \vec{v}\cdot\vec{A}$$

Flux of a Uniform Electric Field

Using the analogy between electric field and fluid flow, we now define electric flux in the same way as we have just defined the volume flow rate of a fluid; we simply replace the fluid velocity $\vec{v}$ by the electric field $\vec{E}$. The symbol that we use for electric flux is Φ_E (the capital Greek letter phi; the subscript E is a reminder that this is *electric* flux). Consider first a flat area A perpendicular to a uniform electric field $\vec{E}$ (Fig. 22.6a). We define the electric flux through this area to be the product of the field magnitude E and the area A:

$$\Phi_E = EA$$

Roughly speaking, we can picture Φ_E in terms of the field lines passing through A. Increasing the area means that more lines of $\vec{E}$ pass through the area, increasing the flux; stronger field means more closely spaced lines of $\vec{E}$ and therefore more lines per unit area, so again the flux increases.

If the area A is flat but not perpendicular to the field $\vec{E}$, then fewer field lines pass through it. In this case the area that counts is the silhouette area that we see when looking in the direction of $\vec{E}$. This is the area $A_\perp$ in Fig. 22.6b and is equal to $A\cos\phi$ (compare to Fig. 22.5b). We generalize our definition of electric flux for a uniform electric field to

$$\Phi_E = EA\cos\phi \qquad \text{(electric flux for uniform } \vec{E}\text{, flat surface)} \qquad (22.1)$$

Since $E\cos\phi$ is the component of $\vec{E}$ perpendicular to the area, we can rewrite Eq. (22.1) as

$$\Phi_E = E_\perp A \qquad \text{(electric flux for uniform } \vec{E}\text{, flat surface)} \qquad (22.2)$$

In terms of the vector area $\vec{A}$ perpendicular to the area, we can write the electric flux as the scalar product of $\vec{E}$ and $\vec{A}$:

$$\Phi_E = \vec{E}\cdot\vec{A} \qquad \text{(electric flux for uniform } \vec{E}\text{, flat surface)} \qquad (22.3)$$

22.6 A flat surface in a uniform electric field. The electric flux Φ_E through the surface equals the scalar product of the electric field $\vec{E}$ and the area vector $\vec{A}$.

(a) Surface is face-on to electric field:
- $\vec{E}$ and $\vec{A}$ are parallel (the angle between $\vec{E}$ and $\vec{A}$ is $\phi = 0$).
- The flux $\Phi_E = \vec{E}\cdot\vec{A} = EA$.

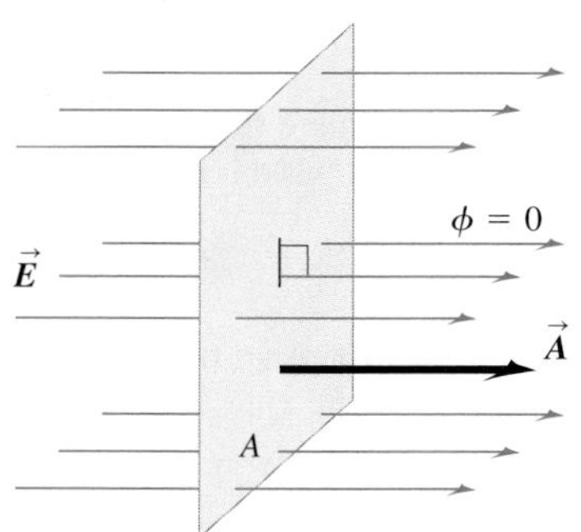

(b) Surface is tilted from a face-on orientation by an angle ϕ:
- The angle between $\vec{E}$ and $\vec{A}$ is ϕ.
- The flux $\Phi_E = \vec{E}\cdot\vec{A} = EA\cos\phi$.

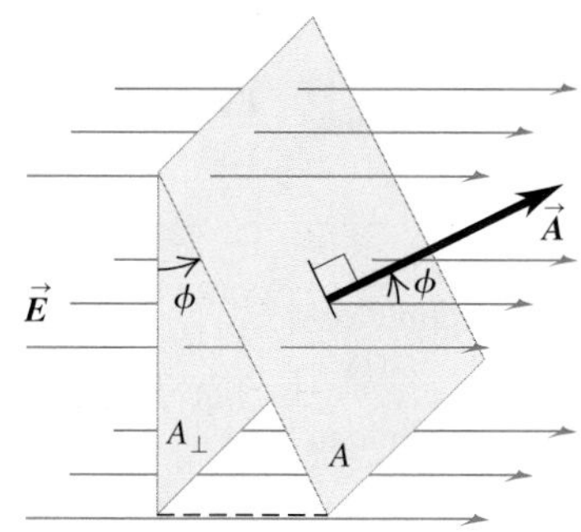

(c) Surface is edge-on to electric field:
- $\vec{E}$ and $\vec{A}$ are perpendicular (the angle between $\vec{E}$ and $\vec{A}$ is $\phi = 90°$).
- The flux $\Phi_E = \vec{E}\cdot\vec{A} = EA\cos 90° = 0$.

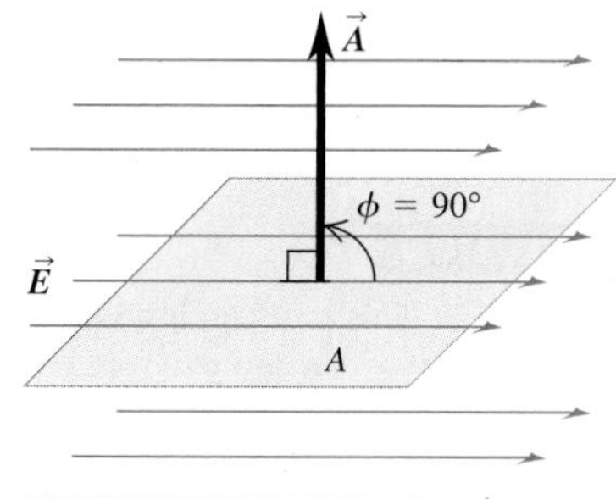

Equations (22.1), (22.2), and (22.3) express the electric flux for a *flat* surface and a *uniform* electric field in different but equivalent ways. The SI unit for electric flux is $1\ \mathrm{N\cdot m^2/C}$. Note that if the area is edge-on to the field, $\vec{E}$ and $\vec{A}$ are perpendicular and the flux is zero (Fig. 22.6c).

We can represent the direction of a vector area $\vec{A}$ by using a *unit vector* $\hat{n}$ perpendicular to the area; $\hat{n}$ stands for "normal." Then

$$\vec{A} = A\hat{n} \tag{22.4}$$

A surface has two sides, so there are two possible directions for $\hat{n}$ and $\vec{A}$. We must always specify which direction we choose. In Section 22.1 we related the charge inside a *closed* surface to the electric flux through the surface. With a closed surface we will always choose the direction of $\hat{n}$ to be *outward,* and we will speak of the flux *out of* a closed surface. Thus what we called "outward electric flux" in Section 22.1 corresponds to a *positive* value of Φ_E, and what we called "inward electric flux" corresponds to a *negative* value of Φ_E.

Flux of a Nonuniform Electric Field

What happens if the electric field $\vec{E}$ isn't uniform but varies from point to point over the area A ? Or what if A is part of a curved surface? Then we divide A into many small elements dA, each of which has a unit vector $\hat{n}$ perpendicular to it and a vector area $d\vec{A} = \hat{n}\,dA$. We calculate the electric flux through each element and integrate the results to obtain the total flux:

$$\Phi_E = \int E\cos\phi\, dA = \int E_\perp\, dA = \int \vec{E}\cdot d\vec{A} \quad \text{(general definition of electric flux)} \tag{22.5}$$

We call this integral the **surface integral** of the component $E_\perp$ over the area, or the surface integral of $\vec{E}\cdot d\vec{A}$. The various forms of the integral all express the same thing in different terms. In specific problems, one form is sometimes more convenient than another. Example 22.3 at the end of this section illustrates the use of Eq. (22.5).

In Eq. (22.5) the electric flux $\int E_\perp\, dA$ is equal to the *average* value of the perpendicular component of the electric field, multiplied by the area of the surface. This is the same definition of electric flux that we were led to in Section 22.1, now expressed more mathematically. In the next section we will see the connection between the total electric flux through *any* closed surface, no matter what its shape, and the amount of charge enclosed within that surface.

Example 22.1 Electric flux through a disk

A disk with radius 0.10 m is oriented with its normal unit vector $\hat{n}$ at an angle of 30° to a uniform electric field $\vec{E}$ with magnitude 2.0×10^3 N/C (Fig. 22.7). (Since this isn't a closed surface, it has no "inside" or "outside." That's why we have to specify the direction of $\hat{n}$ in the figure.) (a) What is the electric flux through the disk? (b) What is the flux through the disk if it is turned so that its normal is perpendicular to $\vec{E}$? (c) What is the flux through the disk if its normal is parallel to $\vec{E}$?

SOLUTION

IDENTIFY: This problem is about a flat surface in a uniform electric field, so we can apply the ideas of this section.

SET UP: The orientation of the disk is like that of the rectangle in Fig. 22.6b. We calculate the electric flux using Eq. (22.1).

EXECUTE: (a) The area is $A = \pi(0.10 \text{ m})^2 = 0.0314 \text{ m}^2$ and the angle between $\vec{E}$ and $\vec{A} = A\hat{n}$ is $\phi = 30°$, so

$$\Phi_E = EA\cos\phi = (2.0 \times 10^3 \text{ N/C})(0.0314 \text{ m}^2)(\cos 30°)$$
$$= 54 \text{ N} \cdot \text{m}^2/\text{C}$$

(b) The normal to the disk is now perpendicular to $\vec{E}$, so $\phi = 90°$, $\cos\phi = 0$, and $\Phi_E = 0$. There is no flux through the disk.

(c) The normal to the disk is parallel to $\vec{E}$, so $\phi = 0$, $\cos\phi = 1$, and the flux has its maximum possible value. From Eq. (22.1),

$$\Phi_E = EA\cos\phi = (2.0 \times 10^3 \text{ N/C})(0.0314 \text{ m}^2)(1)$$
$$= 63 \text{ N} \cdot \text{m}^2/\text{C}$$

EVALUATE: As a check on our results, note that the answer to part (a) is smaller than the answer to part (c). Is this as it should be?

22.7 The electric flux Φ_E through a disk depends on the angle between its normal $\hat{n}$ and the electric field $\vec{E}$.

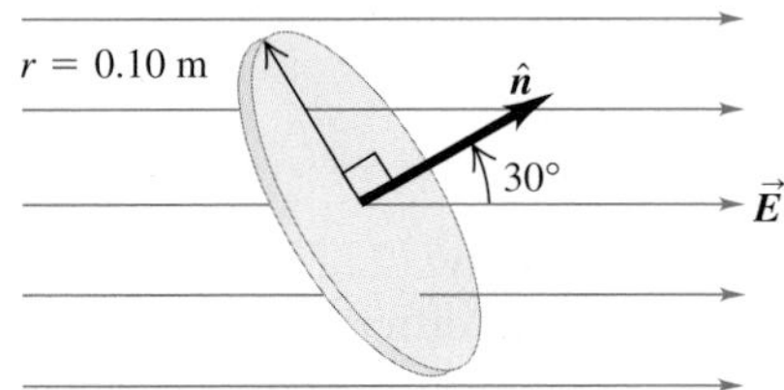

Example 22.2 Electric flux through a cube

A cube of side L is placed in a region of uniform electric field $\vec{E}$. Find the electric flux through each face of the cube and the total flux through the cube when (a) it is oriented with two of its faces perpendicular to the field $\vec{E}$, as in Fig. 22.8a; and (b) when the cube is turned by an angle θ, as in Fig. 22.8b.

SOLUTION

IDENTIFY: In this problem we are to find the electric flux through each face of the cube as well as the total flux (the sum of the fluxes through the six faces).

SET UP: Since $\vec{E}$ is uniform and each of the six faces of the cube is a flat surface, we find the flux through each face using Eqs. (22.3) and (22.4). We then calculate the total flux through the cube by adding the six individual fluxes.

EXECUTE: (a) The unit vectors for each face ($\hat{n}_1$ through $\hat{n}_6$) are shown in the figure; the direction of each unit vector is *outward* from the closed surface of the cube. The angle between $\vec{E}$ and $\hat{n}_1$ is 180°; the angle between $\vec{E}$ and $\hat{n}_2$ is 0°; and the angle between $\vec{E}$ and each of the other four unit vectors is 90°. Each face of the cube has area L^2, so the fluxes through each of the faces are

$$\Phi_{E1} = \vec{E} \cdot \hat{n}_1 A = EL^2 \cos 180° = -EL^2$$
$$\Phi_{E2} = \vec{E} \cdot \hat{n}_2 A = EL^2 \cos 0° = +EL^2$$
$$\Phi_{E3} = \Phi_{E4} = \Phi_{E5} = \Phi_{E6} = EL^2 \cos 90° = 0$$

The flux is negative on face 1, where $\vec{E}$ is directed into the cube, and positive on face 2, where $\vec{E}$ is directed out of the cube. The *total* flux through the cube is the sum of the fluxes through the six faces:

$$\Phi_E = \Phi_{E1} + \Phi_{E2} + \Phi_{E3} + \Phi_{E4} + \Phi_{E5} + \Phi_{E6}$$
$$= -EL^2 + EL^2 + 0 + 0 + 0 + 0 = 0$$

22.8 Electric flux of a uniform field $\vec{E}$ through a cubical box of side L in two orientations.

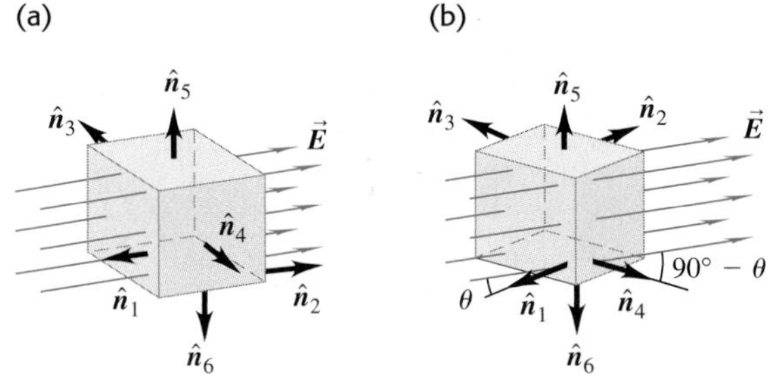

(b) The fluxes through faces 1 and 3 are negative, since $\vec{E}$ is directed into those faces; the field is directed out of faces 2 and 4, so the fluxes through those faces are positive. We find

$$\Phi_{E1} = \vec{E} \cdot \hat{n}_1 A = EL^2 \cos(180° - \theta) = -EL^2 \cos\theta$$
$$\Phi_{E2} = \vec{E} \cdot \hat{n}_2 A = +EL^2 \cos\theta$$
$$\Phi_{E3} = \vec{E} \cdot \hat{n}_3 A = EL^2 \cos(90° + \theta) = -EL^2 \sin\theta$$
$$\Phi_{E4} = \vec{E} \cdot \hat{n}_4 A = EL^2 \cos(90° - \theta) = +EL^2 \sin\theta$$
$$\Phi_{E5} = \Phi_{E6} = EL^2 \cos 90° = 0$$

The total flux $\Phi_E = \Phi_{E1} + \Phi_{E2} + \Phi_{E3} + \Phi_{E4} + \Phi_{E5} + \Phi_{E6}$ through the surface of the cube is again zero.

EVALUATE: It's no surprise that the total flux is zero for both orientations. We came to this same conclusion in our discussion of Fig. 22.3c in Section 22.1. There we observed that there was zero net flux of a uniform electric field through a closed surface that contains no electric charge.

Example 22.3 Electric flux through a sphere

A positive point charge $q = 3.0\ \mu C$ is surrounded by a sphere with radius 0.20 m centered on the charge (Fig. 22.9). Find the electric flux through the sphere due to this charge.

SOLUTION

IDENTIFY: Here the surface is not flat and the electric field is not uniform, so we must use the general definition of electric flux.

SET UP: We use Eq. (22.5) to calculate the electric flux (our target variable). Because the sphere is centered on the point charge, at any point on the spherical surface, $\vec{E}$ is directed out of the sphere perpendicular to the surface. The positive direction for both $\hat{n}$ and $E_{\perp}$ is outward, so $E_{\perp} = E$ and the flux through a surface element dA is $\vec{E} \cdot d\vec{A} = E\,dA$. This greatly simplifies the integral in Eq. (22.5).

EXECUTE: At any point on the sphere the magnitude of $\vec{E}$ is

$$E = \frac{q}{4\pi\epsilon_0 r^2} = (9.0 \times 10^9\ \mathrm{N \cdot m^2/C^2})\frac{3.0 \times 10^{-6}\ \mathrm{C}}{(0.20\ \mathrm{m})^2}$$
$$= 6.75 \times 10^5\ \mathrm{N/C}$$

Because E is the same at every point, it can be taken outside the integral $\Phi_E = \int E\,dA$ in Eq. (22.5). What remains is the integral $\int dA$, which is just the total area $A = 4\pi r^2$ of the spherical surface. Thus the total flux out of the sphere is

$$\Phi_E = EA = (6.75 \times 10^5\ \mathrm{N/C})(4\pi)(0.20\ \mathrm{m})^2$$
$$= 3.4 \times 10^5\ \mathrm{N \cdot m^2/C}$$

22.9 Electric flux through a sphere centered on a point charge.

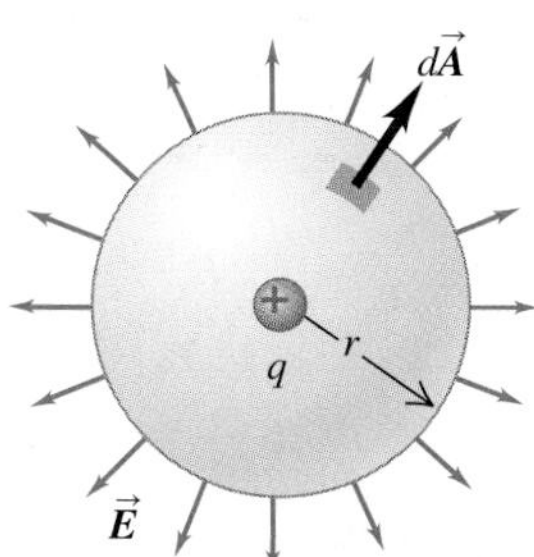

EVALUATE: Notice that we divided by $r^2 = (0.20\ \mathrm{m})^2$ to find E, then multiplied by $r^2 = (0.20\ \mathrm{m})^2$ to find Φ_E; hence the radius r of the sphere cancels out of the result for Φ_E. We would have obtained the same flux with a sphere of radius 2.0 m or 200 m. We came to essentially the same conclusion in our discussion of Fig. 22.4 in Section 22.1, where we considered rectangular closed surfaces of two different sizes enclosing a point charge. There we found that the flux of $\vec{E}$ was independent of the size of the surface; the same result holds true for a spherical surface. Indeed, the flux through *any* surface enclosing a single point charge is independent of the shape or size of the surface, as we'll soon see.

Test Your Understanding of Section 22.2 Rank the following surfaces in order from most positive to most negative electric flux. (i) a flat rectangular surface with vector area $\vec{A} = (6.0\ \mathrm{m^2})\hat{\imath}$ in a uniform electric field $\vec{E} = (4.0\ \mathrm{N/C})\hat{\jmath}$; (ii) a flat circular surface with vector area $\vec{A} = (3.0\ \mathrm{m^2})\hat{\jmath}$ in a uniform electric field $\vec{E} = (4.0\ \mathrm{N/C})\hat{\imath} + (2.0\ \mathrm{N/C})\hat{\jmath}$; (iii) a flat square surface with vector area $\vec{A} = (3.0\ \mathrm{m^2})\hat{\imath} + (7.0\ \mathrm{m^2})\hat{\jmath}$ in a uniform electric field $\vec{E} = (4.0\ \mathrm{N/C})\hat{\imath} - (2.0\ \mathrm{N/C})\hat{\jmath}$; (iv) a flat oval surface with vector area $\vec{A} = (3.0\ \mathrm{m^2})\hat{\imath} - (7.0\ \mathrm{m^2})\hat{\jmath}$ in a uniform electric field $\vec{E} = (4.0\ \mathrm{N/C})\hat{\imath} - (2.0\ \mathrm{N/C})\hat{\jmath}$.

22.3 Gauss's Law

Gauss's law is an alternative to Coulomb's law. While completely equivalent to Coulomb's law, Gauss's law provides a different way to express the relationship between electric charge and electric field. It was formulated by Carl Friedrich Gauss (1777–1855), one of the greatest mathematicians of all time. Many areas of mathematics bear the mark of his influence, and he made equally significant contributions to theoretical physics (Fig. 22.10).

22.10 Carl Friedrich Gauss helped develop several branches of mathematics, including differential geometry, real analysis, and number theory. The "bell curve" of statistics is one of his inventions. Gauss also made state-of-the-art investigations of the earth's magnetism and calculated the orbit of the first asteroid to be discovered.

Point Charge Inside a Spherical Surface

Gauss's law states that the total electric flux through any closed surface (a surface enclosing a definite volume) is proportional to the total (net) electric charge inside the surface. In Section 22.1 we observed this relationship qualitatively for certain special cases; now we'll develop it more rigorously. We'll start with the field of a single positive point charge q. The field lines radiate out equally in all directions. We place this charge at the center of an imaginary spherical surface with radius R. The magnitude E of the electric field at every point on the surface is given by

$$E = \frac{1}{4\pi\epsilon_0}\frac{q}{R^2}$$

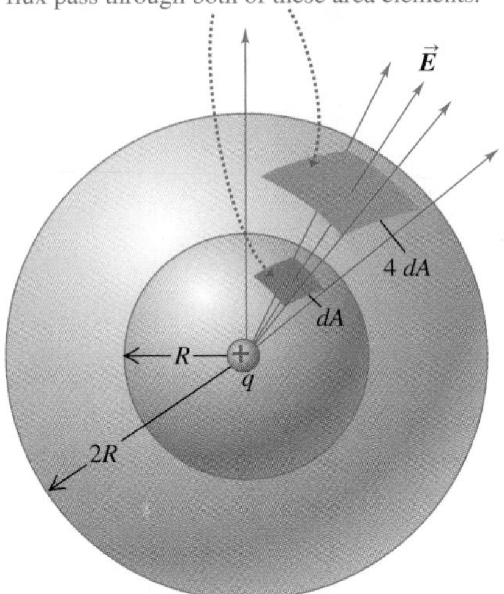

The same number of field lines and the same flux pass through both of these area elements.
$\vec{E}$
4 dA
dA
R
q
2R

22.11 Projection of an element of area dA of a sphere of radius R onto a concentric sphere of radius $2R$. The projection multiplies each linear dimension by 2, so the area element on the larger sphere is $4\,dA$.

At each point on the surface, $\vec{E}$ is perpendicular to the surface, and its magnitude is the same at every point, just as in Example 22.3 (Section 22.2). The total electric flux is the product of the field magnitude E and the total area $A = 4\pi R^2$ of the sphere:

$$\Phi_E = EA = \frac{1}{4\pi\epsilon_0}\frac{q}{R^2}(4\pi R^2) = \frac{q}{\epsilon_0} \tag{22.6}$$

The flux is independent of the radius R of the sphere. It depends only on the charge q enclosed by the sphere.

We can also interpret this result in terms of field lines. Figure 22.11 shows two spheres with radii R and $2R$ centered on the point charge q. Every field line that passes through the smaller sphere also passes through the larger sphere, so the total flux through each sphere is the same.

What is true of the entire sphere is also true of any portion of its surface. In Fig.22.11 an area dA is outlined on the sphere of radius R and then projected onto the sphere of radius $2R$ by drawing lines from the center through points on the boundary of dA. The area projected on the larger sphere is clearly $4\,dA$. But since the electric field due to a point charge is inversely proportional to r^2, the field magnitude is $\frac{1}{4}$ as great on the sphere of radius $2R$ as on the sphere of radius R. Hence the electric flux is the same for both areas and is independent of the radius of the sphere.

Point Charge Inside a Nonspherical Surface

This projection technique shows us how to extend this discussion to nonspherical surfaces. Instead of a second sphere, let us surround the sphere of radius R by a surface of irregular shape, as in Fig. 22.12a. Consider a small element of area dA on the irregular surface; we note that this area is *larger* than the corresponding element on a spherical surface at the same distance from q. If a normal to dA makes an angle ϕ with a radial line from q, two sides of the area projected onto the spherical surface are foreshortened by a factor $\cos\phi$ (Fig. 22.12b). The other two sides are unchanged. Thus the electric flux through the spherical surface element is equal to the flux $E\,dA\cos\phi$ through the corresponding irregular surface element.

We can divide the entire irregular surface into elements dA, compute the electric flux $E\,dA\cos\phi$ for each, and sum the results by integrating, as in Eq. (22.5). Each of the area elements projects onto a corresponding spherical surface element. Thus the *total* electric flux through the irregular surface, given by any of the forms of Eq. (22.5), must be the same as the total flux through a sphere, which Eq.(22.6) shows is equal to q/ϵ_0. Thus, for the irregular surface,

$$\Phi_E = \oint \vec{E}\cdot d\vec{A} = \frac{q}{\epsilon_0} \tag{22.7}$$

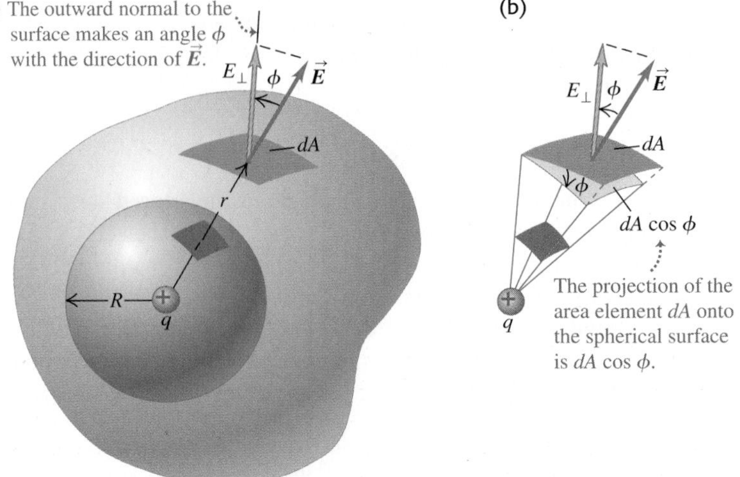

(a) The outward normal to the surface makes an angle ϕ with the direction of $\vec{E}$.
$E_\perp$
ϕ
$\vec{E}$
dA
r
R
q
(b)
$E_\perp$
ϕ
$\vec{E}$
dA
ϕ
dA cos ϕ
The projection of the area element dA onto the spherical surface is dA cos ϕ.
q

22.12 Calculating the electric flux through a nonspherical surface.

Equation (22.7) holds for a surface of *any* shape or size, provided only that it is a *closed* surface enclosing the charge q. The circle on the integral sign reminds us that the integral is always taken over a *closed* surface.

The area elements $d\vec{A}$ and the corresponding unit vectors $\hat{n}$ always point *out of* the volume enclosed by the surface. The electric flux is then positive in areas where the electric field points out of the surface and negative where it points inward. Also, $E_\perp$ is positive at points where $\vec{E}$ points out of the surface and negative at points where $\vec{E}$ points into the surface.

If the point charge in Fig. 22.12 is negative, the $\vec{E}$ field is directed radially *inward;* the angle ϕ is then greater than 90°, its cosine is negative, and the integral in Eq. (22.7) is negative. But since q is also negative, Eq. (22.7) still holds.

For a closed surface enclosing *no* charge,

$$\Phi_E = \oint \vec{E} \cdot d\vec{A} = 0$$

This is the mathematical statement that when a region contains no charge, any field lines caused by charges *outside* the region that enter on one side must leave again on the other side. (In Section 22.1 we came to the same conclusion by considering the special case of a rectangular box in a uniform field.) Figure 22.13 illustrates this point. *Electric field lines can begin or end inside a region of space only when there is charge in that region.*

22.13 A point charge *outside* a closed surface that encloses no charge. If an electric field line from the external charge enters the surface at one point, it must leave at another.

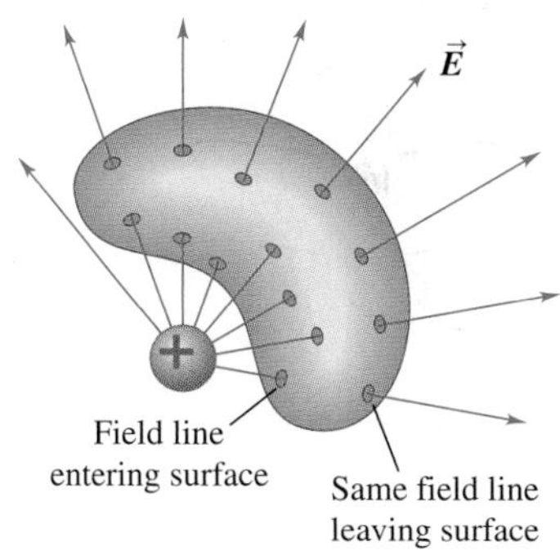

General Form of Gauss's Law

Now comes the final step in obtaining the general form of Gauss's law. Suppose the surface encloses not just one point charge q but several charges q_1, q_2, q_3, ... The total (resultant) electric field $\vec{E}$ at any point is the vector sum of the $\vec{E}$ fields of the individual charges. Let Q_{encl} be the *total* charge enclosed by the surface: $Q_{encl} = q_1 + q_2 + q_3 + \cdots$. Also let $\vec{E}$ be the *total* field at the position of the surface area element $d\vec{A}$, and let $E_\perp$ be its component perpendicular to the plane of that element (that is, parallel to $d\vec{A}$). Then we can write an equation like Eq. (22.7) for each charge and its corresponding field and add the results. When we do, we obtain the general statement of Gauss's law:

$$\Phi_E = \oint \vec{E} \cdot d\vec{A} = \frac{Q_{encl}}{\epsilon_0} \qquad \text{(Gauss's law)} \qquad (22.8)$$

The total electric flux through a closed surface is equal to the total (net) electric charge inside the surface, divided by ϵ_0.

CAUTION Gaussian surfaces are imaginary Remember that the closed surface in Gauss's law is *imaginary;* there need not be any material object at the position of the surface. We often refer to a closed surface used in Gauss's law as a **Gaussian surface.**

Using the definition of Q_{encl} and the various ways to express electric flux given in Eq. (22.5), we can express Gauss's law in the following equivalent forms:

$$\Phi_E = \oint E\cos\phi\, dA = \oint E_\perp\, dA = \oint \vec{E} \cdot d\vec{A} = \frac{Q_{encl}}{\epsilon_0} \qquad \text{(various forms of Gauss's law)} \qquad (22.9)$$

As in Eq. (22.5), the various forms of the integral all express the same thing, the total electric flux through the Gaussian surface, in different terms. One form is sometimes more convenient than another.

As an example, Fig. 22.14a shows a spherical Gaussian surface of radius r around a positive point charge $+q$. The electric field points out of the Gaussian surface, so at every point on the surface $\vec{E}$ is in the same direction as $d\vec{A}$, $\phi = 0$, and

22.14 Spherical Gaussian surfaces around (a) a positive point charge and (b) a negative point charge.

(a) Gaussian surface around positive charge: positive (outward) flux

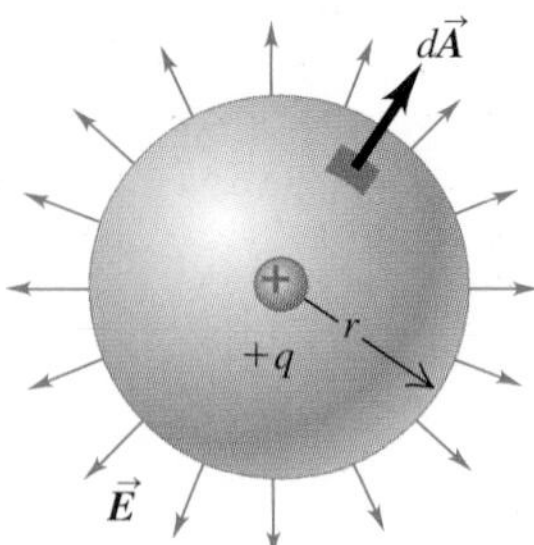

(b) Gaussian surface around negative charge: negative (inward) flux

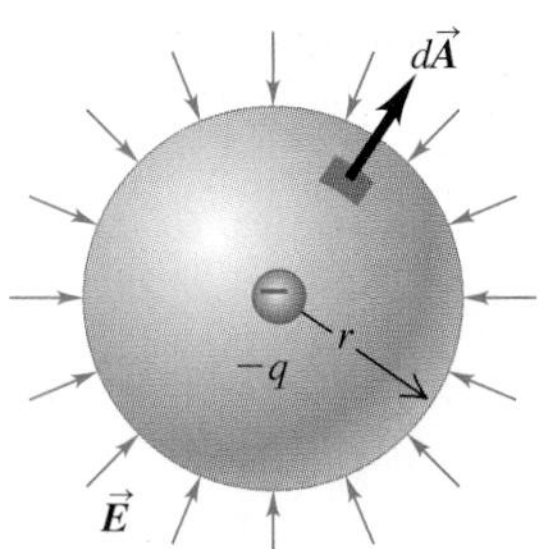

$E_\perp$ is equal to the field magnitude $E = q/4\pi\epsilon_0 r^2$. Since E is the same at all points on the surface, we can take it outside the integral in Eq. (22.9). Then the remaining integral is $\int dA = A = 4\pi r^2$, the area of the sphere. Hence Eq. (22.9) becomes

$$\Phi_E = \oint E_\perp \, dA = \oint \frac{q}{4\pi\epsilon_0 r^2} \, dA = \frac{q}{4\pi\epsilon_0 r^2} \oint dA = \frac{q}{4\pi\epsilon_0 r^2} 4\pi r^2 = \frac{q}{\epsilon_0}$$

The enclosed charge Q_{encl} is just the charge $+q$, so this agrees with Gauss's law. If the Gaussian surface encloses a *negative* point charge as in Fig. 22.14b, then $\vec{E}$ points *into* the surface at each point in the direction opposite $d\vec{A}$. Then $\phi =$ 180° and $E_\perp$ is equal to the negative of the field magnitude: $E_\perp = -E = -|-q|/4\pi\epsilon_0 r^2 = -q/4\pi\epsilon_0 r^2$. Equation (22.9) then becomes

$$\Phi_E = \oint E_\perp \, dA = \oint \left(\frac{-q}{4\pi\epsilon_0 r^2}\right) dA = \frac{-q}{4\pi\epsilon_0 r^2} \oint dA = \frac{-q}{4\pi\epsilon_0 r^2} 4\pi r^2 = \frac{-q}{\epsilon_0}$$

This again agrees with Gauss's law because the enclosed charge in Fig. 22.14b is $Q_{encl} = -q$.

In Eqs. (22.8) and (22.9), Q_{encl} is always the algebraic sum of all the positive and negative charges enclosed by the Gaussian surface, and $\vec{E}$ is the *total* field at each point on the surface. Also note that in general, this field is caused partly by charges inside the surface and partly by charges outside. But as Fig. 22.13 shows, the outside charges do *not* contribute to the total (net) flux through the surface. So Eqs. (22.8) and (22.9) are correct even when there are charges outside the surface that contribute to the electric field at the surface. When $Q_{encl} = 0$, the total flux through the Gaussian surface must be zero, even though some areas may have positive flux and others may have negative flux (see Fig. 22.3b).

Gauss's law is the definitive answer to the question we posed at the beginning of Section 22.1: "If the electric field pattern is known in a given region, what can we determine about the charge distribution in that region?" It provides a relationship between the electric field on a closed surface and the charge distribution within that surface. But in some cases we can use Gauss's law to answer the reverse question: "If the charge distribution is known, what can we determine about the electric field that the charge distribution produces?" Gauss's law may seem like an unappealing way to address this question, since it may look as though evaluating the integral in Eq. (22.8) is a hopeless task. Sometimes it is, but other times it is surprisingly easy. Here's an example in which *no* integration is involved at all; we'll work out several more examples in the next section.

Conceptual Example 22.4 Electric flux and enclosed charge

Figure 22.15 shows the field produced by two point charges $+q$ and $-q$ of equal magnitude but opposite sign (an electric dipole). Find the electric flux through each of the closed surfaces A, B, C, and D.

SOLUTION

The definition of electric flux given in Eq. (22.5) involves a surface integral, and so it might seem that integration is called for. But Gauss's law says that the total electric flux through a closed surface is equal to the total enclosed charge divided by ϵ_0. By inspection of Fig. 22.15, surface A (shown in red) encloses the positive charge, so $Q_{encl} = +q$; surface B (shown in blue) encloses the negative charge, so $Q_{encl} = -q$; surface C (shown in yellow), which encloses *both* charges, has $Q_{encl} = +q + (-q) = 0$; and surface D (shown in purple), which has no charges enclosed within it, also has $Q_{encl} = 0$. Hence without having to do any integration, we can

22.15 The net number of field lines leaving a closed surface is proportional to the total charge enclosed by that surface.

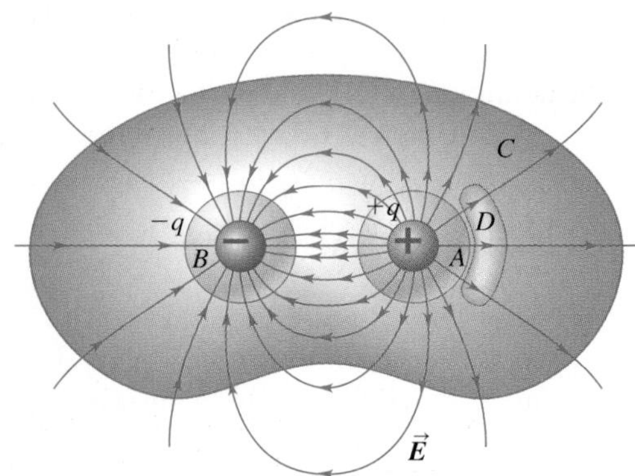

conclude that the total fluxes for the various surfaces are $\Phi_E = +q/\epsilon_0$ for surface A, $\Phi_E = -q/\epsilon_0$ for surface B, and $\Phi_E = 0$ for both surface C and surface D.

These results depend only on the charges enclosed within each Gaussian surface, not on the precise shapes of the surfaces. For example, compare surface C to the rectangular surface shown in Fig. 22.3b, which also encloses both charges of an electric dipole. In that case as well, we concluded that the net flux of $\vec{E}$ was zero; the inward flux on one part of the surface exactly compensates for the outward flux on the remainder of the surface.

We can draw similar conclusions by examining the electric field lines. Surface A encloses only the positive charge; in Fig. 22.15, 18 lines are depicted crossing A in an outward direction. Surface B encloses only the negative charge; it is crossed by these same 18 lines, but in an inward direction. Surface C encloses *both* charges. It is intersected by lines at 16 points; at 8 intersections the lines are outward, and at 8 they are inward. The *net* number of lines crossing in an outward direction is zero, and the net charge inside the surface is also zero. Surface D is intersected at 6 points; at 3 points the lines are outward, and at the other 3 they are inward. The net number of lines crossing in an outward direction and the total charge enclosed are both zero. There are points on the surfaces where $\vec{E}$ is not perpendicular to the surface, but this doesn't affect the counting of the field lines.

Test Your Understanding of Section 22.3 Figure 22.16 shows six point charges that all lie in the same plane. Five Gaussian surfaces—S_1, S_2, S_3, S_4, and S_5—each enclose part of this plane, and Fig. 22.16 shows the intersection of each surface with the plane. Rank these five surfaces in order of the electric flux through them, from most positive to most negative.

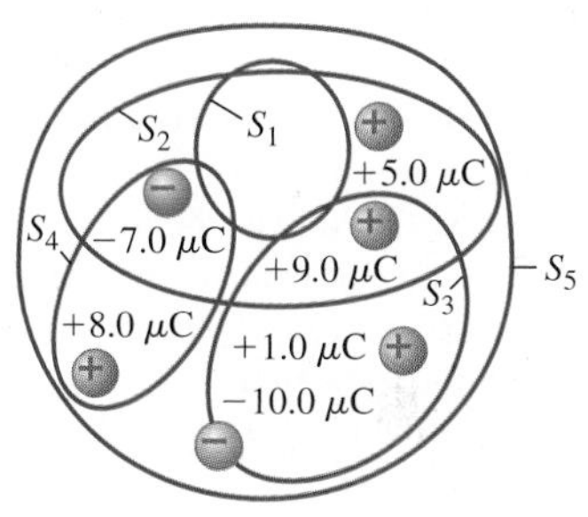

22.16 Five Gaussian surfaces and six point charges.

22.4 Applications of Gauss's Law

Gauss's law is valid for *any* distribution of charges and for *any* closed surface. Gauss's law can be used in two ways. If we know the charge distribution, and if it has enough symmetry to let us evaluate the integral in Gauss's law, we can find the field. Or if we know the field, we can use Gauss's law to find the charge distribution, such as charges on conducting surfaces.

In this section we present examples of both kinds of applications. As you study them, watch for the role played by the symmetry properties of each system. We will use Gauss's law to calculate the electric fields caused by several simple charge distributions; the results are collected in a table in the chapter summary.

In practical problems we often encounter situations in which we want to know the electric field caused by a charge distribution on a conductor. These calculations are aided by the following remarkable fact: *When excess charge is placed on a solid conductor and is at rest, it resides entirely on the surface, not in the interior of the material.* (By *excess* we mean charges other than the ions and free electrons that make up the neutral conductor.) Here's the proof. We know from Section 21.4 that in an electrostatic situation (with all charges at rest) the electric field $\vec{E}$ at every point in the interior of a conducting material is zero. If $\vec{E}$ were *not* zero, the excess charges would move. Suppose we construct a Gaussian surface inside the conductor, such as surface A in Fig. 22.17. Because $\vec{E} = \mathbf{0}$ everywhere on this surface, Gauss's law requires that the net charge inside the surface is zero. Now imagine shrinking the surface like a collapsing balloon until it encloses a region so small that we may consider it as a point P; then the charge at that point must be zero. We can do this anywhere inside the conductor, so *there can be no excess charge at any point within a solid conductor; any excess charge must reside on the conductor's surface.* (This result is for a *solid* conductor. In the next section we'll discuss what can happen if the conductor has cavities in its interior.) We will make use of this fact frequently in the examples that follow.

22.17 Under electrostatic conditions (charges not in motion), any excess charge on a solid conductor resides entirely on the conductor's surface.

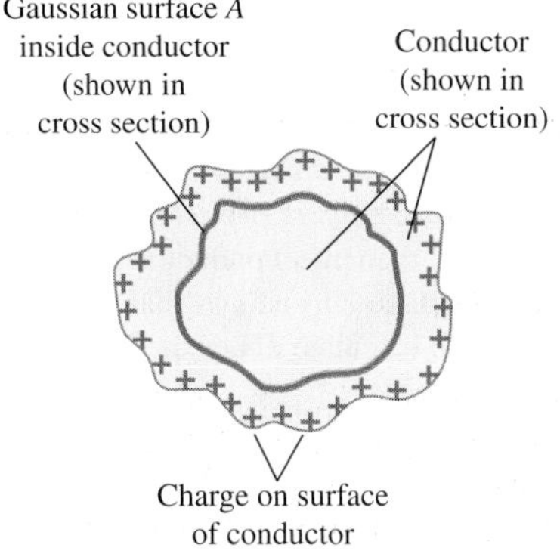

Problem-Solving Strategy 22.1 Gauss's Law

IDENTIFY *the relevant concepts:* Gauss's law is most useful in situations where the charge distribution has spherical or cylindrical symmetry or is distributed uniformly over a plane. In these situations we determine the direction of $\vec{E}$ from the symmetry of the charge distribution. If we are given the charge distribution, we can use Gauss's law to find the magnitude of $\vec{E}$. Alternatively, if we are given the field, we can use Gauss's law to determine the details of the charge distribution. In either case, begin your analysis by asking the question: What is the symmetry?

SET UP *the problem* using the following steps:

1. Select the surface that you will use with Gauss's law. We often call it a *Gaussian surface.* If you are trying to find the field at a particular point, then that point must lie on your Gaussian surface.
2. The Gaussian surface does not have to be a real physical surface, such as a surface of a solid body. Often the appropriate surface is an imaginary geometric surface; it may be in empty space, embedded in a solid body, or both.
3. Usually you can evaluate the integral in Gauss's law (without using a computer) only if the Gaussian surface and the charge distribution have some symmetry property. If the charge distribution has cylindrical or spherical symmetry, choose the Gaussian surface to be a coaxial cylinder or a concentric sphere, respectively.

EXECUTE *the solution* as follows:

1. Carry out the integral in Eq. (22.9). This may look like a daunting task, but the symmetry of the charge distribution and your careful choice of a Gaussian surface make it straightforward.
2. Often you can think of the closed Gaussian surface as being made up of several separate surfaces, such as the sides and ends of a cylinder. The integral $\oint E_\perp \, dA$ over the entire closed surface is always equal to the sum of the integrals over all the separate surfaces. Some of these integrals may be zero, as in points 4 and 5 below.
3. If $\vec{E}$ is *perpendicular* (normal) at every point to a surface with area A, if it points *outward* from the interior of the surface, and if it also has the same *magnitude* at every point on the surface, then $E_\perp = E =$ constant, and $\int E_\perp \, dA$ over that surface is equal to EA. If instead $\vec{E}$ is perpendicular and *inward,* then $E_\perp = -E$ and $\int E_\perp \, dA = -EA$.
4. If $\vec{E}$ is *tangent* to a surface at every point, then $E_\perp = 0$ and the integral over that surface is zero.
5. If $\vec{E} = \mathbf{0}$ at every point on a surface, the integral is zero.
6. In the integral $\oint E_\perp \, dA$, $E_\perp$ is always the perpendicular component of the *total* electric field at each point on the closed Gaussian surface. In general, this field may be caused partly by charges within the surface and partly by charges outside it. Even when there is *no* charge within the surface, the field at points on the Gaussian surface is not necessarily zero. In that case, however, the *integral* over the Gaussian surface—that is, the total electric flux through the Gaussian surface—is always zero.
7. Once you have evaluated the integral, use Eq. (22.9) to solve for your target variable.

EVALUATE *your answer:* Often your result will be a *function* that describes how the magnitude of the electric field varies with position. Examine this function with a critical eye to see whether it makes sense.

Example 22.5 Field of a charged conducting sphere

We place positive charge q on a solid conducting sphere with radius R (Fig. 22.18). Find $\vec{E}$ at any point inside or outside the sphere.

SOLUTION

IDENTIFY: As we discussed earlier in this section, all the charge must be on the surface of the sphere. The system has spherical symmetry.

SET UP: To take advantage of the symmetry, we take as our Gaussian surface an imaginary sphere of radius r centered on the conductor. To calculate the field outside the conductor, we take r to be greater than the conductor's radius R; to calculate the field inside, we take r to be less than R. In either case, the point where we want to calculate $\vec{E}$ lies on the Gaussian surface.

EXECUTE: The role of symmetry deserves careful discussion before we do any calculations. When we say that the system is spherically symmetric, we mean that if we rotate it through any angle about any axis through the center, the system after rotation is indistinguishable from the original unrotated system. The charge is free to move on the conductor, and there is nothing about the con-

22.18 Calculating the electric field of a conducting sphere with positive charge q. Outside the sphere, the field is the same as if all of the charge were concentrated at the center of the sphere.

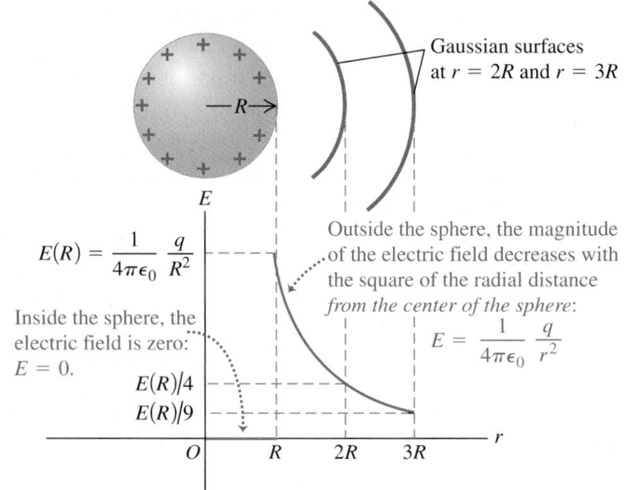

Gaussian surfaces at $r = 2R$ and $r = 3R$
R
E
$E(R) = \frac{1}{4\pi\epsilon_0}\frac{q}{R^2}$
Outside the sphere, the magnitude of the electric field decreases with the square of the radial distance from the center of the sphere:
$E = \frac{1}{4\pi\epsilon_0}\frac{q}{r^2}$
Inside the sphere, the electric field is zero: $E = 0$.
$E(R)/4$
$E(R)/9$
O
R
$2R$
$3R$
r

ductor that would make it tend to concentrate more in some regions than others. So we conclude that the charge is distributed *uniformly* over the surface.

Symmetry also shows that the direction of the electric field must be *radial,* as shown in Fig. 22.18. If we again rotate the system, the field pattern of the rotated system must be identical to that of the original system. If the field had a component at some point that was perpendicular to the radial direction, that component would have to be different after at least some rotations. Thus there can't be such a component, and the field must be radial. For the same reason the magnitude E of the field can depend only on the distance r from the center and must have the same value at all points on a spherical surface concentric with the conductor.

Our choice of a sphere as a Gaussian surface takes advantage of these symmetry properties. We first consider the field outside the conductor, so we choose $r > R$. The entire conductor is within the Gaussian surface, so the enclosed charge is q. The area of the Gaussian surface is $4\pi r^2$; $\vec{E}$ is uniform over the surface and perpendicular to it at each point. The flux integral $\oint E_\perp\, dA$ in Gauss's law is therefore just $E(4\pi r^2)$, and Eq. (22.8) gives

$$E(4\pi r^2) = \frac{q}{\epsilon_0} \quad \text{and}$$

$$E = \frac{1}{4\pi\epsilon_0}\frac{q}{r^2} \quad \text{(outside a charged conducting sphere)}$$

This expression for the field at any point *outside* the sphere $(r > R)$ is the same as for a point charge; the field due to the charged sphere is the same as though the entire charge were concentrated at its center. Just outside the surface of the sphere, where $r = R$,

$$E = \frac{1}{4\pi\epsilon_0}\frac{q}{R^2}$$

(at the surface of a charged conducting sphere)

CAUTION Flux can be positive or negative Remember that we have chosen the charge q to be *positive.* If the charge is negative, the electric field is radially *inward* instead of radially outward, and the electric flux through the Gaussian surface is negative. The electric field magnitudes outside and at the surface of the sphere are given by the same expressions as above, except that q denotes the *magnitude* (absolute value) of the charge.

To find $\vec{E}$ inside the conductor, we use a spherical Gaussian surface with radius $r < R$. The spherical symmetry again tells us that $E(4\pi r^2) = Q_{\text{encl}}/\epsilon_0$. But because all of the charge is on the surface of the conductor, our Gaussian surface (which lies entirely within the conductor) encloses *no* charge. So $Q_{\text{encl}} = 0$ and, therefore, the electric field inside the conductor is zero.

EVALUATE: We already knew that $\vec{E} = \mathbf{0}$ inside the conductor, as it must be inside any solid conductor when the charges are at rest. Figure 22.18 shows E as a function of the distance r from the center of the sphere. Note that in the limit as $R \to 0$, the sphere becomes a point charge; there is then only an "outside," and the field is everywhere given by $E = q/4\pi\epsilon_0 r^2$. Thus we have deduced Coulomb's law from Gauss's law. (In Section 22.3 we deduced Gauss's law from Coulomb's law, so this completes the demonstration of their logical equivalence.)

We can also use this method for a conducting spherical *shell* (a spherical conductor with a concentric spherical hole in the center) if there is no charge inside the hole. We use a spherical Gaussian surface with radius r less than the radius of the hole. If there *were* a field inside the hole, it would have to be radial and spherically symmetric as before, so $E = Q_{\text{encl}}/4\pi\epsilon_0 r^2$. But now there is no enclosed charge, so $Q_{\text{encl}} = 0$ and $E = 0$ inside the hole.

Can you use this same technique to find the electric field in the interspace between a charged sphere and a concentric hollow conducting sphere that surrounds it?

Example 22.6 Field of a line charge

Electric charge is distributed uniformly along an infinitely long, thin wire. The charge per unit length is λ (assumed positive). Find the electric field. (This is an approximate representation of the field of a uniformly charged *finite* wire, provided that the distance from the field point to the wire is much less than the length of the wire.)

SOLUTION

IDENTIFY: The system has *cylindrical* symmetry. The field must point away from the positive charges. To determine the direction of $\vec{E}$ more precisely, as well as how its magnitude can depend on position, we use symmetry as in Example 22.5.

SET UP: Cylindrical symmetry means that we can rotate the system through any angle about its axis, and we can shift it by any amount along the axis; in each case the resulting system is indistinguishable from the original. Hence $\vec{E}$ at each point can't change when either of these operations is carried out. The field can't have any component parallel to the wire; if it did, we would have to explain why the field lines that begin on the wire pointed in one direction parallel to the wire and not the other. Also, the field can't have any component tangent to a circle in a plane perpendicular to the wire with its center on the wire. If it did, we would have to explain why the component pointed in one direction around the wire rather than the other. All that's left is a component radially outward from the wire at each point. So the field lines outside a uniformly charged, infinite wire are *radial* and lie in planes perpendicular to the wire. The field *magnitude* can depend only on the radial distance from the wire.

These symmetry properties suggest that we use as a Gaussian surface a *cylinder* with arbitrary radius r and arbitrary length l, with its ends perpendicular to the wire (Fig. 22.19).

22.19 A coaxial cylindrical Gaussian surface is used to find the electric field outside an infinitely long, charged wire.

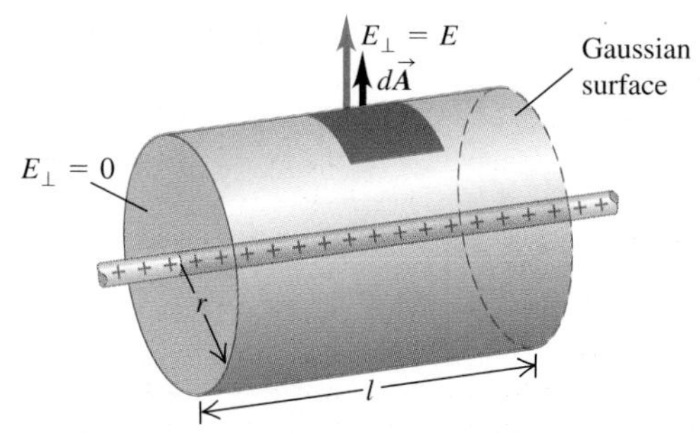

Continued

EXECUTE: We break the surface integral for the flux Φ_E into an integral over each flat end and one over the curved side walls. There is no flux through the ends because $\vec{E}$ lies in the plane of the surface and $E_\perp = 0$. To find the flux through the side walls, note that $\vec{E}$ is perpendicular to the surface at each point, so $E = E_\perp$; by symmetry, E has the same value everywhere on the walls. The area of the side walls is $2\pi rl$. (To make a paper cylinder with radius r and height l, you need a paper rectangle with width $2\pi r$, height l, and area $2\pi rl$.) Hence the total flux Φ_E through the entire cylinder is the sum of the flux through the side walls, which is $(E)(2\pi rl)$, and the zero flux through the two ends. Finally, we need the total enclosed charge, which is the charge per unit length multiplied by the length of wire inside the Gaussian surface, or $Q_{encl} = \lambda l$. From Gauss's law, Eq. (22.8),

$$\Phi_E = (E)(2\pi rl) = \frac{\lambda l}{\epsilon_0} \quad \text{and}$$

$$E = \frac{1}{2\pi\epsilon_0}\frac{\lambda}{r} \quad \text{(field of an infinite line of charge)}$$

This is the same result that we found in Example 21.11 (Section 21.5) by much more laborious means.

We have assumed that λ is *positive.* If it is *negative,* $\vec{E}$ is directed radially inward toward the line of charge, and in the above expression for the field magnitude E we must interpret λ as the *magnitude* (absolute value) of the charge per unit length.

EVALUATE: Note that although the *entire* charge on the wire contributes to the field, only the part of the total charge that is within the Gaussian surface is considered when we apply Gauss's law. This may seem strange; it looks as though we have somehow obtained the right answer by ignoring part of the charge and the field of a *short* wire of length l would be the same as that of a very long wire. But we *do* include the entire charge on the wire when we make use of the *symmetry* of the problem. If the wire is short, the symmetry with respect to shifts along the axis is not present, and the field is not uniform in magnitude over our Gaussian surface. Gauss's law is then no longer useful and *cannot* be used to find the field; the problem is best handled by the integration technique used in Example 21.11.

We can use a Gaussian surface like that in Fig. 22.19 to show that the field at points outside a long, uniformly charged cylinder is the same as though all the charge were concentrated on a line along its axis. We can also calculate the electric field in the space between a charged cylinder and a coaxial hollow conducting cylinder surrounding it. We leave these calculations to you (see Problems 22.37 and 22.40).

Example 22.7 Field of an infinite plane sheet of charge

Find the electric field caused by a thin, flat, infinite sheet on which there is a uniform positive charge per unit area σ.

SOLUTION

IDENTIFY: The field must point away from the positively charged sheet. As in Examples 22.5 and 22.6, before doing calculations we use the symmetry (in this case, *planar* symmetry) to learn more about the direction and position dependence of $\vec{E}$.

SET UP: Planar symmetry means that the charge distribution doesn't change if we slide it in any direction parallel to the sheet. From this we conclude that at each point, $\vec{E}$ is perpendicular to the sheet. The symmetry also tells us that the field must have the same magnitude E at any given distance on either side of the sheet. To take advantage of these symmetry properties, we use as our Gaussian surface a cylinder with its axis perpendicular to the sheet of charge, with ends of area A (Fig. 22.20).

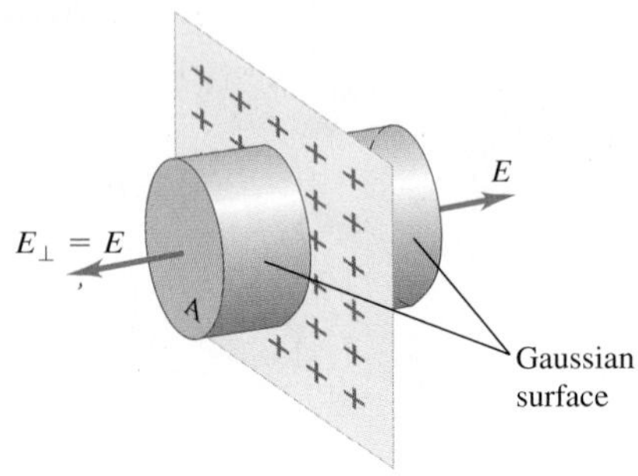

22.20 A cylindrical Gaussian surface is used to find the field of an infinite plane sheet of charge.

EXECUTE: The charged sheet passes through the middle of the cylinder's length, so the cylinder ends are equidistant from the sheet. At each end of the cylinder, $\vec{E}$ is perpendicular to the surface and $E_\perp$ is equal to E; hence the flux through each end is $+EA$.

Because $\vec{E}$ is perpendicular to the charged sheet, it is parallel to the curved *side* walls of the cylinder, so $E_\perp$ at these walls is zero and there is no flux through these walls. The total flux integral in Gauss's law is then $2EA$ (EA from each end and zero from the side walls). The net charge within the Gaussian surface is the charge per unit area multiplied by the sheet area enclosed by the surface, or $Q_{encl} = \sigma A$. Hence Gauss's law, Eq. (22.8), gives

$$2EA = \frac{\sigma A}{\epsilon_0} \quad \text{and}$$

$$E = \frac{\sigma}{2\epsilon_0} \quad \text{(field of an infinite sheet of charge)}$$

This is the same result that we found in Example 21.12 (Section 21.5) using a much more complex calculation. The field is uniform and directed perpendicular to the plane of the sheet. Its magnitude is *independent* of the distance from the sheet. The field lines are therefore straight, parallel to each other, and perpendicular to the sheet.

If the charge density is negative, $\vec{E}$ is directed *toward* the sheet, the flux through the Gaussian surface in Fig. 22.20 is negative, and σ in the expression $E = \sigma/2\epsilon_0$ denotes the magnitude (absolute value) of the charge density.

EVALUATE: The assumption that the sheet is infinitely large is an idealization; nothing in nature is really infinitely large. But the result $E = \sigma/2\epsilon_0$ is a good approximation for points that are close to the sheet (compared to the sheet's dimensions) and not too near its edges. At such points, the field is very nearly uniform and perpendicular to the plane.

Example 22.8 Field between oppositely charged parallel conducting plates

Two large plane parallel conducting plates are given charges of equal magnitude and opposite sign; the charge per unit area is $+\sigma$ for one and $-\sigma$ for the other. Find the electric field in the region between the plates.

SOLUTION

IDENTIFY: The field between and around the plates is approximately as shown in Fig. 22.21a. Because opposite charges attract, most of the charge accumulates at the opposing faces of the plates. A small amount of charge resides on the *outer* surfaces of the plates, and there is some spreading or "fringing" of the field at the edges. But if the plates are very large in comparison to the distance between them, the amount of charge on the outer surfaces is negligibly small, and the fringing can be neglected except near the edges. In this case we can assume that the field is uniform in the interior region between plates, as in Fig. 22.21b, and that the charges are distributed uniformly over the opposing surfaces.

SET UP: To exploit this symmetry, we can use the shaded Gaussian surfaces S_1, S_2, S_3, and S_4. These surfaces are cylinders with ends of area A like the one shown in perspective in Fig. 22.20; they are shown in a side view in Fig. 22.21b. One end of each surface lies within one of the conducting plates.

EXECUTE: For the surface labeled S_1, the left-hand end is within plate 1 (the positive plate). Since the field is zero within the volume of any solid conductor under electrostatic conditions, there is no electric flux through this end. The electric field between the plates is perpendicular to the right-hand end, so on that end, $E_\perp$ is equal to E and the flux is EA; this is positive, since $\vec{E}$ is directed out of the Gaussian surface. There is no flux through the side walls of the cylinder, since these walls are parallel to $\vec{E}$. So the total flux integral in Gauss's law is EA. The net charge enclosed by the cylinder is σA, so Eq. (22.8) yields

$$EA = \frac{\sigma A}{\epsilon_0} \quad \text{and} \quad E = \frac{\sigma}{\epsilon_0} \quad \text{(field between oppositely charged conducting plates)}$$

The field is uniform and perpendicular to the plates, and its magnitude is independent of the distance from either plate. This same result can be obtained by using the Gaussian surface S_4; furthermore, the surfaces S_2 and S_3 can be used to show that $E = 0$ to the left of plate 1 and to the right of plate 2. We leave these calculations to you (see Exercise 22.27).

EVALUATE: We obtained the same results in Example 21.13 (Section 21.5) by using the principle of superposition of electric fields. The fields due to the two sheets of charge (one on each plate) are $\vec{E}_1$ and $\vec{E}_2$; from Example 22.7, both of these have magnitude $\sigma/2\epsilon_0$. The total (resultant) electric field at any point is the vector sum $\vec{E} = \vec{E}_1 + \vec{E}_2$. At points a and c in Fig. 22.21b, $\vec{E}_1$ and $\vec{E}_2$ have opposite directions, and their resultant is zero. This is also true at every point within the material of each plate, consistent with the requirement that with charges at rest there can be no field within a solid conductor. At any point b between the plates, $\vec{E}_1$ and $\vec{E}_2$ have the same direction; their resultant has magnitude $E = \sigma/\epsilon_0$, just as we found above using Gauss's law.

22.21 Electric field between oppositely charged parallel plates.

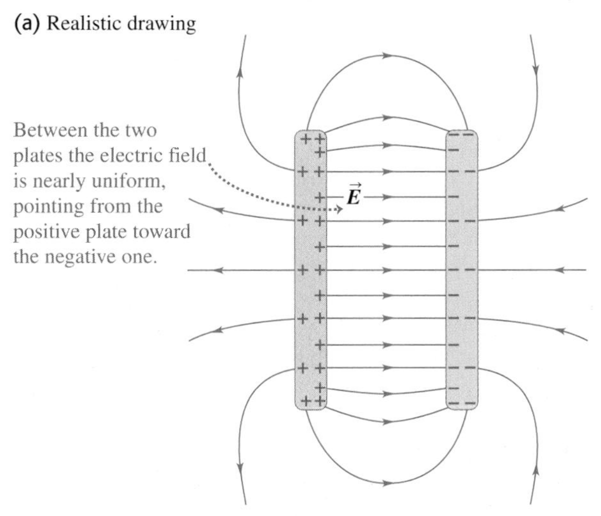
(a) Realistic drawing
Between the two plates the electric field is nearly uniform, pointing from the positive plate toward the negative one.
$\vec{E}$

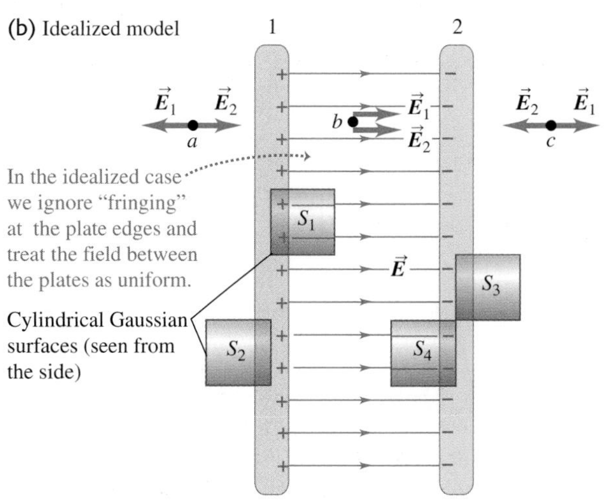
(b) Idealized model
1
2
$\vec{E}_1$ $\vec{E}_2$
a
b
$\vec{E}_1$
$\vec{E}_2$
$\vec{E}_2$ $\vec{E}_1$
c
In the idealized case we ignore "fringing" at the plate edges and treat the field between the plates as uniform.
S_1
$\vec{E}$
S_3
Cylindrical Gaussian surfaces (seen from the side)
S_2
S_4

Example 22.9 Field of a uniformly charged sphere

Positive electric charge Q is distributed uniformly *throughout the volume* of an *insulating* sphere with radius R. Find the magnitude of the electric field at a point P a distance r from the center of the sphere.

SOLUTION

IDENTIFY: As in Example 22.5, the system is spherically symmetric. Hence we can use the conclusions of that example about the direction and magnitude of $\vec{E}$.

SET UP: To make use of the symmetry, we choose as our Gaussian surface a sphere with radius r, concentric with the charge distribution.

EXECUTE: From symmetry the magnitude E of the electric field has the same value at every point on the Gaussian surface, and the direction of $\vec{E}$ is radial at every point on the surface, so $E_\perp = E$. Hence the total electric flux through the Gaussian surface is the product of E and the total area of the surface $A = 4\pi r^2$, that is, $\Phi_E = 4\pi r^2 E$.

The amount of charge enclosed within the Gaussian surface depends on the radius r. Let's first find the field magnitude *inside* the charged sphere of radius R; the magnitude E is evaluated at the radius of the Gaussian surface, so we choose $r < R$. The volume charge density ρ is the charge Q divided by the volume of the entire charged sphere of radius R:

$$\rho = \frac{Q}{4\pi R^3/3}$$

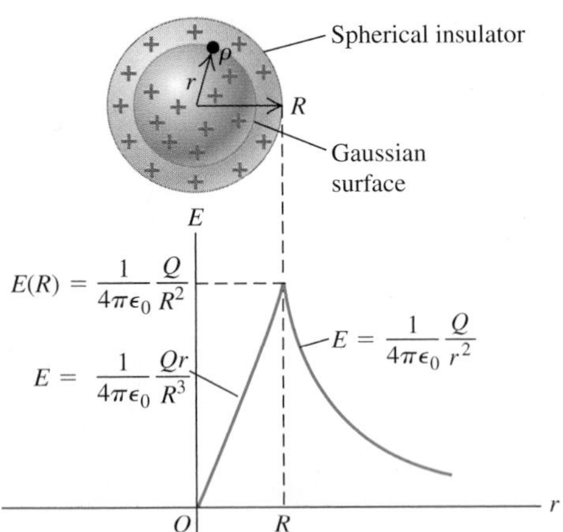

22.22 The magnitude of the electric field of a uniformly charged insulating sphere. Compare this with the field for a conducting sphere (Fig. 22.18).

The volume V_{encl} enclosed by the Gaussian surface is $\frac{4}{3}\pi r^3$, so the total charge Q_{encl} enclosed by that surface is

$$Q_{encl} = \rho V_{encl} = \left(\frac{Q}{4\pi R^3/3}\right)\left(\frac{4}{3}\pi r^3\right) = Q\frac{r^3}{R^3}$$

Then Gauss's law, Eq. (22.8), becomes

$$4\pi r^2 E = \frac{Q}{\epsilon_0}\frac{r^3}{R^3} \quad \text{or}$$

$$E = \frac{1}{4\pi\epsilon_0}\frac{Qr}{R^3} \quad \text{(field inside a uniformly charged sphere)}$$

The field magnitude is proportional to the distance r of the field point from the center of the sphere. At the center $(r = 0)$, $E = 0$.

To find the field magnitude *outside* the charged sphere, we use a spherical Gaussian surface of radius $r > R$. This surface encloses the entire charged sphere, so $Q_{encl} = Q$, and Gauss's law gives

$$4\pi r^2 E = \frac{Q}{\epsilon_0} \quad \text{or}$$

$$E = \frac{1}{4\pi\epsilon_0}\frac{Q}{r^2} \quad \text{(field outside a uniformly charged sphere)}$$

For *any* spherically symmetric charged body the electric field outside the body is the same as though the entire charge were concentrated at the center. (We made this same observation in Example 22.5.)

Figure 22.22 shows a graph of E as a function of r for this problem. For $r < R$, E is directly proportional to r, and for $r > R$, E varies as $1/r^2$. If the charge is negative instead of positive, $\vec{E}$ is radially *inward* and Q in the expressions for E is interpreted as the magnitude (absolute value) of the charge.

EVALUATE: Notice that if we set $r = R$ in either of the two expressions for E (inside or outside the sphere), we get the same result $E = Q/4\pi\epsilon_0 R^2$ for the magnitude of the field at the surface of the sphere. This is because the magnitude E is a *continuous* function of r. By contrast, for the charged conducting sphere of Example 22.5 the electric-field magnitude is *discontinuous* at $r = R$ (it jumps from $E = 0$ just inside the sphere to $E = Q/4\pi\epsilon_0 R^2$ just outside the sphere). In general, the electric field $\vec{E}$ is discontinuous in magnitude, direction, or both wherever there is a *sheet* of charge, such as at the surface of a charged conducting sphere (Example 22.5), at the surface of an infinite charged sheet (Example 22.7), or at the surface of a charged conducting plate (Example 22.8).

The general technique used in this example can be applied to *any* spherically symmetric distribution of charge, whether it is uniform or not. Such charge distributions occur within many atoms and atomic nuclei, which is why Gauss's law is a useful tool in atomic and nuclear physics.

Example 22.10 Field of a hollow charged sphere

A thin-walled, hollow sphere of radius 0.250 m has an unknown amount of charge distributed uniformly over its surface. At a distance of 0.300 m from the center of the sphere, the electric field points directly toward the center of the sphere and has magnitude 1.80×10^2 N/C. How much charge is on the sphere?

SOLUTION

IDENTIFY: The charge distribution is spherically symmetric. As in Examples 22.5 and 22.9, it follows that the electric field is radial everywhere and its magnitude is a function only of the radial distance r from the center of the sphere.

SET UP: We again use a spherical Gaussian surface that is concentric with the charge distribution and that passes through the point of interest at $r = 0.300$ m.

EXECUTE: The charge distribution is the same as if the charge were on the surface of a 0.250-m-radius conducting sphere. Hence we can borrow the results of Example 22.5. A key difference from that example is that because the electric field here is directed toward the sphere, the charge must be *negative*. Furthermore, because the electric field is directed into the Gaussian surface, $E_\perp = -E$ and the flux is $\oint E_\perp \, dA = -E(4\pi r^2)$.

By Gauss's law, the flux is equal to the charge q on the sphere (all of which is enclosed by the Gaussian surface) divided by ϵ_0. Solving for q, we find

$$\begin{aligned} q &= -E(4\pi\epsilon_0 r^2) = -(1.80 \times 10^2 \text{ N/C})(4\pi) \\ &\quad \times (8.854 \times 10^{-12} \text{ C}^2/\text{N} \cdot \text{m}^2)(0.300 \text{ m})^2 \\ &= -8.01 \times 10^{-10} \text{ C} = -0.801 \text{ nC} \end{aligned}$$

EVALUATE: To determine the charge, we had to know the electric field at *all* points on the Gaussian surface so that we could calculate the flux integral. This was possible here because the charge distribution is highly symmetric. If the charge distribution is irregular or lacks symmetry, however, Gauss's law is not very useful for calculating the charge distribution from the field, or vice versa.

Test Your Understanding of Section 22.4 You place a known amount of charge Q on the irregularly shaped conductor shown in Fig. 22.17. If you know the size and shape of the conductor, can you use Gauss's law to calculate the electric field at an arbitrary position outside the conductor?

22.5 Charges on Conductors

We have learned that in an electrostatic situation (in which there is no net motion of charge) the electric field at every point within a conductor is zero and that any excess charge on a solid conductor is located entirely on its surface (Fig. 22.23a). But what if there is a *cavity* inside the conductor (Fig. 22.23b)? If there is no charge within the cavity, we can use a Gaussian surface such as A (which lies completely within the material of the conductor) to show that the *net* charge on the *surface of the cavity* must be zero, because $\vec{E} = \mathbf{0}$ everywhere on the Gaussian surface. In fact, we can prove in this situation that there can't be any charge *anywhere* on the cavity surface. We will postpone detailed proof of this statement until Chapter 23.

Suppose we place a small body with a charge q inside a cavity within a conductor (Fig. 22.23c). The conductor is uncharged and is insulated from the charge q. Again $\vec{E} = \mathbf{0}$ everywhere on surface A, so according to Gauss's law the *total* charge inside this surface must be zero. Therefore there must be a charge $-q$ distributed on the surface of the cavity, drawn there by the charge q inside the cavity. The *total* charge on the conductor must remain zero, so a charge $+q$ must appear either on its outer surface or inside the material. But we showed in Section 22.4 that in an electrostatic situation there can't be any excess charge within the material of a conductor. So we conclude that the charge $+q$ must appear on the outer surface. By the same reasoning, if the conductor originally had a charge q_C, then the total charge on the outer surface must be $q_C + q$ after the charge q is inserted into the cavity.

22.23 Finding the electric field within a charged conductor.

(a) Solid conductor with charge q_C

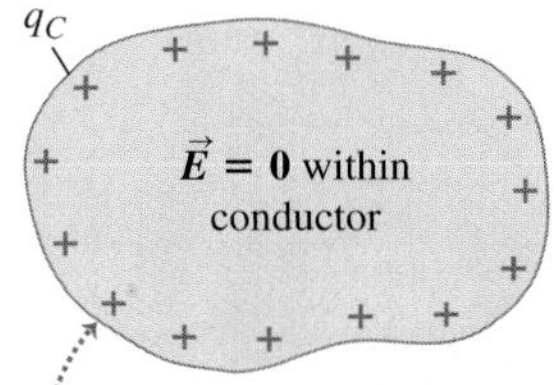

The charge q_C resides entirely on the surface of the conductor. The situation is electrostatic, so $\vec{E} = \mathbf{0}$ within the conductor.

(b) The same conductor with an internal cavity

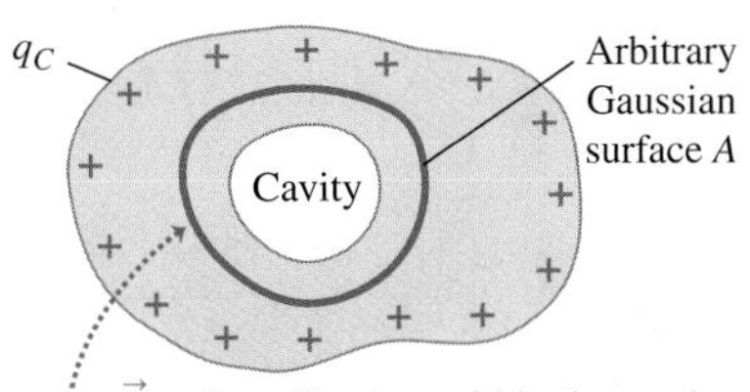

Because $\vec{E} = \mathbf{0}$ at all points within the conductor, the electric field at all points on the Gaussian surface must be zero.

(c) An isolated charge q placed in the cavity

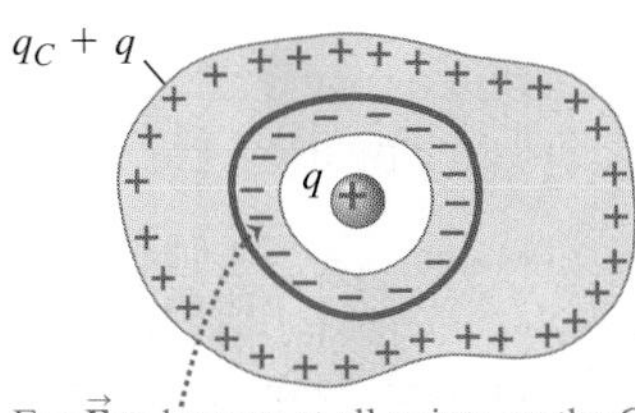

For $\vec{E}$ to be zero at all points on the Gaussian surface, the surface of the cavity must have a total charge $-q$.

Conceptual Example 22.11 A conductor with a cavity

A solid conductor with a cavity carries a total charge of $+7$ nC. Within the cavity, insulated from the conductor, is a point charge of -5 nC. How much charge is on each surface (inner and outer) of the conductor?

SOLUTION

Figure 22.24 shows the situation. If the charge in the cavity is $q = -5$ nC, the charge on the inner cavity surface must be $-q = -(-5\text{ nC}) = +5\text{ nC}$. The conductor carries a *total* charge of $+7$ nC, none of which is in the interior of the material. If $+5$ nC is on the inner surface of the cavity, then there must be $(+7\text{ nC}) - (+5\text{ nC}) = +2$ nC on the outer surface of the conductor.

22.24 Our sketch for this problem. There is zero electric field inside the bulk conductor and hence zero flux through the Gaussian surface shown, so the charge on the cavity wall must be the opposite of the point charge.

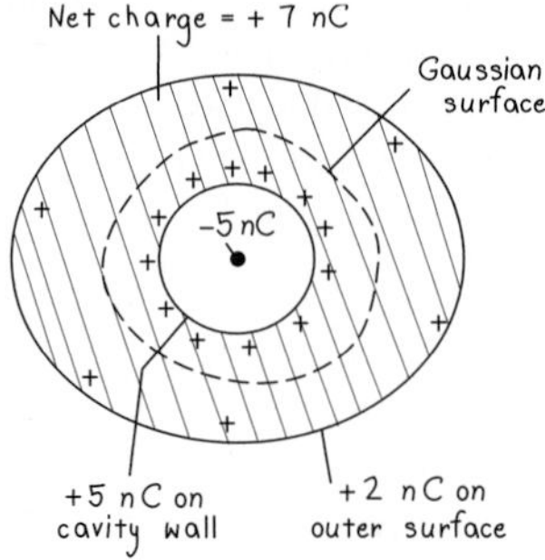
Net charge = + 7 nC
Gaussian surface
-5 nC
+5 nC on cavity wall
+2 nC on outer surface

Testing Gauss's Law Experimentally

We can now consider a historic experiment, shown in Fig. 22.25. We mount a conducting container, such as a metal pail with a lid, on an insulating stand. The container is initially uncharged. Then we hang a charged metal ball from an insulating thread (Fig. 22.25a), lower it into the pail, and put the lid on (Fig. 22.25b). Charges are induced on the walls of the container, as shown. But now we let the ball *touch* the inner wall (Fig. 22.25c). The surface of the ball becomes, in effect, part of the cavity surface. The situation is now the same as Fig. 22.23b; if Gauss's law is correct, the net charge on the cavity surface must be zero. Thus the ball must lose all its charge. Finally, we pull the ball out; we find that it has indeed lost all its charge.

This experiment was performed in the 19th century by the English scientist Michael Faraday, using a metal icepail with a lid, and it is called **Faraday's icepail experiment.** (Similar experiments were carried out in the 18th century by Benjamin Franklin in America and Joseph Priestley in England, although with much less precision.) The result confirms the validity of Gauss's law and therefore of Coulomb's law. Faraday's result was significant because Coulomb's experimental method, using a torsion balance and dividing of charges, was not very precise; it is very difficult to confirm the $1/r^2$ dependence of the electrostatic force with great precision by direct force measurements. By contrast, experiments like Faraday's test the validity of Gauss's law, and therefore of Coulomb's law, with much greater precision.

22.25 (a) A charged conducting ball suspended by an insulating thread outside a conducting container on an insulating stand. (b) The ball is lowered into the container, and the lid is put on. (c) The ball is touched to the inner surface of the container.

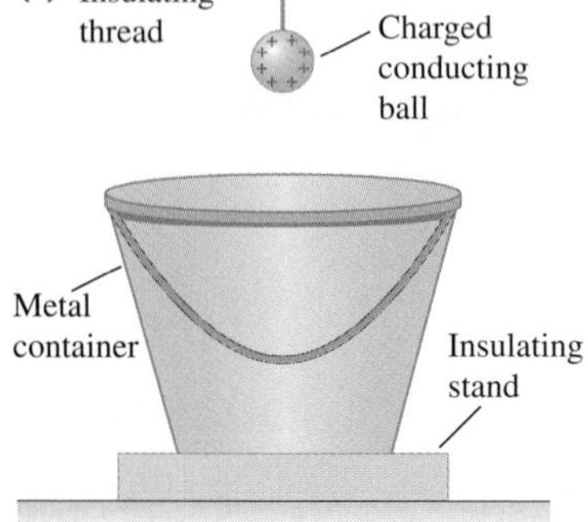
(a)
Insulating thread
Charged conducting ball
Metal container
Insulating stand

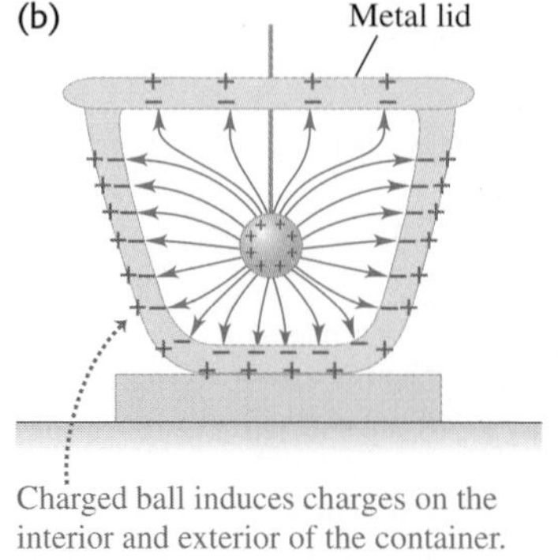
(b)
Metal lid
Charged ball induces charges on the interior and exterior of the container.

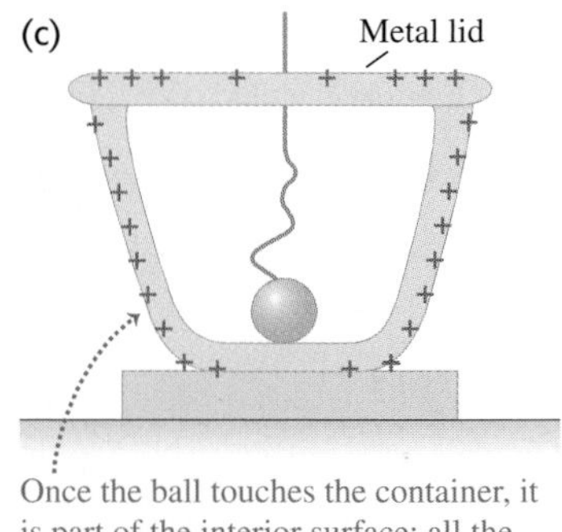
(c)
Metal lid
Once the ball touches the container, it is part of the interior surface; all the charge moves to the container's exterior.

A modern version of Faraday's experiment is shown in Fig. 22.26. The details of the box labeled "Power supply" aren't important; its job is to place charge on the outer sphere and remove it, on demand. The inner box with a dial is a sensitive *electrometer,* an instrument that can detect motion of extremely small amounts of charge between the outer and inner spheres. If Gauss's law is correct, there can never be any charge on the inner surface of the outer sphere. If so, there should be no flow of charge between spheres while the outer sphere is being charged and discharged. The fact that no flow is actually observed is a very sensitive confirmation of Gauss's law and therefore of Coulomb's law. The precision of the experiment is limited mainly by the electrometer, which can be astonishingly sensitive. Experiments have shown that the exponent 2 in the $1/r^2$ of Coulomb's law does not differ from precisely 2 by more than 10^{-16}. So there is no reason to suspect that it is anything other than exactly 2.

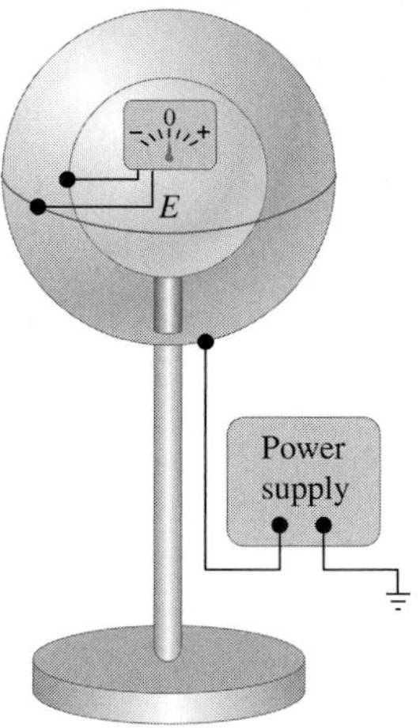

22.26 The outer spherical shell can be alternately charged and discharged by the power supply. If there were any flow of charge between the inner and outer shells, it would be detected by the electrometer inside the inner shell.

The same principle behind Faraday's icepail experiment is used in a *Van de Graaff electrostatic generator* (Fig. 22.27). The charged conducting sphere of Fig. 22.26 is replaced by a charged belt that continuously carries charge to the inside of a conducting shell, only to have it carried away to the outside surface of the shell. As a result, the charge on the shell and the electric field around it can become very large very rapidly. The Van de Graaff generator is used as an accelerator of charged particles and for physics demonstrations.

This principle also forms the basis for *electrostatic shielding.* Suppose we have a very sensitive electronic instrument that we want to protect from stray electric fields that might cause erroneous measurements. We surround the instrument with a conducting box, or we line the walls, floor, and ceiling of the room with a conducting material such as sheet copper. The external electric field redistributes the free electrons in the conductor, leaving a net positive charge on the outer

22.27 Cutaway view of the essential parts of a Van de Graaff electrostatic generator. The electron sink at the bottom draws electrons from the belt, giving it a positive charge; at the top the belt attracts electrons away from the conducting shell, giving the shell a positive charge.

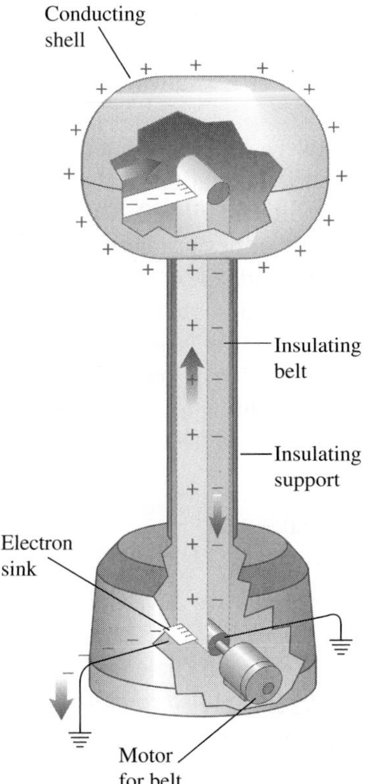

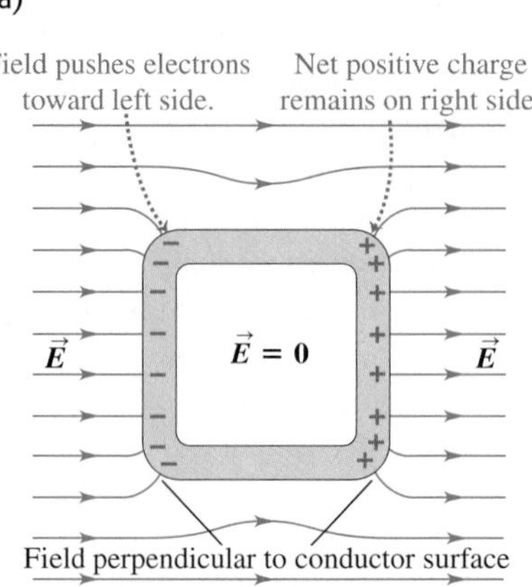

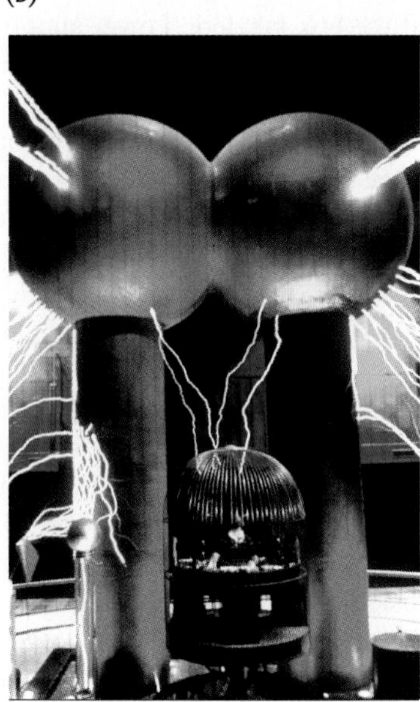

22.28 (a) A conducting box (a Faraday cage) immersed in a uniform electric field. The field of the induced charges on the box combines with the uniform field to give zero total field inside the box. (b) Electrostatic shielding can protect you from a dangerous electric discharge.

surface in some regions and a net negative charge in others (Fig. 22.28). This charge distribution causes an additional electric field such that the *total* field at every point inside the box is zero, as Gauss's law says it must be. The charge distribution on the box also alters the shapes of the field lines near the box, as the figure shows. Such a setup is often called a *Faraday cage.* The same physics tells you that one of the safest places to be in a lightning storm is inside an automobile; if the car is struck by lightning, the charge tends to remain on the metal skin of the vehicle, and little or no electric field is produced inside the passenger compartment.

Field at the Surface of a Conductor

Finally, we note that there is a direct relationship between the $\vec{E}$ field at a point just outside any conductor and the surface charge density σ at that point. In general, σ varies from point to point on the surface. We will show in Chapter 23 that at any such point, the direction of $\vec{E}$ is always *perpendicular* to the surface (see Fig. 22.28a).

To find a relationship between σ at any point on the surface and the perpendicular component of the electric field at that point, we construct a Gaussian surface in the form of a small cylinder (Fig. 22.29). One end face, with area A, lies within the conductor and the other lies just outside. The electric field is zero at all points within the conductor. Outside the conductor the component of $\vec{E}$ perpendicular to the side walls of the cylinder is zero, and over the end face the perpendicular component is equal to $E_\perp$. (If σ is positive, the electric field points out of the conductor and $E_\perp$ is positive; if σ is negative, the field points inward and $E_\perp$ is negative.) Hence the total flux through the surface is $E_\perp A$. The charge enclosed within the Gaussian surface is σA, so from Gauss's law,

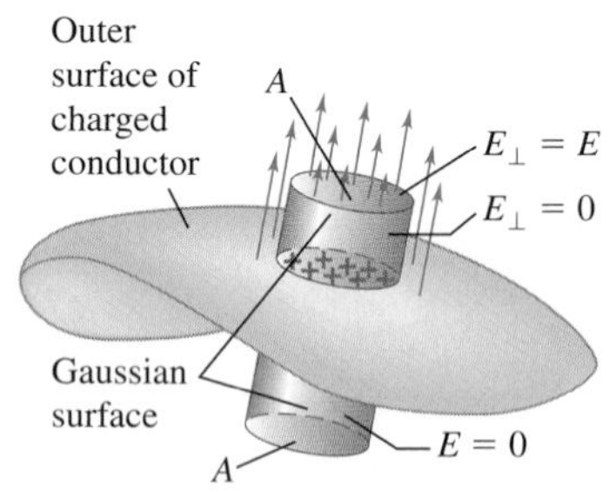

22.29 The field just outside a charged conductor is perpendicular to the surface, and its perpendicular component $E_\perp$ is equal to σ/ϵ_0.

$$E_\perp A = \frac{\sigma A}{\epsilon_0} \quad \text{and} \quad E_\perp = \frac{\sigma}{\epsilon_0} \quad \text{(field at the surface of a conductor)} \tag{22.10}$$

We can check this with the results we have obtained for spherical, cylindrical, and plane surfaces.

We showed in Example 22.8 that the field magnitude between two infinite flat oppositely charged conducting plates also equals σ/ϵ_0. In this case the field magnitude is the same at *all* distances from the plates, but in all other cases it decreases with increasing distance from the surface.

Conceptual Example 22.12 Field at the surface of a conducting sphere

Verify Eq. (22.10) for a conducting sphere with radius R and total charge q.

SOLUTION

In Example 22.5 (Section 22.4) we showed that the electric field just outside the surface is

$$E = \frac{1}{4\pi\epsilon_0}\frac{q}{R^2}$$

The surface charge density is uniform and equal to q divided by the surface area of the sphere:

$$\sigma = \frac{q}{4\pi R^2}$$

Comparing these two expressions, we see that $E = \sigma/\epsilon_0$, as Eq. (22.10) states.

Example 22.13 Electric field of the earth

The earth (a conductor) has a net electric charge. The resulting electric field near the surface can be measured with sensitive electronic instruments; its average value is about 150 N/C, directed toward the center of the earth. (a) What is the corresponding surface charge density? (b) What is the *total* surface charge of the earth?

SOLUTION

IDENTIFY: We are given the electric field magnitude at the surface of the conducting earth, and we are asked to calculate the surface charge density and the total charge on the entire surface of the earth.

SET UP: Given the perpendicular electric field, we determine the surface charge density σ using Eq. (22.10). The total surface charge on the earth is then the product of σ and the earth's surface area.

EXECUTE: (a) We know from the direction of the field that σ is negative (corresponding to $\vec{E}$ being directed *into* the surface, so $E_\perp$ is negative). From Eq. (22.10),

$$\begin{aligned}\sigma = \epsilon_0 E_\perp &= (8.85 \times 10^{-12}\ \text{C}^2/\text{N}\cdot\text{m}^2)(-150\ \text{N/C})\\ &= -1.33 \times 10^{-9}\ \text{C/m}^2 = -1.33\ \text{nC/m}^2\end{aligned}$$

(b) The earth's surface area is $4\pi R_E^2$, where $R_E = 6.38 \times 10^6$ m is the radius of the earth (see Appendix F). The total charge Q is the product $4\pi R_E^2\sigma$, or

$$\begin{aligned}Q &= 4\pi(6.38 \times 10^6\ \text{m})^2(-1.33 \times 10^{-9}\ \text{C/m}^2)\\ &= -6.8 \times 10^5\ \text{C} = -680\ \text{kC}\end{aligned}$$

EVALUATE: You can check our result in part (b) using the result of Example 22.5. Solving for Q, we find

$$\begin{aligned}Q &= 4\pi\epsilon_0 R^2 E_\perp\\ &= \frac{1}{9.0 \times 10^9\ \text{N}\cdot\text{m}^2/\text{C}^2}(6.38 \times 10^6\ \text{m})^2(-150\ \text{N/C})\\ &= -6.8 \times 10^5\ \text{C}\end{aligned}$$

One electron has a charge of -1.60×10^{-19} C. Hence this much excess negative electric charge corresponds to there being $(-6.8 \times 10^5\ \text{C})/(-1.60 \times 10^{-19}\ \text{C}) = 4.2 \times 10^{24}$ excess electrons on the earth, or about 7 moles of excess electrons. This is compensated by an equal *deficiency* of electrons in the earth's upper atmosphere, so the combination of the earth and its atmosphere is electrically neutral.

Test Your Understanding of Section 22.5 A hollow conducting sphere has no net charge. There is a positive point charge q at the center of the spherical cavity within the sphere. You connect a conducting wire from the outside of the sphere to ground. Will you measure an electric field outside the sphere?

CHAPTER 22 SUMMARY

Electric flux: Electric flux is a measure of the "flow" of electric field through a surface. It is equal to the product of an area element and the perpendicular component of $\vec{E}$, integrated over a surface. (See Examples 22.1–22.3.)

$$\Phi_E = \int E\cos\phi \, dA$$

$$= \int E_\perp \, dA = \int \vec{E} \cdot d\vec{A} \quad (22.5)$$

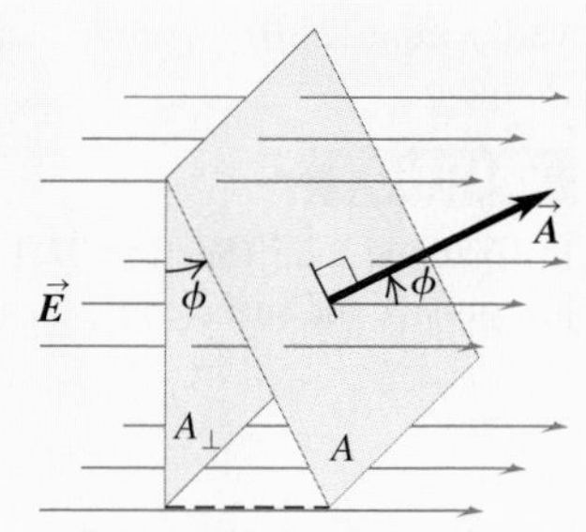

Gauss's law: Gauss's law states that the total electric flux through a closed surface, which can be written as the surface integral of the component of $\vec{E}$ normal to the surface, equals a constant times the total charge Q_{encl} enclosed by the surface. Gauss's law is logically equivalent to Coulomb's law, but its use greatly simplifies problems with a high degree of symmetry. (See Examples 22.4–22.10.)

When excess charge is placed on a conductor and is at rest, it resides entirely on the surface, and $\vec{E} = \mathbf{0}$ everywhere in the material of the conductor. (See Examples 22.11–22.13.)

$$\Phi_E = \oint E\cos\phi \, dA$$

$$= \oint E_\perp \, dA = \oint \vec{E} \cdot d\vec{A}$$

$$= \frac{Q_{encl}}{\epsilon_0} \quad (22.8), (22.9)$$

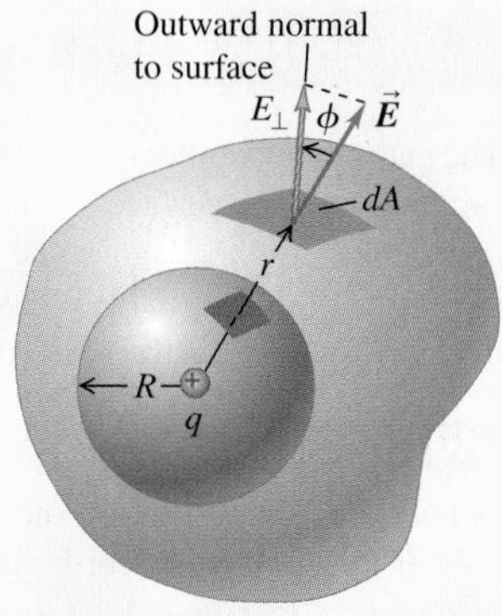

Electric field of various symmetric charge distributions: The following table lists electric fields caused by several symmetric charge distributions. In the table, q, Q, λ, and σ refer to the *magnitudes* of the quantities.

Charge Distribution	Point in Electric Field	Electric Field Magnitude
Single point charge q	Distance r from q	$E = \frac{1}{4\pi\epsilon_0}\frac{q}{r^2}$
Charge q on surface of conducting sphere with radius R	Outside sphere, $r > R$	$E = \frac{1}{4\pi\epsilon_0}\frac{q}{r^2}$
	Inside sphere, $r < R$	$E = 0$
Infinite wire, charge per unit length λ	Distance r from wire	$E = \frac{1}{2\pi\epsilon_0}\frac{\lambda}{r}$
Infinite conducting cylinder with radius R, charge per unit length λ	Outside cylinder, $r > R$	$E = \frac{1}{2\pi\epsilon_0}\frac{\lambda}{r}$
	Inside cylinder, $r < R$	$E = 0$
Solid insulating sphere with radius R, charge Q distributed uniformly throughout volume	Outside sphere, $r > R$	$E = \frac{1}{4\pi\epsilon_0}\frac{Q}{r^2}$
	Inside sphere, $r < R$	$E = \frac{1}{4\pi\epsilon_0}\frac{Qr}{R^3}$
Infinite sheet of charge with uniform charge per unit area σ	Any point	$E = \frac{\sigma}{2\epsilon_0}$
Two oppositely charged conducting plates with surface charge densities $+\sigma$ and $-\sigma$	Any point between plates	$E = \frac{\sigma}{\epsilon_0}$

Key Terms

closed surface, *751*
electric flux, *752*
surface integral, *755*
Gauss's law, *757*
Gaussian surface, *759*
Faraday's icepail experiment, *768*

Answer to Chapter Opening Question ?

No. The electric field inside a cavity within a conductor is zero, so there is no electric effect on the child. (See Section 22.5.)

Answers to Test Your Understanding Questions

22.1 Answer: (iii) Each part of the surface of the box will be three times farther from the charge $+q$, so the electric field will be $(\frac{1}{3})^2 = \frac{1}{9}$ as strong. But the area of the box will increase by a factor of $3^2 = 9$. Hence the electric flux will be multiplied by a factor of $(\frac{1}{9})(9) = 1$. In other words, the flux will be unchanged.

22.2 Answer: (iv), (ii), (i), (iii) In each case the electric field in uniform, so the flux is $\Phi_E = \vec{E} \cdot \vec{A}$. We use the relationships for the scalar products of unit vectors: $\hat{\imath} \cdot \hat{\imath} = \hat{\jmath} \cdot \hat{\jmath} = 1, \hat{\imath} \cdot \hat{\jmath} = 0$. In case (i) we have $\Phi_E = (4.0\text{ N/C})(6.0\text{ m}^2)\hat{\imath} \cdot \hat{\jmath} = 0$ (the electric field and vector area are perpendicular, so there is zero flux). In case (ii) we have $\Phi_E[(4.0\text{ N/C})\hat{\imath} + (2.0\text{ N/C})\hat{\jmath}] \cdot (3.0\text{ m}^2)\hat{\jmath} = (2.0\text{ N/C}) \cdot (3.0\text{ m}^2) = 6.0\text{ N}\cdot\text{m}^2/\text{C}$. Similarly, in case (iii) we have $\Phi_E = [(4.0\text{ N/C})\hat{\imath} - (2.0\text{ N/C})\hat{\jmath}] \cdot [(3.0\text{ m}^2)\hat{\imath} + (7.0\text{ m}^2)\hat{\jmath}] = (4.0\text{ N/C})(3.0\text{ m}^2) - (2.0\text{ N/C})(7.0\text{ m}^2) = -2\text{ N}\cdot\text{m}^2/\text{C}$, and in case (iv) we have $\Phi_E = [(4.0\text{ N/C})\hat{\imath} - (2.0\text{ N/C})\hat{\jmath}] \cdot [(3.0\text{ m}^2)\hat{\imath} - (7.0\text{ m}^2)\hat{\jmath}] = (4.0\text{ N/C})(3.0\text{ m}^2) + (2.0\text{ N/C}) \cdot (7.0\text{ m}^2) = 26\text{ N}\cdot\text{m}^2/\text{C}$.

22.3 Answer: S_2, S_5, S_4, S_1 and S_3 (tie) Gauss's law tells us that the flux through a closed surface is proportional to the amount of charge enclosed within that surface. So an ordering of these surfaces by their fluxes is the same as an ordering by the amount of enclosed charge. Surface S_1 encloses no charge, surface S_2 encloses $9.0\ \mu\text{C} + 5.0\ \mu\text{C} + (-7.0\ \mu\text{C}) = 7.0\ \mu\text{C}$, surface S_3 encloses $9.0\ \mu\text{C} + 1.0\ \mu\text{C} + (-10.0\ \mu\text{C}) = 0$, surface S_4 encloses $8.0\ \mu\text{C} + (-7.0\ \mu\text{C}) = 1.0\ \mu\text{C}$, and surface S_5 encloses $8.0\ \mu\text{C} + (-7.0\ \mu\text{C}) + (-10.0\ \mu\text{C}) + (1.0\ \mu\text{C}) + (9.0\ \mu\text{C}) + (5.0\ \mu\text{C}) = 6.0\ \mu\text{C}$.

22.4 Answer: no You might be tempted to draw a Gaussian surface that is an enlarged version of the conductor, with the same shape and placed so that it completely encloses the conductor. While you know the flux through this Gaussian surface (by Gauss's law, it's $\Phi_E = Q/\epsilon_0$), the direction of the electric field need not be perpendicular to the surface and the magnitude of the field need not be the same at all points on the surface. It's not possible to do the flux integral $\oint E_\perp\, dA$, and we can't calculate the electric field. Gauss's law is useful for calculating the electric field only when the charge distribution is *highly* symmetric.

22.5 Answer: no Before you connect the wire to the sphere, the presence of the point charge will induce a charge $-q$ on the inner surface of the hollow sphere and a charge q on the outer surface (the net charge on the sphere is zero). There will be an electric field outside the sphere due to the charge on the outer surface. Once you touch the conducting wire to the sphere, however, electrons will flow from ground to the outer surface of the sphere to neutralize the charge there (see Fig. 21.7c). As a result the sphere will have no charge on its outer surface and no electric field outside.

PROBLEMS

For instructor-assigned homework, go to www.masteringphysics.com 

Discussion Questions

Q22.1. A rubber balloon has a single point charge in its interior. Does the electric flux through the balloon depend on whether or not it is fully inflated? Explain your reasoning.

Q22.2. Suppose that in Fig. 22.15 both charges were positive. What would be the fluxes through each of the four surfaces in the example?

Q22.3. In Fig. 22.15, suppose a third point charge were placed outside the purple Gaussian surface *C*. Would this affect the electric flux through any of the surfaces *A*, *B*, *C*, or *D* in the figure? Why or why not?

Q22.4. A certain region of space bounded by an imaginary closed surface contains no charge. Is the electric field always zero everywhere on the surface? If not, under what circumstances is it zero on the surface?

Q22.5. A spherical Gaussian surface encloses a point charge q. If the point charge is moved from the center of the sphere to a point away from the center, does the electric field at a point on the surface change? Does the total flux through the Gaussian surface change? Explain.

Q22.6. You find a sealed box on your doorstep. You suspect that the box contains several charged metal spheres packed in insulating material. How can you determine the total net charge inside the box without opening the box? Or isn't this possible?

Q22.7. During the flow of electric current in a conducting wire, one or more electrons from each atom are free to move along the wire, somewhat like water flowing through a pipe. Would you expect to find an electric field outside a wire carrying such a steady flow of electrons? Explain.

Q22.8. If the electric field of a point charge were proportional to $1/r^3$ instead of $1/r^2$, would Gauss's law still be valid? Explain your reasoning. (*Hint:* Consider a spherical Gaussian surface centered on a single point charge.)

Q22.9. Suppose the disk in Example 22.1 (Section 22.2), instead of having its normal vector oriented at just two or three particular angles to the electric field, began to rotate continuously, so that its normal vector was first parallel to the field, then perpendicular to it, then opposite to it, and so on. Sketch a graph of the resulting electric flux versus time, for an entire rotation of 360°.

Q22.10. In a conductor, one or more electrons from each atom are free to roam throughout the volume of the conductor. Does this contradict the statement that any excess charge on a solid conductor must reside on its surface? Why or why not?

Q22.11. You charge up the van de Graaff generator shown in Fig. 22.27, and then bring an identical but uncharged hollow conducting sphere near it, without letting the two spheres touch. Sketch the distribution of charges on the second sphere. What is the net flux through the second sphere? What is the electric field inside the second sphere?

Q22.12. The magnitude of $\vec{E}$ at the surface of an irregularly shaped solid conductor must be greatest in regions where the surface curves most sharply, such as point A in Fig. 22.30, and must be least in flat regions such as point B in Fig. 22.30. Explain why this must be so by considering how electric field lines must be arranged near a conducting surface. How does the surface charge density compare at points A and B? Explain.

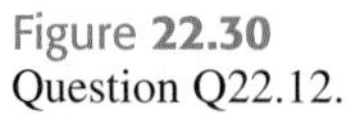
Figure **22.30** Question Q22.12.

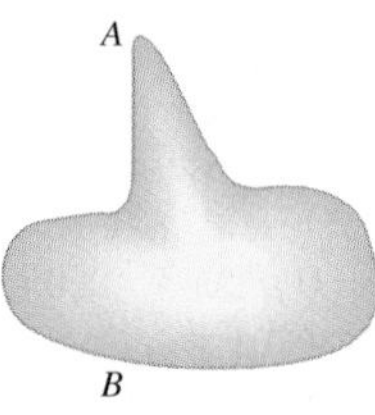

Q22.13. A lightning rod is a rounded copper rod mounted on top of a building and welded to a heavy copper cable running down into the ground. Lightning rods are used to protect houses and barns from lightning; the lightning current runs through the copper rather than through the building. Why? Why should the end of the rod be rounded? (*Hint:* The answer to Discussion Question Q22.12 may be helpful.)

Q22.14. A solid conductor has a cavity in its interior. Would the presence of a point charge inside the cavity affect the electric field outside the conductor? Why or why not? Would the presence of a point charge outside the conductor affect the electric field inside the cavity? Again, why or why not?

Q22.15. Explain this statement: "In a static situation, the electric field at the surface of a conductor can have no component parallel to the surface because this would violate the condition that the charges on the surface are at rest." Would this same statement be valid for the electric field at the surface of an *insulator?* Explain your answer and the reason for any differences between the cases of a conductor and an insulator.

Q22.16. A solid copper sphere has a net positive charge. The charge is distributed uniformly over the surface of the sphere, and the electric field inside the sphere is zero. Then a negative point charge outside the sphere is brought close to the surface of the sphere. Is all the net charge on the sphere still on its surface? If so, is this charge still distributed uniformly over the surface? If it is not uniform, how is it distributed? Is the electric field inside the sphere still zero? In each case justify your answers.

Q22.17. Some modern aircraft are made primarily of composite materials that do not conduct electricity. The U.S. Federal Aviation Administration requires that such aircraft have conducting wires embedded in their surfaces to provide protection when flying near thunderstorms. Explain the physics behind this requirement.

Exercises

Section 22.2 Calculating Electric Flux

22.1. A flat sheet of paper of area $0.250\ \text{m}^2$ is oriented so that the normal to the sheet is at an angle of 60° to a uniform electric field of magnitude 14 N/C. (a) Find the magnitude of the electric flux through the sheet. (b) Does the answer to part (a) depend on the shape of the sheet? Why or why not? (c) For what angle ϕ between the normal to the sheet and the electric field is the magnitude of the flux through the sheet (i) largest and (ii) smallest? Explain your answers.

22.2. A flat sheet is in the shape of a rectangle with sides of lengths 0.400 m and 0.600 m. The sheet is immersed in a uniform electric field of magnitude 75.0 N/C that is directed at 20° from the plane of the sheet (Fig. 22.31). Find the magnitude of the electric flux through the sheet.

Figure **22.31** Exercise 22.2.

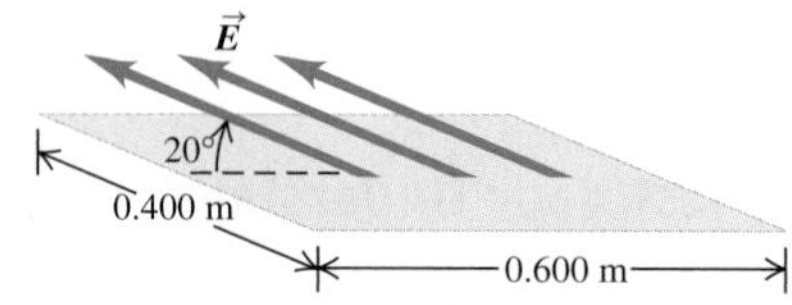

22.3. You measure an electric field of 1.25×10^6 N/C at a distance of 0.150 m from a point charge. (a) What is the electric flux through a sphere at that distance from the charge? (b) What is the magnitude of the charge?

22.4. A cube has sides of length $L = 0.300$ m. It is placed with one corner at the origin as shown in Fig. 22.32. The electric field is not uniform but is given by $\vec{E} = (-5.00\ \text{N/C}\cdot\text{m})x\hat{\imath} + (3.00\ \text{N/C}\cdot\text{m})z\hat{k}$. (a) Find the electric flux through each of the six cube faces S_1, S_2, S_3, S_4, S_5, and S_6. (b) Find the total electric charge inside the cube.

Figure **22.32** Exercises 22.4 and 22.6; Problem 22.32.

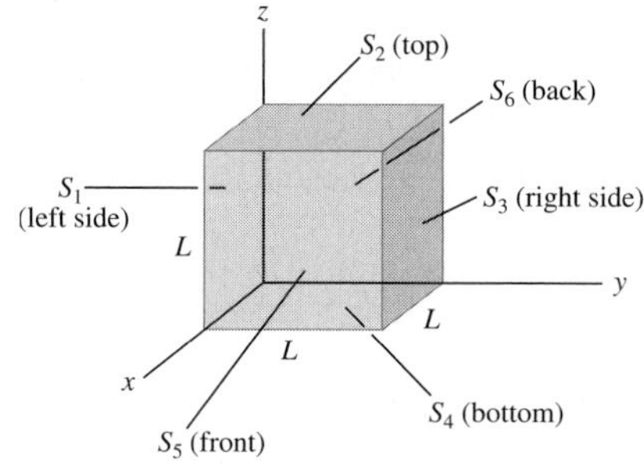

22.5. A hemispherical surface with radius r in a region of uniform electric field $\vec{E}$ has its axis aligned parallel to the direction of the field. Calculate the flux through the surface.

22.6. The cube in Fig. 22.32 has sides of length $L = 10.0$ cm. The electric field is uniform, has magnitude $E = 4.00 \times 10^3$ N/C, and is parallel to the xy -plane at an angle of 36.9° measured from the $+x$-axis toward the $+y$-axis. (a) What is the electric flux through each of the six cube faces S_1, S_2, S_3, S_4, S_5, and S_6? (b) What is the total electric flux through all faces of the cube?

22.7. It was shown in Example 21.11 (Section 21.5) that the electric field due to an infinite line of charge is perpendicular to the line and has magnitude $E = \lambda/2\pi\epsilon_0 r$. Consider an imaginary cylinder with radius $r = 0.250$ m and length $l = 0.400$ m that has an infinite line of positive charge running along its axis. The charge per unit length on the line is $\lambda = 6.00\ \mu\text{C/m}$. (a) What is the electric flux through the cylinder due to this infinite line of charge? (b) What is the flux through the cylinder if its radius is increased to $r = 0.500$ m? (c) What is the flux through the cylinder if its length is increased to $l = 0.800$ m?

Section 22.3 Gauss's Law

22.8. The three small spheres shown in Fig. 22.33 carry charges $q_1 = 4.00$ nC, $q_2 = -7.80$ nC, and $q_3 = 2.40$ nC. Find the net electric flux through each of the following closed surfaces shown in cross section in the figure: (a) S_1; (b) S_2; (c) S_3; (d) S_4; (e) S_5. (f) Do your answers to parts (a)–(e) depend on how the charge is distributed over each small sphere? Why or why not?

Figure **22.33** Exercise 22.8.

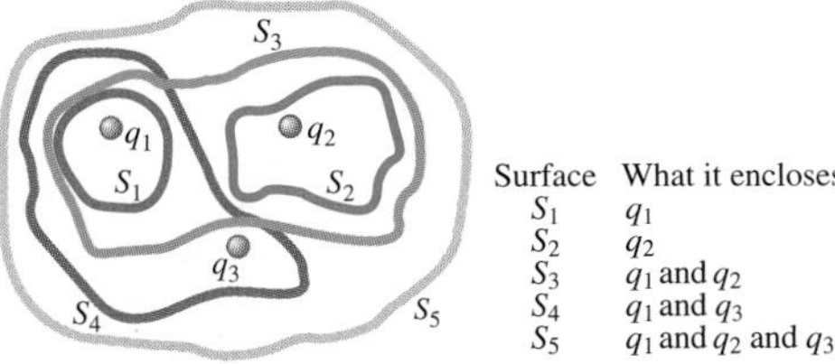

22.9. A charged paint is spread in a very thin uniform layer over the surface of a plastic sphere of diameter 12.0 cm, giving it a charge of $-15.0\ \mu$C. Find the electric field (a) just inside the paint layer; (b) just outside the paint layer; (c) 5.00 cm outside the surface of the paint layer.

22.10. A point charge $q_1 = 4.00$ nC is located on the x-axis at $x = 2.00$ m, and a second point charge $q_2 = -6.00$ nC is on the y-axis at $y = 1.00$ m. What is the total electric flux due to these two point charges through a spherical surface centered at the origin and with radius (a) 0.500 m, (b) 1.50 m, (c) 2.50 m?

22.11. In a certain region of space, the electric field $\vec{E}$ is uniform. (a) Use Gauss's law to prove that this region of space must be electrically neutral; that is, the volume charge density ρ must be zero. (b) Is the converse true? That is, in a region of space where there is no charge, must $\vec{E}$ be uniform? Explain.

22.12. (a) In a certain region of space, the volume charge density ρ has a uniform positive value. Can $\vec{E}$ be uniform in this region? Explain. (b) Suppose that in this region of uniform positive ρ there is a "bubble" within which $\rho = 0$. Can $\vec{E}$ be uniform within this bubble? Explain.

22.13. A 9.60-μC point charge is at the center of a cube with sides of length 0.500 m. (a) What is the electric flux through one of the six faces of the cube? (b) How would your answer to part (a) change if the sides were 0.250 m long? Explain.

22.14. Electric Fields in an Atom. The nuclei of large atoms, such as uranium, with 92 protons, can be modeled as spherically symmetric spheres of charge. The radius of the uranium nucleus is approximately 7.4×10^{-15} m. (a) What is the electric field this nucleus produces just outside its surface? (b) What magnitude of electric field does it produce at the distance of the electrons, which is about 1.0×10^{-10} m? (c) The electrons can be modeled as forming a uniform shell of negative charge. What net electric field do they produce at the location of the nucleus?

22.15. A point charge of $+5.00\ \mu$C is located on the x-axis at $x = 4.00$ m, next to a spherical surface of radius 3.00 m centered at the origin. (a) Calculate the magnitude of the electric field at $x = 3.00$ m. (b) Calculate the magnitude of the electric field at $x = -3.00$ m. (c) According to Gauss's law, the net flux through the sphere is zero because it contains no charge. Yet the field due to the external charge is much stronger on the near side of the sphere (i.e., at $x = 3.00$ m) than on the far side (at $x = -3.00$ m). How, then, can the flux into the sphere (on the near side) equal the flux out of it (on the far side)? Explain. A sketch will help.

Section 22.4 Applications of Gauss's Law and Section 22.5 Charges on Conductors

22.16. A solid metal sphere with radius 0.450 m carries a net charge of 0.250 nC. Find the magnitude of the electric field (a) at a point 0.100 m outside the surface of the sphere and (b) at a point inside the sphere, 0.100 m below the surface.

22.17. On a humid day, an electric field of 2.00×10^4 N/C is enough to produce sparks about an inch long. Suppose that in your physics class, a van de Graaff generator (see Fig. 22.27) with a sphere radius of 15.0 cm is producing sparks 6 inches long. (a) Use Gauss's law to calculate the amount of charge stored on the surface of the sphere before you bravely discharge it with your hand. (b) Assume all the charge is concentrated at the center of the sphere, and use Coulomb's law to calculate the electric field at the surface of the sphere.

22.18. Some planetary scientists have suggested that the planet Mars has an electric field somewhat similar to that of the earth, producing a net electric flux of $3.63 \times 10^{16}\ \text{N} \cdot \text{m}^2/\text{C}$ at the planet's surface. Calculate: (a) the total electric charge on the planet; (b) the electric field at the planet's surface (refer to the astronomical data inside the back cover); (c) the charge density on Mars, assuming all the charge is uniformly distributed over the planet's surface.

22.19. How many excess electrons must be added to an isolated spherical conductor 32.0 cm in diameter to produce an electric field of 1150 N/C just outside the surface?

22.20. The electric field 0.400 m from a very long uniform line of charge is 840 N/C. How much charge is contained in a 2.00-cm section of the line?

22.21. A very long uniform line of charge has charge per unit length 4.80 μC/m and lies along the x-axis. A second long uniform line of charge has charge per unit length $-2.40\ \mu$C/m and is parallel to the x-axis at $y = 0.400$ m. What is the net electric field (magnitude and direction) at the following points on the y-axis: (a) $y = 0.200$ m and (b) $y = 0.600$ m?

22.22. (a) At a distance of 0.200 cm from the center of a charged conducting sphere with radius 0.100 cm, the electric field is 480 N/C. What is the electric field 0.600 cm from the center of the sphere? (b) At a distance of 0.200 cm from the axis of a very long charged conducting cylinder with radius 0.100 cm, the electric field is 480 N/C. What is the electric field 0.600 cm from the axis of the cylinder? (c) At a distance of 0.200 cm from a large uniform sheet of charge, the electric field is 480 N/C. What is the electric field 1.20 cm from the sheet?

22.23. A hollow, conducting sphere with an outer radius of 0.250 m and an inner radius of 0.200 m has a uniform surface charge density of $+6.37 \times 10^{-6}\ \text{C/m}^2$. A charge of $-0.500\ \mu$C is now introduced into the cavity inside the sphere. (a) What is the new charge density on the outside of the sphere? (b) Calculate the strength of the electric field just outside the sphere. (c) What is the electric flux through a spherical surface just inside the inner surface of the sphere?

22.24. A point charge of $-2.00\ \mu$C is located in the center of a spherical cavity of radius 6.50 cm inside an insulating charged solid. The charge density in the solid is $\rho = 7.35 \times 10^{-4}\ \text{C/m}^3$. Calculate the electric field inside the solid at a distance of 9.50 cm from the center of the cavity.

22.25. The electric field at a distance of 0.145 m from the surface of a solid insulating sphere with radius 0.355 m is 1750 N/C. (a) Assuming the sphere's charge is uniformly distributed, what is the charge density inside it? (b) Calculate the electric field inside the sphere at a distance of 0.200 m from the center.

22.26. A conductor with an inner cavity, like that shown in Fig. 22.23c, carries a total charge of +5.00 nC. The charge within the cavity, insulated from the conductor, is −6.00 nC. How much charge is on (a) the inner surface of the conductor and (b) the outer surface of the conductor?

22.27. Apply Gauss's law to the Gaussian surfaces S_2, S_3, and S_4 in Fig. 22.21b to calculate the electric field between and outside the plates.

22.28. A square insulating sheet 80.0 cm on a side is held horizontally. The sheet has 7.50 nC of charge spread uniformly over its area. (a) Calculate the electric field at a point 0.100 mm above the center of the sheet. (b) Estimate the electric field at a point 100 m above the center of the sheet. (c) Would the answers to parts (a) and (b) be different if the sheet were made of a conducting material? Why or why not?

22.29. An infinitely long cylindrical conductor has radius R and uniform surface charge density σ. (a) In terms of σ and R, what is the charge per unit length λ for the cylinder? (b) In terms of σ, what is the magnitude of the electric field produced by the charged cylinder at a distance $r > R$ from its axis? (c) Express the result of part (b) in terms of λ and show that the electric field outside the cylinder is the same as if all the charge were on the axis. Compare your result to the result for a line of charge in Example 22.6 (Section 22.4).

22.30. Two very large, nonconducting plastic sheets, each 10.0 cm thick, carry uniform charge densities $\sigma_1, \sigma_2, \sigma_3$, and σ_4 on their surfaces, as shown in Fig. 22.34. These surface charge densities have the values $\sigma_1 = -6.00\ \mu C/m^2$, $\sigma_2 = +5.00\ \mu C/m^2$, $\sigma_3 = +2.00\ \mu C/m^2$, and $\sigma_4 = +4.00\ \mu C/m^2$. Use Gauss's law to find the magnitude and direction of the electric field at the following points, far from the edges of these sheets: (a) point A, 5.00 cm from the left face of the left-hand sheet; (b) point B, 1.25 cm from the inner surface of the right-hand sheet; (c) point C, in the middle of the right-hand sheet.

Figure 22.34 Exercise 22.30.

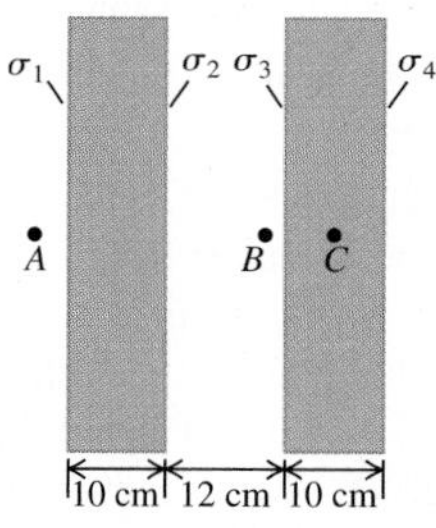

22.31. A negative charge $-Q$ is placed inside the cavity of a hollow metal solid. The outside of the solid is grounded by connecting a conducting wire between it and the earth. (a) Is there any excess charge induced on the inner surface of the piece of metal? If so, find its sign and magnitude. (b) Is there any excess charge on the outside of the piece of metal? Why or why not? (c) Is there an electric field in the cavity? Explain. (d) Is there an electric field within the metal? Why or why not? Is there an electric field outside the piece of metal? Explain why or why not. (e) Would someone outside the solid measure an electric field due to the charge $-Q$? Is it reasonable to say that the grounded conductor has *shielded* the region from the effects of the charge $-Q$? In principle, could the same thing be done for gravity? Why or why not?

Problems

22.32. A cube has sides of length L. It is placed with one corner at the origin as shown in Fig. 22.32. The electric field is uniform and given by $\vec{E} = -B\hat{\imath} + C\hat{\jmath} - D\hat{k}$, where B, C, and D are positive constants. (a) Find the electric flux through each of the six cube faces S_1, S_2, S_3, S_4, S_5, and S_6. (b) Find the electric flux through the entire cube.

22.33. The electric field $\vec{E}$ in Fig. 22.35 is everywhere parallel to the x-axis, so the components E_y and E_z are zero. The x-component of the field E_x depends on x but not on y and z. At points in the yz-plane (where $x = 0$), $E_x = 125$ N/C. (a) What is the electric flux through surface I in Fig. 22.35? (b) What is the electric flux through surface II? (c) The volume shown in the figure is a small section of a very large insulating slab 1.0 m thick. If there is a total charge of −24.0 nC within the volume shown, what are the magnitude and direction of $\vec{E}$ at the face opposite surface I? (d) Is the electric field produced only by charges within the slab, or is the field also due to charges outside the slab? How can you tell?

Figure 22.35 Problem 22.33.

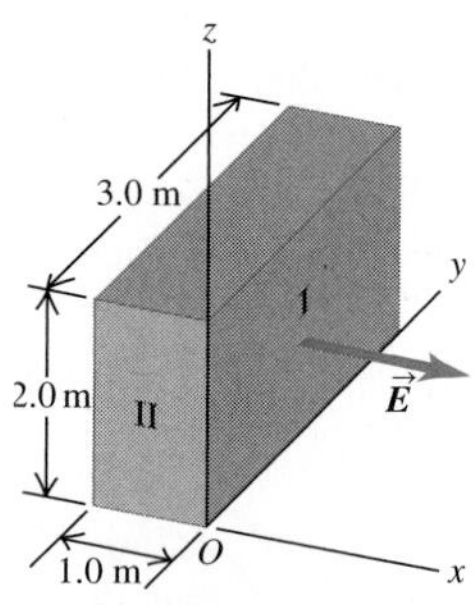

22.34. A flat, square surface with sides of length L is described by the equations

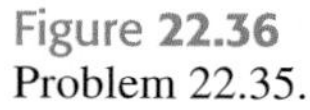

$$x = L \qquad (0 \le y \le L, 0 \le z \le L)$$

(a) Draw this square and show the x-, y-, and z-axes. (b) Find the electric flux through the square due to a positive point charge q located at the origin $(x = 0, y = 0, z = 0)$. (*Hint:* Think of the square as part of a cube centered on the origin.)

22.35. The electric field $\vec{E}_1$ at one face of a parallelepiped is uniform over the entire face and is directed out of the face. At the opposite face, the electric field $\vec{E}_2$ is also uniform over the entire face and is directed into that face (Fig. 22.36). The two faces in question are inclined at 30.0° from the horizontal, while $\vec{E}_1$ and $\vec{E}_2$ are both horizontal; $\vec{E}_1$ has a magnitude of 2.50×10^4 N/C, and $\vec{E}_2$ has a magnitude of 7.00×10^4 N/C. (a) Assuming that no other electric field lines cross the surfaces of the parallelepiped, determine the net charge contained within. (b) Is the electric field produced only by the charges within the parallelepiped, or is the field also due to charges outside the parallelepiped? How can you tell?

Figure 22.36 Problem 22.35.

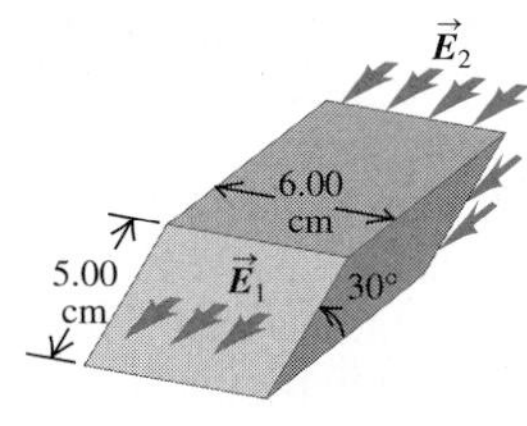

22.36. A long line carrying a uniform linear charge density $+50.0\ \mu C/m$ runs parallel to and 10.0 cm from the surface of a large, flat plastic sheet that has a uniform surface charge density of $-100\ \mu C/m^2$ on one side. Find the location of all points where an α particle would feel no force due to this arrangement of charged objects.

22.37. The Coaxial Cable. A long coaxial cable consists of an inner cylindrical conductor with radius a and an outer coaxial cylinder with inner radius b and outer radius c. The outer cylinder is mounted on insulating supports and has no net charge. The inner cylinder has a uniform positive charge per unit length λ. Calculate the electric field (a) at any point between the cylinders a distance r from the axis and (b) at any point outside the outer cylinder. (c) Graph the magnitude of the electric field as a function of the distance r from the axis of the cable, from $r = 0$ to $r = 2c$. (d) Find the charge per unit length on the inner surface and on the outer surface of the outer cylinder.

22.38. A very long conducting tube (hollow cylinder) has inner radius a and outer radius b. It carries charge per unit length $+\alpha$, where α is a positive constant with units of C/m. A line of charge lies along the axis of the tube. The line of charge has charge per unit length $+\alpha$. (a) Calculate the electric field in terms of α and the distance r from the axis of the tube for (i) $r < a$; (ii) $a < r < b$; (iii) $r > b$. Show your results in a graph of E as a function of r. (b) What is the charge per unit length on (i) the inner surface of the tube and (ii) the outer surface of the tube?

22.39. Repeat Problem 22.38, but now let the conducting tube have charge per unit length $-\alpha$. As in Problem 22.38, the line of charge has charge per unit length $+\alpha$.

22.40. A very long, solid cylinder with radius R has positive charge uniformly distributed throughout it, with charge per unit volume ρ. (a) Derive the expression for the electric field inside the volume at a distance r from the axis of the cylinder in terms of the charge density ρ. (b) What is the electric field at a point outside the volume in terms of the charge per unit length λ in the cylinder? (c) Compare the answers to parts (a) and (b) for $r = R$. (d) Graph the electric-field magnitude as a function of r from $r = 0$ to $r = 3R$.

22.41. A small sphere with a mass of 0.002 g and carrying a charge of 5.00×10^{-8} C hangs from a thread near a very large, charged conducting sheet, as shown in Fig. 22.37. The charge density on the sheet is $2.50 \times 10^{-9}\ \mathrm{C/m^2}$. Find the angle of the thread.

Figure 22.37 Problem 22.41.

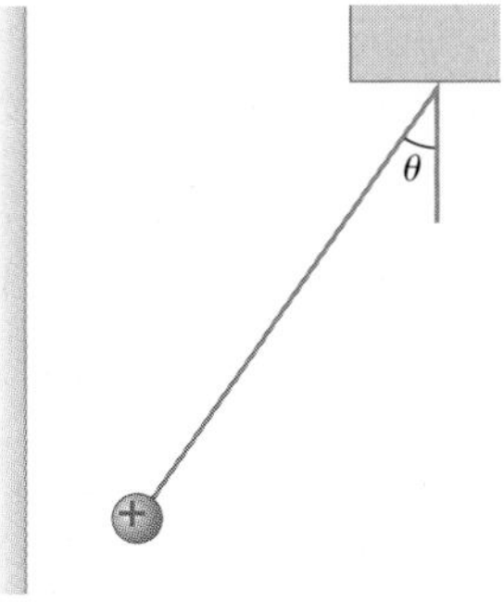

22.42. A Sphere in a Sphere. A solid conducting sphere carrying charge q has radius a. It is inside a concentric hollow conducting sphere with inner radius b and outer radius c. The hollow sphere has no net charge. (a) Derive expressions for the electric-field magnitude in terms of the distance r from the center for the regions $r < a$, $a < r < b$, $b < r < c$, and $r > c$. (b) Graph the magnitude of the electric field as a function of r from $r = 0$ to $r = 2c$. (c) What is the charge on the inner surface of the hollow sphere? (d) On the outer surface? (e) Represent the charge of the small sphere by four plus signs. Sketch the field lines of the system within a spherical volume of radius 2 c.

22.43. A solid conducting sphere with radius R that carries positive charge Q is concentric with a very thin insulating shell of radius $2R$ that also carries charge Q. The charge Q is distributed uniformly over the insulating shell. (a) Find the electric field (magnitude and direction) in each of the regions $0 < r < R$, $R < r < 2R$, and $r > 2R$. (b) Graph the electric-field magnitude as a function of r.

22.44. A conducting spherical shell with inner radius a and outer radius b has a positive point charge Q located at its center. The total charge on the shell is $-3Q$, and it is insulated from its surroundings (Fig. 22.38). (a) Derive expressions for the electric-field magnitude in terms of the distance r from the center for the regions $r < a$, $a < r < b$, and $r > b$. (b) What is the surface charge density on the inner surface of the conducting shell? (c) What is the surface charge density on the outer surface of the conducting shell? (d) Sketch the electric field lines and the location of all charges. (e) Graph the electric-field magnitude as a function of r.

Figure 22.38 Problem 22.44.

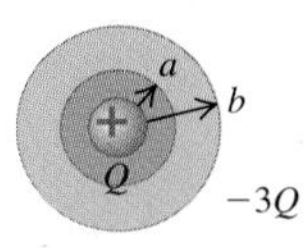

22.45. Concentric Spherical Shells. A small conducting spherical shell with inner radius a and outer radius b is concentric with a larger conducting spherical shell with inner radius c and outer radius d (Fig. 22.39). The inner shell has total charge $+2q$, and the outer shell has charge $+4q$. (a) Calculate the electric field (magnitude and direction) in terms of q and the distance r from the common center of the two shells for (i) $r < a$; (ii) $a < r < b$; (iii) $b < r < c$; (iv) $c < r < d$; (v) $r > d$. Show your results in a graph of the radial component of $\vec{E}$ as a function of r. (b) What is the total charge on the (i) inner surface of the small shell; (ii) outer surface of the small shell; (iii) inner surface of the large shell; (iv) outer surface of the large shell?

Figure 22.39 Problem 22.45.

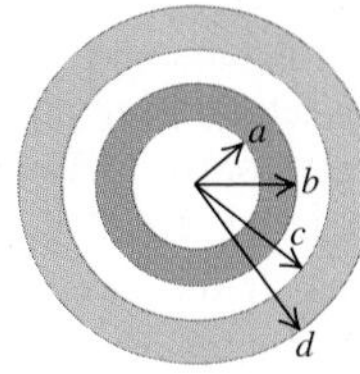

22.46. Repeat Problem 22.45, but now let the outer shell have charge $-2q$. As in Problem 22.45, the inner shell has charge $+2q$.

22.47. Repeat Problem 22.45, but now let the outer shell have charge $-4q$. As in Problem 22.45, the inner shell has charge $+2q$.

22.48. A solid conducting sphere with radius R carries a positive total charge Q. The sphere is surrounded by an insulating shell with inner radius R and outer radius $2R$. The insulating shell has a uniform charge density ρ. (a) Find the value of ρ so that the net charge of the entire system is zero. (b) If ρ has the value found in part (a), find the electric field (magnitude and direction) in each of the regions $0 < r < R$, $R < r < 2R$, and $r > 2R$. Show your results in a graph of the radial component of $\vec{E}$ as a function of r. (c) As a general rule, the electric field is discontinuous only at locations where there is a thin sheet of charge. Explain how your results in part (b) agree with this rule.

22.49. Negative charge $-Q$ is distributed uniformly over the surface of a thin spherical insulating shell with radius R. Calculate the force (magnitude and direction) that the shell exerts on a positive point charge q located (a) a distance $r > R$ from the center of the shell (outside the shell) and (b) a distance $r < R$ from the center of the shell (inside the shell).

22.50. (a) How many excess electrons must be distributed uniformly within the volume of an isolated plastic sphere 30.0 cm in diameter to produce an electric field of 1150 N/C just outside the surface of the sphere? (b) What is the electric field at a point 10.0 cm outside the surface of the sphere?

22.51. A single isolated, large conducting plate (Fig. 22.40) has a charge per unit area σ on its surface. Because the plate is a conductor, the electric field at its surface is perpendicular to the surface and has magnitude $E = \sigma/\epsilon_0$. (a) In Example 22.7 (Section 22.4) it was shown that the field caused by a large, uniformly charged sheet with charge per unit area σ has magnitude $E = \sigma/2\epsilon_0$, exactly *half* as much as for a charged conducting plate. Why is there a difference? (b) Regarding the charge distribution on the conducting plate as being two sheets of charge (one on each surface), each with charge per unit area σ, use the result of Example 22.7 and the principle of superposition to show that $E = 0$ inside the plate and $E = \sigma/\epsilon_0$ outside the plate.

Figure 22.40 Problem 22.51.

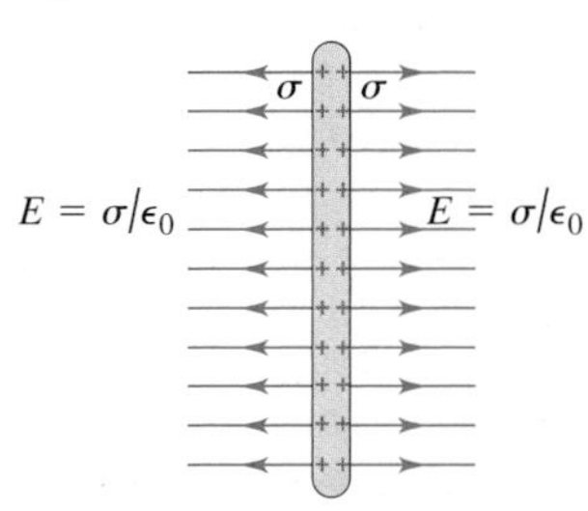

22.52. Thomson's Model of the Atom. In the early years of the 20th century, a leading model of the structure of the atom was that of the English physicist J. J. Thomson (the discoverer of the electron). In Thomson's model, an atom consisted of a sphere of positively charged material in which were embedded negatively charged electrons, like chocolate chips in a ball of cookie dough. Consider such an atom consisting of one electron with mass m and charge $-e$, which may be regarded as a point charge, and a uniformly charged sphere of charge $+e$ and radius R. (a) Explain why the equilibrium position of the electron is at the center of the nucleus. (b) In Thomson's model, it was assumed that the positive material provided little or no resistance to the motion of the electron. If the electron is displaced from equilibrium by a distance less than R, show that the resulting motion of the electron will be simple harmonic, and calculate the frequency of oscillation. (*Hint:* Review the definition of simple harmonic motion in Section 13.2. If it can be shown that the net force on the electron is of this form, then it follows that the motion is simple harmonic. Conversely, if the net force on the electron does not follow this form, the motion is not simple harmonic.) (c) By Thomson's time, it was known that excited atoms emit light waves of only certain frequencies. In his model, the frequency of emitted light is the same as the oscillation frequency of the electron or electrons in the atom. What would the radius of a Thomson-model atom have to be for it to produce red light of frequency 4.57×10^{14} Hz? Compare your answer to the radii of real atoms, which are of the order of 10^{-10} m (see Appendix F for data about the electron). (d) If the electron were displaced from equilibrium by a distance greater than R, would the electron oscillate? Would its motion be simple harmonic? Explain your reasoning. (*Historical note:* In 1910, the atomic nucleus was discovered, proving the Thomson model to be incorrect. An atom's positive charge is not spread over its volume as Thomson supposed, but is concentrated in the tiny nucleus of radius 10^{-14} to 10^{-15} m.)

22.53. Thomson's Model of the Atom, Continued. Using Thomson's (outdated) model of the atom described in Problem 22.52, consider an atom consisting of two electrons, each of charge $-e$, embedded in a sphere of charge $+2e$ and radius R. In equilibrium, each electron is a distance d from the center of the atom (Fig. 22.41). Find the distance d in terms of the other properties of the atom.

Figure 22.41 Problem 22.53.

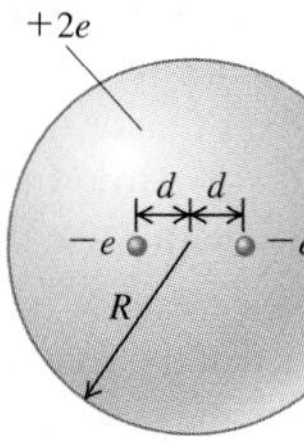

22.54. A Uniformly Charged Slab. A slab of insulating material has thickness $2d$ and is oriented so that its faces are parallel to the yz-plane and given by the planes $x = d$ and $x = -d$. The y- and z-dimensions of the slab are very large compared to d and may be treated as essentially infinite. The slab has a uniform positive charge density ρ. (a) Explain why the electric field due to the slab is zero at the center of the slab $(x = 0)$. (b) Using Gauss's law, find the electric field due to the slab (magnitude and direction) at all points in space.

22.55. A Nonuniformly Charged Slab. Repeat Problem 22.54, but now let the charge density of the slab be given by $\rho(x) = \rho_0(x/d)^2$, where ρ_0 is a positive constant.

22.56. Can Electric Forces Alone Give Stable Equilibrium? In Chapter 21, several examples were given of calculating the force exerted on a point charge by other point charges in its surroundings. (a) Consider a positive point charge $+q$. Give an example of how you would place two other point charges of your choosing so that the net force on charge $+q$ will be zero. (b) If the net force on charge $+q$ is zero, then that charge is in equilibrium. The equilibrium will be *stable* if, when the charge $+q$ is displaced slightly in *any* direction from its position of equilibrium, the net force on the charge pushes it back toward the equilibrium position. For this to be the case, what must the direction of the electric field $\vec{E}$ be due to the other charges at points surrounding the equilibrium position of $+q$? (c) Imagine that the charge $+q$ is moved very far away, and imagine a small Gaussian surface centered on the position where $+q$ was in equilibrium. By applying Gauss's law to this surface, show that it is *impossible* to satisfy the condition for stability described in part (b). In other words, a charge $+q$ cannot be held in stable equilibrium by electrostatic forces alone. This result is known as *Earnshaw's theorem.* (d) Parts (a)–(c) referred to the equilibrium of a positive point charge $+q$. Prove that Earnshaw's theorem also applies to a negative point charge $-q$.

22.57. A nonuniform, but spherically symmetric, distribution of charge has a charge density $\rho(r)$ given as follows:

$$\rho(r) = \rho_0(1 - r/R) \quad \text{for } r \le R$$
$$\rho(r) = 0 \quad \text{for } r \ge R$$

where $\rho_0 = 3Q/\pi R^3$ is a positive constant. (a) Show that the total charge contained in the charge distribution is Q. (b) Show that the electric field in the region $r \ge R$ is identical to that produced by a point charge Q at $r = 0$. (c) Obtain an expression for the electric field in the region $r \le R$. (d) Graph the electric-field magnitude E as a function of r. (e) Find the value of r at which the electric field is maximum, and find the value of that maximum field.

22.58. A nonuniform, but spherically symmetric, distribution of charge has a charge density $\rho(r)$ given as follows:

$$\rho(r) = \rho_0(1 - 4r/3R) \quad \text{for } r \le R$$
$$\rho(r) = 0 \quad \text{for } r \ge R$$

where ρ_0 is a positive constant. (a) Find the total charge contained in the charge distribution. (b) Obtain an expression for the electric field in the region $r \ge R$. (c) Obtain an expression for the electric field in the region $r \le R$. (d) Graph the electric-field magnitude E as a function of r. (e) Find the value of r at which the electric field is maximum, and find the value of that maximum field.

22.59. Gauss's Law for Gravitation. The gravitational force between two point masses separated by a distance r is proportional to $1/r^2$, just like the electric force between two point charges. Because of this similarity between gravitational and electric interactions, there is also a Gauss's law for gravitation. (a) Let $\vec{g}$ be the acceleration due to gravity caused by a point mass m at the origin, so that $\vec{g} = -(Gm/r^2)\hat{r}$. Consider a spherical Gaussian surface with radius r centered on this point mass, and show that the flux of $\vec{g}$ through this surface is given by

$$\oint \vec{g} \cdot d\vec{A} = -4\pi Gm$$

(b) By following the same logical steps used in Section 22.3 to obtain Gauss's law for the electric field, show that the flux of $\vec{g}$ through *any* closed surface is given by

$$\oint \vec{g} \cdot d\vec{A} = -4\pi GM_{\text{encl}}$$

where M_{encl} is the total mass enclosed within the closed surface.

22.60. Applying Gauss's Law for Gravitation. Using Gauss's law for gravitation (derived in part (b) of Problem 22.59), show that the following statements are true: (a) For any spherically symmetric mass distribution with total mass M, the acceleration due to gravity outside the distribution is the same as though all the mass were concentrated at the center. (*Hint:* See Example 22.5 in Section 22.4.) (b) At any point inside a spherically symmetric shell of mass, the acceleration due to gravity is zero. (*Hint:* See Example 22.5.) (c) If we could drill a hole through a spherically symmetric planet to its center, and if the density were uniform, we would find that the magnitude of $\vec{g}$ is directly proportional to the distance r from the center. (*Hint:* See Example 22.9 in Section 22.4.) We proved these results in Section 12.6 using some fairly strenuous analysis; the proofs using Gauss's law for gravitation are *much* easier.

22.61. (a) An insulating sphere with radius a has a uniform charge density ρ. The sphere is not centered at the origin but at $\vec{r} = \vec{b}$. Show that the electric field inside the sphere is given by $\vec{E} = \rho(\vec{r} - \vec{b})/3\epsilon_0$. (b) An insulating sphere of radius R has a spherical hole of radius a located within its volume and centered a distance b from the center of the sphere, where $a < b < R$ (a cross section of the sphere is shown in Fig. 22.42). The solid part of the sphere has a uniform volume charge density ρ. Find the magnitude and direction of the electric field $\vec{E}$ inside the hole, and show that $\vec{E}$ is uniform over the entire hole. [*Hint:* Use the principle of superposition and the result of part (a).]

Figure 22.42 Problem 22.61.

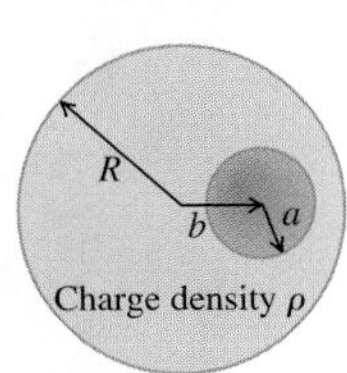

22.62. A very long, solid insulating cylinder with radius R has a cylindrical hole with radius a bored along its entire length. The axis of the hole is a distance b from the axis of the cylinder, where $a < b < R$ (Fig. 22.43). The solid material of the cylinder has a uniform volume charge density ρ. Find the magnitude and direction of the electric field $\vec{E}$ inside the hole, and show that $\vec{E}$ is uniform over the entire hole. (*Hint:* See Problem 22.61.)

Figure 22.43 Problem 22.62.

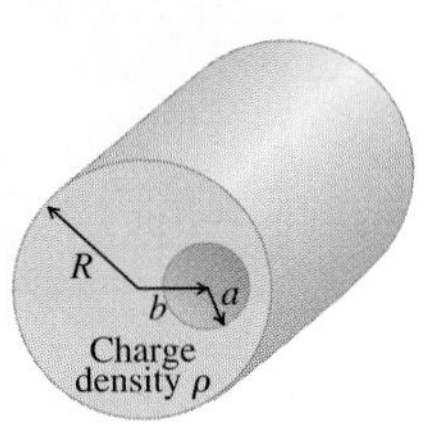

22.63. Positive charge Q is distributed uniformly over each of two spherical volumes with radius R. One sphere of charge is centered at the origin and the other at $x = 2R$ (Fig. 22.44). Find the magnitude and direction of the net electric field due to these two distributions of charge at the following points on the x-axis: (a) $x = 0$; (b) $x = R/2$; (c) $x = R$; (d) $x = 3R$.

Figure 22.44 Problem 22.63.

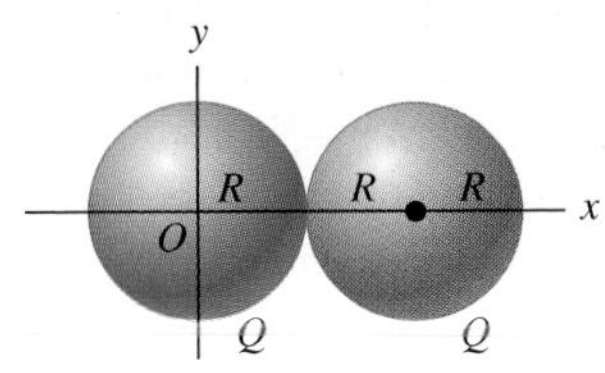

22.64. Repeat Problem 22.63, but now let the left-hand sphere have positive charge Q and let the right-hand sphere have negative charge $-Q$.

22.65. Electric Field Inside a Hydrogen Atom. A hydrogen atom is made up of a proton of charge $+Q = 1.60 \times 10^{-19}$ C and an electron of charge $-Q = -1.60 \times 10^{-19}$ C. The proton may be regarded as a point charge at $r = 0$, the center of the atom. The motion of the electron causes its charge to be "smeared out" into a spherical distribution around the proton, so that the electron is equivalent to a charge per unit volume of

$$\rho(r) = -\frac{Q}{\pi a_0^3} e^{-2r/a_0}$$

where $a_0 = 5.29 \times 10^{-11}$ m is called the *Bohr radius.* (a) Find the total amount of the hydrogen atom's charge that is enclosed within a sphere with radius r centered on the proton. Show that as $r \to \infty$, the enclosed charge goes to zero. Explain this result. (b) Find the electric field (magnitude and direction) caused by the charge of the hydrogen atom as a function of r. (c) Graph the electric-field magnitude E as a function of r.

Challenge Problems

22.66. A region in space contains a total positive charge Q that is distributed spherically such that the volume charge density $\rho(r)$ is given by

$$\begin{aligned} \rho(r) &= \alpha && \text{for } r \le R/2 \\ \rho(r) &= 2\alpha(1 - r/R) && \text{for } R/2 \le r \le R \\ \rho(r) &= 0 && \text{for } r \ge R \end{aligned}$$

Here α is a positive constant having units of C/m^3. (a) Determine α in terms of Q and R. (b) Using Gauss's law, derive an expression for the magnitude of $\vec{E}$ as a function of r. Do this separately for all three regions. Express your answers in terms of the total charge Q. Be sure to check that your results agree on the boundaries of the regions. (c) What fraction of the total charge is contained within the region $r \le R/2$? (d) If an electron with charge $q' = -e$ is oscillating back and forth about $r = 0$ (the center of the distribution) with an amplitude less than $R/2$, show that the motion is simple harmonic. (*Hint:* Review the discussion of simple harmonic motion in Section 13.2. If, and only if, the net force on the electron is proportional to its displacement from equilibrium, then the motion is simple harmonic.) (e) What is the period of the motion in part (d)? (f) If the amplitude of the motion described in part (e) is greater than $R/2$, is the motion still simple harmonic? Why or why not?

22.67. A region in space contains a total positive charge Q that is distributed spherically such that the volume charge density $\rho(r)$ is given by

$$\begin{aligned} \rho(r) &= 3\alpha r/(2R) && \text{for } r \le R/2 \\ \rho(r) &= \alpha[1 - (r/R)^2] && \text{for } R/2 \le r \le R \\ \rho(r) &= 0 && \text{for } r \ge R \end{aligned}$$

Here α is a positive constant having units of C/m^3. (a) Determine α in terms of Q and R. (b) Using Gauss's law, derive an expression for the magnitude of the electric field as a function of r. Do this separately for all three regions. Express your answers in terms of the total charge Q. (c) What fraction of the total charge is contained within the region $R/2 \le r \le R$? (d) What is the magnitude of $\vec{E}$ at $r = R/2$? (e) If an electron with charge $q' = -e$ is released from rest at any point in any of the three regions, the resulting motion will be oscillatory but not simple harmonic. Why? (See Challenge Problem 22.66.)

23 ELECTRIC POTENTIAL

LEARNING GOALS

By studying this chapter, you will learn:

- How to calculate the electric potential energy of a collection of charges.
- The meaning and significance of electric potential.
- How to calculate the electric potential that a collection of charges produces at a point in space.
- How to use equipotential surfaces to visualize how the electric potential varies in space.
- How to use electric potential to calculate the electric field.

? In one type of welding, electric charge flows between the welding tool and the metal pieces that are to be joined together. This produces a glowing arc whose high temperature fuses the pieces together. Why must the tool be held close to the pieces being welded?

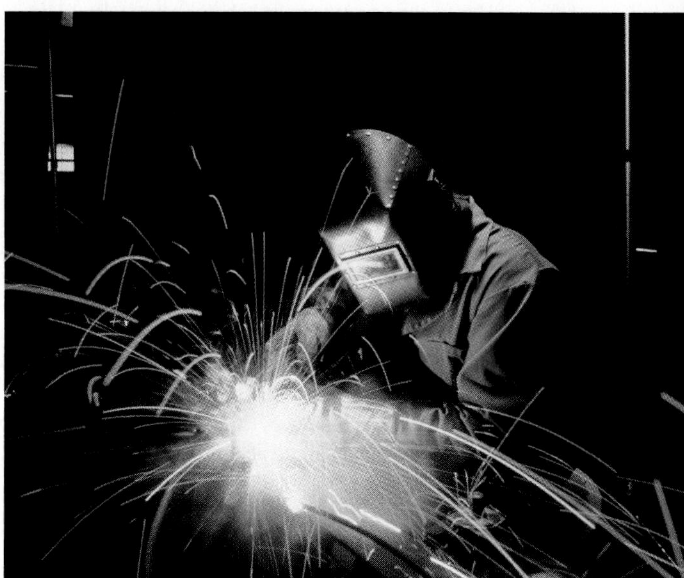

This chapter is about energy associated with electrical interactions. Every time you turn on a light, a CD player, or an electric appliance, you are making use of electrical energy, an indispensable ingredient of our technological society. In Chapters 6 and 7 we introduced the concepts of *work* and *energy* in the context of mechanics; now we'll combine these concepts with what we've learned about electric charge, electric forces, and electric fields. Just as the energy concept made it possible to solve some kinds of mechanics problems very simply, using energy ideas makes it easier to solve a variety of problems in electricity.

When a charged particle moves in an electric field, the field exerts a force that can do *work* on the particle. This work can always be expressed in terms of electric potential energy. Just as gravitational potential energy depends on the height of a mass above the earth's surface, electric potential energy depends on the position of the charged particle in the electric field. We'll describe electric potential energy using a new concept called *electric potential,* or simply *potential.* In circuits, a difference in potential from one point to another is often called *voltage.* The concepts of potential and voltage are crucial to understanding how electric circuits work and have equally important applications to electron beams used in cancer radiotherapy, high-energy particle accelerators, and many other devices.

23.1 Electric Potential Energy

The concepts of work, potential energy, and conservation of energy proved to be extremely useful in our study of mechanics. In this section we'll show that these concepts are just as useful for understanding and analyzing electrical interactions.

Let's begin by reviewing three essential points from Chapters 6 and 7. First, when a force $\vec{F}$ acts on a particle that moves from point a to point b, the work $W_{a\to b}$ done by the force is given by a *line integral:*

$$W_{a\to b} = \int_a^b \vec{F}\cdot d\vec{l} = \int_a^b F\cos\phi\, dl \qquad \text{(work done by a force)} \qquad (23.1)$$

where $d\vec{l}$ is an infinitesimal displacement along the particle's path and ϕ is the angle between $\vec{F}$ and $d\vec{l}$ at each point along the path.

Second, if the force $\vec{F}$ is *conservative,* as we defined the term in Section 7.3, the work done by $\vec{F}$ can always be expressed in terms of a **potential energy** U. When the particle moves from a point where the potential energy is U_a to a point where it is U_b, the change in potential energy is $\Delta U = U_b - U_a$ and the work $W_{a\to b}$ done by the force is

$$W_{a\to b} = U_a - U_b = -(U_b - U_a) = -\Delta U \quad \text{(work done by a conservative force)} \tag{23.2}$$

When $W_{a\to b}$ is positive, U_a is greater than U_b, ΔU is negative, and the potential energy *decreases.* That's what happens when a baseball falls from a high point (a) to a lower point (b) under the influence of the earth's gravity; the force of gravity does positive work, and the gravitational potential energy decreases (Fig. 23.1). When a tossed ball is moving upward, the gravitational force does negative work during the ascent, and the potential energy increases.

Third, the work–energy theorem says that the change in kinetic energy $\Delta K = K_b - K_a$ during any displacement is equal to the *total* work done on the particle. If the only work done on the particle is done by conservative forces, then Eq. (23.2) gives the total work, and $K_b - K_a = -(U_b - U_a)$. We usually write this as

$$K_a + U_a = K_b + U_b \tag{23.3}$$

That is, the total mechanical energy (kinetic plus potential) is *conserved* under these circumstances.

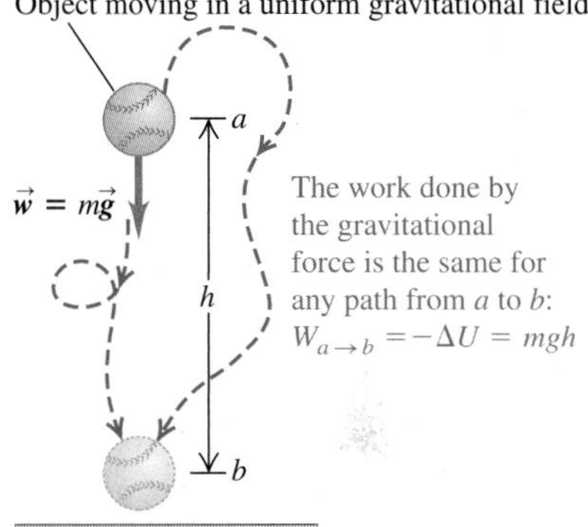
Object moving in a uniform gravitational field
a
w = mg
h
b
The work done by the gravitational force is the same for any path from a to b:
W_{a→b} = −ΔU = mgh

23.1 The work done on a baseball moving in a uniform gravitational field.

Electric Potential Energy in a Uniform Field

Let's look at an electrical example of these basic concepts. In Fig. 23.2 a pair of charged parallel metal plates sets up a uniform, downward electric field with magnitude E. The field exerts a downward force with magnitude $F = q_0E$ on a positive test charge q_0. As the charge moves downward a distance d from point a to point b, the force on the test charge is constant and independent of its location. So the work done by the electric field is the product of the force magnitude and the component of displacement in the (downward) direction of the force:

$$W_{a\to b} = Fd = q_0Ed \tag{23.4}$$

This work is positive, since the force is in the same direction as the net displacement of the test charge.

The y-component of the electric force, $F_y = -q_0E$, is constant, and there is no x- or z-component. This is exactly analogous to the gravitational force on a mass m near the earth's surface; for this force, there is a constant y-component $F_y = -mg$ and the x- and z-components are zero. Because of this analogy, we can conclude that the force exerted on q_0 by the uniform electric field in Fig. 23.2 is *conservative,* just as is the gravitational force. This means that the work $W_{a\to b}$ done by the field is independent of the path the particle takes from a to b. We can represent this work with a *potential-energy* function U, just as we did for gravitational potential energy in Section 7.1. The potential energy for the gravitational force $F_y = -mg$ was $U = mgy$; hence the potential energy for the electric force $F_y = -q_0E$ is

$$U = q_0Ey \tag{23.5}$$

When the test charge moves from height y_a to height y_b, the work done on the charge by the field is given by

$$W_{a\to b} = -\Delta U = -(U_b - U_a) = -(q_0Ey_b - q_0Ey_a) = q_0E(y_a - y_b) \tag{23.6}$$

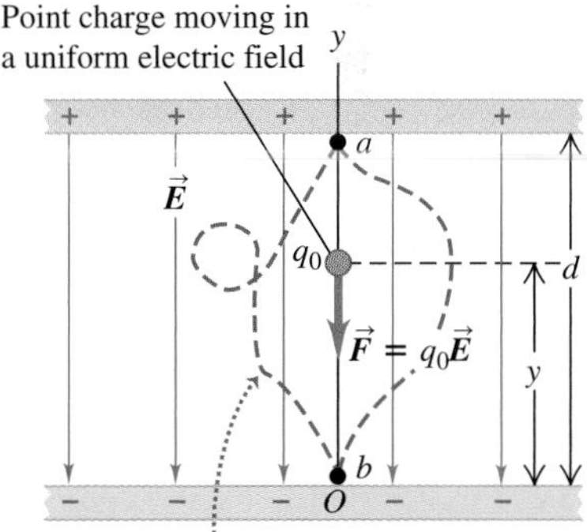
Point charge moving in a uniform electric field
y
a
E
q0
d
F = q0E
y
b
O
The work done by the electric force is the same for any path from a to b:
W_{a→b} = −ΔU = q0Ed

23.2 The work done on a point charge moving in a uniform electric field. Compare with Fig. 23.1.

23.3 A positive charge moving (a) in the direction of the electric field $\vec{E}$ and (b) in the direction opposite $\vec{E}$.

(a) Positive charge moves in the direction of $\vec{E}$:
- Field does *positive* work on charge.
- *U decreases.*

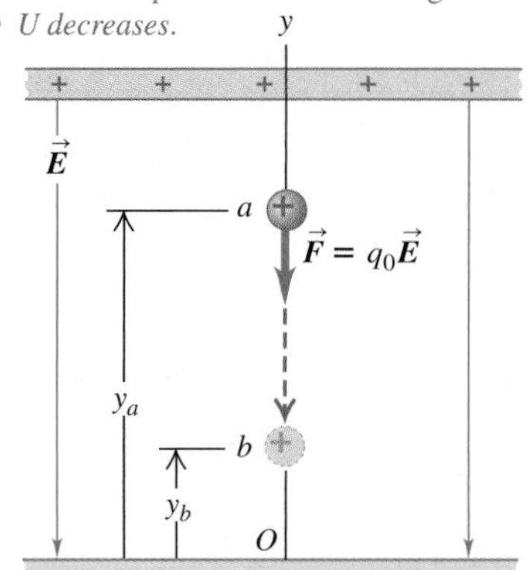

(b) Positive charge moves opposite $\vec{E}$:
- Field does *negative* work on charge.
- *U increases.*

When y_a is greater than y_b (Fig. 23.3a), the positive test charge q_0 moves downward, in the same direction as $\vec{E}$; the displacement is in the same direction as the force $\vec{F} = q_0\vec{E}$, so the field does positive work and U decreases. [In particular, if $y_a - y_b = d$ as in Fig. 23.2, Eq. (23.6) gives $W_{a \to b} = q_0 E d$, in agreement with Eq. (23.4).] When y_a is less than y_b (Fig. 23.3b), the positive test charge q_0 moves upward, in the opposite direction to $\vec{E}$; the displacement is opposite the force, the field does negative work, and U increases.

If the test charge q_0 is *negative,* the potential energy increases when it moves with the field and decreases when it moves against the field (Fig. 23.4).

Whether the test charge is positive or negative, the following general rules apply: *U increases* if the test charge q_0 moves in the direction *opposite* the electric force $\vec{F} = q_0\vec{E}$ (Figs. 23.3b and 23.4a); *U decreases* if q_0 moves in the *same* direction as $\vec{F} = q_0\vec{E}$ (Figs. 23.3a and 23.4b). This is the same behavior as for gravitational potential energy, which increases if a mass m moves upward (opposite the direction of the gravitational force) and decreases if m moves downward (in the same direction as the gravitational force).

CAUTION **Electric potential energy** The relationship between electric potential energy change and motion in an electric field is an important one that we'll use often. It's also a relationship that takes a little effort to truly understand. Take the time to review the preceding paragraph thoroughly and to study Figs. 23.3 and 23.4 carefully. Doing so now will help you tremendously later!

Electric Potential Energy of Two Point Charges

The idea of electric potential energy isn't restricted to the special case of a uniform electric field. Indeed, we can apply this concept to a point charge in *any* electric field caused by a static charge distribution. Recall from Chapter 21 that

23.4 A negative charge moving (a) in the direction of the electric field $\vec{E}$ and (b) in the direction opposite $\vec{E}$. Compare with Fig. 23.3.

(a) Negative charge moves in the direction of $\vec{E}$:
- Field does *negative* work on charge.
- *U increases.*

(b) Negative charge moves opposite $\vec{E}$:
- Field does *positive* work on charge.
- *U decreases.*

we can represent any charge distribution as a collection of point charges. Therefore it's useful to calculate the work done on a test charge q_0 moving in the electric field caused by a single, stationary point charge q.

We'll consider first a displacement along the *radial* line in Fig. 23.5, from point a to point b. The force on q_0 is given by Coulomb's law, and its radial component is

$$F_r = \frac{1}{4\pi\epsilon_0}\frac{qq_0}{r^2} \tag{23.7}$$

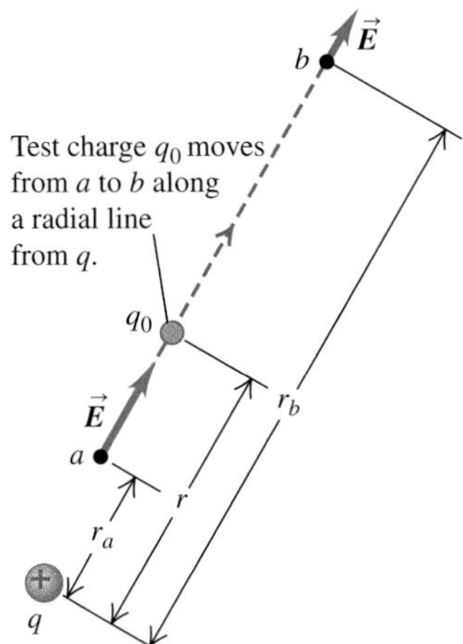

23.5 Test charge q_0 moves along a straight line extending radially from charge q. As it moves from a to b, the distance varies from r_a to r_b.

If q and q_0 have the same sign ($+$ or $-$) the force is repulsive and F_r is positive; if the two charges have opposite signs, the force is attractive and F_r is negative. The force is *not* constant during the displacement, and we have to integrate to calculate the work $W_{a\to b}$ done on q_0 by this force as q_0 moves from a to b. We find

$$W_{a\to b} = \int_{r_a}^{r_b} F_r\,dr = \int_{r_a}^{r_b} \frac{1}{4\pi\epsilon_0}\frac{qq_0}{r^2}\,dr = \frac{qq_0}{4\pi\epsilon_0}\left(\frac{1}{r_a} - \frac{1}{r_b}\right) \tag{23.8}$$

The work done by the electric force for this particular path depends only on the endpoints.

In fact, the work is the same for *all possible* paths from a to b. To prove this, we consider a more general displacement (Fig. 23.6) in which a and b do not lie on the same radial line. From Eq. (23.1) the work done on q_0 during this displacement is given by

$$W_{a\to b} = \int_{r_a}^{r_b} F\cos\phi\,dl = \int_{r_a}^{r_b} \frac{1}{4\pi\epsilon_0}\frac{qq_0}{r^2}\cos\phi\,dl$$

But the figure shows that $\cos\phi\,dl = dr$. That is, the work done during a small displacement $d\vec{l}$ depends only on the change dr in the distance r between the charges, which is the *radial component* of the displacement. Thus Eq. (23.8) is valid even for this more general displacement; the work done on q_0 by the electric field $\vec{E}$ produced by q depends only on r_a and r_b, not on the details of the path. Also, if q_0 returns to its starting point a by a different path, the total work done in the round-trip displacement is zero (the integral in Eq. (23.8) is from r_a back to r_a). These are the needed characteristics for a conservative force, as we defined it in Section 7.3. Thus the force on q_0 is a *conservative* force.

We see that Eqs. (23.2) and (23.8) are consistent if we define $qq_0/4\pi\epsilon_0 r_a$ to be the potential energy U_a when q_0 is at point a, a distance r_a from q, and we define $qq_0/4\pi\epsilon_0 r_b$ to be the potential energy U_b when q_0 is at point b, a distance r_b from

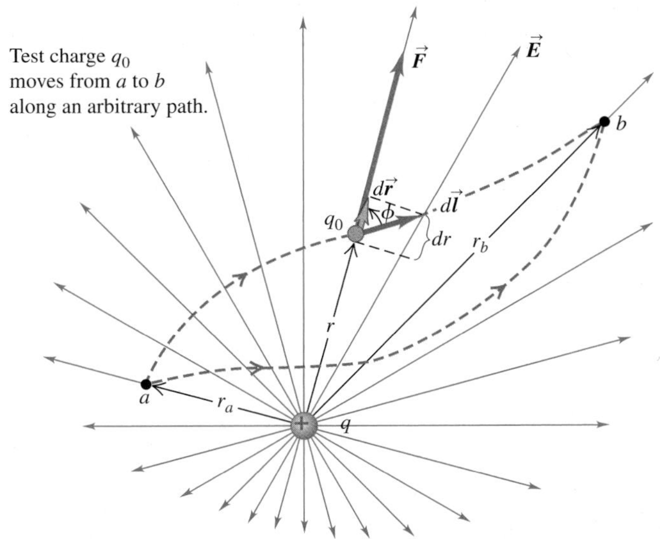

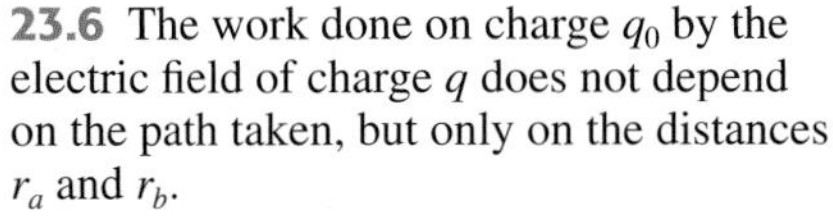

23.6 The work done on charge q_0 by the electric field of charge q does not depend on the path taken, but only on the distances r_a and r_b.

23.7 Graphs of the potential energy U of two point charges q and q_0 versus their separation r.

(a) q and q_0 have the same sign.

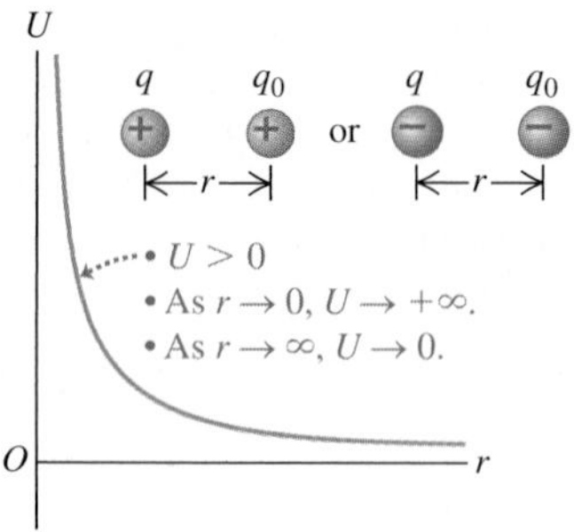

(b) q and q_0 have opposite signs.

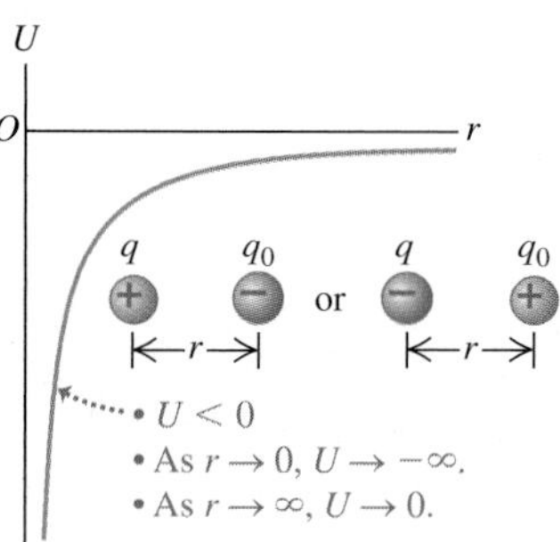

q. Thus the potential energy U when the test charge q_0 is at *any* distance r from charge q is

$$U = \frac{1}{4\pi\epsilon_0}\frac{qq_0}{r} \quad \text{(electric potential energy of two point charges } q \text{ and } q_0\text{)} \tag{23.9}$$

Note that we have *not* assumed anything about the signs of q and q_0; Eq. (23.9) is valid for any combination of signs. The potential energy is positive if the charges q and q_0 have the same sign (Fig. 23.7a) and negative if they have opposite signs (Fig. 23.7b).

CAUTION **Electric potential energy vs. electric force** Be careful not to confuse Eq. (23.9) for the potential energy of two point charges with the similar expression in Eq. (23.7) for the radial component of the electric force that one charge exerts on the other. The potential energy U is proportional to $1/r$, while the force component F_r is proportional to $1/r^2$.

Potential energy is always defined relative to some reference point where $U = 0$. In Eq. (23.9), U is zero when q and q_0 are infinitely far apart and $r = \infty$. Therefore U represents the work that would be done on the test charge q_0 by the field of q if q_0 moved from an initial distance r to infinity. If q and q_0 have the same sign, the interaction is repulsive, this work is positive, and U is positive at any finite separation (Fig. 23.7a). If the charges have opposite signs, the interaction is attractive, the work done is negative, and U is negative (Fig. 23.7b).

We emphasize that the potential energy U given by Eq. (23.9) is a *shared* property of the two charges q and q_0; it is a consequence of the *interaction* between these two bodies. If the distance between the two charges is changed from r_a to r_b, the change in potential energy is the same whether q is held fixed and q_0 is moved or q_0 is held fixed and q is moved. For this reason, we never use the phrase "the electric potential energy *of* a point charge." (Likewise, if a mass m is at a height h above the earth's surface, the gravitational potential energy is a shared property of the mass m and the earth. We emphasized this in Sections 7.1 and 12.3.)

Gauss's law tells us that the electric field outside any spherically symmetric charge distribution is the same as though all the charge were concentrated at the center. Therefore Eq. (23.9) also holds if the test charge q_0 is outside any spherically symmetric charge distribution with total charge q at a distance r from the center.

Example 23.1 Conservation of energy with electric forces

A positron (the antiparticle of the electron) has a mass of 9.11×10^{-31} kg and a charge $+e = +1.60 \times 10^{-19}$ C. Suppose a positron moves in the vicinity of an alpha particle, which has a charge $+2e = 3.20 \times 10^{-19}$ C. The alpha particle is more than 7000 times as massive as the positron, so we assume that it is at rest in some inertial frame of reference. When the positron is 1.00×10^{-10} m from the alpha particle, it is moving directly away from the alpha particle at a speed of 3.00×10^6 m/s. (a) What is the positron's speed when the two particles are 2.00×10^{-10} m apart? (b) What is the positron's speed when it is very far away from the alpha particle? (c) How would the situation change if the moving particle were an electron (same mass as the positron but opposite charge)?

SOLUTION

IDENTIFY: The electric force between the positron and the alpha particle is conservative, so mechanical energy (kinetic plus potential) is conserved.

SET UP: The kinetic and potential energies at any two points a and b are related by Eq. (23.3), $K_a + U_a = K_b + U_b$, and the potential energy at any distance r is given by Eq. (23.9). We are given complete information about the system at a point a where the two charges are 1.00×10^{-10} m apart. We use Eqs. (23.3) and (23.9) to find the speed at two different values of r in parts (a) and (b), and for the case where the charge $+e$ is replaced by $-e$ in part (c).

EXECUTE: (a) In this part, $r_b = 2.00 \times 10^{-10}$ m and we want to find the final speed v_b of the positron. This appears in the expression for the final kinetic energy, $K_b = \frac{1}{2}mv_b^2$; solving the energy-conservation equation for K_b, we have

$$K_b = K_a + U_a - U_b$$

The values of the energies on the right-hand side of this expression are

$$K_a = \frac{1}{2}mv_a^2 = \frac{1}{2}(9.11 \times 10^{-31}\ \text{kg})(3.00 \times 10^6\ \text{m/s})^2$$
$$= 4.10 \times 10^{-18}\ \text{J}$$
$$U_a = \frac{1}{4\pi\epsilon_0}\frac{qq_0}{r_a}$$
$$= (9.0 \times 10^9\ \text{N}\cdot\text{m}^2/\text{C}^2)\frac{(3.20 \times 10^{-19}\ \text{C})(1.60 \times 10^{-19}\ \text{C})}{1.00 \times 10^{-10}\ \text{m}}$$
$$= 4.61 \times 10^{-18}\ \text{J}$$
$$U_b = (9.0 \times 10^9\ \text{N}\cdot\text{m}^2/\text{C}^2)\frac{(3.20 \times 10^{-19}\ \text{C})(1.60 \times 10^{-19}\ \text{C})}{2.00 \times 10^{-10}\ \text{m}}$$
$$= 2.30 \times 10^{-18}\ \text{J}$$

Hence the final kinetic energy is

$$K_b = \frac{1}{2}mv_b^2 = K_a + U_a - U_b$$
$$= 4.10 \times 10^{-18}\ \text{J} + 4.61 \times 10^{-18}\ \text{J} - 2.30 \times 10^{-18}\ \text{J}$$
$$= 6.41 \times 10^{-18}\ \text{J}$$

and the final speed of the positron is

$$v_b = \sqrt{\frac{2K_b}{m}} = \sqrt{\frac{2(6.41 \times 10^{-18}\ \text{J})}{9.11 \times 10^{-31}\ \text{kg}}} = 3.8 \times 10^6\ \text{m/s}$$

The force is repulsive, so the positron speeds up as it moves away from the stationary alpha particle.

(b) When the final positions of the positron and alpha particle are very far apart, the separation r_b approaches infinity and the final potential energy U_b approaches zero. Then the final kinetic energy of the positron is

$$K_b = K_a + U_a - U_b = 4.10 \times 10^{-18}\ \text{J} + 4.61 \times 10^{-18}\ \text{J} - 0$$
$$= 8.71 \times 10^{-18}\ \text{J}$$

and its final speed is

$$v_b = \sqrt{\frac{2K_b}{m}} = \sqrt{\frac{2(8.71 \times 10^{-18}\ \text{J})}{9.11 \times 10^{-31}\ \text{kg}}} = 4.4 \times 10^6\ \text{m/s}$$

Comparing to part (a), we see that as the positron moves from $r = 2.00 \times 10^{-10}$ m to infinity, the additional work done on it by the electric field of the alpha particle increases the speed by only about 16%. This is because the electric force decreases rapidly with distance.

(c) If the moving charge is negative, the force on it is attractive rather than repulsive, and we expect it to slow down rather than speed up. The only difference in the above calculations is that both potential-energy quantities are negative. From part (a), at a distance $r_b = 2.00 \times 10^{-10}$ m we have

$$K_b = K_a + U_a - U_b$$
$$= 4.10 \times 10^{-18}\ \text{J} + (-4.61 \times 10^{-18}\ \text{J}) - (-2.30 \times 10^{-18}\ \text{J})$$
$$= 1.79 \times 10^{-18}\ \text{J}$$
$$v_b = \sqrt{\frac{2K_b}{m}} = 2.0 \times 10^6\ \text{m/s}$$

From part (b), at $r_b = \infty$ the kinetic energy of the electron would seem to be

$$K_b = K_a + U_a - U_b$$
$$= 4.10 \times 10^{-18}\ \text{J} + (-4.61 \times 10^{-18}\ \text{J}) - 0$$
$$= -5.1 \times 10^{-19}\ \text{J}$$

But kinetic energies can *never* be negative! This result means that the electron can never reach $r_b = \infty$; the attractive force brings the electron to a halt at a finite distance from the alpha particle. The electron will then begin to move back toward the alpha particle. You can solve for the distance r_b at which the electron comes momentarily to rest by setting K_b equal to zero in the equation for conservation of mechanical energy.

EVALUATE: It's useful to compare our calculations with Fig. 23.7. In parts (a) and (b), the charges have the same sign; since $r_b > r_a$, the potential energy U_b is less than U_a. In part (c), the charges have opposite signs; since $r_b > r_a$, the potential energy U_b is greater (that is, less negative) than U_a.

Electric Potential Energy with Several Point Charges

Suppose the electric field $\vec{E}$ in which charge q_0 moves is caused by *several* point charges $q_1, q_2, q_3, \ldots$ at distances $r_1, r_2, r_3, \ldots$ from q_0, as in Fig. 23.8. For example, q_0 could be a positive ion moving in the presence of other ions (Fig. 23.9). The total electric field at each point is the *vector sum* of the fields due to the individual charges, and the total work done on q_0 during any displacement is the sum of the contributions from the individual charges. From Eq. (23.9) we conclude that the potential energy associated with the test charge q_0 at point a in Fig. 23.8 is the *algebraic* sum (*not* a vector sum):

$$U = \frac{q_0}{4\pi\epsilon_0}\left(\frac{q_1}{r_1} + \frac{q_2}{r_2} + \frac{q_3}{r_3} + \cdots\right) = \frac{q_0}{4\pi\epsilon_0}\sum_i \frac{q_i}{r_i} \qquad (23.10)$$

(point charge q_0 and collection of charges q_i)

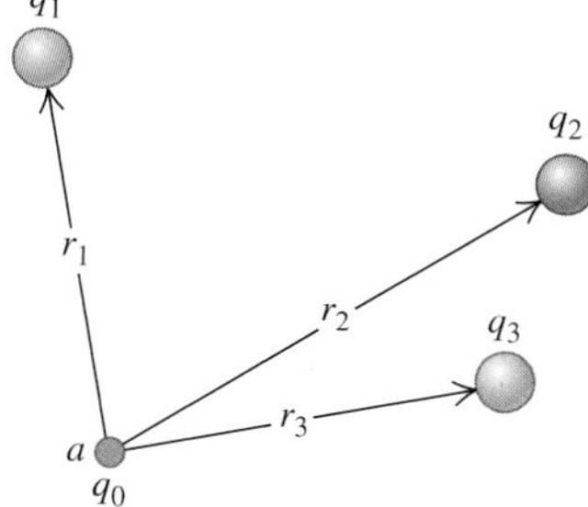

23.8 The potential energy associated with a charge q_0 at point a depends on the other charges q_1, q_2, and q_3 and on their distances r_1, r_2, and r_3 from point a.

When q_0 is at a different point b, the potential energy is given by the same expression, but $r_1, r_2, \ldots$ are the distances from $q_1, q_2, \ldots$ to point b. The work

Example 23.4 Potential due to two point charges

An electric dipole consists of two point charges, $q_1 = +12$ nC and $q_2 = -12$ nC, placed 10 cm apart (Fig. 23.14). Compute the potentials at points a, b, and c by adding the potentials due to either charge, as in Eq. (23.15).

SOLUTION

IDENTIFY: This is the same arrangement of charges as in Example 21.9 (Section 21.5). In that example we calculated electric *field* at each point by doing a *vector* sum. Our target variable in this problem is the electric *potential* V at three points.

SET UP: To find V at each point, we do the *algebraic* sum in Eq. (23.15):

$$V = \frac{1}{4\pi\epsilon_0}\sum_i \frac{q_i}{r_i}$$

EXECUTE: At point a the potential due to the positive charge q_1 is

$$\frac{1}{4\pi\epsilon_0}\frac{q_1}{r_1} = (9.0 \times 10^9\ \text{N}\cdot\text{m}^2/\text{C}^2)\frac{12 \times 10^{-9}\ \text{C}}{0.060\ \text{m}}$$
$$= 1800\ \text{N}\cdot\text{m/C}$$
$$= 1800\ \text{J/C} = 1800\ \text{V}$$

and the potential due to the negative charge q_2 is

$$\frac{1}{4\pi\epsilon_0}\frac{q_2}{r_2} = (9.0 \times 10^9\ \text{N}\cdot\text{m}^2/\text{C}^2)\frac{(-12 \times 10^{-9}\ \text{C})}{0.040\ \text{m}}$$
$$= -2700\ \text{N}\cdot\text{m/C}$$
$$= -2700\ \text{J/C} = -2700\ \text{V}$$

The potential V_a at point a is the sum of these:

$$V_a = 1800\ \text{V} + (-2700\ \text{V}) = -900\ \text{V}$$

By similar calculations you can show that at point b the potential due to the positive charge is +2700 V, the potential due to the negative charge is −770 V, and

$$V_b = 2700\ \text{V} + (-770\ \text{V}) = 1930\ \text{V}$$

23.14 What are the potentials at points a, b, and c due to this electric dipole?

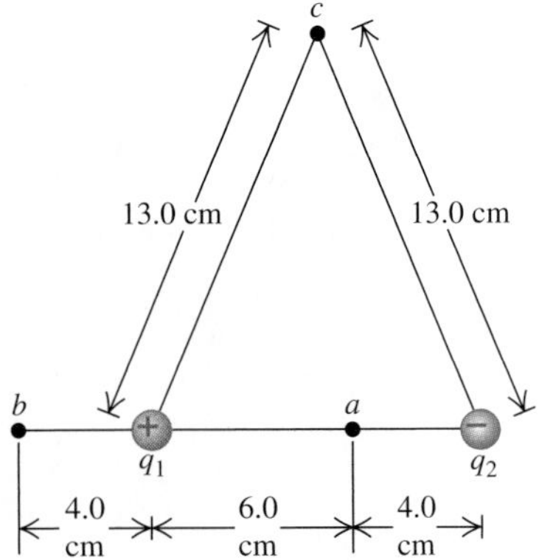

At point c the potential due to the positive charge is

$$\frac{1}{4\pi\epsilon_0}\frac{q_1}{r_1} = (9.0 \times 10^9\ \text{N}\cdot\text{m}^2/\text{C}^2)\frac{12 \times 10^{-9}\ \text{C}}{0.13\ \text{m}} = 830\ \text{V}$$

The potential due to the negative charge is −830 V, and the total potential is zero:

$$V_c = 830\ \text{V} + (-830\ \text{V}) = 0$$

The potential is also equal to zero at infinity (infinitely far from both charges).

EVALUATE: Comparing this example with Example 21.9 shows that it's much easier to calculate electric potential (a scalar) than electric field (a vector). We'll take advantage of this simplification whenever possible.

Example 23.5 Potential and potential energy

Compute the potential energy associated with a point charge of +4.0 nC if it is placed at points a, b, and c in Fig. 23.14.

SOLUTION

IDENTIFY: We know the value of the electric potential at each of these points, and we need to find the potential energy for a point charge placed at each point.

SET UP: For any point charge q, the associated potential energy is $U = qV$. We use the values of V from Example 23.4.

EXECUTE: At point a,

$$U_a = qV_a = (4.0 \times 10^{-9}\ \text{C})(-900\ \text{J/C}) = -3.6 \times 10^{-6}\ \text{J}$$

At point b,

$$U_b = qV_b = (4.0 \times 10^{-9}\ \text{C})(1930\ \text{J/C}) = 7.7 \times 10^{-6}\ \text{J}$$

At point c,

$$U_c = qV_c = 0$$

All of these values correspond to U and V being zero at infinity.

EVALUATE: Note that *no* net work is done on the 4.0-nC charge if it moves from point c to infinity *by any path*. In particular, let the path be along the perpendicular bisector of the line joining the other two charges q_1 and q_2 in Fig. 23.14. As shown in Example 21.9 (Section 21.5), at points on the bisector the direction of $\vec{E}$ is perpendicular to the bisector. Hence the force on the 4.0-nC charge is perpendicular to the path, and no work is done in any displacement along it.

Although we have defined the electron volt in terms of *potential* energy, we can use it for *any* form of energy, such as the kinetic energy of a moving particle. When we speak of a "one-million-electron-volt proton," we mean a proton with a kinetic energy of one million electron volts (1 MeV), equal to $(10^6)(1.602 \times 10^{-19}\ \text{J}) = 1.602 \times 10^{-13}\ \text{J}$ (Fig. 23.13).

23.13 This accelerator at the Fermi National Accelerator Laboratory in Illinois gives protons a kinetic energy of 400 MeV $(4 \times 10^8\ \text{eV})$. Additional acceleration stages increase their kinetic energy to 980 GeV, or 0.98 TeV $(9.8 \times 10^{11}\ \text{eV})$.

Example 23.3 Electric force and electric potential

A proton (charge $+e = 1.602 \times 10^{-19}\ \text{C}$) moves in a straight line from point a to point b inside a linear accelerator, a total distance $d = 0.50\ \text{m}$. The electric field is uniform along this line, with magnitude $E = 1.5 \times 10^7\ \text{V/m} = 1.5 \times 10^7\ \text{N/C}$ in the direction from a to b. Determine (a) the force on the proton; (b) the work done on it by the field; (c) the potential difference $V_a - V_b$.

SOLUTION

IDENTIFY: This problem uses the relationship between electric field (which we are given) and electric force (which is one of our target variables). It also uses the relationship among force, work, and potential energy difference.

SET UP: We are given the electric field, so it is straightforward to find the electric force on the proton. Calculating the work done on the proton by this force is also straightforward because $\vec{E}$ is uniform, which means that the force is constant. Once the work is known, we find the potential difference using Eq. (23.13).

EXECUTE: (a) The force on the proton is in the same direction as the electric field, and its magnitude is

$$F = qE = (1.602 \times 10^{-19}\ \text{C})(1.5 \times 10^7\ \text{N/C}) = 2.4 \times 10^{-12}\ \text{N}$$

(b) The force is constant and in the same direction as the displacement, so the work done on the proton is

$$W_{a\to b} = Fd = (2.4 \times 10^{-12}\ \text{N})(0.50\ \text{m}) = 1.2 \times 10^{-12}\ \text{J}$$
$$= (1.2 \times 10^{-12}\ \text{J})\frac{1\ \text{eV}}{1.602 \times 10^{-19}\ \text{J}}$$
$$= 7.5 \times 10^6\ \text{eV} = 7.5\ \text{MeV}$$

(c) From Eq. (23.13) the potential difference is the work per unit charge, which is

$$V_a - V_b = \frac{W_{a\to b}}{q} = \frac{1.2 \times 10^{-12}\ \text{J}}{1.602 \times 10^{-19}\ \text{C}} = 7.5 \times 10^6\ \text{J/C}$$
$$= 7.5 \times 10^6\ \text{V} = 7.5\ \text{MV}$$

We can get this same result even more easily by remembering that 1 electron volt equals 1 volt multiplied by the charge e. Since the work done is 7.5×10^6 eV and the charge is e, the potential difference is $(7.5 \times 10^6\ \text{eV})/e = 7.5 \times 10^6\ \text{V}$.

EVALUATE: We can check our result in part (c) by using Eq. (23.17) or (23.18) to calculate an integral of the electric field. The angle ϕ between the constant field $\vec{E}$ and the displacement is zero, so Eq. (23.17) becomes

$$V_a - V_b = \int_a^b E\cos\phi\, dl = \int_a^b E\, dl = E\int_a^b dl$$

The integral of dl from a to b is just the distance d, so we again find

$$V_a - V_b = Ed = (1.5 \times 10^7\ \text{V/m})(0.50\ \text{m}) = 7.5 \times 10^6\ \text{V}$$

Example 23.4 Potential due to two point charges

An electric dipole consists of two point charges, $q_1 = +12$ nC and $q_2 = -12$ nC, placed 10 cm apart (Fig. 23.14). Compute the potentials at points a, b, and c by adding the potentials due to either charge, as in Eq. (23.15).

SOLUTION

IDENTIFY: This is the same arrangement of charges as in Example 21.9 (Section 21.5). In that example we calculated electric *field* at each point by doing a *vector* sum. Our target variable in this problem is the electric *potential* V at three points.

SET UP: To find V at each point, we do the *algebraic* sum in Eq. (23.15):

$$V = \frac{1}{4\pi\epsilon_0}\sum_i \frac{q_i}{r_i}$$

EXECUTE: At point a the potential due to the positive charge q_1 is

$$\begin{aligned}\frac{1}{4\pi\epsilon_0}\frac{q_1}{r_1} &= (9.0 \times 10^9\ \text{N}\cdot\text{m}^2/\text{C}^2)\frac{12 \times 10^{-9}\ \text{C}}{0.060\ \text{m}} \\ &= 1800\ \text{N}\cdot\text{m/C} \\ &= 1800\ \text{J/C} = 1800\ \text{V}\end{aligned}$$

and the potential due to the negative charge q_2 is

$$\begin{aligned}\frac{1}{4\pi\epsilon_0}\frac{q_2}{r_2} &= (9.0 \times 10^9\ \text{N}\cdot\text{m}^2/\text{C}^2)\frac{(-12 \times 10^{-9}\ \text{C})}{0.040\ \text{m}} \\ &= -2700\ \text{N}\cdot\text{m/C} \\ &= -2700\ \text{J/C} = -2700\ \text{V}\end{aligned}$$

The potential V_a at point a is the sum of these:

$$V_a = 1800\ \text{V} + (-2700\ \text{V}) = -900\ \text{V}$$

By similar calculations you can show that at point b the potential due to the positive charge is +2700 V, the potential due to the negative charge is −770 V, and

$$V_b = 2700\ \text{V} + (-770\ \text{V}) = 1930\ \text{V}$$

23.14 What are the potentials at points a, b, and c due to this electric dipole?

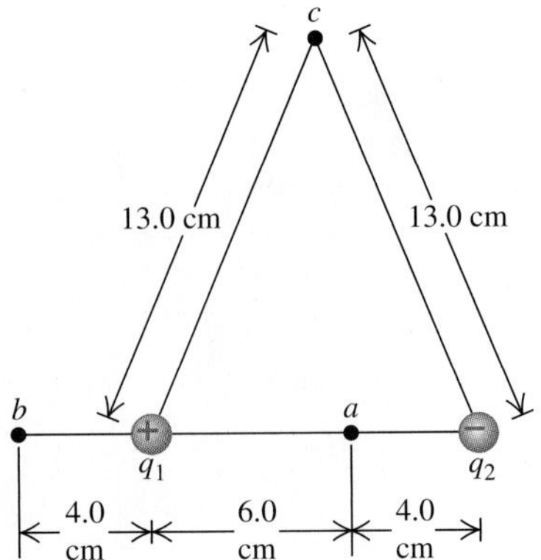

At point c the potential due to the positive charge is

$$\frac{1}{4\pi\epsilon_0}\frac{q_1}{r_1} = (9.0 \times 10^9\ \text{N}\cdot\text{m}^2/\text{C}^2)\frac{12 \times 10^{-9}\ \text{C}}{0.13\ \text{m}} = 830\ \text{V}$$

The potential due to the negative charge is −830 V, and the total potential is zero:

$$V_c = 830\ \text{V} + (-830\ \text{V}) = 0$$

The potential is also equal to zero at infinity (infinitely far from both charges).

EVALUATE: Comparing this example with Example 21.9 shows that it's much easier to calculate electric potential (a scalar) than electric field (a vector). We'll take advantage of this simplification whenever possible.

Example 23.5 Potential and potential energy

Compute the potential energy associated with a point charge of +4.0 nC if it is placed at points a, b, and c in Fig. 23.14.

SOLUTION

IDENTIFY: We know the value of the electric potential at each of these points, and we need to find the potential energy for a point charge placed at each point.

SET UP: For any point charge q, the associated potential energy is $U = qV$. We use the values of V from Example 23.4.

EXECUTE: At point a,

$$U_a = qV_a = (4.0 \times 10^{-9}\ \text{C})(-900\ \text{J/C}) = -3.6 \times 10^{-6}\ \text{J}$$

At point b,

$$U_b = qV_b = (4.0 \times 10^{-9}\ \text{C})(1930\ \text{J/C}) = 7.7 \times 10^{-6}\ \text{J}$$

At point c,

$$U_c = qV_c = 0$$

All of these values correspond to U and V being zero at infinity.

EVALUATE: Note that *no* net work is done on the 4.0-nC charge if it moves from point c to infinity *by any path.* In particular, let the path be along the perpendicular bisector of the line joining the other two charges q_1 and q_2 in Fig. 23.14. As shown in Example 21.9 (Section 21.5), at points on the bisector the direction of $\vec{E}$ is perpendicular to the bisector. Hence the force on the 4.0-nC charge is perpendicular to the path, and no work is done in any displacement along it.

In this expression, r_i is the distance from the ith charge, q_i, to the point at which V is evaluated. Just as the electric field due to a collection of point charges is the *vector* sum of the fields produced by each charge, the electric potential due to a collection of point charges is the *scalar* sum of the potentials due to each charge. When we have a continuous distribution of charge along a line, over a surface, or through a volume, we divide the charge into elements dq, and the sum in Eq. (23.15) becomes an integral:

$$V = \frac{1}{4\pi\epsilon_0}\int\frac{dq}{r} \quad \text{(potential due to a continuous distribution of charge)} \tag{23.16}$$

where r is the distance from the charge element dq to the field point where we are finding V. We'll work out several examples of such cases. The potential defined by Eqs. (23.15) and (23.16) is zero at points that are infinitely far away from *all* the charges. Later we'll encounter cases in which the charge distribution itself extends to infinity. We'll find that in such cases we cannot set $V = 0$ at infinity, and we'll need to exercise care in using and interpreting Eqs. (23.15) and (23.16).

CAUTION **What is electric potential?** Before getting too involved in the details of how to calculate electric potential, you should stop and remind yourself what potential is. The electric *potential* at a certain point is the potential energy that would be associated with a *unit* charge placed at that point. That's why potential is measured in joules per coulomb, or volts. Keep in mind, too, that there doesn't have to be a charge at a given point for a potential V to exist at that point. (In the same way, an electric field can exist at a given point even if there's no charge there to respond to it.)

Finding Electric Potential from Electric Field

When we are given a collection of point charges, Eq. (23.15) is usually the easiest way to calculate the potential V. But in some problems in which the electric field is known or can be found easily, it is easier to determine V from $\vec{E}$. The force $\vec{F}$ on a test charge q_0 can be written as $\vec{F} = q_0\vec{E}$, so from Eq. (23.1) the work done by the electric force as the test charge moves from a to b is given by

$$W_{a\to b} = \int_a^b \vec{F}\cdot d\vec{l} = \int_a^b q_0\vec{E}\cdot d\vec{l}$$

If we divide this by q_0 and compare the result with Eq. (23.13), we find

$$V_a - V_b = \int_a^b \vec{E}\cdot d\vec{l} = \int_a^b E\cos\phi\, dl \quad \text{(potential difference as an integral of } \vec{E}\text{)} \tag{23.17}$$

The value of $V_a - V_b$ is independent of the path taken from a to b, just as the value of $W_{a\to b}$ is independent of the path. To interpret Eq. (23.17), remember that $\vec{E}$ is the electric force per unit charge on a test charge. If the line integral $\int_a^b \vec{E}\cdot d\vec{l}$ is positive, the electric field does positive work on a positive test charge as it moves from a to b. In this case the electric potential energy decreases as the test charge moves, so the potential energy per unit charge decreases as well; hence V_b is less than V_a and $V_a - V_b$ is positive.

As an illustration, consider a positive point charge (Fig. 23.12a). The electric field is directed away from the charge, and $V = q/4\pi\epsilon_0 r$ is positive at any finite distance from the charge. If you move away from the charge, in the direction of $\vec{E}$, you move toward lower values of V; if you move toward the charge, in the direction opposite $\vec{E}$, you move toward greater values of V. For the negative point charge in Fig. 23.12b, $\vec{E}$ is directed toward the charge and $V = q/4\pi\epsilon_0 r$ is negative at any finite distance from the charge. In this case, if you move toward the charge, you are moving in the direction of $\vec{E}$ and in the direction of decreasing (more negative) V. Moving away from the charge, in the direction opposite $\vec{E}$,

23.12 If you move in the direction of $\vec{E}$, electric potential V decreases; if you move in the direction opposite $\vec{E}$, V increases.

(a) A positive point charge

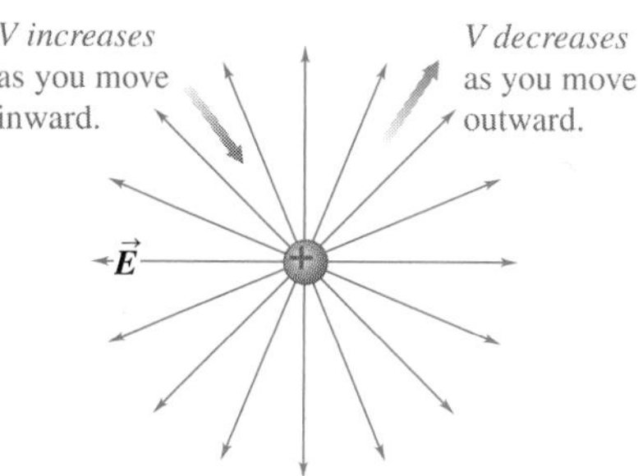
V increases
as you move
inward.
V decreases
as you move
outward.
E

(b) A negative point charge

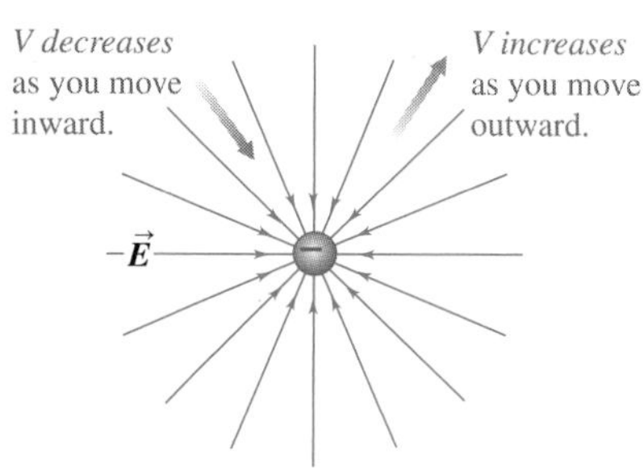
V decreases
as you move
inward.
V increases
as you move
outward.
E

moves you toward increasing (less negative) values of V. The general rule, valid for *any* electric field, is: Moving *with* the direction of $\vec{E}$ means moving in the direction of *decreasing* V, and moving *against* the direction of $\vec{E}$ means moving in the direction of *increasing* V.

Also, a positive test charge q_0 experiences an electric force in the direction of $\vec{E}$, toward lower values of V; a negative test charge experiences a force opposite $\vec{E}$, toward higher values of V. Thus a positive charge tends to "fall" from a high-potential region to a lower-potential region. The opposite is true for a negative charge.

Notice that Eq. (23.17) can be rewritten as

$$V_a - V_b = -\int_b^a \vec{E} \cdot d\vec{l} \tag{23.18}$$

This has a negative sign compared to the integral in Eq. (23.17), and the limits are reversed; hence Eqs. (23.17) and (23.18) are equivalent. But Eq. (23.18) has a slightly different interpretation. To move a unit charge slowly against the electric force, we must apply an *external* force per unit charge equal to $-\vec{E}$, equal and opposite to the electric force per unit charge $\vec{E}$. Equation (23.18) says that $V_a - V_b = V_{ab}$, the potential of a with respect to b, equals the work done per unit charge by this external force to move a unit charge from b to a. This is the same alternative interpretation we discussed under Eq. (23.13).

Equations (23.17) and (23.18) show that the unit of potential difference (1 V) is equal to the unit of electric field (1 N/C) multiplied by the unit of distance (1 m). Hence the unit of electric field can be expressed as 1 *volt per meter* (1 V/m), as well as 1 N/C:

$$1\text{ V/m} = 1\text{ volt/meter} = 1\text{ N/C} = 1\text{ newton/coulomb}$$

In practice, the volt per meter is the usual unit of electric-field magnitude.

Electron Volts

The magnitude e of the electron charge can be used to define a unit of energy that is useful in many calculations with atomic and nuclear systems. When a particle with charge q moves from a point where the potential is V_b to a point where it is V_a, the change in the potential energy U is

$$U_a - U_b = q(V_a - V_b) = qV_{ab}$$

If the charge q equals the magnitude e of the electron charge, 1.602×10^{-19} C, and the potential difference is $V_{ab} = 1$ V, the change in energy is

$$U_a - U_b = (1.602 \times 10^{-19}\text{ C})(1\text{ V}) = 1.602 \times 10^{-19}\text{ J}$$

This quantity of energy is defined to be 1 **electron volt** (1 eV):

$$1\text{ eV} = 1.602 \times 10^{-19}\text{ J}$$

The multiples meV, keV, MeV, GeV, and TeV are often used.

CAUTION **Electron volts vs. volts** Remember that the electron volt is a unit of energy, *not* a unit of potential or potential difference!

When a particle with charge e moves through a potential difference of 1 volt, the change in potential *energy* is 1 eV. If the charge is some multiple of e—say Ne—the change in potential energy in electron volts is N times the potential difference in volts. For example, when an alpha particle, which has charge $2e$, moves between two points with a potential difference of 1000 V, the change in potential energy is $2(1000\text{ eV}) = 2000$ eV. To confirm this, we write

$$\begin{aligned} U_a - U_b = qV_{ab} &= (2e)(1000\text{ V}) = (2)(1.602 \times 10^{-19}\text{ C})(1000\text{ V}) \\ &= 3.204 \times 10^{-16}\text{ J} = 2000\text{ eV} \end{aligned}$$

Example 23.6 Finding potential by integration

By integrating the electric field as in Eq. (23.17), find the potential at a distance r from a point charge q.

SOLUTION

IDENTIFY: This problem asks us to find the electric potential from the electric field.

SET UP: To find the potential V at a distance r from the point charge, we let point a in Eq. (23.17) be at distance r and let point b be at infinity (Fig. 23.15). As usual, we choose the potential to be zero at an infinite distance from the charge.

EXECUTE: To carry out the integral, we can choose any path we like between points a and b. The most convenient path is a straight radial line as shown in Fig. 23.15, so that $d\vec{l}$ is in the radial direction and has magnitude dr. If q is positive, $\vec{E}$ and $d\vec{l}$ are always parallel, so $\phi = 0$ and Eq. (23.17) becomes

$$V - 0 = \int_r^\infty E\,dr = \int_r^\infty \frac{q}{4\pi\epsilon_0 r^2}dr$$

$$= -\frac{q}{4\pi\epsilon_0 r}\bigg|_r^\infty = 0 - \left(-\frac{q}{4\pi\epsilon_0 r}\right)$$

$$V = \frac{q}{4\pi\epsilon_0 r}$$

This agrees with Eq. (23.14). If q is negative, $\vec{E}$ is radially inward while $d\vec{l}$ is still radially outward, so $\phi = 180°$. Since $\cos 180° = -1$, this adds a minus sign to the above result. However, the field magnitude E is always positive, and since q is negative, we must write $E = |q|/4\pi\epsilon_0 r = -q/4\pi\epsilon_0 r$, giving another minus sign. The two minus signs cancel, and the above result for V is valid for point charges of either sign.

23.15 Calculating the potential by integrating $\vec{E}$ for a single point charge.

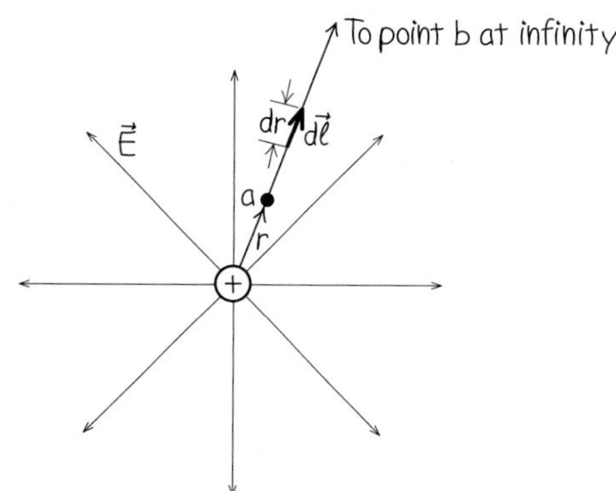

EVALUATE: We can get the same result by using Eq. (21.7) for the electric field, which is valid for either sign of q, and writing $d\vec{l} = \hat{r}dr$:

$$V - 0 = V = \int_r^\infty \vec{E}\cdot d\vec{l}$$

$$= \int_r^\infty \frac{1}{4\pi\epsilon_0}\frac{q}{r^2}\hat{r}\cdot\hat{r}\,dr = \int_r^\infty \frac{q}{4\pi\epsilon_0 r^2}dr$$

$$V = \frac{q}{4\pi\epsilon_0 r}$$

Example 23.7 Moving through a potential difference

In Fig. 23.16 a dust particle with mass $m = 5.0 \times 10^{-9}$ kg $= 5.0\ \mu$g and charge $q_0 = 2.0$ nC starts from rest at point a and moves in a straight line to point b. What is its speed v at point b?

SOLUTION

IDENTIFY: This problem involves the change in speed and hence kinetic energy of the particle, so we can use an energy approach. This problem would be difficult to solve without using energy techniques, since the force that acts on the particle varies in magnitude as the particle moves from a to b.

SET UP: Only the conservative electric force acts on the particle, so mechanical energy is conserved:

$$K_a + U_a = K_b + U_b$$

EXECUTE: For this situation, $K_a = 0$ and $K_b = \frac{1}{2}mv^2$. We get the potential energies (U) from the potentials (V) using Eq. (23.12):

23.16 The particle moves from point a to point b; its acceleration is not constant.

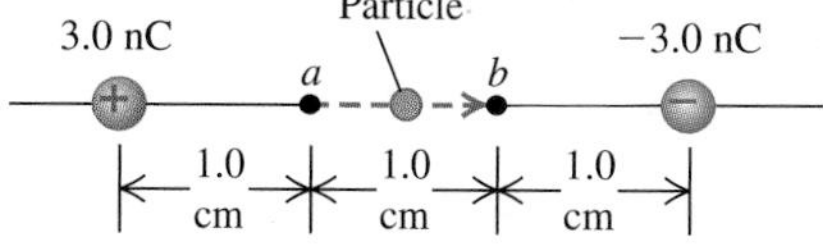

$U_a = q_0V_a$ and $U_b = q_0V_b$. Substituting these into the energy-conservation equation and solving for v, we find

$$0 + q_0V_a = \frac{1}{2}mv^2 + q_0V_b$$

$$v = \sqrt{\frac{2q_0(V_a - V_b)}{m}}$$

Continued

We calculate the potentials using Eq. (23.15), just as we did in Example 23.4:

$$V_a = (9.0 \times 10^9\ \text{N}\cdot\text{m}^2/\text{C}^2) \times \left(\frac{3.0 \times 10^{-9}\ \text{C}}{0.010\ \text{m}} + \frac{(-3.0 \times 10^{-9}\ \text{C})}{0.020\ \text{m}}\right) = 1350\ \text{V}$$

$$V_b = (9.0 \times 10^9\ \text{N}\cdot\text{m}^2/\text{C}^2) \times \left(\frac{3.0 \times 10^{-9}\ \text{C}}{0.020\ \text{m}} + \frac{(-3.0 \times 10^{-9}\ \text{C})}{0.010\ \text{m}}\right) = -1350\ \text{V}$$

$$V_a - V_b = (1350\ \text{V}) - (-1350\ \text{V}) = 2700\ \text{V}$$

Finally,

$$v = \sqrt{\frac{2(2.0 \times 10^{-9}\ \text{C})(2700\ \text{V})}{5.0 \times 10^{-9}\ \text{kg}}} = 46\ \text{m/s}$$

EVALUATE: Our result makes sense: The positive test charge gains speed as it moves away from the positive charge and toward the negative charge. To check unit consistency in the final line of the calculation, note that $1\ \text{V} = 1\ \text{J/C}$, so the numerator under the radical has units of J or $\text{kg}\cdot\text{m}^2/\text{s}^2$.

We can use exactly this same method to find the speed of an electron accelerated across a potential difference of 500 V in an oscilloscope tube or 20 kV in a TV picture tube. The end-of-chapter problems include several examples of such calculations.

Test Your Understanding of Section 23.2 If the electric *potential* at a certain point is zero, does the electric *field* at that point have to be zero? (*Hint:* Consider point c in Example 23.4 and Example 21.9.)

23.3 Calculating Electric Potential

When calculating the potential due to a charge distribution, we usually follow one of two routes. If we know the charge distribution, we can use Eq. (23.15) or (23.16). Or if we know how the electric field depends on position, we can use Eq. (23.17), defining the potential to be zero at some convenient place. Some problems require a combination of these approaches.

As you read through these examples, compare them with the related examples of calculating electric *field* in Section 21.5. You'll see how much easier it is to calculate scalar electric potentials than vector electric fields. The moral is clear: Whenever possible, solve problems using an energy approach (using electric potential and electric potential energy) rather than a dynamics approach (using electric fields and electric forces).

Problem-Solving Strategy 23.1 Calculating Electric Potential

MP

IDENTIFY *the relevant concepts:* Remember that potential is *potential energy per unit charge.* Understanding this statement can get you a long way.

SET UP *the problem* using the following steps:

1. Make a drawing that clearly shows the locations of the charges (which may be point charges or a continuous distribution of charge) and your choice of coordinate axes.
2. Indicate on your drawing the position of the point at which you want to calculate the electric potential V. Sometimes this position will be an arbitrary one (say, a point a distance r from the center of a charged sphere).

EXECUTE *the solution* as follows:

1. To find the potential due to a collection of point charges, use Eq. (23.15). If you are given a continuous charge distribution, devise a way to divide it into infinitesimal elements and then use Eq. (23.16). Carry out the integration, using appropriate limits to include the entire charge distribution. In the integral, be careful about which geometric quantities vary and which are held constant.
2. If you are given the electric field, or if you can find it using any of the methods presented in Chapter 21 or 22, it may be easier to use Eq. (23.17) or (23.18) to calculate the potential difference between points a and b. When appropriate, make use of your freedom to define V to be zero at some convenient place, and choose this place to be point b. (For point charges, this will usually be at infinity. For other distributions of charge—especially those that themselves extend to infinity—it may be convenient or necessary to define V_b to be zero at some finite distance from the charge distribution. This is just like defining U to be zero at ground level in gravitational problems.) Then the potential at any other point, say a, can by found from Eq. (23.17) or (23.18) with $V_b = 0$.
3. Remember that potential is a *scalar* quantity, not a *vector.* It doesn't have components! However, you may have to use components of the vectors $\vec{E}$ and $d\vec{l}$ when you use Eq. (23.17) or (23.18).

EVALUATE *your answer:* Check whether your answer agrees with your intuition. If your result gives V as a function of position, make a graph of this function to see whether it makes sense. If you know the electric field, you can make a rough check of your result for V by verifying that V decreases if you move in the direction of $\vec{E}$.

Example 23.8 A charged conducting sphere

A solid conducting sphere of radius R has a total charge q. Find the potential everywhere, both outside and inside the sphere.

SOLUTION

IDENTIFY: We used Gauss's law in Example 22.5 (Section 22.4) to find the electric field at all points for this charge distribution. We can use that result to determine the potential at all points.

SET UP: We choose the origin at the center of the sphere. Since we know E at all values of the distance r from the center of the sphere, we can determine V as a function of r.

EXECUTE: From Example 22.5, at all points *outside* the sphere the field is the same as if the sphere were removed and replaced by a point charge q. We take $V = 0$ at infinity, as we did for a point charge. Then the potential at a point outside the sphere at a distance r from its center is the same as the potential due to a point charge q at the center:

$$V = \frac{1}{4\pi\epsilon_0}\frac{q}{r}$$

The potential at the surface of the sphere is $V_{\text{surface}} = q/4\pi\epsilon_0 R$.

Inside the sphere, $\vec{E}$ is zero everywhere; otherwise, charge would move within the sphere. Hence if a test charge moves from any point to any other point inside the sphere, no work is done on that charge. This means that the potential is the same at every point inside the sphere and is equal to its value $q/4\pi\epsilon_0 R$ at the surface.

EVALUATE: Figure 23.17 shows the field and potential as a function of r for a positive charge q. In this case the electric field points radially away from the sphere. As you move away from the sphere, in the direction of $\vec{E}$, V decreases (as it should). The electric field at the surface has magnitude $E_{\text{surface}} = |q|/4\pi\epsilon_0 R^2$.

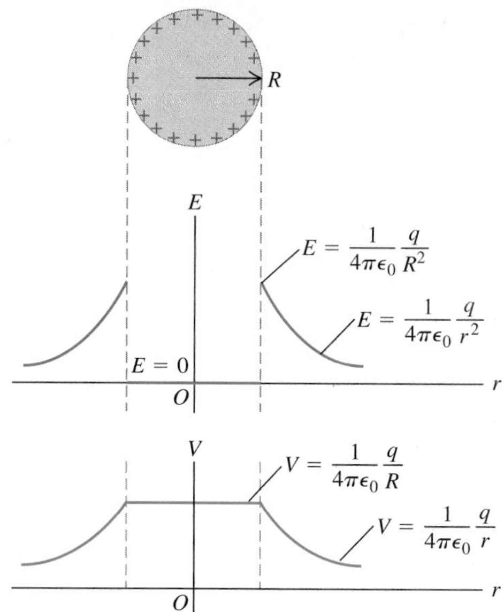

23.17 Electric field magnitude E and potential V at points inside and outside a positively charged spherical conductor.

Ionization and Corona Discharge

The results of Example 23.8 have numerous practical consequences. One consequence relates to the maximum potential to which a conductor in air can be raised. This potential is limited because air molecules become *ionized,* and air becomes a conductor, at an electric-field magnitude of about 3×10^6 V/m. Assume for the moment that q is positive. When we compare the expressions in Example 23.8 for the potential V_{surface} and field magnitude E_{surface} at the surface of a charged conducting sphere, we note that $V_{\text{surface}} = E_{\text{surface}}R$. Thus, if E_{m} represents the electric-field magnitude at which air becomes conductive (known as the *dielectric strength* of air), then the maximum potential V_{m} to which a spherical conductor can be raised is

$$V_{\text{m}} = RE_{\text{m}}$$

For a conducting sphere 1 cm in radius in air, $V_{\text{m}} = (10^{-2}\text{ m})(3 \times 10^6\text{ V/m}) = 30{,}000$ V. No amount of "charging" could raise the potential of a conducting sphere of this size in air higher than about 30,000 V; attempting to raise the potential further by adding extra charge would cause the surrounding air to become ionized and conductive, and the extra added charge would leak into the air.

To attain even higher potentials, high-voltage machines such as Van de Graaff generators use spherical terminals with very large radii (see Fig. 22.27 and the photograph that opens Chapter 22). For example, a terminal of radius $R = 2$ m has a maximum potential $V_{\text{m}} = (2\text{ m})(3 \times 10^6\text{ V/m}) = 6 \times 10^6\text{ V} = 6$ MV. Such machines are sometimes placed in pressurized tanks filled with a gas such as sulfur hexafluoride (SF_6) that has a larger value of E_{m} than does air and, therefore, can withstand even larger fields without becoming conductive.

23.18 The metal mast at the top of the Empire State Building acts as a lightning rod. It is struck by lightning as many as 500 times each year.

Our result in Example 23.8 also explains what happens with a charged conductor with a very *small* radius of curvature, such as a sharp point or thin wire. Because the maximum potential is proportional to the radius, even relatively small potentials applied to sharp points in air produce sufficiently high fields just outside the point to ionize the surrounding air, making it become a conductor. The resulting current and its associated glow (visible in a dark room) are called *corona*. Laser printers and photocopying machines use corona from fine wires to spray charge on the imaging drum (see Fig. 21.2).

A large-radius conductor is used in situations where it's important to *prevent* corona. An example is the metal ball at the end of a car radio antenna, which prevents the static that would be caused by corona. Another example is the blunt end of a metal lightning rod (Fig. 23.18). If there is an excess charge in the atmosphere, as happens during thunderstorms, a substantial charge of the opposite sign can build up on this blunt end. As a result, when the atmospheric charge is discharged through a lightning bolt, it tends to be attracted to the charged lightning rod rather than to other nearby structures that could be damaged. (A conducting wire connecting the lightning rod to the ground then allows the acquired charge to dissipate harmlessly.) A lightning rod with a sharp end would allow less charge buildup and hence would be less effective.

Example 23.9 Oppositely charged parallel plates

Find the potential at any height y between the two oppositely charged parallel plates discussed in Section 23.1 (Fig. 23.19).

SOLUTION

IDENTIFY: From Section 23.1 we know the electric *potential energy* U for a test charge q_0 as a function of y. Our goal here is to find the electric *potential* V due to the charges on the plates as a function of y.

SET UP: From Eq. (23.5), $U = q_0Ey$ at a point a distance y above the bottom plate. We use this expression to determine the potential V at such a point.

EXECUTE: The potential $V(y)$ at coordinate y is the potential energy per unit charge:

$$V(y) = \frac{U(y)}{q_0} = \frac{q_0Ey}{q_0} = Ey$$

We have chosen $U(y)$, and therefore $V(y)$, to be zero at point b, where $y = 0$. Even if we choose the potential to be different from zero at b, it is still true that

$$V(y) - V_b = Ey$$

The potential decreases as we move in the direction of $\vec{E}$ from the upper to the lower plate. At point a, where $y = d$ and $V(y) = V_a$,

$$V_a - V_b = Ed \quad \text{and} \quad E = \frac{V_a - V_b}{d} = \frac{V_{ab}}{d}$$

where V_{ab} is the potential of the positive plate with respect to the negative plate. That is, the electric field equals the potential difference between the plates divided by the distance between them. For a given potential difference V_{ab}, the smaller the distance d between the two plates, the greater the magnitude E of the electric field. (This relationship between E and V_{ab} holds *only* for the planar geometry we have described. It does *not* work for situations such as concentric cylinders or spheres in which the electric field is not uniform.)

23.19 The charged parallel plates from Fig. 23.2

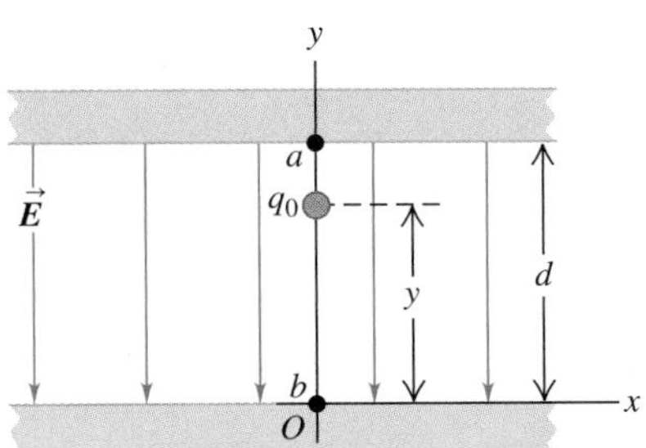

EVALUATE: Our result tells us how to measure the charge density on the charges on the two plates in Fig. 23.19. In Example 22.8 (Section 22.4), we derived the expression $E = \sigma/\epsilon_0$ for the electric field E between two conducting plates having surface charge densities $+\sigma$ and $-\sigma$. Setting this expression equal to $E = V_{ab}/d$ gives

$$\sigma = \frac{\epsilon_0 V_{ab}}{d}$$

The surface charge density on the positive plate is directly proportional to the potential difference between the plates, and its value σ can be determined by measuring V_{ab}. This technique is useful because no instruments are available that read surface charge density directly. On the negative plate the surface charge density is $-\sigma$.

CAUTION **"Zero potential" is arbitrary** You might think that if a conducting body has zero potential, it must necessarily also have zero net charge. But that just isn't so! As an example, the plate at $y = 0$ in Fig. 23.19 has zero potential $(V = 0)$ but has a nonzero charge per unit area $-\sigma$. Remember that there's nothing particularly special about the place where potential is zero; we can *define* this place to be wherever we want it to be.

Example 23.10 An infinite line charge or charged conducting cylinder

Find the potential at a distance r from a very long line of charge with linear charge density (charge per unit length) λ.

SOLUTION

IDENTIFY: One approach to this problem is to divide the line of charge into infinitesimal elements, as we did in Example 21.11 (Section 21.5) to find the electric field produced by such a line. We could then integrate as in Eq. (23.16) to find the net potential V. In this case, however, our task is greatly simplified because we already know the electric field.

SET UP: In both Example 21.11 and Example 22.6 (Section 22.4), we found that the electric field at a distance r from a long straight-line charge (Fig. 23.20a) has only a radial component, given by

$$E_r = \frac{1}{2\pi\epsilon_0}\frac{\lambda}{r}$$

We use this expression to find the potential by integrating $\vec{E}$ as in Eq. (23.17).

EXECUTE: Since the field has only a radial component, the scalar product $\vec{E}\cdot d\vec{l}$ is equal to $E_r dr$. Hence the potential of any point a with respect to any other point b, at radial distances r_a and r_b from the line of charge, is

$$V_a - V_b = \int_a^b \vec{E}\cdot d\vec{l} = \int_a^b E_r dr = \frac{\lambda}{2\pi\epsilon_0}\int_{r_a}^{r_b}\frac{dr}{r} = \frac{\lambda}{2\pi\epsilon_0}\ln\frac{r_b}{r_a}$$

If we take point b at infinity and set $V_b = 0$, we find that V_a is *infinite:*

$$V_a = \frac{\lambda}{2\pi\epsilon_0}\ln\frac{\infty}{r_a} = \infty$$

This shows that if we try to define V to be zero at infinity, then V must be infinite at *any* finite distance from the line charge. This is *not* a useful way to define V for this problem! The difficulty is that the charge distribution itself extends to infinity.

To get around this difficulty, remember that we can define V to be zero at any point we like. We set $V_b = 0$ at point b at an arbitrary radial distance r_0. Then the potential $V = V_a$ at point a at a radial distance r is given by $V - 0 = (\lambda/2\pi\epsilon_0)\ln(r_0/r)$, or

$$V = \frac{\lambda}{2\pi\epsilon_0}\ln\frac{r_0}{r}$$

EVALUATE: According to our result, if λ is positive, then V decreases as r increases. This is as it should be: V decreases as we move in the direction of $\vec{E}$.

From Example 22.6, the expression for E_r with which we started also applies outside a long charged conducting cylinder with charge per unit length λ (Fig. 23.20b). Hence our result also gives the potential for such a cylinder, but only for values of r (the distance from the cylinder axis) equal to or greater than the radius R of the cylinder. If we choose r_0 to be the cylinder radius R, so that $V = 0$ when $r = R$, then at any point for which $r > R$,

$$V = \frac{\lambda}{2\pi\epsilon_0}\ln\frac{R}{r}$$

Inside the cylinder, $\vec{E} = \mathbf{0}$, and V has the same value (zero) as on the cylinder's surface.

23.20 Electric field outside **(a)** a long positively charged wire and **(b)** a long, positively charged cylinder.

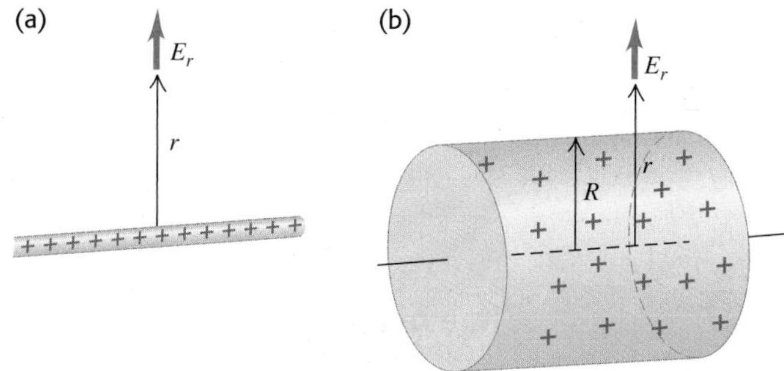

Example 23.11 A ring of charge

Electric charge is distributed uniformly around a thin ring of radius a, with total charge Q (Fig. 23.21). Find the potential at a point P on the ring axis at a distance x from the center of the ring.

SOLUTION

IDENTIFY: We already know the electric field at all points along the x-axis from Example 21.10 (Section 21.5), so we could solve the problem by integrating $\vec{E}$ as in Eq. (23.17) to find V along this axis. Alternatively, we could divide the ring up into infinitesimal segments and use Eq. (23.16) to find V.

SET UP: Figure 23.21 shows that it's far easier to find V on the axis by using the infinitesimal-segment approach. That's because

23.21 All the charge in a ring of charge Q is the same distance r from a point P on the ring axis.

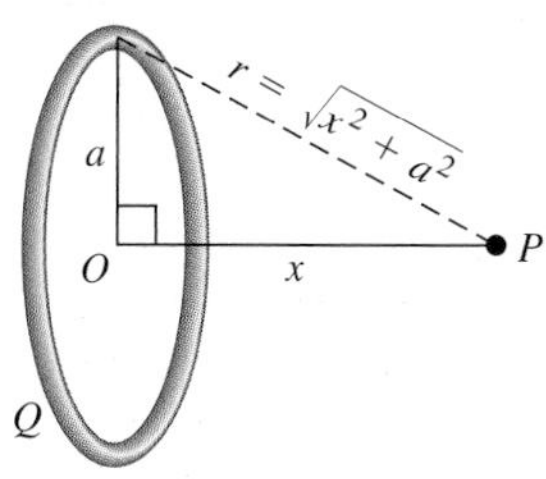

Continued

all parts of the ring (that is, all elements of the charge distribution) are the same distance r from point P.

EXECUTE: Figure 23.21 shows that the distance from each charge element dq on the ring to the point P is $r = \sqrt{x^2 + a^2}$. Hence we can take the factor $1/r$ outside the integral in Eq. (23.16), and

$$V = \frac{1}{4\pi\epsilon_0}\int\frac{dq}{r} = \frac{1}{4\pi\epsilon_0}\frac{1}{\sqrt{x^2 + a^2}}\int dq = \frac{1}{4\pi\epsilon_0}\frac{Q}{\sqrt{x^2 + a^2}}$$

Potential is a *scalar* quantity; there is no need to consider components of vectors in this calculation, as we had to do when we found the electric field at P. So the potential calculation is a lot simpler than the field calculation.

EVALUATE: When x is much larger than a, the above expression for V becomes approximately equal to $V = Q/4\pi\epsilon_0 x$. This corresponds to the potential of a point charge Q at distance x. So when we are very far away from a charged ring, it looks like a point charge. (We drew a similar conclusion about the electric field of a ring in Example 21.10.)

These results for V can also be found by integrating the expression for E_x found in Example 21.10 (see Problem 23.69).

Example 23.12 A line of charge

Electric charge Q is distributed uniformly along a line or thin rod of length $2a$. Find the potential at a point P along the perpendicular bisector of the rod at a distance x from its center.

SOLUTION

IDENTIFY: This is the same situation as in Example 21.11 (Section 21.5), where we found an expression for the electric field $\vec{E}$ at an arbitrary point on the x-axis. We could integrate $\vec{E}$ using Eq. (23.17) to find V. Instead, we'll integrate over the charge distribution using Eq. (23.16) to get a bit more experience with this approach.

SET UP: Figure 23.22 shows the situation. Unlike the situation in Example 23.11, each charge element dQ is a different distance from point P.

EXECUTE: As in Example 21.11, the element of charge dQ corresponding to an element of length dy on the rod is given by $dQ = (Q/2a)dy$. The distance from dQ to P is $\sqrt{x^2 + y^2}$, and the contribution dV that it makes to the potential at P is

$$dV = \frac{1}{4\pi\epsilon_0}\frac{Q}{2a}\frac{dy}{\sqrt{x^2 + y^2}}$$

To get the potential at P due to the entire rod, we integrate dV over the length of the rod from $y = -a$ to $y = a$:

$$V = \frac{1}{4\pi\epsilon_0}\frac{Q}{2a}\int_{-a}^{a}\frac{dy}{\sqrt{x^2 + y^2}}$$

23.22 Our sketch for this problem.

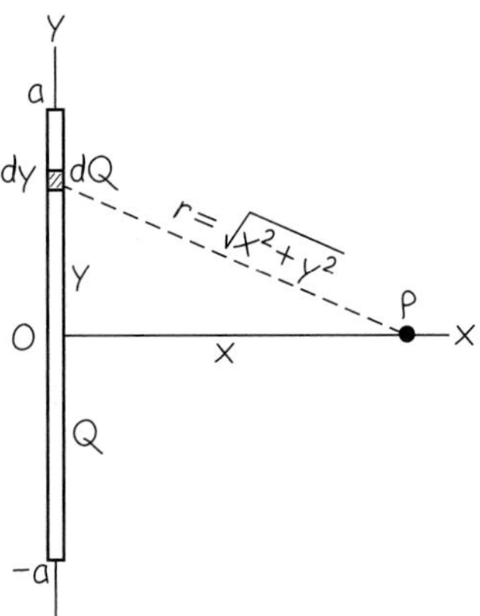

You can look up the integral in a table. The final result is

$$V = \frac{1}{4\pi\epsilon_0}\frac{Q}{2a}\ln\left(\frac{\sqrt{a^2 + x^2} + a}{\sqrt{a^2 + x^2} - a}\right)$$

EVALUATE: We can check our result by letting x approach infinity. In this limit the point P is infinitely far from all of the charge, so we expect V to approach zero; we invite you to verify that it does so.

As in Example 23.11, this problem is simpler than finding $\vec{E}$ at point P because potential is a scalar quantity and no vector calculations are involved.

Test Your Understanding of Section 23.3 If the electric *field* at a certain point is zero, does the electric *potential* at that point have to be zero? (*Hint:* Consider the center of the ring in Example 23.11 and Example 21.10.)

23.4 Equipotential Surfaces

Field lines (see Section 21.6) help us visualize electric fields. In a similar way, the potential at various points in an electric field can be represented graphically by *equipotential surfaces.* These use the same fundamental idea as topographic maps like those used by hikers and mountain climbers (Fig. 23.23). On a topographic map, contour lines are drawn through points that are all at the same elevation. Any number of these could be drawn, but typically only a few contour lines are shown at equal spacings of elevation. If a mass m is moved over the terrain along such a contour line, the gravitational potential energy mgy does not change because the elevation y is constant. Thus contour lines on a topographic map are really curves of constant gravitational potential energy. Contour lines are close together in regions where the terrain is steep and there are large changes in elevation over a small horizontal distance; the contour lines are farther apart where the terrain is gently sloping. A ball allowed to roll downhill will experience the greatest downhill gravitational force where contour lines are closest together.

By analogy to contour lines on a topographic map, an **equipotential surface** is a three-dimensional surface on which the *electric potential* V is the same at every point. If a test charge q_0 is moved from point to point on such a surface, the *electric* potential energy q_0V remains constant. In a region where an electric field is present, we can construct an equipotential surface through any point. In diagrams we usually show only a few representative equipotentials, often with equal potential differences between adjacent surfaces. No point can be at two different potentials, so equipotential surfaces for different potentials can never touch or intersect.

23.23 Contour lines on a topographic map are curves of constant elevation and hence of constant gravitational potential energy.

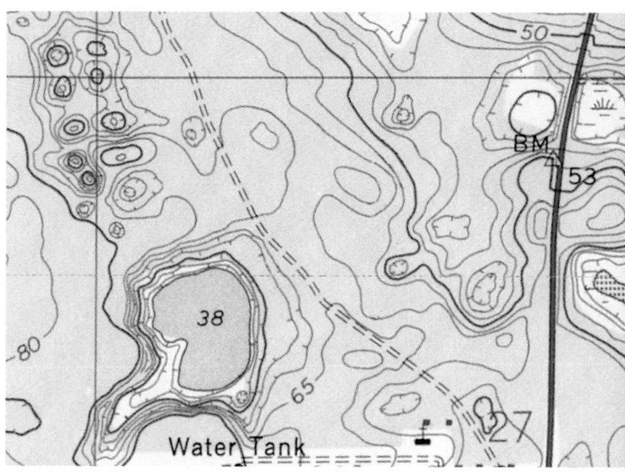

Equipotential Surfaces and Field Lines

Because potential energy does not change as a test charge moves over an equipotential surface, the electric field can do no work on such a charge. It follows that $\vec{E}$ must be perpendicular to the surface at every point so that the electric force $q_0\vec{E}$ is always perpendicular to the displacement of a charge moving on the surface. **Field lines and equipotential surfaces are always mutually perpendicular.** In general, field lines are curves, and equipotentials are curved surfaces. For the special case of a *uniform* field, in which the field lines are straight, parallel, and equally spaced, the equipotentials are parallel *planes* perpendicular to the field lines.

Figure 23.24 shows three arrangements of charges. The field lines in the plane of the charges are represented by red lines, and the intersections of the equipotential surfaces with this plane (that is, cross sections of these surfaces) are shown as blue lines. The actual equipotential surfaces are three-dimensional. At each crossing of an equipotential and a field line, the two are perpendicular.

In Fig. 23.24 we have drawn equipotentials so that there are equal potential differences between adjacent surfaces. In regions where the magnitude of $\vec{E}$ is large, the equipotential surfaces are close together because the field does a rela-

23.24 Cross sections of equipotential surfaces (blue lines) and electric field lines (red lines) for assemblies of point charges. There are equal potential differences between adjacent surfaces. Compare these diagrams to those in Fig. 21.29, which showed only the electric field lines.

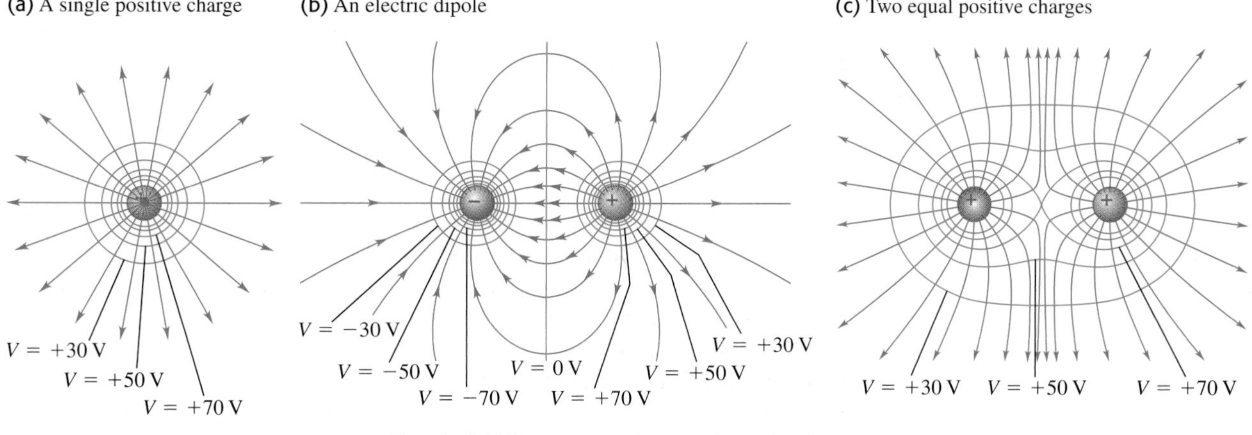

23.25 When charges are at rest, a conducting surface is always an equipotential surface. Field lines are perpendicular to a conducting surface.

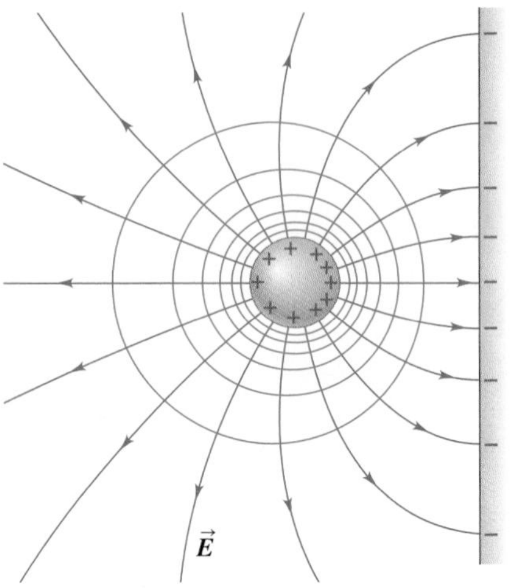

23.26 At all points on the surface of a conductor, the electric field must be perpendicular to the surface. If $\vec{E}$ had a tangential component, a net amount of work would be done on a test charge by moving it around a loop as shown here—which is impossible because the electric force is conservative.

An impossible electric field
If the electric field just outside a conductor had a tangential component $E_{\parallel}$, a charge could move in a loop with net work done.

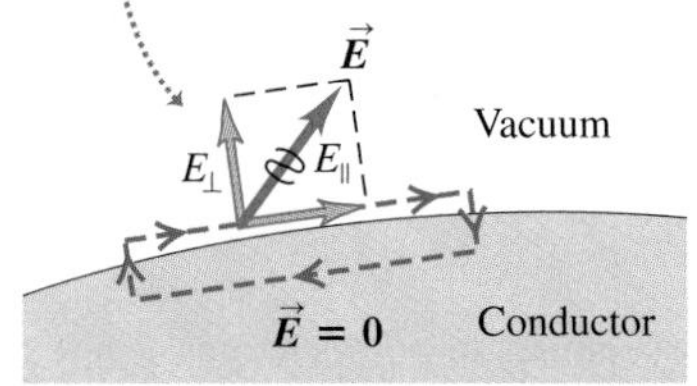

23.27 A cavity in a conductor. If the cavity contains no charge, every point in the cavity is at the same potential, the electric field is zero everywhere in the cavity, and there is no charge anywhere on the surface of the cavity.

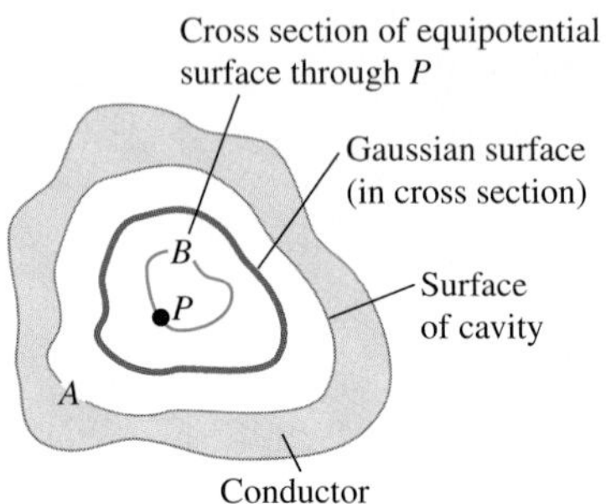

tively large amount of work on a test charge in a relatively small displacement. This is the case near the point charge in Fig. 23.24a or between the two point charges in Fig. 23.24b; note that in these regions the field lines are also closer together. This is directly analogous to the downhill force of gravity being greatest in regions on a topographic map where contour lines are close together. Conversely, in regions where the field is weaker, the equipotential surfaces are farther apart; this happens at larger radii in Fig. 23.24a, to the left of the negative charge or the right of the positive charge in Fig. 23.24b, and at greater distances from both charges in Fig.23.24c. (It may appear that two equipotential surfaces intersect at the center of Fig.23.24c, in violation of the rule that this can never happen. In fact this is a single figure-8–shaped equipotential surface.)

CAUTION ***E* need not be constant over an equipotential surface** On a given equipotential surface, the potential V has the same value at every point. In general, however, the electric-field magnitude E is *not* the same at all points on an equipotential surface. For instance, on the equipotential surface labeled "$V = -30$ V" in Fig. 23.24b, the magnitude E is less to the left of the negative charge than it is between the two charges. On the figure-8–shaped equipotential surface in Fig. 23.24c, $E = 0$ at the middle point halfway between the two charges; at any other point on this surface, E is nonzero.

Equipotentials and Conductors

Here's an important statement about equipotential surfaces: **When all charges are at rest, the surface of a conductor is always an equipotential surface.** Since the electric field $\vec{E}$ is always perpendicular to an equipotential surface, we can prove this statement by proving that **when all charges are at rest, the electric field just outside a conductor must be perpendicular to the surface at every point** (Fig. 23.25). We know that $\vec{E} = \mathbf{0}$ everywhere inside the conductor; otherwise, charges would move. In particular, at any point just inside the surface the component of $\vec{E}$ tangent to the surface is zero. It follows that the tangential component of $\vec{E}$ is also zero just *outside* the surface. If it were not, a charge could move around a rectangular path partly inside and partly outside (Fig. 23.26) and return to its starting point with a net amount of work having been done on it. This would violate the conservative nature of electrostatic fields, so the tangential component of $\vec{E}$ just outside the surface must be zero at every point on the surface. Thus $\vec{E}$ is perpendicular to the surface at each point, proving our statement.

Finally, we can now prove a theorem that we quoted without proof in Section 22.5. The theorem is as follows: In an electrostatic situation, if a conductor contains a cavity and if no charge is present inside the cavity, then there can be no net charge *anywhere* on the surface of the cavity. This means that if you're inside a charged conducting box, you can safely touch any point on the inside walls of the box without being shocked. To prove this theorem, we first prove that *every point in the cavity is at the same potential.* In Fig. 23.27 the conducting surface A of the cavity is an equipotential surface, as we have just proved. Suppose point P in the cavity is at a different potential; then we can construct a different equipotential surface B including point P.

Now consider a Gaussian surface, shown in Fig. 23.27, between the two equipotential surfaces. Because of the relationship between $\vec{E}$ and the equipotentials, we know that the field at every point between the equipotentials is from A toward B, or else at every point it is from B toward A, depending on which equipotential surface is at higher potential. In either case the flux through this Gaussian surface is certainly not zero. But then Gauss's law says that the charge enclosed by the Gaussian surface cannot be zero. This contradicts our initial assumption that there is *no* charge in the cavity. So the potential at P *cannot* be different from that at the cavity wall.

The entire region of the cavity must therefore be at the same potential. But for this to be true, *the electric field inside the cavity must be zero everywhere.*

Finally, Gauss's law shows that the electric field at any point on the surface of a conductor is proportional to the surface charge density σ at that point. We conclude that *the surface charge density on the wall of the cavity is zero at every point.* This chain of reasoning may seem tortuous, but it is worth careful study.

CAUTION **Equipotential surfaces vs. Gaussian surfaces** Don't confuse equipotential surfaces with the Gaussian surfaces we encountered in Chapter 22. Gaussian surfaces have relevance only when we are using Gauss's law, and we can choose *any* Gaussian surface that's convenient. We are *not* free to choose the shape of equipotential surfaces; the shape is determined by the charge distribution.

Test Your Understanding of Section 23.4 Would the shapes of the equipotential surfaces in Fig. 23.24 change if the sign of each charge were reversed?

23.5 Potential Gradient

Electric field and potential are closely related. Equation (23.17), restated here, expresses one aspect of that relationship:

$$V_a - V_b = \int_a^b \vec{E} \cdot d\vec{l}$$

ActivPhysics ONLINE

11.12.3 Electric Potential, Field, and Force

If we know $\vec{E}$ at various points, we can use this equation to calculate potential differences. In this section we show how to turn this around; if we know the potential V at various points, we can use it to determine $\vec{E}$. Regarding V as a function of the coordinates (x, y, z) of a point in space, we will show that the components of $\vec{E}$ are directly related to the *partial derivatives* of V with respect to x, y, and z.

In Eq. (23.17), $V_a - V_b$ is the potential of a with respect to b—that is, the change of potential encountered on a trip from b to a. We can write this as

$$V_a - V_b = \int_b^a dV = -\int_a^b dV$$

where dV is the infinitesimal change of potential accompanying an infinitesimal element $d\vec{l}$ of the path from b to a. Comparing to Eq. (23.17), we have

$$-\int_a^b dV = \int_a^b \vec{E} \cdot d\vec{l}$$

These two integrals must be equal for *any* pair of limits a and b, and for this to be true the *integrands* must be equal. Thus, for *any* infinitesimal displacement $d\vec{l}$,

$$-dV = \vec{E} \cdot d\vec{l}$$

To interpret this expression, we write $\vec{E}$ and $d\vec{l}$ in terms of their components: $\vec{E} = \hat{\imath} E_x + \hat{\jmath} E_y + \hat{k} E_z$ and $d\vec{l} = \hat{\imath}\, dx + \hat{\jmath}\, dy + \hat{k}\, dz$. Then we have

$$-dV = E_x dx + E_y dy + E_z dz$$

Suppose the displacement is parallel to the x-axis, so $dy = dz = 0$. Then $-dV = E_x dx$ or $E_x = -(dV/dx)_{y,\, z \text{ constant}}$, where the subscript reminds us that only x varies in the derivative; recall that V is in general a function of x, y, and z. But this is just what is meant by the partial derivative $\partial V/\partial x$. The y- and z-components of $\vec{E}$ are related to the corresponding derivatives of V in the same way, so we have

$$E_x = -\frac{\partial V}{\partial x} \qquad E_y = -\frac{\partial V}{\partial y} \qquad E_z = -\frac{\partial V}{\partial z} \qquad \text{(components of } \vec{E} \text{ in terms of } V\text{)} \tag{23.19}$$

This is consistent with the units of electric field being V/m. In terms of unit vectors we can write $\vec{E}$ as

$$\vec{E} = -\left(\hat{\imath}\frac{\partial V}{\partial x} + \hat{\jmath}\frac{\partial V}{\partial y} + \hat{k}\frac{\partial V}{\partial z}\right) \quad (\vec{E} \text{ in terms of } V) \tag{23.20}$$

In vector notation the following operation is called the **gradient** of the function f:

$$\vec{\nabla}f = \left(\hat{\imath}\frac{\partial}{\partial x} + \hat{\jmath}\frac{\partial}{\partial y} + \hat{k}\frac{\partial}{\partial z}\right)f \tag{23.21}$$

The operator denoted by the symbol $\vec{\nabla}$ is called "grad" or "del." Thus in vector notation,

$$\vec{E} = -\vec{\nabla}V \tag{23.22}$$

This is read "$\vec{E}$ is the negative of the gradient of V" or "$\vec{E}$ equals negative grad V." The quantity $\vec{\nabla}V$ is called the *potential gradient.*

At each point, the potential gradient points in the direction in which V *increases* most rapidly with a change in position. Hence at each point the direction of $\vec{E}$ is the direction in which V *decreases* most rapidly and is always perpendicular to the equipotential surface through the point. This agrees with our observation in Section 23.2 that moving in the direction of the electric field means moving in the direction of decreasing potential.

Equation (23.22) doesn't depend on the particular choice of the zero point for V. If we were to change the zero point, the effect would be to change V at every point by the same amount; the derivatives of V would be the same.

If $\vec{E}$ is radial with respect to a point or an axis and r is the distance from the point or the axis, the relationship corresponding to Eqs. (23.19) is

$$E_r = -\frac{\partial V}{\partial r} \quad \text{(radial electric field)} \tag{23.23}$$

Often we can compute the electric field caused by a charge distribution in either of two ways: directly, by adding the $\vec{E}$ fields of point charges, or by first calculating the potential and then taking its gradient to find the field. The second method is often easier because potential is a *scalar* quantity, requiring at worst the integration of a scalar function. Electric field is a *vector* quantity, requiring computation of components for each element of charge and a separate integration for each component. Thus, quite apart from its fundamental significance, potential offers a very useful computational technique in field calculations. Below, we present two examples in which a knowledge of V is used to find the electric field.

We stress once more that if we know $\vec{E}$ as a function of position, we can calculate V using Eq. (23.17) or (23.18), and if we know V as a function of position, we can calculate $\vec{E}$ using Eq. (23.19), (23.20), or (23.23). Deriving V from $\vec{E}$ requires integration, and deriving $\vec{E}$ from V requires differentiation.

Example 23.13 Potential and field of a point charge

From Eq. (23.14) the potential at a radial distance r from a point charge q is $V = q/4\pi\epsilon_0 r$. Find the vector electric field from this expression for V.

SOLUTION

IDENTIFY: This problem uses the relationship between the electric potential as a function of position and the electric field vector.

SET UP: By symmetry, the electric field has only a radial component E_r. We use Eq. (23.23) to find this component.

EXECUTE: From Eq. (23.23),

$$E_r = -\frac{\partial V}{\partial r} = -\frac{\partial}{\partial r}\left(\frac{1}{4\pi\epsilon_0}\frac{q}{r}\right) = \frac{1}{4\pi\epsilon_0}\frac{q}{r^2}$$

so the vector electric field is

$$\vec{E} = \hat{r}E_r = \frac{1}{4\pi\epsilon_0}\frac{q}{r^2}\hat{r}$$

EVALUATE: Our result agrees with Eq. (21.7), as it must.

An alternative approach is to ignore the radial symmetry, write the radial distance as $r = \sqrt{x^2 + y^2 + z^2}$, and take the derivatives of V with respect to x, y, and z as in Eq. (23.20). We find

$$\frac{\partial V}{\partial x} = \frac{\partial}{\partial x}\left(\frac{1}{4\pi\epsilon_0}\frac{q}{\sqrt{x^2 + y^2 + z^2}}\right) = -\frac{1}{4\pi\epsilon_0}\frac{qx}{(x^2 + y^2 + z^2)^{3/2}}$$

$$= -\frac{qx}{4\pi\epsilon_0 r^3}$$

and similarly

$$\frac{\partial V}{\partial y} = -\frac{qy}{4\pi\epsilon_0 r^3} \qquad \frac{\partial V}{\partial z} = -\frac{qz}{4\pi\epsilon_0 r^3}$$

From Eq. (23.20), the electric field is

$$\vec{E} = -\left[\hat{\imath}\left(-\frac{qx}{4\pi\epsilon_0 r^3}\right) + \hat{\jmath}\left(-\frac{qy}{4\pi\epsilon_0 r^3}\right) + \hat{k}\left(-\frac{qz}{4\pi\epsilon_0 r^3}\right)\right]$$

$$= \frac{1}{4\pi\epsilon_0}\frac{q}{r^2}\left(\frac{x\hat{\imath} + y\hat{\jmath} + z\hat{k}}{r}\right) = \frac{1}{4\pi\epsilon_0}\frac{q}{r^2}\hat{r}$$

This approach gives us the same answer, but with a bit more effort. Clearly it's best to exploit the symmetry of the charge distribution whenever possible.

Example 23.14 Potential and field of a ring of charge

In Example 23.11 (Section 23.3) we found that for a ring of charge with radius a and total charge Q, the potential at a point P on the ring axis a distance x from the center is

$$V = \frac{1}{4\pi\epsilon_0}\frac{Q}{\sqrt{x^2 + a^2}}$$

Find the electric field at P.

SOLUTION

IDENTIFY: We are given V as a function of x along the x-axis, and we wish to find the electric field at a point on this axis.

SET UP: From the symmetry of the charge distribution shown in Fig. 23.21, the electric field along the symmetry axis of the ring can have only an x-component. We find it using the first of Eqs. (23.19).

EXECUTE: The x-component of the electric field is

$$E_x = -\frac{\partial V}{\partial x} = \frac{1}{4\pi\epsilon_0}\frac{Qx}{(x^2 + a^2)^{3/2}}$$

EVALUATE: This agrees with the result that we obtained in Example 21.10 (Section 21.5).

CAUTION Don't use expressions where they don't apply In this example, V does not appear to be a function of y or z, but it would *not* be correct to conclude that $\partial V/\partial y = \partial V/\partial z = 0$ and $E_y = E_z = 0$ everywhere. The reason is that our expression for V is valid *only for points on the x-axis,* where $y = z = 0$. Hence our expression for E_x is likewise valid on the x-axis only. If we had the complete expression for V valid at *all* points in space, then we could use it to find the components of $\vec{E}$ at any point using Eq. (23.19).

Test Your Understanding of Section 23.5 In a certain region of space the potential is given by $V = A + Bx + Cy^3 + Dxy$, where A, B, C, and D are positive constants. Which of these statements about the electric field $\vec{E}$ in this region of space is correct? (There may be more than one correct answer.) (i) Increasing the value of A will increase the value of $\vec{E}$ at all points; (ii) increasing the value of A will decrease the value of $\vec{E}$ at all points; (iii) $\vec{E}$ has no z-component; (iv) the electric field is zero at the origin $(x = 0, y = 0, z = 0)$.

CHAPTER 23 SUMMARY

Electric potential energy: The electric force caused by any collection of charges at rest is a conservative force. The work W done by the electric force on a charged particle moving in an electric field can be represented by the change in a potential-energy function U.

The electric potential energy for two point charges q and q_0 depends on their separation r. The electric potential energy for a charge q_0 in the presence of a collection of charges q_1, q_2, q_3 depends on the distance from q_0 to each of these other charges. (See Examples 23.1 and 23.2.)

$$W_{a\to b} = U_a - U_b \quad (23.2)$$

$$U = \frac{1}{4\pi\epsilon_0}\frac{qq_0}{r} \quad (23.9)$$

(two point charges)

$$U = \frac{q_0}{4\pi\epsilon_0}\left(\frac{q_1}{r_1} + \frac{q_2}{r_2} + \frac{q_3}{r_3} + \cdots\right) = \frac{q_0}{4\pi\epsilon_0}\sum_i \frac{q_i}{r_i} \quad (23.10)$$

(q_0 in presence of other point charges)

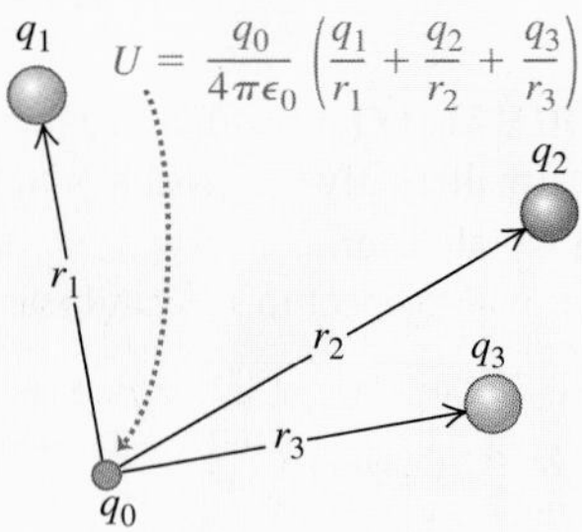

Electric potential: Potential, denoted by V, is potential energy per unit charge. The potential difference between two points equals the amount of work that would be required to move a unit positive test charge between those points. The potential V due to a quantity of charge can be calculated by summing (if the charge is a collection of point charges) or by integrating (if the charge is a distribution). (See Examples 23.3, 23.4, 23.5, 23.7, 23.11, and 23.12.)

The potential difference between two points a and b, also called the potential of a with respect to b, is given by the line integral of $\vec{E}$. The potential at a given point can be found by first finding $\vec{E}$ and then carrying out this integral. (See Examples 23.6, 23.8, 23.9, and 23.10.)

$$V = \frac{U}{q_0} = \frac{1}{4\pi\epsilon_0}\frac{q}{r} \quad (23.14)$$

(due to a point charge)

$$V = \frac{U}{q_0} = \frac{1}{4\pi\epsilon_0}\sum_i \frac{q_i}{r_i} \quad (23.15)$$

(due to a collection of point charges)

$$V = \frac{1}{4\pi\epsilon_0}\int \frac{dq}{r} \quad (23.16)$$

(due to a charge distribution)

$$V_a - V_b = \int_a^b \vec{E}\cdot d\vec{l} = \int_a^b E\cos\phi\, dl \quad (23.17)$$

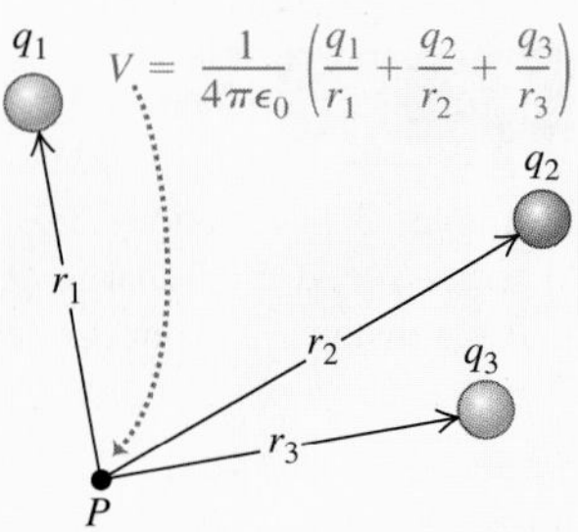

Equipotential surfaces: An equipotential surface is a surface on which the potential has the same value at every point. At a point where a field line crosses an equipotential surface, the two are perpendicular. When all charges are at rest, the surface of a conductor is always an equipotential surface and all points in the interior of a conductor are at the same potential. When a cavity within a conductor contains no charge, the entire cavity is an equipotential region and there is no surface charge anywhere on the surface of the cavity.

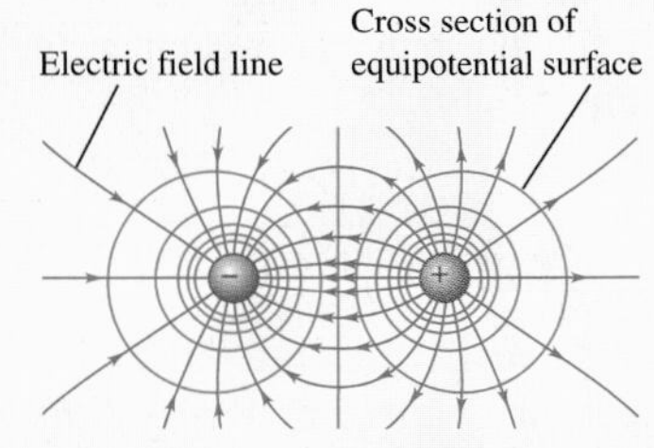

Finding electric field from electric potential: If the potential V is known as a function of the coordinates x, y, and z, the components of electric field $\vec{E}$ at any point are given by partial derivatives of V. (See Examples 23.13 and 23.14.)

$$E_x = -\frac{\partial V}{\partial x} \quad E_y = -\frac{\partial V}{\partial y} \quad E_z = -\frac{\partial V}{\partial z} \quad (23.19)$$

$$\vec{E} = -\left(\hat{\imath}\frac{\partial V}{\partial x} + \hat{\jmath}\frac{\partial V}{\partial y} + \hat{k}\frac{\partial V}{\partial z}\right) \quad (23.20)$$

(vector form)

Key Terms

(electric) potential energy, *781*
(electric) potential, *787*
volt, *787*
voltage, *788*
electron volt, *790*
equipotential surface, *799*
gradient, *802*

Answer to Chapter Opening Question ?

A large, constant potential difference V_{ab} is maintained between the welding tool (a) and the metal pieces to be welded (b). From Example 23.9 (Section 23.3) the electric field between two conductors separated by a distance d has magnitude $E = V_{ab}/d$. Hence d must be small in order for the field magnitude E to be large enough to ionize the gas between the conductors a and b (see Section 23.3) and produce an arc through this gas.

Answers to Test Your Understanding Questions

23.1 Answers: (a) (i), (b) (ii) The three charges q_1, q_2, and q_3 are all positive, so all three of the terms in the sum in Eq. (23.11)—q_1q_2/r_{12}, q_1q_3/r_{13}, and q_2q_3/r_{23}—are positive. Hence the total electric potential energy U is positive. This means that it would take positive work to bring the three charges from infinity to the positions shown in Fig. 21.14, and hence *negative* work to move the three charges from these positions back to infinity.

23.2 Answer: no If $V = 0$ at a certain point, $\vec{E}$ does *not* have to be zero at that point. An example is point c in Figs. 21.23 and 23.14, for which there is an electric field in the $+x$-direction (see Example 21.9 in Section 21.5) even though $V = 0$ (see Example 23.4). This isn't a surprising result because V and $\vec{E}$ are quite different quantities: V is the net amount of work required to bring a unit charge from infinity to the point in question, whereas $\vec{E}$ is the electric force that acts on a unit charge when it arrives at that point.

23.3 Answer: no If $\vec{E} = \mathbf{0}$ at a certain point, V does *not* have to be zero at that point. An example is point O at the center of the charged ring in Figs. 21.24 and 23.21. From Example 21.10 (Section 21.5), the electric field is zero at O because the electric-field contributions from different parts of the ring completely cancel. From Example 23.11, however, the potential at O is *not* zero: This point corresponds to $x = 0$, so $V = (1/4\pi\epsilon_0)(Q/a)$. This value of V corresponds to the work that would have to be done to move a unit positive test charge along a path from infinity to point O; it is nonzero because the charged ring repels the test charge, so positive work must be done to move the test charge toward the ring.

23.4 Answer: no If the positive charges in Fig. 23.24 were replaced by negative charges, and vice versa, the equipotential surfaces would be the same but the sign of the potential would be reversed. For example, the surfaces in Fig. 23.24b with potential $V = +30$ V and $V = -50$ V would have potential $V = -30$ V and $V = +50$ V, respectively.

23.5 Answer: (iii) From Eqs. (23.19), the components of the electric field are $E_x = -\partial V/\partial x = B + Dy$, $E_y = -\partial V/\partial y = 3Cy^2 + Dx$, and $E_z = -\partial V/\partial z = 0$. The value of A has no effect, which means that we can add a constant to the electric potential at all points without changing $\vec{E}$ or the potential difference between two points. The potential does not depend on z, so the z-component of $\vec{E}$ is zero. Note that at the origin the electric field is not zero because it has a nonzero x-component: $E_x = B$, $E_y = 0$, $E_z = 0$.

PROBLEMS

For instructor-assigned homework, go to **www.masteringphysics.com** 

Discussion Questions

Q23.1. A student asked, "Since electrical potential is always proportional to potential energy, why bother with the concept of potential at all?" How would you respond?

Q23.2. The potential (relative to a point at infinity) midway between two charges of equal magnitude and opposite sign is zero. Is it possible to bring a test charge from infinity to this midpoint in such a way that no work is done in any part of the displacement? If so, describe how it can be done. If it is not possible, explain why.

Q23.3. Is it possible to have an arrangement of two point charges separated by a finite distance such that the electric potential energy of the arrangement is the same as if the two charges were infinitely far apart? Why or why not? What if there are three charges? Explain your reasoning.

Q23.4. Since potential can have any value you want depending on the choice of the reference level of zero potential, how does a voltmeter know what to read when you connect it between two points?

Q23.5. If $\vec{E}$ is zero everywhere along a certain path that leads from point A to point B, what is the potential difference between those two points? Does this mean that $\vec{E}$ is zero everywhere along *any* path from A to B? Explain.

Q23.6. If $\vec{E}$ is zero throughout a certain region of space, is the potential necessarily also zero in this region? Why or why not? If not, what *can* be said about the potential?

Q23.7. If you carry out the integral of the electric field $\int \vec{E} \cdot d\vec{l}$ for a *closed* path like that shown in Fig. 23.28, the integral will *always* be equal to zero, independent of the shape of the path and independent of where charges may be located relative to the path. Explain why.

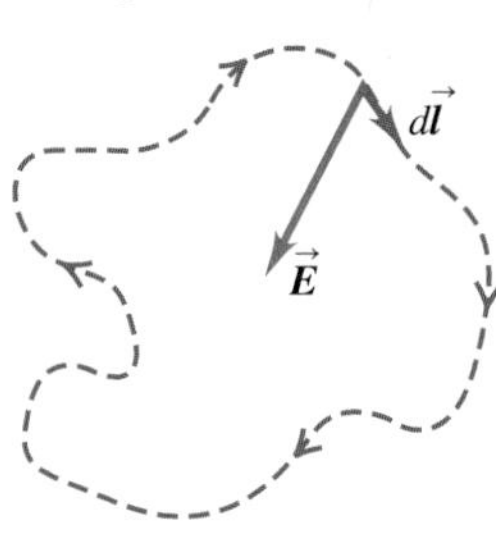

Figure **23.28** Question Q23.7.

Q23.8. The potential difference between the two terminals of an AA battery (used in flashlights and portable stereos) is 1.5 V. If two AA batteries are placed end to end with the positive terminal of one battery touching the negative terminal of the other, what is the potential difference between the terminals at the exposed ends of the combination? What if the two positive terminals are touching each other? Explain your reasoning.

Q23.9. It is easy to produce a potential difference of several thousand volts between your body and the floor by scuffing your shoes across a nylon carpet. When you touch a metal doorknob, you get a mild shock. Yet contact with a power line of comparable voltage would probably be fatal. Why is there a difference?

Q23.10. If the electric potential at a single point is known, can $\vec{E}$ at that point be determined? If so, how? If not, why not?

Q23.11. Because electric field lines and equipotential surfaces are always perpendicular, two equipotential surfaces can never cross; if they did, the direction of $\vec{E}$ would be ambiguous at the crossing points. Yet two equipotential surfaces appear to cross at the center of Fig. 23.24c. Explain why there is no ambiguity about the direction of $\vec{E}$ in this particular case.

Q23.12. The electric field due to a very large sheet of charge is independent of the distance from the sheet, yet the fields due to the individual point charges on the sheet all obey an inverse-square law. Why doesn't the field of the sheet get weaker at greater distances?

Q23.13. We often say that if point A is at a higher potential than point B, A is at positive potential and B is at negative potential. Does it necessarily follow that a point at positive potential is positively charged, or that a point at negative potential is negatively charged? Illustrate your answers with clear, simple examples.

Q23.14. A conducting sphere is to be charged by bringing in positive charge a little at a time until the total charge is Q. The total work required for this process is alleged to be proportional to Q^2. Is this correct? Why or why not?

Q23.15. Three pairs of parallel metal plates (A, B, and C) are connected as shown in Fig. 23.29, and a battery maintains a potential of 1.5 V across ab. What can you say about the potential difference across each pair of plates? Why?

Figure 23.29 Question Q23.15.

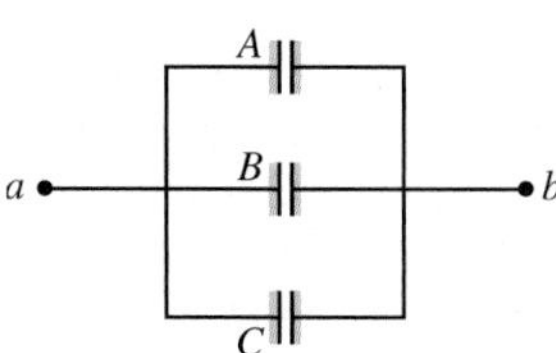

Q23.16. A conducting sphere is placed between two charged parallel plates such as those shown in Fig. 23.2. Does the electric field inside the sphere depend on precisely where between the plates the sphere is placed? What about the electric potential inside the sphere? Do the answers to these questions depend on whether or not there is a net charge on the sphere? Explain your reasoning.

Q23.17. A conductor that carries a net charge Q has a hollow, empty cavity in its interior. Does the potential vary from point to point within the material of the conductor? What about within the cavity? How does the potential inside the cavity compare to the potential within the material of the conductor?

Q23.18. A high-voltage dc power line falls on a car, so the entire metal body of the car is at a potential of 10,000 V with respect to the ground. What happens to the occupants (a) when they are sitting in the car and (b) when they step out of the car? Explain your reasoning.

Q23.19. When a thunderstorm is approaching, sailors at sea sometimes observe a phenomenon called "St. Elmo's fire," a bluish flickering light at the tips of masts. What causes this? Why does it occur at the tips of masts? Why is the effect most pronounced when the masts are wet? (*Hint:* Seawater is a good conductor of electricity.)

Q23.20. A positive point charge is placed near a very large conducting plane. A professor of physics asserted that the field caused by this configuration is the same as would be obtained by removing the plane and placing a negative point charge of equal magnitude in the mirror-image position behind the initial position of the plane. Is this correct? Why or why not? (*Hint:* Inspect Fig. 23.24b.)

Q23.21. In electronics it is customary to define the potential of ground (thinking of the earth as a large conductor) as zero. Is this consistent with the fact that the earth has a net electric charge that is not zero? (Refer to Exercise 21.32.)

Exercises

Section 23.1 Electric Potential Energy

23.1. A point charge $q_1 = +2.40\ \mu C$ is held stationary at the origin. A second point charge $q_2 = -4.30\ \mu C$ moves from the point $x = 0.150$ m, $y = 0$ to the point $x = 0.250$ m, $y = 0.250$ m. How much work is done by the electric force on q_2?

23.2. A point charge q_1 is held stationary at the origin. A second charge q_2 is placed at point a, and the electric potential energy of the pair of charges is $+5.4 \times 10^{-8}$ J. When the second charge is moved to point b, the electric force on the charge does -1.9×10^{-8} J of work. What is the electric potential energy of the pair of charges when the second charge is at point b?

23.3. Energy of the Nucleus. How much work is needed to assemble an atomic nucleus containing three protons (such as Be) if we model it as an equilateral triangle of side 2.00×10^{-15} m with a proton at each vertex? Assume the protons started from very far away.

23.4. (a) How much work would it take to push two protons very slowly from a separation of 2.00×10^{-10} m (a typical atomic distance) to 3.00×10^{-15} m (a typical nuclear distance)? (b) If the protons are both released from rest at the closer distance in part (a), how fast are they moving when they reach their original separation?

23.5. A small metal sphere, carrying a net charge of $q_1 = -2.80\ \mu C$, is held in a stationary position by insulating supports. A second small metal sphere, with a net charge of $q_2 = -7.80\ \mu C$ and mass 1.50 g, is projected toward q_1. When the two spheres are 0.800 m apart, q_2 is moving toward q_1 with speed 22.0 m/s (Fig. 23.30). Assume that the two spheres can be treated as point charges. You can ignore the force of gravity. (a) What is the speed of q_2 when the spheres are 0.400 m apart? (b) How close does q_2 get to q_1?

Figure 23.30 Exercise 23.5.

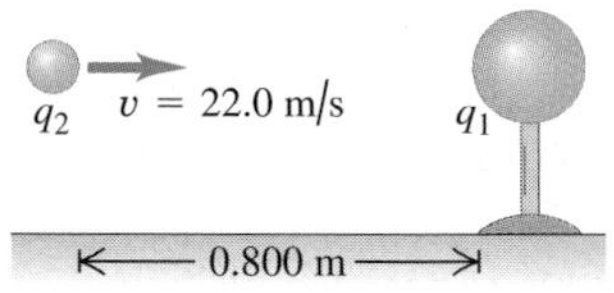

23.6. How far from a -7.20-μC point charge must a $+2.30$-μC point charge be placed for the electric potential energy U of the pair of charges to be -0.400 J? (Take U to be zero when the charges have infinite separation.)

23.7. A point charge $Q = +4.60\ \mu C$ is held fixed at the origin. A second point charge $q = +1.20\ \mu C$ with mass of 2.80×10^{-4} kg is placed on the x-axis, 0.250 m from the origin. (a) What is the electric potential energy U of the pair of charges? (Take U to be zero when the charges have infinite separation.) (b) The second point charge is released from rest. What is its speed when its distance from the origin is (i) 0.500 m; (ii) 5.00 m; (iii) 50.0 m?

23.8. Three equal 1.20-μC point charges are placed at the corners of an equilateral triangle whose sides are 0.500 m long. What is the potential energy of the system? (Take as zero the potential energy of the three charges when they are infinitely far apart.)

23.9. A point charge $q_1 = 4.00$ nC is placed at the origin, and a second point charge $q_2 = -3.00$ nC is placed on the x-axis at $x = +20.0$ cm. A third point charge $q_3 = 2.00$ nC is to be placed on the x-axis between q_1 and q_2. (Take as zero the potential energy of the three charges when they are infinitely far apart.) (a) What is the potential energy of the system of the three charges if q_3 is placed at $x = +10.0$ cm? (b) Where should q_3 be placed to make the potential energy of the system equal to zero?

23.10. Four electrons are located at the corners of a square 10.0 nm on a side, with an alpha particle at its midpoint. How much work is needed to move the alpha particle to the midpoint of one of the sides of the square?

23.11. Three point charges, which initially are infinitely far apart, are placed at the corners of an equilateral triangle with sides d. Two of the point charges are identical and have charge q. If zero net work is required to place the three charges at the corners of the triangle, what must the value of the third charge be?

23.12. Two protons are aimed directly toward each other by a cyclotron accelerator with speeds of 1000 km/s, measured relative to the earth. Find the maximum electrical force that these protons will exert on each other.

Section 23.2 Electric Potential

23.13. A uniform electric field is directed due east. Point B is 2.00 m west of point A, point C is 2.00 m east of point A, and point D is 2.00 m south of A. For each point, B, C, and D, is the potential at that point larger, smaller, or the same as at point A? Give the reasoning behind your answers.

23.14. Identical point charges $q = +5.00\ \mu\text{C}$ are placed at opposite corners of a square. The length of each side of the square is 0.200 m. A point charge $q_0 = -2.00\ \mu\text{C}$ is placed at one of the empty corners. How much work is done on q_0 by the electric force when q_0 is moved to the other empty corner?

23.15. A small particle has charge $-5.00\ \mu\text{C}$ and mass 2.00×10^{-4} kg. It moves from point A, where the electric potential is $V_A = +200$ V, to point B, where the electric potential is $V_B = +800$ V. The electric force is the only force acting on the particle. The particle has speed 5.00 m/s at point A. What is its speed at point B? Is it moving faster or slower at B than at A? Explain.

23.16. A particle with a charge of +4.20 nC is in a uniform electric field $\vec{E}$ directed to the left. It is released from rest and moves to the left; after it has moved 6.00 cm, its kinetic energy is found to be $+1.50 \times 10^{-6}$ J. (a) What work was done by the electric force? (b) What is the potential of the starting point with respect to the end point? (c) What is the magnitude of $\vec{E}$?

23.17. A charge of 28.0 nC is placed in a uniform electric field that is directed vertically upward and has a magnitude of 4.00×10^4 V/m. What work is done by the electric force when the charge moves (a) 0.450 m to the right; (b) 0.670 m upward; (c) 2.60 m at an angle of 45.0° downward from the horizontal?

23.18. Two stationary point charges +3.00 nC and +2.00 nC are separated by a distance of 50.0 cm. An electron is released from rest at a point midway between the two charges and moves along the line connecting the two charges. What is the speed of the electron when it is 10.0 cm from the +3.00-nC charge?

23.19. A point charge has a charge of 2.50×10^{-11} C. At what distance from the point charge is the electric potential (a) 90.0 V and (b) 30.0 V? Take the potential to be zero at an infinite distance from the charge.

23.20. Two charges of equal magnitude Q are held a distance d apart. Consider only points on the line passing through both charges. (a) If the two charges have the same sign, find the location of all points (if there are any) at which (i) the potential (relative to infinity) is zero (is the electric field zero at these points?), and (ii) the electric field is zero (is the potential zero at these points?). (b) Repeat part (a) for two charges having opposite signs.

23.21. Two point charges $q_1 = +2.40$ nC and $q_2 = -6.50$ nC are 0.100 m apart. Point A is midway between them; point B is 0.080 m from q_1 and 0.060 m from q_2 (Fig. 23.31). Take the electric potential to be zero at infinity. Find (a) the potential at point A; (b) the potential at point B; (c) the work done by the electric field on a charge of 2.50 nC that travels from point B to point A.

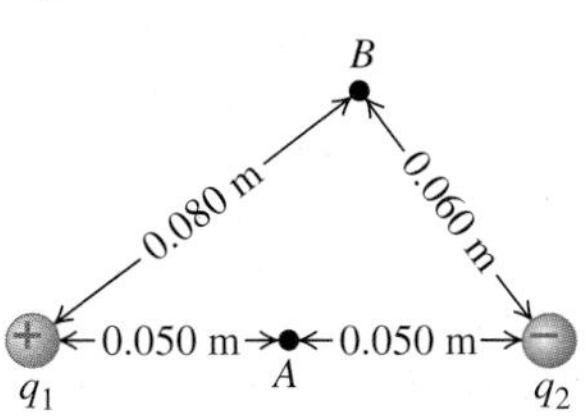

Figure 23.31 Exercise 23.21.

23.22. Two positive point charges, each of magnitude q, are fixed on the y-axis at the points $y = +a$ and $y = -a$. Take the potential to be zero at an infinite distance from the charges. (a) Show the positions of the charges in a diagram. (b) What is the potential V_0 at the origin? (c) Show that the potential at any point on the x-axis is

$$V = \frac{1}{4\pi\epsilon_0}\frac{2q}{\sqrt{a^2 + x^2}}$$

(d) Graph the potential on the x-axis as a function of x over the range from $x = -4a$ to $x = +4a$. (e) What is the potential when $x \gg a$? Explain why this result is obtained.

23.23. A positive charge $+q$ is located at the point $x = 0, y = -a$, and a negative charge $-q$ is located at the point $x = 0, y = +a$. (a) Show the positions of the charges in a diagram. (b) Derive an expression for the potential V at points on the x-axis as a function of the coordinate x. Take V to be zero at an infinite distance from the charges. (c) Graph V at points on the x-axis as a function of x over the range from $x = -4a$ to $x = +4a$. (d) What is the answer to part (b) if the two charges are interchanged so that $+q$ is at $y = +a$ and $-q$ is at $y = -a$?

23.24. Consider the arrangement of charges described in Exercise 23.23. (a) Derive an expression for the potential V at points on the y-axis as a function of the coordinate y. Take V to be zero at an infinite distance from the charges. (b) Graph V at points on the y-axis as a function of y over the range from $y = -4a$ to $y = +4a$. (c) Show that for $y \gg a$, the potential at a point on the positive y-axis is given by $V = -(1/4\pi\epsilon_0)2qa/y^2$. (d) What are the answers to parts (a) and (c) if the two charges are interchanged so that $+q$ is at $y = +a$ and $-q$ is at $y = -a$?

23.25. A positive charge q is fixed at the point $x = 0, y = 0$, and a negative charge $-2q$ is fixed at the point $x = a, y = 0$. (a) Show the positions of the charges in a diagram. (b) Derive an expression for the potential V at points on the x-axis as a function of the coordinate x. Take V to be zero at an infinite distance from the charges. (c) At which positions on the x-axis is $V = 0$? (d) Graph V at points on the x-axis as a function of x in the range from $x = -2a$ to $x = +2a$. (e) What does the answer to part (b) become when $x \gg a$? Explain why this result is obtained.

23.26. Consider the arrangement of point charges described in Exercise 23.25. (a) Derive an expression for the potential V at points on the y-axis as a function of the coordinate y. Take V to be zero at an infinite distance from the charges. (b) At which positions on the y-axis is $V = 0$? (c) Graph V at points on the y-axis as a function of y in the range from $y = -2a$ to $y = +2a$. (d) What does the answer to part (a) become when $y \gg a$? Explain why this result is obtained.

23.27. Before the advent of solid-state electronics, vacuum tubes were widely used in radios and other devices. A simple type of vacuum tube known as a *diode* consists essentially of two electrodes within a highly evacuated enclosure. One electrode, the *cathode,* is maintained at a high temperature and emits electrons from its surface. A potential difference of a few hundred volts is maintained between the cathode and the other electrode, known as the *anode,* with the anode at the higher potential. Suppose that in a particular vacuum tube the potential of the anode is 295 V higher than that of the cathode. An electron leaves the surface of the cathode with zero initial speed. Find its speed when it strikes the anode.

23.28. At a certain distance from a point charge, the potential and electric-field magnitude due to that charge are 4.98 V and 12.0 V/m, respectively. (Take the potential to be zero at infinity.) (a) What is the distance to the point charge? (b) What is the magnitude of the charge? (c) Is the electric field directed toward or away from the point charge?

23.29. A uniform electric field has magnitude E and is directed in the negative x-direction. The potential difference between point a (at $x = 0.60$ m) and point b (at $x = 0.90$ m) is 240 V. (a) Which point, a or b, is at the higher potential? (b) Calculate the value of E. (c) A negative point charge $q = -0.200\ \mu\text{C}$ is moved from b to a. Calculate the work done on the point charge by the electric field.

23.30. For each of the following arrangements of two point charges, find all the points along the line passing through both charges for which the electric potential V is zero (take $V = 0$ infinitely far from the charges) and for which the electric field E is zero: (a) charges $+Q$ and $+2Q$ separated by a distance d, and (b) charges $-Q$ and $+2Q$ separated by a distance d. (c) Are both V and E zero at the same places? Explain.

23.31. (a) An electron is to be accelerated from 3.00×10^6 m/s to 8.00×10^6 m/s. Through what potential difference must the electron pass to accomplish this? (b) Through what potential difference must the electron pass if it is to be slowed from 8.00×10^6 m/s to a halt?

Section 23.3 Calculating Electric Potential

23.32. A total electric charge of 3.50 nC is distributed uniformly over the surface of a metal sphere with a radius of 24.0 cm. If the potential is zero at a point at infinity, find the value of the potential at the following distances from the center of the sphere: (a) 48.0 cm; (b) 24.0 cm; (c) 12.0 cm.

23.33. A uniformly charged thin ring has radius 15.0 cm and total charge +24.0 nC. An electron is placed on the ring's axis a distance 30.0 cm from the center of the ring and is constrained to stay on the axis of the ring. The electron is then released from rest. (a) Describe the subsequent motion of the electron. (b) Find the speed of the electron when it reaches the center of the ring.

23.34. An infinitely long line of charge has linear charge density 5.00×10^{-12} C/m. A proton (mass 1.67×10^{-27} kg, charge $+1.60 \times 10^{-19}$ C) is 18.0 cm from the line and moving directly toward the line at 1.50×10^3 m/s. (a) Calculate the proton's initial kinetic energy. (b) How close does the proton get to the line of charge? (*Hint:* See Example 23.10.)

23.35. A very long wire carries a uniform linear charge density λ. Using a voltmeter to measure potential difference, you find that when one probe of the meter is placed 2.50 cm from the wire and the other probe is 1.00 cm farther from the wire, the meter reads 575 V. (a) What is λ? (b) If you now place one probe at 3.50 cm from the wire and the other probe 1.00 cm farther away, will the voltmeter read 575 V? If not, will it read more or less than 575 V? Why? (c) If you place both probes 3.50 cm from the wire but 17.0 cm from each other, what will the voltmeter read?

23.36. A very long insulating cylinder of charge of radius 2.50 cm carries a uniform linear density of 15.0 nC/m. If you put one probe of a voltmeter at the surface, how far from the surface must the other probe be placed so that the voltmeter reads 175 V?

23.37. A very long insulating cylindrical shell of radius 6.00 cm carries charge of linear density 8.50 μC/m spread uniformly over its outer surface. What would a voltmeter read if it were connected between (a) the surface of the cylinder and a point 4.00 cm above the surface, and (b) the surface and a point 1.00 cm from the central axis of the cylinder?

23.38. A ring of diameter 8.00 cm is fixed in place and carries a charge of +5.00 μC uniformly spread over its circumference. (a) How much work does it take to move a tiny +3.00-μC charged ball of mass 1.50 g from very far away to the center of the ring? (b) Is it necessary to take a path along the axis of the ring? Why? (c) If the ball is slightly displaced from the center of the ring, what will it do and what is the maximum speed it will reach?

23.39. Two very large, parallel metal plates carry charge densities of the same magnitude but opposite signs (Fig. 23.32). Assume they are close enough together to be treated as ideal infinite plates. Taking the potential to be zero at the left surface of the negative plate, sketch a graph of the potential as a function of x. Include *all* regions from the left of the plates to the right of the plates.

Figure 23.32 Exercise 23.39.

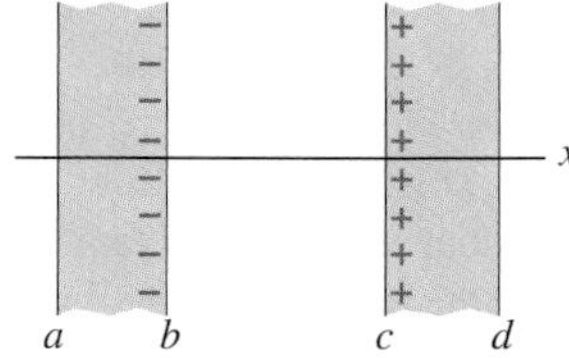

23.40. Two large, parallel conducting plates carrying opposite charges of equal magnitude are separated by 2.20 cm. (a) If the surface charge density for each plate has magnitude 47.0 nC/m², what is the magnitude of $\vec{E}$ in the region between the plates? (b) What is the potential difference between the two plates? (c) If the separation between the plates is doubled while the surface charge density is kept constant at the value in part (a), what happens to the magnitude of the electric field and to the potential difference?

23.41. Two large, parallel, metal plates carry opposite charges of equal magnitude. They are separated by 45.0 mm, and the potential difference between them is 360 V. (a) What is the magnitude of the electric field (assumed to be uniform) in the region between the plates? (b) What is the magnitude of the force this field exerts on a particle with charge +2.40 nC? (c) Use the results of part (b) to compute the work done by the field on the particle as it moves from the higher-potential plate to the lower. (d) Compare the result of part (c) to the change of potential energy of the same charge, computed from the electric potential.

23.42. (a) How much excess charge must be placed on a copper sphere 25.0 cm in diameter so that the potential of its center, relative to infinity, is 1.50 kV? (b) What is the potential of the sphere's surface relative to infinity?

23.43. (a) Show that V for a spherical shell of radius R, that has charge q distributed uniformly over its surface, is the same as V for a solid conductor with radius R and charge q. (b) You rub an inflated balloon on the carpet and it acquires a potential that is 1560 V lower than its potential before it became charged. If the charge is uniformly distributed over the surface of the balloon and if the radius of the balloon is 15 cm, what is the net charge on the balloon? (c) In light of its 1200-V potential difference relative to you, do you think this balloon is dangerous? Explain.

23.44. The electric field at the surface of a charged, solid, copper sphere with radius 0.200 m is 3800 N/C, directed toward the center of the sphere. What is the potential at the center of the sphere, if we take the potential to be zero infinitely far from the sphere?

Section 23.4 Equipotential Surfaces and Section 23.5 Potential Gradient

23.45. A potential difference of 480 V is established between large, parallel, metal plates. Let the potential of one plate be 480 V and the other be 0 V. The plates are separated by $d = 1.70$ cm. (a) Sketch the equipotential surfaces that correspond to 0, 120, 240, 360, and 480 V. (b) In your sketch, show the electric field lines. Does your sketch confirm that the field lines and equipotential surfaces are mutually perpendicular?

23.46. A very large plastic sheet carries a uniform charge density of $-6.00\ \text{nC/m}^2$ on one face. (a) As you move away from the sheet along a line perpendicular to it, does the potential increase or decrease? How do you know, without doing any calculations? Does your answer depend on where you choose the reference point for potential? (b) Find the spacing between equipotential surfaces that differ from each other by 1.00 V. What type of surfaces are these?

23.47. In a certain region of space, the electric potential is $V(x, y, z) = Axy - Bx^2 + Cy$, where A, B, and C are positive constants. (a) Calculate the x-, y-, and z-components of the electric field. (b) At which points is the electric field equal to zero?

23.48. The potential due to a point charge Q at the origin may be written as

$$V = \frac{Q}{4\pi\epsilon_0 r} = \frac{Q}{4\pi\epsilon_0\sqrt{x^2 + y^2 + z^2}}$$

(a) Calculate E_x, E_y, and E_z using Eqs. (23.19). (b) Show that the results of part (a) agrees with Eq. (21.7) for the electric field of a point charge.

23.49. A metal sphere with radius r_a is supported on an insulating stand at the center of a hollow, metal, spherical shell with radius r_b. There is charge $+q$ on the inner sphere and charge $-q$ on the outer spherical shell. (a) Calculate the potential $V(r)$ for (i) $r < r_a$; (ii) $r_a < r < r_b$; (iii) $r > r_b$. (*Hint:* The net potential is the sum of the potentials due to the individual spheres.) Take V to be zero when r is infinite. (b) Show that the potential of the inner sphere with respect to the outer is

$$V_{ab} = \frac{q}{4\pi\epsilon_0}\left(\frac{1}{r_a} - \frac{1}{r_b}\right)$$

(c) Use Eq. (23.23) and the result from part (a) to show that the electric field at any point between the spheres has magnitude

$$E(r) = \frac{V_{ab}}{(1/r_a - 1/r_b)}\frac{1}{r^2}$$

(d) Use Eq. (23.23) and the result from part (a) to find the electric field at a point outside the larger sphere at a distance r from the center, where $r > r_b$. (e) Suppose the charge on the outer sphere is not $-q$ but a negative charge of different magnitude, say $-Q$. Show that the answers for parts (b) and (c) are the same as before but the answer for part (d) is different.

23.50. A metal sphere with radius $r_a = 1.20$ cm is supported on an insulating stand at the center of a hollow, metal, spherical shell with radius $r_b = 9.60$ cm. Charge $+q$ is put on the inner sphere and charge $-q$ on the outer spherical shell. The magnitude of q is chosen to make the potential difference between the spheres 500 V, with the inner sphere at higher potential. (a) Use the result of Exercise 23.49(b) to calculate q. (b) With the help of the result of Exercise 23.49(a), sketch the equipotential surfaces that correspond to 500, 400, 300, 200, 100, and 0 V. (c) In your sketch, show the electric field lines. Are the electric field lines and equipotential surfaces mutually perpendicular? Are the equipotential surfaces closer together when the magnitude of $\vec{E}$ is largest?

23.51. A very long cylinder of radius 2.00 cm carries a uniform charge density of 1.50 nC/m. (a) Describe the shape of the equipotential surfaces for this cylinder. (b) Taking the reference level for the zero of potential to be the surface of the cylinder, find the radius of equipotential surfaces having potentials of 10.0 V, 20.0 V, and 30.0 V. (c) Are the equipotential surfaces equally spaced? If not, do they get closer together or farther apart as r increases?

Problems

23.52. Figure 23.33 shows the potential of a charge distribution as a function of x. Sketch a graph of the electric field E_x over the region shown.

Figure 23.33 Problem 23.52.

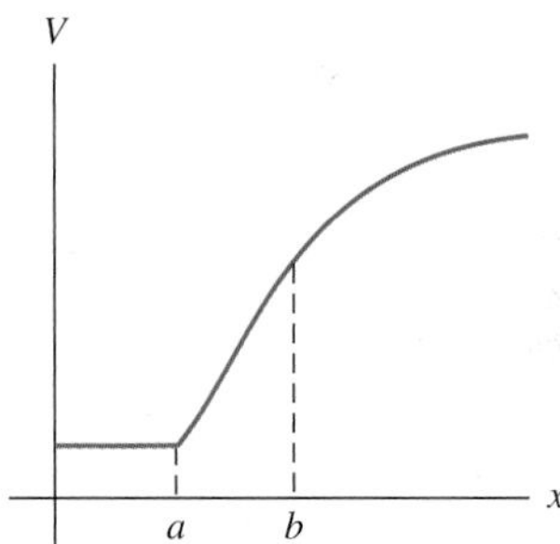

23.53. A particle with charge +7.60 nC is in a uniform electric field directed to the left. Another force, in addition to the electric force, acts on the particle so that when it is released from rest, it moves to the right. After it has moved 8.00 cm, the additional force has done 6.50×10^{-5} J of work and the particle has 4.35×10^{-5} J of kinetic energy. (a) What work was done by the electric force? (b) What is the potential of the starting point with respect to the end point? (c) What is the magnitude of the electric field?

23.54. In the *Bohr model* of the hydrogen atom, a single electron revolves around a single proton in a circle of radius r. Assume that the proton remains at rest. (a) By equating the electric force to the electron mass times its acceleration, derive an expression for the electron's speed. (b) Obtain an expression for the electron's kinetic energy, and show that its magnitude is just half that of the electric potential energy. (c) Obtain an expression for the total energy, and evaluate it using $r = 5.29 \times 10^{-11}$ m. Give your numerical result in joules and in electron volts.

23.55. A vacuum tube diode (see Exercise 23.27) consists of concentric cylindrical electrodes, the negative cathode and the positive anode. Because of the accumulation of charge near the cathode, the electric potential between the electrodes is not a linear function of the position, even with planar geometry, but is given by

$$V(x) = Cx^{4/3}$$

where x is the distance from the cathode and C is a constant, characteristic of a particular diode and operating conditions. Assume that the distance between the cathode and anode is 13.0 mm and the potential difference between electrodes is 240 V. (a) Determine the value of C. (b) Obtain a formula for the electric field between the electrodes as a function of x. (c) Determine the force on an electron when the electron is halfway between the electrodes.

23.56. Two oppositely charged identical insulating spheres, each 50.0 cm in diameter and carrying a uniform charge of magnitude 175 μC, are placed 1.00 m apart center to center (Fig. 23.34). (a) If a voltmeter is connected between the nearest points (a and b) on their surfaces, what will it read? (b) Which point, a or b, is at the higher potential? How can you know this without any calculations?

Figure **23.34** Problem 23.56.

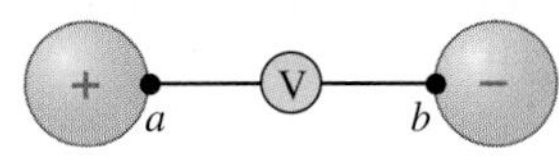

23.57. An Ionic Crystal. Figure 23.35 shows eight point charges arranged at the corners of a cube with sides of length d. The values of the charges are $+q$ and $-q$, as shown. This is a model of one cell of a cubic ionic crystal. In sodium chloride (NaCl), for instance, the positive ions are Na^+ and the negative ions are Cl^-. (a) Calculate the potential energy U of this arrangement. (Take as zero the potential energy of the eight charges when they are infinitely far apart.) (b) In part (a), you should have found that $U < 0$. Explain the relationship between this result and the observation that such ionic crystals exist in nature.

Figure **23.35** Problem 23.57.

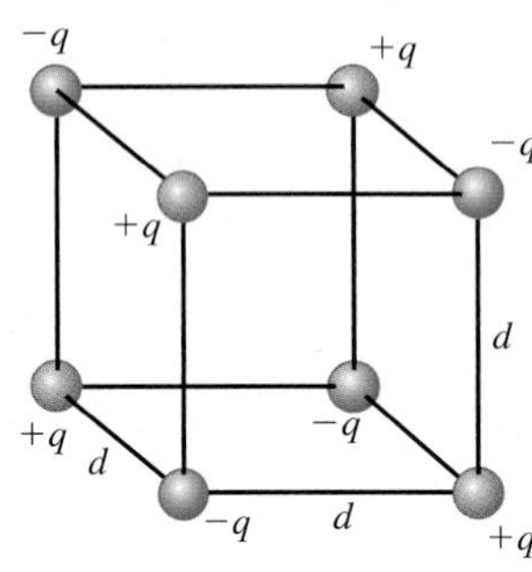

23.58. (a) Calculate the potential energy of a system of two small spheres, one carrying a charge of 2.00 μC and the other a charge of $-3.50\ \mu$C, with their centers separated by a distance of 0.250 m. Assume zero potential energy when the charges are infinitely separated. (b) Suppose that one of the spheres is held in place and the other sphere, which has a mass of 1.50 g, is shot away from it. What minimum initial speed would the moving sphere need in order to escape completely from the attraction of the fixed sphere? (To escape, the moving sphere would have to reach a velocity of zero when it was infinitely distant from the fixed sphere.)

23.59. The H_2^+ Ion. The H_2^+ ion is composed of two protons, each of charge $+e = 1.60 \times 10^{-19}$ C, and an electron of charge $-e$ and mass 9.11×10^{-31} kg. The separation between the protons is 1.07×10^{-10} m. The protons and the electron may be treated as point charges. (a) Suppose the electron is located at the point midway between the two protons. What is the potential energy of the interaction between the electron and the two protons? (Do not include the potential energy due to the interaction between the two protons.) (b) Suppose the electron in part (a) has a velocity of magnitude 1.50×10^6 m/s in a direction along the perpendicular bisector of the line connecting the two protons. How far from the point midway between the two protons can the electron move? Because the masses of the protons are much greater than the electron mass, the motions of the protons are very slow and can be ignored. (*Note:* A realistic description of the electron motion requires the use of quantum mechanics, not Newtonian mechanics.)

23.60. A small sphere with mass 1.50 g hangs by a thread between two parallel vertical plates 5.00 cm apart (Fig. 23.36). The plates are insulating and have uniform surface charge densities $+\sigma$ and $-\sigma$. The charge on the sphere is $q = 8.90 \times 10^{-6}$ C. What potential difference between the plates will cause the thread to assume an angle of 30.0° with the vertical?

Figure **23.36** Problem 23.60.

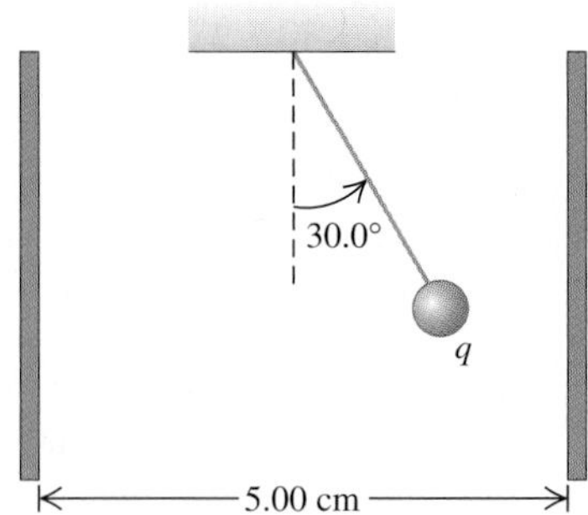

23.61. Coaxial Cylinders. A long metal cylinder with radius a is supported on an insulating stand on the axis of a long, hollow, metal tube with radius b. The positive charge per unit length on the inner cylinder is λ, and there is an equal negative charge per unit length on the outer cylinder. (a) Calculate the potential $V(r)$ for (i) $r < a$; (ii) $a < r < b$; (iii) $r > b$. (*Hint:* The net potential is the sum of the potentials due to the individual conductors.) Take $V = 0$ at $r = b$. (b) Show that the potential of the inner cylinder with respect to the outer is

$$V_{ab} = \frac{\lambda}{2\pi\epsilon_0}\ln\frac{b}{a}$$

(c) Use Eq. (23.23) and the result from part (a) to show that the electric field at any point between the cylinders has magnitude

$$E(r) = \frac{V_{ab}}{\ln(b/a)}\frac{1}{r}$$

(d) What is the potential difference between the two cylinders if the outer cylinder has no net charge?

23.62. A *Geiger counter* detects radiation such as alpha particles by using the fact that the radiation ionizes the air along its path. A thin wire lies on the axis of a hollow metal cylinder and is insulated from it (Fig. 23.37). A large potential difference is established between the wire and the outer cylinder, with the wire at higher potential; this sets up a strong electric field directed radially outward. When ionizing radiation enters the device, it ionizes a few air molecules. The free electrons produced are accelerated by the electric field toward the wire and, on the way there, ionize many more air molecules. Thus a current pulse is produced that can be detected by appropriate electronic circuitry and converted to an audible "click." Suppose the radius of the central wire is 145 μm and the radius of the hollow cylinder is 1.80 cm. What potential difference between the wire and the cylinder produces an

Figure **23.37** Problem 23.62.

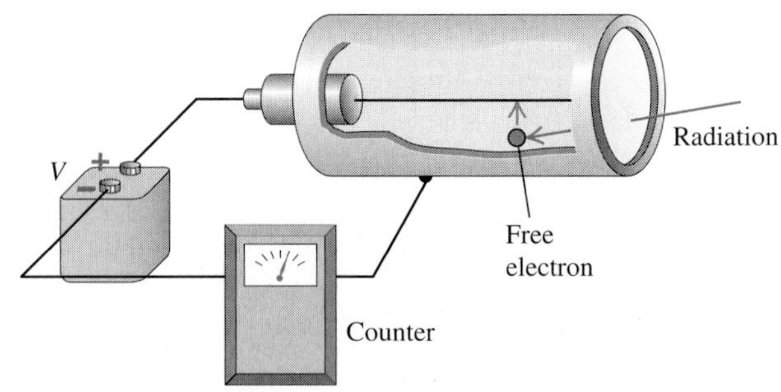

electric field of 2.00×10^4 V/m at a distance of 1.20 cm from the axis of the wire? (The wire and cylinder are both very long in comparison to their radii, so the results of Problem 23.61 apply.)

23.63. Deflection in a CRT. Cathode-ray tubes (CRTs) are often found in oscilloscopes and computer monitors. In Fig. 23.38 an electron with an initial speed of 6.50×10^6 m/s is projected along the axis midway between the deflection plates of a cathode-ray tube. The uniform electric field between the plates has a magnitude of 1.10×10^3 V/m and is upward. (a) What is the force (magnitude and direction) on the electron when it is between the plates? (b) What is the acceleration of the electron (magnitude and direction) when acted on by the force in part (a)? (c) How far below the axis has the electron moved when it reaches the end of the plates? (d) At what angle with the axis is it moving as it leaves the plates? (e) How far below the axis will it strike the fluorescent screen S?

Figure **23.38** Problem 23.63.

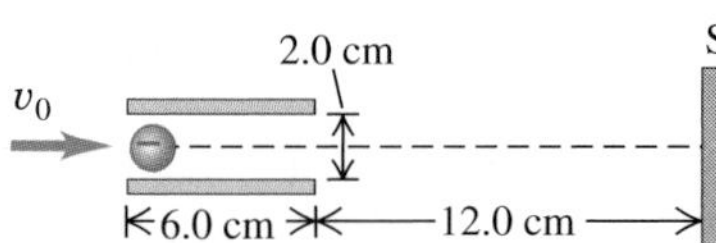

23.64. Deflecting Plates of an Oscilloscope. The vertical deflecting plates of a typical classroom oscilloscope are a pair of parallel square metal plates carrying equal but opposite charges. Typical dimensions are about 3.0 cm on a side, with a separation of about 5.0 mm. The plates are close enough that we can ignore fringing at the ends. Under these conditions: (a) how much charge is on each plate, and (b) how strong is the electric field between the plates? (c) If an electron is ejected at rest from the negative plates, how fast is it moving when it reaches the positive plate?

23.65. *Electrostatic precipitators* use electric forces to remove pollutant particles from smoke, in particular in the smokestacks of coal-burning power plants. One form of precipitator consists of a vertical, hollow, metal cylinder with a thin wire, insulated from the cylinder, running along its axis (Fig. 23.39). A large potential difference is established between the wire and the outer cylinder, with the wire at lower potential. This sets up a strong radial electric field directed inward. The field produces a region of ionized air near the wire. Smoke enters the precipitator at the bottom, ash and dust in it pick up electrons, and the charged pollutants are accelerated toward the outer cylinder wall by the electric field. Suppose the radius of the central wire is 90.0 μm, the radius of the cylinder is 14.0 cm, and a potential difference of 50.0 kV is established between the wire and the cylinder. Also assume that the wire and cylinder are both very long in comparison to the cylinder radius, so the results of Problem 23.61 apply. (a) What is the magnitude of the electric field midway between the wire and the cylinder wall? (b) What magnitude of charge must a 30.0-μg ash particle have if the electric field computed in part (a) is to exert a force ten times the weight of the particle?

Figure **23.39** Problem 23.65.

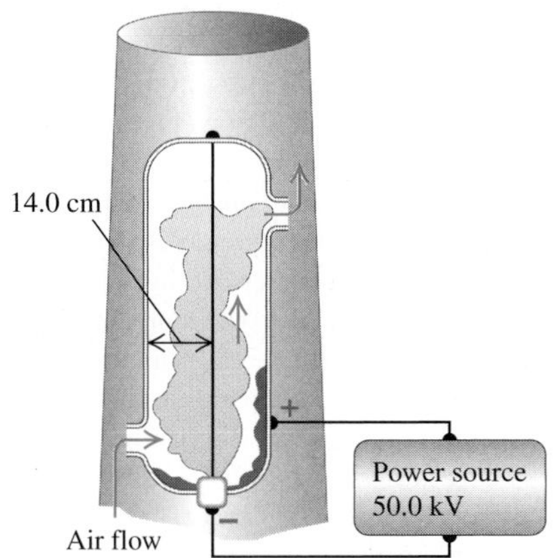

23.66. A disk with radius R has uniform surface charge density σ. (a) By regarding the disk as a series of thin concentric rings, calculate the electric potential V at a point on the disk's axis a distance x from the center of the disk. Assume that the potential is zero at infinity. (*Hint:* Use the result of Example 23.11 in Section 23.3.) (b) Calculate $-\partial V/\partial x$. Show that the result agrees with the expression for E_x calculated in Example 21.12 (Section 21.5).

23.67. (a) From the expression for E obtained in Problem 22.40, find the expressions for the electric potential V as a function of r, both inside and outside the cylinder. Let $V = 0$ at the surface of the cylinder. In each case, express your result in terms of the charge per unit length λ of the charge distribution. (b) Graph V and E as functions of r from $r = 0$ to $r = 3R$.

23.68. Alpha particles $(mass = 6.7 \times 10^{-27}$ kg, charge $= +2e)$ are shot directly at a gold foil target. We can model the gold nucleus as a uniform sphere of charge and assume that the gold does not move. (a) If the radius of the gold nucleus is 5.6×10^{-15} m, what minimum speed do the alpha particles need when they are far away to reach the surface of the gold nucleus? (Ignore relativistic effects.) (b) Give good physical reasons why we can ignore the effects of the orbital electrons when the alpha particle is (i) outside the electron orbits and (ii) inside the electron orbits.

23.69. For the ring of charge described in Example 23.11 (Section 23.3), integrate the expression for E_x found in Example 21.10 (Section 21.5) to find the potential at point P on the ring's axis. Assume that $V = 0$ at infinity. Compare your result to that obtained in Example 23.11 using Eq. (23.16).

23.70. A thin insulating rod is bent into a semicircular arc of radius a, and a total electric charge Q is distributed uniformly along the rod. Calculate the potential at the center of curvature of the arc if the potential is assumed to be zero at infinity.

23.71. Self-Energy of a Sphere of Charge. A solid sphere of radius R contains a total charge Q distributed uniformly throughout its volume. Find the energy needed to assemble this charge by bringing infinitesimal charges from far away. This energy is called the "self-energy" of the charge distribution. (*Hint:* After you have assembled a charge q in a sphere of radius r, how much energy would it take to add a spherical shell of thickness dr having charge dq? Then integrate to get the total energy.)

23.72. (a) From the expression for E obtained in Example 22.9 (Section 22.4), find the expression for the electric potential V as a function of r both inside and outside the uniformly charged sphere. Assume that $V = 0$ at infinity. (b) Graph V and E as functions of r from $r = 0$ to $r = 3R$.

23.73. A solid insulating sphere with radius R has charge Q uniformly distributed throughout its volume. (a) Use the results of Problem 23.72 to find the magnitude of the potential difference between the surface of the sphere and its center. (b) Which is at higher potential, the surface or the center, if (i) Q is positive and (ii) Q is negative?

23.74. An insulating spherical shell with inner radius 25.0 cm and outer radius 60.0 cm carries a charge of $+150.0\ \mu C$ uniformly distributed over its outer surface (see Exercise 23.43). Point a is at the center of the shell, point b is on the inner surface, and point c is on the outer surface. (a) What will a voltmeter read if it is connected between the following points: (i) a and b; (ii) b and c; (iii) c and infinity; (iv) a and c? (b) Which is at higher potential: (i) a or b; (ii) b or c; (iii) a or c? (c) Which, if any, of the answers would change sign if the charges were $-150\ \mu C$?

23.75. Exercise 23.43 shows that, outside a spherical shell with uniform surface charge, the potential is the same as if all the charge were concentrated into a point charge at the center of the sphere. (a) Use this result to show that for two uniformly charged insulating shells, the force they exert on each other and their mutual electrical energy are the same as if all the charge were concentrated at their centers. (*Hint*: See Section 12.6.) (b) Does this same result hold for solid insulating spheres, with charge distributed uniformly throughout their volume? (c) Does this same result hold for the force between two charged conducting shells? Between two charged solid conductors? Explain.

23.76. Two plastic spheres, each carrying charge uniformly distributed throughout its interior, are initially placed in contact and then released. One sphere is 60.0 cm in diameter, has mass 50.0 g and contains $-10.0\ \mu C$ of charge. The other sphere is 40.0 cm in diameter, has mass 150.0 g, and contains $-30.0\ \mu C$ of charge. Find the maximum acceleration and the maximum speed achieved by each sphere (relative to the fixed point of their initial location in space), assuming that no other forces are acting on them. (*Hint:* The uniformly distributed charges behave as though they were concentrated at the centers of the two spheres.)

23.77. Use the electric field calculated in Problem 22.43 to calculate the potential difference between the solid conducting sphere and the thin insulating shell.

23.78. Consider a solid conducting sphere inside a hollow conducting sphere, with radii and charges specified in Problem 22.42. Take $V = 0$ as $r \rightarrow \infty$. Use the electric field calculated in Problem 22.42 to calculate the potential V at the following values of r: (a) $r = c$ (at the outer surface of the hollow sphere); (b) $r = b$ (at the inner surface of the hollow sphere); (c) $r = a$ (at the surface of the solid sphere); (d) $r = 0$ (at the center of the solid sphere).

23.79. Electric charge is distributed uniformly along a thin rod of length a, with total charge Q. Take the potential to be zero at infinity. Find the potential at the following points (Fig. 23.40): (a) point P, a distance x to the right of the rod, and (b) point R, a distance y above the right-hand end of the rod. (c) In parts (a) and (b), what does your result reduce to as x or y becomes much larger than a?

Figure **23.40** Problem 23.79.

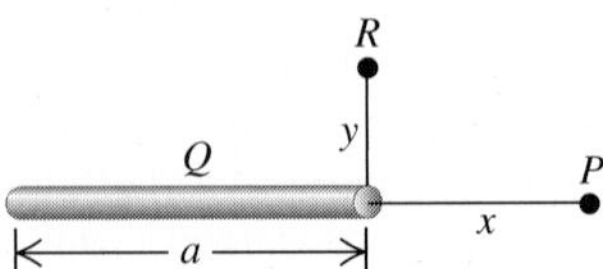

23.80. (a) If a spherical raindrop of radius 0.650 mm carries a charge of -1.20 pC uniformly distributed over its volume, what is the potential at its surface? (Take the potential to be zero at an infinite distance from the raindrop.) (b) Two identical raindrops, each with radius and charge specified in part (a), collide and merge into one larger raindrop. What is the radius of this larger drop, and what is the potential at its surface, if its charge is uniformly distributed over its volume?

23.81. Two metal spheres of different sizes are charged such that the electric potential is the same at the surface of each. Sphere A has a radius three times that of sphere B. Let Q_A and Q_B be the charges on the two spheres, and let E_A and E_B be the electric-field magnitudes at the surfaces of the two spheres. What are (a) the ratio Q_B/Q_A and (b) the ratio E_B/E_A?

23.82. An alpha particle with kinetic energy 11.0 MeV makes a head-on collision with a lead nucleus at rest. What is the distance of closest approach of the two particles? (Assume that the lead nucleus remains stationary and that it may be treated as a point charge. The atomic number of lead is 82. The alpha particle is a helium nucleus, with atomic number 2.)

23.83. A metal sphere with radius R_1 has a charge Q_1. Take the electric potential to be zero at an infinite distance from the sphere. (a) What are the electric field and electric potential at the surface of the sphere? This sphere is now connected by a long, thin conducting wire to another sphere of radius R_2 that is several meters from the first sphere. Before the connection is made, this second sphere is uncharged. After electrostatic equilibrium has been reached, what are (b) the total charge on each sphere; (c) the electric potential at the surface of each sphere (d) the electric field at the surface of each sphere? Assume that the amount of charge on the wire is much less than the charge on each sphere.

23.84. Use the charge distribution and electric field calculated in Problem 22.57. (a) Show that for $r \geq R$ the potential is identical to that produced by a point charge Q. (Take the potential to be zero at infinity.) (b) Obtain an expression for the electric potential valid in the region $r \leq R$.

23.85. Nuclear Fusion in the Sun. The source of the sun's energy is a sequence of nuclear reactions that occur in its core. The first of these reactions involves the collision of two protons, which fuse together to form a heavier nucleus and release energy. For this process, called *nuclear fusion,* to occur, the two protons must first approach until their surfaces are essentially in contact. (a) Assume both protons are moving with the same speed and they collide head-on. If the radius of the proton is 1.2×10^{-15} m, what is the minimum speed that will allow fusion to occur? The charge distribution within a proton is spherically symmetric, so the electric field and potential outside a proton are the same as if it were a point charge. The mass of the proton is 1.67×10^{-27} kg. (b) Another nuclear fusion reaction that occurs in the sun's core involves a collision between two helium nuclei, each of which has 2.99 times the mass of the proton, charge $+2e$, and radius 1.7×10^{-15} m. Assuming the same collision geometry as in part (a), what minimum speed is required for this fusion reaction to take place if the nuclei must approach a center-to-center distance of about 3.5×10^{-15} m? As for the proton, the charge of the helium nucleus is uniformly distributed throughout its volume. (c) In Section 18.3 it was shown that the average translational kinetic energy of a particle with mass m in a gas at absolute temperature T is $\frac{3}{2}kT$, where k is the Boltzmann constant (given in Appendix F). For two protons with kinetic energy equal to this average value to be able to undergo the process described in part (a), what absolute temperature is required? What absolute temperature is required for two average helium nuclei to be able to undergo the process described in part (b)? (At these temperatures, atoms are completely ionized, so nuclei and electrons move separately.) (d) The temperature in the sun's core is about 1.5×10^7 K. How does this compare to the temperatures calculated in part (c)? How can the reactions described in parts (a) and (b) occur at all in the interior of the sun? (*Hint:* See the discussion of the distribution of molecular speeds in Section 18.5.)

23.86. The electric potential V in a region of space is given by

$$V(x, y, z) = A(x^2 - 3y^2 + z^2)$$

where A is a constant. (a) Derive an expression for the electric field $\vec{E}$ at any point in this region. (b) The work done by the field when a 1.50-μC test charge moves from the point $(x, y, z) = (0, 0, 0.250 \text{ m})$ to the origin is measured to be 6.00×10^{-5} J. Determine A. (c) Determine the electric field at the point (0, 0, 0.250 m). (d) Show that in every plane parallel to the xz-plane the equipotential contours are circles. (e) What is the radius of the equipotential contour corresponding to $V = 1280$ V and $y = 2.00$ m?

23.87. Nuclear Fission. The unstable nucleus of uranium-236 can be regarded as a uniformly charged sphere of charge $Q = +92e$ and radius $R = 7.4 \times 10^{-15}$ m. In nuclear fission, this can divide into two smaller nuclei, each with half the charge and half the volume of the original uranium-236 nucleus. This is one of the reactions that occurred in the nuclear weapon that exploded over Hiroshima, Japan, in August 1945. (a) Find the radii of the two "daughter" nuclei of charge $+46e$. (b) In a simple model for the fission process, immediately after the uranium-236 nucleus has undergone fission, the "daughter" nuclei are at rest and just touching, as shown in Fig. 23.41. Calculate the kinetic energy that each of the "daughter" nuclei will have when they are very far apart. (c) In this model the sum of the kinetic energies of the two "daughter" nuclei, calculated in part (b), is the energy released by the fission of one uranium-236 nucleus. Calculate the energy released by the fission of 10.0 kg of uranium-236. The atomic mass of uranium-236 is 236 u, where 1 u = 1 atomic mass unit = 1.66×10^{-24} kg. Express your answer both in joules and in kilotons of TNT (1 kiloton of TNT releases 4.18×10^{12} J when it explodes). (d) In terms of this model, discuss why an atomic bomb could just as well be called an "electric bomb."

Figure 23.41 Problem 23.87.

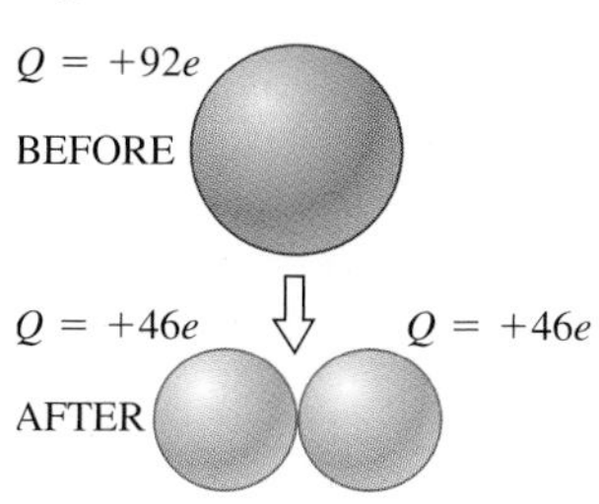

Challenge Problems

23.88. In a certain region, a charge distribution exists that is spherically symmetric but nonuniform. That is, the volume charge density $\rho(r)$ depends on the distance r from the center of the distribution but not on the spherical polar angles θ and ϕ. The electric potential $V(r)$ due to this charge distribution is

$$V(r) = \begin{cases} \dfrac{\rho_0 a^2}{18\epsilon_0}\left[1 - 3\left(\dfrac{r}{a}\right)^2 + 2\left(\dfrac{r}{a}\right)^3\right] & \text{for } r \le a \\ 0 & \text{for } r \ge a \end{cases}$$

where ρ_0 is a constant having units of C/m^3 and a is a constant having units of meters. (a) Derive expressions for $\vec{E}$ for the regions $r \le a$ and $r \ge a$. [*Hint:* Use Eq. (23.23).] Explain why $\vec{E}$ has only a radial component. (b) Derive an expression for $\rho(r)$ in each of the two regions $r \le a$ and $r \ge a$. [*Hint:* Use Gauss's law for two spherical shells, one of radius r and the other of radius $r + dr$. The charge contained in the infinitesimal spherical shell of radius dr is $dq = 4\pi r^2 \rho(r) dr$.] (c) Show that the net charge contained in the volume of a sphere of radius greater than or equal to a is zero. [*Hint:* Integrate the expressions derived in part (b) for $\rho(r)$ over a spherical volume of radius greater than or equal to a.] Is this result consistent with the electric field for $r > a$ that you calculated in part (a)?

23.89. In experiments in which atomic nuclei collide, head-on collisions like that described in Problem 23.82 do happen, but "near misses" are more common. Suppose the alpha particle in Problem 23.82 was not "aimed" at the center of the lead nucleus, but had an initial nonzero angular momentum (with respect to the stationary lead nucleus) of magnitude $L = p_0 b$, where p_0 is the magnitude of the initial momentum of the alpha particle and $b = 1.00 \times 10^{-12}$ m. What is the distance of closest approach? Repeat for $b = 1.00 \times 10^{-13}$ m and $b = 1.00 \times 10^{-14}$ m.

23.90. A hollow, thin-walled insulating cylinder of radius R and length L (like the cardboard tube in a roll of toilet paper) has charge Q uniformly distributed over its surface. (a) Calculate the electric potential at all points along the axis of the tube. Take the origin to be at the center of the tube, and take the potential to be zero at infinity. (b) Show that if $L \ll R$, the result of part (a) reduces to the potential on the axis of a ring of charge of radius R (See Example 23.11 in Section 23.3). (c) Use the result of part (a) to find the electric field at all points along the axis of the tube.

23.91. The Millikan Oil-Drop Experiment. The charge of an electron was first measured by the American physicist Robert Millikan during 1909–1913. In his experiment, oil is sprayed in very fine drops (around 10^{-4} mm in diameter) into the space between two parallel horizontal plates separated by a distance d. A potential difference V_{AB} is maintained between the parallel plates, causing a downward electric field between them. Some of the oil drops acquire a negative charge because of frictional effects or because of ionization of the surrounding air by x rays or radioactivity. The drops are observed through a microscope. (a) Show that an oil drop of radius r at rest between the plates will remain at rest if the magnitude of its charge is

$$q = \frac{4\pi}{3} \frac{\rho r^3 g d}{V_{AB}}$$

where ρ is the density of the oil. (Ignore the buoyant force of the air.) By adjusting V_{AB} to keep a given drop at rest, the charge on that drop can be determined, provided its radius is known. (b) Millikan's oil drops were much too small to measure their radii directly. Instead, Millikan determined r by cutting off the electric field and measuring the *terminal speed* v_t of the drop as it fell. (We discussed the concept of terminal speed in Section 5.3.) The viscous force F on a sphere of radius r moving with speed v through a fluid with viscosity η is given by Stokes's law: $F = 6\pi\eta r v$. When the drop is falling at v_t, the viscous force just balances the weight $w = mg$ of the drop. Show that the magnitude of the charge on the drop is

$$q = 18\pi \frac{d}{V_{AB}} \sqrt{\frac{\eta^3 v_t^3}{2\rho g}}$$

Within the limits of their experimental error, every one of the thousands of drops that Millikan and his coworkers measured had a charge equal to some small integer multiple of a basic charge e. That is, they found drops with charges of $\pm 2e$, $\pm 5e$, and so on, but none with values such as $0.76e$ or $2.49e$. A drop with charge $-e$ has acquired one extra electron; if its charge is $-2e$, it has acquired two extra electrons, and so on. (c) A charged oil drop in a Millikan oil-drop apparatus is observed to fall 1.00 mm at constant speed in 39.3 s if $V_{AB} = 0$. The same drop can be held at rest between two plates separated by 1.00 mm if $V_{AB} = 9.16$ V. How many excess electrons has the drop acquired, and what is the radius of the drop? The viscosity of air is 1.81×10^{-5} N · s/m^2, and the density of the oil is 824 kg/m^3.

23.92. Two point charges are moving to the right along the x-axis. Point charge 1 has charge $q_1 = 2.00\ \mu\text{C}$, mass $m_1 = 6.00 \times 10^{-5}$ kg, and speed v_1. Point charge 2 is to the right of q_1 and has charge $q_2 = -5.00\ \mu\text{C}$, mass $m_2 = 3.00 \times 10^{-5}$ kg, and speed v_2. At a particular instant, the charges are separated by a distance of 9.00 mm and have speeds $v_1 = 400$ m/s and $v_2 = 1300$ m/s. The only forces on the particles are the forces they exert on each other. (a) Determine the speed v_{cm} of the center of mass of the system. (b) The *relative energy* E_{rel} of the system is defined as the total energy minus the kinetic energy contributed by the motion of the center of mass:

$$E_{\text{rel}} = E - \frac{1}{2}(m_1 + m_2)v_{\text{cm}}^2$$

where $E = \frac{1}{2}m_1v_1^2 + \frac{1}{2}m_2v_2^2 + q_1q_2/4\pi\epsilon_0 r$ is the total energy of the system and r is the distance between the charges. Show that $E_{\text{rel}} = \frac{1}{2}\mu v^2 + q_1q_2/4\pi\epsilon_0 r$, where $\mu = m_1m_2/(m_1 + m_2)$ is called the *reduced mass* of the system and $v = v_2 - v_1$ is the relative speed of the moving particles. (c) For the numerical values given above, calculate the numerical value of E_{rel}. (d) Based on the result of part (c), for the conditions given above, will the particles escape from one another? Explain. (e) If the particles do escape, what will be their final relative speed when $r \to \infty$? If the particles do not escape, what will be their distance of maximum separation? That is, what will be the value of r when $v = 0$? (f) Repeat parts (c)–(e) for $v_1 = 400$ m/s and $v_2 = 1800$ m/s when the separation is 9.00 mm.

CAPACITANCE AND DIELECTRICS

24

? The energy used in a camera's flash unit is stored in a capacitor, which consists of two closely spaced conductors that carry opposite charges. If the amount of charge on the conductors is doubled, by what factor does the stored energy increase?

LEARNING GOALS

By studying this chapter, you will learn:

- The nature of capacitors, and how to calculate a quantity that measures their ability to store charge.
- How to analyze capacitors connected in a network.
- How to calculate the amount of energy stored in a capacitor.
- What dielectrics are, and how they make capacitors more effective.

When you set an old-fashioned spring mousetrap or pull back the string of an archer's bow, you are storing mechanical energy as elastic potential energy. A capacitor is a device that stores *electric* potential energy and electric charge. To make a capacitor, just insulate two conductors from each other. To store energy in this device, transfer charge from one conductor to the other so that one has a negative charge and the other has an equal amount of positive charge. Work must be done to move the charges through the resulting potential difference between the conductors, and the work done is stored as electric potential energy.

Capacitors have a tremendous number of practical applications in devices such as electronic flash units for photography, pulsed lasers, air bag sensors for cars, and radio and television receivers. We'll encounter many of these applications in later chapters (particularly Chapter 31, in which we'll see the crucial role played by capacitors in the alternating-current circuits that pervade our technological society). In this chapter, however, our emphasis is on the fundamental properties of capacitors. For a particular capacitor, the ratio of the charge on each conductor to the potential difference between the conductors is a constant, called the *capacitance.* The capacitance depends on the sizes and shapes of the conductors and on the insulating material (if any) between them. Compared to the case in which there is only vacuum between the conductors, the capacitance increases when an insulating material (a *dielectric*) is present. This happens because a redistribution of charge, called *polarization,* takes place within the insulating material. Studying polarization will give us added insight into the electrical properties of matter.

Capacitors also give us a new way to think about electric potential energy. The energy stored in a charged capacitor is related to the electric field in the space between the conductors. We will see that electric potential energy can be regarded as being stored *in the field itself.* The idea that the electric field is itself a storehouse of energy is at the heart of the theory of electromagnetic waves and our modern understanding of the nature of light, to be discussed in Chapter 32.

24.1 Any two conductors a and b insulated from each another form a capacitor.

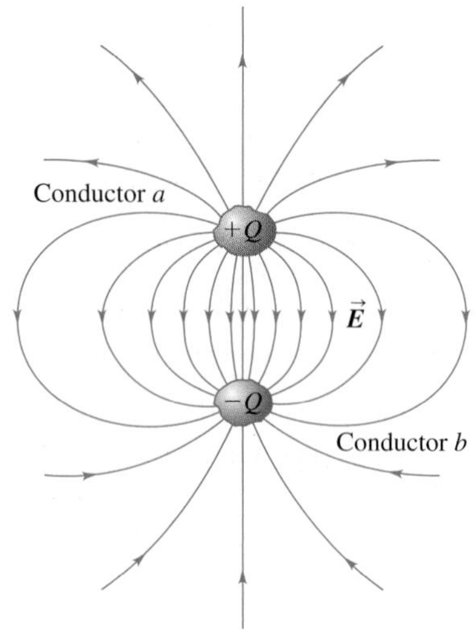

24.1 Capacitors and Capacitance

Any two conductors separated by an insulator (or a vacuum) form a **capacitor** (Fig. 24.1). In most practical applications, each conductor initially has zero net charge and electrons are transferred from one conductor to the other; this is called *charging* the capacitor. Then the two conductors have charges with equal magnitude and opposite sign, and the *net* charge on the capacitor as a whole remains zero. We will assume throughout this chapter that this is the case. When we say that a capacitor has charge Q, or that a charge Q is *stored* on the capacitor, we mean that the conductor at higher potential has charge $+Q$ and the conductor at lower potential has charge $-Q$ (assuming that Q is positive). Keep this in mind in the following discussion and examples.

In circuit diagrams a capacitor is represented by either of these symbols:

⊣⊢ ⊣(⊢

In either symbol the vertical lines (straight or curved) represent the conductors and the horizontal lines represent wires connected to either conductor. One common way to charge a capacitor is to connect these two wires to opposite terminals of a battery. Once the charges Q and $-Q$ are established on the conductors, the battery is disconnected. This gives a fixed *potential difference* V_{ab} between the conductors (that is, the potential of the positively charged conductor a with respect to the negatively charged conductor b) that is just equal to the voltage of the battery.

11.11.6 Electric Potential: Qualitative Introduction

11.12.1 and 11.12.3 Electric Potential, Field and, Force

The electric field at any point in the region between the conductors is proportional to the magnitude Q of charge on each conductor. It follows that the potential difference V_{ab} between the conductors is also proportional to Q. If we double the magnitude of charge on each conductor, the charge density at each point doubles, the electric field at each point doubles, and the potential difference between conductors doubles; however, the *ratio* of charge to potential difference does not change. This ratio is called the **capacitance** C of the capacitor:

$$C = \frac{Q}{V_{ab}} \quad \text{(definition of capacitance)} \tag{24.1}$$

The SI unit of capacitance is called one **farad** (1 F), in honor of the 19th-century English physicist Michael Faraday. From Eq. (24.1), one farad is equal to one *coulomb per volt* (1 C/V):

$$1\ \text{F} = 1\ \text{farad} = 1\ \text{C/V} = 1\ \text{coulomb/volt}$$

CAUTION **Capacitance vs. coulombs** Don't confuse the symbol C for capacitance (which is always in italics) with the abbreviation C for coulombs (which is never italicized).

The greater the capacitance C of a capacitor, the greater the magnitude Q of charge on either conductor for a given potential difference V_{ab} and hence the greater the amount of stored energy. (Remember that potential is potential energy per unit charge.) Thus *capacitance is a measure of the ability of a capacitor to store energy.* We will see that the value of the capacitance depends only on the shapes and sizes of the conductors and on the nature of the insulating material between them. (The above remarks about capacitance being independent of Q and V_{ab} do not apply to certain special types of insulating materials. We won't discuss these materials in this book, however.)

Calculating Capacitance: Capacitors in Vacuum

We can calculate the capacitance C of a given capacitor by finding the potential difference V_{ab} between the conductors for a given magnitude of charge Q and then using Eq. (24.1). For now we'll consider only *capacitors in vacuum;* that is, we'll assume that the conductors that make up the capacitor are separated by empty space.

The simplest form of capacitor consists of two parallel conducting plates, each with area A, separated by a distance d that is small in comparison with their dimensions (Fig. 24.2a). When the plates are charged, the electric field is almost completely localized in the region between the plates (Fig. 24.2b). As we discussed in Example 22.8 (Section 22.4), the field between such plates is essentially *uniform,* and the charges on the plates are uniformly distributed over their opposing surfaces. We call this arrangement a **parallel-plate capacitor.**

We worked out the electric-field magnitude E for this arrangement in Example 21.13 (Section 21.5) using the principle of superposition of electric fields and again in Example 22.8 (Section 22.4) using Gauss's law. It would be a good idea to review those examples. We found that $E = \sigma/\epsilon_0$, where σ is the magnitude (absolute value) of the surface charge density on each plate. This is equal to the magnitude of the total charge Q on each plate divided by the area A of the plate, or $\sigma = Q/A$, so the field magnitude E can be expressed as

$$E = \frac{\sigma}{\epsilon_0} = \frac{Q}{\epsilon_0 A}$$

The field is uniform and the distance between the plates is d, so the potential difference (voltage) between the two plates is

$$V_{ab} = Ed = \frac{1}{\epsilon_0}\frac{Qd}{A}$$

From this we see that the capacitance C of a parallel-plate capacitor in vacuum is

$$C = \frac{Q}{V_{ab}} = \epsilon_0 \frac{A}{d} \quad \text{(capacitance of a parallel-plate capacitor in vacuum)} \qquad (24.2)$$

The capacitance depends only on the geometry of the capacitor; it is directly proportional to the area A of each plate and inversely proportional to their separation d. The quantities A and d are constants for a given capacitor, and ϵ_0 is a universal constant. Thus in vacuum the capacitance C is a constant independent of the charge on the capacitor or the potential difference between the plates. If one of the capacitor plates is flexible, the capacitance C changes as the plate separation d changes. This is the operating principle of a condenser microphone (Fig. 24.3).

When matter is present between the plates, its properties affect the capacitance. We will return to this topic in Section 24.4. Meanwhile, we remark that if the space contains air at atmospheric pressure instead of vacuum, the capacitance differs from the prediction of Eq. (24.2) by less than 0.06%.

In Eq. (24.2), if A is in square meters and d in meters, C is in farads. The units of ϵ_0 are $C^2/N \cdot m^2$, so we see that

$$1\text{ F} = 1\text{ C}^2/\text{N}\cdot\text{m} = 1\text{ C}^2/\text{J}$$

Because $1\text{ V} = 1\text{ J/C}$ (energy per unit charge), this is consistent with our definition $1\text{ F} = 1\text{ C/V}$. Finally, the units of ϵ_0 can be expressed as $1\text{ C}^2/\text{N}\cdot\text{m}^2 = 1\text{ F/m}$, so

$$\epsilon_0 = 8.85 \times 10^{-12}\text{ F/m}$$

24.2 A charged parallel-plate capacitor.

(a) Arrangement of the capacitor plates

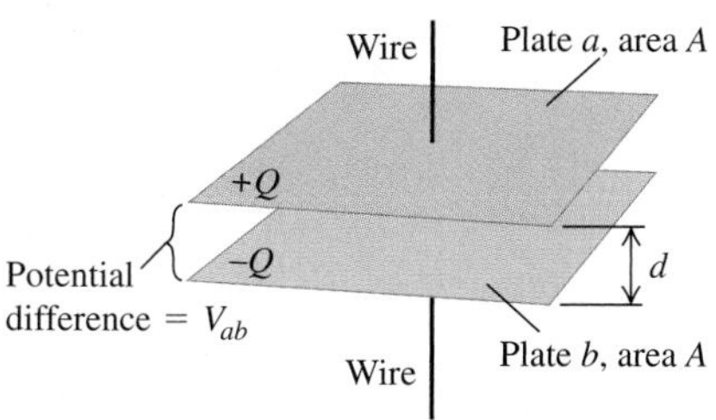

(b) Side view of the electric field $\vec{E}$

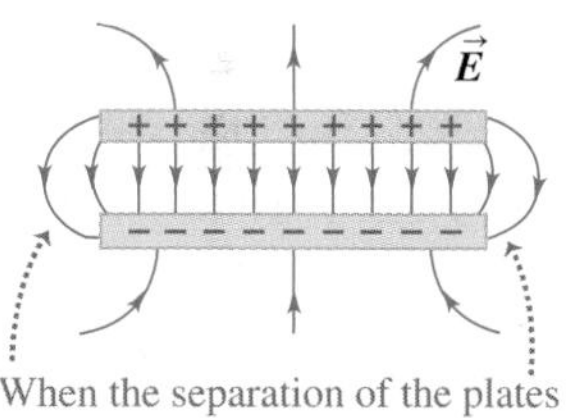

24.3 Inside a condenser microphone is a capacitor with one rigid plate and one flexible plate. The two plates are kept at a constant potential difference V_{ab}. Sound waves cause the flexible plate to move back and forth, varying the capacitance C and causing charge to flow to and from the capacitor in accordance with the relationship $C = Q/V_{ab}$. Thus a sound wave is converted to a charge flow that can be amplified and recorded digitally.

24.4 A commercial capacitor is labeled with the value of its capacitance. For these capacitors, $C = 2200\ \mu\text{F}$, $1000\ \mu\text{F}$, and $470\ \mu\text{F}$.

This relationship is useful in capacitance calculations, and it also helps us to verify that Eq. (24.2) is dimensionally consistent.

One farad is a very large capacitance, as the following example shows. In many applications the most convenient units of capacitance are the *microfarad* $(1\ \mu\text{F} = 10^{-6}\ \text{F})$ and the *picofarad* $(1\ \text{pF} = 10^{-12}\ \text{F})$. For example, the flash unit in a point-and-shoot camera uses a capacitor of a few hundred microfarads (Fig. 24.4), while capacitances in a radio tuning circuit are typically from 10 to 100 picofarads.

For *any* capacitor in vacuum, the capacitance C depends only on the shapes, dimensions, and separation of the conductors that make up the capacitor. If the conductor shapes are more complex than those of the parallel-plate capacitor, the expression for capacitance is more complicated than in Eq. (24.2). In the following examples we show how to calculate C for two other conductor geometries.

Example 24.1 Size of a 1-F capacitor

A parallel-plate capacitor has a capacitance of 1.0 F. If the plates are 1.0 mm apart, what is the area of the plates?

SOLUTION

IDENTIFY: This problem uses the relationship among the capacitance, plate separation, and plate area (our target variable) for a parallel-plate capacitor.

SET UP: We are given the values of C and d for a parallel-plate capacitor, so we use Eq. (24.2) and solve for the target variable A.

EXECUTE: From Eq. (24.2), the area A is

$$A = \frac{Cd}{\epsilon_0} = \frac{(1.0\ \text{F})(1.0 \times 10^{-3}\ \text{m})}{8.85 \times 10^{-12}\ \text{F/m}}$$
$$= 1.1 \times 10^{8}\ \text{m}^2$$

EVALUATE: This corresponds to a square about 10 km (about 6 miles) on a side! This area is about a third larger than Manhattan Island. Clearly this is not a very practical design for a capacitor.

In fact, it's now possible to make 1-F capacitors a few centimeters on a side. The trick is to have an appropriate substance between the plates rather than a vacuum. We'll explore this further in Section 24.4.

Example 24.2 Properties of a parallel-plate capacitor

The plates of a parallel-plate capacitor in vacuum are 5.00 mm apart and 2.00 m^2 in area. A potential difference of 10,000 V (10.0 kV) is applied across the capacitor. Compute (a) the capacitance; (b) the charge on each plate; and (c) the magnitude of the electric field in the space between them.

SOLUTION

IDENTIFY: We are given the plate area A, the plate spacing d, and the potential difference V_{ab} for this parallel-plate capacitor. Our target variables are the capacitance C, charge Q, and electric-field magnitude E.

SET UP: We use Eq. (24.2) to calculate C and then find the charge Q on each plate using the given potential difference V_{ab} and Eq. (24.1). Once we have Q, we find the electric field between the plates using the relationship $E = Q/\epsilon_0 A$.

EXECUTE: (a) From Eq. (24.2),

$$C = \epsilon_0 \frac{A}{d} = \frac{(8.85 \times 10^{-12}\ \text{F/m})(2.00\ \text{m}^2)}{5.00 \times 10^{-3}\ \text{m}}$$
$$= 3.54 \times 10^{-9}\ \text{F} = 0.00354\ \mu\text{F}$$

(b) The charge on the capacitor is

$$Q = CV_{ab} = (3.54 \times 10^{-9}\ \text{C/V})(1.00 \times 10^{4}\ \text{V})$$
$$= 3.54 \times 10^{-5}\ \text{C} = 35.4\ \mu\text{C}$$

The plate at higher potential has charge $+35.4\ \mu\text{C}$ and the other plate has charge $-35.4\ \mu\text{C}$.

(c) The electric-field magnitude is

$$E = \frac{\sigma}{\epsilon_0} = \frac{Q}{\epsilon_0 A} = \frac{3.54 \times 10^{-5}\ \text{C}}{(8.85 \times 10^{-12}\ \text{C}^2/\text{N}\cdot\text{m}^2)(2.00\ \text{m}^2)}$$
$$= 2.00 \times 10^{6}\ \text{N/C}$$

EVALUATE: An alternative way to get the result in part (c) is to recall that the electric field is equal in magnitude to the potential gradient [Eq. (23.22)]. Since the field between the plates is uniform,

$$E = \frac{V_{ab}}{d} = \frac{1.00 \times 10^{4}\ \text{V}}{5.00 \times 10^{-3}\ \text{m}} = 2.00 \times 10^{6}\ \text{V/m}$$

(Remember that the newton per coulomb and the volt per meter are equivalent units.)

Example 24.3 A spherical capacitor

Two concentric spherical conducting shells are separated by vacuum. The inner shell has total charge $+Q$ and outer radius r_a, and the outer shell has charge $-Q$ and inner radius r_b (Fig. 24.5). (The inner shell is attached to the outer shell by thin insulating rods that have negligible effect on the capacitance.) Find the capacitance of this spherical capacitor.

SOLUTION

IDENTIFY: This isn't a parallel-plate capacitor, so we can't use the relationships developed for that particular geometry. Instead, we'll go back to the fundamental definition of capacitance: the magnitude of the charge on either conductor divided by the potential difference between the conductors.

SET UP: We use Gauss's law to find the electric field between the spherical conductors. From this value we determine the potential difference V_{ab} between the two conductors; we then use Eq. (24.1) to find the capacitance $C = Q/V_{ab}$.

EXECUTE: Using the same procedure as in Example 22.5 (Section 22.4), we take as our Gaussian surface a sphere with radius r between the two spheres and concentric with them. Gauss's law, Eq. (22.8), states that the electric flux through this surface is equal to the total charge enclosed within the surface, divided by ϵ_0:

$$\oint \vec{E} \cdot d\vec{A} = \frac{Q_{\text{encl}}}{\epsilon_0}$$

By symmetry, $\vec{E}$ is constant in magnitude and parallel to $d\vec{A}$ at every point on this surface, so the integral in Gauss's law is equal to $(E)(4\pi r^2)$. The total charge enclosed is $Q_{\text{encl}} = Q$, so we have

$$(E)(4\pi r^2) = \frac{Q}{\epsilon_0}$$

$$E = \frac{Q}{4\pi\epsilon_0 r^2}$$

The electric field between the spheres is just that due to the charge on the inner sphere; the outer sphere has no effect. We found in Example 22.5 that the charge on a conducting sphere produces zero field *inside* the sphere, which also tells us that the outer conductor makes no contribution to the field between the conductors.

The above expression for E is the same as that for a point charge Q, so the expression for the potential can also be taken to be the same as for a point charge, $V = Q/4\pi\epsilon_0 r$. Hence the potential of the inner (positive) conductor at $r = r_a$ with respect to that of the outer (negative) conductor at $r = r_b$ is

$$V_{ab} = V_a - V_b = \frac{Q}{4\pi\epsilon_0 r_a} - \frac{Q}{4\pi\epsilon_0 r_b}$$

$$= \frac{Q}{4\pi\epsilon_0}\left(\frac{1}{r_a} - \frac{1}{r_b}\right) = \frac{Q}{4\pi\epsilon_0}\frac{r_b - r_a}{r_a r_b}$$

Finally, the capacitance is

$$C = \frac{Q}{V_{ab}} = 4\pi\epsilon_0 \frac{r_a r_b}{r_b - r_a}$$

As an example, if $r_a = 9.5$ cm and $r_b = 10.5$ cm,

$$C = 4\pi(8.85 \times 10^{-12}\ \text{F/m})\frac{(0.095\ \text{m})(0.105\ \text{m})}{0.010\ \text{m}}$$

$$= 1.1 \times 10^{-10}\ \text{F} = 110\ \text{pF}$$

EVALUATE: We can relate this result to the capacitance of a parallel-plate capacitor. The quantity $4\pi r_a r_b$ is intermediate between the areas $4\pi r_a^2$ and $4\pi r_b^2$ of the two spheres; in fact, it's the *geometric mean* of these two areas, which we can denote by A_{gm}. The distance between spheres is $d = r_b - r_a$, so we can rewrite the above result as $C = \epsilon_0 A_{\text{gm}}/d$. This is exactly the same form as for parallel plates: $C = \epsilon_0 A/d$. The point is that if the distance between spheres is very small in comparison to their radii, they behave like parallel plates with the same area and spacing.

24.5 A spherical capacitor.

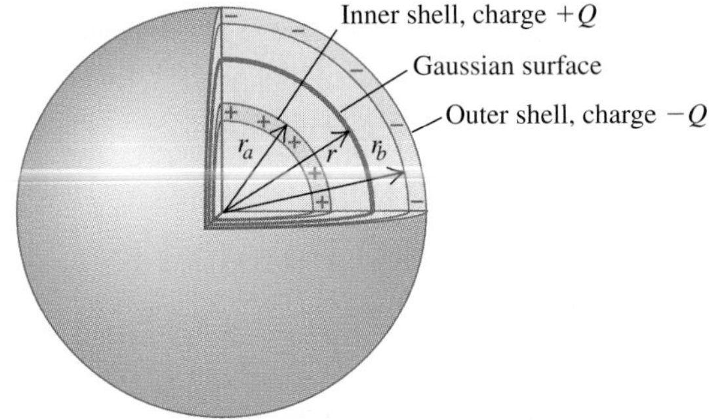

Example 24.4 A cylindrical capacitor

A long cylindrical conductor has a radius r_a and a linear charge density $+\lambda$. It is surrounded by a coaxial cylindrical conducting shell with inner radius r_b and linear charge density $-\lambda$ (Fig. 24.6). Calculate the capacitance per unit length for this capacitor, assuming that there is vacuum in the space between cylinders.

SOLUTION

IDENTIFY: As in Example 24.3, we use the fundamental definition of capacitance.

SET UP: We first find expressions for the potential difference V_{ab} between the cylinders and the charge Q in a length L of the cylinders; we then find the capacitance of a length L using Eq. (24.1). Our target variable is this capacitance divided by L.

EXECUTE: To find the potential difference between the cylinders, we use a result that we worked out in Example 23.10 (Section 23.3). There we found that at a point outside a charged

Continued

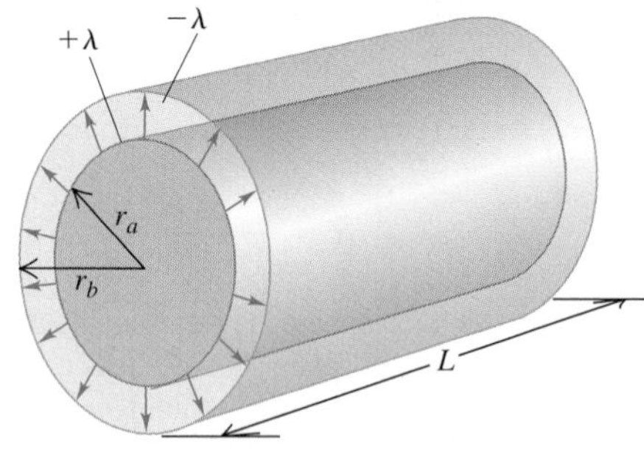

24.6 A long cylindrical capacitor. The linear charge density λ is assumed to be positive in this figure. The magnitude of charge in a length L of either cylinder is λL.

cylinder a distance r from the axis, the potential due to the cylinder is

$$V = \frac{\lambda}{2\pi\epsilon_0} \ln \frac{r_0}{r}$$

where r_0 is the (arbitrary) radius at which $V = 0$. We can use this same result for the potential *between* the cylinders in the present problem because, according to Gauss's law, the charge on the outer cylinder doesn't contribute to the field between cylinders (see Example 24.3). In our case, we take the radius r_0 to be r_b, the radius of the inner surface of the outer cylinder, so that the outer conducting cylinder is at $V = 0$. Then the potential at the outer surface of the inner cylinder (where $r = r_a$) is just equal to the potential V_{ab} of the inner (positive) cylinder a with respect to the outer (negative) cylinder b, or

$$V_{ab} = \frac{\lambda}{2\pi\epsilon_0} \ln \frac{r_b}{r_a}$$

This potential difference is positive (assuming that λ is positive, as in Fig. 24.6) because the inner cylinder is at higher potential than the outer.

The total charge Q in a length L is $Q = \lambda L$, so from Eq. (24.1) the capacitance C of a length L is

$$C = \frac{Q}{V_{ab}} = \frac{\lambda L}{\dfrac{\lambda}{2\pi\epsilon_0} \ln \dfrac{r_b}{r_a}} = \frac{2\pi\epsilon_0 L}{\ln (r_b/r_a)}$$

The capacitance per unit length is

$$\frac{C}{L} = \frac{2\pi\epsilon_0}{\ln (r_b/r_a)}$$

Substituting $\epsilon_0 = 8.85 \times 10^{-12}\ \text{F/m} = 8.85\ \text{pF/m}$, we get

$$\frac{C}{L} = \frac{55.6\ \text{pF/m}}{\ln (r_b/r_a)}$$

EVALUATE: We see that the capacitance of the coaxial cylinders is determined entirely by the dimensions, just as for the parallel-plate case. Ordinary coaxial cables are made like this but with an insulating material instead of vacuum between the inner and outer conductors. A typical cable for TV antennas and VCR connections has a capacitance per unit length of 69 pF/m.

Test Your Understanding of Section 24.1 A capacitor has vacuum in the space between the conductors. If you double the amount of charge on each conductor, what happens to the capacitance? (i) It increases; (ii) it decreases; (iii) it remains the same; (iv) the answer depends on the size or shape of the conductors.

24.2 Capacitors in Series and Parallel

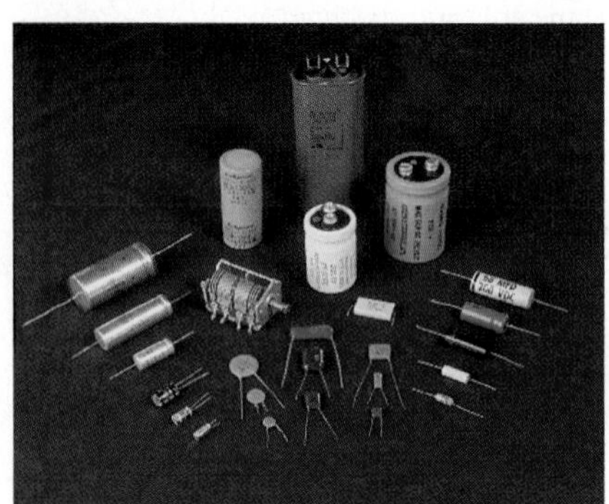

24.7 An assortment of commercially available capacitors.

Capacitors are manufactured with certain standard capacitances and working voltages (Fig. 24.7). However, these standard values may not be the ones you actually need in a particular application. You can obtain the values you need by combining capacitors; many combinations are possible, but the simplest combinations are a series connection and a parallel connection.

Capacitors in Series

Figure 24.8a is a schematic diagram of a **series connection.** Two capacitors are connected in series (one after the other) by conducting wires between points a and b. Both capacitors are initially uncharged. When a constant positive potential difference V_{ab} is applied between points a and b, the capacitors become charged; the figure shows that the charge on *all* conducting plates has the same magnitude. To see why, note first that the top plate of C_1 acquires a positive charge Q. The electric field of this positive charge pulls negative charge up to the bottom plate of C_1 until all of the field lines that begin on the top plate end on the bottom plate. This requires that the bottom plate have charge $-Q$. These negative charges had to come from the top plate of C_2, which becomes positively charged with charge $+Q$. This positive charge then pulls negative charge $-Q$ from the connection at point b onto the bottom plate of C_2. The total charge on the lower plate of C_1 and the upper plate of C_2 together must always be zero because these plates aren't connected to anything except each other. Thus *in a series connection the magnitude of charge on all plates is the same.*

Referring to Fig. 24.8a, we can write the potential differences between points a and c, c and b, and a and b as

$$V_{ac} = V_1 = \frac{Q}{C_1} \qquad V_{cb} = V_2 = \frac{Q}{C_2}$$

$$V_{ab} = V = V_1 + V_2 = Q\left(\frac{1}{C_1} + \frac{1}{C_2}\right)$$

and so

$$\frac{V}{Q} = \frac{1}{C_1} + \frac{1}{C_2} \tag{24.3}$$

24.8 A series connection of two capacitors.

(a) Two capacitors in series

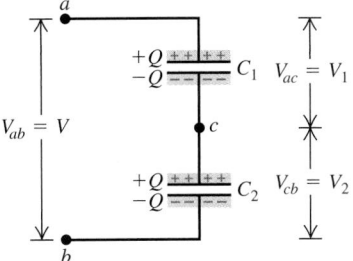

Capacitors in series:
- The capacitors have the same charge Q.
- Their potential differences add: $V_{ac} + V_{cb} = V_{ab}$.

a $+Q$ $-Q$ C_1 $V_{ac} = V_1$ $V_{ab} = V$ c $+Q$ $-Q$ C_2 $V_{cb} = V_2$ b

(b) The equivalent single capacitor

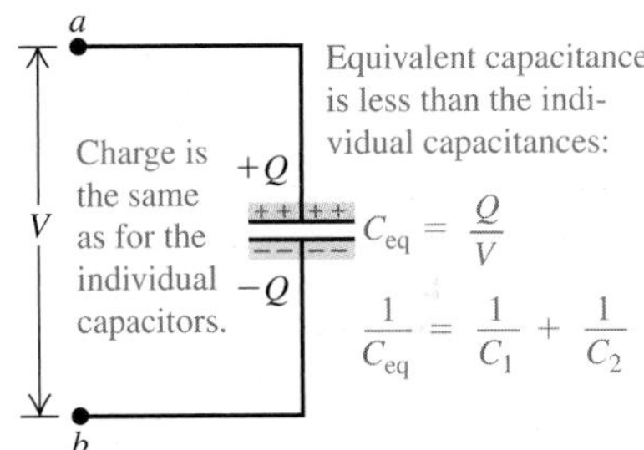

a
Charge is the same as for the individual capacitors.
+Q
V
C_{eq}
−Q
b
Equivalent capacitance is less than the individual capacitances:
$C_{eq} = \frac{Q}{V}$
$\frac{1}{C_{eq}} = \frac{1}{C_1} + \frac{1}{C_2}$

Following a common convention, we use the symbols V_1, V_2, and V to denote the potential *differences* V_{ac} (across the first capacitor), V_{cb} (across the second capacitor), and V_{ab} (across the entire combination of capacitors), respectively.

The **equivalent capacitance** C_{eq} of the series combination is defined as the capacitance of a *single* capacitor for which the charge Q is the same as for the combination, when the potential difference V is the same. In other words, the combination can be replaced by an *equivalent capacitor* of capacitance C_{eq}. For such a capacitor, shown in Fig. 24.8b,

$$C_{eq} = \frac{Q}{V} \quad \text{or} \quad \frac{1}{C_{eq}} = \frac{V}{Q} \tag{24.4}$$

Combining Eqs. (24.3) and (24.4), we find

$$\frac{1}{C_{eq}} = \frac{1}{C_1} + \frac{1}{C_2}$$

We can extend this analysis to any number of capacitors in series. We find the following result for the *reciprocal* of the equivalent capacitance:

$$\frac{1}{C_{eq}} = \frac{1}{C_1} + \frac{1}{C_2} + \frac{1}{C_3} + \cdots \quad \text{(capacitors in series)} \tag{24.5}$$

The reciprocal of the equivalent capacitance of a series combination equals the sum of the reciprocals of the individual capacitances. In a series connection the equivalent capacitance is always *less than* any individual capacitance.

CAUTION Capacitors in series The magnitude of charge is the same on all plates of all the capacitors in a series combination; however, the potential differences of the individual capacitors are *not* the same unless their individual capacitances are the same. The potential differences of the individual capacitors add to give the total potential difference across the series combination: $V_{total} = V_1 + V_2 + V_3 + \cdots$.

Capacitors in Parallel

The arrangement shown in Fig. 24.9a is called a **parallel connection.** Two capacitors are connected in parallel between points a and b. In this case the upper plates of the two capacitors are connected by conducting wires to form an equipotential surface, and the lower plates form another. Hence *in a parallel connection the potential difference for all individual capacitors is the same* and is equal to $V_{ab} = V$. The charges Q_1 and Q_2 are not necessarily equal, however,

24.9 A parallel connection of two capacitors.

(a) Two capacitors in parallel

Capacitors in parallel:
- The capacitors have the same potential V.
- The charge on each capacitor depends on its capacitance: $Q_1 = C_1V$, $Q_2 = C_2V$.

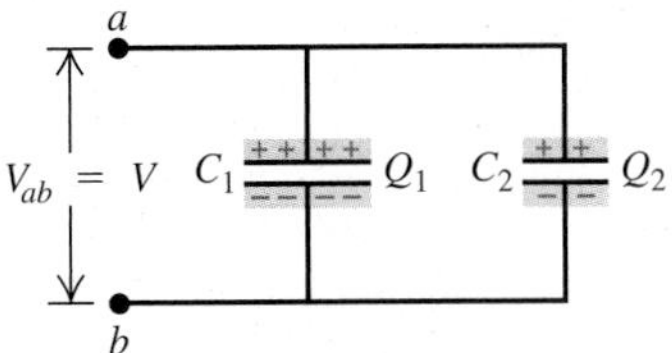

a
$V_{ab} = V$
C_1
Q_1
C_2
Q_2
b

(b) The equivalent single capacitor

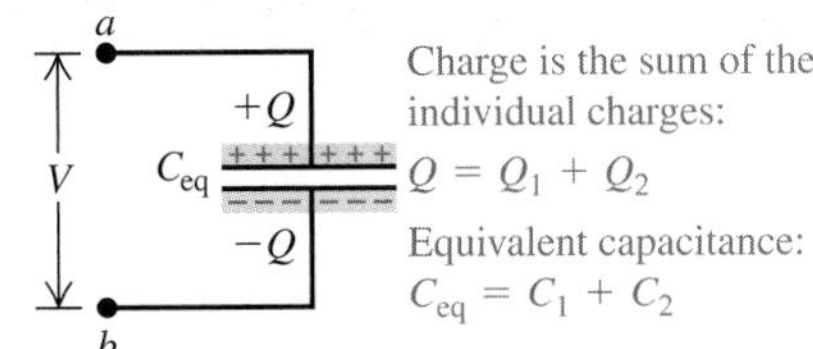

a
+Q
V
C_{eq}
−Q
b
Charge is the sum of the individual charges:
$Q = Q_1 + Q_2$
Equivalent capacitance:
$C_{eq} = C_1 + C_2$

since charges can reach each capacitor independently from the source (such as a battery) of the voltage V_{ab}. The charges are

$$Q_1 = C_1 V \quad \text{and} \quad Q_2 = C_2 V$$

The *total* charge Q of the combination, and thus the total charge on the equivalent capacitor, is

$$Q = Q_1 + Q_2 = (C_1 + C_2)V$$

so

$$\frac{Q}{V} = C_1 + C_2 \tag{24.6}$$

The parallel combination is equivalent to a single capacitor with the same total charge $Q = Q_1 + Q_2$ and potential difference V as the combination (Fig. 24.9b). The equivalent capacitance of the combination, C_{eq}, is the same as the capacitance Q/V of this single equivalent capacitor. So from Eq. (24.6),

$$C_{eq} = C_1 + C_2$$

In the same way we can show that for any number of capacitors in parallel,

$$C_{eq} = C_1 + C_2 + C_3 + \cdots \quad \text{(capacitors in parallel)} \tag{24.7}$$

The equivalent capacitance of a parallel combination equals the *sum* of the individual capacitances. In a parallel connection the equivalent capacitance is always *greater than* any individual capacitance.

CAUTION Capacitors in parallel The potential differences are the same for all the capacitors in a parallel combination; however, the charges on individual capacitors are *not* the same unless their individual capacitances are the same. The charges on the individual capacitors add to give the total charge on the parallel combination: $Q_{total} = Q_1 + Q_2 + Q_3 + \cdots$. [Compare these statements to those in the "Caution" paragraph following Eq. (24.5).]

Problem-Solving Strategy 24.1 Equivalent Capacitance

IDENTIFY *the relevant concepts:* The concept of equivalent capacitance is useful whenever two or more capacitors are connected.

SET UP *the problem* using the following steps:
1. Make a drawing of the capacitor arrangement.
2. Identify whether the capacitors are connected in series or in parallel. With more complicated combinations, you can sometimes identify parts that are simple series or parallel connections.
3. Keep in mind that when we say a capacitor has charge Q, we always mean that the plate at higher potential has charge $+Q$ and the other plate has charge $-Q$.

EXECUTE *the solution* as follows:
1. When capacitors are connected in series, as in Fig. 24.8a, they always have the same charge, assuming that they were uncharged before they were connected. The potential differences are *not* equal unless the capacitances are equal. The total potential difference across the combination is the sum of the individual potential differences.
2. When capacitors are connected in parallel, as in Fig. 24.9a, the potential difference V is always the same for all of the individual capacitors. The charges on the individual capacitors are *not* equal unless the capacitances are equal. The total charge on the combination is the sum of the individual charges.
3. For more complicated combinations, find the parts that are simple series or parallel connections and replace them with their equivalent capacitances, in a step-by-step reduction. If you then need to find the charge or potential difference for an individual capacitor, you may have to retrace your path to the original capacitors.

EVALUATE *your answer:* Check whether your result makes sense. If the capacitors are connected in series, the equivalent capacitance C_{eq} must be *smaller* than any of the individual capacitances. By contrast, if the capacitors are connected in parallel, C_{eq} must be *greater* than any of the individual capacitances.

Example 24.5 Capacitors in series and in parallel

In Figs. 24.8 and 24.9, let $C_1 = 6.0\ \mu\text{F}$, $C_2 = 3.0\ \mu\text{F}$, and $V_{ab} = 18\ \text{V}$. Find the equivalent capacitance, and find the charge and potential difference for each capacitor when the two capacitors are connected (a) in series and (b) in parallel.

SOLUTION

IDENTIFY: This problem uses the ideas discussed in this section about capacitor connections.

SET UP: In both parts, one of the target variables is the equivalent capacitance C_{eq}. For the series combination in part (a), it is given by Eq. (24.5); for the parallel combination in part (b), C_{eq} is given by Eq. (24.6). In each part we find the charge and potential difference using the definition of capacitance, Eq. (24.1), and the rules outlined in the Problem-Solving Strategy 24.1.

EXECUTE: (a) Using Eq. (24.5) for the equivalent capacitance of the series combination (Fig. 24.8a), we find

$$\frac{1}{C_{\text{eq}}} = \frac{1}{C_1} + \frac{1}{C_2} = \frac{1}{6.0\ \mu\text{F}} + \frac{1}{3.0\ \mu\text{F}} \qquad C_{\text{eq}} = 2.0\ \mu\text{F}$$

The charge Q on each capacitor in series is the same as the charge on the equivalent capacitor:

$$Q = C_{\text{eq}}V = (2.0\ \mu\text{F})(18\ \text{V}) = 36\ \mu\text{C}$$

The potential difference across each capacitor is inversely proportional to its capacitance:

$$V_{ac} = V_1 = \frac{Q}{C_1} = \frac{36\ \mu\text{C}}{6.0\ \mu\text{F}} = 6.0\ \text{V}$$

$$V_{cb} = V_2 = \frac{Q}{C_2} = \frac{36\ \mu\text{C}}{3.0\ \mu\text{F}} = 12.0\ \text{V}$$

(b) To find the equivalent capacitance of the parallel combination (Fig. 24.9a), we use Eq. (24.6):

$$C_{\text{eq}} = C_1 + C_2 = 6.0\ \mu\text{F} + 3.0\ \mu\text{F} = 9.0\ \mu\text{F}$$

The potential difference across each of the two capacitors in parallel is the same as that across the equivalent capacitor, 18 V. The charges Q_1 and Q_2 are directly proportional to the capacitances C_1 and C_2, respectively:

$$Q_1 = C_1V = (6.0\ \mu\text{F})(18\ \text{V}) = 108\ \mu\text{C}$$

$$Q_2 = C_2V = (3.0\ \mu\text{F})(18\ \text{V}) = 54\ \mu\text{C}$$

EVALUATE: Note that the equivalent capacitance C_{eq} for the series combination in part (a) is indeed less than either C_1 or C_2, while for the parallel combination in part (b) the equivalent capacitance is indeed greater than either C_1 or C_2.

It's instructive to compare the potential differences and charges in each part of the example. For two capacitors in series, as in part (a), the charge is the same on either capacitor and the *larger* potential difference appears across the capacitor with the *smaller* capacitance. Furthermore, $V_{ac} + V_{cb} = V_{ab} = 18\ \text{V}$, as it must. By contrast, for two capacitors in parallel, as in part (b), each capacitor has the same potential difference and the *larger* charge appears on the capacitor with the *larger* capacitance. Can you show that the total charge $Q_1 + Q_2$ on the parallel combination is equal to the charge $Q = C_{\text{eq}}V$ on the equivalent capacitor?

Example 24.6 A capacitor network

Find the equivalent capacitance of the combination shown in Fig. 24.10a.

SOLUTION

IDENTIFY: The five capacitors in Fig. 24.10a are neither all in series nor all in parallel. We can, however, identify portions of the arrangement that *are* either in series or parallel, which we combine to find the net equivalent capacitance.

SET UP: We use Eq. (24.5) to analyze portions of the network that are series connections and Eq. (24.7) to analyze portions that are parallel connections.

24.10 (a) A capacitor network between points a and b. (b) The 12-μF and 6-μF capacitors in series in (a) are replaced by an equivalent 4-μF capacitor. (c) The 3-μF, 11-μF, and 4-μF capacitors in parallel in (b) are replaced by an equivalent 18-μF capacitor. (d) Finally, the 18-μF and 9-μF capacitors in series in (c) are replaced by an equivalent 6-μF capacitor.

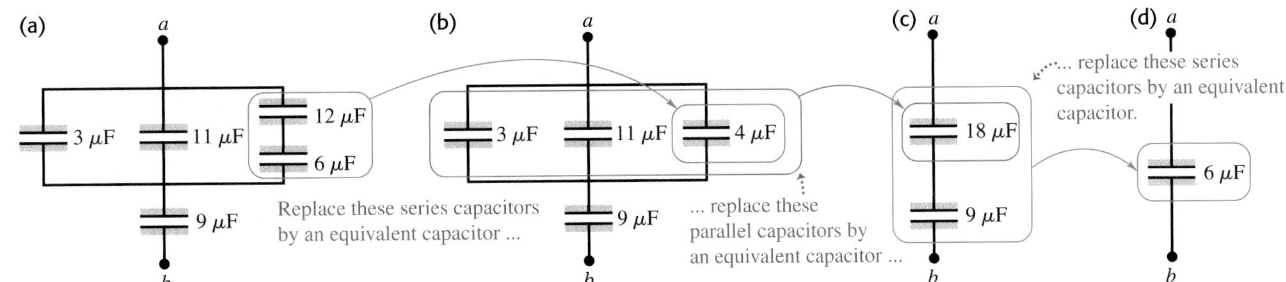

Continued

plates. To develop this relationship, let's find the energy *per unit volume* in the space between the plates of a parallel-plate capacitor with plate area A and separation d. We call this the **energy density,** denoted by u. From Eq. (24.9) the total stored potential energy is $\frac{1}{2}CV^2$ and the volume between the plates is just Ad; hence the energy density is

$$u = \text{Energy density} = \frac{\frac{1}{2}CV^2}{Ad} \tag{24.10}$$

From Eq. (24.2) the capacitance C is given by $C = \epsilon_0 A/d$. The potential difference V is related to the electric field magnitude E by $V = Ed$. If we use these expressions in Eq. (24.10), the geometric factors A and d cancel, and we find

$$u = \frac{1}{2}\epsilon_0 E^2 \quad \text{(electric energy density in a vacuum)} \tag{24.11}$$

Although we have derived this relationship only for a parallel-plate capacitor, it turns out to be valid for any capacitor in vacuum and indeed *for any electric field configuration in vacuum.* This result has an interesting implication. We think of vacuum as space with no matter in it, but vacuum can nevertheless have electric fields and therefore energy. Thus "empty" space need not be truly empty after all. We will use this idea and Eq. (24.11) in Chapter 32 in connection with the energy transported by electromagnetic waves.

CAUTION **Electrical-field energy is electric potential energy** It's a common misconception that electric-field energy is a new kind of energy, different from the electric potential energy described before. This is *not* the case; it is simply a different way of interpreting electric potential energy. We can regard the energy of a given system of charges as being a shared property of all the charges, or we can think of the energy as being a property of the electric field that the charges create. Either interpretation leads to the same value of the potential energy.

Example 24.7 Transferring charge and energy between capacitors

In Fig. 24.12 we charge a capacitor of capacitance $C_1 = 8.0\ \mu\text{F}$ by connecting it to a source of potential difference $V_0 = 120\ \text{V}$ (not shown in the figure). The switch S is initially open. Once C_1 is charged, the source of potential difference is disconnected. (a) What is the charge Q_0 on C_1 if switch S is left open? (b) What is the energy stored in C_1 if switch S is left open? (c) The capacitor of capacitance $C_2 = 4.0\ \mu\text{F}$ is initially uncharged. After we close switch S, what is the potential difference across each capacitor, and what is the charge on each capacitor? (d) What is the total energy of the system after we close switch S?

SOLUTION

IDENTIFY: Initially we have a single capacitor with a given potential difference between its plates. After the switch is closed, one wire connects the upper plates of the two capacitors and another wire connects the lower plates; in other words, the capacitors are connected in parallel.

SET UP: In parts (a) and (b) we find the charge and stored energy for capacitor C_1 using Eqs. (24.1) and (24.9), respectively. In part (c) we use the character of the parallel connection to determine how the charge Q_0 is shared between the two capacitors. In part (d) we again use Eq. (24.9) to find the energy stored in capacitors C_1 and C_2; the total energy is the sum of these values.

24.12 When the switch S is closed, the charged capacitor C_1 is connected to an uncharged capacitor C_2. The center part of the switch is an insulating handle; charge can flow only between the two upper terminals and between the two lower terminals.

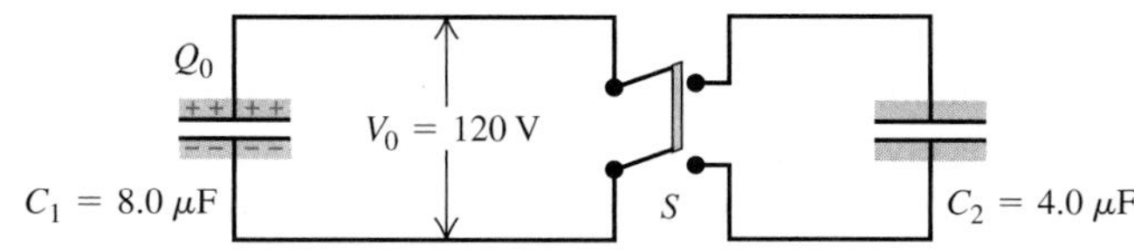

EXECUTE: (a) The charge Q_0 on C_1 is

$$Q_0 = C_1 V_0 = (8.0\ \mu\text{F})(120\ \text{V}) = 960\ \mu\text{C}$$

(b) The energy initially stored in the capacitor is

$$U_{\text{initial}} = \frac{1}{2}Q_0 V_0 = \frac{1}{2}(960 \times 10^{-6}\ \text{C})(120\ \text{V}) = 0.058\ \text{J}$$

(c) When the switch is closed, the positive charge Q_0 becomes distributed over the upper plates of both capacitors and the negative charge $-Q_0$ is distributed over the lower plates of both capacitors. Let Q_1 and Q_2 be the magnitudes of the final charges on the two capacitors. From conservation of charge,

$$Q_1 + Q_2 = Q_0$$

When Q is in coulombs, C in farads (coulombs per volt), and V in volts (joules per coulomb), U is in joules.

The last form of Eq. (24.9), $U = \frac{1}{2}QV$, shows that the total work W required to charge the capacitor is equal to the total charge Q multiplied by the *average* potential difference $\frac{1}{2}V$ during the charging process.

The expression $U = \frac{1}{2}(Q^2/C)$ in Eq. (24.9) shows that a charged capacitor is the electrical analog of a stretched spring with elastic potential energy $U = \frac{1}{2}kx^2$. The charge Q is analogous to the elongation x, and the *reciprocal* of the capacitance, $1/C$, is analogous to the force constant k. The energy supplied to a capacitor in the charging process is analogous to the work we do on a spring when we stretch it.

Equations (24.8) and (24.9) tell us that capacitance measures the ability of a capacitor to store both energy and charge. If a capacitor is charged by connecting it to a battery or other source that provides a fixed potential difference V, then increasing the value of C gives a greater charge $Q = CV$ and a greater amount of stored energy $U = \frac{1}{2}CV^2$. If instead the goal is to transfer a given quantity of charge Q from one conductor to another, Eq. (24.8) shows that the work W required is inversely proportional to C; the greater the capacitance, the easier it is to give a capacitor a fixed amount of charge.

Applications of Capacitors: Energy Storage

Most practical applications of capacitors take advantage of their ability to store and release energy. In electronic flash units used by photographers, the energy stored in a capacitor (see Fig. 24.4) is released by depressing the camera's shutter button. This provides a conducting path from one capacitor plate to the other through the flash tube. Once this path is established, the stored energy is rapidly converted into a brief but intense flash of light. An extreme example of the same principle is the Z machine at Sandia National Laboratories in New Mexico, which is used in experiments in controlled nuclear fusion (Fig. 24.11). A bank of charged capacitors releases more than a million joules of energy in just a few billionths of a second. For that brief space of time, the power output of the Z machine is 2.9×10^{14} W, or about 80 times the electric output of all the electric power plants on earth combined!

?

24.11 The Z machine uses a large number of capacitors in parallel to give a tremendous equivalent capacitance C (see Section 24.2). Hence a large amount of energy $U = \frac{1}{2}CV^2$ can be stored with even a modest potential difference V. The arcs shown here are produced when the capacitors discharge their energy into a target, which is no larger than a spool of thread. This heats the target to a temperature higher than 2×10^9 K.

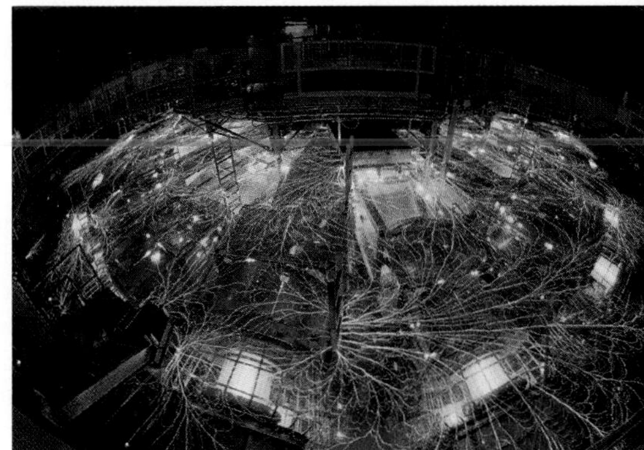

In other applications, the energy is released more slowly. Springs in the suspension of an automobile, help smooth out the ride by absorbing the energy from sudden jolts and releasing that energy gradually; in an analogous way, a capacitor in an electronic circuit can smooth out unwanted variations in voltage due to power surges. And just as the presence of a spring gives a mechanical system a natural frequency at which it responds most strongly to an applied periodic force, so the presence of a capacitor gives an electric circuit a natural frequency for current oscillations. This idea is used in tuned circuits such as those in radio and television receivers, which respond to broadcast signals at one particular frequency and ignore signals at other frequencies. We'll discuss these circuits in detail in Chapter 31.

The energy-storage properties of capacitors also have some undesirable practical effects. Adjacent pins on the underside of a computer chip act like a capacitor, and the property that makes capacitors useful for smoothing out voltage variations acts to retard the rate at which the potentials of the chip's pins can be changed. This tendency limits how rapidly the chip can perform computations, an effect that becomes more important as computer chips become smaller and are pushed to operate at faster speeds.

Electric-Field Energy

We can charge a capacitor by moving electrons directly from one plate to another. This requires doing work against the electric field between the plates. Thus we can think of the energy as being stored *in the field* in the region between the plates. To develop this relationship, let's find the energy *per unit volume* in the space between the plates of a parallel-plate capacitor with plate area A and separation d. We call this the **energy density,** denoted by u. From Eq. (24.9) the total stored potential energy is $\frac{1}{2}CV^2$ and the volume between the plates is just Ad; hence the energy density is

$$u = \text{Energy density} = \frac{\frac{1}{2}CV^2}{Ad} \tag{24.10}$$

From Eq. (24.2) the capacitance C is given by $C = \epsilon_0 A/d$. The potential difference V is related to the electric field magnitude E by $V = Ed$. If we use these expressions in Eq. (24.10), the geometric factors A and d cancel, and we find

$$u = \frac{1}{2}\epsilon_0 E^2 \quad \text{(electric energy density in a vacuum)} \tag{24.11}$$

Although we have derived this relationship only for a parallel-plate capacitor, it turns out to be valid for any capacitor in vacuum and indeed *for any electric field configuration in vacuum.* This result has an interesting implication. We think of vacuum as space with no matter in it, but vacuum can nevertheless have electric fields and therefore energy. Thus "empty" space need not be truly empty after all. We will use this idea and Eq. (24.11) in Chapter 32 in connection with the energy transported by electromagnetic waves.

CAUTION **Electrical-field energy is electric potential energy** It's a common misconception that electric-field energy is a new kind of energy, different from the electric potential energy described before. This is *not* the case; it is simply a different way of interpreting electric potential energy. We can regard the energy of a given system of charges as being a shared property of all the charges, or we can think of the energy as being a property of the electric field that the charges create. Either interpretation leads to the same value of the potential energy.

Example 24.7 Transferring charge and energy between capacitors

In Fig. 24.12 we charge a capacitor of capacitance $C_1 = 8.0\ \mu\text{F}$ by connecting it to a source of potential difference $V_0 = 120$ V (not shown in the figure). The switch S is initially open. Once C_1 is charged, the source of potential difference is disconnected. (a) What is the charge Q_0 on C_1 if switch S is left open? (b) What is the energy stored in C_1 if switch S is left open? (c) The capacitor of capacitance $C_2 = 4.0\ \mu\text{F}$ is initially uncharged. After we close switch S, what is the potential difference across each capacitor, and what is the charge on each capacitor? (d) What is the total energy of the system after we close switch S?

SOLUTION

IDENTIFY: Initially we have a single capacitor with a given potential difference between its plates. After the switch is closed, one wire connects the upper plates of the two capacitors and another wire connects the lower plates; in other words, the capacitors are connected in parallel.

SET UP: In parts (a) and (b) we find the charge and stored energy for capacitor C_1 using Eqs. (24.1) and (24.9), respectively. In part (c) we use the character of the parallel connection to determine how the charge Q_0 is shared between the two capacitors. In part (d) we again use Eq. (24.9) to find the energy stored in capacitors C_1 and C_2; the total energy is the sum of these values.

24.12 When the switch S is closed, the charged capacitor C_1 is connected to an uncharged capacitor C_2. The center part of the switch is an insulating handle; charge can flow only between the two upper terminals and between the two lower terminals.

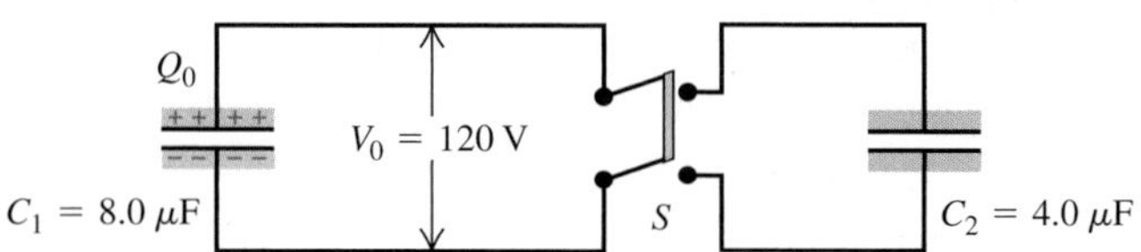

EXECUTE: (a) The charge Q_0 on C_1 is

$$Q_0 = C_1V_0 = (8.0\ \mu\text{F})(120\ \text{V}) = 960\ \mu\text{C}$$

(b) The energy initially stored in the capacitor is

$$U_{\text{initial}} = \frac{1}{2}Q_0V_0 = \frac{1}{2}(960 \times 10^{-6}\ \text{C})(120\ \text{V}) = 0.058\ \text{J}$$

(c) When the switch is closed, the positive charge Q_0 becomes distributed over the upper plates of both capacitors and the negative charge $-Q_0$ is distributed over the lower plates of both capacitors. Let Q_1 and Q_2 be the magnitudes of the final charges on the two capacitors. From conservation of charge,

$$Q_1 + Q_2 = Q_0$$

Example 24.5 Capacitors in series and in parallel

In Figs. 24.8 and 24.9, let $C_1 = 6.0\ \mu\text{F}$, $C_2 = 3.0\ \mu\text{F}$, and $V_{ab} = 18\ \text{V}$. Find the equivalent capacitance, and find the charge and potential difference for each capacitor when the two capacitors are connected (a) in series and (b) in parallel.

SOLUTION

IDENTIFY: This problem uses the ideas discussed in this section about capacitor connections.

SET UP: In both parts, one of the target variables is the equivalent capacitance C_{eq}. For the series combination in part (a), it is given by Eq. (24.5); for the parallel combination in part (b), C_{eq} is given by Eq. (24.6). In each part we find the charge and potential difference using the definition of capacitance, Eq. (24.1), and the rules outlined in the Problem-Solving Strategy 24.1.

EXECUTE: (a) Using Eq. (24.5) for the equivalent capacitance of the series combination (Fig. 24.8a), we find

$$\frac{1}{C_{eq}} = \frac{1}{C_1} + \frac{1}{C_2} = \frac{1}{6.0\ \mu\text{F}} + \frac{1}{3.0\ \mu\text{F}} \qquad C_{eq} = 2.0\ \mu\text{F}$$

The charge Q on each capacitor in series is the same as the charge on the equivalent capacitor:

$$Q = C_{eq}V = (2.0\ \mu\text{F})(18\ \text{V}) = 36\ \mu\text{C}$$

The potential difference across each capacitor is inversely proportional to its capacitance:

$$V_{ac} = V_1 = \frac{Q}{C_1} = \frac{36\ \mu\text{C}}{6.0\ \mu\text{F}} = 6.0\ \text{V}$$

$$V_{cb} = V_2 = \frac{Q}{C_2} = \frac{36\ \mu\text{C}}{3.0\ \mu\text{F}} = 12.0\ \text{V}$$

(b) To find the equivalent capacitance of the parallel combination (Fig. 24.9a), we use Eq. (24.6):

$$C_{eq} = C_1 + C_2 = 6.0\ \mu\text{F} + 3.0\ \mu\text{F} = 9.0\ \mu\text{F}$$

The potential difference across each of the two capacitors in parallel is the same as that across the equivalent capacitor, 18 V. The charges Q_1 and Q_2 are directly proportional to the capacitances C_1 and C_2, respectively:

$$Q_1 = C_1V = (6.0\ \mu\text{F})(18\ \text{V}) = 108\ \mu\text{C}$$

$$Q_2 = C_2V = (3.0\ \mu\text{F})(18\ \text{V}) = 54\ \mu\text{C}$$

EVALUATE: Note that the equivalent capacitance C_{eq} for the series combination in part (a) is indeed less than either C_1 or C_2, while for the parallel combination in part (b) the equivalent capacitance is indeed greater than either C_1 or C_2.

It's instructive to compare the potential differences and charges in each part of the example. For two capacitors in series, as in part (a), the charge is the same on either capacitor and the *larger* potential difference appears across the capacitor with the *smaller* capacitance. Furthermore, $V_{ac} + V_{cb} = V_{ab} = 18$ V, as it must. By contrast, for two capacitors in parallel, as in part (b), each capacitor has the same potential difference and the *larger* charge appears on the capacitor with the *larger* capacitance. Can you show that the total charge $Q_1 + Q_2$ on the parallel combination is equal to the charge $Q = C_{eq}V$ on the equivalent capacitor?

Example 24.6 A capacitor network

Find the equivalent capacitance of the combination shown in Fig. 24.10a.

SOLUTION

IDENTIFY: The five capacitors in Fig. 24.10a are neither all in series nor all in parallel. We can, however, identify portions of the arrangement that *are* either in series or parallel, which we combine to find the net equivalent capacitance.

SET UP: We use Eq. (24.5) to analyze portions of the network that are series connections and Eq. (24.7) to analyze portions that are parallel connections.

24.10 (a) A capacitor network between points a and b. (b) The 12-μF and 6-μF capacitors in series in (a) are replaced by an equivalent 4-μF capacitor. (c) The 3-μF, 11-μF, and 4-μF capacitors in parallel in (b) are replaced by an equivalent 18-μF capacitor. (d) Finally, the 18-μF and 9-μF capacitors in series in (c) are replaced by an equivalent 6-μF capacitor.

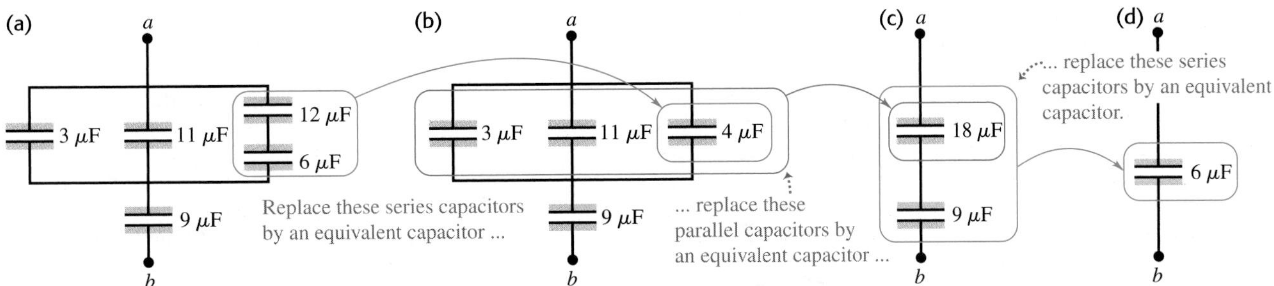

Continued

EXECUTE: We first replace the 12-μF and 6-μF series combination by its equivalent capacitance; calling that C', we use Eq. (24.5):

$$\frac{1}{C'} = \frac{1}{12\ \mu\text{F}} + \frac{1}{6\ \mu\text{F}} \qquad C' = 4\ \mu\text{F}$$

This gives us the equivalent combination shown in Fig. 24.10b. Next we find the equivalent capacitance of the three capacitors in parallel, using Eq. (24.7). Calling their equivalent capacitance C'', we have

$$C'' = 3\ \mu\text{F} + 11\ \mu\text{F} + 4\ \mu\text{F} = 18\ \mu\text{F}$$

This gives us the simpler equivalent combination shown in Fig. 24.10c. Finally, we find the equivalent capacitance C_{eq} of these two capacitors in series (Fig. 24.10d):

$$\frac{1}{C_{eq}} = \frac{1}{18\ \mu\text{F}} + \frac{1}{9\ \mu\text{F}} \qquad C_{eq} = 6\ \mu\text{F}$$

EVALUATE: The equivalent capacitance of the network is 6 μF; that is, if a potential difference V_{ab} is applied across the terminals of the network, the net charge on the network is 6 μF times V_{ab}. How is this net charge related to the charges on the individual capacitors in Fig. 24.10a?

Test Your Understanding of Section 24.2 You want to connect a 4-μF capacitor and an 8-μF capacitor. (a) With which type of connection will the 4-μF capacitor have a greater *potential difference* across it than the 8-μF capacitor? (i) series; (ii) parallel; (iii) either series or parallel; (iv) neither series nor parallel. (b) With which type of connection will the 4-μF capacitor have a greater *charge* than the 8-μF capacitor? (i) series; (ii) parallel; (iii) either series or parallel; (iv) neither series nor parallel.

MP

24.3 Energy Storage in Capacitors and Electric-Field Energy

Many of the most important applications of capacitors depend on their ability to store energy. The electric potential energy stored in a charged capacitor is just equal to the amount of work required to charge it—that is, to separate opposite charges and place them on different conductors. When the capacitor is discharged, this stored energy is recovered as work done by electrical forces.

We can calculate the potential energy U of a charged capacitor by calculating the work W required to charge it. Suppose that when we are done charging the capacitor, the final charge is Q and the final potential difference is V. From Eq. (24.1) these quantities are related by

$$V = \frac{Q}{C}$$

Let q and v be the charge and potential difference, respectively, at an intermediate stage during the charging process; then $v = q/C$. At this stage the work dW required to transfer an additional element of charge dq is

$$dW = v\,dq = \frac{q\,dq}{C}$$

The total work W needed to increase the capacitor charge q from zero to a final value Q is

$$W = \int_0^W dW = \frac{1}{C}\int_0^Q q\,dq = \frac{Q^2}{2C} \qquad \text{(work to charge a capacitor)} \quad (24.8)$$

This is also equal to the total work done by the electric field on the charge when the capacitor discharges. Then q *decreases* from an initial value Q to zero as the elements of charge dq "fall" through potential differences v that vary from V down to zero.

If we define the potential energy of an *uncharged* capacitor to be zero, then W in Eq. (24.8) is equal to the potential energy U of the charged capacitor. The final stored charge is $Q = CV$, so we can express U (which is equal to W) as

$$U = \frac{Q^2}{2C} = \frac{1}{2}CV^2 = \frac{1}{2}QV \qquad \text{(potential energy stored in a capacitor)} \quad (24.9)$$

In the final state, when the charges are no longer moving, both upper plates are at the same potential; they are connected by a conducting wire and so form a single equipotential surface. Both lower plates are also at the same potential, different from that of the upper plates. The final potential difference V between the plates is therefore the same for both capacitors, as we would expect for a parallel connection. The capacitor charges are

$$Q_1 = C_1V \qquad Q_2 = C_2V$$

When we combine these with the preceding equation for conservation of charge, we find

$$V = \frac{Q_0}{C_1 + C_2} = \frac{960\ \mu\text{C}}{8.0\ \mu\text{F} + 4.0\ \mu\text{F}} = 80\ \text{V}$$

$$Q_1 = 640\ \mu\text{C} \qquad Q_2 = 320\ \mu\text{C}$$

(d) The final energy of the system is the sum of the energies stored in each capacitor:

$$U_{\text{final}} = \frac{1}{2}Q_1V + \frac{1}{2}Q_2V = \frac{1}{2}Q_0V$$

$$= \frac{1}{2}(960 \times 10^{-6}\ \text{C})(80\ \text{V}) = 0.038\ \text{J}$$

EVALUATE: The final energy is less than the original energy $U_{\text{initial}} = 0.058$ J; the difference has been converted to energy of some other form. The conductors become a little warmer because of their resistance, and some energy is radiated as electromagnetic waves. We'll study the circuit behavior of capacitors in detail in Chapters 26 and 31.

Example 24.8 Electric-field energy

Suppose you want to store 1.00 J of electric potential energy in a volume of 1.00 m^3 in vacuum. (a) What is the magnitude of the required electric field? (b) If the field magnitude is 10 times larger, how much energy is stored per cubic meter?

SOLUTION

IDENTIFY: We use the relationship between the electric-field magnitude E and the energy density u, which equals the electric-field energy divided by the volume occupied by the field.

SET UP: In part (a) we use the given information to find u, then we use Eq. (24.11) to find the required value of E. This same equation gives us the relationship between changes in E and the corresponding changes in u.

EXECUTE: (a) The desired energy density is $u = 1.00\ \text{J/m}^3$. We solve Eq. (24.11) for E:

$$E = \sqrt{\frac{2u}{\epsilon_0}} = \sqrt{\frac{2(1.00\ \text{J/m}^3)}{8.85 \times 10^{-12}\ \text{C}^2/\text{N}\cdot\text{m}^2}}$$

$$= 4.75 \times 10^5\ \text{N/C} = 4.75 \times 10^5\ \text{V/m}$$

(b) Equation (24.11) shows that u is proportional to E^2. If E increases by a factor of 10, u increases by a factor of $10^2 = 100$, and the energy density is 100 J/m^3.

EVALUATE: The value of E found in part (a) is sizable, corresponding to a potential difference of nearly a half million volts over a distance of 1 meter. We will see in Section 24.4 that the field magnitudes in practical insulators can be as great as this or even larger.

Example 24.9 Two ways to calculate energy stored in a capacitor

The spherical capacitor described in Example 24.3 (Section 24.1) has charges $+Q$ and $-Q$ on its inner and outer conductors. Find the electric potential energy stored in the capacitor (a) by using the capacitance C found in Example 24.3 and (b) by integrating the electric-field energy density.

SOLUTION

IDENTIFY: This problem asks us to think about the energy stored in a capacitor, U, in two different ways: in terms of the work done to put the charges on the two conductors, $U = Q^2/2C$, and in terms of the energy in the electric field between the two conductors. Both descriptions are equivalent, so both must give us the same answer for U.

SET UP: In Example 24.3 we found the capacitance C and the field magnitude E between the conductors. We find the stored energy U in part (a) using the expression for C in Eq. (24.9). In part (b) we use the expression for E in Eq. (24.11) to find the electric-field energy density u between the conductors. The field magnitude depends on the distance r from the center of the capacitor, so u also depends on r. Hence we cannot find U by simply multiplying u by the volume between the conductors; instead, we must integrate u over this volume.

EXECUTE: (a) From Example 24.3, the spherical capacitor has capacitance

$$C = 4\pi\epsilon_0 \frac{r_a r_b}{r_b - r_a}$$

where r_a and r_b are the radii of the inner and outer conducting spheres. From Eq. (24.9) the energy stored in this capacitor is

$$U = \frac{Q^2}{2C} = \frac{Q^2}{8\pi\epsilon_0}\frac{r_b - r_a}{r_a r_b}$$

(b) The electric field in the volume between the two conducting spheres has magnitude $E = Q/4\pi\epsilon_0 r^2$. The electric field is zero inside the inner sphere and is also zero outside the inner surface of the outer sphere, because a Gaussian surface with radius $r < r_a$ or $r > r_b$ encloses zero net charge. Hence the energy density is nonzero only in the space between the spheres ($r_a < r < r_b$). In this region,

$$u = \frac{1}{2}\epsilon_0 E^2 = \frac{1}{2}\epsilon_0\left(\frac{Q}{4\pi\epsilon_0 r^2}\right)^2 = \frac{Q^2}{32\pi^2\epsilon_0 r^4}$$

The energy density is *not* uniform; it decreases rapidly with increasing distance from the center of the capacitor. To find the

Continued

total electric-field energy, we integrate u (the energy per unit volume) over the volume between the inner and outer conducting spheres. Dividing this volume up into spherical shells of radius r, surface area $4\pi r^2$, thickness dr, and volume $dV = 4\pi r^2\,dr$, we have

$$\begin{aligned} U &= \int u\,dV = \int_{r_a}^{r_b}\left(\frac{Q^2}{32\pi^2\epsilon_0 r^4}\right)4\pi r^2\,dr \\ &= \frac{Q^2}{8\pi\epsilon_0}\int_{r_a}^{r_b}\frac{dr}{r^2} = \frac{Q^2}{8\pi\epsilon_0}\left(-\frac{1}{r_b}+\frac{1}{r_a}\right) \\ &= \frac{Q^2}{8\pi\epsilon_0}\,\frac{r_b - r_a}{r_a r_b} \end{aligned}$$

EVALUATE: We obtain the same result for U with either approach, as we must. We emphasize that electric potential energy can be regarded as being associated with either the *charges,* as in part (a), or the *field,* as in part (b); regardless of which viewpoint you choose, the amount of stored energy is the same.

Test Your Understanding of Section 24.3 You want to connect a 4-μF capacitor and an 8-μF capacitor. With which type of connection will the 4-μF capacitor have a greater amount of *stored energy* than the 8-μF capacitor? (i) series; (ii) parallel; (iii) either series or parallel; (iv) neither series nor parallel.

24.4 Dielectrics

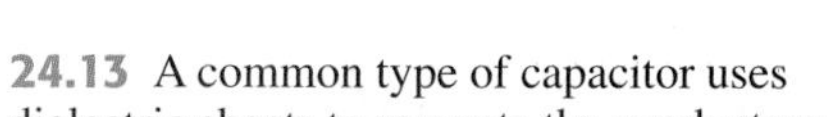

24.13 A common type of capacitor uses dielectric sheets to separate the conductors.

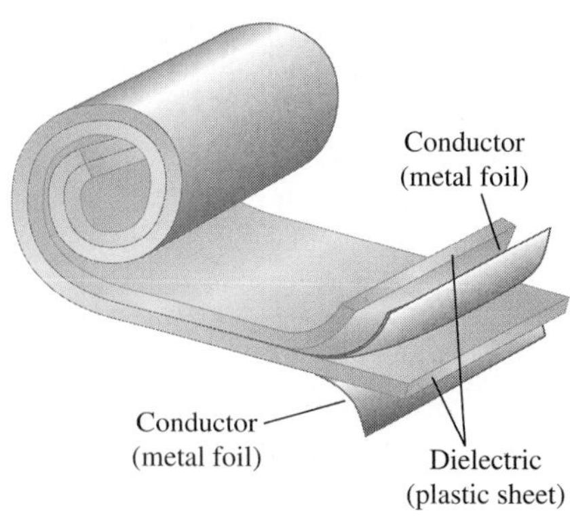

Most capacitors have a nonconducting material, or **dielectric,** between their conducting plates. A common type of capacitor uses long strips of metal foil for the plates, separated by strips of plastic sheet such as Mylar. A sandwich of these materials is rolled up, forming a unit that can provide a capacitance of several microfarads in a compact package (Fig. 24.13).

Placing a solid dielectric between the plates of a capacitor serves three functions. First, it solves the mechanical problem of maintaining two large metal sheets at a very small separation without actual contact.

Second, using a dielectric increases the maximum possible potential difference between the capacitor plates. As we described in Section 23.3, any insulating material, when subjected to a sufficiently large electric field, experiences a partial ionization that permits conduction through it. This is called **dielectric breakdown.** Many dielectric materials can tolerate stronger electric fields without breakdown than can air. Thus using a dielectric allows a capacitor to sustain a higher potential difference V and so store greater amounts of charge and energy.

Third, the capacitance of a capacitor of given dimensions is *greater* when there is a dielectric material between the plates than when there is vacuum. We can demonstrate this effect with the aid of a sensitive *electrometer,* a device that measures the potential difference between two conductors without letting any appreciable charge flow from one to the other. Figure 24.14a shows an electrometer connected across a charged capacitor, with magnitude of charge Q on each plate and potential difference V_0. When we insert an uncharged sheet of dielectric, such as glass, paraffin, or polystyrene, between the plates, experiment shows that the potential difference *decreases* to a smaller value V (Fig. 24.14b). When we remove the dielectric, the potential difference returns to its original value V_0, showing that the original charges on the plates have not changed.

The original capacitance C_0 is given by $C_0 = Q/V_0$, and the capacitance C with the dielectric present is $C = Q/V$. The charge Q is the same in both cases, and V is less than V_0, so we conclude that the capacitance C with the dielectric present is *greater* than C_0. When the space between plates is completely filled by the dielectric, the ratio of C to C_0 (equal to the ratio of V_0 to V) is called the **dielectric constant** of the material, K:

$$K = \frac{C}{C_0} \qquad \text{(definition of dielectric constant)} \qquad (24.12)$$

When the charge is constant, $Q = C_0V_0 = CV$ and $C/C_0 = V_0/V$. In this case, Eq. (24.12) can be rewritten as

$$V = \frac{V_0}{K} \quad \text{(when } Q \text{ is constant)} \tag{24.13}$$

With the dielectric present, the potential difference for a given charge Q is *reduced* by a factor K.

The dielectric constant K is a pure number. Because C is always greater than C_0, K is always greater than unity. Some representative values of K are given in Table 24.1. For vacuum, $K = 1$ by definition. For air at ordinary temperatures and pressures, K is about 1.0006; this is so nearly equal to 1 that for most purposes an air capacitor is equivalent to one in vacuum. Note that while water has a very large value of K, it is usually not a very practical dielectric for use in capacitors. The reason is that while pure water is a very poor conductor, it is also an excellent ionic solvent. Any ions that are dissolved in the water will cause charge to flow between the capacitor plates, so the capacitor discharges.

24.14 Effect of a dielectric between the plates of a parallel-plate capacitor. (a) With a given charge, the potential difference is V_0. (b) With the same charge but with a dielectric between the plates, the potential difference V is smaller than V_0.

(a)

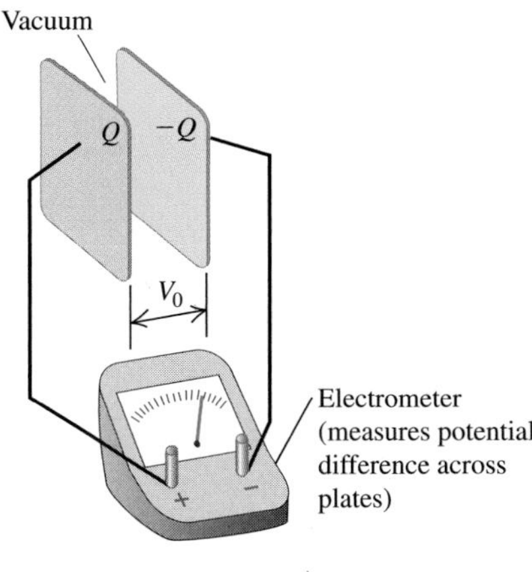
Vacuum
Q
−Q
V0
Electrometer (measures potential difference across plates)
+
−

(b)

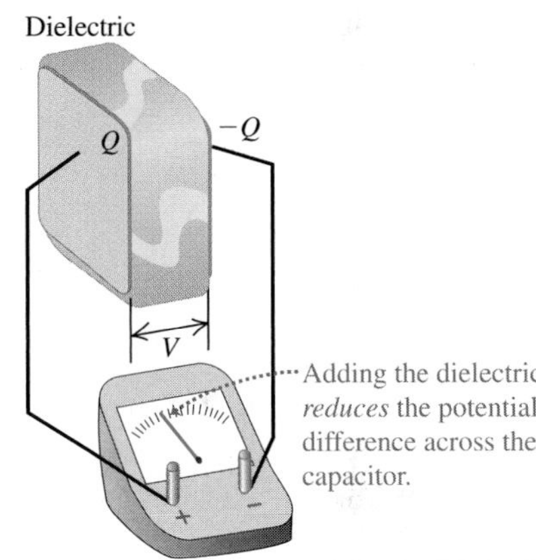
Dielectric
Q
−Q
V
Adding the dielectric *reduces* the potential difference across the capacitor.
+
−

Table 24.1 Values of Dielectric Constant K at 20°C

Material	K	Material	K
Vacuum	1	Polyvinyl chloride	3.18
Air (1 atm)	1.00059	Plexiglas	3.40
Air (100 atm)	1.0548	Glass	5–10
Teflon	2.1	Neoprene	6.70
Polyethylene	2.25	Germanium	16
Benzene	2.28	Glycerin	42.5
Mica	3–6	Water	80.4
Mylar	3.1	Strontium titanate	310

No real dielectric is a perfect insulator. Hence there is always some *leakage current* between the charged plates of a capacitor with a dielectric. We tacitly ignored this effect in Section 24.2 when we derived expressions for the equivalent capacitances of capacitors in series, Eq. (24.5), and in parallel, Eq. (24.7). But if a leakage current flows for a long enough time to substantially change the charges from the values we used to derive Eqs. (24.5) and (24.7), those equations may no longer be accurate.

Induced Charge and Polarization

When a dielectric material is inserted between the plates while the charge is kept constant, the potential difference between the plates decreases by a factor K. Therefore the electric field between the plates must decrease by the same factor. If E_0 is the vacuum value and E is the value with the dielectric, then

$$E = \frac{E_0}{K} \quad \text{(when } Q \text{ is constant)} \tag{24.14}$$

Since the electric-field magnitude is smaller when the dielectric is present, the surface charge density (which causes the field) must be smaller as well. The surface charge on the conducting plates does not change, but an *induced* charge of the opposite sign appears on each surface of the dielectric (Fig. 24.15). The dielectric was originally electrically neutral and is still neutral; the induced surface charges arise as a result of *redistribution* of positive and negative charge within the dielectric material, a phenomenon called **polarization.** We first encountered polarization in Section 21.2, and we suggest that you reread the discussion of Fig. 21.8. We will assume that the induced surface charge is *directly proportional* to the electric-field magnitude E in the material; this is indeed the case for many common dielectrics. (This direct proportionality is analogous to

24.15 Electric field lines with (a) vacuum between the plates and (b) dielectric between the plates.

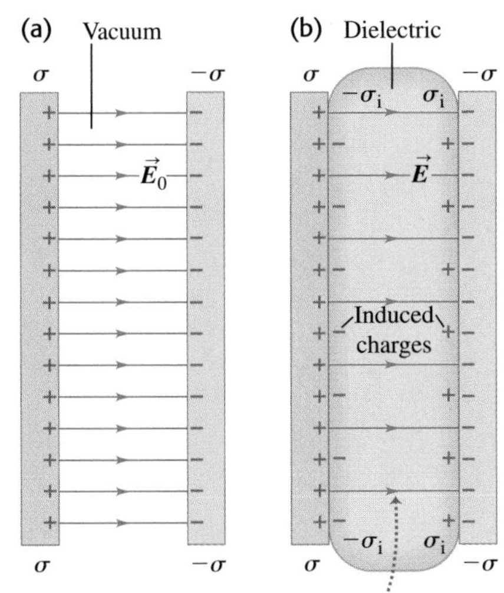
(a) Vacuum
σ
−σ
$\vec{E}_0$
(b) Dielectric
σ
−σ
$-\sigma_i$
σ_i
$\vec{E}$
Induced charges
For a given charge density σ, the induced charges on the dielectric's surfaces reduce the electric field between the plates.

Hooke's law for a spring.) In that case, K is a constant for any particular material. When the electric field is very strong or if the dielectric is made of certain crystalline materials, the relationship between induced charge and the electric field can be more complex; we won't consider such cases here.

We can derive a relationship between this induced surface charge and the charge on the plates. Let's denote the magnitude of the charge per unit area induced on the surfaces of the dielectric (the induced surface charge density) by σ_i. The magnitude of the surface charge density on the capacitor plates is σ, as usual. Then the *net* surface charge on each side of the capacitor has magnitude $(\sigma - \sigma_i)$, as shown in Fig. 24.15b. As we found in Example 21.13 (Section 21.5) and in Example 22.8 (Section 22.4), the field between the plates is related to the net surface charge density by $E = \sigma_{net}/\epsilon_0$. Without and with the dielectric, respectively, we have

$$E_0 = \frac{\sigma}{\epsilon_0} \qquad E = \frac{\sigma - \sigma_i}{\epsilon_0} \tag{24.15}$$

Using these expressions in Eq. (24.14) and rearranging the result, we find

$$\sigma_i = \sigma\left(1 - \frac{1}{K}\right) \qquad \text{(induced surface charge density)} \tag{24.16}$$

This equation shows that when K is very large, σ_i is nearly as large as σ. In this case, σ_i nearly cancels σ, and the field and potential difference are much smaller than their values in vacuum.

The product $K\epsilon_0$ is called the **permittivity** of the dielectric, denoted by ϵ:

$$\epsilon = K\epsilon_0 \qquad \text{(definition of permittivity)} \tag{24.17}$$

In terms of ϵ we can express the electric field within the dielectric as

$$E = \frac{\sigma}{\epsilon} \tag{24.18}$$

The capacitance when the dielectric is present is given by

$$C = KC_0 = K\epsilon_0\frac{A}{d} = \epsilon\frac{A}{d} \qquad \text{(parallel-plate capacitor, dielectric between plates)} \tag{24.19}$$

We can repeat the derivation of Eq. (24.11) for the energy density u in an electric field for the case in which a dielectric is present. The result is

$$u = \frac{1}{2}K\epsilon_0 E^2 = \frac{1}{2}\epsilon E^2 \qquad \text{(electric energy density in a dielectric)} \tag{24.20}$$

In empty space, where $K = 1$, $\epsilon = \epsilon_0$ and Eqs. (24.19) and (24.20) reduce to Eqs. (24.2) and (24.11), respectively, for a parallel-plate capacitor in vacuum. For this reason, ϵ_0 is sometimes called the "permittivity of free space" or the "permittivity of vacuum." Because K is a pure number, ϵ and ϵ_0 have the same units, $C^2/N \cdot m^2$ or F/m.

Equation (24.19) shows that extremely high capacitances can be obtained with plates that have a large surface area A and are separated by a small distance d by a dielectric with a large value of K. In an *electrolytic double-layer capacitor,* tiny carbon granules adhere to each plate: The value of A is the combined surface area of the granules, which can be tremendous. The plates with granules attached are separated by a very thin dielectric sheet. A capacitor of this kind can have a capacitance of 5000 farads yet fit in the palm of your hand (compare Example 24.1 in Section 24.1).

Several practical devices make use of the way in which a capacitor responds to a change in dielectric constant. One example is an electric stud finder, used by home repair workers to locate metal studs hidden behind a wall's surface. It consists of a metal plate with associated circuitry. The plate acts as one half of a capacitor, with the wall acting as the other half. If the stud finder moves over a metal stud, the effective dielectric constant for the capacitor changes, changing the capacitance and triggering a signal.

Problem-Solving Strategy 24.2 Dielectrics

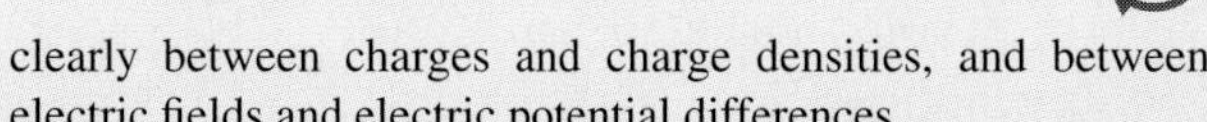

IDENTIFY *the relevant concepts:* The relationships in this section are useful whenever there is an electric field in a dielectric, such as a dielectric between charged capacitor plates. Typically you will be asked to relate the potential difference between the plates, the electric field in the capacitor, the charge density on the capacitor plates, and the induced charge density on the surfaces of the capacitor.

SET UP *the problem* using the following steps:

1. Make a drawing of the situation.
2. Identify the target variables, and choose which of the key equations of this section will help you find those variables.

EXECUTE *the solution* as follows:

1. In problems such as the next example, it is easy to get lost in a blizzard of formulas. Ask yourself at each step what kind of quantity each symbol represents. For example, distinguish clearly between charges and charge densities, and between electric fields and electric potential differences.
2. As you calculate, continually check for consistency of units. This effort is a bit more complex with electrical quantities than it was in mechanics. Distances must always be in meters. Remember that a microfarad is 10^{-6} farad, and so on. Don't confuse the numerical value of ϵ_0 with the value of $1/4\pi\epsilon_0$. There are several alternative sets of units for electric-field magnitude, including N/C and V/m. The units of ϵ_0 are $C^2/N \cdot m^2$ or F/m.

EVALUATE *your answer:* When you check numerical values, remember that with a dielectric present, (a) the capacitance is always greater than without a dielectric; (b) for a given amount of charge on the capacitor, the electric field and potential difference are less than without a dielectric; and (c) the induced surface charge density σ_i on the dielectric is always less in magnitude than the charge density σ on the capacitor plates.

Example 24.10 A capacitor with and without a dielectric

Suppose the parallel plates in Fig. 24.15 each have an area of $2000\ \text{cm}^2\ (2.00 \times 10^{-1}\ \text{m}^2)$ and are $1.00\ \text{cm}\ (1.00 \times 10^{-2}\ \text{m})$ apart. The capacitor is connected to a power supply and charged to a potential difference $V_0 = 3000\ \text{V} = 3.00\ \text{kV}$. It is then disconnected from the power supply, and a sheet of insulating plastic material is inserted between the plates, completely filling the space between them. We find that the potential difference decreases to 1000 V while the charge on each capacitor plate remains constant. Compute (a) the original capacitance C_0; (b) the magnitude of charge Q on each plate; (c) the capacitance C after the dielectric is inserted; (d) the dielectric constant K of the dielectric; (e) the permittivity ϵ of the dielectric; (f) the magnitude of the induced charge Q_i on each face of the dielectric; (g) the original electric field E_0 between the plates; and (h) the electric field E after the dielectric is inserted.

SOLUTION

IDENTIFY: This problem uses most of the relationships we have discussed for capacitors and dielectrics.

SET UP: Most of the target variables can be obtained in several different ways. The methods used below are a representative sample; we encourage you to think of others and compare your results.

EXECUTE: (a) With vacuum between the plates, we use Eq. (24.19) with $K = 1$:

$$C_0 = \epsilon_0 \frac{A}{d} = (8.85 \times 10^{-12}\ \text{F/m}) \frac{2.00 \times 10^{-1}\ \text{m}^2}{1.00 \times 10^{-2}\ \text{m}}$$
$$= 1.77 \times 10^{-10}\ \text{F} = 177\ \text{pF}$$

(b) Using the definition of capacitance, Eq. (24.1),

$$Q = C_0 V_0 = (1.77 \times 10^{-10}\ \text{F})(3.00 \times 10^3\ \text{V})$$
$$= 5.31 \times 10^{-7}\ \text{C} = 0.531\ \mu\text{C}$$

(c) When the dielectric is inserted, the charge remains the same but the potential decreases to $V = 1000$ V. Hence from Eq. (24.1), the new capacitance is

$$C = \frac{Q}{V} = \frac{5.31 \times 10^{-7}\ \text{C}}{1.00 \times 10^3\ \text{V}} = 5.31 \times 10^{-10}\ \text{F} = 531\ \text{pF}$$

(d) From Eq. (24.12), the dielectric constant is

$$K = \frac{C}{C_0} = \frac{5.31 \times 10^{-10}\ \text{F}}{1.77 \times 10^{-10}\ \text{F}} = \frac{531\ \text{pF}}{177\ \text{pF}} = 3.00$$

Alternatively, from Eq. (24.13),

$$K = \frac{V_0}{V} = \frac{3000\ \text{V}}{1000\ \text{V}} = 3.00$$

(e) Using K from part (d) in Eq. (24.17), the permittivity is

$$\epsilon = K\epsilon_0 = (3.00)(8.85 \times 10^{-12}\ \text{C}^2/\text{N} \cdot \text{m}^2)$$
$$= 2.66 \times 10^{-11}\ \text{C}^2/\text{N} \cdot \text{m}^2$$

(f) Multiplying Eq. (24.15) by the area of each plate gives the induced charge $Q_i = \sigma_i A$ in terms of the charge $Q = \sigma A$ on each plate:

$$Q_i = Q\left(1 - \frac{1}{K}\right) = (5.31 \times 10^{-7}\ \text{C})\left(1 - \frac{1}{3.00}\right)$$
$$= 3.54 \times 10^{-7}\ \text{C}$$

Continued

(g) Since the electric field between the plates is uniform, its magnitude is the potential difference divided by the plate separation:

$$E_0 = \frac{V_0}{d} = \frac{3000\ \text{V}}{1.00 \times 10^{-2}\ \text{m}} = 3.00 \times 10^5\ \text{V/m}$$

(h) With the new potential difference after the dielectric is inserted,

$$E = \frac{V}{d} = \frac{1000\ \text{V}}{1.00 \times 10^{-2}\ \text{m}} = 1.00 \times 10^5\ \text{V/m}$$

or, from Eq. (24.17),

$$E = \frac{\sigma}{\epsilon} = \frac{Q}{\epsilon A} = \frac{5.31 \times 10^{-7}\ \text{C}}{(2.66 \times 10^{-11}\ \text{C}^2/\text{N}\cdot\text{m}^2)(2.00 \times 10^{-1}\ \text{m}^2)}$$
$$= 1.00 \times 10^5\ \text{V/m}$$

or, from Eq. (24.15),

$$E = \frac{\sigma - \sigma_i}{\epsilon_0} = \frac{Q - Q_i}{\epsilon_0 A}$$
$$= \frac{(5.31 - 3.54) \times 10^{-7}\ \text{C}}{(8.85 \times 10^{-12}\ \text{C}^2/\text{N}\cdot\text{m}^2)(2.00 \times 10^{-1}\ \text{m}^2)}$$
$$= 1.00 \times 10^5\ \text{V/m}$$

or, from Eq. (24.14),

$$E = \frac{E_0}{K} = \frac{3.00 \times 10^5\ \text{V/m}}{3.00} = 1.00 \times 10^5\ \text{V/m}$$

EVALUATE: It's always useful to check the results by finding them in more than one way, as we did in parts (d) and (h). Our results show that inserting the dielectric increased the capacitance by a factor of $K = 3.00$ and reduced the electric field between the plates by a factor of $1/K = 1/3.00$. It did so by developing induced charges on the faces of the dielectric of magnitude $Q(1 - 1/K) = Q(1 - 1/3.00) = 0.667Q$.

Example 24.11 Energy storage with and without a dielectric

Find the total energy stored in the electric field of the capacitor in Example 24.10 and the energy density, both before and after the dielectric sheet is inserted.

SOLUTION

IDENTIFY: In this problem we have to extend the analysis of Example 24.10 to include the ideas of energy stored in a capacitor and electric-field energy.

SET UP: We use Eq. (24.9) to find the stored energy before and after the dielectric is inserted, and Eq. (24.20) to find the energy density.

EXECUTE: Let the original energy be U_0 and let the energy with the dielectric in place be U. From Eq. (24.9),

$$U_0 = \frac{1}{2}C_0V_0^2 = \frac{1}{2}(1.77 \times 10^{-10}\ \text{F})(3000\ \text{V})^2 = 7.97 \times 10^{-4}\ \text{J}$$

$$U = \frac{1}{2}CV^2 = \frac{1}{2}(5.31 \times 10^{-10}\ \text{F})(1000\ \text{V})^2 = 2.66 \times 10^{-4}\ \text{J}$$

The final energy is one-third of the original energy.

The energy density without the dielectric is given by Eq. (24.20) with $K = 1$:

$$u_0 = \frac{1}{2}\epsilon_0 E_0^2 = \frac{1}{2}(8.85 \times 10^{-12}\ \text{C}^2/\text{N}\cdot\text{m}^2)(3.0 \times 10^5\ \text{N/C})^2$$
$$= 0.398\ \text{J/m}^3$$

With the dielectric in place,

$$u = \frac{1}{2}\epsilon E^2 = \frac{1}{2}(2.66 \times 10^{-11}\ \text{C}^2/\text{N}\cdot\text{m}^2)(1.00 \times 10^5\ \text{N/C})^2$$
$$= 0.133\ \text{J/m}^3$$

The energy density with the dielectric is one-third of the original energy density.

EVALUATE: We can check our answer for u_0 by noting that the volume between the plates is $V = (0.200\ \text{m})^2(0.0100\ \text{m}) = 0.00200\ \text{m}^3$. Since the electric field is uniform between the plates, u_0 is uniform as well and the energy density is just the stored energy divided by the volume:

$$u_0 = \frac{U_0}{V} = \frac{7.97 \times 10^{-4}\ \text{J}}{0.00200\ \text{m}^3} = 0.398\ \text{J/m}^3$$

which agrees with our earlier answer. You should use the same approach to check the value for U, the energy density with the dielectric.

We can generalize the results of this example. When a dielectric is inserted into a capacitor while the charge on each plate remains the same, the permittivity ϵ increases by a factor of K (the dielectric constant), the electric field decreases by a factor of $1/K$, and the energy density $u = \frac{1}{2}\epsilon E^2$ decreases by a factor of $1/K$. Where did the energy go? The answer lies in the fringing field at the edges of a real parallel-plate capacitor. As Fig. 24.16 shows, that field tends to pull the dielectric into the space between the plates, doing work on it as it does so. We could attach a spring to the left end of the dielectric in Fig. 24.16 and use this force to stretch the spring. Because work is done by the field, the field energy density decreases.

24.16 The fringing field at the edges of the capacitor exerts forces $\vec{F}_{-i}$ and $\vec{F}_{+i}$ on the negative and positive induced surface charges of a dielectric, pulling the dielectric into the capacitor.

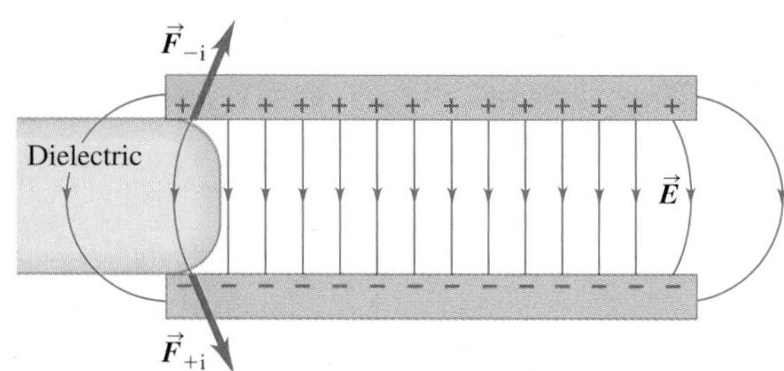

Dielectric Breakdown

We mentioned earlier that when any dielectric material is subjected to a sufficiently strong electric field, *dielectric breakdown* takes place and the dielectric becomes a conductor (Fig. 24.17). This occurs when the electric field is so strong that electrons are ripped loose from their molecules and crash into other molecules, liberating even more electrons. This avalanche of moving charge, forming a spark or arc discharge, often starts quite suddenly.

Because of dielectric breakdown, capacitors always have maximum voltage ratings. When a capacitor is subjected to excessive voltage, an arc may form through a layer of dielectric, burning or melting a hole in it. This arc creates a conducting path (a short circuit) between the conductors. If a conducting path remains after the arc is extinguished, the device is rendered permanently useless as a capacitor.

The maximum electric-field magnitude that a material can withstand without the occurrence of breakdown is called its **dielectric strength.** This quantity is affected significantly by temperature, trace impurities, small irregularities in the metal electrodes, and other factors that are difficult to control. For this reason we can give only approximate figures for dielectric strengths. The dielectric strength of dry air is about 3×10^6 V/m. Values of dielectric strength for a few common insulating materials are shown in Table 24.2. Note that the values are all substantially greater than the value for air. For example, a layer of polycarbonate 0.01 mm thick (about the smallest practical thickness) has 10 times the dielectric strength of air and can withstand a maximum voltage of about $(3 \times 10^7 \text{ V/m})(1 \times 10^{-5} \text{ m}) = 300$ V.

24.17 A very strong electric field caused dielectric breakdown in a block of Plexiglas. The resulting flow of charge etched this pattern into the block.

Table 24.2 Dielectric Constant and Dielectric Strength of Some Insulating Materials

Material	Dielectric Constant, K	Dielectric Strength, E_m (V/m)
Polycarbonate	2.8	3×10^7
Polyester	3.3	6×10^7
Polypropylene	2.2	7×10^7
Polystyrene	2.6	2×10^7
Pyrex glass	4.7	1×10^7

Test Your Understanding of Section 24.4 The space between the plates of an isolated parallel-plate capacitor is filled by a slab of dielectric with dielectric constant K. The two plates of the capacitor have charges Q and $-Q$. You pull out the dielectric slab. If the charges do not change, how does the energy in the capacitor change when you remove the slab? (i) It increases; (ii) it decreases; (iii) it remains the same.

*24.5 Molecular Model of Induced Charge

In Section 24.4 we discussed induced surface charges on a dielectric in an electric field. Now let's look at how these surface charges can arise. If the material were a *conductor,* the answer would be simple. Conductors contain charge that is free to move, and when an electric field is present, some of the charge redistributes itself on the surface so that there is no electric field inside the conductor. But an ideal dielectric has *no* charges that are free to move, so how can a surface charge occur?

To understand this, we have to look again at rearrangement of charge at the *molecular* level. Some molecules, such as H_2O and N_2O, have equal amounts of positive and negative charges but a lopsided distribution, with excess positive charge concentrated on one side of the molecule and negative charge on the other. As we described in Section 21.7, such an arrangement is called an *electric dipole,* and the molecule is called a *polar molecule.* When no electric field is present in a gas or liquid with polar molecules, the molecules are oriented randomly (Fig. 24.18a). When they are placed in an electric field, however, they tend

24.18 Polar molecules (a) without and (b) with an applied electric field $\vec{E}$.

(a)

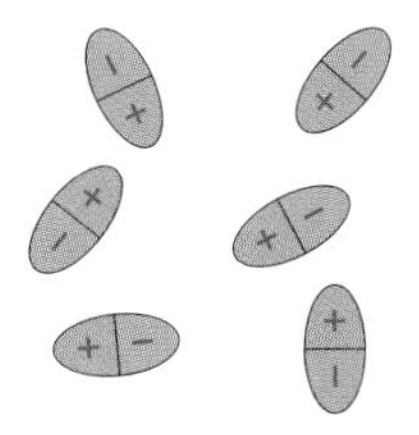

In the absence of an electric field, polar molecules orient randomly.

(b)

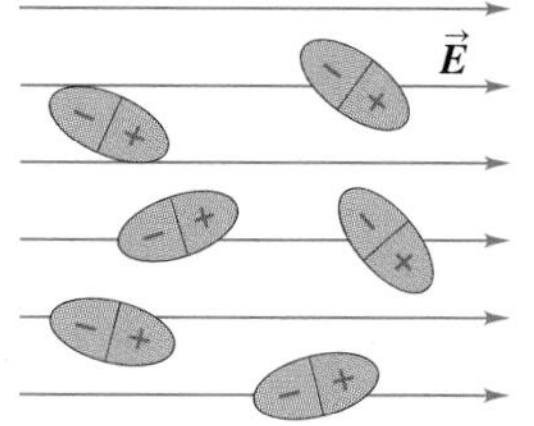

When an electric field is applied, the molecules tend to align with it.

24.19 Nonpolar molecules (a) without and (b) with an applied electric field $\vec{E}$.

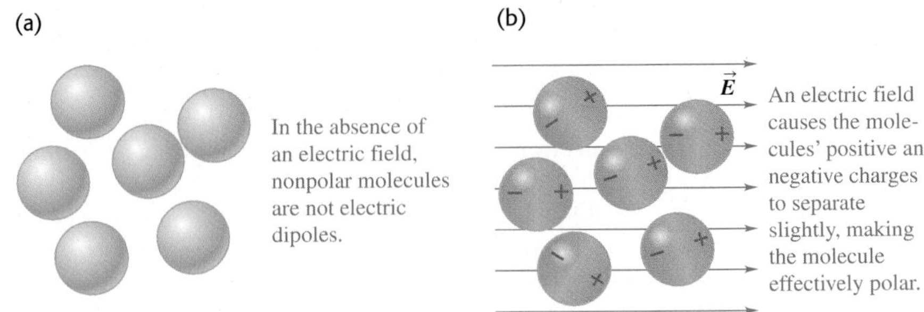

to orient themselves as in Fig. 24.18b, as a result of the electric-field torques described in Section 21.7. Because of thermal agitation, the alignment of the molecules with $\vec{E}$ is not perfect.

Even a molecule that is *not* ordinarily polar *becomes* a dipole when it is placed in an electric field because the field pushes the positive charges in the molecules in the direction of the field and pushes the negative charges in the opposite direction. This causes a redistribution of charge within the molecule (Fig. 24.19). Such dipoles are called *induced* dipoles.

24.20 Polarization of a dielectric in an electric field $\vec{E}$ gives rise to thin layers of bound charges on the surfaces, creating surface charge densities σ_i and $-\sigma_i$. The sizes of the molecules are greatly exaggerated for clarity.

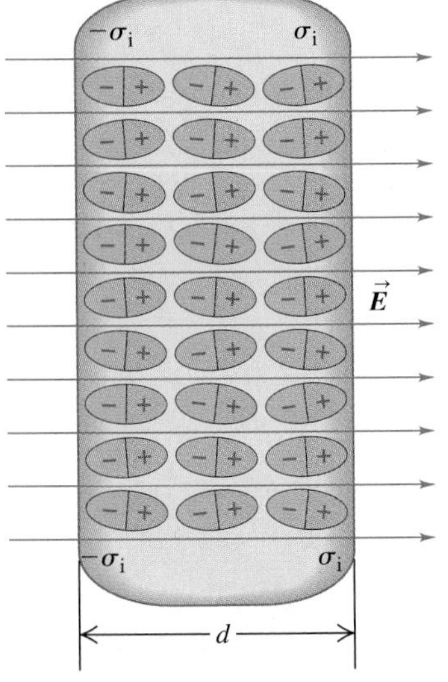

With either polar or nonpolar molecules, the redistribution of charge caused by the field leads to the formation of a layer of charge on each surface of the dielectric material (Fig. 24.20). These layers are the surface charges described in Section 24.4; their surface charge density is denoted by σ_i. The charges are *not* free to move indefinitely, as they would be in a conductor, because each charge is bound to a molecule. They are in fact called **bound charges** to distinguish them from the **free charges** that are added to and removed from the conducting capacitor plates. In the interior of the material the net charge per unit volume remains zero. As we have seen, this redistribution of charge is called *polarization,* and we say that the material is *polarized.*

The four parts of Fig. 24.21 show the behavior of a slab of dielectric when it is inserted in the field between a pair of oppositely charged capacitor plates. Figure 24.21a shows the original field. Figure 24.21b is the situation after the dielectric has been inserted but before any rearrangement of charges has occurred.

24.21 (a) Electric field of magnitude E_0 between two charged plates. (b) Introduction of a dielectric of dielectric constant K. (c) The induced surface charges and their field. (d) Resultant field of magnitude E_0/K.

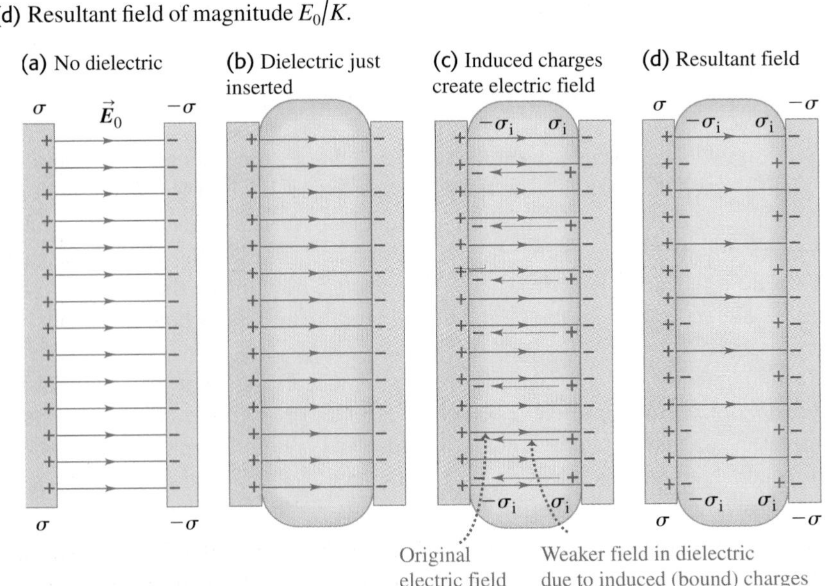

Figure 24.21c shows by thinner arrows the additional field set up in the dielectric by its induced surface charges. This field is *opposite* to the original field, but it is not great enough to cancel the original field completely because the charges in the dielectric are not free to move indefinitely. The resultant field in the dielectric, shown in Fig. 24.21d, is therefore decreased in magnitude. In the field-line representation, some of the field lines leaving the positive plate go through the dielectric, while others terminate on the induced charges on the faces of the dielectric.

As we discussed in Section 21.2, polarization is also the reason a charged body, such as an electrified plastic rod, can exert a force on an *uncharged* body such as a bit of paper or a pith ball. Figure 24.22 shows an uncharged dielectric sphere B in the radial field of a positively charged body A. The induced positive charges on B experience a force toward the right, while the force on the induced negative charges is toward the left. The negative charges are closer to A, and thus are in a stronger field, than are the positive charges. The force toward the left is stronger than that toward the right, and B is attracted toward A, even though its net charge is zero. The attraction occurs whether the sign of A's charge is positive or negative (see Fig. 21.8). Furthermore, the effect is not limited to dielectrics; an uncharged conducting body would be attracted in the same way.

24.22 A neutral sphere B in the radial electric field of a positively charged sphere A is attracted to the charge because of polarization.

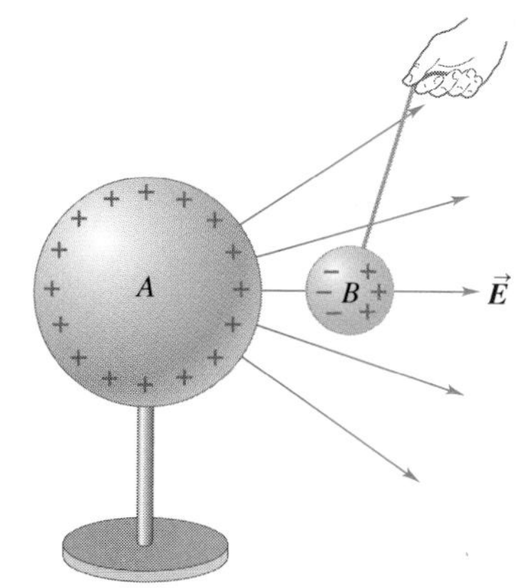

Test Your Understanding of Section 24.5 A parallel-plate capacitor has charges Q and $-Q$ on its two plates. A dielectric slab with $K = 3$ is then inserted into the space between the plates as shown in Fig. 24.21. Rank the following electric-field magnitudes in order from largest to smallest. (i) the field before the slab is inserted; (ii) the resultant field after the slab is inserted; (iii) the field due to the bound charges.

*24.6 Gauss's Law in Dielectrics

We can extend the analysis of Section 24.4 to reformulate Gauss's law in a form that is particularly useful for dielectrics. Figure 24.23 is a close-up view of the left capacitor plate and left surface of the dielectric in Fig. 24.15b. Let's apply Gauss's law to the rectangular box shown in cross section by the purple line; the surface area of the left and right sides is A. The left side is embedded in the conductor that forms the left capacitor plate, and so the electric field everywhere on that surface is zero. The right side is embedded in the dielectric, where the electric field has magnitude E, and $E_{\perp} = 0$ everywhere on the other four sides. The total charge enclosed, including both the charge on the capacitor plate and the induced charge on the dielectric surface, is $Q_{\text{encl}} = (\sigma - \sigma_{\text{i}})A$, so Gauss's law gives

$$EA = \frac{(\sigma - \sigma_{\text{i}})A}{\epsilon_0} \tag{24.21}$$

This equation is not very illuminating as it stands because it relates two unknown quantities: E inside the dielectric and the induced surface charge density σ_{i}. But now we can use Eq. (24.16), developed for this same situation, to simplify this equation by eliminating σ_{i}. Equation (24.16) is

$$\sigma_{\text{i}} = \sigma\left(1 - \frac{1}{K}\right) \quad \text{or} \quad \sigma - \sigma_{\text{i}} = \frac{\sigma}{K}$$

Combining this with Eq. (24.21), we get

$$EA = \frac{\sigma A}{K\epsilon_0} \quad \text{or} \quad KEA = \frac{\sigma A}{\epsilon_0} \tag{24.22}$$

Equation (24.22) says that the flux of $K\vec{E}$, not $\vec{E}$, through the Gaussian surface in Fig. 24.23 is equal to the enclosed *free* charge σA divided by ϵ_0. It turns out

24.23 Gauss's law with a dielectric. This figure shows a close-up of the left-hand capacitor plate in Fig. 24.15b. The Gaussian surface is a rectangular box that lies half in the conductor and half in the dielectric.

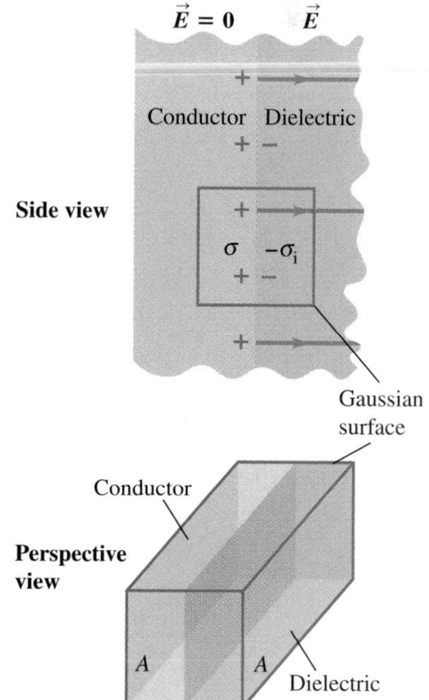

that for *any* Gaussian surface, whenever the induced charge is proportional to the electric field in the material, we can rewrite Gauss's law as

$$\oint K\vec{E} \cdot d\vec{A} = \frac{Q_{\text{encl-free}}}{\epsilon_0} \qquad \text{(Gauss's law in a dielectric)} \qquad (24.23)$$

where $Q_{\text{encl-free}}$ is the total *free* charge (not bound charge) enclosed by the Gaussian surface. The significance of these results is that the right sides contain only the *free* charge on the conductor, not the bound (induced) charge. In fact, although we have not proved it, Eq. (24.23) remains valid even when different parts of the Gaussian surface are embedded in dielectrics having different values of K, provided that the value of K in each dielectric is independent of the electric field (usually the case for electric fields that are not too strong) and that we use the appropriate value of K for each point on the Gaussian surface.

Example 24.12 A spherical capacitor with dielectric

In the spherical capacitor of Example 24.3 (Section 24.1), the volume between the concentric spherical conducting shells is filled with an insulating oil with dielectric constant K. Use Gauss's law to find the capacitance.

SOLUTION

IDENTIFY: This is essentially the same problem as Example 24.3. The only difference is the presence of the dielectric.

SET UP: As we did in Example 24.3, we use a spherical Gaussian surface of radius r between the two spheres. Since a dielectric is present, we use Gauss's law in the form of Eq. (24.23).

EXECUTE: The spherical symmetry of the problem is not changed by the presence of the dielectric, so we have

$$\oint K\vec{E} \cdot d\vec{A} = \oint KE\, dA = KE \oint dA = (KE)\,(4\pi r^2) = \frac{Q}{\epsilon_0}$$

$$E = \frac{Q}{4\pi K\epsilon_0 r^2} = \frac{Q}{4\pi\epsilon r^2}$$

where $\epsilon = K\epsilon_0$ is the permittivity of the dielectric (introduced in Section 24.4). Compared to the case in which there is vacuum between the conducting shells, the electric field is reduced by a factor of $1/K$. The potential difference V_{ab} between the shells is likewise reduced by a factor of $1/K$, and so the capacitance $C = Q/V_{ab}$ is *increased* by a factor of K, just as for a parallel-plate capacitor when a dielectric is inserted. Using the result for the vacuum case in Example 24.3, we find that the capacitance with the dielectric is

$$C = \frac{4\pi K\epsilon_0 r_a r_b}{r_b - r_a} = \frac{4\pi\epsilon r_a r_b}{r_b - r_a}$$

EVALUATE: In this case the dielectric completely fills the volume between the two conductors, so the capacitance is just K times the value with no dielectric. The result is more complicated if the dielectric only partially fills this volume (see Challenge Problem 24.76).

Test Your Understanding of Section 24.6 A single point charge q is imbedded in a dielectric of dielectric constant K. At a point inside the dielectric a distance r from the point charge, what is the magnitude of the electric field? (i) $q/4\pi\epsilon_0 r^2$; (ii) $Kq/4\pi\epsilon_0 r^2$; (iii) $q/4\pi K\epsilon_0 r^2$; (iv) none of these.

CHAPTER 24 SUMMARY

Capacitors and capacitance: A capacitor is any pair of conductors separated by an insulating material. When the capacitor is charged, there are charges of equal magnitude Q and opposite sign on the two conductors, and the potential V_{ab} of the positively charged conductor with respect to the negatively charged conductor is proportional to Q. The capacitance C is defined as the ratio of Q to V_{ab}. The SI unit of capacitance is the farad (F): $1\text{ F} = 1\text{ C/V}$.

A parallel-plate capacitor consists of two parallel conducting plates, each with area A, separated by a distance d. If they are separated by vacuum, the capacitance depends only on A and d. For other geometries, the capacitance can be found by using the definition $C = Q/V_{ab}$. (See Examples 24.1–24.4.)

$$C = \frac{Q}{V_{ab}} \tag{24.1}$$

$$C = \frac{Q}{V_{ab}} = \epsilon_0 \frac{A}{d} \tag{24.2}$$

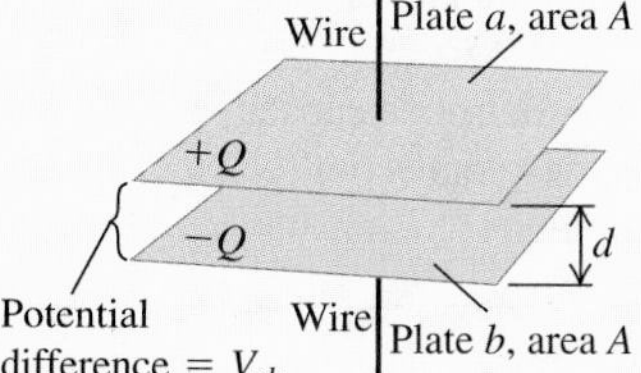

Capacitors in series and parallel: When capacitors with capacitances $C_1, C_2, C_3, \ldots$ are connected in series, the reciprocal of the equivalent capacitance C_{eq} equals the sum of the reciprocals of the individual capacitances. When capacitors are connected in parallel, the equivalent capacitance C_{eq} equals the sum of the individual capacitances. (See Examples 24.5 and 24.6.)

$$\frac{1}{C_{eq}} = \frac{1}{C_1} + \frac{1}{C_2} + \frac{1}{C_3} + \cdots \tag{24.5}$$
(capacitors in series)

$$C_{eq} = C_1 + C_2 + C_3 + \cdots \tag{24.7}$$
(capacitors in parallel)

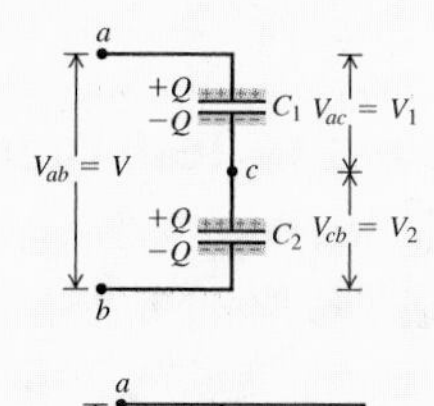

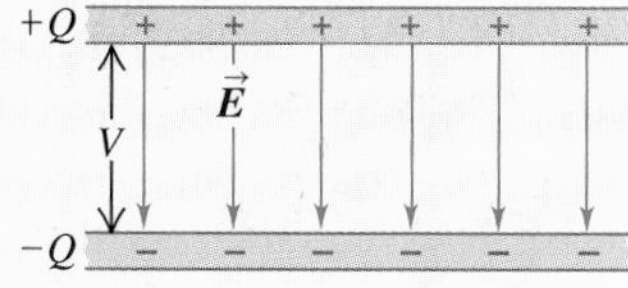

Energy in a capacitor: The energy U required to charge a capacitor C to a potential difference V and a charge Q is equal to the energy stored in the capacitor. This energy can be thought of as residing in the electric field between the conductors; the energy density u (energy per unit volume) is proportional to the square of the electric-field magnitude. (See Examples 24.7–24.9.)

$$U = \frac{Q^2}{2C} = \frac{1}{2}CV^2 = \frac{1}{2}QV \tag{24.9}$$

$$u = \frac{1}{2}\epsilon_0 E^2 \tag{24.11}$$

Dielectrics: When the space between the conductors is filled with a dielectric material, the capacitance increases by a factor K, called the dielectric constant of the material. The quantity $\epsilon = K\epsilon_0$ is called the permittivity of the dielectric. For a fixed amount of charge on the capacitor plates, induced charges on the surface of the dielectric decrease the electric field and potential difference between the plates by the same factor K. The surface charge results from polarization, a microscopic rearrangement of charge in the dielectric. (See Example 24.10.)

Under sufficiently strong fields, dielectrics become conductors, a situation called dielectric breakdown. The maximum field that a material can withstand without breakdown is called its dielectric strength.

In a dielectric, the expression for the energy density is the same as in vacuum but with ϵ_0 replaced by $\epsilon = K\epsilon$. (See Example 24.11.)

Gauss's law in a dielectric has almost the same form as in vacuum, with two key differences: $\vec{E}$ is replaced by $K\vec{E}$ and Q_{encl} is replaced by $Q_{encl\text{-}free}$, which includes only the free charge (not bound charge) enclosed by the Gaussian surface. (See Example 24.12.)

$$C = KC_0 = K\epsilon_0 \frac{A}{d} = \epsilon \frac{A}{d} \tag{24.19}$$
(parallel-plate capacitor filled with dielectric)

$$u = \frac{1}{2}K\epsilon_0 E^2 = \frac{1}{2}\epsilon E^2 \tag{24.20}$$

$$\oint K\vec{E} \cdot d\vec{A} = \frac{Q_{encl\text{-}free}}{\epsilon_0} \tag{24.23}$$

Dielectric between plates

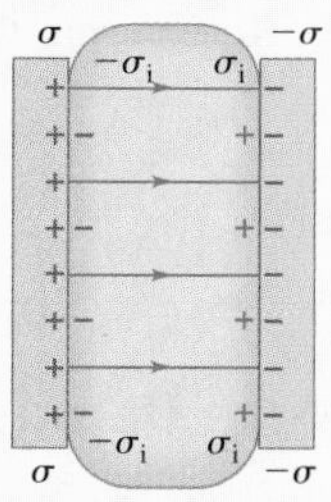

Key Terms

capacitor, *816*
capacitance, *816*
farad, *816*
parallel-plate capacitor, *817*
series connection, *820*
equivalent capacitance, *821*
parallel connection, *821*
energy density, *826*
dielectric, *828*
dielectric breakdown, *828*
dielectric constant, *828*
polarization, *829*
permittivity, *830*
dielectric strength, *833*
bound charge, *834*
free charge, *834*

Answer to Chapter Opening Question ?

Equation (24.9) shows that the energy stored in a capacitor with capacitance C and charge Q is $U = Q^2/2C$. If the charge Q is doubled, the stored energy increases by a factor of $2^2 = 4$. Note that if the value of Q is too great, the electric-field magnitude inside the capacitor will exceed the dielectric strength of the material between the plates and dielectric breakdown will occur (see Section 24.4). This puts a practical limit on the amount of energy that can be stored.

Answers to Test Your Understanding Questions

24.1 Answer: (iii) The capacitance does not depend on the value of the charge Q. Doubling the value of Q causes the potential difference V_{ab} to double, so the capacitance $C = Q/V_{ab}$ remains the same. These statements are true no matter what the geometry of the capacitor.

24.2 Answers: (a) (i), (b) (iv) In a series connection the two capacitors carry the same charge Q but have different potential differences $V_{ab} = Q/C$; the capacitor with the smaller capacitance C has the greater potential difference. In a parallel connection the two capacitors have the same potential difference V_{ab} but carry different charges $Q = CV_{ab}$; the capacitor with the larger capacitance C has the greater charge. Hence a 4-μF capacitor will have a greater potential difference than an 8-μF capacitor if the two are connected in series. The 4-μF capacitor cannot carry more charge than the 8-μF capacitor no matter how they are connected: In a series connection they will carry the same charge, and in a parallel connection the 8-μF capacitor will carry more charge.

24.3 Answer: (i) Capacitors connected in series carry the same charge Q. To compare the amount of energy stored, we use the expression $U = Q^2/2C$ from Eq. (24.9); it shows that the capacitor with the *smaller* capacitance ($C = 4\ \mu$F) has more stored energy in a series combination. By contrast, capacitors in parallel have the same potential difference V, so to compare them we use $U = \frac{1}{2}CV^2$ from Eq. (24.9). It shows that in a parallel combination, the capacitor with the *larger* capacitance ($C = 8\ \mu$F) has more stored energy. (If we had instead used $U = \frac{1}{2}CV^2$ to analyze the series combination, we would have to account for the different potential differences across the two capacitors. Likewise, using $U = Q^2/2C$ to study the parallel combination would require us to account for the different charges on the capacitors.)

24.4 Answers: (i) Here Q remains the same, so we use $U = Q^2/2C$ from Eq. (24.9) for the stored energy. Removing the dielectric lowers the capacitance by a factor of $1/K$; since U is inversely proportional to C, the stored energy *increases* by a factor of K. It takes work to pull the dielectric slab out of the capacitor because the fringing field tries to pull the slab back in (Fig. 24.16). The work that you do goes into the energy stored in the capacitor.

24.5 Answer: (i), (iii), (ii) Equation (24.14) says that if E_0 is the initial electric-field magnitude (before the dielectric slab is inserted), then the resultant field magnitude after the slab is inserted is $E_0/K = E_0/3$. The magnitude of the resultant field equals the difference between the initial field magnitude and the magnitude E_i of the field due to the bound charges (see Fig. 24.21). Hence $E_0 - E_i = E_0/3$ and $E_i = 2E_0/3$.

24.6 Answer: (iii) Equation (24.23) shows that this situation is the same as an isolated point charge in vacuum but with $\vec{E}$ replaced by $K\vec{E}$. Hence KE at the point of interest is equal to $q/4\pi\epsilon_0 r^2$, and so $E = q/4\pi K\epsilon_0 r^2$. As in Example 24.12, filling the space with a dielectric reduces the electric field by a factor of $1/K$.

PROBLEMS

For instructor-assigned homework, go to www.masteringphysics.com 

Discussion Questions

Q24.1. Equation (24.2) shows that the capacitance of a parallel-plate capacitor becomes larger as the plate separation d decreases. However, there is a practical limit to how small d can be made, which places limits on how large C can be. Explain what sets the limit on d. (*Hint:* What happens to the magnitude of the electric field as $d \rightarrow 0$?)

Q24.2. Suppose several different parallel-plate capacitors are charged up by a constant-voltage source. Thinking of the actual movement and position of the charges on an atomic level, why does it make sense that the capacitances are proportional to the surface areas of the plates? Why does it make sense that the capacitances are *inversely* proportional to the distance between the plates?

Q24.3. Suppose the two plates of a capacitor have different areas. When the capacitor is charged by connecting it to a battery, do the charges on the two plates have equal magnitude, or may they be different? Explain your reasoning.

Q24.4. At the Fermi National Accelerator Laboratory (Fermilab) in Illinois, protons are accelerated around a ring 2 km in radius to speeds that approach that of light. The energy for this is stored in capacitors the size of a house. When these capacitors are being charged, they make a very loud creaking sound. What is the origin of this sound?

Q24.5. In the parallel-plate capacitor of Fig. 24.2, suppose the plates are pulled apart so that the separation d is much larger than the size of the plates. (a) Is it still accurate to say that the electric field between the plates is uniform? Why or why not? (b) In the situation shown in Fig. 24.2, the potential difference between the plates is $V_{ab} = Qd/\epsilon_0 A$. If the plates are pulled apart as described above, is V_{ab} more or less than this formula would indicate? Explain your reasoning. (c) With the plates pulled apart as described above, is the capacitance more than, less than, or the same as that given by Eq. (24.2)? Explain your reasoning.

Q24.6. A parallel-plate capacitor is charged by being connected to a battery and is kept connected to the battery. The separation between the plates is then doubled. How does the electric field change? The charge on the plates? The total energy? Explain your reasoning.

Q24.7. A parallel-plate capacitor is charged by being connected to a battery and is then disconnected from the battery. The separation between the plates is then doubled. How does the electric field change? The potential difference? The total energy? Explain your reasoning.

Q24.8. Two parallel-plate capacitors, identical except that one has twice the plate separation of the other, are charged by the same voltage source. Which capacitor has a stronger electric field between the plates? Which capacitor has a greater charge? Which has greater energy density? Explain your reasoning.

Q24.9. The charged plates of a capacitor attract each other, so to pull the plates farther apart requires work by some external force. What becomes of the energy added by this work? Explain your reasoning.

Q24.10. The two plates of a capacitor are given charges $\pm Q$. The capacitor is then disconnected from the charging device so that the charges on the plates can't change, and the capacitor is immersed in a tank of oil. Does the electric field between the plates increase, decrease, or stay the same? Explain your reasoning. How can this field be measured?

Q24.11. As shown in Table 24.1, water has a very large dielectric constant $K = 80.4$. Why do you think water is not commonly used as a dielectric in capacitors?

Q24.12. Is dielectric strength the same thing as dielectric constant? Explain any differences between the two quantities. Is there a simple relationship between dielectric strength and dielectric constant (see Table 24.2)?

Q24.13. A capacitor made of aluminum foil strips separated by Mylar film was subjected to excessive voltage, and the resulting dielectric breakdown melted holes in the Mylar. After this, the capacitance was found to be about the same as before, but the breakdown voltage was much less. Why?

Q24.14. Suppose you bring a slab of dielectric close to the gap between the plates of a charged capacitor, preparing to slide it between the plates. What force will you feel? What does this force tell you about the energy stored between the plates once the dielectric is in place, compared to before the dielectric is in place?

Q24.15. The freshness of fish can be measured by placing a fish between the plates of a capacitor and measuring the capacitance. How does this work? (*Hint:* As time passes, the fish dries out. See Table 24.1.)

Q24.16. *Electrolytic* capacitors use as their dielectric an extremely thin layer of nonconducting oxide between a metal plate and a conducting solution. Discuss the advantage of such a capacitor over one constructed using a solid dielectric between the metal plates.

Q24.17. In terms of the dielectric constant K, what happens to the electric flux through the Gaussian surface shown in Fig. 24.23 when the dielectric is inserted into the previously empty space between the plates? Explain.

Q24.18. A parallel-plate capacitor is connected to a power supply that maintains a fixed potential difference between the plates. (a) If a sheet of dielectric is then slid between the plates, what happens to (i) the electric field between the plates, (ii) the magnitude of charge on each plate, and (iii) the energy stored in the capacitor? (b) Now suppose that before the dielectric is inserted, the charged capacitor is disconnected from the power supply. In this case, what happens to (i) the electric field between the plates, (ii) the magnitude of charge on each plate, (iii) the energy stored in the capacitor? Explain any differences between the two situations.

Q24.19. Liquid dielectrics that have polar molecules (such as water) always have dielectric constants that decrease with increasing temperature. Why?

Q24.20. A conductor is an extreme case of a dielectric, since if an electric field is applied to a conductor, charges are free to move within the conductor to set up "induced charges." What is the dielectric constant of a perfect conductor? Is it $K = 0$, $K \rightarrow \infty$, or something in between? Explain your reasoning.

Exercises

Section 24.1 Capacitors and Capacitance

24.1. A capacitor has a capacitance of 7.28 μF. What amount of charge must be placed on each of its plates to make the potential difference between its plates equal to 25.0 V?

24.2. The plates of a parallel-plate capacitor are 3.28 mm apart, and each has an area of 12.2 cm^2. Each plate carries a charge of magnitude 4.35×10^{-8} C. The plates are in vacuum. (a) What is the capacitance? (b) What is the potential difference between the plates? (c) What is the magnitude of the electric field between the plates?

24.3. A parallel-plate air capacitor of capacitance 245 pF has a charge of magnitude 0.148 μC on each plate. The plates are 0.328 mm apart. (a) What is the potential difference between the plates? (b) What is the area of each plate? (c) What is the electric-field magnitude between the plates? (d) What is the surface charge density on each plate?

24.4. Capacitance of an Oscilloscope. Oscilloscopes have parallel metal plates inside them to deflect the electron beam. These plates are called the *deflecting plates.* Typically, they are squares 3.0 cm on a side and separated by 5.0 mm, with vacuum in between. What is the capacitance of these deflecting plates and hence of the oscilloscope? (*Note:* This capacitance can sometimes have an effect on the circuit you are trying to study and must be taken into consideration in your calculations.)

24.5. A 10.0-μF parallel-plate capacitor with circular plates is connected to a 12.0-V battery. (a) What is the charge on each plate? (b) How much charge would be on the plates if their separation were doubled while the capacitor remained connected to the battery? (c) How much charge would be on the plates if the capacitor were connected to the 12.0-V battery after the radius of each plate was doubled without changing their separation?

24.6. A 10.0-μF parallel-plate capacitor is connected to a 12.0-V battery. After the capacitor is fully charged, the battery is disconnected without loss of any of the charge on the plates. (a) A voltmeter is connected across the two plates without discharging them. What does it read? (b) What would the voltmeter read if (i) the plate separation were doubled; (ii) the radius of each plate were doubled and, but their separation was unchanged?

24.7. How far apart would parallel pennies have to be to make a 1.00-pF capacitor? Does your answer suggest that you are justified in treating these pennies as infinite sheets? Explain.

24.8. A 5.00-pF, parallel-plate, air-filled capacitor with circular plates is to be used in a circuit in which it will be subjected to potentials of up to 1.00×10^2 V. The electric field between the plates is to be no greater than 1.00×10^4 N/C. As a budding electrical engineer for Live-Wire Electronics, your tasks are to (a) design the capacitor by finding what its physical dimensions and separation must be; (b) find the maximum charge these plates can hold.

24.9. A capacitor is made from two hollow, coaxial, iron cylinders, one inside the other. The inner cylinder is negatively charged and the outer is positively charged; the magnitude of the charge on each is 10.0 pC. The inner cylinder has radius 0.50 mm, the outer one has radius 5.00 mm, and the length of each cylinder is 18.0 cm. (a) What is the capacitance? (b) What applied potential difference is necessary to produce these charges on the cylinders?

24.10. A cylindrical capacitor consists of a solid inner conducting core with radius 0.250 cm, surrounded by an outer hollow conducting tube. The two conductors are separated by air, and the length of the cylinder is 12.0 cm. The capacitance is 36.7 pF. (a) Calculate the inner radius of the hollow tube. (b) When the capacitor is charged to 125 V, what is the charge per unit length λ on the capacitor?

24.11. A cylindrical capacitor has an inner conductor of radius 1.5 mm and an outer conductor of radius 3.5 mm. The two conductors are separated by vacuum, and the entire capacitor is 2.8 m long. (a) What is the capacitance per unit length? (b) The potential of the inner conductor is 350 mV higher than that of the outer conductor. Find the charge (magnitude and sign) on both conductors.

24.12. A spherical capacitor is formed from two concentric, spherical, conducting shells separated by vacuum. The inner sphere has radius 15.0 cm and the capacitance is 116 pF. (a) What is the radius of the outer sphere? (b) If the potential difference between the two spheres is 220 V, what is the magnitude of charge on each sphere?

24.13. A spherical capacitor contains a charge of 3.30 nC when connected to a potential difference of 220 V. If its plates are separated by vacuum and the inner radius of the outer shell is 4.00 cm, calculate: (a) the capacitance; (b) the radius of the inner sphere; (c) the electric field just outside the surface of the inner sphere.

Section 24.2 Capacitors in Series and Parallel

24.14. For the system of capacitors shown in Fig. 24.24, find the equivalent capacitance (a) between b and c, and (b) between a and c.

Figure **24.24** Exercise 24.14.

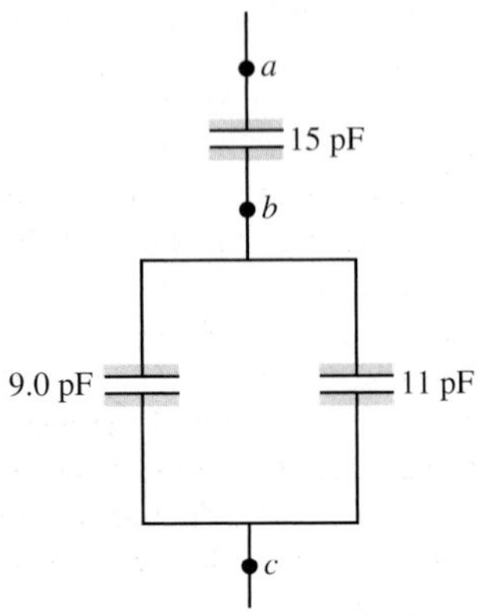

24.15. In Fig. 24.25, each capacitor has $C = 4.00\ \mu\text{F}$ and $V_{ab} = +28.0$ V. Calculate (a) the charge on each capacitor; (b) the potential difference across each capacitor; (c) the potential difference between points a and d.

Figure **24.25** Exercise 24.15.

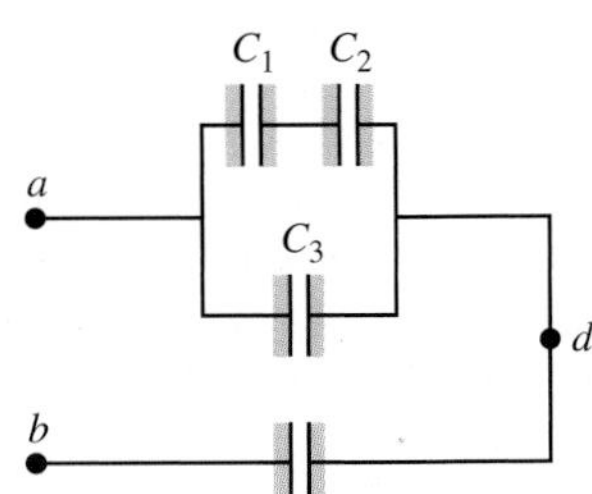

24.16. In Fig. 24.8a, let $C_1 = 3.00\ \mu\text{F}$, $C_2 = 5.00\ \mu\text{F}$, and $V_{ab} = +52.0$ V. Calculate (a) the charge on each capacitor and (b) the potential difference across each capacitor.

24.17. In Fig. 24.9a, let $C_1 = 3.00\ \mu\text{F}$, $C_2 = 5.00\ \mu\text{F}$, and $V_{ab} = +52.0$ V. Calculate (a) the charge on each capacitor and (b) the potential difference across each capacitor.

24.18. In Fig. 24.26, $C_1 = 6.00\ \mu\text{F}$, $C_2 = 3.00\ \mu\text{F}$, and $C_3 = 5.00\ \mu\text{F}$. The capacitor network is connected to an applied potential V_{ab}. After the charges on the capacitors have reached their final values, the charge on C_2 is 40.0 μC. (a) What are the charges on capacitors C_1 and C_3? (b) What is the applied voltage V_{ab}?

Figure **24.26** Exercises 24.18 and 24.19.

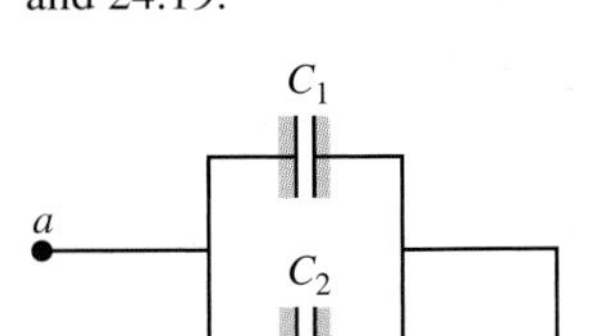

24.19. In Fig. 24.26, $C_1 = 3.00\ \mu\text{F}$ and $V_{ab} = 120$ V. The charge on capacitor C_1 is 150 μC. Calculate the voltage across the other two capacitors.

24.20. Two parallel-plate vacuum capacitors have plate spacings d_1 and d_2 and equal plate areas A. Show that when the capacitors are connected in series, the equivalent capacitance is the same as for a single capacitor with plate area A and spacing $d_1 + d_2$.

24.21. Two parallel-plate vacuum capacitors have areas A_1 and A_2 and equal plate spacings d. Show that when the capacitors are connected in parallel, the equivalent capacitance is the same as for a single capacitor with plate area $A_1 + A_2$ and spacing d.

24.22. Figure 24.27 shows a system of four capacitors, where the potential difference across ab is 50.0 V. (a) Find the equivalent capacitance of this system between a and b. (b) How much charge is stored by this combination of capacitors? (c) How much charge is stored in each of the 10.0-μF and the 9.0-μF capacitors?

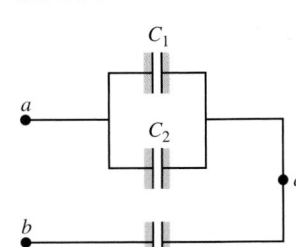

Figure **24.27** Exercise 24.22.

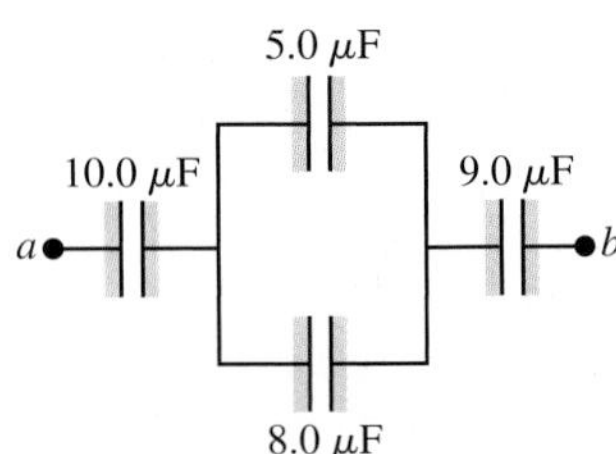

24.23. Suppose the 3-μF capacitor in Fig. 24.10a were removed and replaced by a different one, and that this changed the equivalent capacitance between points a and b to 8 μF. What would be the capacitance of the replacement capacitor?

Section 24.3 Energy Storage in Capacitors and Electric-Field Energy

24.24. A parallel-plate air capacitor has a capacitance of 920 pF. The charge on each plate is 2.55 μC. (a) What is the potential difference between the plates? (b) If the charge is kept constant, what will be the potential difference between the plates if the separation is doubled? (c) How much work is required to double the separation?

24.25. A 5.80-μF, parallel-plate, air capacitor has a plate separation of 5.00 mm and is charged to a potential difference of 400 V. Calculate the energy density in the region between the plates, in units of J/m^3.

24.26. An air capacitor is made from two flat parallel plates 1.50 mm apart. The magnitude of charge on each plate is 0.0180 μC when the potential difference is 200 V. (a) What is the capacitance? (b) What is the area of each plate? (c) What maximum voltage can be applied without dielectric breakdown? (Dielectric breakdown for air occurs at an electric-field strength of 3.0×10^6 V/m.) (d) When the charge is 0.0180 μC, what total energy is stored?

24.27. A 450-μF capacitor is charged to 295 V. Then a wire is connected between the plates. How many joules of thermal energy are produced as the capacitor discharges if all of the energy that was stored goes into heating the wire?

24.28. A capacitor of capacitance C is charged to a potential difference V_0. The terminals of the charged capacitor are then connected to those of an uncharged capacitor of capacitance $C/2$. Compute (a) the original charge of the system; (b) the final potential difference across each capacitor; (c) the final energy of the system; (d) the decrease in energy when the capacitors are connected. (e) Where did the "lost" energy go?

24.29. A parallel-plate vacuum capacitor with plate area A and separation x has charges $+Q$ and $-Q$ on its plates. The capacitor is disconnected from the source of charge, so the charge on each plate remains fixed. (a) What is the total energy stored in the capacitor? (b) The plates are pulled apart an additional distance dx. What is the change in the stored energy? (c) If F is the force with which the plates attract each other, then the change in the stored energy must equal the work $dW = Fdx$ done in pulling the plates apart. Find an expression for F. (d) Explain why F is *not* equal to QE, where E is the electric field between the plates.

24.30. A parallel-plate vacuum capacitor has 8.38 J of energy stored in it. The separation between the plates is 2.30 mm. If the separation is decreased to 1.15 mm, what is the energy stored (a) if the capacitor is disconnected from the potential source so the charge on the plates remains constant, and (b) if the capacitor remains connected to the potential source so the potential difference between the plates remains constant?

24.31. (a) How much charge does a battery have to supply to a 5.0-μF capacitor to create a potential difference of 1.5 V across its plates? How much energy is stored in the capacitor in this case? (b) How much charge would the battery have to supply to store 1.0 J of energy in the capacitor? What would be the potential across the capacitor in that case?

24.32. For the capacitor network shown in Fig. 24.28, the potential difference across ab is 36 V. Find (a) the total charge stored in this network; (b) the charge on each capacitor; (c) the total energy stored in the network; (d) the energy stored in each capacitor; (e) the potential differences across each capacitor.

Figure 24.28 Exercise 24.32.

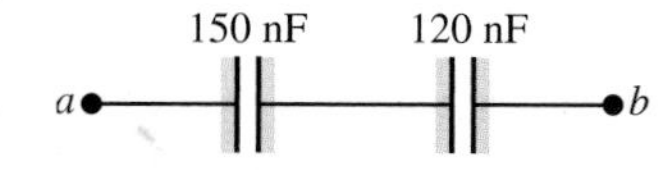

150 nF 120 nF

a b

24.33. For the capacitor network shown in Fig. 24.29, the potential difference across ab is 220 V. Find (a) the total charge stored in this network; (b) the charge on each capacitor; (c) the total energy stored in the network; (d) the energy stored in each capacitor; (e) the potential difference across each capacitor.

Figure 24.29 Exercise 24.33

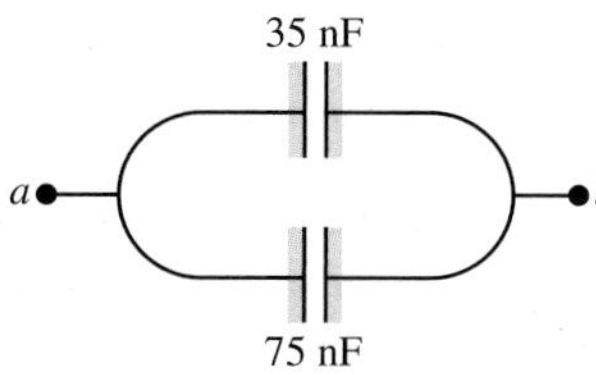

35 nF

a b

75 nF

24.34. A 0.350-m-long cylindrical capacitor consists of a solid conducting core with a radius of 1.20 mm and an outer hollow conducting tube with an inner radius of 2.00 mm. The two conductors are separated by air and charged to a potential difference of 6.00 V. Calculate (a) the charge per length for the capacitor; (b) the total charge on the capacitor; (c) the capacitance; (d) the energy stored in the capacitor when fully charged.

24.35. A cylindrical air capacitor of length 15.0 m stores 3.20×10^{-9} J of energy when the potential difference between the two conductors is 4.00 V. (a) Calculate the magnitude of the charge on each conductor. (b) Calculate the ratio of the radii of the inner and outer conductors.

24.36. A capacitor is formed from two concentric spherical conducting shells separated by vacuum. The inner sphere has radius 12.5 cm, and the outer sphere has radius 14.8 cm. A potential difference of 120 V is applied to the capacitor. (a) What is the energy density at $r = 12.6$ cm, just outside the inner sphere? (b) What is the energy density at $r = 14.7$ cm, just inside the outer sphere? (c) For a parallel-plate capacitor the energy density is uniform in the region between the plates, except near the edges of the plates. Is this also true for a spherical capacitor?

24.37. You have two identical capacitors and an external potential source. (a) Compare the total energy stored in the capacitors when they are connected to the applied potential in series and in parallel. (b) Compare the maximum amount of charge stored in each case. (c) Energy storage in a capacitor can be limited by the maximum electric field between the plates. What is the ratio of the electric field for the series and parallel combinations?

Section 24.4 Dielectrics

24.38. A parallel-plate capacitor has capacitance $C_0 = 5.00$ pF when there is air between the plates. The separation between the plates is 1.50 mm. (a) What is the maximum magnitude of charge Q that can be placed on each plate if the electric field in the region between the plates is not to exceed 3.00×10^4 V/m? (b) A dielectric with $K = 2.70$ is inserted between the plates of the capacitor, completely filling the volume between the plates. Now what is the maximum magnitude of charge on each plate if the electric field between the plates is not to exceed 3.00×10^4 V/m?

24.39. Two parallel plates have equal and opposite charges. When the space between the plates is evacuated, the electric field is $E = 3.20 \times 10^5$ V/m. When the space is filled with dielectric, the electric field is $E = 2.50 \times 10^5$ V/m. (a) What is the charge density on each surface of the dielectric? (b) What is the dielectric constant?

24.40. A budding electronics hobbyist wants to make a simple 1.0-nF capacitor for tuning her crystal radio, using two sheets of aluminum foil as plates, with a few sheets of paper between them as a dielectric. The paper has a dielectric constant of 3.0, and the thickness of one sheet of it is 0.20 mm. (a) If the sheets of paper measure 22×28 cm and she cuts the aluminum foil to the same dimensions, how many sheets of paper should she use between her plates to get the proper capacitance? (b) Suppose for convenience she wants to use a single sheet of posterboard, with the same dielectric constant but a thickness of 12.0 mm, instead of the paper. What area of aluminum foil will she need for her plates to get her 1.0 nF of capacitance? (c) Suppose she goes high-tech and finds a sheet of Teflon of the same thickness as the posterboard to use as a dielectric. Will she need a larger or smaller area of Teflon than of posterboard? Explain.

24.41. The dielectric to be used in a parallel-plate capacitor has a dielectric constant of 3.60 and a dielectric strength of 1.60×10^7 V/m. The capacitor is to have a capacitance of 1.25×10^{-9} F and must be able to withstand a maximum potential difference of 5500 V. What is the minimum area the plates of the capacitor may have?

24.42. Show that Eq. (24.20) holds for a parallel-plate capacitor with a dielectric material between the plates. Use a derivation analogous to that used for Eq. (24.11).

24.43. A capacitor has parallel plates of area 12 cm^2 separated by 2.0 mm. The space between the plates is filled with polystyrene (see Table 24.2). (a) Find the permittivity of polystyrene. (b) Find the maximum permissible voltage across the capacitor to avoid dielectric breakdown. (c) When the voltage equals the value found in part (b), find the surface charge density on each plate and the induced surface-charge density on the surface of the dielectric.

24.44. A constant potential difference of 12 V is maintained between the terminals of a 0.25-μF, parallel-plate, air capacitor. (a) A sheet of Mylar is inserted between the plates of the capacitor, completely filling the space between the plates. When this is done, how much additional charge flows onto the positive plate of the capacitor (see Table 24.1)? (b) What is the total induced charge on either face of the Mylar sheet? (c) What effect does the Mylar sheet have on the electric field between the plates? Explain how you can reconcile this with the increase in charge on the plates, which acts to *increase* the electric field.

24.45. When a 360-nF air capacitor $(1 \text{ nF} = 10^{-9} \text{ F})$ is connected to a power supply, the energy stored in the capacitor is 1.85×10^{-5} J. While the capacitor is kept connected to the power supply, a slab of dielectric is inserted that completely fills the space between the plates. This increases the stored energy by 2.32×10^{-5} J. (a) What is the potential difference between the capacitor plates? (b) What is the dielectric constant of the slab?

24.46. A parallel-plate capacitor has capacitance $C = 12.5$ pF when the volume between the plates is filled with air. The plates are circular, with radius 3.00 cm. The capacitor is connected to a battery and a charge of magnitude 25.0 pC goes onto each plate. With the capacitor still connected to the battery, a slab of dielectric is inserted between the plates, completely filling the space between the plates. After the dielectric has been inserted, the charge on each plate has magnitude 45.0 pC. (a) What is the dielectric constant K of the dielectric? (b) What is the potential difference between the plates before and after the dielectric has been inserted? (c) What is the electric field at a point midway between the plates before and after the dielectric has been inserted?

24.47. A 12.5-μF capacitor is connected to a power supply that keeps a constant potential difference of 24.0 V across the plates. A piece of material having a dielectric constant of 3.75 is placed between the plates, completely filling the space between them. (a) How much energy is stored in the capacitor before and after the dielectric is inserted? (b) By how much did the energy change during the insertion? Did it increase or decrease?

*Section 24.6 Gauss's Law in Dielectrics

***24.48.** A parallel-plate capacitor has plates with area 0.0225 m^2 separated by 1.00 mm of Teflon. (a) Calculate the charge on the plates when they are charged to a potential difference of 12.0 V. (b) Use Gauss's law (Eq. 24.23) to calculate the electric field inside the Teflon. (c) Use Gauss's law to calculate the electric field if the voltage source is disconnected and the Teflon is removed.

***24.49.** A parallel-plate capacitor has the volume between its plates filled with plastic with dielectric constant K. The magnitude of the charge on each plate is Q. Each plate has area A, and the distance between the plates is d. (a) Use Gauss's law as stated in Eq. (24.23) to calculate the magnitude of the electric field in the dielectric. (b) Use the electric field determined in part (a) to calculate the potential difference between the two plates. (c) Use the result of part (b) to determine the capacitance of the capacitor. Compare your result to Eq. (24.12).

Problems

24.50. A parallel-plate air capacitor is made by using two plates 16 cm square, spaced 4.7 mm apart. It is connected to a 12-V battery. (a) What is the capacitance? (b) What is the charge on each plate? (c) What is the electric field between the plates? (d) What is the energy stored in the capacitor? (e) If the battery is disconnected and then the plates are pulled apart to a separation of 9.4 mm, what are the answers to parts (a)–(d)?

24.51. Suppose the battery in Problem 24.50 remains connected while the plates are pulled apart. What are the answers then to parts (a)–(d) after the plates have been pulled apart?

24.52. Cell Membranes. Cell membranes (the walled enclosure around a cell) are typically about 7.5 nm thick. They are partially permeable to allow charged material to pass in and out, as needed. Equal but opposite charge densities build up on the inside and outside faces of such a membrane, and these charges prevent additional charges from passing through the cell wall. We can model a cell membrane as a parallel-plate capacitor, with the membrane itself containing proteins embedded in an organic material to give the membrane a dielectric constant of about 10. (See Fig. 24.30.) (a) What is the capacitance per square centimeter of such a cell wall? (b) In its normal resting state, a cell has a potential difference of 85 mV across its membrane. What is the electric field inside this membrane?

Figure **24.30** Problem 24.52.

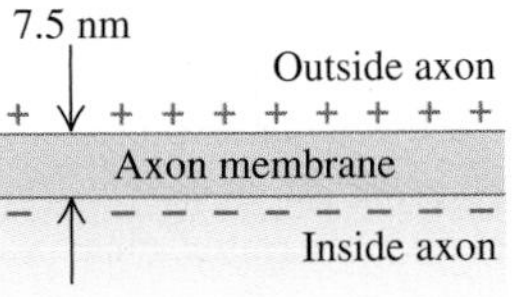

24.53. Electronic flash units for cameras contain a capacitor for storing the energy used to produce the flash. In one such unit, the flash lasts for $\frac{1}{675}$ s with an average light power output of 2.70×10^5 W. (a) If the conversion of electrical energy to light is 95% efficient (the rest of the energy goes to thermal energy), how much energy must be stored in the capacitor for one flash? (b) The capacitor has a potential difference between its plates of 125 V when the stored energy equals the value calculated in part (a). What is the capacitance?

24.54. In one type of computer keyboard, each key holds a small metal plate that serves as one plate of a parallel-plate, air-filled capacitor. When the key is depressed, the plate separation decreases and the capacitance increases. Electronic circuitry detects the change in capacitance and thus detects that the key has been pressed. In one particular keyboard, the area of each metal plate is 42.0 mm^2, and the separation between the plates is 0.700 mm before the key is depressed. (a) Calculate the capacitance before the key is depressed. (b) If the circuitry can detect a change in capacitance of 0.250 pF, how far must the key be depressed before the circuitry detects its depression?

24.55. Consider a cylindrical capacitor like that shown in Fig. 24.6. Let $d = r_b - r_a$ be the spacing between the inner and outer conductors. (a) Let the radii of the two conductors be only slightly different, so that $d \ll r_a$. Show that the result derived in Example 24.4 (Section 24.1) for the capacitance of a cylindrical capacitor then reduces to Eq. (24.2), the equation for the capacitance of a parallel-plate capacitor, with A being the surface area of each cylinder. Use the result that $\ln(1+z) \cong z$ for $|z| \ll 1$. (b) Even though the earth is essentially spherical, its surface appears flat to us because its radius is so large. Use this idea to explain why the result of part (a) makes sense from a purely geometrical standpoint.

24.56. In Fig. 24.9a, let $C_1 = 9.0\ \mu\text{F}$, $C_2 = 4.0\ \mu\text{F}$, and $V_{ab} = 28\ \text{V}$. Suppose the charged capacitors are disconnected from the source and from each other, and then reconnected to each other with plates of *opposite* sign together. By how much does the energy of the system decrease?

24.57. For the capacitor network shown in Fig. 24.31, the potential difference across ab is 12.0 V. Find (a) the total energy stored in this network and (b) the energy stored in the 4.80-μF capacitor.

Figure 24.31 Problem 24.57.

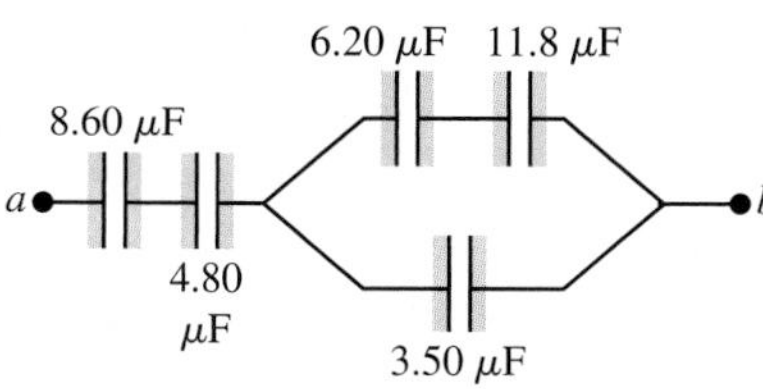

24.58. Several 0.25-μF capacitors are available. The voltage across each is not to exceed 600 V. You need to make a capacitor with capacitance 0.25 μF to be connected across a potential difference of 960 V. (a) Show in a diagram how an equivalent capacitor with the desired properties can be obtained. (b) No dielectric is a perfect insulator that would not permit the flow of any charge through its volume. Suppose that the dielectric in one of the capacitors in your diagram is a moderately good conductor. What will happen in this case when your combination of capacitors is connected across the 960-V potential difference?

24.59. In Fig. 24.32, $C_1 = C_5 = 8.4\ \mu\text{F}$ and $C_2 = C_3 = C_4 = 4.2\ \mu\text{F}$. The applied potential is $V_{ab} = 220\ \text{V}$. (a) What is the equivalent capacitance of the network between points a and b? (b) Calculate the charge on each capacitor and the potential difference across each capacitor.

Figure 24.32 Problem 24.59.

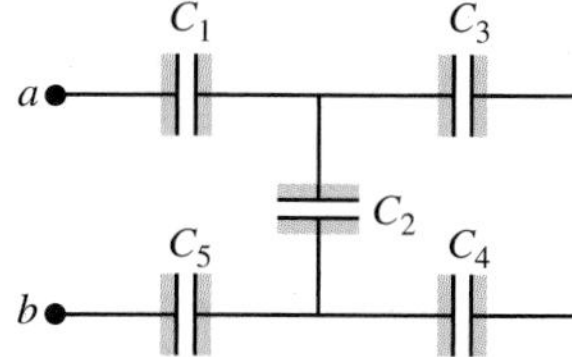

Figure 24.33 Problem 24.60.

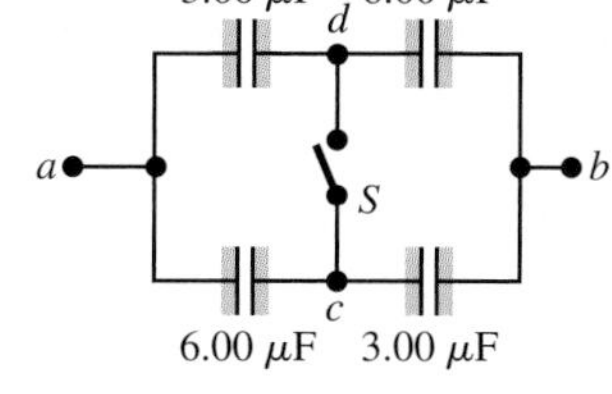

24.60. The capacitors in Fig. 24.33 are initially uncharged and are connected, as in the diagram, with switch S open. The applied potential difference is $V_{ab} = +210\ V$. (a) What is the potential difference V_{cd}? (b) What is the potential difference across each capacitor after switch S is closed? (c) How much charge flowed through the switch when it was closed?

24.61. Three capacitors having capacitances of 8.4, 8.4, and 4.2 μF are connected in series across a 36-V potential difference. (a) What is the charge on the 4.2-μF capacitor? (b) What is the total energy stored in all three capacitors? (c) The capacitors are disconnected from the potential difference without allowing them to discharge. They are then reconnected in parallel with each other, with the positively charged plates connected together. What is the voltage across each capacitor in the parallel combination? (d) What is the total energy now stored in the capacitors?

24.62. Capacitance of a Thundercloud. The charge center of a thundercloud, drifting 3.0 km above the earth's surface, contains 20 C of negative charge. Assuming the charge center has a radius of 1.0 km, and modeling the charge center and the earth's surface as parallel plates, calculate: (a) the capacitance of the system; (b) the potential difference between charge center and ground; (c) the average strength of the electric field between cloud and ground; (d) the electrical energy stored in the system.

24.63. In Fig. 24.34, each capacitance C_1 is 6.9 μF, and each capacitance C_2 is 4.6 μF. (a) Compute the equivalent capacitance of the network between points a and b. (b) Compute the charge on each of the three capacitors nearest a and b when $V_{ab} = 420\ \text{V}$. (c) With 420 V across a and b, compute V_{cd}.

Figure 24.34 Problem 24.63.

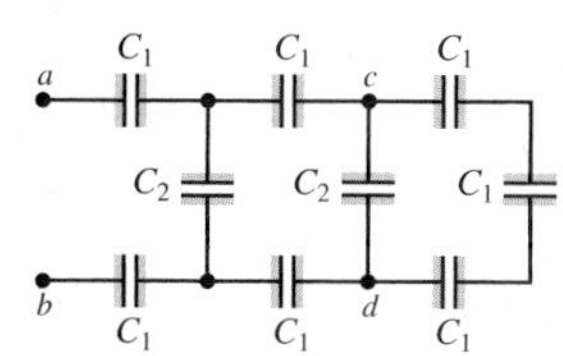

24.64. Each combination of capacitors between points a and b in Fig. 24.35 is first connected across a 120-V battery, charging the combination to 120 V. These combinations are then connected to make the circuits shown. When the switch S is thrown, a surge of charge for the discharging capacitors flows to trigger the signal device. How much charge flows through the signal device?

Figure 24.35 Problem 24.64.

(a)

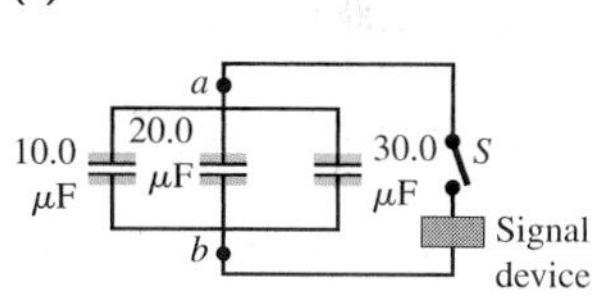

(b)

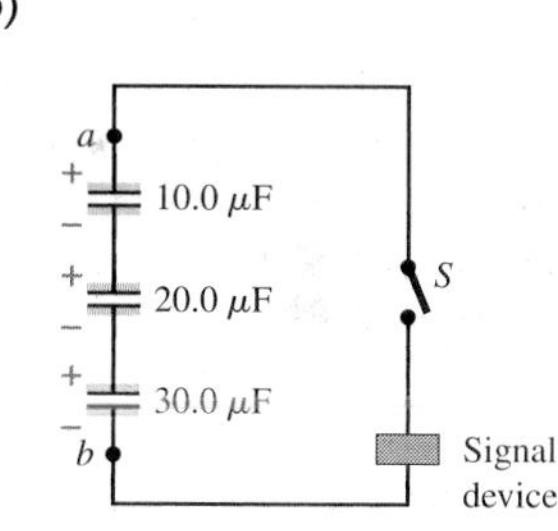

24.65. A parallel-plate capacitor with only air between the plates is charged by connecting it to a battery. The capacitor is then disconnected from the battery, without any of the charge leaving the plates. (a) A voltmeter reads 45.0 V when placed across the capacitor. When a dielectric is inserted between the plates, completely filling the space, the voltmeter reads 11.5 V. What is the dielectric constant of this material? (b) What will the voltmeter read if the dielectric is now pulled partway out so it fills only one-third of the space between the plates?

24.66. An air capacitor is made by using two flat plates, each with area A, separated by a distance d. Then a metal slab having thickness a (less than d) and the same shape and size as the plates is inserted between them, parallel to the plates and not touching either plate (Fig. 24.36). (a) What is the capacitance of this arrangement? (b) Express the capacitance as a multiple of the capacitance C_0 when the metal slab is not present. (c) Discuss what happens to the capacitance in the limits $a \rightarrow 0$ and $a \rightarrow d$.

Figure 24.36 Problem 24.66.

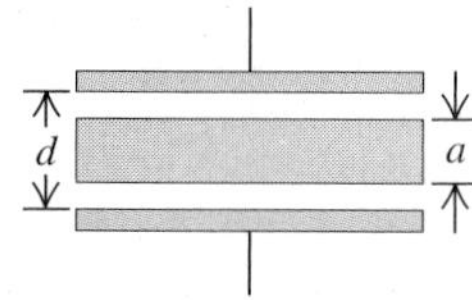

24.67. Capacitance of the Earth. (a) Discuss how the concept of capacitance can also be applied to a *single* conductor. (*Hint:* In the relationship $C = Q/V_{ab}$, think of the second conductor as being located at infinity.) (b) Use Eq. (24.1) to show that $C = 4\pi\epsilon_0 R$ for a solid conducting sphere of radius R. (c) Use your result in part (b) to calculate the capacitance of the earth, which is a good conductor of radius 6380 km. Compare to typical capacitors used in electronic circuits that have capacitances ranging from 10 pF to 100 μF.

24.68. A solid conducting sphere of radius R carries a charge Q. Calculate the electric-field energy density at a point a distance r from the center of the sphere for (a) $r < R$ and (b) $r > R$. (c) Calculate the total electric-field energy associated with the charged sphere. (*Hint:* Consider a spherical shell of radius r and thickness dr that has volume $dV = 4\pi r^2\,dr$, and find the energy stored in this volume. Then integrate from $r = 0$ to $r \rightarrow \infty$.) (d) Explain why the result of part (c) can be interpreted as the amount of work required to assemble the charge Q on the sphere. (e) By using Eq. (24.9) and the result of part (c), show that the capacitance of the sphere is as given in Problem 24.67.

24.69. Earth-Ionosphere Capacitance. The earth can be considered as a single-conductor capacitor (see Problem 24.67). It can also be considered in combination with a charged layer of the atmosphere, the ionosphere, as a spherical capacitor with two plates, the surface of the earth being the negative plate. The ionosphere is at a level of about 70 km, and the potential difference between earth and ionosphere is about 350,000 V. Calculate: (a) the capacitance of this system; (b) the total charge on the capacitor; (c) the energy stored in the system.

24.70. The inner cylinder of a long, cylindrical capacitor has radius r_a and linear charge density $+\lambda$. It is surrounded by a coaxial cylindrical conducting shell with inner radius r_b and linear charge density $-\lambda$ (see Fig. 24.6). (a) What is the energy density in the region between the conductors at a distance r from the axis? (b) Integrate the energy density calculated in part (a) over the volume between the conductors in a length L of the capacitor to obtain the total electric-field energy per unit length. (c) Use Eq. (24.9) and the capacitance per unit length calculated in Example 24.4 (Section 24.1) to calculate U/L. Does your result agree with that obtained in part (b)?

24.71. A parallel-plate capacitor has the space between the plates filled with two slabs of dielectric, one with constant K_1 and one with constant K_2 (Fig. 24.37). Each slab has thickness $d/2$, where d is the plate separation. Show that the capacitance is

Figure 24.37 Problem 24.71.

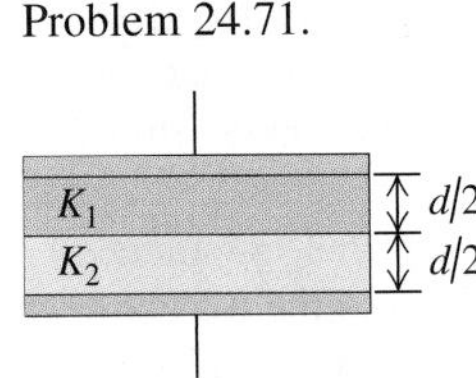

$$C = \frac{2\epsilon_0 A}{d}\left(\frac{K_1 K_2}{K_1 + K_2}\right)$$

24.72. A parallel-plate capacitor has the space between the plates filled with two slabs of dielectric, one with constant K_1 and one with constant K_2 (Fig. 24.38). The thickness of each slab is the same as the plate separation d, and each slab fills half of the volume between the plates. Show that the capacitance is

Figure 24.38 Problem 24.72.

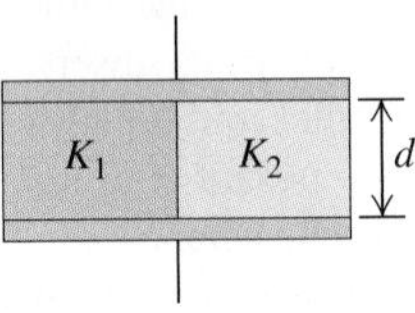

$$C = \frac{\epsilon_0 A(K_1 + K_2)}{2d}$$

Challenge Problems

24.73. Capacitors in networks cannot always be grouped into simple series or parallel combinations. As an example, Fig. 24.39a shows three capacitors C_x, C_y, and C_z in a *delta network*, so called because of its triangular shape. This network has *three* terminals a, b, and c and hence cannot be transformed into a single equivalent capacitor. It can be shown that as far as any effect on the external circuit is concerned, a delta network is equivalent to what is called a *Y network*. For example, the delta network of Fig. 24.39a can be replaced by the Y network of Fig. 24.39b. (The name "Y network" also refers to the shape of the network.) (a) Show that the transformation equations that give C_1, C_2, and C_3 in terms of C_x, and C_y, and C_z are

$$C_1 = (C_xC_y + C_yC_z + C_zC_x)/C_x$$
$$C_2 = (C_xC_y + C_yC_z + C_zC_x)/C_y$$
$$C_3 = (C_xC_y + C_yC_z + C_zC_x)/C_z$$

(*Hint:* The potential difference V_{ac} must be the same in both circuits, as V_{bc} must be. Also, the charge q_1 that flows from point a along the wire as indicated must be the same in both circuits, as must q_2. Obtain a relationship for V_{ac} as a function of q_1 and q_2 and the capacitances for each network, and obtain a separate relationship for V_{bc} as a function of the charges for each network. The coefficients of corresponding charges in corresponding equations must be the same for both networks.) (b) For the network shown in Fig. 24.39c, determine the equivalent capacitance between the terminals at the left end of the network. (*Hint:* Use the delta-Y transformation derived in part (a). Use points a, b, and c to form the delta, and transform the delta into a Y. The capacitors can then be combined using the relationships for series and parallel combinations of capacitors.) (c) Determine the charges of, and the potential differences across, each capacitor in Fig. 24.39c.

Figure 24.39 Challenge Problem 24.73.

(a)

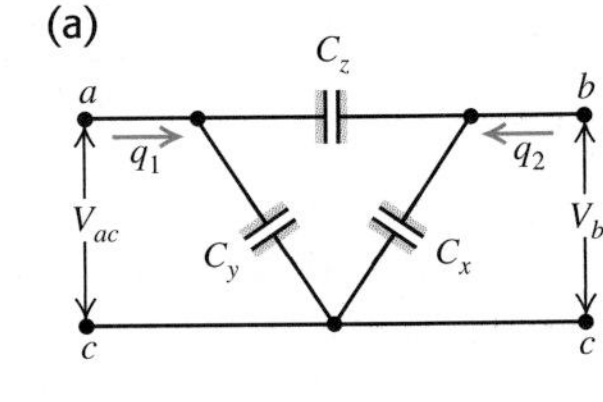

(b)

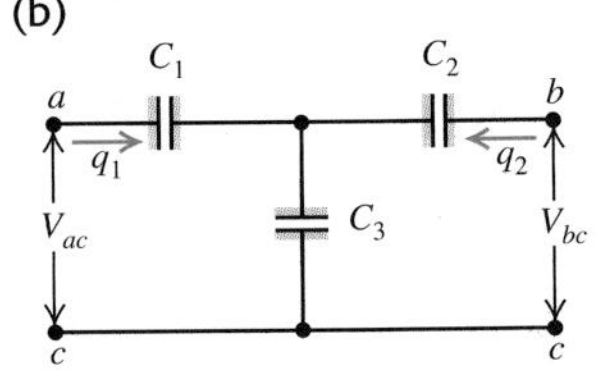

(c)

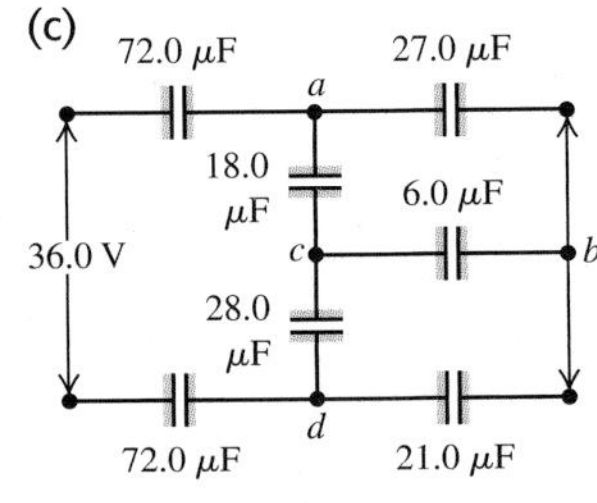

24.74. The parallel-plate air capacitor in Fig. 24.40 consists of two horizontal conducting plates of equal area A. The bottom plate rests on a fixed support, and the top plate is suspended by four

Figure 24.40 Challenge Problem 24.74.

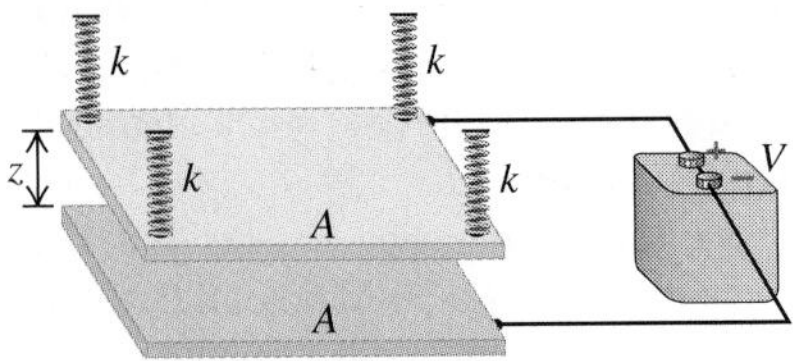

springs with spring constant k, positioned at each of the four corners of the top plate as shown in the figure. When uncharged, the plates are separated by a distance z_0. A battery is connected to the plates and produces a potential difference V between them. This causes the plate separation to decrease to z. Neglect any fringing effects. (a) Show that the electrostatic force between the charged plates has a magnitude $\epsilon_0 AV^2/2z^2$. (*Hint:* See Exercise 24.29.) (b) Obtain an expression that relates the plate separation z to the potential difference V. The resulting equation will be cubic in z. (c) Given the values $A = 0.300\ \text{m}^2$, $z_0 = 1.20$ mm, $k = 25.0$ N/m, and $V = 120$ V, find the two values of z for which the top plate will be in equilibrium. (*Hint:* You can solve the cubic equation by plugging a trial value of z into the equation and then adjusting your guess until the equation is satisfied to three significant figures. Locating the roots of the cubic equation graphically can help you pick starting values of z for this trial-and-error procedure. One root of the cubic equation has a nonphysical negative value.) (d) For each of the two values of z found in part (c), is the equilibrium stable or unstable? For stable equilibrium a small displacement of the object will give rise to a net force tending to return the object to the equilibrium position. For unstable equilibrium a small displacement gives rise to a net force that takes the object farther away from equilibrium.

24.75. Two square conducting plates with sides of length L are separated by a distance D. A dielectric slab with constant K with dimensions $L \times L \times D$ is inserted a distance x into the space between the plates, as shown in Fig. 24.41. (a) Find the capacitance C of this system (see Problem 24.72). (b) Suppose that the capacitor is connected to a battery that maintains a constant potential difference V between the plates. If the dielectric slab is inserted an additional distance dx into the space between the plates, show that the change in stored energy is

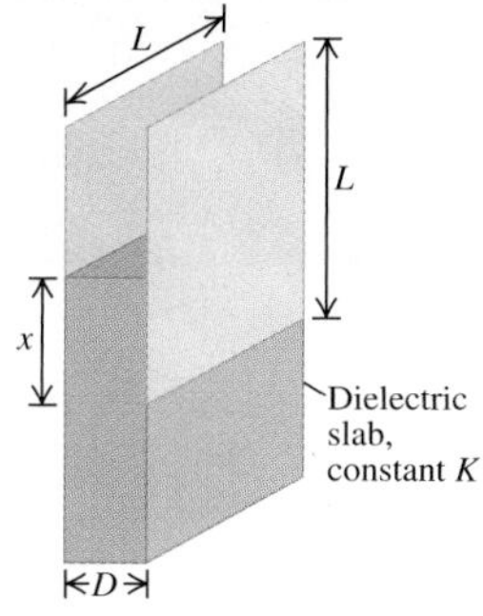

Figure 24.41 Challenge Problem 24.75.

$$dU = +\frac{(K-1)\epsilon_0 V^2 L}{2D}dx$$

(c) Suppose that before the slab is moved by dx, the plates are disconnected from the battery, so that the charges on the plates remain constant. Determine the magnitude of the charge on each plate, and then show that when the slab is moved dx farther into the space between the plates, the stored energy changes by an amount that is the *negative* of the expression for dU given in part (b). (d) If F is the force exerted on the slab by the charges on the plates, then dU should equal the work done *against* this force to move the slab a distance dx. Thus $dU = -F\,dx$. Show that applying this expression to the result of part (b) suggests that the electric force on the slab pushes it *out* of the capacitor, while the result of part (c) suggests that the force pulls the slab *into* the capacitor. (e) Figure 24.16 shows that the force in fact pulls the slab into the capacitor. Explain why the result of part (b) gives an incorrect answer for the direction of this force, and calculate the magnitude of the force. (This method does not require knowledge of the nature of the fringing field.)

24.76. An isolated spherical capacitor has charge $+Q$ on its inner conductor (radius r_a) and charge $-Q$ on its outer conductor (radius r_b). Half of the volume between the two conductors is then filled with a liquid dielectric of constant K, as shown in cross section in Fig. 24.42. (a) Find the capacitance of the half-filled capacitor. (b) Find the magnitude of $\vec{E}$ in the volume between the two conductors as a function of the distance r from the center of the capacitor. Give answers for both the upper and lower halves of this volume. (c) Find the surface density of free charge on the upper and lower halves of the inner and outer conductors. (d) Find the surface density of bound charge on the inner $(r = r_a)$ and outer $(r = r_b)$ surfaces of the dielectric. (e) What is the surface density of bound charge on the flat surface of the dielectric? Explain.

Figure 24.42 Challenge Problem 24.76.

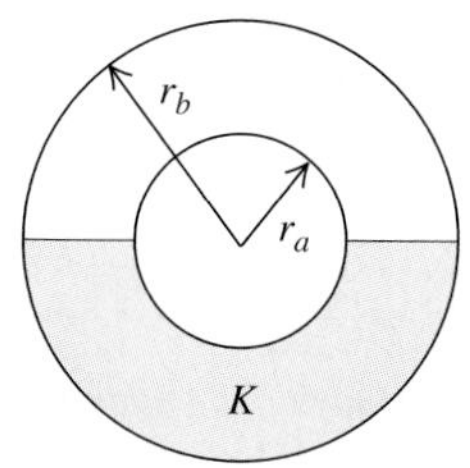

24.77. Three square metal plates A, B, and C, each 12.0 cm on a side and 1.50 mm thick, are arranged as in Fig. 24.43. The plates are separated by sheets of paper 0.45 mm thick and with dielectric constant 4.2. The outer plates are connected together and connected to point b. The inner plate is connected to point a. (a) Copy the diagram and show by plus and minus signs the charge distribution on the plates when point a is maintained at a positive potential relative to point b. (b) What is the capacitance between points a and b?

Figure 24.43 Challenge Problem 24.77.

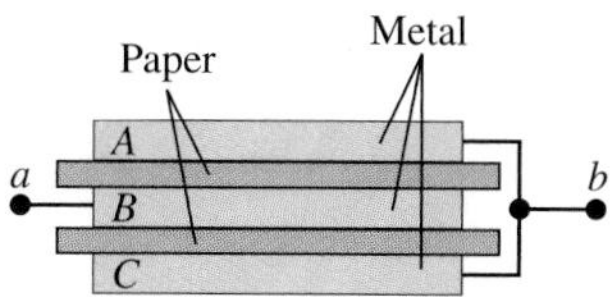

24.78. A fuel gauge uses a capacitor to determine the height of the fuel in a tank. The effective dielectric constant K_{eff} changes from a value of 1 when the tank is empty to a value of K, the dielectric constant of the fuel, when the tank is full. The appropriate electronic circuitry can determine the effective dielectric constant of the combined air and fuel between the capacitor plates. Each of the two rectangular plates has a width w and a length L (Fig. 24.44). The height of the fuel between the plates is h. You can ignore any fringing effects. (a) Derive an expression for K_{eff} as a function of h. (b) What is the effective dielectric constant for a tank $\frac{1}{4}$ full, $\frac{1}{2}$ full, and $\frac{3}{4}$ full if the fuel is gasoline $(K = 1.95)$? (c) Repeat part (b) for methanol $(K = 33.0)$. (d) For which fuel is this fuel gauge more practical?

Figure 24.44 Challenge Problem 24.78.

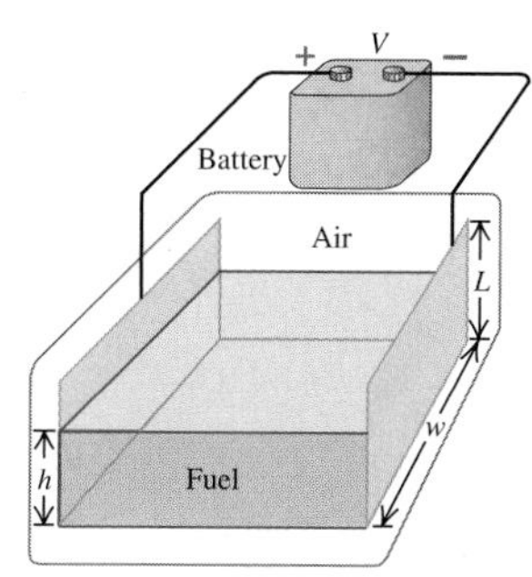

25 CURRENT, RESISTANCE, AND ELECTROMOTIVE FORCE

LEARNING GOALS

By studying this chapter, you will learn:

- The meaning of electric current, and how charges move in a conductor.
- What is meant by the resistivity and conductivity of a substance.
- How to calculate the resistance of a conductor from its dimensions and its resistivity.
- How an electromotive force (emf) makes it possible for current to flow in a circuit.
- How to do calculations involving energy and power in circuits.

? In a flashlight, is the amount of current that flows out of the bulb less than, greater than, or equal to the amount of current that flows into the bulb?

In the past four chapters we studied the interactions of electric charges *at rest;* now we're ready to study charges *in motion.* An *electric current* consists of charges in motion from one region to another. When this motion takes place within a conducting path that forms a closed loop, the path is called an *electric circuit.*

Fundamentally, electric circuits are a means for conveying *energy* from one place to another. As charged particles move within a circuit, electric potential energy is transferred from a source (such as a battery or generator) to a device in which that energy is either stored or converted to another form: into sound in a stereo system or into heat and light in a toaster or light bulb. From a technological standpoint, electric circuits are useful because they allow energy to be transported without any moving parts (other than the moving charged particles themselves). Electric circuits are at the heart of flashlights, CD players, computers, radio and television transmitters and receivers, and household and industrial power distribution systems. The nervous systems of animals and humans are specialized electric circuits that carry vital signals from one part of the body to another.

In Chapter 26 we will see how to analyze electric circuits and will examine some practical applications of circuits. Before we can do so, however, you must understand the basic properties of electric currents. These properties are the subject of this chapter. We'll begin by describing the nature of electric conductors and considering how they are affected by temperature. We'll learn why a short, fat, cold copper wire is a better conductor than a long, skinny, hot steel wire. We'll study the properties of batteries and see how they cause current and energy transfer in a circuit. In this analysis we will use the concepts of current, potential difference (or voltage), resistance, and electromotive force. Finally, we'll look at electric current in a material from a microscopic viewpoint.

25.1 Current

A **current** is any motion of charge from one region to another. In this section we'll discuss currents in conducting materials. The vast majority of technological applications of charges in motion involve currents of this kind.

In electrostatic situations (discussed in Chapters 21 through 24) the electric field is zero everywhere within the conductor, and there is *no* current. However, this does not mean that all charges within the conductor are at rest. In an ordinary metal such as copper or alumium, some of the electrons are free to move within the conducting material. These free electrons move randomly in all directions, somewhat like the molecules of a gas but with much greater speeds, of the order of 10^6 m/s. The electrons nonetheless do not escape from the conducting material, because they are attracted to the positive ions of the material. The motion of the electrons is random, so there is no *net* flow of charge in any direction and hence no current.

Now consider what happens if a constant, steady electric field $\vec{E}$ is established inside a conductor. (We'll see later how this can be done.) A charged particle (such as a free electron) inside the conducting material is then subjected to a steady force $\vec{F} = q\vec{E}$. If the charged particle were moving in *vacuum,* this steady force would cause a steady acceleration in the direction of $\vec{F}$, and after a time the charged particle would be moving in that direction at high speed. But a charged particle moving in a *conductor* undergoes frequent collisions with the massive, nearly stationary ions of the material. In each such collision the particle's direction of motion undergoes a random change. The net effect of the electric field $\vec{E}$ is that in addition to the random motion of the charged particles within the conductor, there is also a very slow net motion or *drift* of the moving charged particles as a group in the direction of the electric force $\vec{F} = q\vec{E}$ (Fig. 25.1). This motion is described in terms of the **drift velocity** $\vec{v}_d$ of the particles. As a result, there is a net current in the conductor.

While the random motion of the electrons has a very fast average speed of about 10^6 m/s, the drift speed is very slow, often on the order of 10^{-4} m/s. Given that the electrons move so slowly, you may wonder why the light comes on immediately when you turn on the switch of a flashlight. The reason is that the electric field is set up in the wire with a speed approaching the speed of light, and electrons start to move all along the wire at very nearly the same time. The time that it takes any individual electron to get from the switch to the light bulb isn't really relevant. A good analogy is a group of soldiers standing at attention when the sergeant orders them to start marching; the order reaches the soldiers' ears at the speed of sound, which is much faster than their marching speed, so all the soldiers start to march essentially in unison.

25.1 If there is no electric field inside a conductor, an electron moves randomly from point P_1 to point P_2 in a time Δt. If an electric field $\vec{E}$ is present, the electric force $\vec{F} = q\vec{E}$ imposes a small drift (greatly exaggerated here) that takes the electron to point P'_2, a distance $v_d\Delta t$ from P_2 in the direction of the force.

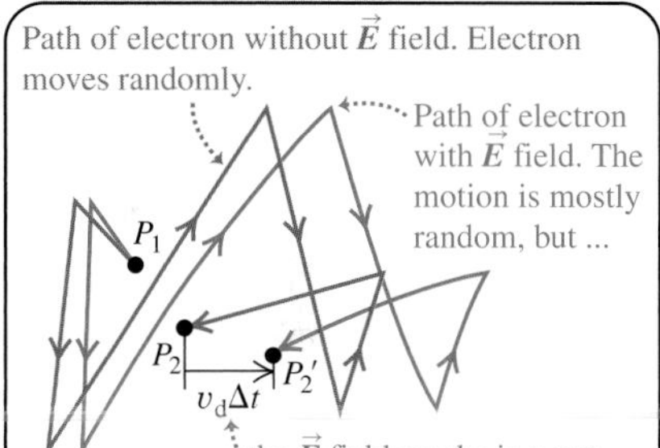
Conductor without internal $\vec{E}$ field
Path of electron without $\vec{E}$ field. Electron moves randomly.
Path of electron with $\vec{E}$ field. The motion is mostly random, but ...
P_1
P_2
P'_2
$v_d\Delta t$
... the $\vec{E}$ field results in a net displacement along the wire.
Conductor with internal $\vec{E}$ field
$\vec{E}$
$\vec{F} = q\vec{E}$
$\vec{E}$
An electron has a negative charge q, so the force on it due to the $\vec{E}$ field is in the direction opposite to $\vec{E}$.

The Direction of Current Flow

The drift of moving charges through a conductor can be interpreted in terms of work and energy. The electric field $\vec{E}$ does work on the moving charges. The resulting kinetic energy is transferred to the material of the conductor by means of collisions with the ions, which vibrate about their equilibrium positions in the crystalline structure of the conductor. This energy transfer increases the average vibrational energy of the ions and therefore the temperature of the material. Thus much of the work done by the electric field goes into heating the conductor, *not* into making the moving charges move ever faster and faster. This heating is sometimes useful, as in an electric toaster, but in many situations is simply an unavoidable by-product of current flow.

In different current-carrying materials, the charges of the moving particles may be positive or negative. In metals the moving charges are always (negative) electrons, while in an ionized gas (plasma) or an ionic solution the moving

25.2 The same current can be produced by (a) positive charges moving in the direction of the electric field $\vec{E}$ or (b) the same number of negative charges moving at the same speed in the direction opposite to $\vec{E}$.

(a)

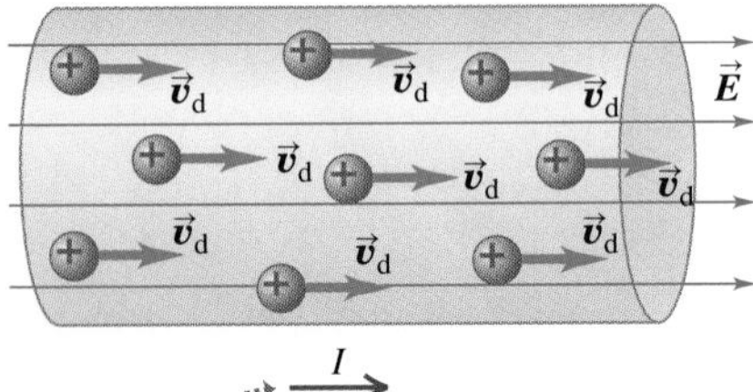

A **conventional current** is treated as a flow of positive charges, regardless of whether the free charges in the conductor are positive, negative, or both.

(b)

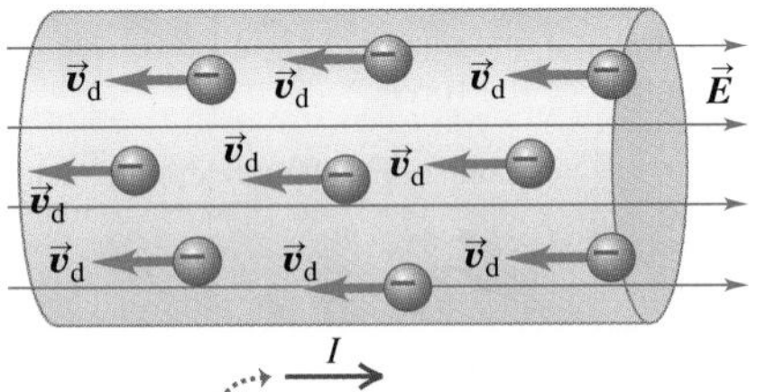

In a metallic conductor, the moving charges are electrons — but the *current* still points in the direction positive charges would flow.

25.3 The current I is the time rate of charge transfer through the cross-sectional area A. The random component of each moving charged particle's motion averages to zero, and the current is in the same direction as $\vec{E}$ whether the moving charges are positive (as shown here) or negative (see Fig. 25.2b).

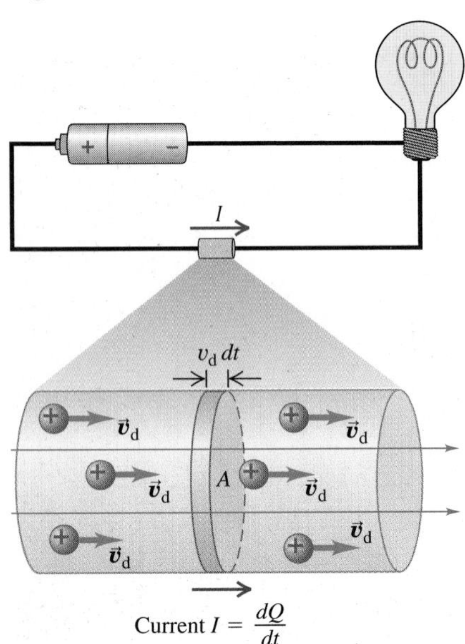

charges may include both electrons and positively charged ions. In a semiconductor material such as germanium or silicon, conduction is partly by electrons and partly by motion of *vacancies,* also known as *holes;* these are sites of missing electrons and act like positive charges.

Fig. 25.2 shows segments of two different current-carrying materials. In Fig. 25.2a the moving charges are positive, the electric force is in the same direction as $\vec{E}$, and the drift velocity $\vec{v}_d$ is from left to right. In Fig. 25.2b the charges are negative, the electric force is opposite to $\vec{E}$, and the drift velocity $\vec{v}_d$ is from right to left. In both cases there is a net flow of positive charge from left to right, and positive charges end up to the right of negative ones. We *define* the current, denoted by I, to be in the direction in which there is a flow of *positive* charge. Thus we describe currents as though they consisted entirely of positive charge flow, even in cases in which we know that the actual current is due to electrons. Hence the current is to the right in both Figs. 25.2a and 25.2b. This choice or convention for the direction of current flow is called **conventional current.** While the direction of the conventional current is *not* necessarily the same as the direction in which charged particles are actually moving, we'll find that the sign of the moving charges is of little importance in analyzing electric circuits.

Fig. 25.3 shows a segment of a conductor in which a current is flowing. We consider the moving charges to be *positive,* so they are moving in the same direction as the current. We define the current through the cross-sectional area A to be *the net charge flowing through the area per unit time.* Thus, if a net charge dQ flows through an area in a time dt, the current I through the area is

$$I = \frac{dQ}{dt} \quad \text{(definition of current)} \tag{25.1}$$

CAUTION Current is not a vector Although we refer to the *direction* of a current, current as defined by Eq. (25.1) is *not* a vector quantity. In a current-carrying wire, the current is always along the length of the wire, regardless of whether the wire is straight or curved. No single vector could describe motion along a curved path, which is why current is not a vector. We'll usually describe the direction of current either in words (as in "the current flows clockwise around the circuit") or by choosing a current to be positive if it flows in one direction along a conductor and negative if it flows in the other direction.

The SI unit of current is the **ampere;** one ampere is defined to be *one coulomb per second* $(1\text{ A} = 1\text{ C/s})$. This unit is named in honor of the French scientist André Marie Ampère (1775–1836). When an ordinary flashlight (D-cell size) is turned on, the current in the flashlight is about 0.5 to 1 A; the current in the wires of a car engine's starter motor is around 200 A. Currents in radio and television circuits are usually expressed in *milliamperes* $(1\text{ mA} = 10^{-3}\text{ A})$ or *microamperes* $(1\ \mu\text{A} = 10^{-6}\text{ A})$, and currents in computer circuits are expressed in *nanoamperes* $(1\text{ nA} = 10^{-9}\text{ A})$ or *picoamperes* $(1\text{ pA} = 10^{-12}\text{ A})$.

Current, Drift Velocity, and Current Density

We can express current in terms of the drift velocity of the moving charges. Let's consider again the situation of Fig. 25.3, a conductor with cross-sectional area A and an electric field $\vec{E}$ directed from left to right. To begin with, we'll assume that the free charges in the conductor are positive; then the drift velocity is in the same direction as the field.

Suppose there are n moving charged particles per unit volume. We call n the **concentration** of particles; its SI unit is m^{-3}. Assume that all the particles move with the same drift velocity with magnitude v_d. In a time interval dt, each particle moves a distance $v_d\,dt$. The particles that flow out of the right end of the shaded cylinder with length $v_d\,dt$ during dt are the particles that were within this cylinder at the beginning of the interval dt. The volume of the cylinder is $Av_d\,dt$, and the number of particles within it is $nAv_d\,dt$. If each particle has a charge q, the charge dQ that flows out of the end of the cylinder during time dt is

$$dQ = q(nAv_d\,dt) = nqv_dA\,dt$$

and the current is

$$I = \frac{dQ}{dt} = nqv_dA$$

The current *per unit cross-sectional area* is called the **current density** J:

$$J = \frac{I}{A} = nqv_d$$

The units of current density are amperes per square meter (A/m^2).

If the moving charges are negative rather than positive, as in Fig. 25.2b, the drift velocity is opposite to $\vec{E}$. But the *current* is still in the same direction as $\vec{E}$ at each point in the conductor. Hence the current I and current density J don't depend on the sign of the charge, and so in the above expressions for I and J we replace the charge q by its absolute value $|q|$:

$$I = \frac{dQ}{dt} = n|q|v_dA \quad \text{(general expression for current)} \quad (25.2)$$

$$J = \frac{I}{A} = n|q|v_d \quad \text{(general expression for current density)} \quad (25.3)$$

The current in a conductor is the product of the concentration of moving charged particles, the magnitude of charge of each such particle, the magnitude of the drift velocity, and the cross-sectional area of the conductor.

We can also define a *vector* current density $\vec{J}$ that includes the direction of the drift velocity:

$$\vec{J} = nq\vec{v}_d \quad \text{(vector current density)} \quad (25.4)$$

There are *no* absolute value signs in Eq. (25.4). If q is positive, $\vec{v}_d$ is in the same direction as $\vec{E}$; if q is negative, $\vec{v}_d$ is opposite to $\vec{E}$. In either case, $\vec{J}$ is in the same direction as $\vec{E}$. Equation (25.3) gives the *magnitude* J of the vector current density $\vec{J}$.

CAUTION **Current density vs. current** Note that current density $\vec{J}$ is a vector, but current I is not. The difference is that the current density $\vec{J}$ describes how charges flow at a certain point, and the vector's direction tells you about the direction of the flow at that point. By contrast, the current I describes how charges flow through an extended object such as a wire. For example, I has the same value at all points in the circuit of Fig. 25.3, but $\vec{J}$ does not: the current density is directed downward in the left-hand side of the loop and upward in the right-hand side. The magnitude of $\vec{J}$ can also vary around a circuit. In Fig. 25.3 the current density magnitude $J = I/A$ is less in the battery (which has a large cross-sectional area A) than in the wires (which have a small cross-sectional area).

In general, a conductor may contain several different kinds of moving charged particles having charges $q_1, q_2, \ldots$, concentrations $n_1, n_2, \ldots$, and drift velocities with magnitudes $v_{d1}, v_{d2}, \ldots$. An example is current flow in an ionic solution (Fig. 25.4). In a sodium chloride solution, current can be carried by both positive sodium ions and negative chlorine ions; the total current I is found by adding up the currents due to each kind of charged particle, using Eq. (25.2). Likewise, the total vector current density $\vec{J}$ is found by using Eq. (25.4) for each kind of charged particle and adding the results.

We will see in Section 25.4 that it is possible to have a current that is *steady* (that is, one that is constant in time) only if the conducting material forms a

25.4 Part of the electric circuit that includes this light bulb passes through a beaker with a solution of sodium chloride. The current in the solution is carried by both positive charges (Na^+ ions) and negative charges (Cl^- ions).

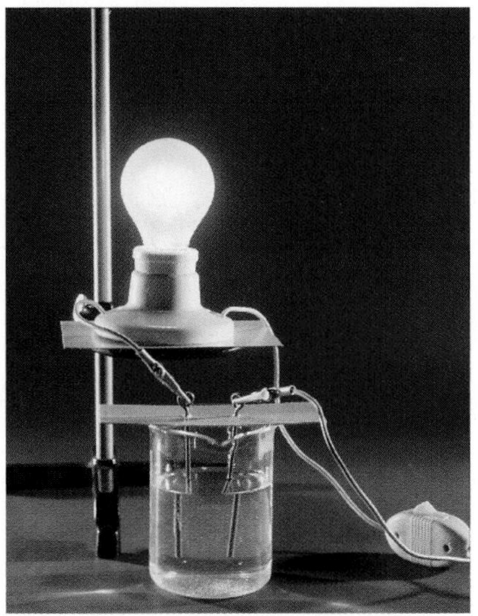

closed loop, called a *complete circuit.* In such a steady situation, the total charge in every segment of the conductor is constant. Hence the rate of flow of charge *out* at one end of a segment at any instant equals the rate of flow of charge *in* at the other end of the segment, and *the current is the same at all cross sections of the circuit.* We'll make use of this observation when we analyze electric circuits later in this chapter.

In many simple circuits, such as flashlights or cordless electric drills, the direction of the current is always the same; this is called *direct current.* But home appliances such as toasters, refrigerators, and televisions use *alternating current,* in which the current continuously changes direction. In this chapter we'll consider direct current only. Alternating current has many special features worthy of detailed study, which we'll examine in Chapter 31.

Example 25.1 Current density and drift velocity in a wire

An 18-gauge copper wire (the size usually used for lamp cords) has a nominal diameter of 1.02 mm. This wire carries a constant current of 1.67 A to a 200-watt lamp. The density of free electrons is 8.5×10^{28} electrons per cubic meter. Find the magnitudes of (a) the current density and (b) the drift velocity.

SOLUTION

IDENTIFY: This problem uses the relationships among current, current density, and drift velocity.

SET UP: We are given the current and the dimensions of the wire, so we use Eq. (25.3) to find the magnitude J of the current density. We then use Eq. (25.3) again to find the drift speed v_d from J and the concentration of electrons.

EXECUTE: (a) The cross-sectional area is

$$A = \frac{\pi d^2}{4} = \frac{\pi(1.02 \times 10^{-3}\ \text{m})^2}{4} = 8.17 \times 10^{-7}\ \text{m}^2$$

The magnitude of the current density is

$$J = \frac{I}{A} = \frac{1.67\ \text{A}}{8.17 \times 10^{-7}\ \text{m}^2} = 2.04 \times 10^6\ \text{A/m}^2$$

(b) Solving Eq. (25.3) for the drift velocity magnitude v_d, we find

$$v_d = \frac{J}{n|q|} = \frac{2.04 \times 10^6\ \text{A/m}^2}{(8.5 \times 10^{28}\ \text{m}^{-3})|-1.60 \times 10^{-19}\ \text{C}|}$$
$$= 1.5 \times 10^{-4}\ \text{m/s} = 0.15\ \text{mm/s}$$

EVALUATE: At this speed an electron would require 6700 s, or about 1 hr 50 min, to travel the length of a wire 1 m long. The speeds of random motion of the electrons are of the order of 10^6 m/s. So in this example the drift speed is around 10^{10} times slower than the speed of random motion. Picture the electrons as bouncing around frantically, with a very slow and sluggish drift!

Test Your Understanding of Section 25.1 Suppose we replaced the wire in Example 25.1 with 12-gauge copper wire, which has twice the diameter of 18-gauge wire. If the current remains the same, what effect would this have on the magnitude of the drift velocity v_d? (i) none—v_d would be unchanged; (ii) v_d would be twice as great; (iii) v_d would be four times greater; (iv) v_d would be half as great; (v) v_d would be one-fourth as great.

25.2 Resistivity

The current density $\vec{J}$ in a conductor depends on the electric field $\vec{E}$ and on the properties of the material. In general, this dependence can be quite complex. But for some materials, especially metals, at a given temperature, $\vec{J}$ is nearly *directly proportional* to $\vec{E}$, and the ratio of the magnitudes of E and J is constant. This relationship, called Ohm's law, was discovered in 1826 by the German physicist Georg Simon Ohm (1787–1854). The word "law" should actually be in quotation marks, since **Ohm's law,** like the ideal-gas equation and Hooke's law, is an *idealized model* that describes the behavior of some materials quite well but is not a general description of *all* matter. In the following discussion we'll assume that Ohm's law is valid, even though there are many situations in which it is not. The situation is comparable to our representation of the behavior of the static and kinetic friction forces; we treated these friction forces as being directly proportional to the normal force, even though we knew that this was at best an approximate description.

Table 25.1 Resistivities at Room Temperature (20 °C)

	Substance	$\rho(\Omega\cdot\text{m})$	Substance	$\rho(\Omega\cdot\text{m})$
Conductors			**Semiconductors**	
Metals	Silver	1.47×10^{-8}	Pure carbon (graphite)	3.5×10^{-5}
	Copper	1.72×10^{-8}	Pure germanium	0.60
	Gold	2.44×10^{-8}	Pure silicon	2300
	Aluminum	2.75×10^{-8}	**Insulators**	
	Tungsten	5.25×10^{-8}	Amber	5×10^{14}
	Steel	20×10^{-8}	Glass	10^{10}–10^{14}
	Lead	22×10^{-8}	Lucite	$>10^{13}$
	Mercury	95×10^{-8}	Mica	10^{11}–10^{15}
Alloys	Manganin (Cu 84%, Mn 12%, Ni 4%)	44×10^{-8}	Quartz (fused)	75×10^{16}
	Constantan (Cu 60%, Ni 40%)	49×10^{-8}	Sulfur	10^{15}
	Nichrome	100×10^{-8}	Teflon	$>10^{13}$
			Wood	10^{8}–10^{11}

We define the **resistivity** ρ of a material as the ratio of the magnitudes of electric field and current density:

$$\rho = \frac{E}{J} \quad \text{(definition of resistivity)} \tag{25.5}$$

The greater the resistivity, the greater the field needed to cause a given current density, or the smaller the current density caused by a given field. From Eq. (25.5) the units of ρ are $(\text{V/m})/(\text{A/m}^2) = \text{V}\cdot\text{m/A}$. As we will discuss in the next section, 1 V/A is called one *ohm* (1 Ω; we use the Greek letter Ω, or omega, which is alliterative with "ohm"). So the SI units for ρ are $\Omega\cdot\text{m}$ (ohm-meters). Table 25.1 lists some representative values of resistivity. A perfect conductor would have zero resistivity, and a perfect insulator would have an infinite resistivity. Metals and alloys have the smallest resistivities and are the best conductors. The resistivities of insulators are greater than those of the metals by an enormous factor, on the order of 10^{22}.

The reciprocal of resistivity is **conductivity.** Its units are $(\Omega\cdot\text{m})^{-1}$. Good conductors of electricity have larger conductivity than insulators. Conductivity is the direct electrical analog of thermal conductivity. Comparing Table 25.1 with Table 17.5 (Thermal Conductivities), we note that good electrical conductors, such as metals, are usually also good conductors of heat. Poor electrical conductors, such as ceramic and plastic materials, are also poor thermal conductors. In a metal the free electrons that carry charge in electrical conduction also provide the principal mechanism for heat conduction, so we should expect a correlation between electrical and thermal conductivity. Because of the enormous difference in conductivity between electrical conductors and insulators, it is easy to confine electric currents to well-defined paths or circuits (Fig. 25.5). The variation in *thermal* conductivity is much less, only a factor of 10^3 or so, and it is usually impossible to confine heat currents to that extent.

Semiconductors have resistivities intermediate between those of metals and those of insulators. These materials are important because of the way their resistivities are affected by temperature and by small amounts of impurities.

A material that obeys Ohm's law reasonably well is called an *ohmic* conductor or a *linear* conductor. For such materials, at a given temperature, ρ is a *constant* that does not depend on the value of E. Many materials show substantial departures from Ohm's-law behavior; they are *nonohmic,* or *nonlinear.* In these materials, J depends on E in a more complicated manner.

Analogies with fluid flow can be a big help in developing intuition about electric current and circuits. For example, in the making of wine or maple syrup, the product is sometimes filtered to remove sediments. A pump forces the fluid through the filter under pressure; if the flow rate (analogous to J) is proportional to the pressure difference between the upstream and downstream sides (analogous to E), the behavior is analogous to Ohm's law.

25.5 The copper "wires," or traces, on this circuit board are printed directly onto the surface of the dark-colored insulating board. Even though the traces are very close to each other (only about a millimeter apart), the board has such a high resistivity (and low conductivity) compared to the copper that no current can flow between the traces.

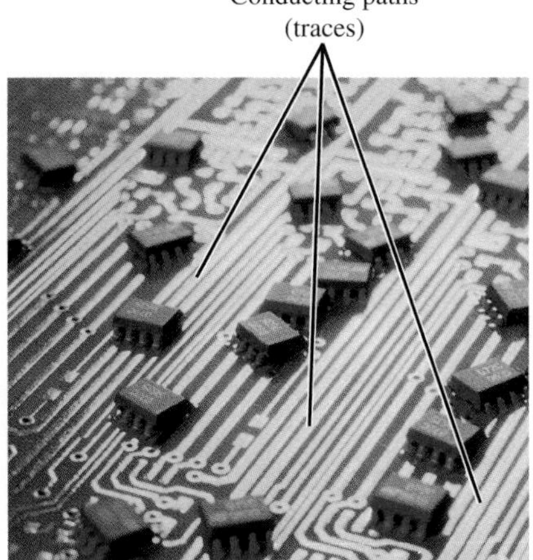

25.6 Variation of resistivity ρ with absolute temperature T for (a) a normal metal, (b) a semiconductor, and (c) a superconductor. In (a) the linear approximation to ρ as a function of T is shown as a green line; the approximation agrees exactly at $T = T_0$, where $\rho = \rho_0$.

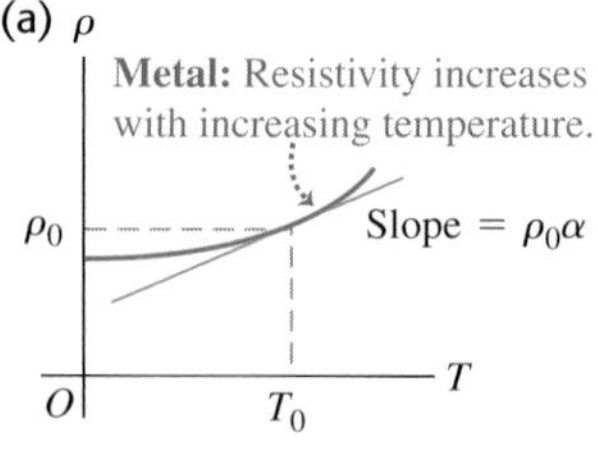
(a) ρ
Metal: Resistivity increases with increasing temperature.
ρ0
Slope = ρ0α
O
T0
T

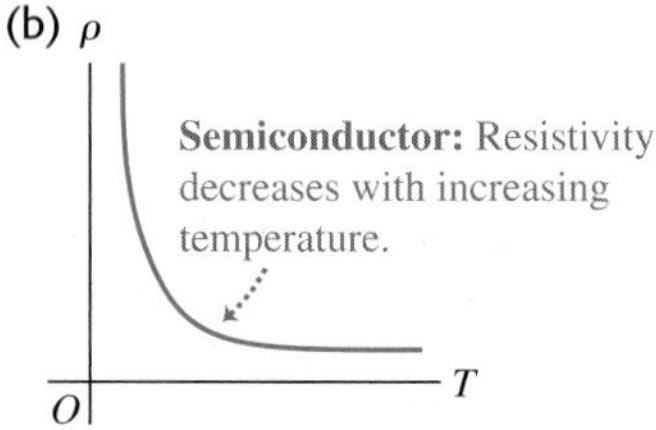
(b) ρ
Semiconductor: Resistivity decreases with increasing temperature.
O
T

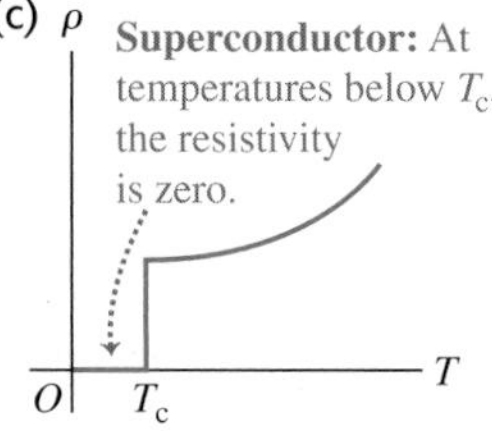
(c) ρ
Superconductor: At temperatures below Tc, the resistivity is zero.
O
Tc
T

Resistivity and Temperature

The resistivity of a *metallic* conductor nearly always increases with increasing temperature, as shown in Fig. 25.6a. As temperature increases, the ions of the conductor vibrate with greater amplitude, making it more likely that a moving electron will collide with an ion as in Fig. 25.1; this impedes the drift of electrons through the conductor and hence reduces the current. Over a small temperature range (up to 100 C° or so), the resistivity of a metal can be represented approximately by the equation

$$\rho(T) = \rho_0[1 + \alpha(T - T_0)] \quad \text{(temperature dependence of resistivity)} \tag{25.6}$$

where ρ_0 is the resistivity at a reference temperature T_0 (often taken as 0°C or 20°C) and $\rho(T)$ is the resistivity at temperature T, which may be higher or lower than T_0. The factor α is called the **temperature coefficient of resistivity.** Some representative values are given in Table 25.2. The resistivity of the alloy manganin is practically independent of temperature.

Table 25.2 Temperature Coefficients of Resistivity (Approximate Values Near Room Temperature)

Material	$\alpha\,[(°C)^{-1}]$	Material	$\alpha\,[(°C)^{-1}]$
Aluminum	0.0039	Lead	0.0043
Brass	0.0020	Manganin	0.00000
Carbon (graphite)	−0.0005	Mercury	0.00088
Constantan	0.00001	Nichrome	0.0004
Copper	0.00393	Silver	0.0038
Iron	0.0050	Tungsten	0.0045

The resistivity of graphite (a nonmetal) *decreases* with increasing temperature, since at higher temperatures, more electrons are "shaken loose" from the atoms and become mobile; hence the temperature coefficient of resistivity of graphite is negative. This same behavior occurs for semiconductors (Fig. 25.6b). Measuring the resistivity of a small semiconductor crystal is therefore a sensitive measure of temperature; this is the principle of a type of thermometer called a *thermistor.*

Some materials, including several metallic alloys and oxides, show a phenomenon called *superconductivity.* As the temperature decreases, the resistivity at first decreases smoothly, like that of any metal. But then at a certain critical temperature T_c a phase transition occurs and the resistivity suddenly drops to zero, as shown in Fig. 25.6c. Once a current has been established in a superconducting ring, it continues indefinitely without the presence of any driving field.

Superconductivity was discovered in 1911 by the Dutch physicist Heike Kamerlingh Onnes (1853–1926). He discovered that at very low temperatures, below 4.2 K, the resistivity of mercury suddenly dropped to zero. For the next 75 years, the highest T_c attained was about 20 K. This meant that superconductivity occurred only when the material was cooled using expensive liquid helium, with a boiling-point temperature of 4.2 K, or explosive liquid hydrogen, with a boiling point of 20.3 K. But in 1986 Karl Müller and Johannes Bednorz discovered an oxide of barium, lanthanum, and copper with a T_c of nearly 40 K, and the race was on to develop "high-temperature" superconducting materials.

By 1987 a complex oxide of yttrium, copper, and barium had been found that has a value of T_c well above the 77 K boiling temperature of liquid nitrogen, a refrigerant that is both inexpensive and safe. The current (2006) record for T_c at atmospheric pressure is 138 K, and materials that are superconductors at room temperature may become a reality. The implications of these discoveries for power-distribution systems, computer design, and transportation are enormous. Meanwhile, superconducting electromagnets cooled by liquid helium are used in particle accelerators and some experimental magnetic-levitation railroads. Superconductors have other exotic properties that require an understanding of magnetism to explore; we will discuss these further in Chapter 29.

Test Your Understanding of Section 25.2 You maintain a constant electric field inside a piece of semiconductor while lowering the semiconductor's temperature. What happens to the current density in the semiconductor? (i) It increases; (ii) it decreases; (iii) it remains the same.

25.3 Resistance

For a conductor with resistivity ρ, the current density $\vec{J}$ at a point where the electric field is $\vec{E}$ is given by Eq. (25.5), which we can write as

$$\vec{E} = \rho\vec{J} \tag{25.7}$$

When Ohm's law is obeyed, ρ is constant and independent of the magnitude of the electric field, so $\vec{E}$ is directly proportional to $\vec{J}$. Often, however, we are more interested in the total current in a conductor than in $\vec{J}$ and more interested in the potential difference between the ends of the conductor than in $\vec{E}$. This is so largely because current and potential difference are much easier to measure than are $\vec{J}$ and $\vec{E}$.

Suppose our conductor is a wire with uniform cross-sectional area A and length L, as shown in Fig. 25.7. Let V be the potential difference between the higher-potential and lower-potential ends of the conductor, so that V is positive. The *direction* of the current is always from the higher-potential end to the lower-potential end. That's because current in a conductor flows in the direction of $\vec{E}$, no matter what the sign of the moving charges (Fig. 25.2), and because $\vec{E}$ points in the direction of *decreasing* electric potential (see Section 23.2). As the current flows through the potential difference, electric potential energy is lost; this energy is transferred to the ions of the conducting material during collisions.

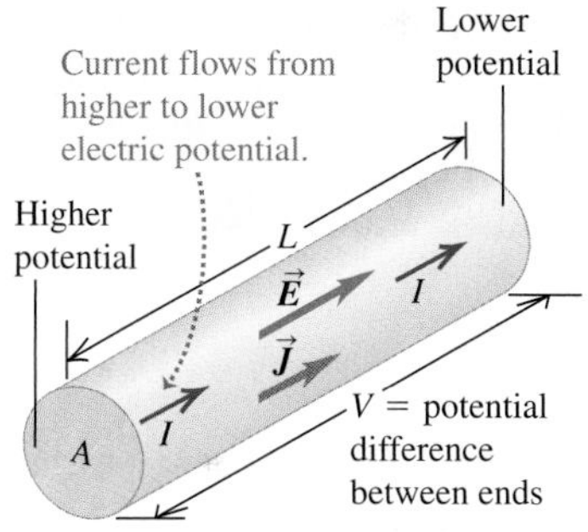

25.7 A conductor with uniform cross section. The current density is uniform over any cross section, and the electric field is constant along the length.

We can also relate the *value* of the current I to the potential difference between the ends of the conductor. If the magnitudes of the current density $\vec{J}$ and the electric field $\vec{E}$ are uniform throughout the conductor, the total current I is given by $I = JA$, and the potential difference V between the ends is $V = EL$. When we solve these equations for J and E, respectively, and substitute the results in Eq. (25.7), we obtain

$$\frac{V}{L} = \frac{\rho I}{A} \quad \text{or} \quad V = \frac{\rho L}{A}I \tag{25.8}$$

This shows that when ρ is constant, the total current I is proportional to the potential difference V.

The ratio of V to I for a particular conductor is called its **resistance** R:

$$R = \frac{V}{I} \tag{25.9}$$

Comparing this definition of R to Eq. (25.8), we see that the resistance R of a particular conductor is related to the resistivity ρ of its material by

$$R = \frac{\rho L}{A} \quad \text{(relationship between resistance and resistivity)} \tag{25.10}$$

If ρ is constant, as is the case for ohmic materials, then so is R.

The equation

$$V = IR \quad \text{(relationship among voltage, current, and resistance)} \tag{25.11}$$

is often called Ohm's law, but it is important to understand that the real content of Ohm's law is the direct proportionality (for some materials) of V to I or of J to E. Equation (25.9) or (25.11) *defines* resistance R for *any* conductor, whether or not it obeys Ohm's law, but only when R is constant can we correctly call this relationship Ohm's law.

Interpreting Resistance

Equation (25.10) shows that the resistance of a wire or other conductor of uniform cross section is directly proportional to its length and inversely proportional to its cross-sectional area. It is also proportional to the resistivity of the material of which the conductor is made.

The flowing-fluid analogy is again useful. In analogy to Eq. (25.10), a narrow water hose offers more resistance to flow than a fat one, and a long hose has more resistance than a short one (Fig. 25.8). We can increase the resistance to flow by stuffing the hose with cotton or sand; this corresponds to increasing the resistivity. The flow rate is approximately proportional to the pressure difference between the ends. Flow rate is analogous to current, and pressure difference is analogous to potential difference ("voltage"). Let's not stretch this analogy too far, though; the water flow rate in a pipe is usually *not* proportional to its cross-sectional area (see Section 14.6).

25.8 A long fire hose offers substantial resistance to water flow. To make water pass through the hose rapidly, the upstream end of the hose must be at much higher pressure than the end where the water emerges. In an analogous way, there must be a large potential difference between the ends of a long wire in order to cause a substantial electric current through the wire.

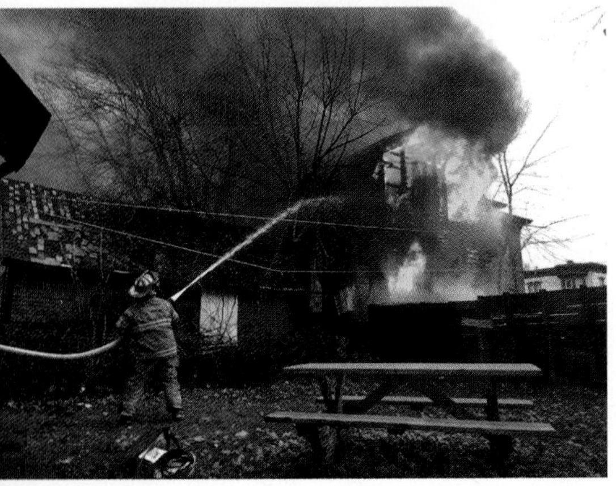

The SI unit of resistance is the **ohm,** equal to one volt per ampere $(1\ \Omega = 1\ \text{V/A})$. The *kilohm* $(1\ \text{k}\Omega = 10^3\ \Omega)$ and the *megohm* $(1\ \text{M}\Omega = 10^6\ \Omega)$ are also in common use. A 100-m length of 12-gauge copper wire, the size usually used in household wiring, has a resistance at room temperature of about 0.5 Ω. A 100-W, 120-V light bulb has a resistance (at operating temperature) of 140 Ω. If the same current I flows in both the copper wire and the light bulb, the potential difference $V = IR$ is much greater across the light bulb, and much more potential energy is lost per charge in the light bulb. This lost energy is converted by the light bulb filament into light and heat. You don't want your household wiring to glow white-hot, so its resistance is kept low by using wire of low resistivity and large cross-sectional area.

Because the resistivity of a material varies with temperature, the resistance of a specific conductor also varies with temperature. For temperature ranges that are not too great, this variation is approximately a linear relationship, analogous to Eq. (25.6):

$$R(T) = R_0[1 + \alpha(T - T_0)] \tag{25.12}$$

In this equation, $R(T)$ is the resistance at temperature T and R_0 is the resistance at temperature T_0, often taken to be 0°C or 20°C. The *temperature coefficient of resistance* α is the same constant that appears in Eq. (25.6) if the dimensions L and A in Eq. (25.10) do not change appreciably with temperature; this is indeed the case for most conducting materials (see Problem 25.67). Within the limits of validity of Eq. (25.12), the *change* in resistance resulting from a temperature change $T - T_0$ is given by $R_0\alpha(T - T_0)$.

Table 25.3 Color Codes for Resistors

Color	Value as Digit	Value as Multiplier
Black	0	1
Brown	1	10
Red	2	10^2
Orange	3	10^3
Yellow	4	10^4
Green	5	10^5
Blue	6	10^6
Violet	7	10^7
Gray	8	10^8
White	9	10^9

A circuit device made to have a specific value of resistance between its ends is called a **resistor.** Resistors in the range 0.01 to $10^7\ \Omega$ can be bought off the shelf. Individual resistors used in electronic circuitry are often cylindrical, a few millimeters in diameter and length, with wires coming out of the ends. The resistance may be marked with a standard code using three or four color bands near one end (Fig. 25.9), according to the scheme shown in Table 25.3. The first two bands (starting with the band nearest an end) are digits, and the third is a power-of-10 multiplier, as shown in Fig. 25.9. For example, green–violet–red means $57 \times 10^2\ \Omega$, or 5.7 kΩ. The fourth band, if present, indicates the precision (tolerance) of the value; no band means ±20%, a silver band ±10%, and a gold band ±5%. Another important characteristic of a resistor is the maximum *power* it can dissipate without damage. We'll return to this point in Section 25.5.

25.9 This resistor has a resistance of 5.7 kΩ with a precision (tolerance) of ±10%.

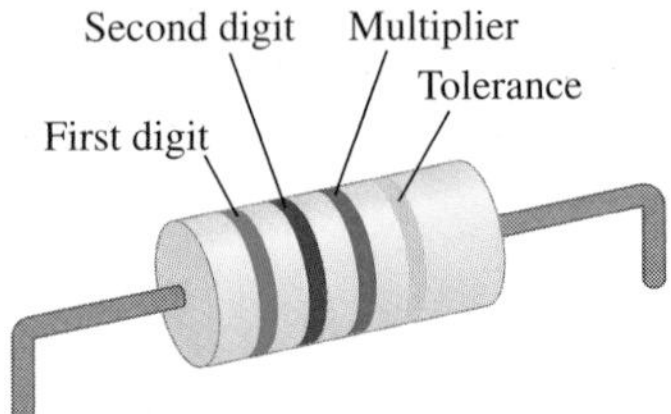

For a resistor that obeys Ohm's law, a graph of current as a function of potential difference (voltage) is a straight line (Fig. 25.10a). The slope of the line is $1/R$. If the sign of the potential difference changes, so does the sign of the current produced; in Fig. 25.7 this corresponds to interchanging the higher- and lower-potential ends of the conductor, so the electric field, current density, and current

25.10 Current–voltage relationships for two devices. Only for a resistor that obeys Ohm's law as in (a) is current I proportional to voltage V.

(a)

Ohmic resistor (e.g., typical metal wire): At a given temperature, current is proportional to voltage.

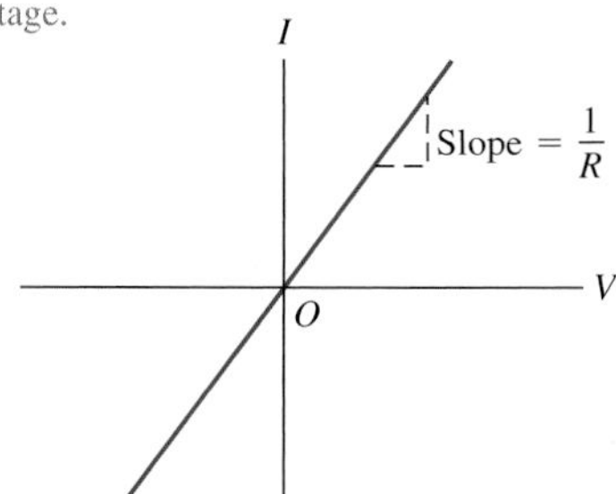

I
Slope = 1/R
V
O

(b)

Semiconductor diode: a nonohmic resistor

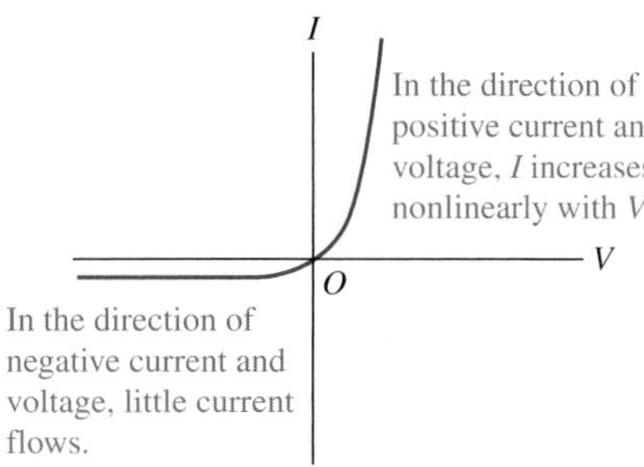

I
In the direction of positive current and voltage, I increases nonlinearly with V.
V
O
In the direction of negative current and voltage, little current flows.

all reverse direction. In devices that do not obey Ohm's law, the relationship of voltage to current may not be a direct proportion, and it may be different for the two directions of current. Figure 25.10b shows the behavior of a semiconductor *diode*, a device used to convert alternating current to direct current and to perform a wide variety of logic functions in computer circuitry. For positive potentials V of the anode (one of two terminals of the diode) with respect to the cathode (the other terminal), I increases exponentially with increasing V; for negative potentials the current is extremely small. Thus a positive potential difference V causes a current to flow in the positive direction, but a potential difference of the other sign causes little or no current. Hence a diode acts like a one-way valve in a circuit.

Example 25.2 Electric field, potential difference, and resistance in a wire

The 18-gauge copper wire in Example 25.1 (Section 25.1) has a diameter of 1.02 mm and a cross-sectional area of $8.20 \times 10^{-7}\ \text{m}^2$. It carries a current of 1.67 A. Find (a) the electric-field magnitude in the wire; (b) the potential difference between two points in the wire 50.0 m apart; (c) the resistance of a 50.0-m length of this wire.

SOLUTION

IDENTIFY: We are given the values of cross-sectional area A and current I. Our target variables are the electric-field magnitude E, potential difference V, and resistance R.

SET UP: The magnitude of the current density is $J = I/A$ and the resistivity ρ is given in Table 25.1. We find the electric-field magnitude by using Eq. (25.5), $E = \rho J$. Once we have found E, the potential difference is simply the product of E and the length of the wire. We find the resistance by using Eq. (25.11).

EXECUTE: (a) From Table 25.1, the resistivity of copper is $1.72 \times 10^{-8}\ \Omega \cdot \text{m}$. Hence, using Eq. (25.5),

$$E = \rho J = \frac{\rho I}{A} = \frac{(1.72 \times 10^{-8}\ \Omega \cdot \text{m})(1.67\ \text{A})}{8.20 \times 10^{-7}\ \text{m}^2}$$
$$= 0.0350\ \text{V/m}$$

(b) The potential difference is given by

$$V = EL = (0.0350\ \text{V/m})(50.0\ \text{m}) = 1.75\ \text{V}$$

(c) From Eq. (25.11) the resistance of a 50.0-m length of this wire is

$$R = \frac{V}{I} = \frac{1.75\ \text{V}}{1.67\ \text{A}} = 1.05\ \Omega$$

EVALUATE: To check our result in part (c), we calculate the resistance using Eq. (25.10):

$$R = \frac{\rho L}{A} = \frac{(1.72 \times 10^{-8}\ \Omega \cdot \text{m})(50.0\ \text{m})}{8.20 \times 10^{-7}\ \text{m}^2} = 1.05\ \Omega$$

We emphasize that the resistance of the wire is *defined* to be the ratio of voltage to current. If the wire is made of nonohmic material, then R is different for different values of V but is always given by $R = V/I$. Resistance is also always given by $R = \rho L/A$; if the material is nonohmic, ρ is not constant but depends on E (or, equivalently, on $V = EL$).

Example 25.3 Temperature dependence of resistance

Suppose the resistance of the wire in Example 25.2 is 1.05 Ω at a temperature of 20°C. Find the resistance at 0°C and at 100°C.

SOLUTION

IDENTIFY: This example concerns how resistance (the target variable) depends on temperature. As Table 25.2 shows, this temperature dependence differs for different substances.

SET UP: Our target variables are the values of the wire resistance R at two temperatures, $T = 0°\text{C}$ and $T = 100°\text{C}$. To find these values we use Eq. (25.12). Note that we are given the resistance $R_0 = 1.05\ \Omega$ at a reference temperature $T_0 = 20°\text{C}$, and we know from Example 25.2 that the wire is made of copper.

EXECUTE: From Table 25.2 the temperature coefficient of resistivity of copper is $\alpha = 0.00393\ (\text{C}°)^{-1}$. From Eq. (25.12), the resistance at $T = 0°\text{C}$ is

$$\begin{aligned} R &= R_0[1 + \alpha(T - T_0)] \\ &= (1.05\ \Omega)\{1 + [0.00393\ (\text{C}°)^{-1}][0°\text{C} - 20°\text{C}]\} \\ &= 0.97\ \Omega \end{aligned}$$

At $T = 100°\text{C}$,

$$\begin{aligned} R &= (1.05\ \Omega)\{1 + [0.00393\ (\text{C}°)^{-1}][100°\text{C} - 20°\text{C}]\} \\ &= 1.38\ \Omega \end{aligned}$$

EVALUATE: The resistance at 100°C is greater than that at 0°C by a factor of $(1.38\ \Omega)/(0.97\ \Omega) = 1.42$. In other words, raising the temperature of ordinary copper wire from 0°C to 100°C increases its resistance by 42%. From Eq. (25.11), $V = IR$, this means that 42% more voltage V is required to produce the same current I at 100°C than at 0°C. This is a substantial effect that must be taken into account in designing electric circuits that are to operate over a wide range of temperatures.

Example 25.4 Calculating resistance

The hollow cylinder shown in Fig. 25.11 has length L and inner and outer radii a and b. It is made of a material with resistivity ρ. A potential difference is set up between the inner and outer surfaces of the cylinder (each of which is an equipotential surface) so that current flows radially through the cylinder. What is the resistance to this radial current flow?

SOLUTION

IDENTIFY: Figure 25.11 shows that the current flows radially from the inside of the conductor toward the outside, *not* along the length of the conductor as in Fig. 25.7. Hence we must use the ideas of this section to derive a new formula for resistance (our target variable) appropriate for radial current flow.

SET UP: We can't use Eq. (25.10) directly because the cross section through which the charge travels is *not* constant; it varies from $2\pi aL$ at the inner surface to $2\pi bL$ at the outer surface. Instead, we calculate the resistance to radial current flow through a thin cylindrical shell of inner radius r and thickness dr. We then combine the resistances for all such shells between the inner and outer radii of the cylinder.

EXECUTE: The area A for the shell is $2\pi rL$, the surface area that the current encounters as it flows outward. The length of the current path through the shell is dr. The resistance dR of this shell, between inner and outer surfaces, is that of a conductor with length dr and area $2\pi rL$:

$$dR = \frac{\rho\, dr}{2\pi rL}$$

The current has to pass successively through all such shells between the inner and outer radii a and b. From Eq. (25.11) the potential difference across one shell is $dV = I\, dR$, and the total potential difference between the inner and outer surfaces is the sum of the potential differences for all shells. The total current is the same through each shell, so the total resistance is the sum of the resistances of all the shells. If the area $2\pi rL$ were constant, we could just integrate dr from $r = a$ to $r = b$ to get the total length of the current path. But the area increases as the current passes through shells of greater radius, so we have to integrate the above expression for dR. The total resistance is thus given by

$$R = \int dR = \frac{\rho}{2\pi L}\int_a^b \frac{dr}{r} = \frac{\rho}{2\pi L}\ln\frac{b}{a}$$

EVALUATE: The conductor geometry shown in Fig. 25.11 plays an important role in your body's nervous system. Each neuron, or nerve cell, has a long extension called a nerve fiber or *axon*. An axon has a cylindrical membrane shaped much like the resistor in Fig. 25.11, with one conducting fluid inside the membrane and another outside it. Ordinarily all of the inner fluid is at the same potential, so no current tends to flow along the length of the axon. If the axon is stimulated at a certain point along its length, however, charged ions flow radially across the cylindrical membrane at that point, as in Fig. 25.11. This flow causes a potential difference between that point and other points along the length of the axon, which makes a nerve signal flow along that length.

25.11 Finding the resistance for radial current flow.

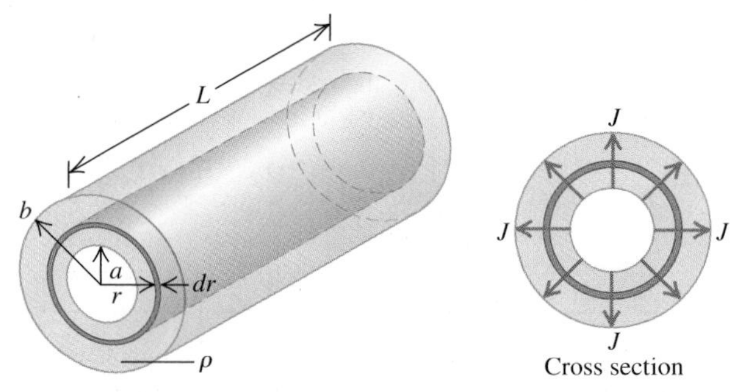

Test Your Understanding of Section 25.3 Suppose you increase the voltage across the copper wire in Examples 25.2 and 25.3. The increased voltage causes more current to flow, which makes the temperature of the wire increase. (The same thing happens to the coils of an electric oven or a toaster when a voltage is applied to them. We'll explore this issue in more depth in Section 25.5.) If you double the voltage across the wire, the current in the wire increases. By what factor does it increase? (i) 2; (ii) greater than 2; (iii) less than 2.

25.4 Electromotive Force and Circuits

For a conductor to have a steady current, it must be part of a path that forms a closed loop or **complete circuit.** Here's why. If you establish an electric field $\vec{E}_1$ inside an isolated conductor with resistivity ρ that is *not* part of a complete circuit, a current begins to flow with current density $\vec{J} = \vec{E}_1/\rho$ (Fig. 25.12a). As a result a net positive charge quickly accumulates at one end of the conductor and a net negative charge accumulates at the other end (Fig. 25.12b). These charges themselves produce an electric field $\vec{E}_2$ in the direction opposite to $\vec{E}_1$, causing the total electric field and hence the current to decrease. Within a very small fraction of a second, enough charge builds up on the conductor ends that the total electric field $\vec{E} = \vec{E}_1 + \vec{E}_2 = \mathbf{0}$ inside the conductor. Then $\vec{J} = \mathbf{0}$ as well, and the current stops altogether (Fig. 25.12c). So there can be no steady motion of charge in such an *incomplete* circuit.

To see how to maintain a steady current in a *complete* circuit, we recall a basic fact about electric potential energy: If a charge q goes around a complete circuit and returns to its starting point, the potential energy must be the same at the end of the round trip as at the beginning. As described in Section 25.3, there is always a *decrease* in potential energy when charges move through an ordinary conducting material with resistance. So there must be some part of the circuit in which the potential energy *increases.*

The problem is analogous to an ornamental water fountain that recycles its water. The water pours out of openings at the top, cascades down over the terraces and spouts (moving in the direction of decreasing gravitational potential energy), and collects in a basin in the bottom. A pump then lifts it back to the top (increasing the potential energy) for another trip. Without the pump, the water would just fall to the bottom and stay there.

25.12 If an electric field is produced inside a conductor that is *not* part of a complete circuit, current flows for only a very short time.

(a) An electric field $\vec{E}_1$ produced inside an isolated conductor causes a current.

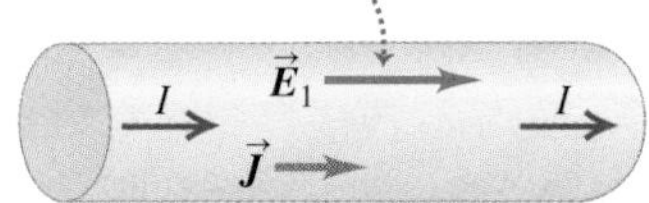

(b) The current causes charge to build up at the ends.

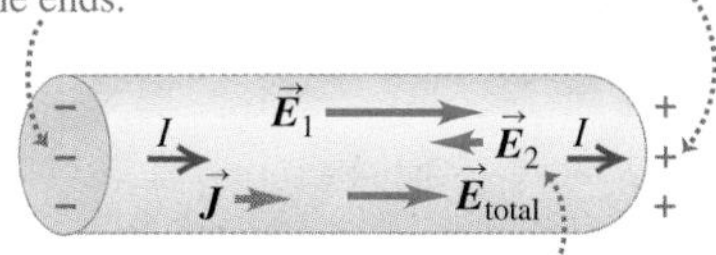

The charge buildup produces an opposing field $\vec{E}_2$, thus reducing the current.

(c) After a very short time $\vec{E}_2$ has the same magnitude as $\vec{E}_1$; then the total field is $\vec{E}_{total} = \mathbf{0}$ and the current stops completely.

$I = 0$ $\vec{E}_1$ $\vec{E}_2$ $\vec{J} = \mathbf{0}$ $\vec{E}_{total} = \mathbf{0}$

Electromotive Force

In an electric circuit there must be a device somewhere in the loop that acts like the water pump in a water fountain (Fig. 25.13). In this device a charge travels "uphill," from lower to higher potential energy, even though the electrostatic force is trying to push it from higher to lower potential energy. The direction of current in such a device is from lower to higher potential, just the opposite of what happens in an ordinary conductor. The influence that makes current flow from lower to higher potential is called **electromotive force** (abbreviated **emf** and pronounced "ee-em-eff"). This is a poor term because emf is *not* a force but an energy-per-unit-charge quantity, like potential. The SI unit of emf is the same as that for potential, the volt $(1\ \text{V} = 1\ \text{J/C})$. A typical flashlight battery has an emf of 1.5 V; this means that the battery does 1.5 J of work on every coulomb of charge that passes through it. We'll use the symbol $\mathcal{E}$ (a script capital E) for emf.

Every complete circuit with a steady current must include some device that provides emf. Such a device is called a **source of emf.** Batteries, electric generators, solar cells, thermocouples, and fuel cells are all examples of sources of emf. All such devices convert energy of some form (mechanical, chemical, thermal, and so on) into electric potential energy and transfer it into the circuit to which the device is connected. An *ideal* source of emf maintains a constant potential

25.13 Just as a water fountain requires a pump, an electric circuit requires a source of electromotive force to sustain a steady current.

12.1 DC Series Circuits (Qualitative)

25.14 Schematic diagram of a source of emf in an "open-circuit" situation. The electric-field force $\vec{F}_e = q\vec{E}$ and the non-electrostatic force $\vec{F}_n$ are shown for a positive charge q.

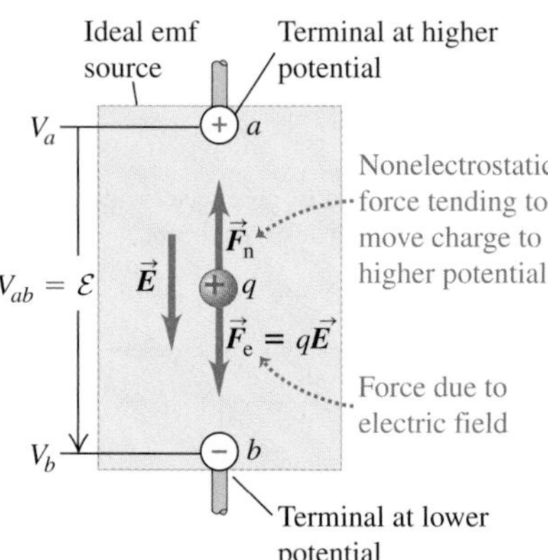

When the emf source is not part of a closed circuit, $F_n = F_e$ and there is no net motion of charge between the terminals.

difference between its terminals, independent of the current through it. We define electromotive force quantitatively as the magnitude of this potential difference. As we will see, such an ideal source is a mythical beast, like the frictionless plane and the massless rope. We will discuss later how real-life sources of emf differ in their behavior from this idealized model.

Fig. 25.14 is a schematic diagram of an ideal source of emf that maintains a potential difference between conductors a and b, called the *terminals* of the device. Terminal a, marked +, is maintained at *higher* potential than terminal b, marked −. Associated with this potential difference is an electric field $\vec{E}$ in the region around the terminals, both inside and outside the source. The electric field inside the device is directed from a to b, as shown. A charge q within the source experiences an electric force $\vec{F}_e = q\vec{E}$. But the source also provides an additional influence, which we represent as a nonelectrostatic force $\vec{F}_n$. This force, operating inside the device, pushes charge from b to a in an "uphill" direction against the electric force $\vec{F}_e$. Thus $\vec{F}_n$ maintains the potential difference between the terminals. If $\vec{F}_n$ were not present, charge would flow between the terminals until the potential difference was zero. The origin of the additional influence $\vec{F}_n$ depends on the kind of source. In a generator it results from magnetic-field forces on moving charges. In a battery or fuel cell it is associated with diffusion processes and varying electrolyte concentrations resulting from chemical reactions. In an electrostatic machine such as a Van de Graaff generator (see Fig. 22.27), an actual mechanical force is applied by a moving belt or wheel.

If a positive charge q is moved from b to a inside the source, the nonelectrostatic force $\vec{F}_n$ does a positive amount of work $W_n = q\mathcal{E}$ on the charge. This displacement is *opposite* to the electrostatic force $\vec{F}_e$, so the potential energy associated with the charge *increases* by an amount equal to qV_{ab}, where $V_{ab} = V_a - V_b$ is the (positive) potential of point a with respect to point b. For the ideal source of emf that we've described, $\vec{F}_e$ and $\vec{F}_n$ are equal in magnitude but opposite in direction, so the total work done on the charge q is zero; there is an increase in potential energy but *no* change in the kinetic energy of the charge. It's like lifting a book from the floor to a high shelf at constant speed. The increase in potential energy is just equal to the non-electrostatic work W_n, so $q\mathcal{E} = qV_{ab}$, or

$$V_{ab} = \mathcal{E} \qquad \text{(ideal source of emf)} \tag{25.13}$$

25.15 Schematic diagram of an ideal source of emf in a complete circuit. The electric-field force $\vec{F}_e = q\vec{E}$ and the non-electrostatic force $\vec{F}_n$ are shown for a positive charge q The current is in the direction from a to b in the external circuit and from b to a within the source.

Potential across terminals creates electric field in circuit, causing charges to move.

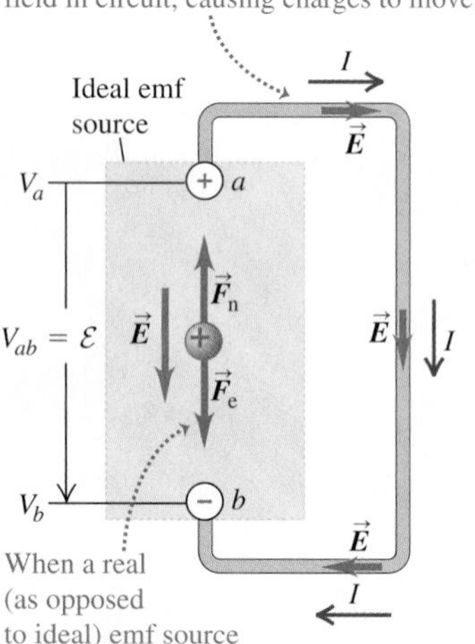

When a real (as opposed to ideal) emf source is connected to a circuit, V_{ab} and thus F_e fall, so that $F_n > F_e$ and $\vec{F}_n$ does work on the charges.

Now let's make a complete circuit by connecting a wire with resistance R to the terminals of a source (Fig. 25.15). The potential difference between terminals a and b sets up an electric field within the wire; this causes current to flow around the loop from a toward b, from higher to lower potential. Where the wire bends, equal amounts of positive and negative charge persist on the "inside" and "outside" of the bend. These charges exert the forces that cause the current to follow the bends in the wire.

From Eq. (25.11) the potential difference between the ends of the wire in Fig. 25.15 is given by $V_{ab} = IR$. Combining with Eq. (25.13), we have

$$\mathcal{E} = V_{ab} = IR \qquad \text{(ideal source of emf)} \tag{25.14}$$

That is, when a positive charge q flows around the circuit, the potential *rise* $\mathcal{E}$ as it passes through the ideal source is numerically equal to the potential *drop* $V_{ab} = IR$ as it passes through the remainder of the circuit. Once $\mathcal{E}$ and R are known, this relationship determines the current in the circuit.

CAUTION **Current is not "used up" in a circuit** It's a common misconception that in a closed circuit, current is something that squirts out of the positive terminal of a battery and is consumed or "used up" by the time it reaches the negative terminal. In fact the current is the *same* at every point in a simple loop circuit like that in Fig. 25.15, even if the thickness of the wires is different at different points in the circuit. This happens because charge is conserved (that is, it can be neither created nor destroyed) and because charge cannot accumulate in the circuit devices we have described. If charge did accumulate, the potential differences would change with time. It's like the flow of water in an ornamental fountain; water flows out of the top of the fountain at the same rate at which it reaches the bottom, no matter what the dimensions of the fountain. None of the water is "used up" along the way!

Internal Resistance

Real sources of emf in a circuit don't behave in exactly the way we have described; the potential difference across a real source in a circuit is *not* equal to the emf as in Eq. (25.14). The reason is that charge moving through the material of any real source encounters *resistance.* We call this the **internal resistance** of the source, denoted by r. If this resistance behaves according to Ohm's law, r is constant and independent of the current I. As the current moves through r, it experiences an associated drop in potential equal to Ir. Thus, when a current is flowing through a source from the negative terminal b to the positive terminal a, the potential difference V_{ab} between the terminals is

$$V_{ab} = \mathcal{E} - Ir \quad \text{(terminal voltage, source with internal resistance)} \tag{25.15}$$

The potential V_{ab}, called the **terminal voltage,** is less than the emf $\mathcal{E}$ because of the term Ir representing the potential drop across the internal resistance r. Expressed another way, the increase in potential energy qV_{ab} as a charge q moves from b to a within the source is now less than the work $q\mathcal{E}$ done by the nonelectrostatic force $\vec{F}_n$, since some potential energy is lost in traversing the internal resistance.

A 1.5-V battery has an emf of 1.5 V, but the terminal voltage V_{ab} of the battery is equal to 1.5 V only if no current is flowing through it so that $I = 0$ in Eq. (25.15). If the battery is part of a complete circuit through which current is flowing, the terminal voltage will be less than 1.5 V. *For a real source of emf, the terminal voltage equals the emf only if no current is flowing through the source* (Fig. 25.16). Thus we can describe the behavior of a source in terms of two properties: an emf $\mathcal{E}$, which supplies a constant potential difference independent of current, in series with an internal resistance r.

25.16 The emf of this battery—that is, the terminal voltage when it's not connected to anything—is 12 V. But because the battery has internal resistance, the terminal voltage of the battery is less than 12 V when it is supplying current to a light bulb.

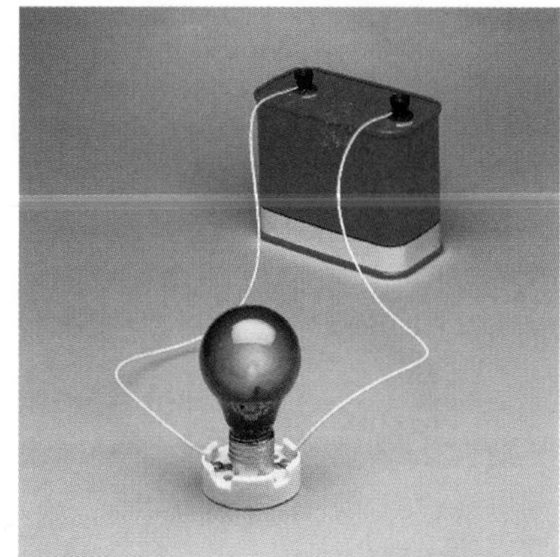

The current in the external circuit connected to the source terminals a and b is still determined by $V_{ab} = IR$. Combining this with Eq. (25.15), we find

$$\mathcal{E} - Ir = IR \quad \text{or} \quad I = \frac{\mathcal{E}}{R + r} \quad \text{(current, source with internal resistance)} \tag{25.16}$$

That is, the current equals the source emf divided by the *total* circuit resistance $(R + r)$.

CAUTION **A battery is not a "current source"** You might have thought that a battery or other source of emf always produces the same current, no matter what circuit it's used in. But as Eq. (25.16) shows, the current that a source of emf produces in a given circuit depends on the resistance R of the external circuit (as well as on the internal resistance r of the source). The greater the resistance, the less current the source will produce. It's analogous to pushing an object through a thick, viscous liquid such as oil or molasses; if you exert a certain steady push (emf), you can move a small object at high speed (small R, large I) or a large object at low speed (large R, small I).

Symbols for Circuit Diagrams

An important part of analyzing any electric circuit is drawing a schematic *circuit diagram.* Table 25.4 shows the usual symbols used in circuit diagrams. We will use these symbols extensively in this chapter and the next. We usually assume that the wires that connect the various elements of the circuit have negligible resistance; from Eq. (25.11), $V = IR$, the potential difference between the ends of such a wire is zero.

Table 25.4 includes two *meters* that are used to measure the properties of circuits. Idealized meters do not disturb the circuit in which they are connected. A **voltmeter,** introduced in Section 23.2, measures the potential difference between its terminals; an idealized voltmeter has infinitely large resistance and measures potential difference without having any current diverted through it. An ammeter measures the current passing through it; an idealized **ammeter** has zero resistance and has no potential difference between its terminals. Because meters act as part of the circuit in which they are connected, these properties are important to remember.

Table 25.4 Symbols for Circuit Diagrams

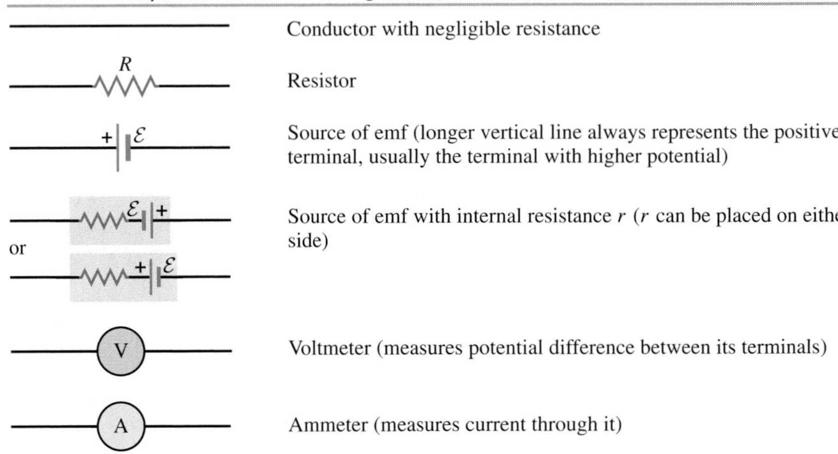

(line)	Conductor with negligible resistance
R	Resistor
+ $\mathcal{E}$	Source of emf (longer vertical line always represents the positive terminal, usually the terminal with higher potential)
$\mathcal{E}$ + or + $\mathcal{E}$	Source of emf with internal resistance r (r can be placed on either side)
V	Voltmeter (measures potential difference between its terminals)
A	Ammeter (measures current through it)

Conceptual Example 25.5 A source in an open circuit

Fig. 25.17 shows a source (a battery) with an emf $\mathcal{E}$ of 12 V and an internal resistance r of 2 Ω. (For comparison, the internal resistance of a commercial 12-V lead storage battery is only a few thousandths of an ohm.) The wires to the left of a and to the right of the ammeter A are not connected to anything. Determine the readings of the idealized voltmeter V and the idealized ammeter A.

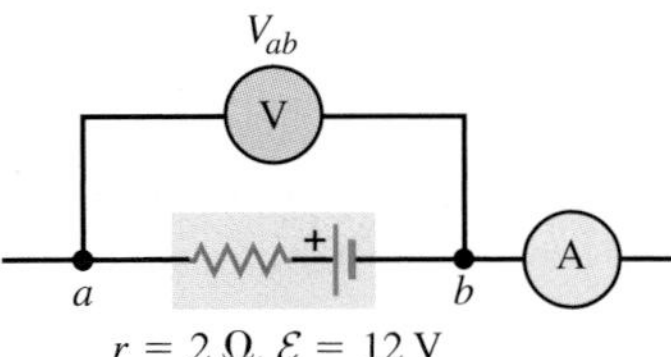

25.17 A source of emf in an open circuit.

SOLUTION

There is no current because there is no complete circuit. (There is no current through our idealized voltmeter, with its infinitely large resistance.) Hence the ammeter A reads $I = 0$. Because there is no current through the battery, there is no potential difference across its internal resistance. From Eq. (25.15) with $I = 0$, the potential difference V_{ab} across the battery terminals is equal to the emf. So the voltmeter reads $V_{ab} = \mathcal{E} = 12$ V. The terminal voltage of a real, nonideal source equals the emf *only* if there is no current flowing through the source, as in this example.

Example 25.6 A source in a complete circuit

Using the battery in Conceptual Example 25.5, we add a 4-Ω resistor to form the complete circuit shown in Fig. 25.18. What are the voltmeter and ammeter readings now?

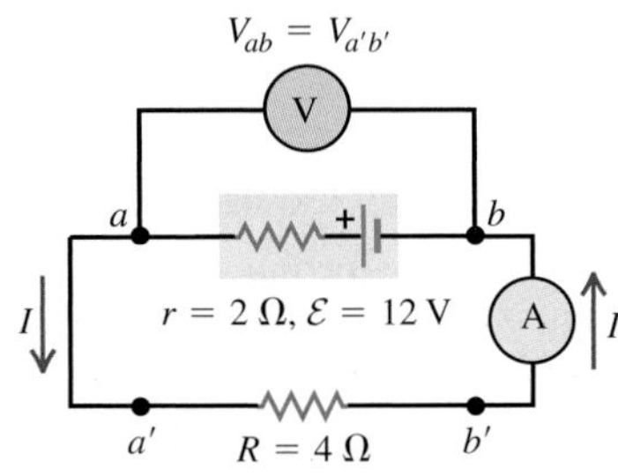

25.18 A source of emf in a complete circuit.

SOLUTION

IDENTIFY Our first target variable is the current I through the circuit $aa'b'b$ (equal to the ammeter reading). The second is the potential difference V_{ab} (equal to the voltmeter reading).

SET UP: We find I using Eq. (25.16). To find V_{ab}, we note that we can regard this either as the potential difference across the source or as the potential difference around the circuit through the external resistor.

EXECUTE: The ideal ammeter has zero resistance, so the resistance external to the source is $R = 4\ \Omega$. From Eq. (25.16), the current through the circuit $aa'b'b$ is

$$I = \frac{\mathcal{E}}{R + r} = \frac{12\ \text{V}}{4\ \Omega + 2\Omega} = 2\ \text{A}$$

The ammeter A reads $I = 2$ A.

Our idealized conducting wires have zero resistance, and the idealized ammeter A also has zero resistance. So there is no potential difference between points a and a' or between points b and b'; that is, $V_{ab} = V_{a'b'}$. We can find V_{ab} by considering a and b either as the terminals of the resistor or as the terminals of the source. Considering them as terminals of the resistor, we use Ohm's law $(V = IR)$:

$$V_{a'b'} = IR = (2\ \text{A})(4\ \Omega) = 8\ \text{V}$$

Considering them as the terminals of the source, we have

$$V_{ab} = \mathcal{E} - Ir = 12\ \text{V} - (2\ A)(2\ \Omega) = 8\ \text{V}$$

Either way, we conclude that the voltmeter reads $V_{ab} = 8$ V.

EVALUATE: With a current flowing through the source, the terminal voltage V_{ab} is less than the emf. The smaller the internal resistance r, the less the difference between V_{ab} and $\mathcal{E}$.

Conceptual Example 25.7 Using voltmeters and ammeters

The voltmeter and ammeter in Example 25.6 are moved to different positions in the circuit. What are the voltmeter and ammeter readings in the situations shown in (a) Fig. 25.19a and (b) Fig. 25.19b?

25.19 Different placements of a voltmeter and an ammeter in a complete circuit.

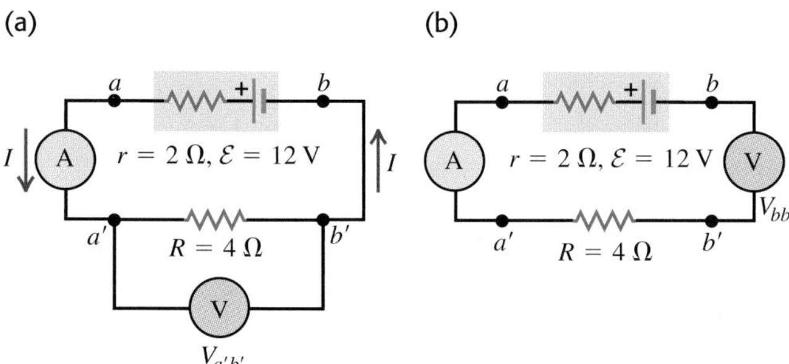

SOLUTION

(a) The voltmeter now measures the potential difference between points a' and b'. But as mentioned in Example 25.6, $V_{ab} = V_{a'b'}$, so the voltmeter reads the same as in Example 25.6: $V_{a'b'} = 8$ V.

CAUTION **Current in a simple loop** You might be tempted to conclude that the ammeter in Fig. 25.19a, which is located "upstream" of the resistor, would have a higher reading than the one located "downstream" of the resistor in Fig. 25.18. But this conclusion is based on the misconception that current is somehow "used up" as it moves through a resistor. As charges move through a resistor, there is a decrease in electric potential energy, but there is *no* change in the current. *The current in a simple loop is the same at every point.* An ammeter placed as in Fig. 25.19a reads the same as one placed as in Fig. 25.18: $I = 2$ A.

(b) There is no current through the voltmeter because it has infinitely large resistance. Since the voltmeter is now part of the circuit, there is no current at all in the circuit, and the ammeter reads $I = 0$.

The voltmeter measures the potential difference $V_{bb'}$ between points b and b'. Since $I = 0$, the potential difference across the resistor is $V_{a'b'} = IR = 0$, and the potential difference between the ends a and a' of the idealized ammeter is also zero. So $V_{bb'}$ is equal to V_{ab}, the terminal voltage of the source. As in Conceptual Example 25.5, there is no current flowing, so the terminal voltage equals the emf, and the voltmeter reading is $V_{ab} = \mathcal{E} = 12$ V.

This example shows that ammeters and voltmeters are circuit elements, too. Moving the voltmeter from the position in Fig. 25.19a to that in Fig. 25.19b changes the current and potential differences in the circuit—in this case rather dramatically. If you want to measure the potential difference between two points in a circuit without disturbing the circuit, use a voltmeter as in Figs. 25.18 or 25.19a, *not* as in Fig. 25.19b.

Example 25.8 A source with a short circuit

Using the same battery as in the preceding three examples, we now replace the 4-Ω resistor with a zero-resistance conductor. What are the meter readings now?

SOLUTION

IDENTIFY: Our target variables are I and V_{ab}, the same as in Example 25.6. The only difference from that example is that the external resistance is now $R = 0$.

SET UP: Figure 25.20 shows the new circuit. There is now a zero-resistance path between points a and b (through the lower loop in Fig. 25.20). Hence the potential difference between these points must be zero, which we can use to help solve the problem.

25.20 Our sketch for this problem.

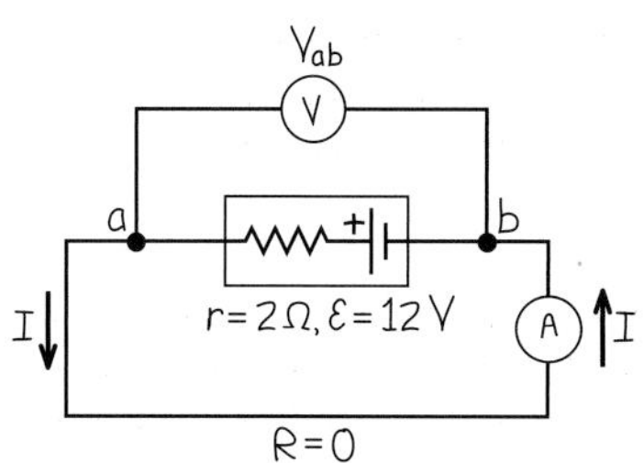

Continued

EXECUTE: We must have $V_{ab} = IR = I(0) = 0$, no matter what the current. Knowing this, we can find the current I from Eq. (25.15):

$$V_{ab} = \mathcal{E} - Ir = 0$$
$$I = \frac{\mathcal{E}}{r} = \frac{12\text{ V}}{2\ \Omega} = 6\text{ A}$$

The ammeter reads $I = 6$ A and the voltmeter reads $V_{ab} = 0$.

EVALUATE: The current has a different value than in Example 25.6, even though the same battery is used. A source does *not* deliver the same current in all situations; the amount of current depends on the internal resistance r and on the resistance of the external circuit.

The situation in this example is called a *short circuit.* The terminals of the battery are connected directly to each other, with no external resistance. The short-circuit current is equal to the emf $\mathcal{E}$ divided by the internal resistance r. *Warning:* A short circuit can be an extremely dangerous situation. An automobile battery or a household power line has very small internal resistance (much less than in these examples), and the short-circuit current can be great enough to melt a small wire or cause a storage battery to explode. Don't try it!

Potential Changes Around a Circuit

The net change in potential energy for a charge q making a round trip around a complete circuit must be zero. Hence the net change in *potential* around the circuit must also be zero; in other words, the algebraic sum of the potential differences and emfs around the loop is zero. We can see this by rewriting Eq. (25.16) in the form

$$\mathcal{E} - Ir - IR = 0$$

A potential gain of $\mathcal{E}$ is associated with the emf, and potential drops of Ir and IR are associated with the internal resistance of the source and the external circuit, respectively. Fig. 25.21 is a graph showing how the potential varies as we go around the complete circuit of Fig. 25.18. The horizontal axis doesn't necessarily represent actual distances, but rather various points in the loop. If we take the potential to be zero at the negative terminal of the battery, then we have a rise $\mathcal{E}$ and a drop Ir in the battery and an additional drop IR in the external resistor, and as we finish our trip around the loop, the potential is back where it started.

In this section we have considered only situations in which the resistances are ohmic. If the circuit includes a nonlinear device such as a diode (see Fig. 25.10b), Eq. (25.16) is still valid but cannot be solved algebraically because R is not a constant. In such a situation, the current I can be found by using numerical techniques (see Challenge Problem 25.84).

Finally, we remark that Eq. (25.15) is not always an adequate representation of the behavior of a source. The emf may not be constant, and what we have

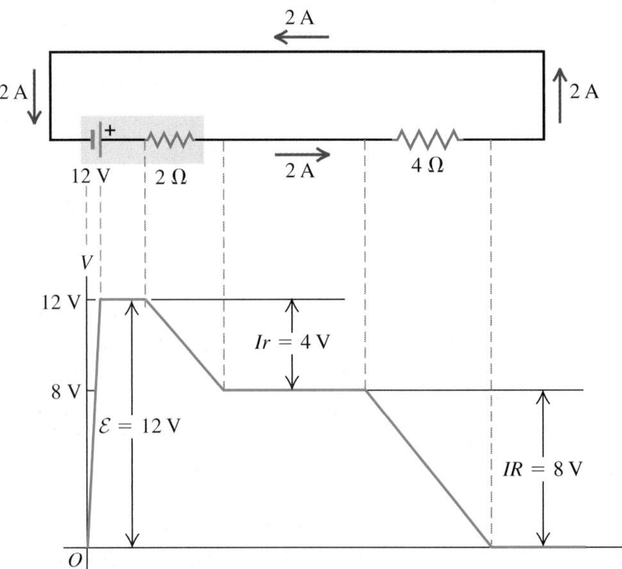

25.21 Potential rises and drops in a circuit.

described as an internal resistance may actually be a more complex voltage–current relationship that doesn't obey Ohm's law. Nevertheless, the concept of internal resistance frequently provides an adequate description of batteries, generators, and other energy converters. The principal difference between a fresh flashlight battery and an old one is not in the emf, which decreases only slightly with use, but in the internal resistance, which may increase from less than an ohm when the battery is fresh to as much as 1000 Ω or more after long use. Similarly, a car battery can deliver less current to the starter motor on a cold morning than when the battery is warm, not because the emf is appreciably less but because the internal resistance increases with decreasing temperature. Cold-climate dwellers take a number of measures to avoid this loss, from using special battery warmers to soaking the battery in warm water on very cold mornings.

Test Your Understanding of Section 25.4 Rank the following circuits in order from highest to lowest current. (i) a 1.4-Ω resistor connected to a 1.5-V battery that has an internal resistance of 0.10 Ω; (ii) a 1.8-Ω resistor connected to a 4.0-V battery that has a terminal voltage of 3.6 V but an unknown internal resistance; (iii) an unknown resistor connected to a 12.0-V battery that has an internal resistance of 0.20 Ω and a terminal voltage of 11.0 V.

25.5 Energy and Power in Electric Circuits

Let's now look at some energy and power relationships in electric circuits. The box in Fig. 25.22 represents a circuit element with potential difference $V_a - V_b = V_{ab}$ between its terminals and current I passing through it in the direction from a toward b. This element might be a resistor, a battery, or something else; the details don't matter. As charge passes through the circuit element, the electric field does work on the charge. In a source of emf, additional work is done by the force $\vec{F}_n$ that we mentioned in Section 25.4.

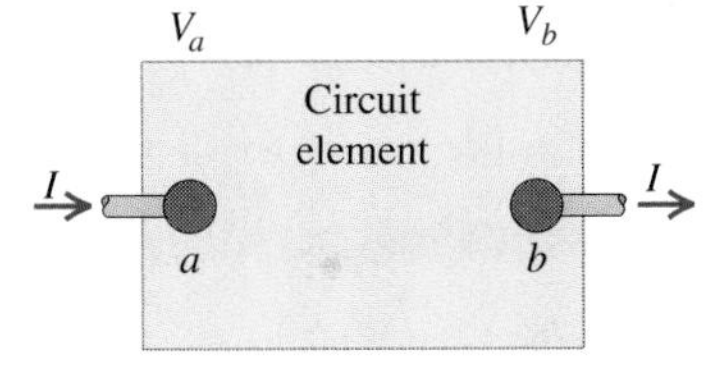

25.22 The power input to the circuit element between a and b is $P = (V_a - V_b)I = V_{ab}I$.

As an amount of charge q passes through the circuit element, there is a change in potential energy equal to qV_{ab}. For example, if $q > 0$ and $V_{ab} = V_a - V_b$ is positive, potential energy decreases as the charge "falls" from potential V_a to lower potential V_b. The moving charges don't gain *kinetic* energy, because the rate of charge flow (that is, the current) out of the circuit element must be the same as the rate of charge flow into the element. Instead, the quantity qV_{ab} represents electrical energy transferred into the circuit element. This situation occurs in the coils of a toaster or electric oven, in which electrical energy is converted to thermal energy.

It may happen that the potential at b is higher than that at a. In this case V_{ab} is negative, and a net transfer of energy *out* of the circuit element occurs. The element then acts as a source, delivering electrical energy into the circuit to which it is attached. This is the usual situation for a battery, which converts chemical energy into electrical energy and delivers it to the external circuit. Thus qV_{ab} can denote either a quantity of energy delivered to a circuit element or a quantity of energy extracted from that element.

In electric circuits we are most often interested in the *rate* at which energy is either delivered to or extracted from a circuit element. If the current through the element is I, then in a time interval dt an amount of charge $dQ = I\,dt$ passes through the element. The potential energy change for this amount of charge is $V_{ab}\,dQ = V_{ab}I\,dt$. Dividing this expression by dt, we obtain the *rate* at which energy is transferred either into or out of the circuit element. The time rate of energy transfer is *power*, denoted by P, so we write

$$P = V_{ab}I \quad \text{(rate at which energy is delivered to or extracted from a circuit element)} \qquad (25.17)$$

The unit of V_{ab} is one volt, or one joule per coulomb, and the unit of I is one ampere, or one coulomb per second. Hence the unit of $P = V_{ab}I$ is one watt, as it should be:

$$(1\ \text{J/C})(1\ \text{C/s}) = 1\ \text{J/s} = 1\ \text{W}$$

Let's consider a few special cases.

Power Inout to a Pure Resistance

If the circuit element in Fig. 25.22 is a resistor, the potential difference is $V_{ab} = IR$. From Eq. (25.17) the electrical power delivered to the resistor by the circuit is

$$P = V_{ab}I = I^2R = \frac{V_{ab}{}^2}{R} \quad \text{(power delivered to a resistor)} \tag{25.18}$$

In this case the potential at a (where the current enters the resistor) is always higher than that at b (where the current exits). Current enters the higher-potential terminal of the device, and Eq. (25.18) represents the rate of transfer of electric potential energy *into* the circuit element.

What becomes of this energy? The moving charges collide with atoms in the resistor and transfer some of their energy to these atoms, increasing the internal energy of the material. Either the temperature of the resistor increases or there is a flow of heat out of it, or both. In any of these cases we say that energy is *dissipated* in the resistor at a rate I^2R. Every resistor has a *power rating,* the maximum power the device can dissipate without becoming overheated and damaged. In practical applications the power rating of a resistor is often just as important a characteristic as its resistance value. Of course, some devices, such as electric heaters, are designed to get hot and transfer heat to their surroundings. But if the power rating is exceeded, even such a device may melt or even explode.

25.23 Energy conversion in a simple circuit.

(a) Diagrammatic circuit

- The emf source converts nonelectrical to electrical energy at a rate $\mathcal{E}I$.
- Its internal resistance *dissipates* energy at a rate I^2r.
- The difference $\mathcal{E}I - I^2r$ is its power output.

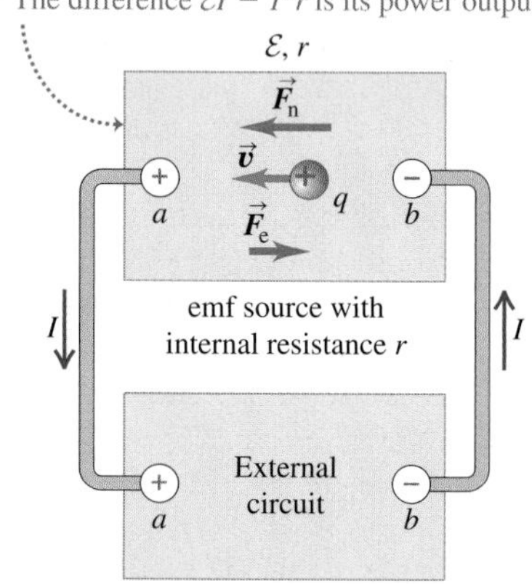

(b) A real circuit of the type shown in (a)

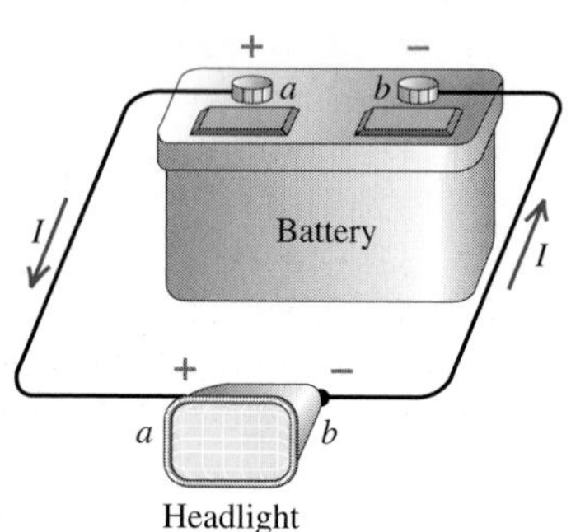

Power Output of a Source

The upper rectangle in Fig. 25.23a represents a source with emf $\mathcal{E}$ and internal resistance r, connected by ideal (resistanceless) conductors to an external circuit represented by the lower box. This could describe a car battery connected to one of the car's headlights (Fig. 25.23b). Point a is at higher potential than point b, so $V_a > V_b$ and V_{ab} is positive. Note that the current I is *leaving* the source at the higher-potential terminal (rather than entering there). Energy is being delivered to the external circuit, and the rate of its delivery to the circuit is given by Eq. (25.17):

$$P = V_{ab}I$$

For a source that can be described by an emf $\mathcal{E}$ and an internal resistance r, we may use Eq. (25.15):

$$V_{ab} = \mathcal{E} - Ir$$

Multiplying this equation by I, we find

$$P = V_{ab}I = \mathcal{E}I - I^2r \tag{25.19}$$

What do the terms $\mathcal{E}I$ and I^2r mean? In Section 25.4 we defined the emf $\mathcal{E}$ as the work per unit charge performed on the charges by the nonelectrostatic force as the charges are pushed "uphill" from b to a in the source. In a time dt, a charge $dQ = I\,dt$ flows through the source; the work done on it by this nonelectrostatic force is $\mathcal{E}\,dQ = \mathcal{E}I\,dt$. Thus $\mathcal{E}I$ is the *rate* at which work is done on the circulating charges by whatever agency causes the nonelectrostatic force in the source. This term represents the rate of conversion of nonelectrical energy to electrical energy within the source. The term I^2r is the rate at which electrical energy is *dissipated* in the internal resistance of the source. The difference $\mathcal{E}I - I^2r$ is the *net* electrical power output of the source—that is, the rate at which the source delivers electrical energy to the remainder of the circuit.

Power Input to a Source

Suppose that the lower rectangle in Fig. 25.23a is itself a source, with an emf *larger* than that of the upper source and with its emf opposite to that of the upper source. Fig. 25.24 shows a practical example, an automobile battery (the upper circuit element) being charged by the car's alternator (the lower element). The current I in the circuit is then *opposite* to that shown in Fig. 25.23; the lower source is pushing current backward through the upper source. Because of this reversal of current, instead of Eq. (25.15) we have for the upper source

$$V_{ab} = \mathcal{E} + Ir$$

and instead of Eq. (25.19), we have

$$P = V_{ab}I = \mathcal{E}I + I^2R \tag{25.20}$$

Work is being done *on,* rather than *by,* the agent that causes the nonelectrostatic force in the upper source. There is a conversion of electrical energy into nonelectrical energy in the upper source at a rate $\mathcal{E}I$. The term I^2r in Eq. (25.20) is again the rate of dissipation of energy in the internal resistance of the upper source, and the sum $\mathcal{E}I + I^2r$ is the total electrical power *input* to the upper source. This is what happens when a rechargeable battery (a storage battery) is connected to a charger. The charger supplies electrical energy to the battery; part of it is converted to chemical energy, to be reconverted later, and the remainder is dissipated (wasted) in the battery's internal resistance, warming the battery and causing a heat flow out of it. If you have a power tool or laptop computer with a rechargeable battery, you may have noticed that it gets warm while it is charging.

25.24 When two sources are connected in a simple loop circuit, the source with the larger emf delivers energy to the other source.

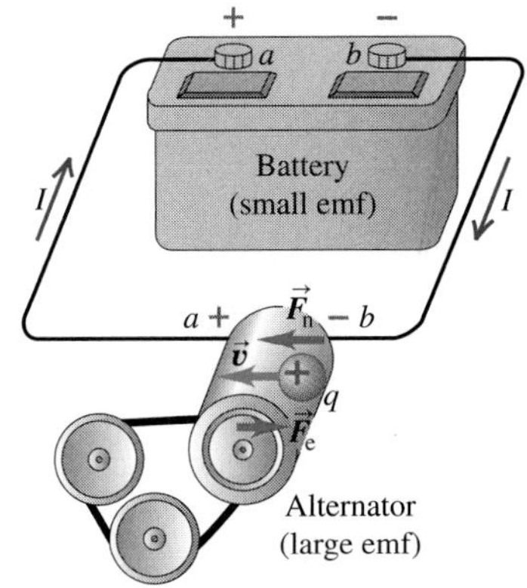

Problem-Solving Strategy 25.1 Power and Energy in Circuits

IDENTIFY *the relevant concepts:*
The ideas of electric power input and output can be applied to any electric circuit. In most cases you'll know when these concepts are needed because the problem will ask you explicitly to consider power or energy.

SET UP *the problem* using the following steps:

1. Make a drawing of the circuit.
2. Identify the circuit elements, including sources of emf and resistors. In later chapters we will add other kinds of circuit elements, including capacitors and inductors (described in Chapter 30).
3. Determine the target variables. Typically they will be the power input or output for each circuit element, or the total amount of energy put into or taken out of a circuit element in a given time.

EXECUTE *the solution* as follows:

1. A source of emf $\mathcal{E}$ delivers power $\mathcal{E}I$ into a circuit when the current I runs through the source from $-$ to $+$. The energy is converted from chemical energy in a battery, from mechanical energy in a generator, or whatever. In this case the source has a *positive* power output to the circuit or, equivalently, a *negative* power input to the source.
2. A source of emf takes power $\mathcal{E}I$ from a circuit—that is, it has a negative power output or, equivalently, a positive power input—when current passes through the source in the direction from $+$ to $-$. This occurs in charging a storage battery, when electrical energy is converted back to chemical energy. In this case the source has a *negative* power output to the circuit or, equivalently, a *positive* power input to the source.
3. No matter what the direction of the current through a resistor, there is always a *positive* power input to the resistor. It removes energy from a circuit at a rate given by $VI = I^2R = V^2/R$, where V is the potential difference across the resistor.
4. There is also a *positive* power input to the internal resistance r of a source, irrespective of the direction of the current. The internal resistance always removes energy from the circuit, converting it into heat at a rate I^2r.
5. You may need to calculate the total energy delivered to or extracted from a circuit element in a given amount of time. If the power into or out of a circuit element is constant, this integral is just the product of power and elapsed time. (In Chapter 26 we will encounter situations in which the power is not constant. In such cases, calculating the total energy requires an integral.)

EVALUATE *your answer:* Check your results, including a check that energy is conserved. This conservation can be expressed in either of two forms: "net power input = net power output" or "the algebraic sum of the power inputs to the circuit elements is zero."

Example 25.9 Power input and output in a complete circuit

For the situation that we analyzed in Example 25.6, find the rate of energy conversion (chemical to electrical) and the rate of dissipation of energy in the battery and the net power output of the battery.

SOLUTION

IDENTIFY: Our target variables are the power output of the source of emf, the power input to the internal resistance, and the net power output of the source.

SET UP: Fig. 25.25 shows the circuit. We use Eq. (25.17) to find the power input or output of a circuit element and Eq. (25.19) to find the source's net power output.

25.25 Our sketch for this problem.

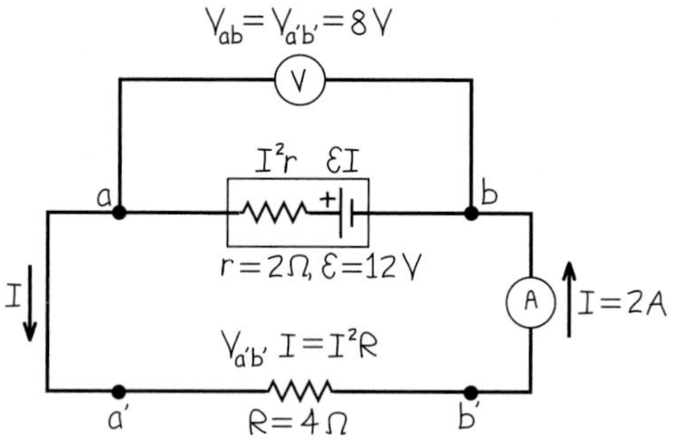

EXECUTE: From Example 25.6 the current in the circuit is $I = 2$ A. The rate of energy conversion in the battery is

$$\mathcal{E}I = (12\text{ V})(2\text{ A}) = 24\text{ W}$$

The rate of dissipation of energy in the battery is

$$I^2r = (2\text{ A})^2(2\ \Omega) = 8\text{ W}$$

The electrical power *output* of the source is the difference between these: $\mathcal{E}I - I^2r = 16$ W.

EVALUATE: The power output is also given by the terminal voltage $V_{ab} = 8$ V (calculated in Example 25.6) multiplied by the current:

$$V_{ab}I = (8\text{ V})(2\text{ A}) = 16\text{ W}$$

The electrical power input to the resistor is

$$V_{a'b'}I = (8\text{ V})(2\text{ A}) = 16\text{ W}$$

This equals the rate of dissipation of electrical energy in the resistor:

$$I^2R = (2\text{ A})^2(4\ \Omega) = 16\text{ W}$$

Note that our results agree with Eq. (25.19), which states that $V_{ab}I = \mathcal{E}I - I^2R$; the left side of this equation equals 16 W, and the right side equals 24 W − 8 W = 16 W. This verifies the consistency of the various power quantities.

Example 25.10 Increasing the resistance

Suppose the 4-Ω resistor in Fig. 25.25 is replaced by an 8-Ω resistor. How does this affect the electrical power dissipated in the resistor?

SOLUTION

IDENTIFY: Our target variable is the power dissipated in the resistor to which the source of emf is connected.

SET UP: The situation is the same as that in Example 25.9, but with a different value of the external resistance R.

EXECUTE: According to Eq. (25.18), the power dissipated in the resistor is given by $P = I^2R$. If you were in a hurry, you might conclude that since R now has twice the value that it had in Example 25.9, the power should also be twice as great, or $2(16\text{ W}) = 32$ W. Or you might instead try to use the formula $P = V_{ab}^2/R$; this formula would lead you to conclude that the power should be one-half as great as in the preceding example, or $(16\text{ W})/2 = 8$ W. Which answer is correct?

In fact, *both* of these conclusions are *incorrect.* The first is incorrect because changing the resistance R also changes the current in the circuit (remember, a source of emf does *not* generate the same current in all situations). The second conclusion is also incorrect because the potential difference V_{ab} across the resistor changes when the current changes. To get the correct answer, we first use the same technique as in Example 25.6 to find the current:

$$I = \frac{\mathcal{E}}{R + r} = \frac{12\text{ V}}{8\ \Omega + 2\ \Omega} = 1.2\text{ A}$$

The greater resistance causes the current to decrease. The potential difference across the resistor is

$$V_{ab} = IR = (1.2\text{ A})(8\ \Omega) = 9.6\text{ V}$$

which is greater than that with the 4-Ω resistor. We can then find the power dissipated in the resistor in either of two ways:

$$P = I^2R = (1.2\text{ A})^2(8\ \Omega) = 12\text{ W} \quad \text{or}$$

$$P = \frac{V_{ab}^2}{R} = \frac{(9.6\text{ V})^2}{8\ \Omega} = 12\text{ W}$$

EVALUATE: Increasing the resistance R causes a *reduction* in the power input to the resistor. In the expression $P = I^2R$ the decrease in current is more important than the increase in resistance; in the expression $P = V_{ab}^2/R$ the increase in resistance is more important than the increase in V_{ab}. This same principle applies to ordinary light bulbs; a 50-W light bulb has a greater resistance than does a 100-W light bulb.

Can you show that replacing the 4-Ω resistor with an 8-Ω resistor decreases both the rate of energy conversion (chemical to electrical) in the battery and the rate of energy dissipation in the battery?

Example 25.11 Power in a short circuit

For the circuit that we analyzed in Example 25.8, find the rates of energy conversion and energy dissipation in the battery and the net power output of the battery.

SOLUTION

IDENTIFY: Our target variables are again the power inputs and outputs associated with the battery.

SET UP: Fig. 25.26 shows the circuit. This is once again the same situation as in Example 25.9, but now the external resistance R is zero.

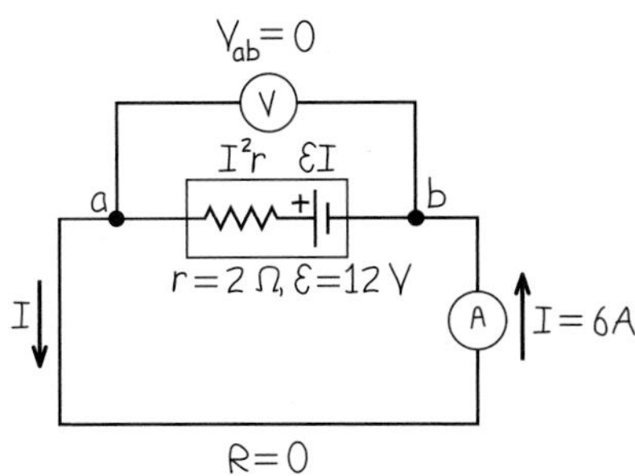

25.26 Our sketch for this problem.

EXECUTE: We found in Example 25.8 that the current in this situation is $I = 6$ A. The rate of energy conversion (chemical to electrical) in the battery is

$$\mathcal{E}I = (12\text{ V})(6\text{ A}) = 72\text{ W}$$

The rate of dissipation of energy in the battery is

$$I^2r = (6\text{ A})^2(2\,\Omega) = 72\text{ W}$$

The net power output of the source, given by $V_{ab}I$, is zero because the terminal voltage V_{ab} is zero.

EVALUATE: With ideal wires and an ideal ammeter so that $R = 0$, *all* of the converted energy is dissipated within the source. This is why a short-circuited battery is quickly ruined and in some cases may even explode.

Test Your Understanding of Section 25.5 Rank the following circuits in order from highest to lowest values of the net power output of the battery. (i) a 1.4-Ω resistor connected to a 1.5-V battery that has an internal resistance of 0.10 Ω; (ii) a 1.8-Ω; resistor connected to a 4.0-V battery that has a terminal voltage of 3.6 V but an unknown internal resistance; (iii) an unknown resistor connected to a 12.0-V battery that has an internal resistance of 0.20 Ω; and a terminal voltage of 11.0 V.

*25.6 Theory of Metallic Conduction

We can gain additional insight into electrical conduction by looking at the microscopic origin of conductivity. We'll consider a very simple model that treats the electrons as classical particles and ignores their quantum-mechanical, wavelike behavior in solids. Using this model, we'll derive an expression for the resistivity of a metal. Even though this model is not entirely correct conceptually, it will still help you to develop an intuitive idea of the microscopic basis of conduction.

In the simplest microscopic model of conduction in a metal, each atom in the metallic crystal gives up one or more of its outer electrons. These electrons are then free to move through the crystal, colliding at intervals with the stationary positive ions. The motion of the electrons is analogous to the motion of molecules of a gas moving through a porous bed of sand, and they are often referred to as an "electron gas."

If there is no electric field, the electrons move in straight lines between collisions, the directions of their velocities are random, and on average they never get anywhere (Fig. 25.27a). But if an electric field is present, the paths curve slightly because of the acceleration caused by electric-field forces. Figure 25.27b shows a few paths of an electron in an electric field directed from right to left. As we mentioned in Section 25.1, the average speed of random motion is of the order of 10^6 m/s, while the average drift speed is *much* slower, of the order of 10^{-4} m/s.

25.27 Random motions of an electron in a metallic crystal (a) with zero electric field and (b) with an electric field that causes drift. The curvatures of the paths are greatly exaggerated.

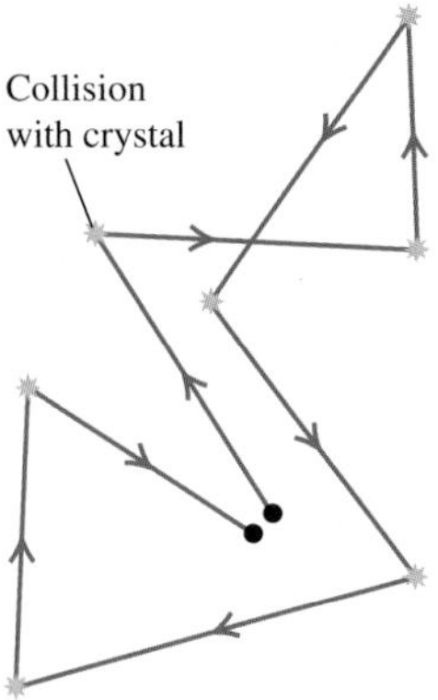
(a) Typical trajectory for an electron in a metallic crystal *without* an internal $\vec{E}$ field
Collision with crystal

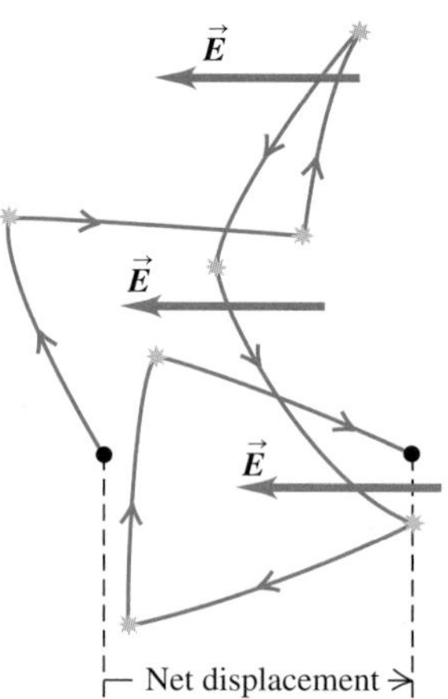
(a) Typical trajectory for an electron in a metallic crystal *with* an internal $\vec{E}$ field
$\vec{E}$
$\vec{E}$
$\vec{E}$
Net displacement

25.28 The motion of a ball rolling down an inclined plane and bouncing off pegs in its path is analogous to the motion of an electron in a metallic conductor with an electric field present.

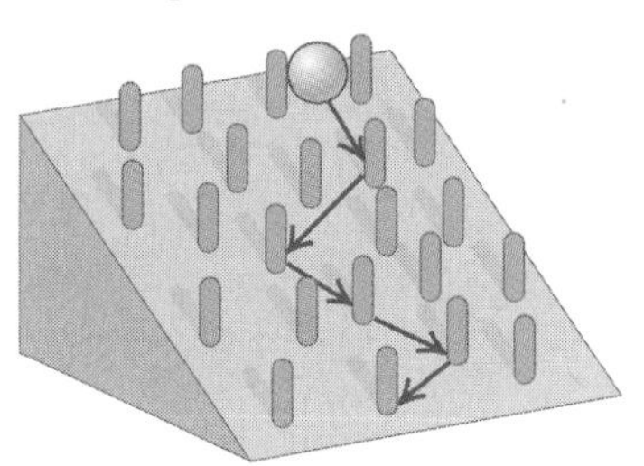

The average time between collisions is called the **mean free time,** denoted by τ. Figure 25.28 shows a mechanical analog of this electron motion.

We would like to derive from this model an expression for the resistivity ρ of a material, defined by Eq. (25.5):

$$\rho = \frac{E}{J} \tag{25.21}$$

where E and J are the magnitudes of electric field and current density. The current density $\vec{J}$ is in turn given by Eq. (25.4):

$$\vec{J} = nq\vec{v}_d \tag{25.22}$$

where n is the number of free electrons per unit volume, q is the charge of each, and $\vec{v}_d$ is their average drift velocity. (We also know that $q = -e$ in an ordinary metal; we'll use that fact later.)

We need to relate the drift velocity $\vec{v}_d$ to the electric field $\vec{E}$. The value of $\vec{v}_d$ is determined by a steady-state condition in which, on average, the velocity *gains* of the charges due to the force of the $\vec{E}$ field are just balanced by the velocity *losses* due to collisions.

To clarify this process, let's imagine turning on the two effects one at a time. Suppose that before time $t = 0$ there is no field. The electron motion is then completely random. A typical electron has velocity $\vec{v}_0$ at time $t = 0$, and the value of $\vec{v}_0$ averaged over many electrons (that is, the initial velocity of an average electron) is zero: $(\vec{v}_0)_{av} = \mathbf{0}$. Then at time $t = 0$ we turn on a constant electric field $\vec{E}$. The field exerts a force $\vec{F} = q\vec{E}$ on each charge, and this causes an acceleration $\vec{a}$ in the direction of the force, given by

$$\vec{a} = \frac{\vec{F}}{m} = \frac{q\vec{E}}{m}$$

where m is the electron mass. *Every* electron has this acceleration.

We wait for a time τ, the average time between collisions, and then "turn on" the collisions. An electron that has velocity $\vec{v}_0$ at time $t = 0$ has a velocity at time $t = \tau$ equal to

$$\vec{v} = \vec{v}_0 + \vec{a}\tau$$

The velocity $\vec{v}_{av}$ of an *average* electron at this time is the sum of the averages of the two terms on the right. As we have pointed out, the initial velocity $\vec{v}_0$ is zero for an average electron, so

$$\vec{v}_{av} = \vec{a}\tau = \frac{q\tau}{m}\vec{E} \tag{25.23}$$

After time $t = \tau$, the tendency of the collisions to decrease the velocity of an average electron (by means of randomizing collisions) just balances the tendency of the $\vec{E}$ field to increase this velocity. Thus the velocity of an average electron, given by Eq. (25.23), is maintained over time and is equal to the drift velocity $\vec{v}_d$:

$$\vec{v}_d = \frac{q\tau}{m}\vec{E}$$

Now we substitute this equation for the drift velocity $\vec{v}_d$ into Eq. (25.22):

$$\vec{J} = nq\vec{v}_d = \frac{nq^2\tau}{m}\vec{E}$$

Comparing this with Eq. (25.21), which we can rewrite as $\vec{J} = \vec{E}/\rho$, and substituting $q = -e$, we see that the resistivity ρ is given by

$$\rho = \frac{m}{ne^2\tau} \tag{25.24}$$

If n and τ are independent of $\vec{E}$, then the resistivity is independent of $\vec{E}$ and the conducting material obeys Ohm's law.

Turning the interactions on one at a time may seem artificial. But the derivation would come out the same if each electron had its own clock and the $t = 0$ times were different for different electrons. If τ is the average time between collisions, then $\vec{v}_d$ is still the average electron drift velocity, even though the motions of the various electrons aren't actually correlated in the way we postulated.

What about the temperature dependence of resistivity? In a perfect crystal with no atoms out of place, a correct quantum-mechanical analysis would let the free electrons move through the crystal with no collisions at all. But the atoms vibrate about their equilibrium positions. As the temperature increases, the amplitudes of these vibrations increase, collisions become more frequent, and the mean free time τ decreases. So this theory predicts that the resistivity of a metal increases with temperature. In a superconductor, roughly speaking, there are no inelastic collisions, τ is infinite, and the resistivity ρ is zero.

In a pure semiconductor such as silicon or germanium, the number of charge carriers per unit volume, n, is not constant but increases very rapidly with increasing temperature. This increase in n far outweighs the decrease in the mean free time, and in a semiconductor the resistivity always decreases rapidly with increasing temperature. At low temperatures, n is very small, and the resistivity becomes so large that the material can be considered an insulator.

Electrons gain energy between collisions through the work done on them by the electric field. During collisions they transfer some of this energy to the atoms of the material of the conductor. This leads to an increase in the material's internal energy and temperature; that's why wires carrying current get warm. If the electric field in the material is large enough, an electron can gain enough energy between collisions to knock off electrons that are normally bound to atoms in the material. These can then knock off more electrons, and so on, possibly leading to an avalanche of current. This is the microscopic basis of dielectric breakdown in insulators.

Example 25.12 Mean free time in copper

Calculate the mean free time between collisions in copper at room temperature.

SOLUTION

IDENTIFY: This problem uses the ideas developed in this section.

SET UP: We can find an expression for mean free time τ in terms of n, ρ, e, and m by rearranging Eq. (25.24). From Example 25.1 and Table 25.1, for copper $n = 8.5 \times 10^{28}\ \text{m}^{-3}$ and $\rho = 1.72 \times 10^{-8}\ \Omega \cdot \text{m}$. Also, $e = 1.60 \times 10^{-19}\ \text{C}$ and $m = 9.11 \times 10^{-31}\ \text{kg}$ for electrons.

EXECUTE: From Eq. (25.24), we get

$$\tau = \frac{m}{ne^2\rho}$$

$$= \frac{9.11 \times 10^{-31}\ \text{kg}}{(8.5 \times 10^{28}\ \text{m}^{-3})(1.60 \times 10^{-19}\ \text{C})^2(1.72 \times 10^{-8}\ \Omega \cdot \text{m})}$$

$$= 2.4 \times 10^{-14}\ \text{s}$$

EVALUATE: Taking the reciprocal of this time, we find that each electron averages about 4×10^{13} collisions every second!

Test Your Understanding of Section 25.6 Which of the following factors will, if increased, make it more difficult to produce a certain amount of current in a conductor? (There may be more than one correct answer.) (i) the mass of the moving charged particles in the conductor; (ii) the number of moving charged particles per cubic meter; (iii) the amount of charge on each moving particle; (iv) the average time between collisions for a typical moving charged particle.

CHAPTER 25 SUMMARY

Current and current density: Current is the amount of charge flowing through a specified area, per unit time. The SI unit of current is the ampere, equal to one coulomb per second $(1\text{ A} = 1\text{ C/s})$. The current I through an area A depends on the concentration n and charge q of the charge carriers, as well as on the magnitude of their drift velocity $\vec{v}_d$. The current density is current per unit cross-sectional area. Current is conventionally described in terms of a flow of positive charge, even when the actual charge carriers are negative or of both signs. (See Example 25.1.)

$$I = \frac{dQ}{dt} = n|q|v_d A \quad (25.2)$$

$$\vec{J} = nq\vec{v}_d \quad (25.4)$$

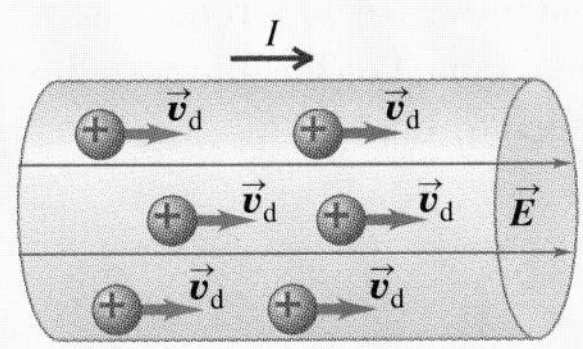

Resistivity: The resistivity ρ of a material is the ratio of the magnitudes of electric field and current density. Good conductors have small resistivity; good insulators have large resistivity. Ohm's law, obeyed approximately by many materials, states that ρ is a constant independent of the value of E. Resistivity usually increases with temperature; for small temperature changes this variation is represented approximately by Eq. (25.6), where α is the temperature coefficient of resistivity.

$$\rho = \frac{E}{J} \quad (25.5)$$

$$\rho(T) = \rho_0[1 + \alpha(T - T_0)] \quad (25.6)$$

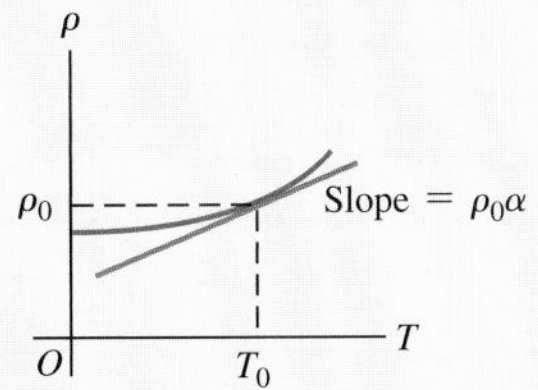

Metal: ρ increases with increasing T.

Resistors: For materials obeying Ohm's law, the potential difference V across a particular sample of material is proportional to the current I through the material. The ratio $V/I = R$ is the resistance of the sample. The SI unit of resistance is the ohm $(1\ \Omega = 1\text{ V/A})$. The resistance of a cylindrical conductor is related to its resistivity ρ, length L, and cross-sectional area A. (See Examples 25.2–25.4.)

$$V = IR \quad (25.11)$$

$$R = \frac{\rho L}{A} \quad (25.10)$$

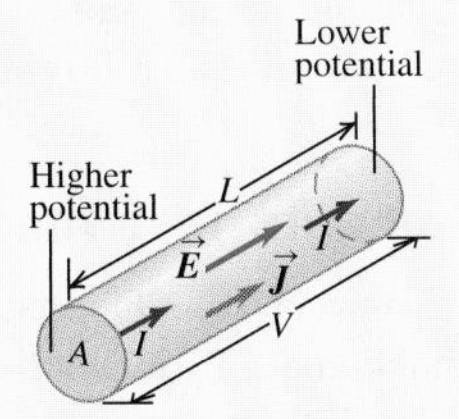

Circuits and emf: A complete circuit has a continuous current-carrying path. A complete circuit carrying a steady current must contain a source of electromotive force (emf) $\mathcal{E}$. The SI unit of electromotive force is the volt (1 V). An ideal source of emf maintains a constant potential difference, independent of current through the device, but every real source of emf has some internal resistance r. The terminal potential difference V_{ab} then depends on current. (See Examples 25.5–25.8.)

$$V_{ab} = \mathcal{E} - Ir \quad (25.15)$$

(source with internal resistance)

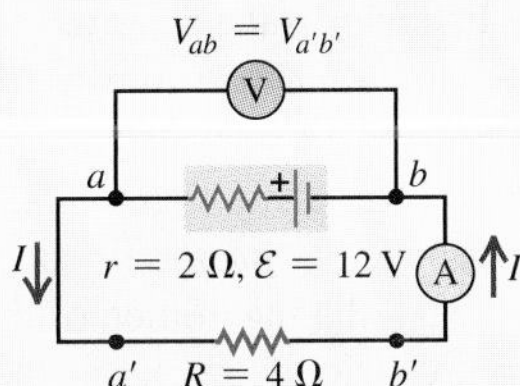

Energy and power in circuits: A circuit element with a potential difference $V_a - V_b = V_{ab}$ and a current I puts energy into a circuit if the current direction is from lower to higher potential in the device, and it takes energy out of the circuit if the current is opposite. The power P (rate of energy transfer) is equal to the product of the potential difference and the current. A resistor always takes electrical energy out of a circuit. (See Examples 25.9–25.11.)

$$P = V_{ab}I \quad (25.17)$$

(general circuit element)

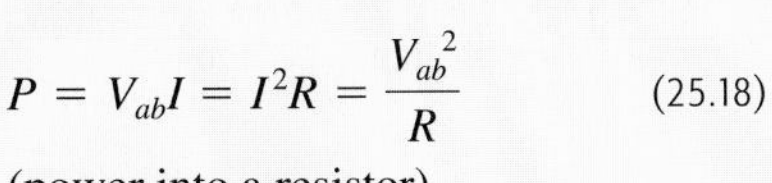

$$P = V_{ab}I = I^2R = \frac{V_{ab}^2}{R} \quad (25.18)$$

(power into a resistor)

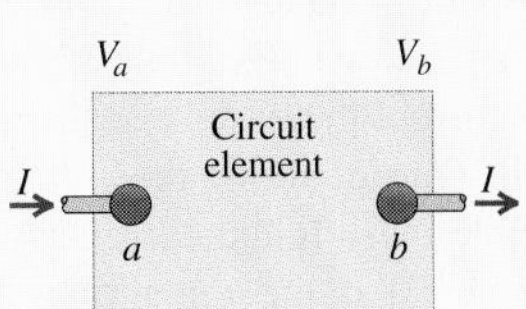

Conduction in metals: The microscopic basis of conduction in metals is the motion of electrons that move freely through the metallic crystal, bumping into ion cores in the crystal. In a crude classical model of this motion, the resistivity of the material can be related to the electron mass, charge, speed of random motion, density, and mean free time between collisions. (See Example 25.12.)

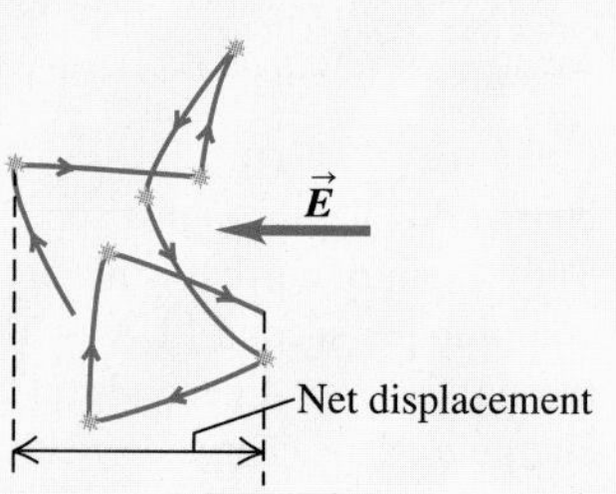

Key Terms

current, *847*
drift velocity, *847*
conventional current, *848*
ampere, *848*
concentration, *848*
current density, *849*
Ohm's law, *850*
resistivity, *851*
conductivity, *851*
temperature coefficient of resistivity, *852*
resistance, *853*
ohm, *854*
resistor, *854*
complete circuit, *857*
electromotive force (emf), *857*
source of emf, *857*
internal resistance, *859*
terminal voltage, *859*
voltmeter, *860*
ammeter, *860*
mean free time, *868*

Answer to Chapter Opening Question ?

The current out equals the current in. In other words, charge must enter the bulb at the same rate as it exits the bulb. It is not "used up" or consumed as it flows through the bulb.

Answers to Test Your Understanding Questions

25.1 Answer: (v) Doubling the diameter increases the cross-sectional area A by a factor of 4. Hence the current density magnitude $J = I/A$ is reduced to $\frac{1}{4}$ of the value in Example 25.1, and the magnitude of the drift velocity $v_d = J/n|q|$ is reduced by the same factor. The new magnitude is $v_d = (0.15\ \text{mm/s})/4 = 0.038\ \text{mm/s}$. This behavior is the same as that of an incompressible fluid, which slows down when it moves from a narrow pipe to a broader one (see Section 14.4).

25.2 Answer (ii) Figure 25.6b shows that the resistivity ρ of a semiconductor increases as the temperature decreases. From Eq. (25.5), the magnitude of the current density is $J = E/\rho$, so the current density decreases as the temperature drops and the resistivity increases.

25.3 Answer (iii) Solving Eq. (25.11) for the current shows that $I = V/R$. If the resistance R of the wire remained the same, doubling the voltage V would make the current I double as well. However, we saw in Example 25.3 that the resistance is *not* constant: As the current increases and the temperature increases, R increases as well. Thus doubling the voltage produces a current that is *less* than double the original current. An ohmic conductor is one for which $R = V/I$ has the same value no matter what the voltage, so the wire is *nonohmic*. (In many practical problems the temperature change of the wire is so small that it can be ignored, so we can safely regard the wire as being ohmic. We do so in almost all examples in this book.)

25.4 Answer: (iii), (ii), (i) For circuit (i), we find the current from Eq. (25.16): $I = \mathcal{E}/(R + r) = (1.5\ \text{V})/(1.4\ \Omega + 0.10\ \Omega) = 1.0\ \text{A}$. For circuit (ii), we note that the terminal voltage $V_{ab} = 3.6\ \text{V}$ equals the voltage IR across the 1.8-Ω resistor: $V_{ab} = IR$, so $I = V_{ab}/R = (3.6\ \text{V})/(1.8\ \Omega) = 2.0\ \text{A}$. For circuit (iii), we use Eq. (25.15) for the terminal voltage: $V_{ab} = \mathcal{E} - Ir$, so $I = (\mathcal{E} - V_{ab})/r = (12.0\ \text{V} - 11.0\ \text{V})/(0.20\ \Omega) = 5.0\ \text{A}$.

25.5 Answer: (iii), (ii), (i) These are the same circuits that we analyzed in Test Your Understanding of Section 25.4. In each case the net power output of the battery is $P = V_{ab}I$, where V_{ab} is the battery terminal voltage. For circuit (i), we found that $I = 1.0\ \text{A}$, so $V_{ab} = \mathcal{E} - Ir = 1.5\ \text{V} - (1.0\ \text{A})(0.10\ \Omega) = 1.4\ \text{V}$, so $P = (1.4\ \text{V})(1.0\ \text{A}) = 1.4\ \text{W}$. For circuit (ii), we have $V_{ab} = 3.6\ \text{V}$ and found that $I = 2.0\ \text{A}$, so $P = (3.6\ \text{V})(2.0\ \text{A}) = 7.2\ \text{W}$. For circuit (iii), we have $V_{ab} = 11.0\ \text{V}$ and found that $I = 5.0\ \text{A}$, so $P = (11.0\ \text{V})(5.0\ \text{A}) = 55\ \text{A}$.

25.6 Answer: (i) The difficulty of producing a certain amount of current increases as the resistivity ρ increases. From Eq. (25.24), $\rho = m/ne^2\tau$, so increasing the mass m will increase the resistivity. That's because a more massive charged particle will respond more sluggishly to an applied electric field and hence drift more slowly. To produce the same current, a greater electric field would be needed. (Increasing n, e, or τ; would decrease the resistivity and make it easier to produce a given current.)

PROBLEMS

For instructor-assigned homework, go to **www.masteringphysics.com** 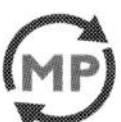

Discussion Questions

Q25.1. The definition of resistivity $(\rho = E/J)$ implies that an electric field exists inside a conductor. Yet we saw in Chapter 21 that there can be no electric field inside a conductor. Is there a contradiction here? Explain.

Q25.2. A cylindrical rod has resistance R. If we triple its length and diameter, what is its resistance, in terms of R?

Q25.3. A cylindrical rod has resistivity ρ. If we triple its length and diameter, what is its resistivity, in terms of ρ?

Q25.4. Two copper wires with different diameters are joined end to end. If a current flows in the wire combination, what happens to electrons when they move from the larger-diameter wire into the smaller-diameter wire? Does their drift speed increase, decrease, or stay the same? If the drift speed changes, what is the force that causes the change? Explain your reasoning.

Q25.5. When is a 1.5-V AAA battery *not* actually a 1.5-V battery? That is, when do its terminals provide a potential difference of less than 1.5 V?

Q25.6. Can the potential difference between the terminals of a battery ever be opposite in direction to the emf? If it can, give an example. If it cannot, explain why not.

Q25.7. A rule of thumb used to determine the internal resistance of a source is that it is the open-circuit voltage divided by the short-circuit current. Is this correct? Why or why not?

Q25.8. Batteries are always labeled with their emf; for instance, an AA flashlight battery is labeled "1.5 volts." Would it also be appropriate to put a label on batteries stating how much current they provide? Why or why not?

Q25.9. We have seen that a coulomb is an enormous amount of charge; it is virtually impossible to place a charge of 1 C on an object. Yet, a current of 10 A, 10 C/s, is quite reasonable. Explain this apparent discrepancy.

Q25.10. Electrons in an electric circuit pass through a resistor. The wire on either side of the resistor has the same diameter. (a) How does the drift speed of the electrons before entering the resistor compare to the speed after leaving the resistor? Explain your reasoning. (b) How does the potential energy for an electron before entering the resistor compare to the potential energy after leaving the resistor? Explain your reasoning.

Q25.11. Current causes the temperature of a real resistor to increase. Why? What effect does this heating have on the resistance? Explain.

Q25.12. Which of the graphs in Fig. 25.29 best illustrates the current I in a real resistor as a function of the potential difference V across it? Explain. (*Hint*: See Discussion Question Q25.11.)

Figure **25.29** Question Q25.12.

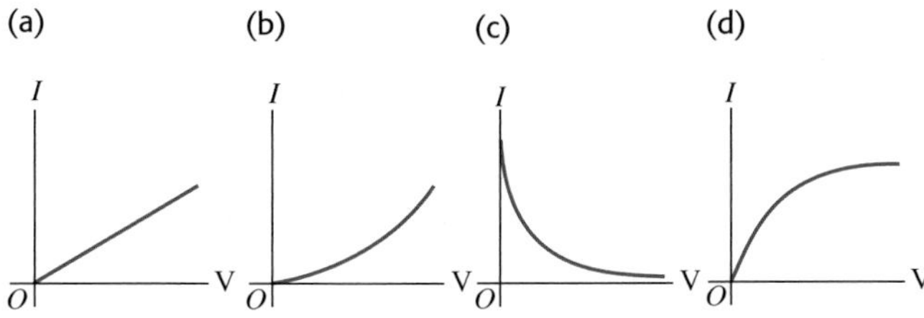

Q25.13. Why does an electric light bulb nearly always burn out just as you turn on the light, almost never while the light is shining?

Q25.14. A light bulb glows because it has resistance. The brightness of a light bulb increases with the electrical power dissipated in the bulb. (a) In the circuit shown in Fig. 25.30a, the two bulbs A and B are identical. Compared to bulb A, does bulb B glow more brightly, just as brightly, or less brightly? Explain your reasoning. (b) Bulb B is removed from the circuit and the circuit is completed as shown in Fig. 25.30b. Compared to the brightness of bulb A in Fig. 25.30a, does bulb A now glow more brightly, just as brightly, or less brightly? Explain your reasoning.

Figure **25.30** Question Q25.14.

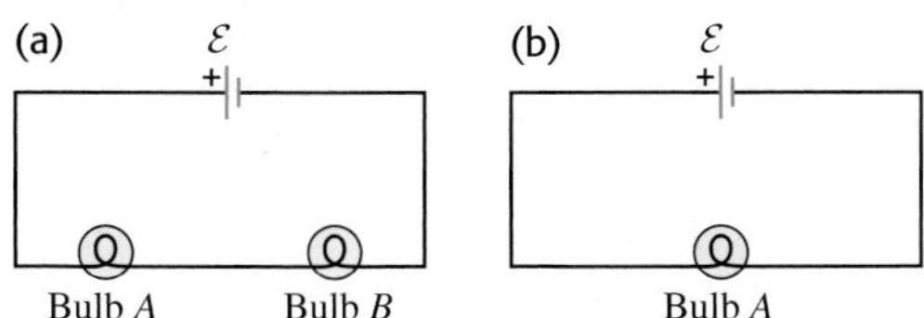

Q25.15. (See Discussion Question Q25.14.) An ideal ammeter A is placed in a circuit with a battery and a light bulb as shown in Fig. 25.31a, and the ammeter reading is noted. The circuit is then reconnected as in Fig. 25.31b, so that the positions of the ammeter and light bulb are reversed. (a) How does the ammeter reading in the situation shown in Fig. 25.31a compare to the reading in the situation shown in Fig. 25.31b? Explain your reasoning. (b) In which situation does the light bulb glow more brightly? Explain your reasoning.

Figure **25.31** Question Q25.15.

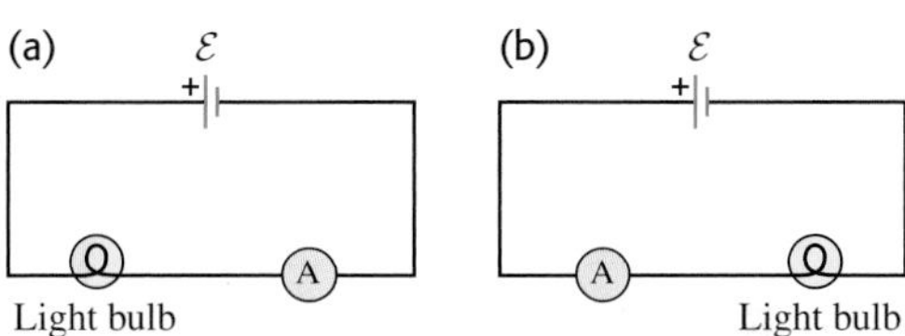

Q25.16. (See Discussion Question Q25.14.) Will a light bulb glow more brightly when it is connected to a battery as shown in Fig. 25.32a, in which an ideal ammeter A is placed in the circuit, or when it is connected as shown in Fig. 25.32b, in which an ideal voltmeter V is placed in the circuit? Explain your reasoning.

Figure **25.32** Question Q25.16.

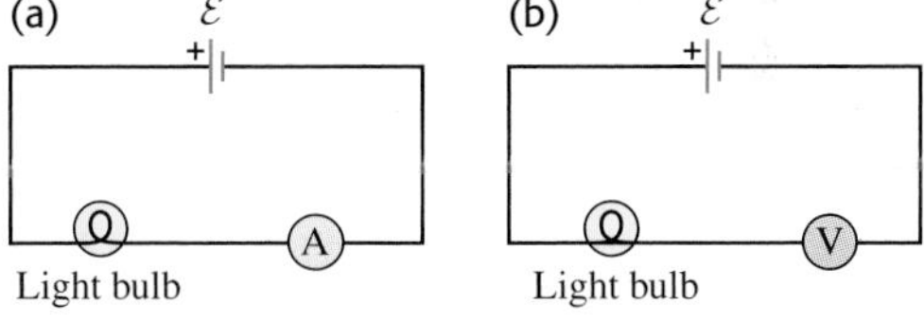

Q25.17. The energy that can be extracted from a storage battery is always less than the energy that goes into it while it is being charged. Why?

Q25.18. Eight flashlight batteries in series have an emf of about 12 V, similar to that of a car battery. Could they be used to start a car with a dead battery? Why or why not?

Q25.19. Small aircraft often have 24-V electrical systems rather than the 12-V systems in automobiles, even though the electrical power requirements are roughly the same in both applications. The explanation given by aircraft designers is that a 24-V system weighs less than a 12-V system because thinner wires can be used. Explain why this is so.

Q25.20. Long-distance, electric-power, transmission lines always operate at very high voltage, sometimes as much as 750 kV. What are the advantages of such high voltages? What are the disadvantages?

Q25.21. Ordinary household electric lines in North America usually operate at 120 V. Why is this a desirable voltage, rather than a value considerably larger or smaller? On the other hand, automobiles usually have 12-V electrical systems. Why is this a desirable voltage?

Q25.22. A fuse is a device designed to break a circuit, usually by melting when the current exceeds a certain value. What characteristics should the material of the fuse have?

Q25.23. High-voltage power supplies are sometimes designed intentionally to have rather large internal resistance as a safety precaution. Why is such a power supply with a large internal resistance safer than a supply with the same voltage but lower internal resistance?

Q25.24. The text states that good thermal conductors are also good electrical conductors. If so, why don't the cords used to connect toasters, irons, and similar heat-producing appliances get hot by conduction of heat from the heating element?

Exercises

Section 25.1 Current

25.1. A current of 3.6 A flows through an automobile headlight. How many coulombs of charge flow through the headlight in 3.0 h?

25.2. A silver wire 2.6 mm in diameter transfers a charge of 420 C in 80 min. Silver contains 5.8×10^{28} free electrons per cubic meter. (a) What is the current in the wire? (b) What is the magnitude of the drift velocity of the electrons in the wire?

25.3. A 5.00-A current runs through a 12-gauge copper wire (diameter 2.05 mm) and through a light bulb. Copper has 8.5×10^{28} free electrons per cubic meter. (a) How many electrons pass through the light bulb each second? (b) What is the current density in the wire? (c) At what speed does a typical electron pass by any given point in the wire? (d) If you were to use wire of twice the diameter, which of the above answers would change? Would they increase or decrease?

25.4. An 18-gauge wire (diameter 1.02 mm) carries a current with a current density of $1.50 \times 10^6 \text{ A/m}^2$. Calculate (a) the current in the wire and (b) the drift velocity of electrons in the wire.

25.5. Copper has 8.5×10^{28} free electrons per cubic meter. A 71.0-cm length of 12-gauge copper wire that is 2.05 mm in diameter carries 4.85 A of current. (a) How much time does it take for an electron to travel the length of the wire? (b) Repeat part (a) for 6-gauge copper wire (diameter 4.12 mm) of the same length that carries the same current. (c) Generally speaking, how does changing the diameter of a wire that carries a given amount of current affect the drift velocity of the electrons in the wire?

25.6. Consider the 18-gauge wire in Example 25.1. How many atoms are in 1.00 m^3 of copper? With the density of free electrons given in the example, how many free electrons are there per copper atom?

25.7. The current in a wire varies with time according to the relationship $I = 55 \text{ A} - (0.65 \text{ A/s}^2)t^2$. (a) How many coulombs of charge pass a cross section of the wire in the time interval between $t = 0$ and $t = 8.0$ s? (b) What constant current would transport the same charge in the same time interval?

25.8. Current passes through a solution of sodium chloride. In 1.00 s, 2.68×10^{16} Na^+ ions arrive at the negative electrode and 3.92×10^{16} Cl^- ions arrive at the positive electrode. (a) What is the current passing between the electrodes? (b) What is the direction of the current?

25.9. Assume that in silver metal there is one free electron per silver atom. Compute the free electron density for silver, and compare it to the value given in Exercise 25.2.

Section 25.2 Resistivity and Section 25.3 Resistance

25.10. (a) At room temperature what is the strength of the electric field in a 12-gauge copper wire (diameter 2.05 mm) that is needed to cause a 2.75-A current to flow? (b) What field would be needed if the wire were made of silver instead?

25.11. A 1.50-m cylindrical rod of diameter 0.500 cm is connected to a power supply that maintains a constant potential difference of 15.0 V across its ends, while an ammeter measures the current through it. You observe that at room temperature (20.0°C) the ammeter reads 18.5 A, while at 92.0°C it reads 17.2 A. You can ignore any thermal expansion of the rod. Find (a) the resistivity and (b) the temperature coefficient of resistivity at 20°C for the material of the rod.

25.12. A copper wire has a square cross section 2.3 mm on a side. The wire is 4.0 m long and carries a current of 3.6 A. The density of free electrons is $8.5 \times 10^{28}/\text{m}^3$. Find the magnitudes of (a) the current density in the wire and (b) the electric field in the wire. (c) How much time is required for an electron to travel the length of the wire?

25.13. In an experiment conducted at room temperature, a current of 0.820 A flows through a wire 3.26 mm in diameter. Find the magnitude of the electric field in the wire if the wire is made of (a) tungsten; and (b) aluminum.

25.14. A wire 6.50 m long with diameter of 2.05 mm has a resistance of 0.0290 Ω. What material is the wire most likely made of?

25.15. A cylindrical tungsten filament 15.0 cm long with a diameter of 1.00 mm is to be used in a machine for which the temperature will range from room temperature (20°C) up to 120°C. It will carry a current of 12.5 A at all temperatures (consult Tables 25.1 and 25.2). (a) What will be the maximum electric field in this filament, and (b) what will be its resistance with that field? (c) What will be the maximum potential drop over the full length of the filament?

25.16. What length of copper wire, 0.462 mm in diameter, has a resistance of 1.00 Ω?

25.17. In household wiring, copper wire 2.05 mm in diameter is often used. Find the resistance of a 24.0-m length of this wire.

25.18. What diameter must a copper wire have if its resistance is to be the same as that of an equal length of aluminum wire with diameter 3.26 mm?

25.19. You need to produce a set of cylindrical copper wires 3.50 m long that will have a resistance of 0.125 Ω each. What will be the mass of each of these wires?

25.20. A tightly coiled spring having 75 coils, each 3.50 cm in diameter, is made of insulated metal wire 3.25 mm in diameter. An ohmmeter connected across its opposite ends reads 1.74 Ω. What is the resistivity of the metal?

25.21. An aluminum cube has sides of length of 1.80 m. What is the resistance between two opposite faces of the cube?

25.22. A battery-powered light bulb has a tungsten filament. When the switch connecting the bulb to the battery is first turned on and the temperature of the bulb is 20°C, the current in the bulb is 0.860 A. After the bulb has been on for 30 s, the current is 0.220 A. What is then the temperature of the filament?

25.23. A rectangular solid of pure germanium measures 12 cm × 12 cm × 25 cm. Assuming that each of its faces is an equipotential surface, what is the resistance between opposite faces that are (a) farthest apart and (b) closest together?

25.24. You apply a potential difference of 4.50 V between the ends of a wire that is 2.50 m in length and 0.654 mm in radius. The resulting current through the wire is 17.6 A. What is the resistivity of the wire?

25.25. A current-carrying gold wire has diameter 0.84 mm. The electric field in the wire is 0.49 V/m. What are (a) the current carried by the wire; (b) the potential difference between two points in the wire 6.4 m apart; (c) the resistance of a 6.4-m length of this wire?

25.26. The potential difference between points in a wire 75.0 cm apart is 0.938 V when the current density is $4.40 \times 10^7\ \text{A/m}^2$. What are (a) the magnitude of $\vec{E}$ in the wire and (b) the resistivity of the material of which the wire is made?

25.27. (a) What is the resistance of a Nichrome wire at 0.0°C if its resistance is 100.00 Ω at 11.5°C? (b) What is the resistance of a carbon rod at 25.8°C if its resistance is 0.0160 Ω at 0.0°C?

25.28. A carbon resistor is to be used as a thermometer. On a winter day when the temperature is 4.0°C, the resistance of the carbon resistor is 217.3 Ω. What is the temperature on a spring day when the resistance is 215.8 Ω? (Take the reference temperature T_0 to be 4.0°C.)

25.29. A strand of wire has resistance 5.60 μΩ. Find the net resistance of 120 such strands if they are (a) placed side by side to form a cable of the same length as a single strand, and (b) connected end to end to form a wire 120 times as long as a single strand.

25.30. A hollow aluminum cylinder is 2.50 m long and has an inner radius of 3.20 cm and an outer radius of 4.60 cm. Treat each surface (inner, outer, and the two end faces) as an equipotential surface. At room temperature, what will an ohmmeter read if it is connected between (a) the opposite faces and (b) the inner and outer surfaces?

Section 25.4 Electromotive Force and Circuits

25.31. A copper transmission cable 100 km long and 10.0 cm in diameter carries a current of 125 A. (a) What is the potential drop across the cable? (b) How much electrical energy is dissipated as thermal energy every hour?

25.32. Consider the circuit shown in Fig. 25.33. The terminal voltage of the 24.0-V battery is 21.2 V. What are (a) the internal resistance r of the battery and (b) the resistance R of the circuit resistor?

Figure **25.33** Exercise 25.32.

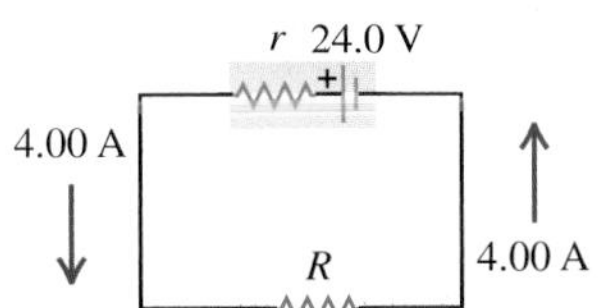

25.33. An idealized voltmeter is connected across the terminals of a battery while the current is varied. Figure 25.34 shows a graph of the voltmeter reading V as a function of the current I through the battery. Find (a) the emf $\mathcal{E}$ and (b) the internal resistance of the battery.

Figure **25.34** Exercise 25.33.

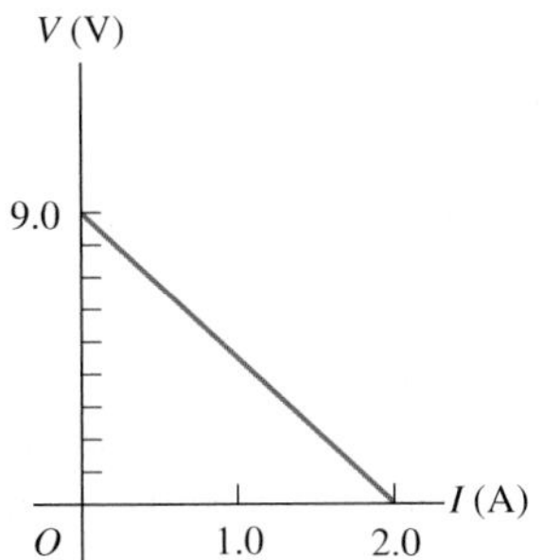

25.34. An idealized ammeter is connected to a battery as shown in Fig. 25.35. Find (a) the reading of the ammeter, (b) the current through the 4.00-Ω resistor, (c) the terminal voltage of the battery.

Figure **25.35** Exercise 25.34.

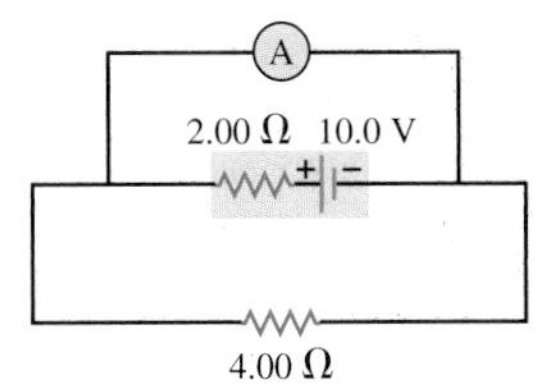

25.35. An ideal voltmeter V is connected to a 2.0-Ω resistor and a battery with emf 5.0 V and internal resistance 0.5 Ω as shown in Fig. 25.36. (a) What is the current in the 2.0-Ω resistor? (b) What is the terminal voltage of the battery? (c) What is the reading on the voltmeter? Explain your answers.

Figure **25.36** Exercise 25.35.

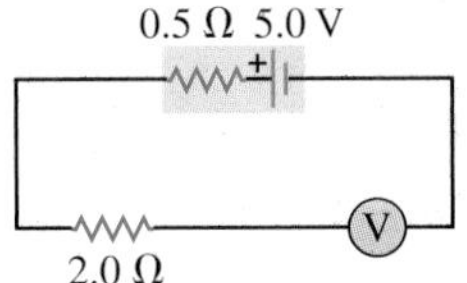

25.36. The circuit shown in Fig. 25.37 contains two batteries, each with an emf and an internal resistance, and two resistors. Find (a) the current in the circuit (magnitude *and* direction); (b) the terminal voltage V_{ab} of the 16.0-V battery; (c) the potential difference V_{ac} of point a with respect to point c. (d) Using Fig. 25.21 as a model, graph the potential rises and drops in this circuit.

Figure **25.37** Exercises 25.36, 25.38, 25.39, and 25.48.

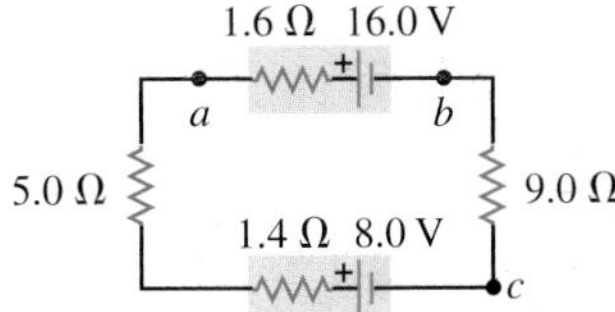

25.37. When switch S in Fig. 25.38 is open, the voltmeter V of the battery reads 3.08 V. When the switch is closed, the voltmeter reading drops to 2.97 V, and the ammeter A reads 1.65 A. Find the emf, the internal resistance of the battery, and the circuit resistance R. Assume that the two meters are ideal, so they don't affect the circuit.

Figure **25.38** Exercise 25.37.

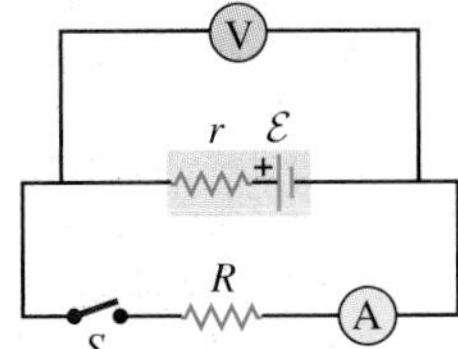

25.38. In the circuit of Fig. 25.37, the 5.0-Ω resistor is removed and replaced by a resistor of unknown resistance R. When this is done, an ideal voltmeter connected across the points b and c reads 1.9 V. Find (a) the current in the circuit and (b) the resistance R. (c) Graph the potential rises and drops in this circuit (see Fig. 25.21).

25.39. In the circuit shown in Fig. 25.37, the 16.0-V battery is removed and reinserted with the opposite polarity, so that its negative terminal is now next to point a. Find (a) the current in the circuit (magnitude *and* direction); (b) the terminal voltage V_{ba} of the 16.0-V battery; (c) the potential difference V_{ac} of point a with respect to point c. (d) Graph the potential rises and drops in this circuit (see Fig. 25.21).

25.40. The following measurements were made on a Thyrite resistor:

I(A)	0.50	1.00	2.00	4.00
V_{ab}(V)	2.55	3.11	3.77	4.58

(a) Graph V_{ab} as a function of I. (b) Does Thyrite obey Ohm's law? How can you tell? (c) Graph the resistance $R = V_{ab}/I$ as a function of I.

25.41. The following measurements of current and potential difference were made on a resistor constructed of Nichrome wire:

I(A)	0.50	1.00	2.00	4.00
V_{ab}(V)	1.94	3.88	7.76	15.52

(a) Graph V_{ab} as a function of I. (b) Does Nichrome obey Ohm's law? How can you tell? (c) What is the resistance of the resistor in ohms?

Section 25.5 Energy and Power in Electric Circuits

25.42. A resistor with a 15.0-V potential difference across its ends develops thermal energy at a rate of 327 W. (a) What is its resistance? (b) What is the current in the resistor?

25.43. Light Bulbs. The power rating of a light bulb (such as a 100-W bulb) is the power it dissipates when connected across a 120-V potential difference. What is the resistance of (a) a 100-W bulb and (b) a 60-W bulb? (c) How much current does each bulb draw in normal use?

25.44. If a "75-W" bulb (see Problem 25.43) is connected across a 220-V potential difference (as is used in Europe), how much power does it dissipate?

25.45. European Light Bulb. In Europe the standard voltage in homes is 220 V instead of the 120 V used in the United States. Therefore a "100-W" European bulb would be intended for use with a 220-V potential difference (see Problem 25.44). (a) If you bring a "100-W" European bulb home to the United States, what should be its U.S. power rating? (b) How much current will the 100-W European bulb draw in normal use in the United States?

25.46. A battery-powered global positioning system (GPS) receiver operating on 9.0 V draws a current of 0.13 A. How much electrical energy does it consume during 1.5 h?

25.47. Consider a resistor with length L, uniform cross-sectional area A, and uniform resistivity ρ that is carrying a current with uniform current density J. Use Eq. (25.18) to find the electrical power dissipated per unit volume, p. Express your result in terms of (a) E and J; (b) J and ρ; (c) E and ρ.

25.48. Consider the circuit of Fig. 25.37. (a) What is the total rate at which electrical energy is dissipated in the 5.00-Ω and 9.00-Ω resistors? (b) What is the power output of the 16.0-V battery? (c) At what rate is electrical energy being converted to other forms in the 8.0-V battery? (d) Show that the power output of the 16.0-V battery equals the overall rate of dissipation of electrical energy in the rest of the circuit.

25.49. The capacity of a storage battery, such as those used in automobile electrical systems, is rated in ampere-hours ($A \cdot h$). A 50-A · h battery can supply a current of 50 A for 1.0 h, or 25 A for 2.0 h, and so on. (a) What total energy can be supplied by a 12-V, 60-A · h battery if its internal resistance is negligible? (b) What volume (in liters) of gasoline has a total heat of combustion equal to the energy obtained in part (a)? (See Section 17.6; the density of gasoline is 900 kg/m^3.) (c) If a generator with an average electrical power output of 0.45 kW is connected to the battery, how much time will be required for it to charge the battery fully?

25.50. In the circuit analyzed in Example 25.9 the 4.0-Ω resistor is replaced by a 8.0-Ω resistor, as in Example 25.10. (a) Calculate the rate of conversion of chemical energy to electrical energy in the battery. How does your answer compare to the result calculated in Example 25.9? (b) Calculate the rate of electrical energy dissipation in the internal resistance of the battery. How does your answer compare to the result calculated in Example 25.9? (c) Use the results of parts (a) and (b) to calculate the net power output of the battery. How does your result compare to the electrical power dissipated in the 8.0-Ω resistor as calculated for this circuit in Example 25.10?

25.51. A 25.0-Ω bulb is connected across the terminals of a 12.0-V battery having 3.50 Ω of internal resistance. What percentage of the power of the battery is dissipated across the internal resistance and hence is not available to the bulb?

25.52. An idealized voltmeter is connected across the terminals of a 15.0-V battery, and a 75.0-Ω appliance is also connected across its terminals. If the voltmeter reads 11.3 V: (a) how much power is being dissipated by the appliance, and (b) what is the internal resistance of the battery?

25.53. In the circuit in Fig. 25.39, find (a) the rate of conversion of internal (chemical) energy to electrical energy within the battery; (b) the rate of dissipation of electrical energy in the battery; (c) the rate of dissipation of electrical energy in the external resistor.

Figure **25.39** Exercise 25.53.

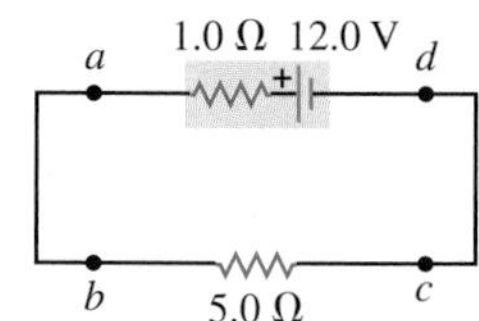

25.54. A typical small flashlight contains two batteries, each having an emf of 1.5 V, connected in series with a bulb having resistance 17 Ω. (a) If the internal resistance of the batteries is negligible, what power is delivered to the bulb? (b) If the batteries last for 5.0 h, what is the total energy delivered to the bulb? (c) The resistance of real batteries increases as they run down. If the initial internal resistance is negligible, what is the combined internal resistance of both batteries when the power to the bulb has decreased to half its initial value? (Assume that the resistance of the bulb is constant. Actually, it will change somewhat when the current through the filament changes, because this changes the temperature of the filament and hence the resistivity of the filament wire.)

25.55. A "540-W" electric heater is designed to operate from 120-V lines. (a) What is its resistance? (b) What current does it draw? (c) If the line voltage drops to 110 V, what power does the heater take? (Assume that the resistance is constant. Actually, it will change because of the change in temperature.) (d) The heater coils are metallic, so that the resistance of the heater decreases with decreasing temperature. If the change of resistance with temperature is taken into account, will the electrical power consumed by the heater be larger or smaller than what you calculated in part (c)? Explain.

*Section 25.6 Theory of Metallic Conduction

***25.56.** Pure silicon contains approximately 1.0×10^{16} free electrons per cubic meter. (a) Referring to Table 25.1, calculate the mean free time τ for silicon at room temperature. (b) Your answer in part (a) is much greater than the mean free time for copper given in Example 25.12. Why, then, does pure silicon have such a high resistivity compared to copper?

Problems

25.57. An electrical conductor designed to carry large currents has a circular cross section 2.50 mm in diameter and is 14.0 m long. The resistance between its ends is 0.104 Ω. (a) What is the resistivity of the material? (b) If the electric-field magnitude in the conductor is 1.28 V/m, what is the total current? (c) If the material has 8.5×10^{28} free electrons per cubic meter, find the average drift speed under the conditions of part (b).

25.58. A plastic tube 25.0 m long and 4.00 cm in diameter is dipped into a silver solution, depositing a layer of silver 0.100 mm thick uniformly over the outer surface of the tube. If this coated tube is then connected across a 12.0-V battery, what will be the current?

25.59. On your first day at work as an electrical technician, you are asked to determine the resistance per meter of a long piece of wire. The company you work for is poorly equipped. You find a battery, a voltmeter, and an ammeter, but no meter for directly measuring resistance (an ohmmeter). You put the leads from the voltmeter across the terminals of the battery, and the meter reads 12.6 V. You cut off a 20.0-m length of wire and connect it to the battery, with an ammeter in series with it to measure the current in the wire. The ammeter reads 7.00 A. You then cut off a 40.0-m length of wire and connect it to the battery, again with the ammeter in series to measure the current. The ammeter reads 4.20 A. Even though the equipment you have available to you is limited, your boss assures you of its high quality: The ammeter has very small resistance, and the voltmeter has very large resistance. What is the resistance of 1 meter of wire?

25.60. A 2.0-mm length of wire is made by welding the end of a 120-cm-long silver wire to the end of an 80-cm-long copper wire. Each piece of wire is 0.60 mm in diameter. The wire is at room temperature, so the resistivities are as given in Table 25.1. A potential difference of 5.0 V is maintained between the ends of the 2.0-m composite wire. (a) What is the current in the copper section? (b) What is the current in the silver section? (c) What is the magnitude of $\vec{E}$ in the copper? (d) What is the magnitude of $\vec{E}$ in the silver? (e) What is the potential difference between the ends of the silver section of wire?

25.61. A 3.00-m length of copper wire at 20°C has a 1.20-m-long section with diameter 1.60 mm and a 1.80-m-long section with diameter 0.80 mm. There is a current of 2.5 mA in the 1.60-mm-diameter section. (a) What is the current in the 0.80-mm-diameter section? (b) What is the magnitude of $\vec{E}$ in the 1.60-mm-diameter section? (c) What is the magnitude of $\vec{E}$ in the 0.80-mm-diameter section? (d) What is the potential difference between the ends of the 3.00-m length of wire?

25.62. Critical Current Density in Superconductors. One problem with some of the newer high-temperature superconductors is getting a large enough current density for practical use without causing the resistance to reappear. The maximum current density for which the material will remain a superconductor is called the critical current density of the material. In 1987, IBM research labs had produced thin films with critical current densities of 1.0×10^5 A/cm^2. (a) How much current could an 18-gauge wire (see Example 25.1 in Section 25.1) of this material carry and still remain superconducting? (b) Researchers are trying to develop superconductors with critical current densities of 1.0×10^6 A/cm^2. What diameter cylindrical wire of such a material would be needed to carry 1000 A without losing its superconductivity?

25.63. A material of resistivity ρ is formed into a solid, truncated cone of height h and radii r_1 and r_2 at either end (Fig. 25.40). (a) Calculate the resistance of the cone between the two flat end faces. (*Hint:* Imagine slicing the cone into very many thin disks, and calculate the resistance of one such disk.) (b) Show that your result agrees with Eq. (25.10) when $r_1 = r_2$.

Figure **25.40** Problem 25.63.

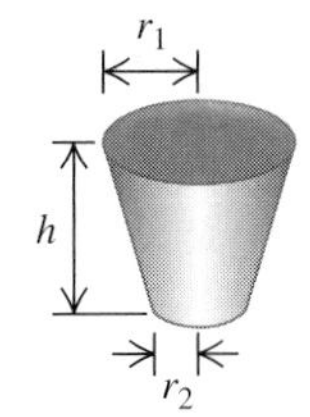

25.64. The region between two concentric conducting spheres with radii a and b is filled with a conducting material with resistivity ρ. (a) Show that the resistance between the spheres is given by

$$R = \frac{\rho}{4\pi}\left(\frac{1}{a} - \frac{1}{b}\right)$$

(b) Derive an expression for the current density as a function of radius, in terms of the potential difference V_{ab} between the spheres. (c) Show that the result in part (a) reduces to Eq. (25.10) when the separation $L = b - a$ between the spheres is small.

25.65. Leakage in a Dielectric. Two parallel plates of a capacitor have equal and opposite charges Q. The dielectric has a dielectric constant K and a resistivity ρ. Show that the "leakage" current I carried by the dielectric is given by $I = Q/K\epsilon_0\rho$.

25.66. In the circuit shown in Fig. 25.41, R is a variable resistor whose value can range from 0 to ∞, and a and b are the terminals of a battery having an emf $\mathcal{E} = 15.0$ V and an internal resistance of 4.00 Ω. The ammeter and voltmeter are both idealized meters. As R varies over its full range of values, what will be the largest and smallest readings of (a) the voltmeter and (b) the ammeter? (c) Sketch qualitative graphs of the readings of both meters as functions of R, as R ranges from 0 to ∞.

Figure **25.41** Problem 25.66.

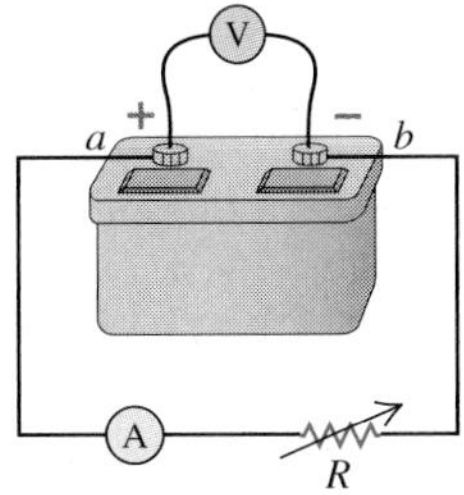

25.67. The temperature coefficient of resistance α in Eq. (25.12) equals the temperature coefficient of resistivity α in Eq. (25.6) only if the coefficient of thermal expansion is small. A cylindrical column of mercury is in a vertical glass tube. At 20°C, the length of the mercury column is 12.0 cm. The diameter of the mercury column is 1.6 mm and doesn't change with temperature because glass has a small coefficient of thermal expansion. The coefficient of volume expansion of the mercury is given in Table 17.2, its resistivity at 20°C is given in Table 25.1, and its temperature coefficient of resistivity is given in Table 25.2. (a) At 20°C, what is the resistance between the ends of the mercury column? (b) The mercury column is heated to 60°C. What is the change in its resistivity? (c) What is the change in its length? Explain why the coefficient of volume expansion, rather than the coefficient of linear expansion, determines the change in length. (d) What is the change in its resistance? (*Hint:* Since the percentage changes in ρ and L are small, you may find it helpful to derive from Eq. (25.10) an equation for ΔR in terms of $\Delta\rho$ and ΔL.) (e) What is the temperature coefficient of resistance α for the mercury column, as defined in Eq. (25.12)? How does this value compare with the temperature coefficient of resistivity? Is the effect of the change in length important?

25.68. (a) What is the potential difference V_{ad} in the circuit of Fig. 25.42? (b) What is the terminal voltage of the 4.00-V battery? (c) A battery with emf 10.30z V and internal resistance 0.50 Ω is inserted in the circuit at d, with its negative terminal connected to the negative terminal of the 8.00-V battery. What is the difference of potential V_{bc} between the terminals of the 4.00-V battery now?

Figure **25.42** Problem 25.68.

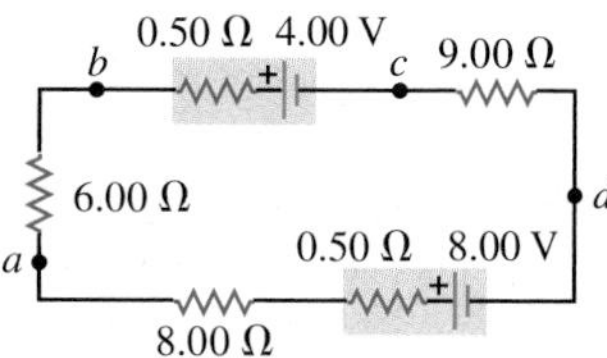

25.69. The potential difference across the terminals of a battery is 8.4 V when there is a current of 1.50 A in the battery from the negative to the positive terminal. When the current is 3.50 A in the reverse direction, the potential difference becomes 9.4 V. (a) What is the internal resistance of the battery? (b) What is the emf of the battery?

25.70. A person with body resistance between his hands of 10 kΩ accidentally grasps the terminals of a 14-kV power supply. (a) If the internal resistance of the power supply is 2000 Ω, what is the current through the person's body? (b) What is the power dissipated in his body? (c) If the power supply is to be made safe by increasing its internal resistance, what should the internal resistance be for the maximum current in the above situation to be 1.00 mA or less?

25.71. The average bulk resistivity of the human body (apart from surface resistance of the skin) is about 5.0 Ω · m. The conducting path between the hands can be represented approximately as a cylinder 1.6 m long and 0.10 m in diameter. The skin resistance can be made negligible by soaking the hands in salt water. (a) What is the resistance between the hands if the skin resistance is negligible? (b) What potential difference between the hands is needed for a lethal shock current of 100 mA? (Note that your result shows that small potential differences produce dangerous currents when the skin is damp.) (c) With the current in part (b), what power is dissipated in the body?

25.72. A typical cost for electric power is 12.0¢ per kilowatt-hour. (a) Some people leave their porch light on all the time. What is the yearly cost to keep a 75-W bulb burning day and night? (b) Suppose your refrigerator uses 400 W of power when it's running, and it runs 8 hours a day. What is the yearly cost of operating your refrigerator?

25.73. A 12.6-V car battery with negligible internal resistance is connected to a series combination of a 3.2-Ω resistor that obeys Ohm's law and a thermistor that does not obey Ohm's law but instead has a current–voltage relationship $V = \alpha I + \beta I^2$, with $\alpha = 3.8\ \Omega$ and $\beta = 1.3\ \Omega/\text{A}$. What is the current through the 3.2-Ω resistor?

25.74. A cylindrical copper cable 1.50 km long is connected across a 220.0-V potential difference. (a) What should be its diameter so that it produces heat at a rate of 50.0 W? (b) What is the electric field inside the cable under these conditions?

25.75. A Nonideal Ammeter. Unlike the idealized ammeter described in Section 25.4, any real ammeter has a nonzero resistance. (a) An ammeter with resistance R_A is connected in series with a resistor R and a battery of emf $\mathcal{E}$ and internal resistance r. The current measured by the ammeter is I_A. Find the current through the circuit if the ammeter is removed so that the battery and the resistor form a complete circuit. Express your answer in terms of I_A, r, R_A, and R. The more "ideal" the ammeter, the smaller the difference between this current and the current I_A. (b) If $R = 3.80\ \Omega$, $\mathcal{E} = 7.50$ V, and $r = 0.45\ \Omega$, find the maximum value of the ammeter resistance R_A so that I_A is within 1.0% of the current in the circuit when the ammeter is absent. (c) Explain why your answer in part (b) represents a *maximum* value.

25.76. A 1.50-m cylinder of radius 1.10 cm is made of a complicated mixture of materials. Its resistivity depends on the distance x from the left end and obeys the formula $\rho(x) = a + bx^2$, where a and b are constants. At the left end, the resistivity is $2.25 \times 10^{-8}\ \Omega \cdot \text{m}$, while at the right end it is $8.50 \times 10^{-8}\ \Omega \cdot \text{m}$. (a) What is the resistance of this rod? (b) What is the electric field at its midpoint if it carries a 1.75-A current? (c) If we cut the rod into two 75.0-cm halves, what is the resistance of each half?

25.77. According to the U.S. National Electrical Code, copper wire used for interior wiring of houses, hotels, office buildings, and industrial plants is permitted to carry no more than a specified maximum amount of current. The table below shows the maximum current I_{max} for several common sizes of wire with varnished cambric insulation. The "wire gauge" is a standard used to describe the diameter of wires. Note that the larger the diameter of the wire, the *smaller* the wire gauge.

Wire gauge	Diameter (cm)	I_{max} (A)
14	0.163	18
12	0.205	25
10	0.259	30
8	0.326	40
6	0.412	60
5	0.462	65
4	0.519	85

(a) What considerations determine the maximum current-carrying capacity of household wiring? (b) A total of 4200 W of power is to be supplied through the wires of a house to the household electrical appliances. If the potential difference across the group of appliances is 120 V, determine the gauge of the thinnest permissible wire that can be used. (c) Suppose the wire used in this house is of the gauge found in part (b) and has total length 42.0 m. At what rate is energy dissipated in the wires? (d) The house is built in a community where the consumer cost of electric energy is \$0.11 per kilowatt-hour. If the house were built with wire of the next larger diameter than that found in part (b), what would be the savings in electricity costs in one year? Assume that the appliances are kept on for an average of 12 hours a day.

25.78. A toaster using a Nichrome heating element operates on 120 V. When it is switched on at 20°C, the heating element carries an initial current of 1.35 A. A few seconds later the current reaches the steady value of 1.23 A. (a) What is the final temperature of the element? The average value of the temperature coefficient of resistivity for Nichrome over the temperature range is $4.5 \times 10^{-4}\ (\text{C}°)^{-1}$. (b) What is the power dissipated in the heating element initially and when the current reaches a steady value?

25.79. In the circuit of Fig. 25.43, find (a) the current through the 8.0-Ω resistor and (b) the total rate of dissipation of electrical energy in the 8.0-Ω resistor and in the internal resistance of the batteries. (c) In one of the batteries, chemical energy is being converted into electrical energy. In which one is this happening, and at what rate? (d) In one of the batteries, electrical energy is being converted into chemical energy. In which one is this happening, and at what rate? (e) Show that the overall rate of production of electrical energy equals the overall rate of consumption of electrical energy in the circuit.

Figure **25.43** Problem 25.79.

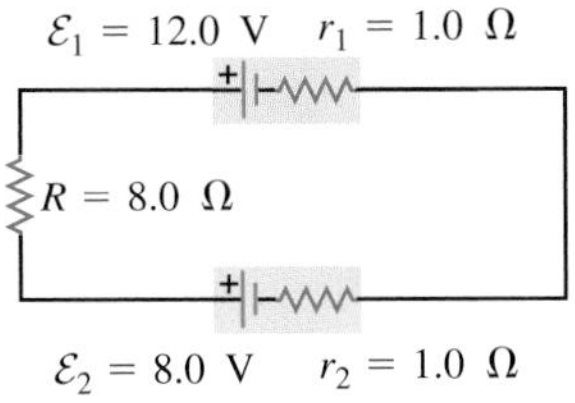

$\mathcal{E}_1 = 12.0$ V $\quad r_1 = 1.0\ \Omega$

$R = 8.0\ \Omega$

$\mathcal{E}_2 = 8.0$ V $\quad r_2 = 1.0\ \Omega$

25.80. A lightning bolt strikes one end of a steel lightning rod, producing a 15,000-A current burst that lasts for 65 μs. The rod is 2.0 m long and 1.8 cm in diameter, and its other end is connected to the ground by 35 m of 8.0-mm-diameter copper wire. (a) Find the potential difference between the top of the steel rod and the lower end of the copper wire during the current burst. (b) Find the total energy deposited in the rod and wire by the current burst.

25.81. A 12.0-V battery has an internal resistance of 0.24 Ω and a capacity of 50.0 A · h (see Exercise 25.49). The battery is charged by passing a 10-A current through it for 5.0 h. (a) What is the terminal voltage during charging? (b) What total electrical energy is supplied to the battery during charging? (c) What electrical energy is dissipated in the internal resistance during charging? (d) The battery is now completely discharged through a resistor, again with a constant current of 10 A. What is the external circuit resistance? (e) What total electrical energy is supplied to the external resistor? (f) What total electrical energy is dissipated in the internal resistance? (g) Why are the answers to parts (b) and (e) not the same?

25.82. Repeat Problem 25.81 with charge and discharge currents of 30 A. The charging and discharging times will now be 1.7 h rather than 5.0 h. What differences in performance do you see?

Challenge Problems

25.83. The *Tolman-Stewart experiment* in 1916 demonstrated that the free charges in a metal have negative charge and provided a quantitative measurement of their charge-to-mass ratio, $|q|/m$. The experiment consisted of abruptly stopping a rapidly rotating spool of wire and measuring the potential difference that this produced between the ends of the wire. In a simplified model of this experiment, consider a metal rod of length L that is given a uniform acceleration $\vec{a}$ to the right. Initially the free charges in the metal lag behind the rod's motion, thus setting up an electric field $\vec{E}$ in the rod. In the steady state this field exerts a force on the free charges that makes them accelerate along with the rod. (a) Apply $\Sigma\vec{F} = m\vec{a}$ to the free charges to obtain an expression for $|q|/m$ in terms of the magnitudes of the induced electric field $\vec{E}$ and the acceleration $\vec{a}$. (b) If all the free charges in the metal rod have the same acceleration, the electric field $\vec{E}$ is the same at all points in the rod. Use this fact to rewrite the expression for $|q|/m$ in terms of the potential V_{bc} between the ends of the rod (Fig. 25.44). (c) If the free charges have negative charge, which end of the rod, b or c, is at higher potential? (d) If the rod is 0.50 m long and the free charges are electrons (charge $q = -1.60 \times 10^{-19}$ C, mass 9.11×10^{-31} kg), what magnitude of acceleration is required to produce a potential difference of 1.0 mV between the ends of the rod? (e) Discuss why the actual experiment used a rotating spool of thin wire rather than a moving bar as in our simplified analysis.

Figure **25.44** Challenge Problem 25.83.

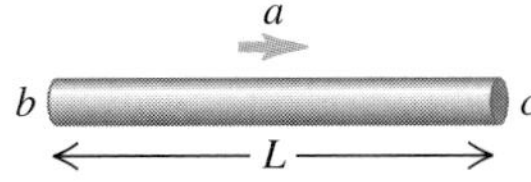

25.84. The current–voltage relationship of a semiconductor diode is given by

$$I = I_S\left[\exp\left(\frac{eV}{kT}\right) - 1\right]$$

where I and V are the current through and the voltage across the diode, respectively. I_S is a constant characteristic of the device, e is the magnitude of the electron charge, k is the Boltzmann constant, and T is the Kelvin temperature. Such a diode is connected in series with a resistor with $R = 1.00\ \Omega$ and a battery with $\mathcal{E} = 2.00$ V. The polarity of the battery is such that the current through the diode is in the forward direction (Fig. 25.45). The battery has negligible internal resistance. (a) Obtain an equation for V. Note that you cannot solve for V algebraically. (b) The value of V must be obtained by using a numerical method. One approach is to try a value of V, see how the left- and right-hand sides of the equation compare for this V, and use this to refine your guess for V. Using $I_S = 1.50$ mA and $T = 293$ K, obtain a solution (accurate to three significant figures) for the voltage drop V across the diode and the current I through it.

Figure **25.45** Challenge Problem 25.84.

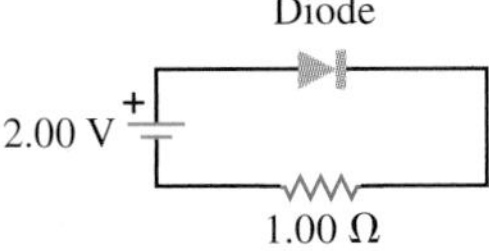

25.85. The resistivity of a semiconductor can be modified by adding different amounts of impurities. A rod of semiconducting material of length L and cross-sectional area A lies along the x-axis between $x = 0$ and $x = L$. The material obeys Ohm's law, and its resistivity varies along the rod according to $\rho(x) = \rho_0 \exp(-x/L)$. The end of the rod at $x = 0$ is at a potential V_0 greater than the end at $x = L$. (a) Find the total resistance of the rod and the current in the rod. (b) Find the electric-field magnitude

$E(x)$ in the rod as a function of x. (c) Find the electric potential $V(x)$ in the rod as a function of x. (d) Graph the functions $\rho(x)$, $E(x)$, and $V(x)$ for values of x between $x = 0$ and $x = L$.

25.86. A source with emf $\mathcal{E}$ and internal resistance r is connected to an external circuit. (a) Show that the power output of the source is maximum when the current in the circuit is one-half the short-circuit current of the source. (b) If the external circuit consists of a resistance R, show that the power output is maximum when $R = r$ and that the maximum power is $\mathcal{E}^2/4r$.

25.87. The temperature coefficient of resistivity α is given by

$$\alpha = \frac{1}{\rho}\frac{d\rho}{dT}$$

where ρ is the resistivity at the temperature T. Equation (25.6) then follows if α is assumed constant and much smaller than $(T - T_0)^{-1}$. (a) If α is not constant but is given by $\alpha = -n/T$, where T is the Kelvin temperature and n is a constant, show that the resistivity is given by $\rho = a/T^n$, where a is a constant. (b) From Fig. 25.10, you can see that such a relationship might be used as a rough approximation for a semiconductor. Using the values of ρ and α for carbon from Tables 25.1 and 25.2, determine a and n. (In Table 25.1, assume that "room temperature" means 293 K). (c) Using your result from part (b), determine the resistivity of carbon at $-196°C$ and $300°C$. (Remember to express T in kelvins.)

DIRECT-CURRENT CIRCUITS

26

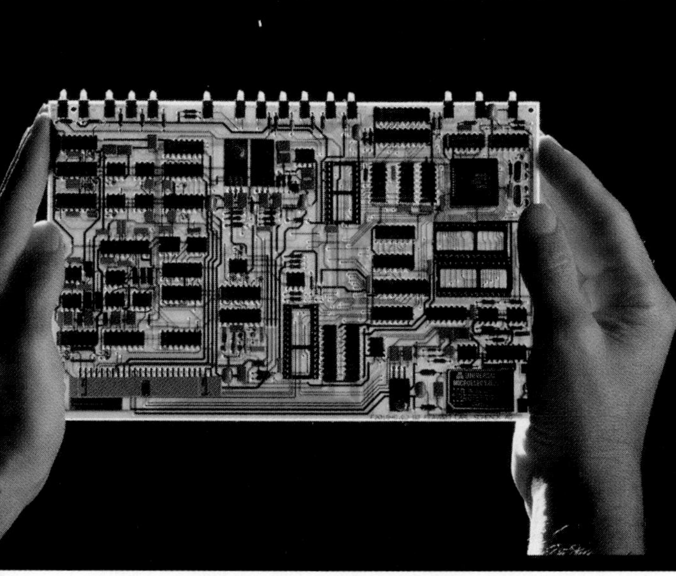

? In a complex circuit like the one on this circuit board, is it possible to connect several resistors with different resistances so that they all have the same potential difference? If so, will the current be the same through all of the resistors?

LEARNING GOALS

By studying this chapter, you will learn:

- How to analyze circuits with multiple resistors in series or parallel.
- Rules that you can apply to any circuit with more than one loop.
- How to use an ammeter, voltmeter, ohmmeter, or potentiometer in a circuit.
- How to analyze circuits that include both a resistor and a capacitor.
- How electric power is distributed in the home.

If you look inside your TV, your computer, or your stereo receiver or under the hood of a car, you will find circuits of much greater complexity than the simple circuits we studied in Chapter 25. Whether connected by wires or integrated in a semiconductor chip, these circuits often include several sources, resistors, and other circuit elements, such as capacitors, transformers, and motors, interconnected in a *network.*

In this chapter we study general methods for analyzing such networks, including how to find unknown voltages, currents, and properties of circuit elements. We'll learn how to determine the equivalent resistance for several resistors connected in series or in parallel. For more general networks we need two rules called *Kirchhoff's rules.* One is based on the principle of conservation of charge applied to a junction; the other is derived from energy conservation for a charge moving around a closed loop. We'll discuss instruments for measuring various electrical quantities. We also look at a circuit containing resistance and capacitance, in which the current varies with time.

Our principal concern in this chapter is with **direct-current** (dc) circuits, in which the direction of the current does not change with time. Flashlights and automobile wiring systems are examples of direct-current circuits. Household electrical power is supplied in the form of **alternating current** (ac), in which the current oscillates back and forth. The same principles for analyzing networks apply to both kinds of circuits, and we conclude this chapter with a look at household wiring systems. We'll discuss alternating-current circuits in detail in Chapter 31.

26.1 Resistors in Series and Parallel

Resistors turn up in all kinds of circuits, ranging from hair dryers and space heaters to circuits that limit or divide current or reduce or divide a voltage. Such circuits often contain several resistors, so it's appropriate to consider *combinations* of resistors. A simple example is a string of light bulbs used for holiday decorations;

12.1 DC Series Circuits (Qualitative)

26.1 Four different ways of connecting three resistors.

(a) R_1, R_2, and R_3 in series

(b) R_1, R_2, and R_3 in parallel

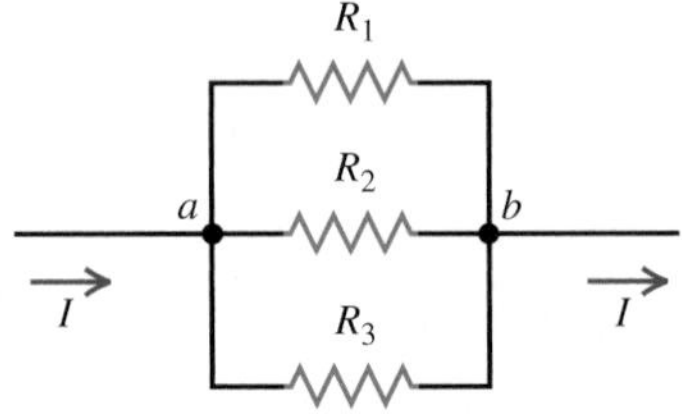

(c) R_1 in series with parallel combination of R_2 and R_3

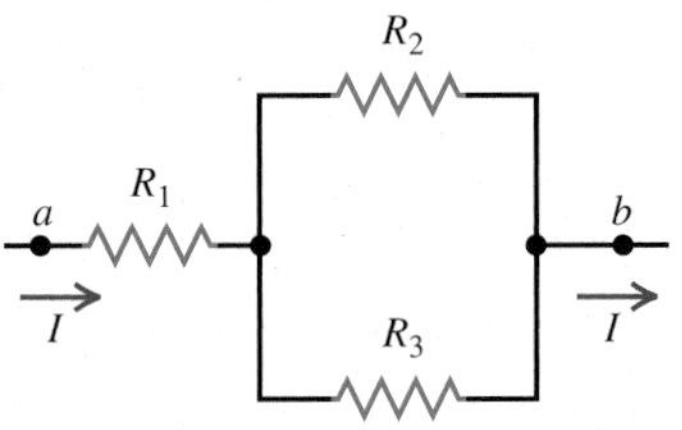

(d) R_1 in parallel with series combination of R_2 and R_3

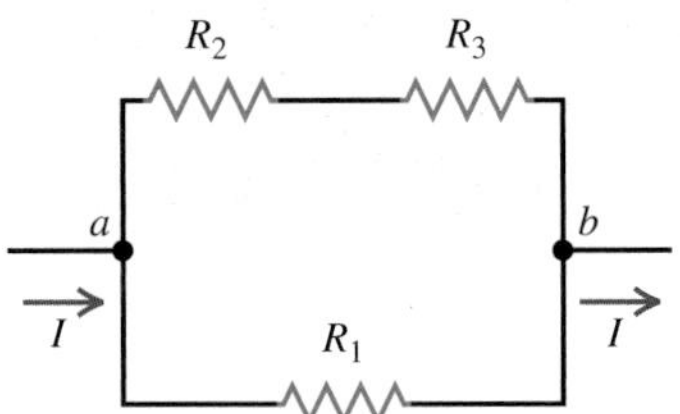

each bulb acts as a resistor, and from a circuit-analysis perspective the string of bulbs is simply a combination of resistors.

Suppose we have three resistors with resistances R_1, R_2, and R_3. Figure 26.1 shows four different ways in which they might be connected between points a and b. When several circuit elements such as resistors, batteries, and motors are connected in sequence as in Fig. 26.1a, with only a single current path between the points, we say that they are connected in **series.** We studied *capacitors* in series in Section 24.2; we found that, because of conservation of charge, capacitors in series all have the same charge if they are initially uncharged. In circuits we're often more interested in the *current,* which is charge flow per unit time.

The resistors in Fig. 26.1b are said to be connected in **parallel** between points a and b. Each resistor provides an alternative path between the points. For circuit elements that are connected in parallel, the *potential difference* is the same across each element. We studied capacitors in parallel in Section 24.2.

In Fig. 26.1c, resistors R_2 and R_3 are in parallel, and this combination is in series with R_1. In Fig. 26.1d, R_2 and R_3 are in series, and this combination is in parallel with R_1.

For any combination of resistors we can always find a *single* resistor that could replace the combination and result in the same total current and potential difference. For example, a string of holiday light bulbs could be replaced by a single, appropriately chosen light bulb that would draw the same current and have the same potential difference between its terminals as the original string of bulbs. The resistance of this single resistor is called the **equivalent resistance** of the combination. If any one of the networks in Fig. 26.1 were replaced by its equivalent resistance R_{eq}, we could write

$$V_{ab} = IR_{eq} \quad \text{or} \quad R_{eq} = \frac{V_{ab}}{I}$$

where V_{ab} is the potential difference between terminals a and b of the network and I is the current at point a or b. To compute an equivalent resistance, we assume a potential difference V_{ab} across the actual network, compute the corresponding current I, and take the ratio V_{ab}/I.

Resistors in Series

We can derive general equations for the equivalent resistance of a series or parallel combination of resistors. If the resistors are in *series,* as in Fig. 26.1a, the current I must be the same in all of them. (As we discussed in Section 25.4, current is *not* "used up" as it passes through a circuit.) Applying $V = IR$ to each resistor, we have

$$V_{ax} = IR_1 \qquad V_{xy} = IR_2 \qquad V_{yb} = IR_3$$

The potential differences across each resistor need not be the same (except for the special case in which all three resistances are equal). The potential difference V_{ab} across the entire combination is the sum of these individual potential differences:

$$V_{ab} = V_{ax} + V_{xy} + V_{yb} = I(R_1 + R_2 + R_3)$$

and so

$$\frac{V_{ab}}{I} = R_1 + R_2 + R_3$$

The ratio V_{ab}/I is, by definition, the equivalent resistance R_{eq}. Therefore

$$R_{eq} = R_1 + R_2 + R_3$$

It is easy to generalize this to any number of resistors:

$$R_{eq} = R_1 + R_2 + R_3 + \cdots \qquad \text{(resistors in series)} \qquad (26.1)$$

The equivalent resistance of *any number* of resistors in series equals the sum of their individual resistances.

The equivalent resistance is *greater than* any individual resistance.

Let's compare this result with Eq. (24.5) for *capacitors* in series. Resistors in series add directly because the voltage across each is directly proportional to its resistance and to the common current. Capacitors in series add reciprocally because the voltage across each is directly proportional to the common charge but *inversely* proportional to the individual capacitance.

Resistors in Parallel

If the resistors are in *parallel,* as in Fig. 26.1b, the current through each resistor need not be the same. But the potential difference between the terminals of each resistor must be the same and equal to V_{ab} (Fig. 26.2). (Remember that the potential difference between any two points does not depend on the path taken between the points.) Let's call the currents in the three resistors I_1, I_2, and I_3. Then from $I = V/R$,

$$I_1 = \frac{V_{ab}}{R_1} \qquad I_2 = \frac{V_{ab}}{R_2} \qquad I_3 = \frac{V_{ab}}{R_3}$$

In general, the current is different through each resistor. Because charge is not accumulating or draining out of point a, the total current I must equal the sum of the three currents in the resistors:

$$I = I_1 + I_2 + I_3 = V_{ab}\left(\frac{1}{R_1} + \frac{1}{R_2} + \frac{1}{R_3}\right) \quad \text{or}$$

$$\frac{I}{V_{ab}} = \frac{1}{R_1} + \frac{1}{R_2} + \frac{1}{R_3}$$

But by the definition of the equivalent resistance R_{eq}, $I/V_{ab} = 1/R_{eq}$, so

$$\frac{1}{R_{eq}} = \frac{1}{R_1} + \frac{1}{R_2} + \frac{1}{R_3}$$

Again it is easy to generalize to *any number* of resistors in parallel:

$$\frac{1}{R_{eq}} = \frac{1}{R_1} + \frac{1}{R_2} + \frac{1}{R_3} + \cdots \quad \text{(resistors in parallel)} \tag{26.2}$$

For *any number* of resistors in parallel, the *reciprocal* of the equivalent resistance equals the *sum of the reciprocals* of their individual resistances.

The equivalent resistance is always *less than* any individual resistance.

We can compare this result with Eq. (24.7) for *capacitors* in parallel. Resistors in parallel add reciprocally because the current in each is proportional to the common voltage across them and *inversely* proportional to the resistance of each. Capacitors in parallel add directly because the charge on each is proportional to the common voltage across them and *directly* proportional to the capacitance of each.

For the special case of *two* resistors in parallel,

$$\frac{1}{R_{eq}} = \frac{1}{R_1} + \frac{1}{R_2} = \frac{R_1 + R_2}{R_1 R_2} \quad \text{and}$$

$$R_{eq} = \frac{R_1 R_2}{R_1 + R_2} \quad \text{(two resistors in parallel)} \tag{26.3}$$

26.2 A car's headlights are connected in parallel. Hence each headlight is exposed to the full potential difference supplied by the car's electrical system, giving maximum brightness. Another advantage is that if one headlight burns out, the other one keeps shining (see Example 26.2).

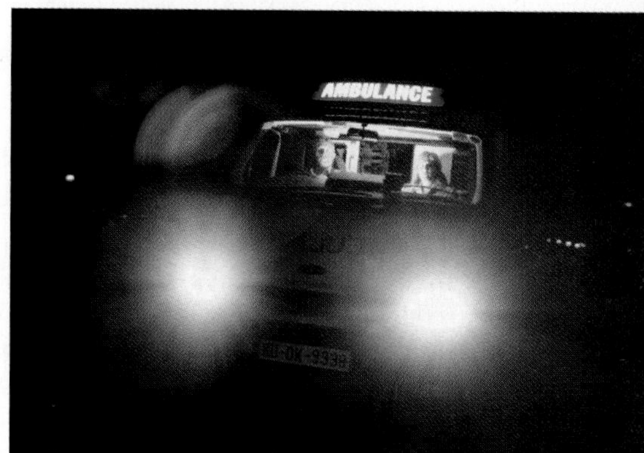

12.2 DC Parallel Circuits

Because $V_{ab} = I_1R_1 = I_2R_2$, it follows that

$$\frac{I_1}{I_2} = \frac{R_2}{R_1} \quad \text{(two resistors in parallel)} \tag{26.4}$$

This shows that the currents carried by two resistors in parallel are *inversely proportional* to their resistances. More current goes through the path of least resistance.

Problem-Solving Strategy 26.1 Resistors in Series and Parallel

IDENTIFY *the relevant concepts:* Many resistor networks are made up of resistors in series, in parallel, or a combination of the two. The key concept is that such a network can be replaced by a single equivalent resistor.

SET UP *the problem* using the following steps:
1. Make a drawing of the resistor network.
2. Determine whether the resistors are connected in series or parallel. Note that you can often consider networks such as those in Figs. 26.1c and 26.1d as combinations of series and parallel arrangements.
3. Determine what the target variables are. They could include the equivalent resistance of the network, the potential difference across each resistor, or the current through each resistor.

EXECUTE *the solution* as follows:
1. Use Eq. (26.1) or (26.2) to find the equivalent resistance for a series or a parallel combination, respectively.
2. If the network is more complex, try reducing it to series and parallel combinations. For example, in Fig. 26.1c we first replace the parallel combination of R_2 and R_3 with its equivalent resistance; this then forms a series combination with R_1. In Fig. 26.1d, the combination of R_2 and R_3 in series forms a parallel combination with R_1.
3. When calculating potential differences, remember that when resistors are connected in series, the total potential difference across the combination equals the sum of the individual potential differences. When resistors are connected in parallel, the potential difference is the same for every resistor and equals the potential difference across the parallel combination.
4. Keep in mind the analogous statements for current. When resistors are connected in series, the current is the same through every resistor and equals the current through the series combination. When resistors are connected in parallel, the total current through the combination equals the sum of the currents through the individual resistors.

EVALUATE *your answer:* Check whether your results are consistent. If resistors are connected in series, the equivalent resistance should be greater than that of any individual resistor; if they are connected in parallel, the equivalent resistance should be less than that of any individual resistor.

Example 26.1 Equivalent resistance

Compute the equivalent resistance of the network in Fig. 26.3a, and find the current in each resistor. The source of emf has negligible internal resistance.

SOLUTION

IDENTIFY: This network of three resistors is a *combination* of series and parallel resistances, just as in Fig. 26.1c. The 6-Ω and

26.3 Steps in reducing a combination of resistors to a single equivalent resistor and finding the current in each resistor.

3-Ω resistors are in parallel, and their combination is in series with the 4-Ω resistor.

SET UP: We first determine the equivalent resistance R_{eq} of this network as a whole. Given this value, we find the current in the emf, which is the same as the current in the 4-Ω resistor. This same current is split between the 6-Ω and 3-Ω resistors; we determine how much goes into each resistor by using the principle that the potential difference must be the same across these two resistors (because they are connected in parallel).

EXECUTE: Figures 26.3b and 26.3c show successive steps in reducing the network to a single equivalent resistance. From Eq.(26.2) the 6-Ω and 3-Ω resistors in parallel in Fig. 26.3a are equivalent to the single 2-Ω resistor in Fig. 26.3b:

$$\frac{1}{R_{eq}} = \frac{1}{6\ \Omega} + \frac{1}{3\ \Omega} = \frac{1}{2\ \Omega}$$

[You can find the same result using Eq. (26.3).] From Eq. (26.1) the series combination of this 2-Ω resistor with the 4-Ω resistor is equivalent to the single 6-Ω resistor in Fig. 26.3c.

To find the current in each resistor of the original network, we reverse the steps by which we reduced the network. In the circuit shown in Fig. 26.3d (identical to Fig. 26.3c), the current is $I = V_{ab}/R = (18\ \text{V})/(6\ \Omega) = 3\ \text{A}$. So the current in the 4-Ω and 2-Ω resistors in Fig. 26.3e (identical to Fig. 26.3b) is also 3 A. The potential difference V_{cb} across the 2-Ω resistor is therefore $V_{cb} = IR = (3\ \text{A})(2\ \Omega) = 6\ \text{V}$. This potential difference must also be 6 V in Fig. 26.3f (identical to Fig. 26.3a). Using $I = V_{cb}/R$, the currents in the 6-Ω and 3-Ω resistors in Fig. 26.3f are $(6\ \text{V})/(6\ \Omega) = 1\ \text{A}$ and $(6\ \text{V})/(3\ \Omega) = 2\ \text{A}$, respectively.

EVALUATE: Note that for the two resistors in parallel between points c and b in Fig. 26.3f, there is twice as much current through the 3-Ω resistor as through the 6-Ω resistor; more current goes through the path of least resistance, in accordance with Eq. (26.4). Note also that the total current through these two resistors is 3 A, the same as it is through the 4-Ω resistor between points a and c.

Example 26.2 Series versus parallel combinations

Two identical light bulbs are to be connected to a source with $\mathcal{E} = 8\ \text{V}$ and negligible internal resistance. Each light bulb has a resistance $R = 2\ \Omega$. Find the current through each bulb, the potential difference across each bulb, and the power delivered to each bulb and to the entire network if the bulbs are connected (a) in series and (b) in parallel. (c) Suppose one of the bulbs burns out; that is, its filament breaks and current can no longer flow through it. What happens to the other bulb in the series case? In the parallel case?

SOLUTION

IDENTIFY: The light bulbs are just resistors in simple series and parallel connections.

SET UP: Figures 26.4a and 26.4b show our sketches of the series and parallel circuits, respectively. Once we have found the current through each light bulb, we can find the power delivered to each bulb using Eq. (25.18), $P = I^2R = V^2/R$.

26.4 Our sketches for this problem.

(a) Light bulbs in series

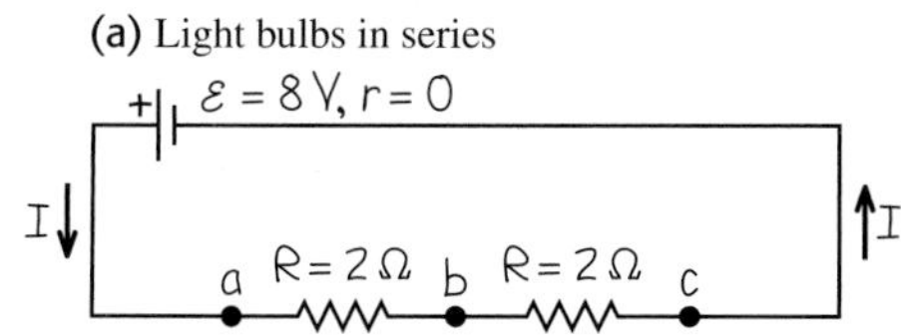

(b) Light bulbs in parallel

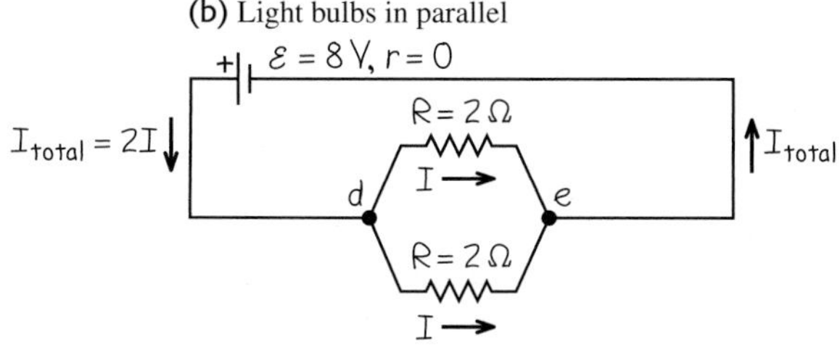

EXECUTE: (a) From Eq. (26.1) the equivalent resistance of the two bulbs between points a and c in Fig. 26.4a is the sum of their individual resistances:

$$R_{eq} = 2R = 2(2\ \Omega) = 4\ \Omega$$

The current is the same through either light bulb in series:

$$I = \frac{V_{ac}}{R_{eq}} = \frac{8\ \text{V}}{4\ \Omega} = 2\ \text{A}$$

Since the bulbs have the same resistance, the potential difference is the same across each bulb:

$$V_{ab} = V_{bc} = IR = (2\ \text{A})(2\ \Omega) = 4\ \text{V}$$

This is one-half of the 8-V terminal voltage of the source. From Eq.(25.18), the power delivered to each light bulb is

$$P = I^2R = (2\ \text{A})^2(2\ \Omega) = 8\ \text{W} \quad \text{or}$$

$$P = \frac{V_{ab}^2}{R} = \frac{V_{bc}^2}{R} = \frac{(4\ \text{V})^2}{2\ \Omega} = 8\ \text{W}$$

The total power delivered to both bulbs is $P_{total} = 2P = 16\ \text{W}$. Alternatively, we can find the total power by using the equivalent resistance $R_{eq} = 4\ \Omega$, through which the current is $I = 2\ \text{A}$ and across which the potential difference is $V_{ac} = 8\ \text{V}$:

$$P_{total} = I^2R_{eq} = (2\ \text{A})^2(4\ \Omega) = 16\ \text{W} \quad \text{or}$$

$$P_{total} = \frac{V_{ac}^2}{R_{eq}} = \frac{(8\ \text{V})^2}{4\ \Omega} = 16\ \text{W}$$

(b) If the light bulbs are in parallel, as in Fig. 26.4b, the potential difference V_{de} across each bulb is the same and equal to 8 V,

Continued

the terminal voltage of the source. Hence the current through each light bulb is

$$I = \frac{V_{de}}{R} = \frac{8\text{ V}}{2\ \Omega} = 4\text{ A}$$

and the power delivered to each bulb is

$$P = I^2R = (4\text{ A})^2(2\ \Omega) = 32\text{ W} \quad \text{or}$$

$$P = \frac{V_{de}^{\ 2}}{R} = \frac{(8\text{ V})^2}{2\ \Omega} = 32\text{ W}$$

Both the potential difference across each bulb and the current through each bulb are twice as great as in the series case. Hence the power delivered to each bulb is *four* times greater, and each bulb glows more brightly than in the series case. If the goal is to produce the maximum amount of light from each bulb, a parallel arrangement is superior to a series arrangement.

The total power delivered to the parallel network is $P_{\text{total}} = 2P = 64\text{ W}$, four times greater than in the series case. The increased power compared to the series case isn't obtained "for free"; energy is extracted from the source four times more rapidly in the parallel case than in the series case. If the source is a battery, it will be used up four times as fast.

We can also find the total power by using the equivalent resistance R_{eq}, given by Eq. (26.2):

$$\frac{1}{R_{\text{eq}}} = 2\left(\frac{1}{2\ \Omega}\right) = 1\ \Omega^{-1} \quad \text{or} \quad R_{\text{eq}} = 1\ \Omega$$

The total current through the equivalent resistor is $I_{\text{total}} = 2I = 2(4\text{ A}) = 8\text{ A}$, and the potential difference across the equivalent resistor is 8 V. Hence the total power is

$$P_{\text{total}} = I^2R_{\text{eq}} = (8\text{ A})^2(1\ \Omega) = 64\text{ W} \quad \text{or}$$

$$P_{\text{total}} = \frac{V_{de}^{\ 2}}{R} = \frac{(8\text{ V})^2}{1\ \Omega} = 64\text{ W}$$

The potential difference across the equivalent resistance is the same for both the series and parallel cases, but for the parallel case the value of R_{eq} is less, and so $P_{\text{total}} = V^2/R_{\text{eq}}$ is greater.

(c) In the series case the same current flows through both bulbs. If one of the bulbs burns out, there will be no current at all in the circuit, and neither bulb will glow.

In the parallel case the potential difference across either bulb remains equal to 8 V even if one of the bulbs burns out. Hence the current through the functional bulb remains equal to 4 A, and the power delivered to that bulb remains equal to 32 W, the same as before the other bulb burned out. This is another of the merits of a parallel arrangement of light bulbs: If one fails, the other bulbs are unaffected. This principle is used in household wiring systems, which we'll discuss in Section 26.5.

EVALUATE: Our calculation isn't completely accurate, because the resistance $R = V/I$ of real light bulbs is *not* a constant independent of the potential difference V across the bulb. (The resistance of the filament increases with increasing operating temperature and hence with increasing V.) But it is indeed true that light bulbs connected in series across a source glow less brightly than when connected in parallel across the same source (Fig. 26.5).

26.5 When connected to the same source, two light bulbs in series (shown at top) draw less power and glow less brightly than when they are in parallel (shown at bottom).

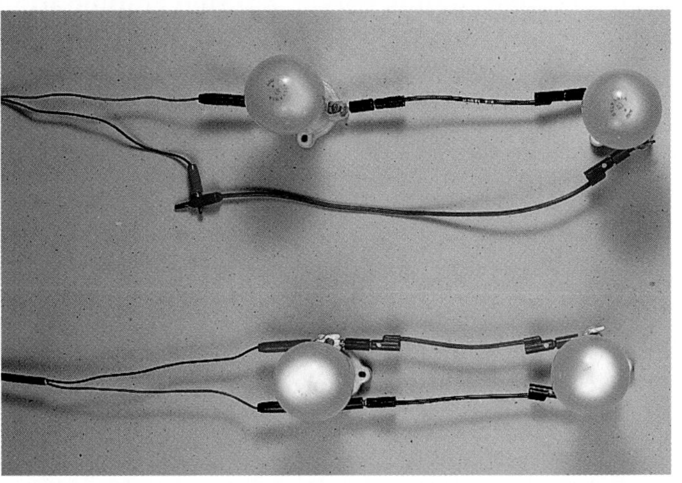

Test Your Understanding of Section 26.1 Suppose all three of the resistors shown in Fig. 26.1 have the same resistance, so $R_1 = R_2 = R_3 = R$. Rank the four arrangements shown in parts (a)–(d) of Fig. 26.1 in order of their equivalent resistance, from highest to lowest.

26.2 Kirchhoff's Rules

Many practical resistor networks cannot be reduced to simple series-parallel combinations. Figure 26.6a shows a dc power supply with emf $\mathcal{E}_1$ charging a battery with a smaller emf $\mathcal{E}_2$ and feeding current to a light bulb with resistance R. Figure 26.6b is a "bridge" circuit, used in many different types of measurement and control systems. (One important application of a "bridge" circuit is described in Problem 26.79.) We don't need any new principles to compute the currents in these networks, but there are some techniques that help us handle such problems systematically. We will describe the techniques developed by the German physicist Gustav Robert Kirchhoff (1824–1887).

First, here are two terms that we will use often. A **junction** in a circuit is a point where three or more conductors meet. Junctions are also called *nodes* or *branch points.* A **loop** is any closed conducting path. In Fig. 26.6a points a and b are junctions, but points c and d are not; in Fig. 26.6b the points a, b, c, and d are junctions, but points e and f are not. The blue lines in Figs. 26.6a and 26.6b show some possible loops in these circuits.

Kirchhoff's rules are the following two statements:

Kirchhoff's junction rule: *The algebraic sum of the currents into any junction is zero.* That is,

$$\sum I = 0 \qquad \text{(junction rule, valid at any junction)} \qquad (26.5)$$

Kirchhoff's loop rule: *The algebraic sum of the potential differences in any loop,* including those associated with emfs and those of resistive elements, *must equal zero.* That is,

$$\sum V = 0 \qquad \text{(loop rule, valid for any closed loop)} \qquad (26.6)$$

The junction rule is based on *conservation of electric charge.* No charge can accumulate at a junction, so the total charge entering the junction per unit time must equal the total charge leaving per unit time (Fig. 26.7a). Charge per unit time is current, so if we consider the currents entering a junction to be positive and those leaving to be negative, the algebraic sum of currents into a junction must be zero. It's like a T branch in a water pipe (Fig. 26.7b); if you have 1 liter per minute coming in one pipe, you can't have 3 liters per minute going out the other two pipes. We may as well confess that we used the junction rule (without saying so) in Section 26.1 in the derivation of Eq. (26.2) for resistors in parallel.

The loop rule is a statement that the electrostatic force is *conservative.* Suppose we go around a loop, measuring potential differences across successive circuit elements as we go. When we return to the starting point, we must find that the *algebraic sum* of these differences is zero; otherwise, we could not say that the potential at this point has a definite value.

Sign Conventions for the Loop Rule

In applying the loop rule, we need some sign conventions. Problem-Solving Strategy 26.2 describes in detail how to use these, but here's a quick overview. We first assume a direction for the current in each branch of the circuit and mark it on a diagram of the circuit. Then, starting at any point in the circuit, we imagine traveling around a loop, adding emfs and IR terms as we come to them. When we travel through a source in the direction from $-$ to $+$, the emf is considered to be *positive;* when we travel from $+$ to $-$, the emf is considered to be *negative* (Fig. 26.8a). When we travel through a resistor in the *same* direction as the assumed current, the IR term is *negative* because the current goes in the direction of decreasing potential. When we travel through a resistor in the direction *opposite* to the assumed current, the IR term is *positive* because this represents a rise of potential (Fig. 26.8b).

26.6 Two networks that cannot be reduced to simple series-parallel combinations of resistors.

(a)

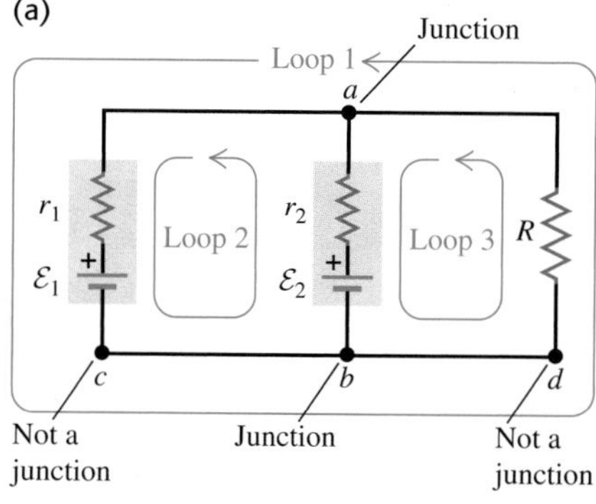

(b)

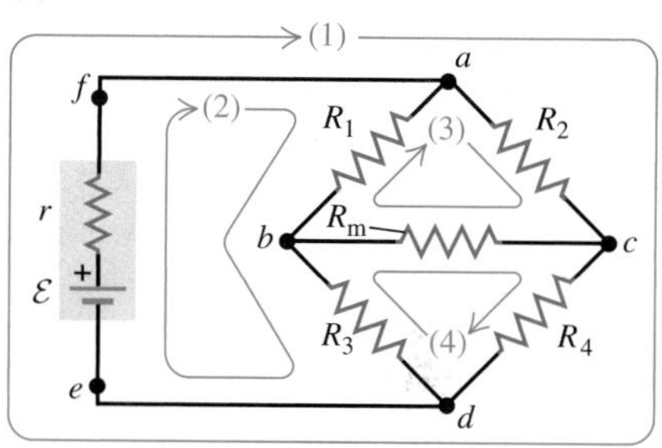

26.7 (a) Kirchhoff's junction rule states that as much current flows into a junction as flows out of it. (b) A water-pipe analogy.

(a) Kirchhoff's junction rule

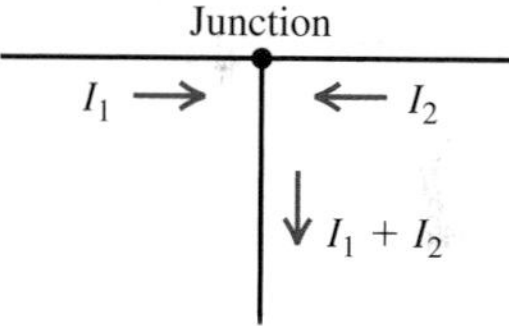

(b) Water-pipe analogy for Kirchhoff's junction rule

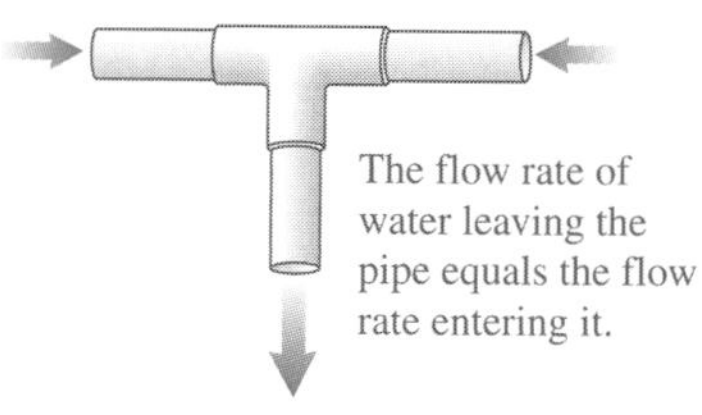

The flow rate of water leaving the pipe equals the flow rate entering it.

(a) Sign conventions for emfs

(b) Sign conventions for resistors

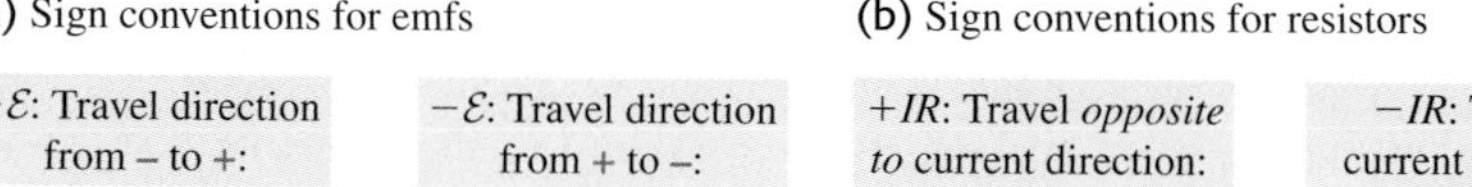

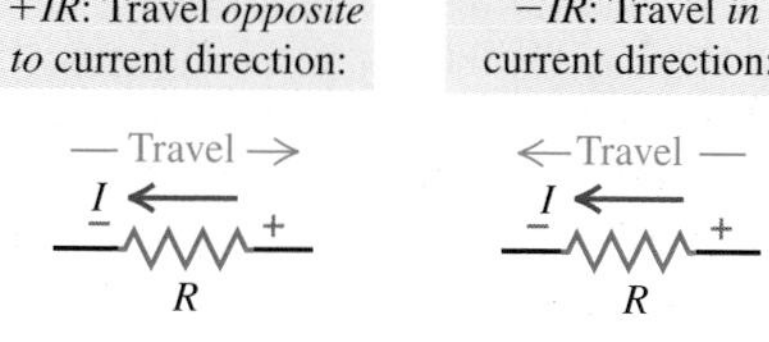

26.8 Use these sign conventions when you apply Kirchhoff's loop rule. In each part of the figure "Travel" is the direction that we imagine going around the loop, which is not necessarily the direction of the current.

Kirchhoff's two rules are all we need to solve a wide variety of network problems. Usually, some of the emfs, currents, and resistances are known, and others are unknown. We must always obtain from Kirchhoff's rules a number of independent equations equal to the number of unknowns so that we can solve the equations simultaneously. Often the hardest part of the solution is not understanding the basic principles but keeping track of algebraic signs!

Problem-Solving Strategy 26.2 Kirchhoff's Rules

IDENTIFY *the relevant concepts:* Kirchhoff's rules are important tools for analyzing any circuit more complicated than a single loop.

SET UP *the problem* using the following steps:

1. Draw a *large* circuit diagram so you have plenty of room for labels. Label all quantities, known and unknown, including an assumed direction for each unknown current and emf. Often you will not know in advance the actual direction of an unknown current or emf, but this doesn't matter. If the actual direction of a particular quantity is opposite to your assumption, the result will come out with a negative sign. If you use Kirchhoff's rules correctly, they will give you the directions as well as the magnitudes of unknown currents and emfs.
2. When you label currents, it is usually best to use the junction rule immediately to express the currents in terms of as few quantities as possible. For example, Fig. 26.9a shows a circuit correctly labeled; Fig. 26.9b shows the same circuit, relabeled by applying the junction rule to point a to eliminate I_3.
3. Determine which quantities are the target variables.

EXECUTE *the solution* as follows:

1. Choose any closed loop in the network and designate a direction (clockwise or counterclockwise) to travel around the loop when applying the loop rule. The direction doesn't have to be the same as any assumed current direction.
2. Travel around the loop in the designated direction, adding potential differences as you cross them. Remember that a positive potential difference corresponds to an increase in potential and a negative potential difference corresponds to a decrease in potential. An emf is counted as positive when you traverse it from $(-)$ to $(+)$, and negative when you go from $(+)$ to $(-)$. An IR term is negative if you travel through the resistor in the same direction as the assumed current and positive if you pass through it in the opposite direction. Figure 26.8 summarizes these sign conventions.
3. Equate the sum in Step 2 to zero.
4. If necessary, choose another loop to get a different relationship among the unknowns, and continue until you have as many independent equations as unknowns or until every circuit element has been included in at least one of the chosen loops.
5. Solve the equations simultaneously to determine the unknowns. This step involves algebra, not physics, but it can be fairly complex. Be careful with algebraic manipulations; one sign error will prove fatal to the entire solution.
6. You can use this same bookkeeping system to find the potential V_{ab} of any point a with respect to any other point b. Start at b and add the potential changes you encounter in going from b to a, using the same sign rules as in Step 2. The algebraic sum of these changes is $V_{ab} = V_a - V_b$.

EVALUATE *your answer:* Check all the steps in your algebra. A useful strategy is to consider a loop other than the ones you used to solve the problem; if the sum of potential drops around this loop isn't zero, you made an error somewhere in your calculations. As always, ask yourself whether the answers make sense.

26.9 Applying the junction rule to point a reduces the number of unknown currents from three to two.

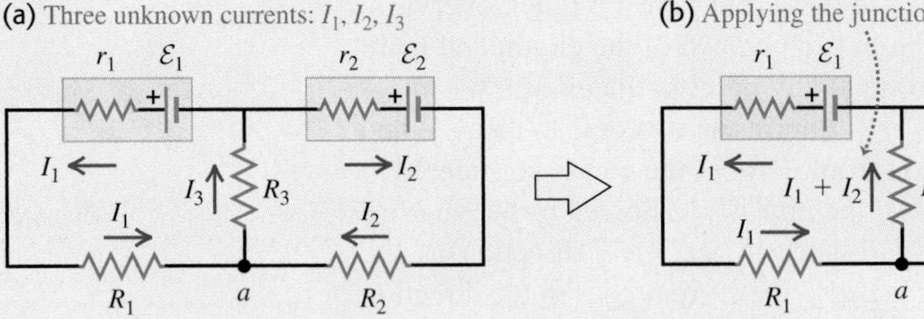

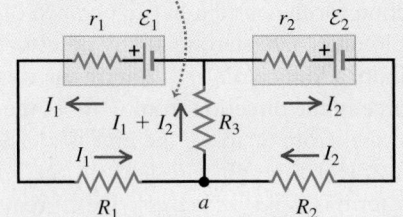

Example 26.3 A single-loop circuit

The circuit shown in Fig. 26.10a contains two batteries, each with an emf and an internal resistance, and two resistors. Find (a) the current in the circuit, (b) the potential difference V_{ab}, and (c) the power output of the emf of each battery.

SOLUTION

IDENTIFY: This single-loop circuit has no junctions, so we don't need Kirchhoff's junction rule to solve for the target variables.

SET UP: To apply the loop rule to the single loop, we first assume a direction for the current; let's assume a counterclockwise direction, as shown in Fig. 26.10a.

EXECUTE: (a) Starting at a and going counterclockwise, we add potential increases and decreases and equate the sum to zero, as in Eq. (26.6). The resulting equation is

$$-I(4\,\Omega) - 4\text{ V} - I(7\,\Omega) + 12\text{ V} - I(2\,\Omega) - I(3\,\Omega) = 0$$

Collecting terms containing I and solving for I, we find

$$8\text{ V} = I(16\ \Omega) \qquad \text{and} \qquad I = 0.5\text{ A}$$

The result for I is positive, showing that our assumed current direction is correct. For an exercise, try assuming the opposite direction for I; you should then get $I = -0.5$ A, indicating that the actual current is opposite to this assumption.

(b) To find V_{ab}, the potential at a with respect to b, we start at b and add potential changes as we go toward a. There are two possible paths from b to a; taking the lower one first, we find

$$V_{ab} = (0.5\text{ A})(7\ \Omega) + 4\text{ V} + (0.5\text{ A})(4\ \Omega) = 9.5\text{ V}$$

Point a is at 9.5 V higher potential than b. All the terms in this sum, including the IR terms, are positive because each represents an *increase* in potential as we go from b toward a. If we use the upper path instead, the resulting equation is

$$V_{ab} = 12\text{ V} - (0.5\text{ A})(2\ \Omega) - (0.5\text{ A})(3\ \Omega) = 9.5\text{ V}$$

Here the IR terms are negative because our path goes in the direction of the current, with potential decreases through the resistors. The result is the same as for the lower path, as it must be in order for the total potential change around the complete loop to be zero. In each case, potential rises are taken to be positive and drops are taken to be negative.

(c) The power output of the emf of the 12-V battery is

$$P = \mathcal{E}I = (12\text{ V})(0.5\text{ A}) = 6\text{ W}$$

and the power output of the emf of the 4-V battery is

$$P = \mathcal{E}I = (-4\text{ V})(0.5\text{ A}) = -2\text{ W}$$

The negative sign in $\mathcal{E}$ for the 4-V battery appears because the current actually runs from the higher-potential side of the battery to the lower-potential side. The negative value of P means that we are *storing* energy in that battery, and it is being *recharged* by the 12-V battery.

EVALUATE: By applying the expression $P = I^2R$ to each of the four resistors in Fig. 26.10a, you should be able to show that the total power dissipated in all four resistors is 4 W. Of the 6 W provided by the emf of the 12-V battery, 2 W goes into storing energy in the 4-V battery and 4 W is dissipated in the resistances.

The circuit shown in Fig. 26.10a is very much like that used when a 12-V automobile battery is used to recharge a run-down battery in another automobile (Fig. 26.10b). The 3-Ω and 7-Ω resistors in Fig. 26.10a represent the resistances of the jumper cables and of the conducting path through the automobile with the run-down battery. (The values of the resistances in actual automobiles and jumper cables are different from those used in this example.)

26.10 (a) In this example we travel around the loop in the same direction as the assumed current, so all the IR terms are negative. The potential decreases as we travel from + to − through the bottom emf but increases as we travel from − to + through the top emf. (b) A real-life example of a circuit of this kind.

(a)

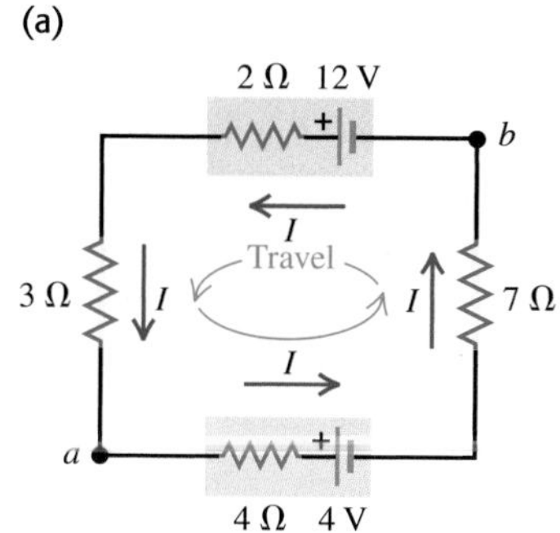

(b)

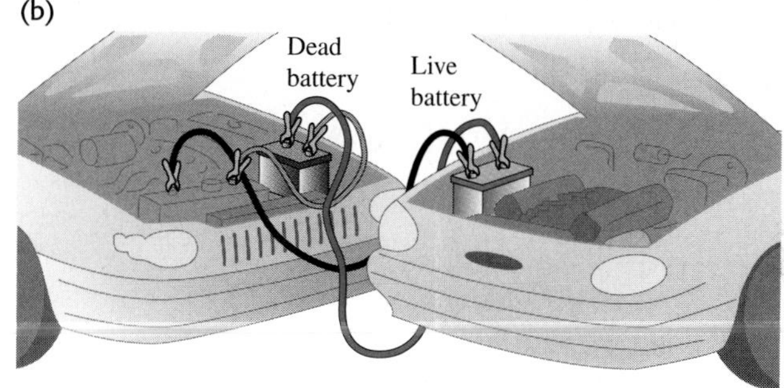

Example 26.4 Charging a battery

In the circuit shown in Fig. 26.11, a 12-V power supply with unknown internal resistance r is connected to a run-down rechargeable battery with unknown emf $\mathcal{E}$ and internal resistance 1 Ω and to an indicator light bulb of resistance 3 Ω carrying a current of 2 A. The current through the run-down battery is 1 A in the direction shown. Find the unknown current I, the internal resistance r, and the emf $\mathcal{E}$.

26.11 In this circuit a power supply charges a run-down battery and lights a bulb. An assumption has been made about the polarity of the emf $\mathcal{E}$ of the run-down battery. Is this assumption correct?

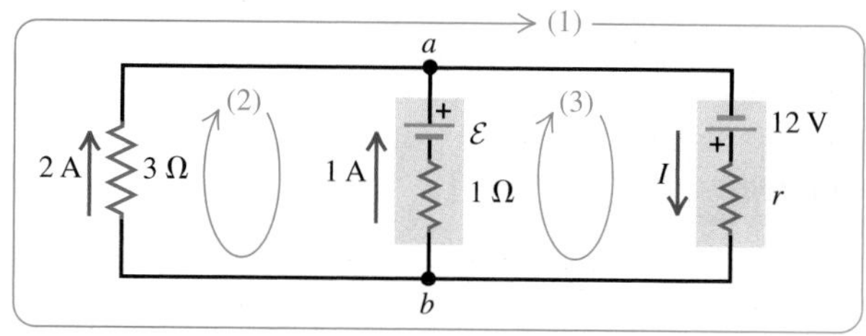

SOLUTION

IDENTIFY: This circuit has more than one loop, so we must apply both the junction rule and the loop rule.

SET UP: We assume the direction of the current through the 12-V power supply to be as shown. There are three target variables, so we need three equations.

EXECUTE: First we apply the junction rule, Eq. (26.5), to point a. We find

$$-I + 1\text{ A} + 2\text{ A} = 0 \qquad \text{so} \qquad I = 3\text{ A}$$

Continued

To determine r, we apply the loop rule, Eq. (26.6), to the outer loop labeled (1); we find

$$12\text{ V} - (3\text{ A})r - (2\text{ A})(3\ \Omega) = 0 \qquad \text{so} \qquad r = 2\ \Omega$$

The terms containing the resistances r and 3 Ω are negative because our loop traverses those elements in the same direction as the current and hence finds potential *drops*. If we had chosen to traverse loop (1) in the opposite direction, every term would have had the opposite sign, and the result for r would have been the same.

To determine $\mathcal{E}$, we apply the loop rule to loop (2):

$$-\mathcal{E} + (1\text{ A})(1\ \Omega) - (2\text{ A})(3\ \Omega) = 0 \qquad \text{so} \qquad \mathcal{E} = -5\text{ V}$$

The term for the 1-Ω resistor is positive because in traversing it in the direction opposite to the current, we find a potential *rise*. The negative value for $\mathcal{E}$ shows that the actual polarity of this emf is opposite to the assumption made in Fig. 26.11; the positive terminal of this source is really on the right side. As in Example 26.3, the battery is being recharged.

EVALUATE: We can check our result for $\mathcal{E}$ by using loop (3), obtaining the equation

$$12\text{ V} - (3\text{ A})(2\ \Omega) - (1\text{ A})(1\ \Omega) + \mathcal{E} = 0$$

from which we again find $\mathcal{E} = -5$ V.

As an additional consistency check, we note that $V_{ba} = V_b - V_a$ equals the voltage across the 3-Ω resistance, which is $(2\text{ A})(3\ \Omega) =$ 6 V. Going from a to b by the top branch, we encounter potential differences $+12\text{ V} - (3\text{ A})(2\ \Omega) = +6\text{ V}$, and going by the middle branch we find $-(-5\text{ V}) + (1\text{ A})(1\ \Omega) = +6\text{ V}$. The three ways of getting V_{ba} give the same results. Make sure that you understand all the signs in these calculations.

Example 26.5 Power in a battery-charging circuit

In the circuit of Example 26.4 (shown in Fig. 26.11), find the power delivered by the 12-V power supply and by the battery being recharged, and find the power dissipated in each resistor.

SOLUTION

IDENTIFY: We use the results of Section 25.5, in which we found that the power delivered *from* an emf to a circuit is $\mathcal{E}I$ and the power delivered *to* a resistor from a circuit is $V_{ab}I = I^2R$.

SET UP: We know the values of each emf, each current, and each resistance from Example 26.4.

EXECUTE: The power output from the emf of the power supply is

$$P_{\text{supply}} = \mathcal{E}_{\text{supply}}I_{\text{supply}} = (12\text{ V})(3\text{ A}) = 36\text{ W}$$

The power dissipated in the power supply's internal resistance r is

$$P_{r\text{-supply}} = I_{\text{supply}}{}^2 r_{\text{supply}} = (3\text{ A})^2(2\ \Omega) = 18\text{ W}$$

so the power supply's *net* power output is $P_{\text{net}} = 36\text{ W} - 18\text{ W} = 18\text{ W}$. Alternatively, from Example 26.4 the terminal voltage of the battery is $V_{ba} = 6$ V, so the net power output is

$$P_{\text{net}} = V_{ba}I_{\text{supply}} = (6\text{ V})(3\text{ A}) = 18\text{ W}$$

The power output of the emf $\mathcal{E}$ of the battery being charged is

$$P_{\text{emf}} = \mathcal{E}I_{\text{battery}} = (-5\text{ V})(1\text{ A}) = -5\text{ W}$$

This is negative because the 1-A current runs through the battery from the higher-potential side to the lower-potential side. (As we mentioned in Example 26.4, the polarity assumed for this battery in Fig. 26.11 was wrong.) We are storing energy in the battery as we charge it. Additional power is dissipated in the battery's internal resistance; this power is

$$P_{r\text{-battery}} = I_{\text{battery}}{}^2 r_{\text{battery}} = (1\text{ A})^2(1\ \Omega) = 1\text{ W}$$

The total power input to the battery is thus $1\text{ W} + |-5\text{ W}| = 6\text{ W}$. Of this, 5 W represents useful energy stored in the battery; the remainder is wasted in its internal resistance.

The power dissipated in the light bulb is

$$P_{\text{bulb}} = I_{\text{bulb}}{}^2 R_{\text{bulb}} = (2\text{ A})^2(3\ \Omega) = 12\text{ W}$$

EVALUATE: As a check, note that all of the power from the supply is accounted for. Of the 18 W of net power from the power supply, 5 W goes to recharge the battery, 1 W is dissipated in the battery's internal resistance, and 12 W is dissipated in the light bulb.

Example 26.6 A complex network

Figure 26.12 shows a "bridge" circuit of the type described at the beginning of this section (see Fig. 26.6b). Find the current in each resistor and the equivalent resistance of the network of five resistors.

SOLUTION

IDENTIFY: This network cannot be represented in terms of series and parallel combinations. Hence we must use Kirchhoff's rules to find the values of the target variables.

SET UP: There are five different currents to determine, but by applying the junction rule to junctions a and b, we can represent them in terms of three unknown currents, as shown in the figure. The current in the battery is $I_1 + I_2$.

26.12 A network circuit with several resistors.

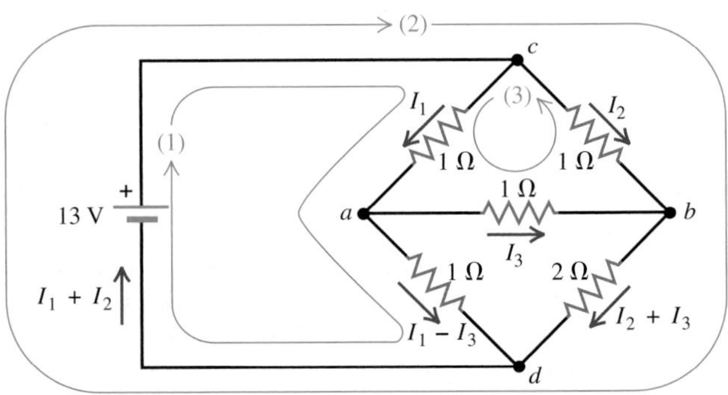

EXECUTE: We apply the loop rule to the three loops shown, obtaining the following three equations:

$$13\text{ V} - I_1(1\,\Omega) - (I_1 - I_3)(1\,\Omega) = 0 \quad (1)$$
$$-I_2(1\,\Omega) - (I_2 + I_3)(2\,\Omega) + 13\text{ V} = 0 \quad (2)$$
$$-I_1(1\,\Omega) - I_3(1\,\Omega) + I_2(1\,\Omega) = 0 \quad (3)$$

This is a set of three simultaneous equations for the three unknown currents. They may be solved by various methods; one straightforward procedure is to solve the third equation for I_2, obtaining $I_2 = I_1 + I_3$, and then substitute this expression into the second equation to eliminate I_2. When this is done, we are left with the two equations

$$13\text{ V} = I_1(2\,\Omega) - I_3(1\,\Omega) \quad (1')$$
$$13\text{ V} = I_1(3\,\Omega) + I_3(5\,\Omega) \quad (2')$$

Now we can eliminate I_3 by multiplying Eq. (1′) by 5 and adding the two equations. We obtain

$$78\text{ V} = I_1(13\,\Omega) \qquad I_1 = 6\text{ A}$$

We substitute this result back into Eq. (1′) to obtain $I_3 = -1$ A, and finally, from Eq. (3) we find $I_2 = 5$ A. The negative value of I_3 tells us that its direction is opposite to our initial assumption.

The total current through the network is $I_1 + I_2 = 11$ A, and the potential drop across it is equal to the battery emf—namely, 13 V. The equivalent resistance of the network is

$$R_{eq} = \frac{13\text{ V}}{11\text{ A}} = 1.2\,\Omega$$

EVALUATE: You can check the results $I_1 = 6$ A, $I_2 = 5$ A, and $I_3 = -1$ A by substituting these values into the three equations (1), (2), and (3). What do you find?

Example 26.7 A potential difference within a complex network

In the circuit of Example 26.6 (Fig. 26.12), find the potential difference V_{ab}.

SOLUTION

IDENTIFY: Our target variable is $V_{ab} = V_a - V_b$, which is the potential at point a with respect to point b.

SET UP: To find V_{ab}, we start at point b and follow a path to point a, adding potential rises and drops as we go. We can follow any of several paths from b to a; the value of V_{ab} must be independent of which path we choose, which gives us a natural way to check our result.

EXECUTE: The simplest path to follow is through the center 1-Ω resistor. We have found $I_3 = -1$ A, showing that the actual current direction in this branch is from right to left. Thus, as we go from b to a, there is a *drop* of potential with magnitude $IR = (1\text{ A})(1\,\Omega) = 1$ V, and $V_{ab} = -1$ V. That is, the potential at point a is 1 V less than that at point b.

EVALUATE: To test our result, let's try a path from b to a that goes through the lower two resistors. The currents through these are

$$I_2 + I_3 = 5\text{ A} + (-1\text{ A}) = 4\text{ A} \quad \text{and}$$
$$I_1 - I_3 = 6\text{ A} - (-1\text{ A}) = 7\text{ A}$$

and so

$$V_{ab} = -(4\text{ A})(2\,\Omega) + (7\text{ A})(1\,\Omega) = -1\text{ V}$$

We suggest that you try some other paths from b to a to verify that they also give this result.

Test Your Understanding of Section 26.2 Subtract Eq. (1) from Eq. (2) in Example 26.6. To which loop in Fig. 26.12 does this equation correspond? Would this equation have simplified the solution of Example 26.6?

26.3 Electrical Measuring Instruments

We've been talking about potential difference, current, and resistance for two chapters, so it's about time we said something about how to *measure* these quantities. Many common devices, including car instrument panels, battery chargers, and inexpensive electrical instruments, measure potential difference (voltage), current, or resistance using a **d'Arsonval galvanometer** (Fig. 26.13). In the following discussion we'll often call it just a *meter.* A pivoted coil of fine wire is placed in the magnetic field of a permanent magnet (Fig. 26.14). Attached to the coil is a spring, similar to the hairspring on the balance wheel of a watch. In the equilibrium position, with no current in the coil, the pointer is at zero. When there is a current in the coil, the magnetic field exerts a torque on the coil that is proportional to the current. (We'll discuss this magnetic interaction in detail in Chapter 27.) As the coil turns, the spring exerts a restoring torque that is proportional to the angular displacement.

Thus the angular deflection of the coil and pointer is directly proportional to the coil current, and the device can be calibrated to measure current. The maximum deflection, typically 90° or so, is called *full-scale deflection.* The essential electrical characteristics of the meter are the current I_{fs} required for

26.13 This ammeter (top) and voltmeter (bottom) are both d'Arsonval galvanometers. The difference has to do with their internal connections (see Fig. 26.15).

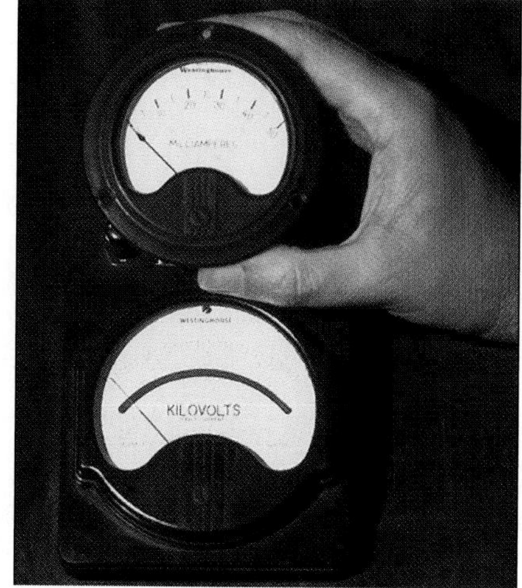

26.14 A d'Arsonval galvanometer, showing a pivoted coil with attached pointer, a permanent magnet supplying a magnetic field that is uniform in magnitude, and a spring to provide restoring torque, which opposes magnetic-field torque.

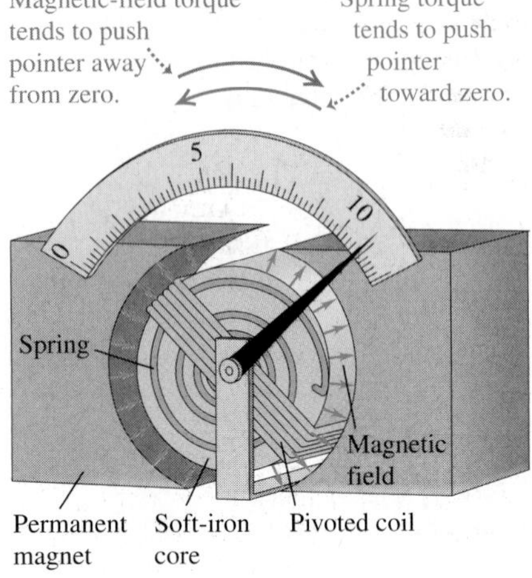

ActivPhysics ONLINE

12.4 Using Ammeters and Voltmeters

full-scale deflection (typically on the order of 10 μA to 10 mA) and the resistance R_c of the coil (typically on the order of 10 to 1000 Ω).

The meter deflection is proportional to the *current* in the coil. If the coil obeys Ohm's law, the current is proportional to the *potential difference* between the terminals of the coil, and the deflection is also proportional to this potential difference. For example, consider a meter whose coil has a resistance $R_c = 20.0\ \Omega$ and that deflects full scale when the current in its coil is $I_{fs} = 1.00$ mA. The corresponding potential difference for full-scale deflection is

$$V = I_{fs}R_c = (1.00 \times 10^{-3}\ \text{A})(20.0\ \Omega) = 0.0200\ \text{V}$$

Ammeters

A current-measuring instrument is usually called an **ammeter** (or milliammeter, microammeter, and so forth, depending on the range). *An ammeter always measures the current passing through it.* An *ideal* ammeter, discussed in Section 25.4, would have *zero* resistance, so including it in a branch of a circuit would not affect the current in that branch. Real ammeters always have some finite resistance, but it is always desirable for an ammeter to have as little resistance as possible.

We can adapt any meter to measure currents that are larger than its full-scale reading by connecting a resistor in parallel with it (Fig. 26.15a) so that some of the current bypasses the meter coil. The parallel resistor is called a **shunt resistor** or simply a *shunt,* denoted as R_{sh}.

Suppose we want to make a meter with full-scale current I_{fs} and coil resistance R_c into an ammeter with full-scale reading I_a. To determine the shunt resistance R_{sh} needed, note that at full-scale deflection the total current through the parallel combination is I_a, the current through the coil of the meter is I_{fs}, and the current through the shunt is the difference $I_a - I_{fs}$. The potential difference V_{ab} is the same for both paths, so

$$I_{fs}R_c = (I_a - I_{fs})R_{sh} \quad \text{(for an ammeter)} \tag{26.7}$$

26.15 Using the same meter to measure (a) current and (b) voltage.

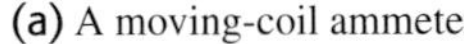

(a) A moving-coil ammeter

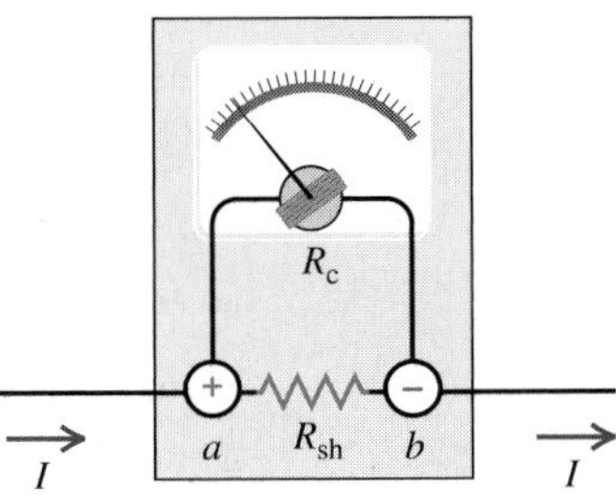

(b) A moving-coil voltmeter

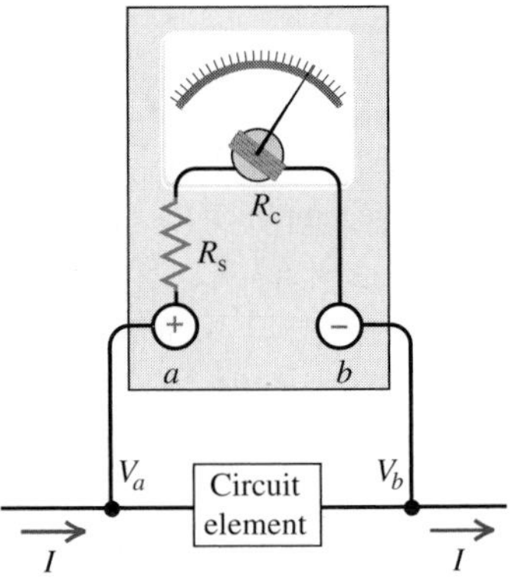

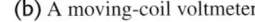

Example 26.8 Designing an ammeter

What shunt resistance is required to make the 1.00-mA, 20.0-Ω meter described above into an ammeter with a range of 0 to 50.0 mA?

SOLUTION

IDENTIFY: Since the meter is being used as an ammeter, its internal connections are as shown in Fig. 26.15a. Our target variable is the shunt resistance R_{sh}.

SET UP: We want the ammeter to be able to handle a maximum current $I_a = 50.0\ \text{mA} = 50.0 \times 10^{-3}$ A. The resistance of the coil is $R_c = 20.0\ \Omega$, and the meter shows full-scale deflection when the current through the coil is $I_{fs} = 1.00 \times 10^{-3}$ A. We find the shunt resistance R_{sh} using Eq. (26.7).

EXECUTE: Solving Eq. (26.7) for R_{sh}, we find

$$R_{sh} = \frac{I_{fs}R_c}{I_a - I_{fs}} = \frac{(1.00 \times 10^{-3}\ \text{A})(20.0\ \Omega)}{50.0 \times 10^{-3}\ \text{A} - 1.00 \times 10^{-3}\ \text{A}}$$
$$= 0.408\ \Omega$$

EVALUATE: It's useful to consider the equivalent resistance R_{eq} of the ammeter as a whole. From Eq. (26.2),

$$\frac{1}{R_{eq}} = \frac{1}{R_c} + \frac{1}{R_{sh}} = \frac{1}{20.0\ \Omega} + \frac{1}{0.408\ \Omega}$$

$$R_{eq} = 0.400\ \Omega$$

The shunt resistance is so small in comparison to the meter resistance that the equivalent resistance is very nearly equal to the shunt resistance. The result is a low-resistance instrument with the desired range of 0 to 50.0 mA. At full-scale deflection, $I = I_a = 50.0$ mA, the current through the galvanometer is 1.00 mA, the current through the shunt resistor is 49.0 mA, and $V_{ab} = 0.0200$ V. If the current I is *less* than 50.0 mA, the coil current and the deflection are proportionally less, but the resistance R_{eq} is still 0.400 Ω.

Voltmeters

This same basic meter may also be used to measure potential difference or *voltage.* A voltage-measuring device is called a **voltmeter** (or millivoltmeter, and so forth, depending on the range). A voltmeter always measures the potential difference between two points, and its terminals must be connected to these points. (Example 25.7 in Section 25.4 described what can happen if a voltmeter is connected incorrectly.) As we discussed in Section 25.4, an ideal voltmeter would have *infinite* resistance, so connecting it between two points in a circuit would not alter any of the currents. Real voltmeters always have finite resistance, but a voltmeter should have large enough resistance that connecting it in a circuit does not change the other currents appreciably.

For the meter described in Example 26.8 the voltage across the meter coil at full-scale deflection is only $I_{fs}R_c = (1.00 \times 10^{-3}\ \text{A})(20.0\ \Omega) = 0.0200$ V. We can extend this range by connecting a resistor R_s in *series* with the coil (Fig. 26.15b). Then only a fraction of the total potential difference appears across the coil itself, and the remainder appears across R_s. For a voltmeter with full-scale reading V_V, we need a series resistor R_s in Fig. 26.15b such that

$$V_V = I_{fs}(R_c + R_s) \qquad \text{(for a voltmeter)} \tag{26.8}$$

Example 26.9 Designing a voltmeter

How can we make a galvanometer with $R_c = 20.0\ \Omega$ and $I_{fs} = 1.00$ mA into a voltmeter with a maximum range of 10.0 V?

SOLUTION

IDENTIFY: Since this meter is being used as a voltmeter, its internal connections are as shown in Fig. 26.15b. Our target variable is the series resistance R_s.

SET UP: The maximum allowable voltage across the voltmeter is $V_V = 10.0$ V. We want this to occur when the current through the coil (of resistance $R_c = 20.0\ \Omega$) is $I_{fs} = 1.00 \times 10^{-3}$ A. We find the series resistance R_s with Eq.(26.8).

EXECUTE: From Eq. (26.8),

$$R_s = \frac{V_V}{I_{fs}} - R_c = \frac{10.0\ \text{V}}{0.00100\ \text{A}} - 20.0\ \Omega = 9980\ \Omega$$

EVALUATE: At full-scale deflection, $V_{ab} = 10.0$ V, the voltage across the meter is 0.0200 V, the voltage across R_s is 9.98 V, and the current through the voltmeter is 0.00100 A. In this case most of the voltage appears across the series resistor. The equivalent meter resistance is $R_{eq} = 20.0\ \Omega + 9980\ \Omega = 10{,}000\ \Omega$. Such a meter is described as a "1000 ohms-per-volt meter," referring to the ratio of resistance to full-scale deflection. In normal operation the current through the circuit element being measured (I in Fig. 26.15b) is much greater than 0.00100 A, and the resistance between points a and b in the circuit is much less than 10,000 Ω. So the voltmeter draws off only a small fraction of the current and disturbs only slightly the circuit being measured.

Ammeters and Voltmeters in Combination

A voltmeter and an ammeter can be used together to measure *resistance* and *power.* The resistance R of a resistor equals the potential difference V_{ab} between its terminals divided by the current I; that is, $R = V_{ab}/I$. The power input P to any circuit element is the product of the potential difference across it and the current through it: $P = V_{ab}I$. In principle, the most straightforward way to measure R or P is to measure V_{ab} and I simultaneously.

With practical ammeters and voltmeters this isn't quite as simple as it seems. In Fig. 26.16a, ammeter A reads the current I in the resistor R. Voltmeter V, however, reads the *sum* of the potential difference V_{ab} across the resistor and the potential difference V_{bc} across the ammeter. If we transfer the voltmeter terminal from c to b, as in Fig. 26.16b, then the voltmeter reads the potential difference V_{ab} correctly, but the ammeter now reads the *sum* of the current I in the resistor and the current I_V in the voltmeter. Either way, we have to correct the reading of one instrument or the other unless the corrections are small enough to be negligible.

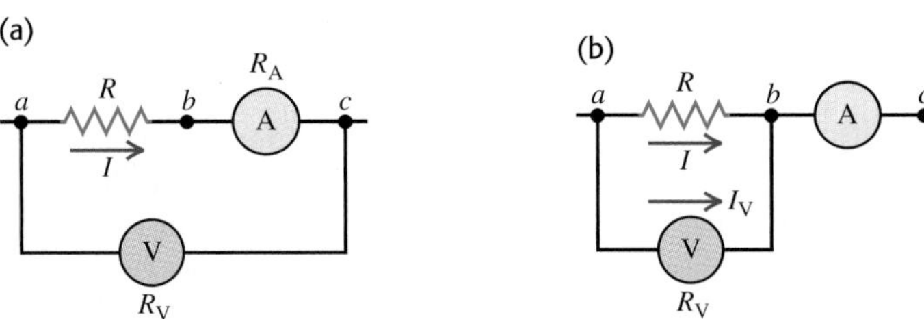

26.16 Ammeter–voltmeter method for measuring resistance.

Example 26.10 Measuring resistance I

Suppose we want to measure an unknown resistance R using the circuit of Fig. 26.16a. The meter resistances are $R_V = 10{,}000\ \Omega$ (for the voltmeter) and $R_A = 2.00\ \Omega$ (for the ammeter). If the voltmeter reads 12.0 V and the ammeter reads 0.100 A, what are the resistance R and the power dissipated in the resistor?

SOLUTION

IDENTIFY: The ammeter reads the current $I = 0.100$ A through the resistor, and the voltmeter reads the potential difference between a and c. If the ammeter were *ideal* (that is, if $R_A = 0$), there would be zero potential difference between b and c, the voltmeter reading $V = 12.0$ V would be equal to the potential difference V_{ab} across the resistor, and the resistance would simply be equal to $R = V/I = (12.0\ \text{V})/(0.100\ \text{A}) = 120\ \Omega$. The ammeter is *not* ideal, however (its resistance is $R_A = 2.00\ \Omega$), so the voltmeter reading V is actually the sum of the potential differences V_{bc} (across the ammeter) and V_{ab} (across the resistor).

SET UP: We use Ohm's law to find the voltage V_{bc} across the ammeter from its known current and resistance. Then we solve for V_{ab} and the resistance R. Given these, we are able to calculate the power P into the resistor.

EXECUTE: From Ohm's law, $V_{bc} = IR_A = (0.100\ \text{A})(2.00\ \Omega) = 0.200\ \text{V}$ and $V_{ab} = IR$. The sum of these is $V = 12.0$ V, so the potential difference across the resistor is $V_{ab} = V - V_{bc} = (12.0\ \text{V}) - (0.200\ \text{V}) = 11.8$ V. Hence the resistance is

$$R = \frac{V_{ab}}{I} = \frac{11.8\ \text{V}}{0.100\ \text{A}} = 118\ \Omega$$

The power dissipated in this resistor is

$$P = V_{ab}I = (11.8\ \text{V})(0.100\ \text{A}) = 1.18\ \text{W}$$

EVALUATE: You can confirm this result for the power by using the alternative formula $P = I^2R$. Do you get the same answer?

Example 26.11 Measuring resistance II

Suppose the meters of Example 26.10 are connected to a different resistor in the circuit shown in Fig. 26.16b, and the readings obtained on the meters are the same as in Example 26.10. What is the value of this new resistance R, and what is the power dissipated in the resistor?

SOLUTION

IDENTIFY: In Example 26.10 the ammeter read the actual current through the resistor, but the voltmeter reading was not the same as the potential difference across the resistor. Now the situation is reversed: The voltmeter reading $V = 12.0$ V shows the actual potential difference V_{ab} across the resistor, but the ammeter reading $I_A = 0.100$ A is *not* equal to the current I through the resistor.

SET UP: Applying the junction rule at b in Fig. 26.16b shows that $I_A = I + I_V$, where I_V is the current through the voltmeter. We find I_V from the given values of V and the voltmeter resistance R_V, and we use this value to find the resistor current I. We then determine the resistance R from I and the voltmeter reading, and calculate the power as in Example 26.10.

EXECUTE: We have $I_V = V/R_V = (12.0\ \text{V})/(10{,}000\ \Omega) = 1.20\ \text{mA}$. The actual current I in the resistor is $I = I_A - I_V = 0.100\ \text{A} - 0.0012\ \text{A} = 0.0988$ A, and the resistance is

$$R = \frac{V_{ab}}{I} = \frac{12.0\ \text{V}}{0.0988\ \text{A}} = 121\ \Omega$$

The power dissipated in the resistor is

$$P = V_{ab}I = (12.0\ \text{V})(0.0988\ \text{A}) = 1.19\ \text{W}$$

EVALUATE: Our results for R and P are not too different than the results of Example 26.10, in which the meters are connected in a different way. That's because the ammeter and voltmeter are nearly ideal: Compared to the resistance R under test, the ammeter resistance R_A is very small and the voltmeter resistance R_V is very large. Nonetheless, the results of the two examples *are* different, which shows that you must account for how ammeters and voltmeters are used when interpreting their readings.

Ohmmeters

An alternative method for measuring resistance is to use a d'Arsonval meter in an arrangement called an **ohmmeter.** It consists of a meter, a resistor, and a source (often a flashlight battery) connected in series (Fig. 26.17). The resistance R to be measured is connected between terminals x and y.

The series resistance R_s is variable; it is adjusted so that when terminals x and y are short-circuited (that is, when $R = 0$), the meter deflects full scale. When nothing is connected to terminals x and y, so that the circuit between x and y is *open* (that is, when $R \rightarrow \infty$), there is no current and hence no deflection. For any intermediate value of R the meter deflection depends on the value of R, and the meter scale can be calibrated to read the resistance R directly. Larger currents correspond to smaller resistances, so this scale reads backward compared to the scale showing the current.

In situations in which high precision is required, instruments containing d'Arsonval meters have been supplanted by electronic instruments with direct digital readouts. These are more precise, stable, and mechanically rugged than d'Arsonval meters. Digital voltmeters can be made with extremely high internal resistance, of the order of 100 MΩ. Figure 26.18 shows a digital *multimeter,* an instrument that can measure voltage, current, or resistance over a wide range.

26.17 Ohmmeter circuit. The resistor R_s has a variable resistance, as is indicated by the arrow through the resistor symbol. To use the ohmmeter, first connect x directly to y and adjust R_s until the meter reads zero. Then connect x and y across the resistor R and read the scale.

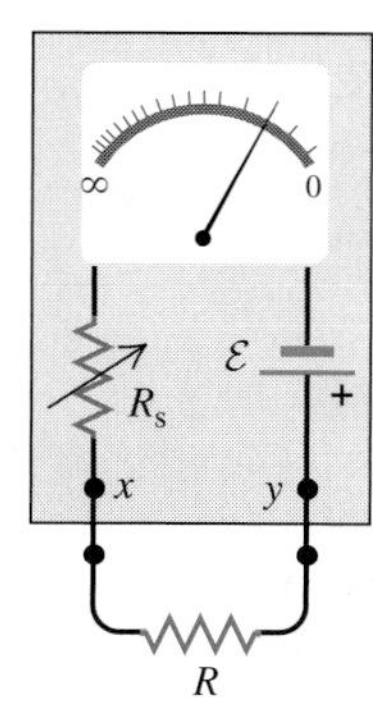

The Potentiometer

The *potentiometer* is an instrument that can be used to measure the emf of a source without drawing any current from the source; it also has a number of other useful applications. Essentially, it balances an unknown potential difference against an adjustable, measurable potential difference.

The principle of the potentiometer is shown schematically in Fig. 26.19a. A resistance wire ab of total resistance R_{ab} is permanently connected to the terminals of a source of known emf $\mathcal{E}_1$. A sliding contact c is connected through the galvanometer G to a second source whose emf $\mathcal{E}_2$ is to be measured. As contact c is moved along the resistance wire, the resistance R_{cb} between points c and b varies; if the resistance wire is uniform, R_{cb} is proportional to the length of wire between c and b. To determine the value of $\mathcal{E}_2$, contact c is moved until a position is found at which the galvanometer shows no deflection; this corresponds to zero current passing through $\mathcal{E}_2$. With $I_2 = 0$, Kirchhoff's loop rule gives

$$\mathcal{E}_2 = IR_{cb}$$

With $I_2 = 0$, the current I produced by the emf $\mathcal{E}_1$ has the same value no matter what the value of the emf $\mathcal{E}_2$. We calibrate the device by replacing $\mathcal{E}_2$ by a source of known emf; then any unknown emf $\mathcal{E}_2$ can be found by measuring the length of wire cb for which $I_2 = 0$ (see Exercise 26.35). Note that for this to work, V_{ab} must be greater than $\mathcal{E}_2$.

The term *potentiometer* is also used for any variable resistor, usually having a circular resistance element and a sliding contact controlled by a rotating shaft and knob. The circuit symbol for a potentiometer is shown in Fig. 26.19b.

26.18 This digital multimeter can be used as a voltmeter (red arc), ammeter (yellow arc), or ohmmeter (green arc).

26.19 (a) Potentiometer circuit. (b) Circuit symbol for a potentiometer (variable resistor).

(a)

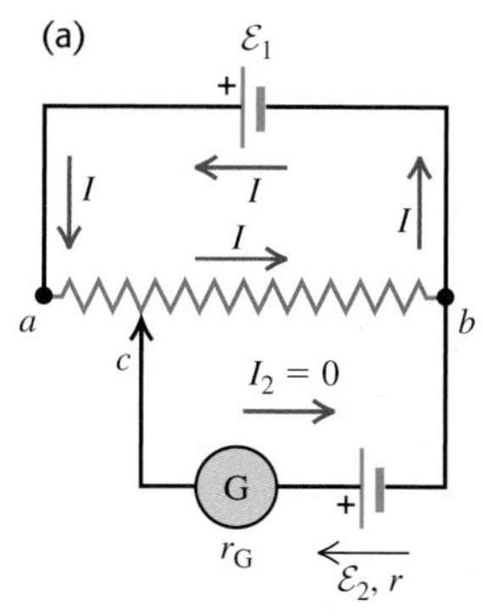

(b)

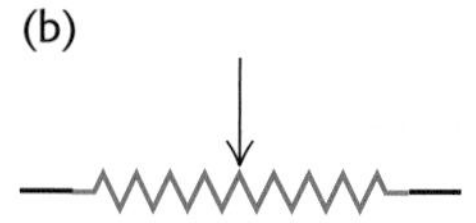

Test Your Understanding of Section 26.3 You want to measure the current through and the potential difference across the 2-Ω resistor shown in Fig. 26.12 (Example 26.6 in Section 26.2). (a) How should you connect an ammeter and a voltmeter to do this? (i) ammeter and voltmeter both in series with the 2-Ω resistor; (ii) ammeter in series with the 2-Ω resistor and voltmeter connected between points b and d; (iii) ammeter connected between points b and d and voltmeter in series with the 2-Ω resistor; (iv) ammeter and voltmeter both connected between points b and d. (b) What resistances should these meters have? (i) Ammeter and voltmeter resistances should both be much greater than 2 Ω; (ii) ammeter resistance should be much greater than 2 Ω and voltmeter resistance should be much less than 2 Ω; (iii) ammeter resistance should be much less than 2 Ω and voltmeter resistance should be much greater than 2 Ω; (iv) ammeter and voltmeter resistances should both be much less than 2 Ω.

26.4 *R-C* Circuits

In the circuits we have analyzed up to this point, we have assumed that all the emfs and resistances are *constant* (time independent) so that all the potentials, currents, and powers are also independent of time. But in the simple act of charging or discharging a capacitor we find a situation in which the currents, voltages, and powers *do* change with time.

Many important devices incorporate circuits in which a capacitor is alternately charged and discharged. These include heart pacemakers (Fig. 26.20), flashing traffic lights, automobile turn signals, and electronic flash units. Understanding what happens in such circuits is thus of great practical importance.

26.20 This colored x-ray image shows a pacemaker surgically implanted in a patient with a malfunctioning sinoatrial node, the part of the heart that generates the electrical signal to trigger heartbeats. To compensate, the pacemaker (located near the collarbone) sends a pulsed electrical signal along the lead to the heart to maintain regular beating.

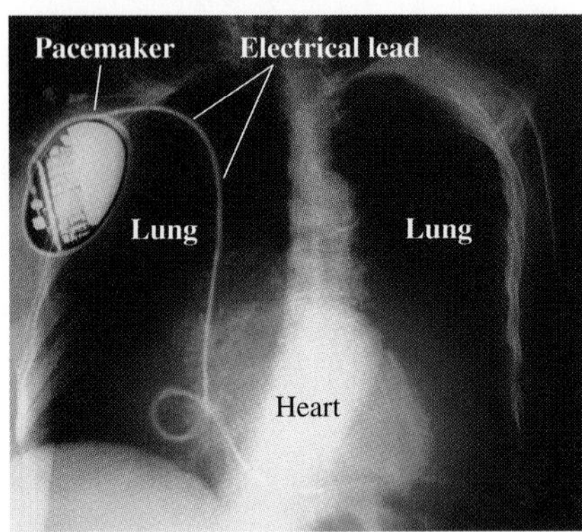

Charging a Capacitor

Figure 26.21 shows a simple circuit for charging a capacitor. A circuit such as this that has a resistor and a capacitor in series is called an ***R-C* circuit.** We idealize the battery (or power supply) to have a constant emf $\mathcal{E}$ and zero internal resistance $(r = 0)$, and we neglect the resistance of all the connecting conductors.

We begin with the capacitor initially uncharged (Fig. 26.21a); then at some initial time $t = 0$ we close the switch, completing the circuit and permitting current around the loop to begin charging the capacitor (Fig. 26.21b). For all practical purposes, the current begins at the same instant in every conducting part of the circuit, and at each instant the current is the same in every part.

CAUTION **Lowercase means time-varying** Up to this point we have been working with constant potential differences (voltages), currents, and charges, and we have used *capital* letters V, I, and Q, respectively, to denote these quantities. To distinguish between quantities that vary with time and those that are constant, we will use *lowercase* letters v, i, and q for time-varying voltages, currents, and charges, respectively. We suggest that you follow this same convention in your own work.

26.21 Charging a capacitor. **(a)** Just before the switch is closed, the charge q is zero. **(b)** When the switch closes (at $t = 0$), the current jumps from zero to $\mathcal{E}/R$. As time passes, q approaches Q_f and the current i approaches zero.

(a) Capacitor initially uncharged

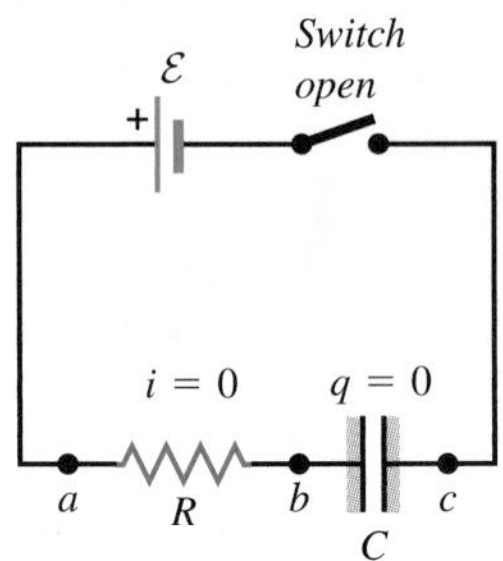

(b) Charging the capacitor

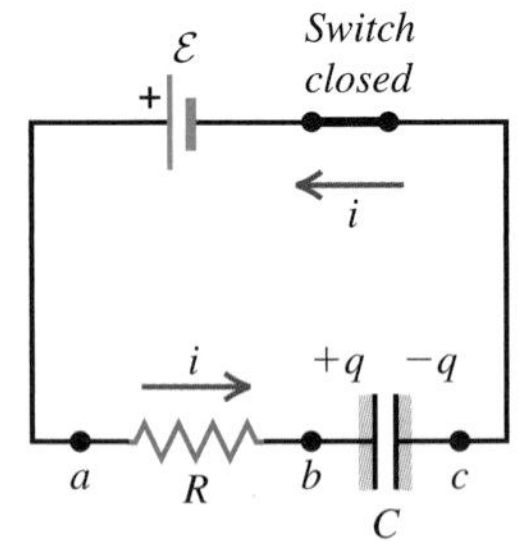

Because the capacitor in Fig. 26.21 is initially uncharged, the potential difference v_{bc} across it is zero at $t = 0$. At this time, from Kirchhoff's loop law, the voltage v_{ab} across the resistor R is equal to the battery emf $\mathcal{E}$. The initial $(t = 0)$ current through the resistor, which we will call I_0, is given by Ohm's law: $I_0 = v_{ab}/R = \mathcal{E}/R$.

As the capacitor charges, its voltage v_{bc} increases and the potential difference v_{ab} across the resistor decreases, corresponding to a decrease in current. The sum of these two voltages is constant and equal to $\mathcal{E}$. After a long time the capacitor becomes fully charged, the current decreases to zero, and the potential difference v_{ab} across the resistor becomes zero. Then the entire battery emf $\mathcal{E}$ appears across the capacitor and $v_{bc} = \mathcal{E}$.

Let q represent the charge on the capacitor and i the current in the circuit at some time t after the switch has been closed. We choose the positive direction for the current to correspond to positive charge flowing onto the left-hand capacitor plate, as in Fig. 26.21b. The instantaneous potential differences v_{ab} and v_{bc} are

$$v_{ab} = iR \qquad v_{bc} = \frac{q}{C}$$

Using these in Kirchhoff's loop rule, we find

$$\mathcal{E} - iR - \frac{q}{C} = 0 \tag{26.9}$$

The potential drops by an amount iR as we travel from a to b and by q/C as we travel from b to c. Solving Eq. (26.9) for i, we find

$$i = \frac{\mathcal{E}}{R} - \frac{q}{RC} \tag{26.10}$$

At time $t = 0$, when the switch is first closed, the capacitor is uncharged, and so $q = 0$. Substituting $q = 0$ into Eq. (26.10), we find that the *initial* current I_0 is given by $I_0 = \mathcal{E}/R$, as we have already noted. If the capacitor were not in the circuit, the last term in Eq. (26.10) would not be present; then the current would be *constant* and equal to $\mathcal{E}/R$.

As the charge q increases, the term q/RC becomes larger and the capacitor charge approaches its final value, which we will call Q_f. The current decreases and eventually becomes zero. When $i = 0$, Eq. (26.10) gives

$$\frac{\mathcal{E}}{R} = \frac{Q_f}{RC} \qquad Q_f = C\mathcal{E} \tag{26.11}$$

Note that the final charge Q_f does not depend on R.

The current and the capacitor charge are shown as functions of time in Fig. 26.22. At the instant the switch is closed $(t = 0)$, the current jumps from zero to its initial value $I_0 = \mathcal{E}/R$; after that, it gradually approaches zero. The capacitor charge starts at zero and gradually approaches the final value given by Eq. (26.11), $Q_f = C\mathcal{E}$.

We can derive general expressions for the charge q and current i as functions of time. With our choice of the positive direction for current (Fig. 26.21b), i equals the rate at which positive charge arrives at the left-hand (positive) plate of the capacitor, so $i = dq/dt$. Making this substitution in Eq. (26.10), we have

$$\frac{dq}{dt} = \frac{\mathcal{E}}{R} - \frac{q}{RC} = -\frac{1}{RC}(q - C\mathcal{E})$$

We can rearrange this to

$$\frac{dq}{q - C\mathcal{E}} = -\frac{dt}{RC}$$

and then integrate both sides. We change the integration variables to q' and t' so that we can use q and t for the upper limits. The lower limits are $q' = 0$ and $t' = 0$:

$$\int_0^q \frac{dq'}{q' - C\mathcal{E}} = -\int_0^t \frac{dt'}{RC}$$

When we carry out the integration, we get

$$\ln\left(\frac{q - C\mathcal{E}}{-C\mathcal{E}}\right) = -\frac{t}{RC}$$

Exponentiating both sides (that is, taking the inverse logarithm) and solving for q, we find

$$\frac{q - C\mathcal{E}}{-C\mathcal{E}} = e^{-t/RC}$$

$$q = C\mathcal{E}(1 - e^{-t/RC}) = Q_f(1 - e^{-t/RC}) \qquad \begin{array}{l}(\textit{R-C} \text{ circuit,}\\ \text{charging capacitor)}\end{array} \tag{26.12}$$

The instantaneous current i is just the time derivative of Eq. (26.12):

$$i = \frac{dq}{dt} = \frac{\mathcal{E}}{R}e^{-t/RC} = I_0 e^{-t/RC} \qquad \begin{array}{l}(\textit{R-C} \text{ circuit,}\\ \text{charging capacitor)}\end{array} \tag{26.13}$$

The charge and current are both *exponential* functions of time. Figure 26.22a is a graph of Eq. (26.13) and Fig. 26.22b is a graph of Eq. (26.12).

26.22 Current i and capacitor charge q as functions of time for the circuit of Fig. 26.21. The initial current is I_0 and the initial capacitor charge is zero. The current asymptotically approaches zero and the capacitor charge asymptotically approaches a final value of Q_f.

(a) Graph of current versus time for a charging capacitor

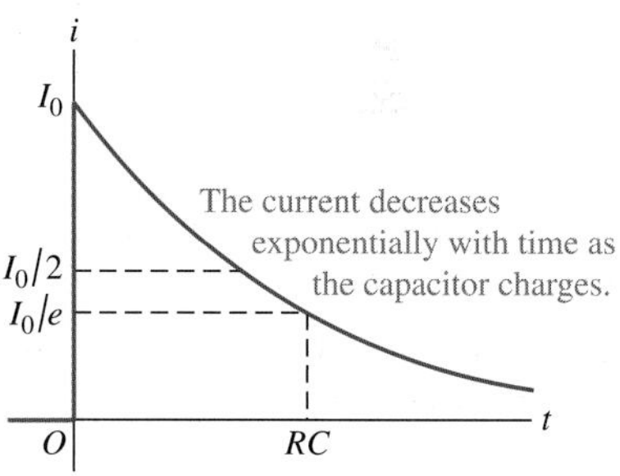

i
I0
I0/2
I0/e
The current decreases exponentially with time as the capacitor charges.
O
RC
t

(b) Graph of capacitor charge versus time for a charging capacitor

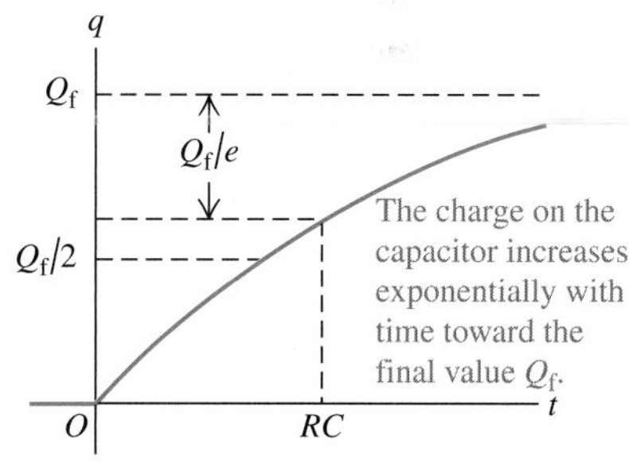

q
Qf
Qf/e
Qf/2
The charge on the capacitor increases exponentially with time toward the final value Qf.
O
RC
t

26.23 Discharging a capacitor. (a) Before the switch is closed at time $t = 0$, the capacitor charge is Q_0 and the current is zero. (b) At time t after the switch is closed, the capacitor charge is q and the current is i. The actual current direction is opposite to the direction shown; i is negative. After a long time, q and i both approach zero.

(a) Capacitor initially charged

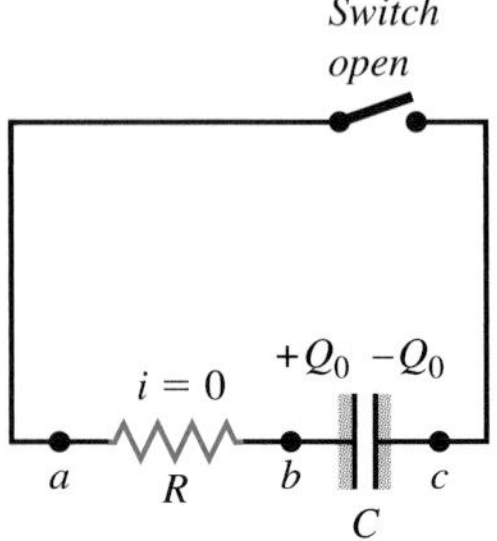

Switch
open
$i = 0$
$+Q_0$ $-Q_0$
a
R
b
C
c

(b) Discharging the capacitor

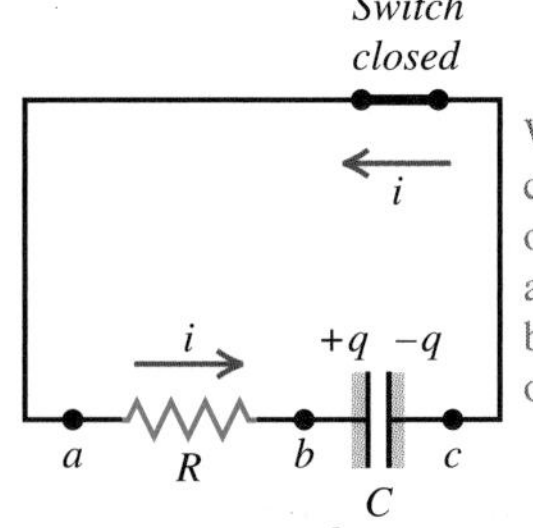

Switch
closed
i
i
$+q$ $-q$
a
R
b
C
c
When the switch is closed, the charge on the capacitor and the current both decrease over time.

26.24 Current i and capacitor charge q as functions of time for the circuit of Fig. 26.23. The initial current is I_0 and the initial capacitor charge is Q_0. Both i and q asymptotically approach zero.

(a) Graph of current versus time for a discharging capacitor

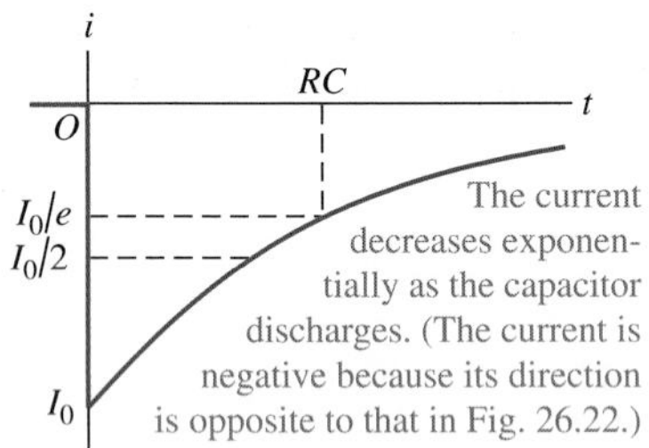

i
RC
O
t
I_0/e
$I_0/2$
I_0
The current decreases exponentially as the capacitor discharges. (The current is negative because its direction is opposite to that in Fig. 26.22.)

(b) Graph of capacitor charge versus time for a discharging capacitor

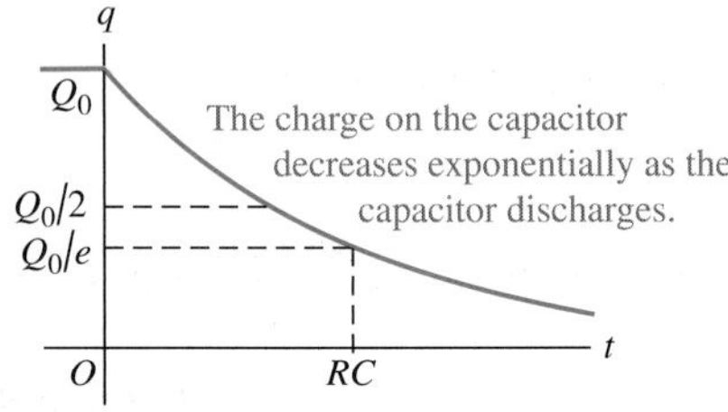

q
Q_0
$Q_0/2$
Q_0/e
O
RC
t
The charge on the capacitor decreases exponentially as the capacitor discharges.

Time Constant

After a time equal to RC, the current in the R-C circuit has decreased to $1/e$ (about 0.368) of its initial value. At this time, the capacitor charge has reached $(1 - 1/e) = 0.632$ of its final value $Q_f = C\mathcal{E}$. The product RC is therefore a measure of how quickly the capacitor charges. We call RC the **time constant,** or the **relaxation time,** of the circuit, denoted by τ:

$$\tau = RC \qquad \text{(time constant for } R\text{-}C \text{ circuit)} \tag{26.14}$$

When τ is small, the capacitor charges quickly; when it is larger, the charging takes more time. If the resistance is small, it's easier for current to flow, and the capacitor charges more quickly. If R is in ohms and C in farads, τ is in seconds.

In Fig. 26.22a the horizontal axis is an *asymptote* for the curve. Strictly speaking, i never becomes exactly zero. But the longer we wait, the closer it gets. After a time equal to 10 RC, the current has decreased to 0.000045 of its initial value. Similarly, the curve in Fig. 26.22b approaches the horizontal dashed line labeled Q_f as an asymptote. The charge q never attains exactly this value, but after a time equal to $10RC$, the difference between q and Q_f is only 0.000045 of Q_f. We invite you to verify that the product RC has units of time.

Discharging a Capacitor

Now suppose that after the capacitor in Fig. 26.21b has acquired a charge Q_0, we remove the battery from our R-C circuit and connect points a and c to an open switch (Fig. 26.23a). We then close the switch and at the same instant reset our stopwatch to $t = 0$; at that time, $q = Q_0$. The capacitor then *discharges* through the resistor, and its charge eventually decreases to zero.

Again let i and q represent the time-varying current and charge at some instant after the connection is made. In Fig. 26.23b we make the same choice of the positive direction for current as in Fig. 26.21b. Then Kirchhoff's loop rule gives Eq. (26.10) but with $\mathcal{E} = 0$; that is,

$$i = \frac{dq}{dt} = -\frac{q}{RC} \tag{26.15}$$

The current i is now negative; this is because positive charge q is leaving the left-hand capacitor plate in Fig. 26.23b, so the current is in the direction opposite to that shown in the figure. At time $t = 0$, when $q = Q_0$, the initial current is $I_0 = -Q_0/RC$.

To find q as a function of time, we rearrange Eq. (26.15), again change the names of the variables to q' and t', and integrate. This time the limits for q' are Q_0 to q. We get

$$\int_{Q_0}^{q} \frac{dq'}{q'} = -\frac{1}{RC}\int_0^t dt'$$

$$\ln\frac{q}{Q_0} = -\frac{t}{RC}$$

$$q = Q_0 e^{-t/RC} \qquad (R\text{-}C \text{ circuit, discharging capacitor}) \tag{26.16}$$

The instantaneous current i is the derivative of this with respect to time:

$$i = \frac{dq}{dt} = -\frac{Q_0}{RC}e^{-t/RC} = I_0 e^{-t/RC} \qquad \begin{pmatrix} R\text{-}C \text{ circuit,} \\ \text{discharging capacitor} \end{pmatrix} \tag{26.17}$$

The current and the charge are graphed in Fig. 26.24; both quantities approach zero exponentially with time. Comparing these results with Eqs. (26.12) and (26.13), we note that the expressions for the current are identical, apart from the sign of I_0.

The capacitor charge approaches zero asymptotically in Eq. (26.16), while the *difference* between q and Q approaches zero asymptotically in Eq. (26.12).

Energy considerations give us additional insight into the behavior of an *R-C* circuit. While the capacitor is charging, the instantaneous rate at which the battery delivers energy to the circuit is $P = \mathcal{E}i$. The instantaneous rate at which electrical energy is dissipated in the resistor is i^2R and the rate at which energy is stored in the capacitor is $iv_{bc} = iq/C$. Multiplying Eq. (26.9) by i, we find

$$\mathcal{E}i = i^2R + \frac{iq}{C} \qquad (26.18)$$

This means that of the power $\mathcal{E}i$ supplied by the battery, part (i^2R) is dissipated in the resistor and part (iq/C) is stored in the capacitor.

The *total* energy supplied by the battery during charging of the capacitor equals the battery emf $\mathcal{E}$ multiplied by the total charge Q_f, or $\mathcal{E}Q_f$. The total energy stored in the capacitor, from Eq. (24.9), is $Q_f\mathcal{E}/2$. Thus, of the energy supplied by the battery, *exactly half* is stored in the capacitor, and the other half is dissipated in the resistor. It is a little surprising that this half-and-half division of energy doesn't depend on C, R, or $\mathcal{E}$. This result can also be verified in detail by taking the integral over time of each of the power quantities in Eq. (26.18). We leave this calculation for your amusement (see Problem 26.87).

ActivPhysics ONLINE

12.6 Capacitance
12.7 Series and Parallel Capacitors
12.8 Circuit Time Constants

Example 26.12 Charging a capacitor

A resistor with resistance 10 MΩ is connected in series with a capacitor with capacitance 1.0 μF and a battery with emf 12.0 V. Before the switch is closed at time $t = 0$, the capacitor is uncharged. (a) What is the time constant? (b) What fraction of the final charge is on the plates at time $t = 46$ s? (c) What fraction of the initial current remains at $t = 46$ s?

SOLUTION

IDENTIFY: This is the same situation as shown in Fig. 26.21, with $R = 10\ \text{M}\Omega$, $C = 1.0\ \mu\text{F}$, and $\mathcal{E} = 12.0$ V. The charge and current vary with time as shown in Fig. 26.22. Our target variables are (a) the time constant, (b) the charge q at $t = 46$ s divided by the final charge Q_f, and (c) the current i at $t = 46$ s divided by the initial current i_0.

SET UP: For a capacitor being charged, the charge is given by Eq. (26.12) and the current by Eq. (26.13). Equation (26.14) gives the time constant.

EXECUTE: (a) From Eq. (26.14), the time constant is

$$\tau = RC = (10 \times 10^6\ \Omega)(1.0 \times 10^{-6}\ \text{F}) = 10\ \text{s}$$

(b) From Eq. (26.12),

$$\frac{q}{Q_f} = 1 - e^{-t/RC} = 1 - e^{-(46\ \text{s})/(10\ \text{s})} = 0.99$$

The capacitor is 99% charged after a time equal to 4.6 RC, or 4.6 time constants.

(c) From Eq. (26.13),

$$\frac{i}{I_0} = e^{-4.6} = 0.010$$

After 4.6 time constants the current has decreased to 1.0% of its initial value.

EVALUATE: The time constant is relatively long because the resistance is very large. The circuit charges more rapidly if a smaller resistance is used.

Example 26.13 Discharging a capacitor

The resistor and capacitor described in Example 26.12 are reconnected as shown in Fig. 26.23. The capacitor is originally given a charge of 5.0 μC and then discharged by closing the switch at $t = 0$. (a) At what time will the charge be equal to 0.50 μC? (b) What is the current at this time?

SOLUTION

IDENTIFY: Now the capacitor is being discharged, so the charge q and current i vary with time as shown in Fig. 26.24. Our target variables are (a) the value of t at which $q = 0.50\ \mu\text{C}$ and (b) the value of i at this time.

SET UP: The charge is given by Eq. (26.16) and the current by Eq. (26.17).

EXECUTE: (a) Solving Eq. (26.16) for the time t gives

$$t = -RC \ln \frac{q}{Q_0}$$

$$= -(10 \times 10^6\ \Omega)(1.0 \times 10^{-6}\ \text{F}) \ln \frac{0.50\ \mu\text{C}}{5.0\ \mu\text{C}} = 23\ \text{s}$$

Continued

This is 2.3 times the time constant $\tau = RC = 10$ s.

(b) From Eq. (26.17), with $Q_0 = 5.0\ \mu\text{C} = 5.0 \times 10^{-6}$ C,

$$i = -\frac{Q_0}{RC}e^{-t/RC} = -\frac{5.0 \times 10^{-6}\ \text{C}}{10\ \text{s}}e^{-2.3} = -5.0 \times 10^{-8}\ \text{A}$$

The current has the opposite sign when the capacitor is discharging than when it is charging.

EVALUATE: We could have saved the effort required to calculate $e^{-t/RC}$ by noticing that at the time in question, $q = 0.10Q_0$; from Eq. (26.16) this means $e^{-t/RC} = 0.10$.

Test Your Understanding of Section 26.4 The energy stored in a capacitor is equal to $q^2/2C$. When a capacitor is discharged, what fraction of the initial energy remains after an elapsed time of one time constant? (i) $1/e$; (ii) $1/e^2$; (iii) $1 - 1/e$; (iv) $(1 - 1/e)^2$; (v) answer depends on how much energy was stored initially.

26.5 Power Distribution Systems

We conclude this chapter with a brief discussion of practical household and automotive electric-power distribution systems. Automobiles use direct-current (dc) systems, while nearly all household, commercial, and industrial systems use alternating current (ac) because of the ease of stepping voltage up and down with transformers. Most of the same basic wiring concepts apply to both. We'll talk about alternating-current circuits in greater detail in Chapter 31.

The various lamps, motors, and other appliances to be operated are always connected in *parallel* to the power source (the wires from the power company for houses, or from the battery and alternator for a car). If appliances were connected in series, shutting one appliance off would shut them all off (see Example 26.2 in Section 26.1). The basic idea of house wiring is shown in Fig. 26.25. One side of the "line," as the pair of conductors is called, is called the *neutral* side; it is always connected to "ground" at the entrance panel. For houses, *ground* is an actual electrode driven into the earth (which is usually a good conductor) or sometimes connected to the household water pipes. Electricians speak of the "hot" side and the "neutral" side of the line. Most modern house wiring systems have *two* hot lines with opposite polarity with respect to the neutral. We'll return to this detail later.

Household voltage is nominally 120 V in the United States and Canada, and often 240 V in Europe. (For alternating current, which varies sinusoidally with time, these numbers represent the *root-mean-square* voltage, which is $1/\sqrt{2}$ times the peak voltage. We'll discuss this further in Section 31.1.) The amount of current I drawn by a given device is determined by its power input P, given by Eq. (25.17): $P = VI$. Hence $I = P/V$. For example, the current in a 100-W light bulb is

$$I = \frac{P}{V} = \frac{100\ \text{W}}{120\ \text{V}} = 0.83\ \text{A}$$

26.25 Schematic diagram of part of a house wiring system. Only two branch circuits are shown; an actual system might have four to thirty branch circuits. Lamps and appliances may be plugged into the outlets. The grounding wires, which normally carry no current, are not shown.

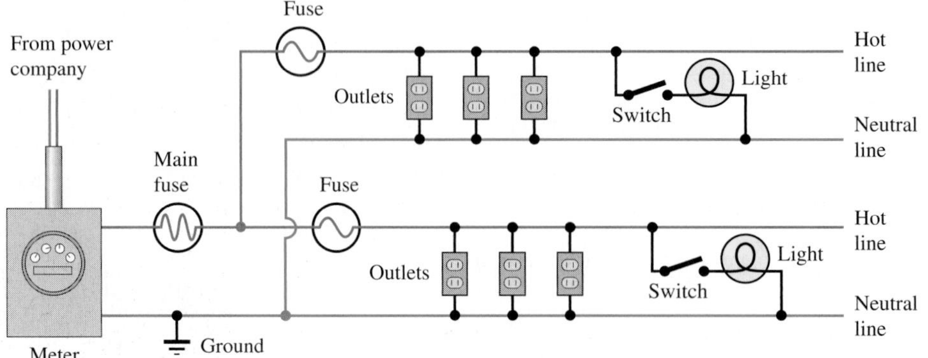

The power input to this bulb is actually determined by its resistance R. Using Eq. (25.18), which states that $P = VI = I^2R = V^2/R$ for a resistor, the resistance of this bulb at operating temperature is

$$R = \frac{V}{I} = \frac{120\ \text{V}}{0.83\ \text{A}} = 144\ \Omega \qquad \text{or} \qquad R = \frac{V^2}{P} = \frac{(120\ \text{V})^2}{100\ \text{W}} = 144\ \Omega$$

Similarly, a 1500-W waffle iron draws a current of $(1500\ \text{W})/(120\ \text{V}) = 12.5\ \text{A}$ and has a resistance, at operating temperature, of $9.6\ \Omega$. Because of the temperature dependence of resistivity, the resistances of these devices are considerably less when they are cold. If you measure the resistance of a 100-W light bulb with an ohmmeter (whose small current causes very little temperature rise), you will probably get a value of about $10\ \Omega$. When a light bulb is turned on, this low resistance causes an initial surge of current until the filament heats up. That's why a light bulb that's ready to burn out nearly always does so just when you turn it on.

Circuit Overloads and Short Circuits

The maximum current available from an individual circuit is limited by the resistance of the wires. As we discussed in Section 25.5, the I^2R power loss in the wires causes them to become hot, and in extreme cases this can cause a fire or melt the wires. Ordinary lighting and outlet wiring in houses usually uses 12-gauge wire. This has a diameter of 2.05 mm and can carry a maximum current of 20 A safely (without overheating). Larger sizes such as 8-gauge (3.26 mm) or 6-gauge (4.11 mm) are used for high-current appliances such as electric ranges and clothes dryers, and 2-gauge (6.54 mm) or larger is used for the main power lines entering a house.

Protection against overloading and overheating of circuits is provided by fuses or circuit breakers. A *fuse* contains a link of lead–tin alloy with a very low melting temperature; the link melts and breaks the circuit when its rated current is exceeded (Fig. 26.26a). A *circuit breaker* is an electromechanical device that performs the same function, using an electromagnet or a bimetallic strip to "trip" the breaker and interrupt the circuit when the current exceeds a specified value (Fig. 26.26b). Circuit breakers have the advantage that they can be reset after they are tripped, while a blown fuse must be replaced. However, fuses are somewhat more reliable in operation than circuit breakers are.

If your system has fuses and you plug too many high-current appliances into the same outlet, the fuse blows. *Do not* replace the fuse with one of larger rating; if you do, you risk overheating the wires and starting a fire. The only safe solution is to distribute the appliances among several circuits. Modern kitchens often have three or four separate 20-A circuits.

Contact between the hot and neutral sides of the line causes a *short circuit.* Such a situation, which can be caused by faulty insulation or by any of a variety of mechanical malfunctions, provides a very low-resistance current path, permitting a very large current that would quickly melt the wires and ignite their insulation if the current were not interrupted by a fuse or circuit breaker (see Example 25.11 in Section 25.5). An equally dangerous situation is a broken wire that interrupts the current path, creating an *open circuit.* This is hazardous because of the sparking that can occur at the point of intermittent contact.

In approved wiring practice, a fuse or breaker is placed *only* in the hot side of the line, never in the neutral side. Otherwise, if a short circuit should develop because of faulty insulation or other malfunction, the ground-side fuse could blow. The hot side would still be live and would pose a shock hazard if you touched the live conductor and a grounded object such as a water pipe. For similar reasons the wall switch for a light fixture is always in the hot side of the line, never the neutral side.

Further protection against shock hazard is provided by a third conductor called the *grounding wire,* included in all present-day wiring. This conductor

26.26 (a) Excess current will melt the thin wire of lead–tin alloy that runs along the length of a fuse, inside the transparent housing. (b) The switch on this circuit breaker will flip if the maximum allowable current is exceeded.

(a)

(b)

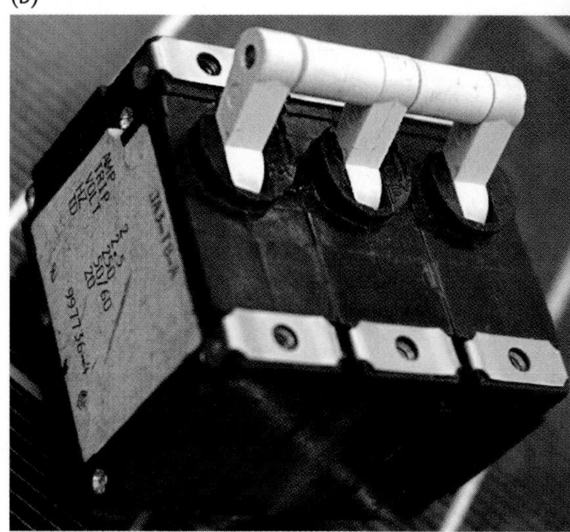

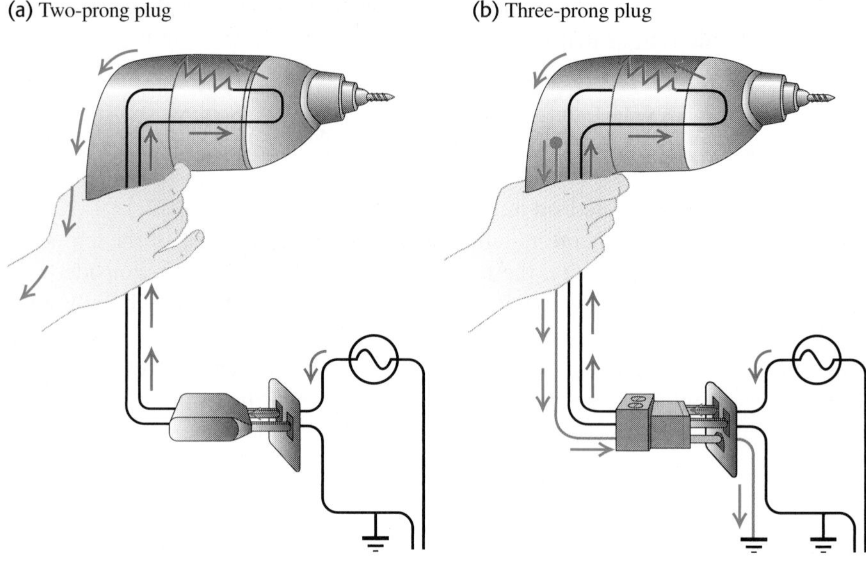

26.27 (a) If a malfunctioning electric drill is connected to a wall socket via a two-prong plug, a person may receive a shock. (b) When the drill malfunctions when connected via a three-prong plug, a person touching it receives no shock, because electric charge flows through the ground wire (shown in green) to the third prong and into the ground rather than into the person's body. If the ground current is appreciable, the fuse blows.

corresponds to the long round or U-shaped prong of the three-prong connector plug on an appliance or power tool. It is connected to the neutral side of the line at the entrance panel. The grounding wire normally carries no current, but it connects the metal case or frame of the device to ground. If a conductor on the hot side of the line accidentally contacts the frame or case, the grounding conductor provides a current path, and the fuse blows. Without the ground wire, the frame could become "live,"—that is, at a potential 120 V above ground. Then if you touched it and a water pipe (or even a damp basement floor) at the same time, you could get a dangerous shock (Fig. 26.27). In some situations, especially outlets located outdoors or near a sink or other water pipes, a special kind of circuit breaker called a *ground-fault interrupter* (GFI or GFCI) is used. This device senses the difference in current between the hot and neutral conductors (which is normally zero) and trips when this difference exceeds some very small value, typically 5 mA.

Household and Automotive Wiring

Most modern household wiring systems actually use a slight elaboration of the system described above. The power company provides *three* conductors (Fig. 26.28). One is neutral; the other two are both at 120 V with respect to the neutral but with opposite polarity, giving a voltage between them of 240 V. The power company calls this a *three-wire line,* in contrast to the 120-V two-wire (plus ground wire) line described above. With a three-wire line, 120-V lamps and appliances can be connected between neutral and either hot conductor, and high-power devices requiring 240 V, such as electric ranges and clothes dryers, are connected between the two hot lines.

To help prevent wiring errors, household wiring uses a standardized color code in which the hot side of a line has black insulation (black and red for the two sides of a 240-V line), the neutral side has white insulation, and the grounding conductor is bare or has green insulation. But in electronic devices and equipment the ground or neutral side of the line is usually black. Beware! (Our illustrations do not follow this standard code but use red for the hot line and blue for neutral.)

All of the above discussion can be applied directly to automobile wiring. The voltage is about 13 V (direct current); the power is supplied by the battery and by the alternator, which charges the battery when the engine is running. The neutral

26.28 Diagram of a typical 120–240-V wiring system in a kitchen. Grounding wires are not shown. For each line, the hot side is shown in red, and the neutral line is shown in blue. (Different colors are used in actual household wiring.)

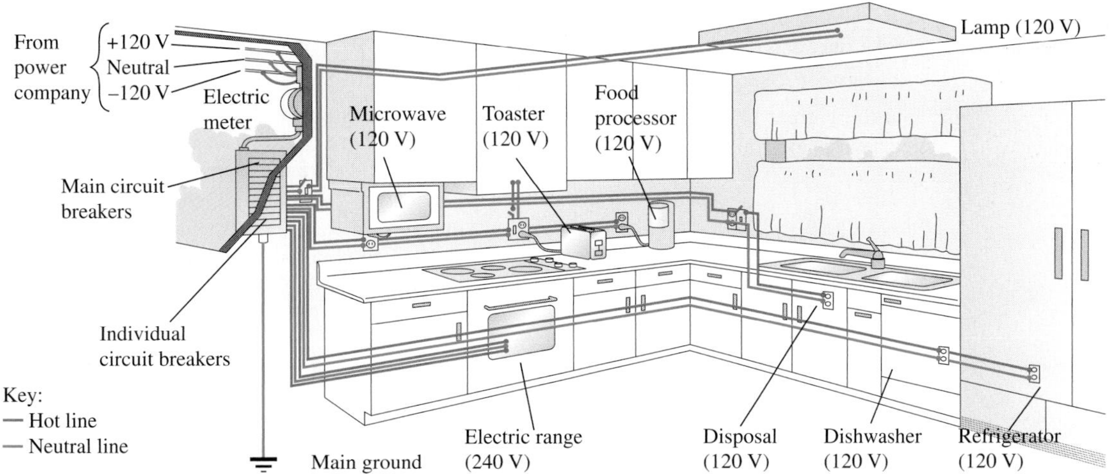

side of each circuit is connected to the body and frame of the vehicle. For this low voltage a separate grounding conductor is not required for safety. The fuse or circuit breaker arrangement is the same in principle as in household wiring. Because of the lower voltage (less energy per charge), more current (a greater number of charges per second) is required for the same power; a 100-W headlight bulb requires a current of about $(100\text{ W})/(13\text{ V}) = 8\text{ A}$.

Although we spoke of *power* in the above discussion, what we buy from the power company is *energy*. Power is energy transferred per unit time, so energy is average power multiplied by time. The usual unit of energy sold by the power company is the kilowatt-hour $(1\text{ kW}\cdot\text{h})$:

$$1\text{ kW}\cdot\text{h} = (10^3\text{ W})(3600\text{ s}) = 3.6\times10^6\text{ W}\cdot\text{s} = 3.6\times10^6\text{ J}$$

One kilowatt-hour typically costs 2 to 10 cents, depending on the location and quantity of energy purchased. To operate a 1500-W (1.5-kW) waffle iron continuously for 1 hour requires 1.5 kW · h of energy; at 10 cents per kilowatt-hour, the energy cost is 15 cents. The cost of operating any lamp or appliance for a specified time can be calculated in the same way if the power rating is known. However, many electric cooking utensils (including waffle irons) cycle on and off to maintain a constant temperature, so the average power may be less than the power rating marked on the device.

Example 26.14 A kitchen circuit

An 1800-W toaster, a 1.3-kW electric frying pan, and a 100-W lamp are plugged into the same 20-A, 120-V circuit. (a) What current is drawn by each device, and what is the resistance of each device? (b) Will this combination blow the fuse?

SOLUTION

IDENTIFY: When plugged into the same circuit, the three devices are in parallel. The voltage across each device is $V = 120\text{ V}$.

SET UP: We find the current I drawn by each device using the relationship $P = VI$, where P is the power input of the device. To find the resistance R for each device we use the relationship $P = V^2/R$.

EXECUTE: (a) To simplify the calculation of current and resistance, we note that $I = P/V$ and $R = V^2/P$. Hence

$$I_{\text{toaster}} = \frac{1800\text{ W}}{120\text{ V}} = 15\text{ A} \qquad R_{\text{toaster}} = \frac{(120\text{ V})^2}{1800\text{ W}} = 8\ \Omega$$

$$I_{\text{frying pan}} = \frac{1300\text{ W}}{120\text{ V}} = 11\text{ A} \qquad R_{\text{frying pan}} = \frac{(120\text{ V})^2}{1300\text{ W}} = 11\ \Omega$$

$$I_{\text{lamp}} = \frac{100\text{ W}}{120\text{ V}} = 0.83\text{ A} \qquad R_{\text{lamp}} = \frac{(120\text{ V})^2}{100\text{ W}} = 144\ \Omega$$

For constant voltage the device with the *least* resistance (in this case the toaster) draws the most current and receives the most power.

Continued

(b) The total current through the line is the sum of the currents drawn by the three devices:

$$I = I_{\text{toaster}} + I_{\text{frying pan}} + I_{\text{lamp}} = 15\text{ A} + 11\text{ A} + 0.83\text{ A} = 27\text{ A}$$

This exceeds the 20-A rating of the line, and the fuse will indeed blow.

EVALUATE: We could also find the current by first finding the equivalent resistance of the three devices in parallel:

$$\frac{1}{R_{\text{eq}}} = \frac{1}{R_{\text{toaster}}} + \frac{1}{R_{\text{frying pan}}} + \frac{1}{R_{\text{lamp}}}$$

$$= \frac{1}{8\ \Omega} + \frac{1}{11\ \Omega} + \frac{1}{144\ \Omega} = 0.22\ \Omega^{-1}$$

$$R_{\text{eq}} = 4.5\ \Omega$$

The total current is then $I = V/R_{\text{eq}} = (120\text{ V})/(4.5\ \Omega) = 27\text{ A}$, as before. A third way to determine I is to use $I = P/V$ and simply divide the total power delivered to all three devices by the voltage:

$$I = \frac{P_{\text{toaster}} + P_{\text{frying pan}} + P_{\text{lamp}}}{V} = \frac{1800\text{ W} + 1300\text{ W} + 100\text{ W}}{120\text{ V}}$$

$$= 27\text{ A}$$

Current demands like these are encountered in everyday life in kitchens, which is why modern kitchens have more than one 20-A circuit. In actual practice, the toaster and frying pan should be connected to different circuits; the current in each circuit would then be safely below the 20-A rating.

Test Your Understanding of Section 26.5 To prevent the fuse in Example 26.14 from blowing, a home electrician replaces the fuse with one rated at 40 A. Is this a reasonable thing to do?

CHAPTER 26 SUMMARY

Resistors in series and parallel: When several resistors $R_1, R_2, R_3, \ldots$, are connected in series, the equivalent resistance R_{eq} is the sum of the individual resistances. The same *current* flows through all the resistors in a series connection. When several resistors are connected in parallel, the reciprocal of the equivalent resistance R_{eq} is the sum of the reciprocals of the individual resistances. All resistors in a parallel connection have the same *potential difference* between their terminals. (See Examples 26.1 and 26.2.)

$$R_{eq} = R_1 + R_2 + R_3 + \cdots \quad (26.1)$$
(resistors in series)

$$\frac{1}{R_{eq}} = \frac{1}{R_1} + \frac{1}{R_2} + \frac{1}{R_3} + \cdots \quad (26.2)$$
(resistors in parallel)

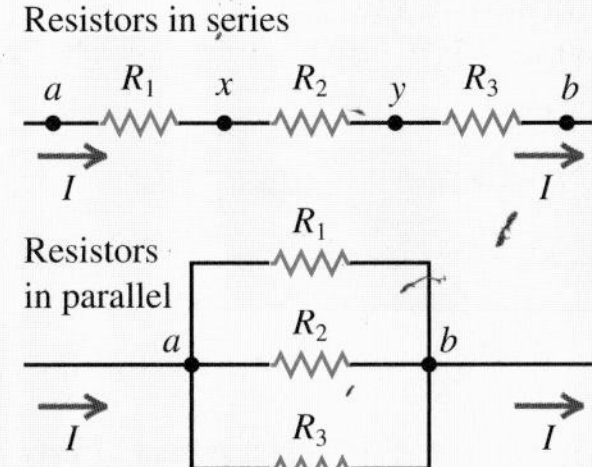

Kirchhoff's rules: Kirchhoff's junction rule is based on conservation of charge. It states that the algebraic sum of the currents into any junction must be zero. Kirchhoff's loop rule is based on conservation of energy and the conservative nature of electrostatic fields. It states that the algebraic sum of potential differences around any loop must be zero. Careful use of consistent sign rules is essential in applying Kirchhoff's rules. (See Examples 26.3–26.7)

$$\sum I = 0 \quad \text{(junction rule)} \quad (26.5)$$

$$\sum V = 0 \quad \text{(loop rule)} \quad (26.6)$$

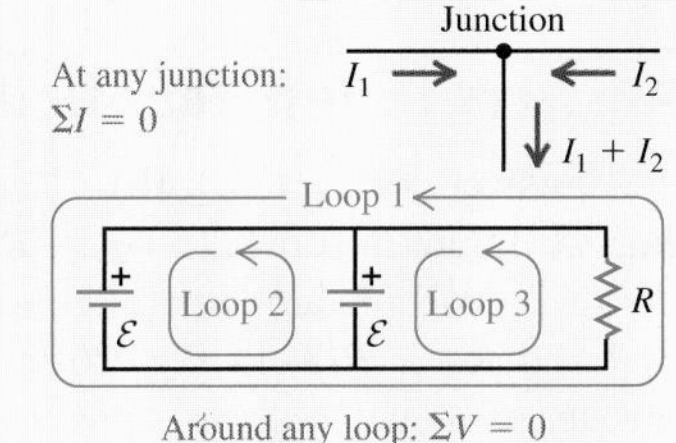

Electrical measuring instruments: In a d'Arsonval galvanometer, the deflection is proportional to the current in the coil. For a larger current range, a shunt resistor is added, so some of the current bypasses the meter coil. Such an instrument is called an ammeter. If the coil and any additional series resistance included obey Ohm's law, the meter can also be calibrated to read potential difference or voltage. The instrument is then called a voltmeter. A good ammeter has very low resistance; a good voltmeter has very high resistance. (See Examples 26.8–26.11.)

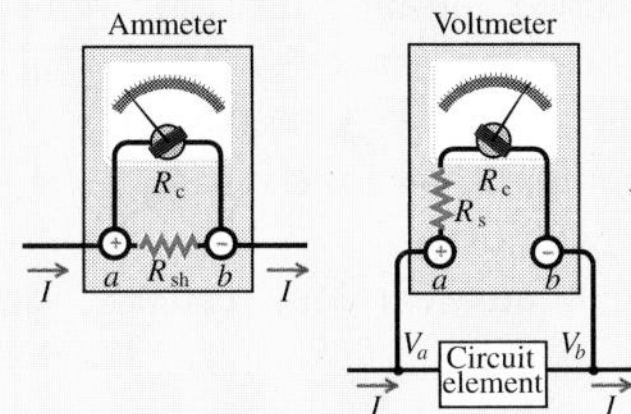

R-C circuits: When a capacitor is charged by a battery in series with a resistor, the current and capacitor charge are not constant. The charge approaches its final value asymptotically and the current approaches zero asymptotically. The charge and current in the circuit are given by Eqs. (26.12) and (26.13). After a time $\tau = RC$, the charge has approached within $1/e$ of its final value. This time is called the time constant or relaxation time of the circuit. When the capacitor discharges, the charge and current are given as functions of time by Eqs. (26.16) and (26.17). The time constant is the same for charging and discharging. (See Examples 26.12 and 26.13.)

Capacitor charging:

$$q = C\mathcal{E}(1 - e^{-t/RC}) = Q_f(1 - e^{-t/RC}) \quad (26.12)$$

$$i = \frac{dq}{dt} = \frac{\mathcal{E}}{R}e^{-t/RC} = I_0 e^{-t/RC} \quad (26.13)$$

Capacitor discharging:

$$q = Q_0 e^{-t/RC} \quad (26.16)$$

$$i = \frac{dq}{dt} = -\frac{Q_0}{RC}e^{-t/RC} = I_0 e^{-t/RC} \quad (26.17)$$

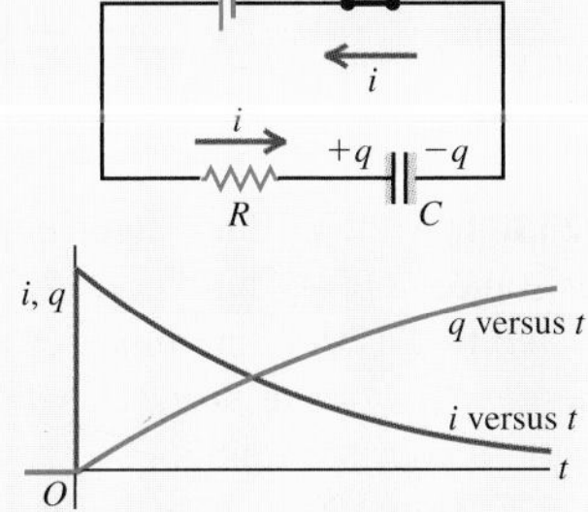

Household wiring: In household wiring systems, the various electrical devices are connected in parallel across the power line, which consists of a pair of conductors, one "hot" and the other "neutral." An additional "ground" wire is included for safety. The maximum permissible current in a circuit is determined by the size of the wires and the maximum temperature they can tolerate. Protection against excessive current and the resulting fire hazard is provided by fuses or circuit breakers. (See Example 26.14.)

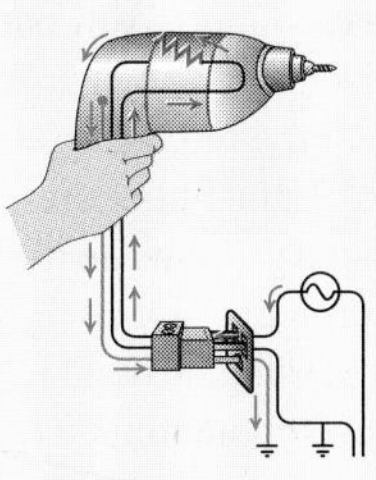

Key Terms

Answer to Chapter Opening Question ?

The potential difference V is the same across resistors connected in parallel. However, there is a different current I through each resistor if the resistances R are different: $I = V/R$.

Answers to Test Your Understanding Questions

26.1 answer: (a), (c), (d), (b) Here's why: The three resistors in Fig. 26.1a are in series, so $R_{eq} = R + R + R = 3R$. In Fig. 26.1b the three resistors are in parallel, so $1/R_{eq} = 1/R + 1/R + 1/R = 3/R$ and $R_{eq} = R/3$. In Fig. 26.1c the second and third resistors are in parallel, so their equivalent resistance R_{23} is given by $1/R_{23} = 1/R + 1/R = 2/R$; hence $R_{23} = R/2$. This combination is in series with the first resistor, so the three resistors together have equivalent resistance $R_{eq} = R + R/2 = 3R/2$. In Fig. 26.1d the second and third resistors are in series, so their equivalent resistance is $R_{23} = R + R = 2R$. This combination is in parallel with the first resistor, so the equivalent resistance of the three-resistor combination is given by $1/R_{eq} = 1/R + 1/2R = 3/2R$. Hence $R_{eq} = 2R/3$.
26.2 answer: loop *cbdac* Equation (2) minus Eq. (1) gives $-I_2(1\ \Omega) - (I_2 + I_3)(2\ \Omega) + (I_1 - I_3)(1\ \Omega) + I_1(1\ \Omega) = 0$. We can obtain this equation by applying the loop rule around the path from c to b to d to a to c in Fig. 26.12. This isn't a new equation, so it would not have helped with the solution of Example 26.6.
26.3 answers: (a) (ii), (b) (iii) An ammeter must always be placed in series with the circuit element of interest, and a voltmeter must always be placed in parallel. Ideally the ammeter would have zero resistance and the voltmeter would have infinite resistance so that their presence would have no effect on either the resistor current or the voltage. Neither of these idealizations is possible, but the ammeter resistance should be much less than 2 Ω and the voltmeter resistance should be much greater than 2 Ω.
26.4 answer: (ii) After one time constant, $t = RC$ and the initial charge Q_0 has decreased to $Q_0e^{-t/RC} = Q_0e^{-RC/RC} = Q_0e^{-1} = Q_0/e$. Hence the stored energy has decreased from $Q_0^2/2C$ to $(Q_0/e)^2/2C = Q_0^2/2Ce^2$, a fraction $1/e^2 = 0.135$ of its initial value. This result doesn't depend on the initial value of the energy.
26.5 answer: no This is a very dangerous thing to do. The fuse will allow currents up to 40 A, double the rated value of the wiring. The amount of power $P = I^2R$ dissipated in a section of wire can therefore be up to four times the rated value, so the wires could get very warm and start a fire.

PROBLEMS

For instructor-assigned homework, go to www.masteringphysics.com

Discussion Questions

Q26.1. In which 120-V light bulb does the filament have greater resistance: a 60-W bulb or a 120-W bulb? If the two bulbs are connected to a 120-V line in series, through which bulb will there be the greater voltage drop? What if they are connected in parallel? Explain your reasoning.

Q26.2. Two 120-V light bulbs, one 25-W and one 200-W, were connected in series across a 240-V line. It seemed like a good idea at the time, but one bulb burned out almost immediately. Which one burned out, and why?

Q26.3. You connect a number of identical light bulbs to a flashlight battery. (a) What happens to the brightness of each bulb as more and more bulbs are added to the circuit if you connect them (i) in series and (ii) in parallel? (b) Will the battery last longer if the bulbs are in series or in parallel? Explain your reasoning.

Q26.4. In the circuit shown in Fig. 26.29, three identical light bulbs are connected to a flashlight battery. How do the brightnesses of the bulbs compare? Which light bulb has the greatest current passing through it? Which light bulb has the greatest potential difference between its terminals? What happens if bulb A is unscrewed? Bulb B? Bulb C? Explain your reasoning.

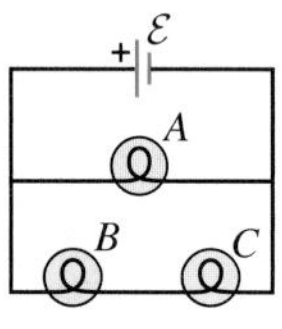

Figure 26.29 Question Q26.4.

Q26.5. If two resistors R_1 and R_2 $(R_2 > R_1)$ are connected in series as shown in Fig. 26.30, which of the following must be true? In each case justify your answer. (a) $I_1 = I_2 = I_3$. (b) The current is greater in R_1 than in R_2. (c) The electrical power consumption is the same for both resistors. (d) The electrical power consumption is greater in R_2 than in R_1. (e) The potential drop is the same across both resistors. (f) The potential at point a is the same as at point c. (g) The potential at point b is lower than at point c. (h) The potential at point c is lower than at point b.

Figure 26.30 Question Q26.5.

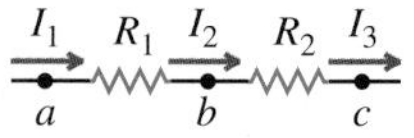

I_1 R_1 I_2 R_2 I_3
a b c

Q26.6. If two resistors R_1 and R_2 $(R_2 > R_1)$ are connected in parallel as shown in Fig. 26.31, which of the following must be true? In each case justify your answer. (a) $I_1 = I_2$. (b) $I_3 = I_4$. (c) The current is greater in R_1 than in R_2. (d) The rate of electrical energy consumption is the same for both resistors. (e) The rate of electrical energy consumption is greater in R_2 than in R_1. (f) $V_{cd} = V_{ef} = V_{ab}$. (g) Point c is at higher potential than point d. (h) Point f is at higher potential than point e. (i) Point c is at higher potential than point e.

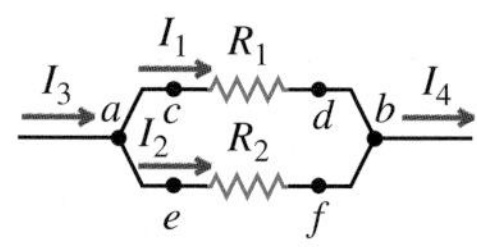

Figure 26.31 Question Q26.6.

Q26.7. Why do the lights on a car become dimmer when the starter is operated?

Q26.8. A resistor consists of three identical metal strips connected as shown in Fig. 26.32. If one of the strips is cut out, does the ammeter reading increase, decrease, or stay the same? Why?

Figure **26.32** Question Q26.8.

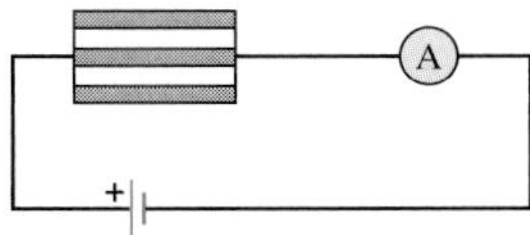

Q26.9. A light bulb is connected in the circuit shown in Fig. 26.33. If we close the switch S, does the bulb's brightness increase, decrease, or remain the same? Explain why.

Figure **26.33** Question Q26.9.

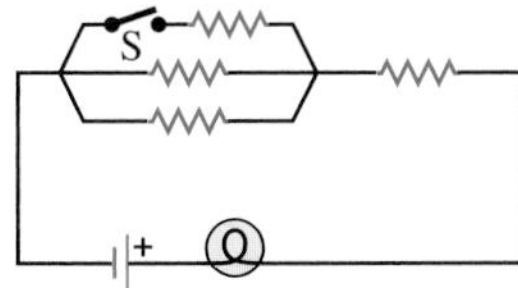

Q26.10. A real battery, having nonnegligible internal resistance, is connected across a light bulb as shown in Fig. 26.34. When the switch S is closed, what happens to the brightness of the bulb? Why?

Figure **26.34** Question Q26.10.

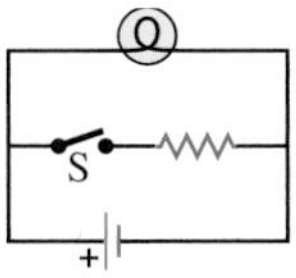

Q26.11. If the battery in Discussion Question Q26.10 is ideal with no internal resistance, what will happen to the brightness of the bulb when S is closed? Why?

Q26.12. For the circuit shown in Fig. 26.35 what happens to the brightness of the bulbs when the switch S is closed if the battery (a) has no internal resistance and (b) has nonnegligible internal resistance? Explain why.

Figure **26.35** Question Q26.12.

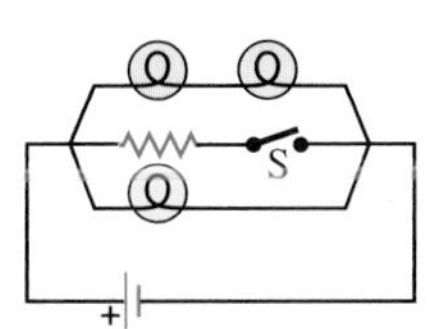

Q26.13. Is it possible to connect resistors together in a way that cannot be reduced to some combination of series and parallel combinations? If so, give examples. If not, state why not.

Q26.14. The direction of current in a battery can be reversed by connecting it to a second battery of greater emf with the positive terminals of the two batteries together. When the direction of current is reversed in a battery, does its emf also reverse? Why or why not?

Q26.15. In a two-cell flashlight, the batteries are usually connected in series. Why not connect them in parallel? What possible advantage could there be in connecting several identical batteries in parallel?

Q26.16. Electric rays (genus *Torpedo*) deliver electric shocks to stun their prey and to discourage predators. (In ancient Rome, physicians practiced a primitive form of electroconvulsive therapy by placing electric rays on their patients to cure headaches and gout.) Figure 26.36a shows *Torpedo* as seen from below. The voltage is produced by thin, waferlike cells called *electrocytes,* each of which acts like a battery with an emf of about 10^{-4} V. Stacks of electrocytes are arranged side by side on the underside of *Torpedo* (Fig. 26.36b); in such a stack, the positive face of each electrocyte touches the negative face of the next electrocyte (Fig. 26.36c). What is the advantage of stacking the electrocytes? Of having the stacks side by side?

Figure **26.36** Question Q26.16.

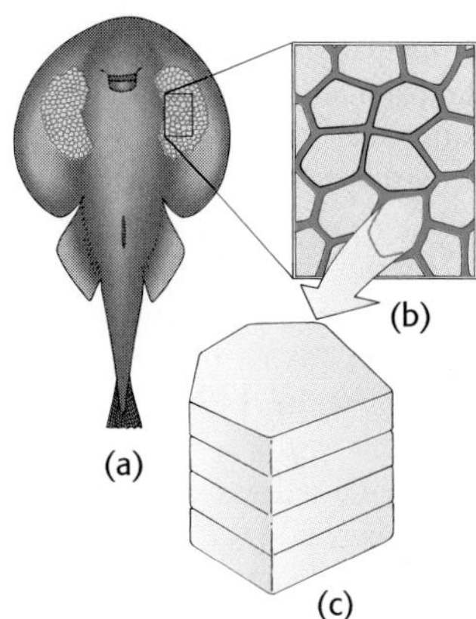

Q26.17. The emf of a flashlight battery is roughly constant with time, but its internal resistance increases with age and use. What sort of meter should be used to test the freshness of a battery?

Q26.18. Is it possible to have a circuit in which the potential difference across the terminals of a battery in the circuit is zero? If so, give an example. If not, explain why not.

Q26.19. Verify that the time constant *RC* has units of time.

Q26.20. For very large resistances it is easy to construct *R-C* circuits that have time constants of several seconds or minutes. How might this fact be used to measure very large resistances, those that are too large to measure by more conventional means?

Q26.21. Whan a capacitor, battery, and resistor are connected in series, does the resistor affect the maximum charge stores on the capacitor? Why or why not? What purpose does the resistor serve?

Q26.22. The greater the diameter of the wire used in household wiring, the greater the maximum current that can safely be carried by the wire. Why is this? Does the maximum permissible current depend on the length of the wire? Does it depend on what the wire is made of? Explain your reasoning.

Exercises

Section 26.1 Resistors in Series and Parallel

26.1. A uniform wire of resistance R is cut into three equal lengths. One of these is formed into a circle and connected between the other two (Fig. 26.37). What is the resistance between the opposite ends a and b?

Figure **26.37** Exercise 26.1.

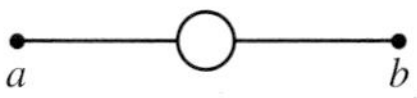

a *b*

26.2. A machine part has a resistor X protruding from an opening in the side. This resistor is connected to three other resistors, as shown in Fig. 26.38. An ohmmeter connected across a and b reads 2.00 Ω. What is the resistance of X?

Figure **26.38** Exercise 26.2.

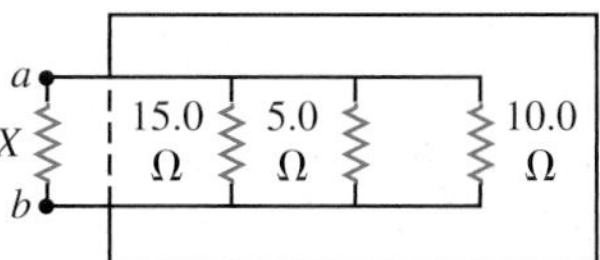

26.3. (a) Prove that when two resistors are connected in parallel, the equivalent resistance of the combination is always smaller than that of the smaller resistor. (b) Generalize your result from part (a) for N resistors.

26.4. A 32-Ω resistor and a 20-Ω resistor are connected in parallel, and the combination is connected across a 240-V dc line. (a) What is the resistance of the parallel combination? (b) What is the total current through the parallel combination? (c) What is the current through each resistor?

26.5. A triangular array of resistors is shown in Fig. 26.39. What current will this array draw from a 35.0-V battery having negligible internal resistance if we connect it across (a) ab; (b) bc; (c) ac? (d) If the battery has an internal resistance of 3.00 Ω, what current will the array draw if the battery is connected across bc?

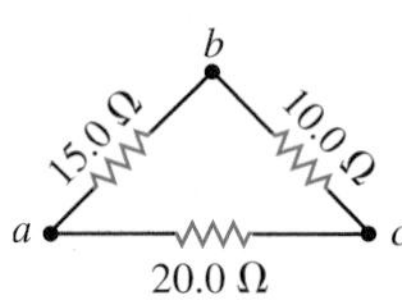

Figure **26.39** Exercise 26.5.

26.6. For the circuit shown in Fig. 26.40 both meters are idealized, the battery has no appreciable internal resistance, and the ammeter reads 1.25 A. (a) What does the voltmeter read? (b) What is the emf $\mathcal{E}$ of the battery?

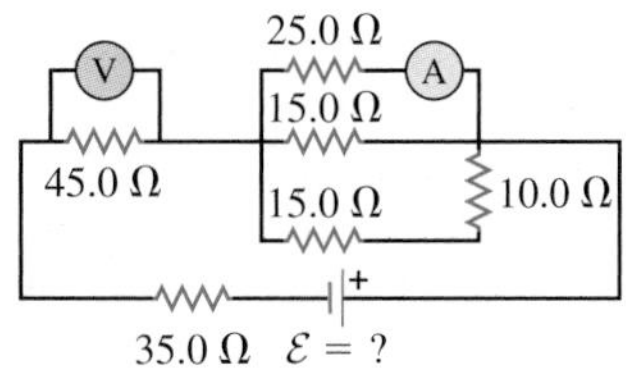

Figure **26.40** Exercise 26.6.

26.7. For the circuit shown in Fig. 26.41 find the reading of the idealized ammeter if the battery has an internal resistance of 3.26 Ω.

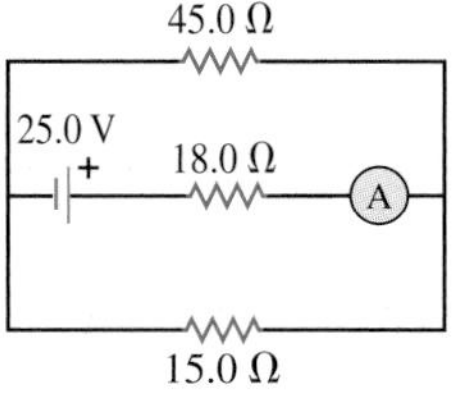

Figure **26.41** Exercise 26.7.

26.8. Three resistors having resistances of 1.60 Ω, 2.40 Ω, and 4.80 Ω are connected in parallel to a 28.0-V battery that has negligible internal resistance. Find (a) the equivalent resistance of the combination; (b) the current in each resistor; (c) the total current through the battery; (d) the voltage across each resistor; (e) the power dissipated in each resistor. (f) Which resistor dissipates the most power: the one with the greatest resistance or the least resistance? Explain why this should be.

26.9. Now the three resistors of Exercise 26.8 are connected in series to the same battery. Answer the same questions for this situation.

26.10. Power Rating of a Resistor. The *power rating* of a resistor is the maximum power the resistor can safely dissipate without too great a rise in temperature and hence damage to the resistor. (a) If the power rating of a 15-kΩ resistor is 5.0 W, what is the maximum allowable potential difference across the terminals of the resistor? (b) A 9.0-kΩ resistor is to be connected across a 120-V potential difference. What power rating is required? (c) A 100.0-Ω and a 150.0-Ω resistor, both rated at 2.00 W, are connected in series across a variable potential difference. What is the greatest this potential difference can be without overheating either resistor, and what is the rate of heat generated in each resistor under these conditions?

26.11. Compute the equivalent resistance of the network in Fig. 26.42, and find the current in each resistor. The battery has negligible internal resistance.

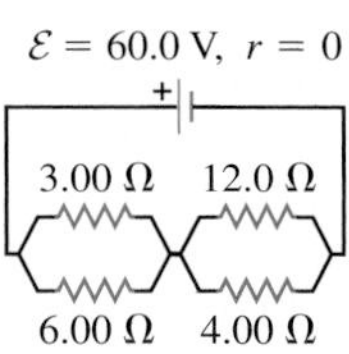

Figure **26.42** Exercise 26.11.

26.12. Compute the equivalent resistance of the network in Fig. 26.43, and find the current in each resistor. The battery has negligible internal resistance.

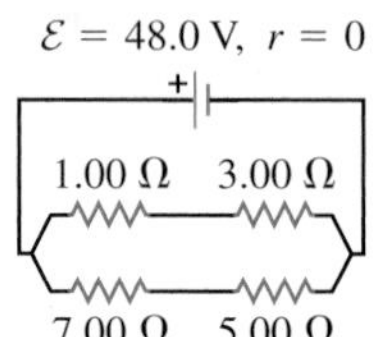

Figure **26.43** Exercise 26.12.

26.13. In the circuit of Fig. 26.44, each resistor represents a light bulb. Let $R_1 = R_2 = R_3 = R_4 = 4.50\ \Omega$ and $\mathcal{E} = 9.00$ V. (a) Find the current in each bulb. (b) Find the power dissipated in each bulb. Which bulb or bulbs glow the brightest? (c) Bulb R_4 is now removed from the circuit, leaving a break in the wire at its position. Now what is the current in each of the remaining bulbs R_1, R_2, and R_3? (d) With bulb R_4 removed, what is the power dissipated in each of the remaining bulbs? (e) Which light bulb(s) glow brighter as a result of removing R_4? Which bulb(s) glow less brightly? Discuss why there are different effects on different bulbs.

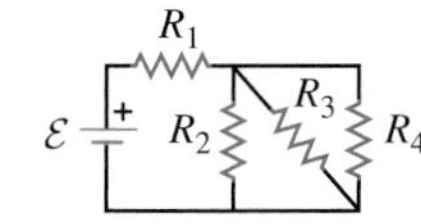

Figure **26.44** Exercise 26.13.

26.14. Consider the circuit shown in Fig. 26.45. The current through the 6.00-Ω resistor is 4.00 A, in the direction shown. What are the currents through the 25.0-Ω and 20.0-Ω resistors?

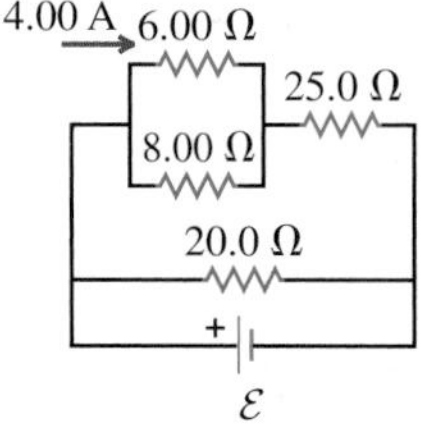

Figure **26.45** Exercise 26.14.

26.15. In the circuit shown in Fig. 26.46, the voltage across the 2.00-Ω resistor is 12.0 V. What are the emf of the battery and the current through the 6.00-Ω resistor?

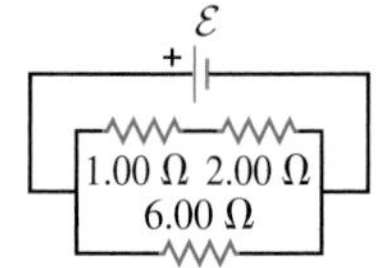

Figure **26.46** Exercise 26.15.

26.16. A Three-Way Light Bulb. A three-way light bulb has three brightness settings (low, medium, and high) but only two filaments. (a) A particular three-way light bulb connected across a 120-V line can dissipate 60 W, 120 W, or 180 W. Describe how the two filaments are arranged in the bulb, and calculate the resistance of each filament. (b) Suppose the filament with the higher resistance burns out. How much power will the bulb dissipate on each of the three brightness settings? What will be the brightness (low, medium, or high) on each setting?

(c) Repeat part (b) for the situation in which the filament with the lower resistance burns out.

26.17. Light Bulbs in Series and in Parallel. Two light bulbs have resistances of 400 Ω and 800 Ω. If the two light bulbs are connected in series across a 120-V line, find (a) the current through each bulb; (b) the power dissipated in each bulb; (c) the total power dissipated in both bulbs. The two light bulbs are now connected in parallel across the 120-V line. Find (d) the current through each bulb; (e) the power dissipated in each bulb; (f) the total power dissipated in both bulbs. (g) In each situation, which of the two bulbs glows the brightest? (h) In which situation is there a greater total light output from both bulbs combined?

26.18. Light Bulbs in Series. A 60-W, 120-V light bulb and a 200-W, 120-V light bulb are connected in series across a 240-V line. Assume that the resistance of each bulb does not vary with current. (*Note:* This description of a light bulb gives the power it dissipates when connected to the stated potential difference; that is, a 25-W, 120-V light bulb dissipates 25 W when connected to a 120-V line.) (a) Find the current through the bulbs. (b) Find the power dissipated in each bulb. (c) One bulb burns out very quickly. Which one? Why?

26.19. In the circuit in Fig. 26.47, a 20.0-Ω resistor is inside 100 g of pure water that is surrounded by insulating styrofoam. If the water is initially at 10.0°C, how long will it take for its temperature to rise to 58.0°C?

Figure 26.47 Exercise 26.19.

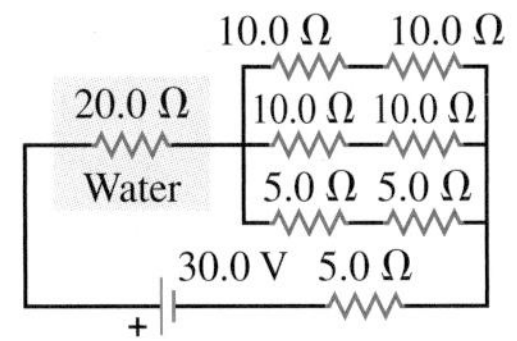

26.20. In the circuit shown in Fig. 26.48, the rate at which R_1 is dissipating electrical energy is 20.0 W. (a) Find R_1 and R_2. (b) What is the emf of the battery? (c) Find the current through both R_2 and the 10.0-Ω resistor. (d) Calculate the total electrical power consumption in all the resistors and the electrical power delivered by the battery. Show that your results are consistent with conservation of energy.

Figure 26.48 Exercise 26.20.

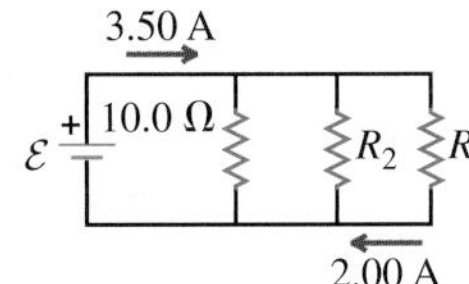

Section 26.2 Kirchhoff's Rules

26.21. In the circuit shown in Fig. 26.49 find (a) the current in resistor R; (b) the resistance R; (c) the unknown emf $\mathcal{E}$. (d) If the circuit is broken at point x, what is the current in resistor R?

Figure 26.49 Exercise 26.21.

26.22. Find the emfs $\mathcal{E}_1$ and $\mathcal{E}_2$ in the circuit of Fig. 26.50, and find the potential difference of point b relative to point a.

Figure 26.50 Exercise 26.22.

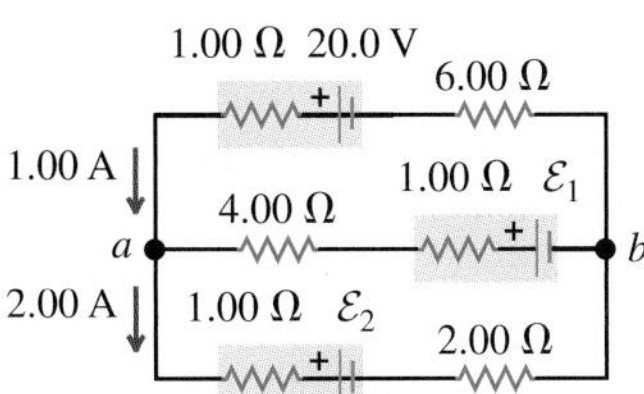

26.23. In the circuit shown in Fig. 26.51, find (a) the current in the 3.00-Ω resistor; (b) the unknown emfs $\mathcal{E}_1$ and $\mathcal{E}_2$; (c) the resistance R. Note that three currents are given.

Figure 26.51 Exercise 26.23.

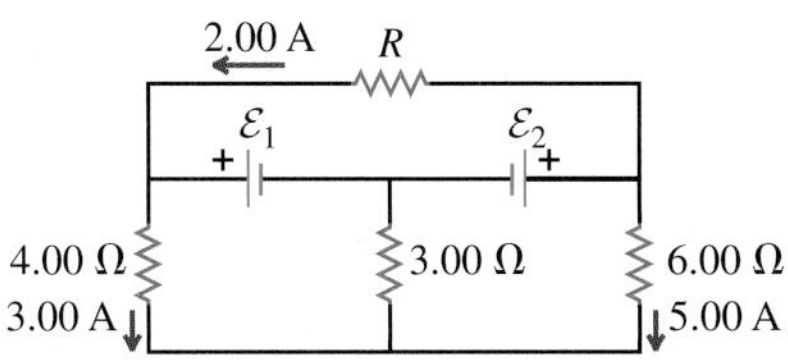

26.24. In the circuit shown in Fig. 26.52, find (a) the current in each branch and (b) the potential difference V_{ab} of point a relative to point b.

Figure 26.52 Exercises 26.24, 26.25, and 26.26.

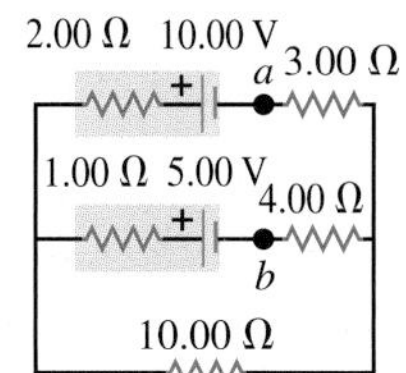

26.25. The 10.00-V battery in Fig. 26.52 is removed from the circuit and reinserted with the opposite polarity, so that its positive terminal is now next to point a. The rest of the circuit is as shown in the figure. Find (a) the current in each branch and (b) the potential difference V_{ab} of point a relative to point b.

26.26. The 5.00-V battery in Fig. 26.52 is removed from the circuit and replaced by a 20.00-V battery, with its negative terminal next to point b. The rest of the circuit is as shown in the figure. Find (a) the current in each branch and (b) the potential difference V_{ab} of point a relative to point b.

26.27. In the circuit shown in Fig. 26.53 the batteries have negligible internal resistance and the meters are both idealized. With the switch S open, the voltmeter reads 15.0 V. (a) Find the emf $\mathcal{E}$ of the battery. (b) What will the ammeter read when the switch is closed?

Figure 26.53 Exercise 26.27.

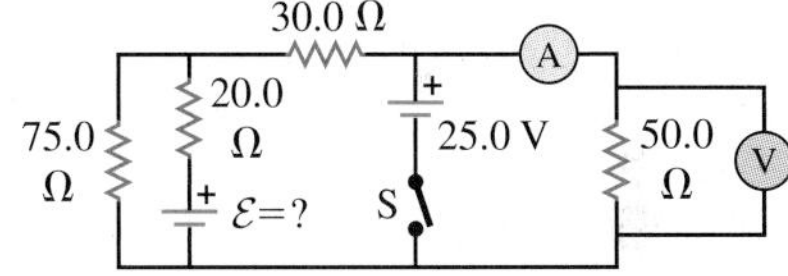

26.28. In the circuit shown in Fig. 26.54 both batteries have insignificant internal resistance and the idealized ammeter reads 1.50 A in the direction shown. Find the emf $\mathcal{E}$ of the battery. Is the polarity shown correct?

Figure 26.54 Exercise 26.28.

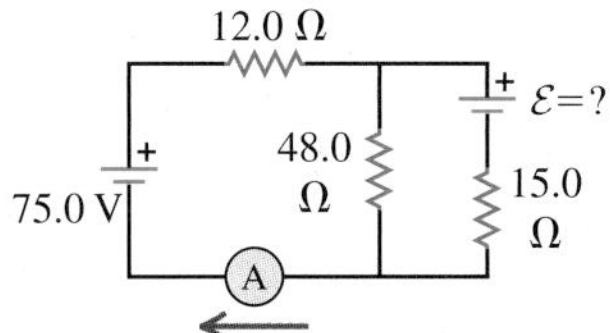

26.29. In the circuit shown in Fig. 26.55 all meters are idealized and the batteries have no appreciable internal resistance. (a) Find the reading of the voltmeter with the switch S open. Which point is at a higher potential: a or b? (b) With the switch closed, find the reading of the voltmeter and the ammeter. Which way (up or down) does the current flow through the switch?

Figure 26.55 Exercise 26.29.

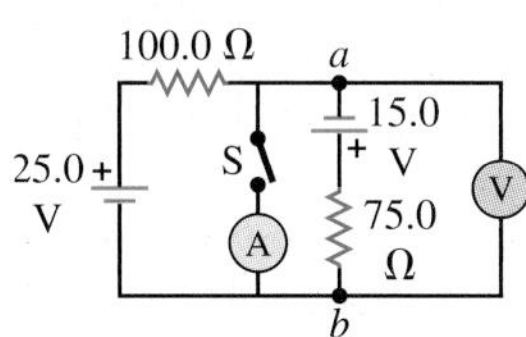

26.30. In the circuit shown in Fig. 26.12 (Example 26.6) the 2-Ω resistor is replaced by a 1-Ω resistor, and the center 1-Ω resistor (through which the current is I_3) is replaced by a resistor of unknown resistance R. The rest of the circuit is as shown in the figure. (a) Calculate the current in each resistor. Draw a diagram of the circuit, and label each resistor with the current through it. (b) Calculate the equivalent resistance of the network. (c) Calculate the potential difference V_{ab}. (d) Your answers in parts (a), (b), and (c) do not depend on the value of R. Explain why.

Section 26.3 Electrical Measuring Instruments

26.31. The resistance of a galvanometer coil is 25.0 Ω, and the current required for full-scale deflection is 500 μA. (a) Show in a diagram how to convert the galvanometer to an ammeter reading 20.0 mA full scale, and compute the shunt resistance. (b) Show how to convert the galvanometer to a voltmeter reading 500 mV full scale, and compute the series resistance.

26.32. The resistance of the coil of a pivoted-coil galvanometer is 9.36 Ω, and a current of 0.0224 A causes it to deflect full scale. We want to convert this galvanometer to an ammeter reading 20.0 A full scale. The only shunt available has a resistance of 0.0250 Ω. What resistance R must be connected in series with the coil (Fig. 26.56)?

Figure 26.56 Exercise 26.32.

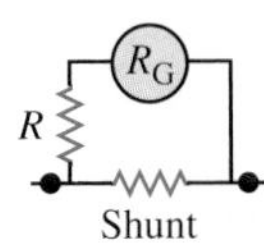

26.33. A circuit consists of a series combination of 6.00-kΩ and 5.00-kΩ resistors connected across a 50.0-V battery having negligible internal resistance. You want to measure the true potential difference (that is, the potential difference without the meter present) across the 5.00-kΩ resistor using a voltmeter having an internal resistance of 10.0 kΩ. (a) What potential difference does the voltmeter measure across the 5.00-kΩ resistor? (b) What is the *true* potential difference across this resistor when the meter is not present? (c) By what percentage is the voltmeter reading in error from the true potential difference?

26.34. A galvanometer having a resistance of 25.0 Ω has a 1.00-Ω shunt resistance installed to convert it to an ammeter. It is then used to measure the current in a circuit consisting of a 15.0-Ω resistor connected across the terminals of a 25.0-V battery having no appreciable internal resistance. (a) What current does the ammeter measure? (b) What should be the *true* current in the circuit (that is, the current without the ammeter present)? (c) By what percentage is the ammeter reading in error from the *true* current?

26.35. Consider the potentiometer circuit of Fig. 26.19a. The resistor between a and b is a uniform wire with length l, with a sliding contact c at a distance x from b. An unknown emf $\mathcal{E}_2$ is measured by sliding the contact until the galvanometer G reads zero. (a) Show that under this condition the unknown emf is given by $\mathcal{E}_2 = (x/l)\mathcal{E}_1$. (b) Why is the internal resistance of the galvanometer not important? (c) Suppose $\mathcal{E}_1 = 9.15$ V and $l = 1.000$ m. The galvanometer G reads zero when $x = 0.365$ m. What is the emf $\mathcal{E}_2$?

26.36. In the ohmmeter of Fig. 26.17, the coil of the meter has resistance $R_c = 15.0\ \Omega$ and the current required for full-scale deflection is $I_{fs} = 3.60$ mA. The source is a flashlight battery with $\mathcal{E} = 1.50$ V and negligible internal resistance. The ohmmeter is to show a meter deflection of one-half of full scale when connected to a resistor with $R = 600\ \Omega$. What series resistance R_s is required?

26.37. In the ohmmeter in Fig. 26.57 M is a 2.50-mA meter of resistance 65.0 Ω. (A 2.50-mA meter deflects full scale when the current through it is 2.50 mA.) The battery B has an emf of 1.52 V and negligible internal resistance. R is chosen so that when the terminals a and b are shorted $(R_x = 0)$, the meter reads full scale. When a and b are open $(R_x = \infty)$, the meter reads zero. (a) What is the resistance of the resistor R? (b) What current indicates a resistance R_x of 200 Ω? (c) What values of R_x correspond to meter deflections of $\frac{1}{4}$, $\frac{1}{2}$, and $\frac{3}{4}$ of full scale if the deflection is proportional to the current through the galvanometer?

Figure 26.57 Exercise 26.37.

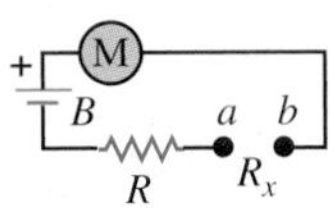

Section 26.4 *R-C* Circuits

26.38. A 4.60-μF capacitor that is initially uncharged is connected in series with a 7.50-kΩ resistor and an emf source with $\mathcal{E} = 125$ V and negligible internal resistance. Just after the circuit is completed, what are (a) the voltage drop across the capacitor; (b) the voltage drop across the resistor; (c) the charge on the capacitor; (d) the current through the resistor? (e) A long time after the circuit is completed (after many time constants) what are the values of the quantities in parts (a)–(d)?

26.39. A capacitor is charged to a potential of 12.0 V and is then connected to a voltmeter having an internal resistance of 3.40 MΩ. After a time of 4.00 s the voltmeter reads 3.0 V. What are (a) the capacitance and (b) the time constant of the circuit?

26.40. A 12.4-μF capacitor is connected through a 0.895-MΩ resistor to a constant potential difference of 60.0 V. (a) Compute the charge on the capacitor at the following times after the connections are made: 0, 5.0 s, 10.0 s, 20.0 s, and 100.0 s. (b) Compute the charging currents at the same instants. (c) Graph the results of parts (a) and (b) for t between 0 and 20 s.

26.41. In the circuit shown in Fig. 26.58 both capacitors are initially charged to 45.0 V. (a) How long after closing the switch S will the potential across each capacitor be reduced to 10.0 V, and (b) what will be the current at that time?

Figure 26.58 Exercise 26.41.

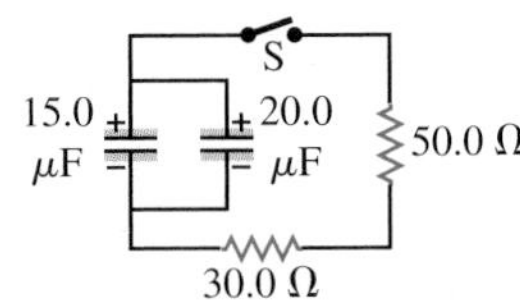

26.42. A resistor and a capacitor are connected in series to an emf source. The time constant for the circuit is 0.870 s. (a) A second capacitor, identical to the first, is added in series. What is the time constant for this new circuit? (b) In the original circuit a second capacitor, identical to the first, is connected in parallel with the first capacitor. What is the time constant for this new circuit?

26.43. An emf source with $\mathcal{E} = 120$ V, a resistor with $R = 80.0\ \Omega$, and a capacitor with $C = 4.00$ μF are connected in series. As the capacitor charges, when the current in the resistor is 0.900 A, what is the magnitude of the charge on each plate of the capacitor?

26.44. A 1.50-μF capacitor is charging through a 12.0-Ω resistor using a 10.0-V battery. What will be the current when the capacitor has acquired $\frac{1}{4}$ of its maximum charge? Will it be $\frac{1}{4}$ of the maximum current?

26.45. In the circuit shown in Fig. 26.59 each capacitor initially has a charge of magnitude 3.50 nC on its plates. After the switch S is closed, what will be the current in the circuit at the instant that the capacitors have lost 80.0% of their initial stored energy?

Figure 26.59 Exercise 26.45.

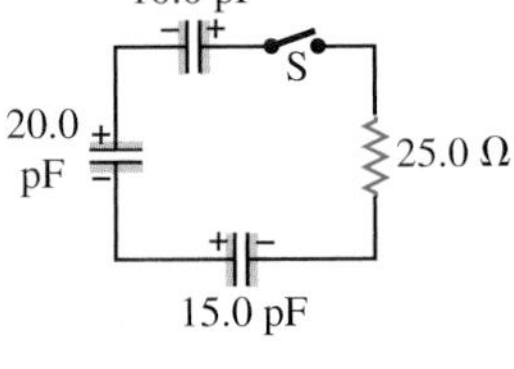

26.46. A 12.0-μF capacitor is charged to a potential of 50.0 V and then discharged through a 175-Ω resistor How long does it take the capacitor to lose (a) half of its charge and (b) half of its stored energy?

26.47. In the circuit in Fig. 26.60 the capacitors are all initially uncharged, the battery has no internal resistance, and the ammeter is idealized. Find the reading of the ammeter (a) just after the switch S is closed and (b) after the switch has been closed for a very long time

Figure 26.60 Exercise 26.47.

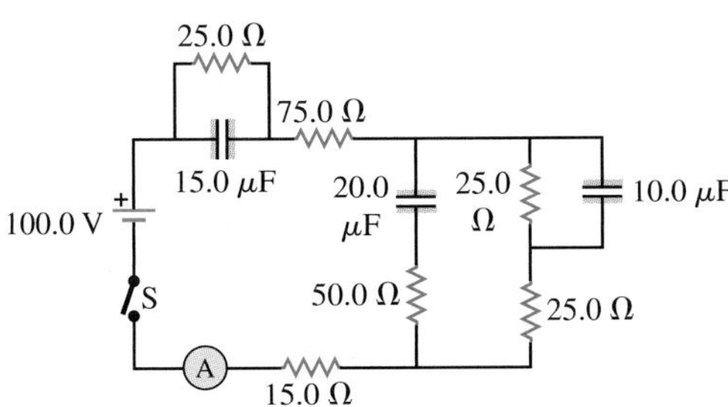

26.48. In the circuit shown in Fig. 26.61, $C = 5.90\ \mu\text{F}$, $\mathcal{E} = 28.0\ \text{V}$, and the emf has negligible resistance. Initially the capacitor is uncharged and the switch S is in position 1. The switch is then moved to position 2, so that the capacitor begins to charge. (a) What will be the charge on the capacitor a long time after the switch is moved to position 2? (b) After the switch has been in position 2 for 3.00 ms, the charge on the capacitor is measured to be 110 μC. What is the value of the resistance R? (c) How long after the switch is moved to position 2 will the charge on the capacitor be equal to 99.0% of the final value found in part (a)?

Figure 26.61 Exercises 26.48 and 26.49.

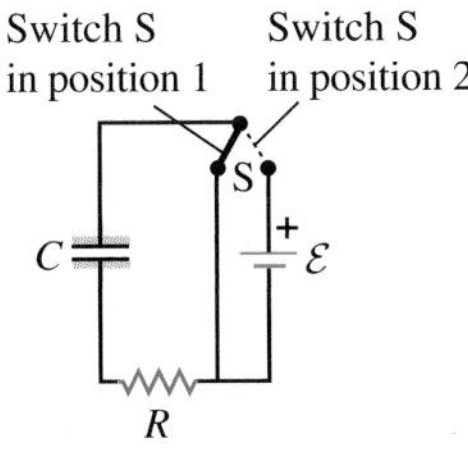

26.49. A capacitor with $C = 1.50 \times 10^{-5}$ F is connected as shown in Fig. 26.61 with a resistor with $R = 980\ \Omega$ and an emf source with $\mathcal{E} = 18.0$ V and negligible internal resistance. Initially the capacitor is uncharged and the switch S is in position 1. The switch is then moved to position 2, so that the capacitor begins to charge. After the switch has been in position 2 for 10.0 ms, the switch is moved back to position 1 so that the capacitor begins to discharge. (a) Compute the charge on the capacitor just *before* the switch is thrown from position 2 back to position 1. (b) Compute the voltage drops across the resistor and across the capacitor at the instant described in part (a). (c) Compute the voltage drops across the resistor and across the capacitor just *after* the switch is thrown from position 2 back to position 1. (d) Compute the charge on the capacitor 10.0 ms after the switch is thrown from position 2 back to position 1.

Section 26.5 Power Distribution Systems

26.50. The heating element of an electric dryer is rated at 4.1 kW when connected to a 240-V line. (a) What is the current in the heating element? Is 12-gauge wire large enough to supply this current? (b) What is the resistance of the dryer's heating element at its operating temperature? (c) At 11 cents per kWh, how much does it cost per hour to operate the dryer?

26.51. A 1500-W electric heater is plugged into the outlet of a 120-V circuit that has a 20-A circuit breaker. You plug an electric hair dryer into the same outlet. The hair dryer has power settings of 600 W, 900 W, 1200 W, and 1500 W. You start with the hair dryer on the 600-W setting and increase the power setting until the circuit breaker trips. What power setting caused the breaker to trip?

26.52. How many 90-W, 120-V light bulbs can be connected to a 20-A, 120-V circuit without tripping the circuit breaker? (See the note in Exercise 26.18.)

26.53. The heating element of an electric stove consists of a heater wire embedded within an electrically insulating material, which in turn is inside a metal casing. The heater wire has a resistance of 20 Ω at room temperature (23.0°C) and a temperature coefficient of resistivity $\alpha = 2.8 \times 10^{-3} (\text{C}°)^{-1}$. The heating element operates from a 120-V line. (a) When the heating element is first turned on, what current does it draw and what electrical power does it dissipate? (b) When the heating element has reached an operating temperature of 280°C (536°F), what current does it draw and what electrical power does it dissipate?

Problems

26.54. A 400-Ω, 2.4-W resistor is needed, but only several 400-Ω, 1.2-W resistors are available (see Exercise 26.10). (a) What two different combinations of the available units give the required resistance and power rating? (b) For each of the resistor networks from part (a), what power is dissipated in each resistor when 2.4 W is dissipated by the combination?

26.55. A 20.0-m-long cable consists of a solid-inner, cylindrical, nickel core 10.0 cm in diameter surrounded by a solid-outer cylindrical shell of copper 10.0 cm in inside diameter and 20.0 cm in outside diameter. The resistivity of nickel is $7.8 \times 10^{-8}\ \Omega \cdot \text{m}$. (a) What is the resistance of this cable? (b) If we think of this cable as a single material, what is its equivalent resistivity?

26.56. Two identical 1.00-Ω wires are laid side by side and soldered together so they touch each other for half of their lengths. What is the equivalent resistance of this combination?

26.57. The two identical light bulbs in Example 26.2 (Section 26.1) are connected in parallel to a different source, one with $\mathcal{E} = 8.0$ V and internal resistance 0.8 Ω. Each light bulb has a resistance $R = 2.0\ \Omega$ (assumed independent of the current through the bulb). (a) Find the current through each bulb, the potential difference across each bulb, and the power delivered to each bulb. (b) Suppose one of the bulbs burns out, so that its filament breaks and current no longer flows through it. Find the power delivered to the remaining bulb. Does the remaining bulb glow more or less brightly after the other bulb burns out than before?

26.58. Each of the three resistors in Fig. 26.62 has a resistance of 2.4 Ω and can dissipate a maximum of 36 W without becoming excessively heated. What is the maximum power the circuit can dissipate?

Figure 26.62 Problem 26.58.

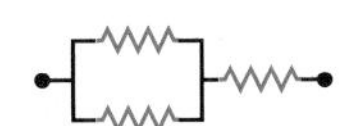

26.59. If an ohmmeter is connected between points a and b in each of the circuits shown in Fig. 26.63, what will it read?

Figure 26.63 Problem 26.59.

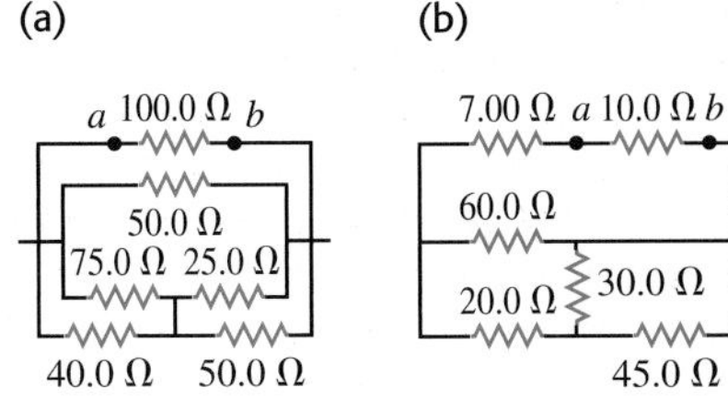

26.60. For the circuit shown in Fig. 26.64 a 20.0-Ω resistor is embedded in a large block of ice at 0.00°C, and the battery has negligible internal resistance. At what rate (in g/s) is this circuit melting the ice? (The latent heat of fusion for ice is 3.34×10^5 J/kg.)

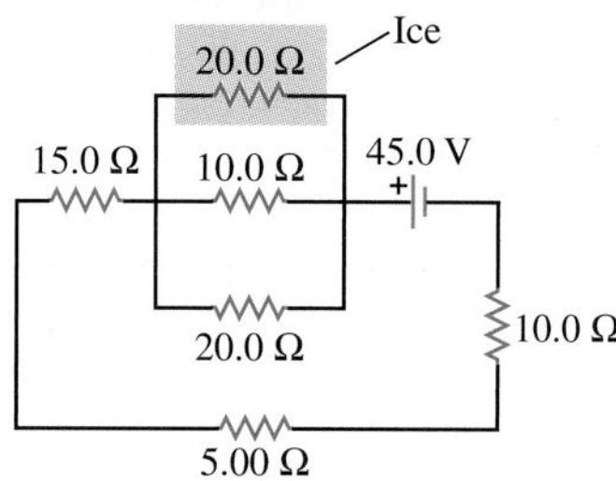

Figure 26.64 Problem 26.60.

26.61. Calculate the three currents I_1, I_2, and I_3 indicated in the circuit diagram shown in Fig. 26.65.

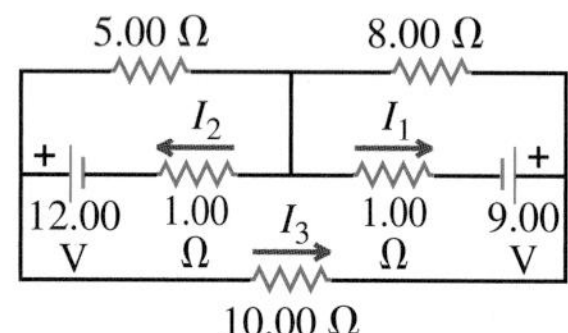

Figure 26.65 Problem 26.61.

26.62. What must the emf $\mathcal{E}$ in Fig. 26.66 be in order for the current through the 7.00-Ω resistor to be 1.80 A? Each emf source has negligible internal resistance.

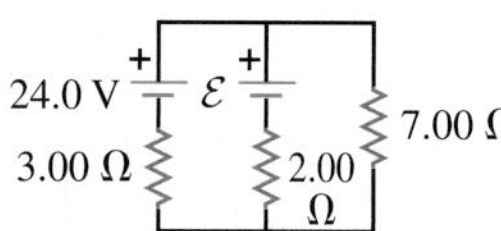

Figure 26.66 Problem 26.62.

26.63. Find the current through each of the three resistors of the circuit shown in Fig. 26.67. The emf sources have negligible internal resistance.

Figure 26.67 Problem 26.63.

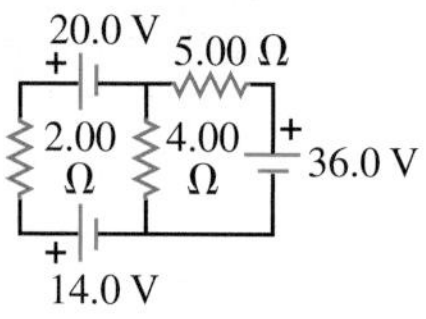

20.0 V 5.00 Ω 2.00 Ω 4.00 Ω 36.0 V 14.0 V

26.64. (a) Find the current through the battery and each resistor in the circuit shown in Fig. 26.68. (b) What is the equivalent resistance of the resistor network?

Figure 26.68 Problem 26.64.

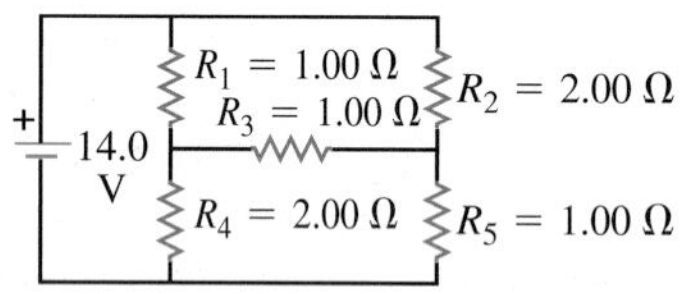

$R_1 = 1.00\ \Omega$ $R_2 = 2.00\ \Omega$ $R_3 = 1.00\ \Omega$ 14.0 V $R_4 = 2.00\ \Omega$ $R_5 = 1.00\ \Omega$

26.65. (a) Find the potential of point a with respect to point b in Fig. 26.69. (b) If points a and b are connected by a wire with negligible resistance, find the current in the 12.0-V battery.

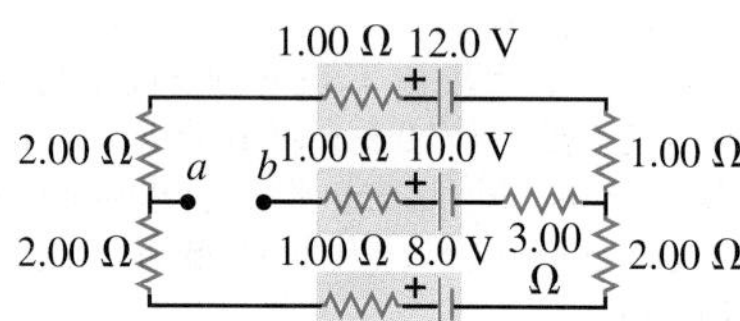

Figure 26.69 Problem 26.65.

26.66. Consider the circuit shown in Fig. 26.70: (a) What must the emf $\mathcal{E}$ of the battery be in order for a current of 2.00 A to flow through the 5.00-V battery as shown? Is the polarity of the battery correct as shown? (b) How long does it take for 60.0 J of thermal energy to be produced in the 10.0-Ω resistor?

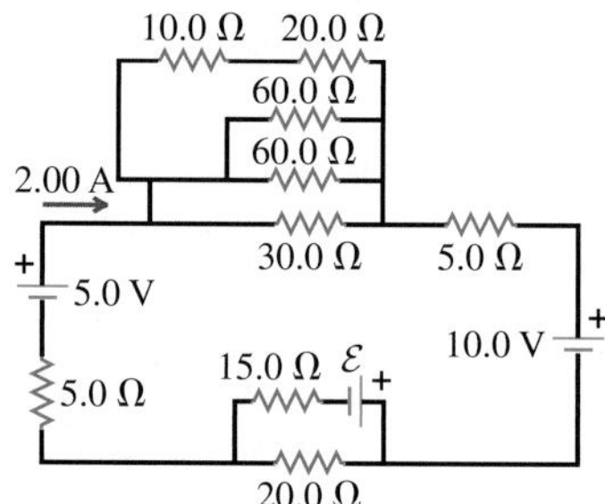

Figure 26.70 Problem 26.66.

26.67. In the circuit shown in Fig. 26.71 the current through the 12.0-V battery is measured to be 70.6 mA in the direction shown. What is the terminal voltage V_{ab} of the 24.0-V battery?

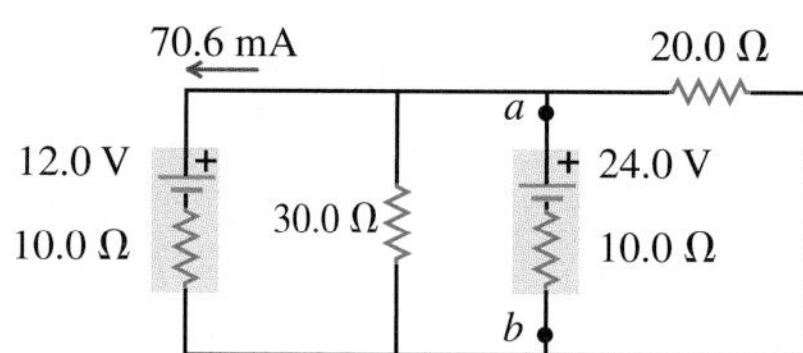

Figure 26.71 Problem 26.67.

26.68. In the circuit shown in Fig. 26.72 all the resistors are rated at a maximum power of 1.00 W. What is the maximum emf $\mathcal{E}$ that the battery can have without burning up any of the resistors?

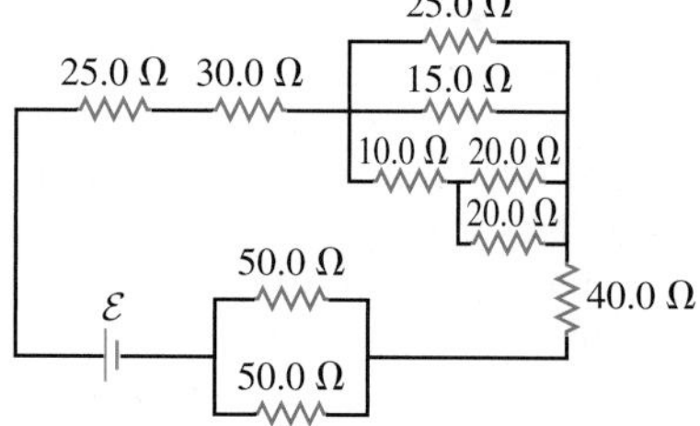

Figure 26.72 Problem 26.68.

26.69. In the circuit shown in Fig. 26.73, the current in the 20.0-V battery is 5.00 A in the direction shown and the voltage across the 8.00-Ω resistor is 16.0 V, with the lower end of the resistor at higher potential. Find (a) the emf (including its polarity) of the battery X; (b) the current I through the 200.0-V battery (including its direction); (c) the resistance R.

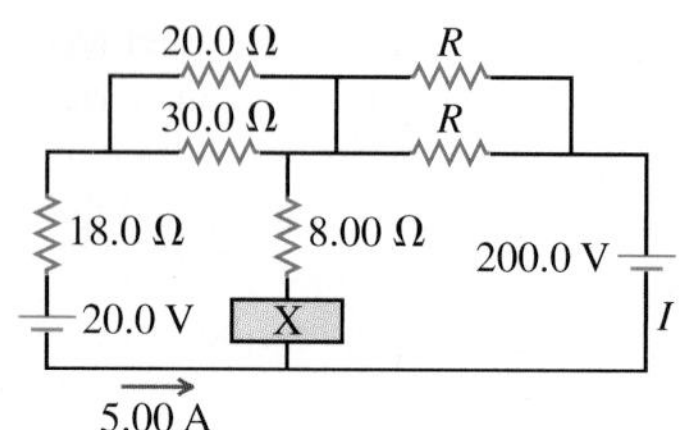

Figure 26.73 Problem 26.69.

26.70. Three identical resistors are connected in series. When a certain potential difference is applied across the combination, the total power dissipated is 27 W. What power would be dissipated if the three resistors were connected in parallel across the same potential difference?

26.71. A resistor R_1 consumes electrical power P_1 when connected to an emf $\mathcal{E}$. When resistor R_2 is connected to the same emf, it consumes electrical power P_2. In terms of P_1 and P_2, what is the total electrical power consumed when they are both connected to this emf source (a) in parallel and (b) in series?

26.72. The capacitor in Fig. 26.74 is initially uncharged. The switch is closed at $t = 0$. (a) Immediately after the switch is closed, what is the current through each resistor? (b) What is the final charge on the capacitor?

Figure **26.74** Problem 26.72.

26.73. Figure 26.75 employs a convention often used in circuit diagrams. The battery (or other power supply) is not shown explicitly. It is understood that the point at the top, labeled "36.0 V," is connected to the positive terminal of a 36.0-V battery having negligible internal resistance, and that the "ground" symbol at the bottom is connected to the negative terminal of the battery. The circuit is completed through the battery, even though it is not shown on the diagram. (a) What is the potential difference V_{ab}, the potential of point a relative to point b, when the switch S is open? (b) What is the current through switch S when it is closed? (c) What is the equivalent resistance when switch S is closed?

Figure **26.75** Problem 26.73.

26.74. (See Problem 26.73.) (a) What is the potential of point a with respect to point b in Fig. 26.76 when switch S is open? (b) Which point, a or b, is at the higher potential? (c) What is the final potential of point b with respect to ground when switch S is closed? (d) How much does the charge on each capacitor change when S is closed?

Figure **26.76** Problem 26.74.

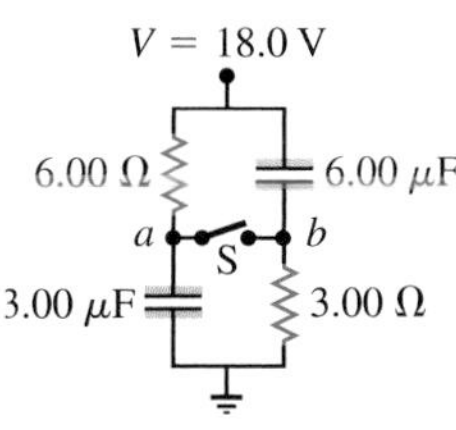

26.75. A Multirange Ammeter. The resistance of the moving coil of the galvanometer G in Fig. 26.77 is 48.0 Ω, and the galvanometer deflects full scale with a current of 0.0200 A. When the meter is connected to the circuit being measured, one connection is made to the post marked + and the other to the post marked with the desired current range. Find the magnitudes of the resistances R_1, R_2, and R_3 required to convert the galvanometer to a multirange ammeter deflecting full scale with currents of 10.0 A, 1.00 A, and 0.100 A.

Figure **26.77** Problem 26.75.

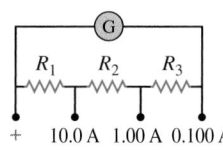

26.76. A Multirange Voltmeter. Figure 26.78 shows the internal wiring of a "three-scale" voltmeter whose binding posts are marked +, 3.00 V, 15.0 V, and 150 V. When the meter is connected to the circuit being measured, one connection is made to the post marked + and the other to the post marked with the desired voltage range. The resistance of the moving coil, R_G, is 40.0 Ω, and a current of 1.00 mA in the coil causes it to deflect full scale. Find the resistances R_1, R_2, and R_3, and the overall resistance of the meter on each of its ranges.

Figure **26.78** Problem 26.76.

26.77. Point a in Fig. 26.79 is maintained at a constant potential of 400 V above ground. (See Problem 26.73.) (a) What is the reading of a voltmeter with the proper range and with resistance 5.00×10^4 Ω when connected between point b and ground? (b) What is the reading of a voltmeter with resistance 5.00×10^6 Ω? (c) What is the reading of a voltmeter with infinite resistance?

Figure **26.79** Problem 26.77.

26.78. A 150-V voltmeter has a resistance of 30,000 Ω. When connected in series with a large resistance R across a 110-V line, the meter reads 68 V. Find the resistance R.

26.79. The Wheatstone Bridge. The circuit shown in Fig. 26.80, called a *Wheatstone bridge,* is used to determine the value of an unknown resistor X by comparison with three resistors M, N, and P whose resistances can be varied. For each setting, the resistance of each resistor is precisely known. With switches K_1 and K_2 closed, these resistors are varied until the current in the galvanometer G is zero; the bridge is then said to be *balanced.* (a) Show that under this condition the unknown resistance is given by $X = MP/N$. (This method permits very high precision in comparing resistors.) (b) If the galvanometer G shows zero deflection when $M = 850.0$ Ω, $N = 15.00$ Ω, and $P = 33.48$ Ω, what is the unknown resistance X?

Figure **26.80** Problem 26.79.

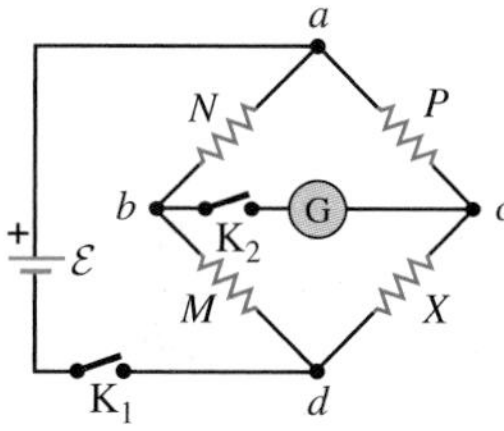

26.80. A certain galvanometer has a resistance of 65.0 Ω and deflects full scale with a current of 1.50 mA in its coil. This is to be replaced with a second galvanometer that has a resistance of 38.0 Ω and deflects full scale with a current of 3.60 μA in its coil. Devise a circuit incorporating the second galvanometer such that the equivalent resistance of the circuit equals the resistance of the first galvanometer, and the second galvanometer deflects full scale when the current through the circuit equals the full-scale current of the first galvanometer.

26.81. A 224-Ω resistor and a 589-Ω resistor are connected in series across a 90.0-V line. (a) What is the voltage across each resistor? (b) A voltmeter connected across the 224-Ω resistor reads 23.8 V. Find the voltmeter resistance. (c) Find the reading of the same voltmeter if it is connected across the 589-Ω resistor. (d) The readings on this voltmeter are lower than the "true" voltages (that is, without the voltmeter present). Would it be possible to design a voltmeter that gave readings *higher* than the "true" voltages? Explain.

26.82. A .2.36-μF capacitor that is initially uncharged is connected in series with a 4.26-Ω resistor and an emf source with $\mathcal{E} = 120$ V and negligible internal resistance. (a) Just after the connection is made, what are (i) the rate at which electrical energy is being dissipated in the resistor; (ii) the rate at which the electrical energy stored in the capacitor is increasing; (iii) the electrical power output of the source? How do the answers to parts (i), (ii), and (iii) compare? (b) Answer the same questions as in part (a) at a long time after the connection is made. (c) Answer the same questions as in part (a) at the instant when the charge on the capacitor is one-half its final value.

26.83. A capacitor that is initially uncharged is connected in series with a resistor and an emf source with $\mathcal{E} = 110$ V and negligible internal resistance. Just after the circuit is completed, the current through the resistor is 6.5×10^{-5} A. The time constant for the circuit is 6.2 s. What are the resistance of the resistor and the capacitance of the capacitor?

26.84. A resistor with $R = 850\ \Omega$ is connected to the plates of a charged capacitor with capacitance $C = 4.62\ \mu$F. Just before the connection is made, the charge on the capacitor is 8.10 mC. (a) What is the energy initially stored in the capacitor? (b) What is the electrical power dissipated in the resistor just after the connection is made? (c) What is the electrical power dissipated in the resistor at the instant when the energy stored in the capacitor has decreased to half the value calculated in part (a)?

26.85. Strictly speaking, Eq. (26.16) implies that an *infinite* amount of time is required to discharge a capacitor completely. Yet for practical purposes, a capacitor may be considered to be fully discharged after a finite length of time. To be specific, consider a capacitor with capacitance C connected to a resistor R to be fully discharged if its charge q differs from zero by no more than the charge of one electron. (a) Calculate the time required to reach this state if $C = 0.920\ \mu$F, $R = 670$ kΩ, and $Q_0 = 7.00\ \mu$C. How many time constants is this? (b) For a given Q_0, is the time required to reach this state always the same number of time constants, independent of the values of C and R? Why or why not?

26.86. An R-C circuit has a time constant RC. (a) If the circuit is discharging, how long will it take for its stored energy to be reduced to $1/e$ of its initial value? (b) If it is charging, how long will it take for the stored energy to reach $1/e$ of its maximum value?

26.87. The current in a charging capacitor is given by Eq. (26.13). (a) The instantaneous power supplied by the battery is $\mathcal{E}i$. Integrate this to find the total energy supplied by the battery. (b) The instantaneous power dissipated in the resistor is i^2R. Integrate this to find the total energy dissipated in the resistor. (c) Find the final energy stored in the capacitor, and show that this equals the total energy supplied by the battery less the energy dissipated in the resistor, as obtained in parts (a) and (b). (d) What fraction of the energy supplied by the battery is stored in the capacitor? How does this fraction depend on R?

26.88. (a) Using Eq. (26.17) for the current in a discharging capacitor, derive an expression for the instantaneous power $P = i^2R$ dissipated in the resistor. (b) Integrate the expression for P to find the total energy dissipated in the resistor, and show that this is equal to the total energy initially stored in the capacitor.

Challenge Problems

26.89. According to the theorem of superposition, the response (current) in a circuit is proportional to the stimulus (voltage) that causes it. This is true even if there are multiple sources in a circuit. This theorem can be used to analyze a circuit without resorting to Kirchhoff's rules by considering the currents in the circuit to be the superposition of currents caused by each source independently. In this way the circuit can be analyzed by computing equivalent resistances rather than by using the (sometimes) more cumbersome method of Kirchhoff's rules. Furthermore, with the superposition theorem it is possible to examine how the modification of a source in one part of the circuit will affect the currents in all parts of the circuit without having to use Kirchhoff's rules to recalculate all of the currents. Consider the circuit shown in Fig. 26.81. If the circuit were redrawn with the 55.0-V and 57.0-V sources replaced by short circuits, the circuit could be analyzed by the method of equivalent resistances without resorting to Kirchhoff's rules, and the current in each branch could be found in a simple manner. Similarly, if the circuit with the 92.0-V and the 55.0-V sources were replaced by short circuits, the circuit could again be analyzed in a simple manner. Finally, if the 92.0-V and the 57.0-V sources were replaced with a short circuit, the circuit could once again be analyzed simply. By superimposing the respective currents found in each of the branches by using the three simplified circuits, we can find the actual current in each branch. (a) Using Kirchhoff's rules, find the branch currents in the 140.0-Ω, 210.0-Ω, and 35.0-Ω resistors. (b) Using a circuit similar to the circuit of Fig. 26.81, but with the 55.0-V and 57.0-V sources replaced by a short circuit, determine the currents in each resistance. (c) Repeat part (b) by replacing the 92.0-V and 55.0-V sources by short circuits, leaving the 57.0-V source intact. (d) Repeat part (b) by replacing the 92.0-V and 57.0-V sources by short circuits, leaving the 55.0-V source intact. (e) Verify the superposition theorem by taking the currents calculated in parts (b), (c), and (d) and comparing them with the currents calculated in part (a). (f) If the 57.0-V source is replaced by an 80.0-V source, what will be the new currents in all branches of the circuit? [*Hint:* Using the superposition theorem, recalculate the partial currents calculated in part (c) using the fact that those currents are proportional to the source that is being replaced. Then superpose the new partial currents with those found in parts (b) and (d).]

Figure 26.81 Challenge Problem 26.89.

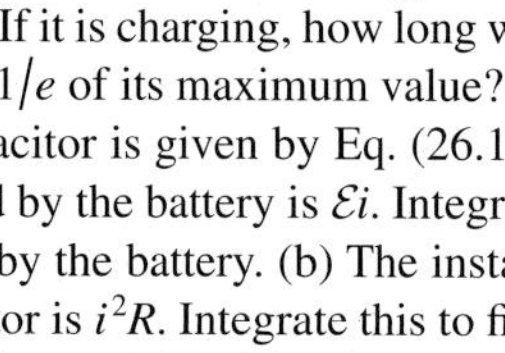

140.0 Ω 35.0 Ω I_1 I_2 I_3 210.0 Ω + 92.0 V + 55.0 V + 57.0 V

26.90. A Capacitor Burglar Alarm. The capacitance of a capacitor can be affected by dielectric material that, although not inside the capacitor, is near enough to the capacitor to be polarized by the fringing electric field that exists near a charged capacitor. This effect is usually of the order of picofarads (pF), but it can be used with appropriate electronic circuitry to detect a change in the dielectric material surrounding the capacitor. Such a dielectric material might be the human body, and the effect described above might be used in the design of a burglar alarm. Consider the simplified circuit shown in Fig. 26.82. The voltage source has emf $\mathcal{E} = 1000$ V, and the capacitor has capacitance $C = 10.0$ pF. The electronic circuitry for detecting the current, represented as an ammeter in the diagram, has negligible resistance and is capable of detecting a current that persists at a level of at least 1.00 μA for at least 200 μs after the capacitance has changed abruptly from C to C'. The burglar alarm is designed to be activated if the capacitance changes by 10%. (a) Determine the charge on the 10.0-pF capacitor when it is fully charged. (b) If the capacitor is fully charged before the intruder is detected, assuming that the time taken for the capacitance to change by 10% is short enough to be ignored, derive an equation that expresses the current through the resistor R as a function of the time t since the capacitance has changed. (c) Determine the range of values of the resistance R that will meet the design specifications of the burglar alarm. What happens if R is too small? Too large? (*Hint:* You will not be able to solve this part analytically but must use numerical methods. Express R as a logarithmic function of R plus known quantities. Use a trial value of R and calculate from the expression

Figure 26.82 Challenge Problem 26.90.

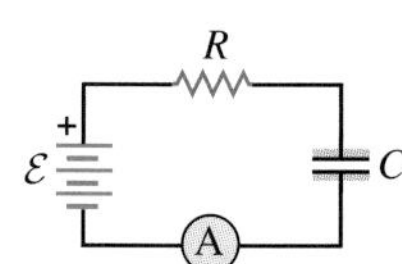

a new value. Continue to do this until the input and output values of R agree to within three significant figures.)

26.91. An Infinite Network. As shown in Fig. 26.83, a network of resistors of resistances R_1 and R_2 extends to infinity toward the right. Prove that the total resistance R_T of the infinite network is equal to

$$R_T = R_1 + \sqrt{R_1^2 + 2R_1R_2}$$

(*Hint:* Since the network is infinite, the resistance of the network to the right of points c and d is also equal to R_T.)

Figure 26.83 Challenge Problems 26.91 and 26.93.

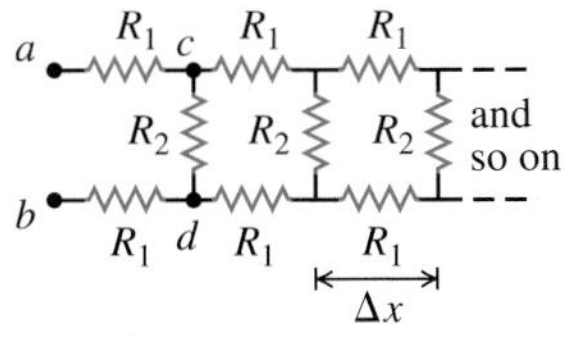

26.92. Suppose a resistor R lies along each edge of a cube (12 resistors in all) with connections at the corners. Find the equivalent resistance between two diagonally opposite corners of the cube (points a and b in Fig. 26.84).

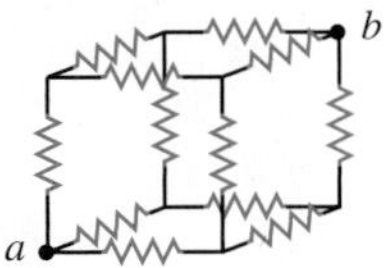

Figure 26.84 Challenge Problem 26.92.

26.93. Attenuator Chains and Axons. The infinite network of resistors shown in Fig. 26.83 is known as an *attenuator chain,* since this chain of resistors causes the potential difference between the upper and lower wires to decrease, or attenuate, along the length of the chain. a) Show that if the potential difference between the points a and b in Fig. 26.83 is V_{ab}, then the potential difference between points c and d is $V_{cd} = V_{ab}/(1 + \beta)$, where $\beta = 2R_1(R_T + R_2)/R_TR_2$ and R_T, the total resistance of the network, is given in Challenge Problem 26.91. (See the hint given in that problem.) (b) If the potential difference between terminals a and b at the left end of the infinite network is V_0, show that the potential difference between the upper and lower wires n segments from the left end is $V_n = V_0/(1 + \beta)^n$. If $R_1 = R_2$, how many segments are needed to decrease the potential difference V_n to less than 1.0% of V_0? (c) An infinite attenuator chain provides a model of the propagation of a voltage pulse along a nerve fiber, or axon. Each segment of the network in Fig. 26.83 represents a short segment of the axon of length Δx. The resistors R_1 represent the resistance of the fluid inside and outside the membrane wall of the axon. The resistance of the membrane to current flowing through the wall is represented by R_2. For an axon segment of length $\Delta x = 1.0\ \mu\text{m}$, $R_1 = 6.4 \times 10^3\ \Omega$ and $R_2 = 8.0 \times 10^8\ \Omega$ (the membrane wall is a good insulator). Calculate the total resistance R_T and β for an infinitely long axon. (This is a good approximation, since the length of an axon is much greater than its width; the largest axons in the human nervous system are longer than 1 m but only about 10^{-7} m in radius.) (d) By what fraction does the potential difference between the inside and outside of the axon decrease over a distance of 2.0 mm? (e) The attenuation of the potential difference calculated in part (d) shows that the axon cannot simply be a passive, current-carrying electrical cable; the potential difference must periodically be reinforced along the axon's length. This reinforcement mechanism is slow, so a signal propagates along the axon at only about 30 m/s. In situations where faster response is required, axons are covered with a segmented sheath of fatty myelin. The segments are about 2 mm long, separated by gaps called the *nodes of Ranvier.* The myelin increases the resistance of a 1.0-μm-long segment of the membrane to $R_2 = 3.3 \times 10^{12}\ \Omega$. For such a myelinated axon, by what fraction does the potential difference between the inside and outside of the axon decrease over the distance from one node of Ranvier to the next? This smaller attenuation means the propagation speed is increased.

27 MAGNETIC FIELD AND MAGNETIC FORCES

LEARNING GOALS

By studying this chapter, you will learn:

- The properties of magnets, and how magnets interact with each other.
- The nature of the force that a moving charged particle experiences in a magnetic field.
- How magnetic field lines are different from electric field lines.
- How to analyze the motion of a charged particle in a magnetic field.
- Some practical applications of magnetic fields in chemistry and physics.
- How to analyze magnetic forces on current-carrying conductors.
- How current loops behave when placed in a magnetic field.

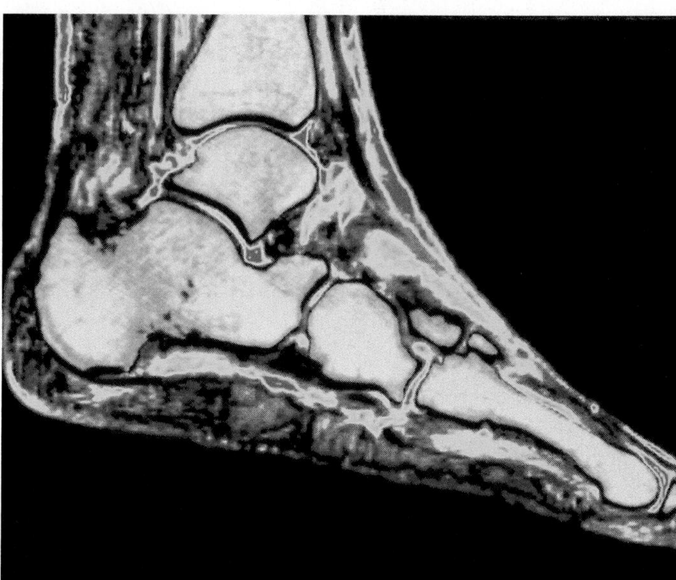

? Magnetic resonance imaging (MRI) makes it possible to see details of soft tissue (such as in the foot shown here) that aren't visible in x-ray images. Yet soft tissue isn't a magnetic material (it's not attracted to a magnet). How does MRI work?

Everybody uses magnetic forces. They are at the heart of electric motors, TV picture tubes, microwave ovens, loudspeakers, computer printers, and disk drives. The most familiar aspects of magnetism are those associated with permanent magnets, which attract unmagnetized iron objects and can also attract or repel other magnets. A compass needle aligning itself with the earth's magnetism is an example of this interaction. But the *fundamental* nature of magnetism is the interaction of moving electric charges. Unlike electric forces, which act on electric charges whether they are moving or not, magnetic forces act only on *moving* charges.

Although electric and magnetic forces are very different from each other, we use the idea of a *field* to describe both kinds of force. We saw in Chapter 21 that the electric force arises in two stages: (1) a charge produces an electric field in the space around it, and (2) a second charge responds to this field. Magnetic forces also arise in two stages. First, a *moving* charge or a collection of moving charges (that is, an electric current) produces a *magnetic* field. Next, a second current or moving charge responds to this magnetic field, and so experiences a magnetic force.

In this chapter we study the second stage in the magnetic interaction—that is, how moving charges and currents *respond* to magnetic fields. In particular, we will see how to calculate magnetic forces and torques, and we will discover why magnets can pick up iron objects like paper clips. In Chapter 28 we will complete our picture of the magnetic interaction by examining how moving charges and currents *produce* magnetic fields.

27.1 Magnetism

Magnetic phenomena were first observed at least 2500 years ago in fragments of magnetized iron ore found near the ancient city of Magnesia (now Manisa, in western Turkey). These fragments were examples of what are now called

permanent magnets; you probably have several permanent magnets on your refrigerator door at home. Permanent magnets were found to exert forces on each other as well as on pieces of iron that were not magnetized. It was discovered that when an iron rod is brought in contact with a natural magnet, the rod also becomes magnetized. When such a rod is floated on water or suspended by a string from its center, it tends to line itself up in a north-south direction. The needle of an ordinary compass is just such a piece of magnetized iron.

Before the relationship of magnetic interactions to moving charges was understood, the interactions of permanent magnets and compass needles were described in terms of *magnetic poles.* If a bar-shaped permanent magnet, or *bar magnet,* is free to rotate, one end points north. This end is called a *north pole* or *N pole;* the other end is a *south pole* or *S pole.* Opposite poles attract each other, and like poles repel each other (Fig. 27.1). An object that contains iron but is not itself magnetized (that is, it shows no tendency to point north or south) is attracted by *either* pole of a permanent magnet (Fig. 27.2). This is the attraction that acts between a magnet and the unmagnetized steel door of a refrigerator. By analogy to electric interactions, we describe the interactions in Figs. 27.1 and 27.2 by saying that a bar magnet sets up a *magnetic field* in the space around it and a second body responds to that field. A compass needle tends to align with the magnetic field at the needle's position.

The earth itself is a magnet. Its north geographic pole is close to a magnetic *south* pole, which is why the north pole of a compass needle points north. The earth's magnetic axis is not quite parallel to its geographic axis (the axis of rotation), so a compass reading deviates somewhat from geographic north. This deviation, which varies with location, is called *magnetic declination* or *magnetic variation.* Also, the magnetic field is not horizontal at most points on the earth's surface; its angle up or down is called *magnetic inclination.* At the magnetic poles the magnetic field is vertical.

Figure 27.3 is a sketch of the earth's magnetic field. The lines, called *magnetic field lines,* show the direction that a compass would point at each location; they are discussed in detail in Section 27.3. The direction of the field at any point can

27.3 A sketch of the earth's magnetic field. The field, which is caused by currents in the earth's molten core, changes with time; geologic evidence shows that it reverses direction entirely at irregular intervals of about a half million years.

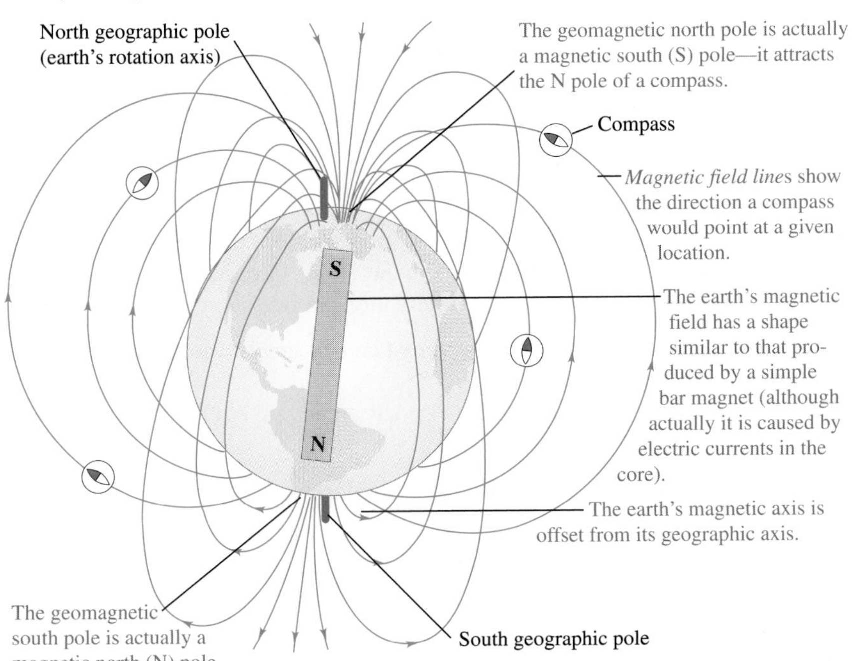
North geographic pole
(earth's rotation axis)
The geomagnetic north pole is actually a magnetic south (S) pole—it attracts the N pole of a compass.
Compass
Magnetic field lines show the direction a compass would point at a given location.
S
The earth's magnetic field has a shape similar to that produced by a simple bar magnet (although actually it is caused by electric currents in the core).
N
The earth's magnetic axis is offset from its geographic axis.
The geomagnetic south pole is actually a magnetic north (N) pole.
South geographic pole

27.1 (a) Two bar magnets attract when opposite poles (N and S, or S and N) are next to each other. (b) The bar magnets repel when like poles (N and N, or S and S) are next to each other.

(a) Opposite poles attract.

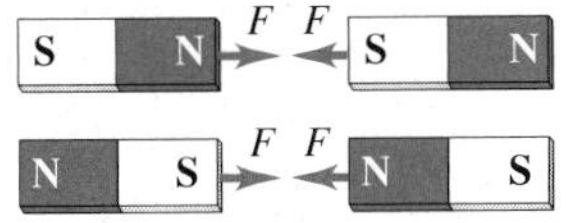
S
N
F F
S
N
N
S
F F
N
S

(b) Like poles repel.

F
S
N
N
S
F
F
N
S
S
N
F

27.2 (a) Either pole of a bar magnet attracts an unmagnetized object that contains iron, such as a nail. (b) A real-life example of this effect.

(a)

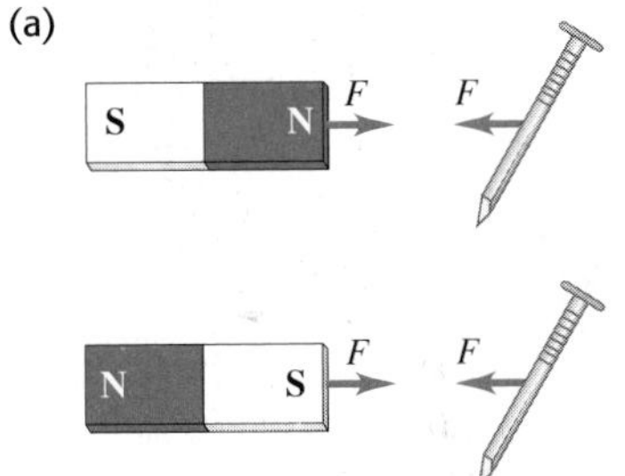
S
N
F
F
N
S
F
F

(b)

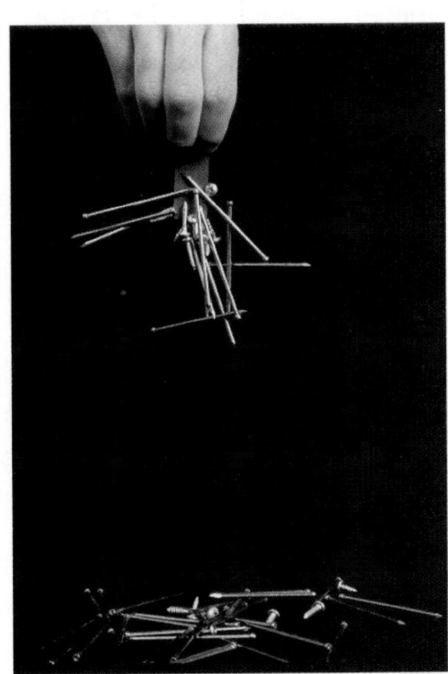

27.4 Breaking a bar magnet. Each piece has a north and south pole, even if the pieces are different sizes. (The smaller the piece, the weaker its magnetism.)

In contrast to electric charges, magnetic poles always come in pairs and can't be isolated.

Breaking a magnet in two ...

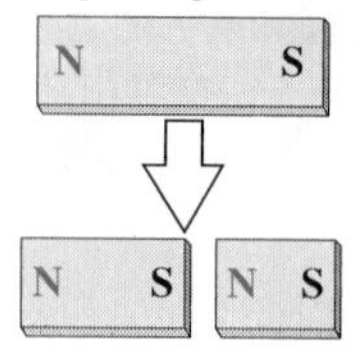

... yields two magnets, not two isolated poles.

27.5 In Oersted's experiment, a compass is placed directly over a horizontal wire (here viewed from above). When the compass is placed directly under the wire, the compass deflection is reversed.

(a)

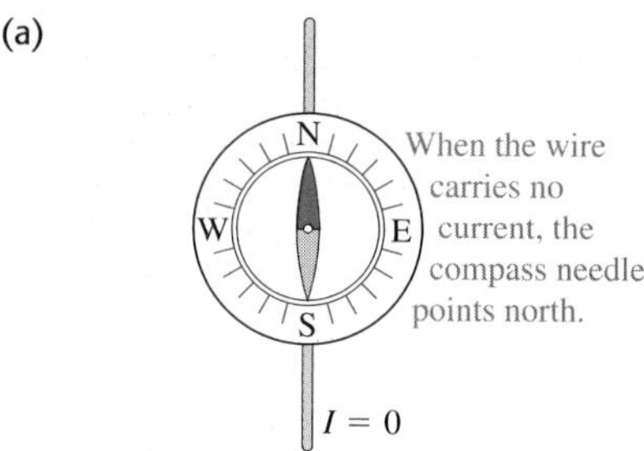

(b)

When the wire carries a current, the compass needle deflects. The direction of deflection depends on the direction of the current.

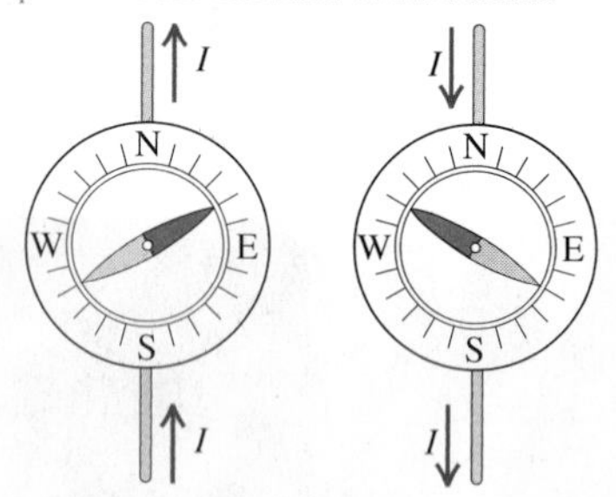

be defined as the direction of the force that the field would exert on a magnetic north pole. In Section 27.2 we'll describe a more fundamental way to define the direction and magnitude of a magnetic field.

Magnetic Poles Versus Electric Charge

The concept of magnetic poles may appear similar to that of electric charge, and north and south poles may seem analogous to positive and negative charge. But the analogy can be misleading. While isolated positive and negative charges exist, there is *no* experimental evidence that a single isolated magnetic pole exists; poles always appear in pairs. If a bar magnet is broken in two, each broken end becomes a pole (Fig. 27.4). The existence of an isolated magnetic pole, or **magnetic monopole,** would have sweeping implications for theoretical physics. Extensive searches for magnetic monopoles have been carried out, but so far without success.

The first evidence of the relationship of magnetism to moving charges was discovered in 1820 by the Danish scientist Hans Christian Oersted. He found that a compass needle was deflected by a current-carrying wire, as shown in Fig. 27.5. Similar investigations were carried out in France by André Ampère. A few years later, Michael Faraday in England and Joseph Henry in the United States discovered that moving a magnet near a conducting loop can cause a current in the loop. We now know that the magnetic forces between two bodies shown in Figs. 27.1 and 27.2 are fundamentally due to interactions between moving electrons in the atoms of the bodies. (There are also *electric* interactions between the two bodies, but these are far weaker than the magnetic interactions because the two bodies are electrically neutral.) Inside a magnetized body such as a permanent magnet, there is a *coordinated* motion of certain of the atomic electrons; in an unmagnetized body these motions are not coordinated. (We'll describe these motions further in Section 27.7, and see how the interactions shown in Figs. 27.1 and 27.2 come about.)

Electric and magnetic interactions prove to be intimately connected. Over the next several chapters we will develop the unifying principles of electromagnetism, culminating in the expression of these principles in *Maxwell's equations.* These equations represent the synthesis of electromagnetism, just as Newton's laws of motion are the synthesis of mechanics, and like Newton's laws they represent a towering achievement of the human intellect.

Test Your Understanding of Section 27.1 Suppose you cut off the part of the compass needle shown in Fig. 27.5a that is painted gray. You discard this part, drill a hole in the remaining red part, and place the red part on the pivot at the center of the compass. Will the red part still swing east and west when a current is applied as in Fig. 27.5b?

27.2 Magnetic Field

To introduce the concept of magnetic field properly, let's review our formulation of *electric* interactions in Chapter 21, where we introduced the concept of *electric* field. We represented electric interactions in two steps:

1. A distribution of electric charge at rest creates an electric field $\vec{E}$ in the surrounding space.
2. The electric field exerts a force $\vec{F} = q\vec{E}$ on any other charge q that is present in the field.

We can describe magnetic interactions in a similar way:

1. A moving charge or a current creates a **magnetic field** in the surrounding space (in addition to its *electric* field).
2. The magnetic field exerts a force $\vec{F}$ on any other moving charge or current that is present in the field.

In this chapter we'll concentrate on the *second* aspect of the interaction: Given the presence of a magnetic field, what force does it exert on a moving charge or a current? In Chapter 28 we will come back to the problem of how magnetic fields are *created* by moving charges and currents.

Like electric field, magnetic field is a *vector field*—that is, a vector quantity associated with each point in space. We will use the symbol $\vec{B}$ for magnetic field. At any position the direction of $\vec{B}$ is defined as the direction in which the north pole of a compass needle tends to point. The arrows in Fig. 27.3 suggest the direction of the earth's magnetic field; for any magnet, $\vec{B}$ points out of its north pole and into its south pole.

Magnetic Forces on Moving Charges

There are four key characteristics of the magnetic force on a moving charge. First, its magnitude is proportional to the magnitude of the charge. If a 1-μC charge and a 2-μC charge move through a given magnetic field with the same velocity, experiments show that the force on the 2-μC charge is twice as great as the force on the 1-μC charge. Second, the magnitude of the force is also proportional to the magnitude, or "strength," of the field; if we double the magnitude of the field (for example, by using two identical bar magnets instead of one) without changing the charge or its velocity, the force doubles.

13.4 Magnetic Force on a Particle

A third characteristic is that the magnetic force depends on the particle's velocity. This is quite different from the electric-field force, which is the same whether the charge is moving or not. A charged particle at rest experiences *no* magnetic force. And fourth, we find by experiment that the magnetic force $\vec{F}$ *does not* have the same direction as the magnetic field $\vec{B}$ but instead is always *perpendicular* to both $\vec{B}$ and the velocity $\vec{v}$. The magnitude F of the force is found to be proportional to the component of $\vec{v}$ perpendicular to the field; when that component is zero (that is, when $\vec{v}$ and $\vec{B}$ are parallel or antiparallel), the force is zero.

Figure 27.6 shows these relationships. The direction of $\vec{F}$ is always perpendicular to the plane containing $\vec{v}$ and $\vec{B}$. Its magnitude is given by

$$F = |q|v_{\perp}B = |q|vB\sin\phi \qquad (27.1)$$

where $|q|$ is the magnitude of the charge and ϕ is the angle measured from the direction of $\vec{v}$ to the direction of $\vec{B}$, as shown in the figure.

This description does not specify the direction of $\vec{F}$ completely; there are always two directions, opposite to each other, that are both perpendicular to the plane of $\vec{v}$ and $\vec{B}$. To complete the description, we use the same right-hand rule that we used to define the vector product in Section 1.10. (It would be a good idea to review that section before you go on.) Draw the vectors $\vec{v}$ and $\vec{B}$ with their tails together, as in Fig. 27.7a. Imagine turning $\vec{v}$ until it points in the direction of $\vec{B}$ (turning through the smaller of the two possible angles). Wrap the fingers of your right hand around the line perpendicular to the plane of $\vec{v}$ and $\vec{B}$ so that they curl around with the sense of rotation from $\vec{v}$ to $\vec{B}$. Your thumb then points in the direction of the force $\vec{F}$ on a *positive* charge. (Alternatively, the direction of the force $\vec{F}$ on a positive charge is the direction in which a right-hand-thread screw would advance if turned the same way.)

This discussion shows that the force on a charge q moving with velocity $\vec{v}$ in a magnetic field $\vec{B}$ is given, both in magnitude and in direction, by

$$\vec{F} = q\vec{v} \times \vec{B} \quad \text{(magnetic force on a moving charged particle)} \qquad (27.2)$$

This is the first of several vector products we will encounter in our study of magnetic-field relationships. It's important to note that Eq. (27.2) was *not* deduced theoretically; it is an observation based on *experiment.*

27.6 The magnetic force $\vec{F}$ acting on a positive charge q moving with velocity $\vec{v}$ is perpendicular to both $\vec{v}$ and the magnetic field $\vec{B}$. For given values of the speed v and magnetic field strength B, the force is greatest when $\vec{v}$ and $\vec{B}$ are perpendicular.

(a)

A charge moving **parallel** to a magnetic field experiences **zero magnetic force.**

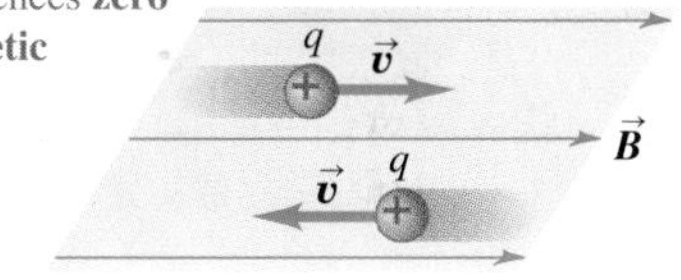

(b)

A charge moving at an angle ϕ to a magnetic field experiences a magnetic force with magnitude $F = |q|v_{\perp}B = |q|vB\sin\phi$.

$\vec{F}$ is perpendicular to the plane containing $\vec{v}$ and $\vec{B}$.

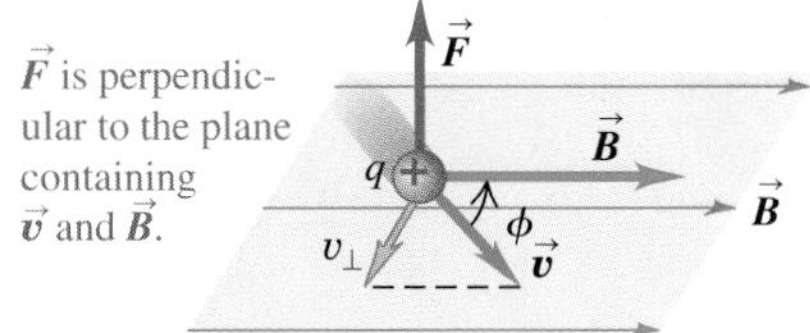

(c)

A charge moving **perpendicular** to a magnetic field experiences a maximal magnetic force with magnitude $F_{max} = qvB$.

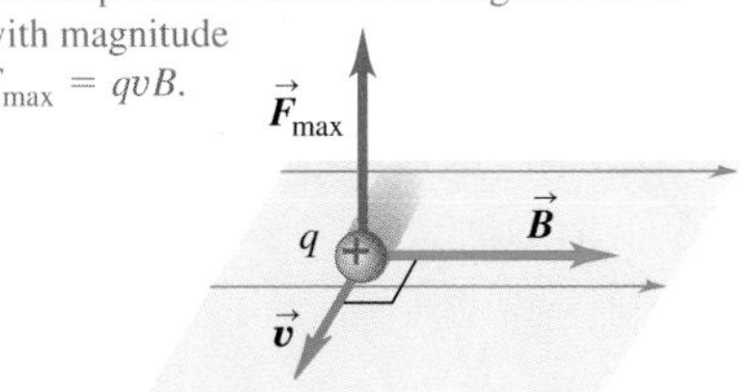

27.7 Finding the direction of the magnetic force on a moving charged particle.

(a)

Right-hand rule for the direction of magnetic force on a **positive** charge moving in a magnetic field:

1. Place the $\vec{v}$ and $\vec{B}$ vectors tail to tail.
2. Imagine turning $\vec{v}$ toward $\vec{B}$ in the $\vec{v}$-$\vec{B}$ plane (through the smaller angle).
3. The force acts along a line perpendicular to the $\vec{v}$-$\vec{B}$ plane. Curl the fingers of your *right hand* around this line in the same direction you rotated $\vec{v}$. Your thumb now points in the direction the force acts.

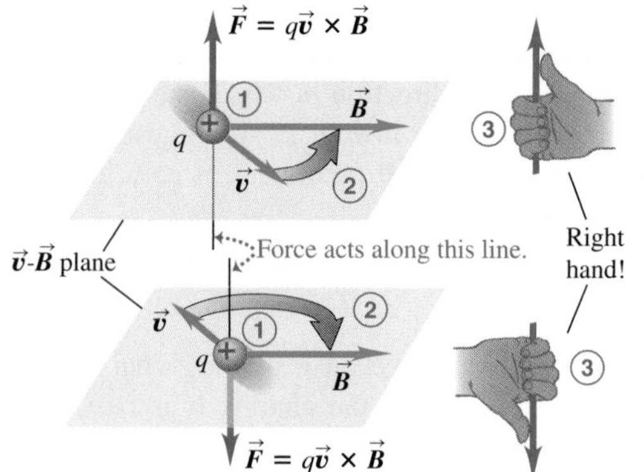

(b)

If the charge is negative, the direction of the force is ***opposite*** to that given by the right-hand rule.

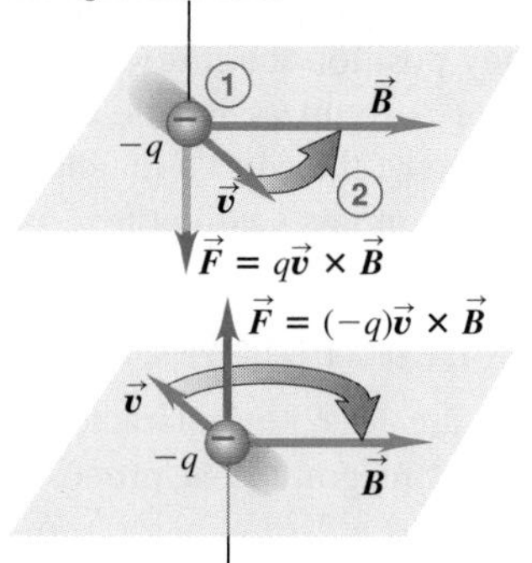

27.8 Two charges of the same magnitude but opposite sign moving with the same velocity in the same magnetic field. The magnetic forces on the charges are equal in magnitude but opposite in direction.

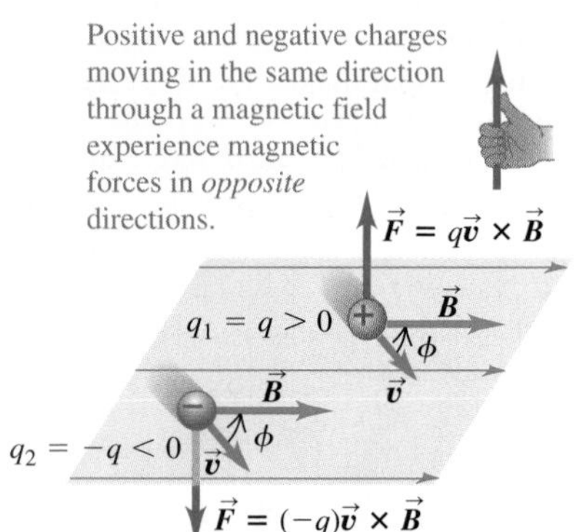

Equation (27.2) is valid for both positive and negative charges. When q is negative, the direction of the force $\vec{F}$ is opposite to that of $\vec{v} \times \vec{B}$ (Fig. 27. 7b). If two charges with equal magnitude and opposite sign move in the same $\vec{B}$ field with the same velocity (Fig. 27.8), the forces have equal magnitude and opposite direction. Figures 27.6, 27.7, and 27.8 show several examples of the relationships of the directions of $\vec{F}$, $\vec{v}$, and $\vec{B}$ for both positive and negative charges. Be sure you understand the relationships shown in these figures.

Equation (27.1) gives the magnitude of the magnetic force $\vec{F}$ in Eq. (27.2). We can express this magnitude in a different but equivalent way. Since ϕ is the angle between the directions of vectors $\vec{v}$ and $\vec{B}$, we may interpret $B\sin\phi$ as the component of $\vec{B}$ perpendicular to $\vec{v}$—that is, $B_\perp$. With this notation the force magnitude is

$$F = |q|vB_\perp \tag{27.3}$$

This form is sometimes more convenient, especially in problems involving *currents* rather than individual particles. We will discuss forces on currents later in this chapter.

From Eq. (27.1) the *units* of B must be the same as the units of F/qv. Therefore the SI unit of B is equivalent to $1\ \text{N} \cdot \text{s/C} \cdot \text{m}$, or, since one ampere is one coulomb per second $(1\ \text{A} = 1\ \text{C/s})$, $1\ \text{N/A} \cdot \text{m}$. This unit is called the **tesla** (abbreviated T), in honor of Nikola Tesla (1857–1943), the prominent Serbian-American scientist and inventor:

$$1\ \text{tesla} = 1\ \text{T} = 1\ \text{N/A} \cdot \text{m}$$

Another unit of B, the **gauss** $(1\ \text{G} = 10^{-4}\ \text{T})$, is also in common use. Instruments for measuring magnetic field are sometimes called *gaussmeters.*

The magnetic field of the earth is of the order of 10^{-4} T or 1 G. Magnetic fields of the order of 10 T occur in the interior of atoms and are important in the analysis of atomic spectra. The largest steady magnetic field that can be produced at present in the laboratory is about 45 T. Some pulsed-current electromagnets can produce fields of the order of 120 T for short time intervals of the order of a millisecond. The magnetic field at the surface of a neutron star is believed to be of the order of 10^8 T.

Measuring Magnetic Fields with Test Charges

To explore an unknown magnetic field, we can measure the magnitude and direction of the force on a *moving* test charge and then use Eq. (27.2) to determine $\vec{B}$. The electron beam in a cathode-ray tube, such as that used in a television set, is a convenient device for making such measurements. The electron gun shoots out a narrow beam of electrons at a known speed. If there is no force to deflect the beam, it strikes the center of the screen.

If a magnetic field is present, in general the electron beam is deflected. But if the beam is parallel or antiparallel to the field, then $\phi = 0$ or π in Eq. (27.1) and $F = 0$; there is no force, and hence no deflection. If we find that the electron beam is not deflected when its direction is parallel to a certain axis as in Fig. 27.9a, the $\vec{B}$ vector must point either up or down along that axis.

If we then turn the tube 90° (Fig. 27.9b), $\phi = \pi/2$ in Eq. (27.1) and the magnetic force is maximum; the beam is deflected in a direction perpendicular to the plane of $\vec{B}$ and $\vec{v}$. The direction and magnitude of the deflection determine the direction and magnitude of $\vec{B}$. We can perform additional experiments in which the angle between $\vec{B}$ and $\vec{v}$ is between zero and 90° to confirm Eq. (27.1) or (27.3) and the accompanying discussion. We note that the electron has a negative charge; the force in Fig. 27.9b is opposite in direction to the force on a positive charge.

When a charged particle moves through a region of space where *both* electric and magnetic fields are present, both fields exert forces on the particle. The total force $\vec{F}$ is the vector sum of the electric and magnetic forces:

$$\vec{F} = q(\vec{E} + \vec{v} \times \vec{B}) \quad (27.4)$$

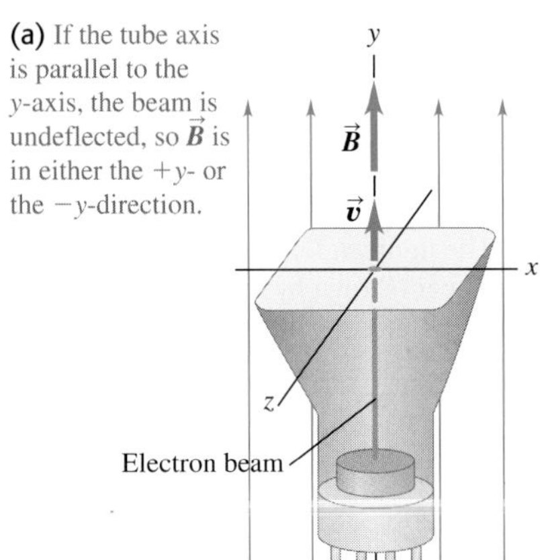

(a) If the tube axis is parallel to the y-axis, the beam is undeflected, so $\vec{B}$ is in either the $+y$- or the $-y$-direction.
y
$\vec{B}$
$\vec{v}$
x
z
Electron beam

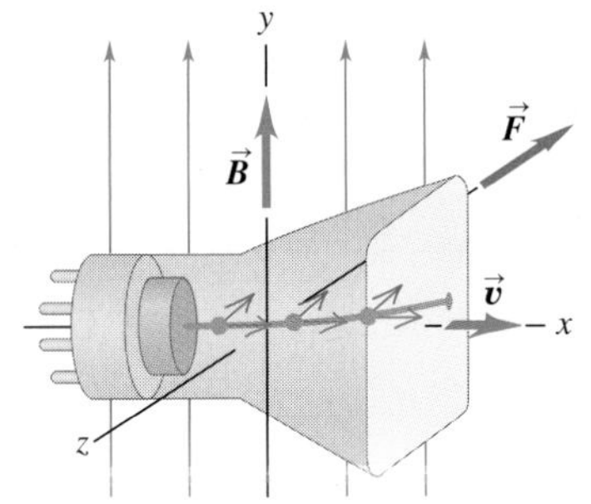

27.9 Determining the direction of a magnetic field using a cathode-ray tube. Because electrons have a negative charge, the magnetic force $\vec{F} = q\vec{v} \times \vec{B}$ in part (b) points opposite to the direction given by the right-hand rule (see Fig. 27.7b).

Problem-Solving Strategy 27.1 Magnetic Forces

IDENTIFY *the relevant concepts:* The right-hand rule allows you to determine the magnetic force on a moving charged particle.

SET UP *the problem* using the following steps:

1. Draw the velocity vector $\vec{v}$ and magnetic field $\vec{B}$ with their tails together so that you can visualize the plane in which these two vectors lie.
2. Identify the angle ϕ between the two vectors.
3. Identify the target variables. This may be the magnitude and direction of the force, or it may be the magnitude or direction of $\vec{v}$ or $\vec{B}$.

EXECUTE *the solution* as follows:

1. Express the magnetic force using Eq. (27.2), $\vec{F} = q\vec{v} \times \vec{B}$. The magnitude of the force is given by Eq. (27.1), $F = qvB\sin\phi$.
2. Remember that $\vec{F}$ is perpendicular to the plane of the vectors $\vec{v}$ and $\vec{B}$. The direction of $\vec{v} \times \vec{B}$ is determined by the right-hand rule; keep referring to Fig. 27.7 until you're sure you understand this rule. If q is negative, the force is *opposite* to $\vec{v} \times \vec{B}$.

EVALUATE *your answer:* Whenever you can, solve the problem in two ways. Do it directly from the geometric definition of the vector product. Then find the components of the vectors in some convenient axis system and calculate the vector product algebraically from the components. Verify that the results agree.

Example 27.1 Magnetic force on a proton

A beam of protons $(q = 1.6 \times 10^{-19}\ \text{C})$ moves at 3.0×10^5 m/s through a uniform magnetic field with magnitude 2.0 T that is directed along the positive z-axis, as in Fig. 27.10. The velocity of each proton lies in the xz-plane at an angle of 30° to the $+z$-axis. Find the force on a proton.

SOLUTION

IDENTIFY: This problem uses the expression for the magnetic force on a moving charged particle.

SET UP: Figure 27.10 shows that the vectors $\vec{v}$ and $\vec{B}$ lie in the xz-plane. The angle between these vectors is 30°. The target variables are the magnitude and direction of the force $\vec{F}$.

27.10 Directions of $\vec{v}$ and $\vec{B}$ for a proton in a magnetic field.

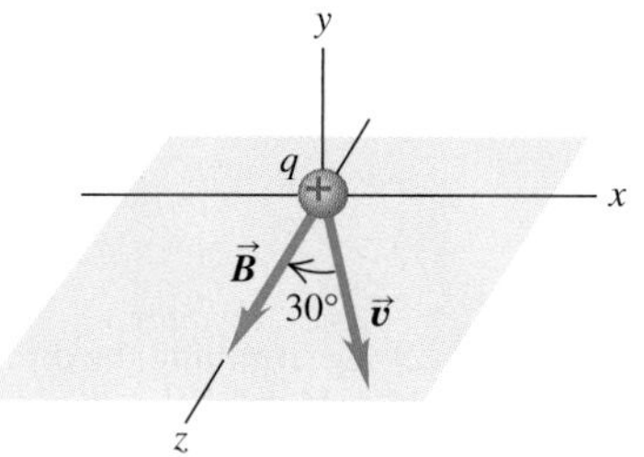

EXECUTE: The charge is positive, so the force is in the same direction as the vector product $\vec{v} \times \vec{B}$. From the right-hand rule, this direction is along the negative y-axis. The magnitude of the force, from Eq. (27.1), is

$$\begin{aligned} F &= qvB\sin\phi \\ &= (1.6 \times 10^{-19}\ \text{C})(3.0 \times 10^5\ \text{m/s})(2.0\ \text{T})(\sin 30°) \\ &= 4.8 \times 10^{-14}\ \text{N} \end{aligned}$$

EVALUATE: We check our result by evaluating the force using vector language and Eq. (27.2). We have

$$\begin{aligned} \vec{v} &= (3.0 \times 10^5\ \text{m/s})(\sin 30°)\hat{\imath} + (3.0 \times 10^5\ \text{m/s})(\cos 30°)\hat{k} \\ \vec{B} &= (2.0\ \text{T})\hat{k} \\ \vec{F} &= q\vec{v} \times \vec{B} \\ &= (1.6 \times 10^{-19}\ \text{C})(3.0 \times 10^5\ \text{m/s})(2.0\ \text{T}) \\ &\quad \times (\sin 30°\,\hat{\imath} + \cos 30°\hat{k}) \times \hat{k} \\ &= (-4.8 \times 10^{-14}\ \text{N})\hat{\jmath} \end{aligned}$$

(Recall that $\hat{\imath} \times \hat{k} = -\hat{\jmath}$ and $\hat{k} \times \hat{k} = \mathbf{0}$.) We again find that the force is in the negative y-direction with magnitude 4.8×10^{-14} N.

If the beam consists of *electrons* rather than protons, the charge is negative $(q = -1.6 \times 10^{-19}\ \text{C})$ and the direction of the force is reversed. The force is now directed along the *positive* y-axis, but the magnitude is the same as before, $F = 4.8 \times 10^{-14}$ N.

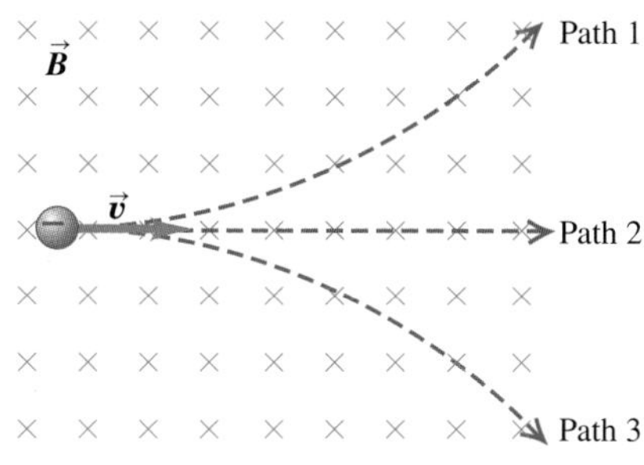

Test Your Understanding of Section 27.2 The figure at left shows a uniform magnetic field $\vec{B}$ directed into the plane of the paper (shown by the blue ×'s). A particle with a negative charge moves in the plane. Which of the three paths—1, 2, or 3—does the particle follow?

27.3 Magnetic Field Lines and Magnetic Flux

27.11 The magnetic field lines of a permanent magnet. Note that the field lines pass through the interior of the magnet.

At each point, the field line is tangent to the magnetic field vector $\vec{B}$.

The more densely the field lines are packed, the stronger the field is at that point.

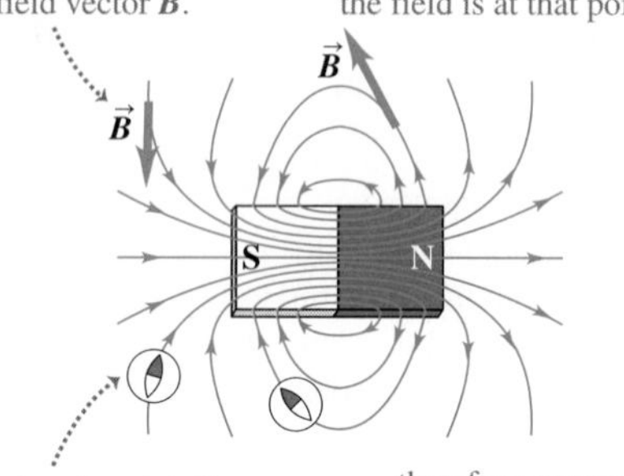

At each point, the field lines point in the same direction a compass would . . .

. . . therefore, magnetic field lines point *away from* N poles and *toward* S poles.

We can represent any magnetic field by **magnetic field lines,** just as we did for the earth's magnetic field in Fig. 27.3. The idea is the same as for the electric field lines we introduced in Section 21.6. We draw the lines so that the line through any point is tangent to the magnetic field vector $\vec{B}$ at that point (Fig. 27.11). Just as with electric field lines, we draw only a few representative lines; otherwise, the lines would fill up all of space. Where adjacent field lines are close together, the field magnitude is large; where these field lines are far apart, the field magnitude is small. Also, because the direction of $\vec{B}$ at each point is unique, field lines never intersect.

CAUTION Magnetic field lines are not "lines of force" Magnetic field lines are sometimes called "magnetic lines of force," but that's not a good name for them; unlike electric field lines, they *do not* point in the direction of the force on a charge (Fig. 27.12). Equation (27.2) shows that the force on a moving charged particle is always perpendicular to the magnetic field, and hence to the magnetic field line that passes through the particle's position. The direction of the force depends on the particle's velocity and the sign of its charge, so just looking at magnetic field lines cannot in itself tell you the direction of the force on an arbitrary moving charged particle. Magnetic field lines *do* have the direction that a compass needle would point at each location; this may help you to visualize them.

Figures 27.11 and 27.13 show magnetic field lines produced by several common sources of magnetic field. In the gap between the poles of the magnet shown in Fig. 27.13a, the field lines are approximately straight, parallel, and equally spaced, showing that the magnetic field in this region is approximately *uniform* (that is, constant in magnitude and direction).

Because magnetic-field patterns are three-dimensional, it's often necessary to draw magnetic field lines that point into or out of the plane of a drawing. To do this we use a dot (·) to represent a vector directed out of the plane and a cross (×) to represent a vector directed into the plane (Fig. 27.13b). Here's a good way to remember these conventions: Think of a dot as the head of an arrow coming directly toward you, and think of a cross as the feathers of an arrow flying directly away from you.

Iron filings, like compass needles, tend to align with magnetic field lines. Hence they provide an easy way to visualize field lines (Fig. 27.14).

27.12 Magnetic field lines are *not* "lines of force."

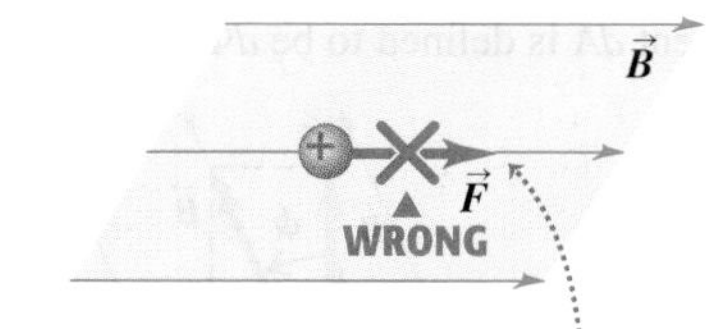
$\vec{B}$
$\vec{F}$
WRONG
Magnetic field lines are *not* "lines of force." The force on a charged particle is not along the direction of a field line.

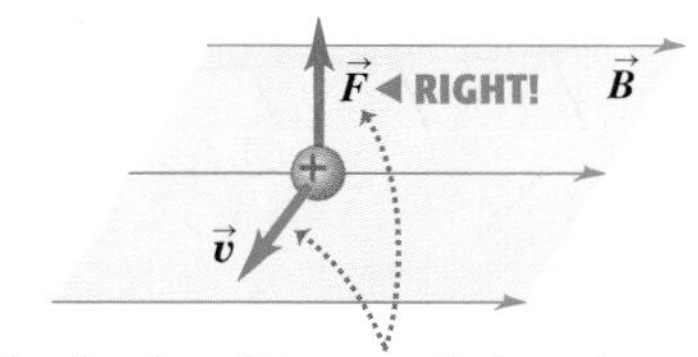
$\vec{F}$ RIGHT!
$\vec{B}$
$\vec{v}$
The direction of the magnetic force depends on the velocity $\vec{v}$, as expressed by the magnetic force law $\vec{F} = q\vec{v} \times \vec{B}$.

27.13 Magnetic field lines produced by several common sources of magnetic field.

(a) Magnetic field of a C-shaped magnet

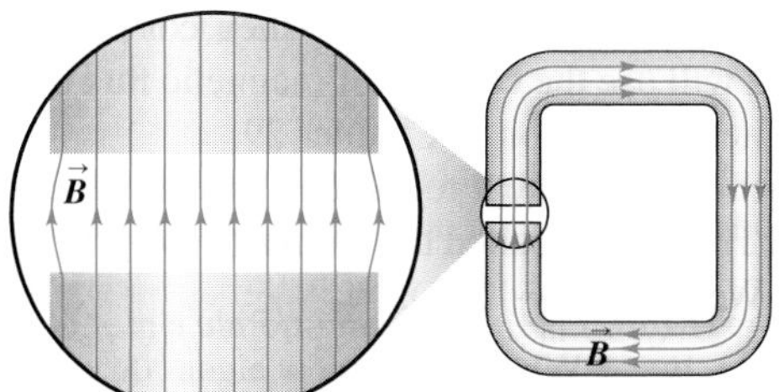
Between flat, parallel magnetic poles, the magnetic field is nearly uniform.
$\vec{B}$
$\vec{B}$

(b) Magnetic field of a straight current-carrying wire

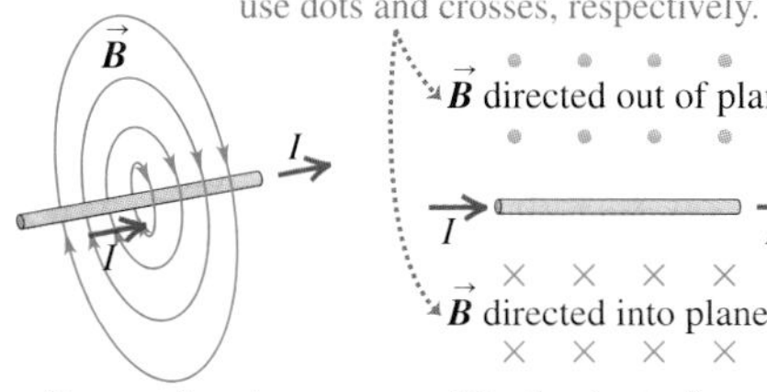
To represent a field coming out of or going into the plane of the paper, we use dots and crosses, respectively.
$\vec{B}$
I
I
$\vec{B}$ directed out of plane
I
I
$\vec{B}$ directed into plane
Perspective view
Wire in plane of paper

(c) Magnetic fields of a current-carrying loop and a current-carrying coil (solenoid)

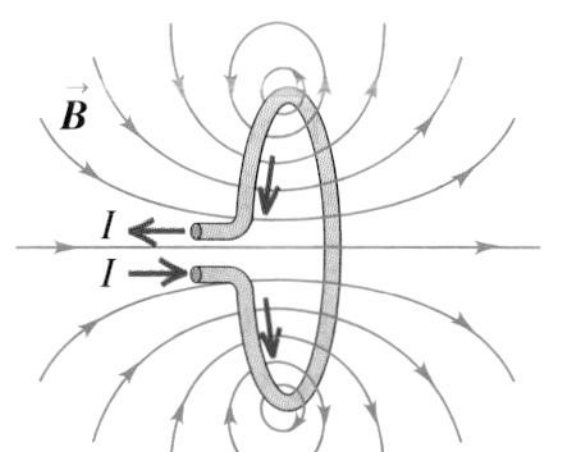
$\vec{B}$
I
I

Notice that the field of the loop and, especially, that of the coil look like the field of a bar magnet (see Fig. 27.11).

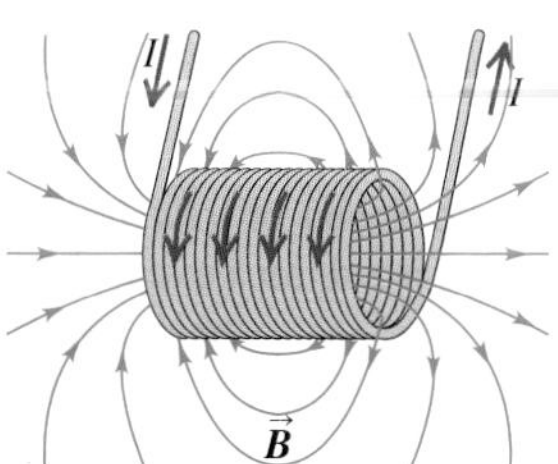
I
I
$\vec{B}$

27.14 (a) Like little compass needles, iron filings line up tangent to magnetic field lines. (b) Drawing of the field lines for the situation shown in (a).

(a)

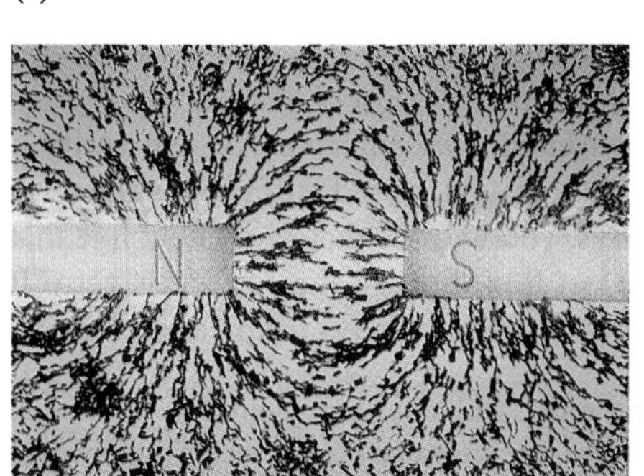
N
S

(b)

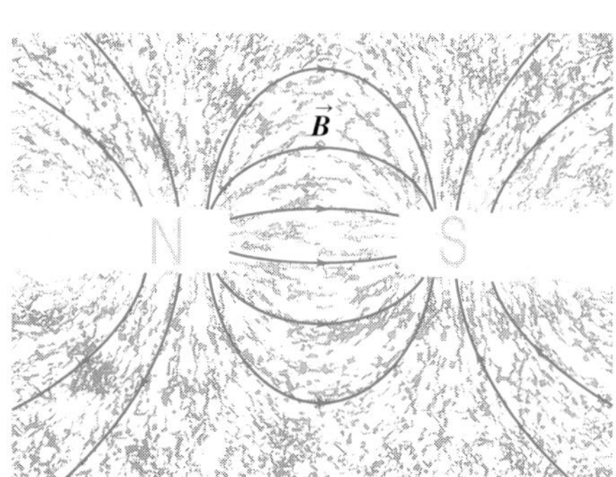
$\vec{B}$
N
S

27.17 A charged particle moves in a plane perpendicular to a uniform magnetic field $\vec{B}$.

(a) The orbit of a charged particle in a uniform magnetic field

A charge moving at right angles to a uniform $\vec{B}$ field moves in a circle at constant speed because $\vec{F}$ and $\vec{v}$ are always perpendicular to each other.

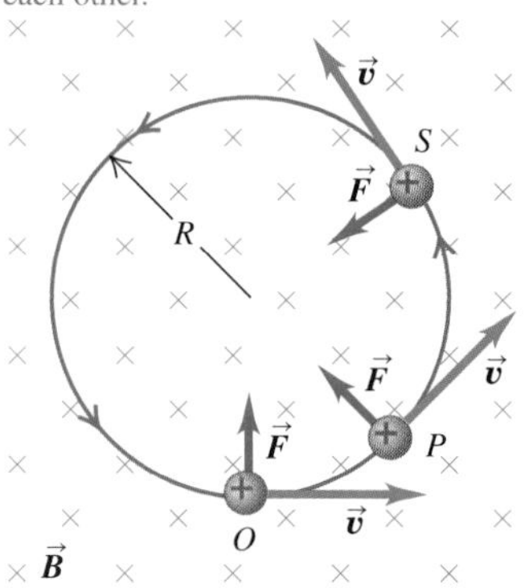

(b) An electron beam (seen as a blue arc) curving in a magnetic field

point O, moving with velocity $\vec{v}$ in a uniform magnetic field $\vec{B}$ directed into the plane of the figure. The vectors $\vec{v}$ and $\vec{B}$ are perpendicular, so the magnetic force $\vec{F} = q\vec{v} \times \vec{B}$ has magnitude $F = qvB$ and a direction as shown in the figure. The force is *always* perpendicular to $\vec{v}$, so it cannot change the *magnitude* of the velocity, only its direction. To put it differently, the magnetic force never has a component parallel to the particle's motion, so the magnetic force can never do *work* on the particle. This is true even if the magnetic field is not uniform.

Motion of a charged particle under the action of a magnetic field alone is always motion with constant speed.

Using this principle, we see that in the situation shown in Fig. 27.17a the magnitudes of both $\vec{F}$ and $\vec{v}$ are constant. At points such as P and S the directions of force and velocity have changed as shown, but their magnitudes are the same. The particle therefore moves under the influence of a constant-magnitude force that is always at right angles to the velocity of the particle. Comparing these conditions with the discussion of circular motion in Sections 3.4 and 5.4, we see that the particle's path is a *circle*, traced out with constant speed v. The centripetal acceleration is v^2/R and the only force acting is the magnetic force, so from Newton's second law,

$$F = |q|vB = m\frac{v^2}{R} \tag{27.10}$$

where m is the mass of the particle. Solving Eq. (27.10) for the radius R of the circular path, we find

$$R = \frac{mv}{|q|B} \quad \text{(radius of a circular orbit in a magnetic field)} \tag{27.11}$$

We can also write this as $R = p/|q|B$, where $p = mv$ is the magnitude of the particle's momentum. If the charge q is negative, the particle moves *clockwise* around the orbit in Fig. 27.17a.

The angular speed ω of the particle can be found from Eq. (9.13), $v = R\omega$. Combining this with Eq. (27.11), we get

$$\omega = \frac{v}{R} = v\frac{|q|B}{mv} = \frac{|q|B}{m} \tag{27.12}$$

The number of revolutions per unit time is $f = \omega/2\pi$. This frequency f is independent of the radius R of the path. It is called the **cyclotron frequency;** in a particle accelerator called a *cyclotron,* particles moving in nearly circular paths are given a boost twice each revolution, increasing their energy and their orbital radii but not their angular speed or frequency. Similarly, one type of *magnetron,* a common source of microwave radiation for microwave ovens and radar systems, emits radiation with a frequency equal to the frequency of circular motion of electrons in a vacuum chamber between the poles of a magnet.

If the direction of the initial velocity is *not* perpendicular to the field, the velocity *component* parallel to the field is constant because there is no force parallel to the field. Then the particle moves in a helix (Fig. 27.18). The radius of the helix is given by Eq. (27.11), where v is now the component of velocity perpendicular to the $\vec{B}$ field.

Motion of a charged particle in a nonuniform magnetic field is more complex. Figure 27.19 shows a field produced by two circular coils separated by some distance. Particles near either coil experience a magnetic force toward the center of the region; particles with appropriate speeds spiral repeatedly from one end of the region to the other and back. Because charged particles can be trapped in such a magnetic field, it is called a *magnetic bottle.* This technique is used to confine very hot plasmas with temperatures of the order of 10^6 K. In a similar way the

27.18 The general case of a charged particle moving in a uniform magnetic field $\vec{B}$. The magnetic field does no work on the particle, so its speed and kinetic energy remain constant.

This particle's motion has components both parallel ($v_\parallel$) and perpendicular ($v_\perp$) to the magnetic field, so it moves in a helical path.

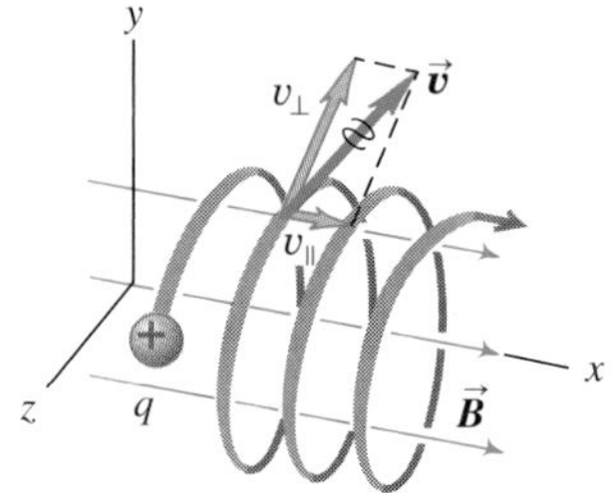

that begin at the north pole of a magnet and end at a south pole. But as Fig. 27.11 shows, the field lines of a magnet actually continue through the interior of the magnet. Like all other magnetic field lines, they form closed loops.

For Gauss's law, which always deals with *closed* surfaces, the vector area element $d\vec{A}$ in Eq. (27.6) always points *out of* the surface. However, some applications of *magnetic* flux involve an *open* surface with a boundary line; there is then an ambiguity of sign in Eq. (27.6) because of the two possible choices of direction for $d\vec{A}$. In these cases we choose one of the two sides of the surface to be the "positive" side and use that choice consistently.

If the element of area dA in Eq. (27.5) is at right angles to the field lines, then $B_\perp = B$; calling the area $dA_\perp$, we have

$$B = \frac{d\Phi_B}{dA_\perp} \tag{27.9}$$

That is, the magnitude of magnetic field is equal to *flux per unit area* across an area at right angles to the magnetic field. For this reason, magnetic field $\vec{B}$ is sometimes called **magnetic flux density.**

Example 27.2 Magnetic flux calculations

Figure 27.16a shows a perspective view of a flat surface with area 3.0 cm^2 in a uniform magnetic field. If the magnetic flux through this area is 0.90 mWb, calculate the magnitude of the magnetic field and find the direction of the area vector.

SOLUTION

IDENTIFY: In many problems we are asked to calculate the flux of a given magnetic field through a given area. In this example, however, we are given the flux, the area, and the direction of the magnetic field. Our target variables are the field magnitude and the direction of the area vector.

27.16 (a) A flat area A in a uniform magnetic field $\vec{B}$. (b) The area vector $\vec{A}$ makes a 60° angle with $\vec{B}$. (If we had chosen $\vec{A}$ to point in the opposite direction, ϕ would have been 120° and the magnetic flux Φ_B would have been negative.)

(a) Perspective view

(b) Our sketch of the problem (edge-on view)

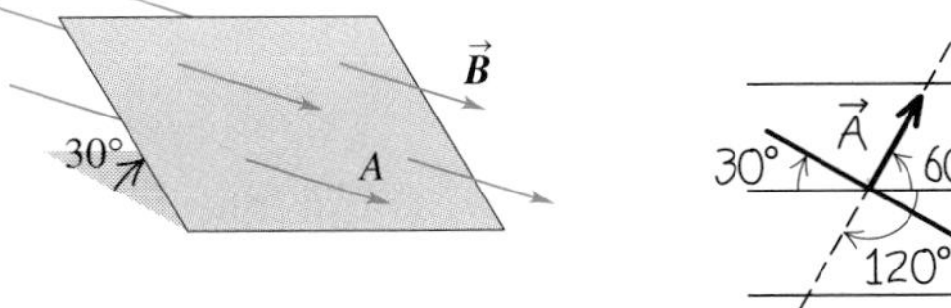

SET UP: Because the magnetic field is uniform, B and ϕ are the same at all points on the surface. Hence we can use Eq. (27.7): $\Phi_B = BA\cos\phi$. Our target variable is B.

EXECUTE: The area A is 3.0×10^{-4} m^2; the direction of $\vec{A}$ is perpendicular to the surface, so ϕ could be either 60° or 120°. But Φ_B, B, and A are all positive, so $\cos\phi$ must also be positive. This rules out 120°, so $\phi = 60°$, and we find

$$B = \frac{\Phi_B}{A\cos\phi} = \frac{0.90 \times 10^{-3}\ \text{Wb}}{(3.0 \times 10^{-4}\ \text{m}^2)(\cos 60°)} = 6.0\ \text{T}$$

The area vector $\vec{A}$ is perpendicular to the area in the direction shown in Fig. 27.16b.

EVALUATE: A good way to check our result is to calculate the product $BA\cos\phi$ to make sure that it is equal to the given value of the magnetic flux Φ_B. Is it?

Test Your Understanding of Section 27.3 Imagine moving along the axis of the current-carrying loop in Fig. 27.13c, starting at a point well to the left of the loop and ending at a point well to the right of the loop. (a) How would the magnetic field strength vary as you moved along this path? (i) It would be the same at all points along the path; (ii) it would increase and then decrease; (iii) it would decrease and then increase. (b) Would the magnetic field direction vary as you moved along the path?

27.4 Motion of Charged Particles in a Magnetic Field

When a charged particle moves in a magnetic field, it is acted on by the magnetic force given by Eq. (27.2), and the motion is determined by Newton's laws. Figure 27.17 shows a simple example. A particle with positive charge q is at

27.17 A charged particle moves in a plane perpendicular to a uniform magnetic field $\vec{B}$.

(a) The orbit of a charged particle in a uniform magnetic field

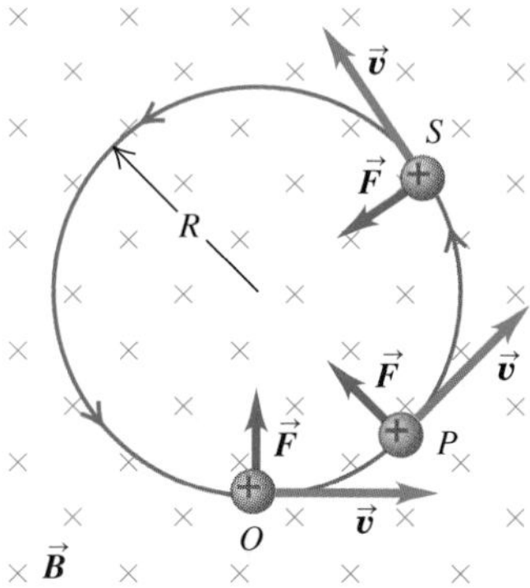
A charge moving at right angles to a uniform $\vec{B}$ field moves in a circle at constant speed because $\vec{F}$ and $\vec{v}$ are always perpendicular to each other.
$\vec{v}$
S
$\vec{F}$
R
$\vec{F}$
$\vec{v}$
$\vec{F}$
P
O
$\vec{v}$
$\vec{B}$

(b) An electron beam (seen as a blue arc) curving in a magnetic field

point O, moving with velocity $\vec{v}$ in a uniform magnetic field $\vec{B}$ directed into the plane of the figure. The vectors $\vec{v}$ and $\vec{B}$ are perpendicular, so the magnetic force $\vec{F} = q\vec{v} \times \vec{B}$ has magnitude $F = qvB$ and a direction as shown in the figure. The force is *always* perpendicular to $\vec{v}$, so it cannot change the *magnitude* of the velocity, only its direction. To put it differently, the magnetic force never has a component parallel to the particle's motion, so the magnetic force can never do *work* on the particle. This is true even if the magnetic field is not uniform.

Motion of a charged particle under the action of a magnetic field alone is always motion with constant speed.

Using this principle, we see that in the situation shown in Fig. 27.17a the magnitudes of both $\vec{F}$ and $\vec{v}$ are constant. At points such as P and S the directions of force and velocity have changed as shown, but their magnitudes are the same. The particle therefore moves under the influence of a constant-magnitude force that is always at right angles to the velocity of the particle. Comparing these conditions with the discussion of circular motion in Sections 3.4 and 5.4, we see that the particle's path is a *circle,* traced out with constant speed v. The centripetal acceleration is v^2/R and the only force acting is the magnetic force, so from Newton's second law,

$$F = |q|vB = m\frac{v^2}{R} \tag{27.10}$$

where m is the mass of the particle. Solving Eq. (27.10) for the radius R of the circular path, we find

$$R = \frac{mv}{|q|B} \quad \text{(radius of a circular orbit in a magnetic field)} \tag{27.11}$$

We can also write this as $R = p/|q|B$, where $p = mv$ is the magnitude of the particle's momentum. If the charge q is negative, the particle moves *clockwise* around the orbit in Fig. 27.17a.

The angular speed ω of the particle can be found from Eq. (9.13), $v = R\omega$. Combining this with Eq. (27.11), we get

$$\omega = \frac{v}{R} = v\frac{|q|B}{mv} = \frac{|q|B}{m} \tag{27.12}$$

The number of revolutions per unit time is $f = \omega/2\pi$. This frequency f is independent of the radius R of the path. It is called the **cyclotron frequency;** in a particle accelerator called a *cyclotron,* particles moving in nearly circular paths are given a boost twice each revolution, increasing their energy and their orbital radii but not their angular speed or frequency. Similarly, one type of *magnetron,* a common source of microwave radiation for microwave ovens and radar systems, emits radiation with a frequency equal to the frequency of circular motion of electrons in a vacuum chamber between the poles of a magnet.

If the direction of the initial velocity is *not* perpendicular to the field, the velocity *component* parallel to the field is constant because there is no force parallel to the field. Then the particle moves in a helix (Fig. 27.18). The radius of the helix is given by Eq. (27.11), where v is now the component of velocity perpendicular to the $\vec{B}$ field.

27.18 The general case of a charged particle moving in a uniform magnetic field $\vec{B}$. The magnetic field does no work on the particle, so its speed and kinetic energy remain constant.

This particle's motion has components both parallel ($v_{\parallel}$) and perpendicular ($v_{\perp}$) to the magnetic field, so it moves in a helical path.

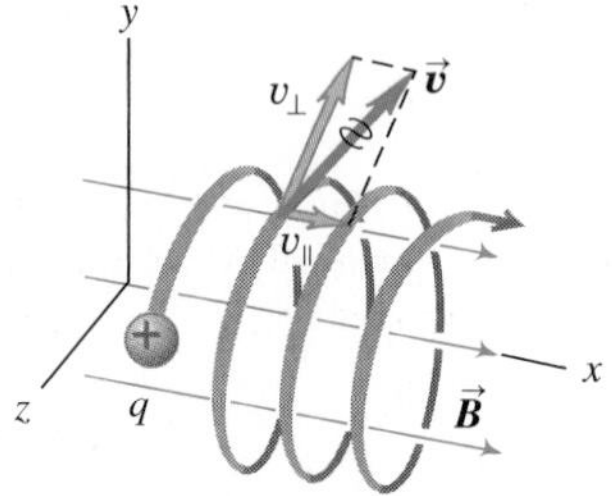
y
$v_{\perp}$
$\vec{v}$
$v_{\parallel}$
x
z
q
$\vec{B}$

Motion of a charged particle in a nonuniform magnetic field is more complex. Figure 27.19 shows a field produced by two circular coils separated by some distance. Particles near either coil experience a magnetic force toward the center of the region; particles with appropriate speeds spiral repeatedly from one end of the region to the other and back. Because charged particles can be trapped in such a magnetic field, it is called a *magnetic bottle.* This technique is used to confine very hot plasmas with temperatures of the order of 10^6 K. In a similar way the

of the force on an arbitrary moving charged particle. Magnetic field lines *do* have the direction that a compass needle would point at each location; this may help you to visualize them.

Figures 27.11 and 27.13 show magnetic field lines produced by several common sources of magnetic field. In the gap between the poles of the magnet shown in Fig. 27.13a, the field lines are approximately straight, parallel, and equally spaced, showing that the magnetic field in this region is approximately *uniform* (that is, constant in magnitude and direction).

Because magnetic-field patterns are three-dimensional, it's often necessary to draw magnetic field lines that point into or out of the plane of a drawing. To do this we use a dot ($\cdot$) to represent a vector directed out of the plane and a cross ($\times$) to represent a vector directed into the plane (Fig. 27.13b). Here's a good way to remember these conventions: Think of a dot as the head of an arrow coming directly toward you, and think of a cross as the feathers of an arrow flying directly away from you.

Iron filings, like compass needles, tend to align with magnetic field lines. Hence they provide an easy way to visualize field lines (Fig. 27.14).

27.12 Magnetic field lines are *not* "lines of force."

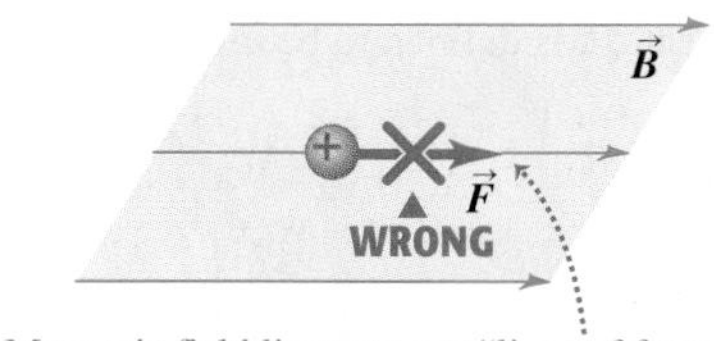
$\vec{B}$
$\vec{F}$
WRONG
Magnetic field lines are *not* "lines of force." The force on a charged particle is not along the direction of a field line.

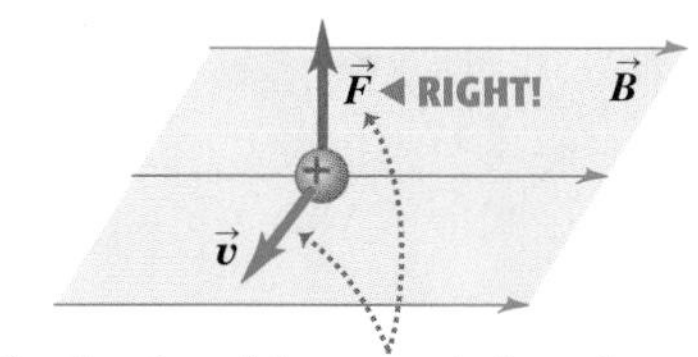
$\vec{F}$ RIGHT!
$\vec{B}$
$\vec{v}$
The direction of the magnetic force depends on the velocity $\vec{v}$, as expressed by the magnetic force law $\vec{F} = q\vec{v} \times \vec{B}$.

27.13 Magnetic field lines produced by several common sources of magnetic field.

(a) Magnetic field of a C-shaped magnet

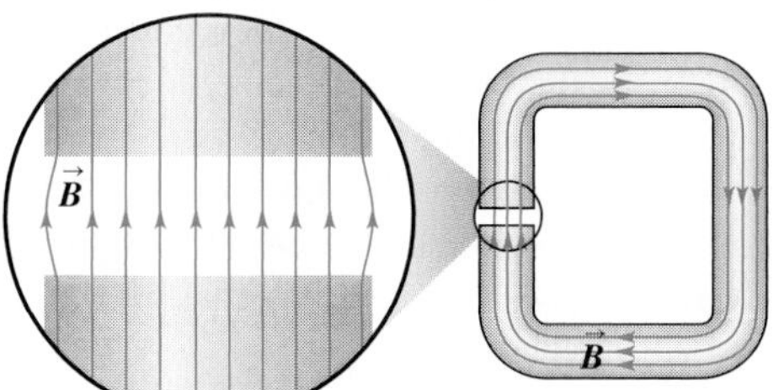
Between flat, parallel magnetic poles, the magnetic field is nearly uniform.
$\vec{B}$
$\vec{B}$

(b) Magnetic field of a straight current-carrying wire

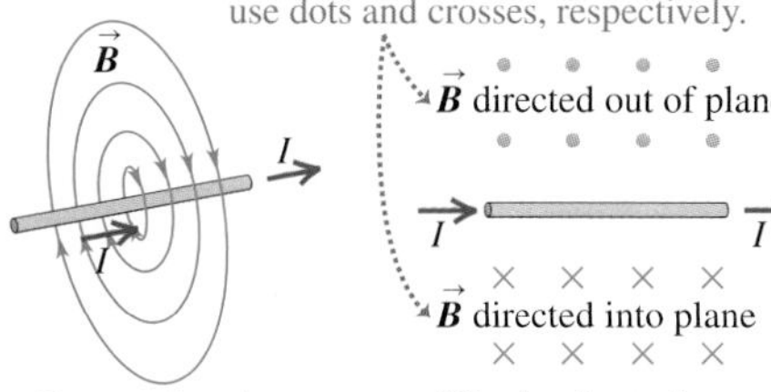
To represent a field coming out of or going into the plane of the paper, we use dots and crosses, respectively.
$\vec{B}$
I
I
$\vec{B}$ directed out of plane
I
I
$\vec{B}$ directed into plane
Perspective view
Wire in plane of paper

(c) Magnetic fields of a current-carrying loop and a current-carrying coil (solenoid)

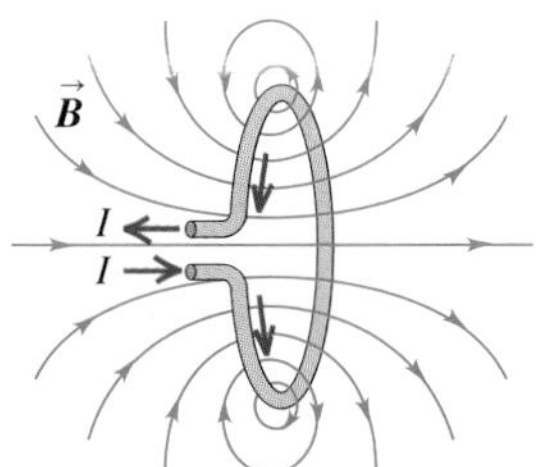
$\vec{B}$
I
I

Notice that the field of the loop and, especially, that of the coil look like the field of a bar magnet (see Fig. 27.11).

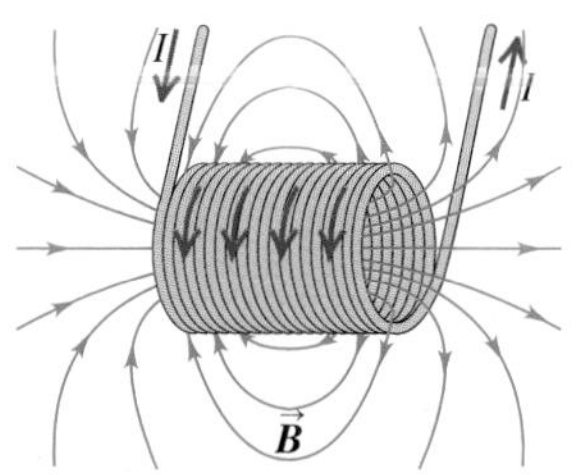
I
I
$\vec{B}$

27.14 (a) Like little compass needles, iron filings line up tangent to magnetic field lines. (b) Drawing of the field lines for the situation shown in (a).

(a)

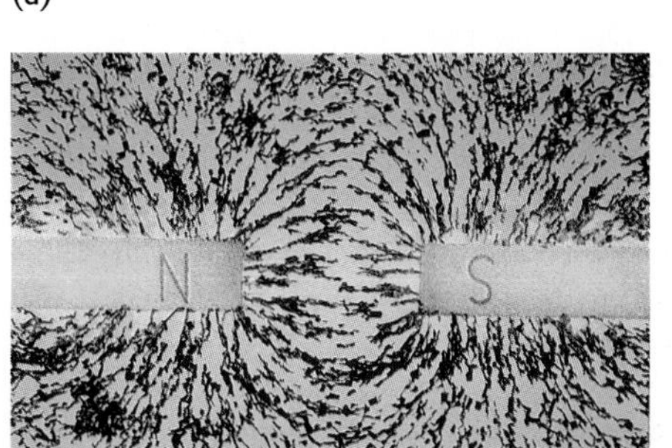
N
S

(b)

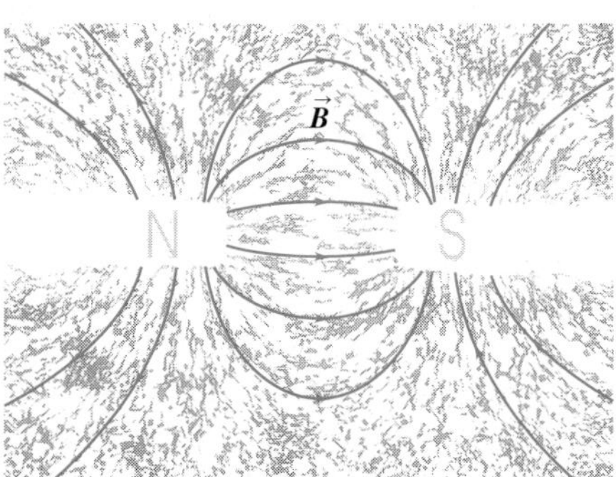
$\vec{B}$
N
S

27.15 The magnetic flux through an area element dA is defined to be $d\Phi_B = B_\perp dA$.

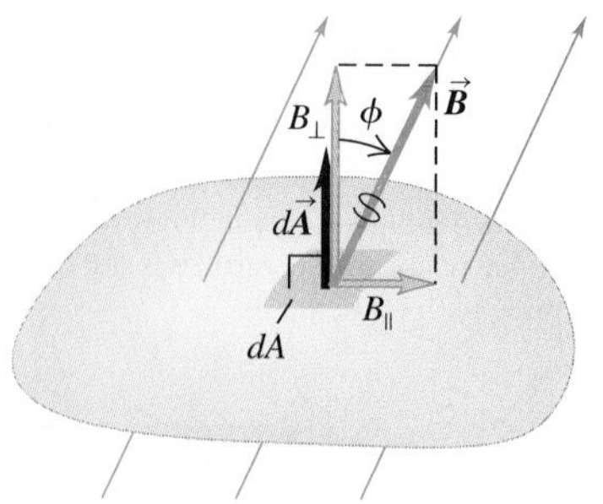

Magnetic Flux and Gauss's Law for Magnetism

We define the **magnetic flux** Φ_B through a surface just as we defined electric flux in connection with Gauss's law in Section 22.2. We can divide any surface into elements of area dA (Fig. 27.15). For each element we determine $B_\perp$, the component of $\vec{B}$ normal to the surface at the position of that element, as shown. From the figure, $B_\perp = B\cos\phi$, where ϕ is the angle between the direction of $\vec{B}$ and a line perpendicular to the surface. (Be careful not to confuse ϕ with Φ_B.) In general, this component varies from point to point on the surface. We define the magnetic flux $d\Phi_B$ through this area as

$$d\Phi_B = B_\perp dA = B\cos\phi\, dA = \vec{B}\cdot d\vec{A} \tag{27.5}$$

The *total* magnetic flux through the surface is the sum of the contributions from the individual area elements:

$$\Phi_B = \int B_\perp dA = \int B\cos\phi\, dA = \int \vec{B}\cdot d\vec{A} \quad \text{(magnetic flux through a surface)} \tag{27.6}$$

(This equation uses the concepts of vector area and surface integral that we introduced in Section 22.2; you may want to review that discussion.)

Magnetic flux is a *scalar* quantity. In the special case in which $\vec{B}$ is uniform over a plane surface with total area A, $B_\perp$ and ϕ are the same at all points on the surface, and

$$\Phi_B = B_\perp A = BA\cos\phi \tag{27.7}$$

If $\vec{B}$ happens to be perpendicular to the surface, then $\cos\phi = 1$ and Eq. (27.7) reduces to $\Phi_B = BA$. We will use the concept of magnetic flux extensively during our study of electromagnetic induction in Chapter 29.

The SI unit of magnetic flux is equal to the unit of magnetic field (1 T) times the unit of area $(1\ \text{m}^2)$. This unit is called the **weber** (1 Wb), in honor of the German physicist Wilhelm Weber (1804–1891):

$$1\ \text{Wb} = 1\ \text{T}\cdot\text{m}^2$$

Also, $1\ \text{T} = 1\ \text{N}/\text{A}\cdot\text{m}$, so

$$1\ \text{Wb} = 1\ \text{T}\cdot\text{m}^2 = 1\ \text{N}\cdot\text{m}/\text{A}$$

In Gauss's law the total *electric* flux through a closed surface is proportional to the total electric charge enclosed by the surface. For example, if the closed surface encloses an electric dipole, the total electric flux is zero because the total charge is zero. (You may want to review Section 22.3 on Gauss's law.) By analogy, if there were such a thing as a single magnetic charge (magnetic monopole), the total *magnetic* flux through a closed surface would be proportional to the total magnetic charge enclosed. But we have mentioned that no magnetic monopole has ever been observed, despite intensive searches. We conclude:

The total magnetic flux through a closed surface is always zero.

Symbolically,

$$\oint \vec{B}\cdot d\vec{A} = 0 \quad \text{(magnetic flux through any closed surface)} \tag{27.8}$$

This equation is sometimes called *Gauss's law for magnetism.* You can verify it by examining Figs. 27.11 and 27.13; if you draw a closed surface anywhere in any of the field maps shown in those figures, you will see that every field line that enters the surface also exits from it; the net flux through the surface is zero. It also follows from Eq. (27.8) that magnetic field lines always form closed loops.

CAUTION **Magnetic field lines have no ends** Unlike electric field lines that begin and end on electric charges, magnetic field lines *never* have end points; such a point would indicate the presence of a monopole. You might be tempted to draw magnetic field lines

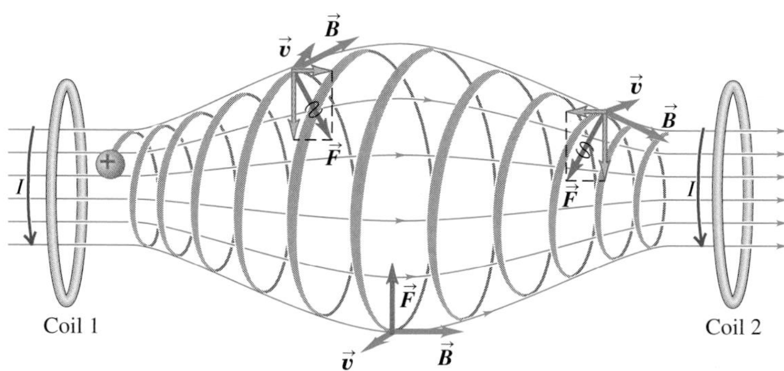

27.19 A magnetic bottle. Particles near either end of the region experience a magnetic force toward the center of the region. This is one way of containing an ionized gas that has a temperature of the order of 10^6 K, which would vaporize any material container.

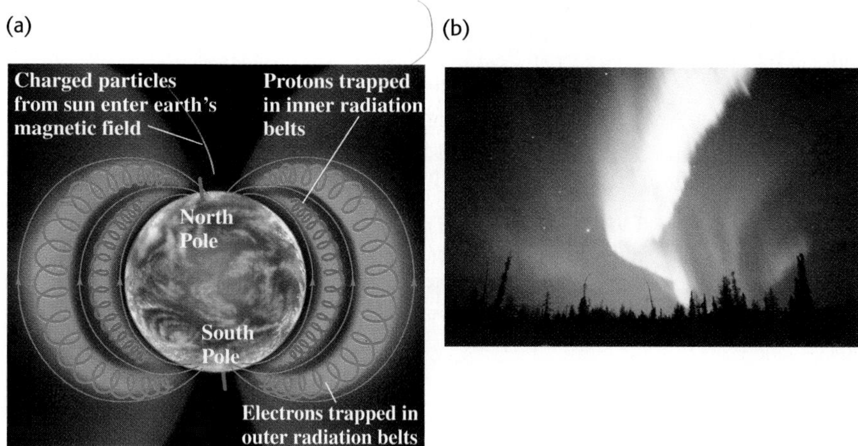

27.20 (a) The Van Allen radiation belts around the earth. Near the poles, charged particles from these belts can enter the atmosphere, producing the aurora borealis ("northern lights") and aurora australis ("southern lights"). (b) A photograph of the aurora borealis.

earth's nonuniform magnetic field traps charged particles coming from the sun in doughnut-shaped regions around the earth, as shown in Fig. 27.20. These regions, called the *Van Allen radiation belts,* were discovered in 1958 using data obtained by instruments aboard the Explorer I satellite.

Magnetic forces on charged particles play an important role in studies of elementary particles. Figure 27.21 shows a chamber filled with liquid hydrogen and with a magnetic field directed into the plane of the photograph. A high-energy gamma ray dislodges an electron from a hydrogen atom, sending it off at high speed and creating a visible track in the liquid hydrogen. The track shows the electron curving downward due to the magnetic force. The energy of the collision also produces another electron and a *positron* (a positively charged electron). Because of their opposite charges, the trajectories of the electron and the positron curve in opposite directions. As these particles plow through the liquid hydrogen, they collide with other charged particles, losing energy and speed. As a result, the radius of curvature decreases as suggested by Eq. (27.11). (The electron's speed is comparable to the speed of light, so Eq. (27.11) isn't directly applicable here.) Similar experiments allow physicists to determine the mass and charge of newly discovered particles.

27.21 This bubble chamber image shows the result of a high-energy gamma ray (which does not leave a track) that collides with an electron in a hydrogen atom. This electron flies off to the right at high speed. Some of the energy in the collision is transformed into a second electron and a positron (a positively charged electron). A magnetic field is directed into the plane of the image, which makes the positive and negative particles curve off in different directions.

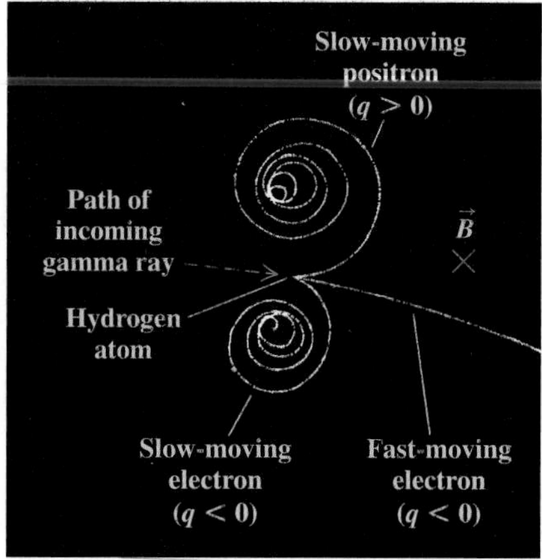

Problem-Solving Strategy 27.2 Motion in Magnetic Fields

IDENTIFY *the relevant concepts:* In analyzing the motion of a charged particle in electric and magnetic fields, you will apply Newton's second law of motion, $\Sigma\vec{F} = m\vec{a}$, with the net force given by $\Sigma\vec{F} = q(\vec{E} + \vec{v} \times \vec{B})$. Often other forces such as gravity can be neglected. Many of the problems are similar to the trajectory and circular-motion problems in Sections 3.3, 3.4, and 5.4; it would be a good idea to review those sections.

SET UP *the problem* using the following steps:

1. Determine the target variable(s).
2. Often the use of components is the most efficient approach. Choose a coordinate system and then express all vector quantities (including $\vec{E}$, $\vec{B}$, $\vec{v}$, $\vec{F}$, and $\vec{a}$) in terms of their components in this system.

Continued

EXECUTE *the solution* as follows:

1. If the particle moves perpendicular to a uniform magnetic field, the trajectory is a circle with a radius and angular speed given by Eqs. (27.11) and (27.12), respectively.
2. If your calculation involves a more complex trajectory, use $\sum \vec{F} = m\vec{a}$ in component form: $\sum F_x = ma_x$, and so forth. This approach is particularly useful when both electric and magnetic fields are present.

EVALUATE *your answer:* Check whether your results are reasonable.

Example 27.3 Electron motion in a microwave oven

A magnetron in a microwave oven emits electromagnetic waves with frequency $f = 2450$ MHz. What magnetic field strength is required for electrons to move in circular paths with this frequency?

SOLUTION

IDENTIFY: The problem refers to circular motion as shown in Fig. 27.17a. Our target variable is the field magnitude B.

SET UP: We use Eq. (27.12) to relate the angular speed in circular motion to the mass and charge of the particle and the magnetic field strength B.

EXECUTE: The angular speed that corresponds to the frequency f is $\omega = 2\pi f = (2\pi)(2450 \times 10^6\ \text{s}^{-1}) = 1.54 \times 10^{10}\ \text{s}^{-1}$. From Eq. (27.12),

$$B = \frac{m\omega}{|q|} = \frac{(9.11 \times 10^{-31}\ \text{kg})(1.54 \times 10^{10}\ \text{s}^{-1})}{1.60 \times 10^{-19}\ \text{C}}$$
$$= 0.0877\ \text{T}$$

EVALUATE: This is a moderate field strength, easily produced with a permanent magnet. Incidentally, 2450-MHz electromagnetic waves are strongly absorbed by water molecules, so they are useful for heating and cooking food.

Example 27.4 Helical particle motion

In a situation like that shown in Fig. 27.18, the charged particle is a proton ($q = 1.60 \times 10^{-19}$ C, $m = 1.67 \times 10^{-27}$ kg) and the uniform magnetic field is directed along the x-axis with magnitude 0.500 T. Only the magnetic force acts on the proton. At $t = 0$ the proton has velocity components $v_x = 1.50 \times 10^5$ m/s, $v_y = 0$, and $v_z = 2.00 \times 10^5$ m/s. (a) At $t = 0$, find the force on the proton and its acceleration. (b) Find the radius of the helical path, the angular speed of the proton, and the *pitch* of the helix (the distance traveled along the helix axis per revolution).

SOLUTION

IDENTIFY: The force is given by $\vec{F} = q\vec{v} \times \vec{B}$ and the acceleration is given by Newton's second law. The force is perpendicular to the velocity, so the speed of the proton does not change. Hence the radius of the helical trajectory is just as given by Eq. (27.11) for circular motion, but with v replaced by the component of velocity perpendicular to $\vec{B}$. The angular speed is given by Eq. (27.12).

SET UP: We use the coordinate system shown in Fig. 27.18. Given the angular speed, we can determine the time required for one revolution; given the velocity parallel to the magnetic field, we can determine the distance traveled along the helix in this time.

EXECUTE: (a) Since $v_y = 0$, the velocity vector is $\vec{v} = v_x\hat{\imath} + v_z\hat{k}$. Using Eq. (27.2) and recalling that $\hat{\imath} \times \hat{\imath} = \mathbf{0}$ and $\hat{k} \times \hat{\imath} = \hat{\jmath}$, we find

$$\vec{F} = q\vec{v} \times \vec{B} = q(v_x\hat{\imath} + v_z\hat{k}) \times B\hat{\imath} = qv_zB\hat{\jmath}$$
$$= (1.60 \times 10^{-19}\ \text{C})(2.00 \times 10^5\ \text{m/s})(0.500\ \text{T})\hat{\jmath}$$
$$= (1.60 \times 10^{-14}\ \text{N})\hat{\jmath}$$

(To check unit consistency, recall from Section 27.2 that 1 T = 1 N/A · m = 1 N · s/C · m.) This may seem like a very weak force, but the resulting acceleration is tremendous because the proton mass is so small:

$$\vec{a} = \frac{\vec{F}}{m} = \frac{1.60 \times 10^{-14}\ \text{N}}{1.67 \times 10^{-27}\ \text{kg}}\hat{\jmath} = (9.58 \times 10^{12}\ \text{m/s}^2)\hat{\jmath}$$

(b) At $t = 0$ the component of velocity perpendicular to $\vec{B}$ is v_z, so

$$R = \frac{mv_z}{|q|B} = \frac{(1.67 \times 10^{-27}\ \text{kg})(2.00 \times 10^5\ \text{m/s})}{(1.60 \times 10^{-19}\ \text{C})(0.500\ \text{T})}$$
$$= 4.18 \times 10^{-3}\ \text{m} = 4.18\ \text{mm}$$

From Eq. (27.12) the angular speed is

$$\omega = \frac{|q|B}{m} = \frac{(1.60 \times 10^{-19}\ \text{C})(0.500\ \text{T})}{1.67 \times 10^{-27}\ \text{kg}} = 4.79 \times 10^7\ \text{rad/s}$$

The time required for one revolution (the period) is $T = 2\pi/\omega = 2\pi/(4.79 \times 10^7\ \text{s}^{-1}) = 1.31 \times 10^{-7}$ s. The pitch is the distance traveled along the x-axis during this time, or

$$v_xT = (1.50 \times 10^5\ \text{m/s})(1.31 \times 10^{-7}\ \text{s})$$
$$= 0.0197\ \text{m} = 19.7\ \text{mm}$$

EVALUATE: The pitch of the helix is almost five times greater than the radius. This helical trajectory is much more "stretched out" than that shown in Fig. 27.18.

Test Your Understanding of Section 27.4 (a) If you double the speed of the charged particle in Fig. 27.17a while keeping the magnetic field the same (as well as the charge and the mass), how does this affect the radius of the trajectory? (i) The radius is unchanged; (ii) the radius is twice as large; (iii) the radius is four times as large; (iv) the radius is $\frac{1}{2}$ as large; (v) the radius is $\frac{1}{4}$ as large. (b) How does this affect the time required for one complete circular orbit? (i) The time is unchanged; (ii) the time is twice as long; (iii) the time is four times as long; (iv) the time is $\frac{1}{2}$ as long; (v) the time is $\frac{1}{4}$ as long.

27.5 Applications of Motion of Charged Particles

This section describes several applications of the principles introduced in this chapter. Study them carefully, watching for applications of Problem-Solving Strategy 27.2 (Section 27.4).

Velocity Selector

In a beam of charged particles produced by a heated cathode or a radioactive material, not all particles move with the same speed. Many applications, however, require a beam in which all the particle speeds are the same. Particles of a specific speed can be selected from the beam using an arrangement of electric and magnetic fields called a *velocity selector.* In Fig. 27.22a a charged particle with mass m, charge q, and speed v enters a region of space where the electric and magnetic fields are perpendicular to the particle's velocity and to each other. The electric field $\vec{E}$ is to the left, and the magnetic field $\vec{B}$ is into the plane of the figure. If q is positive, the electric force is to the left, with magnitude qE, and the magnetic force is to the right, with magnitude qvB. For given field magnitudes E and B, for a particular value of v the electric and magnetic forces will be equal in magnitude; the total force is then zero, and the particle travels in a straight line with constant velocity. For zero total force, $\sum F_y = 0$, we need $-qE + qvB = 0$; solving for the speed v for which there is no deflection, we find

$$v = \frac{E}{B} \tag{27.13}$$

Only particles with speeds equal to E/B can pass through without being deflected by the fields (Fig. 27.22b). By adjusting E and B appropriately, we can select particles having a particular speed for use in other experiments. Because q divides out in Eq. (27.13), a velocity selector for positively charged particles also works for electrons or other negatively charged particles.

27.22 (a) A velocity selector for charged particles uses perpendicular $\vec{E}$ and $\vec{B}$ fields. Only charged particles with $v = E/B$ move through undeflected. (b) The electric and magnetic forces on a positive charge. The forces are reversed if the charge is negative.

(a) Schematic diagram of velocity selector

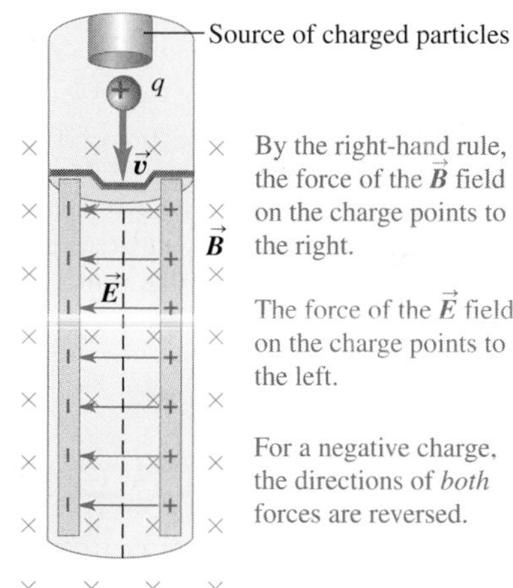

Source of charged particles
q
$\vec{v}$
$\vec{B}$
$\vec{E}$
By the right-hand rule, the force of the $\vec{B}$ field on the charge points to the right.
The force of the $\vec{E}$ field on the charge points to the left.
For a negative charge, the directions of *both* forces are reversed.

(b) Free-body diagram for a positive particle

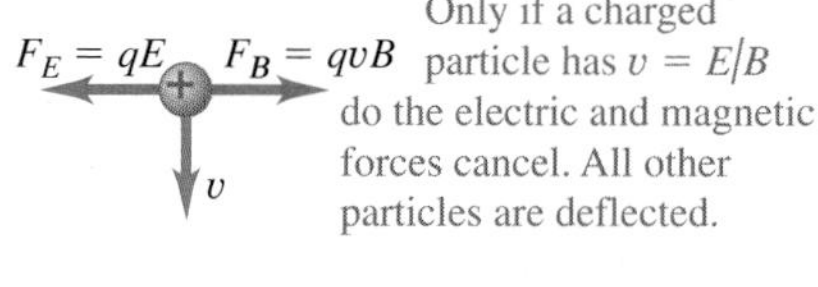

ActivPhysics ONLINE

13.8 Velocity Selector

Thomson's e/m Experiment

In one of the landmark experiments in physics at the end of the 19th century, J. J. Thomson (1856–1940) used the idea just described to measure the ratio of charge to mass for the electron. For this experiment, carried out in 1897 at the Cavendish Laboratory in Cambridge, England, Thomson used the apparatus shown in Fig. 27.23. In a highly evacuated glass container, electrons from the hot cathode are accelerated and formed into a beam by a potential difference V between the two anodes A and A′. The speed v of the electrons is determined by the accelerating potential V. The kinetic energy $\frac{1}{2}mv^2$ equals the loss of electric potential energy eV, where e is the magnitude of the electron charge:

$$\frac{1}{2}mv^2 = eV \quad \text{or} \quad v = \sqrt{\frac{2eV}{m}} \tag{27.14}$$

27.23 Thomson's apparatus for measuring the ratio e/m for the electron.

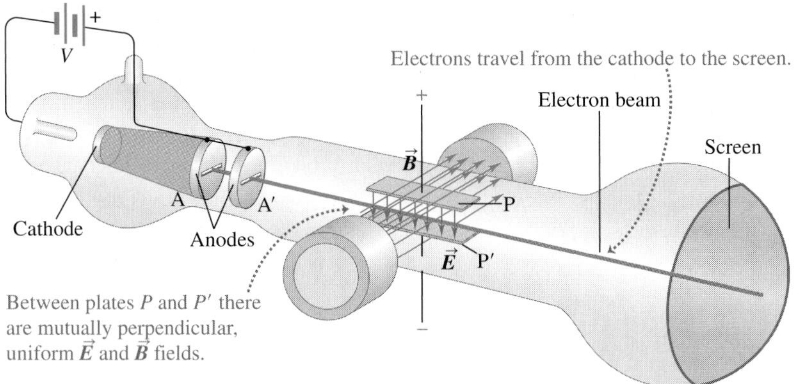

The electrons pass between the plates P and P′ and strike the screen at the end of the tube, which is coated with a material that fluoresces (glows) at the point of impact. The electrons pass straight through the plates when Eq. (27.13) is satisfied; combining this with Eq. (27.14), we get

$$\frac{E}{B} = \sqrt{\frac{2eV}{m}} \quad \text{so} \quad \frac{e}{m} = \frac{E^2}{2VB^2} \tag{27.15}$$

All the quantities on the right side can be measured, so the ratio e/m of charge to mass can be determined. It is *not* possible to measure e or m separately by this method, only their ratio.

The most significant aspect of Thomson's e/m measurements was that he found a *single value* for this quantity. It did not depend on the cathode material, the residual gas in the tube, or anything else about the experiment. This independence showed that the particles in the beam, which we now call electrons, are a common constituent of all matter. Thus Thomson is credited with discovery of the first subatomic particle, the electron. He also found that the *speed* of the electrons in the beam was about one-tenth the speed of light, much greater than any previously measured speed of a material particle.

The most precise value of e/m available as of this writing is

$$e/m = 1.75882012(15) \times 10^{11}\ \text{C/kg}$$

In this expression, (15) indicates the likely uncertainty in the last two digits, 12.

Fifteen years after Thomson's experiments, the American physicist Robert Millikan succeeded in measuring the charge of the electron precisely (see Challenge Problem 23.91). This value, together with the value of e/m, enables us to determine the *mass* of the electron. The most precise value available at present is

$$m = 9.1093826(16) \times 10^{-31}\ \text{kg}$$

27.24 Bainbridge's mass spectrometer utilizes a velocity selector to produce particles with uniform speed v. In the region of magnetic field B', particles with greater mass $(m_2 > m_1)$ travel in paths with larger radius $(R_2 > R_1)$.

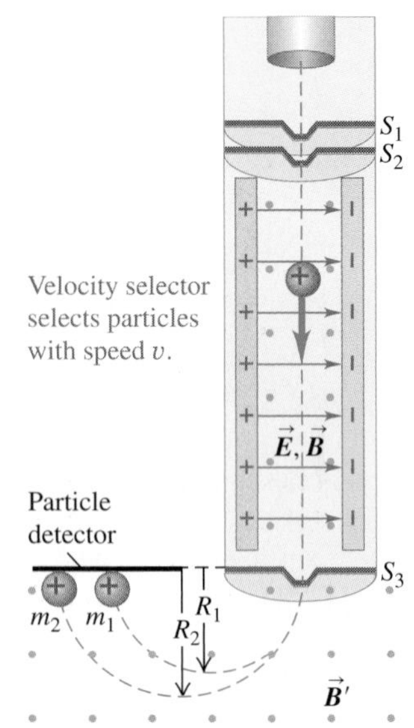

Magnetic field separates particles by mass; the greater a particle's mass, the larger is the radius of its path.

Mass Spectrometers

Techniques similar to Thomson's e/m experiment can be used to measure masses of ions and thus measure atomic and molecular masses. In 1919, Francis Aston (1877–1945), a student of Thomson's, built the first of a family of instruments called **mass spectrometers.** A variation built by Bainbridge is shown in Fig. 27.24. Positive ions from a source pass through the slits S_1 and S_2, forming a narrow beam. Then the ions pass through a velocity selector with crossed $\vec{E}$ and $\vec{B}$ fields, as we have described, to block all ions except those with speeds v equal to E/B. Finally, the ions pass into a region with a magnetic field $\vec{B}'$ perpendicular to the figure, where they move in circular arcs with radius R determined by Eq. (27.11): $R = mv/qB'$. Ions with different masses strike the detector (in

Bainbridge's design, a photographic plate) at different points, and the values of R can be measured. We assume that each ion has lost one electron, so the net charge of each ion is just $+e$. With everything known in this equation except m, we can compute the mass m of the ion.

One of the earliest results from this work was the discovery that neon has two species of atoms, with atomic masses 20 and 22 g/mol. We now call these species **isotopes** of the element. Later experiments have shown that many elements have several isotopes, atoms that are identical in their chemical behavior but different in mass owing to differing numbers of neutrons in their nuclei. This is just one of the many applications of mass spectrometers in chemistry and physics.

ActivPhysics ONLINE
13.7 Mass Spectrometer

Example 27.5 An e/m experiment

You set out to reproduce Thomson's e/m experiment with an accelerating potential of 150 V and a deflecting electric field of magnitude 6.0×10^6 N/C. (a) At what fraction of the speed of light do the electrons move? (b) What magnitude of magnetic field will you need? (c) With this magnetic field, what will happen to the electron beam if you increase the accelerating potential above 150 V?

SOLUTION

IDENTIFY: This is the same situation as depicted in Fig. 27.23.

SET UP: We use Eq. (27.14) to determine the speed of the electrons and Eq. (27.13) to determine the requisite magnetic field.

EXECUTE: (a) From Eq. (27.14), the electron speed v is related to the accelerating potential by:

$$v = \sqrt{2(e/m)V} = \sqrt{2(1.76 \times 10^{11}\ \text{C/kg})(150\ \text{V})}$$
$$= 7.27 \times 10^6\ \text{m/s}$$
$$\frac{v}{c} = \frac{7.27 \times 10^6\ \text{m/s}}{3.00 \times 10^8\ \text{m/s}} = 0.024$$

The electrons are traveling at 2.4% of the speed of light.

(b) From Eq. (27.13),

$$B = \frac{E}{v} = \frac{6.00 \times 10^6\ \text{N/C}}{7.27 \times 10^6\ \text{m/s}} = 0.83\ \text{T}$$

(c) Increasing the accelerating potential V increases the electron speed v. In Fig. 27.23 this doesn't change the upward electric force eE, but it increases the downward magnetic force evB. Therefore the electron beam will be bent *downward* and will hit the end of the tube below the undeflected position.

EVALUATE: The required magnetic field is relatively large. If the maximum available magnetic field B is less than 0.83 T, the electric field strength E would have to be reduced to maintain the desired ratio E/B in Eq. (27.15).

Example 27.6 Finding leaks in a vacuum system

There is almost no helium in ordinary air, so helium sprayed near a leak in a vacuum system will quickly show up in the output of a vacuum pump connected to such a system. You are designing a leak detector that uses a mass spectrometer to detect He^+ ions (charge $+e = +1.60 \times 10^{-19}$ C, mass 6.65×10^{-27} kg). The ions emerge from the velocity selector with a speed of 1.00×10^5 m/s. They are curved in a semicircular path by a magnetic field B' and are detected at a distance of 10.16 cm from the slit S_3 in Fig. 27.24. Calculate the magnitude of the magnetic field B'.

SOLUTION

IDENTIFY: The motion of the ion after it passes through slit S_3 in Fig. 27.24 is just motion in a circular path as described in Section 27.4 (see Fig. 27.17).

SET UP: We use Eq. (27.11) to relate the magnetic field strength B' (the target variable) to the radius of curvature of the path and to the mass, charge, and speed of the ion.

EXECUTE: The distance given is the *diameter* of the semicircular path shown in Fig. 27.24, so the radius is $R = \frac{1}{2}(10.16 \times 10^{-2}\ \text{m}) = 5.08 \times 10^{-2}$ m. From Eq. (27.11), $R = mv/qB'$, we get

$$B' = \frac{mv}{qR} = \frac{(6.65 \times 10^{-27}\ \text{kg})(1.00 \times 10^5\ \text{m/s})}{(1.60 \times 10^{-19}\ \text{C})(5.08 \times 10^{-2}\ \text{m})}$$
$$= 0.0817\ \text{T}$$

EVALUATE: Helium leak detectors are actual devices that are widely used for diagnosing problems with high-vacuum systems. Our result shows that only a small magnetic field is required, which makes it possible to build relatively compact leak detectors.

Test Your Understanding of Section 27.5 In Example 27.6 He^+ ions with charge $+e$ move at 1.00×10^5 m/s in a straight line through a velocity selector. Suppose the He^+ ions were replaced with He^{2+} ions, in which both electrons have been removed from the helium atom and the ion charge is $+2e$. At what speed must the He^{2+} ions travel through the same velocity selector in order to move in a straight line? (i) about 4.00×10^5 m/s; (ii) about 2.00×10^5 m/s; (iii) 1.00×10^5 m/s; (iv) about 0.50×10^5 m/s; (v) about 0.25×10^5 m/s.

27.6 Magnetic Force on a Current-Carrying Conductor

13.5 Magnetic Force on Wire

What makes an electric motor work? The forces that make it turn are forces that a magnetic field exerts on a conductor carrying a current. The magnetic forces on the moving charges within the conductor are transmitted to the material of the conductor, and the conductor as a whole experiences a force distributed along its length. The moving-coil galvanometer that we described in Section 26.3 also uses magnetic forces on conductors.

We can compute the force on a current-carrying conductor starting with the magnetic force $\vec{F} = q\vec{v} \times \vec{B}$ on a single moving charge. Figure 27.25 shows a straight segment of a conducting wire, with length l and cross-sectional area A; the current is from bottom to top. The wire is in a uniform magnetic field $\vec{B}$, perpendicular to the plane of the diagram and directed *into* the plane. Let's assume first that the moving charges are positive. Later we'll see what happens when they are negative.

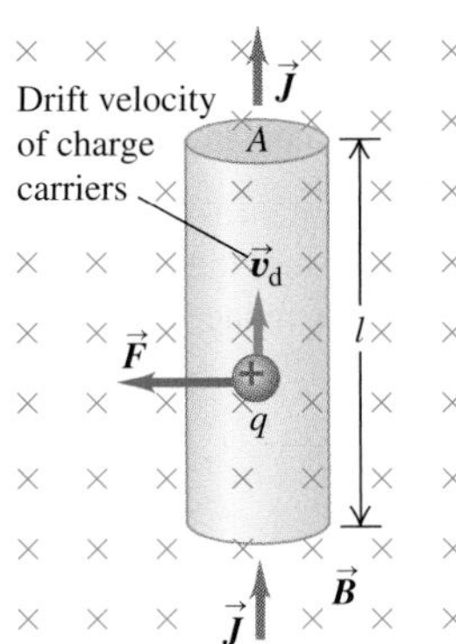

27.25 Forces on a moving positive charge in a current-carrying conductor.

The drift velocity $\vec{v}_d$ is upward, perpendicular to $\vec{B}$. The average force on each charge is $\vec{F} = q\vec{v}_d \times \vec{B}$, directed to the left as shown in the figure; since $\vec{v}_d$ and $\vec{B}$ are perpendicular, the magnitude of the force is $F = qv_dB$.

We can derive an expression for the *total* force on all the moving charges in a length l of conductor with cross-sectional area A using the same language we used in Eqs. (25.2) and (25.3) of Section 25.1. The number of charges per unit volume is n; a segment of conductor with length l has volume Al and contains a number of charges equal to nAl. The total force $\vec{F}$ on *all* the moving charges in this segment has magnitude

$$F = (nAl)(qv_dB) = (nqv_dA)(lB) \tag{27.16}$$

From Eq. (25.3) the current density is $J = nqv_d$. The product JA is the total current I, so we can rewrite Eq. (27.16) as

$$F = IlB \tag{27.17}$$

If the $\vec{B}$ field is not perpendicular to the wire but makes an angle ϕ with it, we handle the situation the same way we did in Section 27.2 for a single charge. Only the component of $\vec{B}$ perpendicular to the wire (and to the drift velocities of the charges) exerts a force; this component is $B_\perp = B\sin\phi$. The magnetic force on the wire segment is then

$$F = IlB_\perp = IlB\sin\phi \tag{27.18}$$

27.26 A straight wire segment of length $\vec{l}$ carries a current I in the direction of $\vec{l}$. The magnetic force on this segment is perpendicular to both $\vec{l}$ and the magnetic field $\vec{B}$.

Force $\vec{F}$ on a straight wire carrying a positive current and oriented at an angle ϕ to a magnetic field $\vec{B}$:
- Magnitude is $F = IlB_\perp = IlB \sin\phi$.
- Direction of $\vec{F}$ is given by the right-hand rule.

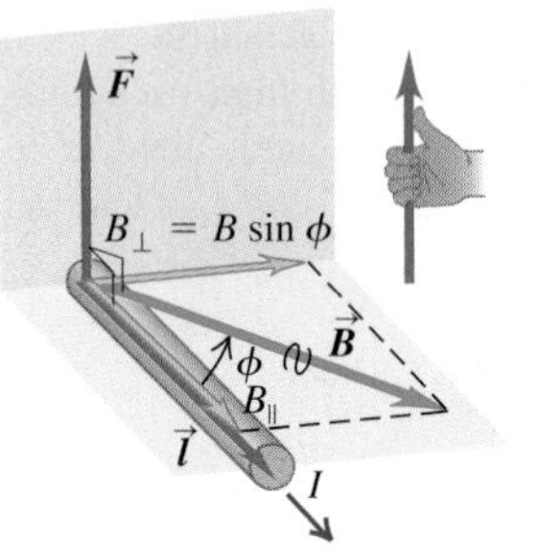

The force is always perpendicular to both the conductor and the field, with the direction determined by the same right-hand rule we used for a moving positive charge (Fig. 27.26). Hence this force can be expressed as a vector product, just like the force on a single moving charge. We represent the segment of wire with a vector $\vec{l}$ along the wire in the direction of the current; then the force $\vec{F}$ on this segment is

$$\vec{F} = I\vec{l} \times \vec{B} \qquad \text{(magnetic force on a straight wire segment)} \qquad (27.19)$$

Figure 27.27 illustrates the directions of $\vec{B}$, $\vec{l}$, and $\vec{F}$ for several cases.

If the conductor is not straight, we can divide it into infinitesimal segments $d\vec{l}$. The force $d\vec{F}$ on each segment is

$$d\vec{F} = I\, d\vec{l} \times \vec{B} \qquad \text{(magnetic force on an infinitesimal wire section)} \qquad (27.20)$$

Then we can integrate this expression along the wire to find the total force on a conductor of any shape. The integral is a *line integral,* the same mathematical operation we have used to define work (Section 6.3) and electric potential (Section 23.2).

CAUTION **Current is not a vector** Recall from Section 25.1 that the current I is not a vector. The direction of current flow is described by $d\vec{l}$, not I. If the conductor is curved, the current I is the same at all points along its length, but $d\vec{l}$ changes direction so that it is always tangent to the conductor.

Finally, what happens when the moving charges are negative, such as electrons in a metal? Then in Fig. 27.25 an upward current corresponds to a downward drift velocity. But because q is now negative, the direction of the force $\vec{F}$ is the same as before. Thus Eqs. (27.17) through (27.20) are valid for *both* positive and negative charges and even when *both* signs of charge are present at once. This happens in some semiconductor materials and in ionic solutions.

A common application of the magnetic forces on a current-carrying wire is found in loudspeakers (Fig. 27.28). The radial magnetic field created by the permanent magnet exerts a force on the voice coil that is proportional to the current in the coil; the direction of the force is either to the left or to the right, depending on the direction of the current. The signal from the amplifier causes the current to oscillate in direction and magnitude. The coil and the speaker cone to which it is attached respond by oscillating with an amplitude proportional to the amplitude of the current in the coil. Turning up the volume knob on the amplifier increases the current amplitude and hence the amplitudes of the cone's oscillation and of the sound wave produced by the moving cone.

27.27 Magnetic field $\vec{B}$, length $\vec{l}$, and force $\vec{F}$ vectors for a straight wire carrying a current I.

(a)

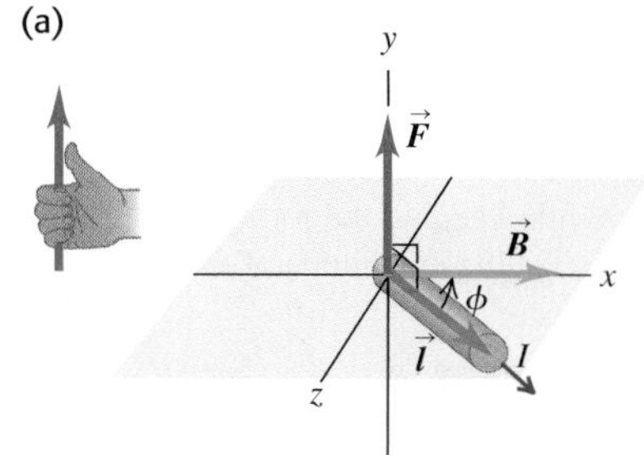

(b)

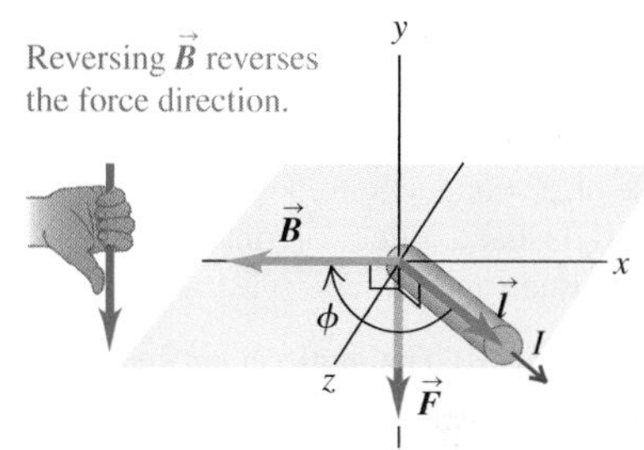

(c)

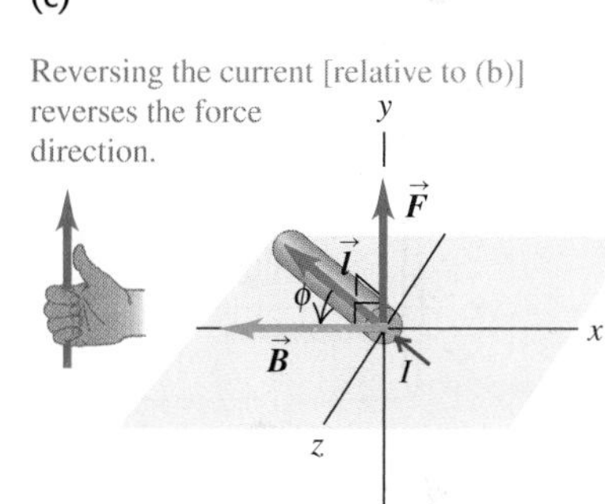

27.28 (a) Components of a loudspeaker. (b) The permanent magnet creates a magnetic field that exerts forces on the current in the voice coil; for a current I in the direction shown, the force is to the right. If the electric current in the voice coil oscillates, the speaker cone attached to the voice coil oscillates at the same frequency.

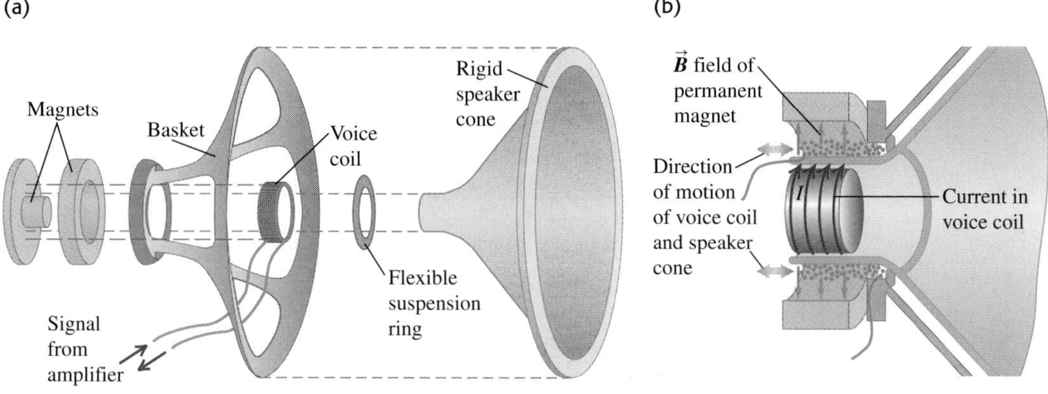

Example 27.7 Magnetic force on a straight conductor

A straight horizontal copper rod carries a current of 50.0 A from west to east in a region between the poles of a large electromagnet. In this region there is a horizontal magnetic field toward the northeast (that is, 45° north of east) with magnitude 1.20 T. (a) Find the magnitude and direction of the force on a 1.00-m section of rod. (b) While keeping the rod horizontal, how should it be oriented to maximize the magnitude of the force? What is the force magnitude in this case?

SOLUTION

IDENTIFY: This is a straight wire segment in a uniform magnetic field, which is the same situation as shown in Fig. 27.26. Our target variables are the force $\vec{F}$ on the rod segment and the angle ϕ for which the force magnitude is greatest.

SET UP: Figure 27.29 shows the situation. We can find the magnitude of the magnetic force using Eq. (27.18) and the direction from the right-hand rule. Alternatively, we can find the force vector (magnitude and direction) using Eq. (27.19).

EXECUTE: (a) The angle ϕ between the directions of current and field is 45°. From Eq. (27.18) we obtain

$$F = IlB\sin\phi = (50.0\text{ A})(1.00\text{ m})(1.20\text{ T})(\sin 45°) = 42.4\text{ N}$$

27.29 Our sketch of the copper rod as seen from overhead.

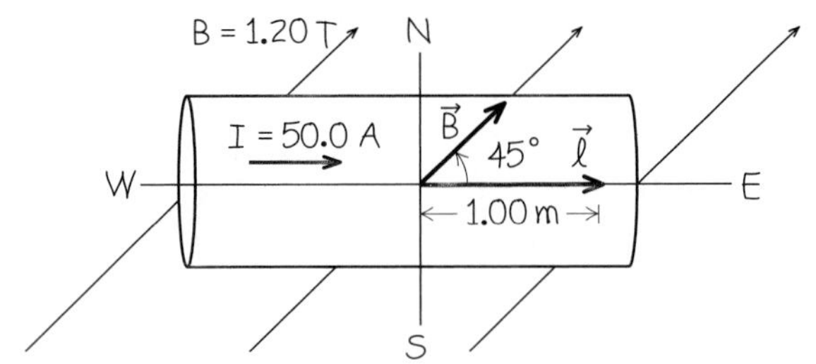

The *direction* of the force is perpendicular to the plane of the current and the field, both of which lie in the horizontal plane. Thus the force must be vertical; the right-hand rule shows that it is vertically *upward* (out of the plane of the figure).

Alternatively, we can use a coordinate system with the x-axis pointing east, the y-axis north, and the z-axis up. Then we have

$$\vec{l} = (1.00\text{ m})\hat{\imath} \qquad \vec{B} = (1.20\text{ T})[(\cos 45°)\hat{\imath} + (\sin 45°)\hat{\jmath}]$$

$$\begin{aligned}\vec{F} &= I\vec{l} \times \vec{B} \\ &= (50\text{ A})(1.00\text{ m})\hat{\imath} \times (1.20\text{ T})[(\cos 45°)\hat{\imath} + (\sin 45°)\hat{\jmath}] \\ &= (42.4\text{ N})\hat{k}\end{aligned}$$

If the conductor is in mechanical equilibrium under the action of its weight and the upward magnetic force, its weight is 42.4 N and its mass is

$$m = \frac{w}{g} = \frac{42.4\text{ N}}{9.8\text{ m/s}^2} = 4.33\text{ kg}$$

(b) The magnitude of the force is maximum if $\phi = 90°$ so that $\vec{l}$ and $\vec{B}$ are perpendicular. To have the force still be upward, we rotate the rod clockwise by 45° from its orientation in Fig. 27.29 so that the current runs toward the southeast. Then the magnetic force has magnitude

$$F = IlB = (50.0\text{ A})(1.00\text{ m})(1.20\text{ T}) = 60.0\text{ N}$$

and the mass of a rod that can be held up against gravity is $m = w/g = (60.0\text{ N})/(9.8\text{ m/s}^2) = 6.12\text{ kg}$.

EVALUATE: This is a simple example of magnetic levitation. Magnetic levitation is also used in special high-speed trains. Conventional electromagnetic technology is used to suspend the train over the tracks; the elimination of rolling friction allows the train to achieve speeds in excess of 400 km/h (250 mi/h).

Example 27.8 Magnetic force on a curved conductor

In Fig. 27.30 the magnetic field $\vec{B}$ is uniform and perpendicular to the plane of the figure, pointing out. The conductor has a straight segment with length L perpendicular to the plane of the figure on the right, with the current opposite to $\vec{B}$; followed by a semicircle with radius R; and finally another straight segment with length L parallel to the x-axis, as shown. The conductor carries a current I. Find the total magnetic force on these three segments of wire.

27.30 What is the total magnetic force on the conductor?

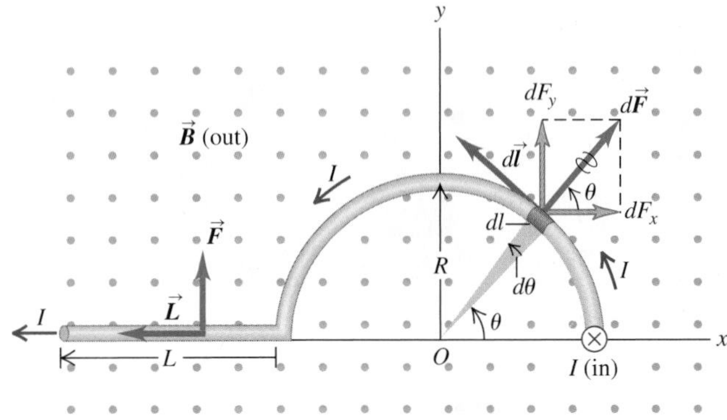

SOLUTION

IDENTIFY: Two of the three segments of wire are straight and the magnetic field is uniform, so we can find the force on these using the ideas of this section. We can analyze the curved segment by first dividing it into a large number of infinitesimal straight segments. We find the force on one such segment and then integrate to find the force on the curved segment as a whole.

SET UP: We find the force on the straight segments using Eq. (27.19) and the force on an infinitesimal part of the curved segment using Eq. (27.20). The total magnetic force on all three segments is the vector sum of the forces on each individual segment.

EXECUTE: Let's do the easy parts (the straight segments) first. There is *no* force on the segment on the right perpendicular to the plane of the figure because it is antiparallel to $\vec{B}$; $\vec{L} \times \vec{B} = \mathbf{0}$, or $\phi = 180°$ and $\sin\phi = 0$. For the straight segment on the left, $\vec{L}$ points to the left (in the direction of the current), perpendicular to

$\vec{B}$. The force has magnitude $F = ILB$, and its direction is up (the $+y$-direction in the figure).

The fun part is the semicircle. The figure shows a segment $d\vec{l}$ with length $dl = R\,d\theta$, at angle θ. The direction of $d\vec{l} \times \vec{B}$ is radially outward from the center; make sure you can verify this direction. Because $d\vec{l}$ and $\vec{B}$ are perpendicular, the magnitude dF of the force on the segment $d\vec{l}$ is just $dF = I\,dl\,B$, so we have

$$dF = I(R\,d\theta)B$$

The components of the force $d\vec{F}$ on segment $d\vec{l}$ are

$$dF_x = IR\,d\theta\,B\cos\theta \qquad dF_y = IR\,d\theta\,B\sin\theta$$

To find the components of the total force, we integrate these expressions, letting θ vary from 0 to π to take in the whole semicircle. We find

$$F_x = IRB\int_0^{\pi}\cos\theta\,d\theta = 0$$

$$F_y = IRB\int_0^{\pi}\sin\theta\,d\theta = 2IRB$$

Finally, adding the forces on the straight and semicircular segments, we find the total force:

$$F_x = 0 \qquad F_y = IB(L + 2R)$$

or

$$\vec{F} = IB(L + 2R)\hat{\jmath}$$

EVALUATE: We could have predicted from symmetry that the x-component of force on the semicircle would be zero. On the right half of the semicircle the x-component of the force is positive (to the right) and on the left half it is negative (to the left); the positive and negative contributions to the integral cancel.

Note that the net force on all three segments together is the same force that would be exerted if we replaced the semicircle with a straight segment along the x-axis. Do you see why?

Test Your Understanding of Section 27.6 The figure at right shows a top view of two conducting rails on which a conducting bar can slide. A uniform magnetic field is directed perpendicular to the plane of the figure as shown. A battery is to be connected to the two rails so that when the switch is closed, current will flow through the bar and cause a magnetic force to push the bar to the right. In which orientation, A or B, should the battery be placed in the circuit?

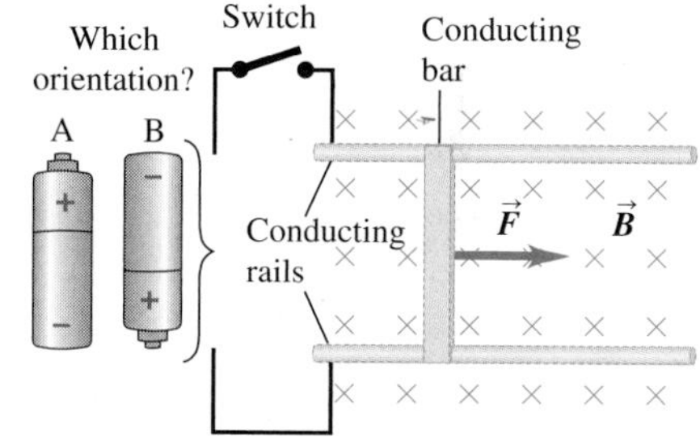

27.7 Force and Torque on a Current Loop

Current-carrying conductors usually form closed loops, so it is worthwhile to use the results of Section 27.6 to find the *total* magnetic force and torque on a conductor in the form of a loop. Many practical devices make use of the magnetic force or torque on a conducting loop, including loudspeakers (see Fig. 27.28) and galvanometers (see Section 26.3). Hence the results of this section are of substantial practical importance. These results will also help us understand the behavior of bar magnets described in Section 27.1.

13.6 Magnetic Torque on a Loop

As an example, let's look at a rectangular current loop in a uniform magnetic field. We can represent the loop as a series of straight line segments. We will find that the total *force* on the loop is zero but that there can be a net *torque* acting on the loop, with some interesting properties.

Figure 27.31a shows a rectangular loop of wire with side lengths a and b. A line perpendicular to the plane of the loop (i.e., a *normal* to the plane) makes an angle ϕ with the direction of the magnetic field $\vec{B}$, and the loop carries a current I. The wires leading the current into and out of the loop and the source of emf are omitted to keep the diagram simple.

The force $\vec{F}$ on the right side of the loop (length a) is to the right, in the $+x$-direction as shown. On this side, $\vec{B}$ is perpendicular to the current direction, and the force on this side has magnitude

$$F = IaB \tag{27.21}$$

A force $-\vec{F}$ with the same magnitude but opposite direction acts on the opposite side of the loop, as shown in the figure.

The sides with length b make an angle $(90° - \phi)$ with the direction of $\vec{B}$. The forces on these sides are the vectors $\vec{F}'$ and $-\vec{F}'$; their magnitude F' is given by

$$F' = IbB\sin(90° - \phi) = IbB\cos\phi$$

The lines of action of both forces lie along the y-axis.

27.31 Finding the torque on a current-carrying loop in a uniform magnetic field.

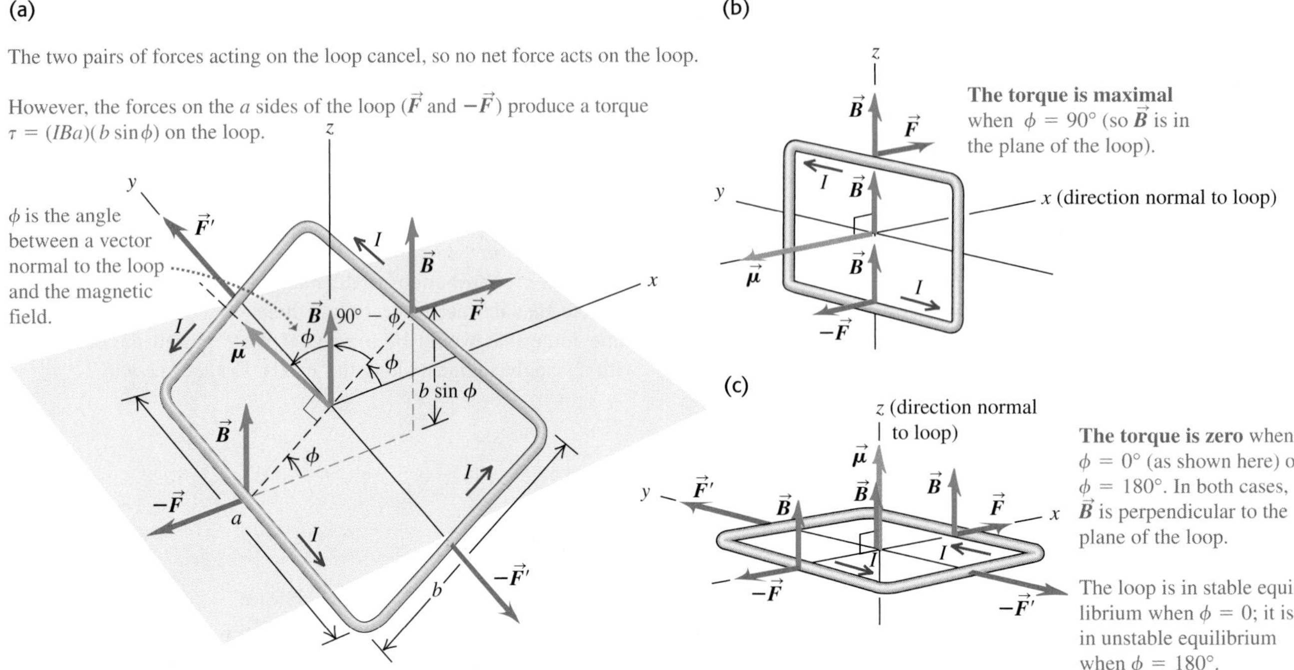
(a)
The two pairs of forces acting on the loop cancel, so no net force acts on the loop.
However, the forces on the a sides of the loop ($\vec{F}$ and $-\vec{F}$) produce a torque $\tau = (IBa)(b\sin\phi)$ on the loop.
ϕ is the angle between a vector normal to the loop and the magnetic field.
$\vec{F}'$
$\vec{B}$
$\vec{F}$
$\vec{\mu}$
$90° - \phi$
$b\sin\phi$
$-\vec{F}$
$-\vec{F}'$
a
b
I
x
y
z
(b)
The torque is maximal when $\phi = 90°$ (so $\vec{B}$ is in the plane of the loop).
x (direction normal to loop)
$\vec{B}$
$\vec{F}$
$\vec{\mu}$
$-\vec{F}$
(c)
z (direction normal to loop)
The torque is zero when $\phi = 0°$ (as shown here) or $\phi = 180°$. In both cases, $\vec{B}$ is perpendicular to the plane of the loop.
The loop is in stable equilibrium when $\phi = 0$; it is in unstable equilibrium when $\phi = 180°$.
$\vec{F}'$
$\vec{B}$
$\vec{F}$
$\vec{\mu}$
$-\vec{F}$
$-\vec{F}'$

The *total* force on the loop is zero because the forces on opposite sides cancel out in pairs.

The net force on a current loop in a uniform magnetic field is zero. However, the net torque is not in general equal to zero.

(You may find it helpful at this point to review the discussion of torque in Section 10.1.) The two forces $\vec{F}'$ and $-\vec{F}'$ in Fig. 27.31a lie along the same line and so give rise to zero net torque with respect to any point. The two forces $\vec{F}$ and $-\vec{F}$ lie along different lines, and each gives rise to a torque about the y-axis. According to the right-hand rule for determining the direction of torques, the vector torques due to $\vec{F}$ and $-\vec{F}$ are both in the $+y$-direction; hence the net vector torque $\vec{\tau}$ is in the $+y$-direction as well. The moment arm for each of these forces (equal to the perpendicular distance from the rotation axis to the line of action of the force) is $(b/2)\sin\phi$, so the torque due to each force has magnitude $F(b/2)\sin\phi$. If we use Eq. (27.21) for F, the magnitude of the net torque is

$$\tau = 2F(b/2)\sin\phi = (IBa)(b\sin\phi) \qquad (27.22)$$

The torque is greatest when $\phi = 90°$, $\vec{B}$ is in the plane of the loop, and the normal to this plane is perpendicular to $\vec{B}$ (Fig. 27.31b). The torque is zero when ϕ is $0°$ or $180°$ and the normal to the loop is parallel or antiparallel to the field (Fig. 27.31c). The value $\phi = 0°$ is a stable equilibrium position because the torque is zero there, and when the loop is rotated slightly from this position, the resulting torque tends to rotate it back toward $\phi = 0°$. The position $\phi = 180°$ is an *unstable* equilibrium position; if displaced slightly from this position, the loop tends to move farther away from $\phi = 180°$. Figure 27.31 shows rotation about the y-axis, but because the net force on the loop is zero, Eq. (27.22) for the torque is valid for *any* choice of axis.

The area A of the loop is equal to ab, so we can rewrite Eq. (27.22) as

$$\tau = IBA\sin\phi \quad \text{(magnitude of torque on a current loop)} \qquad (27.23)$$

The product IA is called the **magnetic dipole moment** or **magnetic moment** of the loop, for which we use the symbol μ (the Greek letter mu):

$$\mu = IA \tag{27.24}$$

It is analogous to the electric dipole moment introduced in Section 21.7. In terms of μ, the magnitude of the torque on a current loop is

$$\tau = \mu B \sin\phi \tag{27.25}$$

where ϕ is the angle between the normal to the loop (the direction of the vector area $\vec{A}$) and $\vec{B}$. The torque tends to rotate the loop in the direction of *decreasing* ϕ—that is, toward its stable equilibrium position in which the loop lies in the *xy*-plane perpendicular to the direction of the field $\vec{B}$ (Fig. 27.31c). A current loop, or any other body that experiences a magnetic torque given by Eq. (27.25), is also called a **magnetic dipole.**

Magnetic Torque: Vector Form

We can also define a vector magnetic moment $\vec{\mu}$ with magnitude IA: this is shown in Fig. 27.31. The direction of $\vec{\mu}$ is defined to be perpendicular to the plane of the loop, with a sense determined by a right-hand rule, as shown in Fig. 27.32. Wrap the fingers of your right hand around the perimeter of the loop in the direction of the current. Then extend your thumb so that it is perpendicular to the plane of the loop; its direction is the direction $\vec{\mu}$ (and of the vector area $\vec{A}$ of the loop). The torque is greatest when $\vec{\mu}$ and $\vec{B}$ are perpendicular and is zero when they are parallel or antiparallel. In the stable equilibrium position, $\vec{\mu}$ and $\vec{B}$ are parallel.

Finally, we can express this interaction in terms of the torque vector $\vec{\tau}$, which we used for *electric*-dipole interactions in Section 21.7. From Eq. (27.25) the magnitude of $\vec{\tau}$ is equal to the magnitude of $\vec{\mu} \times \vec{B}$, and reference to Fig. 27.31 shows that the directions are also the same. So we have

$$\vec{\tau} = \vec{\mu} \times \vec{B} \quad \text{(vector torque on a current loop)} \tag{27.26}$$

This result is directly analogous to the result we found in Section 21.7 for the torque exerted by an *electric* field $\vec{E}$ on an *electric* dipole with dipole moment $\vec{p} \cdot \vec{\tau} = \vec{p} \times \vec{E}$.

27.32 The right-hand rule determines the direction of the magnetic moment of a current-carrying loop. This is also the direction of the loop's area vector $\vec{A}$; $\vec{\mu} = I\vec{A}$ is a vector equation.

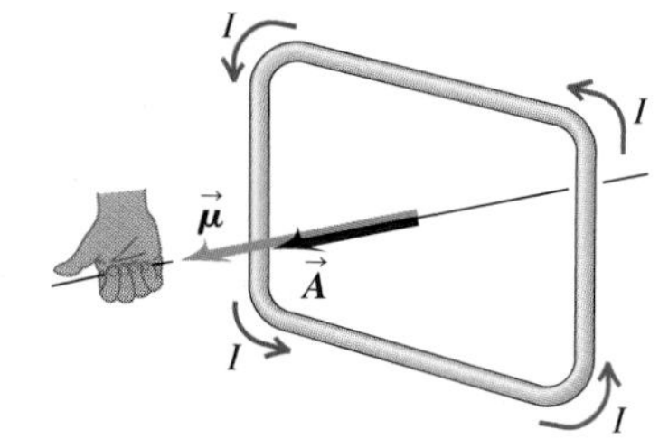

Potential Energy for a Magnetic Dipole

When a magnetic dipole changes orientation in a magnetic field, the field does work on it. In an infinitesimal angular displacement $d\phi$ the work dW is given by $\tau d\phi$, and there is a corresponding change in potential energy. As the above discussion suggests, the potential energy is least when $\vec{\mu}$ and $\vec{B}$ are parallel and greatest when they are antiparallel. To find an expression for the potential energy U as a function of orientation, we can make use of the beautiful symmetry between the electric and magnetic dipole interactions. The torque on an *electric* dipole in an *electric* field is $\vec{\tau} = \vec{p} \times \vec{E}$; we found in Section 21.7 that the corresponding potential energy is $U = -\vec{p} \cdot \vec{E}$. The torque on a *magnetic* dipole in a *magnetic* field is $\vec{\tau} = \vec{\mu} \times \vec{B}$, so we can conclude immediately that the corresponding potential energy is

$$U = -\vec{\mu} \cdot \vec{B} = -\mu B \cos\phi \quad \text{(potential energy for a magnetic dipole)} \tag{27.27}$$

With this definition, U is zero when the magnetic dipole moment is perpendicular to the magnetic field.

Magnetic Torque: Loops and Coils

Although we have derived Eqs. (27.21) through (27.27) for a rectangular current loop, all these relationships are valid for a plane loop of any shape at all. Any planar loop may be approximated as closely as we wish by a very large number of

27.33 The collection of rectangles exactly matches the irregular plane loop in the limit as the number of rectangles approaches infinity and the width of each rectangle approaches zero.

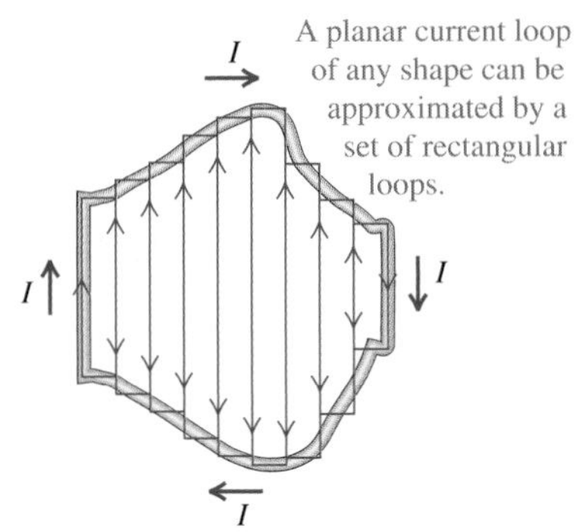

rectangular loops, as shown in Fig. 27.33. If these loops all carry equal currents in the same clockwise sense, then the forces and torques on the sides of two loops adjacent to each other cancel, and the only forces and torques that do not cancel are due to currents around the boundary. Thus all the above relationships are valid for a plane current loop of any shape, with the magnetic moment $\vec{\mu}$ given by $\vec{\mu} = I\vec{A}$.

We can also generalize this whole formulation to a coil consisting of N planar loops close together; the effect is simply to multiply each force, the magnetic moment, the torque, and the potential energy by a factor of N.

An arrangement of particular interest is the **solenoid,** a helical winding of wire, such as a coil wound on a circular cylinder (Fig. 27.34). If the windings are closely spaced, the solenoid can be approximated by a number of circular loops lying in planes at right angles to its long axis. The total torque on a solenoid in a magnetic field is simply the sum of the torques on the individual turns. For a solenoid with N turns in a uniform field B, the magnetic moment is $\mu = NIA$ and

$$\tau = NIAB\sin\phi \tag{27.28}$$

where ϕ is the angle between the axis of the solenoid and the direction of the field. The magnetic moment vector $\vec{\mu}$ is along the solenoid axis. The torque is greatest when the solenoid axis is perpendicular to the magnetic field and zero when they are parallel. The effect of this torque is to tend to rotate the solenoid into a position where its axis is parallel to the field. Solenoids are also useful as *sources* of magnetic field, as we'll discuss in Chapter 28.

27.34 The torque $\vec{\tau} = \vec{\mu} \times \vec{B}$ on this solenoid in a uniform magnetic field is directed straight into the page. An actual solenoid has many more turns, wrapped closely together.

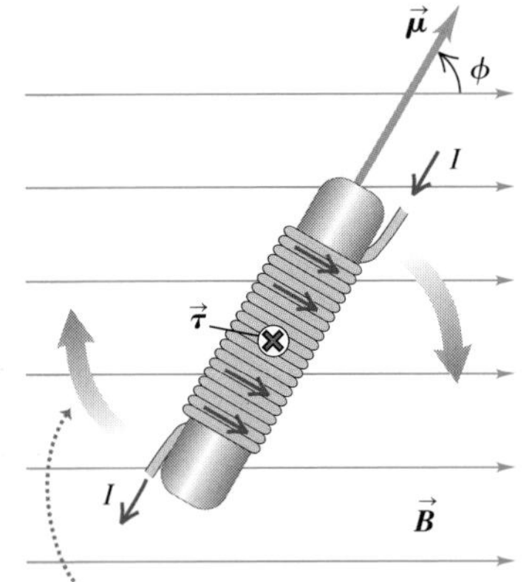

The torque tends to make the solenoid rotate clockwise in the plane of the page, aligning magnetic moment $\vec{\mu}$ with field $\vec{B}$.

The d'Arsonval galvanometer, described in Section 26.3, makes use of a magnetic torque on a coil carrying a current. As Fig. 26.14 shows, the magnetic field is not uniform but is *radial,* so the side thrusts on the coil are always perpendicular to its plane. Thus the angle ϕ in Eq. (27.28) is always 90°, and the magnetic torque is directly proportional to the current, no matter what the orientation of the coil. A restoring torque proportional to the angular displacement of the coil is provided by two hairsprings, which also serve as current leads to the coil. When current is supplied to the coil, it rotates along with its attached pointer until the restoring spring torque just balances the magnetic torque. Thus the pointer deflection is proportional to the current.

An important medical application of the torque on a magnetic dipole is *magnetic resonance imaging* (MRI). A patient is placed in a magnetic field of about 1.5 T, more than 10^4 times stronger than the earth's field. The nucleus of each hydrogen atom in the tissue to be imaged has a magnetic dipole moment, which experiences a torque that aligns it with the applied field. The tissue is then illuminated with radio waves of just the right frequency to flip these magnetic moments out of alignment. The extent to which these radio waves are absorbed in the tissue is proportional to the amount of hydrogen present. Hence hydrogen-rich soft tissue looks quite different from hydrogen-deficient bone, which makes MRI ideal for analyzing details in soft tissue that cannot be seen in x-ray images (see the image that opens this chapter).

Example 27.9 Magnetic torque on a circular coil

A circular coil 0.0500 m in radius, with 30 turns of wire, lies in a horizontal plane. It carries a current of 5.00 A in a counterclockwise sense when viewed from above. The coil is in a uniform magnetic field directed toward the right, with magnitude 1.20 T. Find the magnitudes of the magnetic moment and the torque on the coil.

SOLUTION

IDENTIFY: This problem uses the definition of magnetic moment and the expression for the torque on a magnetic dipole in a magnetic field.

SET UP: Figure 27.35 shows the situation. The magnitude μ of the magnetic moment of a single turn of wire is given in terms of the

27.35 Our sketch for this problem.

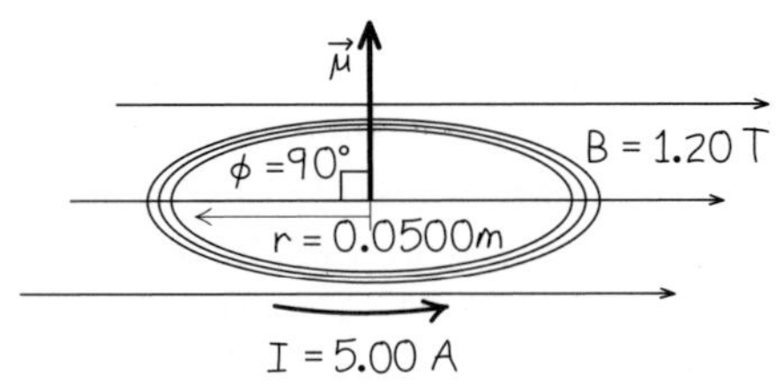

current and coil area by Eq. (27.24). For N turns, the magnetic moment is N times greater. The magnitude τ of the torque is found using Eq. (27.25).

EXECUTE: The area of the coil is

$$A = \pi r^2 = \pi(0.0500\text{ m})^2 = 7.85 \times 10^{-3}\text{ m}^2$$

The magnetic moment of each turn of the coil is

$$\mu = IA = (5.00\text{ A})(7.85 \times 10^{-3}\text{ m}^2) = 3.93 \times 10^{-2}\text{ A}\cdot\text{m}^2$$

and the total magnetic moment of all 30 turns is

$$\mu_{\text{total}} = (30)(3.93 \times 10^{-2}\text{ A}\cdot\text{m}^2) = 1.18\text{ A}\cdot\text{m}^2$$

The angle ϕ between the direction of $\vec{B}$ and the direction of $\vec{\mu}$ (which is along the normal to the plane of the coil) is 90°. From Eq. (27.25),

$$\tau = \mu_{\text{total}}B\sin\phi = (1.18\text{ A}\cdot\text{m}^2)(1.20\text{ T})(\sin 90°) = 1.41\text{ N}\cdot\text{m}$$

Alternatively, from Eq. (27.23), the torque on each turn of the coil is

$$\tau = IBA\sin\phi = (5.00\text{ A})(1.20\text{ T})(7.85 \times 10^{-3}\text{ m}^2)(\sin 90°) = 0.0471\text{ N}\cdot\text{m}$$

and the total torque on the coil is

$$\tau = (30)(0.0471\text{ N}\cdot\text{m}) = 1.41\text{ N}\cdot\text{m}$$

EVALUATE: The torque tends to rotate the right side of the coil down and the left side up, into a position where the normal to its plane is parallel to $\vec{B}$.

Example 27.10 Potential energy for a coil in a magnetic field

If the coil in Example 27.9 rotates from its initial position to a position where its magnetic moment is parallel to $\vec{B}$, what is the change in potential energy?

SOLUTION

IDENTIFY: The initial position is as shown in Fig. 27.35. In the final position, the coil is rotated 90° clockwise so that $\vec{\mu}$ and $\vec{B}$ are parallel $(\phi = 0)$.

SET UP: We calculate the potential energy for each orientation using Eq. (27.27). We then take the difference between the final and initial values to find the change in potential energy.

EXECUTE: From Eq. (27.27), the initial potential energy U_1 is

$$U_1 = -\mu_{\text{total}}B\cos\phi_1 = -(1.18\text{ A}\cdot\text{m}^2)(1.20\text{ T})(\cos 90°) = 0$$

and the final potential energy U_2 is

$$U_2 = -\mu_{\text{total}}B\cos\phi_2 = -(1.18\text{ A}\cdot\text{m}^2)(1.20\text{ T})(\cos 0°) = -1.41\text{ J}$$

The change in potential energy is $\Delta U = U_2 - U_1 = -1.41$ J.

EVALUATE: The potential energy decreases because the rotation is in the direction of the magnetic torque.

Magnetic Dipole in a Nonuniform Magnetic Field

We have seen that a current loop (that is, a magnetic dipole) experiences zero net force in a uniform magnetic field. Figure 27.36 shows two current loops in the *nonuniform* $\vec{B}$ field of a bar magnet; in both cases the net force on the loop is *not* zero. In Fig. 27.36a the magnetic moment $\vec{\mu}$ is in the direction opposite to the field, and the force $d\vec{F} = I\,d\vec{l} \times \vec{B}$ on a segment of the loop has both a radial component and a component to the right. When these forces are summed to find the net force $\vec{F}$ on the loop, the radial components cancel so that the net force is to the right, away from the magnet. Note that in this case the force is toward the region where the field lines are farther apart and the field magnitude B is less. The polarity of the bar magnet is reversed in Fig. 27.36b, so $\vec{\mu}$ and $\vec{B}$ are parallel; now the net force on the loop is to the left, toward the region of greater field magnitude near the magnet. Later in this section we'll use these observations to explain why bar magnets can pick up unmagnetized iron objects.

27.36 Forces on current loops in a nonuniform $\vec{B}$ field. In each case the axis of the bar magnet is perpendicular to the plane of the loop and passes through the center of the loop.

(a) Net force on this coil is away from north pole of magnet.

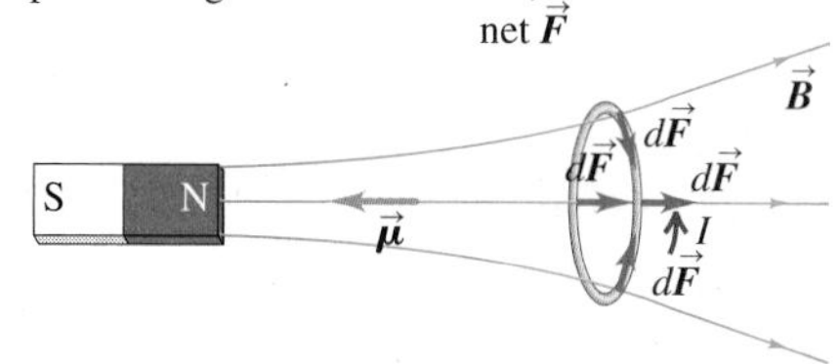

(b) Net force on same coil is toward south pole of magnet.

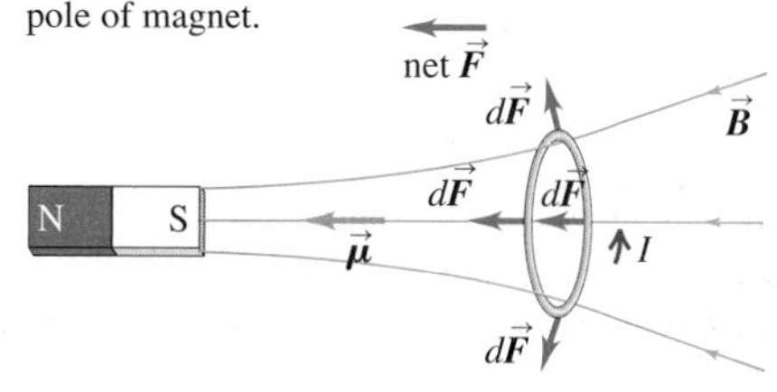

Magnetic Dipoles and How Magnets Work

The behavior of a solenoid in a magnetic field (see Fig. 27.34) resembles that of a bar magnet or compass needle; if free to turn, both the solenoid and the magnet orient themselves with their axes parallel to the $\vec{B}$ field. In both cases this is due to the interaction of moving electric charges with a magnetic field; the difference is that in a bar magnet the motion of charge occurs on the microscopic scale of the atom.

Think of an electron as being like a spinning ball of charge. In this analogy the circulation of charge around the spin axis is like a current loop, and so the electron has a net magnetic moment. (This analogy, while helpful, is inexact; an electron

27.37 (a) An unmagnetized piece of iron. (Only a few representative atomic moments are shown.) (b) A magnetized piece of iron (bar magnet). The net magnetic moment of the bar magnet points from its south pole to its north pole. (c) A bar magnet in a magnetic field.

(a) Unmagnetized iron: magnetic moments are oriented randomly.

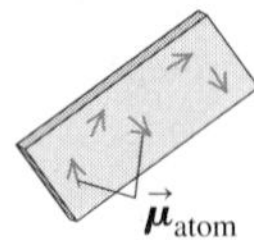

(b) In a bar magnet, the magnetic moments are aligned.

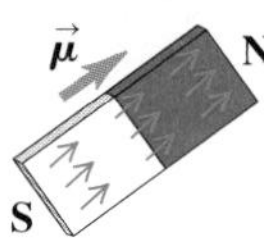

(c) A magnetic field creates a torque on the bar magnet that tends to align its dipole moment with the $\vec{B}$ field.

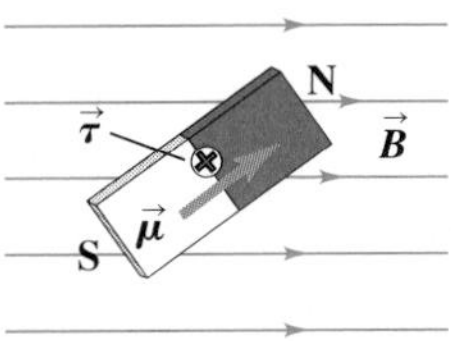

isn't really a spinning sphere. A full explanation of the origin of an electron's magnetic moment involves quantum mechanics, which is beyond our scope here.) In an iron atom a substantial fraction of the electron magnetic moments align with each other, and the atom has a nonzero magnetic moment. (By contrast, the atoms of most elements have little or no net magnetic moment.) In an unmagnetized piece of iron there is no overall alignment of the magnetic moments of the atoms; their vector sum is zero, and the net magnetic moment is zero (Fig. 27.37a). But in an iron bar magnet the magnetic moments of many of the atoms are parallel, and there is a substantial net magnetic moment $\vec{\mu}$ (Fig. 27.37b). If the magnet is placed in a magnetic field $\vec{B}$, the field exerts a torque given by Eq. (27.26) that tends to align $\vec{\mu}$ with $\vec{B}$ (Fig. 27.37c). A bar magnet tends to align with a $\vec{B}$ field so that a line from the south pole to the north pole of the magnet is in the direction of $\vec{B}$; hence the real significance of a magnet's north and south poles is that they represent the head and tail, respectively, of the magnet's dipole moment $\vec{\mu}$.

The torque experienced by a current loop in a magnetic field also explains how an unmagnetized iron object like that in Fig. 27.37a becomes magnetized. If an unmagnetized iron paper clip is placed next to a powerful magnet, the magnetic moments of the paper clip's atoms tend to align with the $\vec{B}$ field of the magnet. When the paper clip is removed, its atomic dipoles tend to remain aligned, and the paper clip has a net magnetic moment. The paper clip can be demagnetized by being dropped on the floor or heated; the added internal energy jostles and re-randomizes the atomic dipoles.

The magnetic-dipole picture of a bar magnet explains the attractive and repulsive forces between bar magnets shown in Fig. 27.1. The magnetic moment $\vec{\mu}$ of a bar magnet points from its south pole to its north pole, so the current loops in Figs. 27.36a and 27.36b are both equivalent to a magnet with its north pole on the left. Hence the situation in Fig. 27.36a is equivalent to two bar magnets with their north poles next to each other; the resultant force is repulsive, just as in Fig. 27.1b. In Fig. 27.36b we again have the equivalent of two bar magnets end to end, but with the south pole of the left-hand magnet next to the north pole of the right-hand magnet. The resultant force is attractive, as in Fig. 27.1a.

Finally, we can explain how a magnet can attract an unmagnetized iron object (see Fig. 27.2). It's a two-step process. First, the atomic magnetic moments of the iron tend to align with the $\vec{B}$ field of the magnet, so the iron acquires a net magnetic dipole moment $\vec{\mu}$ parallel to the field. Second, the nonuniform field of the magnet attracts the magnetic dipole. Figure 27.38a shows an example. The north pole of the magnet is closer to the nail (which contains iron), and the magnetic dipole produced in the nail is equivalent to a loop with a current that circulates in a direction opposite to that shown in Fig. 27.36a. Hence the net magnetic force on the nail is opposite to the force on the loop in Fig. 27.36a, and the nail is attracted toward the magnet. Changing the polarity of the magnet, as in Fig. 27.38b, reverses the directions of both $\vec{B}$ and $\vec{\mu}$. The situation is now equivalent to that shown in Fig. 27.36b; like the loop in that figure, the nail is attracted toward the magnet. Hence a previously unmagnetized object containing iron is attracted to *either* pole of a magnet. By contrast, objects made of brass, aluminum, or wood hardly respond at all to a magnet; the atomic magnetic dipoles of these materials, if present at all, have less tendency to align with an external field.

Our discussion of how magnets and pieces of iron interact has just scratched the surface of a diverse subject known as *magnetic properties of materials.* We'll discuss these properties in more depth in Section 28.8.

27.38 A bar magnet attracts an unmagnetized iron nail in two steps. First, the $\vec{B}$ field of the bar magnet gives rise to a net magnetic moment in the nail. Second, because the field of the bar magnet is not uniform, this magnetic dipole is attracted toward the magnet. The attraction is the same whether the nail is closer to (a) the magnet's north pole or (b) the magnet's south pole.

(a)

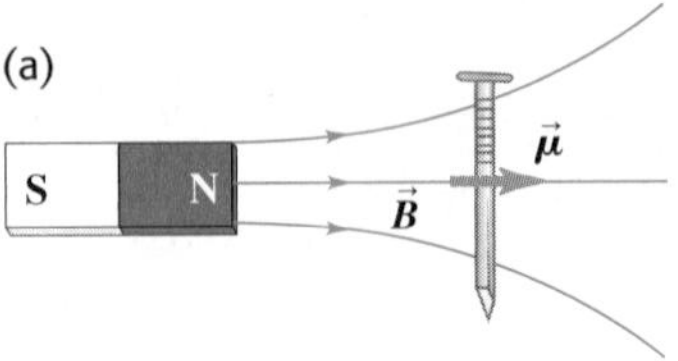

(b)

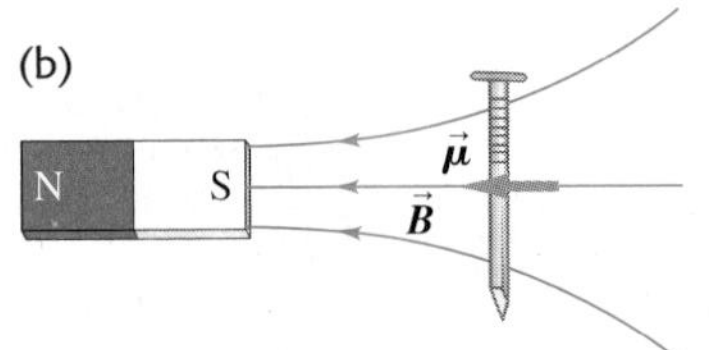

Test Your Understanding of Section 27.7 Figure 27.13c depicts the magnetic field lines due to a circular current-carrying loop. (a) What is the direction of the magnetic moment of this loop? (b) Which side of the loop is equivalent to the north pole of a magnet, and which side is equivalent to the south pole?

*27.8 The Direct-Current Motor

Electric motors play an important role in contemporary society. In a motor a magnetic torque acts on a current-carrying conductor, and electric energy is converted to mechanical energy. As an example, let's look at a simple type of direct-current (dc) motor, shown in Fig. 27.39.

The moving part of the motor is the *rotor,* a length of wire formed into an open-ended loop and free to rotate about an axis. The ends of the rotor wires are attached to circular conducting segments that form a *commutator.* In Fig. 27.39a, each of the two commutator segments makes contact with one of the terminals, or *brushes,* of an external circuit that includes a source of emf. This causes a current to flow into the rotor on one side, shown in red, and out of the rotor on the other side, shown in blue. Hence the rotor is a current loop with a magnetic moment $\vec{\mu}$. The rotor lies between opposing poles of a permanent magnet, so there is a magnetic field $\vec{B}$ that exerts a torque $\vec{\tau} = \vec{\mu} \times \vec{B}$ on the rotor. For the rotor orientation shown in Fig. 27.39a the torque causes the rotor to turn counterclockwise, in the direction that will align $\vec{\mu}$ with $\vec{B}$.

In Fig. 27.39b the rotor has rotated by 90° from its orientation in Fig. 27.39a. If the current through the rotor were constant, the rotor would now be in its equilibrium orientation; it would simply oscillate around this orientation. But here's where the commutator comes into play; each brush is now in contact with *both* segments of the commutator. There is no potential difference between the commutators, so at this instant no current flows through the rotor, and the magnetic moment is zero. The rotor continues to rotate counterclockwise because of its inertia, and current again flows through the rotor as in Fig. 27.39c. But now current enters on the *blue* side of the rotor and exits on the *red* side, just the opposite of the situation in Fig. 27.39a. While the direction of the current has reversed with respect to the rotor, the rotor itself has rotated 180° and the magnetic moment $\vec{\mu}$ is in the same direction with respect to the magnetic field. Hence the magnetic torque $\vec{\tau}$ is in the same direction in Fig. 27.39c as in Fig. 27.39a. Thanks to the commutator, the current reverses after every 180° of rotation, so the torque is always in the direction to rotate the rotor counterclockwise. When the motor has come "up to speed," the average magnetic torque is just balanced by an opposing torque due to air resistance, friction in the rotor bearings, and friction between the commutator and brushes.

The simple motor shown in Fig. 27.39 has only a single turn of wire in its rotor. In practical motors, the rotor has many turns; this increases the magnetic

27.39 Schematic diagram of a simple dc motor. The rotor is a wire loop that is free to rotate about an axis; the rotor ends are attached to the two curved conductors that form the commutator. (The rotor halves are colored red and blue for clarity.) The commutator segments are insulated from one another.

(a) Brushes are aligned with commutator segments.

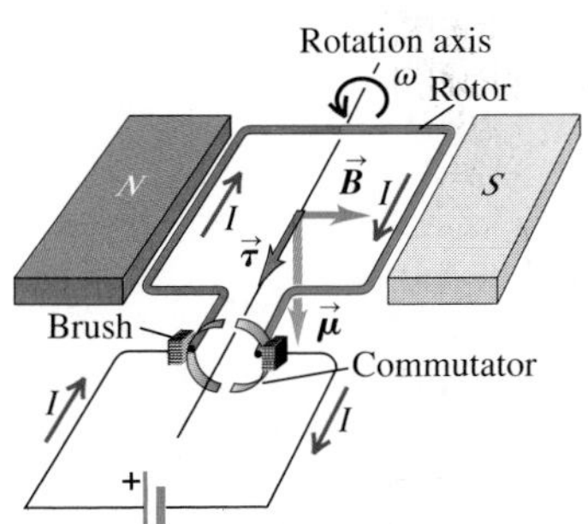

- Current flows into the red side of the rotor and out of the blue side.
- Therefore the magnetic torque causes the rotor to spin counterclockwise.

(b) Rotor has turned 90°.

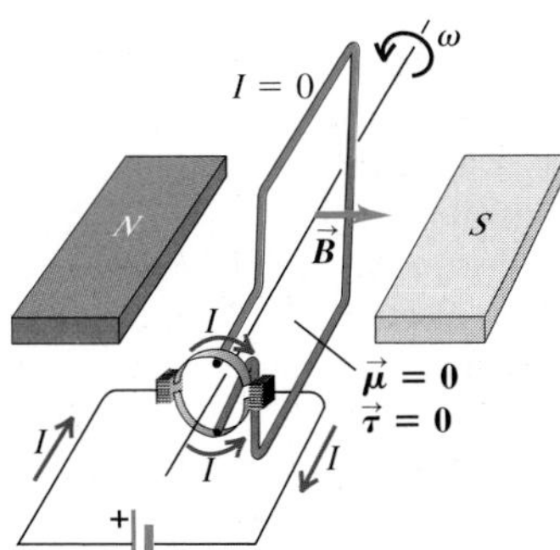

- Each brush is in contact with both commutator segments, so the current bypasses the rotor altogether.
- No magnetic torque acts on the rotor.

(c) Rotor has turned 180°.

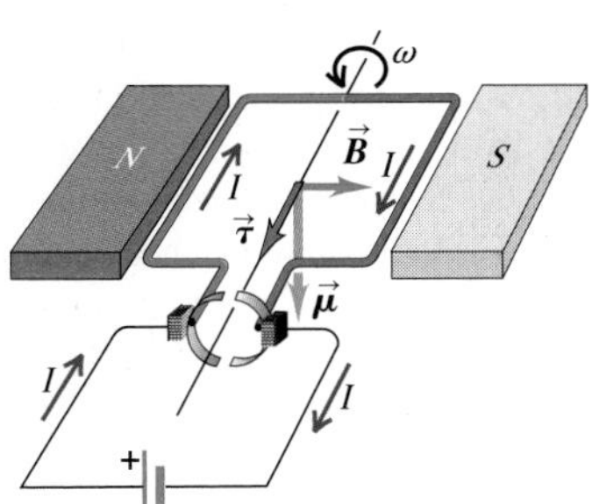

- The brushes are again aligned with commutator segments. This time the current flows into the blue side of the rotor and out of the red side.
- Therefore the magnetic torque again causes the rotor to spin counterclockwise.

27.40 This motor from a computer disk drive has 12 current-carrying coils. They interact with permanent magnets on the turntable (not shown) to make the turntable rotate. (This design is the reverse of the design in Fig. 27.39, in which the permanent magnets are stationary and the coil rotates.) Because there are multiple coils, the magnetic torque is very nearly constant and the turntable spins at a very constant rate.

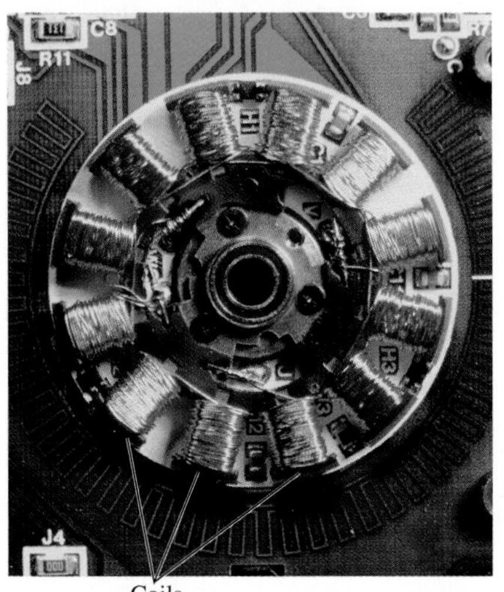

moment and the torque so that the motor can spin larger loads. The torque can also be increased by using a stronger magnetic field, which is why many motor designs use electromagnets instead of a permanent magnet. Another drawback of the simple design in Fig. 27.39 is that the magnitude of the torque rises and falls as the rotor spins. This can be remedied by having the rotor include several independent coils of wire oriented at different angles (Fig. 27.40).

Power for Electric Motors

Because a motor converts electric energy to mechanical energy or work, it requires electric energy input. If the potential difference between its terminals is V_{ab} and the current is I, then the power input is $P = V_{ab}I$. Even if the motor coils have negligible resistance, there must be a potential difference between the terminals if P is to be different from zero. This potential difference results principally from magnetic forces exerted on the currents in the conductors of the rotor as they rotate through the magnetic field. The associated electromotive force $\mathcal{E}$ is called an *induced* emf; it is also called a *back* emf because its sense is opposite to that of the current. In Chapter 29 we will study induced emfs resulting from motion of conductors in magnetic fields.

In a *series* motor the rotor is connected in series with the electromagnet that produces the magnetic field; in a *shunt* motor they are connected in parallel. In a series motor with internal resistance r, V_{ab} is greater than $\mathcal{E}$, and the difference is the potential drop Ir across the internal resistance. That is,

$$V_{ab} = \mathcal{E} + Ir \tag{27.29}$$

Because the magnetic force is proportional to velocity, $\mathcal{E}$ is *not* constant but is proportional to the speed of rotation of the rotor.

Example 27.11 A series dc motor

A dc motor with its rotor and field coils connected in series has an internal resistance of 2.00 Ω. When running at full load on a 120-V line, it draws a current of 4.00 A. (a) What is the emf in the rotor? (b)What is the power delivered to the motor? (c) What is the rate of dissipation of energy in the resistance of the motor? (d) What is the mechanical power developed? (e) What is the efficiency of the motor? (f) What happens if the machine the motor is driving jams and the rotor suddenly stops turning?

SOLUTION

IDENTIFY: This problem uses the ideas of power and potential drop in a series dc motor.

SET UP: We are given the internal resistance $r = 2.00\ \Omega$, the voltage $V_{ab} = 120$ V across the motor, and the current $I = 4.00$ A through the motor. We use Eq. (27.29) to determine the emf $\mathcal{E}$ from these quantities. The power delivered to the motor is $V_{ab}I$, the rate of energy dissipation is I^2r, and the power output by the motor is the difference between the power input and the power dissipated. The efficiency e is the ratio of mechanical power output to electric power input.

EXECUTE: (a) From Eq. (27.29), $V_{ab} = \mathcal{E} + Ir$, we have

$$120\text{ V} = \mathcal{E} + (4.0\text{ A})(2.0\ \Omega) \quad \text{and so} \quad \mathcal{E} = 112\text{ V}$$

(b) The power delivered to the motor from the source is

$$P_{\text{input}} = V_{ab}I = (120\text{ V})(4.0\text{ A}) = 480\text{ W}$$

(c) The power dissipated in the resistance r is

$$P_{\text{dissipated}} = I^2r = (4.0\text{ A})^2(2.0\ \Omega) = 32\text{ W}$$

(d) The mechanical power output is the electric power input minus the rate of dissipation of energy in the motor's resistance (assuming that there are no other power losses):

$$P_{\text{output}} = P_{\text{input}} - P_{\text{dissipated}} = 480\text{ W} - 32\text{ W} = 448\text{ W}$$

(e) The efficiency e is the ratio of mechanical power output to electric power input:

$$e = \frac{P_{\text{output}}}{P_{\text{input}}} = \frac{448\text{ W}}{480\text{ W}} = 0.93 = 93\%$$

(f) With the rotor stalled, the back emf $\mathcal{E}$ (which is proportional to rotor speed) goes to zero. From Eq. (27.29) the current becomes

$$I = \frac{V_{ab}}{r} = \frac{120\text{ V}}{2.0\ \Omega} = 60\text{ A}$$

and the power dissipated in the resistance r becomes

$$P_{\text{dissipated}} = I^2r = (60\text{ A})^2(2\ \Omega) = 7200\text{ W}$$

EVALUATE: If this massive overload doesn't blow a fuse or trip a circuit breaker, the coils will quickly melt. When the motor is first turned on, there's a momentary surge of current until the motor picks up speed. This surge causes greater-than-usual voltage drops ($V = IR$) in the power lines supplying the current. Similar effects are responsible for the momentary dimming of lights in a house when an air conditioner or dishwasher motor starts.

Test Your Understanding of Section 27.8 In the circuit shown in Fig. 27.39, you add a switch in series with the source of emf so that the current can be turned on and off. When you close the switch and allow current to flow, will the rotor begin to turn no matter what its original orientation?

*27.9 The Hall Effect

The reality of the forces acting on the moving charges in a conductor in a magnetic field is strikingly demonstrated by the *Hall effect,* an effect analogous to the transverse deflection of an electron beam in a magnetic field in vacuum. (The effect was discovered by the American physicist Edwin Hall in 1879 while he was still a graduate student.) To describe this effect, let's consider a conductor in the form of a flat strip, as shown in Fig. 27.41. The current is in the direction of the $+x$-axis and there is a uniform magnetic field $\vec{B}$ perpendicular to the plane of the strip, in the $+y$-direction. The drift velocity of the moving charges (charge magnitude $|q|$) has magnitude v_d. Figure 27.41a shows the case of negative charges, such as electrons in a metal, and Fig. 27.41b shows positive charges. In both cases the magnetic force is upward, just as the magnetic force on a conductor is the same whether the moving charges are positive or negative. In either case a moving charge is driven toward the *upper* edge of the strip by the magnetic force $F_z = |q|v_dB$.

27.41 Forces on charge carriers in a conductor in a magnetic field.

(a) Negative charge carriers (electrons)

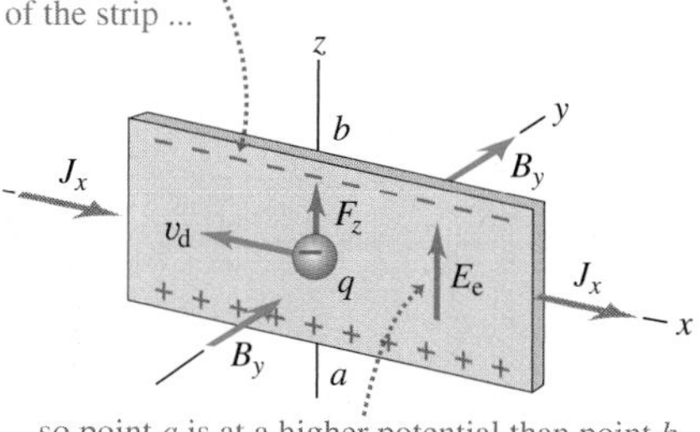
The charge carriers are pushed toward the top of the strip ...
z
b
y
J_x
B_y
F_z
v_d
q
E_e
J_x
x
B_y
a
... so point a is at a higher potential than point b.

(b) Positive charge carriers

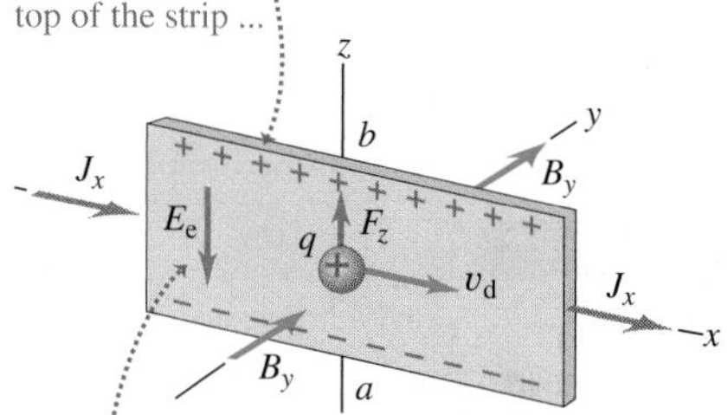
The charge carriers are again pushed toward the top of the strip ...
z
b
y
J_x
B_y
E_e
F_z
q
v_d
J_x
x
B_y
a
... so the polarity of the potential difference is opposite to that for negative charge carriers.

If the charge carriers are electrons, as in Fig. 27.41a, an excess negative charge accumulates at the upper edge of the strip, leaving an excess positive charge at its lower edge. This accumulation continues until the resulting transverse electrostatic field $\vec{E}_e$ becomes large enough to cause a force (magnitude $|q|E_e$) that is equal and opposite to the magnetic force (magnitude $|q|v_dB$). After that, there is no longer any net transverse force to deflect the moving charges. This electric field causes a transverse potential difference between opposite edges of the strip, called the *Hall voltage* or the *Hall emf.* The polarity depends on whether the moving charges are positive or negative. Experiments show that for metals the upper edge of the strip in Fig. 27.41a *does* become negatively charged, showing that the charge carriers in a metal are indeed negative electrons.

However, if the charge carriers are *positive,* as in Fig. 27.41b, then *positive* charge accumulates at the upper edge, and the potential difference is *opposite* to the situation with negative charges. Soon after the discovery of the Hall effect in 1879, it was observed that some materials, particularly some *semiconductors,* show a Hall emf opposite to that of the metals, as if their charge carriers were positively charged. We now know that these materials conduct by a process known as *hole conduction.* Within such a material there are locations, called *holes,* that would normally be occupied by an electron but are actually empty. A missing negative charge is equivalent to a positive charge. When an electron moves in one direction to fill a hole, it leaves another hole behind it. The hole migrates in the direction opposite to that of the electron.

In terms of the coordinate axes in Fig. 27.41b, the electrostatic field $\vec{E}_e$ for the positive-q case is in the $-z$-direction; its z-component E_z is negative. The magnetic field is in the $+y$-direction, and we write it as B_y. The magnetic force (in the $+z$-direction) is qv_dB_y. The current density J_x is in the $+x$-direction. In the steady state, when the forces qE_z and qv_dB_y are equal in magnitude and opposite in direction,

$$qE_z + qv_dB_y = 0 \qquad \text{or} \qquad E_z = -v_dB_y$$

This confirms that when q is positive, E_z is negative. The current density J_x is

$$J_x = nqv_d$$

Eliminating v_d between these equations, we find

$$nq = \frac{-J_x B_y}{E_z} \quad \text{(Hall effect)} \qquad (27.30)$$

Note that this result (as well as the entire derivation) is valid for both positive and negative q. When q is negative, E_z is positive, and conversely.

We can measure J_x, B_y, and E_z, so we can compute the product nq. In both metals and semiconductors, q is equal in magnitude to the electron charge, so the Hall effect permits a direct measurement of n, the concentration of current-carrying charges in the material. The *sign* of the charges is determined by the polarity of the Hall emf, as we have described.

The Hall effect can also be used for a direct measurement of electron drift speed v_d in metals. As we saw in Chapter 25, these speeds are very small, often of the order of 1 mm/s or less. If we move the entire conductor in the opposite direction to the current with a speed equal to the drift speed, then the electrons are at rest with respect to the magnetic field, and the Hall emf disappears. Thus the conductor speed needed to make the Hall emf vanish is equal to the drift speed.

Example 27.12 Using the Hall effect

You place a slab of copper, 2.0 mm thick and 1.50 cm wide, in a uniform magnetic field with magnitude 0.40 T, as shown in Fig. 27.41a. When you run a 75-A current in the $+x$-direction, you find by careful measurement that the potential at the bottom of the slab is 0.81 μV higher than at the top. From this measurement, determine the concentration of mobile electrons in copper.

SOLUTION

IDENTIFY: This problem describes a Hall-effect experiment.

SET UP: We use Eq. (27.30) to determine the mobile electron concentration n.

EXECUTE: First we find the current density J_x and the electric field E_z:

$$J_x = \frac{I}{A} = \frac{75\text{ A}}{(2.0 \times 10^{-3}\text{ m})(1.50 \times 10^{-2}\text{ m})} = 2.5 \times 10^6\text{ A/m}^2$$

$$E_z = \frac{V}{d} = \frac{0.81 \times 10^{-6}\text{ V}}{1.5 \times 10^{-2}\text{ m}} = 5.4 \times 10^{-5}\text{ V/m}$$

Then, from Eq. (27.30),

$$n = \frac{-J_x B_y}{qE_z} = \frac{-(2.5 \times 10^6\text{ A/m}^2)(0.40\text{ T})}{(-1.60 \times 10^{-19}\text{ C})(5.4 \times 10^{-5}\text{ V/m})}$$
$$= 11.6 \times 10^{28}\text{ m}^{-3}$$

EVALUATE: The actual value of n for copper is $8.5 \times 10^{28}\text{ m}^{-3}$, which shows that the simple model of the Hall effect in this section, ignoring quantum effects and electron interactions with the ions, must be used with caution. This example also shows that with good conductors, the Hall emf is very small even with large current densities. Hall-effect devices for magnetic-field measurements and other purposes use semiconductor materials, for which moderate current densities give much larger Hall emfs.

Test Your Understanding of Section 27.9 A copper wire of square cross section is oriented vertically. The four sides of the wire face north, south, east, and west. There is a uniform magnetic field directed from east to west, and the wire carries current downward. Which side of the wire is at the highest electric potential? (i) north side; (ii) south side; (iii) east side; (iv) west side.

CHAPTER 27 SUMMARY

Magnetic forces: Magnetic interactions are fundamentally interactions between moving charged particles. These interactions are described by the vector magnetic field, denoted by $\vec{B}$. A particle with charge q moving with velocity $\vec{v}$ in a magnetic field $\vec{B}$ experiences a force $\vec{F}$ that is perpendicular to both $\vec{v}$ and $\vec{B}$. The SI unit of magnetic field is the tesla $(1\ \text{T} = 1\ \text{N/A}\cdot\text{m})$. (See Example 27.1.)

$$\vec{F} = q\vec{v} \times \vec{B} \qquad (27.2)$$

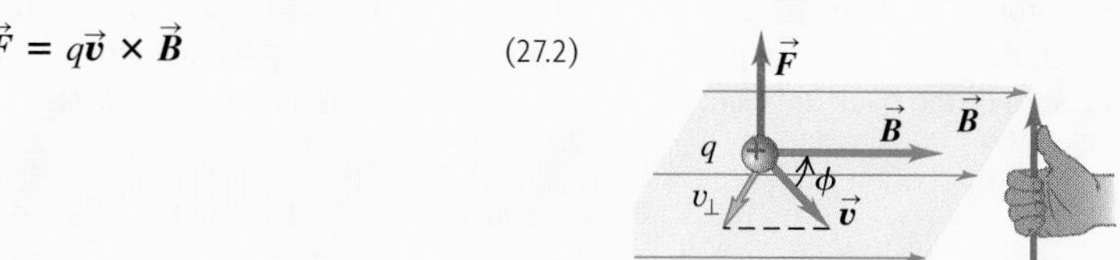

Magnetic field and flux: A magnetic field can be represented graphically by magnetic field lines. At each point a magnetic field line is tangent to the direction of $\vec{B}$ at that point. Where field lines are close together the field magnitude is large, and vice versa. Magnetic flux Φ_B through an area is defined in an analogous way to electric flux. The SI unit of magnetic flux is the weber $(1\ \text{Wb} = 1\ \text{T}\cdot\text{m}^2)$. The net magnetic flux through any closed surface is zero (Gauss's law for magnetism). As a result, magnetic field lines always close on themselves. (See Example 27.2.)

$$\Phi_B = \int B_\perp\, dA = \int B\cos\phi\, dA = \int \vec{B}\cdot d\vec{A} \qquad (27.6)$$

$$\oint \vec{B}\cdot d\vec{A} = 0 \quad \text{(closed surface)} \qquad (27.8)$$

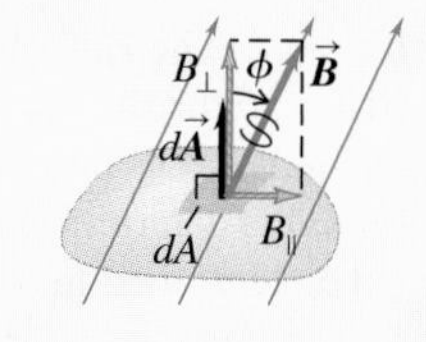

Motion in a magnetic field: The magnetic force is always perpendicular to $\vec{v}$; a particle moving under the action of a magnetic field alone moves with constant speed. In a uniform field, a particle with initial velocity perpendicular to the field moves in a circle with radius R that depends on the magnetic field strength B and the particle mass m, speed v, and charge q. (See Examples 27.3 and 27.4.)

Crossed electric and magnetic fields can be used as a velocity selector. The electric and magnetic forces exactly cancel when $v = E/B$. (See Examples 27.5 and 27.6.)

$$R = \frac{mv}{|q|B} \qquad (27.11)$$

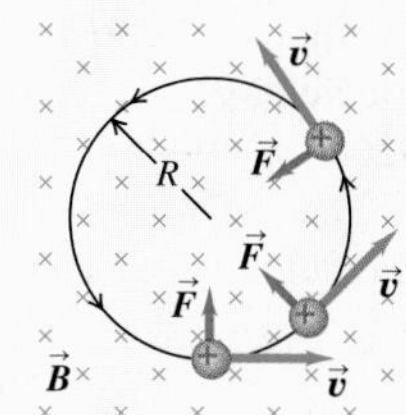

Magnetic force on a conductor: A straight segment of a conductor carrying current I in a uniform magnetic field $\vec{B}$ experiences a force $\vec{F}$ that is perpendicular to both $\vec{B}$ and the vector $\vec{l}$, which points in the direction of the current and has magnitude equal to the length of the segment. A similar relationship gives the force $d\vec{F}$ on an infinitesimal current-carrying segment $d\vec{l}$ (See Examples 27.7 and 27.8.)

$$\vec{F} = I\vec{l} \times \vec{B} \qquad (27.19)$$

$$d\vec{F} = I\, d\vec{l} \times \vec{B} \qquad (27.20)$$

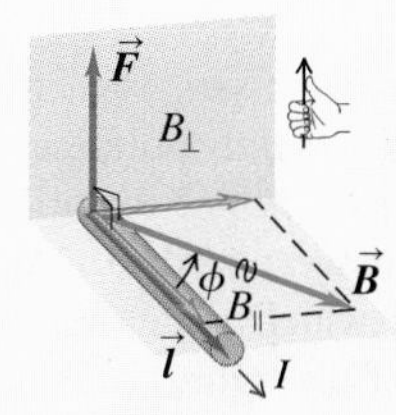

Magnetic torque: A current loop with area A and current I in a uniform magnetic field $\vec{B}$ experiences no net magnetic force, but does experience a magnetic torque of magnitude τ. The vector torque $\vec{\tau}$ can be expressed in terms of the magnetic moment $\vec{\mu} = I\vec{A}$ of the loop, as can the potential energy U of a magnetic moment in a magnetic field $\vec{B}$. The magnetic moment of a loop depends only on the current and the area; it is independent of the shape of the loop. (See Examples 27.9 and 27.10.)

$$\tau = IBA\sin\phi \qquad (27.23)$$

$$\vec{\tau} = \vec{\mu} \times \vec{B} \qquad (27.26)$$

$$U = -\vec{\mu}\cdot\vec{B} = -\mu B\cos\phi \qquad (27.27)$$

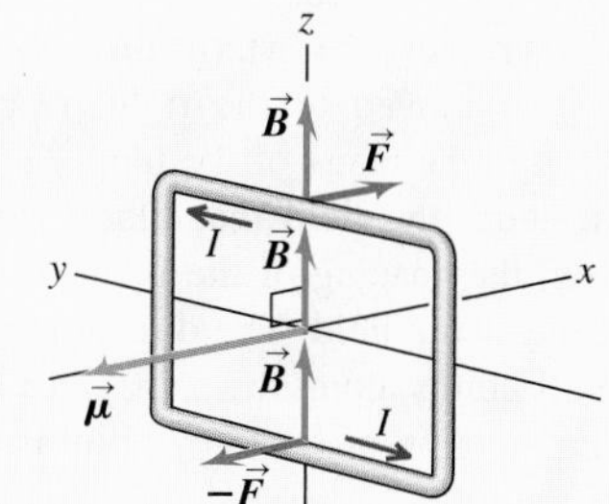

Electric motors: In a dc motor a magnetic field exerts a torque on a current in the rotor. Motion of the rotor through the magnetic field causes an induced emf called a back emf. For a series motor, in which the rotor coil is in parallel with coils that produce the magnetic field, the terminal voltage is the sum of the back emf and the drop Ir across the internal resistance. (See Example 27.11.)

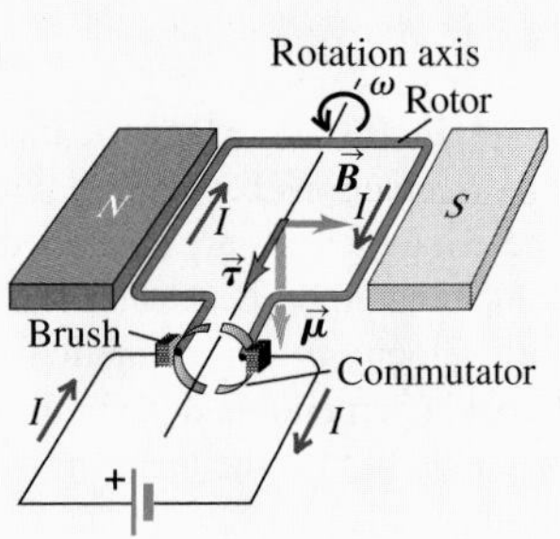

The Hall effect: The Hall effect is a potential difference perpendicular to the direction of current in a conductor, when the conductor is placed in a magnetic field. The Hall potential is determined by the requirement that the associated electric field must just balance the magnetic force on a moving charge. Hall-effect measurements can be used to determine the sign of charge carriers and their concentration n. (See Example 27.12.)

$$nq = \frac{-J_x B_y}{E_z} \qquad (27.30)$$

Key Terms

permanent magnet, *917*
magnetic monopole, *918*
magnetic field, *918*
tesla, *920*
gauss, *920*
magnetic field line, *922*
magnetic flux, *923*
weber, *924*
magnetic flux density, *925*
cyclotron frequency, *926*
mass spectrometer, *930*
isotope, *931*
magnetic dipole moment, *937*
magnetic moment, *937*
magnetic dipole, *937*
solenoid, *938*

Answer to Chapter Opening Question ?

In MRI the nuclei of hydrogen atoms within soft tissue act like miniature current loops whose magnetic moments align with an applied field. See Section 27.7 for details.

Answers to Test Your Understanding Questions

27.1 Answer: yes When a magnet is cut apart, each part has a north and south pole (see Fig. 27.4). Hence the small red part behaves much like the original, full-sized compass needle.

27.2 Answer: path 3 Applying the right-hand rule to the vectors $\vec{v}$ (which points to the right) and $\vec{B}$ (which points into the plane of the figure) says that the force $\vec{F} = q\vec{v} \times \vec{B}$ on a *positive* charge would point *upward.* Since the charge is *negative,* the force points *downward* and the particle follows a trajectory that curves downward.

27.3 Answer: (a) (ii), (b) no The magnitude of $\vec{B}$ would increase as you moved to the right, reaching a maximum as you pass through the plane of the loop. As you moved beyond the plane of the loop, the field magnitude would decrease. You can tell this from the spacing of the field lines: The closer the field lines, the stronger the field. The direction of the field would be to the right at all points along the path, since the path is along a field line and the direction of $\vec{B}$ at any point is tangent to the field line through that point.

27.4 Answers: (a) (ii), (b) (i) The radius of the orbit as given by Eq. (27.11) is directly proportional to the speed, so doubling the particle speed causes the radius to double as well. The particle has twice as far to travel to complete one orbit but is traveling at double the speed, so the time for one orbit is unchanged. This result also follows from Eq. (27.12), which states that the angular speed ω is independent of the linear speed v. Hence the time per orbit, $T = 2\pi/\omega$, likewise does not depend on v.

27.5 Answer: (iii) From Eq. (27.13), the speed $v = E/B$ at which particles travel straight through the velocity selector does not depend on the magnitude or sign of the charge or the mass of the particle. All that is required is that the particles (in this case, ions) have a nonzero charge.

27.6 Answer: A This orientation will cause current to flow clockwise around the circuit and hence through the conducting bar in the direction from the top to the bottom of the figure. From the right-hand rule, the magnetic force $\vec{F} = I\vec{l} \times \vec{B}$ on the bar will then point to the right.

27.7 Answers: (a) to the right; (b) north pole on the right, south pole on the left If you wrap the fingers of your right hand around the coil in the direction of the current, your right thumb points to the right (perpendicular to the plane of the coil). This is the direction of the magnetic moment $\vec{\mu}$. The magnetic moment points from the south pole to the north pole, so the right side of the loop is equivalent to a north pole and the left side is equivalent to a south pole.

27.8 Answer: no The rotor will not begin to turn when the switch is closed if the rotor is initially oriented as shown in Fig. 27.39b. In this case there is no current through the rotor and hence no magnetic torque. This situation can be remedied by using multiple rotor coils oriented at different angles around the rotation axis. With this arrangement, there is always a magnetic torque no matter what the orientation.

27.9 Answer: (ii) The mobile charge carriers in copper are negatively charged electrons, which move upward through the wire to give a downward current. From the right-hand rule, the force on a positively charged particle moving upward in a westward-pointing magnetic field would be to the south; hence the force on a negatively charged particle is to the north. The result is an excess of negative charge on the north side of the wire, leaving an excess of positive charge—and hence a higher electric potential—on the south side.

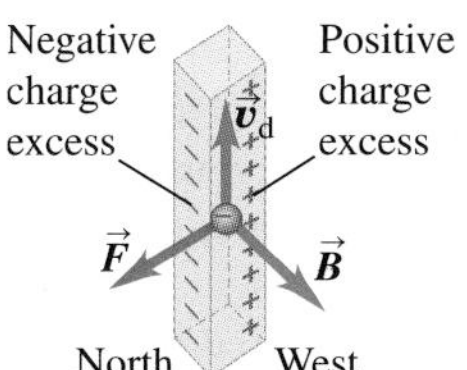

PROBLEMS

For instructor-assigned homework, go to www.masteringphysics.com

Discussion Questions

Q27.1. Can a charged particle move through a magnetic field without experiencing any force? If so, how? If not, why not?

Q27.2. At any point in space, the electric field $\vec{E}$ is defined to be in the direction of the electric force on a positively charged particle at that point. Why don't we similarly define the magnetic field $\vec{B}$ to be in the direction of the magnetic force on a moving, positively charged particle?

Q27.3. Section 27.2 describes a procedure for finding the direction of the magnetic force using your right hand. If you use the same procedure, but with your left hand, will you get the correct direction for the force? Explain.

Q27.4. The magnetic force on a moving charged particle is always perpendicular to the magnetic field $\vec{B}$. Is the trajectory of a moving charged particle always perpendicular to the magnetic field lines? Explain your reasoning.

Q27.5. A charged particle is fired into a cubical region of space where there is a uniform magnetic field. Outside this region, there is no magnetic field. Is it possible that the particle will remain inside the cubical region? Why or why not?

Q27.6. If the magnetic force does no work on a charged particle, how can it have any effect on the particle's motion? Are there other examples of forces that do no work but have a significant effect on a particle's motion?

Q27.7. A charged particle moves through a region of space with constant velocity (magnitude and direction). If the external magnetic field is zero in this region, can you conclude that the external electric field in the region is also zero? Explain. (By "external" we mean fields other than those produced by the charged particle.) If the external electric field is zero in the region, can you conclude that the external magnetic field in the region is also zero?

Q27.8. How might a loop of wire carrying a current be used as a compass? Could such a compass distinguish between north and south? Why or why not?

Q27.9. How could the direction of a magnetic field be determined by making only *qualitative* observations of the magnetic force on a straight wire carrying a current?

Q27.10. A loose, floppy loop of wire is carrying current I. The loop of wire is placed on a horizontal table in a uniform magnetic field $\vec{B}$ perpendicular to the plane of the table. This causes the loop of wire to expand into a circular shape while still lying on the table. In a diagram, show all possible orientations of the current I and magnetic field $\vec{B}$ that could cause this to occur. Explain your reasoning.

Q27.11. Several charges enter a uniform magnetic field directed into the page, (a) What path would a positive charge q moving with a velocity of magnitude v follow through the field? (b) What path would a positive charge q moving with a velocity of magnitude $2v$ follow through the field? (c) What path would a negative charge $-q$ moving with a velocity of magnitude v follow through the field? (d) What path would a neutral particle follow through the field?

Q27.12. Each of the lettered points at the corners of the cube in Fig. 27.42 represents a positive charge q moving with a velocity of magnitude v in the direction indicated. The region in the figure is in a uniform magnetic field $\vec{B}$, parallel to the x-axis and directed toward the right. Which charges experience a force due to $\vec{B}$? What is the direction of the force on each charge?

Figure 27.42 Question Q27.12.

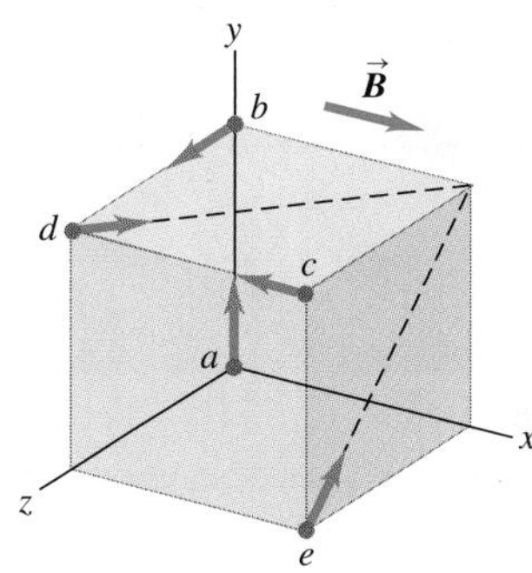

Q27.13. A student claims that if lightning strikes a metal flagpole, the force exerted by the earth's magnetic field on the current in the pole can be large enough to bend it. Typical lightning currents are of the order of 10^4 to 10^5 A. Is the student's opinion justified? Explain your reasoning.

Q27.14. Bubble Chamber I. Certain types of bubble chambers are filled with liquid hydrogen. When a particle (such as an electron or a proton) passes through the liquid, it leaves a track of bubbles, which can be photographed to show the path of the particle. The apparatus is immersed in a known magnetic field, which causes the particle to curve. Figure 27.43 is a trace of a bubble-chamber image showing the path of an electron. (a) How could you determine the *sign* of the charge of a particle from a photograph of its path? (b) How can physicists determine the *momentum* and the *speed* of this electron by using measurements made on the photograph, given that the magnetic field is known and is perpendicular to the plane of the figure? (c) The electron is obviously spiraling into smaller and smaller circles. What properties of the electron must be changing to cause this behavior? Why does this happen? (d) What would be the path of a neutron in a bubble chamber? Why?

Figure 27.43 Question Q27.14.

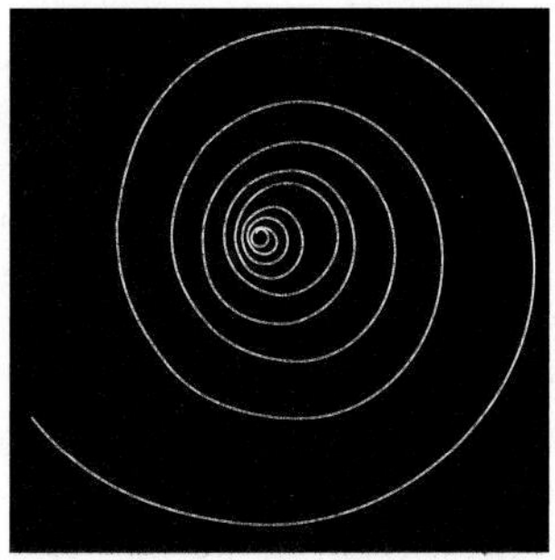

Q27.15. An ordinary loudspeaker such as that shown in Fig. 27.28 should not be placed next to a computer monitor or TV screen. Why not?

Q27.16. Bubble Chamber II. Figure 27.44 show the paths of several particles in a bubble chamber. (See Discussion Question Q27.14.) The two spirals near the top of the photo come from two particles that were created at the same instant due to a high-energy gamma ray. (a) What can you conclude about the *signs* of the charges of these two particles, assuming that the magnetic field is perpendicular to the plane of the photograph and pointing into the paper? (b) Which of the two particles (the right one or the left one) had more initial momentum? How do you know? (c) Why do the paths spiral inward? What causes this to happen?

Figure 27.44 Question Q27.16.

Q27.17. If an emf is produced in a dc motor, would it be possible to use the motor somehow as a generator or source, taking power out of it rather than putting power into it? How might this be done?

Q27.18. When the polarity of the voltage applied to a dc motor is reversed, the direction of motion does *not* reverse. Why not? How *could* the direction of motion be reversed?

Q27.19. In a Hall-effect experiment, is it possible that *no* transverse potential difference will be observed? Under what circumstances might this happen?

Q27.20. Hall-effect voltages are much greater for relatively poor conductors (such as germanium) than for good conductors (such as copper), for comparable currents, fields, and dimensions. Why?

Q27.21. Could an accelerator be built in which *all* the forces on the particles, for steering and for increasing speed, are magnetic forces? Why or why not?

Q27.22. The magnetic force acting on a charged particle can never do work because at every instant the force is perpendicular to the velocity. The torque exerted by a magnetic field can do work on a current loop when the loop rotates. Explain how these seemingly contradictory statements can be reconciled.

Exercises

Section 27.2 Magnetic Field

27.1. A particle with a charge of -1.24×10^{-8} C is moving with instantaneous velocity $\vec{v} = (4.19 \times 10^4 \text{ m/s})\hat{\imath} + (-3.85 \times 10^4 \text{ m/s})\hat{\jmath}$. What is the force exerted on this particle by a magnetic field (a) $\vec{B} = (1.40 \text{ T})\hat{\imath}$ and (b) $\vec{B} = (1.40 \text{ T})\hat{k}$?

27.2. A particle of mass 0.195 g carries a charge of -2.50×10^{-8} C. The particle is given an initial horizontal velocity that is due north and has magnitude 4.00×10^4 m/s. What are the magnitude and direction of the minimum magnetic field that will keep the particle moving in the earth's gravitational field in the same horizontal, northward direction?

27.3. In a 1.25-T magnetic field directed vertically upward, a particle having a charge of magnitude 8.50 μC and initially moving northward at 4.75 km/s is deflected toward the east. (a) What is the sign of the charge of this particle? Make a sketch to illustrate how you found your answer. (b) Find the magnetic force on the particle.

27.4. A particle with mass 1.81×10^{-3} kg and a charge of 1.22×10^{-8} C has, at a given instant, a velocity $\vec{v} = (3.00 \times 10^4 \text{ m/s})\hat{\jmath}$. What are the magnitude and direction of the particle's acceleration produced by a uniform magnetic field $\vec{B} = (1.63 \text{ T})\hat{\imath} + (0.980 \text{ T})\hat{\jmath}$?

27.5. An electron experiences a magnetic force of magnitude 4.60×10^{-15} N when moving at an angle of 60.0° with respect to a magnetic field of magnitude 3.50×10^{-3} T. Find the speed of the electron.

27.6. An electron moves at 2.50×10^6 m/s through a region in which there is a magnetic field of unspecified direction and magnitude 7.40×10^{-2} T. (a) What are the largest and smallest possible magnitudes of the acceleration of the electron due to the magnetic field? (b) If the actual acceleration of the electron is one-fourth of the largest magnitude in part (a), what is the angle between the electron velocity and the magnetic field?

27.7. A particle with charge 7.80 μC is moving with velocity $\vec{v} = -(3.80 \times 10^3 \text{ m/s})\hat{\jmath}$. The magnetic force on the particle is measured to be $\vec{F} = +(7.60 \times 10^{-3}\text{N})\hat{\imath} - (5.20 \times 10^{-3} \text{ N})\hat{k}$. (a) Calculate all the components of the magnetic field you can from this information. (b) Are there components of the magnetic field that are not determined by the measurement of the force? Explain. (c) Calculate the scalar product $\vec{B} \cdot \vec{F}$ What is the angle between $\vec{B}$ and $\vec{F}$?

27.8. A particle with charge -5.60 nC is moving in a uniform magnetic field $\vec{B} = -(1.25 \text{ T})\hat{k}$. The magnetic force on the particle is measured to be $\vec{F} = -(3.40 \times 10^{-7} \text{ N})\hat{\imath} + (7.40 \times 10^{-7} \text{ N})\hat{\jmath}$. (a) Calculate all the components of the velocity of the particle that you can from this information. (b) Are there components of the velocity that are not determined by the measurement of the force? Explain. (c) Calculate the scalar product $\vec{v} \cdot \vec{F}$. What is the angle between $\vec{v}$ and $\vec{F}$?

27.9. A group of particles is traveling in a magnetic field of unknown magnitude and direction. You observe that a proton moving at 1.50 km/s in the $+x$-direction experiences a force of 2.25×10^{-16} N in the $+y$-direction, and an electron moving at 4.75 km/s in the $-z$-direction experiences a force of 8.50×10^{-16} N. (a) What are the magnitude and direction of the magnetic field? (b) What are the magnitude and direction of the magnetic force on an electron moving in the $-y$-direction at 3.2 km/s?

Section 27.3 Magnetic Field Lines and Magnetic Flux

27.10. The magnetic flux through one face of a cube is $+0.120$ Wb. (a) What must the total magnetic flux through the other five faces of the cube be? (b) Why didn't you need to know the dimensions of the cube in order to answer part (a)? (c) Suppose the magnetic flux is due to a permanent magnet like that shown in Fig. 27.11. In a sketch, show where the cube in part (a) might be located relative to the magnet.

27.11. A circular area with a radius of 6.50 cm lies in the xy-plane. What is the magnitude of the magnetic flux through this circle due to a uniform magnetic field $B = 0.230$ T (a) in the $+z$-direction; (b) at an angle of 53.1° from the $+z$-direction; (c) in the $+y$-direction?

27.12. The magnetic field $\vec{B}$ in a certain region is 0.128 T, and its direction is that of the $+z$-axis in Fig. 27.45. (a) What is the magnetic flux across the surface *abcd* in the figure? (b) What is the magnetic flux across the surface *befc*? (c) What is the magnetic flux across the surface *aefd*? (d) What is the net flux through all five surfaces that enclose the shaded volume?

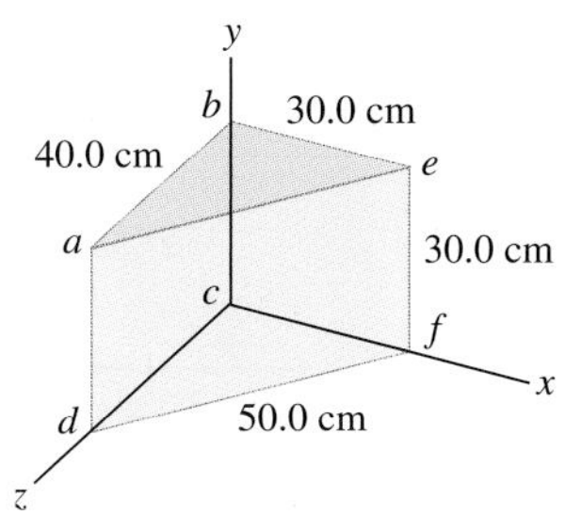

Figure **27.45** Exercise 27.12.

27.13. An open plastic soda bottle with an opening diameter of 2.5 cm is placed on a table. A uniform 1.75-T magnetic field directed upward and oriented 25° from vertical encompasses the bottle. What is the total magnetic flux through the plastic of the soda bottle?

Section 27.4 Motion of Charged Particles in a Magnetic Field

27.14. A particle with charge 6.40×10^{-19} C travels in a circular orbit with radius 4.68 mm due to the force exerted on it by a magnetic field with magnitude 1.65 T and perpendicular to the orbit. (a) What is the magnitude of the linear momentum $\vec{p}$ of the particle? (b) What is the magnitude of the angular momentum $\vec{L}$ of the particle?

27.15. An electron at point A in Fig. 27.46 has a speed v_0 of 1.41×10^6 m/s. Find (a) the magnitude and direction of the magnetic field that will cause the electron to follow the semicircular path from A to B, and (b) the time required for the electron to move from A to B.

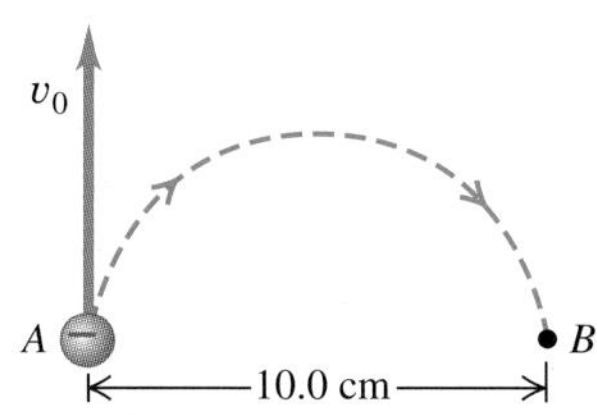

Figure **27.46** Exercise 27.15.

27.16. Repeat Exercise 27.15 for the case in which the particle is a proton rather than an electron.

27.17. A 150-g ball containing 4.00×10^8 excess electrons is dropped into a 125-m vertical shaft. At the bottom of the shaft, the ball suddenly enters a uniform horizontal magnetic field that has magnitude 0.250 T and direction from east to west. If air resistance is negligibly small, find the magnitude and direction of the force that this magnetic field exerts on the ball just as it enters the field.

27.18. An alpha particle (a He nucleus, containing two protons and two neutrons and having a mass of 6.64×10^{-27} kg) traveling horizontally at 35.6 km/s enters a uniform, vertical, 1.10-T magnetic field. (a) What is the diameter of the path followed by this alpha particle? (b) What effect does the magnetic field have on the speed of the particle? (c) What are the magnitude and direction of the acceleration of the alpha particle while it is in the magnetic field? (d) Explain why the speed of the particle does not change even though an unbalanced external force acts on it.

27.19. Fusion Reactor. If two deuterium nuclei (charge $+e$, mass 3.34×10^{-27} kg) get close enough together, the attraction of the strong nuclear force will fuse them to make an isotope of helium, releasing vast amounts of energy. The range of this force is about 10^{-15} m. This is the principle behind the fusion reactor. The deuterium nuclei are moving much too fast to be contained by physical walls, so they are confined magnetically. (a) How fast would two nuclei have to move so that in a head-on collision they would get close enough to fuse? (Treat the nuclei as point charges, and assume that a separation of 1.0×10^{-15} is required for fusion.) (b) What strength magnetic field is needed to make deuterium nuclei with this speed travel in a circle of diameter 2.50 m?

27.20. (a) An ^{16}O nucleus (charge $+8e$) moving horizontally from west to east with a speed of 500 km/s experiences a magnetic force of 0.00320 nN vertically downward. Find the magnitude and direction of the weakest magnetic field required to produce this force. Explain how this same force could be caused by a larger magnetic field. (b) An electron moves in a uniform, horizontal, 2.10-T magnetic field that is toward the west. What must the magnitude and direction of the minimum velocity of the electron be so that the magnetic force on it will be 4.60 pN, vertically upward? Explain how the velocity could be greater than this minimum value and the force still have this same magnitude and direction.

27.21. A deuteron (the nucleus of an isotope of hydrogen) has a mass of 3.34×10^{-27} kg and a charge of $+e$. The deuteron travels in a circular path with a radius of 6.96 mm in a magnetic field with magnitude 2.50 T. (a) Find the speed of the deuteron. (b) Find the time required for it to make half a revolution. (c) Through what potential difference would the deuteron have to be accelerated to acquire this speed?

27.22. In an experiment with cosmic rays, a vertical beam of particles that have charge of magnitude $3e$ and mass 12 times the proton mass enters a uniform horizontal magnetic field of 0.250 T and is bent in a semicircle of diameter 95.0 cm, as shown in Fig. 27.47. (a) Find the speed of the particles and the sign of their charge. (b) Is it reasonable to ignore the gravity force on the particles? (c) How does the speed of the particles as they enter the field compare to their speed as they exit the field?

Figure **27.47** Exercise 27.22.

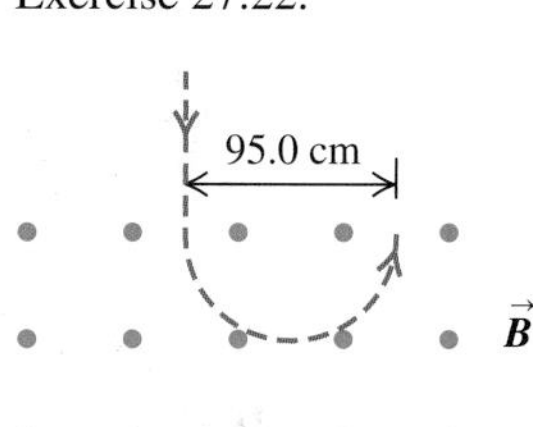

27.23. A physicist wishes to produce electromagnetic waves of frequency 3.0 THz $(1 \text{ THz} = 1 \text{ terahertz} = 10^{12} \text{ Hz})$ using a magnetron (see Example 27.3). (a) What magnetic field would be required? Compare this field with the strongest constant magnetic fields yet produced on earth, about 45 T. (b) Would there be any advantage to using protons instead of electrons in the magnetron? Why or why not?

27.24. A beam of protons traveling at 1.20 km/s enters a uniform magnetic field, traveling perpendicular to the field. The beam exits the magnetic field, leaving the field in a direction perpendicular to its original direction (Fig. 27.48). The beam travels a distance of 1.18 cm *while in the field.* What is the magnitude of the magnetic field?

Figure **27.48** Exercise 27.24.

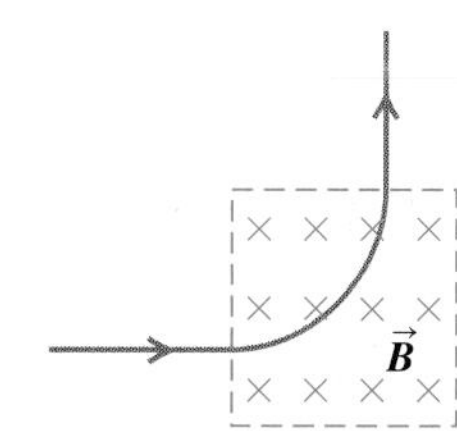

27.25. An electron in the beam of a TV picture tube is accelerated by a potential difference of 2.00 kV. Then it passes through a region of transverse magnetic field, where it moves in a circular arc with radius 0.180 m. What is the magnitude of the field?

27.26. A singly charged ion of ^{7}Li (an isotope of lithium) has a mass of 1.16×10^{-26} kg. It is accelerated through a potential difference of 220 V and then enters a magnetic field with magnitude 0.723 T perpendicular to the path of the ion. What is the radius of the ion's path in the magnetic field?

27.27. A proton $(q = 1.60 \times 10^{-19} \text{ C}, m = 1.67 \times 10^{-27} \text{ kg})$ moves in a uniform magnetic field $\vec{B} = (0.500 \text{ T})\hat{\imath}$. At $t = 0$ the proton has velocity components $v_x = 1.50 \times 10^5$ m/s, $v_y = 0$, and $v_z = 2.00 \times 10^5$ m/s (see Example 27.4). (a) What are the magnitude and direction of the magnetic force acting on the proton? In addition to the magnetic field there is a uniform electric field in the $+x$-direction, $\vec{E} = (+2.00 \times 10^4 \text{ V/m})\hat{\imath}$. (b) Will the proton have a component of acceleration in the direction of the electric field?

(c) Describe the path of the proton. Does the electric field affect the radius of the helix? Explain. (d) At $t = T/2$, where T is the period of the circular motion of the proton, what is the x-component of the displacement of the proton from its position at $t = 0$?

Section 27.5 Applications of Motion of Charged Particles

27.28. (a) What is the speed of a beam of electrons when the simultaneous influence of an electric field of 1.56×10^4 V/m and a magnetic field of 4.62×10^{-3} T, with both fields normal to the beam and to each other, produces no deflection of the electrons? (b) In a diagram, show the relative orientation of the vectors $\vec{v}$, $\vec{E}$, and $\vec{B}$. (c) When the electric field is removed, what is the radius of the electron orbit? What is the period of the orbit?

27.29. A 150-V battery is connected across two parallel metal plates of area 28.5 cm^2 and separation 8.20 mm. A beam of alpha particles (charge $+2e$, mass 6.64×10^{-27} kg) is accelerated from rest through a potential difference of 1.75 kV and enters the region between the plates perpendicular to the electric field. What magnitude and direction of magnetic field are needed so that the alpha particles emerge undeflected from between the plates?

27.30. Crossed $\vec{E}$ and $\vec{B}$ Fields. A particle with initial velocity $\vec{v}_0 = (5.85 \times 10^3 \text{ m/s})\hat{j}$ enters a region of uniform electric and magnetic fields. The magnetic field in the region is $\vec{B} = -(1.35 \text{ T})\hat{k}$. Calculate the magnitude and direction of the electric field in the region if the particle is to pass through undeflected, for a particle of charge (a) +0.640 nC and (b) −0.320 nC. You can ignore the weight of the particle.

27.31. Determining the Mass of an Isotope. The electric field between the plates of the velocity selector in a Bainbridge mass spectrometer (see Fig. 27.22) is 1.12×10^5 V/m, and the magnetic field in both regions is 0.540 T. A stream of singly charged selenium ions moves in a circular path with a radius of 31.0 cm in the magnetic field. Determine the mass of one selenium ion and the mass number of this selenium isotope. (The mass number is equal to the mass of the isotope in atomic mass units, rounded to the nearest integer. One atomic mass unit = 1 u = 1.66×10^{-27} kg.)

27.32. In the Bainbridge mass spectrometer (see Fig. 27.24), the magnetic-field magnitude in the velocity selector is 0.650 T, and ions having a speed of 1.82×10^6 m/s pass through undeflected. (a) What is the electric-field magnitude in the velocity selector? (b) If the separation of the plates is 5.20 mm, what is the potential difference between plates P and P'?

Section 27.6 Magnetic Force on a Current-Carrying Conductor

27.33. A straight 2.00-m, 150-g wire carries a current in a region where the earth's magnetic field is horizontal with a magnitude of 0.55 gauss. (a) What is the minimum value of the current in this wire so that its weight is completely supported by the magnetic force due to earth's field, assuming that no other forces except gravity act on it? Does it seem likely that such a wire could support this size of current? (b) Show how the wire would have to be oriented relative to the earth's magnetic field to be supported in this way.

27.34. An electromagnet produces a magnetic field of 0.550 T in a cylindrical region of radius 2.50 cm between its poles. A straight wire carrying a current of 10.8 A passes through the center of this region and is perpendicular to both the axis of the cylindrical region and the magnetic field. What magnitude of force is exerted on the wire?

27.35. A long wire carrying 4.50 A of current makes two 90° bends, as shown in Fig. 27.49. The bent part of the wire passes through a uniform 0.240-T magnetic field directed as shown in the figure and confined to a limited region of space. Find the magnitude and direction of the force that the magnetic field exerts on the wire.

Figure 27.49 Exercise 27.35.

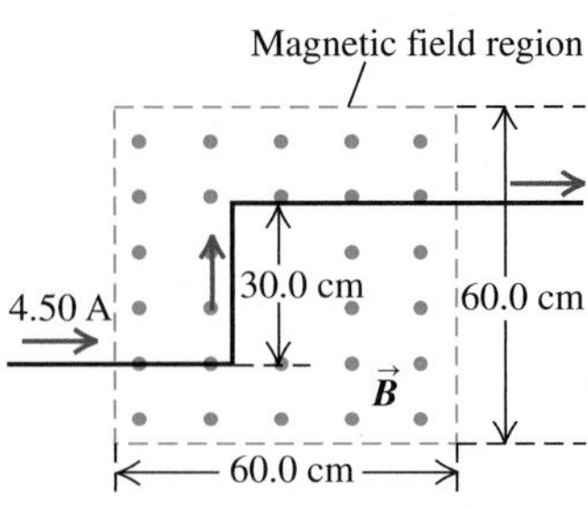

27.36. A straight, vertical wire carries a current of 1.20 A downward in a region between the poles of a large superconducting electromagnet, where the magnetic field has magnitude B = 0.588 T and is horizontal. What are the magnitude and direction of the magnetic force on a 1.00-cm section of the wire that is in this uniform magnetic field, if the magnetic field direction is (a) east; (b) south; (c) 30.0° south of west?

27.37. A horizontal rod 0.200 m long is mounted on a balance and carries a current. At the location of the rod a uniform horizontal magnetic field has magnitude 0.067 T and direction perpendicular to the rod. The magnetic force on the rod is measured by the balance and is found to be 0.13 N. What is the current?

27.38. In Fig. 27.50, a wire carrying current into the plane of the figure is between the north and south poles of two bar magnets. What is the direction of the force exerted by the magnets on the wire?

Figure 27.50 Exercise 27.38.

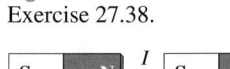

27.39. A thin, 50.0-cm-long metal bar with mass 750 g rests on, but is not attached to, two metallic supports in a uniform 0.450-T magnetic field, as shown in Fig. 27.51. A battery and a 25.0-Ω resistor in series are connected to the supports. (a) What is the highest voltage the battery can have without breaking the circuit at the supports? (b) The battery voltage has the maximum value calculated in part (a). If the resistor suddenly gets partially short-circuited, decreasing its resistance to 2.0 Ω, find the initial acceleration of the bar.

Figure 27.51 Exercise 27.39.

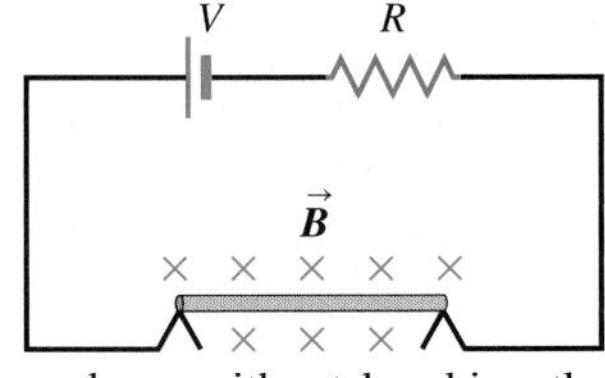

27.40. Magnetic Balance. The circuit shown in Fig. 27.52 is used to make a magnetic balance to weigh objects. The mass m to be measured is hung from the center of the bar that is in a uniform magnetic field of 1.50 T, directed into the plane of the figure. The battery voltage can be adjusted to vary the current in the circuit. The horizontal bar is 60.0 cm long and is made of extremely light-weight material. It is connected to the battery by thin vertical wires that can support no appreciable tension; all the weight of the suspended mass m is supported by the magnetic force on the bar. A resistor with

Figure 27.52 Exercise 27.40.

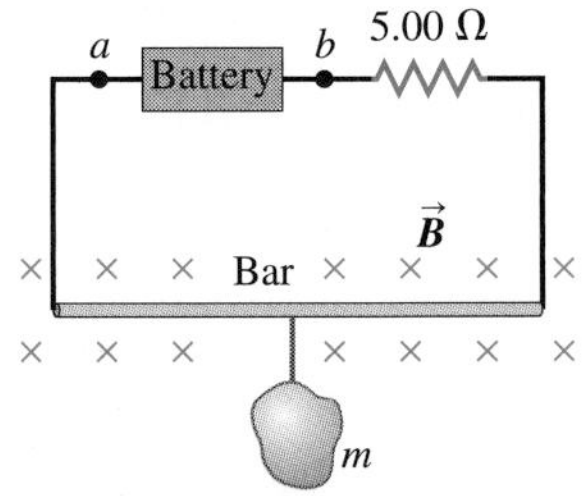

$R = 5.00\ \Omega$ is in series with the bar; the resistance of the rest of the circuit is much less than this. (a) Which point, a or b, should be the positive terminal of the battery? (b) If the maximum terminal voltage of the battery is 175 V, what is the greatest mass m that this instrument can measure?

27.41. Consider the conductor and current in Example 27.8, but now let the magnetic field be parallel to the x-axis. (a) What are the magnitude and direction of the total magnetic force on the conductor? (b) In Example 27.8, the total force is the same as if we replaced the semicircle with a straight segment along the x-axis. Is that still true when the magnetic field is in this different direction? Can you explain why, or why not?

Section 27.7 Force and Torque on a Current Loop

27.42. The plane of a 5.0 cm $\times$ 8.0 cm rectangular loop of wire is parallel to a 0.19-T magnetic field. The loop carries a current of 6.2 A. (a) What torque acts on the loop? (b) What is the magnetic moment of the loop? (c) What is the maximum torque that can be obtained with the same total length of wire carrying the same current in this magnetic field?

27.43. Magnetic Moment of the Hydrogen Atom. In the Bohr model of the hydrogen atom (see Section 38.5), in the lowest energy state the electron orbits the proton at a speed of 2.2×10^6 m/s in a circular orbit of radius 5.3×10^{-11} m. (a) What is the orbital period of the electron? (b) If the orbiting electron is considered to be a current loop, what is the current I? (c) What is the magnetic moment of the atom due to the motion of the electron?

27.44. A rectangular coil of wire, 22.0 cm by 35.0 cm and carrying a current of 1.40 A, is oriented with the plane of its loop perpendicular to a uniform 1.50-T magnetic field, as shown in Fig. 27.53. (a) Calculate the net force and torque that the magnetic field exerts on the coil. (b) The coil is rotated through a 30.0° angle about the axis shown, with the left side coming out of the plane of the figure and the right side going into the plane. Calculate the net force and torque that the magnetic field now exerts on the coil. (*Hint:* In order to help visualize this three-dimensional problem, make a careful drawing of the coil as viewed along the rotation axis.)

Figure 27.53 Exercise 27.44.

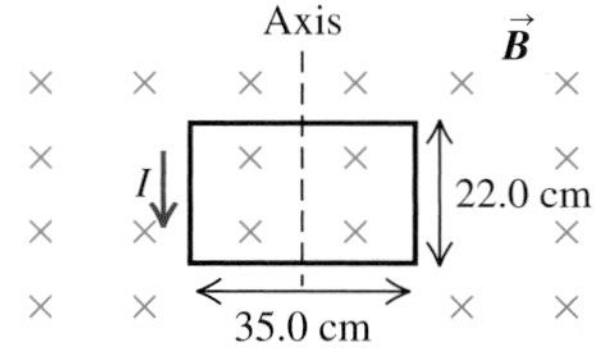

27.45. A uniform rectangular coil of total mass 210 g and dimensions 0.500 m $\times$ 1.00 m is oriented perpendicular to a uniform 3.00-T magnetic field (Fig. 27.54). A current of 2.00 A is suddenly started in the coil. (a) About which axis (A_1 or A_2) will the coil begin to rotate? Why? (b) Find the initial angular acceleration of the coil just after the current is started.

Figure 27.54 Exercise 27.45.

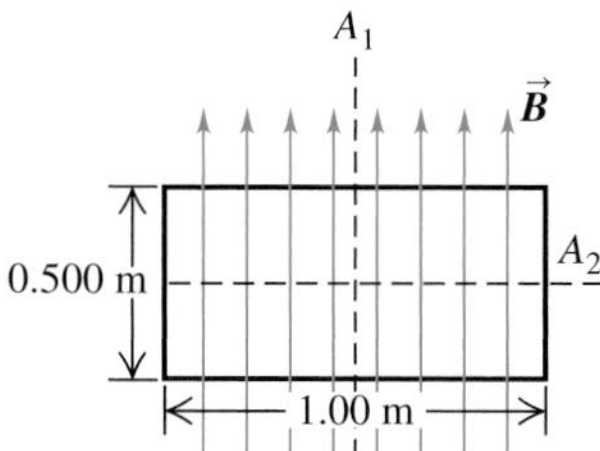

27.46. A circular coil with area A and N turns is free to rotate about a diameter that coincides with the x-axis. Current I is circulating in the coil. There is a uniform magnetic field $\vec{B}$ in the positive y-direction. Calculate the magnitude and direction of the torque $\vec{\tau}$ and the value of the potential energy U, as given in Eq. (27.27), when the coil is oriented as shown in parts (a) through (d) of Fig. 27.55.

Figure 27.55 Exercise 27.46.

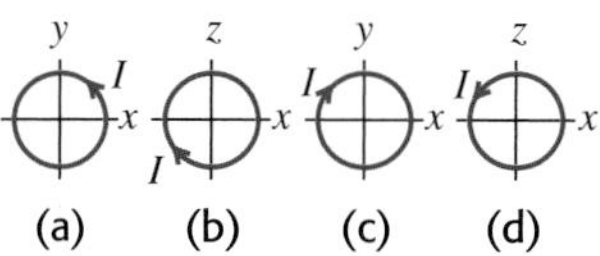

27.47. A coil with magnetic moment $1.45\ \text{A} \cdot \text{m}^2$ is oriented initially with its magnetic moment antiparallel to a uniform 0.835-T magnetic field. What is the change in potential energy of the coil when it is rotated 180° so that its magnetic moment is parallel to the field?

*Section 27.8 The Direct-Current Motor

***27.48.** A dc motor with its rotor and field coils connected in series has an internal resistance of 3.2 Ω. When the motor is running at full load on a 120-V line, the emf in the rotor is 105 V. (a) What is the current drawn by the motor from the line? (b) What is the power delivered to the motor? (c) What is the mechanical power developed by the motor?

***27.49.** In a shunt-wound dc motor with the field coils and rotor connected in parallel (Fig. 27.56), the resistance R_f of the field coils is 106 Ω, and the resistance R_r of the rotor is 5.9 Ω. When a potential difference of 120 V is applied to the brushes and the motor is running at full speed delivering mechanical power, the current supplied to it is 4.82 A. (a) What is the current in the field coils? (b) What is the current in the rotor? (c) What is the induced emf developed by the motor? (d) How much mechanical power is developed by this motor?

Figure 27.56 Exercises 27.49 and 27.50.

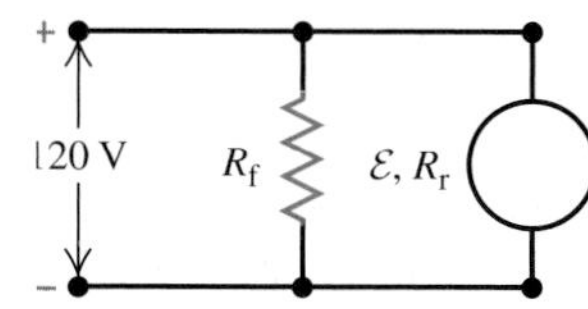

***27.50.** A shunt-wound dc motor with the field coils and rotor connected in parallel (Fig. 27.56) operates from a 120-V dc power line. The resistance of the field windings, R_f, is 218 Ω. The resistance of the rotor, R_r, is 5.9 Ω. When the motor is running, the rotor develops an emf $\mathcal{E}$. The motor draws a current of 4.82 A from the line. Friction losses amount to 45.0 W. Compute (a) the field current; (b) the rotor current; (c) the emf $\mathcal{E}$; (d) the rate of development of thermal energy in the field windings; (e) the rate of development of thermal energy in the rotor; (f) the power input to the motor; (g) the efficiency of the motor.

*Section 27.9 The Hall Effect

***27.51.** Figure 27.57 shows a portion of a silver ribbon with $z_1 = 11.8$ mm and $y_1 = 0.23$ mm, carrying a current of 120 A in the $+x$-direction. The ribbon lies in a uniform magnetic field, in the y-direction, with magnitude 0.95 T. Apply the simplified model of the Hall

Figure 27.57 Exercises 27.51 and 27.52.

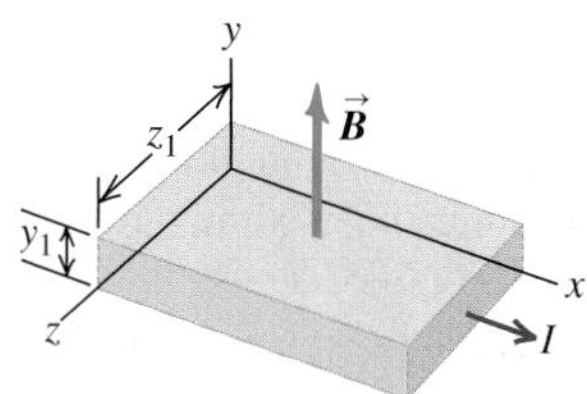

effect presented in Section 27.9. If there are 5.85×10^{28} free electrons per cubic meter, find (a) the magnitude of the drift velocity of the electrons in the x-direction; (b) the magnitude and direction of the electric field in the z-direction due to the Hall effect; (c) the Hall emf.

***27.52.** Let Fig. 27.57 represent a strip of an unknown metal of the same dimensions as those of the silver ribbon in Exercise 27.51. When the magnetic field is 2.29 T and the current is 78.0 A, the Hall emf is found to be 131 μV. What does the simplified model of the Hall effect presented in Section 27.9 give for the density of free electrons in the unknown metal?

Problems

27.53. When a particle of charge $q > 0$ moves with a velocity of $\vec{v}_1$ at 45.0° from the $+x$-axis in the xy-plane, a uniform magnetic field exerts a force $\vec{F}_1$ along the $-z$-axis (Fig. 27.58). When the same particle moves with a velocity $\vec{v}_2$ with the same magnitude as $\vec{v}_1$ but along the $+z$-axis, a force $\vec{F}_2$ of magnitude F_2 is exerted on it along the $+x$-axis. (a) What are the magnitude (in terms of q, v_1, and F_2) and direction of the magnetic field? (b) What is the magnitude of $\vec{F}_1$ in terms of F_2?

Figure **27.58** Problem 27.53.

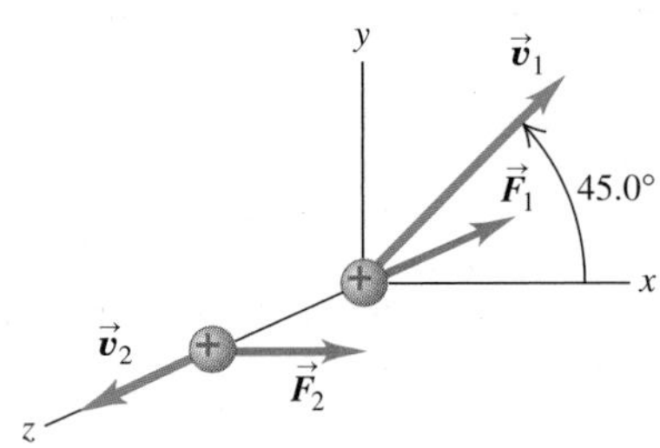

27.54. A particle with charge 9.45×10^{-8} C is moving in a region where there is a uniform magnetic field of 0.450 T in the $+x$-direction. At a particular instant of time the velocity of the particle has components $v_x = -1.68 \times 10^4$ m/s, $v_y = -3.11 \times 10^4$ m/s, and $v_z = 5.85 \times 10^4$ m/s. What are the components of the force on the particle at this time?

27.55. You wish to hit a target from several meters away with a charged coin having a mass of 5.0 g and a charge of +2500 μC. The coin is given an initial velocity of 12.8 m/s, and a downward, uniform electric field with field strength 27.5 N/C exists throughout the region. If you aim directly at the target and fire the coin horizontally, what magnitude and direction of uniform magnetic field are needed in the region for the coin to hit the target?

27.56. A cyclotron is to accelerate protons to an energy of 5.4 MeV. The superconducting electromagnet of the cyclotron produces a 3.5-T magnetic field perpendicular to the proton orbits. (a) When the protons have achieved a kinetic energy of 2.7 MeV, what is the radius of their circular orbit and what is their angular speed? (b) Repeat part (a) when the protons have achieved their final kinetic energy of 5.4 MeV.

27.57. The magnetic poles of a small cyclotron produce a magnetic field with magnitude 0.85 T. The poles have a radius of 0.40 m, which is the maximum radius of the orbits of the accelerated particles. (a) What is the maximum energy to which protons ($q = 1.60 \times 10^{-19}$ C, $m = 1.67 \times 10^{-27}$ kg) can be accelerated by this cyclotron? Give your answer in electron volts and in joules. (b) What is the time for one revolution of a proton orbiting at this maximum radius? (c) What would the magnetic-field magnitude have to be for the maximum energy to which a proton can be accelerated to be twice that calculated in part (a)? (d) For $B = 0.85$ T, what is the maximum energy to which alpha particles ($q = 3.20 \times 10^{-19}$ C, $m = 6.65 \times 10^{-27}$ kg) can be accelerated by this cyclotron? How does this compare to the maximum energy for protons?

27.58. The force on a charged particle moving in a magnetic field can be computed as the vector sum of the forces due to each separate component of the magnetic field. As an example, a particle with charge q is moving with speed v in the $-y$-direction. It is moving in a uniform magnetic field $\vec{B} = B_x\hat{\imath} + B_y\hat{\jmath} + B_z\hat{k}$. (a) What are the components of the force $\vec{F}$ exerted on the particle by the magnetic field? (b) If $q > 0$, what must the signs of the components of $\vec{B}$ be if the components of $\vec{F}$ are all nonnegative? (c) If $q < 0$ and $B_x = B_y = B_z > 0$, find the direction of $\vec{F}$ and find the magnitude of $\vec{F}$ in terms of $|q|$, v, and B_x.

27.59. A uniform, 458-g metal bar 75.0 cm long carries a current I in a uniform, horizontal, 1.55-T magnetic field as shown in Fig. 27.59. The bar is hinged at b but rests unattached at a. What is the largest current that can flow from a to b without breaking the electrical contact at a?

Figure **27.59** Problem 27.59.

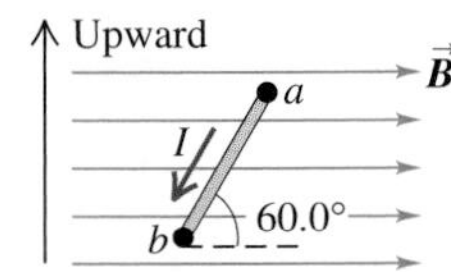

27.60. In the electron gun of a TV picture tube the electrons (charge $-e$, mass m) are accelerated by a voltage V. After leaving the electron gun, the electron beam travels a distance D to the screen; in this region there is a transverse magnetic field of magnitude B and no electric field. (a) Sketch the path of the electron beam in the tube. (b) Show that the approximate deflection of the beam due to this magnetic field is

$$d = \frac{BD^2}{2}\sqrt{\frac{e}{2mV}}$$

(*Hint:* Place the origin at the center of the electron beam's arc and compare an undeflected beam's path to the deflected beam's path.) (c) Evaluate this expression for $V = 750$ V, $D = 50$ cm, and $B = 5.0 \times 10^{-5}$ T (comparable to the earth's field). Is this deflection significant?

27.61. A particle with negative charge q and mass $m = 2.58 \times 10^{-15}$ kg is traveling through a region containing a uniform magnetic field $\vec{B} = -(0.120\ \text{T})\hat{k}$. At a particular instant of time the velocity of the particle is $\vec{v} = (1.05 \times 10^6\ \text{m/s})(-3\hat{\imath} + 4\hat{\jmath} + 12\hat{k})$ and the force $\vec{F}$ on the particle has a magnitude of 1.25 N. (a) Determine the charge q. (b) Determine the acceleration $\vec{a}$ of the particle. (c) Explain why the path of the particle is a helix, and determine the radius of curvature R of the circular component of the helical path. (d) Determine the cyclotron frequency of the particle. (e) Although helical motion is not periodic in the full sense of the word, the x- and y-coordinates do vary in a periodic way. If the coordinates of the particle at $t = 0$ are $(x, y, z) = (R, 0, 0)$, determine its coordinates at a time $t = 2T$, where T is the period of the motion in the xy-plane.

27.62. A long, straight wire containing a semicircular region of radius 0.95 m is placed in a uniform magnetic field of magnitude 2.20 T as shown in Fig. 27.60. What is the net magnetic force acting on the wire when it carries a current of 3.40 A?

Figure **27.60** Problem 27.62.

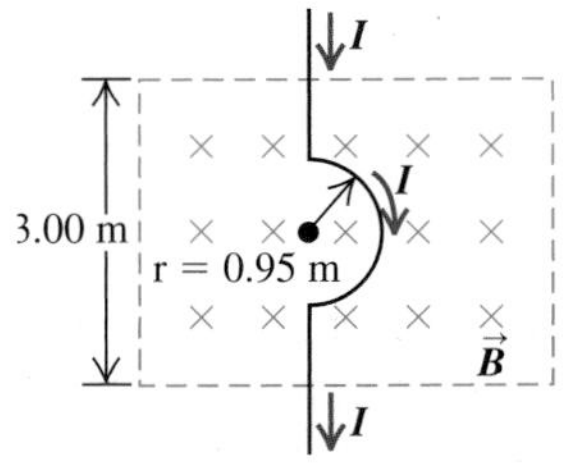

27.63. A magnetic field exerts a torque τ on a round current-carrying loop of wire. What will be the torque on this loop (in terms of τ) if its diameter is tripled?

27.64. A particle of charge $q > 0$ is moving at speed v in the $+z$-direction through a region of uniform magnetic field $\vec{B}$. The magnetic force on the particle is $\vec{F} = F_0(3\hat{\imath} + 4\hat{\jmath})$, where F_0 is a positive constant. (a) Determine the components B_x, B_y, and B_z, or at least as many of the three components as is possible from the information given. (b) If it is given in addition that the magnetic field has magnitude $6F_0/qv$, determine as much as you can about the remaining components of $\vec{B}$.

27.65. Suppose the electric field between the plates P and P' in Fig. 27.24 is 1.88×10^4 V/m and the magnetic field in both regions is 0.701 T. If the source contains the three isotopes of krypton, ^{82}Kr, ^{84}Kr, and ^{86}Kr, and the ions are singly charged, find the distance between the lines formed by the three isotopes on the photographic plate. Assume the atomic masses of the isotopes (in atomic mass units) are equal to their mass numbers, 82, 84, and 86. (One atomic mass unit $= 1$ u $= 1.66 \times 10^{-27}$ kg.)

27.66. Mass Spectrograph. A mass spectrograph is used to measure the masses of ions, or to separate ions of different masses (see Section 27.5). In one design for such an instrument, ions with mass m and charge q are accelerated through a potential difference V. They then enter a uniform magnetic field that is perpendicular to their velocity, and they are deflected in a semicircular path of radius R. A detector measures where the ions complete the semicircle and from this it is easy to calculate R. (a) Derive the equation for calculating the mass of the ion from measurements of B, V, R, and q. (b) What potential difference V is needed so that singly ionized ^{12}C atoms will have $R = 50.0$ cm in a 0.150-T magnetic field? (c) Suppose the beam consists of a mixture of ^{12}C and ^{14}C ions. If V and B have the same values as in part (b), calculate the separation of these two isotopes at the detector. Do you think that this beam separation is sufficient for the two ions to be distinguished? (Make the assumption described in Problem 27.65 for the masses of the ions.)

27.67. A straight piece of conducting wire with mass M and length L is placed on a frictionless incline tilted at an angle θ from the horizontal (Fig. 27.61). There is a uniform, vertical magnetic field $\vec{B}$ at all points (produced by an arrangement of magnets not shown in the figure). To keep the wire from sliding down the incline, a voltage source is attached to the ends of the wire. When just the right amount of current flows through the wire, the wire remains at rest. Determine the magnitude and direction of the current in the wire that will cause the wire to remain at rest. Copy the figure and draw the direction of the current on your copy. In addition, show in a free-body diagram all the forces that act on the wire.

Figure 27.61 Problem 27.67.

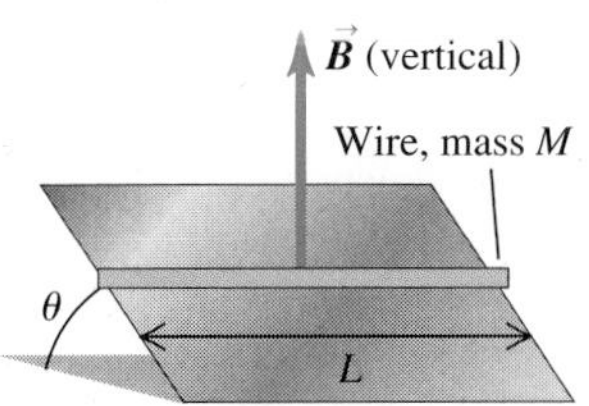

27.68. A 3.00-N metal bar, 1.50 m long and having a resistance of 10.0 Ω, rests horizontally on conducting wires connecting it to the circuit shown in Fig. 27.62. The bar is in a uniform, horizontal, 1.60-T magnetic field and is not attached to the wires in the circuit. What is the acceleration of the bar just after the switch S is closed?

Figure 27.62 Problem 27.68.

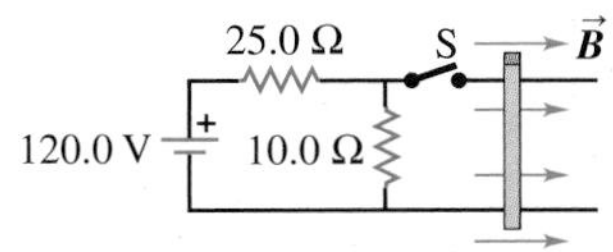

27.69. Two positive ions having the same charge q but different masses m_1 and m_2 are accelerated horizontally from rest through a potential difference V. They then enter a region where there is a uniform magnetic field $\vec{B}$ normal to the plane of the trajectory. (a) Show that if the beam entered the magnetic field along the x-axis, the value of the y-coordinate for each ion at any time t is approximately

$$y = Bx^2\left(\frac{q}{8mV}\right)^{1/2}$$

provided y remains much smaller than x. (b) Can this arrangement be used for isotope separation? Why or why not?

27.70. A plastic circular loop of radius R and a positive charge q is distributed uniformly around the circumference of the loop. The loop is then rotated around its central axis, perpendicular to the plane of the loop, with angular speed ω. If the loop is in a region where there is a uniform magnetic field $\vec{B}$ directed parallel to the plane of the loop, calculate the magnitude of the magnetic torque on the loop.

27.71. Determining Diet. One method for determining the amount of corn in early Native American diets is the *stable isotope ratio analysis* (SIRA) technique. As corn photosynthesizes, it concentrates the isotope carbon-13, whereas most other plants concentrate carbon-12. Overreliance on corn consumption can then be correlated with certain diseases, because corn lacks the essential amino acid lysine. Archaeologists use a mass spectrometer to separate the ^{12}C and ^{13}C isotopes in samples of human remains. Suppose you use a velocity selector to obtain singly ionized (missing one electron) atoms of speed 8.50 km/s, and you want to bend them within a uniform magnetic field in a semicircle of diameter 25.0 cm for the ^{12}C. The measured masses of these isotopes are 1.99×10^{-26} kg (^{12}C) and 2.16×10^{-26} kg (^{13}C). (a) What strength of magnetic field is required? (b) What is the diameter of the ^{13}C semicircle? (c) What is the separation of the ^{12}C and ^{13}C ions at the detector at the end of the semicircle? Is this distance large enough to be easily observed?

27.72. An Electromagnetic Rail Gun. A conducting bar with mass m and length L slides over horizontal rails that are connected to a voltage source. The voltage source maintains a constant current I in the rails and bar, and a constant, uniform, vertical magnetic field $\vec{B}$ fills the region between the rails (Fig. 27.63). (a) Find the magnitude and direction of the net force on the conducting bar. Ignore friction, air resistance, and electrical resistance. (b) If the bar has mass m, find the distance d that the bar must move along the rails from rest to attain speed v. (c) It has been suggested that rail guns based on this principle could accelerate payloads into earth orbit or beyond. Find the distance the bar must travel along the rails if it is to reach the escape speed for the earth (11.2 km/s). Let $B = 0.50$ T, $I = 2.0 \times 10^3$ A, $m = 25$ kg, and $L = 50$ cm. For simplicity asssume the net force on the object is equal to the magnetic force, as in parts (a) and (b), even though gravity plays an important role in an actual launch in space.

Figure 27.63 Problem 27.72.

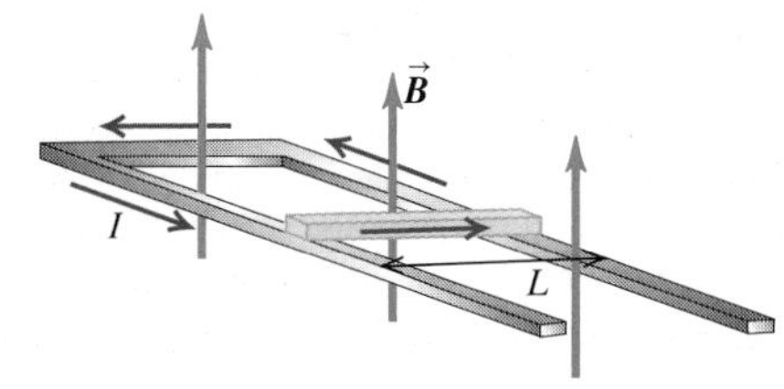

27.73. A long wire carrying a 6.00-A current reverses direction by means of two right-angle bends, as shown in Fig. 27.64. The part of the wire where the bend occurs is in a magnetic field of 0.666 T confined to the circular region of diameter 75 cm, as shown. Find the magnitude and direction of the net force that the magnetic field exerts on this wire.

Figure 27.64 Problem 27.73.

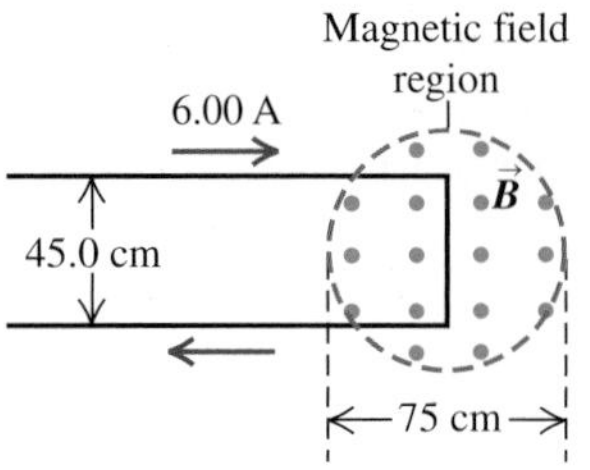

Magnetic field region
6.00 A
45.0 cm
75 cm

27.74. A wire 25.0 cm long lies along the z-axis and carries a current of 9.00 A in the $+z$-direction. The magnetic field is uniform and has components $B_x = -0.242$ T, $B_y = -0.985$ T, and $B_z = -0.336$ T. (a) Find the components of the magnetic force on the wire. (b) What is the magnitude of the net magnetic force on the wire?

27.75. The rectangular loop of wire shown in Fig. 27.65 has a mass of 0.15 g per centimeter of length and is pivoted about side ab on a frictionless axis. The current in the wire is 8.2 A in the direction shown. Find the magnitude and direction of the magnetic field parallel to the y-axis that will cause the loop to swing up until its plane makes an angle of 30.0° with the yz-plane.

Figure 27.65 Problem 27.75.

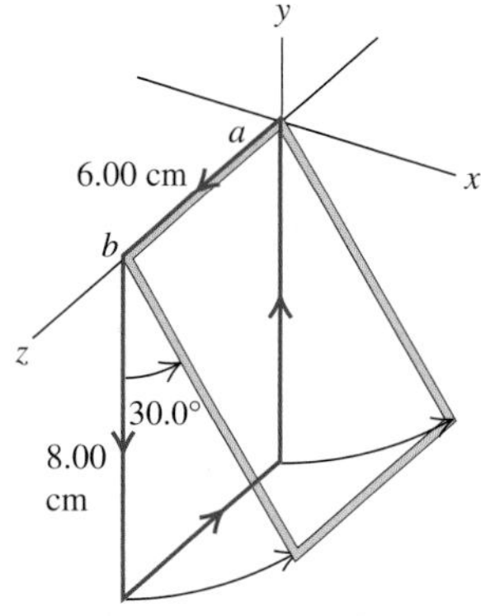

27.76. The rectangular loop shown in Fig. 27.66 is pivoted about the y-axis and carries a current of 15.0 A in the direction indicated. (a) If the loop is in a uniform magnetic field with magnitude 0.48 T in the $+x$-direction, find the magnitude and direction of the torque required to hold the loop in the position shown. (b) Repeat part (a) for the case in which the field is in the $-z$-direction. (c) For each of the above magnetic fields, what torque would be required if the loop were pivoted about an axis through its center, parallel to the y-axis?

Figure 27.66 Problem 27.76.

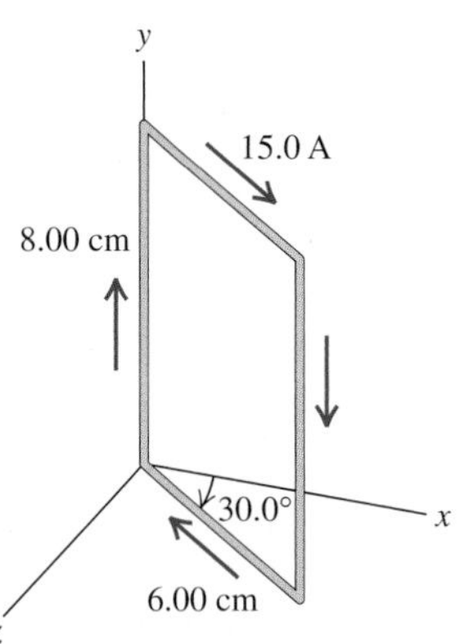

27.77. A thin, uniform rod with negligible mass and length 0.200 m is attached to the floor by a frictionless hinge at point P (Fig. 27.67). A horizontal spring with force constant $k = 4.80$ N/m connects the other end of the rod to a vertical wall. The rod is in a uniform magnetic field $B = 0.340$ T directed into the plane of the figure. There is current $I = 6.50$ A in the rod, in the direction shown. (a) Calculate the torque due to the magnetic force on the rod, for an axis at P. Is it correct to take the total magnetic force to act at the center of gravity of the rod when calculating the torque? Explain. (b) When the rod is in equilibrium and makes an angle of 53.0° with the floor, is the spring stretched or compressed? (c) How much energy is stored in the spring when the rod is in equilibrium?

Figure 27.67 Problem 27.77.

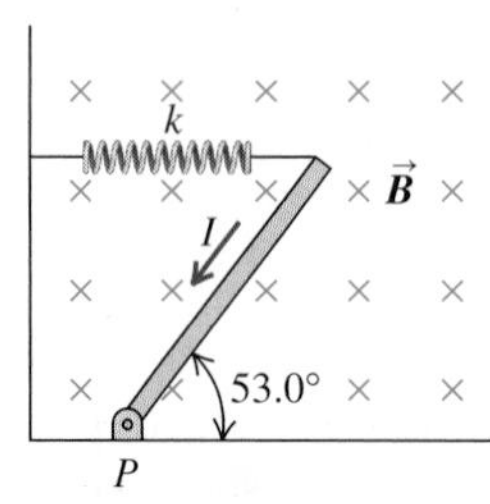

27.78. The triangular loop of wire shown in Fig. 27.68 carries a current $I = 5.00$ A in the direction shown. The loop is in a uniform magnetic field that has magnitude $B = 3.00$ T and the same direction as the current in side PQ of the loop. (a) Find the force exerted by the magnetic field on each side of the triangle. If the force is not zero, specify its direction. (b) What is the net force on the loop? (c) The loop is pivoted about an axis that lies along side PR. Use the forces calculated in part (a) to calculate the torque on each side of the loop (see Problem 27.77). (d) What is the magnitude of the net torque on the loop? Calculate the net torque from the torques calculated in part (c) and also from Eq. (27.28). Do these two results agree? (e) Is the net torque directed to rotate point Q into the plane of the figure or out of the plane of the figure?

Figure 27.68 Problem 27.78.

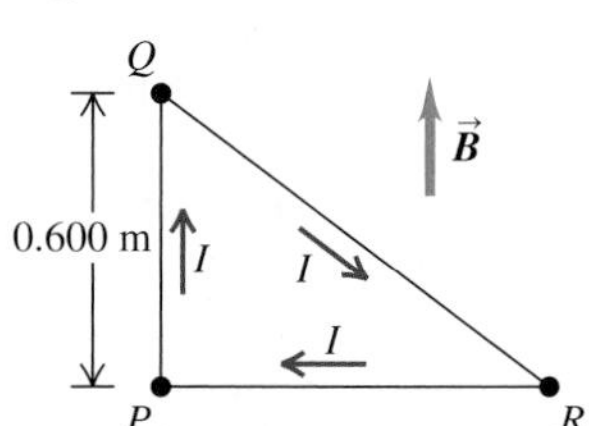

27.79. A Voice Coil. It was shown in Section 27.7 that the net force on a current loop in a *uniform* magnetic field is zero. The magnetic force on the voice coil of a loudspeaker (see Fig. 27.28) is nonzero because the magnetic field at the coil is not uniform. A voice coil in a loudspeaker has 50 turns of wire and a diameter of 1.56 cm, and the current in the coil is 0.950 A. Assume that the magnetic field at each point of the coil has a constant magnitude of 0.220 T and is directed at an angle of 60.0° outward from the normal to the plane of the coil (Fig. 27.69). Let the axis of the coil be in the y-direction. The current in the coil is in the direction shown (counterclockwise as viewed from a point above the coil on the y-axis). Calculate the magnitude and direction of the net magnetic force on the coil.

Figure 27.69 Problem 27.79.

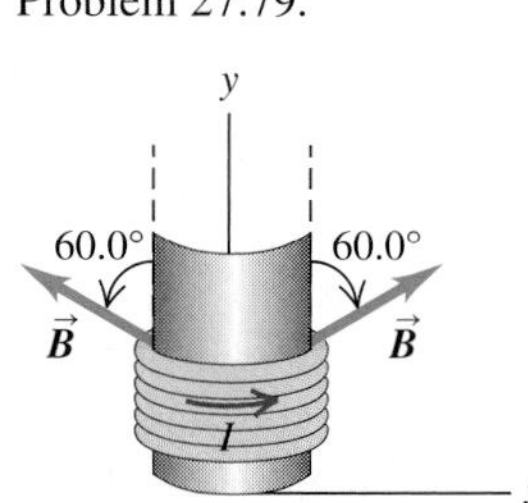

27.80. Paleoclimate. Climatologists can determine the past temperature of the earth by comparing the ratio of the isotope oxygen-18 to the isotope oxygen-16 in air trapped in ancient ice sheets, such as those in Greenland. In one method for separating these isotopes, a sample containing both of them is first singly ionized (one electron is removed) and then accelerated from rest through a potential difference V. This beam then enters a magnetic field B at right angles to the field and is bent into a quarter-circle. A particle detector at the end of the path measures the amount of each isotope, (a) Show that the separation Δr of the two isotopes at the detector is given by

$$\Delta r = \frac{\sqrt{2eV}}{eB}\left(\sqrt{m_{18}} - \sqrt{m_{16}}\right)$$

where m_{16} and m_{18} are the masses of the two oxygen isotopes, (b) The measured masses of the two isotopes are 2.66×10^{-26} kg (^{16}O) and 2.99×10^{-26} kg (^{18}O). If the magnetic field is 0.050 T, what must be the accelerating potential V so that these two isotopes will be separated by 4.00 cm at the detector?

27.81. Force on a Current Loop in a Nonuniform Magnetic Field. It was shown in Section 27.7 that the net force on a current loop in a *uniform* magnetic field is zero. But what if $\vec{B}$ is *not* uniform? Figure 27.70 shows a square loop of wire that lies in the xy-plane. The loop has corners at $(0, 0)$, $(0, L)$, $(L, 0)$, and (L, L) and carries a constant current I in the clockwise direction. The magnetic field has no x-component but has both y- and z-components: $\vec{B} = (B_0 z/L)\hat{\jmath} + (B_0 y/L)\hat{k}$, where B_0 is a positive constant. (a) Sketch the magnetic field lines in the yz-plane. (b) Find the magnitude and direction of the magnetic force exerted on each of the sides of the loop by integrating Eq. (27.20). (c) Find the magnitude and direction of the net magnetic force on the loop.

Figure 27.70 Problems 27.81 and 27.82.

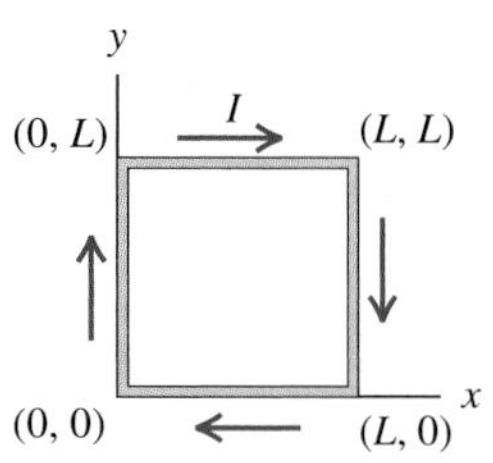

27.82. Torque on a Current Loop in a Nonuniform Magnetic Field. In Section 27.7 the expression for the torque on a current loop was derived assuming that the magnetic field $\vec{B}$ was uniform. But what if $\vec{B}$ is *not* uniform? Figure 27.70 shows a square loop of wire that lies in the xy-plane. The loop has corners at $(0, 0)$, $(0, L)$, $(L, 0)$, and (L, L) and carries a constant current I in the clockwise direction. The magnetic field has no z-component but has both x- and y-components: $\vec{B} = (B_0 y/L)\hat{\imath} + (B_0 x/L)\hat{\jmath}$, where B_0 is a positive constant. (a) Sketch the magnetic field lines in the xy-plane. (b) Find the magnitude and direction of the magnetic force exerted on each of the sides of the loop by integrating Eq. (27.20). (c) If the loop is free to rotate about the x-axis, find the magnitude and direction of the magnetic torque on the loop. (d) Repeat part (c) for the case in which the loop is free to rotate about the y-axis. (e) Is Eq. (27.26), $\vec{\tau} = \vec{\mu} \times \vec{B}$, an appropriate description of the torque on this loop? Why or why not?

27.83. An insulated wire with mass $m = 5.40 \times 10^{-5}$ kg is bent into the shape of an inverted U such that the horizontal part has a length $l = 15.0$ cm. The bent ends of the wire are partially immersed in two pools of mercury, with 2.5 cm of each end below the mercury's surface. The entire structure is in a region containing a uniform 0.00650-T magnetic field directed into the page (Fig. 27.71). An electrical connection from the mercury pools is made through the ends of the wires. The mercury pools are connected to a 1.50-V battery and a switch S. When switch S is closed, the wire jumps 35.0 cm into the air, measured from its initial position. (a) Determine the speed v of the wire as it leaves the mercury. (b) Assuming that the current I through the wire was constant from the time the switch was closed until the wire left the mercury, determine I. (c) Ignoring the resistance of the mercury and the circuit wires, determine the resistance of the moving wire.

Figure 27.71 Problem 27.83.

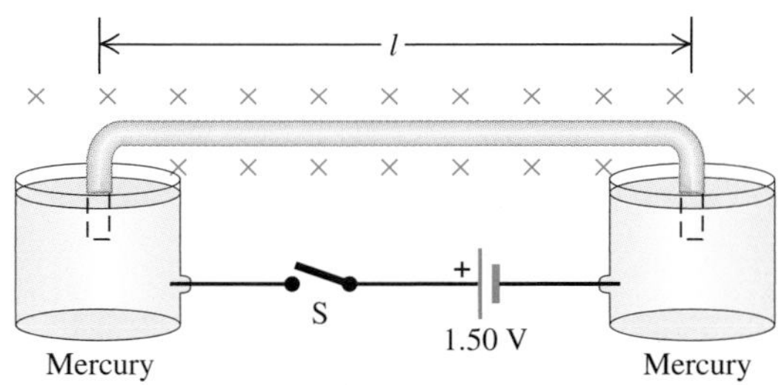

27.84. Derivation of Eq. (27.26) for a Circular Current Loop. A wire ring lies in the xy-plane with its center at the origin. The ring carries a counterclockwise current I (Fig. 27.72). A uniform magnetic field $\vec{B}$ is in the $+x$-direction, $\vec{B} = B_x\hat{\imath}$ (The result is easily extended to $\vec{B}$ in an arbitrary direction.) (a) In Fig. 27.72, show that the element $d\vec{l} = R\,d\theta(-\sin\theta\hat{\imath} + \cos\theta\hat{\jmath})$, and find $d\vec{F} = I\,d\vec{l} \times \vec{B}$. (b) Integrate $d\vec{F}$ around the loop to show that the net force is zero. (c) From part (a), find $d\vec{\tau} = \vec{r} \times d\vec{F}$, where $\vec{r} = R(\cos\theta\hat{\imath} + \sin\theta\hat{\jmath})$ is the vector from the center of the loop to the element $d\vec{l}$. (Note that $d\vec{l}$ is perpendicular to $\vec{r}$.) (d) Integrate $d\vec{\tau}$ over the loop to find the total torque $\vec{\tau}$ on the loop. Show that the result can be written as $\vec{\tau} = \vec{\mu} \times \vec{B}$, where $\mu = IA$. (*Note:* $\int\cos^2 x\,dx = \frac{1}{2}x + \frac{1}{4}\sin 2x$, $\int\sin^2 x\,dx = \frac{1}{2}x - \frac{1}{4}\sin 2x$, and $\int\sin x\cos x\,dx = \frac{1}{2}\sin^2 x$.)

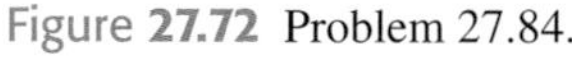

Figure 27.72 Problem 27.84.

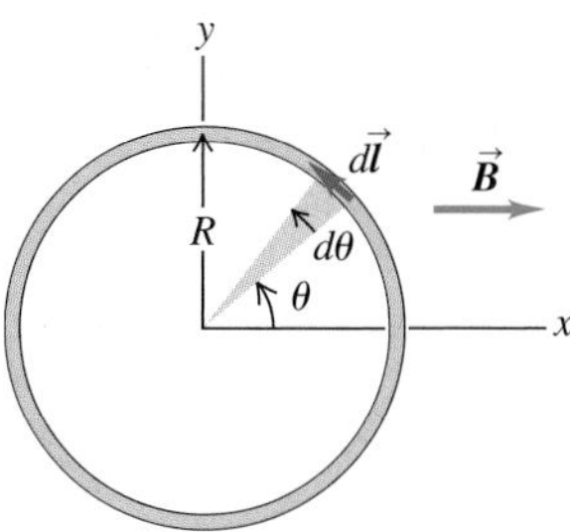

27.85. A circular loop of wire with area A lies in the xy-plane. As viewed along the z-axis looking in the $-z$-direction toward the origin, a current I is circulating clockwise around the loop. The torque produced by an external magnetic field $\vec{B}$ is given by $\vec{\tau} = D(4\hat{\imath} - 3\hat{\jmath})$, where D is a positive constant, and for this orientation of the loop the magnetic potential energy $U = -\vec{\mu} \cdot \vec{B}$ is negative. The magnitude of the magnetic field is $B_0 = 13D/IA$. (a) Determine the vector magnetic moment of the current loop. (b) Determine the components B_x, B_y, and B_z of $\vec{B}$.

27.86. Quark Model of the Neutron. The neutron is a particle with zero charge. Nonetheless, it has a nonzero magnetic moment with z-component $9.66 \times 10^{-27}\ \text{A} \cdot \text{m}^2$. This can be explained by the internal structure of the neutron. A substantial body of evidence indicates that a neutron is composed of three fundamental particles called *quarks*: an "up" (u) quark, of charge $+2e/3$, and two "down" (d) quarks, each of charge $-e/3$. The combination of the three quarks produces a net charge of $2e/3 - e/3 - e/3 = 0$. If the quarks are in motion, they can produce a nonzero magnetic moment. As a very simple model, suppose the u quark moves in a counterclockwise circular path and the d quarks move in a clockwise circular path, all of radius r and all with the same speed v (Fig. 27.73). (a) Determine the current due to the circulation of the u quark. (b) Determine the magnitude of the magnetic moment due to the circulating u quark. (c) Determine the magnitude of the magnetic moment of the three-quark system. (Be careful to use the correct magnetic moment directions.) (d) With what speed v must the quarks move if this model is to reproduce the magnetic moment of the neutron? Use $r = 1.20 \times 10^{-15}$ m (the radius of the neutron) for the radius of the orbits.

Figure 27.73 Problem 27.86.

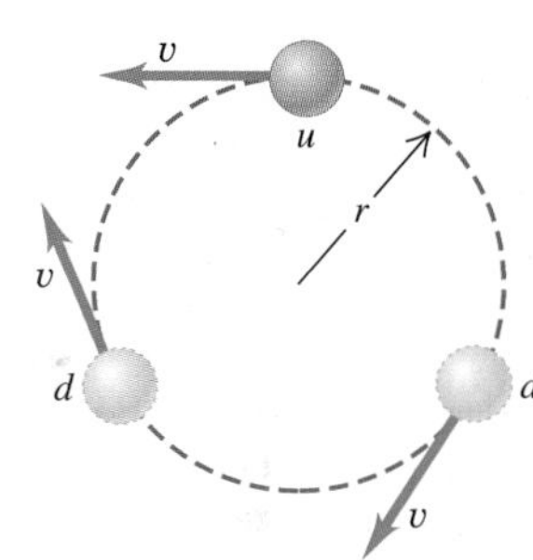

27.87. Using Gauss's Law for Magnetism. In a certain region of space, the magnetic field $\vec{B}$ is not uniform. The magnetic field has both a z-component and a component that points radially away from or toward the z-axis. The z-component is given by $B_z(z) = \beta z$, where β is a positive constant. The radial component B_r depends only on r, the radial distance from the z-axis. (a) Use Gauss's law for magnetism, Eq. (27.8), to find the radial component B_r as a function of r. (*Hint:* Try a cylindrical Gaussian surface of radius r concentric with the z-axis, with one end at $z = 0$ and the other at $z = L$.) (b) Sketch the magnetic field lines.

27.88. A circular ring with area 4.45 cm^2 is carrying a current of 12.5 A. The ring is free to rotate about a diameter. The ring, initially at rest, is immersed in a region of uniform magnetic field given by $\vec{B} = (1.15 \times 10^{-2}\,\text{T})(12\hat{\imath} + 3\hat{\jmath} - 4\hat{k})$. The ring is positioned initially such that its magnetic moment is given by $\vec{\mu}_i = \mu(-0.800\hat{\imath} + 0.600\hat{\jmath})$, where μ is the (positive) magnitude of the magnetic moment. The ring is released and turns through an angle of 90.0°, at which point its magnetic moment is given by $\vec{\mu}_f = -\mu\hat{k}$. (a) Determine the decrease in potential energy. (b) If the moment of inertia of the ring about a diameter is $8.50 \times 10^{-7}\,\text{kg}\cdot\text{m}^2$, determine the angular speed of the ring as it passes through the second position.

Challenge Problems

27.89. A particle with charge 2.15 μC and mass 3.20×10^{-11} kg is initially traveling in the $+y$-direction with a speed $v_0 = 1.45 \times 10^5$ m/s. It then enters a region containing a uniform magnetic field that is directed into, and perpendicular to, the page in Fig. 27.74. The magnitude of the field is 0.420 T. The region extends a distance of 25.0 cm along the initial direction of travel; 75.0 cm from the point of entry into the magnetic field region is a wall. The length of the field-free region is thus 50.0 cm. When the charged particle enters the magnetic field, it follows a curved path whose radius of curvature is R. It then leaves the magnetic field after a time t_1, having been deflected a distance Δx_1. The particle then travels in the field-free region and strikes the wall after undergoing a total deflection Δx. (a) Determine the radius R of the curved part of the path. (b) Determine t_1, the time the particle spends in the magnetic field. (c) Determine Δx_1, the horizontal deflection at the point of exit from the field. (d) Determine Δx, the total horizontal deflection.

Figure 27.74 Challenge Problem 27.89.

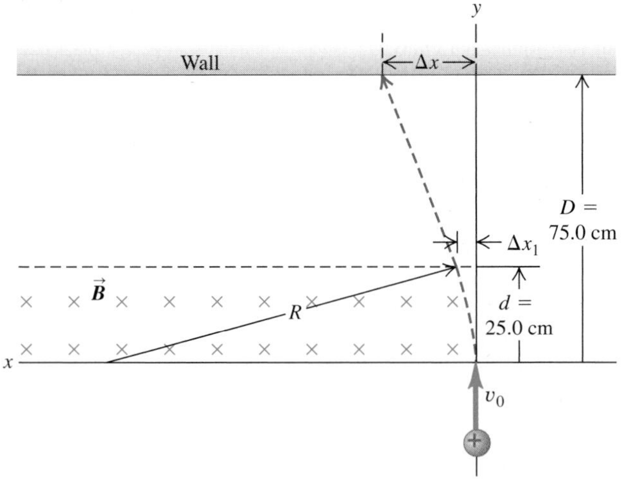

27.90. The Electromagnetic Pump. Magnetic forces acting on conducting fluids provide a convenient means of pumping these fluids. For example, this method can be used to pump blood without the damage to the cells that can be caused by a mechanical pump. A horizontal tube with rectangular cross section (height h, width w) is placed at right angles to a uniform magnetic field with magnitude B so that a length l is in the field (Fig. 27.75). The tube is filled with a conducting liquid, and an electric current of density J is maintained in the third mutually perpendicular direction. (a) Show that the difference of pressure between a point in the liquid on a vertical plane through ab and a point in the liquid on another vertical plane through cd, under conditions in which the liquid is prevented from flowing, is $\Delta p = JlB$. (b) What current density is needed to provide a pressure difference of 1.00 atm between these two points if $B = 2.20$ T and $l = 35.0$ mm?

Figure 27.75 Challenge Problem 27.90.

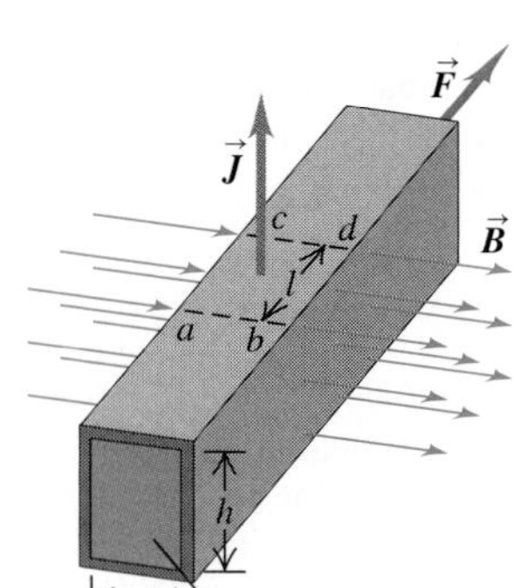

27.91. A Cycloidal Path. A particle with mass m and positive charge q starts from rest at the origin shown in Fig. 27.76. There is a uniform electric field $\vec{E}$ in the $+y$-direction and a uniform magnetic field $\vec{B}$ directed out of the page. It is shown in more advanced books that the path is a *cycloid* whose radius of curvature at the top points is twice the y-coordinate at that level. (a) Explain why the path has this general shape and why it is repetitive. (b) Prove that the speed at any point is equal to $\sqrt{2qEy/m}$. (*Hint:* Use energy conservation.) (c) Applying Newton's second law at the top point and taking as given that the radius of curvature here equals $2y$, prove that the speed at this point is $2E/B$.

Figure 27.76 Challenge Problem 27.91.

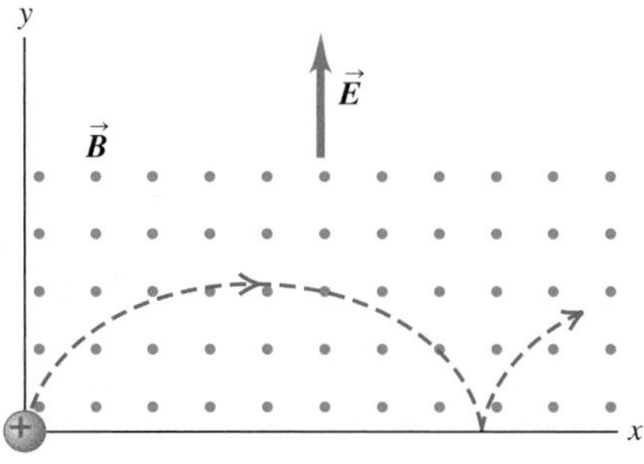

SOURCES OF MAGNETIC FIELD

28

? The immense cylinder in this photograph is actually a current-carrying coil, or solenoid, that generates a uniform magnetic field in its interior as part of an experiment at CERN, the European Laboratory for Particle Physics. If two such solenoids were joined end to end, how much stronger would the magnetic field become?

LEARNING GOALS

By studying this chapter, you will learn:

- The nature of the magnetic field produced by a single moving charged particle.
- How to describe the magnetic field produced by an element of a current-carrying conductor.
- How to calculate the magnetic field produced by a long, straight, current-carrying wire.
- Why wires carrying current in the same direction attract, while wires carrying opposing currents repel.
- How to calculate the magnetic field produced by a current-carrying wire bent into a circle.
- What Ampere's law is, and what it tells us about magnetic fields.
- How to use Ampere's law to calculate the magnetic field of symmetric current distributions.

In Chapter 27 we studied the forces exerted on moving charges and on current-carrying conductors in a magnetic field. We didn't worry about how the magnetic field got there; we simply took its existence as a given fact. But how are magnetic fields *created?* We know that both permanent magnets and electric currents in electromagnets create magnetic fields. In this chapter we will study these sources of magnetic field in detail.

We've learned that a charge creates an electric field and that an electric field exerts a force on a charge. But a *magnetic* field exerts a force only on a *moving* charge. Is it also true that a charge *creates* a magnetic field only when the charge is moving? In a word, yes.

Our analysis will begin with the magnetic field created by a single moving point charge. We can use this analysis to determine the field created by a small segment of a current-carrying conductor. Once we can do that, we can in principle find the magnetic field produced by *any* shape of conductor.

Then we will introduce Ampere's law, which plays a role in magnetism analogous to the role of Gauss's law in electrostatics. Ampere's law lets us exploit symmetry properties in relating magnetic fields to their sources.

Moving charged particles within atoms respond to magnetic fields and can also act as sources of magnetic field. We'll use these ideas to understand how certain magnetic materials can be used to intensify magnetic fields as well as why some materials such as iron act as permanent magnets.

28.1 Magnetic Field of a Moving Charge

Let's start with the basics, the magnetic field of a single point charge q moving with a constant velocity $\vec{v}$. In practical applications, such as the solenoid shown in the photo that opens this chapter, magnetic fields are produced by tremendous numbers of charged particles moving together in a current. But once we understand how to calculate the magnetic field due to a single point charge, it's a small leap to calculate the field due to a current-carrying wire or collection of wires.

As we did for electric fields, we call the location of the moving charge at a given instant the **source point** and the point P where we want to find the field the **field point.** In Section 21.4 we found that at a field point a distance r from a point charge q, the magnitude of the *electric* field $\vec{E}$ caused by the charge is proportional to the charge magnitude $|q|$ and to $1/r^2$, and the direction of $\vec{E}$ (for positive q) is along the line from source point to field point. The corresponding relationship for the *magnetic* field $\vec{B}$ of a point charge q moving with constant velocity has some similarities and some interesting differences.

Experiments show that the magnitude of $\vec{B}$ is also proportional to $|q|$ and to $1/r^2$. But the *direction* of $\vec{B}$ is *not* along the line from source point to field point. Instead, $\vec{B}$ is perpendicular to the plane containing this line and the particle's velocity vector $\vec{v}$, as shown in Fig. 28.1. Furthermore, the field *magnitude* B is also proportional to the particle's speed v and to the sine of the angle ϕ. Thus the magnetic field magnitude at point P is given by

$$B = \frac{\mu_0}{4\pi}\frac{|q|v\sin\phi}{r^2} \tag{28.1}$$

where $\mu_0/4\pi$ is a proportionality constant (μ_0 is read as "mu-nought" or "mu-sub-zero"). The reason for writing the constant in this particular way will emerge shortly. We did something similar with Coulomb's law in Section 21.3.

28.1 (a) Magnetic-field vectors due to a moving positive point charge q. At each point, $\vec{B}$ is perpendicular to the plane of $\vec{r}$ and $\vec{v}$, and its magnitude is proportional to the sine of the angle between them. (b) Magnetic field lines in a plane containing a moving positive charge.

(a) Perspective view

Right-hand rule for the magnetic field due to a positive charge moving at constant velocity: Point the thumb of your right hand in the direction of the velocity. Your fingers now curl around the charge in the direction of the magnetic field lines. (If the charge is negative, the field lines are in the opposite direction.)

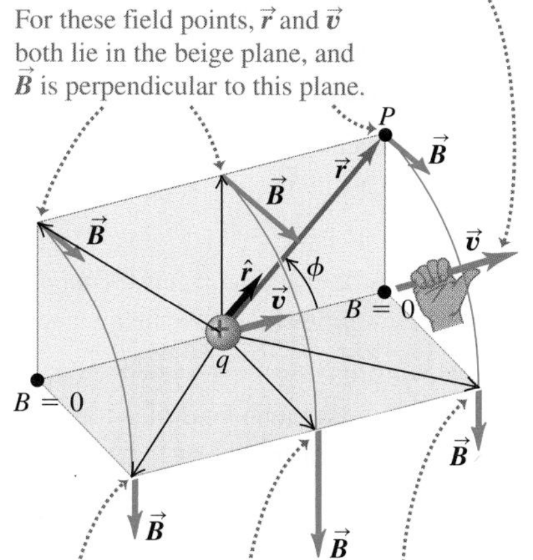
For these field points, $\vec{r}$ and $\vec{v}$ both lie in the beige plane, and $\vec{B}$ is perpendicular to this plane.
P
$\vec{B}$
$\vec{r}$
$\vec{B}$
$\vec{B}$
$\vec{v}$
$\hat{r}$
ϕ
$\vec{v}$
B = 0
q
B = 0
$\vec{B}$
$\vec{B}$
$\vec{B}$

For these field points, $\vec{r}$ and $\vec{v}$ both lie in the gold plane, and $\vec{B}$ is perpendicular to this plane.

(b) View from behind the charge

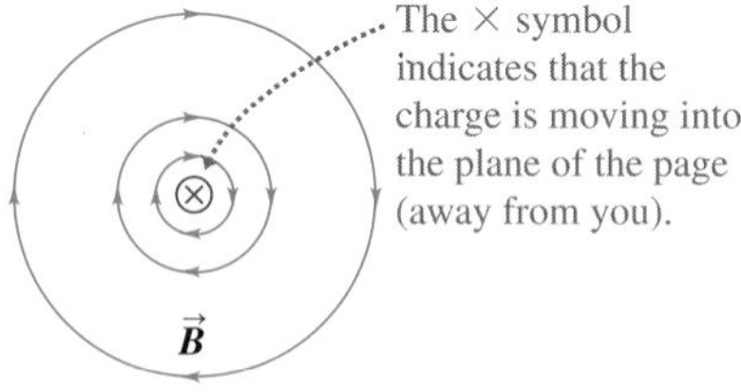
The × symbol indicates that the charge is moving into the plane of the page (away from you).
$\vec{B}$

Moving Charge: Vector Magnetic Field

We can incorporate both the magnitude and direction of $\vec{B}$ into a single vector equation using the vector product. To avoid having to say "the direction from the source q to the field point P" over and over, we introduce a *unit* vector $\hat{r}$ ("r-hat") that points from the source point to the field point. (We used $\hat{r}$ for the same purpose in Section 21.4.) This unit vector is equal to the vector $\vec{r}$ from the source to the field point divided by its magnitude: $\hat{r} = \vec{r}/r$. Then the $\vec{B}$ field of a moving point charge is

$$\vec{B} = \frac{\mu_0}{4\pi}\frac{q\vec{v}\times\hat{r}}{r^2} \quad \text{(magnetic field of a point charge with constant velocity)} \tag{28.2}$$

Figure 28.1 shows the relationship of $\hat{r}$ to P and also shows the magnetic field $\vec{B}$ at several points in the vicinity of the charge. At all points along a line through the charge parallel to the velocity $\vec{v}$, the field is zero because $\sin\phi = 0$ at all such points. At any distance r from q, $\vec{B}$ has its greatest magnitude at points lying in the plane perpendicular to $\vec{v}$ because at all such points, $\phi = 90°$ and $\sin\phi = 1$. If the charge q is negative, the directions of $\vec{B}$ are opposite to those shown in Fig. 28.1.

Moving Charge: Magnetic Field Lines

A point charge in motion also produces an *electric* field, with field lines that radiate outward from a positive charge. The *magnetic* field lines are completely different. The above discussion shows that for a point charge moving with velocity $\vec{v}$, the magnetic field lines are *circles* centered on the line of $\vec{v}$ and lying in planes perpendicular to this line. The field-line directions for a positive charge are given by the following *right-hand rule,* one of several that we will encounter in this chapter for determining the direction of the magnetic field caused by different sources. Grasp the velocity vector $\vec{v}$ with your right hand so that your right thumb points in the direction of $\vec{v}$; your fingers then curl around the line of $\vec{v}$ in the same sense as the magnetic field lines, assuming q is positive. Figure 28.1a shows parts of a few field lines; Fig. 28.1b shows some field lines in a plane through q, perpendicular to $\vec{v}$, as seen by looking in the direction of $\vec{v}$. If the point charge is negative, the directions of the field and field lines are the opposite of those shown in Fig. 28.1.

Equations (28.1) and (28.2) describe the $\vec{B}$ field of a point charge moving with *constant* velocity. If the charge *accelerates,* the field can be much more complicated. We won't need these more complicated results for our purposes. (The moving charged particles that make up a current in a wire accelerate at points where the wire bends and the direction of $\vec{v}$ changes. But because the magnitude v_d of the drift velocity in a conductor is typically very small, the acceleration v_d^2/r is also very small, and the effects of acceleration can be ignored.)

As we discussed in Section 27.2, the unit of B is one tesla (1 T):

$$1\ \mathrm{T} = 1\ \mathrm{N \cdot s/C \cdot m} = 1\ \mathrm{N/A \cdot m}$$

Using this with Eq. (28.1) or (28.2), we find that the units of the constant μ_0 are

$$1\ \mathrm{N \cdot s^2/C^2} = 1\ \mathrm{N/A^2} = 1\ \mathrm{Wb/A \cdot m} = 1\ \mathrm{T \cdot m/A}$$

In SI units the numerical value of μ_0 is exactly $4\pi \times 10^{-7}$. Thus

$$\begin{aligned} \mu_0 &= 4\pi \times 10^{-7}\ \mathrm{N \cdot s^2/C^2} = 4\pi \times 10^{-7}\ \mathrm{Wb/A \cdot m} \\ &= 4\pi \times 10^{-7}\ \mathrm{T \cdot m/A} \end{aligned} \qquad (28.3)$$

It may seem incredible that μ_0 has *exactly* this numerical value! In fact this is a *defined* value that arises from the definition of the ampere, as we'll discuss in Section 28.4.

We mentioned in Section 21.3 that the constant $1/4\pi\epsilon_0$ in Coulomb's law is related to the speed of light c:

$$k = \frac{1}{4\pi\epsilon_0} = (10^{-7}\ \mathrm{N \cdot s^2/C^2})c^2$$

When we study electromagnetic waves in Chapter 32, we will find that their speed of propagation in vacuum, which is equal to the speed of light c, is given by

$$c^2 = \frac{1}{\epsilon_0 \mu_0} \qquad (28.4)$$

If we solve the equation $k = 1/4\pi\epsilon_0$ for ϵ_0, substitute the resulting expression into Eq. (28.4), and solve for μ_0, we indeed get the value of μ_0 stated above. This discussion is a little premature, but it may give you a hint that electric and magnetic fields are intimately related to the nature of light.

Example 28.1 Forces between two moving protons

Two protons move parallel to the x-axis in opposite directions (Fig. 28.2) at the same speed v (small compared to the speed of light c). At the instant shown, find the electric and magnetic forces on the upper proton and determine the ratio of their magnitudes.

SOLUTION

IDENTIFY: The electric force is given by Coulomb's law. To find the magnetic force, we must first find the magnetic field that the lower proton produces at the position of the upper proton.

SET UP: We use Eq. (21.2) for Coulomb's law. Equation (28.2) gives us the magnetic field due to the lower proton, and the magnetic force law, Eq. (27.2), gives us the resulting magnetic force on the upper proton.

EXECUTE: From Coulomb's law, the magnitude of the electric force on the upper proton is

$$F_E = \frac{1}{4\pi\epsilon_0}\frac{q^2}{r^2}$$

28.2 Electric and magnetic forces between two moving protons.

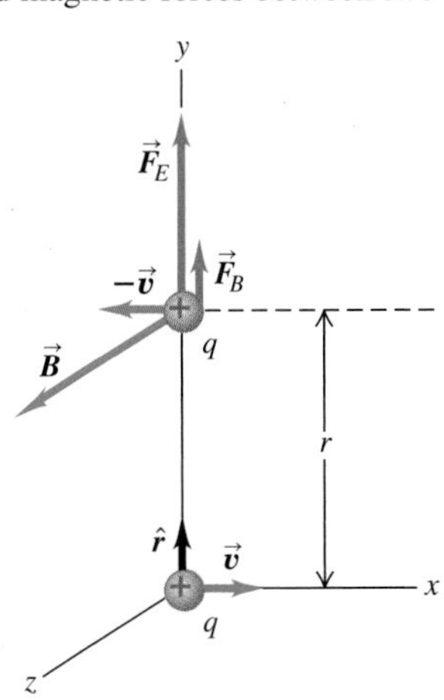

Continued

The forces are repulsive, and the force on the upper proton is vertically upward (in the $+y$-direction).

From the right-hand rule for the cross product $\vec{v} \times \hat{r}$ in Eq. (28.2), the $\vec{B}$-field due to the lower proton at the position of the upper proton is in the $+z$-direction (see Fig. 28.2). From Eq. (28.2), the magnitude of $\vec{B}$ is

$$B = \frac{\mu_0}{4\pi} \frac{qv}{r^2}$$

since $\phi = 90°$. Alternatively, from Eq. (28.2),

$$\vec{B} = \frac{\mu_0}{4\pi} \frac{q(v\hat{\imath}) \times \hat{\jmath}}{r^2} = \frac{\mu_0}{4\pi} \frac{qv}{r^2} \hat{k}$$

The velocity of the upper proton is $-\vec{v}$ and the magnetic force on it is $\vec{F} = q(-\vec{v}) \times \vec{B}$. Combining this with the expressions for $\vec{B}$, we find

$$F_B = \frac{\mu_0}{4\pi} \frac{q^2 v^2}{r^2} \quad \text{or}$$

$$\vec{F}_B = q(-\vec{v}) \times \vec{B} = q(-v\hat{\imath}) \times \frac{\mu_0}{4\pi} \frac{qv}{r^2} \hat{k} = \frac{\mu_0}{4\pi} \frac{q^2 v^2}{r^2} \hat{\jmath}$$

The magnetic interaction in this situation is also repulsive. The ratio of the magnitudes of the two forces is

$$\frac{F_B}{F_E} = \frac{\mu_0 q^2 v^2 / 4\pi r^2}{q^2 / 4\pi\epsilon_0 r^2} = \frac{\mu_0 v^2}{1/\epsilon_0} = \epsilon_0 \mu_0 v^2$$

Using the relationship $\epsilon_0 \mu_0 = 1/c^2$, Eq. (28.4), we can express our result very simply as

$$\frac{F_B}{F_E} = \frac{v^2}{c^2}$$

When v is small in comparison to c, the speed of light, the magnetic force is much smaller than the electric force.

EVALUATE: Note that it is essential to use the same frame of reference in this entire calculation. We have described the velocities and the fields as they appear to an observer who is stationary in the coordinate system of Fig. 28.2. In a coordinate system that moves with one of the charges, one of the velocities would be zero, so there would be *no* magnetic force. The explanation of this apparent paradox provided one of the paths that led to the special theory of relativity.

Test Your Understanding of Section 28.1 (a) If two protons are traveling parallel to each other in the *same* direction and at the same speed, is the magnetic force between them (i) attractive or (ii) repulsive? (b) Is the net force between them (i) attractive, (ii) repulsive, or (iii) zero? (Assume that the protons' speed is much slower than the speed of light.)

28.2 Magnetic Field of a Current Element

Just as for the electric field, there is a **principle of superposition of magnetic fields:**

The total magnetic field caused by several moving charges is the vector sum of the fields caused by the individual charges.

We can use this principle with the results of Section 28.1 to find the magnetic field produced by a current in a conductor.

We begin by calculating the magnetic field caused by a short segment $d\vec{l}$ of a current-carrying conductor, as shown in Fig. 28.3a. The volume of the segment is $A\,dl$, where A is the cross-sectional area of the conductor. If there are n moving charged particles per unit volume, each of charge q, the total moving charge dQ in the segment is

$$dQ = nqA\,dl$$

The moving charges in this segment are equivalent to a single charge dQ, traveling with a velocity equal to the *drift* velocity $\vec{v}_d$. (Magnetic fields due to the *random* motions of the charges will, on average, cancel out at every point.) From Eq. (28.1) the magnitude of the resulting field $d\vec{B}$ at any field point P is

$$dB = \frac{\mu_0}{4\pi} \frac{|dQ| v_d \sin\phi}{r^2} = \frac{\mu_0}{4\pi} \frac{n|q| v_d A\,dl \sin\phi}{r^2}$$

But from Eq. (25.2), $n|q|v_d A$ equals the current I in the element. So

$$dB = \frac{\mu_0}{4\pi} \frac{I\,dl \sin\phi}{r^2} \tag{28.5}$$

Current Element: Vector Magnectic Field

In vector form, using the unit vector $\hat{\boldsymbol{r}}$ as in Section 28.1, we have

$$d\vec{B} = \frac{\mu_0}{4\pi}\frac{I\,d\vec{l} \times \hat{r}}{r^2} \quad \text{(magnetic field of a current element)} \qquad (28.6)$$

where $d\vec{l}$ is a vector with length dl, in the same direction as the current in the conductor.

Equations (28.5) and (28.6) are called the **law of Biot and Savart** (pronounced "Bee-oh" and "Suh-var"). We can use this law to find the total magnetic field $\vec{B}$ at any point in space due to the current in a complete circuit. To do this, we integrate Eq. (28.6) over all segments $d\vec{l}$ that carry current; symbolically,

$$\vec{B} = \frac{\mu_0}{4\pi}\int \frac{I\,d\vec{l} \times \hat{r}}{r^2} \qquad (28.7)$$

In the following sections we will carry out this vector integration for several examples.

Current Element: Magnetic Field Lines

As Fig. 28.3 shows, the field vectors $d\vec{B}$ and the magnetic field lines of a current element are exactly like those set up by a positive charge dQ moving in the direction of the drift velocity $\vec{v}_d$. The field lines are circles in planes perpendicular to $d\vec{l}$ and centered on the line of $d\vec{l}$. Their directions are given by the same right-hand rule that we introduced for point charges in Section 28.1.

We can't verify Eq. (28.5) or (28.6) directly because we can never experiment with an isolated segment of a current-carrying circuit. What we measure experimentally is the *total* $\vec{B}$ for a complete circuit. But we can still verify these equations indirectly by calculating $\vec{B}$ for various current configurations using Eq. (28.7) and comparing the results with experimental measurements.

If matter is present in the space around a current-carrying conductor, the field at a field point P in its vicinity will have an additional contribution resulting from the *magnetization* of the material. We'll return to this point in Section 28.8. However, unless the material is iron or some other ferromagnetic material, the additional field is small and is usually negligible. Additional complications arise if time-varying electric or magnetic fields are present or if the material is a superconductor; we'll return to these topics later.

28.3 (a) Magnetic-field vectors due to a current element $d\vec{l}$. (b) Magnetic field lines in a plane containing the current element $d\vec{l}$. Compare this figure to Fig. 28.1 for the field of a moving point charge.

(a) Perspective view

Right-hand rule for the magnetic field due to a current element: Point the thumb of your right hand in the direction of the current. Your fingers now curl around the current element in the direction of the magnetic field lines.

For these field points, $\vec{r}$ and $d\vec{l}$ both lie in the beige plane, and $d\vec{B}$ is perpendicular to this plane.

For these field points, $\vec{r}$ and $d\vec{l}$ both lie in the gold plane, and $d\vec{B}$ is perpendicular to this plane.

(b) View along the axis of the current element

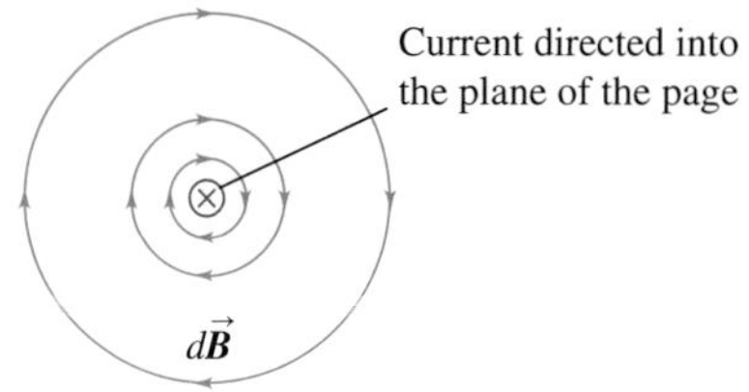

Problem-Solving Strategy 28.1 Magnetic-Field Calculations

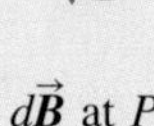

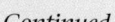

IDENTIFY *the relevant concepts:* The law of Biot and Savart allows you to calculate the magnetic field due to a current-carrying wire of any shape. The idea is to calculate the field due to a representative current element in the wire and then combine the contributions from all such elements to find the total field.

SET UP *the problem* using the following steps:

1. Make a diagram showing a representative current element and the point P at which the field is to be determined (the field point).
2. Draw the current element $d\vec{l}$, being careful that it points in the direction of the current.
3. Draw the unit vector $\hat{r}$. Note that it is always directed *from* the current element (the source point) to the field point P.
4. Identify the target variables. Usually they will be the magnitude and direction of the magnetic field $\vec{B}$.

EXECUTE *the solution* as follows:

1. Use Eq. (28.5) or (28.6) to express the magnetic field $d\vec{B}$ at P from the representative current element.
2. Add up all the $d\vec{B}$'s to find the total field at point P. In some situations the $d\vec{B}$'s at point P have the same direction for all the current elements; then the magnitude of the total $\vec{B}$ field is the sum of the magnitudes of the $d\vec{B}$'s. But often the $d\vec{B}$'s have different directions for different current elements. Then you have to set up a coordinate system and represent each $d\vec{B}$ in terms of its components. The integral for the total $\vec{B}$ is then expressed in terms of an integral for each component.
3. Sometimes you can use the symmetry of the situation to prove that one component of $\vec{B}$ must vanish. Always be alert for ways to use symmetry to simplify the problem.

Continued

4. Look for ways to use the principle of superposition of magnetic fields. Later in this chapter we'll determine the fields produced by certain simple conductor shapes; if you encounter a conductor of a complex shape that can be represented as a combination of these simple shapes, you can use superposition to find the field of the complex shape. Examples include a rectangular loop and a semicircle with straight line segments on both sides.

EVALUATE *your answer:* Often your answer will be a mathematical expression for $\vec{B}$ as a function of the position of the field point. Check the answer by examining its behavior in as many limits as you can.

Example 28.2 Magnetic field of a current segment

A copper wire carries a steady current of 125 A to an electroplating tank. Find the magnetic field caused by a 1.0-cm segment of this wire at a point 1.2 m away from it, if the point is (a) point P_1, straight out to the side of the segment, and (b) point P_2, on a line at 30° to the segment, as shown in Fig. 28.4.

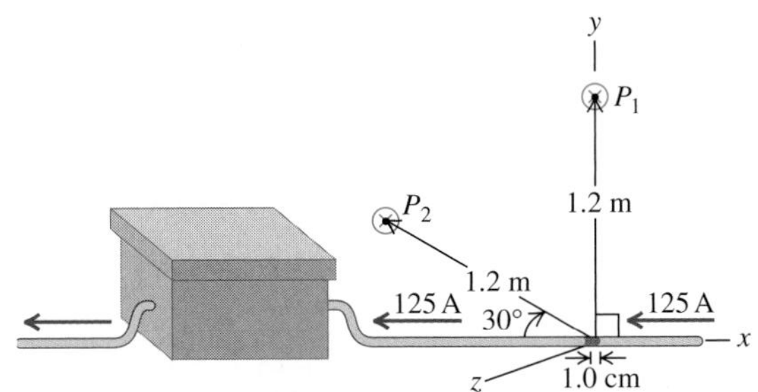

28.4 Finding the magnetic field at two points due to a 1.0-cm segment of current-carrying wire (not shown to scale).

SOLUTION

IDENTIFY: Although Eqs. (28.5) and (28.6) are strictly to be used with infinitesimal current elements only, we may use them here since the segment's 1.0-cm length is much smaller than the 1.2-m distance to the field point.

SET UP: The current element is shown in red in Fig. 28.4 and points in the $-x$-direction (the direction of the current). The unit vector $\hat{r}$ for each field point is directed from the current element toward that point: $\hat{r}$ is in the $+y$-direction for point P_1 and at an angle of 30° above the $-x$-direction for point P_2.

EXECUTE: (a) From the right-hand rule, the direction of $\vec{B}$ at P_1 is *into* the xy-plane of Fig. 28.4. Or, using unit vectors, we note that $d\vec{l} = dl(-\hat{\imath})$. At point P_1, $\hat{r} = \hat{\jmath}$, so in Eq. (28.6),

$$d\vec{l} \times \hat{r} = dl(-\hat{\imath}) \times \hat{\jmath} = dl(-\hat{k})$$

The negative z-direction is *into* the plane.

To find the magnitude of $\vec{B}$, we use Eq. (28.5). At point P_1, the angle between $d\vec{l}$ and $\hat{r}$ is 90°, so

$$\begin{aligned} B &= \frac{\mu_0}{4\pi}\frac{I\,dl\sin\phi}{r^2} \\ &= (10^{-7}\,\mathrm{T\cdot m/A})\frac{(125\,\mathrm{A})(1.0\times10^{-2}\,\mathrm{m})(\sin 90°)}{(1.2\,\mathrm{m})^2} \\ &= 8.7\times10^{-8}\,\mathrm{T} \end{aligned}$$

(b) At point P_2 the direction of $\vec{B}$ is again into the xy-plane of the figure. The angle between $d\vec{l}$ and $\hat{r}$ is 30°, and

$$\begin{aligned} B &= (10^{-7}\,\mathrm{T\cdot m/A})\frac{(125\,\mathrm{A})(1.0\times10^{-2}\,\mathrm{m})(\sin 30°)}{(1.2\,\mathrm{m})^2} \\ &= 4.3\times10^{-8}\,\mathrm{T} \end{aligned}$$

EVALUATE: You can check our results for the direction of $\vec{B}$ by comparing them with Fig. 28.3. The xy-plane in Fig. 28.4 corresponds to the beige plane in Fig. 28.3. However, in the present example the direction of the current and hence of $d\vec{l}$ is the reverse of the direction shown in Fig. 28.3, so the direction of the magnetic field is reversed as well. Hence the field at points in the xy-plane in Fig. 28.4 must point *into,* not out of, that plane. This is just what we concluded above.

Note that these magnetic-field magnitudes are very small; for comparison the magnetic field of the earth is of the order of 10^{-4} T. Note also that the values are not the *total* fields at points P_1 and P_2, but only the contributions from the short segment of conductor described.

Test Your Understanding of Section 28.2 An infinitesimal current element located at the origin ($x = y = z = 0$) carries current I in the positive y-direction. Rank the following locations in order of the strength of the magnetic field that the current element produces at that location, from largest to smallest value. (i) $x = L, y = 0, z = 0$; (ii) $x = 0, y = L, z = 0$; (iii) $x = 0, y = 0, z = L$; (iv) $x = L/\sqrt{2}, y = L/\sqrt{2}, z = 0$.

28.3 Magnetic Field of a Straight Current-Carrying Conductor

ActivPhysics ONLINE
13.1 Magnetic Field of a Wire

An important application of the law of Biot and Savart is finding the magnetic field produced by a straight current-carrying conductor. This result is useful because straight conducting wires are found in essentially all electric and electronic devices. Fig. 28.5 shows such a conductor with length $2a$ carrying a current I. We will find $\vec{B}$ at a point a distance x from the conductor on its perpendicular bisector.

We first use the law of Biot and Savart, Eq. (28.5), to find the field $d\vec{B}$ caused by the element of conductor of length $dl = dy$ shown in Fig. 28.5. From the figure, $r = \sqrt{x^2 + y^2}$ and $\sin\phi = \sin(\pi - \phi) = x/\sqrt{x^2 + y^2}$. The right-hand rule for the vector product $d\vec{l} \times \hat{r}$ shows that the *direction* of $d\vec{B}$ is into the plane of the figure, perpendicular to the plane; furthermore, the directions of the $d\vec{B}$'s from *all* elements of the conductor are the same. Thus in integrating Eq. (28.7), we can just add the *magnitudes* of the $d\vec{B}$'s, a significant simplification.

Putting the pieces together, we find that the magnitude of the total $\vec{B}$ field is

$$B = \frac{\mu_0 I}{4\pi}\int_{-a}^{a}\frac{x\,dy}{(x^2 + y^2)^{3/2}}$$

We can integrate this by trigonometric substitution or by using an integral table. The final result is

$$B = \frac{\mu_0 I}{4\pi}\frac{2a}{x\sqrt{x^2 + a^2}} \qquad (28.8)$$

When the length $2a$ of the conductor is very great in comparison to its distance x from point P, we can consider it to be infinitely long. When a is much larger than x, $\sqrt{x^2 + a^2}$ is approximately equal to a; hence in the limit $a \rightarrow \infty$, Eq. (28.8) becomes

$$B = \frac{\mu_0 I}{2\pi x}$$

The physical situation has axial symmetry about the y-axis. Hence $\vec{B}$ must have the same *magnitude* at all points on a circle centered on the conductor and lying in a plane perpendicular to it, and the *direction* of $\vec{B}$ must be everywhere tangent to such a circle. Thus, at all points on a circle of radius r around the conductor, the magnitude B is

$$B = \frac{\mu_0 I}{2\pi r} \quad \text{(near a long, straight, current-carrying conductor)} \qquad (28.9)$$

Part of the magnetic field around a long, straight, current-carrying conductor is shown in Fig. 28.6.

The geometry of this problem is similar to that of Example 21.11 (Section 21.5), in which we solved the problem of the *electric* field caused by an infinite line of charge. The same integral appears in both problems, and the field magnitudes in both problems are proportional to $1/r$. But the lines of $\vec{B}$ in the magnetic problem have completely different shapes than the lines of $\vec{E}$ in the analogous electrical problem. Electric field lines radiate outward from a positive line charge distribution (inward for negative charges). By contrast, magnetic field lines *encircle* the current that acts as their source. Electric field lines due to charges begin and end at those charges, but magnetic field lines always form closed loops and *never* have end points, irrespective of the shape of the current-carrying conductor that sets up the field. As we discussed in Section 27.3, this is a consequence of Gauss's law for magnetism, which states that the total magnetic flux through *any* closed surface is always zero:

$$\oint \vec{B} \cdot d\vec{A} = 0 \quad \text{(magnetic flux through any closed surface)} \qquad (28.10)$$

This implies that there are no isolated magnetic charges or magnetic monopoles. Any magnetic field line that enters a closed surface must also emerge from that surface.

28.5 Magnetic field produced by a straight current-carrying conductor of length $2a$.

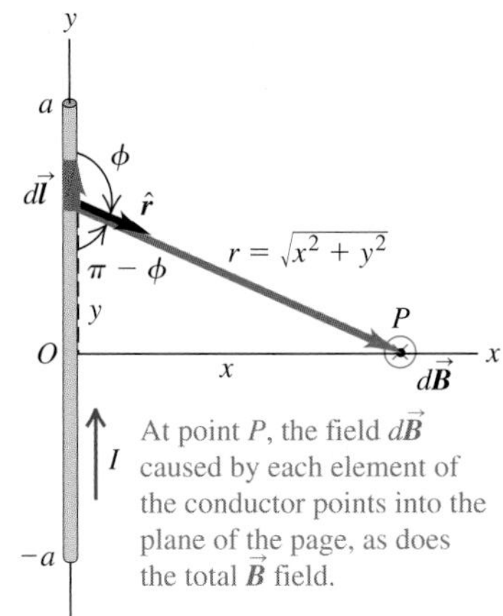

28.6 Magnetic field around a long, straight, current-carrying conductor. The field lines are circles, with directions determined by the right-hand rule.

Right-hand rule for the magnetic field around a current-carrying wire: Point the thumb of your right hand in the direction of the current. Your fingers now curl around the wire in the direction of the magnetic field lines.

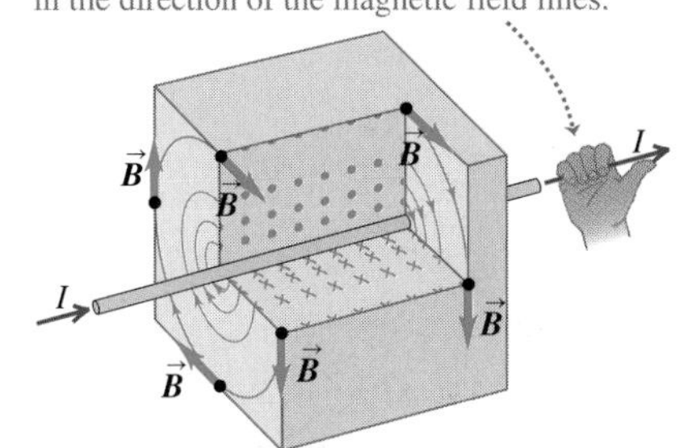

Example 28.3 Magnetic field of a single wire

A long, straight conductor carries a current of 1.0 A. At what distance from the axis of the conductor is the magnetic field caused by the current equal in magnitude to the earth's magnetic field in Pittsburgh (about 0.5×10^{-4} T)?

SOLUTION

IDENTIFY: The straight conductor is described as being long, which means that its length is much greater than the distance from the conductor at which we measure the field. Hence we can use the ideas of this section.

SET UP: The geometry is the same as that in Fig. 28.6, so we use Eq. (28.8). All of the quantities in this equation are known except the target variable, the distance *r*.

EXECUTE: We solve Eq. (28.8) for *r* and insert the appropriate numbers:

$$r = \frac{\mu_0 I}{2\pi B}$$
$$= \frac{(4\pi \times 10^{-7}\ \text{T}\cdot\text{m/A})(1.0\ \text{A})}{(2\pi)(0.5 \times 10^{-4}\ \text{T})} = 4 \times 10^{-3}\ \text{m} = 4\ \text{mm}$$

EVALUATE: Currents of an ampere or so are typical of those found in the wiring of home appliances. This example shows that the magnetic fields produced by these appliances are very weak even at points very close to the wire. At greater distances the field becomes even weaker; for example, at five times the distance $(r = 20\ \text{mm} = 2\ \text{cm} = 2 \times 10^{-2}\ \text{m})$ the field is one-fifth as great $(B = 0.1 \times 10^{-4}\ \text{T})$.

Example 28.4 Magnetic field of two wires

Fig. 28.7a is an end-on view of two long, straight, parallel wires perpendicular to the *xy*-plane, each carrying a current *I* but in opposite directions. (a) Find the magnitude and direction of $\vec{B}$ at points P_1, P_2, and P_3. (b) Find the magnitude and direction of $\vec{B}$ at any point on the *x*-axis to the right of wire 2 in terms of the *x*-coordinate of the point.

SOLUTION

IDENTIFY: We can find the magnetic fields $\vec{B}_1$ and $\vec{B}_2$ due to each wire using the ideas of this section. The principle of superposition of magnetic fields says that the total magnetic field $\vec{B}$ is the vector sum of $\vec{B}_1$ and $\vec{B}_2$.

SET UP: We use Eq. (28.9) to find the magnitude of the fields $\vec{B}_1$ (due to wire 1) and $\vec{B}_2$ (due to wire 2) at any point. We find the directions of these fields using the right-hand rule. The total magnetic field at the point in question is $\vec{B}_{\text{total}} = \vec{B}_1 + \vec{B}_2$.

EXECUTE: (a) Point P_1 is closer to wire 1 (distance 2*d*) than to wire 2 (distance 4*d*), so at this point the field magnitude B_1 is greater than the magnitude B_2:

$$B_1 = \frac{\mu_0 I}{2\pi(2d)} = \frac{\mu_0 I}{4\pi d} \qquad B_2 = \frac{\mu_0 I}{2\pi(4d)} = \frac{\mu_0 I}{8\pi d}$$

The right-hand rule shows that $\vec{B}_1$ is in the negative *y*-direction and $\vec{B}_2$ is in the positive *y*-direction. Since B_1 is the larger magnitude, the total field $\vec{B}_{\text{total}} = \vec{B}_1 + \vec{B}_2$ is in the negative *y*-direction, with magnitude

$$B_{\text{total}} = B_1 - B_2 = \frac{\mu_0 I}{4\pi d} - \frac{\mu_0 I}{8\pi d} = \frac{\mu_0 I}{8\pi d} \qquad \text{(point } P_1\text{)}$$

At point P_2, a distance *d* from both wires, $\vec{B}_1$ and $\vec{B}_2$ are both in the positive *y*-direction, and both have the same magnitude:

$$B_1 = B_2 = \frac{\mu_0 I}{2\pi d}$$

so $\vec{B}_{\text{total}}$ is also in the positive *y*-direction and has magnitude

$$B_{\text{total}} = B_1 + B_2 = \frac{\mu_0 I}{\pi d} \qquad \text{(point } P_2\text{)}$$

Finally, at point P_3 the right-hand rule shows that $\vec{B}_1$ is in the positive *y*-direction and $\vec{B}_2$ is in the negative *y*-direction. This point is farther from wire 1 (distance 3*d*) than from wire 2 (distance *d*), so B_1 is less than B_2:

$$B_1 = \frac{\mu_0 I}{2\pi(3d)} = \frac{\mu_0 I}{6\pi d} \qquad B_2 = \frac{\mu_0 I}{2\pi d}$$

28.7 (a) Two long, straight conductors carrying equal currents in opposite directions. The conductors are seen end-on. (b) Map of the magnetic field produced by the two conductors. The field lines are closest together between the conductors, where the field is strongest.

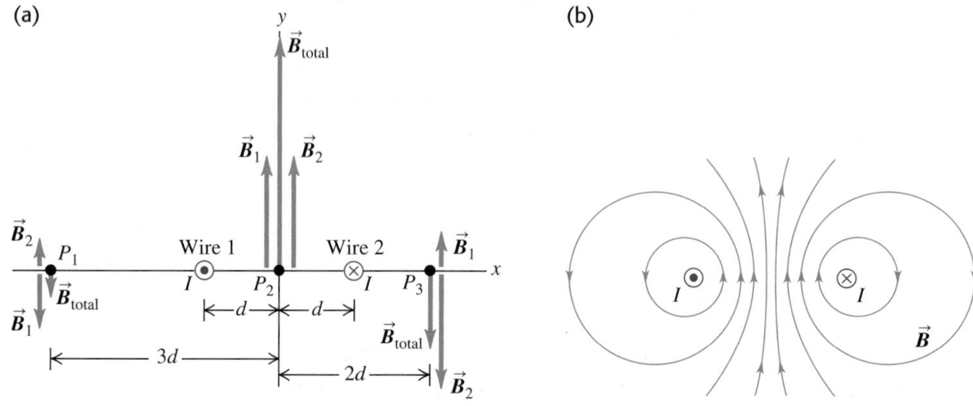

The total field is in the negative y-direction, the same as $\vec{B}_2$, and has magnitude

$$B_{\text{total}} = B_2 - B_1 = \frac{\mu_0 I}{2\pi d} - \frac{\mu_0 I}{6\pi d} = \frac{\mu_0 I}{3\pi d} \qquad \text{(point } P_3\text{)}$$

You should be able to use the right-hand rule to verify for yourself the directions of $\vec{B}_1$ and $\vec{B}_2$ for each point.

The fields $\vec{B}_1$, $\vec{B}_2$, and $\vec{B}_{\text{total}}$ at each of the three points are shown in Fig. 28.7a. The same technique can be used to find $\vec{B}_{\text{total}}$ at any point; for points off the x-axis, caution must be taken in vector addition, since $\vec{B}_1$ and $\vec{B}_2$ need no longer be simply parallel or antiparallel (see Problem 28.60). Figure 28.7b shows some of the magnetic field lines due to this combination of wires.

(b) At any point to the right of wire 2 (that is, for $x > d$), $\vec{B}_1$ and $\vec{B}_2$ are in the same directions as at P_3. As x increases, both $\vec{B}_1$ and $\vec{B}_2$ decrease in magnitude, so $\vec{B}_{\text{total}}$ must decrease as well. The magnitudes of the fields due to each wire are

$$B_1 = \frac{\mu_0 I}{2\pi(x + d)} \qquad \text{and} \qquad B_2 = \frac{\mu_0 I}{2\pi(x - d)}$$

At any field point to the right of wire 2, wire 2 is closer than wire 1, and so $B_2 > B_1$. Hence $\vec{B}_{\text{total}}$ is in the negative y-direction, the same as $\vec{B}_2$, and has magnitude

$$B_{\text{total}} = B_2 - B_1 = \frac{\mu_0 I}{2\pi(x - d)} - \frac{\mu_0 I}{2\pi(x + d)} = \frac{\mu_0 I d}{\pi(x^2 - d^2)}$$

where we combined the two terms using a common denominator.

EVALUATE: At points very far from the wires, so that x is much larger than d, the d^2 term in the denominator can be neglected, and

$$B_{\text{total}} = \frac{\mu_0 I d}{\pi x^2}$$

The magnetic-field magnitude for a single wire decreases with distance in proportion to $1/x$, as shown by Eq. (28.9); for two wires carrying opposite currents, $\vec{B}_1$ and $\vec{B}_2$ partially cancel each other, and so the magnitude of $\vec{B}_{\text{total}}$ decreases more rapidly, in proportion to $1/x^2$. This effect is used in communication systems such as telephone or computer networks. The wiring is arranged so that a conductor carrying a signal in one direction and the conductor carrying the return signal are side by side, as in Fig. 28.7a, or twisted around each other (Fig. 28.8). As a result, the magnetic field caused *outside* the conductors by these signals is greatly reduced and is less likely to exert unwanted forces on other information-carrying currents.

28.8 Computer cables, or cables for audio-video equipment, create little or no magnetic field. This is because within each cable, closely spaced wires carry current in both directions along the length of the cable. The magnetic fields from these opposing currents cancel each other.

Test Your Understanding of Section 28.3 The figure at right shows a circuit that lies on a horizontal table. A compass is placed on top of the circuit as shown. A battery is to be connected to the circuit so that when the switch is closed, the compass needle deflects counterclockwise. In which orientation, A or B, should the battery be placed in the circuit?

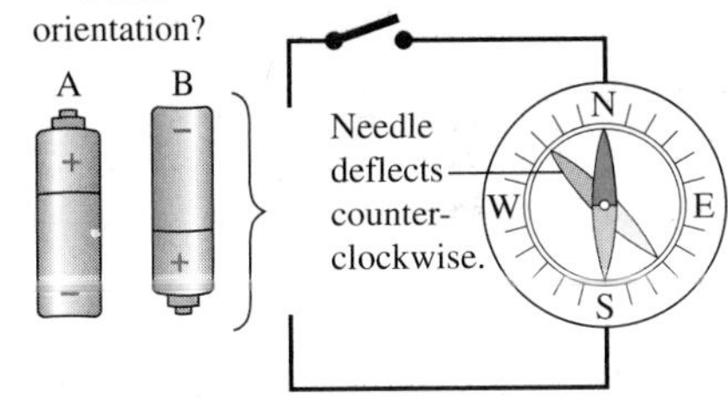

28.4 Force Between Parallel Conductors

In Example 28.4 (Section 28.3) we showed how to use the principle of superposition of magnetic fields to find the total field due to two long current-carrying conductors. Another important aspect of this configuration is the *interaction force* between the conductors. This force plays a role in many practical situations in which current-carrying wires are close to each other, and it also has fundamental significance in connection with the definition of the ampere. Figure 28.9 shows segments of two long, straight, parallel conductors separated by a distance r and carrying currents I and I' in the same direction. Each conductor lies in the magnetic field set up by the other, so each experiences a force. The diagram shows some of the field lines set up by the current in the lower conductor.

From Eq. (28.9) the lower conductor produces a $\vec{B}$ field that, at the position of the upper conductor, has magnitude

$$B = \frac{\mu_0 I}{2\pi r}$$

From Eq. (27.19) the force that this field exerts on a length L of the upper conductor is $\vec{F} = I'\vec{L} \times \vec{B}$, where the vector $\vec{L}$ is in the direction of the current I' and has magnitude L. Since $\vec{B}$ is perpendicular to the length of the conductor and hence to $\vec{L}$, the magnitude of this force is

$$F = I'LB = \frac{\mu_0 I I' L}{2\pi r}$$

and the force *per unit length* F/L is

$$\frac{F}{L} = \frac{\mu_0 I I'}{2\pi r} \quad \text{(two long, parallel, current-carrying conductors)} \quad (28.11)$$

Applying the right-hand rule to $\vec{F} = I'\vec{L} \times \vec{B}$ shows that the force on the upper conductor is directed *downward.*

The current in the upper conductor also sets up a field at the position of the lower one. Two successive applications of the right-hand rule for vector products (one to find the direction of the $\vec{B}$ field due to the upper conductor, as in Section 28.2, and one to find the direction of the force that this field exerts on the lower conductor, as in Section 27.6) show that the force on the lower conductor is *upward.* Thus *two parallel conductors carrying current in the same direction attract each other.* If the direction of either current is reversed, the forces also reverse. *Parallel conductors carrying currents in opposite directions repel each other.*

28.9 Parallel conductors carrying currents in the same direction attract each other. The diagrams show how the magnetic field $\vec{B}$ caused by the current in the lower conductor exerts a force $\vec{F}$ on the upper conductor.

The magnetic field of the lower wire exerts an attractive force on the upper wire. By the same token, the upper wire attracts the lower one.

If the wires had currents in *opposite* directions, they would *repel* each other.

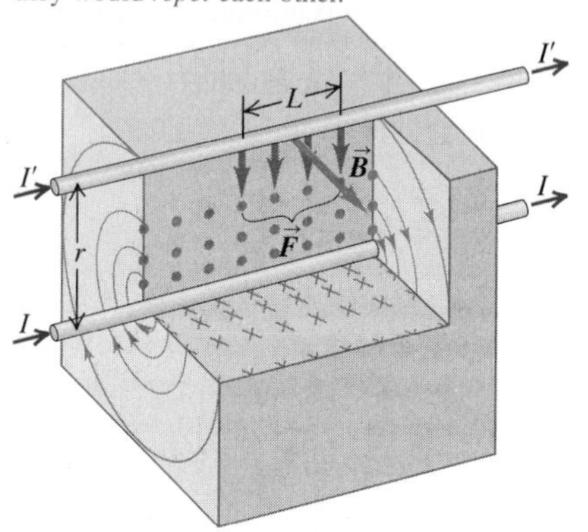

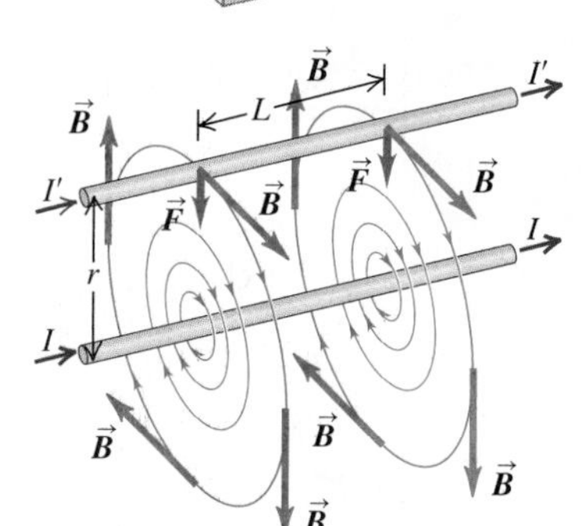

Magnetic Forces and Defining the Ampere

The attraction or repulsion between two straight, parallel, current-carrying conductors is the basis of the official SI definition of the **ampere:**

> ***One ampere*** **is that unvarying current that, if present in each of two parallel conductors of infinite length and one meter apart in empty space, causes each conductor to experience a force of exactly 2 × 10^{-7} newtons per meter of length.**

From Eq. (28.11) you can see that this definition of the ampere is what leads us to choose the value of $4\pi \times 10^{-7}\ \text{T}\cdot\text{m/A}$ for μ_0. It also forms the basis of the SI definition of the coulomb, which is the amount of charge transferred in one second by a current of one ampere.

This is an *operational definition;* it gives us an actual experimental procedure for measuring current and defining a unit of current. In principle we could use this definition to calibrate an ammeter, using only a meter stick and a spring balance. For high-precision standardization of the ampere, coils of wire are used instead of straight wires, and their separation is only a few centimeters. Even more precise measurements of the standardized ampere are possible using a version of the Hall effect (see Section 27.9).

Mutual forces of attraction exist not only between *wires* carrying currents in the same direction, but also between the longitudinal elements of a single current-carrying conductor. If the conductor is a liquid or an ionized gas (a plasma), these forces result in a constriction of the conductor, as if its surface were acted on by an inward pressure. The constriction of the conductor is called the *pinch effect.* The high temperature produced by the pinch effect in a plasma has been used in one technique to bring about nuclear fusion.

Example 28.5 Forces between parallel wires

Two straight, parallel, superconducting wires 4.5 mm apart carry equal currents of 15,000 A in opposite directions. Should we worry about the mechanical strength of these wires?

SOLUTION

IDENTIFY: Whether or not we need to worry about the wires' mechanical strength depends on how much magnetic force each wire exerts on the other.

28.10 Our sketch for this problem.

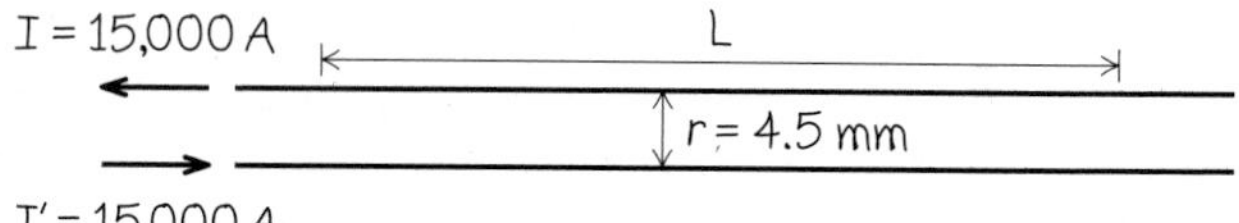

SET UP: Figure 28.10 shows the situation. Our target variable is the magnetic force per unit length of wire, which we find using Eq. (28.11).

EXECUTE: Because the currents are in opposite directions, the two conductors repel each other. From Eq. (28.11) the force per unit length is

$$\frac{F}{L} = \frac{\mu_0 I I'}{2\pi r} = \frac{(4\pi \times 10^{-7}\ \mathrm{T \cdot m/A})(15{,}000\ \mathrm{A})^2}{(2\pi)(4.5 \times 10^{-3}\ \mathrm{m})}$$
$$= 1.0 \times 10^4\ \mathrm{N/m}$$

EVALUATE: This is a large force, more than one ton per meter, so the mechanical strengths of the conductors and insulating materials are certainly a significant consideration. Currents and separations of this magnitude are used in superconducting electromagnets in particle accelerators, and mechanical stress analysis is a crucial part of the design process.

Test Your Understanding of Section 28.4 A solenoid is a wire wound into a helical coil. The figure at right shows a solenoid that carries a current I. (a) Is the *magnetic* force that one turn of the coil exerts on an adjacent turn (i) attractive, (ii) repulsive, or (iii) zero? (b) Is the *electric* force that one turn of the coil exerts on an adjacent turn (i) attractive, (ii) repulsive, or (iii) zero? (c) Is the *magnetic* force between opposite sides of the same turn of the coil (i) attractive, (ii) repulsive, or (iii) zero? (d) Is the *electric* force between opposite sides of the same turn of the coil (i) attractive, (ii) repulsive, or (iii) zero?

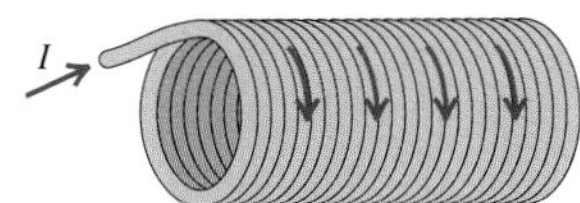

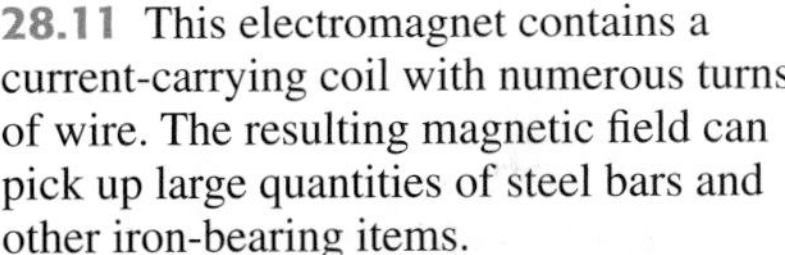

28.5 Magnetic Field of a Circular Current Loop

If you look inside a doorbell, a transformer, an electric motor, or an electromagnet (Fig. 28.11), you will find coils of wire with a large number of turns, spaced so closely that each turn is very nearly a planar circular loop. A current in such a coil is used to establish a magnetic field. So it is worthwhile to derive an expression for the magnetic field produced by a single circular conducting loop carrying a current or by N closely spaced circular loops forming a coil. In Section 27.7 we considered the force and torque on such a current loop placed in an external magnetic field produced by other currents; we are now about to find the magnetic field produced by the loop itself.

Figure 28.12 shows a circular conductor with radius a that carries a current I. The current is led into and out of the loop through two long, straight wires side by side; the currents in these straight wires are in opposite directions, and their magnetic fields very nearly cancel each other (see Example 28.4 in Section 28.3).

We can use the law of Biot and Savart, Eq. (28.5) or (28.6), to find the magnetic field at a point P on the axis of the loop, at a distance x from the center. As the figure shows, $d\vec{l}$ and $\hat{r}$ are perpendicular, and the direction of the field $d\vec{B}$ caused by this particular element $d\vec{l}$ lies in the xy-plane. Since $r^2 = x^2 + a^2$, the magnitude dB of the field due to element $d\vec{l}$ is

$$dB = \frac{\mu_0 I}{4\pi}\frac{dl}{(x^2 + a^2)} \tag{28.12}$$

The components of the vector $d\vec{B}$ are

$$dB_x = dB\cos\theta = \frac{\mu_0 I}{4\pi}\frac{dl}{(x^2 + a^2)}\frac{a}{(x^2 + a^2)^{1/2}} \tag{28.13}$$

$$dB_y = dB\sin\theta = \frac{\mu_0 I}{4\pi}\frac{dl}{(x^2 + a^2)}\frac{x}{(x^2 + a^2)^{1/2}} \tag{28.14}$$

The situation has rotational symmetry about the x-axis, so there cannot be a component of the total field $\vec{B}$ perpendicular to this axis. For every element $d\vec{l}$ there is a corresponding element on the opposite side of the loop, with opposite direction. These two elements give equal contributions to the x-component of $d\vec{B}$, given by Eq. (28.13), but *opposite* components perpendicular to the

28.11 This electromagnet contains a current-carrying coil with numerous turns of wire. The resulting magnetic field can pick up large quantities of steel bars and other iron-bearing items.

28.12 Magnetic field on the axis of a circular loop. The current in the segment $d\vec{l}$ causes the field $d\vec{B}$, which lies in the xy-plane. The currents in other $d\vec{l}$'s cause $d\vec{B}$'s with different components perpendicular to the x-axis; these components add to zero. The x-components of the $d\vec{B}$'s combine to give the total $\vec{B}$ field at point P.

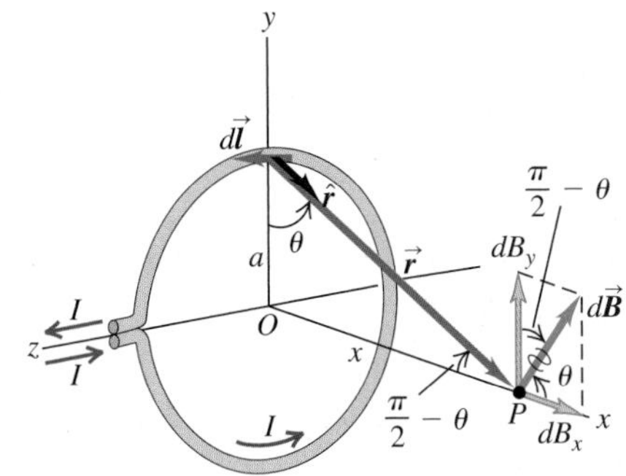

ActivPhysics ONLINE
13.2 Magnetic Field of a Loop

x-axis. Thus all the perpendicular components cancel and only the x-components survive.

To obtain the x-component of the total field $\vec{B}$, we integrate Eq. (28.13), including all the $d\vec{l}$'s around the loop. Everything in this expression except dl is constant and can be taken outside the integral, and we have

$$B_x = \int \frac{\mu_0 I}{4\pi} \frac{a\,dl}{(x^2 + a^2)^{3/2}} = \frac{\mu_0 I a}{4\pi(x^2 + a^2)^{3/2}} \int dl$$

The integral of dl is just the circumference of the circle, $\int dl = 2\pi a$, and we finally get

$$B_x = \frac{\mu_0 I a^2}{2(x^2 + a^2)^{3/2}} \quad \text{(on the axis of a circular loop)} \qquad (28.15)$$

The *direction* of the magnetic field on the axis of a current-carrying loop is given by a right-hand rule. If you curl the fingers of your right hand around the loop in the direction of the current, your right thumb points in the direction of the field (Fig. 28.13).

28.13 The right-hand rule for the direction of the magnetic field produced on the axis of a current-carrying coil.

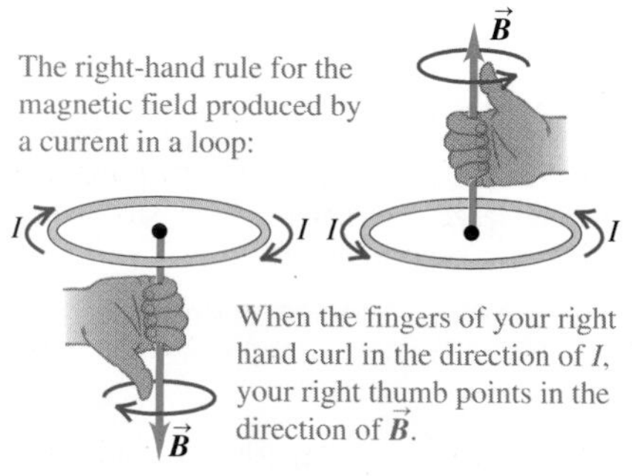
$\vec{B}$
The right-hand rule for the magnetic field produced by a current in a loop:
I
I
I
I
When the fingers of your right hand curl in the direction of I, your right thumb points in the direction of $\vec{B}$.
$\vec{B}$

Magnetic Field on the Axis of a Coil

Now suppose that instead of the single loop in Fig. 28.12 we have a coil consisting of N loops, all with the same radius. The loops are closely spaced so that the plane of each loop is essentially the same distance x from the field point P. Each loop contributes equally to the field, and the total field is N times the field of a single loop:

$$B_x = \frac{\mu_0 N I a^2}{2(x^2 + a^2)^{3/2}} \quad \text{(on the axis of } N \text{ circular loops)} \qquad (28.16)$$

The factor N in Eq. (28.16) is the reason coils of wire, not single loops, are used to produce strong magnetic fields; for a desired field strength, using a single loop might require a current I so great as to exceed the rating of the loop's wire.

Figure 28.14 shows a graph of B_x as a function of x. The maximum value of the field is at $x = 0$, the center of the loop or coil:

$$B_x = \frac{\mu_0 N I}{2a} \quad \text{(at the center of } N \text{ circular loops)} \qquad (28.17)$$

28.14 Graph of the magnetic field along the axis of a circular coil with N turns. When x is much larger than a, the field magnitude decreases approximately as $1/x^3$.

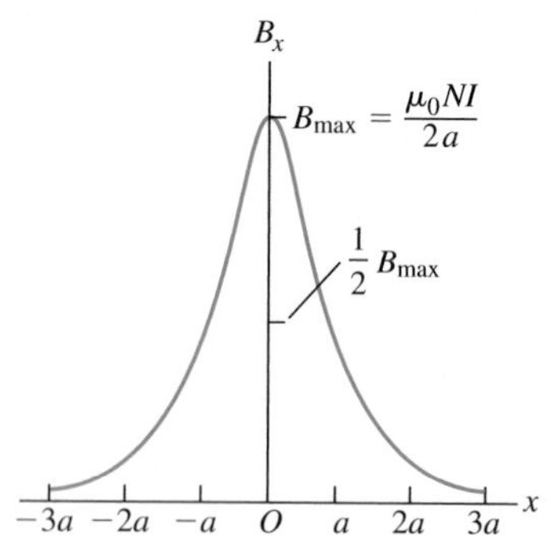
B_x
$B_{max} = \frac{\mu_0 N I}{2a}$
$\frac{1}{2} B_{max}$
x
$-3a$ $-2a$ $-a$ O a $2a$ $3a$

As we go out along the axis, the field decreases in magnitude.

In Section 27.7 we defined the *magnetic dipole moment* μ (or *magnetic moment*) of a current-carrying loop to be equal to IA, where A is the cross-sectional area of the loop. If there are N loops, the total magnetic moment is NIA. The circular loop in Fig. 28.12 has area $A = \pi a^2$, so the magnetic moment of a single loop is $\mu = I\pi a^2$; for N loops, $\mu = NI\pi a^2$. Substituting these results into Eqs. (28.15) and (28.16), we find that both of these expressions can be written as

$$B_x = \frac{\mu_0 \mu}{2\pi(x^2 + a^2)^{3/2}} \quad \text{(on the axis of any number of circular loops)} \qquad (28.18)$$

We described a magnetic dipole in Section 27.7 in terms of its response to a magnetic field produced by currents outside the dipole. But a magnetic dipole is also a *source* of magnetic field; Eq. (28.18) describes the magnetic field *produced* by a magnetic dipole for points along the dipole axis. This field is directly proportional to the magnetic dipole moment μ. Note that the field along the x-axis is in the same direction as the vector magnetic moment $\vec{\mu}$; this is true on both the positive and negative x-axis.

CAUTION **Magnetic field of a coil** Equations (28.15), (28.16), and (28.18) are valid only on the *axis* of a loop or coil. Don't attempt to apply these equations at other points!

Figure 28.15 shows some of the magnetic field lines surrounding a circular current loop (magnetic dipole) in planes through the axis. The directions of the field lines are given by the same right-hand rule as for a long, straight conductor. Grab the conductor with your right hand, with your thumb in the direction of the current; your fingers curl around in the same direction as the field lines. The field lines for the circular current loop are closed curves that encircle the conductor; they are *not* circles, however.

28.15 Magnetic field lines produced by the current in a circular loop. At points on the axis the $\vec{B}$ field has the same direction as the magnetic moment of the loop.

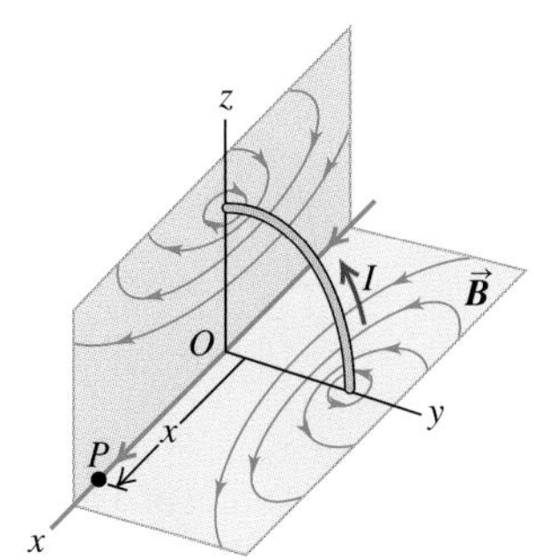

Example 28.6 Magnetic field of a coil

A coil consisting of 100 circular loops with radius 0.60 m carries a current of 5.0 A. (a) Find the magnetic field at a point along the axis of the coil, 0.80 m from the center. (b) Along the axis, at what distance from the center of the coil is the field magnitude $\frac{1}{8}$ as great as it is at the center?

SOLUTION

IDENTIFY: This problem asks about the magnetic field along the axis of a current-carrying coil, so we can use the ideas of this section.

SET UP: We want the field on the axis of the coil, not necessarily at its center, so we use Eq. (28.16). We are given $N = 100$, $I = 5.0$ A, and $a = 0.60$ m. In part (a) our target variable is the magnetic field at a given value of the coordinate x. In part (b) the target variable is the value of x at which the field has $\frac{1}{8}$ of the magnitude that it has at $x = 0$.

EXECUTE: (a) Using $x = 0.80$ m, from Eq. (28.16) we have

$$B_x = \frac{(4\pi \times 10^{-7}\ \text{T}\cdot\text{m/A})(100)(5.0\ \text{A})(0.60\ \text{m})^2}{2[(0.80\ \text{m})^2 + (0.60\ \text{m})^2]^{3/2}}$$
$$= 1.1 \times 10^{-4}\ \text{T}$$

(b) Considering Eq. (28.16), we want to find a value of x such that

$$\frac{1}{(x^2 + a^2)^{3/2}} = \frac{1}{8}\frac{1}{(0^2 + a^2)^{3/2}}$$

To solve this for x, we take the reciprocal of the whole thing and then take the 2/3 power of both sides; the result is

$$x = \pm\sqrt{3}a = \pm 1.04\ \text{m}$$

At a distance of about 1.7 radii from the center, the field has dropped off to $\frac{1}{8}$ its value at the center.

EVALUATE: We can check our answer in part (a) by first finding the magnetic moment and then substituting the result into Eq. (28.18):

$$\mu = NI\pi a^2 = (100)(5.0\ \text{A})\pi(0.60\ \text{m})^2 = 5.7 \times 10^2\ \text{A}\cdot\text{m}^2$$

$$B_x = \frac{(4\pi \times 10^{-7}\ \text{T}\cdot\text{m/A})(5.7 \times 10^2\ \text{A}\cdot\text{m}^2)}{2\pi[(0.80\ \text{m})^2 + (0.60\ \text{m})^2]^{3/2}} = 1.1 \times 10^{-4}\ \text{T}$$

The magnetic moment μ is relatively large, yet this is a rather small field, comparable in magnitude to the earth's magnetic field. This example may give you some idea of the difficulty of producing a field of 1 T or more.

Test Your Understanding of Section 28.5 Figure 28.12 shows the magnetic field $d\vec{B}$ produced at point P by a segment $d\vec{l}$ that lies on the positive y-axis (at the top of the loop). This field has components $dB_x > 0$, $dB_y > 0$, $dB_z = 0$. (a) What are the signs of the components of the field $d\vec{B}$ produced at P by a segment $d\vec{l}$ on the negative y-axis (at the bottom of the loop)? (i) $dB_x > 0$, $dB_y > 0$, $dB_z = 0$; (ii) $dB_x > 0$, $dB_y < 0$, $dB_z = 0$; (iii) $dB_x < 0$, $dB_y > 0$, $dB_z = 0$; (iv) $dB_x < 0$, $dB_y < 0$, $dB_z = 0$; (v) none of these. (b) What are the signs of the components of the field $d\vec{B}$ produced at P by a segment $d\vec{l}$ on the negative z-axis (at the right-hand side of the loop)? (i) $dB_x > 0$, $dB_y > 0$, $dB_z = 0$; (ii) $dB_x > 0$, $dB_y < 0$, $dB_z = 0$; (iii) $dB_x < 0$, $dB_y > 0$, $dB_z = 0$; (iv) $dB_x < 0$, $dB_y < 0$, $dB_z = 0$; (v) none of these.

28.6 Ampere's Law

So far our calculations of the magnetic field due to a current have involved finding the infinitesimal field $d\vec{B}$ due to a current element and then summing all the $d\vec{B}$'s to find the total field. This approach is directly analogous to our *electric-field* calculations in Chapter 21.

For the electric-field problem we found that in situations with a highly symmetric charge distribution, it was often easier to use Gauss's law to find $\vec{E}$. There is likewise a law that allows us to more easily find the *magnetic* fields caused by highly symmetric *current* distributions. But the law that allows us to do this, called *Ampere's law,* is rather different in character from Gauss's law.

Gauss's law for electric fields involves the flux of $\vec{E}$ through a closed surface; it states that this flux is equal to the total charge enclosed within the surface, divided by the constant ϵ_0. Thus this law relates electric fields and charge distributions. By contrast, Gauss's law for *magnetic* fields, Eq. (28.10), is *not* a relationship between magnetic fields and current distributions; it states that the flux of $\vec{B}$ through *any* closed surface is always zero, whether or not there are currents within the surface. So Gauss's law for $\vec{B}$ can't be used to determine the magnetic field produced by a particular current distribution.

Ampere's law is formulated not in terms of magnetic flux, but rather in terms of the *line integral* of $\vec{B}$ around a closed path, denoted by

$$\oint \vec{B} \cdot d\vec{l}$$

We used line integrals to define work in Chapter 6 and to calculate electric potential in Chapter 23. To evaluate this integral, we divide the path into infinitesimal segments $d\vec{l}$, calculate the scalar product of $\vec{B} \cdot d\vec{l}$ for each segment, and sum these products. In general, $\vec{B}$ varies from point to point, and we must use the value of $\vec{B}$ at the location of each $d\vec{l}$. An alternative notation is $\oint B_{\parallel}\, dl$, where $B_{\parallel}$ is the component of $\vec{B}$ parallel to $d\vec{l}$ at each point. The circle on the integral sign indicates that this integral is always computed for a *closed* path, one whose beginning and end points are the same.

28.16 Three integration paths for the line integral of $\vec{B}$ in the vicinity of a long, straight conductor carrying current I *out* of the plane of the page (as indicated by the circle with a dot). The conductor is seen end-on.

(a) Integration path is a circle centered on the conductor; integration goes around the circle counterclockwise.

Result: $\oint \vec{B} \cdot d\vec{l} = \mu_0 I$

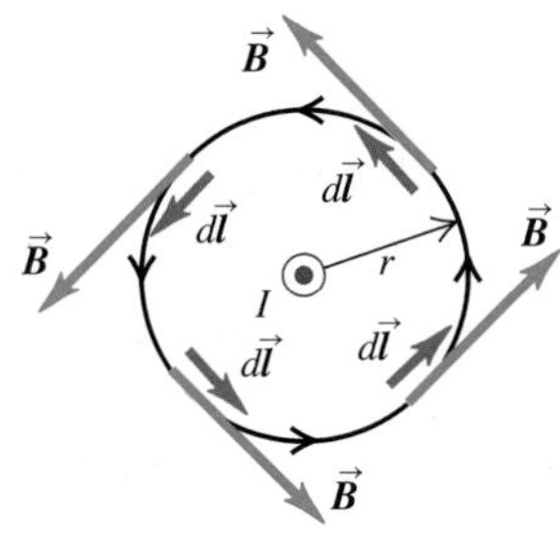

(b) Same integration path as in (a), but integration goes around the circle clockwise.

Result: $\oint \vec{B} \cdot d\vec{l} = -\mu_0 I$

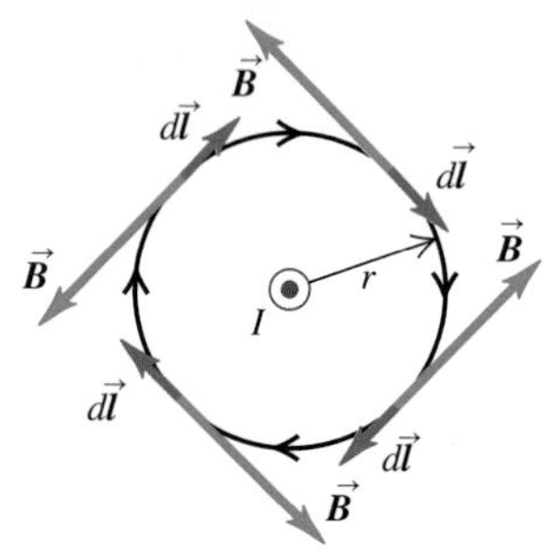

(c) An integration path that does not enclose the conductor.

Result: $\oint \vec{B} \cdot d\vec{l} = 0$

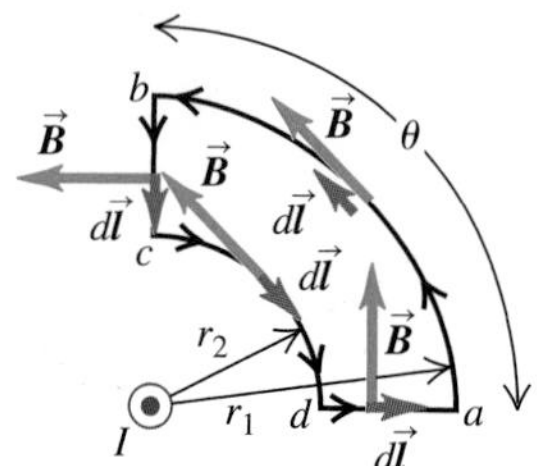

Ampere's Law for a Long, Straight Conductor

To introduce the basic idea of Ampere's law, let's consider again the magnetic field caused by a long, straight conductor carrying a current I. We found in Section 28.3 that the field at a distance r from the conductor has magnitude

$$B = \frac{\mu_0 I}{2\pi r}$$

and that the magnetic field lines are circles centered on the conductor. Let's take the line integral of $\vec{B}$ around one such circle with radius r, as in Figure 28.16a. At every point on the circle, $\vec{B}$ and $d\vec{l}$ are parallel, and so $\vec{B} \cdot d\vec{l} = B\, dl$; since r is constant around the circle, B is constant as well. Alternatively, we can say that $B_{\parallel}$ is constant and equal to B at every point on the circle. Hence we can take B outside of the integral. The remaining integral $\oint dl$ is just the circumference of the circle, so

$$\oint \vec{B} \cdot d\vec{l} = \oint B_{\parallel}\, dl = B \oint dl = \frac{\mu_0 I}{2\pi r}(2\pi r) = \mu_0 I$$

The line integral is thus independent of the radius of the circle and is equal to μ_0 multiplied by the current passing through the area bounded by the circle.

In Fig. 28.16b the situation is the same, but the integration path now goes around the circle in the opposite direction. Now $\vec{B}$ and $d\vec{l}$ are antiparallel, so $\vec{B} \cdot d\vec{l} = -B\, dl$ and the line integral equals $-\mu_0 I$. We get the same result if the integration path is the same as in Fig. 28.16a, but the direction of the current is reversed. Thus the line integral $\oint \vec{B} \cdot d\vec{l}$ equals μ_0 multiplied by the current passing through the area bounded by the integration path, with a positive or negative sign depending on the direction of the current relative to the direction of integration.

There's a simple rule for the sign of the current; you won't be surprised to learn that it uses your right hand. Curl the fingers of your right hand around the integration path so that they curl in the direction of integration (that is, the direction that you use to evaluate $\oint \vec{B} \cdot d\vec{l}$). Then your right thumb indicates the positive current direction. Currents that pass through the integration path in this direction are positive; those in the opposite direction are negative. Using this rule, you should be able to convince yourself that the current is positive in Fig. 28.16a and negative in Fig. 28.16b. Here's another way to say the same thing: Looking at the surface bounded by the integration path, integrate counterclockwise around the path as in Fig. 28.16a. Currents moving toward you through the surface are positive, and those going away from you are negative.

An integration path that does *not* enclose the conductor is used in Fig. 28.16c. Along the circular arc ab of radius r_1, $\vec{B}$ and $d\vec{l}$ are parallel, and $B_\parallel = B_1 = \mu_0 I/2\pi r_1$; along the circular arc cd of radius r_2, $\vec{B}$ and $d\vec{l}$ are antiparallel and $B_\parallel = -B_2 = -\mu_0 I/2\pi r_2$. The $\vec{B}$ field is perpendicular to $d\vec{l}$ at each point on the straight sections bc and da, so $B_\parallel = 0$ and these sections contribute zero to the line integral. The total line integral is then

$$\oint \vec{B} \cdot d\vec{l} = \oint B_\parallel dl = B_1 \int_a^b dl + (0)\int_b^c dl + (-B_2)\int_c^d dl + (0)\int_d^a dl$$

$$= \frac{\mu_0 I}{2\pi r_1}(r_1\theta) + 0 - \frac{\mu_0 I}{2\pi r_2}(r_2\theta) + 0 = 0$$

The magnitude of $\vec{B}$ is greater on arc cd than on arc ab, but the arc length is less, so the contributions from the two arcs exactly cancel. Even though there is a magnetic field everywhere along the integration path, the line integral $\oint \vec{B} \cdot d\vec{l}$ is zero if there is no current passing through the area bounded by the path.

We can also derive these results for more general integration paths, such as the one in Figure 28.17. At the position of the line element $d\vec{l}$, the angle between $d\vec{l}$ and $\vec{B}$ is ϕ, and

$$\vec{B} \cdot d\vec{l} = B\,dl\cos\phi$$

From the figure, $dl\cos\phi = r\,d\theta$, where $d\theta$ is the angle subtended by $d\vec{l}$ at the position of the conductor and r is the distance of $d\vec{l}$ from the conductor. Thus

$$\oint \vec{B} \cdot d\vec{l} = \oint \frac{\mu_0 I}{2\pi r}(r\,d\theta) = \frac{\mu_0 I}{2\pi}\oint d\theta$$

But $\oint d\theta$ is just equal to 2π, the total angle swept out by the radial line from the conductor to $d\vec{l}$ during a complete trip around the path. So we get

$$\oint \vec{B} \cdot d\vec{l} = \mu_0 I \qquad (28.19)$$

This result doesn't depend on the shape of the path or on the position of the wire inside it. If the current in the wire is opposite to that shown, the integral has the opposite sign. But if the path doesn't enclose the wire (Fig. 28.17b), then the net change in θ during the trip around the integration path is zero; $\oint d\theta$ is zero instead of 2π and the line integral is zero.

Ampere's Law: General Statement

Equation (28.19) is almost, but not quite, the general statement of Ampere's law. To generalize it even further, suppose *several* long, straight conductors pass through the surface bounded by the integration path. The total magnetic field $\vec{B}$ at any point on the path is the vector sum of the fields produced by the individual conductors. Thus the line integral of the total $\vec{B}$ equals μ_0 times the *algebraic sum* of the currents. In calculating this sum, we use the sign rule for currents described above. If the integration path does not enclose a particular wire, the

28.17 (a) A more general integration path for the line integral of $\vec{B}$ around a long, straight conductor carrying current I *out* of the plane of the page. The conductor is seen end-on. (b) A more general integration path that does not enclose the conductor.

(a)

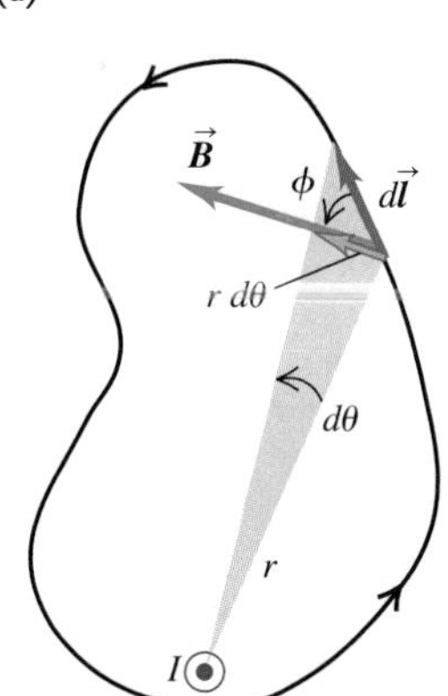

(b)

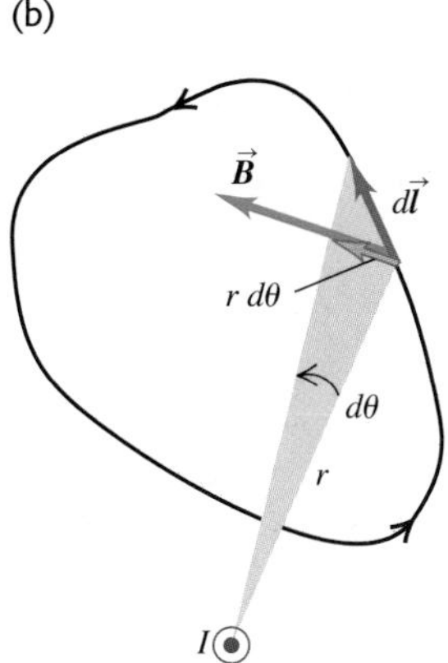

28.18 Ampere's law.

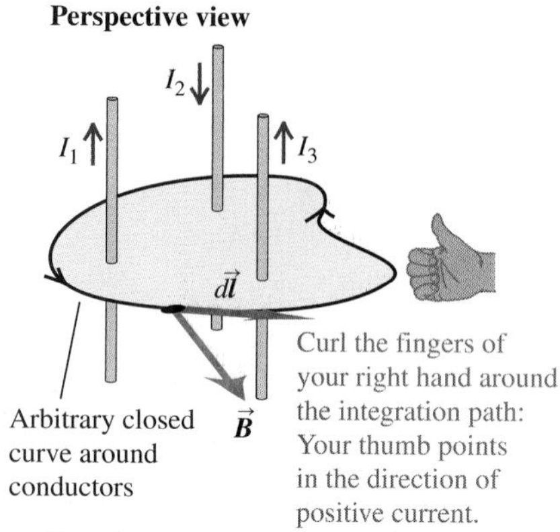

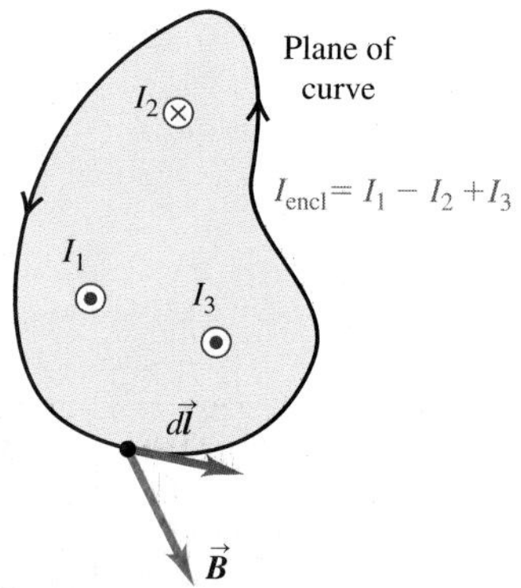

Ampere's law: If we calculate the line integral of the magnetic field around a closed curve, the result equals μ_0 times the total enclosed current: $\oint \vec{B} \cdot d\vec{l} = \mu_0 I_{encl}$

28.19 Two long, straight conductors carrying equal currents in opposite directions. The conductors are seen end-on, and the integration path is counterclockwise. The line integral $\oint \vec{B} \cdot d\vec{l}$ gets zero contribution from the upper and lower segments, a positive contribution from the left segment, and a negative contribution from the right segment; the net integral is zero.

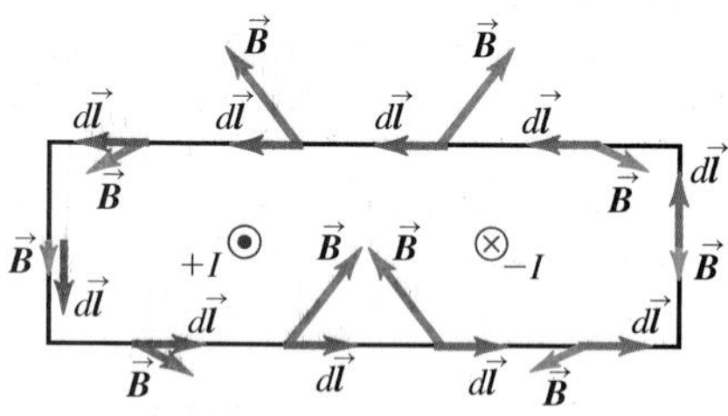

line integral of the $\vec{B}$ field of that wire is zero, because the angle θ for that wire sweeps through a net change of zero rather than 2π during the integration. Any conductors present that are not enclosed by a particular path may still contribute to the value of $\vec{B}$ at every point, but the *line integrals* of their fields around the path are zero.

Thus we can replace I in Eq. (28.19) with I_{encl}, the algebraic sum of the currents *enclosed* or *linked* by the integration path, with the sum evaluated by using the sign rule just described (Fig. 28.18). Our statement of **Ampere's law** is then

$$\oint \vec{B} \cdot d\vec{l} = \mu_0 I_{encl} \qquad \text{(Ampere's law)} \qquad (28.20)$$

While we have derived Ampere's law only for the special case of the field of several long, straight, parallel conductors, Eq. (28.20) is in fact valid for conductors and paths of *any* shape. The general derivation is no different in principle from what we have presented, but the geometry is more complicated.

If $\oint \vec{B} \cdot d\vec{l} = 0$, it *does not* necessarily mean that $\vec{B} = \mathbf{0}$ everywhere along the path, only that the total current through an area bounded by the path is zero. In Figs. 28.16c and 28.17b, the integration paths enclose no current at all; in Fig. 28.19 there are positive and negative currents of equal magnitude through the area enclosed by the path. In both cases, $I_{encl} = 0$ and the line integral is zero.

CAUTION Line integrals of electric and magnetic fields In Chapter 23 we saw that the line integral of the electrostatic field $\vec{E}$ around any closed path is equal to zero; this is a statement that the electrostatic force $\vec{F} = q\vec{E}$ on a point charge q is conservative, so this force does zero work on a charge that moves around a closed path that returns to the starting point. You might think that the value of the line integral $\oint \vec{B} \cdot d\vec{l}$ is similarly related to the question of whether the *magnetic* force is conservative. This isn't the case at all. Remember that the magnetic force $\vec{F} = q\vec{v} \times \vec{B}$ on a moving charged particle is always *perpendicular* to $\vec{B}$, so $\oint \vec{B} \cdot d\vec{l}$ is *not* related to the work done by the magnetic force; as stated in Ampere's law, this integral is related only to the total current through a surface bounded by the integration path. In fact, the magnetic force on a moving charged particle is *not* conservative. A conservative force depends only on the position of the body on which the force is exerted, but the magnetic force on a moving charged particle also depends on the *velocity* of the particle.

In the form we have stated it, Ampere's law turns out to be valid only if the currents are steady and if no magnetic materials or time-varying electric fields are present. In Chapter 29 we will see how to generalize Ampere's law for time-varying fields.

Test Your Understanding of Section 28.6 The figure below shows magnetic field lines through the center of a permanent magnet. The magnet is not connected to a source of emf. One of the field lines is colored red. What can you conclude about the currents inside the permanent magnet within the region enclosed by this field line? (i) There are no currents inside the magnet; (ii) there are currents directed out of the plane of the page; (iii) there are currents directed into the plane of the page; (iv) not enough information given to decide.

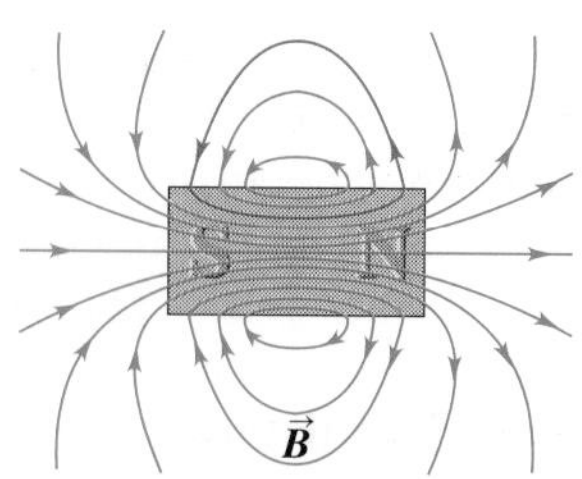

28.7 Applications of Ampere's Law

Ampere's law is useful when we can exploit the symmetry of a situation to evaluate the line integral of $\vec{B}$. Several examples are given below. Problem-Solving Strategy 28.2 is directly analogous to Problem Solving Strategy 22.1 (Section 22.4) for applications of Gauss's law; we suggest you review that strategy now and compare the two methods.

Problem-Solving Strategy 28.2 Ampere's Law

MP

IDENTIFY *the relevant concepts:* Like Gauss's law for electricity, Ampere's law is always true but is most useful in situations where the magnetic field pattern is highly symmetrical. In such situations you can use Ampere's law to find a relationship between the magnetic field as a function of position and the current that generates the field.

SET UP *the problem* using the following steps:

1. Select the integration path you will use with Ampere's law. If you want to determine the magnetic field at a certain point, then the path must pass through that point. The integration path doesn't have to be any actual physical boundary. Usually it is a purely geometric curve; it may be in empty space, embedded in a solid body, or some of each. The integration path has to have enough *symmetry* to make evaluation of the integral possible. If the problem itself has cylindrical symmetry, the integration path will usually be a circle coaxial with the cylinder axis.
2. Determine the target variable(s). Usually this will be the magnitude of the $\vec{B}$ field as a function of position.

EXECUTE *the solution* as follows:

1. Carry out the integral $\oint \vec{B} \cdot d\vec{l}$ along your chosen integration path. If $\vec{B}$ is tangent to all or some portion of the integration path and has the same magnitude B at every point, then its line integral equals B multiplied by the length of that portion of the path. If $\vec{B}$ is perpendicular to some portion of the path, that portion makes no contribution to the integral.
2. In the integral $\oint \vec{B} \cdot d\vec{l}$, $\vec{B}$ is always the *total* magnetic field at each point on the path. This field can be caused partly by currents enclosed by the path and partly by currents outside the path. If *no* net current is enclosed by the path, the field at points on the path need not be zero, but the integral $\oint \vec{B} \cdot d\vec{l}$ is always zero.
3. Determine the current I_{encl} enclosed by the integration path. The sign of this current is given by a right-hand rule. Curl the fingers of your right hand so that they follow the integration path in the direction that you carry out the integration. Your right thumb then points in the direction of positive current. If $\vec{B}$ is tangent to the integration at all points along the path and I_{encl} is positive, then the direction of $\vec{B}$ is the same as the direction of the integration path; if instead I_{encl} is negative, $\vec{B}$ is in the direction opposite to that of the integration.
4. Use Ampere's law $\oint \vec{B} \cdot d\vec{l} = \mu_0 I$ to solve for the target variable.

EVALUATE *your answer:* If your result is an expression for the field magnitude as a function of position, you can check it by examining how the expression behaves in different limits.

Example 28.7 Field of a long, straight, current-carrying conductor

In Section 28.6 we derived Ampere's law using Eq. (28.9) for the field of a long, straight, current-carrying conductor. Reverse this process, and use Ampere's law to find the magnitude *and* direction of $\vec{B}$ for this situation.

SOLUTION

IDENTIFY: This situation has cylindrical symmetry, so we can use Ampere's law to find the magnetic field at all points a distance r from the conductor

SET UP: We take as our integration path a circle with radius r centered on the conductor and in a plane perpendicular to it, as in Fig. 28.16a (Section 28.6). At each point, $\vec{B}$ is tangent to this circle.

EXECUTE: With our choice of integration path, Ampere's law [Eq. (28.20)] becomes

$$\oint \vec{B} \cdot d\vec{l} = \oint B_{\parallel}\, dl = B(2\pi r) = \mu_0 I$$

Equation (28.9), $B = \mu_0 I / 2\pi r$, follows immediately.

Ampere's law determines the direction of $\vec{B}$ as well as its magnitude. Since we go around the integration path in the counterclockwise direction, the positive direction for current is out of the plane of Fig. 28.16a; this is the same as the actual current direction in the figure, so I is positive and the integral $\oint \vec{B} \cdot d\vec{l}$ is also positive. Since the $d\vec{l}$'s run counterclockwise, the direction of $\vec{B}$ must be counterclockwise as well, as shown in Fig. 28.16a.

EVALUATE: Our results are consistent with those in Section 28.6, as they must be.

Example 28.8 Field inside a long cylindrical conductor

A cylindrical conductor with radius R carries a current I. (Fig. 28.20). The current is uniformly distributed over the cross-sectional area of the conductor. Find the magnetic field as a function of the distance r from the conductor axis for points both inside $(r < R)$ and outside $(r > R)$ the conductor.

28.20 To find the magnetic field at radius $r < R$, we apply Ampere's law to the circle enclosing the red area. The current through the red area is $(r^2/R^2)I$. To find the magnetic field at radius $r > R$, we apply Ampere's law to the circle enclosing the entire conductor.

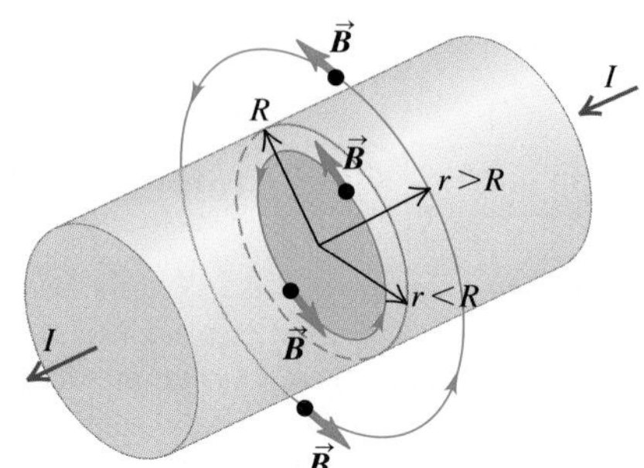

SOLUTION

IDENTIFY: Once again we have a current distribution with cylindrical symmetry. As for a long, straight, skinny current-carrying conductor, the magnetic field lines must be circles concentric with the conductor axis.

SET UP: To find the magnetic field *inside* the conductor, we take as our integration path a circle with radius $r < R$ as shown in Fig. 28.20. *Outside* the conductor, we again use a circle but with a radius $r > R$. In either case, the integration path takes advantage of the circular symmetry of the magnetic field pattern.

EXECUTE: Inside the conductor, $\vec{B}$ has the same magnitude at every point on the circular integration path and is tangent to the path. Thus the magnitude of the line integral is simply $B(2\pi r)$. If we use the right-hand rule for determining the sign of the current, the current through the brown area enclosed by the path is positive; hence $\vec{B}$ points in the same direction as the integration path, as shown. To find the current I_{encl} enclosed by the path, note that the current density (current per unit area) is $J = I/\pi R^2$, so $I_{encl} = J(\pi r^2) = Ir^2/R^2$. Finally, Ampere's law gives

$$B(2\pi r) = \mu_0 \frac{Ir^2}{R^2}$$

$$B = \frac{\mu_0 I}{2\pi} \frac{r}{R^2} \quad \text{(inside the conductor, } r < R) \qquad (28.21)$$

For the circular integration path outside the conductor $(r > R)$, the same symmetry arguments apply and the magnitude of $\oint \vec{B} \cdot d\vec{l}$ is again $B(2\pi r)$. The right-hand rule gives the direction of $\vec{B}$ as shown in Fig. 28.20. For this path, $I_{encl} = I$, the total current in the conductor. Applying Ampere's law gives the same equation as in Example 28.7, with the same result for B:

$$B = \frac{\mu_0 I}{2\pi r} \quad \text{(outside the conductor, } r > R) \qquad (28.22)$$

Outside the conductor, the magnetic field is the same as that of a long, straight conductor carrying current I, independent of the radius R over which the current is distributed. Indeed, the magnetic field outside *any* cylindrically symmetric current distribution is the same as if the entire current were concentrated along the axis of the distribution. This is analogous to the results of Examples 22.5 and 22.9 (Section 22.4), in which we found that the *electric* field outside a spherically symmetric *charged* body is the same as though the entire charge were concentrated at the center.

EVALUATE: Note that at the surface of the conductor $(r = R)$, Eq. (28.21) for $r < R$ and Eq. (28.22) for $r > R$ agree (as they must). Figure 28.21 shows a graph of B as a function of r, both inside and outside the conductor.

28.21 Magnitude of the magnetic field inside and outside a long, straight cylindrical conductor with radius R carrying a current I.

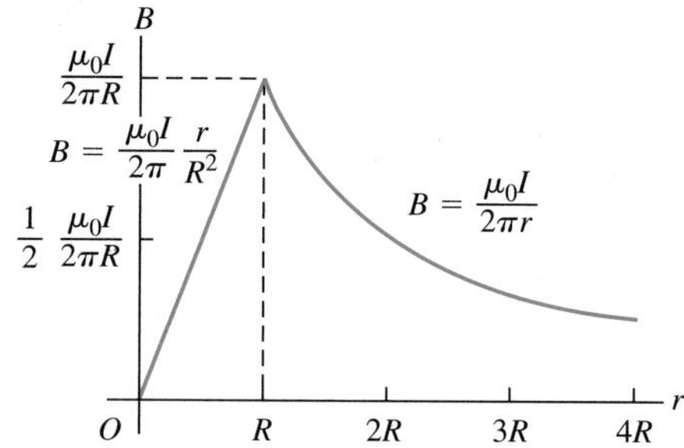

Example 28.9 Field of a solenoid

A solenoid consists of a helical winding of wire on a cylinder, usually circular in cross section. There can be hundreds or thousands of closely spaced turns, each of which can be regarded as a circular loop. There may be several layers of windings. For simplicity, Fig. 28.22 shows a solenoid with only a few turns. All turns carry the same current I, and the total $\vec{B}$ field at every point is the vector sum of the fields caused by the individual turns. The figure shows field lines in the xy- and xz-planes. We draw a set of field lines that are uniformly spaced at the center of the solenoid. Exact calculations show that for a long, closely wound solenoid, half of these field lines emerge from the ends and half "leak out" through the windings between the center and the end.

The field lines near the center of the solenoid are approximately parallel, indicating a nearly uniform $\vec{B}$; outside the solenoid, the

28.22 Magnetic field lines produced by the current in a solenoid. For clarity, only a few turns are shown.

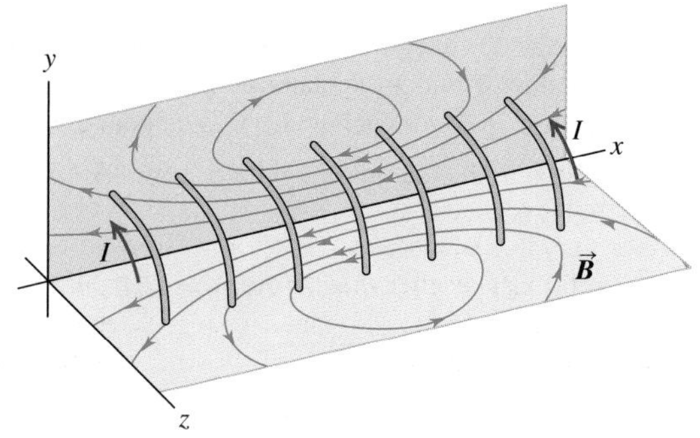

field lines are spread apart, and the magnetic field is weak. If the solenoid is long in comparison with its cross-sectional diameter and the coils are tightly wound, the *internal* field near the midpoint of the solenoid's length is very nearly uniform over the cross section and parallel to the axis, and the *external* field near the midpoint is very small.

Use Ampere's law to find the field at or near the center of such a long solenoid. The solenoid has n turns of wire per unit length and carries a current I.

SOLUTION

IDENTIFY: This is a highly symmetrical situation, with a uniform $\vec{B}$ field inside the solenoid and zero field outside. Hence we can use Ampere's law to find the field inside by using an appropriate choice of integration path.

SET UP: Fig. 28.23 shows the situation and our integration path, rectangle *abcd*. Side *ab*, with length L, is parallel to the axis of the solenoid. Sides *bc* and *da* are taken to be very long so that side *cd* is far from the solenoid; then the field at side *cd* is negligibly small.

EXECUTE: By symmetry, the $\vec{B}$ field along side *ab* is parallel to this side and is constant. In carrying out the Ampere's-law integration, we go along side *ab* in the same direction as $\vec{B}$. So for this side, $B_{\parallel} = +B$ and

$$\int_a^b \vec{B} \cdot d\vec{l} = BL$$

Along sides *bc* and *da*, $B_{\parallel} = 0$ because $\vec{B}$ is perpendicular to these sides; along side *cd*, $B_{\parallel} = 0$ because $\vec{B} = \mathbf{0}$. The integral $\oint \vec{B} \cdot d\vec{l}$ around the entire closed path therefore reduces to BL.

28.23 Our sketch for this problem.

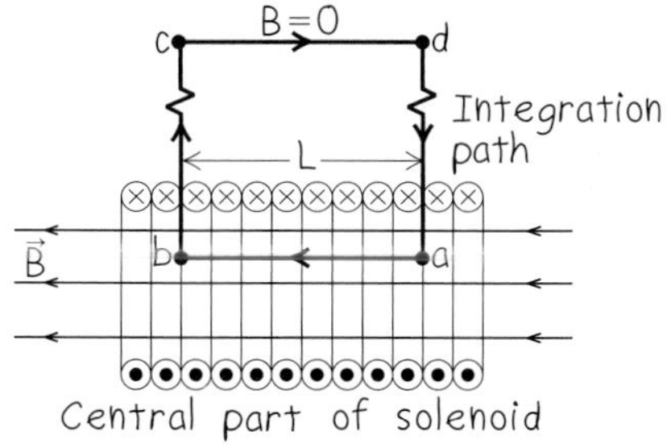

The number of turns in length L is nL. Each of these turns passes once through the rectangle *abcd* and carries a current I, where I is the current in the windings. The total current enclosed by the rectangle is then $I_{encl} = nLI$. From Ampere's law, since the integral $\oint \vec{B} \cdot d\vec{l}$ is positive, I_{encl} must be positive as well; hence the current passing through the surface bounded by the integration path must be in the direction shown in Fig. 28.23. Ampere's law then gives the magnitude B:

$$BL = \mu_0 nLI$$
$$B = \mu_0 nI \qquad \text{(solenoid)} \qquad (28.23)$$

Side *ab* need not lie on the axis of the solenoid, so this calculation also proves that the field is uniform over the entire cross section at the center of the solenoid's length.

EVALUATE: Note that the *direction* of $\vec{B}$ inside the solenoid is in the same direction as the solenoid's vector magnetic moment $\vec{\mu}$. This is the same result that we found in Section 28.5 for a single current-carrying loop.

For points along the axis, the field is strongest at the center of the solenoid and drops off near the ends. For a solenoid that is very long in comparison to its diameter, the field at each end is exactly half as strong as the field at the center. For a short, fat solenoid the relationship is more complicated. Fig. 28.24 shows a graph of B as a function of x for points on the axis of a short solenoid.

28.24 Magnitude of the magnetic field at points along the axis of a solenoid with length $4a$, equal to four times its radius a. The field magnitude at each end is about half its value at the center. (Compare with Fig. 28.14 for the field of N circular loops.)

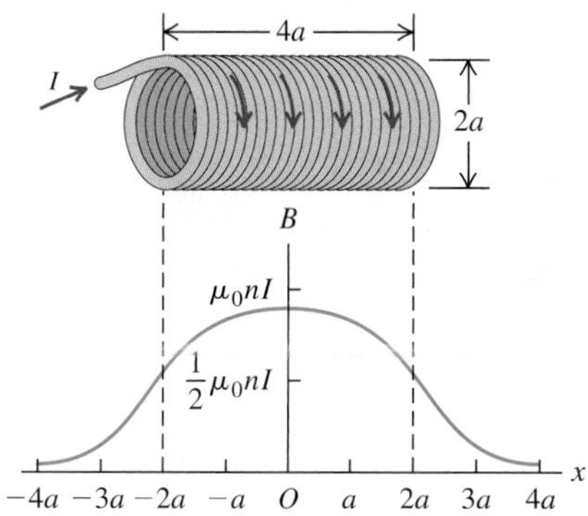

Example 28.10 Field of a toroidal solenoid

Figure 28.25a shows a doughnut-shaped **toroidal solenoid,** also called a *toroid,* wound with N turns of wire carrying a current I. In a practical version the turns would be more closely spaced than they are in the figure. Find the magnetic field at all points.

SOLUTION

IDENTIFY: The flow of current around the toroid's circumference produces a magnetic field component perpendicular to the plane of the figure, just as for the current loop discussed in Section 28.5. But if the coils are very tightly wound, we can consider them as circular loops that carry current between the inner and outer radii of the toroidal solenoid; the flow of current around the toroid's circumference is then negligible, and the perpendicular component of $\vec{B}$ is likewise negligible. In this idealized approximation the circular symmetry of the situation tells us that the magnetic field lines must be circles concentric with the axis of the toroid.

SET UP: To take advantage of this symmetry in finding the field, we choose circular integration paths for use with Ampere's law. Three such paths are shown as black lines in Fig. 28.25b.

EXECUTE: First consider integration path 1 in Fig. 28.25b. If the toroidal solenoid produces any field at all in this region, it must be *tangent* to the path at all points, and $\oint \vec{B} \cdot d\vec{l}$ will equal the product of B and the circumference $l = 2\pi r$ of the path. But the total current enclosed by the path is zero, so from Ampere's law the field $\vec{B}$ must be zero everywhere on this path.

Similarly, if the toroidal solenoid produces any field along path 3, it must also be tangent to the path at all points. Each turn of the winding passes *twice* through the area bounded by this path,

Continued

28.25 **(a)** A toroidal solenoid. For clarity, only a few turns of the winding are shown. **(b)** Integration paths (black circles) used to compute the magnetic field $\vec{B}$ set up by the current (shown as dots and crosses).

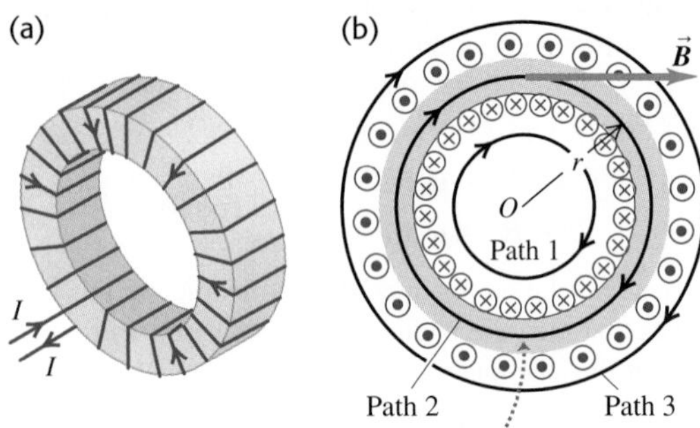

carrying equal currents in opposite directions. The *net* current I_{encl} enclosed within this area is therefore zero, and hence $\vec{B} = \mathbf{0}$ at all points of the path. Conclusion: *The field of an idealized toroidal solenoid is confined completely to the space enclosed by the windings.* We can think of such an idealized toroidal solenoid as a tightly wound solenoid that has been bent into a circle.

Finally, we consider path 2, a circle with radius r. Again by symmetry we expect the $\vec{B}$ field to be tangent to the path, and $\oint \vec{B} \cdot d\vec{l}$ equals $2\pi rB$. Each turn of the winding passes *once* through the area bounded by path 2. The total current enclosed by the path is $I_{\text{encl}} = NI$, where N is the total number of turns in the winding; I_{encl} is positive for the clockwise direction of integration in Fig. 28.25b, so $\vec{B}$ is in the direction shown. Then, from Ampere's law,

$$2\pi rB = \mu_0 NI$$

$$B = \frac{\mu_0 NI}{2\pi r} \quad \text{(toroidal solenoid)} \qquad (28.24)$$

EVALUATE: The magnetic field is *not* uniform over a cross section of the core, because the radius r is larger at the outer side of the section than at the inner side. However, if the radial thickness of the core is small in comparison to r, the field varies only slightly across a section. In that case, considering that $2\pi r$ is the circumferential length of the toroid and that $N/2\pi r$ is the number of turns per unit length n, the field may be written as

$$B = \mu_0 nI$$

just as it is at the center of a long, *straight* solenoid.

In a real toroidal solenoid the turns are not precisely circular loops but rather segments of a bent helix. As a result, the field outside is not strictly zero. To estimate its magnitude, we imagine Fig. 28.25a as being roughly equivalent, for points outside the torus, to a circular loop with a single turn and radius r. Then we can use Eq. (28.17) to show that the field at the *center* of the torus is smaller than the field inside by approximately a factor of N/π.

The equations we have derived for the field in a closely wound straight or toroidal solenoid are strictly correct only for windings in *vacuum.* For most practical purposes, however, they can be used for windings in air or on a core of any nonmagnetic, nonsuperconducting material. In the next section we will show how they are modified if the core is a magnetic material.

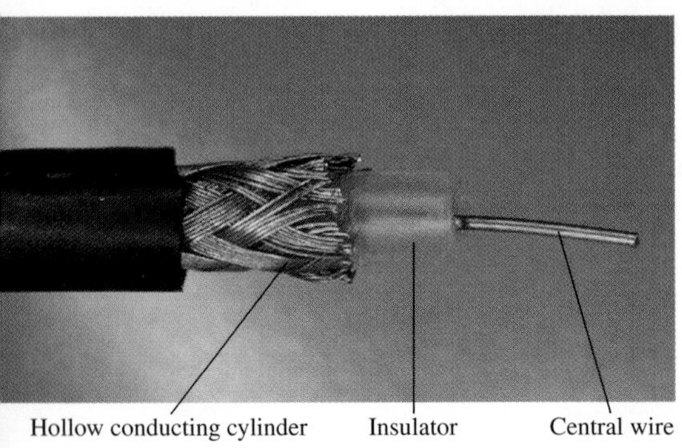

Test Your Understanding of Section 28.7 Consider a conducting wire that runs along the central axis of a hollow conducting cylinder. Such an arrangement, called a *coaxial cable,* has many applications in telecommunications. (The cable that connects a television set to a local cable provider is an example of a coaxial cable.) In such a cable a current I runs in one direction along the hollow conducting cylinder and is spread uniformly over the cylinder's cross-sectional area. An equal current runs in the opposite direction along the central wire. How does the magnitude B of the magnetic field outside such a cable depend on the distance r from the central axis of the cable? (i) B is proportional to $1/r$; (ii) B is proportional to $1/r^2$; (iii) B is zero at all points outside the cable.

*28.8 Magnetic Materials

In discussing how currents cause magnetic fields, we have assumed that the conductors are surrounded by vacuum. But the coils in transformers, motors, generators, and electromagnets nearly always have iron cores to increase the magnetic field and confine it to desired regions. Permanent magnets, magnetic recording tapes, and computer disks depend directly on the magnetic properties of materials; when you store information on a computer disk, you are actually setting up an array of microscopic permanent magnets on the disk. So it is worthwhile to examine some aspects of the magnetic properties of materials. After describing the atomic origins of magnetic properties, we will discuss three broad classes of magnetic behavior that occur in materials; these are called *paramagnetism, diamagnetism,* and *ferromagnetism.*

The Bohr Magneton

As we discussed briefly in Section 27.7, the atoms that make up all matter contain moving electrons, and these electrons form microscopic current loops that produce magnetic fields of their own. In many materials these currents are randomly oriented and cause no net magnetic field. But in some materials an external field (a field produced by currents outside the material) can cause these loops to become oriented preferentially with the field, so their magnetic fields *add* to the external field. We then say that the material is *magnetized.*

Let's look at how these microscopic currents come about. Figure 28.26 shows a primitive model of an electron in an atom. We picture the electron (mass m, charge $-e$) as moving in a circular orbit with radius r and speed v. This moving charge is equivalent to a current loop. In Section 27.7 we found that a current loop with area A and current I has a magnetic dipole moment μ given by $\mu = IA$; for the orbiting electron the area of the loop is $A = \pi r^2$. To find the current associated with the electron, we note that the orbital period T (the time for the electron to make one complete orbit) is the orbit circumference divided by the electron speed: $T = 2\pi r/v$. The equivalent current I is the total charge passing any point on the orbit per unit time, which is just the magnitude e of the electron charge divided by the orbital period T:

$$I = \frac{e}{T} = \frac{ev}{2\pi r}$$

The magnetic moment $\mu = IA$ is then

$$\mu = \frac{ev}{2\pi r}(\pi r^2) = \frac{evr}{2} \qquad (28.25)$$

It is useful to express μ in terms of the *angular momentum* L of the electron. For a particle moving in a circular path, the magnitude of angular momentum equals the magnitude of momentum mv multiplied by the radius r, that is, $L = mvr$ (see Section 10.5). Comparing this with Eq. (28.25), we can write

$$\mu = \frac{e}{2m}L \qquad (28.26)$$

Equation (28.26) is useful in this discussion because atomic angular momentum is *quantized;* its component in a particular direction is always an integer multiple of $h/2\pi$, where h is a fundamental physical constant called *Planck's constant.* (We will discuss the quantization of angular momentum in more detail in Chapter 41.) The numerical value of h is

$$h = 6.626 \times 10^{-34}\ \text{J}\cdot\text{s}$$

The quantity $h/2\pi$ thus represents a fundamental unit of angular momentum in atomic systems, just as e is a fundamental unit of charge. Associated with the quantization of $\vec{L}$ is a fundamental uncertainty in the *direction* of $\vec{L}$ and therefore of $\vec{\mu}$. In the following discussion, when we speak of the magnitude of a magnetic moment, a more precise statement would be "maximum component in a given direction." Thus, to say that a magnetic moment $\vec{\mu}$ is aligned with a magnetic field $\vec{B}$ really means that $\vec{\mu}$ has its maximum possible component in the direction of $\vec{B}$; such components are always quantized.

Equation (28.26) shows that associated with the fundamental unit of angular momentum is a corresponding fundamental unit of magnetic moment. If $L = h/2\pi$, then

$$\mu = \frac{e}{2m}\left(\frac{h}{2\pi}\right) = \frac{eh}{4\pi m} \qquad (28.27)$$

This quantity is called the **Bohr magneton,** denoted by μ_B. Its numerical value is

$$\mu_B = 9.274 \times 10^{-24}\ \text{A}\cdot\text{m}^2 = 9.274 \times 10^{-24}\ \text{J/T}$$

You should verify that these two sets of units are consistent. The second set is useful when we compute the potential energy $U = -\vec{\mu}\cdot\vec{B}$ for a magnetic moment in a magnetic field.

Electrons also have an intrinsic angular momentum, called *spin,* that is not related to orbital motion but that can be pictured in a classical model as spinning

28.26 An electron moving with speed v in a circular orbit of radius r has an angular momentum $\vec{L}$ and an oppositely directed orbital magnetic dipole moment $\vec{\mu}$. It also has a spin angular momentum and an oppositely directed spin magnetic dipole moment.

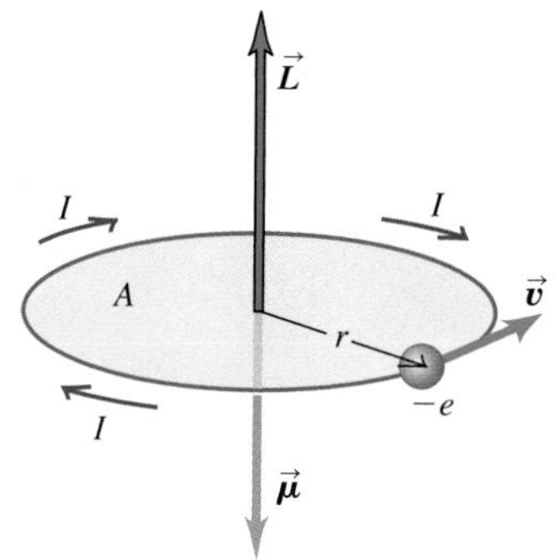

on an axis. This angular momentum also has an associated magnetic moment, and its magnitude turns out to be almost exactly one Bohr magneton. (Effects having to do with quantization of the electromagnetic field cause the spin magnetic moment to be about 1.001 μ_B.)

Paramagnetism

In an atom, most of the various orbital and spin magnetic moments of the electrons add up to zero. However, in some cases the atom has a net magnetic moment that is of the order of μ_B. When such a material is placed in a magnetic field, the field exerts a torque on each magnetic moment, as given by Eq. (27.26): $\vec{\tau} = \vec{\mu} \times \vec{B}$. These torques tend to align the magnetic moments with the field, the position of minimum potential energy, as we discussed in Section 27.7. In this position, the directions of the current loops are such as to *add* to the externally applied magnetic field.

We saw in Section 28.5 that the $\vec{B}$ field produced by a current loop is proportional to the loop's magnetic dipole moment. In the same way, the additional $\vec{B}$ field produced by microscopic electron current loops is proportional to the total magnetic moment $\vec{\mu}_{total}$ per unit volume V in the material. We call this vector quantity the **magnetization** of the material, denoted by $\vec{M}$:

$$\vec{M} = \frac{\vec{\mu}_{total}}{V} \qquad (28.28)$$

The additional magnetic field due to magnetization of the material turns out to be equal simply to $\mu_0\vec{M}$, where μ_0 is the same constant that appears in the law of Biot and Savart and Ampere's law. When such a material completely surrounds a current-carrying conductor, the total magnetic field $\vec{B}$ in the material is

$$\vec{B} = \vec{B}_0 + \mu_0\vec{M} \qquad (28.29)$$

where $\vec{B}_0$ is the field caused by the current in the conductor.

To check that the units in Eq. (28.29) are consistent, note that magnetization $\vec{M}$ is magnetic moment per unit volume. The units of magnetic moment are current times area $(\text{A}\cdot\text{m}^2)$, so the units of magnetization are $(\text{A}\cdot\text{m}^2)/\text{m}^3 = \text{A/m}$. From Section 28.1, the units of the constant μ_0 are $\text{T}\cdot\text{m/A}$. So the units of $\mu_0\vec{M}$ are the same as the units of $\vec{B}$: $(\text{T}\cdot\text{m/A})(\text{A/m}) = \text{T}$.

A material showing the behavior just described is said to be **paramagnetic.** The result is that the magnetic field at any point in such a material is greater by a dimensionless factor K_m, called the **relative permeability** of the material, than it would be if the material were replaced by vacuum. The value of K_m is different for different materials; for common paramagnetic solids and liquids at room temperature, K_m typically ranges from 1.00001 to 1.003.

All of the equations in this chapter that relate magnetic fields to their sources can be adapted to the situation in which the current-carrying conductor is embedded in a paramagnetic material. All that need be done is to replace μ_0 by $K_m\mu_0$. This product is usually denoted as μ and is called the **permeability** of the material:

$$\mu = K_m\mu_0 \qquad (28.30)$$

CAUTION Two meanings of the symbol μ Equation (28.30) involves some really dangerous notation because we have also used μ for magnetic dipole moment. It's customary to use μ for both quantities, but beware: From now on, every time you see a μ, make sure you know whether it is permeability or magnetic moment. You can usually tell from the context.

The amount by which the relative permeability differs from unity is called the **magnetic susceptibility,** denoted by χ_m:

$$\chi_m = K_m - 1 \qquad (28.31)$$

Both K_m and χ_m are dimensionless quantities. Values of magnetic susceptibility for several materials are given in Table 28.1. For example, for aluminum, $\chi_m = 2.2 \times 10^{-5}$ and $K_m = 1.000022$. The first group of materials in the table are paramagnetic; we'll discuss the second group of materials, which are called *diamagnetic,* very shortly.

The tendency of atomic magnetic moments to align themselves parallel to the magnetic field (where the potential energy is minimum) is opposed by random thermal motion, which tends to randomize their orientations. For this reason, paramagnetic susceptibility always decreases with increasing temperature. In many cases it is inversely proportional to the absolute temperature T, and the magnetization M can be expressed as

$$M = C\frac{B}{T} \tag{28.32}$$

This relationship is called *Curie's law,* after its discoverer, Pierre Curie (1859–1906). The quantity C is a constant, different for different materials, called the *Curie constant.*

As we described in Section 27.7, a body with atomic magnetic dipoles is attracted to the poles of a magnet. In most paramagnetic substances this attraction is very weak due to thermal randomization of the atomic magnetic moments. That's why a magnet can't be used to pick up objects made of aluminum (a paramagnetic substance). But at very low temperatures the thermal effects are reduced, the magnetization increases in accordance with Curie's law, and the attractive forces are greater.

Table 28.1 Magnetic Susceptibilities of Paramagnetic and Diamagnetic Materials at $T = 20°C$

Material	$\chi_m = K_m - 1\ (\times 10^{-5})$
Paramagnetic	
Iron ammonium alum	66
Uranium	40
Platinum	26
Aluminum	2.2
Sodium	0.72
Oxygen gas	0.19
Diamagnetic	
Bismuth	−16.6
Mercury	−2.9
Silver	−2.6
Carbon (diamond)	−2.1
Lead	−1.8
Sodium chloride	−1.4
Copper	−1.0

Example 28.11 Magnetic dipoles in a paramagnetic material

Nitric oxide (NO) is a paramagnetic compound. Its molecules have a magnetic moment with a maximum component in any direction of about one Bohr magneton each. In a magnetic field with magnitude $B = 1.5$ T, compare the interaction energy of the magnetic moments with the field to the average translational kinetic energy of the molecules at a temperature of 300 K.

SOLUTION

IDENTIFY: This problem involves both the energy of a magnetic moment in a magnetic field (Chapter 27) and the average translational kinetic energy due to temperature (Chapter 18).

SET UP: In Section 27.7 we derived the equation $U = -\vec{\boldsymbol{\mu}} \cdot \vec{\boldsymbol{B}}$ for the interaction energy of a magnetic moment $\vec{\boldsymbol{\mu}}$ with a $\vec{\boldsymbol{B}}$ field. From Section 18.3 the average translational kinetic energy of a molecule at temperature T is $K = \frac{3}{2}kT$, where k is the Boltzmann constant.

EXECUTE: We can write the interaction energy as $U = -(\mu\cos\phi)B$, where $\mu\cos\phi$ is the component of the magnetic moment $\vec{\boldsymbol{\mu}}$ in the direction of the $\vec{\boldsymbol{B}}$ field. In our case the maximum value of the component $\mu\cos\phi$ is about μ_B, so

$$|U|_{max} \approx \mu_B B = (9.27 \times 10^{-24}\ \text{J/T})(1.5\ \text{T})$$
$$= 1.4 \times 10^{-23}\ \text{J} = 8.7 \times 10^{-5}\ \text{eV}$$

The average translational kinetic energy K is

$$K = \frac{3}{2}kT = \frac{3}{2}(1.38 \times 10^{-23}\ \text{J/K})(300\ \text{K})$$
$$= 6.2 \times 10^{-21}\ \text{J} = 0.039\ \text{eV}$$

EVALUATE: At a temperature of 300 K the magnetic interaction energy is much *smaller* than the random kinetic energy, so we expect only a slight degree of alignment. This is why paramagnetic susceptibilities at ordinary temperature are usually very small.

Diamagnetism

In some materials the total magnetic moment of all the atomic current loops is zero when no magnetic field is present. But even these materials have magnetic effects because an external field alters electron motions within the atoms, causing additional current loops and induced magnetic dipoles comparable to the induced *electric* dipoles we studied in Section 28.5. In this case the additional field caused by these current loops is always *opposite* in direction to that of the external field. (This behavior is explained by Faraday's law of induction, which we will study in Chapter 29. An induced current always tends to cancel the field change that caused it.)

28.27 In this drawing adapted from a magnified photo, the arrows show the directions of magnetization in the domains of a single crystal of nickel. Domains that are magnetized in the direction of an applied magnetic field grow larger.

(a) No field

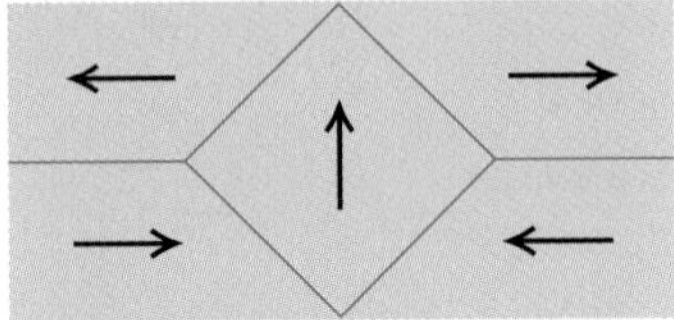

(b) Weak field

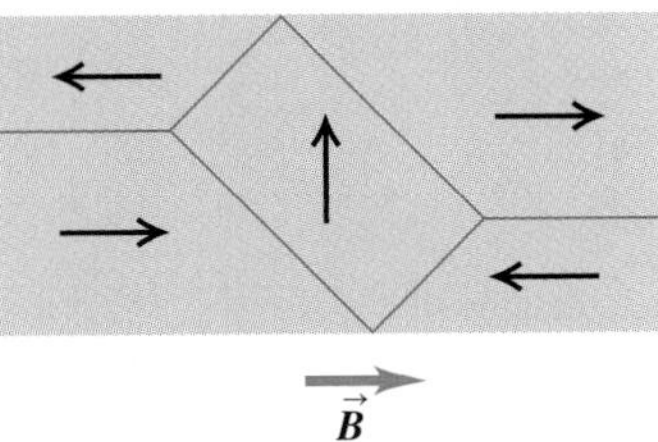

(c) Stronger field

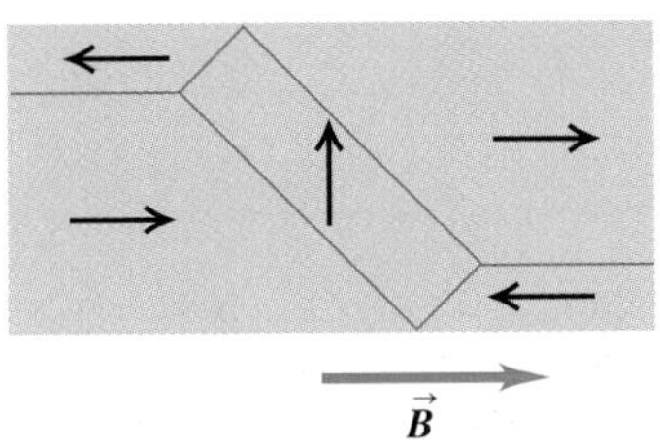

28.28 A magnetization curve for a ferromagnetic material. The magnetization M approaches its saturation value M_{sat} as the magnetic field B_0 (caused by external currents) becomes large.

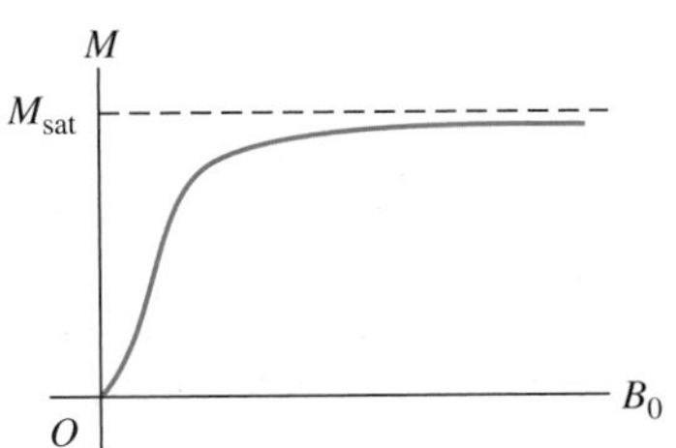

Such materials are said to be **diamagnetic.** They always have negative susceptibility, as shown in Table 28.1, and relative permeability K_m slightly *less* than unity, typically of the order of 0.99990 to 0.99999 for solids and liquids. Diamagnetic susceptibilities are very nearly temperature independent.

Ferromagnetism

There is a third class of materials, called **ferromagnetic** materials, that includes iron, nickel, cobalt, and many alloys containing these elements. In these materials, strong interactions between atomic magnetic moments cause them to line up parallel to each other in regions called **magnetic domains,** even when no external field is present. Figure 28.27 shows an example of magnetic domain structure. Within each domain, nearly all of the atomic magnetic moments are parallel.

When there is no externally applied field, the domain magnetizations are randomly oriented. But when a field $\vec{B}_0$ (caused by external currents) is present, the domains tend to orient themselves parallel to the field. The domain boundaries also shift; the domains that are magnetized in the field direction grow, and those that are magnetized in other directions shrink. Because the total magnetic moment of a domain may be many thousands of Bohr magnetons, the torques that tend to align the domains with an external field are much stronger than occur with paramagnetic materials. The relative permeability K_m is *much* larger than unity, typically of the order of 1,000 to 100,000. As a result, an object made of a ferromagnetic material such as iron is strongly magnetized by the field from a permanent magnet and is attracted to the magnet (see Fig. 27.38). A paramagnetic material such as aluminum is also attracted to a permanent magnet, but K_m for paramagnetic materials is so much smaller for such a material than for ferromagnetic materials that the attraction is very weak. Thus a magnet can pick up iron nails, but not aluminum cans.

As the external field is increased, a point is eventually reached at which nearly *all* the magnetic moments in the ferromagnetic material are aligned parallel to the external field. This condition is called *saturation magnetization;* after it is reached, further increase in the external field causes no increase in magnetization or in the additional field caused by the magnetization.

Figure 28.28 shows a "magnetization curve," a graph of magnetization M as a function of external magnetic field B_0, for soft iron. An alternative description of this behavior is that K_m is not constant but decreases as B_0 increases. (Paramagnetic materials also show saturation at sufficiently strong fields. But the magnetic fields required are so large that departures from a linear relationship between M and B_0 in these materials can be observed only at very low temperatures, 1 K or so.)

For many ferromagnetic materials the relationship of magnetization to external magnetic field is different when the external field is increasing from when it is decreasing. Figure 28.29a shows this relationship for such a material. When the material is magnetized to saturation and then the external field is reduced to zero, some magnetization remains. This behavior is characteristic of permanent magnets, which retain most of their saturation magnetization when the magnetizing field is removed. To reduce the magnetization to zero requires a magnetic field in the reverse direction.

This behavior is called **hysteresis,** and the curves in Fig. 28.29 are called *hysteresis loops.* Magnetizing and demagnetizing a material that has hysteresis involve the dissipation of energy, and the temperature of the material increases during such a process.

Ferromagnetic materials are widely used in electromagnets, transformer cores, and motors and generators, in which it is desirable to have as large a magnetic field as possible for a given current. Because hysteresis dissipates energy, materials that are used in these applications should usually have as narrow a hysteresis loop as possible. Soft iron is often used; it has high permeability without appreciable hysteresis. For permanent magnets a broad hysteresis loop is usually desirable, with large zero-field magnetization and large reverse field needed to demagnetize. Many kinds of steel and many alloys, such as Alnico, are commonly used for permanent magnets. The remaining magnetic field in such a material, after it has been magnetized to near saturation, is typically of the order of 1 T, corresponding to a remaining magnetization $M = B/\mu_0$ of about 800,000 A/m.

28.29 Hysteresis loops. The materials of both (a) and (b) remain strongly magnetized when B_0 is reduced to zero. Since (a) is also hard to demagnetize, it would be good for permanent magnets. Since (b) magnetizes and demagnetizes more easily, it could be used as a computer memory material. The material of (c) would be useful for transformers and other alternating-current devices where zero hysteresis would be optimal.

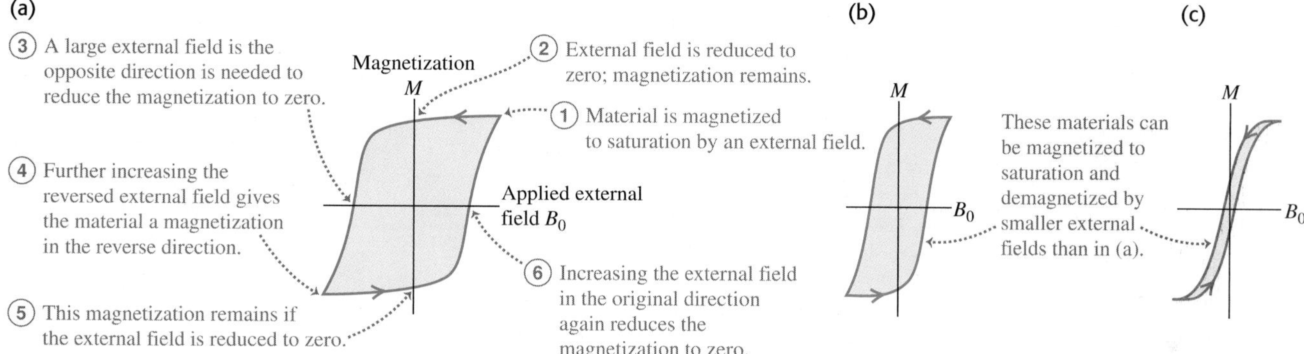

Example 28.12 A ferromagnetic material

A permanent magnet is made of a ferromagnetic material with a magnetization M of about 8×10^5 A/m. The magnet is in the shape of a cube of side 2 cm. (a) Find the magnetic dipole moment of the magnet. (b) Estimate the magnetic field due to the magnet at a point 10 cm from the magnet along its axis.

SOLUTION

IDENTIFY: This problem uses the relationship between magnetization and magnetic dipole moment, as well as the idea that a magnetic dipole produces a magnetic field.

SET UP: We find the magnetic dipole moment from the magnetization, which equals magnetic moment per unit volume. To estimate the magnetic field, we approximate the magnet as a current loop with the same magnetic moment and use the results of Section 28.5.

EXECUTE: (a) The total magnetic moment is the magnetization multiplied by the volume:

$$\mu_{\text{total}} = MV = (8 \times 10^5 \text{ A/m})(2 \times 10^{-2} \text{ m})^3 = 6 \text{ A} \cdot \text{m}^2$$

(b) We found in Section 28.5 that the magnetic field on the axis of a current loop with magnetic moment μ_{total} is given by Eq. (28.18),

$$B = \frac{\mu_0 \mu_{\text{total}}}{2\pi(x^2 + a^2)^{3/2}}$$

where x is the distance from the loop and a is its radius. We can use this same expression here, except that a refers to the size of the permanent magnet. Strictly speaking, there are complications because our magnet does not have the same geometry as a circular current loop. But because $x = 10$ cm is fairly large in comparison to the 2-cm size of the magnet, the term a^2 is negligible in comparison to x^2 and can be ignored. So

$$B \approx \frac{\mu_0 \mu_{\text{total}}}{2\pi x^3} = \frac{(4\pi \times 10^{-7} \text{ T} \cdot \text{m/A})(6 \text{ A} \cdot \text{m}^2)}{2\pi(0.1 \text{ m})^3}$$
$$= 1 \times 10^{-3} \text{ T} = 10 \text{ G}$$

which is about ten times stronger than the magnetic field of the earth. Such a magnet can easily deflect a compass needle.

EVALUATE: Note that we used μ_0, not the permeability μ of the magnetic material, in calculating B. The reason is that we are calculating B at a point *outside* the magnetic material. You would substitute permeability μ for μ_0 only if you were calculating B *inside* a material with relative permeability K_m, for which $\mu = K_m \mu_0$.

Test Your Understanding of Section 28.8 Which of the following materials are attracted to a magnet? (i) sodium; (ii) bismuth; (iii) lead; (iv) uranium.

CHAPTER 28 SUMMARY

Magnetic field of a moving charge: The magnetic field $\vec{B}$ created by a charge q moving with velocity $\vec{v}$ depends on the distance r from the source point (the location of q) to the field point (where $\vec{B}$ is measured). The $\vec{B}$ field is perpendicular to $\vec{v}$ and to $\hat{r}$, the unit vector directed from the source point to the field point. The principle of superposition of magnetic fields states that the total $\vec{B}$ field produced by several moving charges is the vector sum of the fields produced by the individual charges. (See Example 28.1.)

$$\vec{B} = \frac{\mu_0}{4\pi}\frac{q\vec{v} \times \hat{r}}{r^2} \quad (28.2)$$

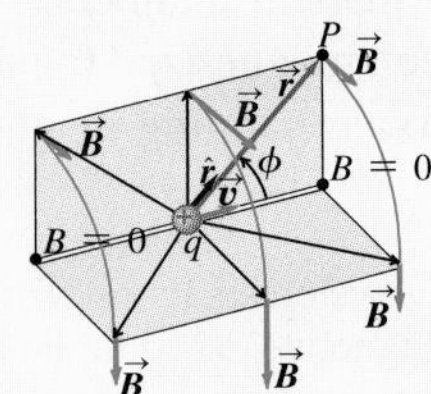

Magnetic field of a current-carrying conductor: The law of Biot and Savart gives the magnetic field $d\vec{B}$ created by an element $d\vec{l}$ of a conductor carrying current I. The field $d\vec{B}$ is perpendicular to both $d\vec{l}$ and $\hat{r}$, the unit vector from the element to the field point. The $\vec{B}$ field created by a finite current-carrying conductor is the integral of $d\vec{B}$ over the length of the conductor. (See Example 28.2.)

$$d\vec{B} = \frac{\mu_0}{4\pi}\frac{I\,d\vec{l} \times \hat{r}}{r^2} \quad (28.6)$$

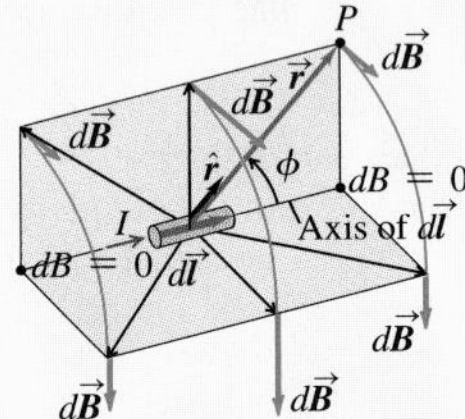

Magnetic field of a long, straight, current-carrying conductor: The magnetic field $\vec{B}$ at a distance r from a long, straight conductor carrying a current I has a magnitude that is inversely proportional to r. The magnetic field lines are circles coaxial with the wire, with directions given by the right-hand rule. (See Examples 28.3 and 28.4.)

$$B = \frac{\mu_0 I}{2\pi r} \quad (28.9)$$

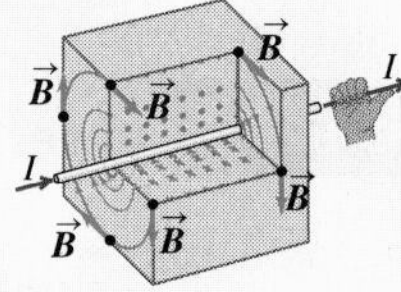

Magnetic force between current-carrying conductors: Two long, parallel, current-carrying conductors attract if the currents are in the same direction and repel if the currents are in opposite directions. The magnetic force per unit length between the conductors depends on their currents I and I' and their separation r. The definition of the ampere is based on this relationship. (See Example 28.5.)

$$\frac{F}{L} = \frac{\mu_0 I I'}{2\pi r} \quad (28.11)$$

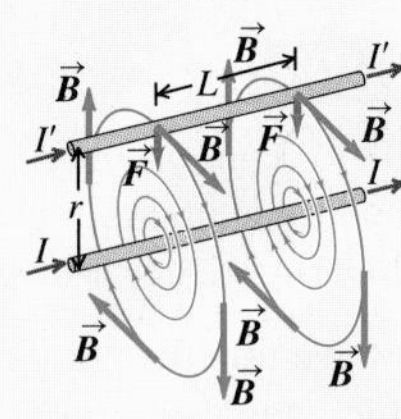

Magnetic field of a current loop: The law of Biot and Savart allows us to calculate the magnetic field produced along the axis of a circular conducting loop of radius a carrying current I. The field depends on the distance x along the axis from the center of the loop to the field point. If there are N loops, the field is multiplied by N. At the center of the loop, $x = 0$. (See Example 28.6.)

$$B_x = \frac{\mu_0 I a^2}{2(x^2 + a^2)^{3/2}} \quad (28.15)$$

(circular loop)

$$B_x = \frac{\mu_0 N I}{2a} \quad (28.17)$$

(center of N circular loops)

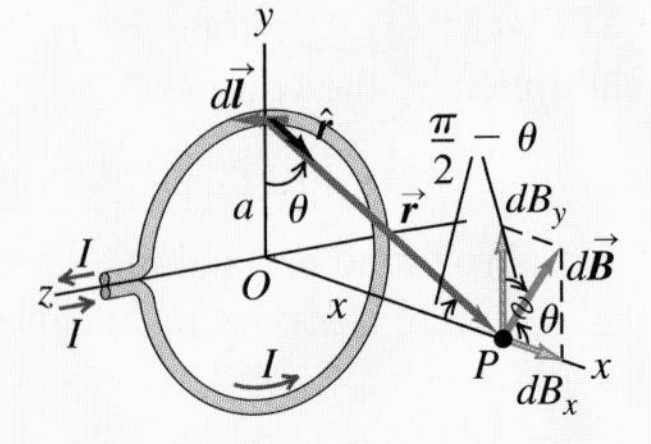

Ampere's law: Ampere's law states that the line integral of $\vec{B}$ around any closed path equals μ_0 times the net current through the area enclosed by the path. The positive sense of current is determined by a right-hand rule. (See Examples 28.7–28.10.)

$$\oint \vec{B} \cdot d\vec{l} = \mu_0 I_{\text{encl}} \quad (28.20)$$

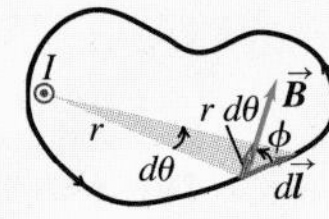

Magnetic fields due to current distributions: The table lists magnetic fields caused by several current distributions. In each case the conductor is carrying current I.

Current Distribution	Point in Magnetic Field	Magnetic-Field Magnitude
Long, straight conductor	Distance r from conductor	$B = \dfrac{\mu_0 I}{2\pi r}$
Circular loop of radius a	On axis of loop	$B = \dfrac{\mu_0 I a^2}{2(x^2 + a^2)^{3/2}}$
	At center of loop	$B = \dfrac{\mu_0 I}{2a}$ (for N loops, multiply these expressions by N)
Long cylindrical conductor of radius R	Inside conductor, $r < R$	$B = \dfrac{\mu_0 I}{2\pi}\dfrac{r}{R^2}$
	Outside conductor, $r > R$	$B = \dfrac{\mu_0 I}{2\pi r}$
Long, closely wound solenoid with n turns per unit length, near its midpoint	Inside solenoid, near center	$B = \mu_0 n I$
	Outside solenoid	$B \approx 0$
Tightly wound toroidal solenoid (toroid) with N turns	Within the space enclosed by the windings, distance r from symmetry axis	$B = \dfrac{\mu_0 N I}{2\pi r}$
	Outside the space enclosed by the windings	$B \approx 0$

***Magnetic materials:** When magnetic materials are present, the magnetization of the material causes an additional contribution to $\vec{B}$. For paramagnetic and diamagnetic materials, μ_0 is replaced in magnetic-field expressions by $\mu = K_m \mu_0$, where μ is the permeability of the material and K_m is its relative permeability. The magnetic susceptibility χ_m is defined as $\chi_m = K_m - 1$. Magnetic susceptibilities for paramagnetic materials are small positive quantities; those for diamagnetic materials are small negative quantities. For ferromagnetic materials, K_m is much larger than unity and is not constant. Some ferromagnetic materials are permanent magnets, retaining their magnetization even after the external magnetic field is removed. (See Examples 28.11 and 28.12.)

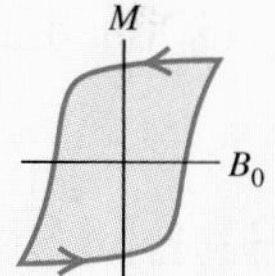

Key Terms

source point, *958*
field point, *958*
principle of superposition of magnetic fields, *960*
law of Biot and Savart, *961*
ampere, *966*
Ampere's law, *972*
toroidal solenoid, *975*
Bohr magneton, *977*
magnetization, *978*
paramagnetic, *978*
relative permeability, *978*
permeability, *978*
magnetic susceptibility, *978*
diamagnetic, *980*
ferromagnetic, *980*
magnetic domain, *980*
hysteresis, *980*

Answer to Chapter Opening Question ?

There would be *no* change in the magnetic field strength. From Example 28.9 (Section 28.7), the field inside a solenoid has magnitude $B = \mu_0 n I$, where n is the number of turns of wire per unit length. Joining two solenoids end to end doubles both the number of turns and the length, so the number of turns per unit length is unchanged.

Answers to Test Your Understanding Questions

28.1 **Answer: (a) (i), (b) (ii)** The situation is the same as shown in Fig. 28.2 except that the upper proton has velocity $\vec{v}$ rather than $-\vec{v}$. The magnetic field due to the lower proton is the same as shown in Fig. 28.2, but the direction of the magnetic force $\vec{F} = q\vec{v} \times \vec{B}$ on the upper proton is reversed. Hence the magnetic force is attractive. Since the speed v is small compared to c, the magnetic force is much smaller in magnitude than the repulsive electric force and the net force is still repulsive.

28.2 **Answer: (i) and (iii) (tie), (iv), (ii)** From Eq. (28.5), the magnitude of the field dB due to a current element of length dl carrying current I is $dB = (\mu/4\pi)(I\,dl \sin\phi/r^2)$. In this expression r is the distance from the element to the field point, and ϕ is the angle between the direction of the current and a vector from the current element to the field point. All four points are the same distance $r = L$ from the current element, so the value of dB is proportional to the value of $\sin\phi$. For the four points the angle is (i) $\phi = 90°$, (ii) $\phi = 0$, (iii) $\phi = 90°$, and (iv) $\phi = 45°$, so the values of $\sin\phi$ are (i) 1, (ii) 0, (iii) 1, and (iv) $1/\sqrt{2}$.

28.3 **Answer: A** This orientation will cause current to flow clockwise around the circuit. Hence current will flow south through the wire that lies under the compass. From the right-hand rule for the magnetic field produced by a long, straight, current-carrying conductor, this will produce a magnetic field that points to the left at the position of the compass (which lies atop the wire). The combination of the northward magnetic field of the earth and the westward field produced by the current gives a net magnetic field to the northwest, so the compass needle will swing counterclockwise to align with this field.

28.4 **Answers: (a) (i), (b) (iii), (c) (ii), (d) (iii)** Current flows in the same direction in adjacent turns of the coil, so the magnetic forces between these turns are attractive. Current flows in opposite directions on opposite sides of the same turn, so the magnetic forces between these sides are repulsive. Thus the magnetic forces on the solenoid turns squeeze them together in the direction along its axis but push them apart radially. The *electric* forces are zero because the wire is electrically neutral, with as much positive charge as there is negative charge.

28.5 **Answers: (a) (ii), (b) (v)** The vector $d\vec{B}$ is in the direction of $d\vec{l} \times \vec{r}$. For a segment on the negative y-axis, $d\vec{l} = -\hat{k}\,dl$ points in the negative z-direction and $\vec{r} = x\hat{\imath} + a\hat{\jmath}$. Hence $d\vec{l} \times \vec{r} = (a\,dl)\hat{\imath} - (x\,dl)\hat{\jmath}$, which has a positive x-component, a negative y-component and zero z-component. For a segment on the negative z-axis, $d\vec{l} = \hat{\jmath}\,dl$ points in the positive y-direction and $\vec{r} = x\hat{\imath} + a\hat{k}$. Hence $d\vec{l} \times \vec{r} = (a\,dl)\hat{\imath} - (x\,dl)\hat{k}$, which has a positive x-component, zero y-component, and a negative z-component.

28.6 **Answer: (ii)** Imagine carrying out the integral $\oint \vec{B} \cdot d\vec{l}$ along an integration path that goes clockwise around the red magnetic field line. At each point along the path the magnetic field $\vec{B}$ and the infinitesimal segment $d\vec{l}$ are both tangent to the path, so $\vec{B} \cdot d\vec{l}$ is positive at each point and the integral $\oint \vec{B} \cdot d\vec{l}$ is likewise positive. It follows from Ampere's law $\oint \vec{B} \cdot d\vec{l} = \mu_0 I_{encl}$ and the right-hand rule that the integration path encloses a current directed out of the plane of the page. There are no currents in the empty space outside the magnet, so there must be currents inside the magnet (see Section 28.8).

28.7 **Answer: (iii)** By symmetry, any $\vec{B}$ field outside the cable must circulate around the cable, with circular field lines like those surrounding the solid cylindrical conductor in Fig. 28.20. Choose an integration path like the one shown in Fig. 28.20 with radius $r > R$, so that the path completely encloses the cable. As in Example 28.8, the integral $\oint \vec{B} \cdot d\vec{l}$ for this path has magnitude $B(2\pi r)$. From Ampere's law this is equal to $\mu_0 I_{encl}$. The net enclosed current I_{encl} is zero because it includes two currents of equal magnitude but opposite direction: one in the central wire and one in the hollow cylinder. Hence $B(2\pi r) = 0$, and so $B = 0$ for any value of r outside the cable. (The field is nonzero *inside* the cable; see Exercise 28.37.)

28.8 **Answer: (i), (iv)** Sodium and uranium are paramagnetic materials and hence are attracted to a magnet, while bismuth and lead are diamagnetic materials that are repelled by a magnet. (See Table 28.1.)

PROBLEMS

For instructor-assigned homework, go to www.masteringphysics.com 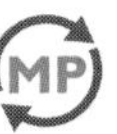

Discussion Questions

Q28.1. A topic of current interest in physics research is the search (thus far unsuccessful) for an isolated magnetic pole, or magnetic *monopole*. If such an entity were found, how could it be recognized? What would its properties be?

Q28.2. Streams of charged particles emitted from the sun during periods of solar activity create a disturbance in the earth's magnetic field. How does this happen?

Q28.3. The text discussed the magnetic field of an infinitely long, straight conductor carrying a current. Of course, there is no such thing as an infinitely long *anything*. How do you decide whether a particular wire is long enough to be considered infinite?

Q28.4. Two parallel conductors carrying current in the same direction attract each other. If they are permitted to move toward each other, the forces of attraction do work. From where does the energy come? Does this contradict the assertion in Chapter 27 that magnetic forces on moving charges do no work? Explain.

Q28.5. Pairs of conductors carrying current into or out of the power-supply components of electronic equipment are sometimes twisted together to reduce magnetic-field effects. Why does this help?

Q28.6. Suppose you have three long, parallel wires arranged so that in cross section they are at the corners of an equilateral triangle. Is there any way to arrange the currents so that all three wires attract each other? So that all three wires repel each other? Explain.

Q28.7. In deriving the force on one of the long, current-carrying conductors in Section 28.4, why did we use the magnetic field due to only one of the conductors? That is, why didn't we use the *total* magnetic field due to *both* conductors?

Q28.8. Two concentric, coplanar, circular loops of wire of different diameter carry currents in the same direction. Describe the nature of the force exerted on the inner loop by the outer loop and on the outer loop by the inner loop.

Q28.9. A current was sent through a helical coil spring. The spring contracted, as though it had been compressed. Why?

Q28.10. What are the relative advantages and disadvantages of Ampere's law and the law of Biot and Savart for practical calculations of magnetic fields?

Q28.11. Magnetic field lines never have a beginning or an end. Use this to explain why it is reasonable for the field of a toroidal solenoid to be confined entirely to its interior, while a straight solenoid *must* have some field outside.

Q28.12. If the magnitude of the magnetic field a distance R from a very long, straight, current-carrying wire is B, at what distance from the wire will the field have magnitude $3B$?

Q28.13. Two very long, parallel wires carry equal currents in opposite directions. (a) Is there any place that their magnetic fields completely cancel? If so, where? If not, why not? (b) How would the answer to part (a) change if the currents were in the same direction?

Q28.14. In the circuit shown in Figure 28.30, when switch S is suddenly closed, the wire L is pulled toward the lower wire carrying current I. Which (a or b) is the positive terminal of the battery? How do you know?

Figure **28.30** Question Q28.14.

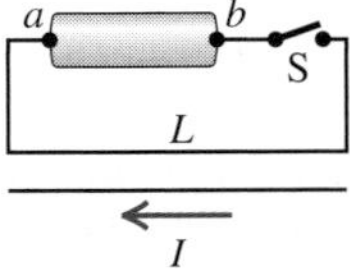

Q28.15. A metal ring carries a current that causes a magnetic field B_0 at the center of the ring and a field B at point P a distance x

from the center along the axis of the ring. If the radius of the ring is doubled, find the magnetic field at the center. Will the field at point P change by the same factor? Why?

***Q28.16.** Why should the permeability of a paramagnetic material be expected to decrease with increasing temperature?

***Q28.17.** If a magnet is suspended over a container of liquid air, it attracts droplets to its poles. The droplets contain only liquid oxygen; even though nitrogen is the primary constituent of air, it is not attracted to the magnet. Explain what this tells you about the magnetic susceptibilities of oxygen and nitrogen, and explain why a magnet in ordinary, room-temperature air doesn't attract molecules of oxygen *gas* to its poles.

***Q28.18.** What features of atomic structure determine whether an element is diamagnetic or paramagnetic? Explain.

***Q28.19.** The magnetic susceptibility of paramagnetic materials is quite strongly temperature dependent, but that of diamagnetic materials is nearly independent of temperature Why the difference?

***Q28.20.** A cylinder of iron is placed so that it is free to rotate around its axis. Initially the cylinder is at rest, and a magnetic field is applied to the cylinder so that it is magnetized in a direction parallel to its axis. If the direction of the *external* field is suddenly reversed, the direction of magnetization will also reverse and the cylinder will begin rotating around its axis. (This is called the *Einstein-de Haas effect.*) Explain why the cylinder begins to rotate.

***Q28.21.** The discussion of magnetic forces on current loops in Section 27.7 commented that no net force is exerted on a complete loop in a uniform magnetic field, only a torque. Yet magnetized materials that contain atomic current loops certainly *do* experience net forces in magnetic fields. How is this discrepancy resolved?

***Q28.22.** Show that the units $A \cdot m^2$ and J/T for the Bohr magneton are equivalent.

Exercises

Section 26.1 Magnetic Field of a Moving Charge

28.1. A $+6.00\text{-}\mu C$ point charge is moving at a constant 8.00×10^6 m/s in the $+y$-direction, relative to a reference frame. At the instant when the point charge is at the origin of this reference frame, what is the magnetic-field vector $\vec{B}$ it produces at the following points: (a) $x = 0.500$ m, $y = 0$, $z = 0$; (b) $x = 0$, $y = -0.500$ m, $z = 0$; (c) $x = 0$, $y = 0$, $z = +0.500$ m; (d) $x = 0$, $y = -0.500$ m, $z = +0.500$ m?

28.2. Fields Within the Atom. In the Bohr model of the hydrogen atom, the electron moves in a circular orbit of radius 5.3×10^{-11} m with a speed of 2.2×10^6 m/s. If we are viewing the atom in such a way that the electron's orbit is in the plane of the paper with the electron moving clockwise, find the magnitude and direction of the electric and magnetic fields that the electron produces at the location of the nucleus (treated as a point).

28.3. An electron moves at $0.100c$ as shown in Fig. 28.31. Find the magnitude and direction of the magnetic field this electon produces at the following points, each 2.00 μm from the electron: (a) points A and B; (b) point C; (c) point D.

Figure 28.31 Exercise 28.3.

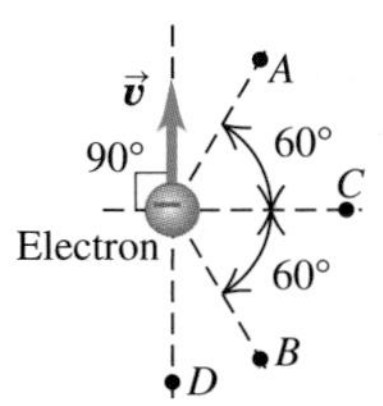

28.4. An alpha particle (charge $+2e$) and an electron move in opposite directions from the same point, each with the speed of 2.50×10^5 m/s (Fig. 28.32). Find the magnitude and direction of the total magnetic field these charges produce at point P, which is 1.75 nm from each of them.

Figure 28.32 Exercise 28.4.

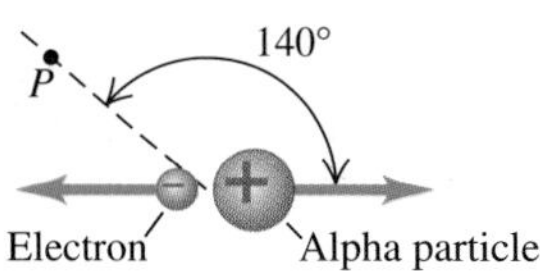

28.5. A $-4.80\text{-}\mu C$ charge is moving at a constant speed of 6.80×10^5 m/s in the $+x$-direction relative to a reference frame. At the instant when the point charge is at the origin, what is the magnetic-field vector it produces at the following points: (a) $x = 0.500$ m, $y = 0$, $z = 0$; (b) $x = 0$, $y = 0.500$ m, $z = 0$; (c) $x = 0.500$ m, $y = 0.500$ m, $z = 0$; (d) $x = 0$, $y = 0$, $z = 0.500$ m?

28.6. Positive point charges $q = +8.00\ \mu C$ and $q' = +3.00\ \mu C$ are moving relative to an observer at point P, as shown in Fig. 28.33. The distance d is 0.120 m, $v = 4.50 \times 10^6$ m/s, and $v' = 9.00 \times 10^6$ m/s. (a) When the two charges are at the locations shown in the figure, what are the magnitude and direction of the net magnetic field they produce at point P? (b) What are the magnitude and direction of the electric and magnetic forces that each charge exerts on the other, and what is the ratio of the magnitude of the electric force to the magnitude of the magnetic force? (c) If the direction of $\vec{v}'$ is reversed, so both charges are moving in the same direction, what are the magnitude and direction of the magnetic forces that the two charges exert on each other?

Figure 28.33 Exercises 28.6 and 28.7.

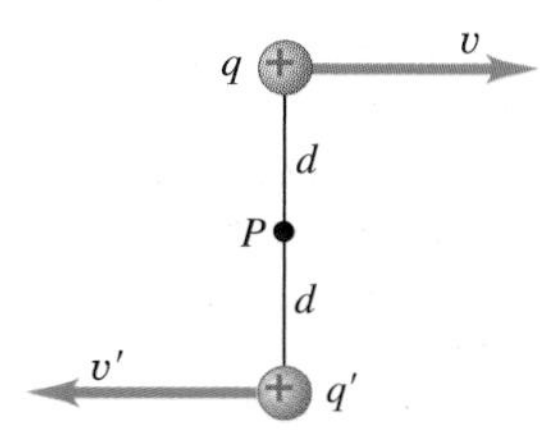

28.7. Figure 28.33 shows two point charges, q and q', moving relative to an observer at point P. Suppose that the lower charge is actually *negative,* with $q' = -q$. (a) Find the magnetic field (magnitude and direction) produced by the two charges at point P if (i) $v' = v/2$; (ii) $v' = v$; (iii) $v' = 2v$. (b) Find the direction of the magnetic force that q exerts on q', and find the direction of the magnetic force that q' exerts on q. (c) If $v = v' = 3.00 \times 10^5$ m/s, what is the ratio of the magnitude of the magnetic force acting on each charge to that of the Coulomb force acting on each charge?

28.8. An electron and a proton are each moving at 845 km/s in perpendicular paths as shown in Fig. 28.34. At the instant when they are at the positions shown in the figure, find the magnitude and direction of (a) the total magnetic field they produce at the origin; (b) the magnetic field the electron produces at the location of the proton; (c) the total electrical force and the total magnetic force that the electron exerts on the proton.

Figure 28.34 Exercise 28.8.

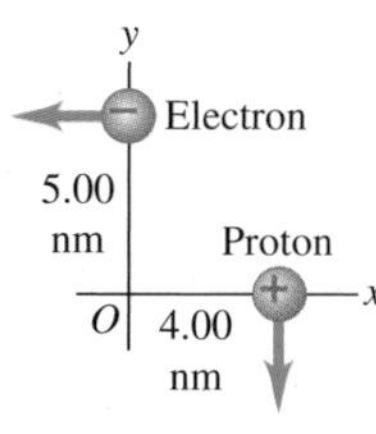

Section 28.2 Magnetic Field of a Current Element

28.9. A straight wire caries a 10.0-A current (Fig. 28.35). $ABCD$ is a rectangle with point D in the middle of a 1.10-mm segment of the wire and point C in the wire. Find the magnitude and direction of the magnetic field due to this segment at (a) point A; (b) point B; (c) point C.

Figure 28.35 Exercise 28.9.

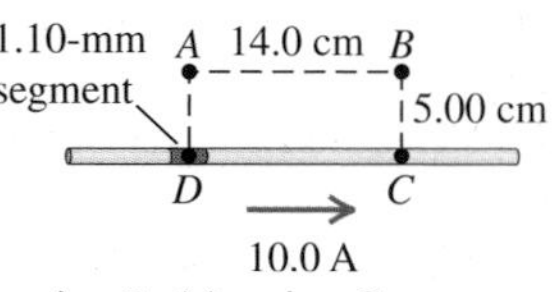

28.10. A long, straight wire, carrying a current of 200 A, runs through a cubical wooden box, entering and leaving through holes in the centers of opposite faces (Fig. 28.36). The length of each side of the box is 20.0 cm. Consider an element dl of the wire 0.100 cm long at the center of the box. Compute the magnitude dB of the magnetic field produced by this element at the points a, b, c, d, and e in Fig. 28.36. Points a, c, and d are at the centers of the faces of the cube; point b is at the midpoint of one edge; and point e is at a corner. Copy the figure and show the directions and relative magnitudes of the field vectors. (*Note:* Assume that the length dl is small in comparison to the distances from the current element to the points where the magnetic field is to be calculated.)

Figure 28.36 Exercise 28.10.

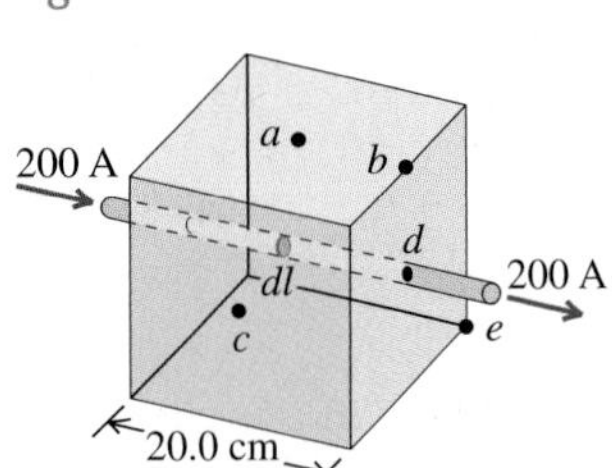

28.11. A long, straight wire lies along the z-axis and carries a 4.00-A current in the $+z$-direction. Find the magnetic field (magnitude and direction) produced at the following points by a 0.500-mm segment of the wire centered at the origin: (a) $x = 2.00$ m, $y = 0$, $z = 0$; (b) $x = 0$, $y = 2.00$ m, $z = 0$; (c) $x = 2.00$ m, $y = 2.00$ m, $z = 0$; (d) $x = 0$, $y = 0$, $z = 2.00$ m.

28.12. Two parallel wires are 5.00 cm apart and carry currents in opposite directions, as shown in Fig. 28.37. Find the magnitude and direction of the magnetic field at point P due to two 1.50-mm segments of wire that are opposite each other and each 8.00 cm from P.

Figure 28.37 Exercise 28.12.

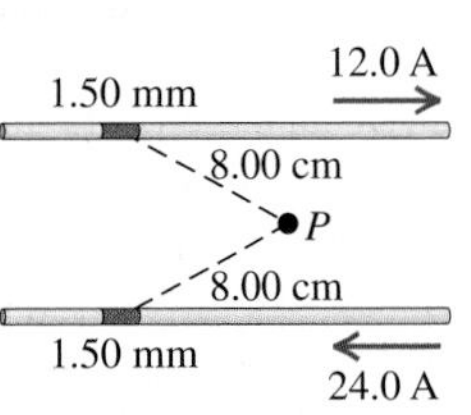

28.13. A wire carrying a 28.0-A current bends through a right angle. Consider two 2.00-mm segments of wire, each 3.00 cm from the bend (Fig. 28.38). Find the magnitude and direction of the magnetic field these two segments produce at point P, which is midway between them.

Figure 28.38 Exercise 28.13.

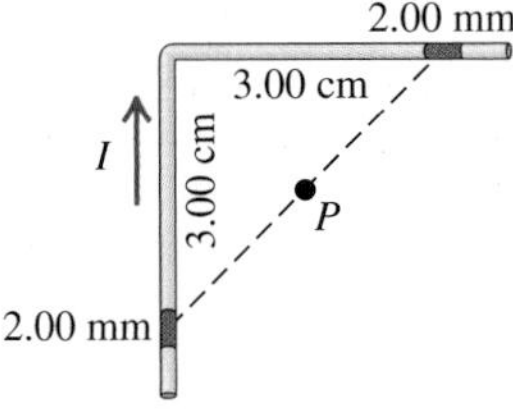

28.14. A square wire loop 10.0 cm on each side carries a clockwise current of 15.0 A. Find the magnitude and direction of the magnetic field at its center due to the four 1.20-mm wire segments at the midpoint of each side.

Section 28.3 Magnetic Field of a Straight Current-Carrying Conductor

28.15. The Magnetic Field from a Lightning Bolt. Lightning bolts can carry currents up to approximately 20 kA. We can model such a current as the equivalent of a very long, straight wire. (a) If you were unfortunate enough to be 5.0 m away from such a lightning bolt, how large a magnetic field would you experience? (b) How does this field compare to one you would experience by being 5.0 cm from a long, straight household current of 10 A?

28.16. A very long, straight horizontal wire carries a current such that 3.50×10^{18} electrons per second pass any given point going from west to east. What are the magnitude and direction of the magnetic field this wire produces at a point 4.00 cm directly above it?

28.17. (a) How large a current would a very long, straight wire have to carry so that the magnetic field 2.00 cm from the wire is equal to 1.00 G (comparable to the earth's northward-pointing magnetic field)? (b) If the wire is horizontal with the current running from east to west, at what locations would the magnetic field of the wire point in the same direction as the horizontal component of the earth's magnetic field? (c) Repeat part (b) except the wire is vertical with the current going upward.

28.18. Two long, straight wires, one above the other, are seperated by a distance $2a$ and are parallel to the x-axis. Let the $+y$-axis be in the plane of the wires in the direction from the lower wire to the upper wire. Each wire carries current I in the $+x$-direction. What are the magnitude and direction of the net magnetic field of the two wires at a point in the plane of the wires (a) midway between them; (b) at a distance a above the upper wire; (c) at a distance a below the lower wire?

28.19. A long, straight wire lies along the y-axis and carries a current $I = 8.00$ A in the $-y$-direction (Fig. 28.39). In addition to the magnetic field due to the current in the wire, a uniform magnetic field $\vec{B}_0$ with magnitude 1.50×10^{-6} T is in the $+x$-direction What is the total field (magnitude and direction) at the following points in the xz-plane: (a) $x = 0$, $z = 1.00$ m; (b) $x = 1.00$ m, $z = 0$; (c) $x = 0$, $z = -0.25$ m?

Figure 28.39 Exercise 28.19.

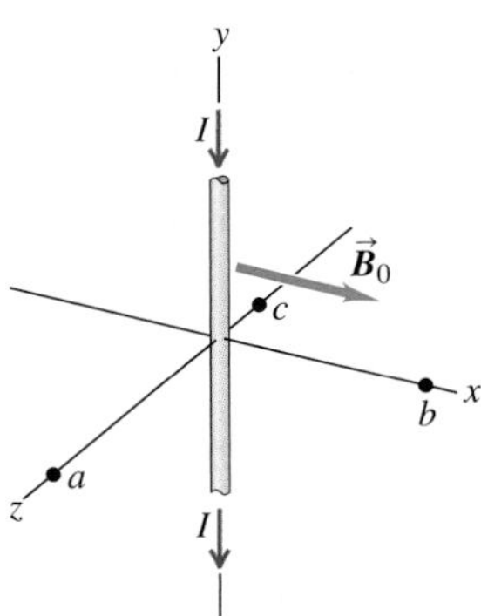

28.20. Effect of Transmission Lines. Two hikers are reading a compass under an overhead transmission line that is 5.50 m above the ground and carries a current of 800 A in a horizontal direction from north to south. (a) Find the magnitude and direction of the magnetic field at a point on the ground directly under the conductor. (b) One hiker suggests they walk on another 50 m to avoid inaccurate compass readings caused by the current. Considering that the magnitude of the earth's field is of the order of 0.5×10^{-4} T, is the current really a problem?

28.21. Two long, straight, parallel wires, 10.0 cm apart, carry equal 4.00-A currents in the same direction, as shown in Fig. 28.40. Find the magnitude and direction of the magnetic field at (a) point P_1, midway between the wires; (b) point P_2, 25.0 cm to the right of P_1; (c) point P_3, 20.0 cm directly above P_1.

Figure 28.40 Exercise 28.21.

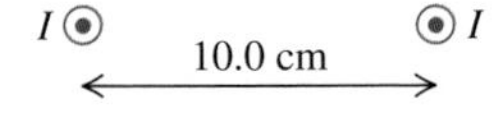

28.22. Two long, parallel transmission lines, 40.0 cm apart, carry 25.0-A and 75.0-A currents. Find all locations where the net magnetic field of the two wires is zero if these currents are in (a) the same direction and (b) the opposite direction.

28.23. Four, long, parallel power lines each carry 100-A currents. A cross-sectional diagram of these lines is a square, 20.0 cm on each side. For each of the three cases shown in Fig. 28.41, calculate the magnetic field at the center of the square.

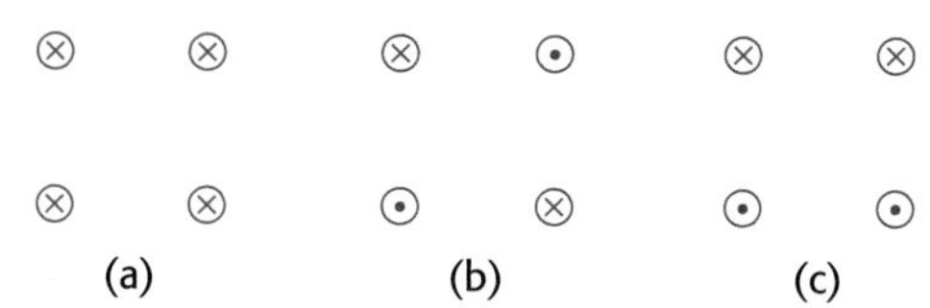

Figure 28.41 Exercise 28.23.

28.24. Four very long, current-carrying wires in the same plane intersect to form a square 40.0 cm on each side, as shown in Fig. 28.42. Find the magnitude and direction of the current I so that the magnetic field at the center of the square is zero.

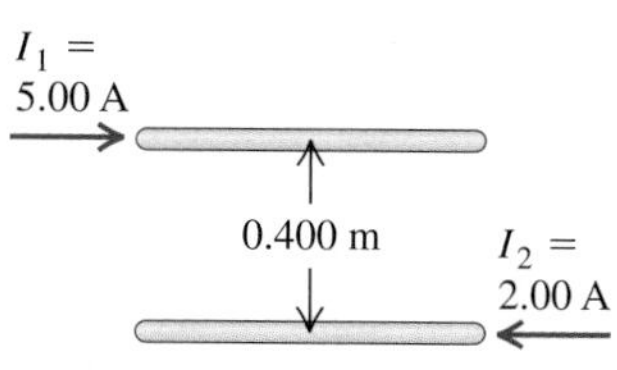

Figure 28.42 Exercise 28.24.

Section 28.4 Force Between Parallel Conductors

28.25. Two long, parallel wires are separated by a distance of 0.400 m (Fig. 28.43). The currents I_1 and I_2 have the directions shown. (a) Calculate the magnitude of the force exerted by each wire on a 1.20-m length of the other. Is the force attractive or repulsive? (b) Each current is doubled, so that I_1 becomes 10.0 A and I_2 becomes 4.00 A. Now what is the magnitude of the force that each wire exerts on a 1.20-m length of the other?

Figure 28.43 Exercise 28.25.

28.26. Two long, parallel wires are separated by a distance of 2.50 cm. The force per unit length that each wire exerts on the other is 4.00×10^{-5} N/m, and the wires repel each other. The current in one wire is 0.600 A. (a) What is the current in the second wire? (b) Are the two currents in the same direction or in opposite directions?

28.27. Lamp Cord Wires. The wires in a household lamp cord are typically 3.0 mm apart center to center and carry equal currents in opposite directions. If the cord carries current to a 100-W light bulb connected across a 120-V potential difference, what force per meter does each wire of the cord exert on the other? Is the force attractive or repulsive? Is this force large enough so it should be considered in the design of lamp cord? (Model the lamp cord as a very long straight wire.)

28.28. Three parallel wires each carry current I in the directions shown in Fig. 28.44. If the separation between adjacent wires is d, calculate the magnitude and direction of the net magnetic force per unit length on each wire.

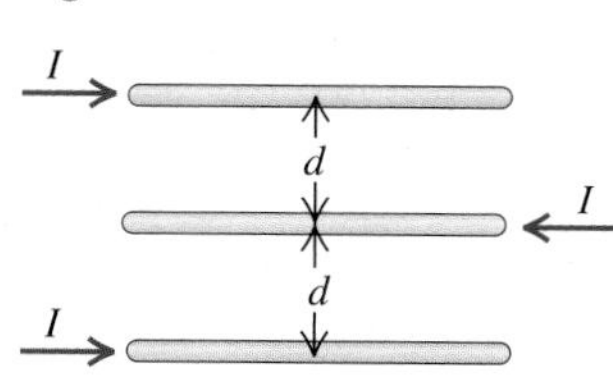

Figure 28.44 Exercise 28.28.

28.29. A long, horizontal wire AB rests on the surface of a table and carries a current I. Horizontal wire CD is vertically above wire AB and is free to slide up and down on the two vertical metal guides C and D (Fig. 28.45). Wire CD is connected through the sliding contacts to another wire that also carries a current I, opposite in direction to the current in wire AB. The mass per unit length of the wire CD is λ. To what equilibrium height h will the wire CD rise, assuming that the magnetic force on it is due entirely to the current in the wire AB?

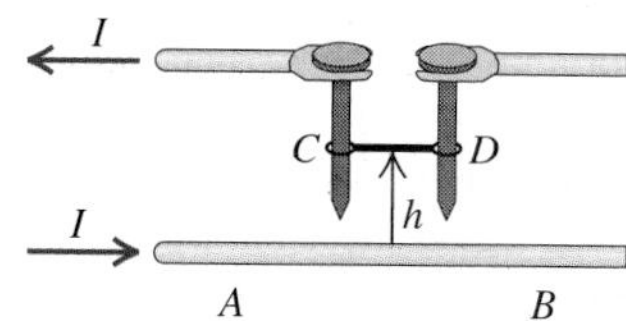

Figure 28.45 Exercise 28.29.

Section 28.5 Magnetic Field of a Circular Current Loop

28.30. Calculate the magnitude and direction of the magnetic field at point P due to the current in the semicircular section of wire shown in Fig. 28.46. (*Hint:* Does the current in the long, straight section of the wire produce any field at P?)

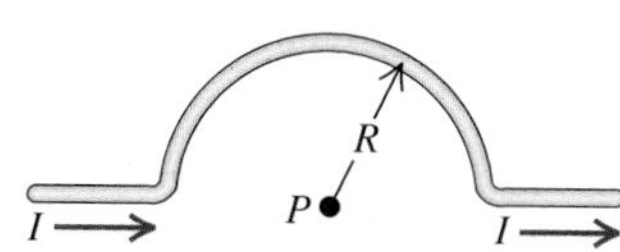

Figure 28.46 Exercise 28.30.

28.31. Calculate the magnitude of the magnetic field at point P of Fig. 28.47 in terms of R, I_1, and I_2. What does your expression give when $I_1 = I_2$?

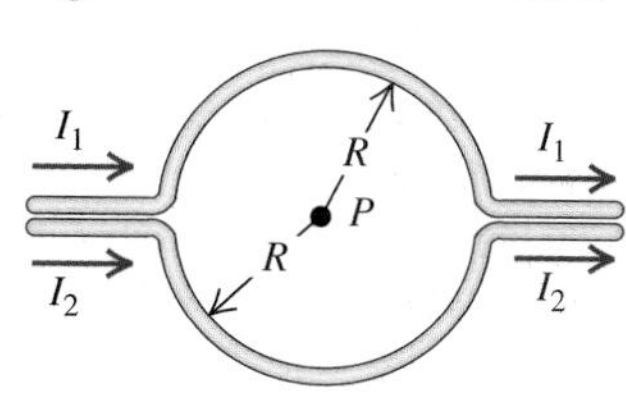

Figure 28.47 Exercise 28.31.

28.32. A closely wound, circular coil with radius 2.40 cm has 800 turns. a) What must the current in the coil be if the magnetic field at the center of the coil is 0.0580 T? b) At what distance x from the center of the coil, on the axis of the coil, is the magnetic field half its value at the center?

28.33. A closely wound, circular coil with a diameter of 4.00 cm has 600 turns and carries a current of 0.500 A. What is the magnitude of the magnetic field (a) at the center of the coil and (b) at a point on the axis of the coil 8.00 cm from its center?

28.34. A closely wound coil has a radius of 6.00 cm and carries a current of 2.50 A. How many turns must it have if, at a point on the coil axis 6.00 cm from the center of the coil, the magnetic field is 6.39×10^{-4} T?

Section 28.6 Ampere's Law

28.35. A closed curve encircles several conductors. The line integral $\oint \vec{B} \cdot d\vec{l}$ around this curve is 3.83×10^{-4} T · m. (a) What is the net current in the conductors? (b) If you were to integrate around the curve in the opposite direction, what would be the value of the line integral? Explain.

28.36. Figure 28.48 shows, in cross section, several conductors that carry currents through the plane of the figure. The currents have the magnitudes $I_1 = 4.0$ A, $I_2 = 6.0$ A, and $I_3 = 2.0$ A, and the directions shown. Four paths, labeled a through d, are shown. What is the line integral $\oint \vec{B} \cdot d\vec{l}$ for each path? Each integral involves going around the path in the counterclockwise direction. Explain your answers.

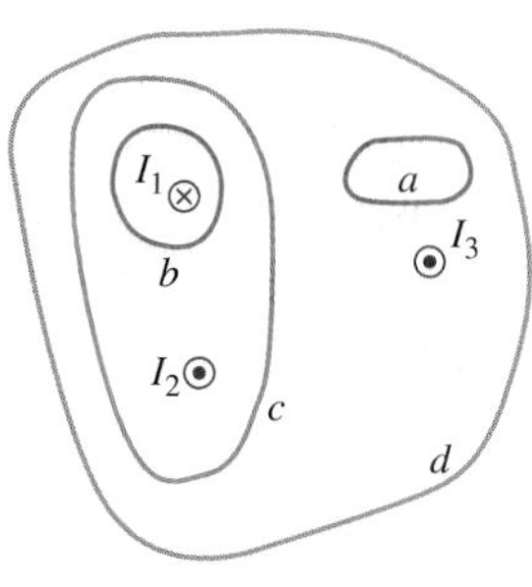

Figure 28.48 Exercise 28.36.

Section 28.7 Applications of Ampere's Law

28.37. Coaxial Cable. A solid conductor with radius a is supported by insulating disks on the axis of a conducting tube with inner radius b and outer radius c (Fig. 28.49). The central conductor and tube carry equal currents I in opposite directions. The currents are distributed uniformly over the cross sections of each conductor. Derive an expression for the magnitude of the magnetic field (a) at points outside the central, solid conductor but inside the tube $(a < r < b)$ and (b) at points outside the tube $(r > c)$.

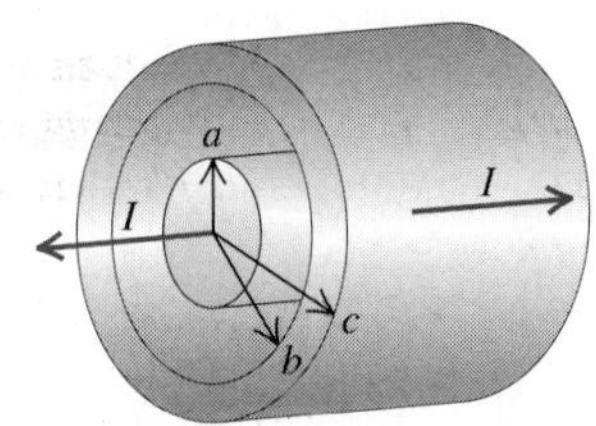

Figure 28.49 Exercise 28.37.

28.38. Repeat Exercise 28.37 for the case in which the current in the central, solid conductor is I_1, the current in the tube is I_2, and these currents are in the same direction rather than in opposite directions.

28.39. A long, straight, cylindrical wire of radius R carries a current uniformly distributed over its cross section. At what location is the magnetic field produced by this current equal to half of its largest value? Consider points inside and outside the wire.

28.40. A 15.0-cm-long solenoid with radius 2.50 cm is closely wound with 600 turns of wire. The current in the windings is 8.00 A. Compute the magnetic field at a point near the center of the solenoid.

28.41. A solenoid is designed to produce a magnetic field of 0.0270 T at its center. It has radius 1.40 cm and length 40.0 cm, and the wire can carry a maximum current of 12.0 A. (a) What minimum number of turns per unit length must the solenoid have? (b) What total length of wire is required?

28.42. As a new electrical technician, you are designing a large solenoid to produce a uniform 0.150 T magnetic field near the center of the solenoid. You have enough wire for 4000 circular turns. This solenoid must be 1.40 m long and 20.0 cm in diameter. What current will you need to produce the necessary field?

28.43. A magnetic field of 37.2 T has been achieved at the MIT Francis Bitter National Magnetic Laboratory. Find the current needed to achieve such a field (a) 2.00 cm from a long, straight wire; (b) at the center of a circular coil of radius 42.0 cm that has 100 turns; (c) near the center of a solenoid with radius 2.40 cm, length 32.0 cm, and 40,000 turns.

28.44. A toroidal solenoid (see Example 28.10) has inner radius $r_1 = 15.0$ cm and outer radius $r_2 = 18.0$ cm. The solenoid has 250 turns and carries a current of 8.50 A. What is the magnitude of the magnetic field at the following distances from the center of the torus: (a) 12.0 cm; (b) 16.0 cm; (c) 20.0 cm?

28.45. A wooden ring whose mean diameter is 14.0 cm is wound with a closely spaced toroidal winding of 600 turns. Compute the magnitude of the magnetic field at the center of the cross section of the windings when the current in the windings is 0.650 A.

*Section 28.8 Magnetic Materials

***28.46.** A toroidal solenoid with 400 turns of wire and a mean radius of 6.0 cm carries a current of 0.25 A. The relative permeability of the core is 80. (a) What is the magnetic field in the core? (b) What part of the magnetic field is due to atomic currents?

***28.47.** A toroidal solenoid with 500 turns is wound on a ring with a mean radius of 2.90 cm. Find the current in the winding that is required to set up a magnetic field of 0.350 T in the ring (a) if the ring is made of annealed iron $(K_m = 1400)$ and (b) if the ring is made of silicon steel $(K_m = 5200)$.

***28.48.** The current in the windings of a toroidal solenoid is 2.400 A. There are 500 turns, and the mean radius is 25.00 cm. The toroidal solenoid is filled with a magnetic material. The magnetic field inside the windings is found to be 1.940 T. Calculate (a) the relative permeability and (b) the magnetic susceptibility of the material that fills the toroid.

***28.49.** A long solenoid with 60 turns of wire per centimeter carries a current of 0.15 A. The wire that makes up the solenoid is wrapped around a solid core of silicon steel $(K_m = 5200)$. (The wire of the solenoid is jacketed with an insulator so that none of the current flows into the core.) (a) For a point inside the core, find the magnitudes of (i) the magnetic field $\vec{B}_0$ due to the solenoid current; (ii) the magnetization $\vec{M}$; (iii) the total magnetic field $\vec{B}$. (b) In a sketch of the solenoid and core, show the directions of the vectors $\vec{B}$, $\vec{B}_0$, and $\vec{M}$ inside the core.

***28.50. Curie's Law.** Experimental measurements of the magnetic susceptibility of iron ammonium alum are given in the table. Graph values of $1/\chi_m$ against Kelvin temperature. Does the material obey Curie's law? If so, what is the Curie constant?

T (°C)	χ_m
−258.15	129×10^{-4}
−173	19.4×10^{-4}
−73	9.7×10^{-4}
27	6.5×10^{-4}

Problems

28.51. A pair of point charges, $q = +8.00\ \mu$C and $q' = -5.00\ \mu$C, are moving as shown in Fig 28.50 with speeds $v = 9.00 \times 10^4$ m/s and $v' = 6.50 \times 10^4$ m/s. When the charges are at the locations shown in the figure, what are the magnitude and direction of (a) the magnetic field produced at the origin and (b) the magnetic force that q' exerts on q?

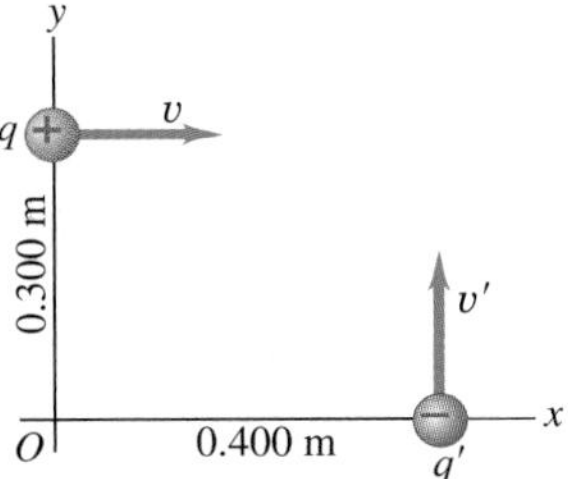

Figure 28.50 Problem 28.51.

28.52. A long, straight wire carries a current of 2.50 A. An electron is traveling in the vicinity of the wire. At the instant when the electron is 4.50 cm from the wire and traveling with a speed of 6.00×10^4 m/s directly toward the wire, what are the magnitude and direction (relative to the direction of the current) of the force that the magnetic field of the current exerts on the electron?

28.53. A long, straight wire carries a 25.0-A current. An electron is fired parallel to this wire with a velocity of 250 km/s in the same direction as the current, 2.00 cm from the wire. (a) Find the magnitude and direction of the electron's initial acceleration. (b) What should be the magnitude and direction of a uniform electric field that will allow the electron to continue to travel parallel to the wire? (c) Is it necessary to include the effects of gravity? Justify your answer.

28.54. In Fig. 28.51 the battery branch of the circuit is very far from the two horizontal segments containing two resistors. These horizontal segments are separated by 5.00 cm, and they are much longer than 5.00 cm. A proton (charge $+e$) is fired at 650 km/s from a point midway between the upper two horizontal segments of the circuit. The initial velocity of the proton is in the plane of the

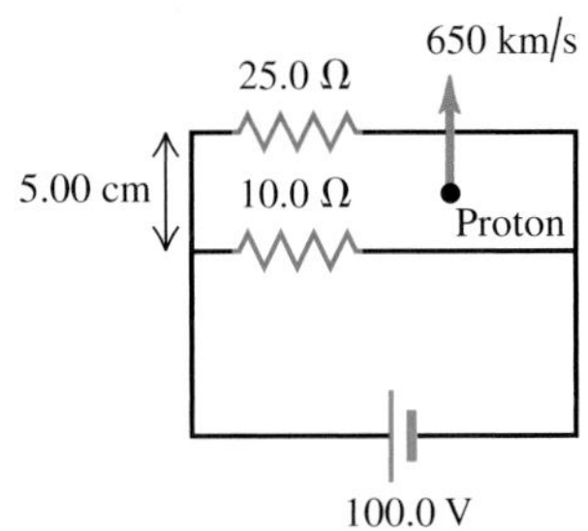

Figure 28.51 Problem 28.54.

circuit and is directed toward the upper wire. Find the magnitude and direction of the initial magnetic force on the proton.

28.55. Two identical circular, wire loops 40.0 cm in diameter each carry a current of 1.50 A in the same direction. These loops are parallel to each other and are 25.0 cm apart. Line ab is normal to the plane of the loops and passes through their centers. A proton is fired at 2400 km/s perpendicular to line ab from a point midway between the centers of the loops. Find the magnitude and direction of the magnetic force these loops exert on the proton just after it is fired.

28.56. Two very long, straight wires carry currents as shown in Fig. 28.52. For each case, find all locations where the net magnetic field is zero.

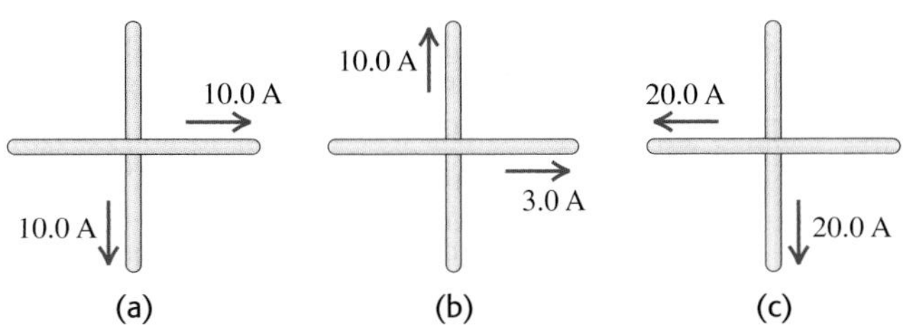

Figure 28.52 Problem 28.56.

28.57. A negative point charge $q = -7.20$ mC is moving in a reference frame. When the point charge is at the origin, the magnetic field it produces at the point $x = 25.0$ cm, $y = 0$, $z = 0$ is $\vec{B} = (6.00\ \mu\text{T})\hat{\jmath}$, and its speed is 800 km/s. (a) What are the x-, y-, and z-components of the velocity $\vec{v}_0$ of the charge? (b) At this same instant, what is the magnitude of the magnetic field that the charge produces at the point $x = 0$, $y = 25.0$ cm, $z = 0$?

28.58. A neophyte magnet designer tells you that he can produce a magnetic field $\vec{B}$ in vacuum that points everywhere in the x-direction and that increases in magnitude with increasing x. That is, $\vec{B} = B_0(x/a)\hat{\imath}$, where B_0 and a are constants with units of teslas and meters, respectively. Use Gauss's law for magnetic fields to show that this claim is *impossible*. (*Hint:* Use a Gaussian surface in the shape of a rectangular box, with edges parallel to the x-, y-, and z-axes.)

28.59. Two long, straight, parallel wires are 1.00 m apart (Fig. 28.53). The wire on the left carries a current I_1 of 6.00 A into the plane of the paper. (a) What must the magnitude and direction of the current I_2 be for the net field at point P to be zero? (b) Then what are the magnitude and direction of the net field at Q? (c) Then what is the magnitude of the net field at S?

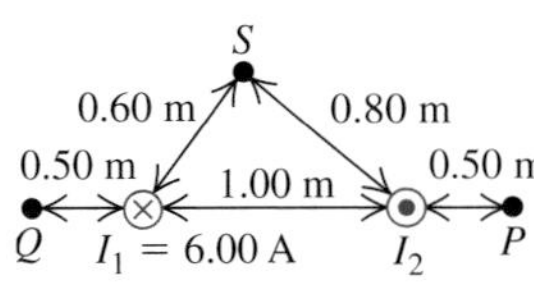

Figure 28.53 Problem 28.59.

28.60. Figure 28.54 shows an end view of two long, parallel wires perpendicular to the xy-plane, each carrying a current I but in opposite directions. (a) Copy the diagram, and draw vectors to show the $\vec{B}$ field of each wire and the net $\vec{B}$ field at point P. (b) Derive the expression for the magnitude of $\vec{B}$ at any point on the x-axis in terms of the x-coordinate of the point. What is the direction of $\vec{B}$? (c) Graph the magnitude of $\vec{B}$ at points on the x-axis. (d) At what value of x is the magnitude of $\vec{B}$ a maximum? (e) What is the magnitude of $\vec{B}$ when $x \gg a$?

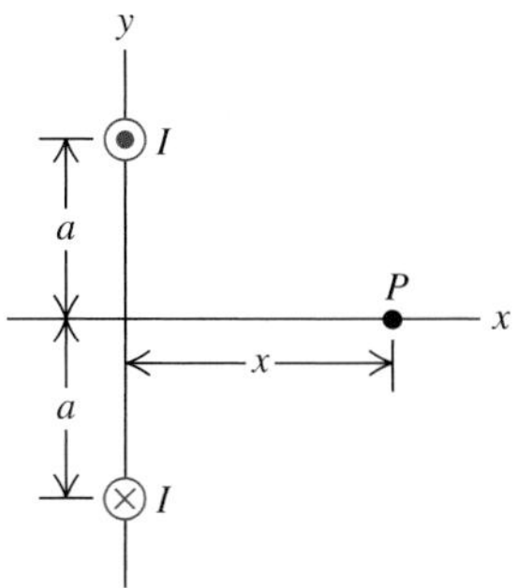

Figure 28.54 Problems 28.60 and 28.61.

28.61. Refer to the situation in Problem 28.60. Suppose that a third long, straight wire, parallel to the other two, passes through point P (see Fig. 28.54) and that each wire carries a current $I = 6.00$ A. Let $a = 40.0$ cm and $x = 60.0$ cm. Find the magnitude and direction of the force per unit length on the third wire, (a) if the current in it is directed into the plane of the figure, and (b) if the current in it is directed out of the plane of the figure.

28.62. A pair of long, rigid metal rods, each of length L, lie parallel to each other on a perfectly smooth table. Their ends are connected by identical, very light conducting springs of force constant k (Fig. 28.55) and negligible unstretched length. If a current I runs through this circuit, the springs will stretch. At what separation will the rods remain at rest? Assume that k is large enough so that the separation of the rods will be much less than L.

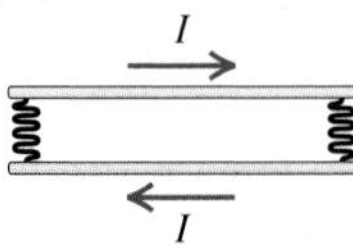

Figure 28.55 Problem 28.62.

28.63. Two long, parallel wires hang by 4.00-cm-long cords from a common axis (Fig. 28.56). The wires have a mass per unit length of 0.0125 kg/m and carry the same current in opposite directions. What is the current in each wire if the cords hang at an angle of 6.00° with the vertical?

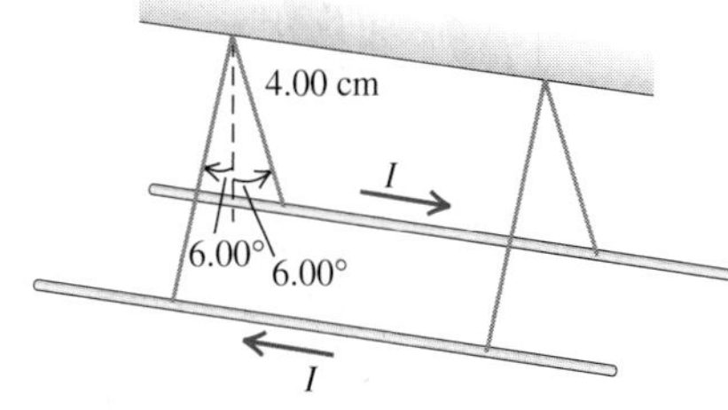

Figure 28.56 Problem 28.63.

28.64. The long, straight wire AB shown in Fig. 28.57 carries a current of 14.0 A. The rectangular loop whose long edges are parallel to the wire carries a current of 5.00 A. Find the magnitude and direction of the net force exerted on the loop by the magnetic field of the wire.

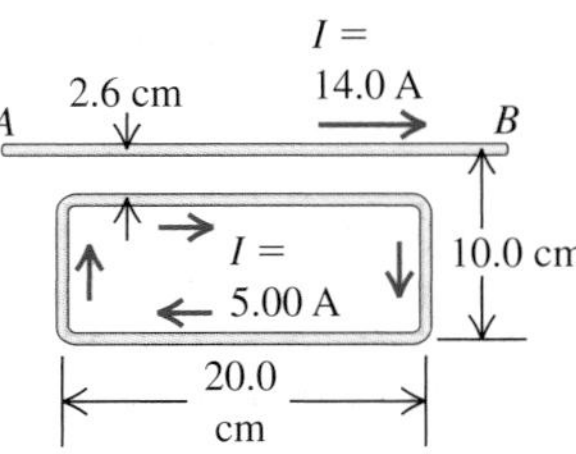

Figure 28.57 Problem 28.64.

29.6 The magnetic flux is becoming **(a)** more positive, **(b)** less positive, **(c)** more negative, and **(d)** less negative. Therefore Φ_B is increasing in **(a)** and **(d)** and decreasing in **(b)** and **(c)**. In **(a)** and **(d)** the emfs are negative (they are opposite to the direction of the curled fingers of your right hand when your right thumb points along $\vec{A}$). In **(b)** and **(c)** the emfs are positive (in the same direction as the curled fingers).

(a)

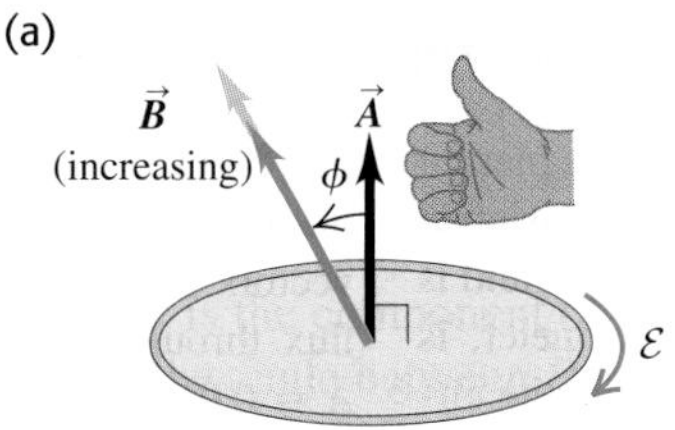

- Flux is positive ($\Phi_B > 0$) ...
- ... and becoming more positive ($d\Phi_B/dt > 0$).
- Induced emf is negative ($\mathcal{E} < 0$).

(b)

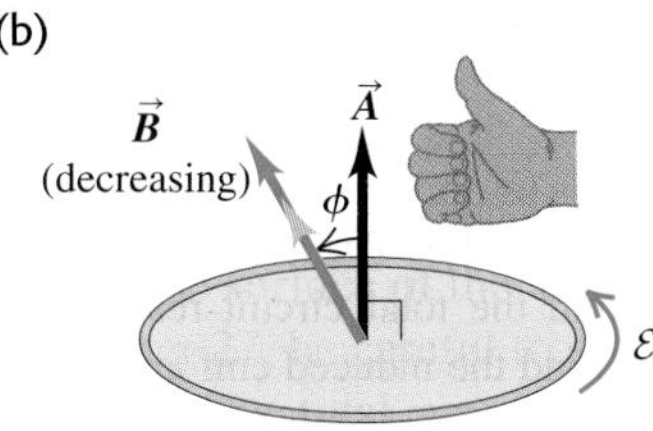

- Flux is positive ($\Phi_B > 0$) ...
- ... and becoming less positive ($d\Phi_B/dt < 0$).
- Induced emf is positive ($\mathcal{E} > 0$).

(c)

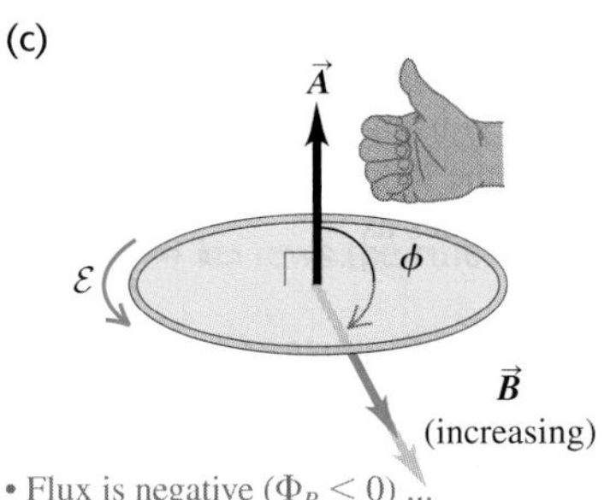

- Flux is negative ($\Phi_B < 0$) ...
- ... and becoming more negative ($d\Phi_B/dt < 0$).
- Induced emf is positive ($\mathcal{E} > 0$).

(d)

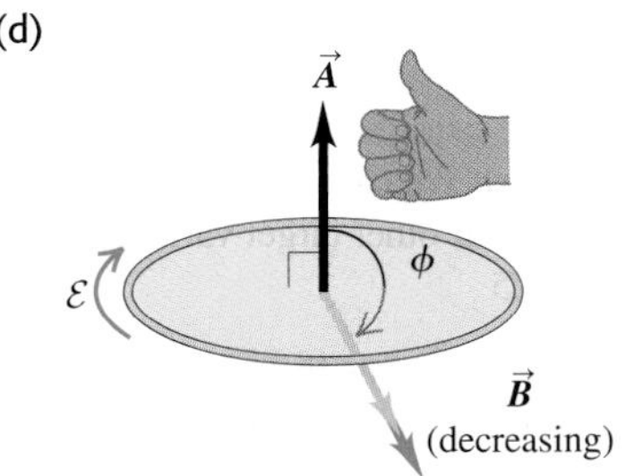

- Flux is negative ($\Phi_B < 0$) ...
- ... and becoming less negative ($d\Phi_B/dt > 0$).
- Induced emf is negative ($\mathcal{E} < 0$).

4. Finally, determine the direction of the induced emf or current using your right hand. Curl the fingers of your right hand around the $\vec{A}$ vector, with your right thumb in the direction of $\vec{A}$. If the induced emf or current in the circuit is *positive,* it is in the same direction as your curled fingers; if the induced emf or current is *negative,* it is in the opposite direction.

In Example 29.1, in which $\vec{A}$ is upward, a positive $\mathcal{E}$ would be directed counterclockwise around the loop, as seen from above. Both $\vec{A}$ and $\vec{B}$ are upward in this example, so Φ_B is positive; the magnitude B is increasing, so $d\Phi_B/dt$ is positive. Hence by Eq. (29.3), $\mathcal{E}$ in Example 29.1 is *negative.* Its actual direction is thus *clockwise* around the loop, as seen from above.

If the loop in Fig. 29.5 is a conductor, an induced current results from this emf; this current is also clockwise, as Fig. 29.5 shows. This induced current produces an additional magnetic field through the loop, and the right-hand rule described in Section 28.6 shows that this field is *opposite* in direction to the increasing field produced by the electromagnet. This is an example of a general rule called *Lenz's law,* which says that any induction effect tends to oppose the change that caused it; in this case the change is the increase in the flux of the electromagnet's field through the loop. (We'll study this law in detail in the next section.)

You should check out the signs of the induced emfs and currents for the list of experiments in Section 29.1. For example, when the loop in Fig. 29.2 is in a constant field and we tilt it or squeeze it to *decrease* the flux through it, the induced emf and current are counterclockwise, as seen from above.

CAUTION **Induced emfs are caused by changes in flux** Since magnetic flux plays a central role in Faraday's law, it's tempting to think that *flux* is the cause of induced emf and that an induced emf will appear in a circuit whenever there is a magnetic field in the region bordered by the circuit. But Eq. (29.3) shows that only a *change* in flux through a circuit, not flux itself, can induce an emf in a circuit. If the flux through a circuit has a constant value, whether positive, negative, or zero, there is no induced emf.

To understand the negative sign, we have to introduce a sign convention for the induced emf $\mathcal{E}$. But first let's look at a simple example of this law in action.

Example 29.1 Emf and current induced in a loop

The magnetic field between the poles of the electromagnet in Figure 29.5 is uniform at any time, but its magnitude is increasing at the rate of 0.020 T/s. The area of the conducting loop in the field is 120 cm^2, and the total circuit resistance, including the meter, is 5.0 Ω. (a) Find the induced emf and the induced current in the circuit. (b) If the loop is replaced by one made of an insulator, what effect does this have on the induced emf and induced current?

SOLUTION

IDENTIFY: The magnetic flux through the loop changes as the magnetic field changes. Hence there will be an induced emf in the loop, and we can find its value (one of our target variables) using Faraday's law. We can determine the current produced in the loop by this emf (our other target variable) using the same techniques as in Chapter 25.

SET UP: We calculate the magnetic flux using Eq. (29.2) and then use Faraday's law given by Eq. (29.3) to determine the resulting induced emf $\mathcal{E}$. Then we calculate the induced current produced by this emf using the relationship $\mathcal{E} = IR$, where R is the total resistance of the circuit that includes the loop.

29.5 A stationary conducting loop in an increasing magnetic field.

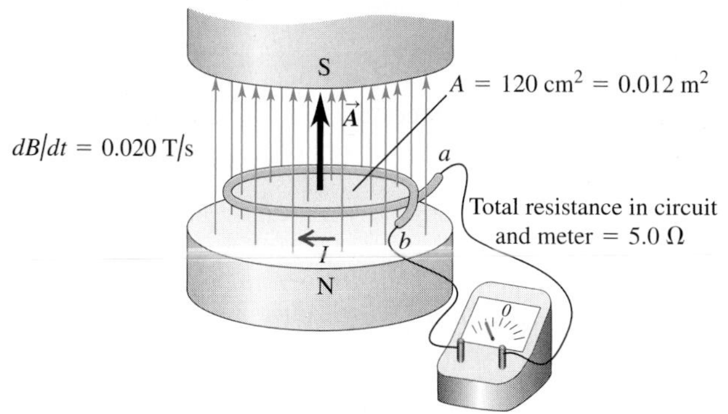

EXECUTE: (a) The vector area of the loop is perpendicular to the plane of the loop; we choose it to be vertically upward. Then the vectors $\vec{A}$ and $\vec{B}$ are parallel. Since $\vec{B}$ is uniform, the magnetic flux through the loop is $\Phi_B = \vec{B} \cdot \vec{A} = BA\cos 0 = BA$. The area $A = 0.012\ \text{m}^2$ is constant, so the rate of change of magnetic flux is

$$\frac{d\Phi_B}{dt} = \frac{d(BA)}{dt} = \frac{dB}{dt}A = (0.020\ \text{T/s})(0.012\ \text{m}^2)$$
$$= 2.4 \times 10^{-4}\ \text{V} = 0.24\ \text{mV}$$

This, apart from a sign that we haven't discussed yet, is the induced emf $\mathcal{E}$. The corresponding induced current is

$$I = \frac{\mathcal{E}}{R} = \frac{2.4 \times 10^{-4}\ \text{V}}{5.0\ \Omega} = 4.8 \times 10^{-5}\ \text{A} = 0.048\ \text{mA}$$

(b) By changing to a loop made of insulator, we've made the resistance of the loop very high. Faraday's law, Eq. (29.3), does not involve the resistance of the circuit in any way, so the induced *emf* does not change. But the *current* will be smaller, as given by the equation $I = \mathcal{E}/R$. If the loop is made of a perfect insulator with infinite resistance, the induced current is zero even though an emf is present. This situation is analogous to an isolated battery whose terminals aren't connected to anything: There is an emf present, but no current flows.

EVALUATE: It's worthwhile to verify unit consistency in this calculation. There are many ways to do this; one is to note that because of the magnetic force relationship $\vec{F} = q\vec{v} \times \vec{B}$, the units of magnetic field are the units of force divided by the units of (charge times velocity): $1\ \text{T} = (1\ \text{N})/(1\ \text{C} \cdot \text{m/s})$. The units of magnetic flux can then be expressed as $(1\ \text{T})(1\ \text{m}^2) = 1\ \text{N} \cdot \text{s} \cdot \text{m/C}$, and the rate of change of magnetic flux as $1\ \text{N} \cdot \text{m/C} = 1\ \text{J/C} = 1\ \text{V}$. Thus the unit of $d\Phi_B/dt$ is the volt, as required by Eq. (29.3). Also recall that the unit of magnetic flux is the weber (Wb): $1\ \text{T} \cdot \text{m}^2 = 1\ \text{Wb}$, so $1\ \text{V} = 1\ \text{Wb/s}$.

Direction of Induced EMF

We can find the direction of an induced emf or current by using Eq. (29.3) together with some simple sign rules. Here's the procedure:

1. Define a positive direction for the vector area $\vec{A}$.
2. From the directions of $\vec{A}$ and the magnetic field $\vec{B}$, determine the sign of the magnetic flux Φ_B and its rate of change $d\Phi_B/dt$. Figure 29.6 shows several examples.
3. Determine the sign of the induced emf or current. If the flux is increasing, so $d\Phi_B/dt$ is positive, then the induced emf or current is negative; if the flux is decreasing, $d\Phi_B/dt$ is negative and the induced emf or current is positive.

29.6 The magnetic flux is becoming (a) more positive, (b) less positive, (c) more negative, and (d) less negative. Therefore Φ_B is increasing in (a) and (d) and decreasing in (b) and (c). In (a) and (d) the emfs are negative (they are opposite to the direction of the curled fingers of your right hand when your right thumb points along $\vec{A}$). In (b) and (c) the emfs are positive (in the same direction as the curled fingers).

(a)

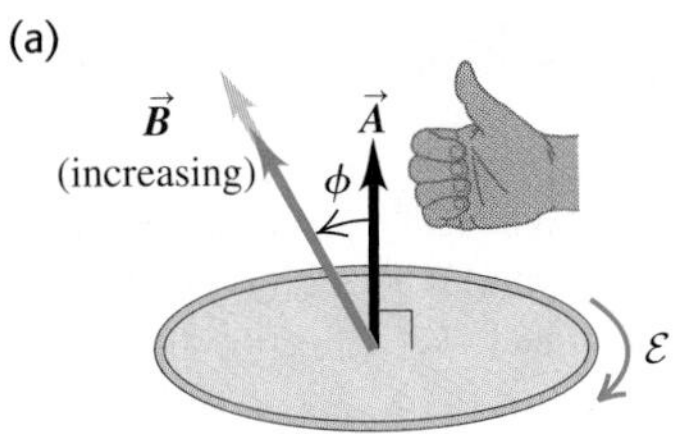

- Flux is positive ($\Phi_B > 0$) ...
- ... and becoming more positive ($d\Phi_B/dt > 0$).
- Induced emf is negative ($\mathcal{E} < 0$).

(b)

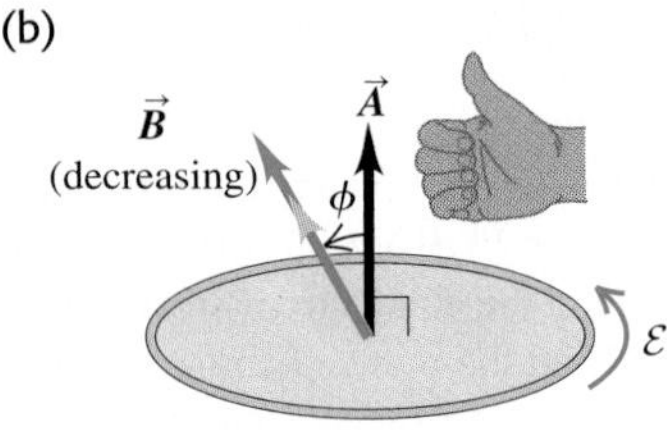

- Flux is positive ($\Phi_B > 0$) ...
- ... and becoming less positive ($d\Phi_B/dt < 0$).
- Induced emf is positive ($\mathcal{E} > 0$).

(c)

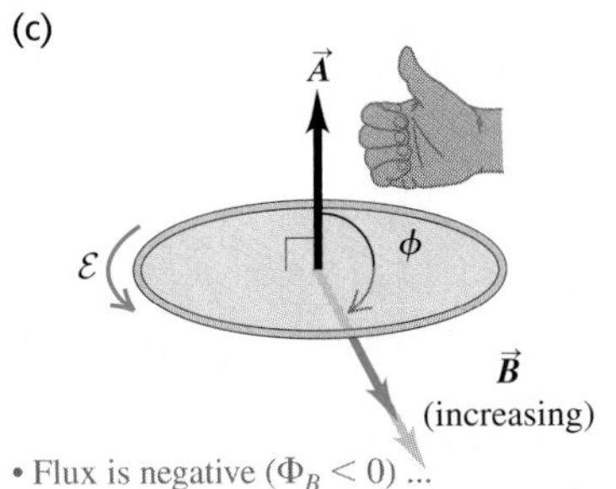

- Flux is negative ($\Phi_B < 0$) ...
- ... and becoming more negative ($d\Phi_B/dt < 0$).
- Induced emf is positive ($\mathcal{E} > 0$).

(d)

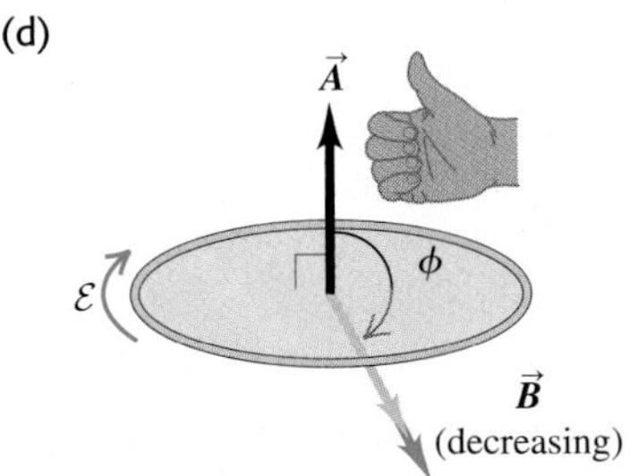

- Flux is negative ($\Phi_B < 0$) ...
- ... and becoming less negative ($d\Phi_B/dt > 0$).
- Induced emf is negative ($\mathcal{E} < 0$).

4. Finally, determine the direction of the induced emf or current using your right hand. Curl the fingers of your right hand around the $\vec{A}$ vector, with your right thumb in the direction of $\vec{A}$. If the induced emf or current in the circuit is *positive,* it is in the same direction as your curled fingers; if the induced emf or current is *negative,* it is in the opposite direction.

In Example 29.1, in which $\vec{A}$ is upward, a positive $\mathcal{E}$ would be directed counterclockwise around the loop, as seen from above. Both $\vec{A}$ and $\vec{B}$ are upward in this example, so Φ_B is positive; the magnitude B is increasing, so $d\Phi_B/dt$ is positive. Hence by Eq. (29.3), $\mathcal{E}$ in Example 29.1 is *negative.* Its actual direction is thus *clockwise* around the loop, as seen from above.

If the loop in Fig. 29.5 is a conductor, an induced current results from this emf; this current is also clockwise, as Fig. 29.5 shows. This induced current produces an additional magnetic field through the loop, and the right-hand rule described in Section 28.6 shows that this field is *opposite* in direction to the increasing field produced by the electromagnet. This is an example of a general rule called *Lenz's law,* which says that any induction effect tends to oppose the change that caused it; in this case the change is the increase in the flux of the electromagnet's field through the loop. (We'll study this law in detail in the next section.)

You should check out the signs of the induced emfs and currents for the list of experiments in Section 29.1. For example, when the loop in Fig. 29.2 is in a constant field and we tilt it or squeeze it to *decrease* the flux through it, the induced emf and current are counterclockwise, as seen from above.

CAUTION **Induced emfs are caused by changes in flux** Since magnetic flux plays a central role in Faraday's law, it's tempting to think that *flux* is the cause of induced emf and that an induced emf will appear in a circuit whenever there is a magnetic field in the region bordered by the circuit. But Eq. (29.3) shows that only a *change* in flux through a circuit, not flux itself, can induce an emf in a circuit. If the flux through a circuit has a constant value, whether positive, negative, or zero, there is no induced emf.

poles of an electromagnet whose magnetic field we can vary. Here's what we observe:

1. When there is no current in the electromagnet, so that $\vec{B} = \mathbf{0}$, the galvanometer shows no current.
2. When the electromagnet is turned on, there is a momentary current through the meter as $\vec{B}$ increases.
3. When $\vec{B}$ levels off at a steady value, the current drops to zero, no matter how large $\vec{B}$ is.
4. With the coil in a horizontal plane, we squeeze it so as to decrease the cross-sectional area of the coil. The meter detects current only *during* the deformation, not before or after. When we increase the area to return the coil to its original shape, there is current in the opposite direction, but only while the area of the coil is changing.
5. If we rotate the coil a few degrees about a horizontal axis, the meter detects current during the rotation, in the same direction as when we decreased the area. When we rotate the coil back, there is a current in the opposite direction during this rotation.
6. If we jerk the coil out of the magnetic field, there is a current during the motion, in the same direction as when we decreased the area.
7. If we decrease the number of turns in the coil by unwinding one or more turns, there is a current during the unwinding, in the same direction as when we decreased the area. If we wind more turns onto the coil, there is a current in the opposite direction during the winding.
8. When the magnet is turned off, there is a momentary current in the direction opposite to the current when it was turned on.
9. The faster we carry out any of these changes, the greater the current.
10. If all these experiments are repeated with a coil that has the same shape but different material and different resistance, the current in each case is inversely proportional to the total circuit resistance. This shows that the induced emfs that are causing the current do not depend on the material of the coil but only on its shape and the magnetic field.

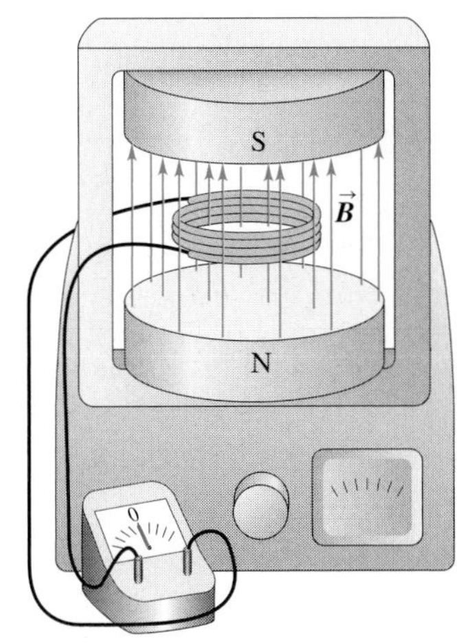

29.2 A coil in a magnetic field. When the $\vec{B}$ field is constant and the shape, location, and orientation of the coil do not change, no current is induced in the coil. A current is induced when any of these factors change.

The common element in all these experiments is changing *magnetic flux* Φ_B through the coil connected to the galvanometer. In each case the flux changes either because the magnetic field changes with time or because the coil is moving through a nonuniform magnetic field. Check back through the list to verify this statement. Faraday's law of induction, the subject of the next section, states that in all of these situations the induced emf is proportional to the *rate of change* of magnetic flux Φ_B through the coil. The *direction* of the induced emf depends on whether the flux is increasing or decreasing. If the flux is constant, there is no induced emf. ?

Induced emfs are not mere laboratory curiosities but have a tremendous number of practical applications. If you are reading these words indoors, you are making use of induced emfs right now! At the power plant that supplies your neighborhood, an electric generator produces an emf by varying the magnetic flux through coils of wire. (In the next section we'll see in detail how this is done.) This emf supplies the voltage between the terminals of the wall sockets in your home, and this voltage supplies the power to your reading lamp. Indeed, any appliance that you plug into a wall socket makes use of induced emfs.

Magnetically induced emfs, just like the emfs discussed in Section 25.4, are always the result of the action of *nonelectrostatic* forces. When these forces are the result of additional electric fields induced by changing magnetic fields, we have to distinguish carefully between electric fields produced by charges (according to Coulomb's law) and those produced by changing magnetic fields. We'll denote these by $\vec{E}_c$ (where c stands for Coulomb or conservative) and $\vec{E}_n$ (where n stands for non-Coulomb or nonconservative), respectively. We'll return to this distinction later in this chapter and the next.

29.3 Calculating the magnetic flux through an area element.

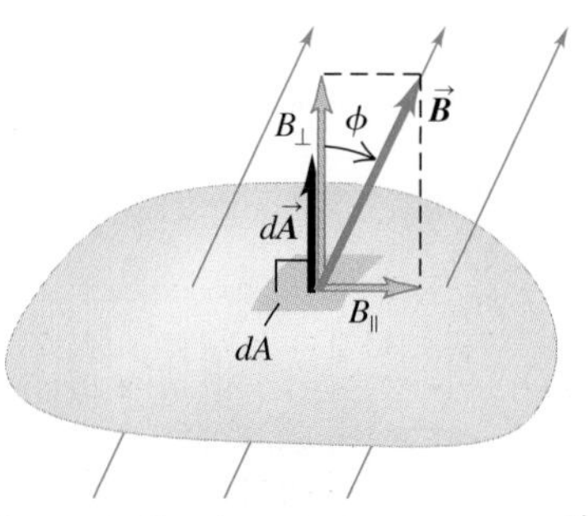

Magnetic flux through element of area $d\vec{A}$:
$d\Phi_B = \vec{B} \cdot d\vec{A} = B_\perp dA = B\, dA \cos\phi$

29.2 Faraday's Law

The common element in all induction effects is changing magnetic flux through a circuit. Before stating the simple physical law that summarizes all of the kinds of experiments described in Section 29.1, let's first review the concept of magnetic flux Φ_B (which we introduced in Section 27.3). For an infinitesimal-area element $d\vec{A}$ in a magnetic field $\vec{B}$ (Figure 29.3), the magnetic flux $d\Phi_B$ through the area is

$$d\Phi_B = \vec{B} \cdot d\vec{A} = B_\perp\, dA = B\, dA \cos\phi$$

where $B_\perp$ is the component of $\vec{B}$ perpendicular to the surface of the area element and ϕ is the angle between $\vec{B}$ and $d\vec{A}$. (As in Chapter 27, be careful to distinguish between two quantities named "phi," ϕ and Φ_B.) The total magnetic flux Φ_B through a finite area is the integral of this expression over the area:

$$\Phi_B = \int \vec{B} \cdot d\vec{A} = \int B\, dA \cos\phi \qquad (29.1)$$

If $\vec{B}$ is uniform over a flat area $\vec{A}$, then

$$\Phi_B = \vec{B} \cdot \vec{A} = BA \cos\phi \qquad (29.2)$$

Figure 29.4 reviews the rules for using Eq. (29.2).

CAUTION **Choosing the direction of $d\vec{A}$ or $\vec{A}$** In Eqs. (29.1) and (29.2) we have to be careful to define the direction of the vector area $d\vec{A}$ or $\vec{A}$ unambiguously. There are always two directions perpendicular to any given area, and the sign of the magnetic flux through the area depends on which one we choose to be positive. For example, in Fig. 29.3 we chose $d\vec{A}$ to point upward so ϕ is less than 90° and $\vec{B} \cdot d\vec{A}$ is positive. We could have chosen instead to have $d\vec{A}$ point downward, in which case ϕ would have been greater than 90° and $\vec{B} \cdot d\vec{A}$ would have been negative. Either choice is equally good, but once we make a choice we must stick with it.

Faraday's law of induction states:

The induced emf in a closed loop equals the negative of the time rate of change of magnetic flux through the loop.

In symbols, Faraday's law is

$$\mathcal{E} = -\frac{d\Phi_B}{dt} \quad \text{(Faraday's law of induction)} \qquad (29.3)$$

29.4 Calculating the flux of a uniform magnetic field through a flat area. (Compare to Fig. 22.6, which shows the rules for calculating the flux of a uniform *electric* field.)

Surface is face-on to magnetic field:
- $\vec{B}$ and $\vec{A}$ are parallel (the angle between $\vec{B}$ and $\vec{A}$ is $\phi = 0$).
- The magnetic flux $\Phi_B = \vec{B} \cdot \vec{A} = BA$.

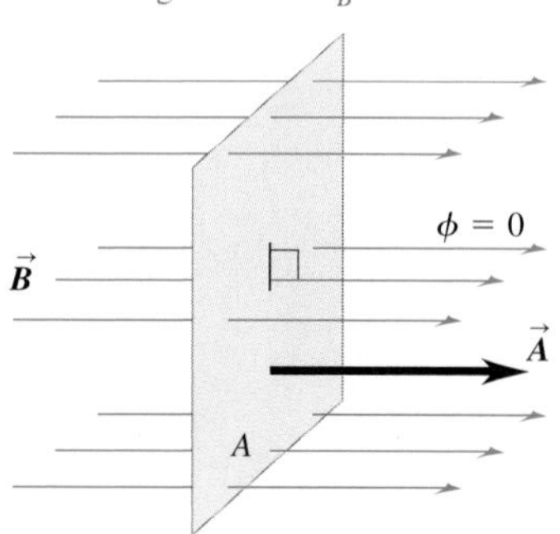

Surface is tilted from a face-on orientation by an angle ϕ:
- The angle between $\vec{B}$ and $\vec{A}$ is ϕ.
- The magnetic flux $\Phi_B = \vec{B} \cdot \vec{A} = BA \cos\phi$.

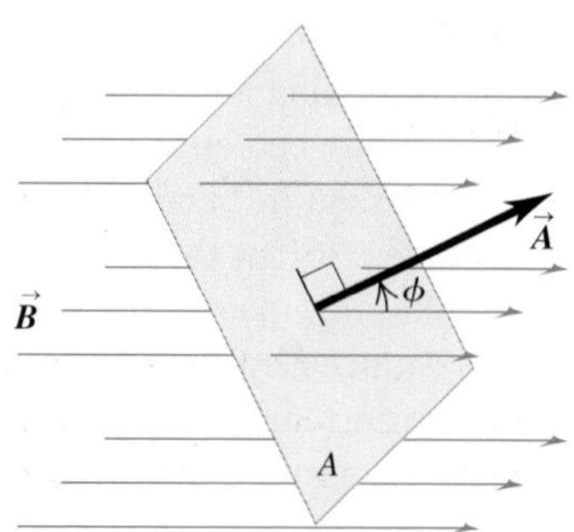

Surface is edge-on to magnetic field:
- $\vec{B}$ and $\vec{A}$ are perpendicular (the angle between $\vec{B}$ and $\vec{A}$ is $\phi = 90°$).
- The magnetic flux $\Phi_B = \vec{B} \cdot \vec{A} = BA \cos 90° = 0$.

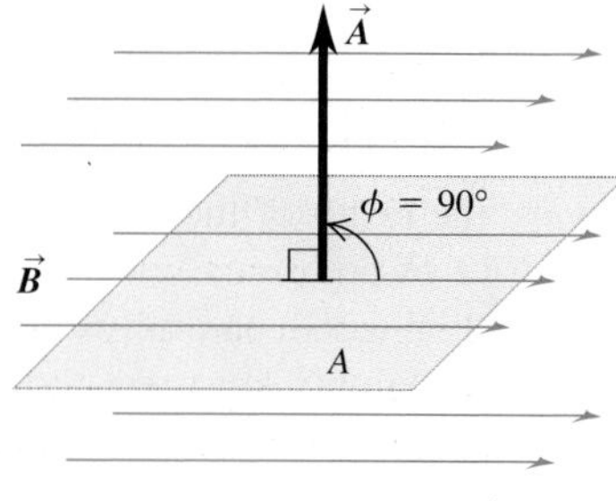

If we have a coil with N identical turns, and if the flux varies at the same rate through each turn, the *total* rate of change through all the turns is N times as large as for a single turn. If Φ_B is the flux through each turn, the total emf in a coil with N turns is

$$\mathcal{E} = -N\frac{d\Phi_B}{dt} \tag{29.4}$$

As we discussed in this chapter's introduction, induced emfs play an essential role in the generation of electric power for commercial use. Several of the following examples explore different methods of producing emfs by the motion of a conductor relative to a magnetic field, giving rise to a changing flux through a circuit.

Problem-Solving Strategy 29.1 Faraday's Law

IDENTIFY: *the relevant concepts:* Faraday's law applies when there is a changing magnetic flux. To use the law, make sure you can identify an area through which there is a flux of magnetic field. This will usually be the area enclosed by a loop, usually made of a conducting material (though not always—see part (b) of Example 29.1). As always, identify the target variable(s).

SET UP *the problem* using the following steps:

1. Faraday's law relates the induced emf to the rate of change of magnetic flux. To calculate this rate of change, you first have to understand what is making the flux change. Is the conductor moving? Is it changing orientation? Is the magnetic field changing? Remember that it's not the flux itself that counts, but its *rate of change.*
2. Choose a direction for the area vector $\vec{A}$ or $d\vec{A}$. The direction must always be perpendicular to the plane of the area. Note that you always have two choices of direction. For instance, if the plane of the area is horizontal, $\vec{A}$ could point straight up or straight down. It's like choosing which direction is the positive one in a problem involving motion in a straight line; it doesn't matter which direction you choose, just so you use it consistently throughout the problem.

EXECUTE *the solution* as follows:

1. Calculate the magnetic flux using Eq. (29.2) if $\vec{B}$ is uniform over the area of the loop or Eq. (29.1) if it isn't uniform, being mindful of the direction you chose for the area vector.
2. Calculate the induced emf using Eq. (29.3) or (29.4). If your conductor has N turns in a coil, don't forget to multiply by N. Remember the sign rule for the positive direction of emf and use it consistently.
3. If the circuit resistance is known, you can calculate the magnitude of the induced current I using $\mathcal{E} = IR$.

EVALUATE *your answer:* Check your results for the proper units, and double-check that you have properly implemented the sign rules for calculating magnetic flux and induced emf.

Example 29.2 Magnitude and direction of an induced emf

A coil of wire containing 500 circular loops with radius 4.00 cm is placed between the poles of a large electromagnet, where the magnetic field is uniform and at an angle of 60° with the plane of the coil. The field decreases at a rate of 0.200 T/s. What are the magnitude and direction of the induced emf?

SOLUTION

IDENTIFY: Our target variable is the emf induced by a varying magnetic flux through the coil. The flux varies because the magnetic field decreases in amplitude.

SET UP: We choose the area vector $\vec{A}$ to be in the direction shown in Figure 29.7. With this choice, the geometry is very similar to Fig. 29.6b. That figure will help us determine the direction of the induced emf.

EXECUTE: The magnetic field is uniform over the loop, so we can calculate the flux using Eq. (29.2): $\Phi_B = BA\cos\phi$, where $\phi = 30°$. In this expression, the only quantity that changes with time is the magnitude B of the field.

CAUTION Remember how ϕ is defined You may have been tempted to say that $\phi = 60°$ in this problem. If so, remember that ϕ is the angle between $\vec{A}$ and $\vec{B}$, *not* the angle between $\vec{B}$ and the plane of the loop.

29.7 Our sketch for this problem.

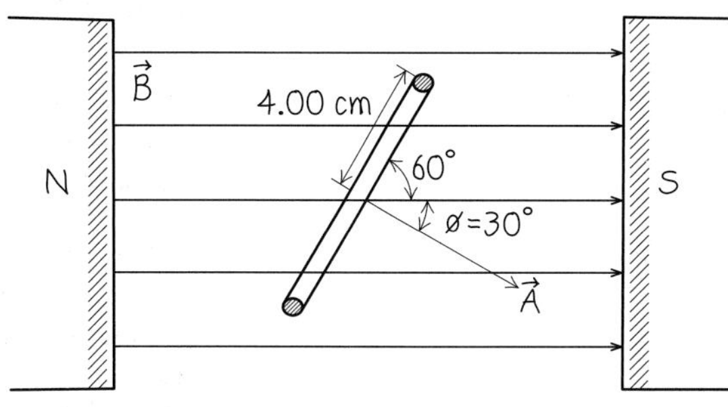

Continued

The rate of change of the flux is $d\Phi_B/dt = (dB/dt)A\cos\phi$. In our problem, $dB/dt = -0.200\ \text{T/s}$ and $A = \pi(0.0400\ \text{m})^2 = 0.00503\ \text{m}^2$, so

$$\begin{aligned}\frac{d\Phi_B}{dt} &= \frac{dB}{dt}A\cos 30^\circ \\ &= (-0.200\ \text{T/s})(0.00503\ \text{m}^2)(0.866) \\ &= -8.71 \times 10^{-4}\ \text{T}\cdot\text{m}^2/\text{s} = -8.71 \times 10^{-4}\ \text{Wb/s}\end{aligned}$$

From Eq. (29.4), the induced emf in the coil of $N = 500$ turns is

$$\begin{aligned}\mathcal{E} &= -N\frac{d\Phi_B}{dt} \\ &= -(500)(-8.71 \times 10^{-4}\ \text{Wb/s}) = 0.435\ \text{V}\end{aligned}$$

Note that the answer is positive. This means that when you point your right thumb in the direction of the area vector $\vec{A}$ (30° above the magnetic field $\vec{B}$), the positive direction for $\mathcal{E}$ is in the direction of the curled fingers of your right hand. Hence the emf in this example is in this same direction (compare Fig. 29.6b). If you were viewing the coil from the left side in Fig. 29.7a and looking in the direction of $\vec{A}$, the emf would be clockwise.

EVALUATE: If the ends of the wire are connected together, the direction of current in the coil is in the same direction as the emf—that is, clockwise as seen from the left side of the coil. A clockwise current gives added magnetic flux through the coil in the same direction as the flux from the electromagnet, and therefore tends to oppose the decrease in total flux. We'll see more examples of this in Section 29.3.

Conceptual Example 29.3 The search coil

One practical way to measure magnetic field strength uses a small, closely wound coil with N turns called a *search coil.* The coil, of area A, is initially held so that its area vector $\vec{A}$ is aligned with a magnetic field with magnitude B. The coil is then either quickly rotated a quarter-turn about a diameter or quickly pulled out of the field. Explain how this device can be used to measure the value of B.

SOLUTION

Initially, the flux through the coil is $\Phi_B = NBA$; when the coil is rotated or pulled from the field, the flux decreases rapidly from NBA to zero. While the flux is decreasing, there is a momentary induced emf, and a momentary induced current occurs in an external circuit connected to the coil. The rate of change of flux through the coil is proportional to the current, or rate of flow of charge, so it is easy to show that the *total* flux change is proportional to the total charge that flows around the circuit. We can build an instrument that measures this total charge, and from this we can compute B. We leave the details as a problem (see Exercise 29.3). Strictly speaking, this method gives only the *average* field over the area of the coil. But if the area is small, this average field is very nearly equal to the field at the center of the coil.

Example 29.4 Generator I: A simple alternator

Figure 29.8a shows a simple version of an *alternator,* a device that generates an emf. A rectangular loop is made to rotate with constant angular speed ω about the axis shown. The magnetic field $\vec{B}$ is uniform and constant. At time $t = 0$, $\phi = 0$. Determine the induced emf.

SOLUTION

IDENTIFY: Again the emf (our target variable) is produced by a varying magnetic flux. In this situation, however, the magnetic field $\vec{B}$ is constant; the flux changes because the direction of $\vec{A}$ changes as the loop rotates.

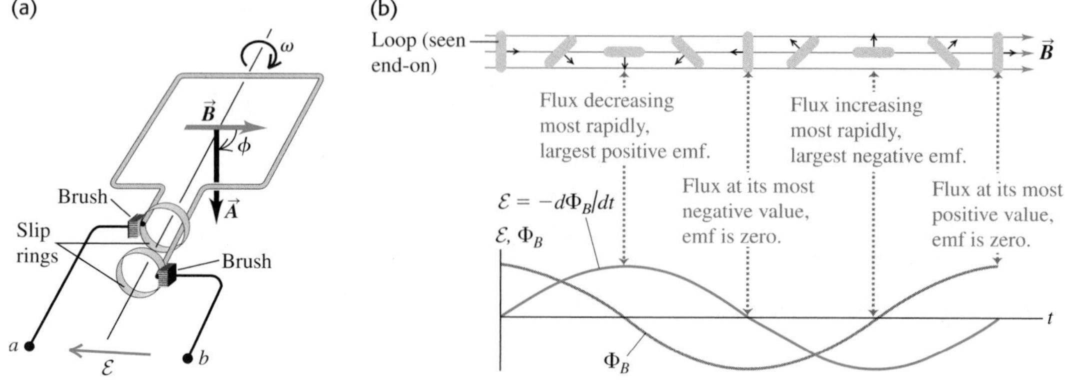

29.8 (a) Schematic diagram of an alternator. A conducting loop rotates in a magnetic field, producing an emf. Connections from each end of the loop to the external circuit are made by means of that end's slip ring. The system is shown at the time when the angle $\phi = \omega t = 90°$. (b) Graph of the flux through the loop and the resulting emf at terminals ab, along with corresponding positions of the loop during one complete rotation.

SET UP: Figure 29.8a shows the direction of the area vector $\vec{A}$. Note that as the loop rotates, the angle ϕ between $\vec{A}$ and $\vec{B}$ increases at a constant rate.

EXECUTE: Again the magnetic field is uniform over the loop, so the magnetic flux is easy to calculate. The rate of change of the angle ϕ is equal to ω, the angular speed of the loop, so we can write $\phi = \omega t$. Hence

$$\Phi_B = BA\cos\phi = BA\cos\omega t$$

The derivative of $\cos\omega t$ is $(d/dt)\cos\omega t = -\omega\sin\omega t$. Hence, by Faraday's law [Eq. (29.3)] the induced emf is

$$\mathcal{E} = -\frac{d\Phi_B}{dt} = \omega BA\sin\omega t$$

EVALUATE: The induced emf $\mathcal{E}$ varies sinusoidally with time (Fig. 29.8b). When the plane of the loop is perpendicular to $\vec{B}$ $(\phi = 0 \text{ or } 180^\circ)$, Φ_B reaches its maximum and minimum values. At these times, its instantaneous rate of change is zero and $\mathcal{E}$ is zero. Also, $\mathcal{E}$ is greatest in absolute value when the plane of the loop is parallel to $\vec{B}$ $(\phi = 90^\circ \text{ or } 270^\circ)$ and Φ_B is changing most rapidly. Finally, we note that the induced emf does not depend on the *shape* of the loop, but only on its area. Because $\mathcal{E}$ is directly proportional to ω and B, some tachometers use the emf in a rotating coil to measure rotational speed. Other devices use an emf of this kind to measure magnetic field.

We can use the alternator as a source of emf in an external circuit by use of two *slip rings,* which rotate with the loop, as shown in Fig. 29.8a. The rings slide against stationary contacts called *brushes,* which are connected to the output terminals a and b. Since the emf varies sinusoidally, the current that results in the circuit is an *alternating* current that also varies sinusoidally in magnitude and direction. An alternator is also called an *alternating-current* (ac) *generator* for this reason. The amplitude of the emf can be increased by increasing the rotation speed, the field magnitude, or the loop area or by using N loops instead of one, as in Eq. (29.4).

Alternators are used in automobiles to generate the currents in the ignition, the lights, and the entertainment system. The arrangement is a little different than in this example; rather than having a rotating loop in a magnetic field, the loop stays fixed and an electromagnet rotates. (The rotation is provided by a mechanical connection between the alternator and the engine.) But the result is the same; the flux through the loop varies sinusoidally, producing a sinusoidally varying emf. Larger alternators of this same type are used in electric power plants (Figure 29.9).

29.9 A commercial alternator uses many loops of wire wound around a barrel-like structure called an armature. The armature and wire remain stationary while electromagnets rotate on a shaft (not shown) through the center of the armature. The resulting induced emf is far larger than would be possible with a single loop of wire.

Example 29.5 Generator II: A DC generator and back emf in a motor

The alternator in Example 29.4 produces a sinusoidally varying emf and hence an alternating current. We can use a similar scheme to make a *direct-current* (dc) *generator* that produces an emf that always has the same sign. A prototype dc generator is shown in Fig. 29.10a. The arrangement of split rings is called a *commutator;* it reverses the connections to the external circuit at angular positions where the emf reverses. The resulting emf is shown in Fig. 29.10b. Commercial dc generators have a large number of coils and commutator segments; this arrangement smooths out the bumps in the emf, so the terminal voltage is not only one-directional but also practically constant. This brush-and-commutator arrangement is the same as that in the direct-current motor we discussed in Section 27.8. The motor's *back emf* is just the emf induced by the changing magnetic flux through its rotating coil. Consider a motor with a square coil 10.0 cm on a side, with 500 turns of wire. If the magnetic field has magnitude 0.200 T, at what rotation speed is the *average* back emf of the motor equal to 112 V?

29.10 (a) Schematic diagram of a dc generator, using a split-ring commutator. The ring halves are attached to the loop and rotate with it. (b) Graph of the resulting induced emf at terminals *ab*. Compare to Fig. 29.8b.

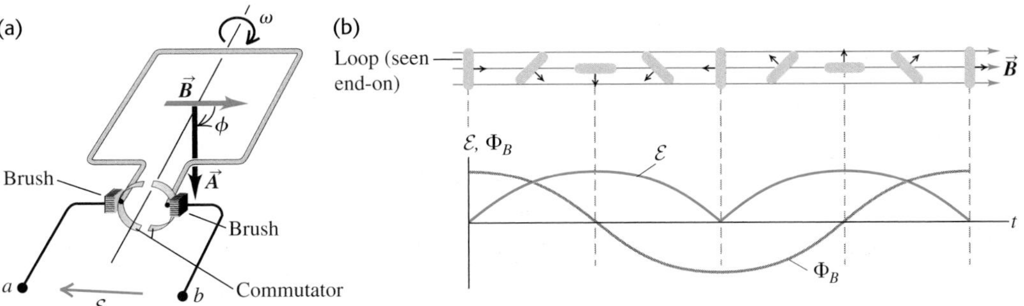

Continued

SOLUTION

IDENTIFY: As far as the rotating loop is concerned, the situation is the same as in Example 29.4 except that we now have N turns of wire. Without the commutator, the emf would alternate between positive and negative values and have an average value of zero (Fig. 29.8b). But with the commutator added, the emf is never negative and its average value is positive (Fig. 29.10b). Using our result from Example 29.4, we'll determine an expression for this average value and solve that expression for the rotational speed ω (our target variable).

SET UP: The setup is the same as in Example 29.4.

EXECUTE: Comparing Figs. 29.8b and 29.10b shows that the back emf of the motor is just the absolute value of the emf found for an alternator in Example 29.4, multiplied by the number of turns N in the coil as in Eq. (29.4):

$$|\mathcal{E}| = N\omega BA|\sin\omega t|$$

To find the *average* back emf, we replace $|\sin\omega t|$ by its average value. The average value of the sine function is found by integrating $\sin\omega t$ over half a cycle, from $t = 0$ to $t = T/2 = \pi/\omega$, and then dividing by the elapsed time π/ω. During this half cycle, the sine function is positive, so $|\sin\omega t| = \sin\omega t$, and we find

$$(|\sin\omega t|)_{\text{av}} = \frac{\int_0^{\pi/\omega}\sin\omega t\,dt}{\pi/\omega} = \frac{2}{\pi}$$

or about 0.64. The average back emf is then

$$\mathcal{E}_{\text{av}} = \frac{2N\omega BA}{\pi}$$

The back emf is proportional to the rotation speed ω, as was stated without proof in Section 27.8. Solving for ω, we obtain

$$\omega = \frac{\pi\mathcal{E}_{\text{av}}}{2NBA}$$
$$= \frac{\pi(112\text{ V})}{2(500)(0.200\text{ T})(0.100\text{ m})^2} = 176\text{ rad/s}$$

We used the relationships $1\text{ V} = 1\text{ Wb/s} = 1\text{ T}\cdot\text{m}^2\text{/s}$ from Example 29.1. We were able to add "radians" to the units of the answer because it is a dimensionless quantity, as we discussed in Chapter 9. The rotation speed can also be written as

$$\omega = 176\text{ rad/s}\frac{1\text{ rev}}{2\pi\text{ rad}}\frac{60\text{ s}}{1\text{ min}} = 1680\text{ rev/min}$$

EVALUATE: The average back emf is directly proportional to ω. Hence the slower the rotation speed, the less the back emf and the greater the possibility of burning out the motor, as we described in Example 27.11 (Section 27.8).

While we have used a very simple model of a generator in this and the preceding example, the same principles apply to the operation of commercial generators.

Example 29.6 Generator III: The slidewire generator

Figure 29.11 shows a U-shaped conductor in a uniform magnetic field $\vec{B}$ perpendicular to the plane of the figure, directed *into* the page. We lay a metal rod with length L across the two arms of the conductor, forming a circuit, and move the rod to the right with constant velocity $\vec{v}$. This induces an emf and a current, which is why this device is called a *slidewire generator*. Find the magnitude and direction of the resulting induced emf.

29.11 A slidewire generator. The magnetic field $\vec{B}$ and the vector area $\vec{A}$ are both directed into the figure. The increase in magnetic flux (caused by an increase in area) induces the emf and current.

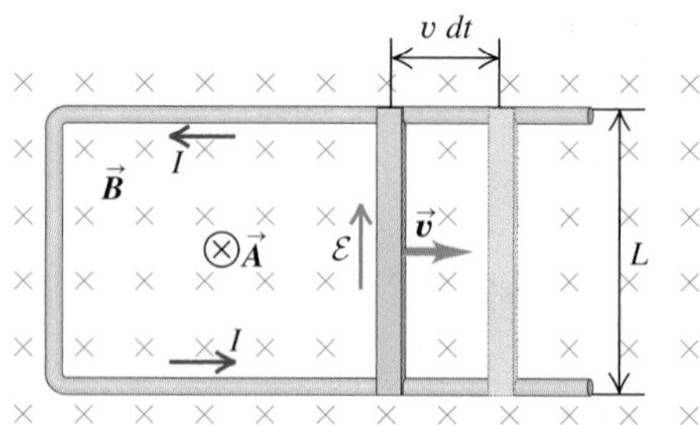

SOLUTION

IDENTIFY: The magnetic flux changes because the area of the loop—bounded on the right by the moving rod—is increasing. Our target variable is the emf $\mathcal{E}$ induced in this expanding loop.

SET UP: The magnetic field is uniform over the area of the loop, so we can again calculate the magnetic flux using $\Phi_B = BA\cos\phi$. We choose the area vector $\vec{A}$ to point straight into the plane of the picture, in the same direction as $\vec{B}$. With this choice a positive emf will be one that is directed clockwise around the loop. (You can check this with the right-hand rule. Using your right hand, point your thumb into the page and curl your fingers as in Fig. 29.6.)

EXECUTE: Since $\vec{B}$ and $\vec{A}$ point in the same direction, the angle $\phi = 0$ and $\Phi_B = BA$. The magnetic field magnitude B is constant, so the induced emf is

$$\mathcal{E} = -\frac{d\Phi_B}{dt} = -B\frac{dA}{dt}$$

To calculate dA/dt, note that in a time dt the sliding rod moves a distance $v\,dt$ (Fig. 29.11) and the loop area increases by an amount $dA = Lv\,dt$. Hence the induced emf is

$$\mathcal{E} = -B\frac{Lv\,dt}{dt} = -BLv$$

The minus sign tells us that the emf is directed *counterclockwise* around the loop. The induced current is also counterclockwise, as shown in the figure.

EVALUATE: Note that the emf is constant if the velocity $\vec{v}$ of the rod is constant. In this case the slidewire generator acts as a *direct-current* generator. It's not a very practical device because the rod eventually moves beyond the U-shaped conductor and loses contact, after which the current stops.

Example 29.7 Work and power in the slidewire generator

In the slidewire generator of Example 29.6, energy is dissipated in the circuit owing to its resistance. Let the resistance of the circuit (made up of the moving slidewire and the U-shaped conductor that connects the ends of the slidewire) at a given point in the slidewire's motion be R. Show that the rate at which energy is dissipated in the circuit is exactly equal to the rate at which work must be done to move the rod through the magnetic field.

SOLUTION

IDENTIFY: Our target variables are the *rates* at which energy is dissipated and at which work is done. This means that we'll be working with the concept of power (recall Section 6.4). Energy is dissipated in the circuit because there is resistance; to describe this we'll need the ideas of Section 25.5. It takes work to move the rod because there is an induced current flowing through it. The magnetic field exerts a force on this current-carrying rod, and whoever is pushing the rod has to do work against this force.

SET UP: We found the induced emf $\mathcal{E}$ in this circuit in Example 29.6. The current I in the circuit equals the absolute value of $\mathcal{E}$ divided by the resistance R, and the rate at which energy is dissipated in the rod is $P_{\text{dissipated}} = I^2R$. The magnetic force on the rod is $\vec{F} = I\vec{L} \times \vec{B}$; the vector $\vec{L}$ points along the rod in the direction of the current. Figure 29.12 shows that this force is opposite to the velocity of the rod, and so to maintain the motion a force of equal magnitude must be applied in the direction of the rod's motion (that is, in the direction of $\vec{v}$). The rate of doing work is equal to the product of the applied force and the speed of the rod: $P_{\text{applied}} = Fv$.

29.12 The magnetic force $\vec{F} = I\vec{L} \times \vec{B}$ that acts on the rod due to the induced current is to the left, opposite to $\vec{v}$.

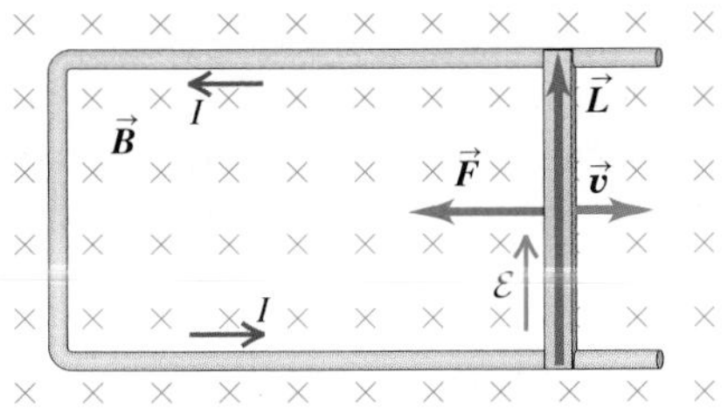

EXECUTE: First we'll calculate $P_{\text{dissipated}}$. From Example 29.6, $\mathcal{E} = -BLv$. Hence the current in the rod is

$$I = \frac{|\mathcal{E}|}{R} = \frac{BLv}{R}$$

and the rate of energy dissipation is

$$P_{\text{dissipated}} = I^2R = \left(\frac{BLv}{R}\right)^2 R = \frac{B^2L^2v^2}{R}$$

To calculate P_{applied}, we first calculate the magnitude of $\vec{F} = I\vec{L} \times \vec{B}$. Since $\vec{L}$ and $\vec{B}$ are perpendicular, this magnitude is

$$F = ILB = \frac{BLv}{R}LB = \frac{B^2L^2v}{R}$$

Hence the rate at which work is done by this applied force is

$$P_{\text{applied}} = Fv = \frac{B^2L^2v^2}{R}$$

EVALUATE: The rate at which work is done is just equal to the rate at which energy is dissipated in the resistance.

CAUTION You can't violate energy conservation You might think that reversing the direction of $\vec{B}$ or of $\vec{v}$ might make it possible to have the magnetic force $\vec{F} = I\vec{L} \times \vec{B}$ be in the *same* direction as $\vec{v}$. This would be a pretty neat trick. Once the rod was moving, the changing magnetic flux would induce an emf and a current, and the magnetic force on the rod would make it move even faster, increasing the emf and current; this would go on until the rod was moving at tremendous speed and producing electric power at a prodigious rate. If this seems too good to be true, not to mention a violation of energy conservation, that's because it is. Reversing $\vec{B}$ also reverses the sign of the induced emf and current and hence the direction of $\vec{L}$, so the magnetic force still opposes the motion of the rod; a similar result holds true if we reverse $\vec{v}$. This behavior is part of Lenz's law, to be discussed in Section 29.3.

Generators As Energy Converters

Example 29.7 shows that the slidewire generator doesn't produce electric energy out of nowhere; the energy is supplied by whatever body exerts the force that keeps the rod moving. All that the generator does is to *convert* that energy into a different form. The equality between the rate at which *mechanical* energy is supplied to a generator and the rate at which *electric* energy is generated holds for all types of generators. This is true in particular for the alternator described in Example 29.4. (We are neglecting the effects of friction in the bearings of an alternator or between the rod and the U-shaped conductor of a slidewire generator. If these are included, the conservation of energy demands that the energy lost to friction is not available for conversion to electric energy. In real generators the friction is kept to a minimum to keep the energy-conversion process as efficient as possible.)

In Chapter 27 we stated that the magnetic force on moving charges can never do work. But you might think that the magnetic force $\vec{F} = I\vec{L} \times \vec{B}$ in Example 29.7 *is* doing (negative) work on the current-carrying rod as it moves, contradicting our earlier statement. In fact, the work done by the magnetic force is actually zero. The moving charges that make up the current in the rod in Fig. 29.12 have a vertical component of velocity, causing a horizontal component of force on these charges. As a result, there is a horizontal displacement of charge within the rod, the left side acquiring a net positive charge and the right side a net negative charge. The result is a horizontal component of electric field, perpendicular to the length of the rod (analogous to the Hall effect, described in Section 27.9). It is this field, in the direction of motion of the rod, that does work on the mobile charges in the rod and hence indirectly on the atoms making up the rod.

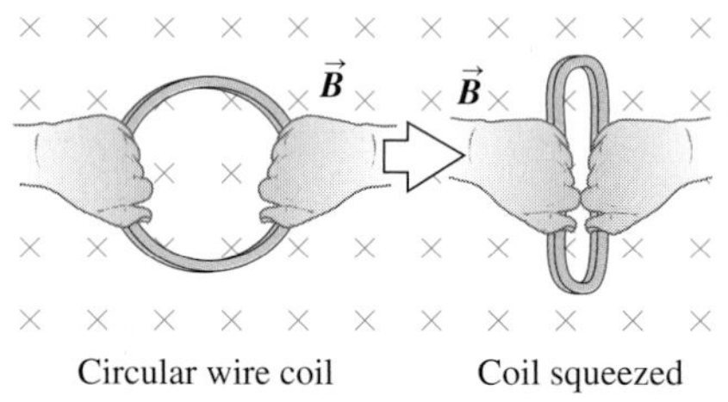

Test Your Understanding of Section 29.2 The figure at left shows a wire coil being squeezed in a uniform magnetic field. (a) While the coil is being squeezed, is the induced emf in the coil (i) clockwise, (ii) counterclockwise, or (iii) zero? (b) Once the coil has reached its final squeezed shape, is the induced emf in the coil (i) clockwise, (ii) counterclockwise, or (iii) zero?

29.3 Lenz's Law

Lenz's law is a convenient alternative method for determining the direction of an induced current or emf. Lenz's law is not an independent principle; it can be derived from Faraday's law. It always gives the same results as the sign rules we introduced in connection with Faraday's law, but it is often easier to use. Lenz's law also helps us gain intuitive understanding of various induction effects and of the role of energy conservation. H. F. E. Lenz (1804–1865) was a Russian scientist who duplicated independently many of the discoveries of Faraday and Henry. **Lenz's law** states:

The direction of any magnetic induction effect is such as to oppose the cause of the effect.

The "cause" may be changing flux through a stationary circuit due to a varying magnetic field, changing flux due to motion of the conductors that make up the circuit, or any combination. If the flux in a stationary circuit changes, as in Examples 29.1 and 29.2, the induced current sets up a magnetic field of its own. Within the area bounded by the circuit, this field is *opposite* to the original field if the original field is *increasing* but is in the *same* direction as the original field if the latter is *decreasing*. That is, the induced current opposes the *change in flux* through the circuit (*not* the flux itself).

If the flux change is due to motion of the conductors, as in Examples 29.3 through 29.7, the direction of the induced current in the moving conductor is such that the direction of the magnetic-field force on the conductor is opposite in direction to its motion. Thus the motion of the conductor, which caused the induced current, is opposed. We saw this explicitly for the slidewire generator in Example 29.7. In all these cases the induced current tries to preserve the *status quo* by opposing motion or a change of flux.

Lenz's law is also directly related to energy conservation. If the induced current in Example 29.7 were in the direction opposite to that given by Lenz's law, the magnetic force on the rod would accelerate it to ever-increasing speed with no external energy source, even though electric energy is being dissipated in the circuit. This would be a clear violation of energy conservation and doesn't happen in nature.

Conceptual Example 29.8 The slidewire generator, revisited

In Fig. 29.11, the induced current in the loop causes an additional magnetic field in the area bounded by the loop. The direction of the induced current is counterclockwise. From the discussion of Section 28.2, we see that the direction of the additional magnetic field caused by this current is *out of* the plane of the figure. Its direction is opposite that of the original magnetic field, so it tends to cancel the effect of that field. This is consistent with the prediction of Lenz's law.

Conceptual Example 29.9 Finding the direction of induced current

In Fig. 29.13 there is a uniform magnetic field $\vec{B}$ through the coil. The magnitude of the field is increasing, and the resulting induced emf causes an induced current. Use Lenz's law to determine the direction of the induced current.

SOLUTION

This situation is the same as in Example 29.1 (Section 29.2). By Lenz's law the induced current must produce a magnetic field $\vec{B}_{\text{induced}}$ inside the coil that is downward, opposing the change in flux. Using the right-hand rule we described in Section 28.5 for the direction of the magnetic field produced by a circular loop, $\vec{B}_{\text{induced}}$ will be in the desired direction if the induced current flows as shown in Fig. 29.13.

Figure 29.14 shows several applications of Lenz's law to the similar situation of a magnet moving near a conducting loop. In each of the four cases shown, the induced current produces a magnetic field of its own, in a direction that opposes the change in flux through the loop due to the magnet's motion.

29.13 The induced current due to the change in $\vec{B}$ is clockwise, as seen from above the loop. The added field $\vec{B}_{\text{induced}}$ that it causes is downward, opposing the change in the upward field $\vec{B}$.

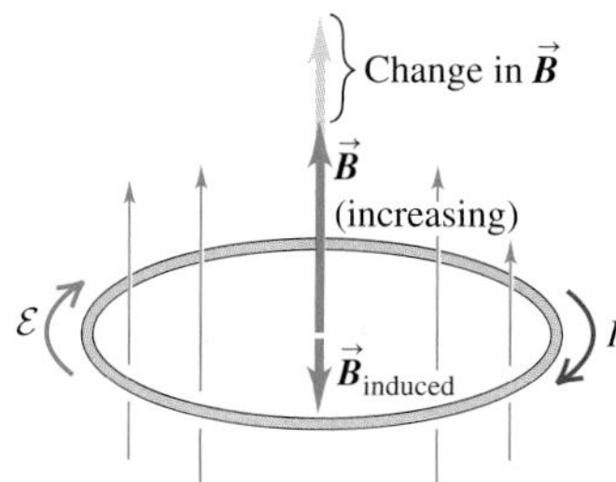

29.14 Directions of induced currents as a bar magnet moves along the axis of a conducting loop. If the bar magnet is stationary, there is no induced current.

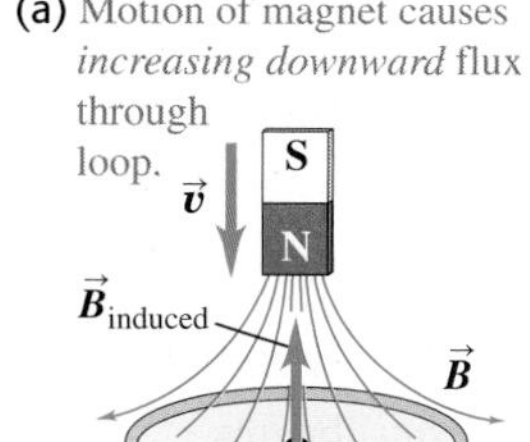

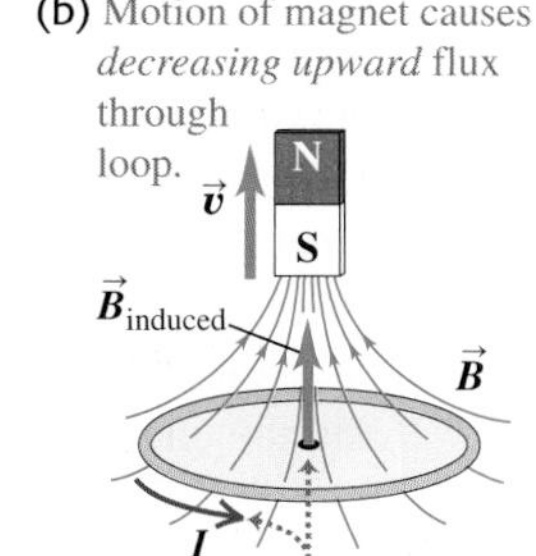

(b) Motion of magnet causes *decreasing upward* flux through loop.

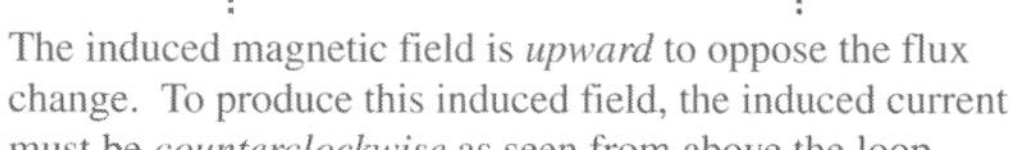

(a) Motion of magnet causes *increasing downward* flux through loop.

The induced magnetic field is *upward* to oppose the flux change. To produce this induced field, the induced current must be *counterclockwise* as seen from above the loop.

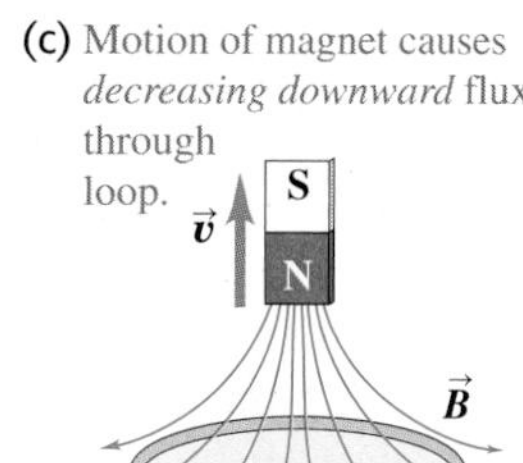

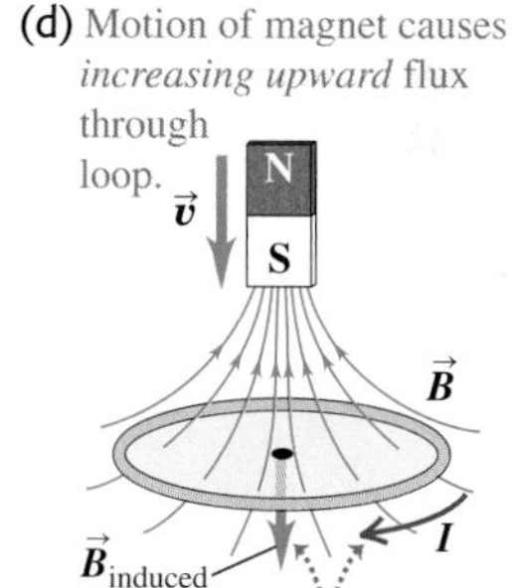

(c) Motion of magnet causes *decreasing downward* flux through loop.

(d) Motion of magnet causes *increasing upward* flux through loop.

Lenz's Law and the Response to Flux Changes

Since an induced current always opposes any change in magnetic flux through a circuit, how is it possible for the flux to change at all? The answer is that Lenz's law gives only the *direction* of an induced current; the *magnitude* of the current depends on the resistance of the circuit. The greater the circuit resistance, the less the induced current that appears to oppose any change in flux and the easier it is for a flux change to take effect. If the loop in Fig. 29.14 were made out of wood (an insulator), there would be almost no induced current in response to changes in the flux through the loop.

Conversely, the less the circuit resistance, the greater the induced current and the more difficult it is to change the flux through the circuit. If the loop in Fig. 29.14 is a good conductor, an induced current flows as long as the magnet moves relative to the loop. Once the magnet and loop are no longer in relative motion, the induced current very quickly decreases to zero because of the nonzero resistance in the loop.

The extreme case occurs when the resistance of the circuit is *zero*. Then the induced current in Fig. 29.14 will continue to flow even after the induced emf has disappeared—that is, even after the magnet has stopped moving relative to the loop. Thanks to this *persistent current,* it turns out that the flux through the loop is exactly the same as it was before the magnet started to move, so the flux through a loop of zero resistance *never* changes. Exotic materials called *superconductors* do indeed have zero resistance; we discuss these further in Section 29.8.

Test Your Understanding of Section 29.3 (a) Suppose the magnet in Fig. 29.14a were stationary and the loop of wire moved upward. Would the induced current in the loop be (i) in the same direction as shown in Fig. 29.14a, (ii) in the direction opposite to that shown in Fig. 29.14a, or (iii) zero? (b) Suppose the magnet and loop of wire in Fig. 29.14a both moved downward at the same velocity. Would the induced current in the loop be (i) in the same direction as shown in Fig. 29.14a, (ii) in the direction opposite to that shown in Fig. 29.14a, or (iii) zero?

29.4 Motional Electromotive Force

29.15 A conducting rod moving in a uniform magnetic field. (a) The rod, the velocity, and the field are mutually perpendicular. (b) Direction of induced current in the circuit.

(a) Isolated moving rod

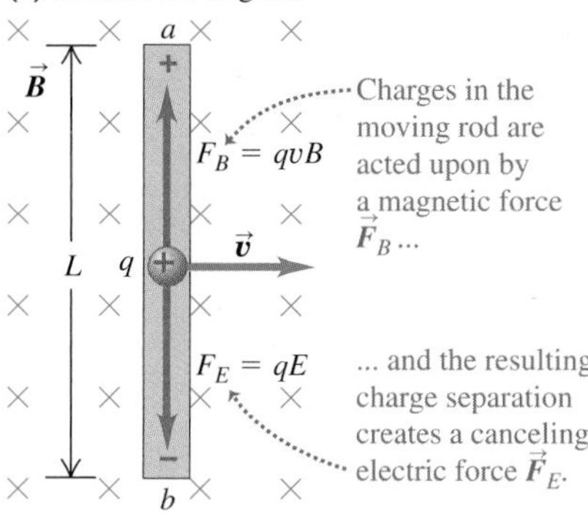

$\vec{B}$
a
b
L
q
$F_B = qvB$
$\vec{v}$
$F_E = qE$
Charges in the moving rod are acted upon by a magnetic force $\vec{F}_B$ ...
... and the resulting charge separation creates a canceling electric force $\vec{F}_E$.

(b) Rod connected to stationary conductor

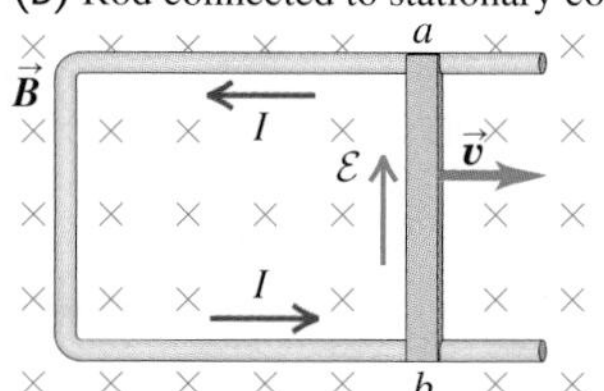

$\vec{B}$
a
b
I
I
$\mathcal{E}$
$\vec{v}$

The motional emf $\mathcal{E}$ in the moving rod creates an electric field in the stationary conductor.

We've seen several situations in which a conductor moves in a magnetic field, as in the generators discussed in Examples 29.4 through 29.7. We can gain additional insight into the origin of the induced emf in these situations by considering the magnetic forces on mobile charges in the conductor. Figure 29.15a shows the same moving rod that we discussed in Example 29.6, separated for the moment from the U-shaped conductor. The magnetic field $\vec{B}$ is uniform and directed into the page, and we move the rod to the right at a constant velocity $\vec{v}$. A charged particle q in the rod then experiences a magnetic force $\vec{F} = q\vec{v} \times \vec{B}$ with magnitude $F = |q|vB$. We'll assume in the following discussion that q is positive; in that case the direction of this force is upward along the rod, from b toward a.

This magnetic force causes the free charges in the rod to move, creating an excess of positive charge at the upper end a and negative charge at the lower end b. This in turn creates an electric field $\vec{E}$ within the rod, in the direction from a toward b (opposite to the magnetic force). Charge continues to accumulate at the ends of the rod until $\vec{E}$ becomes large enough for the downward electric force (with magnitude qE) to cancel exactly the *upward* magnetic force (with magnitude qvB). Then $qE = qvB$ and the charges are in equilibrium.

The magnitude of the potential difference $V_{ab} = V_a - V_b$ is equal to the electric field magnitude E multiplied by the length L of the rod. From the above discussion, $E = vB$, so

$$V_{ab} = EL = vBL \tag{29.5}$$

with point a at higher potential than point b.

Now suppose the moving rod slides along a stationary U-shaped conductor, forming a complete circuit (Fig. 29.15b). No *magnetic* force acts on the charges in the stationary U-shaped conductor, but the charge that was near points a and b redistributes itself along the stationary conductor, creating an *electric* field within it. This field establishes a current in the direction shown. The moving rod has become a source of electromotive force; within it, charge moves from lower to higher potential, and in the remainder of the circuit, charge moves from higher to lower potential. We call this emf a **motional electromotive force,** denoted by $\mathcal{E}$. From the above discussion, the magnitude of this emf is

$$\mathcal{E} = vBL \quad \text{(motional emf; length and velocity perpendicular to uniform } \vec{B}\text{)} \tag{29.6}$$

corresponding to a force per unit charge of magnitude vB acting for a distance L along the moving rod. If the total circuit resistance of the U-shaped conductor and the sliding rod is R, the induced current I in the circuit is given by $vBL = IR$. This is the same result we obtained in Section 29.2 using Faraday's law, and indeed motional emf is a particular case of Faraday's law, one of the several examples described in Section 29.2.

The emf associated with the moving rod in Fig. 29.15 is analogous to that of a battery with its positive terminal at a and its negative terminal at b, although the origins of the two emfs are quite different. In each case a nonelectrostatic force acts on the charges in the device, in the direction from b to a, and the emf is the work per unit charge done by this force when a charge moves from b to a in the device. When the device is connected to an external circuit, the direction of cur-

13.10 Motional EMF

rent is from b to a in the device and from a to b in the external circuit. While we have discussed motional emf in terms of a closed circuit like that in Fig. 29.15b, a motional emf is also present in the isolated moving rod in Fig. 29.15a, in the same way that a battery has an emf even when it's not part of a circuit.

The direction of the induced emf in Fig. 29.15 can be deduced by using Lenz's law, even if (as in Fig. 29.15a) the conductor does not form a complete circuit. In this case we can mentally complete the circuit between the ends of the conductor and use Lenz's law to determine the direction of the current. From this we can deduce the polarity of the ends of the open-circuit conductor. The direction from the $-$ end to the $+$ end within the conductor is the direction the current would have if the circuit were complete.

You should verify that if we express v in meters per second, B in teslas, and L in meters, then $\mathcal{E}$ is in volts. (Recall that $1\text{ V} = 1\text{ J/C}$.)

Motional emf: General Form

We can generalize the concept of motional emf for a conductor with *any* shape, moving in any magnetic field, uniform or not (assuming that the magnetic field at each point does not vary with time). For an element $d\vec{l}$ of conductor, the contribution $d\mathcal{E}$ to the emf is the magnitude dl multiplied by the component of $\vec{v} \times \vec{B}$ (the magnetic force per unit charge) parallel to $d\vec{l}$; that is,

$$d\mathcal{E} = (\vec{v} \times \vec{B}) \cdot d\vec{l}$$

For any closed conducting loop, the total emf is

$$\mathcal{E} = \oint (\vec{v} \times \vec{B}) \cdot d\vec{l} \quad \text{(motional emf: closed conducting loop)} \quad (29.7)$$

This expression looks very different from our original statement of Faraday's law, Eq. (29.3), which stated that $\mathcal{E} = -d\Phi_B/dt$. In fact, though, the two statements are equivalent. It can be shown that the rate of change of magnetic flux through a moving conducting loop is always given by the negative of the expression in Eq. (29.7). Thus this equation gives us an alternative formulation of Faraday's law. This alternative is often more convenient than the original one in problems with *moving* conductors. But when we have *stationary* conductors in changing magnetic fields, Eq. (29.7) *cannot* be used; in this case, $\mathcal{E} = -d\Phi_B/dt$ is the only correct way to express Faraday's law.

Example 29.10 Calculating motional emf

Suppose the moving rod in Fig. 29.15b is 0.10 m long, the velocity v is 2.5 m/s, the total resistance of the loop is 0.030 Ω, and B is 0.60 T. Find $\mathcal{E}$, the induced current, and the force acting on the rod.

SOLUTION

IDENTIFY: The first target variable is the *motional* emf $\mathcal{E}$ due to the rod's motion. We'll find the current from the values of $\mathcal{E}$ and the resistance R. The force on the rod is actually a magnetic force exerted by $\vec{B}$ on the current in the rod.

SET UP: We'll use the motional emf expression developed in this section, the familiar relationship $\mathcal{E} = IR$, and the formula $\vec{F} = I\vec{L} \times \vec{B}$ for the magnetic force on a current-carrying rod of length $L = 0.10$ m.

EXECUTE: From Eq. (29.6) the emf is

$$\mathcal{E} = vBL = (2.5\text{ m/s})(0.60\text{ T})(0.10\text{ m}) = 0.15\text{ V}$$

The resulting induced current in the loop is

$$I = \frac{\mathcal{E}}{R} = \frac{0.15\text{ V}}{0.030\ \Omega} = 5.0\text{ A}$$

The magnetic force on the rod carrying this current is directed *opposite* to the rod's motion. You can see this by applying the right-hand rule for vector products to the formula $\vec{F} = I\vec{L} \times \vec{B}$. The vector $\vec{L}$ points from b to a in Fig. 29.15, in the same direction as the induced current in the rod. Since $\vec{L}$ and $\vec{B}$ are perpendicular, this force has magnitude

$$F = ILB = (5.0\text{ A})(0.10\text{ m})(0.60\text{ T}) = 0.30\text{ N}$$

EVALUATE: We can check our answer for the direction of $\vec{F}$ by using Lenz's law. If we take the area vector $\vec{A}$ to point into the plane of the loop, the magnetic flux is positive and increasing as the rod moves to the right and increases the area of the loop. Lenz's law tells us that a force appears to oppose this increase in flux. Hence the force on the rod is to the left, opposite its motion.

Example 29.11 The Faraday disk dynamo

A conducting disk with radius R, shown in Fig. 29.16, lies in the xy-plane and rotates with constant angular velocity ω about the z-axis. The disk is in a uniform, constant $\vec{B}$ field parallel to the z-axis. Find the induced emf between the center and the rim of the disk.

SOLUTION

IDENTIFY: A motional emf is present because the conducting disk moves relative to the $\vec{B}$ field. The complication is that different parts of the disk move at different speeds v, depending on their distance from the rotation axis. We'll address this by considering small segments of the disk and adding (actually integrating) their contributions to determine our target variable, the emf between the center and the rim.

29.16 A conducting disk with radius R rotating at an angular speed ω in a magnetic field $\vec{B}$. The emf is induced along radial lines of the disk and is applied to an external circuit through the two sliding contacts labeled b.

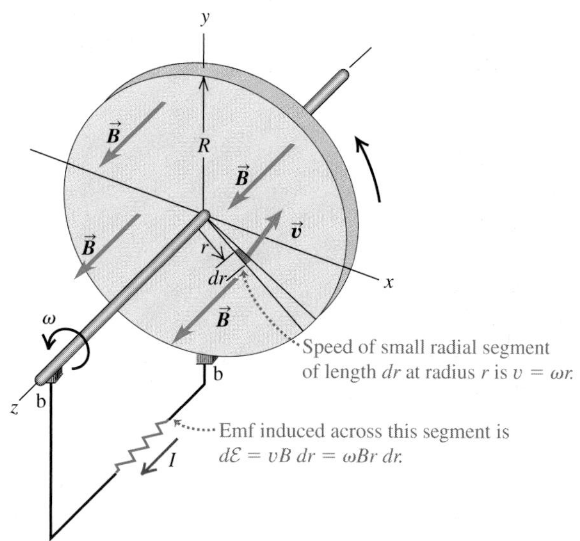

y
R
$\vec{B}$
$\vec{B}$
$\vec{B}$
$\vec{B}$
$\vec{v}$
r
dr
x
ω
b
z
b
Speed of small radial segment of length dr at radius r is $v = \omega r$.
Emf induced across this segment is $d\mathcal{E} = vB\,dr = \omega Br\,dr$.
I

SET UP: Consider the small segment of the disk labeled by its velocity vector $\vec{v}$. The magnetic force per unit charge on this segment is $\vec{v} \times \vec{B}$, which points radially outward from the center of the disk. Hence the induced emf tends to make a current flow radially outward, which tells us that the moving conducting path to think about here is a straight line from the center to the rim. We can find the emf from each small disk segment along this line using the expression $d\mathcal{E} = (\vec{v} \times \vec{B}) \cdot d\vec{l}$ and then integrate to find the total emf.

CAUTION **Speed in a rotating disk** You might be tempted to use Eq. (29.5) and simply multiply vB times the length of the moving conducting path, which is just the radius R. That wouldn't be right, because v has different values at different points along the path.

EXECUTE: Let's consider the motional emf $d\mathcal{E}$ due to a small radial segment at a distance r from the rotation axis. The associated length vector $d\vec{l}$ (of length dr) points radially outward, in the same direction as $\vec{v} \times \vec{B}$. The vectors $\vec{v}$ and $\vec{B}$ are perpendicular, and the magnitude of $\vec{v}$ is $v = \omega r$. Hence the total emf between center and rim is the sum of all such contributions:

$$\mathcal{E} = \int_0^R \omega Br\,dr = \frac{1}{2}\omega BR^2$$

EVALUATE: We can use this device as a source of emf in a circuit by completing the circuit through stationary brushes (b in the figure) that contact the disk and its conducting shaft as shown. The emf in such a disk was studied by Faraday; the device is called *a Faraday disk dynamo* or a *homopolar generator*. Unlike the alternator in Example 29.4, the Faraday disk dynamo is a direct-current generator; it produces an emf that is constant in time. Can you use Lenz's law to show that for the direction of rotation in Fig. 29.16, the current in the external circuit must be in the direction shown?

Test Your Understanding of Section 29.4 The earth's magnetic field points toward (magnetic) north. For simplicity, assume that the field has no vertical component (as is the case near the earth's equator). (a) If you hold a metal rod in your hand and walk toward the east, how should you orient the rod to get the maximum motional emf between its ends? (i) east-west; (ii) north-south; (iii) up-down; (iv) you get the same motional emf with all of these orientations. (b) How should you hold it to get *zero* emf as you walk toward the east? (i) east-west; (ii) north-south; (iii) up-down; (iv) none of these. (c) In which direction should you travel so that the motional emf across the rod is zero no matter how the rod is oriented? (i) west; (ii) north; (iii) south; (iv) straight up; (v) straight down.

29.5 Induced Electric Fields

When a conductor moves in a magnetic field, we can understand the induced emf on the basis of magnetic forces on charges in the conductor, as described in Section 29.4. But an induced emf also occurs when there is a changing flux through a stationary conductor. What is it that pushes the charges around the circuit in this type of situation?

As an example, let's consider the situation shown in Fig. 29.17. A long, thin solenoid with cross-sectional area A and n turns per unit length is encircled at its center by a circular conducting loop. The galvanometer G measures the current in the loop. A current I in the winding of the solenoid sets up a magnetic field $\vec{B}$ along the solenoid axis, as shown, with magnitude B as calculated in Example 28.9 (Section 28.7): $B = \mu_0 nI$, where n is the number of turns per unit length. If we neglect the small field outside the solenoid and take the area vector $\vec{A}$ to point in the same direction as $\vec{B}$, then the magnetic flux Φ_B through the loop is

$$\Phi_B = BA = \mu_0 nIA$$

When the solenoid current I changes with time, the magnetic flux Φ_B also changes, and according to Faraday's law the induced emf in the loop is given by

$$\mathcal{E} = -\frac{d\Phi_B}{dt} = -\mu_0 nA\frac{dI}{dt} \tag{29.8}$$

If the total resistance of the loop is R, the induced current in the loop, which we may call I', is $I' = \mathcal{E}/R$.

But what *force* makes the charges move around the loop? It can't be a magnetic force because the conductor isn't moving in a magnetic field and in fact isn't even *in* a magnetic field. We are forced to conclude that there has to be an **induced electric field** in the conductor *caused by the changing magnetic flux.* This may be a little jarring; we are accustomed to thinking about electric field as being caused by electric charges, and now we are saying that a changing magnetic field somehow acts as a source of electric field. Furthermore, it's a strange sort of electric field. When a charge q goes once around the loop, the total work done on it by the electric field must be equal to q times the emf $\mathcal{E}$. That is, the electric field in the loop *is not conservative,* as we used the term in Chapter 23, because the line integral of $\vec{E}$ around a closed path is not zero. Indeed, this line integral, representing the work done by the induced $\vec{E}$ field per unit charge, is equal to the induced emf $\mathcal{E}$:

$$\oint \vec{E} \cdot d\vec{l} = \mathcal{E} \tag{29.9}$$

From Faraday's law the emf $\mathcal{E}$ is also the negative of the rate of change of magnetic flux through the loop. Thus for this case we can restate Faraday's law as

$$\oint \vec{E} \cdot d\vec{l} = -\frac{d\Phi_B}{dt} \quad \text{(stationary integration path)} \tag{29.10}$$

Note that Faraday's law is always true in the form $\mathcal{E} = -d\Phi_B/dt$; the form given in Eq. (29.10) is valid *only* if the path around which we integrate is *stationary.*

As an example of a situation to which Eq. (29.10) can be applied, consider the stationary circular loop in Fig. 29.17b, which we take to have radius r. Because of cylindrical symmetry, the electric field $\vec{E}$ has the same magnitude at every point on the circle and is tangent to it at each point. (Symmetry would also permit the field to be *radial,* but then Gauss's law would require the presence of a net charge inside the circle, and there is none.) The line integral in Eq. (29.10) becomes simply the magnitude E times the circumference $2\pi r$ of the loop, $\oint \vec{E} \cdot d\vec{l} = 2\pi rE$, and Eq. (29.10) gives

$$E = \frac{1}{2\pi r}\left|\frac{d\Phi_B}{dt}\right| \tag{29.11}$$

The directions of $\vec{E}$ at points on the loop are shown in Fig. 29.17b. We know that $\vec{E}$ has to have the direction shown when $\vec{B}$ in the solenoid is increasing, because

29.17 (a) The windings of a long solenoid carry a current I that is increasing at a rate dI/dt. The magnetic flux in the solenoid is increasing at a rate $d\Phi_B/dt$, and this changing flux passes through a wire loop. An emf $\mathcal{E} = -d\Phi_B/dt$ is induced in the loop, inducing a current I' that is measured by the galvanometer G. (b) Cross-sectional view.

(a)

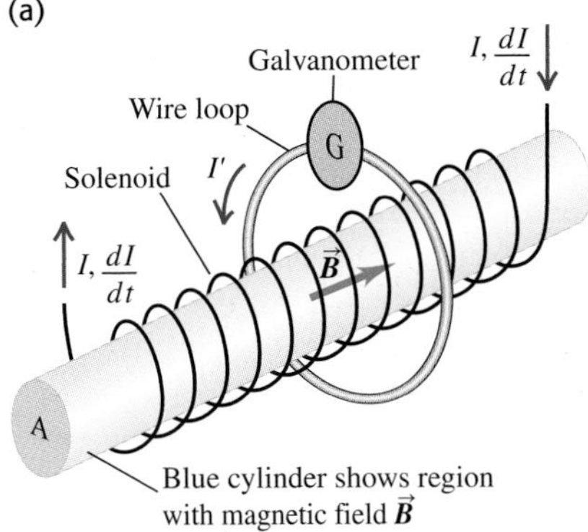

(b)

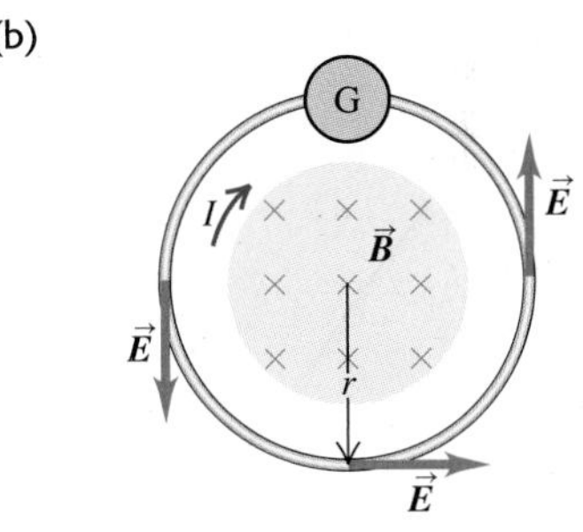

$\oint \vec{E} \cdot d\vec{l}$ has to be negative when $d\Phi_B/dt$ is positive. The same approach can be used to find the induced electric field *inside* the solenoid when the solenoid $\vec{B}$ field is changing; we leave the details to you (see Exercise 29.29).

Nonelectrostatic Electric Fields

Now let's summarize what we've learned. Faraday's law, Eq. (29.3), is valid for two rather different situations. In one, an emf is induced by magnetic forces on charges when a conductor moves through a magnetic field. In the other, a time-varying magnetic field induces an electric field in a stationary conductor and hence induces an emf; in fact, the $\vec{E}$ field is induced even when no conductor is present. This $\vec{E}$ field differs from an electro*static* field in an important way. It is *nonconservative;* the line integral $\oint \vec{E} \cdot d\vec{l}$ around a closed path is not zero, and when a charge moves around a closed path, the field does a nonzero amount of work on it. It follows that for such a field the concept of *potential* has no meaning. We call such a field a **nonelectrostatic field.** In contrast, an electro*static* field is *always* conservative, as we discussed in Section 23.1, and always has an associated potential function. Despite this difference, the fundamental effect of *any* electric field is to exert a force $\vec{F} = q\vec{E}$ on a charge q. This relationship is valid whether $\vec{E}$ is a conservative field produced by a charge distribution or a nonconservative field caused by changing magnetic flux.

So a changing magnetic field acts as a source of electric field of a sort that we *cannot* produce with any static charge distribution. This may seem strange, but it's the way nature behaves. What's more, we'll see in Section 29.7 that a changing *electric* field acts as a source of *magnetic* field. We'll explore this symmetry between the two fields in greater detail in our study of electromagnetic waves in Chapter 32.

If any doubt remains in your mind about the reality of magnetically induced electric fields, consider a few of the many practical applications (Fig. 29.18). In the playback head of a tape deck, currents are induced in a stationary coil as the variously magnetized regions of the tape move past it. Computer disk drives operate on the same principle. Pickups in electric guitars use currents induced in stationary pickup coils by the vibration of nearby ferromagnetic strings. Alternators in most cars use rotating magnets to induce currents in stationary coils. The list goes on and on; whether we realize it or not, magnetically induced electric fields play an important role in everyday life.

29.18 Applications of induced electric fields. (a) Data are stored on a computer hard disk in a pattern of magnetized areas on the surface of the disk. To read these data, a coil on a movable arm is placed next to the spinning disk. The coil experiences a changing magnetic flux, inducing a current whose characteristics depend on the pattern coded on the disk. (b) This hybrid automobile has both a gasoline engine and an electric motor. As the car comes to a halt, the spinning wheels run the motor backward so that it acts as a generator. The resulting induced current is used to recharge the car's batteries. (c) The rotating crankshaft of a piston-engine airplane spins a magnet, inducing an emf in an adjacent coil and generating the spark that ignites fuel in the engine cylinders. This keeps the engine running even if the airplane's other electrical systems fail.

Example 29.12 Induced electric fields

Suppose the long solenoid in Fig. 29.17a is wound with 500 turns per meter and the current in its windings is increasing at the rate of 100 A/s. The cross-sectional area of the solenoid is 4.0 cm^2 = 4.0×10^{-4} m^2. (a) Find the magnitude of the induced emf in the wire loop outside the solenoid. (b) Find the magnitude of the induced electric field within the loop if its radius is 2.0 cm.

SOLUTION

IDENTIFY: As in Fig. 29.17b, the increasing magnetic field inside the solenoid causes a change in the magnetic flux through the wire loop and hence induces an electric field $\vec{E}$ around the loop. Our target variables are the induced emf $\mathcal{E}$ and the magnitude of $\vec{E}$.

SET UP: We use Eq. (29.8) to determine the emf. Determining the field magnitude E is simplified because the loop and the solenoid share the same central axis. Hence, by symmetry, the electric field is tangent to the loop and has the same magnitude all the way around its circumference. This makes it easy to find E from the emf $\mathcal{E}$ using Eq. (29.9).

EXECUTE: (a) From Eq. (29.8), the induced emf is

$$\begin{aligned}\mathcal{E} &= -\frac{d\Phi_B}{dt} = -\mu_0 nA\frac{dI}{dt}\\ &= -(4\pi \times 10^{-7}\ \text{Wb/A}\cdot\text{m})(500\ \text{turns/m})\\ &\quad \times (4.0 \times 10^{-4}\ \text{m}^2)(100\ \text{A/s})\\ &= -25 \times 10^{-6}\ \text{Wb/s} = -25 \times 10^{-6}\ \text{V} = -25\ \mu\text{V}\end{aligned}$$

(b) By symmetry the line integral $\oint \vec{E} \cdot d\vec{l}$ has absolute value $2\pi rE$ (disregarding the direction in which we integrate around the loop). This is equal to the absolute value of the emf, so

$$E = \frac{|\mathcal{E}|}{2\pi r} = \frac{25 \times 10^{-6}\ \text{V}}{2\pi(2.0 \times 10^{-2}\ \text{m})} = 2.0 \times 10^{-4}\ \text{V/m}$$

EVALUATE: In Fig. 29.17b the magnetic flux *into* the plane of the figure is increasing. According to the right-hand rule for induced emf (illustrated in Fig. 29.6), a positive emf would be clockwise around the loop; the negative sign of $\mathcal{E}$ shows that the emf is in the counterclockwise direction. Can you also show this using Lenz's law?

Test Your Understanding of Section 29.5 If you wiggle a magnet back and forth in your hand, are you generating an electric field? If so, is this electric field conservative?

29.19 Eddy currents induced in a rotating metal disk.

(a) Metal disk rotating through a magnetic field

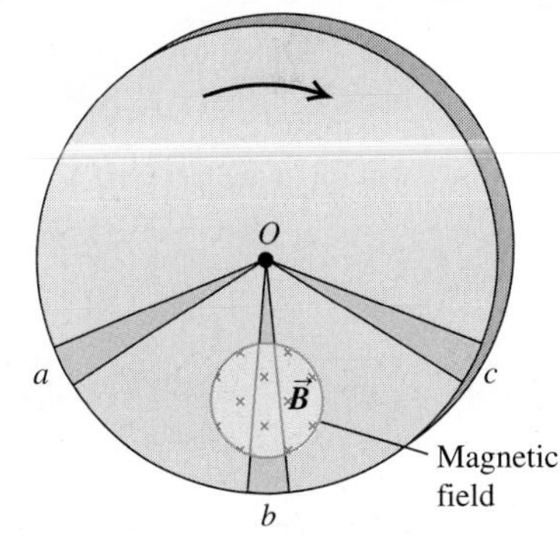

(b) Resulting eddy currents and braking force

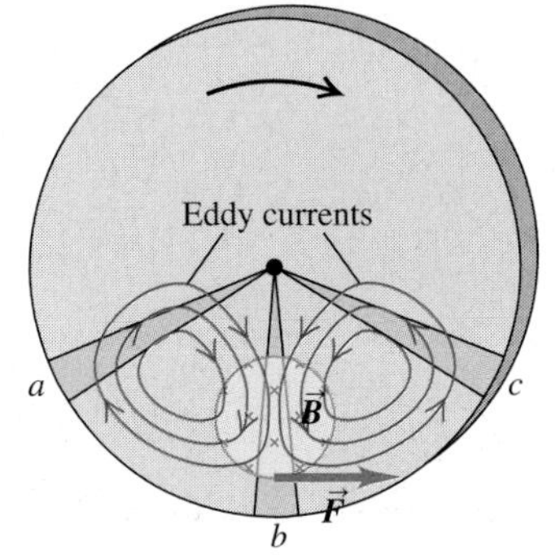

*29.6 Eddy Currents

In the examples of induction effects that we have studied, the induced currents have been confined to well-defined paths in conductors and other components forming a circuit. However, many pieces of electrical equipment contain masses of metal moving in magnetic fields or located in changing magnetic fields. In situations like these we can have induced currents that circulate throughout the volume of a material. Because their flow patterns resemble swirling eddies in a river, we call these **eddy currents.**

As an example, consider a metallic disk rotating in a magnetic field perpendicular to the plane of the disk but confined to a limited portion of the disk's area, as shown in Fig. 29.19a. Sector *Ob* is moving across the field and has an emf induced in it. Sectors *Oa* and *Oc* are not in the field, but they provide return conducting paths for charges displaced along *Ob* to return from *b* to *O*. The result is a circulation of eddy currents in the disk, somewhat as sketched in Fig. 29.19b.

We can use Lenz's law to decide on the direction of the induced current in the neighborhood of sector *Ob*. This current must experience a magnetic force $\vec{F} = I\vec{L} \times \vec{B}$ that *opposes* the rotation of the disk, and so this force must be to the right in Fig. 29.19b. Since $\vec{B}$ is directed into the plane of the disk, the current and hence $\vec{L}$ have downward components. The return currents lie outside the field, so they do not experience magnetic forces. The interaction between the eddy currents

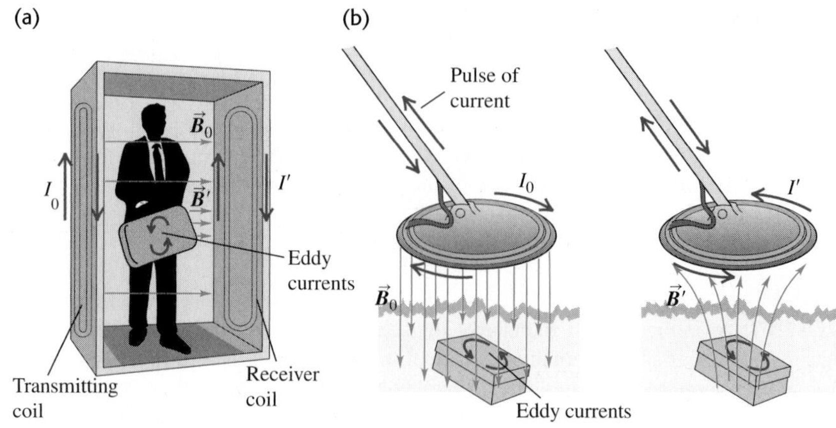

29.20 (a) A metal detector at an airport security checkpoint generates an alternating magnetic field $\vec{B}_0$. This induces eddy currents in a conducting object carried through the detector. The eddy currents in turn produce an alternating magnetic field $\vec{B}'$, and this field induces a current in the detector's receiver coil. (b) Portable metal detectors work on the same principle.

and the field causes a braking action on the disk. Such effects can be used to stop the rotation of a circular saw quickly when the power is turned off. Some sensitive balances use this effect to damp out vibrations. Eddy current braking is used on some electrically powered rapid-transit vehicles. Electromagnets mounted in the cars induce eddy currents in the rails; the resulting magnetic fields cause braking forces on the electromagnets and thus on the cars.

Eddy currents have many other practical uses. The shiny metal disk in the electric power company's meter outside your house rotates as a result of eddy currents. These currents are induced in the disk by magnetic fields caused by sinusoidally varying currents in a coil. In induction furnaces, eddy currents are used to heat materials in completely sealed containers for processes in which it is essential to avoid the slightest contamination of the materials. The metal detectors used at airport security checkpoints (Fig. 29.20a) operate by detecting eddy currents induced in metallic objects. Similar devices (Fig. 29.20b) are used to find buried treasure such as bottlecaps and lost pennies.

A particularly dramatic example of eddy currents in action is Jupiter's moon Io, which is slightly larger than the earth's moon (Fig. 29.21a). Io moves rapidly through Jupiter's intense magnetic field, and this sets up strong eddy currents within Io's interior. These currents dissipate energy at a rate of 10^{12} W, equivalent to setting off a one-kiloton nuclear weapon inside Io every four seconds! This dissipated energy helps to keep Io's interior hot and so helps to cause volcanic eruptions on its surface, like those in Fig. 29.21b. (Gravitational effects from Jupiter cause even more heating.)

Eddy currents also have undesirable effects. In an alternating-current transformer, coils wrapped around an iron core carry a sinusoidally varying current. The resulting eddy currents in the core waste energy through I^2R heating and themselves set up an unwanted opposing emf in the coils. To minimize these effects, the core is designed so that the paths for eddy currents are as narrow as possible. We'll describe how this is done when we discuss transformers in detail in Section 31.6.

29.21 As Jupiter's moon Io moves around its orbit, the planet's powerful magnetic field induces eddy currents within Io. The lower closeup image shows two simultaneous volcanic eruptions on Io, triggered in part by eddy current heating.

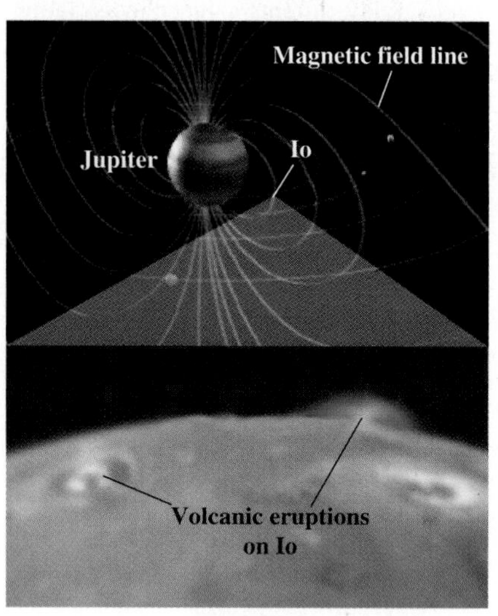

Test Your Understanding of Section 29.6 Suppose that the magnetic field in Fig. 29.19 were directed out of the plane of the figure and the disk were rotating counterclockwise. Compared to the directions of the force $\vec{F}$ and the eddy currents shown in Fig. 29.19b, what would the new directions be? (i) The force $\vec{F}$ and the eddy currents would both be in the same direction; (ii) the force $\vec{F}$ would be in the same direction, but the eddy currents would be in the opposite direction; (iii) the force $\vec{F}$ would be in the opposite direction, but the eddy currents would be in the same direction; (iv) the force $\vec{F}$ and the eddy currents would be in the opposite directions.

29.7 Displacement Current and Maxwell's Equations

We have seen that a varying magnetic field gives rise to an induced electric field. In one of the more remarkable examples of the symmetry of nature, it turns out that a varying *electric* field gives rise to a *magnetic* field. This effect is of tremendous importance, for it turns out to explain the existence of radio waves, gamma rays, and visible light, as well as all other forms of electromagnetic waves.

Generalizing Ampere's Law

To see the origin of the relationship between varying electric fields and magnetic fields, let's return to Ampere's law as given in Section 28.6, Eq. (28.20):

$$\oint \vec{B} \cdot d\vec{l} = \mu_0 I_{\text{encl}}$$

The problem with Ampere's law in this form is that it is *incomplete*. To see why, let's consider the process of charging a capacitor (Fig. 29.22). Conducting wires lead current i_C into one plate and out of the other; the charge Q increases, and the electric field $\vec{E}$ between the plates increases. The notation i_C indicates *conduction* current to distinguish it from another kind of current we are about to encounter, called *displacement* current i_D. We use lowercase i's and v's to denote instantaneous values of currents and potential differences, respectively, that may vary with time.

Let's apply Ampere's law to the circular path shown. The integral $\oint \vec{B} \cdot d\vec{l}$ around this path equals $\mu_0 I_{\text{encl}}$. For the plane circular area bounded by the circle, I_{encl} is just the current i_C in the left conductor. But the surface that bulges out to the right is bounded by the same circle, and the current through that surface is zero. So $\oint \vec{B} \cdot d\vec{l}$ is equal to $\mu_0 i_C$, and at the same time it is equal to zero! This is a clear contradiction.

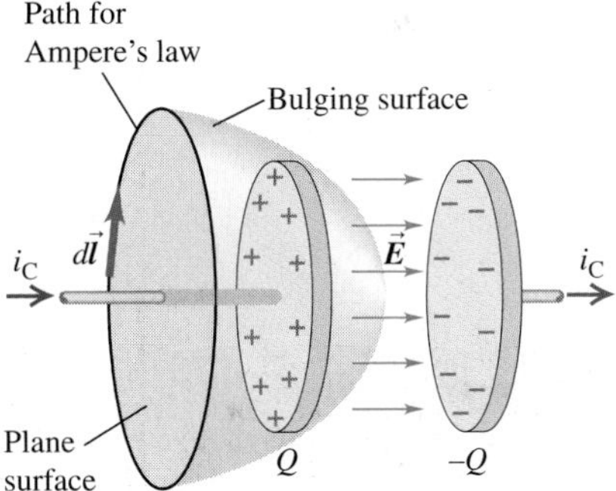

29.22 Parallel-plate capacitor being charged. The conduction current through the plane surface is i_C, but there is no conduction current through the surface that bulges out to pass between the plates. The two surfaces have a common boundary, so this difference in I_{encl} leads to an apparent contradiction in applying Ampere's law.

But something else is happening on the bulged-out surface. As the capacitor charges, the electric field $\vec{E}$ and the electric *flux* Φ_E through the surface are increasing. We can determine their rates of change in terms of the charge and current. The instantaneous charge is $q = Cv$, where C is the capacitance and v is the instantaneous potential difference. For a parallel-plate capacitor, $C = \epsilon_0 A/d$, where A is the plate area and d is the spacing. The potential difference v between plates is $v = Ed$, where E is the electric field magnitude between plates. (We neglect fringing and assume that $\vec{E}$ is uniform in the region between the plates.) If this region is filled with a material with permittivity ϵ, we replace ϵ_0 by ϵ everywhere; we'll use ϵ in the following discussion.

Substituting these expressions for C and v into $q = Cv$, we can express the capacitor charge q as

$$q = Cv = \frac{\epsilon A}{d}(Ed) = \epsilon EA = \epsilon \Phi_E \qquad (29.12)$$

where $\Phi_E = EA$ is the electric flux through the surface.

As the capacitor charges, the rate of change of q is the conduction current, $i_C = dq/dt$. Taking the derivative of Eq. (29.12) with respect to time, we get

$$i_C = \frac{dq}{dt} = \epsilon \frac{d\Phi_E}{dt} \qquad (29.13)$$

Now, stretching our imagination a little, we invent a fictitious **displacement current** i_D in the region between the plates, defined as

$$i_D = \epsilon \frac{d\Phi_E}{dt} \quad \text{(displacement current)} \qquad (29.14)$$

That is, we imagine that the changing flux through the curved surface in Fig. 29.22 is somehow equivalent, in Ampere's law, to a conduction current through that surface. We include this fictitious current, along with the real conduction current i_C, in Ampere's law:

$$\oint \vec{B} \cdot d\vec{l} = \mu_0 (i_C + i_D)_{encl} \qquad \text{(generalized Ampere's law)} \qquad (29.15)$$

Ampere's law in this form is obeyed no matter which surface we use in Fig. 29.22. For the flat surface, i_D is zero; for the curved surface, i_C is zero; and i_C for the flat surface equals i_D for the curved surface. Equation (29.15) remains valid in a magnetic material, provided that the magnetization is proportional to the external field and we replace μ_0 by μ.

The fictitious current i_D was invented in 1865 by the Scottish physicist James Clerk Maxwell (1831–1879), who called it displacement current. There is a corresponding *displacement current density* $j_D = i_D/A$; using $\Phi_E = EA$ and dividing Eq. (29.14) by A, we find

$$j_D = \epsilon \frac{dE}{dt} \qquad (29.16)$$

We have pulled the concept out of thin air, as Maxwell did, but we see that it enables us to save Ampere's law in situations such as that in Fig. 29.22.

Another benefit of displacement current is that it lets us generalize Kirchhoff's junction rule, discussed in Section 26.2. Considering the left plate of the capacitor plate, we have conduction current into it but none out of it. But when we include the displacement current, we have conduction current coming in one side and an equal displacement current coming out the other side. With this generalized meaning of the term "current," we can speak of current going *through* the capacitor.

The Reality of Displacement Current

You might well ask at this point whether displacement current has any real physical significance or whether it is just a ruse to satisfy Ampere's law and Kirchhoff's junction rule. Here's a fundamental experiment that helps to answer that question. We take a plane circular area between the capacitor plates, as shown in Fig. 29.23. If displacement current really plays the role in Ampere's law that we have claimed, then there ought to be a magnetic field in the region between the plates while the capacitor is charging. We can use our generalized Ampere's law, including displacement current, to predict what this field should be.

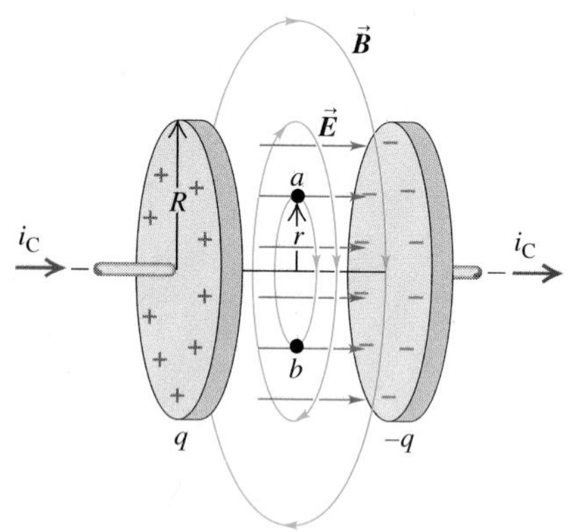

29.23 A capacitor being charged by a current i_C has a displacement current equal to i_C between the plates, with displacement-current density $j_D = \epsilon\, dE/dt$. This can be regarded as the source of the magnetic field between the plates.

To be specific, let's picture round capacitor plates with radius R. To find the magnetic field at a point in the region between the plates at a distance r from the axis, we apply Ampere's law to a circle of radius r passing through the point, with $r < R$. This circle passes through points a and b in Fig. 29.23. The total current enclosed by the circle is j_D times its area, or $(i_D/\pi R^2)(\pi r^2)$. The integral $\oint \vec{B} \cdot d\vec{l}$ in Ampere's law is just B times the circumference $2\pi r$ of the circle, and because $i_D = i_C$ for the charging capacitor, Ampere's law becomes

$$\oint \vec{B} \cdot d\vec{l} = 2\pi r B = \mu_0 \frac{r^2}{R^2} i_C \qquad \text{or}$$

$$B = \frac{\mu_0}{2\pi} \frac{r}{R^2} i_C \qquad (29.17)$$

This result predicts that in the region between the plates $\vec{B}$ is zero at the axis and increases linearly with distance from the axis. A similar calculation shows that *outside* the region between the plates (that is, for $r > R$), $\vec{B}$ is the same as though the wire were continuous and the plates not present at all.

When we *measure* the magnetic field in this region, we find that it really is there and that it behaves just as Eq. (29.17) predicts. This confirms directly the role of displacement current as a source of magnetic field. It is now established beyond reasonable doubt that displacement current, far from being just an artifice, is a fundamental fact of nature. Maxwell's discovery was the bold step of an extraordinary genius.

Maxwell's Equations of Electromagnetism

We are now in a position to wrap up in a single package *all* of the relationships between electric and magnetic fields and their sources. This package consists of four equations, called **Maxwell's equations.** Maxwell did not discover all of these equations single-handedly (though he did develop the concept of displacement current). But he did put them together and recognized their significance, particularly in predicting the existence of electromagnetic waves.

For now we'll state Maxwell's equations in their simplest form, for the case in which we have charges and currents in otherwise empty space. In Chapter 32 we'll discuss how to modify these equations if a dielectric or a magnetic material is present.

Two of Maxwell's equations involve an integral of $\vec{E}$ or $\vec{B}$ over a closed surface. The first is simply Gauss's law for electric fields, Eq. (22.8), which states that the surface integral of $E_\perp$ over any closed surface equals $1/\epsilon_0$ times the total charge Q_{encl} enclosed within the surface:

$$\oint \vec{E} \cdot d\vec{A} = \frac{Q_{encl}}{\epsilon_0} \qquad \text{(Gauss's law for } \vec{E}\text{)} \qquad (29.18)$$

The second is the analogous relationship for *magnetic* fields, Eq. (27.8), which states that the surface integral of $B_\perp$ over any closed surface is always zero:

$$\oint \vec{B} \cdot d\vec{A} = 0 \qquad \text{(Gauss's law for } \vec{B}\text{)} \qquad (29.19)$$

This statement means, among other things, that there are no magnetic monopoles (single magnetic charges) to act as sources of magnetic field.

The third equation is Ampere's law including displacement current. This states that both conduction current i_C and displacement current $\epsilon_0 d\Phi_E/dt$, where Φ_E is electric flux, act as sources of magnetic field:

$$\oint \vec{B} \cdot d\vec{l} = \mu_0 \left(i_C + \epsilon_0 \frac{d\Phi_E}{dt} \right)_{encl} \qquad \text{(Ampere's law)} \qquad (29.20)$$

The fourth and final equation is Faraday's law. It states that a changing magnetic field or magnetic flux induces an electric field:

$$\oint \vec{E} \cdot d\vec{l} = -\frac{d\Phi_B}{dt} \qquad \text{(Faraday's law)} \qquad (29.21)$$

If there is a changing magnetic flux, the line integral in Eq. (29.21) is not zero, which shows that the $\vec{E}$ field produced by a changing magnetic flux is not conservative. Recall that this line integral must be carried out over a *stationary* closed path.

It's worthwhile to look more carefully at the electric field $\vec{E}$ and its role in Maxwell's equations. In general, the total $\vec{E}$ field at a point in space can be the superposition of an electrostatic field $\vec{E}_c$ caused by a distribution of charges at rest and a magnetically induced, nonelectrostatic field $\vec{E}_n$. (The subscript c stands for Coulomb or conservative; the subscript n stands for non-Coulomb, nonelectrostatic, or nonconservative.) That is,

$$\vec{E} = \vec{E}_c + \vec{E}_n$$

The electrostatic part $\vec{E}_c$ is *always* conservative, so $\oint \vec{E}_c \cdot d\vec{l} = 0$. This conservative part of the field does not contribute to the integral in Faraday's law, so we can take $\vec{E}$ in Eq. (29.21) to be the total electric field $\vec{E}$, including both the part $\vec{E}_c$ due to charges and the magnetically induced part $\vec{E}_n$. Similarly, the nonconservative part $\vec{E}_n$ of the $\vec{E}$ field does not contribute to the integral in Gauss's law, because this part of the field is not caused by static charges. Hence $\oint \vec{E}_n \cdot d\vec{A}$ is always zero. We conclude that in all the Maxwell equations, $\vec{E}$ is the total electric field; these equations don't distinguish between conservative and nonconservative fields.

Symmetry in Maxwell's Equations

There is a remarkable symmetry in Maxwell's four equations. In empty space where there is no charge, the first two equations (Eqs. (29.18) and (29.19)) are identical in form, one containing $\vec{E}$ and the other containing $\vec{B}$. When we compare the second two equations, Eq. (29.20) says that a changing electric flux creates a magnetic field, and Eq. (29.21) says that a changing magnetic flux creates an electric field. In empty space, where there is no conduction current, $i_C = 0$ and the two equations have the same form, apart from a numerical constant and a negative sign, with the roles of $\vec{E}$ and $\vec{B}$ exchanged in the two equations.

We can rewrite Eqs. (29.20) and (29.21) in a different but equivalent form by introducing the definitions of electric and magnetic flux, $\Phi_E = \int \vec{E} \cdot d\vec{A}$ and $\Phi_B = \int \vec{B} \cdot d\vec{A}$, respectively. In empty space, where there is no charge or conduction current, $i_C = 0$ and $Q_{encl} = 0$, and we have

$$\oint \vec{B} \cdot d\vec{l} = \epsilon_0 \mu_0 \frac{d}{dt} \int \vec{E} \cdot d\vec{A} \tag{29.22}$$

$$\oint \vec{E} \cdot d\vec{l} = -\frac{d}{dt} \int \vec{B} \cdot d\vec{A} \tag{29.23}$$

Again we notice the symmetry between the roles of $\vec{E}$ and $\vec{B}$ in these expressions.

The most remarkable feature of these equations is that a time-varying field of *either* kind induces a field of the other kind in neighboring regions of space. Maxwell recognized that these relationships predict the existence of electromagnetic disturbances consisting of time-varying electric and magnetic fields that travel or *propagate* from one region of space to another, even if no matter is present in the intervening space. Such disturbances, called *electromagnetic waves,* provide the physical basis for light, radio and television waves, infrared, ultraviolet, x rays, and the rest of the electromagnetic spectrum. We will return to this vitally important topic in Chapter 32.

Although it may not be obvious, *all* the basic relationships between fields and their sources are contained in Maxwell's equations. We can derive Coulomb's law from Gauss's law, we can derive the law of Biot and Savart from Ampere's law, and so on. When we add the equation that defines the $\vec{E}$ and $\vec{B}$ fields in terms of the forces that they exert on a charge q, namely,

$$\vec{F} = q(\vec{E} + \vec{v} \times \vec{B}) \tag{29.24}$$

we have *all* the fundamental relationships of electromagnetism!

Finally, we note that Maxwell's equations would have even greater symmetry between the $\vec{E}$ and $\vec{B}$ fields if single magnetic charges (magnetic monopoles) existed. The right side of Eq. (29.19) would contain the total *magnetic* charge enclosed by the surface, and the right side of Eq. (29.21) would include a magnetic monopole current term. Perhaps you can begin to see why some physicists wish that magnetic monopoles existed; they would help to perfect the mathematical poetry of Maxwell's equations.

The discovery that electromagnetism can be wrapped up so neatly and elegantly is a very satisfying one. In conciseness and generality, Maxwell's equations are in the same league with Newton's laws of motion and the laws of thermodynamics. Indeed, a major goal of science is learning how to express very broad and general relationships in a concise and compact form. Maxwell's synthesis of electromagnetism stands as a towering intellectual achievement, comparable to the Newtonian synthesis we described at the end of Section 12.5 and to the development of relativity and quantum mechanics in the 20th century.

Test Your Understanding of Section 29.7 (a) Which of Maxwell's equations explains how a credit card reader works? (b) Which one describes how a wire carrying a steady current generates a magnetic field?

*29.8 Superconductivity

The most familiar property of a superconductor is the sudden disappearance of all electrical resistance when the material is cooled below a temperature called the *critical temperature,* denoted by T_c. We discussed this behavior and the circumstances of its discovery in Section 25.2. But superconductivity is far more than just the absence of measurable resistance. Superconductors also have extraordinary *magnetic* properties. We'll explore some of these properties in this section.

The first hint of unusual magnetic properties was the discovery that for any superconducting material the critical temperature T_c changes when the material is placed in an externally produced magnetic field $\vec{B}_0$. Figure 29.24 shows this dependence for mercury, the first element in which superconductivity was observed. As the external field magnitude B_0 increases, the superconducting transition occurs at lower and lower temperature. When B_0 is greater than 0.0412 T, *no* superconducting transition occurs. The minimum magnitude of magnetic field that is needed to eliminate superconductivity at a temperature below T_c is called the *critical field,* denoted by B_c.

29.24 Phase diagram for pure mercury, showing the critical magnetic field B_c and its dependence on temperature. Superconductivity is impossible above the critical temperature T_c. The curves for other superconducting materials are similar but with different numerical values.

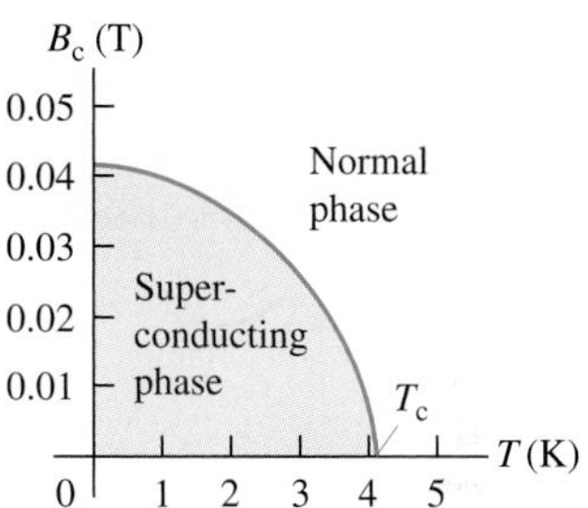
B_c (T)
0.05
0.04
0.03
0.02
0.01
Normal phase
Super-conducting phase
T_c
T (K)
0
1
2
3
4
5

29.25 A superconducting material (a) above the critical temperature and (b), (c) below the critical temperature.

(a) Superconducting material in an external magnetic field $\vec{B}_0$ at $T > T_c$.

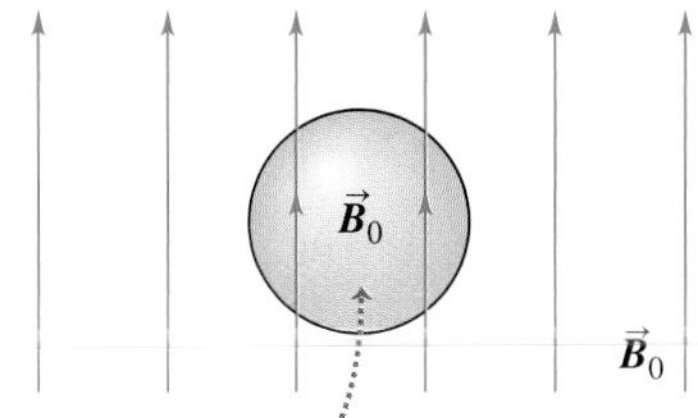
$\vec{B}_0$
$\vec{B}_0$
The field inside the material is very nearly equal to $\vec{B}_0$.

(b) The temperature is lowered to $T < T_c$, so the material becomes superconducting.

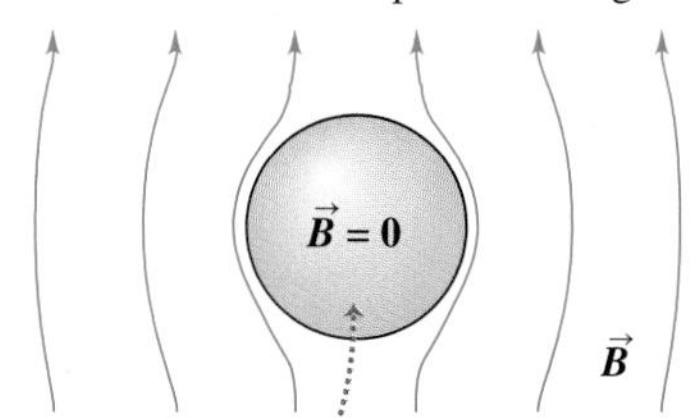
$\vec{B} = 0$
$\vec{B}$
Magnetic flux is expelled from the material, and the field inside it is zero (Meissner effect).

(c) When the external field is turned off at $T < T_c$, the field is zero everywhere.

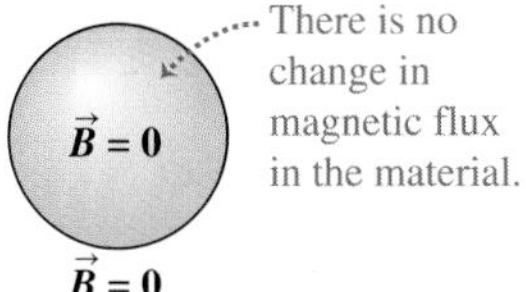
There is no change in magnetic flux in the material.
$\vec{B} = 0$
$\vec{B} = 0$

The Meissner Effect

Another aspect of the magnetic behavior of superconductors appears if we place a homogeneous sphere of a superconducting material in a uniform applied magnetic field $\vec{B}_0$ at a temperature T greater than T_c. The material is then in the normal phase, not the superconducting phase. The field is as shown in Figure 29.25a. Now we lower the temperature until the superconducting transition occurs. (We assume that the magnitude of $\vec{B}_0$ is not large enough to prevent the phase transition.) What happens to the field?

Measurements of the field outside the sphere show that the field lines become distorted as in Fig. 29.25b. There is no longer any field inside the material, except possibly in a very thin surface layer a hundred or so atoms thick. If a coil is wrapped around the sphere, the emf induced in the coil shows that during the superconducting transition the magnetic flux through the coil decreases from its initial value to zero; this is consistent with the absence of field inside the material. Finally, if the field is now turned off while the material is still in its superconducting phase, no emf is induced in the coil, and measurements show no field outside the sphere (Fig. 29.25c).

We conclude that during a superconducting transition in the presence of the field $\vec{B}_0$, all of the magnetic flux is expelled from the bulk of the sphere, and the magnetic flux Φ_B through the coil becomes zero. This expulsion of magnetic flux is called the *Meissner effect.* As shown in Fig. 29.25b, this expulsion crowds the magnetic field lines closer together to the side of the sphere, increasing $\vec{B}$ there.

Superconductor Levitation and Other Applications

29.26 A superconductor (the black slab) exerts a repulsive force on a magnet (the metallic cylinder), supporting the magnet in midair.

The diamagnetic nature of a superconductor has some interesting *mechanical* consequences. A paramagnetic or ferromagnetic material is attracted by a permanent magnet because the magnetic dipoles in the material align with the nonuniform magnetic field of the permanent magnet. (We discussed this in Section 27.7.) For a diamagnetic material the magnetization is in the opposite sense, and a diamagnetic material is *repelled* by a permanent magnet. By Newton's third law the magnet is also repelled by the diamagnetic material. Figure 29.26 shows the repulsion between a specimen of a high-temperature superconductor and a magnet; the magnet is supported ("levitated") by this repulsive magnetic force.

The behavior we have described is characteristic of what are called *type-I superconductors.* There is another class of superconducting materials called *type-II superconductors.* When such a material in the superconducting phase is placed in a magnetic field, the bulk of the material remains superconducting, but thin filaments of material, running parallel to the field, may return to the normal phase. Currents circulate around the boundaries of these filaments, and there *is* magnetic flux inside them. Type-II superconductors are used for electromagnets because they usually have much larger values of B_c than do type-I materials, permitting much larger magnetic fields without destroying the superconducting state. Type-II superconductors have *two* critical magnetic fields: the first, B_{c1}, is the field at which magnetic flux begins to enter the material, forming the filaments just described, and the second, B_{c2}, is the field at which the material becomes normal.

Many important and exciting applications of superconductors are under development. Superconducting electromagnets have been used in research laboratories for several years. Their advantages compared to conventional electromagnets include greater efficiency, compactness, and greater field magnitudes. Once a current is established in the coil of a superconducting electromagnet, no additional power input is required because there is no resistive energy loss. The coils can also be made more compact because there is no need to provide channels for the circulation of cooling fluids. Superconducting magnets routinely attain steady fields of the order of 10 T, much larger than the maximum fields that are available with ordinary electromagnets.

Superconductors are attractive for long-distance electric power transmission and for energy-conversion devices, including generators, motors, and transformers. Very sensitive measurements of magnetic fields can be made with superconducting quantum interference devices (SQUIDs), which can detect changes in magnetic flux of less than 10^{-14} Wb; these devices have applications in medicine, geology, and other fields. The number of potential uses for superconductors has increased greatly since the discovery in 1987 of high-temperature superconductors. These materials have critical temperatures that are above the temperature of liquid nitrogen (about 77 K) and so are comparatively easy to attain. Development of practical applications of superconductor science promises to be an exciting chapter in contemporary technology.

CHAPTER 29 SUMMARY

Faraday's law: Faraday's law states that the induced emf in a closed loop equals the negative of the time rate of change of magnetic flux through the loop. This relationship is valid whether the flux change is caused by a changing magnetic field, motion of the loop, or both. (See Examples 29.1–29.7.)

$$\mathcal{E} = -\frac{d\Phi_B}{dt} \quad (29.3)$$

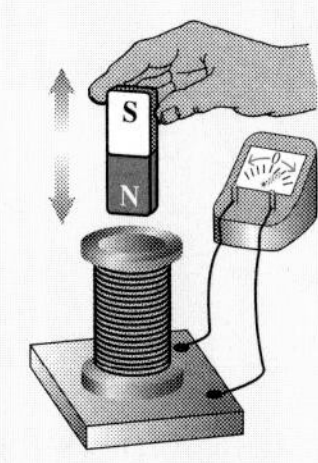

The magnet's motion causes a *changing* magnetic field through the coil, inducing a current in the coil.

Lenz's law: Lenz's law states that an induced current or emf always tends to oppose or cancel out the change that caused it. Lenz's law can be derived from Faraday's law and is often easier to use. (See Examples 29.8 and 29.9.)

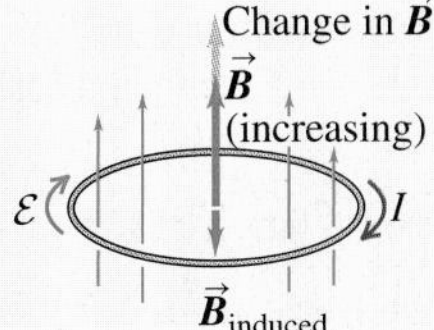

Motional emf: If a conductor moves in a magnetic field, a motional emf is induced. (See Examples 29.10 and 29.11.)

$$\mathcal{E} = vBL \quad (29.6)$$

(conductor with length L moves in uniform $\vec{B}$ field, $\vec{L}$ and $\vec{v}$ both perpendicular to $\vec{B}$ and to each other)

$$\mathcal{E} = \oint (\vec{v} \times \vec{B}) \cdot d\vec{l} \quad (29.7)$$

(all or part of a closed loop moves in a $\vec{B}$ field)

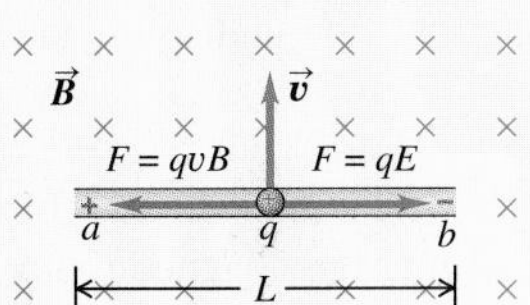

Induced electric fields: When an emf is induced by a changing magnetic flux through a stationary conductor, there is an induced electric field $\vec{E}$ of nonelectrostatic origin. This field is nonconservative and cannot be associated with a potential. (See Example 29.12.)

$$\oint \vec{E} \cdot d\vec{l} = -\frac{d\Phi_B}{dt} \quad (29.10)$$

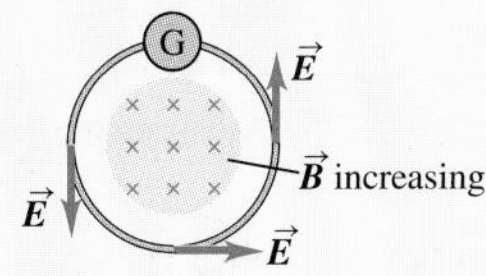

Displacement current and Maxwell's equations: A time-varying electric field generates a displacement current i_D, which acts as a source of magnetic field in exactly the same way as conduction current. The relationships between electric and magnetic fields and their sources can be stated compactly in four equations, called Maxwell's equations. Together they form a complete basis for the relationship of $\vec{E}$ and $\vec{B}$ fields to their sources.

$$i_D = \epsilon \frac{d\Phi_E}{dt} \quad (29.14)$$

(displacement current)

$$\oint \vec{E} \cdot d\vec{A} = \frac{Q_{\text{encl}}}{\epsilon_0} \quad (29.18)$$

(Gauss's law for $\vec{E}$ fields)

$$\oint \vec{B} \cdot d\vec{A} = 0 \quad (29.19)$$

(Gauss's law for $\vec{B}$ fields)

$$\oint \vec{B} \cdot d\vec{l} = \mu_0 \left(i_C + \epsilon_0 \frac{d\Phi_E}{dt} \right)_{\text{encl}} \quad (29.20)$$

(Ampere's law including displacement current)

$$\oint \vec{E} \cdot d\vec{l} = -\frac{d\Phi_B}{dt} \quad (29.21)$$

(Faraday's law)

Key Terms

induced current, *994*
induced emf, *994*
Faraday's law of induction, *996*
Lenz's law, *1004*
motional electromotive force, *1006*
induced electric field, *1009*
nonelectrostatic field, *1010*
eddy currents, *1011*
displacement current, *1013*
Maxwell's equations, *1015*

Answer to Chapter Opening Question ?

As the magnetic stripe moves through the card reader, the coded pattern of magnetization in the stripe causes a varying magnetic flux and hence an induced current in the reader's circuits. If the card does not move, there is no induced emf or current and none of the credit card's information is read.

Answers to Test Your Understanding Questions

29.2 **Answers: (a) (i), (b) (iii)** (a) Initially there is magnetic flux into the plane of the page, which we call positive. While the loop is being squeezed, the flux is becoming less positive ($d\Phi_B/dt < 0$) and so the induced emf is positive as in Fig. 29.6b ($\mathcal{E} = -d\Phi_B/dt > 0$). If you point the thumb of your right hand into the page, your fingers curl clockwise, so this is the direction of positive induced emf. (b) Since the coil's shape is no longer changing, the magnetic flux is not changing and there is no induced emf.

29.3 **Answers: (a) (i), (b) (iii)** In (a), as in the original situation, the magnet and loop are approaching each other and the downward flux through the loop is increasing. Hence the induced emf and induced current are the same. In (b), since the magnet and loop are moving together, the flux through the loop is not changing and no emf is induced.

29.4 **Answers: (a) (iii); (b) (i) or (ii); (c) (ii) or (iii)** You will get the maximum motional emf if you hold the rod vertically, so that its length is perpendicular to both the magnetic field and the direction of motion. With this orientation, $\vec{L}$ is parallel to $\vec{v} \times \vec{B}$. If you hold the rod in any horizontal orientation, $\vec{L}$ will be perpendicular to $\vec{v} \times \vec{B}$ and no emf will be induced. If you walk due north or south, $\vec{v} \times \vec{B} = \mathbf{0}$ and no emf will be induced for any orientation of the rod.

29.5 **Answers: yes, no** The magnetic field at a fixed position changes as you move the magnet. Such induced electric fields are *not* conservative.

29.6 **Answer: (iii)** By Lenz's law, the force must oppose the motion of the disk through the magnetic field. Since the disk material is now moving to the right through the field region, the force $\vec{F}$ is to the left—that is, in the opposite direction to that shown in Fig. 29.19b. To produce a leftward magnetic force $\vec{F} = I\vec{L} \times \vec{B}$ on currents moving through a magnetic field $\vec{B}$ directed out of the plane of the figure, the eddy currents must be moving downward in the figure—that is, in the same direction shown in Fig. 29.19b.

29.7 **Answers: (a) Faraday's law, (b) Ampere's law** A credit card reader works by inducing currents in the reader's coils as the card's magnetized stripe is swiped (see the answer to the chapter opening question). Ampere's law describes how currents of all kinds (both conduction currents and displacement currents) give rise to magnetic fields.

PROBLEMS

For instructor-assigned homework, go to www.masteringphysics.com 

Discussion Questions

Q29.1. A sheet of copper is placed between the poles of an electromagnet with the magnetic field perpendicular to the sheet. When the sheet is pulled out, a considerable force is required, and the force required increases with speed. Explain.

Q29.2. In Fig. 29.8, if the angular speed ω of the loop is doubled, then the frequency with which the induced current changes direction doubles, and the maximum emf also doubles. Why? Does the torque required to turn the loop change? Explain.

Q29.3. Two circular loops lie side by side in the same plane. One is connected to a source that supplies an increasing current; the other is a simple closed ring. Is the induced current in the ring in the same direction as the current in the loop connected to the source, or opposite? What if the current in the first loop is decreasing? Explain.

Q29.4. A farmer claimed that the high-voltage transmission lines running parallel to his fence induced dangerously high voltages on the fence. Is this within the realm of possibility? Explain. (The lines carry alternating current that changes direction 120 times each second.)

Q29.5. A long, straight conductor passes through the center of a metal ring, perpendicular to its plane. If the current in the conductor increases, is a current induced in the ring? Explain.

Q29.6. A student asserted that if a permanent magnet is dropped down a vertical copper pipe, it eventually reaches a terminal velocity even if there is no air resistance. Why should this be? Or should it?

Q29.7. An airplane is in level flight over Antarctica, where the magnetic field of the earth is mostly directed upward away from the ground. As viewed by a passenger facing toward the front of the plane, is the left or the right wingtip at higher potential? Does your answer depend on the direction the plane is flying?

Q29.8. Consider the situation in Exercise 29.19. In part (a), find the direction of the force that the large circuit exerts on the small one. Explain how this result is consistent with Lenz's law.

Q29.9. A metal rectangle is close to a long, straight, current-carrying wire, with two of its sides parallel to the wire. If the current in the long wire is decreasing, is the rectangle repelled by or attracted to the wire? Explain why this result is consistent with Lenz's law.

Q29.10. A square conducting loop is in a region of uniform, constant magnetic field. Can the loop be rotated about an axis along one side and no emf be induced in the loop? Discuss, in terms of the orientation of the rotation axis relative to the magnetic-field direction.

Q29.11. Example 29.7 discusses the external force that must be applied to the slidewire to move it at constant speed. If there were a break in the left-hand end of the U-shaped conductor, how much force would be needed to move the slidewire at constant speed? As in the example, you can ignore friction.

Q29.12. In the situation shown in Fig. 29.16, would it be appropriate to ask how much *energy* an electron gains during a complete trip around the wire loop with current I'? Would it be appropriate to ask what *potential difference* the electron moves through during such a complete trip? Explain your answers.

Q29.13. A metal ring is oriented with the plane of its area perpendicular to a spatially uniform magnetic field that increases at a steady rate. If the radius of the ring is doubled, by what factor do (a) the emf induced in the ring and (b) the electric field induced in the ring change?

Q29.14. For Eq. (29.6), show that if v is in meters per second, B in teslas, and L in meters, then the units of the right-hand side of the equation are joules per coulomb or volts (the correct SI units for $\mathcal{E}$).

Q29.15. Can one have a displacement current as well as a conduction current within a conductor? Explain.

Q29.16. Your physics study partner asks you to consider a parallel-plate capacitor that has a dielectric completely filling the volume between the plates. He then claims that Eqs. (29.13) and (29.14) show that the conduction current in the dielectric equals the displacement current in the dielectric. Do you agree? Explain.

Q29.17. Match the mathematical statements of Maxwell's equations as given in Section 29.7 to these verbal statements. (a) Closed electric field lines are evidently produced only by changing magnetic flux. (b) Closed magnetic field lines are produced both by the motion of electric charge and by changing electric flux. (c) Electric field lines can start on positive charges and end on negative charges. (d) Evidently there are no magnetic monopoles on which to start and end magnetic field lines.

Q29.18. If magnetic monopoles existed, the right-hand side of Eq. (29.21) would include a term proportional to the current of magnetic monopoles. Suppose a steady monopole current is moving in a long straight wire. Sketch the *electric* field lines that such a current would produce.

Q29.19. If magnetic monopoles existed, the right-hand side of Eq. (29.19) would be proportional to the total enclosed *magnetic* charge. Suppose an infinite line of magnetic monopoles were on the x-axis. Sketch the magnetic field lines that this line of monopoles would produce.

Exercises

Section 29.2 Faraday's Law

29.1. A flat, rectangular coil consisting of 50 turns measures 25.0 cm by 30.0 cm. It is in a uniform, 1.20-T, magnetic field, with the plane of the coil parallel to the field. In 0.222 s, it is rotated so that the plane of the coil is perpendicular to the field. (a) What is the change in the magnetic flux through the coil due to this rotation? (b) Find the magnitude of the average emf induced in the coil during this rotation.

29.2. In a physics laboratory experiment, a coil with 200 turns enclosing an area of 12 cm^2 is rotated in 0.040 s from a position where its plane is perpendicular to the earth's magnetic field to a position where its plane is parallel to the field. The earth's magnetic field at the lab location is 6.0×10^{-5} T. (a) What is the total magnetic flux through the coil before it is rotated? After it is rotated? b) What is the average emf induced in the coil?

29.3. Search Coils and Credit Cards. (a) Derive the equation relating the total charge Q that flows through a search coil (Conceptual Example 29.3) to the magnetic-field magnitude B. The search coil has N turns, each with area A, and the flux through the coil is decreased from its initial maximum value to zero in a time Δt. The resistance of the coil is R, and the total charge is $Q = I\Delta t$, where I is the average current induced by the change in flux. (b) In a credit card reader, the magnetic strip on the back of a credit card is rapidly "swiped" past a coil within the reader. Explain, using the same ideas that underlie the operation of a search coil, how the reader can decode the information stored in the pattern of magnetization on the strip. (c) Is it necessary that the credit card be "swiped" through the reader at exactly the right speed? Why or why not?

29.4. A closely wound search coil (Exercise 29.3) has an area of 3.20 cm^2, 120 turns, and a resistance of 60.0 Ω. It is connected to a charge-measuring instrument whose resistance is 45.0 Ω. When the coil is rotated quickly from a position parallel to a uniform magnetic field to a position perpendicular to the field, the instrument indicates a charge of 3.56×10^{-5} C. What is the magnitude of the field?

29.5. A circular loop of wire with a radius of 12.0 cm and oriented in the horizontal xy-plane is located in a region of uniform magnetic field. A field of 1.5 T is directed along the positive z-direction, which is upward. (a) If the loop is removed from the field region in a time interval of 2.0 ms, find the average emf that will be induced in the wire loop during the extraction process. (b) If the coil is viewed looking down on it from above, is the induced current in the loop clockwise or counterclockwise?

29.6. A coil 4.00 cm in radius, containing 500 turns, is placed in a uniform magnetic field that varies with time according to $B = (0.0120\ \text{T/s})t + (3.00 \times 10^{-5}\ \text{T/s}^4)t^4$. The coil is connected to a 600-Ω resistor, and its plane is perpendicular to the magnetic field. You can ignore the resistance of the coil. (a) Find the magnitude of the induced emf in the coil as a function of time. (b) What is the current in the resistor at time $t = 5.00$ s?

29.7. The current in the long, straight wire AB shown in Fig. 29.27 is upward and is increasing steadily at a rate di/dt. (a) At an instant when the current is i, what are the magnitude and direction of the field $\vec{B}$ at a distance r to the right of the wire? (b) What is the flux $d\Phi_B$ through the narrow, shaded strip? (c) What is the total flux through the loop? (d) What is the induced emf in the loop? (e) Evaluate the numerical value of the induced emf if $a = 12.0$ cm, $b = 36.0$ cm, $L = 24.0$ cm, and $di/dt = 9.60$ A/s.

Figure 29.27 Exercise 29.7.

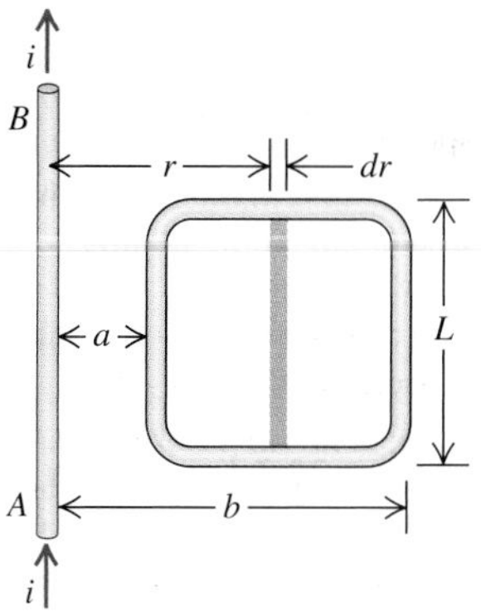

29.8. A flat, circular, steel loop of radius 75 cm is at rest in a uniform magnetic field, as shown in an edge-on view in Fig. 29.28. The field is changing with time, according to $B(t) = (1.4\ \text{T})e^{-(0.057\ \text{s}^{-1})t}$. (a) Find the emf induced in the loop as a function of time. (b) When is the induced emf equal to $\frac{1}{10}$ of its initial value? (c) Find the direction of the current induced in the loop, as viewed from above the loop.

Figure 29.28 Exercise 29.8.

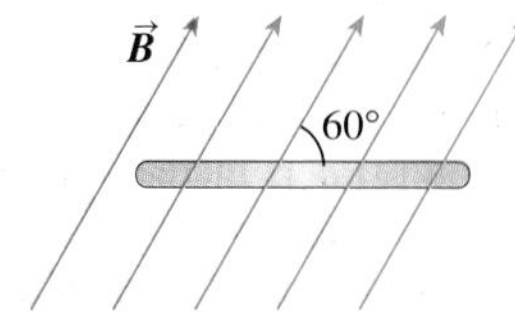

29.9. Shrinking Loop. A circular loop of flexible iron wire has an initial circumference of 165.0 cm, but its circumference is decreasing at a constant rate of 12.0 cm/s due to a tangential pull on the wire. The loop is in a constant, uniform magnetic field

di/dt. The induced electric field at a point near the center of the solenoid and 3.50 cm from its axis is 8.00×10^{-6} V/m. Calculate di/dt.

29.32. A metal ring 4.50 cm in diameter is placed between the north and south poles of large magnets with the plane of its area perpendicular to the magnetic field. These magnets produce an initial uniform field of 1.12 T between them but are gradually pulled apart, causing this field to remain uniform but decrease steadily at 0.250 T/s. (a) What is the magnitude of the electric field induced in the ring? (b) In which direction (clockwise or counterclockwise) does the current flow as viewed by someone on the south pole of the magnet?

29.33. A long, straight solenoid with a cross-sectional area of 8.00 cm^2 is wound with 90 turns of wire per centimeter, and the windings carry a current of 0.350 A. A second winding of 12 turns encircles the solenoid at its center. The current in the solenoid is turned off such that the magnetic field of the solenoid becomes zero in 0.0400 s. What is the average induced emf in the second winding?

Section 29.7 Displacement Current and Maxwell's Equations

29.34. A dielectric of permittivity 3.5×10^{-11} F/m completely fills the volume between two capacitor plates. For $t > 0$ the electric flux through the dielectric is $(8.0 \times 10^3\ \text{V} \cdot \text{m/s}^3)t^3$. The dielectric is ideal and nonmagnetic; the conduction current in the dielectric is zero. At what time does the displacement current in the dielectric equal 21 μA?

29.35. The electric flux through a certain area of a dielectric is $(8.76 \times 10^3\ \text{V} \cdot \text{m/s}^4)t^4$. The displacement current through that area is 12.9 pA at time $t = 26.1$ ms. Calculate the dielectric constant for the dielectric.

29.36. A parallel-plate, air-filled capacitor is being charged as in Fig. 29.23. The circular plates have radius 4.00 cm, and at a particular instant the conduction current in the wires is 0.280 A. (a) What is the displacement current density j_D in the air space between the plates? (b) What is the rate at which the electric field between the plates is changing? (c) What is the induced magnetic field between the plates at a distance of 2.00 cm from the axis? (d) At 1.00 cm from the axis?

29.37. Displacement Current in a Dielectric. Suppose that the parallel plates in Fig. 29.23 have an area of 3.00 cm^2 and are separated by a 2.50-mm-thick sheet of dielectric that completely fills the volume between the plates. The dielectric has dielectric constant 4.70. (You can ignore fringing effects.) At a certain instant, the potential difference between the plates is 120 V and the conduction current i_C equals 6.00 mA. At this instant, what are (a) the charge q on each plate; (b) the rate of change of charge on the plates; (c) the displacement current in the dielectric?

29.38. In Fig. 29.23 the capacitor plates have area 5.00 cm^2 and separation 2.00 mm. The plates are in vacuum. The charging current i_C has a *constant* value of 1.80 mA. At $t = 0$ the charge on the plates is zero. (a) Calculate the charge on the plates, the electric field between the plates, and the potential difference between the plates when $t = 0.500\ \mu$s. (b) Calculate dE/dt, the time rate of change of the electric field between the plates. Does dE/dt vary in time? (c) Calculate the displacement current density j_D between the plates, and from this the total displacement current i_D. How do i_C and i_D compare?

29.39. Displacement Current in a Wire. A long, straight, copper wire with a circular cross-sectional area of 2.1 mm^2 carries a current of 16 A. The resistivity of the material is $2.0 \times 10^{-8}\ \Omega \cdot$ m. (a) What is the uniform electric field in the material? (b) If the current is changing at the rate of 4000 A/s, at what rate is the electric field in the material changing? (c) What is the displacement current density in the material in part (b)? (*Hint:* Since K for copper is very close to 1, use $\epsilon = \epsilon_0$.) (d) If the current is changing as in part (b), what is the magnitude of the magnetic field 6.0 cm from the center of the wire? Note that both the conduction current and the displacement current should be included in the calculation of B. Is the contribution from the displacement current significant?

*Section 29.8 Superconductivity

***29.40.** A long, straight wire made of a type-I superconductor carries a constant current I along its length. Show that the current cannot be uniformly spread over the wire's cross section but instead must all be at the surface.

***29.41.** A type-II superconductor in an external field between B_{c1} and B_{c2} has regions that contain magnetic flux and have resistance, and also has superconducting regions. What is the resistance of a long, thin cylinder of such material?

***29.42.** At temperatures near absolute zero, B_c approaches 0.142 T for vanadium, a type-I superconductor. The normal phase of vanadium has a magnetic susceptibility close to zero. Consider a long, thin vanadium cylinder with its axis parallel to an external magnetic field $\vec{B}_0$ in the $+x$-direction. At points far from the ends of the cylinder, by symmetry, all the magnetic vectors are parallel to the x-axis. At temperatures near absolute zero, what are the resultant magnetic field $\vec{B}$ and the magnetization $\vec{M}$ inside and outside the cylinder (far from the ends) for (a) $\vec{B}_0 = (0.130\ \text{T})\hat{\imath}$ and (b) $\vec{B}_0 = (0.260\ \text{T})\hat{\imath}$?

***29.43.** The compound SiV_3 is a type-II superconductor. At temperatures near absolute zero the two critical fields are $B_{c1} =$ 55.0 mT and $B_{c2} = 15.0$ T. The normal phase of SiV_3 has a magnetic susceptibility close to zero. A long, thin SiV_3 cylinder has its axis parallel to an external magnetic field $\vec{B}_0$ in the $+x$-direction. At points far from the ends of the cylinder, by symmetry, all the magnetic vectors are parallel to the x-axis. At a temperature near absolute zero the external magnetic field is slowly increased from zero. What are the resultant magnetic field $\vec{B}$ and the magnetization $\vec{M}$ inside the cylinder at points far from its ends (a) just before the magnetic flux begins to penetrate the material, and (b) just after the material becomes completely normal?

Problems

29.44. A Changing Magnetic Field. You are testing a new data-acquisition system. This system allows you to record a graph of the current in a circuit as a function of time. As part of the test, you are using a circuit made up of a 4.00-cm-radius, 500-turn coil of copper wire connected in series to a 600-Ω resistor. Copper has resistivity $1.72 \times 10^{-8}\ \Omega \cdot$ m, and the wire used for the coil has diameter 0.0300 mm. You place the coil on a table that is tilted 30.0° from the horizontal and that lies between the poles of an electromagnet. The electromagnet generates a vertically upward magnetic field that is zero for $t < 0$, equal to $(0.120\ \text{T}) \times (1 - \cos \pi t)$ for $0 \leq t \leq 1.00$ s, and equal to 0.240 T for $t > 1.00$ s. (a) Draw the graph that should be produced by your data-acquisition system. (This is a full-featured system, so the graph will include labels and numerical values on its axes.) (b) If you were looking vertically downward at the coil, would the current be flowing clockwise or counterclockwise?

a break in the left-hand end of the U-shaped conductor, how much force would be needed to move the slidewire at constant speed? As in the example, you can ignore friction.

Q29.12. In the situation shown in Fig. 29.16, would it be appropriate to ask how much *energy* an electron gains during a complete trip around the wire loop with current I'? Would it be appropriate to ask what *potential difference* the electron moves through during such a complete trip? Explain your answers.

Q29.13. A metal ring is oriented with the plane of its area perpendicular to a spatially uniform magnetic field that increases at a steady rate. If the radius of the ring is doubled, by what factor do (a) the emf induced in the ring and (b) the electric field induced in the ring change?

Q29.14. For Eq. (29.6), show that if v is in meters per second, B in teslas, and L in meters, then the units of the right-hand side of the equation are joules per coulomb or volts (the correct SI units for $\mathcal{E}$).

Q29.15. Can one have a displacement current as well as a conduction current within a conductor? Explain.

Q29.16. Your physics study partner asks you to consider a parallel-plate capacitor that has a dielectric completely filling the volume between the plates. He then claims that Eqs. (29.13) and (29.14) show that the conduction current in the dielectric equals the displacement current in the dielectric. Do you agree? Explain.

Q29.17. Match the mathematical statements of Maxwell's equations as given in Section 29.7 to these verbal statements. (a) Closed electric field lines are evidently produced only by changing magnetic flux. (b) Closed magnetic field lines are produced both by the motion of electric charge and by changing electric flux. (c) Electric field lines can start on positive charges and end on negative charges. (d) Evidently there are no magnetic monopoles on which to start and end magnetic field lines.

Q29.18. If magnetic monopoles existed, the right-hand side of Eq. (29.21) would include a term proportional to the current of magnetic monopoles. Suppose a steady monopole current is moving in a long straight wire. Sketch the *electric* field lines that such a current would produce.

Q29.19. If magnetic monopoles existed, the right-hand side of Eq. (29.19) would be proportional to the total enclosed *magnetic* charge. Suppose an infinite line of magnetic monopoles were on the x-axis. Sketch the magnetic field lines that this line of monopoles would produce.

Exercises

Section 29.2 Faraday's Law

29.1. A flat, rectangular coil consisting of 50 turns measures 25.0 cm by 30.0 cm. It is in a uniform, 1.20-T, magnetic field, with the plane of the coil parallel to the field. In 0.222 s, it is rotated so that the plane of the coil is perpendicular to the field. (a) What is the change in the magnetic flux through the coil due to this rotation? (b) Find the magnitude of the average emf induced in the coil during this rotation.

29.2. In a physics laboratory experiment, a coil with 200 turns enclosing an area of 12 cm^2 is rotated in 0.040 s from a position where its plane is perpendicular to the earth's magnetic field to a position where its plane is parallel to the field. The earth's magnetic field at the lab location is 6.0×10^{-5} T. (a) What is the total magnetic flux through the coil before it is rotated? After it is rotated? b) What is the average emf induced in the coil?

29.3. Search Coils and Credit Cards. (a) Derive the equation relating the total charge Q that flows through a search coil (Conceptual Example 29.3) to the magnetic-field magnitude B. The search coil has N turns, each with area A, and the flux through the coil is decreased from its initial maximum value to zero in a time Δt. The resistance of the coil is R, and the total charge is $Q = I\Delta t$, where I is the average current induced by the change in flux. (b) In a credit card reader, the magnetic strip on the back of a credit card is rapidly "swiped" past a coil within the reader. Explain, using the same ideas that underlie the operation of a search coil, how the reader can decode the information stored in the pattern of magnetization on the strip. (c) Is it necessary that the credit card be "swiped" through the reader at exactly the right speed? Why or why not?

29.4. A closely wound search coil (Exercise 29.3) has an area of 3.20 cm^2, 120 turns, and a resistance of 60.0 Ω. It is connected to a charge-measuring instrument whose resistance is 45.0 Ω. When the coil is rotated quickly from a position parallel to a uniform magnetic field to a position perpendicular to the field, the instrument indicates a charge of 3.56×10^{-5} C. What is the magnitude of the field?

29.5. A circular loop of wire with a radius of 12.0 cm and oriented in the horizontal xy-plane is located in a region of uniform magnetic field. A field of 1.5 T is directed along the positive z-direction, which is upward. (a) If the loop is removed from the field region in a time interval of 2.0 ms, find the average emf that will be induced in the wire loop during the extraction process. (b) If the coil is viewed looking down on it from above, is the induced current in the loop clockwise or counterclockwise?

29.6. A coil 4.00 cm in radius, containing 500 turns, is placed in a uniform magnetic field that varies with time according to $B = (0.0120\ \text{T/s})t + (3.00 \times 10^{-5}\ \text{T/s}^4)t^4$. The coil is connected to a 600-Ω resistor, and its plane is perpendicular to the magnetic field. You can ignore the resistance of the coil. (a) Find the magnitude of the induced emf in the coil as a function of time. (b) What is the current in the resistor at time $t = 5.00$ s?

29.7. The current in the long, straight wire AB shown in Fig. 29.27 is upward and is increasing steadily at a rate di/dt. (a) At an instant when the current is i, what are the magnitude and direction of the field $\vec{B}$ at a distance r to the right of the wire? (b) What is the flux $d\Phi_B$ through the narrow, shaded strip? (c) What is the total flux through the loop? (d) What is the induced emf in the loop? (e) Evaluate the numerical value of the induced emf if $a = 12.0$ cm, $b = 36.0$ cm, $L = 24.0$ cm, and $di/dt = 9.60$ A/s.

Figure 29.27 Exercise 29.7.

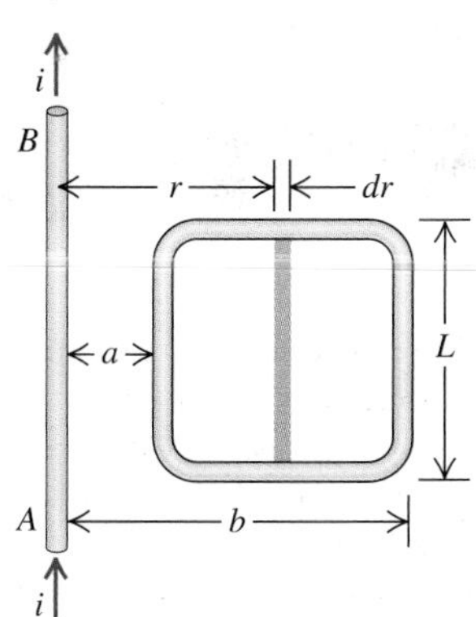

29.8. A flat, circular, steel loop of radius 75 cm is at rest in a uniform magnetic field, as shown in an edge-on view in Fig. 29.28. The field is changing with time, according to $B(t) = (1.4\ \text{T})e^{-(0.057\ \text{s}^{-1})t}$. (a) Find the emf induced in the loop as a function of time. (b) When is the induced emf equal to $\frac{1}{10}$ of its initial value? (c) Find the direction of the current induced in the loop, as viewed from above the loop.

Figure 29.28 Exercise 29.8.

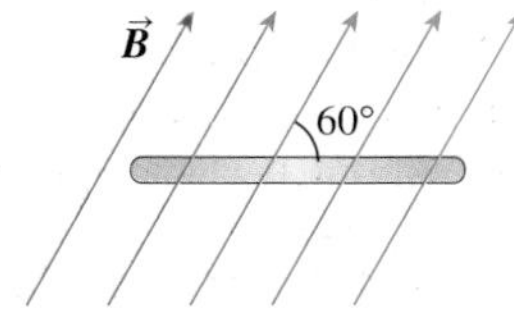

29.9. Shrinking Loop. A circular loop of flexible iron wire has an initial circumference of 165.0 cm, but its circumference is decreasing at a constant rate of 12.0 cm/s due to a tangential pull on the wire. The loop is in a constant, uniform magnetic field oriented perpendicular to the plane of the loop and with magnitude 0.500 T. (a) Find the emf induced in the loop at the instant when 9.0 s have passed. (b) Find the direction of the induced current in the loop as viewed looking along the direction of the magnetic field.

29.10. A rectangle measuring 30.0 cm by 40.0 cm is located inside a region of a spatially uniform magnetic field of 1.25 T, with the field perpendicular to the plane of the coil (Fig. 29.29). The coil is pulled out at a steady rate of 2.00 cm/s traveling perpendicular to the field lines. The region of the field ends abruptly as shown. Find the emf induced in this coil when it is (a) all inside the field; (b) partly inside the field; (c) all outside the field.

Figure **29.29** Exercise 29.10.

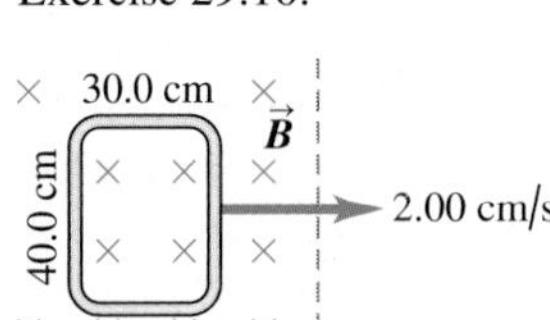

29.11. In a region of space, a magnetic field points in the $+x$-direction (toward the right). Its magnitude varies with position according to the formula $B_x = B_0 + bx$, where B_0 and b are positive constants, for $x \geq 0$. A flat coil of area A moves with uniform speed v from right to left with the plane of its area always perpendicular to this field. (a) What is the emf induced in this coil while it is to the right of the origin? (b) As viewed from the origin, what is the direction (clockwise or counterclockwise) of the current induced in the coil? (c) If instead the coil moved from left to right, what would be the answers to parts (a) and (b)?

29.12. Back emf. A motor with a brush-and-commutator arrangement, as described in Example 29.5, has a circular coil with radius 2.5 cm and 150 turns of wire. The magnetic field has magnitude 0.060 T, and the coil rotates at 440 rev/min. (a) What is the maximum emf induced in the coil? (b) What is the average back emf?

29.13. The armature of a small generator consists of a flat, square coil with 120 turns and sides with a length of 1.60 cm. The coil rotates in a magnetic field of 0.0750 T. What is the angular speed of the coil if the maximum emf produced is 24.0 mV?

29.14. A flat, rectangular coil of dimensions l and w is pulled with uniform speed v through a uniform magnetic field B with the plane of its area perpendicular to the field (Fig. 29.30). (a) Find the emf induced in this coil. (b) If the speed and magnetic field are both tripled, what is the induced emf?

Figure **29.30** Exercise 29.14.

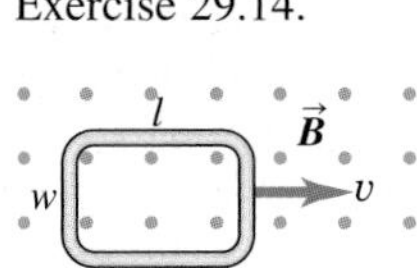

Section 29.3 Lenz's Law

29.15. A circular loop of wire is in a region of spatially uniform magnetic field, as shown in Fig. 29.31. The magnetic field is directed into the plane of the figure. Determine the direction (clockwise or counterclockwise) of the induced current in the loop when (a) B is increasing; (b) B is decreasing; (c) B is constant with value B_0. Explain your reasoning.

Figure **29.31** Exercise 29.15 and 29.30.

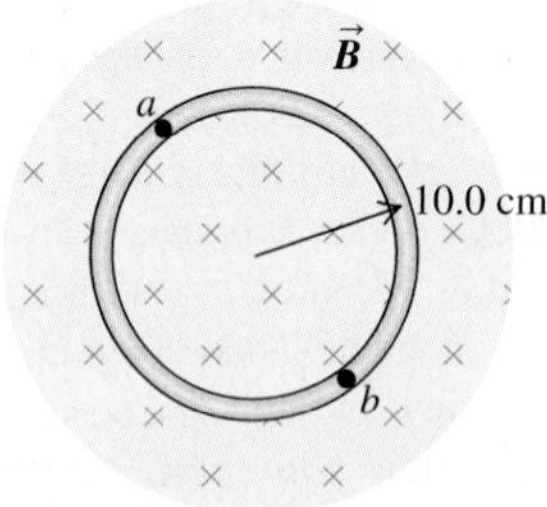

29.16. The current in Fig. 29.32 obeys the equation $I(t) = I_0e^{-bt}$, where $b > 0$. Find the direction (clockwise or counterclockwise) of the current induced in the round coil for $t > 0$.

Figure **29.32** Exercise 29.16.

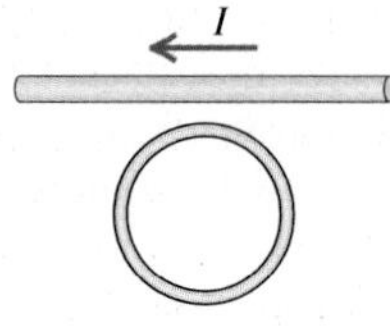

29.17. Using Lenz's law, determine the direction of the current in resistor ab of

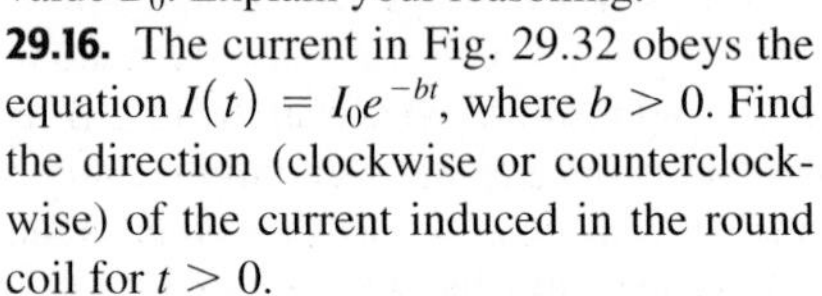

Fig. 29.33 when (a) switch S is opened after having been closed for several minutes; (b) coil B is brought closer to coil A with the switch closed; (c) the resistance of R is decreased while the switch remains closed.

Figure **29.33** Exercise 29.17.

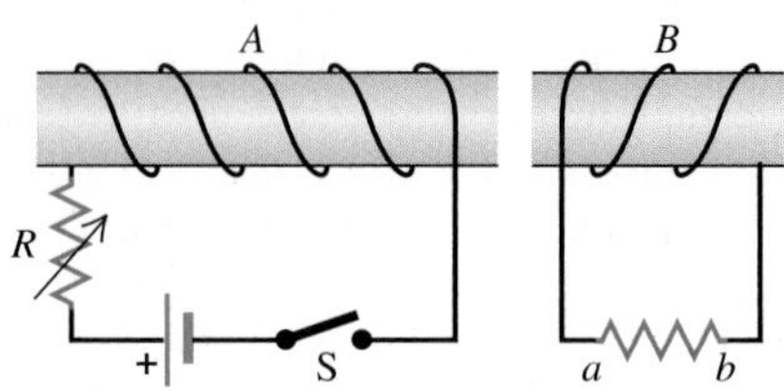

29.18. A cardboard tube is wrapped with two windings of insulated wire wound in opposite directions, as shown in Fig. 29.34. Terminals a and b of winding A may be connected to a battery through a reversing switch. State whether the induced current in the resistor R is from left to right or from right to left in the following circumstances: (a) the current in winding A is from a to b and is increasing; (b) the current in winding A is from b to a and is decreasing; (c) the current in winding A is from b to a and is increasing.

Figure **29.34** Exercise 29.18.

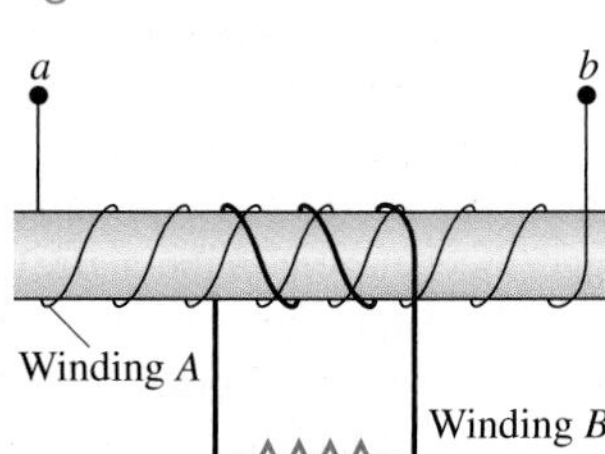

29.19. A small, circular ring is inside a larger loop that is connected to a battery and a switch, as shown in Fig. 29.35. Use Lenz's law to find the direction of the current induced in the small ring (a) just after switch S is closed; (b) after S has been closed a long time; (c) just after S has been reopened after being closed a long time.

Figure **29.35** Exercise 29.19.

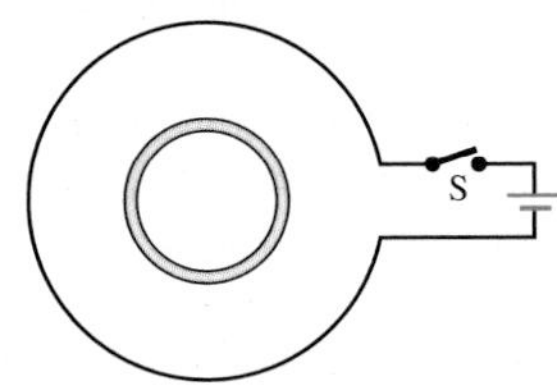

29.20. A 1.50-m-long metal bar is pulled to the right at a steady 5.0 m/s perpendicular to a uniform, 0.750-T magnetic field. The bar rides on parallel metal rails connected through a 25.0-Ω resistor, as shown in Fig. 29.36, so the apparatus makes a complete circuit. You can ignore the resistance of the bar and the rails. (a) Calculate the magnitude of the emf induced in the circuit. (b) Find the direction of the current induced in the circuit (i) using the magnetic force on the charges in the moving bar; (ii) using Faraday's law; (iii) using Lenz's law. (c) Calculate the current through the resistor.

Figure **29.36** Exercise 29.20 and Problem 29.64.

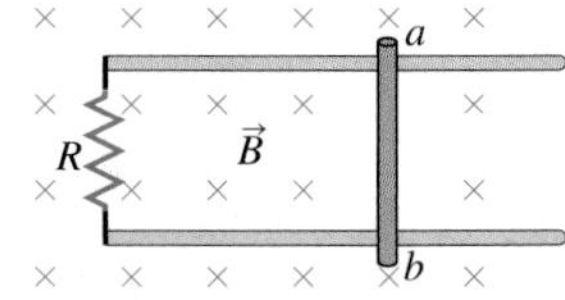

Section 29.4 Motional Electromotive Force

29.21. In Fig. 29.37 a conducting rod of length $L = 30.0$ cm moves in a magnetic field $\vec{B}$ of magnitude 0.450 T directed into the plane of the figure. The rod moves with speed $v = 5.00$ m/s in the direction

shown. (a) what is the potential difference between the ends of the rod? (b) Which point, a to b, is at higher potential? (c) When the charges in the rod are in equilibrium, what are the magnitude and direction of the electric field within the rod? (d) When the charges in the rod are in equilibrium, which point, a or b, has an excess of positive charge? (e) What is the potential difference across the rod if it moves (i) parallel to ab and (ii) directly out of the page?

Figure **29.37** Exercise 29.21.

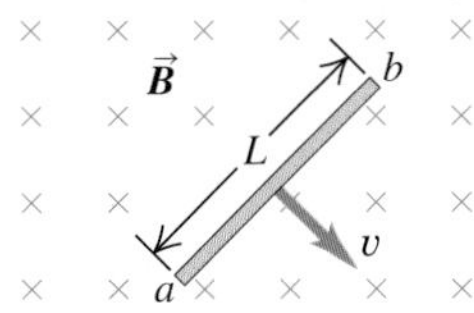

29.22. For the situation in Exercise 29.20, find (a) the motional emf in the bar and (b) the current through the resistor.

29.23. Are Motional emfs a Practical Source of Electricity? How fast (in m/s and mph) would a 5.00-cm copper bar have to move at right angles to a 0.650-T magnetic field to generate 1.50 V (the same as a AA battery) across its ends? Does this seem like a practical way to generate electricity?

29.24. Motional emfs in Transportation. Airplanes and trains move through the earth's magnetic field at rather high speeds, so it is reasonable to wonder whether this field can have a substantial effect on them. We shall use a typical value of 0.50 G for the earth's field (a) The French TGV train and the Japanese "bullet train" reach speeds of up to 180 mph moving on tracks about 1.5 m apart. At top speed moving perpendicular to the earth's magnetic field, what potential difference is induced across the tracks as the wheels roll? Does this seem large enough to produce noticeable effects? (b) The Boeing 747-400 aircraft has a wingspan of 64.4 m and a cruising speed of 565 mph. If there is no wind blowing (so that this is also their speed relative to the ground), what is the maximum potential difference that could be induced between the opposite tips of the wings? Does this seem large enough to cause problems with the plane?

29.25. The conducting rod ab shown in Fig. 29.38 makes contact with metal rails ca and db. The apparatus is in a uniform magnetic field of 0.800 T, perpendicular to the plane of the figure (a) Find the magnitude of the emf induced in the rod when it is moving toward the right with a speed 7.50 m/s. (b) In what direction does the current flow in the rod? (c) If the resistance of the circuit $abdc$ is 1.50 Ω (assumed to be constant), find the force (magnitude and direction) required to keep the rod moving to the right with a constant speed of 7.50 m/s. You can ignore friction. (d) Compare the rate at which mechanical work is done by the force (Fv) with the rate at which thermal energy is developed in the circuit $(I^2 R)$.

Figure **29.38** Exercise 29.25.

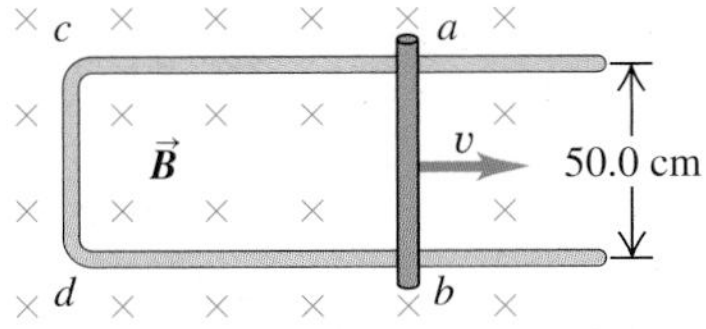

29.26. A square loop of wire with side length L and resistance R is moved at constant speed v across a uniform magnetic field confined to a square region whose sides are twice the length of those of the square loop (Fig. 29.39). (a) Graph the external force F needed to move the loop at constant speed as a function of the coordinate x from $x = -2L$ to $x = +2L$. (The coordinate x is measured from the center of the magnetic-field region to the center of the loop. It is negative when the center of the loop is to the left of the center of the magnetic-field region. Take positive force to be to the right.) (b) Graph the induced current in the loop as a function of x. Take counterclockwise currents to be positive.

Figure **29.39** Exercise 29.26.

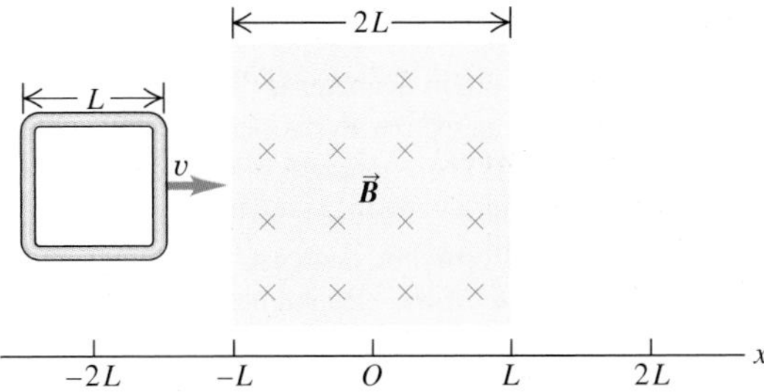

29.27. A 1.41-m bar moves through a uniform, 1.20-T magnetic field with a speed of 2.50 m/s (Fig. 29.40). In each case, find the emf induced between the ends of this bar and identify which, if any, end (a or b) is at the higher potential. The bar moves in the direction of (a) the $+x$-axis; (b) the $-y$-axis; (c) the $+z$-axis. (d) How should this bar move so that the emf across its ends has the greatest possible value with b at a higher potential than a, and what is this maximum emf?

Figure **29.40** Exercise 29.27.

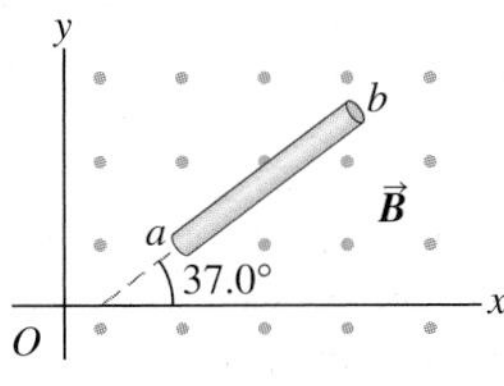

Section 29.5 Induced Electric Fields

29.28. A long, thin solenoid has 900 turns per meter and radius 2.50 cm. The current in the solenoid is increasing at a uniform rate of 60.0 A/s. What is the magnitude of the induced electric field at a point near the center of the solenoid and (a) 0.500 cm from the axis of the solenoid; (b) 1.00 cm from the axis of the solenoid?

29.29. The magnetic field within a long, straight solenoid with a circular cross section and radius R is increasing at a rate of dB/dt. (a) What is the rate of change of flux through a circle with radius r_1 inside the solenoid, normal to the axis of the solenoid, and with center on the solenoid axis? (b) Find the magnitude of the induced electric field inside the solenoid, at a distance r_1 from its axis. Show the direction of this field in a diagram. (c) What is the magnitude of the induced electric field *outside* the solenoid, at a distance r_2 from the axis? (d) Graph the magnitude of the induced electric field as a function of the distance r from the axis from $r = 0$ to $r = 2R$. (e) What is the magnitude of the induced emf in a circular turn of radius $R/2$ that has its center on the solenoid axis? (f) What is the magnitude of the induced emf if the radius in part (e) is R? (g) What is the induced emf if the radius in part (e) is $2R$?

29.30. The magnetic field $\vec{B}$ at all points within the colored circle shown in Fig. 29.31 has an initial magnitude of 0.750 T. (The circle could represent approximately the space inside a long, thin solenoid.) The magnetic field is directed into the plane of the diagram and is decreasing at the rate of −0.0350 T/s. (a) What is the shape of the field lines of the induced electric field shown in Fig. 29.31, within the colored circle? (b) What are the magnitude and direction of this field at any point on the circular conducting ring with radius 0.100 m? (c) What is the current in the ring if its resistance is 4.00 Ω? (d) What is the emf between points a and b on the ring? (e) If the ring is cut at some point and the ends are separated slightly, what will be the emf between the ends?

29.31. A long, thin solenoid has 400 turns per meter and radius 1.10 cm. The current in the solenoid is increasing at a uniform rate

di/dt. The induced electric field at a point near the center of the solenoid and 3.50 cm from its axis is 8.00×10^{-6} V/m. Calculate di/dt.

29.32. A metal ring 4.50 cm in diameter is placed between the north and south poles of large magnets with the plane of its area perpendicular to the magnetic field. These magnets produce an initial uniform field of 1.12 T between them but are gradually pulled apart, causing this field to remain uniform but decrease steadily at 0.250 T/s. (a) What is the magnitude of the electric field induced in the ring? (b) In which direction (clockwise or counterclockwise) does the current flow as viewed by someone on the south pole of the magnet?

29.33. A long, straight solenoid with a cross-sectional area of 8.00 cm^2 is wound with 90 turns of wire per centimeter, and the windings carry a current of 0.350 A. A second winding of 12 turns encircles the solenoid at its center. The current in the solenoid is turned off such that the magnetic field of the solenoid becomes zero in 0.0400 s. What is the average induced emf in the second winding?

Section 29.7 Displacement Current and Maxwell's Equations

29.34. A dielectric of permittivity 3.5×10^{-11} F/m completely fills the volume between two capacitor plates. For $t > 0$ the electric flux through the dielectric is $(8.0 \times 10^3 \text{ V} \cdot \text{m/s}^3)t^3$. The dielectric is ideal and nonmagnetic; the conduction current in the dielectric is zero. At what time does the displacement current in the dielectric equal 21 μA?

29.35. The electric flux through a certain area of a dielectric is $(8.76 \times 10^3 \text{ V} \cdot \text{m/s}^4)t^4$. The displacement current through that area is 12.9 pA at time $t = 26.1$ ms. Calculate the dielectric constant for the dielectric.

29.36. A parallel-plate, air-filled capacitor is being charged as in Fig. 29.23. The circular plates have radius 4.00 cm, and at a particular instant the conduction current in the wires is 0.280 A. (a) What is the displacement current density j_D in the air space between the plates? (b) What is the rate at which the electric field between the plates is changing? (c) What is the induced magnetic field between the plates at a distance of 2.00 cm from the axis? (d) At 1.00 cm from the axis?

29.37. Displacement Current in a Dielectric. Suppose that the parallel plates in Fig. 29.23 have an area of 3.00 cm^2 and are separated by a 2.50-mm-thick sheet of dielectric that completely fills the volume between the plates. The dielectric has dielectric constant 4.70. (You can ignore fringing effects.) At a certain instant, the potential difference between the plates is 120 V and the conduction current i_C equals 6.00 mA. At this instant, what are (a) the charge q on each plate; (b) the rate of change of charge on the plates; (c) the displacement current in the dielectric?

29.38. In Fig. 29.23 the capacitor plates have area 5.00 cm^2 and separation 2.00 mm. The plates are in vacuum. The charging current i_C has a *constant* value of 1.80 mA. At $t = 0$ the charge on the plates is zero. (a) Calculate the charge on the plates, the electric field between the plates, and the potential difference between the plates when $t = 0.500$ μs. (b) Calculate dE/dt, the time rate of change of the electric field between the plates. Does dE/dt vary in time? (c) Calculate the displacement current density j_D between the plates, and from this the total displacement current i_D. How do i_C and i_D compare?

29.39. Displacement Current in a Wire. A long, straight, copper wire with a circular cross-sectional area of 2.1 mm^2 carries a current of 16 A. The resistivity of the material is 2.0×10^{-8} $\Omega \cdot$ m. (a) What is the uniform electric field in the material? (b) If the current is changing at the rate of 4000 A/s, at what rate is the electric field in the material changing? (c) What is the displacement current density in the material in part (b)? (*Hint:* Since K for copper is very close to 1, use $\epsilon = \epsilon_0$.) (d) If the current is changing as in part (b), what is the magnitude of the magnetic field 6.0 cm from the center of the wire? Note that both the conduction current and the displacement current should be included in the calculation of B. Is the contribution from the displacement current significant?

*Section 29.8 Superconductivity

***29.40.** A long, straight wire made of a type-I superconductor carries a constant current I along its length. Show that the current cannot be uniformly spread over the wire's cross section but instead must all be at the surface.

***29.41.** A type-II superconductor in an external field between B_{c1} and B_{c2} has regions that contain magnetic flux and have resistance, and also has superconducting regions. What is the resistance of a long, thin cylinder of such material?

***29.42.** At temperatures near absolute zero, B_c approaches 0.142 T for vanadium, a type-I superconductor. The normal phase of vanadium has a magnetic susceptibility close to zero. Consider a long, thin vanadium cylinder with its axis parallel to an external magnetic field $\vec{B}_0$ in the $+x$-direction. At points far from the ends of the cylinder, by symmetry, all the magnetic vectors are parallel to the x-axis. At temperatures near absolute zero, what are the resultant magnetic field $\vec{B}$ and the magnetization $\vec{M}$ inside and outside the cylinder (far from the ends) for (a) $\vec{B}_0 = (0.130 \text{ T})\hat{\imath}$ and (b) $\vec{B}_0 = (0.260 \text{ T})\hat{\imath}$?

***29.43.** The compound SiV_3 is a type-II superconductor. At temperatures near absolute zero the two critical fields are $B_{c1} =$ 55.0 mT and $B_{c2} = 15.0$ T. The normal phase of SiV_3 has a magnetic susceptibility close to zero. A long, thin SiV_3 cylinder has its axis parallel to an external magnetic field $\vec{B}_0$ in the $+x$-direction. At points far from the ends of the cylinder, by symmetry, all the magnetic vectors are parallel to the x-axis. At a temperature near absolute zero the external magnetic field is slowly increased from zero. What are the resultant magnetic field $\vec{B}$ and the magnetization $\vec{M}$ inside the cylinder at points far from its ends (a) just before the magnetic flux begins to penetrate the material, and (b) just after the material becomes completely normal?

Problems

29.44. A Changing Magnetic Field. You are testing a new data-acquisition system. This system allows you to record a graph of the current in a circuit as a function of time. As part of the test, you are using a circuit made up of a 4.00-cm-radius, 500-turn coil of copper wire connected in series to a 600-Ω resistor. Copper has resistivity 1.72×10^{-8} $\Omega \cdot$ m, and the wire used for the coil has diameter 0.0300 mm. You place the coil on a table that is tilted 30.0° from the horizontal and that lies between the poles of an electromagnet. The electromagnet generates a vertically upward magnetic field that is zero for $t < 0$, equal to $(0.120 \text{ T}) \times (1 - \cos \pi t)$ for $0 \le t \le 1.00$ s, and equal to 0.240 T for $t > 1.00$ s. (a) Draw the graph that should be produced by your data-acquisition system. (This is a full-featured system, so the graph will include labels and numerical values on its axes.) (b) If you were looking vertically downward at the coil, would the current be flowing clockwise or counterclockwise?

29.45. In the circuit shown in Fig. 29.41 the capacitor has capacitance $C = 20\ \mu\text{F}$ and is initially charged to 100 V with the polarity shown. The resistor R_0 has resistance 10 Ω. At time $t = 0$ the switch is closed. The small circuit is not connected in any way to the large one. The wire of the small circuit has a resistance of 1.0 Ω/m and contains 25 loops. The large circuit is a rectangle 2.0 m by 4.0 m, while the small one has dimensions $a = 10.0$ cm and $b = 20.0$ cm. The distance c is 5.0 cm. (The figure is not drawn to scale.) Both circuits are held stationary. Assume that only the wire nearest the small circuit produces an appreciable magnetic field through it. (a) Find the current in the large circuit 200 μs after S is closed. (b) Find the current in the small circuit 200 μs after S is closed. (*Hint:* See Problem 29.7.) (c) Find the direction of the current in the small circuit. (d) Justify why we can ignore the magnetic field from all the wires of the large circuit except for the wire closest to the small circuit.

Figure **29.41** Problem 29.45.

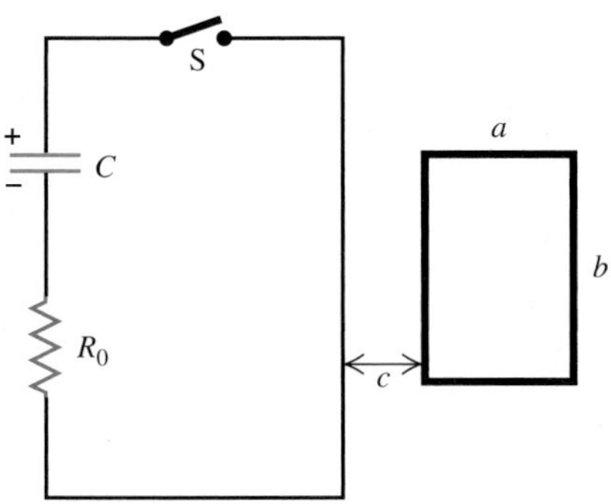

29.46. A flat coil is oriented with the plane of its area at right angles to a spatially uniform magnetic field. The magnitude of this field varies with time according to the graph in Fig. 29.42. Sketch a qualitative (but accurate!) graph of the emf induced in the coil as a function of time. Be sure to identify the times t_1, t_2, and t_3 on your graph.

Figure **29.42** Problem 29.46.

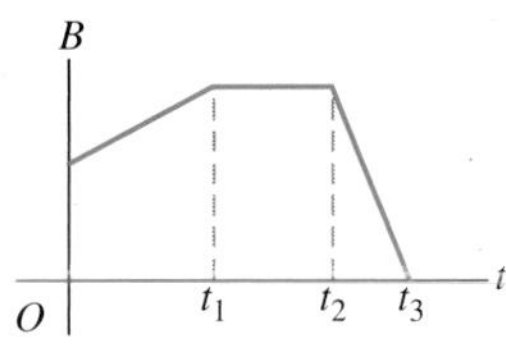

29.47. A circular wire loop of radius a and resistance R initially has a magnetic flux through it due to an external magnetic field. The external field then decreases to zero. A current is induced in the loop while the external field is changing; however, this current does not stop at the instant that the external field stops changing. The reason is that the current itself generates a magnetic field, which gives rise to a flux through the loop. If the current changes, the flux through the loop changes as well, and an induced emf appears in the loop to oppose the change. (a) The magnetic field at the center of the loop of radius a produced by a current i in the loop is given by $B = \mu_0 i/2a$. If we use the crude approximation that the field has this same value at all points within the loop, what is the flux of this field through the loop? (b) By using Faraday's law, Eq. (29.3), and the relationship $\mathcal{E} = iR$, show that after the external field has stopped changing, the current in the loop obeys the differential equation

$$\frac{di}{dt} = -\left(\frac{2R}{\pi\mu_0 a}\right)i$$

(c) If the current has the value i_0 at $t = 0$, the instant that the external field stops changing, solve the equation in part (b) to find i as a function of time for $t > 0$. (*Hint:* In Section 26.4 we encountered a similar differential equation, Eq. (26.15), for the quantity q. This equation for i may be solved in the same way.) (d) If the loop has radius $a = 50$ cm and resistance $R = 0.10\ \Omega$, how long after the external field stops changing will the current be equal to $0.010 i_0$ (that is, $\frac{1}{100}$ of its initial value)? (e) In solving the examples in this chapter, we ignored the effects described in this problem. Explain why this is a good approximation.

29.48. A coil is stationary in a spatially uniform, external, time-varying magnetic field. The emf induced in this coil as a function of time is shown if Fig. 29.43. Sketch a clear qualitative graph of the external magnetic field as a function of time, given that it started from zero. Include the points t_1, t_2, t_3, and t_4 on your graph.

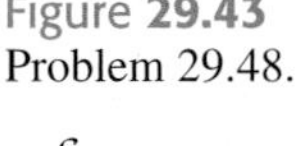
Figure **29.43** Problem 29.48.

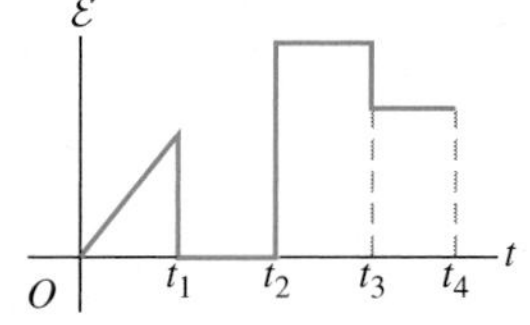

29.49. In Fig. 29.44 the loop is being pulled to the right at constant speed v. A constant current I flows in the long wire, in the direction shown. (a) Calculate the magnitude of the net emf $\mathcal{E}$ induced in the loop. Do this two ways: (i) by using Faraday's law of induction (*Hint:* See Problem 29.7) and (ii) by looking at the emf induced in each segment of the loop due to its motion. (b) Find the direction (clockwise or counterclockwise) of the current induced in the loop. Do this two ways: (i) using Lenz's law and (ii) using the magnetic force on charges in the loop. (c) Check your answer for the emf in part (a) in the following special cases to see whether it is physically reasonable: (i) The loop is stationary; (ii) the loop is very thin, so $a \to 0$; (iii) the loop gets very far from the wire.

Figure **29.44** Problem 29.49.

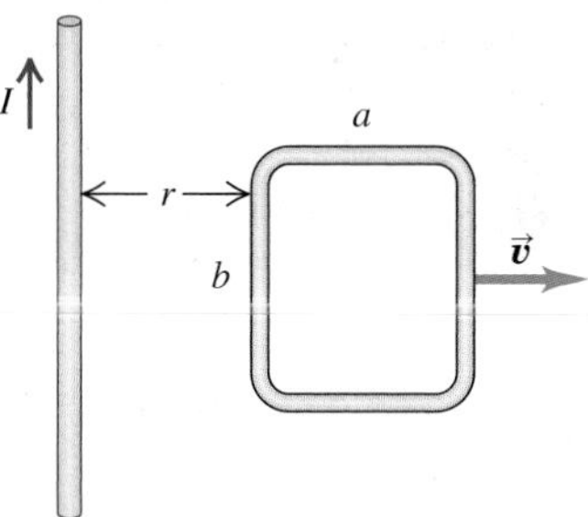

29.50. Suppose the loop in Fig. 29.45 is (a) rotated about the y-axis; (b) rotated about the x-axis; (c) rotated about an edge parallel to the z-axis. What is the maximum induced emf in each case if $A = 600\ \text{cm}^2$, $\omega = 35.0$ rad/s, and $B = 0.450$ T?

Figure **29.45** Problem 29.50.

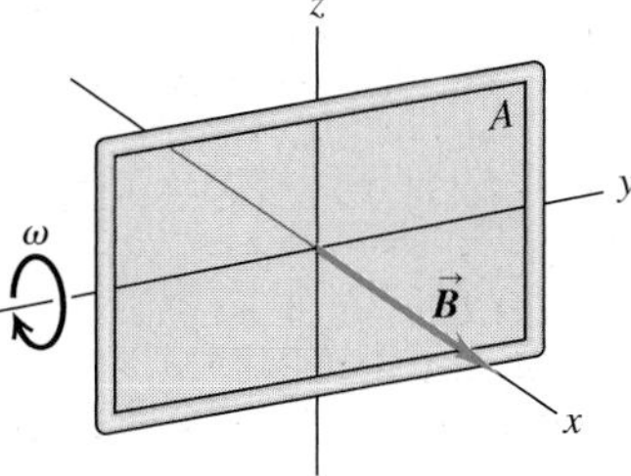

29.51. As a new electrical engineer for the local power company, you are assigned the project of designing a generator of sinusoidal ac voltage with a maximum voltage of 120 V. Besides plenty of wire, you have two strong magnets that can produce a constant uniform magnetic field of 1.5 T over a square area of 10.0 cm on a side when they are 12.0 cm apart. The basic design should consist of a square coil turning in the uniform magnetic field. To have an acceptable coil resistance, the coil can have at most 400 loops. What is the minimum rotation rate (in rpm) of the coil so it will produce the required voltage?

29.52. Make a Generator? You are shipwrecked on a deserted tropical island. You have some electrical devices that you could operate using a generator but you have no magnets. The earth's magnetic field at your location is horizontal and has magnitude 8.0×10^{-5} T, and you decide to try to use this field for a generator by rotating a large circular coil of wire at a high rate. You need to produce a peak emf of 9.0 V and estimate that you can rotate the coil at 30 rpm by turning a crank handle. You also decide that to have an acceptable coil resistance, the maximum number of turns the coil can have is 2000. (a) What area must the coil have? (b) If the coil is circular, what is the maximum translational speed of a point on the coil as it rotates? Do you think this device is feasible? Explain.

29.53. A flexible circular loop 6.50 cm in diameter lies in a magnetic field with magnitude 0.950 T, directed into the plane of the page as shown in Fig. 29.46. The loop is pulled at the points indicated by the arrows, forming a loop of zero area in 0.250 s. (a) Find the average induced emf in the circuit. (b) What is the direction of the current in R: from a to b or from b to a? Explain your reasoning.

Figure **29.46** Problem 29.53.

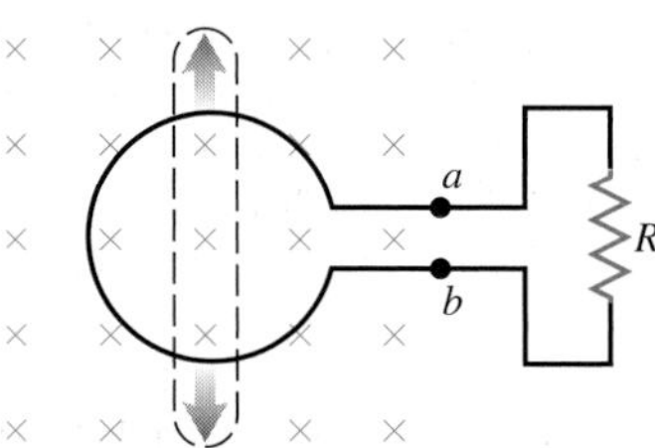

29.54. A Circuit Within a Circuit. Fig. 29.47 shows a small circuit within a larger one, both lying on the surface of a table. The switch is closed at $t = 0$ with the capacitor initially uncharged. Assume that the small circuit has no appreciable effect on the larger one. (a) What is the direction (a to b or to a) of the current in the resistor r (i) the instant after the switch is closed and (ii) one time constant after the switch is closed? (b) Sketch a graph of the current in the small circuit as a function of time, calling clockwise positive.

Figure **29.47** Problem 29.54.

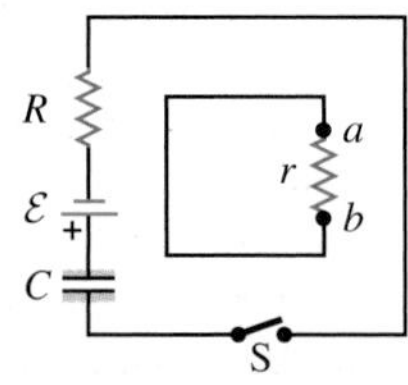

29.55. Terminal Speed. A conducting rod with length L, mass m, and resistance R moves without friction on metal rails as shown in Fig. 29.11. A uniform magnetic field $\vec{B}$ is directed into the plane of the figure. The rod starts from rest and is acted on by a constant force $\vec{F}$ directed to the right. The rails are infinitely long and have negligible resistance. (a) Graph the speed of the rod as a function of time. (b) Find an expression for the terminal speed (the speed when the acceleration of the rod is zero).

29.56. Terminal Speed. A bar of length $L = 0.8$ m is free to slide without friction on horizontal rails, as shown in Fig. 29.48. There is a uniform magnetic field $B = 1.5$ T directed into the plane of the figure. At one end of the rails there is a battery with emf $\mathcal{E} = 12$ V and a switch. The bar has mass 0.90 kg and resistance 5.0 Ω, and all other resistance in the circuit can be ignored. The switch is closed at time $t = 0$. (a) Sketch the speed of the bar as a function of time. (b) Just after the switch is closed, what is the acceleration of the bar? (c) What is the acceleration of the bar when its speed is 2.0 m/s? (d) What is the terminal speed of the bar?

Figure **29.48** Problem 29.56.

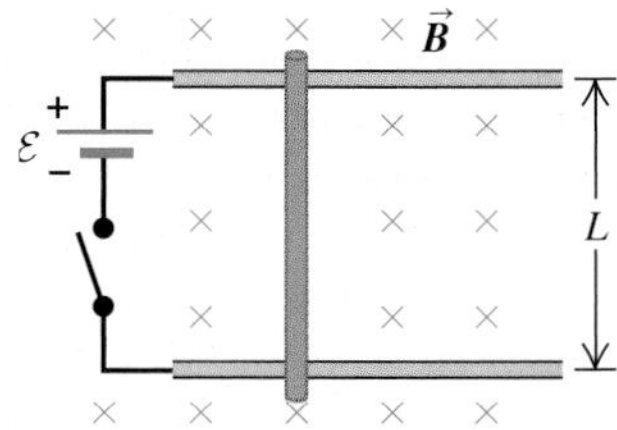

29.57. Antenna emf. A satellite, orbiting the earth at the equator at an altitude of 400 km, has an antenna that can be modeled as a 2.0-m-long rod. The antenna is oriented perpendicular to the earth's surface. At the equator, the earth's magnetic field is essentially horizontal and has a value of 8.0×10^{-5} T; ignore any changes in B with altitude. Assuming the orbit is circular, determine the induced emf between the tips of the antenna.

29.58. emf in a Bullet. At the equator, the earth's magnetic field is approximately horizontal, is directed toward the north, and has a value of 8×10^{-5} T. (a) Estimate the emf induced between the top and bottom of a bullet shot horizontally at a target on the equator if the bullet is shot toward the east. Assume the bullet has a length of 1 cm and a diameter of 0.4 cm and is traveling at 300 m/s. Which is at higher potential: the top or bottom of the bullet? (b) What is the emf if the bullet travels south? (c) What is the emf induced between the front and back of the bullet for any horizontal velocity?

29.59. A very long, cylindrical wire of radius R carries a current I_0 uniformly distributed across the cross section of the wire. Calculate the magnetic flux through a rectangle that has one side of length W running down the center of the wire and another side of length R, as shown in Fig. 29.49 (see Problem 29.7).

Figure **29.49** Problem 29.59.

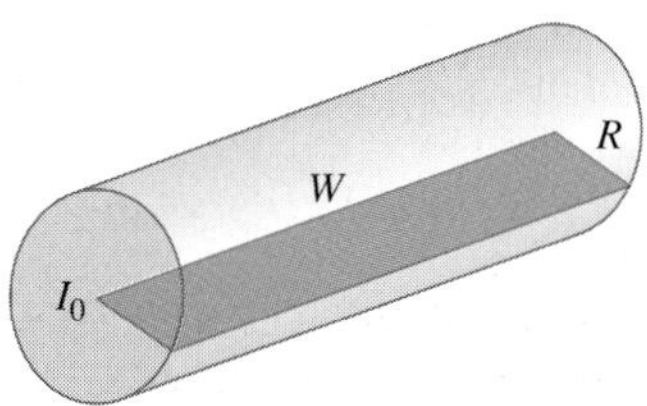

29.60. A circular conducting ring with radius $r_0 = 0.0420$ m lies in the xy-plane in a region of uniform magnetic field $\vec{B} = B_0[1 - 3(t/t_0)^2 + 2(t/t_0)^3]\hat{k}$. In this expression, $t_0 = 0.0100$ s and is constant, t is time, $\hat{k}$ is the unit vector in the $+z$-direction, and $B_0 = 0.0800$ T and is constant. At points a and b (Fig. 29.50) there is a small gap in the ring with wires leading to an external circuit of resistance $R = 12.0$ Ω. There is no magnetic field at the location of the external circuit. (a) Derive an expression, as a function of time, for the total magnetic flux Φ_B through the ring. (b) Determine the emf induced in the ring at time $t = 5.00 \times 10^{-3}$ s. What is the polarity of the emf? (c) Because of the internal resistance of the ring, the current through R at the time given in part (b) is only 3.00 mA. Determine the internal resist-

Figure **29.50** Problem 29.60.

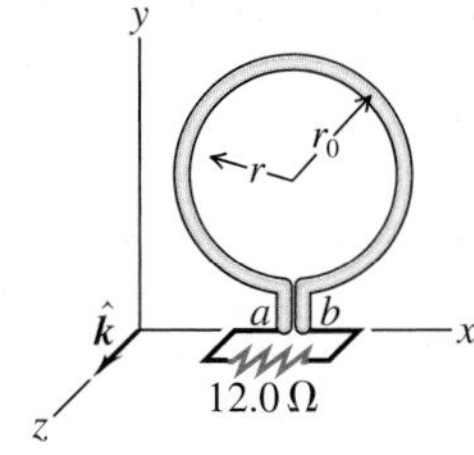

ance of the ring. (d) Determine the emf in the ring at a time $t = 1.21 \times 10^{-2}$ s. What is the polarity of the emf? (e) Determine the time at which the current through R reverses its direction.

29.61. The long, straight wire shown in Fig. 29.51a carries constant current I. A metal bar with length L is moving at constant velocity $\vec{v}$, as shown in the figure. Point a is a distance d from the wire. (a) Calculate the emf induced in the bar. (b) Which point, a or b, is at higher potential? (c) If the bar is replaced by a rectangular wire loop of resistance R (Fig. 29.51b), what is the magnitude of the current induced in the loop?

Figure **29.51** Problem 29.61.

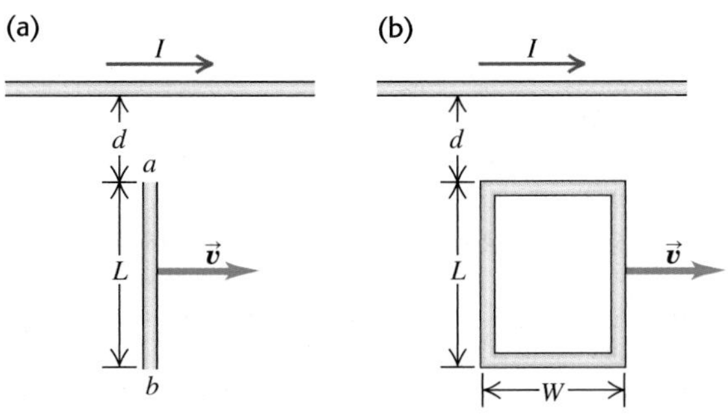

29.62. The cube shown in Fig. 29.52, 50.0 cm on a side, is in a uniform magnetic field of 0.120 T, directed along the positive y-axis. Wires A, C, and D move in the directions indicated, each with a speed of 0.350 m/s. (Wire A moves parallel to the xy-plane, C moves at an angle of 45.0° below the xy-plane, and D moves parallel to the xz-plane.) What is the potential difference between the ends of each wire?

Figure **29.52** Problem 29.62.

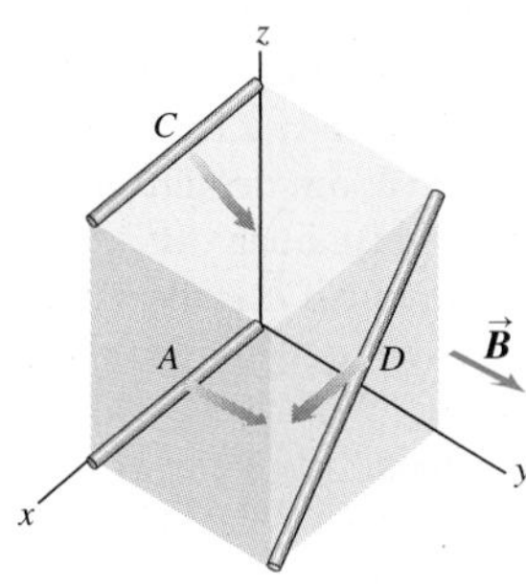

29.63. A slender rod, 0.240 m long, rotates with an angular speed of 8.80 rad/s about an axis through one end and perpendicular to the rod. The plane of rotation of the rod is perpendicular to a uniform magnetic field with a magnitude of 0.650 T. (a) What is the induced emf in the rod? (b) What is the potential difference between its ends? (c) Suppose instead the rod rotates at 8.80 rad/s about an axis through its center and perpendicular to the rod. In this case, what is the potential difference between the ends of the rod? Between the center of the rod and one end?

29.64. A Magnetic Exercise Machine. You have designed a new type of exercise machine with an extremely simple mechanism (Fig. 29.36). A vertical bar of silver (chosen for its low resistivity and because it makes the machine look cool) with length $L = 3.0$ m is free to move left or right without friction on silver rails. The entire apparatus is placed in a horizontal, uniform magnetic field of strength 0.25 T. When you push the bar to the left or right, the bar's motion sets up a current in the circuit that includes the bar. The resistance of the bar and the rails can be neglected. The magnetic field exerts a force on the current-carrying bar, and this force opposes the bar's motion. The health benefit is from the exercise that you do in working against this force. (a) Your design goal is that the person doing the exercise is to do work at the rate of 25 watts when moving the bar at a steady 2.0 m/s. What should be the resistance R? (b) You decide you want to be able to vary the power required from the person, to adapt the machine to the person's strength and fitness. If the power is to be increased to 50 W by altering R while leaving the other design parameters constant, should R be increased or decreased? Calculate the value of R for 50 W. (c) When you start to construct a prototype machine, you find it is difficult to produce a 0.25-T magnetic field over such a large area. If you decrease the length of the bar to 0.20 m while leaving B, v, and R the same as in part (a), what will be the power required of the person?

29.65. A rectangular loop with width L and a slide wire with mass m are as shown in Fig. 29.53. A uniform magnetic field $\vec{B}$ is directed perpendicular to the plane of the loop into the plane of the figure. The slide wire is given an initial speed of v_0 and then released. There is no friction between the slide wire and the loop, and the resistance of the loop is negligible in comparison to the resistance R of the slide wire. (a) Obtain an expression for F, the magnitude of the force exerted on the wire while it is moving at speed v. (b) Show that the distance x that the wire moves before coming to rest is $x = mv_0R/a^2B^2$.

Figure **29.53** Problem 29.65.

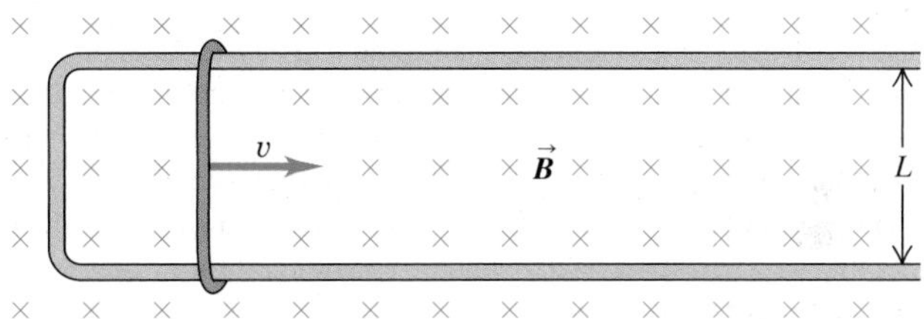

29.66. A 25.0-cm-long metal rod lies in the xy-plane and makes an angle of 36.9° with the positive x-axis and an angle of 53.1° with the positive y-axis. The rod is moving in the $+x$-direction with a speed of 4.20 m/s. The rod is in a uniform magnetic field $\vec{B} = (0.120\text{ T})\hat{\imath} - (0.220\text{ T})\hat{\jmath} - (0.0900\text{ T})\hat{k}$. (a) What is the magnitude of the emf induced in the rod? (b) Indicate in a sketch which end of the rod is at higher potential.

29.67. The magnetic field $\vec{B}$, at all points within a circular region of radius R, is uniform in space and directed into the plane of the page as shown in Fig. 29.54. (The region could be a cross section inside the windings of a long, straight solenoid.) If the magnetic field is increasing at a rate dB/dt, what are the magnitude and direction of the force on a stationary positive point charge q located at points a, b, and c? (Point a is a distance r above the center of the region, point b is a distance r to the right of the center, and point c is at the center of the region.)

Figure **29.54** Problem 29.67.

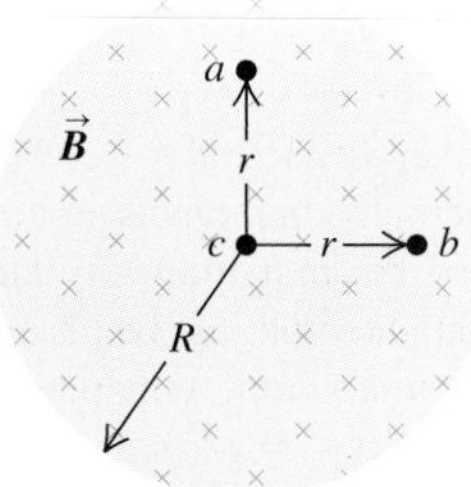

29.68. An airplane propeller of total length L rotates around its center with angular speed ω in a magnetic field that is perpendicular to the plane of rotation. Modeling the propeller as a thin, uniform bar, find the potential difference between (a) the center and either end of the propeller and (b) the two ends. (c) If the field is the earth's field of 0.50 G and the propeller turns at 220 rpm and is 2.0 m long, what is the potential difference between the middle and either end? It this large enough to be concerned about?

29.69. It is impossible to have a uniform electric field that abruptly drops to zero in a region of space in which the magnetic field is constant and in which there are no electric charges. To prove this statement, use the method of contradiction: Assume that such a case *is* possible and then show that your assumption contradicts a law of nature. (a) In the bottom half of a piece of paper, draw evenly spaced horizontal lines representing a uniform electric field to your right. Use dashed lines to draw a rectangle *abcda* with horizontal side *ab* in the electric-field region and horizontal side *cd* in the top half of your paper where $E = 0$. (b) Show that integration around your rectangle contradicts Faraday's law, Eq. (29.21).

29.70. Falling Square Loop. A vertically oriented, square loop of copper wire falls from a region where the field $\vec{B}$ is horizontal, uniform, and perpendicular to the plane of the loop, into a region where the field is zero. The loop is released from rest and initially is entirely within the magnetic-field region. Let the side length of the loop be s and let the diameter of the wire be d. The resistivity of copper is ρ_R and the density of copper is ρ_m. If the loop reaches its terminal speed while its upper segment is still in the magnetic-field region, find an expression for the terminal speed.

29.71. In a region of space where there are no conduction or displacement currents, it is impossible to have a uniform magnetic field that abruptly drops to zero. To prove this statement, use the method of contradiction: Assume that such a case *is* possible, and then show that your assumption contradicts a law of nature. (a) In the bottom half of a piece of paper, draw evenly spaced horizontal lines representing a uniform magnetic field to your right. Use dashed lines to draw a rectangle *abcda* with horizontal side *ab* in the magnetic-field region and horizontal side *cd* in the top half of your paper where $B = 0$. (b) Show that integration around your rectangle contradicts Ampere's law, Eq. (29.15).

29.72. A capacitor has two parallel plates with area A separated by a distance d. The space between plates is filled with a material having dielectric constant K. The material is not a perfect insulator but has resistivity ρ. The capacitor is initially charged with charge of magnitude Q_0 on each plate that gradually discharges by conduction through the dielectric. (a) Calculate the conduction current density $j_C(t)$ in the dielectric. (b) Show that at any instant the displacement current density in the dielectric is equal in magnitude to the conduction current density but opposite in direction, so the *total* current density is zero at every instant.

29.73. A rod of pure silicon (resistivity $\rho = 2300\ \Omega \cdot \text{m}$) is carrying a current. The electric field varies sinusoidally with time according to $E = E_0 \sin \omega t$, where $E_0 = 0.450\ \text{V/m}$, $\omega = 2\pi f$, and the frequency $f = 120$ Hz. (a) Find the magnitude of the maximum conduction current density in the wire. (b) Assuming $\epsilon = \epsilon_0$, find the maximum displacement current density in the wire, and compare with the result of part (a). (c) At what frequency f would the maximum conduction and displacement densities become equal if $\epsilon = \epsilon_0$ (which is not actually the case)? (d) At the frequency determined in part (c), what is the relative *phase* of the conduction and displacement currents?

Challenge Problems

29.74. A square, conducting, wire loop of side L, total mass m, and total resistance R initially lies in the horizontal xy-plane, with corners at $(x, y, z) = (0, 0, 0)$, $(0, L, 0)$, $(L, 0, 0)$, and $(L, L, 0)$. There is a uniform, upward magnetic field $\vec{B} = B\hat{k}$ in the space within and around the loop. The side of the loop that extends from $(0, 0, 0)$ to $(L, 0, 0)$ is held in place on the x-axis; the rest of the loop is free to pivot around this axis. When the loop is released, it begins to rotate due to the gravitational torque. (a) Find the *net* torque (magnitude and direction) that acts on the loop when it has rotated through an angle ϕ from its original orientation and is rotating downward at an angular speed ω. (b) Find the angular acceleration of the loop at the instant described in part (a). (c) Compared to the case with zero magnetic field, does it take the loop a longer or shorter time to rotate through 90°? Explain. (d) Is mechanical energy conserved as the loop rotates downward? Explain.

29.75. A square conducting loop, 20.0 cm on a side, is placed in the same magnetic field as shown in Exercise 29.30. (See Fig. 29.55; the center of the square loop is at the center of the magnetic-field region.) (a) Copy Fig. 29.55, and draw vectors to show the directions and relative magnitudes of the induced electric field $\vec{E}$ at points a, b, and c. (b) Prove that the component of $\vec{E}$ along the loop has the same value at every point of the loop and is equal to that of the ring shown in Fig. 29.31 (see Exercise 29.30). (c) What current is induced in the loop if its resistance is 1.90 Ω? (d) What is the potential difference between points a and b?

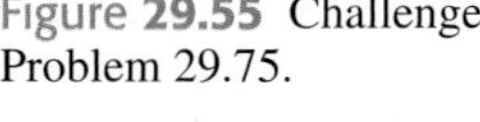
Figure 29.55 Challenge Problem 29.75.

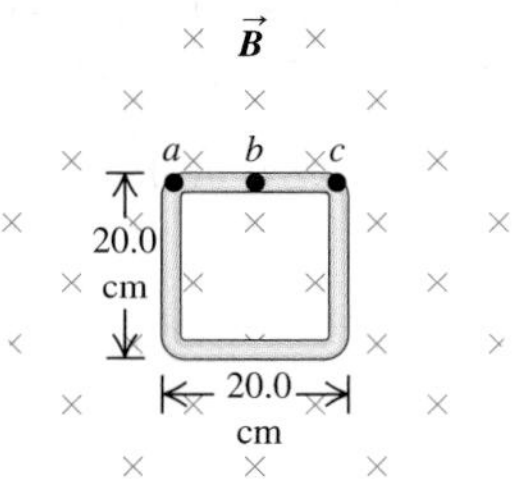

29.76. A uniform, square, conducting loop, 20.0 cm on a side, is placed in the same magnetic field as shown in Exercise 29.30, with side *ac* along a diameter and with point b at the center of the field (Fig. 29.56). (a) Copy Fig. 29.56, and draw vectors to show the direction and relative magnitude of the induced electric field $\vec{E}$ at the lettered points. (b) What is the induced emf in side *ac*? (c) What is the induced emf in the loop? (d) What is the current in the loop if its resistance is 1.90 Ω? (e) What is the potential difference between points a and c? Which is at higher potential?

Figure 29.56 Challenge Problem 29.76.

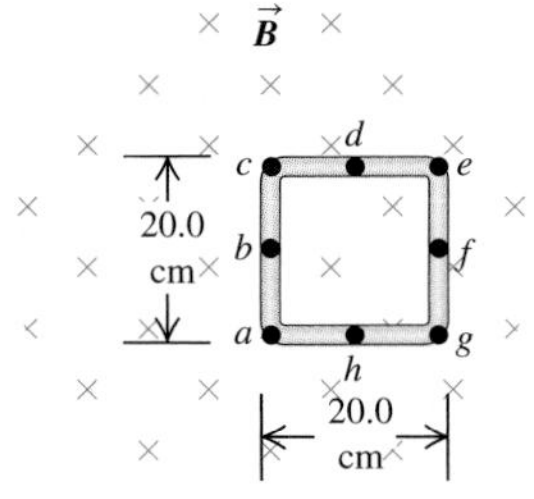

29.77. A metal bar with length L, mass m, and resistance R is placed on frictionless metal rails that are inclined at an angle ϕ above the horizontal. The rails have negligible resistance. A uniform magnetic field of magnitude B is directed downward as shown in Fig. 29.57. The bar is released from rest and slides down the rails. (a) Is the direction of the current induced in the bar from a to b or from b to a? (b) What is the terminal speed of the bar? (c) What is the induced current in the bar when the terminal speed has been reached? (d) After the terminal speed has been reached, at what rate is electrical energy being converted to thermal energy in the resistance of the bar? (e) After the terminal speed has been reached, at what rate is work being done on the bar by gravity? Compare your answer to that in part (d).

Figure 29.57 Challenge Problem 29.77.

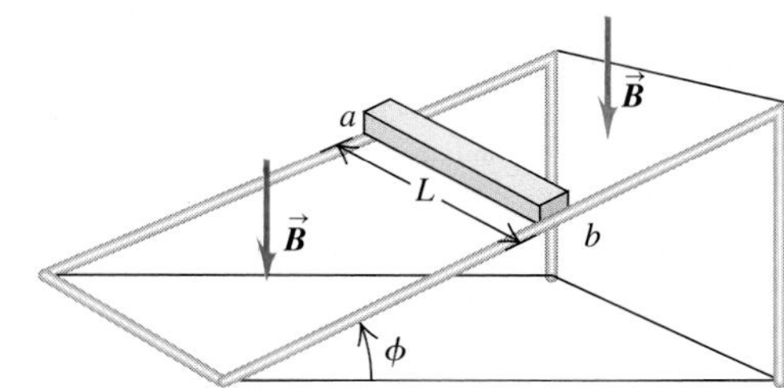

29.78. Consider a uniform metal disk rotating through a perpendicular magnetic field $\vec{B}$, as shown in Fig. 29.19a. The disk has mass m, radius R, and thickness t, is made of a material with resistivity ρ, and is rotating clockwise in Fig. 29.19a with angular speed ω. The magnetic field is directed into the plane of the disk. Suppose that the region to which the magnetic field is confined is not circular, as shown in Fig. 29.19a, but is a small square with sides of length L $(L \ll R)$ centered a distance d from the point O (the center of the disk). The sides of this square are horizontal and vertical in Fig. 29.19a. (a) Show that the current induced within the square is approximately equal to $I = \omega dBLt/\rho$. In which direction does this current flow? (*Hint:* Assume that the resistance to the current is confined to the region of the square. The current also encounters resistance as it flows outside the region to which the magnetic field is confined, as shown in Fig. 29.19b; however, this resistance is relatively small, since the current can flow through such a wide area. Recall Eq. (25.10) for resistance, given in Section 25.3.) (b) Show that the induced current gives rise to a torque of approximate magnitude $\tau = \omega d^2B^2L^2t/\rho$ that opposes the rotation of the disk (that is, a counterclockwise torque). (c) What would be the magnitudes and directions of the induced current and torque if the direction of $\vec{B}$ were still into the plane of the disk but the disk rotated counterclockwise? What if the direction of $\vec{B}$ were out of the plane and the disk rotated counterclockwise?

30 INDUCTANCE

LEARNING GOALS

By studying this chapter, you will learn:

- How a time-varying current in one coil can induce an emf in a second, unconnecetd coil.
- How to relate the induced emf in a circuit to the rate of change of current in the same circuit.
- How to calculate the energy stored in a magnetic field.
- How to analyze circuits that include both a resistor and an inductor (coil).
- Why electrical oscillations occur in circuits that include both an inductor and a capacitor.
- Why oscillations decay in circuits with an inductor, a resistor, and a capacitor.

? Many traffic lights change when a car rolls up to the intersection. How does the light sense the presence of the car?

Take a length of copper wire and wrap it around a pencil to form a coil. If you put this coil in a circuit, does it behave any differently than a straight piece of wire? Remarkably, the answer is yes. In an ordinary gasoline-powered car, a coil of this kind makes it possible for the 12-volt car battery to provide thousands of volts to the spark plugs, which in turn makes it possible for the plugs to fire and make the engine run. Other coils of this type are used to keep fluorescent light fixtures shining. Larger coils placed under city streets are used to control the operation of traffic signals. All of these applications, and many others, involve the *induction* effects that we studied in Chapter 29.

A changing current in a coil induces an emf in an adjacent coil. The coupling between the coils is described by their *mutual inductance.* A changing current in a coil also induces an emf in that same coil. Such a coil is called an *inductor,* and the relationship of current to emf is described by the *inductance* (also called *self-inductance*) of the coil. If a coil is initially carrying a current, energy is released when the current decreases; this principle is used in automotive ignition systems. We'll find that this released energy was stored in the magnetic field caused by the current that was initially in the coil, and we'll look at some of the practical applications of magnetic-field energy.

We'll also take a first look at what happens when an inductor is part of a circuit. In Chapter 31 we'll go on to study how inductors behave in alternating-current circuits; in that chapter we'll learn why inductors play an essential role in modern electronics, including communication systems, power supplies, and many other devices.

30.1 Mutual Inductance

In Section 28.4 we considered the magnetic interaction between two wires carrying *steady* currents; the current in one wire causes a magnetic field, which exerts a force on the current in the second wire. But an additional interaction arises between two circuits when there is a *changing* current in one of the circuits. Consider two neighboring coils of wire, as in Fig. 30.1. A current flowing in coil 1 produces a magnetic field $\vec{B}$ and hence a magnetic flux through coil 2. If the current in coil 1 changes, the flux through coil 2 changes as well; according to Faraday's law, this induces an emf in coil 2. In this way, a change in the current in one circuit can induce a current in a second circuit.

Let's analyze the situation shown in Fig. 30.1 in more detail. We will use lowercase letters to represent quantities that vary with time; for example, a time-varying current is i, often with a subscript to identify the circuit. In Fig. 30.1 a current i_1 in coil 1 sets up a magnetic field (as indicated by the blue lines), and some of these field lines pass through coil 2. We denote the magnetic flux through *each* turn of coil 2, caused by the current i_1 in coil 1, as Φ_{B2}. (If the flux is different through different turns of the coil, then Φ_{B2} denotes the *average* flux.) The magnetic field is proportional to i_1, so Φ_{B2} is also proportional to i_1. When i_1 changes, Φ_{B2} changes; this changing flux induces an emf $\mathcal{E}_2$ in coil 2, given by

$$\mathcal{E}_2 = -N_2 \frac{d\Phi_{B2}}{dt} \tag{30.1}$$

We could represent the proportionality of Φ_{B2} and i_1 in the form $\Phi_{B2} =$ (constant)i_1, but instead it is more convenient to include the number of turns N_2 in the relationship. Introducing a proportionality constant M_{21}, called the **mutual inductance** of the two coils, we write

$$N_2\Phi_{B2} = M_{21}i_1 \tag{30.2}$$

where Φ_{B2} is the flux through a *single* turn of coil 2. From this,

$$N_2 \frac{d\Phi_{B2}}{dt} = M_{21}\frac{di_1}{dt}$$

and we can rewrite Eq. (30.1) as

$$\mathcal{E}_2 = -M_{21}\frac{di_1}{dt} \tag{30.3}$$

That is, a change in the current i_1 in coil 1 induces an emf in coil 2 that is directly proportional to the rate of change of i_1 (Fig. 30.2).

We may also write the definition of mutual inductance, Eq. (30.2), as

$$M_{21} = \frac{N_2\Phi_{B2}}{i_1}$$

If the coils are in vacuum, the flux Φ_{B2} through each turn of coil 2 is directly proportional to the current i_1. Then the mutual inductance M_{21} is a constant that depends only on the geometry of the two coils (the size, shape, number of turns, and orientation of each coil and the separation between the coils). If a magnetic material is present, M_{21} also depends on the magnetic properties of the material. If the material has nonlinear magnetic properties, that is, if the relative permeability K_m (defined in Section 28.8) is not constant and magnetization is not proportional to magnetic field, then Φ_{B2} is no longer directly proportional to i_1. In that case the mutual inductance also depends on the value of i_1. In this discussion we will assume that any magnetic material present has constant K_m so that flux *is* directly proportional to current and M_{21} depends on geometry only.

We can repeat our discussion for the opposite case in which a changing current i_2 in coil 2 causes a changing flux Φ_{B1} and an emf $\mathcal{E}_1$ in coil 1. We might expect that the corresponding constant M_{12} would be different from M_{21} because in general the two coils are not identical and the flux through them is not the same. It turns out, however, that M_{12} is *always* equal to M_{21}, even when the two coils are not symmetric. We call this common value simply the mutual inductance,

30.1 A current i_1 in coil 1 gives rise to a magnetic flux through coil 2.

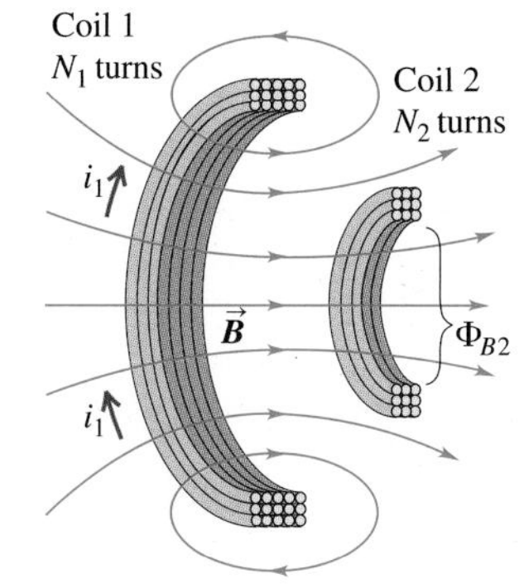
Mutual inductance: If the current in coil 1 is changing, the changing flux through coil 2 induces an emf in coil 2.
Coil 1
N_1 turns
Coil 2
N_2 turns
i_1
$\vec{B}$
Φ_{B2}
i_1

30.2 This electric toothbrush makes use of mutual inductance. The base contains a coil that is supplied with alternating current from a wall socket. This varying current induces an emf in a coil within the toothbrush itself, which is used to recharge the toothbrush battery.

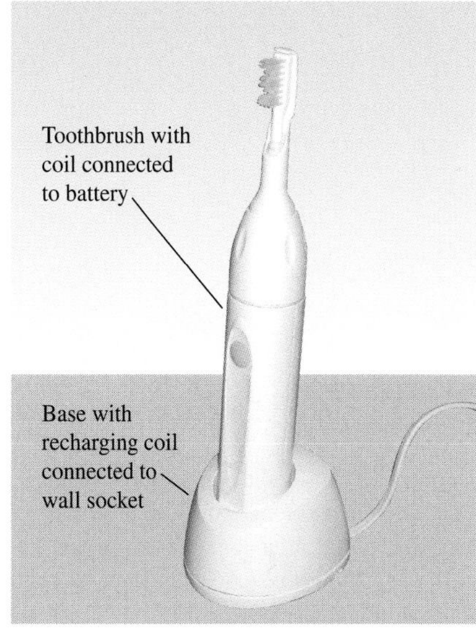
Toothbrush with coil connected to battery
Base with recharging coil connected to wall socket

denoted by the symbol M without subscripts; it characterizes completely the induced-emf interaction of two coils. Then we can write

$$\mathcal{E}_2 = -M\frac{di_1}{dt} \quad \text{and} \quad \mathcal{E}_1 = -M\frac{di_2}{dt} \qquad \text{(mutually induced emfs)} \quad (30.4)$$

where the mutual inductance M is

$$M = \frac{N_2\Phi_{B2}}{i_1} = \frac{N_1\Phi_{B1}}{i_2} \qquad \text{(mutual inductance)} \quad (30.5)$$

The negative signs in Eq. (30.4) are a reflection of Lenz's law. The first equation says that a change in current in coil 1 causes a change in flux through coil 2, inducing an emf in coil 2 that opposes the flux change; in the second equation the roles of the two coils are interchanged.

CAUTION **Only a time-varying current induces an emf** Note that only a *time-varying* current in a coil can induce an emf and hence a current in a second coil. Equations (30.4) show that the induced emf in each coil is directly proportional to the *rate of change* of the current in the other coil, not to the value of the current. A steady current in one coil, no matter how strong, cannot induce a current in a neighboring coil.

The SI unit of mutual inductance is called the **henry** (1 H), in honor of the American physicist Joseph Henry (1797–1878), one of the discoverers of electromagnetic induction. From Eq. (30.5), one henry is equal to *one weber per ampere*. Other equivalent units, obtained by using Eq. (30.4), are *one volt-second per ampere, one ohm-second,* or *one joule per ampere squared:*

$$1\text{ H} = 1\text{ Wb/A} = 1\text{ V}\cdot\text{s/A} = 1\,\Omega\cdot\text{s} = 1\text{ J/A}^2$$

Just as the farad is a rather large unit of capacitance (see Section 24.1), the henry is a rather large unit of mutual inductance. As Example 30.1 shows, typical values of mutual inductance can be in the millihenry (mH) or microhenry (μH) range.

Drawbacks and Uses of Mutual Inductance

Mutual inductance can be a nuisance in electric circuits, since variations in current in one circuit can induce unwanted emfs in other nearby circuits. To minimize these effects, multiple-circuit systems must be designed so that M is as small as possible; for example, two coils would be placed far apart or with their planes perpendicular.

Happily, mutual inductance also has many useful applications. A *transformer,* used in alternating-current circuits to raise or lower voltages, is fundamentally no different from the two coils shown in Fig. 30.1. A time-varying alternating current in one coil of the transformer produces an alternating emf in the other coil; the value of M, which depends on the geometry of the coils, determines the amplitude of the induced emf in the second coil and hence the amplitude of the output voltage. (We'll describe transformers in more detail in Chapter 31 after we've discussed alternating current in greater depth.)

Example 30.1 Calculating mutual inductance

In one form of Tesla coil (a high-voltage generator that you may have seen in a science museum), a long solenoid with length l and cross-sectional area A is closely wound with N_1 turns of wire. A coil with N_2 turns surrounds it at its center (Fig. 30.3). Find the mutual inductance.

SOLUTION

IDENTIFY: Mutual inductance occurs in this situation because a current in one of the coils sets up a magnetic field that causes a flux through the other coil.

30.3 A long solenoid with cross-sectional area A and N_1 turns (shown in black) is surrounded at its center by a coil with N_2 turns (shown in blue).

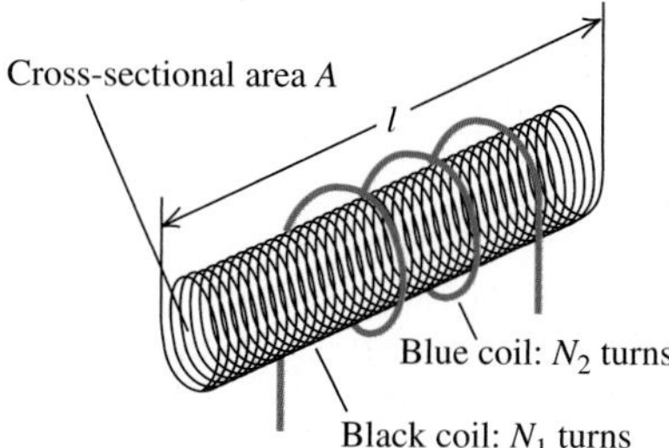

SET UP: We use Eq. (30.5) to determine the mutual inductance M. According to that equation, we need to know either (a) the flux Φ_{B2} through each turn of the outer coil due to a current i_1 in the solenoid or (b) the flux Φ_{B1} through each turn of the solenoid due to a current i_2 in the outer coil. We choose option (a) since from Example 28.9 (Section 28.7) we have a simple expression for the field at the center of a long current-carrying solenoid, given by Eq. (28.23). Note that we are not given a value for the current i_1 in the solenoid. This omission is not cause for alarm, however: The value of the mutual inductance doesn't depend on the value of the current, so the quantity i_1 should cancel out when we calculate M.

EXECUTE: From Example 28.9, a long solenoid carrying current i_1 produces a magnetic field $\vec{B}_1$ that points along the axis of the solenoid. The field magnitude B_1 is proportional to i_1 and to n_1, the number of turns per unit length:

$$B_1 = \mu_0 n_1 i_1 = \frac{\mu_0 N_1 i_1}{l}$$

The flux through a cross section of the solenoid equals $B_1 A$. Since a very long solenoid produces no magnetic field outside of its coil, this is also equal to the flux Φ_{B2} through each turn of the outer, surrounding coil, no matter what the cross-sectional area of the outer coil. From Eq. (30.5) the mutual inductance M is

$$M = \frac{N_2 \Phi_{B2}}{i_1} = \frac{N_2 B_1 A}{i_1} = \frac{N_2}{i_1}\frac{\mu_0 N_1 i_1}{l}A = \frac{\mu_0 A N_1 N_2}{l}$$

EVALUATE: The mutual inductance of any two coils is always proportional to the product $N_1 N_2$ of their numbers of turns. Notice that the mutual inductance M depends only on the geometry of the two coils, not on the current.

Here's a numerical example to give you an idea of magnitudes. Suppose $l = 0.50$ m, $A = 10\text{ cm}^2 = 1.0 \times 10^{-3}\text{ m}^2$, $N_1 = 1000$ turns, and $N_2 = 10$ turns. Then

$$M = \frac{(4\pi \times 10^{-7}\text{ Wb/A}\cdot\text{m})(1.0 \times 10^{-3}\text{ m}^2)(1000)(10)}{0.50\text{ m}}$$
$$= 25 \times 10^{-6}\text{ Wb/A} = 25 \times 10^{-6}\text{ H} = 25\ \mu\text{H}$$

Example 30.2 Emf due to mutual inductance

In Example 30.1, suppose the current i_2 in the outer, surrounding coil is given by $i_2 = (2.0 \times 10^6\text{ A/s})t$ (currents in wires can indeed increase this rapidly for brief periods). (a) At time $t = 3.0\ \mu\text{s}$, what average magnetic flux through each turn of the solenoid is caused by the current in the outer, surrounding coil? (b) What is the induced emf in the solenoid?

SOLUTION

IDENTIFY: In Example 30.1 we found the mutual inductance by relating the current in the solenoid to the flux produced in the outer coil. In this example we are given the current in the outer coil and want to find the resulting flux in the solenoid. The key point is that the mutual inductance is the *same* in either case.

SET UP: Given the value of the mutual inductance $M = 25\ \mu\text{H}$ from Example 30.1, we use Eq. (30.5) to determine the flux Φ_{B1} through each turn of the solenoid caused by a given current i_2 in the outer coil. We then use Eq. (30.4) to determine the emf induced in the solenoid by the time variation of the outer coil's current.

EXECUTE: (a) At time $t = 3.0\ \mu\text{s} = 3.0 \times 10^{-6}$ s, the current in the outer coil (coil 2) is $i_2 = (2.0 \times 10^6\text{ A/s})(3.0 \times 10^{-6}\text{ s}) =$ 6.0 A. To find the average flux through each turn of the solenoid (coil 1), we solve Eq. (30.5) for Φ_{B1}:

$$\Phi_{B1} = \frac{Mi_2}{N_1} = \frac{(25 \times 10^{-6}\text{ H})(6.0\text{ A})}{1000} = 1.5 \times 10^{-7}\text{ Wb}$$

Note that this is an *average* value; the flux can vary considerably between the center and the ends of the solenoid.

(b) The induced emf $\mathcal{E}_1$ is given by Eq. (30.4):

$$\mathcal{E}_1 = -M\frac{di_2}{dt} = -(25 \times 10^{-6}\text{ H})\frac{d}{dt}[(2.0 \times 10^6\text{ A/s})t]$$
$$= -(25 \times 10^{-6}\text{ H})(2.0 \times 10^6\text{ A/s}) = -50\text{ V}$$

EVALUATE: This is a substantial induced emf in response to a very rapid rate of change of current. In an operating Tesla coil, there is a high-frequency alternating current rather than a continuously increasing current as in this example; both di_2/dt and $\mathcal{E}_1$ alternate as well, with amplitudes that can be thousands of times larger than in this example.

Test Your Understanding of Section 30.1 Consider the Tesla coil described in Example 30.1. If you make the solenoid out of twice as much wire, so that it has twice as many turns and is twice as long, how much larger is the mutual inductance? (i) M is four times greater; (ii) M is twice as great; (iii) M is unchanged; (iv) M is $\frac{1}{2}$ as great; (v) M is $\frac{1}{4}$ as great.

30.2 Self-Inductance and Inductors

In our discussion of mutual inductance we considered two separate, independent circuits: A current in one circuit creates a magnetic field and this field gives rise to a flux through the second circuit. If the current in the first circuit changes, the flux through the second circuit changes and an emf is induced in the second circuit.

An important related effect occurs even if we consider only a *single* isolated circuit. When a current is present in a circuit, it sets up a magnetic field that causes a magnetic flux through the *same* circuit; this flux changes when the current changes. Thus any circuit that carries a varying current has an emf induced in it by the variation in *its own* magnetic field. Such an emf is called a **self-induced emf.** By Lenz's law, a self-induced emf always opposes the change in the current that caused the emf and so tends to make it more difficult for variations in current to occur. For this reason, self-induced emfs can be of great importance whenever there is a varying current.

30.4 The current i in the circuit causes a magnetic field $\vec{B}$ in the coil and hence a flux through the coil.

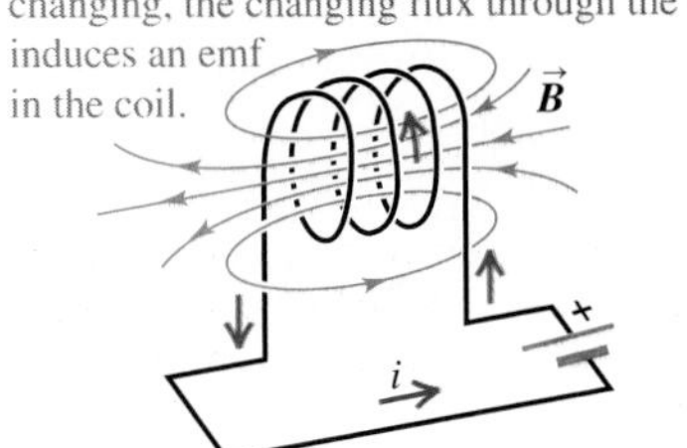

Self-inductance: If the current i in the coil is changing, the changing flux through the coil induces an emf in the coil.
$\vec{B}$
i

Self-induced emfs can occur in *any* circuit, since there is always some magnetic flux through the closed loop of a current-carrying circuit. But the effect is greatly enhanced if the circuit includes a coil with N turns of wire (Fig. 30.4). As a result of the current i, there is an average magnetic flux Φ_B through each turn of the coil. In analogy to Eq. (30.5) we define the **self-inductance** L of the circuit as

$$L = \frac{N\Phi_B}{i} \quad \text{(self-inductance)} \tag{30.6}$$

When there is no danger of confusion with mutual inductance, the self-inductance is called simply the **inductance.** Comparing Eqs. (30.5) and (30.6), we see that the units of self-inductance are the same as those of mutual inductance; the SI unit of self-inductance is one henry.

If the current i in the circuit changes, so does the flux Φ_B; from rearranging Eq. (30.6) and taking the derivative with respect to time, the rates of change are related by

$$N\frac{d\Phi_B}{dt} = L\frac{di}{dt}$$

From Faraday's law for a coil with N turns, Eq. (29.4), the self-induced emf is $\mathcal{E} = -N\,d\Phi_B/dt$, so it follows that

$$\mathcal{E} = -L\frac{di}{dt} \quad \text{(self-induced emf)} \tag{30.7}$$

The minus sign in Eq. (30.7) is a reflection of Lenz's law; it says that the self-induced emf in a circuit opposes any change in the current in that circuit. (Later in this section we'll explore in greater depth the significance of this minus sign.)

Equation (30.7) also states that the self-inductance of a circuit is the magnitude of the self-induced emf per unit rate of change of current. This relationship makes it possible to measure an unknown self-inductance in a relatively simple way: Change the current in the circuit at a known rate di/dt, measure the induced emf, and take the ratio to determine L.

Inductors As Circuit Elements

A circuit device that is designed to have a particular inductance is called an **inductor,** or a *choke.* The usual circuit symbol for an inductor is

Like resistors and capacitors, inductors are among the indispensable circuit elements of modern electronics. Their purpose is to oppose any variations in the current through the circuit. An inductor in a direct-current circuit helps to maintain a steady current despite any fluctuations in the applied emf; in an alternating-current circuit, an inductor tends to suppress variations of the current that are more rapid than desired. In this chapter and the next we will explore the behavior and applications of inductors in circuits in more detail.

To understand the behavior of circuits containing inductors, we need to develop a general principle analogous to Kirchhoff's loop rule (discussed in Section 26.2). To apply that rule, we go around a conducting loop, measuring potential differences across successive circuit elements as we go. The algebraic sum of these differences around any closed loop must be zero because the electric field produced by charges distributed around the circuit is *conservative.* In Section 29.7 we denoted such a conservative field as $\vec{E}_c$.

When an inductor is included in the circuit, the situation changes. The magnetically induced electric field within the coils of the inductor is *not* conservative; as in Section 29.7, we'll denote it by $\vec{E}_n$. We need to think very carefully about the roles of the various fields. Let's assume we are dealing with an inductor whose coils have negligible resistance. Then a negligibly small electric field is required to make charge move through the coils, so the *total* electric field $\vec{E}_c + \vec{E}_n$ within the coils must be zero, even though neither field is individually zero. Because $\vec{E}_c$ is nonzero, we know there have to be accumulations of charge on the terminals of the inductor and the surfaces of its conductors, to produce this field.

Consider the circuit shown in Fig. 30.5; the box contains some combination of batteries and variable resistors that enables us to control the current i in the circuit. According to Faraday's law, Eq. (29.10), the line integral of $\vec{E}_n$ around the circuit is the negative of the rate of change of flux through the circuit, which in turn is given by Eq. (30.7). Combining these two relationships, we get

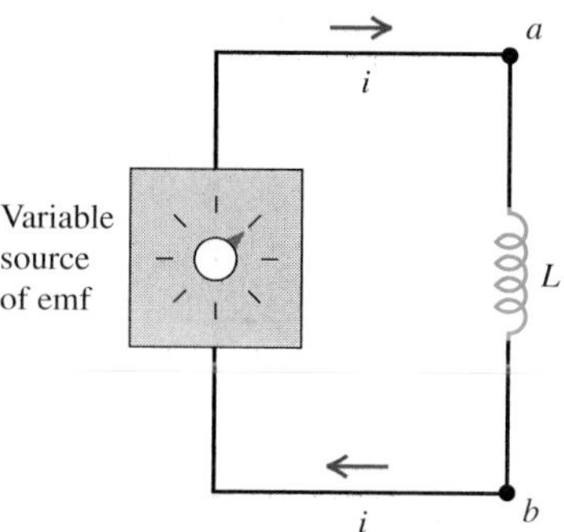

30.5 A circuit containing a source of emf and an inductor. The source is variable, so the current i and its rate of change di/dt can be varied.

$$\oint \vec{E}_n \cdot d\vec{l} = -L\frac{di}{dt}$$

where we integrate clockwise around the loop (the direction of the assumed current). But $\vec{E}_n$ is different from zero only within the inductor. Therefore the integral of $\vec{E}_n$ around the whole loop can be replaced by its integral only from a to b through the inductor; that is,

$$\int_a^b \vec{E}_n \cdot d\vec{l} = -L\frac{di}{dt}$$

Next, because $\vec{E}_c + \vec{E}_n = \mathbf{0}$ at each point within the inductor coils, we can rewrite this as

$$\int_a^b \vec{E}_c \cdot d\vec{l} = L\frac{di}{dt}$$

But this integral is just the potential V_{ab} of point a with respect to point b, so we finally obtain

$$V_{ab} = V_a - V_b = L\frac{di}{dt} \tag{30.8}$$

We conclude that there is a genuine potential difference between the terminals of the inductor, associated with conservative, electrostatic forces, despite the fact that the electric field associated with the magnetic induction effect is nonconservative. Thus we are justified in using Kirchhoff's loop rule to analyze circuits that include inductors. Equation (30.8) gives the potential difference across an inductor in a circuit.

30.6 (a) The potential difference across a resistor depends on the current. (b), (c), (d) The potential difference across an inductor depends on the rate of change of the current.

(a) Resisitor with current i flowing from a to b: potential drops from a to b.

$$V_{ab} = iR > 0$$

(b) Inductor with *constant* current i flowing from a to b: no potential difference.

i constant: $di/dt = 0$

$$V_{ab} = L\frac{di}{dt} = 0$$

$\mathcal{E} = 0$

(c) Inductor with *increasing* current i flowing from a to b: potential drops from a to b.

i increasing: $di/dt > 0$

$$V_{ab} = L\frac{di}{dt} > 0$$

(d) Inductor with *decreasing* current i flowing from a to b: potential increases from a to b.

i decreasing: $di/dt < 0$

$$V_{ab} = L\frac{di}{dt} < 0$$

CAUTION **Self-induced emf opposes changes in current** Note that the self-induced emf does not oppose the current i itself; rather, it opposes any *change* (di/dt) in the current. Thus the circuit behavior of an inductor is quite different from that of a resistor. Figure 30.6 compares the behaviors of a resistor and an inductor and summarizes the sign relationships.

Applications of Inductors

Because an inductor opposes changes in current, it plays an important role in fluorescent light fixtures (Fig. 30.7). In such fixtures, current flows from the wiring into the gas that fills the tube, ionizing the gas and causing it to glow. However, an ionized gas or *plasma* is a highly nonohmic conductor: The greater the current, the more highly ionized the plasma becomes and the lower its resistance. If a sufficiently large voltage is applied to the plasma, the current can grow so much that it damages the circuitry outside the fluorescent tube. To prevent this problem, an inductor or *magnetic ballast* is put in series with the fluorescent tube to keep the current from growing out of bounds.

The ballast also makes it possible for the fluorescent tube to work with the alternating voltage provided by household wiring. This voltage oscillates sinusoidally with a frequency of 60 Hz, so that it goes momentarily to zero 120 times per second. If there were no ballast, the plasma in the fluorescent tube would rapidly deionize when the voltage went to zero and the tube would shut off. With a ballast present, a self-induced emf sustains the current and keeps the tube lit. Magnetic ballasts are also used for this purpose in streetlights (which obtain their light from a glowing vapor of mercury or sodium atoms) and in neon lights. (In compact fluorescent lamps, the magnetic ballast is replaced by a more complicated scheme for regulating current. This scheme utilizes transistors, discussed in Chapter 42.)

The self-inductance of a circuit depends on its size, shape, and number of turns. For N turns close together, it is always proportional to N^2. It also depends on the magnetic properties of the material enclosed by the circuit. In the following examples we will assume that the circuit encloses only vacuum (or air, which from the standpoint of magnetism is essentially vacuum). If, however, the flux is concentrated in a region containing a magnetic material with permeability μ, then in the expression for B we must replace μ_0 (the permeability of vacuum) by $\mu = K_m\mu_0$, as discussed in Section 28.8. If the material is diamagnetic or paramagnetic, this replacement makes very little difference, since K_m is very close to 1. If the material is *ferromagnetic,* however, the difference is of crucial importance. A solenoid wound on a soft iron core having $K_m = 5000$ can have an inductance approximately 5000 times as great as that of the same solenoid with an air core. Ferromagnetic-core inductors are very widely used in a variety of electronic and electric-power applications.

An added complication is that with ferromagnetic materials the magnetization is in general not a linear function of magnetizing current, especially as saturation is approached. As a result, the inductance is not constant but can depend on current in a fairly complicated way. In our discussion we will ignore this complication and assume always that the inductance is constant. This is a reasonable assumption even for a ferromagnetic material if the magnetization remains well below the saturation level.

Because automobiles contain steel, a ferromagnetic material, driving an automobile over a coil causes an appreciable increase in the coil's inductance. ? This effect is used in traffic light sensors, which use a large, current-carrying coil embedded under the road surface near an intersection. The circuitry connected to the coil detects the inductance change as a car drives over. When a preprogrammed number of cars have passed over the coil, the light changes to green to allow the cars through the intersection.

30.7 These fluorescent light tubes are wired in series with an inductor, or ballast, that helps to sustain the current flowing through the tubes.

Example 30.3 Calculating self-inductance

A toroidal solenoid with cross-sectional area A and mean radius r is closely wound with N turns of wire (Fig. 30.8). The toroid is wound on a nonmagnetic core. Determine its self-inductance L. Assume that B is uniform across a cross section (that is, neglect the variation of B with distance from the toroid axis).

SOLUTION

IDENTIFY: Our target variable is the self-inductance L of the toroidal solenoid.

SET UP: We can determine L in one of two ways: either with Eq. (30.6), which requires knowing the flux Φ_B through each turn and the current i in the coil, or from Eq. (30.7), which requires knowing the self-induced emf $\mathcal{E}$ due to a given rate of change of current di/dt. We are not given any information about the emf, so we must use the first approach. We use the results of Example 28.10 (Section 28.7), in which we found the magnetic field in the interior of a toroidal solenoid.

30.8 Determining the self-inductance of a closely wound toroidal solenoid. For clarity, only a few turns of the winding are shown. Part of the toroid has been cut away to show the cross-sectional area A and radius r.

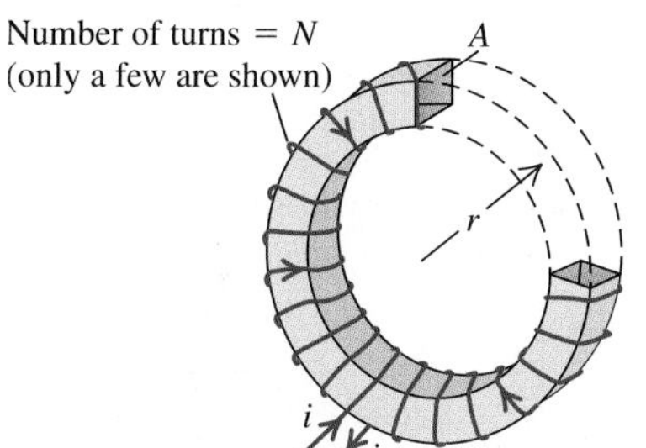

EXECUTE: From Eq. (30.6), the self-inductance is $L = N\Phi_B/i$. From Example 28.10, the field magnitude at a distance r from the toroid axis is $B = \mu_0 Ni/2\pi r$. If we assume that the field has this magnitude over the entire cross-sectional area A, then the magnetic flux through the cross section is

$$\Phi_B = BA = \frac{\mu_0 NiA}{2\pi r}$$

The flux Φ_B is the same through each turn, and the self-inductance L is

$$L = \frac{N\Phi_B}{i} = \frac{\mu_0 N^2 A}{2\pi r} \quad \text{(self-inductance of a toroidal solenoid)}$$

EVALUATE: Suppose $N = 200$ turns, $A = 5.0\ \text{cm}^2 = 5.0 \times 10^{-4}\ \text{m}^2$, and $r = 0.10$ m; then

$$L = \frac{(4\pi \times 10^{-7}\ \text{Wb/A}\cdot\text{m})(200)^2(5.0 \times 10^{-4}\ \text{m}^2)}{2\pi(0.10\ \text{m})}$$
$$= 40 \times 10^{-6}\ \text{H} = 40\ \mu\text{H}$$

Later in this chapter we will use the expression $L = \mu_0 N^2 A/2\pi r$ for the inductance of a toroidal solenoid to help develop an expression for the energy stored in a magnetic field.

Example 30.4 Calculating self-induced emf

If the current in the toroidal solenoid in Example 30.3 increases uniformly from 0 to 6.0 A in 3.0 μs, find the magnitude and direction of the self-induced emf.

SOLUTION

IDENTIFY: We are given L, the self-inductance, and di/dt, the rate of change of the current. Our target variable is the self-induced emf.

SET UP: We calculate the emf using Eq. (30.7).

EXECUTE: The rate of change of the solenoid current is $di/dt = (6.0\ \text{A})/(3.0 \times 10^{-6}\ \text{s}) = 2.0 \times 10^6\ \text{A/s}$. From Eq. (30.7), the magnitude of the induced emf is

$$|\mathcal{E}| = L\left|\frac{di}{dt}\right| = (40 \times 10^{-6}\ \text{H})(2.0 \times 10^6\ \text{A/s}) = 80\ \text{V}$$

The current is increasing, so according to Lenz's law the direction of the emf is opposite to that of the current. This corresponds to the situation in Fig. 30.6c; the emf is in the direction from b to a, like a battery with a as the + terminal and b the − terminal, tending to oppose the current increase from the external circuit.

EVALUATE: This example shows that even a small inductance L can give rise to a substantial induced emf if the current changes rapidly.

Test Your Understanding of Section 30.2 Rank the following inductors in order of the potential difference V_{ab}, from most positive to most negative. In each case the inductor has zero resistance and the current flows from point a through the inductor to point b. (i) The current through a 2.0-μH inductor increases from 1.0 A to 2.0 A in 0.50 s; (ii) the current through a 4.0-μH inductor decreases from 3.0 A to 0 in 2.0 s; (iii) the current through a 1.0-μH inductor remains constant at 4.0 A; (iv) the current through a 1.0-μH inductor increases from 0 to 4.0 A in 0.25 s.

MP

30.3 Magnetic-Field Energy

Establishing a current in an inductor requires an input of energy, and an inductor carrying a current has energy stored in it. Let's see how this comes about. In Fig. 30.5, an increasing current i in the inductor causes an emf $\mathcal{E}$ between its terminals, and a corresponding potential difference V_{ab} between the terminals of the source, with point a at higher potential than point b. Thus the source must be adding energy to the inductor, and the instantaneous power P (rate of transfer of energy into the inductor) is $P = V_{ab}i$.

Energy Stored in an Inductor

We can calculate the total energy input U needed to establish a final current I in an inductor with inductance L if the initial current is zero. We assume that the inductor has zero resistance, so no energy is dissipated within the inductor. Let the current at some instant be i and let its rate of change be di/dt; the current is increasing, so $di/dt > 0$. The voltage between the terminals a and b of the inductor at this instant is $V_{ab} = L\,di/dt$, and the rate P at which energy is being delivered to the inductor (equal to the instantaneous power supplied by the external source) is

$$P = V_{ab}i = Li\frac{di}{dt}$$

The energy dU supplied to the inductor during an infinitesimal time interval dt is $dU = P\,dt$, so

$$dU = Li\,di$$

The total energy U supplied while the current increases from zero to a final value I is

$$U = L\int_0^I i\,di = \frac{1}{2}LI^2 \qquad \text{(energy stored in an inductor)} \qquad (30.9)$$

After the current has reached its final steady value I, $di/dt = 0$ and no more energy is input to the inductor. When there is no current, the stored energy U is zero; when the current is I, the energy is $\frac{1}{2}LI^2$.

When the current decreases from I to zero, the inductor acts as a source that supplies a total amount of energy $\frac{1}{2}LI^2$ to the external circuit. If we interrupt the circuit suddenly by opening a switch or yanking a plug from a wall socket, the current decreases very rapidly, the induced emf is very large, and the energy may be dissipated in an arc across the switch contacts. This large emf is the electrical analog of the large force exerted by a car running into a brick wall and stopping very suddenly.

CAUTION **Energy, resistors, and inductors** It's important not to confuse the behavior of resistors and inductors where energy is concerned (Fig. 30.9). Energy flows into a resistor whenever a current passes through it, whether the current is steady or varying; this energy is dissipated in the form of heat. By contrast, energy flows into an ideal, zero-resistance inductor only when the current in the inductor *increases*. This energy is not dissipated; it is stored in the inductor and released when the current *decreases*. When a steady current flows through an inductor, there is no energy flow in or out.

30.9 A resistor is a device in which energy is irrecoverably dissipated. By contrast, energy stored in a current-carrying inductor can be recovered when the current decreases to zero.

Resistor with current i: energy is *dissipated*.

i a b R

Inductor with current i: energy is *stored*.

i a b L

Magnetic Energy Density

The energy in an inductor is actually stored in the magnetic field within the coil, just as the energy of a capacitor is stored in the electric field between its plates. We can develop relationships for magnetic-field energy analogous to those we obtained for electric-field energy in Section 24.3 [Eqs. (24.9) and (24.11)]. We will concentrate on one simple case, the ideal toroidal solenoid. This system has the advantage that its magnetic field is confined completely to a finite region of space within its core. As in Example 30.3, we assume that the cross-sectional area A is small enough that we can pretend that the magnetic field is uniform over the area. The volume V enclosed by the toroidal solenoid is approximately equal to the circumference $2\pi r$ multiplied by the area A: $V = 2\pi rA$. From Example 30.3, the self-inductance of the toroidal solenoid with vacuum within its coils is

$$L = \frac{\mu_0 N^2 A}{2\pi r}$$

From Eq. (30.9), the energy U stored in the toroidal solenoid when the current is I is

$$U = \frac{1}{2}LI^2 = \frac{1}{2}\frac{\mu_0 N^2 A}{2\pi r}I^2$$

The magnetic field and therefore this energy are localized in the volume $V = 2\pi rA$ enclosed by the windings. The energy *per unit volume,* or *magnetic energy density,* is $u = U/V$:

$$u = \frac{U}{2\pi rA} = \frac{1}{2}\mu_0 \frac{N^2 I^2}{(2\pi r)^2}$$

We can express this in terms of the magnitude B of the magnetic field inside the toroidal solenoid. From Eq. (28.24) in Example 28.10 (Section 28.7), this is

$$B = \frac{\mu_0 NI}{2\pi r}$$

and so

$$\frac{N^2 I^2}{(2\pi r)^2} = \frac{B^2}{\mu_0^2}$$

When we substitute this into the above equation for u, we finally find the expression for **magnetic energy density** in vacuum:

$$u = \frac{B^2}{2\mu_0} \quad \text{(magnetic energy density in vacuum)} \qquad (30.10)$$

This is the magnetic analog of the energy per unit volume in an *electric* field in vacuum, $u = \frac{1}{2}\epsilon_0 E^2$, which we derived in Section 24.3.

When the material inside the toroid is not vacuum but a material with (constant) magnetic permeability $\mu = K_m \mu_0$, we replace μ_0 by μ in Eq. (30.10). The energy per unit volume in the magnetic field is then

$$u = \frac{B^2}{2\mu} \quad \text{(magnetic energy density in a material)} \qquad (30.11)$$

Although we have derived Eq. (30.11) only for one special situation, it turns out to be the correct expression for the energy per unit volume associated with *any* magnetic-field configuration in a material with constant permeability. For vacuum, Eq. (30.11) reduces to Eq. (30.10). We will use the expressions for electric-field and magnetic-field energy in Chapter 32 when we study the energy associated with electromagnetic waves.

30.10 The energy required to fire an automobile spark plug is derived from magnetic-field energy stored in the ignition coil.

Magnetic-field energy plays an important role in the ignition systems of gasoline-powered automobiles. A primary coil of about 250 turns is connected to the car's battery and produces a strong magnetic field. This coil is surrounded by a secondary coil with some 25,000 turns of very fine wire. When it is time for a spark plug to fire (see Fig. 20.5 in Section 20.3), the current to the primary coil is interrupted, the magnetic field quickly drops to zero, and an emf of tens of thousands of volts is induced in the secondary coil. The energy stored in the magnetic field thus goes into a powerful pulse of current that travels through the secondary coil to the spark plug, generating the spark that ignites the fuel–air mixture in the engine's cylinders (Fig. 30.10).

Example 30.5 Storing energy in an inductor

The electric-power industry would like to find efficient ways to store surplus energy generated during low-demand hours to help meet customer requirements during high-demand hours. Perhaps a large inductor can be used. What inductance would be needed to store 1.00 kW · h of energy in a coil carrying a 200-A current?

SOLUTION

IDENTIFY: We are given the required amount of stored energy U and the current I. Our target variable is the self-inductance L.

SET UP: We solve for L using Eq. (30.9)

EXECUTE: We have $I = 200\text{ A}$ and $U = 1.00\text{ kW}\cdot\text{h} = (1.00 \times 10^3\text{ W})(3600\text{ s}) = 3.60 \times 10^6\text{ J}$. Solving Eq. (30.9) for L, we find

$$L = \frac{2U}{I^2} = \frac{2(3.60 \times 10^6\text{ J})}{(200\text{ A})^2} = 180\text{ H}$$

This is more than a *million* times greater than the self-inductance of the toroidal solenoid of Example 30.3 (Section 30.2).

EVALUATE: Conventional wires that are to carry 200 A would have to be of large diameter to keep the resistance low and avoid unacceptable energy losses due to I^2R heating. As a result, a 180-H inductor using conventional wire would be very large (room-size). A superconducting inductor could be much smaller, since the resistance of a superconductor is zero and much thinner wires could be used; one drawback is that the wires would have to be kept at low temperature to remain superconducting, and energy would have to be used to maintain this low temperature. As a result, this scheme is impractical with present technology.

Example 30.6 Magnetic energy density

In a proton accelerator used in elementary particle physics experiments, the trajectories of protons are controlled by bending magnets that produce a magnetic field of 6.6 T. What is the energy density in this field in the vacuum between the poles of such a magnet?

SOLUTION

IDENTIFY: Our target variable is the magnetic energy density u. we are given the magnitude B of the magnetic field.

SET UP: In a vacuum, $\mu = \mu_0$ and the energy density is given by Eq. (30.10).

EXECUTE: The energy density in the magnetic field is

$$u = \frac{B^2}{2\mu_0} = \frac{(6.6\text{ T})^2}{2(4\pi \times 10^{-7}\text{ T}\cdot\text{m/A})} = 1.73 \times 10^7\text{ J/m}^3$$

EVALUATE: As an interesting comparison, the heat of combustion of natural gas, expressed on an energy per unit volume basis, is about $3.8 \times 10^7\text{ J/m}^3$.

Test Your Understanding of Section 30.3 The current in a solenoid is reversed in direction while keeping the same magnitude. (a) Does this change the magnetic field within the solenoid? (b) Does this change the magnetic energy density in the solenoid?

30.4 The *R-L* Circuit

Let's look at some examples of the circuit behavior of an inductor. One thing is clear already; an inductor in a circuit makes it difficult for rapid changes in current to occur, thanks to the effects of self-induced emf. Equation (30.7) shows that the greater the rate of change of current di/dt, the greater the self-induced emf and the greater the potential difference between the inductor terminals. This equation, together with Kirchhoff's rules (see Section 26.2), gives us the principles we need to analyze circuits containing inductors.

ActivPhysics ONLINE
14.1 The *RL* Circuit

Problem-Solving Strategy 30.1 Inductors in Circuits

MP

IDENTIFY *the relevant concepts:* An inductor is just another circuit element, like a source of emf, a resistor, or a capacitor. One key difference is that when an inductor is included in a circuit, all the voltages, currents, and capacitor charges are in general functions of time, not constants as they have been in most of our previous circuit analysis. But Kirchhoff's rules, which we studied in Section 26.2, are still valid. When the voltages and currents vary with time, Kirchhoff's rules hold at each instant of time.

SET UP *the problem* using the following steps:

1. Follow the same procedure described in Problem-Solving Strategy 26.2 in Section 26.2. (Now would be an excellent time to review that strategy.) Draw a large circuit diagram and label all quantities, known and unknown. Apply the junction rule immediately at any junction.
2. Determine which quantities are the target variables.

EXECUTE *the solution* as follows:

1. As in Problem-Solving Strategy 26.2, apply Kirchhoff's loop rule to each loop in the circuit.
2. As in all circuit analysis, getting the correct sign for each potential difference is essential. (You should review the rules given in Problem-Solving Strategy 26.2.) To get the correct sign for the potential difference between the terminals of an inductor, remember Lenz's law and the sign rule described in Section 30.2 in conjunction with Eq. (30.7) and Fig. 30.6. In Kirchhoff's loop rule, when we go through an inductor in the *same* direction as the assumed current, we encounter a voltage *drop* equal to $L\,di/dt$, so the corresponding term in the loop equation is $-L\,di/dt$. When we go through an inductor in the *opposite* direction from the assumed current, the potential difference is reversed and the term to use in the loop equation is $+L\,di/dt$.
3. As always, solve for the target variables.

EVALUATE *your answer:* Check whether your answer is consistent with the way that inductors behave. If the current through an inductor is changing, your result should indicate that the potential difference across the inductor opposes the change. If not, you probably used an incorrect sign somewhere in your calculation.

Current Growth in an *R-L* Circuit

We can learn several basic things about inductor behavior by analyzing the circuit of Fig. 30.11. A circuit that includes both a resistor and an inductor, and possibly a source of emf, is called an ***R-L* circuit.** The inductor helps to prevent rapid changes in current, which can be useful if a steady current is required but the external source has a fluctuating emf. The resistor R may be a separate circuit element, or it may be the resistance of the inductor windings; every real-life inductor has some resistance unless it is made of superconducting wire. By closing switch S_1, we can connect the *R-L* combination to a source with constant emf $\mathcal{E}$. (We assume that the source has zero internal resistance, so the terminal voltage equals the emf.)

30.11 An *R-L* circuit.

Closing switch S_1 connects the *R-L* combination in series with a source of emf $\mathcal{E}$.

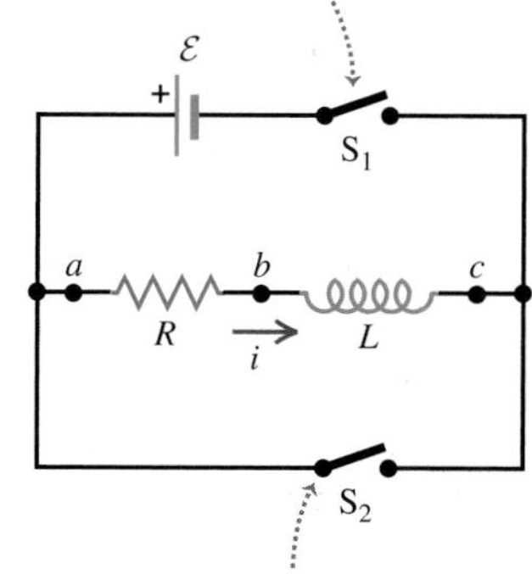

Closing switch S_2 while opening switch S_1 disconnnects the combination from the source.

Suppose both switches are open to begin with, and then at some initial time $t = 0$ we close switch S_1. The current cannot change suddenly from zero to some final value, since di/dt and the induced emf in the inductor would both be infinite. Instead, the current begins to grow at a rate that depends only on the value of L in the circuit.

Let i be the current at some time t after switch S_1 is closed, and let di/dt be its rate of change at that time. The potential difference v_{ab} across the resistor at that time is

$$v_{ab} = iR$$

and the potential difference v_{bc} across the inductor is

$$v_{bc} = L\frac{di}{dt}$$

Note that if the current is in the direction shown in Fig. 30.11 and is increasing, then both v_{ab} and v_{bc} are positive; a is at a higher potential than b, which in turn is at a higher potential than c. (Compare to Figs. 30.6a and c.) We apply Kirchhoff's loop rule, starting at the negative terminal and proceeding counterclockwise around the loop:

$$\mathcal{E} - ir - L\frac{di}{dt} = 0 \tag{30.12}$$

Solving this for di/dt, we find that the rate of increase of current is

$$\frac{di}{dt} = \frac{\mathcal{E} - iR}{L} = \frac{\mathcal{E}}{L} - \frac{R}{L}i \tag{30.13}$$

At the instant that switch S_1 is first closed, $i = 0$ and the potential drop across R is zero. The initial rate of change of current is

$$\left(\frac{di}{dt}\right)_{\text{initial}} = \frac{\mathcal{E}}{L}$$

As we would expect, the greater the inductance L, the more slowly the current increases.

As the current increases, the term $(R/L)i$ in Eq. (30.13) also increases, and the *rate* of increase of current given by Eq. (30.13) becomes smaller and smaller. This means that the current is approaching a final, steady-state value I. When the current reaches this value, its rate of increase is zero. Then Eq. (30.13) becomes

$$\left(\frac{di}{dt}\right)_{\text{final}} = 0 = \frac{\mathcal{E}}{L} - \frac{R}{L}I \quad \text{and}$$

$$I = \frac{\mathcal{E}}{R}$$

The *final* current I does not depend on the inductance L; it is the same as it would be if the resistance R alone were connected to the source with emf $\mathcal{E}$.

30.12 Graph of i versus t for growth of current in an R-L circuit with an emf in series. The final current is $I = \mathcal{E}/R$; after one time constant τ, the current is $1 - 1/e$ of this value.

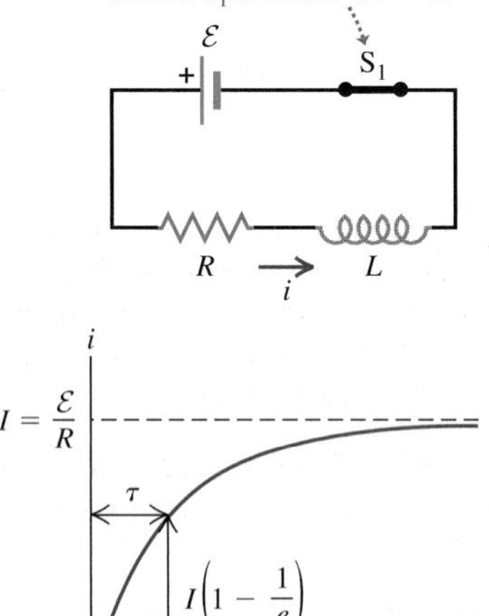

Figure 30.12 shows the behavior of the current as a function of time. To derive the equation for this curve (that is, an expression for current as a function of time), we proceed just as we did for the charging capacitor in Section 26.4. First we rearrange Eq. (30.13) to the form

$$\frac{di}{i - (\mathcal{E}/R)} = -\frac{R}{L}dt$$

This separates the variables, with i on the left side and t on the right. Then we integrate both sides, renaming the integration variables i' and t' so that we can use i and t as the upper limits. (The lower limit for each integral is zero, corresponding to zero current at the initial time $t = 0$.) We get

$$\int_0^i \frac{di'}{i' - (\mathcal{E}/R)} = -\int_0^t \frac{R}{L}dt'$$

$$\ln\left(\frac{i - (\mathcal{E}/R)}{-\mathcal{E}/R}\right) = -\frac{R}{L}t$$

Now we take exponentials of both sides and solve for i. We leave the details for you to work out; the final result is

$$i = \frac{\mathcal{E}}{R}\left(1 - e^{-(R/L)t}\right) \quad \text{(current in an } R\text{-}L \text{ circuit with emf)} \tag{30.14}$$

This is the equation of the curve in Fig. 30.12. Taking the derivative of Eq. (30.14), we find

$$\frac{di}{dt} = \frac{\mathcal{E}}{L}e^{-(R/L)t} \tag{30.15}$$

At time $t = 0$, $i = 0$ and $di/dt = \mathcal{E}/L$. As $t \to \infty$, $i \to \mathcal{E}/R$ and $di/dt \to 0$, as we predicted.

As Fig. 30.12 shows, the instantaneous current i first rises rapidly, then increases more slowly and approaches the final value $I = \mathcal{E}/R$ asymptotically. At a time equal to L/R the current has risen to $(1 - 1/e)$, or about 63%, of its final value. The quantity L/R is therefore a measure of how quickly the current builds toward its final value; this quantity is called the **time constant** for the circuit, denoted by τ:

$$\tau = \frac{L}{R} \quad \text{(time constant for an } R\text{-}L \text{ circuit)} \tag{30.16}$$

In a time equal to 2τ, the current reaches 86% of its final value; in 5τ, 99.3%; and in 10τ, 99.995%. (Compare the discussion in Section 26.4 of charging a capacitor of capacitance C that was in series with a resistor of resistance R; the time constant for that situation was the product RC.)

The graphs of i versus t have the same general shape for all values of L. For a given value of R, the time constant τ is greater for greater values of L. When L is small, the current rises rapidly to its final value; when L is large, it rises more slowly. For example, if $R = 100\ \Omega$ and $L = 10$ H,

$$\tau = \frac{L}{R} = \frac{10\ \text{H}}{100\ \Omega} = 0.10\ \text{s}$$

and the current increases to about 63% of its final value in 0.10 s. (Recall that $1\ \text{H} = 1\ \Omega \cdot \text{s}$.) But if $L = 0.010$ H, $\tau = 1.0 \times 10^{-4}\ \text{s} = 0.10$ ms, and the rise is much more rapid.

Energy considerations offer us additional insight into the behavior of an *R-L* circuit. The instantaneous rate at which the source delivers energy to the circuit is $P = \mathcal{E}i$. The instantaneous rate at which energy is dissipated in the resistor is i^2R, and the rate at which energy is stored in the inductor is $iv_{bc} = Li\,di/dt$ [or, equivalently, $(d/dt)(\frac{1}{2}Li^2) = Li\,di/dt$]. When we multiply Eq. (30.12) by i and rearrange, we find

$$\mathcal{E}i = i^2R + Li\frac{di}{dt} \tag{30.17}$$

Of the power $\mathcal{E}i$ supplied by the source, part (i^2R) is dissipated in the resistor and part $(Li\,di/dt)$ goes to store energy in the inductor. This discussion is completely analogous to our power analysis for a charging capacitor, given at the end of Section 26.4.

Example 30.7 Analyzing an *R-L* circuit

A sensitive electronic device of resistance 175 Ω is to be connected to a source of emf by a switch. The device is designed to operate with a current of 36 mA, but to avoid damage to the device, the current can rise to no more than 4.9 mA in the first 58 μs after the switch is closed. To protect the device, it is connected in series with an inductor as in Fig. 30.11; the switch in question is S_1. (a) What emf must the source have? Assume negligible internal resistance. (b) What inductance is required? (c) What is the time constant?

SOLUTION

IDENTIFY: This problem concerns current growth in an *R-L* circuit, so we can use the ideas of this section.

SET UP: Figure 30.12 shows that the final current is $I = \mathcal{E}/R$. Since the resistance is given, the emf is determined by the requirement that the final current is to be 36 mA. The other requirement is that the current be no more than $i = 4.9$ mA at $t = 58\ \mu$s; to satisfy this, we use Eq. (30.14) for the current as a function of time and solve for the inductance, which is the only unknown quantity. Equation (30.16) then tells us the time constant.

EXECUTE: (a) Using $I = 36\ \text{mA} = 0.036$ A and $R = 175\ \Omega$ in the expression $I = \mathcal{E}/R$ for the final current and solving for the emf, we find

$$\mathcal{E} = IR = (0.036\ \text{A})(175\ \Omega) = 6.3\ \text{V}$$

(b) To find the required inductance, we solve Eq. (30.14) for L. First we multiply through by $(-R/\mathcal{E})$ and then add 1 to both sides to obtain

$$1 - \frac{iR}{\mathcal{E}} = e^{-(R/L)t}$$

Continued

Then we take natural logs of both sides, solve for L, and insert the numbers:

$$L = \frac{-Rt}{\ln(1 - iR/\mathcal{E})}$$
$$= \frac{-(175\ \Omega)(58 \times 10^{-6}\ \text{s})}{\ln[1 - (4.9 \times 10^{-3}\ \text{A})(175\ \Omega)/(6.3\ \text{V})]} = 69\ \text{mH}$$

(c) From Eq. (30.16),

$$\tau = \frac{L}{R} = \frac{69 \times 10^{-3}\ \text{H}}{175\ \Omega} = 3.9 \times 10^{-4}\ \text{s} = 390\ \mu\text{s}$$

EVALUATE: We note that 58 μs is much less than the time constant. In 58 μs the current builds up only from zero to 4.9 mA, a small fraction of its final value of 36 mA; after 390 μs the current equals $(1 - 1/e)$ of its final value, or about $(0.63)(36\ \text{mA}) =$ 23 mA.

Current Decay in an *R-L* Circuit

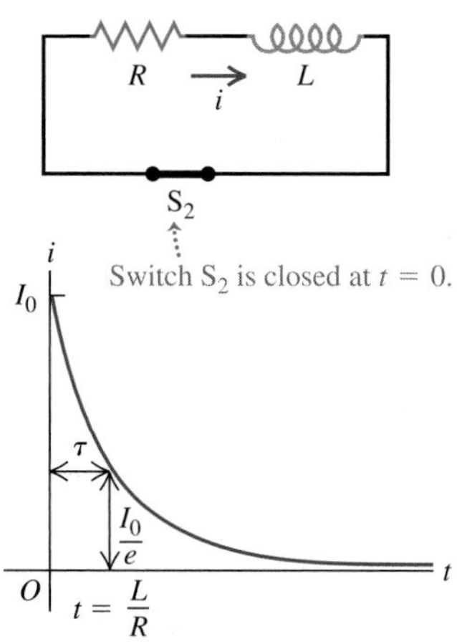

30.13 Graph of i versus t for decay of current in an *R-L* circuit. After one time constant τ, the current is $1/e$ of its initial value.

Now suppose switch S_1 in the circuit of Fig. 30.11 has been closed for a while and the current has reached the value I_0. Resetting our stopwatch to redefine the initial time, we close switch S_2 at time $t = 0$, bypassing the battery. (At the same time we should open S_1 to save the battery from ruin.) The current through R and L does not instantaneously go to zero but decays smoothly, as shown in Fig. 30.13. The Kirchhoff's-rule loop equation is obtained from Eq. (30.12) by simply omitting the $\mathcal{E}$ term. We challenge you to retrace the steps in the above analysis and show that the current i varies with time according to

$$i = I_0 e^{-(R/L)t} \tag{30.18}$$

where I_0 is the initial current at time $t = 0$. The time constant, $\tau = L/R$, is the time for current to decrease to $1/e$, or about 37%, of its original value. In time 2τ it has dropped to 13.5%, in time 5τ to 0.67%, and in 10τ to 0.0045%.

The energy that is needed to maintain the current during this decay is provided by the energy stored in the magnetic field of the inductor. The detailed energy analysis is simpler this time. In place of Eq. (30.17) we have

$$0 = i^2R + Li\frac{di}{dt} \tag{30.19}$$

In this case, $Li\,di/dt$ is negative; Eq. (30.19) shows that the energy stored in the inductor *decreases* at a rate equal to the rate of dissipation of energy i^2R in the resistor.

This entire discussion should look familiar; the situation is very similar to that of a charging and discharging capacitor, analyzed in Section 26.4. It would be a good idea to compare that section with our discussion of the *R-L* circuit.

Example 30.8 Energy in an *R-L* circuit

When the current in an *R-L* circuit is decaying, what fraction of the original energy stored in the inductor has been dissipated after 2.3 time constants?

SOLUTION

IDENTIFY: This problem concerns current decay in an *R-L* circuit as well as the relationship between the current in an inductor and the amount of stored energy.

SET UP: The current i at any time t for this situation is given by Eq. (30.18). The stored energy associated with this current is given by Eq. (30.9), $U = \frac{1}{2}Li^2$.

EXECUTE: From Eq. (30.18), the current i at any time t is

$$i = I_0 e^{-(R/L)t}$$

The energy U in the inductor at *any* time is obtained by substituting this expression into $U = \frac{1}{2}Li^2$. We obtain

$$U = \frac{1}{2}LI_0^2 e^{-2(R/L)t} = U_0 e^{-2(R/L)t}$$

where $U_0 = \frac{1}{2}LI_0^2$ is the energy at the initial time $t = 0$. When $t = 2.3\tau = 2.3L/R$, we have

$$U = U_0 e^{-2(2.3)} = U_0 e^{-4.6} = 0.010\ U_0$$

That is, only 0.010 or 1.0% of the energy initially stored in the inductor remains, so 99.0% has been dissipated in the resistor.

EVALUATE: To get a sense of what this result means, consider the *R-L* circuit we analyzed in Example 30.7, for which the time constant is 390 μs. With $L = 69$ mH $= 0.069$ H and an initial current $I_0 = 36$ mA $= 0.036$ A, the amount of energy in the inductor initially is $U_0 = \frac{1}{2}LI_0^2 = \frac{1}{2}(0.069\text{ H})(0.036\text{ A})^2 = 4.5 \times 10^{-5}$ J. Of this, 99.0% or 4.4×10^{-5} J is dissipated in $2.3(390\ \mu\text{s}) = 9.0 \times 10^{-4}\text{ s} = 0.90$ ms. In other words, this circuit can be powered off almost completely in 0.90 ms, and can be powered on in the same amount of time. The minimum time for a complete on-off cycle is therefore 1.8 ms. For many purposes, such as in fast switching networks for telecommunication, an even shorter cycle time is required. In such cases a smaller time constant $\tau = L/R$ is needed.

Test Your Understanding of Section 30.4 (a) In Fig. 30.11, what are the algebraic signs of the potential differences v_{ab} and v_{bc} when switch S_1 is closed and switch S_2 is open? (i) $v_{ab} > 0, v_{bc} > 0$; (ii) $v_{ab} > 0, v_{bc} < 0$; (iii) $v_{ab} < 0, v_{bc} > 0$; (iv) $v_{ab} < 0, v_{bc} < 0$. (b) What are the signs of v_{ab} and v_{bc} when S_1 is open, S_2 is closed, and current is flowing in the direction shown? (i) $v_{ab} > 0, v_{bc} > 0$; (ii) $v_{ab} > 0, v_{bc} < 0$; (iii) $v_{ab} < 0, v_{bc} > 0$; (iv) $v_{ab} < 0, v_{bc} < 0$.

30.5 The *L-C* Circuit

A circuit containing an inductor and a capacitor shows an entirely new mode of behavior, characterized by *oscillating* current and charge. This is in sharp contrast to the *exponential* approach to a steady-state situation that we have seen with both *R-C* and *R-L* circuits. In the ***L-C* circuit** in Fig. 30.14a we charge the

ActivPhysics ONLINE
14.2 AC Circuits: The *RLC* Oscillator (Questions 1–6)

30.14 In an oscillating *L-C* circuit, the charge on the capacitor and the current through the inductor both vary sinusoidally with time. Energy is transferred between magnetic energy in the inductor (U_B) and electric energy in the capacitor (U_E). As in simple harmonic motion, the total energy E remains constant. (Compare Fig. 13.14 in Section 13.3.)

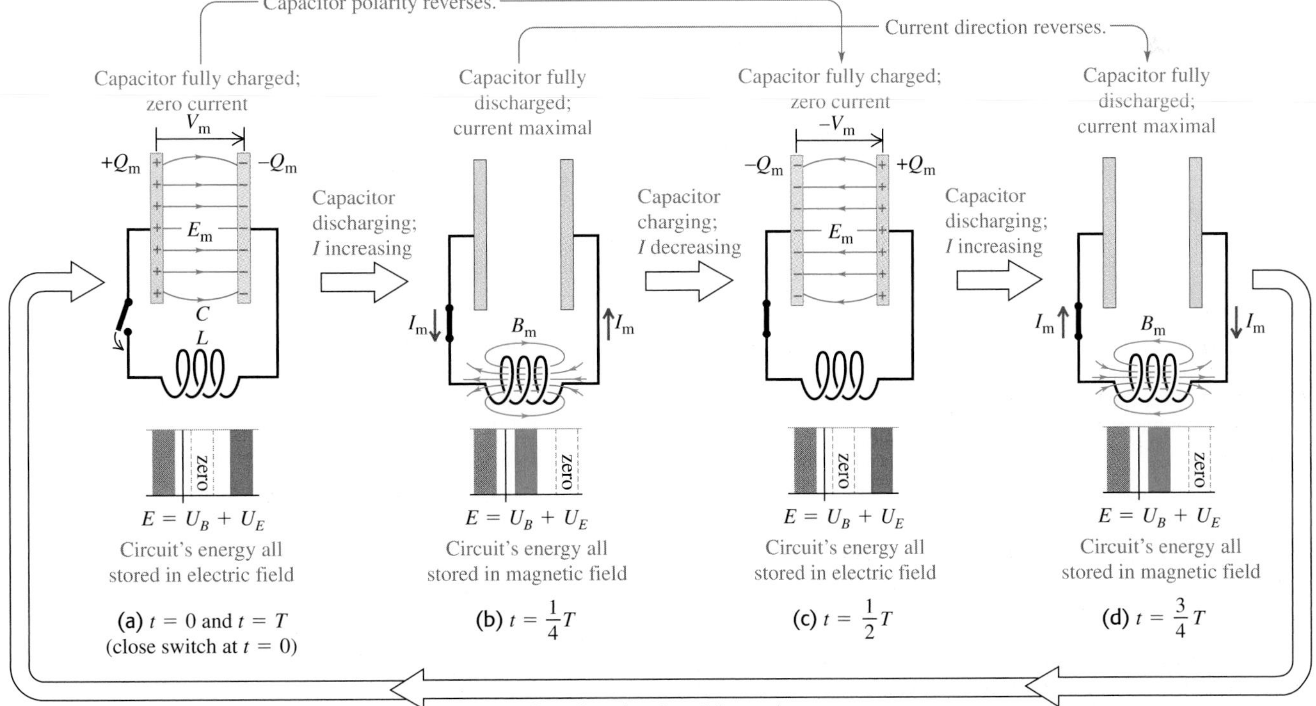

capacitor to a potential difference V_m and initial charge $Q = CV_m$ on its left-hand plate and then close the switch. What happens?

The capacitor begins to discharge through the inductor. Because of the induced emf in the inductor, the current cannot change instantaneously; it starts at zero and eventually builds up to a maximum value I_m. During this buildup the capacitor is discharging. At each instant the capacitor potential equals the induced emf, so as the capacitor discharges, the *rate of change* of current decreases. When the capacitor potential becomes zero, the induced emf is also zero, and the current has leveled off at its maximum value I_m. Figure 30.14b shows this situation; the capacitor has completely discharged. The potential difference between its terminals (and those of the inductor) has decreased to zero, and the current has reached its maximum value I_m.

During the discharge of the capacitor, the increasing current in the inductor has established a magnetic field in the space around it, and the energy that was initially stored in the capacitor's electric field is now stored in the inductor's magnetic field.

Although the capacitor is completely discharged in Fig. 30.14b, the current persists (it cannot change instantaneously), and the capacitor begins to charge with polarity opposite to that in the initial state. As the current decreases, the magnetic field also decreases, inducing an emf in the inductor in the *same* direction as the current; this slows down the decrease of the current. Eventually, the current and the magnetic field reach zero, and the capacitor has been charged in the sense *opposite* to its initial polarity (Fig. 30.14c), with potential difference $-V_m$ and charge $-Q$ on its left-hand plate.

The process now repeats in the reverse direction; a little later, the capacitor has again discharged, and there is a current in the inductor in the opposite direction (Fig. 30.14d). Still later, the capacitor charge returns to its original value (Fig. 30.14a), and the whole process repeats. If there are no energy losses, the charges on the capacitor continue to oscillate back and forth indefinitely. This process is called an **electrical oscillation.**

From an energy standpoint the oscillations of an electrical circuit transfer energy from the capacitor's electric field to the inductor's magnetic field and back. The *total* energy associated with the circuit is constant. This is analogous to the transfer of energy in an oscillating mechanical system from potential energy to kinetic energy and back, with constant total energy. As we will see, this analogy goes much further.

Electrical Oscillations in an *L-C* Circuit

To study the flow of charge in detail, we proceed just as we did for the *R-L* circuit. Figure 30.15 shows our definitions of q and i.

30.15 Applying Kirchhoff's loop rule to the *L-C* circuit. The direction of travel around the loop in the loop equation is shown. Just after the circuit is completed and the capacitor first begins to discharge, as in Fig. 30.14a, the current is negative (opposite to the direction shown).

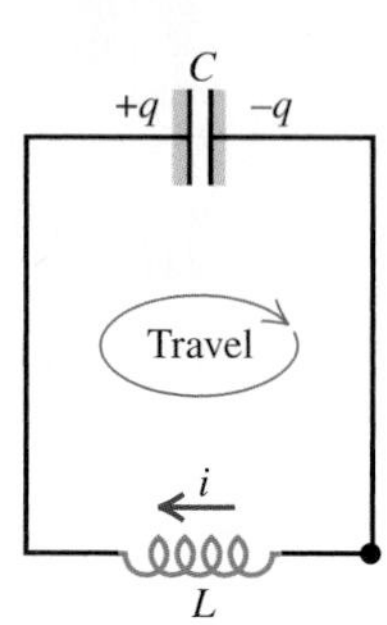

CAUTION Positive current in an *L-C* circuit After examining Fig. 30.14, the positive direction for current in Fig. 30.15 may seem backward to you. In fact we've chosen this direction to simplify the relationship between current and capacitor charge. We define the current at each instant to be $i = dq/dt$, the rate of change of the charge on the left-hand capacitor plate. Hence if the capacitor is initially charged and begins to discharge as in Figs. 30.14a and 30.14b, then $dq/dt < 0$ and the initial current i is negative; the direction of the current is then opposite to the (positive) direction shown in Fig. 30.15.

We apply Kirchhoff's loop rule to the circuit in Fig. 30.15. Starting at the lower-right corner of the circuit and adding voltages as we go clockwise around the loop, we obtain

$$-L\frac{di}{dt} - \frac{q}{C} = 0$$

Since $i = dq/dt$, it follows that $di/dt = d^2q/dt^2$. We substitute this expression into the above equation and divide by $-L$ to obtain

$$\frac{d^2q}{dt^2} + \frac{1}{LC}q = 0 \qquad (L\text{-}C \text{ circuit}) \tag{30.20}$$

Equation (30.20) has exactly the same form as the equation we derived for simple harmonic motion in Section 13.2, Eq. (13.4). That equation is $d^2x/dt^2 = -(k/m)x$, or

$$\frac{d^2x}{dt^2} + \frac{k}{m}x = 0$$

(You should review Section 13.2 before going on with this discussion.) In the L-C circuit the capacitor charge q plays the role of the displacement x, and the current $i = dq/dt$ is analogous to the particle's velocity $v_x = dx/dt$. The inductance L is analogous to the mass m, and the reciprocal of the capacitance, $1/C$, is analogous to the force constant k.

Pursuing this analogy, we recall that the angular frequency $\omega = 2\pi f$ of the harmonic oscillator is equal to $(k/m)^{1/2}$, and the position is given as a function of time by Eq. (13.13),

$$x = A\cos(\omega t + \phi)$$

where the amplitude A and the phase angle ϕ depend on the initial conditions. In the analogous electrical situation the capacitor charge q is given by

$$q = Q\cos(\omega t + \phi) \tag{30.21}$$

and the angular frequency ω of oscillation is given by

$$\omega = \sqrt{\frac{1}{LC}} \qquad \text{(angular frequency of oscillation in an } L\text{-}C \text{ circuit)} \tag{30.22}$$

You should verify that Eq. (30.21) satisfies the loop equation, Eq. (30.20), when ω has the value given by Eq. (30.22). In doing this, you will find that the instantaneous current $i = dq/dt$ is given by

$$i = -\omega Q\sin(\omega t + \phi) \tag{30.23}$$

Thus the charge and current in an L-C circuit oscillate sinusoidally with time, with an angular frequency determined by the values of L and C. The ordinary frequency f, the number of cycles per second, is equal to $\omega/2\pi$ as always. The constants Q and ϕ in Eqs. (30.21) and (30.23) are determined by the initial conditions. If at time $t = 0$ the left-hand capacitor plate in Fig. 30.15 has its maximum charge Q and the current i is zero, then $\phi = 0$. If $q = 0$ at time $t = 0$, then $\phi = \pm\pi/2$ rad.

Energy in an *L-C* Circuit

We can also analyze the L-C circuit using an energy approach. The analogy to simple harmonic motion is equally useful here. In the mechanical problem a body with mass m is attached to a spring with force constant k. Suppose we displace the body a distance A from its equilibrium position and release it from rest at time $t = 0$. The kinetic energy of the system at any later time is $\frac{1}{2}mv_x^2$, and its elastic potential energy is $\frac{1}{2}kx^2$. Because the system is conservative, the sum of these energies equals the initial energy of the system, $\frac{1}{2}kA^2$. We find the velocity v_x at any position x just as we did in Section 13.3, Eq. (13.22):

$$v_x = \pm\sqrt{\frac{k}{m}}\sqrt{A^2 - x^2} \tag{30.24}$$

The *L-C* circuit is also a conservative system. Again let Q be the maximum capacitor charge. The magnetic-field energy $\frac{1}{2}Li^2$ in the inductor at any time corresponds to the kinetic energy $\frac{1}{2}mv^2$ of the oscillating body, and the electric-field energy $q^2/2C$ in the capacitor corresponds to the elastic potential energy $\frac{1}{2}kx^2$ of the spring. The sum of these energies equals the total energy $Q^2/2C$ of the system:

$$\frac{1}{2}Li^2 + \frac{q^2}{2C} = \frac{Q^2}{2C} \tag{30.25}$$

The total energy in the *L-C* circuit is *constant;* it oscillates between the magnetic and the electric forms, just as the constant total mechanical energy in simple harmonic motion is constant and oscillates between the kinetic and potential forms.

Solving Eq. (30.25) for i, we find that when the charge on the capacitor is q, the current i is

$$i = \pm\sqrt{\frac{1}{LC}}\sqrt{Q^2 - q^2} \tag{30.26}$$

You can verify this equation by substituting q from Eq. (30.21) and i from Eq. (30.23). Comparing Eqs. (30.24) and (30.26), we see that current $i = dq/dt$ and charge q are related in the same way as are velocity $v_x = dx/dt$ and position x in the mechanical problem.

The analogies between simple harmonic motion and *L-C* circuit oscillations are summarized in Table 30.1. The striking parallel shown there between mechanical and electrical oscillations is one of many such examples in physics. This parallel is so close that we can solve complicated mechanical and acoustical problems by setting up analogous electrical circuits and measuring the currents and voltages that correspond to the mechanical and acoustical quantities to be determined. This is the basic principle of many analog computers. This analogy can be extended to *damped* oscillations, which we consider in the next section. In Chapter 31 we will extend the analogy further to include *forced* electrical oscillations, which occur in all alternating-current circuits.

Table 30.1 Oscillation of a Mass-Spring System Compared with Electrical Oscillation in an *L-C* Circuit

Mass-Spring System
Kinetic energy $= \frac{1}{2}mv_x^2$
Potential energy $= \frac{1}{2}kx^2$
$\frac{1}{2}mv_x^2 + \frac{1}{2}kx^2 = \frac{1}{2}kA^2$
$v_x = \pm\sqrt{k/m}\sqrt{A^2 - x^2}$
$v_x = dx/dt$
$\omega = \sqrt{\frac{k}{m}}$
$x = A\cos(\omega t + \phi)$

Inductor-Capacitor Circuit
Magnetic energy $= \frac{1}{2}Li^2$
Electric energy $= q^2/2C$
$\frac{1}{2}Li^2 + q^2/2C = Q^2/2C$
$i = \pm\sqrt{1/LC}\sqrt{Q^2 - q^2}$
$i = dq/dt$
$\omega = \sqrt{\frac{1}{LC}}$
$q = Q\cos(\omega t + \phi)$

Example 30.9 An oscillating circuit

A 300-V dc power supply is used to charge a 25-μF capacitor. After the capacitor is fully charged, it is disconnected from the power supply and connected across a 10-mH inductor. The resistance in the circuit is negligible. (a) Find the frequency and period of oscillation of the circuit. (b) Find the capacitor charge and the circuit current 1.2 ms after the inductor and capacitor are connected.

SOLUTION

IDENTIFY: Our target variables are the frequency f and period T, as well as the values of charge q and current i at a given time t.

SET UP: We are given the capacitance C and the inductance L, from which we can calculate the frequency and period using Eq. (30.22). We find the charge and current using Eqs. (30.21) and (30.23). Initially the capacitor is fully charged and the current is zero, as in Fig. 30.14a, so the phase angle is $\phi = 0$ [see the discussion that follows Eq. (30.23)].

EXECUTE: (a) The natural *angular* frequency is

$$\omega = \sqrt{\frac{1}{LC}} = \sqrt{\frac{1}{(10 \times 10^{-3}\,\text{H})(25 \times 10^{-6}\,\text{F})}}$$
$$= 2.0 \times 10^3\ \text{rad/s}$$

The frequency f is $1/2\pi$ times this:

$$f = \frac{\omega}{2\pi} = \frac{2.0 \times 10^3\ \text{rad/s}}{2\pi\ \text{rad/cycle}} = 320\ \text{Hz}$$

The period is the reciprocal of the frequency:

$$T = \frac{1}{f} = \frac{1}{320\ \text{Hz}} = 3.1 \times 10^{-3}\ \text{s} = 3.1\ \text{ms}$$

(b) Since the period of the oscillation is $T = 3.1$ ms, $t = 1.2$ ms equals $0.38T$; this corresponds to a situation intermediate between

Fig. 30.14b ($t = T/4$) and Fig. 30.14c ($t = T/2$). Comparing those figures to Fig. 30.15, we expect the capacitor charge q to be negative (that is, there will be negative charge on the left-hand plate of the capacitor) and the current i to be negative as well (that is, current will be traveling in a counterclockwise direction).

To find the value of q, we use Eq. (30.21). The charge is maximum at $t = 0$, so $\phi = 0$ and $Q = C\mathcal{E} = (25 \times 10^{-6}\text{ F})(300\text{ V}) = 7.5 \times 10^{-3}$ C. The charge q at any time is

$$q = (7.5 \times 10^{-3}\text{ C})\cos\omega t$$

At time $t = 1.2 \times 10^{-3}$ s,

$$\omega t = (2.0 \times 10^3\text{ rad/s})(1.2 \times 10^{-3}\text{ s}) = 2.4\text{ rad}$$
$$q = (7.5 \times 10^{-3}\text{ C})\cos(2.4\text{ rad}) = -5.5 \times 10^{-3}\text{ C}$$

The current i at any time is

$$i = -\omega Q \sin\omega t$$

At time $t = 1.2 \times 10^{-3}$ s,

$$i = -(2.0 \times 10^3\text{ rad/s})(7.5 \times 10^{-3}\text{ C})\sin(2.4\text{ rad}) = -10\text{ A}$$

EVALUATE: Note that the signs of q and i are both negative, as we predicted.

Example 30.10 Energy in an oscillating circuit

Consider again the *L-C* circuit of Example 30.9. 9 (a) Find the magnetic energy and electric energy at $t = 0$. (b) Find the magnetic energy and electric energy at $t = 1.2$ ms.

SOLUTION

IDENTIFY: This problem asks for the magnetic energy (stored in the inductor) and the electric energy (stored in the capacitor) at two different times during the oscillation of the *L-C* circuit.

SET UP: From Example 30.9 we know the values of the capacitor charge q and circuit current i for both of the times of interest. We use them to calculate the magnetic energy stored in the inductor, given by $U_B = \frac{1}{2}Li^2$, and the electric energy stored in the capacitor, given by $U_E = q^2/2C$.

EXECUTE: (a) At $t = 0$ there is no current and $q = Q$. Hence there is no magnetic energy, and all the energy in the circuit is in the form of electric energy in the capacitor:

$$U_B = \frac{1}{2}Li^2 = 0 \qquad U_E = \frac{Q^2}{2C} = \frac{(7.5 \times 10^{-3}\text{ C})^2}{2(25 \times 10^{-6}\text{ F})} = 1.1\text{ J}$$

(b) As we mentioned in Example 30.9, $t = 1.2$ ms corresponds to a situation intermediate between Fig. 30.14b ($t = T/4$) and Fig. 30.14c ($t = T/2$). So we expect the energy to be part magnetic and part electric at this time. From Example 30.9, $i = -10$ A and $q = -5.5 \times 10^{-3}$ C, so

$$U_B = \frac{1}{2}Li^2 = \frac{1}{2}(10 \times 10^{-3}\text{ H})(-10\text{ A})^2 = 0.5\text{ J}$$
$$U_E = \frac{q^2}{2C} = \frac{(-5.5 \times 10^{-3}\text{ C})^2}{2(25 \times 10^{-6}\text{ F})} = 0.6\text{ J}$$

EVALUATE: The magnetic and electric energies are the same at $t = 3T/8 = 0.375T$, exactly halfway between the situations in Figs. 30.14b and 30.14c. The time we are considering here is slightly later and U_B is slightly less than U_E, as we would expect. We emphasize that at *all* times, the *total* energy $E = U_B + U_E$ has the same value, 1.1 J. An *L-C* circuit without resistance is a conservative system; no energy is dissipated.

Test Your Understanding of Section 30.5 One way to think about the energy stored in an *L-C* circuit is to say that the circuit elements do positive or negative work on the charges that move back and forth through the circuit. (a) Between stages (a) and (b) in Fig. 30.14, does the capacitor do positive work or negative work on the charges? (b) What kind of force (electric or magnetic) does the capacitor exert on the charges to do this work? (c) During this process, does the inductor do positive or negative work on the charges? (d) What kind of force (electric or magnetic) does the inductor exert on the charges?

30.6 The *L-R-C* Series Circuit

In our discussion of the *L-C* circuit we assumed that there was no *resistance* in the circuit. This is an idealization, of course; every real inductor has resistance in its windings, and there may also be resistance in the connecting wires. Because of resistance, the electromagnetic energy in the circuit is dissipated and converted to other forms, such as internal energy of the circuit materials. Resistance in an electric circuit is analogous to friction in a mechanical system.

ActivPhysics ONLINE

14.2 AC Circuits: The *RLC* Oscillator (Questions 7–10)

Suppose an inductor with inductance L and a resistor of resistance R are connected in series across the terminals of a charged capacitor, forming an ***L-R-C* series circuit.** As before, the capacitor starts to discharge as soon as the circuit

30.16 Graphs of capacitor charge as a function of time in an *L-R-C* series circuit with initial charge Q.

(a) Underdamped circuit (small resistance R)

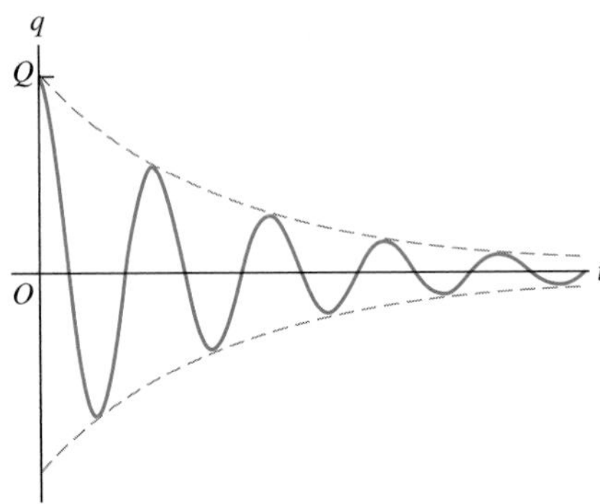

(b) Critically damped circuit (larger resistance R)

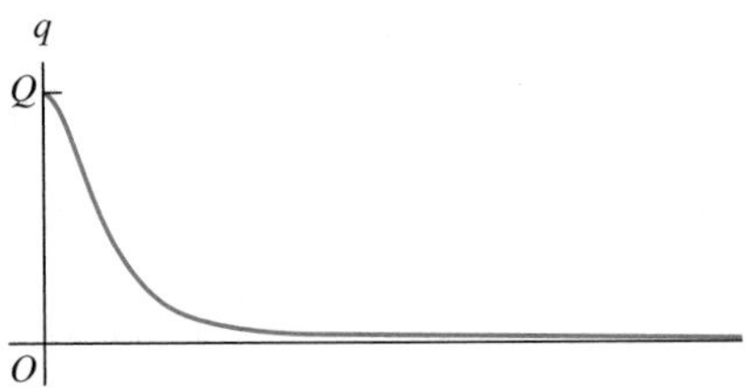

(c) Overdamped circuit (very large resistance R)

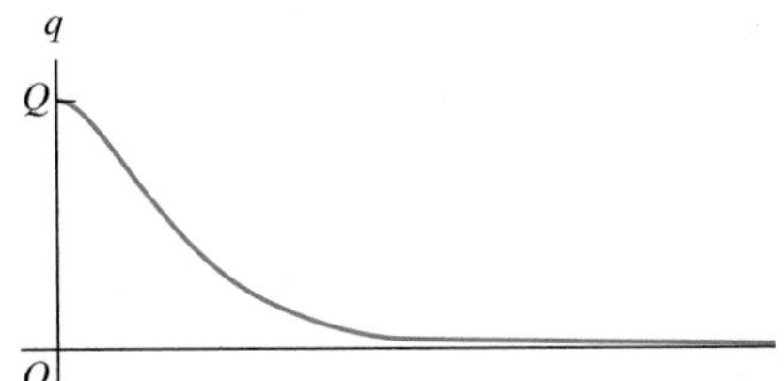

is completed. But because of i^2R losses in the resistor, the magnetic-field energy acquired by the inductor when the capacitor is completely discharged is *less* than the original electric-field energy of the capacitor. In the same way, the energy of the capacitor when the magnetic field has decreased to zero is still smaller, and so on.

If the resistance R is relatively small, the circuit still oscillates, but with **damped harmonic motion** (Fig. 30.16a), and we say that the circuit is **underdamped.** If we increase R, the oscillations die out more rapidly. When R reaches a certain value, the circuit no longer oscillates; it is **critically damped** (Fig. 30.16b). For still larger values of R, the circuit is **overdamped** (Fig. 30.16c), and the capacitor charge approaches zero even more slowly. We used these same terms to describe the behavior of the analogous mechanical system, the damped harmonic oscillator, in Section 13.7.

Analyzing an *L-R-C* Circuit

To analyze *L-R-C* circuit behavior in detail, we consider the circuit shown in Fig. 30.17. It is like the *L-C* circuit of Fig. 30.15 except for the added resistor R; we also show the source that charges the capacitor initially. The labeling of the positive senses of q and i are the same as for the *L-C* circuit.

First we close the switch in the upward position, connecting the capacitor to a source of emf $\mathcal{E}$ for a long enough time to ensure that the capacitor acquires its final charge $Q = C\mathcal{E}$ and any initial oscillations have died out. Then at time $t = 0$ we flip the switch to the downward position, removing the source from the circuit and placing the capacitor in series with the resistor and inductor. Note that the initial current is negative, opposite in direction to the direction of i shown in the figure.

To find how q and i vary with time, we apply Kirchhoff's loop rule. Starting at point a and going around the loop in the direction *abcda*, we obtain the equation

$$-iR - L\frac{di}{dt} - \frac{q}{C} = 0$$

Replacing i with dq/dt and rearranging, we get

$$\frac{d^2q}{dt^2} + \frac{R}{L}\frac{dq}{dt} + \frac{1}{LC}q = 0 \qquad (30.27)$$

30.17 An *L-R-C* series circuit.

When switch S is in this position, the emf charges the capacitor.

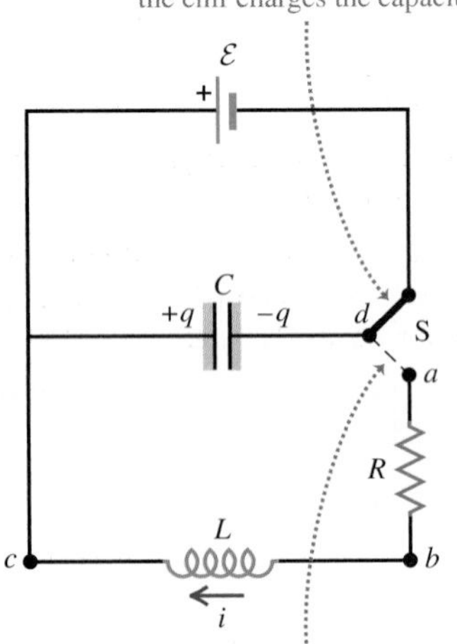

When switch S is moved to this position, the capacitor discharges through the resistor and inductor.

Note that when $R = 0$, this reduces to Eq. (30.20) for an *L-C* circuit.

There are general methods for obtaining solutions of Eq. (30.27). The form of the solution is different for the underdamped (small R) and overdamped (large R) cases. When R^2 is less than $4L/C$, the solution has the form

$$q = Ae^{-(R/2L)t}\cos\left(\sqrt{\frac{1}{LC} - \frac{R^2}{4L^2}}\,t + \phi\right) \qquad (30.28)$$

where A and ϕ are constants. We invite you to take the first and second derivatives of this function and show by direct substitution that it does satisfy Eq. (30.27).

This solution corresponds to the *underdamped* behavior shown in Fig. 30.16a; the function represents a sinusoidal oscillation with an exponentially decaying amplitude. (Note that the exponential factor $e^{-(R/2L)t}$ is *not* the same as the factor $e^{-(R/L)t}$ that we encountered in describing the *R-L* circuit in Section 30.4.) When $R = 0$, Eq. (30.28) reduces to Eq. (30.21) for the oscillations in an *L-C* circuit. If R is not zero, the angular frequency of the oscillation is *less* than $1/(LC)^{1/2}$

because of the term containing R. The angular frequency ω' of the damped oscillations is given by

$$\omega' = \sqrt{\frac{1}{LC} - \frac{R^2}{4L^2}} \quad \text{(underdamped } L\text{-}R\text{-}C \text{ series circuit)} \qquad (30.29)$$

When $R = 0$, this reduces to Eq. (30.22), $\omega = (1/LC)^{1/2}$. As R increases, ω' becomes smaller and smaller. When $R^2 = 4L/C$, the quantity under the radical becomes zero; the system no longer oscillates, and the case of *critical damping* (Fig. 30.16b) has been reached. For still larger values of R the system behaves as in Fig. 30.16c. In this case the circuit is *overdamped,* and q is given as a function of time by the sum of two decreasing exponential functions.

In the *underdamped* case the phase constant ϕ in the cosine function of Eq. (30.28) provides for the possibility of both an initial charge and an initial current at time $t = 0$, analogous to an underdamped harmonic oscillator given both an initial displacement and an initial velocity (see Exercise 30.38).

We emphasize once more that the behavior of the *L-R-C* series circuit is completely analogous to that of the damped harmonic oscillator studied in Section 13.7. We invite you to verify, for example, that if you start with Eq. (13.41) and substitute q for x, L for m, $1/C$ for k, and R for the damping constant b, the result is Eq. (30.27). Similarly, the cross-over point between underdamping and overdamping occurs at $b^2 = 4km$ for the mechanical system and at $R^2 = 4L/C$ for the electrical one. Can you find still other aspects of this analogy?

The practical applications of the *L-R-C* series circuit emerge when we include a sinusoidally varying source of emf in the circuit. This is analogous to the *forced oscillations* that we discussed in Section 13.7, and there are analogous *resonance* effects. Such a circuit is called an *alternating-current (ac) circuit;* the analysis of ac circuits is the principal topic of the next chapter.

Example 30.11 An underdamped *L-R-C* series circuit

What resistance R is required (in terms of L and C) to give an *L-R-C* circuit a frequency that is one-half the undamped frequency?

SOLUTION

IDENTIFY: This problem concerns an underdamped *L-R-C* series circuit (Fig. 30.16a): we want the resistance to be great enough to reduce the oscillation frequency to one-half of the undamped value, but not so great that the oscillator become criticaly damped (Fig. 30.1b) or overdamped (Fig. 30.16c).

SET UP: The angular frequency of an underdamped *L-R-C* series circuit is given by Eq. (30.29); the angular frequency of an undamped *L-C* circuit is given by Eq. (30.22). We use these to solve for the target variable R.

EXECUTE: We want ω' given by Eq. (30.29) to be equal to one-half of ω given by Eq. (30.22):

$$\sqrt{\frac{1}{LC} - \frac{R^2}{4L^2}} = \frac{1}{2}\sqrt{\frac{1}{LC}}$$

When we square both sides and solve for R, we get

$$R = \sqrt{\frac{3L}{C}}$$

For example, adding 35 Ω to the circuit of Example 30.9 would reduce the frequency from 320 Hz to 160 Hz.

EVALUATE: The circuit becomes critically damped with no oscillations when $R = \sqrt{4L/C}$. Our result for R is smaller than that, as it should be; we want the circuit to be underdamped.

Test Your Understanding of Section 30.6 An *L-R-C* series circuit includes a 2.0-Ω resistor. At $t = 0$ the capacitor charge is 2.0 μC. for which of the following values of the inductance and capacitance will the charge on the capacitor *not* oscillate? (i) $L = 3.0\ \mu$H, $C = 6.0\ \mu$F; (ii) $L = 6.0\ \mu$H, $C = 3.0\ \mu$F; (iii) $L = 3.0\ \mu$H, $C = 3.0\ \mu$F.

CHAPTER 30 SUMMARY

Mutual inductance When a changing current i_1 in one circuit causes a changing magnetic flux in a second circuit, an emf $\mathcal{E}_2$ is induced in the second circuit. Likewise, a changing current i_2 in the second circuit induces an emf $\mathcal{E}_1$ in the first circuit. The mutual inductance M depends on the geometry of the two coils and the material between them. If the circuits are coils of wire with N_1 and N_2 turns, M can be expressed in terms of the average flux Φ_{B2} through each turn of coil 2 that is caused by the current i_1 in coil 1, or in terms of the average flux Φ_{B1} through each turn of coil 1 that is caused by the current i_2 in coil 2. The SI unit of mutual inductance is the henry, abbreviated H. (See Examples 30.1 and 30.2.)

$$\mathcal{E}_2 = -M\frac{di_1}{dt} \quad \text{and} \quad \mathcal{E}_1 = -M\frac{di_2}{dt} \tag{30.4}$$

$$M = \frac{N_2\Phi_{B2}}{i_1} = \frac{N_1\Phi_{B1}}{i_2} \tag{30.5}$$

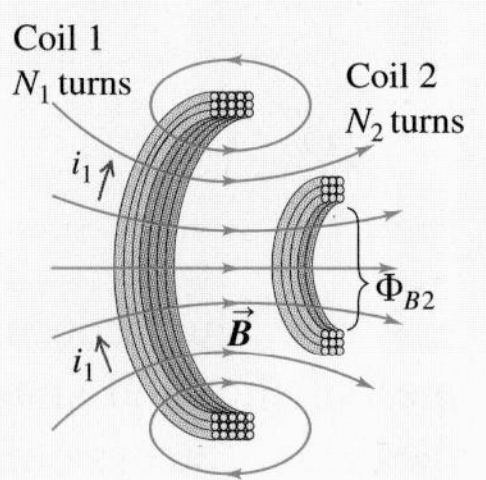

Self-inductance A changing current i in any circuit causes a self-induced emf $\mathcal{E}$. The inductance (or self-inductance) L depends on the geometry of the circuit and the material surrounding it. The inductance of a coil of N turns is related to the average flux Φ_B through each turn caused by the current i in the coil. An inductor is a circuit device, usually including a coil of wire, intended to have a substantial inductance. (See Examples 30.3 and 30.4.)

$$\mathcal{E} = -L\frac{di}{dt} \tag{30.7}$$

$$L = \frac{N\Phi_B}{i} \tag{30.6}$$

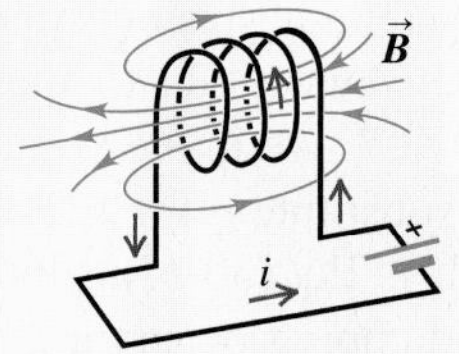

Magnetic-field energy An inductor with inductance L carrying current I has energy U associated with the inductor's magnetic field. The magnetic energy density u (energy per unit volume) is proportional to the square of the magnetic field magnitude. (See Examples 30.5 and 30.6.)

$$U = \frac{1}{2}LI^2 \tag{30.9}$$

$$u = \frac{B^2}{2\mu_0} \quad \text{(in vacuum)} \tag{30.10}$$

$$u = \frac{B^2}{2\mu} \tag{30.11}$$

(in a material with magnetic permeability μ)

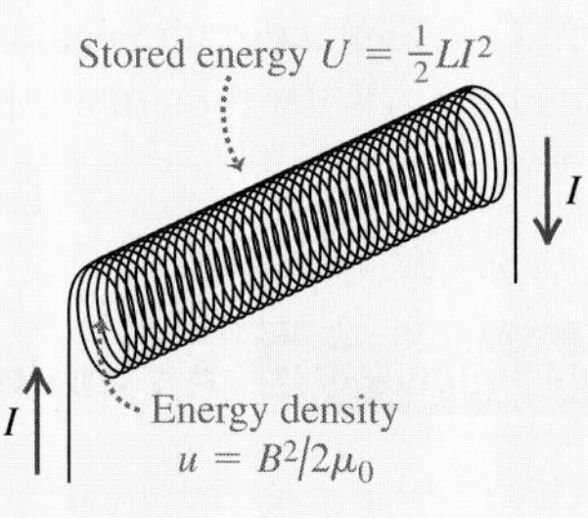

***R-L* circuits** In a circuit containing a resistor R, an inductor L, and a source of emf, the growth and decay of current are exponential. The time constant τ is the time required for the current to approach within a fraction $1/e$ of its final value. (See Examples 30.7 and 30.8.)

$$\tau = \frac{L}{R} \tag{30.16}$$

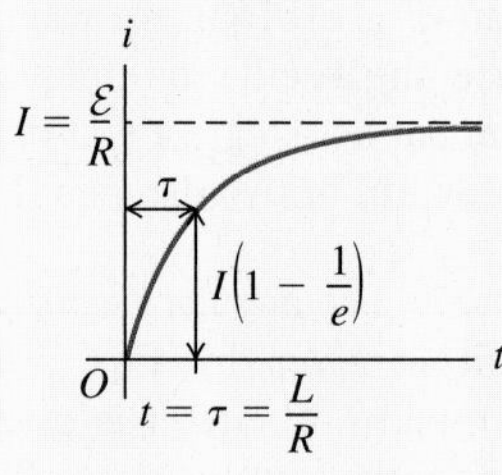

***L-C* circuits:** A circuit that contains inductance L and capacitance C undergoes electrical oscillations with an angular frequency ω that depends on L and C. Such a circuit is analogous to a mechanical harmonic oscillator, with inductance L analogous to mass m, the reciprocal of capacitance $1/C$ to force constant k, charge q to displacement x, and current i to velocity v_x. (See Examples 30.9 and 30.10.)

$$\omega = \sqrt{\frac{1}{LC}} \tag{30.22}$$

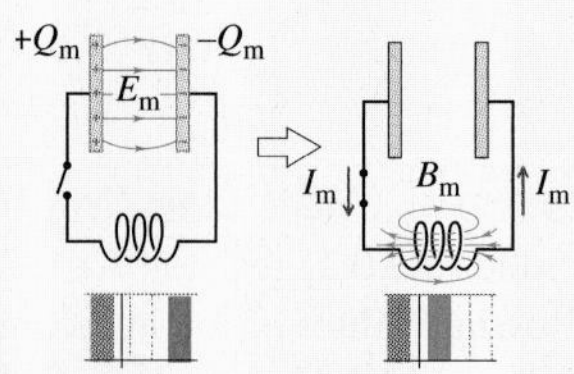

***L-R-C* series circuits:** A circuit that contains inductance, resistance, and capacitance undergoes damped oscillations for sufficiently small resistance. The frequency ω' of damped oscillations depends on the values of L, R, and C. As R increases, the damping increases; if R is greater than a certain value, the behavior becomes overdamped and no longer oscillates. The cross-over between underdamping and overdamping occurs when $R^2 = 4L/C$; when this condition is satisfied, the oscillations are critically damped. (See Example 30.11.)

$$\omega' = \sqrt{\frac{1}{LC} - \frac{R^2}{4L^2}} \quad (30.29)$$

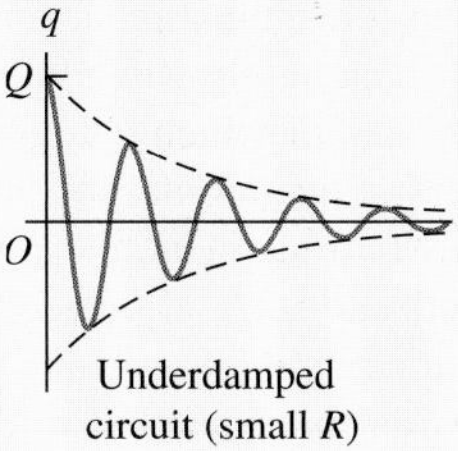

Key Terms

mutual inductance, *1031*
henry, *1032*
self-induced emf, *1034*
inductance (self-inductance), *1034*
inductor, *1034*
magnetic energy density, *1040*
R-L circuit, *1041*
time constant, *1043*
L-C circuit, *1045*
electrical oscillation, *1046*
L-R-C series circuit, *1050*
damped harmonic motion, *1050*
underdamped, *1050*
critically damped, *1050*
overdamped, *1050*

Answer to Chapter Opening Question ?

As explained in Section 30.2, traffic light sensors work by measuring the change in inductance of a coil embedded under the road surface when a car drives over it.

Answers to Test Your Understanding Questions

30.1 Answer: (iii) Doubling both the length of the solenoid (l) and the number of turns of wire in the solenoid (N_1) would have *no* effect on the mutual inductance M. Example 30.1 shows that M depends on the ratio of these quantities, which would remain unchanged. This is because the magnetic field produced by the solenoid depends on the number of turns *per unit length,* and the proposed change has no effect on this quantity.
30.2 Answer: (iv), (i), (iii), (ii) From Eq. (30.8), the potential difference across the inductor is $V_{ab} = L\,di/dt$. For the four cases we find (i) $V_{ab} = (2.0\ \mu\text{H})(2.0\ \text{A} - 1.0\ \text{A})/(0.50\ \text{s}) = 4.0\ \mu\text{V}$; (ii) $V_{ab} = (4.0\ \mu\text{H})(0 - 3.0\ \text{A})/(2.0\ \text{s}) = -6.0\ \mu\text{V}$; (iii) $V_{ab} = 0$ because the rate of change of current is zero; and (iv) $V_{ab} = (1.0\ \mu\text{H})(4.0\ \text{A} - 0)/(0.25\ \text{s}) = 16\ \mu\text{V}$.
30.3 Answers: (a) yes, (b) no Reversing the direction of the current has no effect on the magnetic field magnitude, but it causes the direction of the magnetic field to reverse. It has no effect on the magnetic-field energy density, which is proportional to the square of the *magnitude* of the magnetic field.
30.4 Answers: (a) (i), (b) (ii) Recall that v_{ab} is the potential at a minus the potential at b, and similarly for v_{bc}. For either arrangement of the switches, current flows through the resistor from a to b. The upstream end of the resistor is always at the higher potential, so v_{ab} is positive. With S_1 closed and S_2 open, the current through the inductor flows from b to c and is increasing. The self-induced emf opposes this increase and is therefore directed from c toward b, which means that b is at the higher potential. Hence v_{bc} is positive. With S_1 open and S_2 closed, the inductor current again flows from b to c but is now decreasing. The self-induced emf is directed from b to c in an effort to sustain the decaying current, so c is at the higher potential and v_{bc} is negative.
30.5 Answers: (a) positive, (b) electric, (c) negative, (d) electric The capacitor loses energy between stages (a) and (b), so it does positive work on the charges. It does this by exerting an electric force that pushes current away from the positively charged left-hand capacitor plate and toward the negatively charged right-hand plate. At the same time, the inductor gains energy and does negative work on the moving charges. Although the inductor stores magnetic energy, the force that the inductor exerts is *electric.* This force comes about from the inductor's self-induced emf (see Section 30.2).
30.6 Answers: (i), (iii) There are no oscillations if $R^2 \geq 4L/C$. In each case $R^2 = (2.0\ \Omega)^2 = 4.0\ \Omega^2$. In case (i) $4L/C = 4(3.0\ \mu\text{H})/(6.0\ \mu\text{F}) = 2.0\ \Omega^2$, so there are no oscillations (the system is overdamped); in case (ii) $4L/C = 4(6.0\ \mu\text{H})/(3.0\ \mu\text{F}) = 8.0\ \Omega^2$, so there are oscillations (the system is underdamped); and in case (iii) $4L/C = 4(3.0\ \mu\text{H})/(3.0\ \mu\text{F}) = 4.0\ \Omega^2$, so there are no oscillations (the system is critically damped).

PROBLEMS

For instructor-assigned homework, go to **www.masteringphysics.com** 

Discussion Questions

Q30.1. In an electric trolley or bus system, the vehicle's motor draws current from an overhead wire by means of a long arm with an attachment at the end that slides along the overhead wire. A brilliant electric spark is often seen when the attachment crosses a junction in the wires where contact is momentarily lost. Explain this phenomenon.

Q30.2. A transformer consists basically of two coils in close proximity but not in electrical contact. A current in one coil magnetically induces an emf in the second coil, with properties that can be controlled by adjusting the geometry of the two coils. Such a device will work only with alternating current, however, and not with direct current. Explain.

Q30.3. In Fig. 30.1, if coil 2 is turned 90° so that its axis is vertical, does the mutual inductance increase or decrease? Explain.

Q30.4. The tightly wound toroidal solenoid is one of the few configurations for which it is easy to calculate self-inductance. What features of the toroidal solenoid give it this simplicity?

Q30.5. Two identical, closely wound, circular coils, each having self-inductance L, are placed next to each other, so that they are coaxial and almost touching. If they are connected in series, what is the self-inductance of the combination? What if they are connected in parallel? Can they be connected so that the total inductance is zero? Explain.

Q30.6. Two closely wound circular coils have the same number of turns, but one has twice the radius of the other. How are the self-inductances of the two coils related? Explain your reasoning.

Q30.7. You are to make a resistor by winding a wire around a cylindrical form. To make the inductance as small as possible, it is proposed that you wind half the wire in one direction and the other half in the opposite direction. Would this achieve the desired result? Why or why not?

Q30.8. For the same magnetic field strength B, is the energy density greater in vacuum or in a magnetic material? Explain. Does Eq. (30.11) imply that for a long solenoid in which the current is I the energy stored is proportional to $1/\mu$? And does this mean that for the same current less energy is stored when the solenoid is filled with a ferromagnetic material rather than with air? Explain.

Q30.9. In Section 30.5 Kirchhoff's loop rule is applied to an L-C circuit where the capacitor is initially fully charged and the equation $-L\,di/dt - q/C = 0$ is derived. But as the capacitor starts to discharge, the current increases from zero. The equation says $L\,di/dt = -q/C$, so it says $L\,di/dt$ is negative. Explain how $L\,di/dt$ can be negative when the current is increasing.

Q30.10. In Section 30.5 the relationship $i = dq/dt$ is used in deriving Eq. (30.20). But a flow of current corresponds to a decrease in the charge on the capacitor. Explain, therefore, why this is the correct equation to use in the derivation, rather than $i = -dq/dt$.

Q30.11. In the R-L circuit shown in Fig. 30.11, when switch S_1 is closed, the potential v_{ab} changes suddenly and discontinuously, but the current does not. Explain why the voltage can change suddenly but the current can't.

Q30.12. In the R-L circuit shown in Fig. 30.11, is the current in the resistor always the same as the current in the inductor? How do you know?

Q30.13. Suppose there is a steady current in an inductor. If you attempt to reduce the current to zero instantaneously by quickly opening a switch, an arc can appear at the switch contacts. Why? Is it physically possible to stop the current instantaneously? Explain.

Q30.14. In an R-L-C circuit, what criteria could be used to decide whether the system is overdamped or underdamped? For example, could we compare the maximum energy stored during one cycle to the energy dissipated during one cycle? Explain.

Exercises

Section 30.1 Mutual Inductance

30.1. Two coils have mutual inductance $M = 3.25 \times 10^{-4}$ H. The current i_1 in the first coil increases at a uniform rate of 830 A/s. (a) What is the magnitude of the induced emf in the second coil? Is it constant? (b) Suppose that the current described is in the second coil rather than the first. What is the magnitude of the induced emf in the first coil?

30.2. Two coils are wound around the same cylindrical form, like the coils in Example 30.1. When the current in the first coil is decreasing at a rate of -0.242 A/s, the induced emf in the second coil has magnitude 1.65×10^{-3} V. (a) What is the mutual inductance of the pair of coils? (b) If the second coil has 25 turns, what is the flux through each turn when the current in the first coil equals 1.20 A? (c) If the current in the second coil increases at a rate of 0.360 A/s, what is the magnitude of the induced emf in the first coil?

30.3. From Eq. (30.5) $1\text{ H} = 1\text{ Wb/A}$, and from Eq. (30.4) $1\text{ H} = 1\ \Omega \cdot \text{s}$. Show that these two definitions are equivalent.

30.4. A solenoidal coil with 25 turns of wire is wound tightly around another coil with 300 turns (see Example 30.1). The inner solenoid is 25.0 cm long and has a diameter of 2.00 cm. At a certain time, the current in the inner solenoid is 0.120 A and is increasing at a rate of 1.75×10^3 A/s. For this time, calculate; (a) the average magnetic flux through each turn of the inner solenoid; (b) the mutual inductance of the two solenoids; (c) the emf induced in the outer solenoid by the changing current in the inner solenoid.

30.5. Two toroidal solenoids are wound around the same form so that the magnetic field of one passes through the turns of the other. Solenoid 1 has 700 turns, and solenoid 2 has 400 turns. When the current in solenoid 1 is 6.52 A, the average flux through each turn of solenoid 2 is 0.0320 Wb. (a) What is the mutual inductance of the pair of solenoids? (b) When the current in solenoid 2 is 2.54 A, what is the average flux through each turn of solenoid 1?

Section 30.2 Self-Inductance and Inductors

30.6. A toroidal solenoid has 500 turns, cross-sectional area 6.25 cm^2, and mean radius 4.00 cm. (a) Calcualte the coil's self-inductance. (b) If the current decreases uniformly from 5.00 A to 2.00 A in 3.00 ms, calculate the self-induced emf in the coil. (c) The current is directed from terminal a of the coil to terminal b. Is the direction of the induced emf from a to b or from b to a?

30.7. At the instant when the current in an inductor is increasing at a rate of 0.0640 A/s, the magnitude of the self-induced emf is 0.0160 V. (a) What is the inductance of the inductor? (b) If the inductor is a solenoid with 400 turns, what is the average magnetic flux through each turn when the current is 0.720 A?

30.8. When the current in a toroidal solenoid is changing at a rate of 0.0260 A/s, the magnitude of the induced emf is 12.6 mV. When the current equals 1.40 A, the average flux through each turn of the solenoid is 0.00285 Wb. How many turns does the solenoid have?

30.9. The inductor in Fig. 30.18 has inductance 0.260 H and carries a current in the direction shown that is decreasing at a uniform rate, $di/dt = -0.0180$ A/s. (a) Find the self-induced emf. (b) Which end of the inductor, a or b, is at a higher potential?

Figure 30.18 Exercises 30.9 and 30.10.

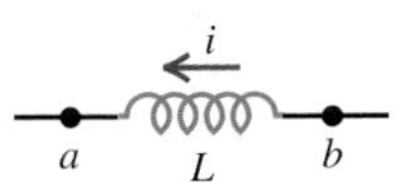

30.10. The inductor shown in Fig. 30.18 has inductance 0.260 H and carries a current in the direction shown. The current is changing at a constant rate. (a) The potential between points a and b is $V_{ab} = 1.04$ V, with point a at higher potential. Is the current increasing or decreasing? b) If the current at $t = 0$ is 12.0 A, what is the current at $t = 2.00$ s?

30.11. Inductance of a Solenoid. A long, straight solenoid has N turns, uniform cross-sectional area A, and length l. Show that the inductance of this solenoid is given by the equation $L = \mu_0 A N^2/l$. Assume that the magnetic field is uniform inside the solenoid and zero outside. (Your answer is approximate because B is actually smaller at the ends than at the center. For this reason, your answer is actually an upper limit on the inductance.)

Section 30.3 Magnetic-Field Energy

30.12. An inductor used in a dc power supply has an inductance of 12.0 H and a resistance of 180 Ω. It carries a current of 0.300 A. (a) What is the energy stored in the magnetic field? (b) At what rate is thermal energy developed in the inductor? (c) Does your answer to part (b) mean that the magnetic-field energy is decreasing with time? Explain.

30.13. An air-filled toroidal solenoid has a mean radius of 15.0 cm and a cross-sectional area of 5.00 cm^2. When the current is 12.0 A, the energy stored is 0.390 J. How many turns does the winding have?

30.14. An air-filled toroidal solenoid has 300 turns of wire, a mean radius of 12.0 cm, and a cross-sectional area of 4.00 cm^2. If the current is 5.00 A, calculate: (a) the magnetic field in the solenoid; (b) the self-inductance of the solenoid; (c) the energy stored in the magnetic field; (d) the energy density in the magnetic field. (e) Check your answer for part (d) by dividing your answer to part (c) by the volume of the solenoid.

30.15. A solenoid 25.0 cm long and with a cross-sectional area of 0.500 cm^2 contains 400 turns of wire and carries a current of 80.0 A. Calculate: (a) the magnetic field in the solenoid; (b) the energy density in the magnetic field if the solenoid is filled with air; (c) the total energy contained in the coil's magnetic field (assume the field is uniform); (d) the inductance of the solenoid.

30.16. It has been proposed to use large inductors as energy storage devices. (a) How much electrical energy is converted to light and thermal energy by a 200-W light bulb in one day? (b) If the amount of energy calculated in part (a) is stored in an inductor in which the current is 80.0 A, what is the inductance?

30.17. Starting from Eq. (30.9), derive in detail Eq. (30.11) for the energy density in a toroidal solenoid filled with a magnetic material.

30.18. It is proposed to store 1.00 kW · h = 3.60×10^6 J of electrical energy in a uniform magnetic field with magnitude 0.600 T. (a) What volume (in vacuum) must the magnetic field occupy to store this amount of energy? (b) If instead this amount of energy is to be stored in a volume (in vacuum) equivalent to a cube 40.0 cm on a side, what magnetic field is required?

Section 30.4 The *R-L* Circuit

30.19. An inductor with an inductance of 2.50 H and a resistance of 8.00 Ω is connected to the terminals of a battery with an emf of 6.00 V and negligible internal resistance. Find (a) the initial rate of increase of current in the circuit; (b) the rate of increase of current at the instant when the current is 0.500 A; (c) the current 0.250 s after the circuit is closed; (d) the final steady-state current.

30.20. A 15.0-Ω resistor and a coil are connected in series with a 6.30-V battery with negligible internal resistance and a closed switch. (a) At 2.00 ms after the switch is opened the current has decayed to 0.210 A. Calculate the inductance of the coil. (b) Calculate the time constant of the circuit. (c) How long after the switch is closed will the current reach 1.00% of its original value?

30.21. A 35.0-V battery with negligible internal resistance, a 50.0-Ω resistor, and a 1.25-mH inductor with negligible resistance are all connected in series with an open switch. The switch is suddenly closed. (a) How long after closing the switch will the current through the inductor reach one-half of its maximum value? (b) How long after closing the switch will the energy stored in the inductor reach one-half of its maximum value?

30.22. In Fig. 30.11, switch S_1 is closed while switch S_2 is kept open. The inductance is $L = 0.115$ H, and the resistance is $R = 120\ \Omega$. (a) When the current has reached its final value, the energy stored in the inductor is 0.260 J. What is the emf $\mathcal{E}$ of the battery? (b) After the current has reached its final value, S_1 is opened and S_2 is closed. How much time does it take for the energy stored in the inductor to decrease to 0.130 J, half the original value?

30.23. Show that L/R has units of time.

30.24. Write an equation corresponding to Eq. (30.13) for the current shown in Fig. 30.11 just after switch S_2 is closed and switch S_1 is opened, if the initial current is I_0. Use integration methods to verify Eq. (30.18).

30.25. In Fig. 30.11, suppose that $\mathcal{E} = 60.0$ V, $R = 240\ \Omega$, and $L = 0.160$ H. With switch S_2 open, switch S_1 is left closed until a constant current is established. Then S_2 is closed and S_1 opened, taking the battery out of the circuit. (a) What is the initial current in the resistor, just after S_2 is closed and S_1 is opened? (b) What is the current in the resistor at $t = 4.00 \times 10^{-4}$ s? (c) What is the potential difference between points b and c at $t = 4.00 \times 10^{-4}$ s? Which point is at a higher potential? (d) How long does it take the current to decrease to half its initial value?

30.26. In Fig. 30.11, suppose that $\mathcal{E} = 60.0$ V, $R = 240\ \Omega$, and $L = 0.160$ H. Initially there is no current in the circuit. Switch S_2 is left open, and switch S_1 is closed. (a) Just after S_1 is closed, what are the potential differences v_{ab} and v_{bc}? (b) A long time (many time constants) after S_1 is closed, what are v_{ab} and v_{bc}? (c) What are v_{ab} and v_{bc} at an intermediate time when $i = 0.150$ A?

30.27. Refer to Exercise 30.19. (a) What is the power input to the inductor from the battery as a function of time if the circuit is completed at $t = 0$? (b) What is the rate of dissipation of energy in the resistance of the inductor as a function of time? (c) What is the rate at which the energy of the magnetic field in the inductor is increasing, as a function of time? (d) Compare the results of parts (a), (b), and (c).

Section 30.5 The *L-C* Circuit

30.28. A 20.0-μF capacitor is charged by a 150.0-V power supply, then disconnected from the power and connected in series with a 0.280-mH inductor. Calculate: (a) the oscillation frequency of the circuit; (b) the energy stored in the capacitor at time $t = 0$ ms (the moment of connection with the inductor); (c) the energy stored in the inductor at $t = 1.30$ ms.

30.29. A 7.50-nF capacitor is charged up to 12.0 V, then disconnected from the power supply and connected in series through a coil. The period of oscillation of the circuit is then measured to be 8.60×10^{-5} s. Calculate: (a) the inductance of the coil; (b) the maximum charge on the capacitor; (c) the total energy of the circuit; (d) the maximum current in the circuit.

30.30. A 18.0-μF capacitor is placed across a 22.5-V battery for several seconds and is then connected across a 12.0-mH inductor that has no appreciable resistance. (a) After the capacitor and inductor are connected together, find the maximum current in the circuit. When the current is a maximum, what is the charge on the capacitor? (b) How long after the capacitor and inductor are connected together does it take for the capacitor to be completely discharged for the first time? For the second time? (c) Sketch graphs of the charge on the capacitor plates and the current through the inductor as functions of time.

30.31. ***L-C* Oscillations.** A capacitor with capacitance 6.00×10^{-5} F is charged by connecting it to a 12.0-V battery. The capacitor is disconnected from the battery and connected across an inductor with $L = 1.50$ H. (a) What are the angular frequency ω of the electrical oscillations and the period of these oscillations (the time for one oscillation)? (b) What is the initial charge on the capacitor? (c) How much energy is initially stored in the capacitor? (d) What is the charge on the capacitor 0.0230 s after the connection to the inductor is made? Interpret the sign of your answer.

(e) At the time given in part (d), what is the current in the inductor? Interpret the sign of your answer. (f) At the time given in part (d), how much electrical energy is stored in the capacitor and how much is stored in the inductor?

30.32. A Radio Tuning Circuit. The minimum capacitance of a variable capacitor in a radio is 4.18 pF. (a) What is the inductance of a coil connected to this capacitor if the oscillation frequency of the *L-C* circuit is 1600×10^3 Hz, corresponding to one end of the AM radio broadcast band, when the capacitor is set to its minimum capacitance? (b) The frequency at the other end of the broadcast band is 540×10^3 Hz. What is the maximum capacitance of the capacitor if the oscillation frequency is adjustable over the range of the broadcast band?

30.33. An *L-C* circuit containing an 80.0-mH inductor and a 1.25-nF capacitor oscillates with a maximum current of 0.750 A. Calculate: (a) the maximum charge on the capacitor and (b) the oscillation frequency of the circuit. (c) Assuming the capacitor had its maximum charge at time $t = 0$, calculate the energy stored in the inductor after 2.50 ms of oscillation.

30.34. In an *L-C* circuit, $L = 85.0$ mH and $C = 3.20\ \mu$F. During the oscillations the maximum current in the inductor is 0.850 mA. (a) What is the maximum charge on the capacitor? (b) What is the magnitude of the charge on the capacitor at an instant when the current in the inductor has magnitude 0.500 mA?

30.35. (a) Using Eqs. (30.21) and (30.23) for an *L-C* circuit, write expressions for the energy stored in the capacitor as a function of time and for the energy stored in the inductor as a function of time. (b) Using Eq. (30.22) and the trigonometric identity $\sin^2 x + \cos^2 x = 1$, show that the total energy in the *L-C* circuit is constant and equal to $Q^2/2C$.

30.36. Show that the differential equation of Eq. (30.20) is satisfied by the function $q = Q\cos(\omega t + \phi)$, with ω given by $1/\sqrt{LC}$.

30.37. Show that $\sqrt{LC}$ has units of time.

Section 30.6 The *L-R-C* Series Circuit

30.38. For the circuit of Fig. 30.17, let $C = 15.0$ nF, $L = 22$ mH, and $R = 75.0\ \Omega$ (a) Calculate the oscillation frequency of the circuit once the capacitor has been charged and the switch has been connected to point *a* (b) How long will it take for the amplitude of the oscillation to decay to 10.0% of its original value? (c) What value of *R* would result in a critically damped circuit?

30.39. (a) In Eq. (13.41), substitute *q* for *x*, *L* for *m*, $1/C$ for *k*, and *R* for the damping constant *b*. Show that the result is Eq. (30.27). (b) Make these same substitutions in Eq. (13.43) and show that Eq. (30.29) results. (c) Make these same substitutions in Eq. (13.42) and show that Eq. (30.28) results.

30.40. (a) Take first and second derivatives with respect to time of *q* given in Eq. (30.28), and show that it is a solution of Eq. (30.27). (b) At $t = 0$ the switch shown in Fig. 30.17 is thrown so that it connects points *d* and *a*; at this time, $q = Q$ and $i = dq/dt = 0$. Show that the constants ϕ and *A* in Eq. (30.28) are given by

$$\tan\phi = -\frac{R}{2L\sqrt{(1/LC) - (R^2/4L^2)}} \quad \text{and} \quad A = \frac{Q}{\cos\phi}$$

30.41. An *L-R-C* circuit has $L = 0.450$ H, $C = 2.50 \times 10^{-5}$ F, and resistance *R*. (a) What is the angular frequency of the circuit when $R = 0$? (b) What value must *R* have to give a 5.0% decrease in angular frequency compared to the value calculated in part (a)?

30.42. Show that the quantity $\sqrt{L/C}$ has units of resistance (ohms).

Problems

30.43. One solenoid is centered inside another. The outer one has a length of 50.0 cm and contains 6750 coils, while the coaxial inner solenoid is 3.0 cm long and 0.120 cm in diameter and contains 15 coils. The current in the outer solenoid is changing at 37.5 A/s. (a) what is the mutual inductance of these solenoids? (b) Find the emf induced in the innner solenoid.

30.44. A coil has 400 turns and self-inductance 3.50 mH. The current in the coil varies with time according to $i = (680\text{ mA})\cos(\pi t/0.0250\text{ s})$. (a) What is the maximum emf induced in the coil? (b) What is the maximum average flux through each turn of the coil? (c) At $t = 0.0180$ s, what is the magnitude of the induced emf?

30.45. A Differentiating Circuit. The current in a resistanceless inductor is caused to vary with time as shown in the graph of Fig. 30.19. (a) Sketch the pattern that would be observed on the screen of an oscilloscope connected to the terminals of the inductor. (The oscilloscope spot sweeps horizontally across the screen at a constant speed, and its vertical deflection is proportional to the potential difference between the inductor terminals.) (b) Explain why a circuit with an inductor can be described as a "differentiating circuit."

Figure 30.19 Problem 30.45

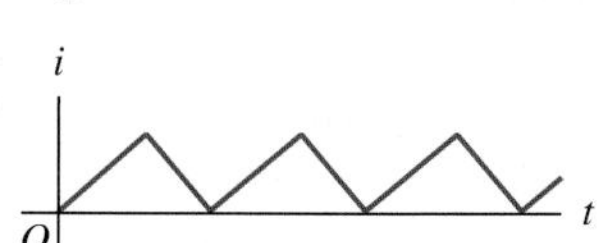

30.46. A 0.250-H inductor carries a time-varying current given by the expression $i = (124\text{ mA})\cos[(240\pi/\text{s})\,t]$. (a) Find an expression for the induced emf as a function of time. Graph the current and induced emf as functions of time for $t = 0$ to $t = \frac{1}{60}$ s. (b) What is the maximum emf? What is the current when the induced emf is a maximum? (c) What is the maximum current? What is the induced emf when the current is a maximum?

30.47. Inductors in Series and Parallel. You are given two inductors, one of self-inductance L_1 and the other of self-inductance L_2. (a) You connect the two inductors in series and arrange them so that their mutual inductance is negligible. Show that the equivalent inductance of the combination is $L_{eq} = L_1 + L_2$. (b) You now connect the two inductors in parallel, again arranging them so that their mutual inductance is negligible. Show that the equivalent inductance of the combination is $L_{eq} = (1/L_1 + 1/L_2)^{-1}$. (*Hint:* For either a series or a parallel combination, the potential difference across the combination is $L_{eq}(di/dt)$, where *i* is the current through the combination. For a parallel combination, *i* is the sum of the currents through the two inductors.)

30.48. A Coaxial Cable. A small solid conductor with radius *a* is supported by insulating, nonmagnetic disks on the axis of a thin-walled tube with inner radius *b*. The inner and outer conductors carry equal currents *i* in opposite directions. (a) Use Ampere's law to find the magnetic field at any point in the volume between the conductors. (b) Write the expression for the flux $d\Phi_B$ through a narrow strip of length *l* parallel to the axis, of width *dr*, at a distance *r* from the axis of the cable and lying in a plane containing the axis. (c) Integrate your expression from part (b) over the volume between the two conductors to find the total flux produced by a current *i* in the central conductor. (d) Show that the inductance of a length *l* of the cable is

$$L = l\frac{\mu_0}{2\pi}\ln\left(\frac{b}{a}\right)$$

(e) Use Eq. (30.9) to calculate the energy stored in the magnetic field for a length *l* of the cable.

30.49. Consider the coaxial cable of Problem 30.48. The conductors carry equal currents i in opposite directions. (a) Use Ampere's law to find the magnetic field at any point in the volume between the conductors. (b) Use the energy density for a magnetic field, Eq. (30.10), to calculate the energy stored in a thin, cylindrical shell between the two conductors. Let the cylindrical shell have inner radius r, outer radius $r + dr$, and length l. (c) integrate your result in part (b) over the volume between the two conductors to find the total energy stored in the magnetic field for a length l of the cable. (d) Use your result in part (c) and Eq. (30.9) to calculate the inductance L of a length l of the cable. Compare your result to L calculated in part (d) of Problem 30.48.

30.50. A toroidal solenoid has a mean radius r and a cross-sectional area A and is wound uniformly with N_1 turns. A second toroidal solenoid with N_2 turns is wound uniformly around the first. The two coils are wound in the same direction. (a) Derive an expression for the inductance L_1 when only the first coil is used and an expression for L_2 when only the second coil is used. (b) Show that $M^2 = L_1 L_2$.

30.51. (a) What would have to be the self-inductance of a solenoid for it to store 10.0 J of energy when a 1.50-A current runs throught it? (b) If this solenoid's cross-sectional diameter is 4.00 cm, and if you could wrap its coils to a density of 10 coils/mm, how long would the solenoid be? (See Exercise 30.11.) Is this a realistic length for ordinary laboratory use?

30.52. An inductor is connected to the terminals of a battery that has an emf of 12.0 V and negligible internal resistance. The current is 4.86 mA at 0.725 ms after the connection is completed. After a long time the current is 6.45 mA. What are (a) the resistance R of the inductor and (b) the inductance L of the inductor?

30.53. Continuation of Exercises 30.19 and 30.27. (a) How much energy is stored in the magnetic field of the inductor one time constant after the battery has been connected? Compute this both by integrating the expression in Exercise 30.27(c) and by using Eq. (30.9), and compare the results. (b) Integrate the expression obtained in Exercise 30.27(a) to find the *total* energy supplied by the battery during the time interval considered in part (a). (c) Integrate the expression obtained in Exercise 30.27(b) to find the *total* energy dissipated in the resistance of the inductor during the same time period. (d) Compare the results obtained in parts (a), (b), and (c).

30.54. Continuation of Exercise 30.25. (a) What is the total energy initially stored in the inductor? (b) At $t = 4.00 \times 10^{-4}$ s, at what rate is the energy stored in the inductor decreasing? (c) At $t = 4.00 \times 10^{-4}$ s, at what rate is electrical energy being converted into thermal energy in the resistor? (d) Obtain an expression for the rate at which electrical energy is being converted into thermal energy in the resistor as a function of time. Integrate this expression from $t = 0$ to $t = \infty$ to obtain the total electrical energy dissipated in the resistor. Compare your result to that of part (a).

30.55. The equation preceding Eq. (30.27) may be converted into an energy relationship. Multiply both sides of this equation by $-i = -dq/dt$. The first term then becomes i^2R. Show that the second term can be written as $d(\frac{1}{2}Li^2)/dt$, and that the third term can be written as $d(q^2/2C)/dt$. What does the resulting equation say about energy conservation in the circuit?

30.56. A 5.00-μF capacitor is initially charged to a potential of 16.0 V. It is then connected in series with a 3.75-mH inductor. (a) What is the total energy stored in this circuit? (b) What is the maximum current in the inductor? What is the charge on the capacitor plates at the instant the current in the inductor is maximal?

30.57. An Electromagnetic Car Alarm. Your latest invention is a car alarm that produces sound at a particularly annoying frequency of 3500 Hz. To do this, the car-alarm circuitry must produce an alternating electric current of the same frequency. That's why your design includes an inductor and a capacitor in series. The maximum voltage across the capacitor is to be 12.0 V (the same voltage as the car battery). To produce a sufficiently loud sound, the capacitor must store 0.0160 J of energy. What values of capacitance and inductance should you choose for your car-alarm circuit?

30.58. An L-C circuit consists of a 60.0-mH inductor and a 250-μF capacitor. The initial charge on the capacitor is 6.00 μC, and the initial current in the inductor is zero. (a) What is the maximum voltage across the capacitor? (b) What is the maximum current in the inductor? (c) What is the maximum energy stored in the inductor? (d) When the current in the inductor has half its maximum value, what is the charge on the capacitor and what is the energy stored in the inductor?

30.59. Solar Magnetic Energy. Magnetic fields within a sunspot can be as strong as 0.4 T. (By comparison, the earth's magnetic field is about 1/10,000 as strong.) Sunspots can be as large as 25,000 km in radius. The material in a sunspot has a density of about 3×10^{-4} kg/m^3. Assume μ for the sunspot material is μ_0. If 100% of the magnetic-field energy stored in a sunspot could be used to eject the sunspot's material away from the sun's surface, at what speed would that material be ejected? Compare to the sun's escape speed, which is about 6×10^5 m/s. (*Hint:* Calcualte the kinetic energy the magnetic field could supply to 1 m^3 of sunspot material.)

30.60. While studying a coil of unknown inductance and internal resistance, you connect it in series with a 25.0-V battery and a 150-Ω resistor. You then place an oscilloscope across one of these circuit elements and use the oscilloscope to measure the voltage across the circuit element as a function of time. The result is shown in Fig. 30.20. (a) Across which circuit element (coil or resistor) is the oscilloscope connected? How do you know this? (b) Find the inductance and the internal resistance of the coil. (c) Carefully make a quantitative sketch showing the voltage versus time you would observe if you put the oscilloscope across the other circuit element (resistor or coil).

Figure 30.20 Problem 30.60.

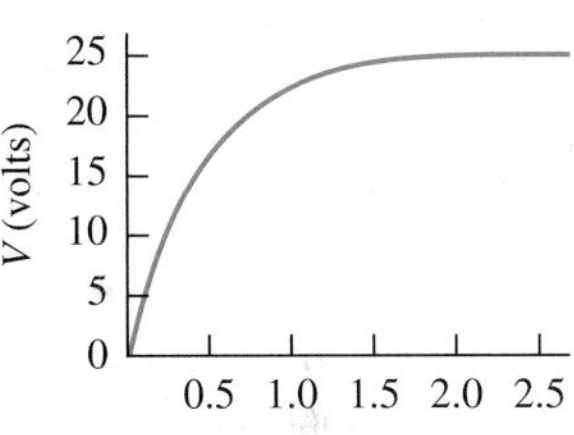

30.61. In the lab, you are trying to find the inductance and internal resistance of a solenoid. You place it in series with a battery of negligible internal resistance, a 10.0-Ω resistor, and a switch. You then put an oscilloscope across one of these circuit elements to measure the voltage across that circuit element as a function of time. You close the switch, and the oscilloscope shows voltage versus time as shown in Fig. 30.21. (a) Across which circuit element (solenoid or resistor) is the oscilloscope connected? How do you know this? (b) Why doesn't the graph approach zero as $t \to \infty$? (c) What is the emf of the battery? (d) Find the maximum current in the circuit. (e) What are the internal resistance and self-inductance of the solenoid?

Figure 30.21 Problem 30.61.

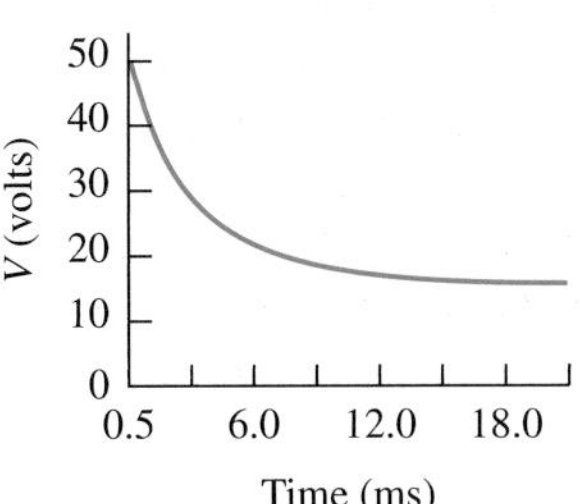

30.62. In the circuit shown in Fig. 30.22, find the reading in each ammeter and voltmeter (a) just after switch S is closed and (b) after S has been closed a very long time.

Figure **30.22** Problem 30.62.

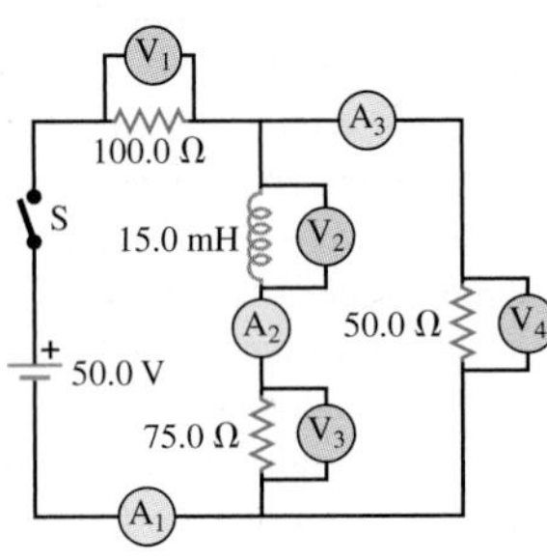

30.63. In the circuit shown in Fig. 30.23, switch S is closed at time $t = 0$ with no charge initially on the capacitor. (a) Find the reading of each ammeter and each voltmeter just after S is closed. (b) Find the reading of each meter after a long time has elapsed. (c) Find the maximum charge on the capacitor. (d) Draw a qualitative graph of the reading of voltmeter V_2 as a function of time.

Figure **30.23** Problem 30.63.

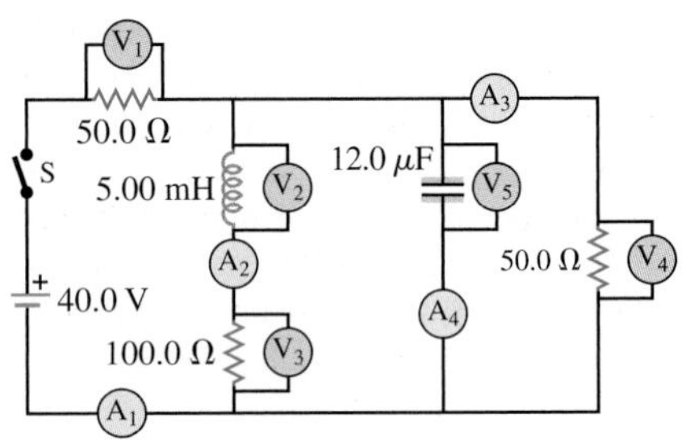

30.64. In the circuit shown in Fig. 30.24 the battery and the inductor have no appreciable internal resistance and there is no current in the circuit. After the switch is closed, find the readings of the ammeter (A) and voltmeters (V_1 and V_2) (a) the instant after the switch is closed and (b) after the switch has been closed for a very long time. (c) Which answers in parts (a) and (b) would change if the inductance were 24.0 mH instead?

Figure **30.24** Problem 30.64.

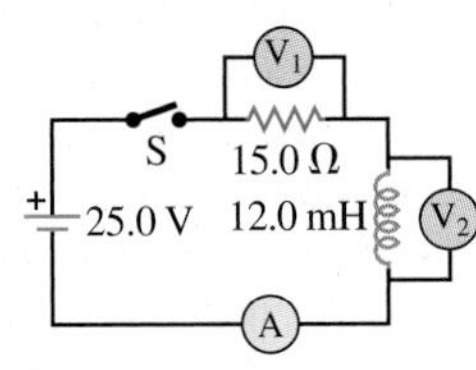

30.65. In the circuit shown in Fig. 30.25, switch S is closed at time $t = 0$. (a) Find the reading of each meter just after S is closed. (b) What does each meter read long after S is closed?

Figure **30.25** Problem 30.65.

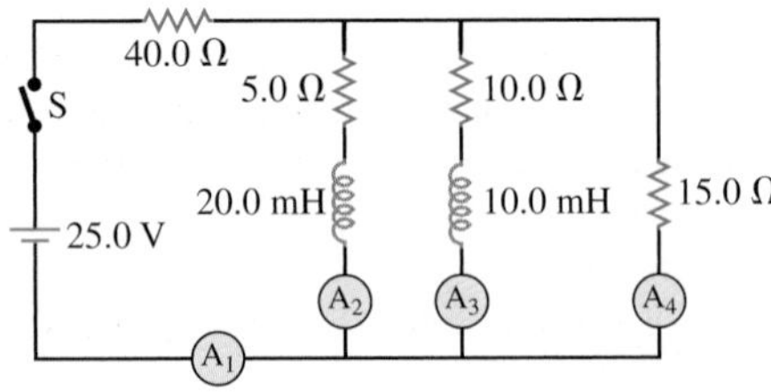

30.66. In the circuit shown in Fig. 30.26, switch S has been closed for a long enough time so that the current reads a steady 3.50 A. Suddenly, switch S_2 is closed and S_1 is opened at the same instant. (a) What is the maximum charge that the capacitor will receive? (b) What is the current in the inductor at this time?

Figure **30.26** Problem 30.66.

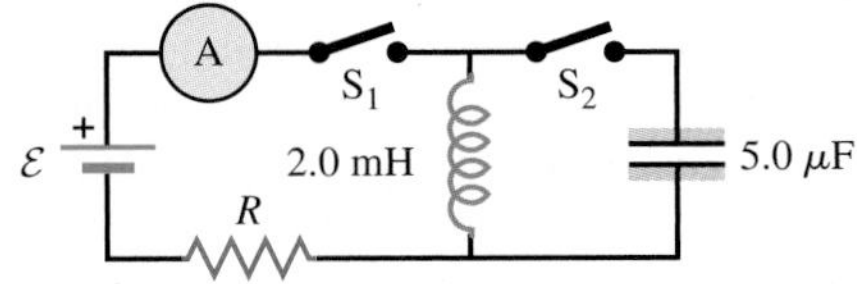

30.67. In the circuit shown in Fig. 30.27, $\mathcal{E} = 60.0$ V, $R_1 = 40.0\ \Omega$, $R_2 = 25.0\ \Omega$, and $L = 0.300$ H. Switch S is closed at $t = 0$. Just after the switch is closed, (a) what is the potential difference v_{ab} across the resistor R_1; (b) which point, a or b, is at a higher potential; (c) what is the potential difference v_{cd} across the inductor L; (d) which point, c or d, is at a higher potential? The switch is left closed a long time and then opened. Just after the switch is opened, (e) what is the potential difference v_{ab} across the resistor R_1; (f) which point, a or b, is at a higher potential; (g) what is the potential difference v_{cd} across the inductor L; (h) which point, c or d, is at a higher potential?

Figure **30.27** Problems 30.67, 30.68, and 30.75.

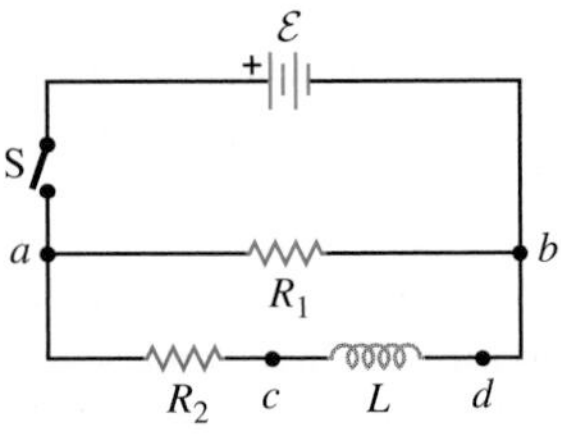

30.68. In the circuit shown in Fig. 30.27, $\mathcal{E} = 60.0$ V, $R_1 = 40.0\ \Omega$, $R_2 = 25.0\ \Omega$, and $L = 0.300$ H. (a) Switch S is closed. At some time t afterward the current in the inductor is increasing at a rate of $di/dt = 50.0$ A/s. At this instant, what are the current i_1 through R_1 and the current i_2 through R_2? (*Hint:* Analyze two separate loops: one containing $\mathcal{E}$ and R_1 and the other containing $\mathcal{E}$, R_2, and L.) (b) After the switch has been closed a long time, it is opened again. Just after it is opened, what is the current through R_1?

30.69. Consider the circuit shown in Fig. 30.28. Let $\mathcal{E} = 36.0$ V, $R_0 = 50.0\ \Omega$, $R = 150\ \Omega$, and $L = 4.00$ H. (a) Switch S_1 is closed and switch S_2 is left open. Just after S_1 is closed, what are the current i_0 through R_0 and the potential differences v_{ac} and v_{cb}? (b) After S_1 has been closed a long time (S_2 is still open) so that the current has reached its final, steady value, what are i_0, v_{ac}, and v_{cb}? (c) Find the expressions for i_0, v_{ac}, and v_{cb} as functions of the time t since S_1 was closed. Your results should agree with part (a) when $t = 0$ and with part (b) when $t \to \infty$. Graph i_0, v_{ac}, and v_{cb} versus time.

Figure **30.28** Problems 30.69 and 30.70.

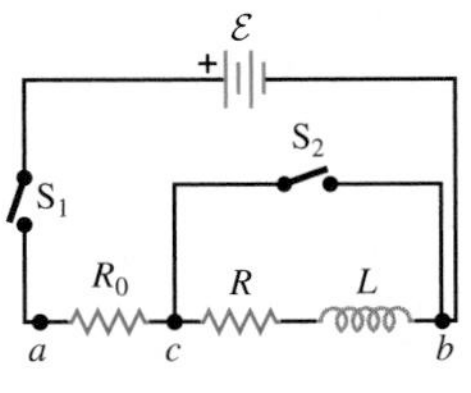

30.70. After the current in the circuit of Fig. 30.28 has reached its final, steady value with switch S_1 closed and S_2 open, switch S_2 is closed, thus short-circuiting the inductor. (Switch S_1 remains closed. See Problem 30.69 for numerical values of the circuit elements.) (a) Just after S_2 is closed, what are v_{ac} and v_{cb}, and what are the currents through R_0, R, and S_2? (b) A long time after S_2 is closed, what are v_{ac} and v_{cb}, and what are the currents through R_0, R, and S_2? (c) Derive expressions for the currents through R_0, R, and S_2 as functions of the time t that has elapsed since S_2 was closed. Your results should agree with part (a) when $t = 0$ and with part (b) when $t \to \infty$. Graph these three currents versus time.

30.71. In the circuit shown in Fig. 30.29, the switch has been open for a long time and is suddenly closed. Neither the battery nor the inductors have any appreciable resistance. Review the results of Problem 30.47. (a) What do the ammeter and voltmeter read just after S is closed? (b) What do the ammeter and the voltmeter read after S has been closed a very long time? (c) What do the ammeter and the voltmeter read 0.115 ms after S is closed?

Figure **30.29** Problem 30.71.

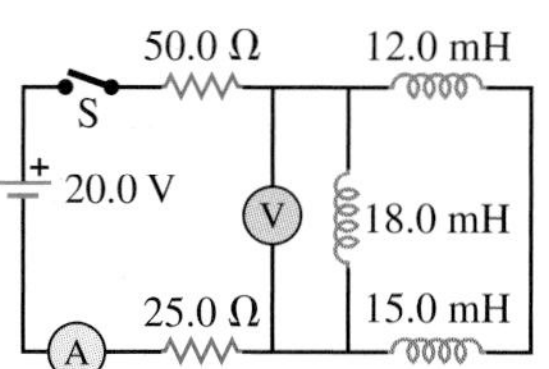

30.72. In the circuit shown in Fig. 30.30, neither the battery nor the inductors have any appreciable resistance, the capacitors are initially uncharged, and the switch S has been in position 1 for a very long time. Review the results of Problem 30.47. (a) What is the current in the circuit? (b) The switch is now suddenly flipped to position 2. Find the maximum charge that each capacitor will receive, and how much time after the switch is flipped it will take them to acquire this charge.

Figure **30.30** Problem 30.72.

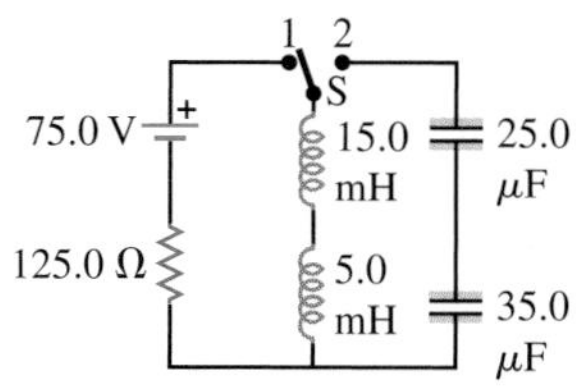

30.73. We have ignored the variation of the magnetic field across the cross section of a toroidal solenoid. Let's now examine the validity of that approximation. A certain toroidal solenoid has a rectangular cross section (Fig. 30.31). It has N uniformly spaced turns, with air inside. The magnetic field at a point inside the toroid is given by the equation derived in Example 28.11 (Section 28.7). *Do not* assume the field is uniform over the cross section. (a) Show that the magnetic flux through a cross section of the toroid is

Figure **30.31** Problem 30.73.

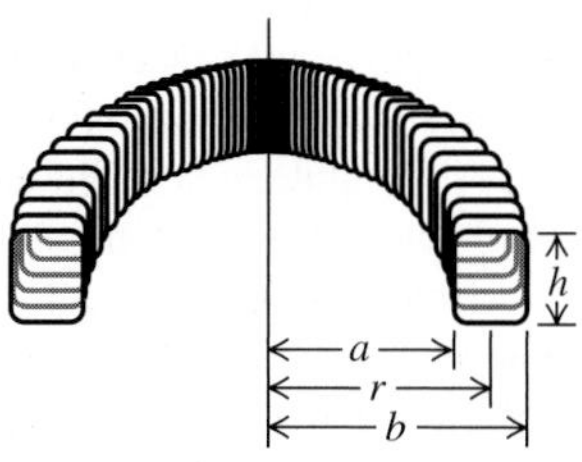

$$\Phi_B = \frac{\mu_0 Nih}{2\pi}\ln\left(\frac{b}{a}\right)$$

(b) Show that the inductance of the toroidal solenoid is given by

$$L = \frac{\mu_0 N^2 h}{2\pi}\ln\left(\frac{b}{a}\right)$$

(c) The fraction b/a may be written as

$$\frac{b}{a} = \frac{a + b - a}{a} = 1 + \frac{b - a}{a}$$

Use the power series expansion $\ln(1 + z) = z + z^2/2 + \cdots$, valid for $|z| < 1$, to show that when $b - a$ is much less than a, the inductance is approximately equal to

$$L = \frac{\mu_0 N^2 h(b - a)}{2\pi a}$$

Compare this result with the result given in Example 30.3 (Section 30.2).

30.74. In Fig. 30.32 the switch is closed, with the capacitor having the polarity shown. Find the direction (clockwise or counter-clockwise) of the current induced in the rectangular wire loop A.

Figure **30.32** Problem 30.74.

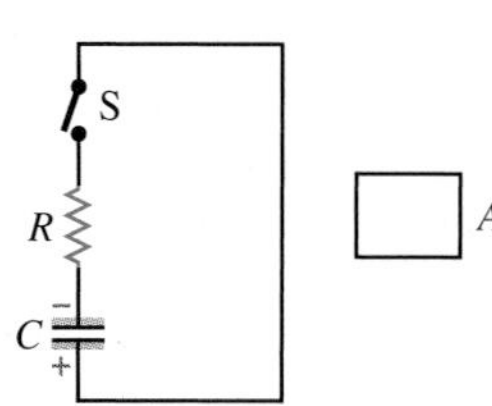

30.75. Demonstrating Inductance. A common demonstration of inductance employs a circuit such as the one shown in Fig. 30.27. Switch S is closed, and the light bulb (represented by resistance R_1) just barely glows. After a period of time, switch S is opened, and the bulb lights up brightly for a short period of time. To understand this effect, think of an inductor as a device that imparts an "inertia" to the current, preventing a discontinuous change in the current through it. (a) Derive, as explicit functions of time, expressions for i_1 (the current through the light bulb) and i_2 (the current through the inductor) after switch S is closed. (b) After a long period of time, the currents i_1 and i_2 reach their steady-state values. Obtain expressions for these steady-state currents. (c) Switch S is now opened. Obtain an expression for the current through the inductor and light bulb as an explicit function of time. (d) You have been asked to design a demonstration apparatus using the circuit shown in Fig. 30.27 with a 22.0-H inductor and a 40.0-W light bulb. You are to connect a resistor in series with the inductor, and R_2 represents the sum of that resistance plus the internal resistance of the inductor. When switch S is opened, a transient current is to be set up that starts at 0.600 A and is not to fall below 0.150 A until after 0.0800 s. For simplicity, assume that the resistance of the light bulb is constant and equals the resistance the bulb must have to dissipate 40.0 W at 120 V. Determine R_2 and $\mathcal{E}$ for the given design considerations. (e) With the numerical values determined in part (d), what is the current through the light bulb just before the switch is opened? Does this result confirm the qualitative description of what is observed in the demonstration?

Challenge Problems

30.76. Consider the circuit shown in Fig. 30.33. The circuit elements are as follows: $\mathcal{E} = 32.0$ V, $L = 0.640$ H, $C = 2.00\ \mu$F, and $R = 400\ \Omega$. At time $t = 0$, switch S is closed. The current through the inductor is i_1, the current through the capacitor branch is i_2, and the charge on the capacitor is q_2. (a) Using Kirchhoff's rules, verify the circuit equations

Figure **30.33** Challenge Problem 30.76.

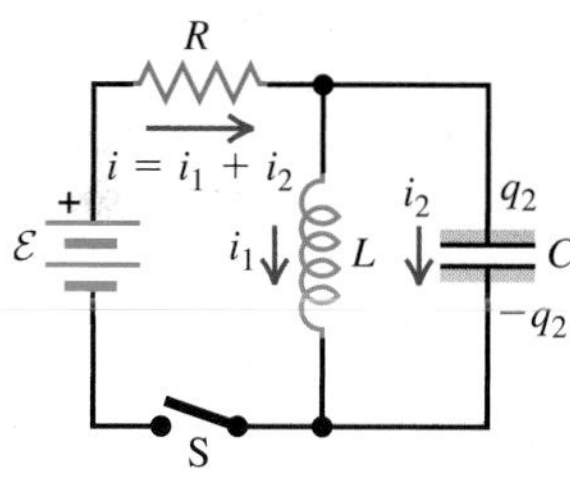

$$R(i_1 + i_2) + L\left(\frac{di_1}{dt}\right) = \mathcal{E}$$

$$R(i_2 + i_2) + \frac{q_2}{C} = \mathcal{E}$$

(b) What are the initial values of i_1, i_2, and q_2? (c) Show by direct substitution that the following solutions for i_1 and q_2 satisfy the circuit equations from part (a). Also, show that they satisfy the initial conditions

$$i_1 = \left(\frac{\mathcal{E}}{R}\right)[1 - e^{-\beta t}(2\omega RC)^{-1}\sin(\omega t) + \cos(\omega t)]$$

$$q_2 = \left(\frac{\mathcal{E}}{\omega R}\right)e^{-\beta t}\sin(\omega t)$$

where $\beta = (2RC)^{-1}$ and $\omega = [(LC)^{-1} - (2RC)^{-2}]^{1/2}$. (d) Determine the time t_1 at which i_2 first becomes zero.

30.77. A Volume Gauge. A tank containing a liquid has turns of wire wrapped around it, causing it to act like an inductor. The liquid content of the tank can be measured by using its inductance to determine the height of the liquid in the tank. The inductance of the tank changes from a value of L_0 corresponding to a relative permeability of 1 when the tank is empty to a value of L_f corresponding to a relative permeability of K_m (the relative permeability of the liquid) when the tank is full. The appropriate electronic circuitry can determine the inductance to five significant figures and thus the effective relative permeability of the combined air and liquid within the rectangular cavity of the tank. The four sides of the tank each have width W and height D (Fig. 30.34). The height of the liquid in the tank is d. You can ignore any fringing effects and assume that the relative permeability of the material of which the tank is made can be ignored. (a) Derive an expression for d as a function of L, the inductance corresponding to a certain fluid height, L_0, L_f, and D. (b) What is the inductance (to five significant figures) for a tank $\frac{1}{4}$ full, $\frac{1}{2}$ full, $\frac{3}{4}$ full, and completely full if the tank contains liquid oxygen? Take $L_0 = 0.63000$ H. The magnetic susceptibility of liquid oxygen is $\chi_m = 1.52 \times 10^{-3}$. (c) Repeat part (b) for mercury. The magnetic susceptibility of mercury is given in Table 28.1. (d) For which material is this volume gauge more practical?

Figure **30.34** Challenge Problem 30.77.

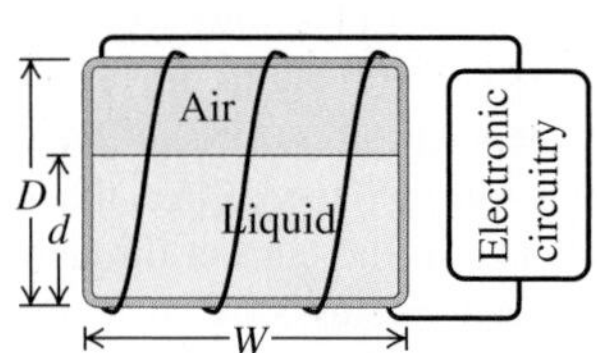

30.78. Two coils are wrapped around each other as shown in Fig. 30.3. The current travels in the same sense around each coil. One coil has self-inductance L_1, and the other coil has self-inductance L_2. The mutual inductance of the two coils is M. (a) Show that if the two coils are connected in series, the equivalent inductance of the combination is $L_{eq} = L_1 + L_2 + 2M$. (b) Show that if the two coils are connected in parallel, the equivalent inductance of the combination is

$$L_{eq} = \frac{L_1 L_2 - M^2}{L_1 + L_2 - 2M}$$

(*Hint:* See the hint for Problem 30.47.)

30.79. Consider the circuit shown in Fig. 30.35. Switch S is closed at time $t = 0$, causing a current i_1 through the inductive branch and a current i_2 through the capacitive branch. The initial charge on the capacitor is zero, and the charge at time t is q_2. (a) Derive expressions for i_1, i_2, and q_2 as functions of time. Express your answers in terms of $\mathcal{E}$, L, C, R_1, R_2, and t. For the remainder of the problem let the circuit elements have the following values: $\mathcal{E} = 48$ V, $L = 8.0$ H, $C = 20\ \mu$F, $R_1 = 25\ \Omega$, and $R_2 = 5000\ \Omega$. (b) What is the initial current through the inductive branch? What is the initial current through the capacitive branch? (c) What are the currents through the inductive and capacitive branches a long time after the switch has been closed? How long is a "long time"? Explain. (d) At what time t_1 (accurate to two significant figures) will the currents i_1 and i_2 be equal? (*Hint:* You might consider using series expansions for the exponentials.) (e) For the conditions given in part (d), determine i_1. (f) The total current through the battery is $i = i_1 + i_2$. At what time t_2 (accurate to two significant figures) will i equal one-half of its final value? (*Hint:* The numerical work is greatly simplified if one makes suitable approximations. A sketch of i_1 and i_2 versus t may help you decide what approximations are valid.)

Figure **30.35** Challenge Problem 30.79.

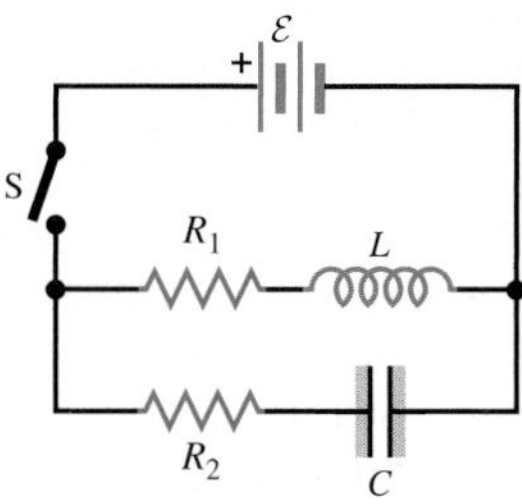

ALTERNATING CURRENT 31

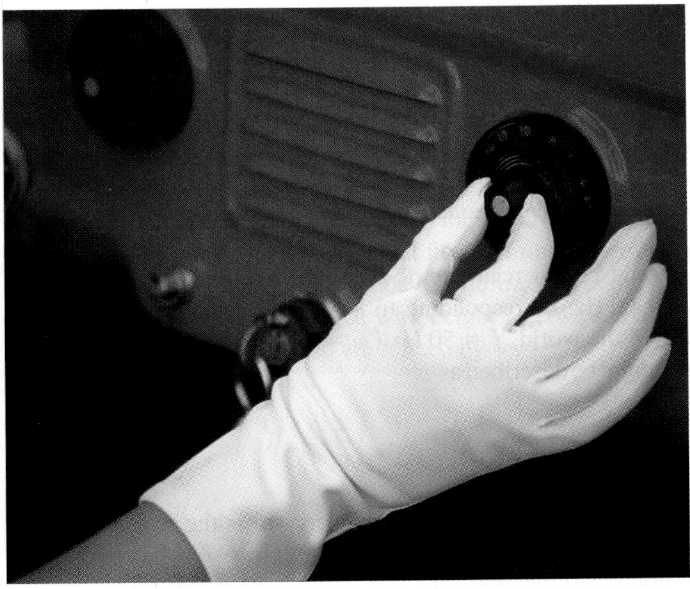

?Waves from a broadcasting station produce an alternating current in the circuits of a radio (like the one in this classic car). If a radio is tuned to a station at a frequency of 1000 kHz, does it also detect the transmissions from a station broadcasting at 600 kHz?

LEARNING GOALS

By studying this chapter, you will learn:

- How phasors make it easy to describe sinusoidally varying quantities.
- How to use reactance to describe the voltage across a circuit element that carries an alternating current.
- How to analyze an *L-R-C* series circuit with a sinusoidal emf.
- What determines the amount of power flowing into or out of an alternating-current circuit.
- How an *L-R-C* series circuit responds to sinusoidal emfs of different frequencies.
- Why transformers are useful, and how they work.

During the 1880s in the United States there was a heated and acrimonious debate between two inventors over the best method of electric-power distribution. Thomas Edison favored direct current (dc)—that is, steady current that does not vary with time. George Westinghouse favored **alternating current (ac),** with sinusoidally varying voltages and currents. He argued that transformers (which we will study in this chapter) can be used to step the voltage up and down with ac but not with dc; low voltages are safer for consumer use, but high voltages and correspondingly low currents are best for long-distance power transmission to minimize i^2R losses in the cables.

Eventually, Westinghouse prevailed, and most present-day household and industrial power-distribution systems operate with alternating current. Any appliance that you plug into a wall outlet uses ac, and many battery-powered devices such as radios and cordless telephones make use of the dc supplied by the battery to create or amplify alternating currents. Circuits in modern communication equipment, including pagers and television, also make extensive use of ac.

In this chapter we will learn how resistors, inductors, and capacitors behave in circuits with sinusoidally varying voltages and currents. Many of the principles that we found useful in Chapters 25, 28, and 30 are applicable, along with several new concepts related to the circuit behavior of inductors and capacitors. A key concept in this discussion is *resonance,* which we studied in Chapter 13 for mechanical systems.

31.1 Phasors and Alternating Currents

To supply an alternating current to a circuit, a source of alternating emf or voltage is required. An example of such a source is a coil of wire rotating with constant angular velocity in a magnetic field, which we discussed in Example 29.4 (Section 29.2). This develops a sinusoidal alternating emf and is the prototype of the commercial alternating-current generator or *alternator* (see Fig. 29.8).

31.5 This wall socket delivers a root-mean-square voltage of 120 V. Sixty times per second, the instantaneous voltage across its terminals varies from $(\sqrt{2})(120\text{ V}) = 170\text{ V}$ to -170 V and back again.

In the same way, the root-mean-square value of a sinusoidal voltage with amplitude (maximum value) V is

$$V_{\text{rms}} = \frac{V}{\sqrt{2}} \quad \text{(root-mean-square value of a sinusoidal voltage)} \quad (31.5)$$

We can convert a rectifying ammeter into a voltmeter by adding a series resistor, just as for the dc case discussed in Section 26.3. Meters used for ac voltage and current measurements are nearly always calibrated to read rms values, not maximum or rectified average. Voltages and currents in power distribution systems are always described in terms of their rms values. The usual household power supply, "120-volt ac," has an rms voltage of 120 V (Fig. 31.5). The voltage amplitude is

$$V = \sqrt{2}V_{\text{rms}} = \sqrt{2}(120\text{ V}) = 170\text{ V}$$

Example 31.1 Current in a personal computer

The plate on the back of a personal computer says that it draws 2.7 A from a 120-V, 60-Hz line. For this computer, what are (a) the average current, (b) the average of the square of the current, and (c) the current amplitude?

SOLUTION

IDENTIFY: This example is about alternating current.

SET UP: In parts (b) and (c) we use the idea that the root-mean-square current, given by Eq. (31.4), is the *square root* of the *mean* (average) of the *square* of the current.

EXECUTE: (a) The average of *any* sinusoidal alternating current, over any whole number of cycles, is zero.

(b) The current given is the rms value: $I_{\text{rms}} = 2.7\text{ A}$. The target variable $(i^2)_{\text{av}}$ is the *mean* of the *square* of the current. The rms current is the square root of this target variable, so

$$I_{\text{rms}} = \sqrt{(i^2)_{\text{av}}} \quad \text{or} \quad (i^2)_{\text{av}} = (I_{\text{rms}})^2 = (2.7\text{ A})^2 = 7.3\text{ A}^2$$

(c) From Eq. (31.4) the current amplitude I is

$$I = \sqrt{2}I_{\text{rms}} = \sqrt{2}(2.7\text{ A}) = 3.8\text{ A}$$

Figure 31.6 shows our graphs of i and i^2.

EVALUATE: Why would we be interested in the average of the square of the current? Recall that the rate at which energy is dissipated in a resistor R equals i^2R. This rate varies if the current is alternating, so it is best described by its average value $(i^2)_{\text{av}}R = I_{\text{rms}}{}^2R$. We make use of this idea in Section 31.4.

31.6 Our graphs of the current i and the square of the current i^2 versus time t.

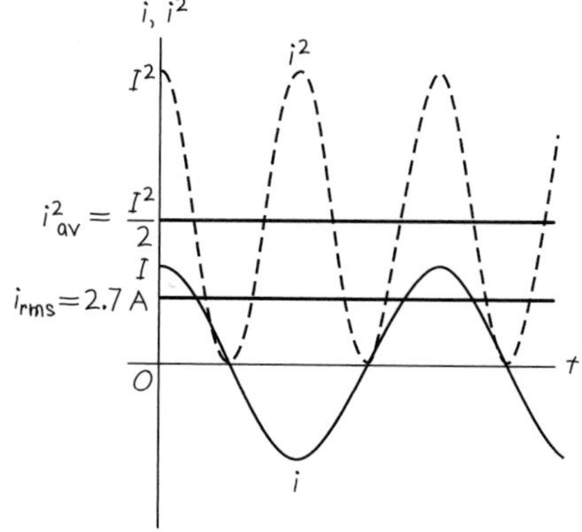

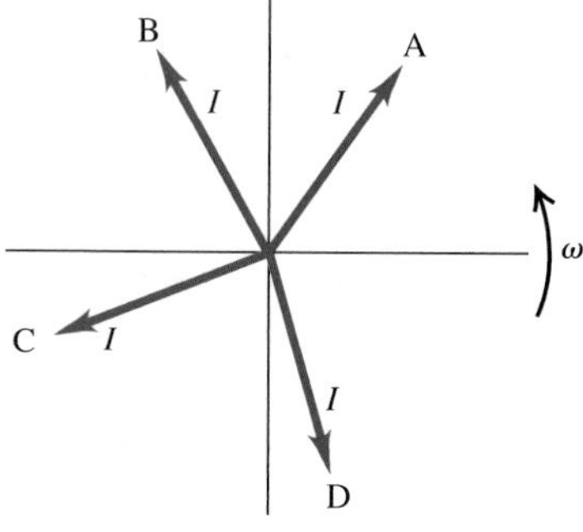

Test Your Understanding of Section 31.1 The figure at left shows four different current phasors with the same angular frequency ω. At the time shown, which phasor corresponds to (a) a positive current that is becoming more positive; (b) a positive current that is decreasing toward zero; (c) a negative current that is becoming more negative; (d) a negative current that is decreasing in magnitude toward zero?

31.2 Resistance and Reactance

In this section we will derive voltage–current relationships for individual circuit elements carrying a sinusoidal current. We'll consider resistors, inductors, and capacitors.

ALTERNATING CURRENT

31

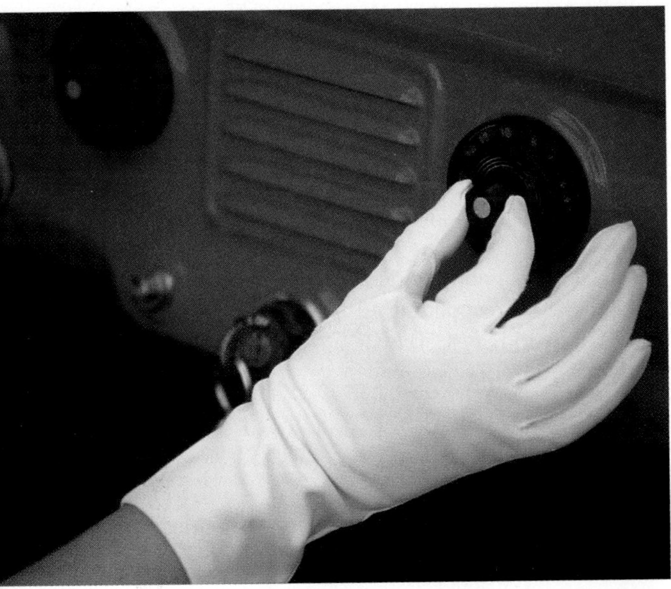

? Waves from a broadcasting station produce an alternating current in the circuits of a radio (like the one in this classic car). If a radio is tuned to a station at a frequency of 1000 kHz, does it also detect the transmissions from a station broadcasting at 600 kHz?

LEARNING GOALS

By studying this chapter, you will learn:

- How phasors make it easy to describe sinusoidally varying quantities.
- How to use reactance to describe the voltage across a circuit element that carries an alternating current.
- How to analyze an *L-R-C* series circuit with a sinusoidal emf.
- What determines the amount of power flowing into or out of an alternating-current circuit.
- How an *L-R-C* series circuit responds to sinusoidal emfs of different frequencies.
- Why transformers are useful, and how they work.

During the 1880s in the United States there was a heated and acrimonious debate between two inventors over the best method of electric-power distribution. Thomas Edison favored direct current (dc)—that is, steady current that does not vary with time. George Westinghouse favored **alternating current (ac),** with sinusoidally varying voltages and currents. He argued that transformers (which we will study in this chapter) can be used to step the voltage up and down with ac but not with dc; low voltages are safer for consumer use, but high voltages and correspondingly low currents are best for long-distance power transmission to minimize i^2R losses in the cables.

Eventually, Westinghouse prevailed, and most present-day household and industrial power-distribution systems operate with alternating current. Any appliance that you plug into a wall outlet uses ac, and many battery-powered devices such as radios and cordless telephones make use of the dc supplied by the battery to create or amplify alternating currents. Circuits in modern communication equipment, including pagers and television, also make extensive use of ac.

In this chapter we will learn how resistors, inductors, and capacitors behave in circuits with sinusoidally varying voltages and currents. Many of the principles that we found useful in Chapters 25, 28, and 30 are applicable, along with several new concepts related to the circuit behavior of inductors and capacitors. A key concept in this discussion is *resonance,* which we studied in Chapter 13 for mechanical systems.

31.1 Phasors and Alternating Currents

To supply an alternating current to a circuit, a source of alternating emf or voltage is required. An example of such a source is a coil of wire rotating with constant angular velocity in a magnetic field, which we discussed in Example 29.4 (Section 29.2). This develops a sinusoidal alternating emf and is the prototype of the commercial alternating-current generator or *alternator* (see Fig. 29.8).

We use the term **ac source** for any device that supplies a sinusoidally varying voltage (potential difference) v or current i. The usual circuit-diagram symbol for an ac source is

A sinusoidal voltage might be described by a function such as

$$v = V\cos\omega t \tag{31.1}$$

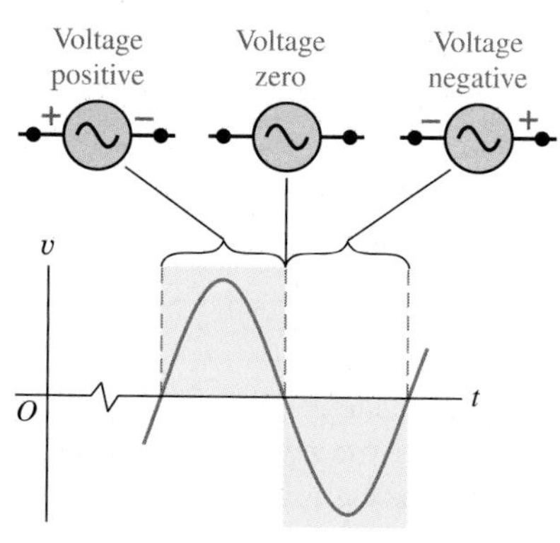

31.1 The voltage across a sinusoidal ac source.

In this expression, v (lowercase) is the *instantaneous* potential difference; V (uppercase) is the maximum potential difference, which we call the **voltage amplitude;** and ω is the *angular frequency,* equal to 2π times the frequency f (Fig. 31.1).

In the United States and Canada, commercial electric-power distribution systems always use a frequency of $f = 60$ Hz, corresponding to $\omega = (2\pi \text{ rad})(60 \text{ s}^{-1}) = 377$ rad/s; in much of the rest of the world, $f = 50$ Hz ($\omega = 314$ rad/s) is used. Similarly, a sinusoidal current might be described as

$$i = I\cos\omega t \tag{31.2}$$

where i (lowercase) is the instantaneous current and I (uppercase) is the maximum current or **current amplitude.**

Phasor Diagrams

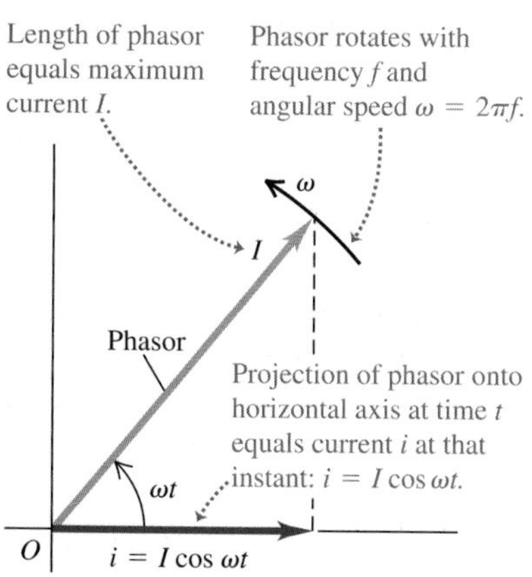

31.2 A phasor diagram.

To represent sinusoidally varying voltages and currents, we will use rotating vector diagrams similar to those we used in the study of simple harmonic motion in Section 13.2 (see Figs. 13.5b and 13.6). In these diagrams the instantaneous value of a quantity that varies sinusoidally with time is represented by the *projection* onto a horizontal axis of a vector with a length equal to the amplitude of the quantity. The vector rotates counterclockwise with constant angular speed ω. These rotating vectors are called **phasors,** and diagrams containing them are called **phasor diagrams.** Figure 31.2 shows a phasor diagram for the sinusoidal current described by Eq. (31.2). The projection of the phasor onto the horizontal axis at time t is $I\cos\omega t$; this is why we chose to use the cosine function rather than the sine in Eq. (31.2).

CAUTION Just what is a phasor? A phasor is not a real physical quantity with a direction in space, such as velocity, momentum, or electric field. Rather, it is a *geometric* entity that helps us to describe and analyze physical quantities that vary sinusoidally with time. In Section 13.2 we used a single phasor to represent the position of a point mass undergoing simple harmonic motion. In this chapter we will use phasors to *add* sinusoidal voltages and currents. Combining sinusoidal quantities with phase differences then becomes a matter of vector addition. We will find a similar use for phasors in Chapters 35 and 36 in our study of interference effects with light.

Rectified Alternating Current

How do we measure a sinusoidally varying current? In Section 26.3 we used a d'Arsonval galvanometer to measure steady currents. But if we pass a *sinusoidal* current through a d'Arsonval meter, the torque on the moving coil varies sinusoidally, with one direction half the time and the opposite direction the other half. The needle may wiggle a little if the frequency is low enough, but its average deflection is zero. Hence a d'Arsonval meter by itself isn't very useful for measuring alternating currents.

To get a measurable one-way current through the meter, we can use *diodes,* which we described in Section 25.3. A diode (or rectifier) is a device that conducts better in one direction than in the other; an ideal diode has zero resistance for one direction of current and infinite resistance for the other. One possible arrangement is shown in Fig. 31.3a. The current through the galvanometer G is always upward, regardless of the direction of the current from the ac source (i.e., which part of the cycle the source is in). The current through G is as shown by the graph in Fig. 31.2b. It pulsates but always has the same direction, and the average meter deflection is *not* zero. This arrangement of diodes is called a *full-wave rectifier circuit.*

The **rectified average current** I_{rav} is defined so that during any whole number of cycles, the total charge that flows is the same as though the current were constant with a value equal to I_{rav}. The notation I_{rav} and the name *rectified average current* emphasize that this is *not* the average of the original sinusoidal current. In Fig. 31.3b the total charge that flows in time t corresponds to the area under the curve of i versus t (recall that $i = dq/dt$, so q is the integral of t); this area must equal the rectangular area with height I_{rav}. We see that I_{rav} is less than the maximum current I; the two are related by

$$I_{rav} = \frac{2}{\pi}I = 0.637I \quad \text{(rectified average value of a sinusoidal current)} \qquad (31.3)$$

(The factor of $2/\pi$ is the average value of $|\cos\omega t|$ or of $|\sin\omega t|$; see Example 29.5 in Section 29.2.) The galvanometer deflection is proportional to I_{rav}. The galvanometer scale can be calibrated to read I, I_{rav}, or, most commonly, I_{rms} (discussed below).

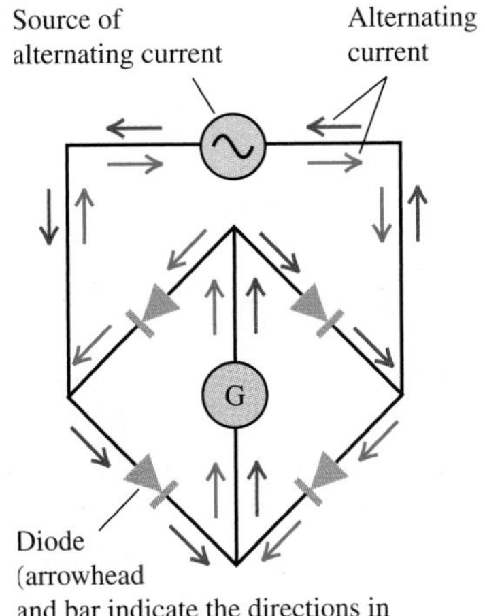
(a) A full-wave rectifier circuit
Source of alternating current
Alternating current
G
Diode (arrowhead and bar indicate the directions in which current can and cannot pass)

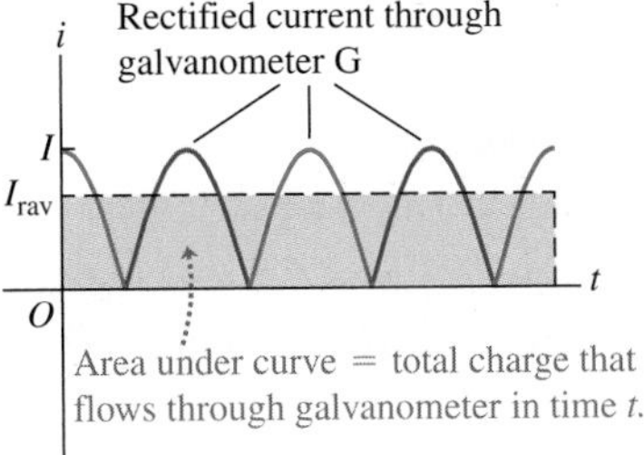
(b) Graph of the full-wave rectified current and its average value, the rectified average current I_{rav}
Rectified current through galvanometer G
i
I
I_{rav}
O
t
Area under curve = total charge that flows through galvanometer in time t.

31.3 (a) A full-wave rectifier circuit. (b) Graph of the resulting current through the galvanometer G.

Root-Mean-Square (rms) Values

A more useful way to describe a quantity that can be either positive or negative is the *root-mean-square (rms) value.* We used rms values in Section 18.3 in connection with the speeds of molecules in a gas. We *square* the instantaneous current i, take the *average* (mean) value of i^2, and finally take the *square root* of that average. This procedure defines the **root-mean-square current,** denoted as I_{rms} (Fig. 31.4). Even when i is negative, i^2 is always positive, so I_{rms} is never zero (unless i is zero at every instant).

Here's how we obtain I_{rms} for a sinusoidal current, like that shown in Fig. 31.4. If the instantaneous current is given by $i = I\cos\omega t$, then

$$i^2 = I^2\cos^2\omega t$$

Using a double-angle formula from trigonometry,

$$\cos^2 A = \frac{1}{2}(1 + \cos 2A)$$

we find

$$i^2 = I^2\frac{1}{2}(1 + \cos 2\omega t) = \frac{1}{2}I^2 + \frac{1}{2}I^2\cos 2\omega t$$

The average of $\cos 2\omega t$ is zero because it is positive half the time and negative half the time. Thus the average of i^2 is simply $I^2/2$. The square root of this is I_{rms}:

$$I_{rms} = \frac{I}{\sqrt{2}} \quad \text{(root-mean-square value of a sinusoidal current)} \qquad (31.4)$$

31.4 Calculating the root-mean-square (rms) value of an alternating current.

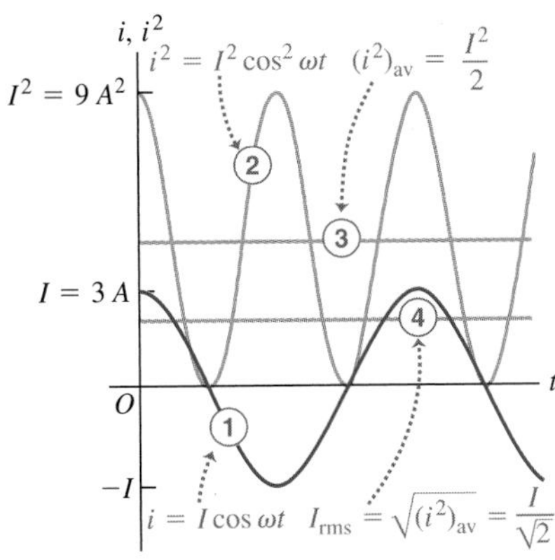
Meaning of the rms value of a sinusoidal quantity (here, ac current with $I = 3$ A):
1 Graph current i versus time.
2 *Square* the instantaneous current i.
3 Take the *average* (mean) value of i^2.
4 Take the *square root* of that average.
i, i^2
$i^2 = I^2\cos^2\omega t$
$(i^2)_{av} = \frac{I^2}{2}$
$I^2 = 9\ A^2$
$I = 3\ A$
O
t
$-I$
$i = I\cos\omega t$
$I_{rms} = \sqrt{(i^2)_{av}} = \frac{I}{\sqrt{2}}$

31.5 This wall socket delivers a root-mean-square voltage of 120 V. Sixty times per second, the instantaneous voltage across its terminals varies from $(\sqrt{2})(120\text{ V}) = 170\text{ V}$ to -170 V and back again.

In the same way, the root-mean-square value of a sinusoidal voltage with amplitude (maximum value) V is

$$V_{rms} = \frac{V}{\sqrt{2}} \quad \text{(root-mean-square value of a sinusoidal voltage)} \quad (31.5)$$

We can convert a rectifying ammeter into a voltmeter by adding a series resistor, just as for the dc case discussed in Section 26.3. Meters used for ac voltage and current measurements are nearly always calibrated to read rms values, not maximum or rectified average. Voltages and currents in power distribution systems are always described in terms of their rms values. The usual household power supply, "120-volt ac," has an rms voltage of 120 V (Fig. 31.5). The voltage amplitude is

$$V = \sqrt{2}V_{rms} = \sqrt{2}(120\text{ V}) = 170\text{ V}$$

Example 31.1 Current in a personal computer

The plate on the back of a personal computer says that it draws 2.7 A from a 120-V, 60-Hz line. For this computer, what are (a) the average current, (b) the average of the square of the current, and (c) the current amplitude?

SOLUTION

IDENTIFY: This example is about alternating current.

SET UP: In parts (b) and (c) we use the idea that the root-mean-square current, given by Eq. (31.4), is the *square root* of the *mean* (average) of the *square* of the current.

EXECUTE: (a) The average of *any* sinusoidal alternating current, over any whole number of cycles, is zero.

(b) The current given is the rms value: $I_{rms} = 2.7$ A. The target variable $(i^2)_{av}$ is the *mean* of the *square* of the current. The rms current is the square root of this target variable, so

$$I_{rms} = \sqrt{(i^2)_{av}} \quad \text{or} \quad (i^2)_{av} = (I_{rms})^2 = (2.7\text{ A})^2 = 7.3\text{ A}^2$$

(c) From Eq. (31.4) the current amplitude I is

$$I = \sqrt{2}I_{rms} = \sqrt{2}(2.7\text{ A}) = 3.8\text{ A}$$

Figure 31.6 shows our graphs of i and i^2.

EVALUATE: Why would we be interested in the average of the square of the current? Recall that the rate at which energy is dissipated in a resistor R equals i^2R. This rate varies if the current is alternating, so it is best described by its average value $(i^2)_{av}R = I_{rms}{}^2R$. We make use of this idea in Section 31.4.

31.6 Our graphs of the current i and the square of the current i^2 versus time t.

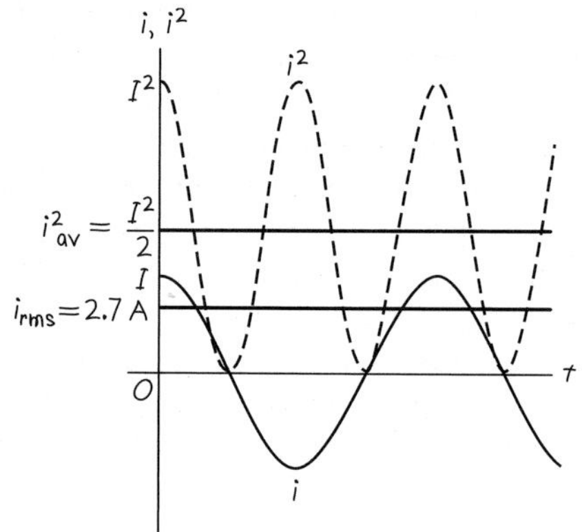

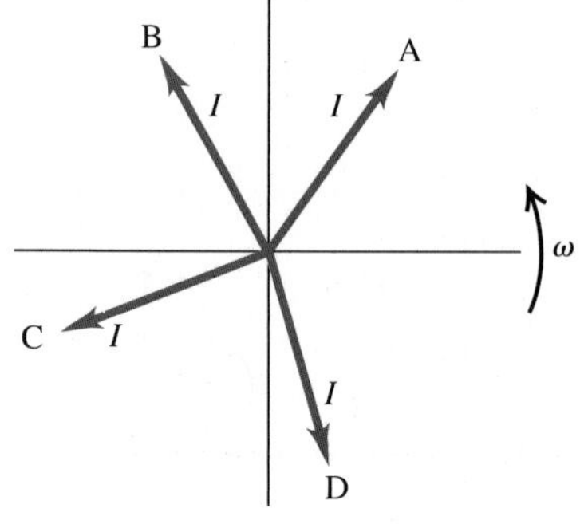

Test Your Understanding of Section 31.1 The figure at left shows four different current phasors with the same angular frequency ω. At the time shown, which phasor corresponds to (a) a positive current that is becoming more positive; (b) a positive current that is decreasing toward zero; (c) a negative current that is becoming more negative; (d) a negative current that is decreasing in magnitude toward zero?

31.2 Resistance and Reactance

In this section we will derive voltage–current relationships for individual circuit elements carrying a sinusoidal current. We'll consider resistors, inductors, and capacitors.

Resistor in an ac Circuit

First let's consider a resistor with resistance R through which there is a sinusoidal current given by Eq. (31.2): $i = I\cos\omega t$. The positive direction of current is counterclockwise around the circuit, as in Fig. 31.7a. The current amplitude (maximum current) is I. From Ohm's law the instantaneous potential v_R of point a with respect to point b (that is, the instantaneous voltage across the resistor) is

$$v_R = iR = (IR)\cos\omega t \tag{31.6}$$

The maximum voltage V_R, the *voltage amplitude,* is the coefficient of the cosine function:

$$V_R = IR \quad \text{(amplitude of voltage across a resistor, ac circuit)} \tag{31.7}$$

Hence we can also write

$$v_R = V_R\cos\omega t \tag{31.8}$$

The current i and voltage v_R are both proportional to $\cos\omega t$, so the current is *in phase* with the voltage. Equation (31.7) shows that the current and voltage amplitudes are related in the same way as in a dc circuit.

Figure 31.7b shows graphs of i and v_R as functions of time. The vertical scales for current and voltage are different, so the relative heights of the two curves are not significant. The corresponding phasor diagram is given in Fig. 31.7c. Because i and v_R are *in phase* and have the same frequency, the current and voltage phasors rotate together; they are parallel at each instant. Their projections on the horizontal axis represent the instantaneous current and voltage, respectively.

31.7 Resistance R connected across an ac source. 

(a) Circuit with ac source and resistor

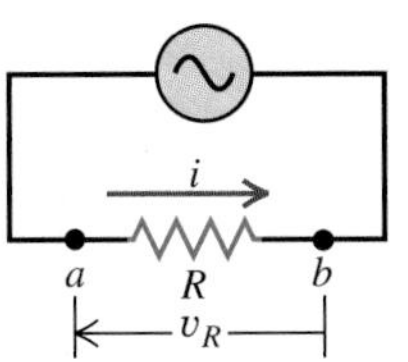

(b) Graphs of current and voltage versus time

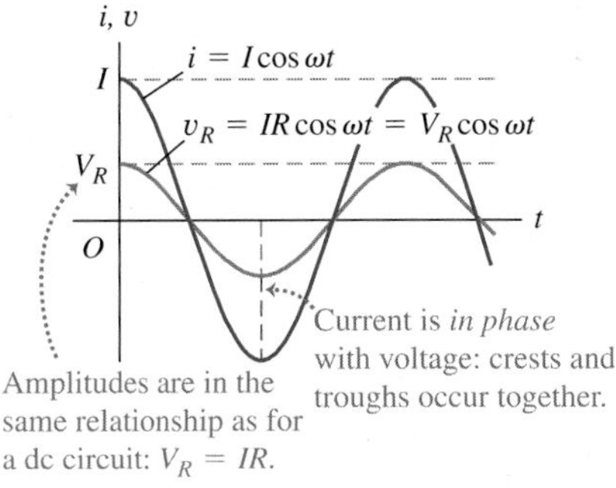

(c) Phasor diagram

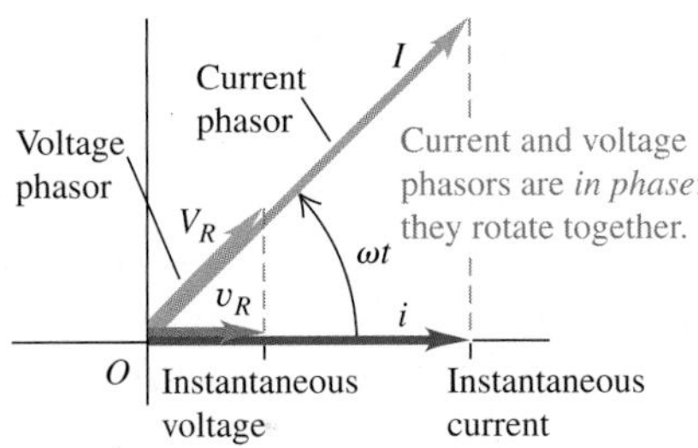

Inductor in an ac Circuit

Next, we replace the resistor in Fig. 31.7 with a pure inductor with self-inductance L and zero resistance (Fig. 31.8a). Again we assume that the current is $i = I\cos\omega t$, with the positive direction of current taken as counterclockwise around the circuit.

Although there is no resistance, there is a potential difference v_L between the inductor terminals a and b because the current varies with time, giving rise to a self-induced emf. The induced emf in the direction of i is given by Eq. (30.7), $\mathcal{E} = -L\,di/dt$; however, the voltage v_L is *not* simply equal to $\mathcal{E}$. To see why, notice that if the current in the inductor is in the positive (counterclockwise) direction from a to b and is increasing, then di/dt is positive and the induced emf is directed to the left to oppose the increase in current; hence point a is at higher potential than is point b. Thus the potential of point a with respect to point b is positive and is given by $v_L = +L\,di/dt$, the *negative* of the induced emf. (You should convince

31.8 Inductance L connected across an ac source. 

(a) Circuit with ac source and inductor

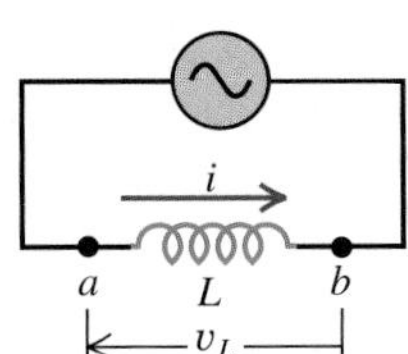

(b) Graphs of current and voltage versus time

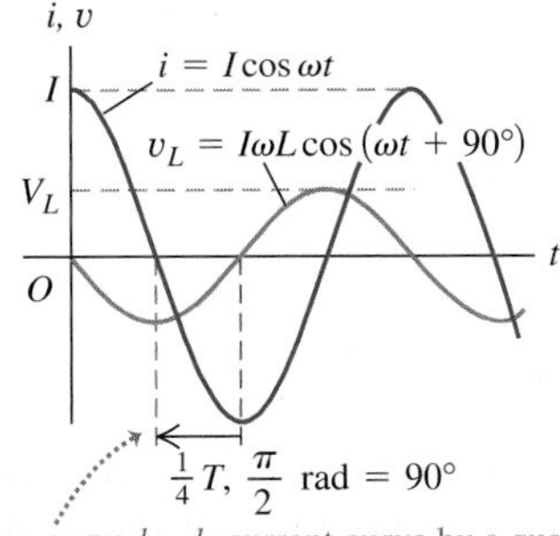

Voltage curve *leads* current curve by a quarter-cycle (corresponding to $\phi = \pi/2$ rad = 90°).

(c) Phasor diagram

Voltage phasor *leads* current phasor by $\phi = \pi/2$ rad = 90°.

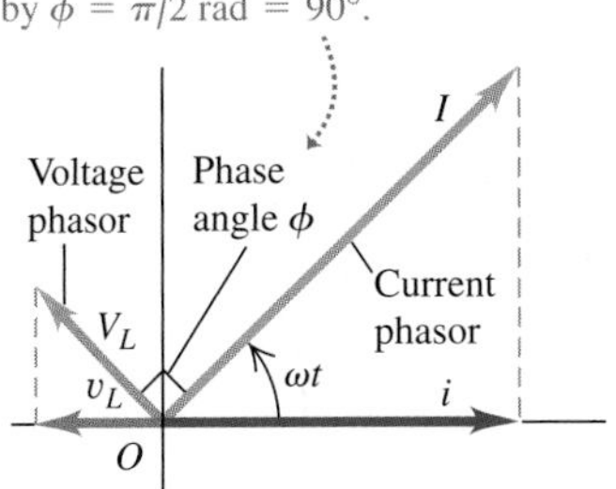

14.3 AC Circuits: The Driven Oscillator (Questions 1–5)

yourself that this expression gives the correct sign of v_L in *all* cases, including i counterclockwise and decreasing, i clockwise and increasing, and i clockwise and decreasing; you should also review Section 30.2.) So we have

$$v_L = L\frac{di}{dt} = L\frac{d}{dt}(I\cos\omega t) = -I\omega L\sin\omega t \tag{31.9}$$

The voltage v_L across the inductor at any instant is proportional to the *rate of change* of the current. The points of maximum voltage on the graph correspond to maximum steepness of the current curve, and the points of zero voltage are the points where the current curve instantaneously levels off at its maximum and minimum values (Fig. 31.8b). The voltage and current are "out of step" or *out of phase* by a quarter-cycle. Since the voltage peaks occur a quarter-cycle earlier than the current peaks, we say that the voltage *leads* the current by 90°. The phasor diagram in Fig. 31.8c also shows this relationship; the voltage phasor is ahead of the current phasor by 90°.

We can also obtain this phase relationship by rewriting Eq. (31.9) using the identity $\cos(A + 90°) = -\sin A$:

$$v_L = I\omega L\cos(\omega t + 90°) \tag{31.10}$$

This result shows that the voltage can be viewed as a cosine function with a "head start" of 90° relative to the current.

As we have done in Eq. (31.10), we will usually describe the phase of the *voltage* relative to the *current,* not the reverse. Thus if the current i in a circuit is

$$i = I\cos\omega t$$

and the voltage v of one point with respect to another is

$$v = V\cos(\omega t + \phi)$$

we call ϕ the **phase angle;** it gives the phase of the *voltage* relative to the *current.* For a pure resistor, $\phi = 0$, and for a pure inductor, $\phi = 90°$.

From Eq. (31.9) or (31.10) the amplitude V_L of the inductor voltage is

$$V_L = I\omega L \tag{31.11}$$

We define the **inductive reactance** X_L of an inductor as

$$X_L = \omega L \quad \text{(inductive reactance)} \tag{31.12}$$

Using X_L, we can write Eq. (31.11) in a form similar to Eq. (31.7) for a resistor $(V_R = IR)$:

$$V_L = IX_L \quad \text{(amplitude of voltage across an inductor, ac circuit)} \tag{31.13}$$

Because X_L is the ratio of a voltage and a current, its SI unit is the ohm, the same as for resistance.

CAUTION Inductor voltage and current are not in phase Keep in mind that Eq. (31.13) is a relationship between the *amplitudes* of the oscillating voltage and current for the inductor in Fig. 31.8a. It does *not* say that the voltage at any instant is equal to the current at that instant multiplied by X_L. As Fig. 31.8b shows, the voltage and current are 90° out of phase. Voltage and current are in phase only for resistors, as in Eq. (31.6).

The Meaning of Inductive Reactance

The inductive reactance X_L is really a description of the self-induced emf that opposes any change in the current through the inductor. From Eq. (31.13), for a given current amplitude I the voltage $v_L = +L\,di/dt$ across the inductor and the self-induced emf $\mathcal{E} = -L\,di/dt$ both have an amplitude V_L that is directly proportional to X_L. According to Eq. (31.12), the inductive reactance and self-induced emf increase with more rapid variation in current (that is, increasing angular frequency ω) and increasing inductance L.

If an oscillating voltage of a given amplitude V_L is applied across the inductor terminals, the resulting current will have a smaller amplitude I for larger values of X_L. Since X_L is proportional to frequency, a high-frequency voltage applied to the inductor gives only a small current, while a lower-frequency voltage of the same amplitude gives rise to a larger current. Inductors are used in some circuit applications, such as power supplies and radio-interference filters, to block high frequencies while permitting lower frequencies or dc to pass through. A circuit device that uses an inductor for this purpose is called a *low-pass filter* (see Problem 31.50).

Example 31.2 An inductor in an ac circuit

Suppose you want the current amplitude in a pure inductor in a radio receiver to be 250 μA when the voltage amplitude is 3.60 V at a frequency of 1.60 MHz (corresponding to the upper end of the AM broadcast band). (a) What inductive reactance is needed? What inductance? (b) If the voltage amplitude is kept constant, what will be the current amplitude through this inductor at 16.0 MHz? At 160 kHz?

SOLUTION

IDENTIFY: We are not told about any other elements of the circuit of which the inductor is part. Nor should we care about those other elements, since from the perspective of this example, all they do is provide the inductor with an oscillating voltage. Hence all of those other circuit elements are lumped into the ac source shown in Fig. 31.8a.

SET UP: We are given the current amplitude I and the voltage amplitude V. Our target variables in part (a) are the inductive reactance X_L at 1.60 MHz and the inductance L, which we find using Eqs. (31.13) and (31.12). Once we know L, we use these same two equations to find the inductive reactance and current amplitude at any other frequency.

EXECUTE: (a) From Eq. (31.13),

$$X_L = \frac{V_L}{I} = \frac{3.60\ \text{V}}{250 \times 10^{-6}\ \text{A}} = 1.44 \times 10^4\ \Omega = 14.4\ \text{k}\Omega$$

From Eq. (31.12), with $\omega = 2\pi f$, we find

$$L = \frac{X_L}{2\pi f} = \frac{1.44 \times 10^4\ \Omega}{2\pi(1.60 \times 10^6\ \text{Hz})} = 1.43 \times 10^{-3}\ \text{H} = 1.43\ \text{mH}$$

(b) Combining Eqs. (31.12) and (31.13), we find that the current amplitude is $I = V_L/X_L = V_L/\omega L = V_L/2\pi f L$. Thus the current amplitude is inversely proportional to the frequency f. Since $I = 250\ \mu\text{A}$ at $f = 1.60$ MHz, the current amplitude at 16.0 MHz (ten times the original frequency) will be one-tenth as great, or 25.0 μA; at 160 kHz = 0.160 MHz (one-tenth of the original frequency) the current amplitude is ten times as great, or 2500 μA = 2.50 mA.

EVALUATE: In general, the lower the frequency of an oscillating voltage applied across an inductor, the greater the amplitude of the oscillating current that results.

Capacitor in an ac Circuit

Finally, we connect a capacitor with capacitance C to the source, as in Fig. 31.9a, producing a current $i = I\cos\omega t$ through the capacitor. Again, the positive direction of current is counterclockwise around the circuit.

CAUTION Alternating current through a capacitor You may object that charge can't really move through the capacitor because its two plates are insulated from each other. True enough, but as the capacitor charges and discharges, there is at each instant a current i into one plate, an equal current out of the other plate, and an equal *displacement* current between the plates just as though the charge were being conducted through the capacitor. (You may want to review the discussion of displacement current in Section 29.7.) Thus we often speak about alternating current *through* a capacitor.

To find the instantaneous voltage v_C across the capacitor—that is, the potential of point a with respect to point b—we first let q denote the charge on the left-hand plate of the capacitor in Fig. 31.9a (so $-q$ is the charge on the right-hand plate). The current i is related to q by $i = dq/dt$; with this definition, positive current corresponds to an increasing charge on the left-hand capacitor plate. Then

$$i = \frac{dq}{dt} = I\cos\omega t$$

Integrating this, we get

$$q = \frac{I}{\omega}\sin\omega t \tag{31.14}$$

31.9 Capacitor C connected across an ac source.

(a) Circuit with ac source and capacitor

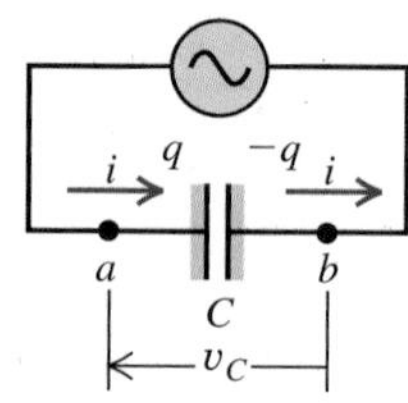

(b) Graphs of current and voltage versus time

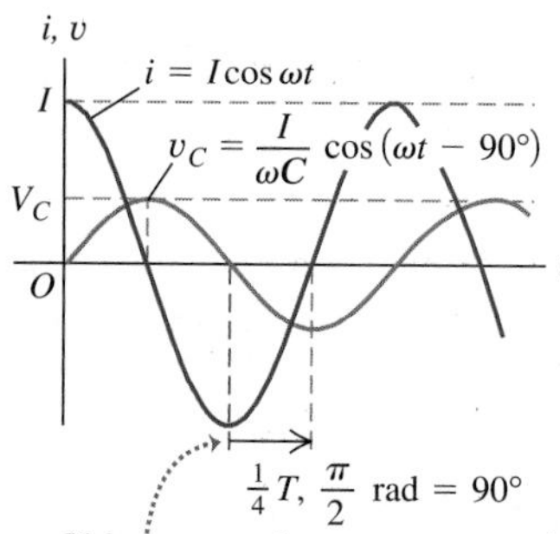

$\frac{1}{4}T$, $\frac{\pi}{2}$ rad = 90°

Voltage curve *lags* current curve by a quarter-cycle (corresponding to $\phi = \pi/2$ rad = 90°).

(c) Phasor diagram

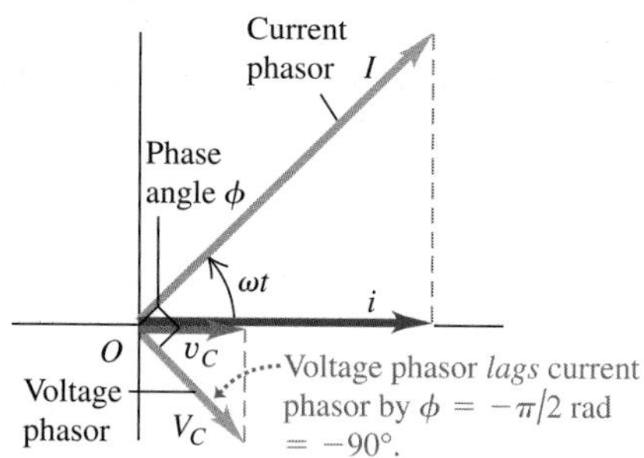

Voltage phasor *lags* current phasor by $\phi = -\pi/2$ rad = −90°.

Also, from Eq. (24.1) the charge q equals the voltage v_C multiplied by the capacitance, $q = Cv_C$. Using this in Eq. (31.14), we find

$$v_C = \frac{I}{\omega C}\sin\omega t \tag{31.15}$$

The instantaneous current i is equal to the rate of change dq/dt of the capacitor charge q; since $q = Cv_C$, i is also proportional to the rate of change of voltage. (Compare to an inductor, for which the situation is reversed and v_L is proportional to the rate of change of i.) Figure 31.9b shows v_C and i as functions of t. Because $i = dq/dt = C\,dv_C/dt$, the current has its greatest magnitude when the v_C curve is rising or falling most steeply and is zero when the v_C curve instantaneously levels off at its maximum and minimum values.

The capacitor voltage and current are out of phase by a quarter-cycle. The peaks of voltage occur a quarter-cycle *after* the corresponding current peaks, and we say that the voltage *lags* the current by 90°. The phasor diagram in Fig. 31.9c shows this relationship; the voltage phasor is behind the current phasor by a quarter-cycle, or 90°.

We can also derive this phase difference by rewriting Eq. (31.15), using the identity $\cos(A - 90°) = \sin A$:

$$v_C = \frac{I}{\omega C}\cos(\omega t - 90°) \tag{31.16}$$

This corresponds to a phase angle $\phi = -90°$. This cosine function has a "late start" of 90° compared with the current $i = I\cos\omega t$.

Equations (31.15) and (31.16) show that the *maximum* voltage V_C (the voltage amplitude) is

$$V_C = \frac{I}{\omega C} \tag{31.17}$$

To put this expression in a form similar to Eq. (31.7) for a resistor, $V_R = IR$, we define a quantity X_C, called the **capacitive reactance** of the capacitor, as

$$X_C = \frac{1}{\omega C} \quad \text{(capacitive reactance)} \tag{31.18}$$

Then

$$V_C = IX_C \quad \text{(amplitude of voltage across a capacitor, ac circuit)} \tag{31.19}$$

The SI unit of X_C is the ohm, the same as for resistance and inductive reactance, because X_C is the ratio of a voltage and a current.

CAUTION **Capacitor voltage and current are not in phase** Remember that Eq. (31.19) for a capacitor, like Eq. (31.13) for an inductor, is *not* a statement about the instantaneous values of voltage and current. The instantaneous values are actually 90° out of phase, as Fig. 31.9b shows. Rather, Eq. (31.19) relates the *amplitudes* of the voltage and current.

The Meaning of Capacitive Reactance

The capacitive reactance of a capacitor is inversely proportional both to the capacitance C and to the angular frequency ω; the greater the capacitance and the higher the frequency, the *smaller* the capacitive reactance X_C. Capacitors tend to pass high-frequency current and to block low-frequency currents and dc, just the opposite of inductors. A device that preferentially passes signals of high frequency is called a *high-pass filter* (see Problem 31.49).

Example 31.3 A resistor and a capacitor in an ac circuit

A 200-Ω resistor is connected in series with a 5.0-μF capacitor. The voltage across the resistor is $v_R = (1.20\ \text{V})\cos(2500\ \text{rad/s})t$. (a) Derive an expression for the circuit current. (b) Determine the capacitive reactance of the capacitor. (c) Derive an expression for the voltage across the capacitor.

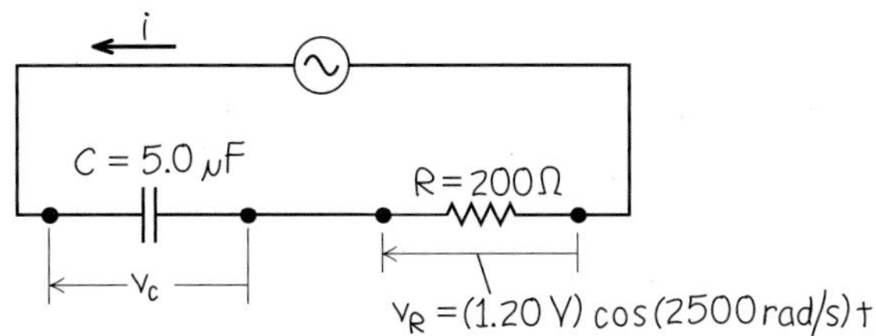

31.10 Our sketch for this problem.

SOLUTION

IDENTIFY: Since this is a series circuit, the current is the same through the capacitor as through the resistor. Our target variables are the current i, capacitive reactance X_C, and capacitor voltage v_C.

SET UP: Figure 31.10 shows the circuit. We find the current through the resistor, and hence through the circuit as a whole, using Eq. (31.6). We use Eq. (31.18) to find the capacitive reactance X_C, Eq. (31.19) to find the voltage amplitude, and Eq. (31.16) to write an expression for the instantaneous voltage across the capacitor.

EXECUTE: (a) Using $v_R = iR$, we find that the current i in the resistor and through the circuit as a whole is

$$i = \frac{v_R}{R} = \frac{(1.20\ \text{V})\cos(2500\ \text{rad/s})t}{200\ \Omega}$$
$$= (6.0 \times 10^{-3}\ \text{A})\cos(2500\ \text{rad/s})t$$

(b) From Eq. (31.18), the capacitive reactance at $\omega = 2500$ rad/s is

$$X_C = \frac{1}{\omega C} = \frac{1}{(2500\ \text{rad/s})(5.0 \times 10^{-6}\ \text{F})} = 80\ \Omega$$

(c) From Eq. (31.19), the amplitude V_C of the voltage across the capacitor is

$$V_C = IX_C = (6.0 \times 10^{-3}\ \text{A})(80\ \Omega) = 0.48\ \text{V}$$

The 80-Ω reactance of the capacitor is 40% of the resistor's 200-Ω resistance, so the value of V_C is 40% of V_R. The instantaneous capacitor voltage v_C is given by Eq. (31.16):

$$v_C = V_C\cos(\omega t - 90°)$$
$$= (0.48\ \text{V})\cos[(2500\ \text{rad/s})t - \pi/2\ \text{rad}]$$

EVALUATE: Although the *current* through the capacitor is the same as through the resistor, the *voltages* across these two devices are different in both amplitude and phase. Note that in the expression for v_C we converted the 90° to $\pi/2$ rad so that all the angular quantities have the same units. In ac circuit analysis, phase angles are often given in degrees, so be careful to convert to radians when necessary.

Comparing ac Circuit Elements

Table 31.1 summarizes the relationships of voltage and current amplitudes for the three circuit elements we have discussed. Note again that *instantaneous* voltage and current are proportional in a resistor, where there is zero phase difference between v_R and i (see Fig. 31.7b). The instantaneous voltage and current are *not* proportional in an inductor or capacitor, because there is a 90° phase difference in both cases (see Figs. 31.8b and 31.9b).

Figure 31.11 shows how the resistance of a resistor and the reactances of an inductor and a capacitor vary with angular frequency ω. Resistance R is independent of frequency, while the reactances X_L and X_C are not. If $\omega = 0$, corresponding to a dc circuit, there is *no* current through a capacitor because $X_C \to \infty$, and there is no inductive effect because $X_L = 0$. In the limit $\omega \to \infty$, X_L also approaches infinity, and the current through an inductor becomes vanishingly small; recall that the self-induced emf opposes rapid changes in current. In this same limit, X_C and the voltage across a capacitor both approach zero; the current changes direction so rapidly that no charge can build up on either plate.

31.11 Graphs of R, X_L, and X_C as functions of angular frequency ω.

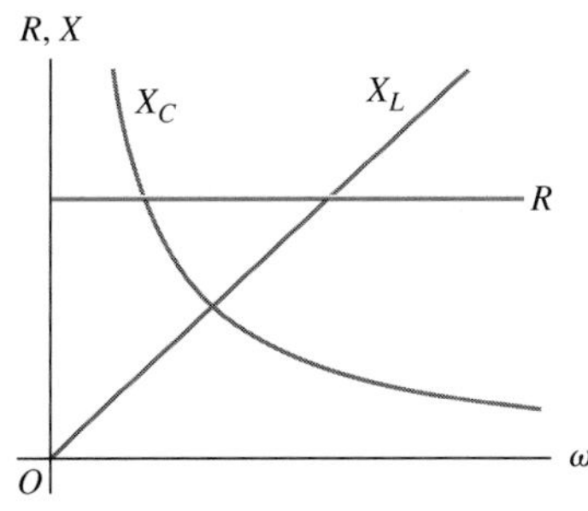

Figure 31.12 shows an application of the above discussion to a loudspeaker system. Low-frequency sounds are produced by the *woofer,* which is a speaker

Table 31.1 Circuit Elements with Alternating Current

Circuit Element	Amplitude Relationship	Circuit Quantity	Phase of v
Resistor	$V_R = IR$	R	In phase with i
Inductor	$V_L = IX_L$	$X_L = \omega L$	Leads i by 90°
Capacitor	$V_C = IX_C$	$X_C = 1/\omega C$	Lags i by 90°

31.12 (a) The two speakers in this loud speaker system are connected in parallel to the amplifier. (b) Graphs of current amplitude in the tweeter and woofer as functions of frequency for a given amplifier voltage amplitude.

(a) A crossover network in a loudspeaker system

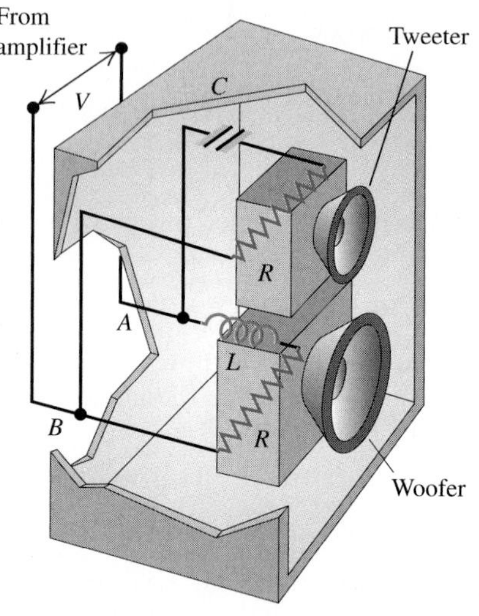
From amplifier
V
C
Tweeter
R
A
L
B
R
Woofer

(b) Graphs of rms current as functions of frequency for a given amplifier voltage

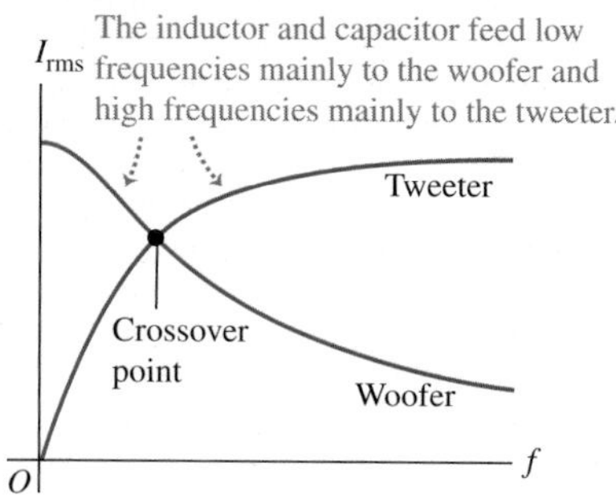
The inductor and capacitor feed low frequencies mainly to the woofer and high frequencies mainly to the tweeter.
I_{rms}
Tweeter
Crossover point
Woofer
O
f

with large diameter; the *tweeter,* a speaker with smaller diameter, produces high-frequency sounds. In order to route signals of different frequency to the appropriate speaker, the woofer and tweeter are connected in parallel across the amplifier output. The capacitor in the tweeter branch blocks the low-frequency components of sound but passes the higher frequencies; the inductor in the woofer branch does the opposite.

Test Your Understanding of Section 31.2 An oscillating voltage of fixed amplitude is applied across a circuit element. If the frequency of this voltage is increased, will the amplitude of the current through the element (i) increase, (ii) decrease, or (iii) remain the same if it is (a) a resistor, (b) an inductor, or (c) a capacitor?

31.3 The *L-R-C* Series Circuit

Many ac circuits used in practical electronic systems involve resistance, inductive reactance, and capacitive reactance. A simple example is a series circuit containing a resistor, an inductor, a capacitor, and an ac source, as shown in Fig. 31.13a. (In Section 30.6 we considered the behavior of the current in an *L-R-C* series circuit *without* a source.)

To analyze this and similar circuits, we will use a phasor diagram that includes the voltage and current phasors for each of the components. In this circuit, because of Kirchhoff's loop rule, the instantaneous *total* voltage v_{ad} across all three components is equal to the source voltage at that instant. We will show that the phasor representing this total voltage is the *vector sum* of the phasors for the individual voltages. Complete phasor diagrams for this circuit are shown in Figs. 31.13b and 31.13c. These may appear complex, but we'll explain them one step at a time.

Let's assume that the source supplies a current i given by $i = I\cos\omega t$. Because the circuit elements are connected in series, the current at any instant is the same at every point in the circuit. Thus a *single phasor I*, with length proportional to the current amplitude, represents the current in *all* circuit elements.

As in Section 31.2, we use the symbols v_R, v_L, and v_C for the instantaneous voltages across R, L, and C, and the symbols V_R, V_L, and V_C for the maximum voltages. We denote the instantaneous and maximum *source* voltages by v and V. Then, in Fig. 31.13a, $v = v_{ad}$, $v_R = v_{ab}$, $v_L = v_{bc}$, and $v_C = v_{cd}$.

We have shown that the potential difference between the terminals of a resistor is *in phase* with the current in the resistor and that its maximum value V_R is given by Eq. (31.7):

$$V_R = IR$$

31.13 An *L-R-C* series circuit with an ac source.

(a) Series *R-L-C* circuit

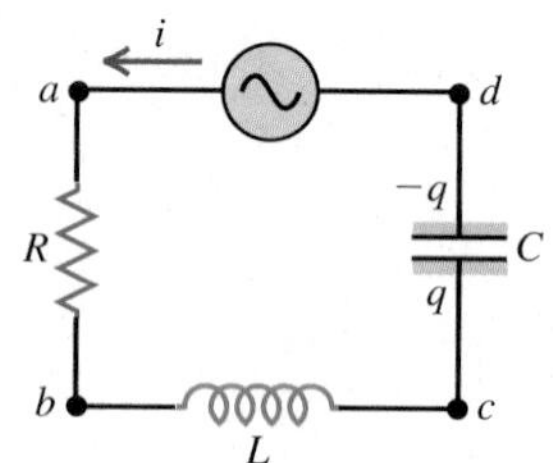
i
a
d
R
−q
q
C
b
c
L

(b) Phasor diagram for the case $X_L > X_C$

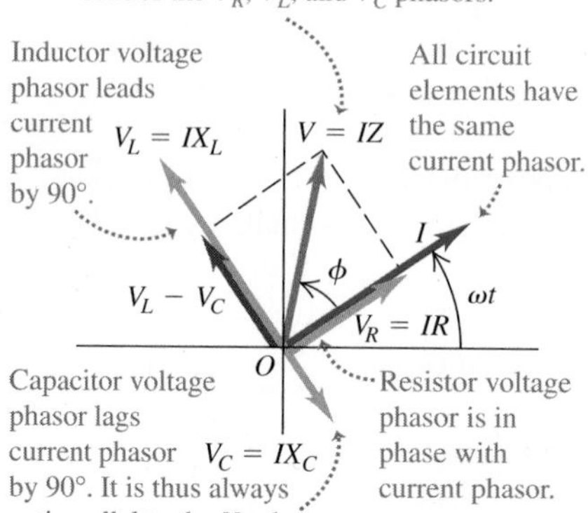
Source voltage phasor is the vector sum of the V_R, V_L, and V_C phasors.
Inductor voltage phasor leads current phasor by 90°.
All circuit elements have the same current phasor.
$V_L = IX_L$
$V = IZ$
I
ϕ
ωt
$V_L - V_C$
$V_R = IR$
O
Capacitor voltage phasor lags current phasor by 90°. It is thus always antiparallel to the V_L phasor.
$V_C = IX_C$
Resistor voltage phasor is in phase with current phasor.

(c) Phasor diagram for the case $X_L < X_C$

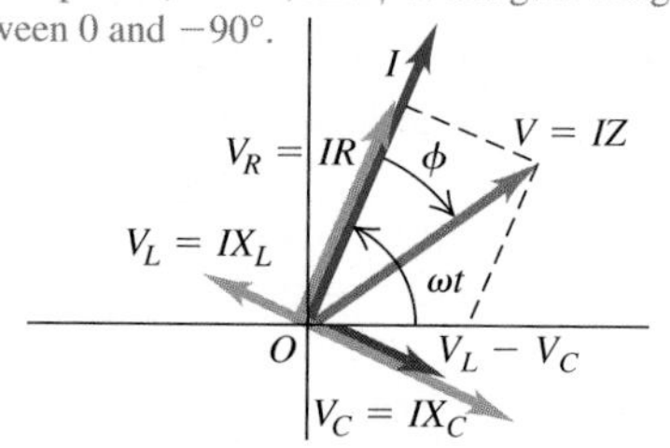
If $X_L < X_C$, the source voltage phasor lags the current phasor, $X < 0$, and ϕ is a negative angle between 0 and −90°.
I
$V_R = IR$
ϕ
$V = IZ$
$V_L = IX_L$
ωt
O
$V_L - V_C$
$V_C = IX_C$

The phasor V_R in Fig. 31.13b, in phase with the current phasor I, represents the voltage across the resistor. Its projection onto the horizontal axis at any instant gives the instantaneous potential difference v_R.

The voltage across an inductor *leads* the current by 90°. Its voltage amplitude is given by Eq. (31.13):

$$V_L = IX_L$$

The phasor V_L in Fig. 31.13b represents the voltage across the inductor, and its projection onto the horizontal axis at any instant equals v_L.

The voltage across a capacitor *lags* the current by 90°. Its voltage amplitude is given by Eq. (31.19):

$$V_C = IX_C$$

The phasor V_C in Fig. 31.13b represents the voltage across the capacitor, and its projection onto the horizontal axis at any instant equals v_C.

The instantaneous potential difference v between terminals a and d is equal at every instant to the (algebraic) sum of the potential differences v_R, v_L, and v_C. That is, it equals the sum of the *projections* of the phasors V_R, V_L, and V_C. But the sum of the projections of these phasors is equal to the *projection* of their *vector sum*. So the vector sum V must be the phasor that represents the source voltage v and the instantaneous total voltage v_{ad} across the series of elements.

To form this vector sum, we first subtract the phasor V_C from the phasor V_L. (These two phasors always lie along the same line, with opposite directions.) This gives the phasor $V_L - V_C$. This is always at right angles to the phasor V_R, so from the Pythagorean theorem the magnitude of the phasor V is

$$V = \sqrt{V_R^2 + (V_L - V_C)^2} = \sqrt{(IR)^2 + (IX_L - IX_C)^2} \quad \text{or}$$

$$V = I\sqrt{R^2 + (X_L - X_C)^2} \tag{31.20}$$

We define the **impedance** Z of an ac circuit as the ratio of the voltage amplitude across the circuit to the current amplitude in the circuit. From Eq. (31.20) the impedance of the *L-R-C* series circuit is

$$Z = \sqrt{R^2 + (X_L - X_C)^2} \tag{31.21}$$

so we can rewrite Eq. (31.20) as

$$V = IZ \quad \text{(amplitude of voltage across an ac circuit)} \tag{31.22}$$

While Eq. (31.21) is valid only for an *L-R-C* series circuit, we can use Eq. (31.22) to define the impedance of *any* network of resistors, inductors, and capacitors as the ratio of the amplitude of the voltage across the network to the current amplitude. The SI unit of impedance is the ohm.

The Meaning of Impedance and Phase Angle

Equation (31.22) has a form similar to $V = IR$, with impedance Z in an ac circuit playing the role of resistance R in a dc circuit. Just as direct current tends to follow the path of least resistance, so alternating current tends to follow the path of lowest impedance (Fig. 31.14). Note, however, that impedance is actually a function of R, L, and C, as well as of the angular frequency ω. We can see this by substituting Eq. (31.12) for X_L and Eq. (31.18) for X_C into Eq. (31.21), giving the following complete expression for Z for a series circuit:

$$\begin{aligned} Z &= \sqrt{R^2 + (X_L - X_C)^2} \\ &= \sqrt{R^2 + [\omega L - (1/\omega C)]^2} \end{aligned} \quad \text{(impedance of an } L\text{-}R\text{-}C \text{ series circuit)} \tag{31.23}$$

14.3 AC Circuits: The Driven Oscillator (Questions 6, 7, and 10)

31.14 This gas-filled glass sphere has an alternating voltage between its surface and the electrode at its center. The glowing streamers show the resulting alternating current that passes through the gas. When you touch the outside of the sphere, your fingertips and the inner surface of the sphere act as the plates of a capacitor, and the sphere and your body together form an *L-R-C* series circuit. The current (which is low enough to be harmless) is drawn to your fingers because the path through your body has a low impedance.

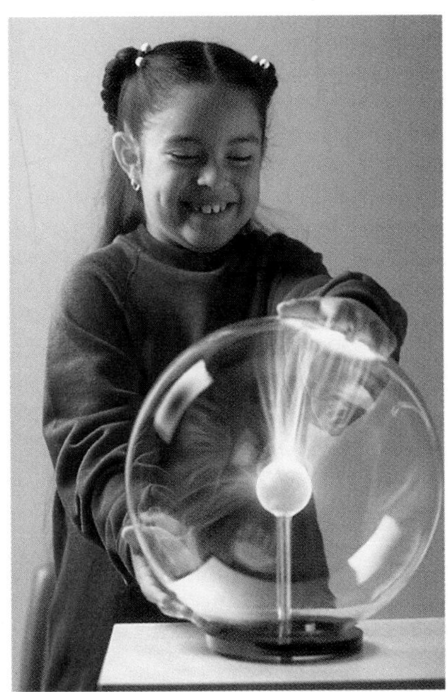

Hence for a given amplitude V of the source voltage applied to the circuit, the amplitude $I = V/Z$ of the resulting current will be different at different frequencies. We'll explore this frequency dependence in detail in Section 31.5.

In the phasor diagram shown in Fig. 31.13b, the angle ϕ between the voltage and current phasors is the phase angle of the source voltage v with respect to the current i; that is, it is the angle by which the source voltage leads the current. From the diagram,

$$\tan\phi = \frac{V_L - V_C}{V_R} = \frac{I(X_L - X_C)}{IR} = \frac{X_L - X_C}{R}$$

$$\tan\phi = \frac{\omega L - 1/\omega C}{R} \quad \text{(phase angle of an } L\text{-}R\text{-}C \text{ series circuit)} \tag{31.24}$$

If the current is $i = I\cos\omega t$, then the source voltage v is

$$v = V\cos(\omega t + \phi) \tag{31.25}$$

Figure 31.13b shows the behavior of a circuit in which $X_L > X_C$. Figure 31.13c shows the behavior when $X_L < X_C$; the voltage phasor V lies on the opposite side of the current phasor I and the voltage *lags* the current. In this case, $X_L - X_C$ is *negative,* $\tan\phi$ is negative, and ϕ is a negative angle between 0 and $-90°$. Since X_L and X_C depend on frequency, the phase angle ϕ depends on frequency as well. We'll examine the consequences of this in Section 31.5.

All of the expressions that we've developed for an L-R-C series circuit are still valid if one of the circuit elements is missing. If the resistor is missing, we set $R = 0$; if the inductor is missing, we set $L = 0$. But if the capacitor is missing, we set $C = \infty$, corresponding to the absence of any potential difference $(v_C = q/C = 0)$ or any capacitive reactance $(X_C = 1/\omega C = 0)$.

In this entire discussion we have described magnitudes of voltages and currents in terms of their *maximum* values, the voltage and current *amplitudes.* But we remarked at the end of Section 31.1 that these quantities are usually described in terms of rms values, not amplitudes. For any sinusoidally varying quantity the rms value is always $1/\sqrt{2}$ times the amplitude. All the relationships between voltage and current that we have derived in this and the preceding sections are still valid if we use rms quantities throughout instead of amplitudes. For example, if we divide Eq. (31.22) by $\sqrt{2}$, we get

$$\frac{V}{\sqrt{2}} = \frac{I}{\sqrt{2}}Z$$

which we can rewrite as

$$V_{\text{rms}} = I_{\text{rms}}Z \tag{31.26}$$

We can translate Eqs. (31.7), (31.13), and (31.19) in exactly the same way.

We have considered only ac circuits in which an inductor, a resistor, and a capacitor are in series. You can do a similar analysis for a *parallel* L-R-C circuit; see Problem 31.54.

Finally, we remark that in this section we have been describing the *steady-state* condition of a circuit, the state that exists after the circuit has been connected to the source for a long time. When the source is first connected, there may be additional voltages and currents, called *transients,* whose nature depends on the time in the cycle when the circuit is initially completed. A detailed analysis of transients is beyond our scope. They always die out after a sufficiently long time, and they do not affect the steady-state behavior of the circuit. But they can cause dangerous and damaging surges in power lines, which is why delicate electronic systems such as computers are often provided with power-line surge protectors.

Problem-Solving Strategy 31.1 Alternating-Current Circuits

IDENTIFY *the relevant concepts:* All of the concepts that we used to analyze direct-current circuits also apply to alternating-current circuits. However, we must be careful to distinguish between the amplitudes of alternating currents and voltages and their instantaneous values. We must also keep in mind the distinctions between resistance (for resistors), reactance (for inductors or capacitors), and impedance (for composite circuits).

SET UP *the problem* using the following steps:

1. Draw a diagram of the circuit and label all known and unknown quantities.
2. Determine the target variables.

EXECUTE *the solution* as follows:

1. Use the relationships derived in Sections 31.2 and 31.3 to solve for the target variables, using the following hints.
2. In ac circuit problems it is nearly always easiest to work with angular frequency ω. If you are given the ordinary frequency f, expressed in Hz, convert it using the relationship $\omega = 2\pi f$.
3. Keep in mind a few basic facts about phase relationships. For a resistor, voltage and current are always *in phase,* and the two corresponding phasors in a phasor diagram always have the same direction. For an inductor, the voltage always *leads* the current by 90° (i.e., $\phi = +90°$), and the voltage phasor is always turned 90° counterclockwise from the current phasor. For a capacitor, the voltage always *lags* the current by 90° (i.e., $\phi = -90°$), and the voltage phasor is always turned 90° clockwise from the current phasor.
4. Remember that with ac circuits, all voltages and currents are sinusoidal functions of time instead of being constant, but Kirchhoff's rules hold nonetheless at each instant. Thus, in a series circuit, the instantaneous current is the same in all circuit elements; in a parallel circuit, the instantaneous potential difference is the same across all circuit elements.
5. Inductive reactance, capacitive reactance, and impedance are analogous to resistance; each represents the ratio of voltage amplitude V to current amplitude I in a circuit element or combination of elements. Keep in mind, however, that phase relationships play an essential role. The effects of resistance and reactance have to be combined by *vector* addition of the corresponding voltage phasors, as in Figs. 31.13b and 31.13c. When you have several circuit elements in series, for example, you can't just *add* all the numerical values of resistance and reactance to get the impedance; that would ignore the phase relationships.

EVALUATE *your answer:* When working with a series *L-R-C* circuit, you can check your results by comparing the values of the inductive reactance X_L and the capacitive reactance X_C. If $X_L > X_C$, then the voltage amplitude across the inductor is greater than that across the capacitor and the phase angle ϕ is positive (between 0 and 90°). If $X_L < X_C$, then the voltage amplitude across the inductor is less than that across the capacitor and the phase angle ϕ is negative (between 0 and −90°).

Example 31.4 An *L-R-C* series circuit I

In the series circuit of Fig. 31.13a, suppose $R = 300\ \Omega$, $L = 60$ mH, $C = 0.50\ \mu$F, $V = 50$ V, and $\omega = 10{,}000$ rad/s. Find the reactances X_L and X_C, the impedance Z, the current amplitude I, the phase angle ϕ, and the voltage amplitude across each circuit element.

SOLUTION

IDENTIFY: This problem uses the ideas developed in Section 31.2 and this section about the behavior of circuit elements in an ac circuit.

SET UP: We use Eqs. (31.12) and (31.18) to determine the reactances and Eq. (31.23) to find the impedance. We then use Eq. (31.22) to find the current amplitude and Eq. (31.24) to calculate the phase angle. Given this information, the relationships in Table 31.1 tell us the voltage amplitudes.

EXECUTE: The inductive and capacitive reactances are

$$X_L = \omega L = (10{,}000 \text{ rad/s})(60 \text{ mH}) = 600\ \Omega$$

$$X_C = \frac{1}{\omega C} = \frac{1}{(10{,}000 \text{ rad/s})(0.50 \times 10^{-6} \text{ F})} = 200\ \Omega$$

The impedance Z of the circuit is

$$Z = \sqrt{R^2 + (X_L - X_C)^2} = \sqrt{(300\ \Omega)^2 + (600\ \Omega - 200\ \Omega)^2} = 500\ \Omega$$

With source voltage amplitude $V = 50$ V the current amplitude is

$$I = \frac{V}{Z} = \frac{50 \text{ V}}{500\ \Omega} = 0.10 \text{ A}$$

The phase angle ϕ is

$$\phi = \arctan\frac{X_L - X_C}{R} = \arctan\frac{400\ \Omega}{300\ \Omega} = 53°$$

From Table 31.1, the voltage amplitudes V_R, V_L, and V_C across the resistor, inductor, and capacitor, respectively, are

$$V_R = IR = (0.10 \text{ A})(300\ \Omega) = 30 \text{ V}$$
$$V_L = IX_L = (0.10 \text{ A})(600\ \Omega) = 60 \text{ V}$$
$$V_C = IX_C = (0.10 \text{ A})(200\ \Omega) = 20 \text{ V}$$

EVALUATE: Note that $X_L > X_C$ and hence the voltage amplitude across the inductor is greater than across the capacitor and ϕ is negative. The value $\phi = -53°$ means that the voltage *leads* the current by 53°; this is like the situation shown in Fig. 31.13b.

Note that the source voltage amplitude $V = 50$ V is *not* equal to the sum of the voltage amplitudes across the separate circuit elements. (That is, $50 \text{ V} \neq 30 \text{ V} + 60 \text{ V} + 20 \text{ V}$.) Make sure you understand why not!

Example 31.5 An *L-R-C* series circuit II

For the *L-R-C* series circuit described in Example 31.4, describe the time dependence of the instantaneous current and each instantaneous voltage.

SOLUTION

IDENTIFY: In Example 31.4 we found the *amplitudes* of the current and voltages. Now our task is to find expressions for the *instantaneous values* of the current and voltages. As we learned in Section 31.2, the voltage across a resistor is in phase with the current but the voltages across an inductor or capacitor are not. We also learned in this section that ϕ is the phase angle between the source voltage and the current.

SET UP: If we describe the current using Eq. (31.2), the voltages are given by Eq. (31.8) for the resistor, Eq. (31.10) for the inductor, Eq. (31.16) for the capacitor, and Eq. (31.25) for the source.

EXECUTE: The current and all of the voltages oscillate with the same angular frequency, $\omega = 10{,}000\ \text{rad/s}$, and hence with the same period, $2\pi/\omega = 2\pi/(10{,}000\ \text{rad/s}) = 6.3 \times 10^{-4}\ \text{s} = 0.63\ \text{ms}$. Using Eq. (31.2), the current is

$$i = I\cos\omega t = (0.10\ \text{A})\cos(10{,}000\ \text{rad/s})t$$

This choice simply means that we choose $t = 0$ to be an instant when the current is maximum. The resistor voltage is *in phase* with the current, so

$$v_R = V_R\cos\omega t = (30\ \text{V})\cos(10{,}000\ \text{rad/s})t$$

The inductor voltage *leads* the current by 90°, so

$$v_L = V_L\cos(\omega t + 90^\circ) = -V_L\sin\omega t = -(60\ \text{V})\sin(10{,}000\ \text{rad/s})t$$

The capacitor voltage *lags* the current by 90°, so

$$v_C = V_C\cos(\omega t - 90^\circ) = V_C\sin\omega t = (20\ \text{V})\sin(10{,}000\ \text{rad/s})t$$

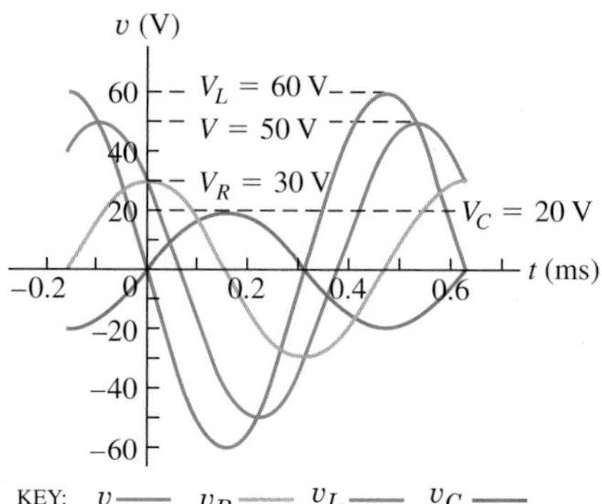

31.15 Graphs of the source voltage v, resistor voltage v_R, inductor voltage v_L, and capacitor voltage v_C as functions of time for the situation of Example 31.4. The current, which is not shown, is in phase with the resistor voltage.

Finally, the source voltage (equal to the voltage across the entire combination of resistor, inductor, and capacitor) *leads* the current by $\phi = 53^\circ$, so

$$\begin{aligned} v &= V\cos(\omega t + \phi) \\ &= (50\ \text{V})\cos\left[(10{,}000\ \text{rad/s})t + \left(\frac{2\pi\ \text{rad}}{360^\circ}\right)(53^\circ)\right] \\ &= (50\ \text{V})\cos[(10{,}000\ \text{rad/s})t + 0.93\ \text{rad}] \end{aligned}$$

EVALUATE: Figure 31.15 graphs the various voltages versus time. The inductor voltage has a larger amplitude than the capacitor voltage because $X_L > X_C$. While the source voltage amplitude V is not equal to the sum of the individual voltage amplitudes V_R, V_L, and V_C, the *instantaneous* source voltage v is always equal to the sum of the instantaneous voltages v_R, v_L, and v_C. You should verify this by measuring the values of the voltages shown in the graph at different values of the time t.

Test Your Understanding of Section 31.3 Rank the following ac circuits in order of their current amplitude, from highest to lowest value. (i) the circuit in Example 31.4; (ii) the circuit in Example 31.4 with the capacitor and inductor both removed; (iii) the circuit in Example 31.4 with the resistor and capacitor both removed; (iv) the circuit in Example 31.4 with the resistor and inductor both removed.

31.4 Power in Alternating-Current Circuits

Alternating currents play a central role in systems for distributing, converting, and using electrical energy, so it's important to look at power relationships in ac circuits. For an ac circuit with instantaneous current i and current amplitude I, we'll consider an element of that circuit across which the instantaneous potential difference is v with voltage amplitude V. The instantaneous power p delivered to this circuit element is

$$p = vi$$

Let's first see what this means for individual circuit elements. We'll assume in each case that $i = I\cos\omega t$.

Power in a Resistor

Suppose first that the circuit element is a *pure resistor R*, as in Fig. 31.7a; then $v = v_R$ and i are *in phase.* We obtain the graph representing p by multiplying the heights of the graphs of v and i in Fig. 31.7b at each instant. This graph is shown by the black curve in Fig. 31.16a. The product vi is always positive because v and i are always either both positive or both negative. Hence energy is supplied *to* the resistor at every instant for both directions of i, although the power is not constant.

The power curve for a pure resistor is symmetrical about a value equal to one-half its maximum value VI, so the *average power* P_{av} is

$$P_{av} = \frac{1}{2}VI \qquad \text{(for a pure resistor)} \tag{31.27}$$

An equivalent expression is

$$P_{av} = \frac{V}{\sqrt{2}}\frac{I}{\sqrt{2}} = V_{rms}I_{rms} \qquad \text{(for a pure resistor)} \tag{31.28}$$

Also, $V_{rms} = I_{rms}R$, so we can express P_{av} by any of the equivalent forms

$$P_{av} = I_{rms}{}^2R = \frac{V_{rms}{}^2}{R} = V_{rms}I_{rms} \qquad \text{(for a pure resistor)} \tag{31.29}$$

Note that the expressions in Eq. (31.29) have the same form as the corresponding relationships for a dc circuit, Eq. (25.18). Also note that they are valid only for pure resistors, not for more complicated combinations of circuit elements.

Power in an Inductor

Next we connect the source to a pure inductor L, as in Fig. 31.8a. The voltage $v = v_L$ leads the current i by 90°. When we multiply the curves of v and i, the product vi is *negative* during the half of the cycle when v and i have *opposite* signs. The power curve, shown in Fig. 31.16b, is symmetrical about the horizontal axis; it is positive half the time and negative the other half, and the average power is zero. When p is positive, energy is being supplied to set up the magnetic field in the inductor; when p is negative, the field is collapsing and the inductor is returning energy to the source. The net energy transfer over one cycle is zero.

31.16 Graphs of current, voltage, and power as functions of time for (a) a pure resistor, (b) a pure inductor, (c) a pure capacitor, and (d) an arbitrary ac circuit that can have resistance, inductance, and capacitance.

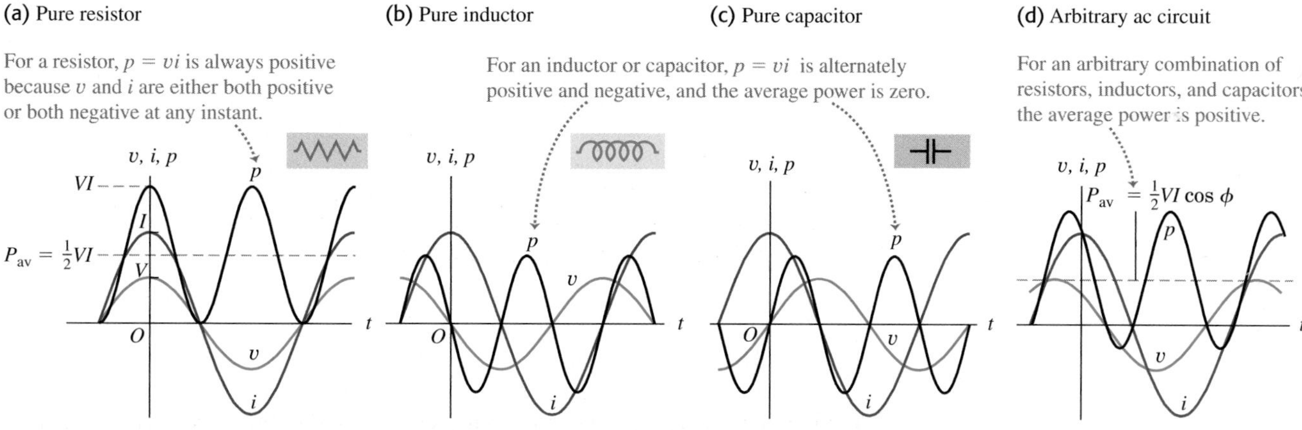
(a) Pure resistor
(b) Pure inductor
(c) Pure capacitor
(d) Arbitrary ac circuit
For a resistor, p = vi is always positive because v and i are either both positive or both negative at any instant.
For an inductor or capacitor, p = vi is alternately positive and negative, and the average power is zero.
For an arbitrary combination of resistors, inductors, and capacitors, the average power is positive.
v, i, p
VI
P_av = ½VI
p
I
V
O
t
v
i
P_av = ½VI cos φ
KEY: Instantaneous current, i
Instantaneous voltage across device, v
Instantaneous power input to device, p

Power in a Capacitor

Finally, we connect the source to a pure capacitor C, as in Fig. 31.9a. The voltage $v = v_C$ lags the current i by 90°. Figure 31.16c shows the power curve; the average power is again zero. Energy is supplied to charge the capacitor and is returned to the source when the capacitor discharges. The net energy transfer over one cycle is again zero.

Power in a General ac Circuit

In *any* ac circuit, with any combination of resistors, capacitors, and inductors, the voltage v across the entire circuit has some phase angle ϕ with respect to the current i. Then the instantaneous power p is given by

$$p = vi = [V\cos(\omega t + \phi)][I\cos\omega t] \qquad (31.30)$$

The instantaneous power curve has the form shown in Fig. 31.16d. The area between the positive loops and the horizontal axis is greater than the area between the negative loops and the horizontal axis, and the average power is positive.

We can derive from Eq. (31.30) an expression for the *average* power P_{av} by using the identity for the cosine of the sum of two angles:

$$\begin{aligned} p &= [V(\cos\omega t\cos\phi - \sin\omega t\sin\phi)][I\cos\omega t] \\ &= VI\cos\phi\cos^2\omega t - VI\sin\phi\cos\omega t\sin\omega t \end{aligned}$$

From the discussion in Section 31.1 that led to Eq. (31.4), we see that the average value of $\cos^2\omega t$ (over one cycle) is $\frac{1}{2}$. The average value of $\cos\omega t\sin\omega t$ is zero because this product is equal to $\frac{1}{2}\sin 2\omega t$, whose average over a cycle is zero. So the average power P_{av} is

$$P_{av} = \frac{1}{2}VI\cos\phi = V_{rms}I_{rms}\cos\phi \quad \text{(average power into a general ac circuit)} \qquad (31.31)$$

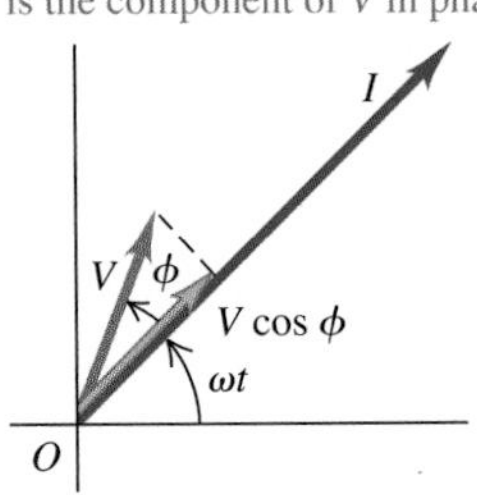

31.17 Using phasors to calculate the average power for an arbitrary ac circuit.

Average power $= \frac{1}{2}I(V\cos\phi)$, where $V\cos\phi$ is the component of V in phase with I.

When v and i are in phase, so $\phi = 0$, the average power equals $\frac{1}{2}VI = V_{rms}I_{rms}$; when v and i are 90° out of phase, the average power is zero. In the general case, when v has a phase angle ϕ with respect to i, the average power equals $\frac{1}{2}I$ multiplied by $V\cos\phi$, the component of the voltage phasor that is *in phase* with the current phasor. Figure 31.17 shows the general relationship of the current and voltage phasors. For the *L-R-C* series circuit, Figs. 31.13b and 31.13c show that $V\cos\phi$ equals the voltage amplitude V_R for the resistor; hence Eq. (31.31) is the average power dissipated in the resistor. On average there is no energy flow into or out of the inductor or capacitor, so none of P_{av} goes into either of these circuit elements.

The factor $\cos\phi$ is called the **power factor** of the circuit. For a pure resistance, $\phi = 0$, $\cos\phi = 1$, and $P_{av} = V_{rms}I_{rms}$. For a pure inductor or capacitor, $\phi = \pm 90°$, $\cos\phi = 0$, and $P_{av} = 0$. For an *L-R-C* series circuit the power factor is equal to R/Z; we leave the proof of this statement to you (see Exercise 31.27).

A low power factor (large angle ϕ of lag or lead) is usually undesirable in power circuits. The reason is that for a given potential difference, a large current is needed to supply a given amount of power. This results in large i^2R losses in the transmission lines. Your electric power company may charge a higher rate to a client with a low power factor. Many types of ac machinery draw a *lagging* current; that is, the current drawn by the machinery lags the applied voltage. Hence the voltage leads the current, so $\phi > 0$ and $\cos\phi < 1$. The power factor can be corrected toward the ideal value of 1 by connecting a capacitor in parallel with the load. The current drawn by the capacitor *leads* the voltage (that is, the voltage across the capacitor lags the current), which compensates for the lagging current in the other branch of the circuit. The capacitor itself absorbs no net power from the line.

Example 31.6 Power in a hair dryer

An electric hair dryer is rated at 1500 W at 120 V. The rated power of this hair dryer, or of any other ac device, is the *average* power drawn by the device, and the rated voltage is the *rms* voltage. Calculate (a) the resistance, (b) the rms current, and (c) the maximum instantaneous power. Assume that the hair dryer is a pure resistor. (The hair dryer's heating element acts as a resistor.)

SOLUTION

IDENTIFY: We assume that the hair dryer is a pure resistor. We are given the average power $P_{av} = 1500\text{ W}$ and the rms voltage $V_{rms} = 120\text{ V}$. Our target variables are the resistance R, the rms current I_{rms}, and the maximum value of the instantaneous power p.

SET UP: We solve Eq. (31.29) to determine the resistance R. We find the rms current from V_{rms} and P_{av} using Eq. (31.28), and we find the maximum instantaneous power from Eq. (31.30).

EXECUTE: (a) From Eq. (31.29), the resistance is

$$R = \frac{V_{rms}^2}{P_{av}} = \frac{(120\text{ V})^2}{1500\text{ W}} = 9.6\ \Omega$$

(b) From Eq. (31.28),

$$I_{rms} = \frac{P_{av}}{V_{rms}} = \frac{1500\text{ W}}{120\text{ V}} = 12.5\text{ A}$$

(c) For a pure resistor, the voltage and current are in phase and the phase angle ϕ is zero. Hence from Eq. (31.30), the instantaneous power is $p = VI\cos^2\omega t$ and the maximum instantaneous power is $p_{max} = VI$. From Eq. (31.27), this is twice the average power P_{av}, so

$$p_{max} = VI = 2P_{av} = 2(1500\text{ W}) = 3000\text{ W}$$

EVALUATE: We can confirm our result in part (b) by using Eq. (31.7): $I_{rms} = V_{rms}/R = (120\text{ V})/(9.6\ \Omega) = 12.5\text{ A}$. Note that some manufacturers of stereo amplifiers state power outputs in terms of the peak value rather than the lower average value, to mislead the unwary consumer.

Example 31.7 Power in an *L-R-C* series circuit

For the *L-R-C* series circuit of Example 31.4, (a) calculate the power factor; and (b) calculate the average power delivered to the entire circuit and to each circuit element.

SOLUTION

IDENTIFY: We can use all of the results found in Example 31.4.

SET UP: The power factor is simply the cosine of the phase angle ϕ, and Eq. (31.31) allows us to find the average power delivered in terms of ϕ and the amplitudes of voltage and current.

EXECUTE: (a) The power factor is $\cos\phi = \cos 53° = 0.60$.

(b) From Eq. (31.31) the average power delivered to the circuit is

$$P_{av} = \frac{1}{2}VI\cos\phi = \frac{1}{2}(50\text{ V})(0.10\text{ A})(0.60) = 1.5\text{ W}$$

EVALUATE: While P_{av} is the average power delivered to the *L-R-C* combination, all of this power is dissipated in the resistor. The average power delivered to a pure inductor or pure capacitor is always zero (see Figs. 31.16b and 31.16c).

Test Your Understanding of Section 31.4 Figure 31.16d shows that during part of a cycle of oscillation, the instantaneous power delivered to the circuit is negative. This means that energy is being extracted from the circuit. (a) Where is the energy extracted from? (i) the resistor; (ii) the inductor; (iii) the capacitor; (iv) the ac source; (v) more than one of these. (b) Where does the energy go? (i) the resistor; (ii) the inductor; (iii) the capacitor; (iv) the ac source; (v) more than one of these.

31.5 Resonance in Alternating-Current Circuits

Much of the practical importance of *L-R-C* series circuits arises from the way in which such circuits respond to sources of different angular frequency ω. For example, one type of tuning circuit used in radio receivers is simply an *L-R-C* series circuit. A radio signal of any given frequency produces a current of the same frequency in the receiver circuit, but the amplitude of the current is *greatest* if the signal frequency equals the particular frequency to which the receiver circuit is "tuned." This effect is called *resonance*. The circuit is designed so that signals at other than the tuned frequency produce currents that are too small to make an audible sound come out of the radio's speakers.

14.3 AC Circuits: The Driven Oscillator (Questions 8, 9, and 11)

31.18 How variations in the angular frequency of an ac circuit affect (a) reactances, resistance, and impedance, and (b) impedance, current amplitude, and phase angle.

(a) Reactance, resistance, and impedance as functions of angular frequency

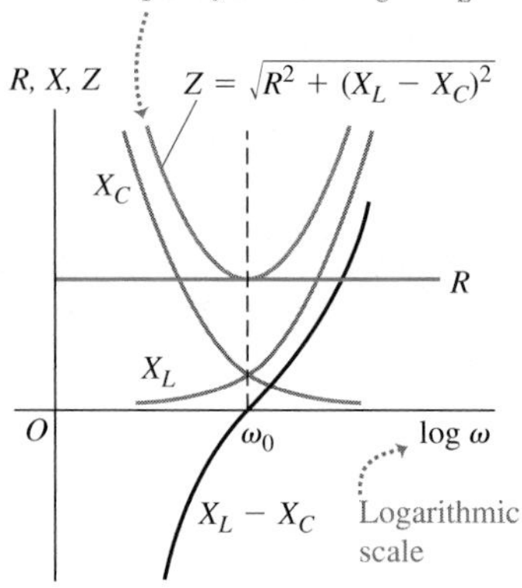
Impedance Z is least at the angular frequency at which $X_C = X_L$.
R, X, Z
$Z = \sqrt{R^2 + (X_L - X_C)^2}$
X_C
R
X_L
O
ω_0
log ω
$X_L - X_C$
Logarithmic scale

(b) Impedance, current, and phase angle as functions of angular frequency

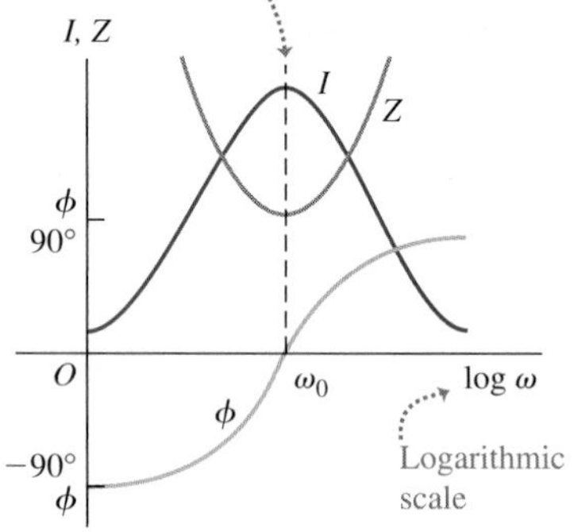
Current peaks at the angular frequency at which impedance is least. This is the *resonance angular frequency* ω_0.
I, Z
I
Z
ϕ
90°
O
ω_0
log ω
ϕ
−90°
ϕ
Logarithmic scale

To see how an L-R-C series circuit can be used in this way, suppose we connect an ac source with constant voltage amplitude V but adjustable angular frequency ω across an L-R-C series circuit. The current that appears in the circuit has the same angular frequency as the source and a current amplitude $I = V/Z$, where Z is the impedance of the L-R-C series circuit. This impedance depends on the frequency, as Eq. (31.23) shows. Figure 31.18a shows graphs of R, X_L, X_C, and Z as functions of ω. We have used a logarithmic angular frequency scale so that we can cover a wide range of frequencies. As the frequency increases, X_L increases and X_C decreases; hence there is always one frequency at which X_L and X_C are equal and $X_L - X_C$ is zero. At this frequency the impedance $Z = \sqrt{R^2 + (X_L - X_C)^2}$ has its *smallest* value, equal simply to the resistance R.

Circuit Behavior at Resonance

As we vary the angular frequency ω of the source, the current amplitude $I = V/Z$ varies as shown in Fig. 31.18b; the *maximum* value of I occurs at the frequency at which the impedance Z is *minimum*. This peaking of the current amplitude at a certain frequency is called **resonance.** The angular frequency ω_0 at which the resonance peak occurs is called the **resonance angular frequency.** This is the angular frequency at which the inductive and capacitive reactances are equal, so at resonance,

$$X_L = X_C \qquad \omega_0 L = \frac{1}{\omega_0 C} \qquad \omega_0 = \frac{1}{\sqrt{LC}} \qquad \text{(}L\text{-}R\text{-}C\text{ series circuit at resonance)} \tag{31.32}$$

Note that this is equal to the natural angular frequency of oscillation of an L-C circuit, which we derived in Section 30.5, Eq. (30.22). The **resonance frequency** f_0 is $\omega_0/2\pi$. This is the frequency at which the greatest current appears in the circuit for a given source voltage amplitude; in other words, f_0 is the frequency to which the circuit is "tuned."

It's instructive to look at what happens to the *voltages* in an L-R-C series circuit at resonance. The current at any instant is the same in L and C. The voltage across an inductor always *leads* the current by 90°, or $\frac{1}{4}$ cycle, and the voltage across a capacitor always *lags* the current by 90°. Therefore the instantaneous voltages across L and C always differ in phase by 180°, or $\frac{1}{2}$ cycle; they have opposite signs at each instant. At the resonance frequency, and *only* at the resonance frequency, $X_L = X_C$ and the voltage amplitudes $V_L = IX_L$ and $V_C = IX_C$ are *equal;* then the instantaneous voltages across L and C add to zero at each instant, and the *total* voltage v_{bd} across the L-C combination in Fig. 31.13a is exactly zero. The voltage across the resistor is then equal to the source voltage. So at the resonance frequency the circuit behaves as if the inductor and capacitor weren't there at all!

The *phase* of the voltage relative to the current is given by Eq. (31.24). At frequencies below resonance, X_C is greater than X_L; the capacitive reactance dominates, the voltage *lags* the current, and the phase angle ϕ is between zero and −90°. Above resonance, the inductive reactance dominates; the voltage *leads* the current, and the phase angle is between zero and +90°. This variation of ϕ with angular frequency is shown in Fig. 31.18b.

Tailoring an ac Circuit

If we can vary the inductance L or the capacitance C of a circuit, we can also vary the resonance frequency. This is exactly how a radio or television receiving set is "tuned" to receive a particular station. In the early days of radio this was accomplished by use of capacitors with movable metal plates whose overlap could be varied to change C. (This is what is being done with the radio tuning knob shown in the photograph that opens this chapter.) A more modern approach is to vary L by using a coil with a ferrite core that slides in or out.

In a series L-R-C circuit the impedance reaches its minimum value and the current its maximum value at the resonance frequency. The middle curve in Fig. 31.19 is a graph of current as a function of frequency for such a circuit, with source voltage amplitude $V = 100$ V, $L = 2.0$ H, $C = 0.50\ \mu$F, and $R = 500\ \Omega$. This curve is called a *response curve* or a *resonance curve*. The resonance angular frequency is $\omega_0 = (LC)^{-1/2} = 1000$ rad/s. As we expect, the curve has a peak at this angular frequency.

The resonance frequency is determined by L and C; what happens when we change R? Figure 31.19 also shows graphs of I as a function of ω for $R = 200\ \Omega$ and for $R = 2000\ \Omega$. The curves are similar for frequencies far away from resonance, where the impedance is dominated by X_L or X_C. But near resonance, where X_L and X_C nearly cancel each other, the curve is higher and more sharply peaked for small values of R and broader and flatter for large values of R. At resonance, $Z = R$ and $I = V/R$, so the maximum height of the curve is inversely proportional to R.

The shape of the response curve is important in the design of radio and television receiving circuits. The sharply peaked curve is what makes it possible to discriminate between two stations broadcasting on adjacent frequency bands. But if the peak is *too* sharp, some of the information in the received signal is lost, such as the high-frequency sounds in music. The shape of the resonance curve is also related to the overdamped and underdamped oscillations that we described in Section 30.6. A sharply peaked resonance curve corresponds to a small value of R and a lightly damped oscillating system; a broad, flat curve goes with a large value of R and a heavily damped system.

In this section we have discussed resonance in an L-R-C *series* circuit. Resonance can also occur in an ac circuit in which the inductor, resistor, and capacitor are connected in *parallel*. We leave the details to you (see Problem 31.55).

Resonance phenomena occur not just in ac circuits, but in all areas of physics. We discussed examples of resonance in *mechanical* systems in Sections 13.8 and 16.5. The amplitude of a mechanical oscillation peaks when the driving-force frequency is close to a natural frequency of the system; this is analogous to the peaking of the current in an L-R-C series circuit. We suggest that you review the sections on mechanical resonance now, looking for the analogies. Other important examples of resonance occur in atomic and nuclear physics and in the study of fundamental particles (high-energy physics).

31.19 Graph of current amplitude I as a function of angular frequency ω for an L-R-C series circuit with $V = 100$ V, $L = 2.0$ H, $C = 0.50\ \mu$F, and three different values of the resistance R.

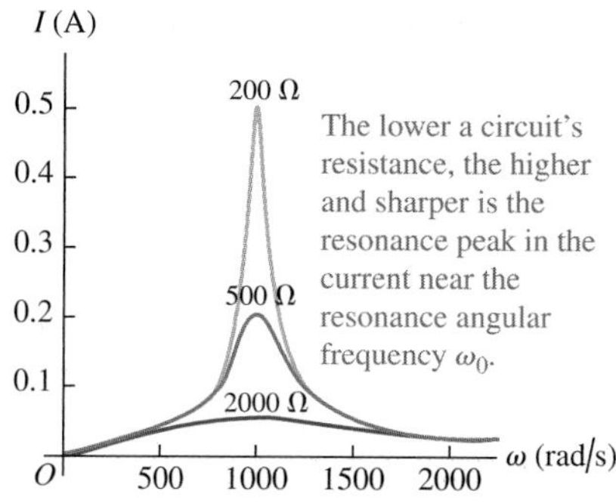

Example 31.8 Tuning a radio

The series circuit in Fig. 31.20 is similar to arrangements that are sometimes used in radio tuning circuits. This circuit is connected to the terminals of an ac source with a constant rms terminal voltage of 1.0 V and a variable frequency. Find (a) the resonance frequency; (b) the inductive reactance, the capacitive reactance, and the impedance at the resonance frequency; (c) the rms current at resonance; and (d) the rms voltage across each circuit element at resonance.

SOLUTION

IDENTIFY: The circuit in Fig. 31.20 is a series L-R-C circuit, but with meters added to measure the rms current and voltages (which are our target variables).

SET UP: Equation (31.32) includes the formula for the resonance angular frequency ω_0, from which we find the resonance frequency f_0. We find the remaining target variables using the results of Sections 31.2 and 31.3.

31.20 A radio tuning circuit at resonance. The circles denote rms current and voltages.

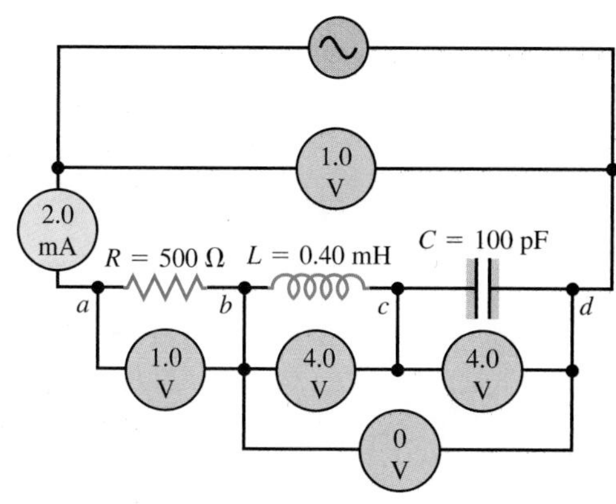

Continued

EXECUTE: (a) The resonance angular frequency is

$$\omega_0 = \frac{1}{\sqrt{LC}} = \frac{1}{\sqrt{(0.40 \times 10^{-3}\ \text{H})(100 \times 10^{-12}\ \text{F})}}$$
$$= 5.0 \times 10^6\ \text{rad/s}$$

The corresponding frequency $f_0 = \omega_0/2\pi$ is

$$f_0 = 8.0 \times 10^5\ \text{Hz} = 800\ \text{kHz}$$

This corresponds to the lower part of the AM radio band.

(b) At this frequency,

$$X_L = \omega L = (5.0 \times 10^6\ \text{rad/s})(0.40 \times 10^{-3}\ \text{H}) = 2000\ \Omega$$

$$X_C = \frac{1}{\omega C} = \frac{1}{(5.0 \times 10^6\ \text{rad/s})(100 \times 10^{-12}\ \text{F})} = 2000\ \Omega$$

Since $X_L = X_C$ and $X_L - X_C = 0$, Eq. (31.23) shows that the impedance Z at resonance is equal to the resistance: $Z = R = 500\ \Omega$.

(c) From Eq. (31.26) the rms current at resonance is

$$I_{\text{rms}} = \frac{V_{\text{rms}}}{Z} = \frac{V_{\text{rms}}}{R} = \frac{1.0\ \text{V}}{500\ \Omega} = 0.0020\ \text{A} = 2.0\ \text{mA}$$

(d) The rms potential difference across the resistor is

$$V_{R\text{-rms}} = I_{\text{rms}}R = (0.0020\ \text{A})(500\ \Omega) = 1.0\ \text{V}$$

The rms potential differences across the inductor and capacitor are, respectively:

$$V_{L\text{-rms}} = I_{\text{rms}}X_L = (0.0020\ \text{A})(2000\ \Omega) = 4.0\ \text{V}$$
$$V_{C\text{-rms}} = I_{\text{rms}}X_C = (0.0020\ \text{A})(2000\ \Omega) = 4.0\ \text{V}$$

EVALUATE: The potential differences across the inductor and the capacitor have equal rms values and amplitudes, but are 180° out of phase and so add to zero at each instant. Note also that at resonance, $V_{R\text{-rms}}$ is equal to the source voltage V_{rms}, while in this example, $V_{L\text{-rms}}$ and $V_{C\text{-rms}}$ are both considerably *larger* than V_{rms}.

Test Your Understanding of Section 31.5 How does the resonance frequency of an *L-R-C* series circuit change if the plates of the capacitor are brought closer together? (i) It increases; (ii) it decreases; (iii) it is unaffected.

31.6 Transformers

One of the great advantages of ac over dc for electric-power distribution is that it is much easier to step voltage levels up and down with ac than with dc. For long-distance power transmission it is desirable to use as high a voltage and as small a current as possible; this reduces i^2R losses in the transmission lines, and smaller wires can be used, saving on material costs. Present-day transmission lines routinely operate at rms voltages of the order of 500 kV. On the other hand, safety considerations and insulation requirements dictate relatively low voltages in generating equipment and in household and industrial power distribution. The standard voltage for household wiring is 120 V in the United States and Canada and 240 V in many other countries. The necessary voltage conversion is accomplished by the use of **transformers.**

How Transformers Work

Figure 31.21 shows an idealized transformer. The key components of the transformer are two coils or *windings,* electrically insulated from each other but wound on the same core. The core is typically made of a material, such as iron, with a very large relative permeability K_m. This keeps the magnetic field lines due to a current in one winding almost completely within the core. Hence almost all of these field lines pass through the other winding, maximizing the *mutual inductance* of the two windings (see Section 30.1). The winding to which power is supplied is called the **primary;** the winding from which power is delivered is called the **secondary.** The circuit symbol for a transformer with an iron core, such as those used in power distribution systems, is

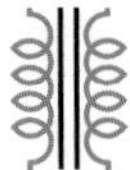

Here's how a transformer works. The ac source causes an alternating current in the primary, which sets up an alternating flux in the core; this induces an emf in each winding, in accordance with Faraday's law. The induced emf in the sec-

31.21 Schematic diagram of an idealized step-up transformer. The primary is connected to an ac source; the secondary is connected to a device with resistance R.

The induced emf *per turn* is the same in both coils, so we adjust the ratio of terminal voltages by adjusting the ratio of turns:

$$\frac{V_2}{V_1} = \frac{N_2}{N_1}$$

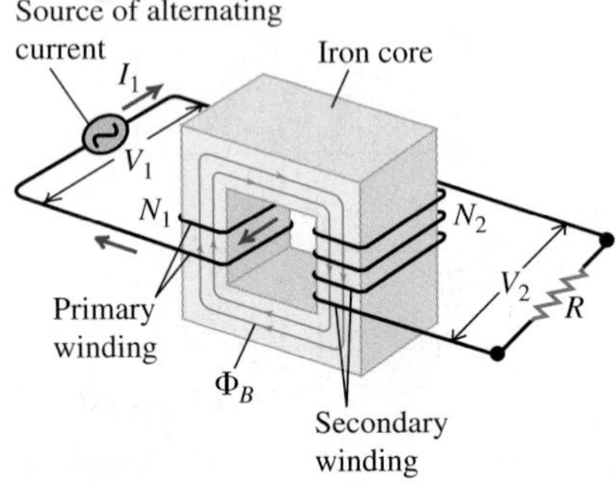

ondary gives rise to an alternating current in the secondary, and this delivers energy to the device to which the secondary is connected. All currents and emfs have the same frequency as the ac source.

Let's see how the voltage across the secondary can be made larger or smaller in amplitude than the voltage across the primary. We neglect the resistance of the windings and assume that all the magnetic field lines are confined to the iron core, so at any instant the magnetic flux Φ_B is the same in each turn of the primary and secondary windings. The primary winding has N_1 turns and the secondary winding has N_2 turns. When the magnetic flux changes because of changing currents in the two coils, the resulting induced emfs are

$$\mathcal{E}_1 = -N_1 \frac{d\Phi_B}{dt} \quad \text{and} \quad \mathcal{E}_2 = -N_2 \frac{d\Phi_B}{dt} \tag{31.33}$$

The flux *per turn* Φ_B is the same in both the primary and the secondary, so Eqs. (31.33) show that the induced emf *per turn* is the same in each. The ratio of the secondary emf $\mathcal{E}_2$ to the primary emf $\mathcal{E}_1$ is therefore equal at any instant to the ratio of secondary to primary turns:

$$\frac{\mathcal{E}_2}{\mathcal{E}_1} = \frac{N_2}{N_1} \tag{31.34}$$

Since $\mathcal{E}_1$ and $\mathcal{E}_2$ both oscillate with the same frequency as the ac source, Eq. (31.34) also gives the ratio of the amplitudes or of the rms values of the induced emfs. If the windings have zero resistance, the induced emfs $\mathcal{E}_1$ and $\mathcal{E}_2$ are equal to the terminal voltages across the primary and the secondary, respectively; hence

$$\frac{V_2}{V_1} = \frac{N_2}{N_1} \quad \text{(terminal voltages of transformer primary and secondary)} \tag{31.35}$$

where V_1 and V_2 are either the amplitudes or the rms values of the terminal voltages. By choosing the appropriate turns ratio N_2/N_1, we may obtain any desired secondary voltage from a given primary voltage. If $N_2 > N_1$, as in Fig. 31.21, then $V_2 > V_1$ and we have a *step-up* transformer; if $N_2 < N_1$, then $V_2 < V_1$ and we have a *step-down* transformer. At a power generating station, step-up transformers are used; the primary is connected to the power source and the secondary is connected to the transmission lines, giving the desired high voltage for transmission. Near the consumer, step-down transformers lower the voltage to a value suitable for use in home or industry (Fig. 31.22).

Even the relatively low voltage provided by a household wall socket is too high for many electronic devices, so a further step-down transformer is necessary. This is the role of an "ac adapter" (also called a "power cube" or "power adapter"), such as those used to recharge a mobile phone or laptop computer from line voltage. Such adapters contain a step-down transformer that converts line voltage to a lower value, typically 3 to 12 volts, as well as diodes to convert alternating current to the direct current that small electronic devices require (Fig. 31.23).

31.22 The cylindrical can near the top of this power pole is a step-down transformer. It converts the high-voltage ac in the power lines to low-voltage (120 V) ac, which is then distributed to the surrounding homes and businesses.

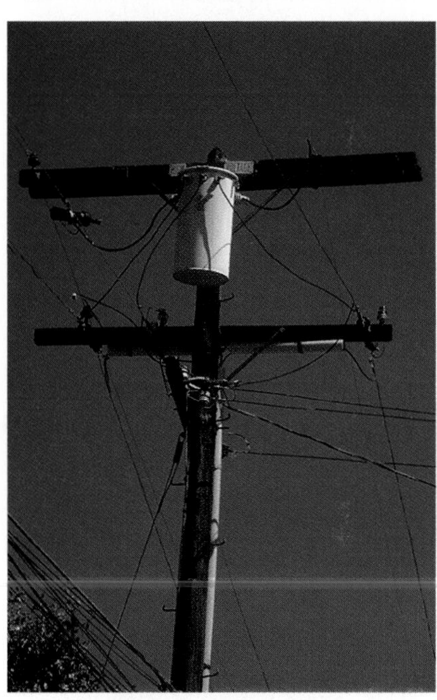

31.23 An ac adapter like this one converts household ac into low-voltage dc for use in electronic devices. It contains a step-down transformer to lower the voltage and diodes to rectify the output current (see Fig. 31.3).

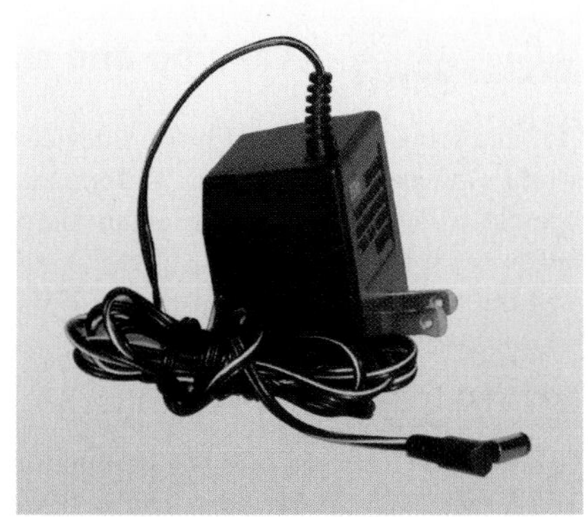

Energy Considerations for Transformers

If the secondary circuit is completed by a resistance R, then the amplitude or rms value of the current in the secondary circuit is $I_2 = V_2/R$. From energy considerations, the power delivered to the primary equals that taken out of the secondary (since there is no resistance in the windings), so

$$V_1 I_1 = V_2 I_2 \quad \text{(currents in transformer primary and secondary)} \tag{31.36}$$

We can combine Eqs. (31.35) and (31.36) and the relationship $I_2 = V_2/R$ to eliminate V_2 and I_2; we obtain

$$\frac{V_1}{I_1} = \frac{R}{(N_2/N_1)^2} \tag{31.37}$$

This shows that when the secondary circuit is completed through a resistance R, the result is the same as if the *source* had been connected directly to a resistance equal to R divided by the square of the turns ratio, $(N_2/N_1)^2$. In other words, the transformer "transforms" not only voltages and currents, but resistances as well. More generally, we can regard a transformer as "transforming" the *impedance* of the network to which the secondary circuit is completed.

Equation (31.37) has many practical consequences. The power supplied by a source to a resistor depends on the resistances of both the resistor and the source. It can be shown that the power transfer is greatest when the two resistances are *equal.* The same principle applies in both dc and ac circuits. When a high-impedance ac source must be connected to a low-impedance circuit, such as an audio amplifier connected to a loudspeaker, the source impedance can be *matched* to that of the circuit by use of a transformer with an appropriate turns ratio N_2/N_1.

Real transformers always have some energy losses. (That's why an ac adapter like the one shown in Fig. 31.23 feels warm to the touch after it's been in use for a while; the transformer is heated by the dissipated energy.) The windings have some resistance, leading to i^2R losses. There are also energy losses through hysteresis in the core (see Section 28.8). Hysteresis losses are minimized by the use of soft iron with a narrow hysteresis loop.

Another important mechanism for energy loss in a transformer core involves eddy currents (see Section 29.6). Consider a section AA through an iron transformer core (Fig. 31.24a). Since iron is a conductor, any such section can be pictured as several conducting circuits, one within the other (Fig. 31.24b). The flux through each of these circuits is continually changing, so eddy currents circulate in the entire volume of the core, with lines of flow that form planes perpendicular to the flux. These eddy currents are very undesirable; they waste energy through i^2R heating and themselves set up an opposing flux.

The effects of eddy currents can be minimized by the use of a *laminated* core, that is, one built up of thin sheets or laminae. The large electrical surface resistance of each lamina, due either to a natural coating of oxide or to an insulating varnish, effectively confines the eddy currents to individual laminae (Fig. 31.24c). The possible eddy-current paths are narrower, the induced emf in each path is smaller, and the eddy currents are greatly reduced. The alternating magnetic field exerts forces on the current-carrying laminae that cause them to vibrate back and forth; this vibration causes the characteristic "hum" of an operating transformer. You can hear this same "hum" from the magnetic ballast of a fluorescent light fixture (see Section 30.2).

Thanks to the use of soft iron cores and lamination, transformer efficiencies are usually well over 90%; in large installations they may reach 99%.

31.24 (a) Primary and secondary windings in a transformer. (b) Eddy currents in the iron core, shown in the cross section at AA. (c) Using a laminated core reduces the eddy currents.

(a) Schematic transformer

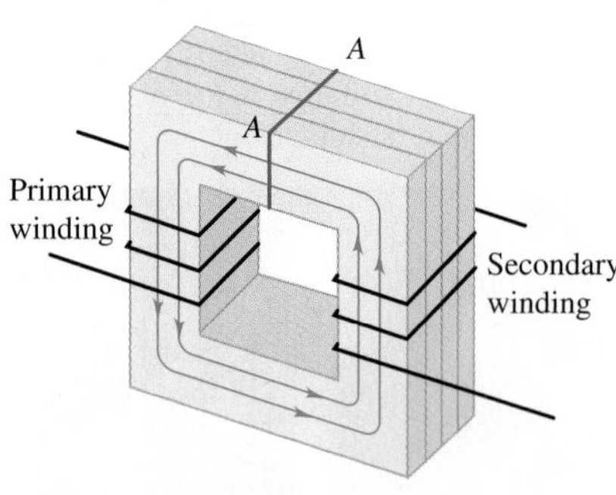

(b) Large eddy currents in solid core

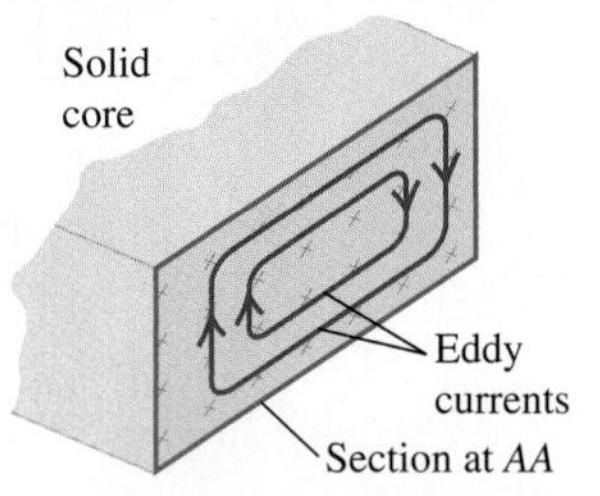

(c) Smaller eddy currents in laminated core

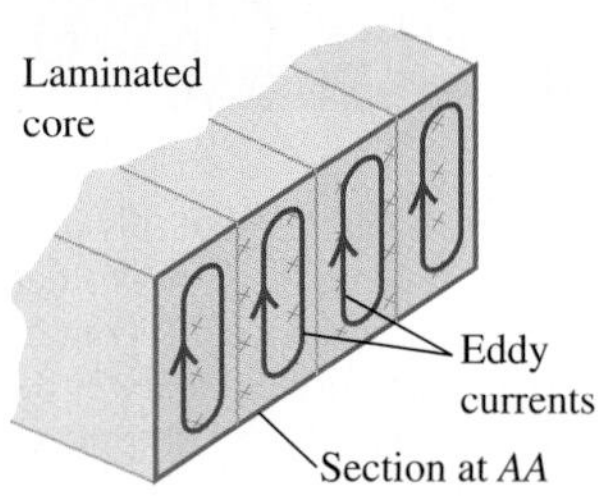

Example 31.9 "Wake up and smell the (transformer)!"

A friend brings back from Europe a device that she claims to be the world's greatest coffeemaker. Unfortunately, it was designed to operate from a 240-V line to obtain the 960 W of power that it needs. (a) What can she do to operate it at 120 V? (b) What current will the coffeemaker draw from the 120-V line? (c) What is the resistance of the coffeemaker? (The voltages are rms values.)

SOLUTION

IDENTIFY: Our friend needs a step-up transformer to convert the 120-V ac available in the home to the 240-V ac that the coffeemaker requires. This problem is about the properties of this transformer.

SET UP: We use Eq. (31.35) to determine the transformer turns ratio N_2/N_1, the relationship $P_{av} = V_{rms}I_{rms}$ for a resistor to find the current draw, and Eq. (31.37) to calculate the resistance.

EXECUTE: (a) To get $V_2 = 240$ V from $V_1 = 120$ V, the required turns ratio is $N_2/N_1 = V_2/V_1 = (240\text{ V})/(120\text{ V}) = 2$. That is, the secondary coil (connected to the coffeemaker) should have twice as many turns as the primary coil (connected to the 120-V line).

(b) The rms current I_1 in the 120-V primary is found by using $P_{av} = V_1 I_1$, where P_{av} is the average power drawn by the coffeemaker and hence the power supplied by the 120-V line. (We're assuming that there are no energy losses in the transformer.) Hence $I_1 = P_{av}/V_1 = (960\text{ W})/(120\text{ V}) = 8.0$ A. The secondary current is then $I_2 = P_{av}/V_2 = (960\text{ W})/(240\text{ V}) = 4.0$ A.

(c) We have $V_1 = 120$ V, $I_1 = 8.0$ A, and $N_2/N_1 = 2$, so

$$\frac{V_1}{I_1} = \frac{120\text{ V}}{8.0\text{ A}} = 15\ \Omega$$

From Eq. (31.37),

$$R = 2^2(15\ \Omega) = 60\ \Omega$$

EVALUATE: As a check, $V_2/R = (240\text{ V})/(60\ \omega) = 4.0\ A = I_2$, the same value obtained previously. you can also check this result for r by using the expression $P_{av} = V_2^2/R$ for the power drawn by the coffeemaker.

Test Your Understanding of Section 31.6 Each of the following four transformers has 1000 turns in its primary coil. Rank the transformers from largest to smallest number of turns in the secondary coil. (i) converts 120-V ac into 6.0-V ac; (ii) converts 120-V ac into 240-V ac; (iii) converts 240-V ac into 6.0-V ac; (iv) converts 240-V ac into 120-V ac.

CHAPTER 31 SUMMARY

Phasors and alternating current: An alternator or ac source produces an emf that varies sinusoidally with time. A sinusoidal voltage or current can be represented by a phasor, a vector that rotates counterclockwise with constant angular velocity ω equal to the angular frequency of the sinusoidal quantity. Its projection on the horizontal axis at any instant represents the instantaneous value of the quantity.

For a sinusoidal current, the rectified average and rms (root-mean-square) currents are proportional to the current amplitude I. Similarly, the rms value of a sinusoidal voltage is proportional to the voltage amplitude V. (See Example 31.1.)

$$I_{rav} = \frac{2}{\pi}I = 0.637I \qquad (31.3)$$

$$I_{rms} = \frac{I}{\sqrt{2}} \qquad (31.4)$$

$$V_{rms} = \frac{V}{\sqrt{2}} \qquad (31.5)$$

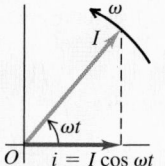

Voltage, current, and phase angle: In general, the instantaneous voltage between two points in an ac circuit is not in phase with the instantaneous current passing through those points. The quantity ϕ is called the phase angle of the voltage relative to the current.

$$i = I\cos\omega t$$
$$v = V\cos(\omega t + \phi) \qquad (31.2)$$

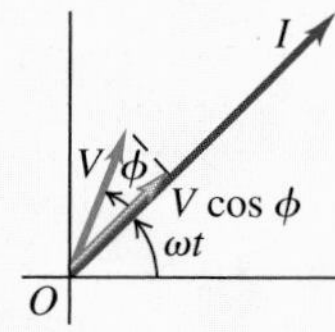

Resistance and reactance: The voltage across a resistor R is in phase with the current. The voltage across an inductor L leads the current by 90° ($\phi = +90°$), while the voltage across a capacitor C lags the current by 90° ($\phi = -90°$). The voltage amplitude across each type of device is proportional to the current amplitude I. An inductor has inductive reactance $X_L = \omega L$, and a capacitor has capacitive reactance $X_C = 1/\omega C$. (See Examples 31.2 and 31.3.)

$$V_R = IR \qquad (31.7)$$

$$V_L = IX_L \qquad (31.13)$$

$$V_C = IX_C \qquad (31.19)$$

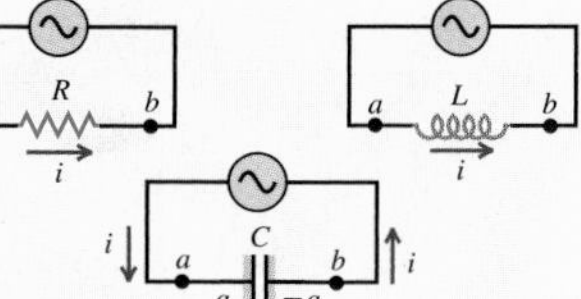

Impedance and the *L-R-C* series circuit: In a general ac circuit, the voltage and current amplitudes are related by the circuit impedance Z. In an L-R-C series circuit, the values of L, R, C, and the angular frequency ω determine the impedance and the phase angle ϕ of the voltage relative to the current. (See Examples 31.4 and 31.5.)

$$V = IZ \qquad (31.22)$$

$$Z = \sqrt{R^2 + (X_L - X_C)^2} = \sqrt{R^2 + [\omega L - (1/\omega C)]^2} \qquad (31.23)$$

$$\tan\phi = \frac{\omega L - 1/\omega C}{R} \qquad (31.24)$$

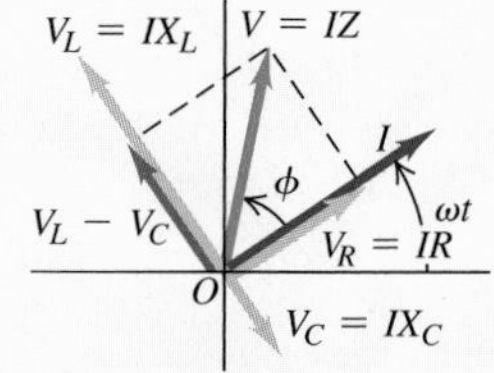

Power in ac circuits: The average power input P_{av} to an ac circuit depends on the voltage and current amplitudes (or, equivalently, their rms values) and the phase angle ϕ of the voltage relative to the current. The quantity $\cos\phi$ is called the power factor.(See Examples 31.6 and 31.7.)

$$P_{av} = \frac{1}{2}VI\cos\phi = V_{rms}I_{rms}\cos\phi \qquad (31.31)$$

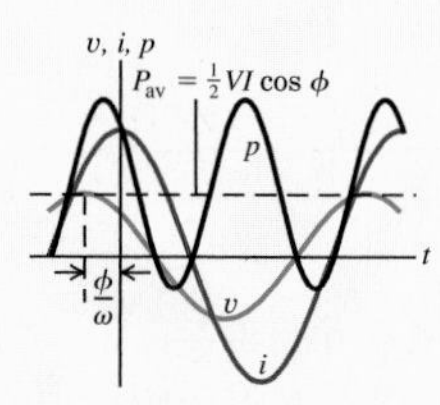

Resonance in ac circuits: In an L-R-C series circuit, the current becomes maximum and the impedance becomes minimum at an angular frequency called the resonance angular frequency. This phenomenon is called resonance. At resonance the voltage and current are in phase, and the impedance Z is equal to the resistance R. (See Example 31.8.)

$$\omega_0 = \frac{1}{\sqrt{LC}} \qquad (31.32)$$

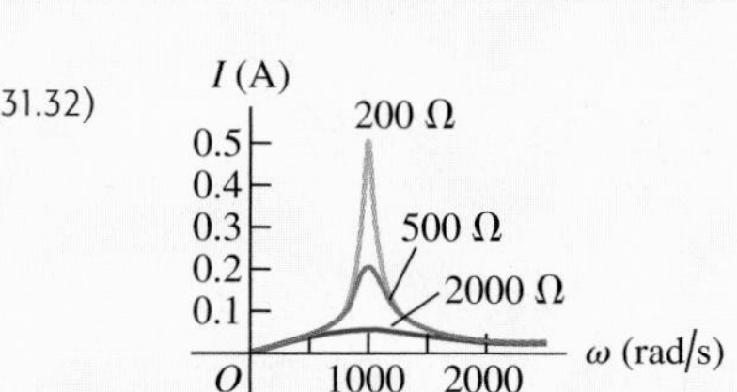

Transformers: A transformer is used to transform the voltage and current levels in an ac circuit. In an ideal transformer with no energy losses, if the primary winding has N_1 turns and the secondary winding has N_2 turns, the amplitudes (or rms values) of the two voltages are related by Eq. (31.35). The amplitudes (or rms values) of the primary and secondary voltages and currents are related by Eq. (31.36). (See Example 31.9.)

$$\frac{V_2}{V_1} = \frac{N_2}{N_1} \quad (31.35)$$

$$V_1 I_1 = V_2 I_2 \quad (31.36)$$

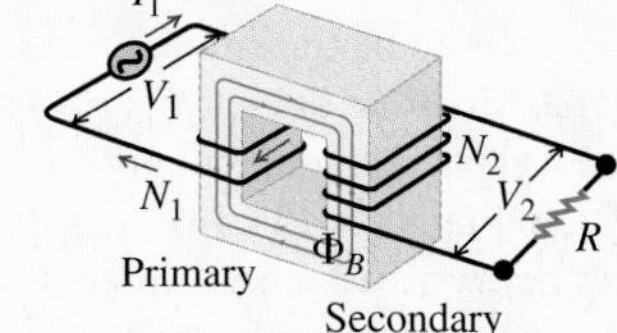

Key Terms

alternating current (ac), *1061*
ac source, *1062*
voltage amplitude, *1062*
current amplitude, *1062*
phasor, *1062*
phasor diagram, *1062*
rectified average current, *1063*
root-mean-square (rms) current, *1063*
phase angle, *1066*
inductive reactance, *1066*
capacitive reactance, *1068*
impedance, *1071*
power factor, *1076*
resonance, *1078*
resonance angular frequency, *1078*
resonance frequency, *1078*
transformer, *1080*
primary, *1080*
secondary, *1080*

Answer to Chapter Opening Question ?

Yes. In fact, the radio simultaneously detects transmissions at *all* frequencies. However, a radio is an *L-R-C* series circuit, and at any given time it is tuned to have a resonance at just one frequency. Hence the response of the radio to that frequency is much greater than its response to any other frequency, which is why you hear only one broadcasting station through the radio's speaker. (You can sometimes hear a second station if its frequency is sufficiently close to the tuned frequency.)

Answers to Test Your Understanding Questions

31.1 Answers: (a) D; (b) A; (c) B; (d) C For each phasor, the actual current is represented by the projection of that phasor onto the horizontal axis. The phasors all rotate counterclockwise around the origin with angular speed ω, so at the instant shown the projection of phasor A is positive but trending toward zero; the projection of phasor B is negative and becoming more negative; the projection of phasor C is negative but trending toward zero; and the projection of phasor D is positive and becoming more positive.

31.2 Answers: (a) (iii); (b) (ii); (c) (i) For a resistor, $V_R = IR$, so $I = V_R/R$. The voltage amplitude V_R and resistance R do not change with frequency, so the current amplitude I remains constant. For an inductor, $V_L = IX_L = I\omega L$, so $I = V_L/\omega L$. The voltage amplitude V_L and inductance L are constant, so the current amplitude I decreases as the frequency increases. For a capacitor, $V_C = IX_C = I/\omega C$, so $I = V_C \omega C$. The voltage amplitude V_C and capacitance C are constant, so the current amplitude I increases as the frequency increases.

31.3 Answer: (iv), (ii), (i), (iii) For the circuit in Example 31.4, $I = V/Z = (50\text{ V})/(500\ \Omega) = 0.10\text{ A}$. If the capacitor and inductor are removed so that only the ac source and resistor remain, the circuit is like that shown in Fig. 31.7a; then $I = V/R = (50\text{ V})/(300\ \Omega) = 0.17\text{ A}$. If the resistor and capacitor are removed so that only the ac source and inductor remain, the circuit is like that shown in Fig. 31.8a; then $I = V/X_L = (50\text{ V})/(600\ \Omega) = 0.083\text{ A}$. Finally, if the resistor and inductor are removed so that only the ac source and capacitor remain, the circuit is like that shown in Fig. 31.9a; then $I = V/X_C = (50\text{ V})/(200\ \Omega) = 0.25\text{ A}$.

31.4 Answers: (a) (v); (b) (iv) The energy cannot be extracted from the resistor, since energy is dissipated in a resistor and cannot be recovered. Instead, the energy must be extracted from either the inductor (which stores magnetic-field energy) or the capacitor (which stores electric-field energy). Positive power means that energy is being transferred from the ac source to the circuit, so *negative* power implies that energy is being transferred back into the source.

31.5 Answer: (ii) The capacitance C increases if the plate spacing is decreased (see Section 24.1). Hence the resonance frequency $f_0 = \omega_0/2\pi = 1/2\pi\sqrt{LC}$ decreases.

31.6 Answer: (ii), (iv), (i), (iii) From Eq. (31.35) the turns ratio is $N_2/N_1 = V_2/V_1$, so the number of turns in the secondary is $N_2 = N_1 V_2/V_1$. Hence for the four cases we have (i) $N_2 = (1000)(6.0\text{ V})/(120\text{ V}) = 50$ turns; (ii) $N_2 = (1000)(240\text{ V})/(120\text{ V}) = 2000$ turns; (iii) $N_2 = (1000)(6.0\text{ V})/(240\text{ V}) = 25$ turns; and (iv) $N_2 = (1000)(120\text{ V})/(240\text{ V}) = 500$ turns. Note that (i), (iii), and (iv) are step-down transformers with fewer turns in the secondary than in the primary, while (ii) is a step-up transformer with more turns in the secondary than in the primary.

PROBLEMS

For instructor-assigned homework, go to **www.masteringphysics.com**

Discussion Questions

Q31.1. Household electric power in most of western Europe is supplied at 240 V, rather than the 120 V that is standard in the United States and Canada. What are the advantages and disadvantages of each system?

Q31.2. The current in an ac power line changes direction 120 times per second, and its average value is zero. Explain how it is possible for power to be transmitted in such a system.

Q31.3. In an ac circuit, why is the average power for an inductor and a capacitor zero, but not for a resistor?

Q31.4. Equation (31.14) was derived by using the relationship $i = dq/dt$ between the current and the charge on the capacitor. In Fig. 31.9a the positive counterclockwise current increases the charge on the capacitor. When the charge on the left plate is positive but decreasing in time, is $i = dq/dt$ still correct or should it be $i = -dq/dt$? Is $i = dq/dt$ still correct when the right-hand plate has positive charge that is increasing or decreasing in magnitude? Explain.

Q31.5. Fluorescent lights often use an inductor, called a ballast, to limit the current through the tubes. Why is it better to use an inductor rather than a resistor for this purpose?

Q31.6. Equation (31.9) says that $v_{ab} = L\,di/dt$ (see Fig. 31.8a). Using Faraday's law, explain why point a is at higher potential than point b when i is in the direction shown in Fig. 31.8a and is increasing in magnitude. When i is counterclockwise and decreasing in magnitude, is $v_{ab} = L\,di/dt$ still correct, or should it be $v_{ab} = -L\,di/dt$? Is $v_{ab} = L\,di/dt$ still correct when i is clockwise and increasing or decreasing in magnitude? Explain.

Q31.7. Is it possible for the power factor of an *L-R-C* series ac circuit to be zero? Justify your answer on *physical* grounds.

Q31.8. In a series *L-R-C* circuit, can the instantaneous voltage across the capacitor exceed the source voltage at that same instant? Can this be true for the instantaneous voltage across the inductor? Across the resistor? Explain.

Q31.9. In a series *L-R-C* circuit, what are the phase angle ϕ and power factor $\cos\phi$ when the resistance is much smaller than the inductive or capacitive reactance and the circuit is operated far from resonance? Explain.

Q31.10. When a series *L-R-C* circuit is connected across a 120-V ac line, the voltage rating of the capacitor may be exceeded even if it is rated at 200 or 400 V. How can this be?

Q31.11. In Example 31.6 (Section 31.4), a hair dryer was treated as a pure resistor. But because there are coils in the heating element and in the motor that drives the blower fan, a hair dryer also has inductance. Qualitatively, does including an inductance increase or decrease the values of R, I_{rms}, and P?

Q31.12. A light bulb and a parallel-plate capacitor with air between the plates are connected in series to an ac source. What happens to the brightness of the bulb when a dielectric is inserted between the plates of the capacitor? Explain.

Q31.13. A coil of wire wrapped on a hollow tube and a light bulb are connected in series to an ac source. What happens to the brightness of the bulb when an iron rod is inserted in the tube?

Q31.14. A circuit consists of a light bulb, a capacitor, and an inductor connected in series to an ac source. What happens to the brightness of the bulb when the inductor is removed? When the inductor is left in the circuit but the capacitor is removed? Explain.

Q31.15. A circuit consists of a light bulb, a capacitor, and an inductor connected in series to an ac source. Is it possible for both the capacitor and the inductor to be removed and the brightness of the bulb to remain the same? Explain.

Q31.16. Can a transformer be used with dc? Explain. What happens if a transformer designed for 120-V ac is connected to a 120-V dc line?

Q31.17. An ideal transformer has N_1 windings in the primary and N_2 windings in its secondary. If you double only the number of secondary windings, by what factor does (a) the voltage amplitude in the secondary change, and (b) the effective resistance of the secondary circuit change?

Q31.18. Some electrical appliances operate equally well on ac or dc, and others work only on ac or only on dc. Give examples of each, and explain the differences.

Exercises

Section 31.1 Phasors and Alternating Currents

31.1. The plate on the back of a certain computer scanner says that the unit draws 0.34 A of current from a 120-V, 60-Hz line. Find (a) the root-mean-square current, (b) the current amplitude, (c) the average current; (d) the average square of the current.

31.2. A sinusoidal current $i = I\cos\omega t$ has an rms value $I_{rms} = 2.10$ A. (a) What is the current amplitude? (b) The current is passed through a full-wave rectifier circuit. What is the rectified average current? (c) Which is larger: I_{rms} or I_{rav}? Explain, using graphs of i^2 and of the rectified current.

31.3. The voltage across the terminals of an ac power supply varies with time according to Eq. (31.1). The voltage amplitude is $V = 45.0$ V. What are (a) the root-mean-square potential difference V_{rms}? and (b) the average potential difference V_{av} between the two terminals of the power supply?

Section 31.2 Resistance and Reactance

31.4. A 2.20-μF capacitor is connected across an ac source whose voltage amplitude is kept constant at 60.0 V but whose frequency can be varied. Find the current amplitude when the angular frequency is (a) 100 rad/s; (b) 1000 rad/s; (c) 10,000 rad/s. (d) Show the results of parts (a) through (c) in a plot of log I versus log ω.

31.5. A 5.00-H inductor with negligible resistance is connected across the ac source of Exercise 31.4. Find the current amplitude when the angular frequency is (a) 100 rad/s; (b) 1000 rad/s; (c) 10,000 rad/s. (d) Show the results of parts (a) through (c) in a plot of log I versus log ω.

31.6. A capacitance C and an inductance L are operated at the same angular frequency. (a) At what angular frequency will they have the same reactance? (b) If $L = 5.00$ mH and $C = 3.50\ \mu$F, what is the numerical value of the angular frequency in part (a), and what is the reactance of each element?

31.7. In each circuit described next, an ac voltage source producing a current $i = I\cos\omega t$ is connected to an additional circuit element. (a) The ac source is connected across a resistor R. Sketch graphs of the current in the circuit and the potential difference across the resistor as functions of time, covering two cycles of oscillation. Put both graphs on the *same* set of axes so you can compare them. (b) Do the same as in part (a), except suppose the resistor is replaced by an inductor L. Sketch the same graphs as in part (a), but this time across the inductor instead of the resistor. (c) Do the same as in part (a), except suppose the resistor is replaced by a capacitor C. Sketch the same graphs as in part (a), except now across the capacitor instead of the resistor. (d) Sketch phasor diagrams for each of the preceding cases.

31.8. (a) Compute the reactance of a 0.450-H inductor at frequencies of 60.0 Hz and 600 Hz. (b) Compute the reactance of a 2.50-μF capacitor at the same frequencies. (c) At what frequency is the reactance of a 0.450-H inductor equal to that of a 2.50-μF capacitor?

31.9. (a) What is the reactance of a 3.00-H inductor at a frequency of 80.0 Hz? (b) What is the inductance of an inductor whose reactance is 120 Ω at 80.0 Hz? (c) What is the reactance of a 4.00-μF capacitor at a frequency of 80.0 Hz? (d) What is the capacitance of a capacitor whose reactance is 120 Ω at 80.0 Hz?

31.10. A Radio Inductor. You want the current amplitude through a 0.450-mH inductor (part of the circuitry for a radio receiver) to be 2.60 mA when a sinusoidal voltage with amplitude 12.0 V is applied across the inductor. What frequency is required?

31.11. Kitchen Capacitance. The wiring for a refrigerator contains a starter capacitor. A voltage of amplitude 170 V and frequency 60.0 Hz applied across the capacitor is to produce a current amplitude of 0.850 A through the capacitor. What capacitance C is required?

31.12. A 250-Ω resistor is connected in series with a 4.80-μF capacitor. The voltage across the capacitor is $v_C = (7.60\text{ V})\sin[(120\text{ rad/s})t]$. (a) Determine the capacitive reactance of the capacitor. (b) Derive an expression for the voltage v_R across the resistor.

31.13. A 150-Ω resistor is connected in series with a 0.250-H inductor. The voltage across the resistor is $v_R = (3.80\text{ V})\cos[(720\text{ rad/s})t]$. (a) Derive an expression for the circuit current. (b) Determine the inductive reactance of the inductor. (c) Derive an expression for the voltage v_L across the inductor.

Section 31.3 The *L-R-C* Series Circuit

31.14. You have a 200-Ω resistor, a 0.400-H inductor, and a 6.00-μF capacitor. Suppose you take the resistor and inductor and make a series circuit with a voltage source that has voltage amplitude 30.0 V and an angular frequency of 250 rad/s. (a) What is the impedance of the circuit? (b) What is the current amplitude? (c) What are the voltage amplitudes across the resistor and across the inductor? (d) What is the phase angle ϕ of the source voltage with respect to the current? Does the source voltage lag or lead the current? (e) Construct the phasor diagram.

31.15. (a) For the *R-L* circuit of Exercise 31.14, graph v, v_R, and v_L versus t for $t = 0$ to $t = 50.0$ ms. The current is given by $i = I\cos\omega t$, so $v = V\cos(\omega t + \phi)$. (b) What are v, v_R, and v_L at $t = 20.0$ ms? Compare $v_R + v_L$ to v at this instant. (c) Repeat part (b) for $t = 40.0$ ms.

31.16. Repeat Exercise 31.14 with the circuit consisting of only the capacitor and the inductor in series. For part (c), calculate the voltage amplitudes across the capacitor and across the inductor.

31.17. Repeat Exercise 31.14 with the circuit consisting of only the resistor and the capacitor in series. For part (c), calculate the voltage amplitudes across the resistor and across the capacitor.

31.18. (a) For the *R-C* circuit of Exercise 31.17, graph v, v_R, and v_C versus t for $t = 0$ to $t = 50.0$ ms. The current is given by $i = I\cos\omega t$, so $v = V\cos(\omega t + \phi)$. (b) What are v, v_R, and v_C at $t = 20.0$ ms? Compare $v_R + v_C$ to v at this instant. (c) Repeat part (b) for $t = 40.0$ ms.

31.19. The resistor, inductor, capacitor, and voltage source described in Exercise 31.14 are connected to form an *L-R-C* series circuit. (a) What is the impedance of the circuit? (b) What is the current amplitude? (c) What is the phase angle of the source voltage with respect to the current? Does the source voltage lag or lead the current? (d) What are the voltage amplitudes across the resistor, inductor, and capacitor? (e) Explain how it is possible for the voltage amplitude across the capacitor to be greater than the voltage amplitude across the source.

31.20. (a) For the *L-R-C* circuit of Exercise 31.19, graph v, v_R, v_L, and v_C versus t for $t = 0$ to $t = 50.0$ ms. The current is given by $i = I\cos\omega t$, so $v = V\cos(\omega t + \phi)$. (b) What are v, v_R, v_L, and v_C at $t = 20.0$ ms? Compare $v_R + v_L + v_C$ to v at this instant. (c) Repeat part (b) for $t = 40.0$ ms.

31.21. Analyzing an *L-R-C* Circuit. You have a 200-Ω resistor, a 0.400-H inductor, a 5.00-μF capacitor, and a variable-frequency ac source with an amplitude of 3.00 V. You connect all four elements together to form a series circuit. (a) At what frequency will the current in the circuit be greatest? What will be the current amplitude at this frequency? (b) What will be the current amplitude at an angular frequency of 400 rad/s? At this frequency, will the source voltage lead or lag the current?

31.22. An *L-R-C* series circuit is constructed using a 175-Ω resistor, a 12.5-μF capacitor, and an 8.00-mH inductor, all connected across an ac source having a variable frequency and a voltage amplitude of 25.0 V. (a) At what angular frequency will the impedance be smallest, and what is the impedance at this frequency? (b) At the angular frequency in part (a), what is the maximum current through the inductor? (c) At the angular frequency in part (a), find the potential difference across the ac source, the resistor, the capacitor, and the inductor at the instant that the current is equal to one-half its greatest positive value. (d) In part (c), how are the potential differences across the resistor, inductor, and capacitor related to the potential difference across the ac source?

31.23. In an *L-R-C* series circuit, the rms voltage across the resistor is 30.0 V, across the capacitor it is 90.0 V, and across the inductor it is 50.0 V. What is the rms voltage of the source?

31.24. Define the reactance X of an *L-R-C* circuit to be $X = X_L - X_C$. (a) Show that $X = 0$ when the angular frequency ω of the current is equal to the resonance angular frequency ω_0. (b) What is the sign of X when $\omega > \omega_0$? (c) What is the sign of X when $\omega < \omega_0$? (d) Graph X versus ω.

Section 31.4 Power in Alternating-Current Circuits

31.25. The power of a certain CD player operating at 120 V rms is 20.0 W. Assuming that the CD player behaves like a pure resistance, find (a) the maximum instantaneous power; (b) the rms current; (c) the resistance of this player.

31.26. In a series *L-R-C* circuit, the components have the following values: $L = 20.0$ mH, $C = 140$ nF, and $R = 350\ \Omega$. The generator has an rms voltage of 120 V and a frequency of 1.25 kHz. Determine (a) the power supplied by the generator; and (b) the power dissipated in the resistor.

31.27. (a) Show that for an *L-R-C* series circuit the power factor is equal to R/Z. (*Hint:* Use the phasor diagram; see Fig. 31.13b.) (b) Show that for any ac circuit, not just one containing pure resistance only, the average power delivered by the voltage source is given by $P_{av} = I_{rms}{}^2R$.

31.28. An *L-R-C* series circuit is connected to a 120-Hz ac source that has $V_{rms} = 80.0$ V. The circuit has a resistance of 75.0 Ω and an impedance at this frequency of 105 Ω. What average power is delivered to the circuit by the source?

31.29. An *L-R-C* series circuit with $L = 0.120$ H, $R = 240\ \Omega$, and $C = 7.30\ \mu$F carries an rms current of 0.450 A with a frequency of 400 Hz. (a) What are the phase angle and power factor for this circuit? (b) What is the impedance of the circuit? (c) What is the rms voltage of the source? (d) What average power is delivered by the source? (e) What is the average rate at which electrical energy is converted to thermal energy in the resistor? (f) What is the average rate at which electrical energy is dissipated (converted to other forms) in the capacitor? (g) In the inductor?

31.30. A series ac circuit contains a 250-Ω resistor, a 15-mH inductor, a 3.5-μF capacitor, and an ac power source of voltage amplitude 45 V operating at an angular frequency of 360 rad/s, (a) What is the power factor of this circuit? (b) Find the average power delivered to the entire circuit. (c) What is the average power delivered to the resistor, to the capacitor, and to the inductor?

Section 31.5 Resonance in Alternating-Current Circuits

31.31. In an L-R-C series circuit, $R = 300\ \Omega$, $L = 0.400$ H, and $C = 6.00 \times 10^{-8}$ F. When the ac source operates at the resonance frequency of the circuit, the current amplitude is 0.500 A. (a) What is the voltage amplitude of the source? (b) What is the amplitude of the voltage across the resistor, across the inductor, and across the capacitor? (c) What is the average power supplied by the source?

31.32. An L-R-C series circuit consists of a source with voltage amplitude 120 V and angular frequency 50.0 rad/s, a resistor with $R = 400\ \Omega$ an inductor with $L = 9.00$ H, and a capacitor with capacitance C. (a) For what value of C will the current amplitude in the circuit be a maximum? (b) When C has the value calculated in part (a), what is the amplitude of the voltage across the inductor?

31.33. In an L-R-C series circuit, $R = 150\ \Omega$, $L = 0.750$ H, and $C = 0.0180\ \mu$F. The source has voltage amplitude $V = 150$ V and a frequency equal to the resonance frequency of the circuit. (a) What is the power factor? (b) What is the average power delivered by the source? (c) The capacitor is replaced by one with $C = 0.0360\ \mu$F and the source frequency is adjusted to the new resonance value. Then what is the average power delivered by the source?

31.34. In an L-R-C series circuit, $R = 400\ \Omega$, $L = 0.350$ H, and $C = 0.0120\ \mu$F. (a) What is the resonance angular frequency of the circuit? (b) The capacitor can withstand a peak voltage of 550 V. If the voltage source operates at the resonance frequency, what maximum voltage amplitude can it have if the maximum capacitor voltage is not exceeded?

31.35. A series circuit consists of an ac source of variable frequency, a 115-Ω resistor, a 1.25-μF capacitor, and a 4.50-mH inductor. Find the impedance of this circuit when the angular frequency of the ac source is adjusted to (a) the resonance angular frequency; (b) twice the resonance angular frequency; (c) half the resonance angular frequency.

31.36. In an L-R-C series circuit, $L = 0.280$ H and $C = 4.00\ \mu$F. The voltage amplitude of the source is 120 V. (a) What is the resonance angular frequency of the circuit? (b) When the source operates at the resonance angular frequency, the current amplitude in the circuit is 1.70 A. What is the resistance R of the resistor? (c) At the resonance angular frequency, what are the peak voltages across the inductor, the capacitor, and the resistor?

Section 31.6 Transformers

31.37. A Step-Down Transformer. A transformer connected to a 120-V (rms) ac line is to supply 12.0 V (rms) to a portable electronic device. The load resistance in the secondary is 5.00 Ω. (a) What should the ratio of primary to secondary turns of the transformer be? (b) What rms current must the secondary supply? (c) What average power is delivered to the load? (d) What resistance connected directly across the 120-V line would draw the same power as the transformer? Show that this is equal to 5.00 Ω times the square of the ratio of primary to secondary turns.

31.38. A Step-Up Transformer. A transformer connected to a 120-V (rms) ac line is to supply 13,000 V (rms) for a neon sign. To reduce shock hazard, a fuse is to be inserted in the primary circuit; the fuse is to blow when the rms current in the secondary circuit exceeds 8.50 mA. (a) What is the ratio of secondary to primary turns of the transformer? (b) What power must be supplied to the transformer when the rms secondary current is 8.50 mA? (c) What current rating should the fuse in the primary circuit have?

31.39. Off to Europe! You plan to take your hair blower to Europe, where the electrical outlets put out 240 V instead of the 120 V seen in the United States. The blower puts out 1600 W at 120 V. (a) What could you do to operate your blower via the 240-V line in Europe? (b) What current will your blower draw from a European outlet? (c) What resistance will your blower appear to have when operated at 240 V?

Problems

31.40. Figure 31.12a shows the crossover network in a loudspeaker system. One branch consists of a capacitor C and a resistor R in series (the tweeter). This branch is in parallel with a second branch (the woofer) that consists of an inductor L and a resistor R in series. The same source voltage with angular frequency ω is applied across each parallel branch. (a) What is the impedance of the tweeter branch? (b) What is the impedance of the woofer branch? (c) Explain why the currents in the two branches are equal when the impedances of the branches are equal. (d) Derive an expression for the frequency f that corresponds to the crossover point in Fig. 31.12b.

31.41. A coil has a resistance of 48.0 Ω. At a frequency of 80.0 Hz the voltage across the coil leads the current in it by 52.3°. Determine the inductance of the coil.

31.42. Five infinite-impedance voltmeters, calibrated to read rms values, are connected as shown in Fig 31.25. Let $R = 200\ \Omega$, $L = 0.400$ H, $C = 6.00\ \mu$F, and $V = 30.0$ V. What is the reading of each voltmeter if (a) $\omega = 200$ rad/s; and (b) $\omega = 1000$ rad/s?

Figure 31.25 Problem 31.42.

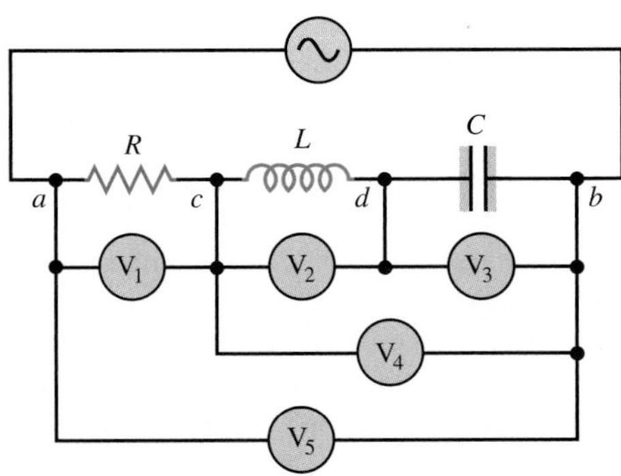

31.43. A sinusoidal current is given by $i = I\cos\omega t$. The full-wave rectified current is shown in Fig. 31.3b. (a) Let t_1 and t_2 be the two smallest positive times at which the rectified current is zero. Express t_1 and t_2 in terms of ω. (b) Find the area under the rectified i versus t curve between t_1 and t_2 by computing the integral $\int_{t_1}^{t_2} i\,dt$. Since $dq = i\,dt$, this area equals the charge that flows during the t_1 to t_2 time interval. (c) Set the result in part (b) equal to $I_{rav}(t_2 - t_1)$ and calculate I_{rav} in terms of the current amplitude I. Compare your answer to Eq. (31.3).

31.44. A large electromagnetic coil is connected to a 120-Hz ac source. The coil has resistance 400 Ω, and at this source frequency the coil has inductive reactance 250 Ω. (a) What is the inductance of the coil? (b) What must the rms voltage of the source be if the coil is to consume an average electrical power of 800 W?

31.45. A series circuit has an impedance of 60.0 Ω and a power factor of 0.720 at 50.0 Hz. The source voltage lags the current. (a) What circuit element, an inductor or a capacitor, should be placed in series with the circuit to raise its power factor? (b) What size element will raise the power factor to unity?

31.46. A circuit consists of a resistor and a capacitor in series with an ac source that supplies an rms voltage of 240 V. At the frequency of the source the reactance of the capacitor is 50.0 Ω. The rms current in the circuit is 3.00 A. What is the average power supplied by the source?

31.47. An *L-R-C* series circuit consists of a 50.0-Ω resistor, a 10.0-μF capacitor, a 3.50-mH inductor, and an ac voltage source of voltage amplitude 60.0 V operating at 1250 Hz. (a) Find the current amplitude and the voltage amplitudes across the inductor, the resistor, and the capacitor. Why can the voltage amplitudes add up to *more* than 60.0 V? (b) If the frequency is now doubled, but nothing else is changed, which of the quantities in part (a) will change? Find the new values for those that do change.

31.48. At a frequency ω_1 the reactance of a certain capacitor equals that of a certain inductor. (a) If the frequency is changed to $\omega_2 = 2\omega_1$, what is the ratio of the reactance of the inductor to that of the capacitor? Which reactance is larger? (b) If the frequency is changed to $\omega_3 = \omega_1/3$, what is the ratio of the reactance of the inductor to that of the capacitor? Which reactance is larger? (c) If the capacitor and inductor are placed in series with a resistor of resistance R to form a series *L-R-C* circuit, what will be the resonance angular frequency of the circuit?

31.49. A High-Pass Filter. One application of *L-R-C* series circuits is to high-pass or low-pass filters, which filter out either the low- or high-frequency components of a signal. A high-pass filter is shown in Fig. 31.26, where the output voltage is taken across the *L-R* combination. (The *L-R* combination represents an inductive coil that also has resistance due to the large length of wire in the coil.) Derive an expression for V_{out}/V_s, the ratio of the output and source voltage amplitudes, as a function of the angular frequency ω of the source. Show that when ω is small, this ratio is proportional to ω and thus is small, and show that the ratio approaches unity in the limit of large frequency.

Figure 31.26 Problem 31.49.

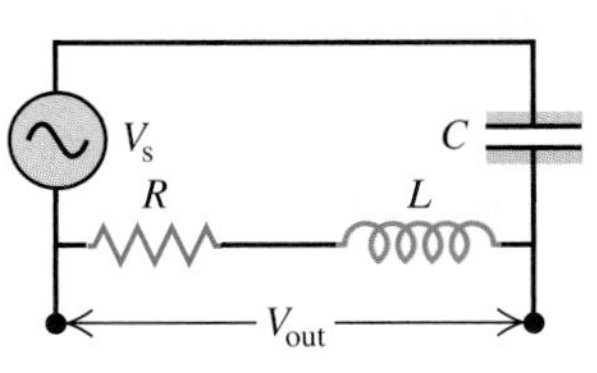

31.50. A Low-Pass Filter. Figure 31.27 shows a low-pass filter (see Problem 31.49); the output voltage is taken across the capacitor in an *L-R-C* series circuit. Derive an expression for V_{out}/V_s, the ratio of the output and source voltage amplitudes, as a function of the angular frequency ω of the source. Show that when ω is large, this ratio is proportional to ω^{-2} and thus is very small, and show that the ratio approaches unity in the limit of small frequency.

Figure 31.27 Problem 31.50.

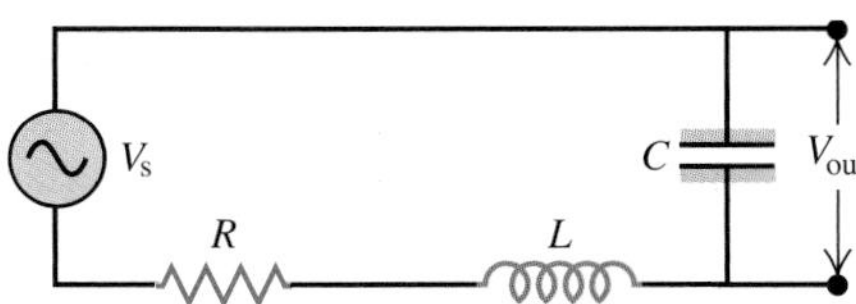

31.51. An *L-R-C* series circuit is connected to an ac source of constant voltage amplitude V and variable angular frequency ω. (a) Show that the current amplitude, as a function of ω, is

$$I = \frac{V}{\sqrt{R^2 + (\omega L - 1/\omega C)^2}}$$

(b) Show that the average power dissipated in the resistor is

$$P = \frac{V^2 R/2}{R^2 + (\omega L - 1/\omega C)^2}$$

(c) Show that I and P are *both* maximum when $\omega = 1/\sqrt{LC}$; that is, when the source frequency equals the resonance frequency of the circuit. (d) Graph P as a function of ω for $V = 100$ V, $R = 200$ Ω, $L = 2.0$ H, and $C = 0.50$ μF. Compare to the light purple curve in Fig. 31.19. Discuss the behavior of I and P in the limits $\omega = 0$ and $\omega \to \infty$.

31.52. An *L-R-C* series circuit is connected to an ac source of constant voltage amplitude V and variable angular frequency ω. Using the results of Problem 31.51, find an expression for (a) the amplitude V_L of the voltage across the inductor as a function of ω; and (b) the amplitude V_C of the voltage across the capacitor as a function of ω. (c) Graph V_L and V_C as functions of ω for $V = 100$ V, $R = 200$ Ω, $L = 2.0$ H, and $C = 0.50$ μF. (d) Discuss the behavior of V_L and V_C in the limits $\omega = 0$ and $\omega \to \infty$. For what value of ω is $V_L = V_C$? What is the significance of this value of ω?

31.53. An *L-R-C* series circuit is connected to an ac source of constant voltage amplitude V and variable angular frequency ω. (a) Show that the time-averaged energy stored in the inductor is $U_B = \frac{1}{4}LI^2$ and the time-averaged energy stored in the capacitor is $U_E = \frac{1}{4}CV^2$. (b) Use the results of Problems 31.51 and 31.52 to find expressions for U_B and U_E as functions of ω. (c) Graph U_B and U_E as functions of ω for $V = 100$ V, $R = 200$ Ω, $L = 2.0$ H, and $C = 0.50$ μF. (d) Discuss the behavior of U_B and U_E in the limits $\omega = 0$ and $\omega \to \infty$. For what value of ω is $U_B = U_E$? What is the significance of this value of ω?

31.54. The *L-R-C* Parallel Circuit. A resistor, inductor, and capacitor are connected in parallel to an ac source with voltage amplitude V and angular frequency ω. Let the source voltage be given by $v = V\cos\omega t$. (a) Show that the instantaneous voltages v_R, v_L, and v_C at any instant are each equal to v and that $i = i_R + i_L + i_C$, where i is the current through the source and i_R, i_L, and i_C are the currents through the resistor, the inductor, and the capacitor, respectively. (b) What are the phases of i_R, i_L, and i_C with respect to v? Use current phasors to represent i, i_R, i_L, and i_C. In a phasor diagram, show the phases of these four currents with respect to v. (c) Use the phasor diagram of part (b) to show that the current amplitude I for the current i through the source is given by $I = \sqrt{I_R^2 + (I_C - I_L)^2}$. (d) Show that the result of part (c) can be written as $I = V/Z$, with $1/Z = \sqrt{1/R^2 + (\omega C - 1/\omega L)^2}$.

31.55. Parallel Resonance. The impedance of an *L-R-C* parallel circuit was derived in Problem 31.54. (a) Show that at the resonance angular frequency $\omega_0 = 1/\sqrt{LC}$, $I_C = I_L$, and I is a *minimum*. (b) Since I is a minimum at resonance, is it correct to say that the power delivered to the resistor is also a minimum at $\omega = \omega_0$? Explain. (c) At resonance, what is the phase angle of the source current with respect to the source voltage? How does this compare to the phase angle for an *L-R-C series* circuit at resonance? (d) Draw the circuit diagram for an *L-R-C* parallel circuit. Arrange the circuit elements in your diagram so that the resistor is closest to the ac source. Justify the following statement: When the angular frequency of the source is $\omega = \omega_0$, there is *no* current flowing between (i) the part of the circuit that includes the source and the resistor and (ii) the part that includes the inductor and capacitor, so you could cut the wires connecting these two parts of the circuit without affecting the currents. (e) Is the statement in part (d) still valid if we consider that any real inductor or capacitor also has some resistance of its own? Explain.

31.56. A 400-Ω resistor and a 6.00-μF capacitor are connected in parallel to an ac generator that supplies an rms voltage of 220 V at an angular frequency of 360 rad/s. Use the results of Problem 31.54. Note that since there is no inductor in the circuit, the $1/\omega L$ term is not present in the expression for Z. Find (a) the current amplitude in the resistor; (b) the current amplitude in the capacitor; (c) the phase angle of the source current with respect to the source voltage; (d) the amplitude of the current through the generator. (e) Does the source current lag or lead the source voltage?

31.57. An *L-R-C* parallel circuit is connected to an ac source of constant voltage amplitude V and variable angular frequency ω. (a) Using the results of Problem 31.54, find expressions for the amplitudes I_R, I_L, and I_C of the currents through the resistor, inductor, and capacitor as functions of ω. (b) Graph I_R, I_L, and I_C as functions of ω for $V = 100$ V, $R = 200\ \Omega$, $L = 2.0$ H, and $C = 0.50\ \mu$F. (c) Discuss the behavior of I_L and I_C in the limits $\omega = 0$ and $\omega \to \infty$. Explain why I_L and I_C behave as they do in these limits. (d) Calculate the resonance frequency (in Hz) of the circuit, and sketch the phasor diagram at the resonance frequency. (e) At the resonance frequency, what is the current amplitude through the source? (f) At the resonance frequency, what is the current amplitude through the resistor, through the inductor, and through the capacitor?

31.58. An *L-R-C* series circuit consists of a 2.50-μF capacitor, a 5.00-mH inductor, and a 75.0-Ω resistor connected across an ac source of voltage amplitude 15.0 V having variable frequency. (a) Under what circumstances is the average power delivered to the circuit equal to $\frac{1}{2}V_{\text{rms}}I_{\text{rms}}$? (b) Under the conditions of part (a), what is the average power delivered to each circuit element and what is the maximum current through the capacitor?

31.59. In an *L-R-C* series circuit the magnitude of the phase angle is 54.0°, with the source voltage lagging the current. The reactance of the capacitor is 350 Ω, and the resistor resistance is 180 Ω. The average power delivered by the source is 140 W. Find (a) the reactance of the inductor; (b) the rms current; (c) the rms voltage of the source.

31.60. An *L-R-C* series circuit has $R = 500\ \Omega$, $L = 2.00$ H, $C = 0.500\ \mu$F, and $V = 100$ V. (a) For $\omega = 800$ rad/s, calculate V_R, V_L, V_C, and ϕ. Using a single set of axes, graph v, v_R, v_L, and v_C as functions of time. Include two cycles of v on your graph. (b) Repeat part (a) for $\omega = 1000$ rad/s. (c) Repeat part (a) for $\omega = 1250$ rad/s.

31.61. In an *L-R-C* series circuit, the source has a voltage amplitude of 120 V, $R = 80.0\ \Omega$, and the reactance of the capacitor is 480 Ω. The voltage amplitude across the capacitor is 360 V. (a) What is the current amplitude in the circuit? (b) What is the impedance? (c) What two values can the reactance of the inductor have? (d) For which of the two values found in part (c) is the angular frequency less than the resonance angular frequency? Explain.

31.62. A series circuit consists of a 1.50-mH inductor, a 125-Ω resistor, and a 25.0-nF capacitor connected across an ac source having an rms voltage of 35.0 V and variable frequency. (a) At what angular frequency will the current amplitude be equal to $\frac{1}{3}$ of its maximum possible value? (b) At the frequency in part (a) what are the current amplitude and the voltage amplitude across each of the circuit elements (including the ac source)?

31.63. The current in a certain circuit varies with time as shown in Fig. 31.28. Find the average current and the rms current in terms of I_0.

Figure **31.28** Problem 31.63.

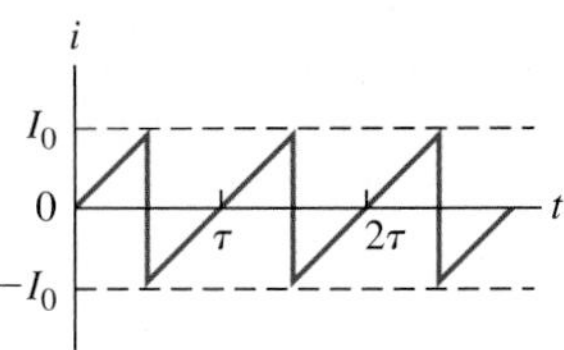

31.64. The Resonance Width. Consider an *L-R-C* series circuit with a 1.80-H inductor, a 0.900-μF capacitor, and a 300-Ω resistor. The source has terminal rms voltage $V_{\text{rms}} = 60.0$ V and variable angular frequency ω. (a) What is the resonance angular frequency ω_0 of the circuit? (b) What is the rms current through the circuit at resonance, $I_{\text{rms-0}}$? (c) For what two values of the angular frequency, ω_1 and ω_2, is the rms current half the resonance value? (d) The quantity $|\omega_1 - \omega_2|$ defines the *resonance width.* Calculate $I_{\text{rms-0}}$ and the resonance width for $R = 300\ \Omega$, $30.0\ \Omega$, and $3.00\ \Omega$. Describe how your results compare to the discussion in Section 31.5.

31.65. An inductor, a capacitor, and a resistor are all connected in series across an ac source. If the resistance, inductance, and capacitance are all doubled, by what factor does each of the following quantities change? Indicate whether they increase or decrease: (a) the resonance angular frequency; (b) the inductive reactance; (c) the capacitive reactance. (d) Does the impedance double?

31.66. A transformer consists of 275 primary windings and 834 secondary windings. If the potential difference across the primary coil is 25.0 V, (a) what is the voltage across the secondary coil, and (b) what is the effective load resistance of the secondary coil if it is connected across a 125-Ω resistor?

31.67. You want to double the resonance angular frequency of a series *R-L-C* circuit by changing only the *pertinent* circuit elements all by the same factor. (a) Which ones should you change? (b) By what factor should you change them?

31.68. A resistance R, capacitance C, and inductance L are connected in series to a voltage source with amplitude V and variable angular frequency ω. If $\omega = \omega_0$, the resonance angular frequency, find (a) the maximum current in the resistor; (b) the maximum voltage across the capacitor; (c) the maximum voltage across the inductor; (d) the maximum energy stored in the capacitor; (e) the maximum energy stored in the inductor. Give your answers in terms of R, C, L, and V.

31.69. Repeat Problem 31.68 for the case $\omega = \omega_0/2$.

31.70. Repeat Problem 31.68 for the case $\omega = 2\omega_0$.

31.71. Finding an Unknown Inductance. Your boss gives you an inductor and asks you to measure its inductance. You have available a resistor, an ac voltmeter of high impedance, a capacitor, and an ac source. Explain how you might use these to determine the inductance, and cite any other piece of equipment you may need. Be sure to explain clearly how to use the equipment and what you need to measure to find the unknown inductance.

31.72. An *L-R-C* series circuit draws 220 W from a 120-V (rms), 50.0-Hz ac line. The power factor is 0.560, and the source voltage leads the current. (a) What is the net resistance R of the circuit? (b) Find the capacitance of the series capacitor that will result in a power factor of unity when it is added to the original circuit. (c) What power will then be drawn from the supply line?

31.73. In an *L-R-C* series circuit the current is given by $i = I\cos\omega t$. The voltage amplitudes for the resistor, inductor, and capacitor are V_R, V_L, and V_C. (a) Show that the instantaneous power into the resistor is $p_R = V_R I \cos^2 \omega t = \frac{1}{2} V_R I(1 + \cos 2\omega t)$. What does this expression give for the average power into the resistor? (b) Show that the instantaneous power into the inductor is $p_L = -V_L I \sin \omega t \cos \omega t = -\frac{1}{2} V_L I \sin 2\omega t$. What does this expression give for the average power into the inductor? (c) Show that the instantaneous power into the capacitor is $p_C = V_C I \sin \omega t \cos \omega t = \frac{1}{2} V_C I \sin 2\omega t$. What does this expression give for the average power into the capacitor? (d) The instantaneous power delivered by the source is shown in Section 31.4 to be $p = VI \cos \omega t (\cos \phi \cos \omega t - \sin \phi \sin \omega t)$. Show that $p_R + p_L + p_C$ equals p at each instant of time.

Challenge Problems

31.74. (a) At what angular frequency is the voltage amplitude across the *resistor* in an *L-R-C* series circuit at maximum value? (b) At what angular frequency is the voltage amplitude across the *inductor* at maximum value? (c) At what angular frequency is the voltage amplitude across the *capacitor* at maximum value? (You may want to refer to the results of Problem 31.52.)

31.75. Complex Numbers in a Circuit. The voltage across a circuit element in an ac circuit is not necessarily in phase with the current through that circuit element. Therefore the voltage amplitudes across the circuit elements in a branch in an ac circuit do not add algebraically. A method that is commonly employed to simplify the analysis of an ac circuit driven by a sinusoidal source is to represent the impedance Z as a *complex* number. The resistance R is taken to be the real part of the impedance, and the reactance $X = X_L - X_C$ is taken to be the imaginary part. Thus, for a branch containing a resistor, inductor, and capacitor in series, the complex impedance is $Z_{\text{cpx}} = R + iX$, where $i^2 = -1$. If the voltage amplitude across the branch is V_{cpx}, we define a *complex* current amplitude by $I_{\text{cpx}} = V_{\text{cpx}}/Z_{\text{cpx}}$. The *actual* current amplitude is the absolute value of the complex current amplitude, that is, $I = (I_{\text{cpx}}{}^* I_{\text{cpx}})^{1/2}$. The phase angle ϕ of the current with respect to the source voltage is given by $\tan \phi = \text{Im}(I_{\text{cpx}})/\text{Re}(I_{\text{cpx}})$. The voltage amplitudes $V_{R\text{-cpx}}$, $V_{L\text{-cpx}}$, and $V_{C\text{-cpx}}$ across the resistance, inductance, and capacitance, respectively, are found by multiplying I_{cpx} by R, iX_L, or $-iX_C$, respectively. From the complex representation for the voltage amplitudes, the voltage across a branch is just the algebraic sum of the voltages across each circuit element; $V_{\text{cpx}} = V_{R\text{-cpx}} + V_{L\text{-cpx}} + V_{C\text{-cpx}}$. The actual value of any current amplitude or voltage amplitude is the absolute value of the corresponding complex quantity. Consider the series *L-R-C* circuit shown in Fig. 31.29. The values of the circuit elements, the source voltage amplitude, and the source angular frequency are as shown. Use the phasor diagram techniques presented in Section 31.1 to solve for (a) the current amplitude; and (b) the phase angle ϕ of the current with respect to the source voltage. (Note that this angle is the negative of the phase angle defined in Fig. 31.13.) Now analyze the same circuit using the complex-number approach. (c) Determine the complex impedance of the circuit, Z_{cpx}. Take the absolute value to obtain Z, the actual impedance of the circuit. (d) Take the voltage amplitude of the source, V_{cpx}, to be real, and find the complex current amplitude I_{cpx}. Find the actual current amplitude by taking the absolute value of I_{cpx}. (e) Find the phase angle ϕ of the current with respect to the source voltage by using the real and imaginary parts of I_{cpx}, as explained above. (f) Find the complex representations of the voltages across the resistance, the inductance, and the capacitance. (g) Adding the answers found in part (f), verify that the sum of these complex numbers is real and equal to 200 V, the voltage of the source.

Figure **31.29** Challenge Problem 31.75.

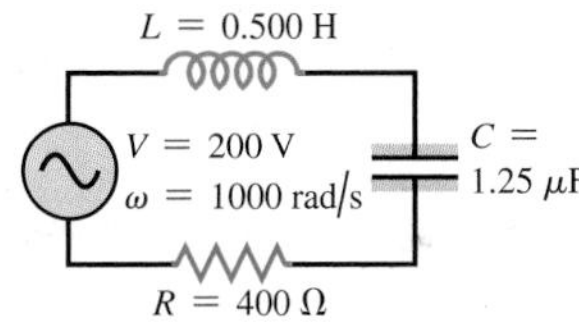

32 ELECTROMAGNETIC WAVES

LEARNING GOALS

By studying this chapter, you will learn:

- Why there are both electric and magnetic fields in a light wave.
- How the speed of light is related to the fundamental constants of electricity and magnetism.
- How to describe the propagation of a sinusoidal electromagnetic wave.
- What determines the amount of power carried by an electromagnetic wave.
- How to describe standing electromagnetic waves.

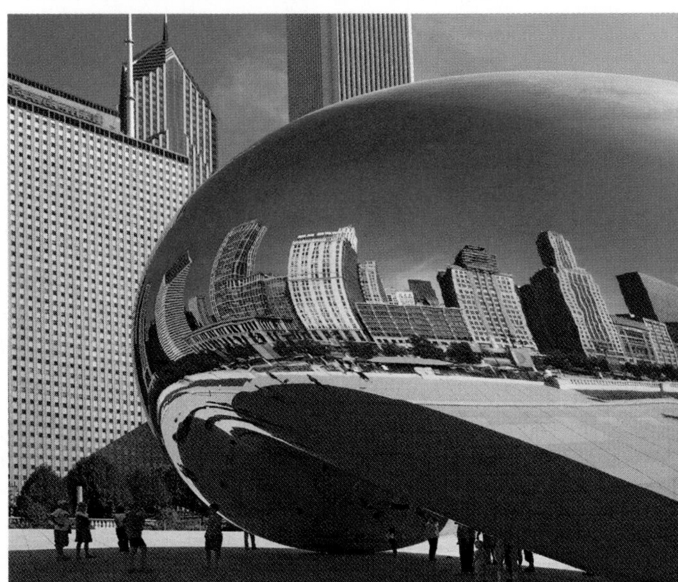

? Metal objects reflect not only visible light but also radio waves. What aspect of metals makes them so reflective?

What is light? This question has been asked by humans for centuries, but there was no answer until electricity and magnetism were unified into the single discipline of *electromagnetism,* as described by Maxwell's equations. These equations show that a time-varying magnetic field acts as a source of electric field and that a time-varying electric field acts as a source of magnetic field. These $\vec{E}$ and $\vec{B}$ fields can sustain each other, forming an *electromagnetic wave* that propagates through space. Visible light emitted by the glowing filament of a light bulb is one example of an electromagnetic wave; other kinds of electromagnetic waves are produced by sources such as TV and radio stations, microwave oscillators for ovens and radar, x-ray machines, and radioactive nuclei.

In this chapter we'll use Maxwell's equations as the theoretical basis for understanding electromagnetic waves. We'll find that these waves carry both energy and momentum. In sinusoidal electromagnetic waves, the $\vec{E}$ and $\vec{B}$ fields are sinusoidal functions of time and position, with a definite frequency and wavelength. The various types of electromagnetic waves—visible light, radio, x rays, and others—differ only in their frequency and wavelength. Our study of optics in the following chapters will be based in part on the electromagnetic nature of light.

Unlike waves on a string or sound waves in a fluid, electromagnetic waves do not require a material medium; the light that you see coming from the stars at night has traveled without difficulty across tens or hundreds of light-years of (nearly) empty space. Nonetheless, electromagnetic waves and mechanical waves have much in common and are described in much the same language. Before reading further in this chapter, you should review the properties of mechanical waves as discussed in Chapters 15 and 16.

32.1 Maxwell's Equations and Electromagnetic Waves

In the last several chapters we studied various aspects of electric and magnetic fields. We learned that when the fields don't vary with time, such as an electric field produced by charges at rest or the magnetic field of a steady current, we can analyze the electric and magnetic fields independently without considering interactions between them. But when the fields vary with time, they are no longer independent. Faraday's law (see Section 29.2) tells us that a time-varying magnetic field acts as a source of electric field, as shown by induced emfs in inductors and transformers. Ampere's law, including the displacement current discovered by Maxwell (see Section 29.7), shows that a time-varying electric field acts as a source of magnetic field. This mutual interaction between the two fields is summarized in Maxwell's equations, presented in Section 29.7.

Thus, when *either* an electric or a magnetic field is changing with time, a field of the other kind is induced in adjacent regions of space. We are led (as Maxwell was) to consider the possibility of an electromagnetic disturbance, consisting of time-varying electric and magnetic fields, that can propagate through space from one region to another, even when there is no matter in the intervening region. Such a disturbance, if it exists, will have the properties of a *wave,* and an appropriate term is **electromagnetic wave.**

Such waves do exist; radio and television transmission, light, x rays, and many other kinds of radiation are examples of electromagnetic waves. Our goal in this chapter is to see how such waves are explained by the principles of electromagnetism that we have studied thus far and to examine the properties of these waves.

Electricity, Magnetism, and Light

As often happens in the development of science, the theoretical understanding of electromagnetic waves evolved along a considerably more devious path than the one just outlined. In the early days of electromagnetic theory (the early 19th century), two different units of electric charge were used: one for electrostatics and the other for magnetic phenomena involving currents. In the system of units used at that time, these two units of charge had different physical dimensions. Their *ratio* had units of velocity, and measurements showed that the ratio had a numerical value that was precisely equal to the speed of light, 3.00×10^8 m/s. At the time, physicists regarded this as an extraordinary coincidence and had no idea how to explain it.

In searching to understand this result, Maxwell (Fig. 32.1) proved in 1865 that an electromagnetic disturbance should propagate in free space with a speed equal to that of light and hence that light waves were likely to be electromagnetic in nature. At the same time, he discovered that the basic principles of electromagnetism can be expressed in terms of the four equations that we now call **Maxwell's equations,** which we discussed in Section 29.7. These four equations are (1) Gauss's law for electric fields; (2) Gauss's law for magnetic fields, showing the absence of magnetic monopoles; (3) Ampere's law, including displacement current; and (4) Faraday's law:

$$\oint \vec{E} \cdot d\vec{A} = \frac{Q_{\text{encl}}}{\epsilon_0} \qquad \text{(Gauss's law)} \qquad (29.18)$$

$$\oint \vec{B} \cdot d\vec{A} = 0 \qquad \text{(Gauss's law for magnetism)} \qquad (29.19)$$

$$\oint \vec{B} \cdot d\vec{l} = \mu_0 \left(i_C + \epsilon_0 \frac{d\Phi_E}{dt} \right)_{\text{encl}} \qquad \text{(Ampere's law)} \qquad (29.20)$$

$$\oint \vec{E} \cdot d\vec{l} = -\frac{d\Phi_B}{dt} \qquad \text{(Faraday's law)} \qquad (29.21)$$

32.1 James Clerk Maxwell (1831–1879) was the first person to truly understand the fundamental nature of light. He also made major contributions to thermodynamics, optics, astronomy, and color photography. Albert Einstein described Maxwell's accomplishments as "the most profound and the most fruitful that physics has experienced since the time of Newton."

These equations apply to electric and magnetic fields *in vacuum.* If a material is present, the permittivity ϵ_0 and permeability μ_0 of free space are replaced by the permittivity ϵ and permeability μ of the material. If the values of ϵ and μ are different at different points in the regions of integration, then ϵ and μ have to be transferred to the left sides of Eqs. (29.18) and (29.20), respectively, and placed inside the integrals. The ϵ in Eq. (29.20) also has to be included in the integral that gives $d\Phi_E/dt$.

According to Maxwell's equations, a point charge at rest produces a static $\vec{E}$ field but no $\vec{B}$ field; a point charge moving with a constant velocity (see Section 28.1) produces both $\vec{E}$ and $\vec{B}$ fields. Maxwell's equations can also be used to show that in order for a point charge to produce electromagnetic waves, the charge must *accelerate.* In fact, it's a general result of Maxwell's equations that *every* accelerated charge radiates electromagnetic energy (Fig. 32.2).

32.2 (a) Every mobile phone, wireless modem, or radio transmitter emits signals in the form of electromagnetic waves that are made by accelerating charges.
(b) Power lines carry a strong alternating current, which means that a substantial amount of charge is accelerating back and forth and generating electromagnetic waves. These waves can produce a buzzing sound from your car radio when you drive near the lines.

Generating Electromagnetic Radiation

One way in which a point charge can be made to emit electromagnetic waves is by making it oscillate in simple harmonic motion, so that it has an acceleration at almost every instant (the exception is when the charge is passing through its equilibrium position). Figure 32.3 shows some of the electric field lines produced by such an oscillating point charge. Field lines are *not* material objects, but you may nonetheless find it helpful to think of them as behaving somewhat like strings that extend from the point charge off to infinity. Oscillating the charge up and down makes waves that propagate outward from the charge along these "strings." Note that the charge does not emit waves equally in all directions; the waves are strongest at 90° to the axis of motion of the charge, while there are *no* waves along this axis. This is just what the "string" picture would lead you to conclude. There is also a *magnetic* disturbance that spreads outward from the charge; this is not shown in Fig. 32.3. Because the electric and magnetic disturbances spread or radiate away from the source, the name **electromagnetic radiation** is used interchangeably with the phrase "electromagnetic waves."

Electromagnetic waves with macroscopic wavelengths were first produced in the laboratory in 1887 by the German physicist Heinrich Hertz. As a source of waves, he used charges oscillating in *L-C* circuits of the sort discussed in Section 30.5; he detected the resulting electromagnetic waves with other circuits tuned to the same frequency. Hertz also produced electromagnetic *standing waves* and measured the distance between adjacent nodes (one half-wavelength) to determine the wavelength. Knowing the resonant frequency of his circuits, he then found the speed of the waves from the wavelength–frequency relationship $v = \lambda f$. He established that their speed was the same as that of light; this verified Maxwell's theoretical prediction directly. The SI unit of frequency is named in honor of Hertz: One hertz (1 Hz) equals one cycle per second.

32.3 Electric field lines of a point charge oscillating in simple harmonic motion, seen at five instants during an oscillation period T. The charge's trajectory is in the plane of the drawings. At $t = 0$ the point charge is at its maximum upward displacement. The arrow shows one "kink" in the lines of $\vec{E}$ as it propagates outward from the point charge. The magnetic field (not shown) comprises circles that lie in planes perpendicular to these figures and concentric with the axis of oscillation.

(a) $t = 0$

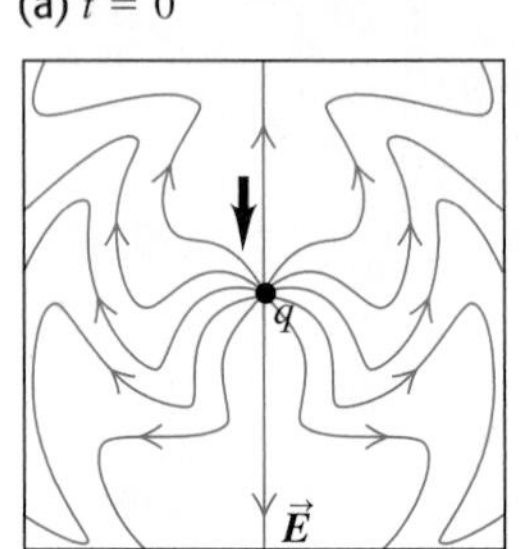

(b) $t = T/4$

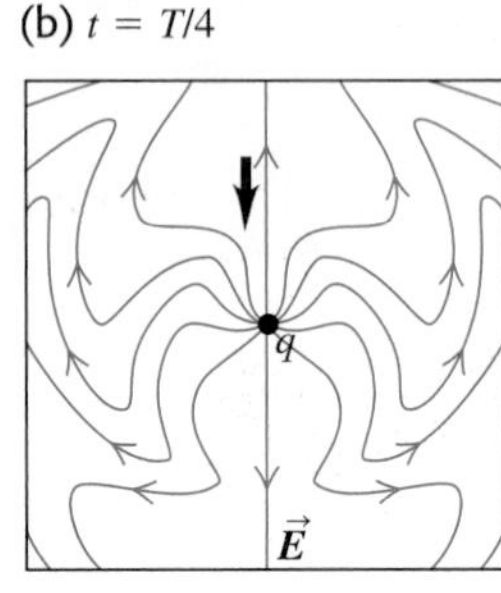

(c) $t = T/2$

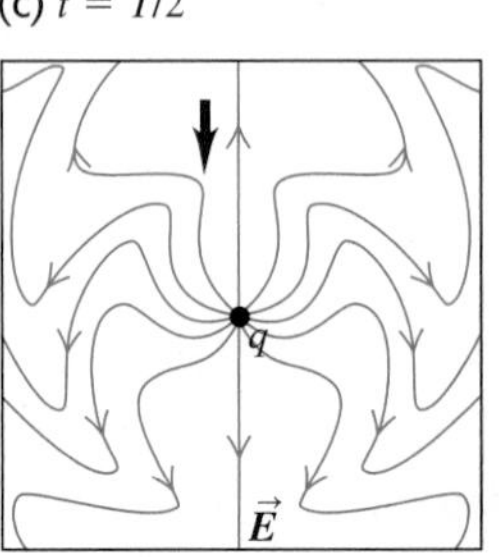

(d) $t = 3T/4$

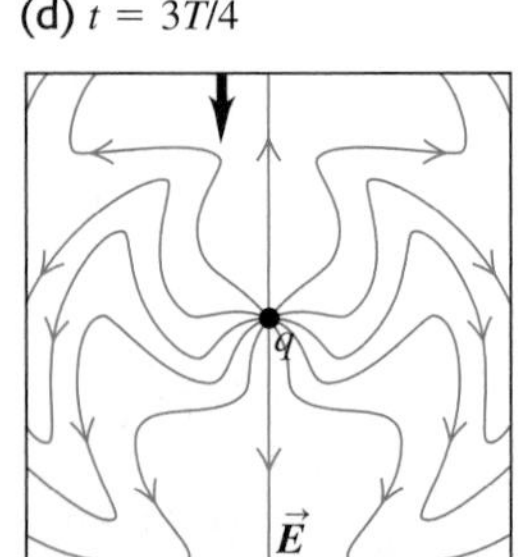

(e) $t = T$

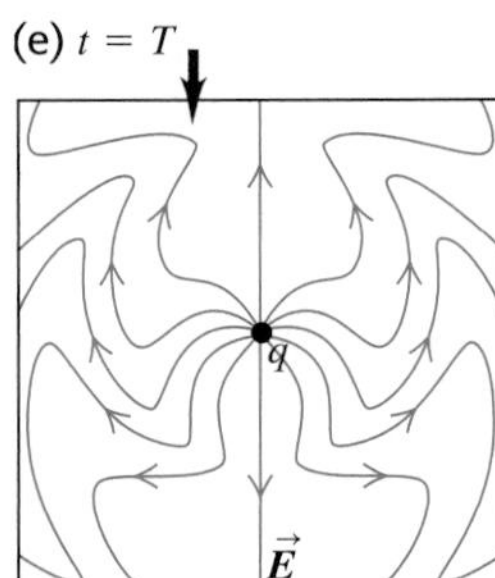

The modern value of the speed of light, which we denote by the symbol c, is 299,792,458 m/s. (Recall from Section 1.3 that this value is the basis of our standard of length: one meter is defined to be the distance that light travels in 1/299,792,458 second.) For our purposes, $c = 3.00 \times 10^8$ m/s is sufficiently accurate.

The possible use of electromagnetic waves for long-distance communication does not seem to have occurred to Hertz. It remained to Marconi and others to make radio communication a familiar household experience. In a radio *transmitter,* electric charges are made to oscillate along the length of the conducting antenna, producing oscillating field disturbances like those shown in Fig. 32.3. Since many charges oscillate together in the antenna, the disturbances are much stronger than those of a single oscillating charge and can be detected at a much greater distance. In a radio *receiver* the antenna is also a conductor; the fields of the wave emanating from a distant transmitter exert forces on free charges within the receiver antenna, producing an oscillating current that is detected and amplified by the receiver circuitry.

For the remainder of this chapter our concern will be with electromagnetic waves themselves, not with the rather complex problem of how they are produced.

The Electromagnetic Spectrum

Electromagnetic waves cover an extremely broad spectrum of wavelength and frequency. This **electromagnetic spectrum** encompasses radio and TV transmission, visible light, infrared and ultraviolet radiation, x rays, and gamma rays. Electromagnetic waves have been detected with frequencies from at least 1 to 10^{24} Hz; the most commonly encountered portion of the spectrum is shown in Fig. 32.4, which gives approximate wavelength and frequency ranges for the various segments. Despite vast differences in their uses and means of production, these are all electromagnetic waves with the same propagation speed (in vacuum) $c = 299{,}792{,}458$ m/s. Electromagnetic waves may differ in frequency f and wavelength λ, but the relationship $c = \lambda f$ in vacuum holds for each.

We can detect only a very small segment of this spectrum directly through our sense of sight. We call this range **visible light.** Its wavelengths range from about 400 to 700 nm (400 to 700×10^{-9} m), with corresponding frequencies from about 750 to 430 THz (7.5 to 4.3×10^{14} Hz). Different parts of the visible spectrum evoke in humans the sensations of different colors. Wavelengths for colors in the visible spectrum are given (very approximately) in Table 32.1.

Ordinary white light includes all visible wavelengths. However, by using special sources or filters, we can select a narrow band of wavelengths within a range of a few nm. Such light is approximately *monochromatic* (single-color) light. Absolutely monochromatic light with only a single wavelength is an unattainable

Table 32.1 Wavelengths of Visible Light

400 to 440 nm	Violet
440 to 480 nm	Blue
480 to 560 nm	Green
560 to 590 nm	Yellow
590 to 630 nm	Orange
630 to 700 nm	Red

32.4 The electromagnetic spectrum. The frequencies and wavelengths found in nature extend over such a wide range that we have to use a logarithmic scale to show all important bands. The boundaries between bands are somewhat arbitrary.

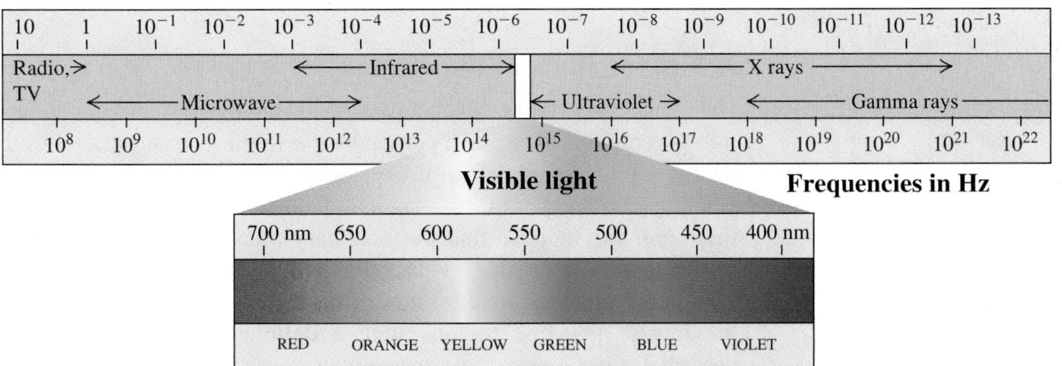

idealization. When we use the expression "monochromatic light with $\lambda =$ 550 nm" with reference to a laboratory experiment, we really mean a small band of wavelengths *around* 550 nm. Light from a *laser* is much more nearly monochromatic than is light obtainable in any other way.

Invisible forms of electromagnetic radiation are no less important than visible light. Our system of global communication, for example, depends on radio waves: AM radio uses waves with frequencies from 5.4×10^5 Hz to 1.6×10^6 Hz, while FM radio broadcasts are at frequencies from 8.8×10^7 Hz to 1.08×10^8 Hz. (Television broadcasts use frequencies that bracket the FM band.) Microwaves are also used for communication (for example, by cellular phones and wireless networks) and for weather radar (at frequencies near 3×10^9 Hz). Many cameras have a device that emits a beam of infrared radiation; by analyzing the properties of the infrared radiation reflected from the subject, the camera determines the distance to the subject and automatically adjusts the focus. Ultraviolet radiation has shorter wavelengths than visible light; as we will learn in Chapter 36, this property allows it to be focused into very narrow beams for high-precision applications such as LASIK eye surgery. X rays are able to penetrate through flesh, which makes them invaluable in dentistry and medicine. The shortest-wavelength electromagnetic radiation, gamma rays, is produced in nature by radioactive materials (see Chapter 43). Gamma rays, which are very energetic, are used in medicine to destroy cancer cells.

Test Your Understanding of Section 32.1 (a) Is it possible to have a purely electric wave propagate through empty space—that is, a wave made up of an electric field but no magnetic field? (b) What about a purely magnetic wave, with a magnetic field but no electric field?

32.2 Plane Electromagnetic Waves and the Speed of Light

We are now ready to develop the basic ideas of electromagnetic waves and their relationship to the principles of electromagnetism. Our procedure will be to postulate a simple field configuration that has wavelike behavior. We'll assume an electric field $\vec{E}$ that has only a y-component and a magnetic field $\vec{B}$ with only a z-component, and we'll assume that both fields move together in the $+x$-direction with a speed c that is initially unknown. (As we go along, it will become clear why we choose $\vec{E}$ and $\vec{B}$ to be perpendicular to the direction of propagation as well as to each other.) Then we will test whether these fields are physically possible by asking whether they are consistent with Maxwell's equations, particularly Ampere's law and Faraday's law. We'll find that the answer is yes, provided that c has a particular value. We'll also show that the *wave equation,* which we encountered during our study of mechanical waves in Chapter 15, can be derived from Maxwell's equations.

32.5 An electromagnetic wave front. The plane representing the wave front moves to the right (in the positive x-direction) with speed c.

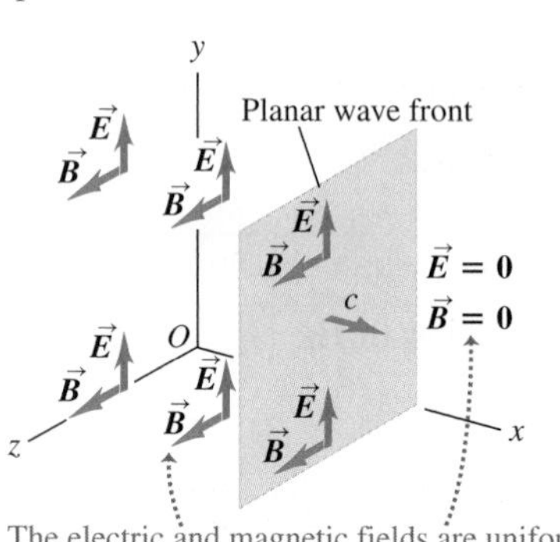
y
Planar wave front
$\vec{E}$
$\vec{B}$
$\vec{E} = 0$
$\vec{B} = 0$
c
O
x
z
The electric and magnetic fields are uniform behind the advancing wave front and zero in front of it.

A Simple Plane Electromagnetic Wave

Using an xyz-coordinate system (Fig. 32.5), we imagine that all space is divided into two regions by a plane perpendicular to the x-axis (parallel to the yz-plane). At every point to the left of this plane there are a uniform electric field $\vec{E}$ in the $+y$-direction and a uniform magnetic field $\vec{B}$ in the $+z$-direction, as shown. Furthermore, we suppose that the boundary plane, which we call the *wave front,* moves to the right in the $+x$-direction with a constant speed c, the value of which we'll leave undetermined for now. Thus the $\vec{E}$ and $\vec{B}$ fields travel to the right into previously field-free regions with a definite speed. The situation, in short, describes a rudimentary electromagnetic wave. A wave such as this, in which at any instant the fields are uniform over any plane perpendicular to the direction of propagation, is called a **plane wave.** In the case shown in Fig. 32.5, the fields are zero for planes to the right of the wave front and have the same values on all planes to the left of the wave front; later we will consider more complex plane waves.

We won't concern ourselves with the problem of actually *producing* such a field configuration. Instead, we simply ask whether it is consistent with the laws of electromagnetism—that is, with Maxwell's equations. We'll consider each of these four equations in turn.

Let us first verify that our wave satisfies Maxwell's first and second equations—that is, Gauss's laws for electric and magnetic fields. To do this, we take as our Gaussian surface a rectangular box with sides parallel to the *xy*, *xz*, and *yz* coordinate planes (Fig. 32.6). The box encloses no electric charge. You can show that the total electric flux and magnetic flux through the box are both zero, even if part of the box is in the region where $E = B = 0$. This would *not* be the case if $\vec{E}$ or $\vec{B}$ had an *x*-component, parallel to the direction of propagation. We leave the proof as a problem (see Problem 32.42). Thus to satisfy Maxwell's first and second equations, the electric and magnetic fields must be perpendicular to the direction of propagation; that is, the wave must be **transverse.**

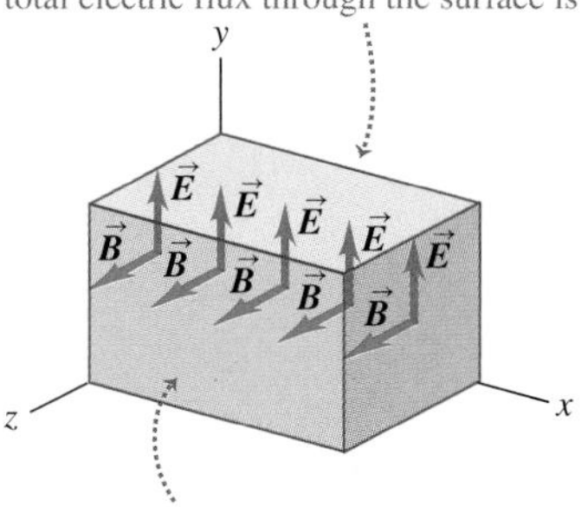

The electric field is the same on the top and bottom sides of the Gaussian surface, so the total electric flux through the surface is zero.
y
E
B
z
x
The magnetic field is the same on the left and right sides of the Gaussian surface, so the total magnetic flux through the surface is zero.

32.6 Gaussian surface for a plane electromagnetic wave.

The next of Maxwell's equations to be considered is Faraday's law:

$$\oint \vec{E} \cdot d\vec{l} = -\frac{d\Phi_B}{dt} \tag{32.1}$$

To test whether our wave satisfies Faraday's law, we apply this law to a rectangle *efgh* that is parallel to the *xy*-plane (Fig. 32.7a). As shown in Fig. 32.7b, a cross section in the *xy*-plane, this rectangle has height *a* and width Δx. At the time shown, the wave front has progressed partway through the rectangle, and $\vec{E}$ is zero along the side *ef*. In applying Faraday's law we take the vector area $d\vec{A}$ of rectangle *efgh* to be in the $+z$-direction. With this choice the right-hand rule requires that we integrate $\vec{E} \cdot d\vec{l}$ *counterclockwise* around the rectangle. At every point on side *ef*, $\vec{E}$ is zero. At every point on sides *fg* and *he*, $\vec{E}$ is either zero or perpendicular to $d\vec{l}$. Only side *gh* contributes to the integral. On this side, $\vec{E}$ and $d\vec{l}$ are opposite, and we obtain

$$\oint \vec{E} \cdot d\vec{l} = -Ea \tag{32.2}$$

Hence, the left-hand side of Eq. (32.1) is nonzero.

To satisfy Faraday's law, Eq. (32.1), there must be a component of $\vec{B}$ in the *z*-direction (perpendicular to $\vec{E}$) so that there can be a nonzero magnetic flux Φ_B through the rectangle *efgh* and a nonzero derivative $d\Phi_B/dt$. Indeed, in our wave, $\vec{B}$ has *only* a *z*-component. We have assumed that this component is in the *positive* *z*-direction; let's see whether this assumption is consistent with Faraday's law. During a time interval *dt* the wave front moves a distance *c dt* to the right in Fig. 32.7b, sweeping out an area *ac dt* of the rectangle *efgh*. During this interval the magnetic flux Φ_B through the rectangle *efgh* increases by $d\Phi_B = B(ac\,dt)$, so the rate of change of magnetic flux is

$$\frac{d\Phi_B}{dt} = Bac \tag{32.3}$$

Now we substitute Eqs. (32.2) and (32.3) into Faraday's law, Eq. (32.1); we get

$$-Ea = -Bac$$

$$E = cB \quad \text{(electromagnetic wave in vacuum)} \tag{32.4}$$

This shows that our wave is consistent with Faraday's law only if the wave speed *c* and the magnitudes of the perpendicular vectors $\vec{E}$ and $\vec{B}$ are related as in

32.7 (a) Applying Faraday's law to a plane wave. (b) In a time *dt*, the magnetic flux through the rectangle in the *xy*-plane increases by an amount $d\Phi_B$. This increase equals the flux through the shaded rectangle with area *ac dt*; that is, $d\Phi_B = Bac\,dt$. Thus $d\Phi_B/dt = Bac$.

(a) In time *dt*, the wave front moves a distance *c dt* in the +*x*-direction.

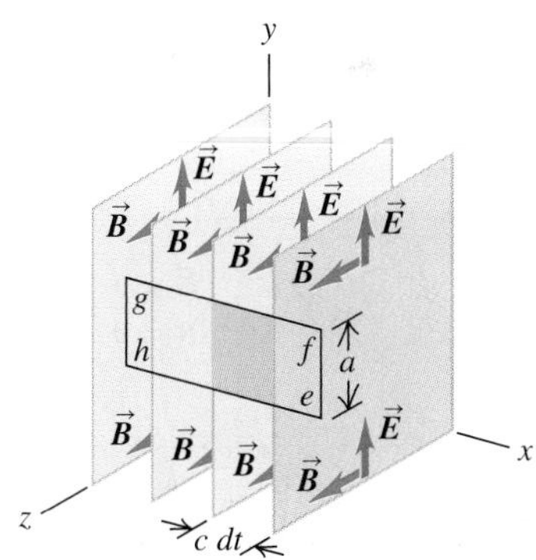

(b) Side view of situation in (a)

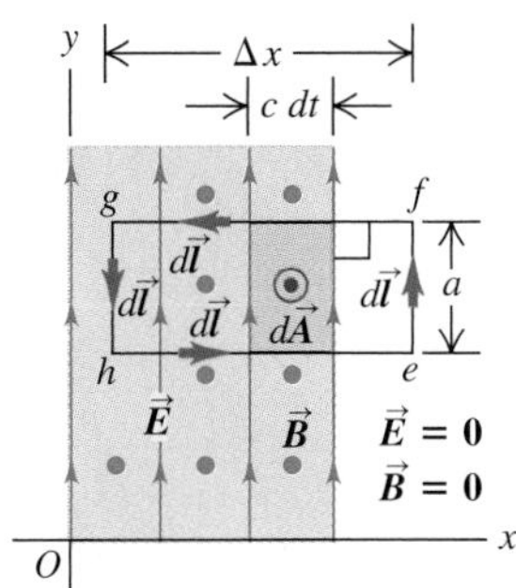

Eq. (32.4). Note that if we had assumed that $\vec{B}$ was in the *negative* z-direction, there would have been an additional minus sign in Eq. (32.4); since E, c, and B are all positive magnitudes, no solution would then have been possible. Furthermore, any component of $\vec{B}$ in the y-direction (parallel to $\vec{E}$) would not contribute to the changing magnetic flux Φ_B through the rectangle *efgh* (which is parallel to the xy-plane) and so would not be part of the wave.

Finally, we carry out a similar calculation using Ampere's law, the remaining member of Maxwell's equations. There is no conduction current $(i_C = 0)$, so Ampere's law is

$$\oint \vec{B} \cdot d\vec{l} = \mu_0 \epsilon_0 \frac{d\Phi_E}{dt} \tag{32.5}$$

32.8 (a) Applying Ampere's law to a plane wave. (Compare to Fig. 32.7a.) (b) In a time dt, the electric flux through the rectangle in the xz-plane increases by an amount $d\Phi_E$. This increase equals the flux through the shaded rectangle with area $ac\,dt$; that is, $d\Phi_E = Eac\,dt$. Thus $d\Phi_E/dt = Eac$.

(a) In time dt, the wave front moves a distance $c\,dt$ in the $+x$-direction.

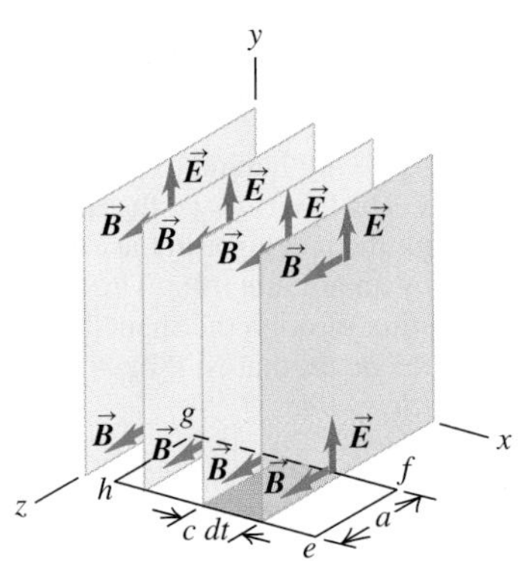

(b) Top view of situation in (a)

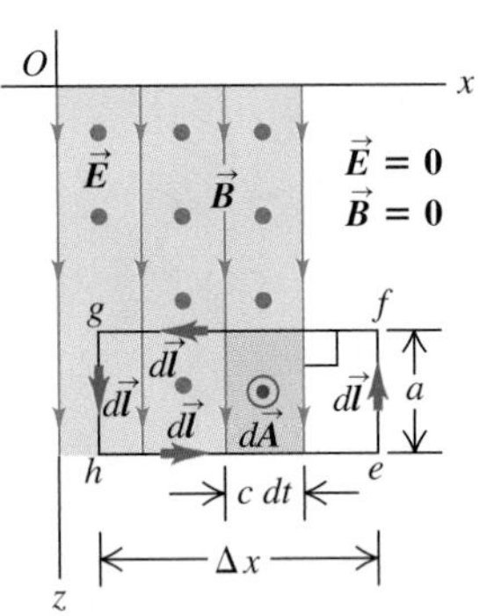

To check whether our wave is consistent with Ampere's law, we move our rectangle so that it lies in the xz-plane, as shown in Fig. 32.8, and we again look at the situation at a time when the wave front has traveled partway through the rectangle. We take the vector area $d\vec{A}$ in the $+y$-direction, and so the right-hand rule requires that we integrate $\vec{B} \cdot d\vec{l}$ counterclockwise around the rectangle. The $\vec{B}$ field is zero at every point along side *ef*, and at each point on sides *fg* and *he* it is either zero or perpendicular to $d\vec{l}$. Only side *gh*, where $\vec{B}$ and $d\vec{l}$ are parallel, contributes to the integral, and we find

$$\oint \vec{B} \cdot d\vec{l} = Ba \tag{32.6}$$

Hence, the left-hand side of Ampere's law, Eq. (32.5), is nonzero; the right-hand side must be nonzero as well. Thus $\vec{E}$ must have a y-component (perpendicular to $\vec{B}$) so that the electric flux Φ_E through the rectangle and the time derivative $d\Phi_E/dt$ can be nonzero. We come to the same conclusion that we inferred from Faraday's law: In an electromagnetic wave, $\vec{E}$ and $\vec{B}$ must be mutually perpendicular.

In a time interval dt the electric flux Φ_E through the rectangle increases by $d\Phi_E = E(ac\,dt)$. Since we chose $d\vec{A}$ to be in the $+y$-direction, this flux change is positive; the rate of change of electric field is

$$\frac{d\Phi_E}{dt} = Eac \tag{32.7}$$

Substituting Eqs. (32.6) and (32.7) into Ampere's law, Eq. (32.5), we find

$$Ba = \epsilon_0 \mu_0 Eac$$

$$B = \epsilon_0 \mu_0 cE \quad \text{(electromagnetic wave in vacuum)} \tag{32.8}$$

Thus our assumed wave obeys Ampere's law only if B, c, and E are related as in Eq. (32.8).

Our electromagnetic wave must obey *both* Ampere's law and Faraday's law, so Eqs. (32.4) and (32.8) must both be satisfied. This can happen only if $\epsilon_0 \mu_0 c = 1/c$, or

$$c = \frac{1}{\sqrt{\epsilon_0 \mu_0}} \quad \text{(speed of electromagnetic waves in vacuum)} \tag{32.9}$$

Inserting the numerical values of these quantities, we find

$$c = \frac{1}{\sqrt{(8.85 \times 10^{-12}\ \mathrm{C^2/N \cdot m^2})(4\pi \times 10^{-7}\ \mathrm{N/A^2})}}$$
$$= 3.00 \times 10^8\ \mathrm{m/s}$$

Our assumed wave is consistent with all of Maxwell's equations, provided that the wave front moves with the speed given above, which you should recognize as the speed of light! Note that the *exact* value of c is defined to be 299,792,458 m/s; the modern value of ϵ_0 is defined to agree with this when used in Eq. (32.9) (see Section 21.3).

Key Properties of Electromagnetic Waves

We chose a simple wave for our study in order to avoid mathematical complications, but this special case illustrates several important features of *all* electromagnetic waves:

1. The wave is *transverse;* both $\vec{E}$ and $\vec{B}$ are perpendicular to the direction of propagation of the wave. The electric and magnetic fields are also perpendicular to each other. The direction of propagation is the direction of the vector product $\vec{E} \times \vec{B}$ (Fig. 32.9).
2. There is a definite ratio between the magnitudes of $\vec{E}$ and $\vec{B}$: $E = cB$.
3. The wave travels in vacuum with a definite and unchanging speed.
4. Unlike mechanical waves, which need the oscillating particles of a medium such as water or air to transmit a wave, electromagnetic waves require no medium. What's "waving" in an electromagnetic wave are the electric and magnetic fields.

32.9 A right-hand rule for electromagnetic waves relates the directions of $\vec{E}$, $\vec{B}$, and the direction of propagation.

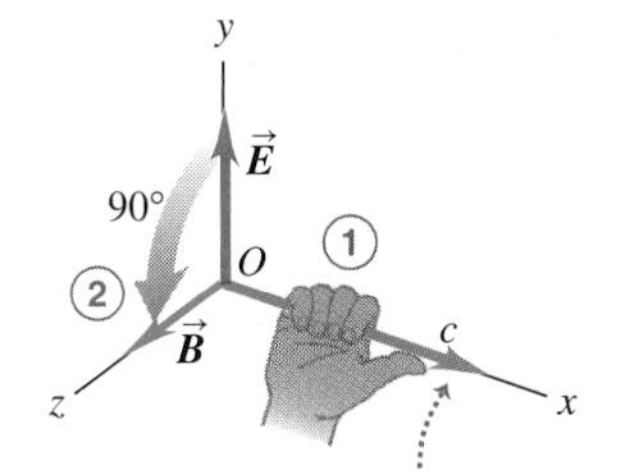
Right-hand rule for an electromagnetic wave:
① Point the thumb of your right hand in the wave's direction of propagation.
② Imagine rotating the $\vec{E}$ field vector 90° in the sense your fingers curl.
That is the direction of the $\vec{B}$ field.
y
$\vec{E}$
90°
O
①
②
c
$\vec{B}$
z
x
Direction of propagation = direction of $\vec{E} \times \vec{B}$.

We can generalize this discussion to a more realistic situation. Suppose we have several wave fronts in the form of parallel planes perpendicular to the x-axis, all of which are moving to the right with speed c. Suppose that the $\vec{E}$ and $\vec{B}$ fields are the same at all points within a single region between two planes, but that the fields differ from region to region. The overall wave is a plane wave, but one in which the fields vary in steps along the x-axis. Such a wave could be constructed by superposing several of the simple step waves we have just discussed (shown in Fig. 32.5). This is possible because the $\vec{E}$ and $\vec{B}$ fields obey the superposition principle in waves just as in static situations: When two waves are superposed, the total $\vec{E}$ field at each point is the vector sum of the $\vec{E}$ fields of the individual waves, and similarly for the total $\vec{B}$ field.

We can extend the above development to show that a wave with fields that vary in steps is also consistent with Ampere's and Faraday's laws, provided that the wave fronts all move with the speed c given by Eq. (32.9). In the limit that we make the individual steps infinitesimally small, we have a wave in which the $\vec{E}$ and $\vec{B}$ fields at any instant vary *continuously* along the x-axis. The entire field pattern moves to the right with speed c. In Section 32.3 we will consider waves in which $\vec{E}$ and $\vec{B}$ are *sinusoidal* functions of x and t. Because at each point the magnitudes of $\vec{E}$ and $\vec{B}$ are related by $E = cB$, the periodic variations of the two fields in any periodic traveling wave must be *in phase.*

Electromagnetic waves have the property of **polarization.** In the above discussion the choice of the y-direction for $\vec{E}$ was arbitrary. We could just as well have specified the z-axis for $\vec{E}$; then $\vec{B}$ would have been in the $-y$-direction. A wave in which $\vec{E}$ is always parallel to a certain axis is said to be **linearly polarized** along that axis. More generally, *any* wave traveling in the x-direction can be represented as a superposition of waves linearly polarized in the y- and z-directions. We will study polarization in greater detail, with special emphasis on polarization of light, in Chapter 33.

*Derivation of the Electromagnetic Wave Equation

Here is an alternative derivation of Eq. (32.9) for the speed of electromagnetic waves. It is more mathematical than our other treatment, but it includes a derivation of the wave equation for electromagnetic waves. This part of the section can be omitted without loss of continuity in the chapter.

32.10 Faraday's law applied to a rectangle with height a and width Δx parallel to the xy-plane.

(a)

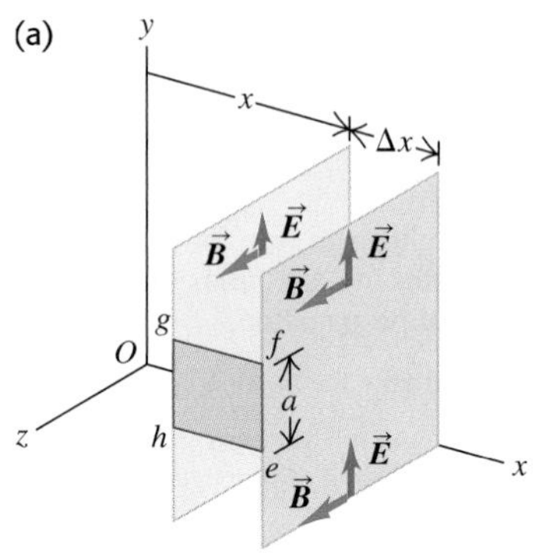

(b) Side view of the situation in (a)

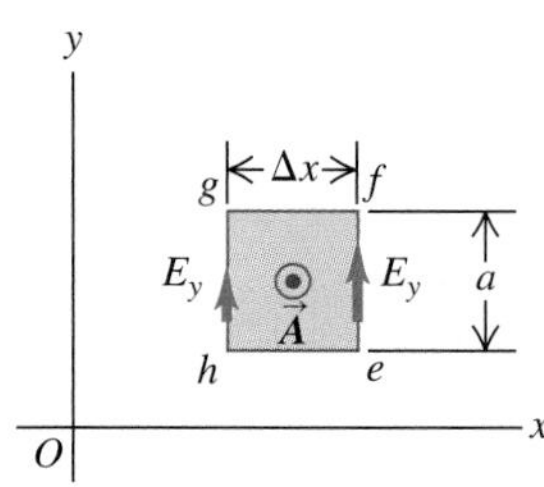

During our discussion of mechanical waves in Section 15.3, we showed that a function $y(x, t)$ that represents the displacement of any point in a mechanical wave traveling along the x-axis must satisfy a differential equation, Eq. (15.12):

$$\frac{\partial^2 y(x, t)}{\partial x^2} = \frac{1}{v^2}\frac{\partial^2 y(x, t)}{\partial t^2} \tag{32.10}$$

This equation is called the **wave equation,** and v is the speed of propagation of the wave.

To derive the corresponding equation for an electromagnetic wave, we again consider a plane wave. That is, we assume that at each instant, E_y and B_z are uniform over any plane perpendicular to the x-axis, the direction of propagation. But now we let E_y and B_z vary continuously as we go along the x-axis; then each is a function of x and t. We consider the values of E_y and B_z on two planes perpendicular to the x-axis, one at x and one at $x + \Delta x$.

Following the same procedure as previously, we apply Faraday's law to a rectangle lying parallel to the xy-plane, as in Fig. 32.10. This figure is similar to Fig. 32.7. Let the left end gh of the rectangle be at position x, and let the right end ef be at position $(x + \Delta x)$. At time t, the values of E_y on these two sides are $E_y(x, t)$ and $E_y(x + \Delta x, t)$, respectively. When we apply Faraday's law to this rectangle, we find that instead of $\oint \vec{E} \cdot d\vec{l} = -Ea$ as before, we have

$$\begin{aligned}\oint \vec{E} \cdot d\vec{l} &= -E_y(x, t)a + E_y(x + \Delta x, t)a \\ &= a[E_y(x + \Delta x, t) - E_y(x, t)]\end{aligned} \tag{32.11}$$

To find the magnetic flux Φ_B through this rectangle, we assume that Δx is small enough that B_z is nearly uniform over the rectangle. In that case, $\Phi_B = B_z(x, t)A = B_z(x, t)a\,\Delta x$, and

$$\frac{d\Phi_B}{dt} = \frac{\partial B_z(x, t)}{\partial t} a\,\Delta x$$

We use partial-derivative notation because B_z is a function of both x and t. When we substitute this expression and Eq. (32.11) into Faraday's law, Eq. (32.1), we get

$$a[E_y(x + \Delta x, t) - E_y(x, t)] = -\frac{\partial B_z}{\partial t} a\,\Delta x$$

$$\frac{E_y(x + \Delta x, t) - E_y(x, t)}{\Delta x} = -\frac{\partial B_z}{\partial t}$$

Finally, imagine shrinking the rectangle down to a sliver so that Δx approaches zero. When we take the limit of this equation as $\Delta x \rightarrow 0$, we get

$$\frac{\partial E_y(x, t)}{\partial x} = -\frac{\partial B_z(x, t)}{\partial t} \tag{32.12}$$

This equation shows that if there is a time-varying component B_z of magnetic field, there must also be a component E_y of electric field that varies with x, and conversely. We put this relationship on the shelf for now; we'll return to it soon.

32.11 Ampere's law applied to a rectangle with height a and width Δx parallel to the xz-plane.

(a)

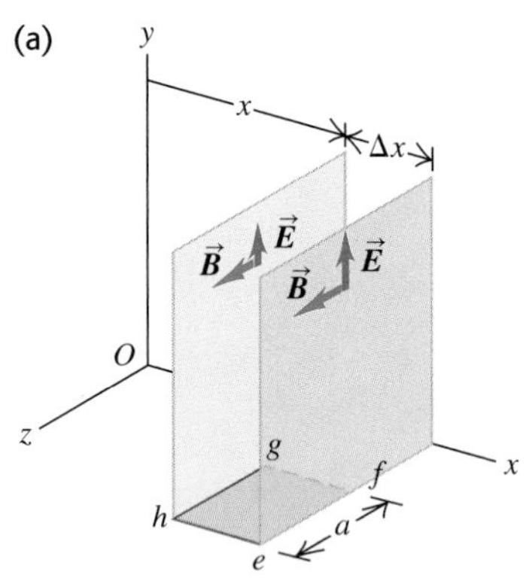

(b) Top view of the situation in (a)

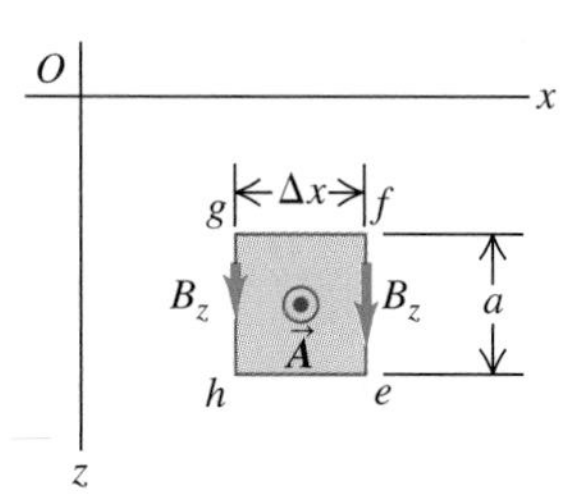

Next we apply Ampere's law to the rectangle shown in Fig. 32.11. The line integral $\oint \vec{B} \cdot d\vec{l}$ becomes

$$\oint \vec{B} \cdot d\vec{l} = -B_z(x + \Delta x, t)a + B_z(x, t)a \tag{32.13}$$

Again assuming that the rectangle is narrow, we approximate the electric flux Φ_E through it as $\Phi_E = E_y(x, t)A = E_y(x, t)a\,\Delta x$. The rate of change of Φ_E, which we need for Ampere's law, is then

$$\frac{d\Phi_E}{dt} = \frac{\partial E_y(x, t)}{\partial t} a\,\Delta x$$

Now we substitute this expression and Eq. (32.13) into Ampere's law, Eq. (32.5):

$$-B_z(x + \Delta x, t)a + B_z(x, t)a = \epsilon_0\mu_0 \frac{\partial E_y(x, t)}{\partial t} a \, \Delta x$$

Again we divide both sides by $a \, \Delta x$ and take the limit as $\Delta x \to 0$. We find

$$-\frac{\partial B_z(x, t)}{\partial x} = \epsilon_0\mu_0 \frac{\partial E_y(x, t)}{\partial t} \tag{32.14}$$

Now comes the final step. We take the partial derivatives with respect to x of both sides of Eq. (32.12), and we take the partial derivatives with respect to t of both sides of Eq. (32.14). The results are

$$-\frac{\partial^2 E_y(x, t)}{\partial x^2} = \frac{\partial^2 B_z(x, t)}{\partial x \partial t}$$

$$-\frac{\partial^2 B_z(x, t)}{\partial x \partial t} = \epsilon_0\mu_0 \frac{\partial^2 E_y(x, t)}{\partial t^2}$$

Combining these two equations to eliminate B_z, we finally find

$$\frac{\partial^2 E_y(x, t)}{\partial x^2} = \epsilon_0\mu_0 \frac{\partial^2 E_y(x, t)}{\partial t^2} \quad \text{(electromagnetic wave equation in vacuum)} \tag{32.15}$$

This expression has the same form as the general wave equation, Eq. (32.10). Because the electric field E_y must satisfy this equation, it behaves as a wave with a pattern that travels through space with a definite speed. Furthermore, comparison of Eqs. (32.15) and (32.10) shows that the wave speed v is given by

$$\frac{1}{v^2} = \epsilon_0\mu_0 \quad \text{or} \quad v = \frac{1}{\sqrt{\epsilon_0\mu_0}}$$

This agrees with Eq. (32.9) for the speed c of electromagnetic waves.

We can show that B_z also must satisfy the same wave equation as E_y, Eq. (32.15). To prove this, we take the partial derivative of Eq. (32.12) with respect to t and the partial derivative of Eq. (32.14) with respect to x and combine the results. We leave this derivation as a problem (see Problem 32.37).

Test Your Understanding of Section 32.2 For each of the following electromagnetic waves, state the direction of the magnetic field. (a) The wave is propagating in the positive z-direction, and $\vec{E}$ is in the positive x-direction; (b) the wave is propagating in the positive y-direction, and $\vec{E}$ is in the negative z-direction; (c) the wave is propagating in the negative x-direction, and $\vec{E}$ is in the positive z-direction.

32.3 Sinusoidal Electromagnetic Waves

10.1 Properties of Mechanical Waves

Sinusoidal electromagnetic waves are directly analogous to sinusoidal transverse mechanical waves on a stretched string, which we studied in Section 15.3. In a sinusoidal electromagnetic wave, $\vec{E}$ and $\vec{B}$ at any point in space are sinusoidal functions of time, and at any instant of time the *spatial* variation of the fields is also sinusoidal.

Some sinusoidal electromagnetic waves are *plane waves;* they share with the waves described in Section 32.2 the property that at any instant the fields are uniform over any plane perpendicular to the direction of propagation. The entire pattern travels in the direction of propagation with speed c. The directions of $\vec{E}$ and $\vec{B}$ are perpendicular to the direction of propagation (and to each other), so the wave is *transverse.* Electromagnetic waves produced by an oscillating point charge, shown in Fig. 32.3, are an example of sinusoidal waves that are *not* plane

32.12 Waves passing through a small area at a sufficiently great distance from a source can be treated as plane waves.

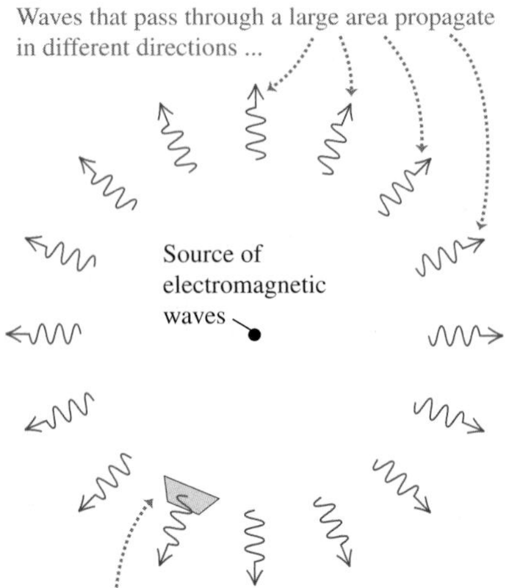
Waves that pass through a large area propagate in different directions ...
Source of electromagnetic waves
... but waves that pass through a small area all propagate in nearly the same direction, so we can treat them as plane waves.

waves. But if we restrict our observations to a relatively small region of space at a sufficiently great distance from the source, even these waves are well approximated by plane waves (Fig. 32.12). In the same way, the curved surface of the (nearly) spherical earth appears flat to us because of our small size relative to the earth's radius. In this section we'll restrict our discussion to plane waves.

The frequency f, the wavelength λ, and the speed of propagation c of any periodic wave are related by the usual wavelength–frequency relationship $c = \lambda f$. If the frequency f is the power-line frequency of 60 Hz, the wavelength is

$$\lambda = \frac{c}{f} = \frac{3 \times 10^8 \text{ m/s}}{60 \text{ Hz}} = 5 \times 10^6 \text{ m} = 5000 \text{ km}$$

which is of the order of the earth's radius! For a wave with this frequency, even a distance of many kilometers includes only a small fraction of a wavelength. But if the frequency is 10^8 Hz (100 MHz), typical of commercial FM radio broadcasts, the wavelength is

$$\lambda = \frac{3 \times 10^8 \text{ m/s}}{10^8 \text{ Hz}} = 3 \text{ m}$$

and a moderate distance can include many complete waves.

Fields of a Sinusoidal Wave

Figure 32.13 shows a linearly polarized sinusoidal electromagnetic wave traveling in the $+x$-direction. The $\vec{E}$ and $\vec{B}$ vectors are shown for only a few points on the positive x-axis. Note that the electric and magnetic fields oscillate in phase: $\vec{E}$ is maximum where $\vec{B}$ is maximum and $\vec{E}$ is zero where $\vec{B}$ is zero. Note also that where $\vec{E}$ is in the $+y$-direction, $\vec{B}$ is in the $+z$-direction; where $\vec{E}$ is in the $-y$-direction, $\vec{B}$ is in the $-z$-direction. At all points the vector product $\vec{E} \times \vec{B}$ is in the direction in which the wave is propagating (the $+x$-direction). We mentioned this in Section 32.2 in the list of characteristics of electromagnetic waves.

32.13 Representation of the electric and magnetic fields as functions of x for a linearly polarized sinusoidal plane electromagnetic wave. One wavelength of the wave is shown at time $t = 0$. The fields are shown only for points along the x-axis.

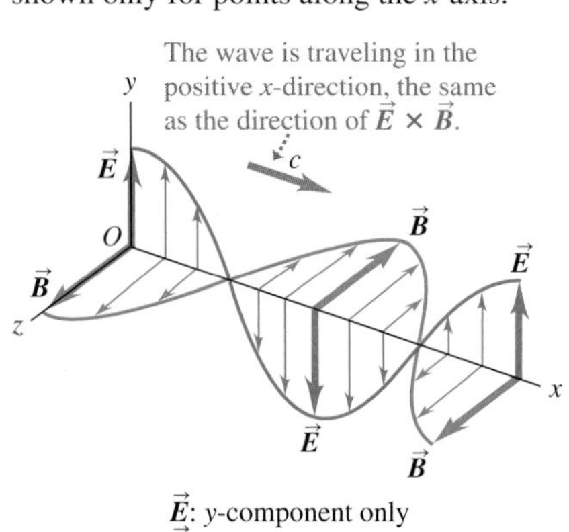
The wave is traveling in the positive x-direction, the same as the direction of $\vec{E} \times \vec{B}$.
y
c
$\vec{E}$
O
$\vec{B}$
z
$\vec{B}$
$\vec{E}$
x
$\vec{E}$
$\vec{B}$
$\vec{E}$: y-component only
$\vec{B}$: z-component only

CAUTION **In a plane wave, $\vec{E}$ and $\vec{B}$ are everywhere** Figure 32.13 may give you the erroneous impression that the electric and magnetic fields exist only along the x-axis. In fact, in a sinusoidal plane wave there are electric and magnetic fields at *all* points in space. Imagine a plane perpendicular to the x-axis (that is, parallel to the yz-plane) at a particular point, at a particular time; the fields have the same values at all points in that plane. The values are different on different planes.

We can describe electromagnetic waves by means of *wave functions,* just as we did in Section 15.3 for waves on a string. One form of the wave function for a transverse wave traveling in the $+x$-direction along a stretched string is Eq. (15.7):

$$y(x, t) = A\cos(kx - \omega t)$$

where $y(x, t)$ is the transverse displacement from its equilibrium position at time t of a point with coordinate x on the string. The quantity A is the maximum displacement, or *amplitude,* of the wave; ω is its *angular frequency,* equal to 2π times the frequency f; and k is the *wave number,* equal to $2\pi/\lambda$, where λ is the wavelength.

Let $E_y(x, t)$ and $B_z(x, t)$ represent the instantaneous values of the y-component of $\vec{E}$ and the z-component of $\vec{B}$, respectively, in Fig. 32.13, and let E_{max} and B_{max} represent the maximum values, or *amplitudes,* of these fields. The wave functions for the wave are then

$$E_y(x, t) = E_{\text{max}}\cos(kx - \omega t) \qquad B_z(x, t) = B_{\text{max}}\cos(kx - \omega t) \qquad (32.16)$$

(sinusoidal electromagnetic plane wave, propagating in $+x$-direction)

We can also write the wave functions in vector form:

$$\vec{E}(x,t) = \hat{\jmath}E_{max}\cos(kx - \omega t)$$
$$\vec{B}(x,t) = \hat{k}B_{max}\cos(kx - \omega t) \quad (32.17)$$

CAUTION The symbol k has two meanings Note the two different k's: the unit vector $\hat{k}$ in the z-direction and the wave number k. Don't get these confused!

The sine curves in Fig. 32.13 represent instantaneous values of the electric and magnetic fields as functions of x at time $t = 0$—that is, $\vec{E}(x, t = 0)$ and $\vec{B}(x, t = 0)$. As time goes by, the wave travels to the right with speed c. Equations (32.16) and (32.17) show that at any point the sinusoidal oscillations of $\vec{E}$ and $\vec{B}$ are *in phase*. From Eq. (32.4) the amplitudes must be related by

$$E_{max} = cB_{max} \quad \text{(electromagnetic wave in vacuum)} \quad (32.18)$$

These amplitude and phase relationships are also required for $E(x,t)$ and $B(x,t)$ to satisfy Eqs. (32.12) and (32.14), which came from Faraday's law and Ampere's law, respectively. Can you verify this statement? (See Problem 32.36.)

Figure 32.14 shows the electric and magnetic fields of a wave traveling in the *negative* x-direction. At points where $\vec{E}$ is in the positive y-direction, $\vec{B}$ is in the *negative* z-direction; where $\vec{E}$ is in the negative y-direction, $\vec{B}$ is in the *positive* z-direction. The wave functions for this wave are

$$E_y(x,t) = E_{max}\cos(kx + \omega t) \quad B_z(x,t) = -B_{max}\cos(kx + \omega t) \quad (32.19)$$

(sinusoidal electromagnetic plane wave, propagating in $-x$-direction)

32.14 Representation of one wavelength of a linearly polarized sinusoidal plane electromagnetic wave traveling in the negative x-direction at $t = 0$. The fields are shown only for points along the x-axis. (Compare with Fig. 32.13.)

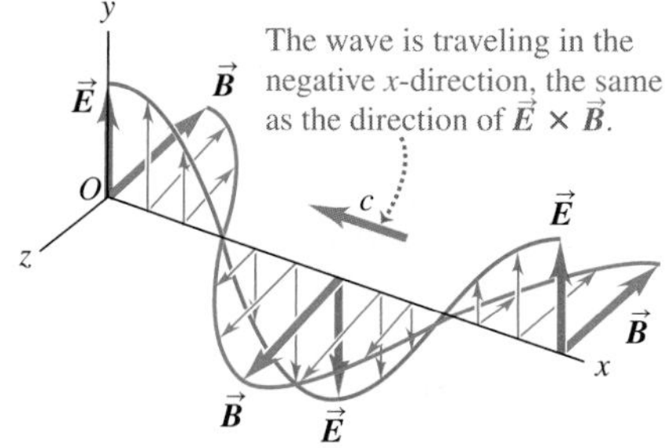

As with the wave traveling in the $+x$-direction, at any point the sinusoidal oscillations of the $\vec{E}$ and $\vec{B}$ fields are *in phase*, and the vector product $\vec{E} \times \vec{B}$ points in the direction of propagation.

The sinusoidal waves shown in Figs. 32.13 and 32.14 are both linearly polarized in the y-direction; the $\vec{E}$ field is always parallel to the y-axis. Example 32.1 concerns a wave that is linearly polarized in the z-direction.

Problem-Solving Strategy 32.1 Electromagnetic Waves

IDENTIFY *the relevant concepts:* Many of the same ideas that apply to mechanical waves (discussed in Chapters 15 and 16) also apply to electromagnetic waves. The new feature is that the wave is described by two quantities, electric field $\vec{E}$ and magnetic field $\vec{B}$, instead of by a single quantity, such as the displacement of a string.

SET UP *the problem* using the following steps:

1. Draw a diagram showing the direction of wave propagation and the directions of $\vec{E}$ and $\vec{B}$.
2. Determine the target variables.

EXECUTE *the solution* as follows:

1. For problems involving electromagnetic waves, the best approach is to concentrate on basic relationships, such as the relationship of $\vec{E}$ to $\vec{B}$ (both magnitude and direction), how the wave speed is determined, the transverse nature of the waves, and so on. Keep these relationships in mind when working through the mathematical details.
2. For sinusoidal electromagnetic waves, you need to use the language developed for sinusoidal mechanical waves in Chapters 15 and 16. Don't hesitate to go back and review that material, including the problem-solving strategies suggested in those chapters.
3. Keep in mind the basic relationships for periodic waves: $v = \lambda f$ and $\omega = vk$. For electromagnetic waves in vacuum, $v = c$. Be careful to distinguish between ordinary frequency f, usually expressed in hertz, and angular frequency $\omega = 2\pi f$, expressed in rad/s. Also remember that the wave number is $k = 2\pi/\lambda$.

EVALUATE *your answer:* Check that your result is reasonable. For electromagnetic waves in vacuum, the magnitude of the magnetic field in teslas is much smaller (by a factor of 3.00×10^8) than the magnitude of the electric field in volts per meter. If your answer suggests otherwise, you probably made an error using the relationship $E = cB$. (We'll see later in this section that the relationship between E and B is different for electromagnetic waves in a material medium.)

Example 32.1 Fields of a laser beam

A carbon dioxide laser emits a sinusoidal electromagnetic wave that travels in vacuum in the negative x-direction. The wavelength is 10.6 μm and the $\vec{E}$ field is parallel to the z-axis, with maximum magnitude of 1.5 MV/m. Write vector equations for $\vec{E}$ and $\vec{B}$ as functions of time and position.

SOLUTION

IDENTIFY: This problem concerns a sinusoidal electromagnetic wave of the sort we have described in this section.

SET UP: Equations (32.19) describe a wave traveling in the negative x-direction with $\vec{E}$ along the y-axis—that is, a wave that is linearly polarized along the y-axis. By contrast, the wave in this example is linearly polarized along the z-axis. At points where $\vec{E}$ is in the positive z-direction, $\vec{B}$ must be in the positive y-direction for the vector product $\vec{E} \times \vec{B}$ to be in the negative x-direction (the direction of propagation). Figure 32.15 shows a wave that satisfies these requirements.

EXECUTE: A possible pair of wave functions that describe the wave shown in Fig. 32.15 are

$$\vec{E}(x, t) = \hat{k}E_{max}\cos(kx + \omega t)$$
$$\vec{B}(x, t) = \hat{j}B_{max}\cos(kx + \omega t)$$

32.15 Our sketch for this problem.

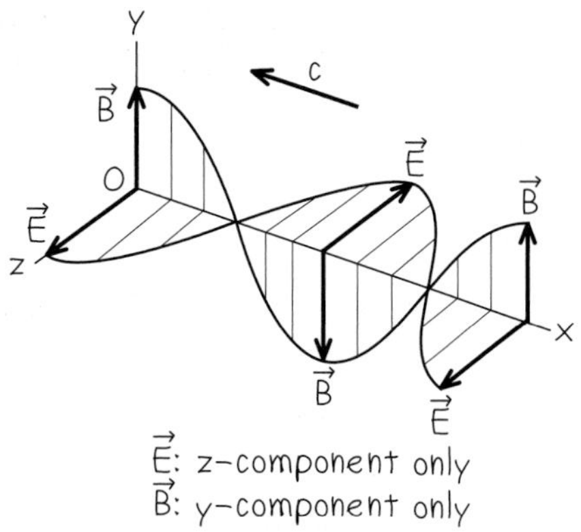

The plus sign in the arguments of the cosine functions indicates that the wave is propagating in the negative x-direction, as it should. Faraday's law requires that $E_{max} = cB_{max}$ [Eq. (32.18)], so

$$B_{max} = \frac{E_{max}}{c} = \frac{1.5 \times 10^6 \text{ V/m}}{3.0 \times 10^8 \text{ m/s}} = 5.0 \times 10^{-3}\text{ T}$$

To check unit consistency, note that 1 V = 1 Wb/s and 1 Wb/m^2 = 1 T.

We have $\lambda = 10.6 \times 10^{-6}$ m, so the wave number and angular frequency are

$$k = \frac{2\pi}{\lambda} = \frac{2\pi \text{ rad}}{10.6 \times 10^{-6}\text{ m}} = 5.93 \times 10^5 \text{ rad/m}$$
$$\omega = ck = (3.00 \times 10^8 \text{ m/s})(5.93 \times 10^5 \text{ rad/m})$$
$$= 1.78 \times 10^{14}\text{ rad/s}$$

Substituting these values into the above wave functions, we get

$$\vec{E}(x, t) = \hat{k}(1.5 \times 10^6 \text{ V/m})\cos[(5.93 \times 10^5 \text{ rad/m})x + (1.78 \times 10^{14}\text{ rad/s})t]$$
$$\vec{B}(x, t) = \hat{j}(5.0 \times 10^{-3}\text{ T})\cos[(5.93 \times 10^5 \text{ rad/m})x + (1.78 \times 10^{14}\text{ rad/s})t]$$

With these equations we can find the fields in the laser beam at any particular position and time by substituting specific values of x and t.

EVALUATE: As we expect, the magnitude B_{max} in teslas is much smaller than the magnitude E_{max} in volts per meter. To check the directions of $\vec{E}$ and $\vec{B}$, note that $\vec{E} \times \vec{B}$ is in the direction of $\hat{k} \times \hat{j} = -\hat{\imath}$. This is as it should be for a wave that propagates in the negative x-direction.

Our expressions for $\vec{E}(x, t)$ and $\vec{B}(x, t)$ are not the only possible solutions. We could always add a phase ϕ to the arguments of the cosine function, so that $kx + \omega t$ would become $kx + \omega t + \phi$. To determine the value of ϕ we would need to know $\vec{E}$ and $\vec{B}$ either as functions of x at a given time t or as functions of t at a given coordinate x. However, the statement of the problem doesn't include this information.

Electromagnetic Waves in Matter

So far, our discussion of electromagnetic waves has been restricted to waves in *vacuum.* But electromagnetic waves can also travel in *matter;* think of light traveling through air, water, or glass. In this subsection we extend our analysis to electromagnetic waves in nonconducting materials—that is, *dielectrics.*

In a dielectric the wave speed is not the same as in vacuum, and we denote it by v instead of c. Faraday's law is unaltered, but in Eq. (32.4), derived from Faraday's law, the speed c is replaced by v. In Ampere's law the displacement current is given not by $\epsilon_0\, d\Phi_E/dt$, where Φ_E is the flux of $\vec{E}$ through a surface, but by $\epsilon\, d\Phi_E/dt = K\epsilon_0\, d\Phi_E/dt$, where K is the dielectric constant and ϵ is the permittivity of the dielectric. (We introduced these quantities in Section 24.4.) Also, the constant μ_0 in Ampere's law must be replaced by $\mu = K_m\mu_0$, where K_m is the relative permeability of the dielectric and μ is its permeability (see Section 28.8). Hence Eqs. (32.4) and (32.8) are replaced by

$$E = vB \qquad \text{and} \qquad B = \epsilon\mu vE \tag{32.20}$$

Following the same procedure as for waves in vacuum, we find that the wave speed v is

$$v = \frac{1}{\sqrt{\epsilon\mu}} = \frac{1}{\sqrt{KK_m}}\frac{1}{\sqrt{\epsilon_0\mu_0}} = \frac{c}{\sqrt{KK_m}} \quad \text{(speed of electromagnetic waves in a dielectric)} \tag{32.21}$$

For most dielectrics the relative permeability K_m is very nearly equal to unity (except for insulating ferromagnetic materials). When $K_m \cong 1$,

$$v = \frac{1}{\sqrt{K}}\frac{1}{\sqrt{\epsilon_0\mu_0}} = \frac{c}{\sqrt{K}}$$

Because K is always greater than unity, the speed v of electromagnetic waves in a dielectric is always *less* than the speed c in vacuum by a factor of $1/\sqrt{K}$ (Fig. 32.16). The ratio of the speed c in vacuum to the speed v in a material is known in optics as the **index of refraction** n of the material. When $K_m \cong 1$,

$$\frac{c}{v} = n = \sqrt{KK_m} \cong \sqrt{K} \tag{32.22}$$

Usually, we can't use the values of K in Table 24.1 in this equation because those values are measured using *constant* electric fields. When the fields oscillate rapidly, there is usually not time for the re-orientating of electric dipoles that occurs with steady fields. Values of K with rapidly varying fields are usually much *smaller* than the values in the table. For example, K for water is 80.4 for steady fields but only about 1.8 in the frequency range of visible light. Thus the dielectric "constant" K is actually a function of frequency, called the *dielectric function* in more advanced treatments.

32.16 The dielectric constant K of water is about 1.8 for visible light, so the speed of visible light in water is slower than in vacuum by a factor of $1/\sqrt{K} = 1/\sqrt{1.8} = 0.75$.

Example 32.2 Electromagnetic waves in different materials

(a) While visiting a jewelry store one evening, you hold a diamond up to the light of a street lamp. The heated sodium vapor in the street lamp emits yellow light with a frequency of 5.09×10^{14} Hz. Find the wavelength in vacuum, the speed of wave propagation in diamond, and the wavelength in diamond. At this frequency, diamond has the properties $K = 5.84$ and $K_m = 1.00$. (b) A radio wave with a frequency of 90.0 MHz (in the FM radio broadcast band) passes from vacuum into an insulating ferrite (a ferromagnetic material used in computer cables to suppress radio interference). Find the wavelength in vacuum, the speed of wave propagation in the ferrite, and the wavelength in the ferrite. At this frequency, the ferrite has the properties $K = 10.0$ and $K_m = 1000$.

SOLUTION

IDENTIFY: We use the relationship among wave speed, wavelength, and frequency. We also use the relationship among the speed of electromagnetic waves in a medium and the values of dielectric constant K and relative permeability K_m for the medium.

SET UP: In each case we find the wavelength in vacuum using $c = \lambda f$. The wave speed v is given by Eq. (32.21). Once we know the value of v, we use $v = \lambda f$ to find the wavelength in the material in question.

EXECUTE: (a) The wavelength in vacuum of the sodium light is

$$\lambda_{\text{vacuum}} = \frac{c}{f} = \frac{3.00 \times 10^8 \text{ m/s}}{5.09 \times 10^{14} \text{ Hz}} = 5.89 \times 10^{-7} \text{ m} = 589 \text{ nm}$$

The wave speed in diamond is

$$v_{\text{diamond}} = \frac{c}{\sqrt{KK_m}} = \frac{3.00 \times 10^8 \text{ m/s}}{\sqrt{(5.84)(1.00)}} = 1.24 \times 10^8 \text{ m/s}$$

This is about two-fifths of the speed in vacuum. The wavelength is proportional to the wave speed and so is reduced by the same factor:

$$\lambda_{\text{diamond}} = \frac{v_{\text{diamond}}}{f} = \frac{1.24 \times 10^8 \text{ m/s}}{5.09 \times 10^{14} \text{ Hz}} = 2.44 \times 10^{-7} \text{ m} = 244 \text{ nm}$$

(b) Following the same steps as in part (a), we find that the wavelength in vacuum of the radio wave is

$$\lambda_{\text{vacuum}} = \frac{c}{f} = \frac{3.00 \times 10^8 \text{ m/s}}{90.0 \times 10^6 \text{ Hz}} = 3.33 \text{ m}$$

The wave speed in the ferrite is

$$v_{\text{ferrite}} = \frac{c}{\sqrt{KK_m}} = \frac{3.00 \times 10^8 \text{ m/s}}{\sqrt{(10.0)(1000)}} = 3.00 \times 10^6 \text{ m/s}$$

Continued

This is only 1% of the speed of light in a vacuum, so the wavelength is likewise 1% as large as the wavelength in vacuum:

$$\lambda_{\text{ferrite}} = \frac{v_{\text{ferrite}}}{f} = \frac{3.00 \times 10^9 \text{ m/s}}{90.0 \times 10^6 \text{ Hz}} = 3.33 \times 10^{-2} \text{ m} = 3.33 \text{ cm}$$

EVALUATE: The speed of light in transparent materials like diamond is typically between c and $0.2c$. As our results in part (b) show, the speed of electromagnetic waves in dense materials like ferrite can be *far* slower than in vacuum.

Test Your Understanding of Section 32.3 The first of Eqs. (32.17) gives the electric field for a plane wave as measured at points along the x-axis. For this plane wave, how does the electric field at points *off* the x-axis differ from the expression in Eqs. (32.17)? (i) The amplitude is different; (ii) the phase is different; (iii) both the amplitude and phase are different; (iv) none of these.

32.4 Energy and Momentum in Electromagnetic Waves

It is a familiar fact that energy is associated with electromagnetic waves; think of the energy in the sun's radiation. Practical applications of electromagnetic waves, such as microwave ovens, radio transmitters, and lasers for eye surgery, all make use of the energy that these waves carry. To understand how to utilize this energy, it's helpful to derive detailed relationships for the energy in an electromagnetic wave.

We begin with the expressions derived in Sections 24.3 and 30.3 for the **energy densities** in electric and magnetic fields; we suggest you review those derivations now. Equations (24.11) and (30.10) show that in a region of empty space where $\vec{E}$ and $\vec{B}$ fields are present, the total energy density u is given by

$$u = \frac{1}{2}\epsilon_0 E^2 + \frac{1}{2\mu_0}B^2 \tag{32.23}$$

where ϵ_0 and μ_0 are, respectively, the permittivity and permeability of free space. For electromagnetic waves in vacuum, the magnitudes E and B are related by

$$B = \frac{E}{c} = \sqrt{\epsilon_0 \mu_0}\,E \tag{32.24}$$

Combining Eqs. (32.23) and (32.24), we can also express the energy density u in a simple electromagnetic wave in vacuum as

$$u = \frac{1}{2}\epsilon_0 E^2 + \frac{1}{2\mu_0}(\sqrt{\epsilon_0 \mu_0}\,E)^2 = \epsilon_0 E^2 \tag{32.25}$$

This shows that in vacuum, the energy density associated with the $\vec{E}$ field in our simple wave is equal to the energy density of the $\vec{B}$ field. In general, the electric-field magnitude E is a function of position and time, as for the sinusoidal wave described by Eqs. (32.16); thus the energy density u of an electromagnetic wave, given by Eq. (32.25), also depends in general on position and time.

Electromagnetic Energy Flow and the Poynting Vector

Electromagnetic waves such as those we have described are *traveling* waves that transport energy from one region to another. For instance, in the wave described in Section 32.2 the $\vec{E}$ and $\vec{B}$ fields advance with time into regions where originally no fields were present and carry the energy density u with them as they advance. We can describe this energy transfer in terms of energy transferred *per unit time per unit cross-sectional area,* or *power per unit area,* for an area perpendicular to the direction of wave travel.

To see how the energy flow is related to the fields, consider a stationary plane, perpendicular to the x-axis, that coincides with the wave front at a certain time. In a time dt after this, the wave front moves a distance $dx = c\,dt$ to the right of the plane. Considering an area A on this stationary plane (Fig. 32.17), we note that the energy in the space to the right of this area must have passed through the area to reach the new location. The volume dV of the relevant region is the base area A times the length $c\,dt$, and the energy dU in this region is the energy density u times this volume:

$$dU = u\,dV = (\epsilon_0 E^2)(Ac\,dt)$$

This energy passes through the area A in time dt. The energy flow per unit time per unit area, which we will call S, is

$$S = \frac{1}{A}\frac{dU}{dt} = \epsilon_0 c E^2 \qquad \text{(in vacuum)} \qquad (32.26)$$

Using Eqs. (32.15) and (32.25), we can derive the alternative forms

$$S = \frac{\epsilon_0}{\sqrt{\epsilon_0\mu_0}}E^2 = \sqrt{\frac{\epsilon_0}{\mu_0}}E^2 = \frac{EB}{\mu_0} \qquad \text{(in vacuum)} \qquad (32.27)$$

The derivation of Eq. (32.27) from Eq. (32.26) is left as a problem (see Exercise 32.29). The units of S are energy per unit time per unit area, or power per unit area. The SI unit of S is $1\ \text{J/s}\cdot\text{m}^2$ or $1\ \text{W/m}^2$.

We can define a *vector* quantity that describes both the magnitude and direction of the energy flow rate:

$$\vec{S} = \frac{1}{\mu_0}\vec{E} \times \vec{B} \qquad \text{(Poynting vector in vacuum)} \qquad (32.28)$$

The vector $\vec{S}$ is called the **Poynting vector;** it was introduced by the British physicist John Poynting (1852–1914). Its direction is in the direction of propagation of the wave (Fig. 32.18). Since $\vec{E}$ and $\vec{B}$ are perpendicular, the magnitude of $\vec{S}$ is $S = EB/\mu_0$; from Eqs. (32.26) and (32.27) this is the energy flow per unit area and per unit time through a cross-sectional area perpendicular to the propagation direction. The total energy flow per unit time (power, P) out of any closed surface is the integral of $\vec{S}$ over the surface:

$$P = \oint \vec{S} \cdot d\vec{A}$$

For the sinusoidal waves studied in Section 32.3, as well as for other more complex waves, the electric and magnetic fields at any point vary with time, so the Poynting vector at any point is also a function of time. Because the frequencies of typical electromagnetic waves are very high, the time variation of the Poynting vector is so rapid that it's most appropriate to look at its *average* value. The magnitude of the average value of $\vec{S}$ at a point is called the **intensity** of the radiation at that point. The SI unit of intensity is the same as for S, $1\ \text{W/m}^2$ (watt per square meter).

Let's work out the intensity of the sinusoidal wave described by Eqs. (32.17). We first substitute $\vec{E}$ and $\vec{B}$ into Eq. (32.28):

$$\begin{aligned}\vec{S}(x,t) &= \frac{1}{\mu_0}\vec{E}(x,t) \times \vec{B}(x,t)\\ &= \frac{1}{\mu_0}[\hat{\jmath}E_{\max}\cos(kx - \omega t)] \times [\hat{k}B_{\max}\cos(kx - \omega t)]\end{aligned}$$

32.17 A wave front at a time dt after it passes through the stationary plane with area A.

At time dt, the volume between the stationary plane and the wave front contains an amount of electromagnetic energy $dU = uAc\,dt$.

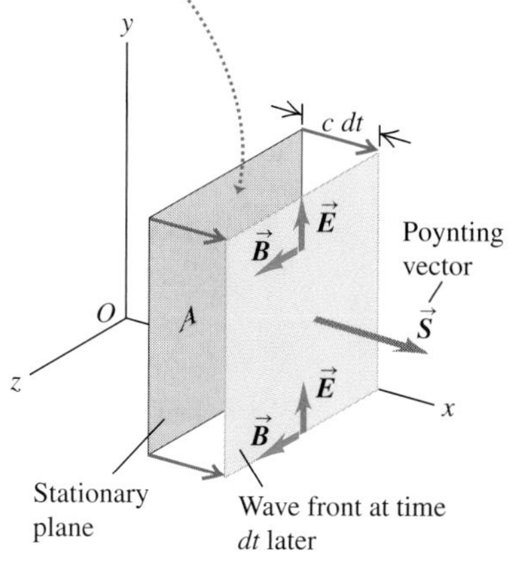

32.18 These rooftop solar panels are tilted to be face-on to the sun—that is, face-on to the Poynting vector of electromagnetic waves from the sun, so that the panels can absorb the maximum amount of wave energy.

$dV = Ac\,dt$. When we substitute this into Eq. (32.30) and rearrange, we find that the momentum flow rate per unit area is

$$\frac{1}{A}\frac{dp}{dt} = \frac{S}{c} = \frac{EB}{\mu_0 c} \quad \text{(flow rate of electromagnetic momentum)} \quad (32.31)$$

This is the momentum transferred per unit surface area per unit time. We obtain the *average* rate of momentum transfer per unit area by replacing S in Eq. (32.31) by $S_{av} = I$.

This momentum is responsible for the phenomenon of **radiation pressure.** When an electromagnetic wave is completely absorbed by a surface, the wave's momentum is also transferred to the surface. For simplicity we'll consider a surface perpendicular to the propagation direction. Using the ideas developed in Section 8.1, we see that the rate dp/dt at which momentum is transferred to the absorbing surface equals the *force* on the surface. The average force per unit area due to the wave, or *radiation pressure* p_{rad}, is the average value of dp/dt divided by the absorbing area A. (We use the subscript "rad" to distinguish pressure from momentum, for which the symbol p is also used.) From Eq. (32.31) the radiation pressure is

$$p_{rad} = \frac{S_{av}}{c} = \frac{I}{c} \quad \text{(radiation pressure, wave totally absorbed)} \quad (32.32)$$

If the wave is totally reflected, the momentum change is twice as great, and the pressure is

$$p_{rad} = \frac{2S_{av}}{c} = \frac{2I}{c} \quad \text{(radiation pressure, wave totally reflected)} \quad (32.33)$$

For example, the value of I (or S_{av}) for direct sunlight, before it passes through the earth's atmosphere, is approximately 1.4 kW/m^2. From Eq. (32.32) the corresponding average pressure on a completely absorbing surface is

$$p_{rad} = \frac{I}{c} = \frac{1.4 \times 10^3\ \text{W/m}^2}{3.0 \times 10^8\ \text{m/s}} = 4.7 \times 10^{-6}\ \text{Pa}$$

From Eq. (32.33) the average pressure on a totally *reflecting* surface is twice this: $2I/c$ or 9.4×10^{-6} Pa. These are very small pressures, of the order of 10^{-10} atm, but they can be measured with sensitive instruments.

The radiation pressure of sunlight is much greater *inside* the sun than at the earth (see Problem 32.43). Inside stars that are much more massive and luminous than the sun, radiation pressure is so great that it substantially augments the gas pressure within the star and so helps to prevent the star from collapsing under its own gravity. In some cases the radiation pressure of stars can have dramatic effects on the material surrounding the stars (Fig. 32.20).

32.20 At the center of this interstellar gas cloud is a group of intensely luminous stars that exert tremendous radiation pressure on their surroundings. Aided by a "wind" of particles emanating from the stars, over the past million years the radiation pressure has carved out a bubble within the cloud 70 light-years across.

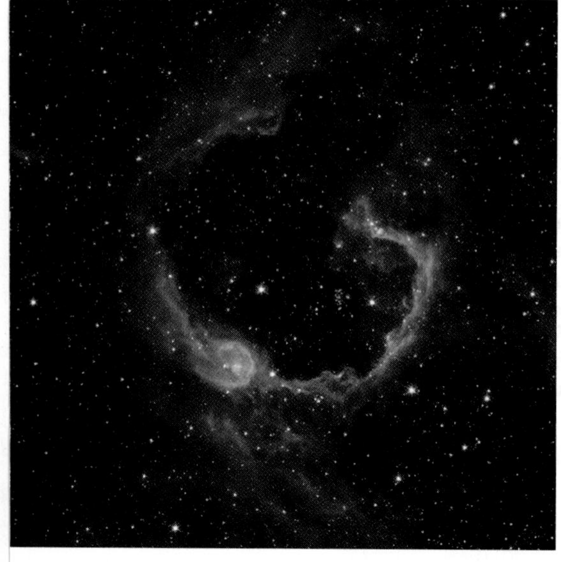

Example 32.5 Power and pressure from sunlight

An earth-orbiting satellite has solar-energy–collecting panels with a total area of 4.0 m^2 (Fig. 32.21). If the sun's radiation is perpendicular to the panels and is completely absorbed, find the average solar power absorbed and the average force associated with radiation pressure.

SOLUTION

IDENTIFY: This problem uses the relationships among intensity, power, radiation pressure, and force.

SET UP: In the above discussion we calculated the intensity I (power per unit area) of sunlight as well as the radiation pressure p_{rad} (force per unit area) of sunlight on an absorbing surface. (We calculated these values for points above the atmosphere, which is where the satellite orbits.) Multiplying each value by the area of the solar panels gives the average power absorbed and the net radiation force on the panels.

From Eq. (32.25),

$$u = \epsilon_0 E^2 = (8.85 \times 10^{-12}\ \mathrm{C^2/N \cdot m^2})(100\ \mathrm{N/C})^2$$
$$= 8.85 \times 10^{-8}\ \mathrm{N/m^2} = 8.85 \times 10^{-8}\ \mathrm{J/m^3}$$

The magnitude of the Poynting vector is

$$S = \frac{EB}{\mu_0} = \frac{(100\ \mathrm{V/m})(3.33 \times 10^{-7}\ \mathrm{T})}{4\pi \times 10^{-7}\ \mathrm{T \cdot m/A}}$$
$$= 26.5\ \mathrm{V \cdot A/m^2} = 26.5\ \mathrm{W/m^2}$$

EVALUATE: We can check our result for S by using an alternative formula from Eq. (32.26):

$$S = \epsilon_0 c E^2$$
$$= (8.85 \times 10^{-12}\ \mathrm{C^2/N \cdot m^2})(3.00 \times 10^8\ \mathrm{m/s})(100\ \mathrm{N/C})^2$$
$$= 26.5\ \mathrm{W/m^2}$$

Since $\vec{E}$ and $\vec{B}$ have the same values at all points behind the wave front, the energy density u and Poynting vector magnitude S likewise have the same value everywhere behind the wave front. In front of the wave front, $\vec{E} = \mathbf{0}$ and $\vec{B} = \mathbf{0}$ and so $u = 0$ and $S = 0$; where there are no fields, there is no field energy.

Example 32.4 Energy in a sinusoidal wave

A radio station on the surface of the earth radiates a sinusoidal wave with an average total power of 50 kW (Fig. 32.19). Assuming that the transmitter radiates equally in all directions above the ground (which is unlikely in real situations), find the amplitudes E_{max} and B_{max} detected by a satellite at a distance of 100 km from the antenna.

SOLUTION

IDENTIFY: This is a sinusoidal wave, so we use the idea that the intensity is equal to the magnitude of the average value of the Poynting vector. We are not given the value of the intensity, but we *are* given the average total power of the transmitter. We use the idea that the intensity is the same as the average power per unit area.

SET UP: Figure 32.19 shows a hemisphere of radius 100 km centered on the transmitter. We divide the average power of the transmitter by the surface area of this hemisphere to find the intensity I at this distance from the transmitter. We then use Eq. (32.29) to find the electric-field magnitude and Eq. (32.4) to find the magnetic-field magnitude.

32.19 A radio station radiates waves into the hemisphere shown.

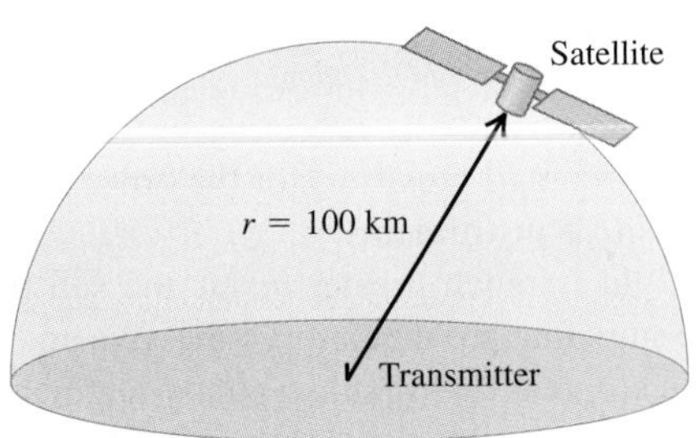

EXECUTE: The surface area of a hemisphere of radius $r = 100\ \mathrm{km} = 1.00 \times 10^5\ \mathrm{m}$ is

$$A = 2\pi R^2 = 2\pi(1.00 \times 10^5\ \mathrm{m})^2 = 6.28 \times 10^{10}\ \mathrm{m^2}$$

All the radiated power passes through this surface, so the average power per unit area (that is, the intensity) is

$$I = \frac{P}{A} = \frac{P}{2\pi R^2} = \frac{5.00 \times 10^4\ \mathrm{W}}{6.28 \times 10^{10}\ \mathrm{m^2}} = 7.96 \times 10^{-7}\ \mathrm{W/m^2}$$

From Eqs. (32.29), $I = S_{av} = E_{max}{}^2/2\mu_0 c$, so

$$E_{max} = \sqrt{2\mu_0 c S_{av}}$$
$$= \sqrt{2(4\pi \times 10^{-7}\ \mathrm{T \cdot m/A})(3.00 \times 10^8\ \mathrm{m/s})(7.96 \times 10^{-7}\ \mathrm{W/m^2})}$$
$$= 2.45 \times 10^{-2}\ \mathrm{V/m}$$

From Eq. (32.4),

$$B_{max} = \frac{E_{max}}{c} = 8.17 \times 10^{-11}\ \mathrm{T}$$

EVALUATE: Note that the magnitude of E_{max} is comparable to fields commonly seen in the laboratory, but B_{max} is extremely small in comparison to $\vec{B}$ fields we saw in previous chapters. For this reason, most detectors of electromagnetic radiation respond to the effect of the electric field, not the magnetic field. Loop radio antennas are an exception.

Electromagnetic Momentum Flow and Radiation Pressure

By using the observation that energy is required to establish electric and magnetic fields, we have shown that electromagnetic waves transport energy. It can also be shown that electromagnetic waves carry *momentum p*, with a corresponding momentum density (momentum dp per volume dV) of magnitude

$$\frac{dp}{dV} = \frac{EB}{\mu_0 c^2} = \frac{S}{c^2} \qquad (32.30)$$

This momentum is a property of the field; it is not associated with the mass of a moving particle in the usual sense.

There is also a corresponding momentum flow rate. The volume dV occupied by an electromagnetic wave (speed c) that passes through an area A in time dt is

$dV = Ac\,dt$. When we substitute this into Eq. (32.30) and rearrange, we find that the momentum flow rate per unit area is

$$\frac{1}{A}\frac{dp}{dt} = \frac{S}{c} = \frac{EB}{\mu_0 c} \quad \text{(flow rate of electromagnetic momentum)} \quad (32.31)$$

This is the momentum transferred per unit surface area per unit time. We obtain the *average* rate of momentum transfer per unit area by replacing S in Eq. (32.31) by $S_{av} = I$.

This momentum is responsible for the phenomenon of **radiation pressure.** When an electromagnetic wave is completely absorbed by a surface, the wave's momentum is also transferred to the surface. For simplicity we'll consider a surface perpendicular to the propagation direction. Using the ideas developed in Section 8.1, we see that the rate dp/dt at which momentum is transferred to the absorbing surface equals the *force* on the surface. The average force per unit area due to the wave, or *radiation pressure* p_{rad}, is the average value of dp/dt divided by the absorbing area A. (We use the subscript "rad" to distinguish pressure from momentum, for which the symbol p is also used.) From Eq. (32.31) the radiation pressure is

$$p_{rad} = \frac{S_{av}}{c} = \frac{I}{c} \quad \text{(radiation pressure, wave totally absorbed)} \quad (32.32)$$

If the wave is totally reflected, the momentum change is twice as great, and the pressure is

$$p_{rad} = \frac{2S_{av}}{c} = \frac{2I}{c} \quad \text{(radiation pressure, wave totally reflected)} \quad (32.33)$$

For example, the value of I (or S_{av}) for direct sunlight, before it passes through the earth's atmosphere, is approximately 1.4 kW/m^2. From Eq. (32.32) the corresponding average pressure on a completely absorbing surface is

$$p_{rad} = \frac{I}{c} = \frac{1.4 \times 10^3\ \text{W/m}^2}{3.0 \times 10^8\ \text{m/s}} = 4.7 \times 10^{-6}\ \text{Pa}$$

From Eq. (32.33) the average pressure on a totally *reflecting* surface is twice this: $2I/c$ or 9.4×10^{-6} Pa. These are very small pressures, of the order of 10^{-10} atm, but they can be measured with sensitive instruments.

The radiation pressure of sunlight is much greater *inside* the sun than at the earth (see Problem 32.43). Inside stars that are much more massive and luminous than the sun, radiation pressure is so great that it substantially augments the gas pressure within the star and so helps to prevent the star from collapsing under its own gravity. In some cases the radiation pressure of stars can have dramatic effects on the material surrounding the stars (Fig. 32.20).

32.20 At the center of this interstellar gas cloud is a group of intensely luminous stars that exert tremendous radiation pressure on their surroundings. Aided by a "wind" of particles emanating from the stars, over the past million years the radiation pressure has carved out a bubble within the cloud 70 light-years across.

Example 32.5 Power and pressure from sunlight

An earth-orbiting satellite has solar-energy–collecting panels with a total area of 4.0 m^2 (Fig. 32.21). If the sun's radiation is perpendicular to the panels and is completely absorbed, find the average solar power absorbed and the average force associated with radiation pressure.

SOLUTION

IDENTIFY: This problem uses the relationships among intensity, power, radiation pressure, and force.

SET UP: In the above discussion we calculated the intensity I (power per unit area) of sunlight as well as the radiation pressure p_{rad} (force per unit area) of sunlight on an absorbing surface. (We calculated these values for points above the atmosphere, which is where the satellite orbits.) Multiplying each value by the area of the solar panels gives the average power absorbed and the net radiation force on the panels.

To see how the energy flow is related to the fields, consider a stationary plane, perpendicular to the x-axis, that coincides with the wave front at a certain time. In a time dt after this, the wave front moves a distance $dx = c\,dt$ to the right of the plane. Considering an area A on this stationary plane (Fig. 32.17), we note that the energy in the space to the right of this area must have passed through the area to reach the new location. The volume dV of the relevant region is the base area A times the length $c\,dt$, and the energy dU in this region is the energy density u times this volume:

$$dU = u\,dV = (\epsilon_0 E^2)(Ac\,dt)$$

This energy passes through the area A in time dt. The energy flow per unit time per unit area, which we will call S, is

$$S = \frac{1}{A}\frac{dU}{dt} = \epsilon_0 c E^2 \qquad \text{(in vacuum)} \qquad (32.26)$$

Using Eqs. (32.15) and (32.25), we can derive the alternative forms

$$S = \frac{\epsilon_0}{\sqrt{\epsilon_0 \mu_0}}E^2 = \sqrt{\frac{\epsilon_0}{\mu_0}}E^2 = \frac{EB}{\mu_0} \qquad \text{(in vacuum)} \qquad (32.27)$$

The derivation of Eq. (32.27) from Eq. (32.26) is left as a problem (see Exercise 32.29). The units of S are energy per unit time per unit area, or power per unit area. The SI unit of S is $1\ \text{J/s}\cdot\text{m}^2$ or $1\ \text{W/m}^2$.

We can define a *vector* quantity that describes both the magnitude and direction of the energy flow rate:

$$\vec{S} = \frac{1}{\mu_0}\vec{E} \times \vec{B} \qquad \text{(Poynting vector in vacuum)} \qquad (32.28)$$

The vector $\vec{S}$ is called the **Poynting vector;** it was introduced by the British physicist John Poynting (1852–1914). Its direction is in the direction of propagation of the wave (Fig. 32.18). Since $\vec{E}$ and $\vec{B}$ are perpendicular, the magnitude of $\vec{S}$ is $S = EB/\mu_0$; from Eqs. (32.26) and (32.27) this is the energy flow per unit area and per unit time through a cross-sectional area perpendicular to the propagation direction. The total energy flow per unit time (power, P) out of any closed surface is the integral of $\vec{S}$ over the surface:

$$P = \oint \vec{S} \cdot d\vec{A}$$

For the sinusoidal waves studied in Section 32.3, as well as for other more complex waves, the electric and magnetic fields at any point vary with time, so the Poynting vector at any point is also a function of time. Because the frequencies of typical electromagnetic waves are very high, the time variation of the Poynting vector is so rapid that it's most appropriate to look at its *average* value. The magnitude of the average value of $\vec{S}$ at a point is called the **intensity** of the radiation at that point. The SI unit of intensity is the same as for S, $1\ \text{W/m}^2$ (watt per square meter).

Let's work out the intensity of the sinusoidal wave described by Eqs. (32.17). We first substitute $\vec{E}$ and $\vec{B}$ into Eq. (32.28):

$$\begin{aligned}\vec{S}(x,t) &= \frac{1}{\mu_0}\vec{E}(x,t) \times \vec{B}(x,t)\\ &= \frac{1}{\mu_0}[\hat{\jmath}E_{\text{max}}\cos(kx-\omega t)] \times [\hat{k}B_{\text{max}}\cos(kx-\omega t)]\end{aligned}$$

32.17 A wave front at a time dt after it passes through the stationary plane with area A.

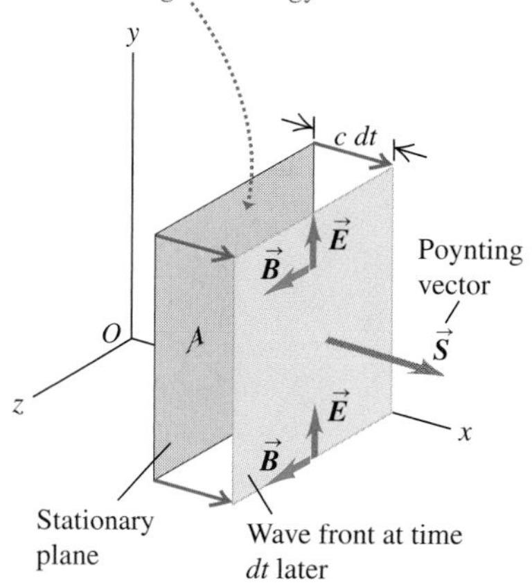

32.18 These rooftop solar panels are tilted to be face-on to the sun—that is, face-on to the Poynting vector of electromagnetic waves from the sun, so that the panels can absorb the maximum amount of wave energy.

The vector product of the unit vectors is $\hat{\jmath} \times \hat{k} = \hat{\imath}$ and $\cos^2(kx - \omega t)$ is never negative, so $\vec{S}(x, t)$ always points in the positive x-direction (the direction of wave propagation). The x-component of the Poynting vector is

$$S_x(x,t) = \frac{E_{max}B_{max}}{\mu_0}\cos^2(kx - \omega t) = \frac{E_{max}B_{max}}{2\mu_0}[1 + \cos 2(kx - \omega t)]$$

The time average value of $\cos 2(kx - \omega t)$ is zero because at any point, it is positive during one half-cycle and negative during the other half. So the average value of the Poynting vector over a full cycle is $\vec{S}_{av} = \hat{\imath}S_{av}$, where

$$S_{av} = \frac{E_{max}B_{max}}{2\mu_0}$$

That is, the magnitude of the average value of $\vec{S}$ for a sinusoidal wave (the intensity I of the wave) is $\frac{1}{2}$ the maximum value. By using the relationships $E_{max} = B_{max}c$ and $\epsilon_0\mu_0 = 1/c^2$, we can express the intensity in several equivalent forms:

$$I = S_{av} = \frac{E_{max}B_{max}}{2\mu_0} = \frac{E_{max}{}^2}{2\mu_0 c} = \frac{1}{2}\sqrt{\frac{\epsilon_0}{\mu_0}}E_{max}{}^2 = \frac{1}{2}\epsilon_0 c E_{max}{}^2 \quad \text{(intensity of a sinusoidal wave in vacuum)} \quad (32.29)$$

We invite you to verify that these expressions are all equivalent.

For a wave traveling in the $-x$-direction, represented by Eqs. (32.19), the Poynting vector is in the $-x$-direction at every point, but its magnitude is the same as for a wave traveling in the $+x$-direction. Verifying these statements is left to you (see Exercise 32.24).

CAUTION **Poynting vector vs. intensity** At any point x, the magnitude of the Poynting vector varies with time. Hence, the *instantaneous* rate at which electromagnetic energy in a sinusoidal plane wave arrives at a surface is not constant. This may seem to contradict everyday experience; the light from the sun, a light bulb, or the laser in a grocery-store scanner appears steady and unvarying in strength. In fact the Poynting vector from these sources *does* vary in time, but the variation isn't noticeable because the oscillation frequency is so high (around 5×10^{14} Hz for visible light). All that you sense is the *average* rate at which energy reaches your eye, which is why we commonly use intensity (the average value of S) to describe the strength of electromagnetic radiation.

Throughout this discussion we have considered only electromagnetic waves propagating in vacuum. If the waves are traveling in a dielectric medium, however, the expressions for energy density [Eq. (32.23)], the Poynting vector [Eq. (32.28)], and the intensity of a sinusoidal wave [Eq. (32.29)] must be modified. It turns out that the required modifications are quite simple: Just replace ϵ_0 with the permittivity ϵ of the dielectric, replace μ_0 with the permeability μ of the dielectric, and replace c with the speed v of electromagnetic waves in the dielectric. Remarkably, the energy densities in the $\vec{E}$ and $\vec{B}$ fields are equal even in a dielectric.

Example 32.3 Energy in a nonsinusoidal wave

For the nonsinusoidal wave described in Section 32.2, suppose that $E = 100\ \text{V/m} = 100\ \text{N/C}$. Find the value of B, the energy density, and the rate of energy flow per unit area S.

SOLUTION

IDENTIFY: In the wave described in Section 32.2, the electric and magnetic fields are uniform behind the wave front. Hence the target variables B, u, and S must also be uniform behind the wave front.

SET UP: Given the value of the magnitude E, we calculate the magnitude B using Eq. (32.4), the energy density u using Eq. 32.25), and the rate of energy flow per unit area S using Eq. (32.27). (Note that we cannot use Eq. (32.29), which applies to sinusoidal waves only.)

EXECUTE: From Eq. (32.4),

$$B = \frac{E}{c} = \frac{100\ \text{V/m}}{3.00 \times 10^8\ \text{m/s}} = 3.33 \times 10^{-7}\ \text{T}$$

EXECUTE: The intensity I (power per unit area) is $1.4 \times 10^3\ \text{W/m}^2$. Although the light from the sun is not a simple sinusoidal wave, we can still use the relationship that the average power P is the intensity I times the area A:

$$P = IA = (1.4 \times 10^3\ \text{W/m}^2)(4.0\ \text{m}^2) = 5.6 \times 10^3\ \text{W} = 5.6\ \text{kW}$$

The radiation pressure of sunlight on an absorbing surface is $p_{rad} = 4.7 \times 10^{-6}\ \text{Pa} = 4.7 \times 10^{-6}\ \text{N/m}^2$. The total force F is the pressure p_{rad} times the area A:

$$F = p_{rad}A = (4.7 \times 10^{-6}\ \text{N/m}^2)(4.0\ \text{m}^2) = 1.9 \times 10^{-5}\ \text{N}$$

32.21 Solar panels on a satellite.

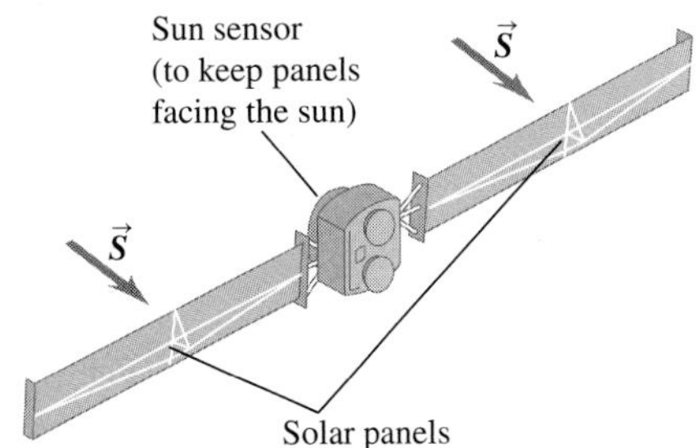

EVALUATE: The absorbed power is quite substantial. Part of it can be used to power the equipment aboard the satellite; the rest goes into heating the panels, either directly or due to inefficiencies in the photocells contained in the panels.

The total radiation force is comparable to the weight (on earth) of a single grain of salt. Over time, however, this small force can have a noticeable effect on the orbit of a satellite like that in Fig. 32.21, and so radiation pressure must be taken into account.

Test Your Understanding of Section 32.4 Figure 32.13 shows one wavelength of a sinusoidal electromagnetic wave at time $t = 0$. For which of the following four values of x is (a) the energy density a maximum; (b) the energy density a minimum; (c) the magnitude of the instantaneous (not average) Poynting vector a maximum; (d) the magnitude of the instantaneous (not average) Poynting vector a minimum? (i) $x = 0$; (ii) $x = \lambda/4$; (iii) $x = \lambda/2$; (iv) $x = 3\lambda/4$.

32.5 Standing Electromagnetic Waves

Electromagnetic waves can be *reflected;* the surface of a conductor (like a polished sheet of metal) or of a dielectric (such as a sheet of glass) can serve as a reflector. The superposition principle holds for electromagnetic waves just as for electric and magnetic fields. The superposition of an incident wave and a reflected wave forms a **standing wave.** The situation is analogous to standing waves on a stretched string, discussed in Section 15.7; you should review that discussion.

Suppose a sheet of a perfect conductor (zero resistivity) is placed in the yz-plane of Fig. 32.22 and a linearly polarized electromagnetic wave, traveling in the negative x-direction, strikes it. As we discussed in Section 23.4, $\vec{E}$ cannot have a component parallel to the surface of a perfect conductor. Therefore in the present situation, $\vec{E}$ must be zero everywhere in the yz-plane. The electric field of the *incident* electromagnetic wave is *not* zero at all times in the yz-plane. But this incident wave induces oscillating currents on the surface of the conductor, and these currents give rise to an additional electric field. The *net* electric field, which is the vector sum of this field and the incident $\vec{E}$, *is* zero everywhere inside and on the surface of the conductor.

The currents induced on the surface of the conductor also produce a *reflected* wave that travels out from the plane in the $+x$-direction. Suppose the incident wave is described by the wave functions of Eqs. (32.19) (a sinusoidal wave traveling in the $-x$-direction) and the reflected wave by the negative of Eqs. (32.16) (a sinusoidal wave traveling in the $+x$-direction). We take the *negative* of the wave given by Eqs. (32.16) so that the incident and reflected electric fields cancel at $x = 0$ (the plane of the conductor, where the total electric field must be zero). The superposition principle states that the total $\vec{E}$ field at any point is the vector sum of the $\vec{E}$ fields of the incident and reflected waves, and similarly for the $\vec{B}$ field. Therefore the wave functions for the superposition of the two waves are

$$E_y(x,t) = E_{max}[\cos(kx + \omega t) - \cos(kx - \omega t)]$$
$$B_z(x,t) = B_{max}[-\cos(kx + \omega t) - \cos(kx - \omega t)]$$

32.22 Representation of the electric and magnetic fields of a linearly polarized electromagnetic standing wave when $\omega t = 3\pi/4$ rad. In any plane perpendicular to the x-axis, E is maximum (an antinode) where B is zero (a node), and vice versa. As time elapses, the pattern does *not* move along the x-axis; instead, at every point the $\vec{E}$ and $\vec{B}$ vectors simply oscillate.

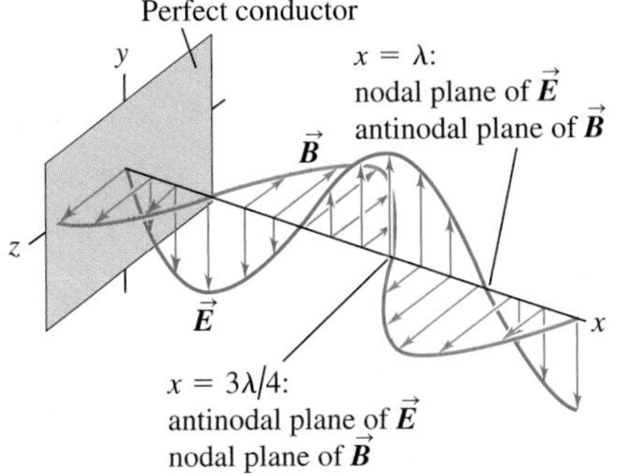

We can expand and simplify these expressions, using the identities

$$\cos(A \pm B) = \cos A \cos B \mp \sin A \sin B$$

The results are

$$E_y(x, t) = -2E_{max} \sin kx \sin \omega t \tag{32.34}$$

$$B_z(x, t) = -2B_{max} \cos kx \cos \omega t \tag{32.35}$$

Equation (32.34) is analogous to Eq. (15.28) for a stretched string. We see that at $x = 0$ the electric field $E_y(x = 0, t)$ is *always* zero; this is required by the nature of the ideal conductor, which plays the same role as a fixed point at the end of a string. Furthermore, $E_y(x, t)$ is zero at *all* times at points in those planes perpendicular to the x-axis for which $\sin kx = 0$; that is, $kx = 0, \pi, 2\pi, \ldots$. Since $k = 2\pi/\lambda$, the positions of these planes are

$$x = 0, \frac{\lambda}{2}, \lambda, \frac{3\lambda}{2}, \ldots \qquad \text{(nodal planes of } \vec{E}\text{)} \tag{32.36}$$

These planes are called the **nodal planes** of the $\vec{E}$ field; they are the equivalent of the nodes, or nodal points, of a standing wave on a string. Midway between any two adjacent nodal planes is a plane on which $\sin kx = \pm 1$; on each such plane, the magnitude of $E(x, t)$ equals the maximum possible value of $2E_{max}$ twice per oscillation cycle. These are the **antinodal planes** of $\vec{E}$, corresponding to the antinodes of waves on a string.

The total magnetic field is zero at all times at points in planes on which $\cos kx = 0$. This occurs where

$$x = \frac{\lambda}{4}, \frac{3\lambda}{4}, \frac{5\lambda}{4}, \ldots \qquad \text{(nodal planes of } \vec{B}\text{)} \tag{32.37}$$

These are the nodal planes of the $\vec{B}$ field; there is an antinodal plane of $\vec{B}$ midway between any two adjacent nodal planes.

Figure 32.22 shows a standing-wave pattern at one instant of time. The magnetic field is *not* zero at the conducting surface $(x = 0)$, and there is no reason it should be. The surface currents that must be present to make $\vec{E}$ exactly zero at the surface cause magnetic fields at the surface. The nodal planes of each field are separated by one half-wavelength. The nodal planes of one field are mid-way between those of the other; hence the nodes of $\vec{E}$ coincide with antinodes of $\vec{B}$, and conversely. Compare this situation to the distinction between pressure nodes and displacement nodes in Section 16.4.

The total electric field is a *sine* function of t, and the total magnetic field is a *cosine* function of t. The sinusoidal variations of the two fields are therefore 90° out of phase at each point. At times when $\sin \omega t = 0$, the electric field is zero *everywhere,* and the magnetic field is maximum. When $\cos \omega t = 0$, the magnetic field is zero everywhere, and the electric field is maximum. This is in contrast to a wave traveling in one direction, as described by Eqs. (32.16) or (32.19) separately, in which the sinusoidal variations of $\vec{E}$ and $\vec{B}$ at any particular point are *in phase.* It is interesting to check that Eqs. (32.34) and (32.35) satisfy the wave equation, Eq. (32.15). They also satisfy Eqs. (32.12) and (32.14) (the equivalents of Faraday's and Ampere's laws); we leave the proofs of these statements to you (see Exercise 32.34).

Standing Waves in a Cavity

Pursuing the stretched-string analogy, we may now insert a second conducting plane, parallel to the first and a distance L from it, along the $+x$-axis. The cavity between the two planes is analogous to a stretched string held at the points $x = 0$ and $x = L$. Both conducting planes must be nodal planes for $\vec{E}$; a standing wave can exist only when the second plane is placed at one of the positions where $E(x, t) = 0$. That is, for a standing wave to exist, L must be an integer multiple of $\lambda/2$. The wavelengths that satisfy this condition are

$$\lambda_n = \frac{2L}{n} \quad (n = 1, 2, 3, \ldots) \tag{32.38}$$

The corresponding frequencies are

$$f_n = \frac{c}{\lambda_n} = n\frac{c}{2L} \quad (n = 1, 2, 3, \ldots) \tag{32.39}$$

Thus there is a set of *normal modes,* each with a characteristic frequency, wave shape, and node pattern (Fig. 32.23). By measuring the node positions, we can measure the wavelength. If the frequency is known, the wave speed can be determined. This technique was first used by Hertz in the 1880s in his pioneering investigations of electromagnetic waves.

A laser has two mirrors; a standing wave is set up in the cavity between the mirrors. One of the mirrors has a small, partially transmitting aperture that allows waves to escape from this end of the laser.

Conducting surfaces are not the only reflectors of electromagnetic waves. Reflections also occur at an interface between two insulating materials with different dielectric or magnetic properties. The mechanical analog is a junction of two strings with equal tension but different linear mass density. In general, a wave incident on such a boundary surface is partly transmitted into the second material and partly reflected back into the first. For example, light is transmitted through a glass window, but its surfaces also reflect light.

32.23 A typical microwave oven sets up a standing electromagnetic wave with $\lambda = 12.2$ cm, a wavelength that is strongly absorbed by the water in food. Because the wave has nodes spaced $\lambda/2 = 6.1$ cm apart, the food must be rotated while cooking. Otherwise, the portion that lies at a node—where the electric-field amplitude is zero—will remain cold.

Example 32.6 Intensity in a standing wave

Calculate the intensity of the standing wave discussed in this section.

SOLUTION

IDENTIFY: The intensity I of the wave is the average value S_{av} of the magnitude of the Poynting vector.

SET UP: We first find the instantaneous value of the Poynting vector and then average it over a whole number of cycles of the wave to determine I.

EXECUTE: Using the wave functions of Eqs. (32.34) and (32.35) in the expression for the Poynting vector $\vec{S}$, Eq. (32.28), we find

$$\begin{aligned}\vec{S}(x, t) &= \frac{1}{\mu_0}\vec{E}(x, t) \times \vec{B}(x, t)\\ &= \frac{1}{\mu_0}[-2\hat{\jmath}E_{max}\sin kx\cos\omega t] \times [-2\hat{k}B_{max}\cos kx\sin\omega t]\\ &= \hat{\imath}\frac{E_{max}B_{max}}{\mu_0}(2\sin kx\cos kx)(2\sin\omega t\cos\omega t)\\ &= \hat{\imath}S_x(x, t)\end{aligned}$$

Using the identity $\sin 2A = 2\sin A\cos A$, we can rewrite $S_x(x, t)$ as

$$S_x(x, t) = \frac{E_{max}B_{max}\sin 2kx\sin 2\omega t}{\mu_0}$$

The average value of a sine function over any whole number of cycles is zero. Thus *the time average of $\vec{S}$ at any point is zero;* $I = S_{av} = 0$.

EVALUATE: This is just what we should expect. We formed our standing wave by superposing two waves with the same frequency and amplitude, traveling in opposite directions. All the energy transferred by one wave is completely cancelled by an equal amount transferred in the opposite direction by the other wave. When we use waves to transmit power, it is important to avoid reflections that give rise to standing waves.

Example 32.7 Standing waves in a cavity

Electromagnetic standing waves are set up in a cavity with two parallel, highly conducting walls separated by 1.50 cm. (a) Calculate the longest wavelength and lowest frequency of electromagnetic standing waves between the walls. (b) For this longest-wavelength standing wave, where in the cavity does $\vec{E}$ have maximum magnitude? Where is $\vec{E}$ zero? Where does $\vec{B}$ have maximum magnitude? Where is $\vec{B}$ zero?

SOLUTION

IDENTIFY: This problem uses the idea that only certain electromagnetic normal modes are possible for electromagnetic waves in a cavity, just as only certain normal modes are possible for standing waves on a string.

SET UP: The longest possible wavelength and lowest possible frequency correspond to the $n = 1$ mode in Eqs. (32.38) and (32.39). We use these equations to determine the values of λ and f. Equations (32.36) and (32.37) then tell us the locations of the nodal planes of $\vec{E}$ and $\vec{B}$; the antinodal planes of each field are midway between adjacent nodal planes.

EXECUTE: (a) From Eq. (32.38), the $n = 1$ wavelength is

$$\lambda_1 = 2L = 2(1.50\text{ cm}) = 3.00\text{ cm}$$

The corresponding frequency is given by Eq. (32.38) with $n = 1$:

$$f_1 = \frac{c}{2L} = \frac{3.00 \times 10^8\text{ m/s}}{2(1.50 \times 10^{-2}\text{ m})} = 1.00 \times 10^{10}\text{ Hz} = 10\text{ GHz}$$

(b) With $n = 1$ there is a single half-wavelength between the walls. The electric field has nodal planes $(\vec{E} = \mathbf{0})$ at the walls and an antinodal plane (where the maximum magnitude of $\vec{E}$ occurs) midway between them. The magnetic field has *antinodal* planes at the walls and a nodal plane midway between them.

EVALUATE: One application of standing waves of this kind is to produce an oscillating $\vec{E}$ field of definite frequency, which in turn is used to probe the behavior of a small sample of material placed inside the cavity. To subject the sample to the strongest possible field, the sample should be placed near the center of the cavity, at the antinode of $\vec{E}$.

Test Your Understanding of Section 32.5 In the standing wave described in Example 32.7, is there any point in the cavity where the energy density is zero at all times? If so, where? If not, why not?

CHAPTER 32 SUMMARY

Maxwell's equations and electromagnetic waves: Maxwell's equations predict the existence of electromagnetic waves that propagate in vacuum at the speed of light c. The electromagnetic spectrum covers frequencies from at least 1 to 10^{24} Hz and a correspondingly broad range of wavelengths. Visible light, with wavelengths from 400 to 700 nm, is only a very small part of this spectrum. In a plane wave, $\vec{E}$ and $\vec{B}$ are uniform over any plane perpendicular to the propagation direction. Faraday's law and Ampere's law both give relationships between the magnitudes of $\vec{E}$ and $\vec{B}$; requiring both of these relationships to be satisfied gives an expression for c in terms of ϵ_0 and μ_0. Electromagnetic waves are transverse; the $\vec{E}$ and $\vec{B}$ fields are perpendicular to the direction of propagation and to each other. The direction of propagation is the direction of $\vec{E} \times \vec{B}$.

$$E = cB \quad (32.4)$$

$$B = \epsilon_0 \mu_0 c E \quad (32.8)$$

$$c = \frac{1}{\sqrt{\epsilon_0 \mu_0}} \quad (32.9)$$

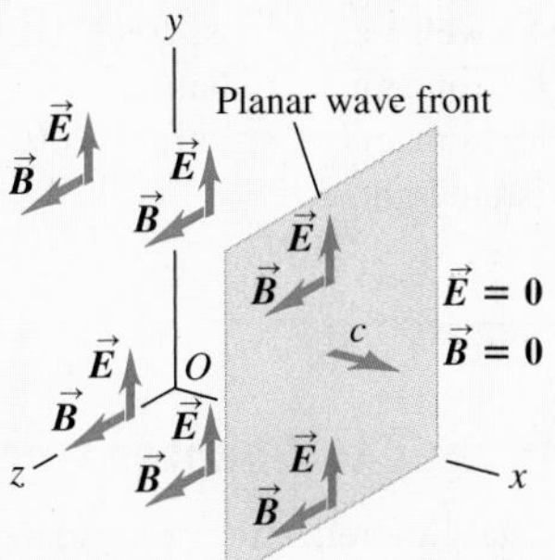

Sinusoidal electromagnetic waves: Equations (32.17) and (32.18) describe a sinusoidal plane electromagnetic wave traveling in vacuum in the $+x$-direction. (See Example 32.1.)

$$\vec{E}(x, t) = \hat{\jmath} E_{max} \cos(kx - \omega t)$$
$$\vec{B}(x, t) = \hat{k} B_{max} \cos(kx - \omega t) \quad (32.17)$$

$$E_{max} = cB_{max} \quad (32.18)$$

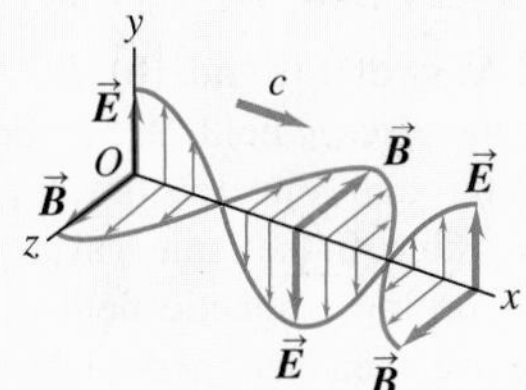

Electromagnetic waves in matter: When an electromagnetic wave travels through a dielectric, the wave speed v is less than the speed of light in vacuum c. (See Example 32.2.)

$$v = \frac{1}{\sqrt{\epsilon\mu}} = \frac{1}{\sqrt{KK_m}} \frac{1}{\sqrt{\epsilon_0\mu_0}} = \frac{c}{\sqrt{KK_m}} \quad (32.21)$$

Energy and momentum in electromagnetic waves: The energy flow rate (power per unit area) in an electromagnetic wave in a vacuum is given by the Poynting vector $\vec{S}$. The magnitude of the time-averaged value of the Poynting vector is called the intensity I of the wave. Electromagnetic waves also carry momentum. When an electromagnetic wave strikes a surface, it exerts a radiation pressure p_{rad}. If the surface is perpendicular to the wave propagation direction and is totally absorbing, $p_{rad} = I/c$; if the surface is a perfect reflector, $p_{rad} = 2I/c$. (See Examples 32.3–32.5.)

$$\vec{S} = \frac{1}{\mu_0} \vec{E} \times \vec{B} \quad (32.28)$$

$$I = S_{av} = \frac{E_{max} B_{max}}{2\mu_0} = \frac{E_{max}^2}{2\mu_0 c} = \frac{1}{2}\sqrt{\frac{\epsilon_0}{\mu_0}} E_{max}^2 = \frac{1}{2}\epsilon_0 c E_{max}^2 \quad (32.29)$$

$$\frac{1}{A}\frac{dp}{dt} = \frac{S}{c} = \frac{EB}{\mu_0 c} \quad (32.31)$$

(flow rate of electromagnetic momentum)

Standing electromagnetic waves: If a perfect reflecting surface is placed at $x = 0$, the incident and reflected waves form a standing wave. Nodal planes for $\vec{E}$ occur at $kx = 0, \pi, 2\pi, \ldots$, and nodal planes for $\vec{B}$ at $kx = \pi/2, 3\pi/2, 5\pi/2, \ldots$. At each point, the sinusoidal variations of $\vec{E}$ and $\vec{B}$ with time are 90° out of phase. (See Examples 32.6 and 32.7.)

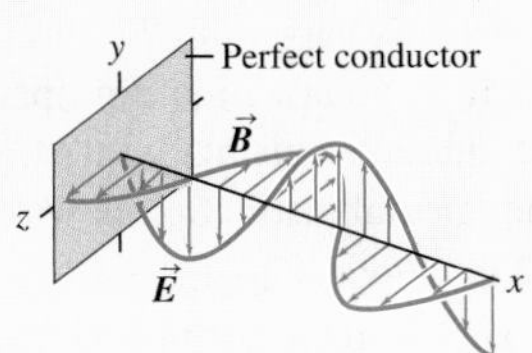

Key Terms

electromagnetic wave, *1093*
Maxwell's equations, *1093*
electromagnetic radiation, *1094*
electromagnetic spectrum, *1095*
visible light, *1095*
plane wave, *1097*
transverse wave, *1097*
polarization, *1099*
linearly polarized, *1099*
wave equation, *1100*
index of refraction, *1105*
energy density, *1106*
Poynting vector, *1107*
intensity, *1107*
radiation pressure, *1110*
standing wave, *1111*
nodal plane, *1112*
antinodal plane, *1112*

Answer to Chapter Opening Question ?

Metals are reflective because they are good conductors of electricity. When an electromagnetic wave strikes a conductor, the electric field of the wave sets up currents on the conductor surface that generate a reflected wave. For a perfect conductor, this reflected wave is just as intense as the incident wave. Tarnished metals are less shiny because their surface is oxidized and less conductive; polishing the metal removes the oxide and exposes the conducting metal.

Answers to Test Your Understanding Questions

32.1 **Answers: (a) no, (b) no** A purely electric wave would have a varying electric field. Such a field necessarily generates a magnetic field through Ampere's law, Eq. (29.20), so a purely electric wave is impossible. In the same way, a purely magnetic wave is impossible: The varying magnetic field in such a wave would automatically give rise to an electric field through Faraday's law, Eq. (29.21).

32.2 **Answers: (a) positive y-direction, (b) negative x-direction, (c) positive y-direction** You can verify these answers by using the right-hand rule to show that $\vec{E} \times \vec{B}$ in each case is in the direction of propagation, or by using the rule shown in Fig. 32.9.

32.3 **Answer: (iv)** In an ideal electromagnetic plane wave, at any instant the fields are the same anywhere in a plane perpendicular to the direction of propagation. The plane wave described by Eqs. (32.17) is propagating in the x-direction, so the fields depend on the coordinate x and time t but do *not* depend on the coordinates y and z.

32.4 **Answers: (a) (i) and (iii), (b) (ii) and (iv), (c) (i) and (iii), (d) (ii) and (iv)** Both the energy density u and the Poynting vector magnitude S are maximum where the $\vec{E}$ and $\vec{B}$ fields have their maximum magnitudes. (The direction of the fields doesn't matter.) From Fig. 32.13, this occurs at $x = 0$ and $x = \lambda/2$. Both u and S have a minimum value of zero; that occurs where $\vec{E}$ and $\vec{B}$ are both zero. From Fig. 32.13, this occurs at $x = \lambda/4$ and $x = 3\lambda/4$.

32.5 **Answer: no** There are places where $\vec{E} = \mathbf{0}$ at all times (at the walls) and the electric energy density $\frac{1}{2}\epsilon_0 E^2$ is always zero. There are also places where $\vec{B} = \mathbf{0}$ at all times (on the plane midway between the walls) and the magnetic energy density $B^2/2\mu_0$ is always zero. However, there are *no* locations where both $\vec{E}$ and $\vec{B}$ are always zero. Hence the energy density at any point in the standing wave is always nonzero.

PROBLEMS

For instructor-assigned homework, go to www.masteringphysics.com 

Discussion Questions

Q32.1. By measuring the electric and magnetic fields at a point in space where there is an electromagnetic wave, can you determine the direction from which the wave came? Explain.

Q32.2. According to Ampere's law, is it possible to have both a conduction current and a displacement current at the same time? Is it possible for the effects of the two kinds of current to cancel each other exactly so that *no* magnetic field is produced? Explain.

Q32.3. Give several examples of electromagnetic waves that are encountered in everyday life. How are they all alike? How do they differ?

Q32.4. Sometimes neon signs located near a powerful radio station are seen to glow faintly at night, even though they are not turned on. What is happening?

Q32.5. Is polarization a property of all electromagnetic waves, or is it unique to visible light? Can sound waves be polarized? What fundamental distinction in wave properties is involved? Explain.

Q32.6. Suppose that a positive point charge q is initially at rest on the x-axis, in the path of the electromagnetic plane wave described in Section 32.2. Will the charge move after the wave front reaches it? If not, why not? If the charge does move, describe its motion qualitatively. (Remember that $\vec{E}$ and $\vec{B}$ have the same value at all points behind the wave front.)

Q32.7. The light beam from a searchlight may have an electric-field magnitude of 1000 V/m, corresponding to a potential difference of 1500 V between the head and feet of a 1.5-m-tall person on whom the light shines. Does this cause the person to feel a strong electric shock? Why or why not?

Q32.8. For a certain sinusoidal wave of intensity I, the amplitude of the magnetic field is B. What would be the amplitude (in terms of B) in a similar wave of twice the intensity?

Q32.9. The magnetic-field amplitude of the electromagnetic wave from the laser described in Example 32.1 (Section 32.3) is about 100 times greater than the earth's magnetic field. If you illuminate a compass with the light from this laser, would you expect the compass to deflect? Why or why not?

Q32.10. Most automobiles have vertical antennas for receiving radio broadcasts. Explain what this tells you about the direction of polarization of $\vec{E}$ in the radio waves used in broadcasting.

Q32.11. If a light beam carries momentum, should a person holding a flashlight feel a recoil analogous to the recoil of a rifle when it is fired? Why is this recoil not actually observed?

Q32.12. A light source radiates a sinusoidal electromagnetic wave uniformly in all directions. This wave exerts an average pressure p on a perfectly reflecting surface a distance R away from it. What average pressure (in terms of p) would this wave exert on a perfectly absorbing surface that was twice as far from the source?

Q32.13. Does an electromagnetic *standing* wave have energy? Does it have momentum? Are your answers to these questions the same as for a *traveling* wave? Why or why not?

Q32.14. When driving on the upper level of the Bay Bridge, westbound from Oakland to San Francisco, you can easily pick up a number of radio stations on your car radio. But when driving eastbound on the lower level of the bridge, which has steel girders on either side to support the upper level, the radio reception is much worse. Why is there a difference?

Exercises

Section 32.2 Plane Electromagnetic Waves and the Speed of Light

32.1. (a) How much time does it take light to travel from the moon to the earth, a distance of 384,000 km? (b) Light from the star Sirius takes 8.61 years to reach the earth. What is the distance from earth to Sirius in kilometers?

32.2. TV Ghosting. In a TV picture, ghost images are formed when the signal from the transmitter travels to the receiver both directly and indirectly after reflection from a building or other large metallic mass. In a 25-inch set, the ghost is about 1.0 cm to the right of the principal image if the reflected signal arrives 0.60 μs after the principal signal. In this case, what is the difference in path lengths for the two signals?

32.3. For an electromagnetic wave propagating in air, determine the frequency of a wave with a wavelength of (a) 5.0 km; (b) 5.0 m; (c) 5.0 μm; (d) 5.0 nm.

32.4. Ultraviolet Radiation. There are two categories of ultraviolet light. Ultraviolet A (UVA) has a wavelength ranging from 320 nm to 400 nm. It is not so harmful to the skin and is necessary for the production of vitamin D. UVB, with a wavelength between 280 nm and 320 nm, is much more dangerous because it causes skin cancer. (a) Find the frequency ranges of UVA and UVB. (b) What are the ranges of the wave numbers for UVA and UVB?

Section 32.3 Sinusoidal Electromagnetic Waves

32.5. A sinusoidal electromagnetic wave having a magnetic field of amplitude 1.25 μT and a wavelength of 432 nm is traveling in the $+x$-direction through empty space. (a) What is the frequency of this wave? (b) What is the amplitude of the associated electric field? (c) Write the equations for the electric and magnetic fields as functions of x and t in the form of Eqs. (32.17).

32.6. An electromagnetic wave of wavelength 435 nm is traveling in vacuum in the $-z$-direction The electric field has amplitude 2.70×10^{-3} V/m and is parallel to the x-axis. What are (a) the frequency and (b) the magnetic-field amplitude? (c) Write the vector equations for $\vec{E}(z, t)$ and $\vec{B}(z, t)$.

32.7. A sinusoidal electromagnetic wave of frequency 6.10×10^{14} Hz travels in vacuum in the $+z$-direction. The $\vec{B}$-field is parallel to the y-axis and has amplitude 5.80×10^{-4} T. Write the vector equations for $\vec{E}(z, t)$ and $\vec{B}(z, t)$.

32.8. The electric field of a sinusoidal electromagnetic wave obeys the equation $E = -(375 \text{ V/m})\sin[(5.97 \times 10^{15} \text{ rad/s})t + (1.99 \times 10^{7} \text{ rad/m})x]$. (a) What are the amplitudes of the electric and magnetic fields of this wave? (b) What are the frequency, wavelength, and period of the wave? Is this light visible to humans? (c) What is the speed of the wave?

32.9. An electromagnetic wave has an electric field given by $\vec{E}(y, t) = -(3.10 \times 10^{5} \text{ V/m})\hat{k}\sin[ky - (12.65 \times 10^{12} \text{ rad/s})t]$. (a) In which direction is the wave traveling? (b) What is the wavelength of the wave? (c) Write the vector equation for $\vec{B}(y, t)$.

32.10. An electromagnetic wave has a magnetic field given by $\vec{B}(x, t) = (8.25 \times 10^{-9} \text{ T})\hat{\jmath}\sin[(1.38 \times 10^{4} \text{ rad/m})x + \omega t]$. (a) In which direction is the wave traveling? (b) What is the frequency f of the wave? (c) Write the vector equation for $\vec{E}(x, t)$.

32.11. Radio station WCCO in Minneapolis broadcasts at a frequency of 830 kHz. At a point some distance from the transmitter, the magnetic-field amplitude of the electromagnetic wave from WCCO is 4.82×10^{-11} T. Calculate (a) the wavelength; (b) the wave number; (c) the angular frequency; (d) the electric-field amplitude.

32.12. The electric-field amplitude near a certain radio transmitter is 3.85×10^{-3} V/m What is the amplitude of $\vec{B}$? How does this compare in magnitude with the earth's field?

32.13. An electromagnetic wave with frequency 5.70×10^{14} Hz propagates with a speed of 2.17×10^{8} m/s in a certain piece of glass. Find (a) the wavelength of the wave in the glass; (b) the wavelength of a wave of the same frequency propagating in air; (c) the index of refraction n of the glass for an electromagnetic wave with this frequency; (d) the dielectric constant for glass at this frequency, assuming that the relative permeability is unity.

32.14. An electromagnetic wave with frequency 65.0 Hz travels in an insulating magnetic material that has dielectric constant 3.64 and relative permeability 5.18 at this frequency. The electric field has amplitude 7.20×10^{-3} V/m. (a) What is the speed of propagation of the wave? (b) What is the wavelength of the wave? (c) What is the amplitude of the magnetic field? (d) What is the intensity of the wave?

Section 32.4 Energy and Momentum in Electromagnetic Waves

32.15. Fields from a Light Bulb. We can reasonably model a 75-W incandescent light-bulb as a sphere 6.0 cm in diameter. Typically, only about 5% of the energy goes to visible light; the rest goes largely to nonvisible infrared radiation. (a) What is the visible-light intensity (in W/m^2) at the surface of the bulb? (b) What are the amplitudes of the electric and magnetic fields at this surface, for a sinusoidal wave with this intensity?

32.16. Consider each of the following electric and magnetic-field orientations. In each case, what is the direction of propagation of the wave? (a) $\vec{E} = E\hat{\imath}$, $\vec{B} = -B\hat{\jmath}$; (b) $\vec{E} = E\hat{\jmath}$, $\vec{B} = B\hat{\imath}$; (c) $\vec{E} = -E\hat{k}$, $\vec{B} = -B\hat{\imath}$; (d) $\vec{E} = E\hat{\imath}$, $\vec{B} = -B\hat{k}$.

32.17. A sinusoidal electromagnetic wave is propagating in a vacuum in the $+z$-direction. If at a particular instant and at a certain point in space the electric field is in the $+x$-direction and has magnitude 4.00 V/m, what are the magnitude and direction of the magnetic field of the wave at this same point in space and instant in time?

32.18. A sinusoidal electromagnetic wave from a radio station passes perpendicularly through an open window that has area 0.500 m^2. At the window, the electric field of the wave has rms value 0.0200 V/m. How much energy does this wave carry through the window during a 30.0-s commercial?

32.19. Testing a Space Radio Transmitter. You are a NASA mission specialist on your first flight aboard the space shuttle. Thanks to your extensive training in physics, you have been assigned to evaluate the performance of a new radio transmitter on board the International Space Station (ISS). Perched on the shuttle's movable arm, you aim a sensitive detector at the ISS, which is 2.5 km away. You find that the electric-field amplitude of the radio waves coming from the ISS transmitter is 0.090 V/m and that the frequency of the waves is 244 MHz. Find the following: (a) the intensity of the radio wave at your location; (b) the magnetic-field amplitude of the wave at your location; (c) the total power output of the ISS radio transmitter. (d) What assumptions, if any, did you make in your calculations?

32.20. The intensity of a cylindrical laser beam is 0.800 W/m^2. The cross-sectional area of the beam is $3.0 \times 10^{-4}\ \text{m}^2$ and the intensity is uniform across the cross section of the beam. (a) What is the average power output of the laser? (b) What is the rms value of the electric field in the beam?

32.21. A space probe 2.0×10^{10} m from a star measures the total intensity of electromagnetic radiation from the star to be $5.0 \times 10^3\ \text{W/m}^2$. If the star radiates uniformly in all directions, what is its total average power output?

32.22. A sinusoidal electromagnetic wave emitted by a cellular phone has a wavelength of 35.4 cm and an electric-field amplitude of 5.40×10^{-2} V/m at a distance of 250 m from the antenna. Calculate (a) the frequency of the wave; (b) the magnetic-field amplitude; (c) the intensity of the wave.

32.23. A monochromatic light source with power output 60.0 W radiates light of wavelength 700 nm uniformly in all directions. Calculate E_{max} and B_{max} for the 700-nm light at a distance of 5.00 m from the source.

32.24. For the electromagnetic wave represented by Eq. (32.19), show that the Poynting vector (a) is in the same direction as the propagation of the wave and (b) has average magnitude given by Eqs. (32.29).

32.25. An intense light source radiates uniformly in all directions. At a distance of 5.0 m from the source, the radiation pressure on a perfectly absorbing surface is 9.0×10^{-6} Pa. What is the total average power output of the source?

32.26. Television Broadcasting. Public television station KQED in San Francisco broadcasts a sinusoidal radio signal at a power of 316 kW. Assume that the wave spreads out uniformly into a hemisphere above the ground. At a home 5.00 km away from the antenna, (a) what average pressure does this wave exert on a totally reflecting surface, (b) what are the amplitudes of the electric and magnetic fields of the wave, and (c) what is the average density of the energy this wave carries? (d) For the energy density in part (c), what percentage is due to the electric field and what percentage is due to the magnetic field?

32.27. If the intensity of direct sunlight at a point on the earth's surface is 0.78 kW/m^2, find (a) the average momentum density (momentum per unit volume) in the sunlight and (b) the average momentum flow rate in the sunlight.

32.28. In the 25-ft Space Simulator facility at NASA's Jet Propulsion Laboratory, a bank of overhead arc lamps can produce light of intensity 2500 W/m^2 at the floor of the facility. (This simulates the intensity of sunlight near the planet Venus.) Find the average radiation pressure (in pascals and in atmospheres) on (a) a totally absorbing section of the floor and (b) a totally reflecting section of the floor. (c) Find the average momentum density (momentum per unit volume) in the light at the floor.

32.29. Verify that all the expressions in Eqs. (32.27) are equivalent to Eq. (32.26).

Section 32.5 Standing Electromagnetic Waves

32.30. An electromagnetic standing wave in air of frequency 750 MHz is set up between two conducting planes 80.0 cm apart. At which positions between the planes could a point charge be placed at rest so that it would *remain* at rest? Explain.

32.31. A standing electromagnetic wave in a certain material has frequency 2.20×10^{10} Hz. The nodal planes of $\vec{B}$ are 3.55 mm apart. Find (a) the wavelength of the wave in this material; (b) the distance between adjacent nodal planes of the $\vec{E}$ field; (c) the speed of propagation of the wave.

32.32. An electromagnetic standing wave in air has frequency 75.0 MHz. (a) What is the distance between nodal planes of the $\vec{E}$ field? (b) What is the distance between a nodal plane of $\vec{E}$ and the closest nodal plane of $\vec{B}$?

32.33. An electromagnetic standing wave in a certain material has frequency 1.20×10^{10} Hz and speed of propagation 2.10×10^8 m/s. (a) What is the distance between a nodal plane of $\vec{B}$ and the closest antinodal plane of $\vec{B}$? (b) What is the distance between an antinodal plane of $\vec{E}$ and the closest antinodal plane of $\vec{B}$? (c) What is the distance between a nodal plane of $\vec{E}$ and the closest nodal plane of $\vec{B}$?

32.34. Show that the electric and magnetic fields for standing waves given by Eqs. (32.34) and (32.35) (a) satisfy the wave equation, Eq. (32.15), and (b) satisfy Eqs. (32.12) and (32.14).

32.35. Microwave Oven. The microwaves in a certain microwave oven have a wavelength of 12.2 cm. (a) How wide must this oven be so that it will contain five antinodal planes of the electric field along its width in the standing wave pattern? (b) What is the frequency of these microwaves? (c) Suppose a manufacturing error occurred and the oven was made 5.0 cm longer than specified in part (a). In this case, what would have to be the frequency of the microwaves for there still to be five antinodal planes of the electric field along the width of the oven?

Problems

32.36. Consider a sinusoidal electromagnetic wave with fields $\vec{E} = E_{max}\hat{\jmath}\sin(kx - \omega t)$ and $\vec{B} = B_{max}\hat{k}\sin(kx - \omega t + \phi)$, with $-\pi \le \phi \le \pi$. Show that if $\vec{E}$ and $\vec{B}$ are to satisfy Eqs. (32.12) and (32.14), then $E_{max} = cB_{max}$ and $\phi = 0$. (The result $\phi = 0$ means the $\vec{E}$ and $\vec{B}$ fields oscillate in phase.)

32.37. Show that the *magnetic* field $B_z(x, t)$ in a plane electromagnetic wave propagating in the $+x$-direction must satisfy Eq. (32.15). (*Hint:* Take the partial derivative of Eq. (32.12) with respect to t and the partial derivative of Eq. (32.14) with respect to x. Then combine the results.)

32.38. For a sinusoidal electromagnetic wave in vacuum, such as that described by Eq. (32.16), show that the *average* energy density in the electric field is the same as that in the magnetic field.

32.39. A satellite 575 km above the earth's surface transmits sinusoidal electromagnetic waves of frequency 92.4 MHz uniformly in all directions, with a power of 25.0 kW. (a) What is the intensity of these waves as they reach a receiver at the surface of the earth directly below the satellite? (b) What are the amplitudes of the electric and magnetic fields at the receiver? (c) If the receiver has a totally absorbing panel measuring 15.0 cm by 40.0 cm oriented with its plane perpendicular to the direction the waves travel, what average force do these waves exert on the panel? Is this force large enough to cause significant effects?

32.40. A plane sinusoidal electromagnetic wave in air has a wavelength of 3.84 cm and an $\vec{E}$-field amplitude of 1.35 V/m. (a) What is the frequency? (b) What is the $\vec{B}$-field amplitude? (c) What is the intensity? (d) What average force does this radiation exert on a totally absorbing surface with area 0.240 m^2 perpendicular to the direction of propagation?

32.41. A small helium-neon laser emits red visible light with a power of 3.20 mW in a beam that has a diameter of 2.50 mm. (a) What are the amplitudes of the electric and magnetic fields of the light? (b) What are the average energy densities associated with the electric field and with the magnetic field? (c) What is the total energy contained in a 1.00-m length of the beam?

32.42. Consider a plane electromagnetic wave such as that shown in Fig. 32.5, but in which $\vec{E}$ and $\vec{B}$ also have components in the x-direction (along the direction of wave propagation). Use Gauss's law for electric and magnetic fields to show that the components E_x and B_x must both be equal to zero so that the fields $\vec{E}$ and $\vec{B}$ are both transverse. (*Hint:* Use a Gaussian surface like that shown in Fig. 32.6. Of the two faces parallel to the yz-plane, choose one to be to the left of the wave front and the other to be to the right of the wave front.)

32.43. The sun emits energy in the form of electromagnetic waves at a rate of 3.9×10^{26} W. This energy is produced by nuclear reactions deep in the sun's interior. (a) Find the intensity of electromagnetic radiation and the radiation pressure on an absorbing object at the surface of the sun (radius $r = R = 6.96 \times 10^5$ km) and at $r = R/2$, in the sun's interior. Ignore any scattering of the waves as they move radially outward from the center of the sun. Compare to the values given in Section 32.4 for sunlight just before it enters the earth's atmosphere. (b) The gas pressure at the sun's surface is about 1.0×10^4 Pa; at $r = R/2$, the gas pressure is calculated from solar models to be about 4.7×10^{13} Pa Comparing with your results in part (a), would you expect that radiation pressure is an important factor in determining the structure of the sun? Why or why not?

32.44. It has been proposed to place solar-power-collecting satellites in earth orbit. The power they collect would be beamed down to the earth as microwave radiation. For a microwave beam with a cross-sectional area of 36.0 m^2 and a total power of 2.80 kW at the earth's surface, what is the amplitude of the electric field of the beam at the earth's surface?

32.45. Two square reflectors, each 1.50 cm on a side and of mass 4.00 g, are located at opposite ends of a thin, extremely light, 1.00-m rod that can rotate without friction and in a vacuum about an axle perpendicular to it through its center (Fig. 32.24). These reflectors are small enough to be treated as point masses in moment-of-inertia calculations. Both reflectors are illuminated on one face by a sinusoidal light wave having an electric field of amplitude 1.25 N/C that falls uniformly on both surfaces and always strikes them perpendicular to the plane of their surfaces. One reflector is covered with a perfectly absorbing coating, and the other is covered with a perfectly reflecting coating. What is the angular acceleration of this device?

Figure 32.24 Problem 32.45.

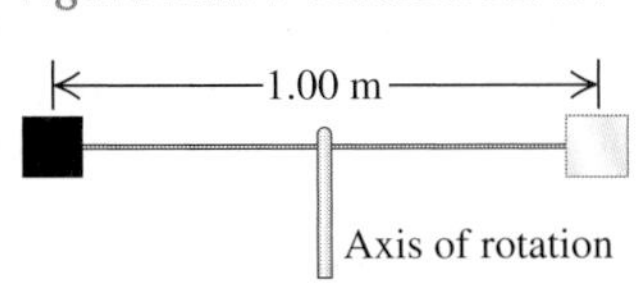

32.46. The plane of a flat surface is perpendicular to the propagation direction of an electromagnetic wave of intensity I. The surface absorbs a fraction w of the incident intensity, where $0 \leq w \leq 1$, and reflects the rest. (a) Show that the radiation pressure on the surface equals $(2 - w)I/c$. (b) Show that this expression gives the correct results for a surface that is (i) totally absorbing and (ii) totally reflective. (c) For an incident intensity of 1.40 kW/m^2, what is the radiation pressure for 90% absorption? For 90% reflection?

32.47. A cylindrical conductor with a circular cross section has a radius a and a resistivity ρ and carries a constant current I. (a) What are the magnitude and direction of the electric-field vector $\vec{E}$ at a point just inside the wire at a distance a from the axis? (b) What are the magnitude and direction of the magnetic-field vector $\vec{B}$ at the same point? (c) What are the magnitude and direction of the Poynting vector $\vec{S}$ at the same point? (The direction of $\vec{S}$ is the direction in which electromagnetic energy flows into or out of the conductor.) (d) Use the result in part (c) to find the rate of flow of energy into the volume occupied by a length l of the conductor. (*Hint:* Integrate $\vec{S}$ over the surface of this volume.) Compare your result to the rate of generation of thermal energy in the same volume. Discuss why the energy dissipated in a current-carrying conductor, due to its resistance, can be thought of as entering through the cylindrical sides of the conductor.

32.48. A source of sinusoidal electromagnetic waves radiates uniformly in all directions. At 10.0 m from this source, the amplitude of the electric field is measured to be 1.50 N/C. What is the electric-field amplitude at a distance of 20.0 cm from the source?

32.49. A circular loop of wire can be used as a radio antenna. If a 18.0-cm-diameter antenna is located 2.50 km from a 95.0-MHz source with a total power of 55.0 kW, what is the maximum emf induced in the loop? (Assume that the plane of the antenna loop is perpendicular to the direction of the radiation's magnetic field and that the source radiates uniformly in all directions.)

32.50. In a certain experiment, a radio transmitter emits sinusoidal electromagnetic waves of frequency 110.0 MHz in opposite directions inside a narrow cavity with reflectors at both ends, causing a standing wave pattern to occur. (a) How far apart are the nodal planes of the magnetic field? (b) If the standing wave pattern is determined to be in its eighth harmonic, how long is the cavity?

32.51. Flashlight to the Rescue. You are the sole crew member of the interplanetary spaceship *T:1339 Vorga,* which makes regular cargo runs between the earth and the mining colonies in the asteroid belt. You are working outside the ship one day while at a distance of 2.0 AU from the sun. [1 AU (astronomical unit) is the average distance from the earth to the sun, 149,600,000 km.] Unfortunately, you lose contact with the ship's hull and begin to drift away into space. You use your spacesuit's rockets to try to push yourself back toward the ship, but they run out of fuel and stop working before you can return to the ship. You find yourself in an awkward position, floating 16.0 m from the spaceship with zero velocity relative to it. Fortunately, you are carrying a 200-W flashlight. You turn on the flashlight and use its beam as a "light rocket" to push yourself back toward the ship. (a) If you, your spacesuit, and the flashlight have a combined mass of 150 kg, how long will it take you to get back to the ship? (b) Is there another way you could use the flashlight to accomplish the same job of returning you to the ship?

32.52. The 19th-century inventor Nikola Tesla proposed to transmit electric power via sinusoidal electromagnetic waves. Suppose power is to be transmitted in a beam of cross-sectional area 100 m^2. What electric- and magnetic-field amplitudes are required to transmit an amount of power comparable to that handled by modern transmission lines (that carry voltages and currents of the order of 500 kV and 1000 A)?

32.53. Global Positioning System (GPS). The GPS network consists of 24 satellites, each of which makes two orbits around the earth per day. Each satellite transmits a 50.0-W (or even less) sinusoidal electromagnetic signal at two frequencies, one of which is 1575.42 MHz. Assume that a satellite transmits half of its power at each frequency and that the waves travel uniformly in a downward hemisphere. (a) What average intensity does a GPS receiver on the ground, directly below the satellite, receive? (*Hint:* First use Newton's laws to find the altitude of the satellite.) (b) What are the amplitudes of the electric and magnetic fields at the GPS receiver in part (a), and how long does it take the signal to reach the receiver? (c) If the receiver is a square panel 1.50 cm on a side that absorbs all of the beam, what average pressure does the signal exert on it? (d) What wavelength must the receiver be tuned to?

32.54. NASA is giving serious consideration to the concept of *solar sailing.* A solar sailcraft uses a large, low-mass sail and the energy and momentum of sunlight for propulsion. (a) Should the sail be absorbing or reflective? Why? (b) The total power output of the sun is 3.9×10^{26} W. How large a sail is necessary to propel a 10,000-kg spacecraft against the gravitational force of the sun? Express your result in square kilometers. (c) Explain why your answer to part (b) is independent of the distance from the sun.

32.55. Interplanetary space contains many small particles referred to as *interplanetary dust.* Radiation pressure from the sun sets a lower limit on the size of such dust particles. To see the origin of this limit, consider a spherical dust particle of radius R and mass density ρ. (a) Write an expression for the gravitational force exerted on this particle by the sun (mass M) when the particle is a distance r from the sun. (b) Let L represent the luminosity of the sun, equal to the rate at which it emits energy in electromagnetic radiation. Find the force exerted on the (totally absorbing) particle due to solar radiation pressure, remembering that the intensity of the sun's radiation also depends on the distance r. The relevant area is the cross-sectional area of the particle, *not* the total surface area of the particle. As part of your answer, explain why this is so. (c) The mass density of a typical interplanetary dust particle is about 3000 kg/m^3. Find the particle radius R such that the gravitational and radiation forces acting on the particle are equal in magnitude. The luminosity of the sun is 3.9×10^{26} W. Does your answer depend on the distance of the particle from the sun? Why or why not? (d) Explain why dust particles with a radius less than that found in part (c) are unlikely to be found in the solar system. [*Hint:* Construct the ratio of the two force expressions found in parts (a) and (b).]

Challenge Problems

32.56. The Classical Hydrogen Atom. The electron in a hydrogen atom can be considered to be in a circular orbit with a radius of 0.0529 nm and a kinetic energy of 13.6 eV. If the electron behaved classically, how much energy would it radiate per second (see Challenge Problem 32.57)? What does this tell you about the use of classical physics in describing the atom?

32.57. Electromagnetic radiation is emitted by accelerating charges. The rate at which energy is emitted from an accelerating charge that has charge q and acceleration a is given by

$$\frac{dE}{dt} = \frac{q^2 a^2}{6\pi\epsilon_0 c^3}$$

where c is the speed of light. (a) Verify that this equation is dimensionally correct. (b) If a proton with a kinetic energy of 6.0 MeV is traveling in a particle accelerator in a circular orbit of radius 0.750 m, what fraction of its energy does it radiate per second? (c) Consider an electron orbiting with the same speed and radius. What fraction of its energy does it radiate per second?

32.58. Electromagnetic waves propagate much differently in *conductors* than they do in dielectrics or in vacuum. If the resistivity of the conductor is sufficiently low (that is, if it is a sufficiently good conductor), the oscillating electric field of the wave gives rise to an oscillating conduction current that is much larger than the displacement current. In this case, the wave equation for an electric field $\vec{E}(x, t) = E_y(x, t)\hat{\jmath}$ propagating in the $+x$-direction within a conductor is

$$\frac{\partial^2 E_y(x, t)}{\partial x^2} = \frac{\mu}{\rho}\frac{\partial E_y(x, t)}{\partial t}$$

where μ is the permeability of the conductor and ρ is its resistivity. (a) A solution to this wave equation is

$$E_y(x, t) = E_{\max} e^{-k_C x} \sin(k_C x - \omega t)$$

where $k_C = \sqrt{\omega\mu/2\rho}$. Verify this by substituting $E_y(x, t)$ into the above wave equation. (b) The exponential term shows that the electric field decreases in amplitude as it propagates. Explain why this happens. (*Hint:* The field does work to move charges within the conductor. The current of these moving charges causes i^2R heating within the conductor, raising its temperature. Where does the energy to do this come from?). (c) Show that the electric-field amplitude decreases by a factor of $1/e$ in a distance $1/k_C = \sqrt{2\rho/\omega\mu}$, and calculate this distance for a radio wave with frequency $f = 1.0$ MHz in copper (resistivity $1.72 \times 10^{-8}\ \Omega \cdot \text{m}$; permeability $\mu = \mu_0$). Since this distance is so short, electromagnetic waves of this frequency can hardly propagate at all into copper. Instead, they are reflected at the surface of the metal. This is why radio waves cannot penetrate through copper or other metals, and why radio reception is poor inside a metal structure.

THE NATURE AND PROPAGATION OF LIGHT

33

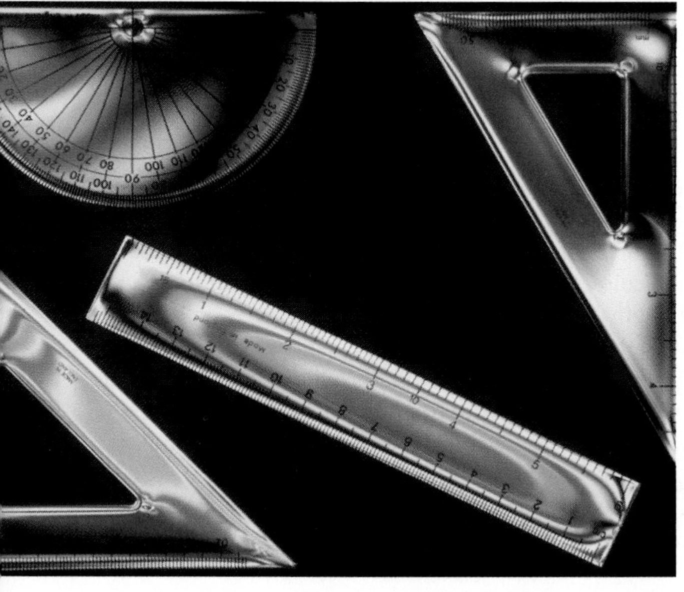

?These drafting tools are made of clear plastic, but a rainbow of colors appears when they are placed between two special filters called polarizers. How does this cause the colors?

LEARNING GOALS

By studying this chapter, you will learn:

- What light rays are, and how they are related to wave fronts.
- The laws that govern the reflection and refraction of light.
- The circumstances under which light is totally reflected at an interface.
- How to make polarized light out of ordinary light.
- How Huygens's principle helps us analyze reflection and refraction.

Blue lakes, ochre deserts, green forests, and multicolored rainbows can be enjoyed by anyone who has eyes with which to see them. But by studying the branch of physics called **optics,** which deals with the behavior of light and other electromagnetic waves, we can reach a deeper appreciation of the visible world. A knowledge of the properties of light allows us to understand the blue color of the sky and the design of optical devices such as telescopes, microscopes, cameras, eyeglasses, and the human eye. The same basic principles of optics also lie at the heart of modern developments such as the laser, optical fibers, holograms, optical computers, and new techniques in medical imaging.

The importance of optics to physics, and to science and engineering in general, is so great that we will devote the next four chapters to its study. In this chapter we begin with a study of the laws of reflection and refraction and the concepts of dispersion, polarization, and scattering of light. Along the way we compare the various possible descriptions of light in terms of particles, rays, or waves, and we introduce Huygens's principle, an important link that connects the ray and wave viewpoints. In Chapter 34 we'll use the ray description of light to understand how mirrors and lenses work, and we'll see how mirrors and lenses are used in optical instruments such as cameras, microscopes, and telescopes. We'll explore the wave characteristics of light further in Chapters 35 and 36.

33.1 The Nature of Light

Until the time of Isaac Newton (1642–1727), most scientists thought that light consisted of streams of particles (called *corpuscles*) emitted by light sources. Galileo and others tried (unsuccessfully) to measure the speed of light. Around

1665, evidence of *wave* properties of light began to be discovered. By the early 19th century, evidence that light is a wave had grown very persuasive.

In 1873, James Clerk Maxwell predicted the existence of electromagnetic waves and calculated their speed of propagation, as we learned in Chapter 32. This development, along with the experimental work of Heinrich Hertz starting in 1887, showed conclusively that light is indeed an electromagnetic wave.

The Two Personalities of Light

The wave picture of light is not the whole story, however. Several effects associated with emission and absorption of light reveal a particle aspect, in that the energy carried by light waves is packaged in discrete bundles called *photons* or *quanta.* These apparently contradictory wave and particle properties have been reconciled since 1930 with the development of quantum electrodynamics, a comprehensive theory that includes *both* wave and particle properties. The *propagation* of light is best described by a wave model, but understanding emission and absorption requires a particle approach.

33.1 An electric heating element emits primarily infrared radiation. But if its temperature is high enough, it also emits a discernible amount of visible light.

The fundamental sources of all electromagnetic radiation are electric charges in accelerated motion. All bodies emit electromagnetic radiation as a result of thermal motion of their molecules; this radiation, called *thermal radiation,* is a mixture of different wavelengths. At sufficiently high temperatures, all matter emits enough visible light to be self-luminous; a very hot body appears "red-hot" (Fig. 33.1) or "white-hot." Thus hot matter in any form is a light source. Familiar examples are a candle flame, hot coals in a campfire, the coils in an electric room heater, and an incandescent lamp filament (which usually operates at a temperature of about 3000°C).

Light is also produced during electrical discharges through ionized gases. The bluish light of mercury-arc lamps, the orange-yellow of sodium-vapor lamps, and the various colors of "neon" signs are familiar. A variation of the mercury-arc lamp is the *fluorescent* lamp (see Fig. 30.7). This light source uses a material called a *phosphor* to convert the ultraviolet radiation from a mercury arc into visible light. This conversion makes fluorescent lamps more efficient than incandescent lamps in transforming electrical energy into light.

33.2 Ophthalmic surgeons use lasers for repairing detached retinas and for cauterizing blood vessels in retinopathy. Pulses of blue-green light from an argon laser are ideal for this purpose, since they pass harmlessly through the transparent part of the eye but are absorbed by red pigments in the retina.

A light source that has attained prominence in the last forty years is the *laser.* In most light sources, light is emitted independently by different atoms within the source; in a laser, by contrast, atoms are induced to emit light in a cooperative, coherent fashion. The result is a very narrow beam of radiation that can be enormously intense and that is much more nearly *monochromatic,* or single-frequency, than light from any other source. Lasers are used by physicians for microsurgery, in CD players and computers to scan the information encoded on a compact disc or CD-ROM, in industry to cut through steel and to fuse high-melting-point materials, and in many other applications (Fig. 33.2).

No matter what its source, electromagnetic radiation travels in vacuum at the same speed. As we saw in Sections 1.3 and 32.1, the speed of light in vacuum is defined to be

$$c = 2.99792458 \times 10^8 \text{ m/s}$$

or 3.00×10^8 m/s to three significant figures. The duration of one second is defined by the cesium clock (see Section 1.3), so one meter is defined to be the distance that light travels in 1/299,792,458 s.

Waves, Wave Fronts, and Rays

We often use the concept of a **wave front** to describe wave propagation. We introduced this concept in Section 32.2 to describe the leading edge of a wave. More generally, we define a wave front as *the locus of all adjacent points at which the phase of vibration of a physical quantity associated with the wave is the same.* That is, at any instant, all points on a wave front are at the same part of the cycle of their variation.

When we drop a pebble into a calm pool, the expanding circles formed by the wave crests, as well as the circles formed by the wave troughs between them, are wave fronts. Similarly, when sound waves spread out in still air from a pointlike source, or when electromagnetic radiation spreads out from a pointlike emitter, any spherical surface that is concentric with the source is a wave front, as shown in Fig. 33.3. In diagrams of wave motion we usually draw only parts of a few wave fronts, often choosing consecutive wave fronts that have the same phase and thus are one wavelength apart, such as crests of water waves. Similarly, a diagram for sound waves might show only the "pressure crests," the surfaces over which the pressure is maximum, and a diagram for electromagnetic waves might show only the "crests" on which the electric or magnetic field is maximum.

We will often use diagrams that show the shapes of the wave fronts or their cross sections in some reference plane. For example, when electromagnetic waves are radiated by a small light source, we can represent the wave fronts as spherical surfaces concentric with the source or, as in Fig. 33.4a, by the circular intersections of these surfaces with the plane of the diagram. Far away from the source, where the radii of the spheres have become very large, a section of a spherical surface can be considered as a plane, and we have a *plane* wave like those discussed in Sections 32.2 and 32.3 (Fig, 33.4b).

To describe the directions in which light propagates, it's often convenient to represent a light wave by **rays** rather than by wave fronts. Rays were used to describe light long before its wave nature was firmly established. In a particle theory of light, rays are the paths of the particles. From the wave viewpoint *a ray is an imaginary line along the direction of travel of the wave.* In Fig. 33.4a the rays are the radii of the spherical wave fronts, and in Fig. 33.4b they are straight lines perpendicular to the wave fronts. When waves travel in a homogeneous isotropic material (a material with the same properties in all regions and in all directions), the rays are always straight lines normal to the wave fronts. At a boundary surface between two materials, such as the surface of a glass plate in air, the wave speed and the direction of a ray may change, but the ray segments in the air and in the glass are straight lines.

The next several chapters will give you many opportunities to see the interplay of the ray, wave, and particle descriptions of light. The branch of optics for which the ray description is adequate is called **geometric optics;** the branch dealing specifically with wave behavior is called **physical optics.** This chapter and the following one are concerned mostly with geometric optics. In Chapters 35 and 36 we will study wave phenomena and physical optics.

Test Your Understanding of Section 33.1 Some crystals are *not* isotropic: Light travels through the crystal at a higher speed in some directions than in others. In a crystal in which light travels at the same speed in the x- and z-directions but at a faster speed in the y-direction, what would be the shape of the wave fronts produced by a light source at the origin? (i) spherical, like those shown in Fig. 33.3; (ii) ellipsoidal, flattened along the y-axis; (iii) ellipsoidal, stretched out along the y-axis.

33.2 Reflection and Refraction

In this section we'll use the *ray* model of light to explore two of the most important aspects of light propagation: **reflection** and **refraction.** When a light wave strikes a smooth interface separating two transparent materials (such as air and glass or water and glass), the wave is in general partly *reflected* and partly *refracted* (transmitted) into the second material, as shown in Fig. 33.5a. For example, when you look into a restaurant window from the street, you see a reflection of the street scene, but a person inside the restaurant can look out through the window at the same scene as light reaches him by refraction.

33.3 Spherical wave fronts of sound spread out uniformly in all directions from a point source in a motionless medium, such as still air, that has the same properties in all regions and in all directions. Electromagnetic waves in vacuum also spread out as shown here.

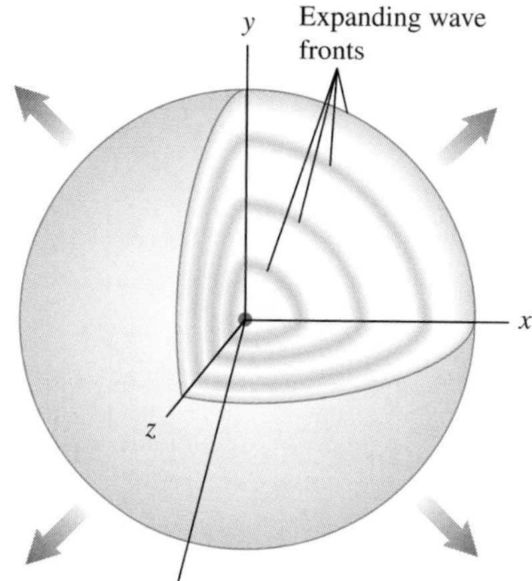
y
Expanding wave fronts
x
z
Point sound source producing spherical sound waves (alternating compressions and rarefactions of air)

33.4 Wave fronts (blue) and rays (purple).

(a)

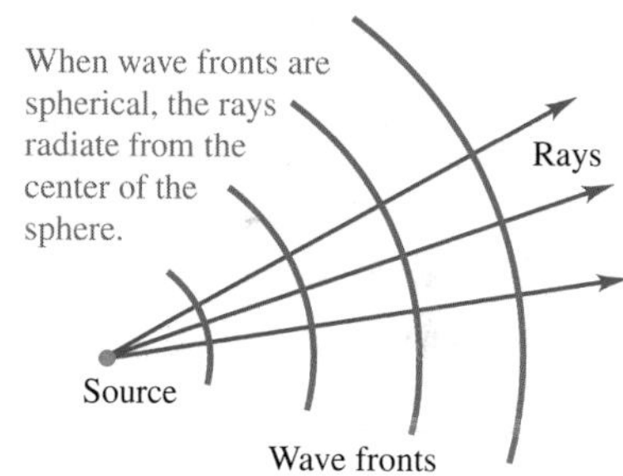
When wave fronts are spherical, the rays radiate from the center of the sphere.
Rays
Source
Wave fronts

(b)

When wave fronts are planar, the rays are perpendicular to the wave fronts and parallel to each other.

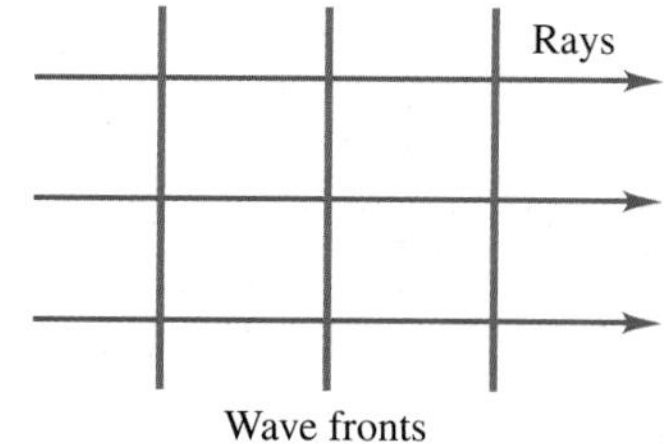
Rays
Wave fronts

ActivPhysics Online
15.1 Reflection and Refraction
15.3 Refraction Applications

33.5 (a) A plane wave is in part reflected and in part refracted at the boundary between two media (in this case, air and glass). The light that reaches the inside of the coffee shop is refracted twice, once entering the glass and once exiting the glass. (b), (c) How light behaves at the interface between the air outside the coffee shop (material a) and the glass (material b). For the case shown here, material b has a larger index of refraction that material a ($n_b > n_a$) and the angle θ_b is smaller than θ_a.

(a) Plane waves reflected and refracted from a window

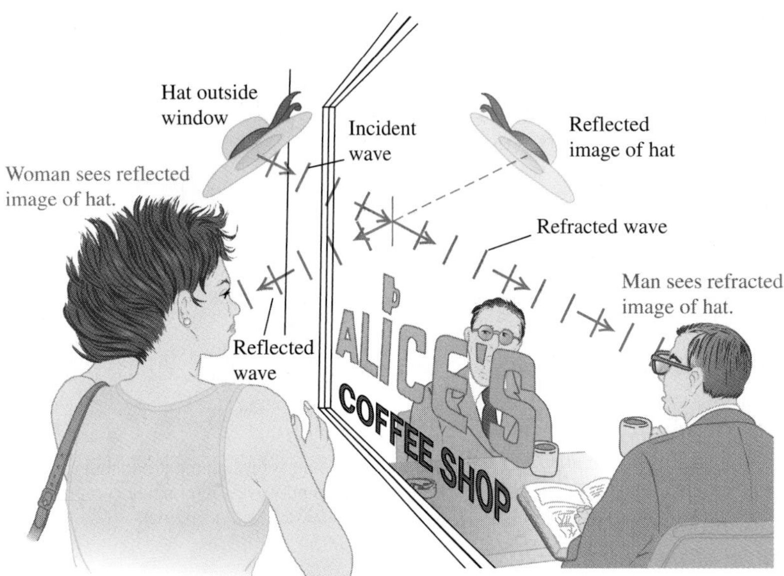

(b) The waves in the outside air and glass represented by rays

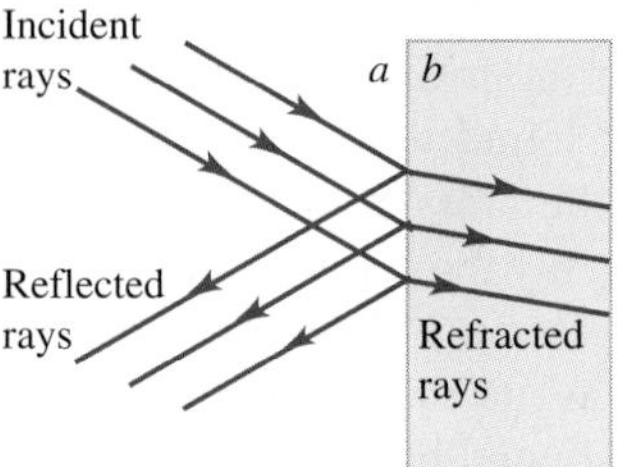

(c) The representation simplified to show just one set of rays

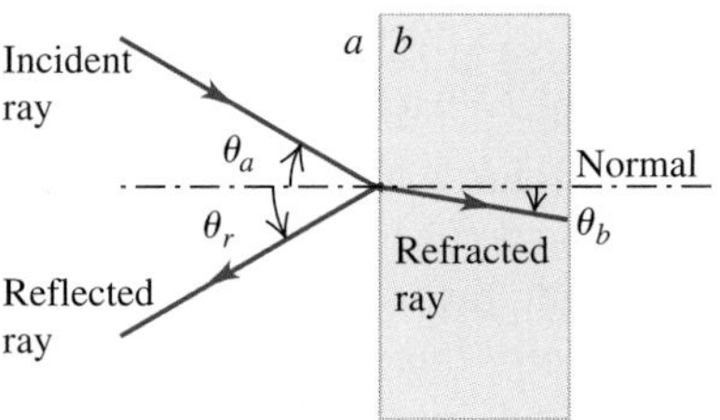

33.6 Two types of reflection.

(a) Specular reflection

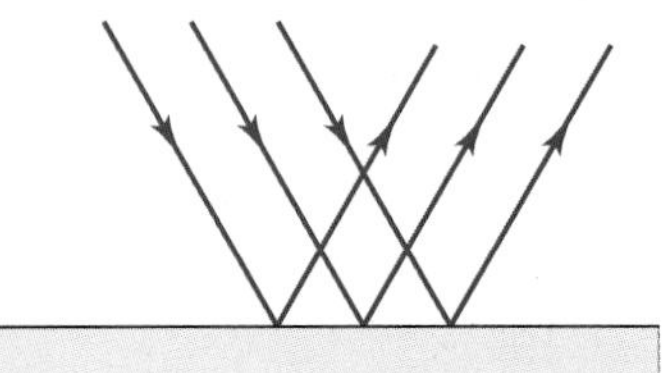

(b) Diffuse reflection

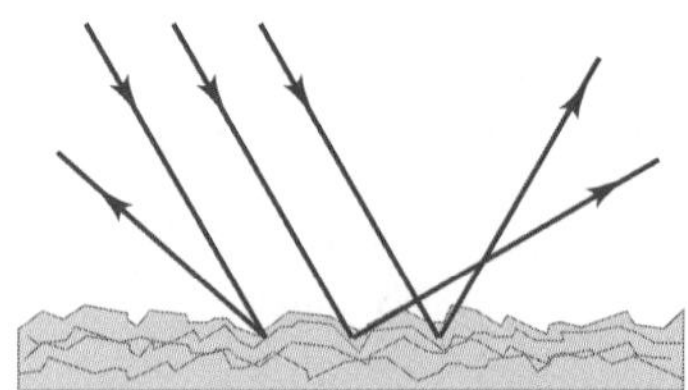

The segments of plane waves shown in Fig. 33.5a can be represented by bundles of rays forming *beams* of light (Fig. 33.5b). For simplicity we often draw only one ray in each beam (Fig. 33.5c). Representing these waves in terms of rays is the basis of geometric optics. We begin our study with the behavior of an individual ray.

We describe the directions of the incident, reflected, and refracted (transmitted) rays at a smooth interface between two optical materials in terms of the angles they make with the *normal* (perpendicular) to the surface at the point of incidence, as shown in Fig. 33.5c. If the interface is rough, both the transmitted light and the reflected light are scattered in various directions, and there is no single angle of transmission or reflection. Reflection at a definite angle from a very smooth surface is called **specular reflection** (from the Latin word for "mirror"); scattered reflection from a rough surface is called **diffuse reflection.** This distinction is shown in Fig. 33.6. Both kinds of reflection can occur with either transparent materials or *opaque* materials that do not transmit light. The vast majority of objects in your environment (including clothing, plants, other people, and this book) are visible to you because they reflect light in a diffuse manner from their surfaces. Our primary concern, however, will be with specular reflection from a very smooth surface such as highly polished glass, plastic, or metal. Unless stated otherwise, when referring to "reflection" we will always mean *specular* reflection.

The **index of refraction** of an optical material (also called the **refractive index**), denoted by n, plays a central role in geometric optics. It is the ratio of the speed of light c in vacuum to the speed v in the material:

$$n = \frac{c}{v} \quad \text{(index of refraction)} \tag{33.1}$$

Light always travels *more slowly* in a material than in vacuum, so the value of n in anything other than vacuum is always greater than unity. For vacuum, $n = 1$.

Since n is a ratio of two speeds, it is a pure number without units. (The relationship of the value of n to the electric and magnetic properties of a material is described in Section 32.3.)

CAUTION **Wave speed and index of refraction** Keep in mind that the wave speed v is *inversely* proportional to the index of refraction n. The greater the index of refraction in a material, the *slower* the wave speed in that material. Failure to remember this point can lead to serious confusion!

The Laws of Reflection and Refraction

Experimental studies of the directions of the incident, reflected, and refracted rays at a smooth interface between two optical materials lead to the following conclusions (Fig. 33.7):

1. **The incident, reflected, and refracted rays and the normal to the surface all lie in the same plane.** The plane of the three rays is perpendicular to the plane of the boundary surface between the two materials. We always draw ray diagrams so that the incident, reflected, and refracted rays are in the plane of the diagram.
2. **The angle of reflection θ_r is equal to the angle of incidence θ_a for all wavelengths and for any pair of materials.** That is, in Fig. 33.5c,

$$\theta_r = \theta_a \quad \text{(law of reflection)} \tag{33.2}$$

This relationship, together with the observation that the incident and reflected rays and the normal all lie in the same plane, is called the **law of reflection.**

3. For monochromatic light and for a given pair of materials, a and b, on opposite sides of the interface, **the ratio of the sines of the angles θ_a and θ_b, where both angles are measured from the normal to the surface, is equal to the inverse ratio of the two indexes of refraction:**

$$\frac{\sin\theta_a}{\sin\theta_b} = \frac{n_b}{n_a} \tag{33.3}$$

or

$$n_a \sin\theta_a = n_b \sin\theta_b \quad \text{(law of refraction)} \tag{33.4}$$

This experimental result, together with the observation that the incident and refracted rays and the normal all lie in the same plane, is called the **law of refraction** or **Snell's law,** after the Dutch scientist Willebrord Snell (1591–1626). There is some doubt that Snell actually discovered it. The discovery that $n = c/v$ came much later.

While these results were first observed experimentally, they can be derived theoretically from a wave description of light. We do this in Section 33.7.

Equations (33.3) and (33.4) show that when a ray passes from one material (a) into another material (b) having a larger index of refraction $(n_b > n_a)$ and hence a slower wave speed, the angle θ_b with the normal is *smaller* in the second material than the angle θ_a in the first; hence the ray is bent *toward* the normal (Fig. 33.8a). When the second material has a *smaller* index of refraction than the first material $(n_b < n_a)$ and hence a faster wave speed, the ray is bent *away from* the normal (Fig. 33.8b).

No matter what the materials on either side of the interface, in the case of *normal* incidence the transmitted ray is not bent at all (Fig. 33.8c). In this case $\theta_a = 0$ and $\sin\theta_a = 0$, so from Eq. (33.4) θ_b is also equal to zero, so the transmitted ray is

33.7 The laws of reflection and refraction.

1. The incident, reflected, and refracted rays and the normal to the surface all lie in the same plane.

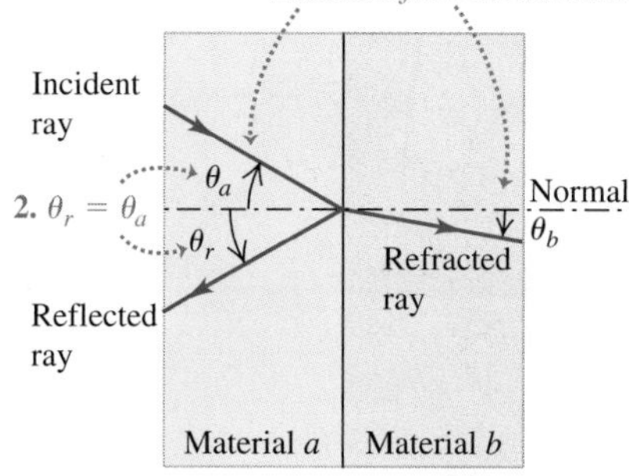

3. When a monochromatic light ray crosses the interface between two given materials a and b, the angles θ_a and θ_b are related to the indexes of refraction of a and b by

$$\frac{\sin\theta_a}{\sin\theta_b} = \frac{n_b}{n_a}$$

33.8 Refraction and reflection in three cases. (a) Material b has a larger index of refraction than material a. (b) Material b has a smaller index of refraction than material a. (c) The incident light ray is normal to the interface between the materials.

(a) A ray entering a material of *larger* index of refraction bends *toward* the normal.

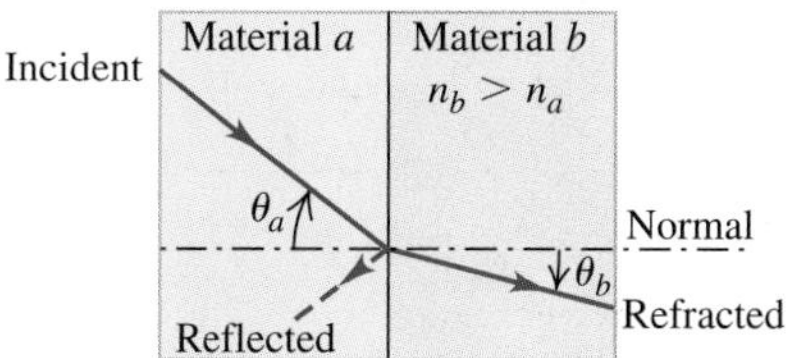

(b) A ray entering a material of *smaller* index of refraction bends *away from* the normal.

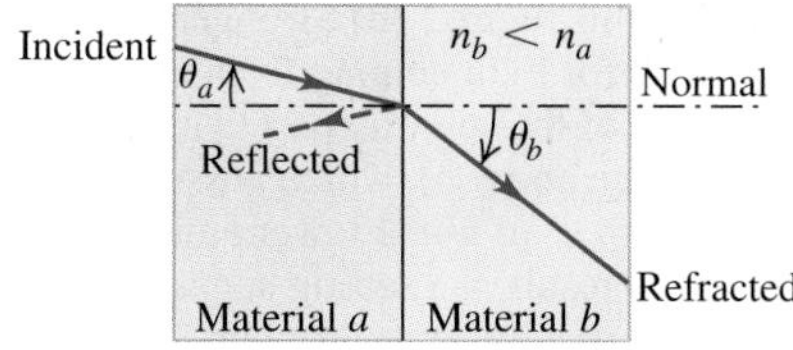

(c) A ray oriented along the normal does not bend, regardless of the materials.

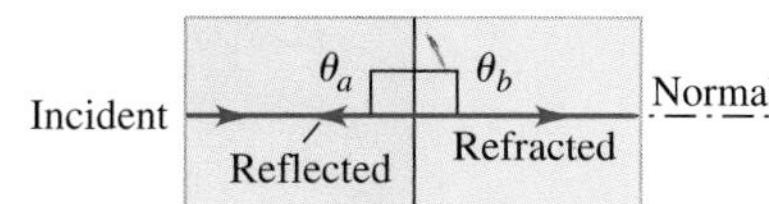

(a) A straight ruler half-immersed in water

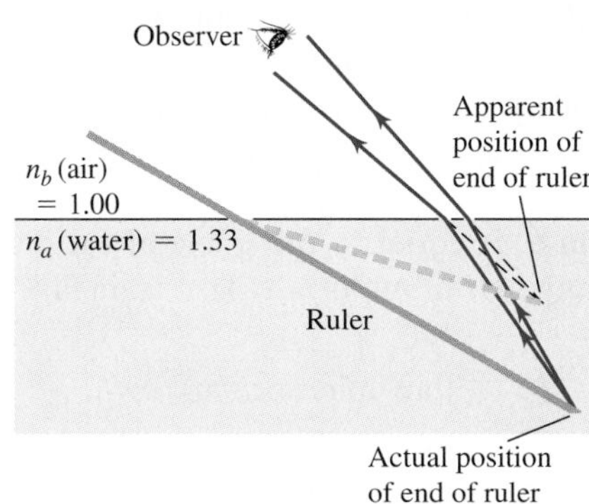

(b) Why the ruler appears bent

33.9 (a) This ruler is actually straight, but it appears to bend at the surface of the water. (b) Light rays from any submerged object bend away from the normal when they emerge into the air. As seen by an observer above the surface of the water, the object appears to be much closer to the surface than it actually is.

also normal to the interface. Equation (33.2) shows that θ_r, too, is equal to zero, so the reflected ray travels back along the same path as the incident ray.

The law of refraction explains why a partially submerged ruler or drinking straw appears bent; light rays coming from below the surface change in direction at the air–water interface, so the rays appear to be coming from a position above their actual point of origin (Fig. 33.9). A similar effect explains the appearance of the setting sun (Fig. 33.10).

An important special case is refraction that occurs at an interface between vacuum, for which the index of refraction is unity by definition, and a material. When a ray passes from vacuum into a material (b), so that $n_a = 1$ and $n_b > 1$, the ray is always bent *toward* the normal. When a ray passes from a material into vacuum, so that $n_a > 1$ and $n_b = 1$, the ray is always bent *away from* the normal.

The laws of reflection and refraction apply regardless of which side of the interface the incident ray comes from. If a ray of light approaches the interface in

(a)

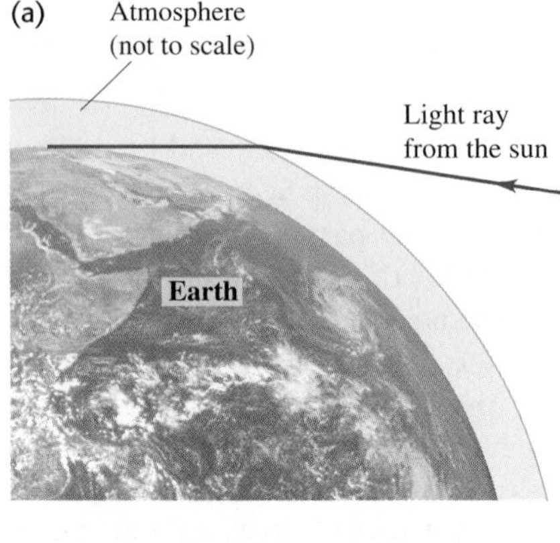

(b)

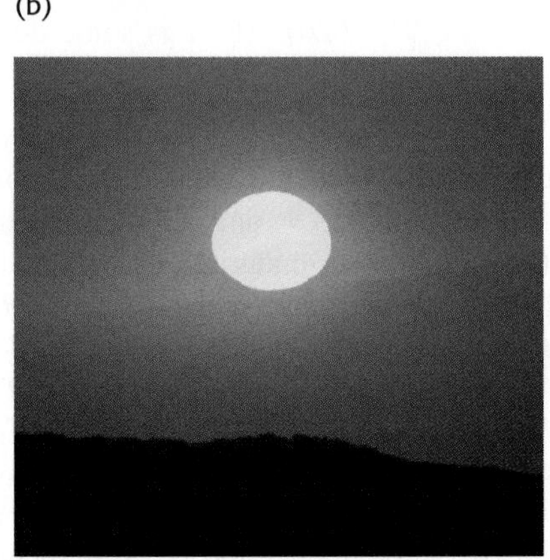

33.10 (a) The index of refraction of air is slightly greater than 1, so light rays from the setting sun bend downward when they enter our atmosphere. (The effect is exaggerated in this figure.) (b) Stronger refraction occurs for light coming from the lower limb of the sun (the part that appears closest to the horizon), which passes through denser air in the lower atmosphere. As a result, the setting sun appears flattened vertically. (See Problem 33.55.)

Fig. 33.8a or 33.8b from the right rather than from the left, there are again reflected and refracted rays; these two rays, the incident ray, and the normal to the surface again lie in the same plane. Furthermore, the path of a refracted ray is *reversible;* it follows the same path when going from b to a as when going from a to b. [You can verify this using Eq. (33.4).] Since reflected and incident rays make the same angle with the normal, the path of a reflected ray is also reversible. That's why when you see someone's eyes in a mirror, they can also see you.

The *intensities* of the reflected and refracted rays depend on the angle of incidence, the two indexes of refraction, and the polarization (that is, the direction of the electric-field vector) of the incident ray. The fraction reflected is smallest at normal incidence $(\theta_a = 0°)$, where it is about 4% for an air–glass interface. This fraction increases with increasing angle of incidence to 100% at grazing incidence, when $\theta_a = 90°$.

It's possible to use Maxwell's equations to predict the amplitude, intensity, phase, and polarization states of the reflected and refracted waves. Such an analysis is beyond our scope, however.

The index of refraction depends not only on the substance but also on the wavelength of the light. The dependence on wavelength is called *dispersion;* we will consider it in Section 33.4. Indexes of refraction for several solids and liquids are given in Table 33.1 for a particular wavelength of yellow light.

The index of refraction of air at standard temperature and pressure is about 1.0003, and we will usually take it to be exactly unity. The index of refraction of a gas increases as its density increases. Most glasses used in optical instruments have indexes of refraction between about 1.5 and 2.0. A few substances have larger indexes; one example is diamond, with 2.417.

Table 33.1 Index of Refraction for Yellow Sodium Light $\lambda_0 = 589$ nm

Substance	Index of Refraction, n
Solids	
Ice (H_2O)	1.309
Fluorite (CaF_2)	1.434
Polystyrene	1.49
Rock salt (NaCl)	1.544
Quartz (SiO_2)	1.544
Zircon $(ZrO_2 \cdot SiO_2)$	1.923
Diamond (C)	2.417
Fabulite $(SrTiO_3)$	2.409
Rutile (TiO_2)	2.62
Glasses (typical values)	
Crown	1.52
Light flint	1.58
Medium flint	1.62
Dense flint	1.66
Lanthanum flint	1.80
Liquids at 20°C	
Methanol (CH_3OH)	1.329
Water (H_2O)	1.333
Ethanol (C_2H_5OH)	1.36
Carbon tetrachloride (CCl_4)	1.460
Turpentine	1.472
Glycerine	1.473
Benzene	1.501
Carbon disulfide (CS_2)	1.628

Index of Refraction and the Wave Aspects of Light

We have discussed how the direction of a light ray changes when it passes from one material to another material with a different index of refraction. It's also important to see what happens to the *wave* characteristics of the light when this happens.

First, the frequency f of the wave does not change when passing from one material to another. That is, the number of wave cycles arriving per unit time must equal the number leaving per unit time; this is a statement that the boundary surface cannot create or destroy waves.

Second, the wavelength λ of the wave *is* different in general in different materials. This is because in any material, $v = \lambda f$; since f is the same in any material as in vacuum and v is always less than the wave speed c in vacuum, λ is also correspondingly reduced. Thus the wavelength λ of light in a material is *less than* the wavelength λ_0 of the same light in vacuum. From the above discussion, $f = c/\lambda_0 = v/\lambda$. Combining this with Eq. (33.1), $n = c/v$, we find

$$\lambda = \frac{\lambda_0}{n} \quad \text{(wavelength of light in a material)} \tag{33.5}$$

When a wave passes from one material into a second material with larger index of refraction, so that $n_b > n_a$, the wave speed decreases. The wavelength $\lambda_b = \lambda_0/n_b$ in the second material is then shorter than the wavelength $\lambda_a = \lambda_0/n_a$ in the first material. If instead the second material has a smaller index of refraction than the first material, so that $n_b < n_a$, then the wave speed increases. Then the wavelength λ_b in the second material is longer than the wavelength λ_a in the first material. This makes intuitive sense; the waves get "squeezed" (the wavelength gets shorter) if the wave speed decreases and get "stretched" (the wavelength gets longer) if the wave speed increases.

Problem-Solving Strategy 33.1 Reflection and Refraction

IDENTIFY *the relevant concepts:* You need to use the ideas of this section, called *geometric optics,* whenever light encounters a boundary between two different materials. In general, part of the light is reflected back into the first material and part is refracted into the second material. These ideas apply to electromagnetic radiation of all frequencies and wavelengths, not just visible light.

SET UP *the problem* using the following steps:

1. In geometric optics problems involving rays and angles, *always* start by drawing a large, neat diagram. Label all known angles and indexes of refraction.
2. Determine the target variables.

EXECUTE *the solution* as follows:

1. Apply the laws of reflection, Eq. (33.2), and refraction, Eq. (33.4). Remember to always measure the angles of incidence, reflection, and refraction from the *normal* to the surface where the reflection and refraction occur, *never* from the surface itself.
2. You will often have to use some simple geometry or trigonometry in working out angular relationships. The sum of the interior angles in a triangle is 180°, an angle and its complement differ by 180°, and so on. Ask yourself, "What information am I given?", "What do I need to know in order to find this angle?", or "What other angles or other quantities can I compute using the information given in the problem?"
3. Remember that the frequency of the light does not change when it moves from one material to another, but the wavelength changes in accordance with Eq. (33.5).

EVALUATE *your answer:* In problems that involve refraction, check that the direction of refraction makes sense. If the second material has a higher index of refraction than the first material, the refracted ray bends toward the normal and the refracted angle is smaller than the incident angle. If the first material has the higher index of refraction, the refracted ray bends away from the normal and the refracted angle is larger than the incident angle. Do your results agree with these rules?

Example 33.1 Reflection and refraction

In Fig. 33.11, material a is water and material b is a glass with index of refraction 1.52. If the incident ray makes an angle of 60° with the normal, find the directions of the reflected and refracted rays.

SOLUTION

IDENTIFY: This is a problem in geometric optics. We are given the incident angle and the index of refraction of each material, and we need to find the reflected and refracted angles.

33.11 Reflection and refraction of light passing from water to glass.

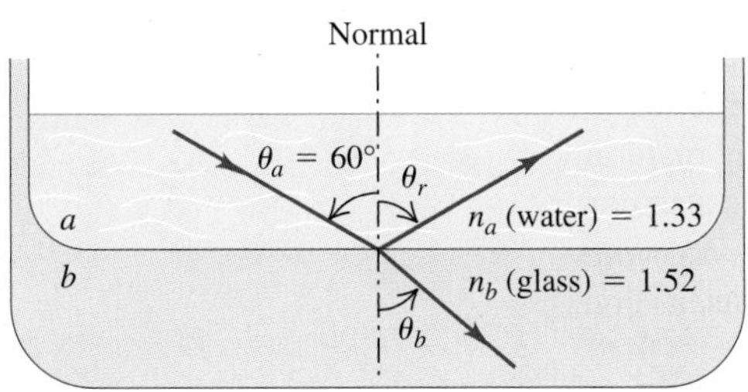

SET UP: Figure 33.11 shows the rays and angles for this situation. The target variables are the reflected angle θ_r and the refracted angle θ_b. Since n_b is greater than n_a, the refracted angle must be smaller than the incident angle θ_a; this is shown in the figure.

EXECUTE: According to Eq. (33.2), the angle the reflected ray makes with the normal is the same as that of the incident ray, so $\theta_r = \theta_a = 60.0°$.

To find the direction of the refracted ray, we use Snell's law, Eq.(33.4), with $n_a = 1.33$, $n_b = 1.52$, and $\theta_a = 60.0°$. We find

$$n_a \sin\theta_a = n_b \sin\theta_b$$

$$\sin\theta_b = \frac{n_a}{n_b}\sin\theta_a = \frac{1.33}{1.52}\sin 60.0° = 0.758$$

$$\theta_b = 49.3°$$

EVALUATE: The second material has a larger refractive index than the first, just like the situation shown in Fig. 33.8a. Hence, the refracted ray is bent toward the normal as the wave slows down upon entering the second material, and $\theta_b < \theta_a$.

Example 33.2 Index of refraction in the eye

The wavelength of the red light from a helium-neon laser is 633 nm in air but 474 nm in the aqueous humor inside your eyeball. Calculate the index of refraction of the aqueous humor and the speed and frequency of the light in this substance.

SOLUTION

IDENTIFY: The key ideas here are the relationship between index of refraction n and wave speed v and the relationship between index of refraction and wavelength λ.

SET UP: We use the definition of index of refraction given by Eq. (33.1), $n = c/v$, as well as Eq. (33.5), $\lambda = \lambda_0/n$. It will also be helpful to use the relationship $v = \lambda f$ among wave speed, wavelength, and frequency.

EXECUTE: The index of refraction of air is very close to unity, so we assume that the wavelengths in air and vacuum are the same. Then the wavelength λ in the material is given by Eq. (33.5) with $\lambda_0 = 633$ nm:

$$\lambda = \frac{\lambda_0}{n} \qquad n = \frac{\lambda_0}{\lambda} = \frac{633\text{ nm}}{474\text{ nm}} = 1.34$$

This is about the same index of refraction as for water. Then $n = c/v$ gives

$$v = \frac{c}{n} = \frac{3.00 \times 10^8 \text{ m/s}}{1.34} = 2.25 \times 10^8 \text{ m/s}$$

Finally, from $v = \lambda f$,

$$f = \frac{v}{\lambda} = \frac{2.25 \times 10^8 \text{ m/s}}{474 \times 10^{-9} \text{ m}} = 4.74 \times 10^{14} \text{ Hz}$$

EVALUATE: Note that while the speed and wavelength have different values in air and in the aqueous humor, the *frequency* in air, f_0, is the same as the frequency f in the aqueous humor:

$$f_0 = \frac{c}{\lambda_0} = \frac{3.00 \times 10^8 \text{ m/s}}{633 \times 10^{-9} \text{ m}} = 4.74 \times 10^{14} \text{ Hz}$$

This illustrates the general rule that when a light wave passes from one material into another, the wave frequency is unchanged.

Example 33.3 A twice-reflected ray

Two mirrors are perpendicular to each other. A ray traveling in a plane perpendicular to both mirrors is reflected from one mirror, then the other, as shown in Fig. 33.12. What is the ray's final direction relative to its original direction?

SOLUTION

IDENTIFY: This problem involves only the law of reflection.

SET UP: There are two reflections in this situation, so we must apply the law of reflection twice.

EXECUTE: For mirror 1 the angle of incidence is θ_1, and this equals the angle of reflection. The sum of interior angles in the triangle shown in the figure is 180°, so we see that the angles of incidence and reflection for mirror 2 are both $90° - \theta_1$. The total change in direction of the ray after both reflections is therefore $2(90° - \theta_1) + 2\theta_1 = 180°$. That is, the ray's final direction is opposite to its original direction.

EVALUATE: An alternative viewpoint is that specular reflection reverses the sign of the component of light velocity perpendicular to the surface but leaves the other components unchanged. We invite you to verify this in detail. You should also be able to use this result to show that when a ray of light is successively reflected by three mirrors forming a corner of a cube (a "corner reflector"), its final direction is again opposite to its original direction. This principle is widely used in tail-light lenses and bicycle reflectors to improve their night-time visibility. Apollo astronauts placed arrays of corner reflectors on the moon. By use of laser beams reflected from these arrays, the earth–moon distance has been measured to within 0.15 m.

33.12 A ray moving in the xy-plane. The first reflection changes the sign of the y-component of its velocity, and the second reflection changes the sign of the x-component. For a different ray with a z-component of velocity, a third mirror (perpendicular to the two shown) could be used to change the sign of that component.

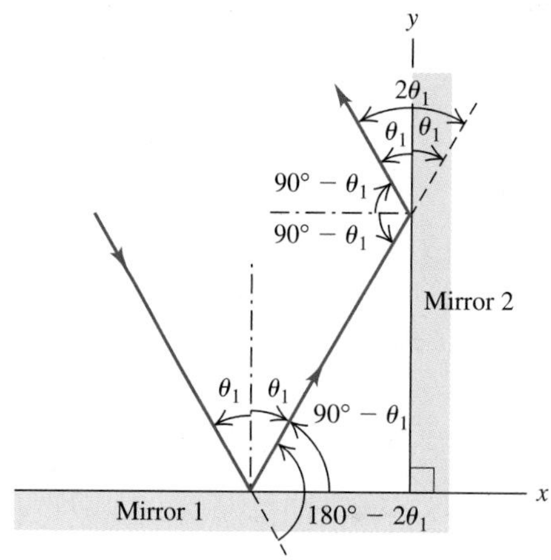

Test Your Understanding of Section 33.2 You are standing on the shore of a lake. You spot a tasty fish swimming some distance below the lake surface. (a) If you want to spear the fish, should you aim the spear (i) above, (ii) below, or (iii) directly at the apparent position of the fish? (b) If instead you use a high-power laser to simultaneously kill and cook the fish, should you aim the laser (i) above, (ii) below, or (iii) directly at the apparent position of the fish?

33.3 Total Internal Reflection

We have described how light is partially reflected and partially transmitted at an interface between two materials with different indexes of refraction. Under certain circumstances, however, *all* of the light can be reflected back from the interface, with none of it being transmitted, even though the second material is transparent. Figure 33.13a shows how this can occur. Several rays are shown radiating from a point source in material a with index of refraction n_a. The rays strike the surface of a second material b with index n_b, where $n_a > n_b$. (For

15.2 Total Internal Reflection

33.13 (a) Total internal reflection. The angle of incidence for which the angle of refraction is 90° is called the critical angle: this is the case for ray 3. The reflected portions of rays 1, 2, and 3 are omitted for clarity. (b) Rays of laser light enter the water in the fishbowl from above; they are reflected at the bottom by mirrors tilted at slightly different angles. One ray undergoes total internal reflection at the air–water interface.

(a) Total internal reflection

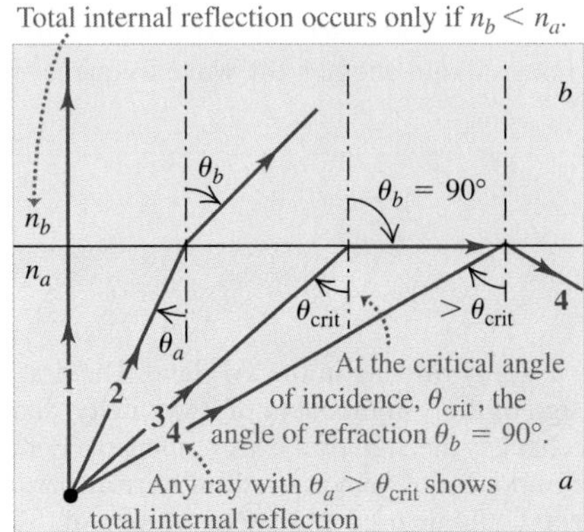
Total internal reflection occurs only if $n_b < n_a$.
b
θ_b
$\theta_b = 90°$
n_b
n_a
θ_a
θ_{crit}
$> \theta_{crit}$
1
2
3
4
4
At the critical angle of incidence, θ_{crit}, the angle of refraction $\theta_b = 90°$.
Any ray with $\theta_a > \theta_{crit}$ shows total internal reflection
a

(b) Total internal reflection demonstrated with a laser, mirrors, and water in a fishbowl

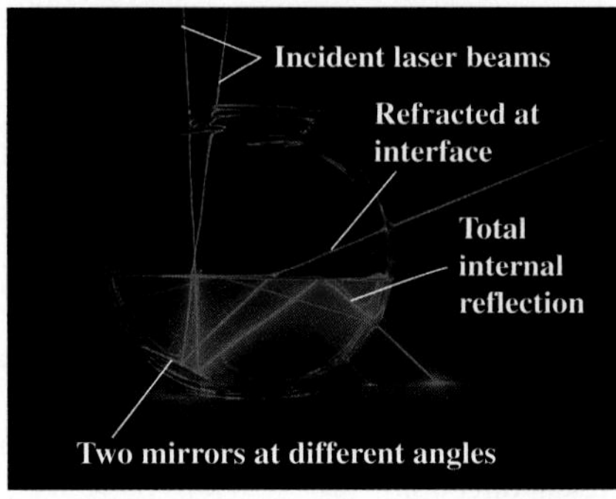
Incident laser beams
Refracted at interface
Total internal reflection
Two mirrors at different angles

instance, materials a and b could be water and air, respectively.) From Snell's law of refraction,

$$\sin\theta_b = \frac{n_a}{n_b}\sin\theta_a$$

Because n_a/n_b is greater than unity, $\sin\theta_b$ is larger than $\sin\theta_a$; the ray is bent *away from* the normal. Thus there must be some value of θ_a *less than* 90° for which Snell's law gives $\sin\theta_b = 1$ and $\theta_b = 90°$. This is shown by ray 3 in the diagram, which emerges just grazing the surface at an angle of refraction of 90°. Compare the diagram in Fig. 33.13a to the photograph of light rays in Fig. 33.13b.

The angle of incidence for which the refracted ray emerges tangent to the surface is called the **critical angle,** denoted by θ_{crit}. (A more detailed analysis using Maxwell's equations shows that as the incident angle approaches the critical angle, the transmitted intensity approaches zero.) If the angle of incidence is *larger* than the critical angle, the sine of the angle of refraction, as computed by Snell's law, would have to be greater than unity, which is impossible. Beyond the critical angle, the ray *cannot* pass into the upper material; it is trapped in the lower material and is completely reflected at the boundary surface. This situation, called **total internal reflection,** occurs only when a ray is incident on the interface with a second material whose index of refraction is *smaller* than that of the material in which the ray is traveling.

We can find the critical angle for two given materials by setting $\theta_b = 90°(\sin\theta_b = 1)$ in Snell's law. We then have

$$\sin\theta_{crit} = \frac{n_b}{n_a} \quad \text{(critical angle for total internal reflection)} \tag{33.6}$$

Total internal reflection will occur if the angle of incidence θ_a is larger than or equal to θ_{crit}.

Applications of Total Internal Reflection

Total internal reflection finds numerous uses in optical technology. As an example, consider glass with index of refraction $n = 1.52$. If light propagating within this glass encounters a glass–air interface, the critical angle is

$$\sin\theta_{crit} = \frac{1}{1.52} = 0.658 \qquad \theta_{crit} = 41.1°$$

(a) Total internal reflection in a Porro prism

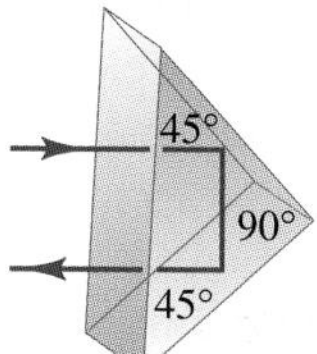

If the incident beam is oriented as shown, total internal reflection occurs on the 45° faces (because, for a glass–air interface, $\theta_{crit} = 41.1°$).

(b) Binoculars use Porro prisms to reflect the light to each eyepiece.

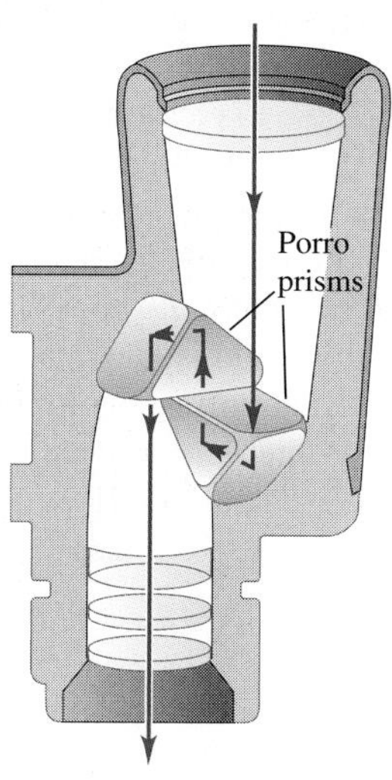

33.14 (a) Total internal reflection in a Porro prism. (b) A combination of two Porro prisms in binoculars.

The light will be *totally reflected* if it strikes the glass–air surface at an angle of 41.1° or larger. Because the critical angle is slightly smaller than 45°, it is possible to use a prism with angles of 45°–45°–90° as a totally reflecting surface. As reflectors, totally reflecting prisms have some advantages over metallic surfaces such as ordinary coated-glass mirrors. While no metallic surface reflects 100% of the light incident on it, light can be *totally* reflected by a prism. The reflecting properties of a prism have the additional advantages of being permanent and unaffected by tarnishing.

A 45°–45°–90° prism, used as in Fig. 33.14a, is called a *Porro* prism. Light enters and leaves at right angles to the hypotenuse and is totally reflected at each of the shorter faces. The total change of direction of the rays is 180°. Binoculars often use combinations of two Porro prisms, as in Fig. 33.14b.

When a beam of light enters at one end of a transparent rod (Fig. 33.15), the light can be totally reflected internally if the index of refraction of the rod is greater than that of the surrounding material. The light is "trapped" within the rod even if the rod is curved, provided that the curvature is not too great. Such a rod is sometimes called a *light pipe.* A bundle of fine glass or plastic fibers behaves in the same way and has the advantage of being flexible. A bundle may consist of thousands of individual fibers, each of the order of 0.002 to 0.01 mm in diameter. If the fibers are assembled in the bundle so that the relative positions of the ends are the same (or mirror images) at both ends, the bundle can transmit an image, as shown in Fig. 33.16.

Fiber-optic devices have found a wide range of medical applications in instruments called *endoscopes,* which can be inserted directly into the bronchial tubes, the bladder, the colon, and so on, for direct visual examination. A bundle of fibers can be enclosed in a hypodermic needle for study of tissues and blood vessels far beneath the skin.

Fiber optics also have applications in communication systems, in which they are used to transmit a modulated laser beam. The rate at which information can be transmitted by a wave (light, radio, or whatever) is proportional to the frequency. To see qualitatively why this is so, consider modulating (modifying) the wave by chopping off some of the wave crests. Suppose each crest represents a binary digit, with a chopped-off crest representing a zero and an unmodified crest representing a one. The number of binary digits we can transmit per unit time is thus proportional to the frequency of the wave. Infrared and visible-light waves have much higher frequency than do radio waves, so a modulated laser beam can transmit an enormous amount of information through a single fiber-optic cable.

33.15 A transparent rod with refractive index greater than that of the surrounding material.

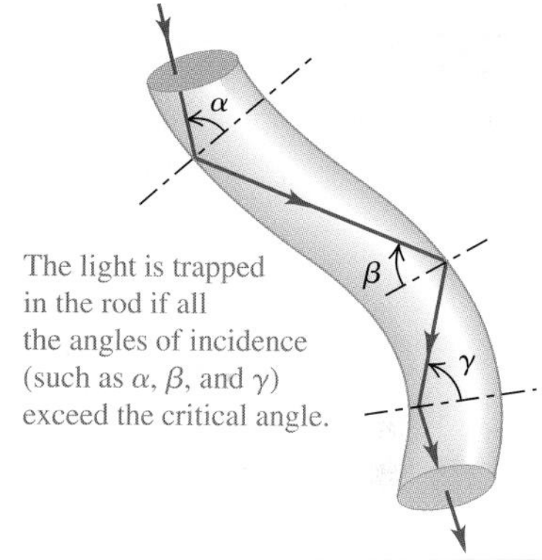

α
β
γ
The light is trapped in the rod if all the angles of incidence (such as α, β, and γ) exceed the critical angle.

33.16 Image transmission by a bundle of optical fibers.

33.17 To maximize their brilliance, diamonds are cut so that there is total internal reflection on their back surfaces.

Another advantage of optical fibers is that they can be made thinner than conventional copper wire, so more fibers can be bundled together in a cable of a given diameter. Hence more distinct signals (for instance, different phone lines) can be sent over the same cable. Because fiber-optic cables are electrical insulators, they are immune to electrical interference from lightning and other sources, and they don't allow unwanted currents between source and receiver. For these and other reasons, fiber-optic cables are playing an increasingly important role in long-distance telephone, television, and Internet communication.

Total internal reflection also plays an important role in the design of jewelry. The brilliance of diamond is due in large measure to its very high index of refraction $(n = 2.417)$ and correspondingly small critical angle. Light entering a cut diamond is totally internally reflected from facets on its back surface, and then emerges from its front surface (Fig. 33.17). "Imitation diamond" gems, such as cubic zirconia, are made from less expensive crystalline materials with comparable indexes of refraction.

Conceptual Example 33.4 A leaky periscope

A periscope for a submarine uses two totally reflecting $45°-45°-90°$ prisms with total internal reflection on the sides adjacent to the $45°$ angles. It springs a leak, and the bottom prism is covered with water. Explain why the periscope no longer works.

SOLUTION

The critical angle for water $(n_b = 1.33)$ on glass $(n_a = 1.52)$ is

$$\theta_{crit} = \arcsin\frac{1.33}{1.52} = 61.0°$$

The $45°$ angle of incidence for a totally reflecting prism is *smaller than* the $61°$ critical angle, so total internal reflection does not occur at the glass–water boundary. Most of the light is transmitted into the water, and very little is reflected back into the prism.

Test Your Understanding of Section 33.3 In which of the following situations is there total internal reflection? (i) Light propagating in water $(n = 1.33)$ strikes a water–air interface at an incident angle of $70°$; (ii) light propagating in glass $(n = 1.52)$ strikes a glass–water interface at an incident angle of $70°$; (iii) light propagating in water strikes a water–glass interface at an incident angle of $70°$.

*33.4 Dispersion

Ordinary white light is a superposition of waves with wavelengths extending throughout the visible spectrum. The speed of light *in vacuum* is the same for all wavelengths, but the speed in a material substance is different for different wavelengths. Therefore the index of refraction of a material depends on wavelength. The dependence of wave speed and index of refraction on wavelength is called **dispersion.**

Figure 33.18 shows the variation of index of refraction n with wavelength for a few common optical materials. Note that the horizontal axis of this figure is the wavelength of the light *in vacuum,* λ_0; the wavelength in the material is given by Eq. (33.5), $\lambda = \lambda_0/n$. In most materials the value of n *decreases* with increasing wavelength and decreasing frequency, and thus n *increases* with decreasing wavelength and increasing frequency. In such a material, light of longer wavelength has greater speed than light of shorter wavelength.

Figure 33.19 shows a ray of white light incident on a prism. The deviation (change of direction) produced by the prism increases with increasing index of refraction and frequency and decreasing wavelength. Violet light is deviated most, and red is deviated least; other colors are in intermediate positions. When it comes out of the prism, the light is spread out into a fan-shaped beam, as shown.

33.18 Variation of index of refraction n with wavelength for different transparent materials. The horizontal axis shows the wavelength λ_0 of the light *in vacuum;* the wavelength in the material is equal to $\lambda = \lambda_0/n$.

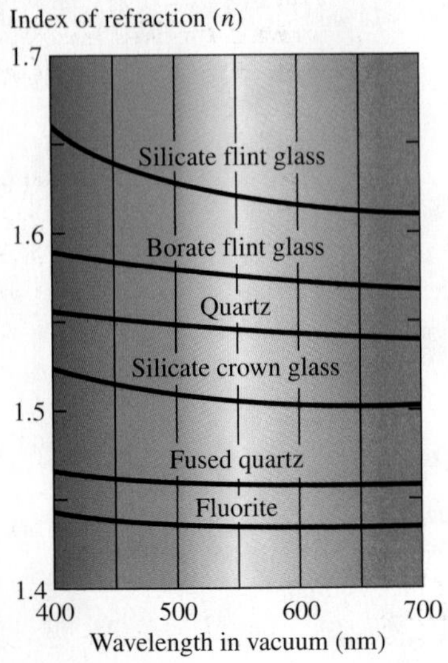

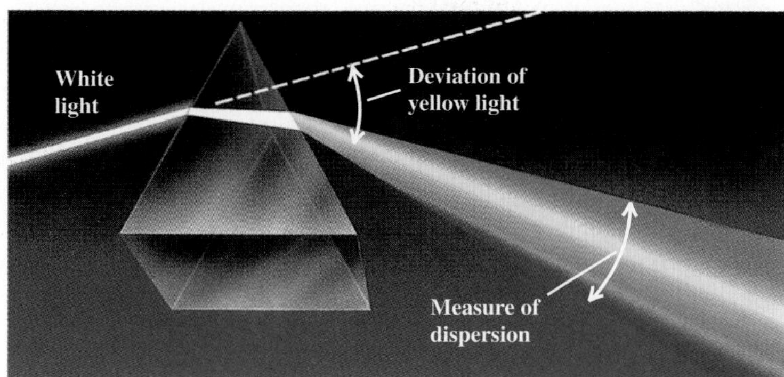

33.19 Dispersion of light by a prism. The band of colors is called a spectrum.

The light is said to be *dispersed* into a spectrum. The amount of dispersion depends on the *difference* between the refractive indexes for violet light and for red light. From Fig. 33.18 we can see that for a substance such as fluorite, the difference between the indexes for red and violet is small, and the dispersion will also be small. A better choice of material for a prism whose purpose is to produce a spectrum would be silicate flint glass, for which there is a larger difference in the value of n between red and violet.

As we mentioned in Section 33.3, the brilliance of diamond is due in part to its unusually large refractive index; another important factor is its large dispersion, which causes white light entering a diamond to emerge as a multicolored spectrum. Crystals of rutile and of strontium titanate, which can be produced synthetically, have about eight times the dispersion of diamond.

Rainbows

When you experience the beauty of a rainbow, as in Fig. 33.20a, you are seeing the combined effects of dispersion, refraction, and reflection. Sunlight comes from behind you, enters a water droplet, is (partially) reflected from the back surface of the droplet, and is refracted again upon exiting the droplet (Fig. 33.20b). A light ray that enters the middle of the raindrop is reflected straight back. All other rays exit the raindrop within an angle Δ of that middle ray, with many rays "piling up" at the angle Δ. What you see is a disk of light of angular radius Δ centered on the down-sun point (the point in the sky opposite the sun); due to the "piling up" of light rays, the disk is brightest around its rim, which we see as a rainbow (Fig. 33.20c). Because no light reaches your eye from angles larger than Δ, the sky looks dark outside the rainbow (see Fig. 33.20a). The value of the angle Δ depends on the index of refraction of the water that makes up the raindrops, which in turn depends on the wavelength (Fig. 33.20d). The bright disk of red light is slightly larger than that for orange light, which in turn is slightly larger than that for yellow light, and so on. As a result, you see the rainbow as a band of colors.

In many cases you can see a second, larger rainbow. It is the result of dispersion, refraction, and *two* reflections from the back surface of the droplet (Fig. 33.20e). Each time a light ray hits the back surface, part of the light is refracted out of the drop (not shown in Fig. 33.20); after two such hits, relatively little light is left inside the drop, which is why the secondary rainbow is noticeably fainter than the primary rainbow. Just as a mirror held up to a book reverses the printed letters, so the second reflection reverses the sequence of colors in the secondary rainbow. You can see this effect in Fig 33.20a.

33.5 Polarization

Polarization is a characteristic of all transverse waves. This chapter is about light, but to introduce some basic polarization concepts, let's go back to the transverse waves on a string that we studied in Chapter 15. For a string that in

16.9 Physical Optics: Polarization

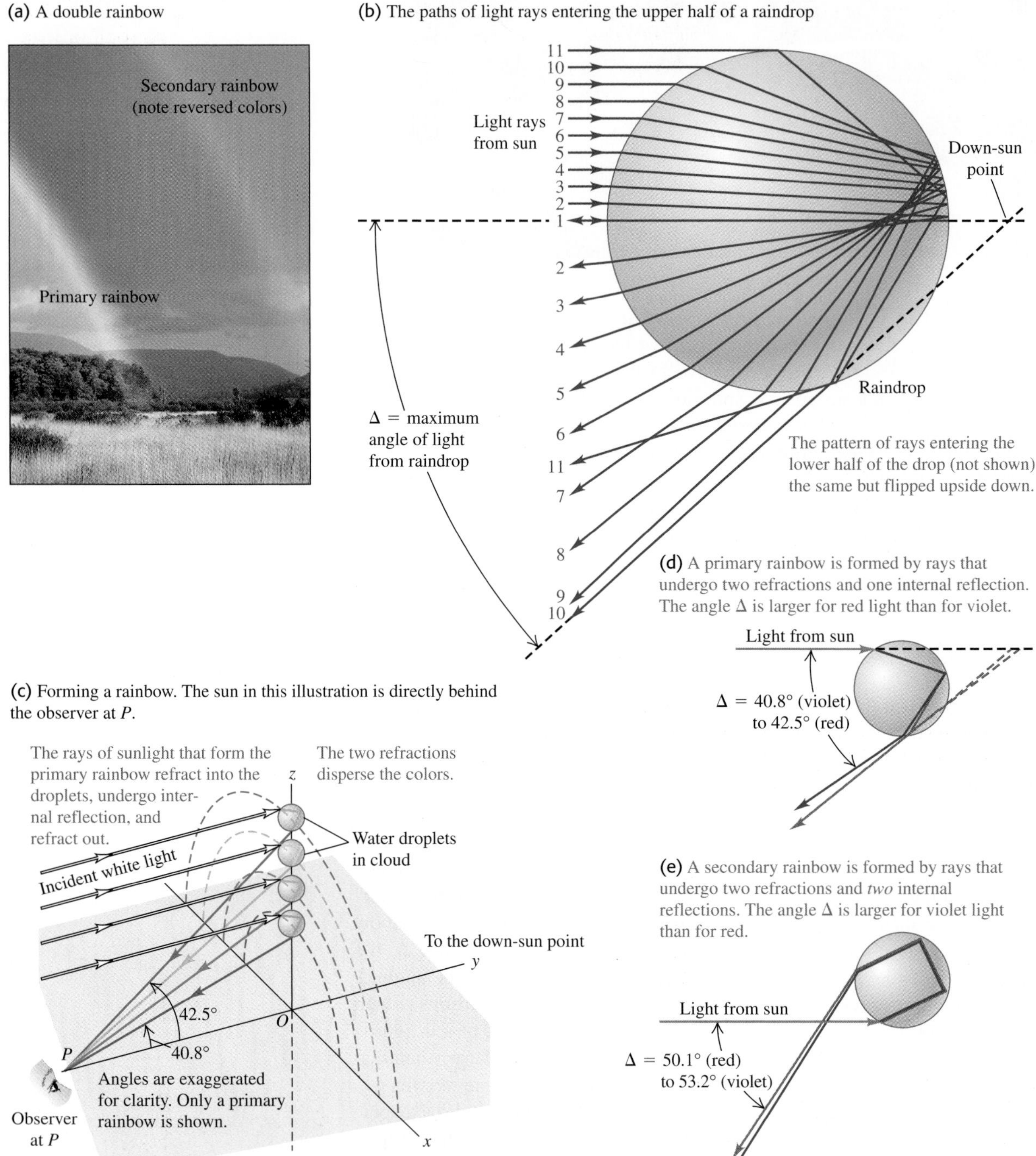

33.20 How rainbows form.

equilibrium lies along the x-axis, the displacements may be along the y-direction, as in Fig. 33.21a. In this case the string always lies in the xy-plane. But the displacements might instead be along the z-axis, as in Fig. 33.21b; then the string always lies in the xz-plane.

When a wave has only y-displacements, we say that it is **linearly polarized** in the y-direction; a wave with only z-displacements is linearly polarized in the z-direction. For mechanical waves we can build a **polarizing filter,** or **polarizer,** that permits only waves with a certain polarization direction to pass. In Fig. 33.21c the string can slide vertically in the slot without friction, but no hori-

33.21 (a), (b) Polarized waves on a string. (c) Making a polarized wave on a string from an unpolarized one using a polarizing filter.

(a) Transverse wave linearly polarized in the y-direction

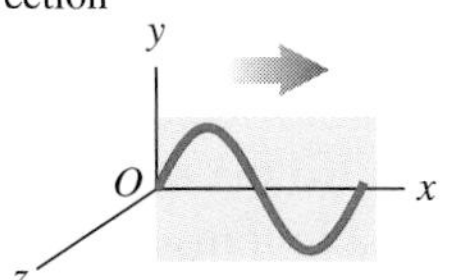

(b) Transverse wave linearly polarized in the z-direction

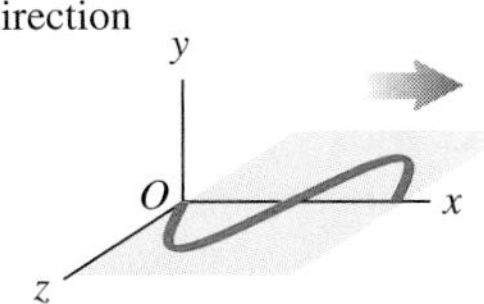

(c) The slot functions as a polarizing filter, passing only components polarized in the y-direction.

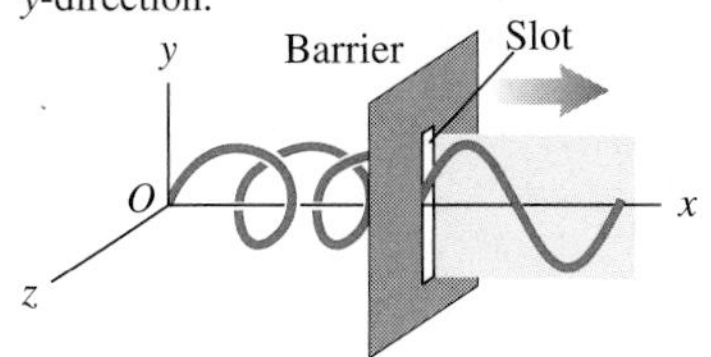

zontal motion is possible. This filter passes waves that are polarized in the y-direction but blocks those that are polarized in the z-direction.

This same language can be applied to electromagnetic waves, which also have polarization. As we learned in Chapter 32, an electromagnetic wave is a *transverse* wave; the fluctuating electric and magnetic fields are perpendicular to each other and to the direction of propagation. We always define the direction of polarization of an electromagnetic wave to be the direction of the *electric*-field vector $\vec{E}$, not the magnetic field, because many common electromagnetic-wave detectors respond to the electric forces on electrons in materials, not the magnetic forces. Thus the electromagnetic wave described by Eq. (32.17),

$$\vec{E}(x, t) = \hat{\jmath}E_{\max}\cos(kx - \omega t)$$
$$\vec{B}(x, t) = \hat{k}B_{\max}\cos(kx - \omega t)$$

is said to be polarized in the y-direction because the electric field has only a y-component.

CAUTION **The meaning of "polarization"** It's unfortunate that the same word "polarization" that is used to describe the direction of $\vec{E}$ in an electromagnetic wave is also used to describe the shifting of electric charge within a body, such as in response to a nearby charged body; we described this latter kind of polarization in Section 21.2 (see Fig. 21.7). You should remember that while these two concepts have the same name, they do not describe the same phenomenon.

Polarizing Filters

Waves emitted by a radio transmitter are usually linearly polarized. The vertical antennas that are used for radio broadcasting emit waves that, in a horizontal plane around the antenna, are polarized in the vertical direction (parallel to the antenna) (Fig. 33.22a). Rooftop TV antennas have horizontal elements in the United States and vertical elements in Great Britain because the transmitted waves have different polarizations.

(a)

(b)

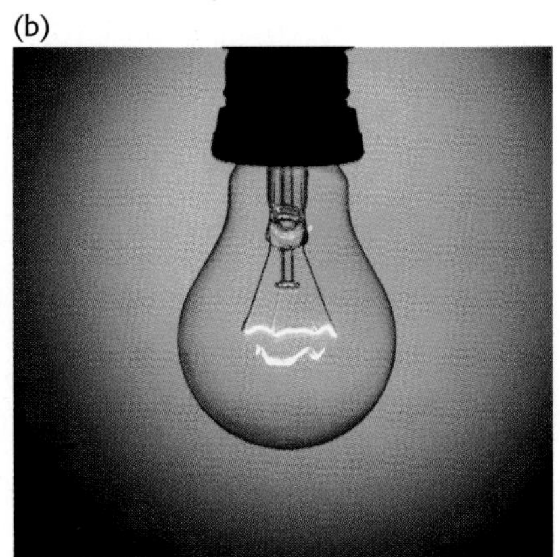

33.22 (a) Electrons in the red and white broadcast antenna oscillate vertically, producing vertically polarized electromagnetic waves that propagate away from the antenna in the horizontal direction. (The small gray antennas are for relaying cellular phone signals.) (b) No matter how this light bulb is oriented, the random motion of electrons in the filament produces unpolarized light waves.

The situation is different for visible light. Light from ordinary sources, such as incandescent light bulbs and fluorescent light fixtures, is *not* polarized (Fig. 33.22b). The "antennas" that radiate light waves are the molecules that make up the sources. The waves emitted by any one molecule may be linearly polarized, like those from a radio antenna. But any actual light source contains a tremendous number of molecules with random orientations, so the emitted light is a random mixture of waves linearly polarized in all possible transverse directions. Such light is called **unpolarized light** or **natural light.** To create polarized light from unpolarized natural light requires a filter that is analogous to the slot for mechanical waves in Fig. 33.21c.

Polarizing filters for electromagnetic waves have different details of construction, depending on the wavelength. For microwaves with a wavelength of a few centimeters, a good polarizer is an array of closely spaced, parallel conducting wires that are insulated from each other. (Think of a barbecue grill with the outer metal ring replaced by an insulating one.) Electrons are free to move along the length of the conducting wires and will do so in response to a wave whose $\vec{E}$ field is parallel to the wires. The resulting currents in the wires dissipate energy by I^2R heating; the dissipated energy comes from the wave, so whatever wave passes through the grid is greatly reduced in amplitude. Waves with $\vec{E}$ oriented perpendicular to the wires pass through almost unaffected, since electrons cannot move through the air between the wires. Hence a wave that passes through such a filter will be predominantly polarized in the direction perpendicular to the wires.

The most common polarizing filter for visible light is a material known by the trade name Polaroid, widely used for sunglasses and polarizing filters for camera lenses. Developed originally by the American scientist Edwin H. Land, this material incorporates substances that have **dichroism,** a selective absorption in which one of the polarized components is absorbed much more strongly than the other (Fig. 33.23). A Polaroid filter transmits 80% or more of the intensity of a wave that is polarized parallel to a certain axis in the material, called the **polarizing axis,** but only 1% or less for waves that are polarized perpendicular to this axis. In one type of Polaroid filter, long-chain molecules within the filter are oriented with their axis perpendicular to the polarizing axis; these molecules preferentially absorb light that is polarized along their length, much like the conducting wires in a polarizing filter for microwaves.

33.23 A Polaroid filter is illuminated by unpolarized natural light (shown by $\vec{E}$ vectors that point in all directions perpendicular to the direction of propagation). The transmitted light is linearly polarized along the polarizing axis (shown by $\vec{E}$ vectors along the polarization direction only).

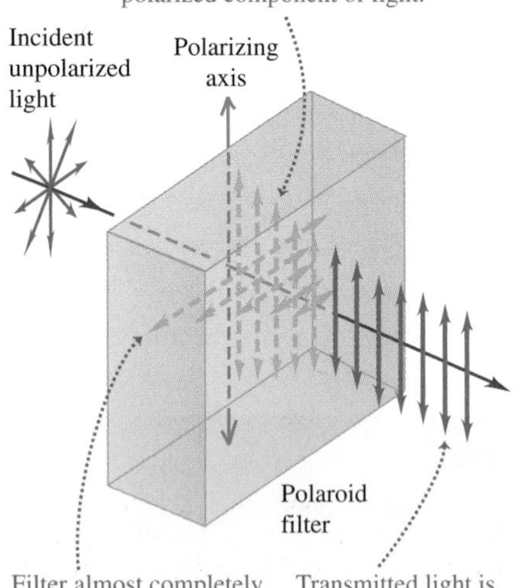
Filter only partially absorbs vertically polarized component of light.
Incident unpolarized light
Polarizing axis
Polaroid filter
Filter almost completely absorbs horizontally polarized component of light.
Transmitted light is linearly polarized in the vertical direction.

Using Polarizing Filters

An *ideal* polarizing filter (polarizer) passes 100% of the incident light that is polarized in the direction of the filter's polarizing axis but completely blocks all light that is polarized perpendicular to this axis. Such a device is an unattainable idealization, but the concept is useful in clarifying the basic ideas. In the following discussion we will assume that all polarizing filters are ideal. In Fig. 33.24 unpolarized light is incident on a flat polarizing filter. The polarizing axis is represented by the blue line. The $\vec{E}$ vector of the incident wave can be represented in terms of components parallel and perpendicular to the polarizer axis; only the component of $\vec{E}$ parallel to the polarizing axis is transmitted. Hence the light emerging from the polarizer is linearly polarized parallel to the polarizing axis.

When unpolarized light is incident on an ideal polarizer as in Fig. 33.24, the intensity of the transmitted light is *exactly half* that of the incident unpolarized light, no matter how the polarizing axis is oriented. Here's why: We can resolve the $\vec{E}$ field of the incident wave into a component parallel to the polarizing axis and a component perpendicular to it. Because the incident light is a random mixture of all states of polarization, these two components are, on average, equal. The ideal polarizer transmits only the component that is parallel to the polarizing axis, so half the incident intensity is transmitted.

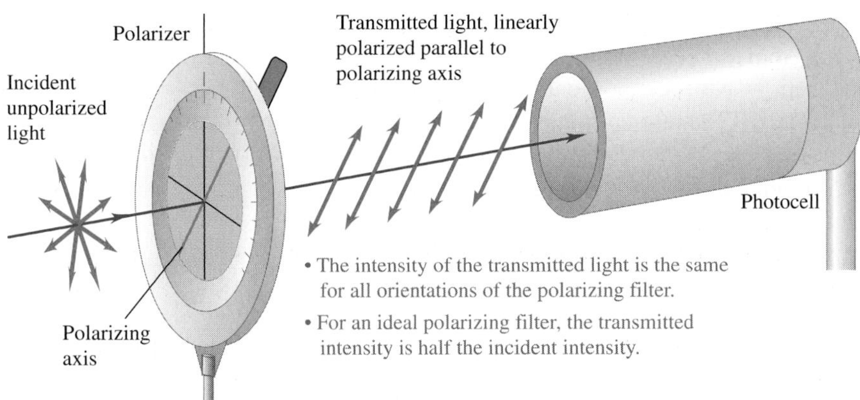
Polarizer
Transmitted light, linearly polarized parallel to polarizing axis
Incident unpolarized light
Photocell
• The intensity of the transmitted light is the same for all orientations of the polarizing filter.
• For an ideal polarizing filter, the transmitted intensity is half the incident intensity.
Polarizing axis

33.24 Unpolarized natural light is incident on the polarizing filter. The photocell measures the intensity of the transmitted linearly polarized light.

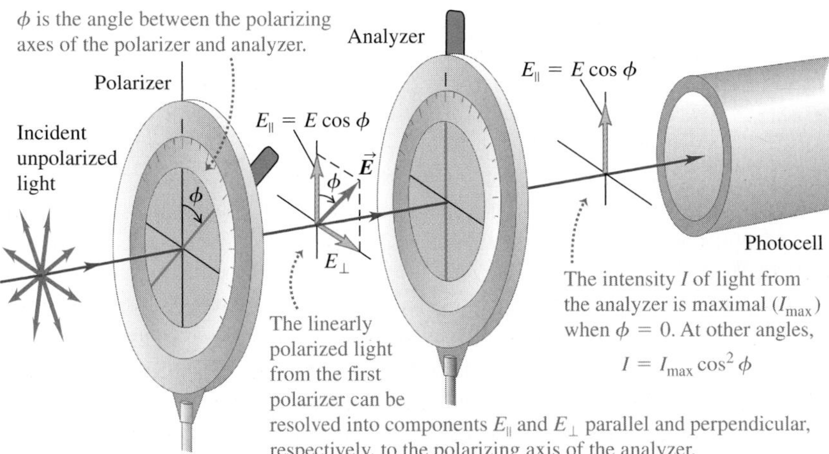
ϕ is the angle between the polarizing axes of the polarizer and analyzer.
Analyzer
Polarizer
$E_{\parallel} = E\cos\phi$
Incident unpolarized light
$E_{\parallel} = E\cos\phi$
$\vec{E}$
ϕ
$E_{\perp}$
Photocell
The intensity I of light from the analyzer is maximal (I_{max}) when $\phi = 0$. At other angles, $I = I_{max}\cos^2\phi$
The linearly polarized light from the first polarizer can be resolved into components $E_{\parallel}$ and $E_{\perp}$ parallel and perpendicular, respectively, to the polarizing axis of the analyzer.

33.25 An ideal analyzer transmits only the electric field component parallel to its transmission direction (that is, its polarizing axis).

What happens when the linearly polarized light emerging from a polarizer passes through a second polarizer, as in Fig. 33.25? Consider the general case in which the polarizing axis of the second polarizer, or *analyzer,* makes an angle ϕ with the polarizing axis of the first polarizer. We can resolve the linearly polarized light that is transmitted by the first polarizer into two components, as shown in Fig. 33.25, one parallel and the other perpendicular to the axis of the analyzer. Only the parallel component, with amplitude $E\cos\phi$, is transmitted by the analyzer. The transmitted intensity is greatest when $\phi = 0$, and it is zero when polarizer and analyzer are *crossed* so that $\phi = 90°$ (Fig. 33.26). To determine the direction of polarization of the light transmitted by the first polarizer, rotate the analyzer until the photocell in Fig. 33.25 measures zero intensity; the polarization axis of the first polarizer is then perpendicular to that of the analyzer.

33.26 These photos show the view through Polaroid sunglasses whose polarizing axes are (left) aligned ($\phi = 0$) and (right) perpendicular ($\phi = 90°$). The transmitted intensity is greatest when the axes are aligned; it is zero when the axes are perpendicular.

To find the transmitted intensity at intermediate values of the angle ϕ, we recall from our energy discussion in Section 32.4 that the intensity of an electromagnetic wave is proportional to the *square* of the amplitude of the wave [see Eq.(32.29)]. The ratio of transmitted to incident *amplitude* is $\cos\phi$, so the ratio of transmitted to incident *intensity* is $\cos^2\phi$. Thus the intensity of the light transmitted through the analyzer is

$$I = I_{max}\cos^2\phi \quad \text{(Malus's law, polarized light passing through an analyzer)} \tag{33.7}$$

where I_{max} is the maximum intensity of light transmitted (at $\phi = 0$) and I is the amount transmitted at angle ϕ. This relationship, discovered experimentally by Etienne Louis Malus in 1809, is called **Malus's law.** Malus's law applies *only* if the incident light passing through the analyzer is already linearly polarized.

Problem-Solving Strategy 33.2 Linear Polarization

MP

IDENTIFY *the relevant concepts:* Remember that in all electromagnetic waves, including light waves, the direction of the $\vec{E}$ field is the direction of polarization and is perpendicular to the propagation direction. When working with polarizers, you are really dealing with components of $\vec{E}$ parallel and perpendicular to the polarizing axis. Everything you know about components of vectors is applicable here.

SET UP *the problem* using the following steps:

1. Just as for problems in geometric optics, you should *always* start by drawing a large, neat diagram. Label all known angles, including the angles of any and all polarizing axes.
2. Determine the target variables.

EXECUTE *the solution* as follows:

1. Remember that a polarizer lets pass only electric-field components parallel to its polarizing axis.
2. If the incident light is linearly polarized and has amplitude E and intensity I_{max}, the light that passes through an ideal polarizer has amplitude $E\cos\phi$ and intensity $I_{max}\cos^2\phi$, where ϕ is the angle between the incident polarization direction and the filter's polarizing axis.
3. Unpolarized light is a random mixture of all possible polarization states, so on the average it has equal components in any two perpendicular directions. When passed through an ideal polarizer, unpolarized light becomes linearly polarized light with half the incident intensity. Partially linearly polarized light is a superposition of linearly polarized and unpolarized light.
4. The intensity (average power per unit area) of a wave is proportional to the *square* of its amplitude. If you find that two waves differ in amplitude by a certain factor, their intensities differ by the square of that factor.

EVALUATE *your answer:* Check your answer for any obvious errors. If your results say that light emerging from a polarizer has greater intensity than the incident light, something's wrong: a polarizer can't add energy to a light wave.

Example 33.5 Two polarizers in combination

In Fig. 33.25 the incident unpolarized light has intensity I_0. Find the intensities transmitted by the first and second polarizers if the angle between the axes of the two filters is 30°.

SOLUTION

IDENTIFY: This problem involves a polarizer (a polarizing filter on which unpolarized light shines, producing polarized light) and an analyzer (a second polarizing filter on which the polarized light shines).

SET UP: The diagram has already been drawn for us in Fig. 33.25. We are given the intensity I_0 of the incident natural light and the angle $\phi = 30°$ between the polarizing axes. Our target variables are the intensities of the light emerging from the first polarizer and of the light emerging from the second polarizer.

EXECUTE: As we explained above, the intensity of the linearly polarized light transmitted by the first filter is $I_0/2$. According to Eq. (33.7) with $\phi = 30°$, the second filter reduces the intensity by a factor of $\cos^2 30° = \frac{3}{4}$. Thus the intensity transmitted by the second polarizer is

$$\left(\frac{I_0}{2}\right)\left(\frac{3}{4}\right) = \frac{3}{8}I_0$$

EVALUATE: Note that the intensity decreases after each passage through a polarizer. The only situation in which the transmitted intensity does *not* decrease is if the polarizer is ideal (so it absorbs none of the light that passes through it) and if the incident light is linearly polarized along the polarizing axis, so $\phi = 0$.

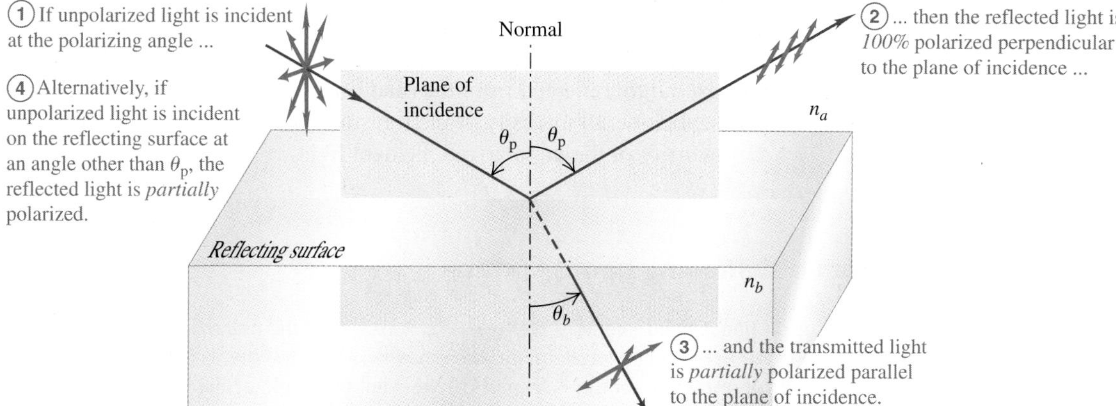
① If unpolarized light is incident at the polarizing angle ...
④ Alternatively, if unpolarized light is incident on the reflecting surface at an angle other than θ_p, the reflected light is *partially* polarized.
Normal
Plane of incidence
θ_p
θ_p
② ... then the reflected light is *100%* polarized perpendicular to the plane of incidence ...
n_a
Reflecting surface
n_b
θ_b
③ ... and the transmitted light is *partially* polarized parallel to the plane of incidence.

33.27 When light is incident on a reflecting surface at the polarizing angle, the reflected light is linearly polarized.

Polarization by Reflection

Unpolarized light can be polarized, either partially or totally, by *reflection.* In Fig. 33.27, unpolarized natural light is incident on a reflecting surface between two transparent optical materials; the plane containing the incident and reflected rays and the normal to the surface is called the **plane of incidence.** For most angles of incidence, waves for which the electric-field vector $\vec{E}$ is perpendicular to the plane of incidence (that is, parallel to the reflecting surface) are reflected more strongly than those for which $\vec{E}$ lies in this plane. In this case the reflected light is *partially polarized* in the direction perpendicular to the plane of incidence.

But at one particular angle of incidence, called the **polarizing angle** θ_p, the light for which $\vec{E}$ lies in the plane of incidence is *not reflected at all* but is completely refracted. At this same angle of incidence the light for which $\vec{E}$ is perpendicular to the plane of incidence is partially reflected and partially refracted. The *reflected* light is therefore *completely* polarized perpendicular to the plane of incidence, as shown in Fig. 33.27. The *refracted* (transmitted) light is *partially* polarized parallel to this plane; the refracted light is a mixture of the component parallel to the plane of incidence, all of which is refracted, and the remainder of the perpendicular component.

In 1812 the British scientist Sir David Brewster discovered that when the angle of incidence is equal to the polarizing angle θ_p, the reflected ray and the refracted ray are perpendicular to each other (Fig. 33.28). In this case the angle of refraction θ_b becomes the complement of θ_p, so $\theta_b = 90° - \theta_p$. From the law of refraction,

$$n_a \sin\theta_p = n_b \sin\theta_b$$

so we find

$$n_a \sin\theta_p = n_b \sin(90° - \theta_p) = n_b \cos\theta_p$$

$$\tan\theta_p = \frac{n_b}{n_a} \quad \text{(Brewster's law for the polarizing angle)} \quad (33.8)$$

This relationship is known as **Brewster's law.** Although discovered experimentally, it can also be *derived* from a wave model using Maxwell's equations.

Polarization by reflection is the reason polarizing filters are widely used in sunglasses (Fig. 33.26). When sunlight is reflected from a horizontal surface, the plane of incidence is vertical, and the reflected light contains a preponderance of

33.28 The significance of the polarizing angle. The open circles represent a component of $\vec{E}$ that is perpendicular to the plane of the figure (the plane of incidence) and parallel to the surface between the two materials.

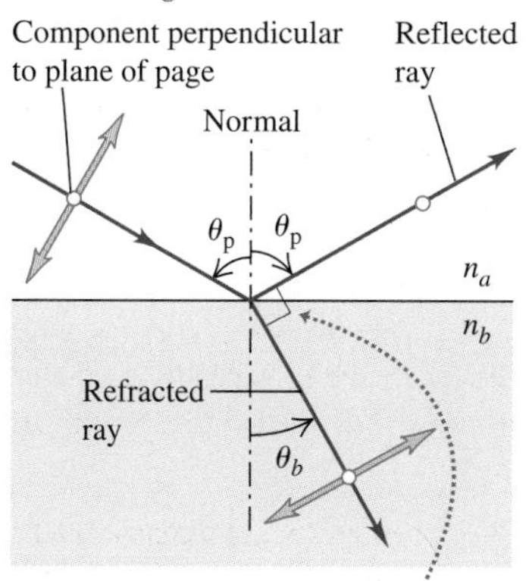
Note: This is a side view of the situation shown in Fig. 33.27.
Component perpendicular to plane of page
Reflected ray
Normal
θ_p
θ_p
n_a
n_b
Refracted ray
θ_b
When light strikes a surface at the polarizing angle, the reflected and refracted rays are perpendicular to each other and
$\tan\theta_p = \frac{n_b}{n_a}$

light that is polarized in the horizontal direction. When the reflection occurs at a smooth asphalt road surface or the surface of a lake, it causes unwanted glare. Vision can be improved by eliminating this glare. The manufacturer makes the polarizing axis of the lens material vertical, so very little of the horizontally polarized light reflected from the road is transmitted to the eyes. The glasses also reduce the overall intensity of the transmitted light to somewhat less than 50% of the intensity of the unpolarized incident light.

Example 33.6 Reflection from a swimming pool's surface

Sunlight reflects off the smooth surface of an unoccupied swimming pool. (a) At what angle of reflection is the light completely polarized? (b) What is the corresponding angle of refraction for the light that is transmitted (refracted) into the water? (c) At night an underwater floodlight is turned on in the pool. Repeat parts (a) and (b) for rays from the floodlight that strike the smooth surface from below.

SOLUTION

IDENTIFY: This problem involves polarization by reflection at an air–water interface in parts (a) and (b) and at a water–air interface in part (c).

SET UP: Figure 33.29 shows our sketches of the light rays for the situation during the day [parts (a) and (b)] and at night [part (c)]. In part (a) we're looking for the polarizing angle for light that is first in air, then in water; we find this with Brewster's law, Eq. (33.8). In part (b) we want the angle of the refracted light for this situation. In part (c) we again want the polarizing angle, but for light that is first in water, then in air. Again we use Eq. (33.8) to determine this angle.

33.29 Our sketches for this problem.

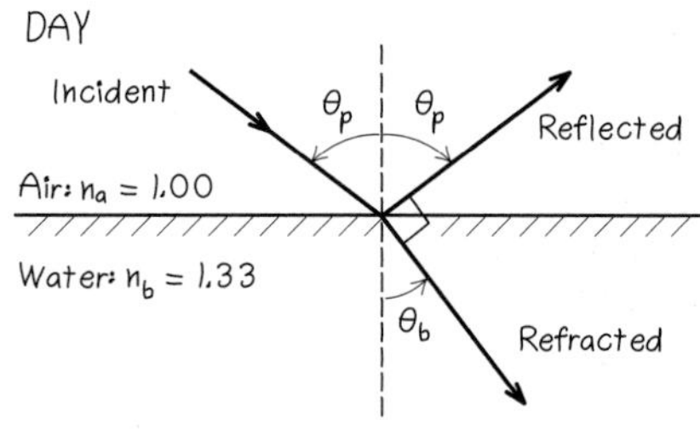

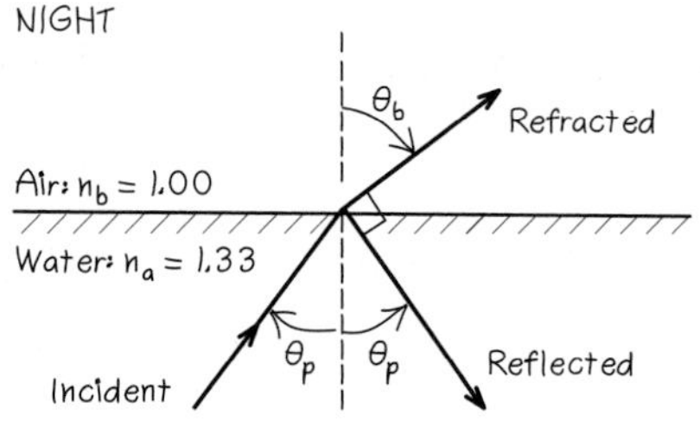

EXECUTE: (a) The top part of Fig. 33.29 shows the situation during the day. Since the light moves from air toward water, we have $n_a = 1.00$ (air) and $n_b = 1.33$ (water). From Eq. (33.8),

$$\theta_p = \arctan\frac{n_b}{n_a} = \arctan\frac{1.33}{1.00} = 53.1^\circ$$

(b) The incident light is at the polarizing angle, so the reflected and refracted rays are perpendicular; hence

$$\theta_p + \theta_b = 90^\circ$$
$$\theta_b = 90^\circ - 53.1^\circ = 36.9^\circ$$

(c) The situation at night is shown in the bottom part of Fig. 33.29. Now the light is *first* in the water, then in the air, so $n_a = 1.33$ and $n_b = 1.00$. Again using Eq. (33.8), we have

$$\theta_p = \arctan\frac{1.00}{1.33} = 36.9^\circ$$
$$\theta_b = 90^\circ - 36.9^\circ = 53.1^\circ$$

EVALUATE: We can check our answer in part (b) using Snell's law, $n_a \sin\theta_a = n_b \sin\theta_b$, or

$$\sin\theta_b = \frac{n_a \sin\theta_p}{n_b} = \frac{1.00 \sin 53.1^\circ}{1.33} = 0.600$$
$$\theta_b = 36.9^\circ$$

Note that the two polarizing angles found in parts (a) and (c) add to 90°. This is *not* an accident; can you see why?

Circular and Elliptical Polarization

Light and other electromagnetic radiation can also have *circular* or *elliptical* polarization. To introduce these concepts, let's return once more to mechanical waves on a stretched string. In Fig. 33.21, suppose the two linearly polarized waves in parts (a) and (b) are in phase and have equal amplitude. When they are superposed, each point in the string has simultaneous y- and z-displacements of equal magnitude. A little thought shows that the resultant wave lies in a plane oriented at 45° to the y- and z-axes (i.e., in a plane making a 45° angle with the *xy*- and *xz*-planes). The amplitude of the resultant wave is larger by a factor of $\sqrt{2}$ than that of either component wave, and the resultant wave is linearly polarized.

But now suppose the two equal-amplitude waves differ in phase by a quarter-cycle. Then the resultant motion of each point corresponds to a superposition of two simple harmonic motions at right angles, with a quarter-cycle phase difference. The *y*-displacement at a point is greatest at times when the *z*-displacement is zero, and vice versa. The motion of the string as a whole then no longer takes place in a single plane. It can be shown that each point on the rope moves in a *circle* in a plane parallel to the *yz*-plane. Successive points on the rope have successive phase differences, and the overall motion of the string has the appearance of a rotating helix. This is shown to the left of the polarizing filter in Fig. 33.21c. This particular superposition of two linearly polarized waves is called **circular polarization.** By convention, the wave is said to be *right circularly polarized* when the sense of motion of a particle of the string, to an observer looking *backward* along the direction of propagation, is *clockwise;* the wave is said to be *left circularly polarized* if the sense of motion is the reverse.

Figure 33.30 shows the analogous situation for an electromagnetic wave. Two sinusoidal waves of equal amplitude, polarized in the *y*- and *z*-directions and with a quarter-cycle phase difference, are superposed. The result is a wave in which the $\vec{E}$ vector at each point has a constant magnitude but *rotates* around the direction of propagation. The wave in Fig. 33.30 is propagating toward you and the $\vec{E}$ vector appears to be rotating clockwise, so it is called a *right circularly polarized* electromagnetic wave. If instead the $\vec{E}$ vector of a wave coming toward you appears to be rotating counterclockwise, it is called a *left circularly polarized* electromagnetic wave.

If the phase difference between the two component waves is something other than a quarter-cycle, or if the two component waves have different amplitudes, then each point on the string traces out not a circle but an *ellipse.* The resulting wave is said to be **elliptically polarized.**

For electromagnetic waves with radio frequencies, circular or elliptical polarization can be produced by using two antennas at right angles, fed from the same transmitter but with a phase-shifting network that introduces the appropriate phase difference. For light, the phase shift can be introduced by use of a material that exhibits *birefringence*—that is, has different indexes of refraction for different directions of polarization. A common example is calcite ($CaCO_3$). When a

33.30 Circular polarization of an electromagnetic wave moving toward you parallel to the *x*-axis. The *y*-component of $\vec{E}$ lags the *z*-component by a quarter-cycle. This phase difference results in right circular polarization.

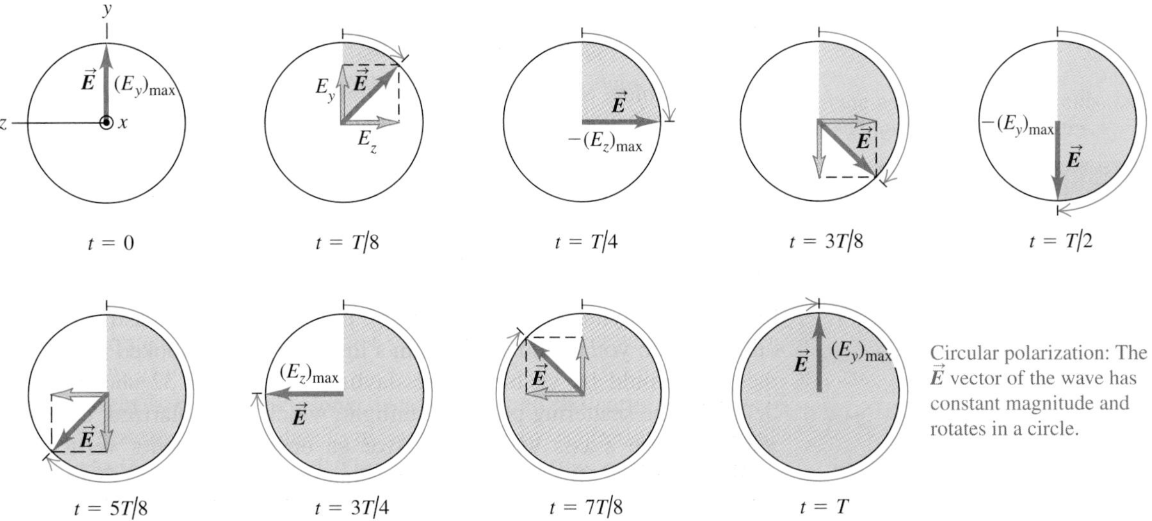

Because skylight is partially polarized, polarizers are useful in photography. The sky in a photograph can be darkened by orienting the polarizer axis to be perpendicular to the predominant direction of polarization of the scattered light. The most strongly polarized light comes from parts of the sky that are 90° away from the sun—for example, from directly overhead when the sun is on the horizon at sunrise or sunset.

33.7 Huygens's Principle

The laws of reflection and refraction of light rays that we introduced in Section 33.2 were discovered experimentally long before the wave nature of light was firmly established. However, we can *derive* these laws from wave considerations and show that they are consistent with the wave nature of light. The same kind of analysis that we use here will be of central importance in Chapters 35 and 36 in our discussion of physical optics.

We begin with a principle called **Huygens's principle.** This principle, stated originally by the Dutch scientist Christiaan Huygens in 1678, is a geometrical method for finding, from the known shape of a wave front at some instant, the shape of the wave front at some later time. Huygens assumed that **every point of a wave front may be considered the source of secondary wavelets that spread out in all directions with a speed equal to the speed of propagation of the wave.** The new wave front at a later time is then found by constructing a surface *tangent* to the secondary wavelets or, as it is called, the *envelope* of the wavelets. All the results that we obtain from Huygens's principle can also be obtained from Maxwell's equations. Thus it is not an independent principle, but it is often very convenient for calculations with wave phenomena.

33.34 Applying Huygens's principle to wave front AA' to construct a new wave front BB'.

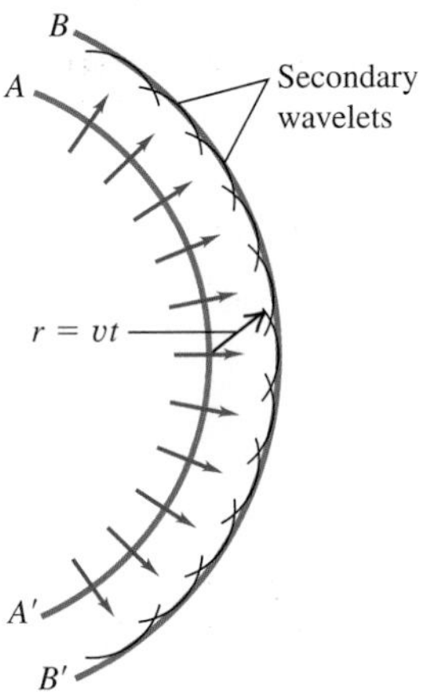

Huygens's principle is shown in Fig. 33.34. The original wave front AA' is traveling outward from a source, as indicated by the arrows. We want to find the shape of the wave front after a time interval t. Let v be the speed of propagation of the wave; then in time t it travels a distance vt. We construct several circles (traces of spherical wavelets) with radius $r = vt$, centered at points along AA'. The trace of the envelope of these wavelets, which is the new wave front, is the curve BB'. We are assuming that the speed v is the same at all points and in all directions.

33.35 Using Huygens's principle to derive the law of reflection.

(a) Successive positions of a plane wave AA' as it is reflected from a plane surface

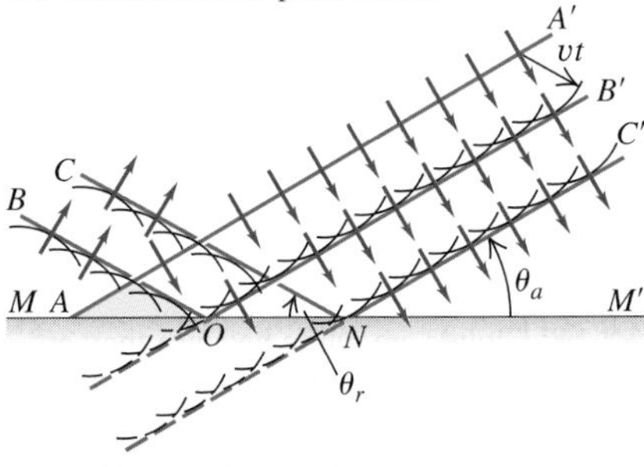

(b) Magnified portion of (a)

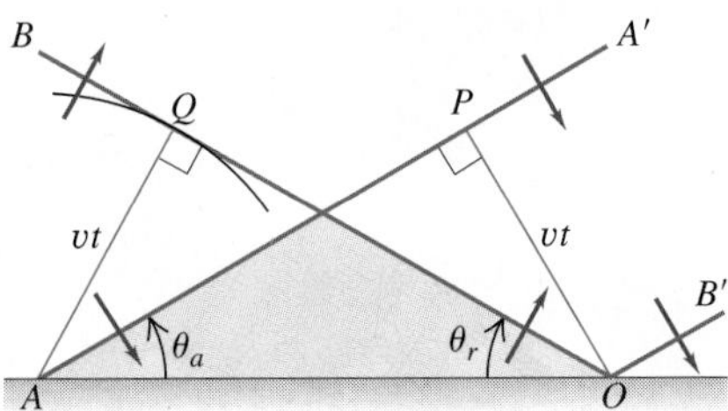

Reflection and Huygens's Principle

To derive the law of reflection from Huygens's principle, we consider a plane wave approaching a plane reflecting surface. In Fig. 33.35a the lines AA', OB', and NC' represent successive positions of a wave front approaching the surface MM'. Point A on the wave front AA' has just arrived at the reflecting surface. We can use Huygens's principle to find the position of the wave front after a time interval t. With points on AA' as centers, we draw several secondary wavelets with radius vt. The wavelets that originate near the upper end of AA' spread out unhindered, and their envelope gives the portion OB' of the new wave front. If the reflecting surface were not there, the wavelets originating near the lower end of AA' would similarly reach the positions shown by the broken circular arcs. Instead, these wavelets strike the reflecting surface.

The effect of the reflecting surface is to *change the direction* of travel of those wavelets that strike it, so the part of a wavelet that would have penetrated the surface actually lies to the left of it, as shown by the full lines. The first such wavelet is centered at point A; the envelope of all such reflected wavelets is the portion OB of the wave front. The trace of the entire wave front at this instant is the bent line BOB'. A similar construction gives the line CNC' for the wave front after another interval t.

33.32 When the sunbathing observer on the left looks up, he sees blue, polarized sunlight that has been scattered by air molecules. The observer on the right sees reddened, unpolarized light when he looks at the sun.

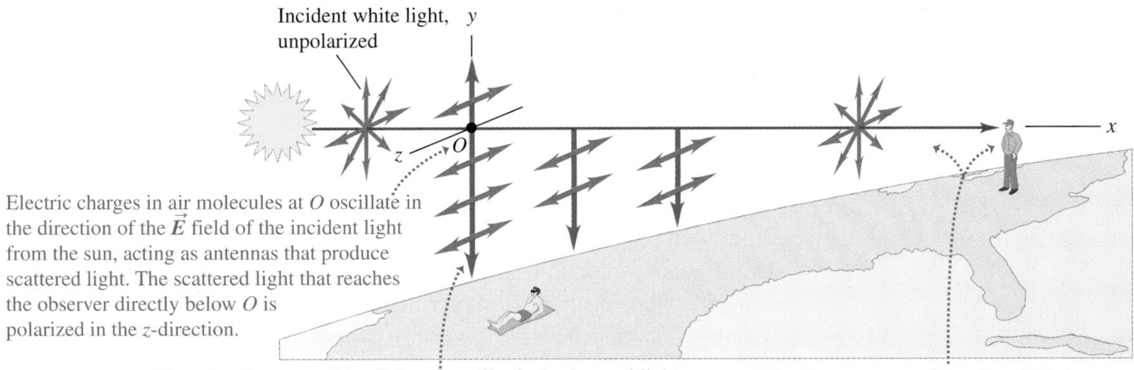
Incident white light, unpolarized
y
x
z
O
Electric charges in air molecules at O oscillate in the direction of the $\vec{E}$ field of the incident light from the sun, acting as antennas that produce scattered light. The scattered light that reaches the observer directly below O is polarized in the z-direction.
Air molecules scatter blue light more effectively than red light; we see the sky overhead by scattered light, so it looks blue.
This observer sees reddened sunlight because most of the blue light has been scattered out.

Since light is a transverse wave, the direction of the electric field in any component of the sunlight lies in the yz-plane, and the motion of the charges takes place in this plane. There is no field, and hence no motion of charges, in the direction of the x-axis.

An incident light wave sets the electric charges in the molecules at point O vibrating along the line of $\vec{E}$. We can resolve this vibration into two components, one along the y-axis and the other along the z-axis. Each component in the incident light produces the equivalent of two molecular "antennas," oscillating with the same frequency as the incident light and lying along the y- and z-axes.

We mentioned in Chapter 32 that an oscillating charge, like those in an antenna, does not radiate in the direction of its oscillation. (See Fig. 32.3 in Section 32.1.) Thus the "antenna" along the y-axis does not send any light to the observer directly below it, although it does emit light in other directions. Therefore the only light reaching this observer comes from the other molecular "antenna," corresponding to the oscillation of charge along the z-axis. This light is linearly polarized, with its electric field along the z-axis (parallel to the "antenna"). The red vectors on the y-axis below point O in Fig. 33.32 show the direction of polarization of the light reaching the observer.

As the original beam of sunlight passes though the atmosphere, its intensity decreases as its energy goes into the scattered light. Detailed analysis of the scattering process shows that the intensity of the light scattered from air molecules increases in proportion to the fourth power of the frequency (inversely to the fourth power of the wavelength). Thus the intensity ratio for the two ends of the visible spectrum is $(700\text{ nm}/400\text{ nm})^4 = 9.4$. Roughly speaking, scattered light contains nine times as much blue light as red, and that's why the sky is blue.

Clouds contain a high concentration of water droplets or ice crystals, which also scatter light. Because of this high concentration, light passing through the cloud has many more opportunities for scattering than does light passing through a clear sky. Thus light of *all* wavelengths is eventually scattered out of the cloud, so the cloud looks white (Fig. 33.33). Milk looks white for the same reason; the scattering is due to fat globules in the milk. If you dilute milk by mixing it with enough water, the concentration of fat globules will be so low that only blue light will be substantially scattered; the dilute solution will look blue, not white. (Nonfat milk, which also has a very low concentration of globules, looks somewhat bluish for this same reason.)

Near sunset, when sunlight has to travel a long distance through the earth's atmosphere, a substantial fraction of the blue light is removed by scattering. White light minus blue light looks yellow or red. This explains the yellow or red hue that we so often see from the setting sun (and that is seen by the observer at the far right of Fig. 33.32).

33.33 Clouds are white because they efficiently scatter sunlight of all wavelengths.

Because skylight is partially polarized, polarizers are useful in photography. The sky in a photograph can be darkened by orienting the polarizer axis to be perpendicular to the predominant direction of polarization of the scattered light. The most strongly polarized light comes from parts of the sky that are 90° away from the sun—for example, from directly overhead when the sun is on the horizon at sunrise or sunset.

33.7 Huygens's Principle

The laws of reflection and refraction of light rays that we introduced in Section 33.2 were discovered experimentally long before the wave nature of light was firmly established. However, we can *derive* these laws from wave considerations and show that they are consistent with the wave nature of light. The same kind of analysis that we use here will be of central importance in Chapters 35 and 36 in our discussion of physical optics.

We begin with a principle called **Huygens's principle.** This principle, stated originally by the Dutch scientist Christiaan Huygens in 1678, is a geometrical method for finding, from the known shape of a wave front at some instant, the shape of the wave front at some later time. Huygens assumed that **every point of a wave front may be considered the source of secondary wavelets that spread out in all directions with a speed equal to the speed of propagation of the wave.** The new wave front at a later time is then found by constructing a surface *tangent* to the secondary wavelets or, as it is called, the *envelope* of the wavelets. All the results that we obtain from Huygens's principle can also be obtained from Maxwell's equations. Thus it is not an independent principle, but it is often very convenient for calculations with wave phenomena.

33.34 Applying Huygens's principle to wave front AA' to construct a new wave front BB'.

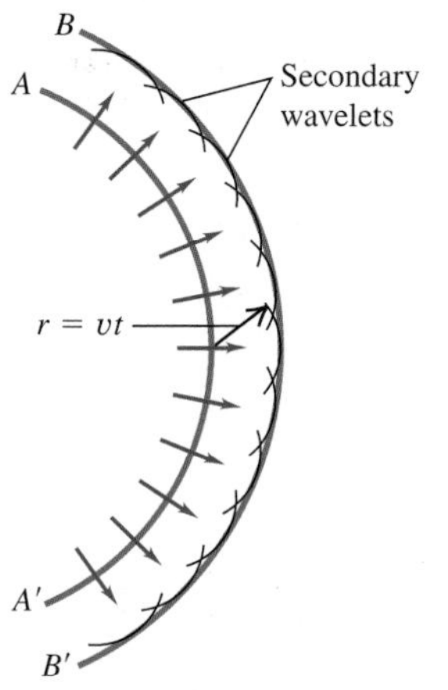

Huygens's principle is shown in Fig. 33.34. The original wave front AA' is traveling outward from a source, as indicated by the arrows. We want to find the shape of the wave front after a time interval t. Let v be the speed of propagation of the wave; then in time t it travels a distance vt. We construct several circles (traces of spherical wavelets) with radius $r = vt$, centered at points along AA'. The trace of the envelope of these wavelets, which is the new wave front, is the curve BB'. We are assuming that the speed v is the same at all points and in all directions.

33.35 Using Huygens's principle to derive the law of reflection.

(a) Successive positions of a plane wave AA' as it is reflected from a plane surface

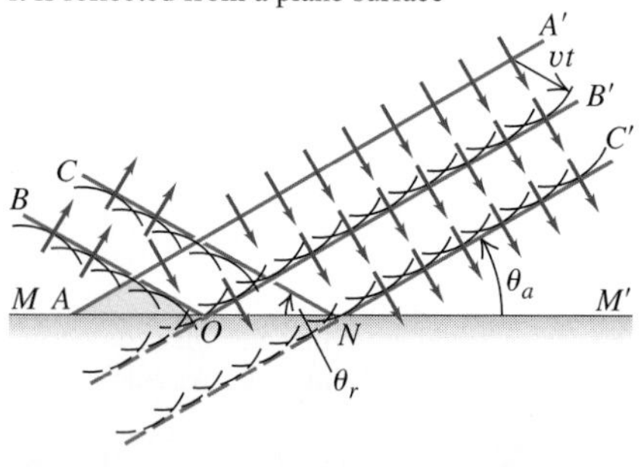

(b) Magnified portion of (a)

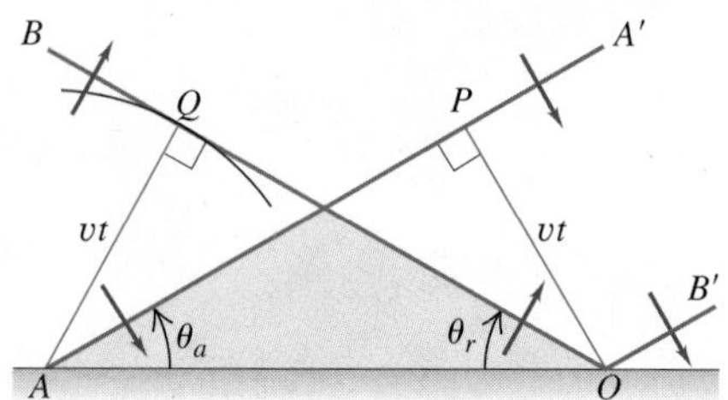

Reflection and Huygens's Principle

To derive the law of reflection from Huygens's principle, we consider a plane wave approaching a plane reflecting surface. In Fig. 33.35a the lines AA', OB', and NC' represent successive positions of a wave front approaching the surface MM'. Point A on the wave front AA' has just arrived at the reflecting surface. We can use Huygens's principle to find the position of the wave front after a time interval t. With points on AA' as centers, we draw several secondary wavelets with radius vt. The wavelets that originate near the upper end of AA' spread out unhindered, and their envelope gives the portion OB' of the new wave front. If the reflecting surface were not there, the wavelets originating near the lower end of AA' would similarly reach the positions shown by the broken circular arcs. Instead, these wavelets strike the reflecting surface.

The effect of the reflecting surface is to *change the direction* of travel of those wavelets that strike it, so the part of a wavelet that would have penetrated the surface actually lies to the left of it, as shown by the full lines. The first such wavelet is centered at point A; the envelope of all such reflected wavelets is the portion OB of the wave front. The trace of the entire wave front at this instant is the bent line BOB'. A similar construction gives the line CNC' for the wave front after another interval t.

xy- and xz-planes). The amplitude of the resultant wave is larger by a factor of $\sqrt{2}$ than that of either component wave, and the resultant wave is linearly polarized.

But now suppose the two equal-amplitude waves differ in phase by a quarter-cycle. Then the resultant motion of each point corresponds to a superposition of two simple harmonic motions at right angles, with a quarter-cycle phase difference. The y-displacement at a point is greatest at times when the z-displacement is zero, and vice versa. The motion of the string as a whole then no longer takes place in a single plane. It can be shown that each point on the rope moves in a *circle* in a plane parallel to the yz-plane. Successive points on the rope have successive phase differences, and the overall motion of the string has the appearance of a rotating helix. This is shown to the left of the polarizing filter in Fig. 33.21c. This particular superposition of two linearly polarized waves is called **circular polarization.** By convention, the wave is said to be *right circularly polarized* when the sense of motion of a particle of the string, to an observer looking *backward* along the direction of propagation, is *clockwise;* the wave is said to be *left circularly polarized* if the sense of motion is the reverse.

Figure 33.30 shows the analogous situation for an electromagnetic wave. Two sinusoidal waves of equal amplitude, polarized in the y- and z-directions and with a quarter-cycle phase difference, are superposed. The result is a wave in which the $\vec{E}$ vector at each point has a constant magnitude but *rotates* around the direction of propagation. The wave in Fig. 33.30 is propagating toward you and the $\vec{E}$ vector appears to be rotating clockwise, so it is called a *right circularly polarized* electromagnetic wave. If instead the $\vec{E}$ vector of a wave coming toward you appears to be rotating counterclockwise, it is called a *left circularly polarized* electromagnetic wave.

If the phase difference between the two component waves is something other than a quarter-cycle, or if the two component waves have different amplitudes, then each point on the string traces out not a circle but an *ellipse.* The resulting wave is said to be **elliptically polarized.**

For electromagnetic waves with radio frequencies, circular or elliptical polarization can be produced by using two antennas at right angles, fed from the same transmitter but with a phase-shifting network that introduces the appropriate phase difference. For light, the phase shift can be introduced by use of a material that exhibits *birefringence*—that is, has different indexes of refraction for different directions of polarization. A common example is calcite ($CaCO_3$). When a

33.30 Circular polarization of an electromagnetic wave moving toward you parallel to the x-axis. The y-component of $\vec{E}$ lags the z-component by a quarter-cycle. This phase difference results in right circular polarization.

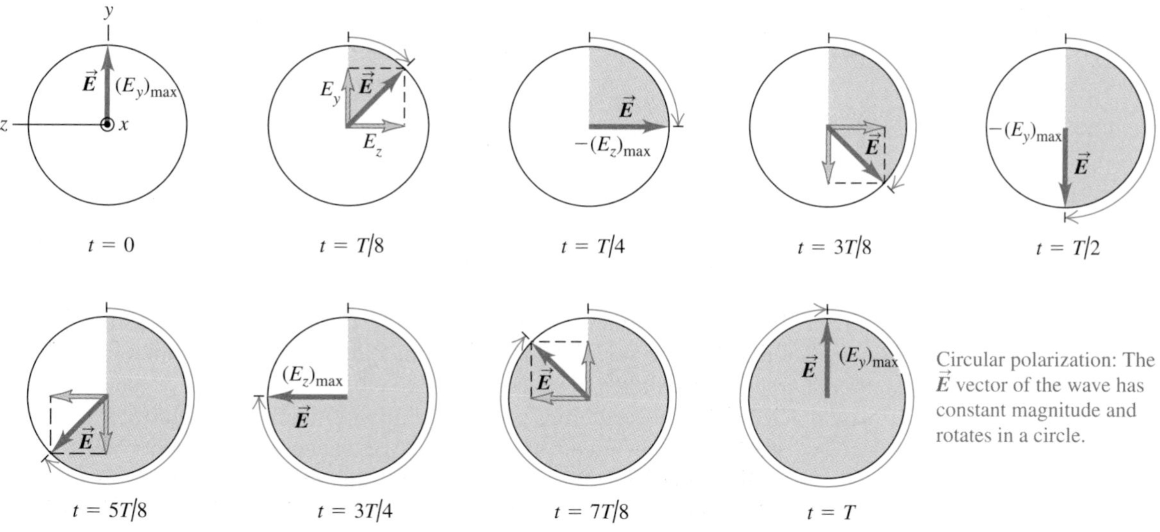

calcite crystal is oriented appropriately in a beam of unpolarized light, its refractive index (for a wavelength in vacuum of 589 nm) is 1.658 for one direction of polarization and 1.486 for the perpendicular direction. When two waves with equal amplitude and with perpendicular directions of polarization enter such a material, they travel with different speeds. If they are in phase when they enter the material, then in general they are no longer in phase when they emerge. If the crystal is just thick enough to introduce a quarter-cycle phase difference, then the crystal converts linearly polarized light to circularly polarized light. Such a crystal is called a *quarter-wave plate.* Such a plate also converts circularly polarized light to linearly polarized light. Can you prove this? (See Problem 33.43.)

33.31 Photoelastic stress analysis of a model of a cross section of a Gothic cathedral. The masonry construction that was used for this kind of building had great strength in compression but very little in tension (see Section 11.4). Inadequate buttressing and high winds sometimes caused tensile stresses in normally compressed structural elements, leading to some spectacular collapses.

Photoelasticity

Some optical materials that are not normally birefringent become so when they are subjected to mechanical stress. This is the basis of the science of *photoelasticity.* Stresses in girders, boiler plates, gear teeth, and cathedral pillars can be analyzed by constructing a transparent model of the object, usually of a plastic material, subjecting it to stress, and examining it between a polarizer and an analyzer in the crossed position. Very complicated stress distributions can be studied by these optical methods. ?

Figure 33.31 is a photograph of a photoelastic model under stress. The polarized light that enters the model can be thought of as having a component along each of the two directions of the birefringent plastic. Since these two components travel through the plastic at different speeds, the light that emerges from the other side of the model can have a different overall direction of polarization. Hence some of this transmitted light will be able to pass through the analyzer even though its polarization axis is at a 90° angle to the polarizer's axis, and the stressed areas in the plastic will appear as bright spots. The amount of birefringence is different for different wavelengths and hence different colors of light; the color that appears at each location in Fig. 33.31 is that for which the transmitted light is most nearly polarized along the analyzer's polarization axis.

Test Your Understanding of Section 33.5 You are taking a photograph of a sunlit high-rise office building. In order to minimize the reflections from the building's windows, you place a polarizing filter on the camera lens. How should you orient the filter? (i) with the polarizing axis vertical; (ii) with the polarizing axis horizontal; (iii) either orientation will minimize the reflections just as well; (iv) neither orientation will have any effect. MP

*33.6 Scattering of Light

The sky is blue. Sunsets are red. Skylight is partially polarized; that's why the sky looks darker from some angles than from others when it is viewed through Polaroid sunglasses. As we will see, a single phenomenon is responsible for all of these effects.

When you look at the daytime sky, the light that you see is sunlight that has been absorbed and then re-radiated in a variety of directions. This process is called **scattering.** (If the earth had no atmosphere, the sky would appear as black in the daytime as it does at night, just as it does to an astronaut in space or on the moon; you would see the sun's light only if you looked directly at it, and the stars would be visible in the daytime.) Figure 33.32 shows some of the details of the scattering process. Sunlight, which is unpolarized, comes from the left along the x-axis and passes over an observer looking vertically upward along the y-axis. (We are viewing the situation from the side.) Consider the molecules of the earth's atmosphere located at point O. The electric field in the beam of sunlight sets the electric charges in these molecules into vibration.

From plane geometry the angle θ_a between the incident *wave front* and the *surface* is the same as that between the incident *ray* and the *normal* to the surface and is therefore the angle of incidence. Similarly, θ_r is the angle of reflection. To find the relationship between these angles, we consider Fig. 33.35b. From O we draw $OP = vt$, perpendicular to AA'. Now OB, by construction, is tangent to a circle of radius vt with center at A. If we draw AQ from A to the point of tangency, the triangles APO and OQA are congruent because they are right triangles with the side AO in common and with $AQ = OP = vt$. The angle θ_a therefore equals the angle θ_r, and we have the law of reflection.

Refraction and Huygens's Principle

We can derive the law of *refraction* by a similar procedure. In Fig. 33.36a we consider a wave front, represented by line AA', for which point A has just arrived at the boundary surface SS' between two transparent materials a and b, with indexes of refraction n_a and n_b and wave speeds v_a and v_b. (The *reflected* waves are not shown in the figure; they proceed as in Fig. 33.35.) We can apply Huygens's principle to find the position of the refracted wave fronts after a time t.

With points on AA' as centers, we draw several secondary wavelets. Those originating near the upper end of AA' travel with speed v_a and, after a time interval t, are spherical surfaces of radius $v_a t$. The wavelet originating at point A, however, is traveling in the second material b with speed v_b and at time t is a spherical surface of radius $v_b t$. The envelope of the wavelets from the original wave front is the plane whose trace is the bent line BOB'. A similar construction leads to the trace CPC' after a second interval t.

The angles θ_a and θ_b between the surface and the incident and refracted wave fronts are the angle of incidence and the angle of refraction, respectively. To find the relationship between these angles, refer to Fig. 33.36b. We draw $OQ = v_a t$, perpendicular to AQ, and we draw $AB = v_b t$, perpendicular to BO. From the right triangle AOQ,

$$\sin\theta_a = \frac{v_a t}{AO}$$

and from the right triangle AOB,

$$\sin\theta_b = \frac{v_b t}{AO}$$

Combining these, we find

$$\frac{\sin\theta_a}{\sin\theta_b} = \frac{v_a}{v_b} \tag{33.9}$$

We have defined the index of refraction n of a material as the ratio of the speed of light c in vacuum to its speed v in the material: $n_a = c/v_a$ and $n_b = c/v_b$. Thus

$$\frac{n_b}{n_a} = \frac{c/v_b}{c/v_a} = \frac{v_a}{v_b}$$

and we can rewrite Eq. (33.9) as

$$\frac{\sin\theta_a}{\sin\theta_b} = \frac{n_b}{n_a} \quad \text{or}$$

$$n_a \sin\theta_a = n_b \sin\theta_b$$

which we recognize as Snell's law, Eq. (33.4). So we have derived Snell's law from a wave theory. Alternatively, we may choose to regard Snell's law as an experimental result that defines the index of refraction of a material; in that case

33.36 Using Huygens's principle to derive the law of refraction. The case $v_b < v_a$ $(n_b > n_a)$ is shown.

(a) Successive positions of a plane wave AA' as it is refracted by a plane surface

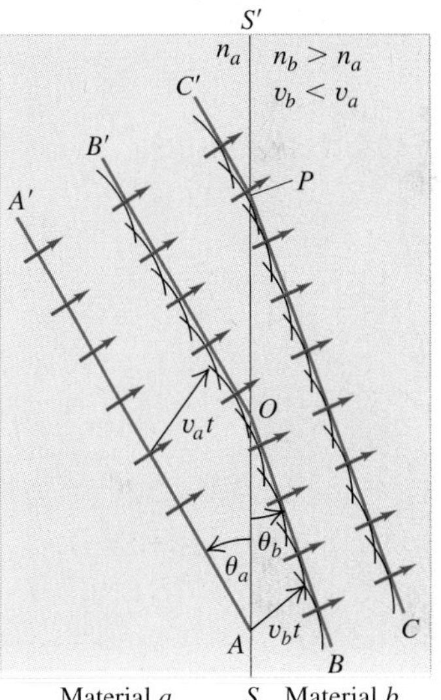

(b) Magnified portion of (a)

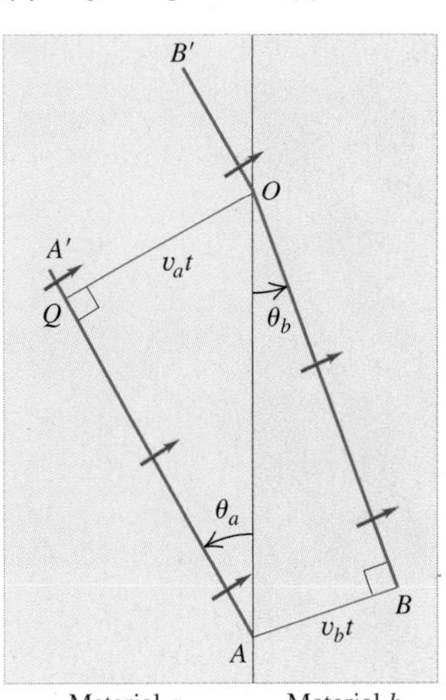

33.37 How mirages are formed.

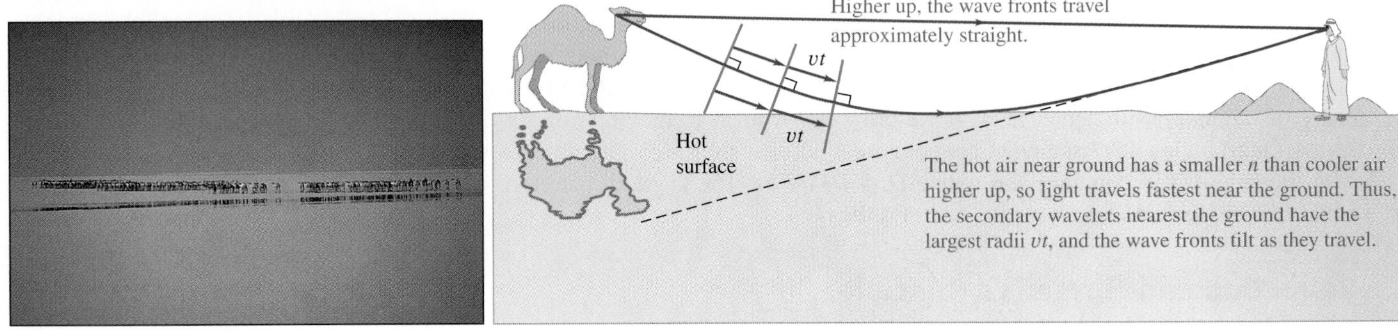

this analysis helps to confirm the relationship $v = c/n$ for the speed of light in a material.

Mirages offer an interesting example of Huygens's principle in action. When the surface of pavement or desert sand is heated intensely by the sun, a hot, less dense, smaller-n layer of air forms near the surface. The speed of light is slightly greater in the hotter air near the ground, the Huygens wavelets have slightly larger radii, the wave fronts tilt slightly, and rays that were headed toward the surface with a large angle of incidence (near 90°) can be bent up as shown in Fig. 33.37. Light farther from the ground is bent less and travels nearly in a straight line. The observer sees the object in its natural position, with an inverted image below it, as though seen in a horizontal reflecting surface. Even when the turbulence of the heated air prevents a clear inverted image from being formed, the mind of the thirsty traveler can interpret the apparent reflecting surface as a sheet of water.

It is important to keep in mind that Maxwell's equations are the fundamental relationships for electromagnetic wave propagation. But it is a remarkable fact that Huygens's principle anticipated Maxwell's analysis by two centuries. Maxwell provided the theoretical underpinning for Huygens's principle. Every point in an electromagnetic wave, with its time-varying electric and magnetic fields, acts as a source of the continuing wave, as predicted by Ampere's and Faraday's laws.

Test Your Understanding of Section 33.7 Sound travels faster in warm air than in cold air. Imagine a weather front that runs north-south, with warm air to the west of the front and cold air to the east. A sound wave traveling in a northeast direction in the warm air encounters this front. How will the direction of this sound wave change when it passes into the cold air? (i) The wave direction will deflect toward the north; (ii) the wave direction will deflect toward the east; (iii) the wave direction will be unchanged.

CHAPTER 33 SUMMARY

Light and its properties: Light is an electromagnetic wave. When emitted or absorbed, it also shows particle properties. It is emitted by accelerated electric charges. The speed of light is a fundamental physical constant.

A wave front is a surface of constant phase; wave fronts move with a speed equal to the propagation speed of the wave. A ray is a line along the direction of propagation, perpendicular to the wave fronts. Representation of light by rays is the basis of geometric optics.

When light is transmitted from one material to another, the frequency of the light is unchanged, but the wavelength and wave speed can change. The index of refraction n of a material is the ratio of the speed of light in vacuum c to the speed v in the material. If λ_0 is the wavelength in vacuum, the same wave has a shorter wavelength λ in a medium with index of refraction n. (See Example 33.2.)

The variation of index of refraction n with wavelength λ is called dispersion. Usually n decreases with increasing λ.

$$n = \frac{c}{v} \quad (33.1)$$

$$\lambda = \frac{\lambda_0}{n} \quad (33.5)$$

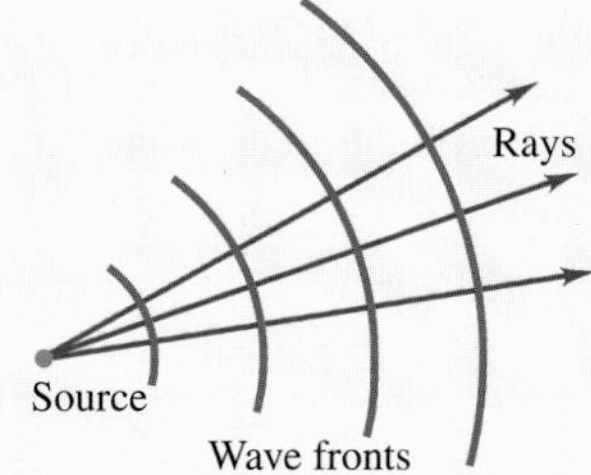

Reflection and refraction: At a smooth interface between two optical materials, the incident, reflected, and refracted rays and the normal to the interface all lie in a single plane called the plane of incidence. The law of reflection states that the angles of incidence and reflection are equal. The law of refraction relates the angles of incidence and refraction to the indexes of refraction of the materials. Angles of incidence, reflection, and refraction are always measured from the normal to the surface. (See Examples 33.1 and 33.3.)

$$\theta_r = \theta_a \quad (33.2)$$
(law of reflection)

$$n_a \sin\theta_a = n_b \sin\theta_b \quad (33.4)$$
(law of refraction)

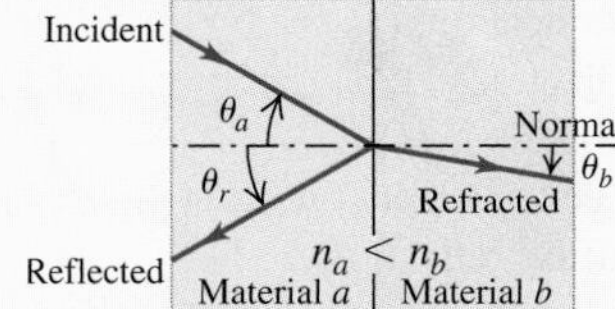

Total internal reflection: When a ray travels in a material of greater index of refraction n_a toward a material of smaller index n_b, total internal reflection occurs at the interface when the angle of incidence exceeds a critical angle θ_{crit}. (See Example 33.4.)

$$\sin\theta_{crit} = \frac{n_b}{n_a} \quad (33.6)$$

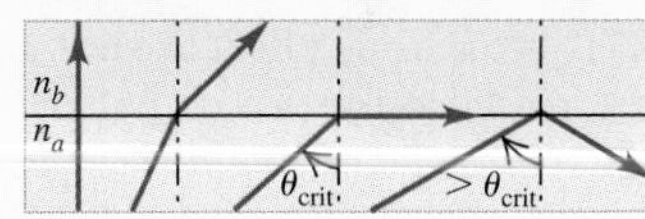

Polarization of light: The direction of polarization of a linearly polarized electromagnetic wave is the direction of the $\vec{E}$ field. A polarizing filter passes waves that are linearly polarized along its polarizing axis and blocks waves polarized perpendicularly to that axis. When polarized light of intensity I_{max} is incident on a polarizing filter used as an analyzer, the intensity I of the light transmitted through the analyzer depends on the angle ϕ between the polarization direction of the incident light and the polarizing axis of the analyzer. (See Example 33.5.)When two linearly polarized waves with a phase difference are superposed, the result is circularly or elliptically polarized light. In this case the $\vec{E}$ vector is not confined to a plane containing the direction of propagation, but rather describes circles or ellipses in planes perpendicular to the propagation direction.

Light is scattered by air molecules. The scattered light is partially polarized.

$$I = I_{max}\cos^2\phi \quad (33.7)$$
(Malus's law)

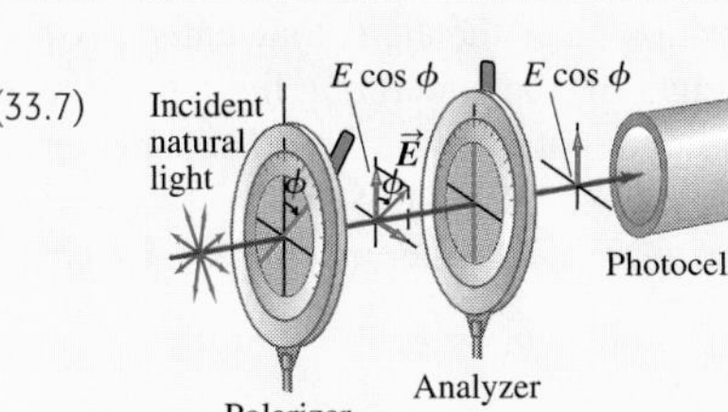

Polarization by reflection: When unpolarized light strikes an interface between two materials, Brewster's law states that the reflected light is completely polarized perpendicular to the plane of incidence (parallel to the interface) if the angle of incidence equals the polarizing angle θ_p. (See Example 33.6.)

$$\tan\theta_p = \frac{n_b}{n_a} \quad (33.8)$$

(Brewster's law)

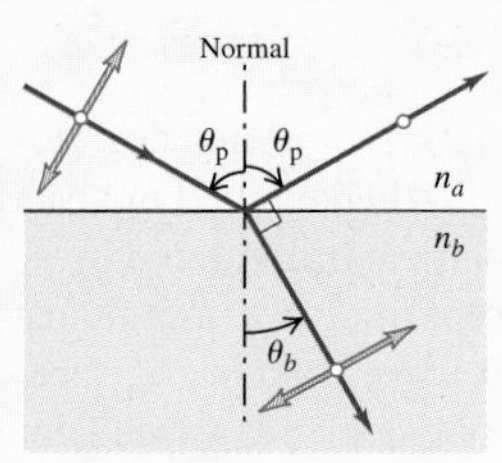

Huygens's principle: Huygens's principle states that if the position of a wave front at one instant is known, then the position of the front at a later time can be constructed by imagining the front as a source of secondary wavelets. Huygens's principle can be used to derive the laws of reflection and refraction.

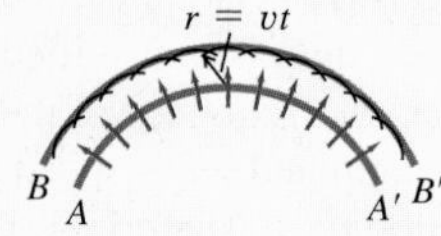

Key Terms

optics, *1121*
wave front, *1122*
ray, *1123*
geometric optics, *1123*
physical optics, *1123*
reflection, *1123*
refraction, *1123*
specular reflection, *1124*
diffuse reflection, *1124*
index of refraction (refractive index), *1124*
law of reflection, *1125*
law of refraction (Snell's law), *1125*
critical angle, *1130*
total internal reflection, *1130*
dispersion, *1132*
linear polarization, *1134*
polarizing filter (polarizer), *1134*
unpolarized light (natural light), *1135*
dichroism, *1136*
polarizing axis, *1136*
Malus's law, *1138*
plane of incidence, *1139*
polarizing angle, *1139*
Brewster's law, *1139*
circular polarization, *1141*
elliptical polarization, *1141*
scattering, *1142*
Huygens's principle, *1144*

Answer to Chapter Opening Question ?

This is the same effect as shown in Fig. 33.31. The drafting tools are placed between two polarizing filters whose polarizing axes are perpendicular. In places where the clear plastic is under stress, the plastic becomes birefringent; that is, light travels through it at a speed that depends on its polarization. The result is that the light that emerges from the plastic has a different polarization than the light that enters. A spot on the plastic appears bright if the emerging light has the same polarization as the second polarizing filter. The amount of birefringence depends on the wavelength of the light as well as the amount of stress on the plastic, so different colors are seen at different locations on the plastic.

Answers to Test Your Understanding Questions

33.1 Answer: (iii) The waves go farther in the y-direction in a given amount of time than in the other directions, so the wave fronts are elongated in the y-direction.

33.2 Answers: (a) (ii), (b) (iii) As shown in the figure, light rays coming from the fish bend away from the normal when they pass from the water $(n = 1.33)$ into the air $(n = 1.00)$. As a result, the fish appears to be higher in the water than it actually is. Hence you should aim a spear *below* the apparent position of the fish. If you use a laser beam, you should aim *at* the apparent position of the fish: The beam of laser light takes the same path from you to the fish as ordinary light takes from the fish to you (though in the opposite direction).

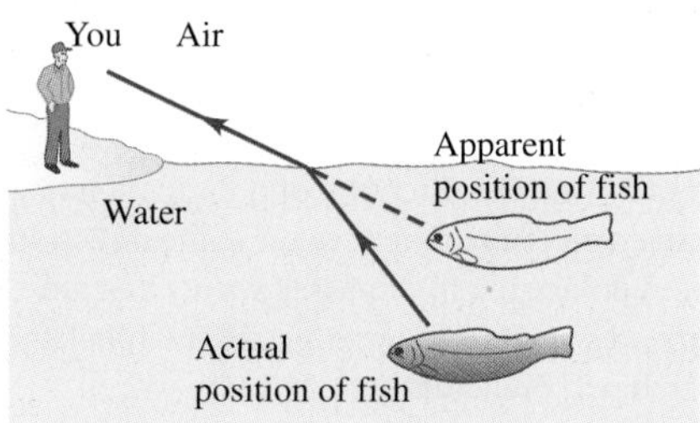

33.3 Answers: (i), (ii) Total internal reflection can occur only if two conditions are met: n_b must be less than n_a, and the critical angle θ_{crit} (where $\sin\theta_{crit} = n_b/n_a$) must be smaller than the angle of incidence θ_a. In the first two cases both conditions are met: The critical angles are (i) $\theta_{crit} = \sin^{-1}(1/1.33) = 48.8°$ and (ii) $\theta_{crit} = \sin^{-1}(1.33/1.52) = 61.0°$, both of which are smaller than $\theta_a = 70°$. In the third case $n_b = 1.52$ is greater than $n_a = 1.33$, so total internal reflection cannot occur for any incident angle.

33.5 Answer: (ii) The sunlight reflected from the windows of the high-rise building is partially polarized in the vertical direction, since each window lies in a vertical plane. The Polaroid filter in front of the lens is oriented with its polarizing axis perpendicular to the dominant direction of polarization of the reflected light.
33.7 Answer: (ii) Huygens's principle applies to waves of all kinds, including sound waves. Hence this situation is exactly like that shown in Fig. 33.36, with material *a* representing the warm air, material *b* representing the cold air in which the waves travel more slowly, and the interface between the materials representing the weather front. North is toward the top of the figure and east is toward the right, so Fig. 33.36 shows that the rays (which indicate the direction of propagation) deflect toward the east.

PROBLEMS

For instructor-assigned homework, go to **www.masteringphysics.com** 

Discussion Questions

Q33.1. Light requires about 8 minutes to travel from the sun to the earth. Is it delayed appreciably by the earth's atmosphere? Explain.
Q33.2. Sunlight or starlight passing through the earth's atmosphere is always bent toward the vertical. Why? Does this mean that a star is not really where it appears to be? Explain.
Q33.3. A beam of light goes from one material into another. On *physical* grounds, explain *why* the wavelength changes but the frequency and period do not.
Q33.4. A student claimed that, because of atmospheric refraction (see Discussion Question Q33.2), the sun can be seen after it has set and that the day is therefore longer than it would be if the earth had no atmosphere. First, what does she mean by saying that the sun can be seen after it has set? Second, comment on the validity of her conclusion.
Q33.5. When hot air rises from a radiator or heating duct, objects behind it appear to shimmer or waver. What causes this?
Q33.6. Devise straightforward experiments to measure the speed of light in a given glass using (a) Snell's law; (b) total internal reflection; (c) Brewster's law.
Q33.7. Sometimes when looking at a window, you see two reflected images slightly displaced from each other. What causes this?
Q33.8. If you look up from underneath toward the surface of the water in your aquarium, you may see an upside-down reflection of your pet fish in the surface of the water. Explain how this can happen.
Q33.9. A ray of light in air strikes a glass surface. Is there a range of angles for which total reflection occurs? Explain.
Q33.10. When light is incident on an interface between two materials, the angle of the refracted ray depends on the wavelength, but the angle of the reflected ray does not. Why should this be?
Q33.11. A salesperson at a bargain counter claims that a certain pair of sunglasses has Polaroid filters; you suspect that the glasses are just tinted plastic. How could you find out for sure?
Q33.12. Does it make sense to talk about the polarization of a *longitudinal* wave, such as a sound wave? Why or why not?
Q33.13. How can you determine the direction of the polarizing axis of a single polarizer?
Q33.14. It has been proposed that automobile windshields and headlights should have polarizing filters to reduce the glare of oncoming lights during night driving. Would this work? How should the polarizing axes be arranged? What advantages would this scheme have? What disadvantages?
Q33.15. When a sheet of plastic food wrap is placed between two crossed polarizers, no light is transmitted. When the sheet is stretched in one direction, some light passes through the crossed polarizers. What is happening?
Q33.16. If you sit on the beach and look at the ocean through Polaroid sunglasses, the glasses help to reduce the glare from sunlight reflecting off the water. But if you lie on your side on the beach, there is little reduction in the glare. Explain why there is a difference.
Q33.17. When unpolarized light is incident on two crossed polarizers, no light is transmitted. A student asserted that if a third polarizer is inserted between the other two, some transmission will occur. Does this make sense? How can adding a third filter *increase* transmission?
Q33.18. For the old "rabbit-ear" style TV antennas, it's possible to alter the quality of reception considerably simply by changing the orientation of the antenna. Why?
Q33.19. In Fig. 33.32, since the light that is scattered out of the incident beam is polarized, why is the transmitted beam not also partially polarized?
Q33.20. You are sunbathing in the late afternoon when the sun is relatively low in the western sky. You are lying flat on your back, looking straight up through Polaroid sunglasses. To minimize the amount of sky light reaching your eyes, how should you lie: with your feet pointing north, east, south, west, or in some other direction? Explain your reasoning.
Q33.21. Light scattered from blue sky is strongly polarized because of the nature of the scattering process described in Section 33.6. But light scattered from white clouds is usually *not* polarized. Why not?
Q33.22. Atmospheric haze is due to water droplets or smoke particles ("smog"). Such haze reduces visibility by scattering light, so that the light from distant objects becomes randomized and images become indistinct. Explain why visibility through haze can be improved by wearing red-tinted sunglasses, which filter out blue light.
Q33.23. The explanation given in Section 33.6 for the color of the setting sun should apply equally well to the *rising* sun, since sunlight travels the same distance through the atmosphere to reach your eyes at either sunrise or sunset. Typically, however, sunsets are redder than sunrises. Why? (*Hint:* Particles of all kinds in the atmosphere contribute to scattering.)
Q33.24. Huygens's principle also applies to sound waves. During the day, the temperature of the atmosphere decreases with increasing altitude above the ground. But at night, when the ground cools, there is a layer of air just above the surface in which the temperature *increases* with altitude. Use this to explain why sound waves from distant sources can be heard more clearly at night than in the daytime. (*Hint:* The speed of sound increases with increasing temperature. Use the ideas displayed in Fig. 33.37 for light.)
Q33.25. Can water waves be reflected and refracted? Give examples. Does Huygens's principle apply to water waves? Explain.

Exercises

Section 33.2 Reflection and Refraction

33.1. Two plane mirrors intersect at right angles. A laser beam strikes the first of them at a point 11.5 cm from their point of intersection, as shown in Fig. 33.38 For what angle of incidence at the first mirror will this ray strike the midpoint of the second mirror (which is 28.0 cm long) after reflecting from the first mirror?

Figure **33.38** Exercise 33.1.

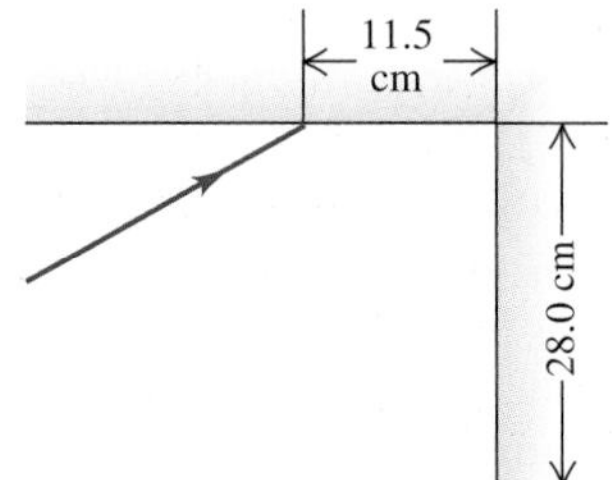

33.2. Three plane mirrors intersect at right angles. A beam of laser light strikes the first of them at an angle θ with respect to the normal (Fig. 33.39). (a) Show that when this ray is reflected off of the other two mirrors and crosses the original ray, the angle α between these two rays will be $\alpha = 180° - 2\theta$. (b) For what angle θ will the two rays be perpendicular when they cross?

Figure **33.39** Exercise 33.2

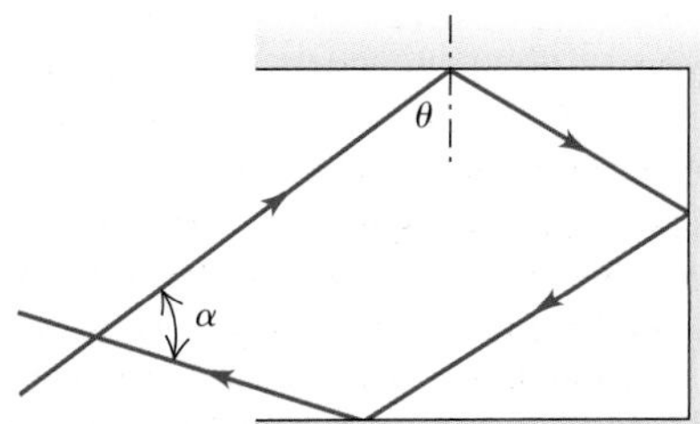

33.3. A beam of light has a wavelength of 650 nm in vacuum. (a) What is the speed of this light in a liquid whose index of refraction at this wavelength is 1.47? (b) What is the wavelength of these waves in the liquid?

33.4. Light with a frequency of 5.80×10^{14} Hz travels in a block of glass that has an index of refraction of 1.52. What is the wavelength of the light (a) in vacuum and (b) in the glass?

33.5. A light beam travels at 1.94×10^8 m/s in quartz. The wavelength of the light in quartz is 355 nm. (a) What is the index of refraction of quartz at this wavelength? (b) If this same light travels through air, what is its wavelength there?

33.6. Light of a certain frequency has a wavelength of 438 nm in water. What is the wavelength of this light in benzene?

33.7. A parallel beam of light in air makes an angle of 47.5° with the surface of a glass plate having a refractive index of 1.66. (a) What is the angle between the reflected part of the beam and the surface of the glass? (b) What is the angle between the refracted beam and the surface of the glass?

33.8. Using a fast-pulsed laser and electronic timing circuitry, you find that light travels 2.50 m within a plastic rod in 11.5 ns. What is the refractive index of the plastic?

33.9. Light traveling in air is incident on the surface of a block of plastic at an angle of 62.7° to the normal and is bent so that it makes a 48.1° angle with the normal in the plastic. Find the speed of light in the plastic.

33.10. (a) A tank containing methanol has walls 2.50 cm thick made of glass of refractive index 1.550. Light from the outside air strikes the glass at a 41.3° angle with the normal to the glass. Find the angle the light makes with the normal in the methanol. (b) The tank is emptied and refilled with an unknown liquid. If light incident at the same angle as in part (a) enters the liquid in the tank at an angle of 20.2° from the normal, what is the refractive index of the unknown liquid?

33.11. (a) Light passes through three parallel slabs of different thicknesses and refractive indexes. The light is incident in the first slab and finally refracts into the third slab. Show that the middle slab has no effect on the final direction of the light. That is, show that the direction of the light in the third slab is the same as if the light had passed directly from the first slab into the third slab. (b) Generalize this result to a stack of N slabs. What determines the final direction of the light in the last slab?

33.12. A horizontal, parallel-sided plate of glass having a refractive index of 1.52 is in contact with the surface of water in a tank. A ray coming from above in air makes an angle of incidence of 35.0° with the normal to the top surface of the glass. (a) What angle does the ray refracted into the water make with the normal to the surface? (b) What is the dependence of this angle on the refractive index of the glass?

33.13. In a material having an index of refraction n, a light ray has frequency f, wavelength λ, and speed v. What are the frequency, wavelength, and speed of this light (a) in vacuum and (b) in a material having refractive index n'? In each case, express your answers in terms of *only* f, λ, v, n, and n'.

33.14. Prove that a ray of light reflected from a plane mirror rotates through an angle of 2θ when the mirror rotates through an angle θ about an axis perpendicular to the plane of incidence.

33.15. A ray of light is incident on a plane surface separating two sheets of glass with refractive indexes 1.70 and 1.58. The angle of incidence is 62.0°, and the ray originates in the glass with $n = 1.70$. Compute the angle of refraction.

33.16. In Example 33.1 the water–glass interface is horizontal. If instead this interface were tilted 15.0° above the horizontal, with the right side higher than the left side, what would be the angle from the vertical of the ray in the glass? (The ray in the water still makes an angle of 60.0° with the vertical.)

Section 33.3 Total Internal Reflection

33.17. Light Pipe. Light enters a solid pipe made of plastic having an index of refraction of 1.60. The light travels parallel to the upper part of the pipe (Fig. 33.40). You want to cut the face AB so that all the light will reflect back into the pipe after it first strikes that face. (a) What is the largest that θ can be if the pipe is in air? (b) If the pipe is immersed in water of refractive index 1.33, what is the largest that θ can be?

Figure **33.40** Exercise 33.17

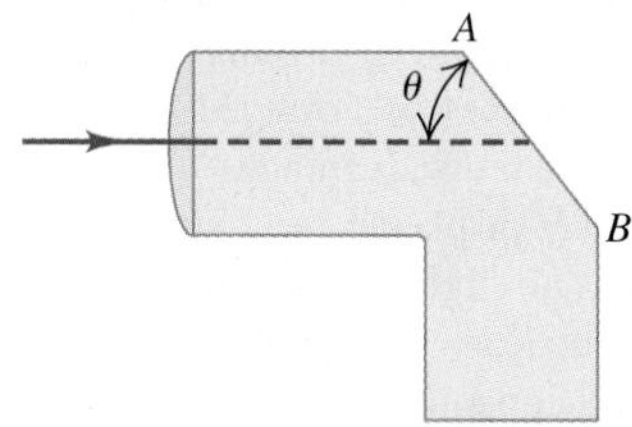

33.18. A beam of light is traveling inside a solid glass cube having index of refraction 1.53. It strikes the surface of the cube from the inside. (a) If the cube is in air, at what minimum angle with the normal inside the glass will this light *not* enter the air at this surface? (b) What would be the minimum angle in part (a) if the cube were immersed in water?

33.19. The critical angle for total internal reflection at a liquid–air interface is 42.5°. (a) If a ray of light traveling in the liquid has an angle of incidence at the interface of 35.0°, what angle does the refracted ray in the air make with the normal? (b) If a ray of light traveling in air has an angle of incidence at the interface of 35.0°, what angle does the refracted ray in the liquid make with the normal?

33.20. At the very end of Wagner's series of operas *Ring of the Nibelung,* Brünnhilde takes the golden ring from the finger of the dead Siegfried and throws it into the Rhine, where it sinks to the bottom of the river. Assuming that the ring is small enough compared to the depth of the river to be treated as a point and that the Rhine is 10.0 m deep where the ring goes in, what is the area of the largest circle at the surface of the water over which light from the ring could escape from the water?

33.21. A ray of light is traveling in a glass cube that is totally immersed in water. You find that if the ray is incident on the glass–water interface at an angle to the normal larger than 48.7°, no light is refracted into the water. What is the refractive index of the glass?

33.22. Light is incident along the normal on face AB of a glass prism of refractive index 1.52, as shown in Fig. 33.41. Find the largest value the angle α can have without any light refracted out of the prism at face AC if (a) the prism is immersed in air and (b) the prism is immersed in water.

Figure 33.41 Exercise 33.22.

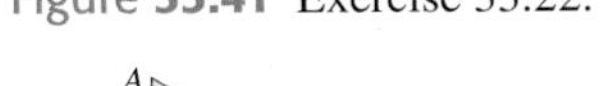
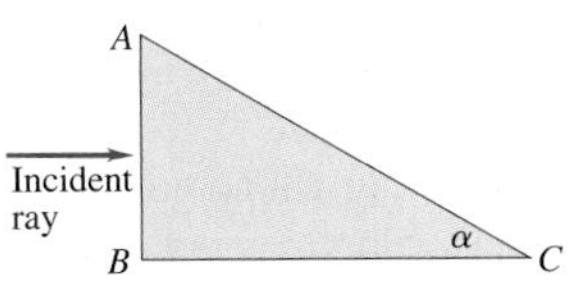

33.23. A ray of light in diamond (index of refraction 2.42) is incident on an interface with air. What is the *largest* angle the ray can make with the normal and not be totally reflected back into the diamond?

Section 33.4 Dispersion

33.24. A beam of light strikes a sheet of glass at an angle of 57.0° with the normal in air. You observe that red light makes an angle of 38.1° with the normal in the glass, while violet light makes a 36.7° angle. (a) What are the indexes of refraction of this glass for these colors of light? (b) What are the speeds of red and violet light in the glass?

Section 33.5 Polarization

33.25. A beam of unpolarized light of intensity I_0 passes through a series of ideal polarizing filters with their polarizing directions turned to various angles as shown in Fig. 33.42. (a) What is the light intensity (in terms of I_0) at points A, B, and C? (b) If we remove the middle filter, what will be the light intensity at point C?

Figure 33.42 Exercise 33.25.

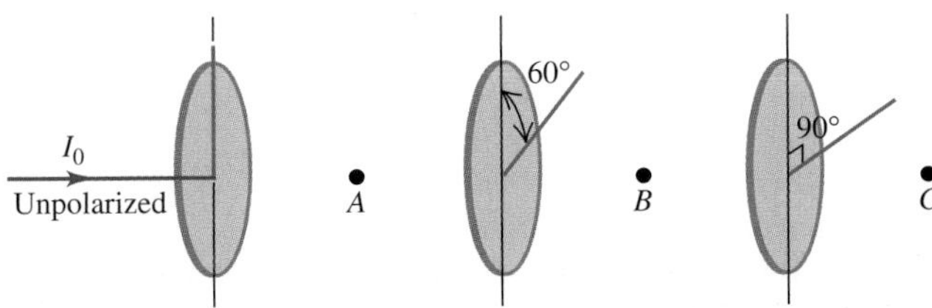

33.26. Light traveling in water strikes a glass plate at an angle of incidence of 53.0°; part of the beam is reflected and part is refracted. If the reflected and refracted portions make an angle of 90.0° with each other, what is the index of refraction of the glass?

33.27. A parallel beam of unpolarized light in air is incident at an angle of 54.5° (with respect to the normal) on a plane glass surface. The reflected beam is completely linearly polarized. (a) What is the refractive index of the glass? (b) What is the angle of refraction of the transmitted beam?

33.28. Light of original intensity I_0 passes through two ideal polarizing filters having their polarizing axes oriented as shown in Fig. 33.43. You want to adjust the angle ϕ so that the intensity at point P is equal to $I_0/10$. (a) If the original light is unpolarized, what should ϕ be? (b) If the original light is linearly polarized in the same direction as the polarizing axis of the first polarizer the light reaches, what should ϕ be?

Figure 33.43 Exercise 33.28.

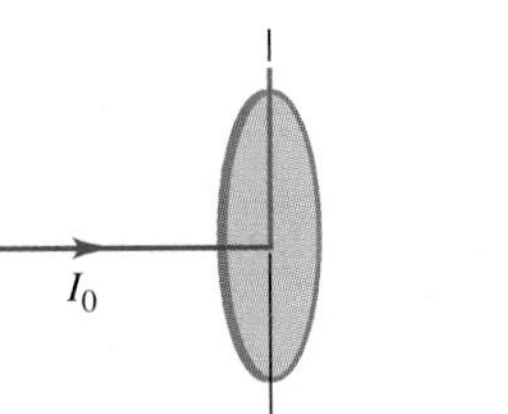

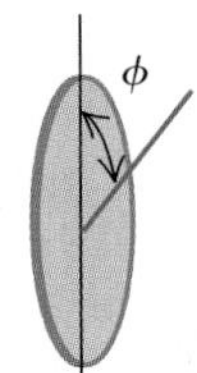

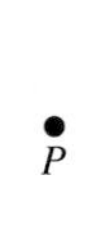

33.29. A beam of polarized light passes through a polarizing filter. When the angle between the polarizing axis of the filter and the direction of polarization of the light is θ, the intensity of the emerging beam is I. If you now want the intensity to be $I/2$, what should be the angle (in terms of θ) between the polarizing angle of the filter and the original direction of polarization of the light?

33.30. The refractive index of a certain glass is 1.66. For what incident angle is light reflected from the surface of this glass completely polarized if the glass is immersed in (a) air and (b) water?

33.31. Unpolarized light of intensity 20.0 W/cm^2 is incident on two polarizing filters. The axis of the first filter is at an angle of 25.0° counterclockwise from the vertical (viewed in the direction the light is traveling), and the axis of the second filter is at 62.0° counterclockwise from the vertical. What is the intensity of the light after it has passed through the second polarizer?

33.32. A polarizer and an analyzer are oriented so that the maximum amount of light is transmitted. To what fraction of its maximum value is the intensity of the transmitted light reduced when the analyzer is rotated through (a) 22.5°; (b) 45.0°; (c) 67.5°?

33.33. Three Polarizing Filters. Three polarizing filters are stacked with the polarizing axes of the second and third at 45.0° and 90.0°, respectively, with that of the first. (a) If unpolarized light of intensity I_0 is incident on the stack, find the intensity and state of polarization of light emerging from each filter. (b) If the second filter is removed, what is the intensity of the light emerging from each remaining filter?

33.34. Three polarizing filters are stacked, with the polarizing axis of the second and third filters at 23.0° and 62.0°, respectively, to that of the first. If unpolarized light is incident on the stack, the light has intensity 75.0 W/cm^2 after it passes through the stack. If the incident intensity is kept constant, what is the intensity of the light after it has passed through the stack if the second polarizer is removed?

*Section 33.6 Scattering of Light

33.35. A beam of white light passes through a uniform thickness of air. If the intensity of the scattered light in the middle of the green part of the visible spectrum is I, find the intensity (in terms of I) of scattered light in the middle of (a) the red part of the spectrum and (b) the violet part of the spectrum. Consult Table 32.1.

Section 33.7 Huygens's Principle

33.36. Bending Around Corners. Traveling particles do not bend around corners, but waves do. To see why, suppose that a plane wave front strikes the edge of a sharp object traveling perpendicular to the surface (Fig. 33.44). Use Huygens's principle to show that this wave will bend around the upper edge of the object. (*Note:* This effect, called *diffraction,* can easily be seen for water waves, but it also occurs for light, as you will see in Chapters 35 and 36. However due to the very short wavelength of visible light, it is not so apparent in daily life.)

Figure 33.44 Exercise 33.36.

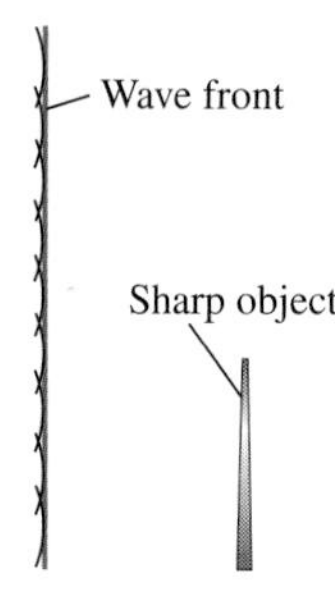

Problems

33.37. The Corner Reflector. An inside corner of a cube is lined with mirrors to make a corner reflector (see Example 33.3 in Section 33.2). A ray of light is reflected successively from each of three mutually perpendicular mirrors; show that its final direction is always exactly opposite to its initial direction.

33.38. A light beam is directed parallel to the axis of a hollow cylindrical tube. When the tube contains only air, it takes the light 8.72 ns to travel the length of the tube, but when the tube is filled with a transparent jelly, it takes the light 2.04 ns longer to travel its length. What is the refractive index of this jelly?

33.39. Light traveling in a material of refractive index n_1 is incident at angle θ_1 with respect to the normal at the interface with a slab of material that has parallel faces and refractive index n_2. After the light passes through this material, it is refracted into a material with refractive index n_3 and in this third material it makes an angle of θ_3 with the normal. (a) Find θ_3 in terms of θ_1 and the refractive indexes of the materials. (b) The ray in the third material is now reversed, so that it is incident on the n_3-to-n_2 interface with the angle θ_3 found in part (a). Show that when the light refracts into the material with refractive index n_1, the angle it makes with the normal is angle θ_1. This shows that the refracted ray is reversible. (c) Are reflected rays also reversible? Explain.

33.40. In a physics lab, light with wavelength 490 nm travels in air from a laser to a photocell in 17.0 ns. When a slab of glass 0.840 m thick is placed in the light beam, with the beam incident along the normal to the parallel faces of the slab, it takes the light 21.2 ns to travel from the laser to the photocell. What is the wavelength of the light in the glass?

33.41. A ray of light is incident in air on a block of a transparent solid whose index of refraction is n. If $n = 1.38$, what is the *largest* angle of incidence θ_a for which total internal reflection will occur at the vertical face (point A shown in Fig. 33.45)?

Figure 33.45 Problem 33.41.

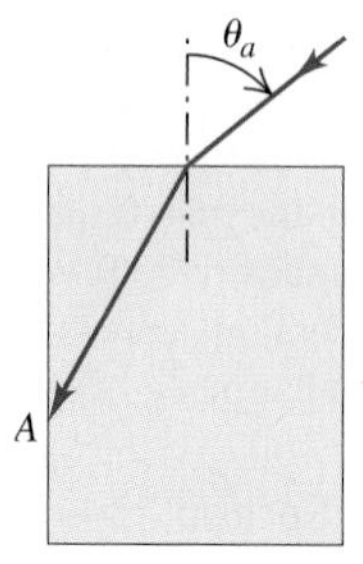

33.42. A light ray in air strikes the right-angle prism shown in Fig. 33.46. This ray consists of two different wavelengths. When it emerges at face AB, it has been split into two different rays that diverge from each other by 8.50°. Find the index of refraction of the prism for each of the two wavelengths.

Figure 33.46 Problem 33.42.

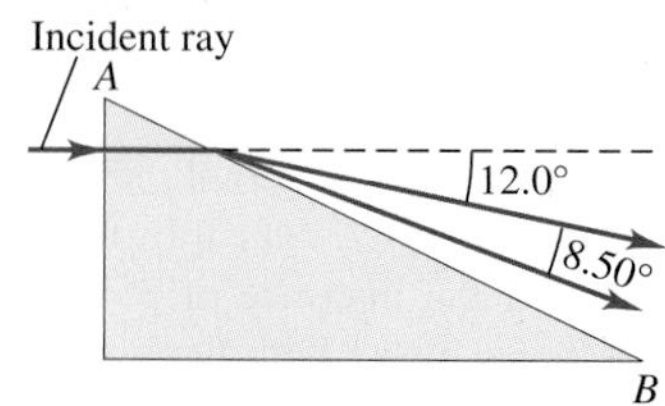

33.43. A quarter-wave plate converts linearly polarized light to circularly polarized light. Prove that a quarter-wave plate also converts circularly polarized light to linearly polarized light.

33.44. A glass plate 2.50 mm thick, with an index of refraction of 1.40, is placed between a point source of light with wavelength 540 nm (in vacuum) and a screen. The distance from source to screen is 1.80 cm. How many wavelengths are there between the source and the screen?

33.45. Old photographic plates were made of glass with a light-sensitive emulsion on the front surface. This emulsion was somewhat transparent. When a bright point source is focused on the front of the plate, the developed photograph will show a halo around the image of the spot. If the glass plate is 3.10 mm thick and the halos have an inner radius of 5.34 mm, what is the index of refraction of the glass? (*Hint:* Light from the spot on the front surface is scattered in all directions by the emulsion. Some of it is then totally reflected at the back surface of the plate and returns to the front surface.)

33.46. After a long day of driving you take a late-night swim in a motel swimming pool. When you go to your room, you realize that you have lost your room key in the pool. You borrow a powerful flashlight and walk around the pool, shining the light into it. The light shines on the key, which is lying on the bottom of the pool, when the flashlight is held 1.2 m above the water surface and is directed at the surface a horizontal distance of 1.5 m from the edge (Fig. 33.47). If the water here is 4.0 m deep, how far is the key from the edge of the pool?

Figure 33.47 Problem 33.46.

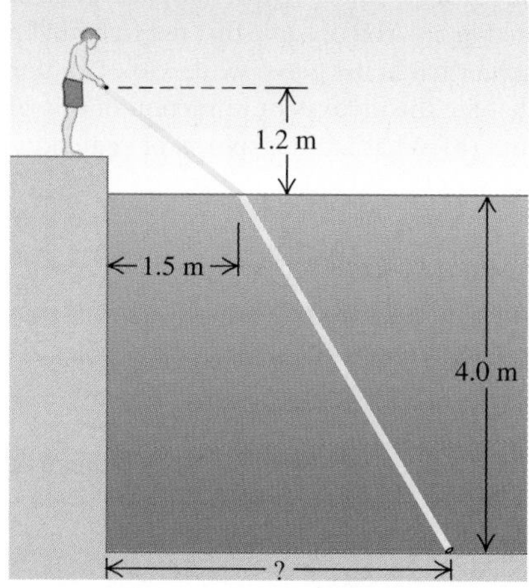

33.47. You sight along the rim of a glass with vertical sides so that the top rim is lined up with the opposite edge of the bottom (Fig. 33.48a). The glass is a thin-walled, hollow cylinder 16.0 cm high with a top and bottom of the glass diameter of 8.0 cm. While you keep your eye in the same position, a friend fills the glass with a transparent liquid, and you then see a dime that is lying at the center of the bottom of the glass (Fig. 33.48b). What is the index of refraction of the liquid?

Figure **33.48** Problem 33.47.

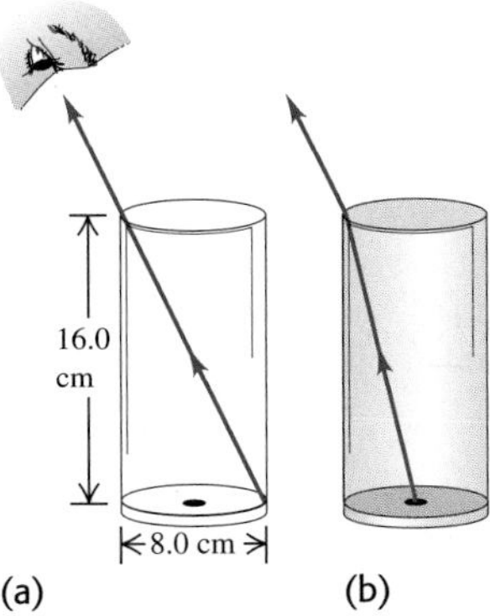

33.48. A beaker with a mirrored bottom is filled with a liquid whose index of refraction is 1.63. A light beam strikes the top surface of the liquid at an angle of 42.5° from the normal. At what angle from the normal will the beam exit from the liquid after traveling down through the liquid, reflecting from the mirrored bottom, and returning to the surface?

33.49. A thin layer of ice $(n = 1.309)$ floats on the surface of water $(n = 1.333)$ in a bucket. A ray of light from the bottom of the bucket travels upward through the water. (a) What is the largest angle with respect to the normal that the ray can make at the ice–water interface and still pass out into the air above the ice? (b) What is this angle after the ice melts?

33.50. A 45°–45°–90° prism is immersed in water. A ray of light is incident normally on one of its shorter faces. What is the minimum index of refraction that the prism must have if this ray is to be totally reflected within the glass at the long face of the prism?

33.51. The prism shown in Fig. 33.49 has a refractive index of 1.66, and the angles A are 25.0°. Two light rays m and n are parallel as they enter the prism. What is the angle between them after they emerge?

Figure **33.49** Problem 33.51.

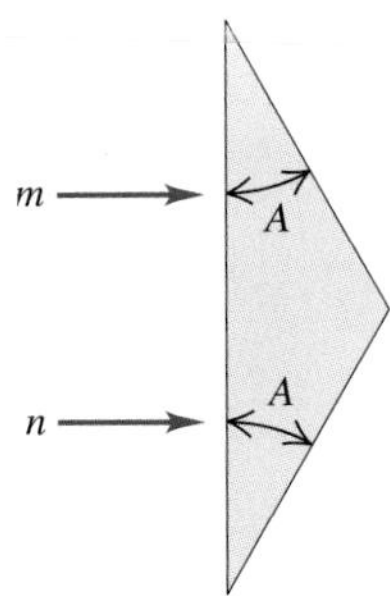

33.52. Light is incident normally on the short face of a 30°–60°–90° prism (Fig. 33.50). A drop of liquid is placed on the hypotenuse of the prism. If the index of the prism is 1.62, find the maximum index that the liquid may have if the light is to be totally reflected.

Figure **33.50** Problem 33.52.

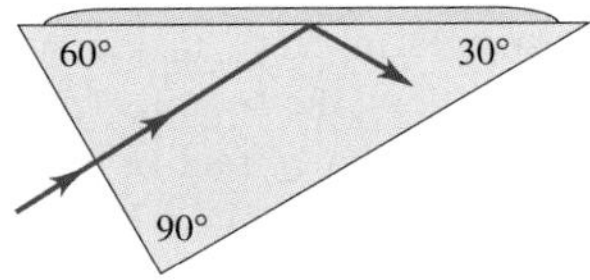

33.53. A horizontal cylindrical tank 2.20 m in diameter is half full of water. The space above the water is filled with a pressurized gas of unknown refractive index. A small laser can move along the curved bottom of the water and aims a light beam toward the center of the water surface (Fig. 33.51). You observe that when the laser has moved a distance $S = 1.09$ m or more (measured along the curved surface) from the lowest point in the water, no light enters the gas. (a) What is the index of refraction of the gas? (b) How long does it take the light beam to travel from the laser to the rim of the tank when (i) $S > 1.09$ m and (ii) $S < 1.09$ m?

Figure **33.51** Problem 33.53.

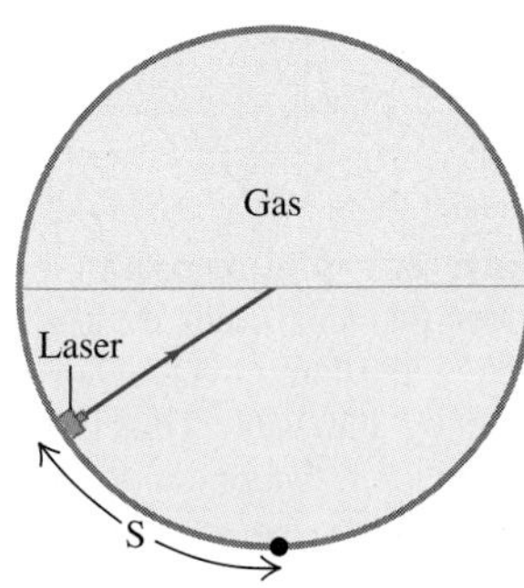

33.54. A large cube of glass has a metal reflector on one face and water on an adjoining face (Fig. 33.52). A light beam strikes the reflector, as shown. You observe that as you gradually increase the angle of the light beam, if $\theta \geq 59.2°$ no light enters the water. What is the speed of light in this glass?

Figure **33.52** Problem 33.54.

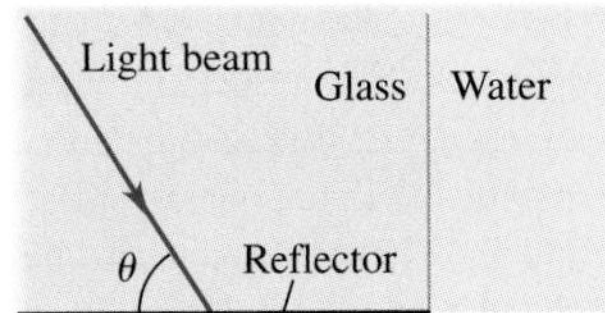

33.55. When the sun is either rising or setting and appears to be just on the horizon, it is in fact *below* the horizon. The explanation for this seeming paradox is that light from the sun bends slightly when entering the earth's atmosphere, as shown in Fig. 33.53. Since our perception is based on the idea that light travels in straight lines, we perceive the light to be coming from an apparent position that is an angle δ above the sun's true position. (a) Make the simplifying assumptions that the atmosphere has uniform density, and hence uniform index of refraction n, and extends to a height h above the earth's surface, at which point it abruptly stops. Show that the angle δ is given by

$$\delta = \arcsin\left(\frac{nR}{R+h}\right) - \arcsin\left(\frac{R}{R+h}\right)$$

where $R = 6378$ km is the radius of the earth. (b) Calculate δ using $n = 1.0003$ and $h = 20$ km. How does this compare to the

Figure **33.53** Problem 33.55.

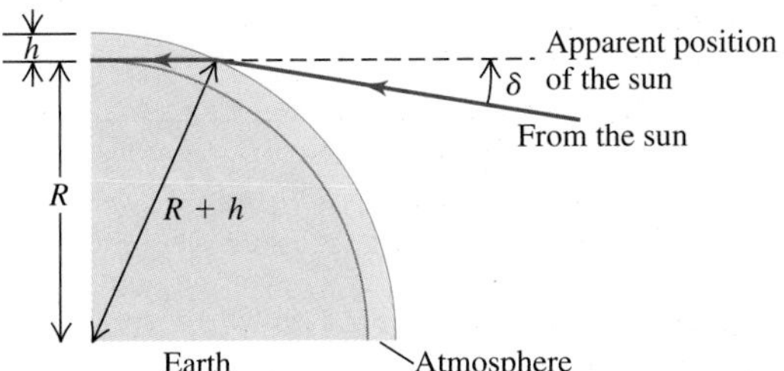

angular radius of the sun, which is about one quarter of a degree? (In actuality a light ray from the sun bends gradually, not abruptly, since the density and refractive index of the atmosphere change gradually with altitude.)

33.56. Fermat's Principle of Least Time. A ray of light traveling with speed c leaves point 1 shown in Fig. 33.54 and is reflected to point 2. The ray strikes the reflecting surface a horizontal distance x from point 1. (a) Show that the time t required for the light to travel from 1 to 2 is

$$t = \frac{\sqrt{y_1^2 + x^2} + \sqrt{y_2^2 + (l - x)^2}}{c}$$

(b) Take the derivative of t with respect to x. Set the derivative equal to zero to show that this time reaches its *minimum* value when $\theta_1 = \theta_2$, which is the law of reflection and corresponds to the actual path taken by the light. This is an example of Fermat's *principle of least time,* which states that among all possible paths between two points, the one actually taken by a ray of light is that for which the time of travel is a *minimum.* (In fact, there are some cases in which the time is a maximum rather than a minimum.)

Figure **33.54** Problem 33.56.

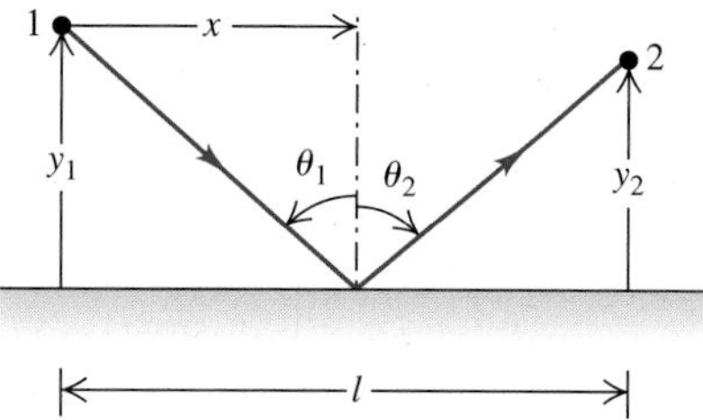

33.57. A ray of light goes from point A in a medium in which the speed of light is v_1 to point B in a medium in which the speed is v_2 (Fig. 33.55). The ray strikes the interface a horizontal distance x to the right of point A. (a) Show that the time required for the light to go from A to B is

$$t = \frac{\sqrt{h_1^2 + x^2}}{v_1} + \frac{\sqrt{h_2^2 + (l - x)^2}}{v_2}$$

(b) Take the derivative of t with respect to x. Set this derivative equal to zero to show that this time reaches its *minimum* value when $n_1 \sin\theta_1 = n_2 \sin\theta_2$. This is Snell's law, and corresponds to the actual path taken by the light. This is another example of Fermat's principle of least time (see Problem 33.56).

Figure **33.55** Problem 33.57.

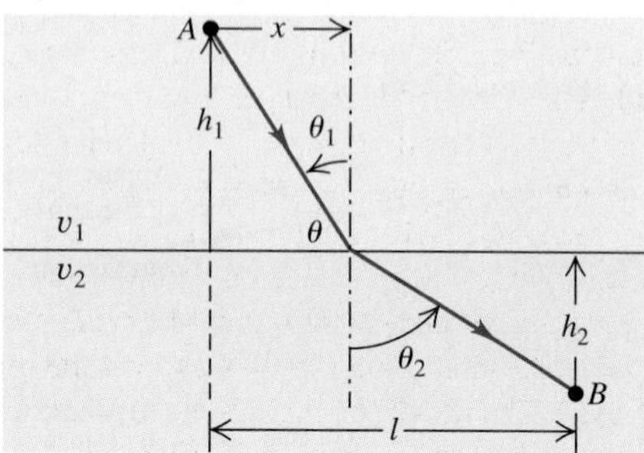

33.58. Light is incident in air at an angle θ_a (Fig. 33.56) on the upper surface of a transparent plate, the surfaces of the plate being plane and parallel to each other. (a) Prove that $\theta_a = \theta'_a$. (b) Show that this is true for any number of different parallel plates. (c) Prove that the lateral displacement d of the emergent beam is given by the relationship

$$d = t\frac{\sin(\theta_a - \theta'_b)}{\cos\theta'_b}$$

where t is the thickness of the plate. (d) A ray of light is incident at an angle of 66.0° on one surface of a glass plate 2.40 cm thick with an index of refraction 1.80. The medium on either side of the plate is air. Find the lateral displacement between the incident and emergent rays.

Figure **33.56** Problem 33.58.

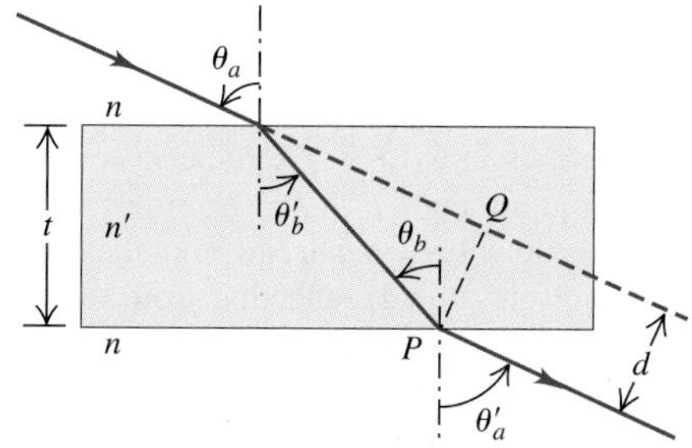

33.59. Light traveling downward is incident on a horizontal film of thickness t, as shown in Fig. 33.57. The incident ray splits into two rays, A and B. Ray A reflects from the top of the film. Ray B reflects from the bottom of the film and then refracts back into the material that is above the film. If the film has parallel faces, show that rays A and B end up parallel to each other.

Figure **33.57** Problem 33.59.

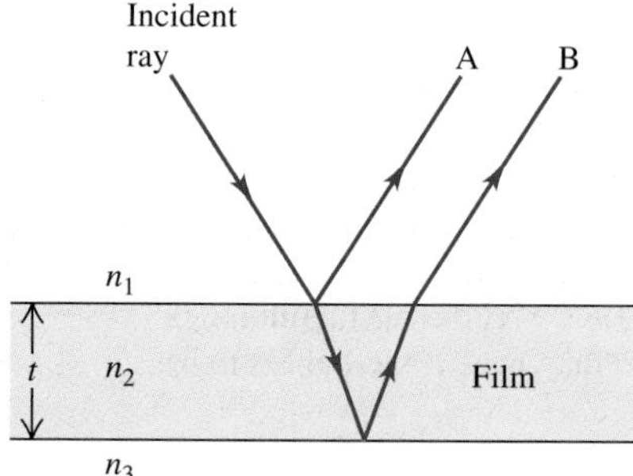

33.60. A thin beam of white light is directed at a flat sheet of silicate flint glass at an angle of 20.0° to the surface of the sheet. Due to dispersion in the glass, the beam is spread out as shown in a spectrum in Fig. 33.58. The refractive index of silicate flint glass versus wavelength is graphed in Fig. 33.18. (a) The rays a and b shown in Fig. 33.58 correspond to the extremes of the visible spectrum. Which corresponds to red and which to violet? Explain your reasoning. (b) For what thickness d of the glass sheet will the spectrum be 1.0 mm wide, as shown (see Problem 33.58)?

Figure 33.58 Problem 33.60.

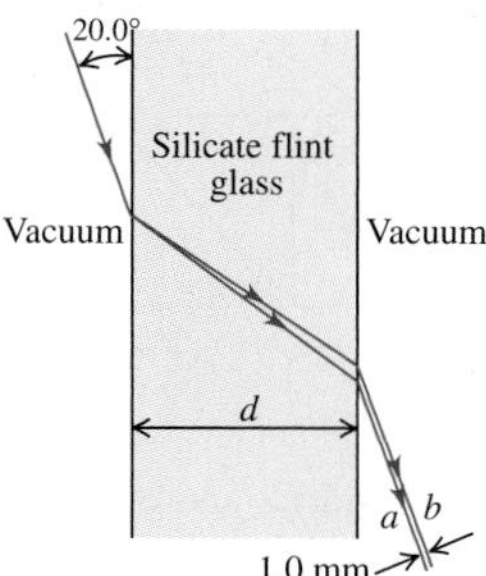

33.61. Angle of Deviation. The incident angle θ_a shown in Fig. 33.59 is chosen so that the light passes symmetrically through the prism, which has refractive index n and apex angle A. (a) Show that the angle of deviation δ (the angle between the initial and final directions of the ray) is given by

$$\sin\frac{A+\delta}{2} = n\sin\frac{A}{2}$$

(When the light passes through symmetrically, as shown, the angle of deviation is a minimum.) (b) Use the result of part (a) to find the angle of deviation for a ray of light passing symmetrically through a prism having three equal angles $(A = 60.0°)$ and $n = 1.52$. (c) A certain glass has a refractive index of 1.61 for red light (700 nm) and 1.66 for violet light (400 nm). If both colors pass through symmetrically, as described in part (a), and if $A = 60.0°$, find the difference between the angles of deviation for the two colors.

Figure 33.59 Problem 33.61.

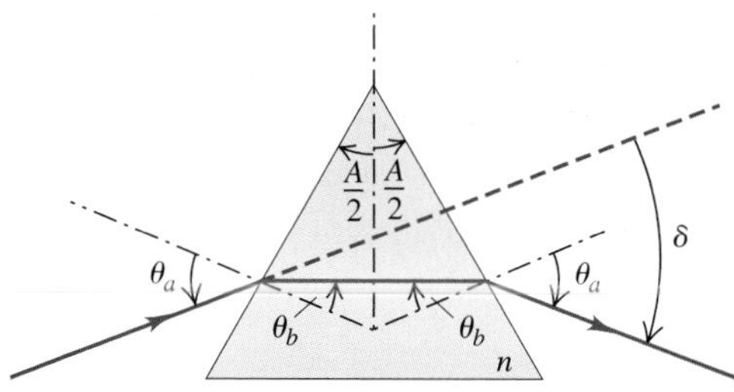

33.62. A beam of unpolarized sunlight strikes the vertical plastic wall of a water tank at an unknown angle. Some of the light reflects from the wall and enters the water (Fig. 33.60). The refractive index of the plastic wall is 1.61. If the light that has been reflected from the wall into the water is observed to be completely polarized, what angle does this beam make with the normal inside the water?

Figure 33.60 Problem 33.62.

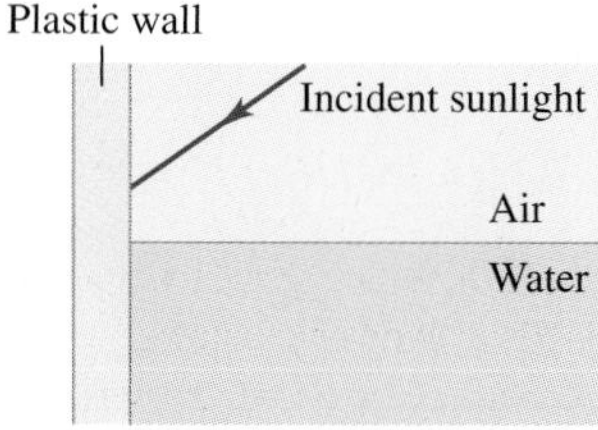

33.63. A beam of light traveling horizontally is made of an unpolarized component with intensity I_0 and a polarized component with intensity I_p. The plane of polarization of the polarized component is oriented at an angle of θ with respect to the vertical. The data in the table give the intensity measured through a polarizer with an orientation of ϕ with respect to the vertical. (a) What is the orientation of the polarized component? (That is, what is the angle θ?) (b) What are the values of I_0 and I_p?

ϕ (°)	I_{total} (W/m^2)	ϕ (°)	I_{total} (W/m^2)
0	18.4	100	8.6
10	21.4	110	6.3
20	23.7	120	5.2
30	24.8	130	5.2
40	24.8	140	6.3
50	23.7	150	8.6
60	21.4	160	11.6
70	18.4	170	15.0
80	15.0	180	18.4
90	11.6		

33.64. A certain birefringent material has indexes of refraction n_1 and n_2 for the two perpendicular components of linearly polarized light passing through it. The corresponding wavelengths are $\lambda_1 = \lambda_0/n_1$ and λ_0/n_2, where λ_0 is the wavelength in vacuum. (a) If the crystal is to function as a quarter-wave plate, the number of wavelengths of each component within the material must differ by $\frac{1}{4}$. Show that the minimum thickness for a quarter-wave plate is

$$d = \frac{\lambda_0}{4(n_1 - n_2)}$$

(b) Find the minimum thickness of a quarter-wave plate made of siderite $(FeO \cdot CO_2)$ if the indexes of refraction are $n_1 = 1.875$ and $n_2 = 1.635$ and the wavelength in vacuum is $\lambda_0 = 589$ nm.

Challenge Problems

33.65. Consider two vibrations of equal amplitude and frequency but differing in phase, one along the x-axis,

$$x = a\sin(\omega t - \alpha)$$

and the other along the y-axis,

$$y = a\sin(\omega t - \beta)$$

These can be written as follows:

$$\frac{x}{a} = \sin\omega t\cos\alpha - \cos\omega t\sin\alpha \qquad (1)$$

$$\frac{y}{a} = \sin\omega t\cos\beta - \cos\omega t\sin\beta \qquad (2)$$

(a) Multiply Eq. (1) by $\sin\beta$ and Eq. (2) by $\sin\alpha$, and then subtract the resulting equations. (b) Multiply Eq. (1) by $\cos\beta$ and Eq. (2) by $\cos\alpha$, and then subtract the resulting equations. (c) Square and add the results of parts (a) and (b). (d) Derive the equation $x^2 + y^2 - 2xy\cos\delta = a^2\sin^2\delta$, where $\delta = \alpha - \beta$. (e) Use the above result to justify each of the diagrams in Fig. 33.61 (next page). In the figure, the angle given is the phase difference between two simple harmonic motions of the same frequency and amplitude, one horizontal (along the x-axis) and the other vertical (along the y-axis). The figure thus shows the resultant motion from the superposition of the two perpendicular harmonic motions.

Figure **33.61** Challenge Problem 33.65.

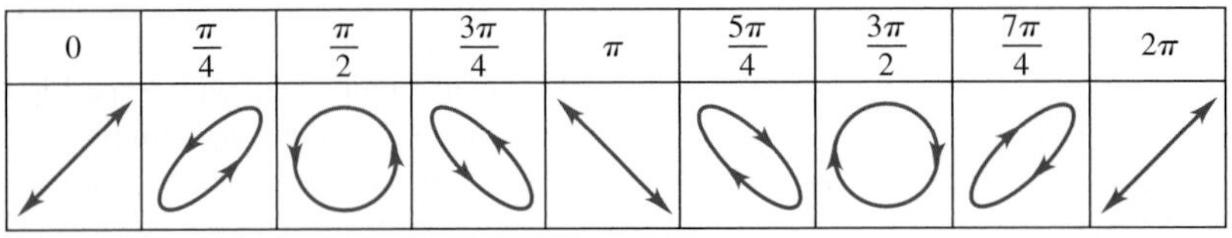

0	$\frac{\pi}{4}$	$\frac{\pi}{2}$	$\frac{3\pi}{4}$	π	$\frac{5\pi}{4}$	$\frac{3\pi}{2}$	$\frac{7\pi}{4}$	2π

33.66. A rainbow is produced by the reflection of sunlight by spherical drops of water in the air. Figure 33.62 shows a ray that refracts into a drop at point A, is reflected from the back surface of the drop at point B, and refracts back into the air at point C. The angles of incidence and refraction, θ_a and θ_b, are shown at points A and C, and the angles of incidence and reflection, θ_a and θ_r, are shown at point B. (a) Show that $\theta_a^B = \theta_b^A$, $\theta_a^C = \theta_b^A$, and $\theta_b^C = \theta_a^A$. (b) Show that the angle in radians between the ray before it enters the drop at A and after it exits at C (the total angular deflection of the ray) is $\Delta = 2\theta_a^A - 4\theta_b^A + \pi$. (*Hint:* Find the angular deflections that occur at A, B, and C, and add them to get Δ.) (c) Use Snell's law to write Δ in terms of θ_a^A and n, the refractive index of the water in the drop. (d) A rainbow will form when the angular deflection Δ is *stationary* in the incident angle θ_a^A—that is, when $d\Delta/d\theta_a^A = 0$. If this condition is satisfied, all the rays with incident angles close to θ_a^A will be sent back in the same direction, producing a bright zone in the sky. Let θ_1 be the value of θ_a^A for which this occurs. Show that $\cos^2\theta_1 = \frac{1}{3}(n^2 - 1)$. (*Hint:* You may find the derivative formula $d(\arcsin u(x))/dx = (1 - u^2)^{-1/2}(du/dx)$ helpful.) (e) The index of refraction in water is 1.342 for violet light and 1.330 for red light. Use the results of parts (c) and (d) to find θ_1 and Δ for violet and red light. Do your results agree with the angles shown in Fig. 33.20d? When you view the rainbow, which color, red or violet, is higher above the horizon?

Figure **33.62** Challenge Problem 33.66.

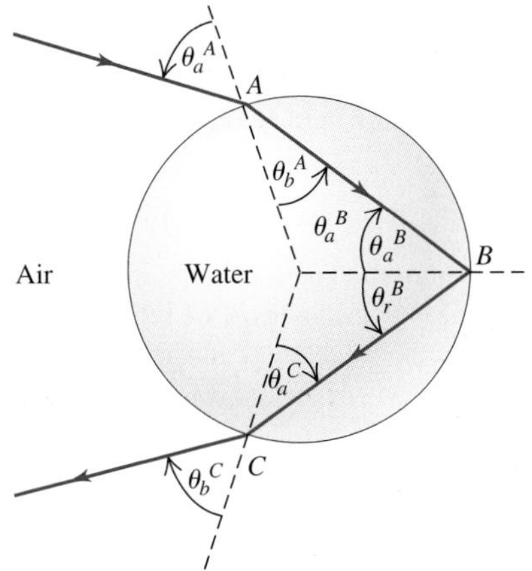

33.67. A *secondary rainbow* is formed when the incident light undergoes two internal reflections in a spherical drop of water as shown in Fig. 33.20e. (See Challenge Problem 33.66.) (a) In terms of the incident angle θ_a^A and the refractive index n of the drop, what is the angular deflection Δ of the ray? That is, what is the angle between the ray before it enters the drop and after it exits? (b) What is the incident angle θ_2 for which the derivative of Δ with respect to the incident angle θ_a^A is zero? (c) The indexes of refraction for red and violet light in water are given in part (e) of Challenge Problem 33.66. Use the results of parts (a) and (b) to find θ_2 and Δ for violet and red light. Do your results agree with the angles shown in Fig. 33.20e? When you view a secondary rainbow, is red or violet higher above the horizon? Explain.

GEOMETRIC OPTICS

34

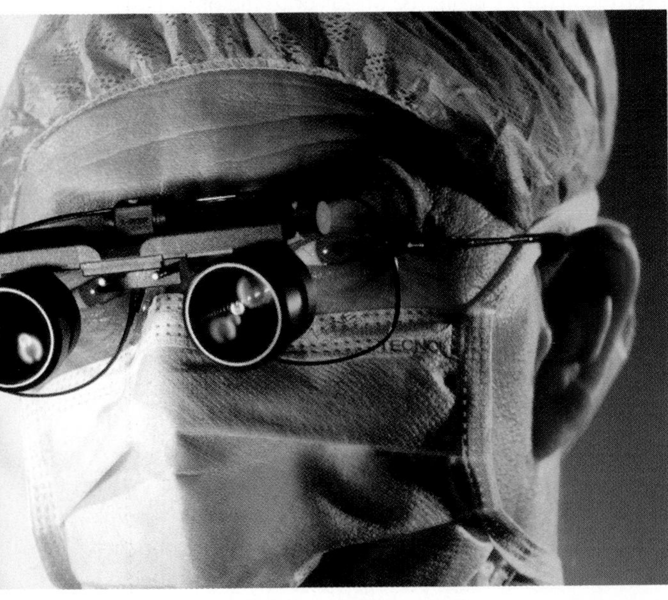

? How do magnifying lenses work? At what distance from the object being examined do they provide the sharpest view?

LEARNING GOALS

By studying this chapter, you will learn:

- How a plane mirror forms an image.
- Why concave and convex mirrors form different kinds of image.
- How images can be formed by a curved interface between two transparent materials.
- What aspects of a lens determine the type of image that it produces.
- What determines the field of view of a camera lens.
- What causes various defects in human vision, and how they can be corrected.
- The principle of the simple magnifier.
- How microscopes and telescopes work.

Your reflection in the bathroom mirror, the view of the moon through a telescope, the patterns seen in a kaleidoscope—all of these are examples of *images.* In each case the object that you're looking at appears to be in a different place than its actual position: Your reflection is on the other side of the mirror, the moon appears to be much closer when seen through a telescope, and objects seen in a kaleidoscope seem to be in many places at the same time. In each case, light rays that come from a point on an object are deflected by reflection or refraction (or a combination of the two), so they converge toward or appear to diverge from a point called an *image point.* Our goal in this chapter is to see how this is done and to explore the different kinds of images that can be made with simple optical devices.

To understand images and image formation, all we need are the ray model of light, the laws of reflection and refraction, and some simple geometry and trigonometry. The key role played by geometry in our analysis is the reason for the name *geometric optics* that is given to the study of how light rays form images. We'll begin our analysis with one of the simplest image-forming optical devices, a plane mirror. We'll go on to study how images are formed by curved mirrors, by refracting surfaces, and by thin lenses. Our results will lay the foundation for understanding many familiar optical instruments, including camera lenses, magnifiers, the human eye, microscopes, and telescopes.

34.1 Reflection and Refraction at a Plane Surface

Before discussing what is meant by an image, we first need the concept of **object** as it is used in optics. By an *object* we mean anything from which light rays radiate. This light could be emitted by the object itself if it is *self-luminous,* like the glowing filament of a light bulb. Alternatively, the light could be emitted by

15.4 Geometric Optics: Plane Mirrors

34.1 Light rays radiate from a point object P in all directions.

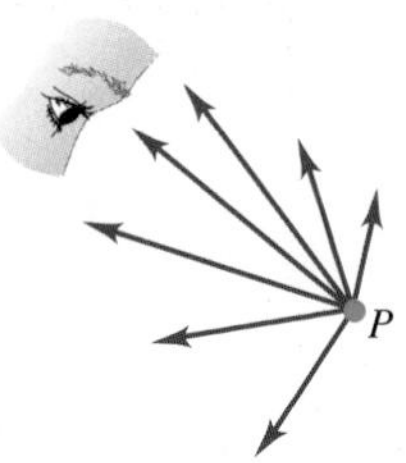

34.2 Light rays from the object at point P are reflected from a plane mirror. The reflected rays entering the eye look as though they had come from image point P'.

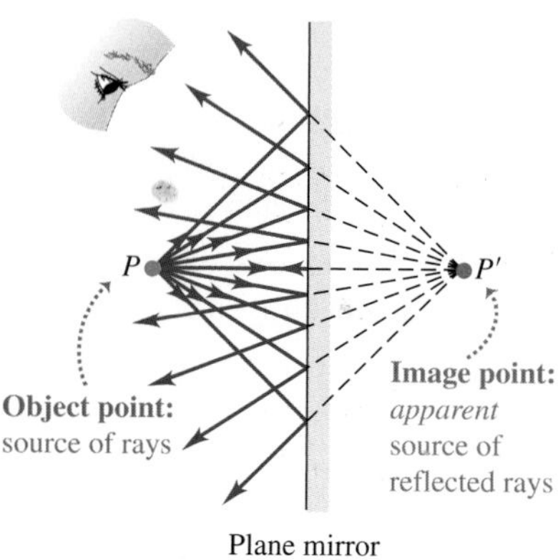

34.3 Light rays from the object at point P are refracted at the plane interface. The refracted rays entering the eye look as though they had come from image point P'.

When $n_a > n_b$, P' is closer to the surface than P; for $n_a < n_b$, the reverse is true.

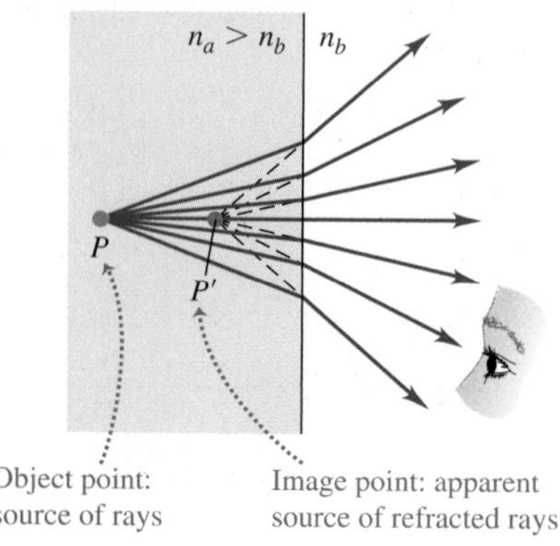

another source (such as a lamp or the sun) and then reflected from the object; an example is the light you see coming from the pages of this book. Figure 34.1 shows light rays radiating in all directions from an object at a point P. For an observer to see this object directly, there must be no obstruction between the object and the observer's eyes. Note that light rays from the object reach the observer's left and right eyes at different angles; these differences are processed by the observer's brain to infer the *distance* from the observer to the object.

The object in Fig. 34.1 is a **point object** that has no physical extent. Real objects with length, width, and height are called **extended objects.** To start with, we'll consider only an idealized point object, since we can always think of an extended object as being made up of a very large number of point objects.

Suppose some of the rays from the object strike a smooth, plane reflecting surface (Fig. 34.2). This could be the surface of a material with a different index of refraction, which reflects part of the incident light, or a polished metal surface that reflects almost 100% of the light that strikes it. We will always draw the reflecting surface as a black line with a shaded area behind it, as in Fig. 34.2. Bathroom mirrors have a thin sheet of glass that lies in front of and protects the reflecting surface; we'll ignore the effects of this thin sheet.

According to the law of reflection, all rays striking the surface are reflected at an angle from the normal equal to the angle of incidence. Since the surface is plane, the normal is in the same direction at all points on the surface, and we have *specular* reflection. After the rays are reflected, their directions are the same as though they had come from point P'. We call point P an *object point* and point P' the corresponding *image point,* and we say that the reflecting surface forms an **image** of point P. An observer who can see only the rays reflected from the surface, and who doesn't know that he's seeing a reflection, *thinks* that the rays originate from the image point P'. The image point is therefore a convenient way to describe the directions of the various reflected rays, just as the object point P describes the directions of the rays arriving at the surface *before* reflection.

If the surface in Fig. 34.2 were *not* smooth, the reflection would be *diffuse,* and rays reflected from different parts of the surface would go in uncorrelated directions (see Fig. 33.6b). In this case there would not be a definite image point P' from which all reflected rays seem to emanate. You can't see your reflection in the surface of a tarnished piece of metal because its surface is rough; polishing the metal smoothes the surface so that specular reflection occurs and a reflected image becomes visible.

An image is also formed by a plane *refracting* surface, as shown in Fig. 34.3. Rays coming from point P are refracted at the interface between two optical materials. When the angles of incidence are small, the final directions of the rays after refraction are the same as though they had come from point P', as shown, and again we call P' an *image point.* In Section 33.2 we described how this effect makes underwater objects appear closer to the surface than they really are (see Fig. 33.9).

In both Figs. 34.2 and 34.3 the rays do not actually pass through the image point P'. Indeed, if the mirror in Fig. 34.2 is opaque, there is no light at all on its right side. If the outgoing rays don't actually pass through the image point, we call the image a **virtual image.** Later we will see cases in which the outgoing rays really *do* pass through an image point, and we will call the resulting image a **real image.** The images that are formed on a projection screen, on the photographic film in a camera, and on the retina of your eye are real images.

Image Formation by a Plane Mirror

Let's concentrate for now on images produced by *reflection;* we'll return to refraction later in the chapter. To find the precise location of the virtual image P' that a plane mirror forms of an object at P, we use the construction shown in Fig. 34.4. The figure shows two rays diverging from an object point P at a distance s to the left of a plane mirror. We call s the **object distance.** The ray PV is incident normally on the mirror (that is, it is perpendicular to the mirror surface), and it returns along its original path.

The ray PB makes an angle θ with PV. It strikes the mirror at an angle of incidence θ and is reflected at an equal angle with the normal. When we extend the two reflected rays backward, they intersect at point P', at a distance s' behind the mirror. We call s' the **image distance.** The line between P and P' is perpendicular to the mirror. The two triangles PVB and $P'VB$ are congruent, so P and P' are at equal distances from the mirror, and s and s' have equal magnitudes. The image point P' is located exactly opposite the object point P as far *behind* the mirror as the object point is from the front of the mirror.

We can repeat the construction of Fig. 34.4 for each ray diverging from P. The directions of *all* the outgoing reflected rays are the same as though they had originated at point P', confirming that P' is the *image* of P. No matter where the observer is located, she will always see the image at the point P'.

34.4 Construction for determining the location of the image formed by a plane mirror. The image point P' is as far behind the mirror as the object point P is in front of it.

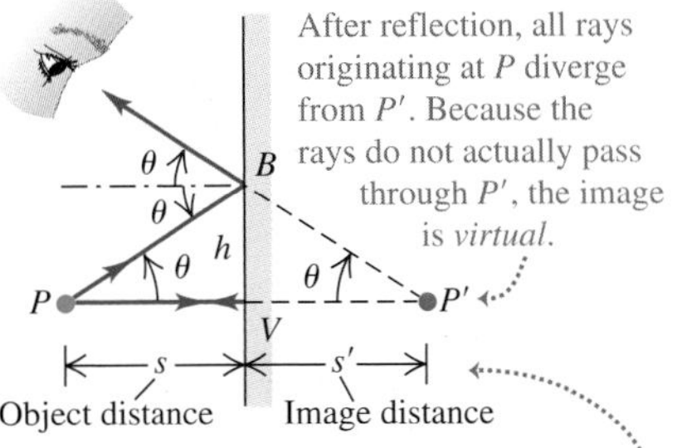

Sign Rules

Before we go further, let's introduce some general sign rules. These may seem unnecessarily complicated for the simple case of an image formed by a plane mirror, but we want to state the rules in a form that will be applicable to *all* the situations we will encounter later. These will include image formation by a plane or spherical reflecting or refracting surface, or by a pair of refracting surfaces forming a lens. Here are the rules:

1. **Sign rule for the object distance:** When the object is on the same side of the reflecting or refracting surface as the incoming light, the object distance s is positive; otherwise, it is negative.
2. **Sign rule for the image distance:** When the image is on the same side of the reflecting or refracting surface as the outgoing light, the image distance s' is positive; otherwise, it is negative.
3. **Sign rule for the radius of curvature of a spherical surface:** When the center of curvature C is on the same side as the outgoing light, the radius of curvature is positive; otherwise, it is negative.

Figure 34.5 illustrates rules 1 and 2 for two different situations. For a mirror the incoming and outgoing sides are always the same; for example, in Figs. 34.2, 34.4, and 34.5a they are both the left side. For the refracting surfaces in Figs. 34.3 and 34.5b the incoming and outgoing sides are on the left and right sides, respectively, of the interface between the two materials. (Note that other textbooks may use different rules.)

In Figs. 34.4 and 34.5a the object distance s is *positive* because the object point P is on the incoming side (the left side) of the reflecting surface. The image distance s' is *negative* because the image point P' is *not* on the outgoing side (the left side) of the surface. The object and image distances s and s' are related simply by

$$s = -s' \qquad \text{(plane mirror)} \tag{34.1}$$

For a plane reflecting or refracting surface, the radius of curvature is infinite and not a particularly interesting or useful quantity; in these cases we really don't need sign rule 3. But this rule will be of great importance when we study image formation by *curved* reflecting and refracting surfaces later in the chapter.

34.5 For both of these situations, the object distance s is positive (rule 1) and the image distance s' is negative (rule 2).

(a) Plane mirror

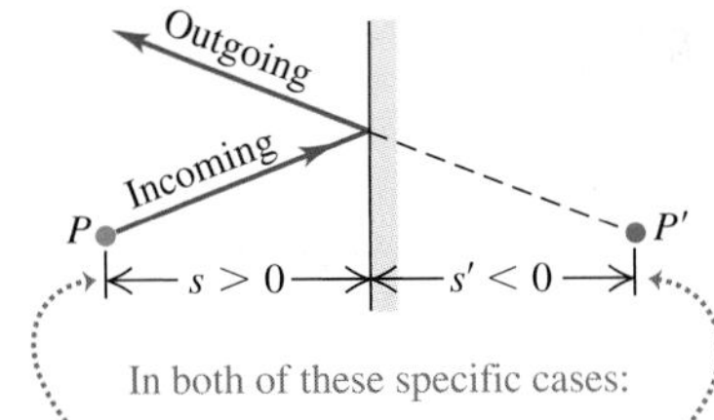

In both of these specific cases:

Object distance s is *positive* because the *object is on the same side as the incoming light.*

Image distance s' is *negative* because the *image is NOT on the same side as the outgoing light.*

(b) Plane refracting interface

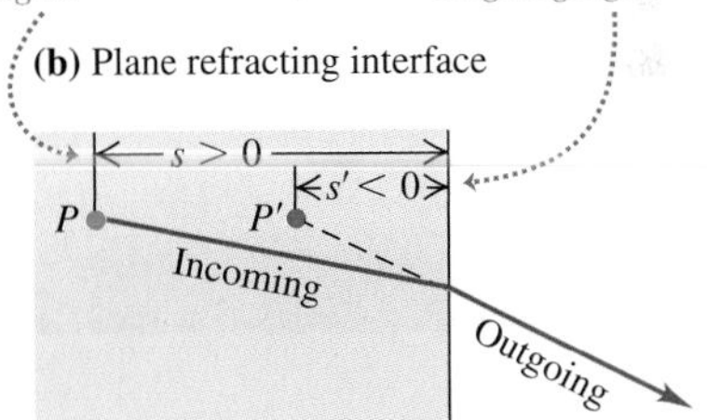

Image of an Extended Object: Plane Mirror

Next we consider an *extended* object with finite size. For simplicity we often consider an object that has only one dimension, like a slender arrow, oriented parallel to the reflecting surface; an example is the arrow PQ in Fig. 34.6. The distance from the head to the tail of an arrow oriented in this way is called its *height;* in Fig. 34.6 the height is y. The image formed by such an extended object is an

34.6 Construction for determining the height of an image formed by reflection at a plane reflecting surface.

For a plane mirror, PQV and $P'Q'V$ are congruent, so $y = y'$ and the object and image are the same size (the lateral magnification is 1).

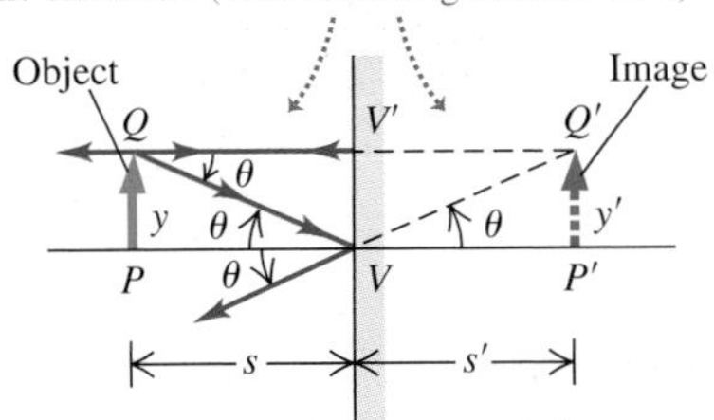

extended image; to each point on the object, there corresponds a point on the image. Two of the rays from Q are shown; *all* the rays from Q appear to diverge from its image point Q' after reflection. The image of the arrow is the line $P'Q'$, with height y'. Other points of the object PQ have image points between P' and Q'. The triangles PQV and $P'Q'V$ are congruent, so the object PQ and image $P'Q'$ have the same size and orientation, and $y = y'$.

The ratio of image height to object height, y'/y, in *any* image-forming situation is called the **lateral magnification** m; that is,

$$m = \frac{y'}{y} \quad \text{(lateral magnification)} \tag{34.2}$$

Thus for a plane mirror the lateral magnification m is unity. When you look at yourself in a plane mirror, your image is the same size as the real you.

In Fig. 34.6 the image arrow points in the *same* direction as the object arrow; we say that the image is **erect.** In this case, y and y' have the same sign, and the lateral magnification m is positive. The image formed by a plane mirror is always erect, so y and y' have both the same magnitude and the same sign; from Eq. (34.2) the lateral magnification of a plane mirror is always $m = +1$. Later we will encounter situations in which the image is **inverted;** that is, the image arrow points in the direction *opposite* to that of the object arrow. For an inverted image, y and y' have *opposite* signs, and the lateral magnification m is *negative.*

The object in Fig. 34.6 has only one dimension. Figure 34.7 shows a *three-dimensional* object and its three-dimensional virtual image formed by a plane mirror. The object and image are related in the same way as a left hand and a right hand.

34.7 The image formed by a plane mirror is virtual, erect, and reversed. It is the same size as the object.

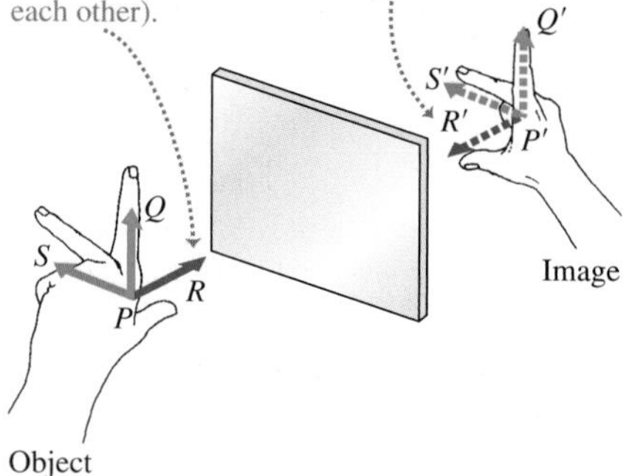

CAUTION Reflections in a plane mirror At this point, you may be asking, "Why does a plane mirror reverse images left and right but not top and bottom?" This question is quite misleading! As Fig. 34.7 shows, the up-down image $P'Q'$ and the left-right image $P'S'$ are parallel to their objects and are not reversed at all. Only the front-back image $P'R'$ is reversed relative to PR. Hence it's most correct to say that a plane mirror reverses *back to front.* To verify this object-image relationship, point your thumbs along PR and $P'R'$, your forefingers along PQ and $P'Q'$, and your middle fingers along PS and $P'S'$. When an object and its image are related in this way, the image is said to be **reversed;** this means that *only* the front-back dimension is reversed.

34.8 The image formed by a plane mirror is reversed; the image of a right hand is a left hand, and so on. (The hand is resting on a horizontal mirror.) Are images of the letters H and A reversed?

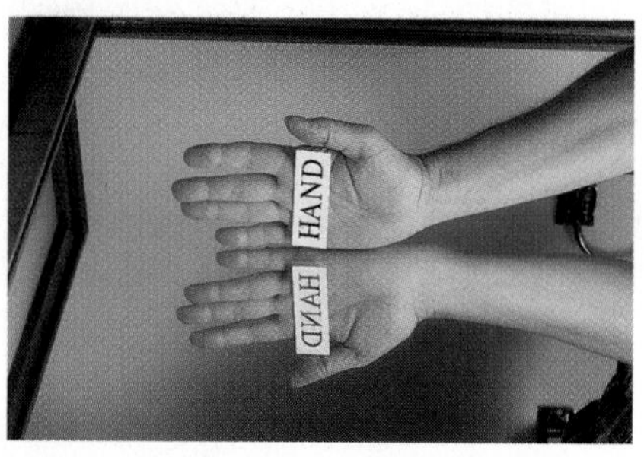

The reversed image of a three-dimensional object formed by a plane mirror is the same *size* as the object in all its dimensions. When the transverse dimensions of object and image are in the same direction, the image is erect. Thus a plane mirror always forms an erect but reversed image. Figure 34.8 illustrates this point.

An important property of all images formed by reflecting or refracting surfaces is that an *image* formed by one surface or optical device can serve as the *object* for a second surface or device. Figure 34.9 shows a simple example. Mirror 1 forms an image P_1' of the object point P, and mirror 2 forms another image P_2', each in the way we have just discussed. But in addition, the image P_1' formed by mirror 1 serves an object for mirror 2, which then forms an image of this object at point P_3' as shown. Similarly, mirror 1 uses the image P_2' formed by mirror 2 as an object and forms an image of it. We leave it to you to show that this image point is also at P_3'. The idea that an image formed by one device can act as the object for a second device is of great importance in geometric optics. We will use it later in this chapter to locate the image formed by two successive curved-surface refractions in a lens. This idea will help us to understand image formation by combinations of lenses, as in a microscope or a refracting telescope.

34.9 Images P_1' and P_2' are formed by a single reflection of each ray from the object at P. Image P_3', located by treating either of the other images as an object, is formed by a double reflection of each ray.

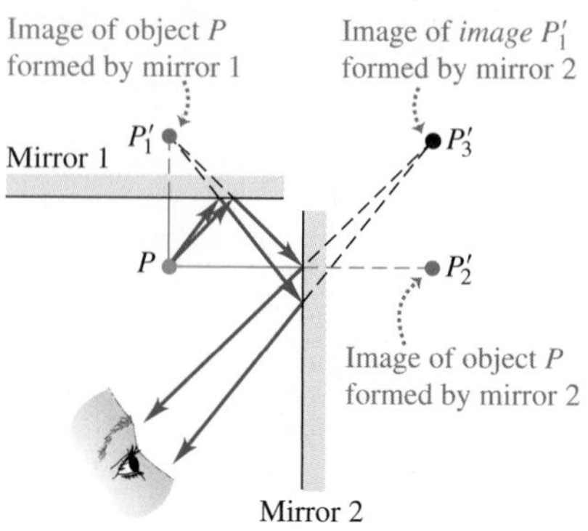

Test Your Understanding of Section 34.1 If you walk directly toward a plane mirror at a speed v, at what speed does your image approach you? (i) slower than v; (ii) v; (iii) faster than v but slower than $2v$; (iv) $2v$; (v) faster than $2v$.

34.2 Reflection at a Spherical Surface

A plane mirror produces an image that is the same size as the object. But there are many applications for mirrors in which the image and object must be of different sizes. A magnifying mirror used when applying makeup gives an image that is *larger* than the object, and surveillance mirrors (used in stores to help spot shoplifters) give an image that is *smaller* than the object. There are also applications of mirrors in which a *real* image is desired, so light rays do indeed pass through the image point P'. A plane mirror by itself cannot perform any of these tasks. Instead, *curved* mirrors are used.

Image of a Point Object: Spherical Mirror

We'll consider the special (and easily analyzed) case of image formation by a *spherical* mirror. Figure 34.10a shows a spherical mirror with radius of curvature R, with its concave side facing the incident light. The **center of curvature** of the surface (the center of the sphere of which the surface is a part) is at C, and the **vertex** of the mirror (the center of the mirror surface) is at V. The line CV is called the **optic axis.** Point P is an object point that lies on the optic axis; for the moment, we assume that the distance from P to V is greater than R.

Ray PV, passing through C, strikes the mirror normally and is reflected back on itself. Ray PB, at an angle α with the axis, strikes the mirror at B, where the angles of incidence and reflection are θ. The reflected ray intersects the axis at point P'. We will show shortly that *all* rays from P intersect the axis at the *same* point P', as in Fig. 34.10b, provided that the angle α is small. Point P' is therefore the *image* of object point P. Unlike the reflected rays in Fig. 34.1, the reflected rays in Fig. 34.10b actually do intersect at point P', then diverge from P' *as if* they had originated at this point. Thus P' is a *real* image.

To see the usefulness of having a real image, suppose that the mirror is in a darkened room in which the only source of light is a self-luminous object at P. If you place a small piece of photographic film at P', all the rays of light coming from point P that reflect off the mirror will strike the same point P' on the film; when developed, the film will show a single bright spot, representing a sharply focused image of the object at point P. This principle is at the heart of most astronomical telescopes, which use large concave mirrors to make photographs of celestial objects. With a *plane* mirror like that in Fig. 34.2, placing a piece of film at the image point P' would be a waste of time; the light rays never actually pass through the image point, and the image can't be recorded on film. Real images are *essential* for photography.

Let's now find the location of the real image point P' in Fig. 34.10a and prove the assertion that all rays from P intersect at P' (provided that their angle with the optic axis is small). The object distance, measured from the vertex V, is s; the image distance, also measured from V, is s'. The signs of s, s', and the radius of curvature R are determined by the sign rules given in Section 34.1. The object point P is on the same side as the incident light, so according to sign rule 1, s is positive. The image point P' is on the same side as the reflected light, so according to sign rule 2, the image distance s' is also positive. The center of curvature C is on the same side as the reflected light, so according to sign rule 3, R, too, is positive; R is always positive when reflection occurs at the *concave* side of a surface Fig. 34.11).

34.10 (a) A concave spherical mirror forms a real image of a point object P on the mirror's optic axis. (b) The eye sees some of the outgoing rays and perceives them as having come from P'.

(a) Construction for finding the position P' of an image formed by a concave spherical mirror

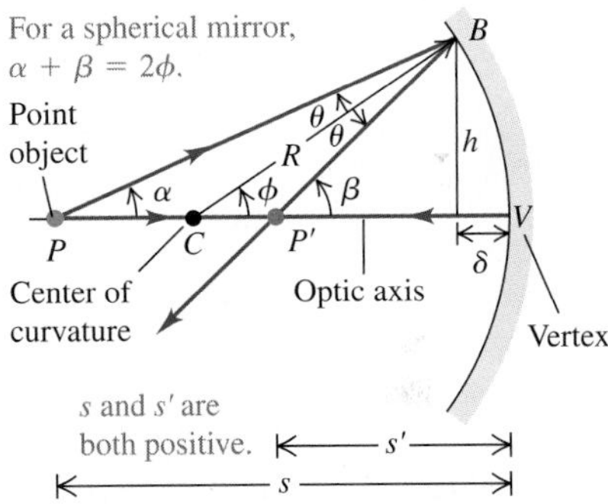

(b) The paraxial approximation, which holds for rays with small α

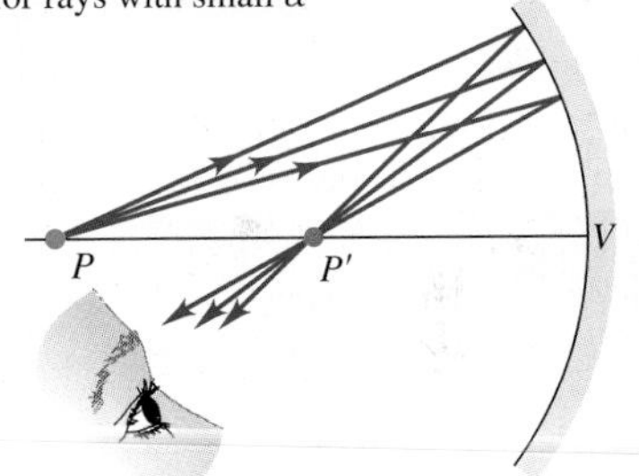

All rays from P that have a small angle α pass through P', forming a real image.

34.11 The sign rule for the radius of a spherical mirror.

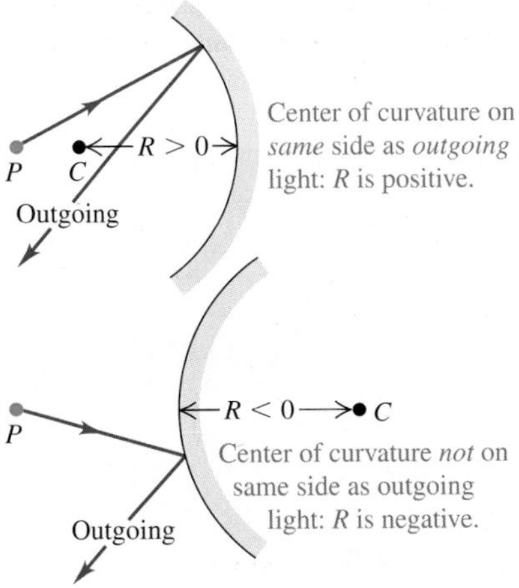

We now use the following theorem from plane geometry: An exterior angle of a triangle equals the sum of the two opposite interior angles. Applying this theorem to triangles PBC and $P'BC$ in Fig. 34.10a, we have

$$\phi = \alpha + \theta \qquad \beta = \phi + \theta$$

Eliminating θ between these equations gives

$$\alpha + \beta = 2\phi \tag{34.3}$$

We may now compute the image distance s'. Let h represent the height of point B above the optic axis, and let δ represent the short distance from V to the foot of this vertical line. We now write expressions for the tangents of α, β, and ϕ, remembering that s, s', and R are all positive quantities:

$$\tan\alpha = \frac{h}{s - \delta} \qquad \tan\beta = \frac{h}{s' - \delta} \qquad \tan\phi = \frac{h}{R - \delta}$$

These trigonometric equations cannot be solved as simply as the corresponding algebraic equations for a plane mirror. However, *if the angle α is small,* the angles β and ϕ are also small. The tangent of an angle that is much less than one radian is nearly equal to the angle itself (measured in radians), so we can replace $\tan\alpha$ by α, and so on, in the equations above. Also, if α is small, we can neglect the distance δ compared with s', s, and R. So for small angles we have the following approximate relationships:

$$\alpha = \frac{h}{s} \qquad \beta = \frac{h}{s'} \qquad \phi = \frac{h}{R}$$

Substituting these into Eq. (34.3) and dividing by h, we obtain a general relationship among s, s', and R:

$$\frac{1}{s} + \frac{1}{s'} = \frac{2}{R} \quad \text{(object–image relationship, spherical mirror)} \tag{34.4}$$

This equation does not contain the angle α. Hence *all* rays from P that make sufficiently small angles with the axis intersect at P' after they are reflected; this verifies our earlier assertion. Such rays, nearly parallel to the axis and close to it, are called **paraxial rays.** (The term **paraxial approximation** is often used for the approximations we have just described.) Since all such reflected light rays converge on the image point, a concave mirror is also called a *converging mirror.*

Be sure you understand that Eq. (34.4), as well as many similar relationships that we will derive later in this chapter and the next, is only *approximately* correct. It results from a calculation containing approximations, and it is valid only for paraxial rays. If we increase the angle α that a ray makes with the optic axis, the point P' where the ray intersects the optic axis moves somewhat closer to the vertex than for a paraxial ray. As a result, a spherical mirror, unlike a plane mirror, does not form a precise point image of a point object; the image is "smeared out." This property of a spherical mirror is called **spherical aberration.** When the primary mirror of the Hubble Space Telescope (Fig. 34.12a) was manufactured, tiny errors were made in its shape that led to an unacceptable amount of spherical aberration (Fig. 34.12b). The performance of the telescope improved dramatically after the installation of corrective optics (Fig. 34.12c).

If the radius of curvature becomes infinite ($R = \infty$), the mirror becomes *plane,* and Eq. (34.4) reduces to Eq. (34.1) for a plane reflecting surface.

34.12 (a), (b) Soon after the Hubble Space Telescope (HST) was placed in orbit in 1990, it was discovered that the concave primary mirror (also called the *objective mirror*) was too shallow by about 1/50 the width of a human hair, leading to spherical aberration of the star's image. (c) After corrective optics were installed in 1993, the effects of spherical aberration were almost completely eliminated.

(a) The 2.4-m-diameter primary mirror of the Hubble Space Telescope

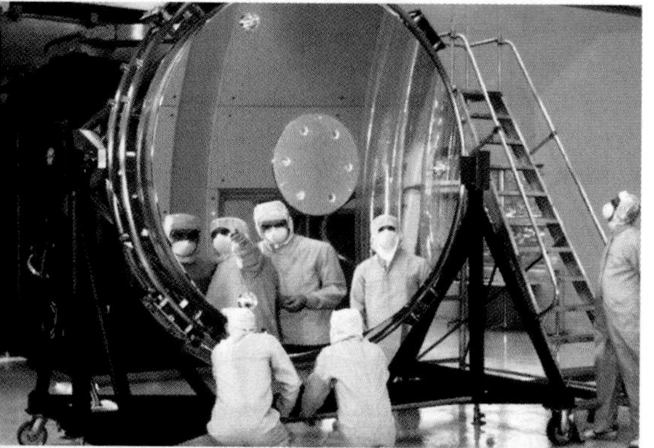

(b) A star seen with the original mirror

(c) The same star with corrective optics

Focal Point and Focal Length

When the object point P is very far from the spherical mirror ($s = \infty$), the incoming rays are parallel. (The star shown in Fig. 34.12c is an example of such a distant object.) From Eq. (34.4) the image distance s' in this case is given by

$$\frac{1}{\infty} + \frac{1}{s'} = \frac{2}{R} \qquad s' = \frac{R}{2}$$

The situation is shown in Fig. 34.13a. The beam of incident parallel rays converges, after reflection from the mirror, to a point F at a distance $R/2$ from the vertex of the mirror. The point F at which the incident parallel rays converge is called the **focal point;** we say that these rays are brought to a focus. The distance from the vertex to the focal point, denoted by f, is called the **focal length.** We see that f is related to the radius of curvature R by

$$f = \frac{R}{2} \quad \text{(focal length of a spherical mirror)} \qquad (34.5)$$

The opposite situation is shown in Fig. 34.13b. Now the *object* is placed at the focal point F, so the object distance is $s = f = R/2$. The image distance s' is again given by Eq. (34.4):

$$\frac{2}{R} + \frac{1}{s'} = \frac{2}{R} \qquad \frac{1}{s'} = 0 \qquad s' = \infty$$

With the object at the focal point, the reflected rays in Fig. 34.13b are parallel to the optic axis; they meet only at a point infinitely far from the mirror, so the image is at infinity.

Thus the focal point F of a spherical mirror has the properties that (1) any incoming ray parallel to the optic axis is reflected through the focal point and (2) any incoming ray that passes through the focal point is reflected parallel to the optic axis. For spherical mirrors these statements are true only for paraxial rays. For parabolic mirrors these statements are *exactly* true; this is why parabolic mirrors are preferred for astronomical telescopes. Spherical or parabolic mirrors are used in flashlights and headlights to form the light from the bulb into a parallel beam. Some solar-power plants use an array of plane mirrors to simulate an approximately spherical concave mirror; light from the sun is collected by the mirrors and directed to the focal point, where a steam boiler is placed. (The concepts of focal point and focal length also apply to lenses, as we'll see in Section 34.4.)

We will usually express the relationship between object and image distances for a mirror, Eq. (34.4), in terms of the focal length f:

$$\frac{1}{s} + \frac{1}{s'} = \frac{1}{f} \quad \text{(object–image relationship, spherical mirror)} \qquad (34.6)$$

34.13 The focal point and focal length of a concave mirror.

(a) All parallel rays incident on a spherical mirror reflect through the focal point.

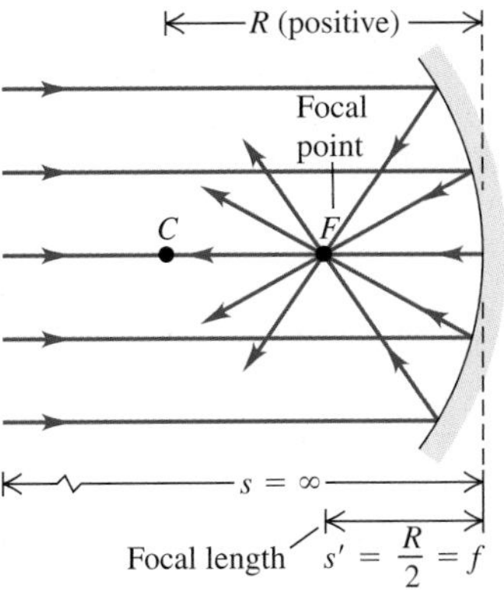

(b) Rays diverging from the focal point reflect to form parallel outgoing rays.

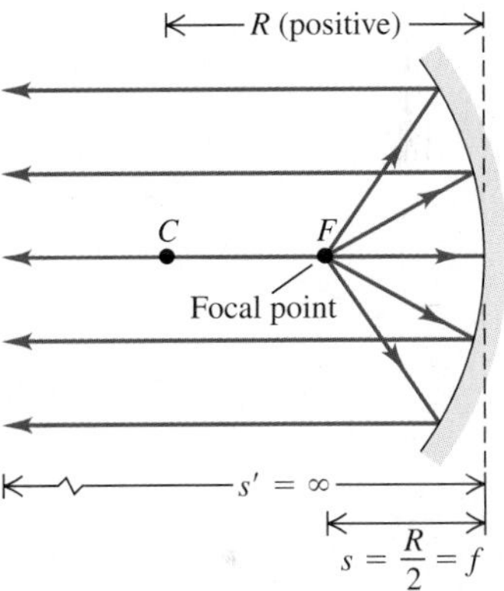

Image of an Extended Object: Spherical Mirror

Now suppose we have an object with *finite* size, represented by the arrow PQ in Fig. 34.14, perpendicular to the optic axis CV. The image of P formed by paraxial rays is at P'. The object distance for point Q is very nearly equal to that for point P, so the image $P'Q'$ is nearly straight and perpendicular to the axis. Note that the object and image arrows have different sizes, y and y', respectively, and that they have opposite orientation. In Eq. (34.2) we defined the *lateral magnification m* as the ratio of image size y' to object size y:

$$m = \frac{y'}{y}$$

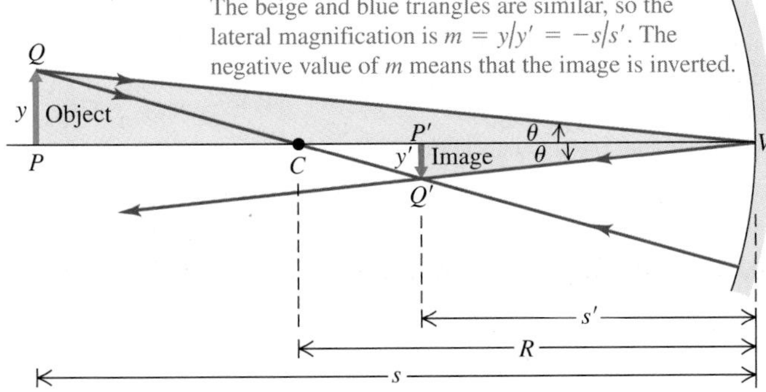

34.14 Construction for determining the position, orientation, and height of an image formed by a concave spherical mirror.

ActivPhysics ONLINE

Because triangles PVQ and $P'VQ'$ in Fig. 34.14 are *similar,* we also have the relationship $y/s = -y'/s'$. The negative sign is needed because object and image are on opposite sides of the optic axis; if y is positive, y' is negative. Therefore

$$m = \frac{y'}{y} = -\frac{s'}{s} \quad \text{(lateral magnification, spherical mirror)} \tag{34.7}$$

If m is positive, the image is erect in comparison to the object; if m is negative, the image is *inverted* relative to the object, as in Fig. 34.14. For a *plane* mirror, $s = -s'$, so $y' = y$ and $m = +1$; since m is positive, the image is erect, and since $|m| = 1$, the image is the same size as the object.

CAUTION **Lateral magnification can be less than 1** Although the ratio of image size to object size is called the *lateral magnification,* the image formed by a mirror or lens may be larger than, smaller than, or the same size as the object. If it is smaller, then the lateral magnification is less than unity in absolute value: $|m| < 1$. The image formed by an astronomical telescope mirror or a camera lens is usually *much* smaller than the object. For example, the image of the bright star shown in Fig. 34.12c is just a few millimeters across, while the star itself is hundreds of thousands of kilometers in diameter.

In our discussion of concave mirrors we have so far considered only objects that lie *outside* or at the focal point, so that the object distance s is greater than or equal to the (positive) focal length f. In this case the image point is on the same side of the mirror as the outgoing rays, and the image is real and inverted. If an object is placed *inside* the focal point of a concave mirror, so that $s < f$, the resulting image is *virtual* (that is, the image point is on the opposite side of the mirror from the object), *erect,* and *larger* than the object. Mirrors used when applying makeup (referred to at the beginning of this section) are concave mirrors; in use, the distance from the face to the mirror is less than the focal length, and an enlarged, erect image is seen. You can prove these statements about concave mirrors by applying Eqs. (34.6) and (34.7) (see Exercise 34.11). We'll also be able to verify these results later in this section, after we've learned some graphical methods for relating the positions and sizes of the object and the image.

Example 34.1 Image formation by a concave mirror I

A concave mirror forms an image, on a wall 3.00 m from the mirror, of the filament of a headlight lamp 10.0 cm in front of the mirror. (a) What are the radius of curvature and focal length of the mirror? (b) What is the height of the image if the height of the object is 5.00 mm?

SOLUTION

IDENTIFY: This problem uses the ideas developed in this section. Our target variables are the radius of curvature R, focal length f, and image height y'.

SET UP: Figure 34.15 shows the situation. We are given the distances from the mirror to the object (s) and from the mirror to the image (s'). We use the object–image relationship given by Eq. (34.6) to determine the focal length f, and then find the radius of curvature R using Eq. (34.5). Equation (34.7) lets us calculate the image height y' from the distances s and s' and the object height y.

EXECUTE: (a) Both the object and the image are on the concave side of the mirror (the reflective side), so both object distance and image distance are positive; we have $s = 10.0$ cm and $s' = 300$ cm. From Eq. (34.4),

34.15 Our sketch for this problem.

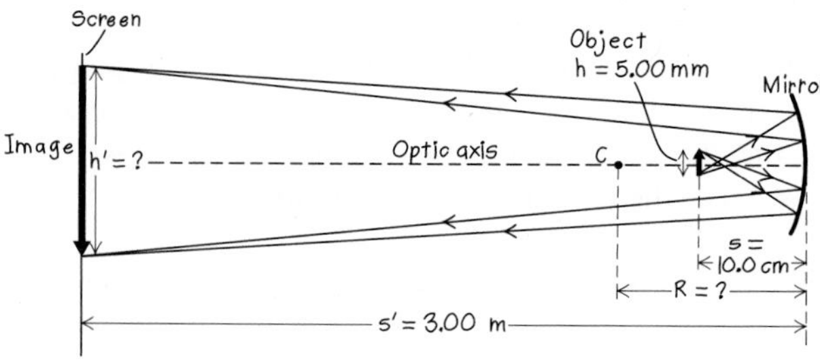

$$\frac{1}{10.0\text{ cm}} + \frac{1}{300\text{ cm}} = \frac{2}{R}$$

$$R = \frac{2}{0.100\text{ cm}^{-1} + 3.33 \times 10^{-3}\text{ cm}^{-1}} = 19.4\text{ cm}$$

The focal length of the mirror is $f = R/2 = 9.7$ cm.

(b) From Eq. (34.7) the lateral magnification is

$$m = \frac{y'}{y} = -\frac{s'}{s} = -\frac{300 \text{ cm}}{10.0 \text{ cm}} = -30.0$$

Because m is negative, the image is inverted. The height of the image is 30.0 times the height of the object, or $(30.0)(5.00 \text{ mm}) = 150 \text{ mm}$.

EVALUATE: Note that the object is placed just outside the focal point ($s = 10.0$ cm compared to $f = 9.7$ cm). This is very similar to what is done in automobile headlights. With the filament close to the focal point, the concave mirror produces a beam of nearly parallel rays.

Conceptual Example 34.2 Image formation by a concave mirror II

In Example 34.1, suppose that the left half of the mirror's reflecting surface is covered with nonreflective soot. What effect will this have on the image of the filament?

SOLUTION

It would be natural to guess that the image would now show only half of the filament. But in fact the image will still show the *entire* filament. The explanation can be seen by examining Fig. 34.10b. Light rays coming from any object point P are reflected from *all* parts of the mirror and converge on the corresponding image point P'. If part of the mirror surface is made nonreflective or is removed altogether, the light rays from the remaining reflective surface still form an image of every part of the object.

The only effect of reducing the reflecting area is that the image becomes dimmer because less light energy reaches the image point. In our example the reflective area of the mirror is reduced by one-half, and the image will be one-half as bright. *Increasing* the reflective area makes the image brighter. To make reasonably bright images of distant stars, astronomical telescopes use mirrors that are up to several meters in diameter. Figure 34.12a shows an example.

Convex Mirrors

In Fig. 34.16a the *convex* side of a spherical mirror faces the incident light. The center of curvature is on the side opposite to the outgoing rays; according to sign rule 3 in Section 34.1, R is negative (see Fig. 34.11). Ray PB is reflected, with the angles of incidence and reflection both equal to θ. The reflected ray, projected backward, intersects the axis at P'. As with a concave mirror, *all* rays from P that are reflected by the mirror diverge from the same point P', provided that the angle α is small. Therefore P' is the image of P. The object distance s is positive, the image distance s' is negative, and the radius of curvature R is *negative* for a *convex* mirror.

Figure 34.16b shows two rays diverging from the head of the arrow PQ and the virtual image $P'Q'$ of this arrow. The same procedure that we used for a concave mirror can be used to show that for a convex mirror,

$$\frac{1}{s} + \frac{1}{s'} = \frac{2}{R}$$

and the lateral magnification is

$$m = \frac{y'}{y} = -\frac{s'}{s}$$

34.16 Image formation by a convex mirror.

(a) Construction for finding the position of an image formed by a convex mirror

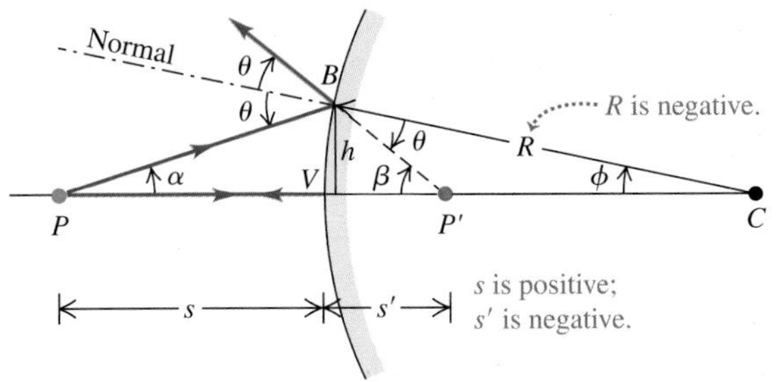

(b) Construction for finding the magnification of an image formed by a convex mirror

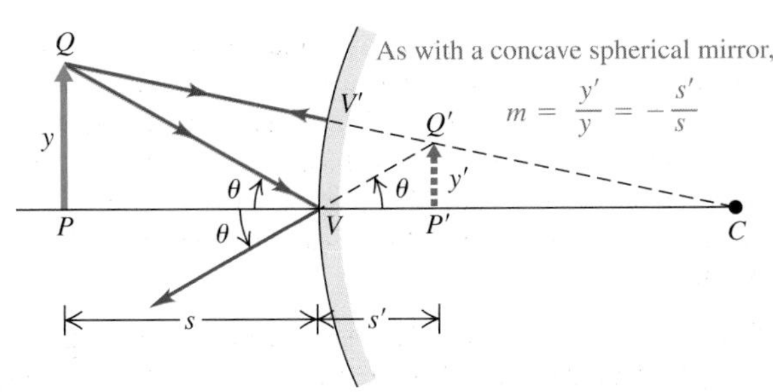

34.17 The focal point and focal length of a convex mirror.

(a) Paraxial rays incident on a convex spherical mirror diverge from a virtual focal point.

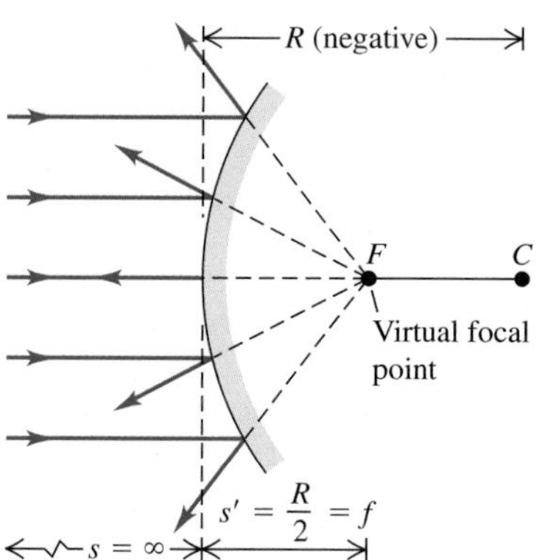

(b) Rays aimed at the virtual focal point are parallel to the axis after reflection.

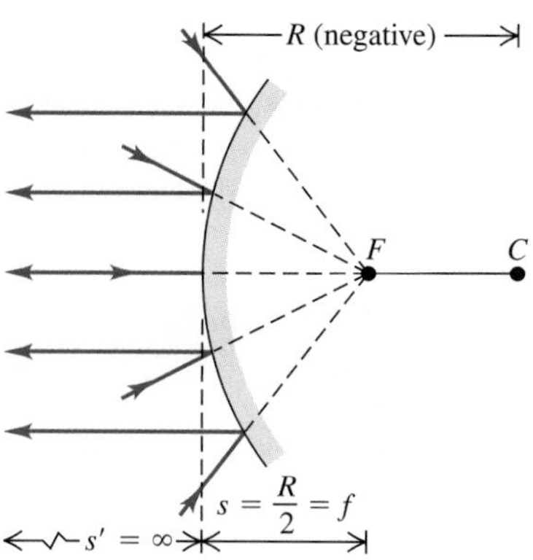

These expressions are exactly the same as Eqs. (34.4) and (34.7) for a concave mirror. Thus when we use our sign rules consistently, Eqs. (34.4) and (34.7) are valid for both concave and convex mirrors.

When R is negative (convex mirror), incoming rays that are parallel to the optic axis are not reflected through the focal point F. Instead, they diverge as though they had come from the point F at a distance f *behind* the mirror, as shown in Fig. 34.17a. In this case, f is the focal length, and F is called a *virtual focal point.* The corresponding image distance s' is negative, so both f and R are negative, and Eq. (34.5), $f = R/2$, holds for convex as well as concave mirrors. In Fig. 34.17b the incoming rays are converging as though they would meet at the virtual focal point F, and they are reflected parallel to the optic axis.

In summary, Eqs. (34.4) through (34.7), the basic relationships for image formation by a spherical mirror, are valid for both concave and convex mirrors, provided that we use the sign rules consistently.

Example 34.3 Santa's image problem

Santa checks himself for soot, using his reflection in a shiny silvered Christmas tree ornament 0.750 m away (Fig. 34.18a). The diameter of the ornament is 7.20 cm. Standard reference works state that he is a "right jolly old elf," so we estimate his height to be 1.6 m. Where and how tall is the image of Santa formed by the ornament? Is it erect or inverted?

SOLUTION

IDENTIFY: Santa is the object, and the surface of the ornament closest to Santa acts as a convex mirror. The relationships among object distance, image distance, focal length, and magnification are the same as for concave mirrors, provided we use the sign rules consistently.

34.18 (a) The ornament forms a virtual, reduced, erect image of Santa. (b) Our sketch of two of the rays forming the image.

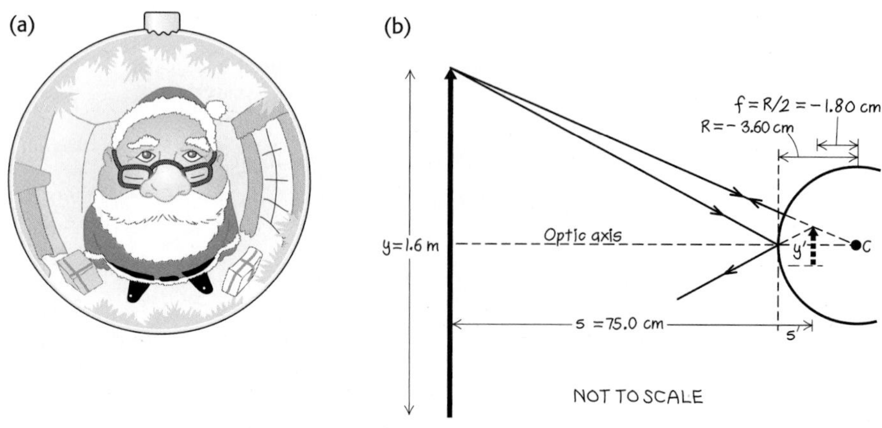

SET UP: Figure 34.18b shows the situation. Since the mirror is convex, its radius of curvature and focal length are negative. The object distance is $s = 0.750\text{ m} = 75.0\text{ cm}$ and Santa's height is $y = 1.6\text{ m}$. We use Eq. (34.6) to determine the image distance s', and then use Eq. (34.7) to find the lateral magnification m and hence the image height y'. The sign of m tells us whether the image is erect or inverted.

EXECUTE: The radius of the convex mirror (half the diameter) is $R = -(7.20\text{ cm})/2 = -3.60\text{ cm}$, and the focal length is $f = R/2 = -1.80\text{ cm}$. From Eq. (34.6),

$$\frac{1}{s'} = \frac{1}{f} - \frac{1}{s} = \frac{1}{-1.80\text{ cm}} - \frac{1}{75.0\text{ cm}}$$
$$s' = -1.76\text{ cm}$$

Because s' is negative, the image is behind the mirror—that is, on the side opposite to the outgoing light (Fig. 34.18b)—and it is virtual. The image is about halfway between the front surface of the ornament and its center.

The lateral magnification m is given by Eq. (34.7):

$$m = \frac{y'}{y} = -\frac{s'}{s} = -\frac{-1.76\text{ cm}}{75.0\text{ cm}} = 0.0234$$

Because m is positive, the image is erect. It is only about 0.0234 as tall as Santa himself:

$$y' = my = (0.0234)(1.6\text{ m}) = 3.8 \times 10^{-2}\text{ m} = 3.8\text{ cm}$$

EVALUATE: When the object distance s is positive, a convex mirror *always* forms an erect, virtual, reduced, reversed image. For this reason, convex mirrors are used for shoplifting surveillance in stores, at blind intersections, and as "wide-angle" rear-view mirrors for cars and trucks (including those that bear the legend "Objects in mirror are closer than they appear").

Graphical Methods for Mirrors

In Examples 34.1 and 34.3, we used Eqs. (34.6) and (34.7) to find the position and size of the image formed by a mirror. We can also determine the properties of the image by a simple *graphical* method. This method consists of finding the point of intersection of a few particular rays that diverge from a point of the object (such as point Q in Fig. 34.19) and are reflected by the mirror. Then (neglecting aberrations) *all* rays from this object point that strike the mirror will intersect at the same point. For this construction we always choose an object point that is *not* on the optic axis. Four rays that we can usually draw easily are shown in Fig. 34.19. These are called **principal rays.**

1. *A ray parallel to the axis,* after reflection, passes through the focal point F of a concave mirror or appears to come from the (virtual) focal point of a convex mirror.
2. *A ray through (or proceeding toward) the focal point F* is reflected parallel to the axis.
3. *A ray along the radius* through or away from the center of curvature C intersects the surface normally and is reflected back along its original path.
4. *A ray to the vertex V* is reflected forming equal angles with the optic axis.

34.19 The graphical method of locating an image formed by spherical mirror. The colors of the rays are for identification only; they do not refer to specific colors of light.

(a) Principal rays for concave mirror

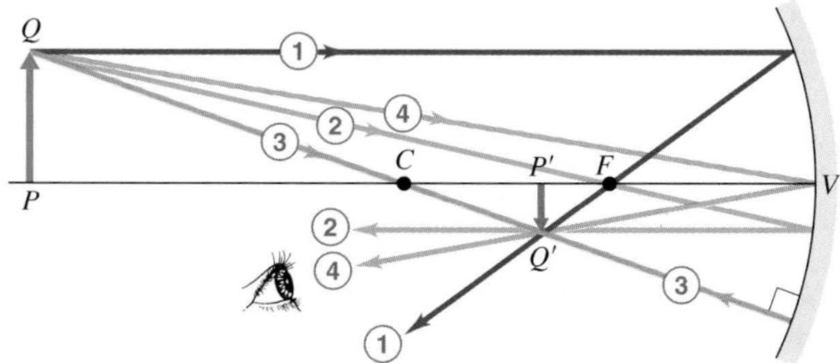

① Ray parallel to axis reflects through focal point.
② Ray through focal point reflects parallel to axis.
③ Ray through center of curvature intersects the surface normally and reflects along its original path.
④ Ray to vertex reflects symmetrically around optic axis.

(b) Principal rays for convex mirror

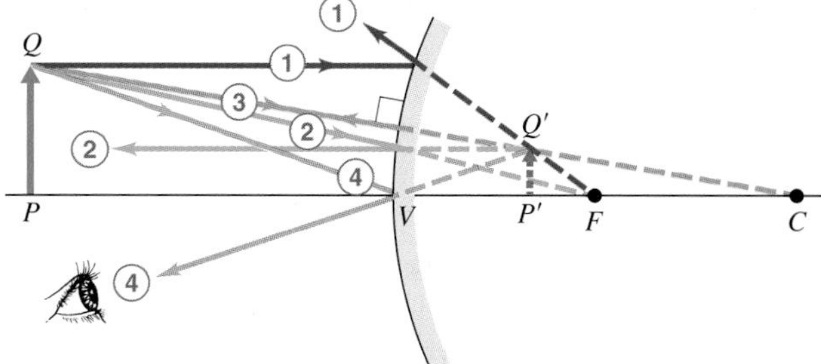

① Reflected parallel ray appears to come from focal point.
② Ray toward focal point reflects parallel to axis.
③ As with concave mirror: Ray radial to center of curvature intersects the surface normally and reflects along its original path.
④ As with concave mirror: Ray to vertex reflects symmetrically around optic axis.

Once we have found the position of the image point by means of the intersection of any two of these principal rays (1, 2, 3, 4), we can draw the path of any other ray from the object point to the same image point.

CAUTION Principal rays are not the only rays Although we've emphasized the principal rays, in fact *any* ray from the object that strikes the mirror will pass through the image point (for a real image) or appear to originate from the image point (for a virtual image). Usually, you only need to draw the principal rays, because these are all you need to locate the image.

Problem-Solving Strategy 34.1 Image Formation by Mirrors

IDENTIFY *the relevant concepts:* There are two different and complementary ways to solve problems involving image formation by mirrors. One approach uses equations, while the other involves drawing a principal-ray diagram. A successful problem solution uses *both* approaches.

SET UP *the problem:* Determine the target variables. The three key quantities are the focal length, object distance, and image distance; typically you'll be given two of these and will have to determine the third.

EXECUTE *the solution* as follows:

1. The principal-ray diagram is to geometric optics what the free-body diagram is to mechanics. In any problem involving image formation by a mirror, *always* draw a principal-ray diagram first if you have enough information. (The same advice should be followed when dealing with lenses in the following sections.)
2. It is usually best to orient your diagrams consistently with the incoming rays traveling from left to right. Don't draw a lot of other rays at random; stick with the principal rays, the ones you know something about. Use a ruler and measure distances carefully! A freehand sketch will *not* give good results.
3. If your principal rays don't converge at a real image point, you may have to extend them straight backward to locate a virtual image point, as in Fig. 34.19b. We recommend drawing the extensions with broken lines. Another useful aid is to color-code the different principal rays, as is done in Fig. 34.19.
4. Check your results using Eq. (34.6), $1/s + 1/s' = 1/f$, and the lateral magnification equation, Eq. (34.7). The results you find using this equation must be consistent with your principal-ray diagram; if not, double check both your calculations and your diagram.
5. Pay careful attention to signs on object and image distances, radii of curvature, and object and image heights. A negative sign on any of these quantities *always* has significance. Use the equations and the sign rules carefully and consistently, and they will tell you the truth! Note that the *same* sign rules (given in Section 34.1) work for all four cases in this chapter: reflection and refraction from plane and spherical surfaces.

EVALUATE *your answer:* You've already checked your results by using both diagrams and equations. But it always helps to take a look back and ask yourself, "Do these results make sense?"

Example 34.4 Concave mirror, different object distances

A concave mirror has a radius of curvature with absolute value 20 cm. Find graphically the image of an object in the form of an arrow perpendicular to the axis of the mirror at each of the following object distances: (a) 30 cm, (b) 20 cm, (c) 10 cm, and (d) 5 cm. Check the construction by *computing* the size and lateral magnification of each image.

SOLUTION

IDENTIFY: This problem asks us to use *both* graphical methods and calculations to find the image made by a mirror. This is a good practice to follow in all problems that involve image formation.

SET UP: We are given the radius of curvature $R = 20$ cm (positive since the mirror is concave) and hence the focal length $f = R/2 = 10$ cm. In each case we are told the object distance s and are asked to find the image distance s' and the lateral magnification $m = -s'/s$.

EXECUTE: Figure 34.20 shows the principal-ray diagrams for the four cases. Study each of these diagrams carefully, comparing each numbered ray with the description above. Several points are worth noting. First, in (b) the object and image distances are equal. Ray 3 cannot be drawn in this case because a ray from Q through the center of curvature C does not strike the mirror. Ray 2 cannot be drawn in (c) because a ray from Q toward F also does not strike the mirror. In this case the outgoing rays are parallel, corresponding to an infinite image distance. In (d) the outgoing rays have no real intersection point; they must be extended backward to find the point from which they appear to diverge—that is, from the *virtual image point* Q'. The case shown in (d) illustrates the general observation that an object placed inside the focal point of a concave mirror produces a virtual image.

Measurements of the figures, with appropriate scaling, give the following approximate image distances: (a) 15 cm; (b) 20 cm; (c) ∞ or $-\infty$ (because the outgoing rays are parallel and do not converge at any finite distance); (d) -10 cm. To *compute* these distances, we use Eq. (34.6) with $f = 10$ cm:

$$\text{(a)}\quad \frac{1}{30\text{ cm}} + \frac{1}{s'} = \frac{1}{10\text{ cm}} \qquad s' = 15\text{ cm}$$

$$\text{(b)}\quad \frac{1}{20\text{ cm}} + \frac{1}{s'} = \frac{1}{10\text{ cm}} \qquad s' = 20\text{ cm}$$

(c) $\frac{1}{10 \text{ cm}} + \frac{1}{s'} = \frac{1}{10 \text{ cm}}$ $\quad s' = \infty \text{ (or } -\infty)$

(d) $\frac{1}{5 \text{ cm}} + \frac{1}{s'} = \frac{1}{10 \text{ cm}}$ $\quad s' = -10 \text{ cm}$

In (a) and (b) the image is real; in (d) it is virtual. In (c) the image is formed at infinity.

The lateral magnifications measured from the figures are approximately (a) $-\frac{1}{2}$; (b) -1; (c) ∞ or $-\infty$ (because the image distance is infinite); (d) $+2$. *Computing* the magnifications from Eq. (34.7), we find:

(a) $m = -\frac{15 \text{ cm}}{30 \text{ cm}} = -\frac{1}{2}$

(b) $m = -\frac{20 \text{ cm}}{20 \text{ cm}} = -1$

(c) $m = -\frac{\infty \text{ cm}}{10 \text{ cm}} = -\infty \text{ (or } +\infty)$

(d) $m = -\frac{-10 \text{ cm}}{5 \text{ cm}} = +2$

In (a) and (b) the image is inverted; in (d) it is erect.

EVALUATE: Notice the trend as the object is moved closer to the mirror. When the object is far from the mirror, as in Fig. 34.20a, the image is smaller than the object, inverted, and real. As the object distance decreases, the image moves farther from the mirror and increases in size (Fig. 34.20b). When the object is at the focal point, the image is at infinity (Fig. 34.20c). If the object is moved inside the focal point, the image becomes larger than the object, erect, and virtual (Fig. 34.20d). You can test these conclusions by looking at objects reflected in the concave bowl of a metal spoon.

34.20 Using principal-ray diagrams to locate the image $P'Q'$ made by a concave mirror.

(a) Construction for $s = 30$ cm

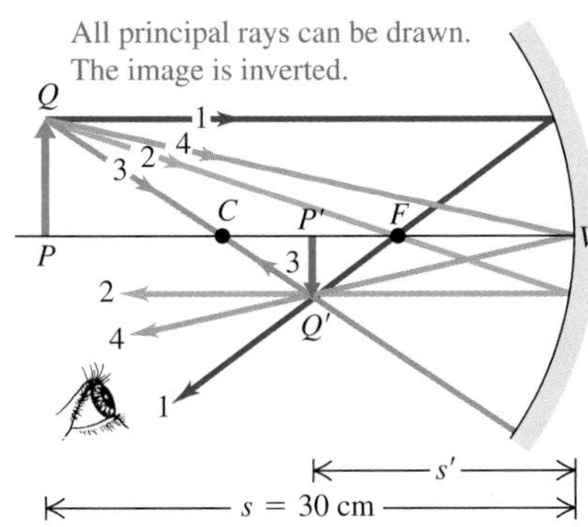

(b) Construction for $s = 20$ cm

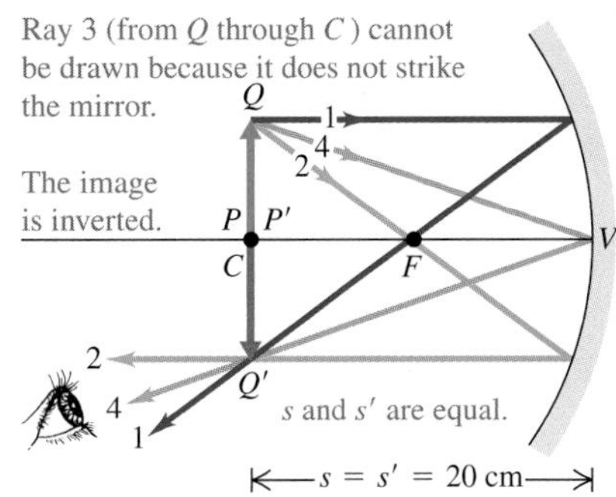

(c) Construction for $s = 10$ cm

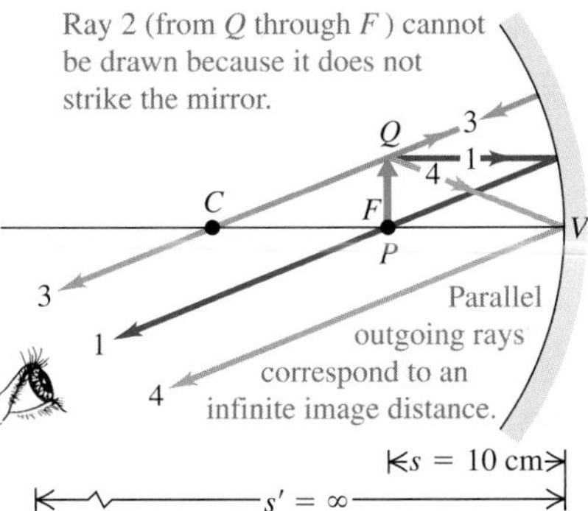

(d) Construction for $s = 5$ cm

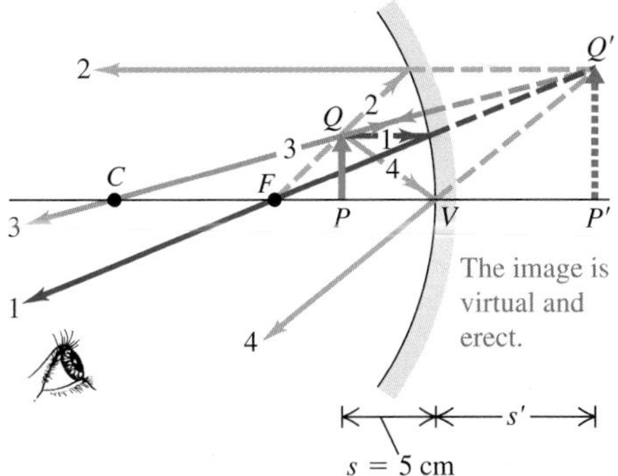

Test Your Understanding of Section 34.2 A cosmetics mirror is designed so that your reflection appears right-side up and enlarged. (a) Is the mirror concave or convex? (b) To see an enlarged image, what should be the distance from the mirror (of focal length f) to your face? (i) $|f|$; (ii) less than $|f|$; (iii) greater than $|f|$.

34.3 Refraction at a Spherical Surface

As we mentioned in Section 34.1, images can be formed by refraction as well as by reflection. To begin with, let's consider refraction at a spherical surface—that is, at a spherical interface between two optical materials with different indexes of refraction. This analysis is directly applicable to some real optical systems, such as the human eye. It also provides a stepping-stone for the analysis of lenses, which usually have *two* spherical (or nearly spherical) surfaces.

Image of a Point Object: Spherical Refracting Surface

In Fig. 34.21 a spherical surface with radius R forms an interface between two materials with different indexes of refraction n_a and n_b. The surface forms an image P' of an object point P; we want to find how the object and image distances (s and s') are related. We will use the same sign rules that we used for spherical mirrors. The center of curvature C is on the outgoing side of the surface, so R is positive. Ray PV strikes the vertex V and is perpendicular to the surface (that is, to the plane that is tangent to the surface at the point of incidence V). It passes into the second material without deviation. Ray PB, making an angle α with the axis, is incident at an angle θ_a with the normal and is refracted at an angle θ_b. These rays intersect at P', a distance s' to the right of the vertex. The figure is drawn for the case $n_a < n_b$. The object and image distances are both positive.

We are going to prove that if the angle α is small, *all* rays from P intersect at the same point P', so P' is the *real image* of P. We use much the same approach as we did for spherical mirrors in Section 34.2. We again use the theorem that an exterior angle of a triangle equals the sum of the two opposite interior angles; applying this to the triangles PBC and $P'BC$ gives

$$\theta_a = \alpha + \phi \qquad \phi = \beta + \theta_b \tag{34.8}$$

From the law of refraction,

$$n_a \sin\theta_a = n_b \sin\theta_b$$

Also, the tangents of α, β, and ϕ are

$$\tan\alpha = \frac{h}{s + \delta} \qquad \tan\beta = \frac{h}{s' - \delta} \qquad \tan\phi = \frac{h}{R - \delta} \tag{34.9}$$

For paraxial rays, θ_a and θ_b are both small in comparison to a radian, and we may approximate both the sine and tangent of either of these angles by the angle itself (measured in radians). The law of refraction then gives

$$n_a\theta_a = n_b\theta_b$$

Combining this with the first of Eqs. (34.8), we obtain

$$\theta_b = \frac{n_a}{n_b}(\alpha + \phi)$$

When we substitute this into the second of Eqs. (34.8), we get

$$n_a\alpha + n_b\beta = (n_b - n_a)\phi \tag{34.10}$$

Now we use the approximations $\tan\alpha = \alpha$, and so on, in Eqs. (34.9) and also neglect the small distance δ; those equations then become

$$\alpha = \frac{h}{s} \qquad \beta = \frac{h}{s'} \qquad \phi = \frac{h}{R}$$

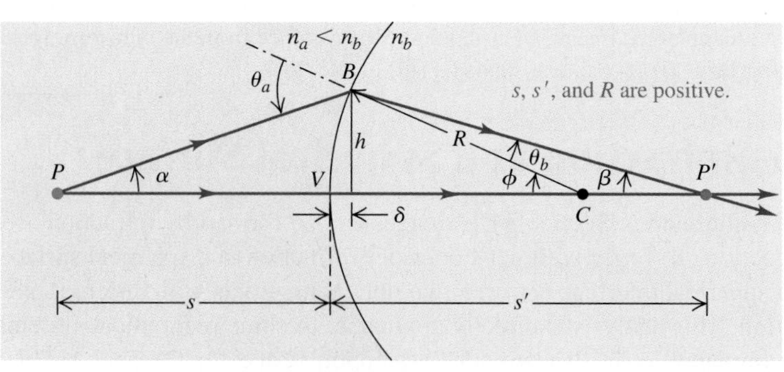

34.21 Construction for finding the position of the image point P' of a point object P formed by refraction at a spherical surface. The materials to the left and right of the interface have refractive indexes n_a and n_b, respectively. In the case shown here, $n_a < n_b$.

Finally, we substitute these into Eq. (34.10) and divide out the common factor h. We obtain

$$\frac{n_a}{s} + \frac{n_b}{s'} = \frac{n_b - n_a}{R} \quad \text{(object–image relationship, spherical refracting surface)} \tag{34.11}$$

This equation does not contain the angle α, so the image distance is the same for *all* paraxial rays emanating from P; this proves our assertion that P' is the image of P.

To obtain the lateral magnification m for this situation, we use the construction in Fig. 34.22. We draw two rays from point Q, one through the center of curvature C and the other incident at the vertex V. From the triangles PQV and $P'Q'V$,

$$\tan\theta_a = \frac{y}{s} \qquad \tan\theta_b = \frac{-y'}{s'}$$

and from the law of refraction,

$$n_a \sin\theta_a = n_b \sin\theta_b$$

For small angles,

$$\tan\theta_a = \sin\theta_a \qquad \tan\theta_b = \sin\theta_b$$

so finally

$$\frac{n_a y}{s} = -\frac{n_b y'}{s'} \qquad \text{or}$$

$$m = \frac{y'}{y} = -\frac{n_a s'}{n_b s} \quad \text{(lateral magnification, spherical refracting surface)} \tag{34.12}$$

Equations (34.11) and (34.12) can be applied to both convex and concave refracting surfaces, provided that you use the sign rules consistently. It doesn't matter whether n_b is greater or less than n_a. To verify these statements, you should construct diagrams like Figs. 34.21 and 34.22 for the following three cases: (i) $R > 0$ and $n_a > n_b$, (ii) $R < 0$ and $n_a < n_b$, and (iii) $R < 0$ and $n_a > n_b$. Then in each case, use your diagram to again derive Eqs. (34.11) and (34.12).

Here's a final note on the sign rule for the radius of curvature R of a surface. For the convex reflecting surface in Fig. 34.16, we considered R negative, but the convex *refracting* surface in Fig. 34.21 has a *positive* value of R. This may seem inconsistent, but it isn't. The rule is that R is positive if the center of curvature C is on the outgoing side of the surface and negative if C is on the other side. For the convex reflecting surface in Fig. 34.16, R is negative because point C is to the right of the surface but outgoing rays are to the left. For the convex refracting surface in Fig. 34.21, R is positive because both C and the outgoing rays are to the right of the surface.

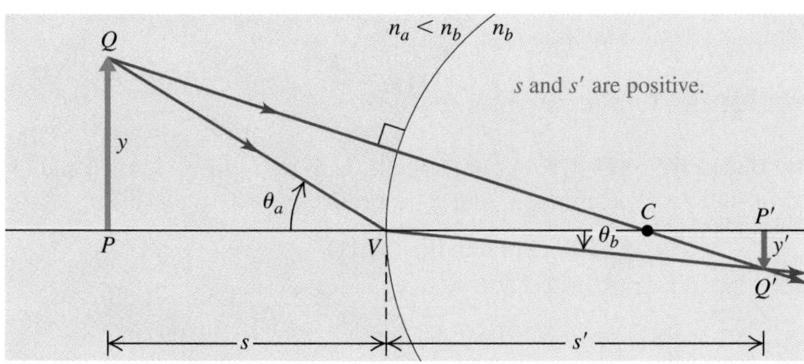

34.22 Construction for determining the height of an image formed by refraction at a spherical surface. In the case shown here, $n_a < n_b$.

34.23 Light rays refract as they pass through the curved surfaces of these water droplets.

Refraction at a curved surface is one reason gardeners avoid watering plants at midday. As sunlight enters a water drop resting on a leaf (Fig. 34.23), the light rays are refracted toward each other as in Figs. 34.21 and 34.22. The sunlight that strikes the leaf is therefore more concentrated and able to cause damage.

An important special case of a spherical refracting surface is a *plane* surface between two optical materials. This corresponds to setting $R = \infty$ in Eq. (34.11). In this case,

$$\frac{n_a}{s} + \frac{n_b}{s'} = 0 \qquad \text{(plane refracting surface)} \tag{34.13}$$

To find the lateral magnification m for this case, we combine this equation with the general relationship, Eq. (34.12), obtaining the simple result

$$m = 1$$

That is, the image formed by a *plane* refracting surface always has the same lateral size as the object, and it is always erect.

An example of image formation by a plane refracting surface is the appearance of a partly submerged drinking straw or canoe paddle. When viewed from some angles, the object appears to have a sharp bend at the water surface because the submerged part appears to be only about three-quarters of its actual distance below the surface. (We commented on the appearance of a submerged object in Section 33.2; see Fig. 33.9.)

Example 34.5 Image formation by refraction I

A cylindrical glass rod in air (Fig. 34.24) has index of refraction 1.52. One end is ground to a hemispherical surface with radius $R = 2.00$ cm. (a) Find the image distance of a small object on the axis of the rod, 8.00 cm to the left of the vertex. (b) Find the lateral magnification.

SOLUTION

IDENTIFY: This problem uses the ideas of refraction at a curved surface. Our target variables are the image distance s' and the lateral magnification m.

SET UP: Here material a is air $(n_a = 1.00)$ and material b is the glass of which the rod is made $(n_b = 1.52)$. We are given $s =$ 8.00 cm; the radius of the spherical surface is positive $(R = +2.00\text{ cm})$ because the center of curvature is on the outgoing side of the surface. We use Eq. (34.11) to determine the image distance and Eq. (34.12) to find the lateral magnification.

34.24 The glass rod in air forms a real image.

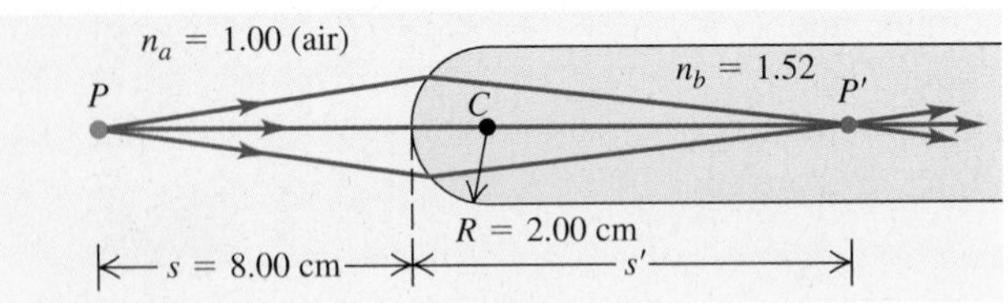

EXECUTE: (a) From Eq. (34.11),

$$\frac{1.00}{8.00\text{ cm}} + \frac{1.52}{s'} = \frac{1.52 - 1.00}{+2.00\text{ cm}}$$

$$s' = +11.3\text{ cm}$$

(b) From Eq. (34.12),

$$m = -\frac{n_a s'}{n_b s} = -\frac{(1.00)(11.3\text{ cm})}{(1.52)(8.00\text{ cm})} = -0.929$$

EVALUATE: Because the image distance s' is positive, the image is formed 11.3 cm to the *right* of the vertex (on the outgoing side), as shown in Fig. 34.24. The value of m tells us that the image is somewhat smaller than the object, and it is inverted. If the object is an arrow 1.000 mm high, pointing upward, the image is an arrow 0.929 mm high, pointing downward.

Example 34.6 Image formation by refraction II

The glass rod in Example 34.5 is immersed in water (index of refraction $n = 1.33$), as shown in Fig. 34.25. The other quantities have the same values as before. Find the image distance and lateral magnification.

SOLUTION

IDENTIFY: The situation is the same as in Example 34.5 except that now $n_a = 1.33$.

SET UP: As in Example 34.5, we use Eqs. (34.11) and (34.12) to determine s' and m, respectively.

EXECUTE: From Eq. (34.11),

$$\frac{1.33}{8.00\text{ cm}} + \frac{1.52}{s'} = \frac{1.52 - 1.33}{+2.00\text{ cm}}$$

$$s' = -21.3\text{ cm}$$

34.25 When immersed in water, the glass rod forms a virtual image.

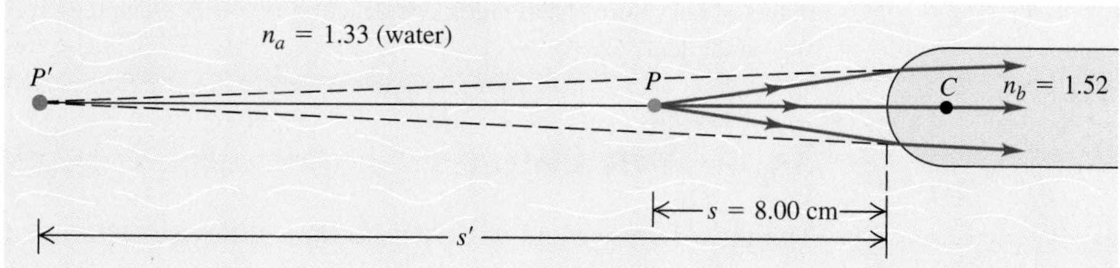

The lateral magnification in this case is

$$m = -\frac{(1.33)(-21.3\text{ cm})}{(1.52)(8.00\text{ cm})} = +2.33$$

EVALUATE: The negative value of s' means that after the rays are refracted by the surface, they are not converging but *appear* to diverge from a point 21.3 cm to the *left* of the vertex. We saw a similar case in the reflection of light from a convex mirror; we call the point a *virtual image.* In this example the surface forms a virtual image 21.3 cm to the left of the vertex. The vertical image is erect (because m is positive) and 2.33 times as large as the object.

Example 34.7 Apparent depth of a swimming pool

Swimming pool owners know that the pool always looks shallower than it really is and that it is important to identify the deep parts conspicuously so that people who can't swim won't jump into water that's over their heads. If a nonswimmer looks straight down into water that is actually 2.00 m (about 6 ft, 7 in.) deep, how deep does it appear to be?

SOLUTION

IDENTIFY: The surface of the water acts as a plane refracting surface.

SET UP: Figure 34.26 shows the situation. To determine the apparent depth of the pool, we imagine that there is an arrow PQ painted on the bottom of the pool. The refracting surface of the pool forms a virtual image $P'Q'$ of this arrow. We use Eq. (34.13) to find the depth of this arrow; it tells us the apparent depth of the pool.

EXECUTE: The object distance is the actual depth of the pool, $s = 2.00$ m. Material a is the water $(n_a = 1.33)$ and material b is air $(n_b = 1.00)$. The position of the image is given by Eq. (34.13):

$$\frac{n_a}{s} + \frac{n_b}{s'} = \frac{1.33}{2.00\text{ m}} + \frac{1.00}{s'} = 0$$

$$s' = -1.50\text{ m}$$

The image distance is negative. From the sign rules in Section 34.1, this means that the image is virtual and on the incoming side of the refracting surface—that is, on the same side as the object. The apparent depth is 1.50 m (about 4 ft, 11 in.), or only three-quarters of the actual depth. A 6-ft nonswimmer who didn't allow for this effect would be in trouble.

EVALUATE: Recall that the lateral magnification for a plane refracting surface is $m = 1$. Hence the image $P'Q'$ of the arrow is the same *horizontal length* as the actual arrow PQ. Only its depth is different. You can see this effect in Fig. 34.27.

34.26 Arrow $P'Q'$ is the virtual image of the underwater arrow PQ. The angles of the ray with the vertical are exaggerated for clarity.

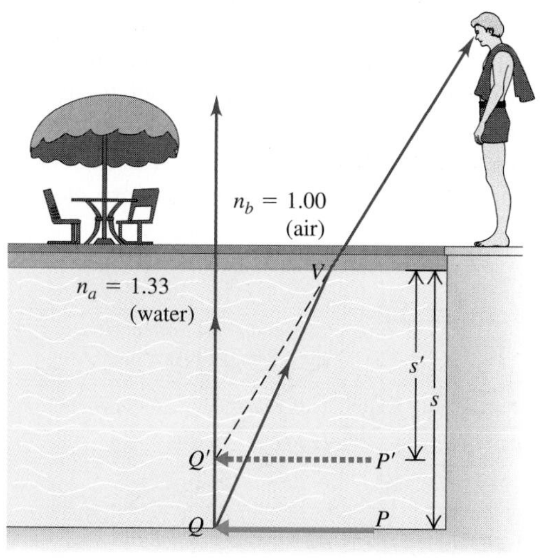

34.27 The submerged portion of this straw appears to be at a shallower depth (closer to the surface) than it actually is.

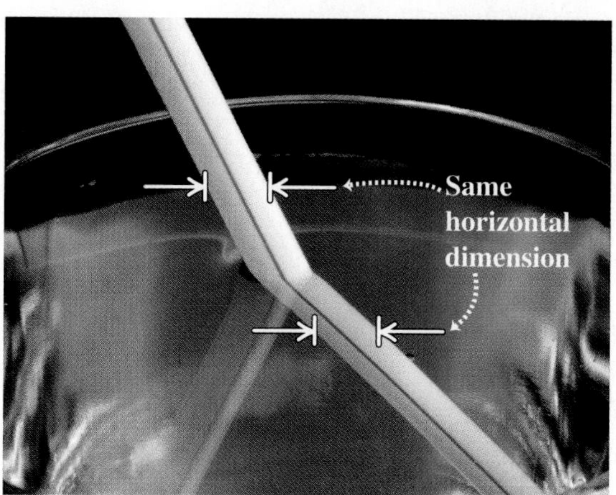

Test Your Understanding of Section 34.3 The water droplets in Fig. 34.23 have radius of curvature R and index of refraction $n = 1.33$. Can they form an image of the sun on the leaf?

34.4 Thin Lenses

ActivPhysics ONLINE
15.9 Thin Lens Ray Diagram
15.10 Converging Thin Lenses
15.11 Diverging Thin Lenses

The most familiar and widely used optical device (after the plane mirror) is the *lens.* A lens is an optical system with two refracting surfaces. The simplest lens has two *spherical* surfaces close enough together that we can neglect the distance between them (the thickness of the lens); we call this a **thin lens.** If you wear eyeglasses or contact lenses while reading, you are viewing these words through a pair of thin lenses. We can analyze thin lenses in detail using the results of Section 34.3 for refraction by a single spherical surface. However, we postpone this analysis until later in the section so that we can first discuss the properties of thin lenses.

Properties of a Lens

A lens of the shape shown in Fig. 34.28 has the property that when a beam of rays parallel to the axis passes through the lens, the rays converge to a point F_2 (Fig. 34.28a) and form a real image at that point. Such a lens is called a **converging lens.** Similarly, rays passing through point F_1 emerge from the lens as a beam of parallel rays (Fig. 34.28b). The points F_1 and F_2 are called the first and second *focal points,* and the distance f (measured from the center of the lens) is called the *focal length.* Note the similarities between the two focal points of a converging lens and the single focal point of a concave mirror (Fig. 34.13). As for a concave mirror, the focal length of a converging lens is defined to be a *positive* quantity, and such a lens is also called a *positive lens.*

The central horizontal line in Fig. 34.28 is called the *optic axis,* as with spherical mirrors. The centers of curvature of the two spherical surfaces lie on and define the optic axis. The two focal lengths in Fig. 34.28, both labeled f, *are always equal* for a thin lens, even when the two sides have different curvatures. We will derive this somewhat surprising result later in the section, when we derive the relationship of f to the index of refraction of the lens and the radii of curvature of its surfaces.

34.28 F_1 and F_2 are the first and second focal points of a converging thin lens. The numerical value of f is positive.

(a)

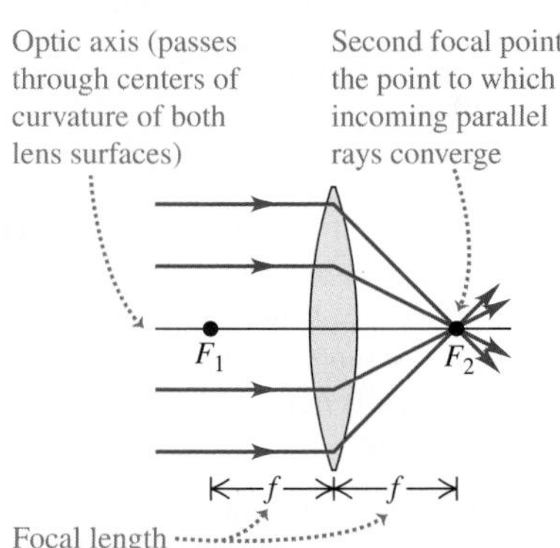
Optic axis (passes through centers of curvature of both lens surfaces)
Second focal point: the point to which incoming parallel rays converge
F_1
F_2
f
f
Focal length
• Measured from lens center
• Always the same on both sides of the lens
• Positive for a converging thin lens

(b)

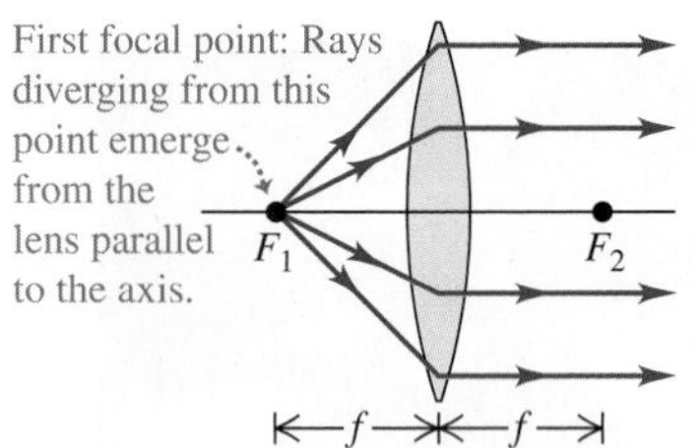
First focal point: Rays diverging from this point emerge from the lens parallel to the axis.
F_1
F_2
f
f

Image of an Extended Object: Converging Lens

Like a concave mirror, a converging lens can form an image of an extended object. Figure 34.29 shows how to find the position and lateral magnification of an image made by a thin converging lens. Using the same notation and sign rules as before, we let s and s' be the object and image distances, respectively, and let y and y' be the object and image heights. Ray QA, parallel to the optic axis before refraction, passes through the second focal point F_2 after refraction. Ray QOQ' passes undeflected straight through the center of the lens because at the center the two surfaces are parallel and (we have assumed) very close together.

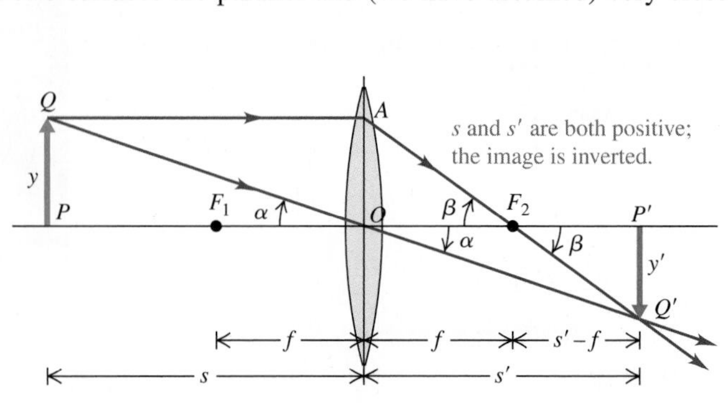
Q
A
s and s' are both positive; the image is inverted.
y
P
F_1
α
O
β
F_2
P'
α
β
y'
Q'
f
f
$s' - f$
s
s'

34.29 Construction used to find image position for a thin lens. To emphasize that the lens is assumed to be very thin, the ray QAQ' is shown as bent at the midplane of the lens rather than at the two surfaces and ray QOQ' is shown as a straight line.

There is refraction where the ray enters and leaves the material but no net change in direction.

The two angles labeled α in Fig. 34.29 are equal. Therefore the two right triangles PQO and $P'Q'O$ are *similar,* and ratios of corresponding sides are equal. Thus

$$\frac{y}{s} = -\frac{y'}{s'} \quad \text{or} \quad \frac{y'}{y} = -\frac{s'}{s} \tag{34.14}$$

(The reason for the negative sign is that the image is below the optic axis and y' is negative.) Also, the two angles labeled β are equal, and the two right triangles OAF_2 and $P'Q'F_2$ are similar, so

$$\frac{y}{f} = -\frac{y'}{s' - f} \quad \text{or}$$

$$\frac{y'}{y} = -\frac{s' - f}{f} \tag{34.15}$$

We now equate Eqs. (34.14) and (34.15), divide by s', and rearrange to obtain

$$\frac{1}{s} + \frac{1}{s'} = \frac{1}{f} \quad \text{(object–image relationship, thin lens)} \tag{34.16}$$

This analysis also gives the lateral magnification $m = y'/y$ for the lens; from Eq. (34.14),

$$m = -\frac{s'}{s} \quad \text{(lateral magnification, thin lens)} \tag{34.17}$$

The negative sign tells us that when s and s' are both positive, as in Fig. 34.29, the image is *inverted,* and y and y' have opposite signs.

Equations (34.16) and (34.17) are the basic equations for thin lenses. They are *exactly* the same as the corresponding equations for spherical mirrors, Eqs. (34.6) and (34.7). As we will see, the same sign rules that we used for spherical mirrors are also applicable to lenses. In particular, consider a lens with a positive focal length (a converging lens). When an object is outside the first focal point F_1 of this lens (that is, when $s > f$), the image distance s' is positive (that is, the image is on the same side as the outgoing rays); this image is real and inverted, as in Fig. 34.29. An object placed inside the first focal point of a converging lens, so that $s < f$, produces an image with a negative value of s'; this image is located on the same side of the lens as the object and is virtual, erect, and larger than the object. You can verify these statements algebraically using Eqs. (34.16) and (34.17); we'll also verify them in the next section, using graphical methods analogous to those introduced for mirrors in Section 34.2.

Figure 34.30 shows how a lens forms a three-dimensional image of a three-dimensional object. Point R is nearer the lens than point P. From Eq. (34.16),

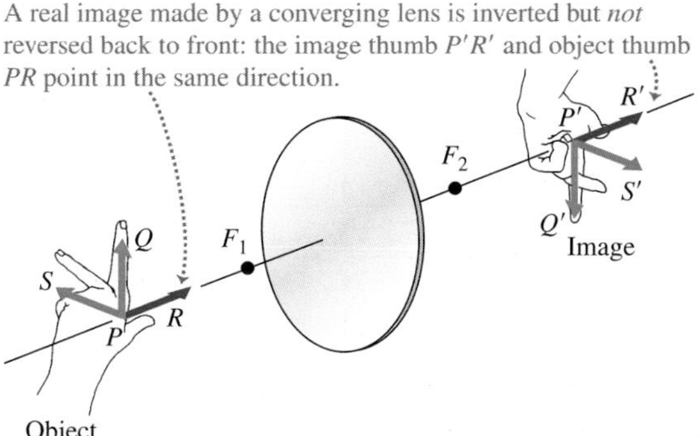
A real image made by a converging lens is inverted but *not* reversed back to front: the image thumb $P'R'$ and object thumb PR point in the same direction.
R'
P'
F₂
S'
Q'
Image
Q
F₁
S
R
P
Object

34.30 The image $S'P'Q'R'$ of a three-dimensional object $SPQR$ is not reversed by a lens.

34.31 F_2 and F_1 are the second and first focal points of a diverging thin lens, respectively. The numerical value of f is negative.

(a)

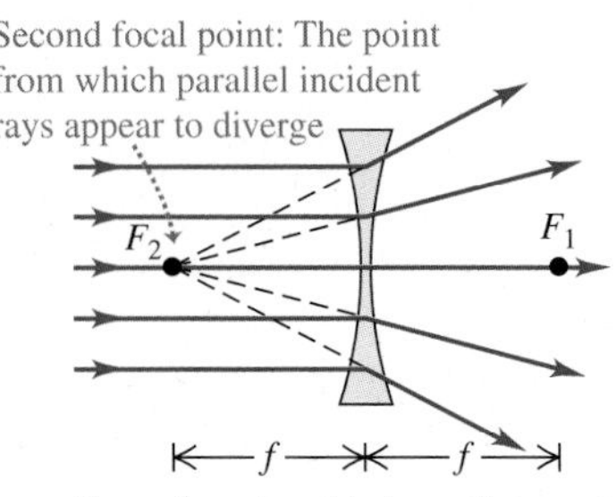

(b)

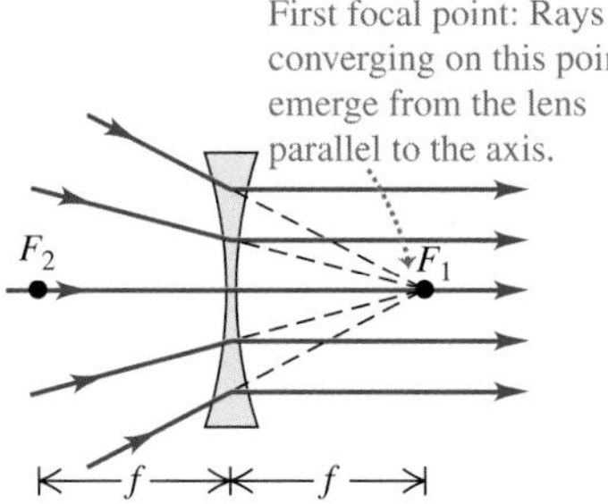

image point R' is farther from the lens than is image point P', and the image $P'R'$ points in the same direction as the object PR. Arrows $P'S'$ and $P'Q'$ are reversed relative to PS and PQ.

Let's compare Fig. 34.30 with Fig. 34.7, which shows the image formed by a plane *mirror.* We note that the image formed by the lens is inverted, but it is *not* reversed front to back along the optic axis. That is, if the object is a left hand, its image is also a left hand. You can verify this by pointing your left thumb along PR, your left forefinger along PQ, and your left middle finger along PS. Then rotate your hand 180°, using your thumb as an axis; this brings the fingers into coincidence with $P'Q'$ and $P'S'$. In other words, an *inverted* image is equivalent to an image that has been rotated by 180° about the lens axis.

Diverging Lenses

So far we have been discussing *converging* lenses. Figure 34.31 shows a **diverging lens;** the beam of parallel rays incident on this lens *diverges* after refraction. The focal length of a diverging lens is a negative quantity, and the lens is also called a *negative lens.* The focal points of a negative lens are reversed, relative to those of a positive lens. The second focal point, F_2, of a negative lens is the point from which rays that are originally parallel to the axis *appear to diverge* after refraction, as in Fig. 34.31a. Incident rays converging toward the first focal point F_1, as in Fig. 34.31b, emerge from the lens parallel to its axis. Comparing with Section 34.2, you can see that a diverging lens has the same relationship to a converging lens as a convex mirror has to a concave mirror.

Equations (34.16) and (34.17) apply to *both* positive and negative lenses. Figure 34.32 shows various types of lenses, both converging and diverging. Here's an important observation: *Any lens that is thicker at its center than at its edges is a converging lens with positive f; and any lens that is thicker at its edges than at its center is a diverging lens with negative f* (provided that the lens has a greater index of refraction than the surrounding material). We can prove this using the *lensmaker's equation,* which it is our next task to derive.

34.32 Various types of lenses.

(a) **Converging lenses**

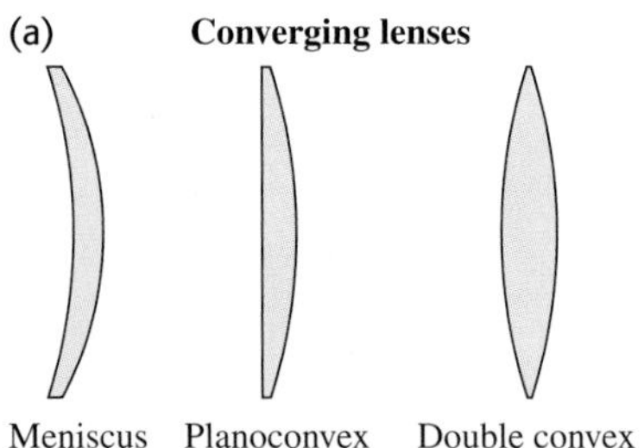

(b) **Diverging lenses**

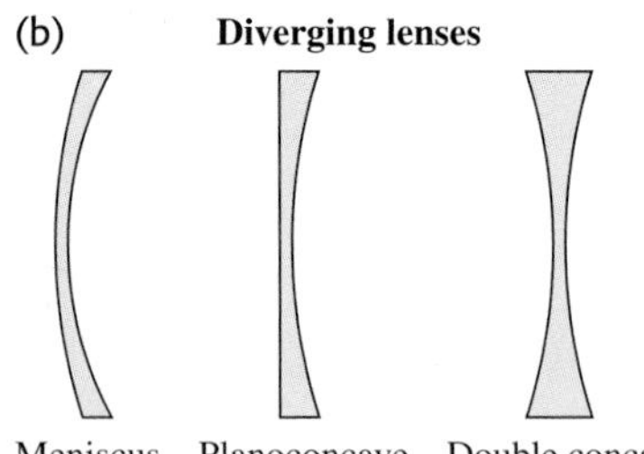

The Lensmaker's Equation

We'll now derive Eq. (34.16) in more detail and at the same time derive the *lensmaker's equation,* which is a relationship among the focal length f, the index of refraction n of the lens, and the radii of curvature R_1 and R_2 of the lens surfaces. We use the principle that an image formed by one reflecting or refracting surface can serve as the object for a second reflecting or refracting surface.

We begin with the somewhat more general problem of two spherical interfaces separating three materials with indexes of refraction n_a, n_b, and n_c, as shown in Fig. 34.33. The object and image distances for the first surface are s_1 and s_1', and those for the second surface are s_2 and s_2'. We assume that the lens is thin, so that the distance t between the two surfaces is small in comparison with the object and

34.33 The image formed by the first surface of a lens serves as the object for the second surface. The distances s_1' and s_2 are taken to be equal; this is a good approximation if the lens thickness t is small.

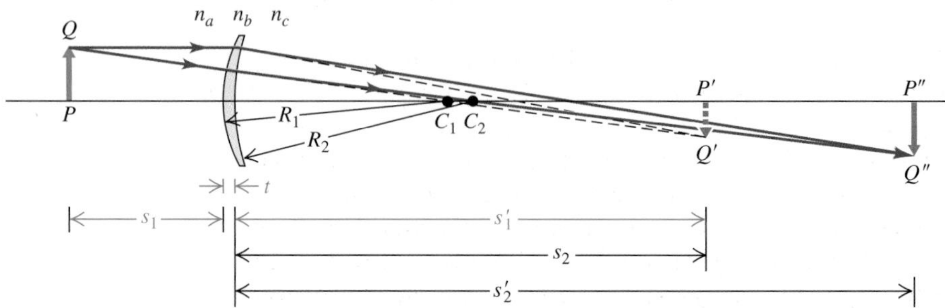

image distances and can therefore be neglected. This is usually the case with eyeglass lenses (Fig. 34.34). Then s_2 and s_1' have the same magnitude but opposite sign. For example, if the first image is on the outgoing side of the first surface, s_1' is positive. But when viewed as an object for the second surface, the first image is *not* on the incoming side of that surface. So we can say that $s_2 = -s_1'$.

We need to use the single-surface equation, Eq. (34.11), twice, once for each surface. The two resulting equations are

$$\frac{n_a}{s_1} + \frac{n_b}{s_1'} = \frac{n_b - n_a}{R_1}$$

$$\frac{n_b}{s_2} + \frac{n_c}{s_2'} = \frac{n_c - n_b}{R_2}$$

Ordinarily, the first and third materials are air or vacuum, so we set $n_a = n_c = 1$. The second index n_b is that of the lens, which we can call simply n. Substituting these values and the relationship $s_2 = -s_1'$, we get

$$\frac{1}{s_1} + \frac{n}{s_1'} = \frac{n - 1}{R_1}$$

$$-\frac{n}{s_1'} + \frac{1}{s_2'} = \frac{1 - n}{R_2}$$

To get a relationship between the initial object position s_1 and the final image position s_2', we add these two equations. This eliminates the term n/s_1', and we obtain

$$\frac{1}{s_1} + \frac{1}{s_2'} = (n - 1)\left(\frac{1}{R_1} - \frac{1}{R_2}\right)$$

Finally, thinking of the lens as a single unit, we call the object distance simply s instead of s_1, and we call the final image distance s' instead of s_2'. Making these substitutions, we have

$$\frac{1}{s} + \frac{1}{s'} = (n - 1)\left(\frac{1}{R_1} - \frac{1}{R_2}\right) \qquad (34.18)$$

Now we compare this with the other thin-lens equation, Eq. (34.16). We see that the object and image distances s and s' appear in exactly the same places in both equations and that the focal length f is given by

$$\frac{1}{f} = (n - 1)\left(\frac{1}{R_1} - \frac{1}{R_2}\right) \qquad \text{(lensmaker's equation for a thin lens)} \qquad (34.19)$$

This is the **lensmaker's equation.** In the process of rederiving the relationship between object distance, image distance, and focal length for a thin lens, we have also derived an expression for the focal length f of a lens in terms of its index of refraction n and the radii of curvature R_1 and R_2 of its surfaces. This can be used to show that all the lenses in Fig. 34.32a are converging lenses with positive focal lengths and that all the lenses in Fig. 34.32b are diverging lenses with negative focal lengths (see Exercise 34.30).

We use all our sign rules from Section 34.1 with Eqs. (34.18) and (34.19). For example, in Fig. 34.35, s, s', and R_1 are positive, but R_2 is negative.

It is not hard to generalize Eq. (34.19) to the situation in which the lens is immersed in a material with an index of refraction greater than unity. We invite you to work out the lensmaker's equation for this more general situation.

We stress that the paraxial approximation is indeed an approximation! Rays that are at sufficiently large angles to the optic axis of a spherical lens will not be brought to the same focus as paraxial rays; this is the same problem of spherical

34.34 These eyeglass lenses satisfy the thin-lens approximation: Their thickness is small compared to the object and image distances.

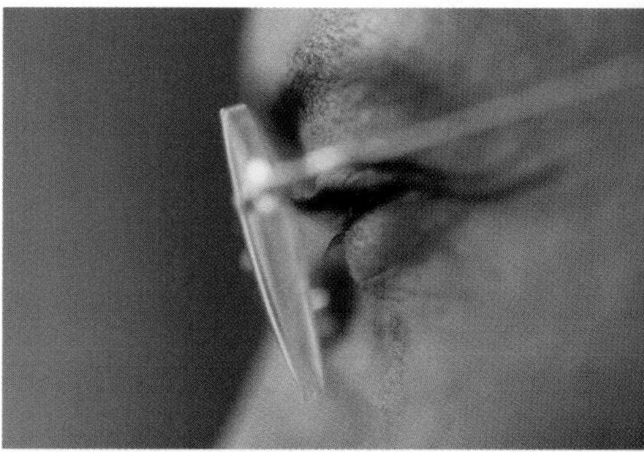

34.35 A converging thin lens with a positive focal length f.

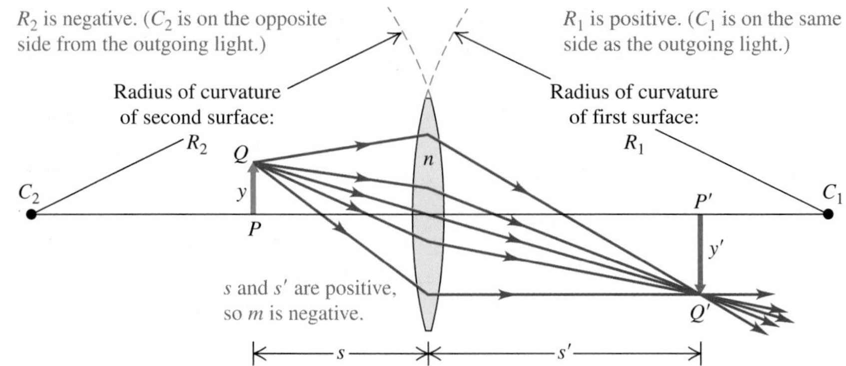

aberration that plagues spherical *mirrors* (see Section 34.2). To avoid this and other limitations of thin spherical lenses, lenses of more complicated shape are used in precision optical instruments.

Example 34.8 Determining the focal length of a lens

(a) Suppose the absolute values of the radii of curvature of the lens surfaces in Fig. 34.35 are both equal to 10 cm and the index of refraction is $n = 1.52$. What is the focal length f of the lens? (b) Suppose the lens in Fig. 34.31 also has $n = 1.52$, and the absolute values of the radii of curvature of its lens surfaces are also both equal to 10 cm. What is the focal length of this lens?

SOLUTION

IDENTIFY: We are asked to find the focal length of (a) a lens that is convex on both sides (Fig. 34.35) and (b) a lens that is concave on both sides (Fig. 34.31).

SET UP: We use the lensmaker's equation, Eq. (34.19), to determine the focal length in each situation. We take account of whether the surfaces are convex or concave by paying careful attention to the signs of the radii of curvature R_1 and R_2.

EXECUTE: (a) Figure 34.35 shows that the center of curvature of the first surface (C_1) is on the outgoing side of the lens, while the center of curvature of the second surface (C_2) is on the *incoming* side. Hence R_1 is positive but R_2 is negative: $R_1 = +10$ cm, $R_2 = -10$ cm. From Eq. (34.19),

$$\frac{1}{f} = (1.52 - 1)\left(\frac{1}{+10\text{ cm}} - \frac{1}{-10\text{ cm}}\right)$$

$$f = 9.6\text{ cm}$$

(b) For a double-concave lens the center of curvature of the first surface is on the *incoming* side, while the center of curvature of the second surface is on the outgoing side. Hence R_1 is negative and R_2 is positive: $R_1 = -10$ cm, $R_2 = +10$ cm. Again using Eq. (34.19),

$$\frac{1}{f} = (1.52 - 1)\left(\frac{1}{-10\text{ cm}} - \frac{1}{+10\text{ cm}}\right)$$

$$f = -9.6\text{ cm}$$

EVALUATE: In part (a) the focal length is positive, so this is a converging lens; this makes sense, since the lens is thicker at its center than at its edges. In part (b) the focal length is *negative,* so this is a *diverging* lens; this also makes sense, since the lens is thicker at its edges than at its center.

Graphical Methods for Lenses

We can determine the position and size of an image formed by a thin lens by using a graphical method very similar to the one we used in Section 34.2 for spherical mirrors. Again we draw a few special rays called *principal rays* that diverge from a point of the object that is *not* on the optic axis. The intersection of these rays, after they pass through the lens, determines the position and size of the image. In using this graphical method, we will consider the entire deviation of a ray as occurring at the midplane of the lens, as shown in Fig. 34.36. This is consistent with the assumption that the distance between the lens surfaces is negligible.

The three principal rays whose paths are usually easy to trace for lenses are shown in Fig. 34.36:

1. *A ray parallel to the axis* emerges from the lens in a direction that passes through the second focal point F_2 of a converging lens, or appears to come from the second focal point of a diverging lens.
2. *A ray through the center of the lens* is not appreciably deviated; at the center of the lens the two surfaces are parallel, so this ray emerges at essentially the same angle at which it enters and along essentially the same line.

34.36 The graphical method of locating an image formed by a thin lens. The colors of the rays are for identification only; they do not refer to specific colors of light. (Compare Fig. 34.19 for spherical mirrors.)

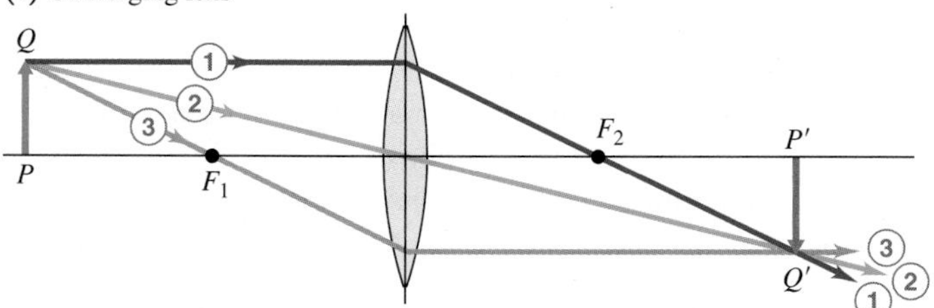

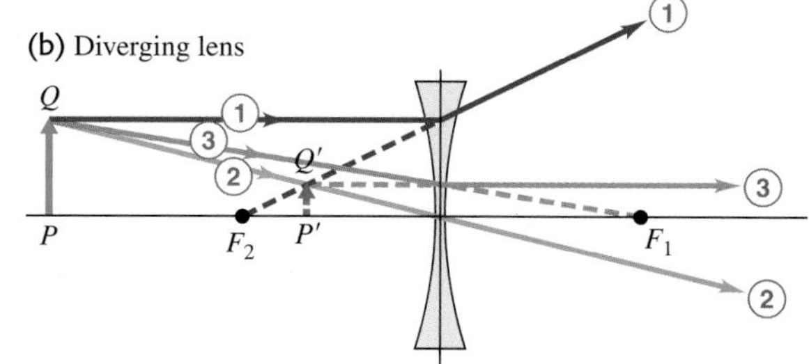

(1) Parallel incident ray refracts to pass through second focal point F_2.
(2) Ray through center of lens does not deviate appreciably.
(3) Ray through the first focal point F_1 emerges parallel to the axis.

(1) Parallel incident ray appears after refraction to have come from the second focal point F_2.
(2) Ray through center of lens does not deviate appreciably.
(3) Ray aimed at the first focal point F_1 emerges parallel to the axis.

3. *A ray through (or proceeding toward) the first focal point* F_1 emerges parallel to the axis.

When the image is real, the position of the image point is determined by the intersection of any two rays 1, 2, and 3 (Fig. 34.36a). When the image is virtual, we extend the diverging outgoing rays backward to their intersection point to find the image point (Fig. 34.36b).

CAUTION **Principal rays are not the only rays** Keep in mind that *any* ray from the object that strikes the lens will pass through the image point (for a real image) or appear to originate from the image point (for a virtual image). (We made a similar comment about image formation by mirrors in Section 34.2.) We've emphasized the principal rays because they're the only ones you need to draw to locate the image.

Figure 34.37 shows principal-ray diagrams for a converging lens for several object distances. We suggest you study each of these diagrams very carefully, comparing each numbered ray with the above description.

34.37 Formation of images by a thin converging lens for various object distances. The principal rays are numbered. (Compare Fig. 34.20 for a concave spherical mirror.)

(a) Object O is outside focal point; image I is real.

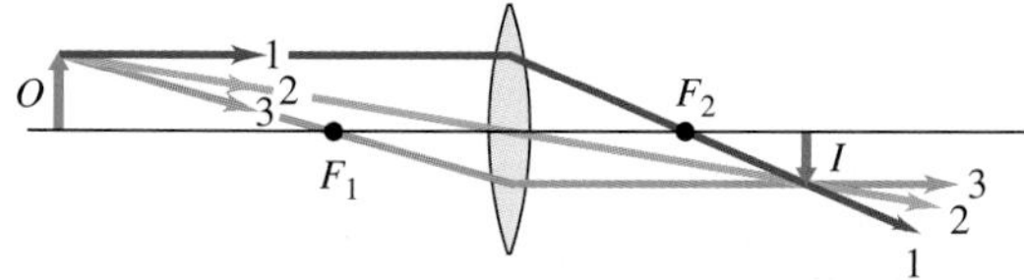

(b) Object O is closer to focal point; image I is real and farther away.

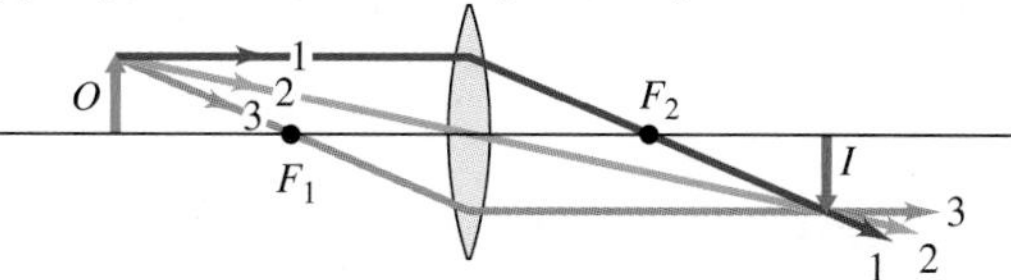

(c) Object O is even closer to focal point; image I is real and even farther away.

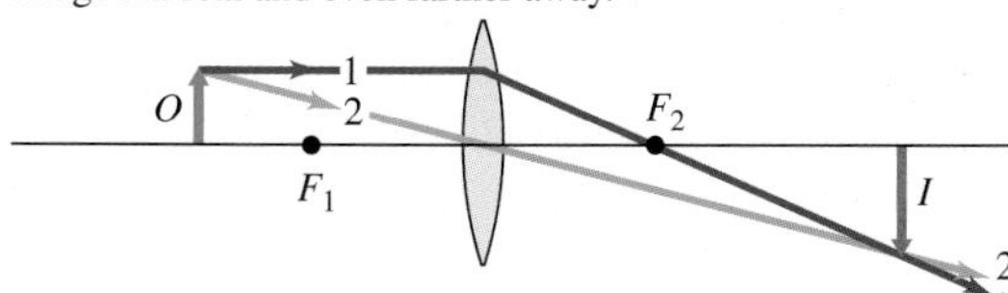

(d) Object O is at focal point; image I is at infinity.

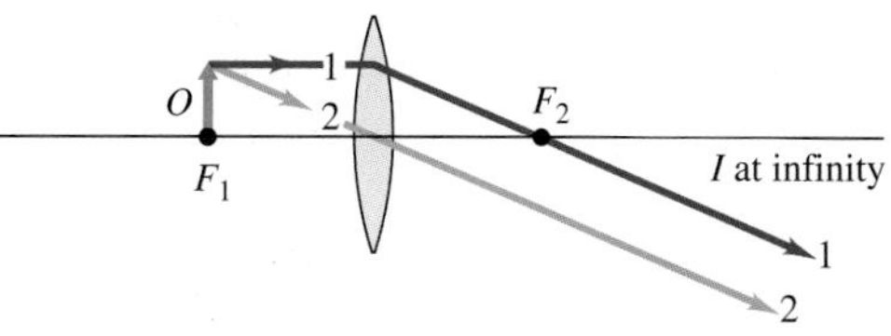

(e) Object O is inside focal point; image I is virtual and larger than object.

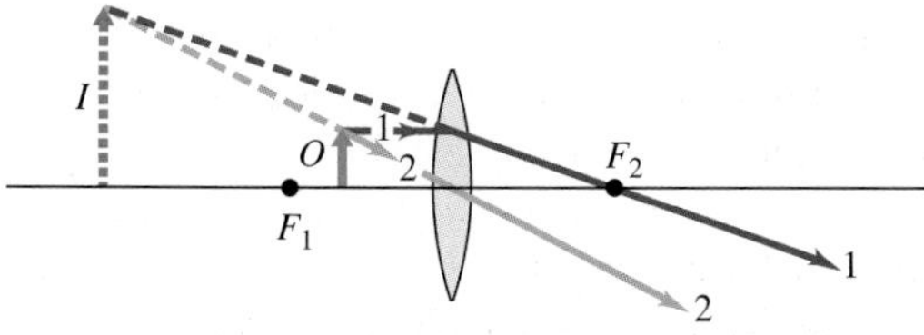

(f) A virtual object O (light rays are *converging* on lens)

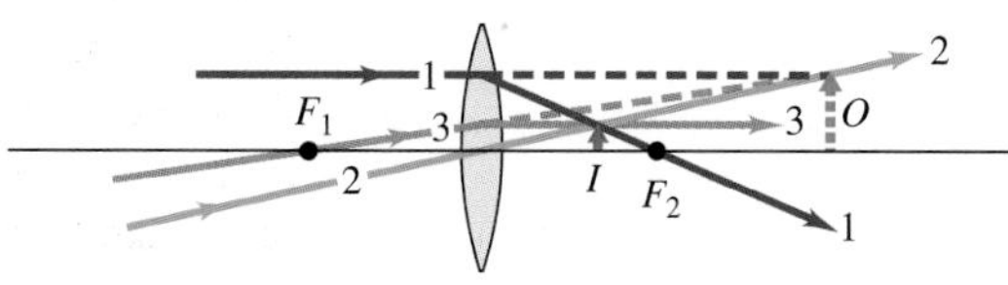

Parts (a), (b), and (c) of Fig. 34.37 help explain what happens in focusing a camera. For a photograph to be in sharp focus, the film must be at the position of the real image made by the camera's lens. The image distance increases as the object is brought closer, so the film is moved farther behind the lens (i.e., the lens is moved farther in front of the film). In Fig. 34.37d the object is at the focal point; ray 3 can't be drawn because it doesn't pass through the lens. In Fig. 34.37e the object distance is less than the focal length. The outgoing rays are divergent, and the image is *virtual;* its position is located by extending the outgoing rays backward, so the image distance s' is negative. Note also that the image is erect and larger than the object. (We'll see the usefulness of this in Section 34.6.) Figure 34.37f corresponds to a *virtual object.* The incoming rays do not diverge from a real object, but are *converging* as though they would meet at the tip of the virtual object O on the right side; the object distance s is negative in this case. The image is real and is located between the lens and the second focal point. This situation can arise if the rays that strike the lens in Fig. 34.37f emerge from another converging lens (not shown) to the left of the figure.

Problem-Solving Strategy 34.2 Image Formation by Thin Lenses

IDENTIFY *the relevant concepts:* Problem-Solving Strategy 34.1 (Section 34.2) for mirrors is equally applicable here, and you should review it now. As for mirrors, you should solve problems involving image formation by lenses using *both* equations and a principal-ray diagram.

SET UP *the problem:* As always, determine the target variables.

EXECUTE *the solution* as follows:

1. Always begin with a principal-ray diagram if you have enough information. Orient your diagrams consistently so that light travels from left to right. Don't just sketch these diagrams; draw the rays with a ruler and measure the distances carefully.
2. Draw the principal rays so they bend at the midplane of the lens, as shown in Fig. 34.36. For a lens there are only three principal rays, compared to four for a mirror. Be sure to draw *all three* whenever possible. The intersection of any two determines the image, but if the third doesn't pass through the same intersection point, you know you have made a mistake. Redundancy can be useful in spotting errors.
3. If the outgoing principal rays don't converge at a real image point, the image is virtual. Then you have to extend the outgoing rays backward to find the virtual image point, which lies on the *incoming* side of the lens.
4. The same sign rules we have used for mirrors and single refracting surfaces (see Section 34.1) are also applicable for thin lenses. Be extremely careful to get your signs right and to interpret the signs of results correctly.
5. Use Eqs. (34.16) and (34.17) to confirm by calculation your graphical results for the image position and size. This gives an extremely useful consistency check.
6. The *image* from one lens or mirror may serve as the *object* for another. In that case, be careful in finding the object and image *distances* for this intermediate image; be sure you include the distance between the two elements (lenses and/or mirrors) correctly.

EVALUATE *your answer:* Cast a critical eye on your diagrams and calculations to make certain that your results are consistent.

Example 34.9 Image location and magnification with a converging lens

A converging lens has a focal length of 20 cm. Find graphically the image location for an object at each of the following distances from the lens: (a) 50 cm; (b) 20 cm; (c) 15 cm; (d) -40 cm. Determine the magnification in each case. Check your results by calculating the image position and lateral magnification from Eqs. (34.16) and (34.17), respectively.

SOLUTION

IDENTIFY: This problem illustrates the usefulness of both graphical and computational methods for problems with thin lenses, just as for problems with curved mirrors.

SET UP: In each case we are given the focal length $f = 20$ cm and the value of the object distance s. Our target variables are the image distance s' and the lateral magnification $m = -s'/s$.

EXECUTE: The appropriate principal-ray diagrams are shown in (a) Fig. 34.37a, (b) Fig. 34.37d, (c) Fig. 34.37e, and (d) Fig. 34.37f. The approximate image distances, from measurements of these diagrams, are 35 cm, $-\infty$, -40 cm, and 15 cm, and the approximate magnifications are $-\frac{2}{3}$, $+\infty$, and $+3$, and $+\frac{1}{3}$, respectively.

Calculating the image positions from Eq. (34.16), we find

$$\text{(a)}\quad \frac{1}{50\text{ cm}} + \frac{1}{s'} = \frac{1}{20\text{ cm}} \qquad s' = 33.3\text{ cm}$$

$$\text{(b)}\quad \frac{1}{20\text{ cm}} + \frac{1}{s'} = \frac{1}{20\text{ cm}} \qquad s' = \pm\infty$$

$$\text{(c)}\quad \frac{1}{15\text{ cm}} + \frac{1}{s'} = \frac{1}{20\text{ cm}} \qquad s' = -60\text{ cm}$$

$$\text{(d)}\quad \frac{1}{-40\text{ cm}} + \frac{1}{s'} = \frac{1}{20\text{ cm}} \qquad s' = 13.3\text{ cm}$$

The graphical results are fairly close to these except for part (c); the accuracy of the diagram in Fig. 34.37e is limited because the rays extended backward have nearly the same direction.

From Eq. (34.17) the lateral magnifications are

$$\text{(a) } m = -\frac{33.3 \text{ cm}}{50 \text{ cm}} = -\frac{2}{3}$$

$$\text{(b) } m = -\frac{\pm\infty \text{ cm}}{20 \text{ cm}} = \pm\infty$$

$$\text{(c) } m = -\frac{-60 \text{ cm}}{15 \text{ cm}} = +4$$

$$\text{(d) } m = -\frac{13.3 \text{ cm}}{-40 \text{ cm}} = +\frac{1}{3}$$

EVALUATE: Note that s' is positive in parts (a) and (d) but negative in part (c). This makes sense: The image is real in parts (a) and (d) but virtual in part (c). The light rays that emerge from the lens in part (b) are parallel and never converge, so the image can be regarded as being at either $+\infty$ or $-\infty$.

The values of magnification tell us that the image is inverted in part (a) and erect in parts (c) and (d), in accordance with the principal-ray diagrams. The infinite value of magnification in part (b) is another way of saying that the image is formed infinitely far away.

Example 34.10 Image formation by a diverging lens

You are given a thin diverging lens. You find that a beam of parallel rays spreads out after passing through the lens, as though all the rays came from a point 20.0 cm from the center of the lens. You want to use this lens to form an erect virtual image that is $\frac{1}{3}$ the height of the object. (a) Where should the object be placed? (b) Draw a principal-ray diagram.

SOLUTION

IDENTIFY: The observation with parallel rays shows that the focal length is $f = -20$ cm. We want the lateral magnification to be $m = +\frac{1}{3}$ (positive because the image is to be erect).

SET UP: We use the given information to determine the ratio s'/s from Eq. (34.17) and then determine the object distance s with Eq. (34.16).

EXECUTE: (a) From Eq. (34.17), $m = +\frac{1}{3} = -s'/s$, so $s' = -s/3$. If we insert this result into Eq. (34.16), we find

$$\frac{1}{s} + \frac{1}{-s/3} = \frac{1}{-20.0 \text{ cm}}$$

$$s = 40.0 \text{ cm}$$

$$s' = -\frac{s}{3} = -\frac{40.0 \text{ cm}}{3} = -13.3 \text{ cm}$$

The image distance is negative, so the object and image are on the same side of the lens.

(b) Figure 34.38 is a principal-ray diagram for this problem, with the rays numbered in the same way as in Fig. 34.36b.

EVALUATE: A diverging lens is often mounted in the front door of a home. It provides the occupant of the home with an erect, reduced image of anyone standing outside the door. The occupant can see the outside person's entire height and decide whether to let him or her in.

34.38 Principal-ray diagram for an image formed by a thin diverging lens.

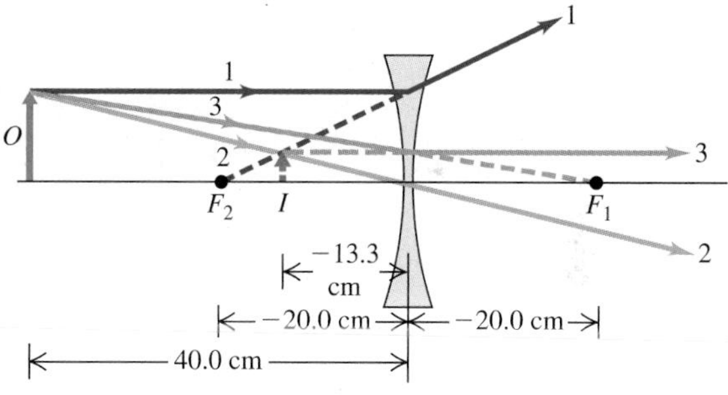

Example 34.11 An image of an image

An object 8.0 cm high is placed 12.0 cm to the left of a converging lens of focal length 8.0 cm. A second converging lens of focal length 6.0 cm is placed 36.0 cm to the right of the first lens. Both lenses have the same optic axis. Find the position, size, and orientation of the image produced by the two lenses in combination. (Combinations of converging lenses are used in telescopes and microscopes, to be discussed in Section 34.7.)

SOLUTION

IDENTIFY: The situation is shown in Fig. 34.39. The object O lies outside the first focal point F_1 of the first lens, so this lens produces a real image I. The light rays that strike the second lens diverge from this real image just as if I was a material object. Hence the *image* made by the *first* lens acts as an *object* for the *second* lens. Our goal is to determine the properties of the final image made by the second lens.

SET UP: We use both graphical and computational methods to determine the properties of the final image.

EXECUTE: In Fig. 34.39 (next page) we have drawn principal rays 1, 2, and 3 from the head of the object arrow O to find the position of the first image I and principal rays 1′, 2′, and 3′ from the head of the first image to find the position of the second image I' made by the second lens (even though rays 2′ and 3′ don't actually exist in this case). Note that the image is inverted *twice,* once by each lens, so the second image I' has the same orientation as the original object.

Continued

To *calculate* the position and size of the second image I', we must first find the position and size of the first image I. Applying Eq. (34.16), $1/s + 1/s' = 1/f$, to the first lens gives

$$\frac{1}{12.0\text{ cm}} + \frac{1}{s_1'} = \frac{1}{8.0\text{ cm}} \qquad s_1' = +24.0\text{ cm}$$

The first image I is 24.0 cm to the right of the first lens. The lateral magnification is $m_1 = -(24.0\text{ cm})/(12.0\text{ cm}) = -2.00$, so the height of the first image is $(-2.0)(8.0\text{ cm}) = -16.0\text{ cm}$.

The first image is 36.0 cm − 24.0 cm = 12.0 cm to the left of the second lens, so the object distance for the second lens is +12.0 cm. Using Eq. (34.16) for the second lens gives the position of the second and final image:

$$\frac{1}{12.0\text{ cm}} + \frac{1}{s_2'} = \frac{1}{6.0\text{ cm}} \qquad s_2' = +12.0\text{ cm}$$

The final image is 12.0 cm to the right of the second lens and 48.0 cm to the right of the first lens. The magnification produced by the second converging lens is $m_2 = -(12.0\text{ cm})/(12.0\text{ cm}) = -1.0$.

EVALUATE: The value of m_2 means that the final image is just as large as the first image but has the opposite orientation. This is also shown in the principal-ray diagram.

34.39 Principal-ray diagram for a combination of two converging lenses. The first lens makes a real image of the object. This real image acts as an object for the second lens.

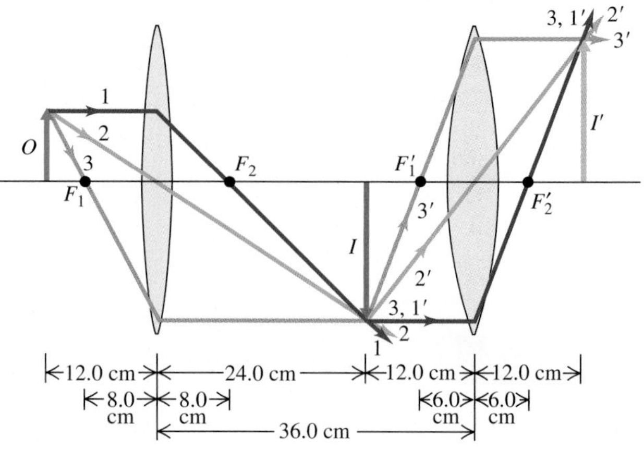

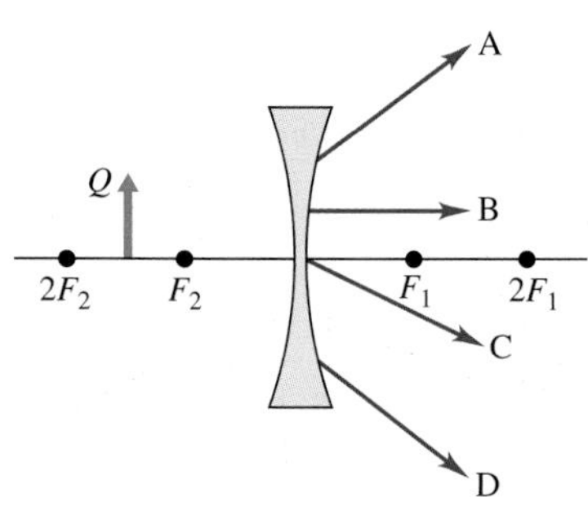

Test Your Understanding of Section 34.4 A diverging lens and an object are positioned as shown in the figure at left. Which of the rays A, B, C, and D could emanate from point Q at the top of the object?

34.5 Cameras

The concept of *image,* which is so central to understanding simple mirror and lens systems, plays an equally important role in the analysis of optical instruments (also called *optical devices*). Among the most common optical devices are cameras, which make an image of an object and record it either electronically or on film.

The basic elements of a **camera** are a light-tight box ("camera" is a Latin word meaning "a room or enclosure"), a converging lens, a shutter to open the lens for a prescribed length of time, and a light-sensitive recording medium (Fig. 34.40). In a digital camera this is an electronic detector called a charge-coupled device (CCD) array; in an older camera, this is photographic film. The lens forms an inverted real image on the recording medium of the object being photographed. High-quality camera lenses have several elements, permitting partial correction of various *aberrations,* including the dependence of

34.40 Key elements of a digital camera.

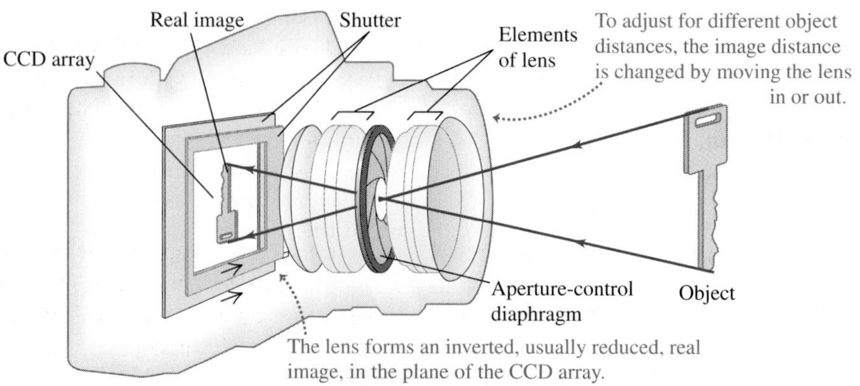

34.41 (a), (b), (c) Three photographs taken with the same camera from the same position in the Boston Public Garden using lenses with focal lengths $f = 28$ mm, 105 mm, and 300 mm. Increasing the focal length increases the image size proportionately. (d) The larger the value of f, the smaller the angle of view. The angles shown here are for a camera with image area 24 mm × 36 mm (corresponding to 35-mm film) and refer to the angle of view along the diagonal dimension of the film.

(a) $f = 28$ mm

(b) $f = 105$ mm

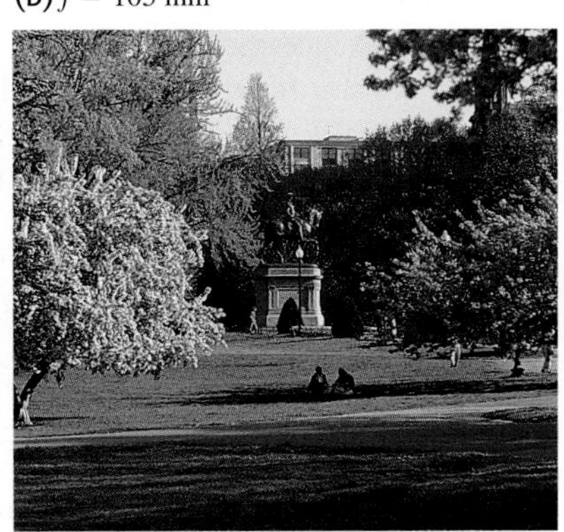

(c) $f = 300$ mm

(d) The angles of view for the photos in (a)–(c)

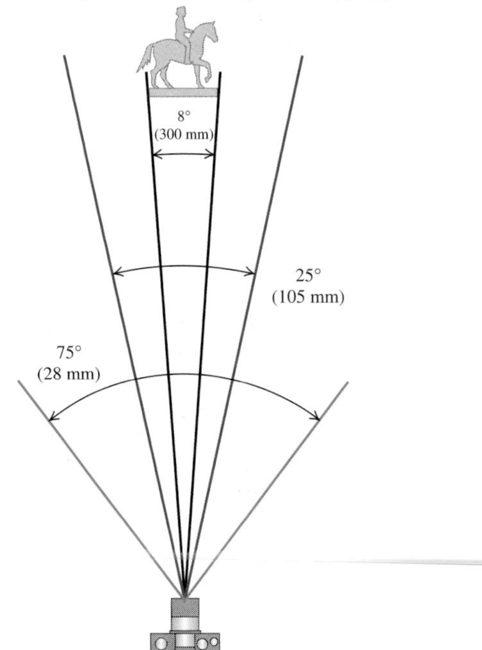

index of refraction on wavelength and the limitations imposed by the paraxial approximation.

When the camera is in proper *focus,* the position of the recording medium coincides with the position of the real image formed by the lens. The resulting photograph will then be as sharp as possible. With a converging lens, the image distance increases as the object distance decreases (see Figs. 34.41a, 34.41b, and 34.41c, and the discussion in Section 34.4). Hence in "focusing" the camera, we move the lens closer to the film for a distant object and farther from the film for a nearby object.

Camera Lenses: Focal Length

The choice of the focal length f for a camera lens depends on the film size and the desired angle of view. Figure 34.41 shows three photographs taken on 35-mm film with the same camera at the same position, but with lenses of different focal lengths. A lens of long focal length, called a *telephoto* lens, gives a small angle of view and a large image of a distant object (such as the statue in Fig. 34.41c); a lens of short focal length gives a small image and a wide angle of view (as in Fig. 34.41a) and is called a *wide-angle* lens. To understand this behavior, recall that the focal length is the distance from the lens to the image when the object is infinitely far away. In general, for *any* object distance, using a lens of longer focal length gives a greater image distance. This also increases the height of the image; as was discussed in Section 34.4, the ratio of the image height y' to the object height y (the *lateral magnification*) is equal in absolute value to the ratio of image distance s' to the object distance s [Eq. (34.17)]:

$$m = \frac{y'}{y} = -\frac{s'}{s}$$

With a lens of short focal length, the ratio s'/s is small, and a distant object gives only a small image. When a lens with a long focal length is used, the image of this same object may entirely cover the area of the film. Hence the longer the focal length, the narrower the angle of view (Fig. 34.41d).

Camera Lenses: f-Number

For the film to record the image properly, the total light energy per unit area reaching the film (the "exposure") must fall within certain limits. This is controlled by the *shutter* and the *lens aperture.* The shutter controls the time interval during which light enters the lens. This is usually adjustable in steps corresponding to factors of about 2, often from 1 s to $\frac{1}{1000}$ s.

The intensity of light reaching the film is proportional to the area viewed by the camera lens and to the effective area of the lens. The size of the area that the lens "sees" is proportional to the square of the angle of view of the lens, and so is roughly proportional to $1/f^2$. The effective area of the lens is controlled by means of an adjustable lens aperture, or *diaphragm,* a nearly circular hole with variable diameter D; hence the effective area is proportional to D^2. Putting these factors together, we see that the intensity of light reaching the film with a particular lens is proportional to D^2/f^2. The light-gathering capability of a lens is commonly expressed by photographers in terms of the ratio f/D, called the ***f*-number** of the lens:

$$f\text{-number} = \frac{\text{Focal length}}{\text{Aperture diameter}} = \frac{f}{D} \tag{34.20}$$

For example, a lens with a focal length $f = 50$ mm and an aperture diameter $D = 25$ mm is said to have an f-number of 2, or "an aperture of $f/2$." The light intensity reaching the film is *inversely* proportional to the square of the f-number.

For a lens with a variable-diameter aperture, increasing the diameter by a factor of $\sqrt{2}$ changes the f-number by $1/\sqrt{2}$ and increases the intensity at the film by a factor of 2. Adjustable apertures usually have scales labeled with successive numbers (often called *f-stops*) related by factors of $\sqrt{2}$, such as

$$f/2 \quad f/2.8 \quad f/4 \quad f/5.6 \quad f/8 \quad f/11 \quad f/16$$

and so on. The larger numbers represent smaller apertures and exposures, and each step corresponds to a factor of 2 in intensity (Fig. 34.42). The actual *exposure* (total amount of light reaching the film) is proportional to both the aperture area and the time of exposure. Thus $f/4$ and $\frac{1}{500}$ s, $f/5.6$ and $\frac{1}{250}$ s, and $f/8$ and $\frac{1}{125}$ s all correspond to the same exposure.

34.42 A camera lens with an adjustable diaphragm.

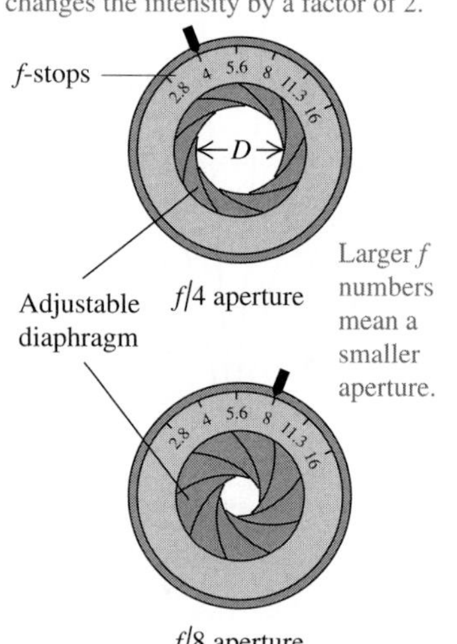

Zoom Lenses and Projectors

Many photographers use a *zoom lens,* which is not a single lens but a complex collection of several lens elements that give a continuously variable focal length, often over a range as great as 10 to 1. Figures 34.43a and 34.43b show a simple system with variable focal length, and Fig. 34.43c shows a typical zoom lens for a single-lens reflex camera. Zoom lenses give a range of image sizes of a given object. It is an enormously complex problem in optical design to keep the image in focus and maintain a constant f-number while the focal length changes. When you vary the focal length of a typical zoom lens, two groups of elements move within the lens and a diaphragm opens and closes.

A *projector* for viewing slides, digital images, or motion pictures operates very much like a camera in reverse. In a movie projector, a lamp shines on the

34.43 A simple zoom lens uses a converging lens and a diverging lens in tandem. **(a)** When the two lenses are close together, the combination behaves like a single lens of long focal length. **(b)** If the two lenses are moved farther apart, the combination behaves like a short-focal-length lens. **(c)** A typical zoom lens for a single-lens reflex camera, containing twelve elements arranged in four groups.

(a) Zoom lens set for long focal length

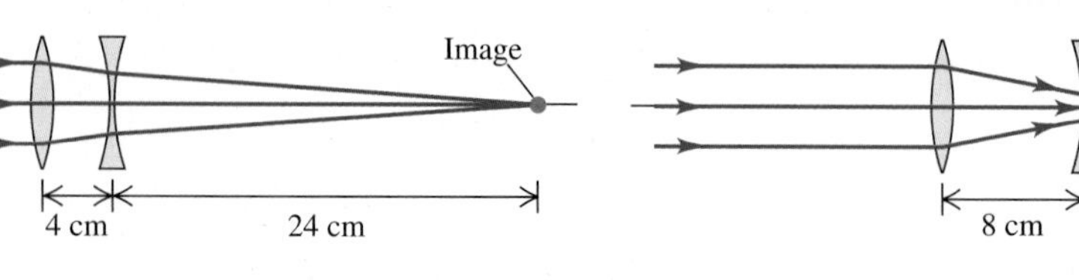

(b) Zoom lens set for short focal length

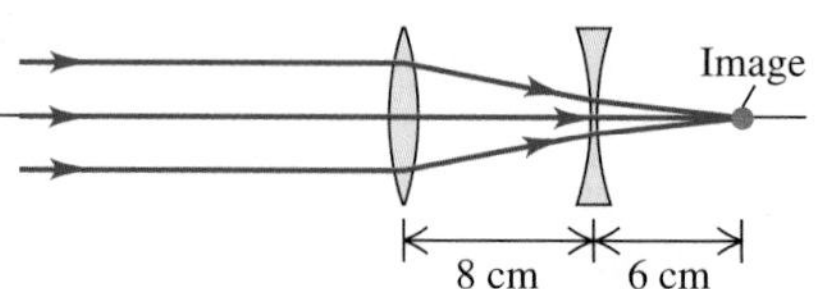

(c) A practical zoom lens

film, which acts as an object for the projection lens. The lens forms a real, enlarged, inverted image of the film on the projection screen. Because the image is inverted, the film goes through the projector upside down so that the image on the screen appears right-side up.

Example 34.12 Photographic exposures

A common telephoto lens for a 35-mm camera has a focal length of 200 mm and a range of *f*-stops from *f*/5.6 to *f*/45. (a) What is the corresponding range of aperture diameters? (b) What is the corresponding range of intensity of the image on the film?

SOLUTION

IDENTIFY: Part (a) of this problem uses the relationship among focal length, aperture diameter, and *f*-number for a lens. Part (b) uses the relationship between intensity and aperture diameter.

SET UP: We use Eq. (34.20) to relate the diameter D (the target variable) to the *f*-number and the focal length $f = 200$ mm. The intensity of the light reaching the film is proportional to D^2/f^2; since f is the same in each case, we conclude that the intensity in this case is proportional to D^2, the square of the aperture diameter.

EXECUTE: (a) From Eq. (34.20) the range of diameters is from

$$D = \frac{f}{f\text{-number}} = \frac{200\text{ mm}}{5.6} = 36\text{ mm}$$

to

$$D = \frac{200\text{ mm}}{45} = 4.4\text{ mm}$$

(b) Because the intensity is proportional to the square of the diameter, the ratio of the intensity at *f*/5.6 to the intensity at *f*/45 is

$$\left(\frac{36\text{ mm}}{4.4\text{ mm}}\right)^2 = \left(\frac{45}{5.6}\right)^2 = 65 \qquad (\text{about } 2^6)$$

EVALUATE: If the correct exposure time at *f*/5.6 is $\frac{1}{1000}$ s, then at *f*/45 it is $(65)\left(\frac{1}{1000}\text{ s}\right) = \frac{1}{15}$ s to compensate for the lower intensity. This illustrates a general rule: The smaller the aperture and the larger the *f*-number, the longer the required exposure time. Nevertheless, many photographers prefer to use small apertures so that only the central part of the lens is used to make the image. This minimizes aberrations that occur near the edges of the lens and gives the sharpest possible images.

Test Your Understanding of Section 34.5 When used with 35-mm film (image area 24 mm × 36 mm), a lens with $f = 50$ mm gives a 45° angle of view and is called a "normal lens." When used with a CCD array that measures 5 mm × 5 mm, this same lens is (i) a wide-angle lens; (ii) a normal lens; (iii) a telephoto lens.

34.6 The Eye

The optical behavior of the eye is similar to that of a camera. The essential parts of the human eye, considered as an optical system, are shown in Fig. 34.44a. The eye is nearly spherical and about 2.5 cm in diameter. The front portion is somewhat more sharply curved and is covered by a tough, transparent membrane called the

34.44 (a) The eye. (b) There are two types of light-sensitive cells on the retina. The rods are more sensitive to light than the cones, but only the cones are sensitive to differences in color. A typical human eye contains about 1.3×10^8 rods and about 7×10^6 cones.

(a) Diagram of the eye

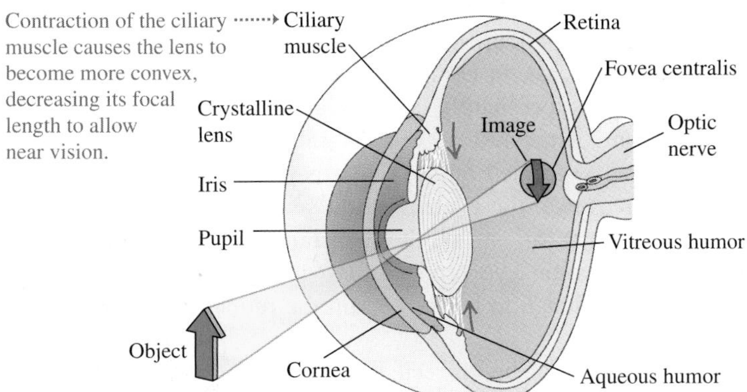

(b) Scanning electron micrograph showing retinal rods and cones in different colors

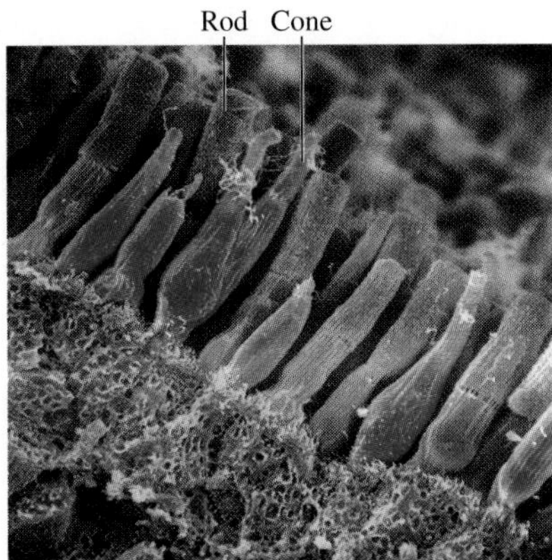

cornea. The region behind the cornea contains a liquid called the *aqueous humor.* Next comes the *crystalline lens,* a capsule containing a fibrous jelly, hard at the center and progressively softer at the outer portions. The crystalline lens is held in place by ligaments that attach it to the ciliary muscle, which encircles it. Behind the lens, the eye is filled with a thin watery jelly called the *vitreous humor.* The indexes of refraction of both the aqueous humor and the vitreous humor are about 1.336, nearly equal to that of water. The crystalline lens, while not homogeneous, has an average index of 1.437. This is not very different from the indexes of the aqueous and vitreous humors. As a result, most of the refraction of light entering the eye occurs at the outer surface of the cornea.

Refraction at the cornea and the surfaces of the lens produces a *real image* of the object being viewed. This image is formed on the light-sensitive *retina,* lining the rear inner surface of the eye. The retina plays the same role as the film in a camera. The *rods* and *cones* in the retina act like an array of miniature photocells (Fig. 34.44b); they sense the image and transmit it via the *optic nerve* to the brain. Vision is most acute in a small central region called the *fovea centralis,* about 0.25 mm in diameter.

In front of the lens is the *iris.* It contains an aperture with variable diameter called the *pupil,* which opens and closes to adapt to changing light intensity. The receptors of the retina also have intensity adaptation mechanisms.

For an object to be seen sharply, the image must be formed exactly at the location of the retina. The eye adjusts to different object distances s by changing the focal length f of its lens; the lens-to-retina distance, corresponding to s', does not change. (Contrast this with focusing a camera, in which the focal length is fixed and the lens-to-film distance is changed.) For the normal eye, an object at infinity is sharply focused when the ciliary muscle is relaxed. To permit sharp imaging on the retina of closer objects, the tension in the ciliary muscle surrounding the lens increases, the ciliary muscle contracts, the lens bulges, and the radii of curvature of its surfaces decrease; this decreases the focal length. This process is called *accommodation.*

The extremes of the range over which distinct vision is possible are known as the *far point* and the *near point* of the eye. The far point of a normal eye is at infinity. The position of the near point depends on the amount by which the ciliary muscle can increase the curvature of the crystalline lens. The range of accommodation gradually diminishes with age because the crystalline lens grows throughout a person's life (it is about 50% larger at age 60 than at age 20) and the ciliary muscles are less able to distort a larger lens. For this reason, the near point gradually recedes as one grows older. This recession of the near point is called *presbyopia.* Table 34.1 shows the approximate position of the near point for an average person at various ages. For example, an average person 50 years of age cannot focus on an object that is closer than about 40 cm.

Table 34.1 Receding of Near Point with Age

Age (years)	Near Point (cm)
10	7
20	10
30	14
40	22
50	40
60	200

34.45 Refractive errors for (a) a normal eye, (b) a myopic (nearsighted) eye, and (c) a hyperopic (farsighted) eye viewing a very distant object. The dashed blue curve indicates the required position of the retina.

(a) Normal eye

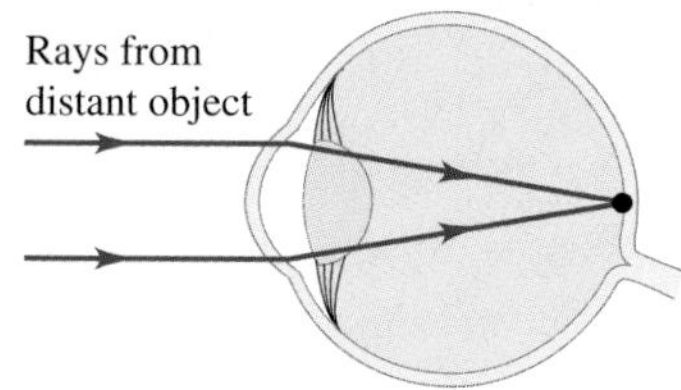
Rays from
distant object

(b) Myopic (nearsighted) eye

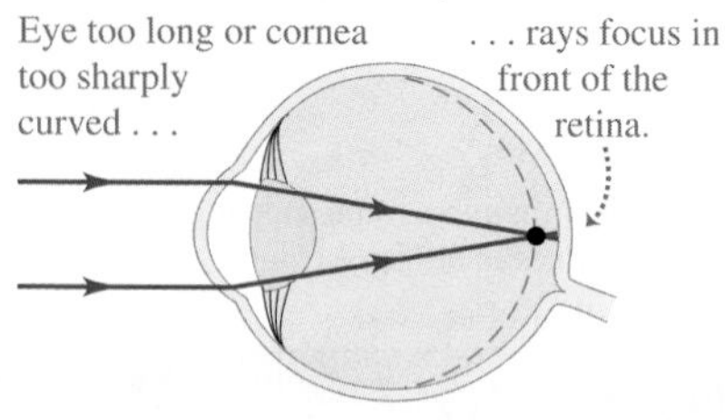
Eye too long or cornea
too sharply
curved . . .
. . . rays focus in
front of the
retina.

(c) Hyperopic (farsighted) eye

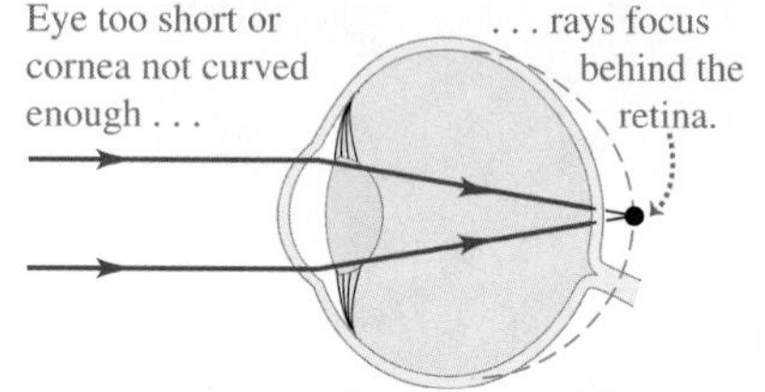
Eye too short or
cornea not curved
enough . . .
. . . rays focus
behind the
retina.

Defects of Vision

Several common defects of vision result from incorrect distance relationships in the eye. A normal eye forms an image on the retina of an object at infinity when the eye is relaxed (Fig. 34.45a). In the *myopic* (nearsighted) eye, the eyeball is too long from front to back in comparison with the radius of curvature of the cornea (or the cornea is too sharply curved), and rays from an object at infinity are focused in front of the retina (Fig. 34.45b). The most distant object for which an image can be formed on the retina is then nearer than infinity. In the *hyperopic* (farsighted) eye, the eyeball is too short or the cornea is not curved enough, and the image of an infinitely distant object is behind the retina (Fig. 34.45c). The myopic eye produces *too much* convergence in a parallel bundle of rays for an image to be formed on the retina; the hyperopic eye, *not enough* convergence.

All of these defects can be corrected by the use of corrective lenses (eyeglasses or contact lenses). The near point of either a presbyopic or a hyperopic

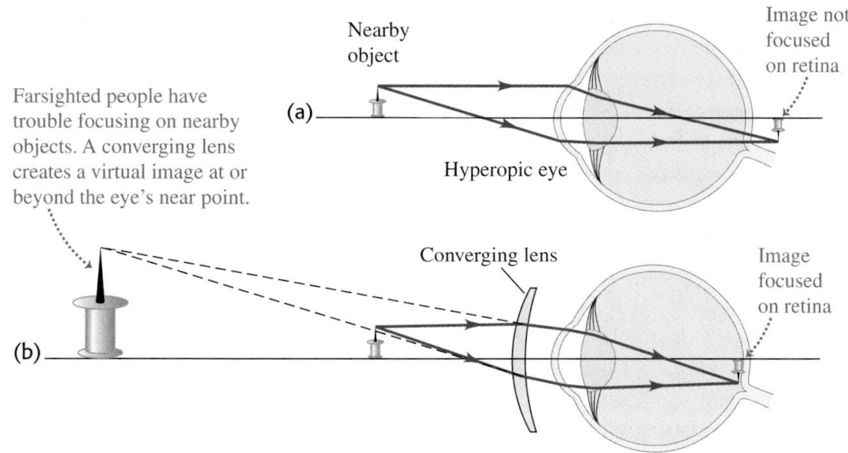
Farsighted people have trouble focusing on nearby objects. A converging lens creates a virtual image at or beyond the eye's near point.
(a)
Nearby object
Image not focused on retina
Hyperopic eye
(b)
Converging lens
Image focused on retina

34.46 (a) An uncorrected hyperopic (farsighted) eye. (b) A positive (converging) lens gives the extra convergence needed for a hyperopic eye to focus the image on the retina.

34.47 (a) An uncorrected myopic (nearsighted) eye. (b) A negative (diverging) lens spreads the rays farther apart to compensate for the excessive convergence of the myopic eye.

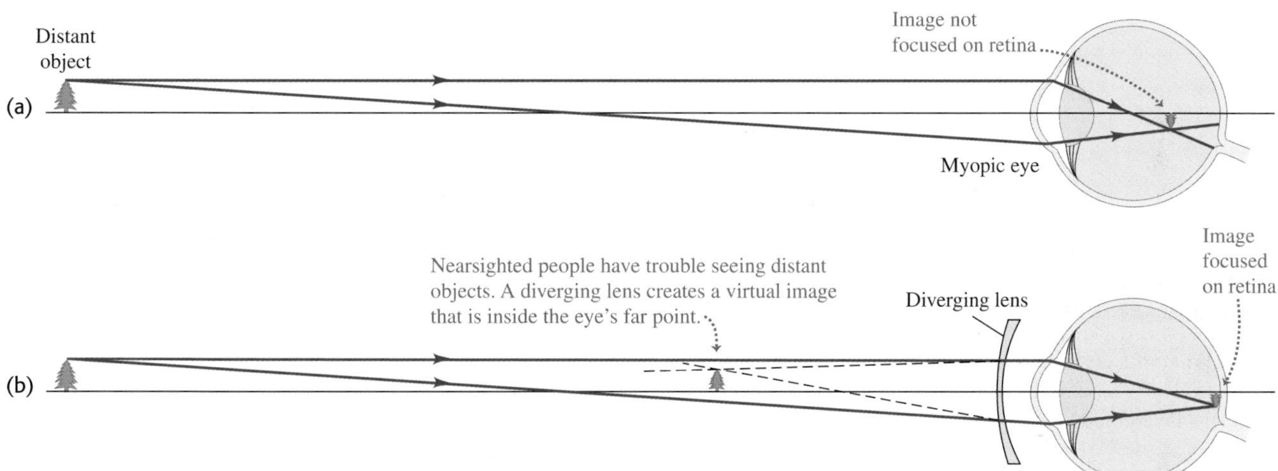
Distant object
(a)
Image not focused on retina
Myopic eye
Nearsighted people have trouble seeing distant objects. A diverging lens creates a virtual image that is inside the eye's far point.
Diverging lens
Image focused on retina
(b)

eye is *farther* from the eye than normal. To see clearly an object at normal reading distance (often assumed to be 25 cm), we need a lens that forms a virtual image of the object at or beyond the near point. This can be accomplished by a converging (positive) lens, as shown in Fig. 34.46. In effect the lens moves the object farther away from the eye to a point where a sharp retinal image can be formed. Similarly, correcting the myopic eye involves using a diverging (negative) lens to move the image closer to the eye than the actual object, as shown in Fig. 34.47.

Astigmatism is a different type of defect in which the surface of the cornea is not spherical but rather more sharply curved in one plane than in another. As a result, horizontal lines may be imaged in a different plane from vertical lines (Fig. 34.48a). Astigmatism may make it impossible, for example, to focus clearly on the horizontal and vertical bars of a window at the same time.

Astigmatism can be corrected by use of a lens with a *cylindrical* surface. For example, suppose the curvature of the cornea in a horizontal plane is correct to focus rays from infinity on the retina but the curvature in the vertical plane is too great to form a sharp retinal image. When a cylindrical lens with its axis horizontal is placed before the eye, the rays in a horizontal plane are unaffected, but the additional divergence of the rays in a vertical plane causes these to be sharply imaged on the retina (Fig. 34.48b).

Lenses for vision correction are usually described in terms of the **power,** defined as the reciprocal of the focal length expressed in meters. The unit of power is the **diopter.** Thus a lens with $f = 0.50$ m has a power of 2.0 diopters,

34.48 One type of astigmatism and how it is corrected.

(a) Vertical lines are imaged in front of the retina.

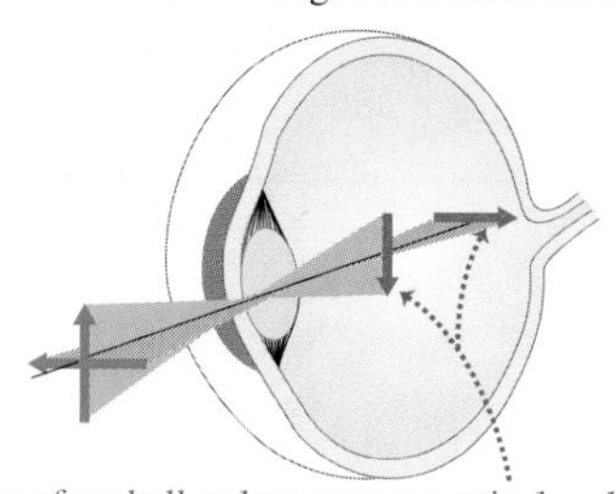

Shape of eyeball or lens causes vertical and horizontal elements to focus at different distances.

(b) A cylindrical lens corrects for astigmatism.

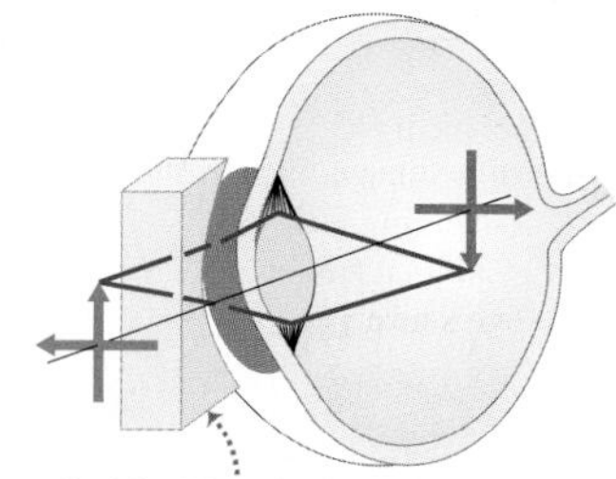

This cylindrical lens is curved in the vertical, but not the horizontal, direction; it changes the focal length of vertical elements.

$f = -0.25$ m corresponds to -4.0 diopters, and so on. The numbers on a prescription for glasses are usually powers expressed in diopters. When the correction involves both astigmatism and myopia or hyperopia, there are three numbers: one for the spherical power, one for the cylindrical power, and an angle to describe the orientation of the cylinder axis.

An alternative approach for correcting many defects of vision is to reshape the cornea. This is often done using a procedure called *laser-assisted in situ keratomileusis,* or LASIK. An incision is made into the cornea and a flap of outer corneal tissue is folded back. A pulsed ultraviolet laser with a beam only 50 μm wide (about $\frac{1}{200}$ the width of a human hair) is then used to vaporize away microscopic areas of the underlying tissue. The flap is then folded back into position, where it conforms to the new shape "carved" by the laser.

Example 34.13 Correcting for farsightedness

The near point of a certain hyperopic eye is 100 cm in front of the eye. To see clearly an object that is 25 cm in front of the eye, what contact lens is required?

SOLUTION

IDENTIFY: We want the lens to form a virtual image of the object at the near point of the eye, 100 cm from it. That is, when $s =$ 25 cm, we want s' to be 100 cm.

SET UP: Figure 34.49 shows the situation. We determine the required focal length of the contact lens using the object-image relationship for a thin lens, Eq. (34.16).

EXECUTE: From Eq. (34.16),

$$\frac{1}{f} = \frac{1}{s} + \frac{1}{s'} = \frac{1}{+25\text{ cm}} + \frac{1}{-100\text{ cm}}$$

$$f = +33\text{ cm}$$

We need a converging lens with focal length $f = 33$ cm. The corresponding power is $1/(0.33\text{ m})$, or $+3.0$ diopters.

EVALUATE: In this example we used a contact lens to correct hyperopia. Had we used eyeglasses, we would have had to account for the separation between the eye and the eyeglass lens, and a somewhat different power would have been required (see Example 34.14).

34.49 Using a contact lens to correct for farsightedness.

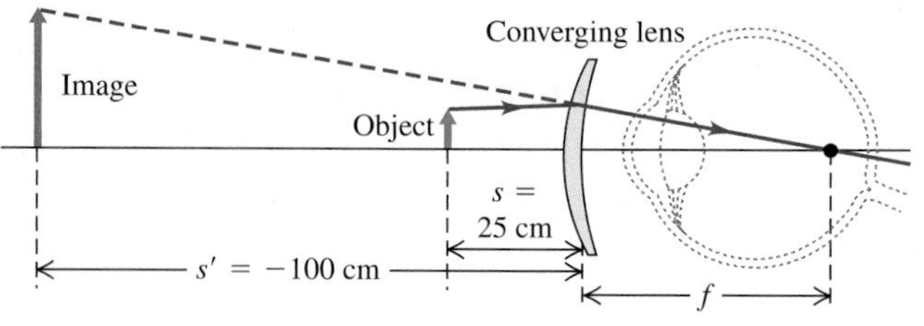

Example 34.14 Correcting for nearsightedness

The far point of a certain myopic eye is 50 cm in front of the eye. To see clearly an object at infinity, what eyeglass lens is required? Assume that the lens is worn 2 cm in front of the eye.

SOLUTION

IDENTIFY: The far point of a myopic eye is nearer than infinity. To see clearly objects beyond the far point, we need a lens that forms a virtual image of such objects no farther from the eye than the far point.

SET UP: Figure 34.50 shows the situation. Assume that the virtual image of the object at infinity is formed at the far point, 50 cm in front of the eye and 48 cm in front of the eyeglass lens. Then when

$s = \infty$, we want s' to be -48 cm. As in Example 34.13, we use the values of s and s' to calculate the required focal length.

EXECUTE: From Eq. (34.16),

$$\frac{1}{f} = \frac{1}{s} + \frac{1}{s'} = \frac{1}{\infty} + \frac{1}{-48\text{ cm}}$$

$$f = -48\text{ cm}$$

We need a *diverging* lens with focal length $-48\text{ cm} = -0.48$ m. The power is -2.1 diopter.

EVALUATE: If a *contact* lens were used instead, we would need $f = -50$ cm and a power of -2.0 diopters. Can you see why?

34.50 Using a contact lens to correct for nearsightedness.

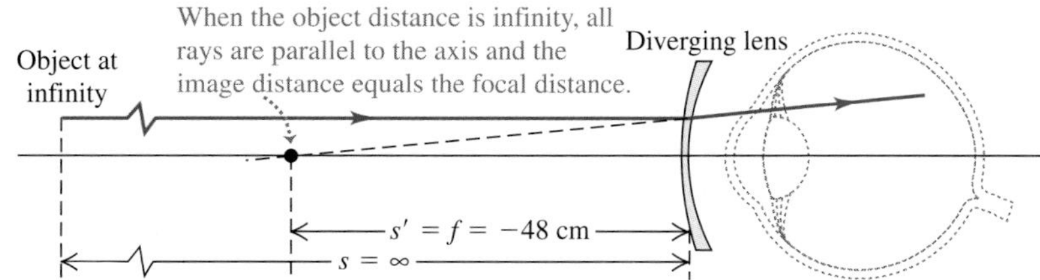

Test Your Understanding of Section 34.6 A certain eyeglass lens is thin at its center, even thinner at its top and bottom edges, and relatively thick at its left and right edges. What defects of vision is this lens intended to correct? (i) hyperopia for objects oriented both vertically and horizontally; (ii) myopia for objects oriented both vertically and horizontally; (iii) hyperopia for objects oriented vertically and myopia for objects oriented horizontally; (iv) hyperopia for objects oriented horizontally and myopia for objects oriented vertically.

34.7 The Magnifier

The apparent size of an object is determined by the size of its image on the retina. If the eye is unaided, this size depends on the *angle* θ subtended by the object at the eye, called its **angular size** (Fig. 34.51a).

To look closely at a small object, such as an insect or a crystal, you bring it close to your eye, making the subtended angle and the retinal image as large as possible. But your eye cannot focus sharply on objects that are closer than the near point, so the angular size of an object is greatest (that is, it subtends the largest possible viewing angle) when it is placed at the near point. In the following discussion we will assume an average viewer for whom the near point is 25 cm from the eye.

34.51 (a) The angular size θ is largest when the object is at the near point. (b) The magnifier gives a virtual image at infinity. This virtual image appears to the eye to be a real object subtending a larger angle θ' at the eye.

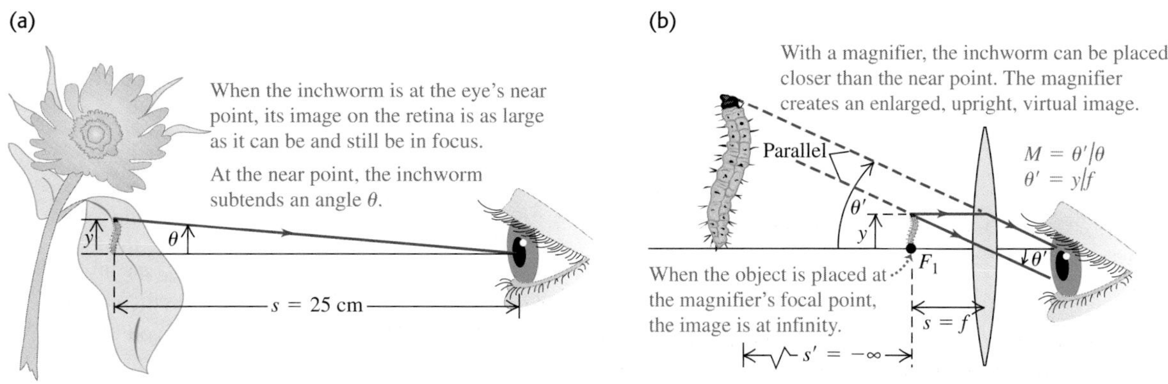

A converging lens can be used to form a virtual image that is larger and farther from the eye than the object itself, as shown in Fig. 34.51b. Then the object can be moved closer to the eye, and the angular size of the image may be substantially larger than the angular size of the object at 25 cm without the lens. A lens used in this way is called a **magnifier,** otherwise known as a *magnifying glass* or a *simple magnifier.* The virtual image is most comfortable to view when it is placed at infinity, so that the ciliary muscle of the eye is relaxed; this means that the object is placed at the focal point F_1 of the magnifier. In the following discussion we assume that this is done.

In Fig. 34.51a the object is at the near point, where it subtends an angle θ at the eye. In Fig. 34.51b a magnifier in front of the eye forms an image at infinity, and the angle subtended at the magnifier is θ'. The usefulness of the magnifier is given by the ratio of the angle θ' (with the magnifier) to the angle θ (without the magnifier). This ratio is called the **angular magnification** M:

$$M = \frac{\theta'}{\theta} \qquad \text{(angular magnification)} \tag{34.21}$$

CAUTION Angular magnification vs. lateral magnification Don't confuse the *angular* magnification M with the *lateral* magnification m. Angular magnification is the ratio of the *angular* size of an image to the angular size of the corresponding object; lateral magnification refers to the ratio of the *height* of an image to the height of the corresponding object. For the situation shown in Fig. 34.51b, the angular magnification is about 3×, since the inchworm subtends an angle about three times larger than that in Fig. 34.51a; hence the inchworm will look about three times larger to the eye. The *lateral* magnification $m = -s'/s$ in Fig. 34.51b is *infinite* because the virtual image is at infinity, but that doesn't mean that the inchworm looks infinitely large through the magnifier! (That's why we didn't attempt to draw an infinitely large inchworm in Fig. 34.51b.) When dealing with a magnifier, M is useful but m is not.

To find the value of M, we first assume that the angles are small enough that each angle (in radians) is equal to its sine and its tangent. Using Fig. 34.451a and drawing the ray in Fig. 34.51b that passes undeviated through the center of the lens, we find that θ and θ' (in radians) are

$$\theta = \frac{y}{25\text{ cm}} \qquad \theta' = \frac{y}{f}$$

Combining these expressions with Eq. (34.21), we find

$$M = \frac{\theta'}{\theta} = \frac{y/f}{y/25\text{ cm}} = \frac{25\text{ cm}}{f} \qquad \begin{pmatrix}\text{angular magnification}\\ \text{for a simple magnifier}\end{pmatrix} \tag{34.22}$$

It may seem that we can make the angular magnification as large as we like by decreasing the focal length f. In fact, the aberrations of a simple double-convex lens set a limit to M of about 3× to 4×. If these aberrations are corrected, the angular magnification may be made as great as 20×. When greater magnification than this is needed, we usually use a compound microscope, discussed in the next section.

Test Your Understanding of Section 34.7 You are examining a gem using a magnifier. If you change to a different magnifier with twice the focal length of the first one, (i) you will have to hold the object at twice the distance and the angular magnification will be twice as great; (ii) you will have to hold the object at twice the distance and the angular magnification will be $\frac{1}{2}$ as great; (iii) you will have to hold the object at $\frac{1}{2}$ the distance and the angular magnification will be twice as great; (iv) you will have to hold the object at $\frac{1}{2}$ the distance and the angular magnification will be $\frac{1}{2}$ as great.

34.8 Microscopes and Telescopes

ActivPhysics Online
15.12 Two-Lens System
15.3 The Telescope and Angular Magnification

Cameras, eyeglasses, and magnifiers use a single lens to form an image. Two important optical devices that use *two* lenses are the microscope and the telescope. In each device a primary lens, or *objective,* forms a real image, and a second lens, or *eyepiece,* is used as a magnifier to make an enlarged, virtual image.

Microscopes

When we need greater magnification than we can get with a simple magnifier, the instrument that we usually use is the **microscope,** sometimes called a *compound microscope.* The essential elements of a microscope are shown in Fig. 34.52a. To analyze this system, we use the principle that an image formed by one optical element such as a lens or mirror can serve as the object for a second element. We used this principle in Section 34.4 when we derived the thin-lens equation by repeated application of the single-surface refraction equation; we used this principle again in Example 34.11 (Section 34.4), in which the image formed by a lens was used as the object of a second lens.

The object O to be viewed is placed just beyond the first focal point F_1 of the **objective,** a converging lens that forms a real and enlarged image I (Fig. 34.52b). In a properly designed instrument this image lies just inside the first focal point F_1' of a second converging lens called the **eyepiece** or *ocular.* (The reason the image should lie just *inside* F_1' is left for you to discover; see Problem 34.108.) The eyepiece acts as a simple magnifier, as discussed in Section 34.7, and forms a final virtual image I' of I. The position of I' may be anywhere between the near

34.52 (a) Elements of a microscope. (b) The object O is placed just outside the first focal point of the objective (the distance s_1 has been exaggerated for clarity). (c) This microscope image shows single-celled organisms about 2×10^{-4} m (0.2 mm) across. Typical light microscopes can resolve features as small as 2×10^{-7} m, comparable to the wavelength of light.

(a) Elements of a microscope

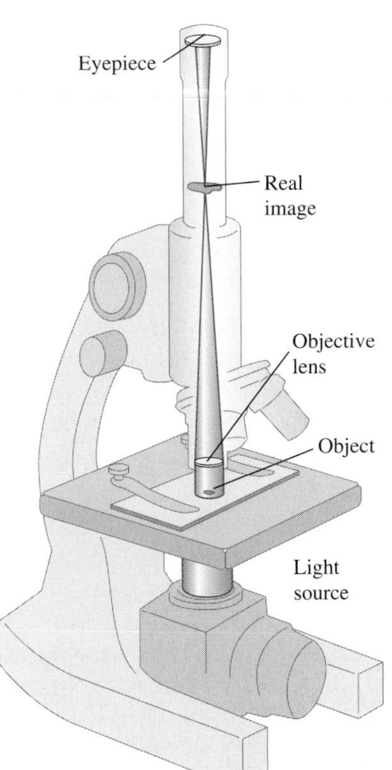
Eyepiece
Real image
Objective lens
Object
Light source

(b) Microscope optics

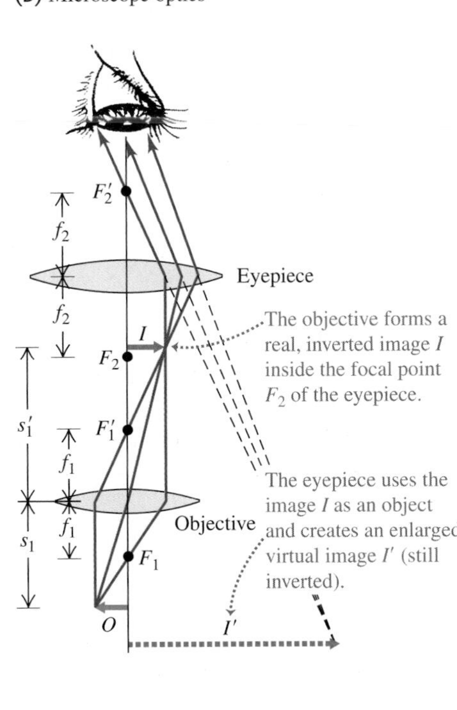
F_2'
f_2
Eyepiece
f_2
I
F_2
The objective forms a real, inverted image I inside the focal point F_2 of the eyepiece.
s_1'
F_1'
f_1
Objective
f_1
s_1
F_1
The eyepiece uses the image I as an object and creates an enlarged, virtual image I' (still inverted).
O
I'

(c) Single-celled freshwater algae (*Micrasterias denticulata*)

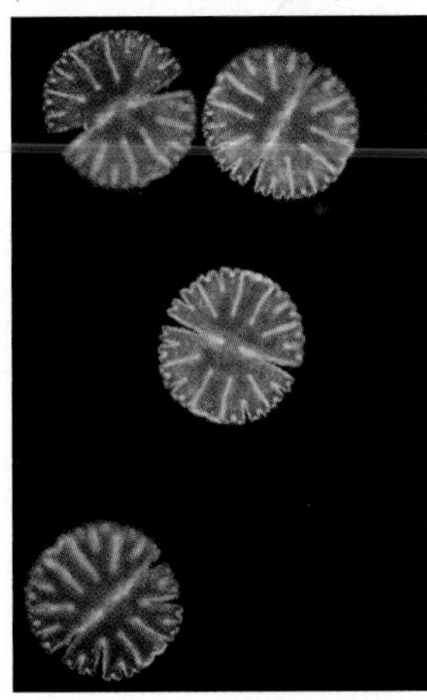

and far points of the eye. Both the objective and the eyepiece of an actual microscope are highly corrected compound lenses with several optical elements, but for simplicity we show them here as simple thin lenses.

As for a simple magnifier, what matters when viewing through a microscope is the *angular* magnification M. The overall angular magnification of the compound microscope is the product of two factors. The first factor is the *lateral* magnification m_1 of the objective, which determines the linear size of the real image I; the second factor is the *angular* magnification M_2 of the eyepiece, which relates the angular size of the virtual image seen through the eyepiece to the angular size that the real image I would have if you viewed it *without* the eyepiece. The first of these factors is given by

$$m_1 = -\frac{s_1'}{s_1} \tag{34.23}$$

where s_1 and s_1' are the object and image distances, respectively, for the objective lens. Ordinarily, the object is very close to the focal point, and the resulting image distance s_1' is very great in comparison to the focal length f_1 of the objective lens. Thus s_1 is approximately equal to f_1, and we can write $m_1 = -s_1'/f_1$.

The real image I is close to the focal point F_1' of the eyepiece, so to find the eyepiece angular magnification, we can use Eq. (34.22): $M_2 = (25\text{ cm})/f_2$, where f_2 is the focal length of the eyepiece (considered as a simple lens). The overall angular magnification M of the compound microscope (apart from a negative sign, which is customarily ignored) is the product of the two magnifications:

$$M = m_1 M_2 = \frac{(25\text{ cm})s_1'}{f_1 f_2} \quad \text{(angular magnification for a microscope)} \tag{34.24}$$

where s_1', f_1, and f_2 are measured in centimeters. The final image is inverted with respect to the object. Microscope manufacturers usually specify the values of m_1 and M_2 for microscope components rather than the focal lengths of the objective and eyepiece.

Equation (34.24) shows that the angular magnification of a microscope can be increased by using an objective of shorter focal length f_1, thereby increasing m_1 and the size of the real image I. Most optical microscopes have a rotating "turret" with three or more objectives of different focal lengths so that the same object can be viewed at different magnifications. The eyepiece should also have a short focal length f_2 to help to maximize the value of M.

To take a photograph using a microscope (called a *photomicrograph* or *micrograph*), the eyepiece is removed and a camera placed so that the real image I falls on the camera's CCD array or film. Figure 34.52c shows such a photograph. In this case what matters is the *lateral* magnification of the microscope as given by Eq. (34.23).

Telescopes

The optical system of a **telescope** is similar to that of a compound microscope. In both instruments the image formed by an objective is viewed through an eyepiece. The key difference is that the telescope is used to view large objects at large distances and the microscope is used to view small objects close at hand. Another difference is that many telescopes use a curved mirror, not a lens, as an objective.

Figure 34.53 shows an *astronomical telescope.* Because this telescope uses a lens as an objective, it is called a *refracting telescope* or *refractor.* The objective lens forms a real, reduced image I of the object. This image is the object for the eyepiece lens, which forms an enlarged, virtual image of I. Objects that are viewed with a telescope are usually so far away from the instrument that the first

34.53 Optical system of an astronomical refracting telescope.

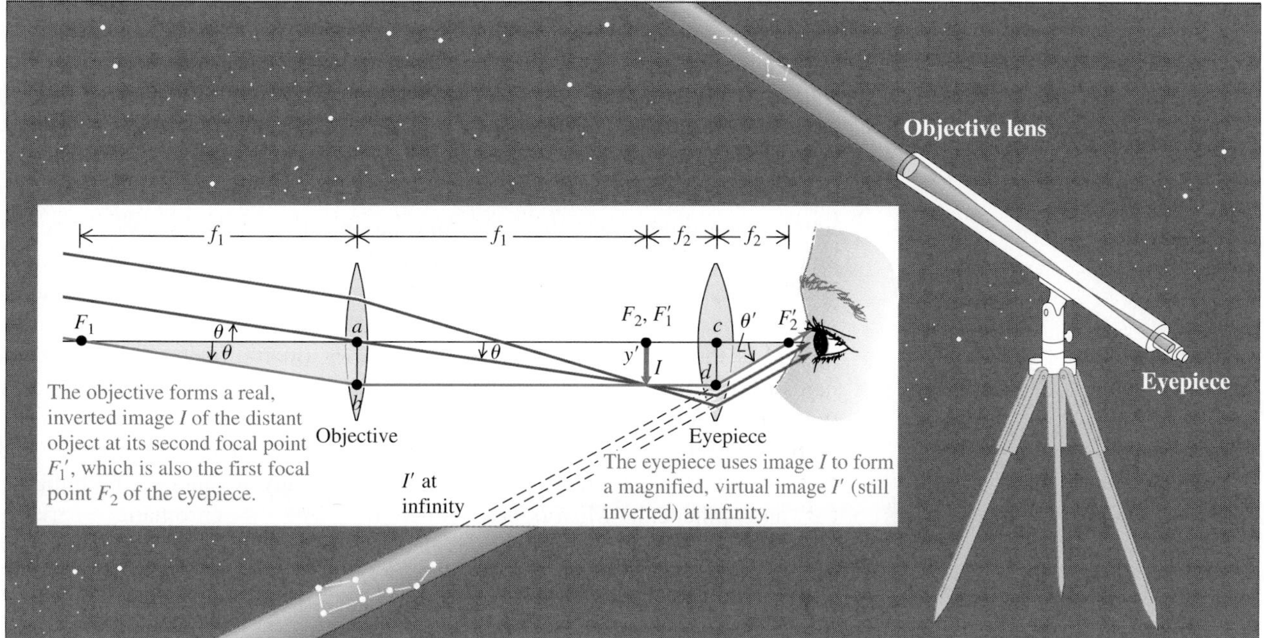

image I is formed very nearly at the second focal point of the objective lens. If the final image I' formed by the eyepiece is at infinity (for most comfortable viewing by a normal eye), the first image must also be at the first focal point of the eyepiece. The distance between objective and eyepiece, which is the length of the telescope, is therefore the *sum* of the focal lengths of objective and eyepiece, $f_1 + f_2$.

The angular magnification M of a telescope is defined as the ratio of the angle subtended at the eye by the final image I' to the angle subtended at the (unaided) eye by the object. We can express this ratio in terms of the focal lengths of objective and eyepiece. In Fig. 34.53 the ray passing through F_1, the first focal point of the objective, and through F_2', the second focal point of the eyepiece, is shown in red. The object (not shown) subtends an angle θ at the objective and would subtend essentially the same angle at the unaided eye. Also, since the observer's eye is placed just to the right of the focal point F_2', the angle subtended at the eye by the final image is very nearly equal to the angle θ'. Because bd is parallel to the optic axis, the distances ab and cd are equal to each other and also to the height y' of the real image I. Because the angles θ and θ' are small, they may be approximated by their tangents. From the right triangles F_1ab and $F_2'cd$,

$$\theta = \frac{-y'}{f_1} \qquad \theta' = \frac{y'}{f_2}$$

and the angular magnification M is

$$M = \frac{\theta'}{\theta} = -\frac{y'/f_2}{y'/f_1} = -\frac{f_1}{f_2} \qquad \text{(angular magnification for a telescope)} \qquad (34.25)$$

The angular magnification M of a telescope is equal to the ratio of the focal length of the objective to that of the eyepiece. The negative sign shows that the final image is inverted. Equation (34.25) shows that to achieve good angular magnification, a *telescope* should have a *long* objective focal length f_1. By contrast, Eq. (34.24) shows that a *microscope* should have a *short* objective focal length. However, a telescope objective with a long focal length should also have a large diameter D so that the f-number f_1/D will not be too large; as described in

Section 34.5, a large f-number means a dim, low-intensity image. Telescopes typically do not have interchangeable objectives; instead, the magnification is varied by using different eyepieces with different focal lengths f_2. Just as for a microscope, smaller values of f_2 give larger angular magnifications.

An inverted image is no particular disadvantage for astronomical observations. When we use a telescope or binoculars—essentially a pair of telescopes mounted side by side—to view objects on the earth, though, we want the image to be right-side up. In prism binoculars, this is accomplished by reflecting the light several times along the path from the objective to the eyepiece. The combined effect of the reflections is to flip the image both horizontally and vertically. Binoculars are usually described by two numbers separated by a multiplication sign, such as 7×50. The first number is the angular magnification M, and the second is the diameter of the objective lenses (in millimeters). The diameter helps to determine the light-gathering capacity of the objective lenses and thus the brightness of the image.

In the *reflecting telescope* (Fig. 34.54a) the objective lens is replaced by a concave mirror. In large telescopes this scheme has many advantages, both theoretical and practical. Mirrors are inherently free of chromatic aberrations (dependence of focal length on wavelength), and spherical aberrations (associated with the paraxial approximation) are easier to correct than with a lens. The reflecting surface is sometimes parabolic rather than spherical. The material of the mirror need not be transparent, and it can be made more rigid than a lens, which has to be supported only at its edges.

The largest reflecting telescopes in the world, the Keck telescopes atop Mauna Kea in Hawaii, each have an objective mirror of overall diameter 10 m made up of 36 separate hexagonal reflecting elements.

34.54 (a), (b), (c) Three designs for reflecting telescopes. (d) This photo shows the interior of the Gemini North telescope, which uses the design shown in (c). The objective mirror is 8 meters in diameter.

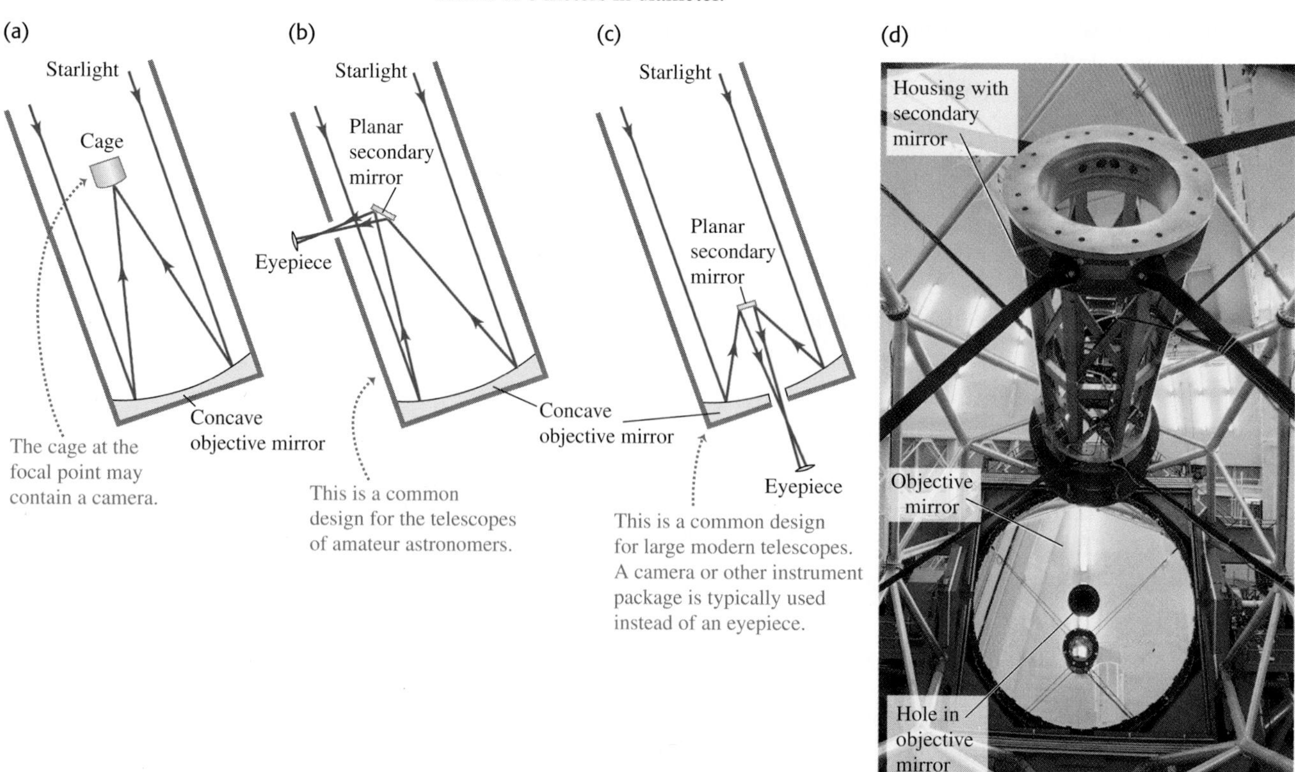

One challenge in designing reflecting telescopes is that the image is formed in front of the objective mirror, in a region traversed by incoming rays. Isaac Newton devised one solution to this problem. A flat secondary mirror oriented at 45° to the optic axis causes the image to be formed in a hole on the side of the telescope, where it can be magnified with an eyepiece (Fig. 34.54b). Another solution uses a secondary mirror that causes the focused light to pass through a hole in the objective mirror (Fig. 34.54c). Large research telescopes, as well as many amateur telescopes, use this design (Fig. 34.54d).

Like a microscope, when a telescope is used for photography the eyepiece is removed and a CCD array or photographic film is placed at the position of the real image formed by the objective. (Some long-focal-length "lenses" for photography are actually reflecting telescopes used in this way.) Most telescopes used for astronomical research are never used with an eyepiece.

Test Your Understanding of Section 34.8 Which gives a lateral magnification of greater absolute value: (i) the objective lens in a microscope (Fig. 34.52); (ii) the objective lens in a refracting telescope (Fig. 34.53); or (iii) not enough information is given to decide?

CHAPTER 34 SUMMARY

Reflection or refraction at a plane surface: When rays diverge from an object point P and are reflected or refracted, the directions of the outgoing rays are the same as though they had diverged from a point P' called the image point. If they actually converge at P' and diverge again beyond it, P' is a real image of P; if they only appear to have diverged from P', it is a virtual image. Images can be either erect or inverted.

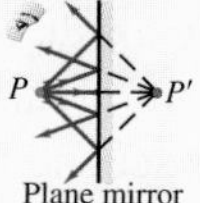

Lateral magnification: The lateral magnification m in any reflecting or refracting situation is defined as the ratio of image height y' to object height y. When m is positive, the image is erect; when m is negative, the image is inverted.

$$m = \frac{y'}{y} \qquad (34.2)$$

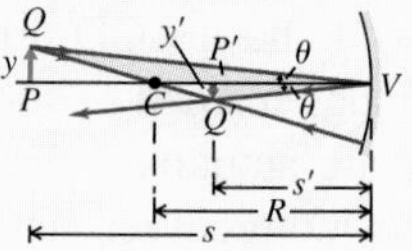

Focal point and focal length: The focal point of a mirror is the point where parallel rays converge after reflection from a concave mirror, or the point from which they appear to diverge after reflection from a convex mirror. Rays diverging from the focal point of a concave mirror are parallel after reflection; rays converging toward the focal point of a convex mirror are parallel after reflection. The distance from the focal point to the vertex is called the focal length, denoted as f. The focal points of a lens are defined similarly.

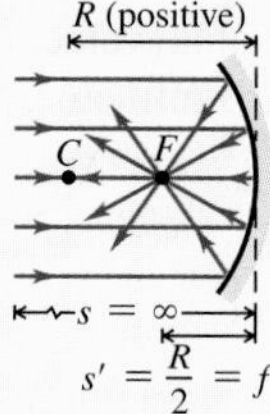

Relating object and image distances: The formulas for object distance s and image distance s' for plane and spherical mirrors and single refracting surfaces are summarized in the table. The equation for a plane surface can be obtained from the corresponding equation for a spherical surface by setting $R = \infty$. (See Examples 34.1–34.7.)

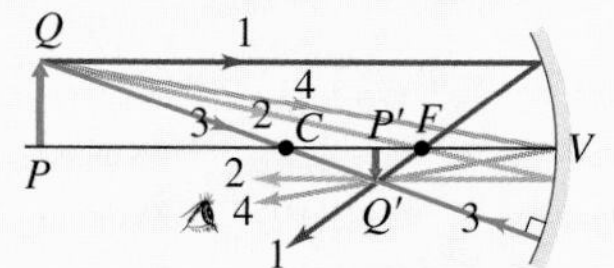

	Plane Mirror	Spherical Mirror	Plane Refracting Surface	Spherical Refracting Surface
Object and image distances	$\frac{1}{s} + \frac{1}{s'} = 0$	$\frac{1}{s} + \frac{1}{s'} = \frac{2}{R} = \frac{1}{f}$	$\frac{n_a}{s} + \frac{n_b}{s'} = 0$	$\frac{n_a}{s} + \frac{n_b}{s'} = \frac{n_b - n_a}{R}$
Lateral magnification	$m = -\frac{s'}{s} = 1$	$m = -\frac{s'}{s}$	$m = -\frac{n_a s'}{n_b s} = 1$	$m = -\frac{n_a s'}{n_b s}$

Object-image relationships derived in this chapter are valid only for rays close to and nearly parallel to the optic axis; these are called paraxial rays. Nonparaxial rays do not converge precisely to an image point. This effect is called spherical aberration.

Thin lenses: The object-image relationships, given by Eq. (34.16), is the same for a thin lens as for a spherical mirror. Equation (34.19), the lensmaker's equation, relates the focal length of a lens to its index of refraction and the radii of curvature of its surfaces. (See Examples 34.8–34.11.)

$$\frac{1}{s} + \frac{1}{s'} = \frac{1}{f} \qquad (34.16)$$

$$\frac{1}{f} = (n - 1)\left(\frac{1}{R_1} - \frac{1}{R_2}\right) \qquad (34.19)$$

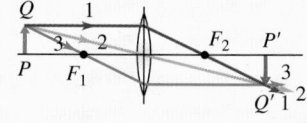

Sign rules: The following sign rules are used with all plane and spherical reflecting and refracting surfaces.

- $s > 0$ when the object is on the incoming side of the surface (a real object); $s < 0$ otherwise.
- $s' > 0$ when the image is on the outgoing side of the surface (a real image); $s' < 0$ otherwise.
- $R > 0$ when the center of curvature is on the outgoing side of the surface; $R < 0$ otherwise.
- $m > 0$ when the image is erect; $m < 0$ when inverted.

Cameras: A camera forms a real, inverted, reduced image of the object being photographed on a light-sensitive surface. The amount of light striking this surface is controlled by the shutter speed and the aperture. The intensity of this light is inversely proportional to the square of the f-number of the lens. (See Example 34.12.)

$$f\text{-number} = \frac{\text{Focal length}}{\text{Aperture diameter}} = \frac{f}{D} \quad (34.20)$$

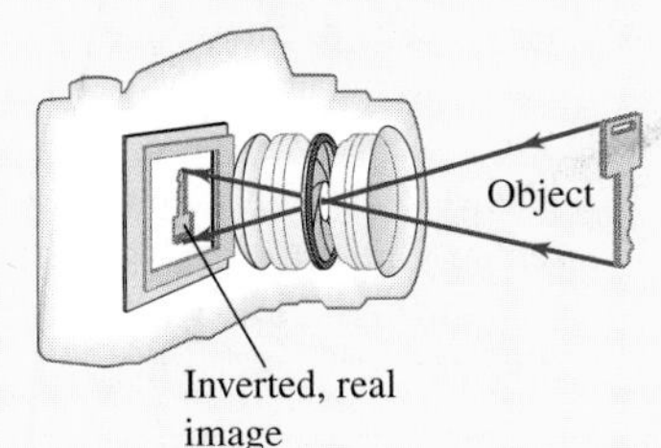

The eye: In the eye, refraction at the surface of the cornea forms a real image on the retina. Adjustment for various object distances is made by squeezing the lens, thereby making it bulge and decreasing its focal length. A nearsighted eye is too long for its lens; a farsighted eye is too short. The power of a corrective lens, in diopters, is the reciprocal of the focal length in meters. (See Examples 34.13 and 34.14.)

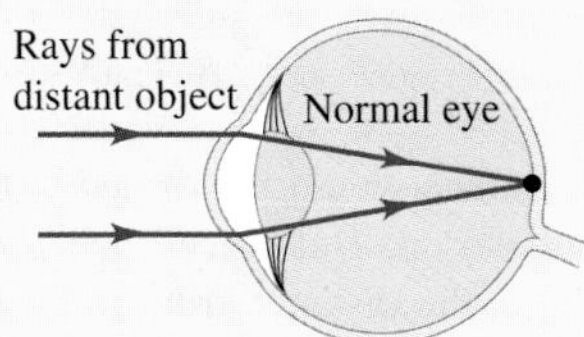

The simple magnifier: The simple magnifier creates a virtual image whose angular size θ' is larger than the angular size θ of the object itself at a distance of 25 cm, the nominal closest distance for comfortable viewing. The angular magnification M of a simple magnifier is the ratio of the angular size of the virtual image to that of the object at this distance.

$$M = \frac{\theta'}{\theta} = \frac{25\text{ cm}}{f} \quad (34.22)$$

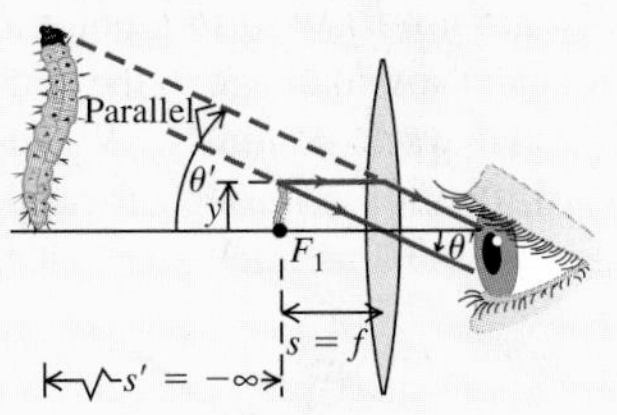

Microscopes and telescopes: In a compound microscope, the objective lens forms a first image in the barrel of the instrument, and the eyepiece forms a final virtual image, often at infinity, of the first image. The telescope operates on the same principle, but the object is far away. In a reflecting telescope, the objective lens is replaced by a concave mirror, which eliminates chromatic aberrations.

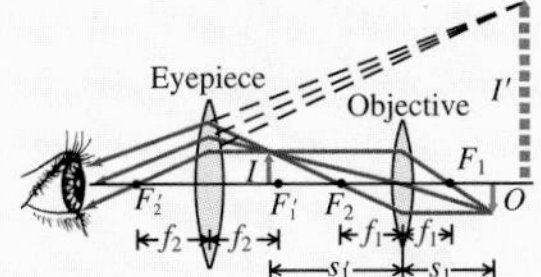

Key Terms

object, *1157*
point object, *1158*
extended object, *1158*
image, *1158*
virtual image, *1158*
real image, *1158*
object distance, *1159*
image distance, *1159*
lateral magnification, *1160*
erect image, *1160*
inverted image, *1160*
reversed image, *1160*
center of curvature, *1161*
vertex, *1161*
optic axis, *1161*
paraxial rays, *1162*
paraxial approximation, *1162*
spherical aberration, *1162*
focal point, *1163*
focal length, *1163*
principal rays, *1167*
thin lens, *1174*
converging lens, *1174*
diverging lens, *1176*
lensmaker's equation, *1177*
camera, *1182*
f-number, *1184*
power, *1187*
diopter, *1187*
angular size, *1189*
magnifier, *1190*
angular magnification, *1190*
microscope, *1191*
objective, *1191*
eyepiece, *1191*
telescope, *1192*

Answer to Chapter Opening Question ?

A magnifying lens (simple magnifier) produces a virtual image with a large angular size that is infinitely far away, so you can see it in sharp focus with your eyes relaxed. (A surgeon doing microsurgery would not appreciate having to strain his eyes while working.) The object should be at the focal point of the lens, so the object and lens are separated by one focal length.

Answers to Test Your Understanding Questions

34.1 Answer: (iv) When you are a distance s from the mirror, your image is a distance s on the other side of the mirror and the distance from you to your image is $2s$. As you move toward the mirror, the distance $2s$ changes at twice the rate of the distance s, so your image moves toward you at speed $2v$.

34.2 Answers: (a) concave, (b) (ii) A convex mirror always produces an erect image, but that image is smaller than the object (see

Fig. 34.16b). Hence a concave mirror must be used. The image will be erect and enlarged only if the distance from the object (your face) to the mirror is less than the focal length of the mirror, as in Fig. 34.20d.

34.3 Answer: no The sun is very far away, so the object distance is essentially infinite: $s = \infty$ and $1/s = 0$. Material a is air ($n_a = 1.00$) and material b is water ($n_b = 1.33$), so the image position s' is given by

$$\frac{n_a}{s} + \frac{n_b}{s'} = \frac{n_b - n_a}{R} \quad \text{or} \quad 0 + \frac{1.33}{s'} = \frac{1.33 - 1.00}{R}$$

$$s' = \frac{1.33}{0.33}R = 4.0R$$

The image would be formed 4.0 drop radii from the front surface of the drop. But since each drop is only a part of a complete sphere, the distance from the front to the back of the drop is less than $2R$. Thus the rays of sunlight never reach the image point, and the drops do not form an image of the sun on the leaf. While the rays are not focused to a point, they are nonetheless concentrated and can cause damage to the leaf.

34.4 Answers: A and C When rays A and D are extended backward, they pass through focal point F_2; thus, before they passed through the lens, they were parallel to the optic axis. The figures show that ray A emanated from point Q, but ray D did not. Ray B is parallel to the optic axis, so before it passed through the lens, it was directed toward focal point F_1. Hence it cannot have come from point Q. Ray C passes through the center of the lens and hence is not deflected by its passage; tracing the ray backward shows that it emanates from point Q.

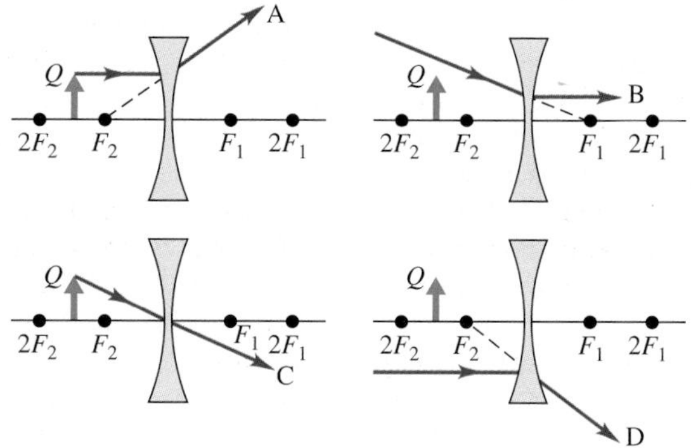

34.5 Answer: (iii) The smaller image area of the CCD array means that the angle of view is decreased for a given focal length. Individual objects make images of the same size in either case; when a smaller light-sensitive area is used, fewer images fit into the area and the field of view is narrower.

34.6 Answer: (iii) This lens is designed to correct for a type of astigmatism. Along the vertical axis, the lens is configured as a converging lens; along the horizontal axis, the lens is configured as a diverging lens. Hence the eye is hyperopic (see Fig. 34.46) for objects that are oriented vertically but myopic for objects that are oriented horizontally (see Fig. 34.47). Without correction, the eye focuses vertical objects behind the retina but horizontal objects in front of the retina.

34.7 Answer: (ii) The object must be held at the focal point, which is twice as far away if the focal length f is twice as great. Equation (24.22) shows that the angular magnification M is inversely proportional to f, so doubling the focal length makes M $\frac{1}{2}$ as great. To improve the magnification, you should use a magnifier with a *shorter* focal length.

34.8 Answer: (i) The objective lens of a microscope is designed to make enlarged images of small objects, so the absolute value of its lateral magnification m is greater than 1. By contrast, the objective lens of a refracting telescope is designed to make *reduced* images. For example, the moon is thousands of kilometers in diameter, but its image may fit on a CCD array a few centimeters across. Thus $|m|$ is much less than 1 for a refracting telescope. (In both cases m is negative because the objective makes an inverted image, which is why the question asks about the absolute value of m.)

PROBLEMS

For instructor-assigned homework, go to www.masteringphysics.com 

Discussion Questions

Q34.1. A spherical mirror is cut in half horizontally. Will an image be formed by the bottom half of the mirror? If so, where will the image be formed?

Q34.2. For the situation shown in Fig. 34.3, is the image distance s' positive or negative? Is the image real or virtual? Explain your answers.

Q34.3. The laws of optics also apply to electromagnetic waves invisible to the eye. A satellite TV dish is used to detect radio waves coming from orbiting satellites. Why is a curved reflecting surface (a "dish") used? The dish is always concave, never convex; why? The actual radio receiver is placed on an arm and suspended in front of the dish. How far in front of the dish should it be placed?

Q34.4. Explain why the focal length of a *plane* mirror is infinite, and explain what it means for the focal point to be at infinity.

Q34.5. If a spherical mirror is immersed in water, does its focal length change? Explain.

Q34.6. For what range of object positions does a concave spherical mirror form a real image? What about a convex spherical mirror?

Q34.7. When a room has mirrors on two opposite walls, an infinite series of reflections can be seen. Discuss this phenomenon in terms of images. Why do the distant images appear fainter?

Q34.8. For a spherical mirror, if $s = f$, then $s' = \infty$, and the lateral magnification m is infinite. Does this make sense? If so, what does it mean?

Q34.9. You may have noticed a small convex mirror next to your bank's ATM. Why is this mirror convex, as opposed to flat or concave? What considerations determine its radius of curvature?

Q34.10. A student claims that she can start a fire on a sunny day using just the sun's rays and a concave mirror. How is this done? Is the concept of image relevant? Can she do the same thing with a convex mirror? Explain.

Q34.11. A person looks at his reflection in the concave side of a shiny spoon. Is it right side up or inverted? Does it matter how far his face is from the spoon? What if he looks in the convex side? (Try this yourself!)

Q34.12. In Example 34.4 (Section 34.2), there appears to be an ambiguity for the case $s = 10$ cm as to whether s' is $+\infty$ or $-\infty$ and whether the image is erect or inverted. How is this resolved? Or is it?

Q34.13. Suppose that in the situation of Example 34.7 of Section 34.3 (see Fig. 34.26) a vertical arrow 2.00 m tall is painted on the side of the pool beneath the water line. According to the calculations in the example, this arrow would appear to the person shown in Fig. 34.26 to be 1.50 m long. But the discussion following Eq. (34.13) states that the magnification for a plane refracting surface is $m = 1$, which suggests that the arrow would appear to the person to be 2.00 m long. How can you resolve this apparent contradiction?

Q34.14. The bottom of the passenger side mirror on your car notes, "Objects in mirror are closer than they appear." Is this true? Why?

Q34.15. How could you very quickly make an approximate measurement of the focal length of a converging lens? Could the same method be applied if you wished to use a diverging lens? Explain.

Q34.16. The focal length of a simple lens depends on the color (wavelength) of light passing through it. Why? Is it possible for a lens to have a positive focal length for some colors and negative for others? Explain.

Q34.17. When a converging lens is immersed in water, does its focal length increase or decrease in comparison with the value in air? Explain.

Q34.18. A spherical air bubble in water can function as a lens. Is it a converging or diverging lens? How is its focal length related to its radius?

Q34.19. Can an image formed by one reflecting or refracting surface serve as an object for a second reflection or refraction? Does it matter whether the first image is real or virtual? Explain.

Q34.20. If a piece of photographic film is placed at the location of a real image, the film will record the image. Can this be done with a virtual image? How might one record a virtual image?

Q34.21. According to the discussion in Section 34.2, light rays are reversible. Are the formulas in the table in this chapter's Summary still valid if object and image are interchanged? What does reversibility imply with respect to the *forms* of the various formulas?

Q34.22. You've entered a survival contest that will include building a crude telescope. You are given a large box of lenses. Which two lenses do you pick? How do you quickly identify them?

Q34.23. You can't see clearly underwater with the naked eye, but you *can* if you wear a face mask or goggles (with air between your eyes and the mask or goggles). Why is there a difference? Could you instead wear eyeglasses (with water between your eyes and the eyeglasses) in order to see underwater? If so, should the lenses be converging or diverging? Explain.

Q34.24. You take a lens and mask it so that light can pass through only the bottom half of the lens. How does the image formed by the masked lens compare to the image formed before masking?

Exercises

Section 34.1 Reflection and Refraction at a Plane Surface

34.1. A candle 4.85 cm tall is 39.2 cm to the left of a plane mirror. Where is the image formed by the mirror, and what is the height of this image?

34.2. The image of a tree just covers the length of a plane mirror 4.00 cm tall when the mirror is held 35.0 cm from the eye. The tree is 28.0 m from the mirror. What is its height?

34.3. As shown in Fig. 34.9, mirror 1 uses the image P_2' formed by mirror 2 as an object and forms an image of it. Show that this image is at point P_3' in the figure.

Section 34.2 Reflection at a Spherical Surface

34.4. A concave mirror has a radius of curvature of 34.0 cm. (a) What is its focal length? (b) If the mirror is immersed in water (refractive index 1.33), what is its focal length?

34.5. An object 0.600 cm tall is placed 16.5 cm to the left of the vertex of a concave spherical mirror having a radius of curvature of 22.0 cm. (a) Draw a principal-ray diagram showing the formation of the image. (b) Determine the position, size, orientation, and nature (real or virtual) of the image.

34.6. Repeat Exercise 34.5 for the case in which the mirror is convex.

34.7. The diameter of Mars is 6794 km, and its minimum distance from the earth is 5.58×10^7 km. When Mars is at this distance, find the diameter of the image of Mars formed by a spherical, concave, telescope mirror with a focal length of 1.75 m.

34.8. An object is 24.0 cm from the center of a silvered spherical glass Christmas tree ornament 6.00 cm in diameter. What are the position and magnification of its image?

34.9. A coin is placed next to the convex side of a thin spherical glass shell having a radius of curvature of 18.0 cm. An image of the 1.5-cm-tall coin is formed 6.00 cm behind the glass shell. Where is the coin located? Determine the size, orientation, and nature (real or virtual) of the image.

34.10. You hold a spherical salad bowl 90 cm in front of your face with the bottom of the bowl facing you. The salad bowl is made of polished metal with a 35-cm radius of curvature. (a) Where is the image of your 2.0-cm-tall nose located? (b) What are the image's size, orientation, and nature (real or virtual)?

34.11. (a) Show that Eq. (34.6) can be written as $s' = sf/(s - f)$ and hence that the lateral magnification, given by Eq. (34.7), can be expressed as $m = f/(f - s)$. (b) Use these formulas for s' and m to graph s' as a function of s for the case $f > 0$ (a concave mirror). (c) For what values of s is s' positive, so that the image is real? (d) For what values of s is s' negative, so that the image is virtual? (e) Where is the image if the object is just inside the focal point (s slightly less than f)? (f) Where is the image if the object is at infinity? (g) Where is the image if the object is next to the mirror ($s = 0$)? (h) Graph m as a function of s for the case of a concave mirror. (i) For which values of s is the image erect and larger than the object? (j) For what values of s is the image inverted? (k) For which values of s is the image smaller than the object? (l) What happens to the size of the image when the object is placed at the focal point?

34.12. Using the formulas for s' and m obtained in part (a) of Exercise 34.11, graph s' as a function of s, and graph m as a function of s, for the case $f < 0$ (a convex mirror), so that $f = -|f|$. (a) For which values of s is s' positive? (b) For what values of s is s' negative? (c) Where is the image if the object is at infinity? (d) Where is the image if the object is next to the mirror ($s = 0$)? For which values of s is the image (e) erect; (f) inverted; (g) larger than the object; (h) smaller than the object?

34.13. Dental Mirror. A dentist uses a curved mirror to view teeth on the upper side of the mouth. Suppose she wants an erect image with a magnification of 2.00 when the mirror is 1.25 cm from a tooth. (Treat this problem as though the object and image lie along a straight line.) (a) What kind of mirror (concave or convex) is needed? Use a ray diagram to decide, without performing any calculations. (b) What must be the focal length and radius of curvature of this mirror? (c) Draw a principal-ray diagram to check your answer in part (b).

34.14. A spherical, concave, shaving mirror has a radius of curvature of 32.0 cm. (a) What is the magnification of a person's face when it is 12.0 cm to the left of the vertex of the mirror? (b) Where is the image? Is the image real or virtual? (c) Draw a principal-ray diagram showing the formation of the image.

Section 34.3 Refraction at a Spherical Surface

34.15. A speck of dirt is embedded 3.50 cm below the surface of a sheet of ice $(n = 1.309)$. What is its apparent depth when viewed at normal incidence?

34.16. A tank whose bottom is a mirror is filled with water to a depth of 20.0 cm. A small fish floats motionless 7.0 cm under the surface of the water. (a) What is the apparent depth of the fish when viewed at normal incidence? (b) What is the apparent depth of the image of the fish when viewed at normal incidence?

34.17. A Spherical Fish Bowl. A small tropical fish is at the center of a water-filled, spherical fish bowl 28.0 cm in diameter. (a) Find the apparent position and magnification of the fish to an observer outside the bowl. The effect of the thin walls of the bowl may be ignored. (b) A friend advised the owner of the bowl to keep it out of direct sunlight to avoid blinding the fish, which might swim into the focal point of the parallel rays from the sun. Is the focal point actually within the bowl?

34.18. The left end of a long glass rod 6.00 cm in diameter has a convex hemispherical surface 3.00 cm in radius. The refractive index of the glass is 1.60. Determine the position of the image if an object is placed in air on the axis of the rod at the following distances to the left of the vertex of the curved end: (a) infinitely far, (b) 12.0 cm; (c) 2.00 cm.

34.19. The glass rod of Exercise 34.18 is immersed in oil $(n = 1.45)$. An object placed to the left of the rod on the rod's axis is to be imaged 1.20 m inside the rod. How far from the left end of the rod must the object be located to form the image?

34.20. The left end of a long glass rod 8.00 cm in diameter, with an index of refraction 1.60, is ground and polished to a convex hemispherical surface with a radius of 4.00 cm. An object in the form of an arrow 1.50 mm tall, at right angles to the axis of the rod, is located on the axis 24.0 cm to the left of the vertex of the convex surface. Find the position and height of the image of the arrow formed by paraxial rays incident on the convex surface. Is the image erect or inverted?

34.21. Repeat Exercise 34.20 for the case in which the end of the rod is ground to a *concave* hemispherical surface with radius 4.00 cm.

34.22. The glass rod of Exercise 34.21 is immersed in a liquid. An object 14.0 cm from the vertex of the left end of the rod and on its axis is imaged at a point 9.00 cm from the vertex inside the liquid. What is the index of refraction of the liquid?

Section 34.4 Thin Lenses

34.23. An insect 3.75 mm tall is placed 22.5 cm to the left of a thin planoconvex lens. The left surface of this lens is flat, the right surface has a radius of curvature of magnitude 13.0 cm, and the index of refraction of the lens material is 1.70. (a) Calculate the location and size of the image this lens forms of the insect. Is it real or virtual? Erect or inverted? (b) Repeat part (a) if the lens is reversed.

34.24. A lens forms an image of an object. The object is 16.0 cm from the lens. The image is 12.0 cm from the lens on the same side as the object. (a) What is the focal length of the lens? Is the lens converging or diverging? (b) If the object is 8.50 mm tall, how tall is the image? Is it erect or inverted? (c) Draw a principal-ray diagram.

34.25. A converging meniscus lens (see Fig. 34.32a) with a refractive index of 1.52 has spherical surfaces whose radii are 7.00 cm and 4.00 cm. What is the position of the image if an object is placed 24.0 cm to the left of the lens? What is the magnification?

34.26. A converging lens with a focal length of 90.0 cm forms an image of a 3.20-cm-tall real object that is to the left of the lens. The image is 4.50 cm tall and inverted. Where are the object and image located in relation to the lens? Is the image real or virtual?

34.27. A converging lens forms an image of an 8.00-mm-tall real object. The image is 12.0 cm to the left of the lens, 3.40 cm tall, and erect. What is the focal length of the lens? Where is the object located?

34.28. A photographic slide is to the left of a lens. The lens projects an image of the slide onto a wall 6.00 m to the right of the slide. The image is 80.0 times the size of the slide. (a) How far is the slide from the lens? (b) Is the image erect or inverted? (c) What is the focal length of the lens? (d) Is the lens converging or diverging?

34.29. A double-convex thin lens has surfaces with equal radii of curvature of magnitude 2.50 cm. Looking through this lens, you observe that it forms an image of a very distant tree at a distance of 1.87 cm from the lens. What is the index of refraction of the lens?

34.30. Six lenses in air are shown in Fig. 34.32. Each lens is made of a material with index of refraction $n > 1$. Considering each lens individually, imagine that light enters the lens from the left. Show that the three lenses shown in Fig. 34.32a have *positive* focal lengths and hence are *converging* lenses. In addition, show that the three lenses in Fig. 34.32b have *negative* focal lengths and hence are *diverging* lenses.

34.31. Exercises 34.11 and 34.12 deal with spherical mirrors. (a) Show that the equations for s' and m derived in part (a) of Exercise 34.11 also apply to a thin lens. (b) A concave mirror is used in Exercise 34.11. Repeat these exercises for a converging lens. Are there any differences in the results when the mirror is replaced by a lens? Explain. (c) A convex mirror is used in Exercise 34.12. Repeat these exercises for a diverging lens. Are there any differences in the results when the mirror is replaced by a lens? Explain.

34.32. A converging lens with a focal length of 12.0 cm forms a virtual image 8.00 mm tall, 17.0 cm to the right of the lens. Determine the position and size of the object. Is the image erect or inverted? Are the object and image on the same side or opposite sides of the lens? Draw a principal-ray diagram for this situation.

34.33. Repeat Exercise 34.32 for the case in which the lens is diverging, with a focal length of -48.0 cm.

34.34. An object is 16.0 cm to the left of a lens. The lens forms an image 36.0 cm to the right of the lens. (a) What is the focal length of the lens? Is the lens converging or diverging? (b) If the object is 8.00 mm tall, how tall is the image? Is it erect or inverted? (c) Draw a principal-ray diagram.

Section 34.5 Cameras

34.35. A camera lens has a focal length of 200 mm. How far from the lens should the subject for the photo be if the lens is 20.4 cm from the film?

34.36. When a camera is focused, the lens is moved away from or toward the film. If you take a picture of your friend, who is standing 3.90 m from the lens, using a camera with a lens with a 85-mm focal length, how far from the film is the lens? Will the whole image of your friend, who is 175 cm tall, fit on film that is 24×36 mm?

34.37. Figure 34.41 shows photographs of the same scene taken with the same camera with lenses of different focal length. If the object is 200 m from the lens, what is the magnitude of the lateral magnification for a lens of focal length (a) 28 mm; (b) 105 mm; (c) 300 mm?

34.38. A photographer takes a photograph of a Boeing 747 airliner (length 70.7 m) when it is flying directly overhead at an altitude of 9.50 km. The lens has a focal length of 5.00 m. How long is the image of the airliner on the film?

34.39. Choosing a Camera Lens. The picture size on ordinary 35-mm camera film is 24 mm $\times$ 36 mm. Focal lengths of lenses available for 35-mm cameras typically include 28, 35, 50 (the "normal" lens), 85, 100, 135, 200, and 300 mm, among others. Which of these lenses should be used to photograph the following objects, assuming that the object is to fill most of the picture area? (a) a building 240 m tall and 160 m wide at a distance of 600 m, and (b) a mobile home 9.6 m in length at a distance of 40.0 m.

34.40. Zoom Lens. Consider the simple model of the zoom lens shown in Fig. 34.43a. The converging lens has focal length $f_1 = 12$ cm, and the diverging lens has focal length $f_2 = -12$ cm. The lenses are separated by 4 cm as shown in Fig. 34.43a. (a) For a distant object, where is the image of the converging lens? (b) The image of the converging lens serves as the object for the diverging lens. What is the object distance for the diverging lens? (c) Where is the final image? Compare your answer to Fig. 34.43a. (d) Repeat parts (a), (b), and (c) for the situation shown in Fig. 34.43b, in which the lenses are separated by 8 cm.

34.41. A camera lens has a focal length of 180.0 mm and an aperture diameter of 16.36 mm. (a) What is the f-number of the lens? (b) If the correct exposure of a certain scene is $\frac{1}{30}$ s at $f/11$, what is the correct exposure at $f/2.8$?

34.42. Recall that the intensity of light reaching film in a camera is proportional to the effective area of the lens. Camera A has a lens with an aperture diameter of 8.00 mm. It photographs an object using the correct exposure time of $\frac{1}{30}$ s. What exposure time should be used with camera B in photographing the same object with the same film if this camera has a lens with an aperture diameter of 23.1 mm?

34.43. Photography. A 35-mm camera has a standard lens with focal length 50 mm and can focus on objects between 45 cm and infinity. (a) Is the lens for such a camera a concave or a convex lens? (b) The camera is focused by rotating the lens, which moves it on the camera body and changes its distance from the film. In what range of distances between the lens and the film plane must the lens move to focus properly over the 45 cm to infinity range?

34.44. You wish to project the image of a slide on a screen 9.00 m from the lens of a slide projector. (a) If the slide is placed 15.0 cm from the lens, what focal length lens is required? (b) If the dimensions of the picture on a 35-mm color slide are 24 mm $\times$ 36 mm, what is the minimum size of the projector screen required to accommodate the image?

Section 34.6 The Eye

34.45. (a) Where is the near point of an eye for which a contact lens with a power of +2.75 diopters is prescribed? (b) Where is the far point of an eye for which a contact lens with a power of -1.30 diopters is prescribed for distant vision?

34.46. Curvature of the Cornea. In a simplified model of the human eye, the aqueous and vitreous humors and the lens all have a refractive index of 1.40, and all the refraction occurs at the cornea, whose vertex is 2.60 cm from the retina. What should be the radius of curvature of the cornea such that the image of an object 40.0 cm from the cornea's vertex is focused on the retina?

34.47. Corrective Lenses. Determine the power of the corrective contact lenses required by (a) a hyperopic eye whose near point is at 60.0 cm and (b) a myopic eye whose far point is at 60.0 cm.

Section 34.7 The Magnifier

34.48. A thin lens with a focal length of 6.00 cm is used as a simple magnifier. (a) What angular magnification is obtainable with the lens if the object is at the focal point? (b) When an object is examined through the lens, how close can it be brought to the lens? Assume that the image viewed by the eye is at the near point, 25.0 cm from the eye, and that the lens is very close to the eye.

34.49. The focal length of a simple magnifier is 8.00 cm. Assume the magnifier is a thin lens placed very close to the eye. (a) How far in front of the magnifier should an object be placed if the image is formed at the observer's near point, 25.0 cm in front of her eye? (b) If the object is 1.00 mm high, what is the height of its image formed by the magnifier?

34.50. You want to view an insect 2.00 mm in length through a magnifier. If the insect is to be at the focal point of the magnifier, what focal length will give the image of the insect an angular size of 0.025 radian?

34.51. You are examining an ant with a magnifying lens that has focal length 5.00 cm. If the image of the ant appears 25.0 cm from the lens, how far is the ant from the lens? On which side of the lens is the image located?

Section 34.8 Microscopes and Telescopes

34.52. Resolution of a Microscope. The image formed by a microscope objective with a focal length of 5.00 mm is 160 mm from its second focal point. The eyepiece has a focal length of 26.0 mm. (a) What is the angular magnification of the microscope? (b) The unaided eye can distinguish two points at its near point as separate if they are about 0.10 mm apart. What is the minimum separation between two points that can be observed (or resolved) through this microscope?

34.53. The focal length of the eyepiece of a certain microscope is 18.0 mm. The focal length of the objective is 8.00 mm. The distance between objective and eyepiece is 19.7 cm. The final image formed by the eyepiece is at infinity. Treat all lenses as thin. (a) What is the distance from the objective to the object being viewed? (b) What is the magnitude of the linear magnification produced by the objective? (c) What is the overall angular magnification of the microscope?

34.54. A certain microscope is provided with objectives that have focal lengths of 16 mm, 4 mm, and 1.9 mm and with eyepieces that have angular magnifications of 5$\times$ and 10$\times$. Each objective forms an image 120 mm beyond its second focal point. Determine (a) the largest overall angular magnification obtainable and (b) the least overall angular magnification obtainable.

34.55. The Yerkes refracting telescope of the University of Chicago has an objective 1.02 m in diameter with an f-number of 19.0. (This is the largest-diameter refracting telescope in the world.) What is its focal length?

34.56. The eyepiece of a refracting telescope (see Fig. 34.53) has a focal length of 9.00 cm. The distance between objective and eyepiece is 1.80 m, and the final image is at infinity. What is the angular magnification of the telescope?

34.57. A telescope is constructed from two lenses with focal lengths of 95.0 cm and 15.0 cm, the 95.0-cm lens being used as the objective. Both the object being viewed and the final image are at infinity. (a) Find the angular magnification for the telescope. (b) Find the height of the image formed by the objective of a building 60.0 m tall, 3.00 km away. (c) What is the angular size of the final image as viewed by an eye very close to the eyepiece?

34.58. Saturn is viewed through the Lick Observatory refracting telescope (objective focal length 18 m). If the diameter of the image of Saturn produced by the objective is 1.7 mm, what angle does Saturn subtend from when viewed from earth?

34.59. A reflecting telescope (Fig. 34.55a) is to be made by using a spherical mirror with a radius of curvature of 1.30 m and an eyepiece with a focal length of 1.10 cm. The final image is at infinity. (a) What should the distance between the eyepiece and the mirror vertex be if the object is taken to be at infinity? (b) What will the angular magnification be?

Figure 34.55 Exercises 34.59 and 34.60 and Problem 34.112.

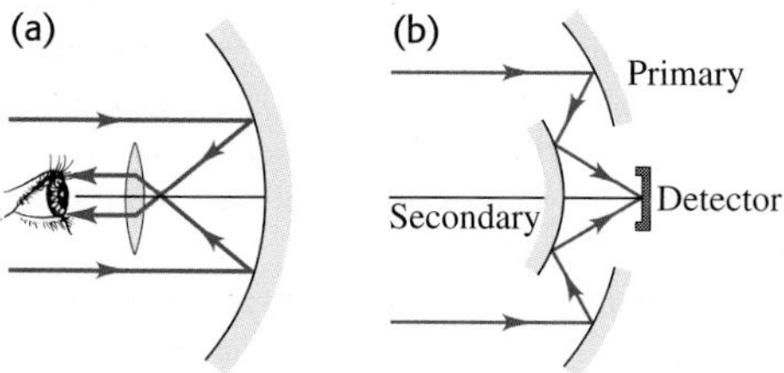

34.60. A Cassegrain telescope is a reflecting telescope that uses two mirrors, the secondary mirror focusing the image through a hole in the primary mirror (similar to that shown in Fig. 34.55b). You wish to focus the image of a distant galaxy onto the detector shown in the figure. If the primary mirror has a focal length of 2.5 m, the secondary mirror has a focal length of -1.5 m and the distance from the vertex of the primary mirror to the detector is 15 cm. What should be the distance between the vertices of the two mirrors?

Problems

34.61. If you run away from a plane mirror at 2.40 m/s, at what speed does your image move away from you?

34.62. An object is placed between two plane mirrors arranged at right angles to each other at a distance d_1 from the surface of one mirror and a distance d_2 from the other. (a) How many images are formed? Show the location of the images in a diagram. (b) Draw the paths of rays from the object to the eye of an observer.

34.63. What is the size of the smallest vertical plane mirror in which a woman of height h can see her full-length image?

34.64. A light bulb is 4.00 m from a wall. You are to use a concave mirror to project an image of the bulb on the wall, with the image 2.25 times the size of the object. How far should the mirror be from the wall? What should its radius of curvature be?

34.65. A concave mirror is to form an image of the filament of a headlight lamp on a screen 8.00 m from the mirror. The filament is 6.00 mm tall, and the image is to be 36.0 cm tall. (a) How far in front of the vertex of the mirror should the filament be placed? (b) What should be the radius of curvature of the mirror?

34.66. Rear-View Mirror. A mirror on the passenger side of your car is convex and has a radius of curvature with magnitude 18.0 cm. (a) Another car is seen in this side mirror and is 13.0 m behind the mirror. If this car is 1.5 m tall, what is the height of the image? (b) The mirror has a warning attached that objects viewed in it are closer than they appear. Why is this so?

34.67. Suppose the lamp filament shown in Example 34.1 (Section 34.2) is moved to a position 8.0 cm in front of the mirror. (a) Where is the image located now? Is it real or virtual? (b) What is the height of the image? Is it erect or inverted? (c) In Example 34.1, the filament is 10.0 cm in front of the mirror, and an image of the filament is formed on a wall 3.00 m from the mirror. If the filament is 8.0 cm from the mirror, can a wall be placed so that an image is formed on it? If so, where should the wall be placed? If not, why not?

34.68. Where must you place an object in front of a concave mirror with radius R so that the image is erect and $2\frac{1}{2}$ times the size of the object? Where is the image?

34.69. Virtual Object. If the light incident from the left onto a convex mirror does not diverge from an object point but instead converges toward a point at a (negative) distance s to the right of the mirror, this point is called a *virtual object.* (a) For a convex mirror having a radius of curvature of 24.0 cm, for what range of virtual-object positions is a real image formed? (b) What is the orientation of this real image? (c) Draw a principal-ray diagram showing the formation of such an image.

34.70. A layer of benzene ($n = 1.50$) 2.60 cm deep floats on water ($n = 1.33$) that is 6.50 cm deep. What is the apparent distance from the upper benzene surface to the bottom of the water layer when it is viewed at normal incidence?

34.71. Sketch the various possible thin lenses that can be obtained by combining two surfaces whose radii of curvature are 4.00 cm and 8.00 cm in absolute magnitude. Which are converging and which are diverging? Find the focal length of each if the surfaces are made of glass with index of refraction 1.60.

34.72. Figure 34.56 shows a small plant near a thin lens. The ray shown is one of the principal rays for the lens. Each square is 2.0 cm along the horizontal direction, but the vertical direction is not to the same scale. Use information from the diagram to answer the following questions: (a) Using only the ray shown, decide what type of lens (converging or diverging) this is. (b) What is the focal length of the lens? (c) Locate the image by drawing the other two principal rays. (d) Calculate where the image should be, and compare this result with the graphical solution in part (c).

Figure 34.56 Problem 34.72.

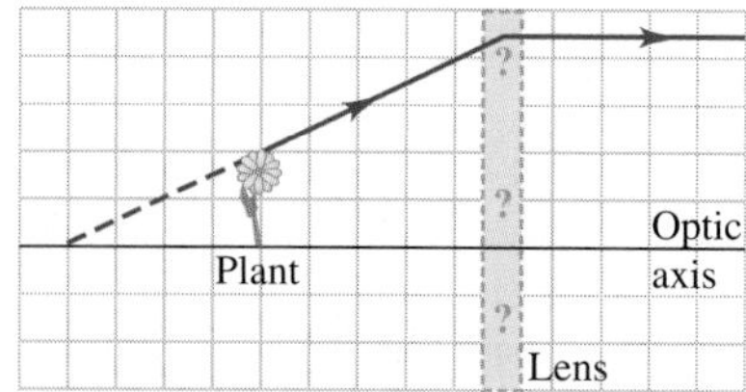

34.73. You are in your car driving on a highway at 25 m/s when you glance in the passenger side mirror (a convex mirror with radius of curvature 150 cm) and notice a truck approaching. If the image of the truck is approaching the vertex of the mirror at a speed of 1.5 m/s when the truck is 2.0 m away, what is the speed of the truck relative to the highway?

34.74. A microscope is focused on the upper surface of a glass plate. A second plate is then placed over the first. To focus on the bottom surface of the second plate, the microscope must be raised 0.780 mm. To focus on the upper surface, it must be raised another 2.50 mm. Find the index of refraction of the second plate.

34.75. Three-Dimensional Image. The *longitudinal* magnification is defined as $m' = ds'/ds$. It relates the longitudinal dimension of a small object to the longitudinal dimension of its image. (a) Show that for a spherical mirror, $m' = -m^2$. What is the significance of the fact that m' is *always* negative? (b) A wire frame in the form of a small cube 1.00 mm on a side is placed with its center on the axis of a concave mirror with radius of curvature 150.0 cm. The sides of the cube are all either parallel or perpendicular to the axis. The cube face toward the mirror is 200.0 cm to the left of the mirror vertex. Find (i) the location of the image of this face and of the opposite face of the cube; (ii) the lateral and longitudinal magnifications; (iii) the shape and dimensions of each of the six faces of the image.

34.76. Refer to Problem 34.75. Show that the longitudinal magnification m' for refraction at a spherical surface is given by

$$m' = -\frac{n_b}{n_a}m^2$$

34.77. Pinhole Camera. A pinhole camera is just a rectangular box with a tiny hole in one face. The film is on the face opposite this hole, and that is where the image is formed. The camera forms an image *without* a lens. (a) Make a clear ray diagram to show how a pinhole camera can form an image on the film without using a lens. (*Hint:* Put an object outside the hole, and then draw rays passing through the hole to the opposite side of the box.) (b) A certain pinhole camera is a box that is 25 cm square and 20.0 cm deep, with the hole in the middle of one of the 25 cm × 25 cm faces. If this camera is used to photograph a fierce chicken that is 18 cm high and 1.5 m in front of the camera, how large is the image of this bird on the film? What is the magnification of this camera?

34.78. A Glass Rod. Both ends of a glass rod with index of refraction 1.60 are ground and polished to convex hemispherical surfaces. The radius of curvature at the left end is 6.00 cm, and the radius of curvature at the right end is 12.0 cm. The length of the rod between vertices is 40.0 cm. The object for the surface at the left end is an arrow that lies 23.0 cm to the left of the vertex of this surface. The arrow is 1.50 mm tall and at right angles to the axis. (a) What constitutes the object for the surface at the right end of the rod? (b) What is the object distance for this surface? (c) Is the object for this surface real or virtual? (*Hint:* See Problem 34.69.) (d) What is the position of the final image? (e) Is the final image real or virtual? Is it erect or inverted with respect to the original object? (f) What is the height of the final image?

34.79. The rod in Problem 34.78 is shortened to a distance of 25.0 cm between its vertices; the curvatures of its ends remain the same. As in Problem 34.78, the object for the surface at the left end is an arrow that lies 23.0 cm to the left of the vertex of this surface. The arrow is 1.50 mm tall and at right angles to the axis. (a) What is the object distance for the surface at the right end of the rod? (b) Is the object for this surface real or virtual? (c) What is the position of the final image? (d) Is the final image real or virtual? Is it erect or inverted with respect to the original object? (e) What is the height of the final image?

34.80. Figure 34.57 shows an object and its image formed by a thin lens. (a) What is the focal length of the lens, and what type of lens (converging or diverging) is it? (b) What is the height of the image? Is it real or virtual?

Figure **34.57** Problem 34.80

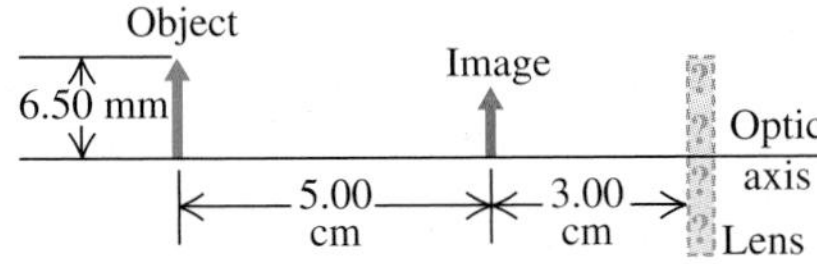

34.81. Figure 34.58 shows an object and its image formed by a thin lens. (a) What is the focal length of the lens, and what type of lens (converging or diverging) is it? (b) What is the height of the image? Is it real or virtual?

Figure **34.58** Problem 34.81

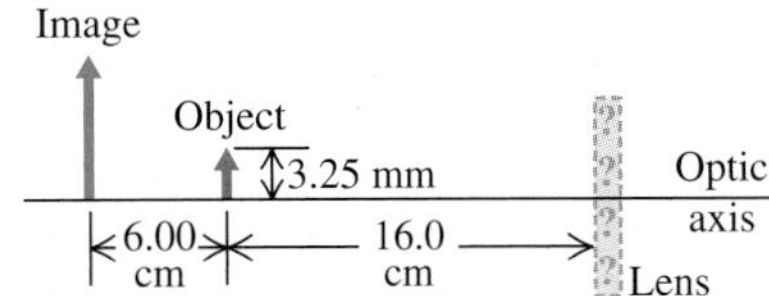

34.82. A transparent rod 30.0 cm long is cut flat at one end and rounded to a hemispherical surface of radius 10.0 cm at the other end. A small object is embedded within the rod along its axis and halfway between its ends, 15.0 cm from the flat end and 15.0 cm from the vertex of the curved end. When viewed from the flat end of the rod, the apparent depth of the object is 9.50 cm from the flat end. What is its apparent depth when viewed from the curved end?

34.83. A solid glass hemisphere of radius 12.0 cm and index of refraction $n = 1.50$ is placed with its flat face downward on a table. A parallel beam of light with a circular cross section 3.80 mm in diameter travels straight down and enters the hemisphere at the center of its curved surface. (a) What is the diameter of the circle of light formed on the table? (b) How does your result depend on the radius of the hemisphere?

34.84. A thick-walled wine goblet sitting on a table can be considered to be a hollow glass sphere with an outer radius of 4.00 cm and an inner radius of 3.40 cm. The index of refraction of the goblet glass is 1.50. (a) A beam of parallel light rays enters the side of the empty goblet along a horizontal radius. Where, if anywhere, will an image be formed? (b) The goblet is filled with white wine $(n = 1.37)$. Where is the image formed?

34.85. Focus of the Eye. The cornea of the eye has a radius of curvature of approximately 0.50 cm, and the aqueous humor behind it has an index of refraction of 1.35. The thickness of the cornea itself is small enough that we shall neglect it. The depth of a typical human eye is around 25 mm. (a) What would have to be the radius of curvature of the cornea so that it alone would focus the image of a distant mountain on the retina, which is at the back of the eye opposite the cornea? (b) If the cornea focused the mountain correctly on the retina as described in part (a), would it also focus the text from a computer screen on the retina if that screen were 25 cm in front of the eye? If not, where would it focus that text: in front of or behind the retina? (c) Given that the cornea has a radius of curvature of about 5.0 mm, where does it actually focus the mountain? Is this in front of or behind the retina? Does this help you see why the eye needs help from a lens to complete the task of focusing?

34.86. A transparent rod 50.0 cm long and with a refractive index of 1.60 is cut flat at the right end and rounded to a hemispherical surface with a 15.0-cm radius at the left end. An object is placed on the axis of the rod 12.0 cm to the left of the vertex of the hemispherical end. (a) What is the position of the final image? (b) What is its magnification?

34.87. What should be the index of refraction of a transparent sphere in order for paraxial rays from an infinitely distant object to be brought to a focus at the vertex of the surface opposite the point of incidence?

34.88. A glass rod with a refractive index of 1.55 is ground and polished at both ends to hemispherical surfaces with radii of 6.00 cm. When an object is placed on the axis of the rod, 25.0 cm to the left of the left-hand end, the final image is formed 65.0 cm to the right of the right-hand end. What is the length of the rod measured between the vertices of the two hemispherical surfaces?

34.89. Two thin lenses with focal lengths of magnitude 15.0 cm, the first diverging and the second converging, are placed 12.00 cm apart. An object 4.00 mm tall is placed 5.00 cm to the left of the first (diverging) lens. (a) Where is the image formed by the first lens located? (b) How far from the object is the final image formed? (c) Is the final image real or virtual? (d) What is the height of the final image? Is the final image erect or inverted?

34.90. The radii of curvature of the surfaces of a thin converging meniscus lens are $R_1 = +12.0$ cm and $R_2 = +28.0$ cm. The index of refraction is 1.60. (a) Compute the position and size of the image of an object in the form of an arrow 5.00 mm tall, perpendicular to the lens axis, 45.0 cm to the left of the lens. (b) A second converging lens with the same focal length is placed 3.15 m to the right of the first. Find the position and size of the final image. Is the final image erect or inverted with respect to the original object? (c) Repeat part (b) except with the second lens 45.0 cm to the right of the first.

34.91. An object to the left of a lens is imaged by the lens on a screen 30.0 cm to the right of the lens. When the lens is moved 4.00 cm to the right, the screen must be moved 4.00 cm to the left to refocus the image. Determine the focal length of the lens.

34.92. For refraction at a spherical surface, the first focal length f is defined as the value of s corresponding to $s' = \infty$, as shown in Fig. 34.59a. The second focal length f' is defined as the value of s' when $s = \infty$, as shown in Fig. 34.59b. (a) Prove that $n_a/n_b = f/f'$. (b) Prove that the general relationship between object and image distance is

$$\frac{f}{s} + \frac{f'}{s'} = 1$$

Figure **34.59** Problem 34.92.

(a)

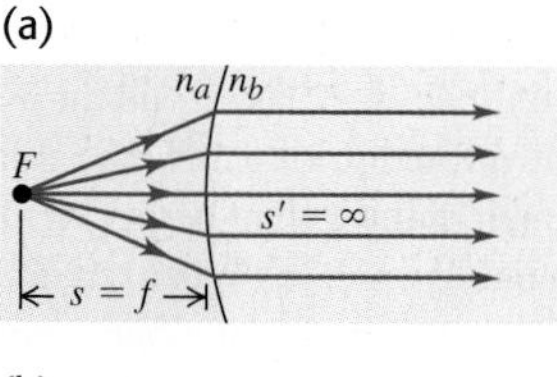

(b)

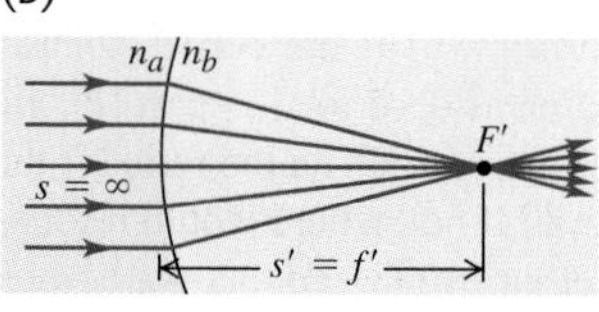

34.93. A convex mirror and a concave mirror are placed on the same optic axis, separated by a distance $L = 0.600$ m. The radius of curvature of each mirror has a magnitude of 0.360 m. A light source is located a distance x from the concave mirror, as shown in Fig. 34.60. (a) What distance x will result in the rays from the source returning to the source after reflecting first from the convex mirror and then from the concave mirror? (b) Repeat part (a), but now let the rays reflect first from the concave mirror and then from the convex one.

Figure **34.60** Problem 34.93.

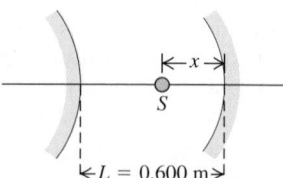

34.94. As shown in Fig. 34.61 the candle is at the center of curvature of the concave mirror, whose focal length is 10.0 cm. The converging lens has a focal length of 32.0 cm and is 85.0 cm to the right of the candle. The candle is viewed looking through the lens from the right. The lens forms two images of the candle. The first is formed by light passing directly through the lens. The second image is formed from the light that goes from the candle to the mirror, is reflected, and then passes through the lens. (a) For each of these two images, draw a principal-ray diagram that locates the image. (b) For each image, answer the following questions: (i) Where is the image? (ii) Is the image real or virtual? (iii) Is the image erect or inverted with respect to the original object?

Figure **34.61** Problem 34.94.

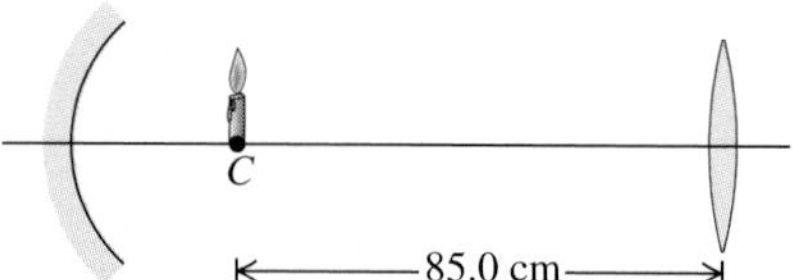

34.95. One end of a long glass rod is ground to a convex hemispherical shape. This glass has an index of refraction of 1.55. When a small leaf is placed 20.0 cm in front of the center of the hemisphere along the optic axis, an image is formed inside the glass 9.12 cm from the spherical surface. Where would the image be formed if the glass were now immersed in water (refractive index 1.33) but nothing else were changed?

34.96. Two Lenses in Contact. (a) Prove that when two thin lenses with focal lengths f_1 and f_2 are placed *in contact,* the focal length f of the combination is given by the relationship

$$\frac{1}{f} = \frac{1}{f_1} + \frac{1}{f_2}$$

(b) A converging meniscus lens (see Fig. 34.32a) has an index of refraction of 1.55 and radii of curvature for its surfaces of 4.50 cm and 9.00 cm. The concave surface is placed upward and filled with carbon tetrachloride (CCl_4), which has $n = 1.46$. What is the focal length of the CCl_4–glass combination?

34.97. Rays from a lens are converging toward a point image P located to the right of the lens. What thickness t of glass with index of refraction 1.60 must be interposed between the lens and P for the image to be formed at P', located 0.30 cm to the right of P? The locations of the piece of glass and of points P and P' are shown in Fig. 34.62.

Figure **34.62** Problem 34.97.

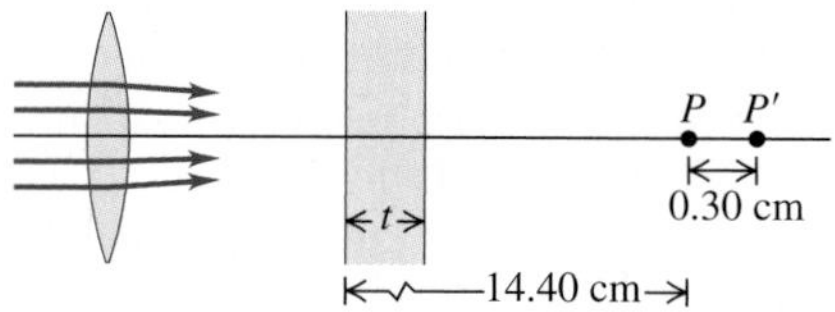

34.98. A Lens in a Liquid. A lens obeys Snell's law, bending light rays at each surface an amount determined by the index of refraction of the lens and the index of the medium in which the lens is located. (a) Equation (34.19) assumes that the lens is surrounded by air. Consider instead a thin lens immersed in a liquid with refractive index n_{liq}. Prove that the focal length f' is then given by Eq. (34.19) with n replaced by n/n_{liq}. (b) A thin lens with index n has focal length f in vacuum. Use the result of part (a) to show that when this lens is immersed in a liquid of index n_{liq}, it will have a new focal length given by

$$f' = \left[\frac{n_{liq}(n-1)}{n - n_{liq}}\right] f$$

34.99. When an object is placed at the proper distance to the left of a converging lens, the image is focused on a screen 30.0 cm to the right of the lens. A diverging lens is now placed 15.0 cm to the right of the converging lens, and it is found that the screen must be moved 19.2 cm farther to the right to obtain a sharp image. What is the focal length of the diverging lens?

34.100. A convex spherical mirror with a focal length of magnitude 24.0 cm is placed 20.0 cm to the left of a plane mirror. An object 0.250 cm tall is placed midway between the surface of the plane mirror and the vertex of the spherical mirror. The spherical mirror forms multiple images of the object. Where are the two images of the object formed by the spherical mirror that are closest to the spherical mirror, and how tall is each image?

34.101. A glass plate 3.50 cm thick, with an index of refraction of 1.55 and plane parallel faces, is held with its faces horizontal and its lower face 6.00 cm above a printed page. Find the position of the image of the page formed by rays making a small angle with the normal to the plate.

34.102. A symmetric, double-convex, thin lens made of glass with index of refraction 1.52 has a focal length in air of 40.0 cm. The lens is sealed into an opening in the left-hand end of a tank filled with water. At the right-hand end of the tank, opposite the lens, is a plane mirror 90.0 cm from the lens. The index of refraction of the water is $\frac{4}{3}$. (a) Find the position of the image formed by the lens–water–mirror system of a small object outside the tank on the lens axis and 70.0 cm to the left of the lens. (b) Is the image real or virtual? (c) Is it erect or inverted? (d) If the object has a height of 4.00 mm, what is the height of the image?

34.103. You have a camera with a 35.0-mm focal length lens and 36.0-mm-wide film. You wish to take a picture of a 12.0-m-long sailboat but find that the image of the boat fills only $\frac{1}{4}$ of the width of the film. (a) How far are you from the boat? (b) How much closer must the boat be to you for its image to fill the width of the film?

34.104. An object is placed 18.0 cm from a screen. (a) At what two points between object and screen may a converging lens with a 3.00-cm focal length be placed to obtain an image on the screen? (b) What is the magnification of the image for each position of the lens?

34.105. Three thin lenses, each with a focal length of 40.0 cm, are aligned on a common axis; adjacent lenses are separated by 52.0 cm. Find the position of the image of a small object on the axis, 80.0 cm to the left of the first lens.

34.106. A camera with a 90-mm-focal-length lens is focused on an object 1.30 m from the lens. To refocus on an object 6.50 m from the lens, by how much must the distance between the lens and the film be changed? To refocus on the more distant object, is the lens moved toward or away from the film?

34.107. The derivation of the expression for angular magnification, Eq. (34.22), assumed a near point of 25 cm. In fact, the near point changes with age as shown in Table 34.1. In order to achieve an angular magnification of 2.0×, what focal length should be used by a person of (a) age 10; (b) age 30; (c) age 60? (d) If the lens that gives $M = 2.0$ for a 10-year-old is used by a 60-year-old, what angular magnification will the older viewer obtain? (e) Does your answer in part (d) mean that older viewers are able to see more highly magnified images than younger viewers? Explain.

34.108. Angular Magnification. In deriving Eq. (34.22) for the angular magnification of a magnifier, we assumed that the object is placed at the focal point of the magnifier so that the virtual image is formed at infinity. Suppose instead that the object is placed so that the virtual image appears at an average viewer's near point of 25 cm, the closest point at which the viewer can bring an object into focus. (a) Where should the object be placed to achieve this? Give your answer in terms of the magnifier focal length f. (b) What angle θ' will an object of height y subtend at the position found in part (a)? (c) Find the angular magnification M with the object at the position found in part (a). The angle θ is the same as in Fig. 34.51a, since it refers to viewing the object *without* the magnifier. (d) For a convex lens with $f = +10.0$ cm, what is the value of M with the object at the position found in part (a)? How many times greater is M in this case than in the case where the image is formed at infinity? (e) In the description of a compound microscope in Section 34.8, it is stated that in a properly designed instrument, the real image formed by the objective lies *just inside* the first focal point F_1' of the eyepiece. What advantages are gained by having the image formed by the objective be just inside F_1', as opposed to precisely at F_1'? What happens if the image formed by the objective is *just outside* F_1'?

34.109. In one form of cataract surgery the person's natural lens, which has become cloudy, is replaced by an artificial lens. The refracting properties of the replacement lens can be chosen so that the person's eye focuses on distant objects. But there is no accommodation, and glasses or contact lenses are needed for close vision. What is the power, in diopters, of the corrective contact lenses that will enable a person who has had such surgery to focus on the page of a book at a distance of 24 cm?

34.110. A Nearsighted Eye. A certain very nearsighted person cannot focus on anything farther than 36.0 cm from the eye. Consider the simplified model of the eye described in Exercise 34.46. If the radius of curvature of the cornea is 0.75 cm when the eye is focusing on an object 36.0 cm from the cornea vertex and the indexes of refraction are as described in Exercise 34.46, what is the distance from the cornea vertex to the retina? What does this tell you about the shape of the nearsighted eye?

34.111. Focal Length of a Zoom Lens. Figure 34.63 shows a simple version of a zoom lens. The converging lens has focal length f_1, and the diverging lens has focal length $f_2 = -|f_2|$. The two lenses are separated by a variable distance d that is always less than f_1. Also, the magnitude of the focal length of the diverging lens satisfies the inequality $|f_2| > (f_1 - d)$. To determine the effective focal length of the combination lens, consider a bundle of parallel rays of radius r_0 entering the converging lens. (a) Show that the radius of the ray bundle decreases to $r_0' = r_0(f_1 - d)/f_1$ at the point that it enters the diverging lens. (b) Show that the final image I' is formed a distance $s_2' = |f_2|(f_1 - d)/(|f_2| - f_1 + d)$ to the right of the diverging lens. (c) If the rays that emerge from the diverging lens and reach the final image point are extended backward to the left of the diverging lens, they will eventually expand to the original radius r_0 at some point Q. The distance from the final image I' to the point Q is the *effective focal length* f of the lens combination; if the combination were replaced by a single lens of focal length f placed at Q, parallel rays would still be

Figure **34.63** Problem 34.111.

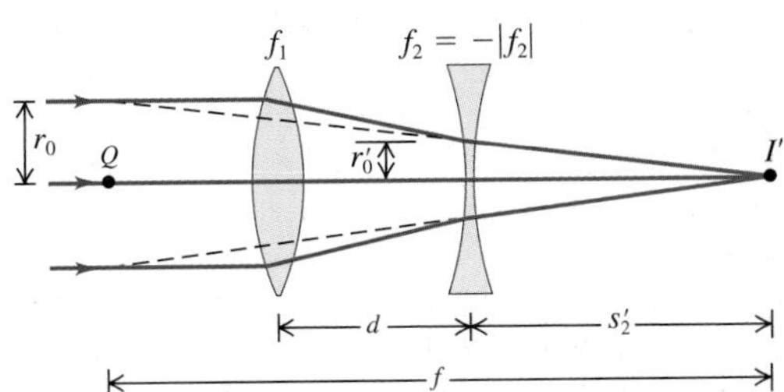

brought to a focus at I'. Show that the effective focal length is given by $f = f_1|f_2|/(|f_2| - f_1 + d)$. (d) If $f_1 = 12.0$ cm, $f_2 = -18.0$ cm, and the separation d is adjustable between 0 and 4.0 cm, find the maximum and minimum focal lengths of the combination. What value of d gives $f = 30.0$ cm?

34.112. A certain reflecting telescope, constructed as shown in Fig. 34.55a, has a spherical mirror with a radius of curvature of 96.0 cm and an eyepiece with a focal length of 1.20 cm. If the angular magnification has a magnitude of 36 and the object is at infinity, find the position of the eyepiece and the position and nature (real or virtual) of the final image. (*Note:* $|M|$ is *not* equal to $|f_1/f_2|$, so the image formed by the eyepiece is *not* at infinity.)

34.113. A microscope with an objective of focal length 8.00 mm and an eyepiece of focal length 7.50 cm is used to project an image on a screen 2.00 m from the eyepiece. Let the image distance of the objective be 18.0 cm. (a) What is the lateral magnification of the image? (b) What is the distance between the objective and the eyepiece?

34.114. The Galilean Telescope. Figure 34.64 is a diagram of a *Galilean telescope,* or *opera glass,* with both the object and its final image at infinity. The image I serves as a virtual object for the eyepiece. The final image is virtual and erect. (a) Prove that the angular magnification is $M = -f_1/f_2$. (b) A Galilean telescope is to be constructed with the same objective lens as in Exercise 34.57. What focal length should the eyepiece have if this telescope is to have the same magnitude of angular magnification as the one in Exercise 34.57? (c) Compare the lengths of the telescopes.

Figure 34.64 Problem 34.114.

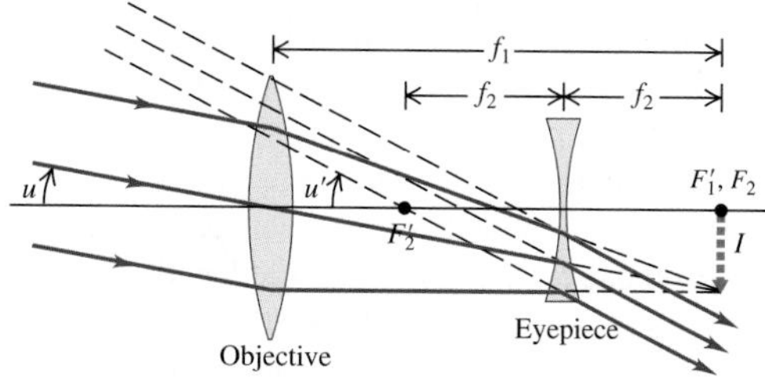

Challenge Problems

34.115. An Object at an Angle. A 16.0-cm-long pencil is placed at a 45.0° angle, with its center 15.0 cm above the optic axis and 45.0 cm from a lens with a 20.0-cm focal length as shown in Fig. 34.65. (Note that the figure is not drawn to scale.) Assume that the diameter of the lens is large enough for the paraxial approximation to be valid. (a) Where is the image of the pencil? (Give the location of the images of the points A, B, and C on the object, which are located at the eraser, point, and center of the pencil, respectively.) (b) What is the length of the image (that is, the distance between the images of points A and B)? (c) Show the orientation of the image in a sketch.

Figure 34.65 Challenge Problem 34.115.

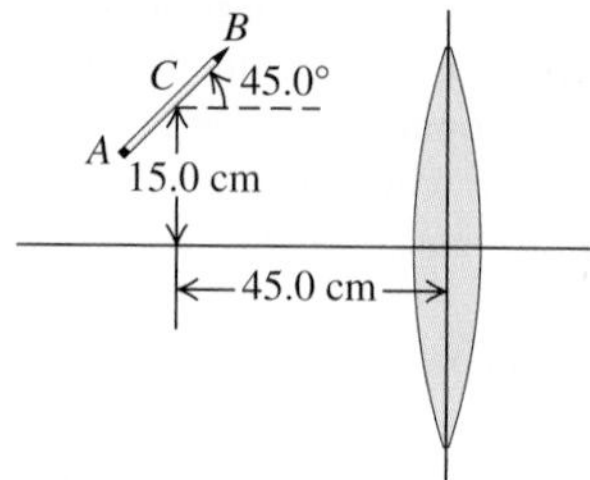

34.116. *Spherical aberration* is a blurring of the image formed by a spherical mirror. It occurs because parallel rays striking the mirror far from the optic axis are focused at a different point than are rays near the axis. This problem is usually minimized by using only the center of a spherical mirror. (a) Show that for a spherical concave mirror, the focus moves toward the mirror as the parallel rays move toward the outer edge of the mirror. (*Hint:* Derive an analytic expression for the distance from the vertex to the focus of the ray for a particular parallel ray. This expression should be in terms of (i) the radius of curvature R of the mirror and (ii) the angle θ between the incident ray and a line connecting the center of curvature of the mirror with the point where the ray strikes the mirror.) (b) What value of θ produces a 2% change in the location of the focus, compared to the location for θ very close to zero?

34.117. (a) For a lens with focal length f, find the smallest distance possible between the object and its real image. (b) Graph the distance between the object and the real image as a function of the distance of the object from the lens. Does your graph agree with the result you found in part (a)?

34.118. Two mirrors are placed together as shown in Fig. 34.66. (a) Show that a point source in front of these mirrors and its two images lie on a circle. (b) Find the center of the circle. (c) In a diagram, show where an observer should stand so as to be able to see both images.

Figure 34.66 Challenge Problem 34.118.

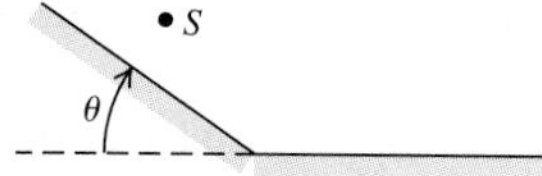

34.119. People with normal vision cannot focus their eyes underwater if they aren't wearing a face mask or goggles and there is water in contact with their eyes (see Discussion Question Q34.23). (a) Why not? (b) With the simplified model of the eye described in Exercise 34.46, what corrective lens (specified by focal length as measured in air) would be needed to enable a person underwater to focus an infinitely distant object? (Be careful—the focal length of a lens underwater is *not* the same as in air! See Problem 34.98. Assume that the corrective lens has a refractive index of 1.62 and that the lens is used in eyeglasses, not goggles, so there is water on both sides of the lens. Assume that the eyeglasses are 2.00 cm in front of the eye.)

INTERFERENCE

35

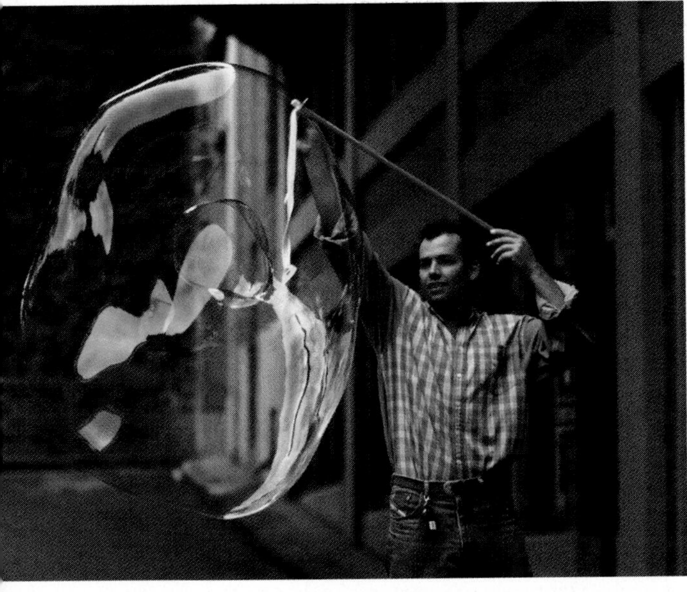

? Soapy water is colorless, but when blown into bubbles it shows vibrant colors. How does the thickness of the bubble walls determine the particular colors that appear?

LEARNING GOALS

By studying this chapter, you will learn:

- What happens when two waves combine, or interfere, in space.
- How to understand the interference pattern formed by the interference of two coherent light waves.
- How to calculate the intensity at various points in an interference pattern.
- How interference occurs when light reflects from the two surfaces of a thin film.
- How interference makes it possible to measure extremely small distances.

An ugly black oil spot on the pavement can become a thing of beauty after a rain, when the oil reflects a rainbow of colors. Multicolored reflections can also be seen from the surfaces of soap bubbles and compact discs. These familiar sights give us a hint that there are aspects of light that we haven't yet explored.

In our discussion of lenses, mirrors, and optical instruments we used the model of *geometric optics,* in which we represent light as *rays,* straight lines that are bent at a reflecting or refracting surface. But many aspects of the behavior of light *can't* be understood on the basis of rays. We have already learned that light is fundamentally a *wave,* and in some situations we have to consider its wave properties explicitly. If two or more light waves of the same frequency overlap at a point, the total effect depends on the *phases* of the waves as well as their amplitudes. The resulting patterns of light are a result of the *wave* nature of light and cannot be understood on the basis of rays. Optical effects that depend on the wave nature of light are grouped under the heading **physical optics.**

In this chapter we'll look at *interference* phenomena that occur when two waves combine. The colors seen in oil films and soap bubbles are a result of interference between light reflected from the front and back surfaces of a thin film of oil or soap solution. Effects that occur when *many* sources of waves are present are called *diffraction* phenomena; we'll study these in Chapter 36. In that chapter we'll see that diffraction effects occur whenever a wave passes through an aperture or around an obstacle. They are important in practical applications of physical optics such as diffraction gratings, x-ray diffraction, and holography.

While our primary concern is with light, interference and diffraction can occur with waves of *any* kind. As we go along, we'll point out applications to other types of waves such as sound and water waves.

35.1 Interference and Coherent Sources

As we discussed in Chapter 15, the term **interference** refers to any situation in which two or more waves overlap in space. When this occurs, the total wave at any point at any instant of time is governed by the **principle of superposition,** which we introduced in Section 15.6 in the context of waves on a string. This principle also applies to electromagnetic waves and is the most important principle in all of physical optics, so make sure you understand it well. The principle of superposition states:

When two or more waves overlap, the resultant displacement at any point and at any instant is found by adding the instantaneous displacements that would be produced at the point by the individual waves if each were present alone.

(In some special physical situations, such as electromagnetic waves propagating in a crystal, this principle may not apply. A discussion of these is beyond our scope.)

We use the term "displacement" in a general sense. With waves on the surface of a liquid, we mean the actual displacement of the surface above or below its normal level. With sound waves, the term refers to the excess or deficiency of pressure. For electromagnetic waves, we usually mean a specific component of electric or magnetic field.

Interference in Two or Three Dimensions

We have already discussed one important case of interference, in which two identical waves propagating in opposite directions combine to produce a *standing wave.* We saw this in Chapters 15 and 16 for transverse waves on a string and for longitudinal waves in a fluid filling a pipe; we described the same phenomenon for electromagnetic waves in Section 32.5. In all of these cases the waves propagated along only a single axis: along a string, along the length of a fluid-filled pipe, or along the propagation direction of an electromagnetic plane wave. But light waves can (and do) travel in *two* or *three* dimensions, as can any kind of wave that propagates in a two- or three-dimensional medium. In this section we'll see what happens when we combine waves that spread out in two or three dimensions from a pair of identical wave sources.

35.1 A "snapshot" of sinusoidal waves of frequency f and wavelength λ spreading out from source S_1 in all directions.

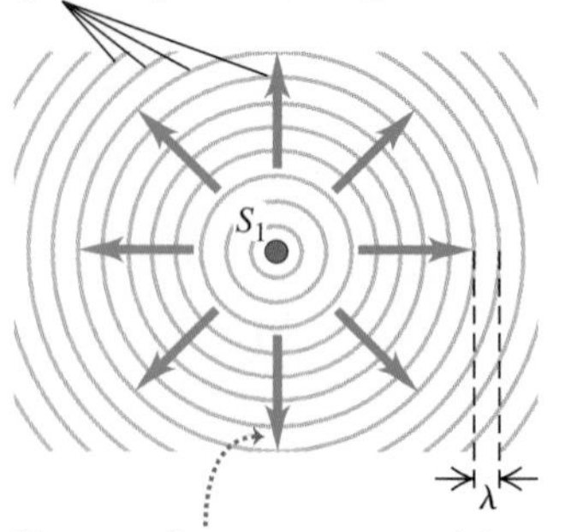

Wave fronts: crests of the wave (frequency f) separated by one wavelength λ
S_1
λ
The wave fronts move outward from source S_1 at the wave speed $v = f\lambda$.

Interference effects are most easily seen when we combine *sinusoidal* waves with a single frequency f and wavelength λ. Figure 35.1 shows a "snapshot" or "freeze-frame" of a *single* source S_1 of sinusoidal waves and some of the wave fronts produced by this source. The figure shows only the wave fronts corresponding to wave *crests,* so the spacing between successive wave fronts is one wavelength. The material surrounding S_1 is uniform, so the wave speed is the same in all directions, and there is no refraction (and hence no bending of the wave fronts). If the waves are two-dimensional, like waves on the surface of a liquid, the circles in Fig. 35.1 represent circular wave fronts; if the waves propagate in three dimensions, the circles represent spherical wave fronts spreading away from S_1.

In optics, sinusoidal waves are characteristic of **monochromatic light** (light of a single color). While it's fairly easy to make water waves or sound waves of a single frequency, common sources of light *do not* emit monochromatic (single-frequency) light. For example, incandescent light bulbs and flames emit a continuous distribution of wavelengths. However, there are several ways to produce *approximately* monochromatic light. For example, some filters block all but a very narrow range of wavelengths. By far the most nearly monochromatic source that is available at present is the *laser.* An example is the helium–neon laser, which emits red light at 632.8 nm with a wavelength range of the order of ± 0.000001 nm, or about one part in 10^9. As we analyze interference and diffraction effects in this chapter and the next, we will assume that we are working with monochromatic waves (unless we explicitly state otherwise).

Constructive and Destructive Interference

Two identical sources of monochromatic waves, S_1 and S_2, are shown in Fig. 35.2a. The two sources produce waves of the same amplitude and the same wavelength λ. In addition, the two sources are permanently *in phase;* they vibrate in unison. They might be two synchronized agitators in a ripple tank, two loudspeakers driven by the same amplifier, two radio antennas powered by the same transmitter, or two small holes or slits in an opaque screen, illuminated by the same monochromatic light source. We will see that if there were not a constant phase relationship between the two sources, the phenomena we are about to discuss would not occur. Two monochromatic sources of the same frequency and with any definite, constant phase relationship (not necessarily in phase) are said to be **coherent.** We also use the term *coherent waves* (or, for light waves, *coherent light*) to refer to the waves emitted by two such sources.

If the waves emitted by the two coherent sources are *transverse,* like electromagnetic waves, then we will also assume that the wave disturbances produced by both sources have the same *polarization* (that is, they lie along the same line). For example, the sources S_1 and S_2 in Fig. 35.2a could be two radio antennas in the form of long rods oriented parallel to the z-axis (perpendicular to the plane of the figure); at any point in the xy-plane the waves produced by both antennas have $\vec{E}$ fields with only a z-component. Then we need only a single scalar function to describe each wave; this makes the analysis much easier.

We position the two sources of equal amplitude, equal wavelength, and (if the waves are transverse) the same polarization along the y-axis in Fig. 35.2a, equidistant from the origin. Consider a point a on the x-axis. From symmetry the two distances from S_1 to a and from S_2 to a are *equal;* waves from the two sources thus require equal times to travel to a. Hence waves that leave S_1 and S_2 in phase arrive at a in phase. The two waves add, and the total amplitude at a is *twice* the amplitude of each individual wave. This is true for *any* point on the x-axis.

Similarly, the distance from S_2 to point b is exactly two wavelengths *greater* than the distance from S_1 to b. A wave crest from S_1 arrives at b exactly two cycles earlier than a crest emitted at the same time from S_2, and again the two waves arrive in phase. As at point a, the total amplitude is the sum of the amplitudes of the waves from S_1 and S_2.

In general, when waves from two or more sources arrive at a point *in phase,* the amplitude of the resultant wave is the *sum* of the amplitudes of the individual waves; the individual waves reinforce each other. This is called **constructive interference** (Fig. 35.2b). Let the distance from S_1 to any point P be r_1, and let the distance from S_2 to P be r_2. For constructive interference to occur at P, the path difference $r_2 - r_1$ for the two sources must be an integral multiple of the wavelength λ:

$$r_2 - r_1 = m\lambda \qquad (m = 0, \pm 1, \pm 2, \pm 3, \dots) \qquad \text{(constructive interference, sources in phase)} \qquad (35.1)$$

In Fig. 35.2a, points a and b satisfy Eq. (35.1) with $m = 0$ and $m = +2$, respectively.

Something different occurs at point c in Fig. 35.2a. At this point, the path difference $r_2 - r_1 = -2.50\lambda$, which is a *half-integral* number of wavelengths. Waves from the two sources arrive at point c exactly a half-cycle out of phase. A crest of one wave arrives at the same time as a crest in the opposite direction (a "trough") of the other wave (Fig. 35.2c). The resultant amplitude is the *difference* between the two individual amplitudes. If the individual amplitudes are equal, then the total amplitude is *zero!* This cancellation or partial cancellation of the

35.2 (a) A "snapshot" of sinusoidal waves spreading out from two coherent sources S_1 and S_2. Constructive interference occurs at point a (equidistant from the two sources) and (b) at point b. (c) Destructive interference occurs at point c.

(a) Two coherent wave sources separated by a distance 4λ

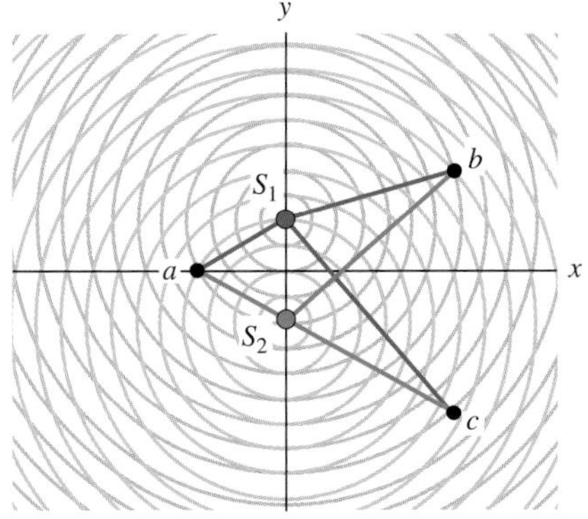

(b) Conditions for constructive interference: Waves interfere constructively if their path lengths differ by an integral number of wavelengths: $r_2 - r_1 = m\lambda$.

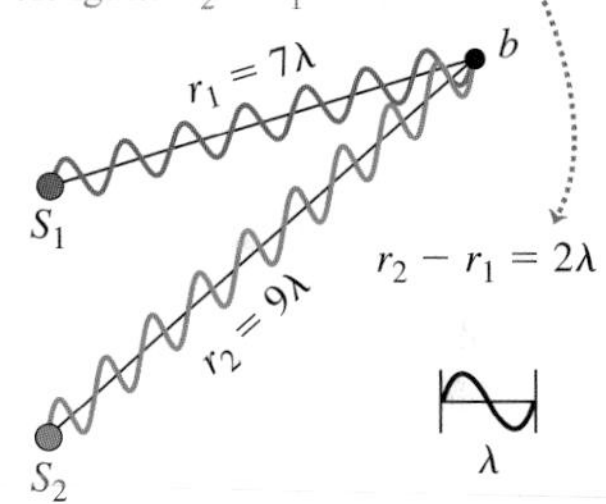

(c) Conditions for destructive interference: Waves interfere destructively if their path lengths differ by a half-integral number of wavelengths: $r_2 - r_1 = (m + \frac{1}{2})\lambda$.

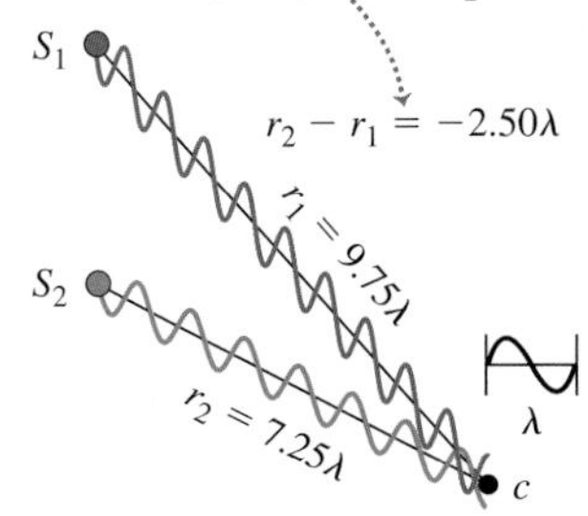

individual waves is called **destructive interference.** The condition for destructive interference in the situation shown in Fig. 35.2a is

$$r_2 - r_1 = \left(m + \frac{1}{2}\right)\lambda \quad (m = 0, \pm 1, \pm 2, \pm 3, \ldots) \quad \text{(destructive interference, sources in phase)} \tag{35.2}$$

The path difference at point c in Fig. 35.2a satisfies Eq. (35.2) with $m = -3$.

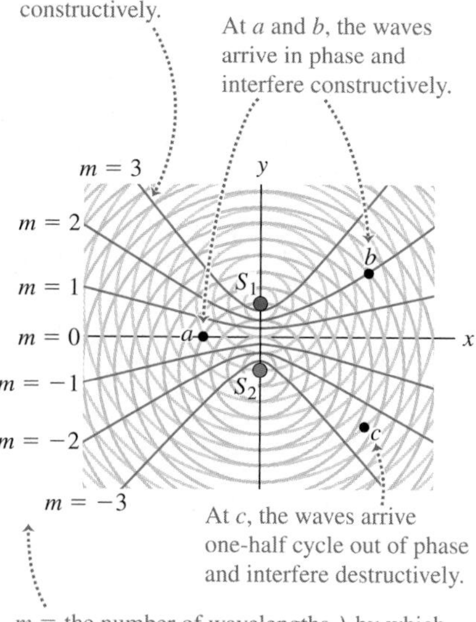
Antinodal curves (red) mark positions where the waves from S_1 and S_2 interfere constructively.
At a and b, the waves arrive in phase and interfere constructively.
$m = 3$
y
$m = 2$
b
$m = 1$
S_1
$m = 0$
a
x
$m = -1$
S_2
$m = -2$
c
$m = -3$
At c, the waves arrive one-half cycle out of phase and interfere destructively.
m = the number of wavelengths λ by which the path lengths from S_1 and S_2 differ.

35.3 The same as Fig. 35.2a, but with red antinodal curves (curves of maximum amplitude) superimposed. All points on each curve satisfy Eq. (35.1) with the value of m shown. The nodal curves (not shown) lie between each adjacent pair of antinodal curves.

Figure 35.3 shows the same situation as in Fig. 35.2a, but with red curves that denote all points on which *constructive* interference occurs. On each curve, the path difference $r_2 - r_1$ is equal to an integer m times the wavelength, as in Eq. (35.1). These curves are called **antinodal curves.** They are directly analogous to *antinodes* in the standing-wave patterns described in Chapters 15 and 16 and Section 32.5. In a standing wave formed by interference between waves propagating in opposite directions, the antinodes are points at which the amplitude is maximum; likewise, the wave amplitude in the situation of Fig. 35.3 is maximum along the antinodal curves. Not shown in Fig. 35.3 are the **nodal curves,** which are the curves denoting points on which *destructive* interference occurs in accordance with Eq. (35.2); these are analogous to the *nodes* in a standing-wave pattern. A nodal curve lies between each two adjacent antinodal curves in Fig. 35.3; one such curve, corresponding to $r_2 - r_1 = -2.50\lambda$, passes through point c.

In some cases, such as two loudspeakers or two radio-transmitter antennas, the interference pattern is three-dimensional. Think of rotating the color curves of Fig. 35.3 around the y-axis; then maximum constructive interference occurs at all points on the resulting surfaces of revolution.

CAUTION **Interference patterns are not standing waves** The interference patterns in Figs. 35.2a and 35.3 are *not* standing waves, though they have some similarities to the standing-wave patterns described in Chapters 15 and 16 and Section 32.5. In a standing wave, the interference is between two waves propagating in opposite directions; a stationary pattern of antinodes and nodes appears, and there is *no* net energy flow in either direction (the energy in the wave is left "standing"). In the situations shown in Figs. 35.2a and 35.3, there is likewise a stationary pattern of antinodal and nodal curves, but there is a net flow of energy *outward* from the two sources. From the energy standpoint, all that interference does is to "channel" the energy flow so that it is greatest along the antinodal curves and least along the nodal curves.

For Eqs. (35.1) and (35.2) to hold, the two sources must have the same wavelength and must *always* be in phase. These conditions are rather easy to satisfy for sound waves (see Example 16.15 in Section 16.6). But with *light* waves there is no practical way to achieve a constant phase relationship (coherence) with two independent sources. This is because of the way light is emitted. In ordinary light sources, atoms gain excess energy by thermal agitation or by impact with accelerated electrons. An atom that is "excited" in such a way begins to radiate energy and continues until it has lost all the energy it can, typically in a time of the order of 10^{-8} s. The many atoms in a source ordinarily radiate in an unsynchronized and random phase relationship, and the light that is emitted from *two* such sources has no definite phase relationship.

However, the light from a single source can be split so that parts of it emerge from two or more regions of space, forming two or more *secondary sources.* Then any random phase change in the source affects these secondary sources equally and does not change their *relative* phase.

The distinguishing feature of light from a *laser* is that the emission of light from many atoms is synchronized in frequency and phase. As a result, the random phase changes mentioned above occur much less frequently. Definite phase relationships are preserved over correspondingly much greater lengths in the beam, and laser light is much more coherent than ordinary light.

Test Your Understanding of Section 35.1 Consider a point in Fig. 35.3 on the positive y-axis above S_1. Does this point lie on (i) an antinodal curve; (ii) a nodal curve; or (iii) neither? (*Hint:* The distance between S_1 and S_2 is 4λ.)

MP

35.2 Two-Source Interference of Light

The interference pattern produced by two coherent sources of *water* waves of the same wavelength can be readily seen in a ripple tank with a shallow layer of water (Fig. 35.4). This pattern is not directly visible when the interference is between *light* waves, since light traveling in a uniform medium cannot be seen. (A shaft of afternoon sunlight in a room is made visible by scattering from airborne dust particles.)

One of the earliest quantitative experiments to reveal the interference of light from two sources was performed in 1800 by the English scientist Thomas Young. We will refer back to this experiment several times in this and later chapters, so it's important to understand it in detail. Young's apparatus is shown in perspective in Fig. 35.5a. A light source (not shown) emits monochromatic light; however, this light is not suitable for use in an interference experiment because emissions from different parts of an ordinary source are not synchronized. To remedy this, the light is directed at a screen with a narrow slit S_0, 1 μm or so wide. The light emerging from the slit originated from only a small region of the light source; thus slit S_0 behaves more nearly like the idealized source shown in Fig. 35.1. (In modern versions of the experiment, a laser is used as a source of coherent light, and the slit S_0 isn't needed.) The light from slit S_0 falls on a screen with two other narrow slits S_1 and S_2, each 1 μm or so wide and a few tens or hundreds of micrometers apart. Cylindrical wave fronts spread out from slit S_0 and reach slits S_1 and S_2 *in phase* because they travel equal distances from S_0. The waves *emerging* from slits S_1 and S_2 are therefore also always in phase, so S_1 and S_2 are *coherent* sources. The interference of waves from S_1 and S_2 produces a pattern in space like that to the right of the sources in Figs. 35.2a and 35.3.

35.4 The concepts of constructive interference and destructive interference apply to these water waves as well as to light waves and sound waves.

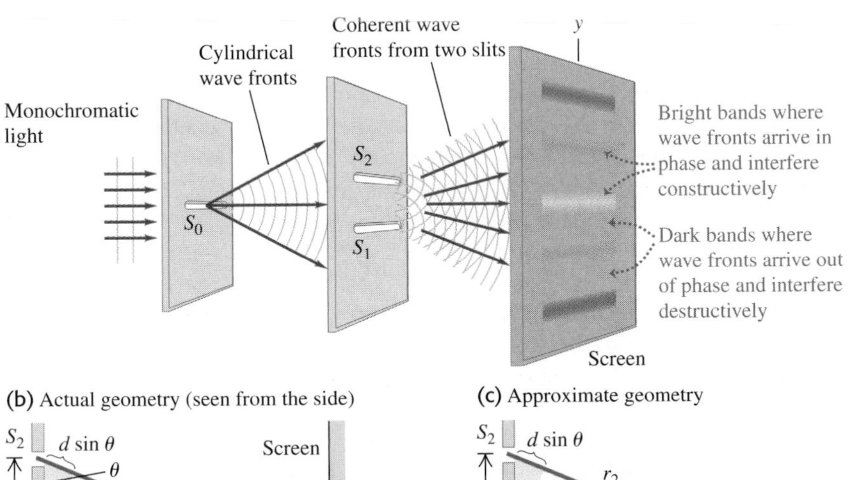
(a) Interference of light waves passing through two slits
Monochromatic light
Cylindrical wave fronts
Coherent wave fronts from two slits
y
S_0
S_2
S_1
Bright bands where wave fronts arrive in phase and interfere constructively
Dark bands where wave fronts arrive out of phase and interfere destructively
Screen
(b) Actual geometry (seen from the side)
S_2
$d \sin\theta$
θ
Screen
d
θ
r_2
y
S_1
r_1
P
R
In real situations, the distance R to the screen is usually very much greater than the distance d between the slits ...

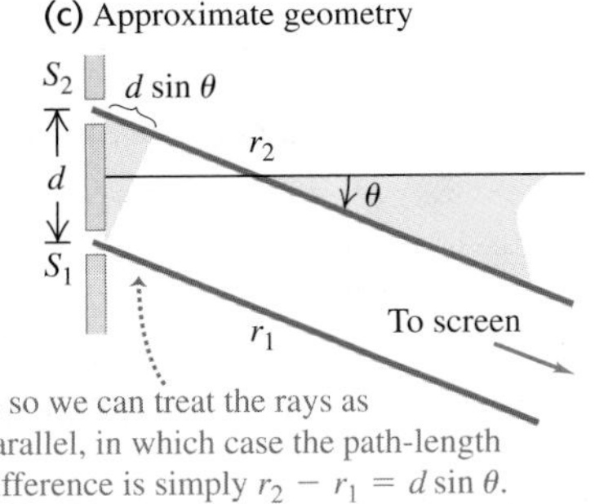
(c) Approximate geometry
S_2
$d \sin\theta$
r_2
d
θ
S_1
r_1
To screen
... so we can treat the rays as parallel, in which case the path-length difference is simply $r_2 - r_1 = d \sin\theta$.

35.5 (a) Young's experiment to show interference of light passing through two slits. A pattern of bright and dark areas appears on the screen (see Fig. 35.6). (b) Geometrical analysis of Young's experiment. For the case shown, $r_2 > r_1$ and both y and θ are positive. If point P is on the other side of the screen's center, $r_2 < r_1$ and both y and θ are negative. (c) Approximate geometry when the distance R to the screen is much greater than the distance d between the slits.

Activ Physics ONLINE
16.1 Two-Source Interference: Introduction
16.1 Two-Source Interference: Qualitative Questions
16.1 Two-Source Interference: Problems

To visualize the interference pattern, a screen is placed so that the light from S_1 and S_2 falls on it (Fig. 35.5b). The screen will be most brightly illuminated at points P, where the light waves from the slits interfere constructively, and will be darkest at points where the interference is destructive.

To simplify the analysis of Young's experiment, we assume that the distance R from the slits to the screen is so large in comparison to the distance d between the slits that the lines from S_1 and S_2 to P are very nearly parallel, as in Fig. 35.5c. This is usually the case for experiments with light; the slit separation is typically a few millimeters, while the screen may be a meter or more away. The difference in path length is then given by

$$r_2 - r_1 = d\sin\theta \qquad (35.3)$$

where θ is the angle between a line from slits to screen (shown in blue in Fig.35.5c) and the normal to the plane of the slits (shown as a thin black line).

Constructive and Destructive Two-Slit Interference

We found in Section 35.1 that constructive interference (reinforcement) occurs at points where the path difference is an integral number of wavelengths, $m\lambda$, where $m = 0, \pm1, \pm2, \pm3, \ldots$. So the bright regions on the screen in Fig. 35.5 occur at angles θ for which

$$d\sin\theta = m\lambda \qquad (m = 0, \pm1, \pm2, \ldots) \qquad \text{(constructive interference, two slits)} \qquad (35.4)$$

Similarly, destructive interference (cancellation) occurs, forming dark regions on the screen, at points for which the path difference is a half-integral number of wavelengths, $(m + \frac{1}{2})\lambda$:

$$d\sin\theta = \left(m + \frac{1}{2}\right)\lambda \qquad (m = 0, \pm1, \pm2, \ldots) \qquad \text{(destructive interference, two slits)} \qquad (35.5)$$

35.6 Photograph of interference fringes produced on a screen in Young's double-slit experiment.

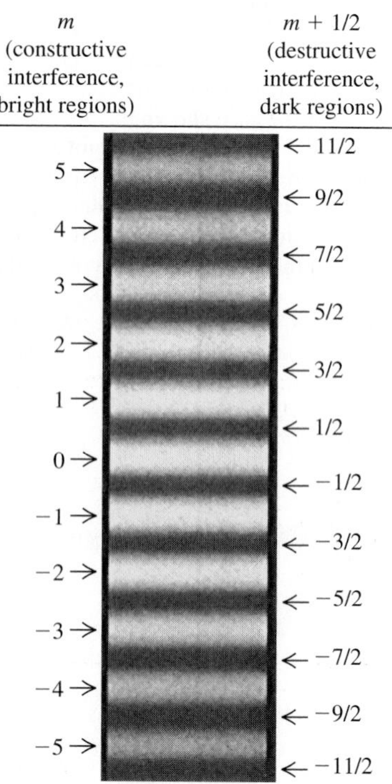

Thus the pattern on the screen of Figs. 35.5a and 35.5b is a succession of bright and dark bands, or **interference fringes,** parallel to the slits S_1 and S_2. A photograph of such a pattern is shown in Fig. 35.6. The center of the pattern is a bright band corresponding to $m = 0$ in Eq. (35.4); this point on the screen is equidistant from the two slits.

We can derive an expression for the positions of the centers of the bright bands on the screen. In Fig. 35.5b, y is measured from the center of the pattern, corresponding to the distance from the center of Fig. 35.6. Let y_m be the distance from the center of the pattern $(\theta = 0)$ to the center of the mth bright band. Let θ_m be the corresponding value of θ; then

$$y_m = R\tan\theta_m$$

In experiments such as this, the distances y_m are often much smaller than the distance R from the slits to the screen. Hence θ_m is very small, $\tan\theta_m$ is very nearly equal to $\sin\theta_m$, and

$$y_m = R\sin\theta_m$$

Combining this with Eq. (35.4), we find that *for small angles only,*

$$y_m = R\frac{m\lambda}{d} \qquad \text{(constructive interference in Young's experiment)} \qquad (35.6)$$

We can measure R and d, as well as the positions y_m of the bright fringes, so this experiment provides a direct measurement of the wavelength λ. Young's experiment was in fact the first direct measurement of wavelengths of light.

CAUTION Equation (35.6) is for small angles only While Eqs. (35.4) and (35.5) are valid at any angle, Eq. (35.6) is valid only for *small* angles. It can be used *only* if the distance R from slits to screen is much greater than the slit separation d and if R is much greater than the distance y_m from the center of the interference pattern to the mth bright fringe.

The distance between adjacent bright bands in the pattern is *inversely* proportional to the distance d between the slits. The closer together the slits are, the more the pattern spreads out. When the slits are far apart, the bands in the pattern are closer together.

While we have described the experiment that Young performed with visible light, the results given in Eqs. (35.4) and (35.5) are valid for *any* type of wave, provided that the resultant wave from two coherent sources is detected at a point that is far away in comparison to the separation d.

Example 35.1 Two-slit interference

In a two-slit interference experiment, the slits are 0.200 mm apart, and the screen is at a distance of 1.00 m. The third bright fringe (not counting the central bright fringe straight ahead from the slits) is found to be displaced 9.49 mm from the central fringe (Fig. 35.7). Find the wavelength of the light used.

SOLUTION

IDENTIFY: This problem asks us to determine the wavelength λ from the dimensions $d = 0.200$ mm (slit separation), $R = 1.00$ m (distance from slits to screen), and $y_m = 9.49$ mm (distance of the third bright fringe from the center of the pattern).

SET UP: The third bright fringe corresponds to $m = 3$ in Eqs. (35.4) and (35.6), as well as to the bright fringe labeled $m = 3$ in Fig. 35.6. To determine the value of the target variable λ, we may use Eq. (35.6) since $R = 1.00$ m is much greater than $d = 0.200$ mm or $y_3 = 9.49$ mm.

EXECUTE: Solving Eq. (35.6) for λ, we find

$$\lambda = \frac{y_m d}{mR} = \frac{(9.49 \times 10^{-3}\ \text{m})(0.200 \times 10^{-3}\ \text{m})}{(3)(1.00\ \text{m})}$$
$$= 633 \times 10^{-9}\ \text{m} = 633\ \text{nm}$$

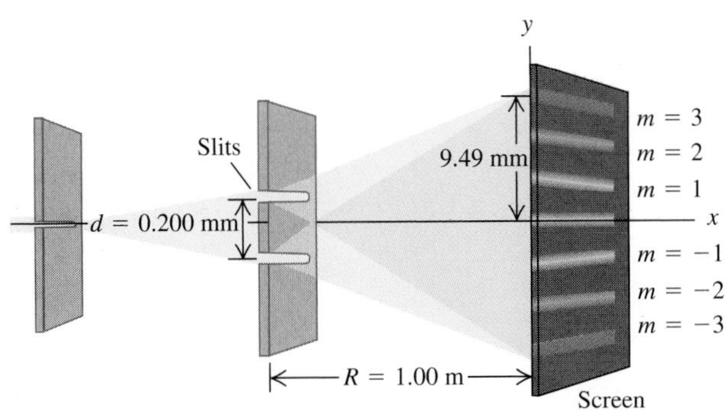

35.7 Using a two-slit interference experiment to measure the wavelength of light.

EVALUATE: This bright fringe could also correspond to $m = -3$; can you show that this gives the same result for λ?

Example 35.2 Broadcast pattern of a radio station

A radio station operating at a frequency of 1500 kHz $= 1.5 \times 10^6$ Hz (near the top end of the AM broadcast band) has two identical vertical dipole antennas spaced 400 m apart, oscillating in phase. At distances much greater than 400 m, in what directions is the intensity greatest in the resulting radiation pattern? (This is not just a hypothetical problem. It is often desirable to beam most of the radiated energy from a radio transmitter in particular directions rather than uniformly in all directions. Pairs or rows of antennas are often used to produce the desired radiation pattern.)

SOLUTION

IDENTIFY: The two antennas, shown in Fig. 35.8, correspond to sources S_1 and S_2 in Fig. 35.5. Hence we can apply the ideas of two-slit interference to this problem.

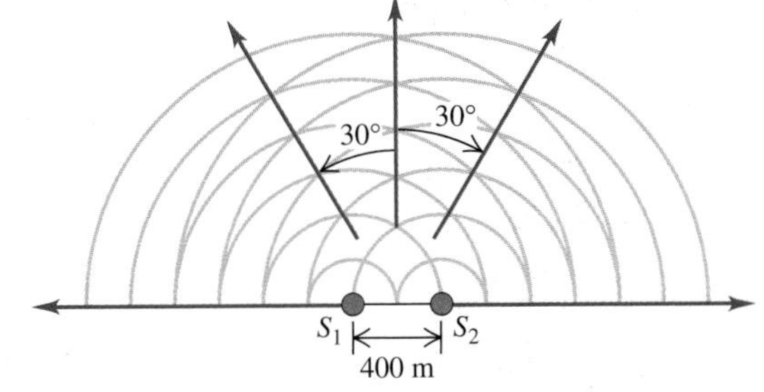

35.8 Two radio antennas broadcasting in phase. The purple arrows indicate the directions of maximum intensity. The waves that are emitted toward the lower half of the figure are not shown.

Continued

SET UP: Since the resultant wave is detected at distances much greater than $d = 400$ m, we may use Eq. (35.4) to give the directions of the intensity *maxima*, the values of θ for which the path difference is zero or a whole number of wavelengths.

EXECUTE: The wavelength is $\lambda = c/f = 200$ m. From Eq. (35.4) with $m = 0, \pm 1$, and ± 2, the intensity maxima are given by

$$\sin\theta = \frac{m\lambda}{d} = \frac{m(200\text{ m})}{400\text{ m}} = \frac{m}{2} \qquad \theta = 0, \pm 30°, \pm 90°$$

In this example, values of m greater than 2 or less than -2 give values of $\sin\theta$ greater than 1 or less than -1, which is impossible. There is *no* direction for which the path difference is three or more wavelengths. Thus values of m of ± 3 and beyond have no physical meaning in this example.

EVALUATE: We can check our result by calculating the angles for *minimum* intensity (destructive interference). There should be one intensity minimum between each pair of intensity maxima, just as in the interference pattern shown in Fig. 35.6. The angles of the intensity minima are given by Eq. (35.5) with $m = -2, -1, 0$, and 1:

$$\sin\theta = \frac{(m + \frac{1}{2})\lambda}{d} = \frac{m + \frac{1}{2}}{2} \qquad \theta = \pm 14.5°, \pm 48.6°$$

(Other values of m have no physical significance in this example.) Note that these angles are intermediate between the angles for intensity maxima, as they should be. Note also that since the angles are not small, the angles for the minima are *not* exactly halfway between the angles for the maxima.

Test Your Understanding of Section 35.2 You shine a tunable laser (whose wavelength can be adjusted by turning a knob) on a pair of closely spaced slits. The light emerging from the two slits produces an interference pattern on a screen like that shown in Fig. 35.6. If you adjust the wavelength so that the laser light changes from red to blue, how will the spacing between bright fringes change? (i) The spacing increases; (ii) the spacing decreases; (iii) the spacing is unchanged; (iv) not enough information is given to decide.

35.3 Intensity in Interference Patterns

In Section 35.2 we found the positions of maximum and minimum intensity in a two-source interference pattern. Let's now see how to find the intensity at *any* point in the pattern. To do this, we have to combine the two sinusoidally varying fields (from the two sources) at a point P in the radiation pattern, taking proper account of the phase difference of the two waves at point P, which results from the path difference. The intensity is then proportional to the square of the resultant electric-field amplitude, as we learned in Chapter 32.

To calculate the intensity, we will assume that the two sinusoidal functions (corresponding to waves from the two sources) have equal amplitude E and that the $\vec{E}$ fields lie along the same line (have the same polarization). This assumes that the sources are identical and neglects the slight amplitude difference caused by the unequal path lengths (the amplitude decreases with increasing distance from the source). From Eq. (32.29), each source by itself would give an intensity $\frac{1}{2}\epsilon_0 cE^2$ at point P. If the two sources are in phase, then the waves that arrive at P differ in phase by an amount proportional to the difference in their path lengths, $(r_2 - r_1)$. If the phase angle between these arriving waves is ϕ, then we can use the following expressions for the two electric fields superposed at P:

$$E_1(t) = E\cos(\omega t + \phi)$$
$$E_2(t) = E\cos\omega t$$

Here is our program. The superposition of the two fields at P is a sinusoidal function with some amplitude E_P that depends on E and the phase difference ϕ. First we'll work on finding the amplitude E_P if E and ϕ are known. Then we'll find the intensity I of the resultant wave, which is proportional to E_P^2. Finally, we'll relate the phase difference ϕ to the path difference, which is determined by the geometry of the situation.

Amplitude in Two-Source Interference

To add the two sinusoidal functions with a phase difference, we use the same *phasor* representation that we used for simple harmonic motion (Section 13.2) and for voltages and currents in ac circuits (Section 31.1). We suggest that you review these sections so that phasors are fresh in your mind. Each sinusoidal function is represented by a rotating vector (phasor) whose projection on the horizontal axis at any instant represents the instantaneous value of the sinusoidal function.

In Fig. 35.9, E_1 is the horizontal component of the phasor representing the wave from source S_1, and E_2 is the horizontal component of the phasor for the wave from S_2. As shown in the diagram, both phasors have the same magnitude E, but E_1 is *ahead* of E_2 in phase by an angle ϕ. Both phasors rotate counterclockwise with constant angular speed ω, and the sum of the projections on the horizontal axis at any time gives the instantaneous value of the total E field at point P. Thus the amplitude E_P of the resultant sinusoidal wave at P is the magnitude of the dark red phasor in the diagram (labeled E_P); this is the *vector sum* of the other two phasors. To find E_P, we use the law of cosines and the trigonometric identity $\cos(\pi - \phi) = -\cos\phi$:

$$E_P^2 = E^2 + E^2 - 2E^2\cos(\pi - \phi)$$
$$= E^2 + E^2 + 2E^2\cos\phi$$

Then, using the identity $1 + \cos\phi = 2\cos^2(\phi/2)$, we obtain

$$E_P^2 = 2E^2(1 + \cos\phi) = 4E^2\cos^2\left(\frac{\phi}{2}\right)$$

$$E_P = 2E\left|\cos\frac{\phi}{2}\right| \quad \text{(amplitude in two-source interference)} \quad (35.7)$$

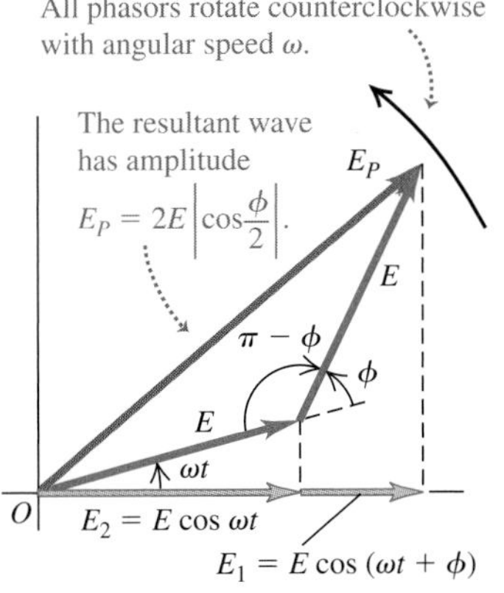
All phasors rotate counterclockwise with angular speed ω.
The resultant wave has amplitude
$E_P = 2E\left|\cos\frac{\phi}{2}\right|$.
E_P
E
$\pi - \phi$
ϕ
E
ωt
O
$E_2 = E\cos\omega t$
$E_1 = E\cos(\omega t + \phi)$

35.9 Phasor diagram for the superposition at a point P of two waves of equal amplitude E with a phase difference ϕ.

You can also obtain this result algebraically without using phasors (see Problem 35.48).

When the two waves are in phase, $\phi = 0$ and $E_P = 2E$. When they are exactly a half-cycle out of phase, $\phi = \pi$ rad $= 180°, \cos(\phi/2) = \cos(\pi/2) = 0$, and $E_P = 0$. Thus the superposition of two sinusoidal waves with the same frequency and amplitude but with a phase difference yields a sinusoidal wave with the same frequency and an amplitude between zero and twice the individual amplitudes, depending on the phase difference.

Intensity in Two-Source Interference

To obtain the intensity I at point P, we recall from Section 32.4 that I is equal to the average magnitude of the Poynting vector, S_{av}. For a sinusoidal wave with electric-field amplitude E_P, this is given by Eq. (32.29) with E_{max} replaced by E_P. Thus we can express the intensity in any of the following equivalent forms:

$$I = S_{av} = \frac{E_P^2}{2\mu_0 c} = \frac{1}{2}\sqrt{\frac{\epsilon_0}{\mu_0}}E_P^2 = \frac{1}{2}\epsilon_0 c E_P^2 \quad (35.8)$$

The essential content of these expressions is that I is proportional to E_P^2. When we substitute Eq. (35.7) into the last expression in Eq. (35.8), we get

$$I = \frac{1}{2}\epsilon_0 c E_P^2 = 2\epsilon_0 c E^2 \cos^2\frac{\phi}{2} \quad (35.9)$$

In particular, the *maximum* intensity I_0, which occurs at points where the phase difference is zero $(\phi = 0)$, is

$$I_0 = 2\epsilon_0 c E^2$$

Note that the maximum intensity I_0 is *four times* (not twice) as great as the intensity $\frac{1}{2}\epsilon_0 c E^2$ from each individual source.

Substituting the expression for I_0 into Eq. (35.9), we can express the intensity I at any point very simply in terms of the maximum intensity I_0:

$$I = I_0 \cos^2 \frac{\phi}{2} \quad \text{(intensity in two-source interference)} \tag{35.10}$$

For some phase angles ϕ the intensity is I_0, four times as great as for an individual wave source, but for other phase angles the intensity is zero. If we average Eq. (35.10) over all possible phase differences, the result is $I_0/2 = \epsilon_0 c E^2$ (the average of $\cos^2(\phi/2)$ is $\frac{1}{2}$). This is just twice the intensity from each individual source, as we should expect. The total energy output from the two sources isn't changed by the interference effects, but the energy is redistributed (as we mentioned in Section 35.1).

Phase Difference and Path Difference

Our next task is to find how the phase difference ϕ between the two fields at point P is related to the geometry of the situation. We know that ϕ is proportional to the difference in path length from the two sources to point P. When the path difference is one wavelength, the phase difference is one cycle, and $\phi = 2\pi \text{ rad} = 360°$. When the path difference is $\lambda/2$, $\phi = \pi \text{ rad} = 180°$, and so on. That is, the ratio of the phase difference ϕ to 2π is equal to the ratio of the path difference $r_2 - r_1$ to λ:

$$\frac{\phi}{2\pi} = \frac{r_2 - r_1}{\lambda}$$

Thus a path difference $(r_2 - r_1)$ causes a phase difference given by

$$\phi = \frac{2\pi}{\lambda}(r_2 - r_1) = k(r_2 - r_1) \quad \text{(phase difference related to path difference)} \tag{35.11}$$

where $k = 2\pi/\lambda$ is the *wave number* introduced in Section 15.3.

If the material in the space between the sources and P is anything other than vacuum, we must use the wavelength *in the material* in Eq. (35.11). If the material has index of refraction n, then

$$\lambda = \frac{\lambda_0}{n} \quad \text{and} \quad k = nk_0 \tag{35.12}$$

where λ_0 and k_0 are the wavelength and the wave number, respectively, in vacuum.

Finally, if the point P is far away from the sources in comparison to their separation d, the path difference is given by Eq. (35.3):

$$r_2 - r_1 = d \sin\theta$$

Combining this with Eq. (35.11), we find

$$\phi = k(r_2 - r_1) = kd \sin\theta = \frac{2\pi d}{\lambda} \sin\theta \tag{35.13}$$

When we substitute this into Eq. (35.10), we find

$$I = I_0 \cos^2\left(\frac{1}{2} kd \sin\theta\right) = I_0 \cos^2\left(\frac{\pi d}{\lambda} \sin\theta\right) \quad \text{(intensity far from two sources)} \tag{35.14}$$

The directions of *maximum* intensity occur when the cosine has the values ± 1—that is, when

$$\frac{\pi d}{\lambda} \sin\theta = m\pi \qquad (m = 0, \pm 1, \pm 2, \dots)$$

35.10 Intensity distribution in the interference pattern from two identical slits.

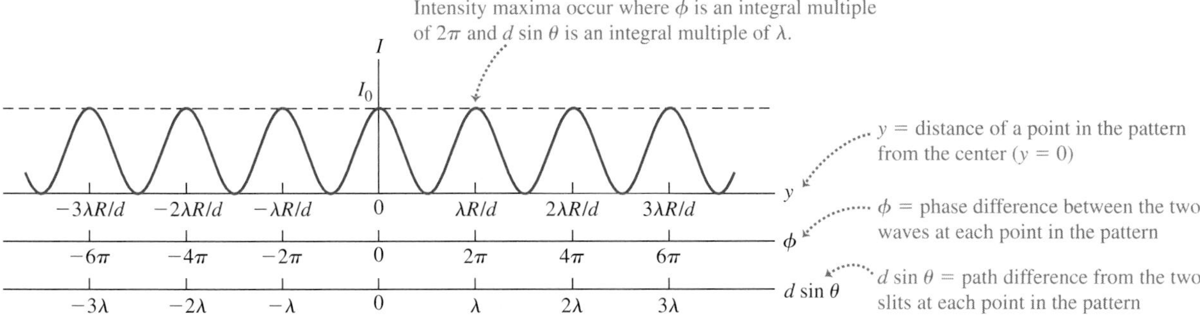
Intensity maxima occur where ϕ is an integral multiple of 2π and $d \sin\theta$ is an integral multiple of λ.
I
I_0
$-3\lambda R/d$ $-2\lambda R/d$ $-\lambda R/d$ 0 $\lambda R/d$ $2\lambda R/d$ $3\lambda R/d$
-6π -4π -2π 0 2π 4π 6π
-3λ -2λ $-\lambda$ 0 λ 2λ 3λ
y
ϕ
$d \sin\theta$
y = distance of a point in the pattern from the center ($y = 0$)
ϕ = phase difference between the two waves at each point in the pattern
$d \sin\theta$ = path difference from the two slits at each point in the pattern

or

$$d \sin\theta = m\lambda$$

in agreement with Eq. (35.4). We leave it to you to show that Eq. (35.5) for the zero-intensity directions can also be derived from Eq. (35.14) (see Exercise 35.24).

As we noted in Section 35.2, in experiments with light we visualize the interference pattern due to two slits by using a screen placed at a distance R from the slits. We can describe positions on the screen with the coordinate y; the positions of the bright fringes are given by Eq. (35.6), where ordinarily $y \ll R$. In that case, $\sin\theta$ is approximately equal to y/R, and we obtain the following expressions for the intensity at *any* point on the screen as a function of y:

$$I = I_0 \cos^2\left(\frac{kdy}{2R}\right) = I_0 \cos^2\left(\frac{\pi dy}{\lambda R}\right) \quad \text{(intensity in two-slit interference)} \quad (35.15)$$

Figure 35.10 shows a graph of Eq. (35.15); we can compare this with the photographically recorded pattern of Fig. 35.6. The peaks in Fig. 35.10 all have the same intensity, while those in Fig. 35.6 fade off as we go away from the center. We'll explore the reasons for this variation in peak intensity in Chapter 36.

Example 35.3 A directional transmitting antenna array

Suppose the two identical radio antennas in Fig. 35.8 are moved to be only 10.0 m apart and the frequency of the radiated waves is increased to $f = 60.0$ MHz. The intensity at a distance of 700 m in the $+x$-direction (corresponding to $\theta = 0$ in Fig. 35.5) is $I_0 = 0.020\ \text{W/m}^2$. (a) What is the intensity in the direction $\theta = 4.0°$? (b) In what direction near $\theta = 0$ is the intensity $I_0/2$? (c) In what directions is the intensity zero?

SOLUTION

IDENTIFY: This problem involves the intensity distribution as a function of *direction*—that is, as a function of angle. (In other problems we are concerned with the intensity as a function of *position* on a screen, as in the interference pattern shown in Fig. 35.6.)

SET UP: Because the 700-m distance from the antennas to the point where the intensity is measured is much greater than the distance between the antennas ($d = 10.0$ m), the amplitudes of the waves from the two antennas are very nearly equal. Hence we can use Eq. (35.14) to relate intensity I and angle θ.

EXECUTE: To use Eq. (35.14), we must first find the wavelength λ using the relationship $c = \lambda f$:

$$\lambda = \frac{c}{f} = \frac{3.00 \times 10^8\ \text{m/s}}{60.0 \times 10^6\ \text{s}^{-1}} = 5.00\ \text{m}$$

The spacing $d = 10.0$ m between the antennas is just twice the wavelength. Equation (35.14) then becomes

$$\begin{aligned} I &= I_0 \cos^2\left(\frac{\pi d}{\lambda}\sin\theta\right) \\ &= (0.020\ \text{W/m}^2)\cos^2\left[\frac{\pi(10.0\ \text{m})}{5.00\ \text{m}}\sin\theta\right] \\ &= (0.020\ \text{W/m}^2)\cos^2[(2.00\pi\ \text{rad})\sin\theta] \end{aligned}$$

(a) When $\theta = 4.0°$,

$$\begin{aligned} I &= (0.020\ \text{W/m}^2)\cos^2[(2.00\pi\ \text{rad})\sin 4.0°] \\ &= 0.016\ \text{W/m}^2 \end{aligned}$$

Continued

principle to show that for normal incidence, the wave reflected at point b in Fig. 35.11a is shifted by a half-cycle, while the wave reflected at d is not (if there is air below the film).

We can summarize this discussion mathematically. If the film has thickness t, the light is at normal incidence and has wavelength λ in the film; if neither or both of the reflected waves from the two surfaces have a half-cycle reflection phase shift, the conditions for constructive and destructive interference are

$$2t = m\lambda \quad (m = 0, 1, 2, \dots) \quad \text{(constructive reflection from thin film, no relative phase shift)} \tag{35.17a}$$

$$2t = \left(m + \frac{1}{2}\right)\lambda \quad (m = 0, 1, 2, \dots) \quad \text{(destructive reflection from thin film, no relative phase shift)} \tag{35.17b}$$

If *one* of the two waves has a half-cycle reflection phase shift, the conditions for constructive and destructive interference are reversed:

$$2t = \left(m + \frac{1}{2}\right)\lambda \quad (m = 0, 1, 2, \dots) \quad \text{(constructive reflection from thin film, half-cycle relative phase shift)} \tag{35.18a}$$

$$2t = m\lambda \quad (m = 0, 1, 2, \dots) \quad \text{(destructive reflection from thin film, half-cycle relative phase shift)} \tag{35.18b}$$

Thin and Thick Films

You may wonder why we have emphasized *thin* films in our discussion. We have done so because of a principle we introduced in Section 35.1: In order for two waves to cause a steady interference pattern, the waves must be *coherent,* with a definite and constant phase relationship. However, the sun and light bulbs emit light in a stream of short bursts, each of which is only a few micrometers long $(1 \text{ micrometer} = 1\ \mu m = 10^{-6}\text{ m})$. If light reflects from the two surfaces of a thin film, the two reflected waves are part of the same burst (Fig. 35.14a). Hence these waves are coherent and interference occurs as we have described. If the film is too thick, however, the two reflected waves will belong to different bursts (Fig. 35.14b). There is no definite phase relationship between different light bursts, so the two waves are incoherent and there is no fixed interference pattern. That's why you see interference colors in light reflected from an oil slick a few micrometers thick (Fig. 35.11b), but you do *not* see such colors in the light reflected from a pane of window glass with a thickness of a few millimeters (a thousand times greater).

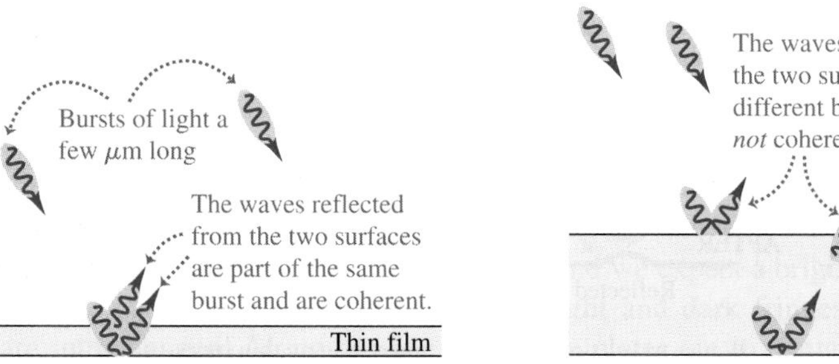

(a) Light reflecting from a thin film
Bursts of light a few μm long
The waves reflected from the two surfaces are part of the same burst and are coherent.
Thin film
(b) Light reflecting from a thick film
The waves reflected from the two surfaces are from different bursts and are *not* coherent.
Thick film

35.14 (a) Light reflecting from a thin film produces a steady interference pattern, but (b) light reflecting from a thick film does not.

dark fringe, not a bright one. This suggests that one or the other of the reflected waves has undergone a half-cycle phase shift during its reflection. In that case the two waves that are reflected at the line of contact are a half-cycle out of phase even though they have the same path length.

In fact, this phase shift can be predicted from Maxwell's equations and the electromagnetic nature of light. The details of the derivation are beyond our scope, but here is the result. Suppose a light wave with electric-field amplitude E_i is traveling in an optical material with index of refraction n_a. It strikes, at normal incidence, an interface with another optical material with index n_b. The amplitude E_r of the wave reflected from the interface is proportional to the amplitude E_i of the incident wave and is given by

$$E_r = \frac{n_a - n_b}{n_a + n_b} E_i \quad \text{(normal incidence)} \tag{35.16}$$

This result shows that the incident and reflected amplitudes have the same sign when n_a is larger than n_b and opposite sign when n_b is larger than n_a. We can distinguish three cases, as shown in Fig. 35.13:

Figure 35.13a: When $n_a > n_b$, light travels more slowly in the first material than in the second. In this case, E_r and E_i have the same sign, and the phase shift of the reflected wave relative to the incident wave is zero. This is analogous to reflection of a transverse mechanical wave on a heavy rope at a point where it is tied to a lighter rope or a ring that can move vertically without friction.

Figure 35.13b: When $n_a = n_b$, the amplitude E_r of the reflected wave is zero. The incident light wave can't "see" the interface, and there is *no* reflected wave.

Figure 35.13c: When $n_a < n_b$, light travels more slowly in the second material than in the first. In this case, E_r and E_i have opposite signs, and the phase shift of the reflected wave relative to the incident wave is π rad (180° or a half-cycle). This is analogous to reflection (with inversion) of a transverse mechanical wave on a light rope at a point where it is tied to a heavier rope or a rigid support.

Let's compare with the situation of Fig. 35.12. For the wave reflected from the upper surface of the air wedge, n_a (glass) is greater than n_b, so this wave has zero phase shift. For the wave reflected from the lower surface, n_a (air) is less than n_b (glass), so this wave has a half-cycle phase shift. Waves that are reflected from the line of contact have no path difference to give additional phase shifts, and they interfere destructively; this is what we observe. You can use the above

35.12 Interference between light waves reflected from the two sides of an air wedge separating two glass plates. The angles and the thickness of the air wedge have been exaggerated for clarity; in the text we assume that the light strikes the upper plate at normal incidence and that the distances h and t are much less than l.

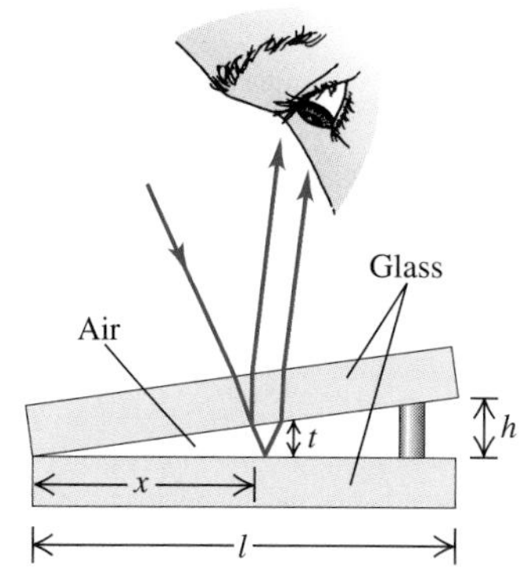

35.13 Upper figures: electromagnetic waves striking an interface between optical materials at normal incidence (shown as a small angle for clarity). Lower figures: mechanical wave pulses on ropes.

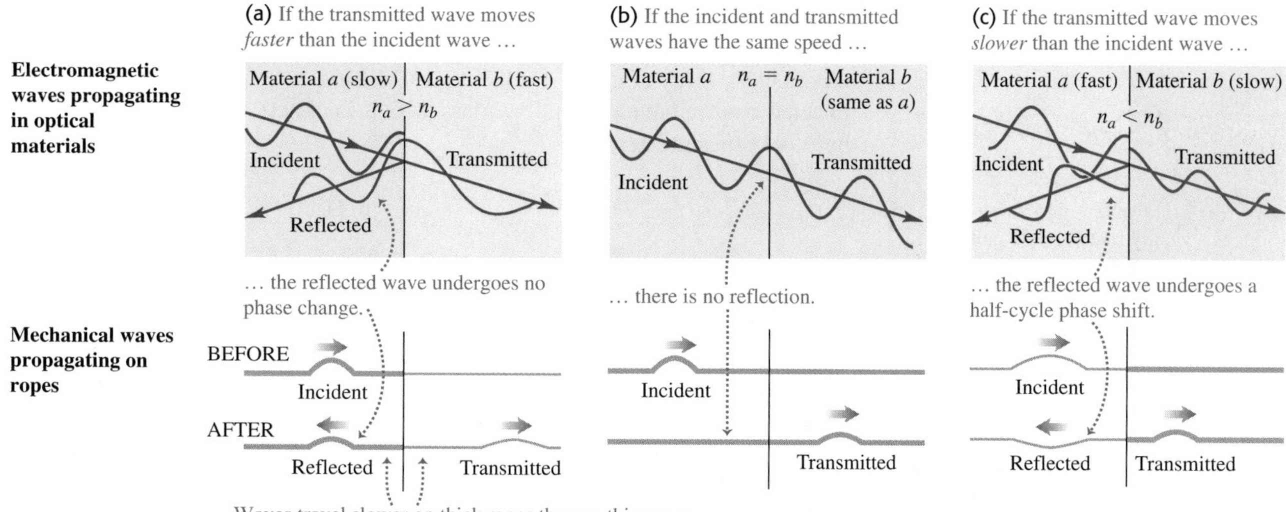

principle to show that for normal incidence, the wave reflected at point b in Fig. 35.11a is shifted by a half-cycle, while the wave reflected at d is not (if there is air below the film).

We can summarize this discussion mathematically. If the film has thickness t, the light is at normal incidence and has wavelength λ in the film; if neither or both of the reflected waves from the two surfaces have a half-cycle reflection phase shift, the conditions for constructive and destructive interference are

$$2t = m\lambda \quad (m = 0, 1, 2, \ldots) \quad \text{(constructive reflection from thin film, no relative phase shift)} \tag{35.17a}$$

$$2t = \left(m + \frac{1}{2}\right)\lambda \quad (m = 0, 1, 2, \ldots) \quad \text{(destructive reflection from thin film, no relative phase shift)} \tag{35.17b}$$

If *one* of the two waves has a half-cycle reflection phase shift, the conditions for constructive and destructive interference are reversed:

$$2t = \left(m + \frac{1}{2}\right)\lambda \quad (m = 0, 1, 2, \ldots) \quad \text{(constructive reflection from thin film, half-cycle relative phase shift)} \tag{35.18a}$$

$$2t = m\lambda \quad (m = 0, 1, 2, \ldots) \quad \text{(destructive reflection from thin film, half-cycle relative phase shift)} \tag{35.18b}$$

Thin and Thick Films

You may wonder why we have emphasized *thin* films in our discussion. We have done so because of a principle we introduced in Section 35.1: In order for two waves to cause a steady interference pattern, the waves must be *coherent,* with a definite and constant phase relationship. However, the sun and light bulbs emit light in a stream of short bursts, each of which is only a few micrometers long $(1 \text{ micrometer} = 1\ \mu m = 10^{-6}\text{ m})$. If light reflects from the two surfaces of a thin film, the two reflected waves are part of the same burst (Fig. 35.14a). Hence these waves are coherent and interference occurs as we have described. If the film is too thick, however, the two reflected waves will belong to different bursts (Fig. 35.14b). There is no definite phase relationship between different light bursts, so the two waves are incoherent and there is no fixed interference pattern. That's why you see interference colors in light reflected from an oil slick a few micrometers thick (Fig. 35.11b), but you do *not* see such colors in the light reflected from a pane of window glass with a thickness of a few millimeters (a thousand times greater).

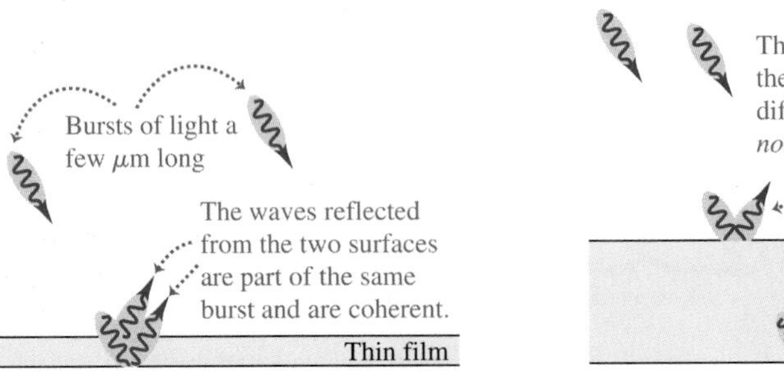
(a) Light reflecting from a thin film
Bursts of light a few μm long
The waves reflected from the two surfaces are part of the same burst and are coherent.
Thin film
(b) Light reflecting from a thick film
The waves reflected from the two surfaces are from different bursts and are not coherent.
Thick film

35.14 (a) Light reflecting from a thin film produces a steady interference pattern, but (b) light reflecting from a thick film does not.

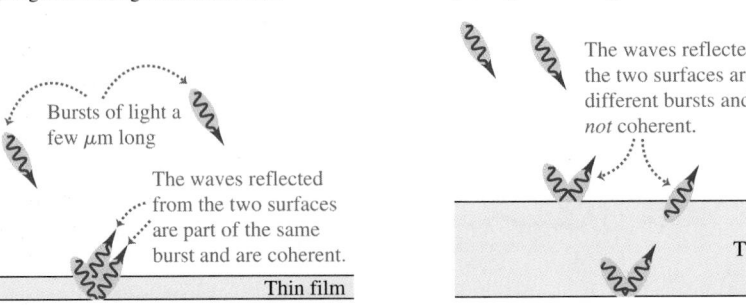

35.10 Intensity distribution in the interference pattern from two identical slits.

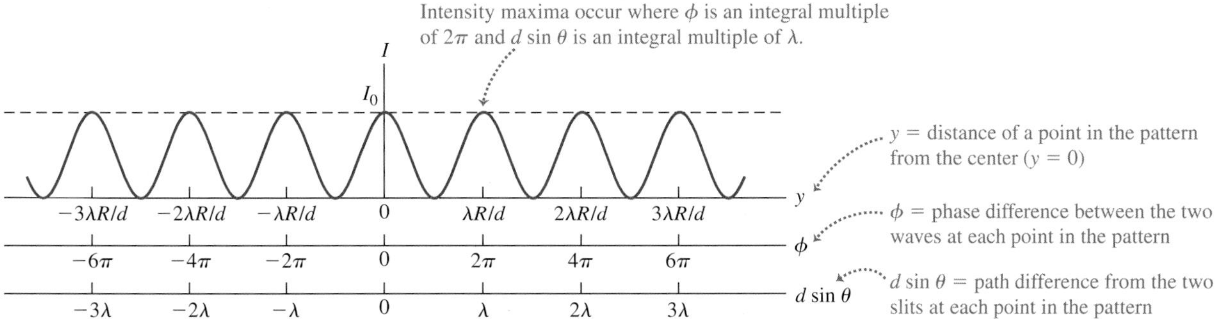

or

$$d\sin\theta = m\lambda$$

in agreement with Eq. (35.4). We leave it to you to show that Eq. (35.5) for the zero-intensity directions can also be derived from Eq. (35.14) (see Exercise 35.24).

As we noted in Section 35.2, in experiments with light we visualize the interference pattern due to two slits by using a screen placed at a distance R from the slits. We can describe positions on the screen with the coordinate y; the positions of the bright fringes are given by Eq. (35.6), where ordinarily $y \ll R$. In that case, $\sin\theta$ is approximately equal to y/R, and we obtain the following expressions for the intensity at *any* point on the screen as a function of y:

$$I = I_0\cos^2\left(\frac{kdy}{2R}\right) = I_0\cos^2\left(\frac{\pi dy}{\lambda R}\right) \quad \text{(intensity in two-slit interference)} \quad (35.15)$$

Figure 35.10 shows a graph of Eq. (35.15); we can compare this with the photographically recorded pattern of Fig. 35.6. The peaks in Fig. 35.10 all have the same intensity, while those in Fig. 35.6 fade off as we go away from the center. We'll explore the reasons for this variation in peak intensity in Chapter 36.

Example 35.3 A directional transmitting antenna array

Suppose the two identical radio antennas in Fig. 35.8 are moved to be only 10.0 m apart and the frequency of the radiated waves is increased to $f = 60.0$ MHz. The intensity at a distance of 700 m in the $+x$-direction (corresponding to $\theta = 0$ in Fig. 35.5) is $I_0 = 0.020\ \text{W/m}^2$. (a) What is the intensity in the direction $\theta = 4.0°$? (b) In what direction near $\theta = 0$ is the intensity $I_0/2$? (c) In what directions is the intensity zero?

SOLUTION

IDENTIFY: This problem involves the intensity distribution as a function of *direction*—that is, as a function of angle. (In other problems we are concerned with the intensity as a function of *position* on a screen, as in the interference pattern shown in Fig. 35.6.)

SET UP: Because the 700-m distance from the antennas to the point where the intensity is measured is much greater than the distance between the antennas ($d = 10.0$ m), the amplitudes of the waves from the two antennas are very nearly equal. Hence we can use Eq. (35.14) to relate intensity I and angle θ.

EXECUTE: To use Eq. (35.14), we must first find the wavelength λ using the relationship $c = \lambda f$:

$$\lambda = \frac{c}{f} = \frac{3.00 \times 10^8\ \text{m/s}}{60.0 \times 10^6\ \text{s}^{-1}} = 5.00\ \text{m}$$

The spacing $d = 10.0$ m between the antennas is just twice the wavelength. Equation (35.14) then becomes

$$I = I_0\cos^2\left(\frac{\pi d}{\lambda}\sin\theta\right)$$
$$= (0.020\ \text{W/m}^2)\cos^2\left[\frac{\pi(10.0\ \text{m})}{5.00\ \text{m}}\sin\theta\right]$$
$$= (0.020\ \text{W/m}^2)\cos^2[(2.00\pi\ \text{rad})\sin\theta]$$

(a) When $\theta = 4.0°$,

$$I = (0.020\ \text{W/m}^2)\cos^2[(2.00\pi\ \text{rad})\sin 4.0°]$$
$$= 0.016\ \text{W/m}^2$$

Continued

This is about 82% of the intensity at $\theta = 0$.

(b) The intensity I equals $I_0/2$ when the cosine in Eq. (35.14) has the value $\pm 1/\sqrt{2}$. This occurs when $2.00\pi \sin\theta = \pm\pi/4$ rad, so that $\sin\theta = \pm(1/8.00) = \pm 0.125$ and $\theta = \pm 7.2°$.

(c) The intensity is zero when $\cos[(2.00\pi \text{ rad})\sin\theta] = 0$. This occurs when $2.00\pi \sin\theta = \pm\pi/2, \pm 3\pi/2, \pm 5\pi/2, \ldots$, or $\sin\theta = \pm 0.250, \pm 0.750, \pm 1.25, \ldots$. Values of $\sin\theta$ greater than 1 have no meaning, and we find

$$\theta = \pm 14.5°, \pm 48.6°$$

EVALUATE: The condition in part (b) that $I = I_0/2$, so that $(2.00\pi \text{ rad})\sin\theta = \pm\pi/4$ rad, is also satisfied when $\sin\theta = \pm 0.375, \pm 0.625$, or ± 0.875 so that $\theta = \pm 22.0°, \pm 38.7°$, or $\pm 61.0°$. (Can you verify this?) It would be incorrect to include these angles in the solution, however, because the problem asked for the angle *near* $\theta = 0$ at which $I = I_0/2$. These additional values of θ aren't the ones we're looking for.

Test Your Understanding of Section 35.3 A two-slit interference experiment uses coherent light of wavelength 5.00×10^{-7} m. Rank the following points in the interference pattern according to the intensity at each point, from highest to lowest. (i) a point that is closer to one slit than the other by 4.00×10^{-7} m; (ii) a point where the light waves received from the two slits are out of phase by 4.00 rad; (iii) a point that is closer to one slit than the other by 7.50×10^{-7} m; (iv) a point where the light waves received by the two slits are out of phase by 2.00 rad.

35.4 Interference in Thin Films

You often see bright bands of color when light reflects from a thin layer of oil floating on water or from a soap bubble (see the photograph that opens this chapter). These are the results of interference. Light waves are reflected from the front and back surfaces of such thin films, and constructive interference between the two reflected waves (with different path lengths) occurs in different places for different wavelengths. Figure 35.11a shows the situation. Light shining on the upper surface of a thin film with thickness t is partly reflected at the upper surface (path *abc*). Light *transmitted* through the upper surface is partly reflected at the lower surface (path *abdef*). The two reflected waves come together at point P on the retina of the eye. Depending on the phase relationship, they may interfere constructively or destructively. Different colors have different wavelengths, so the interference may be constructive for some colors and destructive for others. That's why we see colored rings or fringes in Fig. 35.11b (which shows a thin film of oil floating on water) and in the photograph that opens this chapter (which shows thin films of soap solution that make up the bubble walls). The complex shapes of the colored rings in each photograph result from variations in the thickness of the film.

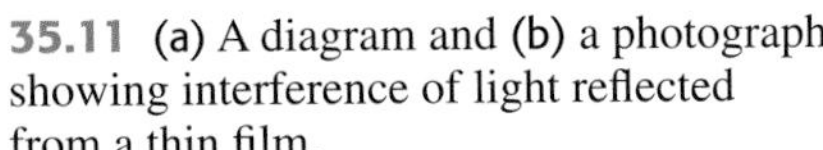

35.11 (a) A diagram and (b) a photograph showing interference of light reflected from a thin film.

(a) Interference between rays reflected from the two surfaces of a thin film

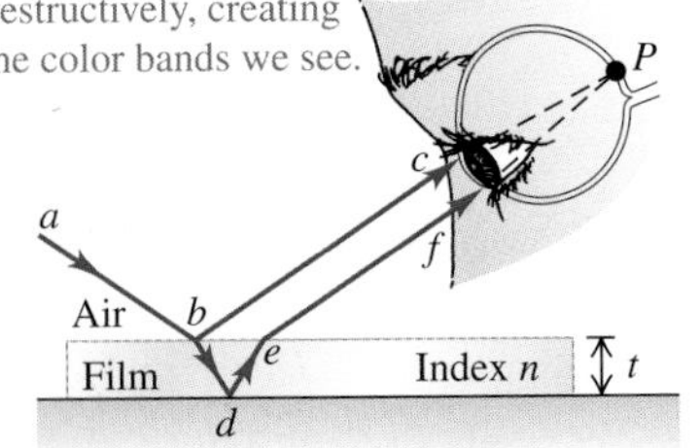
Light reflected from the upper and lower surfaces of the film comes together in the eye at P and undergoes interference.
Some colors interfere constructively and others destructively, creating the color bands we see.
P
a
b
c
d
e
f
Air
Film
Index n
t

(b) The rainbow fringes of an oil slick on water

Thin-Film Interference and Phase Shifts During Reflection

Let's look at a simplified situation in which *monochromatic* light reflects from two nearly parallel surfaces at nearly normal incidence. Figure 35.12 shows two plates of glass separated by a thin wedge, or film, of air. We want to consider interference between the two light waves reflected from the surfaces adjacent to the air wedge, as shown. (Reflections also occur at the top surface of the upper plate and the bottom surface of the lower plate; to keep our discussion simple, we won't include these.) The situation is the same as in Fig. 35.11a except that the film (wedge) thickness is not uniform. The path difference between the two waves is just twice the thickness t of the air wedge at each point. At points where $2t$ is an integer number of wavelengths, we expect to see constructive interference and a bright area; where it is a half-integer number of wavelengths, we expect to see destructive interference and a dark area. Along the line where the plates are in contact, there is practically *no* path difference, and we expect a bright area.

When we carry out the experiment, the bright and dark fringes appear, but they are interchanged! Along the line where the plates are in contact, we find a

Problem-Solving Strategy 35.1 Interference in Thin Films

IDENTIFY *the relevant concepts:* Problems with thin films involve interference of two waves, one reflected from the film's front surface and one reflected from the back surface. Typically you will be asked to relate the wavelength, the index of refraction of the film, and the dimensions of the film.

SET UP *the problem* using the following steps:

1. Make a drawing showing the geometry of the thin film. Your drawing should also depict the materials that adjoin the film; their properties determine whether one or both of the reflected waves have a half-cycle phase shift.
2. Determine the target variable.

EXECUTE *the solution* as follows:

1. Apply the rule for phase changes to each reflected wave. There is a half-cycle phase shift when $n_b > n_a$, and none when $n_b < n_a$.
2. If neither reflected wave undergoes a phase shift, or if both reflected waves do, you can apply Eqs. (35.17). If only one of the reflected waves undergoes a phase shift, you must use Eqs. (35.18).
3. Solve the resulting interference equation for the target variable. If the film consists of anything other than vacuum, be sure to use the wavelength of light *in the film* in your calculations. If the film is anything except vacuum, this is smaller than the wavelength in vacuum by a factor of n. (For air, $n = 1.000$ to four-figure precision.)
4. If you are asked about the wave that is transmitted through the film, keep in mind that *minimum* intensity in the *reflected* wave corresponds to *maximum transmitted* intensity, and vice versa.

EVALUATE *your answer:* You can interpret your results by examining what would happen if the wavelength were changed or if the film had a different thickness.

Example 35.4 Thin-film interference I

Suppose the two glass plates in Fig. 35.12 are two microscope slides 10.0 cm long. At one end they are in contact; at the other end they are separated by a piece of paper 0.0200 mm thick. What is the spacing of the interference fringes seen by reflection? Is the fringe at the line of contact bright or dark? Assume monochromatic light with a wavelength in air of $\lambda = \lambda_0 = 500$ nm.

SOLUTION

IDENTIFY: We'll consider only interference between the light reflected from the upper and lower surfaces of the air wedge between the slides. The glass plate is a millimeter or so thick, so we can ignore interference between the light reflected from the upper and lower surfaces of this plate (see Fig. 35.14b).

SET UP: Figure 35.15 depicts the situation. Light travels more slowly in the glass of the microscope slides than it does in air. Hence the wave reflected from the upper surface of the air wedge has no phase shift (see Fig. 35.13a), while the wave reflected from the lower surface has a half-cycle phase shift (see Fig. 35.13c).

35.15 Our sketch for this problem.

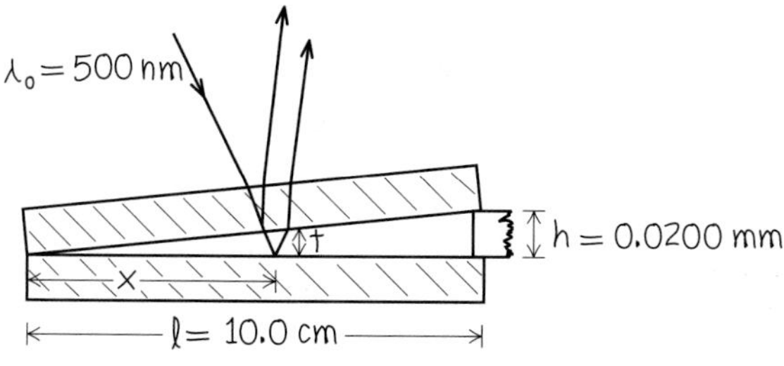

EXECUTE: Since only one of the reflected waves undergoes a phase shift, the condition for *destructive* interference (a dark fringe) is Eq. (35.18b):

$$2t = m\lambda_0 \qquad (m = 0, 1, 2, \ldots)$$

From similar triangles in Fig. 35.15 the thickness t of the air wedge at each point is proportional to the distance x from the line of contact:

$$\frac{t}{x} = \frac{h}{l}$$

Combining this with Eq. (35.18b), we find

$$\frac{2xh}{l} = m\lambda_0$$

$$x = m\frac{l\lambda_0}{2h} = m\frac{(0.100\text{ m})(500 \times 10^{-9}\text{ m})}{(2)(0.0200 \times 10^{-3}\text{ m})} = m(1.25\text{ mm})$$

Successive dark fringes, corresponding to successive integer values of m, are spaced 1.25 mm apart. Substituting $m = 0$ into this equation gives $x = 0$, corresponding to the line of contact between the two slides (at the left-hand side of Fig. 35.15). Hence there is a dark fringe at the line of contact.

EVALUATE: Our result shows that the fringe spacing is proportional to the wavelength of the light used; the fringes would be farther apart with red light (larger λ_0) than with blue light (smaller λ_0). If we use white light, the reflected light at any point is a mixture of wavelengths for which constructive interference occurs; the wavelengths that interfere destructively are weak or absent in the reflected light. (This same effect explains the colors seen when an oil film on water is illuminated by white light, as in Fig. 35.11b).

Example 35.5 Thin-film interference II

In Example 35.4, suppose the glass plates have $n = 1.52$ and the space between plates contains water $(n = 1.33)$ instead of air. What happens now?

SOLUTION

IDENTIFY: The index of refraction of the water film is still less than that of the glass on either side of the film, so the phase shifts are the same as in Example 35.4. The only difference is that the wavelength in water is different than in air.

SET UP: Once again we use Eq. (35.18b) to find the positions of the dark fringes. The wavelengths λ in water is related to the wavelength λ_0 in air (essentially vacuum) by Eq. (33.5), $\lambda = \lambda_0/n$.

EXECUTE: In the film of water $(n = 1.33)$, the wavelength is

$$\lambda = \frac{\lambda_0}{n} = \frac{500\text{ nm}}{1.33} = 376\text{ nm}$$

When we replace λ_0 by λ in the expression from Example 35.4 for the position x of the mth dark fringe, we find that the fringe spacing is reduced by the same factor of 1.33 and is equal to 0.940 mm. Note that there is still a dark fringe at the line of contact.

EVALUATE: Can you see that to return to the same fringe spacing as in Example 35.4, the dimension h in Fig. 35.15 would have to be reduced to $(0.0200\text{ mm})/1.33 = 0.0150$ mm? This shows that what matters in thin-film interference is the *ratio* between the wavelength and the thickness of the film. [You can see this by considering Eqs. (35.17a) and (35.17b).]

Example 35.6 Thin-film interference III

Suppose the upper of the two plates in Example 35.4 is a plastic material with $n = 1.40$, the wedge is filled with a silicone grease having $n = 1.50$, and the bottom plate is a dense flint glass with $n = 1.60$. What happens now?

SOLUTION

IDENTIFY: The geometry is still as shown in Fig. 35.15, but now half-cycle phase shifts occur at *both* surfaces of the wedge of grease (see Fig. 35.13c).

SET UP: Figure 35.16 shows the situation. Since there is a half-cycle phase shift at both surfaces, there is no *relative* phase shift and we must use Eq. (35.17b) to find the positions of the dark fringes.

EXECUTE: The value of λ to use in Eq. (35.17b) is the wavelength in the silicone grease: $\lambda = \lambda_0/n = (500\text{ nm})/1.50 = 333$ nm. You can readily show that the fringe spacing is 0.833 mm. Note that the two reflected waves from the line of contact are in phase (they both undergo the same phase shift), so the line of contact is at a *bright* fringe.

35.16 Our sketch for this problem.

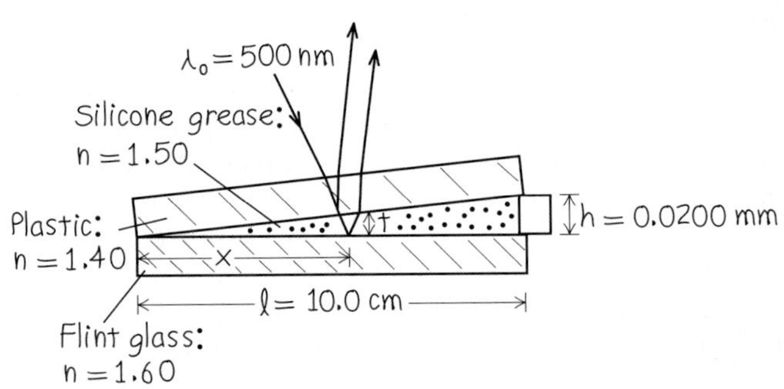

EVALUATE: What would happen if you carefully removed the upper microscope slide so that the grease wedge retained its shape? There would still be half-cycle phase changes at the upper and lower surfaces of the wedge, so the pattern of fringes would be the same as with the upper slide present.

Newton's Rings

Figure 35.17a shows the convex surface of a lens in contact with a plane glass plate. A thin film of air is formed between the two surfaces. When you view the setup with monochromatic light, you see circular interference fringes (Fig. 35.17b). These were studied by Newton and are called **Newton's rings.**

We can use interference fringes to compare the surfaces of two optical parts by placing the two in contact and observing the interference fringes. Figure 35.18 is a photograph made during the grinding of a telescope objective lens. The lower, larger-diameter, thicker disk is the correctly shaped master, and the smaller, upper disk is the lens under test. The "contour lines" are Newton's interference fringes; each one indicates an additional distance between the specimen and the master of one half-wavelength. At 10 lines from the center spot the distance between the two surfaces is five wavelengths, or about 0.003 mm. This

(a) A convex lens in contact with a glass plane

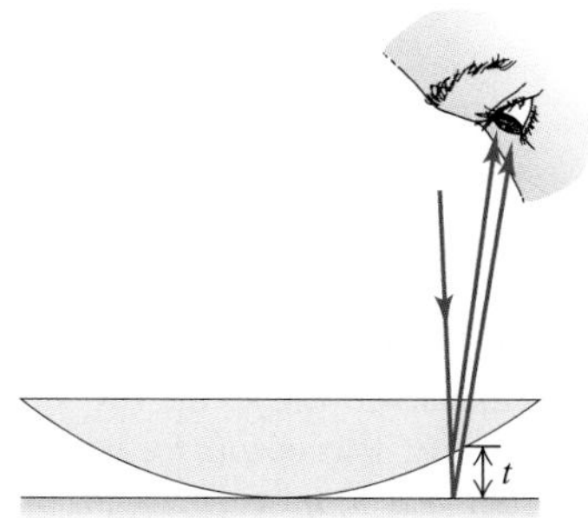
t

(b) Newton's rings: circular interference fringes

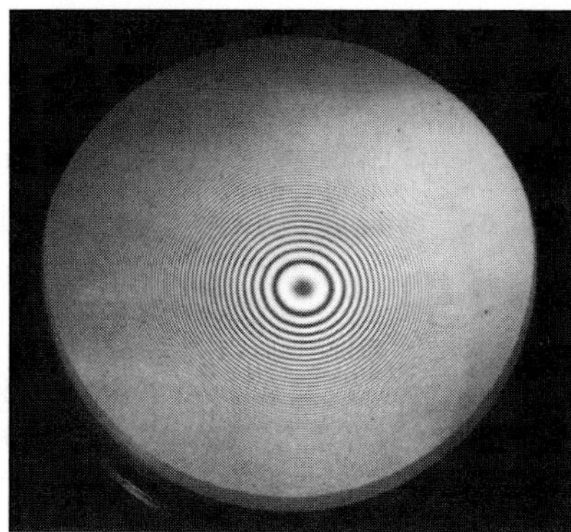

35.17 (a) Air film between a convex lens and a plane surface. The thickness of the film t increases from zero as we move out from the center, giving (b) a series of alternating dark and bright rings for monochromatic light.

isn't very good; high-quality lenses are routinely ground with a precision of less than one wavelength. The surface of the primary mirror of the Hubble Space Telescope was ground to a precision of better than $\frac{1}{50}$ wavelength. Unfortunately, it was ground to incorrect specifications, creating one of the most precise errors in the history of optical technology (see Section 34.2).

35.18 The surface of a telescope objective lens under inspection during manufacture.

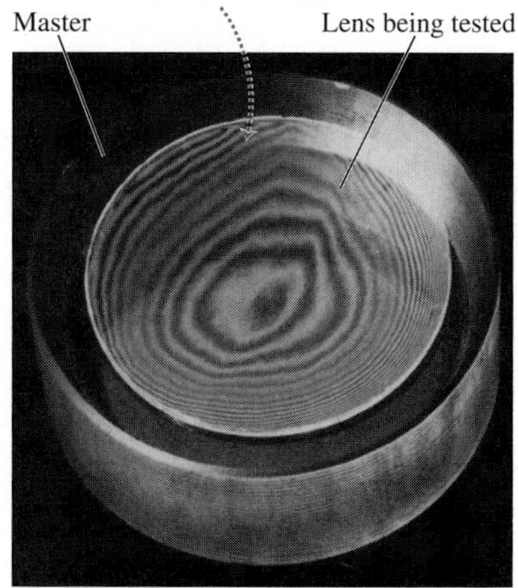
Fringes map lack of fit
between lens and master.
Master
Lens being tested

Nonreflective and Reflective Coatings

Nonreflective coatings for lens surfaces make use of thin-film interference. A thin layer or film of hard transparent material with an index of refraction smaller than that of the glass is deposited on the lens surface, as in Fig. 35.19. Light is reflected from both surfaces of the layer. In both reflections the light is reflected from a medium of greater index than that in which it is traveling, so the same phase change occurs in both reflections. If the film thickness is a quarter (one-fourth) of the wavelength *in the film* (assuming normal incidence), the total path difference is a half-wavelength. Light reflected from the first surface is then a half-cycle out of phase with light reflected from the second, and there is destructive interference.

The thickness of the nonreflective coating can be a quarter-wavelength for only one particular wavelength. This is usually chosen in the central yellow-green portion of the spectrum $(\lambda = 550\text{ nm})$, where the eye is most sensitive. Then there is somewhat more reflection at both longer (red) and shorter (blue) wavelengths, and the reflected light has a purple hue. The overall reflection from a lens or prism surface can be reduced in this way from 4–5% to less than 1%. This treatment is particularly important in eliminating stray reflected light in highly corrected photographic lenses with many individual pieces of glass and many air-glass surfaces. It also increases the net amount of light that is *transmitted* through the lens, since light that is not reflected will be transmitted. The same principle is used to minimize reflection from silicon photovoltaic solar cells $(n = 3.5)$ by use of a thin surface layer of silicon monoxide $(\text{SiO}, n = 1.45)$; this helps to increase the amount of light that actually reaches the solar cells.

35.19 A nonreflective coating has an index of refraction intermediate between those of glass and air.

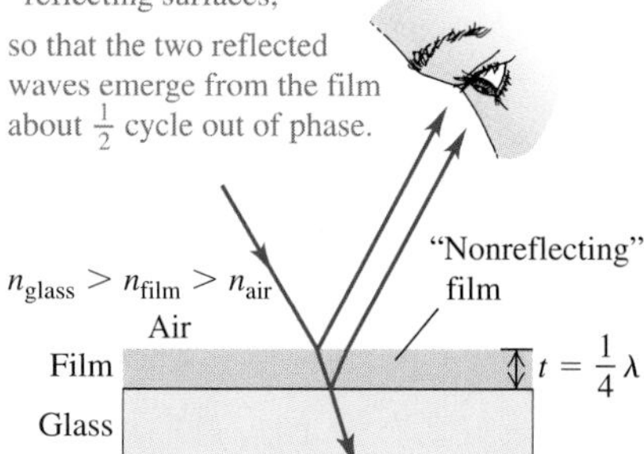
Destructive interference occurs when
• the film is about $\frac{1}{4}\lambda$ thick and
• the light undergoes a phase change at both reflecting surfaces,
so that the two reflected waves emerge from the film about $\frac{1}{2}$ cycle out of phase.
$n_{glass} > n_{film} > n_{air}$
Air
Film
Glass
"Nonreflecting" film
$t = \frac{1}{4}\lambda$

If a quarter-wavelength thickness of a material with an index of refraction *greater* than that of glass is deposited on glass, then the reflectivity is *increased,* and the deposited material is called a **reflective coating.** In this case there is a half-cycle phase shift at the air–film interface but none at the film–glass interface, and reflections from the two sides of the film interfere constructively. For example, a coating with refractive index 2.5 causes 38% of the incident energy to be reflected, compared with 4% or so with no coating. By use of multiple-layer coatings, it is possible to achieve nearly 100% transmission or reflection for particular wavelengths. Some practical applications of these coatings are for color separation in color television cameras and for infrared "heat reflectors" in motion-picture projectors, solar cells, and astronauts' visors. Reflective coatings occur in nature on the scales of herring and other silvery fish; this gives these fish their characteristic shiny appearance (see Problem 35.56).

Example 35.7 A nonreflective coating

A commonly used lens coating material is magnesium fluoride, MgF_2, with $n = 1.38$. What thickness should a nonreflective coating have for 550-nm light if it is applied to glass with $n = 1.52$?

SOLUTION

IDENTIFY: This coating is of the sort depicted in Fig. 35.19.

SET UP: The thickness must be one-quarter of the wavelength in the coating.

EXECUTE: The wavelength of yellow-green light in air is $\lambda_0 = 550$ nm, so its wavelength in the MgF_2 coating is

$$\lambda = \frac{\lambda_0}{n} = \frac{550\text{ nm}}{1.38} = 400\text{ nm}$$

To be a nonreflective film, the coating should have a thickness of one-quarter λ, or 100 nm. This is a very thin film, no more than a few hundred molecules thick.

EVALUATE: Note that such a coating becomes *reflective* if its thickness is equal to one-*half* of a wavelength; then light reflected from the lower surface of the coating travels one wavelength farther than light reflected from the upper surface, so the two waves are in phase and interfere constructively. This occurs for light with a wavelength in MgF_2 of 200 nm and a wavelength in air of $(200\text{ nm})(1.38) = 276$ nm. This is an ultraviolet wavelength (see Section 32.1), so designers of optical lenses with nonreflective coatings need not worry about enhanced reflection of this kind.

Test Your Understanding of Section 35.4 A thin layer of benzene $(n = 1.501)$ ties on top of a sheet of fluorite $(n = 1.434)$. It is illuminated from above with light whose wavelength in benzene is 400 nm. Which of the following possible thicknesses of the benzene layer will maximize the brightness of the reflected light? (i) 100 nm; (ii) 200 nm; (iii) 300 nm; (iv) 400 nm.

35.5 The Michelson Interferometer

An important experimental device that uses interference is the **Michelson interferometer.** In the late 19th century, it helped to provide one of the key experimental underpinnings of the theory of relativity. More recently, Michelson interferometers have been used to make precise measurements of wavelengths and of very small distances, such as the minute changes in thickness of an axon when a nerve impulse propagates along its length. Like the Young two-slit experiment, a Michelson interferometer takes monochromatic light from a single source and divides it into two waves that follow different paths. In Young's experiment, this is done by sending part of the light through one slit and part through another; in a Michelson interferometer a device called a *beam splitter* is used. Interference occurs in both experiments when the two light waves are recombined.

How a Michelson Interferometer Works

The principal components of a Michelson interferometer are shown schematically in Fig. 35.20. A ray of light from a monochromatic source A strikes the beam splitter C, which is a glass plate with a thin coating of silver on its right side. Part of the light (ray 1) passes through the silvered surface and the compensator plate D and is reflected from mirror M_1. It then returns through D and is reflected from the silvered surface of C to the observer. The remainder of the light (ray 2) is reflected from the silvered surface at point P to the mirror M_2 and back through C to the observer's eye. The purpose of the compensator plate D is to ensure that rays 1 and 2 pass through the same thickness of glass; plate D is cut from the same piece of glass as plate C, so their thicknesses are identical to within a fraction of a wavelength.

The whole apparatus in Fig. 35.20 is mounted on a very rigid frame, and the position of mirror M_2 can be adjusted with a fine, very accurate micrometer screw. If the distances L_1 and L_2 are exactly equal and the mirrors M_1 and M_2 are exactly at right angles, the virtual image of M_1 formed by reflection at the silvered

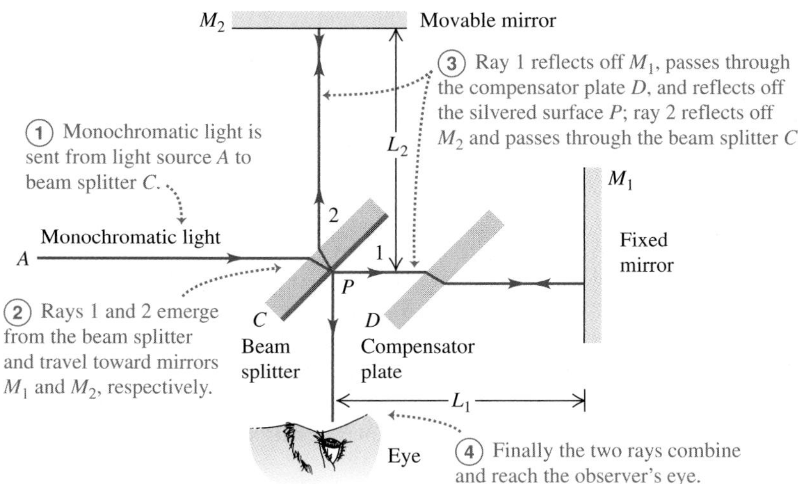

35.20 A schematic Michelson interferometer. The observer sees an interference pattern that results from the difference in path lengths for rays 1 and 2.

surface of plate C coincides with mirror M_2. If L_1 and L_2 are *not* exactly equal, the image of M_1 is displaced slightly from M_2; and if the mirrors are not exactly perpendicular, the image of M_1 makes a slight angle with M_2. Then the mirror M_2 and the virtual image of M_1 play the same roles as the two surfaces of a wedge-shaped thin film (see Section 35.4), and light reflected from these surfaces forms the same sort of interference fringes.

Suppose the angle between mirror M_2 and the virtual image of M_1 is just large enough that five or six vertical fringes are present in the field of view. If we now move the mirror M_2 slowly either backward or forward a distance $\lambda/2$, the difference in path length between rays 1 and 2 changes by λ, and each fringe moves to the left or right a distance equal to the fringe spacing. If we observe the fringe positions through a telescope with a crosshair eyepiece and m fringes cross the crosshairs when we move the mirror a distance y, then

$$y = m\frac{\lambda}{2} \quad \text{or} \quad \lambda = \frac{2y}{m} \qquad (35.19)$$

If m is several thousand, the distance y is large enough that it can be measured with good accuracy, and we can obtain an accurate value for the wavelength λ. Alternatively, if the wavelength is known, a distance y can be measured by simply counting fringes when M_2 is moved by this distance. In this way, distances that are comparable to a wavelength of light can be measured with relative ease.

The Michelson-Morley Experiment

The original application of the Michelson interferometer was to the historic **Michelson-Morley experiment.** Before the electromagnetic theory of light and Einstein's special theory of relativity became established, most physicists believed that the propagation of light waves occurred in a medium called the **ether,** which was believed to permeate all space. In 1887 the American scientists Albert Michelson and Edward Morley used the Michelson interferometer in an attempt to detect the motion of the earth through the ether. Suppose the interferometer in Fig. 35.20 is moving from left to right relative to the ether. According to the ether theory, this would lead to changes in the speed of light in the portions of the path shown as horizontal lines in the figure. There would be fringe shifts relative to the positions that the fringes would have if the instrument were at rest in the ether. Then when the entire instrument was rotated 90°, the other portions of the paths would be similarly affected, giving a fringe shift in the opposite direction.

Michelson and Morley expected that the motion of the earth through the ether would cause a fringe shift of about four-tenths of a fringe when the instrument was rotated. The shift that was actually observed was less than a hundredth of a fringe and, within the limits of experimental uncertainty, appeared to be exactly zero. Despite its orbital motion around the sun, the earth appeared to be *at rest* relative to the ether. This negative result baffled physicists until Einstein developed the special theory of relativity in 1905. Einstein postulated that the speed of a light wave in vacuum has the same magnitude c relative to *all* inertial reference frames, no matter what their velocity may be relative to each other. The presumed ether then plays no role, and the concept of an ether has been abandoned.

The theory of relativity is a well-established cornerstone of modern physics, and we will study it in detail in Chapter 37. In retrospect, the Michelson-Morley experiment gives strong experimental support to the special theory of relativity, and it is often called the most significant "negative-result" experiment ever performed.

Test Your Understanding of Section 35.5 You are observing the pattern of fringes in a Michelson interferometer like that shown in Fig. 35.20. If you change the index of refraction (but not the thickness) of the compensator plate, will the pattern change?

CHAPTER 35 SUMMARY

Interference and coherent sources: Monochromatic light is light with a single frequency. Coherence is a definite, unchanging phase relationship between two waves. The overlap of waves from two coherent sources of monochromatic light forms an interference pattern. The principle of superposition states that the total wave disturbance at any point is the sum of the disturbances from the separate waves.

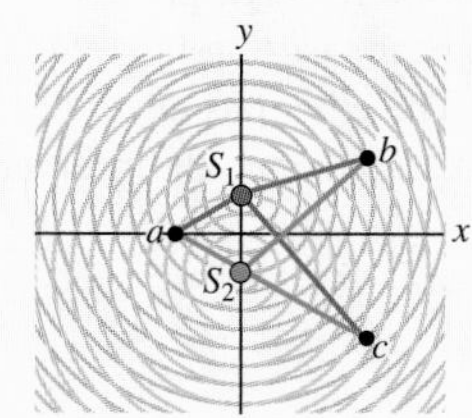

Two-source interference of light: When two sources are in phase, constructive interference occurs at points where the difference in path length from the two sources is zero or an integer number of wavelengths; destructive interference occurs at points where the path difference is a half-integer number of wavelengths. If two sources separated by a distance d are both very far from a point P, and the line from the sources to P makes an angle θ with the line perpendicular to the line of the sources, then the condition for constructive interference at P is Eq. (35.4). The condition for destructive interference is Eq. (35.5). When θ is very small, the position y_m of the mth bright fringe on a screen located a distance R from the sources is given by Eq. (35.6). (See Examples 35.1 and 35.2.)

$$d\sin\theta = m\lambda \quad (m = 0, \pm1, \pm2, \dots)$$
(constructive interference) (35.4)

$$d\sin\theta = \left(m + \frac{1}{2}\right)\lambda$$
$(m = 0, \pm1, \pm2, \dots)$
(destructive interference) (35.5)

$$y_m = R\frac{m\lambda}{d}$$
(bright fringes) (35.6)

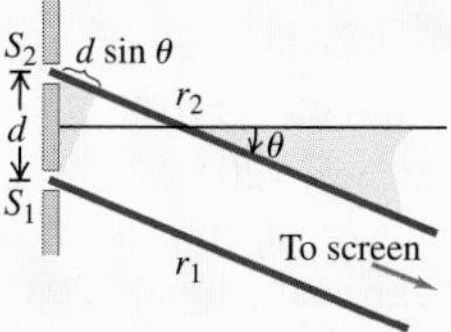

Intensity in interference patterns: When two sinusoidal waves with equal amplitude E and phase difference ϕ are superimposed, the resultant amplitude E_P and intensity I are given by Eqs. (35.7) and (35.10), respectively. If the two sources emit in phase, the phase difference ϕ at a point P (located a distance r_1 from source 1 and a distance r_2 from source 2) is directly proportional to the difference in path length $r_2 - r_1$. (See Example 35.3.)

$$E_P = 2E\left|\cos\frac{\phi}{2}\right| \quad (35.7)$$

$$I = I_0\cos^2\frac{\phi}{2} \quad (35.10)$$

$$\phi = \frac{2\pi}{\lambda}(r_2 - r_1) = k(r_2 - r_1) \quad (35.11)$$

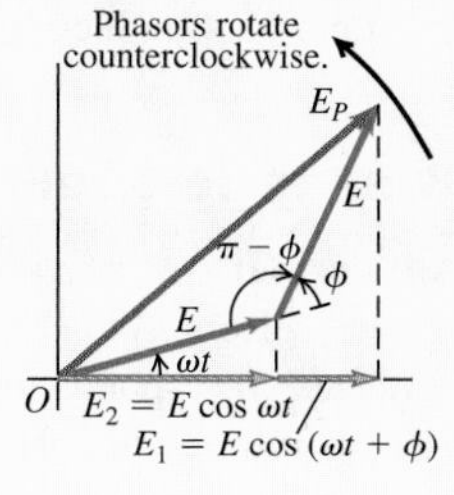

Interference in thin films: When light is reflected from both sides of a thin film of thickness t and no phase shift occurs at either surface, constructive interference between the reflected waves occurs when $2t$ is equal to an integral number of wavelengths. If a half-cycle phase shift occurs at one surface, this is the condition for destructive interference. A half-cycle phase shift occurs during reflection whenever the index of refraction in the second material is greater than that in the first. (See Examples 35.4–35.7.)

$$2t = m\lambda \quad (m = 0, 1, 2, \dots)$$
(constructive reflection from thin film, no relative phase shift) (35.17a)

$$2t = \left(m + \frac{1}{2}\right)\lambda \quad (m = 0, 1, 2, \dots)$$
(destructive reflection from thin film, no relative phase shift) (35.17b)

$$2t = \left(m + \frac{1}{2}\right)\lambda \quad (m = 0, 1, 2, \dots)$$
(constructive reflection from thin film, half-cycle relative phase shift) (35.18a)

$$2t = m\lambda \quad (m = 0, 1, 2, \dots)$$
(destructive reflection from thin film, half-cycle relative phase shift) (35.18b)

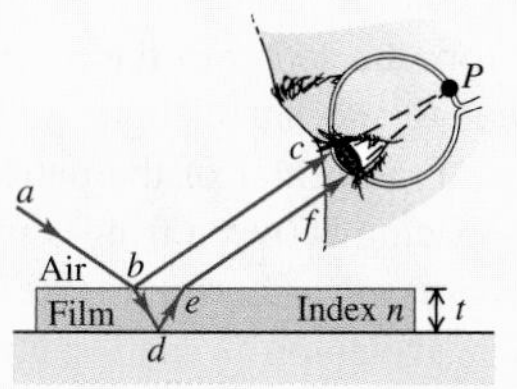

Michelson interferometer: The Michelson interferometer uses a monochromatic light source and can be used for high-precision measurements of wavelengths. Its original purpose was to detect motion of the earth relative to a hypothetical ether, the supposed medium for electromagnetic waves. The ether has never been detected, and the concept has been abandoned; the speed of light is the same relative to all observers. This is part of the foundation of the special theory of relativity.

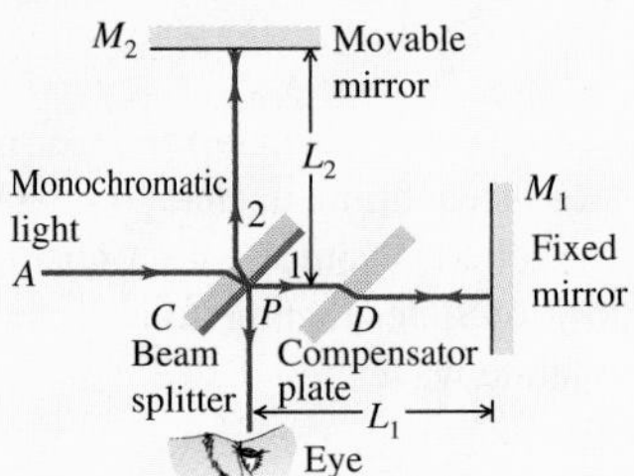

Key Terms

physical optics, *1207*
interference, *1208*
principle of superposition, *1208*
monochromatic light, *1208*
coherent, *1209*
constructive interference, *1209*
destructive interference, *1210*
antinodal curves, *1210*
nodal curves, *1210*
interference fringes, *1212*
Newton's rings, *1222*
nonreflective coating, *1223*
reflective coating, *1223*
Michelson interferometer, *1224*
Michelson-Morley experiment, *1225*
ether, *1225*

Answer to Chapter Opening Question ?

The colors appear due to constructive interference between light waves reflected from the outer and inner surfaces of the soap bubble. The thickness of the bubble walls at each point determines the wavelength of light for which the most constructive interference occurs and hence the color that appears the brightest at that point (see Example 35.4 in Section 35.4).

Answers to Test Your Understanding Questions

35.1 Answer: (i) At any point P on the positive y-axis above S_1, the distance r_2 from S_2 to P is greater than the distance r_1 from S_1 to P by 4λ. This corresponds to $m = 4$ in Eq. (35.1), the equation for constructive interference. Hence all such points make up an antinodal curve.
35.2 Answer: (ii) Blue light has a shorter wavelength than red light (see Section 32.1). Equation (35.6) tells us that the distance y_m from the center of the pattern to the mth bright fringe is proportional to the wavelength λ. Hence all of the fringes will move toward the center of the pattern as the wavelength decreases, and the spacing between fringes will decrease.
35.3 Answer: (i), (iv), (ii), (iii) In cases (i) and (iii) we are given the wavelength λ and path difference $d\sin\theta$. Hence we use Eq. (35.14), $I = I_0\cos^2[(\pi d\sin\theta)/\lambda]$. In parts (ii) and (iii) we are given the phase difference ϕ and we use Eq. (35.10), $I = I_0\cos^2(\phi/2)$. We find:
(i) $I = I_0\cos^2[\pi(4.00 \times 10^{-7}\text{ m})/(5.00 \times 10^{-7}\text{ m})] = I_0\cos^2(0.800\pi\text{ rad}) = 0.655I_0$;
(ii) $I = I_0\cos^2[(4.00\text{ rad})/2] = I_0\cos^2(2.00\text{ rad}) = 0.173I_0$;
(iii) $I = I_0\cos^2[\pi(7.50 \times 10^{-7}\text{ m})/(5.00 \times 10^{-7}\text{ m})] = I_0\cos^2(1.50\pi\text{ rad}) = 0$;
(iv) $I = I_0\cos^2[(2.00\text{ rad})/2] = I_0\cos^2(1.00\text{ rad}) = 0.292I_0$.
35.4 Answers: (i) and (iii) Benzene has a larger index of refraction than air, so light that reflects off the upper surface of the benzene undergoes a half-cycle phase shift. Fluorite has a *smaller* index of refraction than benzene, so light that reflects off the benzene–fluorite interface does not undergo a phase shift. Hence the equation for constructive reflection is Eq. (35.18a), $2t = (m + \frac{1}{2})\lambda$, which we can rewrite as $t = (m + \frac{1}{2})\lambda/2 = (m + \frac{1}{2})(400\text{ mm})/2 = 100\text{ nm}, 300\text{ nm}, 500\text{ nm}, \ldots$.
35.5 Answer: yes Changing the index of refraction changes the wavelength of the light inside the compensator plate, and so changes the nuimber of wavelengths within the thickness of the plate. Hence this has the same effect as changing the distance L_1 from the beam splitter to mirror M_1, which would change the interference pattern.

PROBLEMS

For instructor-assigned homework, go to **www.masteringphysics.com**

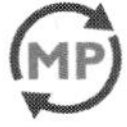

Discussion Questions

Q35.1. A two-slit interference experiment is set up, and the fringes are displayed on a screen. Then the whole apparatus is immersed in the nearest swimming pool. How does the fringe pattern change?
Q35.2. Could an experiment similar to Young's two-slit experiment be performed with sound? How might this be carried out? Does it matter that sound waves are longitudinal and electromagnetic waves are transverse? Explain.
Q35.3. Monochromatic coherent light passing through two thin slits is viewed on a distant screen. Are the bright fringes equally spaced on the screen? If so, why? If not, which ones are closest to being equally spaced?
Q35.4. In a two-slit interference pattern on a distant screen, are the bright fringes midway between the dark fringes? Is this ever a good approximation?
Q35.5. Would the headlights of a distant car form a two-source interference pattern? If so, how might it be observed? If not, why not?

Q35.6. The two sources S_1 and S_2 shown in Fig. 35.3 emit waves of the same wavelength λ and are in phase with each other. Suppose S_1 is a weaker source, so that the waves emitted by S_1 have half the amplitude of the waves emitted by S_2. How would this affect the positions of the antinodal lines and nodal lines? Would there be total reinforcement at points on the antinodal curves? Would there be total cancellation at points on the nodal curves? Explain your answers.

Q35.7. Could the Young two-slit interference experiment be performed with gamma rays? If not, why not? If so, discuss differences in the experimental design compared to the experiment with visible light.

Q35.8. Coherent red light illuminates two narrow slits that are 25 cm apart. Will a two-slit interference pattern be observed when the light from the slits falls on a screen? Explain.

Q35.9. Coherent light with wavelength λ falls on two narrow slits separated by a distance d. If d is less than some minimum value, no dark fringes are observed. Explain. In terms of λ, what is this minimum value of d?

Q35.10. A fellow student, who values memorizing equations above understanding them, combines Eqs. (35.4) and (35.13) to "prove" that ϕ can *only* equal $2\pi m$. How would you explain to this student that ϕ can have values other than $2\pi m$?

Q35.11. If the monochromatic light shown in Fig. 35.5a were replaced by white light, would a two-slit interference pattern be seen on the screen? Explain.

Q35.12. In using the superposition principle to calculate intensities in interference patterns, could you add the intensities of the waves instead of their amplitudes? Explain.

Q35.13. A glass windowpane with a thin film of water on it reflects less than when it is perfectly dry. Why?

Q35.14. A *very* thin soap film $(n = 1.33)$, whose thickness is much less than a wavelength of visible light, looks black; it appears to reflect no light at all. Why? By contrast, an equally thin layer of soapy water $(n = 1.33)$ on glass $(n = 1.50)$ appears quite shiny. Why is there a difference?

Q35.15. Interference can occur in thin films. Why is it important that the films be *thin?* Why don't you get these effects with a relatively *thick* film? Where should you put the dividing line between "thin" and "thick"? Explain your reasoning.

Q35.16. If we shine white light on an air wedge like that shown in Fig. 35.12, the colors that are weak in the light *reflected* from any point along the wedge are strong in the light *transmitted* through the wedge. Explain why this should be so.

Q35.17. Monochromatic light is directed at normal incidence on a thin film. There is destructive interference for the reflected light, so the intensity of the reflected light is very low. What happened to the energy of the incident light?

Q35.18. When a thin oil film spreads out on a puddle of water, the thinnest part of the film looks dark in the resulting interference pattern. What does this tell you about the relative magnitudes of the refractive indexes of oil and water?

Exercises

Section 35.1 Interference and Coherent Sources

35.1. Two coherent sources A and B of radio waves are 5.00 m apart. Each source emits waves with wavelength 6.00 m. Consider points along the line between the two sources. At what distances, if any, from A is the interference (a) constructive and (b) destructive?

35.2. Radio Interference. Two radio antennas A and B radiate in phase. Antenna B is 120 m to the right of antenna A. Consider point Q along the extension of the line connecting the antennas, a horizontal distance of 40 m to the right of antenna B. The frequency, and hence the wavelength, of the emitted waves can be varied. (a) What is the longest wavelength for which there will be destructive interference at point Q? (b) What is the longest wavelength for which there will be constructive interference at point Q?

35.3. A radio transmitting station operating at a frequency of 120 MHz has two identical antennas that radiate in phase. Antenna B is 9.00 m to the right of antenna A. Consider point P between the antennas and along the line connecting them, a horizontal distance x to the right of antenna A. For what values of x will constructive interference occur at point P?

35.4. Two light sources can be adjusted to emit monochromatic light of any visible wavelength. The two sources are coherent, 2.04 μm apart, and in line with an observer, so that one source is 2.04 μm farther from the observer than the other. (a) For what visible wavelengths (400 to 700 nm) will the observer see the brightest light, owing to constructive interference? (b) How would your answers to part (a) be affected if the two sources were not in line with the observer, but were still arranged so that one source is 2.04 μm farther away from the observer than the other? (c) For what visible wavelengths will there be *destructive* interference at the location of the observer?

35.5. Two speakers, emitting identical sound waves of wavelength 2.0 m in phase with each other, and an observer are located as shown in Fig. 35.21. (a) At the observer's location, what is the path difference for waves from the two speakers? (b) Will the sound waves interfere constructively or destructively at the observer's location—or something in between constructive and destructive? (c) Suppose the observer now increases her distance from the speakers to 17.0 m, staying directly in front of the same speaker as initially. Answer the questions of parts (a) and (b) for this new situation.

Figure 35.21 Exercise 35.5

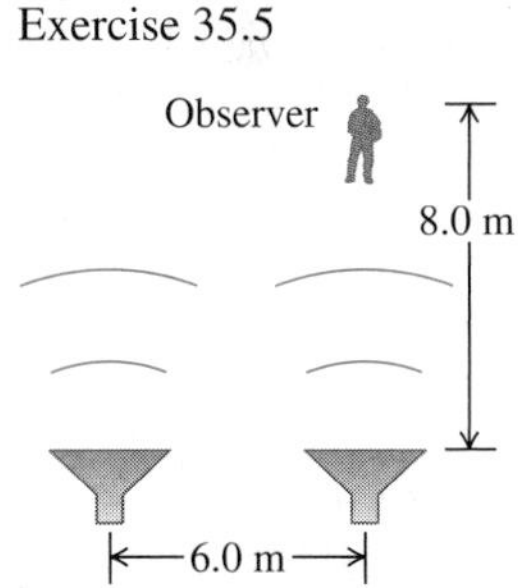

35.6. Figure 35.3 shows the wave pattern produced by two identical, coherent sources emitting waves with wavelength λ and separated by a distance $d = 4\lambda$. (a) Explain why the positive y-axis above S_1 constitutes an antinodal curve with $m = +4$ and why the negative y-axis below S_2 constitutes an antinodal curve with $m = -4$. (b) Draw the wave pattern produced when the separation between the sources is reduced to 3λ. In your drawing, sketch all antinodal curves—that is, the curves on which $r_2 - r_1 = m\lambda$. Label each curve by its value of m. (c) In general, what determines the maximum (most positive) and minimum (most negative) values of the integer m that labels the antinodal lines? (d) Suppose the separation between the sources is increased to $7\frac{1}{2}\lambda$. How many antinodal curves will there be? To what values of m do they correspond? Explain your reasoning. (You should not have to make a drawing to answer these questions.)

35.7. Consider Fig. 35.3, which could represent interference between water waves in a ripple tank. Pick at least three points on the antinodal curve labeled "$m = 3$," and make measurements from the figure to show that Eq. (35.1) is indeed satisfied. Explain what measurements you made and how you measured the wavelength λ.

Section 35.2 Two-Source Interference of Light

35.8. Young's experiment is performed with light from excited helium atoms $(\lambda = 502\text{ nm})$. Fringes are measured carefully on a screen 1.20 m away from the double slit, and the center of the 20th fringe (not counting the central bright fringe) is found to be 10.6 mm from the center of the central bright fringe. What is the separation of the two slits?

35.9. Two slits spaced 0.450 mm apart are placed 75.0 cm from a screen. What is the distance between the second and third dark lines of the interference pattern on the screen when the slits are illuminated with coherent light with a wavelength of 500 nm?

35.10. Coherent light with wavelength 450 nm falls on a double slit. On a screen 1.80 m away, the distance between dark fringes is 4.20 mm. What is the separation of the slits?

35.11. Coherent light from a sodium-vapor lamp is passed through a filter that blocks everything except light of a single wavelength. It then falls on two slits separated by 0.460 mm. In the resulting interference pattern on a screen 2.20 m away, adjacent bright fringes are separated by 2.82 mm. What is the wavelength?

35.12. Coherent light with wavelength 400 nm passes through two very narrow slits that are separated by 0.200 mm and the interference pattern is observed on a screen 4.00 m from the slits. (a) What is the width (in mm) of the central interference maximum? (b) What is the width of the first-order bright fringe?

35.13. Two very narrow slits are spaced 1.80 μm apart and are placed 35.0 cm from a screen. What is the distance between the first and second dark lines of the interference pattern when the slits are illuminated with coherent light with $\lambda = 550$ nm? (*Hint:* The angle θ in Eq. (35.5) is *not* small.)

35.14. Coherent light that contains two wavelengths, 660 nm (red) and 470 nm (blue), passes through two narrow slits separated by 0.300 mm, and the interference pattern is observed on a screen 5.00 m from the slits. What is the distance on the screen between the first-order bright fringes for the two wavelengths?

35.15. Coherent light with wavelength 600 nm passes through two very narrow slits and the interference pattern is observed on a screen 3.00 m from the slits. The first-order bright fringe is at 4.84 mm from the center of the central bright fringe. For what wavelength of light will the first-order dark fringe be observed at this same point on the screen?

35.16. Coherent light of frequency 6.32×10^{14} Hz passes through two thin slits and falls on a screen 85.0 cm away. You observe that the third bright fringe occurs at ± 3.11 cm on either side of the central bright fringe. (a) How far apart are the two slits? (b) At what distance from the central bright fringe will the third dark fringe occur?

35.17. Two thin parallel slits that are 0.0116 mm apart are illuminated by a laser beam of wavelength 585 nm. (a) On a very large distant screen, what is the *total* number of bright fringes (those indicating complete constructive interference), including the central fringe and those on both sides of it? Solve this problem without calculating all the angles! (*Hint:* What is the largest that $\sin\theta$ can be? What does this tell you is the largest value of m?) (b) At what angle, relative to the original direction of the beam, will the fringe that is most distant from the central bright fringe occur?

35.18. An FM radio station has a frequency of 107.9 MHz and uses two identical antennas mounted at the same elevation, 12.0 m apart. The antennas radiate in phase. The resulting radiation pattern has a maximum intensity along a horizontal line perpendicular to the line joining the antennas and midway between them. Assume that the intensity is observed at distances from the antennas that are much greater than 12.0 m. (a) At which other angles (measured from the line of maximum intensity) is the intensity maximum? (b) At which angles is it zero?

Section 35.3 Intensity in Interference Patterns

35.19. In a two-slit interference pattern, the intensity at the peak of the central maximum is I_0. (a) At a point in the pattern where the phase difference between the waves from the two slits is 60.0°, what is the intensity? (b) What is the path difference for 480-nm light from the two slits at a point where the phase angle is 60.0°?

35.20. Coherent sources A and B emit electromagnetic waves with wavelength 2.00 cm. Point P is 4.86 m from A and 5.24 m from B. What is the phase difference at P between these two waves?

35.21. Coherent light with wavelength 500 nm passes through narrow slits separated by 0.340 mm. At a distance from the slits large compared to their separation, what is the phase difference (in radians) in the light from the two slits at an angle of 23.0° from the centerline?

35.22. GPS Transmission. The GPS (Global Positioning System) satellites are approximately 5.18 m across and transmit two low-power signals, one of which is at 1575.42 MHz (in the UHF band). In a series of laboratory tests on the satellite, you put two 1575.42-MHz UHF transmitters at opposite ends of the satellite. These broadcast in phase uniformly in all directions. You measure the intensity at points on a circle that is several hundred meters in radius and centered on the satellite. You measure angles on this circle relative to a point that lies along the centerline of the satellite (that is, the perpendicular bisector of a line which extends from one transmitter to the other). At this point on the circle, the measured intensity is 2.00 W/m^2. (a) At how many other angles in the range $0° < \theta < 90°$ is the intensity also 2.00 W/m^2? (b) Find the four smallest angles in the range $0° < \theta < 90°$ for which the intensity is 2.00 W/m^2. (c) What is the intensity at a point on the circle at an angle of 4.65° from the centerline?

35.23. Two slits spaced 0.260 mm apart are placed 0.700 m from a screen and illuminated by coherent light with a wavelength of 660 nm. The intensity at the center of the central maximum $(\theta = 0°)$ is I_0. (a) What is the distance on the screen from the center of the central maximum to the first minimum? (b) What is the distance on the screen from the center of the central maximum to the point where the intensity has fallen to $I_0/2$?

35.24. Show that Eq. (35.14) gives zero-intensity directions that agree with Eq. (35.5).

35.25. Points A and B are 56.0 m apart along an east-west line. At each of these points, a radio transmitter is emitting a 12.5-MHz signal horizontally. These transmitters are in phase with other and emit their beams uniformly in a horizontal plane. A receiver is taken 0.500 km north of the AB line and initially placed at point C, directly opposite the midpoint of AB. The receiver can be moved only along an east-west direction but, due to its limited sensitivity, it must always remain within a range so that the intensity of the signal it receives from the transmitter is no less than $\frac{1}{4}$ of its maximum value. How far from point C (along an east-west line) can the receiver be moved and always be able to pick up the signal?

35.26. Consider two antennas separated by 9.00 m that radiate in phase at 120 MHz, as described in Exercise 35.3. A receiver placed 150 m from both antennas measures an intensity I_0. The receiver is moved so that it is 1.8 m closer to one antenna than to the other. (a) What is the phase difference ϕ between the two radio waves produced by this path difference? (b) In terms of I_0, what is the intensity measured by the receiver at its new position?

Section 35.4 Interference in Thin Films

35.27. What is the thinnest film of a coating with $n = 1.42$ on glass $(n = 1.52)$ for which destructive interference of the red component (650 nm) of an incident white light beam in air can take place by reflection?

35.28. Nonglare Glass. When viewing a piece of art that is behind glass, one often is affected by the light that is reflected off the front of the glass (called *glare*), which can make it difficult to see the art clearly. One solution is to coat the outer surface of the glass with a film to cancel part of the glare. (a) If the glass has a refractive index of 1.62 and you use TiO_2, which has an index of refraction of 2.62, as the coating, what is the minimum film thickness that will cancel light of wavelength 505 nm? (b) If this coating is too thin to stand up to wear, what other thickness would also work? Find only the three thinnest ones.

35.29. Two rectangular pieces of plane glass are laid one upon the other on a table. A thin strip of paper is placed between them at one edge so that a very thin wedge of air is formed. The plates are illuminated at normal incidence by 546-nm light from a mercury-vapor lamp. Interference fringes are formed, with 15.0 fringes per centimeter. Find the angle of the wedge.

35.30. A plate of glass 9.00 cm long is placed in contact with a second plate and is held at a small angle with it by a metal strip 0.0800 mm thick placed under one end. The space between the plates is filled with air. The glass is illuminated from above with light having a wavelength in air of 656 nm. How many interference fringes are observed per centimeter in the reflected light?

35.31. A uniform film of TiO_2, 1036 nm thick and having index of refraction 2.62, is spread uniformly over the surface of crown glass of refractive index 1.52. Light of wavelength 520.0 nm falls at normal incidence onto the film from air. You want to increase the thickness of this film so that the reflected light cancels. (a) What is the *minimum* thickness of TiO_2 that you must *add* so the reflected light cancels as desired? (b) After you make the adjustment in part (a), what is the path difference between the light reflected off the top of the film and the light that cancels it after traveling through the film? Express your answer in (i) nanometers and (ii) wavelengths of the light in the TiO_2 film.

35.32. A plastic film with index of refraction 1.85 is put on the surface of a car window to increase the reflectivity and thus to keep the interior of the car cooler. The window glass has index of refraction 1.52. (a) What minimum thickness is required if light with wavelength 550 nm in air reflected from the two sides of the film is to interfere constructively? (b) It is found to be difficult to manufacture and install coatings as thin as calculated in part (a). What is the next greatest thickness for which there will also be constructive interference?

35.33. The walls of a soap bubble have about the same index of refraction as that of plain water, $n = 1.33$. There is air both inside and outside the bubble. (a) What wavelength (in air) of visible light is most strongly reflected from a point on a soap bubble where its wall is 290 nm thick? To what color does this correspond (see Fig. 32.4 and Table 32.1)? (b) Repeat part (a) for a wall thickness of 340 nm.

35.34. Light with wavelength 648 nm in air is incident perpendicularly from air on a film 8.76 μm thick and with refractive index 1.35. Part of the light is reflected from the first surface of the film, and part enters the film and is reflected back at the second surface, where the film is again in contact with air. (a) How many waves are contained along the path of this second part of the light in its round trip through the film? (b) What is the phase difference between these two parts of the light as they leave the film?

35.35. Compact Disc Player. A compact disc (CD) is read from the bottom by a semiconductor laser with wavelength 790 nm passing through a plastic substrate of refractive index 1.8. When the beam encounters a pit, part of the beam is reflected from the pit and part from the flat region between the pits, so these two beams interfere with each other (Fig. 35.22). What must the minimum pit depth be so that the part of the beam reflected from a pit cancels the part of the beam reflected from the flat region? (It is this cancellation that allows the player to recognize the beginning and end of a pit. For a fuller explanation of the physics behind CD technology, see the article "The Compact Disc Digital Audio System," by Thomas D. Rossing, in the December 1987 issue of *The Physics Teacher.*)

Figure **35.22** Exercise 35.35.

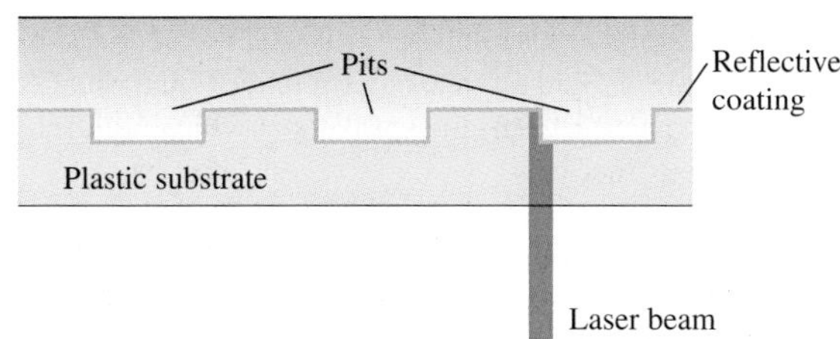

35.36. What is the thinnest soap film (excluding the case of zero thickness) that appears black when illuminated with light with wavelength 480 nm? The index of refraction of the film is 1.33, and there is air on both sides of the film.

Section 35.5 The Michelson Interferometer

35.37. How far must the mirror M_2 (see Fig. 35.20) of the Michelson interferometer be moved so that 1800 fringes of He-Ne laser light ($\lambda = 633$ nm) move across a line in the field of view?

35.38. Jan first uses a Michelson interferometer with the 606-nm light from a krypton-86 lamp. He displaces the movable mirror away from him, counting 818 fringes moving across a line in his field of view. Then Linda replaces the krypton lamp with filtered 502-nm light from a helium lamp and displaces the movable mirror toward her. She also counts 818 fringes, but they move across the line in her field of view opposite to the direction they moved for Jan. Assume that both Jan and Linda counted to 818 correctly. (a) What distance did each person move the mirror? (b) What is the resultant displacement of the mirror?

Problems

35.39. The radius of curvature of the convex surface of a planoconvex lens is 95.2 cm. The lens is placed convex side down on a perfectly flat glass plate that is illuminated from above with red light having a wavelength of 580 nm. Find the diameter of the second bright ring in the interference pattern.

35.40. Newton's rings can be seen when a planoconvex lens is placed on a flat glass surface (see Problem 35.39). For a particular lens with an index of refraction of $n = 1.50$ and a glass plate with an index of $n = 1.80$, the diameter of the third bright ring is 0.850 mm. If water ($n = 1.33$) now fills the space between the lens and the plate, what is the new diameter of this ring?

35.41. Suppose you illuminate two thin slits by monochromatic coherent light in air and find that they produce their first interference *minima* at $\pm 35.20°$ on either side of the central bright spot. You then immerse these slits in a transparent liquid and illuminate them with the same light. Now you find that the first minima occur at $\pm 19.46°$ instead. What is the index of refraction of this liquid?

35.42. A very thin sheet of brass contains two thin parallel slits. When a laser beam shines on these slits at normal incidence and room temperature $(20.0°C)$, the first interference dark fringes occur at $\pm 32.5°$ from the original direction of the laser beam when viewed from some distance. If this sheet is now slowly heated up to 135°C, by how many degrees do these dark fringes change position? Do they move closer together or get farther apart? See Table 17.1 for pertinent information, and ignore any effects that might occur due to change in the thickness of the slits. (*Hint:* Since thermal expansion normally produces very small changes in length, you can use differentials to find the change in the angle.)

35.43. Two speakers, 2.50 m apart, are driven by the same audio oscillator so that each one produces a sound consisting of *two* distinct frequencies, 0.900 kHz and 1.20 kHz. The speed of sound in the room is 344 m/s. Find all the angles relative to the usual center line in front of (and far from) the speakers at which *both* frequencies interfere constructively.

35.44. Two radio antennas radiating in phase are located at points A and B, 200 m apart (Fig. 35.23). The radio waves have a frequency of 5.80 MHz. A radio receiver is moved out from point B along a line perpendicular to the line connecting A and B (line BC shown in Fig. 35.23). At what distances from B will there be *destructive* interference? (*Note:* The distance of the receiver from the sources is not large in comparison to the separation of the sources, so Eq. (35.5) does not apply.)

Figure 35.23 Problem 35.44.

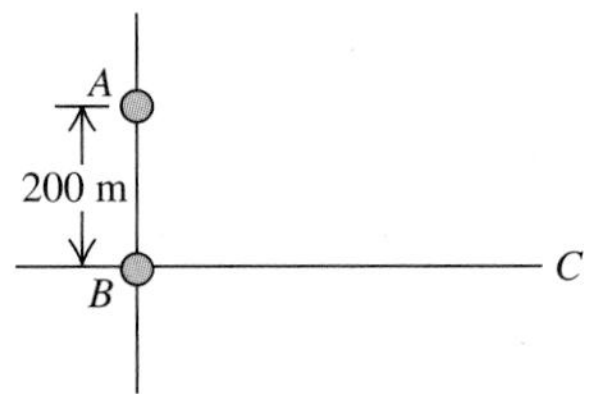

35.45. One round face of a 3.25-m, solid, cylindrical plastic pipe is covered with a thin black coating that completely blocks light. The opposite face is covered with a fluorescent coating that glows when it is struck by light. Two straight, thin, parallel scratches, 0.225 mm apart, are made in the center of the black face. When laser light of wavelength 632.8 nm shines through the slits perpendicular to the black face, you find that the central bright fringe on the opposite face is 5.82 mm wide, measured between the dark fringes that border it on either side. What is the index of refraction of the plastic?

35.46. A uniform thin film of material of refractive index 1.40 coats a glass plate of refractive index 1.55. This film has the proper thickness to cancel normally incident light of wavelength 525 nm that strikes the film surface from air, but it is somewhat greater than the minimum thickness to achieve this cancellation. As time goes by, the film wears away at a steady rate of 4.20 nm per year. What is the minimum number of years before the reflected light of this wavelength is now enhanced instead of cancelled?

35.47. (a) In Fig. 35.3, suppose source S_2 is *not* in phase with S_1, but instead is *out* of phase by $\frac{1}{2}$ cycle. In this situation, Eq. (35.1) is the condition for *destructive* interference, and Eq. (35.2) is the condition for *constructive* interference. Explain why this is so. (b) Suppose S_2 *leads* S_1 by a phase angle ϕ; that is, if the displacement of source S_1 is given by $x_1(t) = A\cos\omega t$, then the displacement of source S_2 is $x_2(t) = A\cos(\omega t + \phi)$. (In the situation of part (a), $\phi = \pi$.) Find expressions for the values of the path difference $r_2 - r_1$ that correspond to constructive interference and to destructive interference.

35.48. The electric fields received at point P from two identical, coherent wave sources are $E_1(t) = E\cos(\omega t + \phi)$ and $E_2(t) = E\cos\omega t$. (a) Use one of the trigonometric identities in Appendix B to show that the resultant wave is $E_P(t) = 2E\cos(\phi/2)\cos(\omega t + \phi/2)$. (b) Show that the amplitude of this resultant wave is given by Eq. (35.7). (c) Use the result of part (a) to show that at an interference maximum, the amplitude of the resultant wave is in phase with the original waves $E_1(t)$ and $E_2(t)$. (d) Use the result of part (a) to show that near an interference minimum, the resultant wave is approximately $\frac{1}{4}$ cycle out of phase with either of the original waves. (e) Show that the *instantaneous* Poynting vector at point P has magnitude $S = 4\epsilon_0 cE^2\cos^2(\phi/2)\cos^2(\omega t + \phi/2)$ and that the *time-averaged* Poynting vector is given by Eq. (35.9).

35.49. Let the two sources S_1 and S_2 shown in Fig. 35.3 be located at $y = d$ and $y = -d$, respectively. (a) Rewrite Eq. (35.1) in terms of the x- and y-coordinates of a point P in Fig. 35.3 at which constructive interference occurs. (b) Your expression in part (a) is the equation for the antinodal curves shown in Fig. 35.3. Show that these curves are hyperbolas. (*Hint:* You may want to review the definition of a hyperbola in analytic geometry.) (c) Repeat part (a) for Eq. (35.2), which describes points at which *destructive* interference occurs, and show that the *nodal* curves (not shown in Fig. 35.3) are also hyperbolas.

35.50. Consider a two-slit interference experiment in which the two slits are of different widths. As measured on a distant screen, the amplitude of the wave from the first slit is E, while the amplitude of the wave from the second slit is $2E$. (a) Show that the intensity at any point in the interference pattern is

$$I = I_0\left(\frac{5}{9} + \frac{4}{9}\cos\phi\right)$$

where ϕ is the phase difference between the two waves as measured at a particular point on the screen and I_0 is the maximum intensity in the pattern. (b) Graph I versus ϕ (like Fig. 35.10). What is the minimum value of the intensity, and for which values of ϕ does it occur?

35.51. A thin uniform film of refractive index 1.750 is placed on a sheet of glass of refractive index 1.50. At room temperature $(20.0°C)$, this film is just thick enough for light with wavelength 582.4 nm reflected off the top of the film to be cancelled by light reflected from the top of the glass. After the glass is placed in an oven and slowly heated to 170°C, you find that the film cancels reflected light with wavelength 588.5 nm. What is the coefficient of linear expansion of the film? (Ignore any changes in the refractive index of the film due to the temperature change.)

35.52. Red light with wavelength 700 nm is passed through a two-slit apparatus. At the same time, monochromatic visible light with another wavelength passes through the same apparatus. As a result, most of the pattern that appears on the screen is a mixture of two colors; however, the center of the third bright fringe $(m = 3)$ of the red light appears pure red, with none of the other color. What are the possible wavelengths of the second type of visible light? Do you need to know the slit spacing to answer this question? Why or why not?

35.53. Consider a two-slit interference pattern, for which the intensity distribution is given by Eq. (35.14). Let θ_m be the angular position of the mth bright fringe, where the intensity is I_0. Assume that θ_m is small, so that $\sin\theta_m \cong \theta_m$. Let θ_m^+ and θ_m^- be the two angles on either side of θ_m for which $I = \frac{1}{2}I_0$. The quantity $\Delta\theta_m = |\theta_m^+ - \theta_m^-|$ is the half-width of the mth fringe. Calculate $\Delta\theta_m$. How does $\Delta\theta_m$ depend on m?

35.54. White light reflects at normal incidence from the top and bottom surfaces of a glass plate $(n = 1.52)$. There is air above and below the plate. Constructive interference is observed for light whose wavelength in air is 477.0 nm. What is the thickness of the plate if the next longer wavelength for which there is constructive interference is 540.6 nm?

35.55. A source S of monochromatic light and a detector D are both located in air a distance h above a horizontal plane sheet of glass, and are separated by a horizontal distance x. Waves reaching D directly from S interfere with waves that reflect off the glass. The distance x is small compared to h so that the reflection is at close to normal incidence. (a) Show that the condition for constructive interference is $\sqrt{x^2 + 4h^2} - x = (m + \frac{1}{2})\lambda$, and the condition for destructive interference is $\sqrt{x^2 + 4h^2} - x = m\lambda$. (*Hint:* Take into account the phase change on reflection.) (b) Let $h = 24$ cm and $x = 14$ cm. What is the longest wavelength for which there will be constructive interference?

35.56. Reflective Coatings and Herring. Herring and related fish have a brilliant silvery appearance that camouflages them while they are swimming in a sunlit ocean. The silveriness is due to *platelets* attached to the surfaces of these fish. Each platelet is made up of several alternating layers of crystalline guanine $(n = 1.80)$ and of cytoplasm $(n = 1.333$, the same as water), with a guanine layer on the outside in contact with the surrounding water (Fig. 35.24). In one typical platelet, the guanine layers are 74 nm thick and the cytoplasm layers are 100 nm thick. (a) For light striking the platelet surface at normal incidence, for which vacuum wavelengths of visible light will all of the reflections R_1, R_2, R_3, R_4, and R_5, shown in Fig. 35.24, be approximately in phase? If white light is shone on this platelet, what color will be most strongly reflected (see Fig. 32.4)? The surface of a herring has very many platelets side by side with layers of different thickness, so that *all* visible wavelengths are reflected. (b) Explain why such a "stack" of layers is more reflective than a single layer of guanine with cytoplasm underneath. (A stack of five guanine layers separated by cytoplasm layers reflects more than 80% of incident light at the wavelength for which it is "tuned.") (c) The color that is most strongly reflected from a platelet depends on the angle at which it is viewed. Explain why this should be so. (You can see these changes in color by examining a herring from different angles. Most of the platelets on these fish are oriented in the same way, so that they are vertical when the fish is swimming.)

Figure 35.24 Problem 35.56.

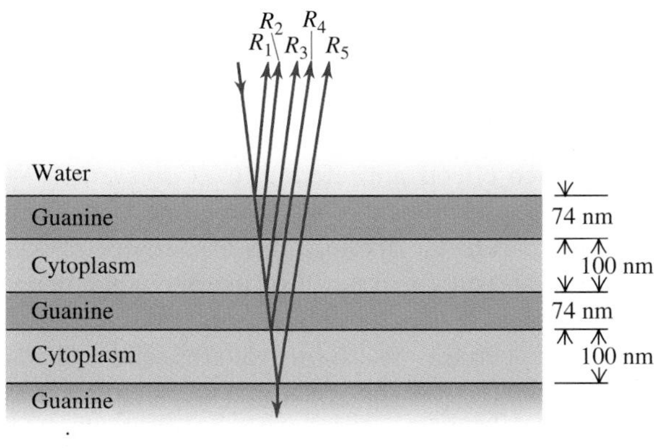

35.57. Two thin parallel slits are made in an opaque sheet of film. When a monochromatic beam of light is shone through them at normal incidence, the first bright fringes in the transmitted light occur in air at $\pm 18.0°$ with the original direction of the light beam on a distant screen when the apparatus is in air. When the apparatus is immersed in a liquid, the same bright fringes now occur at $\pm 12.6°$. Find the index of refraction of the liquid.

35.58. An oil tanker spills a large amount of oil $(n = 1.45)$ into the sea $(n = 1.33)$. (a) If you look down onto the oil spill from overhead, what predominant wavelength of light do you see at a point where the oil is 380 nm thick? What color is the light? (*Hint:* See Table 32.1.) (b) In the water under the slick, what visible wavelength (as measured in air) is predominant in the transmitted light at the same place in the slick as in part (a)?

35.59. In a Young's two-slit experiment a piece of glass with an index of refraction n and a thickness L is placed in front of the upper slit. (a) Describe qualitatively what happens to the interference pattern. (b) Derive an expression for the intensity I of the light at points on a screen as a function of n, L, and θ. Here θ is the usual angle measured from the center of the two slits. That is, determine the equation analogous to Eq. (35.14) but that also involves L and n for the glass plate. (c) From your result in part (b) derive an expression for the values of θ that locate the maxima in the interference pattern [that is, derive an equation analogous to Eq. (35.4)].

35.60. After a laser beam passes through two thin parallel slits, the first completely dark fringes occur at $\pm 15.0°$ with the original direction of the beam, as viewed on a screen far from the slits. (a) What is the ratio of the distance between the slits to the wavelength of the light illuminating the slits? (b) What is the smallest angle, relative to the original direction of the laser beam, at which the intensity of the light is $\frac{1}{10}$ the maximum intensity on the screen?

Challenge Problems

35.61. The index of refraction of a glass rod is 1.48 at $T = 20.0°C$ and varies linearly with temperature, with a coefficient of $2.50 \times 10^{-5}/C°$. The coefficient of linear expansion of the glass is $5.00 \times 10^{-6}/C°$. At 20.0°C the length of the rod is 3.00 cm. A Michelson interferometer has this glass rod in one arm, and the rod is being heated so that its temperature increases at a rate of $5.00\ C°/\text{min}$. The light source has wavelength $\lambda = 589$ nm, and the rod initially is at $T = 20.0°C$. How many fringes cross the field of view each minute?

35.62. Figure 35.25 shows an interferometer known as *Fresnel's biprism.* The magnitude of the prism angle A is extremely small. (a) If S_0 is a very narrow source slit, show that the separation of the two virtual coherent sources S_1 and S_2 is given by $d = 2aA(n - 1)$, where n is the index of refraction of the material of the prism. (b) Calculate the spacing of the fringes of green light with wavelength 500 nm on a screen 2.00 m from the biprism. Take $a = 0.200$ m, $A = 3.50$ mrad, and $n = 1.50$.

Figure 35.25 Challenge Problem 35.62.

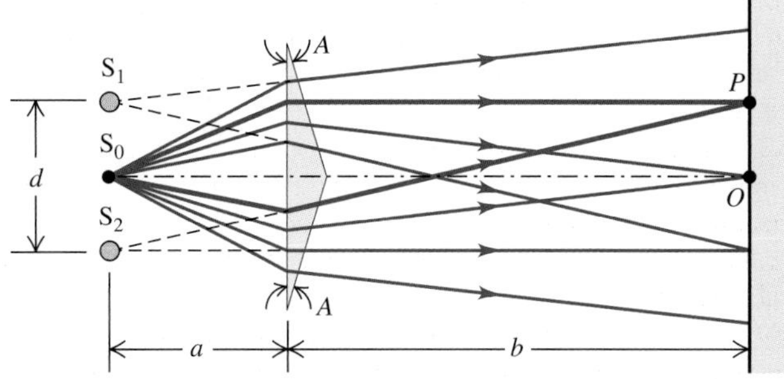

36 DIFFRACTION

LEARNING GOALS

By studying this chapter, you will learn:

- What happens when coherent light shines on an object with an edge or aperture.
- How to understand the diffraction pattern formed when coherent light passes through a narrow slit.
- How to calculate the intensity at various points in a single-slit diffraction pattern.
- What happens when coherent light shines on an array of narrow, closely spaced slits.
- How scientists use diffraction gratings for precise measurements of wavelength.
- How x-ray diffraction reveals the arrangement of atoms in a crystal.
- How diffraction sets limits on the smallest details that can be seen with a telescope.

? The laser used to read a compact disc (CD) has a wavelength of 780 nm, while the laser used to read a DVD has a wavelength of 650 nm. How does this make it possible for a DVD to hold more information than a CD?

Everyone is used to the idea that sound bends around corners. If sound didn't behave this way, you couldn't hear a police siren that's out of sight around a corner or the speech of a person whose back is turned to you. What may surprise you (and certainly surprised many scientists of the early 19th century) is that *light* can bend around corners as well. When light from a point source falls on a straightedge and casts a shadow, the edge of the shadow is never perfectly sharp. Some light appears in the area that we expect to be in the shadow, and we find alternating bright and dark fringes in the illuminated area. In general, light emerging from apertures doesn't behave precisely according to the predictions of the straight-line ray model of geometric optics.

The reason for these effects is that light, like sound, has wave characteristics. In Chapter 35 we studied the interference patterns that can arise when two light waves are combined. In this chapter we'll investigate interference effects due to combining *many* light waves. Such effects are referred to as *diffraction.* We'll find that the behavior of waves after they pass through an aperture is an example of diffraction; each infinitesimal part of the aperture acts as a source of waves, and the resulting pattern of light and dark is a result of interference among the waves emanating from these sources.

Light emerging from arrays of apertures also forms patterns whose character depends on the color of the light and the size and spacing of the apertures. Examples of this effect include the colors of iridescent butterflies and the "rainbow" you see reflected from the surface of a compact disc. We'll explore similar effects with x rays that are used to study the atomic structure of solids and liquids. Finally, we'll look at the physics of a *hologram,* a special kind of interference pattern recorded on photographic film and reproduced. When properly illuminated, it forms a three-dimensional image of the original object.

36.1 Fresnel and Fraunhofer Diffraction

According to geometric optics, when an opaque object is placed between a point light source and a screen, as in Fig. 36.1, the shadow of the object forms a perfectly sharp line. No light at all strikes the screen at points within the shadow, and the area outside the shadow is illuminated nearly uniformly. But as we saw in Chapter 35, the *wave* nature of light causes effects that can't be understood with the simple model of geometric optics. An important class of such effects occurs when light strikes a barrier that has an aperture or an edge. The interference patterns formed in such a situation are grouped under the heading **diffraction.**

An example of diffraction is shown in Fig. 36.2. The photograph in Fig. 36.2a was made by placing a razor blade halfway between a pinhole, illuminated by monochromatic light, and a photographic film. The film recorded the shadow cast by the blade. Figure 36.2b is an enlargement of a region near the shadow of the right edge of the blade. The position of the *geometric* shadow line is indicated by arrows. The area outside the geometric shadow is bordered by alternating bright and dark bands. There is some light in the shadow region, although this is not very visible in the photograph. The first bright band in Fig. 36.2b, just to the right of the geometric shadow, is considerably brighter than in the region of uniform illumination to the extreme right. This simple experiment gives us some idea of the richness and complexity of what might seem to be a simple idea, the casting of a shadow by an opaque object.

We don't often observe diffraction patterns such as Fig. 36.2 in everyday life because most ordinary light sources are not monochromatic and are not point sources. If we use a white frosted light bulb instead of a point source in Fig. 36.1, each wavelength of the light from every point of the bulb forms its own diffraction pattern, but the patterns overlap to such an extent that we can't see any individual pattern.

36.1 A point source of light illuminates a straightedge.

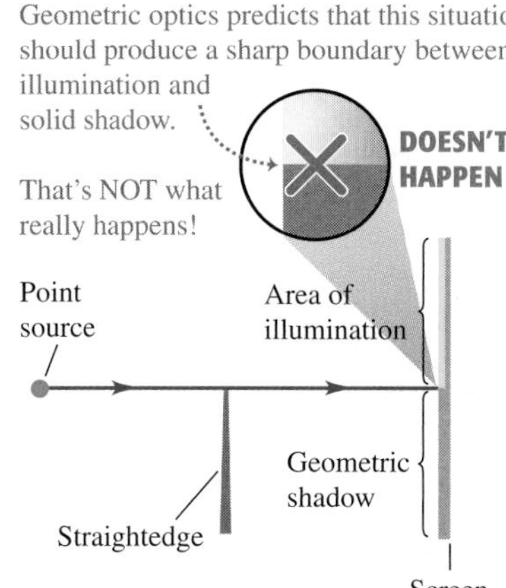
Geometric optics predicts that this situation should produce a sharp boundary between illumination and solid shadow.
DOESN'T HAPPEN
That's NOT what really happens!
Point source
Area of illumination
Geometric shadow
Straightedge
Screen

Diffraction and Huygens's Principle

Diffraction patterns can be analyzed by use of Huygens's principle (see Section 33.7). Let's review that principle briefly. Every point of a wave front can be considered the source of secondary wavelets that spread out in all directions with a speed equal to the speed of propagation of the wave. The position of the wave front at any later time is the *envelope* of the secondary waves at that time. To find the resultant displacement at any point, we combine all the individual displacements

36.2 An example of diffraction.

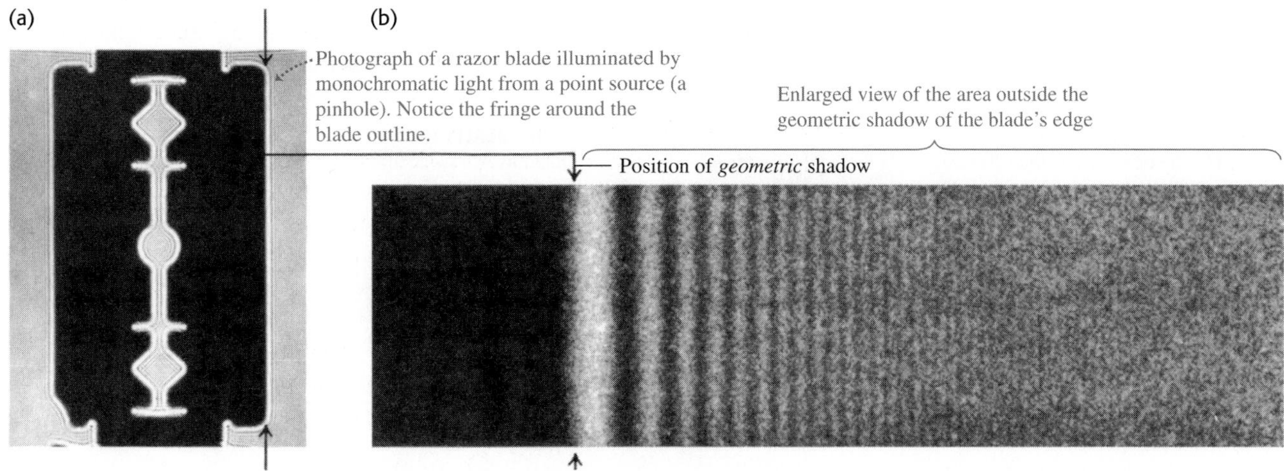
(a)
(b)
Photograph of a razor blade illuminated by monochromatic light from a point source (a pinhole). Notice the fringe around the blade outline.
Enlarged view of the area outside the geometric shadow of the blade's edge
Position of *geometric* shadow

produced by these secondary waves, using the superposition principle and taking into account their amplitudes and relative phases.

In Fig. 36.1, both the point source and the screen are relatively close to the obstacle forming the diffraction pattern. This situation is described as *near-field diffraction* or **Fresnel diffraction,** pronounced "Freh-nell" (after the French scientist Augustin Jean Fresnel, 1788–1827). If the source, obstacle, and screen are far enough away that all lines from the source to the obstacle can be considered parallel and all lines from the obstacle to a point in the pattern can be considered parallel, the phenomenon is called *far-field diffraction* or **Fraunhofer diffraction** (after the German physicist Joseph von Fraunhofer, 1787–1826). We will restrict the following discussion to Fraunhofer diffraction, which is usually simpler to analyze in detail than Fresnel diffraction.

Diffraction is sometimes described as "the bending of light around an obstacle." But the process that causes diffraction is present in the propagation of *every* wave. When part of the wave is cut off by some obstacle, we observe diffraction effects that result from interference of the remaining parts of the wave fronts. Optical instruments typically use only a limited portion of a wave; for example, a telescope uses only the part of a wave that is admitted by its objective lens or mirror. Thus diffraction plays a role in nearly all optical phenomena.

Finally, we emphasize that there is no fundamental distinction between *interference* and *diffraction.* In Chapter 35 we used the term *interference* for effects involving waves from a small number of sources, usually two. *Diffraction* usually involves a *continuous* distribution of Huygens's wavelets across the area of an aperture, or a very large number of sources or apertures. But both categories of phenomena are governed by the same basic physics of superposition and Huygens's principle.

Test Your Understanding of Section 36.1 Can *sound* waves undergo diffraction around an edge?

36.2 Diffraction from a Single Slit

ActivPhysics Online 16.6 Single-Slit Diffraction

In this section we'll discuss the diffraction pattern formed by plane-wave (parallel-ray) monochromatic light when it emerges from a long, narrow slit, as shown in Fig. 36.3. We call the narrow dimension the *width,* even though in this figure it is a vertical dimension.

According to geometric optics, the transmitted beam should have the same cross section as the slit, as in Fig. 36.3a. What is *actually* observed is the pattern shown in Fig. 36.3b. The beam spreads out vertically after passing through the

36.3 (a) The "shadow" of a horizontal slit as incorrectly predicted by geometric optics. (b) A horizontal slit actually produces a diffraction pattern. The slit width has been greatly exaggerated.

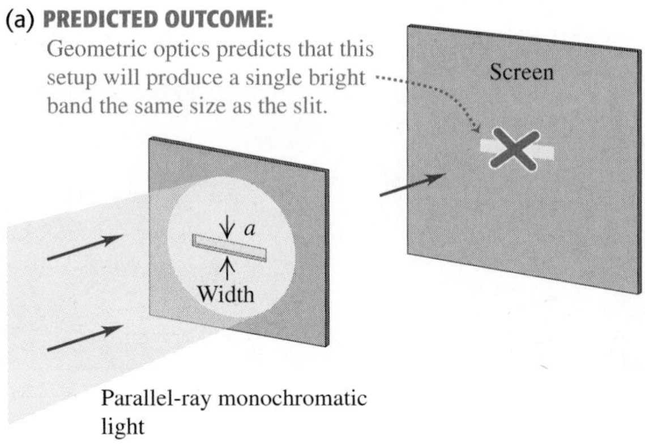
(a) PREDICTED OUTCOME:
Geometric optics predicts that this setup will produce a single bright band the same size as the slit.
Screen
a
Width
Parallel-ray monochromatic light

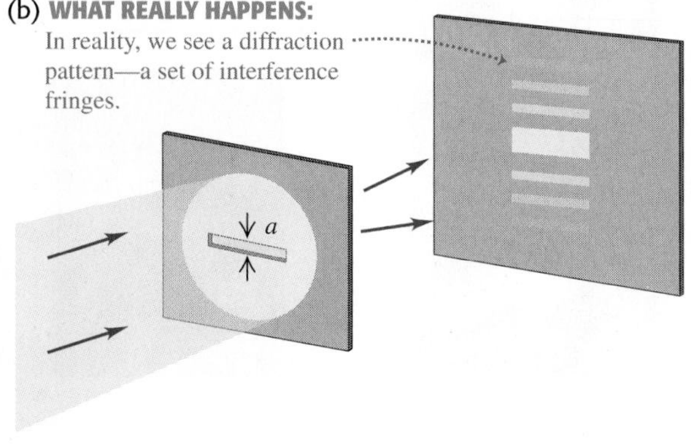
(b) WHAT REALLY HAPPENS:
In reality, we see a diffraction pattern—a set of interference fringes.
a

slit. The diffraction pattern consists of a central bright band, which may be much broader than the width of the slit, bordered by alternating dark and bright bands with rapidly decreasing intensity. About 85% of the power in the transmitted beam is in the central bright band, whose width is found to be *inversely* proportional to the width of the slit. In general, the smaller the width of the slit, the broader the entire diffraction pattern. (The *horizontal* spreading of the beam in Fig. 36.3b is negligible because the horizontal dimension of the slit is relatively large.) You can easily observe a similar diffraction pattern by looking at a point source, such as a distant street light, through a narrow slit formed between your two thumbs held in front of your eye; the retina of your eye corresponds to the screen.

Single-Slit Diffraction: Locating the Dark Fringes

Figure 36.4 shows a side view of the same setup; the long sides of the slit are perpendicular to the figure, and plane waves are incident on the slit from the left. According to Huygens's principle, each element of area of the slit opening can be considered as a source of secondary waves. In particular, imagine dividing the slit into several narrow strips of equal width, parallel to the long edges and perpendicular to the page. Two such strips are shown in Fig. 36.4a. Cylindrical secondary wavelets, shown in cross section, spread out from each strip.

In Fig. 36.4b a screen is placed to the right of the slit. We can calculate the resultant intensity at a point P on the screen by adding the contributions from the individual wavelets, taking proper account of their various phases and amplitudes. It's easiest to do this calculation if we assume that the screen is far enough away that all the rays from various parts of the slit to a particular point P on the screen are parallel, as in Fig. 36.4c. An equivalent situation is Fig. 36.4d, in which the rays to the lens are parallel and the lens forms a reduced image of the same pattern that would be formed on an infinitely distant screen without the lens. We might expect that the various light paths through the lens would introduce additional phase shifts, but in fact it can be shown that all the paths have *equal* phase shifts, so this is not a problem.

The situation of Fig. 36.4b is Fresnel diffraction; those in Figs. 36.4c and 36.4d, where the outgoing rays are considered parallel, are Fraunhofer diffraction. We can derive quite simply the most important characteristics of the Fraunhofer diffraction pattern from a single slit. First consider two narrow strips, one just below the top edge of the drawing of the slit and one at its center, shown in end view in Fig. 36.5. The difference in path length to point P is $(a/2)\sin\theta$, where a is the slit width and θ is the angle between the perpendicular to the slit and a line from the center of the slit to P. Suppose this path difference happens to be equal to $\lambda/2$; then light from these two strips arrives at point P with a half-cycle phase difference, and cancellation occurs.

36.4 Diffraction by a single rectangular slit. The long sides of the slit are perpendicular to the figure.

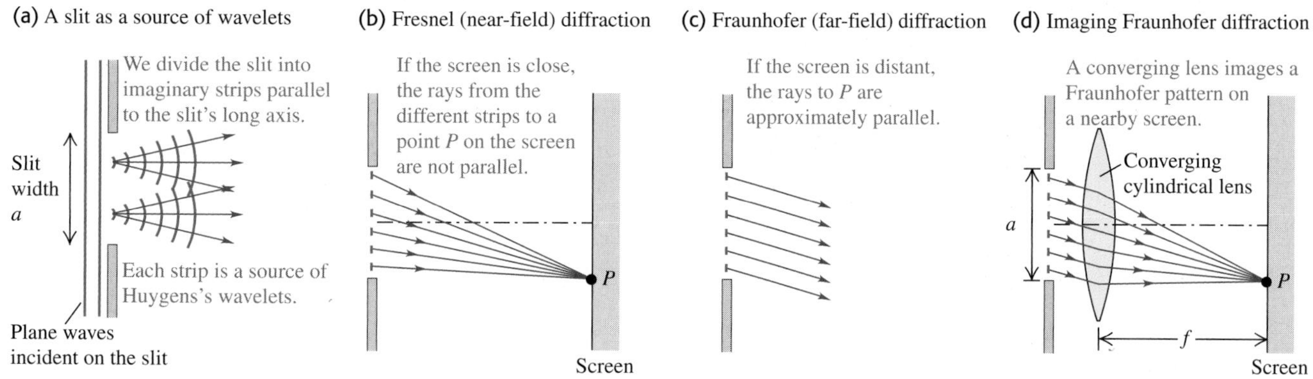
(a) A slit as a source of wavelets
We divide the slit into imaginary strips parallel to the slit's long axis.
Slit width a
Each strip is a source of Huygens's wavelets.
Plane waves incident on the slit
(b) Fresnel (near-field) diffraction
If the screen is close, the rays from the different strips to a point P on the screen are not parallel.
P
Screen
(c) Fraunhofer (far-field) diffraction
If the screen is distant, the rays to P are approximately parallel.
(d) Imaging Fraunhofer diffraction
A converging lens images a Fraunhofer pattern on a nearby screen.
Converging cylindrical lens
a
P
f
Screen

36.5 Side view of a horizontal slit. When the distance x to the screen is much greater than the slit width a, the rays from a distance $a/2$ apart may be considered parallel.

(a)

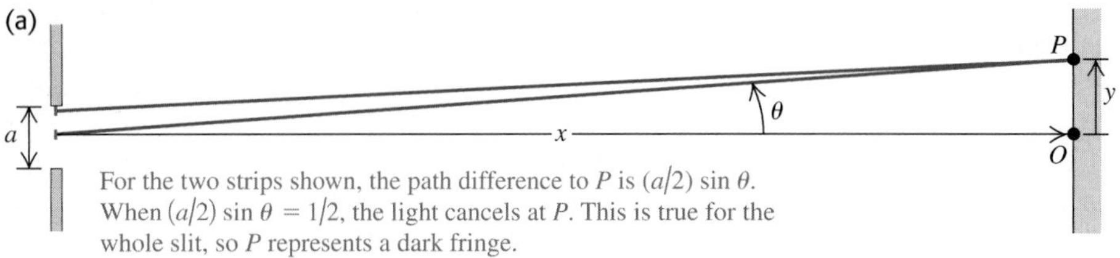

P
y
θ
a
x
O
For the two strips shown, the path difference to P is (a/2) sin θ. When (a/2) sin θ = λ/2, the light cancels at P. This is true for the whole slit, so P represents a dark fringe.

(b) Enlarged view of the top half of the slit

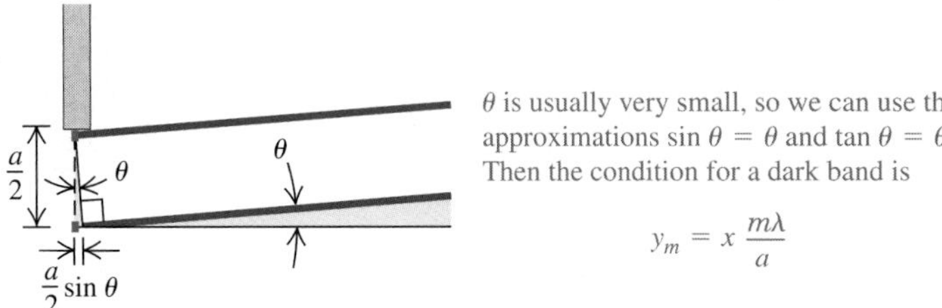

θ is usually very small, so we can use the approximations sin θ = θ and tan θ = θ. Then the condition for a dark band is
y_m = x mλ/a
a/2
θ
θ
a/2 sin θ

Similarly, light from two strips immediately *below* the two in the figure also arrives at P a half-cycle out of phase. In fact, the light from *every* strip in the top half of the slit cancels out the light from a corresponding strip in the bottom half. The result is complete cancellation at P for the combined light from the entire slit, giving a dark fringe in the interference pattern. That is, a dark fringe occurs whenever

$$\frac{a}{2}\sin\theta = \pm\frac{\lambda}{2} \quad \text{or} \quad \sin\theta = \pm\frac{\lambda}{a} \tag{36.1}$$

The plus-or-minus $(\pm)$ sign in Eq. (36.1) says that there are symmetrical dark fringes above and below point O in Fig. 36.5a. The upper fringe $(\theta > 0)$ occurs at a point P where light from the bottom half of the slit travels $\lambda/2$ farther to P than does light from the top half; the lower fringe $(\theta < 0)$ occurs where light from the *top* half travels $\lambda/2$ farther than light from the *bottom* half.

We may also divide the screen into quarters, sixths, and so on, and use the above argument to show that a dark fringe occurs whenever $\sin\theta = \pm 2\lambda/a$, $\pm 3\lambda/a$, and so on. Thus the condition for a *dark* fringe is

$$\sin\theta = \frac{m\lambda}{a} \quad (m = \pm 1, \pm 2, \pm 3, \ldots) \quad \text{(dark fringes in single-slit diffraction)} \tag{36.2}$$

For example, if the slit width is equal to ten wavelengths $(a = 10\lambda)$, dark fringes occur at $\sin\theta = \pm\frac{1}{10}, \pm\frac{2}{10}, \pm\frac{3}{10}, \ldots$. Between the dark fringes are bright fringes. We also note that $\sin\theta = 0$ corresponds to a *bright* band; in this case, light from the entire slit arrives at P in phase. Thus it would be wrong to put $m = 0$ in Eq. (36.2). The central bright fringe is wider than the other bright fringes, as Fig. 36.3 shows. In the small-angle approximation that we will use below, it is exactly *twice* as wide.

With light, the wavelength λ is of the order of 500 nm $= 5 \times 10^{-7}$ m. This is often much smaller than the slit width a; a typical slit width is 10^{-2} cm $= 10^{-4}$ m. Therefore the values of θ in Eq. (36.2) are often so small that the approximation $\sin\theta \approx \theta$ (where θ is in radians) is a very good one. In that case we can rewrite this equation as

$$\theta = \frac{m\lambda}{a} \quad (m = \pm 1, \pm 2, \pm 3, \ldots) \quad \text{(for small angles } \theta\text{)}$$

where θ is in *radians*. Also, if the distance from slit to screen is x, as in Fig. 36.5a, and the vertical distance of the mth dark band from the center of the pattern is y_m, then $\tan\theta = y_m/x$. For small θ we may also approximate $\tan\theta$ by θ (in radians), and we then find

$$y_m = x\frac{m\lambda}{a} \qquad (\text{for } y_m \ll x) \qquad (36.3)$$

Figure 36.6 is a photograph of a single-slit diffraction pattern with the $m = \pm1, \pm2$, and ±3 minima labeled.

CAUTION Single-slit diffraction vs. two-slit interference Equation (36.3) has the same form as the equation for the two-slit pattern, Eq. (35.6), except that in Eq. (36.3) we use x rather than R for the distance to the screen. But Eq. (36.3) gives the positions of the *dark* fringes in a *single-slit* pattern rather than the *bright* fringes in a *double-slit* pattern. Also, $m = 0$ in Eq. (36.2) is *not* a dark fringe. Be careful!

36.6 Photograph of the Fraunhofer diffraction pattern of a single horizontal slit.

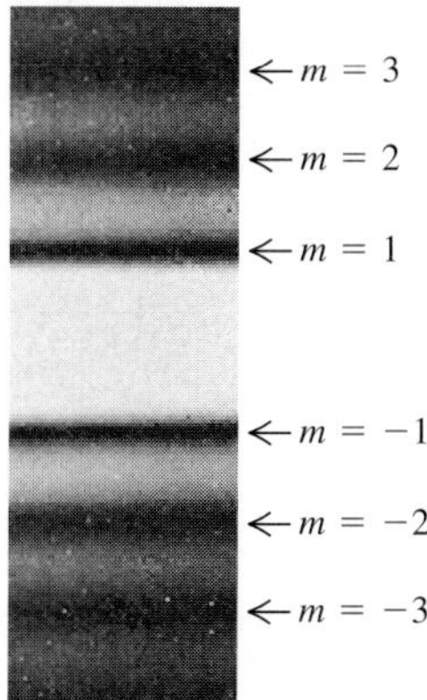

Example 36.1 Single-slit diffraction

You pass 633-nm laser light through a narrow slit and observe the diffraction pattern on a screen 6.0 m away. You find that the distance on the screen between the centers of the first minima outside the central bright fringe is 32 mm (Fig. 36.7). How wide is the slit?

SOLUTION

IDENTIFY: This problem involves the relationship between the dark fringes in a single-slit diffraction pattern and the width of the slit (our target variable).

36.7 A single-slit diffraction experiment.

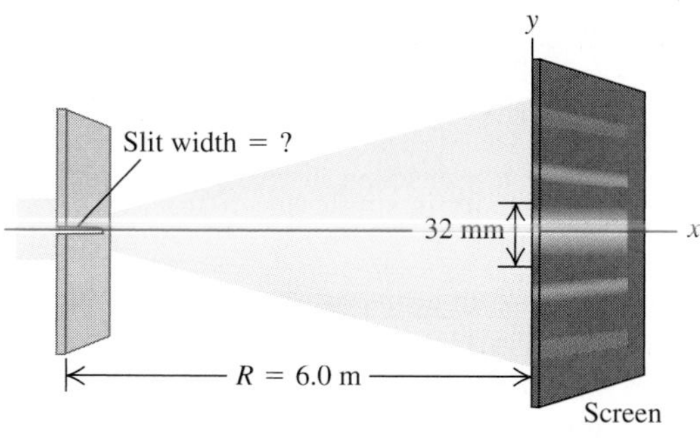

SET UP: The distances between points on the screen are much smaller than the distance from the slit to the screen, so the angle θ shown in Fig. 36.5a is very small. Hence we can use the approximate relationship of Eq. (36.3) to solve for the slit width a (the target variable).

EXECUTE: The first minimum corresponds to $m = 1$ in Eq. (36.3). The distance y_1 from the central maximum to the first minimum on either side is half the distance between the two first minima, so $y_1 = (32\text{ mm})/2$. Substituting these values and solving for a, we find

$$a = \frac{x\lambda}{y_1} = \frac{(6.0\text{ m})(633 \times 10^{-9}\text{ m})}{(32 \times 10^{-3}\text{ m})/2}$$
$$= 2.4 \times 10^{-4}\text{ m} = 0.24\text{ mm}$$

EVALUATE: The angle θ is small only if the wavelength is small compared to the slit width. Since $\lambda = 633\text{ nm} = 6.33 \times 10^{-7}\text{ m}$ and we have found $a = 0.24\text{ mm} = 2.4 \times 10^{-4}\text{ m}$, our result is consistent with this: The wavelength is $(6.33 \times 10^{-7}\text{ m})/(2.4 \times 10^{-4}\text{ m}) = 0.0026$ as large as the slit width.

Can you show that the distance between the *second* minima on the two sides is $2(32\text{ mm}) = 64\text{ mm}$, and so on?

Test Your Understanding of Section 36.2 Rank the following single-slit diffraction experiments in order of the size of the angle from the center of the diffraction pattern to the first dark fringe, from largest to smallest (i) wavelength 400 nm, slit width 0.20 mm; (ii) wavelength 600 nm, slit width 0.20 mm; (iii) wavelength 400 nm, slit width 0.30 mm; (iv) wavelength 600 nm, slit width 0.30 mm.

36.3 Intensity in the Single-Slit Pattern

We can derive an expression for the intensity distribution for the single-slit diffraction pattern by the same phasor-addition method that we used in Section 35.3 to obtain Eqs. (35.10) and (35.14) for the two-slit interference pattern. We again imagine a plane wave front at the slit subdivided into a large number of strips. We superpose the contributions of the Huygens wavelets from all the strips at a point P on a distant screen at an angle θ from the normal to the slit plane

36.8 Using phasor diagrams to find the amplitude of the $\vec{E}$ field in single-slit diffraction. Each phasor represents the $\vec{E}$ field from a single strip within the slit.

(a)

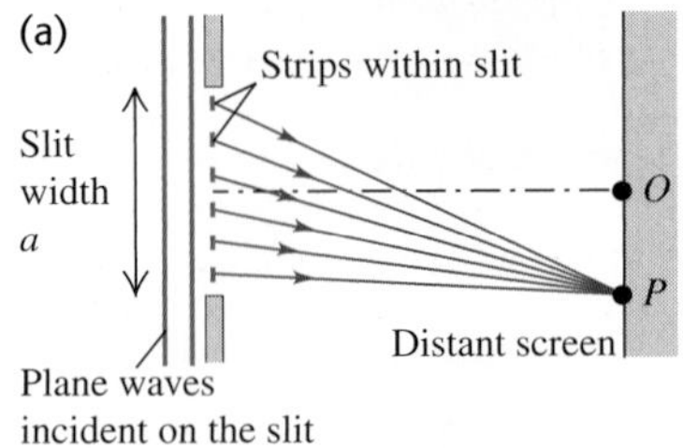

(b) At the center of the diffraction pattern (point O), the phasors from all strips within the slit are in phase.

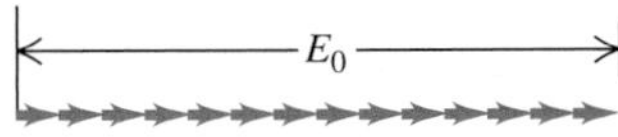

(c) Phasor diagram at a point slightly off the center of the pattern; β = total phase difference between the first and last phasors.

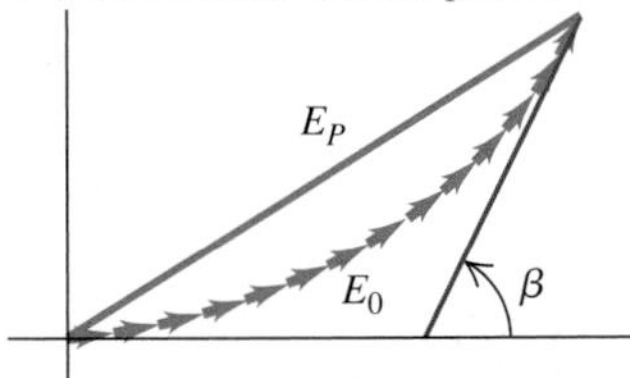

(d) As in (c), but in the limit that the slit is subdivided into infinitely many strips

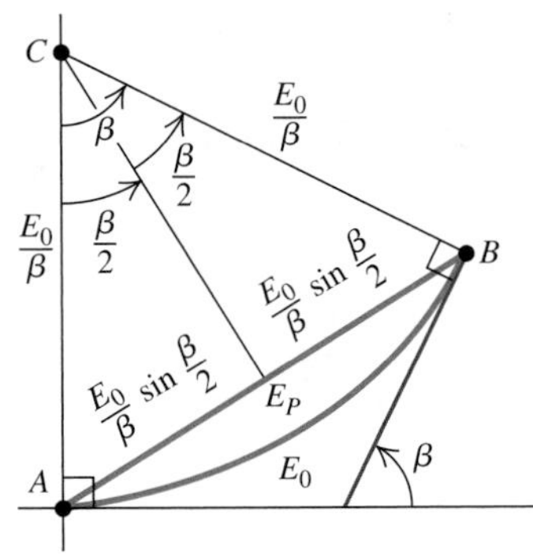

(Fig. 36.8a). To do this, we use a phasor to represent the sinusoidally varying $\vec{E}$ field from each individual strip. The magnitude of the vector sum of the phasors at each point P is the amplitude E_P of the total $\vec{E}$ field at that point. The intensity at P is proportional to E_P^2.

At the point O shown in Figure 36.8a, corresponding to the center of the pattern where $\theta = 0$, there are negligible path differences for $x \gg a$; the phasors are all essentially *in phase* (that is, have the same direction). In Fig. 36.8b we draw the phasors at time $t = 0$ and denote the resultant amplitude at O by E_0. In this illustration we have divided the slit into 14 strips.

Now consider wavelets arriving from different strips at point P in Fig. 36.8a, at an angle θ from point O. Because of the differences in path length, there are now phase differences between wavelets coming from adjacent strips; the corresponding phasor diagram is shown in Fig. 36.8c. The vector sum of the phasors is now part of the perimeter of a many-sided polygon, and E_P, the amplitude of the resultant electric field at P, is the *chord.* The angle β is the total phase difference between the wave from the top strip of Fig. 36.8a and the wave from the bottom strip; that is, β is the phase of the wave received at P from the top strip with respect to the wave received at P from the bottom strip.

We may imagine dividing the slit into narrower and narrower strips. In the limit that there is an infinite number of infinitesimally narrow strips, the curved trail of phasors becomes an *arc of a circle* (Fig. 36.8d), with arc length equal to the length E_0 in Fig. 36.8b. The center C of this arc is found by constructing perpendiculars at A and B. From the relationship among arc length, radius, and angle, the radius of the arc is E_0/β; the amplitude E_P of the resultant electric field at P is equal to the chord AB, which is $2(E_0/\beta)\sin(\beta/2)$. (Note that β *must* be in radians!) We then have

$$E_P = E_0\frac{\sin(\beta/2)}{\beta/2} \qquad \text{(amplitude in single-slit diffraction)} \qquad (36.4)$$

The intensity at each point on the screen is proportional to the square of the amplitude given by Eq. (36.4). If I_0 is the intensity in the straight-ahead direction where $\theta = 0$ and $\beta = 0$, then the intensity I at any point is

$$I = I_0\left[\frac{\sin(\beta/2)}{\beta/2}\right]^2 \qquad \text{(intensity in single-slit diffraction)} \qquad (36.5)$$

We can express the phase difference β in terms of geometric quantities, as we did for the two-slit pattern. From Eq. (35.11) the phase difference is $2\pi/\lambda$ times the path difference. Figure 36.5 shows that the path difference between the ray from the top of the slit and the ray from the middle of the slit is $(a/2)\sin\theta$. The path difference between the rays from the top of the slit and the bottom of the slit is twice this, so

$$\beta = \frac{2\pi}{\lambda}a\sin\theta \qquad (36.6)$$

and Eq. (36.5) becomes

$$I = I_0\left\{\frac{\sin[\pi a(\sin\theta)/\lambda]}{\pi a(\sin\theta)/\lambda}\right\}^2 \qquad \text{(intensity in single-slit diffraction)} \qquad (36.7)$$

This equation expresses the intensity directly in terms of the angle θ. In many calculations it is easier first to calculate the phase angle β, using Eq. (36.6), and then to use Eq. (36.5).

Equation (36.7) is plotted in Fig. 36.9a. Note that the central intensity peak is much larger than any of the others. This means that most of the power in the wave remains within an angle θ from the perpendicular to the slit, where $\sin\theta = \lambda/a$ (the first diffraction minimum). You can see this easily in Fig. 36.9b, which is a photograph of water waves undergoing single-slit diffraction. Note also that the peak intensities in Fig. 36.9a decrease rapidly as we go away from the center of the pattern. (Compare Fig. 36.6, which shows a single-slit diffraction pattern for light.)

The dark fringes in the pattern are the places where $I = 0$. These occur at points for which the numerator of Eq. (36.5) is zero so that β is a multiple of 2π. From Eq. (36.6) this corresponds to

$$\frac{a\sin\theta}{\lambda} = m \qquad (m = \pm 1, \pm 2, \dots)$$

$$\sin\theta = \frac{m\lambda}{a} \qquad (m = \pm 1, \pm 2, \dots) \tag{36.8}$$

This agrees with our previous result, Eq. (36.2). Note again that $\beta = 0$ (corresponding to $\theta = 0$) is *not* a minimum. Equation (36.5) is indeterminate at $\beta = 0$, but we can evaluate the limit as $\beta \to 0$ using L'Hôpital's rule. We find that at $\beta = 0$, $I = I_0$, as we should expect.

Intensity Maxima in the Single-Slit Pattern

We can also use Eq. (36.5) to calculate the positions of the peaks, or *intensity maxima,* and the intensities at these peaks. This is not quite as simple as it may appear. We might expect the peaks to occur where the sine function reaches the value ± 1—namely, where $\beta = \pm\pi, \pm 3\pi, \pm 5\pi$, or in general,

$$\beta \approx \pm(2m + 1)\pi \qquad (m = 0, 1, 2, \dots) \tag{36.9}$$

This is *approximately* correct, but because of the factor $(\beta/2)^2$ in the denominator of Eq. (36.5), the maxima don't occur precisely at these points. When we take the derivative of Eq. (36.5) with respect to β and set it equal to zero to try to find the maxima and minima, we get a transcendental equation that has to be solved numerically. In fact there is *no* maximum near $\beta = \pm\pi$. The first maxima on either side of the central maximum, near $\beta = \pm 3\pi$, actually occur at $\pm 2.860\pi$. The second side maxima, near $\beta = \pm 5\pi$, are actually at $\pm 4.918\pi$, and so on. The error in Eq. (36.9) vanishes in the limit of large m—that is, for intensity maxima far from the center of the pattern.

To find the intensities at the side maxima, we substitute these values of β back into Eq. (36.5). Using the approximate expression in Eq. (36.9), we get

$$I_m \approx \frac{I_0}{\left(m + \dfrac{1}{2}\right)^2 \pi^2} \tag{36.10}$$

where I_m is the intensity of the mth side maximum and I_0 is the intensity of the central maximum. Equation (36.10) gives the series of intensities

$$0.0450I_0 \qquad 0.0162I_0 \qquad 0.0083I_0$$

and so on. As we have pointed out, this equation is only approximately correct. The actual intensities of the side maxima turn out to be

$$0.0472I_0 \qquad 0.0165I_0 \qquad 0.0083I_0 \qquad \dots$$

Note that the intensities of the side maxima decrease very rapidly, as Fig. 36.9a also shows. Even the first side maxima have less than 5% of the intensity of the central maximum.

Width of the Single-Slit Pattern

For small angles the angular spread of the diffraction pattern is inversely proportional to the slit width a or, more precisely, to the ratio of a to the wavelength λ. Figure 36.10 shows graphs of intensity I as a function of the angle θ for three values of the ratio a/λ.

36.9 **(a)** Intensity versus angle in single-slit diffraction. The values of m label intensity minima given by Eq. (36.8). Most of the wave power goes into the central intensity peak (between the $m = 1$ and $m = -1$ intensity minima). **(b)** These water waves passing through a small aperture behave exactly like light waves in single-slit diffraction. Only the diffracted waves within the central intensity peak are visible; the waves at larger angles are too faint to see.

(a)

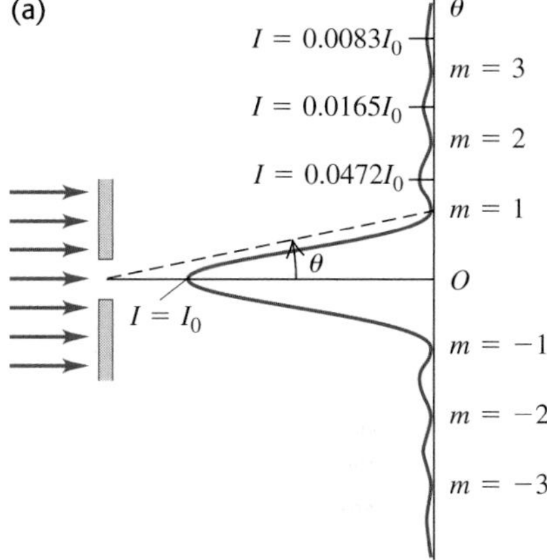

(b)

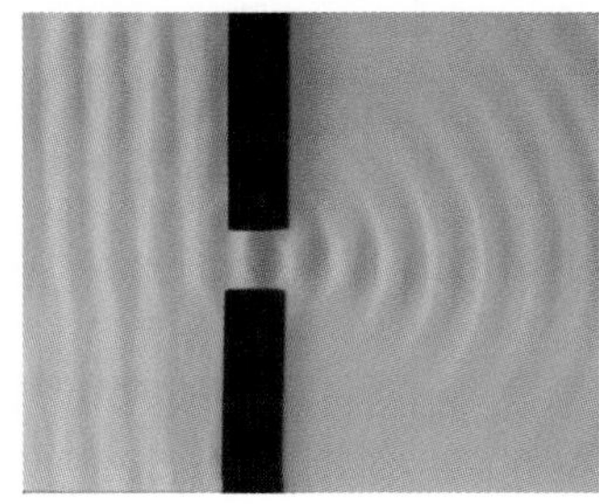

36.10 The single-slit diffraction pattern depends on the ratio of the slit width a to the wavelength λ.

(a) $a = \lambda$

If the slit width is equal to or narrower than the wavelength, only one broad maximum forms.

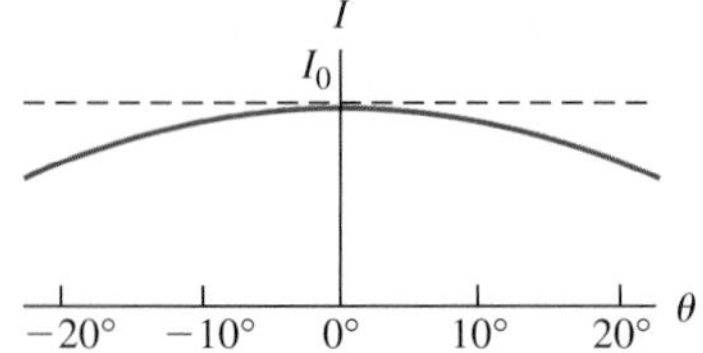

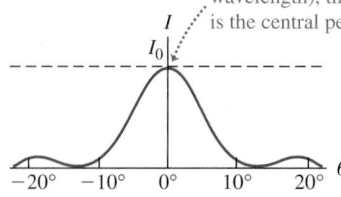

(b) $a = 5\lambda$

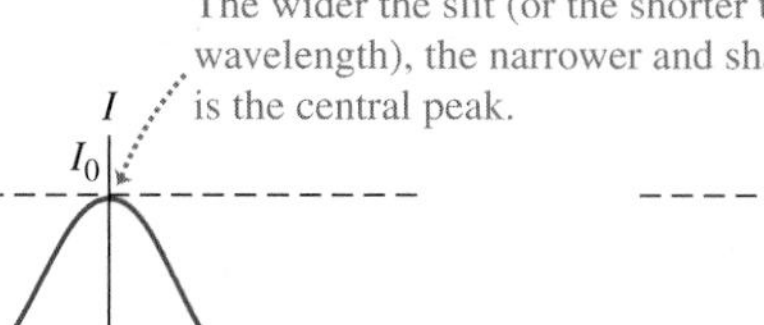

(c) $a = 8\lambda$

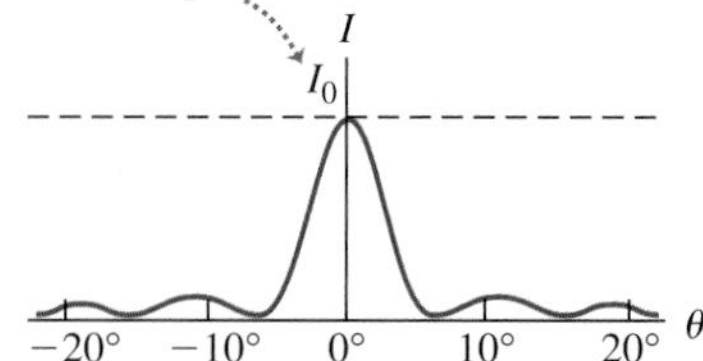

With light waves, the wavelength λ is often much smaller than the slit width a, and the values of θ in Eqs. (36.6) and (36.7) are so small that the approximation $\sin\theta = \theta$ is very good. With this approximation the position θ_1 of the first minimum beside the central maximum, corresponding to $\beta/2 = \pi$, is, from Eq. (36.7),

$$\theta_1 = \frac{\lambda}{a} \tag{36.11}$$

This characterizes the width (angular spread) of the central maximum, and we see that it is *inversely* proportional to the slit width a. When the small-angle approximation is valid, the central maximum is exactly twice as wide as each side maximum. When a is of the order of a centimeter or more, θ_1 is so small that we can consider practically all the light to be concentrated at the geometrical focus. But when a is less than λ, the central maximum spreads over 180°, and the fringe pattern is not seen at all.

It's important to keep in mind that diffraction occurs for *all* kinds of waves, not just light. Sound waves undergo diffraction when they pass through a slit or aperture such as an ordinary doorway. The sound waves used in speech have wavelengths of about a meter or greater, and a typical doorway is less than 1 m wide; in this situation, a is less than λ, and the central intensity maximum extends over 180°. This is why the sounds coming through an open doorway can easily be heard by an eavesdropper hiding out of sight around the corner. In the same way, sound waves can bend around the head of an instructor who faces the blackboard while lecturing (Fig. 36.11). By contrast, there is essentially no diffraction of visible light through such a doorway because the width a is very much greater than the wavelength λ (of order 5×10^{-7} m). You can *hear* around corners because typical sound waves have relatively long wavelengths; you cannot *see* around corners because the wavelength of visible light is very short.

36.11 The sound waves used in speech have a long wavelength (about 1 m) and can easily bend around this instructor's head. By contrast, light waves have very short wavelengths and undergo very little diffraction. Hence you can't *see* around his head!

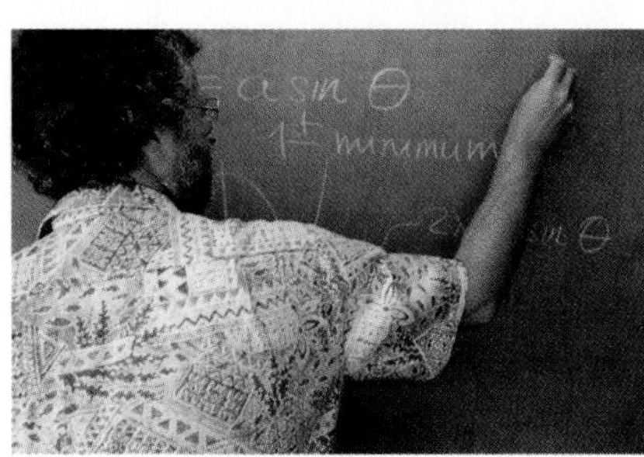

Example 36.2 Single-slit diffraction: Intensity I

(a) In a single-slit diffraction pattern, what is the intensity at a point where the total phase difference between wavelets from the top and bottom of the slit is 66 rad? (b) If this point is 7.0° away from the central maximum, how many wavelengths wide is the slit?

SOLUTION

IDENTIFY: This problem asks us to find the intensity at a point in a single-slit diffraction pattern where there is a specified phase difference between waves coming from the two edges of the slit (Fig. 36.8a). It also asks us to relate phase difference, slit width, wavelength, and the θ shown in Fig. 36.9a.

SET UP: The total phase difference between wavelets from the two edges of the slit is the quantity we called β in Fig. 36.8d. Given $\beta = 66$ rad, we use Eq. (36.5) to find the intensity I at the point in question, and we use Eq. (36.6) to find the slit width a in terms of the wavelength λ.

EXECUTE: (a) Since $\beta = 66$ rad, $\beta/2 = 33$ rad and Eq. (36.5) becomes

$$I = I_0\left[\frac{\sin(33\text{ rad})}{33\text{ rad}}\right]^2 = (9.2 \times 10^{-4})I_0$$

(b) We solve Eq. (36.6) for a:

$$a = \frac{\beta\lambda}{2\pi\sin\theta} = \frac{(66\text{ rad})\lambda}{(2\pi\text{ rad})\sin 7.0^\circ} = 86\lambda$$

For example, for 550-nm light, the slit width a is $(86)(550\text{ nm}) = 4.7 \times 10^{-5}\text{ m} = 0.047\text{ mm}$, or roughly $\frac{1}{20}$ mm.

EVALUATE: To what point in the diffraction pattern does this value of β correspond? To find out, note that $\beta = 66\text{ rad} = 21\pi$. Comparing to Eq. (36.9) shows that this is approximately equal to the value of β at the *tenth* side maximum, well beyond the range shown in Fig. 36.9a (which shows only the first three side maxima). The intensity is very much less than the intensity I_0 at the central maximum. (The *actual* position of this maximum is at $\beta = 65.91\text{ rad} = 20.98\pi$, or approximately midway between the minima at $\beta = 20\pi$ and $\beta = 22\pi$.)

Example 36.3 Single-slit diffraction: Intensity II

In the experiment described in Example 36.1 (Section 36.2), what is the intensity at a point on the screen 3.0 mm from the center of the pattern? The intensity at the center of the pattern is I_0.

SOLUTION

IDENTIFY: This is similar to Example 36.2, except that we are not given the value of the phase difference β at the point in question.

SET UP: We use geometry to determine the angle θ for our point and then use Eq. (36.7) to calculate the intensity I (our target variable).

EXECUTE: Referring to Fig. 36.5a, we have $y = 3.0\text{ mm}$ and $x = 6.0\text{ m}$, so $\tan\theta = y/x = (3.0 \times 10^{-3}\text{ m})/(6.0\text{ m}) = 5.0 \times 10^{-4}$; since this is so small, the values of $\tan\theta$, $\sin\theta$, and θ (in radians) are all nearly the same. Then, using Eq. (36.7), we have

$$\frac{\pi a\sin\theta}{\lambda} = \frac{\pi(2.4 \times 10^{-4}\text{ m})(5.0 \times 10^{-4})}{6.33 \times 10^{-7}\text{ m}} = 0.60$$

$$I = I_0\left(\frac{\sin 0.60}{0.60}\right)^2 = 0.89I_0$$

EVALUATE: Examining Fig. 36.9a shows that an intensity this large can occur only within the central intensity maximum. This checks out; from Example 36.1, the first intensity minimum ($m = 1$ in Fig. 36.9a) is $(32\text{ mm})/2 = 16\text{ mm}$ from the center of the pattern, so the point in question here does, indeed, lie within the central maximum.

Test Your Understanding of Section 36.3 Coherent electromagnetic radiation is sent through a slit of width 0.0100 mm. For which of the following wavelengths will there be *no* points in the diffraction pattern where the intensity is zero? (i) blue light of wavelength 500 nm; (ii) infrared light of wavelength 10.6 μm; (iii) microwaves of wavelength 1.00 mm; (iv) ultraviolet light of wavelength 50.0 nm.

36.4 Multiple Slits

In Sections 35.2 and 35.3 we analyzed interference from two point sources or from two very narrow slits; in this analysis we ignored effects due to the finite (that is, nonzero) slit width. In Sections 36.2 and 36.3 we considered the diffraction effects that occur when light passes through a single slit of finite width. Additional interesting effects occur when we have two slits with finite width or when there are several very narrow slits.

Two Slits of Finite Width

Let's take another look at the two-slit pattern in the more realistic case in which the slits have finite width. If the slits are narrow in comparison to the wavelength, we can assume that light from each slit spreads out uniformly in all directions to the right of the slit. We used this assumption in Section 35.3 to calculate the interference pattern described by Eq. (35.10) or (35.15), consisting of a series of equally spaced, equally intense maxima. However, when the slits have finite width, the peaks in the two-slit interference pattern are modulated by the single-slit diffraction pattern characteristic of the width of each slit.

36.12 Finding the intensity pattern for two slits of finite width.

(a) Single-slit diffraction pattern for a slit width a

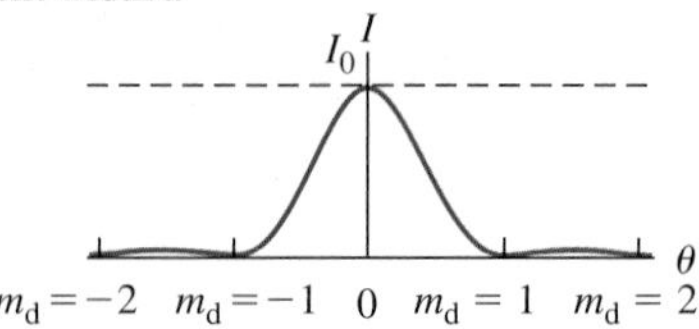

(b) Two-slit interference pattern for narrow slits whose separation d is four times the width of the slit in (a)

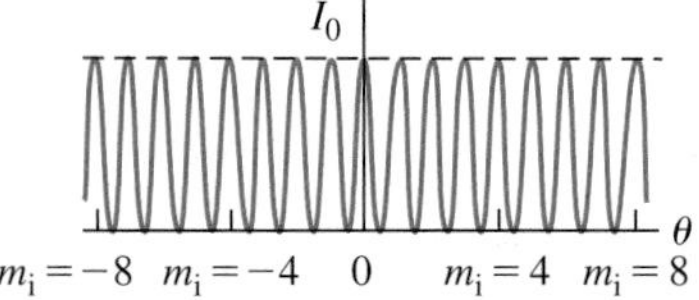

(c) Calculated intensity pattern for two slits of width a and separation $d = 4a$, including both interference and diffraction effects

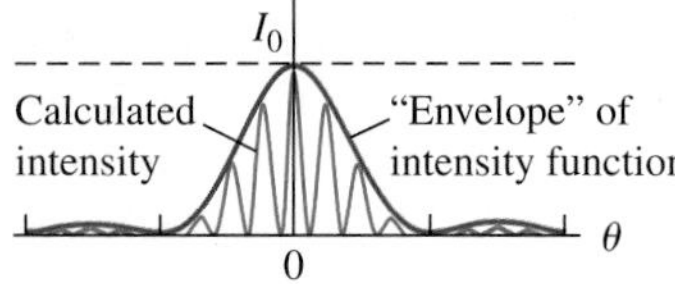

(d) Actual photograph of the pattern calculated in (c)

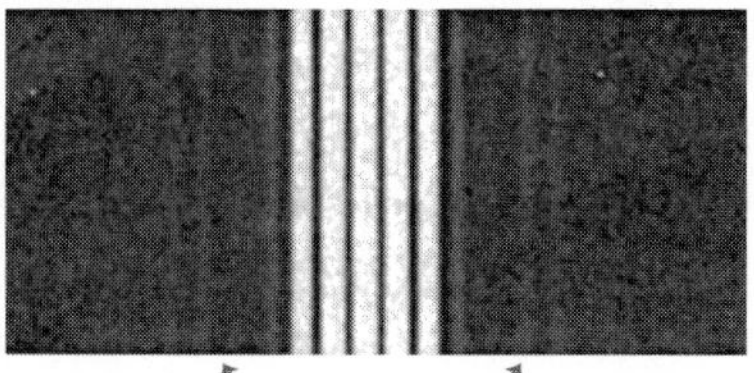

For $d = 4a$, every fourth interference maximum at the sides ($m_i = \pm 4, \pm 8, \ldots$) is missing.

36.13 Multiple-slit diffraction. Here a lens is used to give a Fraunhofer pattern on a nearby screen, as in Fig. 36.4d.

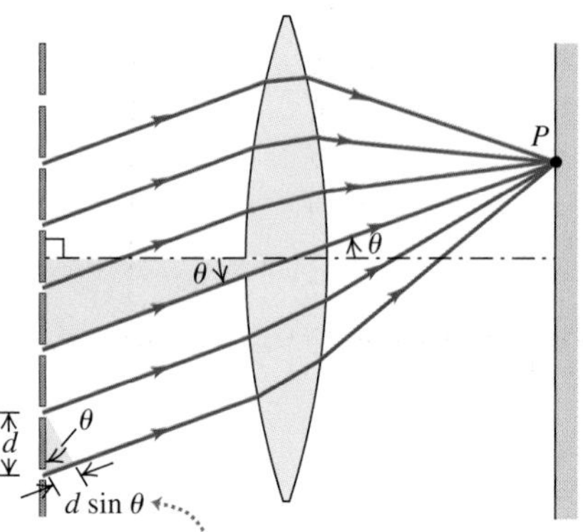

Maxima occur where the path difference for adjacent slits is a whole number of wavelengths: $d \sin \theta = m\lambda$.

Figure 36.12a shows the intensity in a single-slit diffraction pattern with slit width a. The *diffraction minima* are labeled by the integer $m_d = \pm 1, \pm 2, \ldots$ ("d" for "diffraction"). Figure 36.12b shows the pattern formed by two very narrow slits with distance d between slits, where d is four times as great as the single-slit width a in Fig. 36.12a; that is, $d = 4a$. The *interference maxima* are labeled by the integer $m_i = 0, \pm 1, \pm 2, \ldots$ ("i" for "interference"). We note that the spacing between adjacent minima in the single-slit pattern is four times as great as in the two-slit pattern. Now suppose we widen each of the narrow slits to the same width a as that of the single slit in Fig. 36.12a. Figure 36.12c shows the pattern from two slits with width a, separated by a distance (between centers) $d = 4a$. The effect of the finite width of the slits is to superimpose the two patterns—that is, to multiply the two intensities at each point. The two-slit peaks are in the same positions as before, but their intensities are modulated by the single-slit pattern, which acts as an "envelope" for the intensity function. The expression for the intensity shown in Fig. 36.12c is proportional to the product of the two-slit and single-slit expressions, Eqs. (35.10) and (36.5):

$$I = I_0 \cos^2 \frac{\phi}{2} \left[\frac{\sin(\beta/2)}{\beta/2} \right]^2 \quad \text{(two slits of finite width)} \tag{36.12}$$

where, as before,

$$\phi = \frac{2\pi d}{\lambda} \sin\theta \qquad \beta = \frac{2\pi a}{\lambda} \sin\theta$$

Note that in Fig. 36.12c, every fourth interference maximum at the sides is *missing* because these interference maxima $(m_i = \pm 4, \pm 8, \ldots)$ coincide with diffraction minima $(m_d = \pm 1, \pm 2, \ldots)$. This can also be seen in Fig. 36.12d, which is a photograph of an actual pattern with $d = 4a$. You should be able to convince yourself that there will be "missing" maxima whenever d is an integer multiple of a.

Figures 36.12c and 36.12d show that as you move away from the central bright maximum of the two-slit pattern, the intensity of the maxima decreases. This is a result of the single-slit modulating pattern shown in Fig. 36.12a; mathematically, the decrease in intensity arises from the factor $(\beta/2)^2$ in the denominator of Eq. (36.12). This decrease in intensity can also be seen in Fig. 35.6 (Section 35.2). The narrower the slits, the broader the single-slit pattern (as in Fig. 36.10) and the slower the decrease in intensity from one interference maximum to the next.

Shall we call the pattern in Fig. 36.12d *interference* or *diffraction?* It's really both, since it results from superposition of waves coming from various parts of the two apertures. There is no truly fundamental distinction between interference and diffraction.

Several Slits

Next let's consider patterns produced by *several* very narrow slits. As we will see, systems of narrow slits are of tremendous practical importance in *spectroscopy,* the determination of the particular wavelengths of light coming from a source. Assume that each slit is narrow in comparison to the wavelength, so its diffraction pattern spreads out nearly uniformly. Figure 36.13 shows an array of eight narrow slits, with distance d between adjacent slits. Constructive interference occurs for rays at angle θ to the normal that arrive at point P with a path difference between adjacent slits equal to an integer number of wavelengths,

$$d \sin\theta = m\lambda \qquad (m = 0, \pm 1, \pm 2, \ldots)$$

This means that reinforcement occurs when the phase difference ϕ at P for light from adjacent slits is an integer multiple of 2π. That is, the maxima in the pattern occur at the *same* positions as for *two* slits with the same spacing. To this extent the pattern resembles the two-slit pattern.

But what happens *between* the maxima? In the two-slit pattern, there is exactly one intensity minimum located midway between each pair of maxima, corresponding to angles for which the phase difference between waves from the two sources is π, 3π, 5π, and so on. In the eight-slit pattern these are also minima because the light from adjacent slits cancels out in pairs, corresponding to the phasor diagram in Fig. 36.14a. But these are not the only minima in the eight-slit pattern. For example, when the phase difference ϕ from adjacent sources is $\pi/4$, the phasor diagram is as shown in Fig. 36.14b; the total (resultant) phasor is zero, and the intensity is zero. When $\phi = \pi/2$, we get the phasor diagram of Fig. 36.14c, and again both the total phasor and the intensity are zero. More generally, the intensity with eight slits is zero whenever ϕ is an integer multiple of $\pi/4$, *except* when ϕ is a multiple of 2π. Thus there are seven minima for every maximum.

Detailed calculation shows that the eight-slit pattern is as shown in Fig. 36.15b. The large maxima, called *principal maxima,* are in the same positions as for the two-slit pattern of Fig. 36.15a but are much narrower. If the phase difference ϕ between adjacent slits is slightly different from a multiple of 2π, the waves from slits 1 and 2 will be only a little out of phase; however, the phase difference between slits 1 and 3 will be greater, that between slits 1 and 4 will be greater still, and so on. This leads to a partial cancellation for angles that are only slightly different from the angle for a maximum, giving the narrow maxima in Fig. 36.15b. The maxima are even narrower with 16 slits (Fig. 36.15c).

You should show that when there are N slits, there are $(N - 1)$ minima between each pair of principal maxima and a minimum occurs whenever ϕ is an integral multiple of $2\pi/N$ (except when ϕ is an integral multiple of 2π, which gives a principal maximum). There are small *secondary* intensity maxima between the minima; these become smaller in comparison to the principal maxima as N increases. The greater the value of N, the narrower the principal maxima become. From an energy standpoint the total power in the entire pattern is proportional to N. The height of each principal maximum is proportional to N^2, so from energy conservation the width of each principal maximum must be proportional to $1/N$. As we will see in the next section, the narrowness of the principal maxima in a multiple-slit pattern is of great practical importance in physics and astronomy.

36.14 Phasor diagrams for light passing through eight narrow slits. Intensity maxima occur when the phase difference $\phi = 0, 2\pi, 4\pi, \ldots$. Between the maxima at $\phi = 0$ and $\phi = 2\pi$ are seven minima, corresponding to $\phi = \pi/4, \pi/2, 3\pi/4, \pi, 5\pi/4, 3\pi/2$, and $7\pi/4$. Can you draw phasor diagrams for the other minima?

(a) Phasor diagram for $\phi = \pi$

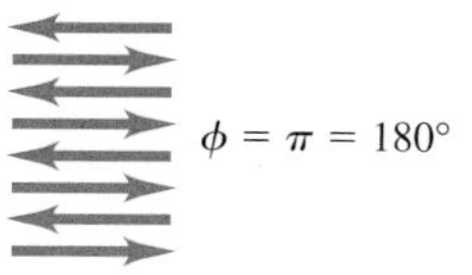

(b) Phasor diagram for $\phi = \frac{\pi}{4}$

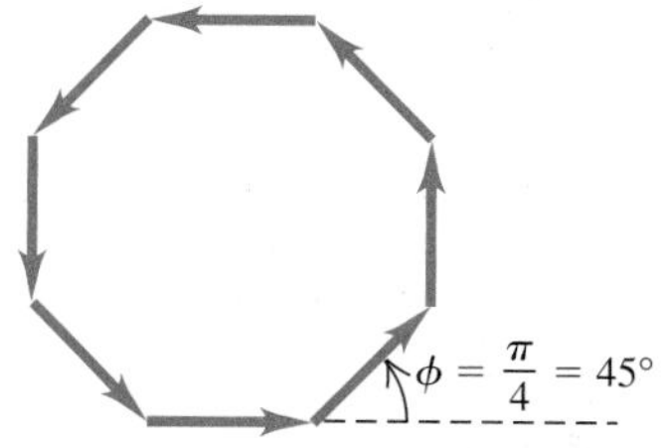

(c) Phasor diagram for $\phi = \frac{\pi}{2}$

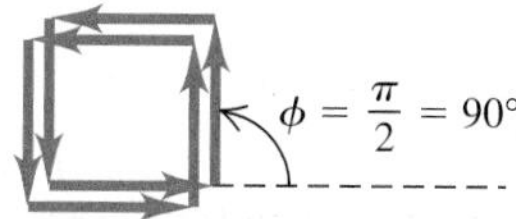

36.15 Interference patterns for N equally spaced, very narrow slits. (a) Two slits. (b) Eight slits. (c) Sixteen slits. The vertical scales are different for each graph; I_0 is the maximum intensity for a single slit, and the maximum intensity for N slits is $N^2 I_0$. The width of each peak is proportional to $1/N$.

(a) $N = 2$: two slits produce one minimum between adjacent maxima.

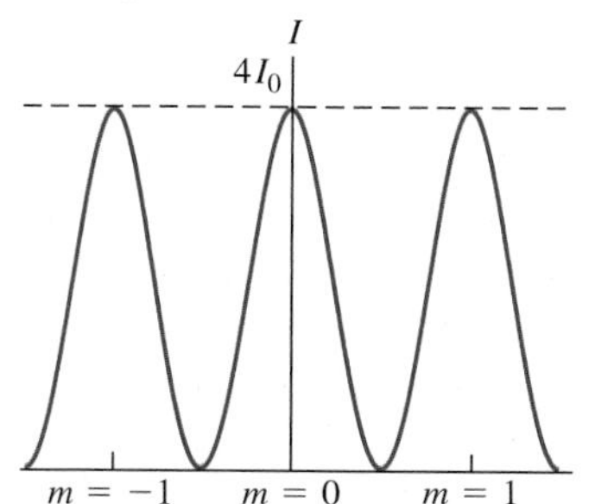

(b) $N = 8$: eight slits produce taller, narrower maxima in the same locations, separated by seven minima.

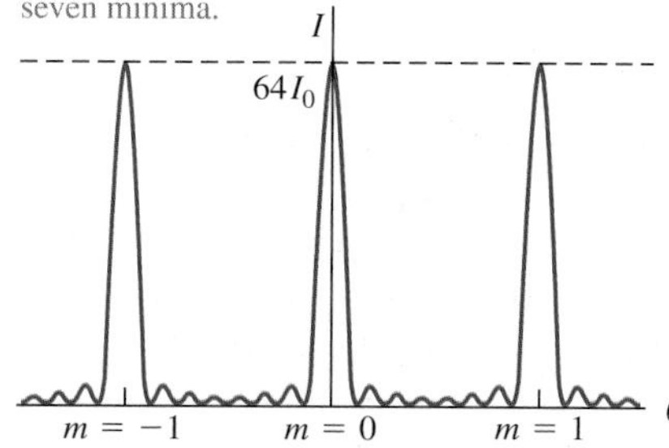

(c) $N = 16$: with 16 slits, the maxima are even taller and narrower, with more intervening minima.

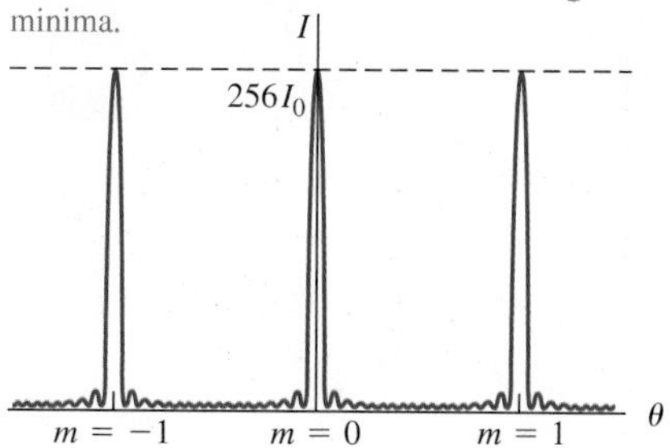

Test Your Understanding of Section 36.4 Suppose two slits, each of width a, are separated by a distance $d = 2.5a$. Are there any missing maxima in the interference pattern produced by these slits? If so, which are missing? If not, why not?

36.16 A portion of a transmission diffraction grating. The separation between the centers of adjacent slits is d.

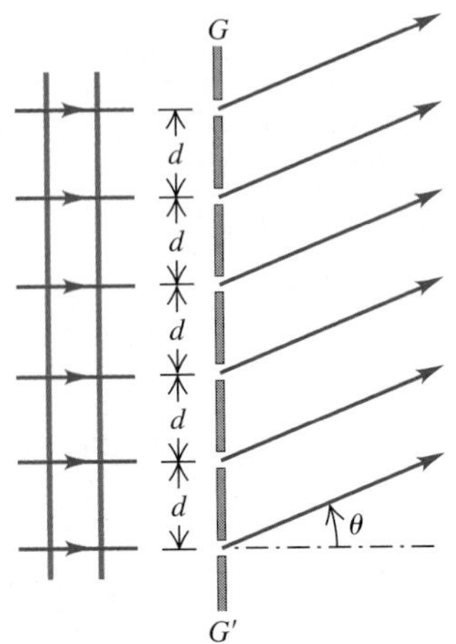

Activ Physics ONLINE

16.4 The Grating: Introduction and Questions

16.5 The Grating: Problems

36.17 The millions of microscopic scales in the wings of the tropical butterfly *Morpho peleides* act as a reflection grating. When viewed at the right angle, these scales strongly reflect blue light. This may be a defense mechanism: The flashes of light from the flapping wings of a *Morpho* could momentarily dazzle predators such as lizards and birds.

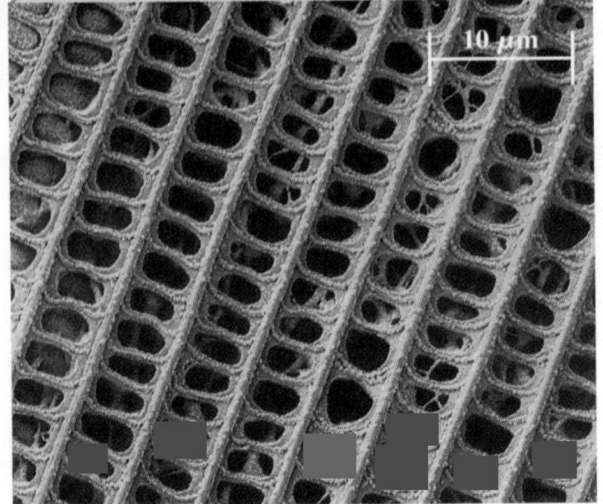

36.5 The Diffraction Grating

We have just seen that increasing the number of slits in an interference experiment (while keeping the spacing of adjacent slits constant) gives interference patterns in which the maxima are in the same positions, but progressively narrower, than with two slits. Because these maxima are so narrow, their angular position, and hence the wavelength, can be measured to very high precision. As we will see, this effect has many important applications.

An array of a large number of parallel slits, all with the same width a and spaced equal distances d between centers, is called a **diffraction grating.** The first one was constructed by Fraunhofer using fine wires. Gratings can be made by using a diamond point to scratch many equally spaced grooves on a glass or metal surface, or by photographic reduction of a pattern of black and white stripes on paper. For a grating, what we have been calling *slits* are often called *rulings* or *lines.*

In Fig. 36.16, GG' is a cross section of a *transmission grating;* the slits are perpendicular to the plane of the page, and an interference pattern is formed by the light that is transmitted through the slits. The diagram shows only six slits; an actual grating may contain several thousand. The spacing d between centers of adjacent slits is called the *grating spacing.* A plane monochromatic wave is incident normally on the grating from the left side. We assume far-field (Fraunhofer) conditions; that is, the pattern is formed on a screen that is far enough away that all rays emerging from the grating and going to a particular point on the screen can be considered to be parallel.

We found in Section 36.4 that the principal intensity maxima with multiple slits occur in the same directions as for the two-slit pattern. These are the directions for which the path difference for adjacent slits is an integer number of wavelengths. So the positions of the maxima are once again given by

$$d\sin\theta = m\lambda \qquad (m = 0, \pm 1, \pm 2, \pm 3, \dots) \qquad \text{(intensity maxima, multiple slits)} \qquad (36.13)$$

The intensity patterns for two, eight, and 16 slits displayed in Fig. 36.15 show the progressive increase in sharpness of the maxima as the number of slits increases.

When a grating containing hundreds or thousands of slits is illuminated by a beam of parallel rays of monochromatic light, the pattern is a series of very sharp lines at angles determined by Eq. (36.13). The $m = \pm 1$ lines are called the *first-order lines,* the $m = \pm 2$ lines the *second-order lines,* and so on. If the grating is illuminated by white light with a continuous distribution of wavelengths, each value of m corresponds to a continuous spectrum in the pattern. The angle for each wavelength is determined by Eq. (36.13); for a given value of m, long wavelengths (the red end of the spectrum) lie at larger angles (that is, are deviated more from the straight-ahead direction) than do the shorter wavelengths at the violet end of the spectrum.

As Eq. (36.13) shows, the sines of the deviation angles of the maxima are proportional to the ratio λ/d. For substantial deviation to occur, the grating spacing d should be of the same order of magnitude as the wavelength λ. Gratings for use with visible light (λ from 400 to 700 nm) usually have about 1000 slits per millimeter; the value of d is the *reciprocal* of the number of slits per unit length, so d is of the order of $\frac{1}{1000}$ mm $=$ 1000 nm.

In a *reflection grating,* the array of equally spaced slits shown in Fig. 36.16 is replaced by an array of equally spaced ridges or grooves on a reflective screen. The reflected light has maximum intensity at angles where the phase difference between light waves reflected from adjacent ridges or grooves is an integral multiple of 2π. If light of wavelength λ is incident normally on a reflection grating with a spacing d between adjacent ridges or grooves, the *reflected* angles at which intensity maxima occur are given by Eq. (36.13). The iridescent colors of certain butterflies arise from microscopic ridges on the butterfly's wings that form a reflection grating (Fig 36.17). When the wings are viewed from different angles, corresponding to varying θ in Eq. (36.13), the wavelength and color that are predominantly reflected to the viewer's eye vary as well.

The rainbow-colored reflections that you see from the surface of a compact disc are a reflection-grating effect (Fig. 36.18). The "grooves" are tiny pits 0.1 μm deep in the surface of the disc, with a uniform radial spacing of $d = 1.60\ \mu\text{m} = 1600$ nm. Information is coded on the CD by varying the *length* of the pits; the reflection-grating aspect of the disc is merely an aesthetic side benefit.

36.18 Microscopic pits on the surface of this compact disc act as a reflection grating, splitting white light into its component colors.

Example 36.4 Width of a grating spectrum

The wavelengths of the visible spectrum are approximately 400 nm (violet) to 700 nm (red). (a) Find the angular width of the first-order visible spectrum produced by a plane grating with 600 slits per millimeter when white light falls normally on the grating. (b) Do the first-order and second-order spectra overlap? What about the second-order and third-order spectra? Do your answers depend on the grating spacing?

SOLUTION

IDENTIFY: The first-, second-, and third-order spectra correspond to $m = 1$, 2, and 3 in Eq. (36.13). This problem asks us to look at the angles spanned by the visible spectrum in each of these orders.

SET UP: We use Eq. (36.13) with $m = 1$ to find the angular deviation θ for 400-nm violet light and 700-nm red light in the first-order spectrum. The difference between these is the angular width of the first-order spectrum, our target variable in part (a). Using the same technique for $m = 2$ and $m = 3$ tells us the maximum and minimum angular deviation for these orders.

EXECUTE: (a) The grating spacing d is

$$d = \frac{1}{600\ \text{slits/mm}} = 1.67 \times 10^{-6}\ \text{m}$$

From Eq. (36.13), with $m = 1$, the angular deviation θ_v of the violet light (400 nm or 400×10^{-9} m) is

$$\sin\theta_v = \frac{400 \times 10^{-9}\ \text{m}}{1.67 \times 10^{-6}\ \text{m}} = 0.240$$

$$\theta_v = 13.9°$$

The angular deviation θ_r of the red light (700 nm) is

$$\sin\theta_r = \frac{700 \times 10^{-9}\ \text{m}}{1.67 \times 10^{-6}\ \text{m}} = 0.419$$

$$\theta_r = 24.8°$$

So the angular width of the first-order visible spectrum is

$$24.8° - 13.9° = 10.9°$$

(b) From Eq. (36.13), with a grating spacing of d the angular deviation θ_{vm} of the 400-nm violet light in the mth-order spectrum is given by

$$\sin\theta_{vm} = \frac{m(400 \times 10^{-9}\ \text{m})}{d}$$
$$= \frac{4.00 \times 10^{-7}\ \text{m}}{d} \quad (m = 1)$$
$$= \frac{8.00 \times 10^{-7}\ \text{m}}{d} \quad (m = 2)$$
$$= \frac{1.20 \times 10^{-6}\ \text{m}}{d} \quad (m = 3)$$

Similarly, the angular deviation θ_{rm} of the 700-nm red light in the mth-order spectrum is given by

$$\sin\theta_{rm} = \frac{m(700 \times 10^{-9}\ \text{m})}{d}$$
$$= \frac{7.00 \times 10^{-7}\ \text{m}}{d} \quad (m = 1)$$
$$= \frac{1.40 \times 10^{-6}\ \text{m}}{d} \quad (m = 2)$$
$$= \frac{2.10 \times 10^{-6}\ \text{m}}{d} \quad (m = 3)$$

The greater the value of $\sin\theta$, the greater the value of θ (for angles between zero and 90°). Hence our results show that for any value of the grating spacing d, the largest angle (at the red end) of the $m = 1$ spectrum is always less than the smallest angle (at the violet end) of the $m = 2$ spectrum, so the first and second orders *never* overlap. By contrast, the largest (red) angle of the $m = 2$ spectrum is always greater than the smallest (violet) angle of the $m = 3$ spectrum, so the second and third orders *always* overlap.

EVALUATE: The fundamental reason the first-order and second-order visible spectra don't overlap is that the human eye is sensitive to only a narrow range of wavelengths. Can you show that if the eye could detect wavelengths from 400 nm to 900 nm (in the near-infrared range), the first and second orders *would* overlap?

36.19 (a) A visible-light photograph of the sun. (b) Sunlight is dispersed into a spectrum by a diffraction grating. Specific wavelengths are absorbed as sunlight passes through the sun's atmosphere, leaving dark lines in the spectrum.

(a)

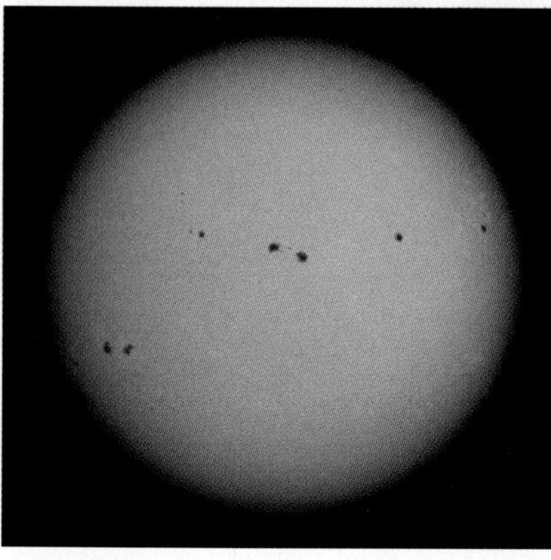

(b)

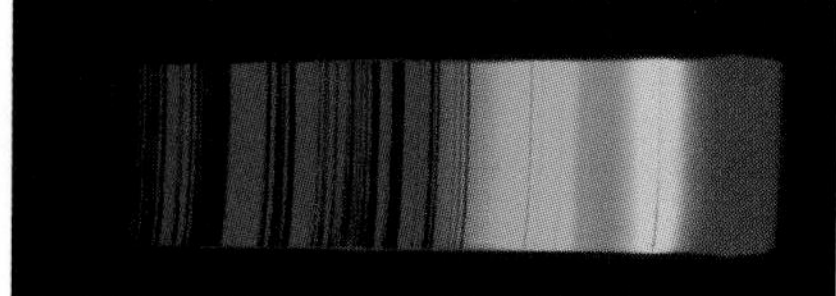

Grating Spectrographs

Diffraction gratings are widely used to measure the spectrum of light emitted by a source, a process called *spectroscopy* or *spectrometry.* Light incident on a grating of known spacing is dispersed into a spectrum. The angles of deviation of the maxima are then measured, and Eq. (36.13) is used to compute the wavelength. With a grating that has many slits, very sharp maxima are produced, and the angle of deviation (and hence the wavelength) can be measured very precisely.

An important application of this technique is to astronomy. As light generated within the sun passes through the sun's atmosphere, certain wavelengths are selectively absorbed. The result is that the spectrum of sunlight produced by a diffraction grating has dark *absorption lines* (Fig. 36.19). Experiments in the laboratory show that different types of atoms and ions absorb light at different wavelengths. By comparing these laboratory results with the wavelengths of absorption lines in the spectrum of sunlight, astronomers can deduce the chemical composition of the sun's atmosphere. The same technique is used to make chemical assays of galaxies that are millions of light-years away.

Figure 36.20 shows one design for a *grating spectrograph* used in astronomy. A transmission grating is used in the figure; in other setups, a reflection grating is used. In older designs a prism was used rather than a grating, and a spectrum was formed by dispersion (see Section 33.4) rather than diffraction. However, there is no simple relationship between wavelength and angle of deviation for a prism, prisms absorb some of the light that passes through them, and they are less effective for many nonvisible wavelengths that are important in astronomy. For these and other reasons, gratings are preferred in precision applications.

Resolution of a Grating Spectrograph

In spectroscopy it is often important to distinguish slightly differing wavelengths. The minimum wavelength difference $\Delta\lambda$ that can be distinguished by a spectrograph is described by the **chromatic resolving power** R, defined as

$$R = \frac{\lambda}{\Delta\lambda} \quad \text{(chromatic resolving power)} \tag{36.14}$$

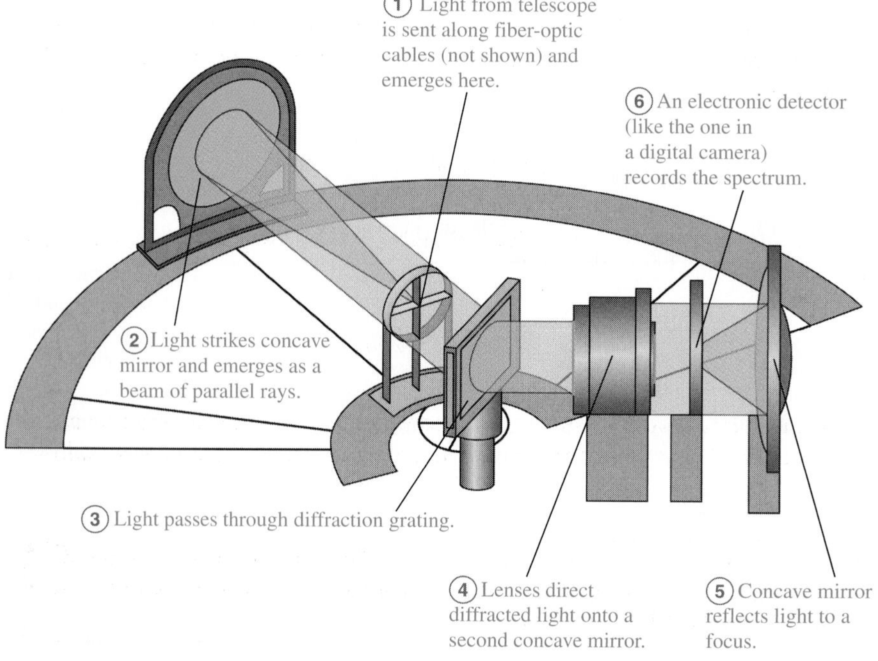

1 Light from telescope is sent along fiber-optic cables (not shown) and emerges here.
6 An electronic detector (like the one in a digital camera) records the spectrum.
2 Light strikes concave mirror and emerges as a beam of parallel rays.
3 Light passes through diffraction grating.
4 Lenses direct diffracted light onto a second concave mirror.
5 Concave mirror reflects light to a focus.

36.20 A schematic diagram of a diffraction-grating spectrograph for use in astronomy. Note that the light does not strike the grating normal to its surface, so the intensity maxima are given by a somewhat different expression than Eq. (36.13). (See Problem 36.66).

As an example, when sodium atoms are heated, they emit strongly at the yellow wavelengths 589.00 nm and 589.59 nm. A spectrograph that can barely distinguish these two lines in the spectrum of sodium light (called the *sodium doublet*) has a chromatic resolving power $R = (589.00 \text{ nm})/(0.59 \text{ nm}) = 1000$. (You can see these wavelengths when boiling water on a gas range. If the water boils over onto the flame, dissolved sodium from table salt emits a burst of yellow light.)

We can derive an expression for the resolving power of a diffraction grating used in a spectrograph. Two different wavelengths give diffraction maxima at slightly different angles. As a reasonable (though arbitrary) criterion, let's assume that we can distinguish them as two separate peaks if the maximum of one coincides with the first minimum of the other.

From our discussion in Section 36.4 the mth-order maximum occurs when the phase difference ϕ for adjacent slits is $\phi = 2\pi m$. The first minimum beside that maximum occurs when $\phi = 2\pi m + 2\pi/N$, where N is the number of slits. The phase difference is also given by $\phi = (2\pi d \sin\theta)/\lambda$, so the angular interval $d\theta$ corresponding to a small increment $d\phi$ in the phase shift can be obtained from the differential of this equation:

$$d\phi = \frac{2\pi d \cos\theta \, d\theta}{\lambda}$$

When $d\phi = 2\pi/N$, this corresponds to the angular interval $d\theta$ between a maximum and the first adjacent minimum. Thus $d\theta$ is given by

$$\frac{2\pi}{N} = \frac{2\pi d \cos\theta \, d\theta}{\lambda} \quad \text{or} \quad d\cos\theta \, d\theta = \frac{\lambda}{N}$$

CAUTION Watch out for different uses of the symbol *d* Don't confuse the spacing d with the differential "d" in the angular interval $d\theta$ or in the phase shift increment $d\phi$!

Now we need to find the angular spacing $d\theta$ between maxima for two slightly different wavelengths. This is easy; we have $d\sin\theta = m\lambda$, so the differential of this equation gives

$$d\cos\theta \, d\theta = m \, d\lambda$$

According to our criterion, the limit or resolution is reached when these two angular spacings are equal. Equating the two expressions for the quantity $(d\cos\theta \, d\theta)$, we find

$$\frac{\lambda}{N} = m \, d\lambda \quad \text{and} \quad \frac{\lambda}{d\lambda} = Nm$$

If $\Delta\lambda$ is small, we can replace $d\lambda$ by $\Delta\lambda$, and the resolving power R is given simply by

$$R = \frac{\lambda}{\Delta\lambda} = Nm \tag{36.15}$$

The greater the number of slits N, the better the resolution; also, the higher the order m of the diffraction-pattern maximum that we use, the better the resolution.

Test Your Understanding of Section 36.5 What minimum number of slits would be required in a grating to resolve the sodium doublet in the fourth order? (i) 250; (ii) 400; (iii) 1000; (iv) 4000.

36.6 X-Ray Diffraction

X rays were discovered by Wilhelm Röntgen (1845–1923) in 1895, and early experiments suggested that they were electromagnetic waves with wavelengths of the order of 10^{-10} m. At about the same time, the idea began to emerge that in a crystalline solid the atoms are arranged in a regular repeating pattern, with spacing between adjacent atoms also of the order of 10^{-10} m. Putting these two ideas together, Max von Laue (1879–1960) proposed in 1912 that a crystal might serve as a kind of three-dimensional diffraction grating for x rays. That is, a beam of x rays might be scattered (that is, absorbed and re-emitted) by the individual atoms in a crystal, and the scattered waves might interfere just like waves from a diffraction grating.

The first **x-ray diffraction** experiments were performed in 1912 by Friederich, Knipping, and von Laue, using the experimental setup sketched in Fig. 36.21a. The scattered x rays *did* form an interference pattern, which they recorded on photographic film. Figure 36.21b is a photograph of such a pattern. These experiments verified that x rays *are* waves, or at least have wavelike properties, and also that the atoms in a crystal *are* arranged in a regular pattern (Fig. 36.22). Since that time, x-ray diffraction has proved to be an invaluable research tool, both for measuring x-ray wavelengths and for studying the structure of crystals and complex molecules.

A Simple Model of X-Ray Diffraction

To better understand x-ray diffraction, we consider first a two-dimensional scattering situation, as shown in Fig. 36.23a, in which a plane wave is incident on a rectangular array of scattering centers. The situation might be a ripple tank with an array of small posts, 3-cm microwaves striking an array of small conducting spheres, or x rays incident on an array of atoms. In the case of electromagnetic waves, the wave induces an oscillating electric dipole moment in each scatterer. These dipoles act like little antennas, emitting scattered waves. The resulting interference pattern is the superposition of all these scattered waves. The situation is different from that with a diffraction grating, in which the waves from all the slits are emitted *in phase* (for a plane wave at normal incidence). Here the scattered waves are *not* all in phase because their distances from the *source* are different. To compute the interference pattern, we have to consider the *total* path differences for the scattered waves, including the distances from source to scatterer and from scatterer to observer.

As Fig. 36.23b shows, the path length from source to observer is the same for all the scatterers in a single row if the two angles θ_a and θ_r are equal. Scattered radia-

36.21 (a) An x-ray diffraction experiment. (b) Diffraction pattern (or *Laue pattern*) formed by directing a beam of x rays at a thin section of quartz crystal.

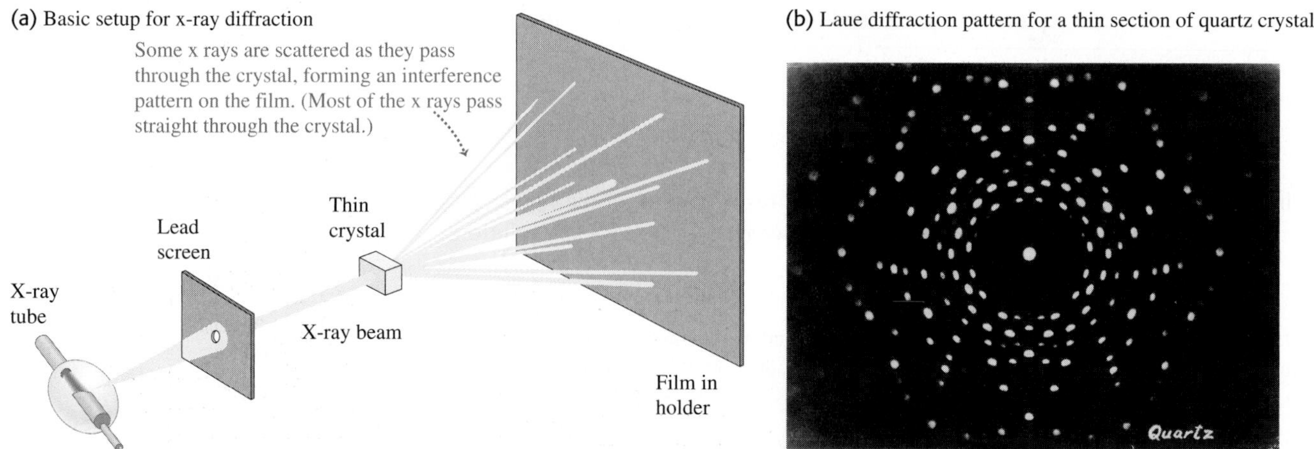
(a) Basic setup for x-ray diffraction
Some x rays are scattered as they pass through the crystal, forming an interference pattern on the film. (Most of the x rays pass straight through the crystal.)
Thin crystal
Lead screen
X-ray tube
X-ray beam
Film in holder
(b) Laue diffraction pattern for a thin section of quartz crystal
Quartz

tion from *adjacent* rows is *also* in phase if the path difference for adjacent rows is an integer number of wavelengths. Figure 36.23c shows that this path difference is $2d\sin\theta$, where θ is the common value of θ_a and θ_r. Therefore the conditions for radiation from the *entire array* to reach the observer in phase are (1) the angle of incidence must equal the angle of scattering and (2) the path difference for adjacent rows must equal $m\lambda$, where m is an integer. We can express the second condition as

$$2d\sin\theta = m\lambda \qquad (m = 1, 2, 3, \dots) \qquad \text{(Bragg condition for constructive interference from an array)} \qquad (36.16)$$

CAUTION **Scattering from an array** In Eq. (36.16) the angle θ is measured with respect to the *surface* of the crystal, rather than with respect to the *normal* to the plane of an array of slits or a grating. Also, note that the path difference in Eq. (36.16) is $2d\sin\theta$, not $d\sin\theta$ as in Eq. (36.13) for a diffraction grating.

In directions for which Eq. (36.16) is satisfied, we see a strong maximum in the interference pattern. We can describe this interference in terms of *reflections* of the wave from the horizontal rows of scatterers in Fig. 36.23a. Strong reflection (constructive interference) occurs at angles such that the incident and scattered angles are equal and Eq. (36.16) is satisfied. Since $\sin\theta$ can never be greater than 1, Eq. (36.16) says that to have constructive interference the quantity $m\lambda$ must be less than $2d$ and so λ must be less than $2d/m$. For example, the value of d in an NaCl crystal (Fig. 36.22) is only 0.282 nm. Hence to have the mth-order maximum present in the diffraction pattern, λ must be less than $2(0.282\text{ nm})/m$; that is, $\lambda < 0.564$ nm for $m = 1$, $\lambda < 0.282$ nm for $m = 2$, $\lambda < 0.188$ nm for $m = 3$, and so on. These are all x-ray wavelengths (see Fig. 32.4), which is why x rays are used for studying crystal structure.

We can extend this discussion to a three-dimensional array by considering *planes* of scatterers instead of *rows*. Figure 36.24 shows two different sets of parallel planes that pass through all the scatterers. Waves from all the scatterers in a

36.22 Model of the arrangement of ions in a crystal of NaCl (table salt). The spacing of adjacent atoms is 0.282 nm. (The electron clouds of the atoms actually overlap slightly.)

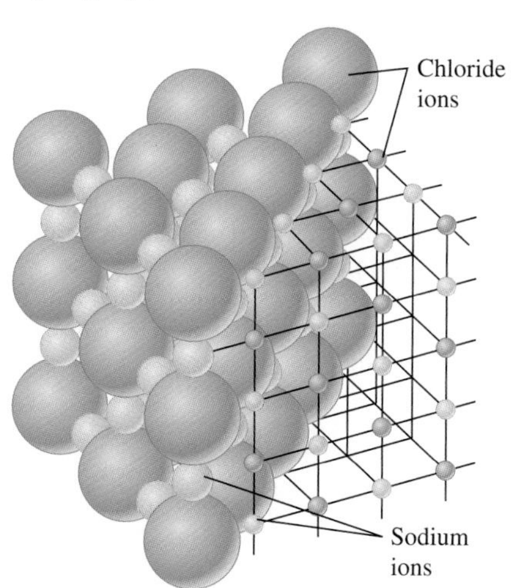

36.23 A two-dimensional model of scattering from a rectangular array. Note that the angles in (b) are measured from the *surface* of the array, not from its normal.

(a) Scattering of waves from a rectangular array

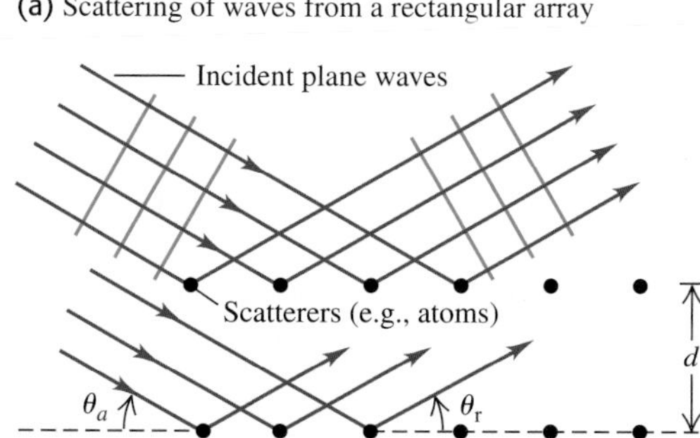

(b) Scattering from adjacent atoms in a row
Interference from adjacent atoms in a row is constructive when the path lengths $a\cos\theta_a$ and $a\cos\theta_r$ are equal, so that the angle of incidence θ_a equals the angle of reflection (scattering) θ_r.

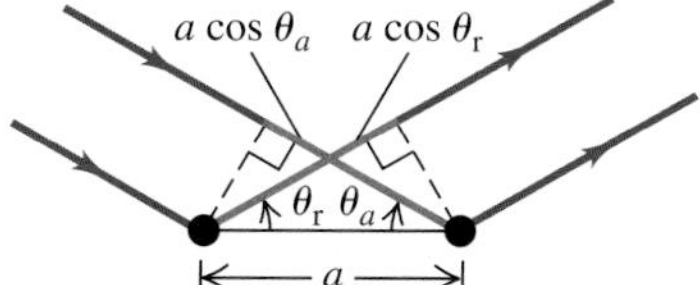

(c) Scattering from atoms in adjacent rows
Interference from atoms in adjacent rows is constructive when the path difference $2d\sin\theta$ is an integral number of wavelengths, as in Eq. (36.16).

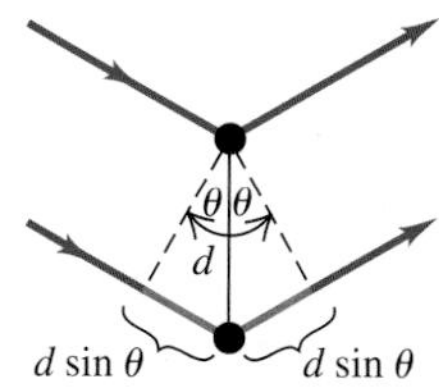

36.24 A cubic crystal and two different families of crystal planes. There are also three sets of planes parallel to the cube faces, with spacing a.

(a) Spacing of planes is $d = a/\sqrt{2}$.

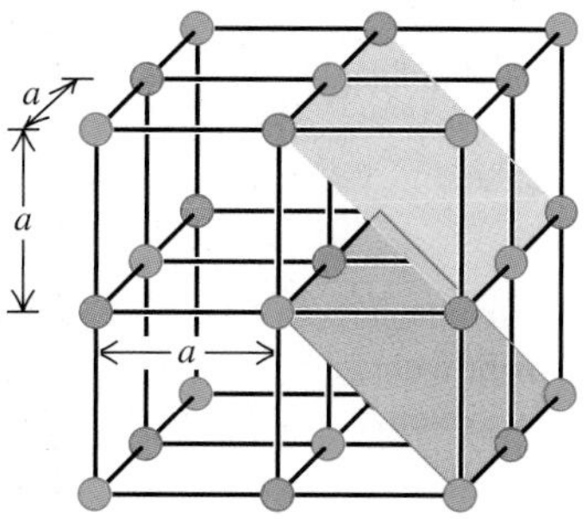

(b) Spacing of planes is $d = a/\sqrt{3}$.

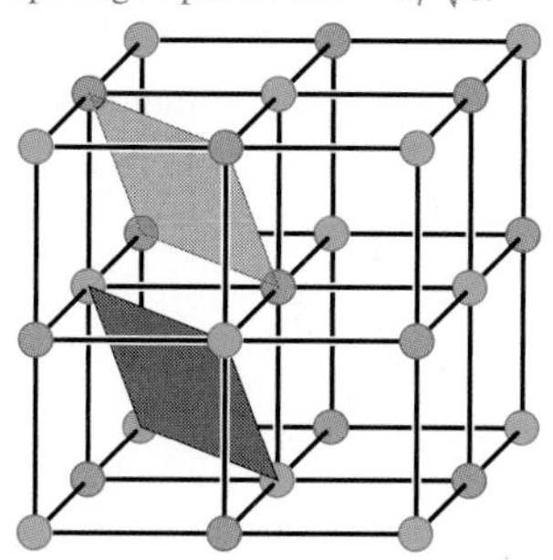

given plane interfere constructively if the angles of incidence and scattering are equal. There is also constructive interference between planes when Eq. (36.16) is satisfied, where d is now the distance between adjacent planes. Because there are many different sets of parallel planes, there are also many values of d and many sets of angles that give constructive interference for the whole crystal lattice. This phenomenon is called **Bragg reflection,** and Eq. (36.16) is called the **Bragg condition,** in honor of Sir William Bragg and his son Laurence Bragg, two pioneers in x-ray analysis.

CAUTION Bragg *reflection* is really Bragg *interference* While we are using the term *reflection,* remember that we are dealing with an *interference* effect. In fact, the reflections from various planes are closely analogous to interference effects in thin films (see Section 35.4).

36.25 The British scientist Rosalind Franklin made this groundbreaking x-ray diffraction image of DNA in 1953. The dark bands arranged in a cross provided the first evidence of the helical structure of the DNA molecule.

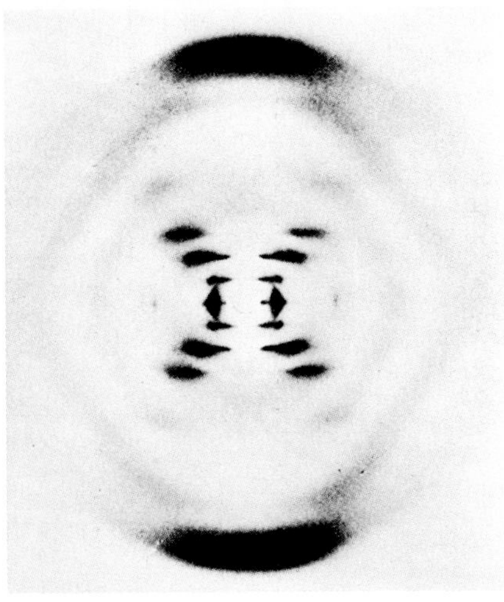

As Fig. 36.21b shows, in x-ray diffraction there is nearly complete cancellation in all but certain very specific directions in which constructive interference occurs and forms bright spots. Such a pattern is usually called an x-ray *diffraction* pattern, although *interference* pattern might be more appropriate.

We can determine the wavelength of x rays by examining the diffraction pattern for a crystal of known structure and known spacing between atoms, just as we determined wavelengths of visible light by measuring patterns from slits or gratings. (The spacing between atoms in simple crystals of known structure, such as sodium chloride, can be found from the density of the crystal and Avogadro's number.) Then, once we know the x-ray wavelength, we can use x-ray diffraction to explore the structure and determine the spacing between atoms in crystals with unknown structure.

X-ray diffraction is by far the most important experimental tool in the investigation of crystal structure of solids. X-ray diffraction also plays an important role in studies of the structures of liquids and of organic molecules. It has been one of the chief experimental techniques in working out the double-helix structure of DNA (Fig. 36.25) and subsequent advances in molecular genetics.

Example 36.5 X-ray diffraction

You direct a beam of x rays with wavelength 0.154 nm at certain planes of a silicon crystal. As you increase the angle of incidence from zero, you find the first strong interference maximum from these planes when the beam makes an angle of 34.5° with the planes. (a) How far apart are the planes? (b) Will you find other interference maxima from these planes at larger angles?

SOLUTION

IDENTIFY: This problem involves Bragg reflection of x rays from the planes of a crystal.

SET UP: In part (a) we use the Bragg condition, Eq. (36.16), to relate the wavelength λ and the angle θ for the $m = 1$ interference maximum (both of which are given) to the spacing d between planes (which is the target variable). Given the value of d, we use the Bragg condition again in part (b) to find the values of θ for interference maxima corresponding to other values of m.

EXECUTE: (a) We solve the Bragg equation, Eq. (36.16), for d and set $m = 1$:

$$d = \frac{m\lambda}{2\sin\theta} = \frac{(1)(0.154\text{ nm})}{2\sin 34.5°} = 0.136\text{ nm}$$

This is the distance between adjacent planes.

(b) To calculate other angles, we solve Eq. (36.16) for $\sin\theta$:

$$\sin\theta = \frac{m\lambda}{2d} = m\frac{0.154\text{ nm}}{2(0.136\text{ nm})} = m(0.566)$$

Values of m of 2 or greater give values of $\sin\theta$ greater than unity, which is impossible. Hence there are *no* other angles for interference maxima for this particular set of crystal planes.

EVALUATE: Our result in part (b) shows that there *would* be a second interference maximum if the quantity $\lambda/2d$ were equal to 0.500 or less. This would be the case if the wavelength of the x rays were less than $2d = 0.272$ nm. How short would the wavelength need to be to have *three* interference maxima?

Test Your Understanding of Section 36.6 You are doing an x-ray diffraction experiment with a crystal in which the atomic planes are 0.200 nm apart. You are using x rays of wavelength 0.100 nm. Will the fifth-order maximum be present in the diffraction pattern?

36.7 Circular Apertures and Resolving Power

ActivPhysics ONLINE

16.7 Circular Hole Diffraction
16.8 Resolving Power

We have studied in detail the diffraction patterns formed by long, thin slits or arrays of slits. But an aperture of *any* shape forms a diffraction pattern. The diffraction pattern formed by a *circular* aperture is of special interest because of its role in limiting how well an optical instrument can resolve fine details. In principle, we could compute the intensity at any point P in the diffraction pattern by dividing the area of the aperture into small elements, finding the resulting wave amplitude and phase at P, and then integrating over the aperture area to find the resultant amplitude and intensity at P. In practice, the integration cannot be carried out in terms of elementary functions. We will simply *describe* the pattern and quote a few relevant numbers.

The diffraction pattern formed by a circular aperture consists of a central bright spot surrounded by a series of bright and dark rings, as shown in Fig. 36.26. We can describe the pattern in terms of the angle θ, representing the angular radius of each ring. If the aperture diameter is D and the wavelength is λ, the angular radius θ_1 of the first *dark* ring is given by

$$\sin\theta_1 = 1.22\frac{\lambda}{D} \quad \text{(diffraction by a circular aperture)} \tag{36.17}$$

The angular radii of the next two dark rings are given by

$$\sin\theta_2 = 2.23\frac{\lambda}{D} \qquad \sin\theta_3 = 3.24\frac{\lambda}{D} \tag{36.18}$$

Between these are bright rings with angular radii given by

$$\sin\theta = 1.63\frac{\lambda}{D}, \qquad 2.68\frac{\lambda}{D}, \qquad 3.70\frac{\lambda}{D} \tag{36.19}$$

and so on. The central bright spot is called the **Airy disk,** in honor of Sir George Airy (1801–1892), Astronomer Royal of England, who first derived the expression for the intensity in the pattern. The angular radius of the Airy disk is that of the first dark ring, given by Eq. (36.17).

The intensities in the bright rings drop off very quickly with increasing angle. When D is much larger than the wavelength λ, the usual case for optical instruments, the peak intensity in the first ring is only 1.7% of the value at the center of the Airy disk, and the peak intensity of the second ring is only 0.4%. Most (85%) of the light energy falls within the Airy disk. Figure 36.27 shows a diffraction pattern from a circular aperture.

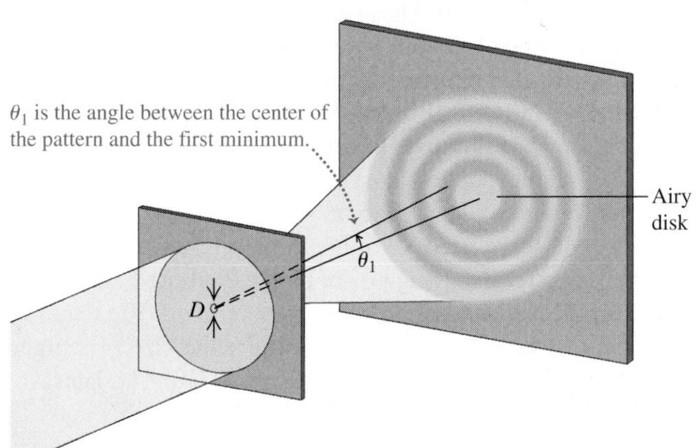

θ_1 is the angle between the center of the pattern and the first minimum.
Airy disk
θ_1
D

36.26 Diffraction pattern formed by a circular aperture of diameter D. The pattern consists of a central bright spot and alternating dark and bright rings. The angular radius θ_1 of the first dark ring is shown. (This diagram is not drawn to scale.)

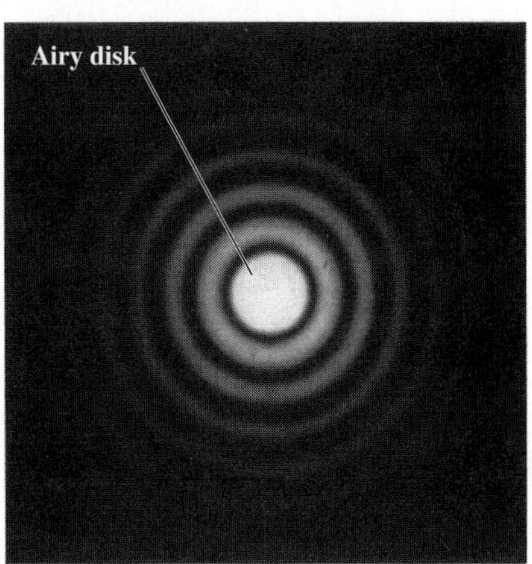

Airy disk

36.27 Photograph of the diffraction pattern formed by a circular aperture.

36.28 Diffraction patterns of four very small ("point") sources of light. The photographs were made with a circular aperture in front of the lens. **(a)** The aperture is so small that the patterns of sources 3 and 4 overlap and are barely resolved by Rayleigh's criterion. Increasing the size of the aperture decreases the size of the diffraction patterns, as shown in **(b)** and **(c)**.

(a) Small aperture

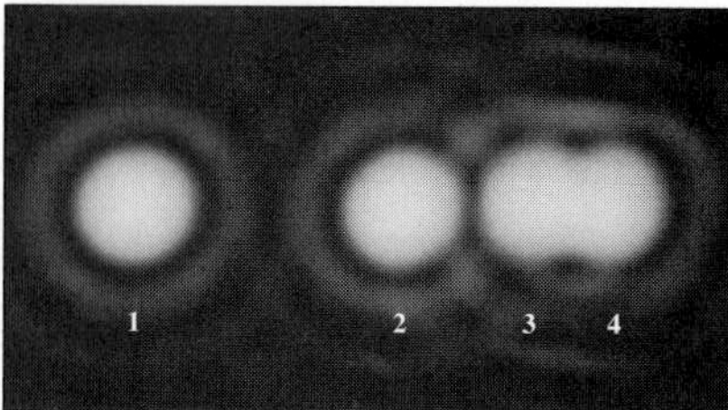

(b) Medium aperture

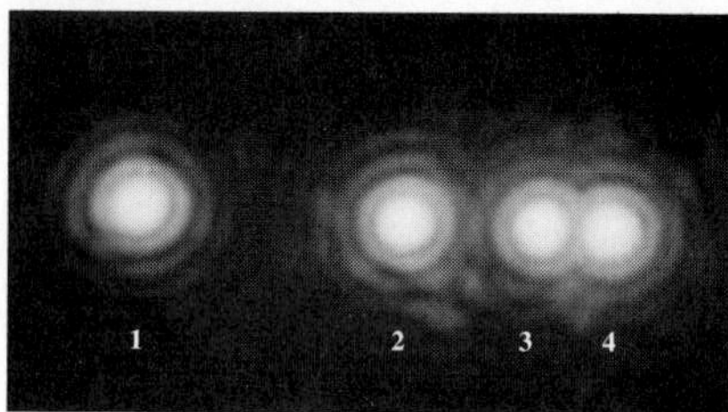

(c) Large aperture

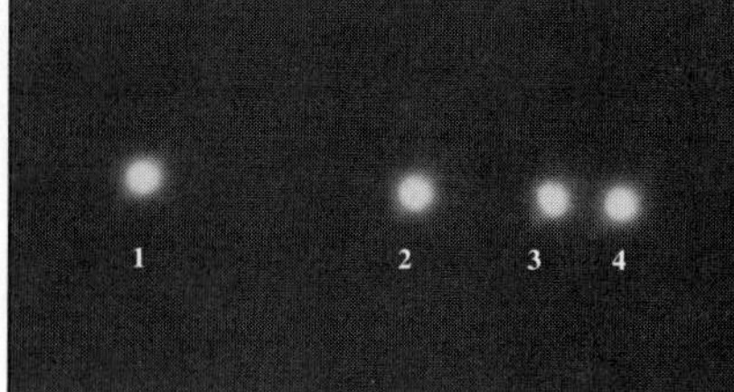

Diffraction and Image Formation

Diffraction has far-reaching implications for image formation by lenses and mirrors. In our study of optical instruments in Chapter 34 we assumed that a lens with focal length f focuses a parallel beam (plane wave) to a *point* at a distance f from the lens. This assumption ignored diffraction effects. We now see that what we get is not a point but the diffraction pattern just described. If we have two point objects, their images are not two points but two diffraction patterns. When the objects are close together, their diffraction patterns overlap; if they are close enough, their patterns overlap almost completely and cannot be distinguished. The effect is shown in Fig. 36.28, which presents the patterns for four very small "point" sources of light. In Fig. 36.28a the image of the left-hand source is well separated from the others, but the images of the middle and right-hand sources have merged. In Fig. 36.28b, with a larger aperture diameter and hence smaller Airy disks, the middle and right-hand images are better resolved. In Fig. 36.28c, with a still larger aperture, they are well resolved.

A widely used criterion for resolution of two point objects, proposed by the English physicist Lord Rayleigh (1842–1919) and called **Rayleigh's criterion,** is that the objects are just barely resolved (that is, distinguishable) if the center of one diffraction pattern coincides with the first minimum of the other. In that case the angular separation of the image centers is given by Eq. (36.17). The angular separation of the *objects* is the same as that of the *images* made by a telescope, microscope, or other optical device. So two point objects are barely resolved, according to Rayleigh's criterion, when their angular separation is given by Eq. (36.17).

The minimum separation of two objects that can just be resolved by an optical instrument is called the **limit of resolution** of the instrument. The smaller the limit of resolution, the greater the *resolution,* or **resolving power,** of the instrument. Diffraction sets the ultimate limits on resolution of lenses. *Geometric* optics may make it seem that we can make images as large as we like. Eventually, though, we always reach a point at which the image becomes larger but does not gain in detail. The images in Fig. 36.28 would not become sharper with further enlargement.

CAUTION **Resolving power vs. chromatic resolving power** Be careful not to confuse the resolving power of an optical instrument with the *chromatic* resolving power of a grating (described in Section 36.5). Resolving power refers to the ability to distinguish the images of objects that appear close to each other, when looking either through an optical instrument or at a photograph made with the instrument. Chromatic resolving power describes how well different wavelengths can be distinguished in a spectrum formed by a diffraction grating.

Rayleigh's criterion combined with Eq. (36.17) shows that resolution (resolving power) improves with larger diameter; it also improves with shorter wavelengths. Ultraviolet microscopes have higher resolution than visible-light microscopes. In electron microscopes the resolution is limited by the wavelengths associated with the electrons, which have wavelike aspects (to be discussed further in Chapter 39). These wavelengths can be made 100,000 times smaller than wavelengths of visible light, with a corresponding gain in resolution. Resolving power also explains the difference in storage capacity between compact discs (CDs) and digital video discs (DVDs). Information is stored in both of these in a series of tiny pits. In order not to lose information in the scanning process, the scanning optics must be able to resolve two adjacent pits so that they do not seem to blend into a single pit (see sources 3 and 4 in Fig. 36.28). The red laser used in a DVD player has a shorter wavelength (650 nm) and hence better resolving power than the infrared laser in a CD player (780 nm). Hence pits can be spaced closer together in a DVD than in a CD, and more information can be stored on a disc of the same size (4.7 gigabytes on a DVD versus 700 megabytes, or 0.7 gigabyte, on a CD). The latest disc storage technology uses a blue-violet laser of 405-nm wavelength; this makes it possible

tion from *adjacent* rows is *also* in phase if the path difference for adjacent rows is an integer number of wavelengths. Figure 36.23c shows that this path difference is $2d\sin\theta$, where θ is the common value of θ_a and θ_r. Therefore the conditions for radiation from the *entire array* to reach the observer in phase are (1) the angle of incidence must equal the angle of scattering and (2) the path difference for adjacent rows must equal $m\lambda$, where m is an integer. We can express the second condition as

$$2d\sin\theta = m\lambda \qquad (m = 1, 2, 3, \ldots) \qquad \text{(Bragg condition for constructive interference from an array)} \qquad (36.16)$$

CAUTION **Scattering from an array** In Eq. (36.16) the angle θ is measured with respect to the *surface* of the crystal, rather than with respect to the *normal* to the plane of an array of slits or a grating. Also, note that the path difference in Eq. (36.16) is $2d\sin\theta$, not $d\sin\theta$ as in Eq. (36.13) for a diffraction grating.

In directions for which Eq. (36.16) is satisfied, we see a strong maximum in the interference pattern. We can describe this interference in terms of *reflections* of the wave from the horizontal rows of scatterers in Fig. 36.23a. Strong reflection (constructive interference) occurs at angles such that the incident and scattered angles are equal and Eq. (36.16) is satisfied. Since $\sin\theta$ can never be greater than 1, Eq. (36.16) says that to have constructive interference the quantity $m\lambda$ must be less than $2d$ and so λ must be less than $2d/m$. For example, the value of d in an NaCl crystal (Fig. 36.22) is only 0.282 nm. Hence to have the mth-order maximum present in the diffraction pattern, λ must be less than $2(0.282\text{ nm})/m$; that is, $\lambda < 0.564$ nm for $m = 1$, $\lambda < 0.282$ nm for $m = 2$, $\lambda < 0.188$ nm for $m = 3$, and so on. These are all x-ray wavelengths (see Fig. 32.4), which is why x rays are used for studying crystal structure.

We can extend this discussion to a three-dimensional array by considering *planes* of scatterers instead of *rows*. Figure 36.24 shows two different sets of parallel planes that pass through all the scatterers. Waves from all the scatterers in a

36.22 Model of the arrangement of ions in a crystal of NaCl (table salt). The spacing of adjacent atoms is 0.282 nm. (The electron clouds of the atoms actually overlap slightly.)

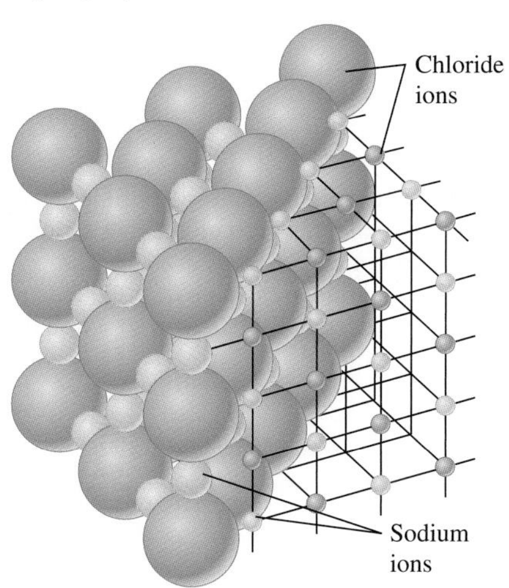

36.23 A two-dimensional model of scattering from a rectangular array. Note that the angles in (b) are measured from the *surface* of the array, not from its normal.

(a) Scattering of waves from a rectangular array

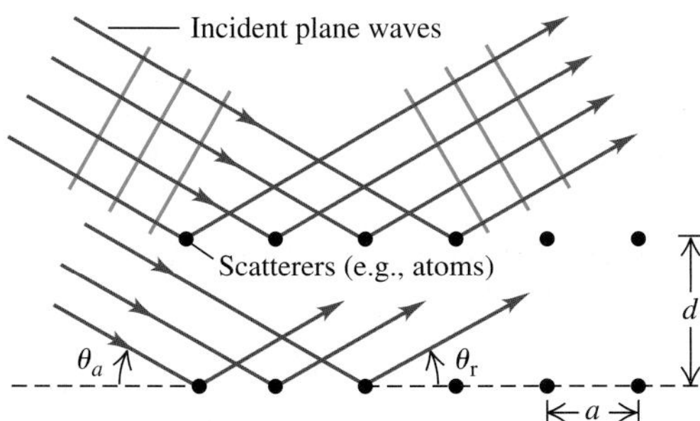

(b) Scattering from adjacent atoms in a row
Interference from adjacent atoms in a row is constructive when the path lengths $a\cos\theta_a$ and $a\cos\theta_r$ are equal, so that the angle of incidence θ_a equals the angle of reflection (scattering) θ_r.

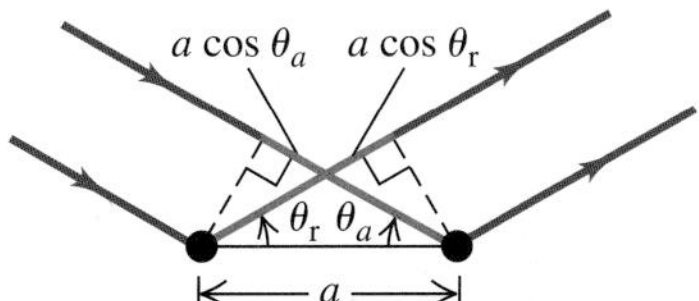

(c) Scattering from atoms in adjacent rows
Interference from atoms in adjacent rows is constructive when the path difference $2d\sin\theta$ is an integral number of wavelengths, as in Eq. (36.16).

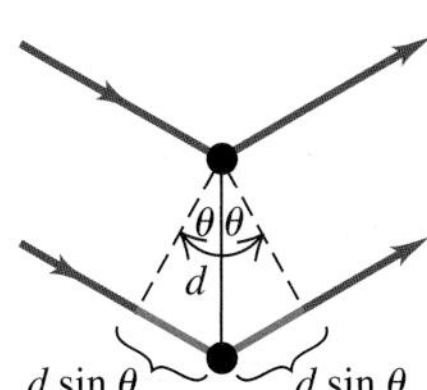

36.24 A cubic crystal and two different families of crystal planes. There are also three sets of planes parallel to the cube faces, with spacing a.

(a) Spacing of planes is $d = a/\sqrt{2}$.

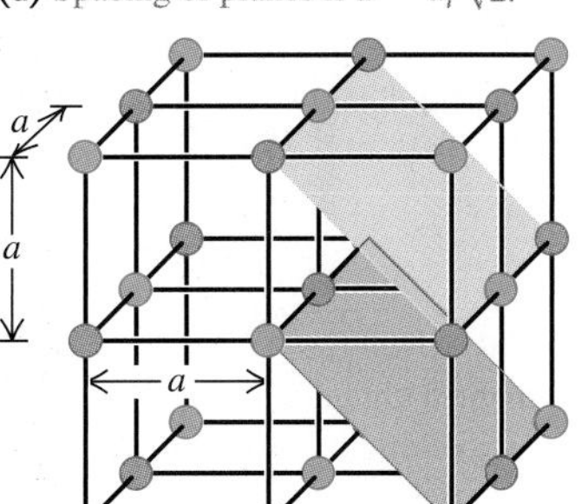

(b) Spacing of planes is $d = a/\sqrt{3}$.

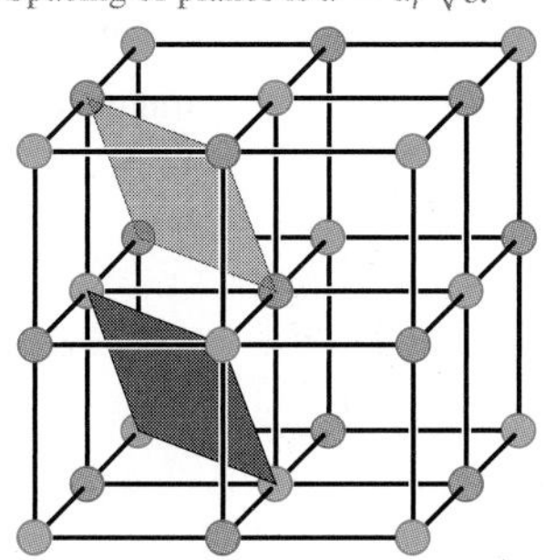

given plane interfere constructively if the angles of incidence and scattering are equal. There is also constructive interference between planes when Eq. (36.16) is satisfied, where d is now the distance between adjacent planes. Because there are many different sets of parallel planes, there are also many values of d and many sets of angles that give constructive interference for the whole crystal lattice. This phenomenon is called **Bragg reflection,** and Eq. (36.16) is called the **Bragg condition,** in honor of Sir William Bragg and his son Laurence Bragg, two pioneers in x-ray analysis.

CAUTION **Bragg *reflection* is really Bragg *interference*** While we are using the term *reflection,* remember that we are dealing with an *interference* effect. In fact, the reflections from various planes are closely analogous to interference effects in thin films (see Section 35.4).

36.25 The British scientist Rosalind Franklin made this groundbreaking x-ray diffraction image of DNA in 1953. The dark bands arranged in a cross provided the first evidence of the helical structure of the DNA molecule.

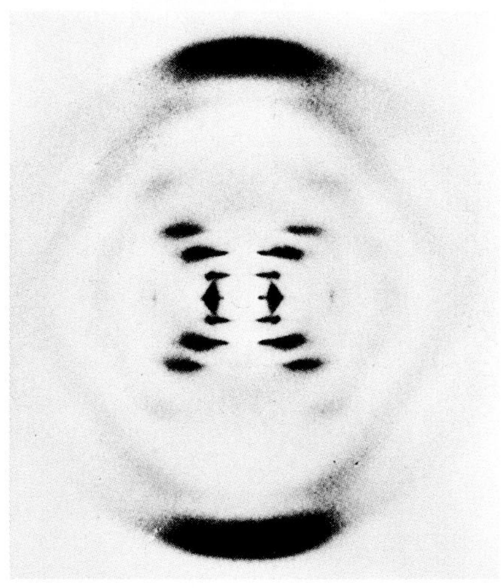

As Fig. 36.21b shows, in x-ray diffraction there is nearly complete cancellation in all but certain very specific directions in which constructive interference occurs and forms bright spots. Such a pattern is usually called an x-ray *diffraction* pattern, although *interference* pattern might be more appropriate.

We can determine the wavelength of x rays by examining the diffraction pattern for a crystal of known structure and known spacing between atoms, just as we determined wavelengths of visible light by measuring patterns from slits or gratings. (The spacing between atoms in simple crystals of known structure, such as sodium chloride, can be found from the density of the crystal and Avogadro's number.) Then, once we know the x-ray wavelength, we can use x-ray diffraction to explore the structure and determine the spacing between atoms in crystals with unknown structure.

X-ray diffraction is by far the most important experimental tool in the investigation of crystal structure of solids. X-ray diffraction also plays an important role in studies of the structures of liquids and of organic molecules. It has been one of the chief experimental techniques in working out the double-helix structure of DNA (Fig. 36.25) and subsequent advances in molecular genetics.

Example 36.5 X-ray diffraction

You direct a beam of x rays with wavelength 0.154 nm at certain planes of a silicon crystal. As you increase the angle of incidence from zero, you find the first strong interference maximum from these planes when the beam makes an angle of 34.5° with the planes. (a) How far apart are the planes? (b) Will you find other interference maxima from these planes at larger angles?

SOLUTION

IDENTIFY: This problem involves Bragg reflection of x rays from the planes of a crystal.

SET UP: In part (a) we use the Bragg condition, Eq. (36.16), to relate the wavelength λ and the angle θ for the $m = 1$ interference maximum (both of which are given) to the spacing d between planes (which is the target variable). Given the value of d, we use the Bragg condition again in part (b) to find the values of θ for interference maxima corresponding to other values of m.

EXECUTE: (a) We solve the Bragg equation, Eq. (36.16), for d and set $m = 1$:

$$d = \frac{m\lambda}{2\sin\theta} = \frac{(1)(0.154\text{ nm})}{2\sin 34.5°} = 0.136\text{ nm}$$

This is the distance between adjacent planes.

(b) To calculate other angles, we solve Eq. (36.16) for $\sin\theta$:

$$\sin\theta = \frac{m\lambda}{2d} = m\frac{0.154\text{ nm}}{2(0.136\text{ nm})} = m(0.566)$$

Values of m of 2 or greater give values of $\sin\theta$ greater than unity, which is impossible. Hence there are *no* other angles for interference maxima for this particular set of crystal planes.

EVALUATE: Our result in part (b) shows that there *would* be a second interference maximum if the quantity $\lambda/2d$ were equal to 0.500 or less. This would be the case if the wavelength of the x rays were less than $2d = 0.272$ nm. How short would the wavelength need to be to have *three* interference maxima?

Test Your Understanding of Section 36.6 You are doing an x-ray diffraction experiment with a crystal in which the atomic planes are 0.200 nm apart. You are using x rays of wavelength 0.100 nm. Will the fifth-order maximum be present in the diffraction pattern?

to use an even smaller pit spacing and hence store even more data (15 to 25 gigabytes) on a disc of the same size as a CD or DVD.

Diffraction is an important consideration for satellite "dishes," parabolic reflectors designed to receive satellite transmission. Satellite dishes have to be able to pick up transmissions from two satellites that are only a few degrees apart, transmitting at the same frequency; the need to resolve two such transmissions determines the minimum diameter of the dish. As higher frequencies are used, the needed diameter decreases. For example, when two satellites 5.0° apart broadcast 7.5-cm microwaves, the minimum dish diameter to resolve them (by Rayleigh's criterion) is about 1.0 m.

One reason for building very large telescopes is to increase the aperture diameter and thus minimize diffraction effects. The effective diameter of a telescope can be increased by using arrays of smaller telescopes. The Very Large Array (VLA) is a collection of 27 radio telescopes that can be spread out in a Y-shaped arrangement 36 km across (Fig. 36.29a). Hence the effective aperture diameter is 36 km, giving the VLA a limit of resolution of less than 3×10^{-7} rad. This is comparable, in the optical realm, to being able to read the bottom line of an eye chart 7 km away! Such an arrangement is called a *radio interferometer* because it makes use of the phase differences between the signals received in different telescopes. The same principle can also be used to improve the resolution of visible-light telescopes (Fig. 36.29b).

36.29 By simultaneously observing the same object with widely separated telescopes, astronomers can obtain far better resolving power than with a single telescope.

(a) **Radio interferometry.** The Very Large Array 80 km west of Socorro, New Mexico, consists of 27 radio dishes that can be moved on tracks; at their greatest separation, their resolution equals that of a single dish 36 km across.

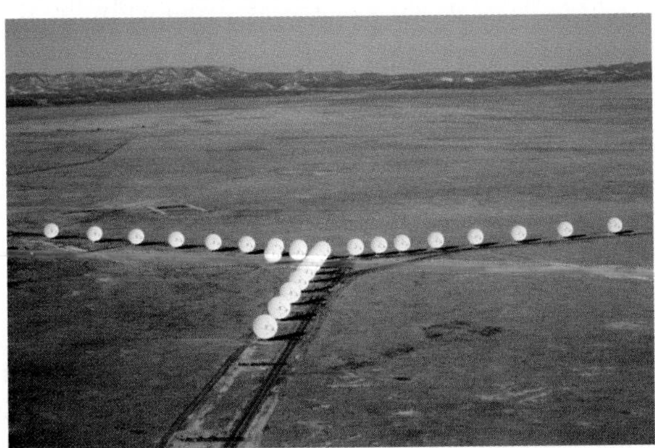

(b) **Optical interferometry.** The four 8.2-m telescopes of the European Southern Observatory's Very Large Telescope in Cerro Paranal, Chile, can be combined optically in pairs. Functioning together, the outer two telescopes have the resolution of a single telescope 130 m across.

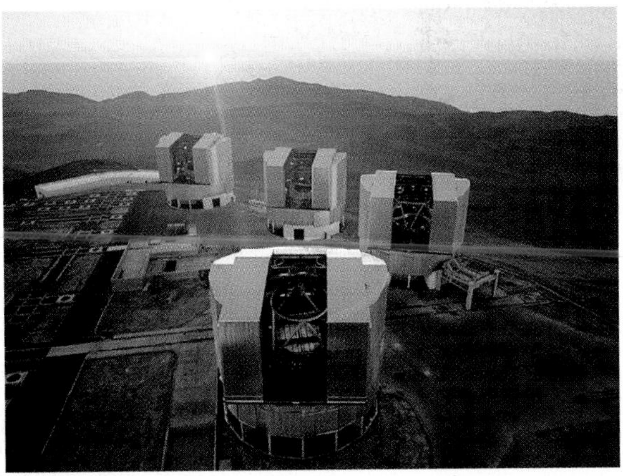

Example 36.6 Resolving power of a camera lens

A camera lens with focal length $f = 50$ mm and maximum aperture $f/2$ forms an image of an object 9.0 m away. (a) If the resolution is limited by diffraction, what is the minimum distance between two points on the object that are barely resolved, and what is the corresponding distance between image points? (b) How does the situation change if the lens is "stopped down" to $f/16$? Assume that $\lambda = 500$ nm in both cases.

SOLUTION

IDENTIFY: This example uses ideas from this section as well as Sections 34.4 (in which we discussed image formation by a lens) and 34.5 (in which the idea of f-number was introduced).

SET UP: From Eq. (34.20) the f-number of a lens is its focal length f divided by the aperture diameter D. We use the information provided to determine D and then use Eq. (36.17) to find the angular separation θ between two barely resolved points on the object. We then use the geometry of image formation by a lens (see Section 34.4) to determine the distance between those points and the distance between the corresponding image points.

EXECUTE: (a) The aperture diameter is $D = f/(f\text{-number}) = (50\text{ mm})/2 = 25\text{ mm} = 25 \times 10^{-3}\text{ m}$. From Eq. (36.17) the

Continued

angular separation θ of two object points that are barely resolved is given by

$$\theta \approx \sin\theta = 1.22\frac{\lambda}{D} = 1.22\frac{500 \times 10^{-9}\text{ m}}{25 \times 10^{-3}\text{ m}}$$
$$= 2.4 \times 10^{-5}\text{ rad}$$

Let y be the separation of the object points, and let y' be the separation of the corresponding image points. We know from our thin-lens analysis in Section 34.4 that, apart from sign, $y/s = y'/s'$. Thus the angular separations of the object points and the corresponding image points are both equal to θ. Because the object distance s is much greater than the focal length $f = 50$ mm, the image distance s' is approximately equal to f. Thus

$$\frac{y}{9.0\text{ m}} = 2.4 \times 10^{-5} \qquad y = 2.2 \times 10^{-4}\text{ m} = 0.22\text{ mm}$$

$$\frac{y'}{50\text{ mm}} = 2.4 \times 10^{-5} \qquad y' = 1.2 \times 10^{-3}\text{ mm}$$
$$= 0.0012\text{ mm} \approx \frac{1}{800}\text{ mm}$$

(b) The aperture diameter is now $(50\text{ mm})/16$, or one-eighth as large as before. The angular separation between barely resolved points is eight times as great, and the values of y and y' are also eight times as great as before:

$$y = 1.8\text{ mm} \qquad y' = 0.0096\text{ mm} = \frac{1}{100}\text{ mm}$$

Only the best camera lenses can approach this resolving power.

EVALUATE: Many photographers use the smallest possible aperture for maximum sharpness, since lens aberrations cause light rays that are far from the optic axis to converge to a different image point than do rays near the axis. Photographers should be aware that, as this example shows, diffraction effects become more significant at small apertures. One cause of fuzzy images has to be balanced against another.

Test Your Understanding of Section 36.7 You have been asked to compare four different proposals for telescopes to be placed in orbit, above the blurring effects of the earth's atmosphere. Rank the proposed telescopes in order of their ability to resolve small details, from best to worst. (i) a radio telescope 100 m in diameter observing at a wavelength of 21 cm; (ii) an optical telescope 2.0 m in diameter observing at a wavelength of 500 nm; (iii) an ultraviolet telescope 1.0 m in diameter observing at a wavelength of 100 nm; (iv) an infrared telescope 2.0 m in diameter observing at a wavelength of 10 μm.

*36.8 Holography

Holography is a technique for recording and reproducing an image of an object through the use of interference effects. Unlike the two-dimensional images recorded by an ordinary photograph or television system, a holographic image is truly three-dimensional. Such an image can be viewed from different directions to reveal different sides and from various distances to reveal changing perspective. If you had never seen a hologram, you wouldn't believe it was possible!

Figure 36.30a shows the basic procedure for making a hologram. We illuminate the object to be holographed with monochromatic light, and we place a photographic film so that it is struck by scattered light from the object and also by direct light from the source. In practice, the light source must be a laser, for reasons we will discuss later. Interference between the direct and scattered light leads to the formation and recording of a complex interference pattern on the film.

To form the images, we simply project light through the developed film, as shown in Fig. 36.30b. Two images are formed: a virtual image on the side of the film nearer the source and a real image on the opposite side.

Holography and Interference Patterns

A complete analysis of holography is beyond our scope, but we can gain some insight into the process by looking at how a single point is holographed and imaged. Consider the interference pattern that is formed on a sheet of photographic negative film by the superposition of an incident plane wave and a spherical wave, as shown in Fig. 36.31a. The spherical wave originates at a point

36.30 (a) A hologram is the record on film of the interference pattern formed with light from the coherent source and light scattered from the object. (b) Images are formed when light is projected through the hologram. The observer sees the virtual image formed behind the hologram.

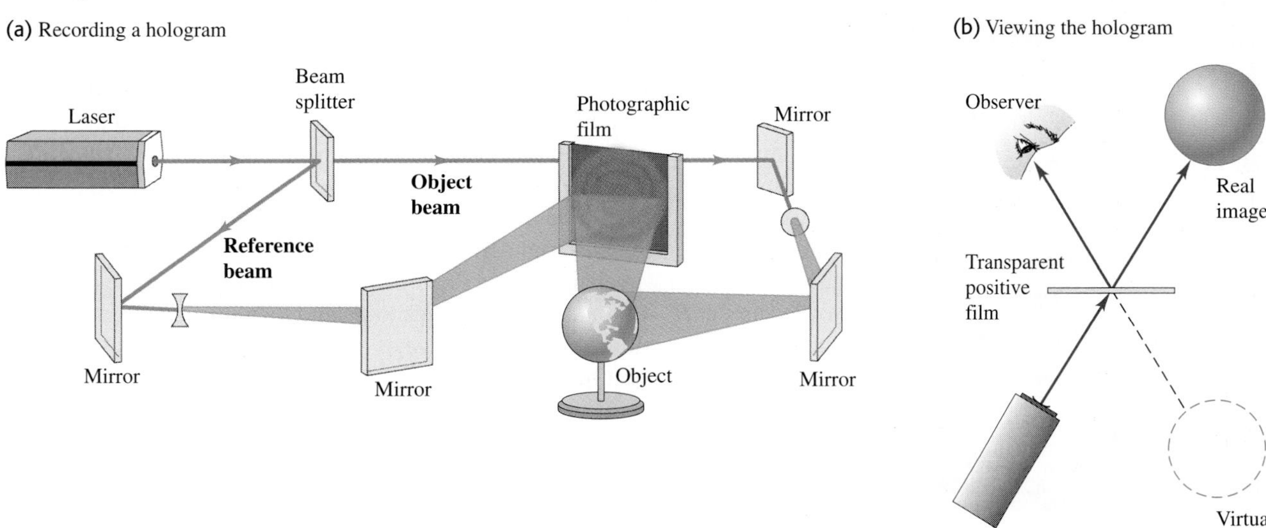

36.31 (a) Constructive interference of the plane and spherical waves occurs in the plane of the film at every point Q for which the distance b_m from P is greater than the distance b_0 from P to O by an integral number of wavelengths $m\lambda$. For the point Q shown, $m = 2$. (b) When a plane wave strikes a transparent positive print of the developed film, the diffracted wave consists of a wave converging to P' and then diverging again and a diverging wave that appears to originate at P. These waves form the real and virtual images, respectively.

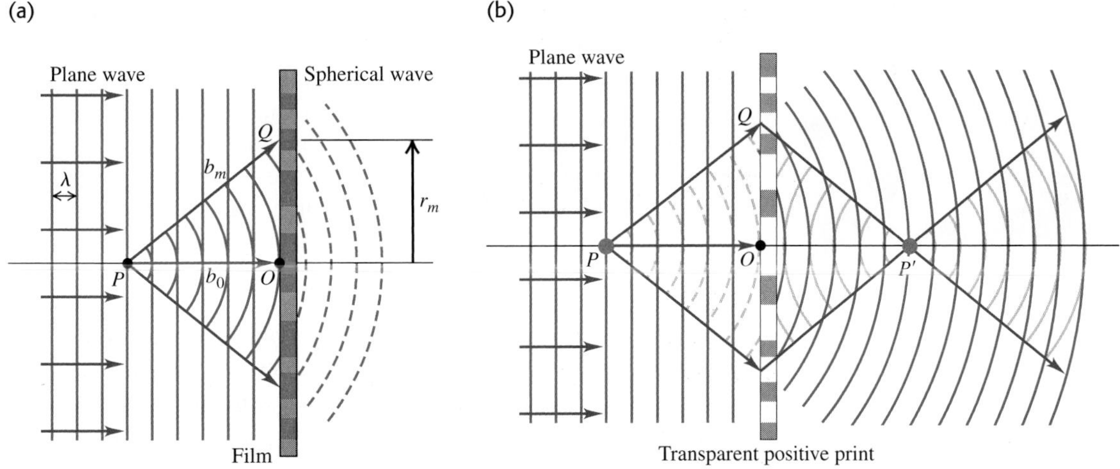

source P at a distance b_0 from the film; P may in fact be a small object that scatters part of the incident plane wave. We assume that the two waves are monochromatic and coherent and that the phase relationship is such that constructive interference occurs at point O on the diagram. Then constructive interference will *also* occur at any point Q on the film that is farther from P than O is by an integer number of wavelengths. That is, if $b_m - b_0 = m\lambda$, where m is an integer, then constructive interference occurs. The points where this condition is satisfied form circles on the film centered at O, with radii r_m given by

$$b_m - b_0 = \sqrt{b_0^2 + r_m^2} - b_0 = m\lambda \qquad (m = 1, 2, 3, \ldots) \qquad (36.20)$$

Solving this for r_m^2, we find

$$r_m^2 = \lambda(2mb_0 + m^2\lambda)$$

36.32 Two views of the same hologram seen from different angles.

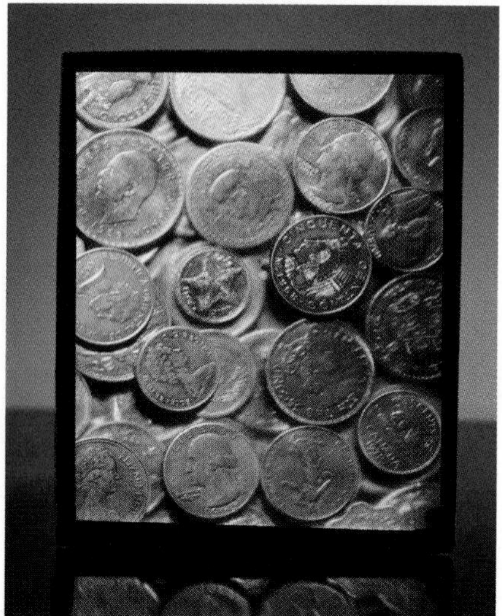

Ordinarily, b_0 is very much larger than λ, so we neglect the second term in parentheses and obtain

$$r_m = \sqrt{2m\lambda b_0} \qquad (m = 1, 2, 3, \ldots) \tag{36.21}$$

The interference pattern consists of a series of concentric bright circular fringes with radii given by Eq. (36.21). Between these bright fringes are dark fringes.

Now we develop the film and make a transparent positive print, so the bright-fringe areas have the greatest transparency on the film. Then we illuminate it with monochromatic plane-wave light of the same wavelength λ that we used initially. In Fig. 36.31b, consider a point P' at a distance b_0 along the axis from the film. The centers of successive bright fringes differ in their distances from P' by an integer number of wavelengths, and therefore a strong *maximum* in the diffracted wave occurs at P'. That is, light converges to P' and then diverges from it on the opposite side. Therefore P' is a *real image* of point P.

This is not the entire diffracted wave, however. The interference of the wavelets that spread out from all the transparent areas forms a second spherical wave that is diverging rather than converging. When this wave is traced back behind the film in Fig. 36.31b, it appears to be spreading out from point P. Thus the total diffracted wave from the hologram is a superposition of a spherical wave converging to form a real image at P' and a spherical wave that diverges as though it had come from the virtual image point P.

Because of the principle of superposition for waves, what is true for the imaging of a single point is also true for the imaging of any number of points. The film records the superposed interference pattern from the various points, and when light is projected through the film, the various image points are reproduced simultaneously. Thus the images of an extended object can be recorded and reproduced just as for a single point object. Figure 36.32 shows photographs of a holographic image from two different angles, showing the changing perspective in this three-dimensional image.

In making a hologram, we have to overcome two practical problems. First, the light used must be *coherent* over distances that are large in comparison to the dimensions of the object and its distance from the film. Ordinary light sources *do not* satisfy this requirement, for reasons that we discussed in Section 35.1. Therefore laser light is essential for making a hologram. (Ordinary white light can be used for *viewing* certain types of hologram, such as those used on credit cards.) Second, extreme mechanical stability is needed. If any relative motion of source, object, or film occurs during exposure, even by as much as a quarter of a wavelength, the interference pattern on the film is blurred enough to prevent satisfactory image formation. These obstacles are not insurmountable, however, and holography has become important in research, entertainment, and a wide variety of technological applications.

CHAPTER 36 SUMMARY

Fresnel and Fraunhofer diffraction: Diffraction occurs when light passes through an aperture or around an edge. When the source and the observer are so far away from the obstructing surface that the outgoing rays can be considered parallel, it is called Fraunhofer diffraction. When the source or the observer is relatively close to the obstructing surface, it is Fresnel diffraction.

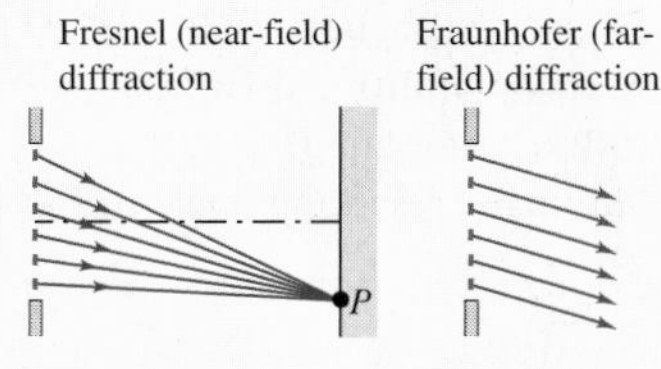

Single-slit diffraction: Monochromatic light sent through a narrow slit of width a produces a diffraction pattern on a distant screen. Equation (36.2) gives the condition for destructive interference (a dark fringe) at a point P in the pattern at angle θ. Equation (36.7) gives the intensity in the pattern as a function of θ. (See Examples 36.1–36.3.)

$$\sin\theta = \frac{m\lambda}{a} \quad (m = \pm 1, \pm 2, \dots) \tag{36.2}$$

$$I = I_0\left\{\frac{\sin[\pi a(\sin\theta)/\lambda]}{\pi a(\sin\theta)/\lambda}\right\}^2 \tag{36.7}$$

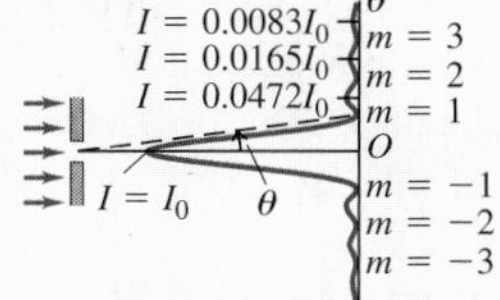

Diffraction gratings: A diffraction grating consists of a large number of thin parallel slits, spaced a distance d apart. The condition for maximum intensity in the interference pattern is the same as for the two-source pattern, but the maxima for the grating are very sharp and narrow. (See Example 36.4.)

$$d\sin\theta = m\lambda \quad (m = 0, \pm 1, \pm 2, \pm 3, \dots) \tag{36.13}$$

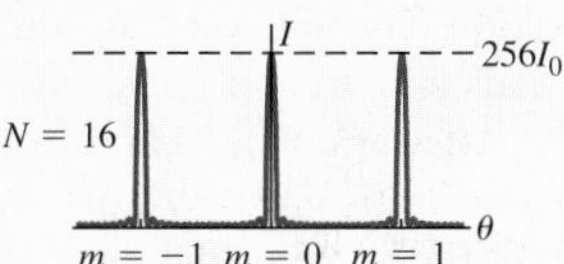

X-ray diffraction: A crystal serves as a three-dimensional diffraction grating for x rays with wavelengths of the same order of magnitude as the spacing between atoms in the crystal. For a set of crystal planes spaced a distance d apart, constructive interference occurs when the angles of incidence and scattering (measured from the crystal planes) are equal and when the Bragg condition [Eq. (36.16)] is satisfied. (See Example 36.5.)

$$2d\sin\theta = m\lambda \quad (m = 1, 2, 3, \dots) \tag{36.16}$$

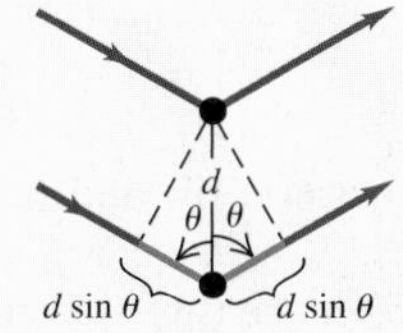

Circular apertures and resolving power: The diffraction pattern from a circular aperture of diameter D consists of a central bright spot, called the Airy disk, and a series of concentric dark and bright rings. Equation (36.17) gives the angular radius θ_1 of the first dark ring, equal to the angular size of the Airy disk. Diffraction sets the ultimate limit on resolution (image sharpness) of optical instruments. According to Rayleigh's criterion, two point objects are just barely resolved when their angular separation θ is given by Eq. (36.17). (See Example 36.6.)

$$\sin\theta_1 = 1.22\frac{\lambda}{D} \tag{36.17}$$

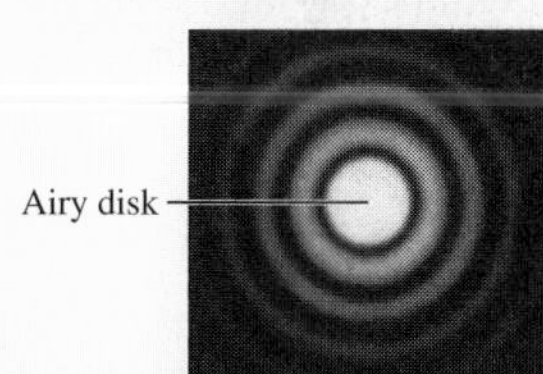

Key Terms

Answer to Chapter Opening Question ?

The shorter wavelength of a DVD scanning laser gives it superior resolving power, so information can be more tightly packed onto a DVD than a CD. See Section 36.7 for details.

Answers to Test Your Understanding Questions

36.1 Answer: yes When you hear the voice of someone standing around a corner, you are hearing sound waves that underwent diffraction. If there were no diffraction of sound, you could hear sounds only from objects that were in plain view.

36.2 Answers: (ii), (i) and (iv) (tie), (iii) The angle θ of the first dark fringe is given by Eq. (36.2) with $m = 1$, or $\sin\theta = \lambda/a$. The larger the value of the ratio λ/a, the larger the value of $\sin\theta$ and hence the value of θ. The ratio λ/a in each case is (i) $(400\text{ nm})/(0.20\text{ mm}) = (4.0 \times 10^{-7}\text{ m})/(2.0 \times 10^{-4}\text{ m}) = 2.0 \times 10^{-3}$; (ii) $(600\text{ nm})/(0.20\text{ mm}) = (6.0 \times 10^{-7}\text{ m})/(2.0 \times 10^{-4}\text{ m}) = 3.0 \times 10^{-3}$; (iii) $(400\text{ nm})/(0.30\text{ mm}) = (4.0 \times 10^{-7}\text{ m})/(3.0 \times 10^{-4}\text{ m}) = 1.3 \times 10^{-3}$; (iv) $(600\text{ nm})/(0.30\text{ mm}) = (6.0 \times 10^{-7}\text{ m})/(3.0 \times 10^{-4}\text{ m}) = 2.0 \times 10^{-3}$.

36.3 Answers: (ii) and (iii) If the slit width a is less than the wavelength λ, there are no points in the diffraction pattern at which the intensity is zero (see Fig. 36.10a). The slit width is $0.0100\text{ mm} = 1.00 \times 10^{-5}\text{ m}$, so this condition is satisfied for (ii) $(\lambda = 10.6\ \mu\text{m} = 10.6 \times 10^{-5}\text{ m})$ and (iii) $(\lambda = 1.00\text{ mm} = 1.00 \times 10^{-3}\text{ m})$ but not for (i) $(\lambda = 500\text{ nm} = 500 \times 10^{-7})$ or (iv) $(\lambda = 50.0\text{ nm} = 5.00 \times 10^{-8}\text{ m})$.

36.4 Answers: yes; $m_i = \pm 5, \pm 10, \ldots$ A "missing maximum" satisfies both $d\sin\theta = m_i\lambda$ (the condition for an interference maximum) and $a\sin\theta = m_d\lambda$ (the condition for a diffraction minimum). Substituting $d = 2.5a$, we can combine these two conditions into the relationship $m_i = 2.5m_d$. This is satisfied for $m_i = \pm 5$ and $m_d = \pm 2$ (the fifth interference maximum is missing because it coincides with the second diffraction minimum), $m_i = \pm 10$ and $m_d = \pm 4$ (the tenth interference maximum is missing because it coincides with the fourth diffraction minimum), and so on.

36.5 Answer: (i) As described in the text, the resolving power needed is $R = Nm = 1000$. In the first order $(m = 1)$ we need $N = 1000$ slits, but in the fourth order $(m = 4)$ we need only $N = R/m = 1000/4 = 250$ slits. (These numbers are only approximate because of the arbitrary nature of our criterion for resolution and because real gratings always have slight imperfections in the shapes and spacings of the slits.)

36.6 Answer: no The angular position of the mth maximum is given by Eq. (36.16), $2d\sin\theta = m\lambda$. With $d = 0.200\text{ nm}$, $\lambda = 0.100\text{ nm}$, and $m = 5$, this gives $\sin\theta = m\lambda/2d = (5)(0.100\text{ nm})/(2)(0.200\text{ nm}) = 1.25$. Since the sine function can never be greater than 1, this means that there is no solution to this equation and the $m = 5$ maximum does not appear.

36.7 Answer: (iii), (ii), (iv), (i) Rayleigh's criterion combined with Eq. (36.17) shows that the smaller the value of the ratio λ/D, the better the resolving power of a telescope of diameter D. For the four telescopes, this ratio is equal to (i) $(21\text{ cm})/(100\text{ m}) = (0.21\text{ m})/(100\text{ m}) = 2.1 \times 10^{-3}$; (ii) $(500\text{ nm})/(2.0\text{ m}) = (5.0 \times 10^{-7}\text{ m})/(2.0\text{ m}) = 2.5 \times 10^{-7}$; (iii) $(100\text{ nm})/(1.0\text{ m}) = (1.0 \times 10^{-7}\text{ m})/(1.0\text{ m}) = 1.0 \times 10^{-7}$; (iv) $(10\ \mu\text{m})/(2.0\text{ m}) = (1.0 \times 10^{-5}\text{ m})/(2.0\text{ m}) = 5.0 \times 10^{-6}$.

PROBLEMS

For instructor-assigned homework, go to **www.masteringphysics.com** 

Discussion Questions

Q36.1. Why can we readily observe diffraction effects for sound waves and water waves, but not for light? Is this because light travels so much faster than these other waves? Explain.

Q36.2. What is the difference between Fresnel and Fraunhofer diffraction? Are they different *physical* processes? Explain.

Q36.3. You use a lens of diameter D and light of wavelength λ and frequency f to form an image of two closely spaced and distant objects. Which of the following will increase the resolving power? (a) Use a lens with a smaller diameter; (b) use light of higher frequency; (c) use light of longer wavelength. In each case justify your answer.

Q36.4. Light of wavelength λ and frequency f passes through a single slit of width a. The diffraction pattern is observed on a screen a distance x from the slit. Which of the following will *decrease* the width of the central maximum? (a) Decrease the slit width; (b) decrease the frequency f of the light; (c) decrease the wavelength λ of the light; (d) decrease the distance x of the screen from the slit. In each case justify your answer.

Q36.5. In a diffraction experiment with waves of wavelength λ, there will be *no* intensity minima (that is, no dark fringes) if the slit width is small enough. What is the maximum slit width for which this occurs? Explain your answer.

Q36.6. The predominant sound waves used in human speech have wavelengths in the range from 1.0 to 3.0 meters. Using the ideas of diffraction, explain how it is possible to hear a person's voice even when he is facing away from you.

Q36.7. In single-slit diffraction, what is $\sin(\beta/2)$ when $\theta = 0$? In view of your answer, why is the single-slit intensity *not* equal to zero at the center?

Q36.8. A rainbow ordinarily shows a range of colors (see Section 33.4). But if the water droplets that form the rainbow are small enough, the rainbow will appear white. Explain why, using diffraction ideas. How small do you think the raindrops would have to be for this to occur?

Q36.9. Some loudspeaker horns for outdoor concerts (at which the entire audience is seated on the ground) are wider vertically than horizontally. Use diffraction ideas to explain why this is more efficient at spreading the sound uniformly over the audience than either a square speaker horn or a horn that is wider horizontally than vertically. Would this still be the case if the audience were seated at different elevations, as in an amphitheater? Why or why not?

Q36.10. Figure 31.12 (Section 31.2) shows a loudspeaker system. Low-frequency sounds are produced by the *woofer,* which is a speaker with large diameter; the *tweeter,* a speaker with smaller diameter, produces high-frequency sounds. Use diffraction ideas to explain why the tweeter is more effective for distributing high-frequency sounds uniformly over a room than is the woofer.

Q36.11. Information is stored on an audio compact disc, CD-ROM, or DVD disc in a series of pits on the disc. These pits are scanned by a laser beam. An important limitation on the amount of information that can be stored on such a disc is the width of the laser beam. Explain why this should be, and explain how using a shorter-wavelength laser allows more information to be stored on a disc of the same size.

Q36.12. With which color of light can the Hubble Space Telescope see finer detail in a distant astronomical object: red, blue, or ultraviolet? Explain your answer.

Q36.13. A typical telescope used by amateur astronomers has a mirror 20 cm in diameter. With such a telescope (and a filter to cut the intensity of sunlight to a safe level for viewing), fine details can be seen on the surface of the sun. Explain why a *radio* telescope would have to be *much* larger to "see" comparable details on the sun.

Q36.14. Could x-ray diffraction effects with crystals be observed by using visible light instead of x rays? Why or why not?

Q36.15. Why is a diffraction grating better than a two-slit setup for measuring wavelengths of light?

Q36.16. One sometimes sees rows of evenly spaced radio antenna towers. A student remarked that these act like diffraction gratings. What did she mean? Why would one want them to act like a diffraction grating?

Q36.17. If a hologram is made using 600-nm light and then viewed with 500-nm light, how will the images look compared to those observed when viewed with 600-nm light? Explain.

Q36.18. A hologram is made using 600-nm light and then viewed by using white light from an incandescent bulb. What will be seen? Explain.

Q36.19. Ordinary photographic film reverses black and white, in the sense that the most brightly illuminated areas become blackest upon development (hence the term *negative*). Suppose a hologram negative is viewed directly, without making a positive transparency. How will the resulting images differ from those obtained with the positive? Explain.

Exercises

Section 36.2 Diffraction from a Single Slit

36.1. Monochromatic light from a distant source is incident on a slit 0.750 mm wide. On a screen 2.00 m away, the distance from the central maximum of the diffraction pattern to the first minimum is measured to be 1.35 mm. Calculate the wavelength of the light.

36.2. Parallel rays of green mercury light with a wavelength of 546 nm pass through a slit covering a lens with a focal length of 60.0 cm. In the focal plane of the lens the distance from the central maximum to the first minimum is 10.2 mm. What is the width of the slit?

36.3. Light of wavelength 585 nm falls on a slit 0.0666 mm wide. (a) On a very large distant screen, how many *totally* dark fringes (indicating complete cancellation) will there be, including both sides of the central bright spot? Solve this problem *without* calculating all the angles! (*Hint:* What is the largest that $\sin\theta$ can be? What does this tell you is the largest that m can be?) (b) At what angle will the dark fringe that is most distant from the central bright fringe occur?

36.4. Light of wavelength 633 nm from a distant source is incident on a slit 0.750 mm wide, and the resulting diffraction pattern is observed on a screen 3.50 m away. What is the distance between the two dark fringes on either side of the central bright fringe?

36.5. Diffraction occurs for all types of waves, including sound waves. High-frequency sound from a distant source with wavelength 9.00 cm passes through a narrow slit 12.0 cm wide. A microphone is placed 40.0 cm directly in front of the center of the slit, corresponding to point O in Fig. 36.5a. The microphone is then moved in a direction perpendicular to the line from the center of the slit to point O. At what distances from O will the intensity detected by the microphone be zero?

36.6. Tsunami! On December 26, 2004, a violent magnitude-9.1 earthquake occurred off the coast of Sumatra. This quake triggered a huge tsunami (similar to a tidal wave) that killed more than 150,000 people. Scientists observing the wave on the open ocean measured the time between crests to be 1.0 h and the speed of the wave to be 800 km/h. Computer models of the evolution of this enormous wave showed that it bent around the continents and spread to all the oceans of the earth. When the wave reached the gaps between continents, it diffracted between them as through a slit. (a) What was the wavelength of this tsunami? (b) The distance between the southern tip of Africa and northern Antarctica is about 4500 km, while the distance between the southern end of Australia and Antarctica is about 3700 km. As an approximation, we can model this wave's behavior by using Fraunhofer diffraction. Find the smallest angle away from the central maximum for which the waves would cancel after going through each of these continental gaps.

36.7. A series of parallel linear water wave fronts are traveling directly toward the shore at 15.0 cm/s on an otherwise placid lake. A long concrete barrier that runs parallel to the shore at a distance of 3.20 m away has a hole in it. You count the wave crests and observe that 75.0 of them pass by each minute, and you also observe that no waves reach the shore at ± 61.3 cm from the point directly opposite the hole, but waves do reach the shore everywhere within this distance. (a) How wide is the hole in the barrier? (b) At what other angles do you find no waves hitting the shore?

36.8. Monochromatic light of wavelength 580 nm passes through a single slit and the diffraction pattern is observed on a screen. Both the source and screen are far enough from the slit for Fraunhofer diffraction to apply. (a) If the first diffraction minima are at $\pm 90.0°$, so the central maximum completely fills the screen, what is the width of the slit? (b) For the width of the slit as calculated in part (a), what is the ratio of the intensity at $\theta = 45.0°$ to the intensity at $\theta = 0$?

36.9. Doorway Diffraction. Sound of frequency 1250 Hz leaves a room through a 1.00-m-wide doorway (see Exercise 36.5). At which angles relative to the centerline perpendicular to the doorway will someone outside the room hear no sound? Use 344 m/s for the speed of sound in air and assume that the source and listener are both far enough from the doorway for Fraunhofer diffraction to apply. You can ignore effects of reflections.

36.10. Light waves, for which the electric field is given by $E_y(x, t) = E_{max} \sin[(1.20 \times 10^7\ \text{m}^{-1})x - \omega t]$, pass through a slit and produce the first dark bands at $\pm 28.6°$ from the center of the diffraction pattern. (a) What is the frequency of this light? (b) How wide is the slit? (c) At which angles will other dark bands occur?

36.11. Parallel rays of light with wavelength 620 nm pass through a slit covering a lens with a focal length of 40.0 cm. The diffraction pattern is observed in the focal plane of the lens, and the distance from the center of the central maximum to the first minimum is 36.5 cm. What is the width of the slit? (*Note:* The angle that locates the first minimum is *not* small.)

36.12. Monochromatic electromagnetic radiation with wavelength λ from a distant source passes through a slit. The diffraction pattern is observed on a screen 2.50 m from the slit. If the width of the central maximum is 6.00 mm, what is the slit width a if the wavelength is (a) 500 nm (visible light); (b) 50.0 μm (infrared radiation); (c) 0.500 nm (x rays)?

36.13. Red light of wavelength 633 nm from a helium–neon laser passes through a slit 0.350 mm wide. The diffraction pattern is observed on a screen 3.00 m away. Define the width of a bright fringe as the distance between the minima on either side. (a) What is the width of the central bright fringe? (b) What is the width of the first bright fringe on either side of the central one?

Section 36.3 Intensity in the Single-Slit Pattern

36.14. Monochromatic light of wavelength $\lambda = 620$ nm from a distant source passes through a slit 0.450 mm wide. The diffraction pattern is observed on a screen 3.00 m from the slit. In terms of the intensity I_0 at the peak of the central maximum, what is the intensity of the light at the screen the following distances from the center of the central maximum: (a) 1.00 mm; (b) 3.00 mm; (c) 5.00 mm?

36.15. A slit 0.240 mm wide is illuminated by parallel light rays of wavelength 540 nm. The diffraction pattern is observed on a screen that is 3.00 m from the slit. The intensity at the center of the central maximum ($\theta = 0°$) is $6.00 \times 10^{-6}\ \text{W/m}^2$. (a) What is the distance on the screen from the center of the central maximum to the first minimum? (b) What is the intensity at a point on the screen midway between the center of the central maximum and the first minimum?

36.16. Laser light of wavelength 632.8 nm falls normally on a slit that is 0.0250 mm wide. The transmitted light is viewed on a distant screen where the intensity at the center of the central bright fringe is $8.50\ \text{W/m}^2$. (a) Find the maximum number of totally dark fringes on the screen, assuming the screen is large enough to show them all. (b) At what angle does the dark fringe that is most distant from the center occur? (c) What is the maximum intensity of the bright fringe that occurs immediately before the dark fringe in part (b)? Approximate the angle at which this fringe occurs by assuming it is midway between the angles to the dark fringes on either side of it.

36.17. A single-slit diffraction pattern is formed by monochromatic electromagnetic radiation from a distant source passing through a slit 0.105 mm wide. At the point in the pattern 3.25° from the center of the central maximum, the total phase difference between wavelets from the top and bottom of the slit is 56.0 rad. (a) What is the wavelength of the radiation? (b) What is the intensity at this point, if the intensity at the center of the central maximum is I_0?

36.18. Consider a single-slit diffraction experiment in which the amplitude of the wave at point O in Fig. 36.5a is E_0. For each of the following cases, draw a phasor diagram like that in Fig. 36.8c and determine *graphically* the amplitude of the wave at the point in question. (*Hint:* Use Eq. (36.6) to determine the value of β for each case.) Compute the intensity and compare to Eq. (36.5). (a) $\sin\theta = \lambda/2a$; (b) $\sin\theta = \lambda/a$; (c) $\sin\theta = 3\lambda/2a$.

36.19. Public Radio station KXPR-FM in Sacramento broadcasts at 88.9 MHz. The radio waves pass between two tall skyscrapers that are 15.0 m apart along their closest walls. (a) At what horizontal angles, relative to the original direction of the waves, will a distant antenna not receive any signal from this station? (b) If the maximum intensity is $3.50\ \text{W/m}^2$ at the antenna, what is the intensity at $\pm 5.00°$ from the center of the central maximum at the distant antenna?

Section 36.4 Multiple Slits

36.20. Diffraction and Interference Combined. Consider the interference pattern produced by two parallel slits of width a and separation d, in which $d = 3a$. The slits are illuminated by normally incident light of wavelength λ. (a) First we ignore diffraction effects due to the slit width. At what angles θ from the central maximum will the next four maxima in the two-slit interference pattern occur? Your answer will be in terms of d and λ. (b) Now we include the effects of diffraction. If the intensity at $\theta = 0$ is I_0, what is the intensity at each of the angles in part (a)? (c) Which double-slit interference maxima are missing in the pattern? (d) Compare your results to those illustrated in Fig. 36.12c. In what ways is your result different?

36.21. Number of Fringes in a Diffraction Maximum. In Fig. 36.12c the central diffraction maximum contains exactly seven interference fringes, and in this case $d/a = 4$. (a) What must the ratio d/a be if the central maximum contains exactly five fringes? (b) In the case considered in part (a), how many fringes are contained within the first diffraction maximum on one side of the central maximum?

36.22. An interference pattern is produced by eight parallel and equally spaced, narrow slits. There is an interference minimum when the phase difference ϕ between light from adjacent slits is $\pi/4$. The phasor diagram is given in Fig. 36.14b. For which pairs of slits is there totally destructive interference?

36.23. An interference pattern is produced by light of wavelength 580 nm from a distant source incident on two identical parallel slits separated by a distance (between centers) of 0.530 mm. (a) If the slits are very narrow, what would be the angular positions of the first-order and second-order, two-slit, interference maxima? (b) Let the slits have width 0.320 mm. In terms of the intensity I_0 at the center of the central maximum, what is the intensity at each of the angular positions in part (a)?

36.24. Monochromatic light illuminates a pair of thin parallel slits at normal incidence, producing an interference pattern on a distant screen. The width of each slit is $\frac{1}{7}$ the center-to-center distance between the slits. (a) Which interference maxima are missing in the pattern on the screen? (b) Does the answer to part (a) depend on the wavelength of the light used? Does the location of the missing maxima depend on the wavelength?

36.25. An interference pattern is produced by four parallel and equally spaced, narrow slits. By drawing appropriate phasor diagrams, show that there is an interference minimum when the phase difference ϕ from adjacent slits is (a) $\pi/2$; (b) π; (c) $3\pi/2$. In each case, for which pairs of slits is there totally destructive interference?

36.26. A diffraction experiment involving two thin parallel slits yields the pattern of closely spaced bright and dark fringes shown in Fig. 36.33. Only the central portion of the pattern is shown in the figure. The bright spots are equally spaced at 1.53 mm center to center (except for the missing spots) on a screen 2.50 m from the slits. The light source was a He-Ne laser producing a wavelength of 632.8 nm. (a) How far apart are the two slits? (b) How wide is each one?

Figure **36.33** Exercise 36.26

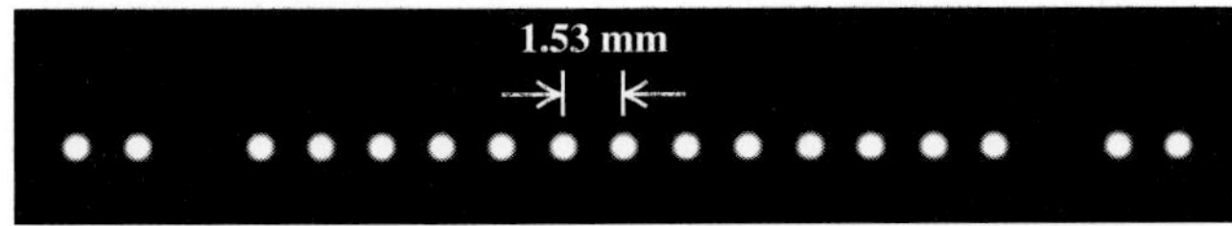

36.27. Laser light of wavelength 500.0 nm illuminates two identical slits, producing an interference pattern on a screen 90.0 cm from the slits. The bright bands are 1.00 cm apart, and the third bright bands on either side of the central maximum are missing in the pattern. Find the width and the separation of the two slits.

Section 36.5 The Diffraction Grating

36.28. Monochromatic light is at normal incidence on a plane transmission grating. The first-order maximum in the interference pattern is at an angle of 8.94°. What is the angular position of the fourth-order maximum?

36.29. If a diffraction grating produces its third-order bright band at an angle of 78.4° for light of wavelength 681 nm, find (a) the number of slits per centimeter for the grating and (b) the angular location of the first-order and second-order bright bands. (c) Will there be a fourth-order bright band? Explain.

36.30. If a diffraction grating produces a third-order bright spot for red light (of wavelength 700 nm) at 65.0° from the central maximum, at what angle will the second-order bright spot be for violet light (of wavelength 400 nm)?

36.31. Visible light passes through a diffraction grating that has 900 slits/cm, and the interference pattern is observed on a screen that is 2.50 m from the grating. (a) Is the angular position of the first-order spectrum small enough for $\sin\theta \approx \theta$ to be a good approximation? (b) In the first-order spectrum, the maxima for two different wavelengths are separated on the screen by 3.00 mm. What is the difference in these wavelengths?

36.32. The wavelength range of the visible spectrum is approximately 400–700 nm. White light falls at normal incidence on a diffraction grating that has 350 slits/mm. Find the angular width of the visible spectrum in (a) the first order and (b) the third order. (*Note:* An advantage of working in higher orders is the greater angular spread and better resolution. A disadvantage is the overlapping of different orders, as shown in Example 36.4.)

36.33. Measuring Wavelengths with a CD. A laser beam of wavelength $\lambda = 632.8$ nm shines at normal incidence on the reflective side of a compact disc. The tracks of tiny pits in which information is coded onto the CD are 1.60 μm apart. For what angles of reflection (measured from the normal) will the intensity of light be maximum?

36.34. (a) What is the wavelength of light that is deviated in the first order through an angle of 13.5° by a transmission grating having 5000 slits/cm? (b) What is the second-order deviation of this wavelength? Assume normal incidence.

36.35. Plane monochromatic waves with wavelength 520 nm are incident normally on a plane transmission grating having 350 slits/mm. Find the angles of deviation in the first, second, and third orders.

36.36. Identifying Isotopes by Spectra. Different isotopes of the same element emit light at slightly different wavelengths. A wavelength in the emission spectrum of a hydrogen atom is 656.45 nm; for deuterium, the corresponding wavelength is 656.27 nm. (a) What minimum number of slits is required to resolve these two wavelengths in second order? (b) If the grating has 500.00 slits/mm, find the angles and angular separation of these two wavelengths in the second order.

36.37. A typical laboratory diffraction grating has 5.00×10^3 lines/cm, and these lines are contained in a 3.50-cm width of grating. (a) What is the chromatic resolving power of such a grating in the first order? (b) Could this grating resolve the lines of the sodium doublet (see Section 36.5) in the first order? (c) While doing spectral analysis of a star, you are using this grating in the *second* order to resolve spectral lines that are very close to the 587.8002-nm spectral line of iron. (i) For wavelengths longer than the iron line, what is the shortest wavelength you could distinguish from the iron line? (ii) For wavelengths shorter than the iron line, what is the longest wavelength you could distinguish from the iron line? (iii) What is the range of wavelengths you could *not* distinguish from the iron line?

36.38. The light from an iron arc includes many different wavelengths. Two of these are at $\lambda = 587.9782$ nm and $\lambda = 587.8002$ nm. You wish to resolve these spectral lines in first order using a grating 1.20 cm in length. What minimum number of slits per centimeter must the grating have?

Section 36.6 X-Ray Diffraction

36.39. X rays of wavelength 0.0850 nm are scattered from the atoms of a crystal. The second-order maximum in the Bragg reflection occurs when the angle θ in Fig. 36.23 is 21.5°. What is the spacing between adjacent atomic planes in the crystal?

36.40. If the planes of a crystal are 3.50 Å (1 Å $= 10^{-10}$ m $=$ 1 Ångstrom unit) apart, (a) what wavelength of electromagnetic waves is needed so that the first strong interference maximum in the Bragg reflection occurs when the waves strike the planes at an angle of 15.0°, and in what part of the electromagnetic spectrum do these waves lie? (See Fig. 32.4.) (b) At what other angles will strong interference maxima occur?

Section 36.7 Circular Apertures and Resolving Power

36.41. Due to blurring caused by atmospheric distortion, the best resolution that can be obtained by a normal, earth-based, visible-light telescope is about 0.3 arcsecond (there are 60 arcminutes in a degree and 60 arcseconds in an arcminute). (a) Using Rayleigh's criterion, calculate the diameter of an earth-based telescope that gives this resolution with 550-nm light. (b) Increasing the telescope diameter beyond the value found in part (a) will increase the light-gathering power of the telescope, allowing more distant and dimmer astronomical objects to be studied, but it will not improve the resolution. In what ways are the Keck telescopes (each of 10-m diameter) atop Mauna Kea in Hawaii superior to the Hale Telescope (5-m diameter) on Palomar Mountain in California? In what ways are they *not* superior? Explain.

36.42. If you can read the bottom row of your doctor's eye chart, your eye has a resolving power of 1 arcminute, equal to $\frac{1}{60}$ degree. If this resolving power is diffraction limited, to what effective diameter of your eye's optical system does this correspond? Use Rayleigh's criterion and assume $\lambda = 550$ nm.

36.43. Two satellites at an altitude of 1200 km are separated by 28 km. If they broadcast 3.6-cm microwaves, what minimum receiving-dish diameter is needed to resolve (by Rayleigh's criterion) the two transmissions?

36.44. The Very Long Baseline Array can resolve (by Rayleigh's criterion) signals from sources separated by 1.0×10^{-8} rad. If the effective diameter of the receiver is 8000 km, what is the wavelength of these signals?

36.45. Monochromatic light with wavelength 620 nm passes through a circular aperture with diameter 7.4 μm. The resulting diffraction pattern is observed on a screen that is 4.5 m from the aperture. What is the diameter of the Airy disk on the screen?

36.46. Photography. A wildlife photographer uses a moderate telephoto lens of focal length 135 mm and maximum aperture $f/4.00$ to photograph a bear that is 11.5 m away. Assume the wavelength is 550 nm. (a) What is the width of the smallest feature on the bear that this lens can resolve if it is opened to its maximum aperture? (b) If, to gain depth of field, the photographer stops the lens down to $f/22.0$, what would be the width of the smallest resolvable feature on the bear?

36.47. Observing Jupiter. You are asked to design a space telescope for earth orbit. When Jupiter is 5.93×10^8 km away (its closest approach to the earth), the telescope is to resolve, by Rayleigh's criterion, features on Jupiter that are 250 km apart. What minimum-diameter mirror is required? Assume a wavelength of 500 nm.

36.48. A converging lens 7.20 cm in diameter has a focal length of 300 mm. If the resolution is diffraction limited, how far away can an object be if points on it 4.00 mm apart are to be resolved (according to Rayleigh's criterion)? Use $\lambda = 550$ nm.

36.49. Hubble Versus Arecibo. The Hubble Space Telescope has an aperture of 2.4 m and focuses visible light (400–700 nm). The Arecibo radio telescope in Puerto Rico is 305 m (1000 ft) in diameter (it is built in a mountain valley) and focuses radio waves of wavelength 75 cm. (a) Under optimal viewing conditions, what is the smallest crater that each of these telescopes could resolve on our moon? (b) If the Hubble Space Telescope were to be converted to surveillance use, what is the highest orbit above the surface of the earth it could have and still be able to resolve the license plate (not the letters, just the plate) of a car on the ground? Assume optimal viewing conditions, so that the resolution is diffraction limited.

36.50. Searching for Starspots. The Hale Telescope on Palomar Mountain in California has a mirror 200 in. (5.08 m) in diameter and it focuses visible light. Given that a large sunspot is about 10,000 mi in diameter, what is the most distant star on which this telescope could resolve a sunspot to see whether other stars have them? (Assume optimal viewing conditions, so that the resolution is diffraction limited.) Are there any stars this close to us, besides our sun?

36.51. Searching for Planets. The Keck Telescopes, on Mauna Kea, Hawaii have a 10.0-m-diameter mirror. Could these telescopes resolve Jupiter-sized planets about our nearest star, Alpha Centauri, which is 4.28 light-years away?

Problems

36.52. Suppose the entire apparatus (slit, screen, and space in between) in Exercise 36.4 is immersed in water $(n = 1.33)$. Then what is the distance between the two dark fringes?

36.53. Consider a single-slit diffraction pattern. The center of the central maximum, where the intensity is I_0, is located at $\theta = 0$. (a) Let θ_+ and θ_- be the two angles on either side of $\theta = 0$ for which $I = \frac{1}{2}I_0$. $\Delta\theta = |\theta_+ - \theta_-|$ is called the *full width at half maximum*, or *FWHM*, of the central diffraction maximum. Solve for $\Delta\theta$ when the ratio between slit width a and wavelength λ is (i) $a/\lambda = 2$; (ii) $a/\lambda = 5$; (iii) $a/\lambda = 10$. (*Hint:* Your equation for θ_+ or θ_- cannot be solved analytically. You must use trial and error or solve it graphically.) (b) The width of the central maximum can alternatively be defined as $2\theta_0$, where θ_0 is the angle that locates the minimum on one side of the central maximum. Calculate $2\theta_0$ for each case considered in part (a), and compare to $\Delta\theta$.

36.54. A loudspeaker having a diaphragm that vibrates at 1250 Hz is traveling at 80.0 m/s directly toward a pair of holes in a very large wall in a region for which the speed of sound is 344 m/s. You observe that the sound coming through the openings first cancels at $\pm 12.7°$ with respect to the original direction of the speaker when observed far from the wall. (a) How far apart are the two openings? (b) At what angles would the sound first cancel if the source stopped moving?

36.55. Measuring Refractive Index. A thin slit illuminated by light of frequency f produces its first dark band at $\pm 38.2°$ in air. When the entire apparatus (slit, screen, and space in between) is immersed in an unknown transparent liquid, the slit's first dark bands occur instead at $\pm 17.4°$. Find the refractive index of the liquid.

36.56. Grating Design. Your boss asks you to design a diffraction grating that will disperse the first-order visible spectrum through an angular range of 15.0° (see Example 36.4 in Section 36.5). (a) What must the number of slits per centimeter be for this grating? (b) At what angles will the first-order visible spectrum begin and end?

36.57. A slit 0.360 mm wide is illuminated by parallel rays of light that have a wavelength of 540 nm. The diffraction pattern is observed on a screen that is 1.20 m from the slit. The intensity at the center of the central maximum $(\theta = 0°)$ is I_0. (a) What is the distance on the screen from the center of the central maximum to the first minimum? (b) What is the distance on the screen from the center of the central maximum to the point where the intensity has fallen to $I_0/2$? (See Problem 36.53, part (a), for a hint about how to solve for the phase angle β.)

36.58. The intensity of light in the Fraunhofer diffraction pattern of a single slit is

$$I = I_0\left(\frac{\sin\gamma}{\gamma}\right)^2$$

where

$$\gamma = \frac{\pi a \sin\theta}{\lambda}$$

(a) Show that the equation for the values of γ at which I is a maximum is $\tan\gamma = \gamma$. (b) Determine the three smallest positive values of γ that are solutions of this equation. (*Hint:* You can use a trial-and-error procedure. Guess a value of γ and adjust your guess to bring $\tan\gamma$ closer to γ. A graphical solution of the equation is very helpful in locating the solutions approximately, to get good initial guesses.)

36.59. Angular Width of a Principal Maximum. Consider N evenly spaced, narrow slits. Use the small-angle approximation $\sin\theta = \theta$ (for θ in radians) to prove the following: For an intensity maximum that occurs at an angle θ, the intensity minima immediately adjacent to this maximum are at angles $\theta + \lambda/Nd$ and $\theta - \lambda/Nd$, so that the angular width of the principal maximum is $2\lambda/Nd$. This is proportional to $1/N$, as we concluded in Section 36.4 on the basis of energy conservation.

36.60. The Expanding Universe. A cosmologist who is studying the light from a galaxy has identified the spectrum of hydrogen but finds that the wavelengths are somewhat shifted from those found in the laboratory. In the lab, the H_α line has a wavelength of 656.3 nm. The cosmologist is using a transmission diffraction grating having 5758 lines/cm in the first order and finds that the first bright fringe for the H_α line occurs at $\pm 23.41°$ from the central spot. How fast is the galaxy moving? Express your answer in m/s and as a percentage of the speed of light. Is it moving toward us or away from us? (*Hint:* See Section 16.8.)

36.61. Phasor Diagram for Eight Slits. An interference pattern is produced by eight equally spaced, narrow slits. Figure 36.14 shows phasor diagrams for the cases in which the phase difference ϕ between light from adjacent slits is $\phi = \pi$, $\phi = \pi/4$, and $\phi = \pi/2$. Each of these cases gives an intensity minimum. The caption for Fig. 36.14 also claims that minima occur for $\phi = 3\pi/4$, $\phi = 5\pi/4$, $\phi = 3\pi/2$, and $\phi = 7\pi/4$. (a) Draw the phasor diagram for each of these four cases, and explain why each diagram proves that there is in fact a minimum. (*Note:* You may find it helpful to use a different colored pencil for each slit!) (b) For each of the four cases $\phi = 3\pi/4$, $\phi = 5\pi/4$, $\phi = 3\pi/2$, and $\phi = 7\pi/4$, for which pairs of slits is there totally destructive interference?

36.62. X-Ray Diffraction of Salt. X rays with a wavelength of 0.125 nm are scattered from a cubic array (of a sodium chloride crystal), for which the spacing of adjacent atoms is $a = 0.282$ nm. (a) If diffraction from planes parallel to a cube face is considered, at what angles θ of the incoming beam relative to the crystal planes will maxima be observed? (b) Repeat part (a) for diffraction produced by the planes shown in Fig. 36.24a, which are separated by $a/\sqrt{2}$.

36.63. At the end of Section 36.4, the following statements were made about an array of N slits. Explain, using phasor diagrams, why each statement is true. (a) A minimum occurs whenever ϕ is an integral multiple of $2\pi/N$, except when ϕ is an integral multiple of 2π (which gives a principal maximum). (b) There are $(N - 1)$ minima between each pair of principal maxima.

36.64. In Eq. (36.12), consider the case in which $d = a$. In a sketch, show that in this case the two slits reduce to a single slit with width $2a$. Then show that Eq. (36.12) reduces to Eq. (36.5) with slit width $2a$.

36.65. What is the longest wavelength that can be observed in the third order for a transmission grating having 6500 slits/cm? Assume normal incidence.

36.66. (a) Figure 36.16 shows plane waves of light incident *normally* on a diffraction grating. If instead the light strikes the grating at an angle of incidence θ' (measured from the normal), show that the condition for an intensity maximum is *not* Eq. (36.13), but rather

$$d(\sin\theta + \sin\theta') = m\lambda \qquad (m = 0, \pm 1, \pm 2, \pm 3, \dots)$$

(b) For the grating described in Example (Section 36.5), with 600 slits/mm, find the angles of the maxima corresponding to $m = 0$, 1, and -1 with red light ($\lambda = 650$ nm) for the cases $\theta' = 0$ (normal incidence) and $\theta' = 20.0°$.

36.67. A diffraction grating has 650 slits/mm. What is the highest order that contains the entire visible spectrum? (The wavelength range of the visible spectrum is approximately 400–700 nm.)

36.68. *Quasars,* an abbreviation for *quasi-stellar radio sources,* are distant objects that look like stars through a telescope but that emit far more electromagnetic radiation than an entire normal galaxy of stars. An example is the bright object below and to the left of center in Fig. 36.34; the other elongated objects in this image are normal galaxies. The leading model for the structure of a quasar is a galaxy with a supermassive black hole at its center. In this model, the radiation is emitted by interstellar gas and dust within the galaxy as this material falls toward the black hole. The radiation is thought to emanate from a region just a few light-years in diameter. (The diffuse glow surrounding the bright quasar shown in Fig. 36.34 is thought to be this quasar's host galaxy.) To investigate this model of quasars and to study other exotic astronomical objects, the Russian Space Agency plans to place a radio telescope in an orbit that extends to 77,000 km from the earth. When the signals from this telescope are combined with signals from the ground-based telescopes of the VLBA, the resolution will be that of a single radio telescope 77,000 km in diameter. What is the size of the smallest detail that this arrangement could resolve in quasar 3C 405, which is 7.2×10^8 light-years from earth, using radio waves at a frequency of 1665 MHz? (*Hint:* Use Rayleigh's criterion.) Give your answer in light-years and in kilometers.

Figure 36.34 Problem 36.68

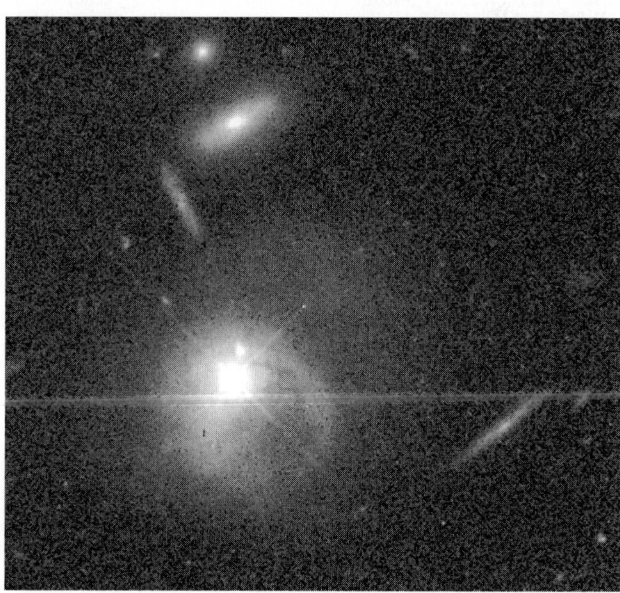

36.69. Phased-Array Radar. In one common type of radar installation, a rotating antenna sweeps a radio beam around the sky. But in a *phased-array* radar system, the antennas remain stationary and the beam is swept electronically. To see how this is done, consider an array of N antennas that are arranged along the horizontal x-axis at $x = 0, \pm d, \pm 2d, \dots, \pm(N - 1)d/2$. (The number N is odd.) Each antenna emits radiation uniformly in all directions in the horizontal xy-plane. The antennas all emit radiation coherently, with the same amplitude E_0 and the same wavelength λ. The relative phase δ of the emission from adjacent antennas can be varied, however. If the antenna at $x = 0$ emits a signal that is given by $E_0 \cos\omega t$, as measured at a point next to the antenna, the antenna at $x = d$ emits a signal given by $E_0 \cos(\omega t + \delta)$, as measured at a point next to that antenna. The corresponding quantity for the antenna at $x = -d$ is $E_0\cos(\omega t - \delta)$; for the antennas at $x = \pm 2d$, it is $E_0\cos(\omega t \pm 2\delta)$; and so on. (a) If $\delta = 0$, the interference pattern at a distance from the antennas is large compared to d and has a principal maximum at $\theta = 0$ (that is, in the $+y$-direction, perpendicular to the line of the antennas). Show that if $d < \lambda$, this is the *only* principal interference maximum in the angular range $-90° < \theta < 90°$. Hence this principal maximum describes a beam emitted in the direction $\theta = 0$. As described in Section 36.4, if N is large, the beam will have a large intensity and be quite narrow. (b) If $\delta \neq 0$, show that the principal intensity maximum described in part (a) is located at

$$\theta = \arcsin\left(\frac{\delta\lambda}{2\pi d}\right)$$

where δ is measured in radians. Thus, by varying δ from positive to negative values and back again, which can easily be done electronically, the beam can be made to sweep back and forth around $\theta = 0$. (c) A weather radar unit to be installed on an airplane emits radio waves at 8800 MHz. The unit uses 15 antennas in an array 28.0 cm long (from the antenna at one end of the array to the antenna at the other end). What must the maximum and minimum values of δ be (that is, the most positive and most negative values) if the radar beam is to sweep 45° to the left or right of the airplane's direction of flight? Give your answer in radians.

36.70. Underwater Photography. An underwater camera has a lens of focal length 35.0 mm and a maximum aperture of $f/2.80$. The film it uses has an emulsion that is sensitive to light of frequency 6.00×10^{14} Hz. If the photographer takes a picture of an object 2.75 m in front of the camera with the lens wide open, what is the width of the smallest resolvable detail on the subject if the object is (a) a fish underwater with the camera in the water and (b) a person on the beach, with the camera out of the water?

36.71. An astronaut in orbit can just resolve two point sources on the earth that are 75.0 m apart. Assume that the resolution is diffraction limited, and use Rayleigh's criterion. What is the astronaut's altitude above the earth? Treat her eye as a circular aperture with a diameter of 4.00 mm (the diameter of her pupil), and take the wavelength of the light to be 500 nm.

36.72. Observing Planets Beyond Our Solar System. NASA is considering a project called *Planet Imager* that would give astronomers the ability to see details on planets orbiting other stars. Using the same principle as the Very Large Array (see Section 36.7), *Planet Imager* will use an array of infrared telescopes spread over thousands of kilometers of space. (Visible light would give even better resolution. Unfortunately, at visible wavelengths, stars are so bright that a planet would be lost in the glare. This is less of a problem at infrared wavelengths.) (a) If *Planet Imager* has an effective diameter of 6000 km and observes infrared radiation at a wavelength of 10 μm, what is the greatest distance at which it would be able to observe details as small as 250 km across (about the size of the greater Los Angeles area) on a planet? Give your answer in light-years (see Appendix E). (*Hint:* Use Rayleigh's criterion.) (b) For comparison, consider the resolution of a single infrared telescope in space that has a diameter of 1.0 m and that observes 10-μm radiation. What is the size of the smallest details that such a telescope could resolve at the distance of the nearest star to the sun, Proxima Centauri, which is 4.22 light-years distant? How does this compare to the diameter of the earth $(1.27 \times 10^4\ \text{km})$? To the average distance from the earth to the sun $(1.50 \times 10^8\ \text{km})$? Would a single telescope of this kind be able to detect the presence of a planet like the earth, in an orbit the size of the earth's orbit, around *any* other star? Explain. (c) Suppose *Planet Imager* is used to observe a planet orbiting the star 70 Virginis, which is 59 light-years from our solar system. A planet (though not an earthlike one) has in fact been detected orbiting this star, not by imaging it directly but by observing the slight "wobble" of the star as both it and the planet orbit their common center of mass. What is the size of the smallest details that *Planet Imager* could hope to resolve on the planet of 70 Virginis? How does this compare to the diameter of the planet, assumed to be comparable to that of Jupiter $(1.38 \times 10^5\ \text{km})$? (Although the planet of 70 Virginis is thought to be at least 6.6 times more massive than Jupiter, its radius is probably not too different from that of Jupiter. The reason is that such large planets are thought to be composed primarily of gases, not rocky material, and hence can be greatly compressed by the mutual gravitational attraction of different parts of the planet.)

Challenge Problems

36.73. It is possible to calculate the intensity in the single-slit Fraunhofer diffraction pattern *without* using the phasor method of Section 36.3. Let y' represent the position of a point within the slit of width a in Fig. 36.5a, with $y' = 0$ at the center of the slit so that the slit extends from $y' = -a/2$ to $y' = a/2$. We imagine dividing the slit up into infinitesimal strips of width dy', each of which acts as a source of secondary wavelets. (a) The amplitude of the total wave at the point O on the distant screen in Fig. 36.5a is E_0. Explain why the amplitude of the wavelet from each infinitesimal strip within the slit is $E_0(dy'/a)$, so that the electric field of the wavelet a distance x from the infinitesimal strip is $dE = E_0(dy'/a)\sin(kx - \omega t)$. (b) Explain why the wavelet from each strip as detected at point P in Fig. 36.5a can be expressed as

$$dE = E_0\frac{dy'}{a}\sin[k(D - y'\sin\theta) - \omega t]$$

where D is the distance from the center of the slit to point P and $k = 2\pi/\lambda$. (c) By integrating the contributions dE from all parts of the slit, show that the total wave detected at point P is

$$\begin{aligned} E &= E_0\sin(kD - \omega t)\frac{\sin[ka(\sin\theta)/2]}{ka(\sin\theta)/2} \\ &= E_0\sin(kD - \omega t)\frac{\sin[\pi a(\sin\theta)/\lambda]}{\pi a(\sin\theta)/\lambda} \end{aligned}$$

(The trigonometric identities in Appendix B will be useful.) Show that at $\theta = 0$, corresponding to point O in Fig. 36.5a, the wave is $E = E_0\sin(Kd - \omega t)$ and has amplitude E_0, as stated in part (a). (d) Use the result of part (c) to show that if the intensity at point O is I_0, then the intensity at a point P is given by Eq. (36.7).

36.74. Intensity Pattern of N Slits. (a) Consider an arrangement of N slits with a distance d between adjacent slits. The slits emit coherently and in phase at wavelength λ. Show that at a time t, the electric field at a distant point P is

$$\begin{aligned} E_P(t) &= E_0\cos(kR - \omega t) + E_0\cos(kR - \omega t + \phi) \\ &+ E_0\cos(kR - \omega t + 2\phi) + \cdots \\ &+ E_0\cos(kR - \omega t + (N-1)\phi) \end{aligned}$$

where E_0 is the amplitude at P of the electric field due to an individual slit, $\phi = (2\pi d\sin\theta)/\lambda$, θ is the angle of the rays reaching P (as measured from the perpendicular bisector of the slit arrangement), and R is the distance from P to the most distant slit. In this problem, assume that R is much larger than d. (b) To carry out the sum in part (a), it is convenient to use the complex-number relationship

$$e^{iz} = \cos z + i \sin z$$

where $i = \sqrt{-1}$. In this expression, $\cos z$ is the *real part* of the complex number e^{iz}, and $\sin z$ is its *imaginary part.* Show that the electric field $E_P(t)$ is equal to the real part of the complex quantity

$$\sum_{n=0}^{N-1} E_0 e^{i(kR - \omega t + n\phi)}$$

(c) Using the properties of the exponential function that $e^A e^B = e^{(A+B)}$ and $(e^A)^n = e^{nA}$, show that the sum in part (b) can be written as

$$E_0\left(\frac{e^{iN\phi} - 1}{e^{i\phi} - 1}\right)e^{i(kR-\omega t)} = E_0\left(\frac{e^{iN\phi/2} - e^{-iN\phi/2}}{e^{i\phi/2} - e^{-i\phi/2}}\right)e^{i[kR-\omega t+(N-1)\phi/2]}$$

Then, using the relationship $e^{iz} = \cos z + i \sin z$, show that the (real) electric field at point P is

$$E_p(t) = \left[E_0 \frac{\sin(N\phi/2)}{\sin(\phi/2)}\right]\cos[kR - \omega t + (N - 1)\phi/2]$$

The quantity in the first square brackets in this expression is the amplitude of the electric field at P. (d) Use the result for the electric-field amplitude in part (c) to show that the intensity at an angle θ is

$$I = I_0\left[\frac{\sin(N\phi/2)}{\sin(\phi/2)}\right]^2$$

where I_0 is the maximum intensity for an individual slit. (e) Check the result in part (d) for the case $N = 2$. It will help to recall that $\sin 2A = 2 \sin A \cos A$. Explain why your result differs from Eq. (35.10), the expression for the intensity in two-source interference, by a factor of 4. (*Hint:* Is I_0 defined in the same way in both expressions?)

36.75. Intensity Pattern of *N* Slits, Continued. Part (d) of Challenge Problem 36.74 gives an expression for the intensity in the interference pattern of N identical slits. Use this result to verify the following statements. (a) The maximum intensity in the pattern is $N^2 I_0$. (b) The principal maximum at the center of the pattern extends from $\phi = -2\pi/N$ to $\phi = 2\pi/N$, so its width is inversely proportional to $1/N$. (c) A minimum occurs whenever ϕ is an integral multiple of $2\pi/N$, except when ϕ is an integral multiple of 2π (which gives a principal maximum). (d) There are $(N - 1)$ minima between each pair of principal maxima. (e) Halfway between two principal maxima, the intensity can be no greater than I_0; that is, it can be no greater than $1/N^2$ times the intensity at a principal maximum.

37 RELATIVITY

LEARNING GOALS

By studying this chapter, you will learn:

- The two postulates of Einstein's special theory of relativity, and what motivates these postulates.
- Why different observers can disagree about whether two events are simultaneous.
- How relativity predicts that moving clocks run slow, and experimental evidence that confirms this.
- How the length of an object changes due to the object's motion.
- How the velocity of an object depends on the frame of reference from which it is observed.
- How the theory of relativity modifies the relationship between velocity and momentum.
- How to solve problems involving work and kinetic energy for particles moving at relativistic speeds.
- Some of the key concepts of Einstein's general theory of relativity.

? At Brookhaven National Laboratory in New York, atomic nuclei are accelerated to 99.995% of the ultimate speed limit of the universe—the speed of light. Is there also an upper limit on the *kinetic energy* of a particle?

When the year 1905 began, Albert Einstein was an unknown 25-year-old clerk in the Swiss patent office. By the end of that amazing year he had published three papers of extraordinary importance. One was an analysis of Brownian motion; a second (for which he was awarded the Nobel Prize) was on the photoelectric effect. In the third, Einstein introduced his **special theory of relativity,** proposing drastic revisions in the Newtonian concepts of space and time.

The special theory of relativity has made wide-ranging changes in our understanding of nature, but Einstein based it on just two simple postulates. One states that the laws of physics are the same in all inertial frames of reference; the other states that the speed of light in vacuum is the same in all inertial frames. These innocent-sounding propositions have far-reaching implications. Here are three: (1) Events that are simultaneous for one observer may not be simultaneous for another. (2) When two observers moving relative to each other measure a time interval or a length, they may not get the same results. (3) For the conservation principles for momentum and energy to be valid in all inertial systems, Newton's second law and the equations for momentum and kinetic energy have to be revised.

Relativity has important consequences in *all* areas of physics, including electromagnetism, atomic and nuclear physics, and high-energy physics. Although many of the results derived in this chapter may run counter to your intuition, the theory is in solid agreement with experimental observations.

37.1 Invariance of Physical Laws

Let's take a look at the two postulates that make up the special theory of relativity. Both postulates describe what is seen by an observer in an *inertial frame of reference,* which we introduced in Section 4.2. The theory is "special" in the sense that it applies to observers in such special reference frames.

Einstein's First Postulate

Einstein's first postulate, called the **principle of relativity,** states: **The laws of physics are the same in every inertial frame of reference.** If the laws differed, that difference could distinguish one inertial frame from the others or make one frame somehow more "correct" than another. Here are two examples. Suppose you watch two children playing catch with a ball while the three of you are aboard a train moving with constant velocity. Your observations of the motion *of the ball,* no matter how carefully done, can't tell you how fast (or whether) the train is moving. This is because Newton's laws of motion are the same in every inertial frame.

Another example is the electromotive force (emf) induced in a coil of wire by a nearby moving permanent magnet. In the frame of reference in which the *coil* is stationary (Fig. 37.1a), the moving magnet causes a change of magnetic flux through the coil, and this induces an emf. In a different frame of reference in which the *magnet* is stationary (Fig. 37.1b), the motion of the coil through a magnetic field induces the emf. According to the principle of relativity, both of these frames of reference are equally valid. Hence the same emf must be induced in both situations shown in Fig. 37.1. As we saw in Chapter 29, this is indeed the case, so Faraday's law is consistent with the principle of relativity. Indeed, *all* of the laws of electromagnetism are the same in every inertial frame of reference.

37.1 The same emf is induced in the coil whether (a) the magnet moves relative to the coil or (b) the coil moves relative to the magnet.

(a)

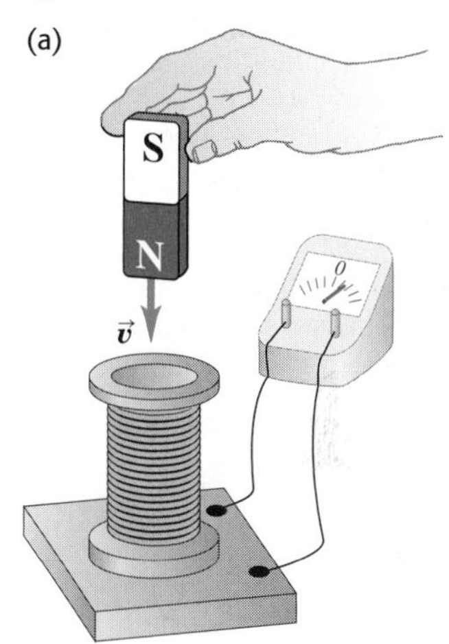

(b)

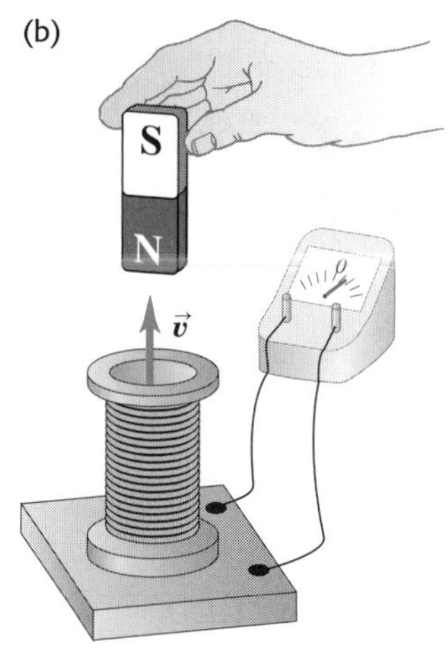

Equally significant is the prediction of the speed of electromagnetic radiation, derived from Maxwell's equations (see Section 32.2). According to this analysis, light and all other electromagnetic waves travel in vacuum with a constant speed, now defined to equal exactly 299,792,458 m/s. (We often use the approximate value $c = 3.00 \times 10^8$ m/s, which is within one part in 1000 of the exact value.) As we will see, the speed of light in vacuum plays a central role in the theory of relativity.

Einstein's Second Postulate

During the 19th century, most physicists believed that light traveled through a hypothetical medium called the *ether,* just as sound waves travel through air. If so, the speed of light measured by observers would depend on their motion relative to the ether and would therefore be different in different directions. The Michelson-Morley experiment, described in Section 35.5, was an effort to detect motion of the earth relative to the ether. Einstein's conceptual leap was to recognize that if Maxwell's equations are valid in all inertial frames, then the speed of light in vacuum should also be the same in all frames and in all directions. In fact, Michelson and Morley detected *no* ether motion across the earth, and the ether concept has been discarded. Although Einstein may not have known about this negative result, it supported his bold hypothesis of the constancy of the speed of light in vacuum.

Einstein's second postulate states: The speed of light in vacuum is the same in all inertial frames of reference and is independent of the motion of the source.

Let's think about what this means. Suppose two observers measure the speed of light in vacuum. One is at rest with respect to the light source, and the other is moving away from it. Both are in inertial frames of reference. According to the principle of relativity, the two observers must obtain the same result, despite the fact that one is moving with respect to the other.

If this seems too easy, consider the following situation. A spacecraft moving past the earth at 1000 m/s fires a missile straight ahead with a speed of 2000 m/s (relative to the spacecraft) (Fig. 37.2). What is the missile's speed relative to the earth? Simple, you say; this is an elementary problem in relative velocity (see Section 3.5). The correct answer, according to Newtonian mechanics, is 3000 m/s. But now suppose the spacecraft turns on a searchlight, pointing in the same direction in which the missile was fired. An observer on the spacecraft measures the

37.2 (a) Newtonian mechanics makes correct predictions about relatively slow-moving objects; (b) it makes incorrect predictions about the behavior of light.

(a)

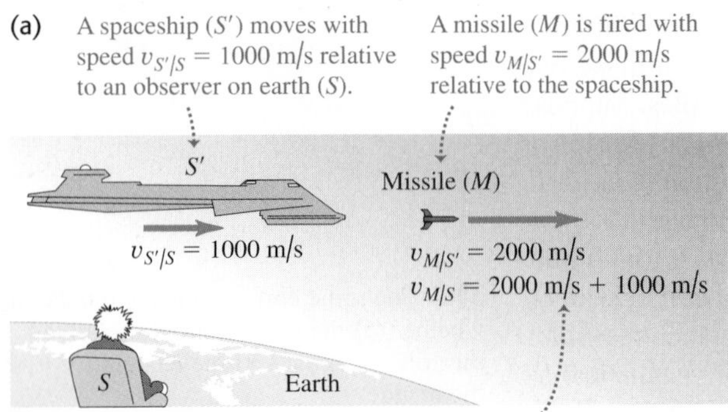
A spaceship (S') moves with speed $v_{S'/S} = 1000$ m/s relative to an observer on earth (S).
A missile (M) is fired with speed $v_{M/S'} = 2000$ m/s relative to the spaceship.
S'
Missile (M)
$v_{S'/S} = 1000$ m/s
$v_{M/S'} = 2000$ m/s
$v_{M/S} = 2000$ m/s + 1000 m/s
S
Earth

NEWTONIAN MECHANICS HOLDS: Newtonian mechanics tells us correctly that the missile moves with speed $v_{M/S} = 3000$ m/s relative to the observer on earth.

(b)

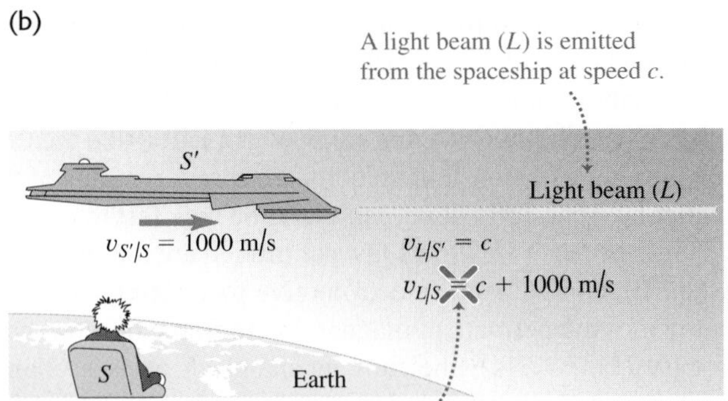
A light beam (L) is emitted from the spaceship at speed c.
S'
Light beam (L)
$v_{S'/S} = 1000$ m/s
$v_{L/S'} = c$
$v_{L/S} = c + 1000$ m/s
S
Earth

NEWTONIAN MECHANICS FAILS: Newtonian mechanics tells us *incorrectly* that the light moves at a speed greater than c relative to the observer on earth ... which would contradict Einstein's second postulate.

speed of light emitted by the searchlight and obtains the value c. According to Einstein's second postulate, the motion of the light after it has left the source cannot depend on the motion of the source. So the observer on earth who measures the speed of this same light must also obtain the value c, *not* $c + 1000$ m/s. This result contradicts our elementary notion of relative velocities, and it may not appear to agree with common sense. But "common sense" is intuition based on everyday experience, and this does not usually include measurements of the speed of light.

The Ultimate Speed Limit

Einstein's second postulate immediately implies the following result:

It is impossible for an inertial observer to travel at *c*, the speed of light in vacuum.

We can prove this by showing that travel at c implies a logical contradiction. Suppose that the spacecraft S' in Fig. 37.2b is moving at the speed of light relative to an observer on the earth, so that $v_{S'/S} = c$. If the spacecraft turns on a headlight, the second postulate now asserts that the earth observer S measures the headlight beam to be also moving at c. Thus this observer measures that the headlight beam and the spacecraft move together and are always at the same point in space. But Einstein's second postulate also asserts that the headlight beam moves at a speed c relative to the spacecraft, so they *cannot* be at the same point in space. This contradictory result can be avoided only if it is impossible for an inertial observer, such as a passenger on the spacecraft, to move at c. As we go through our discussion of relativity, you may find yourself asking the question Einstein asked himself as a 16-year-old student, "What would I see if I were traveling at the speed of light?" Einstein realized only years later that his question's basic flaw was that he could *not* travel at c.

The Galilean Coordinate Transformation

Let's restate this argument symbolically, using two inertial frames of reference, labeled S for the observer on earth and S' for the moving spacecraft, as shown in Fig. 37.3. To keep things as simple as possible, we have omitted the z-axes. The x-axes of the two frames lie along the same line, but the origin O' of frame S' moves relative to the origin O of frame S with constant velocity u along the common x-x'-axis. We on earth set our clocks so that the two origins coincide at time $t = 0$, so their separation at a later time t is ut.

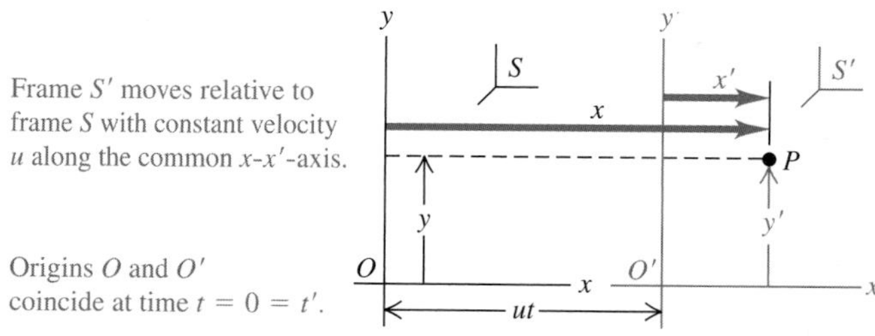
Frame S' moves relative to frame S with constant velocity u along the common x-x'-axis.
Origins O and O' coincide at time $t = 0 = t'$.
y
S
y'
S'
x'
x
P
y
y'
O
x
O'
x'
ut

37.3 The position of particle P can be described by the coordinates x and y in frame of reference S or by x' and y' in frame S'.

CAUTION Choose your inertial frame coordinates wisely Many of the equations derived in this chapter are true *only* if you define your inertial reference frames as stated in the preceding paragraph. For instance, the positive x-direction must be the direction in which the origin O' moves relative to the origin O. In Fig. 37.3 this direction is to the right; if instead O' moves to the left relative to O, you must define the positive x-direction to be to the left.

Now think about how we describe the motion of a particle P. This might be an exploratory vehicle launched from the spacecraft or a pulse of light from a laser. We can describe the *position* of this particle by using the earth coordinates (x, y, z) in S or the spacecraft coordinates (x', y', z') in S'. Figure 37.3 shows that these are simply related by

$$x = x' + ut \qquad y = y' \qquad z = z' \qquad \text{(Galilean coordinate transformation)} \tag{37.1}$$

These equations, based on the familiar Newtonian notions of space and time, are called the **Galilean coordinate transformation.**

If particle P moves in the x-direction, its instantaneous velocity v_x as measured by an observer stationary in S is $v_x = dx/dt$. Its velocity v'_x as measured by an observer stationary in S' is $v'_x = dx'/dt$. We can derive a relationship between v_x and v'_x by taking the derivative with respect to t of the first of Eqs. (37.1):

$$\frac{dx}{dt} = \frac{dx'}{dt} + u$$

Now dx/dt is the velocity v_x measured in S, and dx'/dt is the velocity v'_x measured in S', so we get the *Galilean velocity transformation* for one-dimensional motion:

$$v_x = v'_x + u \qquad \text{(Galilean velocity transformation)} \tag{37.2}$$

Although the notation differs, this result agrees with our discussion of relative velocities in Section 3.5.

Now here's the fundamental problem. Applied to the speed of light in vacuum, Eq. (37.2) says that $c = c' + u$. Einstein's second postulate, supported subsequently by a wealth of experimental evidence, says that $c = c'$. This is a genuine inconsistency, not an illusion, and it demands resolution. If we accept this postulate, we are forced to conclude that Eqs. (37.1) and (37.2) *cannot* be precisely correct, despite our convincing derivation. These equations have to be modified to bring them into harmony with this principle.

The resolution involves some very fundamental modifications in our kinematic concepts. The first idea to be changed is the seemingly obvious assumption that the observers in frames S and S' use the same *time scale,* formally stated as $t = t'$. Alas, we are about to show that this everyday assumption cannot be correct; the two observers *must* have different time scales. We must define the velocity v' in frame S' as $v' = dx'/dt'$, not as dx'/dt; the two quantities are not the same. The difficulty lies in the concept of *simultaneity,* which is our next topic. A careful analysis of simultaneity will help us develop the appropriate modifications of our notions about space and time.

Test Your Understanding of Section 37.1 As a high-speed spaceship flies past you, it fires a strobe light that sends out a pulse of light in all directions. An observer aboard the spaceship measures a spherical wave front that spreads away from the spaceship with the same speed c in all directions. (a) What is the shape of the wave front that *you* measure? (i) spherical; (ii) ellipsoidal, with the longest axis of the ellipsoid along the direction of the spaceship's motion; (iii) ellipsoidal, with the shortest axis of the ellipsoid along the direction of the spaceship's motion; (iv) not enough information is given to decide. (b) Is the wave front centered on the spaceship?

37.2 Relativity of Simultaneity

37.4 An event has a definite position and time—for instance, on the pavement directly below the center of the Eiffel Tower at midnight on New Year's Eve.

Measuring times and time intervals involves the concept of **simultaneity.** In a given frame of reference, an **event** is an occurrence that has a definite position and time (Fig. 37.4). When you say that you awoke at seven o'clock, you mean that two events (your awakening and your clock showing 7:00) occurred *simultaneously.* The fundamental problem in measuring time intervals is this: In general, two events that are simultaneous in one frame of reference are *not* simultaneous in a second frame that is moving relative to the first, even if both are inertial frames.

A Thought Experiment in Simultaneity

This may seem to be contrary to common sense. To illustrate the point, here is a version of one of Einstein's *thought experiments*—mental experiments that follow concepts to their logical conclusions. Imagine a train moving with a speed comparable to c, with uniform velocity (Fig. 37.5). Two lightning bolts strike a passenger car, one near each end. Each bolt leaves a mark on the car and one on the ground at the instant the bolt hits. The points on the ground are labeled A and B in the figure, and the corresponding points on the car are A' and B'. Stanley is stationary on the ground at O, midway between A and B. Mavis is moving with the train at O' in the middle of the passenger car, midway between A' and B'. Both Stanley and Mavis see both light flashes emitted from the points where the lightning strikes.

Suppose the two wave fronts from the lightning strikes reach Stanley at O simultaneously. He knows that he is the same distance from B and A, so Stanley concludes that the two bolts struck B and A simultaneously. Mavis agrees that the two wave fronts reached Stanley at the same time, but she disagrees that the flashes were emitted simultaneously.

Stanley and Mavis agree that the two wave fronts do not reach Mavis at the same time. Mavis at O' is moving to the right with the train, so she runs into the wave front from B' *before* the wave front from A' catches up to her. However, because she is in the middle of the passenger car equidistant from A' and B', her observation is that both wave fronts took the same time to reach her because both moved the same distance at the same speed c. (Recall that the speed of each wave front with respect to *either* observer is c.) Thus she concludes that the lightning bolt at B' struck *before* the one at A'. Stanley at O measures the two events to be simultaneous, but Mavis at O' does not! *Whether or not two events at different x-axis locations are simultaneous depends on the state of motion of the observer.*

You may want to argue that in this example the lightning bolts really *are* simultaneous and that if Mavis at O' could communicate with the distant points without the time delay caused by the finite speed of light, she would realize this. But that would be erroneous; the finite speed of information transmission is not the real issue. If O' is midway between A' and B', then in her frame of reference the time for a signal to travel from A' to O' is the same as that from B' to O'. Two signals arrive simultaneously at O' only if they were emitted simultaneously at A' and B'. In this example they *do not* arrive simultaneously at O', and so Mavis must conclude that the events at A' and B' were *not* simultaneous.

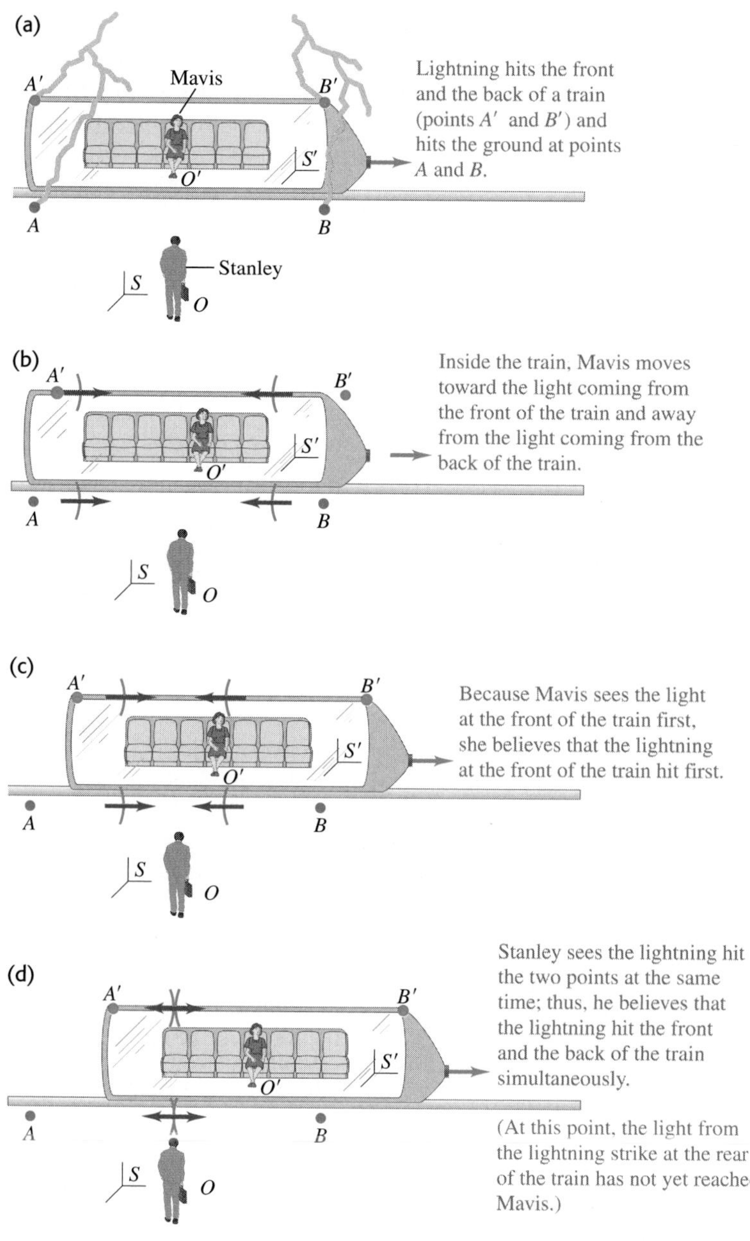
(a)
A′
Mavis
B′
S′
O′
A
B
Stanley
S
O
Lightning hits the front and the back of a train (points A' and B') and hits the ground at points A and B.
(b)
A′
B′
S′
O′
A
B
S
O
Inside the train, Mavis moves toward the light coming from the front of the train and away from the light coming from the back of the train.
(c)
A′
B′
S′
O′
A
B
S
O
Because Mavis sees the light at the front of the train first, she believes that the lightning at the front of the train hit first.
(d)
A′
B′
S′
O′
A
B
S
O
Stanley sees the lightning hit the two points at the same time; thus, he believes that the lightning hit the front and the back of the train simultaneously.
(At this point, the light from the lightning strike at the rear of the train has not yet reached Mavis.)

37.5 A thought experiment in simultaneity.

Furthermore, there is no basis for saying that Stanley is right and Mavis is wrong, or vice versa. According to the principle of relativity, no inertial frame of reference is more correct than any other in the formulation of physical laws. Each observer is correct *in his or her own frame of reference.* In other words, simultaneity is not an absolute concept. Whether two events are simultaneous depends on the frame of reference. As we mentioned at the beginning of this section, simultaneity plays an essential role in measuring time intervals. It follows that *the time interval between two events may be different in different frames of reference.* So our next task is to learn how to compare time intervals in different frames of reference.

Test Your Understanding of Section 37.2 Stanley, who works for the rail system shown in Fig. 37.5, has carefully synchronized the clocks at all of the rail stations. At the moment that Stanley measures all of the clocks striking noon, Mavis is on a high-speed passenger car traveling from Ogdenville toward North Haverbrook. According to Mavis, when the Ogdenville clock strikes noon, what time is it in North Haverbrook? (i) noon; (ii) before noon; (iii) after noon.

37.3 Relativity of Time Intervals

ActivPhysics ONLINE
17.1 Relativity of Time

We can derive a quantitative relationship between time intervals in different coordinate systems. To do this, let's consider another thought experiment. As before, a frame of reference S' moves along the common x-x'-axis with constant speed u relative to a frame S. As discussed in Section 37.1, u must be less than the speed of light c. Mavis, who is riding along with frame S', measures the time interval between two events that occur at the *same* point in space. Event 1 is when a flash of light from a light source leaves O'. Event 2 is when the flash returns to O', having been reflected from a mirror a distance d away, as shown in Fig. 37.6a. We label the time interval Δt_0, using the subscript zero as a reminder that the apparatus is at rest, with zero velocity, in frame S'. The flash of light moves a total distance $2d$, so the time interval is

$$\Delta t_0 = \frac{2d}{c} \tag{37.3}$$

The round-trip time measured by Stanley in frame S is a different interval Δt; in his frame of reference the two events occur at *different* points in space. During the time Δt, the source moves relative to S a distance $u\,\Delta t$ (Fig. 37.6b). In S' the round-trip distance is $2d$ perpendicular to the relative velocity, but the round-trip distance in S is the longer distance $2l$, where

$$l = \sqrt{d^2 + \left(\frac{u\,\Delta t}{2}\right)^2}$$

In writing this expression, we have assumed that both observers measure the same distance d. We will justify this assumption in the next section. The speed of light is the same for both observers, so the round-trip time measured in S is

$$\Delta t = \frac{2l}{c} = \frac{2}{c}\sqrt{d^2 + \left(\frac{u\,\Delta t}{2}\right)^2} \tag{37.4}$$

We would like to have a relationship between Δt and Δt_0 that is independent of d. To get this, we solve Eq. (37.3) for d and substitute the result into Eq. (37.4), obtaining

$$\Delta t = \frac{2}{c}\sqrt{\left(\frac{c\,\Delta t_0}{2}\right)^2 + \left(\frac{u\,\Delta t}{2}\right)^2} \tag{37.5}$$

37.6 (a) Mavis, in frame of reference S', observes a light pulse emitted from a source at O' and reflected back along the same line. (b) How Stanley (in frame of reference S) and Mavis observe the same light pulse. The positions of O' at the times of departure and return of the pulse are shown.

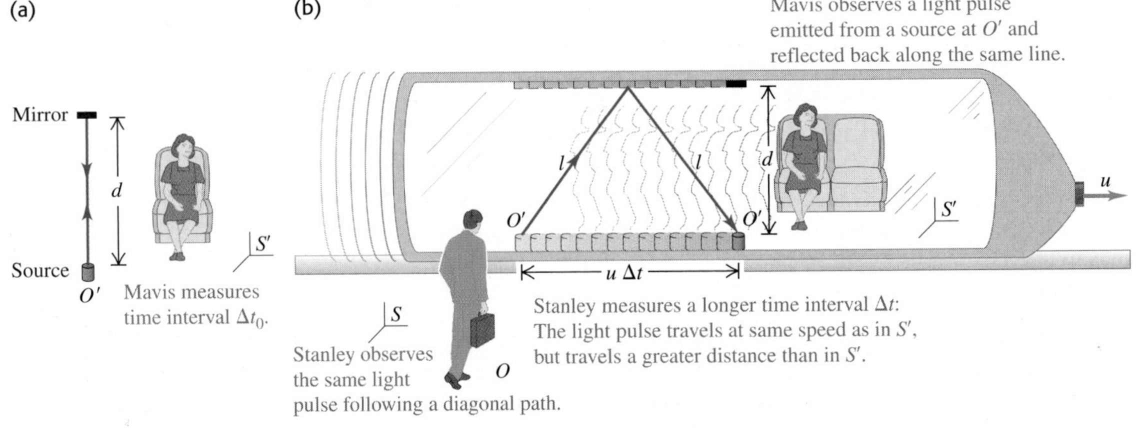
(a)
Mirror
d
Source
O'
S'
Mavis measures time interval Δt₀.
(b)
Mavis observes a light pulse emitted from a source at O′ and reflected back along the same line.
l
l
d
O′
O′
S′
u
u Δt
S
O
Stanley observes the same light pulse following a diagonal path.
Stanley measures a longer time interval Δt: The light pulse travels at same speed as in S′, but travels a greater distance than in S′.

Now we square this and solve for Δt; the result is

$$\Delta t = \frac{\Delta t_0}{\sqrt{1 - u^2/c^2}}$$

Since the quantity $\sqrt{1 - u^2/c^2}$ is less than 1, Δt is greater than Δt_0: Thus Stanley measures a *longer* round-trip time for the light pulse than does Mavis.

Time Dilation

We may generalize this important result. In a particular frame of reference, suppose that two events occur at the same point in space. The time interval between these events, as measured by an observer at rest in this same frame (which we call the *rest frame* of this observer), is Δt_0. Then an observer in a second frame moving with constant speed u relative to the rest frame will measure the time interval to be Δt, where

$$\Delta t = \frac{\Delta t_0}{\sqrt{1 - u^2/c^2}} \quad \text{(time dilation)} \tag{37.6}$$

We recall that no inertial observer can travel at $u = c$ and we note that $\sqrt{1 - u^2/c^2}$ is imaginary for $u > c$. Thus Eq. (37.6) gives sensible results only when $u < c$. The denominator of Eq. (37.7) is always smaller than 1, so Δt is always *larger* than Δt_0. Thus we call this effect **time dilation.**

Think of an old-fashioned pendulum clock that has one second between ticks, as measured by Mavis in the clock's rest frame; this is Δt_0. If the clock's rest frame is moving relative to Stanley, he measures a time between ticks Δt that is longer than one second. In brief, *observers measure any clock to run slow if it moves relative to them* (Fig. 37.7). Note that this conclusion is a direct result of the fact that the speed of light in vacuum is the same in both frames of reference.

37.7 This image shows an exploding star, called a *supernova,* within a distant galaxy. The brightness of a typical supernova decays at a certain rate. But supernovae that are moving away from us at a substantial fraction of the speed of light decay more slowly, in accordance with Eq. (37.6). The decaying supernova is a moving "clock" that runs slow.

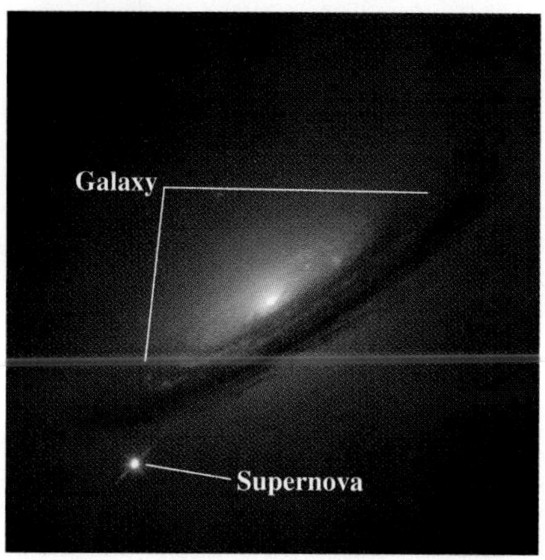

The quantity $1/\sqrt{1 - u^2/c^2}$ in Eq. (37.6) appears so often in relativity that it is given its own symbol γ (the Greek letter gamma):

$$\gamma = \frac{1}{\sqrt{1 - u^2/c^2}} \tag{37.7}$$

In terms of this symbol, we can express the time dilation formula, Eq. (37.6), as

$$\Delta t = \gamma \, \Delta t_0 \quad \text{(time dilation)} \tag{37.8}$$

As a further simplification, u/c is sometimes given the symbol β (the Greek letter beta); then $\gamma = 1/\sqrt{1 - \beta^2}$.

Figure 37.8 shows a graph of γ as a function of the relative speed u of two frames of reference. When u is very small compared to c, u^2/c^2 is much smaller than 1 and γ is very nearly *equal* to 1. In that limit, Eqs. (37.6) and (37.8) approach the Newtonian relationship $\Delta t = \Delta t_0$, corresponding to the same time interval in all frames of reference.

If the relative speed u is great enough that γ is appreciably greater than 1, the speed is said to be *relativistic;* if the difference between γ and 1 is negligibly small, the speed u is called *nonrelativistic.* Thus $u = 6.00 \times 10^7\ \text{m/s} = 0.200c$ (for which $\gamma = 1.02$) is a relativistic speed, but $u = 6.00 \times 10^4\ \text{m/s} = 0.000200c$ (for which $\gamma = 1.00000002$) is a nonrelativistic speed.

37.8 The quantity $\gamma = 1/\sqrt{1 - u^2/c^2}$ as a function of the relative speed u of two frames of reference.

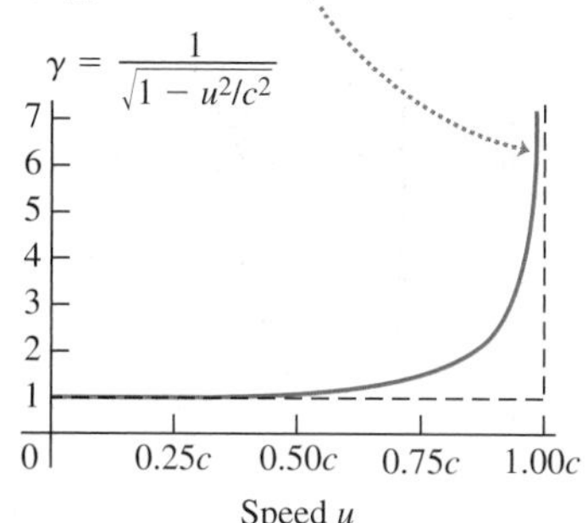

Proper Time

There is only one frame of reference in which a clock is at rest, and there are infinitely many in which it is moving. Therefore the time interval measured between two events (such as two ticks of the clock) that occur at the same point in a particular frame is a more fundamental quantity than the interval between events at different points. We use the term **proper time** to describe the time interval Δt_0 between two events that occur *at the same point.*

CAUTION **Measuring time intervals** It is important to note that the time interval Δt in Eq. (37.6) involves events that occur *at different space points* in the frame of reference S. Note also that any differences between Δt and the proper time Δt_0 are *not* caused by differences in the times required for light to travel from those space points to an observer at rest in S. We assume that our observer is able to correct for differences in light transit times, just as an astronomer who's observing the sun understands that an event seen now on earth actually occurred 500 s ago on the sun's surface. Alternatively, we can use *two* observers, one stationary at the location of the first event and the other at the second, each with his or her own clock. We can synchronize these two clocks without difficulty, as long as they are at rest in the same frame of reference. For example, we could send a light pulse simultaneously to the two clocks from a point midway between them. When the pulses arrive, the observers set their clocks to a prearranged time. (But note that clocks that are synchronized in one frame of reference *are not* in general synchronized in any other frame.)

37.9 A frame of reference pictured as a coordinate system with a grid of synchronized clocks.

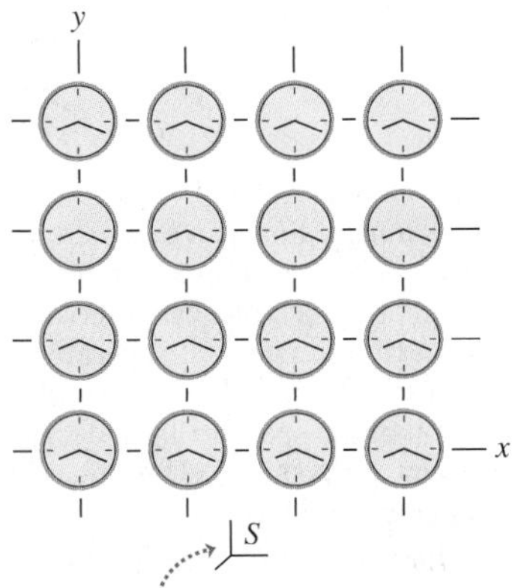

The grid is three dimensional; identical planes of clocks lie in front of and behind the page, connected by grid lines perpendicular to the page.

In thought experiments, it's often helpful to imagine many observers with synchronized clocks at rest at various points in a particular frame of reference. We can picture a frame of reference as a coordinate grid with lots of synchronized clocks distributed around it, as suggested by Fig.37.9. Only when a clock is moving relative to a given frame of reference do we have to watch for ambiguities of synchronization or simultaneity.

Throughout this chapter we will frequently use phrases like "Stanley *observes* that Mavis passes the point $x = 5.00$ m, $y = 0$, $z = 0$ at time 2.00 s." This means that Stanley is using a grid of clocks in his frame of reference, like the grid shown in Fig. 37.9, to record the time of an event. We could restate the phrase as "When Mavis passes the point at $x = 5.00$ m, $y = 0$, $z = 0$, the clock at that location in Stanley's frame of reference reads 2.00 s." We will avoid using phrases like "Stanley *sees* that Mavis is a certain point at a certain time," because there is a time delay for light to travel to Stanley's eye from the position of an event.

Problem-Solving Strategy 37.1 Time Dilation

MP

IDENTIFY *the relevant concepts:* The concept of time dilation is used whenever we compare the time intervals between events as measured by observers in different inertial frames of reference.

SET UP *the problem* using the following steps:
1. To describe a time interval, you must first decide what two events define the beginning and the end of the interval. You must also identify the two frames of reference in which the time interval is measured.
2. Determine what the target variable is.

EXECUTE *the solution* as follows:
1. In many problems involving time dilation, the time interval between events as measured in one frame of reference is the *proper* time Δt_0. The proper time is the time interval between two events in a frame of reference in which the two events occur at the same point in space. The dilated time Δt is the longer time interval between the same two events as measured in a frame of reference that has a speed u relative to the first frame. The two events occur at different points as measured in the second frame. You will need to decide in which frame the time interval is Δt_0 and in which frame it is Δt.
2. Use Eq. (37.6) or (37.8) to relate Δt_0 and Δt, and then solve for the target variable.

EVALUATE *your answer:* Note that Δt is never smaller than Δt_0, and u is never greater than c. If your results suggest otherwise, you need to rethink your calculation.

Example 37.1 Time dilation at 0.990*c*

High-energy subatomic particles coming from space interact with atoms in the earth's upper atmosphere, producing unstable particles called *muons.* A muon decays with a mean lifetime of 2.20×10^{-6} s as measured in a frame of reference in which it is at rest. If a muon is moving at $0.990c$ (about 2.97×10^8 m/s) relative to the earth, what will you (an observer on earth) measure its mean lifetime to be?

SOLUTION

IDENTIFY: This problem concerns the muon's lifetime, which is the time interval between two events: the production of the muon and its subsequent decay. This lifetime is measured by two different observers: one who observes the muon at rest and another (you) who observes it moving at $0.990c$.

SET UP: Let S be your frame of reference on earth, and let S' be the muon's frame of reference. The target variable is the interval between these events as measured in S.

EXECUTE: The time interval between the two events as measured in S', 2.20×10^{-6} s, is a *proper* time, since the two events occur at the same position relative to the muon. Hence $\Delta t_0 = 2.20 \times 10^{-6}$ s. The muon moves relative to the earth between the two events, so the two events occur at different positions as measured in S and the time interval in that frame is Δt (the target variable). From Eq. (37.6),

$$\Delta t = \frac{\Delta t_0}{\sqrt{1 - u^2/c^2}} = \frac{2.20 \times 10^{-6}\ \text{s}}{\sqrt{1 - (0.990)^2}} = 15.6 \times 10^{-6}\ \text{s}$$

EVALUATE: Our result predicts that the mean lifetime of the muon in the earth frame (Δt) is about seven times longer than in the muon's frame (Δt_0). This prediction has been verified experimentally; indeed, it was the first experimental confirmation of the time dilation formula, Eq. (37.6).

Example 37.2 Time dilation at jetliner speeds

An airplane flies from San Francisco to New York (about 4800 km, or 4.80×10^6 m) at a steady speed of 300 m/s (about 670 mi/h). How much time does the trip take, as measured by an observer on the ground? By an observer in the plane?

SOLUTION

IDENTIFY: Here we are interested in what our two observers measure for the time interval between the airplane departing from San Francisco and landing in New York.

SET UP: The target variables are the time intervals between these events as measured in the frame of reference of the ground S and in the frame of reference of the airplane S'.

EXECUTE: The two events occur at different positions (San Francisco and New York) as measured in S, so the time interval measured by ground observers corresponds to Δt in Eq. (37.6). To find it, we simply divide the distance by the speed:

$$\Delta t = \frac{4.80 \times 10^6\ \text{m}}{300\ \text{m/s}} = 1.60 \times 10^4\ \text{s} \qquad (\text{about } 4\tfrac{1}{2} \text{ hours})$$

In the airplane's frame S', San Francisco and New York passing under the plane occur at the same point (the position of the plane). The time interval in the airplane is a proper time, corresponding to Δt_0 in Eq. (37.6). We have

$$\frac{u^2}{c^2} = \frac{(300\ \text{m/s})^2}{(3.00 \times 10^8\ \text{m/s})^2} = 1.00 \times 10^{-12}$$

From Eq. (37.6),

$$\Delta t_0 = (1.60 \times 10^4\ \text{s})\sqrt{1 - 1.00 \times 10^{-12}}$$

The radical can't be evaluated with adequate precision with an ordinary calculator. But we can approximate it using the binomial theorem (see Appendix B):

$$(1 - 1.00 \times 10^{-12})^{1/2} = 1 - \left(\frac{1}{2}\right)(1.00 \times 10^{-12}) + \cdots$$

The remaining terms are of the order of 10^{-24} or smaller and can be discarded. The approximate result for Δt_0 is

$$\Delta t_0 = (1.60 \times 10^4\ \text{s})(1 - 0.50 \times 10^{-12})$$

The proper time Δt_0, measured in the airplane, is very slightly less (by less than one part in 10^{12}) than the time measured on the ground.

EVALUATE: We don't notice such effects in everyday life. But present-day atomic clocks (see Section 1.3) can attain a precision of about one part in 10^{13}. A cesium clock traveling a long distance in an airliner has been used to measure this effect and thereby verify Eq. (37.6) even at speeds much less than c.

Example 37.3 Just when is it proper?

Mavis boards a spaceship and then zips past Stanley on earth at a relative speed of $0.600c$. At the instant she passes, both start timers. (a) At the instant when Stanley measures that Mavis has traveled 9.00×10^7 m past him, what does Mavis's timer read? (b) At the instant when Mavis reads 0.400 s on her timer, what does Stanley read on his?

SOLUTION

IDENTIFY: This problem involves time dilation for two *different* sets of events: the starting and stopping of Mavis's timer, and the starting and stopping of Stanley's timer.

SET UP: Let S be Stanley's frame of reference, and let S' be Mavis's frame of reference. The two events of interest in part (a) are when Mavis passes Stanley and when Stanley measures Mavis as having traveled a distance of 9.00×10^7 m; the target variables are the time intervals between these two events as measured in S and in S'. The two events in part (b) are when Mavis passes Stanley and when Mavis measures an elapsed time of 0.400 s; the target variable is the time interval between these two events as measured in S. As we will see, understanding this example hinges on understanding the difference between these two pairs of events.

EXECUTE: (a) The two events, Mavis passing the earth and Mavis reaching $x = 9.00 \times 10^7$ m as measured by Stanley, occur at different positions in Stanley's frame but at the same position in Mavis's frame. Hence the time interval in Stanley's frame S is Δt, while the time interval in Mavis's frame S' is the proper time Δt_0. As measured

Continued

by Stanley, Mavis moves at $0.600c = 0.600(3.00 \times 10^8 \text{ ms}) = 1.80 \times 10^8 \text{ m/s}$ and travels the 9.00×10^7 m in a time $\Delta t = (9.00 \times 10^7 \text{ m})/(1.80 \times 10^8 \text{ m/s}) = 0.500$ s. From Eq. (37.6), Mavis's timer reads an elapsed time of

$$\Delta t_0 = \Delta t \sqrt{1 - u^2/c^2} = 0.500 \text{ s}\sqrt{1 - (0.600)^2} = 0.400 \text{ s}$$

(b) It is tempting—but wrong—to answer that Stanley's timer reads 0.500 s. We are now considering a *different* pair of events, the starting and the reading of Stanley's timer, that both occur at the same point in Stanley's earth frame S. These two events occur at different positions in Mavis's frame S', so the time interval of 0.400 s that she measures between these events is equal to Δt. (In her frame, Stanley passes her at time zero and is a distance behind her of $(1.80 \times 10^8 \text{ m/s})(0.400 \text{ s}) = 7.20 \times 10^7$ m at time 0.400 s.) The time on Stanley's timer is now the proper time:

$$\Delta t_0 = \Delta t \sqrt{1 - u^2/c^2} = 0.400 \text{ s}\sqrt{1 - (0.600)^2} = 0.320 \text{ s}$$

EVALUATE: If the difference between 0.500 s and 0.320 s still troubles you, consider the following: Stanley, taking proper account of the transit time of a signal from $x = 9.00 \times 10^7$ m, says that Mavis passed that point and his timer read 0.500 s at the same instant. But Mavis says that those two events occurred at different positions and were *not* simultaneous—she passed the point at the instant his timer read 0.320 s. This example shows the relativity of simultaneity.

The Twin Paradox

Equations (37.6) and (37.8) for time dilation suggest an apparent paradox called the **twin paradox.** Consider identical twin astronauts named Eartha and Astrid. Eartha remains on earth while her twin Astrid takes off on a high-speed trip through the galaxy. Because of time dilation, Eartha observes Astrid's heartbeat and all other life processes proceeding more slowly than her own. Thus to Eartha, Astrid ages more slowly; when Astrid returns to earth she is younger (has aged less) than Eartha.

Now here is the paradox: All inertial frames are equivalent. Can't Astrid make exactly the same arguments to conclude that Eartha is in fact the younger? Then each twin measures the other to be younger when they're back together, and that's a paradox.

To resolve the paradox, we recognize that the twins are *not* identical in all respects. While Eartha remains in an approximately inertial frame at all times, Astrid must *accelerate* with respect to that inertial frame during parts of her trip in order to leave, turn around, and return to earth. Eartha's reference frame is always approximately inertial; Astrid's is often far from inertial. Thus there is a real physical difference between the circumstances of the two twins. Careful analysis shows that Eartha is correct; when Astrid returns, she *is* younger than Eartha.

Test Your Understanding of Section 37.3 Samir (who is standing on the ground) starts his stopwatch at the instant that Maria flies past him in her spaceship at a speed of $0.600c$. At the same instant, Maria starts her stopwatch. (a) As measured in Samir's frame of reference, what is the reading on Maria's stopwatch at the instant that Samir's stopwatch reads 10.0 s? (i) 10.0 s; (ii) less than 10.0 s; (iii) more than 10.0 s. (b) As measured in Maria's frame of reference, what is the reading on Samir's stopwatch at the instant that Maria's stopwatch reads 10.0 s? (i) 10.0 s; (ii) less than 10.0 s; (iii) more than 10.0 s.

MP

37.4 Relativity of Length

ActivPhysics ONLINE
17.2 Relativity of Length

Not only does the time interval between two events depend on the observer's frame of reference, but the *distance* between two points may also depend on the observer's frame of reference. The concept of simultaneity is involved. Suppose you want to measure the length of a moving car. One way is to have two assistants make marks on the pavement at the positions of the front and rear bumpers. Then you measure the distance between the marks. But your assistants have to make their marks *at the same time.* If one marks the position of the front bumper at one time and the other marks the position of the rear bumper half a second later, you won't get the car's true length. Since we've learned that simultaneity isn't an absolute concept, we have to proceed with caution.

Lengths Parallel to the Relative Motion

To develop a relationship between lengths that are measured parallel to the direction of motion in various coordinate systems, we consider another thought experiment. We attach a light source to one end of a ruler and a mirror to the other end. The ruler is at rest in reference frame S', and its length in this frame is l_0 (Fig. 37.10a). Then the time Δt_0 required for a light pulse to make the round trip from source to mirror and back is

$$\Delta t_0 = \frac{2l_0}{c} \tag{37.9}$$

This is a proper time interval because departure and return occur at the same point in S'.

In reference frame S the ruler is moving to the right with speed u during this travel of the light pulse (Fig. 37.10b). The length of the ruler in S is l, and the time of travel from source to mirror, as measured in S, is Δt_1. During this interval the ruler, with source and mirror attached, moves a distance $u\,\Delta t_1$. The total length of path d from source to mirror is not l, but rather

$$d = l + u\,\Delta t_1 \tag{37.10}$$

The light pulse travels with speed c, so it is also true that

$$d = c\,\Delta t_1 \tag{37.11}$$

Combining Eqs. (37.10) and (37.11) to eliminate d, we find

$$c\,\Delta t_1 = l + u\,\Delta t_1 \quad \text{or}$$

$$\Delta t_1 = \frac{l}{c - u} \tag{37.12}$$

(Dividing the distance l by $c - u$ does *not* mean that light travels with speed $c - u$, but rather that the distance the pulse travels in S is greater than l.)

In the same way we can show that the time Δt_2 for the return trip from mirror to source is

$$\Delta t_2 = \frac{l}{c + u} \tag{37.13}$$

(a)

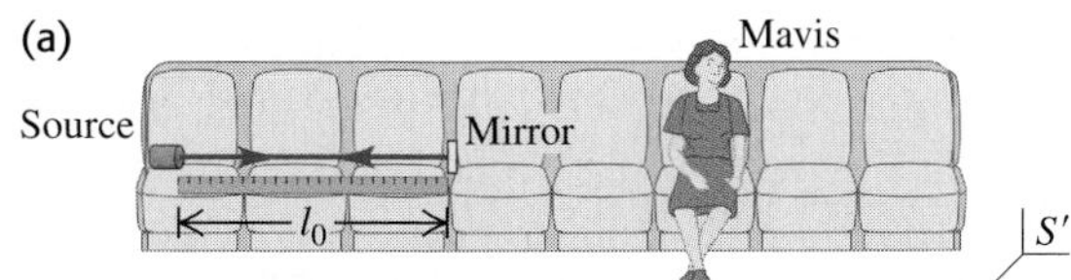

The ruler is stationary in Mavis's frame of reference S'. The light pulse travels a distance l_0 from the light source to the mirror.

(b)

Mavis

d

l

$u\,\Delta t_1$

u

S'

S

Stanley

The ruler moves at speed u in Stanley's frame of reference S. The light pulse travels a distance l (the length of the ruler measured in S) plus an additional distance $u\,\Delta t_1$ from the light source to the mirror.

37.10 (a) A ruler is at rest in Mavis's frame S'. A light pulse is emitted from a source at one end of the ruler, reflected by a mirror at the other end, and returned to the source position. (b) Motion of the light pulse as measured in Stanley's frame S.

The *total* time $\Delta t = \Delta t_1 + \Delta t_2$ for the round trip, as measured in S, is

$$\Delta t = \frac{l}{c - u} + \frac{l}{c + u} = \frac{2l}{c(1 - u^2/c^2)} \tag{37.14}$$

We also know that Δt and Δt_0 are related by Eq. (37.6) because Δt_0 is a proper time in S'. Thus EQ. (37.9) for the round-trip time in the rest frame S' of the ruler becomes

$$\Delta t \sqrt{1 - \frac{u^2}{c^2}} = \frac{2l_0}{c} \tag{37.15}$$

Finally, combining Eqs. (37.14) and (37.15) to eliminate Δt and simplifying, we obtain

$$l = l_0 \sqrt{1 - \frac{u^2}{c^2}} = \frac{l_0}{\gamma} \quad \text{(length contraction)} \tag{37.16}$$

[We have used the quantity $\gamma = 1/\sqrt{1 - u^2/c^2}$ defined in Eq. (37.7).] Thus the length l measured in S, in which the ruler is moving, is *shorter* than the length l_0 measured in its rest frame S'.

CAUTION **Length contraction is real** This is *not* an optical illusion! The ruler really is shorter in reference frame S than it is in S'.

A length measured in the frame in which the body is at rest (the rest frame of the body) is called a **proper length;** thus l_0 is a proper length in S', and the length measured in any other frame moving relative to S' is *less than* l_0. This effect is called **length contraction.**

When u is very small in comparison to c, γ approaches 1. Thus in the limit of small speeds we approach the Newtonian relationship $l = l_0$. This and the corresponding result for time dilation show that Eqs. (37.1), the Galilean coordinate transformation, are usually sufficiently accurate for relative speeds much smaller than c. If u is a reasonable fraction of c, however, the quantity $\sqrt{1 - u^2/c^2}$ can be appreciably less than 1. Then l can be substantially smaller than l_0, and the effects of length contraction can be substantial (Fig. 37.11).

37.11 The speed at which electrons traverse the 3-km beam line of the Stanford Linear Accelerator Center is slower than c by less than 1 cm/s. As measured in the reference frame of such an electron, the beam line (which extends from the top to the bottom of this photograph) is only about 15 cm long!

Lengths Perpendicular to the Relative Motion

We have derived Eq. (37.16) for lengths measured in the direction *parallel* to the relative motion of the two frames of reference. Lengths that are measured *perpendicular* to the direction of motion are *not* contracted. To prove this, consider two identical meter sticks. One stick is at rest in frame S and lies along the positive y-axis with one end at O, the origin of S. The other is at rest in frame S' and lies along the positive y'-axis with one end at O', the origin of S'. Frame S' moves in the positive x-direction relative to frame S. Observers Stanley and Mavis, at rest in S and S' respectively, station themselves at the 50-cm mark of their sticks. At the instant the two origins coincide, the two sticks lie along the same line. At this instant, Mavis makes a mark on Stanley's stick at the point that coincides with her own 50-cm mark, and Stanley does the same to Mavis's stick.

Suppose for the sake of argument that Stanley observes Mavis's stick as longer than his own. Then the mark Stanley makes on her stick is *below* its center. In that case, Mavis will think Stanley's stick has become shorter, since half of its length coincides with *less* than half her stick's length. So Mavis observes moving sticks getting shorter and Stanley observes them getting longer. But this implies an asymmetry between the two frames that contradicts the basic postulate of relativity that tells us all inertial frames are equivalent. We conclude that consistency with the postulates of relativity requires that both observers measure the rulers as having the *same* length, even though to each observer one of them is stationary and the other is

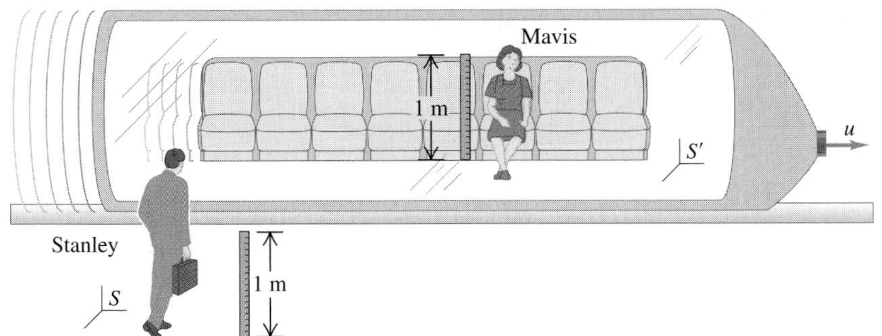

37.12 The meter sticks are perpendicular to the relative velocity. For any value of u, both Stanley and Mavis measure either meter stick to have a length of 1 meter.

moving (Fig. 37.12). So *there is no length contraction perpendicular to the direction of relative motion of the coordinate systems.* We used this result in our derivation of Eq. (37.6) in assuming that the distance d is the same in both frames of reference.

For example, suppose a moving rod of length l_0 makes an angle θ_0 with the direction of relative motion (the x-axis) as measured in its rest frame. Its length component in that frame parallel to the motion, $l_0 \cos\theta_0$, is contracted to $(l_0 \cos\theta_0)/\gamma$. However, its length component perpendicular to the motion, $l_0 \sin\theta_0$, remains the same.

Problem-Solving Strategy 37.2 Length Contraction

IDENTIFY *the relevant concepts:* The concept of length contraction is used whenever we compare the length of an object as measured by observers in different inertial frames of reference.

SET UP *the problem* using the following steps:

1. Decide what defines the length in question. If the problem statement describes an object such as a ruler, it is just the distance between the ends of the object. If, however, the problem is about a distance between two points with no object between them, it can help to envision a ruler or rod that extends from one point to the other.
2. Determine what the target variable is.

EXECUTE *the solution* as follows:

1. Determine the reference frame in which the object in question is at rest. In this frame, the length of the object is its proper length l_0. In a second reference frame moving at speed u relative to the first frame, the object has contracted length l.
2. Keep in mind that length contraction occurs only for lengths parallel to the direction of relative motion of the two frames. Any length that is perpendicular to the relative motion is the same in both frames.
3. Use Eq. (37.16) to relate l and l_0, and then solve for the target variable.

EVALUATE *your answer:* Check that your answers make sense: l is never larger than l_0, and u is never greater than c.

Example 37.4 How long is the spaceship?

A spaceship flies past earth at a speed of $0.990c$. A crew member on board the spaceship measures its length, obtaining the value 400 m. What length do observers measure on earth?

SOLUTION

IDENTIFY: This problem asks us to relate the length of the spaceship—that is, the distance from its nose to its tail—as measured by observers in two different frames of reference: one on board the spaceship and the other on earth.

SET UP: The length in question is along the direction of relative motion (Fig. 37.13), so there will be length contraction as measured in one of the frames of reference. Our target variable is the length measured in the earth frame.

EXECUTE: The 400-m length of the spaceship is the *proper* length l_0 because it is measured in the frame in which the spaceship is

37.13 Measuring the length of a moving spaceship.

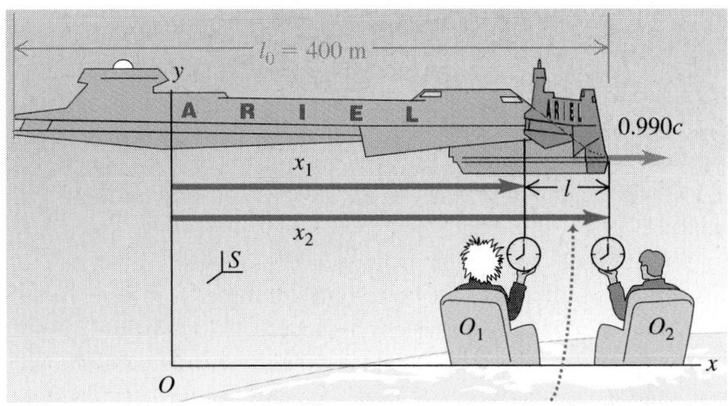

The two observers on earth (S) must measure x_2 and x_1 simultaneously to obtain the correct length $l = x_2 - x_1$ in their frame of reference.

Continued

at rest. We want to find the length l measured by observers on earth. From Eq. (37.16),

$$l = l_0\sqrt{1 - \frac{u^2}{c^2}} = (400\text{ m})\sqrt{1 - (0.990)^2}$$
$$= 56.4\text{ m}$$

EVALUATE: This answer makes sense: The spaceship is shorter in a frame in which it is in motion than in a frame in which it is at rest. To measure the length l, two observers with synchronized clocks could measure the positions of the two ends of the spaceship simultaneously in the earth's reference frame, as shown in Fig. 37.13. (These two measurements will *not* appear simultaneous to an observer in the spaceship.)

Example 37.5 How far apart are the observers?

The two observers mentioned in Example 37.4 are 56.4 m apart on the earth. How far apart does the spaceship crew measure them to be?

SOLUTION

IDENTIFY: The two sets of observers are the same as in Example 37.4, but now the distance being measured is the separation between the two earth observers.

SET UP: The distance between the earth observers as measured on earth is a *proper* length, since the two observers are at rest in the earth frame. (Think of a length of pipe 56.4 m long that extends from O_1 to O_2 in Fig. 37.13. This pipe is at rest in the earth frame, so its length is a proper length.) The earth is moving relative to the spaceship at $0.990c$, so the spaceship crew will measure a distance shorter than 56.4 m between the two earth observers. The value that they measure is our target variable.

EXECUTE: With $l_0 = 56.4$ m and $u = 0.990c$, the length l that the crew members measure is

$$l = l_0\sqrt{1 - \frac{u^2}{c^2}} = (56.4\text{ m})\sqrt{1 - (0.990)^2}$$
$$= 7.96\text{ m}$$

EVALUATE: This answer does *not* say that the crew measures their spaceship to be both 400 m long and 7.96 m long. The observers on earth measure the spaceship to have a contracted length of 56.4 m because they are 56.4 m apart when they measure the positions of the ends at what they measure to be the same instant. (Viewed from the spaceship frame, the observers do not measure those positions simultaneously.) The crew then measures the 56.4 m proper length to be contracted to 7.96 m. The key point is that the measurements made in Example 37.4 (in which the earth observers measure the distance between the ends of the spaceship) are different from those made in this example (in which the spaceship crew measures the distance between the earth observers).

Conceptual Example 37.6 Moving with a muon

As was stated in Example 37.1, a muon has, on average, a proper lifetime of 2.20×10^{-6} s and a dilated lifetime of 15.6×10^{-6} s in a frame in which its speed is $0.990c$. Multiplying constant speed by time to find distance gives $0.990(3.00 \times 10^8\text{ m/s}) \times (2.20 \times 10^{-6}\text{ s}) = 653\text{ m}$ and $0.990(3.00 \times 10^8\text{ m/s}) \times (15.6 \times 10^{-6}\text{ s}) = 4630\text{ m}$. Interpret these two distances.

SOLUTION

If an average muon moves at $0.990c$ past observers, they will measure it to be created at one point and then to decay 15.6×10^{-6} s later at another point 4630 m away. For example, this muon could be created level with the top of a mountain and then move straight down to decay at its base 4630 m below.

However, an observer moving with an average muon will say that it traveled only 653 m because it existed for only 2.20×10^{-6} s. To show that this answer is completely consistent, consider the mountain. The 4630-m distance is its height, a proper length in the direction of motion. Relative to the observer traveling with this muon, the mountain moves up at $0.990c$ with the 4630-m length contracted to

$$l = l_0\sqrt{1 - \frac{u^2}{c^2}} = (4630\text{ m})\sqrt{1 - (0.990)^2}$$
$$= 653\text{ m}$$

Thus we see that length contraction is consistent with time dilation. The same is true for an electron moving at speed u in a linear accelerator (see Fig. 37.11). Compared to the values measured by a physicist standing alongside the accelerator, an observer riding along with the electron would measure the accelerator's length and the time to travel that length to both be shorter by a factor of $\sqrt{1 - u^2/c^2}$.

How an Object Moving Near c Would Appear

Let's think a little about the visual appearance of a moving three-dimensional body. If we could see the positions of all points of the body simultaneously, it would appear to shrink only in the direction of motion. But we *don't* see all the points simultaneously; light from points farther from us takes longer to reach us than does light from points near to us, so we see the farther points at the positions they had at earlier times.

Suppose we have a rectangular rod with its faces parallel to the coordinate planes. When we look end-on at the center of the closest face of such a rod at rest, we see only that face. (See the center rod in computer-generated Fig. 37.14a). But when that rod is moving past us toward the right at an appreciable fraction of the speed of light, we may also see its left side because of the earlier-time effect just described. That is, we can see some points that we couldn't see when the rod was at rest because the rod moves out of the way of the light rays from those points to us. Conversely, some light that can get to us when the rod is at rest is blocked by the moving rod. Because of all this, the rods in Figs. 37.14b and 37.14c appear rotated and distorted.

37.14 Computer simulation of the appearance of an array of 25 rods with square cross section. The center rod is viewed end-on. The simulation ignores color changes in the array caused by the Doppler effect (see Section 37.6).

(a) Array at rest

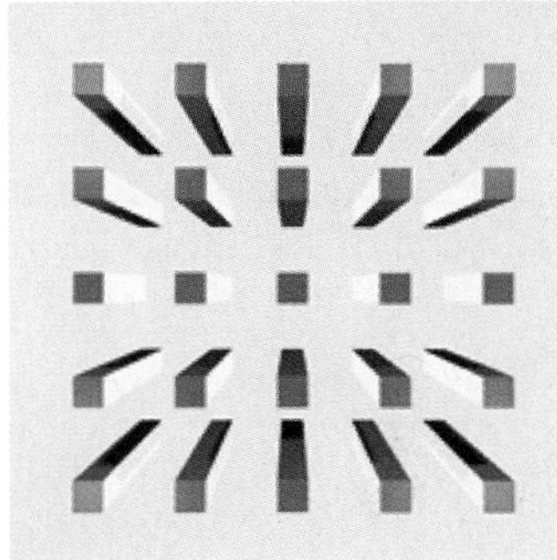

(b) Array moving to the right at $0.2c$

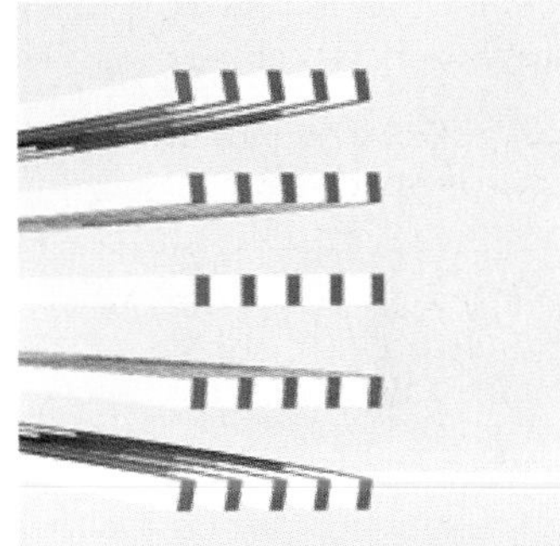

(c) Array moving to the right at $0.9c$

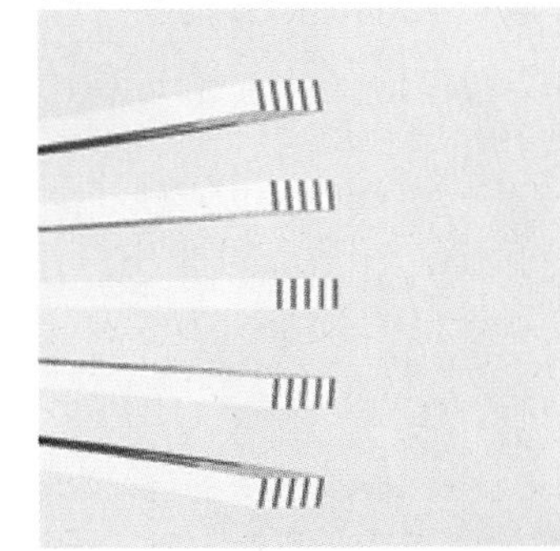

Test Your Understanding of Section 37.4 A miniature spaceship is flying past you, moving horizontally at a substantial fraction of the speed of light. At a certain instant, you observe that the nose and tail of the spaceship align exactly with the two ends of a meter stick that you hold in your hands. Rank the following distances in order from longest to shortest: (i) the proper length of the meter stick; (ii) the proper length of the spaceship; (iii) the length of the spaceship measured in your frame of reference; (iv) the length of the meter stick measured in the spaceship's frame of reference.

37.5 The Lorentz Transformations

In Section 37.1 we discussed the Galilean coordinate transformation equations, Eqs. (37.1). They relate the coordinates (x, y, z) of a point in frame of reference S to the coordinates (x', y', z') of the point in a second frame S'. The second frame moves with constant speed u relative to S in the positive direction along the common x-x'-axis. This transformation also assumes that the time scale is the same in the two frames of reference, as expressed by the additional relationship $t = t'$. This Galilean transformation, as we have seen, is valid only in the limit when u approaches zero. We are now ready to derive more general transformations that are consistent with the principle of relativity. The more general relationships are called the **Lorentz transformations.**

The Lorentz Coordinate Transformation

Our first question is this: When an event occurs at point (x, y, z) at time t, as observed in a frame of reference S, what are the coordinates (x', y', z') and time t' of the event as observed in a second frame S' moving relative to S with constant speed u in the $+x$-direction?

To derive the coordinate transformation, we refer to Fig. 37.15 (next page), which is the same as Fig. 37.3. As before, we assume that the origins coincide at the initial time $t = 0 = t'$. Then in S the distance from O to O' at time t is still ut. The coordinate x' is a *proper length* in S', so in S it is contracted by the factor $1/\gamma = \sqrt{1 - u^2/c^2}$, as in Eq. (37.16). Thus the distance x from O to P, as seen in S, is not simply $x = ut + x'$, as in the Galilean coordinate transformation, but

$$x = ut + x'\sqrt{1 - \frac{u^2}{c^2}} \tag{37.17}$$

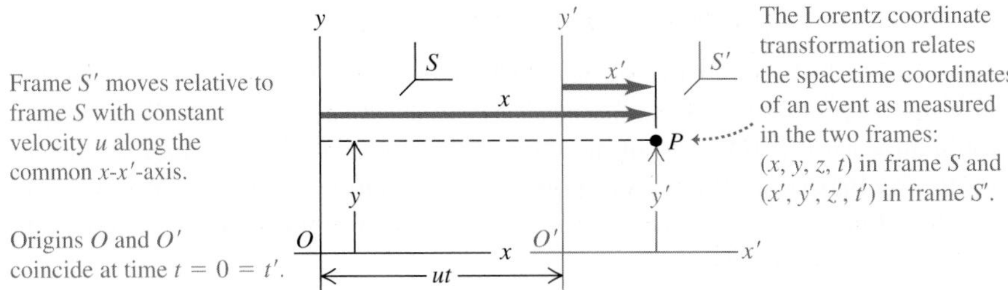
Frame S' moves relative to frame S with constant velocity u along the common x-x'-axis.
Origins O and O' coincide at time $t = 0 = t'$.
The Lorentz coordinate transformation relates the spacetime coordinates of an event as measured in the two frames: (x, y, z, t) in frame S and (x', y', z', t') in frame S'.
y
y'
S
S'
x'
x
P
y
y'
O
O'
x
x'
ut

37.15 As measured in frame of reference S, x' is contracted to x'/γ, so $x = ut + x'/\gamma$ and $x' = \gamma(x - ut)$.

Solving this equation for x', we obtain

$$x' = \frac{x - ut}{\sqrt{1 - u^2/c^2}} \tag{37.18}$$

Equation (37.18) is part of the Lorentz coordinate transformation; another part is the equation giving t' in terms of x and t. To obtain this, we note that the principle of relativity requires that the *form* of the transformation from S to S' be identical to that from S' to S. The only difference is a change in the sign of the relative velocity component u. Thus from Eq. (37.17) it must be true that

$$x' = -ut' + x\sqrt{1 - \frac{u^2}{c^2}} \tag{37.19}$$

We now equate Eqs. (37.18) and (37.19) to eliminate x'. This gives us an equation for t' in terms of x and t. We leave the algebraic details for you to work out; the result is

$$t' = \frac{t - ux/c^2}{\sqrt{1 - u^2/c^2}} \tag{37.20}$$

As we discussed previously, lengths perpendicular to the direction of relative motion are not affected by the motion, so $y' = y$ and $z' = z$.

Collecting all these transformation equations, we have

$$\begin{aligned} x' &= \frac{x - ut}{\sqrt{1 - u^2/c^2}} = \gamma(x - ut) \\ y' &= y \\ z' &= z \\ t' &= \frac{t - ux/c^2}{\sqrt{1 - u^2/c^2}} = \gamma(t - ux/c^2) \end{aligned} \quad \text{(Lorentz coordinate transformation)} \tag{37.21}$$

These equations are the *Lorentz coordinate transformation,* the relativistic generalization of the Galilean coordinate transformation, Eqs. (37.1) and $t = t'$. For values of u that approach zero, the radicals in the denominators and γ approach 1, and the ux/c^2 term approaches zero. In this limit, Eqs. (37.21) become identical to Eqs. (37.1) along with $t = t'$. In general, though, both the coordinates and time of an event in one frame depend on its coordinates and time in another frame. *Space and time have become intertwined; we can no longer say that length and time have absolute meanings independent of the frame of reference.* For this reason, we refer to time and the three dimensions of space collectively as a four-dimensional entity called **spacetime,** and we call (x, y, z, t) together the **spacetime coordinates** of an event.

The Lorentz Velocity Transformation

We can use Eqs. (37.21) to derive the relativistic generalization of the Galilean velocity transformation, Eq. (37.2). We consider only one-dimensional motion along the x-axis and use the term "velocity" as being short for the "x-component of the velocity." Suppose that in a time dt a particle moves a distance dx, as measured in frame S. We obtain the corresponding distance dx' and time dt' in S' by taking differentials of Eqs. (37.21):

$$dx' = \gamma(dx - u\,dt)$$
$$dt' = \gamma(dt - u\,dx/c^2)$$

We divide the first equation by the second and then divide the numerator and denominator of the result by dt to obtain

$$\frac{dx'}{dt'} = \frac{\dfrac{dx}{dt} - u}{1 - \dfrac{u}{c^2}\dfrac{dx}{dt}}$$

Now dx/dt is the velocity v_x in S, and dx'/dt' is the velocity v'_x in S', so we finally obtain the relativistic generalization

$$v'_x = \frac{v_x - u}{1 - uv_x/c^2} \quad \text{(Lorentz velocity transformation)} \qquad (37.22)$$

When u and v_x are much smaller than c, the denominator in Eq. (37.22) approaches 1, and we approach the nonrelativistic result $v'_x = v_x - u$. The opposite extreme is the case $v_x = c$; then we find

$$v'_x = \frac{c - u}{1 - uc/c^2} = \frac{c(1 - u/c)}{1 - u/c} = c$$

This says that anything moving with velocity $v_x = c$ measured in S also has velocity $v'_x = c$ measured in S', despite the relative motion of the two frames. So Eq. (37.22) is consistent with Einstein's postulate that the speed of light in vacuum is the same in all inertial frames of reference.

The principle of relativity tells us there is no fundamental distinction between the two frames S and S'. Thus the expression for v_x in terms of v'_x must have the same form as Eq. (37.22), with v_x changed to v'_x, and vice versa, and the sign of u reversed. Carrying out these operations with Eq. (37.22), we find

$$v_x = \frac{v'_x + u}{1 + uv'_x/c^2} \quad \text{(Lorentz velocity transformation)} \qquad (37.23)$$

This can also be obtained algebraically by solving Eq. (37.22) for v_x. Both Eqs. (37.22) and (37.23) are *Lorentz velocity transformations* for one-dimensional motion.

CAUTION Use the correct reference frame coordinates Keep in mind that the Lorentz transformation equations given by Eqs. (37.21), (37.22), and (37.23) assume that frame S' is moving in the positive x-direction with velocity u relative to frame S. You should always set up your coordinate system to follow this convention.

When u is less than c, the Lorentz velocity transformations show us that a body moving with a speed less than c in one frame of reference always has a speed less than c in *every other* frame of reference. This is one reason for concluding that no material body may travel with a speed equal to or greater than that of light in vacuum, relative to *any* inertial frame of reference. The relativistic generalizations of energy and momentum, which we will explore later, give further support to this hypothesis.

Problem-Solving Strategy 37.3 Lorentz Transformations

IDENTIFY *the relevant concepts:* The Lorentz *coordinate* transformation tells you how to relate the spacetime coordinates of an event in one inertial frame of reference to the spacetime coordinates of the same event in a second inertial frame. The Lorentz *velocity* transformation relates the velocity of an object in one inertial frame to its velocity in a second inertial frame.

SET UP *the problem* using the following steps:

1. Determine what the target variable is.
2. Define the two inertial frames S and S'. Remember that S' moves relative to S at a constant velocity u in the $+x$-direction.
3. If the coordinate transformation equations are needed, make a list of spacetime coordinates in the two frames, such as x_1, x_1', t_1, t_1', and so on. Label carefully which of these you know and which you don't.
4. In velocity-transformation problems, clearly identify the velocities u (the relative velocity of the two frames of reference), v_x (the velocity of the object relative to S), and v_x' (the velocity of the object relative to S').

EXECUTE *the solution* as follows:

1. In a coordinate-transformation problem, use Eqs. (37.21) to solve for the spacetime coordinates of the event as measured in S' in terms of the corresponding values in S. (If you need to solve for the spacetime coordinates in S in terms of the corresponding values in S', you can easily convert the expressions in Eqs. (37.21): Replace all of the primed quantities with unprimed ones, and vice versa, and replace u with $-u$.)
2. In a velocity-transformation problem, use either Eq. (37.22) or Eq. (37.23), as appropriate, to solve for the target variable.

EVALUATE *your answer:* Don't be discouraged if some of your results don't seem to make sense or if they disagree with "common sense." It takes time to develop intuition about relativity; you'll gain it with experience. (One result that would definitely be in error is a speed greater than c.)

Example 37.7 Was it received before it was sent?

Winning an interstellar race, Mavis pilots her spaceship across a finish line in space at a speed of $0.600c$ relative to that line. A "hooray" message is sent from the back of her ship (event 2) at the instant (in her frame of reference) that the front of her ship crosses the line (event 1). She measures the length of her ship to be 300 m. Stanley is at the finish line and is at rest relative to it. When and where does he measure events 1 and 2 to occur?

SOLUTION

IDENTIFY: This example involves the Lorentz coordinate transformation.

SET UP: Our derivation of this transformation assumes that the origins of frames S and S' coincide at $t = 0 = t'$. Thus for simplicity we fix the origin of S at the finish line and the origin of S' at the front of the spaceship so that Stanley and Mavis measure event 1 to be at $x = 0 = x'$ and $t = 0 = t'$.

Mavis in S' measures her spaceship to be 300 m long, so she has the "hooray" sent from 300 m behind her spaceship's front at the instant she measures the front to cross the finish line. That is, she measures event 2 at $x' = -300$ m and $t' = 0$.

Our target variables are the coordinate x and time t of event 2 that Stanley measures in S.

EXECUTE: To most easily solve for the target variables, we modify the first and last of Eqs. (37.21) to give x and t as functions of x' and t'. We do so by using the principle of relativity in the same way that we obtained Eq. (37.23) from Eq. (37.22). We remove the primes from x' and t', add primes to x and t, and replace each u with $-u$. The results are

$$x = \gamma(x' + ut') \qquad \text{and} \qquad t = \gamma(t' + ux'/c^2)$$

From Eq. (37.7), $\gamma = 1.25$ for $u = 0.600c = 1.80 \times 10^8$ m/s. We also substitute $x' = -300$ m, $t' = 0$, $c = 3.00 \times 10^8$ m/s, and $u = 1.80 \times 10^8$ m/s in the equations for x and t to find $x = -375$ m at $t = -7.50 \times 10^{-7}$ s $= -0.750$ μs for event 2.

EVALUATE: Mavis says that the events are simultaneous, but Stanley disagrees. In fact, he says that the "hooray" was sent *before* Mavis crossed the finish line. This does not mean that the effect preceded the cause. The fastest that Mavis can send a signal the length of her ship is $300\text{ m}/(3.00 \times 10^8\text{ m/s}) = 1.00\ \mu\text{s}$. She cannot send a signal from the front at the instant it crosses the finish line that would cause a "hooray" to be broadcast from the back at the same instant. She would have to send that signal from the front at least 1.00 μs before then, so she had to slightly anticipate her success.

Note that relativity *is* consistent. In his frame, Stanley measures Mavis's ship to be $l_0/\gamma = 300\text{ m}/1.25 = 240$ m long with its back at $x = -375$ m at $t = -0.750\ \mu\text{s} = -7.50 \times 10^{-7}$ s when the "hooray" is sent. At that instant he thus measures the front of her 240-m-long ship to be a distance of $(375 - 240)\text{ m} = 135$ m from the finish line. However, since $(1.80 \times 10^8\text{ m/s})(7.50 \times 10^{-7}\text{ s}) = 135$ m, the front does cross the line at $t = 0$.

Example 37.8 Relative velocities

(a) A spaceship moving away from the earth with speed $0.900c$ fires a robot space probe in the same direction as its motion, with speed $0.700c$ relative to the spaceship. What is the probe's velocity relative to the earth? (b) A scoutship tries to catch up with the spaceship by traveling at $0.950c$ relative to the earth. What is the velocity of the scoutship relative to the spaceship?

SOLUTION

IDENTIFY: This example uses the Lorentz velocity transformation.

SET UP: Let the earth's frame of reference be S, and let the spaceship's frame of reference be S' (Fig. 37.16). The relative velocity of the two frames is $u = 0.700c$. The target variable in part (a) is the velocity of the probe relative to S; the target variable in part (b) is the velocity of the scoutship relative to S'.

37.16 The spaceship, robot space probe, and scoutship.

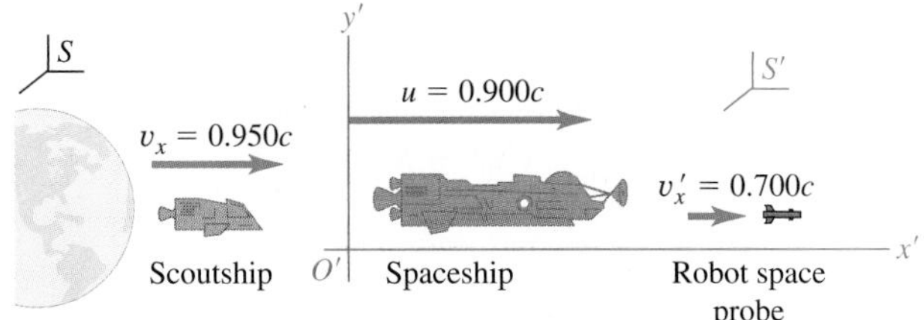
S
y'
S'
u = 0.900c
v_x = 0.950c
v'_x = 0.700c
x'
Scoutship
O'
Spaceship
Robot space probe

EXECUTE: (a) We are given the velocity of the probe relative to the spaceship, $v'_x = 0.700c$. We use Eq. (37.23) to determine its velocity v_x relative to the earth:

$$v_x = \frac{v'_x + u}{1 + uv'_x/c^2} = \frac{0.700c + 0.900c}{1 + (0.900c)(0.700c)/c^2} = 0.982c$$

(b) We are given the velocity of the scoutship relative to the earth, $v_x = 0.950c$. We use Eq. (37.22) to determine its velocity v'_x relative to the spaceship:

$$v'_x = \frac{v_x - u}{1 - uv_x/c^2} = \frac{0.950c - 0.900c}{1 - (0.900c)(0.950c)/c^2} = 0.345c$$

EVALUATE: It's instructive to compare our results to what we would have obtained had we used the Galilean velocity transformation formula, Eq. (37.2). In part (a) we would have found the probe's velocity relative to the earth to be $v_x = v'_x + u = 0.700c + 0.900c = 1.600c$. This value is greater than the speed of light and so must be incorrect. In part (b) we would have found the scoutship's velocity relative to the spaceship to be $v'_x = v_x - u = 0.950c - 0.900c = 0.050c$; the relativistically correct value, $v'_x = 0.345c$, is almost seven times greater than the incorrect Galilean value.

Test Your Understanding of Section 37.5 (a) In frame S events P_1 and P_2 occur at the same x-, y-, and z-coordinates, but event P_1 occurs before event P_2. In frame S', which event occurs first? (b) In frame S events P_3 and P_4 occur at the same time t and the same y- and z-coordinates, but event P_3 occurs at a less positive x-coordinate than event P_4. In frame S', which event occurs first?

*37.6 The Doppler Effect for Electromagnetic Waves

An additional important consequence of relativistic kinematics is the Doppler effect for electromagnetic waves. In our previous discussion of the Doppler effect (see Section 16.8) we quoted without proof the formula, Eq. (16.30), for the frequency shift that results from motion of a source of electromagnetic waves relative to an observer. We can now derive that result.

Here's a statement of the problem. A source of light is moving with constant speed u toward Stanley, who is stationary in an inertial frame (Fig. 37.17). As measured in its rest frame, the source emits light waves with frequency f_0 and period $T_0 = 1/f_0$. What is the frequency f of these waves as received by Stanley?

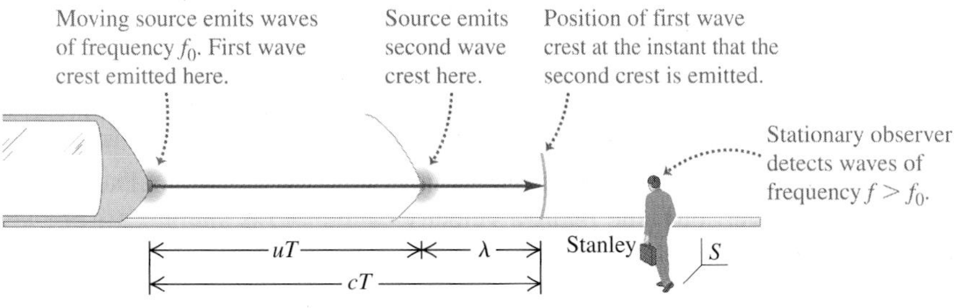
Moving source emits waves of frequency f_0. First wave crest emitted here.
Source emits second wave crest here.
Position of first wave crest at the instant that the second crest is emitted.
Stationary observer detects waves of frequency $f > f_0$.
uT
λ
cT
Stanley
S

37.17 The Doppler effect for light. A light source moving at speed u relative to Stanley emits a wave crest, then travels a distance uT toward an observer and emits the next crest. In Stanley's reference frame S, the second crest is a distance λ behind the first crest.

37.20 Graph of the magnitude of the momentum of a particle of rest mass m as a function of speed v. Also shown is the Newtonian prediction, which gives correct results only at speeds much less than c.

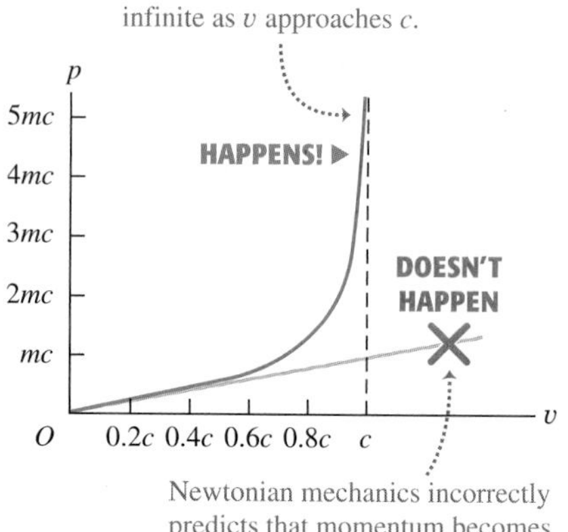
Relativistic momentum becomes infinite as v approaches c.
p
$5mc$
$4mc$
$3mc$
$2mc$
mc
HAPPENS!
DOESN'T HAPPEN
O
$0.2c$ $0.4c$ $0.6c$ $0.8c$ c
v
Newtonian mechanics incorrectly predicts that momentum becomes infinite only if v becomes infinite.

material particle for a particle that has a nonzero rest mass. When such a particle has a velocity $\vec{v}$, its **relativistic momentum** $\vec{p}$ is

$$\vec{p} = \frac{m\vec{v}}{\sqrt{1 - v^2/c^2}} \quad \text{(relativistic momentum)} \tag{37.27}$$

When the particle's speed v is much less than c, this is approximately equal to the Newtonian expression $\vec{p} = m\vec{v}$, but in general the momentum is greater in magnitude than mv (Figure 37.20). In fact, as v approaches c, the momentum approaches infinity.

Relativity, Newton's Second Law, and Relativistic Mass

What about the relativistic generalization of Newton's second law? In Newtonian mechanics the most general form of the second law is

$$\vec{F} = \frac{d\vec{p}}{dt} \tag{37.28}$$

That is, the net force $\vec{F}$ on a particle equals the time rate of change of its momentum. Experiments show that this result is still valid in relativistic mechanics, provided that we use the relativistic momentum given by Eq. 37.27. That is, the relativistically correct generalization of Newton's second law is

$$\vec{F} = \frac{d}{dt}\frac{m\vec{v}}{\sqrt{1 - v^2/c^2}} \tag{37.29}$$

Because momentum is no longer directly proportional to velocity, the rate of change of momentum is no longer directly proportional to the acceleration. As a result, *constant force does not cause constant acceleration.* For example, when the net force and the velocity are both along the x-axis, Eq. 37.29 gives

$$F = \frac{m}{(1 - v^2/c^2)^{3/2}}a \quad (\vec{F} \text{ and } \vec{v} \text{ along the same line}) \tag{37.30}$$

where a is the acceleration, also along the x-axis. Solving Eq. 37.30 for the acceleration a gives

$$a = \frac{F}{m}\left(1 - \frac{v^2}{c^2}\right)^{3/2}$$

We see that as a particle's speed increases, the acceleration caused by a given force continuously *decreases.* As the speed approaches c, the acceleration approaches zero, no matter how great a force is applied. Thus it is impossible to accelerate a particle with nonzero rest mass to a speed equal to or greater than c. We again see that the speed of light in vacuum represents an ultimate speed limit.

Equation (37.27) for relativistic momentum is sometimes interpreted to mean that a rapidly moving particle undergoes an increase in mass. If the mass at zero velocity (the rest mass) is denoted by m, then the "relativistic mass" m_{rel} is given by

$$m_{\text{rel}} = \frac{m}{\sqrt{1 - v^2/c^2}}$$

Indeed, when we consider the motion of a system of particles (such as rapidly moving ideal-gas molecules in a stationary container), the total rest mass of the system is the sum of the relativistic masses of the particles, not the sum of their rest masses.

However, if blindly applied, the concept of relativistic mass has its pitfalls. As Eq. (37.29) shows, the relativistic generalization of Newton's second law is *not* $\vec{F} = m_{\text{rel}}\vec{a}$, and we will show in Section 37.8 that the relativistic kinetic energy of

Example 37.9 A jet from a black hole

A number of galaxies have supermassive black holes at their centers (see Section 12.8). As material swirls around such a black hole, it is heated, becomes ionized, and generates strong magnetic fields. The resulting magnetic forces steer some of the material into high-speed jets that blast out of the galaxy and into intergalactic space (Figure 37.19). The blue light we observe from the jet in Fig. 37.19 has a frequency of 6.66×10^{14} Hz, but in the frame of reference of the jet material the light has a frequency of 5.55×10^{13} Hz (in the infrared region of the electromagnetic spectrum). At what speed is the jet material moving toward us?

37.19 This image shows a fast-moving jet 5000 light-years in length emanating from the center of the galaxy M87. The light from the jet is emitted by fast-moving electrons spiraling around magnetic field lines (see Fig. 27.16).

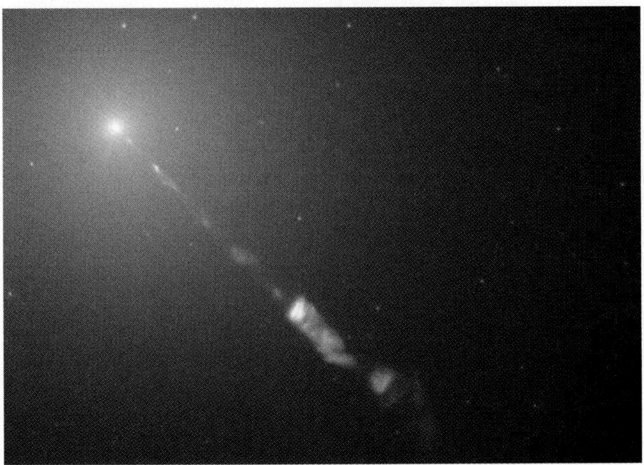

SOLUTION

IDENTIFY: This problem involves the Doppler effect for electromagnetic waves.

SET UP: The frequency we observe is $f = 6.66 \times 10^{14}$ Hz, and the frequency in the frame of the source is $f_0 = 5.55 \times 10^{13}$ Hz. Since $f > f_0$, the source is approaching us and therefore we use Eq. (37.25) to find the target variable u.

EXECUTE: We need to solve Eq. (37.25) for u. That takes a little algebra; we'll leave it as an exercise for you to show that the result is

$$u = \frac{(f/f_0)^2 - 1}{(f/f_0) + 1}c$$

We have $f/f_0 = (6.66 \times 10^{14}\text{ Hz})/(5.55 \times 10^{13}\text{ Hz}) = 12.0$, so we find

$$u = \frac{(12.0)^2 - 1}{(12.0)^2 + 1}c = 0.986c$$

EVALUATE: Because the frequency shift is quite substantial, it would have been erroneous to use the approximate expression $\Delta f/f = u/c$. Had you tried to do so, you would have found $u = c\,\Delta f/f_0 = c(6.66 \times 10^{14}\text{ Hz} - 5.55 \times 10^{13}\text{ Hz})/(5.55 \times 10^{13}\text{ Hz}) = 11.0c$. This result cannot be correct because the jet material cannot travel faster than light.

37.7 Relativistic Momentum

Newton's laws of motion have the same form in all inertial frames of reference. When we use transformations to change from one inertial frame to another, the laws should be *invariant* (unchanging). But we have just learned that the principle of relativity forces us to replace the Galilean transformations with the more general Lorentz transformations. As we will see, this requires corresponding generalizations in the laws of motion and the definitions of momentum and energy.

The principle of conservation of momentum states that *when two bodies interact, the total momentum is constant,* provided that the net external force acting on the bodies in an inertial reference frame is zero (for example, if they form an isolated system, interacting only with each other). If conservation of momentum is a valid physical law, it must be valid in *all* inertial frames of reference. Now, here's the problem: Suppose we look at a collision in one inertial coordinate system S and find that momentum is conserved. Then we use the Lorentz transformation to obtain the velocities in a second inertial system S'. We find that if we use the Newtonian definition of momentum $(\vec{p} = m\vec{v})$, momentum is *not* conserved in the second system! If we are convinced that the principle of relativity and the Lorentz transformation are correct, the only way to save momentum conservation is to generalize the *definition* of momentum.

We won't derive the correct relativistic generalization of momentum, but here is the result. Suppose we measure the mass of a particle to be m when it is at rest relative to us: We often call m the **rest mass.** We will use the term

37.20 Graph of the magnitude of the momentum of a particle of rest mass m as a function of speed v. Also shown is the Newtonian prediction, which gives correct results only at speeds much less than c.

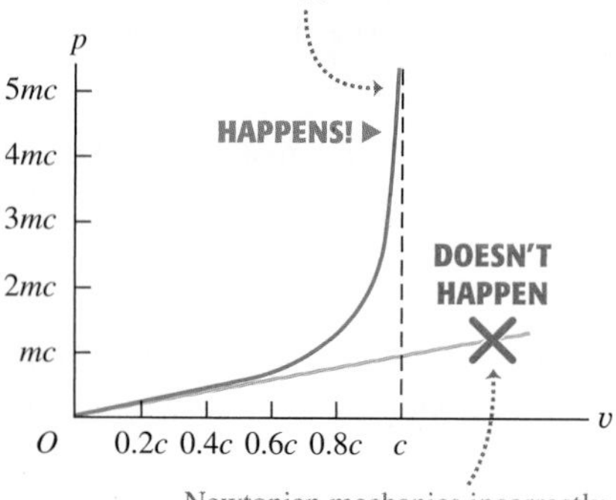

Relativistic momentum becomes infinite as v approaches c.
p
$5mc$
$4mc$
$3mc$
$2mc$
mc
HAPPENS!
DOESN'T HAPPEN
O
$0.2c$ $0.4c$ $0.6c$ $0.8c$ c
v
Newtonian mechanics incorrectly predicts that momentum becomes infinite only if v becomes infinite.

material particle for a particle that has a nonzero rest mass. When such a particle has a velocity $\vec{v}$, its **relativistic momentum** $\vec{p}$ is

$$\vec{p} = \frac{m\vec{v}}{\sqrt{1 - v^2/c^2}} \quad \text{(relativistic momentum)} \tag{37.27}$$

When the particle's speed v is much less than c, this is approximately equal to the Newtonian expression $\vec{p} = m\vec{v}$, but in general the momentum is greater in magnitude than mv (Figure 37.20). In fact, as v approaches c, the momentum approaches infinity.

Relativity, Newton's Second Law, and Relativistic Mass

What about the relativistic generalization of Newton's second law? In Newtonian mechanics the most general form of the second law is

$$\vec{F} = \frac{d\vec{p}}{dt} \tag{37.28}$$

That is, the net force $\vec{F}$ on a particle equals the time rate of change of its momentum. Experiments show that this result is still valid in relativistic mechanics, provided that we use the relativistic momentum given by Eq. 37.27. That is, the relativistically correct generalization of Newton's second law is

$$\vec{F} = \frac{d}{dt}\frac{m\vec{v}}{\sqrt{1 - v^2/c^2}} \tag{37.29}$$

Because momentum is no longer directly proportional to velocity, the rate of change of momentum is no longer directly proportional to the acceleration. As a result, *constant force does not cause constant acceleration.* For example, when the net force and the velocity are both along the x-axis, Eq. 37.29 gives

$$F = \frac{m}{(1 - v^2/c^2)^{3/2}}a \quad (\vec{F} \text{ and } \vec{v} \text{ along the same line}) \tag{37.30}$$

where a is the acceleration, also along the x-axis. Solving Eq. 37.30 for the acceleration a gives

$$a = \frac{F}{m}\left(1 - \frac{v^2}{c^2}\right)^{3/2}$$

We see that as a particle's speed increases, the acceleration caused by a given force continuously *decreases.* As the speed approaches c, the acceleration approaches zero, no matter how great a force is applied. Thus it is impossible to accelerate a particle with nonzero rest mass to a speed equal to or greater than c. We again see that the speed of light in vacuum represents an ultimate speed limit.

Equation (37.27) for relativistic momentum is sometimes interpreted to mean that a rapidly moving particle undergoes an increase in mass. If the mass at zero velocity (the rest mass) is denoted by m, then the "relativistic mass" m_{rel} is given by

$$m_{rel} = \frac{m}{\sqrt{1 - v^2/c^2}}$$

Indeed, when we consider the motion of a system of particles (such as rapidly moving ideal-gas molecules in a stationary container), the total rest mass of the system is the sum of the relativistic masses of the particles, not the sum of their rest masses.

However, if blindly applied, the concept of relativistic mass has its pitfalls. As Eq. (37.29) shows, the relativistic generalization of Newton's second law is *not* $\vec{F} = m_{rel}\vec{a}$, and we will show in Section 37.8 that the relativistic kinetic energy of

Let T be the time interval between *emission* of successive wave crests as observed in Stanley's reference frame. Note that this is *not* the interval between the *arrival* of successive crests at his position, because the crests are emitted at different points in Stanley's frame. In measuring only the frequency f he receives, he does not take into account the difference in transit times for successive crests. Therefore the frequency he receives is *not* $1/T$. What is the equation for f?

During a time T the crests ahead of the source move a distance cT, and the source moves a shorter distance uT in the same direction. The distance λ between successive crests—that is, the wavelength—is thus $\lambda = (c - u)T$, as measured in Stanley's frame. The frequency that he measures is c/λ. Therefore

$$f = \frac{c}{(c - u)T} \tag{37.24}$$

So far we have followed a pattern similar to that for the Doppler effect for sound from a moving source (see Section 16.8). In that discussion our next step was to equate T to the time T_0 between emissions of successive wave crests by the source. However, due to time dilation it is *not* relativistically correct to equate T to T_0. The time T_0 is measured in the rest frame of the source, so it is a proper time. From Eq. (37.6), T_0 and T are related by

$$T = \frac{T_0}{\sqrt{1 - u^2/c^2}} = \frac{cT_0}{\sqrt{c^2 - u^2}}$$

or, since $T_0 = 1/f_0$,

$$\frac{1}{T} = \frac{\sqrt{c^2 - u^2}}{cT_0} = \frac{\sqrt{c^2 - u^2}}{c} f_0$$

Remember, $1/T$ is not equal to f. We must substitute this expression for $1/T$ into Eq. 37.24 to find f:

$$f = \frac{c}{c - u} \frac{\sqrt{c^2 - u^2}}{c} f_0$$

Using $c^2 - u^2 = (c - u)(c + u)$ gives

$$f = \sqrt{\frac{c + u}{c - u}} f_0 \quad \text{(Doppler effect, electromagnetic waves, source approaching observer)} \tag{37.25}$$

This shows that when the source moves *toward* the observer, the observed frequency f is *greater* than the emitted frequency f_0. The difference $f - f_0 = \Delta f$ is called the Doppler frequency shift. When u/c is much smaller than 1, the fractional shift $\Delta f/f$ is also small and is approximately equal to u/c:

$$\frac{\Delta f}{f} = \frac{u}{c}$$

When the source moves *away from* the observer, we change the sign of u in Eq. 37.25 to get

$$f = \sqrt{\frac{c - u}{c + u}} f_0 \quad \text{(Doppler effect, electromagnetic waves, source moving away from observer)} \tag{37.26}$$

This agrees with Eq. (16.30), which we quoted previously, with minor notation changes.

With light, unlike sound, there is no distinction between motion of source and motion of observer; only the *relative* velocity of the two is significant. The last four paragraphs of Section 16.8 discuss several practical applications of the Doppler effect with light and other electromagnetic radiation; we suggest you review those paragraphs now. Figure 37.18 shows one common application.

37.18 This handheld radar gun emits a radio beam of frequency f_0, which in the frame of reference of an approaching car has a higher frequency f given by Eq. (37.25). The reflected beam also has frequency f in the car's frame, but has an even higher frequency f' in the police officer's frame. The radar gun calculates the car's speed by comparing the frequencies of the emitted beam and the doubly Doppler-shifted reflected beam. (Compare Example 16.19 in Section 16.8.)

Example 37.8 Relative velocities

(a) A spaceship moving away from the earth with speed $0.900c$ fires a robot space probe in the same direction as its motion, with speed $0.700c$ relative to the spaceship. What is the probe's velocity relative to the earth? (b) A scoutship tries to catch up with the spaceship by traveling at $0.950c$ relative to the earth. What is the velocity of the scoutship relative to the spaceship?

SOLUTION

IDENTIFY: This example uses the Lorentz velocity transformation.

SET UP: Let the earth's frame of reference be S, and let the spaceship's frame of reference be S' (Fig. 37.16). The relative velocity of the two frames is $u = 0.700c$. The target variable in part (a) is the velocity of the probe relative to S; the target variable in part (b) is the velocity of the scoutship relative to S'.

37.16 The spaceship, robot space probe, and scoutship.

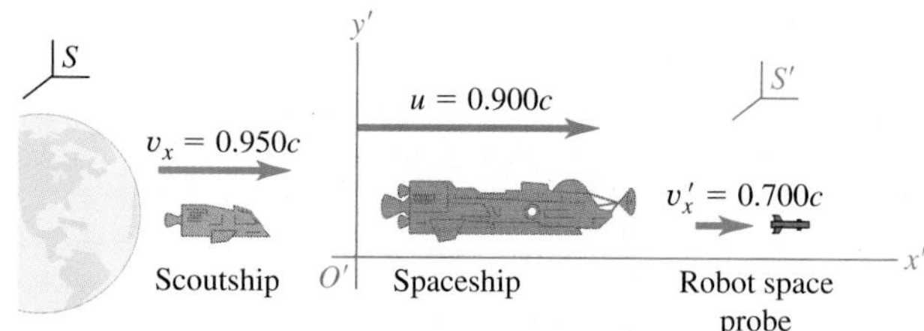

y'
S
S'
u = 0.900c
v_x = 0.950c
v'_x = 0.700c
x'
Scoutship
O'
Spaceship
Robot space probe

EXECUTE: (a) We are given the velocity of the probe relative to the spaceship, $v'_x = 0.700c$. We use Eq. (37.23) to determine its velocity v_x relative to the earth:

$$v_x = \frac{v'_x + u}{1 + uv'_x/c^2} = \frac{0.700c + 0.900c}{1 + (0.900c)(0.700c)/c^2} = 0.982c$$

(b) We are given the velocity of the scoutship relative to the earth, $v_x = 0.950c$. We use Eq. (37.22) to determine its velocity v'_x relative to the spaceship:

$$v'_x = \frac{v_x - u}{1 - uv_x/c^2} = \frac{0.950c - 0.900c}{1 - (0.900c)(0.950c)/c^2} = 0.345c$$

EVALUATE: It's instructive to compare our results to what we would have obtained had we used the Galilean velocity transformation formula, Eq. (37.2). In part (a) we would have found the probe's velocity relative to the earth to be $v_x = v'_x + u = 0.700c + 0.900c = 1.600c$. This value is greater than the speed of light and so must be incorrect. In part (b) we would have found the scoutship's velocity relative to the spaceship to be $v'_x = v_x - u = 0.950c - 0.900c = 0.050c$; the relativistically correct value, $v'_x = 0.345c$, is almost seven times greater than the incorrect Galilean value.

Test Your Understanding of Section 37.5 (a) In frame S events P_1 and P_2 occur at the same x-, y-, and z-coordinates, but event P_1 occurs before event P_2. In frame S', which event occurs first? (b) In frame S events P_3 and P_4 occur at the same time t and the same y- and z-coordinates, but event P_3 occurs at a less positive x-coordinate than event P_4. In frame S', which event occurs first?

*37.6 The Doppler Effect for Electromagnetic Waves

An additional important consequence of relativistic kinematics is the Doppler effect for electromagnetic waves. In our previous discussion of the Doppler effect (see Section 16.8) we quoted without proof the formula, Eq. (16.30), for the frequency shift that results from motion of a source of electromagnetic waves relative to an observer. We can now derive that result.

Here's a statement of the problem. A source of light is moving with constant speed u toward Stanley, who is stationary in an inertial frame (Fig. 37.17). As measured in its rest frame, the source emits light waves with frequency f_0 and period $T_0 = 1/f_0$. What is the frequency f of these waves as received by Stanley?

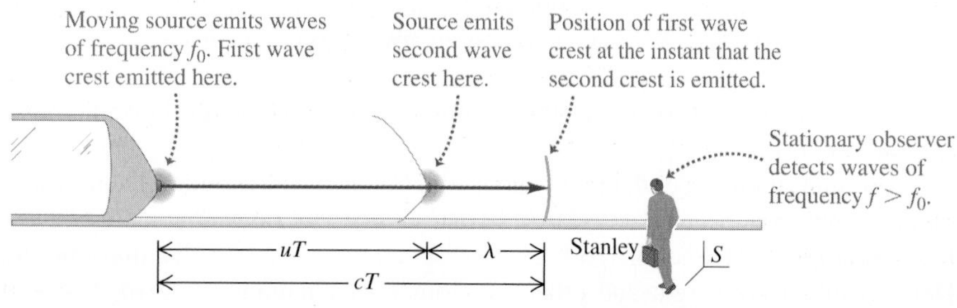

Moving source emits waves of frequency f_0. First wave crest emitted here.
Source emits second wave crest here.
Position of first wave crest at the instant that the second crest is emitted.
Stationary observer detects waves of frequency $f > f_0$.
uT
λ
Stanley
S
cT

37.17 The Doppler effect for light. A light source moving at speed u relative to Stanley emits a wave crest, then travels a distance uT toward an observer and emits the next crest. In Stanley's reference frame S, the second crest is a distance λ behind the first crest.

a particle is *not* $K = \frac{1}{2}m_{rel}v^2$. The use of relativistic mass has its supporters and detractors, some quite strong in their opinions. We will mostly deal with individual particles, so we will sidestep the controversy and use Eq. (37.27) as the generalized definition of momentum with m as a constant for each particle, independent of its state of motion.

We will use the abbreviation

$$\gamma = \frac{1}{\sqrt{1 - v^2/c^2}}$$

We used this abbreviation in Section 37.3 with v replaced by u, the relative speed of two coordinate systems. Here v is the speed of a particle in a particular coordinate system—that is, the speed of the particle's *rest frame* with respect to that system. In terms of γ, Eqs. (37.27) and (37.30) become

$$\vec{p} = \gamma m\vec{v} \qquad \text{(relativistic momentum)} \qquad (37.31)$$

$$F = \gamma^3 ma \qquad (\vec{F} \text{ and } \vec{v} \text{ along the same line}) \qquad (37.32)$$

In linear accelerators (used in medicine as well as nuclear and elementary-particle physics; see Fig. 37.11) the net force $\vec{F}$ and the velocity $\vec{v}$ of the accelerated particle are along the same straight line. But for much of the path in most *circular* accelerators the particle moves in uniform circular motion at constant speed v. Then the net force and velocity are perpendicular, so the force can do no work on the particle and the kinetic energy and speed remain constant. Thus the denominator in Eq. (37.29) is constant, and we obtain

$$F = \frac{m}{(1 - v^2/c^2)^{1/2}}a = \gamma ma \qquad (\vec{F} \text{ and } \vec{v} \text{ perpendicular}) \qquad (37.33)$$

Recall from Section 3.4 that if the particle moves in a circle, the net force and acceleration are directed inward along the radius r, and $a = v^2/r$.

What about the general case in which $\vec{F}$ and $\vec{v}$ are neither along the same line nor perpendicular? Then we can resolve the net force $\vec{F}$ at any instant into components parallel to and perpendicular to $\vec{v}$. The resulting acceleration will have corresponding components obtained from Eqs. (37.32) and (37.33). Because of the different γ^3 and γ factors, the acceleration components will not be proportional to the net force components. That is, *unless the net force on a relativistic particle is either along the same line as the particle's velocity or perpendicular to it, the net force and acceleration vectors are not parallel.*

Example 37.10 Relativistic dynamics of an electron

An electron (rest mass 9.11×10^{-31} kg, charge -1.60×10^{-19} C) is moving opposite to an electric field of magnitude $E = 5.00 \times 10^5$ N/C. All other forces are negligible in comparison to the electric field force. (a) Find the magnitudes of momentum and of acceleration at the instants when $v = 0.010c$, $0.90c$, and $0.99c$. (b) Find the corresponding accelerations if a net force of the same magnitude is perpendicular to the velocity.

SOLUTION

IDENTIFY: In addition to the expressions from this section for relativistic momentum and acceleration, we need the relationship between electric force and electric field from Chapter 21.

SET UP: In part (a) we use Eq. 37.31 to determine the magnitude of momentum and Eq. 37.32 to determine the magnitude of acceleration due to a force along the same line as the velocity. In part (b) the force is perpendicular to the velocity, so we use Eq. 37.33 to determine the magnitude of acceleration.

EXECUTE: (a) To find both the magnitude of momentum and the magnitude of acceleration, we need the values of $\gamma = \sqrt{1 - v^2/c^2}$ for each of the three speeds. We find $\gamma = 1.00$, 2.29, and 7.09. The values of the momentum magnitude p are

$$\begin{aligned} p_1 &= \gamma_1 m v_1 \\ &= (1.00)(9.11 \times 10^{-31}\text{ kg})(0.010)(3.00 \times 10^8\text{m/s}) \\ &= 2.7 \times 10^{-24}\text{ kg} \cdot \text{m/s at } v_1 = 0.010c \\ p_2 &= (2.29)(9.11 \times 10^{-31}\text{ kg})(0.90)(3.00 \times 10^8\text{ m/s}) \\ &= 5.6 \times 10^{-22}\text{ kg} \cdot \text{m/s at } v_2 = 0.90c \end{aligned}$$

Continued

$$p_3 = (7.09)(9.11 \times 10^{-31}\ \text{kg})(0.99)(3.00 \times 10^8\ \text{m/s})$$
$$= 1.9 \times 10^{-21}\ \text{kg}\cdot\text{m/s at } v_3 = 0.99c$$

From Chapter 21, the magnitude of the force on the electron is

$$F = |q|E = (1.60 \times 10^{-19}\ \text{C})(5.00 \times 10^5\ \text{N/C})$$
$$= 8.00 \times 10^{-14}\ \text{N}$$

From Eq. (37.32), $a = F/\gamma^3 m$. When $v = 0.010c$ and $\gamma = 1.00$,

$$a_1 = \frac{8.00 \times 10^{-14}\ \text{N}}{(1.00)^3(9.11 \times 10^{-31}\ \text{kg})} = 8.8 \times 10^{16}\ \text{m/s}^2$$

The accelerations at the two higher speeds are smaller by factors of γ^3:

$$a_2 = 7.3 \times 10^{15}\ \text{m/s}^2 \qquad a_3 = 2.5 \times 10^{14}\ \text{m/s}^2$$

These last two accelerations are only 8.3% and 0.28%, respectively, of the values predicted by nonrelativistic mechanics.

(b) From Eq. (37.33), $a = F/\gamma m$ if $\vec{F}$ and $\vec{v}$ are perpendicular. When $v = 0.010c$ and $\gamma = 1.00$,

$$a_1 = \frac{8.00 \times 10^{-14}\ \text{N}}{(1.00)(9.11 \times 10^{-31}\ \text{kg})} = 8.8 \times 10^{16}\ \text{m/s}^2$$

The accelerations at the two higher speeds are smaller by a factor of γ:

$$a_2 = 3.8 \times 10^{16}\ \text{m/s}^2 \qquad a_3 = 1.2 \times 10^{16}\ \text{m/s}^2$$

These accelerations are larger than the corresponding ones in part (a) by factors of γ^2.

EVALUATE: Our results in part (a) show that at higher speeds, the relativistic values of momentum differ more and more from the nonrelativistic values computed using $p = mv$. Note that the momentum at $0.99c$ is more than three times as great as at $0.90c$ because of the increase in the factor γ.

Our results also show that the acceleration drops off very quickly as v approaches c. At the Stanford Linear Accelerator Center, an essentially constant electric force is used to accelerate electrons to a speed only slightly less than c. If the acceleration were constant as predicted by Newtonian mechanics, this speed would be attained after the electrons had traveled a mere 1.5 cm. In fact, because of the decrease of acceleration with speed, a path length of 3 km is needed.

Test Your Understanding of Section 37.7 According to relativistic mechanics, when you double the speed of a particle, the magnitude of its momentum increases by (i) a factor of 2; (ii) a factor greater than 2; (iii) a factor between 1 and 2 that depends on the mass of the particle.

37.8 Relativistic Work and Energy

When we developed the relationship between work and kinetic energy in Chapter 6, we used Newton's laws of motion. When we generalize these laws according to the principle of relativity, we need a corresponding generalization of the equation for kinetic energy.

Relativistic Kinetic Energy

We use the work–energy theorem, beginning with the definition of work. When the net force and displacement are in the same direction, the work done by that force is $W = \int F\,dx$. We substitute the expression for F from Eq. (37.30), the applicable relativistic version of Newton's second law. In moving a particle of rest mass m from point x_1 to point x_2,

$$W = \int_{x_1}^{x_2} F\,dx = \int_{x_1}^{x_2} \frac{ma\,dx}{(1 - v^2/c^2)^{3/2}} \tag{37.34}$$

To derive the generalized expression for kinetic energy K as a function of speed v, we would like to convert this to an integral on v. To do this, first remember that the kinetic energy of a particle equals the net work done on it in moving it from rest to the speed v: $K = W$. Thus we let the speeds be zero at point x_1 and v at point x_2. So as not to confuse the variable of integration with the final speed, we change v to v_x in Eq. 37.34. That is, v_x is the varying x-component of the velocity of the particle as the net force accelerates it from rest to a speed v. We also realize that dx and dv_x are the infinitesimal changes in x and v_x, respectively, in the time interval dt. Because $v_x = dx/dt$ and $a = dv_x/dt$, we can rewrite $a\,dx$ in Eq. (37.34) as

$$a\,dx = \frac{dv_x}{dt}dx = dx\frac{dv_x}{dt} = \frac{dx}{dt}dv_x = v_x dv_x$$

Making these substitutions gives us

$$K = W = \int_0^v \frac{mv_x dv_x}{(1 - v_x^2/c^2)^{3/2}} \tag{37.35}$$

We can evaluate this integral by a simple change of variable; the final result is

$$K = \frac{mc^2}{\sqrt{1 - v^2/c^2}} - mc^2 = (\gamma - 1)mc^2 \quad \text{(relativistic kinetic energy)} \tag{37.36}$$

As v approaches c, the kinetic energy approaches infinity. If Eq. 37.36 is correct, it must also approach the Newtonian expression $K = \frac{1}{2}mv^2$ when v is much smaller than c (Fig. 37.21). To verify this, we expand the radical, using the binomial theorem in the form

$$(1 + x)^n = 1 + nx + n(n - 1)x^2/2 + \cdots$$

In our case, $n = -\frac{1}{2}$ and $x = -v^2/c^2$, and we get

$$\gamma = \left(1 - \frac{v^2}{c^2}\right)^{-1/2} = 1 + \frac{1}{2}\frac{v^2}{c^2} + \frac{3}{8}\frac{v^4}{c^4} + \cdots$$

Combining this with $K = (\gamma - 1)mc^2$, we find

$$\begin{aligned} K &= \left(1 + \frac{1}{2}\frac{v^2}{c^2} + \frac{3}{8}\frac{v^4}{c^4} + \cdots - 1\right)mc^2 \\ &= \frac{1}{2}mv^2 + \frac{3}{8}\frac{mv^4}{c^2} + \cdots \end{aligned} \tag{37.37}$$

When v is much smaller than c, all the terms in the series in Eq. (37.37) except the first are negligibly small, and we obtain the Newtonian expression $\frac{1}{2}mv^2$.

37.21 Graph of the kinetic energy of a particle of rest mass m as a function of speed v. Also shown is the Newtonian prediction, which gives correct results only at speeds much less than c.

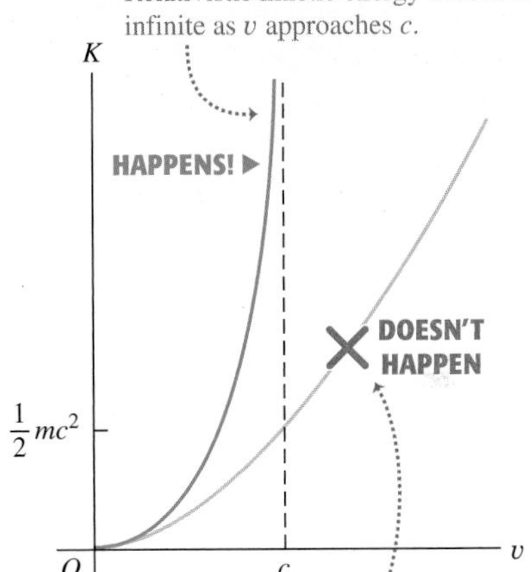
Relativistic kinetic energy becomes infinite as v approaches c.
K
HAPPENS!
DOESN'T HAPPEN
$\frac{1}{2}mc^2$
O
c
v
Newtonian mechanics incorrectly predicts that kinetic energy becomes infinite only if v becomes infinite.

Rest Energy and $E = mc^2$

Equation (37.36) for the kinetic energy of a moving particle includes a term $mc^2/\sqrt{1 - v^2/c^2}$ that depends on the motion and a second energy term mc^2 that is independent of the motion. It seems that the kinetic energy of a particle is the difference between some **total energy** E and an energy mc^2 that it has even when it is at rest. Thus we can rewrite Eq. (37.36) as

$$E = K + mc^2 = \frac{mc^2}{\sqrt{1 - v^2/c^2}} = \gamma mc^2 \quad \text{(total energy of a particle)} \tag{37.38}$$

For a particle at rest $(K = 0)$, we see that $E = mc^2$. The energy mc^2 associated with rest mass m rather than motion is called the **rest energy** of the particle.

There is in fact direct experimental evidence that rest energy really does exist. The simplest example is the decay of a neutral *pion*. This is an unstable subatomic particle of rest mass m_π; when it decays, it disappears and electromagnetic radiation appears. If a neutral pion has no kinetic energy before its decay, the total energy of the radiation after its decay is found to equal exactly $m_\pi c^2$. In many other fundamental particle transformations the sum of the rest masses of the particles changes. In every case there is a corresponding energy change, consistent with the assumption of a rest energy mc^2 associated with a rest mass m.

Historically, the principles of conservation of mass and of energy developed quite independently. The theory of relativity shows that they are actually two special cases of a single broader conservation principle, the *principle of conservation of mass and energy.* In some physical phenomena, neither the sum of the rest masses of the particles nor the total energy other than rest energy is separately conserved, but there is a more general conservation principle: In an isolated system, when the sum of the rest masses changes, there is always a change in $1/c^2$ times the total energy other than the rest energy. This change is equal in magnitude but opposite in sign to the change in the sum of the rest masses.

37.22 Although the control room of a nuclear power plant is very complex, the physical principle whereby such a plant operates is a simple one: Part of the rest energy of atomic nuclei is converted to thermal energy, which in turn is used to produce steam to drive electric generators.

This more general mass-energy conservation law is the fundamental principle involved in the generation of power through nuclear reactions. When a uranium nucleus undergoes fission in a nuclear reactor, the sum of the rest masses of the resulting fragments is *less than* the rest mass of the parent nucleus. An amount of energy is released that equals the mass decrease multiplied by c^2. Most of this energy can be used to produce steam to operate turbines for electric power generators (Fig. 37.22).

We can also relate the total energy E of a particle (kinetic energy plus rest energy) directly to its momentum by combining Eq. (37.27) for relativistic momentum and Eq. (37.38) for total energy to eliminate the particle's velocity. The simplest procedure is to rewrite these equations in the following forms:

$$\left(\frac{E}{mc^2}\right)^2 = \frac{1}{1 - v^2/c^2} \quad \text{and} \quad \left(\frac{p}{mc}\right)^2 = \frac{v^2/c^2}{1 - v^2/c^2}$$

Subtracting the second of these from the first and rearranging, we find

$$E^2 = (mc^2)^2 + (pc)^2 \qquad \text{(total energy, rest energy, and momentum)} \qquad (37.39)$$

Again we see that for a particle at rest $(p = 0)$, $E = mc^2$.

Equation (37.39) also suggests that a particle may have energy and momentum even when it has no rest mass. In such a case, $m = 0$ and

$$E = pc \qquad \text{(zero rest mass)} \qquad (37.40)$$

In fact, zero rest mass particles do exist. Such particles always travel at the speed of light in vacuum. One example is the *photon,* the quantum of electromagnetic radiation (to be discussed in Chapter 38). Photons are emitted and absorbed during changes of state of an atomic or nuclear system when the energy and momentum of the system change.

Example 37.11 Energetic electrons

(a) Find the rest energy of an electron $(m = 9.109 \times 10^{-31}\,\text{kg}$, $q = -e = -1.602 \times 10^{-19}\,\text{C})$ in joules and in electron volts. (b) Find the speed of an electron that has been accelerated by an electric field, from rest, through a potential increase of 20.0 kV (typical of TV picture tubes) or of 5.00 MV (a high-voltage x-ray machine).

SOLUTION

IDENTIFY: This problem uses the ideas of rest energy, relativistic kinetic energy, and (from Chapter 23) electric potential energy.

SET UP: We use the relationship $E = mc^2$ to find the rest energy and Eq. (37.38) to find the speed that gives the stated total energy.

EXECUTE: (a) The rest energy is

$$\begin{aligned} mc^2 &= (9.109 \times 10^{-31}\,\text{kg})(2.998 \times 10^8\,\text{m/s})^2 \\ &= 8.187 \times 10^{-14}\,\text{J} \end{aligned}$$

From the definition of the electron volt in Section 23.2, $1\,\text{eV} = 1.602 \times 10^{-19}\,\text{J}$. Using this, we find

$$\begin{aligned} mc^2 &= (8.187 \times 10^{-14}\,\text{J})\frac{1\,\text{eV}}{1.602 \times 10^{-19}\,\text{J}} \\ &= 5.11 \times 10^5\,\text{eV} = 0.511\,\text{MeV} \end{aligned}$$

(b) In calculations such as this, it is often convenient to work with the quantity γ defined from the modified Eq. (37.7):

$$\gamma = \frac{1}{\sqrt{1 - v^2/c^2}}$$

Solving this for v, we get

$$v = c\sqrt{1 - (1/\gamma)^2}$$

The total energy E of the accelerated electron is the sum of its rest energy mc^2 and the kinetic energy eV_{ba} that it gains from the work done on it by the electric field in moving from point a to point b:

$$E = \gamma mc^2 = mc^2 + eV_{ba} \quad \text{or}$$

$$\gamma = 1 + \frac{eV_{ba}}{mc^2}$$

An electron accelerated through a potential increase of $V_{ba} = 20.0\text{ kV}$ gains an amount of energy 20.0 keV, so for this electron we have

$$\gamma = 1 + \frac{20.0 \times 10^3\text{ eV}}{0.511 \times 10^6\text{ eV}} \quad \text{or}$$

$$= 1.039$$

and

$$v = c\sqrt{1 - (1/1.039)^2} = 0.272c$$

$$= 8.15 \times 10^7\text{ m/s}$$

Repeating the calculation for $V_{ba} = 5.00\text{ MV}$, we find $eV_{ba}/mc^2 = 9.78$, $\gamma = 10.78$, and $v = 0.996c$.

EVALUATE: These results make sense: With $V_{ba} = 20.0\text{ kV}$, the added kinetic energy of 20.0 keV is less than 4% of the rest energy of 0.511 MeV, and the final speed is about one-fourth of the speed of light. With $V_{ba} = 5.00\text{ MV}$, the added kinetic energy of 5.00 MeV is much greater than the rest energy and the speed is close to c.

CAUTION **Three electron energies** The electron that accelerated from rest through a potential increase of 5.00 MV had a kinetic energy of 5.00 MeV. By convention we call such an electron a "5.00-MeV electron." A 5.00-MeV electron has a rest energy of 0.511 MeV (as do all electrons), a kinetic energy of 5.00 MeV, and a total energy of 5.51 MeV. Be careful not to confuse these different energies.

Example 37.12 A relativistic collision

Two protons (each with $M = 1.67 \times 10^{-27}\text{ kg}$) are initially moving with equal speeds in opposite directions. They continue to exist after a head-on collision that also produces a neutral pion of mass $m = 2.40 \times 10^{-28}\text{ kg}$ (Fig. 37.23). If the protons and the pion are at rest after the collision, find the initial speed of the protons. Energy is conserved in the collision.

SOLUTION

IDENTIFY: This problem uses the idea of relativistic total energy, which is conserved in the collision.

SET UP: We equate the (unknown) total energy of the two protons before the collision to the combined rest energies of the two protons and the pion after the collision. We then use Eq. (37.38) to solve for the speed of each proton.

EXECUTE: The total energy of each proton before the collision is γMc^2. By conservation of energy,

$$2(\gamma Mc^2) = 2(Mc^2) + mc^2$$

$$\gamma = 1 + \frac{m}{2M} = 1 + \frac{2.40 \times 10^{-28}\text{ kg}}{2(1.67 \times 10^{-27}\text{ kg})} = 1.072$$

so

$$v = c\sqrt{1 - (1/\gamma)^2} = 0.360c$$

37.23 In this collision the kinetic energy of two protons is transformed into the rest energy of a new particle, a pion.

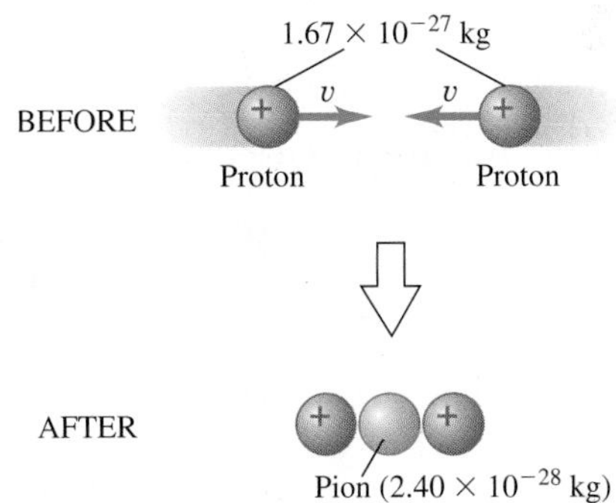

EVALUATE: The initial kinetic energy of each proton is $(\gamma - 1)Mc^2 = 0.072Mc^2$. The rest energy of a proton is 938 MeV, so the kinetic energy is $(0.072)(938\text{ MeV}) = 67.5\text{ MeV}$. (These are "67.5-MeV protons.") You can verify that the rest energy of the pion is twice this, or 135 MeV. All the kinetic energy "lost" in this completely inelastic collision is transformed into the rest energy of the pion.

Test Your Understanding of Section 37.8 A proton is accelerated from rest by a constant force that always points in the direction of the particle's motion. Compared to the amount of kinetic energy that the proton gains during the first meter of its travel, how much kinetic energy does the proton gain during one meter of travel while it is moving at 99% of the speed of light? (i) the same amount; (ii) a greater amount; (iii) a smaller amount.

37.9 Newtonian Mechanics and Relativity

The sweeping changes required by the principle of relativity go to the very roots of Newtonian mechanics, including the concepts of length and time, the equations of motion, and the conservation principles. Thus it may appear that we have destroyed the foundations on which Newtonian mechanics is built. In one sense this is true, yet the Newtonian formulation is still accurate whenever speeds are small in comparison with the speed of light in vacuum. In such cases, time dilation, length contraction, and the modifications of the laws of motion are so small that they are unobservable. In fact, every one of the principles of Newtonian mechanics survives as a special case of the more general relativistic formulation.

The laws of Newtonian mechanics are not *wrong;* they are *incomplete.* They are a limiting case of relativistic mechanics. They are *approximately* correct when all speeds are small in comparison to c, and they become exactly correct in the limit when all speeds approach zero. Thus relativity does not completely destroy the laws of Newtonian mechanics but *generalizes* them. Newton's laws rest on a very solid base of experimental evidence, and it would be very strange to advance a new theory that is inconsistent with this evidence. This is a common pattern in the development of physical theory. Whenever a new theory is in partial conflict with an older, established theory, the new must yield the same predictions as the old in areas in which the old theory is supported by experimental evidence. Every new physical theory must pass this test, called the **correspondence principle.**

37.24 Without information from outside the spaceship, the astronaut cannot distinguish situation (b) from situation (c).

(a) An astronaut is about to drop her watch in a spaceship.

(b) In gravity-free space, the floor accelerates upward at $a = g$ and hits the watch.

(c) On the earth's surface, the watch accelerates downward at $a = g$ and hits the floor.

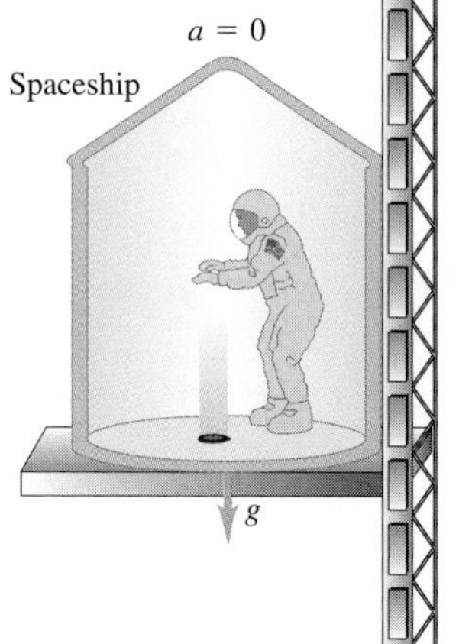

The General Theory of Relativity

At this point we may ask whether the special theory of relativity gives the final word on mechanics or whether *further* generalizations are possible or necessary. For example, inertial frames have occupied a privileged position in our discussion. Can the principle of relativity be extended to noninertial frames as well?

Here's an example that illustrates some implications of this question. A student decides to go over Niagara Falls while enclosed in a large wooden box. During her free fall she can float through the air inside the box. She doesn't fall to the floor because both she and the box are in free fall with a downward acceleration of 9.8 m/s^2. But an alternative interpretation, from her point of view, is that she doesn't fall to the floor because her gravitational interaction with the earth has suddenly been turned off. As long as she remains in the box and it remains in free fall, she cannot tell whether she is indeed in free fall or whether the gravitational interaction has vanished.

A similar problem occurs in a space station in orbit around the earth. Objects in the space station *seem* to be weightless, but without looking outside the station there is no way to determine whether gravity has been turned off or whether the station and all its contents are accelerating toward the center of the earth. Figure 37.24 makes a similar point for a spaceship that is not in free fall but may be accelerating relative to an inertial frame or be at rest on the earth's surface.

These considerations form the basis of Einstein's **general theory of relativity.** If we cannot distinguish experimentally between a uniform gravitational field at a particular location and a uniformly accelerated reference frame, then there cannot be any real distinction between the two. Pursuing this concept, we may try to represent *any* gravitational field in terms of special characteristics of the coordinate system. This turns out to require even more sweeping revisions of our space-time concepts than did the special theory of relativity. In the general theory of relativity the geometric properties of space are affected by the presence of matter (Fig. 37.25).

The general theory of relativity has passed several experimental tests, including three proposed by Einstein. One test has to do with understanding the rotation of the axes of the planet Mercury's elliptical orbit, called the *precession of the perihelion.* (The perihelion is the point of closest approach to the sun.) A second test concerns the apparent bending of light rays from distant stars when they pass near the sun. The third test is the *gravitational red shift,* the increase in wave-

37.25 A two-dimensional representation of curved space. We imagine the space (a plane) as being distorted as shown by a massive object (the sun). Light from a distant star (solid line) follows the distorted surface on its way to the earth. The dashed line shows the direction from which the light *appears* to be coming. The effect is greatly exaggerated; for the sun, the maximum deviation is only 0.00048°.

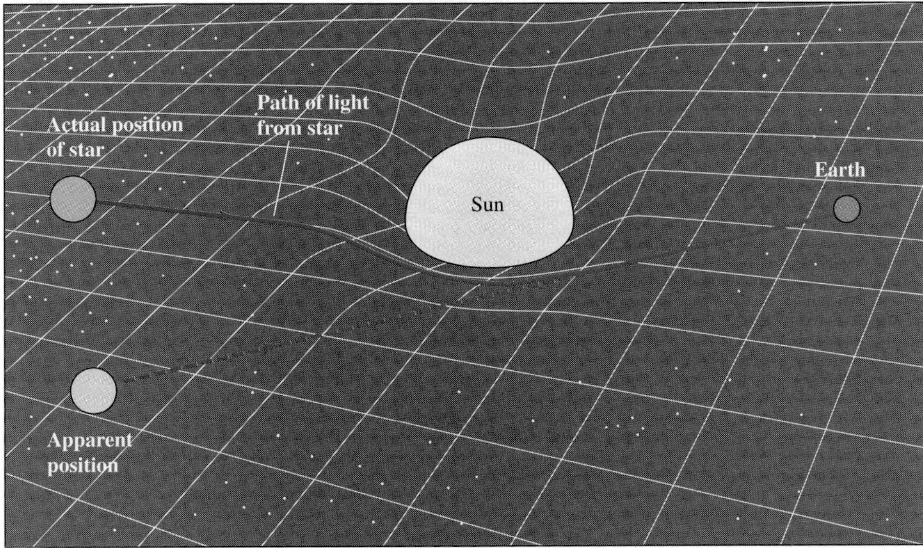

length of light proceeding outward from a massive source. Some details of the general theory are more difficult to test, but this theory has played a central role in investigations of the formation and evolution of stars, black holes, and studies of the evolution of the universe.

The general theory of relativity may seem to be an exotic bit of knowledge with little practical application. In fact, this theory plays an essential role in the global positioning system (GPS), which makes it possible to determine your position on the earth's surface to within a few meters using a handheld receiver (Fig. 37.26). The heart of the GPS system is a collection of more than two dozen satellites in very precise orbits. Each satellite emits carefully timed radio signals, and a GPS receiver simultaneously detects the signals from several satellites. The receiver then calculates the time delay between when each signal was emitted and when it was received, and uses this information to calculate the receiver's position. To ensure the proper timing of the signals, it's necessary to include corrections due to the special theory of relativity (because the satellites are moving relative to the receiver on earth) as well as the general theory (because the satellites are higher in the earth's gravitational field than the receiver). The corrections due to relativity are small—less than one part in 10^9—but are crucial to the superb precision of the GPS system.

37.26 A GPS receiver uses radio signals from the orbiting GPS satellites to determine its position. To account for the effects of relativity, the receiver must be tuned to a slightly higher frequency (10.23 MHz) than the frequency emitted by the satellites (10.22999999543 MHz).

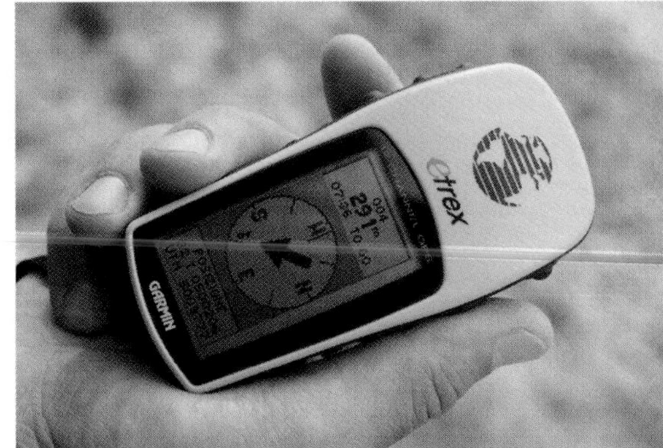

CHAPTER 37 SUMMARY

Invariance of physical laws, simultaneity: All of the fundamental laws of physics have the same form in all inertial frames of reference. The speed of light in vacuum is the same in all inertial frames and is independent of the motion of the source. Simultaneity is not an absolute concept; events that are simultaneous in one frame are not necessarily simultaneous in a second frame moving relative to the first.

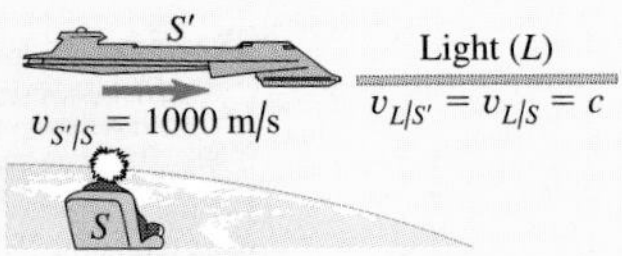

Time dilation: If two events occur at the same space point in a particular frame of reference, the time interval Δt_0 between the events as measured in that frame is called a proper time interval. If this frame moves with constant velocity u relative to a second frame, the time interval Δt between the events as observed in the second frame is longer than Δt_0. This effect is called time dilation. (Examples 37.1–37.3.)

$$\Delta t = \frac{\Delta t_0}{\sqrt{1 - u^2/c^2}} = \gamma\,\Delta t_0 \quad (37.6), (37.8)$$

$$\gamma = \frac{1}{\sqrt{1 - u^2/c^2}} \quad (37.7)$$

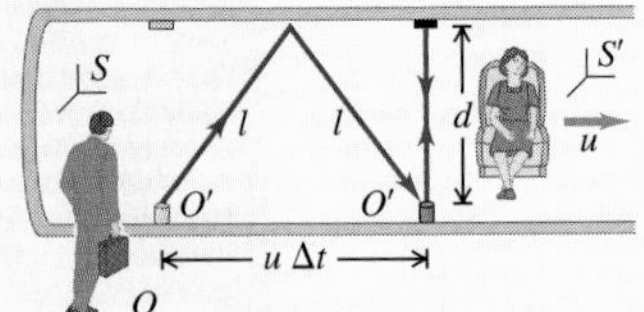

Length contraction: If two points are at rest in a particular frame of reference, the distance l_0 between the points as measured in that frame is called a proper length. If this frame moves with constant velocity u relative to a second frame and the distances are measured parallel to the motion, the distance l between the points as measured in the second frame is shorter than l_0. This effect is called length contraction. (See Examples 37.4–37.6.)

$$l = l_0\sqrt{1 - u^2/c^2} = \frac{l_0}{\gamma} \quad (37.16)$$

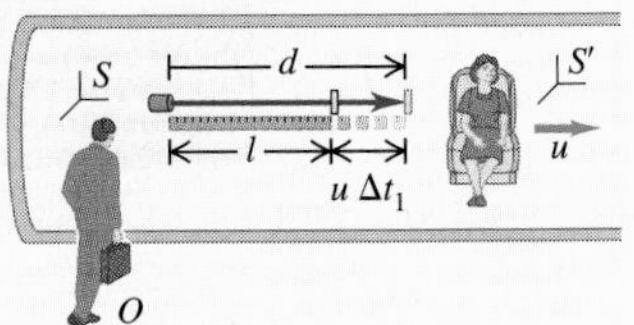

The Lorentz transformations: The Lorentz coordinate transformations relate the coordinates and time of an event in an inertial frame S to the coordinates and time of the same event as observed in a second inertial frame S' moving at velocity u relative to the first. For one-dimensional motion, a particle's velocities v_x in S and v'_x in S' are related by the Lorentz velocity transformation. (See Examples 37.7 and 37.8.)

$$x' = \frac{x - ut}{\sqrt{1 - u^2/c^2}} = \gamma(x - ut)$$

$$y' = y \qquad z' = z$$

$$t' = \frac{t - ux/c^2}{\sqrt{1 - u^2/c^2}} = \gamma(t - ux/c^2) \quad (37.21)$$

$$v'_x = \frac{v_x - u}{1 - uv_x/c^2} \quad (37.22)$$

$$v_x = \frac{v'_x + u}{1 + uv'_x/c^2} \quad (37.23)$$

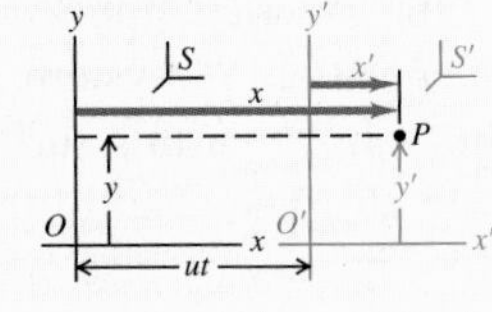

The Doppler effect for electromagnetic waves: The Doppler effect is the frequency shift in light from a source due to the relative motion of source and observer. For a source moving toward the observer with speed u, Eq. (37.25) gives the received frequency f in terms of the emitted frequency f_0. (See Example 37.9.)

$$f = \sqrt{\frac{c + u}{c - u}}\,f_0 \quad (37.25)$$

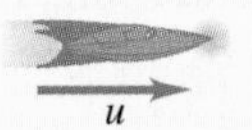

Moving source emits light of frequency f_0.

Stationary observer detects light of frequency $f > f_0$.

Relativistic momentum and energy: For a particle of rest mass m moving with velocity $\vec{v}$, the relativistic momentum $\vec{p}$ is given by Eq. (37.27) or (37.31) and the relativistic kinetic energy K is given by Eq. (37.36). The total energy E is the sum of the kinetic energy and the rest energy mc^2. The total energy can also be expressed in terms of the magnitude of momentum p and rest mass m. (See Examples 37.10–37.12.)

$$\vec{p} = \frac{m\vec{v}}{\sqrt{1 - v^2/c^2}} = \gamma m\vec{v} \quad (37.27), (37.31)$$

$$K = \frac{mc^2}{\sqrt{1 - v^2/c^2}} - mc^2 = (\gamma - 1)mc^2 \quad (37.36)$$

$$E = K + mc^2 = \frac{mc^2}{\sqrt{1 - v^2/c^2}} = \gamma mc^2 \quad (37.38)$$

$$E^2 = (mc^2)^2 + (pc)^2 \quad (37.39)$$

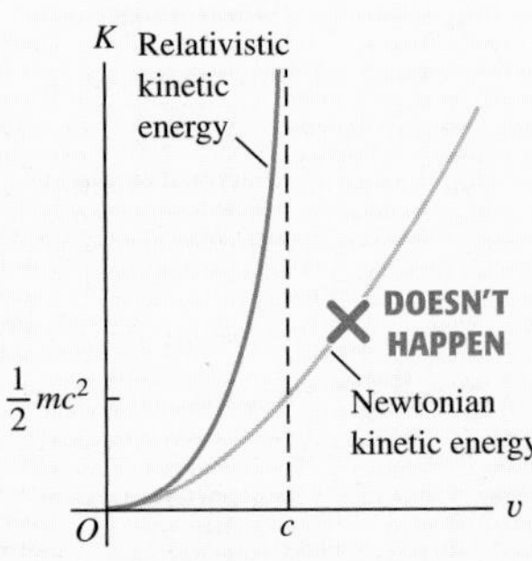

Newtonian mechanics and the special and general theories of relativity: The special theory of relativity is a generalization of Newtonian mechanics. All the principles of Newtonian mechanics are present as limiting cases when all the speeds are small compared to c. Further generalization to include noninertial frames of reference and their relationship to gravitational fields leads to the general theory of relativity.

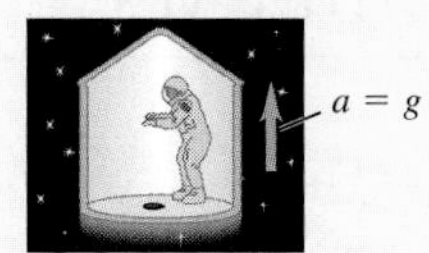

Key Terms

special theory of relativity, *1268*
principle of relativity, *1269*
Galilean coordinate transformation, *1271*
simultaneity, *1272*
event, *1272*
time dilation, *1275*
proper time, *1276*
twin paradox, *1278*
proper length, *1280*
length contraction, *1280*
Lorentz transformations, *1283*
spacetime, *1284*
spacetime coordinates, *1284*
rest mass, *1289*
relativistic momentum, *1290*
total energy, *1293*
rest energy, *1293*
correspondence principle, *1296*
general theory of relativity, *1296*

Answer to Chapter Opening Question ?

No. While the speed of light c is the ultimate "speed limit" for any particle, there is *no* upper limit on a particle's kinetic energy (see Fig. 37.21). As the speed approaches c, a small increase in speed corresponds to a large increase in kinetic energy.

Answers to Test Your Understanding Questions

37.1 answers: (a) (i), (b) no You, too, will measure a spherical wave front that expands at the same speed c in all directions. This is a consequence of Einstein's second postulate. The wave front that you measure is *not* centered on the current position of the spaceship; rather, it is centered on the point P where the spaceship was located at the instant that it emitted the light pulse. For example, suppose the spaceship is moving at speed $c/2$. When your watch shows that a time t has elapsed since the pulse of light was emitted, your measurements will show that the wave front is a sphere of radius ct centered on P and that the spaceship is a distance $ct/2$ from P.

37.2 answer: (iii) In Mavis's frame of reference, the two events (the Ogdenville clock striking noon and the North Haverbrook clock striking noon) are not simultaneous. Figure 37.5 shows that the event toward the front of the rail car occurs first. Since the rail car is moving toward North Haverbrook, that clock struck noon before the one on Ogdenville. So, according to Mavis, it is after noon in North Haverbrook.

37.3 answers: (a) (ii), (b) (ii) The statement that moving clocks run slow refers to any clock that is moving relative to an observer. Maria and her stopwatch are moving relative to Samir, so Samir measures Maria's stopwatch to be running slow and to have ticked off fewer seconds than his own stopwatch. Samir and his stopwatch are moving relative to Maria, so she likewise measures Samir's stopwatch to be running slow. Each observer's measurement is correct for his or her own frame of reference. *Both* observers conclude that a moving stopwatch runs slow. This is consistent with the principle of relativity (see Section 37.1), which states that the laws of physics are the same in all inertial frames of reference.

37.4 answer: (ii), (i) and (iii) (tie), (iv) You measure the rest length of the stationary meter stick and the contracted length of the moving spaceship to both be 1 meter. The rest length of the spaceship is greater than the contracted length that you measure, and so must be greater than 1 meter. A miniature observer on board the spaceship would measure a contracted length for the meter stick of less than 1 meter. Note that in your frame of reference the nose and tail of the spaceship can simultaneously align with the two ends of the meter stick, since in your frame of reference they have the same length of 1 meter. In the spaceship's frame these two alignments cannot happen simultaneously because the meter stick is shorter than the spaceship. Section 37.2 tells us that this shouldn't be a surprise; two events that are simultaneous to one observer may not be simultaneous to a second observer moving relative to the first one.

37.5 answers: (a) P_1, (b) P_4 (a) The last of Eqs. (37.21) tells us the times of the two events in S': $t_1' = \gamma(t_1 - ux_1/c^2)$ and $t_2' = \gamma(t_2 - ux_2/c^2)$. In frame S the two events occur at the same x-coordinate, so $x_1 = x_2$, and event P_1 occurs before event P_2, so $t_1 < t_2$. Hence you can see that $t_1' < t_2'$ and event P_1 happens before P_2 in frame S', too. This says that if event P_1 happens before P_2 in a frame of reference S where the two events occur at the same position, then P_1 happens before P_2 in any other frame moving relative to S. (b) In frame S the two events occur at different x-coordinates such that $x_3 < x_4$, and events P_3 and P_4 occur at the same time, so $t_3 = t_4$. Hence you can see that $t_3' = \gamma(t_3 - ux_3/c^2)$ is greater than $t_4' = \gamma(t_4 - ux_4/c^2)$, so event P_4 happens before P_3 in frame S'. This says that even though the two events are simultaneous in frame S, they need not be simultaneous in a frame moving relative to S.

37.7 answer: (ii) Equation (37.27) tells us that the magnitude of momentum of a particle with mass m and speed v is $p = mv/\sqrt{1 - v^2/c^2}$. If v increases by a factor of 2, the numerator mv increases by a factor of 2 *and* the denominator $\sqrt{1 - v^2/c^2}$ decreases. Hence p increases by a factor greater than 2. (Note that in order to double the speed, the initial speed must be less than $c/2$. That's because the speed of light is the ultimate speed limit.)

37.8 answer: (i) As the proton moves a distance s, the constant force of magnitude F does work $W = Fs$ and increases the kinetic energy by an amount $\Delta K = W = Fs$. This is true no matter what the speed of the proton before moving this distance. Thus the constant force increases the proton's kinetic energy by the same amount during the first meter of travel as during any subsequent meter of travel. (It's true that as the proton approaches the ultimate speed limit of c, the increase in the proton's *speed* is less and less with each subsequent meter of travel. That's not what the question is asking, however.)

PROBLEMS

Discussion Questions

Q37.1. You are standing on a train platform watching a high-speed train pass by. A light inside one of the train cars is turned on and then a little later it is turned off. (a) Who can measure the proper time interval for the duration of the light: you or a passenger on the train? (b) Who can measure the proper length of the train car, you or a passenger on the train? (c) Who can measure the proper length of a sign attached to a post on the train platform, you or a passenger on the train? In each case explain your answer.

Q37.2. If simultaneity is not an absolute concept, does that mean that we must discard the concept of causality? If event A is to *cause* event B, A must occur first. Is it possible that in some frames, A appears to be the cause of B, and in others, B appears to be the cause of A? Explain.

Q37.3. A rocket is moving to the right at $\frac{1}{2}$ the speed of light relative to the earth. A light bulb in the center of a room inside the rocket suddenly turns on. Call the light hitting the front end of the room event A and the light hitting the back of the room event B (Fig. 37.27). Which event occurs first, A or B or are they simultaneous, as viewed by (a) an astronaut riding in the rocket and (b) a person at rest on the earth?

Figure **37.27** Question Q37.3.

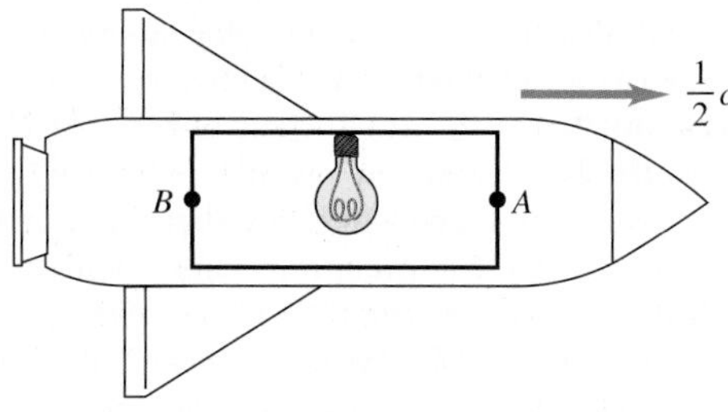

Q37.4. What do you think would be different in everyday life if the speed of light were 10 m/s instead of 3.00×10^8 m/s?

Q37.5. The average life span in the United States is about 70 years. Does this mean that it is impossible for an average person to travel a distance greater than 70 light-years away from the earth? (A light-year is the distance light travels in a year.) Explain.

Q37.6. You are holding an elliptical serving platter. How would you need to travel for the serving platter to appear round to another observer?

Q37.7. Two events occur at the same space point in a particular inertial frame of reference and are simultaneous in that frame. Is it possible that they may not be simultaneous in a different inertial frame? Explain.

Q37.8. A high-speed train passes a train platform. Larry is a passenger on the train, Adam is standing on the train platform, and David is riding a bicycle toward the platform in the same direction as the train is traveling. Compare the length of a train car as measured by Larry, Adam, and David.

Q37.9. The theory of relativity sets an upper limit on the speed that a particle can have. Are there also limits on the energy and momentum of a particle? Explain.

Q37.10. A student asserts that a material particle must always have a speed slower than that of light, and a massless particle must always move at exactly the speed of light. Is she correct? If so, how do massless particles such as photons and neutrinos acquire this speed? Can't they start from rest and accelerate? Explain.

Q37.11. The speed of light relative to still water is 2.25×10^8 m/s. If the water is moving past us, the speed of light we measure depends on the speed of the water. Do these facts violate Einstein's second postulate? Explain.

Q37.12. When a monochromatic light source moves toward an observer, its wavelength appears to be shorter than the value measured when the source is at rest. Does this contradict the hypothesis that the speed of light is the same for all observers? Explain.

Q37.13. In principle, does a hot gas have more mass than the same gas when it is cold? Explain. In practice, would this be a measurable effect? Explain.

Q37.14. Why do you think the development of Newtonian mechanics preceded the more refined relativistic mechanics by so many years?

Exercises

Section 37.2 Relativity of Simultaneity

37.1. Suppose the two lightning bolts shown in Fig. 37.5a are simultaneous to an observer on the train. Show that they are *not* simultaneous to an observer on the ground. Which lightning strike does the ground observer measure to come first?

Section 37.3 Relativity of Time Intervals

37.2. The positive muon (μ^+), an unstable particle, lives on average 2.20×10^{-6} s (measured in its own frame of reference) before decaying. (a) If such a particle is moving, with respect to the laboratory, with a speed of $0.900c$, what average lifetime is measured in the laboratory? (b) What average distance, measured in the laboratory, does the particle move before decaying?

37.3. How fast must a rocket travel relative to the earth so that time in the rocket "slows down" to half its rate as measured by earth-based observers? Do present-day jet planes approach such speeds?

37.4. A spaceship flies past Mars with a speed of $0.985c$ relative to the surface of the planet. When the spaceship is directly overhead, a signal light on the Martian surface blinks on and then off. An observer on Mars measures that the signal light was on for 75.0 μs. (a) Does the observer on Mars or the pilot on the spaceship measure the proper time? (b) What is the duration of the light pulse measured by the pilot of the spaceship?

37.5. The negative pion (π^-) is an unstable particle with an average lifetime of 2.60×10^{-8} s (measured in the rest frame of the pion). (a) If the pion is made to travel at very high speed relative to a laboratory, its average lifetime is measured in the laboratory to be 4.20×10^{-7} s. Calculate the speed of the pion expressed as a fraction of c. (b) What distance, measured in the laboratory, does the pion travel during its average lifetime?

37.6. As you pilot your space utility vehicle at a constant speed toward the moon, a race pilot flies past you in her spaceracer at a constant speed of $0.800c$ relative to you. At the instant the spaceracer passes you, both of you start timers at zero. (a) At the instant when you measure that the spaceracer has traveled 1.20×10^8 m past you, what does the race pilot read on her timer? (b) When the race pilot reads the value calculated in part (a) on her timer, what does she measure to be your distance from her? (c) At the instant when the race pilot reads the value calculated in part (a) on her timer, what do you read on yours?

37.7. A spacecraft flies away from the earth with a speed of 4.80×10^6 m/s relative to the earth and then returns at the same speed. The spacecraft carries an atomic clock that has been carefully synchronized with an identical clock that remains at rest on earth. The spacecraft returns to its starting point 365 days (1 year) later, as measured by the clock that remained on earth. What is the difference in the elapsed times on the two clocks, measured in hours? Which clock, the one in the spacecraft or the one on earth, shows the shortest elapsed time?

37.8. An alien spacecraft is flying overhead at a great distance as you stand in your backyard. You see its searchlight blink on for 0.190 s. The first officer on the spacecraft measures that the searchlight is on for 12.0 ms. (a) Which of these two measured times is the proper time? (b) What is the speed of the spacecraft relative to the earth expressed as a fraction of the speed of light c?

Section 37.4 Relativity of Length

37.9. A spacecraft of the Trade Federation flies past the planet Coruscant at a speed of $0.600c$. A scientist on Coruscant measures the length of the moving spacecraft to be 74.0 m. The spacecraft later lands on Coruscant, and the same scientist measures the length of the now stationary spacecraft. What value does she get?

37.10. A meter stick moves past you at great speed. Its motion relative to you is parallel to its long axis. If you measure the length of the moving meter stick to be 1.00 ft $(1 \text{ ft} = 0.3048 \text{ m})$—for example, by comparing it to a 1-foot ruler that is at rest relative to you—at what speed is the meter stick moving relative to you?

37.11. Why Are We Bombarded by Muons? Muons are unstable subatomic particles that decay to electrons with a mean lifetime of 2.2 μs. They are produced when cosmic rays bombard the upper atmosphere about 10 km above the earth's surface, and they travel very close to the speed of light. The problem we want to address is why we see any of them at the earth's surface. (a) What is the greatest distance a muon could travel during its 2.2-μs lifetime? (b) According to your answer in part (a), it would seem that muons could never make it to the ground. But the 2.2-μs lifetime is measured in the frame of the muon, and muons are moving very fast. At a speed of $0.999c$. what is the mean lifetime of a muon as measured by an observer at rest on the earth? How far would the muon travel in this time? Does this result explain why we find muons in cosmic rays? (c) From the point of view of the muon, it still lives for only 2.2 μs, so how does it make it to the ground? What is the thickness of the 10 km of atmosphere through which the muon must travel, as measured by the muon? It is now clear how the muon is able to reach the ground?

37.12. An unstable particle is created in the upper atmosphere from a cosmic ray and travels straight down toward the surface of the earth with a speed of $0.99540c$ relative to the earth. A scientist at rest on the earth's surface measures that the particle is created at an altitude of 45.0 km. (a) As measured by the scientist, how much time does it take the particle to travel the 45.0 km to the surface of the earth? (b) Use the length-contraction formula to calculate the distance from where the particle is created to the surface of the earth as measured in the particle's frame. (c) In the particle's frame, how much time does it take the particle to travel from where it is created to the surface of the earth? Calculate this time both by the time dilation formula and from the distance calculated in part (b). Do the two results agree?

37.13. As measured by an observer on the earth, a spacecraft runway on earth has a length of 3600 m. (a) What is the length of the runway as measured by a pilot of a spacecraft flying past at a speed of 4.00×10^7 m/s relative to the earth? (b) An observer on earth measures the time interval from when the spacecraft is directly over one end of the runway until it is directly over the other end. What result does she get? (c) The pilot of the spacecraft measures the time it takes him to travel from one end of the runway to the other end. What value does he get?

Section 37.5 The Lorentz Transformations

37.14. Solve Eqs. (37.21) to obtain x and t in terms of x' and t', and show that the resulting transformation has the same form as the original one except for a change of sign for u.

37.15. An observer in frame S' is moving to the right ($+x$-direction) at speed $u = 0.600c$ away from a stationary observer in frame S. The observer in S' measures the speed v' of a particle moving to the right away from her. What speed v does the observer in S measure for the particle if (a) $v' = 0.400c$; (b) $v' = 0.900c$; (c) $v' = 0.990c$?

37.16. Space pilot Mavis zips past Stanley at a constant speed relative to him of $0.800c$. Mavis and Stanley start timers at zero when the front of Mavis's ship is directly above Stanley. When Mavis reads 5.00 s on her timer, she turns on a bright light under the front of her spaceship. (a) Use the Lorentz coordinate transformation derived in Exercise 37.14 and Example 37.7 to calculate x and t as measured by Stanley for the event of turning on the light. (b) Use the time dilation formula, Eq. (37.6), to calculate the time interval between the two events (the front of the spaceship passing overhead and turning on the light) as measured by Stanley. Compare to the value of t you calculated in part (a). (c) Multiply the time interval by Mavis's speed, both as measured by Stanley, to calculate the distance she has traveled as measured by him when the light turns on. Compare to the value of x you calculated in part (a).

37.17. A pursuit spacecraft from the planet Tatooine is attempting to catch up with a Trade Federation cruiser. As measured by an observer on Tatooine, the cruiser is traveling away from the planet with a speed of $0.600c$. The pursuit ship is traveling at a speed of $0.800c$ relative to Tatooine, in the same direction as the cruiser. (a) For the pursuit ship to catch the cruiser, should the speed of the cruiser relative to the pursuit ship be positive or negative? (b) What is the speed of the cruiser relative to the pursuit ship?

37.18. Equation 37.23 gives the transformation for only the x-component of an object's velocity. Suppose the object considered in the derivation also moved in the y/y'-direction. Find an expression for u_y in terms of the components of u', v, and c, which represents the transformation for the y-component of the velocity. (*Hint:* Apply the Lorentz transformations and relationships like $u_x = dx/dt$, $u'_x = dx'/dt'$, and so on, to the y-components.)

37.19. Two particles are created in a high-energy accelerator and move off in opposite directions. The speed of one particle, as measured in the laboratory, is $0.650c$, and the speed of each particle relative to the other is $0.950c$. What is the speed of the second particle, as measured in the laboratory?

37.20. Two particles in a high-energy accelerator experiment are approaching each other head-on, each with a speed of $0.9520c$ as measured in the laboratory. What is the magnitude of the velocity of one particle relative to the other?

37.21. Two particles in a high-energy accelerator experiment approach each other head-on with a relative speed of $0.890c$. Both particles travel at the same speed as measured in the laboratory. What is the speed of each particle, as measured in the laboratory?

37.22. An enemy spaceship is moving toward your starfighter with a speed, as measured in your frame, of $0.400c$. The enemy ship fires a missile toward you at a speed of $0.700c$ relative to the enemy ship (Fig. 37.28). (a) What is the speed of the missile relative to you? Express your answer in terms of the speed of light. (b) If you measure that the enemy ship is 8.00×10^6 km away from you when the missile is fired, how much time, measured in your frame, will it take the missile to reach you?

Figure **37.28** Exercise 37.22.

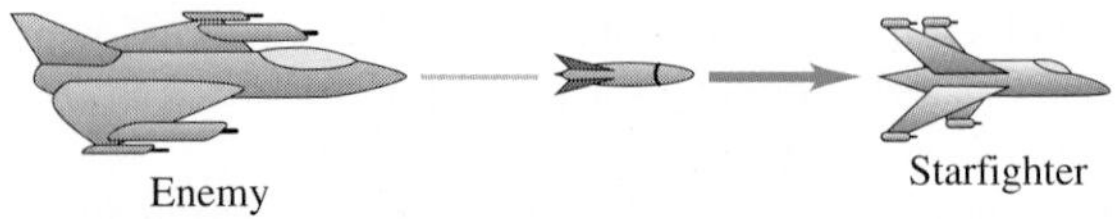

37.23. An imperial spaceship, moving at high speed relative to the planet Arrakis, fires a rocket toward the planet with a speed of $0.920c$ relative to the spaceship. An observer on Arrakis measures that the rocket is approaching with a speed of $0.360c$. What is the speed of the spaceship relative to Arrakis? Is the spaceship moving toward or away from Arrakis?

*Section 37.6 The Doppler Effect for Electromagnetic Waves

***37.24.** Rewrite Eq. 37.25 to find the relative velocity u between the electromagnetic source and an observer in terms of the ratio of the observed frequency and the source frequency of light. What relative velocity u will produce (a) a 5.0% decrease in frequency and (b) an increase by a factor of 5 of the observed light?

***37.25. Tell It to the Judge.** (a) How fast must you be approaching a red traffic light $(\lambda = 675 \text{ nm})$ for it to appear yellow $(\lambda = 575 \text{ nm})$? Express your answer in terms of the speed of light. (b) If you used this as a reason not to get a ticket for running a red light, how much of a fine would you get for speeding? Assume that the fine is \$1.00 for each kilometer per hour that your speed exceeds the posted limit of 90 km/h.

***37.26.** Show that when the source of electromagnetic waves moves away from us at $0.600c$, the frequency we measure is half the value measured in the rest frame of the source.

Section 37.7 Relativistic Momentum

37.27. (a) A particle with mass m moves along a straight line under the action of a force F directed along the same line. Evaluate the derivative in Eq. (37.29) to show that the acceleration $a = dv/dt$ of the particle is given by $a = (F/m)(1 - v^2/c^2)^{3/2}$. (b) Evaluate the derivative in Eq. (37.29) to find the expression for the magnitude of the acceleration in terms of F, m, and v/c if the force is perpendicular to the velocity.

37.28. When Should you Use Relativity? As you have seen, relativistic calculations usually involve the quantity γ. When γ is appreciably greater than 1, we must use relativistic formulas instead of Newtonian ones. For what speed v (in terms of c) is the value of γ (a) 1.0% greater than 1; (b) 10% greater than 1; (c) 100% greater than 1?

37.29. (a) At what speed is the momentum of a particle twice as great as the result obtained from the nonrelativistic expression mv? Express your answer in terms of the speed of light. (b) A force is applied to a particle along its direction of motion. At what speed is the magnitude of force required to produce a given acceleration twice as great as the force required to produce the same acceleration when the particle is at rest? Express your answer in terms of the speed of light.

37.30. Relativistic Baseball. Calculate the magnitude of the force required to give a 0.145-kg baseball an acceleration $a = 1.00 \text{ m/s}^2$ in the direction of the baseball's initial velocity when this velocity has a magnitude of (a) 10.0 m/s; (b) $0.900c$; (c) $0.990c$. (d) Repeat parts (a), (b), and (c) if the force and acceleration are perpendicular to the velocity.

Section 37.8 Relativistic Work and Energy

37.31. What is the speed of a particle whose kinetic energy is equal to (a) its rest energy and (b) five times its rest energy?

37.32. Annihilation. In proton–antiproton annihilation a proton and an antiproton (a negatively charged proton) collide and disappear, producing electromagnetic radiation. If each particle has a mass of 1.67×10^{-27} kg and they are at rest just before the annihilation, find the total energy of the radiation. Give your answers in joules and in electron volts.

37.33. A proton (rest mass $1.67 \times 10^{\times 27}$ kg) has total energy that is 4.00 times its rest energy. What are (a) the kinetic energy of the proton; (b) the magnitude of the momentum of the proton; (c) the speed of the proton?

37.34. (a) How much work must be done on a particle with mass m to accelerate it (a) from rest to a speed of $0.090c$ and (b) from a speed of $0.900c$ to a speed of $0.990c$? (Express the answers in terms of mc^2.) (c) How do your answers in parts (a) and (b) compare?

37.35. (a) By what percentage does your rest mass increase when you climb 30 m to the top of a ten-story building? Are you aware of this increase? Explain. (b) By how many grams does the mass of a 12.0-g spring with force constant 200 N/cm change when you compress it by 6.0 cm? Does the mass increase or decrease? Would you notice the change in mass if you were holding the spring? Explain.

37.36. A 60.0-kg person is standing at rest on level ground. How fast would she have to run to (a) double her total energy and (b) increase her total energy by a factor of 10?

37.37. An Antimatter Reactor. When a particle meets its antiparticle, they annihilate each other and their mass is converted to light energy. The United States uses approximately 1.0×10^{19} J of energy per year. (a) If all this energy came from a futuristic antimatter reactor, how much mass of matter and antimatter fuel would be consumed yearly? (b) If this fuel had the density of iron (7.86 g/cm^3) and were stacked in bricks to form a cubical pile, how high would it be? (Before you get your hopes up, antimatter reactors are a *long* way in the future—if they ever will be feasible.)

37.38. A ψ ("psi") particle has mass 5.52×10^{-27} kg. Compute the rest energy of the ψ particle in MeV.

37.39. A particle has rest mass 6.64×10^{-27} kg and momentum $2.10 \times 10^{-18} \text{ kg} \cdot \text{m/s}$. (a) What is the total energy (kinetic plus rest energy) of the particle? (b) What is the kinetic energy of the particle? (c) What is the ratio of the kinetic energy to the rest energy of the particle?

37.40. Starting from Eq. (37.39), show that in the classical limit $(pc \ll mc^2)$ the energy approaches the classical kinetic energy $\frac{1}{2}mv^2$ plus the rest mass energy mc^2.

37.41. Compute the kinetic energy of a proton (mass 1.67×10^{-27} kg using both the nonrelativistic and relativistic expressions, and compute the ratio of the two results (relativistic divided by nonrelativistic) for speeds of (a) 8.00×10^7 m/s and (b) 2.85×10^8 m/s.

37.42. What is the kinetic energy of a proton moving at (a) $0.100c$; (b) $0.500c$; (c) $0.900c$? How much work must be done to (d) increase the proton's speed from $0.100c$ to $0.500c$ and (e) increase the proton's speed from $0.500c$ to $0.900c$? (f) How do the last two results compare to results obtained in the nonrelativistic limit?

37.43. (a) Through what potential difference does an electron have to be accelerated, starting from rest, to achieve a speed of $0.980c$? (b) What is the kinetic energy of the electron at this speed? Express your answer in joules and in electron volts.

37.44. Creating a Particle. Two protons (each with rest mass $M = 1.67 \times 10^{-27}$ kg) are initially moving with equal speeds in opposite directions. The protons continue to exist after a collision that also produces an η^0 particle (see Chapter 44). The rest mass of the η^0 is $m = 9.75 \times 10^{-28}$ kg. (a) If the two protons and the η^0 are all at rest after the collision, find the initial speed of the protons, expressed as a fraction of the speed of light. (b) What is the kinetic energy of each proton? Express your answer in MeV. (c) What is the rest energy of the η^0, expressed in MeV? (d) Discuss the relationship between the answers to parts (b) and (c).

37.45. Find the speed of a particle whose relativistic kinetic energy is 50% greater than the Newtonian value for the same speed.

37.46. Energy of Fusion. In a hypothetical nuclear fusion reactor, two deuterium nuclei combine or "fuse" to form one helium nucleus. The mass of a deuterium nucleus, expressed in atomic mass units (u), is 2.0136 u; the mass of a helium nucleus is 4.0015 u ($1 \text{ u} = 1.6605402 \times 10^{-27}$ kg). (a) How much energy is released when 1.0 kg of deuterium undergoes fusion? (b) The annual consumption of electrical energy in the United States is of the order of 1.0×10^{19} J. How much deuterium must react to produce this much energy?

37.47. The sun produces energy by nuclear fusion reactions, in which matter is converted into energy. By measuring the amount of energy we receive from the sun, we know that it is producing energy at a rate of 3.8×10^{26} W. (a) How many kilograms of matter does the sun lose each second? Approximately how many tons of matter is this? (b) At this rate, how long would it take the sun to use up all its mass?

37.48. A 0.100-μg speck of dust is accelerated from rest to a speed of $0.900c$ by a constant 1.00×10^6 N force. (a) If the nonrelativistic form of Newton's second law ($\sum F = ma$) is used, how far does the object travel to reach its final speed? (b) Using the correct relativistic treatment of Section 37.8, how far does the object travel to reach its final speed? (c) Which distance is greater? Why?

Problems

37.49. After being produced in a collision between elementary particles, a positive pion (π^+) must travel down a 1.20-km-long tube to reach an experimental area. A π^+ particle has an average lifetime (measured in its rest frame) of 2.60×10^{-8} s; the π^+ we are considering has this lifetime. (a) How fast must the π^+ travel if it is not to decay before it reaches the end of the tube? (Since u will be very close to c, write $u = (1 - \Delta)c$ and give your answer in terms of Δ rather than u.) (b) The π^+ has a rest energy of 139.6 MeV. What is the total energy of the π^+ at the speed calculated in part (a)?

37.50. A cube of metal with sides of length a sits at rest in a frame S with one edge parallel to the x-axis. Therefore, in S the cube has volume a^3. Frame S' moves along the x-axis with a speed u. As measured by an observer in frame S', what is the volume of the metal cube?

37.51. The starships of the Solar Federation are marked with the symbol of the federation, a circle, while starships of the Denebian Empire are marked with the empire's symbol, an ellipse whose major axis is 1.40 times longer than its minor axis ($a = 1.40b$ in Fig. 37.29). How fast, relative to an observer, does an empire ship have to travel for its marking to be confused with the marking of a federation ship?

Figure 37.29 Problem 37.51.

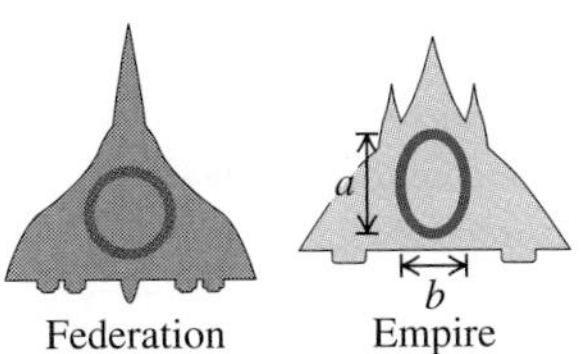

37.52. A space probe is sent to the vicinity of the star Capella, which is 42.2 light-years from the earth. (A light-year is the distance light travels in a year.) The probe travels with a speed of $0.9910c$. An astronaut recruit on board is 19 years old when the probe leaves the earth. What is her biological age when the probe reaches Capella?

37.53. A particle is said to be *extremely relativistic* when its kinetic energy is much greater than its rest energy. (a) What is the speed of a particle (expressed as a fraction of c) such that the total energy is ten times the rest energy? (b) What is the percentage difference between the left and right sides of Eq. (37.39) if $(mc^2)^2$ is neglected for a particle with the speed calculated in part (a)?

37.54. Everyday Time Dilation. Two atomic clocks are carefully synchronized. One remains in New York, and the other is loaded on an airliner that travels at an average speed of 250 m/s and then returns to New York. When the plane returns, the elapsed time on the clock that stayed behind is 4.00 h. By how much will the readings of the two clocks differ, and which clock will show the shorter elapsed time? (*Hint:* Since $u \ll c$, you can simplify $\sqrt{1 - u^2/c^2}$ by a binomial expansion.)

37.55. The Large Hadron Collider (LHC). Physicists and engineers from around the world have come together to build the largest accelerator in the world, the Large Hadron Collider (LHC) at the CERN Laboratory in Geneva, Switzerland. The machine will accelerate protons to kinetic energies of 7 TeV in an underground ring 27 km in circumference. (For the latest news and more information on the LHC, visit www.cern.ch.) (a) What speed v will protons reach in the LHC? (Since v is very close to c, write $v = (1 - \Delta)c$ and give your answer in terms of Δ.) (b) Find the relativistic mass, m_{rel}, of the accelerated protons in terms of their rest mass.

37.56. A nuclear bomb containing 8.00 kg of plutonium explodes. The sum of the rest masses of the products of the explosion is less than the original rest mass by one part in 10^4. (a) How much energy is released in the explosion? (b) If the explosion takes place in 4.00 μs, what is the average power developed by the bomb? (c) What mass of water could the released energy lift to a height of 1.00 km?

37.57. Čerenkov Radiation. The Russian physicist P. A. Čerenkov discovered that a charged particle traveling in a solid with a speed exceeding the speed of light in that material radiates electromagnetic radiation. (This is analogous to the sonic boom produced by an aircraft moving faster than the speed of sound in air; see Section 16.9. Čerenkov shared the 1958 Nobel Prize for this discovery.) What is the minimum kinetic energy (in electron volts) that an electron must have while traveling inside a slab of crown glass ($n = 1.52$) in order to create this Čerenkov radiation?

37.58. A photon with energy E is emitted by an atom with mass m, which recoils in the opposite direction. (a) Assuming that the motion of the atom can be treated nonrelativistically, compute the recoil speed of the atom. (b) From the result of part (a), show that the recoil speed is much less than c whenever E is much less than the rest energy mc^2 of the atom.

37.59. In an experiment, two protons are shot directly toward each other, each moving at half the speed of light relative to the laboratory. (a) What speed does one proton measure for the other proton? (b) What would be the answer to part (a) if we used only nonrelativistic Newtonian mechanics? (c) What is the kinetic energy of each proton as measured by (i) an observer at rest in the laboratory and (ii) an observer riding along with one of the protons? (d) What would be the answers to part (c) if we used only nonrelativistic Newtonian mechanics?

37.60. For the protons in Problem 37.59, suppose that their speed is such that each proton measures a speed of half the speed of light for the other proton. (a) What does an observer in the laboratory measure for the speeds of these protons? (b) What is the kinetic energy of each proton as measured by (i) an observer in the lab and (ii) the other proton?

37.61. Frame S' has an x-component of velocity u relative to frame S, and at $t = t' = 0$ the two frames coincide (see Fig. 37.3). A light pulse with a spherical wave front is emitted at the origin of S' at time $t' = 0$. Its distance x' from the origin after a time t' is given by $x'^2 = c^2t'^2$. Use the Lorentz coordinate transformation to transform this equation to an equation in x and t, and show that the result is $x^2 = c^2t^2$; that is, the motion appears exactly the same in frame of reference S as it does in S'; the wave front is observed to be spherical in both frames.

37.62. In certain radioactive beta decay processes, the beta particle (an electron) leaves the atomic nucleus with a speed of 99.95% the speed of light relative to the decaying nucleus. If this nucleus is moving at 75.00% the speed of light, find the speed of the emitted electron relative to the laboratory reference frame if the electron is emitted (a) in the same direction that the nucleus is moving and (b) in the opposite direction from the nucleus's velocity. (c) In each case in parts (a) and (b), find the kinetic energy of the electron as measured in (i) the laboratory frame and (ii) the reference frame of the decaying nucleus.

37.63. A particle with mass m accelerated from rest by a constant force F will, according to Newtonian mechanics, continue to accelerate without bound; that is, as $t \to \infty$, $v \to \infty$. Show that according to relativistic mechanics, the particle's speed approaches c as $t \to \infty$. [*Note:* A useful integral is $\int (1 - x^2)^{-3/2}\, dx = x/\sqrt{1 - x^2}$.]

37.64. Two events are observed in a frame of reference S to occur at the same space point, the second occurring 1.80 s after the first. In a second frame S' moving relative to S, the second event is observed to occur 2.35 s after the first. What is the difference between the positions of the two events as measured in S'?

37.65. Two events observed in a frame of reference S have positions and times given by (x_1, t_1) and (x_2, t_2), respectively. (a) Frame S' moves along the x-axis just fast enough that the two events occur at the same position in S'. Show that in S', the time interval $\Delta t'$ between the two events is given by

$$\Delta t' = \sqrt{(\Delta t)^2 - \left(\frac{\Delta x}{c}\right)^2}$$

where $\Delta x = x_2 - x_1$ and $\Delta t = t_2 - t_1$. Hence show that if $\Delta x > c\,\Delta t$, there is *no* frame S' in which the two events occur at the same point. The interval $\Delta t'$ is sometimes called the *proper time interval* for the events. Is this term appropriate? (b) Show that if $\Delta x > c\,\Delta t$, there is a different frame of reference S' in which the two events occur *simultaneously*. Find the distance between the two events in S'; express your answer in terms of Δx, Δt, and c. This distance is sometimes called a *proper length*. Is this term appropriate? (c) Two events are observed in a frame of reference S' to occur simultaneously at points separated by a distance of 2.50 m. In a second frame S moving relative to S' along the line joining the two points in S', the two events appear to be separated by 5.00 m. What is the time interval between the events as measured in S? [*Hint:* Apply the result obtained in part (b).]

37.66. Albert in Wonderland. Einstein and Lorentz, being avid tennis players, play a fast-paced game on a court where they stand 20.0 m from each other. Being very skilled players, they play without a net. The tennis ball has mass 0.0580 kg. You can ignore gravity and assume that the ball travels parallel to the ground as it travels between the two players. Unless otherwise specified, all measurements are made by the two men. (a) Lorentz serves the ball at 80.0 m/s. What is the ball's kinetic energy? (b) Einstein slams a return at 1.80×10^8 m/s. What is the ball's kinetic energy? (c) During Einstein's return of the ball in part (a), a white rabbit runs beside the court in the direction from Einstein to Lorentz. The rabbit has a speed of 2.20×10^8 m/s relative to the two men. What is the speed of the rabbit relative to the ball? (d) What does the rabbit measure as the distance from Einstein to Lorentz? (e) How much time does it take for the rabbit to run 20.0 m, according to the players? (f) The white rabbit carries a pocket watch. He uses this watch to measure the time (as he sees it) for the distance from Einstein to Lorentz to pass by under him. What time does he measure?

***37.67.** One of the wavelengths of light emitted by hydrogen atoms under normal laboratory conditions is $\lambda = 656.3$ nm, in the red portion of the electromagnetic spectrum. In the light emitted from a distant galaxy this same spectral line is observed to be Doppler-shifted to $\lambda = 953.4$ nm, in the infrared portion of the spectrum. How fast are the emitting atoms moving relative to the earth? Are they approaching the earth or receding from it?

***37.68. Measuring Speed by Radar.** A baseball coach uses a radar device to measure the speed of an approaching pitched baseball. This device sends out electromagnetic waves with frequency f_0 and then measures the shift in frequency Δf of the waves reflected from the moving baseball. If the fractional frequency shift produced by a baseball is $\Delta f/f_0 = 2.86 \times 10^{-7}$, what is the baseball's speed in km/h? (*Hint:* Are the waves Doppler-shifted a second time when reflected off the ball?)

37.69. Space Travel? Travel to the stars requires hundreds or thousands of years, even at the speed of light. Some people have suggested that we can get around this difficulty by accelerating the rocket (and its astronauts) to very high speeds so that they will age less due to time dilation. The fly in this ointment is that it takes a great deal of energy to do this. Suppose you want to go to the immense red giant Betelgeuse, which is about 500 light-years away. (A light-year is the distance that light travels in a year.) You plan to travel at constant speed in a 1000-kg rocket ship (a little over a ton), which, in reality, is far too small for this purpose. In each case that follows, calculate the time for the trip, as measured by people on earth and by astronauts in the rocket ship, the energy needed in joules, and the energy needed as a percentage of U.S. yearly use (which is 1.0×10^{19} J). For comparison, arrange your results in a table showing v_{rocket}, t_{earth}, t_{rocket}, E (in J), and E

(as % of U.S. use). The rocket ship's speed is (a) 0.50c; (b) 0.99c; (c) 0.9999c. On the basis of your results, does it seem likely that any government will invest in such high-speed space travel any time soon?

***37.70.** A spaceship moving at constant speed u relative to us broadcasts a radio signal at constant frequency f_0. As the spaceship approaches us, we receive a higher frequency f; after it has passed, we receive a lower frequency. (a) As the spaceship passes by, so it is instantaneously moving neither toward nor away from us, show that the frequency we receive is not f_0, and derive an expression for the frequency we do receive. Is the frequency we receive higher or lower than f_0? (*Hint:* In this case, successive wave crests move the same distance to the observer and so they have the same transit time. Thus f equals $1/T$. Use the time dilation formula to relate the periods in the stationary and moving frames.) (b) A spaceship emits electromagnetic waves of frequency $f_0 = 345$ MHz as measured in a frame moving with the ship. The spaceship is moving at a constant speed $0.758c$ relative to us. What frequency f do we receive when the spaceship is approaching us? When it is moving away? In each case what is the shift in frequency, $f - f_0$? (c) Use the result of part (a) to calculate the frequency f and the frequency shift $(f - f_0)$ we receive at the instant that the ship passes by us. How does the shift in frequency calculated here compare to the shifts calculated in part (b)?

***37.71. The Pole and Barn Paradox.** Suppose a *very* fast runner $(v = 0.600c)$ holding a long, horizontal pole runs through a barn open at both ends. The length of the pole (in its rest frame) is 6.00 m, and the length of the barn (in *its* rest frame) is 5.00 m. In the barn's reference frame, the pole will undergo length contraction and can all fit inside the barn at the same time. But in the runner's reference frame, the *barn* will undergo length contraction and the entire pole can *never* be entirely within the barn at any time! Explain the resolution of this paradox.

37.72. The French physicist Armand Fizeau was the first to measure the speed of light accurately. He also found experimentally that the speed, relative to the lab frame, of light traveling in a tank of water that is itself moving at a speed V relative to the lab frame is

$$v = \frac{c}{n} + kV$$

where $n = 1.333$ is the index of refraction of water. Fizeau called k the dragging coefficient and obtained an experimental value of $k = 0.44$. What value of k do you calculate from relativistic transformations?

Challenge Problems

37.73. Lorentz Transformation for Acceleration. Using a method analogous to the one in the text to find the Lorentz transformation formula for velocity, we can find the Lorentz transformation for *acceleration*. Let frame S' have a constant x-component of velocity u relative to frame S. An object moves relative to frame S along the x-axis with instantaneous velocity v_x and instantaneous acceleration a_x. (a) Show that its instantaneous acceleration in frame S' is

$$a'_x = a_x\left(1 - \frac{u^2}{c^2}\right)^{3/2}\left(1 - \frac{uv_x}{c^2}\right)^{-3}$$

[*Hint:* Express the acceleration in S' as $a'_x = dv'_x/dt'$. Then use Eq. (37.21) to express dt' in terms of dt and dx, and use Eq. (37.22) to express dv'_x in terms of u and dv_x. The velocity of the object in S is $v_x = dx/dt$.] (b) Show that the acceleration in frame S can be expressed as

$$a_x = a'_x\left(1 - \frac{u^2}{c^2}\right)^{3/2}\left(1 + \frac{uv'_x}{c^2}\right)^{-3}$$

where $v'_x = dx'/dt'$ is the velocity of the object in frame S'.

37.74. A Realistic Version of the Twin Paradox. A rocket ship leaves the earth on January 1, 2100. Stella, one of a pair of twins born in the year 2075, pilots the rocket (reference frame S'); the other twin, Terra, stays on the earth (reference frame S). The rocket ship has an acceleration of constant magnitude g in its own reference frame (this makes the pilot feel at home, since it simulates the earth's gravity). The path of the rocket ship is a straight line in the $+x$-direction in frame S. (a) Using the results of Challenge Problem 37.73, show that in Terra's earth frame S, the rocket's acceleration is

$$\frac{du}{dt} = g\left(1 - \frac{u^2}{c^2}\right)^{3/2}$$

where u is the rocket's instantaneous velocity in frame S. (b) Write the result of part (a) in the form $dt = f(u)\,du$, where $f(u)$ is a function of u, and integrate both sides. (*Hint:* Use the integral given in Problem 37.63.) Show that in Terra's frame, the time when Stella attains a velocity v_{1x} is

$$t_1 = \frac{v_{1x}}{g\sqrt{1 - v_{1x}^2/c^2}}$$

(c) Use the time dilation formula to relate dt and dt' (infinitesimal time intervals measured in frames S and S', respectively). Combine this result with the result of part (a) and integrate as in part (b) to show the following: When Stella attains a velocity v_{1x} relative to Terra, the time t'_1 that has elapsed in frame S' is

$$t'_1 = \frac{c}{g}\,\text{arctanh}\left(\frac{v_{1x}}{c}\right)$$

Here arctanh is the inverse hyperbolic tangent. (*Hint:* Use the integral given in Challenge Problem 5.124.) (d) Combine the results of parts (b) and (c) to find t_1 in terms of t'_1, g, and c alone. (e) Stella accelerates in a straight-line path for five years (by her clock), slows down at the same rate for five years, turns around, accelerates for five years, slows down for five years, and lands back on the earth. According to Stella's clock, the date is January 1, 2120. What is the date according to Terra's clock?

***37.75. Determining the Masses of Stars.** Many of the stars in the sky are actually *binary stars,* in which two stars orbit about their common center of mass. If the orbital speeds of the stars are high enough, the motion of the stars can be detected by the Doppler shifts of the light they emit. Stars for which this is the case are called *spectroscopic binary stars.* Figure 37.30 (next page) shows the simplest case of a spectroscopic binary star: two identical stars, each with mass m, orbiting their center of mass in a circle of radius R. The plane of the stars' orbits is edge-on to the line of sight of an observer on the earth. (a) The light produced by heated hydrogen gas in a laboratory on the earth has a frequency of 4.568110×10^{14} Hz. In the light received from the stars by a telescope on the earth, hydrogen light is observed to vary in frequency between 4.567710×10^{14} Hz and 4.568910×10^{14} Hz. Determine whether the binary star system as a whole is moving toward or

Figure 37.30 Challenge Problem 37.75.

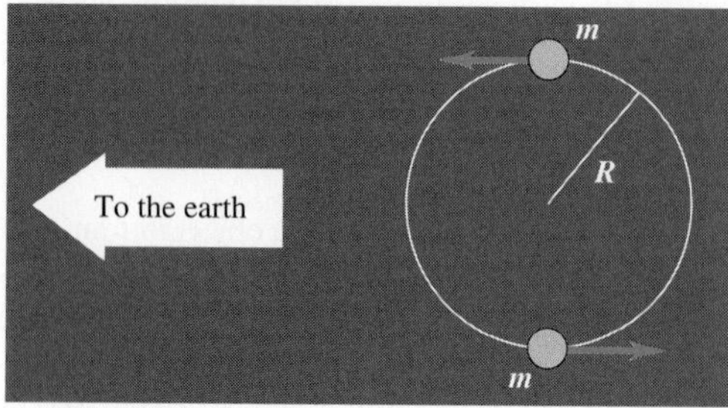

away from the earth, the speed of this motion, and the orbital speeds of the stars. (*Hint:* The speeds involved are much less than c, so you may use the approximate result $\Delta f/f = u/c$ given in Section 37.6.) (b) The light from each star in the binary system varies from its maximum frequency to its minimum frequency and back again in 11.0 days. Determine the orbital radius R and the mass m of each star. Give your answer for m in kilograms and as a multiple of the mass of the sun, 1.99×10^{30} kg. Compare the value of R to the distance from the earth to the sun, 1.50×10^{11} m. (This technique is actually used in astronomy to determine the masses of stars. In practice, the problem is more complicated because the two stars in a binary system are usually not identical, the orbits are usually not circular, and the plane of the orbits is usually tilted with respect to the line of sight from the earth.)

37.76. Relativity and the Wave Equation. (a) Consider the Galilean transformation along the x-direction: $x' = x - vt$ and $t' = t$. In frame S the wave equation for electromagnetic waves in a vacuum is

$$\frac{\partial^2 E(x,t)}{\partial x^2} - \frac{1}{c^2}\frac{\partial^2 E(x,t)}{\partial t^2} = 0$$

where E represents the electric field in the wave. Show that by using the Galilean transformation the wave equation in frame S' is found to be

$$\left(1 - \frac{v^2}{c^2}\right)\frac{\partial^2 E(x',t')}{\partial x'^2} + \frac{2v}{c^2}\frac{\partial^2 E(x',t')}{\partial x'\partial t'} - \frac{1}{c^2}\frac{\partial^2 E(x',t')}{\partial t'^2} = 0$$

This has a different form than the wave equation in S. Hence the Galilean transformation *violates* the first relativity postulate that all physical laws have the same form in all inertial reference frames. (*Hint:* Express the derivatives $\partial/\partial x$ and $\partial/\partial t$ in terms of $\partial/\partial x'$ and $\partial/\partial t'$ by use of the chain rule.) (b) Repeat the analysis of part (a), but use the Lorentz coordinate transformations, Eqs. (37.21), and show that in frame S' the wave equation has the same form as in frame S:

$$\frac{\partial^2 E(x',t')}{\partial x^2} - \frac{1}{c^2}\frac{\partial^2 E(x',t')}{\partial t'^2} = 0$$

Explain why this shows that the speed of light in vacuum is c in both frames S and S'.

37.77. Kaon Production. In high-energy physics, new particles can be created by collisions of fast-moving projectile particles with stationary particles. Some of the kinetic energy of the incident particle is used to create the mass of the new particle. A proton–proton collision can result in the creation of a negative kaon (K^-) and a positive kaon (K^+):

$$p + p \rightarrow p + p + \mathrm{K}^- + \mathrm{K}^+$$

(a) Calculate the minimum kinetic energy of the incident proton that will allow this reaction to occur if the second (target) proton is initially at rest. The rest energy of each kaon is 493.7 MeV, and the rest energy of each proton is 938.3 MeV. (*Hint:* It is useful here to work in the frame in which the total momentum is zero. See Problem 8.100, but note that here the Lorentz transformation must be used to relate the velocities in the laboratory frame to those in the zero-total-momentum frame.) (b) How does this calculated minimum kinetic energy compare with the total rest mass energy of the created kaons? (c) Suppose that instead the two protons are both in motion with velocities of equal magnitude and opposite direction. Find the minimum combined kinetic energy of the two protons that will allow the reaction to occur. How does this calculated minimum kinetic energy compare with the total rest mass energy of the created kaons? (This example shows that when colliding beams of particles are used instead of a stationary target, the energy requirements for producing new particles are reduced substantially.)

APPENDIX A

THE INTERNATIONAL SYSTEM OF UNITS

The Système International d'Unités, abbreviated SI, is the system developed by the General Conference on Weights and Measures and adopted by nearly all the industrial nations of the world. The following material is adapted from B. N. Taylor, ed., National Institute of Standards and Technology Spec. Pub. 811 (U.S. Govt. Printing Office, Washington, DC, 1995). See also **http://physics.nist.gov/cuu**

Quantity	Name of unit	Symbol	
	SI base units		
length	meter	m	
mass	kilogram	kg	
time	second	s	
electric current	ampere	A	
thermodynamic temperature	kelvin	K	
amount of substance	mole	mol	
luminous intensity	candela	cd	
	SI derived units		**Equivalent units**
area	square meter	m^2	
volume	cubic meter	m^3	
frequency	hertz	Hz	s^{-1}
mass density (density)	kilogram per cubic meter	kg/m^3	
speed, velocity	meter per second	m/s	
angular velocity	radian per second	rad/s	
acceleration	meter per second squared	m/s^2	
angular acceleration	radian per second squared	rad/s^2	
force	newton	N	$kg \cdot m/s^2$
pressure (mechanical stress)	pascal	Pa	N/m^2
kinematic viscosity	square meter per second	m^2/s	
dynamic viscosity	newton-second per square meter	$N \cdot s/m^2$	
work, energy, quantity of heat	joule	J	$N \cdot m$
power	watt	W	J/s
quantity of electricity	coulomb	C	$A \cdot s$
potential difference, electromotive force	volt	V	J/C, W/A
electric field strength	volt per meter	V/m	N/C
electric resistance	ohm	Ω	V/A
capacitance	farad	F	$A \cdot s/V$
magnetic flux	weber	Wb	$V \cdot s$
inductance	henry	H	$V \cdot s/A$
magnetic flux density	tesla	T	Wb/m^2
magnetic field strength	ampere per meter	A/m	
magnetomotive force	ampere	A	
luminous flux	lumen	lm	$cd \cdot sr$
luminance	candela per square meter	cd/m^2	
illuminance	lux	lx	lm/m^2
wave number	1 per meter	m^{-1}	
entropy	joule per kelvin	J/K	
specific heat capacity	joule per kilogram-kelvin	$J/kg \cdot K$	
thermal conductivity	watt per meter-kelvin	$W/m \cdot K$	

Quantity	Name of unit	Symbol	Equivalent units
radiant intensity	watt per steradian	W/sr	
activity (of a radioactive source)	becquerel	Bq	s^{-1}
radiation dose	gray	Gy	J/kg
radiation dose equivalent	sievert	Sv	J/kg
	SI supplementary units		
plane angle	radian	rad	
solid angle	steradian	sr	

Definitions of SI Units

meter (m) The *meter* is the length equal to the distance traveled by light, in vacuum, in a time of 1/299,792,458 second.

kilogram (kg) The *kilogram* is the unit of mass; it is equal to the mass of the international prototype of the kilogram. (The international prototype of the kilogram is a particular cylinder of platinum-iridium alloy that is preserved in a vault at Sévres, France, by the International Bureau of Weights and Measures.)

second (s) The *second* is the duration of 9,192,631,770 periods of the radiation corresponding to the transition between the two hyperfine levels of the ground state of the cesium-133 atom.

ampere (A) The *ampere* is that constant current that, if maintained in two straight parallel conductors of infinite length, of negligible circular cross section, and placed 1 meter apart in vacuum, would produce between these conductors a force equal to 2×10^{-7} newton per meter of length.

kelvin (K) The *kelvin,* unit of thermodynamic temperature, is the fraction 1/273.16 of the thermodynamic temper-ature of the triple point of water.

ohm (Ω) The *ohm* is the electric resistance between two points of a conductor when a constant difference of potential of 1 volt, applied between these two points, produces in this conductor a current of 1 ampere, this conductor not being the source of any electromotive force.

coulomb (C) The *coulomb* is the quantity of electricity transported in 1 second by a current of 1 ampere.

candela (cd) The *candela* is the luminous intensity, in a given direction, of a source that emits monochromatic radiation of frequency 540×10^{12} hertz and that has a radiant intensity in that direction of 1/683 watt per steradian.

mole (mol) The *mole* is the amount of substance of a system that contains as many elementary entities as there are carbon atoms in 0.012 kg of carbon 12. The elementary entities must be specified and may be atoms, molecules, ions, electrons, other particles, or specified groups of such particles.

newton (N) The *newton* is that force that gives to a mass of 1 kilogram an acceleration of 1 meter per second per second.

joule (J) The *joule* is the work done when the point of application of a constant force of 1 newton is displaced a distance of 1 meter in the direction of the force.

watt (W) The *watt* is the power that gives rise to the production of energy at the rate of 1 joule per second.

volt (V) The *volt* is the difference of electric potential between two points of a conducting wire carrying a constant current of 1 ampere, when the power dissipated between these points is equal to 1 watt.

weber (Wb) The *weber* is the magnetic flux that, linking a circuit of one turn, produces in it an electromotive force of 1 volt as it is reduced to zero at a uniform rate in 1 second.

lumen (lm) The *lumen* is the luminous flux emitted in a solid angle of 1 steradian by a uniform point source having an intensity of 1 candela.

farad (F) The *farad* is the capacitance of a capacitor between the plates of which there appears a difference of potential of 1 volt when it is charged by a quantity of electricity equal to 1 coulomb.

henry (H) The *henry* is the inductance of a closed circuit in which an electromotive force of 1 volt is produced when the electric current in the circuit varies uniformly at a rate of 1 ampere per second.

radian (rad) The *radian* is the plane angle between two radii of a circle that cut off on the circumference an arc equal in length to the radius.

steradian (sr) The *steradian* is the solid angle that, having its vertex in the center of a sphere, cuts off an area of the surface of the sphere equal to that of a square with sides of length equal to the radius of the sphere.

SI Prefixes The names of multiples and submultiples of SI units may be formed by application of the prefixes listed in Appendix F.

APPENDIX B

USEFUL MATHEMATICAL RELATIONS

Algebra

$$a^{-x} = \frac{1}{a^x} \qquad a^{(x+y)} = a^x a^y \qquad a^{(x-y)} = \frac{a^x}{a^y}$$

Logarithms: If $\log a = x$, then $a = 10^x$. $\log a + \log b = \log(ab)$ $\log a - \log b = \log(a/b)$ $\log(a^n) = n \log a$

If $\ln a = x$, then $a = e^x$. $\ln a + \ln b = \ln(ab)$ $\ln a - \ln b = \ln(a/b)$ $\ln(a^n) = n \ln a$

Quadratic formula: If $ax^2 + bx + c = 0$, $x = \dfrac{-b \pm \sqrt{b^2 - 4ac}}{2a}$.

Binomial Theorem

$$(a+b)^n = a^n + na^{n-1}b + \frac{n(n-1)a^{n-2}b^2}{2!} + \frac{n(n-1)(n-2)a^{n-3}b^3}{3!} + \cdots$$

Trigonometry

In the right triangle ABC, $x^2 + y^2 = r^2$.

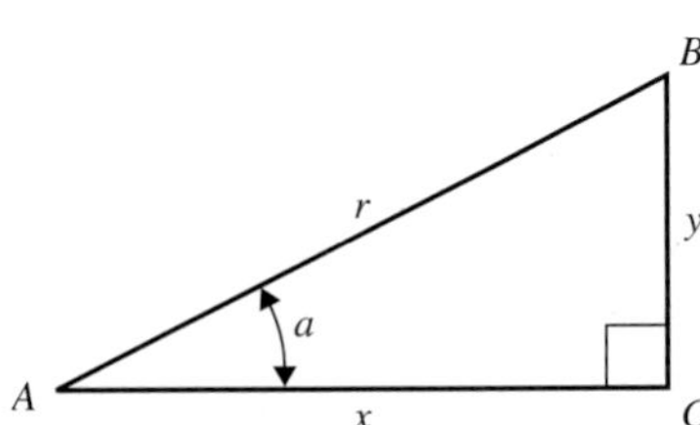

Definitions of the trigonometric functions: $\sin a = y/r$ $\cos a = x/r$ $\tan a = y/x$

Identities:

$$\sin^2 a + \cos^2 a = 1 \qquad \tan a = \frac{\sin a}{\cos a}$$

$$\sin 2a = 2 \sin a \cos a \qquad \cos 2a = \cos^2 a - \sin^2 a = 2\cos^2 a - 1 = 1 - 2\sin^2 a$$

$$\sin \tfrac{1}{2}a = \sqrt{\frac{1 - \cos a}{2}} \qquad \cos \tfrac{1}{2}a = \sqrt{\frac{1 + \cos a}{2}}$$

$$\sin(-a) = -\sin a \qquad \sin(a \pm b) = \sin a \cos b \pm \cos a \sin b$$

$$\cos(-a) = \cos a \qquad \cos(a \pm b) = \cos a \cos b \mp \sin a \sin b$$

$$\sin(a \pm \pi/2) = \pm \cos a \qquad \sin a + \sin b = 2 \sin \tfrac{1}{2}(a+b) \cos \tfrac{1}{2}(a-b)$$

$$\cos(a \pm \pi/2) = \mp \sin a \qquad \cos a + \cos b = 2 \cos \tfrac{1}{2}(a+b) \cos \tfrac{1}{2}(a-b)$$

Geometry

Circumference of circle of radius r: $C = 2\pi r$
Area of circle of radius r: $A = \pi r^2$
Volume of sphere of radius r: $V = 4\pi r^3/3$
Surface area of sphere of radius r: $A = 4\pi r^2$
Volume of cylinder of radius r and height h: $V = \pi r^2 h$

Calculus

Derivatives:

$$\frac{d}{dx}x^n = nx^{n-1}$$

$$\frac{d}{dx}\sin ax = a\cos ax$$

$$\frac{d}{dx}\cos ax = -a\sin ax$$

$$\frac{d}{dx}e^{ax} = ae^{ax}$$

$$\frac{d}{dx}\ln ax = \frac{1}{x}$$

$$\int \frac{dx}{\sqrt{a^2 - x^2}} = \arcsin\frac{x}{a}$$

$$\int \frac{dx}{\sqrt{x^2 + a^2}} = \ln\left(x + \sqrt{x^2 + a^2}\right)$$

$$\int \frac{dx}{x^2 + a^2} = \frac{1}{a}\arctan\frac{x}{a}$$

$$\int \frac{dx}{(x^2 + a^2)^{3/2}} = \frac{1}{a^2}\frac{x}{\sqrt{x^2 + a^2}}$$

$$\int \frac{x\,dx}{(x^2 + a^2)^{3/2}} = -\frac{1}{\sqrt{x^2 + a^2}}$$

Integrals:

$$\int x^n\,dx = \frac{x^{n+1}}{n+1} \quad (n \neq -1)$$

$$\int \frac{dx}{x} = \ln x$$

$$\int \sin ax\,dx = -\frac{1}{a}\cos ax$$

$$\int \cos ax\,dx = \frac{1}{a}$$

$$\int e^{ax}\,dx = \frac{1}{a}e^{ax}$$

Power series (convergent for range of x shown):

$$(1 + x)^n = 1 + nx + \frac{n(n-1)x^2}{2!} + \frac{n(n-1)(n-2)}{3!}x^3 + \cdots \quad (|x| < 1)$$

$$\sin x = x - \frac{x^3}{3!} + \frac{x^5}{5!} - \frac{x^7}{7!} + \cdots \quad (\text{all } x)$$

$$\cos x = 1 - \frac{x^2}{2!} + \frac{x^4}{4!} - \frac{x^6}{6!} + \cdots \quad (\text{all } x)$$

$$\tan x = x + \frac{x^3}{3} + \frac{2x^2}{15} + \frac{17x^7}{315} + \cdots \quad (|x| < \pi/2)$$

$$e^x = 1 + x + \frac{x^2}{2!} + \frac{x^3}{3!} + \cdots \quad (\text{all } x)$$

$$\ln(1 + x) = x - \frac{x^2}{2} + \frac{x^3}{3} - \frac{x^4}{4} + \cdots \quad (|x| < 1)$$

APPENDIX C

THE GREEK ALPHABET

Name	Capital	Lowercase	Name	Capital	Lowercase
Alpha	A	α	Nu	N	ν
Beta	B	β	Xi	Ξ	ξ
Gamma	Γ	γ	Omicron	O	o
Delta	Δ	δ	Pi	Π	π
Epsilon	E	ϵ	Rho	P	ρ
Zeta	Z	ζ	Sigma	Σ	σ
Eta	H	η	Tau	T	τ
Theta	Θ	θ	Upsilon	Υ	υ
Iota	I	ι	Phi	Φ	ϕ
Kappa	K	κ	Chi	X	χ
Lambda	Λ	λ	Psi	Ψ	ψ
Mu	M	μ	Omega	Ω	ω

APPENDIX D

PERIODIC TABLE OF THE ELEMENTS

Group / Period	1	2	3	4	5	6	7	8	9	10	11	12	13	14	15	16	17	18
1	1 **H** 1.008																	2 **He** 4.003
2	3 **Li** 6.941	4 **Be** 9.012											5 **B** 10.811	6 **C** 12.011	7 **N** 14.007	8 **O** 15.999	9 **F** 18.998	10 **Ne** 20.180
3	11 **Na** 22.990	12 **Mg** 24.305											13 **Al** 26.982	14 **Si** 28.086	15 **P** 30.974	16 **S** 32.065	17 **Cl** 35.453	18 **Ar** 39.948
4	19 **K** 39.098	20 **Ca** 40.078	21 **Sc** 44.956	22 **Ti** 47.867	23 **V** 50.942	24 **Cr** 51.996	25 **Mn** 54.938	26 **Fe** 55.845	27 **Co** 58.933	28 **Ni** 58.693	29 **Cu** 63.546	30 **Zn** 65.409	31 **Ga** 69.723	32 **Ge** 72.64	33 **As** 74.922	34 **Se** 78.96	35 **Br** 79.904	36 **Kr** 83.798
5	37 **Rb** 85.468	38 **Sr** 87.62	39 **Y** 88.906	40 **Zr** 91.224	41 **Nb** 92.906	42 **Mo** 95.94	43 **Tc** (98)	44 **Ru** 101.07	45 **Rh** 102.906	46 **Pd** 106.42	47 **Ag** 107.868	48 **Cd** 112.411	49 **In** 114.818	50 **Sn** 118.710	51 **Sb** 121.760	52 **Te** 127.60	53 **I** 126.904	54 **Xe** 131.293
6	55 **Cs** 132.905	56 **Ba** 137.327	71 **Lu** 174.967	72 **Hf** 178.49	73 **Ta** 180.948	74 **W** 183.84	75 **Re** 186.207	76 **Os** 190.23	77 **Ir** 192.217	78 **Pt** 195.078	79 **Au** 196.967	80 **Hg** 200.59	81 **Tl** 204.383	82 **Pb** 207.2	83 **Bi** 208.980	84 **Po** (209)	85 **At** (210)	86 **Rn** (222)
7	87 **Fr** (223)	88 **Ra** (226)	103 **Lr** (262)	104 **Rf** (261)	105 **Db** (262)	106 **Sg** (266)	107 **Bh** (264)	108 **Hs** (269)	109 **Mt** (268)	110 **Ds** (271)	111 **Rg** (272)	112 **Uub** (285)	113 **Uut** (284)	114 **Uuq** (289)	115 **Uup** (288)	116 **Uuh** (292)	117 **Uus**	118 **Uuo**

Lanthanoids	57 **La** 138.905	58 **Ce** 140.116	59 **Pr** 140.908	60 **Nd** 144.24	61 **Pm** (145)	62 **Sm** 150.36	63 **Eu** 151.964	64 **Gd** 157.25	65 **Tb** 158.925	66 **Dy** 162.500	67 **Ho** 164.930	68 **Er** 167.259	69 **Tm** 168.934	70 **Yb** 173.04
Actinoids	89 **Ac** (227)	90 **Th** (232)	91 **Pa** (231)	92 **U** (238)	93 **Np** (237)	94 **Pu** (244)	95 **Am** (243)	96 **Cm** (247)	97 **Bk** (247)	98 **Cf** (251)	99 **Es** (252)	100 **Fm** (257)	101 **Md** (258)	102 **No** (259)

For each element the average atomic mass of the mixture of isotopes occurring in nature is shown. For elements having no stable isotope, the approximate atomic mass of the longest-lived isotope is shown in parentheses. For elements that have been predicted but not yet detected, no atomic mass is given. All atomic masses are expressed in atomic mass units ($1 \text{ u} = 1.66053886(28) \times 10^{-27}$ kg), equivalent to grams per mole (g/mol).

APPENDIX E

UNIT CONVERSION FACTORS

Length

1 m = 100 cm = 1000 mm = 10^6 μm = 10^9 nm
1 km = 1000 m = 0.6214 mi
1 m = 3.281 ft = 39.37 in.
1 cm = 0.3937 in.
1 in. = 2.540 cm
1 ft = 30.48 cm
1 yd = 91.44 cm
1 mi = 5280 ft = 1.609 km
1 Å = 10^{-10} m = 10^{-8} cm = 10^{-1} nm
1 nautical mile = 6080 ft
1 light year = 9.461×10^{15} m

Area

1 cm^2 = 0.155 in.^{2}
1 m^2 = 10^4 cm^2 = 10.76 ft^2
1 in.^{2} = 6.452 cm^2
1 ft = 144 in.^{2} = 0.0929 m^2

Volume

1 liter = 1000 cm^3 = 10^{-3} m^3 = 0.03531 ft^3 = 61.02 in.^{3}
1 ft^3 = 0.02832 m^3 = 28.32 liters = 7.477 gallons
1 gallon = 3.788 liters

Time

1 min = 60 s
1 h = 3600 s
1 d = 86,400 s
1 y = 365.24 d = 3.156×10^7 s

Angle

1 rad = 57.30° = 180°/π
1° = 0.01745 rad = π/180 rad
1 revolution = 360° = 2π rad
1 rev/min (rpm) = 0.1047 rad/s

Speed

1 m/s = 3.281 ft/s
1 ft/s = 0.3048 m/s
1 mi/min = 60 mi/h = 88 ft/s
1 km/h = 0.2778 m/s = 0.6214 mi/h
1 mi/h = 1.466 ft/s = 0.4470 m/s = 1.609 km/h
1 furlong/fortnight = 1.662×10^{-4} m/s

Acceleration

1 m/s^2 = 100 cm/s^2 = 3.281 ft/s^2
1 cm/s^2 = 0.01 m/s^2 = 0.03281 ft/s^2
1 ft/s^2 = 0.3048 m/s^2 = 30.48 cm/s^2
1 mi/h · s = 1.467 ft/s^2

Mass

1 kg = 10^3 g = 0.0685 slug
1 g = 6.85×10^{-5} slug
1 slug = 14.59 kg
1 u = 1.661×10^{-27} kg
1 kg has a weight of 2.205 lb when g = 9.80 m/s^2

Force

1 N = 10^5 dyn = 0.2248 lb
1 lb = 4.448 N = 4.448×10^5 dyn

Pressure

1 Pa = 1 N/m^2 = 1.450×10^{-4}lb/in.^{2} = 0.209 lb/ft^2
1 bar = 10^5 Pa
1 lb/in.^{2} = 6895 Pa
1 lb/ft^2 = 47.88 Pa
1 atm = 1.013×10^5 Pa = 1.013 bar
= 14.7 lb/in.^{2} = 2117 lb/ft^2
1 mm Hg = 1 torr = 133.3 Pa

Energy

1 J = 10^7ergs = 0.239 cal
1 cal = 4.186 J (based on 15° calorie)
1 ft · lb = 1.356 J
1 Btu = 1055 J = 252 cal = 778 ft · lb
1 eV = 1.602×10^{-19} J
1 kWh = 3.600×10^6 J

Mass–Energy Equivalence

1 kg ↔ 8.988×10^{16} J
1 u ↔ 931.5 MeV
1 eV ↔ 1.074×10^{-9} u

Power

1 W = 1 J/s
1 hp = 746 W = 550 ft · lb/s
1 Btu/h = 0.293 W

APPENDIX F

NUMERICAL CONSTANTS

Fundamental Physical Constants*

Name	Symbol	Value
Speed of light	c	2.99792458×10^{8} m/s
Magnitude of charge of electron	e	$1.60217653(14) \times 10^{-19}$ C
Gravitational constant	G	$6.6742(10) \times 10^{-11}\ \mathrm{N \cdot m^2/kg^2}$
Planck's constant	h	$6.6260693(11) \times 10^{-34}\ \mathrm{J \cdot s}$
Boltzmann constant	k	$1.3806505(24) \times 10^{-23}$ J/K
Avogadro's number	N_A	$6.0221415(10) \times 10^{23}$ molecules/mol
Gas constant	R	$8.314472(15)\ \mathrm{J/mol \cdot K}$
Mass of electron	m_e	$9.1093826(16) \times 10^{-31}$ kg
Mass of proton	m_p	$1.67262171(29) \times 10^{-27}$ kg
Mass of neutron	m_n	$1.67492728(29) \times 10^{-27}$ kg
Permeability of free space	μ_0	$4\pi \times 10^{-7}\ \mathrm{Wb/A \cdot m}$
Permittivity of free space	$\epsilon_0 = 1/\mu_0 c^2$	$8.854187817 \ldots \times 10^{-12}\ \mathrm{C^2/N \cdot m^2}$
	$1/4\pi\epsilon_0$	$8.987551787 \ldots \times 10^{9}\ \mathrm{N \cdot m^2/C^2}$

Other Useful Constants*

Mechanical equivalent of heat		4.186 J/cal (15° calorie)
Standard atmospheric pressure	1 atm	1.01325×10^{5} Pa
Absolute zero	0 K	−273.15°C
Electron volt	1 eV	$1.60217653(14) \times 10^{-19}$ J
Atomic mass unit	1 u	$1.66053886(28) \times 10^{-27}$ kg
Electron rest energy	$m_e c^2$	0.510998918(44) MeV
Volume of ideal gas (0°C and 1 atm)		22.413996(39) liter/mol
Acceleration due to gravity (standard)	g	$9.80665\ \mathrm{m/s^2}$

*Source: National Institute of Standards and Technology (**http://physics.nist.gov/cuu**). Numbers in parentheses show the uncertainty in the final digits of the main number; for example, the number 1.6454(21) means 1.6454 ± 0.0021. Values shown without uncertainties are exact.

Astronomical Data[†]

Body	Mass (kg)	Radius (m)	Orbit radius (m)	Orbit period
Sun	1.99×10^{30}	6.96×10^{8}	—	—
Moon	7.35×10^{22}	1.74×10^{6}	3.84×10^{8}	27.3 d
Mercury	3.30×10^{23}	2.44×10^{6}	5.79×10^{10}	88.0 d
Venus	4.87×10^{24}	6.05×10^{6}	1.08×10^{11}	224.7 d
Earth	5.97×10^{24}	6.38×10^{6}	1.50×10^{11}	365.3 d
Mars	6.42×10^{23}	3.40×10^{6}	2.28×10^{11}	687.0 d
Jupiter	1.90×10^{27}	6.91×10^{7}	7.78×10^{11}	11.86 y
Saturn	5.68×10^{26}	6.03×10^{7}	1.43×10^{12}	29.45 y
Uranus	8.68×10^{25}	2.56×10^{7}	2.87×10^{12}	84.02 y
Neptune	1.02×10^{26}	2.48×10^{7}	4.50×10^{12}	164.8 y
Pluto[‡]	1.31×10^{22}	1.15×10^{6}	5.91×10^{12}	247.9 y

[†]Source: NASA Jet Propulsion Laboratory Solar System Dynamics Group (**http://ssd.jpl.nasa.gov**), and P. Kenneth Seidelmann, ed., ***Explanatory Supplement to the Astronomical Almanac*** (University Science Books, Mill Valley, CA, 1992), pp. 704–706. For each body, "radius" is its radius at its equator and "orbit radius" is its average distance from the sun (for the planets) or from the earth (for the moon).

[‡]In August 2006, the International Astronomical Union reclassified Pluto and other small objects that orbit the sun as "dwarf planets."

Prefixes for Powers of 10

Power of ten	Prefix	Abbreviation	Pronunciation
10^{-24}	yocto-	y	*yoc*-toe
10^{-21}	zepto-	z	*zep*-toe
10^{-18}	atto-	a	*at*-toe
10^{-15}	femto-	f	*fem*-toe
10^{-12}	pico-	p	*pee*-koe
10^{-9}	nano-	n	*nan*-oe
10^{-6}	micro-	μ	*my*-crow
10^{-3}	milli-	m	*mil*-i
10^{-2}	centi-	c	*cen*-ti
10^{3}	kilo-	k	*kil*-oe
10^{6}	mega-	M	*meg*-a
10^{9}	giga-	G	*jig*-a or *gig*-a
10^{12}	tera-	T	*ter*-a
10^{15}	peta-	P	*pet*-a
10^{18}	exa-	E	*ex*-a
10^{21}	zetta-	Z	*zet*-a
10^{24}	yotta-	Y	*yot*-a

Examples:

1 femtometer = 1 fm = 10^{-15} m

1 picosecond = 1 ps = 10^{-12} s

1 nanocoulomb = 1 nC = 10^{-9} C

1 microkelvin = 1 μK = 10^{-6} K

1 millivolt = 1 mV = 10^{-3} V

1 kilopascal = 1 kPa = 10^{3} Pa

1 megawatt = 1 MW = 10^{6} W

1 gigahertz = 1 GHz = 10^{9} Hz

ANSWERS TO ODD-NUMBERED PROBLEMS

Chapter 1

1.1 a) 1.61 km b) 3.28×10^3 ft
1.3 1.02 ns
1.5 5.36 L
1.7 31.7 y
1.9 a) 23.4 km/L b) 1.42 tanks
1.11 9.0 cm
1.13 a) 1.1×10^{-3}% b) no
1.15 a) 0.1% b) 0.008% c) 0.03%
1.17 a) $28 \pm 0.3\ \text{cm}^3$ b) 170 ± 20
1.19 a) no b) no c) no d) no e) no
1.21 10^6
1.23 10^9
1.25 \$70 million
1.29 \$$9 \times 10^{14}$; about \$$3 \times 10^6$
1.31 7.8 km, 38° north of east
1.33 144 m, 41° south of west
1.35 $A_x = 0$, $A_y = -8.00$ m; $B_x = 7.50$ m, $B_y = 13.0$ m; $C_x = -10.9$ m, $C_y = -5.07$ m; $D_x = -7.99$ m, $D_y = 6.02$ m
1.37 1190 N; 13.4° above forward direction
1.39 a) 9.01 m, 33.7° b) 9.01 m, 33.7° c) 22.3 m, 250.3° d) 22.3 m, 70.3°
1.41 5.06 km, 20.2° north of west
1.43 a) 2.48 cm, 18.3° b) 4.10 cm, 83.7° c) 4.10 cm, 263.7°
1.45 781 N, 166°
1.47 $\vec{A} = -(8.00\ \text{m})\hat{\jmath}$; $\vec{B} = (7.50\ \text{m})\hat{\imath} + (13.0\ \text{m})\hat{\jmath}$; $\vec{C} = -(10.9\ \text{m})\hat{\imath} + (-5.07\ \text{m})\hat{\jmath}$; $\vec{D} = (-7.99\ \text{m})\hat{\imath} + (6.02\ \text{m})\hat{\jmath}$
1.49 a) $\vec{A} = (1.23\ \text{m})\hat{\imath} + (3.38\ \text{m})\hat{\jmath}$; $\vec{B} = (-2.08\ \text{m})\hat{\imath} + (-1.20\ \text{m})\hat{\jmath}$ b) $\vec{C} = (12.01\ \text{m})\hat{\imath} + (14.94\ \text{m})\hat{\jmath}$ c) 19.17 m; 51.2°
1.51 a) no b) no; yes c) ± 0.20
1.53 a) $-104\ \text{m}^2$ b) $-148\ \text{m}^2$ c) $40.6\ \text{m}^2$
1.55 a) 165° b) 28° c) 90°
1.57 a) 63.9 m; $-\hat{k}$ b) 63.9 m; $+\hat{k}$
1.59 a) $4.61\ \text{cm}^2$; $-z$ b) $4.61\ \text{cm}^2$; $+z$
1.61 a) 1.65×10^4 km b) 2.6 earth radii
1.63 10^{28}
1.65 a) 2.94 cm b) 1.82 cm
1.67 a) 10^{50} b) 10^{57} c) 10^{79}
1.69 149 N; 32.2° north of east
1.71 b) $A_x = 3.03$ cm, $A_y = 8.10$ cm c) 8.65 cm; 69.5° from the $+x$-axis toward the $+y$-axis
1.73 144 m, 41° south of west
1.75 a) 46 N, 139°
1.77 a) (87, 258) b) 136 pixels, 25° below straight left
1.79 380 km, 28.8° south of east
1.81 160 N, 13° below horizontal
1.83 a) 911 m; 8.9° west of south
1.87 b) 90°
1.89 a) $A = 5.39$, $B = 4.36$ b) $-5.00\hat{\imath} + 2.00\hat{\jmath} + 7.00\hat{k}$ c) 8.83; yes
1.93 a) 54.7° b) 35.3°
1.95 $C_x = 8.0$, $C_y = 6.1$
1.97 b) 72.2
1.99 38.5 yd, 24.6° to right of downfield
1.101 a) 76 ly b) 129°

Chapter 2

2.1 a) 197 m/s b) 169 m/s
2.3 1 h 10 min
2.5 a) 17.1 s b) faster: 106 m; slower: 94 m
2.7 250 km
2.9 a) 12.0 m/s b) 0 m/s, 15.0 m/s, 12.0 m/s c) 13.3 s
2.11 a) 2.3 m/s, 2.3 m/s b) 2.3 m/s, 0.33 m/s
2.13 a) no b) (i) $12.8\ \text{m/s}^2$ (ii) $3.5\ \text{m/s}^2$ (iii) $0.72\ \text{m/s}^2$; yes
2.15 a) 2.00 cm/s, 50.0 cm, $-0.125\ \text{cm/s}^2$ b) 16.0 s c) 32.0 s d) 6.20 s, 1.22 cm/s; 25.8 s, -1.22 cm/s; 36.4 s, -2.55 cm/s
2.17 a) $3\ \text{m/s}^2$ b) $10\ \text{m/s}^2$ c) depends on positive coordinate direction
2.21 a) 5.0 m/s b) $1.43\ \text{m/s}^2$
2.23 a) $675\ \text{m/s}^2$ b) 0.067 s
2.25 1.70
2.27 a) (i) $5.59\ \text{m/s}^2$ (ii) $7.74\ \text{m/s}^2$ b) (i) 179 m (ii) 12,800 m
2.29 a) $+2.7$ cm/s, -1.3 cm/s b) $-1.3\ \text{cm/s}^2$ c) 22.5 cm; 25.5 cm
2.31 a) 0, $6.3\ \text{m/s}^2$, $-11.2\ \text{m/s}^2$ b) 100 m, 230 m, 320 m
2.33 a) 1.80×10^4 m/s b) 0.957 c) 6 h 11 min
2.35 b) 1 s, 3 s d) 2 s e) 3 s f) 1 s
2.37 a) A: $20.5\ \text{m/s}^2$; B: $3.8\ \text{m/s}^2$; C: $53\ \text{m/s}^2$ b) 721 km
2.39 a) 2.94 m/s b) 0.599 s
2.41 a) $t = \sqrt{2d/g}$ b) 0.190 s
2.43 a) 646 m b) 16.4 s, 112 m/s
2.45 a) 25.6 m/s b) 31.6 m c) 15.2 m/s
2.47 a) $249\ \text{m/s}^2$ b) 25.4 c) 101 m d) no
2.49 $0.0868\ \text{m/s}^2$
2.51 a) $x(t) = (0.250\ \text{m/s}^3)t^3 - (0.0100\ \text{m/s}^4)t^4$; $v_x(t) = (0.750\ \text{m/s}^3)t^2 - (0.0400\ \text{m/s}^4)t^3$ b) 39.1 m/s
2.53 a) 30.0 cm/s
2.55 b) 0.627 s, 1.60 s c) negative at 0.627 s, positive at 1.60 s d) 1.11 s e) 2.45 m f) 2.00 s, 0 s
2.57 a) 82 km/h b) 31 km/h
2.59 a) $3.5\ \text{m/s}^2$ b) 0 c) $1.5\ \text{m/s}^2$
2.61 a) 92.0 m b) 92.0 m
2.63 a) 464 m/s b) 2.99×10^4 m/s c) 7.48
2.65 50.0 m
2.67 $4.6\ \text{m/s}^2$
2.69 a) 6.17 s b) 24.8 m c) $v_{\text{truck}} = 13.0$ m/s, $v_{\text{auto}} = 21.0$ m/s
2.71 a) 7.85 cm/s b) 5.00 cm/s, horizontal from the initial to final position
2.73 a) 15.9 s b) 393 m c) 29.5 m/s
2.75 a) -4.00 m/s b) 12.0 m/s
2.77 a) $2.64H$ b) $2.64T$
2.79 a) no b) yes; 14.4 m/s; not physically attainable
2.81 a) $6.79 \times 10^4 g$ b) 1.45 m/s c) $H/4$
2.83 a) 7.59 m/s b) 5.14 m c) 1.60 s
2.85 a) 7.7 m/s b) 0.78 s c) 0.59 s d) 1.3 m
2.87 270 m
2.89 a) 20.5 m/s b) yes
2.91 a) 947 m b) 393 m
2.93 a) A b) 2.27 s, 5.73 s c) 1.00 s, 4.33 s d) 2.67 s
2.95 a) 9.55 s, 4.78 m b) 1.62 m/s d) 8.38 m/s e) no f) 3.69 m/s, 21.7 s, 80.0 m
2.97 a) 8.18 m/s b) (i) 0.411 m (ii) 1.15 km c) 9.80 m/s d) 4.90 m/s

Chapter 3

3.1 a) $v_{\text{av-}x} = 1.4$ m/s, $v_{\text{av-}y} = -1.3$ m/s b) 1.9 m/s, $-43°$
3.3 a) 7.1 cm/s, 45° b) 5.0 cm/s, 90°; 7.1 cm/s; 45°; 11 cm/s, 27°
3.5 b) $a_{\text{av-}x} = -8.67\ \text{m/s}^2$, $a_{\text{av-}y} = -2.33\ \text{m/s}^2$ c) $8.98\ \text{m/s}^2$, 195°
3.7 b) $\vec{v} = \alpha\hat{\imath} + (-2\beta)\hat{\jmath}$; $\vec{a} = -2\beta\hat{\jmath}$ c) $v = 5.4$ m/s, $-63°$; $a = 2.4\ \text{m/s}^2$, $-90°$ d) speeding up and turning right
3.9 b) 0.600 m b) 0.385 m c) $v_x = 1.10$ m/s, $v_y = -3.43$ m/s; $v = 3.60$ m/s, 72.2° below the horizontal
3.11 3.32 m
3.13 a) 30.6 m/s b) 36.3 m/s
3.15 $1.29\ \text{m/s}^2$
3.17 a) 40.0 m/s, 69.3 m/s b) 7.07 s c) 245 m d) 565 m e) $a_x = 0$, $a_y = -9.80\ \text{m/s}^2$; $v_x = 40.0$ m/s, $v_y = 0$
3.19 a) 0.682 s, 2.99 s b) 24.0 m/s, 11.3 m/s; 24.0 m/s, -11.3 m/s c) 30.0 m/s, $-36.9°$
3.21 a) 1.5 m b) -0.89 m/s
3.23 a) 13.6 m b) 34.6 m/s c) 103 m
3.25 a) 296 m b) 176 m c) 198 m d) horizontal: 15 m/s; vertical: 58.8 m/s e) horizontal: 15 m/s; vertical: 78.8 m/s
3.27 795 m
3.29 a) $0.034\ \text{m/s}^2$, $0.0034g$ b) $1.4h$
3.31 a) 3.07 s b) 1.68 s
3.33 a) $3.50\ \text{m/s}^2$, upward b) $3.50\ \text{m/s}^2$, downward c) 12.6 s
3.35 a) 32.9 m/s b) $27.7\ \text{m/s}^2$ c) 35.5 rpm
3.37 a) 14 s b) 70 s
3.39 0.36 m/s, 38° west of south
3.41 a) 4.7 m/s, 25° south of east b) 190 s c) 380 m
3.43 b) -7.1 m/s, -42 m/s c) 43 m/s, 9.5° west of south
3.45 a) $A = 0$, $B = 2.00\ \text{m/s}^2$, $C = 50.0$ m, $D = 0.50\ \text{m/s}^3$ b) $\vec{a} = (4.00\ \text{m/s}^2)\hat{\imath}$, $v = 0$ c) $v_x = 40.0$ m/s, $v_y = 150$ m/s, $v = 155$ m/s c) $\vec{r} = (200\ \text{m})\hat{\imath} + (550\ \text{m})\hat{\jmath}$
3.47 a) 124 m b) 280 m
3.49 22 m/s
3.51 40 m/s
3.53 274 m
3.55 a) 42.8 m/s b) 42.0 m
3.57 a) $\sqrt{2gh}$ b) 30.0° c) $6.93h$
3.59 c) less than 45°
3.61 b) 15°, 75°
3.63 a) 17.8 m/s b) in river, 28.4 m from the near bank
3.65 a) 81.6 m b) in cart c) 245 m d) 53.1°
3.67 a) 49 m/s b) 50 m
3.69 a) 2000 m b) 2180 m
3.71 a) 38.5 m/s b) (i) 25.0 m/s, 0 (ii) 25.0 m/s, 38.5 m/s c) (i) 0° (ii) 57.0° d) 499 m
3.73 $\pm 25.4°$
3.77 b) $v_x = R\omega(1 - \cos\omega t)$, $v_y = R\omega\sin\omega t$, $a_x = R\omega^2\sin\omega t$, $a_y = R\omega^2\cos\omega t$ c) $t = 0, 2\pi/\omega, 4\pi/\omega, \ldots$; $x = 0, 2\pi R, 4\pi R, \ldots$; $y = 0$; $a = R\omega^2$ in the $+y$ direction d) no
3.79 a) $2.50g$ b) $0.614n$
3.81 a) 44.7 km/h, 26.6° west of south b) 10.5° north of west
3.83 a) 0.659 s b) (i) 9.10 m/s (ii) 6.46 m/s c) 3.00 m, 2.13 m
3.85 7.39 m/s, 12.4° north of east
3.87 a) 80 m b) 1.6×10^{-3} c) overall effect is to reduce radius
3.89 a) $\left(\dfrac{2v_0^2}{g}\right)[\tan(\theta + \phi) - \tan\theta]\dfrac{\cos^2(\theta + \phi)}{\cos\theta}$ b) $\dfrac{\pi}{4} - \dfrac{\theta}{2}$
3.91 $\Delta t = 0.5$ s: $9.589\ \text{m/s}^2$, 118.6°; $\Delta t = 0.1$ s: $9.983\ \text{m/s}^2$, 95.73°; $\Delta t = 0.05$ s: $9.996\ \text{m/s}^2$, 92.86°
3.93 a) 1.5 km/h b) 3.5 km/h

Chapter 4

4.1 a) 0° b) 90° c) 180°
4.3 7.1 N to the right, 7.1 N downward
4.5 494 N, 31.7°
4.7 $2.2\ \text{m/s}^2$
4.9 16.0 kg
4.11 a) 3.13 m, 3.13 m/s b) 21.9 m, 6.25 m/s
4.13 a) 45.0 N; $t = 2$ s to 4 s b) 2 s to 4 s c) 0, 6 s
4.15 a) $A = 100$ N, $B = 12.5\ \text{N/s}^2$ b) (i) 21.6 N, $2.70\ \text{m/s}^2$ (ii) 134 N, $16.8\ \text{m/s}^2$ c) $26.6\ \text{m/s}^2$
4.17 2.94×10^3 N
4.19 a) 4.49 kg b) 4.49 kg, 8.13 N
4.21 825 N, blocks

4.23 a) gravity exerted by earth on bottle; force of air on bottle b) gravity exerted by bottle on earth; force of bottle on air
4.25 7.4×10^{-23} m/s^2
4.27 b) yes
4.29 yes, in part (a)
4.31 b) 142 N
4.33 c) force exerted by the ground on the truck
4.35 1840 N, 135°
4.37 a) 17 N, 90° clockwise from $+x$-direction b) 840 N
4.39 a) 4.8 m/s b) 16 m/s^2 c) 2360 N
4.41 b) 5.83 m/s^2
4.43 a) 2.50 m/s^2 b) 10.0 N c) to the right; F d) 25.0 N
4.45 a) 2.93 m/s^2 b) 11.1 m/s^2
4.47 b) 79.6 N
4.49 a) mg b) mg c) $m(g + |\vec{a}|)$ d) $m(g - |\vec{a}|)$
4.51 a) 7.80 m/s b) 50.6 m/s^2 c) 4532 N, 6.16mg
4.53 a) w b) 0 c) $w/2$
4.55 b) 1390 N
4.57 b) (i) 3.5 m/s^2 (ii) 8.0 N
4.59 $-6mBt$

Chapter 5

5.1 a) 25.0 N b) 50.0 N
5.3 a) 990 N, 735 N b) 926 N
5.5 48°
5.7 4.10×10^3 N
5.9 a) A: 0.732w; B: 0.897w; C: w b) A: 2.73w; B: 3.35w; C: w
5.11 a) 337 N b) 343 N
5.13 a) 470 N b) 163 N
5.15 b) 1.22mg c) 0.70mg
5.17 a) 4610 m/s^2, 470g b) 9.70×10^5 N, 471w c) 18.7 ms
5.19 b) 2.96 m/s^2 c) 191 N; more than the bricks, less than the counterweight
5.21 b) 2.50 m/s^2 c) 1.37 kg d) $T = 0.745w$
5.23 a) 0.832 m/s^2 b) 17.3 s
5.25 1.38°
5.29 a) 22 N b) 3.1 m
5.31 a) 0.710, 0.472 b) 258 N c) (i) 51.8 N (ii) 4.97 m/s^2
5.33 a) 57.1 N b) 146 N, up the ramp
5.35 11 times farther
5.37 a) $\mu_k(m_A + m_B)g$ b) $\mu_k m_A g$
5.39 3.82 m/s^2
5.41 a) 0.218 m/s b) 11.7 N
5.43 a) $\mu_k mg/(\cos\theta - \mu_k \sin\theta)$ b) $1/\tan\theta = \mu_k$
5.45 b) 8.75 N c) 30.8 N d) 1.54 m/s^2
5.47 a) 0.44 kg/m b) 42 m/s
5.49 a) 3.61 m/s b) bottom c) 3.33 m/s
5.51 a) 21.0°; no b) car: 1.18×10^4 N; truck: 2.36×10^4 N
5.53 upper cable: 1410 N; horizontal cable: 8360 N
5.55 a) 1.49 rev/min b) 0.918 rev/min
5.57 a) 138 km/h b) 3580 N
5.59 2.43 m/s
5.61 a) rope making 60° angle b) 6400 N
5.63 a) $Mg/(2\sin\theta)$ b) $Mg/(2\tan\theta)$ c) $T \to \infty$
5.65 a) $m_1(\sin\alpha + \mu_k\cos\alpha)$ b) $m_1(\sin\alpha - \mu_k\cos\alpha)$ c) $m_1(\sin\alpha - \mu_s\cos\alpha) < m_2 < m_1(\sin\alpha + \mu_s\cos\alpha)$
5.67 a) 1.44 N b) 1.80 N
5.69 a) 1.3×10^{-4} N; 62.5w b) 2.9×10^{-4} N at 1.2 ms c) 1.2 m/s
5.71 1040 N
5.73 a) 11 m/s b) 7.5 m/s
5.75 0.40
5.77 a) $g\left(\dfrac{m_B + m_{\text{rope}}d/L}{m_A + m_B + m_{\text{rope}}}\right)$; increases b) 0.63 m c) will not work for any value of d
5.79 a) 66 N, northward b) 59 N, southward
5.81 a) 294 N, 152 N, 152 N b) 40.0 N
5.83 2.52 N
5.85 a) 12.9 kg b) 47.2 N in left-hand cord, 101 N in right-hand cord
5.87 $a_1 = 2m_2g/(4m_1 + m_2)$; $a_2 = 2m_2g/(4m_1 + m_2)$
5.89 1.46 m above the floor
5.91 g/μ_s
5.93 b) 0.450
5.95 0.34
5.97 a) 170 m b) 18 m/s, 41 mi/h c) 25 m/s, 56 mi/h
5.99 a) move up b) remains constant c) remains constant d) stop
5.101 a) 6.00 m/s^2 b) 0.380 m/s^2 c) 7.36 m/s d) 8.18 m/s e) 7.78 m, 6.29 m/s, 1.38 m/s^2 f) 3.14 s
5.103 1/3
5.105 a) $v_y(t) = v_t + (v_0 - v_t)e^{-kt/m}$ b) $v_y(t) = v_t(\sin\beta - 0.015\cos\beta)^{1/2}$
5.107 a) 0.015; 0.036 N · s^2/m^2 b) 29 m/s c) ratio is $(\sin\beta - 0.015\cos\beta)^{1/2}$
5.109 a) 120 N b) 3.79 m/s
5.111 b) 0.28 c) no
5.113 a) right b) 120 m
5.115 a) 81.1° b) no c) bead rides at bottom of hoop ($\beta = 0$)
5.119 $T_{\max} = 2\pi\sqrt{\left(\dfrac{h\tan\beta}{g}\right)\left(\dfrac{\sin\beta + \mu_s\cos\beta}{\cos\beta - \mu_s\sin\beta}\right)}$; $T_{\min} = 2\pi\sqrt{\left(\dfrac{h\tan\beta}{g}\right)\left(\dfrac{\sin\beta - \mu_s\cos\beta}{\cos\beta + \mu_s\sin\beta}\right)}$
5.121 $(M + m)g\tan\alpha$
5.123 a) $F = \dfrac{\mu_k w}{\cos\theta + \mu_k\sin\theta}$ b) $\theta = \tan^{-1}(\mu_k) = 14.0°$
5.125 a) $a_3 = g\left(\dfrac{-4m_1m_2 + m_2m_3 + m_3m_1}{4m_1m_2 + m_2m_3 + m_3m_1}\right)$ b) $a_B = -a_3$ c) $a_1 = g\left(\dfrac{4m_1m_2 - 3m_2m_3 + m_3m_1}{4m_1m_2 + m_2m_3 + m_3m_1}\right)$ d) $a_2 = g\left(\dfrac{4m_1m_2 + m_2m_3 - 3m_3m_1}{4m_1m_2 + m_2m_3 + m_3m_1}\right)$ e) $T_A = \frac{1}{2}T_C$ f) $T_C = \dfrac{8gm_1m_2m_3}{4m_1m_2 + m_2m_3 + m_3m_1}$ g) $a_1 = a_2 = a_3 = a_B = 0$, $T_C = 2m_2g$, $T_A = m_2g$; yes
5.127 $\cos^2\beta$

Chapter 6

6.1 a) 3.60 J b) −0.900 J c) 2.70 J
6.3 a) 74 N b) 330 J c) −330 J d) zero; zero e) zero
6.5 a) −1750 J b) no
6.7 a) (i) 9.00 J (ii) −9.00 J b) (i) 0 (ii) 9.00 J (iii) −9.00 J (iv) 0 c) zero for each block
6.9 a) (i) zero (ii) zero b) (i) zero (ii) −25.1 J
6.11 a) 1.0×10^{16} J b) about 2 times greater
6.13 a) 42.85V b) 1836K
6.15 a) 43.2 m/s b) 101 m/s c) 5.80 m d) 3.53 m/s e) 7.35 m
6.17 $(2gh[1 + \mu_k/\tan\alpha])^{1/2}$
6.19 a) 9D b) $D/3$
6.21 32.0 N
6.23 a) 4.48 m/s b) 3.61 m/s
6.25 a) 4.96 m/s b) a = 1.43 m/s^2; v = 4.96 m/s; same
6.27 a) $v_0^2/2\mu_k g$ b) 1/2 c) 4 d) 2
6.29 a) 48.0 N, 64.0 N b) 0.360 J, 0.640 J
6.31 a) 2.8 m/s b) 3.5 m/s
6.33 8.5 cm
6.35 a) 1.76 b) 0.67 m/s
6.37 a) 4.0 J b) zero c) −1.0 J d) 3.0 J e) −1.0 J
6.39 a) 2.83 m/s b) 2.40 m/s
6.41 a) 5.65 cm b) no; 0.57 J
6.43 3.6×10^5 J; 100 m/s
6.45 $4.0 \times 10^{13}P$
6.47 743 W, 0.995 hp
6.49 a) 1.4 b) 0.38
6.51 a) 5.4×10^9 J b) 0.72 MW
6.53 2.96×10^4 W
6.55 877 J
6.57 a) 532 J b) −315 J c) zero d) −203 J e) 14.7 J f) 1.21 m/s
6.59 a) $1/\sin\alpha$ b) $W_{\text{in}} = W_{\text{out}}$
6.61 a) 2.59×10^{12} J b) 4800 J
6.63 b) $k_{\text{eff}} = k_1 + k_2 + \cdots + k_N$
6.65 a) $k\left(\dfrac{1}{x_2} - \dfrac{1}{x_1}\right)$; negative b) $k\left(\dfrac{1}{x_1} - \dfrac{1}{x_2}\right)$; positive c) same magnitude and opposite sign, since net work is zero
6.67 a) 5.11 m b) 0.304 c) 10.3 m
6.69 a) 0.15 N b) 9.4 N c) 0.44 J
6.71 a) 2.56 m/s b) 5.28 N c) 19.7 J
6.73 a) −910 J b) 3.17×10^3 J
6.75 1.0×10^5 N/m
6.77 1.1 m from where spring is released
6.79 a) 1.02×10^4 N/m, 8.16 m
6.81 a) 0.600 m b) 1.50 m/s
6.83 0.786
6.85 1.5 m
6.87 a) 1.10×10^5 J b) 1.30×10^5 J c) 3.99 kW
6.89 3.6 h
6.91 1.30×10^3 m^3/s
6.93 a) 1.26×10^5 J b) 1.46 W
6.95 a) 2.4 MW b) 61 MW c) 6.0 MW
6.97 a) 513 W b) 355 W c) 52.1 W
6.99 a) 358 N b) 47.2 hp c) 4.06 hp d) 2.03%
6.101 a) $\frac{1}{3}MV^2$ b) 6.1 m/s c) 3.9 m/s d) K_{ball} = 0.40 J, K_{spring} = 0.60 J
6.103 a) 2.0×10^5 J b) 2.8×10^5 J c) 2.8×10^5 J d) 5 km/h

Chapter 7

7.1 a) 6.6×10^5 J b) -7.7×10^5 J
7.3 a) 820 N b) (i) zero (ii) 740 J
7.5 a) 24.0 m/s b) 24.0 m/s c) part (b)
7.7 2.5 m/s
7.9 a) (i) zero (ii) 0.98 J b) 2.8 m/s c) constant: gravity; not constant: normal, friction d) 5.0 N
7.11 −5400 J
7.13 a) 880 J b) −157 J c) 471 J d) 253 J e) a = 3.16 m/s^2; v = 7.11 m/s; ΔK = 253 J; same
7.15 a) 80.0 J b) 5.00 J
7.17 a) (i) 4U_0 (ii) $U_0/4$ b (i) $x_0\sqrt{2}$ (ii) $x_0/\sqrt{2}$
7.19 a) 6.32 cm b) 12 cm
7.21 ±0.092 m
7.23 a) 3.03 m/s; as mass leaves spring b) 95.9 m/s^2; just after mass is released
7.25 a) 4.46×10^5 N/m b) 0.128 m
7.27 a) −308 J b) −616 J c) nonconservative
7.29 a) −3.6 J b) −3.6 J c) −7.2 J d) nonconservative
7.31 a) $\frac{1}{2}k(x_1^2 - x_2^2)$ b) $-\frac{1}{2}k(x_1^2 - x_2^2)$; zero c) $-\frac{1}{2}k(x_3^2 - x_1^2)$; $-\frac{1}{2}k(x_2^2 - x_3^2)$; $-\frac{1}{2}k(x_2^2 - x_1^2)$; same
7.33 2.46 N, $+x$-direction
7.35 c) attracts
7.37 a) $F(r) = (12a/r^{13}) - (6b/r^7)$ b) $(2a/b)^{1/6}$; stable c) $b^2/4a$ d) $a = 6.68 \times 10^{-138}$ J · m^{12}, $b = 6.41 \times 10^{-78}$ J · m^6
7.39 a) zero, 637 N b) 2.99 m/s
7.41 a) no b) yes, \$150
7.43 0.41
7.45 a) 15.9 J b) 4.0 J c) 3.0 J
7.47 a) 20.0 m from left-hand edge of horizontal section b) −78.4 J
7.49 a) 22.2 m/s b) 16.4 m c) no
7.51 0.602 m
7.53 15.5 m/s
7.55 4.4 m/s
7.57 a) $x_0\sqrt{k/m}$ b) kx_0/m c) $x = 0$, $x = -x_0$ d) x_0 e) system oscillates and never stops
7.59 a) 7.00 m/s b) 2.94 N
7.61 a) $mg(1 - h/d)$ b) 440 N

c) $\sqrt{2gh(1 - y/d)}$
7.63 48.2°
7.65 a) 0.392 b) −0.832 J
7.67 a) $U(x) = (30.0\ \text{N/m})x^2 + (6.00\ \text{N/m}^2)x^3$ b) 7.85 m/s
7.69 7.01 m/s
7.71 a) $m(g + a)^2/2gh$ b) $2gh/(g + a)$
7.73 119 J
7.75 a) 3.87 m/s b) 0.10 m
7.77 a) $F_x = -m\omega_0^2 x$, $F_y = -m\omega_0^2 x$, b) $\frac{1}{2}m\omega_0^2(x^2 + y^2)$ c) (i) $\frac{1}{2}m\omega_0^2(x_0^2 + y_0^2)$ (ii) $\frac{1}{2}m\omega_0^2(x_0^2 + y_0^2)$
7.79 a) 4.4×10^{12} J b) $2.7 \times 10^3\ \text{m}^3$; 0.90 mm
7.81 c) attracts
7.83 a) −50.6 J b) −67.5 J c) nonconservative
7.85 a) no b) $x_0 = F/k$ d) no e) $3F/k, -F/k$ f) $v_{max} = 2F/\sqrt{mk}$ at $x = x_0 = F/k$
7.87 b) $v(x) = \left[\frac{2\alpha}{mx_0^2}\left(\frac{x_0}{x} - \left[\frac{x_0}{x}\right]^2\right)\right]^{1/2}$
c) $x = 2x_0$, $v = \sqrt{\alpha/2mx_0^2}$ d) zero
e) $v(x) = \left[\frac{2\alpha}{mx_0^2}\left(\frac{x_0}{x} - \left[\frac{x_0}{x}\right]^2 - \frac{2}{9}\right)\right]^{1/2}$
f) first case: x_0, ∞; second case: $3x_0/2$, $3x_0$

Chapter 8

8.1 a) 1.20×10^5 kg · m/s b) i) 60.0 m/s ii) 26.8 m/s
8.3 b) baseball, 0.525 c) woman, 0.643
8.5 a) 22.5 kg · m/s, to the left b) 838 J
8.7 562 N, no
8.9 a) 10.8 m/s, to the right b) 0.75 m/s, to the left
8.11 a) 500 N/s² b) 5810 kg · m/s c) 2.70 m/s
8.13 a) 2.50 N · s b) i) +6.25 m/s, to the right b) ii) 3.75 m/s, to the right
8.15 a) 6.79 m/s b) 55.2 J
8.17 a) 0.790 m/s b) −0.0023 J
8.19 0.866 kg · m/s
8.21 a) 0.0559 m/s b) 0.0313 m/s
8.23 3.65×10^5 m/s
8.25 a) 7.20 m/s b) −680 J
8.27 3.56 m/s
8.29 a) 0.846 m/s b) 2.10 J
8.31 a) 1.4×10^{-6} km/h, which is not noticeable. b) 6.7×10^{-8} km/h, which is not noticeable.
8.33 5.9 m/s at 32° east of north
8.35 a) Both cars have the same change in momentum, but the smaller car has a greater velocity change. b) 2.5 Δv c) Those in the smaller car
8.37 19.5 m/s (car), 21.9 m/s (truck)
8.39 a) 2.93 cm b) 866 J c) 1.73 J
8.41 a) 0.333 m/s, 3.33 J b) −1.33 m/s (*A*), +0.67 m/s (*B*)
8.43 a) −0.100 m/s (*A*), 0.500 m/s (*B*) b) 0.009 kg · m/s for both c) -4.5×10^{-4} J (*A*), 4.5×10^{-4} J (*B*), same magnitudes because the collision is elastic
8.45 a) 1/3 b) 1/9 c) 10
8.47 $x_{cm} = 0.044$ m, $y_{cm} = 0.056$ m
8.49 2520 km from the center of Pluto
8.51 0.700 m upward and 0.700 m to the right
8.53 0.47 m/s
8.55 $F_x = (-1.50\ \text{N/s})t$, $F_y = 0.25$ N, $F_z = 0$
8.57 a) 53 g b) 5.22 N
8.59 2.4 km/s
8.61 45.1
8.63 a) 0.47 N · s b) 237 N
8.65 a) $J_x = -1.14$ N · s, $J_y = 0.33$ N · s b) $v_{2x} = 0.0500$ m/s, $v_{2y} = 1.78$ m/s
8.67 2.67 m/s (convertible), 3.46 m/s (SUV)
8.69 a) $v_{Cx} = 1.75$ m/s, $v_{Cy} = 0.26$ m/s b) −0.092 J
8.71 15.0 m/s
8.73 36.4 N
8.75 a) 2.60 m/s b) 325 m/s
8.77 a) 5.28 m/s b) 5.7 m
8.79 68.8°
8.81 102 N
8.83 a) 0.222 b) −291 J c) 0.784 J
8.85 b) $M = m$ c) zero
8.87 a) 9.35 m/s b) 3.29 m/s
8.89 b) $\frac{1}{2}Mv_{cm}^2$
8.91 a) 3.56 m/s b) 5.22 m/s c) 4.67 m/s
8.93 0.00544%
8.95 1.61×10^{-22} kg · m/s, to the left
8.97 *A*: 13.6 m/s; *B*: 6.34 m/s, 65.0°
8.99 a) $(L/2)\cos(\alpha/2)$, along axis from apex b) $(L/3)$, along bisector from bottom c) $L/\sqrt{8}$ along bisector d) $L/\sqrt{12}$ from each side
8.101 0.400 m/s
8.103 a) 1.40 kg: 14.3 m/s; 0.28 kg: 71.6 m/s b) 347 m
8.105 222 m/s, 1.01×10^3 m/s; $v_{Kr} = 1.5v_{Ba}$
8.107 a) zero b) 1 d) 0.87 m f) 0.089 m
8.109 a) yes b) no; kinetic energy decreases by 4.8×10^3 J
8.111 a) $1.37v_{ex}$ b) $1.18v_{ex}$ c) $2.38v_{ex}$ d) 2.94 km/s
8.113 b) $2L/3$
8.115 a) $l^2\lambda g/32$ b) $l^2\lambda g/32$

Chapter 9

9.1 a) 34.4° b) 6.27 cm c) 1.05 m
9.3 a) *A*: rad/s; *B*: rad/s³ b) (i) 0 (ii) 15.0 rad/s² c) 9.50 rad
9.5 a) $\omega_z(t) = (0.400\ \text{rad/s}) + (0.0360\ \text{rad/s}^3)t^2$ b) 0.400 rad/s c) $\omega_z = 1.30$ rad/s; $\omega_{av\text{-}z} = 0.700$ rad/s
9.7 a) $a = \pi/4$ rad, $b = 2.00$ rad/s, $c = -0.139\ \text{rad/s}^3$ b) zero c) 19.5 rad; 9.35 rad/s
9.9 a) 2.25 rad/s b) 4.69 rad
9.11 a) 24.0 s b) 68.8 rev
9.13 10.5 rad/s
9.15 a) 300 rpm b) 75.0 s; 312 rev
9.17 9.00 rev
9.19 a) 540 rad b) 12.3 s c) −8.17 rad/s²
9.21 a) 1.99×10^{-7} rad/s b) 7.27×10^{-5} rad/s c) 2.99×10^4 m/s d) 464 m/s e) 0.0337 m/s²; zero
9.23 a) 15.1 m/s² b) 15.1 m/s²
9.25 a) 0.180 m/s²; 0; 0.180 m/s² b) 0.180 m/s²; 0.377 m/s²; 0.418 m/s² c) 0.180 m/s²; 0.754 m/s²; 0.775 m/s²
9.27 10.7 cm; no
9.29 a) 0.831 m/s b) 109 m/s²
9.31 a) 2.29 b) 1.51 c) 15.7 m/s, 108*g*
9.33 2.99 cm
9.35 a) (i) 0.469 kg · m² (ii) 0.117 kg · m² (iii) zero b) (i) 0.0433 kg · m² (ii) 0.0722 kg · m² c) (i) 0.0288 kg · m² (ii) 0.0144 kg · m²
9.37 a) 0.0640 kg · m² b) 0.0320 kg · m² c) 0.0320 kg · m²
9.39 0.193 kg · m²
9.41 8.52 kg · m²
9.43 a) 3.15×10^{23} J b) 158 y; no
9.45 0.600 kg · m²
9.47 7.35×10^4 J
9.49 a) 67.3 cm b) 45.5%
9.51 a) f^5 b) 6.37×10^8 J
9.53 −88.2 J
9.55 on an axis parallel to a diameter and $(2/\sqrt{15})R$ from the center of the sphere
9.57 $\frac{1}{3}M(a^2 + b^2)$
9.59 a) $ML^2/12$ b) $ML^2/12$
9.61 $MR^2/2$
9.63 a) $\gamma L^2/2$ b) $ML^2/2$; larger c) $ML^2/6$; one-third result of (b)
9.65 in 128 d
9.67 a) 0.600 m/s³ b) $\alpha = (2.40\ \text{rad/s}^3)t$ c) 3.54 s d) 17.7 rad
9.69 a) 0.050 rad/s² b) 0.300 rad/s c) 5.40 m/s² e) 6.18 m/s²; 7.66×10^3 N f) 60.9°
9.71 a) 1.70 m/s b) 84.8 rad/s
9.73 b) 2.00 m/s² d) 0.208 kg · m²
9.77 a) 7.36 m b) 327 m/s²
9.79 a) 2.14×10^{29} J b) 2.66×10^{33} J
9.81 a) $Mb^2/6$ b) 182 J
9.83 a) −0.784 J b) 5.42 rad/s c) 5.42 rad/s d) particle speed = 4.43 m/s
9.85 $\sqrt{(2gd)(m_B - \mu_k m_A)/(m_A + m_B + I/R^2)}$
9.87 $\sqrt{(g/R)(1 - \cos\beta)}$
9.89 a) 2.25×10^{-3} kg · m² b) 3.40 m/s c) 4.95 m/s
9.91 7.23 m
9.93 a) $(247/512)MR^2$ b) $(383/512)MR^2$
9.95 b) $\frac{1}{4}M(R_1^2 + R_2^2)$
9.97 a) $\frac{3}{5}MR^2$ b) larger
9.99 b) 5.97×10^{24} kg c) $0.334MR^2$
9.101 a) $s = r_0\theta + \beta\theta^2/2$ b) $\theta = (1/\beta)[\sqrt{r_0^2 + 2\beta vt} - r_0]$ c) $\omega_z = \frac{v}{\sqrt{r_0^2 + 2\beta vt}}$, $\alpha_z = \frac{\beta v^2}{(r_0^2 + 2\beta vt)^{3/2}}$; no d) $r_0 = 2.50$ cm, $\beta = 0.247\ \mu\text{m/rad}$; 2.13×10^4 rev

Chapter 10

10.1 a) 40.0 N · m, out of the page b) 34.6 N, out of the page c) 20.0 N · m, out of the page d) 17.3 N · m, into the page e) zero f) zero
10.3 2.50 N · m, counterclockwise
10.5 b) into page c) $(-1.05\ \text{N}\cdot\text{m})\hat{k}$
10.7 13.1 N · m
10.9 a) 14.8 rad/s² b) 1.52 s
10.11 7.47 N
10.13 0.482
10.15 a) 7.5 N in horizontal part, 18.2 N in hanging part b) 0.0160 kg · m²
10.17 a) 2.65 rad/s² b) no c) 3.31 m/s²; no
10.19 a) 1.80 m/s b) 7.13 J c) (i) 3.60 m/s, to the right (ii) 0 (iii) 2.55 m/s, 45° below horizontal d) (i) 1.80 m/s, to the right (ii) 1.80 m/s, to the left (iii) 1.80 m/s, downward
10.21 a) 1/3 b) 2/7 c) 2/5 d) 5/13
10.23 a) 0.613 b) no, requires $\mu_s = 0.858$ c) no slipping
10.25 11.7 m
10.27 a) 0.309 rad/s b) 100 J c) 6.67 W
10.29 a) 0.38 N · m b) 160 rad c) 59 J d) 59 J
10.31 b) 65.6 N
10.33 a) 358 N · m b) 1.79×10^3 N c) 83.8 m/s
10.35 a) 115 kg · m²/s, into the page b) 125 kg · m²/s², out of the page
10.37 4.71×10^{-6} kg · m²/s
10.39 4.6×10^3 rad/s
10.41 1.14 rev/s
10.43 0.60 rev
10.45 a) 0.120 rad/s b) 3.20×10^{-4} J; work done by bug
10.47 a) 5.88 rad/s
10.49 a) 1.62 N b) 1.80×10^3 rev/min
10.51 a) halved b) doubled c) halved d) doubled e) unchanged
10.53 a) 67.6 N b) 62.9 N c) 3.27 s
10.55 a) 840 rpm b) 75 mph c) 60 mph
10.57 a) 16.3 rad/s² b) no; decreases c) 5.70 rad/s
10.59 a) at $x = l$ b) at $x = l$ c) at $x = (l/2)(1 + [2h/l]^2)$ for $l > 2h$; at $x = l$ for $l < 2h$
10.61 a) FR b) FR; yes c) $\sqrt{4F/MR}$ d) $2F/M$ e) $4F/M$
10.63 a) 266 N b) 4.71 rad/s²
10.65 a) 2.88 m/s² b) 6.13 m/s²; greater in case (b)
10.67 239 N
10.69 $a = \frac{2g}{2 + (R/b)^2}$; $\alpha = \frac{2g}{2b + R^2/b}$; $T = \frac{2mg}{2(b/R)^2 + 1}$
10.71 clockwise; clockwise; clockwise
10.73 a) 1.41 s; 70.5 m/s b) *t* larger, *v* smaller
10.75 29.0 m/s
10.77 a) 26.0 m/s b) unchanged
10.79 a) $\sqrt{20hy/7}$ b) no c) rolling friction d) $\sqrt{8hy/3}$

10.81 b) R = radius of wheel, T = period of wheel's rotation
c) $v_x = \frac{2\pi R}{T}\left[1 - \cos\left(\frac{2\pi t}{T}\right)\right]$,
$v_y = \frac{2\pi R}{T}\sin\left(\frac{2\pi t}{T}\right)$; $a_x = \left(\frac{2\pi R}{T}\right)^2 R\sin\left(\frac{2\pi t}{T}\right)$,
$a_y = \left(\frac{2\pi R}{T}\right)^2 R\cos\left(\frac{2\pi t}{T}\right)$
d) $t = 0, T, 2T, \ldots$; $a_x = 0$, $a_y = \frac{4\pi^2 R}{T^2}$
e) $\frac{4\pi^2 R}{T^2}$, independent of time

10.83 $g/3$
10.85 1.87 m
10.87 a) $6v/19L$ b) $3/19$
10.89 a) 5.46 rad/s b) 3.17 cm c) 1.01×10^3 m/s
10.91 a) 2.00 rad/s b) 6.57 rad/s
10.93 0.30 rad/s, clockwise
10.97 -4.2×10^{-16} rad/s per year; decreasing
10.101 a) $a = +\mu_k g$, $\alpha = -2\mu_k g/R$ b) $\omega_0^2 R^2/18\mu_k g$ c) $-M\omega_0^2 R^2/6$
10.103 a) $mv_1^2 r_1^2/r^3$ b) $(mv_1^2/2)[(r_1/r_2)^2 - 1]$ c) same

Chapter 11

11.1 29.8 cm
11.3 20.0 kg
11.5 5450 N
11.7 a) 1000 N, 1.20 m from end where 400-N force is applied b) 800 N, 1.25 m from end where 400-N force is applied
11.9 a) 550 N b) 0.614 m from A
11.11 a) 1920 N b) 1140 N
11.13 a) $T = 2.60w$; $F_{pivot} = 3.28w$ at 37.6° b) $T = 4.10w$; $F_{pivot} = 5.38w$ at 48.8°
11.15 140 N by each hinge
11.17 246 N; 0.34 m behind front feet
11.19 $T_{left} = 270$ N, $T_{right} = 304$ N, $\theta = 40°$
11.21 a) 0.800 m b) clockwise c) 0.800 m, clockwise
11.23 1.4 mm
11.25 2.00×10^{11} Pa
11.27 a) upper: 3.1×10^{-3}; lower: 2.0×10^{-3} b) upper: 1.6 mm; lower: 0.98 mm
11.29 9.1×10^6 N
11.31 a) 3.33×10^6 Pa b) 1.33×10^5 Pa
11.33 a) 4.8×10^9 Pa; 2.1×10^{-10} Pa^{-1}
11.35 b) 6.60×10^5 N c) 1.8 mm
11.37 3.41×10^7 Pa
11.39 10.2 m/s^2
11.41 a) 525 N b) 222 N, 328 N c) 1.48
11.43 wing force: 7300 N upward; tail force: 600 N downward
11.45 a) 140 N b) 6 cm to the right
11.47 a) 424 N b) 170 N
11.49 120 N to the right, 160 N upward
11.53 b) $(Mg/2)\sin\theta$
11.55 a) $V = mg + w$, $H = T = (w + mg/4)\cot\theta$ b) 950 N c) 4.00°
11.57 7600 N
11.59 a) 2700 N b) 19
11.61 a) 4.90 m b) 60 N
11.63 a) $\theta = \arctan(h/d)$; $T = (Wd/2)\sqrt{h^2 + d^2}$ b) $\frac{Whd}{2(h^2 + d^2)}$; $W\frac{2h^2 + d^2}{2(h^2 + d^2)}$
11.65 a) 1150 N b) 1940 N c) 918 N d) 0.473
11.67 person above: 590 N; person below: 1370 N; above
11.69 a) $w_{max} = T_{max} hD/(L\sqrt{h^2 + D^2})$
11.71 a) 7140 N; tall walls b) 7900 N
11.73 a) 268 N b) 232 N c) 366 N
11.75 a) A: 0.424 N; B: 1.47 N; C 0.424 N b) 0.848 N
11.77 a) tips at 27°, slips at 31°; the bale tips before it slips b) tips at 27° slips at 22° the bale slips before it tips
11.79 a) $F_A = 80$ N, $F_B = 870$ N b) 1.92 m
11.81 a) 3.7 kN, 2.0 kN vertically upward
11.83 a) $0.012w$ b) less c) 25.0°; tips
11.85 a) 5.4 mm b) 4.2 mm
11.87 a) 0.70 m from wire A b) 0.45 m from wire B
11.89 a) 1.63 m b) brass: 2.00×10^8 Pa; nickel: 4.00×10^8 Pa c) brass: 2.2×10^{-3}; nickel: 1.9×10^{-3}
11.91 a) 0.36 mm b) 0.045 mm c) 0.33 mm
11.93 a) $(F\cos^2\theta)/A$ b) $(F\sin 2\theta)/2A$ c) 0 d) 45°
11.95 a) 600 N b) 13.5 kN c) slide: $\mu_s w/(\sin\theta - \mu_s\cos\theta)$; tip: $w/[(\frac{1}{9})\cos\theta + 2\sin\theta]$; 66°
11.97 the lesser of $h^2/L + L/2$ and L
11.99 $[(A^2 x/F) - k_O V_O]/V_S$
11.101 a) 0.662 mm b) 2.20×10^{-2} J c) 8.33×10^{-3} J d) -3.04×10^{-2} J e) 3.04×10^{-2} J

Chapter 12

12.1 2.18
12.3 0.026 mm
12.5 a) 2.59×10^8 m b) no
12.7 a) 2.40×10^{-3} N b) 3.6×10^{-6}
12.9 a) 6.30×10^{20} N, toward sun b) 4.77×10^{20} N, 24.6° toward earth from sun c) 2.37×10^{20} N, toward sun
12.11 a) 0.366 m from mass m b) (i) unstable (ii) stable
12.13 2.1×10^{-9} m/s^2, down
12.15 1.38×10^7 m
12.17 a) 0.37 m/s^2 b) 1700 kg/m^3
12.19 610 N; 83% of weight at surface
12.21 5.98×10^{24} kg
12.23 0.83 m/s; yes
12.25 a) 5.02×10^3 m/s b) 6.06×10^4 m/s
12.27 a) 7.46×10^3 m/s b) 1.68 h
12.29 2.01×10^{30} kg
12.31 a) 4.7 m/s; yes b) 2.2 h
12.33 a) 8.3×10^4 m/s b) 1.3×10^6 s
12.35 a) 4.45×10^{12} m, 4.55×10^{12} m b) 248 y
12.39 a) (i) 5.31×10^{-9} N (ii) 2.67×10^{-9} N
12.41 a) $-GMm/\sqrt{a^2 + x^2}$ c) $GMmx/(a^2 + x^2)^{3/2}$ toward center of ring e) $-GMm/a$, zero
12.43 a) 53 N b) 52 N
12.45 1.39×10^{-9}
12.47 a) 4.3×10^{37} kg, $2.1 \times 10^7 M_{sun}$ b) no c) 6.3×10^{10} m; yes
12.49 a) 9.67×10^{-12} N, midway between x and y axes b) 3.02×10^{-5} m/s
12.51 b) 5.39×10^{-13} N · m, clockwise
12.53 b) (i) 1.63×10^{-5} m/s, 4.08×10^{-6} m/s (ii) 2.04×10^{-5} m/s c) 31.9 m
12.55 a) 3.58×10^7 m
12.57 1.8×10^2 m/s
12.59 a) 1.39×10^7 m b) 3.59×10^7 m
12.61 $0.01R_E = 64$ km
12.63 0.28%
12.65 6.06×10^3 km/h
12.67 $\sqrt{2Gm_E h/(R_E^2 + hR_E)}$
12.69 a) 13.7 km/s b) 13.3 km/s c) 13.2 km/s
12.71 a) (i) 2.8 y (ii) 6.1 y b) 4.90×10^8 km c) 4.22×10^8 km
12.73 a) $GM^2/4R^2$ b) $\sqrt{GM/4R}$, $4\pi\sqrt{R^3/GM}$ c) $GM^2/4R$
12.75 6.8×10^4 m/s
12.77 a) 7.91×10^3 s b) 1.53 c) 8.43×10^3 m/s, 5.51×10^3 m/s d) 2.41×10^3 m/s, 3.26×10^3; perigee
12.79 3.22×10^9 J
12.81 9.36 m/s^2
12.83 $\frac{GmM}{x(x + L)}$
12.85 a) $U(r) = \frac{Gm_E m}{2R_E^3} r^2$ b) 7.90×10^3 m/s
12.87 a) against the direction of motion in all cases b) 2.24×10^7 s c) 44.1°
12.89 $F = \frac{2GMm}{a^2}\left[1 - \frac{x}{\sqrt{a^2 + x^2}}\right]$, toward the center of the disk

Chapter 13

13.1 a) 4.54×10^{-3} s, 1.38×10^3 rad/s b) 2.27×10^{-3} s, 2.76×10^3 rad/s
13.3 5.53×10^3 rad/s, 1.14×10^{-3} s
13.5 0.0500 s
13.7 a) 0.167 s b) 37.7 rad/s c) 8.44×10^{-2} kg
13.9 a) 0.375 s b) 2.66 Hz c) 16.7 rad/s
13.11 a) 0.98 m b) $\pi/2$ rad c) $x(t) = (-0.98\text{ m})\sin([12.2\text{ rad/s}]t)$
13.13 a) -2.71 m/s^2 b) $x(t) = (1.46\text{ cm})\cos([15.7\text{ rad/s}]t + 0.715\text{ rad})$, $v_x(t) = (-22.9\text{ cm/s})\sin([15.7\text{ rad/s}]t + 0.715\text{ rad})$, $a_x(t) = (-359\text{ cm/s}^2)\cos([15.7\text{ rad/s}]t + 0.715\text{ rad})$
13.15 120 kg
13.17 a) 0.253 kg b) 1.22 cm c) 3.05 N
13.19 a) 1.51 s b) 26.0 N/m c) 0.308 m/s d) 1.92 N e) -0.0125 m; 0.303 m/s; 0.216 m/s^2
13.21 a) 1.48 m/s b) 2.96×10^{-5} J
13.23 a) 1.20 m/s b) 1.11 m/s c) 36 m/s^2 d) 13.5 m/s^2 e) 0.36 J
13.25 $m = 3M$; $\frac{3}{4}$
13.27 0.240 m
13.29 a) 0.0778 m b) 1.28 Hz c) 0.624 m/s
13.31 a) 4.06 cm b) 1.21 m/s c) 29.8 rad/s
13.33 b) 23.9 cm; 1.45 Hz
13.35 a) 2.7×10^{-8} kg · m^2 b) 4.3×10^{-6} N · m/rad
13.37 5.12×10^{-2} kg · m^2
13.41 a) 0.25 s b) 0.25 s
13.43 0.407 swings/s
13.45 2.00 m
13.47 10.7 m/s^2
13.49 0.129 kg · m^2
13.53 A: $2\pi\sqrt{L/g}$; B: $(4\pi\sqrt{2}/3)\sqrt{L/g} = 0.943T_A$; pendulum A
13.55 A: $2\pi\sqrt{L/g}$; B: $2\pi\sqrt{\frac{11L}{10g}} = 1.05T_A$; pendulum B
13.57 a) 0.393 Hz b) 1.73 kg/s
13.59 a) A b) magnitude $= bA/2m$, in $-x$-direction; slope is negative c) $a_x(0) = A\left(\frac{b^2}{2m^2} - \frac{k}{m}\right)$; if $b < \sqrt{2mk}$, $a(0) < 0$; if $b = \sqrt{2mk}$, $a(0) = 0$; if $b > \sqrt{2mk}$, $a(0) > 0$
13.61 a) kg/s b) (i) $5.0F_{max}/k$ (ii) $2.5F_{max}/k$
13.63 a) 6.72×10^3 m/s^2 b) 3.02 kN c) 18.3 m/s, 75.6 J d) 17.6 kW e) 12.1 kN, 36.7 m/s, 302 J, 141 kW
13.65 a) all unchanged b) 1/4 as large c) halved d) $1/\sqrt{5}$ as great e) U: unchanged; K: 1/5 as large
13.67 a) 24.4 cm b) 0.220 s c) 1.19 m/s
13.69 a) 0.318 Hz, 0.500 m, 3.14 s b) 1.57 s
13.71 $\frac{1}{2\pi}\sqrt{\frac{3\sqrt{2}}{5}}\sqrt{\frac{g}{L}} = 0.921\left(\frac{1}{2\pi}\sqrt{\frac{g}{L}}\right)$
13.73 a) 1.49 s b) -2.12×10^{-4} s per s; shorter c) 0.795 s
13.75 a) 0.150 m/s b) 0.112 m/s^2, downward c) 0.700 s d) 4.38 m
13.77 a) 2.6 m/s b) 0.21 m c) 0.49 s
13.79 9.08×10^{24} kg
13.81 1.17 s
13.83 a) yes c) 2.40×10^3 s d) no
13.87 c) -7.57×10^{-19} J e) 8.39×10^{12} Hz
13.89 0.705 Hz; 14.5°
13.91 $2\pi\sqrt{M/3k}$
13.93 $\frac{1}{4\pi}\sqrt{\frac{3g}{\sqrt{2}L}}$
13.95 c) 0.430 m
13.97 a) $k_{eff} = k_1 + k_2$ b) $k_{eff} = k_1 + k_2$ c) $k_{eff} = \frac{k_1 k_2}{k_1 + k_2}$ d) $\sqrt{2}$

13.99 a) $Mv^2/6$ c) $\omega = \sqrt{3k/M}$; $M' = M/3$
13.101 579 N/m

Chapter 14

14.1 $w = 41.8$ N; no
14.3 7.02×10^3 kg/m^3; yes
14.5 1.6
14.7 61.7 N
14.9 a) 1.86×10^6 Pa b) 184 m
14.11 0.581
14.13 a) absolute: 46.7 lb/in.^{2} = 3.22×10^5 Pa = 3.18 atm; gauge: 32.0 *lb/in.*^{2} = 2.21×10^5 Pa = 2.18 atm b) no c) 432 cm^2
14.15 6.27×10^6 Pa = 61.9 atm
14.17 6.0×10^4 Pa
14.19 1.41×10^5 Pa; 4.03×10^4 Pa
14.21 2.3×10^5 N
14.23 a) 637 Pa b) (i) 1170 Pa (ii) 1170 Pa
14.25 1.66×10^5 Pa = 1.64 atm
14.27 6.43×10^{-4} m^3, 2.78×10^3 kg/m^3
14.29 a) $\rho < \rho_{\text{fluid}}$ c) submerged: ρ/ρ_{fluid}; above: $(\rho_{\text{fluid}} - \rho)/\rho_{\text{fluid}}$ d) 32%
14.31 a) 116 Pa b) 921 Pa c) 0.822 kg, 822 kg/m^3
14.33 1.91×10^3 kg/m^3
14.35 9.6 m/s
14.37 a) 17.0 m/s b) 0.317 m
14.39 28.4 m/s
14.41 1.47×10^5 Pa
14.43 12,600 N
14.45 2.03×10^4 Pa
14.47 a) $(p_0 - p)\pi D^2/4$ b) 776 N
14.49 a) 5.9×10^5 N b) 1.76×10^5 N
14.51 c) independent of surface area
14.53 $(p - p_0)VR^2/Gmd$
14.55 a) 12,700 kg/m^3, 3140 kg/m^3
14.57 a) 1470 Pa b) 13.9 cm
14.59 9.8×10^6 kg; yes
14.61 a) 30% b) 70%
14.63 4.66×10^{-4} m^3; 5.27 kg
14.65 a) 1.10×10^4 m^3 b) 112 kN
14.67 a) 0.107 m b) 2.42 s
14.69 a) $H/2$ b) H
14.71 0.0958 kg
14.73 33.5 N
14.75 b) 12.2 N c) 11.8 N
14.77 b) 2.52×10^{-4} m^3, 0.124
14.79 risen by 5.57×10^{-4} m
14.81 a) $1 - \rho_B/\rho_L$ b) $(\rho_L - \rho_B)L/(\rho_L - \rho_W)$ c) 4.60 cm
14.83 a) la/g b) $\omega^2 l^2/2g$
14.87 a) $2\sqrt{h(H-h)}$ b) h
14.89 a) 0.200 m^3/s b) 6.97×10^4 Pa
14.91 $3h_1$
14.93 a) $r = r_0(1 + 2gy/v_0^2)^{-1/4}$ b) 1.10 m
14.95 a) 80.4 N
14.97 a) $\sqrt{2gh}$ b) $(p_a/\rho g) - h$

Chapter 15

15.1 a) 0.439 m; 1.28 ms b) 0.219 m
15.3 220 m/s = 800 km/h
15.5 a) 4.3×10^{14} Hz to 7.5×10^{14} Hz; 1.3×10^{-15} s to 2.3×10^{-15} s b) no
15.7 a) $f = 25.0$ Hz, $T = 0.0400$ s, $k = 19.6$ rad/m b) $y(x,t) = (0.0700\text{ m})\cos 2\pi\left(\frac{x}{0.320\text{ m}} + \frac{t}{0.0400\text{ s}}\right)$ c) +0.0495 m d) 0.0050 s
15.9 c) $-x$-direction for both d) $v_y(x,t) = \omega A\cos(kx + \omega t)$, $a_y(x,t) = -\omega^2 A\sin(kx + \omega t)$
15.11 a) 4.0 mm b) 0.040 s c) 0.14 m, 3.6 m/s d) 0.24 m, 6.0 m/s e) no
15.13 b) $+x$-direction
15.15 a) 16.3 m/s b) 0.136 m c) both increase by factor of $\sqrt{2}$
15.17 0.390 s
15.19 a) 10.0 m/s b) 0.250 m c) $y(x,t) = (3.00\text{ cm})\cos[(8.00\pi\text{ rad/s})x - (80.0\pi\text{ rad/s})t]$ d) 1890 m/s^2 e) yes
15.21 a) 95 km b) 2.5×10^{-7} W/m^2 c) 1.1×10^5 W
15.23 a) 0.050 W/m^2 b) 2.2×10^4 J
15.25 707 W
15.33 a) $(1.33\text{ m})n$, $n = 0, 1, 2, 3, \ldots$ b) $(1.33\text{ m})(n + \frac{1}{2})$, $n = 0, 1, 2, 3, \ldots$
15.39 a) 96.0 m/s b) 461 N c) 1.13 m/s, 426 m/s^2
15.41 a) 2.80 cm c) 277 cm d) 185 cm, 0.126 s, 1470 cm/s e) 280 cm/s f) $y(x,t) = (5.60\text{ cm})\sin[(0.0907\text{ rad/cm})x]\sin([133\text{ rad/s}]t)$
15.43 a) $y(x,t) = (4.60\text{ mm})\sin[(6.98\text{ rad/m})x]\sin([742\text{ rad/s}]t)$ b) 3rd c) 39.4 Hz
15.45 a) 45.0 cm b) no
15.47 a) 311 m/s b) 246 Hz c) 245 Hz, 1.40 m
15.49 a) 20.0 Hz, 126 rad/s, 3.49 rad/m b) $y(x,t) = (2.50\text{ mm})\cos[(3.49\text{ rad/m})x - (126\text{ rad/s})t]$ c) $y(t) = (2.50\text{ mm})\cos[(126\text{ rad/s})t]$ d) $y(t) = (2.50\text{ mm})\cos[3\pi/2 - (126\text{ rad/s})t]$ e) 0.314 m/s f) -2.50 mm, 0
15.51 a) $(7L/2)\sqrt{\mu_1/F}$ b) no
15.53 a) $(2\pi A/\lambda)\sqrt{FL/M}$ b) increase by a factor of 4
15.55 a) $4\pi^2 F\Delta x/\lambda^2$
15.57 a) 1, 0; 2, +; 3, −; 4, 0; 5, −; 6, + b) 1, −; 2, +; 3, −; 4, +; 5, −; 6, 0 c) (a): answers would reverse sign; (b): no change
15.61 c) C/B
15.63 b) k decreases by a factor of $2\sqrt{2}$; ω decreases by a factor of $\sqrt{2}$
15.65 a) 7.07 cm b) 400.0 W
15.67 $\alpha = (v_1^2 - v_2^2)\rho/Y\Delta T$
15.69 $n(0.800\text{ Hz})$, $n = 1, 2, 3, \ldots$
15.71 c) yes
15.73 c) $2A$, $2A\omega$, $2A\omega^2$
15.75 230 N
15.77 a) 0, L b) 0, $L/2$, L d) no
15.79 a) 148 N b) 26%
15.81 b) $\frac{1}{2}\mu\omega^2 A^2\sin^2(kx - \omega t)$ e) $\frac{1}{2}Fk^2A^2\sin^2(kx - \omega t)$
15.83 $\pi/\omega\sqrt{2}$
15.85 a) 99.4 N c) -4.25 Hz, falls

Chapter 16

16.1 a) 0.344 m b) 1.2×10^{-5} m c) 6.9 m, 50 Hz
16.3 a) 7.78 Pa b) 77.8 Pa c) 778 Pa
16.5 a) 1.33×10^{10} Pa b) 9.47×10^{10} Pa
16.7 90.8 m
16.9 81.5°C
16.11 0.208 s
16.13 $Y/900$
16.15 a) 9.44×10^{-11} m; 0.434 m b) 5.66×10^{-9} m; 0.101 m c) air; $A_{\text{air}}/A_{\text{water}} = 60.0$
16.17 a) 1.94 Pa b) 4.58×10^{-3} W/m^2 c) 96.6 dB
16.19 a) 4.4×10^{-12} W/m^2 b) 6.39 dB c) 5.8×10^{-11} m
16.21 14.0 dB
16.23 a) 20.0
16.25 a) *fundamental:* displacement node at 0.60 m, pressure nodes at 0 and 1.20 m; *first overtone:* displacement nodes at 0.30 m and 0.90 m, pressure nodes at 0. 0.60 m, and 1.20 m; *second overtone:* displacement nodes at 0.20 m, 0.60 m, and 1.00 m, pressure nodes at 0, 0.40 m, 0.80 m, and 1.20 m b) *fundamental:* displacement node at 0, pressure node at 1.20 m; *first overtone:* displacement nodes at 0 and 0.80 m, pressure nodes at 0.40m and 1.20 m, and; *second overtone:* displacement nodes at 0, 0.48 m, and 0.96 m, pressure nodes at 0.24 m, 0.72 m, 1.20 m
16.27 506 Hz, 1520 Hz, 2530 Hz
16.29 a) 267 Hz b) no
16.31 a) 614 Hz b) 1.23 kHz
16.33 a) 172 Hz b) 86 Hz
16.35 0.125 m
16.37 a) 4 beats/s b) 3.0×10^{-8} m, 0
16.39 1.3 Hz
16.41 780 m/s
16.43 a) 375 Hz b) 371 Hz c) 4 Hz
16.45 a) 0.25 m/s b) 0.91 m
16.47 19.8 m/s
16.49 26.8 Hz
16.51 $0.095c$; toward us
16.53 a) 36.0° b) 2.23 s
16.55 a) 1.00 b) 8.00 c) 47.3 nm
16.57 b) $3f_0$ c) $v = 4Lf_0$
16.59 flute harmonic $3N(N = 1, 3, \ldots)$ resonates with string harmonic $4N$
16.61 a) stopped b) $n = 7$, $n = 9$ c) 43.9 cm
16.63 a) $v/(2L)$, v/L, $3v/(2L)$
16.65 a) 375 m/s b) 1.39 c) 0.8 cm
16.67 a) $n(77.3\text{ Hz})$, $n = 1, 2, 3, \ldots$
16.69 1.27
16.71 a) 548 Hz b) 652 Hz
16.73 a) $I = 2\pi^2\sqrt{\rho B}f^2(\Delta R)^2$ b) $P = 8\pi^3\sqrt{\rho B}f^2R^2(\Delta R)^2$ c) $A = (R/d)\Delta R$, $p_{\max} = 2\pi\sqrt{\rho B}(Rf/d)\Delta R$, $I = 2\pi^2\sqrt{\rho B}(fR/d)^2(\Delta R)^2$
16.75 a) 6.74 cm b) 147 Hz
16.77 b) 2.0 m/s
16.79 a) 1.2×10^6 m/s b) 3.6×10^{16} m = 3.8 ly c) 5.2×10^3 ly; 4100 BCE
16.81 a) $f_0\left(\frac{2v_W}{v - v_W}\right)$ b) $f_0\left(\frac{2v_W}{v + v_W}\right)$
16.83 d) 9.69 cm/s; 6.67×10^2 m/s^2

Chapter 17

17.1 −81.0°F b) 134.1°F c) 88.0°F
17.3 38 F°
17.5 a) −18.0 F° b) −10.0 C°
17.7 a) 104.4°F; yes b) 54°F
17.9 a) 216.5 K b) 325.9 K c) 205.4 K
17.11 a) −210°C b) 63 K
17.13 0.964 atm
17.15 a) −282°C b) no, 4.76×10^4 Pa
17.17 0.39 m
17.19 a) 1.9014 cm b) 1.8964 cm
17.21 2.3×10^{-5} (C°)$^{-1}$
17.23 11 L
17.25 1.7×10^{-5} (C°)$^{-1}$
17.27 a) 1.431 cm^2 b) 1.437 cm^2
17.29 0.261 mm
17.31 a) 3.2×10^{-5} (C°)$^{-1}$ b) 2.5×10^9 Pa
17.33 5.79×10^5 J
17.35 240 J/kg · K
17.37 1.4×10^3 s
17.39 1.21×10^{-2} C°
17.41 45.1 C°
17.43 a) 114 C° b) 6.35 C°
17.45 a) 215 J/kg · K b) water c) too small
17.47 8 min
17.49 3.64×10^4 J = 8.69×10^3 cal = 34.5 Btu
17.51 2.39×10^4 Btu/h = 7.01×10^3 W
17.53 357 m/s
17.55 3.45 L
17.57 5.50×10^5 J
17.59 0.0940 kg
17.61 2.10 kg
17.63 190 g
17.65 a) 222 K/m b) 10.7 W c) 73.3°C
17.67 a) −5.8°C b) 11 W/m^2
17.69 7.1×10^2 Btu = 7.5×10^5 J
17.71 105.5°C
17.73 a) 21.3 kW b) 6.44 kW
17.75 167 W
17.77 2.1 cm^2
17.79 a) 35.2°M b) 39.6 C°
17.81 b) 5.0×10^{-3} cm^3, −23 kg/m^3
17.83 37.5°C
17.85 35.0°C
17.87 23.0 cm, 7.0 cm

17.89 b) 1.9×10^8 Pa
17.91 a) 87°C b) −80°C
17.93 20.2°C
17.95 a) 54.3
17.97 a) 83.6 J b) 1.86 J/mol · K c) 5.60 J/mol · K
17.99 a) 2.7×10^7 J b) 6.89 K c) 19.3 K
17.101 2.53 cm
17.103 a) 86.1°C b) no ice, 0.130 kg liquid water, no steam
17.105 a) 100°C b) 0.0214 kg steam, 0.219 kg liquid water
17.107 1.743 kg
17.109 a) 94 W b) 1.3
17.111 2.9
17.113 a) 6.0×10^5 s (about 170 h) d) 1.5×10^{10} s (about 500 y); no
17.115 0.106 W/m · K
17.117 5.82×10^{-3} kg
17.119 a) 69.6°C
17.121 1.76 C°
17.123 a) 103°C b) 27 W
17.125 a) the reverse b) 1.2×10^{-4} c) 5.2 s d) to within 1.93 C°
17.127 a) (i) 280 W (ii) 0.248 W (iii) 2.10×10^3 W (iv) 116 W; radiation from the sun b) 3.72 L/h c) 1.4 L/h

Chapter 18

18.1 a) 56.2 mol b) 6.81×10^6 Pa = 67.2 atm
18.3 0.959 atm
18.5 a) 3×10^{27} molecules b) 3×10^{19} molecules/cm^3
18.7 503.0°C
18.9 3.36×10^5 Pa
18.11 0.159 L
18.13 1.05 atm
18.15 a) 70.2°C b) yes
18.17 850 m
18.19 density at sea level is 1.2% larger
18.21 2.28×10^4 Pa
18.23 a) $8720 b) 3.88 cm
18.25 a) 8.2×10^{-17} atm b) no
18.27 55.6 mol, 3.35×10^{25} molecules
18.29 a) 9.00×10^{-5} m^3 b) 3.10×10^{-10} m c) about the same
18.31 b) 1.004
18.33 a) could be true b) could be true c) not true d) must be true e) could be true
18.35 a) 1.9×10^6 m/s; no, 0.64% of c b) 7.3×10^{10} K
18.37 a) 6.21×10^{-21} J b) 2.34×10^5 m^2/s^2 c) 484 m/s d) 2.57×10^{-13} kg · m/s e) 1.24×10^{-19} N f) 1.24×10^{-17} Pa g) 8.15×10^{21} molecules h) 2.45×10^{22} molecules
18.39 3800°C
18.41 a) 1560 J b) 935 J
18.43 a) 741 J/kg · K b) 5.65 kg; 4850 L
18.45 a) 924 J/kg · K b) Table 17.3 gives 910 J/kg · K
18.49 a) 337 m/s b) 380 m/s c) 412 m/s
18.51 a) 610 Pa; solid → vapor b) 2.21×10^7 Pa; solid → liquid → vapor
18.53 no; no
18.55 0.213 kg
18.57 a) −178°C b) 1.17×10^{26} molecules/m^3 c) Titan's is 4.7 times Earth's
18.59 1.92 atm
18.61 a) 31 b) 8.41×10^3 N c) 7.8×10^3 N
18.63 a) 26.2 m/s b) 16.1 m/s, 5.44 m/s c) 1.74 m
18.65 5.0×10^{27}
18.67 a) same translational kinetic energy; A has greater rms speed b) B c) 4250°C d) B
18.69 b) 303 mol/m^3 c) van der Waals
18.71 a) 4.65×10^{-26} kg b) 6.11×10^{-21} J c) 2.04×10^{24} molecules d) 1.24×10^4 J
18.73 b) r_2 c) $r_1 = R_0/2^{16}$, $r_2 = R_0$, $r_1/r_2 = 2^{-16}$ d) U_0
18.75 a) 517 m/s b) 299 m/s
18.77 b) 1.40×10^5 K, 1.01×10^4 K c) 6.37×10^3 K, 4.59×10^2 K
18.79 a) 1.24×10^{-14} kg b) 4.16×10^{11} c) 2.95×10^{-6} m, no
18.81 a) $2R$ b) less
18.83 CO_2: 20.79 J/mol · K, 0.270; SO_2: 24.94 J/mol · K, 0.205; H_2S: 24.94 J/mol · K, 0.039
18.87 b) $0.0420N$ c) $(2.94 \times 10^{-21})N$ d) $0.0297N$, $(2.08 \times 10^{-21})N$ e) $0.0595N$, $(4.15 \times 10^{-21})N$
18.89 42.6%
18.91 a) 4.5×10^{11} m b) 703 m/s, 6.4×10^8 s (about 20 y). no c) 1.4×10^{-14} Pa d) about 650 m/s; evaporate f) 2×10^5 K; no
18.93 d) $T_c = 8a/27Rb$, $(V/n)_c = 3b$ e) $p_c = a/27b^2$ f) 8/3 g) 3.28, 3.44, 4.35

Chapter 19

19.1 b) 1330 J
19.3 b) −6540 J
19.5 a) 0.88 atm
19.7 a) $(p_1 - p_2)(V_2 - V_1)$ b) negative of work done in reverse direction
19.9 a) 3.78×10^4 J b) 7.72×10^4 J c) no
19.11 a) 410 J b) rises
19.13 a) 16.4 min b) 139 m/s = 501 km/h
19.15 a) internal energy b) ab c) none
19.17 a) positive b) I: positive; II: negative c) into d) I: into; II: out of
19.19 a) 1.67×10^5 J b) 2.03×10^6 J
19.21 b) 208 J c) on the piston d) 712 J e) 920 J f) 208 J
19.23 a) 948 K b) 900 K
19.25 2/5
19.27 a) 25.0 C° b) 17.9 C° c) a
19.29 a) −605 J b) 0 c) yes, 605 J, liberates
19.31 a) 747 J b) 1.30
19.33 a) 4.76×10^5 Pa b) -1.06×10^4 J c) 1.59; heated
19.35 5.1×10^3 J; increases; increases
19.37 b) 224 J c) $Q = 0$ d) −224 J
19.39 11.6°C
19.41 a) increases b) 4800 J
19.43 a) 45.0 J b) liberates 65.0 J c) $Q_{ad} = 23.0$ J, $Q_{ab} = 22.0$ J
19.45 a) same b) absorbs 4000 J c) absorbs 8000 J
19.47 b) −2460 J
19.49 a) 1173 K b) 1.22×10^4 J c) 4.26×10^4 J d) 4.57×10^4 J
19.51 −0.226 m^3
19.53 a) 4.32×10^{-4} m^3 b) 648 J c) 7.15×10^5 J d) 7.14×10^5 J e) no substantial difference
19.55 3.4×10^5 J/kg
19.57 b) 11.9 C°
19.59 a) 0.173 m b) 206°C c) 7.46×10^4 J
19.61 a) $Q = 300$ J, $\Delta U = 0$ b) $Q = 0$, $\Delta U = -300$ J c) $Q = 750$ J, $\Delta U = 450$ J
19.63 a) $W = 738$ J, $Q = 2588$ J, $\Delta U = 1850$ J b) $W = 0$, $Q = -1850$ J, $\Delta U = -1850$ J c) 0
19.65 a) $W = -187$ J, $Q = -654$ J, $\Delta U = -467$ J b) $W = 113$ J, $Q = 0$, $\Delta U = -113$ J c) $W = 0$, $Q = 580$ J, $\Delta U = 580$ J
19.67 a) 360 K, 2.67×10^5 Pa b) 1.14 L

Chapter 20

20.1 a) 6500 J b) 34%
20.3 a) 23% b) 12,400 J c) 0.350 g d) 222 kW = 298 hp
20.5 a) 25% b) 970 MW
20.7 13.8
20.9 a) 1.62×10^4 J b) 5.02×10^4 J
20.11 a) 767 W b) 7.27
20.13 a) 215 J b) 378 K c) 39.1%
20.15 a) 4.2×10^4 J b) 715 K
20.17 a) 492 J b) 212 W c) 5.4
20.19 a) 400 W b) 10.7 c) 36.9 kg
20.21 4500 J
20.23 37.1 hp
20.25 a) 428 J/K b) −392 J/K c) 36 J/K
20.27 a) irreversible b) $+1.25 \times 10^4$ J/K; it is consistent
20.29 6.31 J/K
20.31 a) 6.05×10^3 J/K b) five time greater for vaporization
20.33 gallium: +6.63 J/K; hand: −6.48 J/K; greater for gallium
20.35 a) no b) 18.3 J/K c) 18.3 J/K
20.37 a) 0.200 b) 8000 J
20.39 a) 27.8 K b) 15.3 K
20.41 b) absorbed: bc; rejected: ab, ca c) $T_a = T_b = 241$ K, $T_c = 481$ K d) $Q_{net} = W_{net} = 610$ J e) 8.7%
20.43 a) enters: 2.10×10^4 J; leaves: 1.66×10^4J b) 4.4×10^3 J; 21% c) maximum is $e = 67\%$
20.45 a) 7.0% b) 3.0×10^6 J/s; 2.8×10^6 J/s c) 6×10^5 kg/h = 6×10^5 L/h
20.47 a) $p_1 = 2.00$ atm, $V_1 = 4.00$ L; $p_2 = 2.00$ atm, $V_2 = 6.00$ L; $p_3 = 1.11$ atm, $V_3 = 6.00$ L; $p_4 = 1.67$ atm, $V_4 = 4.00$ L b) (i) $Q = 1422$ J, $W = 405$ J (ii) $Q = -1355$ J, $W = 0$ (iii) $Q = W = -274$ J (iv) $Q = 339$ J, $W = 0$ c) 131 J d) 7.5%; $e_{Carnot} = 44\%$
20.49 a) $a \to b$: $Q = 2.25 \times 10^5$ J, $W = 0.90 \times 10^5$ J, $\Delta U = 1.35 \times 10^5$ J; $b \to c$: $Q = -2.40 \times 10^5$ J, $W = 0$, $\Delta U = -2.40 \times 10^5$ J; $c \to a$: $Q = 0.45 \times 10^5$ J, $W = -0.60 \times 10^5$ J, $\Delta U = 1.05 \times 10^5$ J b) $Q = W = 0.30 \times 10^5$ J, $\Delta U = 0$ c) 11.1%
20.51 $\left(\frac{T_H - T'}{T_H}\right)\left(\frac{T' - T_C}{T'}\right)$; less
20.53 a) 122 J, 78 J b) 5.10×10^{-4} m^3 c) $p_b = 2.32 \times 10^6$ Pa, $V_b = 4.81 \times 10^{-5}$ m^3, $T_b = 771$ K; $p_c = 4.00 \times 10^6$ Pa, $V_c = 4.81 \times 10^{-5}$ m^3, $T_c = 1333$ K; $p_d = 1.47 \times 10^5$ Pa, $V_d = 5.10 \times 10^{-4}$ m^3, $T_d = 518$ K d) $e = 61.1\%$; $e_{Carnot} = 77.5\%$
20.55 b) 6.20×10^4 J c) 3.42×10^4 J d) before: 6.20×10^4J; after: 3.42×10^4 J
20.57 a) 88.5 J b) 17.7 J
20.59 a) $b \to c$: $nC_V \ln(T_c/T_b)$; $d \to a$: $nC_V \ln(T_a/T_d)$ b) $nC_V \ln\left(\frac{T_c T_a}{T_b T_d}\right)$
20.61 a) −143 J/K b) +196 J/K c) zero d) +53 J/K

Chapter 21

21.1 a) 2.0×10^{10} b) 8.58×10^{-13}
21.3 2.10×10^{28} electrons, 3.35×10^9 C
21.5 3.71×10^3 m
21.7 a) 7.42×10^{-7} C on each sphere b) 3.71×10^{-7} C on one and 1.48×10^{-6} C on the other
21.9 1.43×10^{13}, away from each other
21.11 a) 2.20×10^4 m/s
21.13 +0.750 nC
21.15 1.8×10^{-4} N, +x-direction
21.17 $x = -0.144$ m
21.19 2.58×10^{-6} N, −y-direction
21.21 b) $F_x = 0$, $F_y = +2kqQa/(a^2 + x^2)^{3/2}$ c) $2kqQ/a^2$, +y-direction
21.23 b) $kq^2(1 + 2\sqrt{2})/2L^2$
21.25 a) 4.40×10^{-16} N b) 2.63×10^{11} m/s^2 c) 2.63×10^5 m/s
21.27 a) 3.31×10^6 N/C, to the left b) 1.42×10^{-8} s c) 1.80×10^3 N/C, to the right
21.29 a) −21.9μC b) 1.02×10^{-7} N/C
21.31 a) 8.75×10^3 N/C,to the right b) 6.54×10^3 N/C,to the right c) 1.40×10^{-15} N,to the right
21.33 a) 364 N/C b) no, 2.73 μm downward
21.35 1.79×10^6 m/s
21.37 a) $mg = 8.93 \times 10^{-30}$ N; $F_e = 1.60 \times 10^{-15}$ N; yes b) 1.63×10^{-16} kg = $1.79 \times 10^{14} m_e$ c) no
21.39 a) $-\hat{j}$ b) $(\hat{\imath} + \hat{j})/\sqrt{2}$ c) $-0.390\hat{\imath} + 0.921\hat{j}$
21.41 a) 6.33×10^5 m/s b) 1.59×10^4 m/s

21.43 a) 0 b) $E_x = -2kq(x^2 + a^2)/(x^2 - a^2)^2$, for $x < -a$; $E_x = +2kq(x^2 + a^2)/(x^2 - a^2)^2$, for $x > +a$

21.45 a) (i) 574 N/C, $+x$-direction
(ii) 268 N/C, $-x$-direction
(iii) 404 N/C, $-x$-direction
b) (i) 9.20×10^{-17} N, $-x$-direction
(ii) 4.30×10^{-17} N, $+x$-direction
(iii) 6.48×10^{-17} N, $+x$-direction

21.47 1.04×10^7 N/C, to the left

21.49 a) $E_x = E_y = E = 0$
b) $E_x = +2.66 \times 10^3$ N/C, $E_y = 0$; $E = 2.66 \times 10^3$ N/C, $+x$-direction
c) $E_x = +129$ N/C, $E_y = -510$ N/C; $E = 526$ N/C, 284° clockwise from $+x$-axis
d) $E_x = 0$, $E_y = E = +1.38 \times 10^3$ N/C, $+y$-direction

21.51 a) $E_x = -4.79 \times 10^3$ N/C, $E_y = 0$; $E = 4.79 \times 10^3$ N/C, $-x$-direction
b) $E_x = +2.13 \times 10^3$ N/C, $E_y = 0$; $E = 2.13 \times 10^3$ N/C, $+x$-direction

21.53 a) $\vec{E} = \dfrac{2k\lambda}{x\sqrt{x^2/a^2 + 1}}\hat{\imath}$ b) $\vec{E} = \dfrac{2k\lambda}{x}\hat{\imath}$

21.55 a) $(7.0\,\text{N/C})\hat{\imath}$ b) $(1.75 \times 10^{-5}\,\text{N})\hat{\imath}$

21.57 a) 0 b) 0 c) σ/ϵ_0 directed downward

21.59 a) yes b) no

21.61 An infinite line of charge has a radial field in the plane through the wire, and constant in the plane of the wire, mirror-imaged about the wire

21.63 a) 1.4×10^{-11} C · m from q_1 toward q_2
b) 860 N/C

21.65 b) This also gives the correct expression for E_y since y appears in the full expression's denominator squared, so the signs carry through correctly.

21.67 b) Opposite charges are closest so the dipoles attract.

21.69 a) The torque is zero when $\vec{p}$ is aligned either in the *same* direction as $\vec{E}$ or in the *opposite* directions
b) The stable orientation is when $\vec{p}$ is aligned in the *same* direction as $\vec{E}$

21.71 1680 N, from + 5.00 μC charge toward -5.00 μC charge
b) 22.3 N · m, clockwise

21.73 a) $\sqrt{\dfrac{kqQ}{m\pi^2a^3}}$ b) accelerating along the y-axis away from origin

21.75 b) 2.80×10^{-6}C c) 39.5°

21.77 a) 2.09×10^{21} N b) 5.90×10^{23} m/s^2 c) no

21.79 a) $6kq^2/L^2$, away from vacant corner
b) $(3kq^2/2L^2)(1 + 2\sqrt{2})$, toward center of square

21.81 a) 6.0×10^{23}
b) $F_g = 4.1 \times 10^{-31}$ N, $F_e = 5.1 \times 10^5$ N
c) yes for F_e and no for F_g

21.83 a) $(2kq/x^2)[1 - (1 + a^2/x^2)^{-3/2}]$, $-x$-direction
b) $3kqa^2/x^4$

21.85 a) 3.5×10^{20} b) 1.6 C; 2.4×10^{10} N

21.87 a) $(mv_0^2\sin^2\alpha)/2eE$ b) $(mv_0^2\sin 2\alpha)/eE$
c) $h_{\text{max}} = 0.418$ m, $d = 2.89$ m

21.89 a) $E_x = \dfrac{kQ}{a}\left(\dfrac{1}{r} - \dfrac{1}{a + r}\right)$, $E_y = 0$
b) $\dfrac{kqQ}{a}\left(\dfrac{1}{x - a} - \dfrac{1}{x}\right)\hat{\imath}$

21.91 a) $-(7850\,\text{N/C})\hat{\imath}$ b) smaller c) 18 cm

21.93 a) $+(0.89\,\text{N/C})\hat{\imath}$ b) smaller c) (i) 1.2%
(ii) 4.5%

21.95 a) $F = \dfrac{2kqQ}{a}\left(\dfrac{1}{y} - \dfrac{1}{\sqrt{a^2 + y^2}}\right)$, $-x$-direction
b) $F = \dfrac{kqQ}{a}\left(\dfrac{1}{x - a} - \dfrac{1}{x + a} - \dfrac{2}{x}\right)$, $+x$-direction

21.97 $E_x = E_y = 2kQ/a^2$

21.99 a) 6.25×10^4 N/C, 225° measured counterclockwise from $+x$-axis
b) 1.00×10^{-14} N, 45° measured counterclockwise from $+x$-axis

21.101 a) 1.19×10^6 N/C, to the left
b) 1.19×10^5 N/C, to the left
c) 1.19×10^5 N/C, to the right

21.103 $\vec{E} = \dfrac{\sigma}{2\epsilon_0}\left[-\dfrac{x}{|x|}\hat{\imath} + \dfrac{z}{|z|}\hat{k}\right]$

21.105 b) $q_1 < 0$, $q_2 > 0$ c) 0.844 μC d) 56.2 N

21.107 a) $\dfrac{kQ}{L}\left[\dfrac{1}{x + a/2} - \dfrac{1}{x + L + a/2}\right]$

Chapter 22

22.1 a) 1.75 N·m^2/C b) no c) i) 0 ii) 90°

22.3 a) 3.53×10^5 N · m^2/C b) 3.13×10^{-6}C

22.5 $\Phi = E\pi r^2$

22.7 a) 2.71×10^5 N · m^2/C
b) 2.71×10^5 N · m^2/C
c) 5.42×10^5 N · m^2/C

22.9 a) zero b) 3.75×10^7 N/C radially inward
c) 1.11×10^7 N/C radially inward

22.11 b) no

22.13 a) 1.81×10^5 N · m^2/C b) no change

22.15 a) 4.50×10^4 N/C b) 9.18×10^2 N/C

22.17 a) 3.00×10^{-7} C b) 1.20×10^5 N/C

22.19 a) $q = 3.27 \times 10^{-9}$ C b) $n_e = 2.04 \times 10^{10}$

22.21 8.06×10^5 N/C, toward negatively charged sphere

22.23 a) 5.73×10^{-6} C/m^2 b) 6.48×10^5 N/C
c) -5.65×10^4 N · m^2/C

22.25 a) 2.59×10^{-7} C/m^3 b) 1.96×10^3 N/C

22.27 a) $\mathbf{E} = \sigma/\epsilon_0$ b) 0

22.29 a) $\lambda = 2\pi r\sigma$ b) $\sigma R/r\epsilon_0$

22.31 a) yes; $+Q$ b) no c) yes d) no; no
e) no; yes; no

22.33 a) 750 N · m^2/C b) 0 c) 577 N/C

22.35 a) -5.98×10^{-10} C

22.37 a) $\lambda/2\pi\epsilon_0 r$, radially outward
b) $\lambda/2\pi\epsilon_0 r$, radially outward
d) inner: $-\lambda$; outer: $+\lambda$

22.39 a) i) $\alpha/2\pi\epsilon_0 r$, radially outward ii) 0 iii) 0
b) i) $-\alpha$ ii) 0

22.41 $\theta = 19.8°$

22.43 a) $0 < r < R$, $E = 0$
$R < r < 2R$, $E = Q/4\pi\epsilon_0 r^2$, radially outward;
$r > 2R$, $E = 2Q/4\pi\epsilon_0 r^2$, radially outward

22.45 a) i) 0 ii) 0 iii) $q/2\pi\epsilon_0 r^2$, radially outward
iv) 0 v) $3q/2\pi\epsilon_0 r^2$, radially outward b) i) 0
ii) $+2q$ iii) $-2q$ iv) $+6q$

22.47 a) i) 0 ii) 0 iii) $q/2\pi\epsilon_0 r^2$, radially outward
iv) 0 v) $q/2\pi\epsilon_0 r^2$, radially inward b) i) 0
ii) $+2q$ iii) $-2q$ iv) $-2q$

22.49 a) $Qq/4\pi\epsilon_0 r^2$, toward the center of the shell
b) 0

22.51 a) The given σ is on both sides, so E is twice as great b) $\Phi = (\sigma A)/\epsilon_0$, but $E_{\text{out}} = \sigma/\epsilon_0$, so $E_{\text{in}} = 0$

22.53 $d = R/2$

22.55 b) for $|x| \le d$: $\vec{E} = (\rho_0 x^3/3\epsilon_0 d^2)\hat{\imath}$;
for $|x| \ge d$: $\vec{E} = (\rho_0 d/3\epsilon_0)(x/|x|)\hat{\imath}$

22.57 c) $E(r) = \dfrac{Q}{\pi\epsilon_0 R}\left(\dfrac{r}{R} - \dfrac{3r^2}{4R^2}\right)$
e) $E_{\text{max}} = Q/3\pi\epsilon_0 R^2$ *at* $r = 2R/3$

22.59 a) $\Phi = 4\pi Gm$ b) $\Phi = -4\pi GM_{\text{encl}}$

22.61 $\rho\vec{b}/3\epsilon_0$

22.63 a) $-(Q/16\pi\epsilon_0 R^2)\hat{\imath}$ b) $(Q/72\pi\epsilon_0 R^2)\hat{\imath}$

22.65 a) $Q(r) = Qe^{-2r/a_0}[2(r/a_0)^2 + 2(r/a_0) + 1]$
b) $E = \dfrac{kQe^{-2r/a_0}}{r^2}[2(r/a_0)^2 + 2(r/a_0) + 1]$

22.67 c) 0.807

Chapter 23

23.3 3.46×10^{-13} J

23.5 a) 12.5 m/s b) 0.323 m

23.7 a) 0.198 J b) i) 26.6 m/s ii) 36.7 m/s
iii) 37.6 m/s

23.9 a) -3.60×10^{-7} J b) $x = 0.0743$ m

23.11 $-q/2$

23.13 B: larger C: smaller D: same

23.15 7.42 m/s; faster

23.17 a) 0 b) $+7.50 \times 10^{-4}$ J
c) -2.06×10^{-3} J

23.19 a) 2.50 mm b) 7.49 mm

23.21 a) -737 V b) -704 V c) $+8.2 \times 10^{-8}$ J

23.23 b) 0 d) 0

23.25 b) $V = \dfrac{q}{4\pi\epsilon_0}\left(\dfrac{1}{|x|} - \dfrac{2}{|x - a|}\right)$

23.27 1.02×10^7m/s

23.29 a) b b) 800 V/m c) -4.8×10^{-5} J

23.31 a) increase of 156 V b) decrease of 182 V

23.33 a) oscillatory b) 1.67×10^7 m/s

23.35 a) $\lambda = 9.51$ C/m b) no. less.
V decreases in direction of $\vec{E}$.
$\lambda > 0$: V inversely proportional to r c) 0

23.37 a) 7.81×10^4 V b) 0

23.41 a) 8.00 kV/m b) 1.92×10^{-7} N
c) 8.64×10^{-7} J d) -8.64×10^{-7} J

23.43 b) -20 nC c) no

23.47 a) $E_x = -Ay + 2Bx$, $E_y = -Ax - C$, $E_z = 0$
b) $x = -C/A$, $y = -2BC/A^2$, any value of z

23.49 a) i) for $r < r_a$, $V = \dfrac{q}{4\pi\epsilon_0}\left(\dfrac{1}{r_a} - \dfrac{1}{r_b}\right)$
ii) for $r_a < r < r_b$, $V = \dfrac{q}{4\pi\epsilon_0}\left(\dfrac{1}{r} - \dfrac{1}{r_b}\right)$
iii) for $r > r_b$, $V = 0$
b) $V_{ab} = \dfrac{q}{4\pi\epsilon_0}\left(\dfrac{1}{r_a} - \dfrac{1}{r_b}\right)$
c) for $r_a < r < r_b$, $E = \dfrac{V_{ab}}{\left(\frac{1}{r_a} - \frac{1}{r_b}\right)}\dfrac{1}{r^2}$
d) $E = 0$

23.51 a) concentric cylinders
b) 10 V: 2.90×10^{-2} m; 20 V: 4.20×10^{-2} m

23.53 a) -2.15×10^{-5} J b) $W_E = +2829$ V
c) $E = 3.54 \times 10^4$ V/m

23.55 a) 7.85×10^4 V/m$^{4/3}$
b) $\vec{E} = (-1.0 \times 10^5\,\text{V/m}^{4/3})x^{1/3}\hat{\imath}$
c) $\vec{F} = (3.13 \times 10^{-15}\,\text{N})\hat{\imath}$

23.57 a) $-1.46q^2/\pi\epsilon_0 d$

23.59 a) -8.62×10^{-18} J b) 2.87×10^{-11} m

23.61 a) i) $V = (\lambda/2\pi\epsilon_0)\ln(b/a)$
ii) $V = (\lambda/2\pi\epsilon_0)\ln(b/r)$ iii) $V = 0$
d) $(\lambda/2\pi\epsilon_0)\ln(b/a)$

23.63 a) 1.76×10^{-16} N, downward
b) 1.93×10^{14} m/s, downward c) 8.24 mm
d) 15.4° e) 4.12 cm

23.65 a) 9.71×10^4 V/m b) 3.03×10^{-11} C

23.67 a) $r \le R$: $V = \left(\dfrac{\lambda}{4\pi\epsilon_0}\right)[1 - (r/R)^2]$;
$r \ge R$: $V = -\left(\dfrac{\lambda}{2\pi\epsilon_0}\right)\ln(r/R)$

23.69 $Q/4\pi\epsilon_0\sqrt{x^2 + a^2}$

23.71 $Q^2/8\pi\epsilon_0 R$

23.73 a) $Q/8\pi\epsilon_0 R$ b) i) center c) ii) surface

23.75 b) yes c) no

23.77 $Q/8\pi\epsilon_0 R$

23.79 a) $(Q/4\pi\epsilon_0 a)\ln[1 + (a/x)]$
b) $(Q/4\pi\epsilon_0 a)\ln\left[(a/y) + \sqrt{1 + (a/y)^2}\right]$
c) in (a), $(Q/4\pi\epsilon_0 x)$ in (b), $(Q/4\pi\epsilon_0 y)$

23.81 a) 1/3 b) 3

23.83 a) $E = Q_1/4\pi\epsilon_0 R_1^2$; $V = Q_1/4\pi\epsilon_0 R_1$
b) sphere 1: $Q_1R_1/(R_1 + R_2)$;
sphere 2: $Q_1R_2/(R_1 + R_2)$
c) $V = Q_1/4\pi\epsilon_0(R_1 + R_2)$ for either sphere
d) sphere 1: $E = Q_1/4\pi\epsilon_0 R_1(R_1 + R_2)$;
sphere 2: $E = Q_1/4\pi\epsilon_0 R_2(R_1 + R_2)$

23.85 a) 7.6×10^6 m/s b) 7.3×10^6 m/s
c) 2.3×10^9 K; 6.9×10^9 K

23.87 a) 5.9×10^{-15} m b) 4.14×10^{-11} J
c) 2.55×10^{25} nuclei

23.89 a) 1.01×10^{-12} m, 1.11×10^{-13} m,
2.54×10^{-14} m

23.91 c) 3 electrons, 0.507 μm

Chapter 24

24.1 1.82×10^{-4} C

24.3 a) 604 V b) 9.1×10^{-3} m^2
c) 1.84×10^6 V/m d) 1.63×10^{-5} C/m^2

24.5 a) 120 μC b) $C = \epsilon_0 A/d$ c) 480 μC

24.7 2.8 mm

24.9 a) 4.35×10^{-12} F b) 2.30 V

24.11 a) 6.56×10^{-11} F/m b) 6.43×10^{-11} C
24.13 a) 1.50×10^{-11} F b) 3.08 cm
c) 3.13×10^4 N/C
24.15 a) $C_{eq} = 2.40\ \mu F$; $Q_{total} = 6.72 \times 10^{-5}$ C;
$Q_{12} = 2.24 \times 10^{-5}$C; $Q_3 = 4.48 \times 10^{-5}$ C;
$Q_1 = Q_2 = Q_{12} = 2.24 \times 10^{-5}$ C
24.17 a) $Q_1 = 1.56 \times 10^{-5}$ C; $Q_1 = 2.6 \times 10^{-4}$ C
b) 52.0 V
24.19 $V_2 = 50$ V; $V_3 = 70$ V
24.21 $C_{eq} = \dfrac{\epsilon_0 A}{d_1 + d_2}$
24.23 57 μF
24.25 0.0283 J/m^3
24.27 19.6 J
24.29 a) $Q^2x/2\epsilon_0 A$ b) $(Q^2/2\epsilon_0 A)dx$ c) $Q^2/2\epsilon_0 A$
24.31 b) yes c) flat sheets parallel to the plates
24.33 a) 24.2 μC
b) $V = 220$ V: $Q_{35} = 7.7\ \mu$C, $Q_{75} = 16.5\ \mu$C
c) 2.66 mJ d) 35 nF: 0.85 mJ; 75 nF: 1.81 mJ
e) 220V for each capacitor
24.35 a) 1.60 nC b) 8.0
24.37 a) $U_{parallel} = 4U_{series}$ b) $Q_{parallel} = 2Q_{series}$
c) $E_{parallel} = 2E_{series}$
24.39 a) 6.20×10^{-7} C/m^2 b) 1.28
24.41 0.0135 m^2
24.43 a) 2.3×10^{-11} C^2/N·m^2 b) 40 kV
c) $\sigma = 4.6 \times 10^{-4}$ C/m^2, $\sigma_i = 2.8 \times 10^{-4}$ C/m^2
24.45 a) 10.1 V b) 2.25
24.47 a) 3.6 mJ; 13.5 mJ b) increased by 9.9 mJ
24.49 a) $Q/k\epsilon_0 A$ b) $Qd/k\epsilon_0 A$ c) $k\epsilon_0 A/d$
24.51 a) 2.4×10^{-11} F b) 2.9×10^{-10} C
c) 1.3×10^3 d) 1.7×10^{-9} J
24.53 a) 421 J b) 5.39×10^{-9} F
24.55 for $d \ll r_a$: $C \approx \dfrac{\epsilon_0 A}{d}$
24.57 a) $U_{tot} = 158\ \mu$J b) $U_{4.5} = 72.1\ \mu$J
24.59 a) 2.5 μF b) $Q_1 = 5.5 \times 10^{-4}$ C, $V_1 = 66$ V;
$Q_2 = 3.7 \times 10^{-4}$ C, $V_2 = 88$ V;
$Q_3 = 1.8 \times 10^{-4}$ C, $V_3 = 44$ V;
$Q_4 = 1.8 \times 10^{-4}$ C, $V_4 = 44$ V;
$Q_5 = 5.5 \times 10^{-4}$ C, $V_5 = 66$ V
24.61 a) 76 μC b) 1.4×10^{-3} J c) 11 V
d) 1.2×10^{-3} J
24.63 a) 2.3 μF b) $C_1 = 9.7 \times 10^{-4}$ C;
$C_2 = 6.4 \times 10^{-4}$ C c) 47 V
24.65 a) 3.91 b) 22.8 V
24.67 c) 710 μF
24.69 a) 6.5×10^{-2} F b) $Q = 2.3 \times 10^4$ C
c) 4.0×10^9 J
24.71 $C_{eq} = \dfrac{2\epsilon_0 A}{d}\left(\dfrac{K_1 K_2}{K_1 + K_2}\right)$
24.73 b) 14 μF c) 72.0 μF: 505 μC, 7.02 V;
28.0 μF: 259 μC, 9.24 V;
18.0 μF: 229 μC, 12.7 V;
27.0 μF: 276 μC, 10.2 V;
6.0 μF: 14.9 μC, 2.49 V
24.75 a) $(\epsilon_0 L/D)[L + (K - 1)x]$
24.77 b) 2.38×10^{-9} F

Chapter 25

25.1 3.89×10^4 C
25.3 a) 3.13×10^{19} b) $J = 1.51 \times 10^6$A/m^2
c) $v_d = 1.11 \times 10^{-4}$m/s
d) J would decrease; v_d would decrease
25.5 a) 110min b) 442min c) $v_d \propto 1/d$
25.7 a) 329 C b) 41.1 A c) 1333 min
25.9 5.86×10^{28} e$^-$/m^3
25.11 a) 1.216Ω·m @ 20 °C
25.13 a) tungsten $E = 5.16 \times 10^{-3}$ V/m
b) aluminum $E = 2.70 \times 10^{-3}$ V/m
25.15 a) $E_{max} = 1.21$ V/m b) $R = 1.45 \times 10^{-2}$ Ω
c) $V_{max} = 1.82 \times 10^{-1}$ V = 0.182 V
25.17 0.125 Ω
25.19 15 g
25.21 1.53×10^{-8} Ω
25.23 a) 1.53×10^{-8} Ω b) $R = 2.4$ Ω
25.25 a) 11.1 A b) 3.13 V c) 0.28 Ω
25.27 a) 99.54 Ω b) 0.0158 Ω
25.29 a) 4.67×10^{-8} Ω b) 6.74×10^{-4} Ω
25.31 a) 0.219 Ω b) $P = 3422$ J/s, $E = 1.23 \times 10^7$ J
25.33 a) $\mathcal{E} = 9.0$ V b) $r = 4.5$ Ω
25.35 a) $I = 0$ b) $\mathcal{E} = 5.0$ V c) 5.0 V
25.37 a) $\mathcal{E} = 3.08$ V b) $r = 0.067$ Ω c) 1.8 Ω
25.39 a) 1.41 A b) −13.7 V c) −1.0 V
25.41 b) yes; linear
25.43 a) 144 Ω b) 2.40×10^2 Ω
c) 100 W bulb, $I = 0.833$ A
d) 120 W bulb, $I = 0.500$ A
25.45 a) 29.8 W b) 0.248 A
25.47 a) $P = JE$ b) $p = J^2\rho$ c) $p = E^2/\rho$
25.49 a) 2.59×10^6 J b) 0.062 L c) 1.6 h
25.51 12.3%
25.53 a) 24 W b) 4.0 W c) 20 W
25.55 a) 26.7 Ω b) 4.5 A c) 454 W
25.57 a) 3.65×10^{-8} Ω·m b) 172 A
c) 2.58×10^{-3} m/s
25.59 0.060 Ω
25.61 a) 2.5 mA b) 2.14×10^{-5} V/m
c) 8.55×10^{-5} V/m d) 1.80×10^{-4} V
25.63 a) $R = \dfrac{\rho h}{\pi r_1 r_2}$ b) $R = \dfrac{\rho L}{A}$
25.65 $I = \dfrac{Q}{\kappa\epsilon_0\rho}$
25.67 a) 0.057 Ω b) 3.34×10^{-8}Ω·m c) 0.86 mm
d) 2.40×10^{-3} Ω
e) 1.1×10^{-3} (°C)$^{-1}$
25.69 a) 0.2 Ω b) 8.7 V
25.71 a) 1000 Ω b) 100 V c) 10 W
25.73 1.42 A
25.75 a) $I_A\left(1 + \dfrac{R_A}{r + R}\right)$ b) 0.0425 Ω
25.77 b) 8-gauge c) 106 W
d) 66 W, 175 kWh, \$19.25
25.79 a) 0.40 A b) 1.6 W c) 4.8 W d) 3.2 W
25.81 a) $\dfrac{a}{E}$ b) 2.59×10^6 J c) 4.32×10^5 J
d) 0.96 Ω e) 1.73×10^6 J
25.83 a) $I = \dfrac{v_0 A}{\rho_0 L(1 - e^{-1})}$
b) $E(x) = \dfrac{v_0 e^{-x/L}}{L(1 - e^{-1})}$
c) $V(x) = V_0\dfrac{(e^{-x/L} - e^{-1})}{(1 - e^{-1})}$

Chapter 26

26.1 $\dfrac{3R}{4}$
26.3 a) $R_q < R_1$ b) $R_{eq} < R_1$
26.5 a) $I = 3.50$ A b) $I = 4.50$ A c) $I = 3.15$ A
d) $I = 3.25$ A
26.7 0.769 A
26.9 a) 8.8 Ω b) 3.18 A c) 3.18 A
d) $V_{2.4} = 7.64$ V; $V_{1.6} = 5.09$ V; $V_{4.8} = 15.3$ V
26.11 $R_{eq} = 5.00$ Ω; $I_{total} = 12.0$ A; $I_{12} = 3.00$ A;
$I_4 = 9.00$ A; $I_3 = 8.00$ A; $I_6 = 4.00$ A
26.13 a) $I_1 = 1.50$ A, $I_2 = I_3 = I_4 = 0.50$ A
b) $P_1 = 10.1$ W, $P_2 = P_3 = P_4 = 1.12$ W;
c) $I_1 = 1.33$ A, $I_2 = I_3 = 0.667$ A
d) $P_1 = 8.00$ W, $P_2 = P_3 = 2.00$ W
e) $R_2 + R_3$ is brighter; R_1 is dimmer
26.15 a) 18.0 V; 3.00 A
26.17 a) 0.100 A for each
b) 400-Ω bulb: 4.00 W; 800-Ω bulb: 8.00 W
c) 400-Ω bulb: 0.300 A; 800-Ω bulb: 0.150 A
d) 400-Ω bulb: 36.0 W; 800-Ω bulb: 18.0 W; total: 54.0 W
e) in series, 800-Ω bulb is brighter; in parallel, 400-Ω bulb is brighter and total light output is greater
26.19 1010 s
26.21 a) 2.00 A b) 5.00 Ω c) 42.0 V d) 3.50 A
26.23 a) 8.00 A b) $\mathcal{E}_1 = 36.0$ V, $\mathcal{E}_2 = 54.0$ V
c) 9.00 Ω
26.25 a) 1.60 A, 1.40 *A*, 0.20 *A* b) 10.4 V
26.27 a) $\mathcal{E} = 36.40$ V b) 0.500 A
26.29 a) −2.14 V, *a* is at a higher potential
b) $I_{100} = 0.250$ A; $I_{75} = 0.200$ A;
$I_A = 0.500$ A downward; V = 0
26.31 a) 0.641 Ω b) 975 Ω
26.33 a) 17.8 V b) 22.7 V c) 27.5%
26.35 c) 3.34 V
26.37 a) 543 Ω b) 1.88 mA c) 203 Ω
26.39 a) $C = 8.49 \times 10^{-7}$ F b) $\tau = 2.89$ s
26.41 a) $t = 4.21 \times 10^{-3}$ s b) $I = 0.125$ A
26.43 190 μC
26.45 $I = 13.6$ A
26.47 a) 0.938 A b) 0.606 A
26.49 a) 1.33×10^{-4} C
b) $v_R = 9.12$ V, $v_C = 8.88$ V
c) $v_R = v_C = 8.88$ V d) 6.75×10^{-5} C
26.51 900 W
26.53 a) 6.0 A, 720 W b) 3.5 A, 420 W
26.55 a) 13.6 μΩ $= 1.36 \times 10^{-5}$ Ω
b) 2.14×10^{-8} Ω
26.57 a) 9.9 W b) 16.3 W, brighter
26.59 a) 18.7 Ω b) 7.5 Ω
26.61 $I_1 = 0.848$ A, $I_2 = 2.14$ A, $I_3 = 0.171$ A
26.63 2.00-Ω resistor: 5.21 A; 4-Ω resistor: 1.11 A;
5-Ω resistor: 6.32 A
26.65 a) 0.222 V b) 0.464 A
26.67 12.7 V
26.69 a) 186 V, upper terminal +
b) 3.00 A from − to + terminal
c) 20.0 Ω
26.71 a) $P_1 + P_2$ b) $\dfrac{P_1 P_2}{(P_1 + P_2)}$
26.73 a) −12.0 V b) 1.71 V c) 4.20 V
26.75 $R_3 = 10.8$ Ω, $R_2 = 1.08$ Ω, $R_1 = 0.12$ Ω
26.77 a) 114.4 V b) 263 V c) 266 V
26.79 b) 1897 Ω
26.81 a) 224-Ω resistor: 24.8 V; 589-Ω: 65.2 V
b) 3.87 kΩ c) 62.6 V d) no

Chapter 27

27.1 a) $(-6.68 \times 10^{-4}\ \text{N})\hat{k}$
b) $(+6.68 \times 10^{-4}\ \text{N})\hat{\imath} + (7.27 \times 10^{-4}\ \text{N})\hat{\jmath}$
27.3 a) positive b) 5.05×10^{-2}N
27.5 9.47×10^6 m/s
27.7 a) $\vec{B}_x = -0.175$ T, $\vec{B}_z = -0.256$ T
b) yes, $\vec{B}_y$ d) zero, 90°
27.9 a) $\vec{B} = 1.46$ T at 40.0° from the $+x$-axis, toward the z-axis in the xz plane
b) $\vec{F} = 7.48 \times 10^{-16}$ N, at 50° from the $+x$-axis toward the $+z$-axis
27.11 a) 3.05×10^{-3} Wb b) 1.83×10^{-3} Wb c) 0
27.13 -7.79×10^{-4} Wb
27.15 a) 1.60×10^{-4} T, into the page
b) 1.11×10^{-7} s
27.17 7.93×10^{-10} N, south
27.19 a) 1.2×10^7 m/s b) 0.10 T
27.21 a) 8.35×10^5 m/s b) 2.62×10^{-8} s
c) 7.26 kV
27.23 a) 107 T b) no
27.25 a) 8.38×10^{-4}T
27.27 a) no b) 1.40 cm
27.29 $B = 4.45 \times 10^{-2}$T
27.31 1.29×10^{-25} kg, 78
27.33 a) 1.34×10^4 A b) horizontal
27.35 $F = 0.724$ N, at 63.4° below the $+x$-axis
27.37 9.7 A
27.39 a) 817 V b) 113 m/s^2
27.41 a) $-(ILB)\hat{\jmath}$ b) yes
27.43 a) 1.5×10^{-16}s b) 1.1 mA
c) 9.3×10^{-24}A·m^2
27.45 a) rotates about axis A_z b) $\alpha = 294$ rad/s^2
27.47 −2.42 J
27.49 a) 1.13 A b) 3.69 A c) 98.2 V d) 362 W
27.51 a) 4.7 mm/s
b) 4.5×10^{-3} V/m in the $+z$-direction
c) 53 μV
27.53 a) F_2/qv_1 in the $-y$-direction b) $F_2/\sqrt{2}$
27.55 $\vec{B} = 3.68$ T at a right angle to v_i
27.57 a) 8.9×10^{-17} J $= 5.5 \times 10^5$eV
b) 7.7×10^{-8}s c) 1.2 T d) same as in (a)
27.59 4.46 A
27.61 a) -1.98×10^{-6}C
b) $(9.69 \times 10^{14}$ m/s$)(4\hat{\imath} + 3\hat{\jmath})$
c) $R = 5.69$ cm
d) 1.47×10^7 Hz e) $(R,0,1.72\ \text{m})$
27.63 9τ

27.65 1.6 mm
27.67 $(Mg\tan\theta/LB)$, right to left
27.71 a) 8.46×10^{-3} T b) 0.271 m c) 2.14×10^{-2} m
27.73 1.80 N to the left
27.75 0.0242 T, in the $+y$-direction
27.77 a) 0.0442 N·m clockwise b) stretched c) 7.98×10^{-3} J
27.79 0.444 N, in the $-y$-direction
27.81 b) side $(0, 0)$ to $(0, L)$: $(B_0IL/2)\hat{\imath}$; side $(0, L)$ to (L, L): $(-B_0IL)\hat{\jmath}$; side (L, L) to $(L, 0)$: $(-B_0IL/2)\hat{\imath}$; side $(L, 0)$ to $(0, 0)$: 0 c) $(-B_0IL)\hat{\jmath}$
27.83 2.52 m/s b) 7.60 A c) 0.197 Ω
27.85 a) $\vec{\mu} = -IA\hat{k}$ b) $B_x = 3D/IA$, $B_y = 4D/IA$, $B_z = -12D/IA$
27.87 $-\beta r/2$
27.89 a) 5.14 m b) 1.72×10^{-6} s c) 6.09 mm d) 3.04 cm

Chapter 28

28.1 a) $(-1.92 \times 10^{-5}\,\text{T})\hat{k}$ b) 0
28.3 a) $\vec{B} = 6.00 \times 10^{-10}$ T out of the paper b) $\vec{B} = 1.20 \times 10^{-9}$ T out of the paper c) 0
28.5 a) 0 b) $(-1.31 \times 10^{-6}\,\text{T})\hat{k}$ out of the paper c) $(-4.62 \times 10^{-7}\,\text{T})\hat{k}$ d) $(1.31 \times 10^{-6}\,\text{T})\hat{\jmath}$
28.7 a) attractive b) 1.00×10^{-6}
28.9 a) 4.00×10^{-7} T out of the paper b) 1.52×10^{-8} T out of the paper c) 0
28.11 a) $(5.00 \times 10^{-11}\,\text{T})\hat{\jmath}$ b) $(-5.00 \times 10^{-11}\,\text{T})\hat{\imath}$ c) $(-1.77 \times 10^{-11}\,\text{T})\hat{k}$ d) 0
28.13 1.76×10^{-5} T into the paper
28.15 a) 8.0×10^{-4} T b) 4.00×10^{-5} T, 20 times larger
28.17 a) 10.0 A b) above the wire c) directly east of the wire.
28.19 a) $(-1.0 \times 10^{-7}\,\text{T})\hat{\imath}$ b) $(2.19 \times 10^{-6}\,\text{T})$, $\theta = 46.8°$ from x toward z c) $(7.9 \times 10^{-6}\,\text{T})\hat{\imath}$
28.21 a) 0 b) 6.67×10^{-6} T c) 7.53×10^{-6} T to the left
28.23 a) 0 b) 0 c) 4.0×10^{-4} T to the left
28.25 a) 6.00×10^{-6} N, repulsive b) 2.40×10^{-5} N
28.27 4.6×10^{-5} N/m, repulsive but negligible
28.29 $\mu_0 I^2/2\pi\lambda g$
28.31 $m_0|I_1 - I_2|/4R,0$
28.33 a) 9.42×10^{-3} T b) 1.34×10^{-4} T
28.35 a) 305 A b) -3.83×10^{-4} T·m
28.37 a) $\dfrac{\mu_0 I}{2\pi r}$ b) 0
28.39 $B = \dfrac{\mu_0 I}{2\pi r}$; $r = R/2$; $r = 2R$
28.41 a) 1790 turns/m b) 63.0 m
28.43 a) 3.72×10^{6} A b) 2.49×10^{5} A c) 237 A
28.45 1.11×10^{-3} T
28.47 a) 0.0725 A b) 0.0195 A
28.49 a) i) 1.1×10^{-3} T ii) 4.7×10^{-6} A/m iii) 5.9 T
28.51 a) 1.00×10^{-6} T into the paper b) $(7.49 \times 10^{-8}\,\text{N})\hat{\jmath}$
28.53 a) 1.1×10^{13} m/s², away from the wire b) 62.5 N/C, away from the wire c) $mg \approx 10^{-29}$ N, negligible
28.55 5.75×10^{-6} T; 2.21×10^{-21} N perpendicular to line ab and to velocity
28.57 a) ± 607 m/s b) 9.2×10^{-6} T
28.59 a) 2.00 A out of the paper b) 2.13×10^{-6} T, to the right c) 2.06×10^{-6} T
28.61 a) 1.11×10^{-5} N/m b) out of page: 1.11×10^{-5} N/m upward
28.63 23.2 A
28.65 a) $\mu_0\pi NN'II'a^2a'^2(\sin\theta)/2x^3$ b) $-\mu_0\pi NN'II'a^2a'^2(\cos\theta)/2x^3$
28.67 a) $(\mu_0 NIa^2/2)[((x + a/2)^2 + a^2)^{-3/2} + ((x - a/2)^2 + a^2)^{-3/2}]$ c) $(\mu_0 NI/a)(4/5)^{3/2}$ d) 0.0202 T e) 0, 0
28.69 $\mu_0 I/8R$, out of the paper
28.71 a) $3I/2\pi R^3$ b) i) $\mu_0 Ir^2/2\pi R^3$ ii) $\mu_0 I/2\pi r$
28.73 zero
28.75 $16a/3$
28.77 b) $\mu_0 I_0/2\pi r$ c) $(I_0 r^2/a^2)(2 - r^2/a^2)$ d) $(\mu_0 I_0 r/2\pi a^2)(2 - r^2/a^2)$
28.79 $\mu_0 I$
28.81 a) $\mu_0 nI/2$, in the $+x$-direction b) $\mu_0 nI/2$, in the $-x$-direction
28.83 7.73×10^{-23} J/T $= 0.0833\,\mu_B$
28.85 c) 6.15 mm
28.87 $\mu_0 Qn/a$

Chapter 29

29.1 a) 4.50 Wb b) 20.3 V
29.3 a) $Q = NBA/R$ b) no
29.5 a) +34 V b) counterclockwise
29.7 a) $I = i{:}B = \dfrac{\mu_0 i}{2\pi r}$ into the page b) $d\Phi_B = \dfrac{\mu_0 i}{2\pi r}L\,dr$ c) $\Phi_B = \dfrac{\mu_0 iL}{2\pi}\ln(b/a)$ d) $\mathcal{E} = \dfrac{\mu_0 L}{2\pi}\ln(b/a)\dfrac{di}{dt}$
29.9 a) 5.44 mV b) clockwise
29.11 a) $\mathcal{E} = +Abv$ b) clockwise c) $\mathcal{E} = -Abv$ d) counterclockwise
29.13 10.4 rad/s
29.15 a) counterclockwise b) clockwise c) $I = 0$
29.17 a) a to b b) b to a c) b to a
29.19 a) clockwise b) 0 c) counterclockwise
29.21 a) $V_{ab} = 0.675$ V b) b at higher potential than a c) $E = 2.25$ V/m from b to a d) b has excess of positive charge e) i) 0 ii) 0
29.23 46.2 m/s; no
29.25 a) 3.00 V b) clockwise c) 0.800 N to the right d) 6.00 W $= P_{\text{mech}} = P_{\text{elec}}$
29.27 a) 4.23 V b) 4.23 V c) 0 d) for width $w \ll L$, it does not matter. $\mathcal{E} = 4.23$ V as long as the longitudinal axis of the rod is in the x-y plane.
29.29 a) $\pi r_1^2\dfrac{dB}{dt}$ b) $\dfrac{r_1}{2}\dfrac{dB}{dt}$ c) $\dfrac{R^2}{2r_2}\dfrac{dB}{dt}$ e) $\dfrac{\pi R^2}{4}\dfrac{dB}{dt}$ f) $\pi R^2\dfrac{dB}{dt}$ g) $\pi R^2\dfrac{dB}{dt}$
29.31 9.21 A/s
29.33 9.50×10^{-4} V
29.35 $K = 2.34$
29.37 a) 5.99×10^{-10} C b) 6.00×10^{-3} A c) 6.00×10^{-3} A
29.39 a) 0.15 V/m b) 38 V/m·s c) 3.4×10^{-10}A/m² d) $B_D = 2.38 \times 10^{-21}$ T, negligible; $B_C = 5.33 \times 10^{-5}$ T
29.41 For any continuous superconducting path, $R_{\text{total}} = 0$
29.43 a) $-(4.38 \times 10^{4}\,\text{A/m})\hat{\imath}$ b) $(15.0\,\text{T})\hat{\imath}$
29.45 a) 3.7 A b) 54 μA c) counterclockwise
29.47 a) $\dfrac{\mu_0 i\pi a}{2C}$ c) $i = i_0\exp(-2Rt/\mu_0\pi a)$ d) 45 μs
29.49 a) $\mu_0 Iabv/2\pi r(a + r)$ b) clockwise
29.51 191 rpm
29.53 a) 0.126 V b) a to b
29.55 b) FR/B^2L^2
29.57 1.2 V
29.59 $\dfrac{\mu_0 IW}{4\pi}$
29.61 a) $(\mu_0 IV/2\pi)\ln((L + d)/d)$ b) a c) 0
29.63 a) 0.165 V b) 0.165 V c) 0; 0.0142 V
29.65 a) B^2a^2V/R
29.67 a) $(qr/2)\dfrac{dB}{dt}$, to the left b) $(qr/2)\dfrac{dB}{dt}$, upward c) 0
29.73 a) 1.96×10^{-4}A/m² b) 3.00×10^{-9}A/m² c) 7.82×10^{6} Hz
29.75 b) $\dfrac{a}{2}\dfrac{dB}{dt}$ c) 7.37×10^{-4} A d) 1.75×10^{-4} V
29.77 a) a to b b) $v_t = \dfrac{Rmg\tan\theta}{L^2B^2\cos\theta}$ c) $\dfrac{mg\tan\theta}{LB}$ d) $\dfrac{Rm^2g^2(\tan\theta)^2}{L^2B^2}$ e) same as (d)

Chapter 30

30.1 a) 0.270 V, yes b) 0.270 V
30.5 a) 1.96 H b) 7.12×10^{-3} Wb
30.7 a) 0.250 H b) 4.5×10^{-4} Wb
30.9 a) 4.68 mV b) a
30.11 $\dfrac{\mu_0 N^2 A}{l}$
30.13 2850
30.15 a) 1.61×10^{-1} T b) 1.03×10^{4} J/m³ c) 0.129 J d) 4.03×10^{-5} H
30.19 a) 2.40 A/s b) 0.800 A/s c) 0.413 A d) 0.750 A
30.21 a) 17.3μs b) 30.7μs
30.25 a) 0.250 A b) 0.137 A c) 32.9 V, c d) 4.62×10^{-4} s
30.27 a) $(4.50\,\text{W})[1 - \exp(-(3.20\,\text{s}^{-1})t)]$ b) $(4.50\,\text{W})[1 - \exp(-(3.20\,\text{s}^{-1})t)]^2$ c) $(4.50\,\text{W})[\exp(-(3.20\,\text{s}^{-1})t) - \exp(-(6.40\,\text{s}^{-1})t)]$
30.29 a) 25.0 mH b) 9.00×10^{-8} C c) 5.40×10^{-7} J d) 6.57 mA
30.31 a) 105 rad/s, 59.6 ms b) 7.20×10^{-4} C c) 4.32×10^{-3} J d) -543 μC e) -49.9 mA f) 2.45×10^{-3} J, capacitor; 1.87×10^{-3} J, inductor
30.33 a) $f = 2.13 \times 10^{3}$ Hz b) $V_E = 0.225$ J c) $V_B = 0.223$ J
30.35 a) $U_C = (Q^2/2C)\cos^2(\omega t + \phi)$; $U_L = (Q^2/2C)\sin^2(\omega t + \phi)$
30.37 $\sqrt{LC} = \sqrt{(\text{V}\cdot\text{s/A})(\text{A}\cdot\text{s/V})} = \sqrt{\text{s}^2} = \text{s}$
30.41 a) 298 rad/s b) 83.8 Ω
30.43 a) $m = 4.80 \times 10^{-6}$ H b) $\mathcal{E} = \pm 1.80 \times 10^{-4}$ V
30.49 a) $\dfrac{\mu_0 i}{2\pi r}$ b) $\left(\dfrac{\mu_0 i^2 l}{4\pi r}\right)dr$ c) $\left(\dfrac{\mu_0 i^2 l}{4\pi}\right)\ln(b/a)$
30.51 a) $L = 8.89$ H b) $l = 56.3$ m; no
30.53 a) 0.281 J b) 0.517 J c) 0.236 J
30.57 222 μF; 9.31 μH
30.59 2×10^{4} m/s
30.61 a) solenoid c) 50 V d) 3.5 A e) 4.3 Ω;43 mH
30.63 a) $V_1 = 40.0$ V; $A_1 = A_4 = 0.80$ A, all others are zero b) $V_1 = 24.0$ V, $V_2 = 0$, $V_3 = V_4 = V_5 = 16.0$; $A_1 = 0.48$ A, $A_2 = 0.16$ A, $A_3 = 0.32$ A, $A_4 = 0$ c) 192 μC
30.65 a) $A_1 = A_4 = 0.45$ A, $A_2 = A_3 = 0$ b) $A_1 = 0.58$ A, $A_2 = 0.32$ A, $A_3 = 0.16$ A, $A_4 = 0.11$ A
30.67 a) 60.0 V b) a c) 60.0 V d) c e) -96.0 V f) b g) -156 V h) d
30.69 a) $i_0 = 0$, $V_{ac} = 0$, $V_{cb} = 36.0$ V b) $i_0 = 0.180$ A, $V_{ac} = 9.0$ V, $V_{cb} = 27.0$ V c) $i_0 = (0.180\,\text{A})[1 - \exp(-(50.0\text{s}^{-1})t)]$, $V_{ac} = (9.00\,\text{V})[1 - \exp(-(50.0\text{s}^{-1})t)]$, $V_{cb} = 27.0\,\text{V} + (9.00\,\text{V})\exp(-(50.0\,\text{s}^{-1})t)$
30.71 a) 0; 20 V b) 0.267 A; 0 c) 0.147 A; 9.0 V
30.75 a) $i_1 = \mathcal{E}/R_1$, $i_2 = (\mathcal{E}/R_2)[1 - \exp(-R_2t/L)]$ b) $i_1 = \mathcal{E}/R_1$, $i_2 = \mathcal{E}/R_2$ c) $i = (\mathcal{E}/R_2)\exp(-(R_1 + R_2)t/L)$
30.77 a) $d = [(L - L_0)/(L_F - L_0)]D$ b) 0.63024 H, 0.63048 H, 0.63072 H, 0.63096 H c) 0.63000 H, 0.62999 H, 0.62999 H, 0.62998 H
30.79 a) $i_1 = (\mathcal{E}/R_1)[1 - \exp(R_1t/L)]$, $i_2 = (\mathcal{E}/R_2)\exp(-t/R_2C)$, $q_2 = C\mathcal{E}[1 - \exp(-t/R_2C)]$ b) 0, 9.6 mA c) 1.9 A, 0 d) 1.6 ms e) 9.4 mA f) 0.22 s

Chapter 31

31.1 a) $I_{rms} = 0.34$ A b) $I = 0.48$ A c) 0 d) $(i^2)_{av} = 0.12\ A^2$
31.3 a) 31.8 V b) 0
31.5 a) 0.0132 A b) 0.132 A c) 1.32 A
31.9 a) 1.51 kΩ b) 0.239 H c) 497 Ω d)16.6 μF
31.11 13.3 μF
31.13 a) $i = (0.0253\ \text{A})\cos[(720\ \text{rad/s})t]$ b) 180 Ω c) $v_L = (-4.56\ \text{V})\sin[(720\ \text{rad/s})t]$
31.15 b) $v = 20.5$ V, $v_r = 7.6$ V, $v_L = 12.9$ V c) $v = -15.2$ V, $v_R = -22.5$ V, $v_L = 7.3$ V
31.17 a) 696 Ω b) 0.0431 A c) $v_R = 8.62$ V, $v_c = 28.7$ V d) −73.3°
31.19 a) 601 Ω b) 49.9 mA c) −70.6°, lags d) $v_R = 9.98$ V, $v_L = 4.99$ V, $v_c = 33.3$ V
31.21 a) 113 Hz; 15 mA b) 7.61 mA; lag
31.23 50.0 V
31.25 a) $P_{max} = 40.0$ W b) $I_{rms} = 0.167$ A c) $R = 7.20 \times 10^2\ \Omega$
31.29 a) + 45.8°,0.697 b) 344 Ω c) 155 V d) 48.6 W e) 48.6 W f) 0 g) 0
31.31 a) 150 V b) 150 V, 1290 V, 1290 V c) 37.5 W
31.33 a) 1.00 b) 75.0 W c) 75.0 W
31.35 a) $Z = 115\ \Omega$ b) $Z = 146\ \Omega$ c) $Z = 146\ \Omega$
31.37 a) 10 b) 2.40 A c) 28.8 A d) 500 Ω
31.39 a) $N_2 = \frac{1}{3}N_1$ b) 13 A c) 9.0 Ω
31.41 0.124 H
31.43 a) $t_1 = \pi/2\omega$, $t_2 = 3\pi/2\omega$ b) $2I/\omega$ c) $I_{rav} = 2I/\omega$
31.45 a) inductor b) 0.133 H
31.47 a) $I = 1.15$ A, $V_L = 31.6$ V, $V_R = 57.5$ V, $V_C = 14.7$ V b) $I = 0.860$ A, $V_L = 47.3$ V, $V_R = 43.0$ V, $V_C = 5.47$ V
31.49 $\sqrt{(R^2 + \omega^2L^2)/[R^2 + (\omega L - 1/\omega C)^2]}$
31.53 b) $V_B = LV^2/4[R^2 + (\omega L - 1/\omega C)^2]$, $V_E = V^2/4\omega C[R^2 + (\omega L - 1/\omega C)^2]$ d) $\omega = 0$; $U_B = 0$; $U_E = CV^2/4$; $\omega \to \infty$; both U_B and $U_E \to 0$; $U_B = U_E$ at $\omega = \omega_0 = 1/\sqrt{LC}$
31.57 a) $I_R = V/R$, $I_L = V/\omega L$, $I_C = \omega CV$ c) $\omega = 0$: $I_L \to \infty$, $I_C \to 0$; $\omega \to \infty$: $I_L = 0$, $I_C \to \infty$ d) 159 Hz e) 0.50 A f) $I_R = 0.50$ A, $I_L = I_C = 0.050$ A
31.59 a) 102 Ω b) 0.882 A c) 270 V
31.61 a) 0.750 A b) 160 Ω c) 619 Ω, 341 Ω d) 341 Ω
31.63 $i_{av} = 0$, $i_{rms} = I_0/\sqrt{3}$
31.65 a) ω_0 decreases by $\frac{1}{2}$ b) X_C doubles c) X_C decreases by $\frac{1}{2}$ d) no
31.67 a) L and C b) factor of $\frac{1}{2}$
31.69 a) $V/\sqrt{R^2 + 9L/4C}$ b) $[2V/\sqrt{R^2 + 9L/4C}]\sqrt{L/C}$ c) $[V/2\sqrt{R^2 + 9L/4C}]\sqrt{L/C}$ d) $2LV^2/(R^2 + 9L/4C)$ e) $LV^2/2(R^2 + 9L/4C)$
31.73 a) $V_RI/2$ b) 0 c) 0
31.75 a) 0.400 A b) 36.9° c) $Z_{cpx} = (400\ \Omega) - i(300\ \Omega)$, $Z = 500\ \Omega$ d) $I_{cpx} = (0.320\ A) - i(240\ A)$

Chapter 32

32.1 a) 1.28 s b) 8.15×10^{15} km
32.3 a) 6.0×10^4 Hz b) 6.0×10^7 Hz c) 6.0×10^{13} Hz d) 6.0×10^{16} Hz
32.5 a) $f = 6.94 \times 10^{14}$ Hz b) $E_{max} = 375$ V/m
32.7 $\vec{E}(z,t) = (1.74 \times 10^5\ \text{V/m})\hat{\imath} \times \cos[(1.28 \times 10^7\ \text{rad/m})z - (3.83 \times 10^{15}\ \text{rad/s})t]$ $\vec{B}(z,t) = (5.80 \times 10^{-4}\ \text{T})\hat{\jmath} \times \cos[(1.28 \times 10^7\ \text{rad/m})z - (3.83 \times 10^{15}\ \text{rad/s})t]$
32.9 a) $+y$-direction b) 7.11×10^{-4} m c) $\vec{B}(y,t) = (-1.03 \times 10^{-2}\ \text{T})\hat{\imath} \times \sin[(8.84 \times 10^3\ \text{rad/m})y - (2.65 \times 10^{12}\ \text{rad/s})t]$
32.11 a) 361 m b) 0.0174 rad/m c) 5.22×10^6 rad/s d) 0.0144 V/m
32.13 a) 381 nm b) 526 nm c) 1.38 d) 1.91
32.15 a) 330 W/m² b) 500 V/m; 1.7 μT
32.17 1.33×10^{-8} T, + y-direction
32.19 a) 1.1×10 W/m² b) 3.0×10^{-10} T c) 840 W; assuming isotropic transmission
32.21 2.5×10^{25} J
32.23 $E_{max} = 12.0$V/m, $B_{max} = 4.00 \times 10^{-8}$ T
32.25 8.5×10^5 W
32.27 a) 8.68×10^{-15} kg/m²·s b) 2.60×10^{-6} kg/m·s²
32.29 $S = \epsilon_0 cE^2$
32.31 a) 7.10 mm b) 3.55 mm c) 1.56×10^8 m/s
32.33 a) 4.38 mm b) 1.38 mm c) 4.38 mm
32.35 a) $L = 30.5$ cm b) $f = 2.46 \times 10^9$ Hz c) $L = 35.5$ cm: $f = 2.11 \times 10^9$ Hz
32.39 a) $I = 0.00602$ W/m² b) 2.13 N/C, 7.10×10^{-9}T c) 1.20×10^{-12} N
32.41 a) $E_{max} = 701$V/m, $B_{max} = 2.34 \times 10^{-6}$T b) $\mu_E = \mu_B = 1.09 \times 10^{-6}$J/m³ c) 1.07×10^{-11} J
32.43 a) $r = R$: $I = 6.4 \times 10^7$ W/m², $p_{rod} = 0.21$ Pa; $r = R/2$: $I = 2.6 \times 10^8$ W/m², $p_{rod} = 0.85$ Pa
32.45 7.78×10^{-13} rad/s
32.47 a) $I\rho/\pi a^2$ in direction of current b) current out of page: $\mu_0 I/2\pi a$, clockwise c) $I^2\rho/2\pi^2a^3$, radially inward d) $I^2\rho l/\pi a^2 = I^2R$
32.49 0.0368 V
32.51 a) 23.6 h b) throw it
32.53 a) 2.66×10^7 m b) 0.0673 s c) 6.50×10^{-23} Pa d) 0.190 m
32.55 a) $4\pi R^3\rho Gm^3/3r^2$ b) $LR^2/4r^2c$ c) 1.90^{-7} m, independent of r
32.57 b) 1.4×10^{-11} s⁻¹ c) 2.6×10^{-8} s⁻¹

Chapter 33

33.1 39.4°
33.3 a) 1.55 b) 549 nm
33.5 a) 5.17×10^{-7} m b) 3.40×10^{-7} m
33.7 a) 47.5° b) 66.0°
33.9 2.51×10^8 m/s
33.13 a) frequency = f; wavelength = $n\lambda$; speed = $nf\lambda = nv$ b) frequency = f; wavelength = $\left(\frac{n}{n'}\right)\lambda$; speed = $\left(\frac{n}{n'}\right)f\lambda = \left(\frac{n}{n'}\right)v$
33.15 71.8°
33.17 a) 51.3° b) 33.8°
33.19 a) 58.1° b) 22.8°
33.21 1.77
33.23 24.4°
33.25 a) A: $I_0/2$ B: $I_0/8$ C: $3I_0/32$ b) 0
33.27 a) 1.40 b) 35.5°
33.29 $\alpha = \arccos\left(\frac{\cos\theta}{\sqrt{2}}\right) = \cos^{-1}\left(\frac{\cos\theta}{\sqrt{2}}\right)$
33.31 6.38 W/m²
33.33 a) first: $I = I_0/2$, second: $I = 0.25I_0$, third: $I = 0.125I_0$ all linearly polarized along the axis of their respective filters.
33.35 a) $I_R = 0.374I$ b) $I_V = 2.35I$
33.39 a) $\sin\theta_3 = (n_1\sin\theta_1)/n_3$ c) yes
33.41 72.0°
33.45 1.53
33.47 1.8
33.49 a) 48.6° b) 48.6°
33.51 39.1°
33.53 a) $n = 1.11$ b) i) 9.75 ns ii) 4.07 ns; total = 8.95 ns
33.55 b) 0.22°
33.61 b) 38.9° c) 5.0°
33.63 a) 35° b) 10.1 W/m², 19.9 W/m²
33.67 a) $\Delta = 2\theta_a^A - 6\sin^{-1}\left(\frac{1}{n}\sin\theta_a^A\right) + 2\pi$ b) $\cos^2\theta_2 = (n^2 - 1)/8$ c) red: $\theta_2 = 71.9°$; $\Delta = 230.1°$; violet: $\theta_2 = 71.6°$, $\Delta = 233.2°$; violet

Chapter 34

34.1 39.2 cm to right of mirror; 4.85 cm
34.3 image at (x_0, y_0)
34.5 b) 33.0 cm to left of vertex, 1.20 cm tall, inverted, real
34.7 0.213 mm
34.9 18.0 m from convex side of glass shell, 0.50 cm tall, erect, virtual
34.11 a) $m = \dfrac{f}{(f - s)}$ c) $s > f$ d) $s < f$ e) $-\infty$ f) $s = f$ g) $s' = 0$ i) $s < f$ j) $s > f$ k) $s > 2f$ l) it becomes infinite
34.13 a) concave b) $f = 2.50$ cm, $R = 5.00$ cm
34.15 2.67 cm
34.17 a) at the center of the ball, $m = +1.33$ b) no
34.19 $s = 0.395$ m
34.21 8.35 cm to left of vertex, 0.326 mm, erect
34.23 a) 1.06 m to right of lens, 17.7 mm tall, real, inverted b) all same as (a)
34.25 71.2 cm to right of lens, $m = -2.97$
34.27 $f = 3.69$ cm, object is 2.82 cm to left of lens
34.29 $n = 1.67$
34.33 Object is 26.3 cm from lens with height 1.24 cm; image is erect; same side
34.35 10.2 m
34.37 a) 1.4×10^{-4} b) 5.25×10^{-4} c) 1.50×10^{-3}
34.39 a) 85 mm b) 135 mm
34.41 a) 11 b) 2.160×10^{-3} s
34.43 a) convex b) 50 mm to 56 mm
34.45 a) 80.0 cm b) 76.9 cm
34.47 a) +2.33 diopters b) −1.67 diopters
34.49 a) 6.06 cm b) 4.12 mm
34.51 4.17 cm from lens; image is located on same side as ant
34.53 a) 8.37 mm b) 21.4 c) 297
34.55 19.4 m
34.57 a) −6.33 b) 1.90 cm c) 0.126 rad = 7.22°
34.59 a) 66.1 cm b) −59.1
34.61 4.80 m/s
34.63 $n/2$
34.65 a) 13.3 cm b) 26.2 cm
34.67 a) 46.2 cm from mirror, on opposite side of mirror; virtual b) 2.88 cm, erect c) no
34.69 a) $-12.0\ \text{cm} < s < 0$ b) erect
34.71 $f = \pm 4.4$ cm, ±13.3 cm
34.73 $v = 31$ m/s
34.75 b) i) 120.00 cm from mirror, 119.96 cm from mirror ii) $m = -0.600$, $m' = -0.360$ c) faces perpendicular to axis: squares with side 0.600 mm: faces parallel to axis: rectangles with sides of length 0.360 mm (parallel to axis) and 0.600 mm (perpendicular to axis)
34.77 b) image = 2.4 cm high; $m = -0.13$
34.79 a) −3.3 cm b) virtual c) 1.9 cm to right of vertex at right end of rod d) real, inverted e) 105 mm
34.81 a) $f = 58.7$ cm, converging b) $h = 4.47$ mm, virtual
34.83 a) 2.53 mm
34.85 a) $R = 8.8$ mm b) no. behind the retina c) $s' = 14$ mm from the cornea. In front of the retina. Yes. The lens needs to complete the focusing.
34.87 2.00
34.89 a) 3.75 cm to left of first lens b) 332 cm c) real d) $h = 60.0$ mm. inverted.
34.91 10.6 cm
34.93 a) 0.24 m b) 0.24 m
34.95 Inside the glass, 72.1 cm from the spherical surface
34.97 0.80 cm
34.99 −26.7 cm
34.101 1.24 cm above page
34.103 a) 46.7 m b) 35.0 m
34.105 134 cm to left of object

Chapter 35

35.1 a) 2.50 m b) 1.00 m, 4.00 m
35.3 0.75 m, 2.00 m, 3.25 m, 4.50 m, 5.75 m, 7.00 m, 8.25 m

35.5 a) 2.0 m b) constructively
c) 1.0 m; destructively
35.9 0.83 mm
35.11 590 nm
35.13 12.6 cm
35.15 1200 nm
35.17 a) $m = 19$, 39 bright fringes
b) $m = \pm 19, \theta = \pm 73.3°$
35.19 a) $0.750I_0$ b) 80 nm
35.21 1670 rad
35.23 a) 0.888 mm b) 0.444 mm
35.25 71.4 m
35.27 114 nm
35.29 0.0235°
35.31 a) $\Delta T = 56$ nm b) i) 2180 nm
ii) 198.5 nm; 11.0 wavelengths
35.33 a) 514 nm; green b) 603 nm; orange
35.35 0.11 μm
35.37 0.570 mm
35.39 1.82 mm
35.41 $n = 1.730$
35.43 27.3°, 66.5°
35.45 $n = 1.57$
35.47 b) constructive: $r_2 - r_1 = (m + \phi/2\pi)\lambda$,
$m = 0, \pm 1, \pm 2, \pm 3, \ldots$;
destructive: $r_2 - r_1 = \left(m + \frac{1}{2} + \phi/2\pi\right)\lambda$,
$m = 0, \pm 1, \pm 2, \pm 3, \ldots$
35.49 a) $\sqrt{x^2 + (y + d)^2} - \sqrt{x^2 + (y - d)^2} = m\lambda$
c) $\sqrt{x^2 + (y + d)^2} - \sqrt{x^2 + (y - d)^2} = \left(m + \frac{1}{2}\right)\lambda$
35.51 $6.8 \times 10^{-5}\ (\text{C°})^{-1}$
35.53 $\lambda/2d$, independent of m
35.55 b) 72 cm
35.57 $n = 1.42$
35.59 a) pattern moves down the screen
b) $I = I_0 \cos^2[(\pi/\lambda)(d\sin\theta + (n - 1)L)]$
c) $d\sin\theta = m\lambda - (n - 1)L$
35.61 14.0

Chapter 36

36.1 506 nm
36.3 $m_{\text{max}} = 113$; 226 dark fringes
36.5 ± 45.4 cm
36.9 $\pm 16.0°, \pm 33.4°, \pm 55.6°$
36.11 0.920 μm
36.13 a) 10.8 mm b) 5.4 mW
36.15 a) 6.75 mm b) $2.43 \times 10^{-6}\ \text{W/m}^2$
36.17 a) 668 nm b) $9.36 \times 10^{-5} I_0$
36.19 a) $\pm 13.0°, \pm 26.7°, \pm 42.4°, \pm 64.1°$
b) $I = 2.08\ \text{W/m}^2$
36.21 a) 3 b) 2
36.23 a) $\pm 0.0627°$ b) $0.249I_0$ c) $0.0256I_0$
36.25 cases (i), (iii): slits 1 and 3 and slits 2 and 4; case (ii): slits 1 and 2 and slits 3 and 4
36.27 $a = 1.50 \times 10^4$ nm in width;
$d = 4.50 \times 10^4$ nm in separation
36.29 a) 4790 b) 19.0°, 40.7° c) no
36.31 a) yes b) 13.3 nm
36.33 23.3°, 52.3°
36.35 10.5°, 21.3°, 33.1°
36.37 a) $R = 17{,}500$ b) yes
c) i) 587.8170 nm ii) 587.7834 nm
iii) 587.7834 nm $< \lambda <$ 587.8170 nm
36.39 0.232 nm
36.41 a) 0.461 m
36.43 1.9 m
36.45 92 cm
36.47 1.45 m
36.49 a) Hubble: 77 m; Arecibo: 1.1×10^6 m
b) 1500 km
36.51 no
36.53 a) i) 25.6° ii) 10.2° iii) 5.1° b) i) 60.0°
ii) 23.1° iii) 11.5°
36.55 2.07
36.57 a) 1.80 mm b) 0.798 mm
36.59 $\Delta\theta_{\pm} = \dfrac{2\lambda}{dN}$
36.61 b) for $3\pi/2$: any two slits separated by one other slit; for the other cases: any two slits separated by three other slits
36.65 513 nm
36.67 second order
36.69 c) ± 2.6 rad
36.71 492 km

Chapter 37

37.1 Flash at AA'
37.3 2.60×10^8 m/s
37.5 a) $0.998c$ b) 126 m
37.7 1.12 h, clock on spacecraft
37.9 92.5 m
37.11 a) 6.6×10^2 m
b) 4.92×10^{-5} s, 1.48×10^4 m; yes c) 447 m
37.13 a) 3.57 km b) 9.00×10^{-5} s
c) 8.92×10^{-5} s
37.15 a) $0.806c$ b) $0.974c$ c) $0.997c$
37.17 $0.385c$
37.19 $0.784c$
37.21 $v = 0.611c$
37.23 $0.837c$, away
37.25 a) $0.159c$ b) \$$1.72 \times 10^8$
37.27 b) $a = (F/m)(1 - v^2/c^2)^{1/2}$
37.29 a) $a = (\sqrt{3}/2)c = 0.866c$
b) $c\sqrt{1 - \left(\frac{1}{2}\right)^{2/3}} = 0.608c$
37.31 a) $(\sqrt{3}/2)c = 0.866c$ b) $\sqrt{35/36}c = 0.986c$
37.33 a) 4.50×10^{-10} J
b) 1.94×10^{-18} kg · m/s
c) $0.968c$
37.35 a) 3.3×10^{-14} %; no
b) 4.0×10^{-16} kg; increases; no
37.37 a) 1.1×10^2 kg b) 0.24 m
37.39 a) 8.68×10^{-10} J b) 2.71×10^{-10} J c) 0.453
37.41 a) nonrelativistic: 5.34×10^{-12} J;
relativistic: 5.65×10^{-12} J;1.06
b) nonrelativistic: 6.78×10^{-11} J;
relativistic: 3.31×10^{-10} J; 4.88
37.43 a) 2.06×10^6 V b) 3.30×10^{-13} J
c) 2.06 MeV
37.45 $v = 0.652c$
37.47 a) 4.2×10^9 kg/s; 4.6×10^6 tons
b) 1.5×10^{13} y
37.49 a) $\Delta = 2.11 \times 10^{-5}$ b) 2.15×10^4 MeV
37.51 $0.700c$
37.53 a) $0.995c$ b) 1.0%
37.55 a) $v = (1 - 9 \times 10^{-9})c$ b) $m_{\text{rel}} = 7 \times 10^3 m$
37.57 1.68×10^5 eV
37.59 a) $0.800c$ b) $1.00c$ c) i) 2.33×10^{-11} J
ii) 1.00×10^{-10} J
d) i) 1.88×10^{-11} J ii) 4.81×10^{-11} J
37.65 b) $\Delta x' = \sqrt{(\Delta x)^2 - (c\Delta t)^2}$
c) 1.44×10^{-8} s
37.67 $0.357c$, receding
37.69 a) 140% b) 5500% c) 63000%
37.75 a) 13.1 km/s, toward
b) 5.96×10^9 m = 0.040 Earth-sun distance (AU); 5.55×10^{29} kg = $0.279m_{\text{sun}}$
37.77 a) $0.7554c$ b) 2.526
c) center of momentum: less energy

PHOTO CREDITS

About the Author Hugh D. Young; John P. Surey

Chapter 1 Opener: NASA; 1.1a: G. Ross/Photo Researchers, Inc.; 1.1b: NASA; 1.4: National Institute of Standards and Technology (NIST); 1.5a: R. Williams (STScI), the HDF-S Team, and NASA; 1.5b: SOHO (ESA & NASA); 1.5c: Courtesy of NASA/JPL/Caltech; 1.5d: Photodisc Green/Getty Images; 1.5e: Chad Baker/PhotoDisc/Getty Images; 1.5f: Purdue University. Veeco Instruments, Inc.; 1.5g: SPL/Photo Researchers; 1.6: Pearson Addison Wesley, San Francisco, California; 1.7: ND-Viollet/Roger Viollet/Liaison Agency, Inc.

Chapter 2 Opener: Mike Hewitt/Getty Images; 2.4: Pete Saloutos/Corbis; 2.5: DiMaggio/Kalish/Corbis; 2.22: Richard Megna/Fundamental Photographs; 2.26: Corbis

Chapter 3 Opener: Schlegelmilch/Corbis; 3.8: PhotoAlto/Getty Images; 3.16: Richard Megna/Fundamental Photographs; 3.19a: Richard Megna/ Fundamental Photographs; 3.19b: Stuart Westmorland/Getty Images; 3.31: AFP/Getty Images

Chapter 4 Opener: Balfour Studios/Alamy; 4.12: Wayne Eastep/Getty Images; 4.17: AFP/Getty Images; 4.20: James H. Robinson/Animals Animals; 4.29: E. Klaswitter/Corbis

Chapter 5 Opener: Kevin Schafer/Peter Arnold; 5.11: NASA/Photo Researchers; 5.16: AFP/Getty Images; 5.26b: Jump Run Productions/Getty Images; 5.38b: Helen Hansma, University of California, Santa Barbara; 5.38:d David Malin, Anglo-Australian Observatory

Chapter 6 Opener: Stephen Dalton/Photo Researchers; 6.1: Christina Hoehn/Getty Images; 6.13: Corbis; 6.26: Hulton Archive/Getty Images; 6.27a: Jeffrey H. Whitesell, Airliners of America; 6.27b: Jeffrey H. Whitesell, Airliners of America

Chapter 7 Opener: Mark A. Johnson/Corbis; 7.1: Purestock/Alamy; 7.3a: Dennis O'Clair/Getty Images; 7.5: Joe McBride/Corbis; 7.12: Phil Mislinski/ Omni-Photo Communications; 7.15: Arco Images/Alamy; 7.21: The Picture House/Alamy

Chapter 8 Opener: Getty Images; 8.2: David Woods/Corbis; 8.4: Jim Cummins/Getty Images; 8.6a: Andrew Davidhazy; 8.16: Getty Images; 8.21: David Leah/Getty Images; 8.29: Richard Megna/Fundamental Photographs; 8.33: NASA

Chapter 9 Opener: George Hall/Corbis; 9.19: Jose Azel/Aurora Photos; 9.38: NASA

Chapter 10 Opener: Reuters/Corbis; 10.7: Corbis; 10.14: picturesbyrob/Alamy; 10.17: Pete Saloutos/Corbis; 10.22: Lester Lefkowitz/Getty Images; 10.28: Gerard Lacz/Natural History Photographic Agency

Chapter 11 Opener: Ruth Tomlinson/Getty Images; 11.3: Jeremy Woodhouse/Getty Images; 11.12a: Walter Bibikow/Getty Images; 11.12b: Jonathan Blair/Corbis; 11.12c: Photodisc Green/Getty Images

Chapter 12 Opener: NASA/JPL/Space Science Institute; 12.3: NASA/JPL/Caltech; 12.6: NASA; 12.7: George Hall/Corbis; 12.13: NASA; 12.16: NASA; 12.17a: NASA; 12.17b: NASA; 12.18: NASA; 12.21: Smithsonian Astrophysical Observatory; 12.27: NASA/Johnson Space Center; 12.28: NASA; 12.29: NASA; 12.30: Keck/UCLA Galactic Center Group

Chapter 13 Opener: Mark Antman/The Image Works; 13.7: American Diagnostic Corporation; 13.21a: Frank Herholdt/Getty Images; 13.25: Christopher Griffin/Alamy; 13.29a: AP/Wide World Photos; 13.29b: AP/Wide World Photos

Chapter 14 Opener: Digital Vision/AGE Fotostock; 14.2: Nicholas Pinturas/Getty Images; 14.7: Cenco Physics; 14.10b: Photodisc Green/Getty Images; 14.15: Robert B. Suter, Vassar College; 14.20: Pearson Addison Wesley; 14.21: Cordelia Molloy/Photo Researchers; 14.28: Digital Vision/AGE Fotostock; 14.30a: Photodisc Green/Getty Images; 14.30b: Colin Barker/ Getty Images; 14.31f: The Harold E. Edgerton 1992 Trust, Palm Press, Inc.

Chapter 15 Opener: David Hume Kennerly/Getty Images; 15.2: Tony Arruza/Corbis; 15.12: R. Dolan/Camerique/H. Armstrong Roberts; 15.18: Reproduced from *PSSC Physics*, 2nd ed. (1965), D.C. Heath & Company with Educational Development Center, Inc., Newton Massachusets; 15.25: Photodisc Green/Getty Images; 15.27: National Optical Astronomy Observatories

Chapter 16 Opener: John Powell/The Image Works; 16.5a: Lisa Pines/Getty Images; 16.5c: David Young-Wolff/PhotoEdit Inc.; 16.6: Dorling Kindersley; 16.9: Bernard Benoit/Photo Researchers; 16.10: Eastcott-Momatiuk/The Image Works; 16.20: Martin Bough/Fundamental Photographs; 16.25: David Young-Wolff/PhotoEdit Inc.;16.28: Mark Reinstein/The Image Works; 16.36: NASA/Robert A. Hoover, Dryden Flight Research Center

Chapter 17 Opener: Cameramann/The Image Works; 17.4: Exergen Corporation; 17.11: NASA/Jim Ross, Dryden Flight Research Center; 17.13: Marshall Henrichs; 17.18: Paul Seheult/Corbis; 17.19: Adam Hart-Davis/Photo Researchers; 17.20: Richard Megna/Fundamental Photographs; 17.22: John Giustina/Getty Images; 17.24: Russ Underwood, Lockheed Martin Missiles & Space Company, Inc.; 17.28: Nancy Rogers; 17.29: Dr. Arthur Tucker/Photo Researchers

Chapter 18 Opener: James Marshall/The Image Works; 18.2: John Powell/ The Image Works; 18.10: Park Scientific Instruments; 18.13: Stone/Getty Images; 18.14: Tatsuyuki Tayama/The Image Works; 18.16: David Grossman/ The Image Works; 18.25: PhotoDisc/Getty Images; 18.28: Royal Observatory, Edinburgh/Anglo-AustralianObsevatory; 18.30: David Malin, Anglo-Australian Observatory

Chapter 19 Opener: Richard A. Cooke III/Getty Images; 19.1: John P. Surey; 19.2a: PhotoDisc/StockTrek/Getty Images; 19.2b: Lawrence Migdale/Photo Researchers; 19.10: John Kelly/Getty Images; 19.14: Tom Branch/Photo Researchers; 19.15: Patrick Watson/The Image Works; 19.32: Thomas Eisner and Daniel Aneshansley

Chapter 20 Opener: Stock Food/Getty Images; 20.2: Bruno Perousse/AGE Fotostock; 20.12: Bill Bachman/Photo Researchers; 20.16: Mark Wagner/Getty Images; 20.17: Erich Schrempp/Photo Researchers; 20.21: Paul Silverman/Fundamental Photographs; Summary: Paul Silverman/Fundamental Photographs

Chapter 21 Opener: Ilja C. Hendel/The Image Works; 21.5: Journal-Courier/The Image Works; 21.8a: Richard Megna/Fundamental Photographs; 21.30a: Reproduced from *PSSC Physics*, 2nd ed. (1965), D.C. Heath & Company with Education Development Center, Inc., Newton, Massachusetts; 21.31b: Tony Craddock/Photo Researchers

Chapter 22 Opener: Department of Energy/Photo Researchers; 22.10: AKG London Ltd.; 22.28b: Russ Kinne/Comstock

Chapter 23 Opener: Ted Kurihara/Getty Images; 23.9: NASA/JPL/Caltech; 23.11: © Lester V. Berman/Corbis: 23/13: Fermilab Visual Media Services; 23.18: Hulton Archive/Keystone/Getty Images; 23.23: U.S. Geological Survey, Denver

Chapter 24 Opener: Digital Vision/Agefotostock; 24.3: Design Pics/ Indexstock; 24.4: Andrew Lambert/Photo Researchers; 24.7: Paul Silverman/ Fundamental Photographs; 24.11: Sandia National Laboratories; 24.17: Stanford Linear Accelerator/Science Photo Library/Photo Researchers

Chapter 25 Opener: David Sacks/Getty Images; 25.4: Fundamental Photographs; 25.5: PhotoDisc/Getty Images; 25.8: Mitch Wojnarowicz/The Image Works; 25.13: Doug Scott/Agefotostock

Chapter 26 Opener: Maximilian Stock/Photo Researchers; 26.2: Corbis; 26.5: John P. Surey; 26.13: John P. Surey; 26.18: Richard Megna/Fundamental Photographs; 26.20: Mehau Kulyk/Photo Researchers; 26.26a: Banana Stock/Alamy; 26.26b: Wikipedia

Chapter 27 Opener: Simon Fraser/Photo Researchers; 27.2b: Bill Aron/PhotoEdit Inc.; 27.20: Cenco; 27.20b: Paul McCormick/Getty Images; 27.21: Lawrence Berkeley National Laboratory; 27.40: Jeremy Burgess/Photo Researchers

Chapter 28 Opener: David Parker/Photo Researchers; 28.8: Definitive Stock; 28.11: Jeremy Walker/Photo Researchers; Test Your Understanding, page 976: Mark Antman/The Image Works

Chapter 29 Opener: James Leynse/Corbis; 29.9: Maximilian Stock Ltd./Photo Researchers; 29.18a: Photodisc Red/Getty Images; 29.18b: Toyota/AP Wide World; 29.18c: CIRRUS Design Corporation; 29.20b: NASA/JPL/Caltech; 29.26: Ken Gatherum, Boeing Computer Services

Chapter 30 Opener: Martin Barraud/Getty Images; 30.7: Photodisc/Getty Images; 30.10: John Walsh/Photo Researchers

Chapter 31 Opener: John P. Surey & Caroline J. Robillard; 31.5: Rubberball/Getty Images; 31.14: Lawrence Migdale/Photo Researchers; 31.22: John P. Surey; 31.23: Roger A. Freedman

Chapter 32 Opener: David Davis Photoproductions; 32.1: Bettmann/Corbis; 32.2a: Peter Barrett/Masterfile; 32.2b: Malcolm Fife/Getty Images; 32.16: The Image Bank/Getty Images; 32.18: Volker Steger/Photo Researchers; 32.20: NASA/JPL-Caltech/E.Churchwell (University of Wisconsin-Madison); 32.23: Michael Porsche/Corbis

Chapter 33 Opener: Peter Aprahamian/Photo Researchers; 33.1: Michael Newman/PhotoEdit; 33.2: National Institutes of Health/Photo Researchers; 33.9: Roger A. Freedman; 33.10a: NASA/John F. Kennedy Space Center; 33.10b: Spencer Grant/PhotoEdit; 33.13b: Susan Schwartzenberg, The Exploratorium; 33.16: Barry S. Blanchard; 33.17: Matthias Kulka/Masterfile; 33.20a: Randy O' Rourke/Corbis; 33.22a: Dougal Walters/Getty Images; 33.22b: Pixtal/AGE Fotostock; 33.26: Diane Hirsch/Fundamental Photographs; 33.31: Sepp Seitz/Woodfin Camp & Associates; 33.33: Dennis Frates/Alamy; 33.37a: K. Nomachi/Photo Researchers

Chapter 34 Opener: Tek Image/Photo Researchers; 34.8: Marshall Henrichs; 34.12a: NASA; 34.12b-c: NASA Headquarters; 34.23: PhotoLink/Getty Images; 34.27: Richard Megna/Fundamental Photographs; 34.34: PhotoDisc/Getty Images; 34.41a-c: Marshall Henrichs; 34.43c: THK Photo Products, Inc.; 34.44b: Omikron/Photo Researchers; 34.52c: Jan Hinsch/Photo Researchers; 34.54d: National Optical Astronomy Observatories

Chapter 35 Opener: Paul A. Souders/Corbis; 35.11: Peter Aprahamian/Photo Researchers; 35.17b: Bausch & Lomb Incorporated; 35.18: Bausch & Lomb Incorporated

Chapter 36 Opener: Digital Vision/Getty Images; 36.2a-b: From Sears, Zemansky, and Young, *College Physics*, 7th Ed., ©1991, Pearson Addison Wesley; 36.6: Pearson Addison Welsey; 36.9b: Richard Megna/Fundamental Photographs; 36.11: Dane Hornsleth; 36.12b: Pearson Addision Wesley; 36.17: Tom Boyden Photography; 36.18: Photodisc Green/Getty Images; 36.19a: NSO/AURA/NSF; 36.19b: Physics Dept., Imperial College/Photo Researchers; 36.21b: Estate of Bertram Eugene Warren; 36.25: Science Photo Library/Photo Researchers; 36.27: From Sears, Zemansky, and Young, *College Physics*, 7th Ed., ©1991 by Pearson Addison Wesley; 36.28a-c: From Sears, Zemansky, and Young, *College Physics*, 7th Ed., ©1991 by Pearson Addison Wesley; 36.29a: National Radio Astronomy Observatory/Associated Universities, Inc./National Science Foundation; 36.29b: European Southern Observatory; 36.32: Paul Silverman/Fundamental Photographs

Chapter 37 Opener: Brookhaven National Laboratory/Corbis; 37.4: Güven Güner/Alamy; 37.7: NASA/John F. Kennedy Space Center; 37.11: Jack Fields/Photo Researchers; 37.18: Adam Hart-Davis/Photo Researchers; 37.19: NASA and The Hubble Heritage Team (STScI/AURA); 37.22: Digital Vision/Getty Images; 37.26: Mauro Fermariello/Photo Researchers

INDEX

Note: Pages in **bold** locate figures; pages in *italic* locate tables.

A

D

E

I

N

Q

R

SOUTH AMERICA
NORTH AMERICA
CARIBBEAN SEA
ATLANTIC OCEAN
Barranquilla
Cartagena
Maracaibo
Caracas
Barquisimeto
VENEZUELA
Medellín
Manizales
Bogotá
Cali
COLOMBIA
Georgetown
GUYANA
Paramaribo
SURINAME
Cayenne
French Guiana (France)
GUIANA HIGHLANDS
N
Equator
Quito
ECUADOR
Guayaquil
AMAZON BASIN
Negro
Amazon
Manaus
Belém
Fortaleza
Madeira
Tapajós
Xingu
Tocantins
Natal
João Pessoa
Recife
Maceió
Aracaju
Salvador
São Francisco
Trujillo
PERU
Lima
Callao
A N D E S
BRAZIL
MATO GROSSO PLATEAU
Brasília
BRAZILIAN HIGHLANDS
Goiânia
BOLIVIA
La Paz
Lake Titicaca
Cochabamba
Santa Cruz
Sucre
GRAN CHACO
PARAGUAY
Campo Grande
Ribeirão Preto
Belo Horizonte
Campinas
Rio de Janeiro
Londrina
São Paulo
Tropic of Capricorn
Asunción
Curitiba
SOUTH PACIFIC OCEAN
Salta
San Miguel de Tucumán
CHILE
Resistencia
M O U N T A I N S
Pôrto Alegre
Córdoba
Mendoza
Rosario
Valparaíso
Santiago
URUGUAY
Buenos Aires
Montevideo
La Plata
ARGENTINA
SOUTH ATLANTIC OCEAN
PAMPAS
Concepción
Bahía Blanca
Mar del Plata
Temuco
P A T A G O N I A
Strait of Magellan
Tierra del Fuego
Falkland Islands (U.K.)
South Georgia Island (U.K.)
Cape Horn
National capital
0 250 500 miles
0 250 500 kilometers
Lambert Equal-Area Projection
20°
10°
0°
10°
20°
30°
40°
50°
100°
90°
80°
70°
60°
50°
40°
30°
20°

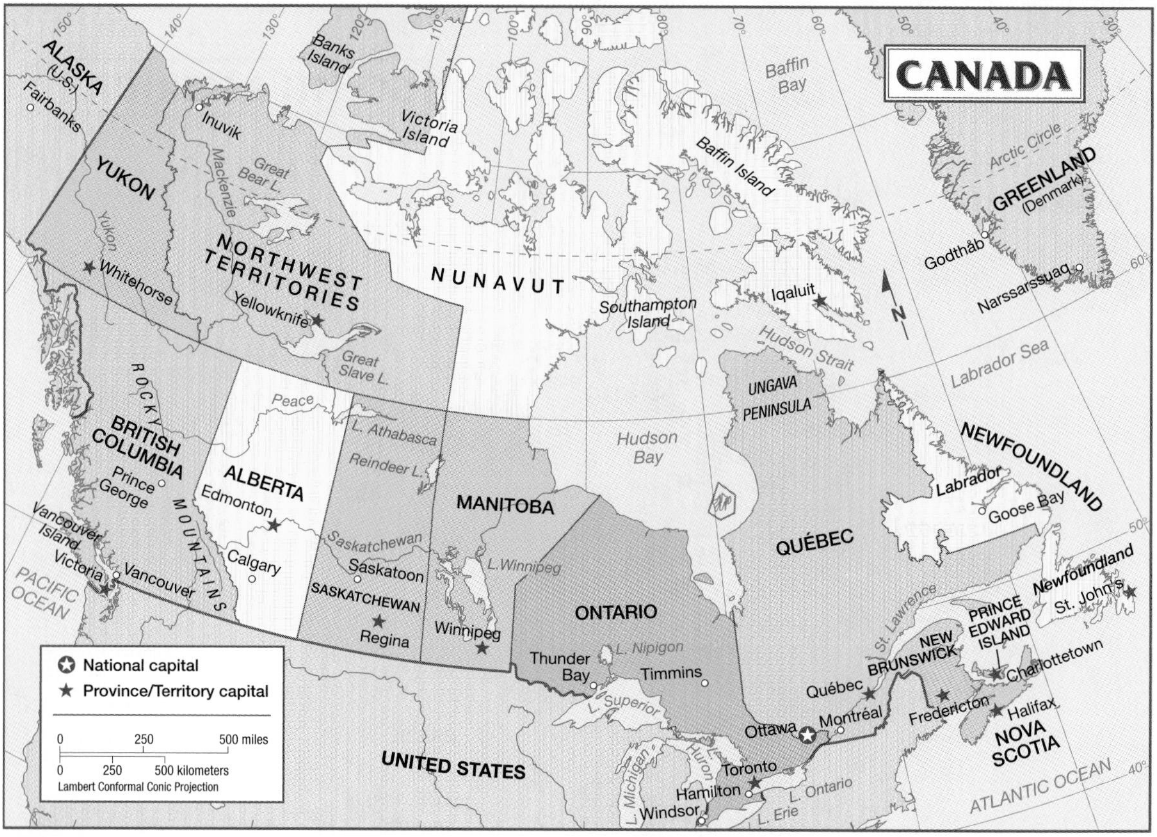

CANADA

ALASKA (U.S.)
Fairbanks
Banks Island
Victoria Island
Baffin Bay
Inuvik
YUKON
Mackenzie
Great Bear L.
Yukon
Whitehorse
NORTHWEST TERRITORIES
Yellowknife
NUNAVUT
Baffin Island
Southampton Island
Iqaluit
GREENLAND (Denmark)
Arctic Circle
Godthåb
Narssarssuaq
Hudson Strait
Great Slave L.
ROCKY MOUNTAINS
UNGAVA PENINSULA
Labrador Sea
Peace
L. Athabasca
Reindeer L.
Hudson Bay
BRITISH COLUMBIA
Prince George
ALBERTA
Edmonton
MANITOBA
NEWFOUNDLAND
Labrador
Goose Bay
QUÉBEC
Vancouver Island
Victoria
Vancouver
Calgary
Saskatchewan
Saskatoon
L. Winnipeg
PACIFIC OCEAN
SASKATCHEWAN
Regina
Winnipeg
ONTARIO
St. Lawrence
Newfoundland
St. John's
PRINCE EDWARD ISLAND
Charlottetown
NEW BRUNSWICK
Fredericton
Halifax
NOVA SCOTIA
Thunder Bay
L. Nipigon
Timmins
Québec
L. Superior
Ottawa
Montréal
UNITED STATES
L. Michigan
L. Huron
Toronto
Hamilton
L. Ontario
Windsor
L. Erie
ATLANTIC OCEAN

National capital
Province/Territory capital

0 250 500 miles
0 250 500 kilometers
Lambert Conformal Conic Projection

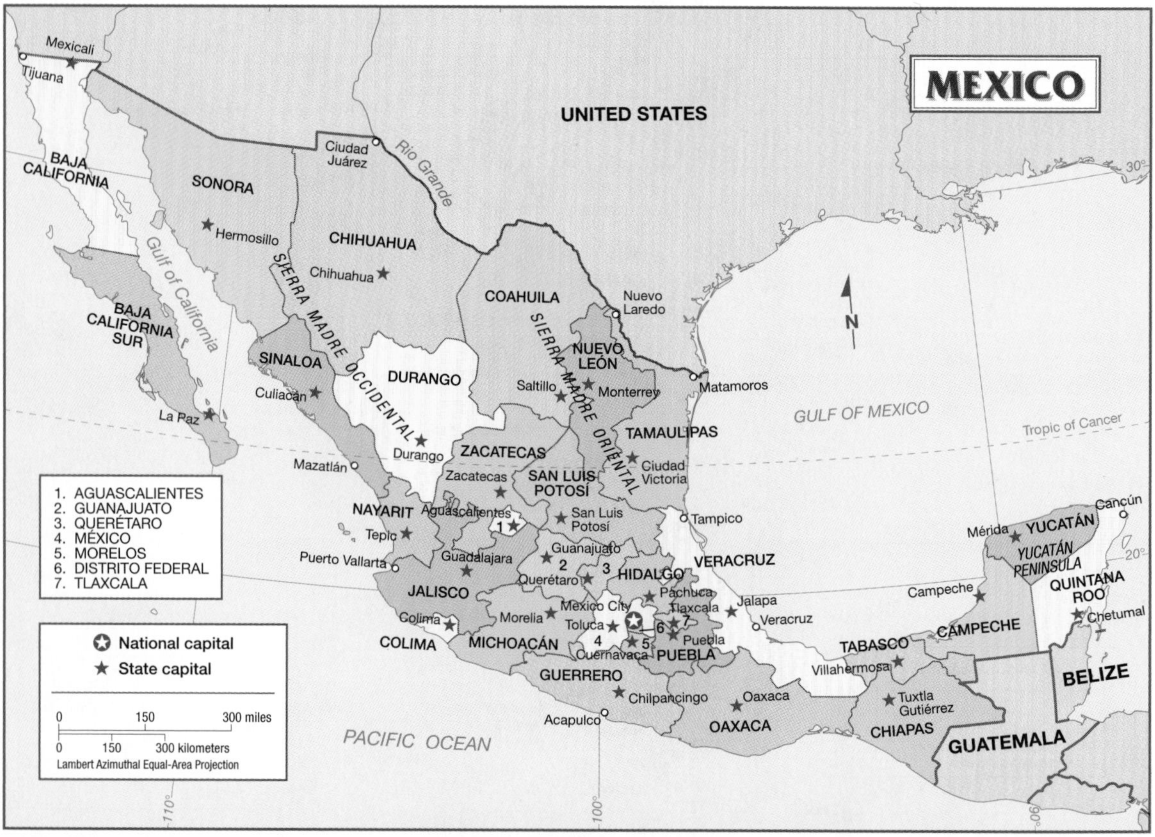

MEXICO

Mexicali
Tijuana
UNITED STATES
Ciudad Juárez
Rio Grande
BAJA CALIFORNIA
SONORA
Hermosillo
CHIHUAHUA
Chihuahua
Gulf of California
SIERRA MADRE OCCIDENTAL
COAHUILA
Nuevo Laredo
BAJA CALIFORNIA SUR
SIERRA MADRE ORIENTAL
NUEVO LEÓN
SINALOA
DURANGO
Saltillo
Monterrey
Matamoros
Culiacán
La Paz
GULF OF MEXICO
Tropic of Cancer
TAMAULIPAS
Durango
ZACATECAS
Mazatlán
Ciudad Victoria
Zacatecas
SAN LUIS POTOSÍ
NAYARIT
Aguascalientes
San Luis Potosí
Tampico
Cancún
Mérida
YUCATÁN
Tepic
Puerto Vallarta
Guadalajara
Guanajuato
VERACRUZ
YUCATÁN PENINSULA
HIDALGO
Querétaro
Pachuca
Campeche
QUINTANA ROO
JALISCO
Tlaxcala
Jalapa
Mexico City
Morelia
Colima
Toluca
Veracruz
Chetumal
CAMPECHE
COLIMA
MICHOACÁN
Cuernavaca
Puebla
PUEBLA
TABASCO
Villahermosa
BELIZE
GUERRERO
Chilpancingo
Oaxaca
Tuxtla Gutiérrez
Acapulco
OAXACA
CHIAPAS
GUATEMALA
PACIFIC OCEAN

1. AGUASCALIENTES
2. GUANAJUATO
3. QUERÉTARO
4. MÉXICO
5. MORELOS
6. DISTRITO FEDERAL
7. TLAXCALA

National capital
State capital

0 150 300 miles
0 150 300 kilometers
Lambert Azimuthal Equal-Area Projection